NATIONAL BANK NOTES

A Guide with Prices

THIRD EDITION

by Don. C. Kelly, Ph.D.

Professor of Physics, Emeritus
Miami University
Oxford, Ohio

National Bank Notes

A Guide with Prices

Third Edition

Published by

The Paper Money Institute, Inc.
P O Box 85
Oxford, Ohio 45056
(513)523-6861

ISBN 0-9656255-0-8

Printed in the United States of America 987654321

DEDICATION

This work is dedicated to four gentlemen who have made it easier and more fun to collect national bank notes.

To John Hickman for bringing to life the rich heritage preserved in nationals.

To Peter Huntoon for sharing his knowledge, his insights, and his experiences.

To Louis W. Van Belkum for his inspired efforts that made it possible to study national bank notes in a systematic fashion.

To Melvin Owen Warns for his unselfish efforts to help collectors and for his tenacity in recording surviving small size notes.

DEDICATION

John Hickman was born and raised in Macon, Georgia, where he was a member of the class of 1944 at Lanier High School. During World War II, John served in the United States Navy. For many years he acted as the Iowa distributor for two Chicago companies, selling check protectors and other bank equipment. These endeavours led him to the study of National Bank Notes, a field which he enriched greatly.

In 1965 John formed a partnership with John T. Waters. Together they pioneered the collecting of nationals by geographic location, rather than by treasury signature combinations. This greatly expanded the market for nationals and gave us the vigorous collecting environment we enjoy today. It was during his association with Waters that John began his prodigious census of nationals. What began as a few scraps of paper in a shirt box grew to a computer database containing records of over 150,000 national bank notes.

John Hickman was the man behind the William R. Higgins Jr. Foundation Museum and Library located in Okoboji, Iowa. This unique museum, a mecca for national bank note enthusiasts, houses the most complete collection of Iowa nationals and major collections of Missouri and Minnesota notes.

Anyone who met John Hickman knows that he had a way with words! John's colorful language leaps out at us from many auction catalogs and price lists. "A peach of a note", "little more than pocket change", and "a flaming rarity" are but a few of the insightful phrases now used freely by many others. Whereas another person would look at a worn note with a corner off and apologize for its condition, John would extoll its virtues and pronounce it "98% Fine."

Collectors of nationals owe John Hickman a great debt. He gave us a priceless legacy of information, he skillfully explained the history we hold in our hands, and he showed us how much fun it can be to collect. And always, he served us generous portions with a verve that made us smile. John Hickman - truly a peach, most definitely much more than pocket change, and certainly a flaming rarity of a man.

Peter Huntoon is a prolific writer, having authored more than 200 articles on United States national bank notes and small size varieties. Most of his articles are based on original research undertaken at various government archives in Washington, DC. He was one of the authors of **The National Bank Note Issues of 1929-1935**, and wrote **Territorials, a Guide to U. S. Territorial National Bank Notes.** Pete's latest effort, **United States Large Size National Bank Notes**, is a collection of essays which explain how national bank notes worked within the context of the legislation which authorized them.

Huntoon was born in West Orange, New Jersey, in 1942, and moved to Tucson, Arizona, in 1959. He earned a doctorate in hydrology from the University of Arizona in 1970, and moved on to university teaching and research, first at the University of Nebraska at Lincoln from 1970 to 1974, and then at the University of Wyoming where he has remained. His research specialty is ground water exploration.

He has published widely in the scientific hydrology and geology literature. Probably he is best known professionally for production of a series of geologic maps for the Grand Canyon of Arizona, and Canyonlands of Utah, which took over a decade and a half to produce. He has won teaching awards for a humanities course he teaches entitled Fission, Fusion, Psychosis, which is a multidisciplinary examination of the atomic bombings of Japan.

He got into paper money seriously in 1963, early enough to enjoy the pleasure of finding notes reasonably available and underpriced, but before the national bank note road map was very well defined. He specialized early in the national bank notes from Arizona, his home at the time, and continues to build the most comprehensive collection of Arizona notes, including territorials.

Huntoon was in on the ground floor of the modern era of national bank note collecting. This can be defined as the 1965 - 1975 period during which Louis Van Belkum assembled circulation and issuance data for the national banks, and John Hickman, and his partner John Waters, greatly expanded the commercial market for nationals by focusing on location rather than treasury signatures. Huntoon emerged as a primary source for the unfolding explosion in national bank note information.

Louis W. Van Belkum was born in Grand Rapids, Michigan in 1942. He became an ardent researcher of fractional currency while still a youngster. Lou began collecting Michigan national bank notes in 1964 when he was teaching in the Grand Rapids school system. In 1968, Lou authored **National Bank Notes of the Note Issuing Period 1863-1935**. This book lists national banks by state, charter number, and town name. In addition it gives key information such as the circulation of the bank and the date it liquidated or entered receivership. Lou's slim volume became a "shopping guide" for the growing numbers of collectors and dealers scouring coin shows and shops for nationals. In 1970 Lou co-authored **The National Bank Note Issues of 1929-1935**, the "blue book" which became a source of inspiration and information for the growing number of small size national enthusiasts.

More than anyone else, Louis Van Belkum is responsible for making it possible to study national bank notes in a systematic way. Beginning in 1968, Lou and his wife Barbara began regular pilgrimages to the National Archives. At first, Lou's study of the Comptroller of the Currency ledgers was focused on the Lazy Twos issued to Michigan banks. When Gerome Walton learned of Lou's work he contracted with him to obtain the issue information for all of the Nebraska national banks. Shortly thereafter Lou and Barbara made the momentous decision to systematically abstract information about all national bank note issues and redemptions. To appreciate the magnitude of their efforts, imagine that you had to record, by hand, information which ultimately filled nearly 5000 typed pages - and then organize it by state and charter number. This project was completed in 1979. The fruits of their labors make up the heart of this book.

Lou and Barbara now reside in Las Vegas, Nevada where he works for the county as a computer systems programer. In recent years their spare time has been divided between the enjoyments of being grandparents and a study of modern gambling casino tokens.

Melvin Owen Warns was born in Toledo, Ohio in 1902. He graduated from Columbia University (College of Pharmacy) and New York University (School of Merchandise Statistics). During World War II he served as a Senior Lieutenant with Fleet Wing 15.

Owen's interest in National Bank Notes resulted from a 1935 visit to the Bureau of Engraving and Printing. At the time Owen was part of a group studying the Bureau's air mail stamp issues. The Director of the Bureau led them through the facilities then being used to produce the small size nationals, and commented that these issues soon would end. Fascinated by the pre-printed 12-subject sheets and the interchangeable bank titles, Owen decided to embark on a study of these notes. Imagine being there when nationals were rolling off the presses. What a thrill!

Owen Warns is best known as the author of **The Nevada Sixteen National Banks and Their Mining Camps** (1974), and as Editor, with authors Peter Huntoon and Louis Van Belkum, of **The National Bank Issues of 1929 - 1935** (1970).

One of the features of the latter book was a listing of all national banks which issued small size nationals. The denominations reported by collectors were identified for each bank. This listing served as a starting point for Owen's regular updates which appeared in **Paper Money**, the journal of the Society of Paper Money Collectors. He sifted through correspondence from hundreds of dealers and collectors, serving as a magnet for information as he chronicled the dwindling number of unreported banks. Owen's efforts helped to popularize small size nationals at a time when they were greatly underappreciated.

Owen's collecting interests were not limited to small size nationals. Inspired by the sale of the Albert A. Grinnell collection of paper money, he formed a collection of notes from the first one hundred charter number banks. He also collected notes from the Milwaukee, Wisconsin area where he resided.

NATIONAL BANK NOTES

Preface

The first edition of **National Bank Notes, A Guide With Prices** was published in 1980 and was revised and enlarged in the second edition in 1985. This third edition has been thoroughly revamped and updated with new information and features.

Chapter 1 gives an overview of United States paper money from the early Colonial issues to the present day Federal Reserve notes. Chapter 2 tells the story of how citizens in a small town organized and operated a national bank. Chapter 3 is a tutorial which describes and illustrates the different types of nationals.

Chapter 4 presents a complete listing of the notes issued by all national banks. The listing is alphabetic by state. In response to the urgings of many collectors and dealers the arrangement within each state has been changed from numeric by charter number to alphabetic by town name. **Census data on surviving notes are presented for all 12,635 note-issuing national banks. Values are given for each type and denomination of note issued by every bank.**

A census of uncut sheets of nationals is presented in Chapter 5, with most sheets being identified by serial number. Chapter 6, developed with the help of Harry Jones, describes and evaluates national bank error notes. A census of major errors is included. Chapter 7 deals with counterfeit nationals and nationals which were stolen before being put into circulation. Chapter 7 was developed with the help of Bob Cochran. Many of the counterfeits, which created problems for merchants and citizens a century ago, still fool collectors and dealers.

The name of every town with a note-issuing national bank is given in Chapter 8. The list is arranged alphabetically by town and state. Chapter 9 lists the charter numbers, town, and state for all note-issuing national banks, in charter number order.

Early publications on paper money did not single out national bank notes for special attention. A monograph by George Blake (1948) presented helpful information on large size national bank notes. The first edition of Robert Friedberg's **Paper Money of the United States** (1953) listed the different types of nationals by signature combinations. Its illustrations helped collectors identify the different types. A 1956 booklet by Walter Dillistin (Dillistin 1956) presented a superb study of nationals. Dillistin's work still makes good reading.

The Society of Paper Money Collectors was founded in 1961. Collectors have benefitted greatly from the publication of many articles dealing with nationals in the Society's journal, **Paper Money.** The Society sponsored the definitive work, **The National Bank Note Issues of 1929-1935** (1970) by Huntoon, Van Belkum, and Warns. This work put small size nationals "on the map." More recently, the Society sponsored publication of Peter Huntoon's **United States Large Size National Bank Notes** (1996).

Louis Van Belkum gave collectors their first roadmap for collecting nationals by location when he authored **National Banks of the Note Issuing Period 1863-1935** (1968). This slim volume listed national banks by state, charter number, town, and title. It gave a circulation figure that served as a crude guide to rarity.

In 1976 Lou and his wife Barbara completed the Herculean task of assembling a listing of the notes issued to each bank - the data which form the heart of this guide. Those who have wrestled with the massive Comptroller of the Currency ledgers housed in the stacks at the National Archives can appreciate the magnitude of the Van Belkums' efforts. The data were made available to collectors and dealers on a state-by-state basis. For a while these state "breakdowns" were as eagerly sought by collectors and dealers as the notes themselves. Recognizing the great value of information, collectors and dealers bought, sold, and traded until they had the complete study - nearly 5000 pages of photocopied material. It was an exciting time that ushered in a new level of sophistication and a heightened appreciation of the rarity of many issues. There is much to be learned from these data. They deserve to be pondered, digested, and interpreted.

Even before the dissemination of Lou's information, collectors and dealers sought to learn which notes had survived. John Hickman began a census of nationals which grew to over 150,000 notes before his passing in 1995. Both John Hickman and the author were fortunate to have the help of many serious collectors, particularly Frank Bennett, Robert Bolduc, Robert Hearn, Peter Huntoon, Robert Kvederas, Roman Latimer, W. K. (Bill) Raymond, Gilmore Sem, Gerome Walton, and Owen Warns.

What does the future hold for national bank note enthusiasts? By the year 2001 the census will hold 300,000 notes. The census will be part of a database which also contains the names of the officers whose signatures appear on the notes. This information will be distributed on CD ROM and perhaps over the World Wide Web.

The author has spent more than thirty years teaching Physics to legions of energetic and enthusiastic youngsters at Miami University. Early on he learned a prime dictum of teaching: "Tell them what you're going to tell them, tell them, and then tell them what you told them." In short, some things bear repetition. The careful reader of this work will find repetition has crept in from time to time. This is not an apology, just an explanation. Some things bear repetition.

Suggestions for improvements are welcome.

Oxford, Ohio
October, 1996

Don. C. Kelly

Table of Contents

ACKNOWLEDGMENTS

The author wishes to thank Louis Van Belkum for his help in making this work complete and accurate.

Bob Cochran and Harry E. Jones shared their extensive knowledge base and made important contributions to Chapters 6 and 7.

I am also deeply appreciative of the help given by my family. My wife Jane and my daughter Linda helped with the tedious work of proof reading and typing. My sons Stewart and Jim provided computer expertise. Bridget Kelly supplied inspiration.

Dr. Peter Huntoon and Doug Walcutt read preliminary versions of portions of this edition and made important contributions to its content. Bob Cochran, Ken McDannel, James Sharp, Pete Simpson, and William Youngerman made helpful comments and suggestions.

A number of people provided notes or note images for the illustrations. My thanks to Tom Durkin, Keith Edison, Larry Falater, Martin Gengerke, Bruce Hagen of R. M. Smythe, Joe Hensley, Gene Hessler, Peter Huntoon, Harry E. Jones, Art Kagin, Roman L. Latimer, Art Leister, Dean Oakes, Vernon Oswald, and William Youngerman. Lynn Vosloh was particularly helpful with photos of notes and proofs in the National Numismatic Collections. The William R. Higgins, Jr. National Bank Note Museum and Research Library provided research facilities.

Mr. Jeff Sabo of Miami University did a masterful job in creating photos used for the dust jacket and illustrations.

Neil Holsing and Joyce Buttery of Miami University provided timely solutions to vexatious eleventh hour word processing and page makeup problems.

The author is especially indebted to a number of people who, in varying degrees, inspired this work. These people have helped me in many ways over the years. They share with me a great respect and a great passion for national bank notes, those bits of history that passed from hand to hand, and are now in our hands.

Amon Carter, Jr. (deceased)
Bob Cochran
Charles Dean
William Donlon (deceased)
Gene Hessler
Joe Hensley
John Hickman (deceased)
James J. Hoskovec
Peter Huntoon
Curtis Iversen (deceased)
Dr. Glenn Jackson (deceased)
Harry E. Jones
Art Kagin
Allen Karn
Lyn Knight
Art Leister
Glenn Martin
Joe McCandless
Ken McDannel
Dean Oakes
Vernon Oswald
Morey Perlmutter
William K. Raymond
Louis Van Belkum
M. Owen Warns
John Wildi

CONTRIBUTING EDITORS

One of the most difficult questions relating to national bank notes is, "What's it worth?" Most national bank notes can be classified as "rare" by any normal standard. Notes are unknown for roughly 10 percent of the note-issuing banks and many other banks are represented by a single note. These extreme rarities are the most difficult to evaluate. The valuations in this guide should be treated as figures at which bargaining can begin.

The valuations are based on the collective experience of the Contributing Editors listed below, a veritable "Who's Who" of collectors and dealers.

Bob Azpiazu
Frank Bennett
Inell Nelson Clark
Neil Clasen
Bob Cochran
Phil Darby
Charles Dean
Richard Deavers
Tom Denly
Keith Edison
Larry Falater
Dennis Forgue
Dustinn Gibson
Bob Hearn
Joe Hensley
Howard Herz
Shawn Hewitt
Ron Horstman
Lowell Horwedel
James J. Hoskovec
Mark Hotz
Peter Huntoon
Harry E. Jones
Richard Jones
Glen Jorde
Lyn F. Knight
Col. Robert Kvederas
Tim Kyzivat
Dr. Wallace Lee
Art Leister
Bill Litt
Gerald Loegler
Don Mark
Glenn Martin
Ken McDannel
Vernon Oswald
Alex Perakis
Peter Plath
John Rowe III
Joe Sande
Gilmore Sem
James Sharp
Stephen Thayer (Pete) Simpson
James A. Sparks, Jr.
Rick Stelzer
Jerry Swanson
Leon Thornton
Frank Trask
Gerome Walton
George Warner
Dale White
William Youngerman

CONTRIBUTORS

The census figures in this guide are based on a database of nearly 200,000 national bank notes. The value of an accurate and extensive census in arriving at meaningful valuations is obvious. The census, which is an ongoing project, was assembled with the help of many collectors and dealers.

The individuals listed below have aided me in various ways. Many have sent me photocopies or lists of nationals. Some have sent computer disks with data for thousands of notes. Others have smiled politely as they handed me a stack of notes, knowing that I wanted information, not a bill of sale. Whether large or small, their contributions are important, for they allow us to form a quantitative picture of the pool of notes we share. Thank you, very much.

Darrell Abel
Paul Abel
Carl Agostini
Paul Alford
Johnny Allen
Fred Angus
Joe Apelman
A A Armstrong
David Arnold
Wil Arnold
Bob Azpiazu
Jeff Bachmann
John W. Baker, Jr
R J Balbaton
Joe Ballentine
Pat Barnes
Tom Bartholomew
Frank Bennett
Sam Bettis
David Bick
Gary Bleichner
Robert Bolduc
A. Bongiovanni
Larry Booth
Q David Bowers
Norman Brand
Bob Brantley
Gerry Briggs
Hy Brown
Norb Brown
Terry A. Bryan
R K Burke
Jim Carr
Tim Carr
Steve Catt
Inell Nelson Clark
Frank Clark III
Neil Clasen
Bob Cochran
Howard Cohen
Ken Cooper
Bruce Countryman
Mike Crabb
Dean Crnkovich
James Cross
Daryl Crotts
Charles Culleiton
Jim Davis
Charles Dean
Richard Deavers
Diane Decker
George Decker
Charles Deibel
Lloyd Deierling
John DeMaris
Tom Denly
Ken Denski
Thom Dixon
David Dmytryka
Joseph Donovan
Ken Dudley
Charles V. Duncan
Roger Durand
Tom Durkin
Mark Dwyer
William Dwyer
Keith Edison
James Ehrhardt
Fred Emerson
Clyde Englehardt
Dale Ennis
Ron Etter
Jim Fairfield
James Fairfield, Jr.
Larry Falater
William Farmer
Ed Fischer
Don Fisher
Jack Fisher
George Fitzgerald
Kevin Foley
Dennis Forgue
Dave Forsythe
John Foster
Ralph Foster
Richard Frost
Martin Gengerke
Fred Gerhardt
Dustinn Gibson
Don Gilletti
Ted Gilliom
Len Glazer
Stephen Goldsmith
David Grant
Jim Greene
Richard Gross
Bruce Hagen
Dave Halaiko
Ken Hallenbeck
Dale Harrington
Marc Harrison
Bob Hastings
John Hay
Bob Hearn
Rodney Heckman
Dave Heinsohn
John Heleva
Patrick Heller
Leon Hendrickson
Joe Hensley
Ed Herman
Howard Herz
Bill Herzog
Mary Herzog
Shawn Hewitt
John Hickman
Rick Hickman
Don Higgins
Tony Hill
Elizabeth T. Himes
Bob Hoebake
George Hohman
Dave Horman
Ron Horstman
Lowell Horwedel
James J. Hoskovec
Mark Hotz
Christopher Howard
Frank Howard
Dennis Huff
Bill Humrickhouse
Peter Huntoon
Arri Jacob
Don Jensen
James S Johnson
Harry E. Jones
Marie Jones
Richard Jones
Glen Jorde
Michael Kaczka
Art Kagin
Paul Kagin
Albert Kaminsky, Jr
Allen Karn

Ed Karn
Willis Karner
Jonathan Kern
Debbie Knight
Eric Knight
Lyn Knight
Dave Koble
Charles Koehler
Dave Kokochak
Robert Kotcher
Robert Kravitz
Ed Krivoniak
Jeff Krump
Robert Kvederas
Tim Kyzivat
John Lahey
Tim Larsen
Roman Latimer
Dr Wallace Lee
Art Leister
Betty Leister
R E Leisy
Wayne Liechty
Charles Litman
William Litt
Mike Little
Gerald Loegler
Jerry Lorenzen
Walter Lototski
Ed Lowe
Fred Maples
Don Mark
Glenn Martin
Jim Mason
Dominick Mattera
Edwin Maughan
Edward Maxwell
Joe McCandless
Harry McDaniel
Michael McDaniel
Ken McDannel
George McDuffie
Mark Mendelson
Richard Merlau
Tim Messerley
David Meyers
Casper Migas
Allen Mincho
Cliff Mishler
Stanley Morycz
Ken Mote
William Mross
Keith Muth
Gregory Myers
John Nickell
Frank Nowak
Lawrence O'Neal
Dean Oakes
Fred Ockers
Helen Oswald
Vernon Oswald
John Parker
Dan Parvis
Worth Paschal
Huston Pearson
Alex Perakis
Eustolio Perez
Leroy Pieper
Peter Plath
Mike Polizzi
Bruce Potter
Gary Potter
Jim Potter
Michael Powers
Ronald Rahl
Clarence Rareshide
Lou Rasera
W K Raymond
Mike Robelin
Ed Rothberg
Eugene Rowe
John Rowe, III
Bob Rozycki
Jim Sabia
Joe Sande
Robert Sawyer
Byrd Saylor, III
Mike Scacci
Ron Schieber
Bob Schmidt
Stephen Schroeder
Gil Sem
Armand Shank
Bill Sharp
James Sharp
Lynn Shaw
John Sheaffer, Jr
Austin Sheheen
Hugh Shull
Leon Silverman
Pete Simpson
Marc Skinner
Leonard Smith
Richard Smith
Gary Snover
James Sorn
Jim Sparks
Kim Stallings
William Stanczyk
Bob Steele
Robert Steinberg
Rick Stelzer
Leland Stickle
John Stone
Dave Stouffer
Ralph Stratman
Mark Strumpf
Don Sullivan
A R Sundell
Jerry Swanson
Fred Swick
Allan Teal
David Thomas
Leon Thornton
Frank Trask
Cam Troilo
Thomas Tullis
Jeff Tyler
Richard Ulbrich
Dan Urbanski
Louis Van Belkum
Albert Van Der Werth
Philip Varnum
P A Vaughn
Brad Vautrinot
James Vermeulen
Eric Vicker
Don Vosburgh
Doug Walcutt
Gerome Walton
Ray Waltz
Mel Weinstein
Harold B. Weitz
Sol Weitz
Chip West
Jim West
Mickey West
Dale White
Harlan White
John White
John Wilson
Nancy Wilson
Ron Winegarden
Wendell Wolka
Daniel Yawczak
Ron Yeager
Ted Young
William Youngerman

About the Author

Don. C. Kelly was born and raised in the northeast Ohio village of Poland. While in high school he began collecting stamps and covers of The Confederate States of America. Five years of schooling at Miami University in Oxford, Ohio was followed by three more at Yale University, where he received a doctorate in theoretical physics. As a graduate student in the late nineteen fifties, he spent far too much time at the Collectors Shop in New Haven, where his interests expanded to classic United States stamps and Colonial Connecticut coppers.

His interest in paper money began in 1960 following his return to Miami University as a faculty member. His first national was a beat up $20 1902 Plain Back from Youngstown, Ohio, acquired on a trip to Chicago in 1963. The intervening thirty three years have seen his Ohio collection grow to over 2000 notes. Don's collection contains notes from 328 of the 336 Ohio banks which issued small size notes. The dust jacket of this work betrays his fondness for notes from towns and banks with unusual names.

The idea for a guide book for national bank notes became a reality in 1981 when the First Edition of this work was published. In 1982 the Professional Numismatists Guild honored Kelly as an outstanding author of a numismatic work by presenting him with the Robert Friedberg Award. Following publication of the Second Edition in 1985 Kelly was honored with the Nathan Gold Memorial Award for the Advancement of Paper Money Collecting.

He resides in Oxford, Ohio where he retired after serving for thirty four years as Professor of Physics at Miami University. His interests include travel, recreational computing, and discus throwing.

NATIONAL BANK NOTES

Chapter 1

HISTORICAL INTRODUCTION: UNITED STATES PAPER MONEY

The Four Paper Money Eras

This chapter presents a brief history of the many types of paper money issued in the United States. Four overlapping time periods, or Eras, are used to organize this history: **Colonial Era, State Bank Era, National Bank Era, and Federal Reserve Bank Era.**

The Colonial Era runs from 1690, when the first paper money was issued, until 1782 when the Bank of North America was chartered, signaling the rise of private and state banks. The State Bank Era lasted until the Civil War prompted our Federal government to establish the National Bank System. National Bank notes were issued from 1863 until 1935. Soon after its creation in 1913 the Federal Reserve System became dominant in American banking. The time periods covered by these four paper money eras are as follows:

Colonial Era 1690 - 1782
State Bank Era 1782 - 1865
National Bank Era 1863 - 1935
Federal Reserve Bank Era 1913 - present

The Colonial Era

The earliest issue of paper money in what is today the United States was in the Colony of Massachusetts in 1690. There were no banks as we know them today. The colony issued bills of credit to pay soldiers who had returned from a military expedition. The bills could be used to pay taxes and could be exchanged for provisions held by the colony.

The practice of using bills of credit - paper money - spread to other colonies where they were likewise used to pay military expenses and to fund public works. In some cases the notes were issued to individuals who provided land as security. These were to be repaid with interest. Such notes were generally retired when received for taxes by the issuing authority.

This "Sword in Hand" note issued in colonial Massachusetts features a defiant patriot.

The paper money experiment was continued by the Continental Congress. There were eleven issues of Continental paper money, the first dated May 10, 1775, the last, January 1, 1779. Following independence in 1776 the designation on the notes changed from "United Colonies" to "United States."

This $4 note dated May 10, 1775 was authorized by the Continental Congress

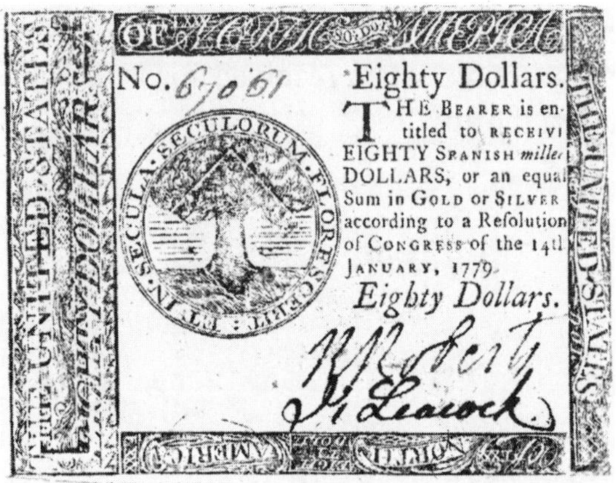

The United States Congress authorized this $80 note dated Jan 14, 1779.

Even though the Continental Congress endowed Continental Currency with legal tender status, its value fell steadily throughout the war. So great was its depreciation that the phrase "Not Worth a Continental" is still recognized as synonymous with "totally worthless."

Throughout its history, continental paper money has been pursued by collectors delighted by notes with patriotic mottoes, nature print backs, and pen signatures of our forefathers.

Colonial paper money makes a wonderful collectable, but the colonial paper money "experiment" was largely a failure. It taught our forefathers how **not** to finance government.

The State Bank Era

The first true bank in the United States was the Bank of North America. It was chartered by Congress and went into business in 1782 at Philadelphia. Its first president was Robert Morris, revered as the person who financed the American Revolution. The Bank of North America issued paper money like the fractional note illustrated here.

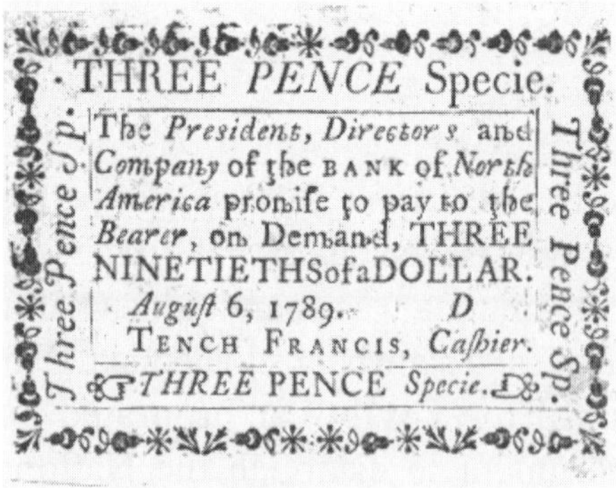

The Bank of North America issued this 3 pence note dated Aug 6, 1789.

The first half of the 19th century saw a flood of paper money issued by private banks and branch banks of state banking systems.

A note issued in 1839 by the Fort Wayne Branch of the State Bank of Indiana. The Cashier was Hugh McCulloch, who became our nation's first Comptroller of the Currency.

In addition to state-chartered banks there were two attempts to establish a national banking system during the first half of the nineteenth century. The first Bank of the United States was the brain child of Alexander Hamilton, our nation's first Secretary of the Treasury. It began operation in 1791 and established branches in cities ranging from Boston to New Orleans. Although it was a commercial success its charter was not renewed in 1811 because of political opposition. Paper money issued by the bank was still being redeemed in 1825. The assets of the bank were acquired by Stephen Girard who continued the business as the Girard Bank.

The War of 1812 created an extraordinary demand for "specie" - gold or silver coins. Local and state banks were ill-equipped to supply this need. People hoarded gold, silver, and even copper coins during times of financial stress. Merchants were forced to issue paper money, referred to as "scrip", in order to carry on everyday business.

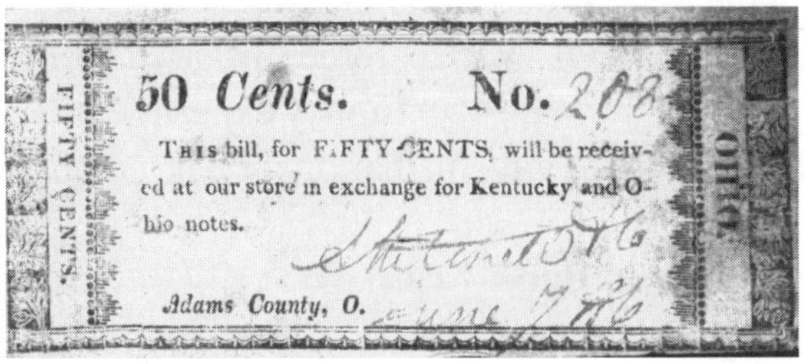

Merchants issued paper scrip like this when people hoarded coins during financial panics.

It became apparent that a national bank was needed to maintain our nation's credit. The second Bank of the United States opened for business in 1816 and issued notes redeemable in coin. The second Bank of the United States enjoyed early commercial success but was unloved by politically powerful state bank interests. Andrew Jackson campaigned against the Bank and vowed to abolish it if elected President. In 1833 President Jackson fulfilled his promise and ordered that public money no longer be deposited in the Bank of the United States, thereby dooming it. When its national charter was not renewed in 1836 the bank continued as a state-chartered bank. It failed in 1841, following the financial panic of 1837.

The State Bank Era was marked by some of the most colorful bank notes ever produced. The notes were called "demand notes" because they carried a promise to pay the face value of the note in gold or silver "on demand", that is, whenever the note was presented at the bank. The promise to pay often went unfulfilled and the State Bank Era spawned classic frauds. In the 1840's some states instituted "free banking" systems. The times were so good and the demand for circulating notes so great it was decided that banks could issue paper money backed by state bonds. These bonds could be bought on margin. With a few thousand dollars a group of speculators could buy bonds, deposit them with the state Treasurer and obtain a bank charter. Once chartered the bank could issue paper money up to the value of the bonds. Some of the newly printed bank notes were promptly used to pay the balance due on the bonds. This procedure could be repeated again and again. The bankers received interest on the bonds. In one instance an investment of $10,000 was leveraged into $600,000 worth of interest-paying bonds. The large volume of bank notes in circulation caused no problem so long as the good times lasted. The notes were a convenience and circulated freely. However, many canals and turnpikes on the midwestern frontier turned out to be poor investments. Land speculations turned sour and the bonds lost most of their value. A wave of bank failures followed and much of the bond-backed paper money became virtually worthless.

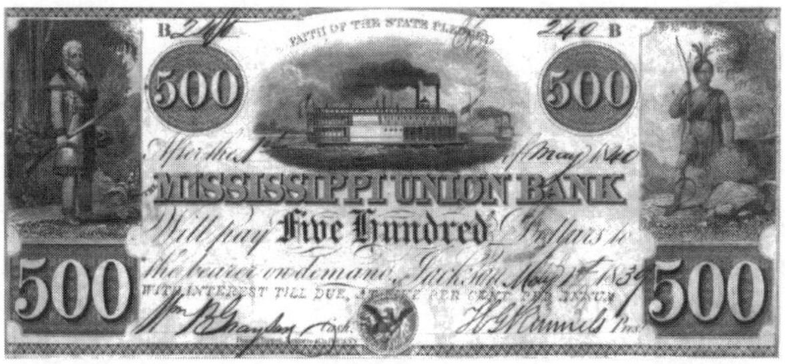

This bond-backed note issued by a Mississippi bank in 1839 is a collector's dream. The vignettes show a majestic river boat and Daniel Boone. The bank failed and the state reneged on its pledge to redeem the bonds.

Wildcat Banking

"Wildcat banking" was another colorful chapter in the State Bank Era. An opportunist would have bank notes engraved and printed at little expense. The location of the bank would be in a place so remote that only wildcats would venture there. He would then ride to distant points and put the notes into circulation, obtaining goods of value in return. If he were lucky a transaction might gain for him hard money or notes of legitimate banks. The worthless notes might circulate for a considerable time before it was realized that no such bank existed. Harold Bowen's classic study of Michigan bank notes (Bowen 1956) relates a story about one such bank. "A story is told of a stranger who lost his way in the wilderness of Shiawassee County. Night was falling and his prospects looked grim indeed. Following an old wood road to a small clearing, he was astonished to see a frame building with a conspicuous sign. (Exchange Bank, Shiawassee) Here lurked a Michigan wildcat in its native haunts."

A wildcat bank note.

In one variation on this scheme bankers would loan money in the form of bank notes made payable at some remote branch of the bank - so remote that the notes might never be presented for payment. In the meantime the banker would collect interest on the loan.

Counterfeit bank notes abounded in the State Bank Era. There were numerous weekly publications describing counterfeit notes. Indeed, no surviving genuine notes are known for many banks of the era. The abundance of counterfeits and frauds left the public with a healthy distrust of banks and paper money.

Confederate Paper Money

The provisional government of The Confederate States of America was formed at Montgomery, Alabama on February 8, 1861. Its Secretary of the Treasury, C. G. Memminger, oversaw the issue of $2,000,000 in denominations of $50, $100, $500, and $1000. Subsequent issues increased in dollar volume, ending with a $200,000,000 issue authorized by the Act of February 17, 1864.

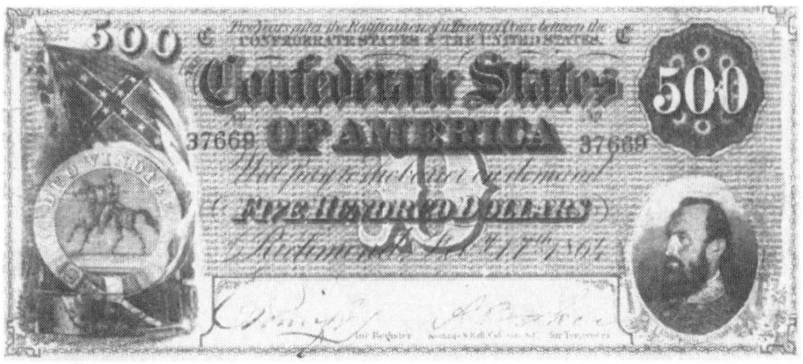

General Stonewall Jackson appears on this Confederate States note, dated February 17, 1864.

The issues of the Confederacy mark a transition from the State Bank Era to the National Bank Era. It took the Civil War to force America to once again try a national paper money experiment. This new experiment gave us national bank notes.

The National Bank Era

The challenge of financing the Civil War left its imprint on the paper money of this era. In 1862 Congress authorized the issue of $150,000,000 of paper money called **United States Notes**.

This $1 United States Note, issued in 1862, bears the likeness of Salmon P. Chase, Lincoln's Secretary of the Treasury, and the "father" of our national banking system.

The legislators made them legal tenders, a controversial move, and viewed them as a temporary "war measure." These "temporary" United States Notes continued to be issued until 1970 and still circulate today.

A Series 1966A $100 United States Note. This note, issued in 1970, marked the final series of United States Notes.

The main subject of this guide, **National Bank Notes**, also were viewed as a temporary expedient, justified only by the extreme conditions brought on by the war. They were authorized by the Act of February 25, 1863. As was the case with United States Notes, "temporary" turned into "lengthy." The last national bank notes were delivered to the First National Bank of Chillicothe, Ohio on July 10, 1935.

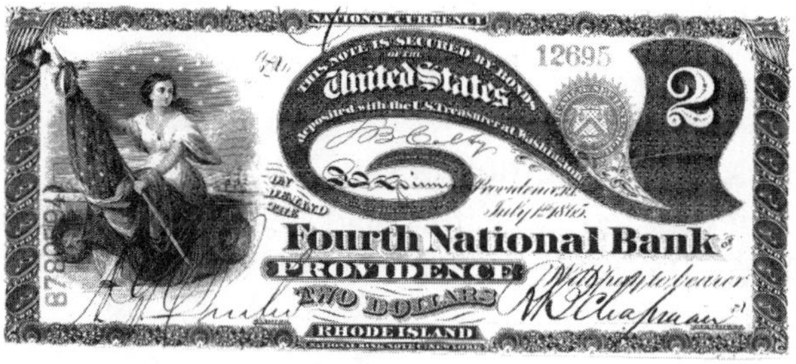

This "Lazy Two" national bank note takes its name from the large reclining "2". Issues of nationals began in 1863.

A note from the last shipment of nationals.

Silver Certificates were the third major type of paper money issued during the National Bank Era. These notes, as their name suggests, were redeemable in silver. They were first issued in 1886 and continued to be issued until 1965.

Silver Certificates were first issued in 1886. The back of this $5 note featured five silver dollars dated 1886.

The last Silver Certificates were Series 1957B and were issued until 1965.

Several other types of paper money were in use during the National Bank Era, including Demand Notes, Refunding Certificates, Gold Certificates, Compound Interest Notes, Coin Notes, and Fractional Currency. Each of these issues is a story in itself. We pass them by with the comment that each had only a minor financial impact. In other words, these types comprised a total dollar volume that was insignificant compared to the three major paper money issues.

Shortcomings of the national bank system became painfully evident during financial panics which struck almost regularly. The national bank currency was **inelastic** - it was not possible to quickly increase or decrease the amount of currency in circulation. Following the Panic of 1907 steps were taken to provide a more elastic currency. These steps resulted in the Federal Reserve Bank System.

The Federal Reserve Bank Era

The Federal Reserve Bank Era began in 1913 and continues today. The passage of the Federal Reserve Bank Act on December 23, 1913 gave our nation a central bank, a "banker's bank." The United States was divided into twelve Federal Reserve districts. District banks were created by requiring each national bank to purchase stock equal to 3 per cent of its capital and surplus. This pool of funds can be tapped by member banks. When a member bank needs funds quickly it puts up "commercial paper" (short term loans) as collateral and borrows from the "Fed."

Two distinct types of paper money have been issued through the Federal Reserve System. These two varieties have similar-sounding names: **Federal Reserve Bank Notes** and **Federal Reserve Notes**. The first type, Federal Reserve Bank Notes, are no longer issued. Like the national bank notes issued by national banks, Federal Reserve Bank Notes were backed by United States Bonds deposited with the Treasurer of the United States. So far as note issues were concerned, the district Federal Reserve Banks functioned as **regional national banks**. Federal Reserve Bank Notes were issued by all twelve district branches. Denominations issued were $1, $2, $5, $10, $20, and $50. Not all denominations were issued by all branches.

The design of this $2 Federal Reserve Bank Note explains why collectors call them "Battleship Twos."

Small size Federal Reserve Bank Notes also were issued. In the midst of the Great Depression, President Franklin Roosevelt declared a bank "holiday." All of the nation's banks remained closed from Monday March 6, 1933 through Thursday March 9, 1933. There had been "runs" on virtually all banks. Even though most were financially secure, they literally began to run out of money. Emergency legislation enacted on March 9, 1933 authorized the issue of Federal Reserve Bank Notes to meet the unprecedented demands for currency. There was not enough time to design new plates so existing stocks of National Bank Notes were used. These were overprinted with the Federal Reserve District bank name. Like their large size kin, each is an obligation on a Federal Reserve District bank, not on the United States Treasury.

Small size Federal Reserve Bank Notes were issued in denominations of $5, $10, $20, $50, and $100, following the "bank holiday" in 1933.

The long weekend of March 10-12, 1933 saw millions of these notes printed. On Monday March 13, 1933, those banks deemed financially secure reopened and deliveries of the new Federal Reserve Bank Notes began. The emergency was relieved and collectors had yet another type of United States paper money to add to their collections.

The bank notes we use today are called Federal Reserve Notes. They were first issued in 1914. Their size was reduced in 1929 giving us the form of paper money we deal with in daily transactions. At one time Federal Reserve Notes were redeemable in gold, a luxury no longer supported. Federal Reserve Notes are obligations on the United States Treasury and are distributed through the Federal Reserve System. Federal Reserve Notes have been issued in denominations ranging from $1 to $10,000. Currently, the highest denomination being issued is the $100 note. Design changes began in 1996, the $100 note being the first to undergo a makeover. The new designs incorporate high-tech anti-counterfeiting devices.

Large size Federal Reserve Notes were issued for all twelve districts. This $5 note was the lowest denomination issued.

This small size $10,000 Federal Reserve Note was the highest denomination issued.

The many forms of paper money issued during the four eras beginning in 1690 and continuing today are avidly collected. Monographs and catalogs dealing with the many different types of United States paper money are listed in the Bibliography. In the next chapter we present a story that explains how citizens went about starting a national bank and how they maintained the circulation of national bank notes.

NATIONAL BANK NOTES

Chapter 2

NATIONAL BANKING: ORGANIZATION AND OPERATION

This chapter describes the steps taken to organize a national bank and the means by which the bank maintained its national bank note circulation. We develop our story through the actions of citizens living in the town of Smokey Hollow, a quaint hamlet in the rolling hills of Meigs County in southeast Ohio. Situated on a bluff overlooking the Ohio River, Smokey Hollow is blessed with fertile land and clean water. A railroad runs through town, serving the farmers who bring their grain to the local elevator. The railroad and the river also enable area timber cutters to move their harvest to markets in Cincinnati and Pittsburgh.

Main Street in Smokey Hollow, Ohio.

How to Organize a National Bank

What Smokey Hollow does not have is its own bank. To remedy this situation fourteen prominent citizens decide to form a national banking association named The Smokey Hollow National Bank. The group elects five directors. Mr. Stephen Thayer Simpson is chosen as secretary of the association. Other directors include Mrs. Jane Williams, who is to serve as the Cashier of the bank, and Judge Joseph Hensley who will be President of the bank. Secretary Simpson spearheads the organization efforts. He is pleased to learn that the steps involved in starting a national bank are quite simple. Any group of five or more "natural persons" may apply to organize a national banking association. The term "natural person" is used to distinguish an individual from a corporation or other business group. Secretary Simpson writes to the Comptroller of the Currency in Washington, DC, requesting the necessary forms, and asking that the chosen name be reserved. The Comptroller's office responds by sending two forms, an **organization certificate** and an **articles of association** form. The Comptroller's office advises that the chosen name will be reserved for fifteen days, enough time for the forms to be completed, notarized, and returned.

Secretary Simpson completes the organization certificate by filling in the name of the bank, the names and addresses of the shareholders, the amount of stock to be held by each, and the location of its office of "**discount and deposit**". The word "deposit" is familiar in connection with banking activity. We are all acquainted with the act of making deposits in savings or checking accounts. The word "discount" as it is used in banking refers to the practice of charging a fee for a short-term loan. To see how banking discounts work, let us suppose that the Smokey Hollow timber mill receives an order from a Cincinnati furniture manufacturer. The timber is processed and the newly minted lumber is dispatched by barge. The price of the lumber is to be $10,000, and the timber mill operator needs to be paid. He needs to pay his help and the owner of the stand of timber which was harvested. He needs the money **right away**, not next month or the month after. He goes to the Smokey Hollow National Bank and borrows the money. He borrows by giving the bank a **bill of exchange** for the lumber. Rather than send the Cincinnati firm a bill and wait a month or more for it to be paid, he **sells** the bill of exchange to his Smokey Hollow banker. The banker **discounts** the bill of exchange, that is, he pays less than $10,000. The amount of the discount might be one-half percent ($50) if the bill is to be paid within 30 days. The Smokey Hollow National Bank credits $9,950 to the timber mill account, thereby earning a gross profit of $50. The Smokey Hollow bank in turn sends the bill of exchange to The First National Bank of Cincinnati, one of its **correspondent banks,** where it will be **rediscounted**. That is, the Smokey Hollow National Bank sells the bill of exchange to the First National Bank of Cincinnati. The Cincinnati banker credits $9,985 to the Smokey Hollow National Bank account. This leaves the Smokey Hollow bank with a profit of $35. The Cincinnati furniture manufacturer is presented the bill and pays for it with a check for $10,000 drawn on its account with the First National Bank of Cincinnati. This leaves the First National Bank of Cincinnati with a profit of $15. All of the parties in the transaction have now been paid, even though no cash ever changed hands. The two banks have earned profits by "discounting" loans. In summary, the term "discount" in banking parlance refers to the practice of charging an up front fee for a short-term loan.

The Comptroller of the Currency dispatches a bank examiner to Smokey Hollow to investigate the prospects for the proposed bank. The examiner considers matters such as the experience and resources of the organizers and proposed officers, the adequacy of existing banking facilities, the outlook for the growth and development of the town in which the bank is to be located, and the prospects for success of the proposed bank. In cases where there is local opposition to the proposed bank, the examiner interviews those for and against its establishment. With no opposition and solid financial backing the Smokey Hollow association wins high marks from the examiner.

The Smokey Hollow association has subscribed $25,000, to be divided into 250 shares of stock with a par (face) value of $100 each. The articles of association form is an agreement defining the rules under which the association will operate, such as the number of directors and the place and date of their annual meetings. Each shareholder signs two copies of the forms, which are then notarized. One set is retained by the bank and the other is returned to the Comptroller.

In less than a month the Comptroller rules favorably on their application and the Smokey Hollow national banking association is notified that they should proceed with the sale of stock. The paid in capital of the bank is $25,000. The 250 shares with a par value of $100 each are actually sold for $120 each. The $20 premium gives the bank a surplus of $5000.

United States bonds with a par value of at least $25,000 must be purchased and deposited with the Treasurer of the United States in order for the bank to order circulating national bank notes. The bonds are purchased on the open market at a premium over their par value.

Bond-Backed Circulation

The idea of paper money backed by bonds became popular in the state banking era, notably in the 1840-1860 period. The basic idea is that the banker would use "sound" money to purchase interest-bearing bonds and deposit these with a government authority. The banker could then issue paper money with a total value based on the value of the bonds. The paper money was in the form of "demand notes". The notes bore an obligation to pay the bearer "on demand", that is, when presented at the bank. Should the banker fail to redeem the notes on demand, the government could sell the bonds and redeem the notes. Bond-backed state banknotes enjoyed some successes but lost the confidence of the public when speculation and inflation rendered the bonds worthless in some states. Our national currency, backed by United States bonds, never suffered any such embarrassments. National bank notes are legal money to this day.

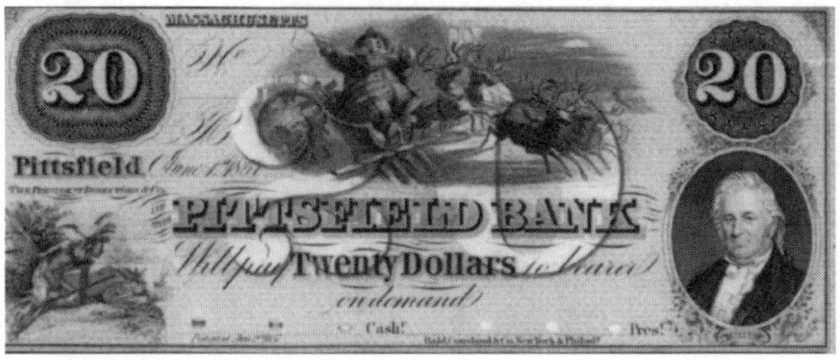

Santa and his team appear on this demand note. The words "Will pay Twenty Dollars to bearer on demand" appear below the center of the note.

The bonds are purchased by the Smokey Hollow bankers and forwarded to the Treasurer's office, where their receipt is acknowledged. Shortly thereafter the Comptroller's office sends a certificate authorizing The Smokey Hollow National Bank to commence business. The year is 1904. The certificate carries charter number 7085, the number assigned to identify the bank and its circulating national bank notes. The bank orders $25,000 worth of national currency, in denominations of $5, $10, and $20.

When the first shipment of $25,000 worth of nationals reaches Smokey Hollow there is great excitement in the bank and throughout the town. The national currency was shipped to the bank in uncut sheets of four notes each. Cashier Williams and President Hensley sign each of the four $5 notes in one sheet and the three $10 notes and one $20 note in another sheet. The notes in these two sheets bear serial number one and are imprinted with a bright red Treasury seal. With much ceremony the sheets are cut into individual notes and displayed for the approval of the assembled shareholders and public. Cashier Williams and President Hensley each retain one of the $5 notes for their personal archives. The $25,000 shipment quickly works its way into circulation in the prosperous economy of Smokey Hollow. Keeping their notes in circulation was important to national banks, a point we'll touch on shortly.

Reserves and Redemptions

In addition to the bonds which backed the national bank notes, there were two other security features of the national banking system. One was the reserve requirement, the other was the redemption fund.

A national bank was required to keep on hand a reserve of at least 15 percent of its deposits. This reserve must be in "legal money", either legal tender United States Notes or gold and silver coins. With deposits of $10,000 the reserve for the Smokey Hollow bank was $1500. In larger so-called **reserve cities** such as Chicago, St Louis, and New York, the reserve requirement was 25 percent.

The word "redemption" is used often in the various National Banking Acts and Comptroller reports. Each national bank was required to maintain a deposit equal to 5 percent of its circulation in the U. S. Treasurer's redemption fund. This money had to be paid in legal tenders. National bank notes did not enjoy legal tender status, although they were convertible into legal tender notes. The Smokey Hollow National Bank had a circulation of $25,000 so its redemption fund balance was set at $1250.

To see how and why the redemption fund would be tapped, let us suppose that the Smokey Hollow National Bank accumulated $1000 in nationals from other banks. It would generally not want to hold these in its vault very long - for two reasons. First, it was required to maintain reserves in legal tender notes or coin. It could not use its own nationals or those of any other national bank for this purpose because the nationals were not legal tenders. So, the Smokey Hollow bank would send the $1000 worth of nationals in for redemption, receiving legal tender United States Notes in exchange. Of course, the Smokey Hollow bankers could simply pay out the $1000 in other bank's notes in the course of business. They didn't want to do this for reason number two: They'd much prefer to pay out their own nationals. After all, the Smokey Hollow bankers had used their gold and legal tenders to buy the United States bonds that backed their nationals. The bonds drew interest, typically 2 percent per year, but the bankers could have kept their legal tenders and loaned the money at perhaps 6 percent interest. In order to profit from their national bank status the Smokey Hollow bankers had to get their own nationals into circulation and keep them there. Occasionally, one sees bank checks dated in the 1870's and 1880's with the wording "Payable in National Currency". This was just another way for a bank to keep its own nationals out of its vault. For these same reasons, other national banks did not want to hold Smokey Hollow nationals, and these would be sent for redemption regularly. When Smokey Hollow notes were returned to the Treasury for redemption the Smokey Hollow redemption account was charged accordingly. Each national banking association was notified regularly as to the amount of their notes presented for redemption. When the sum of redemptions reached $500 the bank had to replenish the redemption fund with a deposit of legal money. Once reimbursed the Treasury returned to the bank those notes fit for circulation. Notes unfit for circulation were sent to the Comptroller and destroyed. New notes of the current series were then sent by the Comptroller to the bank, thereby maintaining the bank's circulation.

Note that replacements or destructions of notes passed through the Comptroller's office. Such notes had to be recorded by the Comptroller who was responsible for seeing that the bank's circulation was maintained. The Treasury could handle redemptions and returns of notes fit for circulation since these did not involve any change in the bank's circulation.

Fractions of notes could be redeemed. Full value was allowed when at least three-fifths of a note was presented. Half the face value was allowed when at least two-fifths but less than three-fifths of a note was presented.

Profit on Circulation

We can begin to appreciate the financial allure of national bank status and the note-issuing privilege. If the bank could loan its notes at 6 percent and earn 2 percent on the bonds backing the notes it made a profit on its circulation. There was an annual tax ranging from one-quarter percent to one-half percent on the circulation, and other expenses associated with purchasing the bonds and with printing and redeeming the notes. Typically national banks earned profits on their circulations ranging from one-half percent to one and one-half percent. For the Smokey Hollow National Bank this amounted to only a few hundred dollars each year. For a national bank with a million dollar circulation it could amount to $10,000 or more.

Times Change

For over twenty years the village of Smokey Hollow and its bank prospered, along with the rest of the nation. But in 1923 and 1924, Nature's abundance was so great that farm commodity prices plunged. Unable to sell their crops at a profit, many local farmers were unable to pay off the loans they made to finance their operations. Their bad luck forced the Smokey Hollow bank to foreclose mortgages on a few farms and generally cut back on the farm loan activity. With loan demand flagging, the need for circulation fell and the Smokey Hollow bankers found their once-heralded nationals were piling up in the vault. The general economy of the country was quite healthy and United States bonds were selling at a healthy premium over their par value. It was decided to reduce the circulation of the bank from $25,000 to $15,000. This was accomplished by returning $10,000 worth of Smokey Hollow nationals to the U. S. Treasurer. The $10,000 bond which the Treasurer then released was transferred to an agent in New York City, and sold for $11,400. This money was promptly loaned to a New York City bank at the rate of 4 percent. The New York bank in turn used the funds to help finance the construction of an ocean-going steamship.

This pattern was repeated from time to time across many parts of our country. Money which ordinarily would have been loaned locally ended up financing commerce somewhere else. At times it was not a drought or local hardship which caused money to flow to New York City and other financial centers. When the demand for capital became great enough as it did often in an era of industrial expansion, bankers sent their nationals to the Treasurer, redeemed their bonds, sold them, and loaned the money far from home. This sometimes caused resentment to the point that disappointed farmers banded together and started their own local banks.

In these days of trillion dollar national debt it is hard to imagine that there were times when the United States government ran a surplus and reduced the national debt by buying up United States bonds in the open market. This drove the bond price skyward, giving national bankers yet another reason to reduce their circulations and sell their bonds.

Early in 1929 the bank learned that there would soon be a change in the size of the banknotes. The Smokey Hollow nationals and all other forms of United States currency would be reduced in size. Scarcely a week after the bank placed its order for the new style nationals a letter was received from a gentleman named George Blake in far off New Jersey. Mr. Blake offered to purchase the first sheets of new notes received by the bank, those bearing serial number one. It was decided to sell the sheets to Mr. Blake who offered to pay a premium of $11 over the face value for the $10 and $20 sheets.

Although the drought subsided, boom times never returned to Smokey Hollow. The growth of industrial cities came at the expense of rural hamlets like Smokey Hollow. Young people decided to forego a quiet and sometimes uncertain life on the farm and move to cities where jobs were plentiful and life was upbeat.

Depression and Liquidation

Soon another spectre would appear on the economic horizon. It would be called The Great Depression. And it would mean the end of the Smokey Hollow National Bank and its issue of national bank notes.

Early in 1933 the folks in Smokey Hollow became nervous when several nearby city banks went broke. They began to withdraw their savings from the Smokey Hollow National Bank in favor of a backyard tin can. At the height of the emergency, President Franklin Roosevelt declared a bank "holiday". All of the nation's banks remained closed from Monday March 6, 1933 through Thursday March 9, 1933. Much to the amazement and bewilderment of the citizens of Smokey Hollow their national bank failed to reopen on March 11, 1933. The bank examiner had declared "a deficiency in assets".

A receiver was appointed and he proceeded to liquidate the assets of the Smokey Hollow National Bank. The Smokey Hollow nationals on hand were returned to the Treasury and used to redeem the bonds on deposit, and the bonds were then sold. In the final analysis the bank was not in terribly bad shape. It was more a matter of too little opportunity to earn a fair return on the capital invested in the bank. All savings accounts were paid in full and stockholders were paid $1.06 for every $1 in stock which they held.

Epitaph

The bank fixtures and the building were sold to a local realtor who eventually rented the building to a family who wanted to start a grocery store. This venture lasted only a few years. The realtor then converted the building into a hotel which made ends meet by renting rooms cheaply to railroad workers. When World War II broke out the Smokey Hollow economy picked up. The logging industry and the railroad once again brought new faces to the town's businesses.

One day a guest at the Smokey Hollow Diner paid his check with a $5 bill. Lo and behold it was a $5 Smokey Hollow national! A young lady named Linda was tending the cash register and she had never seen such strange looking money. She thought it must be a fake of some kind. Two older patrons assured her that the money was real, a ghost from Smokey Hollow's past. One of them explained that in earlier days there were thousands of banks like the one in Smokey Hollow, each with notes bearing the name of the town and bank. "We had a lot of home town paper money in those days", the old-timer mused. Each time Linda rang up a sale she studied the Smokey Hollow note. She recognized the signatures of Mrs. Williams and Judge Hensley, now well up in their years. Later, when the last customer left and it was time to close, Linda took one more longing look at the note. She thought to herself, "This is really neat!" It was Friday night and payday, all rolled into one at the diner. Linda asked the owner if she could have the $5 Smokey Hollow national as part of her $18 wages. When the owner frowned she pleaded, "Please, I want to start a collection of these. They're magical!" The owner looked at the note, shrugged his shoulders, and handed it to her. She beamed, thanked him profusely, and gave him a big hug. As she turned and happily skipped out the door the owner looked at his wife and said, "Why on Earth would anyone want to collect national bank notes?"

Chapter 3

NATIONAL BANK NOTES: HOME TOWN PAPER MONEY

Introduction

On February 25, 1863 Abraham Lincoln signed legislation entitled "An Act to provide a national Currency, secured by a Pledge of United States Stocks, and to provide for the Circulation and Redemption thereof." This Act, which became known as the National Currency Act, provided for the establishment of National Banks and the currency which forms the main subject of this Guide.

Collectors use the terms "national bank notes" or simply "nationals" to refer to the notes circulated by national banks. National bank notes were issued by over 12,000 banks between 1863 and 1935. There were several reasons for creating the national banking system, but two stand out:

(1) The number of private and state banks was growing haphazardly. Bank fraud was commonplace. The public's faith in paper money - never strong -. was at a new low.

(2) In order to finance the Civil War, the Federal government needed new and broadly based markets for its bonds. Like many before and since, the government went to the people with money - the bankers.

The requirements for achieving national bank status changed during the note-issuing period. One feature remained constant throughout the note-issuing era: **The value of the notes which a national bank could circulate was directly related to the value of securities it deposited with the Treasurer of the United States.**

Bond-Backed Circulation

The idea of paper money backed by bonds became popular in the state banking era, notably in the 1840-1860 period. The basic idea is that the banker would use "sound" money to purchase interest-bearing bonds and deposit these with a government authority. The banker could then issue paper money based on the value of the bonds. During most of the note-issuing period national banks were required to back their notes with United States bonds purchased in the open market.

The first firm to be appointed as a bond subscription agent was the banking house of Jay Cooke & Co in Philadelphia. The first series of bonds used to back nationals paid six percent interest. They became known as "five-twenties" because they were redeemable at the pleasure of the government after five years and payable after twenty years. The interest on the bonds was payable **in gold** at six-month intervals. Jay Cooke was so successful in his efforts to sell the first issue of bonds that his banking house was rewarded with the first national bank charter, becoming The First National Bank of Philadelphia, charter number one.

We're number one!

Once the bonds were purchased and deposited with the Treasurer of the United States, a bank could circulate national bank notes with a value up to 90 percent of the par value of the bonds. For example, if a bank deposited $50,000 worth of bonds it could circulate up to $45,000 worth of its national bank notes. **The circulating privilege had the effect of nearly doubling the money supply**. For every dollar paid in, the government had a dollar to spend and the banker had 90 cents to loan.

The Gold Standard Act of March 14, 1900 contained a provision which allowed national banks to circulate notes with a value up to 100 percent of the value of bonds on deposit. For a brief period, 1908-1915, securities other than United States Bonds could be used to back circulating notes. As we will see, all nationals display a clause which spells out the type of securities which back the notes.

Reserves and Reserve Cities

In addition to the bonds deposited as security for their notes, a national bank had to maintain cash reserves for the purpose of redeeming its own nationals. Initially the reserve was set at fifteen percent of the bank's combined circulation and deposits. For example, if a bank's circulation and deposits totaled $50,000 it had to have on hand a minimum of $7500 in legal tender notes, this being deemed an adequate reserve for redeeming its own notes.

National banks in some of the larger cities, called "Reserve Cities", were required to maintain reserves of twenty five percent of their combined circulation and deposits. These banks were often "correspondent" banks for the smaller "country" banks. The Reserve Cities created by the Act of June 3, 1864 were Saint Louis, Louisville, Chicago, Detroit, Milwaukee, New Orleans, Cincinnati, Cleveland, Pittsburgh, Baltimore, Philadelphia, Boston, New York, Albany, Leavenworth, San Francisco, and Washington City.

Redemption Fund

The Act of June 20, 1874 changed the reserve requirements. Only deposits were subject to the fifteen percent reserve requirement. There were no reserves on circulation. At the same time a redemption fund was established. Every national bank was required to maintain an account with the Treasurer of the United States for the purpose of redeeming its notes presented for redemption. The account balance was to be maintained at five percent of a bank's circulation. Thus, if a bank issued $50,000 in nationals it was required to maintain a balance of $2500 in its redemption account.

Business Expenses

National banks had to pay a tax to offset expenses related to engraving plates and printing and distributing notes. This tax rate depended on the type of United States bonds used to secure the notes. The Act of February 25, 1863 set an annual tax rate equal to one percent of a bank's circulation. The Act of December 21, 1905 made Panama Canal bonds eligible as security for nationals. These bonds paid only two percent interest, but circulation backed by their deposit was taxed at just one-half percent per year. They became the "bonds of choice" for securing national bank notes.

The People in Charge

Salmon Chase conceived our National Banking System.

The Secretary of the Treasury is our nation's chief financial officer. The man who conceived the idea of our national banking system was Salmon Portland Chase, the Secretary of the Treasury under Abraham Lincoln. Chase had been Governor of Ohio during a period when the State Bank of Ohio developed as a very successful state-chartered system. Chase proposed a nationally-chartered system based on the best features of state banks. Many state and independent bankers opposed the idea of a national banking system, fearing that it would be far too strong a competitor. The Civil War emergency tipped congressional sentiment in favor of Chase's plan.

The National Currency Act was approved by Congress and signed into law by President Lincoln on February 25, 1863. A key feature of the Act was the requirement that national banks purchase United States bonds, which would be used to secure their circulating notes. With one stroke Chase's vision gave us a stable paper currency and created a huge market for United States bonds.

Department of the Treasury officers with roles in the national bank note story included the Comptroller of the Currency, the Treasurer of the United States, and the Register of the Treasury. The Comptroller decided if applications for national bank status should be approved. His office was in charge of accepting orders for national bank notes, issuing notes, and destroying worn or mutilated notes deemed unfit for circulation. The Comptroller's office was created as a result of the National Currency Act. The first Comptroller was Hugh McCulloch, revered by the bankers for his famous pronouncement, "In case of a dispute, favor the bank". His appointment as the Comptroller was a strange twist of fate, for he had opposed the national bank system while serving as President of the State Bank of Indiana.

Hugh McCulloch as he appears on the $20 Series 1902 nationals.

McCulloch quickly recognized shortcomings in the original National Currency Act. His suggested changes became law under the Act of June 3, 1864, which became known as the National Bank Act.

During the national bank era the duties of the Treasurer included seeing to it that United States bonds were purchased or redeemed in accordance with provisions of the National Bank Act. The Register served as an auditor, maintaining records of transactions involving bonds and national bank notes. National bank notes carry the printed signatures of the Treasurer and Register.

Table A lists the Comptrollers and their dates in office during the national bank note era.

Table A. Comptrollers of the Currency

Name	Term Begins	Term Ends
Hugh McCulloch	May 9, 1863	Mar 8, 1865
Freeman Clarke	Mar 21, 1865	July 24, 1866
Hiland R Hulburd	Feb 1, 1867	Apr 3, 1872
John Jay Knox	Apr 25, 1872	Apr 30, 1884
Henry W Cannon	May 12, 1884	Mar 1, 1886
William Trenholm	Apr 20, 1886	Apr 30, 1869
Wedward S Lacey	May 1, 1889	June 30, 1892
A Barton Hepburn	Aug 2, 1892	Apr 25, 1893
James H Eckles	Apr 26, 1893	Dec 31, 1897
Charles G Dawes	Jan 1, 1898	Sept 30, 1901
William B Ridgely	Oct 1, 1901	Mar 28, 1908
Lawrence O Murray	Apr 28, 1908	Apr 27, 1913
John S Williams	Feb 2, 1914	Mar 2, 1921
D R Crissinger	Mar 17, 1921	Apr 30, 1923
Henry M Dawes	May 1, 1923	Dec 17, 1924
Joseph W McIntosh	Dec 20, 1924	Nov 20, 1928
John W Pole	Nov 21, 1928	Sept 20, 1932
J F T O'Connor	May 11, 1933	

Nationals Wane in Importance

The importance of national bank notes reached its zenith in 1913 when a record 1.1 billion dollars worth of nationals were in circulation. In 1913 the United States was fast becoming an industrial giant. The explosive growth of the American economy demanded a more flexible banking system. In December 1913 the Federal Reserve Act was passed by Congress, an event which marked the beginning of the end for national bank notes. The national bank note era ended on August 1, 1935 when the last bonds with the circulation privilege were called in for redemption. The last nationals issued went to The First National Bank of Chillicothe, Ohio on July 10, 1935.

Themes for Collecting Nationals

There are many features of nationals which appeal to collectors, and there are numerous themes for collecting. Perhaps the most distinctive feature of a national is that it bears the name of the bank, and the name of the town and state (or territory) in which the bank was located. The thrill of acquiring a national from a hometown bank has launched more than one collection. Notes bearing serial number 1 are very popular. Notes with unusual bank or town names are avidly collected. The nationals illustrated here show a few of the many themes for a collection.

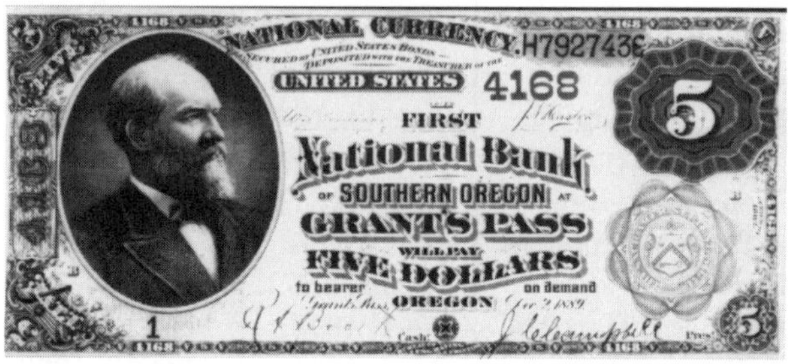

A note with everything!

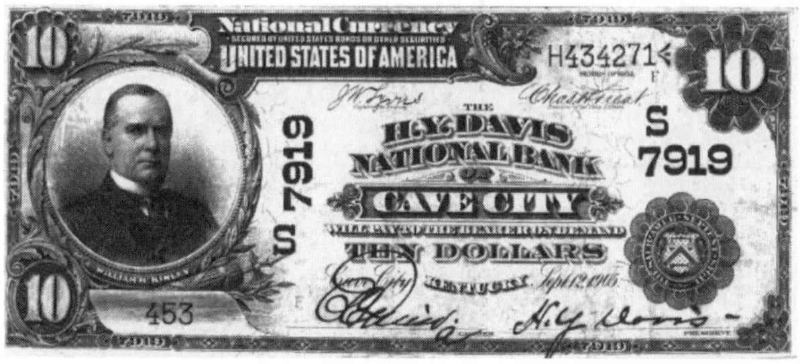

Hardin Young Davis signed this note as President.

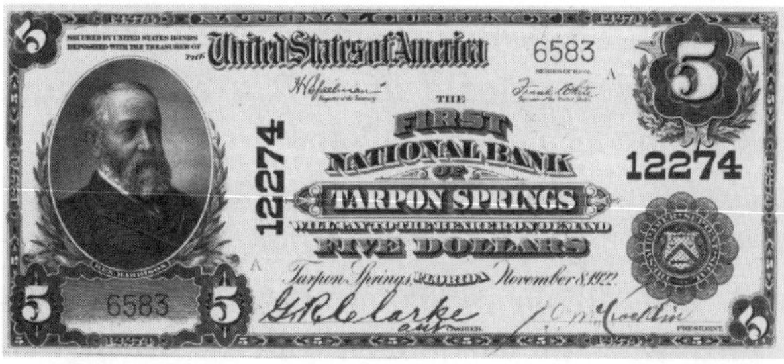

Tarpon Springs, Florida was the home port for generations of sponge fishermen of Greek lineage.

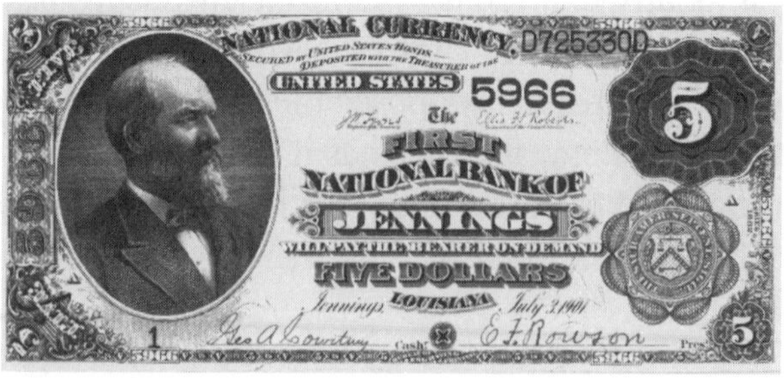

Serial #1 notes have always had great collector appeal.

Large Size and Small Size Nationals

Collectors classify notes into groups based on note designs and the time frame of their issue. These groups are described in detail later in this chapter. The most obvious distinction between groups is the size of notes. Prior to July 1929 national bank notes and other forms of United States paper money were "large size", with dimensions approximately 7.5 inches by 3 inches. In July 1929 the dimensions of United States paper money were reduced to the current size of approximately 6.3 inches by 2.6 inches. Modern size nationals are referred to as "small size" notes.

Honey Grove, Texas: Population 1973

Small size note from popular location.

Key Features of a National Bank Note

All national bank notes share certain features. The illustration below points out key features of large size national bank notes, the type issued before July 1929. Details of these features are discussed in the text which follows.

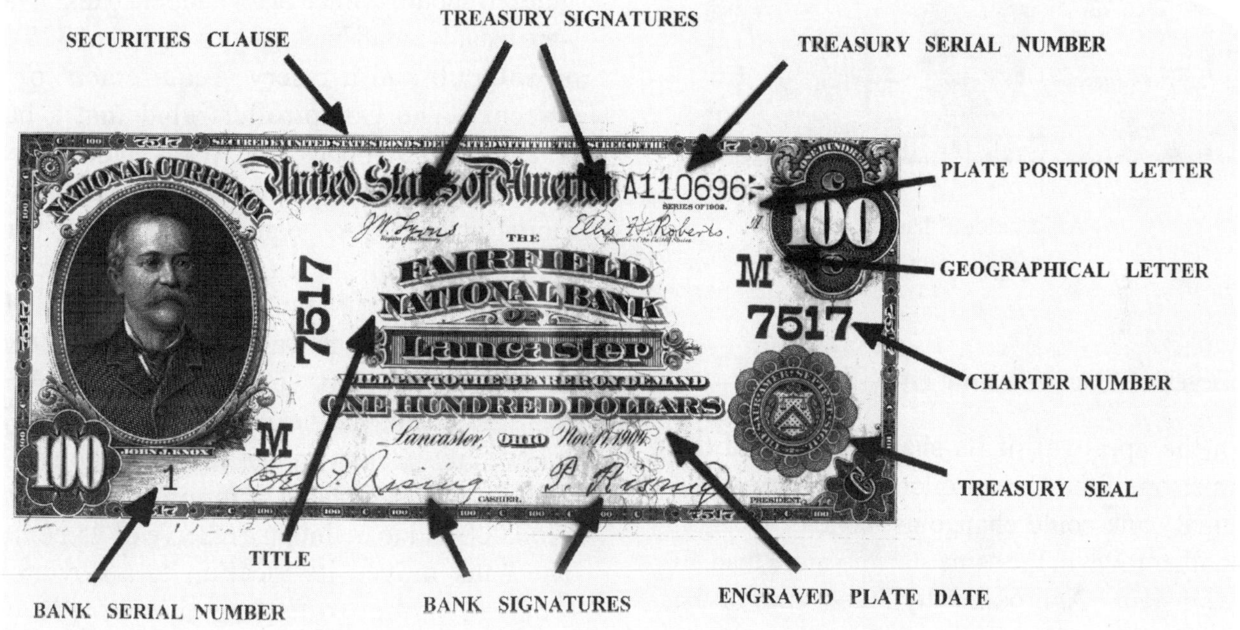

1. Title

Early on, Secretary Chase dictated that only **numerical titles** should be used (McCulloch 1888). That is, banks could use only the titles First National Bank, Second National Bank, etc. Many of the proud Eastern bankers refused to trade their long-established names for a number and declined to apply for national bank charters. They voiced their displeasure to Comptroller Hugh McCulloch who convinced Chase to permit greater flexibility in the choice of title. A name requirement was included in the Act of June 3, 1864. Henceforth the title need only include the words “national” and “bank”. An act of Congress permitted one exception; The Bank of North America became a national bank without the word “national” in its title.

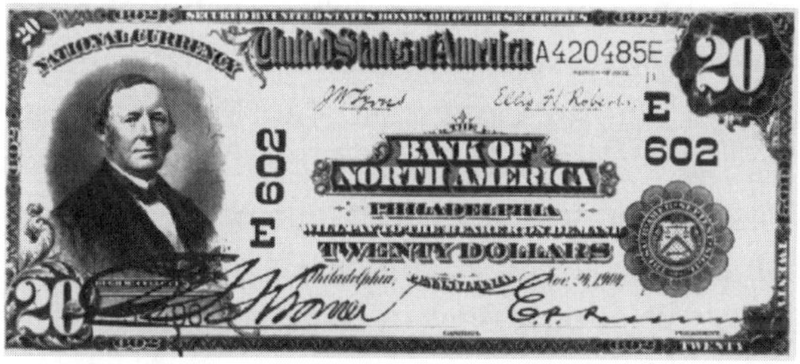

The exception to the rule.

Forbidden Titles

The Act of May 24, 1926 forbade the use of the words “United States”, “Federal”, or “Reserve” in the bank title. A grandfather clause permitted existing banks to continue using these words in their titles. Some collectors seek to assemble a collection of these “forbidden titles”. The word

"Reserve" was used in the title of four note-issuing national banks. The word "Federal" was used by six national banks and "United States" was used by thirty three national banks.

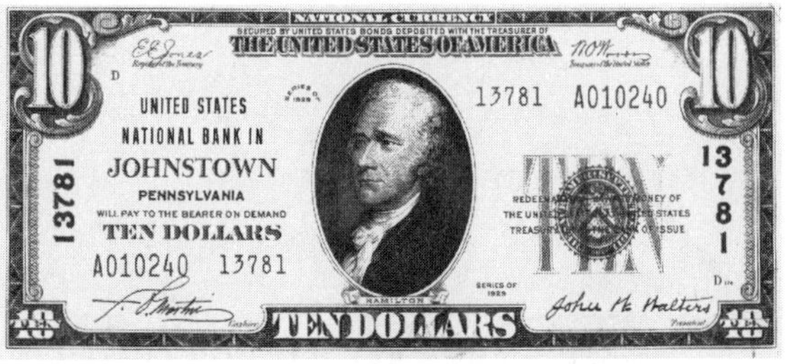

A "forbidden" title

Changes of Location and Title

With the approval of its shareholders and the permission of the Comptroller of the Currency, a national bank could change its name or location to another town in the same state no more than 30 miles distant. Approximately 10 per cent of the note-issuing national banks changed their title at least once, mostly when they took on trust company responsibilities.

There are four instances where national banks moved across state lines, actions which required special acts of Congress. In 1873, The East Chester National Bank of Mount Vernon, New York moved to Evansville, Indiana, changing its name to the German National Bank. In 1874, The Citizens National Bank of Hagerstown, Maryland moved to Washington, DC, changing its name to The Citizens National Bank of Washington City, DC.

Two other change-of-state moves amounted to little more than crossing the street. In 1897, The Interstate National Bank of Kansas City, Kansas changed its location to Kansas City, Missouri. In 1906, The American National Bank of Graham, Virginia changed its name and location to The American National Bank of Bluefield, West Virginia.

In all four cases there was no change of charter number and national bank notes were issued with both the old and new titles.

A national bank was free to move its location within the town or city in which it was located with the approval of the shareholders and the Comptroller. However, as cities grew they often annexed suburbs which had a national bank. These were usually small banks with a capital of $25,000 or $50,000 and a reserve requirement of 15 percent. The Comptroller ruled that a bank organized in a suburb which was later annexed could move its location only if it increased its capital and reserves required of national banks organized within the city. One particular case involved the First National Bank of Capitol Hill, Oklahoma. The bank was organized in 1909 with a capital of $25,000. The town of Capitol Hill was subsequently annexed by Oklahoma City, a reserve city. Banks organized in Oklahoma City were required to have a minimum capital of $200,000 and to maintain a reserve of 25 percent. The bank moved its location to a downtown location without meeting the reserve city requirements. The Comptroller sued for forfeiture of its charter. The bank responded by liquidating in July 1913.

In one instance a special act of Congress allowed a national bank to change its charter number. The Third National Bank of Cincinnati, Ohio received charter number 20 when it was organized in 1863. It was reorganized in 1882 as Charter 2730. In 1908 it merged with the Fifth National Bank of Cincinnati which held charter number 2798. The new bank changed its title to The Fifth-Third National Bank and did business under charter number 2798. In 1913 a special act of Congress allowed the Fifth-Third National Bank to take charter number 20, the number originally assigned to the Third National Bank. The prestige of a low charter number was not to be ignored!

Geographical location or local industry often provided inspiration for a bank title. The titles chosen show us that bankers exercised their imaginations and bared their vanities.

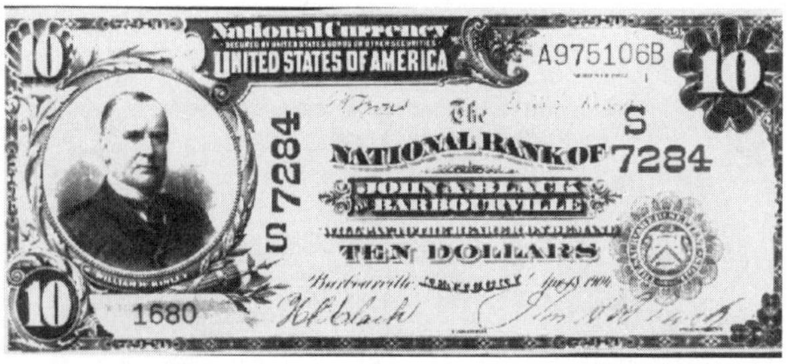

John A. Black signed this note as President of the bank bearing his name.

Local industry often was reflected in a national bank title.

Oil wells are still operating in the area near Sistersville, West Virginia

2. Charter Number

Each national bank was assigned an identification number, called a **charter number**. Most national bank notes have the charter number overprinted on them. The Act of June 20, 1874 required that charter numbers be imprinted on national bank notes. The imprinted charter number made it easier to sort notes turned in for redemption.

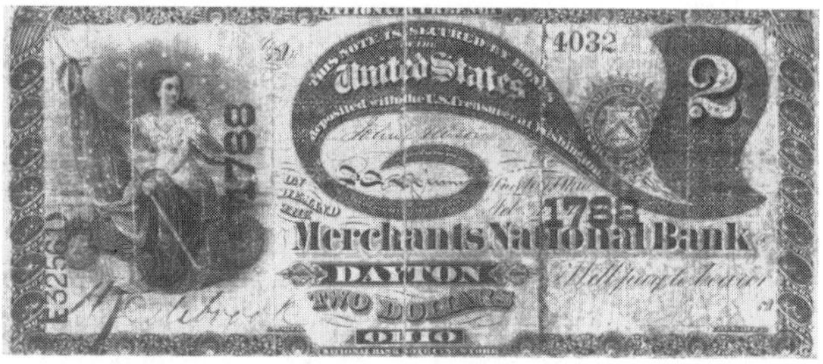

Two notes issued by the same bank. The note above - with charter number imprinted - also carries the higher serial number, showing that it was issued later than the note below which lacks the charter number.

Portion of a Series 1882 note showing the engraved charter number at two of six border positions.

The Act of July 12, 1882, included provisions for new national currency designs. The new designs have the charter number engraved at six positions on the faces of the notes. This aided in the redemption of pieces of notes.

Small size nationals have the charter number overprinted twice in black. In 1933 the charter number overprinting was changed, giving us the so-called "Type 2" notes. On Type 2 notes the charter number is overprinted twice in black and twice in brown.

Type 1 note at top has the charter number twice in black. Type 2 note at bottom has the charter number twice in black and twice in brown.

3. Bank Signatures

The Act of February 25, 1863 required that national bank notes be signed by the Cashier and the President or Vice President of the bank. The Act of July 28, 1892 changed this requirement, allowing redemption of notes without signatures or with forged signatures. Although it is not unusual to find the signature of an Assistant Cashier or a Vice President, most nationals bear the signatures of the Cashier and President. Some notes carry oversized signatures, referred to as "vanity" signatures.

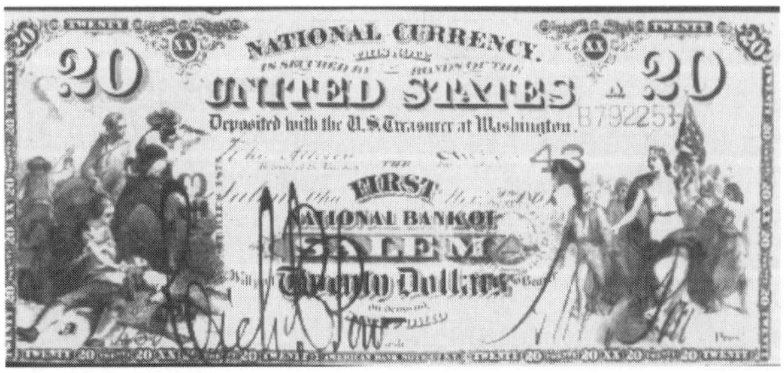

Vanity signatures adorn this national.

Early issues are pen signed. Later issues usually have rubber-stamped signatures. A few banks with large circulations found it economically feasible to send uncut sheets of their notes to a local print shop where the signatures were overprinted and the notes separated.

The Act of March 3, 1919 permitted the bank signatures to be engraved on the printing plate. Most nationals have two engraved guide lines near the bottom, above which the bank officer signatures were applied. The lines were removed when signatures were engraved on the plate.

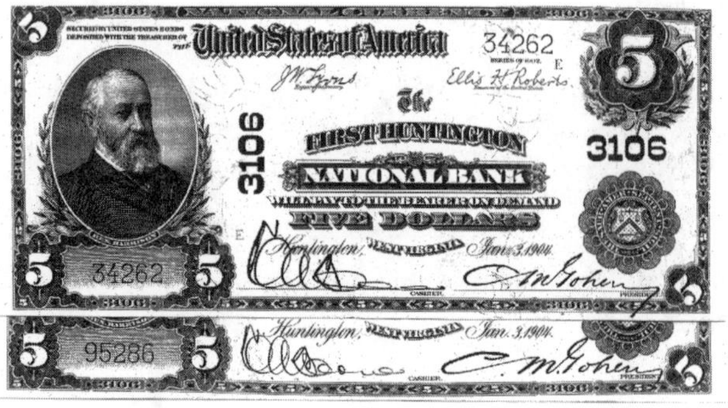

The upper note has overprinted signatures. The lower note has engraved signatures and lacks the guide lines.

All small size notes have printed facsimile signatures. In a few instances the same person was both Cashier and President and notes display dual signatures.

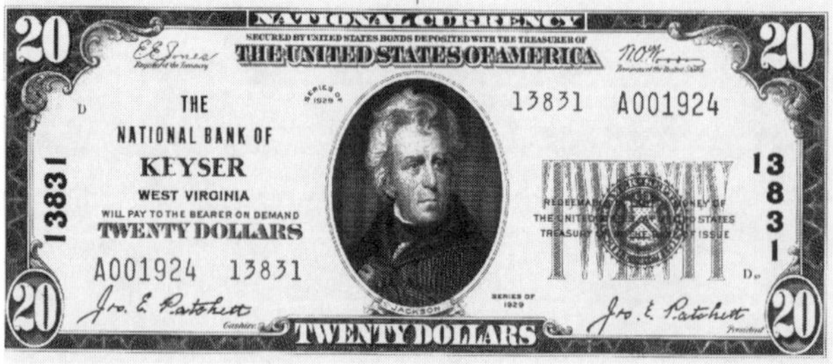

Joseph E Patchett served as Cashier and President of The National Bank of Keyser, West Virginia.

4. Treasury Signatures

The engraved signatures of the Register of the Treasury and of the Treasurer of the United States appear on all nationals. During the note-issuing period there were 34 different signature combinations. These combinations are listed in Table B, along with their terms in office. The signatures of the current Register and Treasurer were engraved on the plates of newly-organized banks. When politics or death caused a change in the office holders, signatures on existing plates were not changed. For example, the Lyons-Roberts signature combination appears on many notes printed between 1902 and 1929, even though the term of these officers ended in June, 1905. Peter Huntoon (Huntoon 1995) has untangled some of the procedures used in assigning Treasury signature combinations on large size notes. The Woods-Jones signature combination appears on all small size nationals.

Table B displays the Register-Treasurer combinations during the National Bank Era.

Table B. Register-Treasurer (1861-1933)

Register-Treasurer	Term Begins	Term Ends
Lucius E Chittenden - Francis E Spinner	Apr 17, 1861	Aug 10, 1864
S B Colby - Francis E Spinner	Aug 11, 1864	Sept 21, 1867
Noah L Jeffries - Francis E Spinner	Oct 5, 1867	Mar 15, 1869
John Allison - Francis E Spinner	Apr 3, 1869	June 30, 1875
John Allison - John C New	June 30, 1875	July 1, 1876
John Allison - A U Wyman	July 1, 1876	June 30, 1877
John Allison - James Gilfillan	July 1, 1877	Mar 23, 1878
Glenni W Scofield -James Gilfillan	Apr 1, 1878	May 20, 1881
Blanche Kelso Bruce - James Gilfillan	May 21, 1881	Mar 31, 1883
Blanche Kelso Bruce - A U Wyman	Apr 1, 1883	Apr 30, 1885
Blanche Kelso Bruce - Conrad N Jordan	May 1, 1885	June 5, 1885
William S Rosecrans - Conrad N Jordan	June 8, 1885	May 23, 1887
William S Rosecrans - James W Hyatt	May 24, 1887	May 10, 1889
William S Rosecrans - J N Huston	May 11, 1889	Apr 21, 1891
William S Rosecrans - Enos H Nebeker	Apr 25, 1891	May 31, 1893
William S Rosecrans - Daniel N Morgan	June 1, 1893	June 19, 1893
James F Tillman - Daniel N Morgan	July 1, 1893	June 30, 1897
James F Tillman - Ellis H Roberts	July 1, 1897	Dec 2, 1897
Blanche Kelso Bruce - Ellis H Roberts	Dec 3, 1897	Mar 17, 1898
Judson W Lyons - Ellis H Roberts	Apr 7, 1898	June 30, 1905
Judson H Lyons - Charles H Treat	July 1, 1905	Apr 1, 1906
William T Vernon - Charles H Treat	June 12, 1906	Oct 30, 1909
William T Vernon - Lee McClung	Nov 1, 1909	Mar 14, 1911
James C Napier - Lee McClung	Mar 15, 1911	Nov 21, 1912
James C Napier - Carmi A Thompson	Nov 22, 1912	Mar 31, 1913
James C Napier - John Burke	Apr 1, 1913	Oct 1, 1913
Gabe E Parker - John Burke	Oct 1, 1913	Dec 31, 1914
Houston B Teehee - John Burke	Mar 24, 1915	Nov 20, 1919
William J Elliott - John Burke	Nov 21, 1919	Jan 5, 1921
William J Elliott - Frank White	May 2, 1921	Jan 24, 1922
Harley V Speelman - Frank White	Jan 25, 1922	Sept 30, 1927
Walter O Woods - Frank White	Oct 1, 1927	May 1, 1928
Walter O Woods - H T Tate	May 31, 1928	Jan 17, 1929
Edward E Jones - Walter O Woods	Jan 22, 1929	May 31, 1933

5. Securities Clause

All nationals carry a securities clause on their face specifying the form of security backing them. From 1863 until 1908 national banks had to deposit United States bonds as security for their nationals. In 1908 the Aldrich-Vreeland emergency currency act was passed, allowing other securities to be used to back the issue of nationals.

These "other securities" included municipal and state bonds and certain types of commercial loans. The securities clause was changed on nationals issued between 1908 and 1915. In 1915 the Aldrich-Vreeland act expired after which only United States bonds could be used for security. In many instances plates with the "other securities" clause were used to print notes well after the expiration of the Aldrich-Vreeland act. The figure shows the two forms of the securities clause as they appear on Series 1882 nationals.

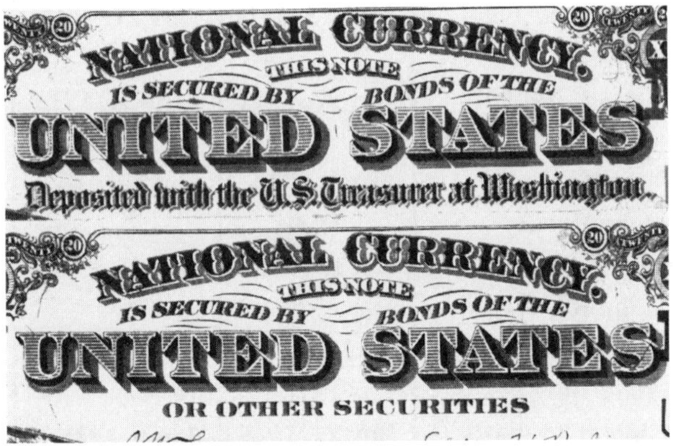

Top: Standard form of securities clause.
Bottom: Form authorized during the 1908-1915 period, when securities other than United States bonds could be used to back the issue of nationals.

6. Serial Numbers

Large size notes issued before September 1925 carry two different serial numbers. At the upper right is the **Treasury serial number**. This number reflects the running total of sheets of a particular plate combination printed for all banks

At the lower left is the **Bank serial number**. The Bank serial number reflects the running total of sheets of that plate combination printed for each particular bank. Beginning in September 1925, there is no Treasury serial number. Instead, the Bank serial number appears twice. On $1 and $2 nationals the Bank serial number is at the upper right and the Treasury serial number is at the left end of the note.

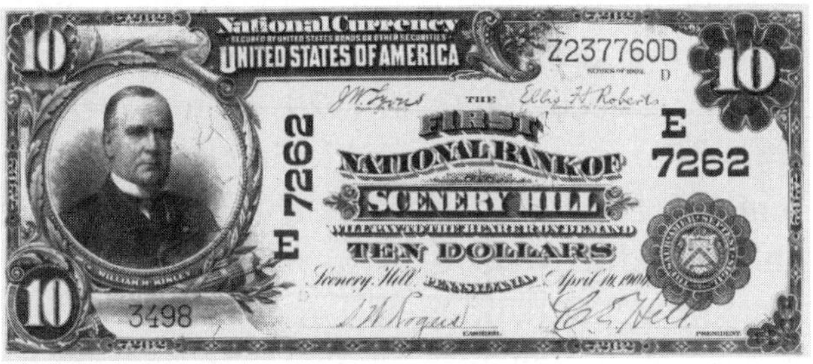

Above: A note issued before September 1925 bearing Treasury and bank serial numbers.
Below: A note issued after September 1925 with duplicate bank serial numbers.

Small size nationals were issued with two types of serial numbers. On Type 1 notes, issued between July 1929 and May 1933, the serials are **sheet** numbers which have a prefix and a suffix letter. On Type 2 notes, issued starting in May 1933, the serials are **note** numbers which have only a prefix letter.

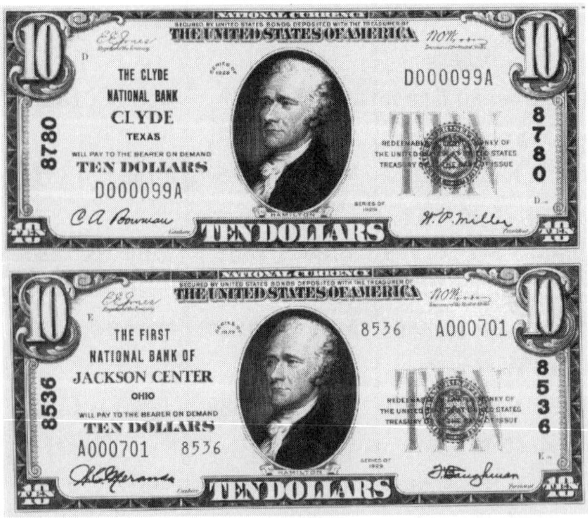

Top: Type 1 serial has prefix and suffix letters.
Bottom: Type 2 has prefix letter only.

7. Plate Position Letter

A **plate position letter**, sometimes referred to as a check letter, appears on the face of all nationals. This letter identifies the position of a note in the sheet. Thus, although the notes in a sheet of nationals carry the **same serial number**, each note of a particular denomination has a **different plate position letter.** As a result, no two notes in the sheet are identical. For example, the position letters A, B, C, and D were assigned to the first plate of 4-subject $5 notes. If a new plate was made to replace one that was worn out or damaged, new position letters were assigned. When a new plate was made the position letters were advanced to E, F, G, and H.

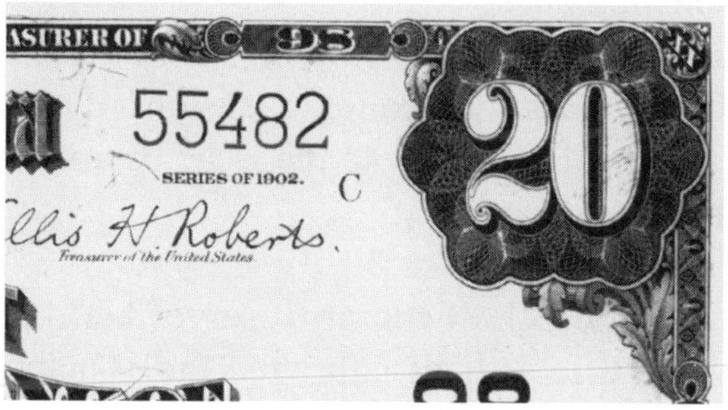

The plate position letter "C" appears twice on the face of this national. Locations vary with the series and denomination.

8. Engraved Plate Date

All large size nationals carry an engraved plate date on their face. Most plate dates are either the date when the bank was organized, or a 20-year or 40-year anniversary of its organization, or the date marking a title change (Huntoon 1995). Collectors who use the plate date as their focus have uncovered many special dates, including January 1, February 14, February 29, March 17, and December 25. A personal challenge for date-minded collectors is to locate a note whose plate date coincides with their birth day.

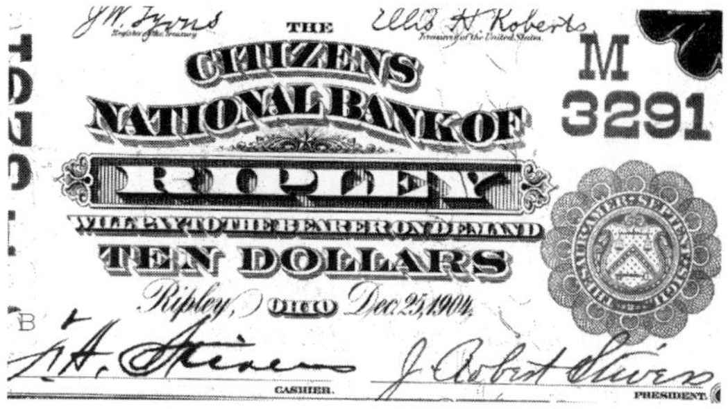

Christmas date appears on this Ripley, Ohio 1902 Red Seal.

9. Treasury Seal

The seal adopted by the Treasury appears on all nationals. The size, color, and surrounding embellishments changed during the note-issuing period, but the basic design remained unchanged. On the earliest nationals the seal is red and is surrounded by a circle with 34 spikes, one for each state of the Union. In 1882 a new series of note designs brought a change of the seal color, first to brown, and then to blue. In 1902 a third series of note designs used red seals, which were later changed to blue. Small size notes have a brown seal.

Treasury Seals on small size (UL), Brown Back (UR), Series 1902 (LL), and Original Series (LR)

10. Geographical Letter

The Gold Standard Act of March 14, 1900 spawned the organization of a flood of new banks, making the task of sorting notes in the redemption bureau increasingly burdensome. To aid the sorting, the country was divided into six geographical areas. A **geographical letter** corresponding to the area in which the bank was located was overprinted on the face of the notes. The table shows the geographical letters and the regions they encompass.

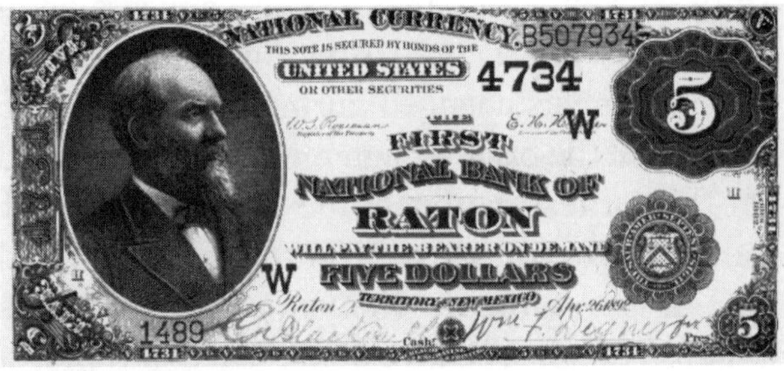

The geographical letter made it easier to sort notes sent for redemption. The "W" overprinted twice on this New Mexico Territory note signifies its Western location.

Notes issued between March 17, 1902 and March 14, 1924 were overprinted with the appropriate geographical letter. The use of geographical letters ended because more efficient sorting methods rendered them unnecessary.

Letter	Area	States
N	New England	CT, ME, MA, NH, RI, VT
E	Eastern	DE, DC, MD, NJ, NY, PA
M	Midwest	IL, IN, IA, MI, MN, MO, OH, WI
S	Southern	AL, AR, FL, GA, KY, LA, MS, NC, PR, SC, TN, TX, VA, WV
W	Western	CO, KS, MT, NE, NM, ND, OK, SD, WY
P	Pacific	AK, AZ, CA, HI, ID, NV, OR, UT, WA

The Eleven Types of National Bank Notes

In this section we describe and illustrate the distinctive features used to classify the eleven types of national bank notes. Our story of national bank note types is punctuated by references to various legislative acts which affected the notes issued. Legislation during the note-issuing period had three main effects on national banks and the notes they issued.

1) Some legislative acts changed the requirements for organizing a national bank. For the most part these acts made it easier to form a national bank or made it possible to increase the circulation of an existing bank.

2) Certain acts allowed for extensions of a bank's corporate life, and led to the issue of notes with different designs.

3) One act, the Federal Reserve Act, had an adverse effect. It discouraged the issuance of national bank notes and marked the beginning of the end of the national bank era.

THE FIRST ISSUE OF NATIONALS

The National Currency Act of February 25, 1863 provided for organization of national banks with a capital of $50,000 or more. The act endowed a national bank with a corporate lifespan of 20 years or less, beginning with the **date of the act**. A total of 489 banks organized under the provisions of the act. Of these, 98 banks chose a 19-year lifespan, starting from their organization date. This unfortunate choice would force many of them to liquidate 19 years later because Congress did not approve legislation extending their charters in a timely fashion. The problems facing these banks in 1882 will be touched on in more detail later.

The banks were required to purchase United States Bonds. By depositing these bonds with the Treasurer of the United States a bank could circulate national bank notes in amounts up to 90 percent of the value of the bonds. National bank notes in the denominations of $5, $10, $20, $50, $100, $500, and $1000 were authorized, and all denominations were issued. The act permitted both national banks and state banks to purchase bonds and to circulate such notes. However, no state bank exercised the privilege, which was withdrawn by the Act of June 3, 1864.

An important provision of the Act of June 3, 1864 concerned the duration and starting time for corporate lifespan. The act specified a 20-year lifetime beginning on the **date of organization** of the bank. This change in the starting time for the charter "clock" remained in effect throughout the note-issuing era. The act also authorized four new denominations, $1, $2, $3, and $10,000. Only the $1 and $2 denominations were issued. The Act of June 3, 1864 also stipulated that the bonds deposited with the Treasurer must be United States interest bearing bonds.

The Act of March 3, 1865 levied an annual tax of 10 percent on all state bank notes in circulation after July 1, 1866. This drove these notes to extinction and ended the state bank era.

Laws alone cannot tell the story of national bank notes - there are many human facets as well. It was the inspired efforts of Spencer Morton Clark which resulted in the beautiful designs of our first national bank notes. Clark is best known as the person responsible for the law forbidding the image of a living American from appearing on obligations of the United States government. Clark placed his own image on the 5 cent note of the third issue of fractional currency and thereby incurred the displeasure of Congress.

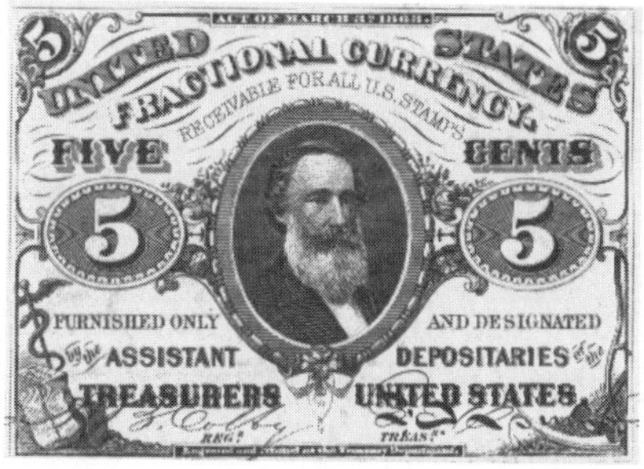

Spencer M. Clark as he appears on our fractional currency.

Fortunately for collectors, this move by Clark came after he spearheaded efforts that produced the first nationals. Clark suggested note designs that would inform and inspire the American public. His suggestions for a "National Picture Currency" led to the adopted designs, which include paintings in the United States Capitol (Morris, 1963, 1964).

The original designs were used for three series of notes; Original Series notes, Series 1875 notes, and National Gold Bank notes.

I. Original Series Notes (designated as "Original Series" in this guide)

Original Series notes were printed from 1863 to 1875 in denominations of $1, $2, $5, $10, $20, $50, $100, $500, and $1000. The earliest issues of original series notes did not bear the bank charter number.

Most Original Series notes show a seal at the left side of the back. In most cases this is the state seal. Some territorial notes show the territorial seal, but most depict an American eagle.

II. Series 1875 Notes (designated as "Series 1875" in this guide)

The basic designs of Series 1875 notes are the same as those of the Original Series. The Act of June 30, 1874 required that notes carry the bank charter number. On Series 1875 notes this number is imprinted twice, in red, on the face of the note. Additionally, Series 1875 notes have a red surcharge "Series 1875" next to one of the charter number imprints. This overprint was simply a way of indicating that note production had moved to the Bureau of Engraving and Printing.

The illustrations show faces and backs of Original Series and Series 1875 notes. Hessler (1996) has identified the titles of the vignettes appearing on the faces and backs of the notes and the artisans who designed and engraved them.

Three bank note companies shared in the production of the Original Series notes. The $5 notes were printed by the Continental Bank Note Co. The American Bank Note Co. printed the $10, $20, $50 and $100 notes. The $500 and $1000 notes were printed by the National Bank Note Co. The $1 and $2 notes resulted from cooperative efforts of the American and National companies. These three companies were based in New York City, where the notes were printed and overprinted with the bank serial number. The notes were then shipped to Washington, D.C. where the Bureau imprinted the Treasury seal and the Treasury serial number.

Concordia

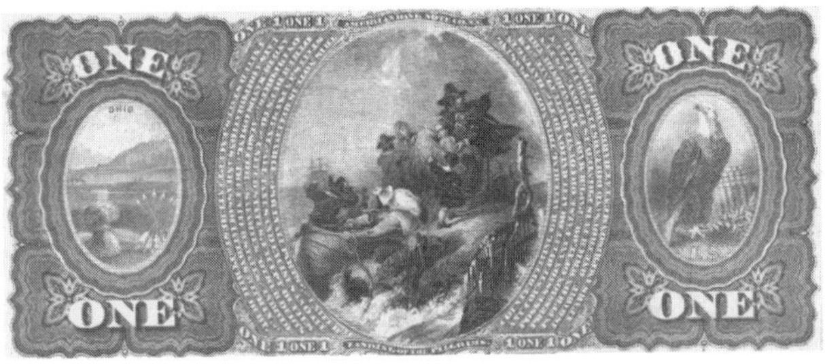

The Landing of the Pilgrims

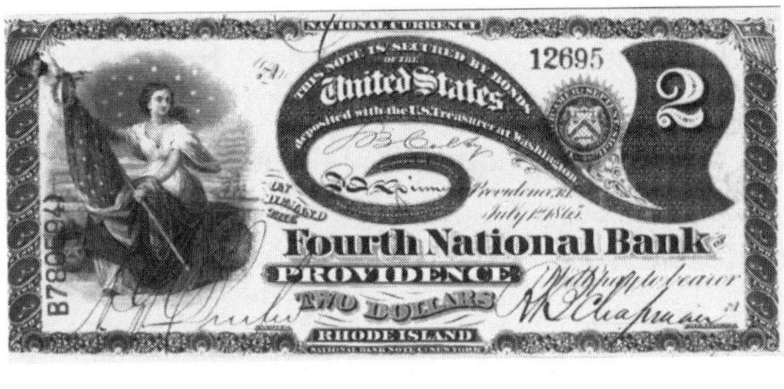

Stars and Stripes

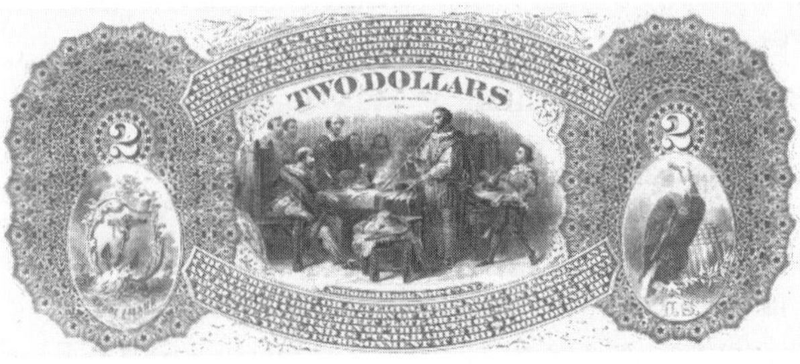

Sir Walter Raleigh Exhibiting Corn and Tobacco

Columbus in Sight of Land and America Presented to the Old World

The Landing of Columbus

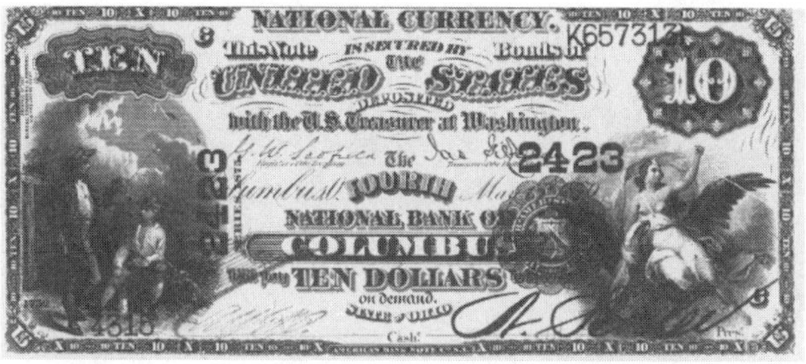

Franklin and Electricity and America Seizing Lightning

DeSoto Discovering the Mississippi

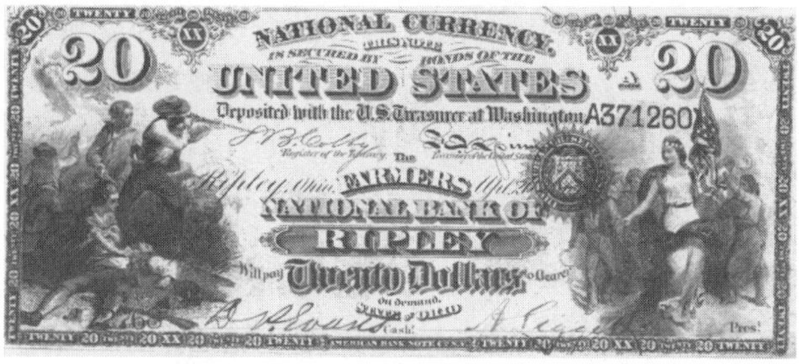

Battle of Lexington and Loyalty

Baptism of Pocahontas

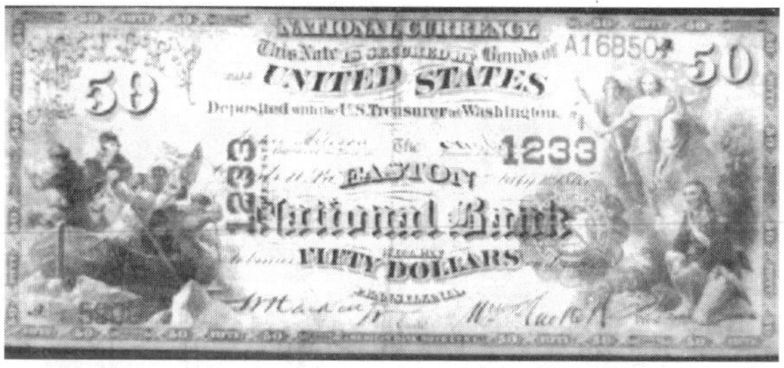

Washington Crossing the Delaware and Washington at Prayer at Valley Forge

Embarkation of the Pilgrims

Battle of Lake Erie and The Union

Signing of the Declaration of Independence

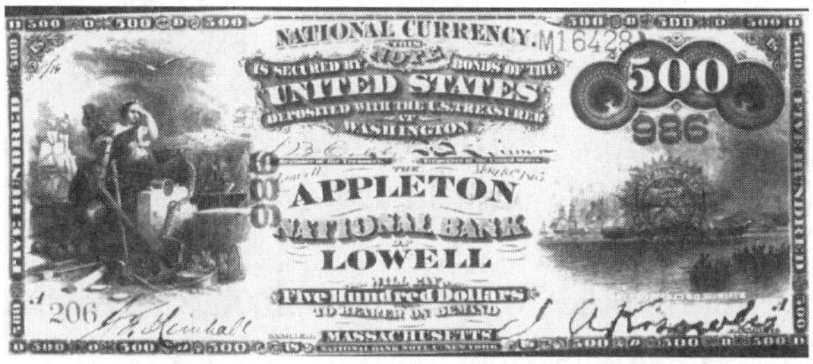

Civilization and Arrival of the Sirius

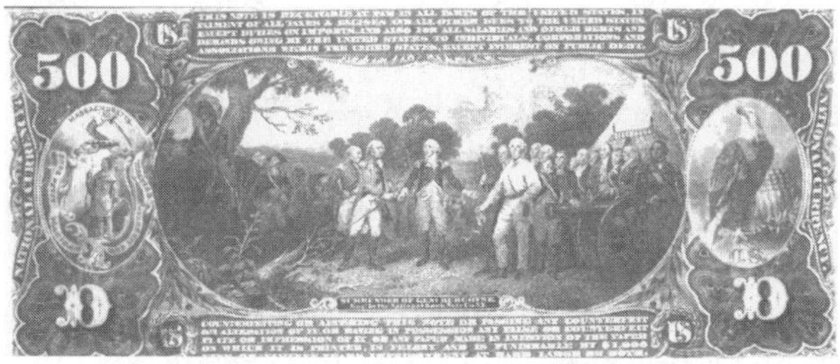

Surrender of Burgoyne to Gates

General Scott's Entrance into Mexico City

Washington Resigning his Commission

The First National Bank of Washington, D.C. (Charter 26) was the first bank to receive and circulate nationals. The first shipment consisted of 1000 sheets of four $5 notes and was issued by the Comptroller on December 21, 1863. One of the $5 notes from the first sheet has survived. It carries bank serial number 1 and Treasury serial number 9.

Other notable "firsts" were the First National Bank of Davenport, Iowa, the first national bank to open for business (June 29, 1863), and the First National Bank of Philadelphia, Pennsylvania, which received charter number 1 on June 20, 1863.

Never-Issued Series of 1873 Nationals

The expense of sorting worn or mutilated notes before returning them to the Treasury for redemption ultimately fell to the large banks in New York and other money centers. This was an expense that the banks did not care to bear so they simply put worn and mutilated notes back into circulation. Congress got fed up with the complaints and lit a fire under the Treasury with an appropriation contained in the Act of March 3, 1873. Congress authorized the expenditure of $600,000 for the purpose of "replacing worn and mutilated circulating notes of national banking associations, and for engraving and preparing, in such manner and of such form and design as the Secretary of the Treasury may prescribe, new circulating notes for such associations to replace notes of a design and denomination now successfully counterfeited.....". The legislation specified that the national banks should bear the cost of preparing the new plates.

In his annual report of 1873 the Comptroller of the Currency, John J. Knox, complained that the appropriation was passed "without report from any committee and no recommendation was made by the Treasury Department for the authorization of a new issue of national bank notes at the expense of the national banks." He argued that new designs would not solve the problem. So long as the banks were to bear the expense of redeeming worn notes, they would avoid that expense by putting them back into circulation.

Comptroller John J Knox appears on the $100 Series 1902 nationals.

The Secretary of the Treasury ordered that new designs be prepared. Meanwhile, Comptroller Knox took steps to avoid the necessity of using them. Knox pointed out that counterfeiting was not a serious problem, especially since the plates used to produce most of them had been seized by the Secret Service. Rather than replace all of the nationals, Knox proposed a simpler and far less costly solution - suspend further issues of those notes which had been successfully counterfeited. The production of $10 notes was suspended from October 14, 1873 until June 29, 1874.

The Act of June 20, 1874 contained a provision which helped alleviate the filthy money problem. It specified that notes unfit for circulation "when received by any assistant treasurer, or at any designated depository of the United States, be forwarded to the Treasurer of the United States for redemption..." The large city banks were "designated depositories" and this provision allowed them to send **unsorted** notes to the Treasury. If the Treasury was to take over the sorting tasks they needed clerks to do the job. The Act of March 3, 1875 contained a provision authorizing the Treasurer and Comptroller to employ clerical forces for the job of redeeming circulating notes. This move gave the Treasury a redemption agency with the muscle needed to remove worn and mutilated nationals from circulation and replace them with new notes. The Act of June 20, 1874 had provided that charter numbers should be overprinted on all national bank notes issued thereafter. This greatly simplified the new redemption agency's task of sorting the notes.

Proof of a never-issued note prepared following passage of the Act of March 3, 1873 (National Numismatic Collections).

Although new designs for circulating notes were engraved by the National Bank Note Co., and trial impressions were made, none was ever issued.

In summary, Congress solved the problem of filthy circulating notes by having the Treasury set up a redemption agency to take over the task of sorting notes. This satisfied the banks who, no longer having to bear the expense, were happy to send in worn and mutilated notes. The Treasury satisfied the public by replacing nearly two-thirds of the circulating nationals in one year.

Private to Federal

In July, 1875 there began a shift of production from the private bank note companies in New York City to the Bureau of Engraving and Printing in Washington, DC. The face plates for the Series of 1875 notes were sent to the Bureau of Engraving and Printing. The backs were printed in New York, then sent to the Bureau where the faces were printed and imprinted with seal, charter number, and serial numbers. The Continental Bank Note Co., which printed the $5 notes, lost its contract and transferred both face and back plates to the Bureau. In an unusual arrangement, the Columbian Bank Note Co. in Washington was then contracted to print the central vignette on the backs of the $5 notes. All other printing and overprinting operations for the $5 notes were performed at the Bureau. In 1877 contracts with the private bank note companies expired and the Bureau assumed all phases of currency production.

The Act of March 3, 1875 contained two significant specifications. It required that notes be printed on a "distinctive" paper. Between 1879 and 1935 The Crane Paper Co. of Dalton, Massachusetts supplied all of the paper used for our national currency. The act also specified that no notes with denominations of less than $5 should circulate after the resumption of specie payments. On January 1, 1879 specie payments resumed. Issues of $1 and $2 nationals ended 21 days later. On January 22, 1879 there was a flurry of shipments of $1 and $2 notes to several hundred banks. The $1 and $2 nationals had a relatively short life span of 14 years, the first notes having been issued April 1, 1865 to The First National Bank of Akron, Ohio.

Black Charter Numbers

A rare charter number variety appears on $5 notes of the Original Series and Series 1875 issues for a few banks. These rare notes are referred to as **black charter number** notes. They were printed from plates which had the charter number **engraved** on the face plate. The charter number, like the rest of the engraved face design, appears in black. Research by Huntoon, Raymond, and Hickman (1984) revealed that the black charter number plates originated at the Continental Bank Note Co. between November 15, 1873 and May 15, 1874. Black charter number notes printed by the Continental Bank Note Co. were Original Series.

In 1875 all Continental plates were transferred to the Bureau of Engraving and Printing. The Bureau altered the plates by adding its logo and by changing the Treasury signatures. Most black charter number notes known to collectors are Series 1875, and were produced at the Bureau.

Black charter number $5 notes are known for the following eight banks (numbers in parentheses indicate the numbers of notes reported):

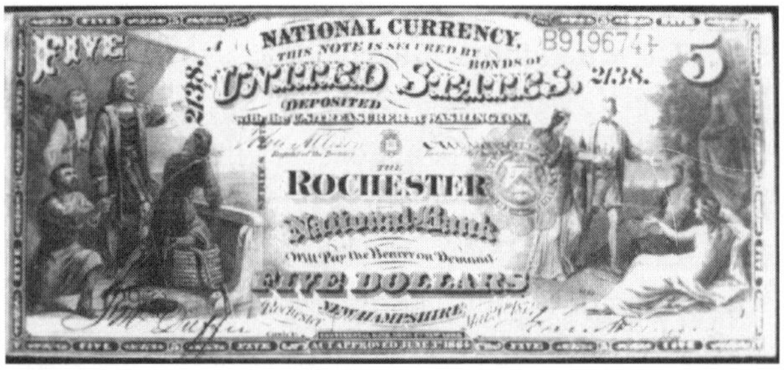

Black charter number - a rare variety which has the charter number engraved on the face plate.

Ch 1830 Merchants NB, Minneapolis, MN (1)
Ch 2129 First NB of Central City,
Colorado Territory (16)
Ch 2130 First NB of Red Oak, IA (3)
Ch 2132 Kellogg Citizens NB, Green Bay, WI (2)
Ch 2137 First NB of Boyertown, PA (5)
Ch 2138 Rochester NB, Rochester, NH (4)
Ch 2141 NB of Pontiac, IL (5)
Ch 2142 NB of Schwenksville, PA (1)

Black charter number notes are known to have been issued by the following two banks, although no notes have been reported:

Ch 1644 FNB of Houston, TX
Ch 2135 Commercial NB, Charlotte, NC

The research of Huntoon, Raymond, and Hickman indicates that black charter number notes were probably issued by the following four banks:

Ch 2131 Green Lane NB, Green Lane, PA
Ch 2133 First NB, DePere, WI
Ch 2134 Peoples NB, Pueblo, Colorado Territory
Ch 2140 First NB, Golden, Colorado Territory

III. National Gold Bank Notes (designated as "Gold Bank Note" in this guide)

Only a few west coast national banks were organized under the original National Currency Act. The West was hard money country - gold and silver dominated the circulating media. All forms of paper money were suspect - whether private banknotes or federal issues. The western preference for gold inspired the National Gold Banks, authorized by the Act of July 12, 1870.

National Gold Bank Notes were issued in the denominations of $5, $10, $20, $50, $100, $500, and $1000. The face designs of the Gold Bank notes are very similar to the Original Series faces - with one prominent distinction. Boldly displayed on the face is the phrase "Redeemable in Gold Coin".

The central vignette on the back, common to all denominations, shows a group of gold coins. Of the ten National Gold Banks that issued notes, nine were organized in California. The Kidder National Gold Bank of Boston, Massachusetts (Charter 1699) received $50, $100, $500, and $1000 gold bank notes, but records indicate that all were returned to the Comptroller of the Currency. Proof impressions of the faces of the $50 and $100 notes of the Kidder bank were sold at public auction in

1980. The Kidder bank was the only National Gold Bank to issue $1000 Gold Bank notes. A total of 610 $500 Gold Bank notes were issued by three California Gold Banks, but none is known to collectors.

National Gold Bank notes were issued in both the "Original Series" and the "Series 1875" formats. Most were printed on a yellowish paper - designed to remind the public that they were "as good as gold" - they could be redeemed in gold coin.

Gold Bank notes have survived in a significantly higher proportion than have their regular national bank note counterparts. Unfortunately the average condition of the survivors is deplorably low. The fact that the notes were redeemable in gold at a time when other forms of federal paper were only "promises" probably explains their longevity and excessive wear. Very few of the approximately 800 known Gold Bank notes are in conditions better than Fine.

National Gold Banks never had any real impact on western banking, in part because the law under which they operated put the Gold Banks at a disadvantage to other national banks. The Gold Banks secured their notes with United States Bonds, but could issue notes only up to 80 percent of the value of the bonds, in contrast to the 90 percent limit for regular national banks. Furthermore, a National Gold Bank was required to keep on hand gold or silver coin with a value equal to 25 percent of its outstanding note circulation. It soon became clear that gold-backed national currency had no special allure to the public. Bankers seeking to organize national banks wisely opted for regular national bank status. The final blow to Gold Bank notes came on January 1, 1879 when the government resumed specie payments. The act made all federal paper money redeemable in silver or gold coin. **Gold Bank notes no longer enjoyed a preferred status**. The Act of February 14, 1880 permitted National Gold Banks to convert to regular National Banks. The existing Gold Banks wisely exercised the privilege, changing their titles to show the change in their status.

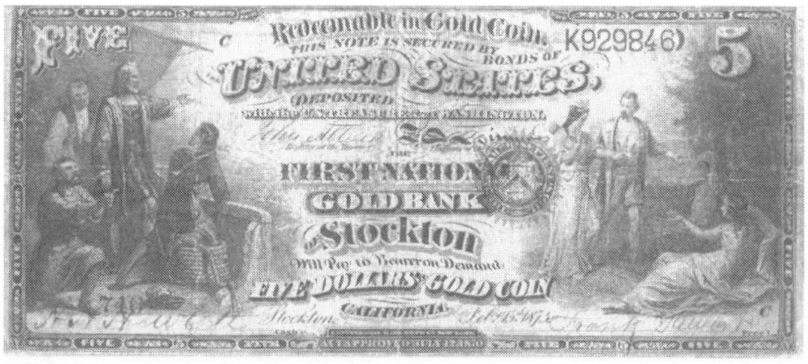

"Redeemable in Gold Coin" distinguishes Gold Bank Notes from other First Issue notes.

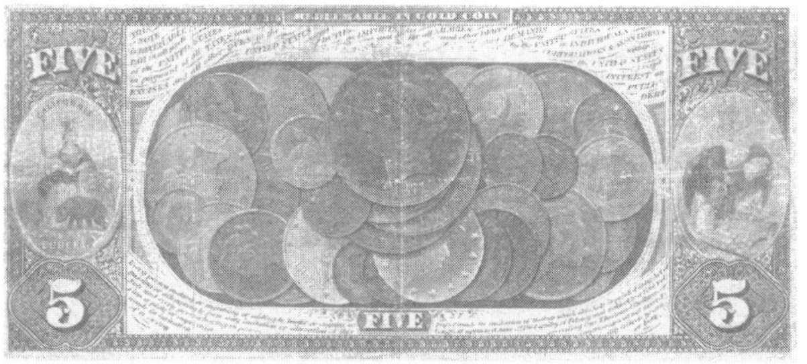

The gold coins vignette on the backs of Gold Bank Notes is the same for all denominations.

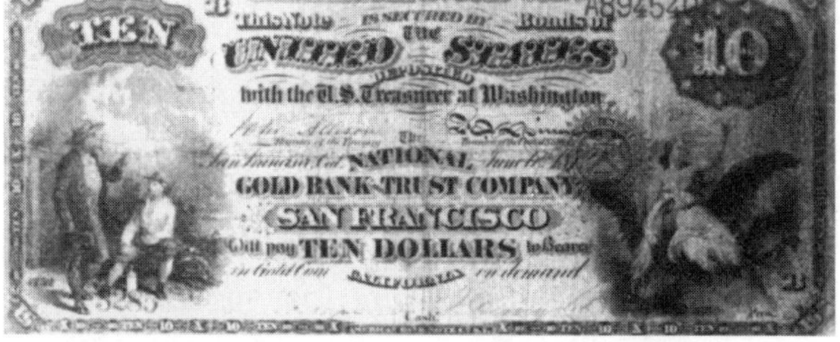

(National Numismatic Collections)

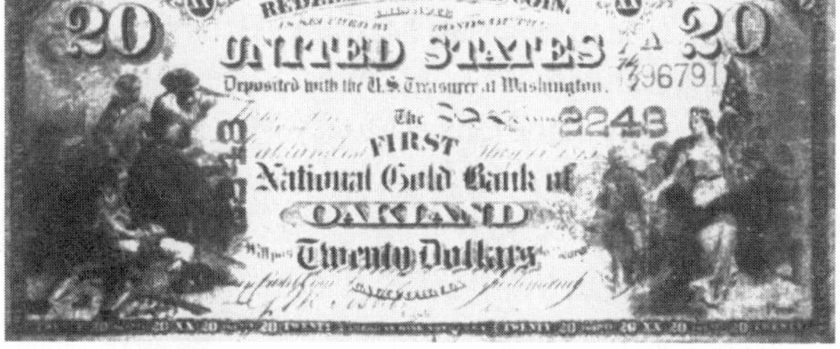

(National Numismatic Collections)

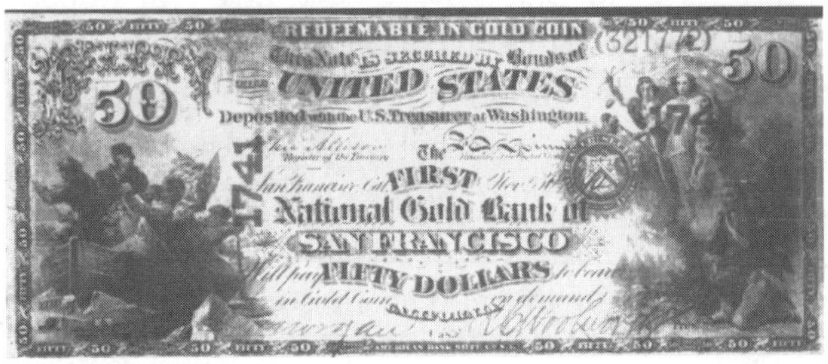

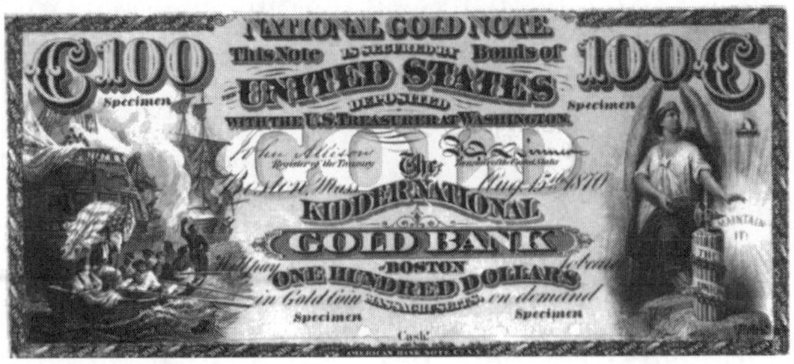

Specimen of Kidder Gold Bank $100

The $500 and $1000 Nationals

In an era when $1000 might exceed the annual income of a working person, the $500 and $1000 national bank notes represented enormous purchasing power. These two denominations offer a challenge to the collector and to the researcher. The Comptroller records tell the facts but not the story.

The first $500 notes were delivered to the Comptroller October 14, 1864, for The Merchants National Bank of Boston (Charter 475). The first $1000 notes were delivered November 28, 1864, for two New York City banks, The Fourth National Bank (Charter 290) and The Ninth National Bank (Charter 387). Deliveries of $500 and $1000 nationals ended in April, 1884.

The table shows the breakdown of issues by state. A total of 24,579 $500 notes and 7,454 $1000 notes were issued. A total of 173 $500 notes are officially unredeemed. Four notes have been reported - two from the same bank! Three of the survivors are well known to collectors:

$500 Original Series. Appleton NB of Lowell, MA (Ch 986). Treasury serial M16428, Bank Serial 206. Colby-Spinner Treasury signatures. Plate date May 10, 1865. Formerly in the Chase Money Museum, this note is now part of the Smithsonian Institution National Numismatic Collections.

$500 Original Series. Appleton NB of Lowell, MA (Ch 986). Treasury serial M16419, Bank Serial 197. Colby-Spinner Treasury signatures. Plate date May 10, 1865. This note also was once part of the Chase collection.

$500 Series 1875. First NB of New York, NY (Ch 29). Treasury Serial A1815, Bank Serial 865. Allison-New signatures. Plate date May 25, 1876. Ex-Amon Carter collection.

$500 and $1000 Nationals by State

State	$500	$1000
Alabama	292	
California	610	
Louisiana	720	
Maine	569	
Maryland	910	142
Massachusetts	10,948	1,567
New York	8,610	5,367
Pennsylvania	1,405	248
Rhode Island	515	130
Totals	**24,579**	**7,454**

Treasury records indicate that 21 $1000 notes are unredeemed, but no survivors have been confirmed. There is strong anecdotal evidence that one $1000 national is held by a government institution and there are rumors of another note held privately. It is extremely unlikely that 21 of the issued 7,454 notes were lost or accidentally destroyed. In fact, there is quantitative evidence that only about one note in every one thousand notes of that era suffered the fate of being lost or

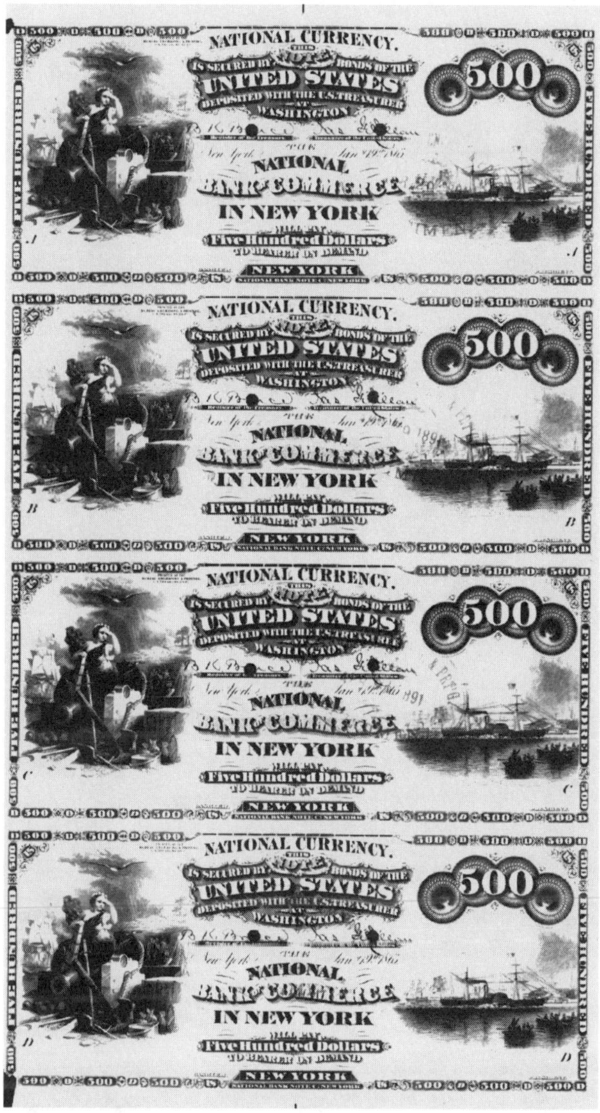

Proof sheet for the 4x$500 combination
(National Numismatic Collections)

destroyed. This suggests that there should be several survivors. It has been suggested that some $500 and $1000 nationals were redeemed and destroyed with Silver Certificates and United States Notes of the same denominations, that is, that they were not correctly accounted for in the Comptroller's records. Time may tell.

A total of 685 $500 Gold Bank notes were issued, 75 to the Kidder bank and 610 to three California banks. None is known to collectors. Considering the relatively high survival rate of Gold Bank notes it would not be a total surprise if a $500 Gold Bank note surfaced.

SERIES 1882 NOTES

The Act of July 12, 1882 provided for a series of new note designs with denominations of $5, $10, $20, $50, and $100. Existing national banks had their corporate lives extended 20 years. Newly organized banks and those extended began receiving the new Series 1882 notes.

Congressional actions resulted in **three distinct types of Series 1882 notes**, 1882 Brown Backs, 1882 Date Backs, and 1882 Value Backs.

IV. Series 1882 Brown Back Notes (designated as "Brown Back" in this guide)

The illustrations show faces and backs of each Brown Back denomination. The name stems from the fact that the backs are printed in brown. The Treasury seal on the face is also brown. On the back, the charter number is printed in skeleton form in blue green. Most Brown Backs show the state seal at the left side of the back. Exceptions include Nebraska, on which the territorial seal was used, and Iowa, which used an eagle on early Brown Back issues. Most territorial Brown Backs do not have a territorial seal. They have an American eagle in panels at both ends. Exceptions include Idaho Territory Brown Backs which do carry the territorial seal.

The charter number is printed in brown on the face of Brown Backs, and engraved six times around the border. The latter feature made it possible to identify the bank from parts of notes sent for redemption. "Series 1882" is overprinted in brown on the face of all denominations except the $5 notes.

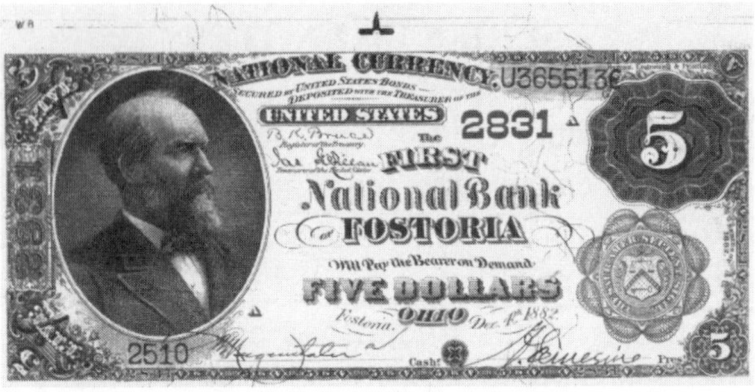

President James A. Garfield

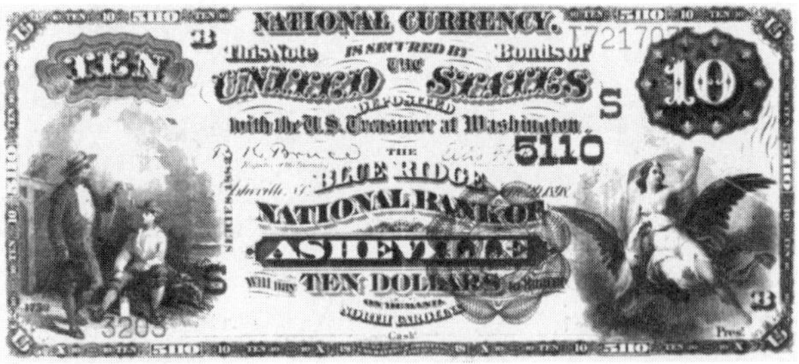

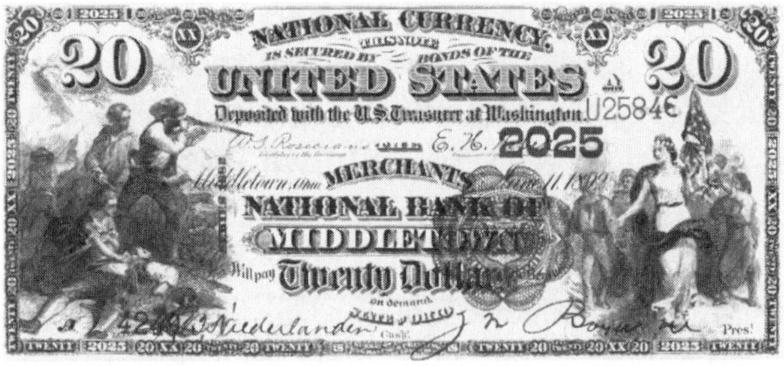

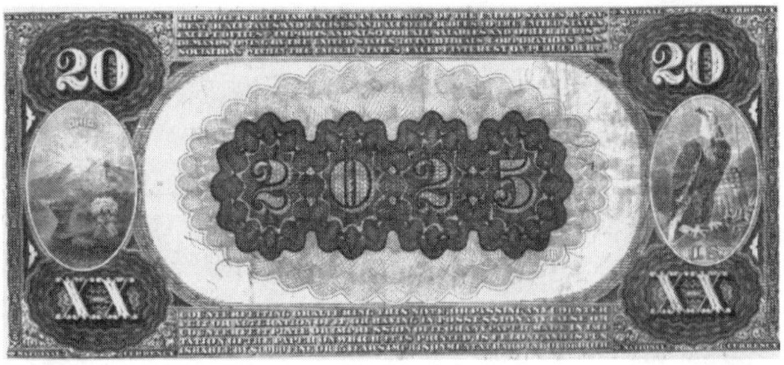

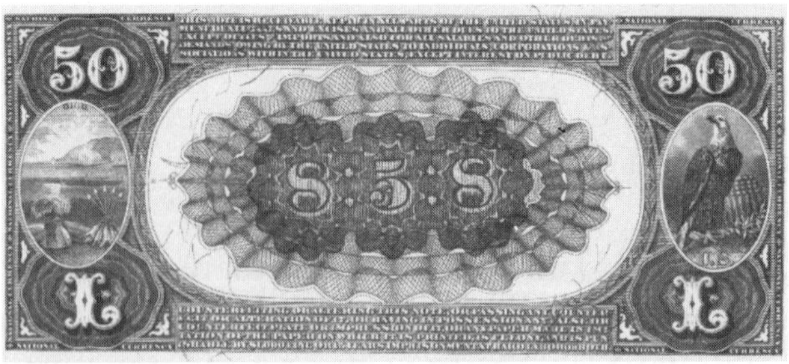

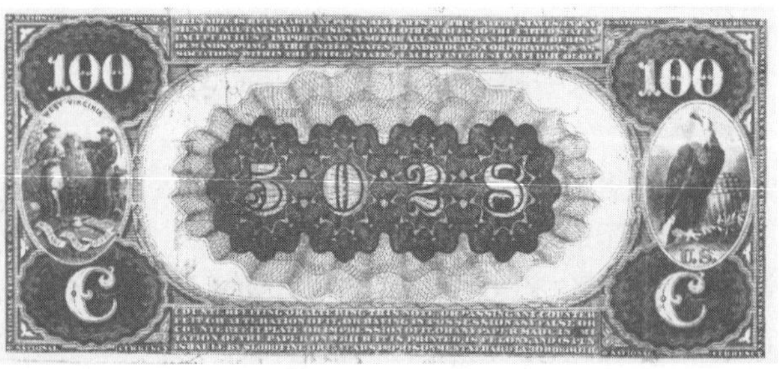

There are two distinct orientations for the overprinted charter number on 1882 Brown Backs. On notes other than the $5 denomination, issued before September 1890, the charter number is vertical. On later issues the charter number is horizontal. The reason for this change is uncertain, but workers sorting notes for redemption probably found the horizontal format easier to read.

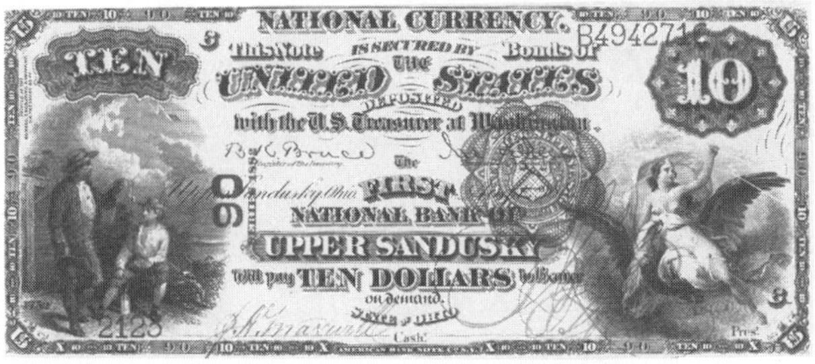

Vertical charter number

The first shipment of Brown Backs from the Bureau of Engraving and Printing was made August 1, 1882. This shipment consisted of 1000 sheets of $10 and $20 notes for The First National Bank of Washington, Iowa (Ch 2656). The first $5 Brown Backs printed were issued to The National Bank of Commerce of Cleveland, Ohio (Ch 2662). By some miracle one of the notes from the first sheet of $5 Brown Backs has survived for collectors. It is a well-used note, not one tucked away as a presentation piece. The initial shipment of $50 and $100 Brown Backs went from the Bureau to the Comptroller on September 15, 1882. These notes were issued to The First National Bank of Chicago, Illinois (Ch 2670).

The Aldrich-Vreeland Act

The National Bank system gave our nation a secure currency. However, two shortcomings became evident. One problem was associated with economic prosperity, the other with financial panic.

The National Bank system made it possible for banks to increase or decrease their circulations. It was envisioned that during periods of economic growth the banks would prosper and use part of their profits to buy additional United States Bonds. These bonds could then be deposited to secure additional circulation, enabling the banks to finance economic expansion. Unfortunately, economic prosperity often had just the opposite effect. The price of United States Bonds tended to rise when capital was in demand. A bank could earn more by reducing its circulation and selling its bonds on the open market than it could realize by buying more bonds and loaning out the added circulation.

A series of financial panics during the National Bank Era called attention to the **inelastic** nature of the money supply - it was not possible to **quickly** increase the amount of money. During panics the need for additional money needed to be met in a matter of days. The impatience of depositors wanting their money was not satisfied by the means then available. The Panic of 1907 caused many bank failures and finally convinced Congress to takes steps to meet such financial emergencies. On May 30, 1908 Congress passed the Emergency Currency Act, which became known as the Aldrich-Vreeland Act. This act permitted national banks to issue national bank notes backed by securities other than United States Bonds. These "other securities" could be short-term loans or other obligations payable to the member banks, generally within six months of the time they were deposited, or they could be local or state bonds.

V. Series 1882 Date Back Notes, with Blue Seal and "1882-1908" on Back

(designated as "1882 Date Back" in this guide.)

After May 30, 1908, banks which had been issuing Series 1882 Brown Backs began issuing a new type of national, the 1882 Date Back. Faces of 1882 Date Backs carry wording that describes the broader types of permitted securities. On notes issued prior to the Aldrich-Vreeland Act the wording is "Secured By United States Bonds Deposited With The U. S. Treasurer at Washington". The changed wording is "Secured By United States Bonds Or Other Securities". The face designs are basically the same as those of the Brown Backs. The Treasury seal and the charter number are overprinted in blue. The dates "1882-1908" fill the central area of the backs, which are printed in green. There is no state seal.

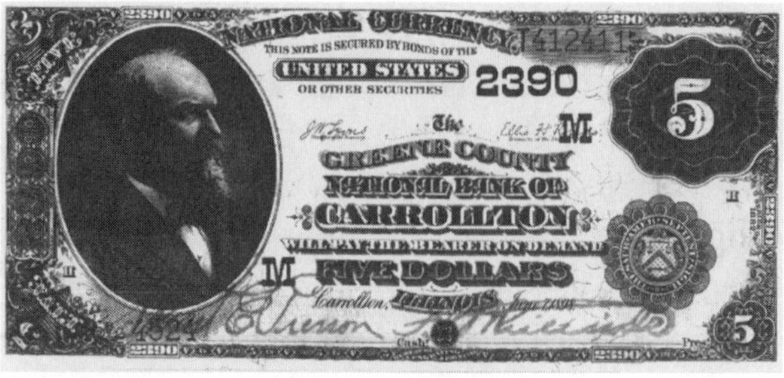

1882 Value Back

VI. Series 1882 Value Back Notes, with Denomination Spelled Out on Back

(designated as "1882 Value Back" in this guide)

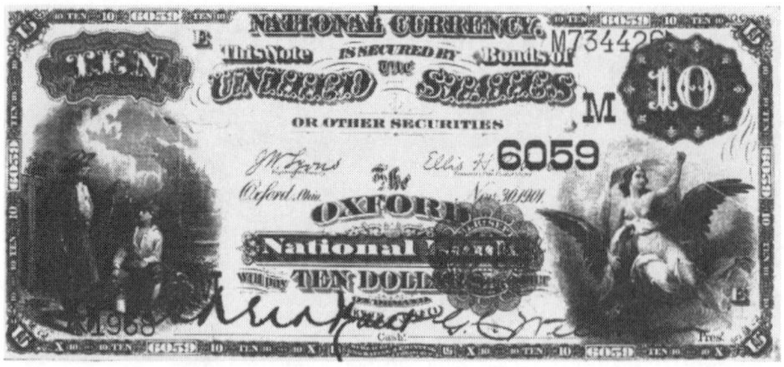

1882 Date Back

The Aldrich-Vreeland Act expired on June 30, 1915. After that date national banks were no longer permitted to use "other securities" to secure their notes - only United States Bonds could be deposited. Banks that were issuing 1882 Date Backs began to issue 1882 Value Backs. On 1882 Value Backs the denomination is spelled out across the central portion of the back, replacing the "1882-1908" of the 1882 Date Backs. The face designs are basically the same as those of the 1882 Date Backs. The "Other Securities" clause was removed only in cases where a new plate was made. As a result, 1882 Value Backs which show the "Other Securities" clause are more plentiful than those which lack this clause. The issue of 1882 Value Backs ended in 1922.

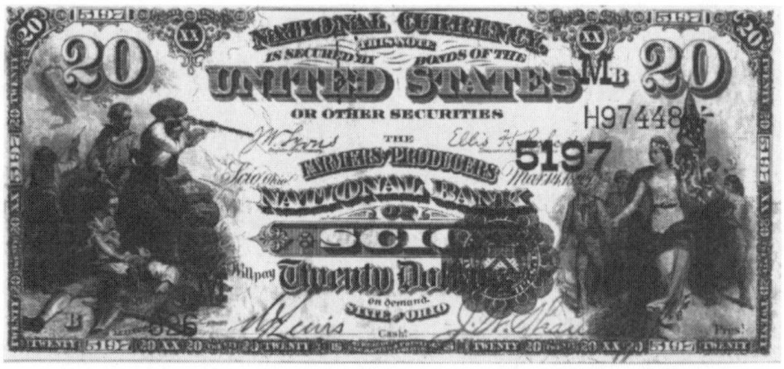

1882 Date Back

On all denominations except the $5 notes, "Series 1882" is overprinted in blue on the face. This overprint is not present on 1882 Date Backs. Thus, excepting the $5 notes, an 1882 Value Back can be identified by its face!

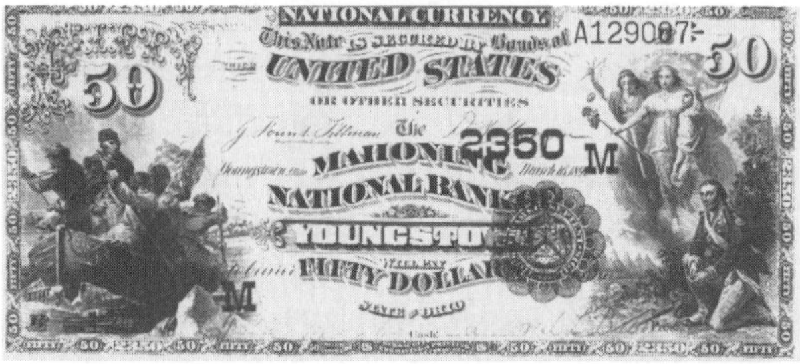

1882 Date Back

All 1882 Value Backs are scarce, but the $50 and $100 value backs are extremely rare. They were issued by just two banks, The Winters National Bank of Dayton, Ohio (Ch 2604) and The Canal-Commercial National Bank of New Orleans, Louisiana (Ch 5649).

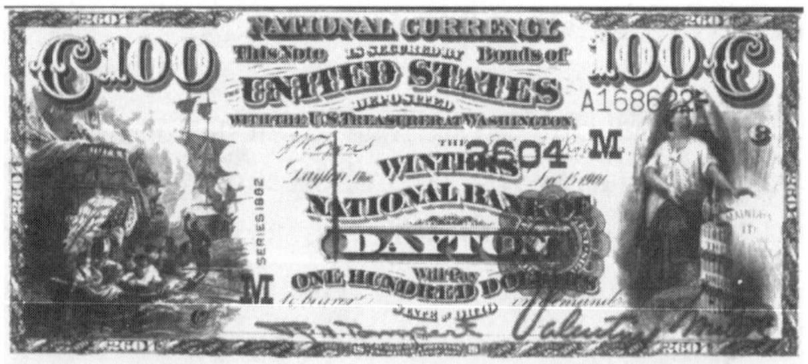

1882 Value Back (National Numismatic Collections)

The illustrations show the backs for all denominations of 1882 Date Backs and 1882 Value Backs. Face designs are shown for the $10, $20, and $50 1882 Date Backs, and $5 and $100 1882 Value Backs.

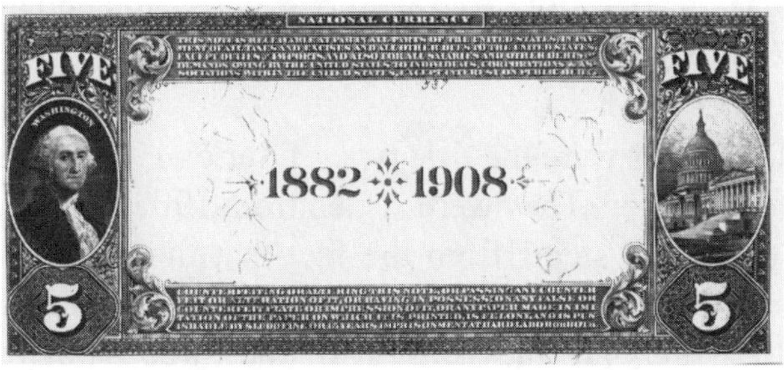
NATIONAL CURRENCY
FIVE
FIVE
1882 1908
5
5

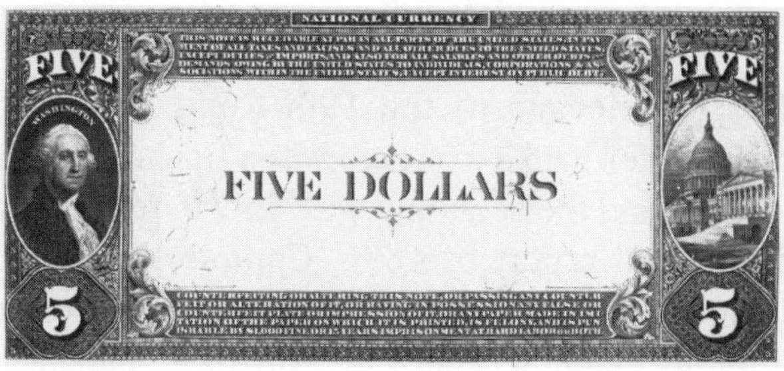
NATIONAL CURRENCY
FIVE
FIVE
FIVE DOLLARS
5
5

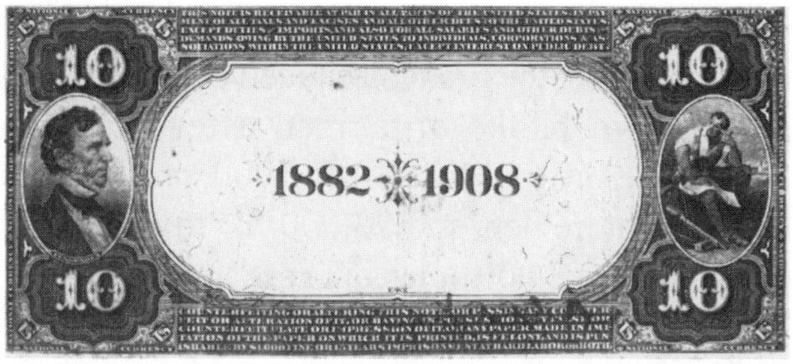
10
10
1882 1908
10
10

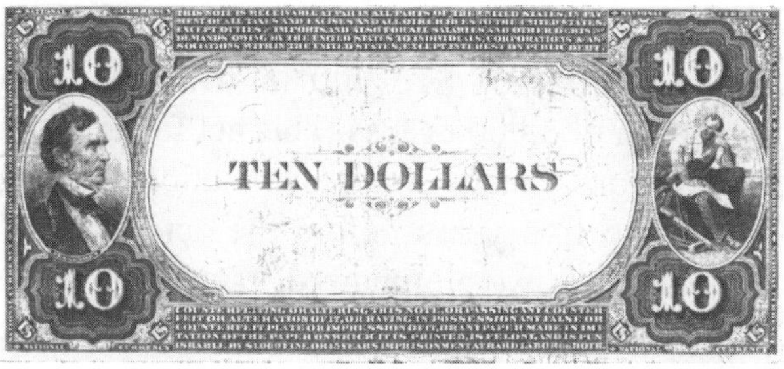
10
10
TEN DOLLARS
10
10

20
20
1882 1908
XX
XX

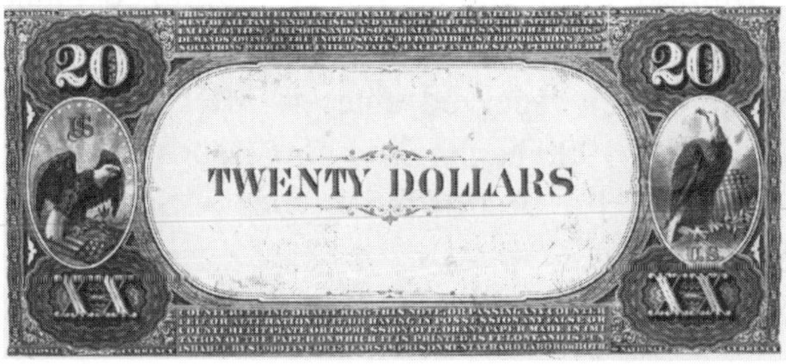
20
20
TWENTY DOLLARS
XX
XX

50
50
1882 1908

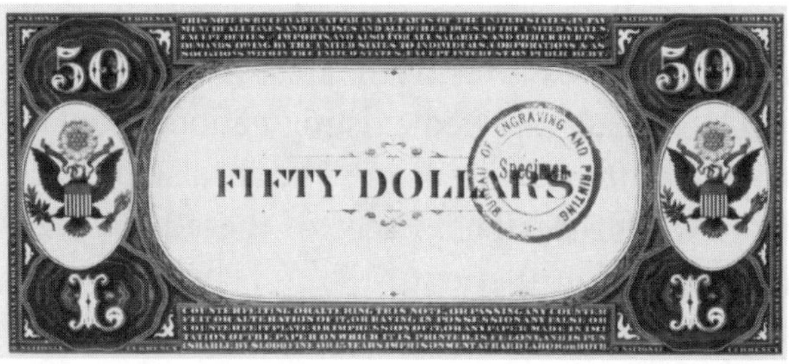
50
50
FIFTY DOLLARS
BUREAU OF ENGRAVING AND PRINTING
Specimen

100
100
1882 1908

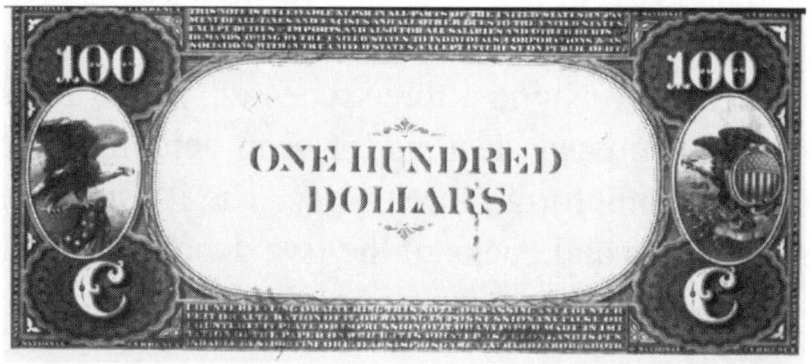
100
100
ONE HUNDRED
DOLLARS

The Gold Standard Act

The last decade of the 19th Century proved difficult for bankers. There was a financial panic in 1893 and the economy was slow to recover. In his annual report of 1896, Comptroller of the Currency Eckles urged Congress to reduce the minimum capital needed to form a national bank. Congress responded in 1900. The Gold Standard Act of March 14, 1900 contained a provision which permitted the organization of national banks with a capital of $25,000 in towns with a population of 3,000 or less. This act fostered the organization of many small town national banks. During the five years before the act only 257 national banks were organized. During the five years following the act, 2300 national banks were organized.

Although some of the newly organized banks issued 1882 Brown Backs, most of the small town banks which received charters after the Act of March 14, 1900 began their note issues with 1902 Red Seals, the first of three types of Series 1902 notes.

SERIES 1902 NOTES

The third distinctive series of designs for national bank notes was a result of The Act of April 12, 1902. This act allowed existing national banks to receive a 20-year extension. The act also provided for new note designs. Faces of these notes carry the designation "Series of 1902". Newly organized banks and those receiving extensions began issuing Series 1902 notes.

Series 1902 notes were issued until July, 1929 when the transition to small size notes began. Collectors recognize three types of Series 1902 notes. The basic designs for each denomination are the same for all three types. The illustrations show faces and backs of the five denominations.

VII. Series 1902 Red Seal Notes (designated as "1902 Red Seal" in this guide)

Red Seals were the first type of Series 1902 notes to be issued. They were issued from 1902 to 1908. The name stems from the fact that the Treasury seal and charter number are overprinted in red. Red seals are the scarcest of the three types of Series 1902 notes. They are generally found with pen signatures of the bank officers.

Red seals were the first notes received by the many small-town banks organized after the Gold Standard Act of March 14, 1900 reduced the capital requirement to $25,000 for towns with a population of 3,000 or less. These 'mom and pop' bankers were understandably proud when they received their first notes and hundreds of serial number 1 red seals were signed and saved - to the everlasting delight of collectors.

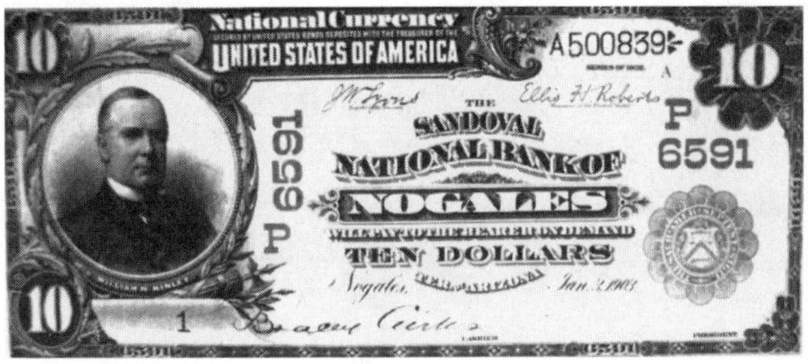

One of over 5,000 serial #1 notes in the census

The first 1902 Red Seals were shipped from the Bureau to the Comptroller on March 17, 1902. These notes were for The Paintsville National Bank, Paintsville, Kentucky (Ch 6100). The first shipment consisted of 120 sheets of $10 and $20 notes. On April 18, 1902 the Comptroller received the first $5 Red Seals - 250 sheets - for The First National Bank of Litchfield, Minnesota (Ch 6118). The first shipment of $50 and $100 Red Seals was September 9, 1902, for The First National Bank of Chicago, Illinois (Ch 2670).

1902 Plain Back

1902 Plain Back

1902 Blue Seal

1902 Date Back

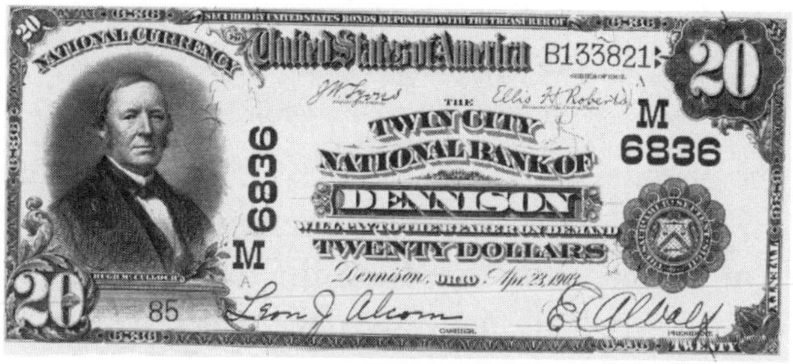

1902 Red Seal

1902 Red Seal

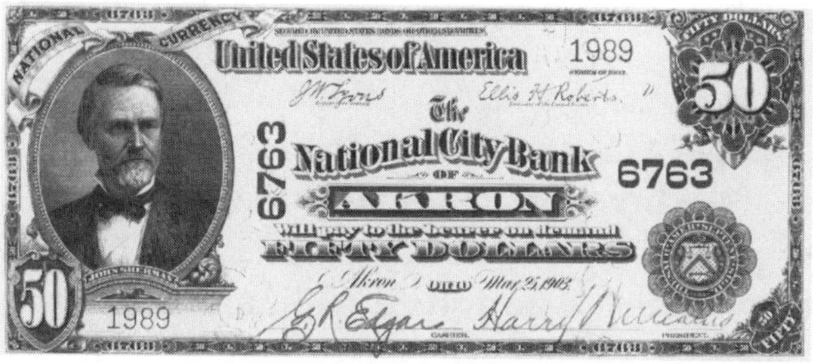

1902 Blue Seal

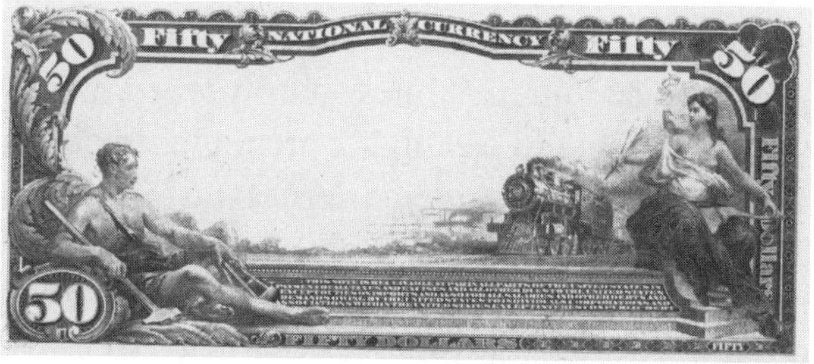

1902 Plain Back

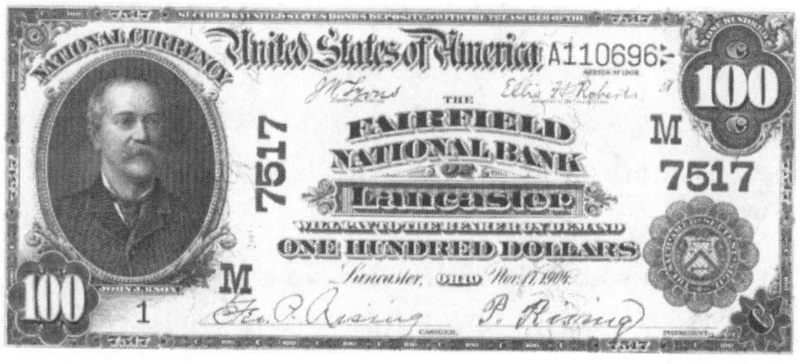

1902 Red Seal

1902 Red Seal

VIII. Series 1902 Blue Seal Notes, dated "1902-1908" on Back (designated as "1902 Date Back" in this guide)

Banks which were issuing 1902 Red Seals in 1908 switched to 1902 Date Backs as a consequence of the Aldrich-Vreeland Act. Most 1902 Date Backs were issued between 1908 and 1915. The faces have the charter number and Treasury seal imprinted in blue. The change in allowed security is noted by the words "Secured by United States Bonds Or Other Securities". The back designs are like those of the 1902 Red Seals, but the dates "1902 - 1908" have been added.

Although the 1882 Date Backs and 1902 Date Backs owe their existence to the Aldrich-Vreeland Act, most were issued under the security of United States Bonds, not by the pledge of short term securities. Notes backed by short term securities were subject to very heavy taxation. The ordinary circulation was subject to an annual tax of one-half percent or one percent, depending on the interest rate paid on the bonds. Circulation backed by other securities was taxed at the rate of five percent per year for the first month. The rate increased by one percent each month up to a maximum of ten percent per year. The logic behind these steep rates was that banks, which quickly raised interest rates sharply when money was scarce, should pay higher premiums to obtain such funds. The Aldrich-Vreeland plan was designed to get money into circulation quickly in times of financial emergency and then get it out of circulation just as quickly when the crisis had passed.

The Aldrich-Vreeland Act served its purpose only once during its brief lifetime. In July 1914, at the outset of World War I, there was a sudden and large outflow of gold from the United States to Europe. Foreign investors sold their American stocks and wanted to be paid in gold. In one week the gold reserves of New York City banks fell by over forty million dollars. A few large banks formed associations and issued nationals backed by "other securities". In the year that followed over 382 million dollars in emergency money was placed in circulation. Because of the onerous interest these notes were quickly redeemed once the crisis passed. By July 1915 virtually all of the emergency notes had been redeemed.

IX. Series 1902 Blue Seal, Plain Back
(designated as "1902 Plain Back" in this guide)

These notes replaced the 1902 Date Backs when the Aldrich-Vreeland Act expired on June 30, 1915. The charter number and Treasury seal are imprinted in blue, as they are on the 1902 Date Backs. The backs do not show any dates, being identical with the backs of the 1902 Red Seals. The 1902 Plain Backs were issued from 1915 to 1929 and are the most plentiful type of large size national.

Reorganized Banks

The original National Currency Act of February 25, 1863 limited corporate lifetimes to no more than 20 years, starting from the **date of the act**. The framers of the act viewed the national banking system as an experiment and they wanted to limit the experiment to twenty years. The manner in which a bank chose to satisfy this requirement had to be spelled out at the time it was organized. Some banks organized during the first year after passage of the act chose a corporate lifetime of 19 years **starting from the date of their organization**. Nineteen years later in early 1882 these banks were forced to liquidate because legislation extending their charters was not passed until July 12, 1882.

The First National Bank of Fremont, Ohio was typical of these "19-year" banks. It first organized as Charter 5 on May 23, 1863, so it would have been forced to liquidate no later than May 23, 1882. The Act of July 12, 1882 would have come too late to extend its charter. The First National Bank of Fremont, and many similarly affected banks, found a way out of their dilemma by applying for new charters. They reorganized under a new charter number before their forced liquidation. The First National Bank of Fremont (Charter 5) liquidated May 22, 1882 but continued in business under its reorganized Charter 2703. Generally, these reorganized banks continued doing business under the same title, at the same location, and with the same officers.

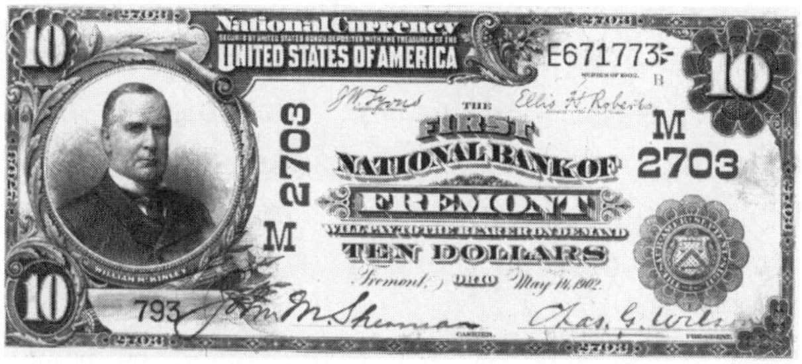

1902 Red Seal issued by Charter 2703, the reorganized successor of Charter 5.

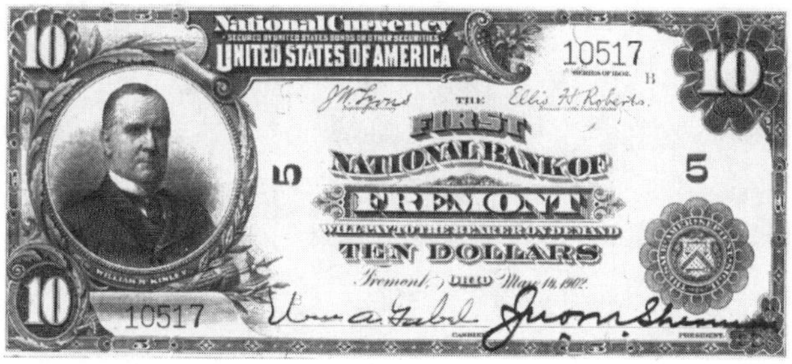

Issued after charter 5 was retaken.

Many of these reorganized banks later retook their original charter numbers because of the prestige of a low charter number. The illustrations show a $10 Red Seal issued by the Fremont bank during its Charter 2703 period. The bank retook Charter 5 on February 23, 1910. The illustrations show a $10 1902 Plain Back issued under the retaken Charter 5.

Second Issue Series 1902 Notes

The major impact of the Acts of July 12, 1882 and April 12, 1902 was to extend the corporate lives of existing banks for 20 years. These acts contained stipulations that extended banks should begin issuing distinctly different notes. It was this provision which earlier gave collectors Series 1882 Brown Backs and Series 1902 Red Seals. Banks which extended in late 1921 and early 1922 satisfied the "distinctly different" condition by issuing **Series 1902 notes with a new plate date and new Register-Treasurer signatures**. The new plate date was approximately 20 years later than the date on the first Series 1902 issues of the bank. Serial numbering started over with #1.The illustration shows a second issue Series 1902 note from the Montgomery National Bank of Mt. Sterling, Kentucky. The plate date is March 1, 1922, exactly 20 years later than the plate date on the first Series 1902 issues of the bank. In this guide these issues are designated as Series 1902 Plain Backs with the added notation (dated 1921) or (dated 1922).

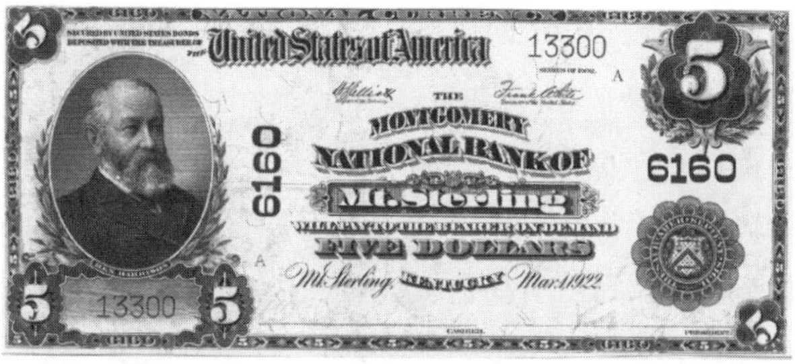

Second issue Series 1902 note. The plate date is March 1, 1922, exactly 20 years after the plate date on the first issue of Series 1902 notes for this bank.

The Act of July 1, 1922 extended the lifetimes of all banks for 99 years, which had the effect of ending the need for new plates or series changes.

SMALL SIZE NATIONALS

The change from large size notes to small size notes took place in July, 1929. The transition affected all types of federal currency. The change to small size notes, nationals and other types, was made for two reasons: They were cheaper to produce and the Treasury wanted to adopt a **uniform design** for all forms of paper money.

To understand the desire for a uniform design, consider the situation in the 1920 era before the switch to small size notes. In addition to National Bank notes the Bureau of Engraving and Printing was producing Silver Certificates, Gold Certificates, United States Notes, and Federal Reserve Notes. Each series had different designs for the same denomination, which tended to confuse the public. After the transition to small size currency all types of notes of a given denomination had the same basic design. For example, all small size $10 notes had the same central portrait of Hamilton, the same counters on the corners, and the same back design.

The illustrations show the large size $10 Silver Certificate, $10 Gold Certificate, and Federal Reserve Note being used in 1929, and the corresponding small size notes. The uniformity of design of the small size notes is apparent.

By 1929, large size nationals were being printed from 4-subject plates on hand presses. Individual face plates had to be made for each national bank. This required the Bureau to keep a huge number of plates on hand. The number of notes printed at any one time for a given bank tended to be small. Small size nationals allowed several economies of scale. To avoid maintaining a huge inventory of plates for individual banks the Bureau used a three-step process. First, 12-subject sheets were printed with the standard back and face designs, but without the bank name or charter number. The

Large size $10 Silver Certificate

Small size $10 Silver Certificate

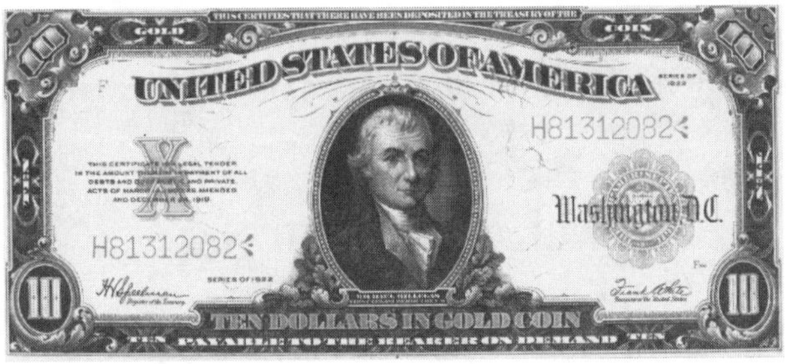

Large size $10 Gold Certificate

Small size $10 Gold Certificate

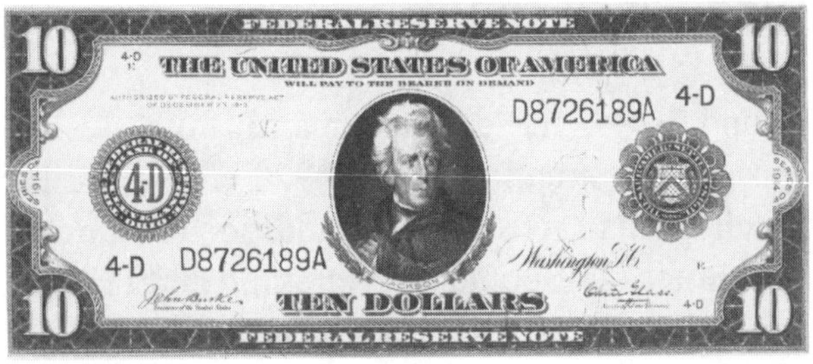

Large size $10 Federal Reserve Note

Small size $10 Federal Reserve Note

Bureau could stockpile these 'one-size fits all' sheets, which required just one plate design for each denomination. The 12-subject sheets were then cut into 6-note sheets. When the Bureau received an order for a specific bank it would take the second step and overprint the name of the bank, the town and state, the officers' signatures, and the charter number, all in black. In a third operation the serial numbers and Treasury seal were overprinted in brown. Notes were sent to the banks as uncut sheets of 6 notes.

Sheet of six small size nationals, the form in which they were shipped to banks.

Small size nationals were issued in denominations of $5, $10, $20, $50, and $100. Authorized but never issued were $10,000 notes. The back designs of the notes are the same as those of the familiar small size Federal Reserve Notes, first placed in circulation in 1929. The faces bear the inscription "Series 1929". Small size nationals bear two pairs of printed signatures. At the top left is the signature of E. E. Jones, Register of the Treasury. At the top right is the signature of W. O. Woods, Treasurer of the United States. These signatures were engraved on the face plates. The bank signatures appear at the lower left and lower right. Generally, these are the facsimile signatures of the Cashier and President of the national bank. These signatures were overprinted along with the bank name and charter number.

There are two distinct types of small size nationals. Their basic designs are identical, but their overprintings differ.

X. Series 1929 Type 1 Notes (designated as "Type 1" in this guide)

The Type 1 notes were issued from July 1929 to May 1933. The charter number is imprinted twice in black. The serials are sheet numbers and have both a prefix and suffix letter.

XI. Series 1929 Type 2 Notes (designated as "Type 2" in this guide)

Type 2 notes were issued from 1933 to 1935. The charter number is imprinted four times, twice in black and twice in brown. The serials have a prefix letter but no suffix letter. The prefix letter is "A" on all Type 2 issues, with one exception. The Bank of America National Trust & Savings Association of San Francisco, California issued Type 2 notes with prefix "A" and prefix "B".

Type 2 notes are scarcer than Type 1 notes. The Type 2 $50 and $100 notes are particularly elusive in uncirculated condition. The illustrations show a mixture of Type 1 and Type 2 faces.

Abraham Lincoln

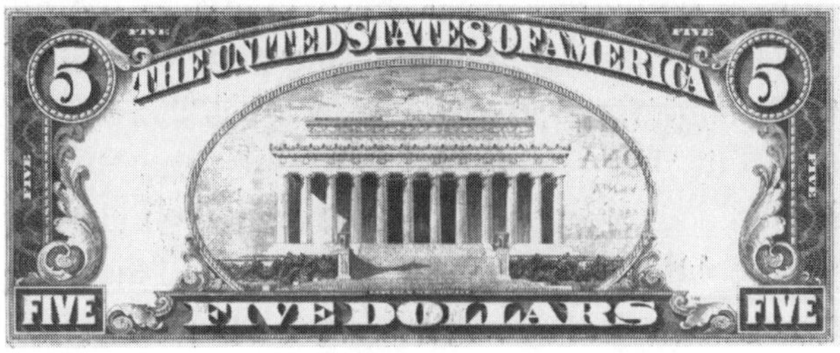

Lincoln Memorial

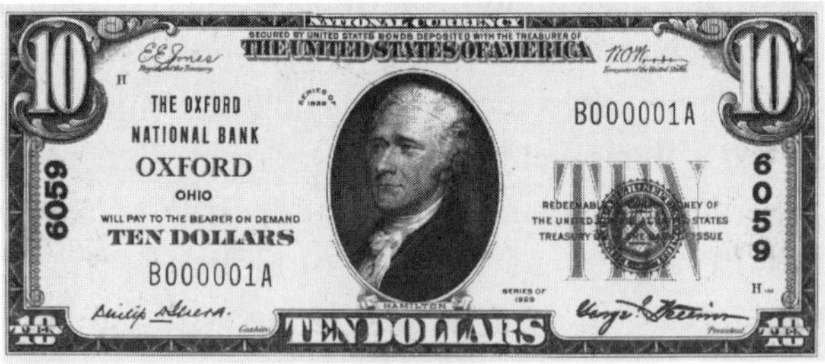

Alexander Hamilton

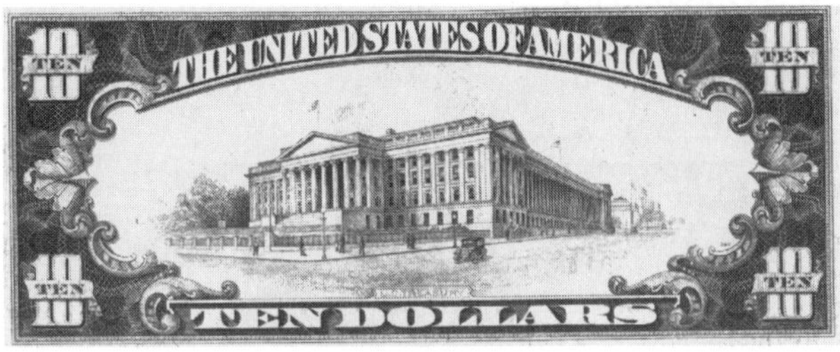

U. S. Treasury

Andrew Jackson

White House

U. S. Grant

U. S. Capitol

Benjamin Franklin

Independence Hall

On August 17, 1929 the last large size nationals were printed by the Bureau. By this time several million sheets of small size nationals had already rolled off the Bureau presses, filling the orders of banks switching to the new format.

On June 22, 1929 the Bureau of Engraving and Printing delivered the first small size notes to the Comptroller of the Currency. These were $5 notes for the First National Bank of Fremont, Ohio, Charter 5. The Comptroller made the earliest deliveries to numerous banks on July 15, 1929. Almost six years later the last small size nationals went to the First National Bank of Chillicothe, Ohio, Charter 128, on July 10, 1935. Nearly three billion dollars worth of small size nationals were sent to national banks during this six year span.

Reorganized Banks During the Small Size Era

During the small size era the Great Depression gripped America and many banks failed. The Federal Reserve System was equipped to combat a short term panic but not a long term depression. During this period a flurry of reorganizations took place. Some banks found it desirable to voluntarily liquidate and immediately reorganize. Generally this was done to strengthen the financial backing of the bank. Bad loans were written off and financially weak shareholders were eased out. The reorganized bank was required to have a title differing from that of the liquidated bank even when there was no change in location. This requirement explains why so many of these reorganized banks had names that differed in the most minor way from their predecessors. For example, The Farmers and Merchants National Bank **of** Bellaire, Ohio (Charter 7327) went into voluntary liquidation on January 13, 1934. It was reorganized in February 1934 as The Farmers and Merchants National Bank **in** Bellaire (Charter 13996). This minor title change preserved the bank's public recognition while also satisfying the new-name policy.

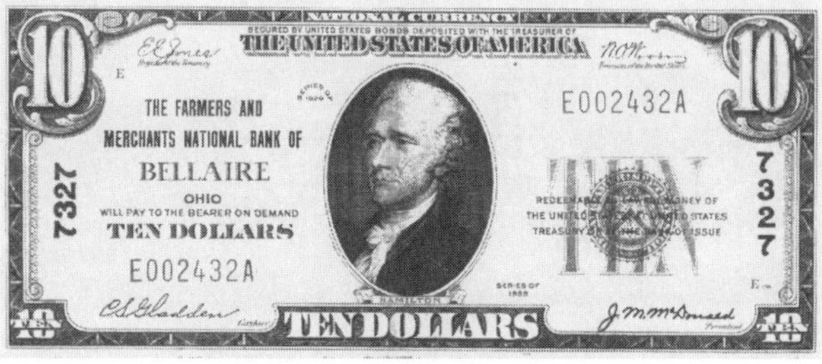

Original title of the Bellaire bank

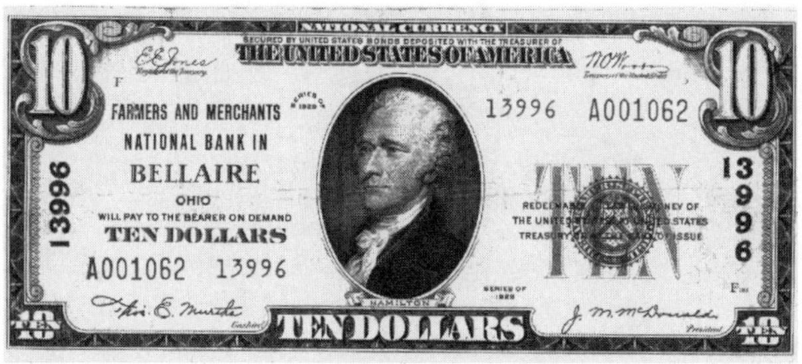

Minor title change for the reorganized Bellaire bank

Territorials

National bank notes issued under territorial status are highly prized by collectors. In many instances a bank issued both territorial and state notes. Territorial notes are listed with the corresponding state issues in Chapter 4. In particular, national banks of Oklahoma Territory and Indian Territory are included in the Oklahoma listings. Dakota Territory banks are included with the North Dakota and South Dakota issues.

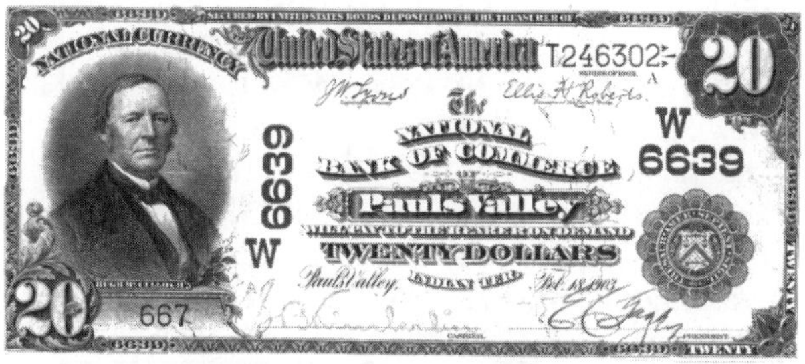

Indian Territory Red Seal

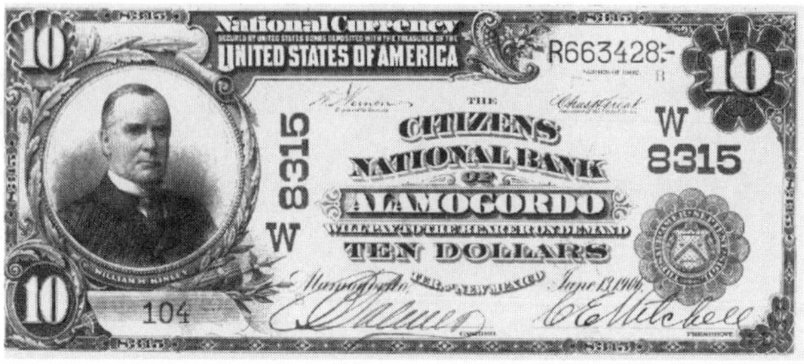

New Mexico Territory Red Seal

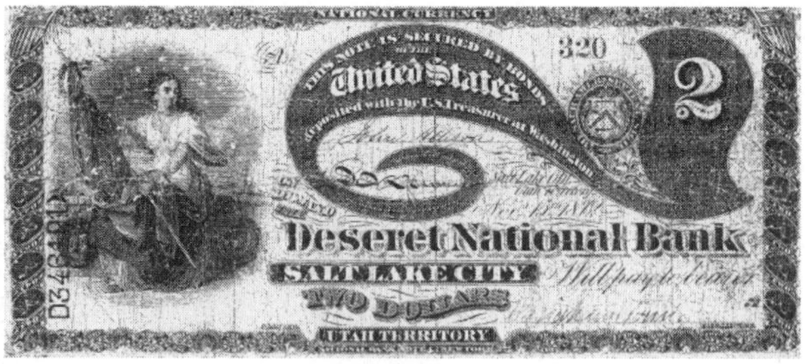

Brigham Young signed this Utah Territory note as President of the Deseret National Bank.

In a number of instances a national bank continued to issue notes with a territorial imprint after statehood. Collectors regard a note as a territorial if the note carries the territorial designation, regardless of when it was issued. Peter Huntoon (1995) has set forth definitive details concerning territorial nationals.

Territory	Created	Statehood
Alaska	May 17, 1884*	Jan 3, 1959
Arizona	Feb 24, 1863	Feb 14, 1912
Colorado	Feb 28, 1861	Aug 1, 1876
Dakota	Mar 2, 1861	Nov 2, 1889**
Hawaii	Apr 30, 1900	Aug 21, 1959
Idaho	Mar 3, 1861	Jul 3, 1890
Indian	May 30, 1854	Nov 16, 1907
Montana	May 26, 1864	Nov 8, 1889
Nebraska	May 30, 1854	Mar 1, 1867
New Mexico	Sep 9, 1850	Jan 6, 1912
Oklahoma	May 2, 1890	Nov 16, 1907
Porto Rico	Dec 10, 1898	Jul 25, 1952***
Utah	Sep 9, 1850	Jan 6, 1896
Washington	Mar 2, 1853	Nov 11, 1889
Wyoming	Jul 25, 1868	Jul 10, 1890

* District status May 17, 1884; Territory Aug 24, 1912
** Partitioned into North Dakota and South Dakota
*** Became Commonwealth July 25, 1952

How Many Survivors?

How many national bank notes have survived for us to collect? Not enough! Most survivors are now in the hands of collectors and dealers. A few have been impounded in government collections. Others are held by families of the bank officers whose signatures appear on the notes. Thanks to the diligent work of a number of people, it is possible to make a good estimate of the number of nationals which have escaped redemption and natural disasters.

John Hickman documented over 160,000 nationals. He had the help of collectors like Frank Bennett, Robert Bolduc, Robert Hearn, Peter Huntoon, Robert Kvederas, Roman Latimer, William K. Raymond, Gilmore Sem, and Gerome Walton, who diligently tracked notes from their favorite states. Three years ago the author began to assemble a census of all nationals. He too has benefitted from the work and advice of the collectors above, and indirectly from that of John Hickman. Many others have contributed in varying degrees to my census. Their names are chronicled in the Acknowledgments. At this writing there are nearly 200,000 notes in the census. One recurring feature is apparent: On average, there are approximately 20 notes per bank for all of the states for which solid census work has been done. There were 12,635 note-issuing national banks. An average of 20 notes per bank works out to a total of approximately 250,000 notes. Allowing for as-yet unrecorded notes it seems likely that the number of surviving nationals lies between 300,000 and 400,000.

John Hickman never ceased to marvel at the flow of newly-discovered nationals. He once confided to the author that he expected that the total would reach 35,000 or so, certainly not more than 50,000. At that point he had over 135,000 notes in his census. He said, "If I'd known there were so many I never would have started to count them." Those who knew John recognize that he was kidding! He'd have counted every one, with pleasure and great zeal!

The End of the National Bank Era

The Aldrich-Vreeland Act of 1908 was an inadequate solution to the problem of a flexible money supply. A more viable solution came on December 23, 1913 when Congress passed the Federal Reserve Act. This act created the Federal Reserve system and marked the beginning of the end for national bank notes. The "Fed" became a cheaper and more efficient means of regulating the supply of currency.

Two provisions of the Federal Reserve Act discouraged the issuing of nationals. The act permitted national banks to organize without depositing bonds. Of course such banks could not issue notes. Furthermore, the act permitted existing national banks to sell their bonds to the Federal Reserve. The banks could then reduce their circulations by an equal amount. The act had a dramatic impact on the number of national banks which issued notes. A total of 10,472 national banks were organized before 1914. All but 30 of these banks issued notes. Nearly 4000 national banks were organized between 1914 and the end of the note-issuing period. Over 1600 of these banks did not issue notes.

Thousands of well-managed national banks survived the Great Depression. However, their note-issuing role became unnecessary as the Federal Reserve became dominant as America's central bank.

How did the end of national bank note issues come about? The Federal Home Loan Act of July 22, 1932 contained a provision that ultimately killed the issue of nationals. The act specified that the types of bonds then being used to secure nationals would lose that privilege three years after passage of the act. Thus, note-issuing privileges ended on July 22, 1935. The bonds then being used to back nationals were 2% Consols of 1930 and 2% Panama Canal Bonds. In March, 1935 the Treasury announced that it would withdraw the circulation privileges for the 2% Consols of 1930 on July 1, 1935 and for the 2% Panama Canal Bonds on August 1, 1935. On the announced dates the Treasury sold the bonds and placed the proceeds in the Redemption Fund. This ended the National Bank Era.

The highest charter number bank to issue notes was The Liberty National Bank & Trust Co. of Louisville, Kentucky, Charter 14320. The last shipment of nationals was made July 10, 1935 to The First National Bank of Chillicothe, Ohio, Charter 128.

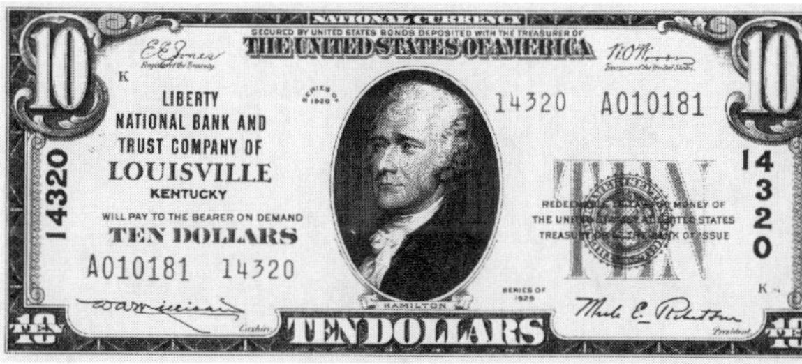

The Liberty National Bank & Trust Co of Louisville, Kentucky had the highest charter number of the note-issuing national banks.

NATIONAL BANK NOTES

Chapter 4

NATIONAL BANK NOTE DATA AND VALUES

This chapter presents a state-by-state listing of notes issued by every national bank. A value is assigned to each variety of note issued by every bank. The listings are arranged **alphabetically by state**. Within each state the banks are arranged in **alphabetic order**, first by **town name**, and second by **bank title.**

This chapter also presents a **TYPE NOTE PRICE GUIDE** which lists retail values for nationals by type in four grades.

Data Listings

The type of information given for each bank is illustrated by the listing for The Oxford National Bank of Oxford, Ohio, which is reproduced below.

6059 **Butler**
OXFORD NB, OXFORD
{{ 8 L U + 17 S }}
Chartered 12/21/01

Brown Back			<$VALUE
3x10-20		1-3700	<$500
1882 Date Back			
3x10-20		1-2160	<$500
1882 Value Back			
3x10-20		2161-2190	<$500
1902 Plain Back			
3x50-100		1-523	<$600/$750
1929 Small Size			
5	Type 1	1-130	<$275
10	Type 1	1-40	<$275
50	Type 1	1-171	<$350
100	Type 1	1-32	<$500
Total Issue			$502,050
Out in 1935			$50,000
Large out 1935			$3,380

Following the charter number (6059) is the County in which the town is located (Butler). The original title of the bank appears below the charter number. **The number of notes currently in our census of nearly 200,000 notes is indicated in brackets below the bank title.** For The Oxford National Bank the brackets show

{{ 8 L U + 17 S }}

This means that the census contains 8 large size notes, 17 single small size notes, and 1 uncut sheet of small size notes. If there are more than 50 notes in the census, the listing will show **50+** rather than the actual number.

An **{{ UNREPORTED }}** citation indicates that notes are currently unknown. The census is not equally mature for all states - a low number inside the brackets may not signal great rarity. Readers are urged to report notes to the author.

Key dates and events in the history of the bank follow the census line. Changes of title that appeared on notes are indicated. Each listing shows the types of notes issued, the sheet format, and the range of issued serial numbers.

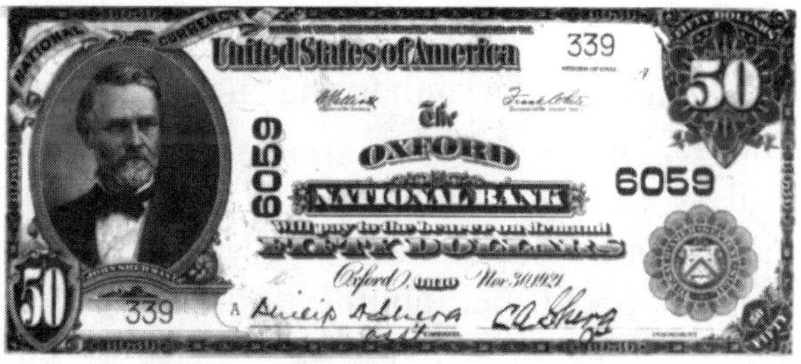

1902 Plain Back $50 from Oxford, Ohio.

For example, the 1902 Plain Back listings for the Oxford National Bank are

3x50-100 1-523 <$600/$750

The "3x50-100" means that notes were issued in sheets containing three \$50 and one \$100. The "1-523" means that 523 **sheets** were issued to the bank, with serial numbers 1 through 523. This means that there were 523 \$100 notes issued and 1569 \$50 notes issued. The last entry on the line, <\$600/\$750, indicates the values of a \$50 note and a \$100 note.

Note Values

Every national bank note is worth more than its face value. Rarity, condition, and demand are primary factors affecting value. In this guide a value is given for each variety of note issued by every bank. Values are positioned to the right of the serial number range, following the angle bracket. Where space does not permit, values are shown on the following line. The values listed on the line

3x50-100 1-523 <\$600/\$750

mean that a \$50 note is valued at \$600, and a \$100 note is valued at \$750. In many instances different denominations carry the same value. For the Oxford NB, the Brown Back listing is

3x10-20 1-3700 <\$500

which indicates that a value of \$500 applies to a \$10 note or a \$20 note.

The values assigned are based on the collective experience of the author and the Contributing Editors, the distinguished group of collectors and dealers listed in the Acknowledgments. Neither the author nor the Contributing Editors have any illusions about their abilities to assign prices to nationals. Accordingly, the values listed should be viewed as figures at which bargaining can begin.

Collectors generally recognize at least 9 full grades: Poor, Fair, Good, Very Good, Fine, Very Fine, Extremely Fine, About Uncirculated, and Uncirculated. See **Paper Money Grades** (p 53) for a brief explanation of grades.

Values in this guide refer to notes in FINE condition. A note in FINE condition shows obvious signs of circulation. It may have numerous folds but generally retains some of its original body, and it is not damaged, nor repaired, nor doctored.

Larger or smaller values would apply depending on condition. A useful rule of thumb is that the value of a note changes by approximately 25 percent for a change of one full grade. Thus, a \$50 note valued at \$600 in Fine would be worth approximately \$450 in Very Good (one full grade lower than Fine) and approximately \$750 in Very Fine (one full grade higher than Fine). Consult **TYPE NOTE PRICE GUIDE** (p 55) for further insights on how condition affects values. Nationals in uncut sheet form command a premium over the values of the individual notes. See Chapter 5 for evaluations of uncut sheets of notes.

A note from the last sheet of \$100 notes delivered to the Oxford National Bank.

The small size \$100 note shown carries bank serial number D000032A. The data show that 32 sheets of small size \$100 notes were issued. Each sheet contained six notes. The note shown is from the last sheet delivered to the bank. It consisted of notes with the serials A000032A, B000032A, C000032A, D000032A, E000032A, and F000032A. The listing shows that a small size \$100 note in FINE condition has a value of \$500.

Following the listing of notes issued and their values are lines showing the total face value of all notes issued by the bank, the face value of all notes unredeemed in 1935 (or some other key date), and the face value of all large size notes unredeemed in 1935 (or some other key date). In the case of the Oxford National Bank the total face value of notes issued was $502,050. In 1935 the bank had a total of $50,000 worth of nationals in circulation, of which $3,380 were large size notes. In the years following 1935, most of the $50,000 worth of notes wore out and were sent for redemption. A few were saved for us to collect. The face value of the 31 notes known to have survived is under $600. The survival story for the Oxford bank is the typical pattern - a few saved and many redeemed. Hoards of new notes have survived for only a tiny fraction of the 12,635 note-issuing charters.

Type 2 Serial Numbering

From 1863 until 1933 the serial numbers were the same for each note in a sheet. Plate position letters distinguished the different subjects. In 1933 the serial numbering of small size nationals was changed, creating the Type 2 notes. The serial numbers are different for each note in a Type 2 sheet. For example, the first sheet of Type 2 notes issued to a bank carried the serials A000001, A000002, A000003, A000004, A000005, and A000006. **For Type 2 notes the listings in this guide give the range of serial numbers**. For example, if the listing reads

5 Type 2 1-606 <$125

then 606 notes were issued (101 sheets) with serials from A000001 to A000606.

Rarity Versus Availability

In some instances the number of notes in the census suggests that a note should sell for a price well below the value listed. Often an unusual town name or bank title enhances the value of a note. In some cases, all or most of the reported notes are part of an uncirculated hoard. If there are 50 notes in the census and 45 are uncirculated, the value listed is representative of the 5 circulated examples. This value would be higher than it would be if all 50 notes were circulated.

Rarity is a key factor in assessing value. However, availability is sometimes equally or more important than rarity in matters of value. For example, if the census shows eighteen notes and twelve are tightly held by the family of the bank president, then only six are available for collectors. Of these six, perhaps only one or two will come on the market over a ten-year period. Under these circumstances, **availability dictates value**. The census figure may be deceptive because it reflects **rarity** rather than **availability**.

Type Note Price Guide

While many collectors pursue nationals on a geographical or topical basis, others collect by "type". That is, they seek notes of each of the eleven types in one or more denominations. High grade notes are not widely available because most served their intended purpose - a circulating medium of exchange. A few hoards of uncirculated notes have surfaced, mostly of the lower denominations.

The values quoted in the **TYPE NOTE PRICE GUIDE** (p 55) are values for notes from the most readily available banks. Notes from rarer banks command higher prices than those listed here. Consult the state listings for values of notes from specific banks.

Paper Money Grades

Values are given for four different grades. Grading paper money is decidedly subjective and experience is a great teacher. Key characteristics of each of the four grades are as follows:

Very Good (VG): Limp, but complete and with no significant damage.

Very Fine (VF): Several folds, bright with significant body.

About Uncirculated (AU): Perhaps one light fold, no real circulation.

Choice Crisp Uncirculated (Ch CU): Fresh, bright, no folds, minimal handling marks.

Pinholes are found in many nationals and a few pinholes would not lower the grade. Pen-signed and rubber-stamped signatures are often weak or missing.

This detraction may lower the value of a note but does not alter its grade. **Harshly laundered or "doctored" notes usually sell at substantial discounts from the values listed here.**

Values have been assigned to all denominations of all types. No $500 Gold Bank notes are known to collectors and no $1000 nationals have ever sold publicly. Thus, the values listed for these are simply estimates of the price which a note might command. In a few instances, values are left blank where notes are unknown in the listed grades.

Abbreviations

The following abbreviations have been used:

Assoc	Association
B	Bank
N	National
F	First
Ch	Charter
C	Company
T	Trust

The three most frequently appearing combinations are NB (National Bank), FNB (First National Bank), and TC (Trust Company).

Terminology

The following terminology is used repeatedly:

"not marked". Records for Series 1882 and Series 1902 issues are incomplete. As a result the type of note (1882 Date Back or Value Back, 1902 Date Back or Plain Back) is uncertain.

"assumed circulation". In many instances one national bank was absorbed or succeeded by another. The successor bank assumed responsibility for redeeming any notes still in circulation.

"Outstanding includes". When one national bank absorbed or succeeded another it assumed responsibility for the outstanding notes of that bank. This fact explains the seemingly paradoxical listings which show a total outstanding circulation greater than the total issue by the successor bank - or - an outstanding circulation of large size notes for a charter that did not issue large size notes.

"Total Issue". This figure is the total face value of notes issued under that particular charter number.

"Out at close". This figure indicates the face value of notes unredeemed when the bank closed, or was liquidated, or went into receivership.

"Out in 1935". This figure indicates the face value of notes unredeemed in 1935. It includes both large size and small size notes.

"Large out". This figure indicates the face value of unredeemed large size notes in the year of closing ("Large out at close"), or at the time specified (e.g. "Large out 1935").

NATIONAL BANK NOTES TYPE NOTE PRICE GUIDE

DENOMINATION / TYPE	GRADE			
ORIGINAL/SERIES 1875 NOTES	VG	VF	AU	Choice CU
$1 Original Series/Series 1875	$165/$175	$400/$400	$750/$750	$1500/$1500
$2 Original Series/Series 1875	$550/$550	$1500/$1500	$2500/$2500	$5000/$5000
$5 Original Series/Series 1875	$225/$200	$500/$500	$1000/$1000	$2000/$2000
$5 Black Charter Orig/Series 1875	$3750/$3500	$5500/$5000	$8500/$7500	$15,000/$12,500
$10 Original Series/Series 1875	$500/$400	$1000/$800	$2250/$1750	$4500/$3500
$20 Original Series/Series 1875	$1000/$750	$1750/$1500	$3250/$2750	$6500/$5000
$50 Original Series or Series 1875	$3000	$7500	$15,000	$25,000
$100 Original Series or Series 1875	$3000	$8000	$17,500	$30,000
$500 Original or Series 1875	$125,000	$200,000	$250,000	$300,000
$1000 Original or Series 1875	$200,000	$275,000	$300,000	$350,000
GOLD BANK NOTES	VG	VF	AU	Choice CU
$5 Original Series only	$900	$2750	$10,000	---
$10 Original Series/Series 1875	$2500/$3000	$6000/$7500	---	---
$20 Original Series/Series 1875	$4000/$4500	$8500/$10,000	---	---
$50 Original Series or Series 1875	$25,000	$50,000	---	---
$100 Original Series or Series 1875	$25,000	$50,000	---	---
$500 Original Series only (Unknown)	$200,000	$300,000	---	---
SERIES 1882 NOTES	VG	VF	AU	Choice CU
$5 1882 Brown B/Date B/Value B	$100/$100/$110	$175/$175/$250	$400/$400$/625	$800/$800/$1250
$10 1882 Brown B/Date B/Value B	$110/$110/$125	$200/$175/$250	$450/$450/$750	$900/$900/$1500
$20 1882 Brown B/Date B/Value B	$135/$135/$160	$250/$225/$300	$625/$625/$900	$1250/$1250/$1800
$50 1882 Brown B/Date B/Value B	$1000/$850/$25,000	$2000/$1750/$35,000	$3250/$3500/$40,000	$6500/$7500/$65,000
$100 1882 Brown B/Date B/Value B	$1000/$900/$25,000	$2250/$2000/$40,000	$3500/$3750/$50,000	$7500/$8500/$75,000
SERIES 1902 NOTES	VG	VF	AU	Choice CU
$5 1902 Red Seal/Date B/Plain B	$75/$30/$30	$135/$50/$50	$300/$175/$125	$600/$350/$275
$10 1902 Red Seal/Date B/Plain B	$85/$35/$35	$175/$60/$60	$500/$225/$135	$850/$450/$275
$20 1902 Red Seal/Date B/Plain B	$115/$40/$40	$225/$75/$70	$625/$300/$125	$1250/$600/$350
$50 1902 Red Seal/Date B/Plain B	$1250/$225/$225	$2500/$450/$450	$4000/$1000/$1000	$6500/$2000/$2000
$100 1902 Red Seal/Date B/Plain B	$1375/$250/$250	$2750/$500/$500	$4000/$1000/$1000	$6500/$2250/$2250
SMALL SIZE NOTES	VG	VF	AU	Choice CU
$5 1929 Small Size Type 1/Type 2	$12/$12	$20/$20	$30/$30	$60/$70
$10 1929 Small Size Type 1/Type 2	$15/$15	$25/$25	$35/$35	$70/$80
$20 1929 Small Size Type 1/Type 2	$25/$25	$35/$35	$45/$50	$90/$110
$50 1929 Small Size Type 1/Type 2	$65/$85	$100/$200	$165/$500	$325/$1250
$100 1929 Small Size Type 1/Type 2	$120/$135	$140/$350	$200/$600	$350/$1500

STATE CAPITALS AND NUMBERS OF ISSUING CHARTERS

STATE	CAPITAL	Number of Issuing Charters	Number of Small Size Charters
Alabama	Montgomery	164	107
Alaska	Juneau	3	3
Arizona	Phoenix	27	11
Arkansas	Little Rock	114	69
California	Sacramento	415	172
Colorado	Denver	185	93
Connecticut	Hartford	117	57
Delaware	Dover	28	16
District of Columbia	Washington	27	11
Florida	Tallahassee	109	54
Georgia	Atlanta	165	79
Hawaii	Honolulu	5	1
Idaho	Boise	86	28
Illinois	Springfield	718	469
Indiana	Indianapolis	409	224
Iowa	Des Moines	496	249
Kansas	Topeka	400	212
Kentucky	Frankfort	238	141
Louisiana	Baton Rouge	87	38
Maine	Augusta	120	58
Maryland	Annapolis	138	91
Massachusetts	Boston	346	145
Michigan	Lansing	278	145
Minnesota	Saint Paul	434	248
Mississippi	Jackson	66	34
Missouri	Jefferson City	265	119
Montana	Helena	124	44
Nebraska	Lincoln	349	152
Nevada	Carson City	16	10
New Hampshire	Concord	78	58
New Jersey	Trenton	342	257
New Mexico	Santa Fe	63	23
New York	Albany	901	522
North Carolina	Raleigh	127	63
North Dakota	Bismarck	223*	111
Ohio	Columbus	648	336
Oklahoma	Oklahoma City	557**	214
Oregon	Salem	127	79
Pennsylvania	Harrisburg	1196	899
Porto Rico	San Juan	1	
Rhode Island	Providence	67	12
South Carolina	Columbia	97	42
South Dakota	Pierre	177*	75
Tennessee	Nashville	196	105
Texas	Austin	917	510
Utah	Salt Lake City	34	17
Vermont	Montpelier	80	48
Virginia	Richmond	224	151
Washington	Olympia	183	84
West Virginia	Charleston	177	130
Wisconsin	Madison	240	157
Wyoming	Cheyenne	51	23
	TOTALS	**12,635**	**6,996**

*Includes Dakota Territory **Includes Indian Territory

NATIONAL BANK NOTES

ALABAMA

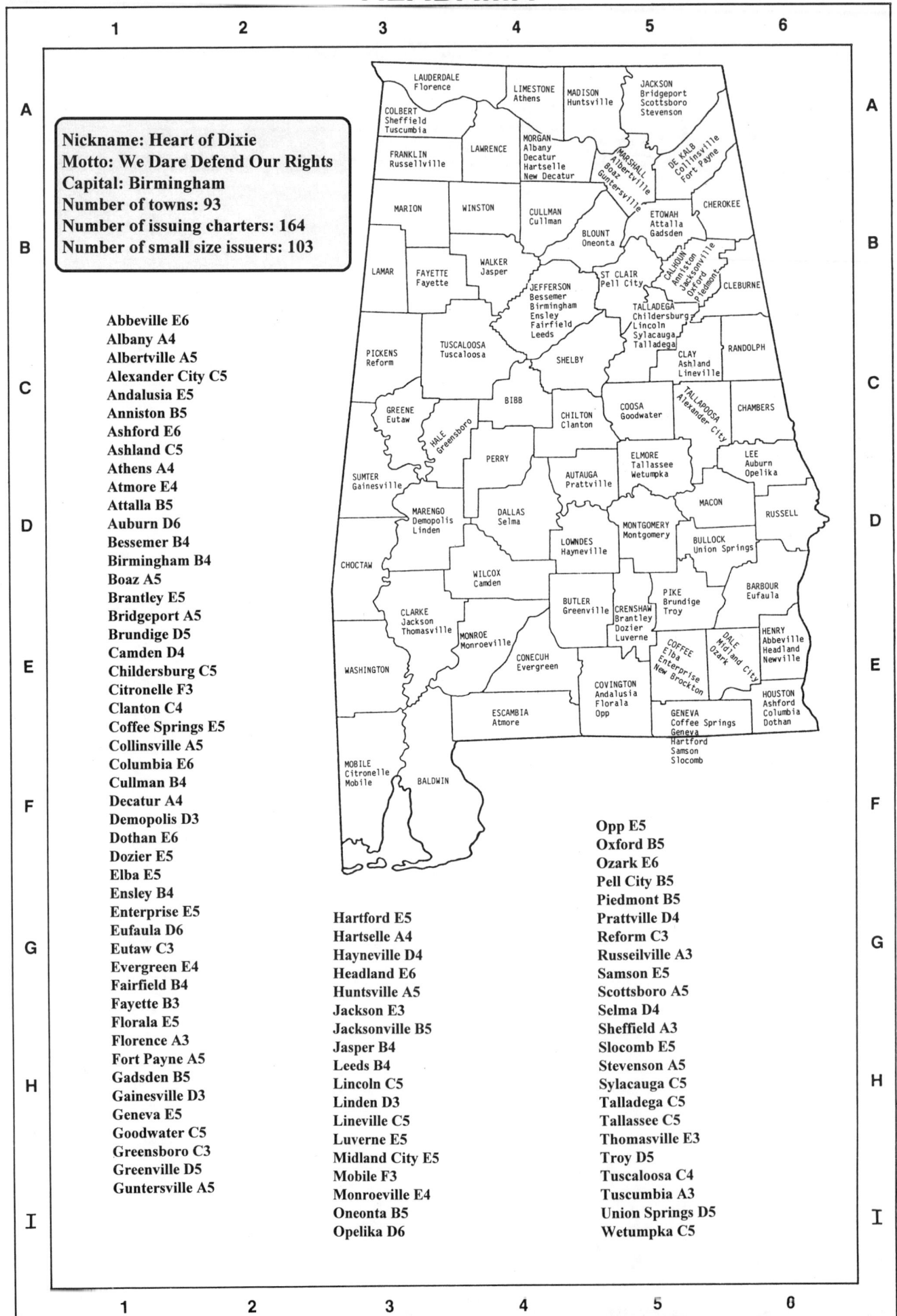

Nickname: Heart of Dixie
Motto: We Dare Defend Our Rights
Capital: Birmingham
Number of towns: 93
Number of issuing charters: 164
Number of small size issuers: 103

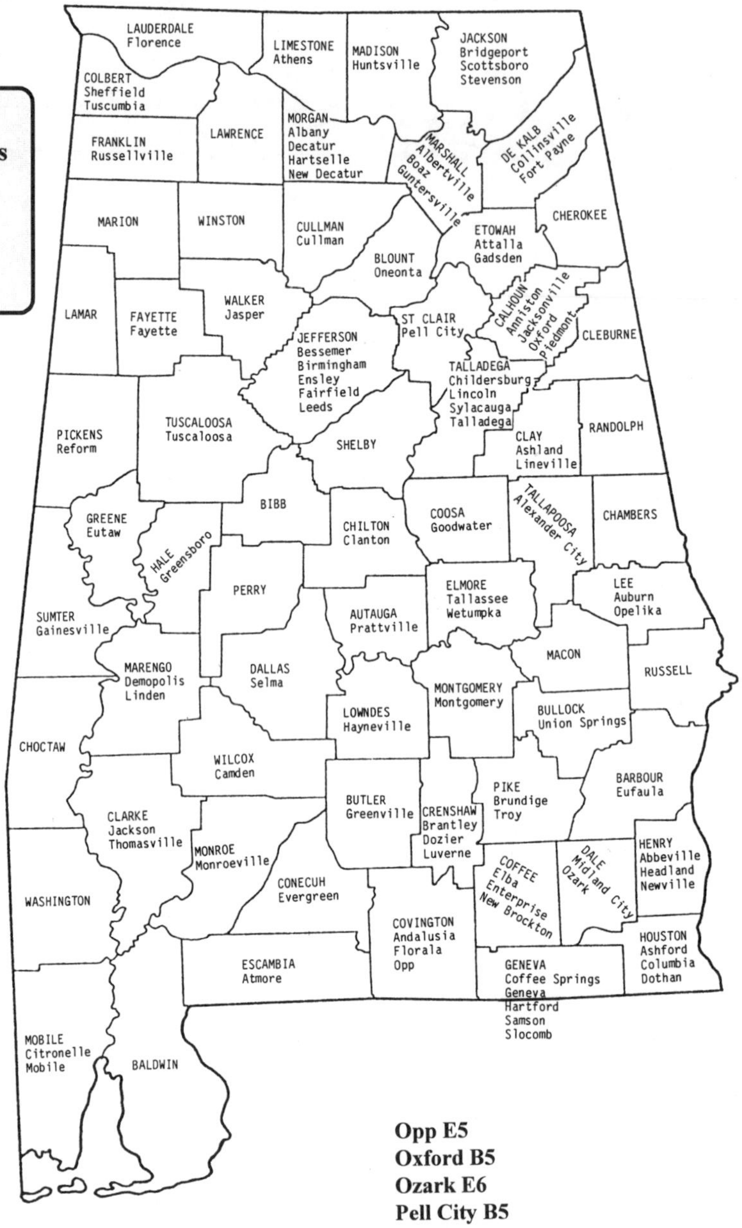

Abbeville E6
Albany A4
Albertville A5
Alexander City C5
Andalusia E5
Anniston B5
Ashford E6
Ashland C5
Athens A4
Atmore E4
Attalla B5
Auburn D6
Bessemer B4
Birmingham B4
Boaz A5
Brantley E5
Bridgeport A5
Brundige D5
Camden D4
Childersburg C5
Citronelle F3
Clanton C4
Coffee Springs E5
Collinsville A5
Columbia E6
Cullman B4
Decatur A4
Demopolis D3
Dothan E6
Dozier E5
Elba E5
Ensley B4
Enterprise E5
Eufaula D6
Eutaw C3
Evergreen E4
Fairfield B4
Fayette B3
Florala E5
Florence A3
Fort Payne A5
Gadsden B5
Gainesville D3
Geneva E5
Goodwater C5
Greensboro C3
Greenville D5
Guntersville A5
Hartford E5
Hartselle A4
Hayneville D4
Headland E6
Huntsville A5
Jackson E3
Jacksonville B5
Jasper B4
Leeds B4
Lincoln C5
Linden D3
Lineville C5
Luverne E5
Midland City E5
Mobile F3
Monroeville E4
Oneonta B5
Opelika D6
Opp E5
Oxford B5
Ozark E6
Pell City B5
Piedmont B5
Prattville D4
Reform C3
Russeilville A3
Samson E5
Scottsboro A5
Selma D4
Sheffield A3
Slocomb E5
Stevenson A5
Sylacauga C5
Talladega C5
Tallassee C5
Thomasville E3
Troy D5
Tuscaloosa C4
Tuscumbia A3
Union Springs D5
Wetumpka C5

5987 Henry
FNB OF ABBEVILLE
{{ 9 L }}
Organized 8/17/01
Receivership 11/14/24
Brown Back <$VALUE
3x10-20 1-5700 <$600
1882 Date Back
3x10-20 1-9100 <$500
1882 Value Back
3x10-20 9101-13412 <$500
1902 Plain Back
3x10-20 1-4530 <$250
Total Issue $1,182,100
Out at close $98,500

10959 Henry
HENRY NB OF ABBEVILLE
{{ 3 L }}
Organized 2/21/17
Receivership 8/16/29
1902 Plain Back <$VALUE
3x10-20 1-4356 <$750
Total Issue $217,800
Out at close $16,850

Central NB of Albany
SEE Ch 10423
Central NB of New Decatur

Morgan County NB of Albany
SEE Ch 6380
Morgan County NB of New Decatur

11820 Marshall
ALBERTVILLE NB, ALBERTVILLE
{{ 4 L 12 S }}
Chartered 8/20
1902 Plain Back <$VALUE
4x5 1-25740 <$500
1929 Small Size
5 Type 1 1-9518 <$125
5 Type 2 1-19758 <$135
Total Issue $899,130
Out in 1935 $50,000
Large out 1935 $1,050

11819 Marshall
FNB OF ALBERTVILLE
{{ 15 S }}
Chartered 8/20
1929 Small Size <$VALUE
10 Type 1 1-3970 <$100
10 Type 2 1-14410 <$110
Total Issue $382,300
Out in 1935 $100,000

7417 Tallapoosa
FNB OF ALEXANDER CITY
{{ 3 L U + 10 S }}
Chartered 9/04
1902 Red Seal <$VALUE
4x5 1-1550 <$1250
3x10-20 1-1260 <$1250
1902 Date Back
4x5 1-4450 <$600
3x10-20 1-3500 <$600
1902 Plain Back
4x5 4451-13273 <$600
3x10-20 3501-9271 <$600
1929 Small Size
5 Type 1 1-3104 <$200
10 Type 1 1-1738 <$200
20 Type 1 1-464 <$200
5 Type 2 1-9076 <$225
10 Type 2 1-4776 <$225
20 Type 2 1-1332 <$225
Total Issue $1,195,870
Out in 1935 $100,000
Large out 1935 $3,200

11955 Covington
ANDALUSIA NB, ANDALUSIA
{{ 14 L 16 S }}
Organized 4/9/21
Receivership 10/5/32
1902 Plain Back <$VALUE
4x5 1-29140 <$125
3x10-20 1-19825 <$125
1929 Small Size
5 Type 1 1-7349 <$75
10 Type 1 1-3774 <$75
20 Type 1 1-1037 <$75
Total Issue $2,145,400
Out at close $200,000
Large out at close $12,340

5970 Covington
FNB OF ANDALUSIA
{{ 5 L 2 S }}
Chartered 9/01
Liquidated 5/30/32
Brown Back <$VALUE
3x10-20 1-2500 <$750
1882 Date Back
3x10-20 1-6600 <$750
1882 Value Back
3x10-20 6601-8167 <$750
1902 Plain Back
3x10-20 1-5646 <$350
1929 Small Size
10 Type 1 1-1060 <$500
20 Type 1 1-304 <$500
Total Issue $915,730
Out at close $50,000
Large out at close $3,880

Anniston City NB, Anniston
SEE Ch 4250
Anniston NB, Anniston

4250 Calhoun
ANNISTON NB, ANNISTON
Chartered 1890
2nd title: Anniston City NB 1/5/11
3rd title: Anniston NB 7/1/18
FIRST TITLE {{ 3 L }}
Brown Back <$VALUE
4x5 1-7800 <$600
3x10-20 1-3800 <$600
50-100 1-522 <$2500
1882 Date Back
4x5 1-1042 <$500
3x10-20 1-1058 <$500
1902 Date Back
4x5 1-885 <$250
3x10-20 1-1022* <$250
* 689-1000 not issued
SECOND TITLE {{ 3 L }}
1902 Date Back
4x5 1-8000 <$250
3x10-20 1-13300 <$250
1902 Plain Back
3x10-20 13301-17000 <$250
THIRD TITLE {{ 18 L 19 S }}
1902 Plain Back
4x5 1-36181 <$110
3x10-20 1-24587 <$110
1929 Small Size
5 Type 1 1-9768 <$70
10 Type 1 1-5320 <$70
20 Type 1 1-1210 <$75
5 Type 2 1-9938 <$75
10 Type 2 1-5021 <$75
20 Type 2 1-1260 <$80
Total Issue $4,396,750
Out in 1935 $100,000
Large out 1935 $10,920

6021 Calhoun
CITY NB OF ANNISTON
{{ UNREPORTED }}
Chartered 11/01
Liquidated 12/30/10
Brown Back <$VALUE
3x10-20 1-1800 <$2000
1882 Date Back
3x10-20 1-1588 <$2000
Total Issue $169,400
Out in 1911 $22,950

11753 Calhoun
COMMERCIAL NB OF ANNISTON
{{ 15 L 24 S }}
Chartered 6/20
1902 Plain Back <$VALUE
4x5 1-48492 <$100
3x10-20 1-30600 <$100
1929 Small Size
5 Type 1 1-15980 <$60
10 Type 1 1-8130 <$60
20 Type 1 1-1900 <$60
5 Type 2 1-17648 <$60
10 Type 2 1-9512 <$60
20 Type 2 1-2043 <$60
Total Issue $3,919,260
Out in 1935 $225,000
Large out 1935 $8,800

3041 Calhoun
FNB OF ANNISTON
{{ 10 L 2U + 14 S }}
Chartered 1883
Brown Back <$VALUE
3x10-20 1-4893 <$700
1902 Red Seal
3x10-20 1-4400 <$1000
1902 Date Back
3x10-20 1-11400 <$250
1902 Plain Back
3x10-20 11401-29012 <$250
1929 Small Size
10 Type 1 1-3470 <$75
20 Type 1 1-858 <$75
10 Type 2 1-5315 <$85
20 Type 2 1-1537 <$85
Total Issue $2,310,300
Out in 1935 $98,800
Large out 1935 $5,995

10102 Houston
FNB OF ASHFORD
{{ 2 L 0 S }}
Chartered 11/11
1902 Date Back <$VALUE
3x10-20 1-750 <$1000
1902 Plain Back
3x10-20 751-1625 <$1000
1929 Small Size
10 Type 1 1-254 <$850
20 Type 1 1-67 <$850
Total Issue $104,530
Out in 1935 $6,250
Large out 1935 $220

9580 Clay
FNB OF ASHLAND
{{ 3 L 9 S }}
Chartered 11/09
1902 Date Back <$VALUE
4x10 1-5250* <$600
1902 Plain Back
4x10 5501-18653* <$600
* 5251-5500 not marked
1929 Small Size
10 Type 1 1-3004 <$150
10 Type 2 1-6200 <$150
Total Issue $988,360
Out in 1935 $47,200
Large out 1935 $1,990

6146 Limestone
FNB OF ATHENS
{{ 2 L }}
Chartered 3/02
Liquidated 1/11/27
1902 Red Seal <$VALUE
4x5 1-1225 <$1500
3x10-20 1-1180 <$1500
1902 Date Back
4x5 1-4125 <$750
3x10-20 1-3170 <$750
1902 Plain Back (dated 1902)
4x5 4126-7735 <$750
3x10-20 3171-5238 <$750
1902 Plain Back (dated 1922)
4x5 1-3330 <$750
3x10-20 1-2334 <$750
Total Issue $683,400
Out at close $48,800

10697 Escambia
FNB OF ATMORE
{{ 2 L 6 S }}
Chartered 2/15
1902 Date Back <$VALUE
4x10 1-875 <$850
1902 Plain Back
4x10 876-6415 <$850
1929 Small Size
10 Type 1 1-1306 <$300
10 Type 2 1-5693 <$300
Total Issue $391,890
Out in 1935 $50,000
Large out 1935 $850

7951 Etowah
FNB OF ATTALLA
{{ UNREPORTED }}
Organized 10/05
Receivership 4/24/06
1902 Red Seal <$VALUE
4x5 1-525 <$2500
3x10-20 1-420 <$2500
Total Issue $31,500
Out in 1915 $590

12455 Lee
FNB OF AUBURN
{{ 1 L 4 S }}
Chartered 10/23
1902 Plain Back <$VALUE
4x5 1-8433 <$1500
1929 Small Size
5 Type 1 1-3558 <$650
5 Type 2 1-7980 <$650
Total Issue $315,300
Out in 1935 $20,000
Large out at close $435

6961 Jefferson
BESSEMER NB, BESSEMER
Organized 8/25/03
Receivership 12/28/33
2nd title:FNB in Bessemer 5/29/20
FIRST TITLE {{ 3 L }}
1902 Red Seal <$VALUE
3x10-20 1-4025 <$1000
1902 Date Back
3x10-20 1-12600 <$350
1902 Plain Back
3x10-20 12601-15000 <$350
SECOND TITLE {{ 5 L 10 S }}
1902 Plain Back
4x10 1-23133 <$300
1929 Small Size
10 Type 1 1-6738 <$125
10 Type 2 1-1652 <$150
Total Issue $2,297,370
Out at close $78,565
Large out at close $3,785

11905 Jefferson
CITY NB OF BESSEMER
{{ 5 L 4 S }}
Organized 12/6/20
Receivership 1/12/31
1902 Plain Back <$VALUE
4x5 1-10655 <$300
3x10-20 1-6821 <$300
1929 Small Size
5 Type 1 1-2507 <$300
10 Type 1 1-1149 <$300
20 Type 1 1-373 <$300
Total Issue $743,060
Out at close $100,000
Large out at close $7,980

13789 Jefferson
FNB AT BESSEMER
{{ 4 S }}
Chartered 9/33
1929 Small Size <$VALUE
10 Type 2 1-11280 <$350
Total Issue $112,800
Out in 1935 $43,330

FNB in Bessemer
SEE Ch 6961
Bessemer NB, Bessemer

4220 Jefferson
FNB OF BESSEMER
{{ UNREPORTED }}
Chartered 1/25/90
Liquidated 9/10/94
Brown Back <$VALUE
50-100 1-151 <$3500
Total Issue $22,650
Out in 1910 $550

3587 Jefferson
ALABAMA NB OF BIRMINGHAM
{{ UNREPORTED }}
Chartered 11/10/86
Liquidated 1/10/05
Brown Back <$VALUE
3x10-20 1-4778 <$1250
50-100 1-1463 <$3000
Total Issue $458,350
Out in 1910 $18,345

3734 Jefferson
AMERICAN NB OF BIRMINGHAM
{{ UNREPORTED }}
Chartered 6/23/87
Liquidated 3/22/92
Brown Back <$VALUE
3x10-20 1-1656 <$1500
Total Issue $82,800
Out in 1910 $670

American-Traders NB of Birmingham
SEE Ch 7020
Traders NB of Birmingham

3442 Jefferson
BERNEY NB OF BIRMINGHAM
{{ 1 L }}
Chartered 1/28/86
Liquidated 3/11/01
Brown Back <$VALUE
3x10-20 1-4202 <$1750
Total Issue $210,100
Out in 1910 $2,880

3679 Jefferson
BIRMINGHAM NB, BIRMINGHAM
{{ UNREPORTED }}
Chartered 4/23/87
Liquidated 5/2/92
Brown Back <$VALUE
50-100 1-599 <$3000
Total Issue $89,850
Out in 1910 $500

3993 Jefferson
CITY NB OF BIRMINGHAM
{{ 1 L }}
Chartered 3/18/89
Liquidated 1/8/95
Brown Back <$VALUE
50-100 1-334 <$2500
Total Issue $50,100
Out in 1910 $850

12906 Jefferson
ENSLEY NB OF BIRMINGHAM
{{ 12 L 8 S }}
Chartered 3/26
Liquidated 11/10/32
1902 Plain Back <$VALUE
4x5 1-22886 <$125
4x10 1-13169 <$125
1929 Small Size
5 Type 1 1-12991 <$110
10 Type 1 1-6955 <$125
Total Issue $984,480
Out at close $200,000
Large out at close $4,860

3185 Jefferson
FNB OF BIRMINGHAM
{{ 50+ L 50+ S }}
Chartered 1884
Brown Back <$VALUE
3x10-20 1-12068 <$500
1902 Red Seal
3x10-20 1-38500 <$500
1902 Date Back
4x5 1-115000 <$50
3x10-20 1-87400 <$60/$65
1902 Plain Back
4x5 115001-424771 <$50
3x10-20 87401-275620 <$65
1929 Small Size
5 Type 1 1-172042 <$15
10 Type 1 1-101360 <$20
20 Type 1 1-34040 <$30
5 Type 2 1-48830 <$20
10 Type 2 1-40249 <$20
20 Type 2 1-11190 <$30
Total Issue $41,002,920
Out in 1935 $2,500,000
Large out 1935 $98,595
Outstanding includes Ch 7020

2065 Jefferson
NB OF BIRMINGHAM
{{ 2 L }}
Chartered 11/27/72
Liquidated 5/14/84
Original Series <$VALUE
3x1-2 1-1900 <$1500/$4000
4x5 1-2775 <$1500
Series 1875
4x5 1-4490 <$1500
Total Issue $154,800
Out in 1910 $826

7020 Jefferson
TRADERS NB OF BIRMINGHAM
Chartered 10/03
Closed 6/30/30
2nd title:American-Traders NB of Birmingham 7/11/27
FIRST TITLE {{ 10 L }}
1902 Red Seal <$VALUE
4x5 1-3295 <$600
3x10-20 1-2607 <$600
1902 Date Back
4x5 1-10380 <$125
3x10-20 1-9308 <$125
1902 Plain Back
4x5 10381-54468 <$125
3x10-20 9309-38754 <$125
SECOND TITLE {{ 36 L 10 S }}
1902 Plain Back
4x5 1-126175 <$100
4x10 1-47332 <$100
3x10-20 1-61382 <$100
1929 Small Size
5 Type 1 1-51620 <$100
10 Type 1 1-23070 <$100
20 Type 1 1-7200 <$100
Total Issue $14,505,990
Out at close $2,750,000
Large out at close $239,950
Ch 3185 assumed circulation

13358 Jefferson
WOODLAWN-AMERICAN NB OF BIRMINGHAM
{{ 2U + 15 S }}
Chartered 7/29
Liquidated 5/8/35
1929 Small Size <$VALUE
5 Type 1 1-5402 <$40
10 Type 1 1-2860 <$40
20 Type 1 1-754 <$50
5 Type 2 1-9392 <$45
10 Type 2 1-5324 <$50
20 Type 2 1-1240 <$60
Total Issue $549,140
Out in 1935 $100,000

10441 Marshall
FNB OF BOAZ
{{ UNREPORTED }}
Chartered 9/13
Liquidated 8/4/16
1902 Date Back <$VALUE
4x10 1-572 <$2000
Total Issue $22,880
Out in 1916 $9,000

11870 Marshall
NB OF BOAZ
{{ 2 L 7 S }}
Chartered 11/20
1902 Plain Back <$VALUE
4x5 1-12056 <$850
1929 Small Size
5 Type 1 1-4516 <$225
5 Type 2 1-10380 <$225
Total Issue $428,500
Out in 1935 $25,000
Large out 1935 $550

7991 Crenshaw
FNB OF BRANTLEY
{{ 1 L 0 S }}
Organized 11/6/05
Receivership 2/17/30
1902 Red Seal <$VALUE
3x10-20 1-540 <$1500
1902 Date Back
3x10-20 1-1690 <$1000
1902 Plain Back
3x10-20 1691-3603 <$1000
1929 Small Size
10 Type 1 1-120 <$750
20 Type 1 1-3 <$800
Total Issue $214,710
Out at close $12,780
Large out at close $9,740

11168 Jackson
AMERICAN NB OF BRIDGEPORT
{{ 2 L 3 S }}
Chartered 4/18
1902 Plain Back <$VALUE
3x10-20 1-4593 <$850
1929 Small Size
10 Type 1 1-902 <$450
20 Type 1 1-224 <$450
10 Type 2 1-1173 <$450
20 Type 2 1-293 <$450
Total Issue $328,240
Out in 1935 $25,000
Large out 1935 $1,160

4591 Jackson
FNB OF BRIDGEPORT
{{ UNREPORTED }}
Chartered 6/30/91
Liquidated 1/1/97
Brown Back <$VALUE
3x10-20 1-469 <$2000
Total Issue $23,450
Out in 1910 $410

CONDITION affects Value. The Values shown are for notes in FINE condition.

7429 Pike
FNB OF BRUNDIDGE
{{ 6 L 8 S }}
Chartered 10/04
1902 Red Seal <$VALUE
4x5 1-2060 <$1000
3x10-20 1-1626 <$1000
1902 Date Back
4x5 1-4300 <$400
3x10-20 1-3320 <$400
1902 Plain Back
4x5 4301-13125 <$400
3x10-20 3321-9260 <$400
1929 Small Size
5 Type 1 1-1984 <$275
10 Type 1 1-1124 <$275
20 Type 1 1-278 <$275
5 Type 2 1-3490 <$300
10 Type 2 1-2101 <$300
20 Type 2 1-528 <$300
Total Issue $1,057,340
Out in 1935 $50,000
Large out 1935 $2,360

8217 Wilcox
CAMDEN NB, CAMDEN
{{ 1 L 4 S }}
Chartered 5/06
1902 Red Seal <$VALUE
3x10-20 1-400 <$2500
1902 Date Back
3x10-20 1-1060 <$1500
1902 Plain Back
3x10-20 1061-2535 <$1500
1929 Small Size
10 Type 1 1-316 <$400
20 Type 1 1-106 <$400
10 Type 2 1-178 <$400
20 Type 2 1-55 <$400
Total Issue $181,310
Out in 1935 $10,000
Large out 1935 $890

10066 Talladega
FNB OF CHILDERSBURG
{{ UNREPORTED }}
Chartered 8/11
Liquidated 3/10/19
1902 Date Back <$VALUE
3x10-20 1-1840 <$1500
1902 Plain Back
3x10-20 1841-2625 <$1500
Total Issue $131,250
Out at close $25,000

6835 Mobile
FNB OF CITRONELLE
{{ UNREPORTED }}
Organized 6/13/03
Receivership 3/25/16
1902 Red Seal <$VALUE
3x10-20 1-1350 <$2000
1902 Date Back
3x10-20 1-1873 <$1500
Total Issue $161,150
Out at close $24,700

11515 Chilton
FNB OF CLANTON
{{ 3 L 5 S }}
Chartered 11/19
1902 Plain Back <$VALUE
4x5 1-4876 <$750
4x10 1-2387 <$750
3x10-20 1-2166 <$750
1929 Small Size
5 Type 1 1-1310 <$400
10 Type 1 1-714 <$400
20 Type 1 1-204 <$400
5 Type 2 1-2028 <$450
10 Type 2 1-1140 <$450
20 Type 2 1-396 <$450
Total Issue $437,380
Out in 1935 $29,600
Large out at close $1,100

11259 Geneva
FNB OF COFFEE SPRINGS
{{ 1 L 0 S }}
Organized 10/28/18
Receivership 3/13/30
1902 Plain Back <$VALUE
4x5 1-9121 <$1500
1929 Small Size
5 Type 1 1-145 <$1000
Total Issue $186,770
Out at close $6,900
Large out at close $2,550

11337 De Kalb
FNB OF COLLINSVILLE
{{ 5 L 8 S }}
Chartered 4/19
1902 Plain Back <$VALUE
4x5 1-29393 <$375
1929 Small Size
5 Type 1 1-8678 <$225
5 Type 2 1-9276 <$225
Total Issue $894,580
Out in 1935 $25,000
Large out 1935 $1,870

8095 Houston
FNB OF COLUMBIA
{{ UNREPORTED }}
Chartered 2/06
Liquidated 4/3/16
1902 Red Seal <$VALUE
3x10-20 1-500 <$2500
1902 Date Back
3x10-20 1-2497 <$1500
Total Issue $149,850
Out in 1916 $14,270

7097 Cullman
FNB OF CULLMAN
{{ UNREPORTED }}
Chartered 1/14/04
Liquidated 12/4/05
1902 Red Seal <$VALUE
3x10-20 1-191 <$3000
Total Issue $9,550
Out in 1910 $540

9614 Cullman
LEETH NB OF CULLMAN
{{ 12 L 50+ S }}
Chartered 12/09
1902 Date Back <$VALUE
4x10 1-3200 <$275
1902 Plain Back
4x10 3201-27782 <$275
1929 Small Size
10 Type 1 1-6278 <$85
10 Type 2 1-10896 <$85
Total Issue $1,596,920
Out in 1935 $100,000
Large out 1935 $3,360

Central NB of Decatur
SEE Ch 10423
Central NB of New Albany

Morgan County NB of Decatur
SEE Ch 6380
Morgan County NB of
New Decatur

10336 Morgan
CITY NB OF DECATUR
Organized 2/2/13
Receivership 1/18/32
2nd title: FNB in Decatur
9/26/30
FIRST TITLE {{ 10 L 5 S }}
1902 Date Back <$VALUE
4x5 1-7650 <$150
4x10 1-7675 <$150
1902 Plain Back
4x5 7651-54697 <$150
4x10 7676-43822 <$150
1929 Small Size
5 Type 1 1-5534 <$150
10 Type 1 1-2888 <$150
SECOND TITLE {{ 3U + 14 S }}
1929 Small Size
5 Type 1 1-4313 <$85
10 Type 1 1-1955 <$85
Total Issue $3,432,810
Out at close $200,000
Large out at close $12,020

FNB in Decatur
SEE Ch 10336
City NB of Decatur

3699 Morgan
FNB OF DECATUR
{{ 1 L }}
Chartered 1887
Liquidated 6/21/13
Brown Back <$VALUE
3x10-20 1-3773 <$1250
1902 Red Seal
4x5 1-900 <$1500
4x10 1-425 <$1500
1902 Date Back
4x5 1-4683 <$850
4x10 1-4029 <$850
Total Issue $510,470
Out in 1913 $58,250

10035 Marengo
COMMERCIAL NB OF
DEMOPOLIS
{{ 9 L 12 S }}
Chartered 6/11
1902 Date Back <$VALUE
4x5 1-6900 <$175
3x10-20 1-5900 <$175
1902 Plain Back
4x5 6901-24592 <$175
3x10-20 5901-17295 <$175
1929 Small Size
5 Type 1 1-4736 <$100
10 Type 1 1-2572 <$100
20 Type 1 1-514 <$110
5 Type 2 1-7338 <$125
10 Type 2 1-3456 <$125
20 Type 2 1-737 <$135
Total Issue $1,800,660
Out in 1935 $75,000
Large out 1935 $4,350

4394 Marengo
FNB OF DEMOPOLIS
{{ 1 L }}
Chartered 8/13/90
Liquidated 3/9/07
Brown Back <$VALUE
50-100 1-432 <$3000
Total Issue 64,800
Out in 1910 $3,650

5909 Houston
DOTHAN NB, DOTHAN
{{ 18 L }}
Organized 7/6/01
Receivership 1/30/30
Brown Back <$VALUE
3x10-20 1-8400 <$350
1882 Date Back
4x5 1-20000 <$300
3x10-20 1-12900 <$300
1882 Value Back
4x5 20001-31500 <$300
3x10-20 12901-19300 <$300
1902 Plain Back
4x5 1-11415 <$85
3x10-20 1-6568 <$85/$100
Total Issue $2,571,700
Out at close $17,820

5249 Houston
FNB OF DOTHAN
{{ 20 L 32 S }}
Chartered 1/29/00
Brown Back <$VALUE
4x5 1-8375 <$400
3x10-20 1-9175 <$400
1882 Date Back
4x5 1-22850 <$350
3x10-20 1-17720 <$350
1882 Value Back
4x5 22851-29747 <$350
3x10-20 17721-21848 <$350
1902 Plain Back
4x5 1-16851 <$75
3x10-20 1-10460 <$75/$85
1929 Small Size
5 Type 1 1-11234 <$45
10 Type 1 1-5796 <$45
20 Type 1 1-1684 <$55
5 Type 2 1-19332 <$45
10 Type 2 1-9552 <$45
20 Type 2 1-1644 <$55
Total Issue $4,285,530
Out in 1935 $250,000
Large out 1935 $8,210

7932 Houston
HOUSTON NB OF DOTHAN
{{ 11 L 6 S }}
Organized 9/22/05
Receivership 10/15/31
1902 Red Seal <$VALUE
3x10-20 1-2100 <$1250
1902 Date Back
4x5 1-8400 <$350
3x10-20 1-7480 <$350
1902 Plain Back
4x5 8401-31835 <$350
3x10-20 7481-22251 <$350
1929 Small Size
5 Type 1 1-3524 <$225
10 Type 1 1-1539 <$225
20 Type 1 1-425 <$225
Total Issue $2,103,310
Out at close $127,000
Large out at close $14,035

7938 Houston
THIRD NB OF DOTHAN
{{ UNREPORTED }}
Chartered 10/05
Liquidated 2/3/14
1902 Red Seal <$VALUE
3x10-20 1-2000 <$1500
1902 Date Back
3x10-20 1-1634 <$1000
Total Issue $181,700
Out in 1914 $17,500

9681 Crenshaw
FNB OF DOZIER
{{ 0 L 4 S }}
Chartered 3/10
1902 Date Back <$VALUE
3x10-20 1-1260 <$1250
1902 Plain Back
3x10-20 1261-1732 <$1250
1929 Small Size
10 Type 1 1-900 <$325
20 Type 1 1-244 <$325
10 Type 2 1-1579 <$350
20 Type 2 1-406 <$350
Total Issue $193,790
Out in 1935 $30,000
Large out 1935 $620

6897 Coffee
FNB OF ELBA
{{ 5 L 12 S }}
Organized 7/20/03
Receivership 10/6/31
1902 Red Seal <$VALUE
3x10-20 1-3000 <$1000
1902 Date Back
3x10-20 1-4600 <$300
1902 Plain Back
3x10-20 4601-13629 <$300
1929 Small Size
10 Type 1 1-850 <$125
20 Type 1 1-233 <$125
Total Issue $910,410
Out at close $50,000
Large out at close $6,560

5962 Jefferson
FNB OF ENSLEY
{{ 1 L }}
Chartered 9/12/01
Liquidated 5/5/06
Brown Back <$VALUE
4x5 1-1755 <$1500
3x10-20 1-1479 <$1500
Total Issue $109,050
Out in 1910 $4,645

10421 Coffee
FARMERS & MERCHANTS NB OF
ENTERPRISE
{{ 8 L 10 S }}
Organized 7/2/13
Receivership 1/11/32
1902 Date Back <$VALUE
4x5 1-2370 <$300
4x10 1-2290 <$300
1902 Plain Back
4x5 2371-21774 <$300
4x10 2291-26747 <$300
1929 Small Size
10 Type 1 1-5202 <$150
Total Issue $1,817,480
Out at close $150,000
Large out at close $10,600
Outstanding includes Ch 10457

6319 Coffee
FNB OF ENTERPRISE
{{ 7 L 3 S }}
Organized 6/21/02
Receivership 7/18/32
1902 Red Seal <$VALUE
3x10-20 1-3100 <$1250
1902 Date Back
3x10-20 1-5500 <$350
1902 Plain Back
3x10-20 5501-14069 <$350
1929 Small Size
10 Type 1 1-880 <$350
20 Type 1 1-213 <$350
Total Issue $936,810
Out at close $50,000
Large out at close $5,140

5024 Barbour
COMMERCIAL NB OF EUFAULA
{{ 12 L 4 S }}
Organized 9/3/95
Receivership 10/27/31
Brown Back <$VALUE
3x10-20 1-5270 <$600
1882 Date Back
3x10-20 1-7457 <$500
1902 Date Back
3x10-20 1-16997 <$175
1929 Small Size
10 Type 1 1-1867 <$175
20 Type 1 1-562 <$175
Total Issue $1,665,660
Out at close $100,000
Large out at close $12,310

3622 Barbour
EAST ALABAMA NB OF
EUFAULA
{{ 9 L }}
Chartered 12/23/86
Receivership 7/1/29
Brown Back <$VALUE
4x5 1-5398 <$700
3x10-20 1-613 <$700
1902 Red Seal
3x10-20 1-390 <$1000
1902 Date Back
3x10-20 1-7900 <$275
1902 Plain Back
3x10-20 7901-19429 <$275
Total Issue $1,129,560
Out at close $70,450

2309 Barbour
EUFAULA NB, EUFAULA
{{ 1 L }}
Chartered 11/30/75
Receivership 10/21/01
Series 1875 <$VALUE
3x1-2 1-1620 <$2000/$4000
4x5 1-9223 <$2000
Brown Back
4x5 1-1868 <$1500
3x10-20 1-306 <$1500
Total Issue $245,220
Out in 1915 $1,451

3931 Greene
FNB OF EUTAW
{{ 10 L U + 13 S }}
Organized 10/5/88
Receivership 8/23/33
Brown Back <$VALUE
50-100 1-1380 <$2500
1902 Date Back
4x10 1-12150 <$275
1902 Plain Back
4x10 12151-37826 <$275
1929 Small Size
10 Type 1 1-6174 <$125
10 Type 2 1-479 <$125
Total Issue $2,095,270
Out at close $99,995
Large out at close $5,185

7687 Conecuh
FNB OF EVERGREEN
{{ 8 L 0 S }}
Chartered 4/05
Liquidated 6/10/30
1902 Red Seal <$VALUE
3x10-20 1-1200 <$1000
1902 Date Back
3x10-20 1-2120 <$500
1902 Plain Back
3x10-20 2121-6226 <$500
1929 Small Size
10 Type 1 1-251 <$750
20 Type 1 1-22 <$750
Total Issue $389,000
Out at close $24,430
Large out at close $6,730

11766 Jefferson
FAIRFIELD AMERICAN NB,
FAIRFIELD
{{ 16 S }}
Chartered 6/20 as FNB of Fairfield, under which there was no issue. Issuing title adopted 3/12/30.
Liquidated 5/9/35
1929 Small Size <$VALUE
5 Type 1 1-2978 <$150
10 Type 1 1-1528 <$150
5 Type 2 1-20898 <$165
10 Type 2 1-9360 <$165
Total Issue $439,110
Out at close $100,000

10377 Fayette
FNB OF FAYETTE
{{ 5 L 10 S }}
Chartered 4/13
1902 Date Back <$VALUE
4x5 1-1500 <$160
3x10-20 1-1100 <$450
3x50-100 1-120 <$1250/$1500
1902 Plain Back
4x5 1501-16067 <$450
3x10-20 1101-10855 <$450
1929 Small Size
5 Type 1 1-4742 <$175
10 Type 1 1-2490 <$165
20 Type 1 1-716 <$185
5 Type 2 1-8292 <$200
10 Type 2 1-5056 <$200
20 Type 2 1-1332 <$200
Total Issue $1,390,330
Out in 1935 $100,000
Large out at close $3,150

8910 Covington
FNB OF FLORALA
{{ 8 L 1 S }}
Organized 9/4/07
Receivership 1/13/30
1902 Red Seal <$VALUE
3x10-20 1-400 <$1250
1902 Date Back
3x10-20 1-4440 <$450
1902 Plain Back
3x10-20 4441-21696 <$450
1929 Small Size
10 Type 1 1-598 <$600
20 Type 1 1-50 <$600
Total Issue $1,146,680
Out at close $86,075
Large out at close $44,195

3981 Lauderdale
FNB OF FLORENCE
{{ 10 L 29 S }}
Chartered 1889
Brown Back <$VALUE
4x5 1-5645 <$750
3x10-20 1-1956 <$750
1902 Date Back
4x5 1-4700 <$250
3x10-20 1-3580 <$250
1902 Plain Back
4x5 4701-23775 <$250
3x10-20 3581-16240 <$250
1929 Small Size
5 Type 1 1-6000 <$125
10 Type 1 1-4814 <$125
20 Type 1 1-1194 <$125
5 Type 2 1-24760 <$150
10 Type 2 1-14747 <$150
20 Type 2 1-4752 <$150
Total Issue $2,476,630
Out in 1935 $299,995
Large out 1935 $4,695

4135 Lauderdale
FLORENCE NB, FLORENCE
{{ UNREPORTED }}
Chartered 10/3/89
Receivership 7/23/91
Brown Back <$VALUE
3x10-20 1-290 <$2000
Total Issue $14,500
Out in 1915 $180

4064 De Kalb
FNB OF FORT PAYNE
{{ UNREPORTED }}
Chartered 7/2/89
Receivership 1/26/94
Brown Back <$VALUE
3x10-20 1-429 <$2000
Total Issue $21,450
Out in 1915 $80

11451 De Kalb
FNB OF FORT PAYNE
{{ 4 L 13 S }}
Chartered 9/19
1902 Plain Back <$VALUE
4x5 1-28529 <$600
1929 Small Size
5 Type 1 1-8290 <$150
5 Type 2 1-20880 <$165
Total Issue $923,680
Out in 1935 $50,000
Large out 1935 $1,040

13412 Etowah
AMERICAN NB OF GADSDEN
{{ 14 S }}
Chartered 12/31/29
1929 Small Size <$VALUE
5 Type 2 1-20988 <$75
10 Type 2 1-16632 <$75
20 Type 2 1-4296 <$75
Total Issue $357,180
Out in 1935 $125,000

3663 Etowah
FNB OF GADSDEN
{{ 10 L 18 S }}
Organized 3/29/87
Liquidated 8/21/33
Brown Back <$VALUE
3x10-20 1-3397 <$750
1902 Red Seal
3x10-20 1-2000 <$1000
1902 Date Back
3x10-20 1-9100 <$250
1902 Plain Back
3x10-20 9101-29734 <$250
1929 Small Size
10 Type 1 1-5592 <$75
20 Type 1 1-1560 <$85
10 Type 2 1-1449 <$110
20 Type 2 1-211 <$125
Total Issue $2,297,980
Out at close $250,000
Large out at close $4,370
Ch 13728 assumed circulation

13728 Etowah
FNB OF GADSDEN
{{ 4 S }}
Chartered 7/33
1929 Small Size <$VALUE
10 Type 2 1-3587 <$400
20 Type 2 1-1034 <$400
Total Issue $56,550
Out in 1935 $101,150
Outstanding includes Ch 3663

8560 Etowah
GADSDEN NB, GADSDEN
{{ 10 L 6 S }}
Organized 1/25/07
Receivership 12/1/32
1902 Red Seal <$VALUE
3x10-20 1-2400 <$1000
1902 Date Back
3x10-20 1-10200 <$275
1902 Plain Back
3x10-20 10201-32214 <$275
1929 Small Size
10 Type 1 1-2787 <$250
20 Type 1 1-788 <$250
Total Issue $1,992,480
Out at close $102,740
Large out at close $6,160

1822 Sumter
GAINESVILLE NB, GAINESVILLE
{{ 2 L }}
Chartered 5/20/71
Liquidated 11/25/79
Original Series <$VALUE
3x1-2 1-3000 <$1500/$4000
4x5 1-1500 <$2000
3x10-20 1-1500<$2500/$3500
Series 1875
3x10-20 1-1284<$2000/$3000
Total Issue $184,200
Out in 1910 $1,227

10307 Geneva
FARMERS NB OF GENEVA
{{ 2 L 0 S }}
Organized 12/20/12
Receivership 10/25/33
1902 Date Back <$VALUE
3x10-20 1-1520 <$750
1902 Plain Back
3x10-20 1521-2930 <$750
1929 Small Size
10 Type 1 1-360 <$750
20 Type 1 1-108 <$750
Total Issue $181,060
Out at close $12,500
Large out at close $770

5714 Geneva
FNB OF GENEVA
{{ 4 L }}
Chartered 2/15/01
Liquidated 5/1/09
Brown Back <$VALUE
3x10-20 1-3100 <$750
1882 Date Back
3x10-20 1-40 <$750
Total Issue $157,000
Out in 1910 $15,060

12960 Coosa
FNB OF GOODWATER
{{ 2 L 5 S }}
Chartered 7/26
1902 Plain Back <$VALUE
4x5 1-5170 <$1250
1929 Small Size
5 Type 1 1-4122 <$500
5 Type 2 1-9984 <$500
Total Issue $276,980
Out in 1935 $25,000
Large out 1935 $460

5693 Hale
FNB OF GREENSBORO
{{ 14 L 5 S }}
Organized 1/15/01
Receivership 7/21/31
Brown Back <$VALUE
4x5 1-4300 <$400
3x10-20 1-3570 <$400
1882 Date Back
4x5 1-8100 <$350
3x10-20 1-6000 <$350
1882 Value Back
4x5 8101-13675 <$350
3x10-20 6001-8566 <$350
1902 Plain Back
3x10-20 1-13803 <$225
1929 Small Size
10 Type 1 1-1690 <$200
20 Type 1 1-551 <$200
Total Issue $1,823,970
Out at close $50,000
Large out at close $13,980

5572 Butler
FNB OF GREENVILLE
{{ 11 L 14 S }}
Chartered 9/10/00
Brown Back <$VALUE
4x5 1-2400 <$450
3x10-20 1-2600 <$450
1882 Date Back
4x5 1-7700 <$400
3x10-20 1-6000 <$400
1882 Value Back
4x5 7701-10820 <$400
3x10-20 6001-7656 <$400
1902 Plain Back
3x10-20 1-13092 <$250
1929 Small Size
10 Type 1 1-7704 <$100
20 Type 1 1-2268 <$100
10 Type 2 1-12535 <$110
20 Type 2 1-3024 <$110
Total Issue $2,352,030
Out in 1935 $250,000
Large out 1935 $4,800

10990 Marshall
FNB OF GUNTERSVILLE
{{ 2 L 12 S }}
Chartered 5/17
1902 Plain Back <$VALUE
3x10-20 1-7181 <$750
1929 Small Size
10 Type 1 1-1962 <$175
20 Type 1 1-492 <$175
10 Type 2 1-3516 <$200
20 Type 2 1-888 <$200
Total Issue $588,730
Out in 1935 $50,000
Large out 1935 $1,430

7592 Geneva
FNB OF HARTFORD
{{ 1 L 3 S }}
Chartered 2/05
1902 Red Seal <$VALUE
3x10-20 1-620 <$2000
1902 Date Back
3x10-20 1-1670 <$1250
1902 Plain Back
3x10-20 1671-3603 <$1250
1929 Small Size
10 Type 1 1-766 <$400
20 Type 1 1-180 <$400
10 Type 2 1-1381 <$400
20 Type 2 1-284 <$400
Total Issue $298,200
Out in 1935 $29,270
Large out 1935 $730

8067 Morgan
FNB OF HARTSELLE
{{ 9 L 5 S }}
Organized 1/15/06
Receivership 2/16/31
1902 Red Seal <$VALUE
4x5 1-425 <$1250
3x10-20 1-930 <$1250
1902 Date Back
4x5 1-4275 <$400
3x10-20 1-3080 <$400
1902 Plain Back
4x5 4276-22206 <$400
3x10-20 3081-15359 <$400
1929 Small Size
5 Type 1 1-2241 <$350
10 Type 1 1-1055 <$350
20 Type 1 1-270 <$350
Total Issue $1,430,000
Out at close $100,000
Large out at close $10,600

7975 Lowndes
FNB OF HAYNEVILLE
{{ UNREPORTED }}
Chartered 11/11/05
Liquidated 10/11/06
1902 Red Seal <$VALUE
3x10-20 1-220 <$2500
Total Issue $11,000
Out in 1910 $530

11445 Henry
FARMERS & MERCHANTS NB OF HEADLAND
{{ 1 L }}
Organized 8/25/19
Liquidated 2/7/35
1902 Plain Back <$VALUE
4x5 1-4420 <$1000
3x10-20 1-2706 <$1000
Total Issue $223,700
Out at close $365

7424 Henry
FNB OF HEADLAND
{{ 10 L 10 S }}
Organized 9/28/04
Liquidated 8/10/34
1902 Red Seal <$VALUE
3x10-20 1-2300 <$1000
1902 Date Back
4x5 1-5000 <$275
3x10-20 1-7000 <$275
1902 Plain Back
4x5 5001-30049 <$275
3x10-20 7001-18214 <$275
1929 Small Size
5 Type 1 1-1520 <$150
10 Type 1 1-2340 <$150
20 Type 1 1-846 <$150
10 Type 2 1-2184 <$175
20 Type 2 1-399 <$175
Total Issue $1,944,020
Out at close $100,000
Large out at close $5,635

13752 Henry
HEADLAND NB, HEADLAND
{{ 3 S }}
Chartered 8/33
1929 Small Size <$VALUE
5 Type 2 1-4176 <$350
10 Type 2 1-1956 <$350
20 Type 2 1-600 <$350
Total Issue $52,440
Out in 1935 $22,280

4689 Madison
FARMERS & MERCHANTS NB OF HUNTSVILLE
{{ UNREPORTED }}
Chartered 1/25/92
Liquidated 3/16/05
Brown Back <$VALUE
3x10-20 1-1912 <$2000
Total Issue $95,600
Out in 1910 $2,850

4067 Madison
FNB OF HUNTSVILLE
{{ 6 L 14 S }}
Chartered 1889
Brown Back <$VALUE
3x10-20 1-3817 <$1000
1902 Date Back
4x5 1-5000 <$500
3x10-20 1-7900 <$500
1902 Plain Back
4x5 5001-18697 <$500
3x10-20 7901-17101 <$500
1929 Small Size
5 Type 1 1-5256 <$150
10 Type 1 1-2762 <$150
20 Type 1 1-642 <$165
5 Type 2 1-8162 <$175
10 Type 2 1-4570 <$175
20 Type 2 1-1392 <$185
Total Issue $1,934,630
Out in 1935 $100,000
Large out 1935 $2,170

8765 Madison
HENDERSON NB OF HUNTSVILLE
{{ 12 L 50+ S }}
Chartered 6/07
1902 Red Seal <$VALUE
4x5 1-1750 <$1000
3x10-20 1-1400 <$1000
1902 Date Back
4x5 1-8500 <$300
3x10-20 1-6600 <$300
1902 Plain Back
4x5 8501-28325 <$300
3x10-20 6601-19854 <$300
1929 Small Size
5 Type 1 1-4506 <$85
10 Type 1 1-2470 <$85
20 Type 1 1-716 <$85
5 Type 2 1-5834 <$85
10 Type 2 1-3713 <$85
20 Type 2 1-1155 <$75
Total Issue $2,122,900
Out in 1935 $100,000
Large out 1935 $4,320

1560 Madison
NB OF HUNTSVILLE
{{ 2 L }}
Chartered 9/15/65
Liquidated 7/3/89
Original Series <$VALUE
4x5 1-2450 <$1250
3x10-20 1-2120<$1750/$2500
Series 1875
4x5 1-1730 <$1250
3x10-20 1-1514<$1750/$2000
Brown Back
3x10-20 1-1033 <$1000
Total Issue $316,950
Out in 1910 $1,765

5983 Clarke
FNB OF JACKSON
{{ 1 L }}
Chartered 10/01
Liquidated 4/18/10
Brown Back <$VALUE
3x10-20 1-500 <$2000
1882 Date Back
3x10-20 1-38 <$2000
Total Issue $26,900
Out in 1910 $4,550

FNB of Jacksonville
SEE Ch 4319
Tredegar NB of Jacksonville

4319 Calhoun
TREDEGAR NB OF JACKSONVILLE
Organized 5/6/90
Receivership 3/6/34
2nd title: FNB of Jacksonville 4/7/13
FIRST TITLE {{ 4 L }}
Brown Back <$VALUE
4x5 1-4925 <$600
3x10-20 1-2120 <$600
1882 Date Back
4x5 1-7421 <$500
3x10-20 1-479 <$500
1902 Date Back
4x5 1-1620 <$300
3x10-20 1-1380 <$300
SECOND TITLE {{ 2 L 4 S }}
1902 Date Back
4x5 1-625 <$300
3x10-20 1-510 <$300
1902 Plain Back
4x5 626-6078 <$300
3x10-20 511-3771 <$300
1929 Small Size
5 Type 1 1-1246 <$225
10 Type 1 1-580 <$225
20 Type 1 1-174 <$225
5 Type 2 1-378 <$250
10 Type 2 1-329 <$250
20 Type 2 1-49 <$250
Total Issue $754,000
Out in 1934 $25,000

7746 Walker
FNB OF JASPER
{{ 10 L 10 S }}
Chartered 5/05
1902 Red Seal <$VALUE
4x5 1-500 <$1250
3x10-20 1-400 <$1250
1902 Date Back
4x5 1-3975 <$350
3x10-20 1-3040 <$350
1902 Plain Back
4x5 3976-20165 <$350
3x10-20 3041-13959 <$350
1929 Small Size
5 Type 1 1-4958 <$175
10 Type 1 1-2820 <$175
20 Type 1 1-778 <$175
5 Type 2 1-10078 <$225
10 Type 2 1-6035 <$225
20 Type 2 1-1540 <$225
Total Issue $1,684,090
Out in 1935 $100,000
Large out 1935 $3,175

13359 Jefferson
LEEDS-AMERICAN NB, LEEDS
{{ 11 S }}
Chartered 7/29
Liquidated 5/10/35
1929 Small Size <$VALUE
5 Type 1 1-3284 <$175
10 Type 1 1-1362 <$175
5 Type 2 1-3740 <$200
10 Type 2 1-1764 <$200
Total Issue $216,580
Out in 1935 $25,000

10131 Talladega
FNB OF LINCOLN
{{ 3 L 3 S }}
Organized 1/23/12
Receivership 12/1/32
1902 Date Back <$VALUE
3x10-20 1-1650 <$1000
1902 Plain Back
3x10-20 1651-6854 <$1000
1929 Small Size
10 Type 1 1-797 <$500
20 Type 1 1-200 <$500
Total Issue $414,520
Out at close $24,760
Large out at close $2,090

7148 Marengo
FNB OF LINDEN
{{ 2 L 7 S }}
Chartered 2/04
1902 Red Seal <$VALUE
3x10-20 1-1160 <$1500
1902 Date Back
3x10-20 1-1510 <$850
1902 Plain Back
3x10-20 1511-4765 <$850
1929 Small Size
10 Type 1 1-698 <$250
20 Type 1 1-198 <$250
10 Type 2 1-3209 <$250
20 Type 2 1-562 <$250
Total Issue $405,220
Out in 1935 $50,000
Large out 1935 $1,440

8856 Clay
CITIZENS NB OF LINEVILLE
{{ 1 L }}
Chartered 9/07
Liquidated 6/30/24
1902 Red Seal <$VALUE
3x10-20 1-263 <$2000
1902 Date Back
3x10-20 1-6850 <$1250
1902 Plain Back
3x10-20 6851-15534 <$1250
Total Issue $631,880
Out at close $60,000

7516 Clay
FNB OF LINEVILLE
{{ UNREPORTED }}
Organized 12/16/04
Receivership 11/24/05
1902 Red Seal <$VALUE
3x10-20 1-137 <$3000
Total Issue $6,850
Out in 1910 $130

7551 Clay
LINEVILLE NB, LINEVILLE
{{ 5 L 10 S }}
Chartered 1/05
1902 Red Seal <$VALUE
3x10-20 1-800 <$1000
1902 Date Back
3x10-20 1-3610 <$400
1902 Plain Back
3x10-20 3611-12958 <$400
1929 Small Size
10 Type 1 1-1718 <$200
20 Type 1 1-442 <$200
10 Type 2 1-2923 <$200
20 Type 2 1-519 <$200
Total Issue $883,630
Out in 1935 $47,680
Large out 1935 $2,320

7992 Crenshaw
FNB OF LUVERNE
{{ 1 L 0 S }}
Chartered 12/05
Liquidated 9/9/30
1902 Red Seal <$VALUE
3x10-20 1-340 <$2500
1902 Date Back
3x10-20 1-1000* <$1500
1902 Plain Back
3x10-20 1501-2083* <$1500
* 1001-1500 not marked
1929 Small Size
10 Type 1 1-107 <$850
20 Type 1 1-6 <$850
Total Issue $128,290
Out at close $7,500
Large out at close $1,250

8458 Dale
FNB OF MIDLAND CITY
{{ 3 L 4 S }}
Organized 11/27/06
Receivership 9/28/31
1902 Red Seal <$VALUE
3x10-20 1-890 <$1250
1902 Date Back
3x10-20 1-3770 <$600
1902 Plain Back
3x10-20 3771-12375 <$600
1929 Small Size
10 Type 1 1-609 <$275
20 Type 1 1-181 <$275
Total Issue $721,510
Out at close $34,995
Large out at close $5,105

Alabama NB of Mobile
SEE Ch 1817
N Commercial B of Mobile

13414 Mobile
AMERICAN NB & TC OF MOBILE
{{ 2U + 40 S }}
Chartered 1/4/30
1929 Small Size <$VALUE
5 Type 1 1-8542 <$20
10 Type 1 1-5366 <$20
20 Type 1 1-1230 <$30
5 Type 2 1-33494 <$20
10 Type 2 1-18237 <$20
20 Type 2 1-3150 <$30
Total Issue $1,138,660
Out in 1935 $287,840

7062 Mobile
B OF MOBILE, N BANKING ASSOC., MOBILE
{{ 1 L }}
Chartered 12/03
Liquidated 8/7/17
1902 Red Seal <$VALUE
4x5 1-2925 <$1500
3x10-20 1-2330 <$1500
1902 Date Back
4x5 1-8200 <$850
3x10-20 1-5520 <$850
1902 Plain Back
4x5 8201-8710 <$850
3x10-20 5521-5812 <$850
Total Issue $639,000
Out at close $100,000

5219 Mobile
CITY NB OF MOBILE
{{ UNREPORTED }}
Chartered 9/5/99
Liquidated 3/31/03
Brown Back <$VALUE
3x10-20 1-5518 <$2000
Total Issue $275,900
Out in 1910 $9,165

CONDITION affects Value. The Values shown are for notes in FINE condition.

****
1595 Mobile
FNB OF MOBILE
{{ 33 L 50+ S }}
Chartered 1865
Original Series <$VALUE
3x1-2 1-6060 <$1500/$4000
4x5 1-3150 <$1500
3x10-20 1-8590<$2000/$3500
Series 1875
3x10-20 1-3584<$2000/$3000
500 1-292 <$150,000
Brown Back
3x10-20 1-8996 <$500
1902 Red Seal
3x10-20 1-30000 <$750
1902 Date Back
3x10-20 1-20000 <$60
1902 Plain Back
4x5 1-8585 <$60
3x10-20 20001-89778 <$60
1929 Small Size
5 Type 1 1-40932 <$15
10 Type 1 1-22190 <$20
20 Type 1 1-6070 <$30
5 Type 2 1-68250 <$15
10 Type 2 1-38388 <$20
20 Type 2 1-11220 <$30
Total Issue $10,345,690
Out in 1935 $1,000,000
Large out 1935 $10,245
****
13097 Mobile
MERCHANTS NB OF MOBILE
{{ 18 L 50+ S }}
Chartered 6/30/27
1902 Plain Back <$VALUE
4x5 1-40105 <$50
3x10-20 1-19943 <$50/$60
1929 Small Size
5 Type 1 1-40836 <$15
10 Type 1 1-22382 <$20
20 Type 1 1-6216 <$30
5 Type 2 1-72410 <$15
10 Type 2 1-35449 <$20
20 Type 2 1-10875 <$30
Total Issue $6,047,210
Out in 1935 $1,000,000
Large out 1935 $12,050
****
13195 Mobile
MOBILE NB, MOBILE
{{ 6 L 8 S }}
Chartered 3/31/28
Liquidated 12/8/31
1902 Plain Back <$VALUE
4x5 1-22469 <$175
1929 Small Size
5 Type 1 1-16258 <$125
Total Issue $937,120
Out at close $200,000
Large out at close $4,145
****
1817 Mobile
N COMMERCIAL B OF MOBILE
Chartered 5/13/71
Receivership 4/17/93
2nd title: Alabama NB of Mobile 2/28/91
FIRST TITLE {{ 1 L }}
Original Series <$VALUE
4x5 1-3700 <$2000
3x10-20 1-2720<$2500/$3500
50-100 1-1600 <$8500
Series 1875
3x10-20 1-900 <$2500/$3500
50-100 1-2084 <$8500
SECOND TITLE {{ 1 L }}
Brown Back
4x5 1-1184 <$1250
Total Issue $831,280
Out in 1915 $3,435
****
12642 Monroe
FNB OF MONROEVILLE
{{ 1 L 8 S }}
Chartered 2/25
1902 Plain Back <$VALUE
4x5 1-2426 <$1500
3x10-20 1-1276 <$1500
1929 Small Size
5 Type 1 1-1176 <$300
10 Type 1 1-610 <$300
20 Type 1 1-146 <$300
5 Type 2 1-4728 <$300
10 Type 2 1-2712 <$300
20 Type 2 1-660 <$300
Total Issue $265,680
Out in 1935 $50,000
Large out 1935 $620
****

****
12993 Montgomery
ALABAMA NB OF MONTGOMERY
{{ 11 L 20 S }}
Chartered 10/26
1902 Plain Back <$VALUE
4x5 1-58950 <$110
1929 Small Size
5 Type 2 1-32628 <$50
10 Type 2 1-17664 <$50
20 Type 2 1-4704 <$60
Total Issue $1,612,860
Out in 1935 $300,000
Large out 1935 $4,780
****
7141 Montgomery
AMERICAN NB OF MONTGOMERY
{{ UNREPORTED }}
Chartered 2/16/04
Liquidated 12/30/05
1902 Red Seal <$VALUE
50-100 1-423 <$5000
Total Issue $63,450
Out in 1910 $5,750
****
Capital NB of Montgomery
SEE Ch 8460
New Farley NB of Montgomery
****
8284 Montgomery
EXCHANGE NB OF MONTGOMERY
{{ 18 L }}
Chartered 6/06
Liquidated 4/24/26
1902 Red Seal <$VALUE
4x5 1-9000 <$650
3x10-20 1-6600 <$650
1902 Date Back
4x5 1-26000 <$65
3x10-20 1-19700 <$65/$75
1902 Plain Back
4x5 26001-69270 <$65
3x10-20 19701-45640<$65/$75
Total Issue $4,177,400
Out at close $300,000
Ch 1814 assumed circulation
****
4180 Montgomery
FARLEY NB OF MONTGOMERY
Chartered 12/18/89
Liquidated 7/16/06
2nd title: Merchants & Planters Farley NB 4/9/03
FIRST TITLE {{ 1 L }}
Brown Back <$VALUE
3x10-20 1-450 <$1250
50-100 1-1029 <$3000/$3500
SECOND TITLE {{ 2 L }}
Brown Back
3x10-20 1-13228 <$1000
Total Issue $838,250
Out in 1910 $55,360
****
1814 Montgomery
FNB OF MONTGOMERY
{{ 31 L 50 S }}
Chartered 4/28/71
Original Series <$VALUE
4x5 1-1250 <$1000
3x10-20 1-1000<$1750/$2500
50-100 1-1000 <$7500
Series 1875
4x5 1-112 <$1000
3x10-20 1-154 <$1500/$2000
50-100 1-1306 <$7500
Brown Back
3x10-20 1-31600 <$400
1882 Date Back
3x10-20 1-18854 <$300
1902 Date Back
3x10-20 1-45500 <$85
1902 Plain Back
3x10-20 45501-114366 <$85
1929 Small Size
5 Type 2 1-78280 <$40
10 Type 2 1-52430 <$45
20 Type 2 1-27549 <$55
Total Issue $10,138,520
Out in 1935 $750,000
Large out 1935 $30,225
Outstanding includes Ch 8284
****
5877 Montgomery
FOURTH NB OF MONTGOMERY
{{ 31 L }}
Organized 5/24/01
Receivership 9/6/30
Brown Back <$VALUE
3x10-20 1-18400 <$300
1882 Date Back
3x10-20 1-48500 <$300
1882 Value Back
3x10-20 48501-74070 <$300
1902 Plain Back
3x10-20 1-33034 <$75
Total Issue $6,275,200
Out at close $38,585
****
2029 Montgomery
MERCHANTS & PLANTERS NB OF MONTGOMERY
{{ 2 L }}
Chartered 8/19/72
Liquidated 5/19/03
Original Series <$VALUE
4x5 1-1000 <$1500
3x10-20 1-1040<$2500/$3500
50-100 1-500 <$8500
Series 1875
3x10-20 1-1542<$2500/$3500
50-100 1-300 <$8500
Brown Back
3x10-20 1-2291 <$1250
Total Issue $383,650
Out in 1910 $4,630
****
Merchants & Planters Farley NB of Montgomery
SEE Ch 4180
Farley NB of Montgomery
****
8460 Montgomery
NEW FARLEY NB OF MONTGOMERY
Chartered 12/06
Liquidated 2/15/22
2nd title: Capital NB of Montgomery 8/25/16
FIRST TITLE {{ 2 L }}
1902 Red Seal <$VALUE
3x10-20 1-6000 <$1250
1902 Date Back
3x10-20 1-18900 <$600
1902 Plain Back
3x10-20 18901-19825 <$600
SECOND TITLE {{ 4 L }}
1902 Plain Back
3x10-20 1-11044 <$350
Total Issue $1,843,450
Out at close $197,100
****
10457 Coffee
FNB OF NEW BROCKTON
{{ UNREPORTED }}
Chartered 10/13
Liquidated 3/12/23
1902 Date Back <$VALUE
4x5 1-1300 <$2000
4x10 1-1300 <$2000
1902 Plain Back
4x5 1301-3585 <$2000
4x10 1301-2779 <$2000
Total Issue $182,860
Out at close $22,000
Ch 10421 assumed circulation
****
10423 Morgan
CENTRAL NB OF NEW DECATUR
Organized 7/10/13
Liquidated 11/6/30
2nd title:Central NB of Albany 3/23/17
3rd title:Central NB of Decatur 12/8/27
FIRST TITLE {{ 1 L }}
1902 Date Back <$VALUE
4x5 1-3165 <$500
3x10-20 1-2534 <$500
1902 Plain Back
4x5 3166-3945 <$500
3x10-20 2535-3115 <$500
SECOND TITLE {{ 9 L }}
1902 Plain Back
4x5 1-30432 <$200
3x10-20 1-20588 <$200
THIRD TITLE {{ 2 L 7 S }}
1902 Plain Back
3x10-20 1-6180 <$450
1929 Small Size
10 Type 1 1-2903 <$200
20 Type 1 1-781 <$200
Total Issue $2,449,590
Out at close $200,000
Large out at close $25,990
****
6380 Morgan
MORGAN COUNTY NB OF NEW DECATUR
Chartered 8/02
2nd title:Morgan County NB of Albany 3/16/17
3rd title:Morgan County NB of Decatur 3/26/28
FIRST TITLE {{ 2 L }}
1902 Red Seal <$VALUE
4x5 1-2375 <$1000
3x10-20 1-1613 <$1000
1902 Date Back
4x5 1-4500 <$500
3x10-20 1-3540 <$500
1902 Plain Back
4x5 4501-5575 <$500
3x10-20 3541-4298 <$500
SECOND TITLE {{ 9 L }}
1902 Plain Back
4x5 1-25656 <$175
3x10-20 1-16963 <$175
THIRD TITLE {{ 1 L 14 S }}
1902 Plain Back
4x5 1-7054 <$350
1929 Small Size
5 Type 1 1-16176 <$85
5 Type 2 1-39684 <$85
Total Issue $2,640,600
Out in 1935 $100,000
Large out 1935 $5,425
****
9927 Henry
FNB OF NEWVILLE
{{ 3 L 2 S }}
Chartered 2/11
Liquidated 4/21/31
1902 Date Back <$VALUE
3x10-20 1-2130 <$750
1902 Plain Back
3x10-20 2131-6608 <$750
1929 Small Size
10 Type 1 1-325 <$600
20 Type 1 1-115 <$600
Total Issue $363,700
Out at close $25,000
Large out at close $3,360
****
12006 Blount
FNB OF ONEONTA
{{ 2 L 7 S }}
Chartered 8/21
1902 Plain Back <$VALUE
4x5 1-8539 <$850
1929 Small Size
5 Type 1 1-3408 <$300
5 Type 2 1-8496 <$300
Total Issue $315,500
Out in 1935 $20,000
Large out 1935 $290
****
9550 Lee
FARMERS NB OF OPELIKA
{{ 14 L 3U + 26 S }}
Chartered 9/09
1902 Date Back <$VALUE
4x5 1-7650 <$150
3x10-20 1-5800 <$150
1902 Plain Back
4x5 7651-45219 <$150
3x10-20 5801-37264 <$150
1929 Small Size
5 Type 1 1-8130 <$50
10 Type 1 1-4386 <$50
20 Type 1 1-1476 <$60
5 Type 2 1-8950 <$60
10 Type 2 1-4009 <$60
20 Type 2 1-1244 <$70
Total Issue $3,561,480
Out in 1935 $99,995
Large out 1935 $8,555
****
3452 Lee
FNB OF OPELIKA
{{ 15 L 15 S }}
Chartered 1886
Brown Back <$VALUE
4x5 1-4554 <$500
3x10-20 1-5151 <$500
1902 Red Seal
3x10-20 1-2800 <$1000
1902 Date Back
3x10-20 1-11400 <$150
1902 Plain Back
3x10-20 11401-28069 <$150
1929 Small Size
10 Type 1 1-3422 <$70
20 Type 1 1-854 <$85
10 Type 2 1-4171 <$85
20 Type 2 1-1248 <$85
Total Issue $2,266,550
Out in 1935 $100,000
Large out 1935 $6,380
****
11635 Lee
NB OF OPELIKA
{{ 18 L 22 S }}
Chartered 3/20
1902 Plain Back <$VALUE
4x5 1-20419 <$110
3x10-20 1-14395 <$110
1929 Small Size
5 Type 1 1-5328 <$50
10 Type 1 1-2898 <$50
20 Type 1 1-768 <$60
5 Type 2 1-9708 <$50
10 Type 2 1-4620 <$50
20 Type 2 1-1524 <$60
Total Issue $1,679,230
Out in 1935 $125,000
Large out 1935 $4,480
****
7985 Covington
FNB OF OPP
{{ 12 L 32 S }}
Chartered 11/05
1902 Red Seal <$VALUE
3x10-20 1-1000 <$1000
1902 Date Back
3x10-20 1-5700 <$275
1902 Plain Back
3x10-20 5701-30534 <$275
1929 Small Size
10 Type 1 1-6392 <$85
20 Type 1 1-1704 <$85
10 Type 2 1-6182 <$100
20 Type 2 1-1155 <$100
Total Issue $2,249,620
Out in 1935 $100,000
Large out 1935 $9,360
****
7073 Calhoun
FNB OF OXFORD
{{ U + 10 L 3 S }}
Organized 12/14/03
Receivership 10/10/33
1902 Red Seal <$VALUE
4x5 1-250 <$1000
3x10-20 1-210 <$1000
1902 Date Back
4x5 1-1300 <$375
3x10-20 1-1020 <$375
1902 Plain Back
4x5 1301-7234 <$375
3x10-20 1021-4562 <$375
1929 Small Size
5 Type 1 1-1040 <$325
10 Type 1 1-600 <$325
20 Type 1 1-194 <$350
5 Type 2 1-752 <$400
10 Type 2 1-82 <$400
20 Type 2 1-65 <$400
Total Issue $484,640
Out at close $25,000
Large out at close $1,765
****
9925 Calhoun
OXFORD NB, OXFORD
{{ UNREPORTED }}
Chartered 1/11
Liquidated 5/3/15
1902 Date Back <$VALUE
3x10-20 1-2608 <$1500
Total Issue $130,400
Out at close $34,000
****
7629 Dale
FNB OF OZARK
{{ 3 L }}
Organized 2/13/05
Receivership 10/23/24
1902 Red Seal <$VALUE
3x10-20 1-380 <$2000
1902 Date Back
3x10-20 1-3490 <$850
1902 Plain Back
3x10-20 3491-6880 <$850
Total Issue $363,000
Out at close $32,400
****
9506 St Clair
FNB OF PELL CITY
{{ 1 L }}
Chartered 8/09
Liquidated 1/8/18
1902 Date Back <$VALUE
4x5 1-1250 <$1250
3x10-20 1-2040 <$1250
1902 Plain Back
4x5 1251-1265 <$1250
3x10-20 2041-2599 <$1250
Total Issue $155,250
Out at close $25,000
****
7464 Calhoun
FNB OF PIEDMONT
{{ 3 L 7 S }}
Chartered 11/04
1902 Red Seal <$VALUE
3x10-20 1-983 <$1500
1902 Date Back
3x10-20 1-2250 <$750
1902 Plain Back
3x10-20 2251-12250 <$750
1929 Small Size
10 Type 1 1-1710 <$300
20 Type 1 1-466 <$300
10 Type 2 1-1459 <$325
20 Type 2 1-412 <$325
Total Issue $843,150
Out in 1935 $25,000
Large out 1935 $2,530
****
9055 Autauga
FNB OF PRATTVILLE
{{ 1 L 0 S }}
Organized 2/24/08
Receivership 6/1/31
1902 Red Seal <$VALUE
4x5 1-400 <$2000
3x10-20 1-340 <$2000
1902 Date Back
4x5 1-1750 <$1000
3x10-20 1-1280 <$1000
1902 Plain Back
4x5 1751-3758 <$1000
3x10-20 1281-2588 <$1000
1929 Small Size
5 Type 1 1-352 <$750
10 Type 1 1-162 <$750
20 Type 1 1-31 <$750
Total Issue $253,560
Out at close $12,500
Large out at close $1,450
****
11233 Pickens
FNB OF REFORM
{{ 1 L }}
Chartered 8/18
Liquidated 11/4/24
1902 Plain Back <$VALUE
4x5 1-2965 <$1500
Total Issue $59,300
Out at close $10,000
****
11846 Franklin
FNB OF RUSSELLVILLE
{{ 1 L U + 2 S }}
Organized 9/13/20
1902 Plain Back <$VALUE
4x5 1-2656 <$1250
1929 Small Size
5 Type 1 1-1028 <$500
5 Type 2 1-1524 <$500
Total Issue $91,580
Out in 1935 $5,000
****
8028 Geneva
FNB OF SAMSON
{{ UNREPORTED }}
Organized 12/22/06
Receivership 1/8/30
1902 Red Seal <$VALUE
3x10-20 1-500 <$2500
1902 Date Back
3x10-20 1-1520 <$2000
1902 Plain Back
3x10-20 1521-3314 <$2000
1929 Small Size
10 Type 1 1-93 <$850
20 Type 1 1-6 <$850
Total Issue $197,000
Out at close $12,500
Large out at close $6,200
****
8963 Jackson
FNB OF SCOTTSBORO
{{ 2 L 5 S }}
Chartered 12/07
1902 Red Seal <$VALUE
4x5 1-600 <$1250
4x10 1-600 <$1250
1902 Date Back
4x5 1-2025 <$750
4x10 1-2025 <$750
1902 Plain Back
4x5 2026-7339 <$750
4x10 2026-5931 <$750
1929 Small Size
5 Type 1 1-1882 <$350
10 Type 1 1-804 <$325
5 Type 2 1-4020 <$350
10 Type 2 1-1884 <$350
Total Issue $563,660
Out in 1935 $24,150
****

<$VALUEs are for notes in FINE condition. Value changes by approximately 25% for a change of one full grade.

****
1736 Dallas
CITY NB OF SELMA
{{ 50+ L 37 S }}
Chartered 11/70
Original Series <$VALUE
4x5 1-2500 <$600
3x10-20 1-5500<$1500/$2500
50-100 1-634 <$8500
Series 1875
4x5 1-185 <$600
3x10-20 1-3300<$1500/$2250
50-100 1-4563 <$8500
Brown Back
4x5 1-9700 <$300
50-100 1-12128 <$2000
1882 Date Back
4x5 1-6160 <$250
50-100 1-1541 <$2000
1902 Date Back
4x5 1-19000 <$100
4x10 1-15250 <$100
3x50-100 1-1000<$850/$1000
1902 Plain Back
4x5 19001-73479 <$100
4x10 15251-78149 <$100
1929 Small Size
10 Type 1 1-24590 <$35
10 Type 2 1-46223 <$35
Total Issue $10,423,970
Out in 1935 $396,800
Large out 1935 $25,640
****
1537 Dallas
FNB OF SELMA
{{ 1 L }}
Organized 8/24/65
Receivership 4/30/67
Original Series <$VALUE
4x5 1-4250 <$2000
Total Issue $85,000
Out in 1915 $375
****
7084 Dallas
SELMA NB, SELMA
{{ 12 L 24 S }}
Chartered 1/04
1902 Red Seal <$VALUE
4x5 1-8500 <$800
3x10-20 1-7400 <$800
1902 Date Back
4x5 1-19000 <$125
3x10-20 1-13500 <$125
1902 Plain Back
4x5 19001-55858 <$125
3x10-20 13501-37580 <$125
1929 Small Size
5 Type 1 1-8886 <$40
10 Type 1 1-4730 <$40
20 Type 1 1-1238 <$50
5 Type 2 1-14436 <$40
10 Type 2 1-8820 <$50
20 Type 2 1-2016 <$60
Total Issue $4,435,800
Out in 1935 $200,000
Large out 1935 $10,915
****
3617 Colbert
FNB OF SHEFFIELD
{{ 1 L }}
Chartered 1/14/87
Receivership 12/23/89
Brown Back <$VALUE
4x5 1-1035 <$2000
3x10-20 1-224 <$2000
Total Issue $31,900
Out in 1915 $260
****
6759 Colbert
SHEFFIELD NB, SHEFFIELD
{{ 6 L 8 S }}
Chartered 5/03
1902 Red Seal <$VALUE
3x10-20 1-3200 <$1500
1902 Date Back
3x10-20 1-4760 <$600
1902 Plain Back
3x10-20 4761-13383 <$600
1929 Small Size
10 Type 1 1-1624 <$300
20 Type 1 1-388 <$300
10 Type 2 1-2738 <$300
20 Type 2 1-776 <$300
Total Issue $1,016,050
Out in 1935 $50,000
Large out at close $2,510
****

****
7871 Geneva
FNB OF SLOCOMB
{{ UNREPORTED }}
Chartered 8/05
Liquidated 1/28/16
1902 Red Seal <$VALUE
3x10-20 1-1150 <$2000
1902 Date Back
3x10-20 1-2398 <$1250
Total Issue $177,400
Out in 1916 $14,940
****
7940 Geneva
SLOCOMB NB, SLOCOMB
{{ 2 L U + 10 S }}
Chartered 10/05
1902 Red Seal <$VALUE
3x10-20 1-1400 <$1250
1902 Date Back
3x10-20 1-3210 <$750
1902 Plain Back
3x10-20 3211-9197 <$750
1929 Small Size
5 Type 1 1-294 <$225
10 Type 1 1-996 <$225
20 Type 1 1-266 <$250
5 Type 2 1-2372 <$250
10 Type 2 1-1412 <$250
20 Type 2 1-345 <$275
Total Issue $663,230
Out in 1935 $32,900
Large out 1935 $1,400
****
9855 Jackson
FNB OF STEVENSON
{{ 1 L 6 S }}
Chartered 9/10
1902 Date Back <$VALUE
3x10-20 1-1100* <$1250
1902 Plain Back
3x10-20 1201-5296* <$1250
* 1101-1200 not marked
1929 Small Size
10 Type 1 1-864 <$325
20 Type 1 1-266 <$325
10 Type 2 1-1002 <$350
20 Type 2 1-204 <$375
Total Issue $362,660
Out in 1935 $25,000
Large out 1935 $750
****
10879 Talladega
CITY NB OF SYLACAUGA
{{ 5 L 14 S }}
Chartered 7/16
1902 Plain Back <$VALUE
4x5 1-17075 <$250
3x10-20 1-10865 <$250
1929 Small Size
5 Type 1 1-3902 <$75
10 Type 1 1-2108 <$75
20 Type 1 1-586 <$90
5 Type 2 1-7620 <$90
10 Type 2 1-4068 <$90
20 Type 2 1-1020 <$100
Total Issue $1,297,790
Out in 1935 $75,000
Large out at close $2,460
****
7451 Talladega
FNB OF SYLACAUGA
{{ 5 L 2 S }}
Organized 10/10/04
Receivership 7/27/32
1902 Red Seal <$VALUE
4x5 1-1325 <$1000
3x10-20 1-980 <$1000
1902 Date Back
4x5 1-2800 <$300
3x10-20 1-1480 <$300
1902 Plain Back
4x5 2801-10517 <$300
3x10-20 1481-6839 <$300
1929 Small Size
5 Type 1 1-2146 <$300
10 Type 1 1-1010 <$300
20 Type 1 1-289 <$325
Total Issue $787,450
Out at close $48,075
Large out at close $3,025
****

****
7484 Talladega
MERCHANTS & PLANTERS NB OF SYLACAUGA
{{ 8 L 10 S }}
Chartered 11/04
1902 Red Seal <$VALUE
4x5 1-2100 <$850
3x10-20 1-1735 <$850
1902 Date Back
4x5 1-4150 <$200
3x10-20 1-3000 <$200
1902 Plain Back
4x5 4151-14670 <$200
3x10-20 3001-9777 <$200
1929 Small Size
5 Type 1 1-2648 <$100
10 Type 1 1-1334 <$100
20 Type 1 1-358 <$100
5 Type 2 1-5884 <$125
10 Type 2 1-3228 <$100
20 Type 2 1-780 <$125
Total Issue $1,190,740
Out in 1935 $49,995
Large out 1935 $2,700
****
3899 Talladega
FNB OF TALLADEGA
{{ UNREPORTED }}
Chartered 6/16/88
Liquidated 2/19/07
Brown Back <$VALUE
3x10-20 1-3869 <$1500
Total Issue $193,450
Out in 1910 $7,170
****
4838 Talladega
ISBELL NB OF TALLADEGA
{{ 13 L 8 S }}
Chartered 1893
Brown Back <$VALUE
3x10-20 1-5350 <$600
1882 Date Back
3x10-20 1-2475 <$500
1902 Date Back
3x10-20 1-1900 <$175
1902 Plain Back
3x10-20 1901-11654 <$175
1929 Small Size
10 Type 1 1-1902 <$125
20 Type 1 1-440 <$125
5 Type 2 1-72 <$150
10 Type 2 1-3511 <$150
20 Type 2 1-828 <$150
Total Issue $1,192,900
Out in 1935 $50,000
Large out 1935 $3,255
****
7558 Talladega
TALLADEGA NB, TALLADEGA
{{ 12 L 18 S }}
Chartered 1/05
1902 Red Seal <$VALUE
3x10-20 1-4550 <$850
1902 Date Back
3x10-20 1-17300 <$200
1902 Plain Back
3x10-20 17301-42043 <$200
1929 Small Size
5 Type 1 1-2176 <$85
10 Type 1 1-5768 <$75
20 Type 1 1-1228 <$75
5 Type 2 1-22652 <$85
10 Type 2 1-10676 <$85
Total Issue $3,126,390
Out in 1935 $150,000
Large out 1935 $7,850
****
10766 Elmore
FNB OF TALLASSEE
{{ 2 L 1 S }}
Organized 7/14/15
Receivership 3/6/30
1902 Plain Back <$VALUE
4x5 1-5698 <$850
3x10-20 1-3508 <$850
1929 Small Size
5 Type 1 1-366 <$750
10 Type 1 1-129 <$750
20 Type 1 1-15 <$750
Total Issue $309,880
Out at close $24,400
Large out at close $4,280
****

****
7371 Clarke
CITIZENS NB OF THOMASVILLE
{{ UNREPORTED }}
Chartered 4/25/04
Liquidated 6/1/07
1902 Red Seal <$VALUE
3x10-20 1-828 <$2500
Total Issue $41,400
Out in 1910 $3,730
****
5664 Clarke
FNB OF THOMASVILLE
{{ UNREPORTED }}
Chartered 1/3/01
Liquidated 6/1/07
Brown Back <$VALUE
3x10-20 1-1092 <$2000
Total Issue $54,600
Out in 1910 $4,360
****
7044 Pike
FARMERS & MERCHANTS NB OF TROY
{{ 12 L 8 S }}
Chartered 11/03
Closed 8/14/31
1902 Red Seal <$VALUE
4x5 1-5675 <$850
3x10-20 1-4955 <$850
1902 Date Back
4x5 1-14250 <$275
3x10-20 1-10800 <$275
1902 Plain Back
4x5 14251-34831 <$275
3x10-20 10801-24027 <$275
1929 Small Size
5 Type 1 1-2998 <$175
10 Type 1 1-1468 <$175
20 Type 1 1-410 <$175
Total Issue $2,486,440
Out at close $128,600
Large out at close $12,400
Ch 5593 assumed circulation
****
F Farmers & Merchants NB of Troy
SEE Ch 5593
FNB of Troy
****
5593 Pike
FNB OF TROY
Chartered 10/10/00
2nd title: F Farmers & Merchants NB 8/14/31
FIRST TITLE {{ 12 L 3 S }}
Brown Back <$VALUE
4x5 1-3380 <$600
3x10-20 1-2728 <$600
1882 Date Back
4x5 1-8950 <$500
3x10-20 1-6560 <$500
1882 Value Back
4x5 8951-13290 <$500
3x10-20 6561-8964 <$500
1902 Plain Back
4x5 1-13362 <$200
3x10-20 1-9234 <$200
1929 Small Size
5 Type 1 1-2634 <$200
10 Type 1 1-1506 <$200
20 Type 1 1-344 <$200
SECOND TITLE {{ 31 S }}
1929 Small Size
5 Type 1 1-5036 <$75
10 Type 1 1-3226 <$75
20 Type 1 1-686 <$85
5 Type 2 1-35316 <$75
10 Type 2 1-11276 <$75
20 Type 2 1-3412 <$85
Total Issue $2,642,140
Out in 1935 $300,000
Large out 1935 $9,930
Outstanding includes Ch 7044
****
6173 Tuscaloosa
CITY NB OF TUSCALOOSA
{{ 13 L 21 S }}
Chartered 3/02
1902 Red Seal <$VALUE
4x5 1-2300 <$1000
3x10-20 1-3180 <$1000
1902 Date Back
4x5 1-6950 <$175
3x10-20 1-5360 <$175
1902 Plain Back (dated 1902)
4x5 6951-16100 <$175
3x10-20 5361-10461 <$175
1902 Plain Back (dated 1922)
4x5 1-67521 <$175
1929 Small Size
5 Type 1 1-9192 <$75
10 Type 1 1-4668 <$70
20 Type 1 1-1070 <$75
5 Type 2 1-19800 <$80
10 Type 2 1-11004 <$80
20 Type 2 1-3132 <$90
Total Issue $3,356,390
Out in 1935 $200,000
Large out 1935 $5,120
****
1853 Tuscaloosa
FNB OF TUSCALOOSA
{{ 12 L 16 S }}
Chartered 7/28/71
Original Series <$VALUE
3x1-2 1-1500 <$1250/$4000
4x5 1-2875 <$1000
Series 1875
4x5 1-8015 <$1000
Brown Back
3x10-20 1-4540 <$450
1882 Date Back
4x5 1-2430 <$400
3x10-20 1-3136 <$400
1902 Date Back
4x5 1-6500* <$150
4x10 1-6250** <$150
1902 Plain Back
4x5 7251-38818* <$150
4x10 7001-30036** <$150
* 6501-7250 not marked
** 6251-7000 not marked
1929 Small Size
5 Type 1 1-12286 <$75
10 Type 1 1-6048 <$75
5 Type 2 1-7276 <$75
10 Type 2 1-4183 <$75
Total Issue $3,445,170
Out in 1935 $75,000
****
3678 Tuscaloosa
MERCHANTS NB OF TUSCALOOSA
{{ UNREPORTED }}
Chartered 4/23/87
Liquidated 1/19/07
Brown Back <$VALUE
4x5 1-5938 <$1750
50-100 1-374 <$3500
Total Issue $174,860
Out in 1910 $5,675
****
11281 Colbert
FNB OF TUSCUMBIA
{{ 4 L 7 S }}
Organized 12/17/18
Receivership 6/18/34
1902 Plain Back <$VALUE
4x5 1-7676 <$750
4x10 1-6492 <$750
1929 Small Size
5 Type 1 1-2504 <$300
10 Type 1 1-1404 <$300
5 Type 2 1-1692 <$325
10 Type 2 1-1345 <$325
20 Type 2 1-132 <$350
Total Issue $597,110
Out at close $38,550
Large out at close $900
****
12962 Bullock
AMERICAN NB OF UNION SPRINGS
{{ 1 L 12 S }}
Chartered 7/26
1902 Plain Back <$VALUE
4x5 1-1999 <$1000
3x10-20 1-976 <$1000
1929 Small Size
5 Type 1 1-3556 <$175
10 Type 1 1-1708 <$175
5 Type 2 1-7430 <$200
10 Type 2 1-3864 <$200
Total Issue $363,970
Out in 1935 $50,000
Large out 1935 $750
****

****
7467 Bullock
FNB OF UNION SPRINGS
{{ 5 L 7 S }}
Chartered 11/04
1902 Red Seal <$VALUE
4x5 1-1115 <$1500
3x10-20 1-854 <$1500
1902 Date Back
4x5 1-3275 <$500
3x10-20 1-2520 <$500
1902 Plain Back
4x5 3276-8082 <$500
3x10-20 2521-5336 <$500
1929 Small Size
5 Type 1 1-1782 <$200
10 Type 1 1-886 <$200
20 Type 1 1-250 <$200
5 Type 2 1-4436 <$225
10 Type 2 1-2537 <$225
20 Type 2 1-672 <$225
Total Issue $691,050
Out in 1935 $50,000
Large out 1935 $1,150
****
7568 Elmore
FNB OF WETUMPKA
{{ 0 L 4 S }}
Chartered 1/05
1902 Red Seal <$VALUE
4x5 1-887 <$2000
3x10-20 1-705 <$2000
1902 Date Back
4x5 1-2175 <$1000
3x10-20 1-1540 <$1000
1902 Plain Back
4x5 2176-5829 <$1000
3x10-20 1541-4015 <$1000
1929 Small Size
5 Type 1 1-1090 <$450
10 Type 1 1-548 <$450
20 Type 1 1-170 <$450
5 Type 2 1-1842 <$500
10 Type 2 1-1066 <$500
20 Type 2 1-309 <$500
Total Issue $482,350
Out in 1935 $25,000
Large out 1935 $840
****

ALASKA — ARIZONA

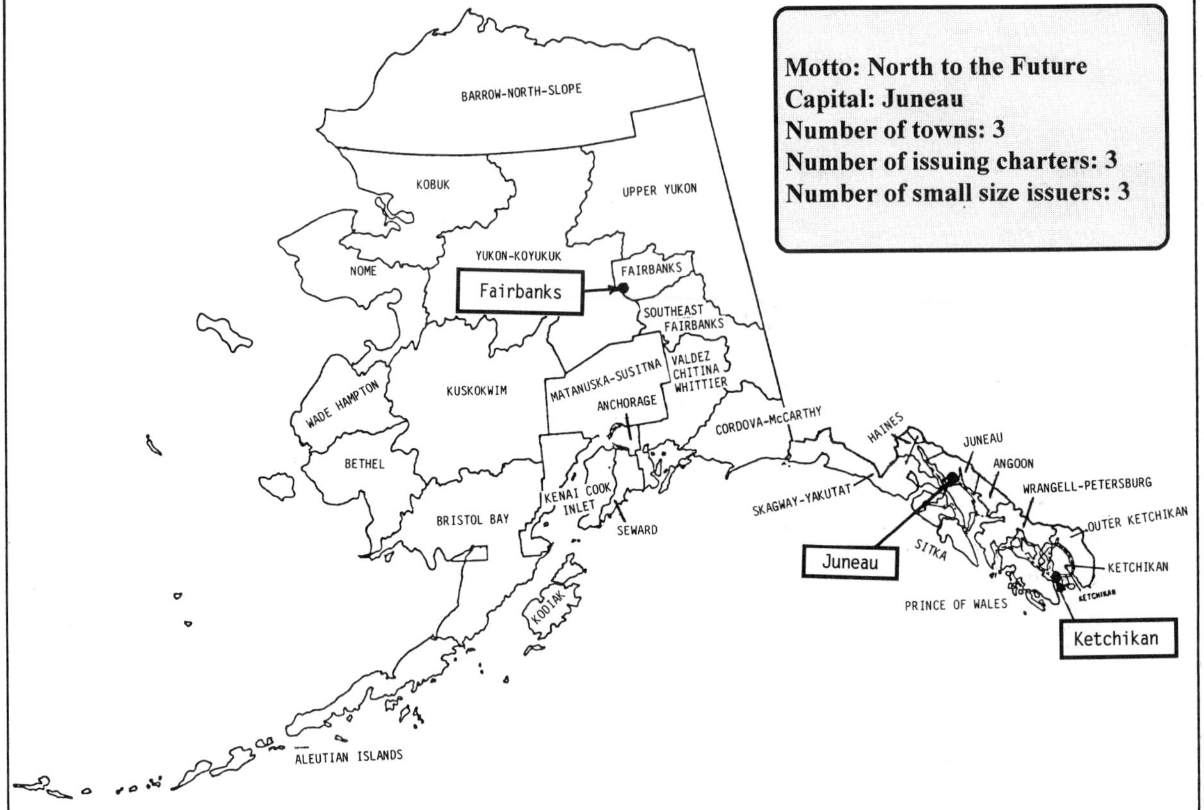

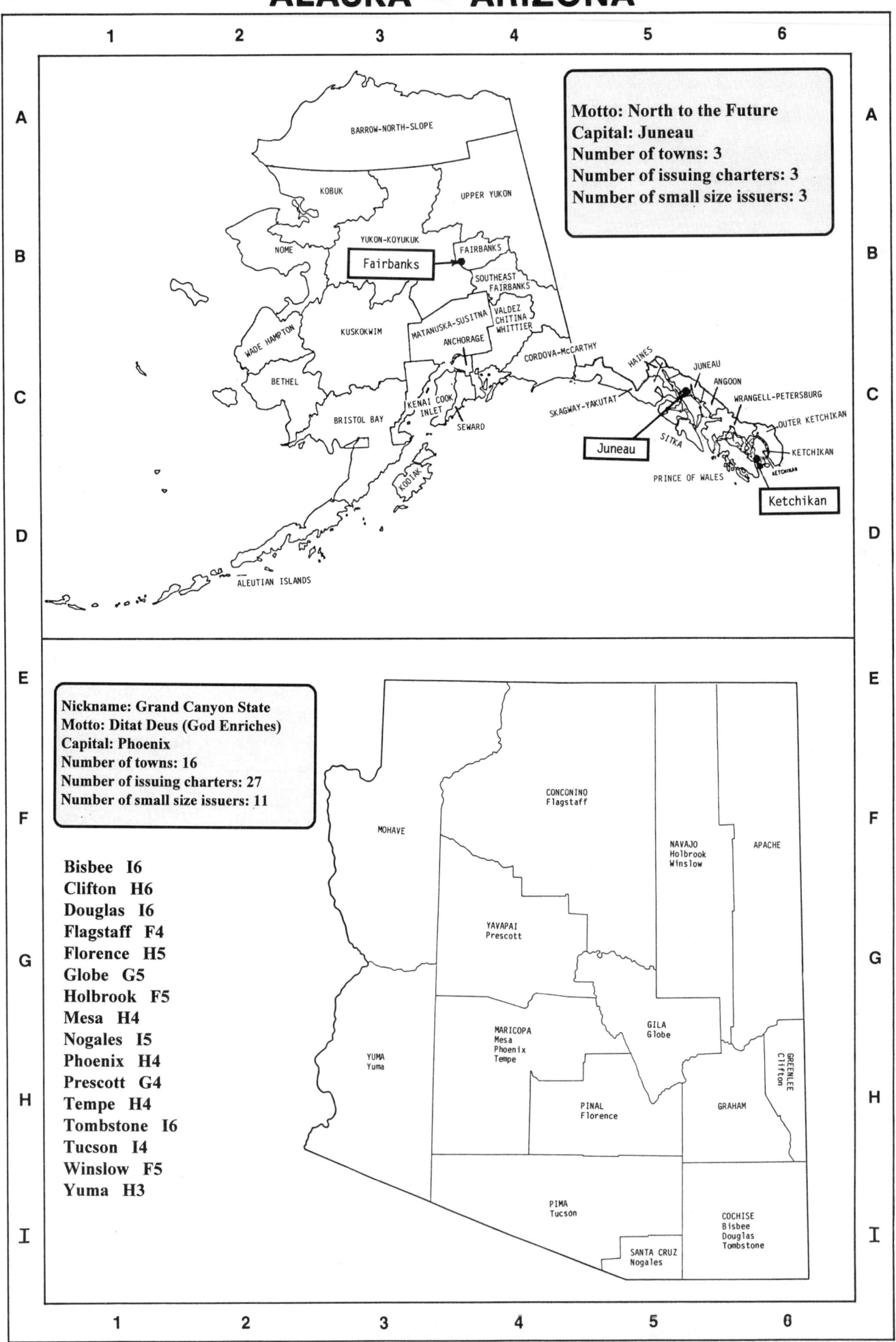

Motto: North to the Future
Capital: Juneau
Number of towns: 3
Number of issuing charters: 3
Number of small size issuers: 3

Nickname: Grand Canyon State
Motto: Ditat Deus (God Enriches)
Capital: Phoenix
Number of towns: 16
Number of issuing charters: 27
Number of small size issuers: 11

Bisbee I6
Clifton H6
Douglas I6
Flagstaff F4
Florence H5
Globe G5
Holbrook F5
Mesa H4
Nogales I5
Phoenix H4
Prescott G4
Tempe H4
Tombstone I6
Tucson I4
Winslow F5
Yuma H3

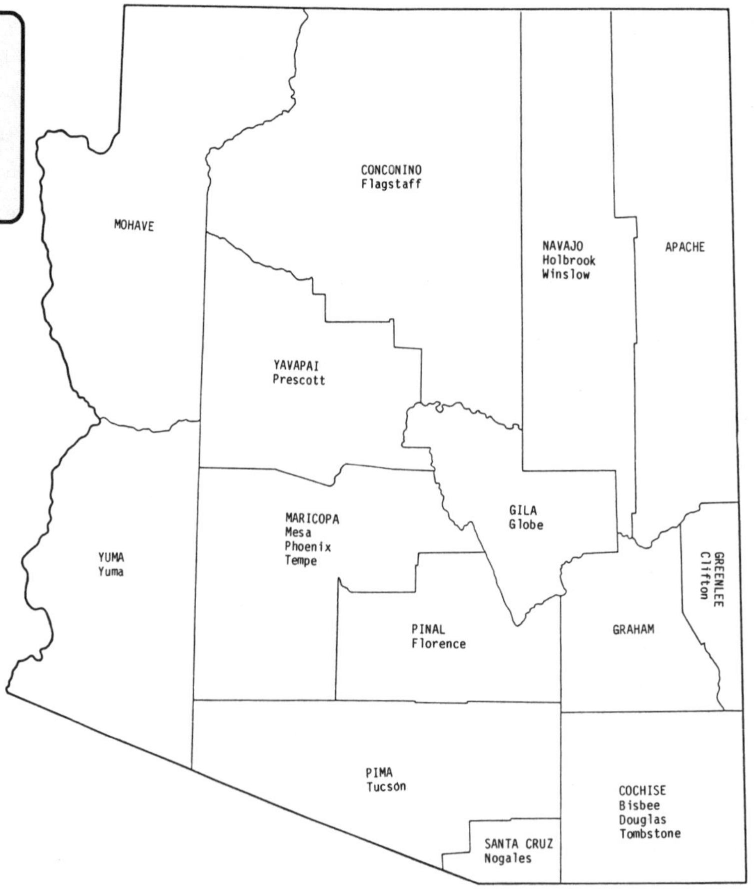

ALASKA

7718 Fairbanks
FNB OF FAIRBANKS
{{ 3U + 50+ L U + 11 S }}
Chartered 5/05
1902 Red Seal <$VALUE
4x5 1-1600 <$6500
3x10-20 1-1460<$7000/$7500
1902 Date Back
4x5 1-2600 <$6000
3x10-20 1-1960 <$6000
1902 Plain Back
4x5 2601-6460 <$6000
3x10-20 1961-4836 <$6000
1929 Small Size
5 Type 1 1-1050 <$6000
10 Type 1 1-520 <$6000
20 Type 1 1-170 <$6000
5 Type 2 1-2086 <$6000
10 Type 2 1-1034 <$6000
20 Type 2 1-324 <$6500
Total Issue $586,350
Out in 1935 $49,245
Large out 1935 $5,580

5117 Juneau
FNB OF JUNEAU
{{ 8 L 10 S }}
Chartered 1898
Brown Back <$VALUE
3x10-20 1-770 <$40,000
1882 Date Back
3x10-20 1-928 <$35,000
1902 Plain Back
3x10-20 1-1556 <$8000
1929 Small Size
10 Type 1 1-834 <$7000
20 Type 1 1-208 <$7000
10 Type 2 1-1671 <$7000
20 Type 2 1-176 <$7500
Total Issue $257,930
Out in 1935 $50,000
Large out 1935 $930

12578 Ketchikan
FNB OF KETCHIKAN
{{ 24 S }}
Chartered 9/24
1929 Small Size <$VALUE
5 Type 1 1-2302 <$6000
10 Type 1 1-1274 <$6000
20 Type 1 1-330 <$6000
5 Type 2 1-4910 <$6000
10 Type 2 1-1801 <$6000
20 Type 2 1-600 <$6000
Total Issue $239,660
Out in 1935 $61,500

CONDITION affects Value. The Values shown are for notes in FINE condition.

ARIZONA

7182 Cochise
FNB OF BISBEE
{{ UNREPORTED }}
Chartered 3/04
Receivership 3/24/08
TERRITORIAL ISSUES
1902 Red Seal <$VALUE
3x10-20 1-1672 <$10,000
Total Issue $83,600
Out in 1916 $1,280

5821 Greenlee
FNB OF CLIFTON
Chartered 5/20/01
Receivership 4/2/23
TERRITORIAL ISSUES {{ 1 L }}
Brown Back <$VALUE
3x10-20 1-1960 <$8000
1882 Date Back
3x10-20 1-1250 <$7500
STATE ISSUES {{ 10 L }}
1882 Date Back
3x10-20 1-950* <$1250
1882 Value Back
3x10-20 1251-2895* <$1250
* 951-1250 not marked
1902 Plain Back
3x10-20 1-1192 <$1000
Total Issue $364,850
Out at close $45,400

6633 Cochise
FNB OF DOUGLAS
Chartered 2/03
TERRITORIAL ISSUES {{ 2 L }}
1902 Red Seal <$VALUE
3x10-20 1-2460 <$8000
1902 Date Back
4x5 1-2583 <$7500
3x10-20 1-1700 <$7500
STATE ISSUES {{ 4 L }}
1902 Date Back
4x5 1-1500 <$1750
3x10-20 1-940 <$1750
1902 Plain Back
4x5 1501-7694 <$1750
3x10-20 941-4648 <$1750
Total Issue $645,940
Out in 1935 $1,705

11120 Concino
FNB OF FLAGSTAFF
{{ 9 L 1 S }}
Chartered 12/17
Liquidated 1/7/31
1902 Plain Back <$VALUE
4x5 1-8660 <$1250
3x10-20 1-5770 <$1250
1929 Small Size
5 Type 1 1-795 <$1500
10 Type 1 1-407 <$1500
20 Type 1 1-110 <$1500
Total Issue $523,170
Out at close $44,480
Large out at close $6,430

10998 Pinal
FNB OF FLORENCE
{{ 5 L }}
Chartered 5/17
Receivership 12/5/33
1902 Plain Back <$VALUE
4x10 1-4748 <$1500
Total Issue $189,920
Out at close $920

6579 Gila
FNB OF GLOBE
Chartered 1/03
Liquidated 9/30/24
TERRITORIAL ISSUES {{ 2 L }}
1902 Red Seal <$VALUE
3x10-20 1-3312 <$8500
1902 Date Back
3x10-20 1-5300 <$7500
STATE ISSUES {{ 6 L }}
1902 Date Back
3x10-20 1-2800 <$1500
1902 Plain Back
3x10-20 2801-13263 <$1500
Total Issue $1,093,750
Out at close $97,800

8193 Gila
GLOBE NB, GLOBE
{{ 1 L }}
Chartered 4/06
Liquidated 1/11/10
TERRITORIAL ISSUES
1902 Red Seal <$VALUE
4x5 1-1250 <$8500
3x10-20 1-1250 <$8500
1902 Date Back
4x5 1-538 <$7500
3x10-20 1-480 <$7500
Total Issue $122,260
Out in 1910 $44,150

12198 Navajo
FNB OF HOLBROOK
{{ 10 L 2 S }}
Chartered 5/22
1902 Plain Back <$VALUE
4x5 1-3837 <$1250
1929 Small Size
5 Type 1 1-1434 <$1500
5 Type 2 1-2332 <$1500
Total Issue $131,420
Out in 1935 $9,800
Large out 1935 $340

11130 Maricopa
FNB OF MESA
{{ 2 L 20 S }}
Chartered 1/18
Receivership 6/27/32
1902 Plain Back <$VALUE
3x10-20 1-3232 <$2500
1929 Small Size
10 Type 1 1-2340 <$400
20 Type 1 1-646 <$400
Total Issue $379,520
Out at close $100,000
Large out at close $3,210

FNB of Nogales
SEE Ch 6591
Sandoval NB of Nogales

11012 Santa Cruz
NOGALES NB, NOGALES
{{ 9 L 3 S }}
Chartered 6/17
Receivership 12/11/31
1902 Plain Back <$VALUE
3x10-20 1-8960 <$1000
1929 Small Size
10 Type 1 1-955 <$750
20 Type 1 1-263 <$750
Total Issue $536,860
Out at close $48,860
Large out at close $5,930

6591 Santa Cruz
SANDOVAL NB OF NOGALES
Chartered 1/03
2nd title: FNB of Nogales 1/04
TERRITORIAL ISSUES
FIRST TITLE {{ 4 L }}
1902 Red Seal <$VALUE
3x10-20 1-131 <$7500
SECOND TITLE {{ 1 L }}
1902 Red Seal
3x10-20 1-1525 <$7500
1902 Date Back
3x10-20 1-2240 <$7000
STATE ISSUES {{ 2 L 20 S }}
1902 Date Back
3x10-20 1-1500 <$1750
1902 Plain Back
3x10-20 1501-4040 <$1750
1929 Small Size
10 Type 1 1-3444 <$275
20 Type 1 1-884 <$275
10 Type 2 1-3752 <$325
20 Type 2 1-845 <$375
Total Issue $763,940
Out in 1935 $84,900
Large out 1935 $1,270

11559 Maricopa
COMMERCIAL NB OF PHOENIX
{{ 8 L }}
Chartered 12/19
Liquidated 7/30/31
1902 Plain Back <$VALUE
4x5 1-15300 <$600
Total Issue $306,000
Out at close $1,175

FNB of Arizona at Phoenix
SEE Ch 3728
NB of Arizona at Phoenix

3054 Maricopa
FNB OF PHOENIX
{{ UNREPORTED }}
Chartered 1883
Liquidated 4/7/84
TERRITORIAL ISSUES
Brown Back <$VALUE
4x5 1-562 <$10,000
Total Issue $11,240
Out in 1910 $85

3728 Maricopa
NB OF ARIZONA AT PHOENIX
Chartered 6/18/87
2nd title: FNB of Arizona at Phoenix 7/17/26
TERRITORIAL ISSUES {{ 4 L }}
Brown Back <$VALUE
3x10-20 1-5105 <$6000
1902 Red Seal
3x10-20 1-1000 <$6000
1902 Date Back
3x10-20 1-5300 <$5000
STATE ISSUES {{ 9 L }}
1902 Date Back
3x10-20 1-7000 <$600
1902 Plain Back
3x10-20 7001-29700 <$600
SECOND TITLE {{ 4 L 50+ S }}
1902 Plain Back
3x10-20 1-5298 <$750
1929 Small Size
10 Type 1 1-8780 <$200
20 Type 1 1-2576 <$200
10 Type 2 1-12867 <$225
20 Type 2 1-3052 <$250
Total Issue $3,345,780
Out in 1935 $300,005
Large out 1935 $7,675

4729 Maricopa
PHOENIX NB, PHOENIX
Chartered 4/92
TERRITORIAL ISSUES {{ 2 L }}
Brown Back <$VALUE
3x10-20 1-10020 <$6500
1882 Date Back
3x10-20 1-3766 <$6000
STATE ISSUES {{ 17 L 44 S }}
1902 Date Back
3x10-20 1-6800 <$500
1902 Plain Back
3x10-20 6801-32499 <$500
1929 Small Size
10 Type 1 1-4136 <$200
20 Type 1 1-3974 <$200
Total Issue $3,039,290
Out in 1935 $400,460
Large out 1935 $6,720

13262 Yavapai
FNB IN PRESCOTT
{{ U + 8 S }}
Chartered 12/28
Liquidated 3/25/33
1929 Small Size <$VALUE
5 Type 1 1-340 <$750
10 Type 1 1-275 <$750
20 Type 1 1-71 <$1000
Total Issue $35,220
Out at close $35,000

3122 Yavapai
FNB OF PRESCOTT
{{ UNREPORTED }}
Chartered 1884
Liquidated 4/9/85
TERRITORIAL ISSUES
Brown Back <$VALUE
3x10-20 1-225 <$10,000
Total Issue $11,250
Out in 1910 $90

4851 Yavapai
PRESCOTT NB, PRESCOTT
Chartered 1892
Liquidated 10/25/16
TERRITORIAL ISSUES {{ 8 L }}
Brown Back <$VALUE
4x5 1-8775 <$7000
3x10-20 1-5430 <$7000
1882 Date Back
4x5 1-4500 <$6000
3x10-20 1-3200 <$6000
STATE ISSUES {{ 1 L }}
1882 Date Back
4x5 1-150 <$3500
3x10-20 1-120 <$3500
1902 Date Back
4x5 1-3000 <$1750
3x10-20 1-2400 <$1750
1902 Plain Back
4x5 3001-3996 <$1750
3x10-20 2401-2678 <$1750
Total Issue $919,820
Out at close $97,995

5720 Maricopa
TEMPE NB, TEMPE
Chartered 2/16/01
Liquidated 6/29/35
TERRITORIAL ISSUES {{ 1 L }}
Brown Back <$VALUE
3x10-20 1-520 <$7500
1882 Date Back
3x10-20 1-910 <$6500
STATE ISSUES {{ 4 L 8 S }}
1882 Date Back
3x10-20 1-380 <$2500
1882 Value Back
3x10-20 381-639 <$2500
1902 Plain Back
3x10-20 1-1615 <$1750
1929 Small Size
10 Type 1 1-874 <$550
20 Type 1 1-246 <$550
10 Type 2 1-1572 <$600
20 Type 2 1-528 <$600
Total Issue $292,440
Out at close $44,400
Large out at close $650

6439 Cochise
FNB OF TOMBSTONE
Chartered 9/25/02
Liquidated 5/21/26
TERRITORIAL ISSUES {{ 2 L }}
1902 Red Seal <$VALUE
3x10-20 1-476 <$12,500
1902 Date Back
3x10-20 1-460 <$10,000
STATE ISSUES {{ 8 L }}
1902 Date Back
3x10-20 1-260 <$7500
1902 Plain Back
3x10-20 261-2139 <$7500
Total Issue $153,750
Out at close $20,000

4440 Pima
ARIZONA NB OF TUCSON
Chartered 1890
Liquidated 8/4/28
TERRITORIAL ISSUES {{ 3 L }}
Brown Back <$VALUE
50-100 1-633 <$12,500
1882 Date Back
50-100 1-236 <$10,000
1902 Date Back
3x10-20 1-1500 <$6000
STATE ISSUES {{ 9 L }}
1902 Date Back
3x10-20 1-2600 <$850
1902 Plain Back
3x10-20 2601-11600 <$850
Total Issue $785,350
Out at close $15,945

4287 Pima
CONSOLIDATED NB OF TUCSON
Chartered 1890
TERRITORIAL ISSUES {{ 3 L }}
Brown Back <$VALUE
3x10-20 1-2400 <$6500
50-100 1-240 <$12,500
1882 Date Back
3x10-20 1-569 <$6000
1902 Date Back
3x10-20 1-1000 <$5000
50-100 1-740 <$8500
STATE ISSUES {{ 30 L 50+ S }}
1902 Date Back
3x10-20 1-2400 <$450
1902 Plain Back
4x5 1-7470 <$450
3x10-20 2401-26473 <$450
1929 Small Size
5 Type 1 1-15412 <$200
10 Type 1 1-7838 <$200
20 Type 1 1-2626 <$200
5 Type 2 1-12388 <$200
10 Type 2 1-5859 <$200
20 Type 2 1-2099 <$200
Total Issue $3,228,770
Out in 1935 $193,530
Large out 1935 $7,310

2639 Pima
FNB OF TUCSON
{{ 3 L }}
Chartered 1882
Liquidated 1/31/85
TERRITORIAL ISSUES
Series 1875 <$VALUE
4x5 1-2120 <$15,000
Total Issue $42,400
Out in 1910 $335

11159 Pima
TUCSON NB, TUCSON
{{ UNREPORTED }}
Chartered 3/18
Receivership 11/14/23
1902 Plain Back <$VALUE
3x10-20 1-6148 <$3500
Total Issue $307,400
Out at close $67,300

12581 Navajo
FNB OF WINSLOW
{{ 11 L 18 S }}
Chartered 9/24
1902 Plain Back <$VALUE
4x5 1-4300 <$750
3x10-20 1-2680 <$850
1929 Small Size
5 Type 1 1-2020 <$400
10 Type 1 1-938 <$400
20 Type 1 1-272 <$400
5 Type 2 1-2692 <$450
10 Type 2 1-1704 <$450
20 Type 2 1-396 <$450
Total Issue $407,940
Out in 1935 $49,600
Large out 1935 $1,150

7591 Yuma
FNB OF YUMA
Chartered 2/05
Liquidated 11/20/29
TERRITORIAL ISSUES {{ 0 L }}
1902 Red Seal <$VALUE
3x10-20 1-360 <$7500
1902 Date Back
3x10-20 1-2000 <$6500
STATE ISSUES {{ 8 L }}
1902 Date Back
3x10-20 1-2040 <$1250
1902 Plain Back
3x10-20 2041-13672 <$1250
Total Issue $801,600
Out at close $7,350

9608 Yuma
YUMA NB, YUMA
Chartered 12/09
Liquidated 6/22/29
TERRITORIAL ISSUES {{ 0 L }}
1902 Date Back <$VALUE
3x10-20 1-2600 <$6500
STATE ISSUES {{ 10 L }}
1902 Date Back
4x5 1-1650 <$1000
3x10-20 1-1320 <$1000
1902 Plain Back
4x5 1651-11390 <$1000
3x10-20 1321-7732 <$1000
Total Issue $744,400
Out at close $42,700

<$VALUEs are for notes in FINE condition. Value changes by approximately 25% for a change of one full grade.

ARKANSAS

Nickname: Land of Opportunity
Motto: Regnat Populus (The People Rule)
Capital: Little Rock
Number of towns: 71
Number of issuing charters: 114
Number of small size issuers: 69

Arkadelphia D5
Ashdown E4
Batesville B7
Benton C6
Bentonville A4
Berryville A5
Camden E5
Clarksville B5
Conway C6
Corning A8
Cotton Plant C7
Dardanelle C5
Dequeen D7
Dewitt D4
Earle C8
El Dorado E6
Eudora E7
Eureka Springs A5
Fayetteville B4
Fordyce D6
Forrest City C8
Fort Smith C4
Gentry A4
Gravette A4
Green Forest A5
Greenwood C4
Gurdon A8
Harrison A5
Hartford C4
Heber Springs B6
Helena D8
Holly Grove C7
Hope E5
Horatio D4
Hot Springs C5
Huntsville B4
Huttig E6
Jonesboro B8
Judsonia C7
Lake Village E7
Lamar B5
Leslie B6
Lewisville E5
Lincoln B4
Little Rock C6
Malvern D5
Mansfield C4
Marked Tree B8
Marshall B6
Mcghee D7
Mena D4
Morrilton B6
Nashville D4
Newark B7
Newport B7
Paragould A8
Paris C4
Perry C5
Pine Bluff D6
Prairie Grove B4
Rector A8
Rogers A4
Russellville B5
Siloam Springs A4
Springdale B4
Stuttgart D7
Texarkana E4
Van Buren B4
Waldron C4
Walnut Ridge A7
Wynne C8

10087 Clark
CITIZENS NB OF ARKADELPHIA
{{ 4 L 8 S }}
Chartered 9/11
1902 Date Back <$VALUE
3x10-20 1-2400 <$850
1902 Plain Back
3x10-20 2401-9290 <$850
1929 Small Size
10 Type 1 1-1126 <$325
20 Type 1 1-320 <$325
10 Type 2 1-2568 <$350
20 Type 2 1-664 <$375
Total Issue $609,480
Out in 1935 $47,500
Large out 1935 $2,150

13534 Little River
FNB IN ASHDOWN
{{ 3 S }}
Chartered 4/31
1929 Small Size <$VALUE
5 Type 1 1-588 <$500
10 Type 1 1-242 <$500
20 Type 1 1-76 <$550
5 Type 2 1-1256 <$600
10 Type 2 1-869 <$600
20 Type 2 1-250 <$600
Total Issue $61,250
Out in 1935 $24,200
Large out 1935 $530
Outstanding includes Ch 10486

10486 Little River
FNB OF ASHDOWN
{{ 5 L 2 S }}
Chartered 2/14
Liquidated 5/19/31
1902 Date Back <$VALUE
4x5 1-500 <$850
3x10-20 1-400 <$850
1902 Plain Back
4x5 501-3995 <$850
3x10-20 401-2504 <$850
1929 Small Size
5 Type 1 1-584 <$600
10 Type 1 1-282 <$600
20 Type 1 1-82 <$600
Total Issue $249,380
Out at close $23,910
Large out at close $530
Ch 13534 assumed circulation

7556 Independence
FNB OF BATESVILLE
{{ 2U + 28 L 3 S }}
Chartered 1/05
Liquidated 5/31/30
1902 Red Seal <$VALUE
4x5 1-2325 <$1500
3x10-20 1-1440 <$1500
1902 Date Back
4x5 1-4600 <$250
3x10-20 1-3610 <$250
1902 Plain Back
4x5 4601-20667 <$250
3x10-20 3611-14318 <$250
1929 Small Size
5 Type 1 1-114 <$600
10 Type 1 1-558 <$600
20 Type 1 1-85 <$600
Total Issue $1,324,840
Out at close $99,995
Large out at close $27,965
Outstanding includes Ch 8864

8864 Independence
MAXFIELD NB OF BATESVILLE
Chartered 9/07
Liquidated 7/20/12
2nd title:NB of Batesville 3/9/08
FIRST TITLE {{ 1 L }}
1902 Red Seal <$VALUE
4x5 1-205 <$2500
4x10 1-210 <$2500
SECOND TITLE {{ 3 L }}
1902 Red Seal
4x5 1-300 <$2000
4x10 1-300 <$2000
1902 Date Back
4x5 1-1988 <$850
4x10 1-1734 <$850
Total Issue $139,620
Out at close $50,000
Ch 7556 assumed circulation

NB of Batesville
SEE Ch 8864
Maxfield NB of Batesville

9494 Saline
FNB OF BENTON
{{ UNREPORTED }}
Chartered 7/09
Liquidated 7/12/19
1902 Date Back <$VALUE
3x10-20 1-1350 <$2500
1902 Plain Back
3x10-20 1351-1474 <$2500
Total Issue $73,700
Out at close $11,800

8135 Benton
BENTON COUNTY NB OF BENTONVILLE
{{ 8 L 3 S }}
Organized 2/28/06
Receivership 12/16/30
1902 Red Seal <$VALUE
4x5 1-1900 <$2000
3x10-20 1-1520 <$2000
1902 Date Back
4x5 1-4050 <$500
3x10-20 1-2960 <$500
1902 Plain Back
4x5 4051-13925 <$500
3x10-20 2961-8672 <$500
1929 Small Size
5 Type 1 1-892 <$600
10 Type 1 1-461 <$600
20 Type 1 1-121 <$600
Total Issue $895,040
Out at close $58,500
Large out at close $10,790

7523 Benton
FNB OF BENTONVILLE
{{ 7 L 4 S }}
Chartered 12/04
Liquidated 7/18/30
1902 Red Seal <$VALUE
4x5 1-2150 <$2000
3x10-20 1-1540 <$2000
1902 Date Back
4x5 1-3500 <$500
3x10-20 1-2420 <$500
1902 Plain Back
4x5 3501-10740 <$500
3x10-20 2421-7097 <$500
1929 Small Size
5 Type 1 1-689 <$600
10 Type 1 1-337 <$600
20 Type 1 1-49 <$600
Total Issue $736,420
Out at close $13,220
Large out at close $5,250

10406 Carroll
FNB OF BERRYVILLE
{{ 4 L 2U + 14 S }}
Chartered 6/13
1902 Date Back <$VALUE
3x10-20 1-1600 <$600
1902 Plain Back
3x10-20 1601-8723 <$600
1929 Small Size
5 Type 1 1-314 <$250
10 Type 1 1-1532 <$225
20 Type 1 1-394 <$250
5 Type 2 1-2416 <$275
10 Type 2 1-1260 <$275
Total Issue $609,450
Out in 1935 $52,700
Large out 1935 $2,520

4066 Ouachita
CAMDEN NB, CAMDEN
Chartered 7/2/89
Receivership 4/16/34
2nd title: FNB of Camden 2/19/23
FIRST TITLE {{ 2 L }}
Brown Back <$VALUE
4x5 1-2805 <$1500
50-100 1-187 <$5000
1902 Date Back
4x5 1-1125 <$750
50-100 1-170 <$2500
3x50-100 1-41 <$2500
1902 Plain Back
4x5 1126-2275 <$750
SECOND TITLE {{ 4 L 13 S }}
1902 Plain Back
4x5 1-8072 <$750
1929 Small Size
5 Type 1 1-10482 <$200
5 Type 2 1-16126 <$225
Total Issue $721,930
Out at close $110,000
Large out at close $1,135

14096 Ouachita
CITIZENS NB OF CAMDEN
{{ 6 S }}
Chartered 4/34
1929 Small Size <$VALUE
5 Type 2 1-5470 <$600
10 Type 2 1-4500 <$600
Total Issue $72,350
Out in 1935 $50,000

FNB of Camden
SEE Ch 4066
Camden NB, Camden

11580 Johnson
FARMERS NB OF CLARKSVILLE
{{ 5 L 9 S }}
Organized 1/10/20
1902 Plain Back <$VALUE
3x10-20 1-4716 <$600
1929 Small Size
10 Type 1 1-1090 <$250
20 Type 1 1-318 <$250
10 Type 2 1-1470 <$250
20 Type 2 1-502 <$250
Total Issue $364,100
Out in 1935 $40,500
Large out 1935 $2,070
Outstanding includes Ch 12238

9633 Johnson
FNB OF CLARKSVILLE
{{ 4 L 0 S }}
Organized 11/27/09
Receivership 11/18/29
1902 Date Back <$VALUE
4x5 1-1950 <$750
4x10 1-1975 <$750
1902 Plain Back
4x5 1951-7466 <$750
4x10 1976-5918 <$750
1929 Small Size
5 Type 1 1-163 <$1000
10 Type 1 1-51 <$1000
Total Issue $393,990
Out at close $25,000
Large out at close $17,050

13719 Faulkner
FNB OF CONWAY
{{ 3 S }}
Chartered 6/33
1929 Small Size <$VALUE
5 Type 2 1-4620 <$500
10 Type 2 1-1718 <$500
20 Type 2 1-588 <$500
Total Issue $52,040
Out in 1935 $24,350

7311 Clay
FNB OF CORNING
{{ UNREPORTED }}
Organized 6/7/04
Liquidated 7/30/30
1902 Red Seal <$VALUE
3x10-20 1-620 <$3000
1902 Date Back
3x10-20 1-421 <$2500
Total Issue $52,050
Out at close $200

10723 Woodruff
FNB OF COTTON PLANT
{{ 3 L }}
Organized 3/6/15
Receivership 4/7/22
1902 Date Back <$VALUE
3x10-20 1-500 <$1500
1902 Plain Back
3x10-20 501-4052 <$1500
Total Issue $202,600
Out at close $50,000

11276 Yell
FNB OF DARDANELLE
{{ 2 L }}
Organized 11/26/18
Liquidated 10/29/34
1902 Plain Back <$VALUE
4x5 1-7600 <$1500
Total Issue $152,000
Out at close $575

5929 Sevier
FNB OF DeQUEEN
{{ 6 L 6 S }}
Chartered 7/31/01
Brown Back <$VALUE
3x10-20 1-400 <$1500
1882 Date Back
3x10-20 1-1620* <$1500
1882 Value Back
3x10-20 1721-3078* <$1500
* 1621-1720 not marked
1902 Plain Back
3x10-20 1-2553 <$500
1929 Small Size
10 Type 1 1-774 <$350
20 Type 1 1-194 <$350
10 Type 2 1-1018 <$375
20 Type 2 1-175 <$400
Total Issue $384,950
Out in 1935 $24,350
Large out 1935 $1,610

10178 Arkansas
FNB OF DeWITT
{{ 6 L 9 S }}
Chartered 4/12
1902 Date Back <$VALUE
3x10-20 1-2620* <$500
1902 Plain Back
3x10-20 2871-11169* <$500
* 2621-2870 not marked
1929 Small Size
10 Type 1 1-1396 <$250
20 Type 1 1-360 <$250
10 Type 2 1-1831 <$300
20 Type 2 1-532 <$300
Total Issue $714,360
Out in 1935 $48,700
Large out 1935 $3,120

9324 Crittenden
FNB OF EARLE
{{ UNREPORTED }}
Chartered 1/09
Liquidated 2/19/10
1902 Date Back <$VALUE
4x10 1-792 <$2500
Total Issue $31,680
Out in 1910 $11,790

7323 Union
CITIZENS NB OF EL DORADO
{{ 2 L }}
Chartered 6/04
Closed 6/4/21
1902 Red Seal <$VALUE
3x10-20 1-1282 <$2000
1902 Date Back
3x10-20 1-3250 <$850
1902 Plain Back
3x10-20 3251-4626 <$850
Total Issue $295,400
Out at close $32,500
Ch 7046 assumed circulation

7046 Union
FNB OF EL DORADO
{{ 4 L 2U + 9 S }}
Chartered in 1903 as NB of El Dorado, under which there was no issue. Issuing title adopted 1/04.
1902 Red Seal <$VALUE
3x10-20 1-556 <$1500
1902 Date Back
3x10-20 1-1300 <$600
1902 Plain Back
3x10-20 1301-8130 <$600
1929 Small Size
10 Type 1 1-1152 <$160
20 Type 1 1-298 <$175
10 Type 2 1-2028 <$200
20 Type 2 1-670 <$225
Total Issue $572,860
Out in 1935 $43,110
Large out 1935 $2,260
Outstanding includes Ch 7323

12813 Chicot
FNB OF EUDORA
{{ 3 S }}
Organized 8/15/25
Receivership 9/12/31
1929 Small Size <$VALUE
5 Type 1 1-862 <$600
10 Type 1 1-425 <$600
Total Issue $51,360
Out at close $20,000

8495 Carroll
FNB OF EUREKA SPRINGS
{{ 3 L 2 S }}
Organized 1/2/07
Receivership 1/6/31
1902 Red Seal <$VALUE
4x5 1-350 <$2500
3x10-20 1-300 <$2500
1902 Date Back
4x5 1-1100 <$1000
3x10-20 1-820 <$1000
1902 Plain Back
4x5 1101-5329 <$1000
3x10-20 821-3266 <$1000
1929 Small Size
5 Type 1 1-418 <$750
10 Type 1 1-179 <$750
20 Type 1 1-81 <$750
Total Issue $324,880
Out at close $28,860
Large out at close $4,870

8786 Washington
ARKANSAS NB OF FAYETTEVILLE
{{ 15 L 7 S }}
Organized 6/8/07
Liquidated 1/13/31
1902 Red Seal <$VALUE
4x5 1-2000 <$1500
3x10-20 1-1600 <$1500
1902 Date Back
4x5 1-7000 <$275
3x10-20 1-4900 <$275
1902 Plain Back
4x5 7001-22260 <$275
3x10-20 4901-15353 <$275
1929 Small Size
5 Type 1 1-1488 <$250
10 Type 1 1-723 <$250
20 Type 1 1-225 <$275
Total Issue $1,447,870
Out at close $80,505
Large out at close $15,850

7346 Washington
FNB OF FAYETTEVILLE
{{ 23 L U + 25 S }}
Organized 6/3/04
1902 Red Seal <$VALUE
4x5 1-3086 <$1500
3x10-20 1-2258 <$1500
1902 Date Back
4x5 1-7850 <$250
3x10-20 1-5800 <$250
1902 Plain Back
4x5 7851-23924 <$250
3x10-20 5801-17260 <$250
1929 Small Size
5 Type 1 1-3824 <$110
10 Type 1 1-2262 <$100
20 Type 1 1-642 <$110
5 Type 2 1-5740 <$135
10 Type 2 1-3716 <$125
20 Type 2 1-750 <$135
Total Issue $1,924,440
Out in 1935 $99,240
Large out 1935 $7,190

7952 Washington
NB OF FAYETTEVILLE
{{ 1 L }}
Chartered 10/18/05
Liquidated 3/17/08
1902 Red Seal <$VALUE
4x5 1-1640 <$3000
3x10-20 1-1100 <$3000
Total Issue $87,800
Out in 1910 $11,730

9501 Dallas
FNB OF FORDYCE
{{ 2 L U + 8 S }}
Chartered 8/09
1902 Date Back <$VALUE
4x5 1-2500 <$1000
3x10-20 1-2000 <$1000
1902 Plain Back
4x5 2501-5863 <$1000
3x10-20 2001-3995 <$1000
1929 Small Size
5 Type 1 1-2102 <$250
10 Type 1 1-1278 <$250
20 Type 1 1-364 <$250
5 Type 2 1-3198 <$300
10 Type 2 1-1945 <$300
20 Type 2 1-302 <$325
Total Issue $541,860
Out in 1935 $45,000
Large out 1935 $900

10550 St Francis
FNB OF FORREST CITY
{{ 6 L }}
Chartered 5/14
Liquidated 5/6/29
1902 Date Back <$VALUE
3x10-20 1-1200 <$600
1902 Plain Back
3x10-20 1201-10333 <$600
Total Issue $516,650
Out at close $44,400

13637 St Francis
NB OF EASTERN ARKANSAS OF FORREST CITY
{{ 5 S }}
Chartered 10/1/32
1929 Small Size <$VALUE
5 Type 1 1-748 <$375
10 Type 1 1-416 <$350
20 Type 1 1-128 <$375
5 Type 2 1-3870 <$400
10 Type 2 1-2304 <$400
20 Type 2 1-552 <$400
Total Issue $116,190
Out in 1935 $47,050

3634 Sebastian
AMERICAN NB OF FORT SMITH
{{ 12 L }}
Chartered 2/7/87
Receivership 4/1/16
Brown Back <$VALUE
4x5 1-10071 <$1250
3x10-20 1-3771 <$1250
1902 Red Seal
4x5 1-2832 <$1500
4x10 1-834 <$1500
1902 Date Back
4x5 1-13050 <$300
4x10 1-12350 <$300
1902 Plain Back
4x5 13051-14017 <$300
4x10 12351-13338 <$300
Total Issue $1,293,830
Out in 1916 $124,560

10609 Sebastian
CITY NB OF FORT SMITH
{{ 16 L 21 S }}
Organized 7/17/14
1902 Date Back <$VALUE
4x10 1-3000 <$250
1902 Plain Back
4x10 3001-48155 <$250
1929 Small Size
10 Type 1 1-9734 <$100
10 Type 2 1-11832 <$110
Total Issue $2,628,560
Out in 1935 $132,210
Large out 1935 $7,610

1631 Sebastian
FNB OF FORT SMITH
{{ UNREPORTED }}
Organized 2/6/66
Receivership 5/2/72
Original Series <$VALUE
4x5 1-1900 <$5000
3x10-20 1-140 <$6000/$7500
Total Issue $45,000
Out in 1916 $450

FNB of Fort Smaith
SEE Ch 1950
NB of Western Arkansas, Fort Smith

4995 Sebastian
FORT SMITH NB, FORT SMITH
{{ 1 L }}
Chartered 5/1/95
Liquidated 12/9/97
Brown Back <$VALUE
50-100 1-204 <$5000
Total Issue $30,600
Out in 1910 $850

<$VALUEs are for notes in **FINE** condition. Value changes by approximately **25%** for a change of one full grade.

****
7240 Sebastian
MERCHANTS NB OF
FORT SMITH
{{ 29 L 50+ S }}
Chartered 4/04
1902 Red Seal <$VALUE
3x10-20 1-4250 <$1500
1902 Date Back
3x10-20 1-22500 <$125
1902 Plain Back
3x10-20 22501-97895 <$125
1929 Small Size
10 Type 1 1-12766 <$75
20 Type 1 1-4030 <$75
10 Type 2 1-19765 <$80
20 Type 2 1-4035 <$85
Total Issue $6,635,160
Out in 1935 $438,300
Large out 1935 $24,200
****
1950 Sebastian
NB OF WESTERN ARKANSAS,
FORT SMITH
Chartered 3/29/72
2nd title: FNB of
Fort Smith 12/24/87
FIRST TITLE {{ 1 L }}
Original Series <$VALUE
3x1-2 1-1640 <$5000/$7500
4x5 1-3065 <$5000
Series 1875
4x5 1-759 <$5000
100-100 1-478 <$15,000
SECOND TITLE {{ 35 L 50+ S }}
Series 1875
100-100 1-101 <$15,000
Brown Back
50-100 1-1974 <$5000
1882 Date Back
3x10-20 1-3599 <$1000
50-100 1-710 <$5000
1902 Date Back
3x10-20 1-11500 <$125
1902 Plain Back
3x10-20 11501-85450 <$125
1929 Small Size
10 Type 1 1-14716 <$65
20 Type 1 1-3870 <$70
10 Type 2 15304 <$70
20 Type 2 1-3925 <$75
Total Issue $6,634,430
Out in 1935 $423,400
Large out 1935 $25,210
****
12340 Benton
FNB OF GENTRY
{{ 1 L 4 S }}
Chartered 3/23
Liquidated 6/15/34
1902 Plain Back <$VALUE
4x5 1-1695 <$1500
3x10-20 1-994 <$1500
1929 Small Size
5 Type 1 1-840 <$650
10 Type 1 1-390 <$650
20 Type 1 1-108 <$650
5 Type 2 1-128 <$700
10 Type 2 1-45 <$700
Total Issue $146,250
Out at close $19,650
Large out at close $290
****
8237 Benton
FNB OF GRAVETTE
{{ 6 L 8 S }}
Chartered 5/06
1902 Red Seal <$VALUE
3x10-20 1-650 <$2000
1902 Date Back
3x10-20 1-1970 <$800
1902 Plain Back
3x10-20 1971-5242 <$800
1929 Small Size
10 Type 1 1-626 <$375
20 Type 1 1-170 <$375
10 Type 2 1-920 <$400
20 Type 2 1-281 <$400
Total Issue $367,380
Out in 1935 $25,000
Large out 1935 $1,530
****
10422 Carroll
FNB OF GREEN FOREST
{{ 1 L 2 S }}
Organized 6/7/13
Liquidated 6/23/31
1902 Date Back <$VALUE
3x10-20 1-475 <$2500
1902 Plain Back
3x10-20 476-976 <$2500
1929 Small Size
10 Type 1 1-86 <$1250
20 Type 1 1-10 <$1250
Total Issue $55,160
Out at close $5,830
Large out at close $1,040
****
10983 Sebastian
CITIZENS NB OF GREENWOOD
Organized 3/24/17
2nd title:FNB in Greenwood
12/6/19
FIRST TITLE {{ 1 L }}
1902 Plain Back <$VALUE
4x10 1-1375 <$1250
SECOND TITLE {{ 2 L 7 S }}
1902 Plain Back
4x10 1-4567 <$1000
1929 Small Size
10 Type 1 1-1306 <$275
10 Type 2 1-2208 <$300
Total Issue $338,120
Out in 1935 $23,340
Large out 1935 $870
****
FNB in Greenwood
SEE Ch 10983
Citizens NB of Greenwood
****
6786 Sebastian
FNB OF GREENWOOD
{{ 1 L }}
Chartered 5/18/03
Liquidated 5/20/05
1902 Red Seal <$VALUE
4x5 1-160 <$3000
3x10-20 1-139 <$3000
Total Issue $10,150
Out in 1910 $470
****
13210 Clay
FNB OF GURDON
{{ 5 L 3U + 6 S }}
Chartered 5/28
1902 Plain Back <$VALUE
4x5 1-480 <$850
1929 Small Size
5 Type 1 1-2182 <$400
5 Type 2 1-5906 <$400
Total Issue $104,590
Out in 1935 $18,835
Large out 1935 $85
****
12291 Boone
CITIZENS NB OF HARRISON
{{ 4 L }}
Chartered 1/23
Liquidated 6/30/29
1902 Plain Back <$VALUE
4x5 1-2385 <$850
3x10-20 1-1450 <$850
Total Issue $120,200
Out at close $16,150
****
FNB in Harrison
SEE Ch 10801
Peoples NB of Harrison
****
5890 Boone
FNB OF HARRISON
{{ 1 L }}
Chartered 7/1/01
Liquidated 12/19/01
Brown Back <$VALUE
3x10-20 1-125 <$3000
Total Issue $6,250
Out in 1910 $150
****
10801 Boone
PEOPLES NB OF HARRISON
Organized 11/9/15
Receivership 1/10/35
2nd title:FNB in Harrison
2/4/22
FIRST TITLE {{ 1 L }}
1902 Plain Back <$VALUE
4x5 1-2265 <$1250
3x10-20 1-1394 <$1250
SECOND TITLE {{ 3 L 2 S }}
1902 Plain Back
4x5 1-2330 <$750
3x10-20 1-1376 <$750
1929 Small Size
5 Type 1 1-417 <$600
10 Type 1 1-193 <$600
20 Type 1 1-45 <$600
Total Issue $259,890
Out at close $3,610
Large out at close $1,390

****
11830 Sebastian
FARMERS & MINERS NB OF
HARTFORD
Organized 7/27/20
Liquidated 11/8/34
2nd title: New FNB of
Hartford 2/17/25
3rd title:FNB in Hartford
2/4/26
FIRST TITLE {{ 2 L }}
1902 Plain Back <$VALUE
4x5 1-6150 <$1000
SECOND TITLE {{ 1 L }}
1902 Plain Back
4x5 1-1318 <$1000
THIRD TITLE {{ 1 L 3 S }}
1902 Plain Back
4x5 1-3882 <$1000
1929 Small Size
5 Type 1 1-3216 <$500
5 Type 2 1-4454 <$500
Total Issue $345,750
Out at close $22,095
Large out at close $685
****
FNB in Hartford
SEE Ch 11830
Farmers & Miners NB of
Hartford
****
11748 Sebastian
FNB OF HARTFORD
{{ 2 L }}
Chartered 6/20
Liquidated 11/29/24
1902 Plain Back <$VALUE
4x5 1-1845 <$1750
3x10-20 1-1372 <$1750
Total Issue $105,500
Out at close $20,700
****
New FNB of Hartford
SEE Ch 11830
Farmers & Miners NB of
Hartford
****
11180 Cleburne
FNB OF HEBER SPRINGS
{{ UNREPORTED }}
Chartered 5/18
Liquidated 3/14/19
1902 Plain Back <$VALUE
4x5 1-500 <$3000
Total Issue $10,000
Out at close $9,700
****
3662 Phillips
FNB OF HELENA
{{ 10 L }}
Chartered 3/29/87
Liquidated 5/28/29
Brown Back <$VALUE
4x5 1-8870 <$1500
3x10-20 1-1338 <$1500
1902 Red Seal
4x5 1-580 <$2000
3x10-20 1-468 <$2000
1902 Date Back
4x5 1-5500 <$350
3x10-20 1-4220 <$350
1902 Plain Back
4x5 5501-11925 <$350
3x10-20 4221-8787 <$350
Total Issue $957,150
Out at close $29,900
****
13520 Phillips
PHILLIPS NB OF HELENA
{{ U + 6 S }}
Chartered 1/31
1929 Small Size <$VALUE
5 Type 1 1-4938 <$250
5 Type 2 1-44874 <$250
Total Issue $372,510
Out in 1935 $94,550
****
12296 Monroe
FNB OF HOLLY GROVE
{{ 2 L 1 S }}
Organized 12/7/22
Receivership 2/27/34
1902 Plain Back <$VALUE
4x5 1-3652 <$1750
1929 Small Size
5 Type 1 1-1404 <$1000
5 Type 2 1-428 <$1000
Total Issue $117,300
Out at close $10,000
Large out at close $250
****

****
10579 Hempstead
CITIZENS NB OF HOPE
{{ 8 L 26 S }}
Chartered 7/14
1902 Date Back <$VALUE
4x5 1-2500 <$375
4x10 1-2500 <$375
1902 Plain Back
4x5 2501-19118 <$375
4x10 2501-15959 <$375
1929 Small Size
5 Type 1 1-4288 <$110
10 Type 1 1-2092 <$100
20 Type 1 1-582 <$110
5 Type 2 1-6108 <$125
10 Type 2 1-3761 <$125
20 Type 2 1-1212 <$125
Total Issue $1,437,110
Out in 1935 $97,050
Large out 1935 $2,220
****
12533 Hempstead
FNB OF HOPE
{{ 23 S }}
Organized 4/15/24
1929 Small Size <$VALUE
5 Type 1 1-6368 <$110
10 Type 1 1-3358 <$100
5 Type 2 1-11204 <$125
10 Type 2 1-5739 <$125
Total Issue $505,930
Out in 1935 $77,300
****
8594 Hempstead
HOPE NB, HOPE
{{ 3 L }}
Chartered 3/07
Liquidated 1/13/25
1902 Red Seal <$VALUE
4x5 1-350 <$2000
4x10 1-340 <$2000
1902 Date Back
4x5 1-3300 <$850
4x10 1-3300 <$850
1902 Plain Back
4x5 3301-8042 <$850
4x10 3301-7140 <$850
Total Issue $467,040
Out at close $21,800
****
10447 Sevier
FNB OF HORATIO
{{ UNREPORTED }}
Chartered 9/13
Liquidated 3/1/29
1902 Date Back <$VALUE
3x10-20 1-500 <$2500
1902 Plain Back
3x10-20 501-1268 <$2500
Total Issue $63,400
Out at close $5,000
****
2832 Garland
ARKANSAS NB OF
HOT SPRINGS
{{ 3 L 15 S }}
Organized 11/20/82
Brown Back <$VALUE
4x5 1-6670 <$1500
3x10-20 1-461 <$1500
1902 Red Seal
3x10-20 1-1430 <$2000
1902 Date Back
3x10-20 1-2043 <$850
1929 Small Size
5 Type 1 1-2056 <$200
10 Type 1 1-1038 <$200
5 Type 2 1-14010 <$200
10 Type 2 1-7008 <$200
Total Issue $594,190
Out in 1935 $77,950
Large out 1935 $200
****
7531 Garland
CITIZENS NB OF
HOT SPRINGS
{{ 2 L }}
Chartered 12/04
Liquidated 3/10/26
1902 Red Seal <$VALUE
3x10-20 1-1100 <$2500
1902 Date Back
3x10-20 1-2800 <$1000
1902 Plain Back
3x10-20 2801-4982 <$1000
Total Issue $304,100
Out at close $23,100
****

****
2887 Garland
HOT SPRINGS NB,
HOT SPRINGS
{{ 1 L }}
Organized 2/17/83
Receivership 6/2/84
Brown Back <$VALUE
3x10-20 1-900 <$2500
Total Issue $45,000
Out in 1916 $190
****
8952 Madison
FNB OF HUNTSVILLE
{{ 2 L 11 S }}
Organized 10/29/07
1902 Red Seal <$VALUE
4x5 1-250 <$2500
3x10-20 1-200 <$2500
1902 Date Back
4x5 1-1350 <$1000
3x10-20 1-1040 <$1000
1902 Plain Back
4x5 1351-3790 <$1000
3x10-20 1041-2466 <$1000
1929 Small Size
5 Type 1 1-692 <$400
10 Type 1 1-336 <$400
20 Type 1 1-96 <$400
5 Type 2 1-3936 <$400
10 Type 2 1-2536 <$400
20 Type 2 1-696 <$400
Total Issue $325,500
Out in 1935 $49,300
Large out 1935 $1,480
****
10060 Union
FNB OF HUTTIG
{{ 2 L 4 S }}
Organized 7/8/11
Receivership 11/8/33
1902 Date Back <$VALUE
3x10-20 1-700* <$1000
1902 Plain Back
3x10-20 781-3806* <$1000
* 701-780 not marked
1929 Small Size
10 Type 1 1-758 <$450
20 Type 1 1-224 <$450
10 Type 2 1-12 <$500
20 Type 2 1-30 <$500
Total Issue $263,380
Out at close $25,000
Large out at close $1,290
****
8086 Craighead
FNB OF JONESBORO
{{ 2 L }}
Organized 12/20/05
Receivership 6/4/26
1902 Red Seal <$VALUE
3x10-20 1-1200 <$2500
1902 Date Back
3x10-20 1-3900 <$1000
1902 Plain Back
3x10-20 3901-8294 <$1000
Total Issue $474,700
Out at close $40,000
****
10439 White
FNB OF JUDSONIA
{{ 1 L }}
Organized 9/2/13
Receivership 6/29/20
1902 Date Back <$VALUE
4x5 1-1050 <$1500
3x10-20 1-840 <$1500
1902 Plain Back
4x5 1051-2760 <$1500
3x10-20 841-1847 <$1500
Total Issue $147,550
Out at close $28,200
****
13632 Chicot
FNB IN LAKE VILLAGE
{{ U + 9 S }}
Chartered 8/32
1929 Small Size <$VALUE
5 Type 1 1-1646 <$225
5 Type 2 1-15960 <$225
Total Issue $129,150
Out in 1935 $43,475
Outstanding includes Ch 11262
****

****
11262 Chicot
FNB OF LAKE VILLAGE
{{ 5 L 5 S }}
Organized 11/4/18
Liquidated 9/12/32
1902 Plain Back <$VALUE
4x5 1-10133 <$500
4x10 1-8126 <$500
1929 Small Size
5 Type 1 1-1881 <$350
10 Type 1 1-831 <$350
Total Issue $633,990
Out at close $48,200
Large out 1935 $2,475
Ch 13632 assumed circulation
****
12238 Johnson
FNB OF LAMAR
{{ 3 L 0 S }}
Chartered 7/22
Liquidated 4/29/30
1902 Plain Back <$VALUE
4x5 1-2005 <$1250
3x10-20 1-1052 <$1250
1929 Small Size
5 Type 1 1-150 <$1250
10 Type 1 1-59 <$1250
20 Type 1 1-8 <$1250
Total Issue $101,700
Out at close $12,840
Large out at close $4,250
Ch 11580 assumed circulation
****
10138 Searcy
FNB OF LESLIE
{{ 2 L }}
Chartered 2/12
Liquidated 6/25/17
1902 Date Back <$VALUE
4x5 1-2330 <$1500
3x10-20 1-1868 <$1500
1902 Plain Back
4x5 2331-3185 <$1500
3x10-20 1869-2325 <$1500
Total Issue $179,950
Out at close $48,900
****
9354 Lafayette
FNB OF LEWISVILLE
{{ 3 L 10 S }}
Chartered 3/09
1902 Date Back <$VALUE
3x10-20 1-2420 <$850
1902 Plain Back
3x10-20 2421-6761 <$850
1929 Small Size
10 Type 1 1-758 <$350
20 Type 1 1-178 <$350
10 Type 2 1-1596 <$375
20 Type 2 1-276 <$400
Total Issue $426,370
Out in 1935 $24,150
Large out 1935 $1,040
****
11825 Washington
FNB OF LINCOLN
{{ 1 L }}
Organized 7/27/20
Receivership 2/9/27
1902 Plain Back <$VALUE
4x5 1-2925 <$2500
Total Issue $58,500
Out at close $11,600
****
14000 Pulaski
COMMERCIAL NB OF
LITTLE ROCK
{{ 24 S }}
Chartered 2/12/34
1929 Small Size <$VALUE
5 Type 2 1-45336 <$100
10 Type 2 1-18216 <$100
20 Type 2 1-4932 <$100
Total Issue $507,480
Out in 1935 $293,000
****
9037 Pulaski
ENGLAND NB OF LITTLE ROCK
{{ 12 L }}
Organized 2/6/08
Receivership 11/1/26
1902 Red Seal <$VALUE
3x10-20 1-2750 <$1500
1902 Date Back
3x10-20 1-11000 <$250
1902 Plain Back
3x10-20 11001-37568 <$250
Total Issue $2,015,900
Out at close $178,700
****

****
3300 Pulaski
EXCHANGE NB OF
LITTLE ROCK
{{ 15 L }}
Chartered 1885
Liquidated 2/21/30
Brown Back <$VALUE
3x10-20 1-5711 <$1250
1902 Red Seal
3x10-20 1-2700 <$1500
1902 Date Back
3x10-20 1-12100 <$250
1902 Plain Back
3x10-20 12101-27450 <$250
Total Issue $1,793,050
Out at close $13,295
****
FNB of Little Rock
SEE Ch 1648
Merchants NB of Little Rock
****
3318 Pulaski
GERMAN NB OF LITTLE ROCK
{{ 1 L }}
Chartered 1885
Liquidated 4/26/19
Brown Back <$VALUE
50-100 1-1490 <$5000
1902 Red Seal
50-100 1-586 <$7500
1902 Date Back
4x5 1-5150 <$1500
3x10-20 1-4025 <$1500
50-100 1-563 <$2500
Total Issue $700,100
Out at close $46,700
****
1648 Pulaski
MERCHANTS NB OF
LITTLE ROCK
Chartered 4/12/66
Receivership 2/6/93
2nd title: FNB of
Little Rock 2/15/86
FIRST TITLE {{ 3 L }}
Original Series <$VALUE
3x1-2 1-2860 <$5000/$7500
4x5 1-3485 <$5000
3x10-20 1-4400<$6000/$7500
Series 1875
4x5 1-1200 <$5000
3x10-20 1-5229<$6000/$7500
SECOND TITLE {{ 1 L }}
Brown Back
50-100 1-1333 <$5000
Total Issue $789,400
Out in 1916 $4,104
****
6902 Pulaski
STATE NB OF LITTLE ROCK
{{ 10 L }}
Chartered 7/03
Liquidated 7/9/14
1902 Red Seal <$VALUE
4x5 1-10000 <$1500
3x10-20 1-10325 <$1500
1902 Date Back
4x5 1-16040 <$300
3x10-20 1-8865 <$300
Total Issue $1,480,300
Out in 1916 $64,660
****
7634 Hot Spring
FNB OF MALVERN
{{ 3 L 4 S }}
Organized 2/7/05
Receivership 10/15/34
1902 Red Seal <$VALUE
3x10-20 1-356 <$2500
1902 Date Back
3x10-20 1-660 <$1250
1902 Plain Back
3x10-20 661-4752 <$1250
1929 Small Size
5 Type 1 1-1116 <$500
10 Type 1 1-510 <$500
20 Type 1 1-142 <$500
5 Type 2 1-990 <$550
10 Type 2 1-552 <$550
Total Issue $346,990
Out at close $24,500
Large out at close $1,140
****
11195 Sebastian
FNB OF MANSFIELD
{{ 5 L 6 S }}
Organized 4/23/18
Receivership 11/3/33
1902 Plain Back <$VALUE
4x5 1-14337 <$800
1929 Small Size
5 Type 1 1-3132 <$500
5 Type 2 1-1472 <$500
Total Issue $388,060
Out at close $24,050
Large out at close $1,140
****
11196 Sebastian
NB OF MANSFIELD
{{ 1 L 9 S }}
Chartered 6/18
1902 Plain Back <$VALUE
3x10-20 1-1944 <$1500
1929 Small Size
10 Type 1 1-334 <$300
20 Type 1 1-118 <$300
10 Type 2 1-249 <$325
20 Type 2 1-45 <$325
Total Issue $134,790
Out in 1935 $12,500
Large out 1935 $580
****
11122 Poinsett
FNB OF MARKED TREE
{{ 5 L }}
Organized 12/17/17
Receivership 11/30/26
1902 Plain Back <$VALUE
3x10-20 1-7626 <$1500
Total Issue $381,300
Out at close $48,300
****
10795 Searcy
ARKANSAS NB OF MARSHALL
{{ UNREPORTED }}
Chartered 10/15
Liquidated 2/16/21
1902 Plain Back <$VALUE
4x5 1-1690 <$2500
3x10-20 1-1038 <$2500
Total Issue $85,700
Out at close $23,600
****
10794 Searcy
FNB OF MARSHALL
{{ 2 L }}
Chartered 10/15
Liquidated 9/24/23
1902 Plain Back <$VALUE
3x10-20 1-5760 <$1250
Total Issue $230,400
Out at close $47,800
****
13280 Desha
FNB IN McGEHEE
{{ 4 L 5 S }}
Chartered 2/11/29
Liquidated 7/1/31
1902 Plain Back <$VALUE
4x5 1-6018 <$850
1929 Small Size
5 Type 1 1-7529 <$400
Total Issue $346,230
Out at close $91,600
Large out at close $1,110
****
7163 Polk
FNB OF MENA
{{ 3 L }}
Organized 2/29/04
Receivership 12/15/28
1902 Red Seal <$VALUE
3x10-20 1-2020 <$2000
1902 Date Back
3x10-20 1-4000 <$850
1902 Plain Back
3x10-20 4001-10188 <$850
Total Issue $610,400
Out at close $19,230
****
7829 Polk
NB OF MENA
{{ UNREPORTED }}
Chartered 7/05
Liquidated 11/1/10
1902 Red Seal <$VALUE
4x5 1-1215 <$3000
3x10-20 1-886 <$3000
1902 Date Back
4x5 1-210 <$2000
3x10-20 1-127 <$2000
Total Issue $79,150
Out in 1911 $15,090
****
13693 Polk
PLANTERS NB OF MENA
{{ 7 S }}
Chartered 5/33
1929 Small Size <$VALUE
5 Type 2 1-6804 <$350
10 Type 2 1-3599 <$350
20 Type 2 1-1003 <$350
Total Issue $90,070
Out in 1935 $40,550
****
10434 Conway
FNB OF MORRILTON
{{ 3 L }}
Chartered 8/13
Liquidated 5/13/29
1902 Date Back <$VALUE
4x10 1-1200 <$1000
1902 Plain Back
4x10 1201-10034 <$1000
Total Issue $401,360
Out at close $18,050
****
11113 Howard
FNB OF NASHVILLE
{{ 2 S }}
Chartered 12/17 as FNB of
Mineral Springs, under which
there was no issue. Issuing
title adopted 3/10/31.
1929 Small Size <$VALUE
5 Type 2 1-10600 <$750
Total Issue $53,000
Out in 1935 $18,800
****
9022 Independence
FNB OF NEWARK
{{ 7 L U + 12 S }}
Chartered2/08
1902 Red Seal <$VALUE
4x5 1-625 <$1750
4x10 1-625 <$1750
1902 Date Back
4x5 1-1475* <$450
4x10 1-1425** <$450
1902 Plain Back
4x5 1626-6335* <$450
4x10 1526-5046** <$450
* 1476-1625 not marked
** 1426-1525 not marked
1929 Small Size
5 Type 1 1-1378 <$350
10 Type 1 1-706 <$350
5 Type 2 1-1614 <$350
10 Type 2 1-1125 <$350
Total Issue $469,060
Out in 1935 $24,400
Large out 1935 $1,320
****
6758 Jackson
FNB OF NEWPORT
{{ 18 L 9 S }}
Chartered 5/03
1902 Red Seal <$VALUE
4x5 1-2772 <$1750
3x10-20 1-1961 <$1750
1902 Date Back
4x5 1-3100 <$375
3x10-20 1-2420 <$375
1902 Plain Back
4x5 3101-11079 <$375
3x10-20 2421-7573 <$375
1929 Small Size
5 Type 1 1-1560 <$250
10 Type 1 1-964 <$250
20 Type 1 1-264 <$250
5 Type 2 1-3224 <$275
10 Type 2 1-1455 <$275
20 Type 2 1-340 <$300
Total Issue $926,510
Out in 1935 $42,750
Large out 1935 $3,900
****
6846 Greene
FNB OF PARAGOULD
{{ 5 L }}
Chartered 6/03
Liquidated 3/20/28
1902 Red Seal <$VALUE
4x5 1-1400 <$1750
3x10-20 1-1095 <$1750
1902 Date Back
4x5 1-3300 <$650
3x10-20 1-2880 <$650
1902 Plain Back
4x5 3301-10435 <$650
3x10-20 2881-7517 <$650
Total Issue $667,300
Out at close $41,450
Ch 13155 assumed circulation
****
10004 Greene
NB OF COMMERCE OF
PARAGOULD
{{ 9 L 16 S }}
Chartered 4/11
1902 Date Back <$VALUE
4x5 1-3100* <$400
3x10-20 1-2420** <$400
1902 Plain Back
4x5 3501-11895* <$400
3x10-20 2721-8037** <$400
* 3101-3500 not marked
** 2421-2720 not marked
1929 Small Size
5 Type 1 1-2830 <$150
10 Type 1 1-1826 <$150
20 Type 1 1-438 <$150
5 Type 2 1-5652 <$165
10 Type 2 1-2986 <$165
20 Type 2 1-961 <$175
Total Issue $964,110
Out in 1935 $83,000
Large out 1935 $3,100
****
13155 Greene
NEW FNB OF PARAGOULD
{{ 2 L 8 S }}
Chartered 12/27
1902 Plain Back <$VALUE
3x10-20 1-1069 <$1250
1929 Small Size
10 Type 1 1-1330 <$225
20 Type 1 1-364 <$250
10 Type 2 1-1673 <$300
20 Type 2 1-411 <$300
Total Issue $201,880
Out in 1935 $49,150
Large out 1935 $3,440
Outstanding includes Ch 6846
****
11592 Logan
FNB OF PARIS
{{ 4 L 9 S }}
Chartered 2/20
Liquidated 8/15/34
1902 Plain Back <$VALUE
4x10 1-15162 <$600
1929 Small Size
10 Type 1 1-3906 <$250
10 Type 2 1-406 <$275
Total Issue $844,900
Out in 1935 $27,770
Large out 1935 $1,920
Ch 14209 assumed circulation
****
6706 Perry
FNB OF PERRY
{{ UNREPORTED }}
Chartered 3/31/03
Liquidated 3/1/17
1902 Red Seal <$VALUE
3x10-20 1-1000 <$3000
1902 Date Back
3x10-20 1-708 <$2500
Total Issue $85,400
Out at close $8,300
****
2776 Jefferson
FNB OF PINE BLUFF
{{ 1 L }}
Chartered 9/18/82
Receivership 11/20/86
Brown Back <$VALUE
4x5 1-2435 <$2500
Total Issue $48,700
Out in 1916 $400
****
10768 Jefferson
NB OF ARKANSAS AT
PINE BLUFF
{{ 5 L 4 S }}
Organized 8/12/15
Receivership 7/21/30
1902 Plain Back <$VALUE
3x10-20 1-16073 <$600
1929 Small Size
10 Type 1 1-1078 <$500
20 Type 1 1-226 <$500
Total Issue $895,450
Out at close $98,920
Large out at close $19,650
****
14056 Jefferson
NB OF COMMERCE OF
PINE BLUFF
{{ 5 S }}
Chartered 3/34
1929 Small Size <$VALUE
5 Type 2 1-2916 <$500
10 Type 2 1-1451 <$500
20 Type 2 1-1513 <$500
Total Issue $59,350
Out in 1935 $49,000
****
6680 Jefferson
SIMMONS NB OF PINE BLUFF
{{ 12 L 24 S }}
Chartered 3/03
1902 Red Seal <$VALUE
3x10-20 1-4450 <$1500
1902 Date Back
3x10-20 1-12000 <$175
1902 Plain Back
3x10-20 12001-39709 <$175
1929 Small Size
10 Type 1 1-5926 <$75
20 Type 1 1-1588 <$80
10 Type 2 1-6014 <$100
20 Type 2 1-1692 <$100
Total Issue $2,848,050
Out in 1935 $175,350
Large out 1935 $8,990
****
8030 Washington
FNB OF PRAIRIE GROVE
{{ 7 L }}
Chartered 1/06
Liquidated 1/8/29
1902 Red Seal <$VALUE
4x5 1-700 <$2000
3x10-20 1-560 <$2000
1902 Date Back
4x5 1-1675 <$650
3x10-20 1-1260 <$650
1902 Plain Back
4x5 1676-5330 <$650
3x10-20 1261-3405 <$650
Total Issue $318,850
Out at close $22,400
****
10853 Clay
FNB OF RECTOR
{{ 3 L 1 S }}
Organized 4/17/16
Receivership 12/3/30
1902 Plain Back <$VALUE
3x10-20 1-4372 <$1250
1929 Small Size
10 Type 1 1-280 <$1000
20 Type 1 1-64 <$1000
Total Issue $243,080
Out at close $24,520
Large out at close $4,870
****
10750 Benton
AMERICAN NB OF ROGERS
{{ 8 L 11 S }}
Chartered 6/15
1902 Plain Back <$VALUE
4x5 1-10993 <$600
3x10-20 1-5049 <$600
1929 Small Size
5 Type 1 1-1444 <$250
10 Type 1 1-1002 <$250
20 Type 1 1-286 <$250
5 Type 2 1-1728 <$275
10 Type 2 1-1327 <$275
20 Type 2 1-295 <$300
Total Issue $637,880
Out in 1935 $44,000
Large out 1935 $1,830
****
7789 Benton
FNB OF ROGERS
{{ 7 L 2 S }}
Organized 5/19/05
Receivership 1/13/31
1902 Red Seal <$VALUE
4x5 1-1000 <$1750
3x10-20 1-620 <$1750
1902 Date Back
4x5 1-3800 <$600
3x10-20 1-2880 <$600
1902 Plain Back
4x5 3801-11271 <$600
3x10-20 2881-7715 <$600
1929 Small Size
5 Type 1 1-779 <$500
10 Type 1 1-386 <$500
20 Type 1 1-124 <$500
Total Issue $723,580
Out at close $48,320
Large out at close $9,120
****
4582 Pope
FNB OF RUSSELLVILLE
{{ 1 L }}
Chartered 6/13/91
Liquidated 12/30/97
Brown Back <$VALUE
3x10-20 1-536 <$3000
Total Issue $26,800
Out in 1910 $340
****
9871 Benton
FARMERS NB OF
SILOAM SPRINGS
Organized 9/26/10
Liquidated 1/21/29
2nd title:FNB of Siloam
Springs 3/2/12
FIRST TITLE {{ 1 L }}
1902 Date Back <$VALUE
4x5 1-1315 <$1250
3x10-20 1-1033 <$1250
SECOND TITLE {{ 6 L }}
1902 Date Back
4x5 1-1950 <$600
3x10-20 1-1460 <$600
1902 Plain Back
4x5 1951-9175 <$600
3x10-20 1461-6289 <$600
Total Issue $575,900
Out at close $49,100
Ch 13274 assumed circulation
****
13274 Benton
FNB IN SILOAM SPRINGS
{{ U + 13 L 3 S }}
Chartered 1/29
Liquidated 12/8/30
1902 Plain Back <$VALUE
4x5 1-840 <$650
1929 Small Size
5 Type 1 1-2169 <$750
Total Issue $81,870
Out at close $18,860
Large out at close $5,810
Outstanding includes Ch 9871
Ch 13506 assumed circulation
****
FNB of Siloam Springs
SEE Ch 9871
Farmers NB of Siloam Springs
****
8763 Washington
FNB OF SPRINGDALE
{{ 9 L 12 S }}
Organized 5/23/07
1902 Red Seal <$VALUE
4x5 1-725 <$2000
3x10-20 1-580 <$2000
1902 Date Back
4x5 1-3400 <$600
3x10-20 1-2390 <$600
1902 Plain Back
4x5 3401-10775 <$600
3x10-20 2391-7302 <$600
1929 Small Size
5 Type 1 1-1776 <$250
10 Type 1 1-1018 <$250
20 Type 1 1-280 <$250
5 Type 2 1-2602 <$275
10 Type 2 1-1365 <$275
20 Type 2 1-454 <$275
Total Issue $807,800
Out in 1935 $52,110
Large out 1935 $3,560
****
10459 Arkansas
FNB OF STUTTGART
{{ U + 2 L 1 S }}
Chartered 11/11/13
Liquidated 3/31/30
1902 Date Back <$VALUE
4x5 1-750 <$1250
3x10-20 1-600 <$1250
1902 Plain Back
4x5 751-5507 <$1250
3x10-20 601-3329 <$1250
1929 Small Size
5 Type 1 1-283 <$850
10 Type 1 1-110 <$850
20 Type 1 1-20 <$850
Total Issue $294,080
Out at close $25,000
Large out at close $8,110
****

****
4401 Miller
GATE CITY NB OF TEXARKANA
{{ 2 L }}
Chartered 8/19/90
Liquidated 6/30/94
Brown Back <$VALUE
4x5 1-1063 <$3000
Total Issue $21,260
Out in 1910 $185
****
7138 Miller
STATE NB OF TEXARKANA
{{ 19 L 34 S }}
Chartered 2/04
1902 Red Seal <$VALUE
3x10-20 1-1440 <$1500
1902 Date Back
3x10-20 1-12200 <$225
1902 Plain Back
3x10-20 12201-44704 <$225
1929 Small Size
10 Type 1 1-13280 <$65
20 Type 1 1-2950 <$75
10 Type 2 1-4160 <$75
20 Type 2 1-900 <$85
Total Issue $3,517,600
Out in 1935 $180,500
Large out 1935 $1,300
****
7361 Crawford
FNB OF VAN BUREN
{{ 14 L 6 S }}
Chartered 8/04
Liquidated 3/21/30
1902 Red Seal <$VALUE
3x10-20 1-640 <$2000
1902 Date Back
3x10-20 1-4200 <$400
1902 Plain Back
3x10-20 4201-16854 <$400
1929 Small Size
10 Type 1 1-724 <$500
20 Type 1 1-145 <$500
Total Issue $935,540
Out at close $100,000
Large out at close $39,490
****
5849 Scott
FNB OF WALDRON
{{ 3 L 2 S }}
Organized 5/17/01
Receivership 4/22/31
Brown Back <$VALUE
3x10-20 1-420 <$2000
1882 Date Back
3x10-20 1-1020* <$1750
1882 Value Back
3x10-20 1121-1993* <$1750
* 1021-1120 not marked
1902 Plain Back
3x10-20 1-2075 <$1000
1929 Small Size
10 Type 1 1-249 <$750
20 Type 1 1-75 <$750
Total Issue $248,340
Out at close $18,750
Large out at close $2,800
****
9332 Lawrence
FNB OF WALNUT RIDGE
{{ 3 L }}
Chartered 2/09
Liquidated 12/31/21
1902 Date Back <$VALUE
4x5 1-2275 <$1000
3x10-20 1-1700 <$1000
1902 Plain Back
4x5 2276-4370 <$1000
3x10-20 1701-2894 <$1000
Total Issue $232,100
Out at close $25,000
****
11312 Lawrence
FNB OF LAWRENCE COUNTY AT WALNUT RIDGE
{{ 3 S }}
Chartered 3/19 as FNB of Black Rock, under which there was no issue. Issuing title adopted 9/16/33.
1929 Small Size <$VALUE
5 Type 2 1-1240 <$750
10 Type 2 1-670 <$750
20 Type 2 1-305 <$750
50 Type 2 1-128 <$1250
100 Type 2 1-72 <$1250
Total Issue $32,600
Out in 1935 $22,600
****

****
12083 Lawrence
PLANTERS NB OF WALNUT RIDGE
{{ 3 L 1 S }}
Organized 8/24/21
Receivership 11/11/30
1902 Plain Back <$VALUE
4x5 1-9737 <$1500
1929 Small Size
5 Type 1 1-1225 <$1250
Total Issue $231,490
Out at close $25,000
****
10807 Cross
FNB OF WYNNE
{{ 3 S }}
Chartered 12/15
1929 Small Size <$VALUE
5 Type 1 1-898 <$600
10 Type 1 1-450 <$600
5 Type 2 1-4056 <$650
10 Type 2 1-1632 <$650
Total Issue $90,540
Out in 1935 $20,020
****

CONDITION affects Value. The Values shown are for notes in FINE condition.

NATIONAL BANK NOTES

CALIFORNIA

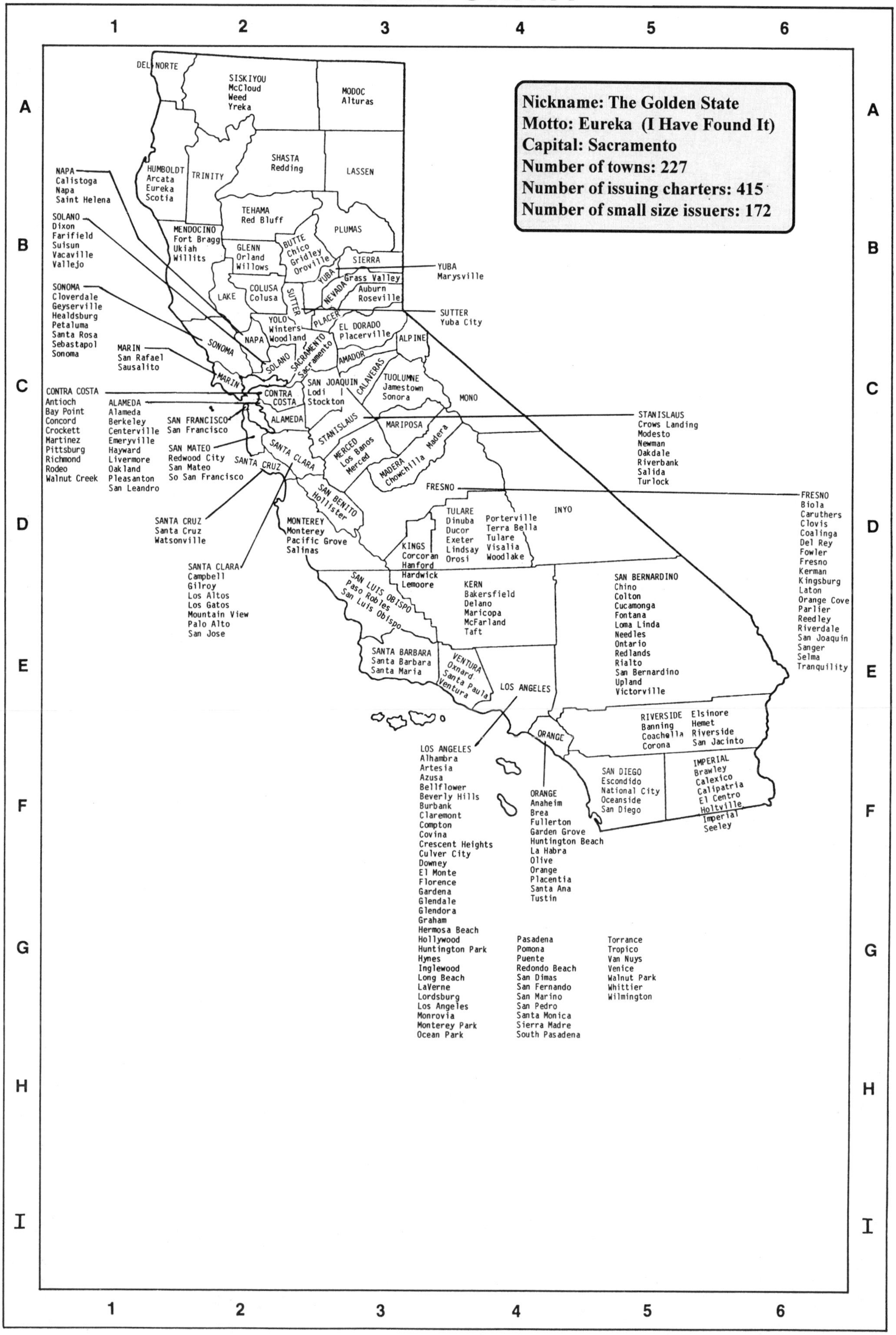
Nickname: The Golden State
Motto: Eureka (I Have Found It)
Capital: Sacramento
Number of towns: 227
Number of issuing charters: 415
Number of small size issuers: 172
1 2 3 4 5 6
A B C D E F G H I
DEL NORTE
SISKIYOU McCloud Weed Yreka
MODOC Alturas
HUMBOLDT Arcata Eureka Scotia
TRINITY
SHASTA Redding
LASSEN
TEHAMA Red Bluff
PLUMAS
MENDOCINO Fort Bragg Ukiah Willits
GLENN Orland Willows
BUTTE Chico Gridley Oroville
SIERRA
YUBA
NEVADA Grass Valley
Auburn Roseville
YUBA Marysville
LAKE
COLUSA Colusa
SUTTER
SUTTER Yuba City
YOLO Winters Woodland
PLACER
EL DORADO Placerville
ALPINE
NAPA
NAPA Calistoga Napa Saint Helena
SOLANO Dixon Farifield Suisun Vacaville Vallejo
SONOMA Cloverdale Geyserville Healdsburg Petaluma Santa Rosa Sebastapol Sonoma
MARIN San Rafael Sausalito
SONOMA
SOLANO
SACRAMENTO Sacramento
AMADOR
MARIN
CALAVERAS
TUOLUMNE Jamestown Sonora
MONO
SAN JOAQUIN Lodi Stockton
CONTRA COSTA
CONTRA COSTA Antioch Bay Point Concord Crockett Martinez Pittsburg Richmond Rodeo Walnut Creek
ALAMEDA Alameda Berkeley Centerville Emeryville Hayward Livermore Oakland Pleasanton San Leandro
SAN FRANCISCO San Francisco
SAN MATEO Redwood City San Mateo So San Francisco
ALAMEDA
STANISLAUS
STANISLAUS Crows Landing Modesto Newman Oakdale Riverbank Salida Turlock
MARIPOSA
SANTA CLARA
SANTA CRUZ
MERCED Los Banos Merced
MADERA Chowchilla
Madera
FRESNO
FRESNO Biola Caruthers Clovis Coalinga Del Rey Fowler Fresno Kerman Kingsburg Laton Orange Cove Parlier Reedley Riverdale San Joaquin Sanger Selma Tranquility
SAN BENITO Hollister
SANTA CRUZ Santa Cruz Watsonville
MONTEREY Monterey Pacific Grove Salinas
TULARE Dinuba Ducor Exeter Lindsay Orosi
Porterville Terra Bella Tulare Visalia Woodlake
INYO
KINGS Corcoran Hanford Hardwick Lemoore
SANTA CLARA Campbell Gilroy Los Altos Los Gatos Mountain View Palo Alto San Jose
SAN LUIS OBISPO Paso Robles San Luis Obispo
KERN Bakersfield Delano Maricopa McFarland Taft
SAN BERNARDINO Chino Colton Cucamonga Fontana Loma Linda Needles Ontario Redlands Rialto San Bernardino Upland Victorville
SANTA BARBARA Santa Barbara Santa Maria
VENTURA Oxnard Santa Paula Ventura
LOS ANGELES
RIVERSIDE Banning Coachella Corona
Elsinore Hemet Riverside San Jacinto
ORANGE
LOS ANGELES Alhambra Artesia Azusa Bellflower Beverly Hills Burbank Claremont Compton Covina Crescent Heights Culver City Downey El Monte Florence Gardena Glendale Glendora Graham Hermosa Beach Hollywood Huntington Park Hynes Inglewood Long Beach LaVerne Lordsburg Los Angeles Monrovia Monterey Park Ocean Park
Pasadena Pomona Puente Redondo Beach San Dimas San Fernando San Marino San Pedro Santa Monica Sierra Madre South Pasadena
Torrance Tropico Van Nuys Venice Walnut Park Whittier Wilmington
ORANGE Anaheim Brea Fullerton Garden Grove Huntington Beach La Habra Olive Orange Placentia Santa Ana Tustin
SAN DIEGO Escondido National City Oceanside San Diego
IMPERIAL Brawley Calexico Calipatria El Centro Holtville Imperial Seeley

9220 Alameda
ALAMEDA NB, ALAMEDA
{{ 5 L }}
Chartered 8/08
Liquidated 6/30/21
1902 Date Back <$VALUE
4x5 1-7400 <$500
3x10-20 1-5720 <$500
1902 Plain Back
4x5 7401-13550 <$500
3x10-20 5721-9240 <$500
Total Issue $733,000
Out at close $96,600

10150 Alameda
CITIZENS NB OF ALAMEDA
{{ 16 L }}
Chartered 3/12
Liquidated 12/29/27
1902 Date Back <$VALUE
4x5 1-5150 <$150
3x10-20 1-3840 <$150
1902 Plain Back
4x5 5151-20140 <$150
3x10-20 3841-13683 <$150
Total Issue $1,086,950
Out at close $78,800

11942 Alameda
COMMERCIAL NB OF ALAMEDA
{{ 14 L 11 S }}
Chartered 3/21
1902 Plain Back <$VALUE
4x5 1-29220 <$150
1929 Small Size
5 Type 1 1-8432 <$125
5 Type 2 1-19804 <$125
Total Issue $936,380
Out in 1935 $65,000
Large out 1935 $2,135

2431 Alameda
FNB OF ALAMEDA
{{ 1 L }}
Chartered 8/26/79
Liquidated 9/4/88
Series 1875 <$VALUE
4x5 1-3666 <$3000
3x10-20 1-1523<$3500/$4000
Total Issue $149,470
Out in 1910 $885

Alhambra NB, Alhambra
SEE Ch 9966
NB of Alhambra

8490 Los Angeles
FNB OF ALHAMBRA
{{ 5 L 5 S }}
Chartered 1/07
Liquidated 7/25/32
1902 Red Seal <$VALUE
3x10-20 1-750 <$1500
1902 Date Back
3x10-20 1-2470 <$750
1902 Plain Back
3x10-20 2471-6695 <$750
1929 Small Size
10 Type 1 1-497 <$400
20 Type 1 1-140 <$400
Total Issue $418,870
Out at close $24,700
Large out at close $1,780

9966 Los Angeles
NB OF ALHAMBRA
{{ UNREPORTED }}
Chartered 3/11
Liquidated 1/11/15
2nd title: Alhambra NB
5/27/13
FIRST TITLE
1902 Date Back <$VALUE
4x5 1-531 <$2500
4x10 1-447 <$2500
SECOND TITLE
1902 Date Back
4x5 1-210 <$2500
3x10-20 1-170 <$2500
Total Issue $41,200
Out in 1915 $4,650

7219 Modoc
FNB OF ALTURAS
{{ 5 L }}
Chartered 4/04
Liquidated 5/29/30
1902 Red Seal <$VALUE
3x10-20 1-1800 <$1250
50-100 1-333 <$7500/$8500
1902 Date Back
3x10-20 1-5500 <$600
3x50-100 1-219 <$1500
1902 Plain Back
3x10-20 5501-14816 <$600
3x50-100 220-342 <$1500
Total Issue $966,250
Out at close $20,395

10228 Orange
ANAHEIM NB, ANAHEIM
Organized 6/26/12
Receivership 1/15/34
2nd title:Anaheim FNB
10/1/30
FIRST TITLE {{ 7 L 2U + 7 S }}
1902 Date Back <$VALUE
3x10-20 1-2260 <$400
1902 Plain Back
3x10-20 2261-11386 <$400
1929 Small Size
10 Type 1 1-622 <$200
20 Type 1 1-202 <$200
SECOND TITLE {{ 5 S }}
1929 Small Size
10 Type 1 1-650 <$200
20 Type 1 1-188 <$200
Total Issue $692,420
Out at close $49,500
Large out at close $2,440

6481 Orange
FNB OF ANAHEIM
{{ 6 L 4 S }}
Chartered 11/7/02
Liquidated 1/16/30
1902 Red Seal <$VALUE
3x10-20 1-895 <$1250
1902 Date Back
3x10-20 1-4480 <$450
1902 Plain Back
3x10-20 4481-18883 <$450
1929 Small Size
10 Type 1 1-413 <$400
20 Type 1 1-141 <$400
Total Issue $1,030,600
Out at close $86,675
Large out at close $44,975

11823 Orange
GOLDEN STATE NB OF
ANAHEIM
{{ UNREPORTED }}
Chartered 8/20
Liquidated 6/18/25
1902 Plain Back <$VALUE
3x10-20 1-726 <$2500
Total Issue $36,300
Out at close $8,600

9892 Contra Costa
FNB OF ANTIOCH
{{ 5 L 2U + 9 S }}
Chartered 11/10
1902 Date Back <$VALUE
3x10-20 1-850 <$500
1902 Plain Back
3x10-20 851-4586 <$500
1929 Small Size
10 Type 1 1-860 <$250
20 Type 1 1-186 <$250
10 Type 2 1-1028 <$250
20 Type 2 1-209 <$250
Total Issue $317,680
Out in 1935 $23,500
Large out 1935 $540

10372 Humboldt
FNB OF ARCATA
{{ 3 L }}
Chartered 4/13
Liquidated 4/3/28
1902 Date Back <$VALUE
4x5 1-830 <$650
3x10-20 1-668 <$650
1902 Plain Back
4x5 831-2390 <$650
3x10-20 669-1588 <$650
Total Issue $127,200
Out at close $7,300

8063 Los Angeles
FNB OF ARTESIA
{{ 6 L 1 S }}
Chartered 1/06
Receivership 7/18/32
1902 Red Seal <$VALUE
4x5 1-850 <$1250
3x10-20 1-680 <$1250
1902 Date Back
4x5 1-2175 <$500
3x10-20 1-1520 <$500
1902 Plain Back
4x5 2176-7520 <$500
3x10-20 1521-4574 <$500
1929 Small Size
5 Type 1 1-677 <$650
10 Type 1 1-316 <$650
20 Type 1 1-107 <$650
Total Issue $482,210
Out at close $25,000
Large out at close $2,260

9227 Placer
FNB OF AUBURN
{{ 2 L }}
Chartered 8/08
Liquidated 1/8/29
1902 Date Back <$VALUE
4x5 1-1400 <$1250
3x10-20 1-1520 <$1250
1902 Plain Back
3x10-20 1521-6882 <$1250
Total Issue $372,100
Out at close $10,150

8065 Los Angeles
FNB OF AZUSA
{{ 4 L U + 19 S }}
Chartered 1/06
1902 Red Seal <$VALUE
4x5 1-939 <$1250
3x10-20 1-734 <$1250
1902 Date Back
4x5 1-2525 <$600
3x10-20 1-1620 <$600
1902 Plain Back
4x5 2526-7714 <$600
3x10-20 1621-4587 <$600
1929 Small Size
5 Type 1 1-310 <$175
10 Type 1 1-2386 <$150
20 Type 1 1-680 <$150
5 Type 2 1-4152 <$175
10 Type 2 1-2144 <$175
20 Type 2 1-708 <$175
Total Issue $729,530
Out in 1935 $81,075
Large out 1935 $1,075

8074 Los Angeles
UNITED STATES NB OF AZUSA
{{ 1 L }}
Chartered 2/06
Liquidated 12/30/16
1902 Red Seal <$VALUE
4x5 1-1410 <$1500
3x10-20 1-1136 <$1500
1902 Date Back
4x5 1-4525 <$1250
3x10-20 1-2800 <$1250
1902 Plain Back
4x5 4526-5225 <$1250
3x10-20 2801-3215 <$1250
Total Issue $350,250
Out at close $48,800

FNB in Bakersfield
SEE Ch 10357
NB of Bakersfield

6044 Kern
FNB OF BAKERSFIELD
{{ 9 L }}
Chartered 12/11/01
Closed 5/15/19
Brown Back <$VALUE
4x5 1-2310 <$750
3x10-20 1-1816 <$750
50-100 1-60 <$3500
1882 Date Back
4x5 1-8750 <$600
3x10-20 1-6000 <$600
50-100 1-100 <$3000
3x50-100 1-192 <$3000
1882 Value Back
4x5 8751-13180 <$750
3x10-20 6001-7762 <$750
Total Issue $860,700
Out at close $150,000

11327 Kern
FNB OF BAKERSFIELD
{{ 3 L }}
Chartered 4/19 as Producers
NB of Bakersfield, under
which there was no issue.
Issuing title adopted
5/15/19.
Liquidated 5/3/22
1902 Plain Back <$VALUE
4x5 1-25275 <$500
3x10-20 1-14102 <$500
Total issue $1,210,600
Out at close $400,000
Outstanding includes Ch 6044

10357 Kern
NB OF BAKERSFIELD
Chartered 4/13
Liquidated 5/6/35
2nd title:FNB in
Bakersfield 5/3/24
FIRST TITLE {{ 4 L }}
1902 Date Back <$VALUE
4x5 1-3250 <$400
3x10-20 1-2600 <$400
1902 Plain Back
4x5 3251-11600 <$400
3x10-20 2601-7770 <$400
SECOND TITLE {{ 0 L 5U+32 S }}
1902 Plain Back
4x5 1-1170 <$600
3x10-20 1-1465 <$600
1929 Small Size
5 Type 1 1-6160 <$100
10 Type 1 1-4228 <$100
20 Type 1 1-1554 <$100
50 Type 1 1-230 <$175
100 Type 1 1-114 <$250
5 Type 2 1-16772 <$125
10 Type 2 1-8855 <$125
20 Type 2 1-2625 <$125
Total Issue $1,704,420
Out at close $502,125
Large out at close $2,125

9459 Riverside
FNB OF BANNING
{{ 8 L 2U + 4 S }}
Chartered 6/09
Liquidated 7/5/35
1902 Date Back <$VALUE
4x5 1-1800 <$400
3x10-20 1-1300 <$400
1902 Plain Back
4x5 1801-6545 <$400
3x10-20 1301-4142 <$400
1929 Small Size
5 Type 1 1-932 <$300
10 Type 1 1-442 <$300
20 Type 1 1-150 <$300
5 Type 2 1-1244 <$350
10 Type 2 1-531 <$350
20 Type 2 1-138 <$350
Total Issue $424,770
Out at close $20,950
Large out at close $1,060

11561 Contra Costa
FNB OF BAY POINT
{{ 2 L }}
Organized 12/19/19
Receivership 3/18/32
1902 Plain Back <$VALUE
4x5 1-3060 <$1250
Total Issue $61,200
Out at close $350

12754 Los Angeles
COMMERCIAL NB OF
BELLFLOWER
{{ 2 S }}
Chartered 6/25
Liquidated 11/29/32
1929 Small Size <$VALUE
10 Type 1 1-428 <$750
20 Type 1 1-135 <$750
Total Issue $41,880
Out at close $25,000
Ch 12328 assumed circulation

12328 Los Angeles
FNB OF BELLFLOWER
{{ 6 L 1 S }}
Organized 1/6/23
1902 Plain Back <$VALUE
4x5 1-3452 <$500
1929 Small Size
5 Type 1 1-1222 <$850
5 Type 2 1-4598 <$850
Total Issue $128,690
Out in 1935 $27,585
Large out 1935 $635
Outstanding includes Ch 12754

7849 Alameda
BERKELEY NB, BERKELEY
{{ 4 L }}
Chartered 7/05
Liquidated 5/22/15
1902 Red Seal <$VALUE
3x10-20 1-4225 <$1250
1902 Date Back
3x10-20 1-8942 <$400
Total Issue $658,350
Out at close $109,800

11495 Alameda
COLLEGE NB OF BERKELEY
{{ 7 L }}
Chartered 10/19
Liquidated 7/27/29
1902 Plain Back <$VALUE
3x10-20 1-20458 <$400
Total Issue $1,022,900
Out at close $17,075

12320 Alameda
FNB IN BERKELEY
{{ 10 L }}
Chartered 1/23
Liquidated 1/13/31
1902 Plain Back <$VALUE
4x5 1-11505 <$250
3x10-20 1-7964 <$250
Total Issue $628,300
Out at close $6,375

5380 Alameda
FNB OF BERKELEY
{{ 11 L }}
Chartered 5/29/00
Liquidated 3/4/22
Brown Back <$VALUE
4x5 1-5300 <$600
3x10-20 1-7480 <$600
1882 Date Back
4x5 1-6000* <$500
3x10-20 1-4800** <$500
3x50-100 1-355 <$2500
1882 Value Back
4x5 8501-11350* <$600
3x10-20 6001-7473** <$600
* 6001-8500 not marked
** 4801-6000 not marked
1902 Plain Back
4x5 1-11685 <$350
3x10-20 1-4466 <$350
3x50-100 1-58 <$850/$1000
Total Issue $1,640,900
Out at close $279,795

11461 Los Angeles
FNB OF BEVERLY HILLS
{{ 17 L 16 S }}
Organized 7/7/19 as The
Beverly Hills NB, under
which there was no issue.
Issuing title adopted
11/18/19.
Receivership 6/7/32
1902 Plain Back <$VALUE
4x5 1-29619 <$375
1929 Small Size
5 Type 1 1-32504 <$175
Total issue $1,567,500
Out at close $400,000
Large out at close $5,125
Outstanding includes Ch 12909

12909 Los Angeles
LIBERTY NB OF
BEVERLY HILLS
{{ 4 L }}
Chartered 4/26
Liquidated 8/31/27
1902 Plain Back <$VALUE
4x5 1-1250 <$750
3x10-20 1-1536 <$750
Total Issue $101,800
Out at close $100,000
Ch 11461 assumed circulation

11769 Fresno
FNB OF BIOLA
{{ UNREPORTED }}
Chartered 6/20
Liquidated 10/27/22
1902 Plain Back <$VALUE
3x10-20 1-478 <$3000
Total Issue $23,900
Out at close $9,500

9673 Imperial
FNB OF BRAWLEY
{{ 2 L }}
Chartered 2/10
Liquidated 9/12/22
1902 Date Back <$VALUE
4x5 1-1700 <$1250
3x10-20 1-1375 <$1250
1902 Plain Back
4x5 1701-6625 <$1250
3x10-20 1376-4261 <$1250
Total Issue $345,550
Out at close $65,300

13877 Orange
OILFIELDS NB IN BREA
{{ 3U + 12 S }}
Chartered 12/33
1929 Small Size <$VALUE
5 Type 2 1-2820 <$300
10 Type 2 1-1935 <$300
Total Issue $33,450
Out in 1935 $18,550

13001 Orange
OILFIELDS NB OF BREA
{{ 2 L 5 S }}
Chartered 10/26
Liquidated 3/2/34
1902 Plain Back <$VALUE
4x5 1-3841 <$1250
1929 Small Size
5 Type 1 1-6380 <$400
5 Type 2 1-846 <$400
Total Issue $272,450
Out at close $33,210
Large out at close $320

10099 Los Angeles
FNB OF BURBANK
{{ 1 L }}
Chartered 11/11
Liquidated 1/20/23
1902 Date Back <$VALUE
4x5 1-825 <$1500
3x10-20 1-630 <$1500
1902 Plain Back
4x5 826-1855 <$1500
3x10-20 631-1259 <$1500
Total Issue $100,050
Out at close $11,500

9705 Imperial
CALEXICO NB, CALEXICO
{{ UNREPORTED }}
Chartered 3/10
Liquidated 3/5/21
1902 Date Back <$VALUE
4x5 1-1450 <$2000
4x10 1-1700 <$2000
1902 Plain Back
4x5 1451-2738 <$2000
4x10 1701-2545 <$2000
Total Issue $156,560
Out at close $20,000
Ch 9686 assumed circulation

9686 Imperial
FNB OF CALEXICO
{{ 9 L }}
Organized 1/27/10
Receivership 7/24/28
1902 Date Back <$VALUE
4x5 1-1250 <$750
3x10-20 1-1000 <$750
1902 Plain Back
4x5 1251-13339 <$750
3x10-20 1001-8287 <$750
Total Issue $681,130
Out at close $37,295
Outstanding includes Ch 9705

10687 Imperial
FNB OF CALIPATRIA
{{ UNREPORTED }}
Chartered 1/15
Liquidated 9/12/22
1902 Date Back <$VALUE
4x5 1-250 <$2000
3x10-20 1-200 <$2000
1902 Plain Back
4x5 251-795 <$2000
3x10-20 201-497 <$2000
Total Issue $40,750
Out at close $6,250

9551 Napa
CALISTOGA NB, CALISTOGA
{{ 1 L 2U + 12 S }}
Chartered 10/09
1902 Date Back <$VALUE
4x5 1-1600 <$1250
3x10-20 1-1260 <$1250
1902 Plain Back
4x5 1601-6365 <$1250
3x10-20 1261-4218 <$1250
1929 Small Size
5 Type 1 1-894 <$275
10 Type 1 1-482 <$275
20 Type 1 1-138 <$275
5 Type 2 1-1156 <$300
10 Type 2 1-706 <$300
20 Type 2 1-120 <$300
Total Issue $425,740
Out in 1935 $21,500
Large out 1935 $840

****
7388 Napa
FNB OF CALISTOGA
{{ UNREPORTED }}
Chartered 9/3/04
Liquidated 2/16/07
1902 Red Seal <$VALUE
4x5 1-510 <$3000
3x10-20 1-354 <$3000
Total Issue $27,900
Out in 1910 $1,725
****
11572 Santa Clara
GROWERS NB OF CAMPBELL
{{ 3 L }}
Chartered 1/20
Liquidated 9/29/23
1902 Plain Back <$VALUE
4x5 1-3040 <$1250
3x10-20 1-2302 <$1250
Total Issue $175,900
Out at close $47,200
****
11330 Fresno
FNB OF CARUTHERS
{{ 3 L 4 S }}
Chartered 4/19
1902 Plain Back <$VALUE
3x10-20 1-4260 <$1250
1929 Small Size
10 Type 1 1-830 <$450
20 Type 1 1-190 <$450
10 Type 2 1-784 <$450
20 Type 2 1-251 <$450
Total issue $298,460
Out in 1935 $24,750
Large out 1935 $630
****
11743 Alameda
FNB OF CENTERVILLE
{{ 4 L }}
Chartered 5/20
Liquidated 9/30/21
1902 Plain Back <$VALUE
4x5 1-635 <$1250
Total Issue $12,700
Out at close $5,700
****
9294 Butte
BUTTE COUNTY NB OF CHICO
{{ 2 L }}
Chartered 12/08
Liquidated 10/20/22
1902 Date Back <$VALUE
4x5 1-4400 <$750
3x10-20 1-4040 <$750
50-100 1-240 <$1500
1902 Plain Back
4x5 4401-6250 <$750
3x10-20 4041-5146 <$750
Total Issue $418,300
Out at close $49,300
****
8798 Butte
FNB OF CHICO
Organized 7/8/07
Receivership 7/18/33
2nd title: FN T & Savings B of Chico 6/11/28
FIRST TITLE {{ 6 L }}
1902 Red Seal <$VALUE
3x10-20 1-1160 <$1250
1902 Date Back
3x10-20 1-3900 <$400
1902 Plain Back
3x10-20 3901-16326 <$400
SECOND TITLE {{ 0 L 16 S }}
1902 Plain Back
3x10-20 1-2151 <$500
1929 Small Size
10 Type 1 1-3755 <$125
20 Type 1 1-1075 <$125
Total Issue $1,336,150
Out at close $150,000
Large out at close $5,500
****
13711 Butte
FNB OF CHICO
{{ 2U + 11 S }}
Chartered 6/33
1929 Small Size <$VALUE
5 Type 2 1-18604 <$175
10 Type 2 1-8970 <$175
20 Type 2 1-2844 <$175
Total Issue $239,600
Out in 1935 $146,700
****
FN T & Savings B of Chico
SEE Ch 8798
FNB of Chico
****
10271 San Bernardino
FNB OF CHINO
{{ 3 L }}
Chartered 10/12
Liquidated 2/14/29
1902 Date Back <$VALUE
4x5 1-650* <$850
3x10-20 1-840** <$850
1902 Plain Back
4x5 801-5425* <$850
3x10-20 901-3714** <$850
* 651-800 not marked
** 841-900 not marked
Total Issue $294,200
Out at close $9,700
****
11151 Madera
CHOWCHILLA NB, CHOWCHILLA
{{ 2 L }}
Chartered 2/18
Liquidated 1/12/26
1902 Plain Back <$VALUE
3x10-20 1-4674 <$1500
Total Issue $233,700
Out at close $18,100
****
10208 Los Angeles
CLAREMONT NB, CLAREMONT
{{ UNREPORTED }}
Chartered 6/12
Liquidated 7/1/18
1902 Date Back <$VALUE
4x5 1-1300 <$2000
3x10-20 1-1040 <$2000
1902 Plain Back
4x5 1301-2290 <$2000
3x10-20 1041-1582 <$2000
Total Issue $124,900
Out at close $29,000
Ch 9467 assumed circulation
****
9467 Los Angeles
FNB OF CLAREMONT
{{ 4 L 13 S }}
Chartered 7/09
1902 Date Back <$VALUE
3x10-20 1-2280 <$650
1902 Plain Back
3x10-20 2281-10461 <$650
1929 Small Size
10 Type 1 1-1282 <$275
20 Type 1 1-366 <$275
10 Type 2 1-1737 <$300
20 Type 2 1-263 <$300
Total Issue $666,520
Out in 1935 $46,000
Large out 1935 $2,100
Outstanding includes Ch 10208
****
11282 Sonoma
FNB OF CLOVERDALE
{{ 5 L 8 S }}
Chartered 12/18
1902 Plain Back <$VALUE
3x10-20 1-4612 <$650
1929 Small Size
5 Type 1 1-2046 <$300
10 Type 1 1-1090 <$300
20 Type 1 1-284 <$300
5 Type 2 1-1322 <$350
10 Type 2 1-900 <$350
20 Type 2 1-180 <$350
Total issue $410,670
Out in 1935 $30,000
Large out 1935 $1,100
****
10213 Fresno
FNB OF CLOVIS
{{ 2 L }}
Chartered 6/12
1902 Date Back <$VALUE
4x5 1-400* <$1500
3x10-20 1-335** <$1500
1902 Plain Back
4x5 501-2503* <$1500
3x10-20 416-1648** <$1500
* 401-500 not marked
** 336-415 not marked
Total Issue $132,460
Out in 1935 $475
****
10292 Riverside
FNB OF COACHELLA
{{ 0 L 2 S }}
Organized 10/28/12
Liquidated 2/15/35
1902 Date Back <$VALUE
4x5 1-425 <$2000
4x10 1-425 <$2000
1902 Plain Back
4x5 426-1892 <$2000
4x10 426-1600 <$2000
1929 Small Size
5 Type 1 1-449 <$750
10 Type 1 1-217 <$750
Total Issue $128,330
Out at close $6,160
Large out at close $555
Ch 14317 assumed circulation
****
9323 Fresno
FNB OF COALINGA
{{ 2 L }}
Chartered 1/09
Liquidated 11/6/22
1902 Date Back <$VALUE
4x5 1-4250 <$1250
3x10-20 1-3220 <$1250
1902 Plain Back
4x5 4251-8995 <$1250
3x10-20 3221-5987 <$1250
Total Issue $479,250
Out at close $47,000
****
13356 San Bernardino
CITIZENS NB OF COLTON
{{ 9 S }}
Chartered 7/29
1929 Small Size <$VALUE
5 Type 1 1-5582 <$225
5 Type 2 1-13616 <$225
Total Issue $235,540
Out in 1935 $50,000
Small out 1935 $47,765
Outstanding includes Ch 8608
****
8608 San Bernardino
COLTON NB, COLTON
{{ 6 L }}
Organized 3/6/07
Liquidated 7/24/29
1902 Red Seal <$VALUE
3x10-20 1-700 <$1250
1902 Date Back
3x10-20 1-4400 <$450
1902 Plain Back
3x10-20 4401-12752 <$450
Total Issue $672,600
Out in 1935 $2,235
Ch 13356 assumed circulation
****
3573 San Bernardino
FNB OF COLTON
{{ 10 L }}
Chartered 10/18/86
Liquidated 2/26/30
Brown Back <$VALUE
50-100 1-1102 <$3500
1902 Red Seal
4x5 1-1000 <$1250
3x10-20 1-450 <$1250
1902 Date Back
4x5 1-3600 <$400
3x10-20 1-2840 <$400
1902 Plain Back
4x5 3601-12351 <$400
3x10-20 2841-8855 <$400
Total Issue $897,570
Out at close $9,590
****
10072 Colusa
FNB OF COLUSA
{{ 1 L }}
Organized 7/1/11
Receivership 11/22/22
1902 Date Back <$VALUE
4x5 1-1700 <$1500
3x10-20 1-1300 <$1500
1902 Plain Back
4x5 1701-3270 <$1500
3x10-20 1301-2197 <$1500
Total Issue $175,250
Out at close $19,700
****
8085 Los Angeles
FNB OF COMPTON
{{ 4 L }}
Chartered 2/06
Liquidated 5/3/26
1902 Red Seal <$VALUE
3x10-20 1-950 <$1500
1902 Date Back
3x10-20 1-2130* <$750
1902 Plain Back
3x10-20 2331-5402* <$750
* 2131-2330 not marked
Total Issue $317,600
Out at close $22,400
****
9945 Contra Costa
FNB OF CONCORD
{{ 1 L }}
Chartered 3/11
Liquidated 3/22/24
1902 Date Back <$VALUE
4x5 1-500 <$2000
3x10-20 1-395 <$2000
1902 Plain Back
4x5 501-1705 <$2000
3x10-20 396-1125 <$2000
Total Issue $90,350
Out at close $12,200
****
14230 Kings
FNB IN CORCORAN
{{ 1 S }}
Chartered 7/34
1929 Small Size <$VALUE
5 Type 2 1-1620 <$1250
Total Issue $8,100
Out in 1935 $21,140
Small out 1935 $20,000
Outstanding includes Ch 9546
****
9546 Kings
FNB OF CORCORAN
{{ 2 L U + 5 S }}
Chartered 9/09
Liquidated 9/14/34
1902 Date Back <$VALUE
3x10-20 1-2400 <$850
1902 Plain Back
3x10-20 2401-6810 <$850
1929 Small Size
10 Type 1 1-664 <$350
20 Type 1 1-190 <$350
10 Type 2 1-427 <$350
20 Type 2 1-70 <$350
Total Issue $408,810
Out at close $19,890
Large out 1935 $1,140
Ch 14230 assumed circulation
****
8436 Riverside
CORONA NB, CORONA
{{ 1 L }}
Organized 10/23/06
Receivership 11/10/25
1902 Red Seal <$VALUE
3x10-20 1-307 <$2000
1902 Date Back
3x10-20 1-1300 <$1250
1902 Plain Back
3x10-20 1301-4195 <$1250
Total Issue $225,100
Out at close $18,400
****
7867 Riverside
FNB OF CORONA
{{ 14 L 2U + 22 S }}
Chartered 8/05
Receivership 11/10/25
1902 Red Seal <$VALUE
3x10-20 1-550 <$750
1902 Date Back
3x10-20 1-3800 <$200
1902 Plain Back
3x10-20 3801-16539 <$200
1929 Small Size
5 Type 1 1-4710 <$100
10 Type 1 1-2128 <$100
20 Type 1 1-144 <$125
5 Type 2 1-7898 <$125
10 Type 2 1-3362 <$125
Total Issue $1,213,820
Out in 1935 $81,250
Large out 1935 $3,150
****
8222 Los Angeles
COVINA NB, COVINA
{{ 3 L 2U + 5 S }}
Chartered 5/06
1902 Red Seal <$VALUE
3x10-20 1-1450 <$2000
1902 Date Back
3x10-20 1-4000 <$850
1902 Plain Back
3x10-20 4001-11071 <$850
1929 Small Size
10 Type 1 1-620 <$400
20 Type 1 1-182 <$400
10 Type 2 1-2026 <$400
20 Type 2 1-487 <$400
Total Issue $715,090
Out in 1935 $29,580
Large out 1935 $1,690
****
5830 Los Angeles
FNB OF COVINA
{{ U + 11 L 6 S }}
Chartered 5/22/01
Brown Back <$VALUE
4x5 1-1050 <$1250
3x10-20 1-1220 <$1250
1882 Date Back
4x5 1-2550 <$1250
3x10-20 1-1960 <$1250
1882 Value Back
4x5 2551-3985 <$1250
3x10-20 1961-2685 <$1250
1902 Plain Back
3x10-20 1-3148 <$600
1929 Small Size
10 Type 1 1-1340 <$400
20 Type 1 1-374 <$400
10 Type 2 1-2093 <$400
20 Type 2 1-435 <$400
Total Issue $608,260
Out in 1935 $43,850
Large out 1935 $1,590
****
11880 Los Angeles
WEST HOLLYWOOD NB OF CRESCENT HEIGHTS
{{ UNREPORTED }}
Chartered 11/20 as Crescent Heights NB, under which there was no issue. Issuing title adopted 11/20/22.
Liquidated 12/18/26
1902 Plain Back <$VALUE
4x10 1-1632 <$3000
Total Issue $65,280
Out at close $23,800
****
11326 Contra Costa
FNB OF CROCKETT
{{ 7 L 7 S }}
Chartered 3/19
1902 Plain Back <$VALUE
4x5 1-7040 <$500
4x10 1-6899 <$500
1929 Small Size
5 Type 1 1-2778 <$275
10 Type 1 1-1500 <$275
5 Type 2 1-2806 <$275
10 Type 2 1-1320 <$275
Total Issue $617,330
Out in 1935 $25,700
Large out 1935 $1,400
****
9765 Stanislaus
FNB OF CROWS LANDING
{{ 2 L 3 S }}
Chartered 6/10
1902 Date Back <$VALUE
4x5 1-615 <$2000
3x10-20 1-494 <$2000
1902 Plain Back
4x5 616-1355 <$2000
3x10-20 495-1009 <$2000
1929 Small Size
5 Type 1 1-295 <$1250
10 Type 1 1-161 <$1250
20 Type 1 1-41 <$1250
Total Issue $100,980
Out in 1935 $6,250
Large out 1935 $330
****
7152 San Bernardino
FNB OF CUCAMONGA
{{ 2 L 3 S }}
Chartered 2/04
Liquidated 10/2/34
1902 Red Seal <$VALUE
3x10-20 1-886 <$2000
1902 Date Back
3x10-20 1-2410 <$1250
1902 Plain Back
3x10-20 2411-6890 <$1250
1929 Small Size
5 Type 1 1-104 <$650
10 Type 1 1-566 <$650
20 Type 1 1-170 <$650
5 Type 2 1-730 <$650
10 Type 2 1-438 <$650
Total Issue $454,310
Out at close 22,850
Large out at close $1,400
****
11732 Los Angeles
FNB OF CULVER CITY
{{ 7 S }}
Organized 5/24/20
Receivership 1/23/32
1929 Small Size <$VALUE
5 Type 1 1-2909 <$400
10 Type 1 1-1318 <$400
20 Type 1 1-429 <$400
Total Issue $217,830
Out at close $95,260
****
11041 Fresno
FNB OF DEL REY
{{ 11 L 1 S }}
Chartered 7/17
1902 Plain Back <$VALUE
3x10-20 1-4449 <$750
1929 Small Size
10 Type 1 1-738 <$1000
20 Type 1 1-212 <$1000
10 Type 2 1-696 <$1000
20 Type 2 1-252 <$1000
Total Issue $304,170
Out in 1935 $24,580
Large out 1935 $1,020
****
FNB in Delano
SEE Ch 10387
FNB of McFarland
****
9195 Kern
FNB OF DELANO
{{ 3 L }}
Organized 7/1/08
Receivership 1/14/27
1902 Date Back <$VALUE
4x5 1-1750 <$850
3x10-20 1-1360 <$850
1902 Plain Back
4x5 1751-13645 <$850
3x10-20 1361-9334 <$850
Total Issue $739,600
Out at close $96,400
****
9158 Tulare
FNB OF DINUBA
{{ 1 L }}
Organized 5/12/08
Receivership 7/9/26
1902 Date Back <$VALUE
3x10-20 1-1770* <$1500
1902 Plain Back
3x10-20 2131-3554* <$1500
* 1771-2130 not marked
Total Issue $177,700
Out at close $9,800
****
9156 Tulare
UNITED STATES NB OF DINUBA
{{ 1 L }}
Organized 5/2/08
Receivership 3/25/27
1902 Date Back <$VALUE
4x5 1-2125 <$1500
3x10-20 1-1610 <$1500
1902 Plain Back
4x5 2126-6140 <$1500
3x10-20 1611-3949 <$1500
Total Issue $320,250
Out at close $24,500
****
10120 Solano
FNB OF DIXON
{{ 2 L 6 S }}
Chartered 1/12
1902 Date Back <$VALUE
4x5 1-1925 <$850
3x10-20 1-1300 <$850
3x50-100 1-40 <$2000
1902 Plain Back
4x5 1926-11280 <$850
3x10-20 1301-7339 <$850
1929 Small Size
5 Type 1 1-1778 <$300
10 Type 1 1-1018 <$300
20 Type 1 1-288 <$300
5 Type 2 1-3852 <$300
10 Type 2 1-1783 <$300
20 Type 2 1-480 <$300
Total Issue $798,220
Out in 1935 $49,450
Large out 1935 $2,530
****
11701 Los Angeles
FNB OF DOWNEY
{{ 2 L 7 S }}
Chartered 5/20
1902 Plain Back <$VALUE
3x10-20 1-2886 <$1500
1929 Small Size
10 Type 1 1-676 <$350
20 Type 1 1-172 <$350
10 Type 2 1-1148 <$350
20 Type 2 1-384 <$350
Total Issue $224,660
Out in 1935 $25,000
Large out 1935 $720
****

<$VALUEs are for notes in FINE condition. Value changes by approximately 25% for a change of one full grade.

****
10301 Tulare
FNB OF DUCOR
{{ 4 L 2 S }}
Chartered 12/12
Liquidated 6/18/31
1902 Date Back <$VALUE
3x10-20 1-480 <$650
1902 Plain Back
3x10-20 481-4694 <$650
1929 Small Size
10 Type 1 1-402 <$600
20 Type 1 1-108 <$600
Total Issue $271,780
Out at close $23,740
Large out at close $2,460
****
9349 Imperial
EL CENTRO NB, EL CENTRO
{{ UNREPORTED }}
Chartered 2/09
Liquidated 6/22/20
1902 Date Back <$VALUE
3x10-20 1-2760 <$1500
1902 Plain Back
3x10-20 2761-4236 <$1500
Total Issue $211,800
Out at close $12,050
****
9350 Imperial
FNB OF EL CENTRO
{{ 2 L }}
Chartered 2/09
Liquidated 4/23/25
1902 Date Back <$VALUE
3x10-20 1-5100 <$850
1902 Plain Back
3x10-20 5101-11577 <$850
Total Issue $578,850
Out at close $76,700
Outstanding includes Ch 6027
****
6993 Los Angeles
FNB OF EL MONTE
{{ 4 L 10 S }}
Chartered 10/03
1902 Red Seal <$VALUE
3x10-20 1-620 <$1500
1902 Date Back
3x10-20 1-990 <$650
1902 Plain Back
3x10-20 991-9452 <$650
1929 Small Size
10 Type 1 1-1870 <$250
20 Type 1 1-486 <$250
10 Type 2 1-366 <$275
20 Type 2 1-310 <$275
Total Issue $683,980
Out in 1935 $51,110
Large out 1935 $1,810
****
11922 Riverside
FNB OF ELSINORE
{{ 3 L 8 S }}
Chartered 1/21
1902 Plain Back <$VALUE
3x10-20 1-2632 <$750
1929 Small Size
10 Type 1 1-1376 <$300
20 Type 1 1-340 <$300
10 Type 2 1-682 <$300
20 Type 2 1-156 <$300
Total Issue $264,900
Out in 1935 $27,450
Large out 1935 $1,240
****
9410 Alameda
FNB OF EMERYVILLE
{{ 1 L }}
Chartered 5/09
Liquidated 10/7/22
1902 Date Back <$VALUE
3x10-20 1-2050* <$1500
1902 Plain Back
3x10-20 2171-3864* <$1500
* 2051-2170 not marked
Total Issue $193,200
Out at close $21,300
****
8040 San Diego
ESCONDIDO NB, ESCONDIDO
{{ 3 L }}
Chartered 1/06
Liquidated 7/31/26
1902 Red Seal <$VALUE
3x10-20 1-1820 <$1500
1902 Date Back
3x10-20 1-3600 <$750
1902 Plain Back
3x10-20 3601-10063 <$750
Total Issue $594,150
Out at close $50,000
****

****
13029 San Diego
FNB IN ESCONDIDO
{{ UNREPORTED }}
Chartered 1/27
Liquidated 6/1/29
1902 Plain Back <$VALUE
4x5 1-1172 <$2000
Total Issue $23,440
Out at close $3,140
****
7801 San Diego
FNB OF ESCONDIDO
{{ 5 L }}
Chartered 6/23/05
Liquidated 4/24/24
1902 Red Seal <$VALUE
4x5 1-250 <$1250
3x10-20 1-200 <$1250
1902 Date Back
4x5 1-3475 <$600
3x10-20 1-2560 <$600
1902 Plain Back
4x5 3476-9475 <$600
3x10-20 2561-6040 <$600
Total Issue $506,500
Out at close $44,600
****
5986 Humboldt
FNB OF EUREKA
{{ 36 L 16 S }}
Chartered 10/7/01
Liquidated 1/6/31
Brown Back <$VALUE
4x5 1-3400 <$600
3x10-20 1-3740 <$600
50-100 1-1000 <$3000
1882 Date Back
4x5 1-1500 <$500
3x10-20 1-7200 <$500
50-100 1-900 <$2500
3x50-100 1-400 <$2500
1882 Value Back
4x5 1501-3645 <$600
3x10-20 7201-13801 <$600
1902 Plain Back
4x5 1-34720 <$200
3x10-20 1-21351 <$200
1929 Small Size
5 Type 1 1-5100 <$200
10 Type 1 1-2231 <$200
20 Type 1 1-597 <$200
Total Issue $3,523,400
Out at close $253,075
Large out at close $36,915
Outstanding includes Ch 10528
****
10528 Humboldt
HUMBOLDT NB OF EUREKA
{{ 6 L }}
Chartered 5/14
Closed 7/1/21
1902 Plain Back <$VALUE
4x5 1-8295 <$500
3x10-20 1-5442 <$500
Total Issue $438,000
Out at close $100,000
Ch 5986 assumed circulation
****
9370 Tulare
FNB OF EXETER
{{ 4 L }}
Chartered 3/09
Liquidated 1/8/29
1902 Date Back <$VALUE
3x10-20 1-1060* <$750
50-100 1-160 <$2000
3x50-100 1-59 <$2000
1902 Plain Back
3x10-20 1341-4596* <$750
* 1061-1340 not marked
Total Issue $268,550
Out at close $12,700
****
10984 Solano
FNB OF FAIRFIELD
{{ 8 S }}
Chartered 4/17
1929 Small Size <$VALUE
10 Type 1 1-624 <$300
20 Type 1 1-212 <$300
10 Type 2 1-1833 <$300
20 Type 2 1-500 <$300
Total Issue $91,210
Out in 1935 $50,000
****
12624 Los Angeles
FLORENCE NB, FLORENCE
{{ 6 L 0 S }}
Chartered 1/25
Liquidated 11/14/29
1902 Plain Back <$VALUE
3x10-20 1-2806 <$800
1929 Small Size
10 Type 1 1-116 <$1250
20 Type 1 1-6 <$1250
Total Issue $147,980
Out at close $29,930
Large out at close $22,250
****
12976 San Bernardino
FNB OF FONTANA
{{ 11 S }}
Chartered 8/26
1929 Small Size <$VALUE
5 Type 1 1-1760 <$275
10 Type 1 1-962 <$275
20 Type 1 1-272 <$275
5 Type 2 1-704 <$300
10 Type 2 1-335 <$300
20 Type 2 1-90 <$300
Total Issue $151,830
Out in 1935 $25,000
****
13787 Mendocino
COAST NB IN FORT BRAGG
{{ 3 S }}
Chartered 9/33
1929 Small Size <$VALUE
10 Type 2 1-2184 <$450
20 Type 2 1-698 <$450
Total Issue $35,800
Out in 1935 $24,400
****
Coast NB of Fort Bragg
SEE Ch 9626
FNB of Fort Bragg
****
9626 Mendocino
FNB OF FORT BRAGG
Organized 9/30/09
Receivership 11/7/33
2nd title Coast NB of
Fort Bragg 9/5/22
FIRST TITLE {{ 2 L }}
1902 Date Back <$VALUE
4x5 1-3775 <$850
3x10-20 1-2860 <$850
1902 Plain Back
4x5 3776-7580 <$850
3x10-20 2861-5198 <$850
SECOND TITLE {{ 3 L 7 S }}
1902 Plain Back
3x10-20 1-4555 <$750
1929 Small Size
10 Type 1 1-1249 <$350
20 Type 1 1-343 <$350
Total Issue $755,350
Out at close $50,000
Large out at close $3,280
****
7390 Fresno
FNB OF FOWLER
{{ UNREPORTED }}
Chartered 9/04
Liquidated 1/10/28
1902 Red Seal <$VALUE
3x10-20 1-400 <$3000
1902 Date Back
3x10-20 1-960 <$2000
1902 Plain Back
3x10-20 961-7353 <$2000
Total Issue $387,650
Out at close $6,760
****
10312 Fresno
FOWLER NB, FOWLER
{{ 1 L }}
Chartered 1/13
Liquidated 11/14/14
1902 Date Back <$VALUE
3x10-20 1-807 <$2000
Total Issue $40,350
Out in 1915 $9,050
****
5162 Fresno
FARMERS NB OF FRESNO
{{ 15 L }}
Chartered 12/27/98
Liquidated 5/6/20
Brown Back <$VALUE
3x10-20 1-5117 <$750
50-100 1-831 <$3000
1882 Date Back
3x10-20 1-20500 <$650
50-100 1-600 <$2500
3x50-100 1-300 <$2500
1882 Value Back
3x10-20 20501-25513 <$750
1902 Plain Back
4x5 1-4500 <$300
3x10-20 1-2200 <$300
Total Issue $2,021,150
Out at close $261,800
****

****
FNB in Fresno
SEE Ch 11473
Growers NB of Fresno
****
3321 Fresno
FNB OF FRESNO
{{ 12 L }}
Chartered 1885
Liquidated 10/24/21
Brown Back <$VALUE
3x10-20 1-2564 <$1000
1902 Red Seal
4x5 1-5500 <$1000
50-100 1-1483 <$7500/$8500
1902 Date Back
4x5 1-24500 <$250
3x10-20 1-11000 <$250
50-100 1-2200 <$1000
3x50-100 1-500 <$1000
1902 Plain Back
4x5 24501-42109 <$250
3x10-20 11001-21073 <$250
Total Issue $2,811,480
Out at close $265,100
****
3870 Fresno
FRESNO NB, FRESNO
{{ 4 L }}
Chartered 4/20/88
Liquidated 1/10/17
Brown Back <$VALUE
4x5 1-3175 <$1250
50-100 1-1528 <$3000
1902 Red Seal
50-100 1-160 <$7500/$8500
1902 Date Back
50-100 1-1000 <$1000
3x50-100 1-1146 <$1000
Total Issue $753,200
Out at close $194,750
****
11473 Fresno
GROWERS NB OF FRESNO
Organized 9/29/19
Receivership 7/7/30
2nd title:FNB in Fresno
5/21/23
FIRST TITLE {{ 7 L }}
1902 Plain Back <$VALUE
3x10-20 1-11800 <$500
SECOND TITLE {{ 9 L 8 S }}
1902 Plain Back
3x10-20 1-13814 <$300
1929 Small Size
10 Type 1 1-2180 <$200
20 Type 1 1-538 <$200
Total Issue $1,476,060
Out at close $200,000
Large out at close $25,150
****
8718 Fresno
UNION NB OF FRESNO
{{ 5 L }}
Chartered 5/07
Liquidated 3/14/23
1902 Red Seal <$VALUE
3x10-20 1-2625 <$1000
1902 Date Back
3x10-20 1-12600 <$400
1902 Plain Back
3x10-20 12601-21341 <$400
Total Issue $1,198,300
Out at close $50,000
****
9538 Orange
FARMERS & MERCHANTS NB OF
FULLERTON
{{ 1 L }}
Chartered 9/09
Liquidated 6/15/25
1902 Date Back <$VALUE
3x10-20 1-2430 <$1250
1902 Plain Back
3x10-20 2431-5221 <$1250
Total Issue $261,050
Out at close $22,300
****
5654 Orange
FNB OF FULLERTON
{{ 7 L }}
Chartered 12/26/00
Liquidated 11/1/24
Brown Back <$VALUE
3x10-20 1-3800 <$1250
1882 Date Back
3x10-20 1-3840 <$750
1882 Value Back
3x10-20 3841-5990 <$850
1902 Plain Back
3x10-20 1-4641 <$400
Total Issue $721,550
Out at close $97,520
****

****
12764 Orange
FN T & SAVINGS B OF
FULLERTON
{{ 3 L 20 S }}
Chartered 6/25 as New FNB,
under which there was no
issue. Issuing title
adopted 5/14/27.
1902 Plain Back <$VALUE
4x5 1-2103 <$650
4x10 1-1591 <$650
1929 Small Size
5 Type 1 1-5476 <$125
10 Type 1 1-3008 <$125
5 Type 2 1-7614 <$135
10 Type 2 1-4042 <$135
Total Issue $528,950
Out in 1935 $82,750
Large out 1935 $490
****
11251 Orange
FNB OF GARDEN GROVE
{{ 5 L 3 S }}
Chartered 9/18
1902 Plain Back <$VALUE
4x5 1-27983 <$750
1929 Small Size
5 Type 1 1-6034 <$500
5 Type 2 1-7800 <$500
Total issue $779,680
Out in 1935 $24,940
Large out 1935 $1,430
****
10453 Los Angeles
FNB OF GARDENA
{{ 11 L }}
Chartered 10/13
Liquidated 11/16/29
1902 Date Back <$VALUE
4x5 1-800 <$600
3x10-20 1-680 <$600
1902 Plain Back
4x5. 801-8390 <$600
3x10-20 681-5848 <$600
Total Issue $460,200
Out at close $35,300
****
11678 Sonoma
FNB OF GEYSERVILLE
{{ 2 L }}
Chartered 4/20
Liquidated 2/6/29
1902 Plain Back <$VALUE
3x10-20 1-2853 <$1500
Total Issue $142,650
Out at close $9,480
****
10166 Santa Clara
FNB OF GILROY
{{ 1 L }}
Chartered 3/12
Liquidated 1/16/18
1902 Date Back <$VALUE
3x10-20 1-2640* <$1500
1902 Plain Back
3x10-20 3001-4043* <$1500
* 2641-3000 not marked
Total Issue $202,150
Out at close $71,900
****
FNB in Glendale
SEE Ch 10412
FNB of Tropico
****
7987 Los Angeles
FNB OF GLENDALE
{{ 5 L }}
Chartered 11/05
Liquidated 7/6/22
1902 Red Seal <$VALUE
4x5 1-850 <$1500
3x10-20 1-625 <$1500
1902 Date Back
4x5 1-2025 <$750
3x10-20 1-1390 <$750
1902 Plain Back
4x5 2026-4400 <$750
3x10-20 1391-2688 <$750
Total Issue $270,650
Out at close $23,895
****
Glendale NB, Glendale
SEE Ch 10412
FNB of Tropico
****
8652 Los Angeles
FNB OF GLENDORA
{{ 2 L 2U + 6 S }}
Chartered 4/07
1902 Red Seal <$VALUE
4x5 1-625 <$2000
3x10-20 1-500 <$2000
1902 Date Back
4x5 1-2225 <$1250
3x10-20 1-1440 <$1250
1902 Plain Back
4x5 2226-6018 <$1250
3x10-20 1441-3953* <$1250
* Sheet 3768 destroyed
1929 Small Size
5 Type 1 1-800 <$400
10 Type 1 1-400 <$400
20 Type 1 1-96 <$400
5 Type 2 1-1622 <$450
10 Type 2 1-653 <$450
20 Type 2 1-200 <$450
Total Issue $433,670
Out in 1935 $20,700
Large out 1935 $1,220
****
12673 Los Angeles
GRAHAM NB, GRAHAM
{{ 2 L 1 S }}
Chartered 4/25
Liquidated 11/14/29
1902 Plain Back <$VALUE
3x10-20 1-2652 <$2500
1929 Small Size
10 Type 1 1-114 <$1500
20 Type 1 1-73 <$1500
Total Issue $148,200
Out at close $47,120
Large out at close $31,520
****
12433 Nevada
FNB IN GRASS VALLEY
{{ 6 L 10 S }}
Chartered 9/23
Liquidated 5/22/34
1902 Plain Back <$VALUE
4x5 1-3985 <$650
3x10-20 1-3455 <$650
1929 Small Size
5 Type 1 1-1918 <$300
10 Type 1 1-932 <$300
20 Type 1 1-280 <$300
5 Type 2 1-126 <$350
10 Type 2 1-47 <$350
20 Type 2 1-70 <$350
Total Issue $402,010
Out at close $39,090
Large out at close $1,790
****
3648 Nevada
FNB OF GRASS VALLEY
{{ UNREPORTED }}
Chartered 3/16/87
Liquidated 9/18/88
Brown Back <$VALUE
4x5 1-90 <$5000
3x10-20 1-109 <$5000
50-100 1-30 <$7500
Total Issue $11,750
Out in 1910 $50
****
11164 Butte
FNB OF GRIDLEY
{{ 2 L }}
Organized 3/14/18
Receivership 1/29/21
1902 Plain Back <$VALUE
3x10-20 1-1542 <$1500
Total issue $77,100
Out at close $36,000
****
7658 Kings
FARMERS & MERCHANTS NB OF
HANFORD
{{ 2 L }}
Chartered 3/05
Liquidated 6/30/22
1902 Red Seal <$VALUE
4x5 1-900 <$1500
3x10-20 1-840 <$1500
1902 Date Back
4x5 1-4100 <$750
3x10-20 1-2920 <$750
1902 Plain Back
4x5 4101-6430 <$750
3x10-20 2921-4272 <$750
Total Issue $402,200
Out at close $23,600
****

****
5863 Kings
FNB OF HANFORD
{{ 5 L 14 S }}
Chartered 6/17/01
Liquidated 3/1/35
Brown Back <$VALUE
3x10-20 1-2040 <$1000
50-100 1-100 <$3000
1882 Date Back
3x10-20 1-3000 <$850
50-100 1-200 <$2500
3x50-100 1-88 <$2500
1882 Value Back
3x10-20 3001-4535 <$850
1902 Plain Back
3x10-20 1-2558 <$450
3x50-100 1-331 <$850/$1000
1929 Small Size
10 Type 1 1-1200 <$185
20 Type 1 1-454 <$185
50 Type 1 1-158 <$325
100 Type 1 1-44 <$400
10 Type 2 1-3570 <$200
20 Type 2 1-986 <$200
Total Issue $862,100
Out at close $146,000
Large out at close $3,840
****
6873 Kings
HANFORD NB, HANFORD
{{ 4 L }}
Chartered 7/03
Liquidated 5/3/24
1902 Red Seal <$VALUE
3x10-20 1-752 <$1500
1902 Date Back
3x10-20 1-2860 <$600
1902 Plain Back
3x10-20 2861-4263 <$600
Total Issue $250,750
Out at close $24,400
****
10364 Kings
FNB OF HARDWICK
{{ 2 L 2 S }}
Chartered 4/13
Liquidated 2/13/34
1902 Date Back <$VALUE
3x10-20 1-500 <$1500
1902 Plain Back
3x10-20 501-1382 <$1500
1929 Small Size
10 Type 1 1-206 <$600
20 Type 1 1-39 <$600
Total Issue $86,140
Out at close $5,890
Large out at close $270
****
10018 Alameda
FNB OF HAYWARD
{{ 2 L }}
Chartered 5/11
Liquidated 9/12/21
1902 Date Back <$VALUE
4x5 1-1375 <$1500
3x10-20 1-1100 <$1500
1902 Plain Back
4x5 1376-3185 <$1500
3x10-20 1101-2155 <$1500
Total Issue $171,450
Out at close $24,600
****
10184 Sonoma
FNB OF HEALDSBURG
{{ 16 L 0 S }}
Chartered 5/12
Liquidated 1/7/30
1902 Date Back <$VALUE
4x5 1-2000 <$300
3x10-20 1-1500 <$300
1902 Plain Back
4x5 2001-15740 <$300
3x10-20 1501-11324 <$300
1929 Small Size
5 Type 1 1-477 <$750
10 Type 1 1-138 <$750
20 Type 1 1-50 <$750
Total Issue $909,590
Out at close $112,090
****
10204 Sonoma
HEALDSBURG NB, HEALDSBURG
{{ 3 L }}
Chartered 5/12
Liquidated 11/30/25
1902 Date Back <$VALUE
4x5 1-2550 <$600
3x10-20 1-1960 <$600
1902 Plain Back
4x5 2551-17625 <$600
3x10-20 1961-12844 <$600
Total Issue $994,700
Out at close $150,000
****

****
10764 Riverside
FNB OF HEMET
{{ 2 L 10 S }}
Chartered 8/15
Liquidated 7/19/34
1902 Plain Back <$VALUE
4x5 1-2590 <$1500
3x10-20 1-1628 <$1500
1929 Small Size
5 Type 1 1-5868 <$275
5 Type 2 1-2420 <$275
Total Issue $321,340
Out at close $24,430
Large out at close $440
****
12209 Los Angeles
FNB OF HERMOSA BEACH
{{ 6 L 5 S }}
Organized 3/10/22
Receivership 12/29/32
1902 Plain Back <$VALUE
4x5 1-5610 <$600
3x10-20 1-4105 <$600
1929 Small Size
5 Type 1 1-1547 <$375
10 Type 1 1-742 <$375
20 Type 1 1-243 <$375
Total Issue $437,540
Out at close $49,640
Large out at close $2,260
****
12271 Los Angeles
NB OF HERMOSA BEACH
{{ 7 L 0 S }}
Chartered 11/22
Liquidated 1/3/30
1902 Plain Back <$VALUE
4x5 1-18899 <$650
1929 Small Size
5 Type 1 1-1152 <$1250
Total Issue $412,540
Out at close $46,160
Large out at close $11,600
****
9378 San Benito
FNB OF HOLLISTER
{{ 7 L }}
Chartered 4/09
Liquidated 12/8/27
1902 Date Back <$VALUE
3x10-20 1-4400 <$500
1902 Plain Back
4x5 1-5355 <$500
3x10-20 4401-15434 <$500
Total Issue $878,800
Out at close $94,100
****
13510 San Benito
HOLLISTER NB, HOLLISTER
{{ 4 S }}
Chartered 12/30
1929 Small Size <$VALUE
5 Type 1 1-1342 <$400
10 Type 1 1-552 <$400
20 Type 1 1-240 <$400
5 Type 2 1-2974 <$400
10 Type 2 1-1848 <$400
20 Type 2 1-468 <$400
Total Issue $144,890
Out in 1935 $48,650
****
7543 Los Angeles
FNB OF HOLLYWOOD
{{ 6 L }}
Chartered 1/05
Liquidated 6/30/22
1902 Red Seal <$VALUE
4x5 1-1250 <$1500
3x10-20 1-1225 <$1500
1902 Date Back
4x5 1-1875 <$750
3x10-20 1-1350 <$750
1902 Plain Back
4x5 1876-3730 <$750
3x10-20 1351-2557 <$750
Total Issue $288,700
Out at close $22,700
****
7803 Los Angeles
HOLLYWOOD NB, HOLLYWOOD
{{ UNREPORTED }}
Chartered 6/05
Liquidated 11/15/19
1902 Red Seal <$VALUE
3x10-20 1-1100 <$3000
1902 Date Back
3x10-20 1-2050 <$2000
1902 Plain Back
3x10-20 2051-2708 <$2000
Total Issue $190,400
Out at close $22,700
****

****
9770 Imperial
FNB OF HOLTVILLE
{{ 3 L 7 S }}
Chartered 6/10
1902 Date Back <$VALUE
4x5 1-3240 <$850
3x10-20 1-2534 <$850
1902 Plain Back
4x5 3241-11164 <$850
3x10-20 2535-7456 <$850
1929 Small Size
5 Type 1 1-1782 <$350
10 Type 1 1-982 <$350
20 Type 1 1-284 <$350
5 Type 2 1-3276 <$375
Total Issue $758,920
Out in 1935 $27,045
Large out 1935 $2,045
****
7868 Orange
FNB OF HUNTINGTON BEACH
{{ UNREPORTED }}
Chartered 6/05
Liquidated 9/20/21
1902 Red Seal <$VALUE
3x10-20 1-2000 <$3000
1902 Date Back
3x10-20 1-1900 <$2000
1902 Plain Back
3x10-20 1901-5400 <$2000
Total Issue $370,000
Out at close $60,950
****
11925 Los Angeles
NB OF HUNTINGTON PARK
{{ 2 L }}
Chartered 2/21
Liquidated 4/9/26
1902 Plain Back <$VALUE
3x10-20 1-6372 <$1500
Total Issue $318,600
Out at close $64,000
****
9919 Los Angeles
FNB OF HYNES
{{ 4 L 7 S }}
Organized 12/5/10
1902 Date Back <$VALUE
3x10-20 1-1000 <$850
1902 Plain Back
3x10-20 1001-5718 <$850
1929 Small Size
10 Type 1 1-1314 <$400
20 Type 1 1-374 <$400
10 Type 2 1-55 <$425
Total Issue $410,170
Out in 1935 $24,650
Large out 1935 $1,380
****
6027 Imperial
FNB OF IMPERIAL
{{ 5 L }}
Chartered 11/19/01
Liquidated 2/24/23
Brown Back <$VALUE
4x5 1-1250 <$1000
3x10-20 1-900 <$1000
1882 Date Back
4x5 1-3800* <$850
3x10-20 1-2840** <$850
1882 Value Back
4x5 3951-6892* <$850
3x10-20 2961-4708** <$850
* 3801-3950 not marked
** 2841-2960 not marked
1902 Plain Back
4x5 1-1010 <$650
3x10-20 1-654 <$650
Total Issue $496,140
Out at close $38,300
Ch 9350 assumed circulation
****
9093 Los Angeles
FNB OF INGLEWOOD
{{ UNREPORTED }}
Chartered 4/08
Liquidated 4/24/26
1902 Red Seal <$VALUE
3x10-20 1-570 <$3000
1902 Date Back
3x10-20 1-2149 <$2000
Total Issue $135,950
Out at close $760
****
10362 Tuolumne
JAMESTOWN NB, JAMESTOWN
{{ 2 L }}
Chartered 4/13
Liquidated 11/10/30
1902 Date Back <$VALUE
4x5 1-1000 <$850
3x10-20 1-810 <$850

1902 Plain Back
4x5 1001-5205 <$850
3x10-20 811-3395 <$850
Total Issue $273,850
Out at close $2,100
****
10284 Tuolumne
UNION NB OF JAMESTOWN
{{ UNREPORTED }}
Chartered 10/12
Liquidated 5/21/14
1902 Date Back <$VALUE
3x10-20 1-805 <$2500
Total Issue $40,250
Out in 1914 $18,280
****
9234 Fresno
FNB OF KERMAN
{{ UNREPORTED }}
Chartered 9/08
Liquidated 11/16/22
1902 Date Back <$VALUE
3x10-20 1-785 <$3000
1902 Plain Back
3x10-20 786-1133 <$3000
Total Issue $56,650
Out at close $5,950
****
8409 Fresno
FNB OF KINGSBURG
{{ 1 L }}
Organized 9/14/06
Receivership 11/9/26
1902 Red Seal <$VALUE
50-100 1-200 <$7500/$8500
1902 Date Back
50-100 1-120 <$2000
3x50-100 1-331 <$2000
Total Issue $130,750
Out at close $24,750
****
11827 Orange
FNB OF LA HABRA
{{ 2 L }}
Chartered 8/20
Liquidated 3/8/28
1902 Plain Back <$VALUE
4x5 1-3525 <$1500
3x10-20 1-2063 <$1500
Total Issue $173,650
Out at close $19,600
****
9818 Fresno
FNB OF LATON
{{ 1 L }}
Chartered 7/10
1902 Date Back <$VALUE
4x5 1-525 <$1500
3x10-20 1-420 <$1500
1902 Plain Back
4x5 526-2680 <$1500
3x10-20 421-1607 <$1500
Total Issue $133,950
Out in 1935 $285
****
FNB of LaVerne
SEE Ch 9599
FNB of Lordsburg
****
7779 Kings
FNB OF LEMOORE
{{ 2 L 21 S }}
Chartered 6/05
Liquidated 5/14/35
1902 Red Seal <$VALUE
3x10-20 1-300 <$1500
1902 Date Back
3x10-20 1-1180 <$850
1902 Plain Back
3x10-20 1181-2991 <$850
1929 Small Size
10 Type 1 1-2364 <$165
20 Type 1 1-524 <$165
10 Type 2 1-6083 <$185
20 Type 2 1-2296 <$185
Total Issue $476,020
Out at close $136,950
Large out at close $690
****
7965 Tulare
FNB OF LINDSAY
{{ 2 L }}
Chartered 10/05
Liquidated 11/24/23
1902 Red Seal <$VALUE
3x10-20 1-190 <$1500
50-100 1-70 <$7500/$8500
1902 Date Back
3x10-20 1-1500 <$850
50-100 1-120 <$1500

1902 Plain Back
3x10-20 1501-2786 <$850
Total Issue $177,300
Out at close $18,800
****
9710 Tulare
LINDSAY NB, LINDSAY
{{ 1 L }}
Chartered 3/10
Liquidated 6/30/22
1902 Date Back <$VALUE
3x10-20 1-1620 <$1250
1902 Plain Back
3x10-20 1621-4325 <$1250
Total Issue $216,250
Out at close $47,000
****
9914 Alameda
FARMERS & MERCHANTS NB OF LIVERMORE
{{ UNREPORTED }}
Chartered 1/11
Liquidated 4/12/17
1902 Date Back <$VALUE
4x5 1-2925 <$2000
3x10-20 1-2290 <$2000
1902 Plain Back
4x5 2926-3720 <$2000
3x10-20 2291-2860 <$2000
Total Issue $217,400
Out at close $46,400
****
8002 Alameda
FNB OF LIVERMORE
{{ 3 L }}
Chartered 12/05
Liquidated 5/17/23
1902 Red Seal <$VALUE
4x5 1-225 <$1250
3x10-20 1-186 <$1250
1902 Date Back
4x5 1-3175 <$700
3x10-20 1-2460 <$700
1902 Plain Back
4x5 3176-7780 <$700
3x10-20 2461-5177 <$700
Total Issue $428,250
Out at close $48,900
****
12112 San Joaquin
CITIZENS NB OF LODI
{{ 8 L }}
Chartered 2/22
Closed 12/31/25
1902 Plain Back <$VALUE
3x10-20 1-5338 <$300
3x50-100 1-620 <$650/750
Total Issue $421,900
Out at close $200,000
Outstanding includes Ch 11126
****
7719 San Joaquin
FNB OF LODI
{{ 16 L }}
Chartered 5/05
Liquidated 10/28/25
1902 Red Seal <$VALUE
4x5 1-1000 <$1000
3x10-20 1-1425 <$1000
1902 Date Back
4x5 1-2500 <$250
3x10-20 1-2100 <$250
50-100 1-200 <$750/$850
3x50-100 1-660 <$750/$850
1902 Plain Back
4x5 2501-3500 <$250
3x10-20 2101-9922 <$250
Total Issue $1,034,350
Out at close $191,550
****
11126 San Joaquin
LODI NB, LODI
{{ 8 L }}
Chartered 12/17
Liquidated 3/29/28
1902 Plain Back <$VALUE
3x10-20 1-18653 <$350
Total Issue $932,650
Out at close $233,900
Outstanding includes Ch 12112
****
13332 San Bernardino
FNB OF LOMA LINDA
{{ 2U + 11 S }}
Chartered 5/29
Liquidated 6/11/35
1929 Small Size <$VALUE
5 Type 1 1-828 <$500
10 Type 1 1-378 <$500
20 Type 1 1-128 <$500
5 Type 2 1-1798 <$500
Total Issue $71,870
Out at close $20,300
****

****
6749 Los Angeles
AMERICAN NB OF LONG BEACH
{{ 1 L }}
Chartered 4/28/03
Liquidated 6/30/04
1902 Red Seal <$VALUE
3x10-20 1-1124 <$2000
Total Issue $56,200
Out in 1910 $1,810
****
California FNB of Long Beach
SEE Ch 11873
California NB of Long Beach
****
11873 Los Angeles
CALIFORNIA NB OF LONG BEACH
Chartered 11/20
2nd title:California FNB of Long Beach 6/10/29
FIRST TITLE {{ 11 L }}
1902 Plain Back <$VALUE
3x10-20 1-26212 <$225
SECOND TITLE {{ 32 S }}
1929 Small Size
10 Type 1 1-6798 <$75
20 Type 1 1-1914 <$100
10 Type 2 1-2271 <$125
20 Type 2 1-350 <$175
Total Issue $1,977,870
Out in 1935 $289,910
Large out 1935 $4,960
****
8870 Los Angeles
CITY NB IN LONG BEACH
{{ 7 L }}
Chartered 9/07
Liquidated 6/30/22
1902 Red Seal <$VALUE
4x5 1-2000 <$1000
3x10-20 1-1600 <$1000
1902 Date Back
4x5 1-7950 <$300
3x10-20 1-4960 <$300
1902 Plain Back
4x5 7951-28560 <$300
3x10-20 4961-6560 <$300
Total Issue $1,019,200
Out at close $87,900
****
8510 Los Angeles
EXCHANGE NB OF LONG BEACH
Chartered 1/07
Liquidated 7/21/24
2nd title:Long Beach NB 12/21/21
FIRST TITLE {{ 8 L }}
1902 Red Seal <$VALUE
4x5 1-1100 <$1000
4x10 1-1200 <$1000
1902 Date Back
4x5 1-8850 <$300
4x10 1-8200 <$300
1902 Plain Back
4x5 8851-20050 <$300
4x10 8201-20200 <$300
SECOND TITLE {{ 2 L }}
1902 Plain Back
3x10-20 1-6774 <$500
Total Issue $1,617,700
Out at close $180,500
****
5456 Los Angeles
FNB OF LONG BEACH
{{ 20 L }}
Chartered 6/26/00
Liquidated 3/1/29
Brown Back <$VALUE
3x10-20 1-11000 <$850
1882 Date Back
3x10-20 1-2400 <$850
1882 Value Back
3x10-20 2401-2659 <$1000
1902 Plain Back
3x10-20 1-24442 <$200
Total Issue $1,905,050
Out at close $178,950
****
Long Beach NB, Long Beach
SEE Ch 8510
Exchange NB of Long Beach
****

****

6730 Los Angeles
NB OF LONG BEACH
{{ 8 L }}
Chartered 4/03
Liquidated 2/26/21
1902 Red Seal <$VALUE
4x5 1-6000 <$800
3x10-20 1-5200 <$800
1902 Date Back
4x5 1-11500* <$300
3x10-20 1-7500** <$300
1902 Plain Back
4x5 12001-28000* <$300
3x10-20 7901-10300** <$300
* 11501-12000 not marked
** 7501-7900 not marked
Total Issue $1,455,000
Out at close $139,000

****

12819 Los Angeles
SEASIDE NB OF LONG BEACH
{{ 4 L 6 S }}
Organized 8/29/25
Receivership 2/17/32
1902 Plain Back <$VALUE
4x5 1-5810 <$600
3x10-20 1-4688 <$600
1929 Small Size
5 Type 1 1-2743 <$225
10 Type 1 1-1362 <$225
20 Type 1 1-347 <$225
Total Issue $556,250
Out at close $97,900
Large out at close $4,330

****

9599 Los Angeles
FNB OF LORDSBURG
Organized 11/9/09
2nd title:FNB of LaVerne 11/9/17
FIRST TITLE {{ 4 L }}
1902 Date Back <$VALUE
3x10-20 1-2110* <$750
1902 Plain Back
3x10-20 2231-2629* <$750
* 2111-2230 not marked
SECOND TITLE {{ 6 L 5 S }}
1902 Plain Back
4x10 1-5623 <$500
1929 Small Size
10 Type 1 1-1162 <$350
10 Type 2 1-1736 <$350
Total Issue $443,450
Out in 1935 $24,600
Large out 1935 $1,830

****

11522 Santa Clara
FNB OF LOS ALTOS
{{ 5 L 6 S }}
Chartered 11/19
1902 Plain Back <$VALUE
3x10-20 1-3619 <$800
1929 Small Size
10 Type 1 1-788 <$400
20 Type 1 1-180 <$400
10 Type 2 1-965 <$400
20 Type 2 1-205 <$400
Total Issue $263,580
Out in 1935 $25,000
Large out 1935 $880

****

6545 Los Angeles
AMERICAN NB OF LOS ANGELES
{{ 10 L }}
Chartered 12/19/02
Liquidated 9/1/09
1902 Red Seal <$VALUE
4x5 1-36250 <$400
3x10-20 1-25000 <$400
1902 Date Back
4x5 1-12995 <$250
3x10-20 1-1796 <$250
Total Issue $2,324,700
Out in 1910 $367,325

****

8827 Los Angeles
CENTRAL NB OF LOS ANGELES
Chartered 8/07
Liquidated 5/15/20
2nd title:Security NB of Los Angeles 9/2/13
FIRST TITLE {{ 4 L }}
1902 Red Seal <$VALUE
4x5 1-1600 <$600
3x10-20 1-1000 <$600
50-100 1-120 <$7500/$8500
1902 Date Back
4x5 1-2670 <$350
3x10-20 1-1752 <$350
50-100 1-96 <$1250
SECOND TITLE {{ 0 L }}
1902 Date Back
4x5 1-2000 <$1000
3x10-20 1-1800 <$1000
3x50-100 1-560 <$1500
1902 Plain Back
3x10-20 1801-1957 <$1000
Total Issue $580,750
Out at close $112,050

****

5927 Los Angeles
CITIZENS NB OF LOS ANGELES
Chartered 7/31/01
2nd title:Citizens NT & Savings B of Los Angeles 3/21/28
FIRST TITLE {{ 50 L }}
Brown Back <$VALUE
50-100 1-3500 <$2250/$2500
1882 Date Back
4x5 1-49000 <$125
3x10-20 1-30400 <$125/$175
50-100 1-2400 <$1750/$2000
3x50-100 1-4288<$1750/$2000
1882 Value Back
4x5 49001-74675 <$150
3x10-20 30401-48559 <$175
1902 Plain Back
4x5 1-70094 <$45
3x10-20 1-36773 <$50/$60
3x50-100 1-2210 <$400/$500
SECOND TITLE {{ 11 L 50+ S }}
1902 Plain Back
4x5 1-6978 <$45
3x10-20 1-5008 <$50/$60
3x50-100 1-515 <$400/$500
1929 Small Size
5 Type 1 1-24546 <$15
10 Type 1 1-17254 <$20
20 Type 1 1-6142 <$30
50 Type 1 1-1466 <$100
100 Type 1 1-844 <$150
5 Type 2 1-52206 <$15
10 Type 2 1-27846 <$20
20 Type 2 1-5800 <$30
Total Issue $14,300,540
Out in 1935 $1,756,150
Large out 1935 $46,160

****

6864 Los Angeles
COMMERCIAL NB OF LOS ANGELES
Chartered 7/03
Liquidated 3//15/27
2nd title:Commercial NT & Savings B of Los Angeles 8/19/25
FIRST TITLE {{ 24 L }}
1902 Red Seal <$VALUE
3x10-20 1-7500 <$500
1902 Date Back
3x10-20 1-22100 <$65
1902 Plain Back 65
3x10-20 22101-86500 <$75
SECOND TITLE {{ 11 L }}
1902 Plain Back
3x10-20 1-23655 <$75
Total Issue $5,882,750
Out at close $1,000,000

****

6617 Los Angeles
FARMERS & MERCHANTS NB OF LOS ANGELES
{{ 50+ L 50+ S }}
Chartered 2/03
1902 Red Seal <$VALUE
4x5 1-69795 <$300
3x10-20 1-45082 <$300
50-100 1-1334 <$7500/$8500
1902 Date Back
4x5 1-113000 <$40
3x10-20 1-72000 <$50/$60
50-100 1-1000 <$350/$450
3x50-100 1-2900 <$350/$450
1902 Plain Back
4x5 113001-347894 <$40
3x10-20 72001-217283 <$50/$60
1929 Small Size
5 Type 1 1-53802 <$15
10 Type 1 1-27380 <$20
20 Type 1 1-8486 <$30
50 Type 1 1-1020 <$100
100 Type 1 1-522 <$150
5 Type 2 1-144384 <$15
10 Type 2 1-77085 <$20
20 Type 2 1-18460 <$30
Total Issue $29,303,480
Out in 1935 $2,652,595
Large out 1935 $66,095

****

2491 Los Angeles
FNB OF LOS ANGELES
Chartered 9/80
2nd title:Los Angeles-FNT & Savings B 9/1/27
3rd title:Security-FNB 3/30/29
FIRST TITLE {{ 50+ L }}
Series 1875 <$VALUE
3x10-20 1-8451<$2000/$3000
Brown Back
4x5 1-21000 <$150
3x10-20 1-43200 <$175/$200
1882 Date Back
4x5 1-89000 <$150
3x10-20 1-61300 <$175/$200
1882 Value Back
4x5 89001-139500 <$150
3x10-20 61301-91300 <$160/$200
1902 Plain Back
3x10-20 1-182408 <$50/$60
SECOND TITLE {{ 30 L }}
1902 Plain Back
3x10-20 1-39856 <$50/$60
3x50-100 1-3343 <$350/$450
THIRD TITLE {{ 50+ S }}
1929 Small Size
5 Type 1 1-81322 <$15
10 Type 1 1-99284 <$20
20 Type 1 1-42762 <$30
50 Type 1 1-6816 <$85
100 Type 1 1-2970 <$150
5 Type 2 1-348682 <$15
10 Type 2 1-268720 <$20
20 Type 2 1-68850 <$30
Total Issue $45,469,050
Out in 1935 $10,184,150
Large out 1935 $91,110

****

12804 Los Angeles
HOLLYWOOD NB OF LOS ANGELES
{{ 25 S }}
Chartered 8/25 as NB of Hollywood in Los Angeles, under which there was no issue. Issuing title adopted 1/17/27.
Liquidated 3/26/34
1929 Small Size <$VALUE
5 Type 1 1-5674 <$85
10 Type 1 1-2794 <$75
20 Type 1 1-900 <$85
5 Type 2 1-758 <$110
10 Type 2 1-490 <$110
Total Issue $454,550
Out at close $162,750

****

Los Angeles-FNT & Savings B of Los Angeles
SEE Ch 2491
FNB of Los Angeles

****

2938 Los Angeles
LOS ANGELES NB, LOS ANGELES
{{ 5 L }}
Chartered 4/30/83
Liquidated 10/21/05
Brown Back <$VALUE
3x10-20 1-176310 <$850
50-100 1-4002 <$2500
1902 Red Seal
4x5 1-3772 <$650
3x10-20 1-5481 <$650
50-100 1-700 <$7500/$8500
Total Issue $1,936,290
Out in 1910 $71,050

****

Merchants NB of Los Angeles
Merchants NT & Savings B of Los Angeles
SEE Ch 3538
Southern California NB of Los Angeles

****

4096 Los Angeles
N B OF CALIFORNIA AT LOS ANGELES
{{ 36 L }}
Chartered 8/21/89
Liquidated 5/26/17
Brown Back <$VALUE
4x5 1-47150 <$250
3x10-20 1-15300 <$250
1882 Date Back
4x5 1-622 <$250
3x10-20 1-950 <$250
1902 Date Back
4x5 1-37750 <$65
3x10-20 1-26800 <$65
1902 Plain Back
4x5 37751-45520 <$65
3x10-20 26801-32221 <$65
Total Issue $4,289,390
Out at close $500,000
Ch 4096 assumed circulation

****

8117 Los Angeles
NB OF COMMERCE IN LOS ANGELES
{{ UNREPORTED }}
Chartered 3/06
Liquidated 2/3/13
1902 Red Seal <$VALUE
4x5 1-5000 <$2000
3x10-20 1-4900 <$2000
1902 Date Back
4x5 1-8630 <$1500
3x10-20 1-6476 <$1500
Total Issue $841,400
Out in 1913 $85,150

****

NB of Commerce of Los Angeles
SEE Ch 12755
Peoples NB of Los Angeles

****

12410 Los Angeles
N CITY B OF LOS ANGELES
{{ 16 L }}
Chartered 7/23
Liquidated 8/17/28
1902 Plain Back <$VALUE
4x5 1-26485 <$85
3x10-20 1-15616 <$85
3x50-100 1-2929 <$350/$450
Total Issue $2,042,750
Out at close $840,950

****

12454 Los Angeles
PACIFIC NB OF LOS ANGELES
{{ 44 L 2 S }}
Chartered 10/23
Liquidated 3/18/30
1902 Plain Back <$VALUE
4x5 1-22900 <$50
3x10-20 1-15572 <$60
3x50-100 1-2366 <$400/$450
1929 Small Size
5 Type 1 1-1017* <$600
* E001017A & F001017A not issued
Total Issue $1,858,600
Out at close $309,520
Large out at close $292,420

****

12755 Los Angeles
PEOPLES NB OF LOS ANGELES
Chartered 6/25
Liquidated 11/1/32
2nd title:NB of Commerce of Los Angeles 6/27/28
FIRST TITLE {{ 6 L }}
1902 Plain Back <$VALUE
4x5 1-18429 <$200
SECOND TITLE {{ 9 L 3 S }}
1902 Plain Back
4x5 1-11386 <$125
4x10 1-7801 <$125
1929 Small Size
5 Type 1 1-6052 <$250
10 Type 1 1-2533 <$250
Total Issue $1,241,880
Out at close $19,730
Large out at close $6,055

****

12545 Los Angeles
SEABOARD NB OF LOS ANGELES
{{ U + 50+ S }}
Chartered 5/24
1929 Small Size <$VALUE
5 Type 1 1-36574 <$20
10 Type 1 1-20052 <$25
20 Type 1 1-8022 <$35
5 Type 2 1-63104 <$20
10 Type 2 1-35775 <$25
20 Type 2 1-4345 <$35
Total Issue $4,023,150
Out in 1935 $945,590

****

Security-FNB of Los Angeles
SEE Ch 2491
FNB of Los Angeles

****

Security NB of Los Angeles
SEE Ch 8827
Central NB of Los Angeles

****

3538 Los Angeles
SOUTHERN CALIFORNIA NB OF LOS ANGELES
Chartered 7/22/86
Liquidated 12/31/28
2nd title:Merchants NB 7/22/95
3rd title:Merchants N T & Savings B 10/8/26
FIRST TITLE {{ 0 L }}
Brown Back <$VALUE
3x10-20 1-2670 <$1000
SECOND TITLE {{ 29 L }}
Brown Back
3x10-20 1-1904 <$400
50-100 1-2882 <$2000/$2250
1902 Red Seal
3x10-20 1-4500 <$400
1902 Date Back
3x10-20 1-29200 <$60
1902 Plain Back
3x10-20 29201-127051 <$60
THIRD TITLE {{ 19 L }}
1902 Plain Back
3x10-20 1-23284 <$60
Total Issue $8,402,750
Out at close $849,995
Outstanding includes Ch 4096

****

5993 Los Angeles
SOUTHWESTERN NB OF LOS ANGELES
{{ 1 L }}
Chartered 10/16/01
Liquidated 10/7/05
Brown Back <$VALUE
3x10-20 1-9463 <$1000
Total Issue $473,150
Out in 1910 $34,860

****

7632 Los Angeles
UNITED STATES NB OF LOS ANGELES
{{ 20 L }}
Chartered 3/05
Receivership 8/18/31
1902 Red Seal <$VALUE
4x5 1-8575 <$400
3x10-20 1-5570 <$400
1902 Date Back
4x5 1-13915 <$100
3x10-20 1-10834 <$100
1902 Plain Back
4x5 13916-45256 <$100
3x10-20 10835-30830 <$100
Total Issue $2,896,620
Out at close $13,485

****

13187 Los Angeles
WESTERN NB IN LOS ANGELES
Chartered 3/28 as NB for Savings in Los Angeles, under which there was no issue. Issuing title adopted 2/11/29.
Liquidated 3/13/31
2nd title:Central NB in Los Angeles 7/31/30
FIRST TITLE {{ 6 S }}
1929 Small Size <$VALUE
5 Type 1 1-3724 <$200
10 Type 1 1-1924 <$200
20 Type 1 1-640 <$200
SECOND TITLE {{ 1 S }}
1929 Small Size
5 Type 1 1-988 <$500
10 Type 1 1-457 <$500
20 Type 1 1-75 <$500
Total Issue $370,020
Out at close $171,340

****

9933 Merced
FNB OF LOS BANOS
{{ 5 L }}
Chartered 2/11
Liquidated 11/2/21
1902 Date Back <$VALUE
4x5 1-1210 <$600
3x10-20 1-931 <$600
1902 Plain Back
4x5 1211-2950 <$600
3x10-20 932-1899 <$600
Total Issue $153,950
Out at close $15,200

****

10091 Santa Clara
FNB OF LOS GATOS
{{ 3 L 15 S }}
Organized 9/15/11
1902 Date Back <$VALUE
3x50-100 1-779 <$1250
1902 Plain Back
3x50-100 780-959 <$1250
1929 Small Size
5 Type 1 1-1460 <$200
10 Type 1 1-850 <$200
20 Type 1 1-252 <$200
5 Type 2 1-3168 <$225
10 Type 2 1-1644 <$225
20 Type 2 1-336 <$225
Total Issue $403,790
Out in 1935 $47,850
Large out 1935 $3,150

****

10197 Madera
COMMERCIAL NB OF MADERA
{{ UNREPORTED }}
Chartered 5/12
Liquidated 10/3/17
1902 Date Back <$VALUE
3x10-20 1-860 <$2500
Total Issue $43,000
Out at close $10,900

****

7336 Madera
FNB OF MADERA
{{ UNREPORTED }}
Chartered 7/04
Liquidated 3/27/35
1902 Red Seal <$VALUE
50-100 1-113 <$7500/$8500
1902 Date Back
50-100 1-180 <$2500
3x50-100 1-113 <$2500
Total Issue $72,200
Out at close $600

****

9957 Kern
FNB OF MARICOPA
{{ 1 L }}
Chartered 3/11
Liquidated 4/15/15
1902 Date Back <$VALUE
3x10-20 1-1427 <$1500
Total Issue $71,350
Out in 1915 $14,750

****

8692 Contra Costa
FNB OF CONTRA COSTA COUNTY AT MARTINEZ
{{ 6 L }}
Chartered 5/07
Liquidated 5/18/23
1902 Red Seal <$VALUE
4x5 1-450 <$1250
3x10-20 1-380 <$1250
1902 Date Back
4x5 1-3450 <$450
3x10-20 1-2600 <$450
1902 Plain Back
4x5 3451-8565 <$450
3x10-20 2601-5576 <$450
Total Issue $478,100
Out at close $50,000

****

12511 Contra Costa
NB OF MARTINEZ
{{ 4 L }}
Chartered 3/24
Liquidated 4/12/27
1902 Plain Back <$VALUE
4x5 1-2690 <$650
3x10-20 1-1642 <$650
Total Issue $135,900
Out at close $42,100

****

11123 Yuba
FNB OF MARYSVILLE
{{ 4 L 0 S }}
Chartered 12/17
Liquidated 6/29/31
1902 Plain Back <$VALUE
4x5 1-14847 <$750
1929 Small Size
5 Type 1 1-1631 <$750
Total issue $345,870
Out at close $24,460
Large out at close $1,860

****

CONDITION affects Value. The Values shown are for notes in FINE condition.

9479 Siskiyou
McCLOUD NB, McCLOUD
{{ 4 L 2U + 4 S }}
Chartered 7/09
Liquidated 10/15/35
1902 Date Back <$VALUE
4x5 1-2150 <$600
3x10-20 1-1570 <$600
1902 Plain Back
4x5 2151-7393 <$600
3x10-20 1571-4578 <$600
1929 Small Size
5 Type 1 1-986 <$350
10 Type 1 1-492 <$350
20 Type 1 1-142 <$350
5 Type 2 1-1216 <$400
10 Type 2 1-756 <$400
20 Type 2 1-255 <$400
Total Issue $471,640
Out in 1935 $21,700
Large out 1935 $1,255

10387 Kern
FNB OF McFARLAND
Chartered 5/13
2nd title:FNB in Delano 6/22/34
FIRST TITLE {{ 2 L U + 2 S }}
1902 Date Back <$VALUE
4x5 1-625 <$1000
3x10-20 1-500 <$1000
1902 Plain Back
4x5 626-2635 <$1000
3x10-20 501-1594 <$1000
1929 Small Size
5 Type 1 1-628 <$500
10 Type 1 1-372 <$500
20 Type 1 1-96 <$500
5 Type 2 1-1596 <$500
10 Type 2 1-648 <$500
20 Type 2 1-204 <$500
SECOND TITLE {{ 0 S }}
1929 Small Size
5 Type 2 1-374 <$750
10 Type 2 1-125 <$750
20 Type 2 1-95 <$750
Total Issue $208,640
Out in 1935 $24,800
Large out 1935 $390

10352 Merced
FARMERS & MERCHANTS NB OF MERCED
{{ 8 L }}
Organized 1/4/13
Receivership 9/23/26
1902 Date Back <$VALUE
4x5 1-3650 <$400
3x10-20 1-2940 <$400
1902 Plain Back
4x5 3651-15865 <$400
3x10-20 2941-10730 <$400
Total Issue $853,800
Out at close $19,600

13028 Merced
FNB IN MERCED
{{ U + 9 S }}
Chartered 1/27
1929 Small Size <$VALUE
5 Type 2 1-14388 <$200
10 Type 2 1-6638 <$200
20 Type 2 1-2196 <$200
Total Issue $182,240
Out in 1935 $98,600

3733 Merced
FNB OF MERCED
{{ UNREPORTED }}
Chartered 6/23/87
Liquidated 6/30/91
Brown Back <$VALUE
3x10-20 1-1434 <$3000
Total Issue $71,700
Out in 1910 $470

9437 Merced
FNB OF MERCED
{{ 3 L }}
Chartered 6/09
Liquidated 1/14/16
1902 Date Back <$VALUE
4x5 1-7060 <$600
3x10-20 1-6460 <$600
1902 Plain Back
3x10-20 6461-6650 <$600
Total Issue $473,700
Out in 1916 $82,295

10988 Stanislaus
CALIFORNIA NB OF MODESTO
{{ 1 L }}
Organized 2/23/17
Receivership 4/13/21
1902 Plain Back <$VALUE
3x10-20 1-2572 <$1500
Total issue $128,600
Out at close $48,500

3136 Stanislaus
FNB OF MODESTO
{{ 6 L }}
Chartered 1884
Liquidated 7/10/20
Brown Back <$VALUE
3x10-20 1-5134 <$1000
1902 Red Seal
3x10-20 1-4200 <$1250
1902 Date Back
4x5 1-6750 <$500
3x10-20 1-6900 <$500
1902 Plain Back
3x10-20 6901-13292 <$500
Total Issue $1,266,300
Out at close $189,495

7705 Los Angeles
AMERICAN NB OF MONROVIA
Chartered 4/05
Liquidated 3/7/27
2nd title:NB of Monrovia 2/4/16
3rd title:FNB in Monrovia 5/8/24
FIRST TITLE {{ 2 L }}
1902 Red Seal <$VALUE
4x5 1-750 <$1500
3x10-20 1-620 <$1500
1902 Date Back
4x5 1-4150 <$850
3x10-20 1-2940 <$850
1902 Plain Back
4x5 4151-4300 <$850
3x10-20 2941-2996 <$850
SECOND TITLE {{ 2 L }}
1902 Plain Back
4x5 1-5950 <$850
3x10-20 1-3610 <$850
THIRD TITLE {{ 1 L }}
1902 Plain Back
4x5 1-5815 <$850
Total Issue $697,600
Out at close $47,100

FNB in Monrovia
SEE Ch 7705
American NB of Monrovia

3743 Los Angeles
FNB OF MONROVIA
{{ 3 L }}
Chartered 7/2/87
Liquidated 4/7/24
Brown Back <$VALUE
4x5 1-3673 <$1250
3x10-20 1-933 <$1250
1902 Red Seal
4x5 1-350 <$1500
3x10-20 1-200 <$1500
1902 Date Back
4x5 1-3100 <$650
3x10-20 1-2580 <$650
1902 Plain Back
4x5 3101-7140 <$650
3x10-20 2581-4656 <$650
Total Issue $512,710
Out at close $35,000

NB of Monrovia
SEE Ch 7705
American NB of Monrovia

7058 Monterey
FNB OF MONTEREY
{{ 3 L U + 24 S }}
Chartered 12/03
1902 Red Seal <$VALUE
3x10-20 1-1200 <$1500
1902 Date Back
3x10-20 1-1710* <$850
1902 Plain Back
3x10-20 1951-5896* <$850
* 1711-1950 not marked
1929 Small Size
10 Type 1 1-2264 <$200
20 Type 1 1-470 <$200
10 Type 2 1-4593* <$200
20 Type 2 1-1210 <$200
* 475-480 not issued
Total Issue $617,110
Out in 1935 $97,150
Large out 1935 $1,380

12061 Los Angeles
FNB OF MONTEREY PARK
{{ 1 S }}
Organized 11/3/21
Receivership 2/9/32
1929 Small Size <$VALUE
5 Type 1 1-433 <$850
10 Type 1 1-202 <$850
Total Issue $25,110
Out at close $25,000

11532 Santa Clara
FARMERS & MERCHANTS NB OF MOUNTAIN VIEW
{{ 3 L }}
Chartered 12/19
Liquidated 3/31/27
1902 Plain Back <$VALUE
3x10-20 1-5666 <$850
Total Issue $283,300
Out at close $44,100

10324 Santa Clara
FNB OF MOUNTAIN VIEW
{{ 7 L 8 S }}
Chartered 2/13
1902 Date Back <$VALUE
3x10-20 1-900 <$650
1902 Plain Back
3x10-20 901-9296 <$650
1929 Small Size
10 Type 1 1-1296 <$350
20 Type 1 1-356 <$350
10 Type 2 1-649 <$350
20 Type 2 1-125 <$350
Total Issue $594,150
Out in 1935 $26,470
Large out 1935 $1,920

7176 Napa
FNB OF NAPA
{{ 7 L 50+ S }}
Chartered 3/04
1902 Red Seal <$VALUE
4x5 1-2380 <$1000
3x10-20 1-1668 <$1000
1902 Date Back
4x5 1-3650 <$500
3x10-20 1-2470 <$500
1902 Plain Back
4x5 3651-15877 <$500
3x10-20 2471-11614 <$500
1929 Small Size
5 Type 1 1-3568 $125
10 Type 1 1-2056 $125
20 Type 1 1-486 $125
5 Type 2 1-4606 $125
10 Type 2 1-2715 $125
20 Type 2 1-670 $125
Total Issue $1,381,540
Out in 1935 $85,450
Large out 1935 $3,645

9512 San Diego
PEOPLES NB OF NATIONAL CITY
{{ 1 L }}
Organized 6/21/09
Receivership 11/7/21
1902 Date Back <$VALUE
3x10-20 1-1650 <$1500
1902 Plain Back
3x10-20 1651-3276 <$1500
Total Issue $163,800
Out at close $25,000

4873 San Bernardino
NEEDLES NB, NEEDLES
{{ UNREPORTED }}
Chartered 3/6/93
Receivership 1/19/95
Brown Back <$VALUE
3x10-20 1-299 <$5000
Total Issue $14,950
Out in 1916 $40

9760 Stanislaus
FNB OF NEWMAN
{{ 1 L }}
Organized 5/25/10
Receivership 1/31/20
1902 Date Back <$VALUE
4x5 1-1150 <$2000
3x10-20 1-880 <$2000
1902 Plain Back
4x5 1151-1185 <$2000
3x10-20 881-928 <$2000
Total Issue $70,100
Out at close $12,500

7502 Stanislaus
FNB OF OAKDALE
{{ 12 L U + 13 S }}
Chartered 12/04
1902 Red Seal <$VALUE
4x5 1-3300 <$1000
3x10-20 1-1840 <$1000
1902 Date Back
4x5 1-4050* <$350
3x10-20 1-3040** <$350
1902 Plain Back
4x5 4451-22730* <$350
3x10-20 3361-15701** <$350
* 4051-4450 not marked
** 3041-3360 not marked
1929 Small Size
5 Type 1 1-3382 <$200
10 Type 1 1-1942 <$200
20 Type 1 1-568 <$200
5 Type 2 1-6984 <$225
10 Type 2 1-3561 <$225
20 Type 2 1-870 <$225
Total Issue $1,771,720
Out in 1935 $98,700
Large out 1935 $5,170

9502 Alameda
CENTRAL NB OF OAKLAND
{{ 50+ L 50+ S }}
Organized 8/4/09
Receivership 5/8/33
1902 Date Back <$VALUE
4x5 1-21000 <$50
3x10-20 1-16800 <$60/$70
50-100 1-8500 <$350/$400
3x50-100 1-7000 <$350/$400
1902 Plain Back
4x5 21001-119079 <$50
3x10-20 16801-95162<$60/$70
1929 Small Size
5 Type 1 1-41484 <$20
10 Type 1 1-16595 <$20
20 Type 1 1-5563 <$30
Total Issue $13,072,460
Out at close $1,149,900
Large out at close $72,100

FNB in Oakland
SEE Ch 12665
New FNB in Oakland

FNB of Oakland
See Ch 2248
FN Gold B of Oakland

2248 Alameda
FN GOLD B OF OAKLAND
Chartered 4/10/75
Liquidated 10/11/24
2nd title: FNB of Oakland 2/80
FIRST TITLE {{ 15 L }}
GOLD BANK NOTES <$VALUE
Original Series Gold Notes
3x10-20 1-1600<$3500/$5000
Series 1875 Gold Notes
3x10-20 1-12 <$4000/$6000
SECOND TITLE {{ 40 L }}
Series 1875
3x10-20 1-6405<$3000/$3500
Brown Back
4x5 1-7500 <$350
3x10-20 1-9500 <$350
50-100 1-1784 <$2500
1882 Date Back
4x5 1-23935 <$350
3x10-20 1-14396 <$350
50-100 1-700 <$2000/$2250
3x50-100 1-1528<$2000/$2250
1902 Date Back
4x5 1-8250 <$75
3x10-20 1-6700 <$75
1902 Plain Back
4x5 8251-73435 <$75
3x10-20 6701-45241 <$75
Total Issue $6,709,700
Out at close $985,895

12665 Alameda
NEW FNB IN OAKLAND
Chartered 3/25
Liquidated 12/6/34
2nd title:FNB in Oakland 8/10/26
FIRST TITLE {{ 5 L }}
1902 Plain Back <$VALUE
4x5 1-9440 <$250
SECOND TITLE {{ 22 L 42 S }}
1902 Plain Back
4x5 1-15495 <$50
3x10-20 1-10295 <$50/$60
3x50-100 1-1669 <$400/$450
1929 Small Size
5 Type 1 1-17136 <$15
10 Type 1 1-6682 <$20
20 Type 1 1-2062 <$30
50 Type 1 1-350 <$100
100 Type 1 1-114 <$150
5 Type 2 1-10318 <$20
10 Type 2 1-3935 <$25
20 Type 2 1-1550 <$35
Total Issue $2,888,480
Out at close $400,085
Large out at close $10,820

Union NB of Oakland
SEE Ch 2266
Union N Gold B of Oakland

2266 Alameda
UNION N GOLD B OF OAKLAND
Chartered 5/20/75
Receivership 4/14/09
2nd title: Union NB of Oakland 2/80
FIRST TITLE {{ 5 L }}
GOLD BANK NOTES <$VALUE
Original Series Gold Notes
3x10-20 1-500<$8000/$10,000
50-100 1-100 <$35,000
SECOND TITLE {{ 8 L }}
Series 1875
3x10-20 1-5935<$2500/$3500
Brown Back
4x5 1-4000 <$600
3x10-20 1-1834 <$600
50-100 1-1721 <$2250/$2500
1882 Date Back
4x5 1-775 <$600
Total Issue $702,750
Out in 1916 $9,470

7690 Los Angeles
FNB OF OCEAN PARK
{{ 5 L }}
Chartered 4/05
Liquidated 3/1/27
1902 Red Seal <$VALUE
3x10-20 1-1575 <$1500
1902 Date Back
3x10-20 1-4600 <$750
1902 Plain Back
3x10-20 4601-11756 <$750
Total Issue $666,550
Out at close $47,900

8069 San Diego
FNB OF OCEANSIDE
{{ 2 L }}
Chartered 1/06
Receivership 2/15/33
1902 Red Seal <$VALUE
3x10-20 1-400 <$2000
1902 Date Back
4x5 1-2050 <$1250
3x10-20 1-1600 <$1250
1902 Plain Back
4x5 2051-5965 <$1250
3x10-20 1601-3789 <$1250
Total Issue $328,750
Out at close $1,110

10891 Orange
FNB OF OLIVE
{{ 5 L 6 S }}
Chartered 7/25/16
Receivership 1/26/34
1902 Plain Back <$VALUE
3x10-20 1-2945 <$850
1929 Small Size
10 Type 1 1-372 <$450
20 Type 1 1-116 <$450
10 Type 2 1-31 <$500
20 Type 2 1-15 <$500
Total Issue $184,000
Out at close $15,000
Large out at close $710

13092 San Bernardino
CITIZENS NB OF ONTARIO
{{ 3 L 15 S }}
Chartered 6/27
1902 Plain Back <$VALUE
3x10-20 1-4134 <$500
1929 Small Size
10 Type 1 1-2814 <$135
20 Type 1 1-806 <$135
10 Type 2 1-1400 <$165
20 Type 2 1-390 <$175
Total Issue $494,060
Out in 1935 $66,480
Large out 1935 $1,280

6268 San Bernardino
FNB OF ONTARIO
{{ 12 L U + 24 S }}
Organized 4/2/02
1902 Red Seal <$VALUE
3x10-20 1-1820 <$850
1902 Date Back
3x10-20 1-4400 <$350
1902 Plain Back (dated 1902)
3x10-20 4401-9000 <$350
1902 Plain Back (dated 1922)
3x10-20 1-11276 <$350
1929 Small Size
5 Type 1 1-4650 <$75
10 Type 1 1-2640 <$75
20 Type 1 1-416 <$85
5 Type 2 1-5816 <$85
10 Type 2 1-1905 <$85
Total Issue 1,500,750
Out in 1935 $67,370
Large out 1935 $4,870

9935 San Bernardino
ONTARIO NB, ONTARIO
{{ 11 L }}
Chartered 2/11
Liquidated 3/8/27
1902 Date Back <$VALUE
3x10-20 1-3540 <$300
1902 Plain Back
3x10-20 3541-17703 <$300
Total Issue $885,150
Out at close $125,800

8181 Orange
FNB OF ORANGE
{{ 10 L 29 S }}
Chartered 4/06
1902 Red Seal <$VALUE
3x10-20 1-288 <$1500
1902 Date Back
3x10-20 1-2780 <$400
1902 Plain Back
3x10-20 2781-23879 <$400
1929 Small Size
5 Type 1 1-35126 <$100
5 Type 2 1-46140 <$100
Total Issue $2,492,830
Out in 1935 $275,160
Large out 1935 $7,830
Outstanding includes Ch 9878

9878 Orange
NB OF ORANGE
{{ 9 L }}
Chartered 10/10
Closed 6/30/27
1902 Date Back <$VALUE
3x10-20 1-2920* <$400
1902 Plain Back
3x10-20 3421-16844* <$400
* 2921-3420 not marked
Total Issue $842,200
Out at close $97,900
Ch 8181 assumed circulation

11616 Fresno
FNB OF ORANGE COVE
{{ 4 L U + 10 S }}
Chartered 2/20
1902 Plain Back <$VALUE
4x5 1-3550 <$750
3x10-20 1-2389 <$750
1929 Small Size
5 Type 1 1-924 <$350
10 Type 1 1-494 <$350
20 Type 1 1-132 <$375
5 Type 2 1-1474 <$400
10 Type 2 1-708 <$400
20 Type 2 1-204 <$400
Total Issue $282,180
Out in 1935 $25,000
Large out 1935 $1,330

10378 Glenn
FNB OF ORLAND
{{ 4 L 4 S }}
Chartered 4/13
Liquidated 1/30/33
1902 Date Back <$VALUE
4x5 1-1000 <$650
3x10-20 1-820 <$650
1902 Plain Back
4x5 1001-6585 <$650
3x10-20 821-4680 <$650
1929 Small Size
5 Type 1 1-820 <$450
10 Type 1 1-399 <$450
20 Type 1 1-107 <$500
Total Issue $427,080
Out at close $24,320
Large out at close $2,250

****

9167 Tulare
FNB OF OROSI
{{ UNREPORTED }}
Chartered 6/08
Liquidated 11/10/10
1902 Date Back <$VALUE
4x5 1-700 <$2500
3x10-20 1-583 <$2500
Total Issue $43,150
Out in 1911 $9,560

****

10328 Tulare
NB OF OROSI
{{ 0 L 1 S }}
Chartered 2/13
Liquidated 8/6/30
1902 Date Back <$VALUE
3x10-20 1-660 <$2000
1902 Plain Back
3x10-20 661-2864 <$2000
1929 Small Size
10 Type 1 1-137 <$1250
20 Type 1 1-12 <$1250
Total Issue $152,860
Out at close $11,180
Large out at close $2,230

****

6919 Butte
FNB OF OROVILLE
{{ 0 L 3 S }}
Chartered 8/03
1902 Red Seal <$VALUE
3x10-20 1-650 <$2500
1902 Date Back
3x10-20 1-1300* <$2000
1902 Plain Back
3x10-20 1421-3222* <$2000
* 1301-1421 not marked
1929 Small Size
10 Type 1 1-392 <$450
20 Type 1 1-118 <$450
10 Type 2 1-276 <$500
20 Type 2 1-50 <$500
Total Issue $235,040
Out in 1935 $12,350
Large out 1935 $720

****

10282 Butte
RIDEOUT SMITH NB OF OROVILLE
{{ 3 L }}
Chartered 10/12
Liquidated 4/12/22
1902 Date Back <$VALUE
3x10-20 1-5000 <$1250
1902 Plain Back
3x10-20 5001-5678 <$1250
Total Issue $283,900
Out at close $49,200

****

9481 Ventura
FNB OF OXNARD
{{ 2 L }}
Chartered 7/09
Liquidated 6/30/22
1902 Date Back <$VALUE
4x5 1-5850 <$1500
3x10-20 1-4580 <$1500
1902 Plain Back
4x5 5851-8190 <$1500
3x10-20 4581-6046 <$1500
Total Issue $466,100
Out at close $46,100

****

13375 Monterey
FNB OF PACIFIC GROVE
{{ 3U + 24 S }}
Chartered 9/29
1929 Small Size <$VALUE
5 Type 1 1-2066 <$250
10 Type 1 1-1026 <$250
20 Type 1 1-432 <$250
5 Type 2 1-5556 <$250
10 Type 2 1-3265 <$250
20 Type 2 1-1270 <$250
Total Issue $261,210
Out in 1935 $97,300

****

7069 Santa Clara
FNB OF PALO ALTO
{{ 4 L }}
Chartered 12/03
Liquidated 6/12/28
1902 Red Seal <$VALUE
3x10-20 1-1120 <$2000
1902 Date Back
3x10-20 1-2100* <$1250
1902 Plain Back
3x10-20 2401-6840* <$1250
* 2101-2400 not marked
Total Issue $398,000
Out at close $26,350

****

13212 Santa Clara
PALO ALTO NB, PALO ALTO
{{ 3U + 31 S }}
Chartered 5/28
1929 Small Size <$VALUE
5 Type 1 1-2570 <$225
10 Type 1 1-1304 <$225
20 Type 1 1-422 <$250
5 Type 2 1-12174 <$250
10 Type 2 1-5480 <$250
20 Type 2 1-1595 <$250
Total Issue $353,550
Out in 1935 $124,800

****

10124 Fresno
FNB OF PARLIER
{{ 9 L }}
Chartered 1/12
1902 Date Back <$VALUE
3x10-20 1-1200 <$450
1902 Plain Back
3x10-20 1201-11113 <$450
Total Issue $555,650
Out in 1935 $1,420

****

9366 Los Angeles
CROWN CITY NB OF PASADENA
{{ 2 L }}
Chartered 3/09
Liquidated 6/20/14
1902 Date Back <$VALUE
3x10-20 1-7303 <$1500
Total Issue $365,150
Out in 1914 $78,050

****

3499 Los Angeles
FNB OF PASADENA
{{ 13 L 13 S }}
Chartered 1886
Liquidated 9/1/34
Brown Back <$VALUE
4x5 1-3825 <$800
3x10-20 1-5494 <$800
1902 Red Seal
4x5 1-2650 <$1000
3x10-20 1-1340 <$1000
1902 Date Back
4x5 1-12200 <$275
3x10-20 1-9940 <$275
1902 Plain Back
4x5 12201-27880 <$275
3x10-20 9941-20636 <$275
1929 Small Size
5 Type 1 1-3634 <$135
10 Type 1 1-2058 <$135
20 Type 1 1-494 <$135
5 Type 2 1-1112 <$185
10 Type 2 1-380 <$185
20 Type 2 1-145 <$185
Total Issue $2,364,640
Out at close $82,550
Large out at close $5,355

****

11425 Los Angeles
NB & TC OF PASADENA
{{ 5 L }}
Chartered 8/19
Liquidated 10/11/21
1902 Plain Back <$VALUE
4x5 1-27000 <$375
Total issue $540,000
Out at close $281,180
Outstanding includes Ch 10082

****

10082 Los Angeles
NB OF COMMERCE OF PASADENA
Chartered 9/11
Closed 10/27/19
2nd title: NB of Pasadena 6/9/14
FIRST TITLE {{ 3 L }}
1902 Date Back <$VALUE
3x10-20 1-4532 <$400
SECOND TITLE {{ 7 L }}
1902 Date Back
3x10-20 1-5500 <$250
1902 Plain Back
4x5 1-14327 <$250
3x10-20 5501-12611 <$250
Total Issue $1,143,690
Out at close $300,000
Outstanding includes Ch 3568
Ch 11425 assumed circulation

****

NB of Pasadena
SEE Ch 10082
NB of Commerce of Pasadena

****

3568 Los Angeles
PASADENA NB, PASADENA
{{ 12 L }}
Chartered 10/11/86
Liquidated 6/20/14
Brown Back <$VALUE
4x5 1-3115 <$750
3x10-20 1-4117 <$750
1902 Red Seal
4x5 1-2750 <$850
3x10-20 1-1900 <$850
1902 Date Back
4x5 1-13843 <$250
3x10-20 1-9087 <$250
Total Issue $1,149,360
Out at close $199,995
Ch 10082 assumed circulation

****

12385 Los Angeles
PASADENA NB, PASADENA
Organized 5/14/23
2nd title:Pasadena - FNB 12/1/34
FIRST TITLE {{ 10 L 10 S }}
1902 Plain Back <$VALUE
4x5 1-21947 <$250
1929 Small Size
5 Type 1 1-11736 <$165
5 Type 2 1-25524 <$165
SECOND TITLE {{ 0 S }}
1929 Small Size
5 Type 2 1-1292 <$500
Total Issue $925,100
Out in 1935 $82,200
Large out 1935 $1,370

****

Pasadena-FNB, Pasadena
SEE Ch 12385
Pasadena NB, Pasadena

****

10167 Los Angeles
SECURITY NB OF PASADENA
{{ 24 L 2U + 34 S }}
Chartered 3/12
1902 Date Back <$VALUE
3x10-20 1-5800 <$150
1902 Plain Back
3x10-20 5801-44559 <$150
1929 Small Size
5 Type 1 1-2056 <$75
10 Type 1 1-7838 <$75
20 Type 1 1-1926 <$75
5 Type 2 1-19034 <$75
10 Type 2 1-10601 <$75
Total Issue $3,192,210
Out in 1935 $296,900
Large out 1935 $9,880

****

9121 Los Angeles
UNION NB OF PASADENA
{{ 6 L }}
Chartered 5/08
Liquidated 6/17/21
1902 Red Seal <$VALUE
4x5 1-2500 <$850
3x10-20 1-2000 <$850
1902 Date Back
4x5 1-6500* <$400
3x10-20 1-4700 <$400
1902 Plain Back
4x5 6901-12995* <$400
3x10-20 4701-8890 <$400
* 6501-6900 not marked
Total Issue $854,400
Out at close $97,695

****

FNB in Paso Robles
SEE Ch 12172
Paso Robles NB, Paso Robles

****

9844 San Luis Obispo
FNB OF PASO ROBLES
{{ 2 L }}
Chartered 9/10
Liquidated 4/12/22
1902 Date Back <$VALUE
4x5 1-650 <$1250
3x10-20 1-520 <$1250
1902 Plain Back
4x5 651-2305 <$1250
3x10-20 521-1557 <$1250
Total Issue $123,950
Out at close $49,300

****

12172 San Luis Obispo
PASO ROBLES NB, PASO ROBLES
Chartered 4/22
2nd title:FNB in Paso Robles 1/26/26
FIRST TITLE {{ 1 L }}
1902 Plain Back <$VALUE
4x10 1-4250 <$1250
SECOND TITLE {{ 4 L 9 S }}
1902 Plain Back
3x10-20 1-2760 <$650
1929 Small Size
10 Type 1 1-1364 <$300
20 Type 1 1-396 <$300
10 Type 2 1-1854 <$325
20 Type 2 1-516 <$325
Total Issue $466,220
Out in 1935 $44,650
Large out 1935 $1,540

****

FNB of Petaluma
SEE Ch 2193
FN Gold B of Petaluma

****

2193 Sonoma
FN GOLD B OF PETALUMA
Chartered 10/12/74
Liquidated 9/25/94
2nd title: FNB of Petaluma 4/17/84
FIRST TITLE {{ 18 L }}
GOLD BANK NOTES <$VALUE
Original Series Gold Notes
3x10-20 1-2000<$3500/$5000
50-100 1-400 <$35,000
Series 1875 Gold Notes
3x10-20 1-363 <$4000/$6000
SECOND TITLE {{ 0 L }}
Series 1875
3x10-20 1-2866<$3500/$5000
Total Issue $321,450
Out in 1910 $930

****

6904 Sonoma
PETALUMA NB, PETALUMA
{{ 16 L }}
Chartered 7/03
Liquidated 1/27/23
1902 Red Seal <$VALUE
4x5 1-4500 <$750
3x10-20 1-3580 <$750
1902 Date Back
4x5 1-11250 <$350
3x10-20 1-8400 <$350
1902 Plain Back
4x5 11251-28785 <$350
3x10-20 8401-19281 <$350
Total Issue $1,808,750
Out at close $190,800

****

9918 Sonoma
SONOMA COUNTY NB AT PETALUMA
{{ 22 L }}
Chartered 1/11
Liquidated 3/1/29
1902 Date Back <$VALUE
4x5 1-12250 <$250
3x10-20 1-9200 <$250
1902 Plain Back
4x5 12251-42510 <$250
3x10-20 9201-28672 <$250
Total Issue $2,283,800
Out at close $75,395

****

11359 Contra Costa
FNB OF PITTSBURG
{{ 1 L }}
Chartered 5/19
Liquidated 5/4/27
1902 Plain Back <$VALUE
3x10-20 1-6128 <$2000
Total issue $306,400
Out at close $40,800

****

10092 Orange
PLACENTIA NB, PLACENTIA
{{ 3 L }}
Chartered 10/11
Liquidated 3/12/26
1902 Date Back <$VALUE
4x5 1-1400 <$800
3x10-20 1-1120 <$800
1902 Plain Back
4x5 1401-6030 <$800
3x10-20 1121-3941 <$800
Total Issue $317,650
Out at close $23,000

****

12056 El Dorado
PLACERVILLE NB, PLACERVILLE
{{ 5 L 8 S }}
Chartered 12/21
Liquidated 5/22/34
1902 Plain Back <$VALUE
4x5 1-18921 <$600
1929 Small Size
5 Type 1 1-6388 <$350
5 Type 2 1-2040 <$350
Total Issue $580,260
Out at close $27,630
Large out at close $1,660

****

9897 Alameda
FNB OF PLEASANTON
{{ 1 L 3U + 7 S }}
Chartered 12/10
1902 Date Back <$VALUE
4x5 1-1110 <$1500
3x10-20 1-871 <$1500
1902 Plain Back
4x5 1111-4600 <$1500
3x10-20 872-3056 <$1500
1929 Small Size
5 Type 1 1-778 <$300
10 Type 1 1-384 <$300
20 Type 1 1-118 <$325
5 Type 2 1-1700 <$325
10 Type 2 1-763 <$325
20 Type 2 1-264 <$350
Total Issue $326,750
Out in 1935 $23,850
Large out 1935 $930

****

American NB of Pomona
SEE Ch 4663
NB of Pomona

****

3518 Los Angeles
FNB OF POMONA
{{ 29 L 45 S }}
Organized 6/8/86
Brown Back <$VALUE
4x5 1-10129 <$600
3x10-20 1-3268 <$600
1902 Red Seal
4x5 1-1825 <$750
3x10-20 1-1170 <$750
1902 Date Back
4x5 1-12750 <$150
3x10-20 1-9300 <$150
1902 Plain Back
4x5 12751-38011 <$150
3x10-20 9301-24832 <$150
1929 Small Size
5 Type 1 1-5346 <$85
10 Type 1 1-3046 <$85
20 Type 1 1-800 <$85
5 Type 2 1-6492 <$100
10 Type 2 1-3396 <$100
20 Type 2 1-1020 <$110
Total Issue $2,988,760
Out in 1935 $146,530
Large out 1935 $8,230

****

4663 Los Angeles
NB OF POMONA
Chartered 1891
Liquidated 3/25/26
2nd title: American NB of Pomona 12/12/04
FIRST TITLE {{ 0 L }}
Brown Back <$VALUE
4x5 1-3592 <$1250
3x10-20 1-1292 <$1250
SECOND TITLE {{ 12 L }}
Brown Back
3x10-20 1-3000 <$850
1882 Date Back
3x10-20 1-3037 <$750
1902 Date Back
3x10-20 1-4600 <$300
1902 Plain Back
3x10-20 4601-16129 <$300
Total Issue $1,244,740
Out at close $85,700

****

6808 Tulare
FNB OF PORTERVILLE
{{ 2 L 2 S }}
Chartered 6/03
Liquidated 11/24/30
1902 Red Seal <$VALUE
3x10-20 1-2250 <$1500
1902 Date Back
3x10-20 1-3700 <$750
1902 Plain Back
3x10-20 3701-12132 <$750
1929 Small Size
10 Type 1 1-540 <$500
20 Type 1 1-169 <$500
Total Issue $771,780
Out at close $47,780
Large out at close $7,500

****

9894 Los Angeles
FNB OF PUENTE
{{ 7 L 11 S }}
Chartered 11/10
Liquidated 9/20/34
1902 Date Back <$VALUE
4x5 1-650 <$400
4x10 1-650 <$400
1902 Plain Back
4x5 651-11178 <$400
4x10 651-8901 <$400
1929 Small Size
5 Type 1 1-2676 <$175
10 Type 1 1-1490 <$175
5 Type 2 1-1368 <$200
10 Type 2 1-696 <$200
Total Issue $763,080
Out at close $43,330
Large out at close $1,430

****

FNB of Red Bluff
SEE Ch 10114
Red Bluff NB, Red Bluff

****

10114 Tehama
RED BLUFF NB, RED BLUFF
Chartered 12/11
Liquidated 3/22/28
2nd title:FNB of Red Bluff 7/1/25
FIRST TITLE {{ 4 L }}
1902 Date Back <$VALUE
4x5 1-4965 <$650
3x10-20 1-3774 <$650
1902 Plain Back
4x5 4966-16865 <$650
3x10-20 3775-11154 <$650
SECOND TITLE {{ 1 L }}
1902 Plain Back
4x5 1-2285 <$850
3x10-20 1-2249 <$850
Total Issue $1,053,150
Out at close $73,400

****

10100 Shasta
NORTHERN CALIFORNIA NB OF REDDING
{{ 4 L U + 10 S }}
Chartered 11/11
Liquidated 12/11/34
1902 Date Back <$VALUE
4x5 1-1950 <$500
3x10-20 1-1560 <$500
1902 Plain Back
4x5 1951-12120 <$500
3x10-20 1561-7393 <$500
3x50-100 1-531 <$750/$850
1929 Small Size
5 Type 1 1-1686 <$175
10 Type 1 1-1134 <$175
20 Type 1 1-308 <$175
50 Type 1 1-126 <$300
100 Type 1 1-44 <$350
5 Type 2 1-1962 <$200
10 Type 2 1-870 <$200
20 Type 2 1-265 <$200
Total Issue $988,390
Out at close $98,200
Large out at close $5,970

****

10070 Shasta
REDDING NB, REDDING
{{ 12 L }}
Chartered 8/11
Liquidated 1/14/26
1902 Date Back <$VALUE
4x5 1-5915 <$350
3x10-20 1-4214 <$350
1902 Plain Back
4x5 5916-17810 <$350
3x10-20 4215-12056 <$350
Total Issue $959,000
Out at close $96,500

****

8073 San Bernardino
CITIZENS NB OF REDLANDS
{{ 5 L }}
Chartered 2/06
Liquidated 2/11/16
1902 Red Seal <$VALUE
4x5 1-2000 <$1000
3x10-20 1-1950 <$1000
1902 Date Back
4x5 1-14515 <$450
3x10-20 1-11169 <$450
Total Issue $986,250
Out at close $200,000
Ch 3892 assumed circulation

****

12316 San Bernardino
FNB IN REDLANDS
{{ 6 L }}
Chartered 2/23
Liquidated 4/6/28
1902 Plain Back <$VALUE
4x5 1-18620 <$400
Total Issue $372,400
Out at close $4,575

****

****
3892 San Bernardino
FNB OF REDLANDS
{{ 12 L }}
Chartered 5/29/88
Liquidated 6/30/22
Brown Back <$VALUE
4x5 1-4676 <$850
3x10-20 1-3203 <$850
1902 Red Seal
4x5 1-750 <$1000
3x10-20 1-700 <$1000
1902 Date Back
4x5 1-8000 <$350
3x10-20 1-6000 <$350
1902 Plain Back
4x5 8001-22504 <$350
3x10-20 6001-14089 <$350
Total Issue $1,458,200
Out at close $161,000
Outstanding includes Ch 8073
****
7259 San Bernardino
REDLANDS NB, REDLANDS
{{ 4 L }}
Chartered 5/04
Liquidated 5/14/22
1902 Red Seal <$VALUE
4x5 1-3825 <$1250
3x10-20 1-2760 <$1250
1902 Date Back
4x5 1-12000 <$600
3x10-20 1-9000 <$600
1902 Plain Back
4x5 12001-37350 <$600
3x10-20 9001-11400 <$600
Total Issue $1,531,500
Out at close $112,615
****
7895 Los Angeles
FARMERS & MERCHANTS NB OF REDONDO
{{ 2 L }}
Chartered 8/05
Liquidated 3/11/27
1902 Red Seal <$VALUE
4x5 1-1660 <$1500
3x10-20 1-1236 <$1500
1902 Date Back
4x5 1-4200 <$850
3x10-20 1-2980 <$850
1902 Plain Back
4x5 4201-12265 <$850
3x10-20 2981-8117 <$850
Total Issue $746,150
Out at close $46,000
****
8143 Los Angeles
FNB OF REDONDO
{{ 9 L 15 S }}
Chartered 3/06
Liquidated 3/17/33
1902 Red Seal <$VALUE
4x5 1-950 <$1250
3x10-20 1-665 <$1250
1902 Date Back
4x5 1-1850 <$500
3x10-20 1-1350 <$500
1902 Plain Back
4x5 1851-11920 <$500
3x10-20 1351-8524 <$500
1929 Small Size
5 Type 1 1-3337 <$275
10 Type 1 1-1766 <$275
20 Type 1 1-380 <$300
Total Issue $968,520
Out at close $86,510
Large out at close $2,080
****
7279 San Mateo
FNB OF SAN MATEO COUNTY AT REDWOOD CITY
{{ 28 L 2U + 48 S }}
Chartered 5/04
1902 Red Seal <$VALUE
4x5 1-2000 <$850
3x10-20 1-1656 <$850
1902 Date Back
4x5 1-4550 <$275
3x10-20 1-3360 <$275
1902 Plain Back
4x5 4551-17755 <$275
3x10-20 3361-11946 <$275
1929 Small Size
5 Type 1 1-6560 <$100
10 Type 1 1-3340 <$100
20 Type 1 1-846 <$100
5 Type 2 1-10786 <$110
10 Type 2 1-5881 <$110
20 Type 2 1-2049 <$110
Total Issue $1,727,640
Out in 1935 $168,400
Large out 1935 $2,260
****

****
8857 Fresno
FNB OF REEDLEY
{{ 1 L }}
Chartered 9/07
Liquidated 10/31/21
1902 Red Seal <$VALUE
3x10-20 1-73 <$2000
50-100 1-41 <$7500/$8500
1902 Date Back
3x10-20 1-1000 <$1500
50-100 1-80 <$2500
1902 Plain Back
3x10-20 1001-1771 <$1500
Total Issue $110,350
Out at close $16,500
****
9688 Fresno
REEDLEY NB, REEDLEY
{{ 2 L }}
Chartered 3/10
Liquidated 7/26/27
1902 Date Back <$VALUE
3x10-20 1-1360 <$1250
1902 Plain Back
3x10-20 1361-4173 <$1250
Total Issue $208,650
Out at close $17,800
****
11867 San Bernardino
CITIZENS NB OF RIALTO
{{ 1 L 0 S }}
Chartered 11/20
Liquidated 1/13/31
1902 Plain Back <$VALUE
4x5 1-4197 <$1500
1929 Small Size
10 Type 1 1-556 <$850
Total Issue $117,300
Out at close $21,340
Large out at close $850
Ch 8768 assumed circulation
****
8768 San Bernardino
FNB OF RIALTO
{{ 5 L 7 S }}
Organized 7/3/06
Receivership 8/2/33
1902 Red Seal <$VALUE
3x10-20 1-700 <$1250
1902 Date Back
3x10-20 1-1820 <$600
1902 Plain Back
3x10-20 1821-6212 <$600
1929 Small Size
10 Type 1 1-1038 <$350
20 Type 1 1-240 <$350
Total Issue $436,680
Out at close $50,000
Large out at close $1,720
Outstanding includes Ch 11867
****
12341 Contra Costa
FNB IN RICHMOND
{{ 13 L 12 S }}
Chartered 3/23
1902 Plain Back <$VALUE
4x5 1-9950 <$300
3x10-20 1-7793 <$300
1929 Small Size
5 Type 1 1-4028 <$200
10 Type 1 1-1958 <$200
20 Type 1 1-538 <$200
5 Type 2 1-3810 <$225
10 Type 2 1-1762 <$225
20 Type 2 1-370 <$250
Total Issue $935,600
Out in 1935 $52,500
Large out 1935 $3,150
****
9735 Contra Costa
FNB OF RICHMOND
{{ 4 L }}
Chartered 4/10
Liquidated 10/7/22
1902 Date Back <$VALUE
4x5 1-6250 <$600
3x10-20 1-4660 <$600
1902 Plain Back
4x5 6251-14775 <$600
3x10-20 4661-9894 <$600
Total Issue $790,200
Out at close $91,100
****
10427 Stanislaus
FNB OF RIVERBANK
{{ 1 L }}
Organized 6/26/13
Receivership 12/28/25
1902 Date Back <$VALUE
4x5 1-550 <$1500
3x10-20 1-440 <$1500
1902 Plain Back
4x5 551-2945 <$1500
3x10-20 441-1931 <$1500
Total Issue $155,450
Out at close $12,100
****
10200 Fresno
FNB OF RIVERDALE
{{ 1 L 1 S }}
Chartered 5/12
1902 Date Back <$VALUE
3x10-20 1-400* <$1500
1902 Plain Back
3x10-20 521-1482* <$1500
* 401-520 not marked
1929 Small Size
10 Type 1 1-210 <$850
20 Type 1 1-54 <$850
Total Issue $93,180
Out in 1935 $5,650
Large out 1935 $350
****
8907 Riverside
CITIZENS NB OF RIVERSIDE
Chartered 10/07
2nd title:Citizens NT & Savings B 1/21/28
FIRST TITLE {{ 9 L }}
1902 Red Seal <$VALUE
4x5 1-1850 <$850
4x10 1-1850 <$850
1902 Date Back
4x5 1-12500 <$175
4x10 1-11250 <$175
1902 Plain Back
4x5 12501-39515 <$175
4x10 11251-32460 <$175
SECOND TITLE {{ 6 L 50+ S }}
1902 Plain Back
4x5 1-11718 <$175
1929 Small Size
5 Type 1 1-24526 <$50
10 Type 1 1-7744 <$50
20 Type 1 1-1918 <$50
5 Type 2 1-26674 <$60
10 Type 2 1-15204 <$60
20 Type 2 1-3816 <$60
Total Issue $4,266,370
Out in 1935 $500,000
Large out 1935 $6,245
****
FNB in Riverside
SEE Ch 8377
NB of Riverside
****
3348 Riverside
FNB OF RIVERSIDE
{{ 7 L }}
Chartered 1885
Liquidated 5/6/16
Brown Back <$VALUE
4x5 1-2620 <$850
3x10-20 1-1830 <$850
1902 Red Seal
4x5 1-3850 <$1000
3x10-20 1-3000 <$1000
1902 Date Back
4x5 1-27350 <$300
3x10-20 1-19300 <$300
1902 Plain Back
4x5 27351-29460 <$300
3x10-20 19301-20655 <$300
Total Issue $1,992,850
Out in 1916 $207,000
****
8377 Riverside
NB OF RIVERSIDE
Chartered 9/06
2nd title:FNB in Riverside 1/16/23
FIRST TITLE {{ 5 L }}
1902 Red Seal <$VALUE
3x10-20 1-2700 <$850
1902 Date Back
3x10-20 1-8000 <$225
1902 Plain Back
3x10-20 8001-16000 <$225
SECOND TITLE {{ 7 L 2U+19 S }}
1902 Plain Back
4x5 1-17422 <$225
3x10-20 1-11646 <$225
1929 Small Size
5 Type 1 1-7274 <$60
10 Type 1 1-4036 <$60
20 Type 1 1-1040 <$75
5 Type 2 1-8894 <$75
10 Type 2 1-4928 <$85
20 Type 2 1-1155 <$85
Total Issue $2,567,770
Out in 1935 $175,650
Large out 1935 $6,605
****

****
6833 Riverside
ORANGE GROWERS NB, RIVERSIDE
{{ UNREPORTED }}
Chartered 6/03
Receivership 3/23/04
1902 Red Seal <$VALUE
3x10-20 1-512 <$3000
Total Issue $25,600
Out in 1916 $250
****
4757 Riverside
RIVERSIDE NB, RIVERSIDE
{{ UNREPORTED }}
Chartered 6/13/92
Liquidated 10/20/94
Brown Back <$VALUE
3x10-20 1-1248 <$3000
Total Issue $62,400
Out in 1910 $730
****
11201 Contra Costa
FNB OF RODEO
{{ 2 L }}
Chartered 7/18
Liquidated 3/1/28
1902 Plain Back <$VALUE
4x5 1-3897 <$1500
4x10 1-2884 <$1500
Total issue $193,300
Out at close $10,400
****
FNB of Roseville
SEE Ch 11961
Roseville NB, Roseville
****
11992 Placer
RAILROAD NB OF ROSEVILLE
{{ 3 L }}
Chartered 7/21
Liquidated 12/23/24
1902 Plain Back <$VALUE
4x5 1-9600 <$1250
Total Issue $192,000
Out at close $42,350
****
11961 Placer
ROSEVILLE NB, ROSEVILLE
Chartered 4/21
Liquidated 3/10/27
2nd title:FNB of Roseville 2/8/24
FIRST TITLE {{ 0 L }}
1902 Plain Back <$VALUE
4x5 1-2800 <$1500
3x10-20 1-1970 <$1500
SECOND TITLE {{ 2 L }}
1902 Plain Back
4x5 1-2115 <$1250
3x10-20 1-1424 <$1250
Total Issue $268,000
Out at close $46,500
****
8504 Sacramento
CALIFORNIA NB OF SACRAMENTO
{{ 50+ L 50+ S }}
Organized 12/18/06
Receivership 1/21/33
1902 Red Seal <$VALUE
4x5 1-23125 <$250
3x10-20 1-11910 <$250
50-100 1-2280 <$7500/$8500
1902 Date Back
4x5 1-68830 <$50
3x10-20 1-51000 <$50/$60
50-100 1-1000 <$750/$850
3x50-100 1-1000 <$750/$850
1902 Plain Back
3x10-20 51001-180077 <$50/$60
1929 Small Size
10 Type 1 1-27647 <$25
20 Type 1 1-7391 <$35
Total Issue $14,726,190
Out at close $1,701,580
Large out at close $64,770
****
10107 Sacramento
CAPITAL NB OF SACRAMENTO
{{ U + 42 L U + 40 S }}
Chartered 11/11
1902 Date Back <$VALUE
4x5 1-8100 <$85
3x10-20 1-6360 <$85
1902 Plain Back
4x5 8101-97388 <$85
3x10-20 6361-65955 <$85
1929 Small Size
5 Type 1 1-22122 <$35
10 Type 1 1-10512 <$35
20 Type 1 1-2406 <$45
5 Type 2 1-23820 <$40
10 Type 2 1-15715 <$40
20 Type 2 1-4384 <$50
Total Issue $7,192,540
Out in 1935 $423,900
Large out 1935 $20,025
****
7776 Sacramento
FORT SUTTER NB OF SACRAMENTO
{{ 7 L }}
Chartered 6/05
Liquidated 8/20/20
1902 Red Seal <$VALUE
4x5 1-5750 <$850
3x10-20 1-4680 <$850
50-100 1-590 <$7500/$8500
1902 Date Back
4x5 1-1665 <$400
3x10-20 1-12234 <$400
50-100 1-200 <$1250/$1500
3x50-100 1-250<$1250/$1500
1902 Plain Back
3x10-20 12235-19629 <$400
Total Issue $1,544,750
Out at close $184,600
****
11875 Sacramento
MERCHANTS NB OF SACRAMENTO
{{ 13 L 16 S }}
Chartered 11/20
1902 Plain Back <$VALUE
4x5 1-19980 <$150
3x10-20 1-12843 <$150
3x50-100 1-1050 <$750/$850
1929 Small Size
5 Type 1 1-4034 <$75
10 Type 1 1-1796 <$75
20 Type 1 1-646 <$85
50 Type 1 1-294 <$175
100 Type 1 1-90 <$275
5 Type 2 1-7304 <$85
10 Type 2 1-3631 <$85
20 Type 2 1-1140 <$85
Total Issue $1,848,380
Out in 1935 $197,750
Large out 1935 $9,450
****
NB of D O Mills & Co, Sacramento
SEE Ch 2014
N Gold B of D O Mills & Co, Sacramento
****
2014 Sacramento
N GOLD B OF D O MILLS & CO, SACRAMENTO
Chartered 7/19/72
Liquidated 4/10/26
2nd title: NB of D O Mills & Co. 9/83
FIRST TITLE {{ 40 L }}
GOLD BANK NOTES <$VALUE
Original Series Gold Notes
4x5 1-1990 <$1500
3x10-20 1-1241<$3500/$5000
4x20 1-600 <$5000
50-100 1-604 <$35,000
500 1-60 <$250,000
SECOND TITLE {{ 44 L }}
Series 1875
3x10-20 1-3223<$3000/$3500
Brown Back
4x5 1-13500 <$350
3x10-20 1-9500 <$350
50-100 1-4460 <$2250/$2500
1882 Date Back
4x5 1-9115 <$300
3x10-20 1-11975 <$300
50-100 1-339 <$2000/$2250
1902 Date Back
3x10-20 1-14000 <$85
3x50-100 1-3494 <$450/$500
1902 Plain Back
4x5 1-30255 <$85
3x10-20 14001-29596 <$85
Total Issue $5,635,900
Out at close $408,850
****
3757 Napa
CARVER NB OF ST HELENA
Chartered 7/23/87
Liquidated 2/9/28
2nd title:FNB of St Helena 4/1/20
FIRST TITLE {{ 3 L }}
Brown Back <$VALUE
3x10-20 1-3025 <$1500
1902 Red Seal
3x10-20 1-500 <$1500
1902 Date Back
3x10-20 1-3700 <$850
1902 Plain Back
3x10-20 3701-5600 <$850
SECOND TITLE {{ 1 L }}
1902 Plain Back
3x10-20 1-4735 <$1500
Total Issue $693,000
Out at close $40,450
****
FNB of St Helena
SEE Ch 3757
Carver NB of St Helena
****
11601 Stanislaus
FNB OF SALIDA
{{ 3 L 2 S }}
Chartered 2/20
Liquidated 6/26/31
1902 Plain Back <$VALUE
3x10-20 1-3755 <$850
1929 Small Size
10 Type 1 1-365 <$600
20 Type 1 1-118 <$600
Total Issue $223,810
Out at close $22,120
Large out at close $2,040
****
5074 Monterey
FNB OF SALINAS
{{ 3 L }}
Chartered 1897
Liquidated 6/20/23
Brown Back <$VALUE
4x5 1-1050 <$1250
3x10-20 1-1230 <$1250
1882 Date Back
4x5 1-1822 <$1250
3x10-20 1-1437 <$1250
1902 Plain Back
3x10-20 1-1644 <$750
Total Issue $272,990
Out at close $21,500
****
13380 Monterey
SALINAS NB, SALINAS
{{ 24 S }}
Chartered 10/29
1929 Small Size <$VALUE
5 Type 1 1-4274 <$150
10 Type 1 1-2206 <$150
20 Type 1 1-418 <$165
5 Type 2 1-15050 <$175
10 Type 2 1-7608 <$175
20 Type 2 1-2340 <$175
Total Issue $508,870
Out in 1935 $180,200
****
10931 San Bernardino
AMERICAN NB OF SAN BERNARDINO
{{ 10 L 35 S }}
Organized 10/9/16
1902 Plain Back <$VALUE
3x10-20 1-20780 <$225
1929 Small Size
10 Type 1 1-4224 <$75
20 Type 1 1-1096 <$75
10 Type 2 1-4173 <$85
20 Type 2 1-1070 <$85
Total Issue $1,487,090
Out in 1935 $113,790
Large out 1935 $3,610
****
8618 San Bernardino
FARMERS NB OF SAN BERNARDINO
{{ 4 L }}
Chartered 3/07
Liquidated 3/15/24
1902 Red Seal <$VALUE
3x10-20 1-1550 <$1250
1902 Date Back
3x10-20 1-8200 <$600
1902 Plain Back
3x10-20 8201-18694 <$600
Total Issue $1,012,200
Out at close $87,650
****
3527 San Bernardino
FNB OF SAN BERNARDINO
{{ 2 L }}
Chartered 7/3/86
Receivership 1/29/95
Brown Back <$VALUE
4x5 1-575 <$2000
3x10-20 1-1098 <$2000
Total Issue $66,400
Out in 1916 $455
****

****
3818 San Bernardino
SAN BERNARDINO NB,
SAN BERNARDINO
{{ 9 L 15 S }}
Chartered 11/26/87
Receivership 6/21/32
Brown Back <$VALUE
4x5 1-1525 <$1000
3x10-20 1-5463 <$1000
1902 Red Seal
3x10-20 1-1000 <$1250
1902 Date Back
3x10-20 1-7900 <$400
1902 Plain Back
3x10-20 7901-26012 <$400
1929 Small Size
10 Type 1 1-1997 <$160
20 Type 1 1-555 <$175
Total Issue $1,840,670
Out at close $99,000
Large out at close $10,120
****
7418 San Diego
AMERICAN NB OF SAN DIEGO
{{ 4 L }}
Chartered 10/04
Liquidated 12/29/17
1902 Red Seal <$VALUE
4x5 1-2420 <$1000
3x10-20 1-1957 <$1000
1902 Date Back
4x5 1-15250 <$500
3x10-20 1-11200 <$500
1902 Plain Back
4x5 15251-19070 <$500
3x10-20 11201-13177 <$500
Total Issue $1,186,500
Out at close $200,000
****
3828 San Diego
CALIFORNIA NB OF
SAN DIEGO
{{ UNREPORTED }}
Chartered 12/29/87
Receivership 12/18/91
Brown Back <$VALUE
50-100 1-463 <$4000
Total Issue $69,450
Out in 1916 $100
****
3056 San Diego
CONSOLIDATED NB OF
SAN DIEGO
{{ 1 L }}
Chartered 9/22/83
Receivership 7/24/93
Brown Back <$VALUE
3x10-20 1-3215 <$2000
Total Issue $160,750
Out in 1916 $630
****
3050 San Diego
FNB OF SAN DIEGO
Chartered 1883
2nd title:FNT & Savings B of San Diego 8/31/27
FIRST TITLE **{{ 28 L }}**
Brown Back <$VALUE
4x5 1-3162 <$650
50-100 1-1047 <$2500
1902 Red Seal
4x5 1-3600 <$750
3x10-20 1-4650 <$750
1902 Date Back
4x5 1-14500 <$125
3x10-20 1-9800 <$125
1902 Plain Back
4x5 14501-45500 <$125
3x10-20 9801-105939 <$125
SECOND TITLE **{{ 47 S }}**
1929 Small Size
5 Type 1 1-4108 <$50
10 Type 1 1-10220 <$50
20 Type 1 1-4108 <$60
5 Type 2 1-17776 <$60
10 Type 2 1-6575 <$60
20 Type 2 1-1850 <$70
Total Issue $8,152,770
Out in 1935 $458,550
Large out 1935 $18,860
****
FNT & Savings B of San Diego
SEE Ch 3050
FNB of San Diego
****
9483 San Diego
MARINE NB OF SAN DIEGO
{{ 1 L }}
Chartered 7/09
Liquidated 3/18/16
1902 Date Back <$VALUE
4x5 1-1955 <$1500
3x10-20 1-1486 <$1500

Total Issue $113,400
Out in 1916 $15,555
****
4886 San Diego
MERCHANTS NB OF SAN DIEGO
{{ 12 L }}
Chartered 1893
Liquidated 12/18/22
Brown Back <$VALUE
4x5 1-6050 <$500
3x10-20 1-2500 <$500
1882 Date Back
4x5 1-3843 <$500
3x10-20 1-3122 <$500
1902 Date Back
4x5 1-5750 <$250
3x10-20 1-4600 <$250
3x50-100 1-644 <$850/$1000
1902 Plain Back
4x5 5751-17555 <$250
3x10-20 4601-11618 <$250
Total Issue $1,571,960
Out at close $245,700
****
6869 San Diego
NB OF COMMERCE, SAN DIEGO
{{ 1 L }}
Chartered 7/7/03
Liquidated 10/12/07
1902 Red Seal <$VALUE
3x10-20 1-6515 <$1500
Total Issue $325,750
Out in 1910 $23,625
****
3780 San Diego
SAN DIEGO NB, SAN DIEGO
{{ UNREPORTED }}
Chartered 8/23/87
Liquidated 11/7/88
Brown Back <$VALUE
50-100 1-154 <$4000
Total Issue $23,100
Out in 1910 $100
****
10435 San Diego
UNION NB OF SAN DIEGO
{{ 6 L }}
Chartered 8/13
Liquidated 3/17/27
1902 Date Back <$VALUE
3x10-20 1-7820 <$300
1902 Plain Back
3x10-20 7821-36235 <$300
Total Issue $1,811,750
Out at close $195,495
****
10391 San Diego
UNITED STATES NB OF
SAN DIEGO
{{ 9 L 13 S }}
Chartered 5/13
1902 Date Back <$VALUE
4x5 1-3750* <$250
3x10-20 1-2500** <$250
3x50-100 1-120 <$850/$1000
1902 Plain Back
4x5 4251-15600* <$250
3x10-20 2901-9926** <$250
* 3751-4250 not marked
** 2501-2900 not marked
1929 Small Size
10 Type 1 1-1232 <$100
20 Type 1 1-414 <$100
10 Type 2 1-3072 <$125
20 Type 2 1-820 <$125
Total Issue $1,009,020
Out in 1935 $101,390
Large out 1935 $2,790
****
10068 Los Angeles
FNB OF SAN DIMAS
{{ 2 L 2U + 12 S }}
Chartered 8/11
1902 Date Back <$VALUE
4x5 1-2250 <$1500
3x10-20 1-2070 <$1500
1902 Plain Back
4x5 2251-11745 <$1500
3x10-20 2071-8189 <$1500
1929 Small Size
5 Type 1 1-1604 <$275
10 Type 1 1-908 <$275
20 Type 1 1-272 <$275
5 Type 2 1-2946 <$300
10 Type 2 1-1674 <$300
20 Type 2 1-336 <$300
Total Issue $817,780
Out in 1935 $48,350
Large out 1935 $2,260
****

****
9575 Los Angeles
FNB OF SAN FERNANDO
{{ 4 L }}
Chartered 11/09
Liquidated 8/12/25
1902 Date Back <$VALUE
4x5 1-825* <$800
3x10-20 1-520** <$800
1902 Plain Back
4x5 1076-1730* <$800
3x10-20 721-1123** <$800
* 826-1075 not marked
** 521-720 not marked
Total Issue $90,750
Out at close $6,400
****
10273 Los Angeles
SAN FERNANDO NB,
SAN FERNANDO
{{ 2 L }}
Chartered 10/12
Liquidated 1/1/23
1902 Date Back <$VALUE
4x5 1-415 <$1500
3x10-20 1-334 <$1500
1902 Plain Back
4x5 416-810 <$1500
3x10-20 335-557 <$1500
Total Issue $44,050
Out at close $6,300
****
6426 San Francisco
AMERICAN NB OF
SAN FRANCISCO
{{ 36 L }}
Chartered 9/17/02
Liquidated 8/18/23
1902 Red Seal <$VALUE
4x5 1-39795 <$250
3x10-20 1-40082 <$250
1902 Date Back
4x5 1-41330 <$50
3x10-20 1-71168 <$65
3x50-100 1-5000 <$600/$700
1902 Plain Back
4x5 41331-77690 <$50
3x10-20 71169-106803 <$65
Total Issue $10,943,950
Out at close $1,538,895
****
Anglo California NB of
San Francisco
Anglo & London Paris NB of
San Francisco
SEE Ch 9174
London-Paris NB of
San Francisco
****
9655 San Francisco
B OF CALIFORNIA, N ASSOC,
SAN FRANCISCO
{{ 50+ L 50+ S }}
Chartered 2/10
1902 Date Back <$VALUE
4x5 1-409165 <$50
3x10-20 1-302334 <$60
3x50-100 1-8000 <$400/$450
1902 Plain Back
4x5 409166-675438 <$50
3x10-20 302335-437437 <$60
1929 Small Size
5 Type 1 1-93620 <$20
10 Type 1 1-32690 <$25
20 Type 1 1-11178 <$35
5 Type 2 1-188586 <$20
10 Type 2 1-53707 <$25
20 Type 2 1-18826 <$35
Total Issue $45,348,490
Out in 1935 $1,755,850
Large out 1935 $129,700
****
B of America NT & Savings
Assoc, San Francisco
SEE Ch 13044
B of Italy NT & Savings
Assoc, San Francisco
****
13044 San Francisco
B OF ITALY N T & SAVINGS
ASSOC, SAN FRANCISCO
Chartered 3/1/27
2nd title:B of America N T & Savings Assoc 11/1/30
FIRST TITLE **{{ 50+ L 50+ S }}**
1902 Plain Back <$VALUE
4x5 1-282343 <$60
4x10 1-94566 <$65
3x10-20 1-95212 <$65/$75
3x50-100 1-9081 <$400/$500
1929 Small Size
5 Type 1 1-131088 <$25
10 Type 1 1-57094 <$30
20 Type 1 1-24522 <$40
50 Type 1 1-5940 <$110
100 Type 1 1-2366 <$165

SECOND TITLE **{{ 50+ S }}**
1929 Small Size
5 Type 1 1-634826 <$15
10 Type 1 1-393722 <$20
20 Type 1 1-129054 <$30
50 Type 1 1-11178 <$85
100 Type 1 1-4572 <$135
5 Type 2 A1-A999996 <$20
and B1-B172602 <$30
10 Type 2 1-762420 <$20
20 Type 2 1-435444 <$30
50 Type 2 1-60308 <$175
100 Type 2 1-41112 <$200
Total Issue $123,536,720
Out in 1935 $38,673,070
Large out 1935 $147,120
****
13016 San Francisco
BROTHERHOOD NB OF
SAN FRANCISCO
Chartered 12/26
Liquidated 8/11/32
2nd title:City NB of San Francisco 5/15/29
FIRST TITLE **{{ 12 L }}**
1902 Plain Back <$VALUE
4x5 1-33062 <$200
SECOND TITLE **{{ 20 S }}**
1929 Small Size
10 Type 1 1-7248 <$60
20 Type 1 1-2192 <$65
Total Issue $1,359,160
Out at close $582,960
Large out at close $4,370
****
3592 San Francisco
CALIFORNIA NB OF
SAN FRANCISCO
{{ UNREPORTED }}
Chartered 11/23/86
Receivership 1/14/89
Brown Back <$VALUE
3x10-20 1-1136 <$2500
Total Issue $56,800
Out in 1916 $160
****
7713 San Francisco
CITIZENS NB OF
SAN FRANCISCO
{{ 3 L }}
Chartered 4/27/05
Liquidated 6/1/07
1902 Red Seal <$VALUE
4x5 1-4755 <$750
3x10-20 1-3226 <$750
50-100 1-150 <$7500/$8500
Total Issue $278,900
Out in 1910 $24,375
****
City NB of San Francisco
SEE Ch 13016
Brotherhood NB of
San Francisco
****
Crocker FNB of San Francisco
SEE Ch 1741
FN Gold B of San Francisco
****
Crocker NB of San Francisco
SEE Ch 3555
Crocker-Woolworth NB of
San Francisco
****
3555 San Francisco
CROCKER-WOOLWORTH NB OF
SAN FRANCISCO
Chartered 9/9/86
2nd title:Crocker NB 8/31/06
FIRST TITLE **{{ 13 L }}**
Brown Back <$VALUE
3x10-20 1-33588 <$250
50-100 1-1624 <$2250/$2500
SECOND TITLE **{{ 2U + 50+ L }}**
1902 Red Seal
4x5 1-20000 <$350
3x10-20 1-15000 <$350
50-100 1-1000 <$7500/$8500
1902 Date Back
4x5 1-123330 <$50
3x10-20 1-80668 <$60
50-100 1-1000 <$400/$450
3x50-100 1-9594 <$400/$450
1902 Plain Back
4x5 123331-251326 <$50
3x10-20 80669-154310 <$60
Total Issue $18,513,520
Out at close $1,891,800
Ch 1741 assumed circulation
****
FNB of San Francisco
SEE Ch 1741
FN Gold B of San Francisco
****

****
1741 San Francisco
FN GOLD B OF
SAN FRANCISCO
Chartered 11/30/70
2nd title: FNB of San Francisco 2/25/84
3rd title: Crocker FNB 5/31/34
FIRST TITLE **{{ 50+ L }}**
GOLD BANK NOTES <$VALUE
Original Series Gold Notes
4x5 1-8250 <$1350
4x10 1-4501 <$3500
4x20 1-2812 <$5000
50-100 1-2000 <$35,000
500 1-300 <$250,000
Series 1875 Gold Notes
4x20 1-900 <$6000
50-100 1-620 <$35,000
SECOND TITLE **{{ 50+ L }}**
Series 1875
4x5 1-250 <$2500
3x10-20 1-4599<$3000/$3500
50-100 1-4339 <$15,000
Brown Back
4x5 1-105150 <$150
3x10-20 1-78940 <$150/$200
50-100 1-1214 <$2000/$2250
1882 Date Back
4x5 1-17727 <$125
3x10-20 1-12964 <$125/$150
50-100 1-234 <$1750/$2000
1902 Date Back
4x5 1-146500 <$50
3x10-20 1-111400 <$60
1902 Plain Back
4x5 146501-181467 <$50
3x10-20 111401-135365 <$60
THIRD TITLE **{{ 50+ L 50+ S }}**
1902 Plain Back
4x5 1-241639 <$50
3x10-20 1-159064 <$60
3x50-100 1-7239 <$350/$400
1929 Small Size
5 Type 1 1-140280 <$15
10 Type 1 1-78366 <$20
20 Type 1 1-27668 <$30
50 Type 1 1-5358 <$85
100 Type 1 1-1656 <$135
5 Type 2 1-241816 <$15
10 Type 2 1-126393 <$20
20 Type 2 1-31450 <$30
Total Issue $52,267,590
Out in 1935 $5,043,840
Large out 1935 $277,795
Outstanding includes Ch 3555
****
6592 San Francisco
GERMANIA NB OF
SAN FRANCISCO
{{ 2 L }}
Chartered 1/26/03
Liquidated 8/1/07
1902 Red Seal <$VALUE
4x5 1-3745 <$1000
3x10-20 1-1969 <$1000
50-100 1-295 <$7500/$8500
Total Issue $217,600
Out in 1910 $15,840
****
9174 San Francisco
LONDON-PARIS NB OF
SAN FRANCISCO
Chartered 6/08
2nd title:Anglo & London Paris NB 3/17/09
3rd title:Anglo California NB 6/30/32
FIRST TITLE **{{ 9 L }}**
1902 Date Back <$VALUE
4x5 1-21140 <$125
3x10-20 1-15372 <$125
50-100 1-600 <$600/$700
SECOND TITLE **{{ 50+ L 50+ S }}**
1902 Date Back
4x5 1-190500* <$50
3x10-20 1-150000 <$60
50-100 1-4000 <$350/$400
3x50-100 1-11000<$350/$400
1902 Plain Back
4x5 210501-779461* <$50
3x10-20 150001-545820 <$60
* 190501-210500 not marked
1929 Small Size
5 Type 1 1-170672 <$15
10 Type 1 1-93758 <$20
20 Type 1 1-29424 <$30
THIRD TITLE **{{ 50+ S }}**
1929 Small Size
5 Type 1 1-63752 <$15
10 Type 1 1-47378 <$20
20 Type 1 1-25384 <$30
5 Type 2 1-674052 <$15
10 Type 2 1-379589 <$20
20 Type 2 1-62905 <$30

Total Issue $78,013,710
Out in 1935 $8,374,260
Large out 1935 $180,375
****
9683 San Francisco
MERCANTILE NB OF
SAN FRANCISCO
{{ 45 L }}
Chartered 3/10
Liquidated 7/3/20
1902 Date Back <$VALUE
4x5 1-137500 <$60
3x10-20 1-96000 <$65
50-100 1-4400 <$400/$500
1902 Plain Back
4x5 137501-204265 <$60
3x10-20 96001-132540 <$65
Total Issue $11,372,300
Out at close $1,868,800
****
8487 San Francisco
MERCHANTS NB OF
SAN FRANCISCO
{{ 2 L }}
Chartered 12/06
Liquidated 5/31/12
1902 Red Seal <$VALUE
4x5 1-8000 <$1000
3x10-20 1-6000 <$1000
1902 Date Back
4x5 1-13270 <$750
3x10-20 1-15492 <$750
Total Issue $1,500,000
Out at close $499,995
Ch 9882 assumed circulation
****
Merchants NB of San Francisco
SEE Ch 9882
Western Metropolis NB of
San Francisco
****
1994 San Francisco
N GOLD B & TC,
SAN FRANCISCO
{{ 17 L }}
Chartered 6/3/72
Liquidated 9/1/79
GOLD BANK NOTES <$VALUE
Original Series Gold Notes
4x5 1-4460 <$1500
3x10-20 1-4223<$3500/$5000
50-100 1-2856 <$35,000
500 1-250 <$250,000
Total Issue $853,750
Out in 1910 $9,545
****
7894 San Francisco
NB OF THE PACIFIC,
SAN FRANCISCO
{{ 3 L }}
Chartered 8/30/05
Liquidated 10/1/09
1902 Red Seal <$VALUE
4x5 1-8125 <$800
3x10-20 1-6575 <$800
50-100 1-190 <$7500/$8500
1902 Date Back
4x5 1-1315 <$500
3x10-20 1-2323 <$500
Total Issue $662,200
Out in 1910 $129,215
****
5105 San Francisco
NEVADA NB OF
SAN FRANCISCO
Chartered 1897
Liquidated 12/31/23
2nd title:Wells-Fargo Nevada NB of San Francisco 4/19/05
FIRST TITLE **{{ 36 L }}**
Brown Back <$VALUE
4x5 1-96000 <$165
3x10-20 1-85607 <$165/$200
50-100 1-3720 <$2000/$2250
SECOND TITLE **{{ 50+ L }}**
Brown Back
4x5 1-177500 <$150
4x10 1-26250 <$150
3x10-20 1-91000 <$150/$200
1882 Date Back
4x5 1-412500 <$125
4x10 1-315000 <$125
3x10-20 1-76000 <$125/$150
1882 Value Back
4x5 412501-536000 <$165
4x10 315001-423500 <$165
1902 Plain Back
4x5 1-478499 <$50
3x10-20 1-302241 <$60
Total Issue $72,050,380
Out at close $5,687,990
****

12579 San Francisco
PACIFIC NB OF
SAN FRANCISCO
{{ 40 L 50+ S }}
Chartered 9/24
1902 Plain Back <$VALUE
4x5 1-65000 <$75
3x10-20 1-44103 <$85
1929 Small Size
5 Type 1 1-39930 <$20
10 Type 1 1-22284 <$25
20 Type 1 1-5566 <$35
5 Type 2 1-28098 <$20
10 Type 2 1-13895 <$30
20 Type 2 1-1925 <$40
Total Issue $7,022,590
Out in 1935 $510,800
Large out 1935 $18,205

5096 San Francisco
SAN FRANCISCO NB,
SAN FRANCISCO
{{ 50+ L }}
Chartered 1897
Liquidated 8/1/10
Brown Back <$VALUE
4x5 1-26500 <$200
3x10-20 1-25660 <$200/$250
50-100 1-1980 <$2000/$2250
1882 Date Back
4x5 1-13778 <$200
3x10-20 1-7043 <$200/$250
50-100 1-713 <$1750/$2000
Total Issue $2,844,660
Out in 1910 $896,495

9141 San Francisco
SEABOARD NB OF
SAN FRANCISCO
{{ 15 L }}
Organized 5/22/08
Liquidated 10/4/20
1902 Date Back <$VALUE
4x5 1-20160 <$125
3x10-20 1-23781 <$125
3x50-100 1-1400 <$400/$500
Total Issue $1,942,250
Out at close $131,800

7691 San Francisco
UNITED STATES NB OF
SAN FRANCISCO
{{ 3 L }}
Chartered 4/1 5/05
Liquidated 12/31/08
1902 Red Seal <$VALUE
4x5 1-7250 <$850
3x10-20 1-5085 <$850
1902 Date Back
4x5 1-340 <$600
Total Issue $406,050
Out in 1910 $46,335

Wells-Fargo Nevada NB of
San Francisco
SEE Ch 5105
Nevada NB of San Francisco

9882 San Francisco
WESTERN METROPOLIS NB OF
SAN FRANCISCO
Chartered 10/10
Liquidated 3/14/23
2nd title: Merchants NB
6/1/12
FIRST TITLE {{ 5 L }}
1902 Date Back <$VALUE
4x5 1-22270 <$400
3x10-20 1-10526 <$400
3x50-100 1-1600 <$750/$850
SECOND TITLE {{ 36 L }}
1902 Date Back
4x5 1-47700* <$100
3x10-20 1-36680** <$100
3x50-100 1-5314 <$400/$450
1902 Plain Back
4x5 61701-82600* <$100
3x10-20 41681-54425**<$100
* 47701-61700 not marked
** 36681-41680 not marked
Total Issue $7,073,450
Out at close $937,750
Outstanding includes Ch 8487

5688 San Francisco
WESTERN NB OF
SAN FRANCISCO
{{ 26 L }}
Chartered 1/21/01
Liquidated 10/31/10
Brown Back <$VALUE
4x5 1-39050 <$250
3x10-20 1-25080 <$250
50-100 1-2000 <$2250/$2500
1882 Date Back
4x5 1-20155 <$225
3x10-20 1-12168 <$225
50-100 1-146 <$2250/$2500
Total Issue $3,368,400
Out at close $1,000,000

7997 Riverside
FNB OF SAN JACINTO
{{ 10 L 12 S }}
Chartered 12/05
1902 Red Seal <$VALUE
4x5 1-1025 <$1250
3x10-20 1-820 <$1250
1902 Date Back
4x5 1-5950 <$500
3x10-20 1-4320 <$500
1902 Plain Back
4x5 5951-15577 <$500
3x10-20 4321-10399 <$500
1929 Small Size
5 Type 1 1-1820 <$250
10 Type 1 1-880 <$250
20 Type 1 1-258 <$250
5 Type 2 1-802 <$275
10 Type 2 1-485 <$275
20 Type 2 1-110 <$275
Total Issue $1,042,410
Out in 1935 $26,930
Large out 1935 $2,340

11484 Fresno
FNB OF SAN JOAQUIN
{{ 5 L }}
Chartered 10/19
Liquidated 3/27/28
1902 Plain Back <$VALUE
4x5 1-9642 <$750
Total Issue $192,840
Out at close $21,000

2158 Santa Clara
FARMERS N GOLD B OF
SAN JOSE
Chartered 7/21/74
2nd title: FNB of San Jose
2/80
FIRST TITLE {{ 50 L }}
GOLD BANK NOTES <$VALUE
Original Series Gold Notes
4x5 1-2007 <$1350
3x10-20 1-2849<$3500/$5000
50-100 1-400 <$35,000
SECOND TITLE {{ 31 L 50+ S }}
Series 1875
3x10-20 1-3000<$3000/$3500
50-100 1-1540 <$15,000
Brown Back
50-100 1-3274 <$2250/$2500
1882 Date Back
4x5 1-2190 <$250
4x10 1-2086 <$250
50-100 1-1000 <$2000/$2250
3x50-100 1-1047
<$2000/$2250
1902 Date Back
3x10-20 1-3000 <$60
3x50-100 1-2960 <$400/$500
1902 Plain Back
3x10-20 3001-17120 <$60
3x50-100 2961-3788
<$400/$500
1929 Small Size
5 Type 1 1-1038 <$85
10 Type 1 1-5706 <$85
20 Type 1 1-2086 <$85
50 Type 1 1-674 <$150
100 Type 1 1-136 <$225
5 Type 2 1-25634 <$85
10 Type 2 1-12535 <$85
20 Type 2 1-3096 <$85
Total Issue $4,679,740
Out in 1935 $588,800
Large out 1935 $26,610

FNB of San Diego
SEE Ch 2158
Farmers N Gold B of San Jose

3715 Santa Clara
GARDEN CITY NB OF
SAN JOSE
{{ UNREPORTED }}
Chartered 6/3/87
Liquidated 7/1/93
Brown Back <$VALUE
3x10-20 1-1050 <$3000
Total Issue $52,500
Out in 1910 $480

13338 Santa Clara
SAN JOSE NB, SAN JOSE
{{ 3U + 36 S }}
Chartered 6/12/29
Liquidated 3/8/35
1929 Small Size <$VALUE
5 Type 1 1-2474 <$85
10 Type 1 1-1444 <$85
20 Type 1 1-738 <$85
50 Type 1 1-420 <$165
100 Type 1 1-212 <$225
5 Type 2 1-5902 <$100
10 Type 2 1-2930* <$100
20 Type 2 1-655 <$100
* 1311-1316 not issued
Total Issue $574,470
Out at close $384,050

13217 Alameda
FNB IN SAN LEANDRO
{{ 21 S }}
Chartered 6/28
1929 Small Size <$VALUE
5 Type 1 1-3842 <$135
10 Type 1 1-2090 <$135
20 Type 1 1-732 <$135
5 Type 2 1-1858 <$175
10 Type 2 1-990 <$175
20 Type 2 1-350 <$185
Total Issue $354,690
Out in 1935 $46,400

9800 Alameda
FNB OF SAN LEANDRO
{{ 2 L }}
Chartered 6/10
Liquidated 10/3/24
1902 Date Back <$VALUE
3x10-20 1-3300* <$850
1902 Plain Back
3x10-20 3551-8043* <$850
* 3301-3550 not marked
Total Issue $402,150
Out at close $48,595

12802 Alameda
SAN LEANDRO NB,
SAN LEANDRO
{{ 6 L }}
Chartered 8/25
Liquidated 5/12/27
1902 Plain Back <$VALUE
3x10-20 1-3554 <$600
Total Issue $177,700
Out at close $81,600

3826 San Luis Obispo
FNB OF SAN LUIS OBISPO
{{ 1 L }}
Chartered 12/24/87
Liquidated 8/27/92
Brown Back <$VALUE
3x10-20 1-1067 <$2500
Total Issue $53,350
Out in 1910 $270

7877 San Luis Obispo
UNION NB OF
SAN LUIS OBISPO
{{ 8 L }}
Chartered 8/05
Liquidated 9/6/22
1902 Red Seal <$VALUE
3x10-20 1-2640 <$1250
1902 Date Back
3x10-20 1-7500 <$500
1902 Plain Back
3x10-20 7501-14599 <$500
Total Issue $861,950
Out at close $94,895

13335 Los Angeles
SAN MARINO NB, SAN MARINO
{{ 3U + 8 S }}
Chartered 6/29 as Arcadia
NB of San Marino, under
which there was no issue.
Issuing title adopted
3/30/31.
Liquidated 8/1/35
1929 Small Size <$VALUE
5 Type 1 1-834 <$275
10 Type 1 1-514 <$275
20 Type 1 1-116 <$275
5 Type 2 1-3466 <$325
10 Type 2 1-2044 <$325
20 Type 2 1-528 <$325
Total Issue $118,110
Out in 1935 $45,600

9424 San Mateo
NB OF SAN MATEO
{{ 8 L 25 S }}
Chartered 6/09
1902 Date Back <$VALUE
4x5 1-2700 <$500
3x10-20 1-2120 <$500
1902 Plain Back
4x5 2701-11625 <$500
3x10-20 2121-8225 <$500
1929 Small Size
5 Type 1 1-1814 <$150
10 Type 1 1-1020 <$150
20 Type 1 1-260 <$150
5 Type 2 1-2260 <$185
10 Type 2 1-1333 <$185
20 Type 2 1-406 <$185
Total Issue $823,320
Out in 1935 $49,050
Large out 1935 $2,280

7057 Los Angeles
FNB OF SAN PEDRO
{{ 7 L }}
Chartered 12/03
Liquidated 1/24/29
1902 Red Seal <$VALUE
3x10-20 1-1975 <$1250
1902 Date Back
3x10-20 1-4000 <$600
1902 Plain Back
3x10-20 4001-12873 <$600
Total Issue $742,400
Out at close $41,600

12640 Marin
FNB IN SAN RAFAEL
{{ 8 S }}
Chartered 2/25
1929 Small Size <$VALUE
5 Type 1 1-1794 <$550
10 Type 1 1-1482 <$550
20 Type 1 1-304 <$550
5 Type 2 1-6636 <$600
10 Type 2 1-2976 <$600
20 Type 2 1-828 <$600
Total Issue $258,720
Out in 1935 $96,580

10177 Marin
MARIN COUNTY NB OF
SAN RAFAEL
{{ 7 L }}
Chartered 4/12
Liquidated 4/12/24
1902 Date Back <$VALUE
4x5 1-2550* <$1500
3x10-20 1-2040** <$1500
1902 Plain Back
4x5 2801-7595* <$1500
3x10-20 2201-5264** <$1500
* 2551-2800 not marked
** 2041-2200 not marked
Total Issue $415,100
Out at close $45,600

9308 Fresno
FNB OF SANGER
{{ 7 L }}
Chartered 1/09
Liquidated 2/3/23
1902 Date Back <$VALUE
50-100 1-180 <$1500
3x50-100 1-249 <$1500
Total Issue $89,250
Out at close $25,000

11869 Orange
AMERICAN NB OF SANTA ANA
{{ 5 L }}
Chartered 11/20
Liquidated 4/22/25
1902 Plain Back <$VALUE
3x10-20 1-11318 <$450
Total Issue $565,900
Out at close $107,300

9904 Orange
CALIFORNIA NB OF
SANTA ANA
{{ 6 L }}
Chartered 12/10
Liquidated 2/16/23
1902 Date Back <$VALUE
4x5 1-4915 <$450
3x10-20 1-3534 <$450
1902 Plain Back
4x5 4916-15010 <$450
3x10-20 3535-9508 <$450
Total Issue $775,600
Out at close $88,900

13200 Orange
COMMERCIAL NB OF
SANTA ANA
{{ 6 L 10 S }}
Chartered 4/28
1902 Plain Back <$VALUE
4x5 1-3030 <$500
1929 Small Size
5 Type 1 1-7086 <$200
5 Type 2 1-8898 <$200
10 Type 2 1-4943 <$200
Total Issue $367,100
Out in 1935 $100,000
Large out 1935 $290

7980 Orange
FARMERS & MERCHANTS NB OF
SANTA ANA
{{ 4 L }}
Chartered 11/05
Closed 3/10/19
1902 Red Seal <$VALUE
3x10-20 1-3412 <$1000
1902 Date Back
3x10-20 1-15500 <$500
1902 Plain Back
3x10-20 15501-19859 <$500
Total Issue $1,163,550
Out at close $199,995
Outstanding includes Ch 3520

3520 Orange
FNB OF SANTA ANA
{{ 46 L 50+ S }}
Chartered 1882
Brown Back <$VALUE
3x10-20 1-9945 <$700
1902 Red Seal
3x10-20 1-4000 <$850
1902 Date Back
3x10-20 1-20500 <$100
1902 Plain Back
3x10-20 20501-103220 <$100
1929 Small Size
10 Type 1 1-13660 <$40
20 Type 1 1-3734 <$50
10 Type 2 1-570 <$75
20 Type 2 1-260 <$75
Total Issue $7,124,830
Out in 1935 $262,970
Large out 1935 $23,630
Outstanding includes Ch 7980

FNB of Santa Barbara
SEE Ch 2104
FN Gold B of Santa Barbara

2104 Santa Barbara
FN GOLD B OF
SANTA BARBARA
Chartered 5/7/73
2nd title: FNB of
Santa Barbara 8/80
3rd title: FNT & Savings B
of Santa Barbara 6/21/27
FIRST TITLE {{ 17 L }}
GOLD BANK NOTES <$VALUE
Original Series Gold Notes
4x5 1-500 <$1750
3x10-20 1-800 <$3500/$5000
50-100 1-200 <$35,000
SECOND TITLE {{ 28 L }}
Series 1875
3x10-20 1-1184<$3000/$4000
50-100 1-374 <$15,000
Brown Back
4x5 1-3000 <$450
3x10-20 1-1849 <$500
50-100 1-917 <$2500
1882 Date Back
4x5 1-3925 <$400
3x10-20 1-2376 <$450
50-100 1-35 <$$2000/$2250
1902 Date Back
4x5 1-2500 <$150
3x10-20 1-2000 <$150
1902 Plain Back
4x5 2501-43196 <$150
3x10-20 2001-10660 <$150
THIRD TITLE {{ 8 L 50+ S }}
1902 Plain Back
4x5 1-19154 <$150
1929 Small Size
5 Type 1 1-31142 <$50
5 Type 2 1-82160 <$50
Total Issue $3,812,910
Out in 1935 $294,700
Large out 1935 $11,700

FNT & Savings B of
Santa Barbara
SEE Ch 2104
FN Gold B of Santa Barbara

2456 Santa Barbara
SANTA BARBARA COUNTY NB,
SANTA BARBARA
Chartered 2/21/80
2nd title:County NB & TC of
Santa Barbara 5/22/20
FIRST TITLE {{ 10 L }}
Series 1875 <$VALUE
3x10-20 1-1841<$3000/$3500
Brown Back
50-100 1-483 <$2500
1882 Date Back
50-100 1-800 <$2000/$2250
3x50-100 1-683<$2000/$2250
SECOND TITLE {{ 13 L 21 S }}
1902 Plain Back
3x50-100 1-2610 <$400/$500
1929 Small Size
5 Type 1 1-622 <$150
10 Type 1 1-312 <$150
50 Type 1 1-662 <$225
100 Type 1 1-184 <$275
5 Type 2 1-84 <$200
10 Type 2 1-250 <$200
Total Issue $1,457,050
Out in 1935 $237,150
Large out 1935 $11,600

County FNB of Santa Cruz
SEE Ch 9745
Santa Cruz County NB of
Santa Cruz

10571 Santa Cruz
FARMERS & MERCHANTS NB OF
SANTA CRUZ
{{ 14 S }}
Chartered 6/14
1929 Small Size <$VALUE
10 Type 1 1-1232 <$185
20 Type 1 1-420 <$200
10 Type 2 1-3851 <$200
20 Type 2 1-1210 <$200
Total Issue $187,030
Out in 1935 $93,050

8403 Santa Cruz
FNB OF SANTA CRUZ
{{ 5 L }}
Chartered 10/06
Liquidated 4/12/27
1902 Red Seal <$VALUE
4x5 1-2000 <$1000
3x10-20 1-1050 <$1000
50-100 1-550 <$7500/$8500
1902 Date Back
4x5 1-5850 <$500
3x10-20 1-3760 <$500
50-100 1-200 <$850/$1000
1902 Plain Back
4x5 5851-18215 <$500
3x10-20 3761-11911 <$500
Total Issue $1,164,850
Out at close $86,695

9745 Santa Cruz
SANTA CRUZ COUNTY NB OF
SANTA CRUZ
Chartered 5/10
2nd title:County FNB of
Santa Cruz 8/1/27
FIRST TITLE {{ 13 L }}
1902 Date Back <$VALUE
4x5 1-4125 <$300
3x10-20 1-4500 <$300
50-100 1-250 <$750/$850
3x50-100 1-160 <$750/$850
1902 Plain Back
4x5 4126-15202 <$300
3x10-20 4501-14537 <$300
SECOND TITLE {{ 7 L 18 S }}
1902 Plain Back
4x5 1-4263 <$300
3x10-20 1-3214 <$300
1929 Small Size
5 Type 1 1-5052 <$125
10 Type 1 1-2782 <$125
20 Type 1 1-802 <$125
5 Type 2 1-8896 <$150
10 Type 2 1-5271 <$150
20 Type 2 1-1490 <$150
Total Issue $1,896,060
Out in 1935 $150,000
Large out 1935 $4,050

****
7480 Santa Barbara
FNB OF SANTA MARIA
{{ 6 L }}
Chartered 11/04
Liquidated 2/21/28
1902 Red Seal <$VALUE
4x5 1-400 <$1500
3x10-20 1-320 <$1500
1902 Date Back
4x5 1-2250 <$600
3x10-20 1-3400 <$600
1902 Plain Back
4x5 2251-2900 <$600
3x10-20 3401-16515 <$600
Total Issue $907,750
Out at close $86,950
****
12787 Los Angeles
AMERICAN NB OF
SANTA MONICA
{{ 6 L 23 S }}
Chartered 7/25
1902 Plain Back <$VALUE
4x5 1-9987 <$600
1929 Small Size
5 Type 1 1-5132 <$150
10 Type 1 1-622 <$150
5 Type 2 1-11472 <$150
10 Type 2 1-2592 <$150
Total Issue $474,300
Out in 1935 $72,100
Large out 1935 $720
****
3845 Los Angeles
FNB OF SANTA MONICA
{{ 1 L }}
Chartered 2/16/88
Liquidated 6/17/93
Brown Back <$VALUE
3x10-20 1-425 <$2500
Total Issue $21,250
Out in 1910 $130
****
FNB of Santa Monica
SEE Ch 6945
Merchants NB of Santa Monica
****
6945 Los Angeles
MERCHANTS NB OF
SANTA MONICA
Chartered 9/03
Liquidated 4/3/28
2nd title:FNB of
Santa Monica 12/30/22
FIRST TITLE {{ 3 L }}
1902 Red Seal <$VALUE
4x5 1-2600 <$1500
3x10-20 1-1892 <$1500
1902 Date Back
4x5 1-3900 <$750
3x10-20 1-2680 <$750
1902 Plain Back
4x5 3901-9000 <$750
3x10-20 2681-5540 <$750
SECOND TITLE {{ 5 L }}
1902 Plain Back
3x10-20 1-6809 <$600
Total Issue $944,050
Out at close $85,245
****
4120 Ventura
FNB OF SANTA PAULA
Chartered 9/13/89
Liquidated 2/23/24
2nd title: FNB & TC of
Santa Paula 7/13/21
FIRST TITLE {{ 4 L }}
Brown Back <$VALUE
4x5 1-3010 <$1500
3x10-20 1-5251 <$1500
1902 Date Back
4x5 1-5200 <$650
3x10-20 1-3940 <$650
1902 Plain Back
4x5 5201-10200 <$650
3x10-20 3941-7080 <$650
SECOND TITLE {{ 2 L }}
1902 Plain Back
4x5 1-2375 <$650
3x10-20 1-1586 <$650
Total Issue $1,007,550
Out at close $71,900
****
12201 Sonoma
FNB OF SANTA ROSA
{{ 5 L }}
Chartered 5/22 as American
NB, under which there was
no issue. Issuing title
adopted 6/14/23.
Liquidated 2/6/29
1902 Plain Back <$VALUE
4x5 1-4300 <$750
3x10-20 1-2708 <$750
Total Issue $221,400
Out at close $35,500
****
3558 Sonoma
SANTA ROSA NB, SANTA ROSA
{{ 4 L }}
Chartered 9/15/86
Receivership 10/18/18
Brown Back <$VALUE
3x10-20 1-7372 <$1500
1902 Red Seal
50-100 1-1000 <$7500/$8500
1902 Date Back
50-100 1-1800 <$1000/$1250
3x50-100 1-742<$1000/$1250
Total Issue $974,100
Out at close $149,000
****
12453 Marin
FNB OF SAUSALITO
{{ 1 L }}
Chartered 10/23
Liquidated 3/15/27
1902 Plain Back <$VALUE
4x5 1-3900 <$3500
3x10-20 1-1664 <$3500
Total Issue $161,200
Out at close $46,400
****
9787 Humboldt
FNB OF SCOTIA
{{ 1 L 13 S }}
Chartered 6/10
1902 Date Back <$VALUE
4x5 1-800 <$1500
4x10 1-800 <$1500
1902 Plain Back
4x5 801-8989 <$1500
4x10 801-7001 <$1500
1929 Small Size
5 Type 1 1-3198 <$250
10 Type 1 1-1830 <$250
5 Type 2 1-3884 <$275
10 Type 2 1-2155 <$275
Total Issue $706,530
Out in 1935 $36,810
Large out 1935 $1,730
****
9648 Sonoma
FNB OF SEBASTOPOL
{{ 0 L 3 S }}
Chartered 1/10
Liquidated 12/27/33
1902 Date Back <$VALUE
4x5 1-2075 <$1500
3x10-20 1-1740 <$1500
1902 Plain Back
4x5 2076-6290 <$1500
3x10-20 1741-4152 <$1500
1929 Small Size
5 Type 1 1-933 <$450
10 Type 1 1-526 <$450
20 Type 1 1-144 <$500
Total Issue $410,230
Out at close $24,200
Large out at close $1,200
****
11161 Sonoma
SEBASTOPOL NB, SEBASTOPOL
{{ 5 L 10 S }}
Chartered 3/18
1902 Plain Back <$VALUE
3x10-20 1-8020 <$650
1929 Small Size
10 Type 1 1-2070 <$250
20 Type 1 1-514 <$250
10 Type 2 1-2522 <$275
20 Type 2 1-803 <$275
Total issue $628,160
Out in 1935 $67,450
Large out 1935 $2,230
****
10462 Imperial
FNB OF SEELEY
{{ UNREPORTED }}
Organized 9/5/13
Receivership 1/30/22
1902 Date Back <$VALUE
3x10-20 1-500 <$2500
1902 Plain Back
3x10-20 501-749 <$2500
Total Issue $37,450
Out at close $6,250
****
5395 Fresno
FNB OF SELMA
{{ 4 L }}
Chartered 6/4/00
Liquidated 2/28/28
Brown Back <$VALUE
50-100 1-582 <$3000
1882 Date Back
50-100 1-440 <$2500
3x50-100 1-334 <$2500
1902 Plain Back
3x10-20 1-4465 <$1000
Total Issue $460,050
Out at close $43,100
****
10293 Fresno
SELMA NB, SELMA
{{ UNREPORTED }}
Chartered 12/12
Liquidated 2/9/22
1902 Date Back <$VALUE
3x10-20 1-1060 <$2500
1902 Plain Back
3x10-20 1061-3747 <$2500
Total Issue $187,350
Out at close $47,400
****
8707 Los Angeles
FNB OF SIERRA MADRE
{{ 1 L }}
Chartered 5/07
Liquidated 11/4/22
1902 Red Seal <$VALUE
4x5 1-650 <$3000
3x10-20 1-520 <$3000
1902 Date Back
4x5 1-1825 <$2000
3x10-20 1-1240 <$2000
1902 Plain Back
4x5 1826-4010 <$2000
3x10-20 1241-2488 <$2000
Total Issue $243,600
Out at close $18,400
****
10259 Sonoma
FNB OF SONOMA
{{ 1 L }}
Chartered 9/12
Liquidated 1/27/23
1902 Date Back <$VALUE
4x5 1-1015 <$2000
3x10-20 1-814 <$2000
1902 Plain Back
4x5 1016-2430 <$2000
3x10-20 815-1661 <$2000
Total Issue $131,650
Out at close $20,000
****
7202 Tuolumne
FNB OF SONORA
{{ 15 L 14 S }}
Chartered 4/6/04
Liquidated 12/19/32
1902 Red Seal <$VALUE
4x5 1-2000 <$1000
3x10-20 1-1750 <$1000
1902 Date Back
4x5 1-6650 <$375
3x10-20 1-5320 <$375
1902 Plain Back
4x5 6651-32195 <$375
3x10-20 5321-21432 <$375
1929 Small Size
5 Type 1 1-4567 <$225
10 Type 1 1-2086 <$225
20 Type 1 1-571 <$225
Total Issue $2,173,690
Out at close $123,780
Large out at close $10,700
Outstanding includes Ch 10461
****
10461 Tuolumne
SONORA NB, SONORA
{{ UNREPORTED }}
Chartered 11/18/13
Liquidated 6/4/17
1902 Date Back <$VALUE
4x5 1-1580 <$2000
3x10-20 1-1268 <$2000
1902 Plain Back
4x5 1581-2775 <$2000
3x10-20 1269-2212 <$2000
Total Issue $166,100
Out at close $44,550
Ch 7202 assumed circulation
****
12797 Los Angeles
FNB IN SOUTH PASADENA
{{ 9 L }}
Chartered 7/25
Liquidated 1/16/29
1902 Plain Back <$VALUE
4x5 1-5517 <$600
3x10-20 1-1890 <$600
Total Issue $185,940
Out at close $78,290
****
8544 Los Angeles
FNB OF SOUTH PASADENA
{{ UNREPORTED }}
Chartered 2/07
Liquidated 7/7/22
1902 Red Seal <$VALUE
4x5 1-725 <$2000
3x10-20 1-600 <$2000
1902 Date Back
4x5 1-1925 <$1500
3x10-20 1-1390 <$1500
1902 Plain Back
4x5 1926-4150 <$1500
3x10-20 1391-2743 <$1500
Total Issue $264,650
Out at close $20,600
****
12364 San Mateo
CITIZENS NB OF
SOUTH SAN FRANCISCO
{{ UNREPORTED }}
Chartered 4/23
Liquidated 3/14/27
1902 Plain Back <$VALUE
4x5 1-4990 <$2500
Total Issue $99,800
Out at close $21,000
****
2077 San Joaquin
FN GOLD B OF STOCKTON
{{ 42 L }}
Chartered 1/27/73
Liquidated 1/14/79
GOLD BANK NOTES <$VALUE
Original Series Gold Notes
4x5 1-1000 <$1500
3x10-20 1-5000<$3500/$5000
50-100 1-867 <$35,000
Series 1875 Gold Notes
3x10-20 1-293 <$4000/$6000
Total Issue $414,700
Out in 1910 $10,125
****
2412 San Joaquin
FNB OF STOCKTON
{{ 8 L 10 S }}
Chartered 2/20/79
Series 1875 <$VALUE
3x10-20 1-6306<$3000/$3500
50-100 1-2592 <$15,000
Brown Back
3x10-20 1-1761 <$1250
50-100 1-1113 <$3000
1882 Date Back
3x10-20 1-4300 <$1000
50-100 1-200 <$2500
3x50-100 1-73 <$2500
1882 Value Back
3x10-20 3201-4893 <$1250
1902 Plain Back
3x10-20 1-6198 <$600
3x50-100 1-362<$1000/$1250
1929 Small Size
10 Type 1 1-885 <$350
20 Type 1 1-323 <$350
50 Type 1 1-145 <$500
100 Type 1 1-46 <$650
Total Issue $1,815,360
Out in 1935 $78,600
Large out 1935 $7,350
****
10817 San Joaquin
SAN JOAQUIN VALLEY NB OF
STOCKTON
{{ 7 L }}
Chartered 1/16
Liquidated 1/24/18
1902 Plain Back <$VALUE
4x5 1-11355 <$650
3x10-20 1-9382 <$650
3x50-100 1-600<$1250/$1500
Total Issue $846,200
Out at close $469,650
****
2794 San Joaquin
STOCKTON NB, STOCKTON
{{ 1 L }}
Chartered 1882
Liquidated 10/1/83
Brown Back <$VALUE
4x5 1-750 <$3500
3x10-20 1-999 <$3500
50-100 1-167 <$5000
Total Issue $90,000
Out in 1910 $460
****
11684 Solano
B OF SUISUN, N ASSOC,
SUISUN
{{ 7 S }}
Chartered 4/20
1929 Small Size <$VALUE
10 Type 1 1-1232 <$350
20 Type 1 1-416 <$375
10 Type 2 1-4442 <$375
20 Type 2 1-1015 <$375
Total Issue $188,560
Out in 1935 $100,000
****
10149 Solano
FNB OF SUISUN
{{ 2 L }}
Chartered 2/12
Liquidated 12/9/27
1902 Date Back <$VALUE
4x5 1-3300 <$1000
3x10-20 1-3140 <$1000
1902 Plain Back
4x5 3301-15450 <$1000
3x10-20 3141-10488 <$1000
Total Issue $833,400
Out at close $57,450
****
10088 Kern
FNB OF TAFT
{{ UNREPORTED }}
Chartered 9/11
Liquidated 1/15/16
1902 Date Back <$VALUE
3x10-20 1-1600 <$2500
1902 Plain Back
3x10-20 1601-1648 <$2500
Total Issue $82,400
Out in 1916 $6,960
****
9889 Tulare
FNB OF TERRA BELLA
{{ 3 L 3 S }}
Organized 9/28/10
Receivership 5/5/31
1902 Date Back <$VALUE
4x5 1-1500 <$1500
4x10 1-1425 <$1500
1902 Plain Back
4x5 1501-7209 <$1500
3x10-20 1426-5641 <$1500
1929 Small Size
10 Type 1 1-708 <$750
20 Type 1 1-314 <$750
Total Issue $409,900
Out at close $24,580
Large out at close $2,480
****
10396 Los Angeles
FNB OF TORRANCE
{{ 6 L 8 S }}
Chartered 5/13
Liquidated 8/6/34
1902 Date Back <$VALUE
3x10-20 1-1150 <$1000
1902 Plain Back
3x10-20 1151-9933 <$1000
1929 Small Size
10 Type 1 1-1402 <$350
20 Type 1 1-400 <$350
10 Type 2 1-592 <$400
20 Type 2 1-75 <$400
Total Issue $636,190
Out at close $48,030
Large out 1935 $1,670
Ch 14202 assumed circulation
****
14202 Los Angeles
TORRANCE NB, TORRANCE
{{ 1 S }}
Chartered 6/34
1929 Small Size <$VALUE
5 Type 2 1-1570 <$1250
10 Type 2 1-561 <$1250
20 Type 2 1-252 <$1250
Total Issue $18,500
Out in 1935 $50,000
Small out 1935 $48,330
Outstanding includes Ch 10396
****
11433 Fresno
FNB OF TRANQUILITY
{{ 3 L 0 S }}
Organized 7/15/19
Receivership 2/27/30
1902 Plain Back <$VALUE
3x10-20 1-8043 <$1500
1929 Small Size
10 Type 1 1-401 <$1250
20 Type 1 1-53 <$1250
Total Issue $432,570
Out at close $50,000
Large out at close $19,580
****
10412 Los Angeles
FNB OF TROPICO
Organized 6/13/13
Liquidated 12/17/34
2nd title:Glendale NB,
Glendale 1/17/19
3rd title:FNB in Glendale,
11/14/22
FIRST TITLE {{ 3 L }}
1902 Date Back <$VALUE
3x10-20 1-500 <$1500
SECOND TITLE {{ 1 L }}
1902 Plain Back
3x10-20 1-295 <$1500
THIRD TITLE {{ 1 L 1 S }}
1902 Plain Back
3x10-20 1-552 <$1500
1929 Small Size
10 Type 1 1-180 <$1250
20 Type 1 1-42 <$1250
Total Issue $83,190
Out at close $5,040
Large out at close $360
****
8626 Tulare
FNB OF TULARE
{{ 6 L }}
Chartered 4/07
Liquidated 5/16/28
1902 Red Seal <$VALUE
4x5 1-500 <$1250
3x10-20 1-200 <$1250
50-100 1-75 <$7500/$8500
1902 Date Back
4x5 1-5550 <$650
3x10-20 1-3480 <$650
3x50-100 1-220<$1000/$1250
1902 Plain Back
4x5 5551-15445 <$650
3x10-20 3481-9390 <$650
Total Issue $864,650
Out at close $47,350
****
10201 Tulare
NB OF TULARE
{{ UNREPORTED }}
Chartered 5/12
Liquidated 6/30/22
1902 Date Back <$VALUE
4x5 1-2250 <$1500
3x10-20 1-2000 <$1500
1902 Plain Back
4x5 2251-6260 <$1500
3x10-20 2001-4252 <$1500
Total Issue $337,800
Out at close $46,100
****
7738 Stanislaus
FNB OF TURLOCK
{{ 1 L }}
Chartered 5/13/05
Liquidated 3/19/07
1902 Red Seal <$VALUE
3x10-20 1-677 <$2500
Total Issue $33,850
Out in 1910 $2,880
****
10134 Orange
FNB OF TUSTIN
{{ 3 L 3U + 11 S }}
Chartered 1/12
1902 Date Back <$VALUE
3x10-20 1-600* <$850
1902 Plain Back
3x10-20 1201-10023* <$850
* 601-1200 not marked
1929 Small Size
10 Type 1 1-1354 <$250
20 Type 1 1-380 <$250
5 Type 2 1-5340 <$250
Total Issue $654,690
Out in 1935 $48,690
Large out 1935 $1,270
****
10977 Mendocino
FNB OF UKIAH
{{ 7 L 2 S }}
Chartered 4/17
Liquidated 9/23/31
1902 Plain Back <$VALUE
4x5 1-7870 <$600
3x10-20 1-5415 <$600
1929 Small Size
5 Type 1 1-1009 <$600
10 Type 1 1-551 <$600
20 Type 1 1-154 <$600
Total issue $509,960
Out at close $47,480
Large out at close $4,160
****
9570 San Bernardino
COMMERCIAL NB OF UPLAND
{{ 4 L }}
Chartered 10/09
Liquidated 12/12/27
1902 Date Back <$VALUE
4x5 1-1800 <$650
3x10-20 1-1400 <$650
1902 Plain Back
4x5 1801-8840 <$650
3x10-20 1401-5912 <$650
Total Issue $472,400
Out at close $32,050
****

****
8266 San Bernardino
FNB OF UPLAND
{{ 5 L 12 S }}
Chartered 6/06
1902 Red Seal <$VALUE
3x10-20 1-400 <$1250
1902 Date Back
3x10-20 1-1240 <$600
1902 Plain Back
3x10-20 1241-8381 <$600
1929 Small Size
5 Type 1 1-1464 <$275
10 Type 1 1-1012 <$275
20 Type 1 1-286 <$275
5 Type 2 1-2216 <$300
10 Type 2 1-1367 <$300
20 Type 2 1-444 <$300
Total Issue $611,640
Out in 1935 $50,000
Large out 1935 $1,620
****
9795 Solano
FNB OF VACAVILLE
{{ 6 L 7 S }}
Chartered 6/10
Liquidated 11/22/32
1902 Date Back <$VALUE
3x10-20 1-3000* <$750
1902 Plain Back
3x10-20 3251-11726* <$750
* 3001-3250 not marked
1929 Small Size
10 Type 1 1-1116 <$400
20 Type 1 1-322 <$400
Total Issue $691,900
Out at close $45,435
Large out at close $2,065
****
9573 Solano
FNB OF VALLEJO
{{ 8 L }}
Chartered 11/09
Liquidated 12/23/25
1902 Date Back <$VALUE
4x5 1-7750 <$400
3x10-20 1-5880 <$400
1902 Plain Back
4x5 7751-20630 <$400
3x10-20 5881-14222 <$400
Total Issue $1,123,700
Out at close $87,300
****
13368 Solano
MECHANICS & MERCHANTS NB OF VALLEJO
{{ 21 S }}
Chartered 8/29
1929 Small Size <$VALUE
5 Type 1 1-2410 <$150
10 Type 1 1-1382 <$150
20 Type 1 1-352 <$175
5 Type 2 1-6872 <$200
10 Type 2 1-3659 <$200
20 Type 2 1-1188 <$200
Total Issue $292,170
Out in 1935 $83,800
****
11206 Solano
VALLEJO COMMERCIAL NB, VALLEJO
{{ 8 L }}
Chartered 7/18
Liquidated 5/18/34
1902 Plain Back <$VALUE
4x5 1-16425 <$400
3x10-20 1-10718 <$400
Total issue $864,400
Out at close $3,285
****
10168 Los Angeles
FNB OF VAN NUYS
{{ UNREPORTED }}
Chartered 3/12
Liquidated 11/10/21
1902 Date Back <$VALUE
4x5 1-2580 <$2500
3x10-20 1-1373 <$2500
3x50-100 1-107 <$3500
1902 Plain Back
4x5 2581-9500 <$2500
3x10-20 1374-5486 <$2500
Total Issue $491,050
Out at close $84,900
****

****
10233 Los Angeles
FNB OF VENICE
{{ 1 L 2 S }}
Organized 1/3/12
Receivership 12/23/31
1902 Date Back <$VALUE
3x10-20 1-1110 <$2500
1902 Plain Back
3x10-20 1111-3489 <$2500
1929 Small Size
10 Type 1 1-287 <$1000
20 Type 1 1-67 <$1000
Total Issue $199,710
Out at close $15,000
Large out at close $1,600
****
7210 Ventura
FNB OF VENTURA
{{ 23 L 3 S }}
Chartered 4/04
Liquidated 6/9/31
1902 Red Seal <$VALUE
4x5 1-3060 <$1000
3x10-20 1-2460 <$1000
1902 Date Back
4x5 1-10600 <$275
3x10-20 1-8080 <$275
1902 Plain Back
4x5 10601-41120 <$275
3x10-20 8081-27254 <$275
1929 Small Size
5 Type 1 1-1933 <$400
10 Type 1 1-917 <$400
20 Type 1 1-285 <$450
Total Issue $2,516,510
Out at close $57,760
Large out at close $14,480
****
9685 Ventura
NB OF VENTURA
{{ 8 L }}
Chartered 3/10
Liquidated 3/5/18
1902 Date Back <$VALUE
4x5 1-12250 <$350
3x10-20 1-9800 <$350
1902 Plain Back
4x5 12251-16960 <$350
3x10-20 9801-12765 <$350
Total Issue $977,450
Out at close $192,000
****
12996 Ventura
UNION NB OF VENTURA
{{ 5 L 40 S }}
Chartered 10/26
1902 Plain Back <$VALUE
3x10-20 1-6145 <$400
1929 Small Size
10 Type 1 1-5856 <$75
20 Type 1 1-1508 <$75
10 Type 2 1-7202 <$85
20 Type 2 1-2348 <$85
Total Issue $958,550
Out in 1935 $171,000
Large out 1935 $1,555
****
11005 San Bernardino
FNB OF VICTORVILLE
{{ 2 L 3 S }}
Organized 5/1/17
Receivership 12/21/31
1902 Plain Back <$VALUE
3x10-20 1-4691 <$1250
1929 Small Size
10 Type 1 1-469 <$600
20 Type 1 1-119 <$600
Total Issue $276,970
Out at close $24,640
Large out at close $2,150
****
7063 Tulare
FNB OF VISALIA
{{ 1 L }}
Chartered 12/03
Liquidated 6/30/22
1902 Red Seal <$VALUE
4x5 1-900 <$2000
3x10-20 1-860 <$2000
50-100 1-120 <$7500/$8500
1902 Date Back
4x5 1-3525 <$1250
3x10-20 1-2300 <$1250
50-100 1-100 <$2000
3x50-100 1-412 <$2000
1902 Plain Back
4x5 3526-7235 <$1250
3x10-20 2301-4186 <$1250
Total Issue $551,000
Out at close $97,000
****

****
9173 Tulare
NB OF VISALIA
{{ 13 L }}
Chartered 6/08
Liquidated 6/4/21
1902 Date Back <$VALUE
4x5 1-16500 <$350
3x10-20 1-11400 <$350
1902 Plain Back
4x5 16501-27250 <$350
3x10-20 11401-17400 <$350
Total Issue $1,415,000
Out at close $152,600
****
12678 Tulare
NEW FNB IN VISALIA
{{ 2 L }}
Chartered 4/25
Liquidated 1/8/29
1902 Plain Back <$VALUE
3x10-20 1-4714 <$1250
Total Issue $235,700
Out at close $47,700
****
10281 Contra Costa
FNB OF WALNUT CREEK
{{ 3 L }}
Chartered 10/12
Liquidated 8/3/22
1902 Date Back <$VALUE
4x5 1-1250 <$1500
3x10-20 1-1000 <$1500
1902 Plain Back
4x5 1251-3150 <$1500
3x10-20 1001-2071 <$1500
Total Issue $166,550
Out at close $24,300
****
12572 Los Angeles
WALNUT PARK NB, WALNUT PARK
{{ 3 S }}
Organized 8/6/24
Receivership 1/11/32
1929 Small Size <$VALUE
5 Type 1 1-1316 <$850
10 Type 1 1-658 <$850
20 Type 1 1-156 <$850
Total Issue $97,680
Out at close $48,620
****
9621 Santa Cruz
PAJARO VALLEY NB OF WATSONVILLE
{{ 5 L 10 S }}
Chartered 12/09
1902 Date Back <$VALUE
4x5 1-2225 <$850
3x10-20 1-1740 <$850
1902 Plain Back
4x5 2226-8565 <$850
3x10-20 1741-6879 <$850
1929 Small Size
5 Type 1 1-2826 <$375
10 Type 1 1-1516 <$375
20 Type 1 1-390 <$400
5 Type 2 1-5698 <$400
10 Type 2 1-2935 <$400
20 Type 2 1-785 <$400
Total Issue $811,330
Out in 1935 $82,400
Large out 1935 $2,250
****
9873 Siskiyou
FNB OF WEED
{{ 8 L U + 28 S }}
Chartered 10/10
1902 Date Back <$VALUE
4x5 1-1550 <$1000
3x10-20 1-1190 <$1000
1902 Plain Back
4x5 1551-6600 <$1000
3x10-20 1191-4159 <$1000
1929 Small Size
5 Type 1 1-1202 <$300
10 Type 1 1-808 <$300
20 Type 1 1-234 <$300
5 Type 2 1-2788 <$300
10 Type 2 1-1601 <$300
20 Type 2 1-456 <$300
Total Issue $491,640
Out in 1935 $47,950
Large out 1935 $1,370
****

****
5588 Los Angeles
FNB OF WHITTIER
Chartered 10/2/00
Liquidated 2/11/29
2nd title:FNT & Savings B of Whittier 5/16/27
FIRST TITLE {{ 12 L }}
Brown Back <$VALUE
4x5 1-2190 <$750
3x10-20 1-1814 <$750
1882 Date Back
4x5 1-8400 <$750
3x10-20 1-5820 <$750
1882 Value Back
4x5 8401-13800 <$750
3x10-20 5821-8540 <$750
1902 Plain Back
4x5 1-11273 <$400
3x10-20 1-7156 <$400
SECOND TITLE {{ 3 L }}
1902 Plain Back
4x5 1-3065 <$500
4x10 1-563 <$500
3x10-20 1-764 <$500
Total Issue $1,542,780
Out at close $96,250
****
FNT & Savings B of Whittier
SEE Ch 5588
FNB of Whittier
****
7999 Los Angeles
WHITTIER NB, WHITTIER
Chartered 12/05
2nd title: Whittier NT & Savings B 6/30/30
FIRST TITLE {{ 11 L 13 S }}
1902 Red Seal <$VALUE
4x5 1-1730 <$1000
3x10-20 1-1388 <$1000
1902 Date Back
4x5 1-9350 <$350
3x10-20 1-6260 <$350
1902 Plain Back
4x5 9351-27825 <$350
3x10-20 6261-18592 <$350
1929 Small Size
5 Type 1 1-1532 <$150
10 Type 1 1-780 <$150
20 Type 1 1-262 <$165
SECOND TITLE {{ U + 20 S }}
1929 Small Size
5 Type 1 1-4268 <$125
10 Type 1 1-3214 <$125
20 Type 1 1-800 <$125
5 Type 2 1-12648 <$150
10 Type 2 1-1743 <$150
20 Type 2 1-765 <$150
Total Issue $2,227,150
Out in 1935 $150,835
Large out 1935 $4,835
****
Whittier NT & Savings B
SEE Ch 7999
Whittier NB, Whittier
****
11566 Mendocino
FNB OF WILLITS
{{ 4 L 1 S }}
Chartered 12/19
Liquidated 6/5/31
1902 Plain Back <$VALUE
3x10-20 1-4037 <$750
1929 Small Size
10 Type 1 1-699 <$750
20 Type 1 1-196 <$750
Total Issue $267,310
Out at close $41,600
Large out at close $4,480
****
9713 Glenn
FNB OF WILLOWS
{{ 5 L 10 S }}
Chartered 3/10
1902 Date Back <$VALUE
4x5 1-3400 <$650
3x10-20 1-2900 <$650
1902 Plain Back
4x5 3401-16885 <$650
3x10-20 2901-11672 <$650
1929 Small Size
5 Type 1 1-2990 <$300
10 Type 1 1-1550 <$300
20 Type 1 1-400 <$300
5 Type 2 1-3916 <$300
10 Type 2 1-2220 <$300
20 Type 2 1-648 <$300
Total Issue $1,206,740
Out in 1935 $74,000
Large out 1935 $2,420
****

****
9515 Los Angeles
FNB OF WILMINGTON
{{ 6 L }}
Chartered 8/09
Liquidated 2/23/24
1902 Date Back <$VALUE
4x5 1-2100 <$600
3x10-20 1-1600 <$600
1902 Plain Back
4x5 2101-6120 <$600
3x10-20 1601-4346 <$600
Total Issue $339,700
Out at close $49,300
****
10133 Yolo
FNB OF WINTERS
{{ 5 L }}
Chartered 1/12
Liquidated 3/15/27
1902 Date Back <$VALUE
4x5 1-3900 <$500
3x10-20 1-3040 <$500
1902 Plain Back
4x5 3901-15105 <$500
3x10-20 3041-9737 <$500
Total Issue $788,950
Out at close $67,100
****
13312 Yolo
WINTERS NB, WINTERS
{{ 5U + 7 S }}
Chartered 4/29
1929 Small Size <$VALUE
5 Type 1 1-1358 <$250
10 Type 1 1-774 <$250
20 Type 1 1-262 <$275
5 Type 2 1-2282 <$275
10 Type 2 1-1770 <$275
20 Type 2 1-540 <$300
Total Issue $158,530
Out in 1935 $43,700
****
10309 Tulare
FNB OF WOODLAKE
{{ U + 0 L 0 S }}
Organized 12/7/12
Receivership 12/2/32
1902 Date Back <$VALUE
3x10-20 1-500 <$2000
1902 Plain Back
3x10-20 501-1444 <$2000
1929 Small Size
10 Type 1 1-186 <$1250
20 Type 1 1-31 <$1250
Total Issue $87,080
Out at close $7,000
Large out at close $460
****
10878 Yolo
B OF WOODLAND N ASSOCIATION, WOODLAND
{{ 31 S }}
Chartered 7/16
1929 Small Size <$VALUE
5 Type 1 1-8738 <$135
10 Type 1 1-4554 <$135
20 Type 1 1-1210 <$150
5 Type 2 1-13418 <$165
10 Type 2 1-8622 <$165
20 Type 2 1-1584 <$175
Total Issue $865,570
Out in 1935 $200,000
****
9493 Yolo
FNB OF WOODLAND
{{ 5 L }}
Chartered 7/09
Liquidated 8/3/22
1902 Date Back <$VALUE
4x5 1-6850 <$600
3x10-20 1-5340 <$600
1902 Plain Back
4x5 6851-18310 <$600
3x10-20 5341-11974 <$600
Total Issue $964,900
Out at close $124,995
****
13340 Yreka
FNB IN YREKA
{{ 3U + 8 S }}
Chartered 6/29
1929 Small Size <$VALUE
5 Type 1 1-1574 <$275
10 Type 1 1-884 <$275
20 Type 1 1-272 <$300
5 Type 2 1-3976 <$300
10 Type 2 1-2124 <$300
20 Type 2 1-420 <$325
Total Issue $182,420
Out in 1935 $48,750
****

****
10731 Yreka
FNB OF YREKA
{{ 5 L }}
Chartered 4/15
Liquidated 4/24/28
1902 Plain Back <$VALUE
3x10-20 1-6819 <$650
Total Issue $340,950
Out at close $46,750
****
10299 Sutter
FNB OF YUBA CITY
{{ 2 L }}
Chartered 12/12
Liquidated 4/3/28
1902 Date Back <$VALUE
3x10-20 1-1440 <$1500
1902 Plain Back
3x10-20 1441-4948 <$1500
Total Issue $247,400
Out at close $17,900
****

CONDITION affects Value. The Values shown are for notes in FINE condition.

COLORADO

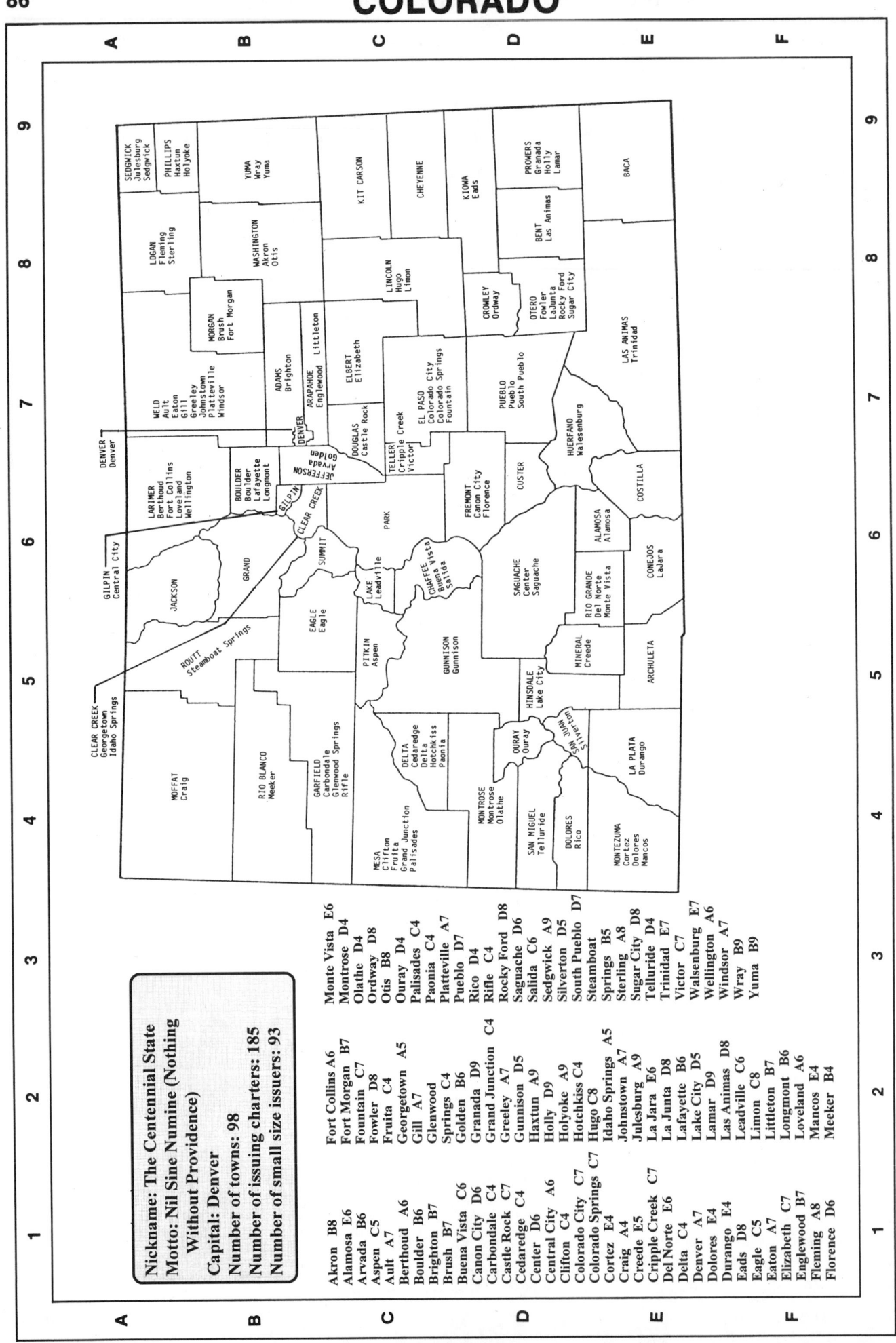

Nickname: The Centennial State
Motto: Nil Sine Numine (Nothing Without Providence)
Capital: Denver
Number of towns: 98
Number of issuing charters: 185
Number of small size issuers: 93

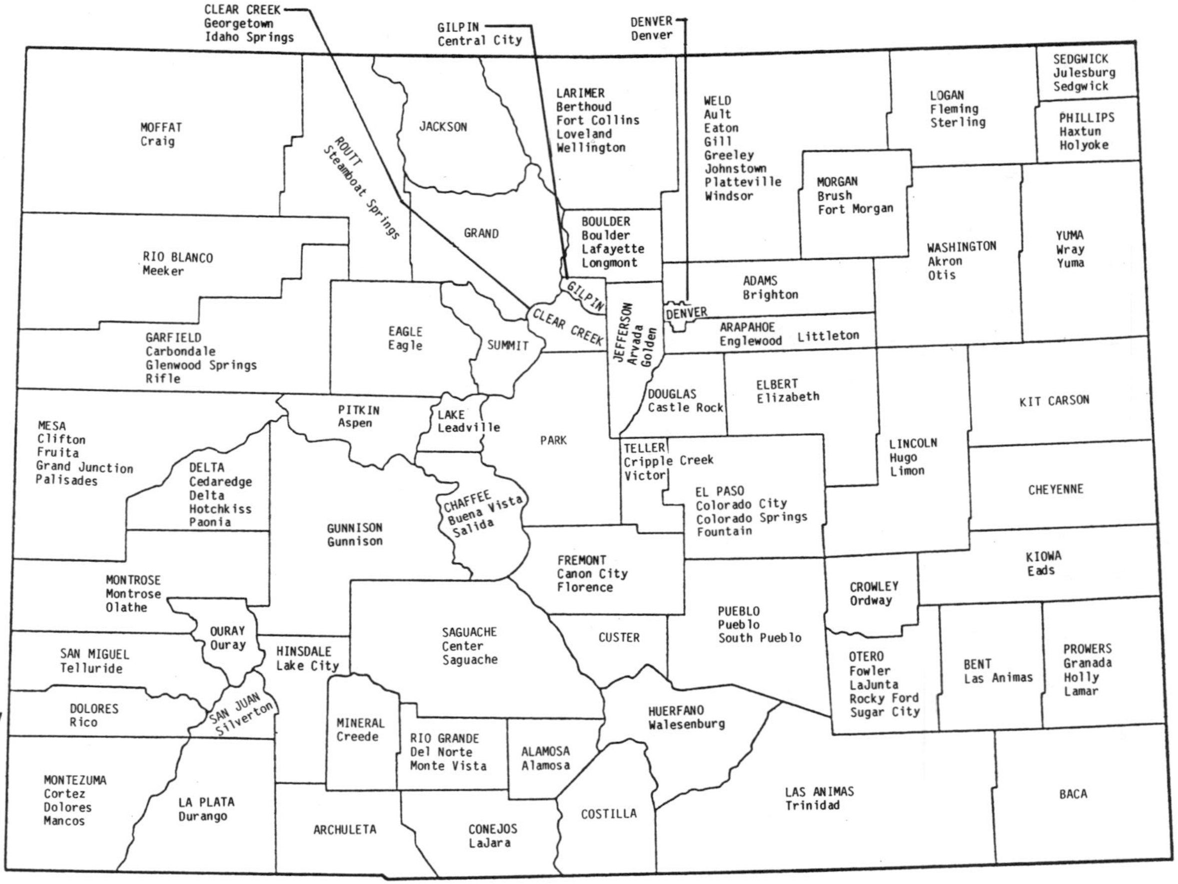

Akron B8
Alamosa E6
Arvada B6
Aspen C5
Ault A7
Berthoud A6
Boulder B6
Brighton B7
Brush B7
Buena Vista C6
Canon City D6
Carbondale C4
Castle Rock C7
Cedaredge C4
Center D6
Central City A6
Clifton C4
Colorado City C7
Colorado Springs C7
Cortez E4
Craig A4
Creede E5
Cripple Creek C7
Del Norte E6
Delta C4
Denver A7
Dolores E4
Durango E4
Eads D8
Eagle C5
Eaton A7
Elizabeth C7
Englewood B7
Fleming A8
Florence D6
Fort Collins A6
Fort Morgan B7
Fountain C7
Fowler D8
Fruita C4
Georgetown A5
Gill A7
Glenwood Springs C4
Golden B6
Granada D9
Grand Junction C4
Greeley A7
Gunnison D5
Haxtun A9
Holly D9
Holyoke A9
Hotchkiss C4
Hugo C8
Idaho Springs A5
Johnstown A7
Julesburg A9
La Jara E6
La Junta D8
Lafayette B6
Lake City D5
Lamar D9
Las Animas D8
Leadville C6
Limon C8
Littleton B7
Longmont B6
Loveland A6
Mancos E4
Meeker B4
Monte Vista E6
Montrose D4
Olathe D4
Ordway D8
Otis B8
Ouray D4
Palisades C4
Paonia C4
Platteville A7
Pueblo D7
Rico D4
Rifle C4
Rocky Ford D8
Saguache D6
Salida C6
Sedgwick A9
Silverton D5
South Pueblo D7
Steamboat Springs B5
Sterling A8
Sugar City D8
Telluride D4
Trinidad E7
Victor C7
Walsenburg E7
Wellington A6
Windsor A7
Wray B9
Yuma B9

****
10901 Washington
CITIZENS NB OF AKRON
{{ 4 L 6 S }}
Chartered 9/16
1902 Plain Back <$VALUE
4x10 1-3099 <$750
1929 Small Size
10 Type 1 1-670 <$350
10 Type 2 1-1039 <$375
Total Issue $174,550
Out in 1935 $15,000
Large out 1935 $960
****
8548 Washington
FNB OF AKRON
{{ 2 L }}
Organized 2/4/07
Receivership 8/26/26
1902 Red Seal <$VALUE
4x10 1-250 <$3000
1902 Date Back
4x10 1-1600 <$1500
1902 Plain Back
4x10 1601-4553 <$1500
Total Issue $192,120
Out at close $19,800
****
8541 Alamosa
ALAMOSA NB, ALAMOSA
{{ 0 L 1 S }}
Organized 1/14/07
1902 Red Seal <$VALUE
3x10-20 1-180 <$4000
1902 Date Back
3x10-20 1-720 <$3000
1902 Plain Back
3x10-20 721-1294 <$3000
1929 Small Size
10 Type 1 1-218 <$750
20 Type 1 1-53 <$750
Total Issue $93,140
Out in 1935 $6,250
Large out 1935 $230
****
7904 Alamosa
AMERICAN NB OF ALAMOSA
{{ 5 L 10 S }}
Chartered 9/05
1902 Red Seal <$VALUE
3x10-20 1-2112 <$1750
1902 Date Back
3x10-20 1-4900 <$600
1902 Plain Back
3x10-20 4901-10831 <$600
1929 Small Size
10 Type 1 1-1316 <$225
20 Type 1 1-370 <$225
10 Type 2 1-1563 <$250
20 Type 2 1-333 <$250
Total Issue $792,800
Out in 1935 $50,000
Large out 1935 $1,920
****
3114 Alamosa
FNB OF ALAMOSA
{{ 1 L }}
Chartered 1/26/84
Liquidated 7/1/97
Brown Back <$VALUE
4x5 1-2982 <$3000
Total Issue $59,540
Out in 1910 $450
****
7501 Jefferson
FNB OF ARVADA
{{ 3 L 3 S }}
Chartered 12/04
1902 Red Seal <$VALUE
4x5 1-500 <$2000
3x10-20 1-756 <$2000
1902 Date Back
4x5 1-1625 <$1250
3x10-20 1-1180 <$1250
1902 Plain Back
4x5 1626-2356 <$1250
3x10-20 1181-1606 <$1250
1929 Small Size
5 Type 1 1-272 <$600
10 Type 1 1-138 <$600
20 Type 1 1-32 <$600
Total Issue $195,500
Out in 1935 $6,250
Large out 1935 $700
****

<$VALUEs are for notes in FINE condition. Value changes by approximately 25% for a change of one full grade.

****
4733 Pitkin
ASPEN NB, ASPEN
{{ UNREPORTED }}
Chartered 4/25/92
Liquidated 4/9/94
Brown Back <$VALUE
4x5 1-672 <$5000
3x10-20 1-364 <$3000
Total Issue $31,640
Out in 1910 $325
****
3485 Pitkin
FNB OF ASPEN
{{ 3 L }}
Chartered 4/9/86
Liquidated 2/1/98
Brown Back <$VALUE
4x5 1-5290 <$3000
Total Issue $105,800
Out in 1910 $1,040
****
8815 Pitkin
PEOPLES NB OF ASPEN
{{ UNREPORTED }}
Chartered 8/1/07
Liquidated 9/21/08
1902 Red Seal <$VALUE
3x10-20 1-142 <$5000
Total Issue $7,100
Out in 1910 $2,310
****
8167 Weld
FARMERS NB OF AULT
{{ 4 L 6 S }}
Chartered 4/06
1902 Red Seal <$VALUE
3x10-20 1-440 <$2000
1902 Date Back
3x10-20 1-2900* <$1000
1902 Plain Back
3x10-20 3401-6216* <$1000
* 2901-3400 not marked
1929 Small Size
10 Type 1 1-602 <$450
20 Type 1 1-182 <$450
10 Type 2 1-1083 <$500
20 Type 2 1-264 <$500
Total Issue $406,870
Out in 1935 $25,000
Large out 1935 $1,470
****
8088 Weld
FNB OF AULT
{{ 2 L }}
Chartered 2/06
Liquidated 4/29/29
1902 Red Seal <$VALUE
4x5 1-350 <$2500
3x10-20 1-280 <$2500
1902 Date Back
4x5 1-1400 <$1500
3x10-20 1-1080 <$1500
1902 Plain Back
4x5 1401-1920 <$1500
3x10-20 1081-1415 <$1500
Total Issue $130,150
Out in 1925 $10,000
****
7995 Larimer
BERTHOUD NB, BERTHOUD
{{ 6 L 12 S }}
Chartered 12/05
1902 Red Seal <$VALUE
3x10-20 1-1900 <$2000
1902 Date Back
3x10-20 1-3440 <$600
1902 Plain Back
3x10-20 3441-10769 <$600
1929 Small Size
10 Type 1 1-1304 <$200
20 Type 1 1-360 <$200
10 Type 2 1-1352 <$225
20 Type 2 1-285 <$225
Total Issue $774,110
Out in 1935 $50,000
Large out 1935 $2,990
****
8033 Larimer
FNB OF BERTHOUD
{{ UNREPORTED }}
Chartered 1/06
Liquidated 1/21/29
1902 Red Seal <$VALUE
3x10-20 1-300 <$3500
1902 Date Back
3x10-20 1-560 <$2500
1902 Plain Back
3x10-20 561-1198 <$2500
Total Issue $74,900
Out at close $6,250
****

****
3246 Boulder
BOULDER NB, BOULDER
{{ 2 L }}
Organized 8/19/84
Receivership 3/28/34
Brown Back <$VALUE
3x10-20 1-1532 <$2000
1902 Red Seal
3x10-20 1-470 <$2000
1902 Date Back
3x10-20 1-1300 <$1250
1902 Plain Back
3x10-20 1301-2291 <$1250
Total Issue $214,650
Out at close $900
****
14021 Boulder
FNB IN BOULDER
{{ 5 S }}
Chartered 2/34
1929 Small Size <$VALUE
5 Type 2 1-106 <$600
50 Type 2 1-138 <$1000
100 Type 2 1-60 <$1250
Total Issue $13,430
Out in 1935 $87,980
Outstanding includes Ch 2352
****
2352 Boulder
FNB OF BOULDER
{{ 8 L 15 S }}
Chartered 8/18/77
Liquidated 4/19/34
Series 1875 <$VALUE
4x5 1-8079 <$2500
Brown Back
50-100 1-1355 <$3000/$3500
1882 Date Back
50-100 1-600 <$2500/$3000
3x50-100 1-397<$2500/$3000
1902 Plain Back
3x50-100 1-1375<$1250/$1500
1929 Small Size
50 Type 1 1-285 <$300
100 Type 1 1-66 <$400
Total Issue $1,022,930
Out at close $99,970
Large out at close $13,770
Ch 14021 assumed circulation
****
2355 Boulder
N STATE B OF BOULDER
{{ 5 L 7 S }}
Chartered 5/4/77
Series 1875 <$VALUE
4x5 1-6720 <$2500
Brown Back
3x10-20 1-2300 <$1500
1882 Date Back
3x10-20 1-2052* <$1200
* 1801-2052 not marked
1902 Plain Back
3x10-20 1-3515 <$600
1929 Small Size
10 Type 1 1-983 <$300
20 Type 1 1-210 <$300
Total Issue $611,930
Out in 1935 $28,850
Large out 1935 $2,060
****
7577 Adams
FNB OF BRIGHTON
{{ 4 L 4 S }}
Organized 12/31/04
Receivership 12/2/31
1902 Red Seal <$VALUE
4x5 1-415 <$2000
3x10-20 1-1000 <$2000
1902 Date Back
4x5 1-775 <$1250
3x10-20 1-1830 <$1250
1902 Plain Back
4x5 776-6196 <$1250
3x10-20 1831-2840 <$1250
1929 Small Size
5 Type 1 1-2050 <$500
Total Issue $385,720
Out at close $24,220
Large out at close $910
****
6437 Morgan
FNB OF BRUSH
{{ 4 L U + 6 S }}
Chartered 9/02
1902 Red Seal <$VALUE
4x5 1-900 <$2000
3x10-20 1-680 <$2000
1902 Date Back
4x5 1-1900 <$750
3x10-20 1-1470 <$750
1902 Plain Back
4x5 1901-4485 <$750
3x10-20 1471-3012 <$750
1929 Small Size
5 Type 1 1-684 <$375
10 Type 1 1-324 <$375
5 Type 2 1-2126 <$400
10 Type 2 1-1035 <$400
Total Issue $353,240
Out in 1935 $21,440
Large out 1935 $1,130
****
8520 Morgan
STOCKMAN'S NB OF BRUSH
{{ 1 L }}
Organized 12/22/06
Receivership 3/1/26
1902 Red Seal <$VALUE
4x5 1-300 <$3000
4x10 1-300 <$3000
1902 Date Back
4x5 1-850 <$1500
4x10 1-850 <$1500
1902 Plain Back
4x5 851-2160 <$1500
4x10 851-1635 <$1500
Total Issue $126,600
Out at close $9,800
****
8735 Chaffee
FNB OF BUENA VISTA
{{ 1 L 5 S }}
Organized 5/13/07
Receivership 11/6/31
1902 Red Seal <$VALUE
3x10-20 1-300 <$3000
1902 Date Back
3x10-20 1-860 <$2000
1902 Plain Back
3x10-20 861-2068 <$2000
1929 Small Size
10 Type 1 1-176 <$500
20 Type 1 1-28 <$500
Total Issue $132,320
Out at close $9,520
Large out at close $1,530
****
3879 Fremont
FNB OF CANON CITY
{{ 5 L }}
Chartered 1888
Brown Back <$VALUE
4x5 1-3276 <$2500
3x10-20 1-944 <$2500
1902 Red Seal
4x5 1-250 <$2500
3x10-20 1-400 <$2500
1902 Date Back
4x5 1-3650 <$1000
3x10-20 1-2520 <$1000
1902 Plain Back
4x5 3651-9050 <$1000
3x10-20 2521-5789 <$1000
Total Issue $608,170
Out in 1935 $2,715
****
8433 Fremont
FREMONT COUNTY NB OF
CANON CITY
{{ 7 L }}
Chartered 11/06
1902 Red Seal <$VALUE
4x5 1-2250 <$1750
3x10-20 1-1800 <$1750
1902 Date Back
4x5 1-5200 <$750
3x10-20 1-3900 <$750
1902 Plain Back
4x5 5201-16145 <$750
3x10-20 3901-11139 <$750
Total Issue $1,014,850
Out in 1935 $4,140
****
9009 Garfield
FNB OF CARBONDALE
{{ 2 L U + 9 S }}
Chartered 1/08
1902 Red Seal <$VALUE
4x5 1-300 <$2500
3x10-20 1-240 <$2500
1902 Date Back
4x5 1-925 <$1500
3x10-20 1-720 <$1500
1902 Plain Back
4x5 926-4734 <$1500
3x10-20 721-2853 <$1500
1929 Small Size
5 Type 1 1-814 <$300
10 Type 1 1-412 <$300
20 Type 1 1-138 <$300
5 Type 2 1-1574 <$350
10 Type 2 1-840 <$350
20 Type 2 1-192 <$350
Total Issue $341,140
Out in 1935 $24,650
Large out 1935 $1,120
****

****
6556 Douglas
FNB OF DOUGLAS COUNTY AT
CASTLE ROCK
{{ 3 L 3 S }}
Organized 12/12/02
Receivership 12/18/33
1902 Red Seal <$VALUE
3x10-20 1-456 <$3000
1902 Date Back
3x10-20 1-980 <$1750
1902 Plain Back
3x10-20 981-2702 <$1750
1929 Small Size
10 Type 1 1-303 <$750
20 Type 1 1-96 <$750
Total Issue $187,600
Out at close $12,500
Large out at close $780
****
10272 Delta
FNB OF CEDAREDGE
{{ 4 L U + 5 S }}
Chartered 10/12
1902 Date Back <$VALUE
3x10-20 1-500 <$1250
1902 Plain Back
3x10-20 501-3415 <$1250
1929 Small Size
5 Type 1 1-312 <$400
10 Type 1 1-494 <$400
20 Type 1 1-150 <$400
5 Type 2 1-1422 <$450
10 Type 2 1-722 <$450
20 Type 2 1-205 <$450
Total Issue $246,180
Out in 1935 $25,000
Large out 1935 $1,210
****
9743 Saguache
FNB OF CENTER
{{ 1 L }}
Chartered 5/10
1902 Date Back <$VALUE
3x10-20 1-1510* <$3000
1902 Plain Back
3x10-20 1911-3105* <$3000
* 1511-1910 not marked
Total Issue $155,250
Out in 1935 $360
****
2129 Gilpin
FNB OF CENTRAL CITY
Organized 9/15/73
Receivership 10/9/33
TERRITORIAL ISSUES {{ 16 L }}
Original Series <$VALUE
3x1-2 1-2100 <$3500/$6000
4x5 1-2475 <$4000
Series 1875
3x1-2 1-1220 <$3500/$6000
4x5 1-9050 <$3500
STATE ISSUES {{ 3 L 5 S }}
Series 1875
4x5 9051-9105 <$3500
Brown Back
4x5 1-2175 <$1750
3x10-20 1-840 <$1750
1882 Date Back
4x5 1-1007 <$1500
3x10-20 1-709 <$1500
1902 Date Back
4x5 1-700 <$850
3x10-20 1-560 <$850
1902 Plain Back
4x5 701-3817 <$850
3x10-20 561-2382 <$850
1929 Small Size
5 Type 1 1-864 <$450
10 Type 1 1-389 <$450
20 Type 1 1-123 <$450
Total Issue $648,750
Out at close $25,000
Large out at close $3,820
****
1652 Gilpin
ROCKY MOUNTAIN NB OF
CENTRAL CITY
Chartered 1866
Liquidated 1/1/16
TERRITORIAL ISSUES {{ 1 L }}
Original Series <$VALUE
4x5 1-4400 <$4000
Series 1875
4x5 1-7707 <$4000
STATE ISSUES {{ 2 L }}
Brown Back
4x5 1-5035 <$2500
3x10-20 1-617 <$2500
1902 Red Seal
3x10-20 1-300 <$3000
1902 Date Back
3x10-20 1-815 <$1500
Total Issue $429,440
Out at close $11,000
****

****
9875 Mesa
FNB OF CLIFTON
{{ UNREPORTED }}
Organized 10/20/10
Receivership 11/29/13
1902 Date Back <$VALUE
4x5 1-580 <$3500
3x10-20 1-425 <$3500
Total Issue $32,850
Out in 1915 $2,715
****
6238 El Paso
FNB OF COLORADO CITY
Chartered 5/02
Liquidated 2/16/32
2nd title: City NB of
Colorado Springs 5/10/18
FIRST TITLE {{ 2 L }}
1902 Red Seal <$VALUE
3x10-20 1-2500 <$3500
1902 Date Back
3x10-20 1-3840 <$2500
1902 Plain Back
3x10-20 3841-4990 <$2500
SECOND TITLE {{U+4 L U+ 4 S}}
1902 Plain Back (dated 1902)
3x10-20 1-1800 <$750
1902 Plain Back (dated 1922)
3x10-20 1-4297 <$750
1929 Small Size
10 Type 1 1-791 <$350
20 Type 1 1-265 <$350
Total Issue $758,610
Out at close $50,000
Large out at close $5,490
****
City NB of Colorado Springs
SEE Ch 6238
FNB of Colorado City
****
8572 El Paso
COLORADO SPRINGS NB,
COLORADO SPRINGS
{{ 11 L 16 S }}
Chartered 3/07
1902 Red Seal <$VALUE
3x10-20 1-2250 <$1500
1902 Date Back
4x5 1-6665 <$200
3x10-20 1-4600 <$200
1902 Plain Back
4x5 6666-22657 <$200
3x10-20 4601-15147 <$200
1929 Small Size
5 Type 1 1-3454 <$100
10 Type 1 1-2128 <$100
20 Type 1 1-456 <$125
5 Type 2 1-4868 <$125
10 Type 2 1-3109 <$125
20 Type 2 1-780 <$135
Total Issue $1,680,040
Out in 1935 $100,000
Large out 1935 $5,460
****
5283 El Paso
EL PASO NB OF
COLORADO SPRINGS
{{ 4 L }}
Chartered 4/11/00
Liquidated 1/9/17
Brown Back <$VALUE
3x10-20 1-11600 <$1500
1882 Date Back
3x10-20 1-14000 <$1500
1882 Value Back
3x10-20 14001-15034 <$1500
Total Issue $1,331,700
Out at close $200,000
****
3913 El Paso
EXCHANGE NB OF
COLORADO SPRINGS
{{ 6 L 31 S }}
Chartered 1888
Brown Back <$VALUE
3x10-20 1-9417 <$1250
1902 Date Back
4x5 1-10750 <$350
3x10-20 1-12000 <$350
1902 Plain Back
3x10-20 12001-13906 <$350
1929 Small Size
5 Type 2 1-16970 <$75
10 Type 2 1-8850 <$75
20 Type 2 1-4004 <$85
50 Type 2 1-1391 <$300
100 Type 2 1-733 <$400
Total Issue $1,702,860
Out in 1935 $300,000
Large out 1935 $4,570
****

2179 El Paso
FNB OF COLORADO SPRINGS
Chartered 9/8/74
TERRITORIAL ISSUES {{ 0 L }}
Original Series <$VALUE
4x5 1-1350 <$4000
Series 1875
4x5 1-4975 <$4000
STATE ISSUES {{26 L U+36 S}}
Series 1875
4x5 4976-6428 <$2500
Brown Back
4x5 1-5600 <$1250
3x10-20 1-9400 <$1250
1882 Date Back
4x5 1-7990 <$1000
3x10-20 1-7600 <$1000
1902 Date Back
4x5 1-2500 <$150
3x10-20 1-2000 <$150
1902 Plain Back
4x5 2501-33600 <$150
3x10-20 2001-22528 <$150
1929 Small Size
5 Type 1 1-7620 <$50
10 Type 1 1-3990 <$50
20 Type 1 1-1006 <$65
5 Type 2 1-12206 <$65
10 Type 2 1-5916 <$65
20 Type 2 1-1536 <$75
Total Issue $3,815,390
Out in 1935 $199,995
Large out 1935 $11,995

8967 Montezuma
CORTEZ NB OF CORTEZ
{{ UNREPORTED }}
Chartered 12/07
Liquidated 7/9/15
2nd title: FNB of Cortez 10/6/08
FIRST TITLE
1902 Red Seal <$VALUE
3x10-20 1-210 <$5000
SECOND TITLE
1902 Date Back
3x10-20 1-711 <$4000
Total Issue $46,050
Out in 1915 $8,300

FNB of Cortez
SEE Ch 8967
Cortez NB of Cortez

9100 Montezuma
MONTEZUMA VALLEY NB OF CORTEZ
{{ 4 L 10 S }}
Organized 2/26/08
Receivership 8/18/33
1902 Red Seal <$VALUE
4x5 1-250 <$2500
3x10-20 1-200 <$2500
1902 Date Back
4x5 1-2075 <$1000
3x10-20 1-1620 <$1000
1902 Plain Back
4x5 2076-6700 <$1000
3x10-20 1621-4523 <$1000
1929 Small Size
5 Type 1 1-974 <$350
10 Type 1 1-476 <$350
20 Type 1 1-152 <$350
Total Issue $451,170
Out at close $30,000
Large out at close $1,620

10558 Moffat
FNB OF CRAIG
{{ 2 L 2 S }}
Organized 5/28/14
Receivership 2/18/32
1902 Date Back <$VALUE
4x5 1-415 <$1750
3x10-20 1-334 <$1750
1902 Plain Back
4x5 416-2091 <$1750
3x10-20 335-1259 <$1750
1929 Small Size
5 Type 1 1-241 <$750
10 Type 1 1-127 <$750
20 Type 1 1-23 <$750
Total Issue $122,380
Out at close $10,000
Large out at close $1,125

4716 Mineral
FNB OF CREEDE
{{ UNREPORTED }}
Chartered 3/29/92
Liquidated 12/31/95
Brown Back <$VALUE
4x5 1-1123 <$5000
Total Issue $22,460
Out in 1910 $255

4845 Teller
FNB OF CRIPPLE CREEK
{{ 3 L }}
Chartered 1893
Brown Back <$VALUE
3x10-20 1-1400 <$5000
50-100 1-450 <$7500/$8500
1882 Date Back
3x10-20 1-1635 <$4500
50-100 1-14 <$6500/$7500
1902 Date Back
3x10-20 1-1500 <$3000
1902 Plain Back
3x10-20 1501-5311 <$3000
Total Issue $486,900
Out in 1935 $2,875

4264 Rio Grande
FNB OF DEL NORTE
{{ 1 L }}
Chartered 3/18/90
Receivership 1/14/93
Brown Back <$VALUE
4x5 1-838 <$4000
Total Issue $16,760
Out in 1915 $140

8675 Delta
DELTA NB, DELTA
{{ 4 L }}
Chartered 5/07
Liquidated 10/5/23
1902 Red Seal <$VALUE
3x10-20 1-1200 <$2500
1902 Date Back
3x10-20 1-3800 <$1000
1902 Plain Back
3x10-20 3801-7360 <$1000
Total Issue $428,000
Out at close $50,000

5467 Delta
FNB OF DELTA
{{ 6 L }}
Organized 5/22/00
Receivership 9/25/29
Brown Back <$VALUE
3x10-20 1-1600 <$1750
1882 Date Back
3x10-20 1-3500 <$1500
1882 Value Back
3x10-20 3501-5052 <$1500
1902 Plain Back
3x10-20 1-5233 <$600
Total Issue $594,250
Out at close $49,600

4159 Denver
AMERICAN NB OF DENVER
{{ UNREPORTED }}
Chartered 11/13/89
Liquidated 4/1/99
Brown Back <$VALUE
4x5 1-5900 <$3000
50-100 1-756 <$4000
Total Issue $231,400
Out in 1910 $6,070

12517 Denver
AMERICAN NB OF DENVER
{{ U + 12 L U + 34 S }}
Chartered 3/24
1902 Plain Back <$VALUE
4x5 1-64823 <$125
1929 Small Size
5 Type 1 1-35610 <$50
5 Type 2 1-72096 <$50
Total Issue $2,725,240
Out in 1935 $250,000
Large out 1935 $3,990

Capitol NB of Denver
SEE Ch 6355
Continental NB of Denver

8774 Denver
CENTRAL NB OF DENVER
{{ 1 L }}
Chartered 6/07
Liquidated 4/10/12
1902 Red Seal <$VALUE
3x10-20 1-1500 <$1500
1902 Date Back
3x10-20 1-3491 <$750
Total Issue $249,550
Out in 1912 $88,890

1955 Denver
CITY NB OF DENVER
{{ 2 L }}
Chartered 4/9/72
Liquidated 1/7/95
TERRITORIAL ISSUES
Original Series <$VALUE
3x1-2 1-2600 <$3500/$6000
4x5 1-3250 <$3500
3x10-20 1-900 <$4500/$5000
Series 1875
3x1-2 1-100 <$3500/$6000
4x5 1-4994 <$3500
3x10-20 1-3861<$4500/$5000
STATE ISSUES
Brown Back
3x10-20 1-754 <$1500
Total Issue $454,130
Out in 1910 $2,779

1651 Denver
COLORADO NB OF DENVER
Chartered 8/66
TERRITORIAL ISSUES {{ 10 L }}
Original Series <$VALUE
3x1-2 1-3830 <$3500/$6000
4x5 1-5250 <$3500
2x10-20-50 1-415 <$4000/$5000/$8500
Series 1875
4x5 1-17234 <$3500
STATE ISSUES {{ 41 L 50+ S }}
Brown Back
3x10-20 1-4140 <$750
50-100 1-8066 <$3000/$3500
1902 Red Seal
50-100 1-2666 <$6000
1902 Date Back
50-100 1-5667 <$650/$750
3x50-100 1-1000 <$650/$750
1929 Small Size
5 Type 1 1-16240 <$35
10 Type 1 1-8144 <$40
100 Type 1 1-420 <$250
5 Type 2 1-90924 <$40
10 Type 2 1-51621 <$45
Total Issue $5,621,700
Out in 1935 $1,000,000
Large out 1935 $17,349

4113 Denver
COMMERCIAL NB OF DENVER
{{ UNREPORTED }}
Chartered 9/6/89
Receivership 10/24/93
Brown Back <$VALUE
3x10-20 1-1522 <$2500
Total Issue $76,100
Out in 1915 $440

6355 Denver
CONTINENTAL NB OF DENVER
{{ UNREPORTED }}
Chartered 7/02
Liquidated 5/11/12
2nd title: Capitol NB of Denver 3/3/03
FIRST TITLE
1902 Red Seal <$VALUE
4x5 1-800 <$2000
3x10-20 1-715 <$2000
SECOND TITLE
1902 Red Seal
4x5 1-2830 <$2000
3x10-20 1-2168 <$2000
1902 Date Back
4x5 1-3037 <$1000
3x10-20 1-1898 <$1000
Total Issue $372,390
Out at close $120,000
Ch 1016 assumed circulation

3269 Denver
DENVER NB, DENVER
{{ 50+ L U + 50+ S }}
Chartered 1884
Brown Back <$VALUE
4x5 1-17790 <$650
3x10-20 1-19249 <$650
50-100 1-134 <$2500/$3000
1902 Red Seal
4x5 1-17500 <$850
3x10-20 1-9800 <$850
1902 Date Back
4x5 1-66250 <$85
3x10-20 1-53200 <$85
1902 Plain Back
4x5 66251-115872 <$85
3x10-20 53201-83525 <$85
1929 Small Size
10 Type 1 1-11519 <$30
20 Type 1 1-9576 <$35
Total Issue $10,512,300
Out in 1935 $1,500,000
Large out 1935 $25,065

11564 Denver
DROVERS NB OF DENVER
{{ 8 L }}
Organized 12/18/19
Receivership 12/24/25
1902 Plain Back <$VALUE
4x5 1-14825 <$250
3x10-20 1-7420 <$250
3x50-100 1-760 <$750/$850
Total Issue $857,500
Out at close $200,000

10064 Denver
FEDERAL NB OF DENVER
{{ 6 L }}
Chartered 8/11
Liquidated 11/8/15
1902 Date Back <$VALUE
4x5 1-11290 <$350
3x10-20 1-8172 <$350
Total Issue $634,400
Out in 1916 $92,635

1016 Denver
FNB OF DENVER
Chartered 4/17/65
TERRITORIAL ISSUES {{ 10 L }}
Original Series <$VALUE
3x1-2 1-1000 <$3500/$6000
4x5 1-1250 <$3500
3x10-20 1-4400<$4000/$4500
50-100 1-340 <$8500
Series 1875
4x5 1-350 <$3500
3x10-20 1-1475<$4000/$4500
50-100 1-1333 <$8500
STATE ISSUES {{ 41 L 50+ S }}
Brown Back
4x5 1-13600 <$650
3x10-20 1-5196 <$650/$700
50-100 1-9452 <$2500/$3000
1902 Red Seal
4x5 1-32100 <$850
3x10-20 1-8800 <$850
50-100 1-2320 <$6000
1902 Date Back
4x5 1-57500 <$85
3x10-20 1-54600 <$85
50-100 1-1000 <$600/$700
3x50-100 1-1000 <$600/$700
1902 Plain Back
4x5 57501-89300 <$85
3x10-20 54601-74299 <$85
1929 Small Size
5 Type 1 1-14204 <$35
10 Type 1 1-10160 <$40
20 Type 1 1-3602 <$45
50 Type 1 1-616 <$125
100 Type 1 1-316 <$200
5 Type 2 1-69626 <$35
10 Type 2 1-31093 <$40
20 Type 2 1-11105 <$45
Total Issue $12,585,770
Out in 1935 $1,500,000
Large out 1935 $36,680
Outstanding includes Ch 6355

2351 Denver
GERMAN NB OF DENVER
{{ 3 L }}
Chartered 4/9/77
Receivership 7/6/94
Series 1875 <$VALUE
4x5 1-3055 <$2000
3x10-20 1-5576<$3000/$3500
Total Issue $339,900
Out in 1915 $1,750

9887 Denver
HAMILTON NB OF DENVER
{{ 5 L }}
Chartered 11/10
Liquidated 2/25/24
1902 Date Back <$VALUE
4x5 1-9850 <$350
3x10-20 1-7300 <$350
1902 Plain Back
4x5 9851-36345 <$350
3x10-20 7301-22770 <$350
Total Issue $1,865,400
Out at close $350,000

2523 Denver
MERCHANTS NB OF DENVER
{{ 1 L }}
Chartered 1881
Liquidated 12/24/81
Series 1875 <$VALUE
4x10 1-1800 <$3000
Total Issue $72,000
Out in 1910 $300

4358 Denver
NB OF COMMERCE, DENVER
{{ 2 L }}
Chartered 7/8/90
Liquidated 11/14/08
Brown Back <$VALUE
3x10-20 1-2160 <$1500
50-100 1-6576 <$3000/$3500
1882 Date Back
3x10-20 1-98 <$1500
Total Issue $1,099,300
Out in 1910 $229,500

13098 Denver
N CITY B OF DENVER
{{ 2U + 13 S }}
Chartered 7/1/27 as West Side NB of Denver, under which there was no issue. Issuing title adopted 9/16/29.
1929 Small Size <$VALUE
5 Type 1 1-1765 <$75
10 Type 1 1-1110 <$75
20 Type 1 1-368 <$85
100 Type 1 1-50 <$325
Total Issue $193,710
Out in 1935 $50,000

4084 Denver
PEOPLES NB OF DENVER
{{ UNREPORTED }}
Organized 7/30/89
Receivership 12/20/99
Brown Back <$VALUE
50-100 1-816 <$4000
Total Issue $122,400
Out in 1915 $900

2694 Denver
STATE NB OF DENVER
{{ UNREPORTED }}
Organized 5/16/82
Liquidated 2/1/96
Series 1875 <$VALUE
3x10-20 1-3520<$3000/$3500
Total Issue $176,000
Out in 1910 $1,050

4382 Denver
UNION NB OF DENVER
{{ UNREPORTED }}
Chartered 7/30/90
Receivership 8/2/95
Brown Back <$VALUE
3x10-20 1-5343 <$2500
Total Issue $267,150
Out in 1915 $1,790

7408 Denver
UNITED STATES NB OF DENVER
{{ 2U + 25 L 2U + 50+ S }}
Chartered 9/04
1902 Red Seal <$VALUE
3x10-20 1-8500 <$850
1902 Date Back
3x10-20 1-36500 <$110
1902 Plain Back
3x10-20 36501-90198 <$110
1929 Small Size
10 Type 1 1-11520 <$30
20 Type 1 1-3774 <$40
5 Type 2 1-324 <$45
10 Type 2 1-18901 <$45
20 Type 2 1-4493 <$55
Total Issue $6,359,470
Out in 1935 $472,000
Large out 1935 $23,655

10770 Montezuma
FNB OF DOLORES
{{ 2 L }}
Chartered 8/15
Liquidated 5/2/27
1902 Plain Back <$VALUE
4x5 1-4920 <$1500
Total Issue $98,400
Out at close $19,600

9797 La Plata
BURNS NB OF DURANGO
{{ 6 L 12 S }}
Chartered 6/10
1902 Date Back <$VALUE
3x10-20 1-4900* <$400
1902 Plain Back
3x10-20 5701-15772* <$400
* 4901-5700 not marked
1929 Small Size
10 Type 1 1-1904 <$150
20 Type 1 1-578 <$150
10 Type 2 1-2083 <$175
20 Type 2 1-414 <$175
Total Issue $1,001,310
Out in 1935 $50,000
Large out 1935 $5,430

4126 La Plata
DURANGO NB, DURANGO
{{ UNREPORTED }}
Chartered 9/23/89
Liquidated 1/6/90
Brown Back <$VALUE
3x10-20 1-225 <$4000
Total Issue $11,250
All notes reportedly redeemed

2637 La Plata
FNB OF DURANGO
{{ 7 L 10 S }}
Chartered 1882
Series 1875 <$VALUE
3x10-20 1-2708<$2500/$3000
Brown Back
3x10-20 1-4820 <$1250
1882 Date Back
3x10-20 1-6400 <$1000
1882 Value Back
3x10-20 6401-10994 <$1000
1902 Plain Back
3x50-100 1-449 <$650/$750
1929 Small Size
50 Type 1 1-231 <$225
100 Type 1 1-70 <$325
Total Issue $1,149,650
Out in 1935 $50,000
Large out 1935 $6,050

4776 La Plata
SMELTER NB OF DURANGO
{{ UNREPORTED }}
Chartered 7/13/92
Liquidated 12/14/96
Brown Back <$VALUE
4x5 1-1225 <$4000
Total Issue $24,500
Out in 1910 $215

14213 Kiowa
FNB IN EADS
{{ 2U + 2 S }}
Chartered 7/34
1929 Small Size <$VALUE
5 Type 2 1-618 <$600
10 Type 2 1-226 <$600
20 Type 2 1-101 <$600
Total Issue $7,370
Out in 1935 $24,630
Outstanding includes Ch 8412

CONDITION affects Value. The Values shown are for notes in FINE condition.

8412 Kiowa
FNB OF EADS
{{ 3 L 11 S }}
Organized 9/10/06
Liquidated 9/15/34
1902 Red Seal <$VALUE
4x10 1-300 <$2500
1902 Date Back
4x10 1-825 <$1250
1902 Plain Back
4x10 826-1044 <$1250
1929 Small Size
5 Type 1 1-262 <$350
10 Type 1 1-526 <$350
20 Type 1 1-106 <$350
5 Type 2 1-636 <$450
20 Type 2 1-72 <$450
Total Issue $110,520
Out at close $25,000
Large out 1935 $370
Ch 14213 assumed circulation

9013 Eagle
FNB OF EAGLE COUNTY,
EAGLE
{{ UNREPORTED }}
Chartered 2/08
1902 Red Seal <$VALUE
3x10-20 1-300 <$5000
1902 Date Back
3x10-20 1-2110 <$3500
1902 Plain Back
3x10-20 2111-4512 <$3500
Total Issue $240,600
Out in 1935 $840

8658 Weld
EATON NB, EATON
{{ UNREPORTED }}
Chartered 4/07
Liquidated 12/26/31
1902 Red Seal <$VALUE
4x5 1-250 <$4000
3x10-20 1-200 <$4000
1902 Date Back
4x5 1-1350 <$3000
3x10-20 1-1060 <$3000
1902 Plain Back
4x5 1351-1870 <$3000
3x10-20 1061-1380 <$3000
Total Issue $121,400
Out at close $970

6057 Weld
FNB OF EATON
{{ 6 L }}
Chartered 12/7/01
Receivership 2/26/34
Brown Back <$VALUE
3x10-20 1-700 <$1750
1882 Date Back
3x10-20 1-4800 <$1500
1882 Value Back
3x10-20 4801-10551 <$1500
1902 Plain Back
3x10-20 1-2774 <$500
Total Issue $701,250
Out at close $3,965

8271 Elbert
FNB OF ELIZABETH
{{ 1 L }}
Chartered 6/06
Liquidated 12/19/14
1902 Red Seal <$VALUE
3x10-20 1-950 <$3500
1902 Date Back
3x10-20 1-1451 <$2500
Total Issue $120,050
Out in 1915 $12,600

9907 Arapahoe
FNB OF ENGLEWOOD
{{ 7 L 8 S }}
Organized 11/18/10
1902 Date Back <$VALUE
4x5 1-1785 <$600
3x10-20 1-1331 <$600
1902 Plain Back
4x5 1786-6165 <$600
3x10-20 1332-3898 <$600
1929 Small Size
5 Type 1 1-980 <$300
10 Type 1 1-444 <$300
20 Type 1 1-142 <$300
5 Type 2 1-1184 <$350
10 Type 2 1-800 <$350
20 Type 2 1-204 <$350
Total Issue $409,280
Out in 1935 $25,000
Large out 1935 $1,830

11571 Logan
FNB OF FLEMING
{{ 3 L 6 S }}
Chartered 1/20
1902 Plain Back <$VALUE
3x10-20 1-1764 <$1250
1929 Small Size
10 Type 1 1-392 <$400
20 Type 1 1-122 <$400
10 Type 2 1-261 <$450
20 Type 2 1-45 <$450
Total Issue $129,870
Out in 1935 $15,000
Large out 1935 $720

5381 Fremont
FNB OF FLORENCE
{{ 3 L 8 S }}
Chartered 5/31/00
Brown Back <$VALUE
3x10-20 1-1710 <$2500
1882 Date Back
3x10-20 1-2450 <$2250
1882 Value Back
3x10-20 2451-3050 <$2250
1902 Plain Back
3x10-20 1-3313 <$1250
1929 Small Size
10 Type 1 1-768 <$300
20 Type 1 1-234 <$300
10 Type 2 1-668 <$350
20 Type 2 1-177 <$350
Total Issue $488,030
Out in 1935 $31,000
Large out 1935 $1,570

14146 Larimer
FNB IN FORT COLLINS
{{ 5 S }}
Chartered 5/34
1929 Small Size <$VALUE
10 Type 2 1-3170 <$500
20 Type 2 1-1085 <$500
Total Issue $53,400
Out in 1935 $50,000

2622 Larimer
FNB OF FORT COLLINS
{{ 20 L U + 25 S }}
Organized 12/21/81
Liquidated 7/14/34
Series 1875 <$VALUE
3x10-20 1-2427<$2500/$3000
Brown Back
3x10-20 1-5700 <$850
1882 Date Back
3x10-20 1-9000 <$750
1882 Value Back
3x10-20 9001-16088 <$750
1902 Plain Back
3x10-20 1-13803 <$165
1929 Small Size
10 Type 1 1-3654 <$65
20 Type 1 1-1028 <$75
10 Type 2 1-2452 <$85
20 Type 2 1-297 <$100
Total Issue $2,273,960
Out at close $150,000
Large out at close $9,040

5503 Larimer
FORT COLLINS NB,
FORT COLLINS
{{ U + 11 L 22 S }}
Organized 6/11/00
Receivership 2/23/33
Brown Back <$VALUE
3x10-20 1-2900 <$850
1882 Date Back
4x5 1-7500* <$750
3x10-20 1-4700** <$750
1882 Value Back
4x5 8001-12050* <$750
3x10-20 5101-7315** <$750
* 7501-8000 not marked
** 4701-5100 not marked
1902 Plain Back
4x5 1-11565 <$175
3x10-20 1-8188 <$175
1929 Small Size
5 Type 1 1-3448 <$75
10 Type 1 1-1790 <$75
20 Type 1 1-391 <$85
Total Issue $1,650,210
Out at close $100,000
Large out at close $8,465

7837 Larimer
POUDRE VALLEY NB OF
FORT COLLINS
{{ 18 L 33 S }}
Chartered 7/05
1902 Red Seal <$VALUE
4x5 1-5865 <$1000
3x10-20 1-4304 <$1000
1902 Date Back
4x5 1-11250 <$175
3x10-20 1-7500 <$175
1902 Plain Back
4x5 11251-34670 <$175
3x10-20 7501-21548 <$175
1929 Small Size
5 Type 1 1-4976 <$60
10 Type 1 1-2870 <$60
20 Type 1 1-692 <$65
5 Type 2 1-9320 <$60
10 Type 2 1-4584 <$65
20 Type 2 1-1392 <$75
Total Issue $2,628,120
Out in 1935 $150,000
Large out at close $8,145

7004 Morgan
FNB OF FORT MORGAN
{{ 16 L 32 S }}
Organized 10/5/03
1902 Red Seal <$VALUE
3x10-20 1-2050 <$1000
1902 Date Back
3x10-20 1-8200 <$200
1902 Plain Back
3x10-20 8201-22830 <$200
1929 Small Size
10 Type 1 1-4094 <$75
20 Type 1 1-1006 <$75
10 Type 2 1-3531 <$85
20 Type 2 1-700 <$85
Total Issue $1,659,670
Out in 1935 $50,000
Large out 1935 $5,430

7832 Morgan
MORGAN COUNTY NB OF
FORT MORGAN
{{ 4 L }}
Chartered 7/05
Liquidated 8/1/27
1902 Red Seal <$VALUE
4x5 1-860 <$1500
3x10-20 1-690 <$1500
1902 Date Back
4x5 1-4150 <$750
3x10-20 1-2920 <$750
1902 Plain Back
4x5 4151-10377 <$750
3x10-20 2921-6984 <$750
Total Issue $608,440
Out at close $50,000

6772 El Paso
FNB OF FOUNTAIN
{{ 2 L 2 S }}
Organized 4/20/03
Receivership 8/1/30
1902 Red Seal <$VALUE
3x10-20 1-1500 <$3500
1902 Date Back
3x10-20 1-1900 <$2000
1902 Plain Back
3x10-20 1901-5586 <$2000
1929 Small Size
10 Type 1 1-273 <$850
20 Type 1 1-39 <$850
Total Issue $375,360
Out at close $25,000
Large out at close $5,610

7637 Otero
FNB OF FOWLER
{{ 2 L 4 S }}
Chartered 3/05
1902 Red Seal <$VALUE
3x10-20 1-356 <$3500
1902 Date Back
3x10-20 1-860 <$2000
1902 Plain Back
3x10-20 861-1791 <$2000
1929 Small Size
10 Type 1 1-274 <$650
20 Type 1 1-75 <$700
Total Issue $132,790
Out in 1935 $8,250
Large out 1935 $140

8840 Mesa
FNB OF FRUITA
{{ 3 L 6 S }}
Chartered 8/07
Liquidated 2/23/35
1902 Red Seal <$VALUE
3x10-20 1-600 <$2500
1902 Date Back
3x10-20 1-1970 <$1250
1902 Plain Back
3x10-20 1971-5486 <$1250
1929 Small Size
10 Type 1 1-674 <$375
20 Type 1 1-170 <$400
10 Type 2 1-922 <$450
20 Type 2 1-140 <$450
Total Issue $377,160
Out at close $25,000
Large out at close $1,390

1991 Clear Creek
FNB OF GEORGETOWN
{{ UNREPORTED }}
Chartered 5/31/72
Receivership 8/18/77
TERRITORIAL ISSUES
Original Series <$VALUE
4x5 1-1250 <$6000
3x10-20 1-1204 <$6500
Total Issue $85,200
Out in 1915 $290

2394 Clear Creek
MERCHANTS NB OF
GEORGETOWN
{{ UNREPORTED }}
Chartered 8/16/78
Liquidated 6/22/82
Series 1875 <$VALUE
4x5 1-3670 <$5000
Total Issue $73,400
Out in 1910 $505

2199 Clear Creek
MINERS NB OF GEORGETOWN
{{ 1 L }}
Chartered 10/30/74
Receivership 1/24/76
TERRITORIAL ISSUES
Original Series <$VALUE
4x5 1-1000 <$5000
3x10-20 1-500 <$6000
Total Issue $45,000
Out in 1915 $245

9697 Weld
FNB OF GILL
{{ UNREPORTED }}
Chartered 3/14/10
Liquidated 4/1/14
1902 Date Back <$VALUE
4x5 1-545 <$3500
3x10-20 1-447 <$3500
Total Issue $33,250
Out in 1914 $6,100

6957 Garfield
CITIZENS NB OF
GLENWOOD SPRINGS
{{ 5 L }}
Organized 9/9/03
Receivership 12/29/32
1902 Red Seal <$VALUE
4x5 1-1230 <$2000
3x10-20 1-984 <$2000
1902 Date Back
4x5 1-3750 <$650
3x10-20 1-2740 <$650
1902 Plain Back
4x5 3751-9480 <$650
3x10-20 2741-6240 <$650
Total Issue $575,400
Out at close $2,905

3661 Garfield
FNB OF GLENWOOD SPRINGS
{{ 5 L }}
Chartered 1887
Brown Back <$VALUE
4x5 1-6800 <$2000
50-100 1-259 <$3500/$4000
1902 Red Seal
3x10-20 1-250 <$2000
1902 Date Back
3x10-20 1-4200 <$650
1902 Plain Back
3x10-20 4201-8383 <$650
Total Issue $606,500
Out in 1935 $2,685

3722 Garfield
GLENWOOD NB OF
GLENWOOD SPRINGS
{{ UNREPORTED }}
Chartered 6/13/87
Liquidated 5/23/91
Brown Back <$VALUE
4x5 1-2361 <$4000
Total Issue $47,220
Out in 1910 $350

2140 Jefferson
FNB OF GOLDEN
{{ UNREPORTED }}
Chartered 3/26/74
Liquidated 8/25/75
TERRITORIAL ISSUES
Original Series <$VALUE
4x5 1-1475 <$7500
Total Issue $29,500
Out in 1910 $160

Rubey NB of Golden
SEE Ch 6497
Woods-Rubey NB of Golden

6497 Jefferson
WOODS-RUBEY NB OF GOLDEN
Organized 10/28/02
Receivership 9/21/33
2nd title: Rubey NB 9/1/16
FIRST TITLE {{ 0 L }}
1902 Red Seal <$VALUE
4x5 1-3015 <$4000
3x10-20 1-2174 <$4000
1902 Date Back
4x5 1-2750 <$3000
3x10-20 1-1670 <$3000
SECOND TITLE {{ 2 L 4 S }}
1902 Plain Back
3x10-20 1-1522 <$2000
1929 Small Size
10 Type 1 1-282 <$650
20 Type 1 1-83 <$650
Total Issue $410,480
Out at close $12,500
Large out at close $1,610

7809 Prowers
FNB OF GRANADA
{{ UNREPORTED }}
Chartered 6/05
Liquidated 8/27/15
1902 Red Seal <$VALUE
3x10-20 1-600 <$5000
1902 Date Back
3x10-20 1-823 <$3500
Total Issue $71,150
Out at close $9,900

13902 Mesa
FNB IN GRAND JUNCTION
{{ 7 S }}
Chartered 12/33
1929 Small Size <$VALUE
5 Type 2 1-4356 <$350
10 Type 2 1-2184 <$350
20 Type 2 1-636 <$350
50 Type 2 1-120 <$650
Total Issue $62,340
Out in 1935 $49,190

3860 Mesa
FNB OF GRAND JUNCTION
{{ UNREPORTED }}
Chartered 3/29/88
Liquidated 10/30/97
Brown Back <$VALUE
4x5 1-2187 <$4000
Total Issue $43,740
Out in 1910 $360

6137 Mesa
GRAND VALLEY NB OF
GRAND JUNCTION
{{ 7 L }}
Chartered 2/4/02
Liquidated 2/13/34
1902 Red Seal <$VALUE
3x10-20 1-4900 <$1750
1902 Date Back
3x10-20 1-7200 <$600
1902 Plain Back (dated 1902)
3x10-20 7201-12543 <$600
1902 Plain Back (dated 1922)
3x10-20 1-4576 <$600
Total Issue $1,100,950
Out at close $4,135

7766 Mesa
MESA COUNTY NB OF
GRAND JUNCTION
{{ 1 L }}
Organized 5/31/05
Receivership 11/29/13
1902 Red Seal <$VALUE
4x5 1-3540 <$3000
3x10-20 1-2834 <$3000
1902 Date Back
4x5 1-4995 <$2000
3x10-20 1-3598 <$2000
Total Issue $492,300
Out in 1915 $25,395

10038 Weld
CITY NB OF GREELEY
{{ UNREPORTED }}
Chartered 6/11
Liquidated 3/22/15
1902 Date Back <$VALUE
4x5 1-1130 <$2500
3x10-20 1-924 <$2500
Total Issue $68,800
Out at close $25,000
Ch 7604 assumed circulation

3178 Weld
FNB OF GREELEY
{{ 16 L 24 S }}
Chartered 1884
Brown Back <$VALUE
4x5 1-3108 <$1000
3x10-20 1-2203 <$1000
1902 Red Seal
3x10-20 1-2550 <$1250
1902 Date Back
4x5 1-7350 <$165
3x10-20 1-4960 <$165
1902 Plain Back
4x5 7351-23067 <$165
3x10-20 4961-15094 <$165
1929 Small Size
5 Type 1 1-3794 <$70
10 Type 1 1-2040 <$70
20 Type 1 1-448 <$80
5 Type 2 1-4416 <$70
10 Type 2 1-2308 <$70
20 Type 2 1-867 <$85
Total Issue $1,868,330
Out in 1935 $100,000
Large out 1935 $6,100

4437 Weld
GREELEY NB, GREELEY
Chartered 1890
Liquidated 2/14/34
2nd title: Greeley Union NB
4/23/26
FIRST TITLE {{ 6 L }}
Brown Back <$VALUE
3x10-20 1-2490 <$1000
1882 Date Back
3x10-20 1-655 <$850
1902 Date Back
3x10-20 1-3500 <$300
1902 Plain Back
3x10-20 3501-13308 <$300
SECOND TITLE {{ 12 L 50+ S }}
1902 Plain Back
3x10-20 1-5862 <$175
1929 Small Size
5 Type 1 1-3288 <$40
10 Type 1 1-3812 <$50
20 Type 1 1-1052 <$60
Total Issue $1,569,350
Out at close $175,000
Large out at close $10,885
Outstanding includes Ch 7604

13928 Weld
GREELEY NB, GREELEY
{{ 10 S }}
Chartered 1/34
1929 Small Size <$VALUE
5 Type 2 1-10484 <$200
10 Type 2 1-5628 <$200
Total Issue $108,700
Out in 1935 $65,500

Greeley Union NB of Greeley
SEE Ch 4437
Greeley NB, Greeley

<$VALUEs are for notes in FINE condition. Value changes by approximately 25% for a change of one full grade.

****
7604 Weld
UNION NB OF GREELEY
{{ 3 L }}
Chartered 2/05
Closed 4/23/26
1902 Red Seal <$VALUE
3x10-20 1-700 <$1250
1902 Date Back
3x10-20 1-4400 <$600
1902 Plain Back
3x10-20 4401-12378 <$600
Total Issue $653,900
Out at close $74,000
Outstanding includes Ch 10038
****
2686 Gunnison
FNB OF GUNNISON
{{ 7 L 10 S }}
Chartered 1882
Series 1875 <$VALUE
4x5 1-4374 <$2500
3x10-20 1-657 <$3000/$3500
1902 Red Seal
3x10-20 1-2575 <$2000
1902 Date Back
3x10-20 1-3340 <$600
1902 Plain Back
3x10-20 3341-9437 <$600
1929 Small Size
10 Type 1 1-1174 <$275
20 Type 1 1-328 <$275
10 Type 2 1-1285 <$325
20 Type 2 1-281 <$350
Total Issue $849,200
Out in 1935 $50,000
Large out 1935 $2,425
****
2975 Gunnison
IRON NB OF GUNNISON
{{ UNREPORTED }}
Chartered 1883
Liquidated 12/8/84
Brown Back <$VALUE
3x10-20 1-245 <$4000
Total Issue $12,250
Out in 1910 $90
****
11099 Phillips
FNB OF HAXTUN
{{ 4 L 14 S }}
Chartered 11/17
Liquidated 2/20/31
1902 Plain Back <$VALUE
3x10-20 1-2695 <$850
3x50-100 1-460<$1250/$1500
1929 Small Size
10 Type 1 1-549 <$165
20 Type 1 1-135 <$175
Total Issue $298,890
Out at close $50,000
Large out at close $12,130
****
7704 Prowers
FNB OF HOLLY
{{ 3 L 4 S }}
Chartered 4/05
1902 Red Seal <$VALUE
3x10-20 1-260 <$2500
1902 Date Back
3x10-20 1-1320* <$1000
1902 Plain Back
3x10-20 1441-2807* <$1000
* 1321-1440 not marked
1929 Small Size
10 Type 1 1-492 <$500
20 Type 1 1-146 <$500
10 Type 2 1-184 <$550
20 Type 2 1-45 <$600
Total Issue $203,130
Out in 1933 $21,500
Large out 1935 $770
****
9278 Phillips
FNB OF HOLYOKE
{{ 2 L 4 S }}
Chartered 11/08
1902 Date Back <$VALUE
3x10-20 1-1420 <$2000
1902 Plain Back
3x10-20 1421-2640 <$2000
1929 Small Size
10 Type 1 1-306 <$550
20 Type 1 1-106 <$550
10 Type 2 1-89 <$650
20 Type 2 1-10 <$700
Total Issue $164,170
Out in 1935 $12,500
Large out 1935 $880
****

****
5976 Delta
FNB OF HOTCHKISS
{{ 2 L 2 S }}
Chartered 9/01
Liquidated 7/19/30
Brown Back <$VALUE
3x10-20 1-870 <$3000
1882 Date Back
3x10-20 1-1790* <$2500
1882 Value Back
3x10-20 1891-3089* <$2500
* 1791-1890 not marked
1902 Plain Back
3x10-20 1-2346 <$1750
1929 Small Size
10 Type 1 1-237 <$750
20 Type 1 1-38 <$800
Total Issue $334,030
Out at close $25,000
Large out at close $6,390
****
8489 Lincoln
FNB OF HUGO
{{ 6 L 8 S }}
Chartered 12/06
1902 Red Seal <$VALUE
3x10-20 1-700 <$2000
1902 Date Back
3x10-20 1-1990 <$750
1902 Plain Back
3x10-20 1991-5580 <$750
1929 Small Size
10 Type 1 1-648 <$350
20 Type 1 1-172 <$350
10 Type 2 1-710 <$400
20 Type 2 1-175 <$400
Total Issue $384,120
Out in 1935 $25,000
Large out 1935 $1,780
****
10786 Lincoln
HUGO NB, HUGO
{{ 1 L }}
Chartered 10/15
Liquidated 5/17/27
1902 Plain Back <$VALUE
4x5 1-550 <$2500
3x10-20 1-1392 <$2500
Total Issue $66,680
Out at close $10,000
****
2962 Clear Creek
FNB OF IDAHO SPRINGS
{{ 6 L }}
Organized 5/19/83
Receivership 12/23/31
Brown Back <$VALUE
3x10-20 1-2343 <$3000
1902 Red Seal
4x5 1-750 <$3000
3x10-20 1-1000 <$3000
1902 Date Back
4x5 1-3700 <$750
3x10-20 1-2740 <$750
1902 Plain Back
4x5 3701-6550 <$750
3x10-20 2741-7250 <$750
Total Issue $675,650
Out at close $4,835
****
5989 Clear Creek
MERCHANTS & MINERS NB OF IDAHO SPRINGS
{{ 1 L }}
Chartered 10/01
Liquidated 4/1/18
Brown Back <$VALUE
3x10-20 1-770 <$3500
1882 Date Back
3x10-20 1-1176 <$3000
Total Issue $97,300
Out in 1917 $1,250
****
8636 Weld
FNB OF JOHNSTOWN
{{ 3 L U + 8 S }}
Chartered 4/07
1902 Red Seal <$VALUE
3x10-20 1-800 <$2500
1902 Date Back
3x10-20 1-1920 <$1000
1902 Plain Back
3x10-20 1921-4872 <$1000
1929 Small Size
10 Type 1 1-624 <$300
20 Type 1 1-212 <$300
10 Type 2 1-1632 <$325
20 Type 2 1-380 <$350
Total Issue $370,400
Out in 1935 $60,000
Large out 1935 $1,590
****

****
9603 Sedgwick
CITIZENS NB OF JULESBURG
{{ 2 L }}
Organized 9/29/09
Receivership 6/12/24
1902 Date Back <$VALUE
4x5 1-1765 <$1500
3x10-20 1-1334 <$1500
1902 Plain Back
4x5 1766-4200 <$1500
3x10-20 1335-2709 <$1500
Total Issue $219,450
Out at close $24,000
****
8205 Sedgwick
FNB OF JULESBURG
{{ 5 L 12 S }}
Chartered 5/06
1902 Red Seal <$VALUE
3x10-20 1-750 <$2000
1902 Date Back
3x10-20 1-3550 <$750
1902 Plain Back
3x10-20 3551-10557 <$750
1929 Small Size
10 Type 1 1-1148 <$225
20 Type 1 1-350 <$225
10 Type 2 1-1010 <$250
20 Type 2 1-318 <$275
Total Issue $692,690
Out in 1935 $50,000
Large out 1935 $2,050
****
9840 Conejos
FNB OF LA JARA
{{ 3 L 8 S }}
Chartered 9/10
1902 Date Back <$VALUE
3x10-20 1-600 <$1250
1902 Plain Back
3x10-20 601-1850 <$1250
1929 Small Size
5 Type 1 1-148 <$325
10 Type 1 1-810 <$325
20 Type 1 1-234 <$325
5 Type 2 1-3288 <$350
10 Type 2 1-1596 <$350
Total Issue $206,020
Out in 1935 $40,000
Large out 1935 $840
****
4507 Otero
FNB OF LA JUNTA
{{ 7 L 8 S }}
Organized 11/19/90
Receivership 6/18/34
Brown Back <$VALUE
4x5 1-3600 <$1750
3x10-20 1-1100 <$1750
1882 Date Back
4x5 1-779 <$1500
3x10-20 1-692 <$1500
1902 Date Back
4x5 1-2075 <$500
3x10-20 1-1980 <$500
3x50-100 1-50 <$900/$1000
1902 Plain Back
4x5 2076-9595 <$500
3x10-20 1981-6994 <$500
1929 Small Size
5 Type 1 1-1770 <$225
10 Type 1 1-980 <$225
20 Type 1 1-262 <$250
5 Type 2 1-308 <$275
10 Type 2 1-160 <$300
Total Issue $877,760
Out at close $50,000
Large out at close $3,630
****
8909 Boulder
FNB OF LAFAYETTE
{{ 3 L 6 S }}
Organized 9/21/07
Receivership 5/9/32
1902 Red Seal <$VALUE
3x10-20 1-700 <$2000
1902 Date Back
3x10-20 1-1870 <$1000
1902 Plain Back
3x10-20 1871-4954 <$1000
1929 Small Size
10 Type 1 1-435 <$400
20 Type 1 1-143 <$425
Total Issue $325,960
Out at close $24,520
Large out at close $2,650
****

****
2354 Hinsdale
FNB OF LAKE CITY
{{ UNREPORTED }}
Chartered 4/30/77
Liquidated 6/15/78
Series 1875 <$VALUE
4x5 1-1350 <$6000
Total Issue $27,000
Out in 1910 $135
****
3749 Prowers
FNB OF LAMAR
{{ 1 L 4 S }}
Chartered 1887
Brown Back <$VALUE
4x5 1-3073 <$3500
3x10-20 1-504 <$3500
1902 Red Seal
3x10-20 1-250 <$3500
1902 Date Back
3x10-20 1-1260 <$2000
1902 Plain Back
3x10-20 1261-2268 <$2000
1929 Small Size
10 Type 1 1-316 <$500
20 Type 1 1-106 <$500
10 Type 2 1-206 <$550
20 Type 2 1-72 <$600
Total Issue $247,740
Out in 1935 $12,495
Large out 1935 $605
****
9036 Prowers
LAMAR NB, LAMAR
{{ 3 L 13 S }}
Organized 1/29/08
Liquidated 10/10/34
1902 Red Seal <$VALUE
3x10-20 1-375 <$2000
1902 Date Back
3x10-20 1-1400 <$850
1902 Plain Back
3x10-20 1401-7394 <$850
1929 Small Size
10 Type 1 1-1348 <$125
20 Type 1 1-392 <$150
10 Type 2 1-652 <$175
20 Type 2 1-206 <$200
Total Issue $527,010
Out at close $50,000
Large out at close $2,110
Ch 14254 assumed circulation
****
6030 Bent
FNB OF LAS ANIMAS
{{ 5 L 11 S }}
Chartered 11/01
Brown Back <$VALUE
3x10-20 1-1000 <$2000
1882 Date Back
3x10-20 1-2150 <$1750
1882 Value Back
3x10-20 2151-4496 <$1750
1902 Plain Back
3x10-20 1-4886 <$750
1929 Small Size
10 Type 1 1-1330 <$225
20 Type 1 1-362 <$250
10 Type 2 1-2254 <$250
20 Type 2 1-515 <$275
Total Issue $675,180
Out in 1935 $50,000
Large out 1935 $2,780
****
3949 Lake
AMERICAN NB OF LEADVILLE
{{ 5 L }}
Chartered 1888
Closed 7/13/25
Brown Back <$VALUE
4x5 1-8448 <$1500
3x10-20 1-1980 <$1500
50-100 1-956 <$3000/$3500
1902 Date Back
4x5 1-3750 <$600
3x10-20 1-5700 <$600
1902 Plain Back
3x10-20 5701-12275 <$600
Total Issue $1,100,110
Out at close $100,000
Ch 3746 assumed circulation
****
3746 Lake
CARBONATE NB OF LEADVILLE
{{ 10 L }}
Chartered 1887
Liquidated 7/11/34
Brown Back <$VALUE
4x5 1-8498 <$1250
3x10-20 1-3526 <$1250
50-100 1-514 <$3000/$3500

1902 Red Seal
4x5 1-750 <$1250
3x10-20 1-400 <$1250
50-100 1-400 <$6000
1902 Date Back
4x5 1-4750 <$400
3x10-20 1-3200 <$400
50-100 1-200 <$750/$850
1902 Plain Back
4x5 4751-10545 <$400
3x10-20 3201-7154 <$400
Total Issue $1,116,960
Out at close $12,320
Outstanding includes Ch 3949
****
2420 Lake
FNB OF LEADVILLE
{{ 3 L }}
Chartered 3/19/79
Receivership 1/24/84
Series 1875 <$VALUE
4x5 1-5385 <$2500
Total Issue $107,700
Out in 1915 $715
****
11504 Lincoln
FNB OF LIMON
{{ 2 L 6 S }}
Chartered 11/19
1902 Plain Back <$VALUE
4x5 1-12075 <$1000
1929 Small Size
10 Type 1 1-690 <$350
20 Type 1 1-222 <$350
10 Type 2 1-728 <$400
20 Type 2 1-231 <$400
Total Issue $321,440
Out in 1935 $25,000
Large out 1935 $865
****
7533 Arapahoe
FNB OF LITTLETON
{{ 4 L 5 S }}
Organized 12/9/04
Receivership 1/12/33
1902 Red Seal <$VALUE
3x10-20 1-1100 <$2000
1902 Date Back
3x10-20 1-1890 <$850
1902 Plain Back
3x10-20 1891-5655 <$850
1929 Small Size
10 Type 1 1-578 <$450
20 Type 1 1-144 <$450
Total Issue $389,710
Out at close $25,000
Large out at close $2,370
****
11949 Arapahoe
LITTLETON NB, LITTLETON
{{ 2 L 5 S }}
Chartered 3/21
1902 Plain Back <$VALUE
4x5 1-8328 <$1500
1929 Small Size
5 Type 1 1-3332 <$450
5 Type 2 1-8098 <$450
Total Issue $307,010
Out in 1935 $25,000
Large out 1935 $625
****
11253 Boulder
AMERICAN NB OF LONGMONT
Chartered 9/18
2nd title: FNB of Longmont 3/29/27
FIRST TITLE {{ 2 L }}
1902 Plain Back <$VALUE
4x5 1-15300 <$1000
SECOND TITLE {{ 21 S }}
1929 Small Size
10 Type 1 1-1232 <$100
20 Type 1 1-418 <$110
10 Type 2 1-3951 <$110
20 Type 2 1-770 <$115
Total Issue $484,990
Out in 1935 $100,000
Large out at close $5,730
Ch 4653 assumed circulation
****
4653 Boulder
FARMERS NB OF LONGMONT
{{ 3 L }}
Chartered 1891
Closed 3/29/27
Brown Back <$VALUE
3x10-20 1-2950 <$2500
1882 Date Back
3x10-20 1-1264 <$2500
1902 Date Back
3x50-100 1-889<$1250/$1500
Total Issue $432,950
Out in 1925 $50,000
****

****
3354 Boulder
FNB OF LONGMONT
{{ UNREPORTED }}
Chartered 6/17/85
Liquidated 3/15/00
Brown Back <$VALUE
3x10-20 1-1000 <$4000
Total Issue $50,000
Out in 1910 $500
****
FNB of Longmont
SEE Ch 11253
American NB of Longmont
****
7839 Boulder
LONGMONT NB, LONGMONT
{{ 5 L 2U + 6 S }}
Chartered 7/05
1902 Red Seal <$VALUE
3x10-20 1-2000 <$1500
1902 Date Back
3x10-20 1-3700 <$650
1902 Plain Back
3x10-20 3701-10813 <$650
1929 Small Size
10 Type 1 1-1292 <$200
20 Type 1 1-370 <$225
10 Type 2 1-1597 <$225
20 Type 2 1-260 <$250
Total Issue $783,740
Out in 1935 $50,000
Large out 1935 $2,990
****
7648 Larimer
FNB OF LOVELAND
{{ 6 L 10 S }}
Chartered 3/05
Liquidated 8/20/32
1902 Red Seal <$VALUE
3x10-20 1-2200 <$1500
1902 Date Back
3x10-20 1-3540 <$500
1902 Plain Back
3x10-20 3541-10741 <$500
1929 Small Size
10 Type 1 1-981 <$350
20 Type 1 1-247 <$350
Total Issue $735,550
Out at close $50,000
Large out at close $5,230
Ch 13624 assumed circulation
****
13624 Larimer
FNB OF LOVELAND
{{ 8 S }}
Chartered 7/32
1929 Small Size <$VALUE
10 Type 1 1-210 <$350
20 Type 1 1-64 <$350
10 Type 2 1-1938 <$375
20 Type 2 1-406 <$375
Total Issue $47,780
Out in 1935 $41,910
Outstanding includes Ch 7648
****
8116 Larimer
LOVELAND NB, LOVELAND
{{ 7 L }}
Organized 2/14/06
Receivership 10/22/25
1902 Red Seal <$VALUE
3x10-20 1-3100 <$1500
1902 Date Back
3x10-20 1-7800 <$450
1902 Plain Back
3x10-20 7801-17378 <$450
Total Issue $1,023,900
Out at close $100,000
9674 Montezuma
FNB OF MANCOS
{{ 5 L 8 S }}
Organized 1/18/10
Receivership 10/9/33
1902 Date Back <$VALUE
4x5 1-3400 <$650
3x10-20 1-2550 <$650
1902 Plain Back
4x5 3401-11014 <$650
3x10-20 2551-7745 <$650
1929 Small Size
5 Type 1 1-1556 <$300
10 Type 1 1-904 <$300
20 Type 1 1-250 <$300
5 Type 2 1-296 <$350
10 Type 2 1-225 <$350
20 Type 2 1-30 <$350
Total Issue $742,780
Out at close $50,000
Large out at close $3,895
****

****
7435 Rio Blanco
FNB OF MEEKER
{{ 1 L }}
Organized 8/6/04
1902 Red Seal <$VALUE
3x10-20 1-500 <$3500
1902 Date Back
3x10-20 1-1020 <$2500
1902 Plain Back
3x10-20 1021-1634 <$2500
Total Issue $106,700
Out in 1935 $370
****
7228 Rio Grande
FNB OF MONTE VISTA
{{ 6 L 3 S }}
Organized 4/8/04
Receivership 2/8/32
1902 Red Seal <$VALUE
3x10-20 1-376 <$2500
1902 Date Back
3x10-20 1-1220 <$1000
1902 Plain Back
3x10-20 1221-4816 <$1000
1929 Small Size
10 Type 1 1-436 <$600
20 Type 1 1-113 <$650
Total Issue $299,320
Out at close $24,000
Large out at close $3,280
****
4007 Montrose
FNB OF MONTROSE
{{ 9 L 9 S }}
Organized 2/21/89
Brown Back <$VALUE
4x5 1-5275 <$1500
3x10-20 1-2080 <$1500
1882 Date Back
4x5 1-346 <$1500
3x10-20 1-27 <$1500
1902 Date Back
4x5 1-4950 <$350
3x10-20 1-3960 <$350
1902 Plain Back
4x5 4951-16605 <$350
3x10-20 3961-11290 <$350
1929 Small Size
5 Type 1 1-2704 <$175
10 Type 1 1-1270 <$175
20 Type 1 1-352 <$185
5 Type 2 1-4200 <$200
10 Type 2 1-2127 <$200
20 Type 2 1-636 <$200
Total Issue $1,368,920
Out in 1935 $76,000
Large out 1935 $5,165
****
7288 Montrose
MONTROSE NB, MONTROSE
{{ 2 L 3 S }}
Chartered 6/04
1902 Red Seal <$VALUE
4x5 1-600 <$2500
3x10-20 1-480 <$2500
1902 Date Back
4x5 1-1450 <$1500
3x10-20 1-1140 <$1500
1902 Plain Back
4x5 1451-3165 <$1500
3x10-20 1141-2298 <$1500
1929 Small Size
5 Type 1 1-416 <$500
10 Type 1 1-294 <$500
20 Type 1 1-86 <$525
5 Type 2 1-520 <$550
10 Type 2 1-312 <$550
20 Type 2 1-48 <$600
Total Issue $261,320
Out in 1935 $15,000
Large out 1935 $930
****
9719 Montrose
FNB OF OLATHE
{{ 3 L 9 S }}
Chartered 4/10
1902 Date Back <$VALUE
3x10-20 1-2090 <$1000
1902 Plain Back
3x10-20 2091-5616 <$1000
1929 Small Size
5 Type 1 1-240 <$300
10 Type 1 1-564 <$300
20 Type 1 1-160 <$325
5 Type 2 1-2296 <$350
Total Issue $358,020
Out in 1935 $25,000
Large out 1935 $1,390
****

****
8695 Crowley
FNB OF ORDWAY
{{ 1 L 2 S }}
Chartered 5/07
1902 Red Seal <$VALUE
3x10-20 1-300 <$3500
1902 Date Back
3x10-20 1-920 <$2500
1902 Plain Back
3x10-20 921-2216 <$2500
1929 Small Size
10 Type 1 1-295 <$800
20 Type 1 1-97 <$850
Total Issue $155,140
Out in 1935 $10,000
Large out 1935 $540
****
10852 Washington
FNB OF OTIS
{{ 1 L 6 S }}
Chartered 5/16
1902 Plain Back <$VALUE
4x10 1-2234 <$2500
1929 Small Size
10 Type 1 1-522 <$400
10 Type 2 1-249 <$450
Total Issue $123,170
Out in 1935 $10,000
Large out 1935 $360
****
4109 Ouray
FNB OF OURAY
{{ UNREPORTED }}
Chartered 9/2/89
Liquidated 1/23/95
Brown Back <$VALUE
4x5 1-1352 <$5000
Total Issue $27,040
Out in 1910 $185
****
8004 Mesa
PALISADES NB, PALISADES
{{ 3 L 8 S }}
Organized 10/17/05
1902 Red Seal <$VALUE
3x10-20 1-870 <$2500
1902 Date Back
3x10-20 1-1860 <$1250
1902 Plain Back
3x10-20 1861-5581 <$1250
1929 Small Size
10 Type 1 1-630 <$400
20 Type 1 1-184 <$400
10 Type 2 1-1189 <$400
20 Type 2 1-170 <$450
Total Issue $397,720
Out in 1935 $25,000
Large out 1935 $1,210
****
6671 Delta
FNB OF PAONIA
{{ 4 L 16 S }}
Organized 1/6/03
1902 Red Seal <$VALUE
3x10-20 1-850 <$2000
1902 Date Back
3x10-20 1-1490 <$850
1902 Plain Back
3x10-20 1491-5217 <$850
1929 Small Size
10 Type 1 1-640 <$225
20 Type 1 1-178 <$225
10 Type 2 1-546 <$200
20 Type 2 1-192 <$250
Total Issue $372,410
Out in 1935 $25,000
Large out 1935 $1,160
****
8755 Weld
FNB OF PLATTEVILLE
{{ UNREPORTED }}
Chartered 6/07
Liquidated 4/15/11
1902 Red Seal <$VALUE
4x10 1-468 <$5000
1902 Date Back
4x10 1-386 <$3500
Total Issue $34,160
Out in 1911 $8,050
****
9451 Weld
PLATTEVILLE NB,
PLATTEVILLE
{{ 1 L }}
Chartered 6/09
1902 Date Back <$VALUE
4x10 1-975 <$2500
1902 Plain Back
4x10 976-1850 <$2500
Total Issue $74,000
Out in 1935 $230
****

****
4108 Pueblo
AMERICAN NB OF PUEBLO
Organized 8/31/89
Receivership 3/30/15
2nd title: Mercantile NB of Pueblo 6/1/98
FIRST TITLE {{ 0 L }}
Brown Back <$VALUE
3x10-20 1-650 <$3000
50-100 1-591 <$3500/$4000
SECOND TITLE {{ 3 L }}
Brown Back
4x5 1-2000 <$1500
50-100 1-1431 <$2500/$3000
1882 Date Back
4x5 1-735 <$1250
1902 Date Back
4x5 1-4125 <$500
50-100 1-800 <$650/$750
3x50-100 1-41 <$650/$750
Total Issue $603,250
Out in 1916 $52,640
****
Central NB of Pueblo
SEE Ch 2541
South Pueblo NB, South Pueblo
****
1833 Pueblo
FNB OF PUEBLO
Chartered 6/5/71
TERRITORIAL ISSUES {{ 11 L }}
Original Series <$VALUE
3x1-2 1-1500 <$3500/$6000
4x5 1-3375 <$3500
Series 1875
4x5 1-12750 <$3500
STATE ISSUES {{ U + 13 L 33 S }}
Series 1875
4x5 12751-12899 <$2500
Brown Back
50-100 1-6725 <$2500/$3000
1882 Date Back
4x5 1-2770 <$600
1902 Date Back
3x10-20 1-3000 <$200
3x50-100 1-4000 <$350/$400
1902 Plain Back
3x50-100 4001-4692 <$350/$400
1929 Small Size
50 Type 1 1-1210 <$125
100 Type 1 1-451 <$185
Total Issue $3,353,730
Out in 1935 $500,000
Large out 1935 $30,350
****
Mercantile NB of Pueblo
SEE Ch 4108
American NB of Pueblo
****
2134 Pueblo
PEOPLES NB OF PUEBLO
{{ 1 L }}
Chartered 2/10/74
Liquidated 1/12/75
TERRITORIAL ISSUES
Original Series <$VALUE
3x1-2 1-900 <$4000/$6500
4x5 1-1125 <$4500
Total Issue $27,000
Out in 1910 $165
****
4498 Pueblo
PUEBLO NB, PUEBLO
{{ 1 L }}
Chartered 1/19/91
Liquidated 10/20/02
Brown Back <$VALUE
3x10-20 1-5074 <$2500
Total Issue $253,700
Out in 1910 $5,250
****
2310 Pueblo
STOCK GROWERS NB OF PUEBLO
{{ UNREPORTED }}
Chartered 12/8/75
Liquidated 6/1/98
TERRITORIAL ISSUES
Series 1875 <$VALUE
4x10 1-1250 <$5000
STATE ISSUES
Series 1875
4x10 1251-2866 <$4000
Brown Back
50-100 1-124 <$4500
Total Issue $133,240
Out in 1910 $1,170
****
Western NB of Pueblo
SEE Ch 2546
Western NB of South Pueblo
****

****
4334 Dolores
FNB OF RICO
{{ 1 L }}
Chartered 6/4/90
Liquidated 4/30/95
Brown Back <$VALUE
3x10-20 1-471 <$4000
Total Issue $23,550
Out in 1910 $240
****
6178 Garfield
FNB OF RIFLE
{{ 2 L }}
Organized 12/5/01
Receivership 12/24/25
1902 Red Seal <$VALUE
4x5 1-425 <$4000
3x10-20 1-340 <$4000
1902 Date Back
4x5 1-2150 <$2500
3x10-20 1-1690 <$2500
1902 Plain Back (dated 1901)
4x5 2151-3565 <$2500
3x10-20 1691-2377 <$2500
1902 Plain Back (dated 1921)
4x5 1-1265 <$2500
3x10-20 1-828 <$2500
Total Issue $282,350
Out at close $24,500
****
7082 Otero
FNB OF ROCKY FORD
{{ 1 L }}
Organized 10/23/03
Receivership 4/5/24
1902 Red Seal <$VALUE
3x10-20 1-732 <$3000
1902 Date Back
3x10-20 1-1430 <$1750
1902 Plain Back
3x10-20 1431-2154 <$1750
Total Issue $144,300
Out at close $14,100
****
9117 Otero
ROCKY FORD NB, ROCKY FORD
{{ 6 L 12 S }}
Chartered 4/08
1902 Red Seal <$VALUE
4x5 1-625 <$1750
3x10-20 1-500 <$1750
1902 Date Back
4x5 1-2150 <$600
3x10-20 1-1640 <$600
1902 Plain Back
4x5 2151-10269 <$600
3x10-20 1641-6882 <$600
1929 Small Size
5 Type 1 1-2024 <$275
10 Type 1 1-948 <$275
20 Type 1 1-250 <$275
5 Type 2 1-2530 <$300
10 Type 2 1-1812 <$300
20 Type 2 1-348 <$325
Total Issue $772,310
Out in 1935 $50,000
Large out at close $2,450
****
9997 Saguache
FNB OF SAGUACHE
Chartered 4/11
2nd title: Saguache County NB of Saguache 8/12/27
FIRST TITLE {{ 0 L }}
1902 Date Back <$VALUE
3x10-20 1-1480 <$2500
1902 Plain Back
3x10-20 1481-2579 <$2500
SECOND TITLE {{ 0 L U + 12 S }}
1902 Plain Back
3x10-20 1-340 <$2500
1929 Small Size
5 Type 1 1-1570 <$200
10 Type 1 1-978 <$200
20 Type 1 1-276 <$225
5 Type 2 1-3928 <$250
10 Type 2 1-1593 <$250
20 Type 2 1-543 <$275
Total Issue $331,280
Out in 1935 $60,000
Large out 1935 $910
****
Saguache County NB of Saguache
SEE Ch 9997
FNB of Saguache
****

****
7888 Chaffee
COMMERCIAL NB OF SALIDA
{{ 3 L 3 S }}
Chartered 8/05
Liquidated 5/22/31
1902 Red Seal <$VALUE
4x5 1-485 <$2500
3x10-20 1-368 <$2500
1902 Date Back
4x5 1-1225 <$1250
3x10-20 1-920 <$1250
1902 Plain Back
4x5 1226-2810 <$1250
3x10-20 921-1931 <$1250
1929 Small Size
5 Type 1 1-246 <$600
10 Type 1 1-113 <$600
20 Type 1 1-26 <$650
Total Issue $198,130
Out at close $25,000
Large out at close $1,860
****
4172 Chaffee
FNB OF SALIDA
{{ 5 L 21 S }}
Chartered 12/5/89
Brown Back <$VALUE
4x5 1-2875 <$1750
50-100 1-190 <$3000/$3500
1902 Date Back
4x5 1-1500* <$450
3x10-20 1-1200** <$450
1902 Plain Back
4x5 1701-5615* <$450
3x10-20 1361-3774** <$450
* 1501-1700 not marked
** 1201-1360 not marked
1929 Small Size
5 Type 1 1-4066 <$125
10 Type 1 1-1938 <$125
20 Type 1 1-498 <$135
5 Type 2 1-5420 <$150
10 Type 2 1-3138 <$150
20 Type 2 1-972 <$165
Total Issue $762,940
Out in 1935 $100,000
Large out 1935 $2,290
Outstanding includes Ch 8951
****
8951 Chaffee
MERCHANTS NB OF SALIDA
{{ UNREPORTED }}
Chartered 11/07
Liquidated 7/1/12
1902 Red Seal <$VALUE
3x10-20 1-375 <$3500
1902 Date Back
3x10-20 1-380 <$3000
Total Issue $37,750
Out at close $12,500
Ch 4172 assumed circulation
****
9045 Sedgwick
FNB OF SEDGWICK
{{ 3 L 8 S }}
Chartered 2/08
1902 Red Seal <$VALUE
4x10 1-300 <$2500
1902 Date Back
4x10 1-2850 <$1000
1902 Plain Back
4x10 2851-7894 <$1000
1929 Small Size
10 Type 1 1-1152 <$300
10 Type 2 1-1344 <$350
Total Issue $410,320
Out in 1935 $25,000
Large out 1935 $1,060
****
2930 San Juan
FNB OF SILVERTON
{{ 0 L 1 S }}
Chartered 1883
Liquidated 3/1/34
Brown Back <$VALUE
3x10-20 1-1367 <$4500
1902 Red Seal
3x10-20 1-600 <$5000
1902 Date Back
3x10-20 1-1270 <$3000
1902 Plain Back
3x10-20 1271-2532 <$3000
1929 Small Size
10 Type 1 1-304 <$850
20 Type 1 1-102 <$900
10 Type 2 1-44 <$1000
20 Type 2 1-27 <$1000
Total Issue $256,410
Out at close $13,000
Large out at close $1,170
****

****
7784 San Juan
SILVERTON NB, SILVERTON
{{ UNREPORTED }}
Organized 6/12/05
Receivership 4/9/15
1902 Red Seal <$VALUE
3x10-20 1-940 <$5000
1902 Date Back
3x10-20 1-1666 <$3500
Total Issue $130,300
Out in 1915 $17,600
****
2541 Pueblo
SOUTH PUEBLO NB,
SOUTH PUEBLO
{{ UNREPORTED }}
Chartered 7/6/81
Liquidated 1/15/98
2nd title: Central NB of Pueblo 1889
FIRST TITLE
Series 1875 <$VALUE
3x10-20 1-842 <$5000
SECOND TITLE
Series 1875
50-100 1-191 <$8500
Total Issue $70,750
Out in 1910 $660
****
2546 Pueblo
WESTERN NB OF
SOUTH PUEBLO
Chartered 1881
2nd title: Western NB of Pueblo 2/6/93
FIRST TITLE {{ 1 L }}
Series 1875 <$VALUE
4x5 1-6019 <$3000
SECOND TITLE {{ 10 L 18 S }}
Series 1875
4x5 1-3300 <$2500
Brown Back
3x10-20 1-4500 <$1000
1882 Date Back
3x10-20 1-6400 <$850
1882 Value Back
3x10-20 6401-9998 <$850
1902 Plain Back
3x10-20 1-9435 <$250
1929 Small Size
10 Type 1 1-2786 <$100
20 Type 1 1-712 <$100
10 Type 2 1-2818 <$125
20 Type 2 1-829 <$125
Total Issue $1,680,390
Out in 1935 $100,000
Large out at close $6,825
****
6454 Routt
FNB OF STEAMBOAT SPRINGS
{{ 1 L 2 S }}
Organized 9/12/02
Receivership 11/17/31
1902 Red Seal <$VALUE
4x5 1-556 <$5000
3x10-20 1-414 <$5000
1902 Date Back
4x5 1-800 <$3500
3x10-20 1-620 <$3500
1902 Plain Back
4x5 801-2469 <$3500
3x10-20 621-1500 <$3500
1929 Small Size
5 Type 1 1-217 <$2000
10 Type 1 1-106 <$2000
20 Type 1 1-33 <$2000
Total Issue $173,030
Out at close $10,000
Large out at close $1,250
****
9454 Logan
FARMERS NB OF STERLING
{{ UNREPORTED }}
Chartered 6/09
Liquidated 6/28/21
1902 Date Back <$VALUE
3x10-20 1-1500 <$3500
1902 Plain Back
3x10-20 1501-1605 <$3500
Total Issue $80,250
Out at close $12,500
****

****

5624 Logan
FNB OF STERLING
{{ 6 L }}
Organized 10/29/00
Receivership 4/5/24
Brown Back <$VALUE
4x5 1-525 <$1500
3x10-20 1-440 <$1500
1882 Date Back
4x5 1-7650 <$1250
3x10-20 1-5720 <$1250
1882 Value Back
4x5 7651-12367 <$1250
3x10-20 5721-8316 <$1250
1902 Plain Back
4x5 1-4050 <$400
3x10-20 1-3054 <$400
Total Issue $929,340
Out at close $98,300

****

7973 Logan
LOGAN COUNTY NB OF STERLING
{{ 6 L }}
Organized 10/11/05
Receivership 1/26/25
1902 Red Seal <$VALUE
3x10-20 1-1312 <$1750
1902 Date Back
3x10-20 1-3700 <$750
1902 Plain Back
3x10-20 3701-17302 <$750
Total Issue $930,700
Out at close $100,000

****

6472 Crowley
CITIZENS NB OF SUGAR CITY
{{ 1 L }}
Chartered 10/27/02
Liquidated 3/31/05
1902 Red Seal <$VALUE
4x5 1-275 <$7500
3x10-20 1-236 <$7500
Total Issue $17,300
Out in 1910 $580

****

4417 San Miguel
FNB OF TELLURIDE
{{ 5 L }}
Chartered 1890
Liquidated 12/27/24
Brown Back <$VALUE
4x5 1-4425 <$2500
3x10-20 1-1600 <$2500
1882 Date Back
4x5 1-206 <$2250
3x10-20 1-55 <$2250
1902 Date Back
3x10-20 1-1900 <$1250
1902 Plain Back
3x10-20 1901-5402 <$1250
Total Issue $445,470
Out at close $50,000

****

2300 Las Animas
FNB OF TRINIDAD
Chartered 9/24/75
Liquidated 9/4/34
TERRITORIAL ISSUES {{ 1 L }}
Series 1875 <$VALUE
4x5 1-1350 <$4000
STATE ISSUES {{ 11 L 12 S }}
Series 1875
4x5 1351-8761 <$2500
Brown Back
50-100 1-2361 <$3000/$3500
1882 Date Back
50-100 1-1300 <$2500/$3000
3x50-100 1-197<$2500/$3000
1902 Date Back
3x50-100 1-2560 <$450/$500
1902 Plain Back
3x50-100 2561-3165
<$450/$500
1929 Small Size
5 Type 1 1-530 <$125
10 Type 1 1-140 <$125
50 Type 1 1-492 <$200
100 Type 1 1-144 <$250
Total Issue $1,823,130
Out at close $200,000
Large out at close $25,100

****

3450 Las Animas
TRINIDAD NB, TRINIDAD
{{ 15 L 16 S }}
Organized 1/23/86
Liquidated 6/4/34
Brown Back <$VALUE
3x10-20 1-6622 <$1000
1902 Red Seal
3x10-20 1-2800 <$1000
1902 Date Back
3x10-20 1-7100 <$200
1902 Plain Back
3x10-20 7101-20826 <$200
1929 Small Size
10 Type 1 1-2355 <$100
20 Type 1 1-558 <$100
Total Issue $1,720,660
Out at close $100,000
Large out at close $8,890

****

5586 Teller
FNB OF VICTOR
{{ UNREPORTED }}
Organized 9/25/00
Receivership 11/4/03
Brown Back <$VALUE
3x10-20 1-974 <$5000
50-100 1-211 <$6000
Total Issue $80,350
Out in 1915 $1,410

****

7022 Huerfano
FNB OF WALSENBURG
{{ UNREPORTED }}
Chartered 10/03
1902 Red Seal <$VALUE
3x10-20 1-750 <$4500
1902 Date Back
3x10-20 1-1346 <$3500
Total Issue $104,800
Out in 1935 $400

****

7793 Larimer
FNB OF WELLINGTON
{{ 3 L 4 S }}
Organized 6/3/05
Receivership 1/24/33
1902 Red Seal <$VALUE
3x10-20 1-256 <$2500
1902 Date Back
3x10-20 1-2560 <$1000
1902 Plain Back
3x10-20 2561-6286 <$1000
1929 Small Size
10 Type 1 1-551 <$500
20 Type 1 1-149 <$500
Total Issue $378,040
Out at close $25,000
Large out at close $2,250

****

9120 Weld
FARMERS NB OF WINDSOR
{{ UNREPORTED }}
Chartered 4/08
Liquidated 2/1/13
1902 Date Back <$VALUE
3x10-20 1-401 <$3500
Total Issue $20,050
Out in 1913 $3,300

****

8296 Weld
FNB OF WINDSOR
{{ 2 L }}
Chartered 7/06
1902 Red Seal <$VALUE
3x10-20 1-900 <$2500
1902 Date Back
3x10-20 1-1070 <$1500
1902 Plain Back
3x10-20 1071-1590 <$1500
Total Issue $124,500
Out in 1935 $510

****

8752 Yuma
FNB OF WRAY
{{ 3 L U + 8 S }}
Chartered 6/07
1902 Red Seal <$VALUE
3x10-20 1-240 <$2000
1902 Date Back
3x10-20 1-2000 <$850
1902 Plain Back
3x10-20 2001-6264 <$850
1929 Small Size
10 Type 1 1-706 <$250
20 Type 1 1-232 <$275
10 Type 2 1-486 <$300
20 Type 2 1-30 <$325
Total Issue $400,860
Out in 1935 $30,000
Large out 1935 $2,160

****

9676 Yuma
NB OF WRAY
{{ 2 L 6 S }}
Chartered 2/10
1902 Date Back <$VALUE
3x10-20 1-2380 <$1000
1902 Plain Back
3x10-20 2381-6512 <$1000
1929 Small Size
10 Type 1 1-682 <$300
20 Type 1 1-230 <$325
10 Type 2 1-498 <$375
20 Type 2 1-160 <$400
Total Issue $402,300
Out in 1935 $30,000
Large out 1935 $1,870

****

10093 Yuma
FNB OF YUMA
{{ 5 L 4 S }}
Chartered 10/16/11
Receivership 10/16/31
1902 Date Back <$VALUE
3x10-20 1-1600 <$850
1902 Plain Back
3x10-20 1601-5086 <$850
1929 Small Size
10 Type 1 1-344 <$500
20 Type 1 1-105 <$500
Total Issue $287,540
Out at close $25,000
Large out at close $3,910

****

CONDITION affects Value. The Values shown are for notes in FINE condition.

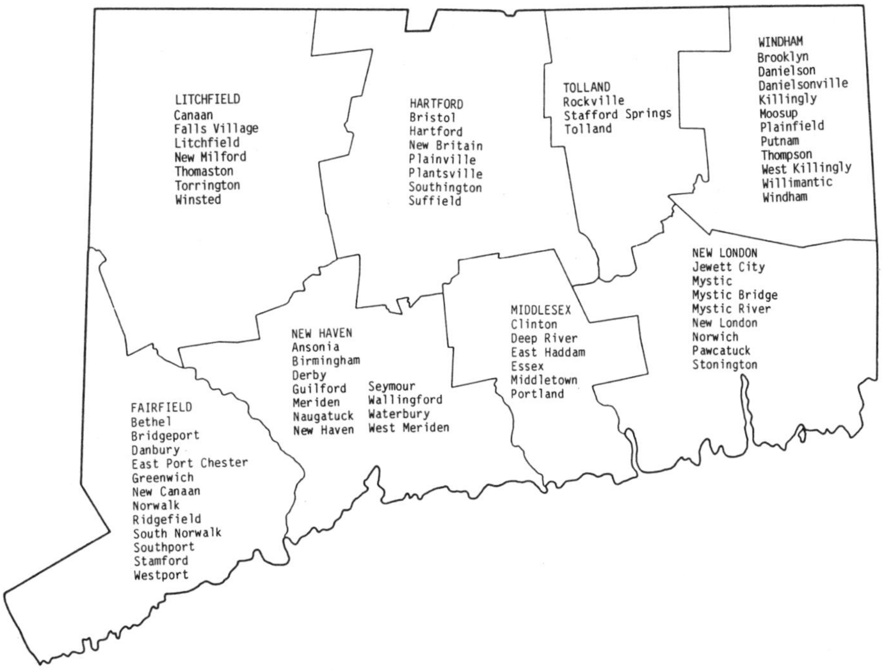

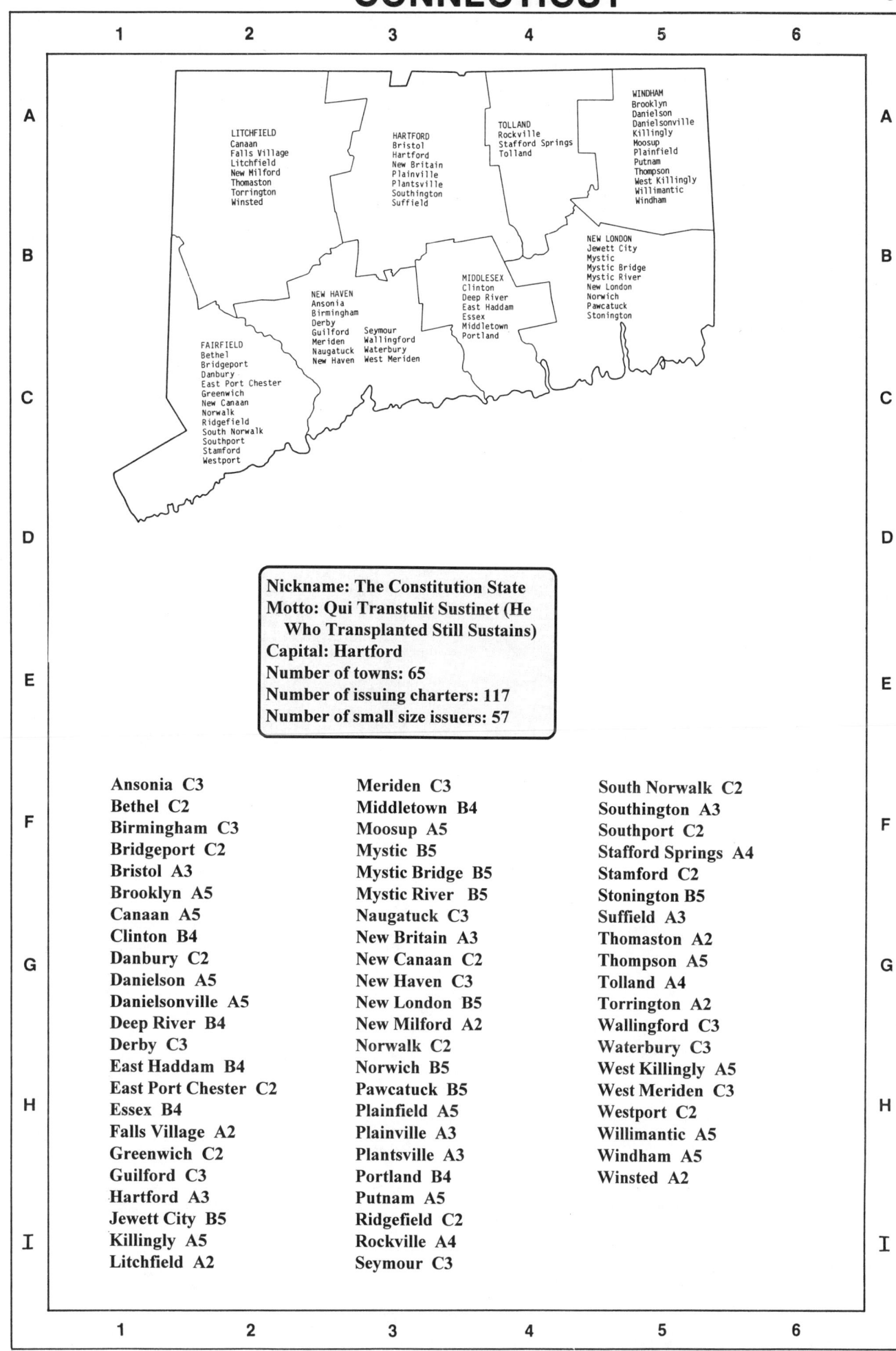

Nickname: The Constitution State
Motto: Qui Transtulit Sustinet (He Who Transplanted Still Sustains)
Capital: Hartford
Number of towns: 65
Number of issuing charters: 117
Number of small size issuers: 57

Ansonia C3
Bethel C2
Birmingham C3
Bridgeport C2
Bristol A3
Brooklyn A5
Canaan A5
Clinton B4
Danbury C2
Danielson A5
Danielsonville A5
Deep River B4
Derby C3
East Haddam B4
East Port Chester C2
Essex B4
Falls Village A2
Greenwich C2
Guilford C3
Hartford A3
Jewett City B5
Killingly A5
Litchfield A2
Meriden C3
Middletown B4
Moosup A5
Mystic B5
Mystic Bridge B5
Mystic River B5
Naugatuck C3
New Britain A3
New Canaan C2
New Haven C3
New London B5
New Milford A2
Norwalk C2
Norwich B5
Pawcatuck B5
Plainfield A5
Plainville A3
Plantsville A3
Portland B4
Putnam A5
Ridgefield C2
Rockville A4
Seymour C3
South Norwalk C2
Southington A3
Southport C2
Stafford Springs A4
Stamford C2
Stonington B5
Suffield A3
Thomaston A2
Thompson A5
Tolland A4
Torrington A2
Wallingford C3
Waterbury C3
West Killingly A5
West Meriden C3
Westport C2
Willimantic A5
Windham A5
Winsted A2

****
1093 New Haven
ANSONIA NB, ANSONIA
{{ 8 L 4 S }}
Chartered 5/65
Original Series <$VALUE
3x1-2 1-1200 <$650/$1500
4x5 1-3600 <$750
3x10-20 1-1000 <$850/$1250
50-100 1-270 <$4000
Series 1875
4x5 1-8100 <$750
3x10-20 1-3900 <$850/$1250
Brown Back
3x10-20 1-8363 <$500
1902 Red Seal
3x10-20 1-1900 <$600
1902 Date Back
3x10-20 1-5800 <$300
1902 Plain Back
3x10-20 5801-12485 <$300
1929 Small Size
10 Type 1 1-1316 <$275
20 Type 1 1-326 <$275
10 Type 2 1-2361 <$300
20 Type 2 1-565 <$300
Total Issue $1,815,890
Out in 1935 $48,900
Large out 1935 $4,650
****
10289 Fairfield
BETHEL NB, BETHEL
{{ 3 L 6 S }}
Chartered 11/07/12
1902 Date Back <$VALUE
4x5 1-1375 <$600
4x10 1-1375 <$600
1902 Plain Back
4x5 1376-7374 <$600
4x10 1376-5634 <$600
1929 Small Size
5 Type 1 1-1552 <$275
10 Type 1 1-602 <$275
5 Type 2 1-2874 <$300
10 Type 2 1-1504 <$300
Total Issue $484,930
Out in 1935 $24,600
Large out 1935 $910
****
1141 Fairfield
FNB OF BETHEL
{{ UNREPORTED }}
Organized 5/15/65
Receivership 2/28/68
Original Series <$VALUE
4x5 1-915 <$2000
4x10 1-200 <$2500
Total Issue $26,300
Out in 1916 $130
****
1098 New Haven
BIRMINGHAM NB, BIRMINGHAM
Chartered 1865
2nd title:Birmingham NB of Derby 1905
FIRST TITLE {{ 6 L }}
Original Series <$VALUE
3x1-2 1-3520 <$400/$1250
4x5 1-3000 <$500
3x10-20 1-4800 <$750/$1250
50-100 1-1467 <$4000
Series 1875
4x5 1-6500 <$500
3x10-20 1-5898 <$750/$1000
Brown Back
4x5 1-21547 <$400
3x10-20 1-15040 <$400
SECOND TITLE {{ 20 L 23 S }}
1902 Red Seal
4x5 1-7750 <$350
3x10-20 1-5000 <$350
1902 Date Back
4x5 1-30500 <$125
3x10-20 1-21600 <$125
1902 Plain Back
4x5 30501-95640 <$125
3x10-20 21601-60686 <$125
1929 Small Size
5 Type 1 1-11626 <$60
10 Type 1 1-6112 <$60
20 Type 1 1-1634 <$65
5 Type 2 1-19570 <$65
10 Type 2 1-9756 <$65
20 Type 2 1-3360 <$75
Total Issue $8,672,660
Out in 1935 $290,700
Large out 1935 $17,240
****

****
910 Fairfield
BRIDGEPORT NB, BRIDGEPORT
{{ 6 L }}
Chartered 3/18/65
Liquidated 7/20/09
Original Series <$VALUE
3x1-2 1-2700 <$400/$1000
4x5 1-4750 <$500
3x10-20 1-3807 <$750/$1250
50-100 1-484 <$4000
Series 1875
3x1-2 1-400 <$400/$1000
4x5 1-3680 <$500
3x10-20 1-5520 <$650/$1000
50-100 1-40 <$4000
Brown Back
4x5 1-19150 <$300
3x10-20 1-12625 <$300/$350
50-100 1-200 <$1250/$1500
1902 Red Seal
4x5 1-10750 <$400
4x10 1-2000 <$400
3x10-20 1-3000 <$400
1902 Date Back
4x5 1-982 <$200
4x10 1-1310 <$200
3x10-20 1-1344 <$200
Total Issue $2,360,540
Out in 1910 $69,350
****
921 Fairfield
CITY NB OF BRIDGEPORT
{{ 8 L }}
Chartered 3/21/65
Liquidated 9/20/29
Original Series <$VALUE
3x1-2 1-2600 <$350/$1000
4x5 1-3850 <$400
3x10-20 1-5254 <$750/$1250
50-100 1-1262 <$4000
Series 1875
4x5 1-4995 <$400
3x10-20 1-5000 <$650/$1000
Brown Back
3x10-20 1-12032 <$300/$350
1902 Red Seal
3x10-20 1-8500 <$400
1902 Date Back
3x10-20 1-26400 <$175
1902 Plain Back
3x10-20 26401-28078 <$175
Total Issue $3,322,400
Out at close 10,650
****
927 Fairfield
CONNECTICUT NB OF BRIDGEPORT
{{ 15 L }}
Chartered 3/23/65
Closed 1/29/21
Original Series <$VALUE
3x1-2 1-10600 <$300/$850
4x5 1-10800 <$350
3x10-20 1-3248 <$750/$1250
Series 1875
4x5 1-7100 <$350
3x10-20 1-6060 <$650/$1000
Brown Back
4x5 1-8950 <$200
3x10-20 1-15820 <$200/$250
1902 Red Seal
3x10-20 1-14000 <$350
1902 Date Back
3x10-20 1-29820 <$125
1902 Plain Back
3x10-20 29821-49338 <$125
Total Issue $5,013,300
Out at close $298,800
Ch 335 assumed circulation
****
335 Fairfield
FNB OF BRIDGEPORT
Chartered 3/64
2nd title: F-Bridgeport NB 7/21/09
3rd title: FNB of Bridgeport 1/29/21
4th title: FNB & TC of Bridgeport 11/1/29
FIRST TITLE {{ 5 L }}
Original Series <$VALUE
3x1-2 1-8000 <$300/$850
4x5 1-7000 <$350
3x10-20 1-2500 <$750/$1250
50-100 1-700 <$4000
Series 1875
3x10-20 1-4002 <$650/$1000
50-100 1-396 <$4000
Brown Back
4x5 1-3000 <$250
3x10-20 1-17476 <$250
50-100 1-1000 <$1250/$1500
1902 Red Seal
4x5 1-16500 <$350
3x10-20 1-9300 <$350
1902 Date Back
4x5 1-3286 <$100
3x10-20 1-1319 <$100
SECOND TITLE {{ 14 L }}
1902 Date Back
4x5 1-50550 <$75
4x10 1-49100 <$75
1902 Plain Back
4x5 50551-103550 <$75
4x10 49101-86600 <$75
THIRD TITLE {{ 24 L 3 S }}
1902 Plain Back
4x5 1-112381 <$65
4x10 1-50773 <$65
3x10-20 1-51632 <$65/$75
1929 Small Size
5 Type 1 1-3884 <$125
10 Type 1 1-1948 <$125
20 Type 1 1-652 <$125
FOURTH TITLE {{ U + 42 S }}
1929 Small Size
5 Type 1 1-35834 <$20
10 Type 1 1-16776 <$25
20 Type 1 1 -4708 <$35
5 Type 2 1-25890 <$30
10 Type 2 1-13254 <$35
20 Type 2 1-3545 <$45
Total Issue $18,366,180
Out in 1935 $408,490
Large out 1935 $51,665
Outstanding includes Ch 927 and Ch 928
****
928 Fairfield
PEQUONNOCK NB OF BRIDGEPORT
{{ 7 L }}
Chartered 3/23/65
Liquidated 12/3/13
Original Series <$VALUE
3x1-2 1-4000 <$450/$1250
4x5 1-7115 <$500
3x10-20 1-3400 <$750/$1250
Series 1875
3x1-2 1-920 <$450/$1250
4x5 1-6000 <$500
3x10-20 1-4900 <$750/$1250
Brown Back
4x5 1-7043 <$400
3x10-20 1-4812 <$400/$450
50-100 1-67 <$1250/$1500
1902 Red Seal
3x10-20 1-2000 <$500
1902 Date Back
4x5 1-3345 <$250
3x10-20 1-11709 <$250
Total Issue $1,845,760
Out at close $149,995
Ch 335 assumed circulation
****
2250 Hartford
BRISTOL NB, BRISTOL
{{ 19 L }}
Chartered 4/21/75
Liquidated 6/21/29
Original Series <$VALUE
3x10-20 1-1800 <$750/$1250
Series 1875
3x10-20 1-3366 <$650/$1000
Brown Back
4x5 1-2750 <$250
3x10-20 1-8340 <$250/$300
1882 Date Back
4x5 1-9315 <$250
3x10-20 1-6061 <$250/$300
1902 Date Back
4x5 1-1665 <$125
3x10-20 1-1334 <$125
1902 Plain Back
4x5 1666-31235 <$125
3x10-20 1335-22788 <$125
Total Issue $2,983,750
Out at close $198,750
****
1360 Windham
WINDHAM COUNTY NB OF BROOKLYN
Chartered 1865
2nd title:Windham County NB of Danielsonville 4/95
3rd title:Windham County NB of Danielson 5/17/05
FIRST TITLE {{ 10 L }}
Original Series <$VALUE
3x1-2 1-3200 <$350/$1000
4x5 1-5250 <$400
3x10-20 1-1410 <$750/$1250
Series 1875
3x1-2 1-1500 <$350/$1000
4x5 1-3290 <$400
3x10-20 1-1672 <$650/$1000
Brown Back
4x5 1-1894 <$300
3x10-20 1-1159 <$300/$350
SECOND TITLE {{ 2 L }}
Brown Back
4x5 1-1335 <$600
3x10-20 1-1505 <$600
THIRD TITLE {{2U+7 L U+19 S}}
1902 Red Seal
4x5 1-1150 <$500
3x10-20 1-880 <$500
1902 Date Back
4x5 1-4050 <$250
3x10-20 1-2920 <$250
1902 Plain Back
4x5 4051-13110 <$250
3x10-20 2921-8814 <$250
1929 Small Size
5 Type 1 1-3252 <$60
10 Type 1 1-1512 <$60
20 Type 1 1-424 <$70
5 Type 2 1-7664 <$75
10 Type 2 1-3828 <$75
20 Type 2 1-1332 <$85
Total Issue $1,658,480
Out in 1935 $146,600
Large out 1935 $2,930
****
8511 Litchfield
CANAAN NB, CANAAN
{{ 2 L 5 S }}
Organized 10/30/06
1902 Red Seal <$VALUE
3x10-20 1-375 <$1500
1902 Date Back
3x10-20 1-1400* <$750
1902 Plain Back
3x10-20 1561-5314* <$750
* 1401-1560 not marked
1929 Small Size
10 Type 1 1-726 <$275
20 Type 1 1-194 <$275
5 Type 2 1-2442 <$300
10 Type 2 1-2388 <$300
20 Type 2 1-192 <$325
Total Issue $391,220
Out in 1935 $50,000
Large out 1935 $1,350
****
1314 Middlesex
CLINTON NB, CLINTON
{{ 18 L 9 S }}
Organized 4/27/65
Original Series <$VALUE
3x1-2 1-1700 <$300/$850
4x5 1-2850 <$400
3x10-20 1-800 <$750/$1250
Series 1875
3x1-2 1-100 <$300/$850
4x5 1-2696 <$400
3x10-20 1-1773 <$650/$1000
Brown Back
4x5 1-3665 <$250
3x10-20 1-6849 <$250/$300
1902 Red Seal
4x5 1-3225 <$275
3x10-20 1-1900 <$275/$325
1902 Date Back
4x5 1-5900 <$125
3x10-20 1-4440 <$125
1902 Plain Back
4x5 5901-20450 <$125
3x10-20 4441-13782 <$125
1929 Small Size
5 Type 1 1-2928 <$150
10 Type 1 1-1386 <$150
20 Type 1 1-410 <$175
5 Type 2 1-4176 <$175
10 Type 2 1-2292 <$175
20 Type 2 1-684 <$185
Total Issue $2,199,600
Out in 1935 $71,070
Large out 1935 $4,900
****
943 Fairfield
DANBURY NB, DANBURY
{{ 24 L 20 S }}
Chartered 3/28/65
Original Series <$VALUE
3x1-2 1-17000 <$275/$850
4x5 1-14075 <$350
3x10-20 1-3600 <$750/$1250
50-100 1-500 <$4000
Series 1875
3x1-2 1-3560 <$275/$850
4x5 1-13000 <$350
3x10-20 1-4500 <$650/$1000
Brown Back
4x5 1-13943 <$200
3x10-20 1-9166 <$200/$250
50-100 1-200 <$1250/$1500
1902 Red Seal
4x5 1-9250 <$250
3x10-20 1-6700 <$250
1902 Date Back
4x5 1-20250 <$100
3x10-20 1-14600 <$100
1902 Plain Back
4x5 20251-62720 <$100
3x10-20 14601-42477 <$100
1929 Small Size
5 Type 1 1-8534 <$60
10 Type 1 1-4202 <$60
20 Type 1 1-1174 <$70
5 Type 2 1-16212 <$70
10 Type 2 1-7884 <$70
20 Type 2 1-2340 <$80
Total Issue $6,645,430
Out in 1935 $205,210
Large out 1935 $18,360
****
1132 Fairfield
N PAHQUIOQUE B OF DANBURY
Chartered 1865
2nd title:City NB 1/21/03
3rd title:City NB & TC 3/24/28
FIRST TITLE {{ 2 L }}
Original Series <$VALUE
3x1-2 1-1400 <$750/$1500
4x5 1-8150 <$850
3x10-20 1-4900<$1000/$1500
50-100 1-834 <$4000
Series 1875
4x5 1-3500 <$850
3x10-20 1-4740<$1000/$1500
Brown Back
3x10-20 1-12527 <$750
SECOND TITLE {{ 8 L }}
Brown Back
3x10-20 1-2803 <$400
1902 Red Seal
3x10-20 1-8500 <$400
1902 Date Back
4x5 1-7000 <$175
3x10-20 1-17000 <$175
1902 Plain Back
3x10-20 17001-47700 <$175
THIRD TITLE {{ 0 L 5 S }}
1902 Plain Back
3x10-20 1-247 <$300
1929 Small Size
10 Type 1 1-1166 <$225
20 Type 1 1-338 <$225
10 Type 2 1-1700 <$250
20 Type 2 1-340 <$250
Total Issue $4,710,270
Out in 1935 $48,600
Large out 1935 $10,050
****
Windham County NB of Danielson
SEE Ch 1360
Windham County NB of Brooklyn
****
Windham County NB of Danielsonville
SEE Ch 1360
Windham County NB of Brooklyn
****
1139 Middlesex
DEEP RIVER NB, DEEP RIVER
{{ 14 L 18 S }}
Chartered 1865
Original Series <$VALUE
3x1-2 1-1600 <$500/$1250
4x5 1-5150 <$600
3x10-20 1-2600 <$750/$1250
Series 1875
3x1-2 1-1000 <$500/$1250
4x5 1-4085 <$600
3x10-20 1-2788 <$750/$1250
Brown Back
4x5 1-10475 <$400
3x10-20 1-5710 <$400
1902 Red Seal
4x5 1-3000 <$500
3x10-20 1-2000 <$500
1902 Date Back
4x5 1-4200 <$225
3x10-20 1-3560 <$225
1902 Plain Back
4x5 4201-28880 <$225
3x10-20 3561-18385 <$225
1929 Small Size
5 Type 1 1-5428 <$100
10 Type 1 1-3014 <$100
20 Type 1 1-810 <$110
5 Type 2 1-8120 <$125
10 Type 2 1-5189 <$125
20 Type 2 1-1344 <$125
Total Issue $3,179,200
Out in 1935 $149,995
Large out 1935 $7,510
****

****
Birminghman NB of Derby
SEE Ch 1098
Birmingham NB of Birmingham
****
7812 Middlesex
NB OF NEW ENGLAND OF EAST HADDAM
{{ 1 L }}
Chartered 6/05
1902 Red Seal <$VALUE
3x10-20 1-2400 <$1500
1902 Date Back
3x10-20 1-4680* <$1000
1902 Plain Back
3x10-20 4881-8548* <$1000
* 4681-4880 not marked
Total Issue $547,400
Out in 1935 $930
****
1480 Middlesex
NB OF NEW ENGLAND, EAST HADDAM
{{ 5 L }}
Chartered 7/22/65
Liquidated 6/27/05
Original Series <$VALUE
3x1-2 1-5300 <$500/$1250
4x5 1-6900 <$600
3x10-20 1-1650 <$750/$1250
Series 1875
4x5 1-5940 <$600
3x10-20 1-2634 <$750/$1250
Brown Back
4x5 1-10906 <$500
3x10-20 1-4087 <$500
Total Issue $919,970
Out in 1910 $6,268
Succeeded by Ch 7812
****
12973 Fairfield
BYRAM NB OF EAST PORT CHESTER
{{ 1 L 5 S }}
Chartered 8/26
1902 Plain Back <$VALUE
3x10-20 1-923 <$1000
1929 Small Size
10 Type 1 1-804 <$325
20 Type 1 1-222 <$325
10 Type 2 1-1684 <$350
20 Type 2 1-380 <$375
Total Issue $145,470
Out in 1935 $20,400
Large out 1935 $400
****
8936 Middlesex
ESSEX NB, ESSEX
{{ 3 L 9 S }}
Chartered 10/07
1902 Red Seal <$VALUE
4x10 1-1050 <$1000
1902 Date Back
4x10 1-3350* <$600
1902 Plain Back
4x10 3501-9926* <$600
* 3351-3500 not marked
1929 Small Size
10 Type 1 1-1240 <$200
10 Type 2 1-1812 <$200
Total Issue $531,560
Out in 1935 $24,500
Large out 1935 $810
****
1084 Middlesex
SAYBROOK NB OF ESSEX
{{ UNREPORTED }}
Chartered 4/65
Liquidated 2/20/85
Original Series <$VALUE
4x5 1-4425 <$1250
3x10-20 1-2530<$1500/$2000
Series 1875
4x5 1-45 <$1250
3x10-20 1-1256<$1500/$2000
Total Issue $278,700
Out in 1910 $1,290
****

****

1214 Litchfield
N IRON B OF FALLS VILLAGE
{{ 4 L 9 S }}
Chartered 1865
Original Series <$VALUE
4x5 1-5125 <$750
3x10-20 1-2860 <$850/$1250
Series 1875
4x5 1-3930 <$750
3x10-20 1-3234 <$850/$1250
Brown Back
3x10-20 1-5658 <$600
1902 Red Seal
3x10-20 1-1900 <$750
1902 Date Back
3x10-20 1-4640 <$400
1902 Plain Back
3x10-20 4641-12362 <$400
1929 Small Size
10 Type 1 1-1348 <$225
20 Type 1 1-380 <$225
10 Type 2 1-1839 <$250
20 Type 2 1-444 <$250
Total Issue $1,635,550
Out in 1935 $48,700
Large out 1935 $5,270

****

8243 Fairfield
GREENWICH NB, GREENWICH
{{ U + 4 L }}
Chartered 6/06
Liquidated 1/20/23
1902 Red Seal <$VALUE
3x10-20 1-1875 <$1000
1902 Date Back
3x10-20 1-7000 <$600
1902 Plain Back
3x10-20 7001-10214 <$600
Total Issue $604,450
Out at close $48,700

****

5358 New Haven
GUILFORD NB, GUILFORD
{{ 3 L }}
Chartered 5/19/00
Liquidated 5/13/14
Brown Back <$VALUE
4x5 1-1190 <$1250
3x10-20 1-864 <$1250
1882 Date Back
4x5 1-860 <$1250
3x10-20 1-625 <$1250
Total Issue $115,450
Out in 1914 $8,500

****

756 Hartford
AETNA NB OF HARTFORD
{{ 8 L }}
Chartered 1/26/65
Liquidated 4/26/15
Original Series <$VALUE
4x5 1-12000 <$400
3x10-20 1-6100 <$750/$1250
50-100 1-1784 <$4000
Series 1875
4x5 1-12000 <$400
3x10-20 1-6200 <$750/$1250
50-100 1-834 <$4000
Brown Back
4x5 1-17239 <$300
3x10-20 1-8228 <$300/$350
1902 Red Seal
4x5 1-20750 <$400
3x10-20 1-11300 <$400
50-100 1-900 <$2250/$2500
1902 Date Back
4x5 1-39525 <$200
3x10-20 1-24843 <$200
50-100 1-1300 <$650/$750
3x50-100 1-56 <$650/$750
Total Issue $5,600,530
Out at close $515,095
Ch 1338 assumed circulation

****

1165 Hartford
AMERICAN NB OF HARTFORD
{{ 5 L }}
Chartered 1865
Liquidated 5/15/12
Original Series <$VALUE
4x5 1-17250 <$500
3x10-20 1-8500 <$750/$1250
50-100 1-600 <$4000
Series 1875
4x5 1-18750 <$500
3x10-20 1-13905 <$650/$1000
50-100 1-300 <$4000
Brown Back
4x5 1-9848 <$400
3x10-20 1-8422 <$400
50-100 1-607 <$1250/$1500
1902 Red Seal
4x5 1-18250 <$450
3x10-20 1-10800 <$450
50-100 1-1300 <$2250/$2500
1902 Date Back
4x5 1-28010 <$275
3x10-20 1-14787 <$275
50-100 1-67 <$650/$750
Total Issue $5,093,960
Out at close $500,000
Ch 670 assumed circulation

****

13038 Hartford
CAPITOL NB OF HARTFORD
Chartered 2/27
2nd title: Capitol NB &TC 5/6/27
FIRST TITLE **{{ 5U + 4 L }}**
1902 Plain Back <$VALUE
4x5 1-3550 <$200
4x10 1-725 <$200
SECOND TITLE **{{ 2U + 33 S }}**
1929 Small Size
5 Type 1 1-32570 <$25
10 Type 1 1-16960 <$30
5 Type 2 1-49440 <$35
Total Issue $2,341,900
Out in 1935 $222,065
Large out 1935 $715

****

486 Hartford
CHARTER OAK NB OF HARTFORD
{{ 10 L }}
Chartered 7/64
Liquidated 2/15/15
Original Series <$VALUE
3x1-2 1-5000 <$350/$1000
4x5 1-9500 <$450
3x10-20 1-9500 <$750/$1250
50-100 1-1100 <$4000
Series 1875
3x1-2 1-1860 <$350/$1000
4x5 1-3055 <$450
3x10-20 1-5291 <$750/$1250
50-100 1-491 <$4000
Brown Back
4x5 1-4450 <$300
3x10-20 1-5498 <$300/$350
50-100 1-200 <$1250/$1500
1902 Red Seal
4x5 1-4000 <$400
3x10-20 1-3400 <$400
50-100 1-400 <$2250/$2500
1902 Date Back
4x5 1-34315 <$200
3x10-20 1-23211 <$200
50-100 1-1300 <$650/$750
3x50-100 1-220 <$650/$750
Total Issue $4,064,350
Out at close $499,995
Ch 670 assumed circulation

****

1377 Hartford
CITY NB OF HARTFORD
{{ 8 L }}
Chartered 1865
Liquidated 6/9/85
Original Series <$VALUE
3x1-2 1-6800 <$300/$1000
4x5 1-9300 <$350
3x10-20 1-3920 <$750/$1250
50-100 1-710 <$4000
Series 1875
3x1-2 1-2300 <$300/$1000
4x5 1-6645 <$350
3x10-20 1-2829 <$600/$1000
50-100 1-247 <$4000
Total Issue $845,400
Out in 1910 $4,998

****

10796 Hartford
COLONIAL NB OF HARTFORD
{{ 4 L }}
Chartered 10/15
Liquidated 2/11/20
1902 Plain Back <$VALUE
4x5 1-41205 <$350
3x10-20 1-25554 <$350
Total Issue $2,101,800
Out at close $455,300

****

1321 Hartford
FARMERS & MECHANICS NB OF HARTFORD
{{ 15 L }}
Chartered 1865
Liquidated 4/9/10
Original Series <$VALUE
3x1-2 1-3000 <$275/$850
4x5 1-17695 <$350
3x10-20 1-5000 <$750/$1250
3x50-100 1-260 <$4000
Series 1875
3x1-2 1-13000 <$275/$850
4x5 1-10750 <$350
3x10-20 1-8130 <$600/$1000
3x50-100 1-940 <$4000
Brown Back
4x5 1-8834 <$200
3x10-20 1-4371 <$200/$225
1902 Red Seal
4x5 1-1900 <$300
3x10-20 1-1240 <$300
1902 Date Back
4x5 1-340 <$150
3x10-20 1-595 <$150
Total Issue $2,137,180
Out in 1910 $32,197

****

121 Hartford
FNB OF HARTFORD
{{ 32 L 50+ S }}
Chartered 11/63
Original Series <$VALUE
3x1-2 1-12600 <$275/$850
4x5 1-18255 <$350
4x10 1-9000 <$650
3x20-50 1-2390 <$1250/$4000
Series 1875
3x1-2 1-1200 <$275/$850
4x5 1-7000 <$350
4x10 1-4625 <$600
3x20-50 1-2000 <$1000/$4000
Brown Back
4x5 1-10453 <$150
3x10-20 1-9265 <$150/$200
50-100 1-400 <$1250/$1500
1902 Red Seal
4x5 1-16300 <$175
4x10 1-3000 <$175
3x10-20 1-9880 <$175/$200
1902 Date Back
4x5 1-30000 <$50
4x10 1-22500 <$50
3x10-20 1-2300 <$50/$60
1902 Plain Back
4x5 30001-200273 <$50
4x10 22501-155606 <$50
1929 Small Size
5 Type 1 1-45018 <$15
10 Type 1 1-21530 <$20
5 Type 2 1-108448 <$15
10 Type 2 1-47887* <$20
* 9925-9930 not issued
Total Issue $17,322,400
Out in 1935 $750,820
Large out 1935 $50,635
Outstanding includes Ch 361

****

1338 Hartford
HARTFORD NB, HARTFORD
Chartered 1865
2nd title: Hartford-Aetna NB 5/28/15
3rd title: Hartford NB & TC 5/21/27
FIRST TITLE **{{ 26 L }}**
Original Series <$VALUE
3x1-2 1-17050 <$275/$850
4x5 1-10500 <$350
3x10-20 1-8812 <$750/$1250
3x50-100 1-1040 <$4000
Series 1875
4x5 1-8520 <$350
3x10-20 1-2942 <$650/$1000
Brown Back
4x5 1-15149 <$150
3x10-20 1-6867 <$150/$200
1902 Red Seal
4x5 1-27000 <$150
4x10 1-8500 <$150
3x10-20 1-8700 <$150/$200
1902 Date Back
4x5 1-65075 <$50
4x10 1-61047 <$50
3x10-20 1-4000 <$50/$60
SECOND TITLE **{{ 41 L }}**
1902 Plain Back
4x5 1-220555 <$50
3x10-20 1-110685 <$50/$60
THIRD TITLE **{{ 14 L 50+ S }}**
1902 Plain Back
4x5 1-15015 <$60
3x10-20 1-25143 <$60/$75
1929 Small Size
5 Type 1 1-34194 <$15
10 Type 1 1-20794 <$20
20 Type 1 1-5854 <$30
5 Type 2 1-57250 <$15
10 Type 2 1-28158 <$20
20 Type 2 1-7358 <$30
Total Issue $22,411,790
Out in 1935 $877,250
Large out 1935 $58,210
Outstanding includes Ch 756

****

1300 Hartford
MERCANTILE NB OF HARTFORD
{{ UNREPORTED }}
Chartered 6/17/65
Liquidated 7/20/97
Original Series <$VALUE
4x5 1-5370 <$1000
3x10-20 1-6400 <$1250/$1500
50-100 1-1464 <$4000
Series 1875
4x5 1-360 <$1000
3x10-20 1-2020 <$1250/$1500
Brown Back
4x5 1-16421 <$850
Total Issue $1,083,620
Out in 1910 $5,465

****

361 Hartford
N EXCHANGE B OF HARTFORD
{{ 28 L }}
Chartered 4/64
Liquidated 10/21/16
Original Series <$VALUE
3x1-2 1-5200 <$250/$850
4x5 1-15250 <$275
4x10 1-11100 <$650
3x20-50 1-2500 <$1250/$4000
Series 1875
3x1-2 1-1946 <$250/$850
4x5 1-8842 <$275
4x10 1-6750 <$650
3x20-50 1-933 <$1250/$4000
Brown Back
4x5 1-24175 <$150
3x10-20 1-12427 <$150/$200
50-100 1-2033 <$1250/$1500
1902 Red Seal
4x5 1-34000 <$175
3x10-20 1-12960 <$175/$225
50-100 1-980 <$2250/$2500
1902 Date Back
4x5 1-46900* <$50
3x10-20 1-29100** <$50/$60
50-100 1-450 <$400/$500
1902 Plain Back
4x5 48901-51645* <$50
3x10-20 30701-32341* <$50/$60
* 46901-48900 not marked
** 29101-30700 not marked
Total Issue $7,211,450
Out at close $482,600

****

670 Hartford
PHOENIX NB OF HARTFORD
{{ 39 L }}
Chartered 12/64
Liquidated 7/30/26
Original Series <$VALUE
3x1-2 1-25000 <$275/$850
4x5 1-17475 <$300
4x10 1-8700 <$650
3x20-50 1-4270 <$1250/$4000
100-100 1-789 <$4000
Series 1875
4x5 1-5492 <$300
4x10 1-4323 <$600
3x20-50 1-1564 <$1000/$4000
Brown Back
3x10-20 1-5842 <$175/$225
1902 Red Seal
4x5 1-5750 <$150
3x10-20 1-3700 <$150/$200
1902 Date Back
4x5 1-25350 <$40
3x10-20 1-18660 <$40/$50
1902 Plain Back
4x5 25351-153885 <$40
3x10-20 18661-100965 <$40/$50
Total Issue $10,622,850
Out at close $225,355
Outstanding includes Ch 486 and Ch 1165

****

1478 New London
JEWETT CITY NB, JEWETT CITY
{{ UNREPORTED }}
Chartered 7/22/65
Liquidated 10/4/72
Original Series <$VALUE
4x5 1-1790 <$2000
3x10-20 1-449 <$2000/$2500
Total Issue $58,250
Out in 1910 $375

****

****

709 Litchfield
FNB OF LITCHFIELD
{{ U + 12 L 18 S }}
Chartered 1/65
Original Series <$VALUE
3x1-2 1-3700 <$400/$1000
4x5 1-7600 <$450
4x10 1-3100 <$750
3x20-50 1-1144 <$1250/$4000
Series 1875
4x5 1-6692 <$450
4x10 1-3938 <$650
Brown Back
4x5 1-17371 <$300
3x10-20 1-9146 <$300/$350
1902 Red Seal
3x10-20 1-4400 <$400
1902 Date Back
3x10-20 1-8100 <$200
1902 Plain Back
3x10-20 8101-25078 <$200
1929 Small Size
10 Type 1 1-2882 <$60
20 Type 1 1-686 <$70
10 Type 2 1-3721 <$65
20 Type 2 1-948 <$75
Total Issue $3,301,730
Out in 1935 $96,700
Large out 1935 $8,170

****

FNB of Meriden
SEE Ch 250
FNB of West Meriden

****

720 New Haven
HOME NB OF MERIDEN
{{ 19 L 2U + 26 S }}
Chartered 1/65
Original Series <$VALUE
3x1-2 1-8600 <$275/$850
4x5 1-7000 <$300
3x10-20 1-5600 <$750/$1250
Series 1875
4x5 1-5250 <$300
3x10-20 1-13300 <$600/$1000
Brown Back
4x5 1-21000 <$250
3x10-20 1-39247 <$250/$275
1902 Red Seal
4x5 1-18000 <$300
3x10-20 1-10100 <$300
1902 Date Back
4x5 1-37000 <$60
3x10-20 1-26000 <$60/$75
1902 Plain Back
4x5 37001-113167 <$60
3x10-20 26001-80622 <$60/$75
1929 Small Size
10 Type 1 1-13734 <$50
20 Type 1 1-3772 <$60
10 Type 2 1-21504 <$60
20 Type 2 1-5830 <$65
Total Issue $12,383,110
Out in 1935 $418,500
Large out 1935 $24,070

****

1382 New Haven
MERIDEN NB, MERIDEN
{{ 13 L 20 S }}
Chartered 1865
Original Series <$VALUE
3x1-2 1-2000 <$400/$1000
4x5 1-7650 <$400
3x10-20 1-3000 <$750/$1250
Series 1875
3x1-2 1-660 <$400/$1000
4x5 1-10615 <$400
3x10-20 1-5729 <$750/$1250
Brown Back
4x5 1-13265 <$275
3x10-20 1-11457 <$275/$325
1902 Red Seal
4x5 1-9000 <$325
3x10-20 1-5800 <$325/$375
1902 Date Back
4x5 1-16915 <$175
3x10-20 1-11634 <$175
1902 Plain Back
4x5 16916-57015 <$175
3x10-20 11635-38333 <$175
1929 Small Size
5 Type 1 1-8278 <$60
10 Type 1 1-3918 <$60
20 Type 1 1-1002 <$65
5 Type 2 1-4812 <$75
10 Type 2 1-2384 <$75
20 Type 2 1-465 <$80
Total Issue $5,841,010
Out in 1935 $183,680
Large out 1935 $11,665

****

****

1340 Middlesex
CENTRAL NB OF MIDDLETOWN
{{ 12 L 22 S }}
Organized 6/14/65
Original Series <$VALUE
3x1-2 1-1000 <$350/$1000
4x5 1-3650 <$400
3x10-20 1-2900 <$750/$1250
50-100 1-100 <$4000
Series 1875
4x5 1-3250 <$400
3x10-20 1-3498 <$650/$1000
50-100 1-68 <$4000
Brown Back
4x5 1-6648 <$300
3x10-20 1-12217 <$300/$350
1902 Red Seal
4x5 1-6250 <$350
3x10-20 1-3700 <$350/$400
1902 Date Back
4x5 1-12750 <$175
3x10-20 1-9500 <$175
1902 Plain Back
4x5 12751-46973 <$175
3x10-20 9801-32251 <$175
1929 Small Size
5 Type 1 1-8102 <$50
10 Type 1 1-3590 <$50
20 Type 1 1-1110 <$60
5 Type 2 1-12618 <$65
10 Type 2 1-7050 <$65
20 Type 2 1-2160 <$75
Total Issue $4,862,370
Out in 1935 $193,350
Large out 1935 $9,870

****

397 Middlesex
FNB OF MIDDLETOWN
{{ 3 L 7 S }}
Chartered 4/64
Liquidated 12/29/33
Original Series <$VALUE
3x1-2 1-1200 <$500/$1250
4x5 1-4000 <$600
3x10-20 1-4400 <$750/$1250
Series 1875
3x1-2 1-120 <$500/$1250
4x5 1-500 <$600
3x10-20 1-3130 <$750/$1250
Brown Back
3x10-20 1-9241 <$500
1902 Red Seal
3x10-20 1-3200 <$600
1902 Date Back
3x10-20 1-5800 <$350
1902 Plain Back
3x10-20 5801-12674 <$350
1929 Small Size
5 Type 1 1-402 <$250
10 Type 1 1-1830 <$250
20 Type 1 1-512 <$275
Total Issue $1,912,150
Out at close $93,660
Large out at close $4,510

****

845 Middlesex
MIDDLESEX COUNTY NB OF MIDDLETOWN
{{ 4 L }}
Chartered 2/27/65
Liquidated 2/5/16
Original Series <$VALUE
3x1-2 1-3000 <$600/$1250
4x5 1-7500 <$750
3x10-20 1-3900 <$850/$1250
50-100 1-200 <$4000
Series 1875
4x5 1-5500 <$750
3x10-20 1-6600 <$850/$1250
50-100 1-100 <$4000
Brown Back
4x5 1-2285 <$500
3x10-20 1-6759 <$500
1902 Red Seal
3x10-20 1-2500 <$600
1902 Date Back
4x5 1-12745 <$350
3x10-20 1-10600 <$350
1902 Plain Back
3x10-20 10601-11113 <$350
Total Issue $2,164,200
Out in 1916 $133,150

****

<$VALUEs are for notes in FINE condition. Value changes by approximately 25% for a change of one full grade.

****
1216 Middlesex
MIDDLETOWN NB, MIDDLETOWN
Organized 5/23/65
2nd title: Middletown NB & TC 7/23/28 {NO NOTE ISSUE}
3rd title:Middletown NB 3/28/32
FIRST TITLE {{ 45 L }}
Original Series <$VALUE
3x1-2 1-12100 <$300/$850
4x5 1-8625 <$350
4x10 1-5075 <$650
3x20-50 1-909 <$1250/$4000
Series 1875
4x5 1-8900 <$350
4x10 1-7863 <$600
3x20-50 1-1210<$1000/$4000
Brown Back
4x5 1-45143 <$175
3x10-20 1-29699 <$175/$225
50-100 1-200 <$1250/$1500
1902 Red Seal
4x5 1-13750 <$250
3x10-20 1-8200 <$250/$300
1902 Date Back
4x5 1-30250 <$60
3x10-20 1-24200 <$60/$75
1902 Plain Back
4x5 30251-103623 <$60
3x10-20 24201-65952 <$60/$75
THIRD TITLE {{ U + 9 S }}
1929 Small Size
5 Type 1 1-2050 <$150
10 Type 1 1-1034 <$135
5 Type 2 1-9112 <$160
10 Type 2 1-5370 <$150
Total Issue $9,857,280
Out in 1935 $98,640
Large out 1935 $24,740
****
Plainfield NB of Moosup
SEE Ch 10145
Plainfield NB of Plainfield
****
1268 New London
MYSTIC NB, MYSTIC
{{ 1 L }}
Chartered 6/14/65
Liquidated 7/7/87
Original Series <$VALUE
3x1-2 1-600 <$1250/$2000
4x5 1-3500 <$1250
3x10-20 1-400 <$1500/$2000
Series 1875
3x1-2 1-1560 <$1250/$2000
4x5 1-5130 <$1250
Brown Back
4x5 1-1684 <$1250
Total Issue $237,080
Out in 1910 $1,072
****
251 New London
FNB OF MYSTIC BRIDGE
{{ UNREPORTED }}
Chartered 2/12/64
Liquidated 5/21/94
Original Series <$VALUE
3x1-2 1-2000 <$1500/$2500
4x5 1-5500 <$1500
4x10 1-2900 <$2000
3x20-50 1-900*<$2500/$4000
* 301-500 not issued
Series 1875
3x1-2 1-912 <$1500/$2500
4x5 1-2600 <$1500
4x10 1-1400 <$2000
3x20-50 1-300 <$2500/$4000
Brown Back
4x5 1-3002 <$1500
3x10-20 1-2916 <$1500
Total Issue $664,400
Out in 1910 $3,611
****
645 New London
MYSTIC RIVER NB, MYSTIC RIVER
{{ 11 L 19 S }}
Chartered 12/64
Original Series <$VALUE
3x1-2 1-5000 <$650/$1500
4x5 1-4000 <$650
3x10-20 1-2000 <$850/$1250
Series 1875
3x1-2 1-700 <$650/$1500
4x5 1-2500 <$650
3x10-20 1-1854 <$850/$1250
Brown Back
4x5 1-6001 <$400
3x10-20 1-10307 <$400/$450
1902 Red Seal
4x5 1-2750 <$500
3x10-20 1-3100 <$500
1902 Date Back
4x5 1-9250 <$225
3x10-20 1-6080 <$225
1902 Plain Back
4x5 9251-27525 <$225
3x10-20 6081-18161 <$225
1929 Small Size
5 Type 1 1-3452 <$100
10 Type 1 1-1958 <$100
20 Type 1 1-522 <$110
5 Type 2 1-5344 <$125
10 Type 2 1-3154 <$125
20 Type 2 1-829 <$135
Total Issue $2,942,280
Out in 1935 $97,400
Large out 1935 $6,400
****
3020 New Haven
NAUGATUCK NB, NAUGATUCK
{{ 5 L 3 S }}
Chartered 1883
Brown Back <$VALUE
4x5 1-6298 <$600
3x10-20 1-8553 <$600
1902 Red Seal
3x10-20 1-5800 <$750
1902 Date Back
3x10-20 1-8700 <$375
1902 Plain Back
3x10-20 8701-20421 <$375
1929 Small Size
5 Type 2 1-8220 <$400
10 Type 2 1-4120 <$400
20 Type 2 1-1505 <$400
Total Issue $1,977,060
Out in 1935 $100,025
Large out 1935 $3,625
****
12846 Hartford
CITY NB OF NEW BRITAIN
{{ 5 L 8 S }}
Chartered 11/25
Liquidated 3/12/32
1902 Plain Back <$VALUE
3x10-20 1-13063 <$750
1929 Small Size
10 Type 1 1-1797 <$225
20 Type 1 1-510 <$225
Total Issue $822,170
Out at close $85,600
Large out at close $7,040
Ch 1184 assumed circulation
****
3668 Hartford
MECHANICS NB OF NEW BRITAIN
{{ UNREPORTED }}
Chartered 4/6/87
Liquidated 4/20/07
Brown Back <$VALUE
4x5 1-8605 <$1500
3x10-20 1-10589 <$1500
1902 Red Seal
3x10-20 1-72 <$2000
Total Issue $705,150
Out in 1910 $4,400
****
1184 Hartford
NEW BRITAIN NB, NEW BRITAIN
{{ 4 L 7 S }}
Chartered 1865
Original Series <$VALUE
3x1-2 1-8050 <$650/$1250
4x5 1-8925 <$750
3x10-20 1-2050 <$850/$1250
50-100 1-150 <$4000
Series 1875
3x1-2 1-320 <$650/$1250
4x5 1-5165 <$750
3x10-20 1-3120 <$850/$1250
50-100 1-100 <$4000
Brown Back
4x5 1-11750 <$600
3x10-20 1-10500 <$600
50-100 1-100 <$1750/$2000
1902 Red Seal
4x5 1-8730 <$750
3x10-20 1-6608 <$750
1902 Date Back
4x5 1-23024 <$375
3x10-20 1-15185 <$375
1929 Small Size
10 Type 1 1-1904 <$200
Total Issue $3,233,620
Out in 1935 $51,924
Large out 1935 $9,184
Outstanding includes Ch 12846
****
1249 Fairfield
FNB OF NEW CANAAN
Chartered 1865
2nd title:FNB & TC of New Canaan 5/17/29
FIRST TITLE {{ 11 L }}
Original Series <$VALUE
4x5 1-5400 <$600
3x10-20 1-1250 <$850/$1250
Series 1875
4x5 1-9740 <$600
Brown Back
4x5 1-29213 <$400
1902 Red Seal
4x5 1-4600 <$500
3x10-20 1-2420 <$500
1902 Date Back
4x5 1-9450 <$225
3x10-20 1-7040 <$225
1902 Plain Back
4x5 9451-28970 <$225
3x10-20 7041-19926 <$225
SECOND TITLE {{ 9 S }}
1929 Small Size
5 Type 1 1-3860 <$150
10 Type 1 1-1942 <$150
20 Type 1 1-494 <$150
5 Type 2 1-7754 <$175
10 Type 2 1-3773 <$175
20 Type 2 1-996 <$175
Total Issue $3,302,330
Out in 1935 $97,800
Large out 1935 $7,785
****
2 New Haven
FNB OF NEW HAVEN*
Chartered 6/63
Liquidated 5/6/82
*Reorganized as Ch 2682 which retook Ch 2 3/19/09
2nd title: FNB & TC of New Haven 7/2/28
FIRST TITLE {{ 41 L }}
Original Series <$VALUE
4x5 1-2500 <$600
4x10 1-7175 <$800
3x20-50 1-1598<$1250/$4000
Series 1875
4x10 1-7646 <$800
3x20-50 1-1000<$1250/$4000
1902 Date Back
3x10-20 1-12340 <$60/$75
1902 Plain Back (dated 1909)
4x5 1-43000 <$60
3x10-20 12341-44140 <$60/$75
1902 Plain Back (dated 1922)
4x5 1-107419 <$60
3x10-20 1-47876 <$60/$75
SECOND TITLE {{13 L 5U+50 S}}
1902 Plain Back
4x5 1-9916 <$150
3x10-20 1-6177 <$150
1929 Small Size
5 Type 1 1-33050 <$25
10 Type 1 1-14800 <$30
20 Type 1 1-5422 <$40
5 Type 2 1-55696 <$30
10 Type 2 1-9595 <$35
20 Type 2 1-4144 <$45
Total Issue $12,032,420
Out in 1935 $629,217
Large out 1935 $47,210
Outstanding includes Ch 796, Ch 1128, and Ch 2682
****
2682 New Haven
FNB OF NEW HAVEN
{{ UNREPORTED }}
Chartered 5/6/82
RETOOK Ch 2 3/19/09
Brown Back <$VALUE
3x10-20 1-20819 <$1250
1902 Red Seal
3x10-20 1-6500 <$1500
1902 Date Back
3x10-20 1-298 <$1000
Total Issue $1,380,850
Out in 1909 $50,000
****
1128 New Haven
MERCHANTS NB OF NEW HAVEN
{{ 17 L U + 19 S }}
Chartered 1865
Liquidated 7/20/32
Original Series <$VALUE
4x5 1-10050 <$400
3x10-20 1-7430 <$750/$1250
50-100 1-1700 <$4000
Series 1875
3x10-20 1-16000<$750/$1250
Brown Back
4x5 1-9000 <$275
3x10-20 1-16326 <$275/$325
50-100 1-500 <$1250/$1500
1902 Red Seal
4x5 1-5600 <$300
3x10-20 1-3100 <$300/$350
50-100 1-220 <$2250/$2500
1902 Date Back
4x5 1-8100 <$125
3x10-20 1-6300 <$125
50-100 1-100 <$450/$500
3x50-100 1-400 <$450/$500
1902 Plain Back
4x5 8101-33815 <$125
3x10-20 6301-17804 <$125
3x50-100 401-562<$450/$500
1929 Small Size
5 Type 1 1-12159 <$40
10 Type 1 1-5166 <$40
20 Type 1 1-1579 <$50
50 Type 1 1-507 <$275
100 Type 1 1-154 <$325
Total Issue $5,829,510
Out at close $476,955
Large out at close $20,715
Ch 2682 assumed circulation
****
1202 New Haven
N TRADESMEN'S B OF NEW HAVEN
Organized 5/26/65
Liquidated 1/15/34
2nd title:N Tradesmen's B & TC 3/15/23
FIRST TITLE {{ 14 L }}
Original Series <$VALUE
4x5 1-4150 <$500
3x10-20 1-7010 <$750/$1250
50-100 1-314 <$4000
Series 1875
4x5 1-6030 <$500
3x10-20 1-8888 <$650/$1000
Brown Back
4x5 1-9865 <$250
3x10-20 1-12342 <$250/$300
1902 Red Seal
4x5 1-2500 <$300
3x10-20 1-7000 <$300/$350
1902 Date Back
4x5 1-21000 <$125
3x10-20 1-12000 <$125
1902 Plain Back
4x5 21001-67500 <$125
3x10-20 12001-36400 <$125
SECOND TITLE {{ 2 L U+17 S }}
1902 Plain Back
4x5 1-16049 <$175
3x10-20 1-9442 <$175
1929 Small Size
5 Type 1 1-8806 <$50
10 Type 1 1-4084 <$50
20 Type 1 1-1497 <$60
Total Issue $6,911,940
Out at close $295,500
Large out at close $21,035
****
1245 New Haven
NEW HAVEN COUNTY NB, NEW HAVEN
{{ 7 L }}
Chartered 1865
Liquidated 8/28/15
Original Series <$VALUE
3x1-2 1-4000 <$400/$1000
4x5 1-5750 <$500
3x10-20 1-6200 <$750/$1250
50-100 1-700 <$4000
Series 1875
3x10-20 1-8000 <$750/$1250
50-100 1-248 <$4000
Brown Back
3x10-20 1-24300 <$300/$350
50-100 1-467 <$1250/$1500
1902 Red Seal
3x10-20 1-9000 <$500
1902 Date Back
3x10-20 1-22702 <$275
Total Issue $3,857,350
Out at close $246,400
Ch 1243 assumed circulation
****
1243 New Haven
NEW HAVEN NB, NEW HAVEN
Chartered 1865
2nd title:New Haven N Banking Assoc 8/14/15
FIRST TITLE {{ 6 L }}
Original Series <$VALUE
3x1-2 1-2508 <$400/$1000
4x5 1-19659 <$500
3x10-20 1-8400 <$750/$1250
50-100 1-600 <$4000
Series 1875
4x5 1-5000 <$500
3x10-20 1-9202 <$650/$1000
50-100 1-1800 <$4000
Brown Back
4x5 1-22000 <$300
3x10-20 1-29800 <$300/$325
1902 Red Seal
4x5 1-14000 <$350
3x10-20 1-11300 <$350/$400
1902 Date Back
4x5 1-44587 <$150
3x10-20 1-30500 <$150
1902 Plain Back
3x10-20 30501-30707 <$150
SECOND TITLE {{ 20 L 17 S }}
1902 Plain Back
4x5 1-113430 <$60
3x10-20 1-69350 <$60/$75
1929 Small Size
5 Type 1 1-6550 <$45
10 Type 1 1-3504 <$40
20 Type 1 1-872 <$50
5 Type 2 1-8600 <$50
10 Type 2 1-4454 <$55
20 Type 2 1-1078 <$65
Total Issue $13,304,490
Out in 1935 $164,620
Large out 1935 $34,930
Outstanding includes Ch 1245
****
227 New Haven
SECOND NB OF NEW HAVEN
{{ 28 L }}
Chartered 2/64
Original Series <$VALUE
4x5 1-12700 <$400
4x10 1-17075 <$650
3x20-50 1-7020<$1250/$4000
Series 1875
4x5 1-11753 <$400
4x10 1-11140 <$660
3x20-50 1-2491<$1000/$4000
Brown Back
4x5 1-46202 <$175
3x10-20 1-30445 <$175/$225
50-100 1-400 <$1250/$1500
1902 Red Seal
4x5 1-26000 <$250
3x10-20 1-21200 <$250
1902 Date Back
4x5 1-61750 <$75
3x10-20 1-41700 <$75
1902 Plain Back
4x5 61751-183257 <$75
3x10-20 41701-104068 <$75
Total Issue $15,618,700
Out in 1935 $35,985
****
13704 New Haven
TRADESMEN'S NB OF NEW HAVEN
{{ 14 S }}
Chartered 6/33
1929 Small Size <$VALUE
5 Type 2 1-21480 <$50
10 Type 2 1-10028 <$50
20 Type 2 1-3058 <$60
Total Issue $268,840
Out in 1935 $136,500
****
796 New Haven
YALE NB OF NEW HAVEN
{{ 11 L }}
Chartered 2/1 4/65
Liquidated 12/31/17
Original Series <$VALUE
3x1-2 1-4700 <$400/$1000
4x5 1-11275 <$500
4x10 1-6975 <$650
4x20 1-2425 <$1250
50-100 1-917 <$4000
Series 1875
3x1-2 1-2000 <$400/$1000
4x5 1-3500 <$500
4x10 1-4125 <$650
4x20 1-4062 <$1250
50-100 1-2369 <$4000
Brown Back
4x5 1-5480 <$300
3x10-20 1-9487 <$300/$350
50-100 1-1413 <$1250/$1500
1902 Red Seal
4x5 1-9250 <$350
3x10-20 1-10200 <$350/$400
1902 Date Back
4x5 1-40415* <$175
3x10-20 1-25534** <$175
1902 Plain Back
4x5 41666-43045* <$175
3x10-20 26535-27569**<$175
* 40416-41665 not marked
** 25535-26534 not marked
Total Issue $5,515,110
Out at close $167,300
Ch 2682 assumed circulation
****
196 New London
FNB OF NEW LONDON
{{ UNREPORTED }}
Chartered 1/64
Liquidated 1/9/77
Original Series <$VALUE
4x5 1-4110 <$2000
4x10 1-2500 <$2500
Total Issue $182,200
Out in 1910 $1,395
****
666 New London
NB OF COMMERCE OF NEW LONDON
{{ 24 L 50+ S }}
Chartered 12/64
Original Series <$VALUE
3x1-2 1-2300 <$300/$1000
4x5 1-3625 <$350
3x10-20 1-2100 <$750/$1250
50-100 1-550 <$4000
Series 1875
3x1-2 1-1930 <$300/$1000
4x5 1-4460 <$350
3x10-20 1-1395 <$600/$1000
50-100 1-43 <$4000
Brown Back
4x5 1-10594 <$150
3x10-20 1-6397 <$150/$200
50-100 1-468 <$1250/$1500
1902 Red Seal
4x5 1-12415 <$225
3x10-20 1-8434 <$225/$250
1902 Date Back
4x5 1-15250 <$60
3x10-20 1-10100 <$60/$75
1902 Plain Back
4x5 15251-51647 <$60
3x10-20 10101-32438 <$60/$75
1929 Small Size
5 Type 1 1-10970 <$30
10 Type 1 1-5904 <$35
20 Type 1 1-1372 <$45
5 Type 2 1-17532 <$35
10 Type 2 1-8525 <$40
Total Issue $5,394,210
Out in 1935 $191,420
Large out 1935 $9,230
****
1175 New London
N UNION B OF NEW LONDON
{{ 2 L }}
Chartered 1865
Liquidated 1/10/82
Original Series <$VALUE
3x1-2 1-2000 <$750/$1500
4x5 1-2000 <$850
3x10-20 1-1410<$1000/$1500
50-100 1-960 <$4000
Series 1875
50-100 1-588 <$4000
Total Issue $352,700
Out in 1910 $1,394
****
978 New London
N WHALING B OF NEW LONDON
{{ 11 L 2U + 39 S }}
Chartered 4/5/65
Original Series <$VALUE
3x1-2 1-8300 <$500/$1250
4x5 1-11700 <$600
3x10-20 1-1300 <$750/$1250
Series 1875
4x5 1-2500 <$600
3x10-20 1-2400 <$750/$1250
Brown Back
3x10-20 1-5084 <$400/$450
1902 Red Seal
3x10-20 1-1460 <$500
1902 Date Back
3x10-20 1-4100 <$225
1902 Plain Back
3x10-20 4101-9479 <$225
1929 Small Size
5 Type 1 1-3526 <$50
10 Type 1 1-2594 <$50
20 Type 1 1-208 <$60
5 Type 2 1-14004 <$60
10 Type 2 1-8172 <$60
Total Issue $1,749,770
Out in 1935 $146,550
Large out 1935 $4,440
****

****
1037 New London
NEW LONDON CITY NB,
NEW LONDON
{{ 28 L 24 S }}
Chartered 4/65
Original Series <$VALUE
3x1-2 1-2800 <$350/$1000
4x5 1-2800 <$350
3x10-20 1-600 <$750/$1250
Series 1875
3x1-2 1-200 <$350/$1000
4x5 1-2855 <$350
3x10-20 1-934 <$650/$1000
Brown Back
4x5 1-8697 <$175
3x10-20 1-5444 <$175/$225
1902 Red Seal
4x5 1-4000 <$200
3x10-20 1-2700 <$200/$250
1902 Date Back
4x5 1-10000 <$60
3x10-20 1-6880 <$60/$75
1902 Plain Back
4x5 10001-44748 <$60
3x10-20 6881-29908<$60/$75
1929 Small Size
5 Type 1 1-7512 <$40
10 Type 1 1-4100 <$40
20 Type 1 1-1064 <$55
5 Type 2 1-13022 <$40
10 Type 2 1-7076* <$45
20 Type 2 1-2340 <$60
* 5257-5262 not issued
Total Issue $4,037,950
Out in 1935 $193,750
Large out 1935 $8,390
****
1193 Litchfield
FNB OF NEW MILFORD
{{ 9 L 13 S }}
Chartered 1865
Original Series <$VALUE
3x1-2 1-1000 <$400/$1000
4x5 1-2650 <$500
4x10 1-1350 <$750
3x20-50 1-950 <$1250/$4000
Series 1875
4x5 1-350 <$500
4x10 1-625 <$750
3x20-50 1-1504<$1250/$4000
Brown Back
3x10-20 1-8039 <$350/$400
1902 Red Seal
3x10-20 1-5650 <$500
1902 Date Back
3x10-20 1-16300 <$225
1902 Plain Back
3x10-20 16301-54022 <$225
1929 Small Size
10 Type 1 1-5816 <$80
20 Type 1 1-1640 <$90
10 Type 2 1-7228 <$90
20 Type 2 1-1956 <$100
Total Issue $4,456,650
Out in 1935 $162,750
Large out 1935 $10,150
****
2342 Fairfield
CENTRAL NB OF NORWALK
{{ 4 L }}
Chartered 8/29/76
Liquidated 10/27/17
Series 1875 <$VALUE
4x5 1-20521 <$650
Brown Back
3x10-20 1-3750 <$500
1882 Date Back
3x10-20 1-8660* <$550
1882 Value Back
3x10-20 9061-9360* <$600
* 8661-9060 not marked
1902 Plain Back
3x10-20 1-558 <$400
Total Issue $1,093,820
Out at close $50,500
****
754 Fairfield
FAIRFIELD COUNTY NB OF
NORWALK
{{ 12 L }}
Chartered 1/25/65
Liquidated 9/30/22
Original Series <$VALUE
3x1-2 1-7000 <$400/$1000
4x5 1-6500 <$500
4x10 1-3250 <$750
3x20-50 1-700 <$1250/$4000
100-100 1-100 <$4000
Series 1875
4x5 1-7322 <$500
4x10 1-6159 <$750
3x20-50 1-1100<$1250/$4000
100-100 1-231 <$4000
Brown Back
4x5 1-16500 <$300
3x10-20 1-14100 <$300/$350
1902 Red Seal
4x5 1-6700 <$400
3x10-20 1-5520 <$400/$450
1902 Date Back
4x5 1-15500 <$175
3x10-20 1-12200 <$175
1902 Plain Back
4x5 15501-26780 <$175
3x10-20 12201-19626 <$175
Total Issue $3,913,900
Out at close $140,000
****
942 Fairfield
NB OF NORWALK
{{ 20 L 19 S }}
Chartered 3/28/65
Original Series <$VALUE
3x1-2 1-7000 <$300/$850
4x5 1-9905 <$400
3x10-20 1-5000 <$750/$1250
50-100 1-175 <$4000
Series 1875
4x5 1-12500 <$400
3x10-20 1-4000 <$650/$1000
50-100 1-117 <$4000
Brown Back
4x5 1-28125 <$175
3x10-20 1-18993 <$175/$225
1902 Red Seal
4x5 1-8250 <$225
3x10-20 1-5600 <$225/$275
1902 Date Back
4x5 1-22750 <$85
3x10-20 1-18300 <$85
1902 Plain Back
4x5 22751-71955 <$85
3x10-20 18301-50019 <$85
1929 Small Size
5 Type 1 1-8724 <$40
10 Type 1 1-5058 <$40
20 Type 1 1-1308 <$50
5 Type 2 1-15976 <$40
10 Type 2 1-8898 <$45
20 Type 2 1-2003 <$55
Total Issue $7,805,180
Out in 1935 $192,495
Large out 1935 $17,225
****
65 New London
FNB OF NORWICH
{{ UNREPORTED }}
Chartered 8/63
Liquidated 5/2/64
Original Series <$VALUE
4x10 1-250 <$2500
Total Issue $10,000
All notes reportedly redeemed
****
458 New London
FNB OF NORWICH
{{ 12 L }}
Organized 6/6/64
Receivership 5/7/13
Original Series <$VALUE
3x1-2 1-7440 <$400/$1000
4x5 1-11650 <$400
4x10 1-9600 <$750
3x20-100 1-1481<$1250/$4000
Series 1875
4x5 1-3483 <$400
4x10 1-3612 <$750
Brown Back
4x5 1-33193 <$250
3x10-20 1-14849 <$250/$275
1902 Red Seal
4x5 1-10550 <$300
3x10-20 1-8480 <$300/$350
1902 Date Back
4x5 1-13223 <$175
3x10-20 1-8279 <$175
Total Issue $3,825,000
Out in 1916 $31,562
****
1481 New London
MERCHANTS NB OF NORWICH
{{ 3 L }}
Chartered 1865
Closed 10/1/28
Original Series <$VALUE
3x1-2 1-2200 <$650/$1500
4x5 1-3000 <$750
3x10-20 1-2800 <$850/$1250
50-100 1-360 <$4000
Series 1875
4x5 1-1815 <$750
3x10-20 1-1824 <$850/$1250
50-100 1-210 <$4000
Brown Back
4x5 1-13855 <$500
3x10-20 1-7488 <$500
1902 Red Seal
4x5 1-3750 <$600
3x10-20 1-2700 <$600
1902 Date Back
4x5 1-7330* <$350
3x10-20 1-5748** <$350
1902 Plain Back
4x5 7831-18575* <$350
3x10-20 6109-12879** <$350
* 7331-7830 not marked
** 5749-6108 not marked
Total Issue $2,300,950
Out at close $14,855
Ch 1187 assumed circulation
****
1358 New London
NORWICH NB, NORWICH
{{ UNREPORTED }}
Chartered 6/29/65
Liquidated 3/15/89
Original Series <$VALUE
4x5 1-2000 <$1000
3x10-20 1-700 <$1500/$2000
3x50-100 1-1066 <$4000
Series 1875
4x5 1-760 <$1000
3x10-20 1-211 <$1500/$2000
3x50-100 1-929 <$4000
Brown Back
3x10-20 1-1241 <$1000
50-100 1-115 <$1750/$2000
Total Issue $678,800
Out in 1910 $3,150
****
224 New London
SECOND NB OF NORWICH
{{ 2 L }}
Chartered 2/1/64
Liquidated 2/24/03
Original Series <$VALUE
4x5 1-3800 <$850
4x10 1-2575 <$1000
3x20-50 1-1400<$1500/$4000
Series 1875
4x5 1-1800 <$850
4x10 1-1800 <$1000
3x20-50 1-1758<$1500/$4000
Brown Back
4x5 1-6373 <$750
3x10-20 1-5750 <$750
Total Issue $1,049,340
Out in 1910 $6,065
****
1379 New London
SHETUCKET NB OF NORWICH
{{ 1 L }}
Chartered 1865
Liquidated 5/18/85
Original Series <$VALUE
3x1-2 1-3000 <$1000/$2000
4x5 1-3600 <$1000
3x10-20 1-1400<$1500/$2000
Series 1875
4x5 1-750 <$1000
3x10-20 1-2098<$1500/$2000
Total Issue $276,900
Out in 1910 $1,323
****
657 New London
THAMES NB OF NORWICH
{{ 50+ L }}
Chartered 12/64
Liquidated 8/2/29
Original Series <$VALUE
3x1-2 1-20000 <$250/$850
4x5 1-32200 <$275
4x10 1-11500 <$650
3x20-50 1-4609<$1250/$4000
100-100 1-500 <$4000
Series 1875
3x1-2 1-3806 <$250/$850
4x5 1-23000 <$275
4x10 1-12925 <$600
3x20-50 1-2761<$1000/$4000
Brown Back
4x5 1-204732 <$125
3x10-20 1-59696 <$125/$150
1902 Red Seal
4x5 1-26900 <$125
3x10-20 1-21240 <$125/$150
1902 Date Back
4x5 1-8350 <$35
3x10-20 1-6660 <$35/$45
1902 Plain Back
4x5 8351-33245 <$35
3x10-20 6661-16780<$35/$45
Total Issue $13,294,070
Out at close $92,750
****
1187 New London
UNCAS NB OF NORWICH
{{ 11 L }}
Chartered 1865
Original Series <$VALUE
3x1-2 1-5000 <$400/$1250
4x5 1-6000 <$500
3x10-20 1-2400 <$750/$1250
50-100 1-500 <$4000
Series 1875
3x1-2 1-4480 <$400/$1250
4x5 1-5350 <$500
3x10-20 1-3280 <$750/$1250
50-100 1-200 <$4000
Brown Back
4x5 1-8621 <$350
3x10-20 1-5459 <$350/$400
1902 Red Seal
4x5 1-3630 <$450
3x10-20 1-2548 <$450/$500
1902 Date Back
4x5 1-7700 <$225
4x10 1-5520 <$225
1902 Plain Back
4x5 7701-16900 <$225
4x10 5521-11148 <$225
Total Issue $2,204,170
Out in 1935 $13,506
Outstanding includes Ch 1481
****
919 New London
PAWCATUCK NB, PAWCATUCK
{{ 3 L }}
Chartered 3/21/65
Liquidated 4/8/04
Original Series <$VALUE
3x1-2 1-2400 <$750/$1500
4x5 1-3185 <$850
3x10-20 1-1100<$1000/$1500
Series 1875
3x1-2 1-300 <$750/$1500
4x5 1-3065 <$850
3x10-20 1-1586<$1000/$1500
Brown Back
3x10-20 1-5323 <$750
Total Issue $538,950
Out in 1910 $5,156
****
10145 Windham
FNB OF PLAINFIELD
Organized 2/5/12
2nd title:Plainfield NB of
Moosup 8/24/34
FIRST TITLE {{ 4 L 2 S }}
1902 Date Back <$VALUE
3x10 20 1 1130 <$600
1902 Plain Back
3x10-20 1131-10340 <$500
1929 Small Size
10 Type 1 1-1348 <$400
20 Type 1 1-388 <$400
10 Type 2 1-768 <$450
20 Type 2 1-324 <$450
SECOND TITLE {{ 0 S }}
1929 Small Size
10 Type 2 1-848 <$850
20 Type 2 1-88 <$850
Total Issue $668,840
Out in 1935 $49,050
Large out 1935 $1,750
****
9313 Hartford
FNB OF PLAINVILLE
{{ UNREPORTED }}
Chartered 1/09
Liquidated 12/14/15
1902 Date Back <$VALUE
3x10-20 1-2850 <$1500
Total Issue $142,500
Out in 1916 $13,500
****
12637 Hartford
PLANTSVILLE NB,
PLANTSVILLE
{{ 1 L 5 S }}
Chartered 2/25
1902 Plain Back <$VALUE
4x5 1-2607 <$1000
1929 Small Size
5 Type 1 1-1320 <$325
5 Type 2 1-2904 <$350
Total Issue $106,260
Out in 1935 $8,550
Large out 1935 $260
****
1013 Middlesex
FNB OF PORTLAND
{{ 13 L }}
Chartered 4/65
Liquidated 3/2/25
Original Series <$VALUE
4x5 1-2250 <$600
3x10-20 1-4000 <$750/$1250
Series 1875
4x5 1-3050 <$600
3x10-20 1-3194 <$750/$1250
Brown Back
4x5 1-15478 <$350
3x10-20 1-7584 <$350/$400
1902 Red Seal
4x5 1-3750 <$450
3x10-20 1-2400 <$450/$500
1902 Date Back
4x5 1-8680 <$225
3x10-20 1-6568 <$225
1902 Plain Back
4x5 8681-21953 <$225
3x10-20 6569-14447 <$225
Total Issue $2,510,870
Out at close $94,850
****
448 Windham
FNB OF PUTNAM
{{ 4 L }}
Organized 3/23/64
Receivership 8/13/24
Original Series <$VALUE
3x1-2 1-3300 <$650/$1500
4x5 1-2500 <$750
3x10-20 1-2252<$1000/$1500
50-100 1-652 <$4000
Series 1875
4x5 1-5320 <$750
3x10-20 1-1300<$1000/$1500
Brown Back
4x5 1-18669 <$650
3x10-20 1-984 <$650
1902 Red Seal
4x5 1-4000 <$750
3x10-20 1-4100 <$750
1902 Date Back
4x5 1-8400 <$375
3x10-20 1-4880 <$375
1902 Plain Back
4x5 8401-11880 <$375
3x10-20 4881-7001 <$375
Total Issue $1,743,530
Out at close $50,000
****
Thompson NB of Putnam
SEE Ch 1477
Thompson NB of Thompson
****
5309 Fairfield
FNB OF RIDGEFIELD
Chartered 4/27/00
2nd title:FNB & TC of
Ridgefield 1/8/20
FIRST TITLE {{ 7 L }}
Brown Back <$VALUE
4x5 1-1940 <$450
3x10-20 1-1404 <$450/$500
1882 Date Back
4x5 1-2600 <$450
3x10-20 1-1860 <$450/$500
1882 Value Back
4x5 2601-4200 <$600
3x10-20 1861-2720 <$600
SECOND TITLE {{ 7 L 3 S }}
1902 Plain Back
4x5 1-4052 <$275
3x10-20 1-2404 <$275
1929 Small Size
5 Type 1 1-922 <$350
10 Type 1 1-510 <$350
20 Type 1 1-160 <$350
5 Type 2 1-1272 <$400
10 Type 2 1-636 <$400
20 Type 2 1-204 <$400
Total Issue $624,500
Out in 1935 $24,670
Large out 1935 $1,380
****
186 Tolland
FNB OF ROCKVILLE
{{ 6 L 3 S }}
Chartered 1/64
Liquidated 7/26/30
Original Series <$VALUE
3x1-2 1-6600 <$600/$1250
4x5 1-7325 <$650
3x10-20 1-3220 <$850/$1250
50-100 1-150 <$4000
Series 1875
4x5 1-6755 <$650
3x10-20 1-2140 <$850/$1250
Brown Back
4x5 1-12598 <$500
3x10-20 1-5602 <$500
1902 Red Seal
4x5 1-2944 <$600
3x10-20 1-2122 <$600
1902 Date Back
4x5 1-4950 <$300
3x10-20 1-3740 <$300
1902 Plain Back
4x5 4951-11188 <$300
3x10-20 3741-8309 <$300
1929 Small Size
5 Type 1 1-710 <$350
10 Type 1 1-267 <$350
20 Type 1 1-33 <$375
Total Issue $1,982,630
Out at close $45,800
Large out at close $11,710
****
509 Tolland
ROCKVILLE NB, ROCKVILLE
{{ 4 L 7 S }}
Chartered 9/64
Liquidated 12/12/33
Original Series <$VALUE
4x5 1-13750 <$750
3x10-20 1-6000<$1000/$1500
Series 1875
4x5 1-2500 <$750
3x10-20 1-7697<$1000/$1500
Brown Back
4x5 1-12050 <$500
3x10-20 1-10072 <$500
1902 Red Seal
4x5 1-2000 <$600
3x10-20 1-1600 <$600
1902 Date Back
4x5 1-5200 <$350
3x10-20 1-4140 <$350
1902 Plain Back
4x5 5201-5850 <$350
3x10-20 4141-18735 <$350
1929 Small Size
10 Type 1 1-2510 <$150
20 Type 1 1-656 <$175
10 Type 2 1-441 <$200
20 Type 2 1-130 <$200
Total Issue $3,164,530
Out at close $97,750
Large out at close $9,820
****
5499 New Haven
VALLEY NB OF SEYMOUR
{{ 2 L }}
Chartered 7/16/00
Liquidated 8/12/05
Brown Back <$VALUE
4x5 1-1840 <$1250
3x10-20 1-1718 <$1250
Total Issue $122,700
Out in 1910 $2,795
****
2643 Fairfield
CITY NB OF SOUTH NORWALK
{{ 13 L 8 S }}
Chartered 1882
Series 1875 <$VALUE
4x5 1-3747 <$500
3x10-20 1-8245 <$750/$1250
Brown Back
4x5 1-6600 <$300
3x10-20 1-5080 <$300/$350
1882 Date Back
4x5 1-10100 <$300
3x10-20 1-6360 <$300/$350
1882 Value Back
4x5 10101-11907 <$400
3x10-20 6361-11660 <$400
1902 Plain Back
4x5 1-11907 <$175
3x10-20 1-8396 <$175
1929 Small Size
5 Type 1 1-4002 <$125
10 Type 1 1-2124 <$125
20 Type 1 1-510 <$150
5 Type 2 1-6826 <$175
10 Type 2 1-3862 <$175
20 Type 2 1-1164 <$175
Total Issue $2,911,860
Out in 1935 $96,700
Large out 1935 $5,130
****

****
502 Fairfield
FNB OF SOUTH NORWALK
{{ 5 L }}
Chartered 8/24/64
Liquidated 2/28/01
Original Series <$VALUE
3x1-2 1-4700 <$500/$1250
4x5 1-6600 <$600
3x10-20 1-3790 <$850/$1250
Series 1875
4x5 1-6690 <$600
3x10-20 1-2520 <$850/$1250
Brown Back
4x5 1-5220 <$450
3x10-20 1-4235 <$450/$500
Total Issue $920,950
Out in 1910 $4,393
****
2814 Hartford
SOUTHINGTON NB, SOUTHINGTON
{{ 2 L }}
Chartered 1882
Liquidated 4/19/16
Brown Back <$VALUE
4x5 1-11215 <$1000
3x10-20 1-495 <$1000
1902 Red Seal
3x10-20 1-1670 <$1250
1902 Date Back
3x10-20 1-2455 <$750
Total Issue $455,300
Out in 1916 $15,335
****
660 Fairfield
SOUTHPORT NB, SOUTHPORT
{{ 6 L }}
Organized 12/29/64
Receivership 5/19/03
Original Series <$VALUE
3x1-2 1-6500 <$650/$1500
4x5 1-4250 <$750
3x10-20 1-1700 <$850/$1500
Series 1875
3x1-2 1-360 <$650/$1500
4x5 1-3045 <$750
3x10-20 1-2234 <$850/$1500
Brown Back
3x10-20 1-10969 <$650
Total Issue $925,350
Out in 1916 $5,285
****
3914 Tolland
FNB OF STAFFORD SPRINGS
{{ 9 L 2 S }}
Chartered 7/27/88
Liquidated 12/27/33
Brown Back <$VALUE
4x5 1-9033 <$600
3x10-20 1-2734 <$600
1902 Date Back
4x5 1-4125 <$300
3x10-20 1-3380 <$300
1902 Plain Back
4x5 4126-12887 <$300
3x10-20 3381-9519 <$300
1929 Small Size
5 Type 1 1-1793 <$400
10 Type 1 1-958 <$400
20 Type 1 1-265 <$450
Total Issue $1,194,120
Out at close $48,980
Large out at close $3,940
****
686 Tolland
STAFFORD NB OF STAFFORD SPRINGS
{{ 3 L }}
Chartered 6/7/65
Receivership 10/17/87
Original Series <$VALUE
3x1-2 1-4000 <$850/$1500
4x5 1-6500 <$1000
3x10-20 1-2200<$1250/$2000
50-100 1-417 <$4000
Series 1875
3x1-2 1-2900 <$850/$1500
4x5 1-2750 <$1000
3x10-20 1-3337<$1250/$2000
50-100 1-664 <$4000
Brown Back
4x5 1-3105 <$850
3x10-20 1-860 <$850
50-100 1-105 <$1750/$2000
Total Issue $779,350
Out in 1916 $2,855
****
4 Fairfield
FNB OF STAMFORD
Chartered 6/63
2nd title: F-Stamford NB 7/12/19
3rd title: F-Stamford NB & TC 1/2/30
FIRST TITLE {{ 29 L }}
Original Series <$VALUE
3x1-2 1-8000 <$650/$1500
4x5 1-11250 <$750
3x10-20 1-2800<$1000/$1500
Series 1875
3x1-2 1-4000 <$650/$1500
4x5 1-4040 <$750
3x10-20 1-3458<$1000/$1500
Brown Back
4x5 1-7050 <$400
3x10-20 1-21449 <$400/$450
1902 Red Seal
3x10-20 1-12900 <$500
1902 Date Back
3x10-20 1-20100 <$150
1902 Plain Back
3x10-20 20101-28600 <$150
SECOND TITLE {{17 L U+16 S }}
1902 Plain Back
3x10-20 1-57096 <$150
1929 Small Size
10 Type 1 1-4592 <$50
20 Type 1 1-1542 <$60
THIRD TITLE {{ 4U + 16 S }}
1929 Small Size
5 Type 1 1-16274 <$50
10 Type 1 1-12820 <$60
5 Type 2 1-19944 <$50
10 Type 2 1-19682 <$60
Total Issue $8,836,470
Out in 1935 $662,225
Large out 1935 $30,205
Outstanding includes Ch 1038
****
12400 Fairfield
PEOPLES NB OF STAMFORD
{{ 6 L 9 S }}
Chartered 6/23
Liquidated 3/1/33
1902 Plain Back <$VALUE
4x5 1-14025 <$450
3x10-20 1-9219 <$450
1929 Small Size
5 Type 1 1-5426 <$200
10 Type 1 1-2662 <$200
20 Type 1 1-746 <$200
Total Issue $1,153,470
Out at close $132,050
Large out at close $6,390
****
1038 Fairfield
STAMFORD NB, STAMFORD
{{ 9 L }}
Chartered 4/65
Closed 7/12/19
Original Series <$VALUE
3x1-2 1-3000 <$600/$1250
4x5 1-5600 <$750
3x10-20 1-1800<$1000/$1500
50-100 1-815 <$4000
Series 1875
3x1-2 1-2020 <$600/$1250
4x5 1-5250 <$750
3x10-20 1-4000<$1000/$1500
Brown Back
4x5 1-26438 <$350
3x10-20 1-12937 <$350/$400
50-100 1-1345 <$1500/$1750
1902 Red Seal
4x5 1-17500 <$450
3x10-20 1-8780 <$450
50-100 1-1040 <$2250/$2500
1902 Date Back
4x5 1-38750 <$225
3x10-20 1-23800 <$225
50-100 1-400 <$500/$600
3x50-100 1-732 <$500/$600
1902 Plain Back
4x5 38751-48957 <$225
3x10-20 23801-39318 <$225
Total Issue $5,714,750
Out at close $200,000
Ch 4 assumed circulation
****
735 New London
FNB OF STONINGTON
{{ 18 L 10 S }}
Chartered 1/21/65
Original Series <$VALUE
3x1-2 1-8500 <$400/$1000
4x5 1-12700 <$500
3x10-20 1-1800 <$750/$1250
50-100 1-140 <$4000
Series 1875
3x1-2 1-2000 <$400/$1000
4x5 1-5750 <$500
3x10-20 1-4198 <$750/$1250
Brown Back
4x5 1-7095 <$350
3x10-20 1-6887 <$350
1902 Red Seal
4x5 1-2000 <$400
3x10-20 1-1300 <$400
1902 Date Back
4x5 1-3925 <$150
3x10-20 1-3100 <$150
1902 Plain Back
4x5 3926-11825 <$150
3x10-20 3101-8321 <$150
1929 Small Size
5 Type 1 1-1718 <$150
10 Type 1 1-976 <$150
20 Type 1 1-248 <$175
5 Type 2 1-2352 <$200
10 Type 2 1-1068 <$200
20 Type 2 1-300 <$225
Total Issue $2,154,500
Out in 1935 $48,950
Large out 1935 $6,070
****
497 Hartford
FNB OF SUFFIELD
{{ 7 L 13 S }}
Chartered 8/64
Original Series <$VALUE
3x1-2 1-2000 <$500/$1250
4x5 1-10250 <$600
3x10-20 1-2500 <$750/$1250
50-100 1-100 <$4000
Series 1875
3x1-2 1-1680 <$500/$1250
4x5 1-8500 <$600
3x10-20 1-2400 <$750/$1250
50-100 1-200 <$4000
Brown Back
4x5 1-15099 <$450
3x10-20 1-6768 <$450/$500
50-100 1-560 <$1500/$1750
1902 Red Seal
4x5 1-4250 <$500
3x10-20 1-3000 <$500
1902 Date Back
4x5 1-9000 <$250
3x10-20 1-6300 <$250
1902 Plain Back
4x5 9001-27387 <$250
3x10-20 6301-18401 <$250
1929 Small Size
5 Type 1 1-3884 <$85
10 Type 1 1-1956 <$85
20 Type 1 1-494 <$100
5 Type 2 1-4580 <$110
10 Type 2 1-2710 <$110
20 Type 2 1-804 <$125
Total Issue $3,469,810
Out in 1935 $96,045
Large out 1935 $10,615
****
3964 Litchfield
THOMASTON NB, THOMASTON
{{ 1 L 4 S }}
Chartered 1/17/89
Brown Back <$VALUE
4x5 1-3721 <$1500
3x10-20 1-745 <$1500
1902 Date Back
3x10-20 1-1480* <$1250
1902 Plain Back
3x10-20 1601-3407* <$1250
* 1481-1600 not marked
1929 Small Size
10 Type 1 1-310 <$350
20 Type 1 1-104 <$350
10 Type 2 1-1439 <$375
20 Type 2 1-422 <$400
Total Issue $335,930
Out in 1935 $24,550
Large out 1935 $670
****
1477 Windham
THOMPSON NB, THOMPSON
{{ UNREPORTED }}
Chartered 7/22/65
Liquidated 4/24/89
2nd title: Thompson NB of Putnam 3/28/93
FIRST TITLE
Original Series <$VALUE
3x1-2 1-4160 <$1500/$2500
4x5 1-3825 <$1500
3x10-20 1-860 <$1500/$2000
Series 1875
4x5 1-2190 <$1500
3x10-20 1-1140<$1500/$2000
Brown Back
3x10-20 1-1370 <$1500
SECOND TITLE
Brown Back
3x10-20 1-870 <$2000
Total Issue $353,400
Out in 1910 $2,177
****
1385 Tolland
TOLLAND COUNTY NB, TOLLAND
{{ 7 L }}
Chartered 1865
Liquidated 6/6/85
Original Series <$VALUE
3x1-2 1-5500 <$500/$1250
4x5 1-3500 <$600
3x10-20 1-600 <$750/$1250
Series 1875
3x1-2 1-108 <$500/$1250
4x5 1-3670 <$600
3x10-20 1-1362 <$750/$1250
Total Issue $269,540
Out in 1910 $1,632
****
5231 Litchfield
BROOKS NB OF TORRINGTON
{{ 1 L }}
Chartered 11/4/99
Liquidated 3/31/17
Brown Back <$VALUE
4x5 1-2025 <$1250
3x10-20 1-1570 <$1250
1882 Date Back
4x5 1-305 <$1250
3x10-20 1-60 <$1250
Total Issue $128,100
Out at close $1,000
****
5235 Litchfield
TORRINGTON NB, TORRINGTON
Chartered 12/9/99
2nd title: Torrington NB & TC 2/8/30
FIRST TITLE {{ 17 L 6 S }}
Brown Back <$VALUE
4x5 1-5175 <$275
3x10-20 1-3410 <$275/$325
1882 Date Back
4x5 1-8400 <$300
3x10-20 1-5740 <$300/$350
1882 Value Back
4x5 8401-13200 <$300
3x10-20 5741-8380<$300/$350
1902 Plain Back
4x5 1-16370 <$175
4x10 1-12546 <$175
1929 Small Size
5 Type 1 1-2050 <$100
10 Type 1 1-1036 <$100
SECOND TITLE {{ 36 S }}
1929 Small Size
5 Type 1 1-7240 <$50
10 Type 1 1-6250 <$50
5 Type 2 1-43758 <$50
10 Type 2 1-23820 <$50
Total Issue $2,959,090
Out in 1935 $393,950
Large out 1935 $3,410
****
2599 New Haven
FNB OF WALLINGFORD
{{ 16 L 18 S }}
Chartered 1881
Series 1875 <$VALUE
4x5 1-14655 <$500
3x10-20 1-8070 <$600/$1000
Brown Back
4x5 1-8100 <$325
3x10-20 1-6860 <$325/$375
1882 Date Back
4x5 1-13000 <$350
3x10-20 1-10100 <$350/$400
1882 Value Back
4x5 13001-24878 <$350
3x10-20 10101-17312 <$350/$400
1902 Plain Back
3x50-100 1-2884 <$400/$500
1929 Small Size
5 Type 1 1-6328 <$50
10 Type 1 1-3152 <$60
50 Type 1 1-248 <$300
100 Type 1 1-84 <$400
5 Type 2 1-9986 <$60
10 Type 2 1-4447 <$70
Total Issue $3,883,920
Out in 1935 $173,250
Large out 1935 $11,790
****
791 New Haven
CITIZENS NB OF WATERBURY
{{ 9 L }}
Chartered 2/9/65
Closed 11/11/22
Original Series <$VALUE
3x1-2 1-5500 <$400/$1000
4x5 1-5395 <$500
3x10-20 1-3930 <$750/$1250
50-100 1-1224 <$4000
Series 1875
3x1-2 1-1980 <$400/$1000
4x5 1-4000 <$500
3x10-20 1-3888 <$750/$1250
50-100 1-1434 <$4000
Brown Back
4x5 1-6190 <$300
3x10-20 1-4634 <$300/$350
50-100 1-1304 <$1250/$1500
1902 Red Seal
4x5 1-7500 <$350
3x10-20 1-5500 <$350/$400
50-100 1-267 <$2250/$2500
1902 Date Back
4x5 1-19750 <$175
3x10-20 1-14200 <$175
50-100 1-400 <$500/$600
3x50-100 1-69 <$500/$600
1902 Plain Back
4x5 19751-21277 <$175
3x10-20 14201-15395* <$175
* 15162, 15178, 15195 not issued
Total Issue $3,303,440
Out at close $33,150
Ch 2494 assumed circulation
****
3768 New Haven
FOURTH NB OF WATERBURY
{{ 1 L }}
Chartered 8/2/87
Liquidated 11/18/07
Brown Back <$VALUE
3x10-20 1-8863 <$1250
Total Issue $443,150
Out in 1910 $14,050
****
2494 New Haven
MANUFACTURERS NB OF WATERBURY
Chartered 10/25/80
2nd title: Citizens & Manufacturers NB of Waterbury 11/11/22
FIRST TITLE {{ 3 L }}
Series 1875 <$VALUE
4x5 1-9295 <$750
3x10-20 1-2718 <$850/$1250
Brown Back
3x10-20 1-4620 <$600
50-100 1-860 <$1500/$1750
1882 Date Back
3x10-20 1-7556 <$600
50-100 1-400 <$1750/$2000
3x50-100 1-200 <$1750/$2000
SECOND TITLE {{ 15 S }}
1929 Small Size
5 Type 1 1-418 <$85
10 Type 1 1-1230 <$65
20 Type 1 1-408 <$75
5 Type 2 1-4916 <$85
10 Type 2 1-2397 <$85
Total Issue $1,353,450
Out in 1935 $88,070
Large out 1935 $9,970
Outstanding includes Ch 791
****
780 New Haven
WATERBURY NB, WATERBURY
{{ 5 L 2U + 33 S }}
Chartered 2/2/65
Original Series <$VALUE
3x1-2 1-5000 <$500/$1250
4x5 1-6000 <$600
3x10-20 1-9200 <$750/$1250
50-100 1-2700 <$4000
Series 1875
3x10-20 1-3000 <$750/$1250
50-100 1-2400 <$4000
Brown Back
3x10-20 1-6191 <$450
50-100 1-3217 <$1250/$1500
1902 Red Seal
4x5 1-3750 <$500
3x10-20 1-2200 <$500
50-100 1-534 <$2250/$2500
1902 Date Back
4x5 1-7250 <$250
3x10-20 1-5300 <$250
50-100 1-390 <$500/$600
3x50-100 1-100 <$500/$600
1902 Plain Back
4x5 7251-8770 <$250
3x10-20 5301-6483 <$250
3x50-100 101-117<$500/$600
1929 Small Size
5 Type 1 1-8030 <$35
10 Type 1 1-4812 <$35
20 Type 1 1-1454 <$45
50 Type 1 1-188 <$275
100 Type 1 1-98 <$375
5 Type 2 1-15964 <$45
10 Type 2 1-9455 <$45
20 Type 2 1-2580 <$50
Total Issue $4,209,770
Out in 1935 $331,950
Large out 1935 $6,740
****
450 Windham
FNB OF KILLINGLY AT WEST KILLINGLY
Chartered 6/1/64
Liquidated 4/11/98
2nd title: FNB of Killingly 1884
FIRST TITLE {{ 9 L }}
Original Series <$VALUE
3x1-2 1-2000 <$500/$1250
4x5 1-5450 <$600
3x10-20 1-2000 <$750/$1250
Series 1875
3x1-2 1-740 <$500/$1250
4x5 1-1500 <$600
3x10-20 1-1450 <$750/$1250
SECOND TITLE {{ 3 L }}
Brown Back
4x5 1-5193 <$450
3x10-20 1-3244 <$450/$500
Total Issue $591,260
Out in 1910 $3,660
****
250 New Haven
FNB OF WEST MERIDEN
Chartered 2/64
Liquidated 12/18/33
2nd title: FNB of Meriden 3/1/81
FIRST TITLE {{ 8 L }}
Original Series <$VALUE
3x1-2 1-10824 <$400/$1000
4x5 1-17775 <$500
4x10 1-5000 <$750
Series 1875
4x5 1-7125 <$500
4x10 1-8037 <$750
SECOND TITLE {{ 17 L 25 S }}
Series 1875
4x5 1-5000 <$500
3x10-20 1-2000 <$750/$1250
Brown Back
4x5 1-38444 <$325
3x10-20 1-10083 <$325/$350
1902 Red Seal
4x5 1-14750 <$350
4x10 1-1500 <$350
3x10-20 1-6400 <$350/$400
1902 Date Back
4x5 1-20415 <$125
4x10 1-14500 <$125
3x10-20 1-534 <$125
1902 Plain Back
4x5 20416-60777 <$125
4x10 14501-46732 <$125
3x10-20 535-1134 <$125
1929 Small Size
5 Type 1 1-11036 <$40
10 Type 1 1-5322 <$40
5 Type 2 1-3590 <$45
10 Type 2 1-718 <$50
Total Issue $7,038,680
Out at close $186,955
Large out at close $16,555
****

CONDITION affects Value. The Values shown are for notes in FINE condition.

****

394 Fairfield
FNB OF WESTPORT
{{ 10 L }}
Chartered 4/64
Liquidated 7/31/13
Original Series <$VALUE
3x1-2 1-9500 <$450/$1250
4x5 1-17500 <$600
3x10-20 1-3000 <$850/$1250
Series 1875
3x1-2 1-7000 <$450/$1250
4x5 1-9750 <$600
3x10-20 1-2925 <$850/$1250
Brown Back
4x5 1-18750 <$400
3x10-20 1-4950 <$400/$450
1902 Red Seal
4x5 1-5750 <$500
3x10-20 1-3900 <$500
1902 Date Back
4x5 1-5082 <$250
3x10-20 1-3556 <$250
Total Issue $2,135,690
Out in 1910 $73,700

****

2388 Windham
FNB OF WILLIMANTIC
{{ 2 L }}
Chartered 6/20/78
Receivership 4/23/95
Series 1875 <$VALUE
4x5 1-3098 <$1250
3x10-20 1-4251<$1500/$2000
Total Issue $274,510
Out in 1916 $980

****

Windham NB, Willimantic
SEE Ch 1614
Windham NB, Windham

****

1614 Windham
WINDHAM NB, WINDHAM
Chartered 1865
2nd title and location:
Windham NB, Willimantic
2/10/79
FIRST TITLE {{ 0 L }}
Original Series <$VALUE
4x5 1-3700 , <$1000
3x10-20 1-1966<$1250/$1500
50-100 1-100 <$4000
Series 1875
4x5 1-1500 <$1000
SECOND TITLE {{ 18 L 19 S }}
Series 1875
4x5 1501-2958 <$600
3x10-20 1-2219 <$750/$1250
Brown Back
4x5 1-7592 <$250
3x10-20 1-7280 <$250/$275
1902 Red Seal
4x5 1-4330 <$350
3x10-20 1-2868 <$350
1902 Date Back
4x5 1-5250 <$125
3x10-20 1-4200 <$125
1902 Plain Back
4x5 5251-21392 <$125
3x10-20 4201-14706 <$125
1929 Small Size
5 Type 1 1-3926 <$50
10 Type 1 1-1836 <$50
20 Type 1 1-450 <$60
5 Type 2 1-4142 <$65
10 Type 2 1-2387 <$65
20 Type 2 1-813 <$70
Total Issue $2,609,170
Out in 1935 $86,495
Large out 1935 $6,365

****

2414 Litchfield
FNB OF WINSTED
{{ 9 L 8 S }}
Chartered 2/27/79
Series 1875 <$VALUE
4x5 1-3478 <$600
3x10-20 1-3753 <$750/$1250
Brown Back
4x5 1-1350 <$400
3x10-20 1-1805 <$400
1882 Date Back
4x5 1-2800 <$450
3x10-20 1-2080 <$450
1882 Value Back
4x5 2801-3445 <$500
3x10-20 2081-2398 <$500
1902 Plain Back
3x10-20 1-4060 <$275
1929 Small Size
10 Type 1 1-764 <$175
20 Type 1 1-234 <$175
10 Type 2 1-1206 <$200
20 Type 2 1-247 <$200
Total Issue $857,180
Out in 1935 $29,050
Large out 1935 $1,750

****

1494 Litchfield
HURLBUT NB OF WINSTED
{{ 25 L 34 S }}
Chartered 1865
Original Series <$VALUE
3x1-2 1-3000 <$350/$850
4x5 1-8250 <$400
3x10-20 1-3800 <$750/$1250
50-100 1-150 <$4000
Series 1875
3x1-2 1-1520 <$350/$850
4x5 1-3495 <$400
3x10-20 1-2590 <$750/$1250
50-100 1-50 <$4000
Brown Back
4x5 1-9645 <$200
3x10-20 1-8006 <$200/$250
1902 Red Seal
4x5 1-6500 <$225
3x10-20 1-4400 <$225/$275
1902 Date Back
4x5 1-16600 <$60
4x10 1-11800 <$60/$75
1902 Plain Back
4x5 16601-44608 <$60
4x10 11801-39767 <$60/$75
1929 Small Size
10 Type 1 1-5544 <$45
20 Type 1 1-1458 <$55
10 Type 2 1-8557 <$50
20 Type 2 1-2231 <$60
Total Issue $5,068,500
Out in 1935 $193,750
Large out 1935 $9,280

****

2419 Litchfield
WINSTED NB, WINSTED
{{ UNREPORTED }}
Chartered 3/15/79
Liquidated 4/12/87
Series 1875 <$VALUE
4x5 1-2655 <$1500
3x10-20 1-857 <$1750/$2000
Total Issue $95,950
Out in 1910 $235

****

<$VALUEs are for notes in **FINE** condition. Value changes by approximately **25%** for a change of one full grade.

DAKOTA TERRITORY

The Dakota Territory was divided November 2, 1889 to form the states of North Dakota and South Dakota. Notes issued by Dakota Territory National Banks will be found in the North Dakota or South Dakota listings. Listed below are the charter numbers and town names for Dakota Territory issuers.

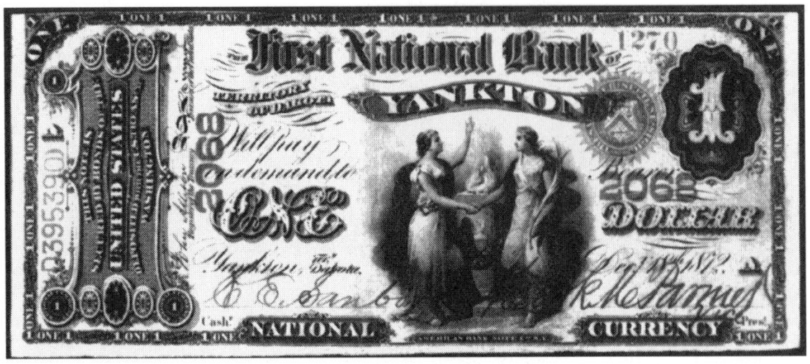

Dakota Territory Ace

NORTH DAKOTA

Charter	Town	Charter	Town
2377	Fargo	3096	Grafton
2434	Bismarck	3169	Bismarck
2514	Fargo	3301	Grand Forks
2548	Valley City	3331	Jamestown
2564	Grand Forks	3397	Devils Lake
2570	Grand Forks	3400	Hillsboro
2578	Jamestown	3411	Hillsboro
2580	Jamestown	3436	Park River
2585	Mandan	3438	Pembina
2624	Wahpeton	3504	Grand Forks
2650	Valley City	3602	Fargo
2677	Bismarck	3669	Lisbon
2792	Casselton	3673	Mayville
2840	Grafton	3714	Devils Lake
2854	Larimore	4009	Minot
2986	Bismarck	4106	Wahpeton
		4143	Lakota

SOUTH DAKOTA

Charter	Town	Charter	Town
2068	Yankton	3349	Watertown
2391	Deadwood	3352	Columbia
2461	Deadwood	3393	Sioux Falls
2465	Sioux Falls	3398	Redfield
2645	Mitchell	3401	Rapid City
2819	Huron	3414	Watertown
2823	Sioux Falls	3435	DeSmet
2830	Canton	3437	Ashton
2843	Sioux Falls	3479	Clark
2911	Chamberlain	3508	Dell Rapids
2935	Watertown	3522	Doland
2941	Pierre	3552	Deadwood
2980	Aberdeen	3578	Mitchell
2989	Huron	3586	Sioux Falls
3087	Brookings	3597	Madison
3130	Plankinton	3636	Huron
3149	Madison	3675	Parker
3151	Madison	3739	Sturgis
3237	Rapid City	3932	Aberdeen
3267	Huron	4104	Pierre
3326	Aberdeen		

Nickname: The First State
Motto: Liberty and Independence
Capital: Dover
Number of towns: 21
Number of issuing charters: 28
Number of small size issuers: 16

Dagsboro
Delaware City
Delmar
Dover
Felton
Frankford
Frederica
Georgetown
Harrington
Laurel
Lewes
Middletown
Milford
Newark
Newport
Odessa
Seaford
Selbyville
Smyrna
Wilmington
Wyoming

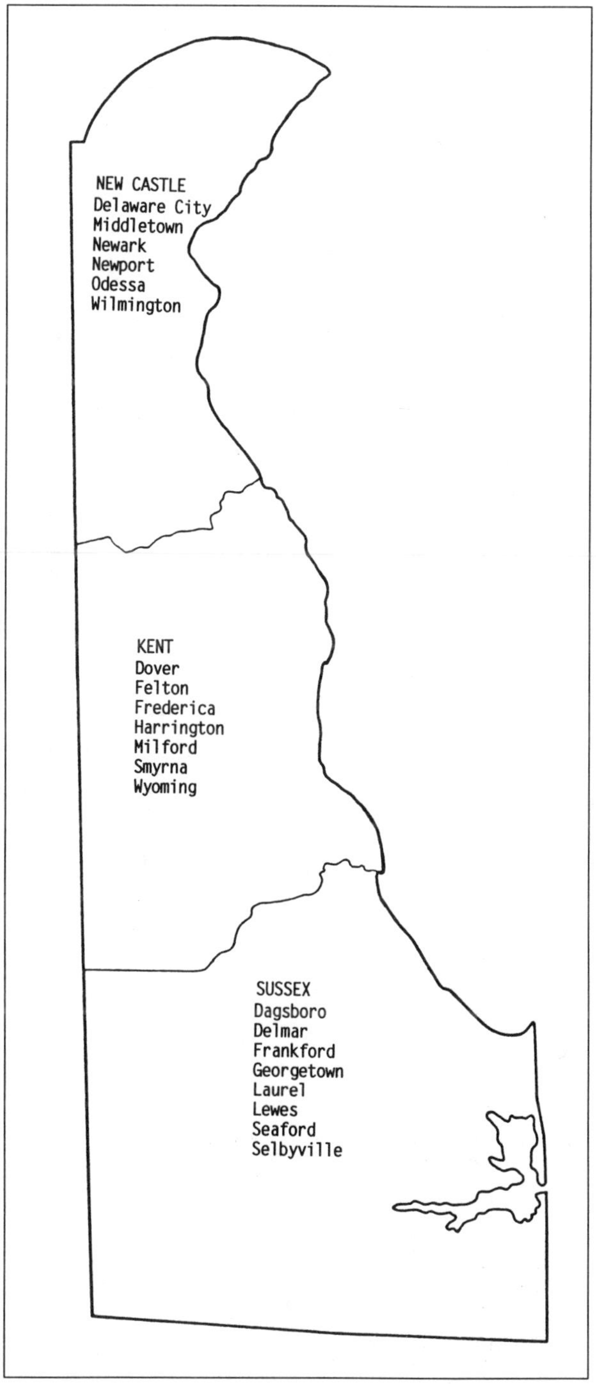

****
8972 Sussex
FNB OF DAGSBORO
{{4 L U+11 S}}
Chartered 12/07
1902 Red Seal <$VALUE
4x10 1-500 <$3500
1902 Date Back
4x10 1-2600 <$850
1902 Plain Back
4x10 2601-9098 <$850
1929 Small Size
10 Type 1 1-1328 <$400
10 Type 2 1-2016 <$400
Total Issue $483,760
Out in 1935 $25,000
Large out 1935 $790
****
1332 New Castle
DELAWARE CITY NB,
DELAWARE CITY
{{12 L 8 S}}
Chartered 1865
Original Series <$VALUE
3x1-2 1-1000 <$1750/$3500
4x5 1-2700 <$1500
3x10-20 1-800 <$2000/$3000
Series 1875
4x5 1-250 <$1500
3x10-20 1-1766<$2000/$3000
Brown Back
4x5 1-650 <$1500
3x10-20 1-5712 <$1500
1902 Red Seal
3x10-20 1-1760 <$3500
1902 Date Back
4x5 1-4500 <$450
3x10-20 1-2940 <$450
1902 Plain Back
4x5 4501-14047 <$450
3x10-20 2941-9213 <$450
1929 Small Size
5 Type 1 1-2124 <$350
10 Type 1 1-1242 <$350
20 Type 1 1-358 <$350
5 Type 2 1-3764 <$400
10 Type 2 1-2058 <$400
20 Type 2 1-513 <$400
Total Issue $1,551,350
Out in 1935 $60,000
Large out 1935 $3,480
****
7211 Sussex
FNB OF DELMAR
{{0 L 5 S}}
Chartered 4/04
1902 Red Seal <$VALUE
3x10-20 1-650 <$5000
1902 Date Back
3x10-20 1-1170* <$2500
1902 Plain Back
3x10-20 1271-3091* <$2500
* 1171-1270 not marked
1929 Small Size
10 Type 1 1-314 <$750
20 Type 1 1-104 <$750
10 Type 2 1-272 <$750
20 Type 2 1-72 <$750
Total Issue $222,530
Out in 1935 $9,650
Large out 1935 $240
****
1567 Kent
FNB OF DOVER
{{12 L 50+ S}}
Chartered 1865
Original Series <$VALUE
3x1-2 1-1805 <$1750/$3500
4x5 1-3500 <$1500
3x10-20 1-2500<$2000/$3000
Series 1875
4x5 . 1-470 <$1500
3x10-20 1-2214<$2000/$3000
Brown Back
3x10-20 1-2341 <$1500
50-100 1-1178 <$5000
1902 Red Seal
4x5 1-1500 <$3500
3x10-20 1-700 <$3500
50-100 1-367 <$6500
1902 Date Back
4x5 1-5600 <$600
3x10-20 1-4060 <$600
50-100 1-100 <$1750/$2000
1902 Plain Back
4x5 5601-25736 <$600
3x10-20 4061-16990 <$600
1929 Small Size
5 Type 1 1-4348 <$175
10 Type 1 1-2066 <$175
20 Type 1 1-530 <$175
5 Type 2 1-6270 <$150
10 Type 2 1-3163 <$150
20 Type 2 1-886 <$175
Total Issue $2,515,845
Out in 1935 $100,000
Large out 1935 $5,900
****
9132 Kent
FNB OF FELTON
{{3 L}}
Chartered 5/08
Liquidated 4/30/17
1902 Date Back <$VALUE
3x10-20 1-4050* <$1500
1902 Plain Back
3x10-20 4176-4785* <$1500
* 4051-4175 not marked
Total Issue $191,400
Out at close $25,000
****
8918 Sussex
FNB OF FRANKFORD
{{1 L 5 S}}
Chartered 10/07
1902 Red Seal <$VALUE
3x10-20 1-470 <$4000
1902 Date Back
3x10-20 1-1720* <$2000
1902 Plain Back
3x10-20 1821-5253* <$2000
* 1721-1820 not marked
1929 Small Size
10 Type 1 1-586 <$650
20 Type 1 1-160 <$650
10 Type 2 1-654 <$650
20 Type 2 1-85 <$650
Total Issue $348,750
Out in 1935 $20,000
Large out 1935 $610
****
5421 Kent
FNB OF FREDERICA
{{2 L}}
Chartered 6/13/00
Liquidated 11/30/20
Brown Back <$VALUE
4x5 1-1670 <$2000
50-100 1-510 <$5000
1882 Date Back
4x5 1-1975* <$2000
3x10-20 1-650** <$2000
50-100 1-220 <$4000
3x50-100 1-40 <$4000
1882 Value Back
4x5 2076-3610* <$2500
* 1976-2075 not marked
** 651-1638 not marked
1902 Plain Back
4x5 1-200 <$1500
4x10 1-95 <$1500
Total Issue $298,420
Out at close $24,400
****
5930 Sussex
FNB OF GEORGETOWN
{{2 L}}
Chartered 8/1/01
Liquidated 9/30/18
Brown Back <$VALUE
3x10-20 1-1230 <$2000
1882 Date Back
3x10-20 1-1420* <$2000
1882 Value Back
3x10-20 1721-2444* <$2000
* 1421-1720 not marked
Total Issue $183,700
Out at close $28,500
****
3883 Kent
FNB OF HARRINGTON
{{3 L 3 S}}
Chartered 5/9/88
Brown Back <$VALUE
50-100 1-512 <$5000
1902 Red Seal
50-100 1-60 <$6500
1902 Date Back
50-100 1-300 <$1750/$2000
3x50-100 1-170 <$1750/$2000
1902 Plain Back
3x50-100 171-233
<$1750/$2000
1929 Small Size
10 Type 1 1-584 <$750
10 Type 2 1-1012 <$750
Total Issue $234,210
Out in 1935 $12,350
Large out 1935 $1,140
****

****
6726 Sussex
PEOPLES NB OF LAUREL
{{ 5 L 9 S }}
Organized 3/2/03
Receivership 1/18/32
1902 Red Seal <$VALUE
3x10-20 1-650 <$3500
1902 Date Back
3x10-20 1-2050 <$850
1902 Plain Back
3x10-20 2051-11421 <$850
1929 Small Size
10 Type 1 1-2210 <$350
20 Type 1 1-612 <$350
5 Type 2 1-12460 <$350
Total Issue $871,890
Out in 1935 $100,000
Large out 1935 $1,930
****
5148 Sussex
LEWES NB, LEWES
{{ 6 L }}
Chartered 1898
Liquidated 5/12/15
Brown Back <$VALUE
4x5 1-1425 <$1500
3x10-20 1-820 <$1500
1882 Date Back
4x5 1-4503 <$1250
3x10-20 1-3376 <$1250
Total Issue $328,360
Out in 1915 $31,100
****
1181 New Castle
CITIZENS NB OF MIDDLETOWN
{{ 9 L }}
Chartered 1865
Liquidated 1/15/18
Original Series <$VALUE
3x1-2 1-1440 <$1750/$3500
4x5 1-2900 <$1500
3x10-20 1-1600<$2000/$3000
Series 1875
3x10-20 1-2216<$2000/$3000
Brown Back
3x10-20 1-9185 <$1500
1902 Red Seal
3x10-20 1-2900 <$3500
1902 Date Back
3x10-20 1-7100 <$500
1902 Plain Back
3x10-20 7101-8895 <$500
Total Issue $1,305,000
Out at close $80,000
****
3019 New Castle
PEOPLES NB OF MIDDLETOWN
{{ 8 L }}
Organized 6/2/83
Receivership 12/14/28
Brown Back <$VALUE
3x10-20 1-6029 <$1500
1902 Red Seal
3x10-20 1-2810 <$3500
1902 Date Back
3x10-20 1-4900 <$500
1902 Plain Back
3x10-20 4901-13721 <$500
Total Issue $1,128,000
Out at close $50,500
****
2340 Kent
FNB OF MILFORD
Chartered 7/27/76
2nd title:FNB & TC of Milford 12/31/28
FIRST TITLE {{ 18 L }}
Series 1875 <$VALUE
4x5 1-4020 <$1500
3x10-20 1-3349<$2000/$2500
Brown Back
3x10-20 1-5600 <$1500
1882 Date Back
4x5 1-5250 <$1250
3x10-20 1-2940 <$1250
1882 Value Back
4x5 5251-5500 <$2000
3x10-20 2941-3220 <$2000
1902 Plain Back
4x5 1-13726 <$500
3x10-20 1-8339 <$500
SECOND TITLE {{ 0 L 23 S }}
1902 Plain Back
4x5 1-398 <$600
3x10-20 1-362 <$600
1929 Small Size
5 Type 1 1-3406 <$150
10 Type 1 1-1566 <$135
20 Type 1 1-412 <$150
5 Type 2 1-4598 <$175
10 Type 2 1-2071 <$175
20 Type 2 1-925 <$175
Total Issue $1,824,160
Out in 1935 $80,000
Large out 1935 $4,500
****
1536 New Castle
NB OF NEWARK
{{ 3 L }}
Chartered 1865
Liquidated 6/24/13
Original Series <$VALUE
4x5 1-5125 <$2500
Series 1875
4x5 1-5610 <$2500
Brown Back
3x10-20 1-2989 <$2000
1902 Red Seal
3x10-20 1-1350 <$4000
1902 Date Back
4x5 1-2095 <$1250
3x10-20 1-1184 <$1250
Total Issue $532,750
Out in 1913 $22,200
****
997 New Castle
NEWPORT NB, NEWPORT
{{ 10 L }}
Chartered 4/8/65
Liquidated 2/7/28
Original Series <$VALUE
4x5 1-2500 <$1500
3x10-20 1-1550<$2000/$3000
Series 1875
3x10-20 1-2040<$2000/$3000
Brown Back
3x10-20 1-8922 <$1500
1902 Red Seal
3x10-20 1-3200 <$3500
1902 Date Back
3x10-20 1-6900 <$750
1902 Plain Back
3x10-20 6901-20007 <$750
Total Issue $1,835,950
Out at close $75,000
****
1281 New Castle
NEW CASTLE COUNTY NB OF ODESSA
{{ 16 L 17 S }}
Chartered 1865
Original Series <$VALUE
3x1-2 1-4360 <$1750/$3500
4x5 1-2950 <$1500
3x10-20 1-1100<$2000/$2500
Series 1875
3x1-2 1-800 <$1750/$3500
4x5 1-1960 <$1500
3x10-20 1-1644<$2000/$2500
Brown Back
4x5 1-2723 <$1500
3x10-20 1-7966 <$1500
1902 Red Seal
4x5 1-2550 <$2500
3x10-20 1-1800 <$2500
1902 Date Back
4x5 1-6400* <$450
3x10-20 1-4320** <$450
1902 Plain Back
4x5 6751-21971* <$450
3x10-20 4601-14070** <$450
* 6401-6750 not marked
** 4321-4600 not marked
1929 Small Size
5 Type 1 1-3032 <$225
10 Type 1 1-1630 <$200
20 Type 1 1-440 <$225
5 Type 2 1-5540 <$250
10 Type 2 1-2775 <$250
20 Type 2 1-590 <$250
Total issue $2,306,740
Out in 1935 $75,000
Large out 1935 $5,640
****
795 Sussex
FNB OF SEAFORD
{{ 4 L 16 S }}
Chartered 2/10/65
Original Series <$VALUE
4x5 1-1472 <$1500
3x10-20 1-1085<$2000/$3000
Series 1875
3x10-20 1-1246<$2000/$3000
Brown Back
3x10-20 1-4050 <$1500
1902 Red Seal
3x10-20 1-2000 <$3500
1902 Date Back
3x10-20 1-3940 <$750
1902 Plain Back
3x10-20 3941-7580 <$750
1929 Small Size
10 Type 1 1-1404 <$225
20 Type 1 1-420 <$225
10 Type 2 1-10053 <$225
20 Type 2 1-2600 <$225
Total Issue $1,114,660
Out in 1935 $150,000
Large out 1935 $1,650
****
3693 Sussex
SUSSEX NB OF SEAFORD
{{ UNREPORTED }}
Chartered 5/3/87
Liquidated 3/30/18
Brown Back <$VALUE
4x5 1-3530 <$2500
3x10-20 1-573 <$2500
1902 Red Seal
3x10-20 1-200 <$4000
1902 Date Back
3x10-20 1-2820 <$2000
Total Issue $315,150
Out at close $50,000
****
6718 Sussex
SELBYVILLE NB, SELBYVILLE
{{ 2 L }}
Chartered 4/03
Liquidated 5/15/17
1902 Red Seal <$VALUE
3x10-20 1-3000 <$3500
1902 Date Back
3x10-20 1-4300 <$1500
1902 Plain Back
3x10-20 4301-5036 <$1500
Total Issue $401,800
Out at close $50,000
****
2336 Kent
FRUIT GROWERS NB OF SMYRNA
Chartered 6/23/76
2nd title:Fruit Growers NB & TC of Smyrna 12/1/25
FIRST TITLE {{ 5 L }}
Series 1875 <$VALUE
4x5 1-1398 <$2000
3x10-20 1-4322<$2500/$3000
Brown Back
3x10-20 1-1900 <$2000
1882 Date Back
3x10-20 1-1672 <$1500
1902 Plain Back
3x10-20 1-4227 <$750
SECOND TITLE {{ 4 L 14 S }}
1902 Plain Back
3x10-20 1-2631 <$750
1929 Small Size
10 Type 1 1-1596 <$275
20 Type 1 1-442 <$275
10 Type 2 1-2559 <$300
20 Type 2 1-580 <$300
Total Issue $951,550
Out in 1935 $50,000
Large out 1935 $1,500
****
2381 Kent
NB OF SMYRNA
{{ 11 L 10 S }}
Chartered 4/4/78
Series 1875 <$VALUE
4x5 1-3000 <$1500
3x10-20 1-4741<$2000/$3000
Brown Back
3x10-20 1-5020 <$1500
50-100 1-1274 <$5000
1882 Date Back
3x10-20 1-4104 <$1250
50-100 1-160 <$4000
3x50-100 1-768 <$4000
1902 Plain Back
3x50-100 1-1781<$1750/$2000
1929 Small Size
5 Type 1 1-962 <$250
10 Type 1 1-720 <$250
20 Type 1 1-222 <$275
50 Type 1 1-250 <$750
100 Type 1 1-84 <$1000
Total Issue $1,829,700
Out in 1935 $100,000
Large out 1935 $6,840
****

****
3395 New Castle
CENTRAL NB OF WILMINGTON
{{ 20 L 33 S }}
Chartered 1885
Brown Back <$VALUE
3x10-20 1-6388 <$1500
1902 Red Seal
3x10-20 1-8500 <$3500
1902 Date Back
3x10-20 1-19600 <$300
1902 Plain Back
3x10-20 19601-60120 <$300
1929 Small Size
10 Type 1 1-6114 <$110
20 Type 1 1-1832 <$110
10 Type 2 1-8932 <$125
20 Type 2 1-3265 <$125
Total Issue $4,491,700
Out in 1935 $193,200
****
473 New Castle
FNB OF WILMINGTON
{{ 3 L }}
Chartered 1864
Liquidated 11/16/12
Original Series <$VALUE
4x5 1-4500 <$1500
3x10-20 1-3300<$2000/$3000
3x50-100 1-2260 <$10,000
Series 1875
3x10-20 1-1400<$2000/$3000
3x50-100 1-1588 <$10,000
Brown Back
3x10-20 1-1017 <$1500
50-100 1-4545 <$5000
1902 Red Seal
4x5 1-2750 <$3500
3x10-20 1-3300 <$3500
1902 Date Back
4x5 1-4250 <$750
3x10-20 1-3051 <$750
Total Issue $2,477,150
Out in 1913 $41,715
****
1420 New Castle
NB OF DELAWARE AT WILMINGTON
{{ 14 L 2 S }}
Chartered 1865
Liquidated 1/4/30
Original Series <$VALUE
4x5 1-2800 <$1500
3x10-20 1-1540<$2000/$3000
50-100 1-450 <$10,000
Series 1875
4x5 1-240 <$1500
3x10-20 1-656 <$2000/$3000
50-100 1-482 <$10,000
Brown Back
4x5 1-1375 <$1500
3x10-20 1-1020 <$1500
50-100 1-1102 <$5000
1902 Red Seal
4x5 1-1400 <$3500
3x10-20 1-820 <$3500
50-100 1-1120 <$6500
1902 Date Back
4x5 1-2250 <$500
3x10-20 1-1000 <$500
50-100 1-500 <$1750/$2000
3x50-100 1-2040 <$1750/$2000
1902 Plain Back
4x5 2251-17605 <$500
3x10-20 1001-5093 <$500
1929 Small Size
5 Type 1 1-1018 <$750
10 Type 1 1-260 <$750
20 Type 1 1-73 <$750
Total issue $2,037,850
Out at close $106,160
Large out at close $51,260
****
1190 New Castle
NB OF WILMINGTON & BRANDYWINE, WILMINGTON
{{ 8 L }}
Chartered 1865
Liquidated 11/16/12
Original Series <$VALUE
3x1-2 1-5000 <$1750/$3500
4x5 1-7150 <$1500
3x10-20 1-2400<$2000/$3000
50-100 1-485 <$10,000
Series 1875
4x5 1-7125 <$1500
3x10-20 1-2429<$2000/$3000
50-100 1-434 <$10,000
Brown Back
4x5 1-7855 <$1500
3x10-20 1-3744 <$1500
50-100 1-983 <$5000
1902 Red Seal
4x5 1-6000 <$3500
3x10-20 1-2600 <$3500
50-100 1-300 <$6500
1902 Date Back
4x5 1-7710 <$650
3x10-20 1-5377 <$650
50-100 1-73 <$1750/$2000
Total Issue $1,910,550
Out in 1913 $47,367
****
1390 New Castle
UNION NB OF WILMINGTON
{{ 12 L 19 S }}
Chartered 1865
Original Series <$VALUE
4x5 1-4000 <$1500
3x10-20 1-3307<$2000/$3000
50-100 1-484 <$10,000
Series 1875
3x10-20 1-6382<$2000/$3000
Brown Back
4x5 1-4180 <$1500
50-100 1-1906 <$5000
1902 Red Seal
3x10-20 1-6500 <$3500
1902 Date Back
3x10-20 1-9000 <$400
1902 Plain Back
3x10-20 9001-27217 <$400
1929 Small Size
10 Type 1 1-4854 <$125
20 Type 1 1-1334 <$150
10 Type 2 1-9257 <$150
20 Type 2 1-3168 <$175
Total Issue $3,425,050
Out in 1935 $200,000
Large out 1935 $8,040
****
9428 Kent
FNB OF WYOMING
{{ 2 L 9 S }}
Chartered 6/09
1902 Date Back <$VALUE
3x10-20 1-2830 <$1500
1902 Plain Back
3x10-20 2831-7667 <$1500
1929 Small Size
10 Type 1 1-784 <$500
20 Type 1 1-194 <$500
10 Type 2 1-866 <$550
20 Type 2 1-240 <$550
Total issue $467,120
Out in 1935 $25,000
Large out 1935 $720
****

CONDITION affects Value. The Values shown are for notes in FINE condition.

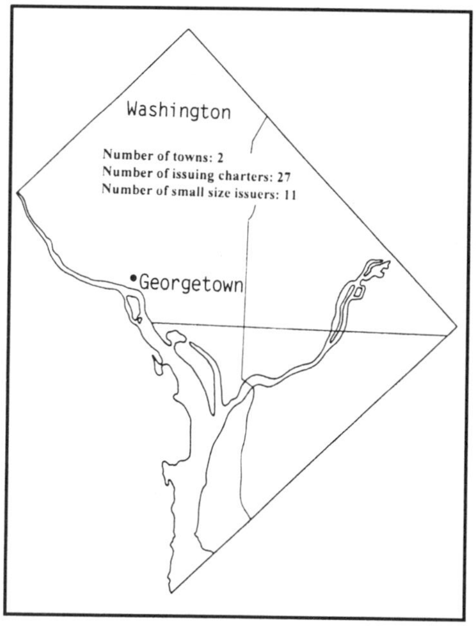

****

1928
FARMERS & MECHANICS NB OF GEORGETOWN
Chartered 1/24/72
Closed 12/15/28
2nd title:Farmers & Mechanics NB of Washington 1/14/25
FIRST TITLE **{{ 40 L }}**
Original Series <$VALUE
4x5 1-250 <$1500
3x10-20 1-6000 <$1750/$2250
50-100 1-300 <$10,000
Series 1875
4x5 1-4250 <$1250
3x10-20 1-10915<$1500/$2000
Brown Back
3x10-20 1-28800 <$450/$500
1882 Date Back
3x10-20 1-8680 <$450/$500
1902 Date Back
3x10-20 1-13000 <$175
1902 Plain Back
3x10-20 13001-48400 <$175
SECOND TITLE **{{ 9 L }}**
1902 Plain Back
4x5 1-40230 <$175
Total Issue $6,079,350
Out at close $83,960
Ch 5046 assumed circulation

****

682
NB OF COMMERCE OF GEORGETOWN
{{ UNREPORTED }}
Chartered 12/31/64
Liquidated 10/28/69
Original Series <$VALUE
4x5 1-2065 <$2000
3x10-20 1-1000<$2500/$3500
Total Issue $91,300
Out in 1910 $865

****

6716
AMERICAN NB OF WASHINGTON
{{ 24 L }}
Chartered 4/03
Closed 10/31/22
1902 Red Seal <$VALUE
4x5 1-14000 <$500
3x10-20 1-18250 <$500/$600
1902 Date Back
4x5 1-55665 <$125
3x10-20 1-39834 <$125
1902 Plain Back
4x5 55666-110345 <$125
3x10-20 39835-74996 <$125
Total Issue $7,149,200
Out at close $584,395
Ch 10316 assumed circulation

****

2382
CENTRAL NB OF WASHINGTON
{{ U + 14 L }}
Chartered 4/15/78
Liquidated 3/28/07
Series 1875 <$VALUE
3x10-20 1-11600<$2000/$2500
Brown Back
4x5 1-2080 <$600
3x10-20 1-23364 <$500/$600
Total Issue $1,789,800
Out in 1910 $54,835

****

1893
CITIZENS NB OF WASHINGTON CITY
Chartered 10/18/71 as The **Citizens NB of Hagerstown, Maryland.** Relocated to Washington 5/1/74
Liquidated 11/7/04
FIRST TITLE **(Maryland)**
{{ UNREPORTED }}
Original Series <$VALUE
3x1-2 1-1000 <$2000/$4000
4x5 1-530 <$2000
3x10-20 1-620 <$2500/$3500
SECOND TITLE **(Washington)**
{{ 7 L }}
Original Series
3x1-2 1-1720 <$2000/$4000
4x5 1-2500 <$1750
3x10-20 1-3000 <$2500/$3500
Series 1875
4x5 1-8566 <$1500
3x10-20 1-7661<$2000/$2500
Brown Back
4x5 1-7000 <$500
3x10-20 1-1858 <$500/$600
Total Issue $1,042,470
Out in 1910 $8,041

****

3625
COLUMBIA NB OF WASHINGTON
{{ 26 L 29 S }}
Chartered 1/27/87
Brown Back <$VALUE
3x10-20 1-17260 <$500
1902 Red Seal
3x10-20 1-4000 <$600
1902 Date Back
3x10-20 1-19000 <$125
1902 Plain Back
3x10-20 19001-72361 <$125
1929 Small Size
10 Type 1 1-8312 <$40
20 Type 1 1-2164 <$50
5 Type 2 1-324 <$100
10 Type 2 1-11210 <$60
20 Type 2 1-2876 <$70
Total Issue $5,610,690
Out in 1935 $240,300
Large out 1935 $12,045

****

7446
COMMERCIAL NB OF WASHINGTON
{{ U + 50+ L 40 S }}
Organized 10/18/04
Receivership 2/28/33
1902 Red Seal <$VALUE
3x10-20 1-22200 <$450/$500
1902 Date Back
3x10-20 1-61500 <$85
1902 Plain Back
3x10-20 61501-281555 <$85
1929 Small Size
10 Type 1 1-31009 <$35
20 Type 1 1-8830 <$50
Total Issue $18,107,890
Out at close $984,400
Large out at close $76,620
Outstanding includes Ch 7936

****

9545
DISTRICT NB OF WASHINGTON
{{ 39 L 31 S }}
Organized 9/8/09
Receivership 11/6/33
1902 Date Back <$VALUE
4x5 1-37940* <$85
4x10 1-35175** <$85
1902 Plain Back
4x5 40941-155555* <$85
4x10 37176-130637** <$85
* 37941-40940 not marked
** 35176-37175 not marked
1929 Small Size
5 Type 1 1-3404 <$125
10 Type 1 1-22496 <$50
20 Type 1 1-7598 <$55
Total Issue $10,700,220
Out at close $903,000
Large out at close $22,990

****

Farmers & Mechanics NB of Washington
SEE Ch 1928
Farmers & Mechanics NB of Georgetown

****

10825
DUPONT NB OF WASHINGTON
{{ 4 L }}
Chartered 2/16
Liquidated 4/1/22
1902 Plain Back <$VALUE
3x10-20 1-19728 <$500
Total Issue $986,400
Out at close $200,000

****

Federal-American NB of Washington
SEE Ch 10316
Federal NB of Washington

****

10316
FEDERAL NB OF WASHINGTON
Organized 1/15/13
Receivership 10/31/33
2nd title:Federal-American NB 10/31/22
FIRST TITLE **{{ 20 L }}**
1902 Date Back <$VALUE
3x10-20 1-12700 <$150
1902 Plain Back
3x10-20 12701-25300 <$150
SECOND TITLE **{{ 9 L 0 S }}**
1902 Plain Back
3x50-100 1-3361 <$600/$750
1929 Small Size
5 Type 1 1-164 <$750
10 Type 1 1-23 <$750
20 Type 1 1-2 <$800
Total Issue $2,111,790
Out at close $49,815
Large out at close $43,585
Outstanding includes Ch 6716

****

26
FNB OF WASHINGTON
{{ 3 L }}
Organized 7/16/63
Receivership 9/19/73
Original Series <$VALUE
3x1-2 1-54 <$2500/$5000
4x5 1-19155 <$2000
2x10-2x20 1-1728 <$2500/$3500
50-100 1-1621 <$10,000
Total Issue $730,200
Out in 1916 $5,956

****

10504
FRANKLIN NB OF WASHINGTON
{{ 21 L 20 S }}
Organized 4/3/14
1902 Date Back <$VALUE
3x10-20 1-8300 <$125
1902 Plain Back
3x10-20 8301-68395 <$125
1929 Small Size
10 Type 1 1-7708 <$75
20 Type 1 1-2190 <$85
10 Type 2 1-4292 <$100
20 Type 2 1-1577 <$125
Total Issue $4,219,490
Out in 1935 $96,230
Large out 1935 $7,720

****

2358
GERMAN-AMERICAN NB OF WASHINGTON
{{ 2 L }}
Chartered 5/14/77
Receivership 11/1/78
Series 1875 <$VALUE
3x1-2 1-1500 <$2500/$5000
4x5 1-3110 <$2500
Total Issue $69,700
Out in 1916 $270

****

13782
HAMILTON NB OF WASHINGTON
{{ 2U + 30 S }}
Chartered 9/33
1929 Small Size <$VALUE
5 Type 2 1-111612 <$50
10 Type 2 1-74312 <$50
20 Type 2 1-17328 <$60
Total Issue $1,647,740
Out in 1935 $795,500

****

4247
LINCOLN NB OF WASHINGTON
{{ 13 L 49 S }}
Chartered 1890
Brown Back <$VALUE
3x10-20 1-11160 <$500/$600
1882 Date Back
3x10-20 1-1008 <$500/$600
1902 Date Back
3x10-20 1-10100 <$200
1902 Plain Back
3x10-20 10101-38889 <$200
1929 Small Size
10 Type 1 1-2980 <$100
20 Type 1 1-1492 <$100
10 Type 2 1-3041 <$150
20 Type 2 1-2413 <$150
Total Issue $2,989,360
Out in 1935 $118,200
Large out 1935 $3,570

****

627
MERCHANTS NB OF WASHINGTON
{{ UNREPORTED }}
Organized 12/14/64
Receivership 5/8/66
Original Series <$VALUE
4x5 1-3000 <$2500
3x10-20 1-2400<$2500/$3000
Total Issue $180,000
Out in 1916 $505

****

3425
NB OF WASHINGTON
{{ 43 L 50+ S }}
Chartered 1885
1902 Red Seal <$VALUE
4x5 1-16000 <$500
3x10-20 1-13800 <$500/$600
1902 Date Back
4x5 1-20000 <$85
3x10-20 1-110400 <$85
1902 Plain Back
3x10-20 110401-277180 <$85
1929 Small Size
10 Type 1 1-21014 <$30
20 Type 1 1-7620 <$40
10 Type 2 1-20227 <$35
20 Type 2 1-5710 <$45
Total Issue $17,760,710
Out in 1935 $943,260
Large out 1935 $32,970

****

526
NB OF THE METROPOLIS OF WASHINGTON
{{ 2 L }}
Chartered 10/4/64
Liquidated 11/28/66
Original Series <$VALUE
3x1-2 1-4000 <$2000/$4000
4x5 1-2000 <$1500
3x10-20 1-1520 <$2250/$2750
50-100 1-360 <$10,000
Total Issue $190,000
Out in 1910 $2,669

****

875
NB OF THE REPUBLIC OF WASHINGTON
{{ 5 L }}
Chartered 3/10/65
Liquidated 8/11/97
Original Series <$VALUE
3x1-2 1-900 <$2000/$4000
4x5 1-3750 <$1500
3x10-20 1-4400 <$2250/$2750
50-100 1-300 <$10,000
Series 1875
4x5 1-515 <$1500
3x10-20 1-5100<$2000/$2500
50-100 1-30 <$10,000
Brown Back
3x10-20 1-7070 <$500/$600
50-100 1-1163 <$5000
Total Issue $1,142,250
Out in 1910 $8,376

****

4107
N CAPITAL B OF WASHINGTON
{{ 9 L }}
Chartered 8/30/89
Brown Back <$VALUE
50-100 1-2797 <$5000
1902 Date Back
3x10-20 1-11700 <$200
1902 Plain Back
3x10-20 11701-30126 <$200
Total Issue $1,925,850
Out in 1935 $4,170

****

7936
N CITY B OF WASHINGTON
{{ 1 L }}
Chartered 10/05
Liquidated 5/1/11
1902 Red Seal <$VALUE
3x10-20 1-8500 <$1250
1902 Date Back
3x10-20 1-12780 <$850
Total Issue $1,064,000
Out at close $289,200
Ch 7446 assumed circulation

****

1069
N METROPOLITAN B OF WASHINGTON
Chartered 1865
2nd title:N Metropolitan Citizens B of Washington 11/7/04
3rd title:N Metropolitan B of Washington 1/10/06
FIRST TITLE **{{ 6 L }}**
Original Series <$VALUE
4x5 1-6500 <$1500
3x10-20 1-6662 <$2250/$2750
50-100 1-1516 <$10,000
Series 1875
4x5 1-500 <$1500
3x10-20 1-450 <$2000/$2500
50-100 1-52 <$10,000
Brown Back
4x5 1-21465 <$400
3x10-20 1-12857 <$400/$450
SECOND TITLE **{{ 6 L }}**
Brown Back
3x10-20 1-2000 <$400/$450
1902 Red Seal
4x5 1-9100 <$500
3x10-20 1-6054 <$500/$600
THIRD TITLE
{{ 2U + 50+ L U + 27 S }}
1902 Red Seal
4x5 1-27000 <$500
3x10-20 1-14100 <$500/$600
1902 Date Back
4x5 1-20000 <$100
3x10-20 1-71200 <$75
1902 Plain Back
3x10-20 71201-197319 <$75
1929 Small Size
10 Type 1 1-11031 <$35
20 Type 1 1-3116 <$50
Total Issue $14,934,380
Out in 1935 $162,293
Large out 1935 $40,310

****

N Metropolitan Citizens B of Washington
SEE Ch 1069
N Metropolitan B of Washington

****

4522
OHIO NB OF WASHINGTON
{{ UNREPORTED }}
Chartered 2/19/91
Liquidated 12/31/97
Brown Back <$VALUE
3x10-20 1-3008 <$1500
Total Issue $150,400
Out in 1910 $1,670

****

5046
RIGGS NB OF WASHINGTON
{{ 50+ L 50+ S }}
Chartered 1896
Brown Back <$VALUE
4x5 1-45750 <$325
3x10-20 1-39500 <$325/$375
1882 Date Back
4x5 1-85830 <$275
3x10-20 1-68668 <$275/$325
3x50-100 1-849 <$3500
1882 Value Back
4x5 85831-98827 <$1250
1902 Plain Back
4x5 1-23550 <$65
3x10-20 1-32687 <$65/$75
1929 Small Size
5 Type 1 1-46875 <$40
10 Type 1 1-22643 <$25
20 Type 1 1-20859 <$35
Total Issue $15,885,450
Out in 1935 $1,999,955
Large out 1935 $30,665
Outstanding includes Ch 1928

****

2038
SECOND NB OF WASHINGTON
{{ 40 L 20 S }}
Chartered 9/3/72
Original Series <$VALUE
4x5 1-3000 <$1500
3x10-20 1-3600 <$2250/$2750
Series 1875
4x5 1-1230 <$1500
3x10-20 1-3719<$2000/$2500
Brown Back
3x10-20 1-21460 <$350/$400
1882 Date Back
4x5 1-25330 <$300
3x10-20 1-21742 <$300/$350
1902 Date Back
4x5 1-24300 <$85
3x10-20 1-17980 <$75
1902 Plain Back
4x5 24301-109865 <$85
3x10-20 17981-70761 <$75
1929 Small Size
5 Type 1 1-8902 <$60
10 Type 1 1-4146 <$50
20 Type 1 1-1182 <$60
5 Type 2 1-34412 <$60
10 Type 2 1-19960 <$60
20 Type 2 1-9322 <$70
Total Issue $10,068,360
Out in 1935 $225,385
Large out 1935 $18,505

****

4244
TRADERS NB OF WASHINGTON
{{ 6 L }}
Chartered 2/27/90
Liquidated 4/21/08
Brown Back <$VALUE
4x5 1-6005 <$500
3x10-20 1-9058 <$500/$600
50-100 1-457 <$5000
Total Issue $641,550
Out in 1910 $27,230

****

4195
WEST END NB OF WASHINGTON
{{ 1 L }}
Chartered 1/7/90
Liquidated 4/23/03
Consolidated with Ch 1893
Brown Back <$VALUE
3x10-20 1-3279 <$1500
50-100 1-341 <$5000
Total Issue $215,100
Out in 1910 $2,595

****

<$VALUEs are for notes in **FINE** condition. Value changes by approximately **25%** for a change of one full grade.

FLORIDA

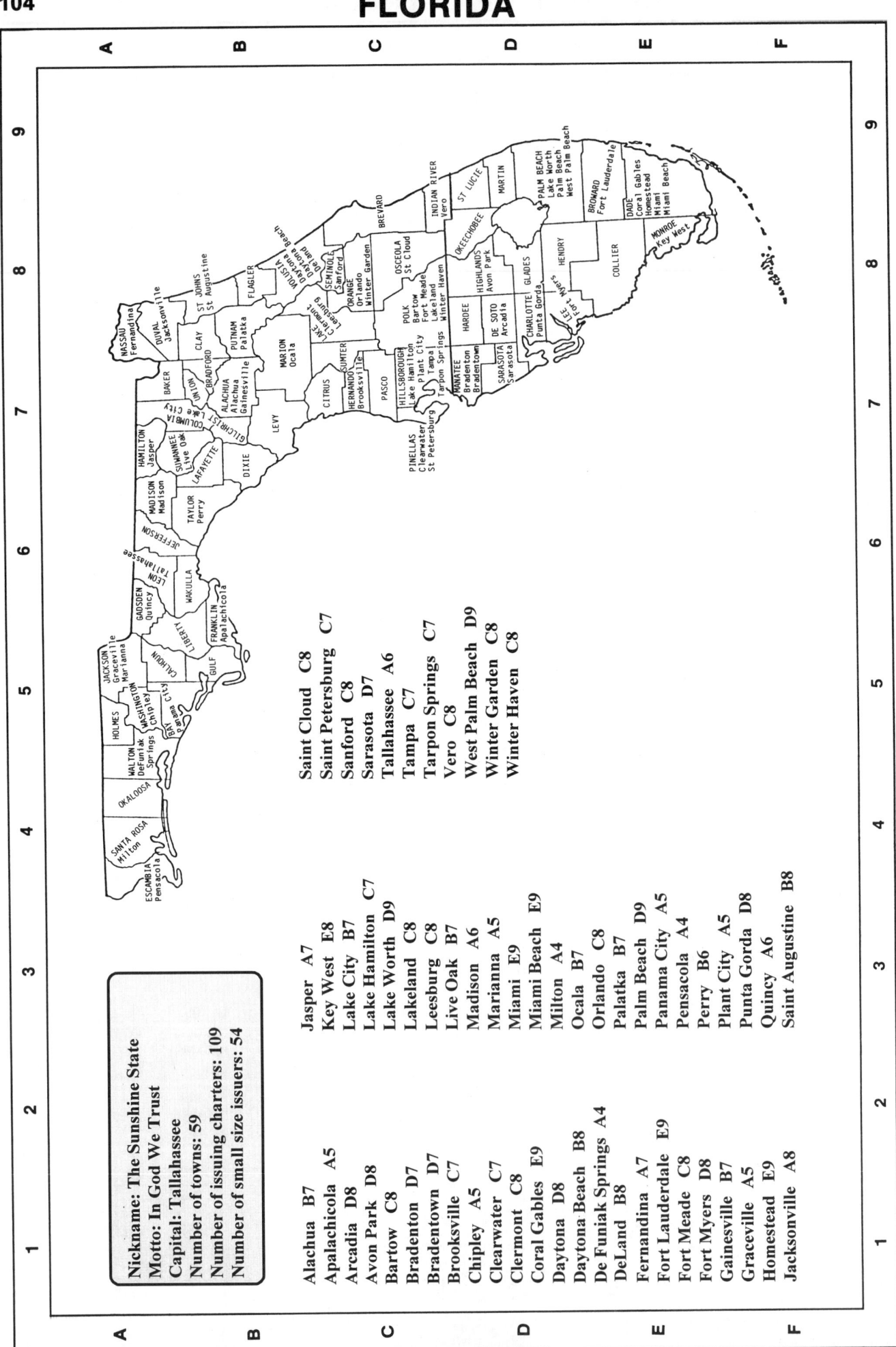

Nickname: The Sunshine State
Motto: In God We Trust
Capital: Tallahassee
Number of towns: 59
Number of issuing charters: 109
Number of small size issuers: 54

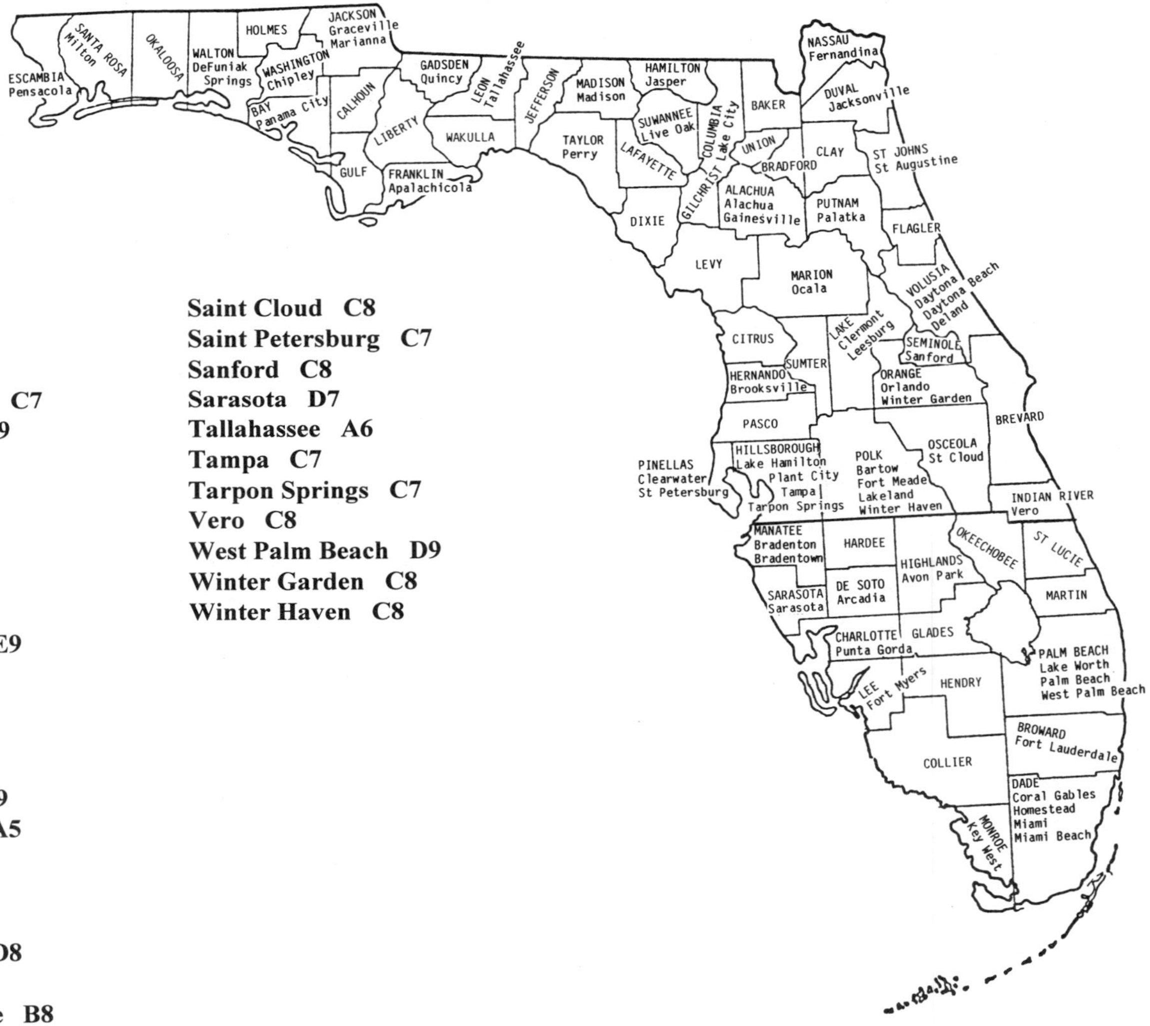

Alachua B7
Apalachicola A5
Arcadia D8
Avon Park D8
Bartow C8
Bradenton D7
Bradentown D7
Brooksville C7
Chipley A5
Clearwater C7
Clermont C8
Coral Gables E9
Daytona D8
Daytona Beach B8
De Funiak Springs A4
DeLand B8
Fernandina A7
Fort Lauderdale E9
Fort Meade C8
Fort Myers D8
Gainesville B7
Graceville A5
Homestead E9
Jacksonville A8
Jasper A7
Key West E8
Lake City B7
Lake Hamilton C7
Lake Worth D9
Lakeland C8
Leesburg C8
Live Oak B7
Madison A6
Marianna A5
Miami E9
Miami Beach E9
Milton A4
Ocala B7
Orlando C8
Palatka B7
Palm Beach D9
Panama City A5
Pensacola A4
Perry B6
Plant City A5
Punta Gorda D8
Quincy A6
Saint Augustine B8
Saint Cloud C8
Saint Petersburg C7
Sanford C8
Sarasota D7
Tallahassee A6
Tampa C7
Tarpon Springs C7
Vero C8
West Palm Beach D9
Winter Garden C8
Winter Haven C8

****
8980 Alachua
FNB OF ALACHUA
{{ 3 L 5 S }}
Chartered 1/08
1902 Red Seal <$VALUE
4x10 1-800 <$3000
1902 Date Back
4x10 1-3350 <$1250
1902 Plain Back
4x10 3351-9206 <$1250
1929 Small Size
10 Type 1 1-1280 <$650
10 Type 2 1-2821 <$650
Total Issue $505,250
Out in 1935 $25,000
Large out 1935 $1,030
****
6274 Franklin
FNB OF APALACHICOLA
{{ 3 L }}
Chartered 5/02
Liquidated 2/15/11
1902 Red Seal <$VALUE
4x5 1-1650 <$3000
3x10-20 1-2160 <$3000
1902 Date Back
4x5 1-1410 <$1500
3x10-20 1-1070 <$1500
Total Issue $222,700
Out in 1911 $27,550
****
8728 De Soto
DESOTO NB OF ARCADIA
{{ 7 L 19 S }}
Chartered 6/07
1902 Red Seal <$VALUE
3x10-20 1-450 <$2500
1902 Date Back
3x10-20 1-3450 <$750
1902 Plain Back
3x10-20 3451-12709 <$750
1929 Small Size
10 Type 1 1-1518 <$300
20 Type 1 1-390 <$300
10 Type 2 1-5288 <$325
20 Type 2 1-1087 <$325
Total Issue $870,450
Out in 1935 $75,000
Large out 1935 $2,540
****
5534 De Soto
FNB OF ARCADIA
{{ 7 L 6 S }}
Organized 6/15/00
Receivership 1/26/32
Brown Back <$VALUE
4x5 1-550 <$2500
3x10-20 1-460 <$2500
1882 Date Back
4x5 1-4875 <$2000
3x10-20 1-3820 <$2000
1882 Value Back
4x5 4876-7885 <$2000
3x10-20 3821-5390 <$2000
1902 Plain Back
3x10-20 1-9482 <$750
1929 Small Size
10 Type 1 1-1222 <$500
20 Type 1 1-369 <$500
Total Issue $1,052,900
Out at close $69,280
Large out at close $8,860
****
10826 Highlands
FNB OF AVON PARK
{{ 2 L }}
Organized 2/10/16
Receivership 2/18/29
1902 Plain Back <$VALUE
4x5 1-3435 <$2500
3x10-20 1-2066 <$2500
Total Issue $172,000
Out at close $16,250
****
13389 Polk
FLORIDA NB OF BARTOW
{{ 20 S }}
Chartered 10/29
1929 Small Size <$VALUE
5 Type 1 1-1898 <$275
10 Type 1 1-930 <$275
20 Type 1 1-284 <$275
5 Type 2 1-9848 <$300
10 Type 2 1-5376 <$300
20 Type 2 1-1272 <$300
Total Issue $275,260
Out in 1935 $100,000
****

****
4627 Polk
POLK COUNTY NB OF BARTOW
{{ 1 L }}
Chartered 1891
Liquidated 11/8/29
Brown Back <$VALUE
50-100 1-454 <$7500
1882 Date Back
50-100 1-144 <$7500
1902 Date Back
3x50-100 1-570 <$2500
1902 Plain Back
3x50-100 571-606 <$2500
Total Issue $241,200
Out at close $8,050
****
FNB of Bradenton
SEE Ch 10245
FNB of Bradentown
****
10245 Manatee
FNB OF BRADENTOWN
Chartered 8/12
2nd title: FNB of Bradenton
4/25/29
FIRST TITLE {{ 4 L }}
1902 Date Back <$VALUE
3x10-20 1-2440* <$1250
1902 Plain Back
3x10-20 2641-9436* <$1250
* 2441-2640 not marked
SECOND TITLE {{ 12 S }}
1929 Small Size
10 Type 1 1-1916 <$375
20 Type 1 1-494 <$375
10 Type 2 1-4062 <$400
20 Type 2 1-1295 <$400
Total Issue $712,560
Out in 1935 $85,000
Large out 1935 $2,300
****
13320 Hernando
FNB IN BROOKSVILLE
{{ 2U + 9 S }}
Organized 4/26/29
1929 Small Size <$VALUE
5 Type 1 1-1938 <$400
10 Type 1 1-940 <$400
20 Type 1 1-280 <$400
5 Type 2 1-3560 <$400
10 Type 2 1-1610 <$400
20 Type 2 1-423 <$400
Total Issue $190,500
Out in 1935 $39,990
****
9891 Hernando
FNB OF BROOKSVILLE
{{ 2U + 1 L }}
Chartered 11/10
Liquidated 10/16/29
1902 Date Back <$VALUE
3x10-20 1-2260 <$1250
1902 Plain Back
3x10-20 2261-10366 <$1250
Total Issue $518,300
Out in 1935 $1,860
Ch 13320 assumed circulation
****
7778 Washington
FNB OF CHIPLEY
{{ 9 L 2 S }}
Chartered 6/05
Liquidated 1/13/31
1902 Red Seal <$VALUE
3x10-20 1-580 <$2500
1902 Date Back
3x10-20 1-4820 <$750
1902 Plain Back
3x10-20 4821-13467 <$750
1929 Small Size
10 Type 1 1-611 <$800
20 Type 1 1-177 <$800
Total Issue $760,250
Out at close $50,000
Large out at close $7,670
****
12905 Pinellas
FNB OF CLEARWATER
{{ 3 L 22 S }}
Chartered 3/26
1902 Plain Back <$VALUE
4x5 1-1634 <$1000
3x10-20 1-974 <$1000
1929 Small Size
5 Type 1 1-1950 <$325
10 Type 1 1-1422 <$325
20 Type 1 1-418 <$325
5 Type 2 1-7760 <$350
10 Type 2 1-4116 <$350
20 Type 2 1-1212 <$350
Total Issue $379,560
Out in 1935 $100,000
Large out 1935 $310
****

****
11921 Lake
FNB OF CLERMONT
{{ 2 L }}
Chartered 1/21
Liquidated 6/21/30
1902 Plain Back <$VALUE
4x5 1-2840 <$2000
3x10-20 1-1598 <$2000
Total Issue $136,700
Out at close $2,570
****
13008 Dade
CORAL GABLES FNB,
CORAL GABLES
{{ 11 S }}
Chartered 11/26
1929 Small Size <$VALUE
5 Type 1 1-1144 <$525
10 Type 1 1-1244 <$525
20 Type 1 1-360 <$525
5 Type 2 1-7004 <$525
10 Type 2 1-2505 <$525
20 Type 2 1-728 <$550
Total Issue $226,790
Out in 1935 $100,000
****
10545 Volusia
FNB OF DAYTONA
{{ 3 L }}
Organized 5/19/14
Liquidated 8/2/23
1902 Date Back <$VALUE
3x10-20 1-1500 <$1500
1902 Plain Back
3x10-20 1501-6351 <$1500
Total Issue $317,550
Out at close $50,000
****
12546 Volusia
F ATLANTIC NB OF
DAYTONA BEACH
{{ 16 S }}
Chartered 6/24 as FNB of Seabreeze, under which there was no issue. Issuing title adopted 8/18/30.
1929 Small Size <$VALUE
5 Type 1 1-1932 <$400
10 Type 1 1-1238 <$400
20 Type 1 1-522 <$400
5 Type 2 1-4758 <$400
10 Type 2 1-2866 <$400
20 Type 2 1-640 <$400
Total Issue $260,130
Out in 1935 $100,000
****
7404 Walton
FNB OF DE FUNIAK SPRINGS
{{ 6 L 9 S }}
Chartered 9/04
1902 Red Seal <$VALUE
4x5 1-500 <$3000
3x10-20 1-400 <$3000
1902 Date Back
4x5 1-2900 <$1000
3x10-20 1-2240 <$1000
1902 Plain Back
4x5 2901-9536 <$1000
3x10-20 2241-6135 <$1000
1929 Small Size
5 Type 1 1-1558 <$500
10 Type 1 1-972 <$500
20 Type 1 1-270 <$525
5 Type 2 1-2902 <$550
10 Type 2 1-1524 <$550
20 Type 2 1-420 <$550
Total Issue $703,080
Out in 1935 $50,000
Large out 1935 $1,760
****
13388 Volusia
BARNETT NB OF DeLAND
{{ 18 S }}
Chartered 10/29
1929 Small Size <$VALUE
5 Type 1 1-1390 <$350
10 Type 1 1-1388 <$350
20 Type 1 1-378 <$350
5 Type 2 1-7152 <$350
10 Type 2 1-3325 <$350
20 Type 2 1-953 <$350
Total Issue $258,410
Out in 1935 $79,850
****
9657 Volusia
FNB OF DeLAND
{{ 20 L }}
Organized 1/5/10
Receivership 7/12/29
1902 Date Back <$VALUE
4x5 1-1150* <$450
3x10-20 1-960** <$450
1902 Plain Back
4x5 1251-16195* <$450
3x10-20 1041-11527** <$450
* 1151-1250 not marked
** 961-1040 not marked
Total Issue $900,250
Out at close $100,000
****
10024 Nassau
CITIZENS NB OF FERNANDINA
{{ 1 L }}
Chartered 5/11
Liquidated 8/10/18
1902 Date Back <$VALUE
3x10-20 1-2250 <$1500
1902 Plain Back
3x10-20 2251-3646 <$1500
Total Issue $182,300
Out at close $50,000
****
4558 Nassau
FNB OF FERNANDINA
{{ 12 L 18 S }}
Chartered 1891
Brown Back <$VALUE
4x5 1-2500 <$2500
3x10-20 1-5910 <$2500
1882 Date Back
4x5 1-2470 <$2000
3x10-20 1-1921 <$2000
1902 Date Back
4x5 1-5850 <$750
3x10-20 1-4460 <$750
1902 Plain Back
4x5 5851-24387 <$750
3x10-20 4461-17402 <$750
1929 Small Size
5 Type 1 1-4354 <$400
10 Type 1 1-2344 <$400
20 Type 1 1-526 <$400
5 Type 2 1-7580 <$400
10 Type 2 1-4320 <$400
20 Type 2 1-1152 <$400
Total Issue $2,287,310
Out in 1935 $100,000
Large out 1935 $5,965
****
12020 Broward
FNB OF FORT LAUDERDALE
{{ 3 L }}
Organized 9/20/21
Receivership 12/15/28
1902 Plain Back <$VALUE
4x5 1-1003 <$2000
4x10 1-877 <$2000
Total Issue $55,140
Out in 1927 $12,200
****
10386 Polk
FNB OF FORT MEADE
{{ UNREPORTED }}
Chartered 5/13
Liquidated 11/3/19
1902 Date Back <$VALUE
3x10-20 1-1400 <$3000
1902 Plain Back
3x10-20 1401-2262 <$3000
Total Issue $113,100
Out at close $25,000
****
14195 Lee
FNB IN FORT MYERS
{{ 2 S }}
Chartered 6/34
1929 Small Size <$VALUE
5 Type 2 1-2110 <$1000
10 Type 2 1-1321 <$1000
Total Issue $23,760
Out in 1935 $50,000
Outstanding includes Ch 9035
****
9035 Lee
FNB OF FORT MYERS
{{ 4 L 12 S }}
Organized 1/29/08
Liquidated 8/11/34
1902 Red Seal <$VALUE
4x5 1-625 <$3000
3x10-20 1-500 <$3000
1902 Date Back
4x5 1-4250 <$1000
3x10-20 1-3040 <$1000
1902 Plain Back
4x5 4251-13081 <$1000
3x10-20 3041-8756 <$1000
1929 Small Size
5 Type 1 1-2082 <$500
10 Type 1 1-984 <$500
20 Type 1 1-276 <$525
5 Type 2 1-1726 <$550
10 Type 2 1-860 <$550
20 Type 2 1-192 <$550
Total Issue $912,610
Out in 1934 $50,000
Large out 1935 $2,350
Ch 14195 assumed circulation
****

****
10310 Alachua
FLORIDA NB OF GAINESVILLE
{{ 8 L }}
Chartered 1/13
Liquidated 8/19/22
1902 Date Back <$VALUE
4x5 1-6750 <$750
3x10-20 1-5400 <$750
1902 Plain Back
4x5 6751-25220 <$750
3x10-20 5401-16533 <$750
Total Issue $1,331,050
Out at close $200,000
****
3894 Alachua
FNB OF GAINESVILLE
{{ 19 L 26 S }}
Chartered 1888
Brown Back <$VALUE
4x5 1-6214 <$2000
3x10-20 1-2558 <$2000
1902 Red Seal
4x5 1-750 <$2250
3x10-20 1-700 <$2250
1902 Date Back
4x5 1-7500 <$600
3x10-20 1-5700 <$600
1902 Plain Back
4x5 7501-26307 <$600
3x10-20 5701-18491 <$600
1929 Small Size
5 Type 1 1-4204 <$300
10 Type 1 1-1958 <$300
20 Type 1 1-644 <$300
5 Type 2 1-3112 <$300
10 Type 2 1-1484 <$300
20 Type 2 1-215 <$325
Total Issue $2,108,450
Out in 1935 $100,000
Large out 1935 $5,875
****
8802 Alachua
GAINESVILLE NB,
GAINESVILLE
{{ 4 L }}
Chartered 7/07
Liquidated 12/27/18
1902 Red Seal <$VALUE
3x10-20 1-2500 <$2500
1902 Date Back
4x5 1-8250 <$1000
3x10-20 1-6400 <$1000
1902 Plain Back
4x5 8251-11065 <$1000
3x10-20 6401-7805 <$1000
Total Issue $736,550
Out at close $100,000
****
7423 Jackson
FNB OF GRACEVILLE
{{ 6 L 2 S }}
Organized 9/26/04
Receivership 10/27/31
1902 Red Seal <$VALUE
3x10-20 1-1500 <$2500
1902 Date Back
3x10-20 1-2870 <$1000
1902 Plain Back
3x10-20 2871-8957 <$1000
1929 Small Size
5 Type 1 1-82 <$800
10 Type 1 1-612 <$800
20 Type 1 1-182 <$800
Total Issue $583,870
Out at close $35,000
Large out at close $4,600
****
13641 Dade
FNB OF HOMESTEAD
{{ 3U + 12 S }}
Chartered 10/32
1929 Small Size <$VALUE
5 Type 1 1-828 <$350
10 Type 1 1-106 <$350
5 Type 2 1-4476 <$375
10 Type 2 1-1930 <$375
Total Issue $72,880
Out in 1935 $18,100
****
6888 Duval
ATLANTIC NB OF
JACKSONVILLE
{{ 38 L 50+ S }}
Chartered 7/03
1902 Red Seal <$VALUE
4x5 1-16000 <$1750
3x10-20 1-10100 <$1750
50-100 1-2000 <$7500
1902 Date Back
4x5 1-31000 <$150
3x10-20 1-21100 <$150
50-100 1-200 <$800/$1000
1902 Plain Back
4x5 31001-123270 <$150
3x10-20 21101-75900 <$150
1929 Small Size
5 Type 1 1-45550 <$50
10 Type 1 1-33878* <$50
20 Type 1 1-8766 <$65
100 Type 1 1-378 <$250
5 Type 2 1-17102 <$65
10 Type 2 1-5100 <$65
20 Type 2 1-780 <$75
* 29490 not issued
Total Issue $12,245,350
Out in 1934 $500,000
Large out 1935 $24,275
****
9049 Duval
BARNETT NB OF
JACKSONVILLE
{{ 30 L 50+ S }}
Chartered 3/08
1902 Red Seal <$VALUE
4x5 1-6250 <$1750
3x10-20 1-5000 <$1750
1902 Date Back
4x5 1-29750 <$165
3x10-20 1-25000 <$165
1902 Plain Back
4x5 29751-101880 <$165
3x10-20 25001-71889 <$165
1929 Small Size
5 Type 1 1-16466 <$50
10 Type 1 1-19790 <$50
20 Type 1 1-5420 <$60
5 Type 2 1-55504 <$60
10 Type 2 1-28731 <$60
20 Type 2 1-7835 <$60
Total Issue $9,060,360
Out in 1935 $1,000,000
Large out 1935 $18,385
****
2174 Duval
FNB OF FLORIDA,
JACKSONVILLE
{{ UNREPORTED }}
Chartered 8/24/74
Receivership 3/14/03
Original Series <$VALUE
4x10 1-1125 <$8500
Series 1875
4x10 1-3497 <$8500
Brown Back
50-100 1-699 <$8500
Total Issue $289,730
Out in 1915 $2,710
****
8321 Duval
FLORIDA NB OF
JACKSONVILLE
{{ 34 L 50+ S }}
Chartered 8/06
1902 Red Seal <$VALUE
4x5 1-4150 <$1500
4x10 1-6675 <$1500
1902 Date Back
4x5 1-48000* <$150
4x10 1-46500** <$150
1902 Plain Back
4x5 50001-157275* <$150
4x10 48501-132484** <$150
* 48001-50000 not marked
** 46501-48500 not marked
1929 Small Size
5 Type 1 1-31916* <$40
10 Type 1 1-22880** <$40
5 Type 2 1-220212 <$45
10 Type 2 1-127464 <$45
* 9478-9500 not issued
** 4578-4772 not issued
Total Issue $13,490,450
Out in 1935 $1,500,000
Large out 1935 $22,385
****
9628 Duval
FOURTH NB OF JACKSONVILLE
{{ 2 L }}
Chartered 1/10
Liquidated 12/29/13
1902 Date Back <$VALUE
4x5 1-19290 <$750
3x10-20 1-14590 <$750
Total Issue $1,115,300
Out in 1914 $156,680
****
10136 Duval
HEARD NB OF JACKSONVILLE
{{ 3U + 8 L }}
Organized 2/2/12
Receivership 1/17/17
1902 Date Back <$VALUE
4x5 1-44000 <$500
4x10 1-43250 <$500
1902 Plain Back
4x5 44001-47088 <$500
4x10 43251-46440 <$500
Total Issue $2,799,360
Out at close $583,400
****

4332 Duval
MERCHANTS NB OF JACKSONVILLE
{{ UNREPORTED }}
Chartered 6/2/90
Receivership 3/17/97
Brown Back <$VALUE
4x5 1-3221 <$3000
Total Issue $64,420
Out in 1915 $335

3869 Duval
NB OF JACKSONVILLE
{{ 3 L }}
Chartered 4/20/88
Liquidated 4/14/08
Brown Back <$VALUE
4x5 1-10790 <$2500
4x10 1-1676 <$2500
50-100 1-1840 <$7500
Total Issue $555,840
Out in 1910 $37,515

3327 Duval
NB OF THE STATE OF FLORIDA, JACKSONVILLE
{{ 1 L }}
Chartered 3/30/85
Liquidated 9/8/03
Brown Back <$VALUE
3x10-20 1-4700 <$3000
Total Issue $235,000
Out in 1910 $4,930

7757 Hamilton
FNB OF JASPER
{{ 3 L 0 S }}
Organized 1/17/05
Receivership 5/13/30
1902 Red Seal <$VALUE
3x10-20 1-520 <$3000
1902 Date Back
3x10-20 1-3050 <$1250
1902 Plain Back
3x10-20 3051-8279 <$1250
1929 Small Size
10 Type 1 1-328 <$1500
20 Type 1 1-19 <$1500
Total Issue $463,110
Out at close $29,040
Large out at close $7,770

4672 Monroe
FNB OF KEY WEST
{{ 18 L 19 S }}
Chartered 1891
Brown Back <$VALUE
4x5 1-5900 <$2250
3x10-20 1-2300 <$2250
1882 Date Back
4x5 1-3108 <$2000
3x10-20 1-1896 <$2000
1902 Date Back
4x5 1-3250 <$650
3x10-20 1-2700 <$650
1902 Plain Back
4x5 3251-14650 <$650
3x10-20 2701-10859 <$650
1929 Small Size
5 Type 1 1-3460 <$375
10 Type 1 1-1724 <$375
20 Type 1 1-452 <$375
5 Type 2 1-4972 <$400
10 Type 2 1-2912 <$400
20 Type 2 1-775 <$400
Total Issue $1,556,870
Out in 1935 $100,000
Large out 1935 $7,605

7942 Monroe
ISLAND CITY NB OF KEY WEST
{{ 1 L }}
Organized 10/7/05
Receivership 7/29/15
1902 Red Seal <$VALUE
4x5 1-3520 <$4000
3x10-20 1-2617 <$4000
1902 Date Back
4x5 1-4900 <$3000
3x10-20 1-3966 <$3000
Total Issue $497,550
Out in 1915 $83,800

7540 Columbia
FNB OF LAKE CITY
{{ 3 L 2U + 12 S }}
Chartered 12/04
1902 Red Seal <$VALUE
4x5 1-1565 <$3000
3x10-20 1-1284 <$3000
1902 Date Back
4x5 1-3100 <$1250
3x10-20 1-2400 <$1250
1902 Plain Back
4x5 3101-11285 <$1250
3x10-20 2401-7418 <$1250
1929 Small Size
5 Type 1 1-1692 <$450
10 Type 1 1-912 <$450
20 Type 1 1-234 <$475
5 Type 2 1-4042 <$500
10 Type 2 1-2148 <$500
20 Type 2 1-528 <$525
Total Issue $877,910
Out in 1935 $50,000
Large out 1935 $1,925

11703 Hillsborough
FNB OF LAKE HAMILTON
{{ 2 L }}
Chartered 5/20
Liquidated 8/4/23
1902 Plain Back <$VALUE
3x10-20 1-1248 <$2000
Total Issue $62,400
Out at close $25,000

11716 Palm Beach
FNB OF LAKE WORTH
{{ 2 L }}
Organized 4/19/20
Receivership 4/2/27
1902 Plain Back <$VALUE
4x5 1-8515 <$1500
Total Issue $170,300
Out at close $32,300

9811 Polk
FNB OF LAKELAND
{{ 6 L }}
Organized 6/9/10
Receivership 5/15/29
1902 Date Back <$VALUE
3x10-20 1-2540 <$1500
1902 Plain Back
3x10-20 2541-4340 <$1500
3x50-100 1-1222 <$2000
Total Issue $522,500
Out in 1922 $100,000

13370 Polk
FLORIDA NB OF LAKELAND
{{ 4U + 18 S }}
Chartered 9/29
1929 Small Size <$VALUE
5 Type 1 1-1646 <$300
10 Type 1 1-830 <$300
20 Type 1 1-212 <$325
5 Type 2 1-8316 <$300
10 Type 2 1-4248 <$300
20 Type 2 1-1080 <$325
Total Issue $230,280
Out in 1935 $97,160

11038 Lake
FNB OF LEESBURG
{{ 8 L 12 S }}
Chartered 7/17
1902 Plain Back <$VALUE
4x5 1-10087 <$850
4x10 1-7792 <$850
1929 Small Size
5 Type 1 1-2938 <$450
10 Type 1 1-1698 <$450
5 Type 2 1-7332 <$450
10 Type 2 1-3120 <$450
Total Issue $771,300
Out in 1935 $50,000
Large out 1935 $890

6055 Suwannee
FNB OF LIVE OAK
{{ 7 L U + 12 S }}
Chartered 12/01
Brown Back <$VALUE
4x5 1-800 <$2250
3x10-20 1-590 <$2250
1882 Date Back
4x5 1-3825 <$2000
3x10-20 1-3020 <$2000
1882 Value Back
4x5 3826-6545 <$2000
3x10-20 3021-4715 <$2000
1902 Plain Back
4x5 1-4065 <$850
3x10-20 1-2931 <$850
1929 Small Size
5 Type 1 1-1814 <$450
10 Type 1 1-956 <$450
20 Type 1 1-264 <$475
5 Type 2 1-3660 <$450
10 Type 2 1-2148 <$450
20 Type 2 1-576 <$475
Total Issue $834,760
Out in 1935 $50,000
Large out 1935 $1,140

7190 Madison
FNB OF MADISON
{{ 7 L }}
Chartered 3/04
Liquidated 6/30/23
1902 Red Seal <$VALUE
4x5 1-2515 <$3000
3x10-20 1-2733 <$3000
1902 Date Back
4x5 1-6500 <$1000
3x10-20 1-4560 <$1000
1902 Plain Back
4x5 6501-13480 <$1000
3x10-20 4561-8939 <$1000
Total Issue $903,500
Out at close $75,000

6110 Jackson
FNB OF MARIANNA
{{ 7 L 10 S }}
Chartered 1/02
1902 Red Seal <$VALUE
4x5 1-1370 <$2500
3x10-20 1-1092 <$2500
1902 Date Back
4x5 1-4150 <$850
3x10-20 1-3260 <$850
1902 Plain Back (dated 1902)
4x5 4151-7625 <$850
3x10-20 3261-5343 <$850
1902 Plain Back (dated 1922)
4x5 1-18589 <$850
1929 Small Size
5 Type 1 1-7252 <$500
5 Type 2 1-13296 <$600
Total Issue $1,157,470
Out in 1935 $50,000
Large out 1935 $3,840

6370 Dade
FNB OF MIAMI
{{ 8 L 50+ S }}
Chartered 8/02
1902 Red Seal <$VALUE
4x5 1-2250 <$2500
3x10-20 1-2200 <$2500
1902 Date Back
4x5 1-11170 <$850
3x10-20 1-7600 <$850
1902 Plain Back
4x5 11171-23550 <$850
3x10-20 7601-16245 <$850
1929 Small Size
5 Type 1 1-11654 <$100
10 Type 1 1-6184 <$100
20 Type 1 1-2650 <$100
50 Type 1 1-766 <$200
100 Type 1 1-370 <$300
5 Type 2 1-20736 <$110
10 Type 2 1-3508 <$110
Total Issue $3,067,470
Out in 1933 $1,186,500
Large out 1935 $3,950

13570 Dade
FLORIDA NB & TC OF MIAMI
{{ 41 S }}
Chartered 8/31
1929 Small Size <$VALUE
5 Type 1 1-11314 <$100
10 Type 1 1-3116 <$100
20 Type 1 1-736 <$100
5 Type 2 1-86750 <$110
10 Type 2 1-15248 <$110
Total Issue $1,200,930
Out in 1935 $400,000

6774 Dade
FORT DALLAS NB OF MIAMI
{{ UNREPORTED }}
Chartered 5/6/03
Receivership 7/5/07
1902 Red Seal <$VALUE
4x5 1-1880 <$4000
3x10-20 1-1421 <$4000
Total Issue $108,650
Out in 1915 $1,945

13828 Dade
MERCANTILE NB OF MIAMI BEACH
{{ 6 S }}
Chartered 11/6/33
1929 Small Size <$VALUE
5 Type 2 1-17334 <$500
10 Type 2 1-7977 <$500
Total Issue $166,440
Out in 1935 $66,200

12047 Dade
MIAMI BEACH FNB, MIAMI BEACH
{{ 32 S }}
Chartered 11/21
1929 Small Size <$VALUE
5 Type 1 1-8304 <$175
10 Type 1 1-4534 <$175
20 Type 1 1-1394 <$175
5 Type 2 1-3272 <$200
10 Type 2 1-3275 <$200
20 Type 2 1-625 <$200
Total Issue $750,050
Out in 1933 $300,000

13968 Santa Rosa
FNB IN MILTON
{{ 4 S }}
Chartered 1/34
1929 Small Size <$VALUE
5 Type 2 1-6444 <$750
Total Issue $32,220
Out in 1935 $25,000
Outstanding includes Ch 7034

7034 Santa Rosa
FNB OF MILTON
{{ 4 L 4 S }}
Chartered 11/03
Liquidated 3/27/34
1902 Red Seal <$VALUE
4x5 1-975 <$3000
3x10-20 1-792 <$3000
1902 Date Back
4x5 1-1975 <$1000
3x10-20 1-1540 <$1000
1902 Plain Back
4x5 1976-13191 <$1000
3x10-20 1541-2220 <$1000
1929 Small Size
5 Type 1 1-3376 <$600
5 Type 2 1-2194 <$600
Total Issue $546,170
Out at close $25,000
Large out at close $1,550
Ch 13968 assumed circulation

6825 Marion
CENTRAL NB OF OCALA
{{ 1 L }}
Chartered 6/9/03
Liquidated 2/16/07
1902 Red Seal <$VALUE
4x5 1-450 <$3500
3x10-20 1-350 <$3500
Total Issue $26,500
Out in 1910 $1,695

3470 Marion
FNB OF OCALA
{{ UNREPORTED }}
Chartered 3/16/86
Receivership 4/22/95
Brown Back <$VALUE
4x5 1-2166 <$4000
Total Issue $43,320
Out in 1915 $200

3815 Marion
MERCHANTS NB OF OCALA
{{ 1 L }}
Chartered 11/21/87
Receivership 2/3/97
Brown Back <$VALUE
4x5 1-2699 <$3000
3x10-20 1-400 <$3000
Total Issue $73,980
Out in 1915 $375

10578 Marion
MUNROE & CHAMBLISS NB OF OCALA
{{ 6 L 16 S }}
Chartered 7/14
1902 Date Back <$VALUE
3x10-20 1-1600 <$1000
1902 Plain Back
3x10-20 1601-9787 <$1000
1929 Small Size
10 Type 1 1-1386 <$425
20 Type 1 1-372 <$450
5 Type 2 1-6434 <$450
10 Type 2 1-2578 <$450
20 Type 2 1-1192 <$450
Total Issue $698,940
Out in 1935 $50,000
Large out 1935 $1,220

9926 Marion
OCALA NB, OCALA
{{ 16 L 15 S }}
Organized 1/17/11
1902 Date Back <$VALUE
4x5 1-5350 <$500
3x10-20 1-4260 <$500
1902 Plain Back
4x5 5351-19344 <$500
3x10-20 4261-13170 <$500
1929 Small Size
5 Type 1 1-3288 <$400
10 Type 1 1-1566 <$400
20 Type 1 1-406 <$400
5 Type 2 1-5688 <$450
10 Type 2 1-2898 <$450
20 Type 2 1-840 <$450
Total Issue $1,374,520
Out in 1935 $75,000
Large out 1935 $3,830

3802 Orange
CITIZENS NB OF ORLANDO
{{ UNREPORTED }}
Chartered 10/12/87
Liquidated 3/22/93
Brown Back <$VALUE
4x5 1-2114 <$4000
Total Issue $42,280
Out in 1910 $270

FNB in Orlando
FNB & TC in Orlando
SEE Ch 10069
Peoples NB of Orlando

3469 Orange
FNB OF ORLANDO
{{ 4 L }}
Chartered 3/16/86
Receivership 11/29/95
Brown Back <$VALUE
4x5 1-3940 <$2500
Total Issue $78,800
Out in 1915 $535

10069 Orange
PEOPLES NB OF ORLANDO
Organized 8/1/11
Receivership 2/27/34
2nd title: FNB in Orlando 1/22/20
3rd title: FNB & TC in Orlando 2/9/28
FIRST TITLE {{ 2 L }}
1902 Date Back <$VALUE
4x5 1-1850 <$1000
3x10-20 1-1520 <$1000
1902 Plain Back
4x5 1851-2650 <$1000
3x10-20 1521-1940 <$1000
SECOND TITLE {{ 4 L }}
1902 Plain Back
4x5 1-7206 <$850
3x10-20 1-4509 <$850
THIRD TITLE {{ 1 L 9 S }}
1902 Plain Back
4x5 1-800 <$1000
3x10-20 1-844 <$1000
1929 Small Size
5 Type 1 1-1750 <$550
10 Type 1 1-1020 <$550
20 Type 1 1-248 <$575
5 Type 2 1-1272 <$600
10 Type 2 1-636 <$600
20 Type 2 1-182 <$600
Total Issue $737,590
Out at close $50,000
Large out at close $2,670

3223 Putnam
FNB OF PALATKA
{{ 1 L }}
Chartered 7/15/84
Receivership 8/7/91
Brown Back <$VALUE
4x5 1-3667 <$3000
Total Issue $73,340
Out in 1915 $430

13214 Putnam
PALATKA ATLANTIC NB, PALATKA
{{ 26 S }}
Chartered 6/28
1929 Small Size <$VALUE
5 Type 1 1-624 <$350
10 Type 1 1-106 <$350
20 Type 1 1-42 <$350
50 Type 1 1-6 <$650
100 Type 1 1-4 <$750
5 Type 2 1-5864 <$400
10 Type 2 1-2054 <$400
20 Type 2 1-675 <$400
Total Issue $97,680
Out in 1935 $32,300

3266 Putnam
PALATKA NB, PALATKA
{{ UNREPORTED }}
Chartered 11/20/84
Receivership 6/3/87
Brown Back <$VALUE
4x5 1-875 <$3500
3x10-20 1-200 <$3500
Total Issue $27,500
Out in 1915 $185

4813 Putnam
PUTNAM NB OF PALATKA
{{ 5 L 4 S }}
Organized 10/22/92
Receivership 12/31/32
Brown Back <$VALUE
50-100 1-1044 <$7500
1882 Date Back
50-100 1-460 <$7500
3x50-100 1-12 <$7500
1902 Date Back
3x10-20 1-1500 <$850
1902 Plain Back
3x10-20 1501-9395 <$850
1929 Small Size
10 Type 1 1-1145 <$525
20 Type 1 1-312 <$550
Total Issue $804,490
Out at close $49,460
Large out at close $6,470

12275 Palm Beach
FNB OF PALM BEACH
{{ 1 L }}
Chartered 11/22
Liquidated 2/5/24
1902 Plain Back <$VALUE
4x5 1-1950 <$2000
Total Issue $39,000
Out at close $25,000

10346 Bay
FNB OF PANAMA CITY
{{ 8 L 6 S }}
Organized 2/26/13
Receivership 2/12/31
1902 Date Back <$VALUE
4x10 1-2150 <$600
1902 Plain Back
4x10 2151-33466 <$600
1929 Small Size
10 Type 1 1-1963 <$600
Total Issue $1,456,420
Out in 1929 $125,000
Large out at close $12,550

5603 Escambia
AMERICAN NB OF PENSACOLA
{{ 37 L 50+ S }}
Chartered 10/22/00
Brown Back <$VALUE
4x5 1-11880 <$1250
4x10 1-3375 <$1250
3x10-20 1-6148 <$1250
1882 Date Back
4x5 1-20250 <$1000
4x10 1-19000 <$1000
3x10-20 1-400 <$1000
1882 Value Back
4x5 20251-41708 <$1250
4x10 19001-34542 <$1250
1902 Plain Back
3x10-20 1-80011 <$150
1929 Small Size
10 Type 1 1-23430 <$50
20 Type 1 1-6330 <$60
10 Type 2 1-28545 <$50
20 Type 2 1-11400 <$60
Total Issue $9,595,240
Out in 1935 $800,000
Large out 1935 $34,170
Outstanding includes Ch 10535

Citizens & Peoples NB of Pensacola
SEE Ch 9007
Peoples NB of Pensacola

4837 Escambia
CITIZENS NB OF PENSACOLA
{{ 4 L }}
Chartered 1893
Liquidated 9/6/11
Brown Back <$VALUE
3x10-20 1-2570 <$2000
1882 Date Back
3x10-20 1-746 <$1750
Total Issue $165,800
Out in 1911 $23,800
Ch 9007 assumed circulation

2490 Escambia
FNB OF PENSACOLA
{{ 26 L }}
Organized 8/10/80
Receivership 1/22/14
Series 1875 <$VALUE
4x5 1-7399 <$4000
Brown Back
4x5 1-9665 <$1250
3x10-20 1-12034 <$1250
1882 Date Back
4x5 1-26925 <$850
3x10-20 1-23717 <$850
Total Issue $2,667,330
Out in 1915 $120,015

10535 Escambia
NB OF COMMERCE OF PENSACOLA
{{ 7 L }}
Chartered 5/14
Liquidated 7/31/17
1902 Date Back <$VALUE
4x5 1-7500 <$500
3x10-20 1-6000 <$500
1902 Plain Back
4x5 7501-12265 <$500
3x10-20 6001-9288 <$500
Total Issue $709,700
Out at close $300,000
Ch 5603 assumed circulation

9007 Escambia
PEOPLES NB OF PENSACOLA
Chartered 1/08
2nd title: Citizens & Peoples NB 9/11/11
FIRST TITLE {{ 0 L }}
1902 Red Seal <$VALUE
4x5 1-1900 <$2500
4x10 1-1900 <$2500
1902 Date Back
4x5 1-2724 <$750
4x10 1-2538 <$750
SECOND TITLE {{ 16 L 31 S }}
1902 Date Back
4x5 1-6250 <$225
4x10 1-6500* <$225
1902 Plain Back
4x5 6251-42740 <$225
4x10 7251-32697* <$225
* 6501-7250 not marked
1929 Small Size
5 Type 1 1-11976 <$75
10 Type 1 1-6630 <$75
5 Type 2 1-20108 <$75
10 Type 2 1-11529 <$75
Total Issue $3,405,590
Out in 1935 $200,000
Large out 1935 $8,095
Outstanding includes Ch 4837

7865 Taylor
FNB OF PERRY
{{ 5 L 2 S }}
Organized 7/11/05
Receivership 10/25/30
1902 Red Seal <$VALUE
4x5 1-815 <$3000
3x10-20 1-694 <$3000
1902 Date Back
4x5 1-2175 <$1000
3x10-20 1-1580 <$1000
1902 Plain Back
4x5 2176-11972 <$1000
3x10-20 1581-8177 <$1000
1929 Small Size
5 Type 1 1-832 <$800
10 Type 1 1-428 <$800
20 Type 1 1-133 <$800
Total Issue $765,890
Out at close $50,000
Large out at close $7,150

10236 Hillsborough
FNB OF PLANT CITY
{{ 1 L }}
Chartered 8/12
Liquidated 2/4/19
1902 Date Back <$VALUE
4x5 1-2300 <$1500
3x10-20 1-1840 <$1500
1902 Plain Back
4x5 2301-3840 <$1500
3x10-20 1841-2805 <$1500
Total Issue $217,050
Out at close $50,000

10512 Charlotte
FNB OF PUNTA GORDA
{{ 4 L }}
Organized 4/6/14
Receivership 2/18/29
1902 Date Back <$VALUE
4x5 1-400 <$1500
4x10 1-400 <$1500
1902 Plain Back
4x5 401-4981 <$1500
4x10 401-3638 <$1500
Total Issue $245,140
Out at close $22,000

7253 Gadsden
FNB OF QUINCY
{{ 11 L }}
Organized 5/4/04
Receivership 2/11/25
1902 Red Seal <$VALUE
4x5 1-2400 <$2500
3x10-20 1-1920 <$2500
1902 Date Back
4x5 1-8750 <$750
3x10-20 1-6160 <$750
1902 Plain Back
4x5 8751-19535 <$750
3x10-20 6161-13338 <$750
Total Issue $1,201,600
Out at close $100,000

3462 St Johns
FNB OF SAINT AUGUSTINE
{{ 15 L }}
Organized 2/16/86
Receivership 7/25/29
Brown Back <$VALUE
4x5 1-7550 <$2000
3x10-20 1-2424 <$2000
50-100 1-1030 <$7500
1902 Red Seal
4x5 1-1750 <$2250
3x10-20 1-1300 <$2250
1902 Date Back
4x5 1-8000 <$600
3x10-20 1-6700 <$600
1902 Plain Back
4x5 8001-32599 <$600
3x10-20 6701-22059 <$600
Total Issue $2,281,630
Out at close $130,000

11420 St Johns
SAINT AUGUSTINE NB, SAINT AUGUSTINE
{{ 7 L 7 S }}
Chartered 8/19
1902 Plain Back <$VALUE
4x5 1-29525 <$600
1929 Small Size
5 Type 1 1-7670 <$400
5 Type 2 1-14724 <$450
Total Issue $894,220
Out in 1935 $50,000
Large out 1935 $1,810

9707 Osceola
FNB OF SAINT CLOUD
{{ 3 L }}
Organized 3/24/10
Receivership 1/2/18
1902 Date Back <$VALUE
4x5 1-1765 <$1250
3x10-20 1-1345 <$1250
Total Issue $102,550
Out at close $17,100

12623 Pinellas
ALEXANDER NB OF SAINT PETERSBURG
{{ 5 L }}
Chartered 1/25
Liquidated 10/19/27
1902 Plain Back <$VALUE
4x5 1-25055 <$850
Total Issue $501,100
Out at close $200,000

Central NB of Saint Petersburg
Central NB & TC of Saint Petersburg
SEE Ch 7796
NB of Saint Petersburg

7730 Pinellas
FNB OF SAINT PETERSBURG
{{ 9 L }}
Organized 4/26/05
Receivership 6/9/30
1902 Red Seal <$VALUE
3x10-20 1-1250 <$2500
1902 Date Back
3x10-20 1-3000 <$750
1902 Plain Back
4x5 1-25070 <$750
3x10-20 3001-21695 <$750
Total Issue $1,648,650
Out at close $15,360

7796 Pinellas
NB OF SAINT PETERSBURG
Organized 4/18/05
Receivership 4/21/31
2nd title: Central NB 1/21/10
3rd title: Central NB & TC 1/16/22
FIRST TITLE {{ 1 L }}
1902 Red Seal <$VALUE
4x5 1-1625 <$2500
3x10-20 1-1306 <$2500
1902 Date Back
4x5 1-445 <$850
3x10-20 1-186 <$850
SECOND TITLE {{ 4 L }}
1902 Date Back
3x10-20 1-6400 <$750
1902 Plain Back
3x10-20 6401-13300 <$750
THIRD TITLE {{ 4 L }}
1902 Plain Back
3x10-20 1-7891 <$750
Total Issue $1,175,550
Out at close $6,105

3798 Seminole
FNB OF SANFORD
{{ 5 L }}
Organized 4/19/87
Receivership 7/15/29
Brown Back <$VALUE
4x5 1-2334 <$3000
3x10-20 1-213 <$3000
1902 Red Seal
4x10 1-125 <$3500
1902 Date Back
4x10 1-1150 <$1250
1902 Plain Back
4x10 1151-3545 <$1250
3x50-100 1-278 <$2500
Total Issue $273,630
Out at close $3,820

13157 Seminole
SANFORD ATLANTIC NB OF SANFORD
{{ 22 S }}
Chartered 12/27
1929 Small Size <$VALUE
5 Type 1 1-3108 <$250
10 Type 1 1-1388 <$250
20 Type 1 1-372 <$250
5 Type 2 1-6925 <$275
10 Type 2 1-3280 <$275
20 Type 2 1-893 <$275
Total Issue $306,445
Out in 1935 $100,000

12751 Sarasota
AMERICAN NB OF SARASOTA
{{ 1 L }}
Organized 4/7/25
Receivership 5/15/28
1902 Plain Back <$VALUE
3x10-20 1-4444 <$2000
Total Issue $222,200
Out at close $95,850

10414 Sarasota
FNB OF SARASOTA
{{ 1 L }}
Chartered 6/13
Liquidated 11/20/23
1902 Date Back <$VALUE
3x10-20 1-500 <$2500
1902 Plain Back
3x10-20 501-1295 <$2500
Total Issue $64,750
Out at close $12,500

13352 Sarasota
PALMER NB & TC OF SARASOTA
{{ 8U + 24 S }}
Chartered 7/29
1929 Small Size <$VALUE
5 Type 1 1-1536 <$400
10 Type 1 1-756 <$400
20 Type 1 1-258 <$400
5 Type 2 1-24 <$400
10 Type 2 1-65 <$400
20 Type 2 1-65 <$400
Total Issue $124,470
Out in 1935 $41,250

4132 Leon
FNB OF TALLAHASSEE
{{ 3 L }}
Chartered 1889
Liquidated 7/12/16
Brown Back <$VALUE
50-100 1-967 <$30,000
1902 Date Back
50-100 1-500 <$10,000
3x50-100 1-20 <$10,000
Total Issue $225,050
Out in 1916 $45,250

7153 Hillsborough
AMERICAN NB OF TAMPA
{{ 6 L }}
Chartered 3/04
Liquidated 11/22/19
1902 Red Seal <$VALUE
3x10-20 1-4250 <$1750
1902 Date Back
3x10-20 1-23500 <$500
1902 Plain Back
3x10-20 23501-31142 <$500
Total Issue $1,769,600
Out in 1919 $244,500

4949 Hillsborough
EXCHANGE NB OF TAMPA
{{ 20 L 39 S }}
Chartered 1894
Brown Back <$VALUE
4x5 1-6665 <$1500
3x10-20 1-2974 <$1500
1882 Date Back
4x5 1-11764 <$1000
3x10-20 1-8049 <$1000
1902 Date Back
4x5 1-4015 <$165
3x10-20 1-3394 <$165
1902 Plain Back
4x5 4016-44000 <$165
3x10-20 3395-29346 <$165
1929 Small Size
5 Type 1 1-9142 <$60
10 Type 1 1-4290 <$60
20 Type 1 1-1192 <$60
5 Type 2 1-13578 <$75
10 Type 2 1-6610 <$75
20 Type 2 1-2219 <$75
Total Issue $4,120,100
Out in 1935 $200,000
Large out 1935 $7,325

3497 Hillsborough
FNB OF TAMPA
{{ 36 L 50+ S }}
Chartered 4/86
Brown Back <$VALUE
4x5 1-3607 <$1250
50-100 1-353 <$6500
1902 Red Seal
4x5 1-11000 <$1250
3x10-20 1-3300 <$1250
50-100 1-2106 <$7500
1902 Date Back
4x5 1-23250 <$165
3x10-20 1-21900 <$165
1902 Plain Back
4x5 23251-95642 <$165
3x10-20 21901-72491 <$165
1929 Small Size
5 Type 1 1-38524 <$45
10 Type 1 1-23754 <$45
20 Type 1 1-7280 <$50
5 Type 2 1-92852 <$50
10 Type 2 1-46378 <$50
20 Type 2 1-12171 <$60
Total Issue $10,989,400
Out in 1935 $1,350,000
Large out 1935 $41,435
Outstanding includes Ch 10958

4478 Hillsborough
GULF NB OF TAMPA
{{ UNREPORTED }}
Chartered 12/2/90
Receivership 7/14/93
Brown Back <$VALUE
3x10-20 1-315 <$4000
Total Issue $15,750
Out in 1915 $60

10958 Hillsborough
N CITY B OF TAMPA
{{ 19 L }}
Organized 2/21/17
Receivership 5/20/32
1902 Plain Back <$VALUE
4x5 1-92765 <$175
3x10-20 1-60629 <$175
Total Issue $4,886,750
Out in 1929 $500,000
Ch 3497 assumed circulation

4539 Hillsborough
TAMPA NB, TAMPA
{{ UNREPORTED }}
Chartered 3/26/91
Liquidated 5/2/92
Brown Back <$VALUE
4x5 1-612 <$4000
Total Issue $12,240
Out in 1910 $80

12274 Pinellas
FNB OF TARPON SPRINGS
{{ 5 L }}
Organized 11/8/22
Receivership 10/26/33
1902 Plain Back <$VALUE
4x5 1-6732 <$2000
Total Issue $134,640
Out at close $515

11156 Indian River
FNB OF VERO
{{ 2 L }}
Chartered 3/18
Liquidated 3/1/23
1902 Plain Back <$VALUE
4x5 1-6185 <$2000
Total Issue $123,700
Out at close $25,000

12057 Palm Beach
AMERICAN NB OF WEST PALM BEACH
{{ 1 L }}
Chartered 12/21
Liquidated 2/5/24
1902 Plain Back <$VALUE
3x10-20 1-2336 <$2000
Total Issue $116,800
Out at close $25,000

11073 Palm Beach
FNB OF WEST PALM BEACH
{{ 2 L }}
Chartered 9/17
Liquidated 2/5/24
1902 Plain Back <$VALUE
4x5 1-5385 <$2000
3x10-20 1-2766 <$2000
Total Issue $246,000
Out at close $100,000

13300 Palm Beach
WEST PALM BEACH ATLANTIC NB, WEST PALM BEACH
{{ 8 S }}
Chartered 3/29
1929 Small Size <$VALUE
5 Type 1 1-2000 <$600
10 Type 1 1-990 <$600
20 Type 1 1-252 <$600
5 Type 2 1-6290 <$600
10 Type 2 1-2769 <$600
20 Type 2 1-855 <$600
Total Issue $225,880
Out in 1935 $53,250

11389 Orange
FNB OF WINTER GARDEN
{{ 5 L 4 S }}
Organized 6/20/19
1902 Plain Back <$VALUE
3x10-20 1-4720 <$850
1929 Small Size
10 Type 1 1-1438 <$600
20 Type 1 1-420 <$600
10 Type 2 1-1182 <$600
20 Type 2 1-310 <$600
Total Issue $390,700
Out in 1935 $25,000
Large out 1935 $1,040

13383 Polk
AMERICAN NB IN WINTER HAVEN
{{ U + 11 S }}
Chartered 10/29
1929 Small Size <$VALUE
5 Type 1 1-1784 <$400
10 Type 1 1-928 <$400
5 Type 2 1-4236 <$400
10 Type 2 1-1925 <$400
Total Issue $149,630
Out in 1935 $25,000
Outstanding includes Ch 12100

American NB of Winter Haven
SEE Ch 12100
NB of Winter Haven

13437 Polk
EXCHANGE NB OF WINTER HAVEN
{{ 17 S }}
Chartered 3/30 as Snell NB in Winter Haven, under which there was no issue. Issuing title adopted 4/11/32.
1929 Small Size <$VALUE
5 Type 1 1-2042 <$300
10 Type 1 1-736 <$300
20 Type 1 1-558 <$300
5 Type 2 1-6936 <$325
10 Type 2 1-3705 <$325
20 Type 2 1-905 <$325
Total Issue $262,210
Out in 1935 $80,650

12100 Polk
NB OF WINTER HAVEN
Chartered 1/22
Liquidated 11/22/29
2nd title: American NB of Winter Haven 4/15/26
FIRST TITLE {{ 4 L }}
1902 Plain Back <$VALUE
4x5 1-7631 <$850
3x10-20 1-1986 <$850
SECOND TITLE {{ 6 L 2 S }}
1902 Plain Back
4x5 1-4356 <$750
4x10 1-3461 <$750
1929 Small Size
5 Type 1 1-424 <$750
10 Type 1 1-137* <$750
*E000137A, F000137A not issued
Total Issue $498,400
Out at close $48,870
Large out 1935 $2,255
Ch 13383 assumed circulation

10379 Polk
SNELL NB OF WINTER HAVEN
{{ UNREPORTED }}
Organized 4/22/13
Receivership 1/19/33
1902 Date Back <$VALUE
3x10-20 1-600 <$2000
1902 Plain Back
3x10-20 601-2113 <$2000
1929 Small Size
10 Type 1 1-73 <$1500
20 Type 1 1-4 <$1500
Total Issue $110,510
Out at close $6,700
Large out at close $1,840

<$VALUEs are for notes in FINE condition. Value changes by approximately 25% for a change of one full grade.

GEORGIA

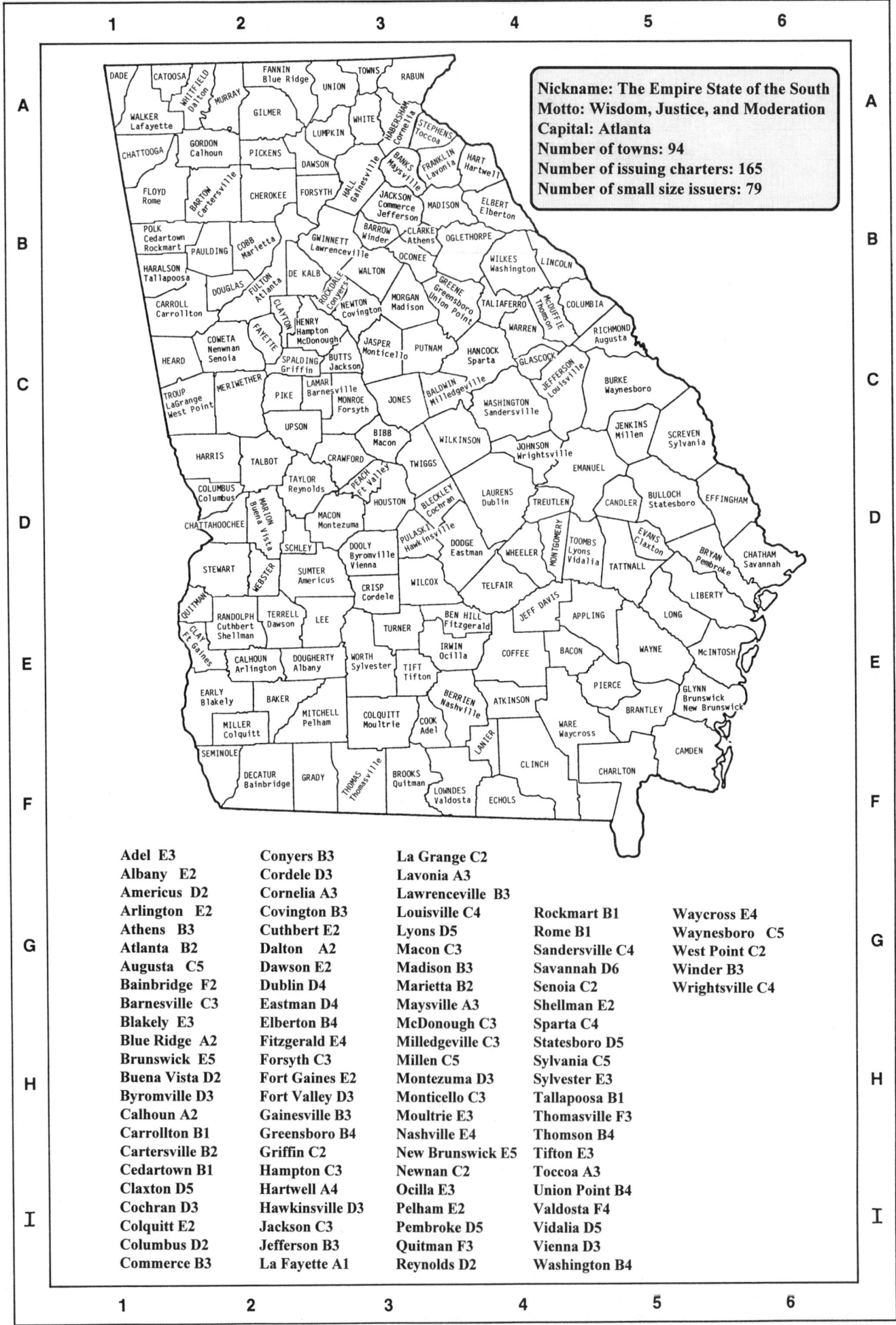

Nickname: The Empire State of the South
Motto: Wisdom, Justice, and Moderation
Capital: Atlanta
Number of towns: 94
Number of issuing charters: 165
Number of small size issuers: 79

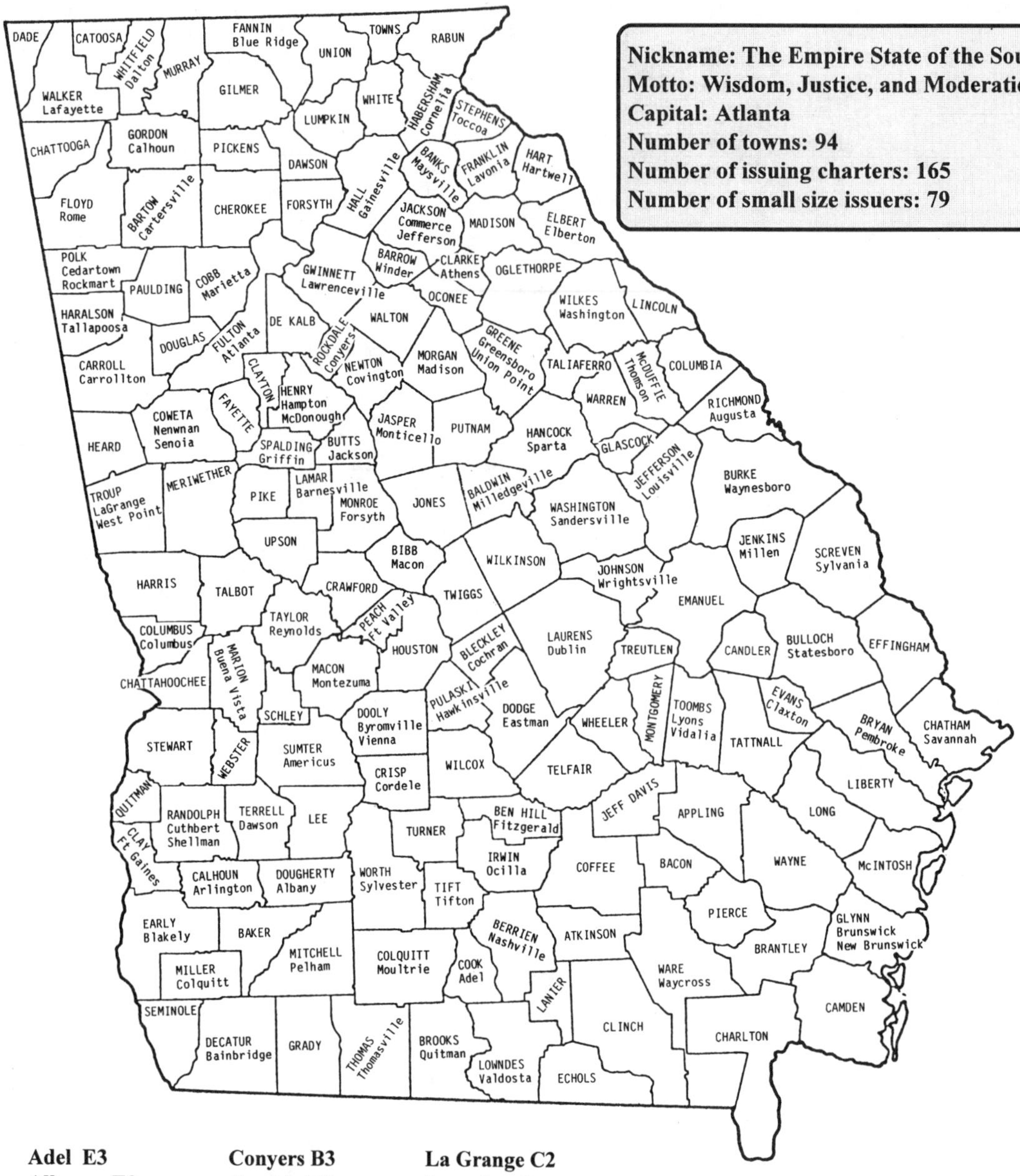

Adel E3
Albany E2
Americus D2
Arlington E2
Athens B3
Atlanta B2
Augusta C5
Bainbridge F2
Barnesville C3
Blakely E3
Blue Ridge A2
Brunswick E5
Buena Vista D2
Byromville D3
Calhoun A2
Carrollton B1
Cartersville B2
Cedartown B1
Claxton D5
Cochran D3
Colquitt E2
Columbus D2
Commerce B3
Conyers B3
Cordele D3
Cornelia A3
Covington B3
Cuthbert E2
Dalton A2
Dawson E2
Dublin D4
Eastman D4
Elberton B4
Fitzgerald E4
Forsyth C3
Fort Gaines E2
Fort Valley D3
Gainesville B3
Greensboro B4
Griffin C2
Hampton C3
Hartwell A4
Hawkinsville D3
Jackson C3
Jefferson B3
La Fayette A1
La Grange C2
Lavonia A3
Lawrenceville B3
Louisville C4
Lyons D5
Macon C3
Madison B3
Marietta B2
Maysville A3
McDonough C3
Milledgeville C3
Millen C5
Montezuma D3
Monticello C3
Moultrie E3
Nashville E4
New Brunswick E5
Newnan C2
Ocilla E3
Pelham E2
Pembroke D5
Quitman F3
Reynolds D2
Rockmart B1
Rome B1
Sandersville C4
Savannah D6
Senoia C2
Shellman E2
Sparta C4
Statesboro D5
Sylvania C5
Sylvester E3
Tallapoosa B1
Thomasville F3
Thomson B4
Tifton E3
Toccoa A3
Union Point B4
Valdosta F4
Vidalia D5
Vienna D3
Washington B4
Waycross E4
Waynesboro C5
West Point C2
Winder B3
Wrightsville C4

****
9777 Cook
FNB OF ADEL
{{ 1 L }}
Chartered 6/10
Liquidated 6/10/19
1902 Date Back <$VALUE
4x5 1-1975 <$1250
3x10-20 1-1630 <$1250
1902 Plain Back
4x5 1976-2960 <$1250
3x10-20 1631-2147 <$1250
Total Issue $166,550
Out at close $25,000
****
Albany Exchange NB, Albany
SEE Ch 5512
Albany NB, Albany
****
5512 Dougherty
ALBANY NB, ALBANY
Chartered 7/23/00
2nd title:Albany Exchange NB 4/11/22
FIRST TITLE {{ 7 L }}
Brown Back <$VALUE
3x10-20 1-3600 <$600
1882 Date Back
3x10-20 1-5240 <$600
1882 Value Back
3x10-20 5241-7242 <$600
1902 Plain Back
3x10-20 1-4400 <$225
SECOND TITLE {{ 6 L 20 S }}
1902 Plain Back
3x10-20 1-11940 <$225
1929 Small Size
10 Type 1 1-4912 <$85
20 Type 1 1-1346 <$100
10 Type 2 1-7193 <$110
20 Type 2 1-2084 <$110
Total Issue $1,928,950
Out in 1935 $150,000
Large out 1935 $7,470
****
Citizens FNB of Albany
SEE Ch 3872
FNB of Albany
****
7777 Dougherty
CITIZENS NB OF ALBANY
{{ 1 L }}
Chartered 6/9/05
Liquidated 5/1/05
1902 Red Seal <$VALUE
3x10-20 1-1880 <$2000
Total Issue $94,000
Out in 1910 $8,500
****
13223 Dougherty
CITY NB OF ALBANY
{{ 9 L 20 S }}
Chartered 7/28
1902 Plain Back <$VALUE
4x5 1-2508 <$225
3x10-20 1-1508 <$225
1929 Small Size
5 Type 1 1-4474 <$100
10 Type 1 1-2046 <$100
20 Type 1 1-826 <$100
5 Type 2 1-8148 <$110
10 Type 2 1-4748 <$110
20 Type 2 1-1332 <$110
Total Issue $596,520
Out in 1935 $100,000
Large out 1935 $1,160
****
3872 Dougherty
FNB OF ALBANY
Chartered 4/21/88
Liquidated 8/28/24
2nd title: Citizens FNB of Albany 5/1/08
FIRST TITLE {{ 1 L }}
Brown Back <$VALUE
3x10-20 1-4212 <$850
SECOND TITLE {{ 4 L }}
1902 Red Seal
3x10-20 1-1100 <$1500
50-100 1-300 <$1500
1902 Date Back
3x10-20 1-13350 <$350
50-100 1-400 <$1000
1902 Plain Back
3x10-20 13351-21710 <$350
Total Issue $1,456,100
Out at close $150,000
Outstanding includes Ch 9729
****

****
9729 Dougherty
GEORGIA NB OF ALBANY
{{ 10 L }}
Chartered 4/10
Liquidated 1/12/26
1902 Date Back <$VALUE
4x5 1-7850 <$250
3x10-20 1-6560 <$250
1902 Plain Back
4x5 7851-36710 <$250
3x10-20 6561-23642 <$250
Total Issue $1,916,300
Out at close $300,000
Outstanding includes Ch 3872
Ch 12863 assumed circulation
****
12863 Dougherty
NEW GEORGIA NB OF ALBANY
{{ 5 L }}
Organized 12/22/25
Receivership 1/4/28
1902 Plain Back <$VALUE
3x10-20 1-6938 <$400
Total Issue $346,900
Out at close $197,995
Outstanding includes Ch 9729 and Ch 3872
****
6336 Dougherty
THIRD NB OF ALBANY
{{ UNREPORTED }}
Chartered 7/12/02
Liquidated 3/31/08
1902 Red Seal <$VALUE
4x5 1-250 <$2000
3x10-20 1-694 <$2000
Total Issue $39,700
Out in 1910 $2,285
****
8305 Sumter
AMERICUS NB, AMERICUS
{{ 2 L }}
Organized 7/14/06
Receivership 2/3/14
1902 Red Seal <$VALUE
3x10-20 1-3750 <$1500
1902 Date Back
3x10-20 1-6999 <$750
Total Issue $537,450
Out in 1916 $15,560
****
2009 Sumter
FNB OF AMERICUS
{{ UNREPORTED }}
Chartered 7/8/72
Liquidated 6/17/81
Original Series <$VALUE
3x1-2 1-2000 <$2000/$4500
4x5 1-2375 <$2000
Series 1875
3x1-2 1-1620 <$2000/$4500
4x5 1-2545 <$2000
Total Issue $116,500
Out in 1910 $692
****
2839 Sumter
PEOPLES NB OF AMERICUS
{{ UNREPORTED }}
Chartered 12/16/82
Liquidated 4/15/99
Brown Back <$VALUE
3x10-20 1-1657 <$1500
Total Issue $82,850
Out in 1910 $620
****
8314 Calhoun
FNB OF ARLINGTON
{{ 3 L 0 S }}
Organized 7/16/06
Receivership 3/8/32
1902 Red Seal <$VALUE
3x10-20 1-400 <$2000
1902 Date Back
3x10-20 1-1500 <$750
1902 Plain Back
3x10-20 1501-3048 <$750
1929 Small Size
10 Type 1 1-259 <$750
20 Type 1 1-41 <$750
Total Issue $192,860
Out at close $9,460
Large out at close $1,050
****

****
6525 Clarke
GEORGIA NB OF ATHENS
{{ 18 L }}
Chartered 12/9/02
Receivership 4/17/25
1902 Red Seal <$VALUE
4x5 1-6672 <$1000
3x10-20 1-5254 <$1000
1902 Date Back
4x5 1-18750 <$165
3x10-20 1-14090 <$165
1902 Plain Back
4x5 18751-52703 <$165
3x10-20 14091-34782 <$165
Total Issue $3,189,300
Out at close $200,000
****
1639 Clarke
NB OF ATHENS
{{ 25 L 24 S }}
Chartered 1866
Original Series <$VALUE
3x1-2 1-3400 <$1750/$4500
4x5 1-2350 <$1750
3x10-20 1-2100<$2000/$2500
Series 1875
3x10-20 1-1884<$2000/$2500
Brown Back
3x10-20 1-5826 <$500
1902 Red Seal
3x10-20 1-1800 <$1000
1902 Date Back
3x10-20 1-7100 <$150
1902 Plain Back
3x10-20 7101-46814 <$150
1929 Small Size
10 Type 1 1-7442 <$65
20 Type 1 1-2142 <$75
10 Type 2 1-1496 <$100
20 Type 2 1-430 <$125
Total Issue $3,712,320
Out in 1935 $100,000
Large out 1935 $12,340
****
9105 Fulton
AMERICAN NB OF ATLANTA
{{ 12 L }}
Chartered 4/08
Liquidated 12/2/16
1902 Red Seal <$VALUE
4x5 1-5000 <$1000
4x10 1-5625 <$1000
1902 Date Back
4x5 1-60088* <$200
4x10 1-56969 <$200
* 58001-60088 not marked
Total Issue $3,805,520
Out in 1916 $500,000
****
1559 Fulton
ATLANTA NB, ATLANTA
Organized 9/2/65
2nd title:Atlanta & Lowry NB 2/6/24
3rd title:FNB of Atlanta 11/23/29
FIRST TITLE {{ 38 L }}
Original Series <$VALUE
4x5 1-4900 <$1500
3x10-20 1-6280<$2000/$2500
Series 1875
3x10-20 1-5338<$2000/$2500
Brown Back
3x10-20 1-14573 <$300/$350
1902 Red Seal
3x10-20 1-12200 <$850
1902 Date Back
4x5 1-71250 <$40
3x10-20 1-59000 <$50
1902 Plain Back
4x5 71251-186250 <$40
3x10-20 59001-130800 <$50
SECOND TITLE {{ 46 L 10 S }}
1902 Plain Back
4x5 1-101227 <$40
3x10-20 1-57503 <$50
1929 Small Size
5 Type 1 1-9988 <$65
10 Type 1 1-5022 <$65
20 Type 1 1-1690 <$75
THIRD TITLE {{ 50+ S }}
1929 Small Size
5 Type 1 1-122852 <$15
10 Type 1 1-67342 <$20
20 Type 1 1-22914 <$30
5 Type 2 1-185512 <$15
10 Type 2 1-77736 <$20
20 Type 2 1-38635 <$30
Total Issue $30,939,380
Out in 1933 $4,848,930
Large out 1935 $164,170
Outstanding includes Ch 5045
****

****
Atlanta & Lowry NB, Atlanta
SEE Ch 1559
Atlanta NB, Atlanta
****
5490 Fulton
CAPITAL CITY NB OF ATLANTA
{{ 1 L }}
Chartered 7/9/00
Liquidated 5/16/03
Brown Back <$VALUE
4x5 1-1425 <$1250
3x10-20 1-1104 <$1250
Total Issue $83,700
Out in 1910 $1,955
****
FNB of Atlanta
SEE Ch 1559
Atlanta NB, Atlanta
****
5045 Fulton
FOURTH NB OF ATLANTA
{{ 50+ L 9 S }}
Chartered 1896
Closed 11/23/29
Brown Back <$VALUE
4x5 1-28165 <$250
3x10-20 1-23234 <$250/$300
1882 Date Back
4x5 1-63500 <$250
3x10-20 1-40652 <$250/$300
1902 Plain Back
4x5 1-214036 <$40
3x10-20 1-136071 <$40/$50
1929 Small Size
5 Type 1 1-7441 <$150
10 Type 1 1-3052 <$150
20 Type 1 1-1020 <$150
Total Issue $16,640,620
Out at close $1,199,995
Large out at close $671,245
Ch 1559 assumed circulation
****
9617 Fulton
FULTON NB OF ATLANTA
{{ 36 L 28 S }}
Chartered 12/09
1902 Date Back <$VALUE
4x5 1-28750 <$50
3x10-20 1-22100 <$50/$60
1902 Plain Back
4x5 28751-121805 <$50
3x10-20 22101-77418<$50/$60
1929 Small Size
5 Type 1 1-14128 <$40
10 Type 1 1-7460 <$40
20 Type 1 1-1770 <$50
5 Type 2 1-26782 <$50
10 Type 2 1-14326 <$50
20 Type 2 1-3360 <$60
Total Issue $7,735,210
Out in 1935 $300,000
Large out 1935 $17,820
****
2424 Fulton
GATE CITY NB OF ATLANTA
{{ UNREPORTED }}
Chartered 5/3/79
Liquidated 7/25/93
Series 1875 <$VALUE
3x10-20 1-6374<$2500/$3000
50-100 1-839 <$8500
Total Issue $444,550
Out in 1910 $1,900
****
1605 Fulton
GEORGIA NB OF ATLANTA
{{ 2 L }}
Chartered 1865
Liquidated 5/31/77
Original Series <$VALUE
3x1-2 1-2160 <$1750/$4500
4x5 1-4400 <$1500
3x10-20 1-800 <$2000/$2500
Series 1875
4x5 1-155 <$1500
3x10-20 1-42 <$2000/$2500
Total Issue $144,000
Out in 1910 $1,143
****
5318 Fulton
LOWRY NB OF ATLANTA
{{ 50+ L }}
Chartered 5/1/00
Liquidated 1/2/23
Brown Back <$VALUE
4x5 1-36450 <$225
3x10-20 1-28020 <$225/$275
1882 Date Back
4x5 1-100000 <$175
3x10-20 1-71934 <$175/$225
1882 Value Back
4x5 100001-137957 <$175
3x10-20 71935-94818 <$175/$225
1902 Plain Back
4x5 1-45385 <$40
3x10-20 1-31630 <$40/$50
Total Issue $12,119,240
Out in 1922 $982,900
****
2064 Fulton
STATE NB OF ATLANTA
{{ UNREPORTED }}
Chartered 11/20/72
Liquidated 8/31/76
Original Series <$VALUE
4x5 1-2390 <$1500
3x10-20 1-1176<$2000/$2500
50-100 1-300 <$8500
Total Issue $151,600
Out in 1910 $415
****
5030 Fulton
THIRD NB OF ATLANTA
{{ 27 L }}
Chartered 1896
Liquidated 10/30/19
Brown Back <$VALUE
4x5 1-8250 <$250
3x10-20 1-16346 <$250/$300
1882 Date Back
4x5 1-38855 <$200
3x10-20 1-27897 <$200/$250
1902 Plain Back
4x5 1-25550 <$50
3x10-20 1-15348 <$50/$60
Total Issue $4,432,650
Out at close $700,000
****
1703 Richmond
MERCHANTS & PLANTERS NB OF AUGUSTA
{{ UNREPORTED }}
Chartered 8/26/70
Liquidated 3/30/75
Original Series <$VALUE
4x5 1-2590 <$2000
3x10-20 1-2298<$2500/$3500
50-100 1-350 <$8500
Total Issue $219,200
Out in 1910 $1,115
****
1613 Richmond
NB OF AUGUSTA
{{ 8 L }}
Chartered 1865
Liquidated 7/1/12
Original Series <$VALUE
4x5 1-6500 <$1000
3x10-20 1-7500<$1500/$2000
20 7501-9500 <$2000
3x10-20 9501-13500 <$1500/$2000
50-100 1-600 <$8500
Series 1875
4x5 1-2250 <$1000
3x10-20 1-4600<$1500/$2000
50-100 1-3000 <$8500
Brown Back
4x5 1-3000 <$450
3x10-20 1-8369 <$450/$500
1902 Red Seal
3x10-20 1-4100 <$1000
1902 Date Back
3x10-20 1-7115 <$250
Total Issue $2,599,200
Out at close $146,200
****
1860 Richmond
N EXCHANGE B OF AUGUSTA
{{ 50+ L 31 S }}
Chartered 8/10/71
Original Series <$VALUE
4x5 1-6500 <$1000
3x10-20 1-2300<$1500/$2000
50-100 1-800 <$8500
Series 1875
4x5 1-2466 <$1000
3x10-20 1-2687<$1500/$2000
50-100 1-1981 <$8500
Brown Back
4x5 1-12150 <$350
3x10-20 1-25840 <$350
1882 Date Back
4x5 1-9905 <$350
3x10-20 1-8355 <$350
1902 Date Back
4x5 1-21500 <$40
4x10 1-21500 <$40/$50
1902 Plain Back
4x5 21501-102173 <$40
4x10 21501-85076 <$40/$50
1929 Small Size
5 Type 1 1-22082 <$40
10 Type 1 1-12744 <$40
5 Type 2 1-28908 <$45
10 Type 2 1-31976 <$50
Total Issue $10,334,570
Out in 1935 $400,000
Large out 1935 $23,120
****
6004 Decatur
FNB OF BAINBRIDGE
{{ 10 L 20 S }}
Chartered 10/31/01
Brown Back <$VALUE
4x5 1-1415 <$500
3x10-20 1-1934 <$500
1882 Date Back
4x5 1-6800 <$500
3x10-20 1-5360 <$500
1882 Value Back
4x5 6801-11595 <$500
3x10-20 5361-8020 <$500
1902 Plain Back
4x5 1-16091 <$250
3x10-20 1-10349 <$250
1929 Small Size
5 Type 1 1-5910 <$110
10 Type 1 1-2776 <$110
20 Type 1 1-704 <$110
5 Type 2 1-7472 <$125
10 Type 2 1-4530 <$125
20 Type 2 1-959 <$125
Total Issue $2,127,350
Out in 1935 $125,000
Large out 1935 $5,940
****
12404 Lamar
CITIZENS NB OF BARNESVILLE
{{ UNREPORTED }}
Organized 6/15/23
Receivership 8/29/35
1902 Plain Back <$VALUE
4x5 1-3557 <$1500
1929 Small Size
5 Type 1 1-236 <$750
Total Issue $78,220
Out at close $8,370
Large out at close $1,290
****
6243 Lamar
FNB OF BARNESVILLE
{{ 7 L 5 S }}
Chartered 5/7/02
1902 Red Seal <$VALUE
4x5 1-1800 <$1250
3x10-20 1-1435 <$1250
1902 Date Back
4x5 1-4350 <$400
3x10-20 1-3160 <$400
1902 Plain Back (dated 1902)
4x5 4351-8650 <$400
3x10-20 3161-5760 <$400
1902 Plain Back (dated 1922)
4x5 1-3798 <$400
3x10-20 1-3779 <$400
1929 Small Size
5 Type 1 1-2062 <$250
10 Type 1 1-1124 <$250
20 Type 1 1-296 <$275
5 Type 2 1-4352 <$275
10 Type 2 1-2133 <$275
20 Type 2 1-684 <$275
Total Issue $1,055,250
Out in 1935 $50,000
Large out 1935 $3,560
****
7018 Early
FNB OF BLAKELY
{{ 5 L 6 S }}
Chartered 10/03
1902 Red Seal <$VALUE
3x10-20 1-2213 <$1500
1902 Date Back
4x5 1-3000 <$450
3x10-20 1-5000 <$450
1902 Plain Back
4x5 3001-8690 <$450
3x10-20 5001-8814 <$450
1929 Small Size
5 Type 1 1-1688 <$250
10 Type 1 1-902 <$250
20 Type 1 1-236 <$275
5 Type 2 1-3060 <$275
10 Type 2 1-1716 <$275
20 Type 2 1-444 <$275
Total Issue $899,570
Out in 1934 $38,950
Large out 1935 $2,350
****

****
6079 Fanin
NORTH GEORGIA NB OF
BLUE RIDGE
{{ 5 L }}
Chartered 1/2/02
Liquidated 6/15/16
Brown Back <$VALUE
4x5 1-1650 <$1000
3x10-20 1-1240 <$1000
1882 Date Back
4x5 1-3410 <$1000
3x10-20 1-2699 <$1000
Total Issue $298,150
Out in 1916 $25,295
****
4944 Glynn
NB OF BRUNSWICK
{{ 47 L 2U + 20 S }}
Chartered 1894
Brown Back <$VALUE
4x5 1-7750 <$400
3x10-20 1-7250 <$400
1882 Date Back
4x5 1-9875 <$400
3x10-20 1-6811 <$400
1902 Date Back
4x5 1-4250 <$60
3x10-20 1-3600 <$60/$75
1902 Plain Back
4x5 4251-35351 <$60
3x10-20 3601-22771<$60/$75
1929 Small Size
5 Type 1 1-6416 <$100
10 Type 1 1-3546 <$100
20 Type 1 1-894 <$110
5 Type 2 1-11712 <$110
10 Type 2 1-6168 <$110
20 Type 2 1-1596 <$120
Total Issue $3,565,800
Out in 1935 $150,000
Large out 1935 $8,580
****
3753 Glynn
OGLETHORPE NB OF
BRUNSWICK
{{ UNREPORTED }}
Chartered 7/16/87
Receivership 6/12/93
Brown Back <$VALUE
3x10-20 1-1458 <$2000
Total Issue $72,900
Out in 1916 $350
****
7963 Marion
FNB OF BUENA VISTA
{{ 4 L }}
Organized 10/12/05
Receivership 1/26/25
1902 Red Seal <$VALUE
3x10-20 1-1100 <$1500
1902 Date Back
3x10-20 1-4100 <$600
1902 Plain Back
3x10-20 4101-9484 <$600
Total Issue $529,200
Out at close $48,400
****
9607 Dooly
BYROM NB OF BYROMVILLE
{{ 2 L }}
Chartered 12/09
Liquidated 5/23/18
1902 Date Back <$VALUE
4x5 1-1350 <$850
3x10-20 1-1100 <$850
1902 Plain Back
4x5 1351-1565 <$850
3x10-20 1101-1251 <$850
Total Issue $93,850
Out at close $6,250
****
7549 Gordon
CALHOUN NB, CALHOUN
{{ 3 L 6 S }}
Chartereu 1/05
1902 Red Seal <$VALUE
4x5 1-1750 <$1500
3x10-20 1-1540 <$1500
1902 Date Back
4x5 1-4300 <$600
3x10-20 1-3020 <$600
1902 Plain Back
4x5 4301-13581 <$600
3x10-20 3021-8492 <$600
1929 Small Size
5 Type 1 1-1402 <$250
10 Type 1 1-848 <$250
20 Type 1 1-210 <$250
5 Type 2 1-4376 <$275
10 Type 2 1-2592 <$275
20 Type 2 1-612 <$275
Total Issue $986,400
Out in 1935 $50,000
Large out 1935 $2,290
****
5264 Carroll
FNB OF CARROLLTON
{{ 21 L 3 S }}
Chartered 3/9/00
Liquidated 1/13/31
Brown Back <$VALUE
3x10-20 1-2630 <$600
1882 Date Back
3x10-20 1-10400 <$600
1882 Value Back
3x10-20 10401-13493 <$600
1902 Plain Back
3x10-20 1-14243 <$200
1929 Small Size
10 Type 1 1-1213 <$350
20 Type 1 1-368 <$375
Total Issue $1,635,240
Out at close $100,000
Large out at close $17,330
****
12635 Bartow
CARTERSVILLE NB,
CARTERSVILLE
{{ 12 L }}
Chartered 2/25
Closed 7/5/29
1902 Plain Back <$VALUE
4x5 1-9490 <$225
3x10-20 1-6213 <$225
Total Issue $500,450
Out at close $100,000
Ch 4012 assumed circulation
****
4012 Bartow
FNB OF CARTERSVILLE
{{ 9 L 25 S }}
Chartered 4/18/89
Brown Back <$VALUE
4x5 1-3628 <$600
3x10-20 1-1189 <$600
1902 Date Back
4x5 1-3725 <$250
3x10-20 1-2970 <$250
1902 Plain Back
4x5 3726-14219 <$250
3x10-20 2971-9967 <$250
1929 Small Size
5 Type 1 1-8484 <$85
10 Type 1 1-4420 <$85
20 Type 1 1-1132 <$100
5 Type 2 1-16500 <$110
10 Type 2 1-8129 <$110
20 Type 2 1-1962 <$110
Total Issue $1,773,330
Out in 1935 $200,000
Large out 1935 $5,565
Outstanding includes Ch 12635
****
4075 Polk
FNB OF CEDARTOWN
{{ 1 L }}
Chartered 7/16/89
Receivership 7/26/93
Brown Back <$VALUE
3x10-20 1-554 <$1500
Total Issue $27,700
Out in 1916 $210
****
11833 Polk
LIBERTY NB OF CEDARTOWN
{{ 2 L 19 S }}
Chartered 9/20
1902 Plain Back <$VALUE
4x5 1-4382 <$850
3x10-20 1-2778 <$850
1929 Small Size
5 Type 1 1-2728 <$150
10 Type 1 1-1476 <$150
20 Type 1 1-456 <$165
5 Type 2 1-9444 <$175
10 Type 2 1-4428 <$175
20 Type 2 1-1284 <$175
Total Issue $568,780
Out in 1935 $100,000
Large out 1935 $560
****
10333 Evans
FNB OF CLAXTON
{{ 0 L 3 S }}
Organized 2/10/13
Liquidated 9/17/34
1902 Date Back <$VALUE
3x10-20 1-800 <$1500
1902 Plain Back
3x10-20 801-1687 <$1500
1929 Small Size
10 Type 1 1-176 <$500
20 Type 1 1-45 <$500
Total Issue $100,310
Out at close $6,250
Large out at close $540
****
7567 Bleckley
FNB OF COCHRAN
{{ 1 L }}
Chartered 1/05
Liquidated 2/21/16
1902 Red Seal <$VALUE
3x10-20 1-1240 <$2000
1902 Date Back
3x10-20 1-2470 <$1000
1902 Plain Back
3x10-20 2471-2496 <$1000
Total Issue $186,800
Out in 1916 $13,105
****
9254 Miller
COLQUITT NB, COLQUITT
{{ UNREPORTED }}
Chartered 10/08
Liquidated 6/15/17
1902 Date Back <$VALUE
4x5 1-1400 <$1500
3x10-20 1-1112 <$1500
Total Issue $83,600
Out at close $10,000
Ch 6498 assumed circulation
****
6498 Miller
FNB OF COLQUITT
{{ 3 L }}
Chartered 11/21/02
Receivership 8/14/23
1902 Red Seal <$VALUE
3x10-20 1-676 <$1500
1902 Date Back
3x10-20 1-1580 <$650
1902 Plain Back
3x10-20 1581-2105 <$650
Total Issue $139,050
Out at close $9,700
Outstanding includes Ch 9254
****
1630 Columbus
CHATTAHOOCHE NB OF
COLUMBUS
{{ UNREPORTED }}
Chartered 1/22/66
Receivership 12/7/95
Original Series <$VALUE
4x5 1-3850 <$2000
3x10-20 1-1900<$2500/$3000
Series 1875
4x5 1-500 <$2000
3x10-20 1-2550<$2500/$3000
Brown Back
3x10-20 1-2728 <$1500
Total Issue $445,900
Out in 1916 $2,160
****
FNB of Columbus
SEE Ch 2338
NB of Columbus
****
4691 Columbus
FOURTH NB OF COLUMBUS
{{ 10 L 10 S }}
Chartered 1892
Brown Back <$VALUE
3x10-20 1-6800 <$450
50-100 1-1327 <$2500
1882 Date Back
3x10-20 1-3551 <$450
1902 Date Back
3x10-20 1-19000 <$200
1902 Plain Back
3x10-20 19001-54185 <$200
1929 Small Size
5 Type 2 1-10912 <$85
10 Type 2 1-11622 <$85
20 Type 2 1-6566 <$85
Total Issue $3,727,950
Out in 1935 $200,000
Large out 1935 $3,385
****
2338 Columbus
NB OF COLUMBUS
Chartered 7/15/76
2nd title:FNB of Columbus
4/1/20
FIRST TITLE {{ 16 L }}
Series 1875 <$VALUE
4x5 1-2300 <$1500
3x10-20 1-3667<$2000/$2500
50-100 1-500 <$8500
Brown Back
4x5 1-10400 <$400
4x10 1-3625 <$400
3x10-20 1-5200 <$400
1882 Date Back
4x5 1-19014 <$400
4x10 1-19761 <$400
1902 Plain Back
4x5 1-10030 <$150
4x10 1-7185 <$150
SECOND TITLE {{ 14 L 18 S }}
1902 Plain Back
4x5 1-34125 <$150
4x10 1-29863 <$150
1929 Small Size
5 Type 1 1-13874 <$75
10 Type 1 1-7148 <$75
5 Type 2 1-31500 <$85
10 Type 2 1-17952 <$85
Total Issue $5,635,210
Out in 1935 $200,000
Large out 1935 $10,385
****
3937 Columbus
THIRD NB OF COLUMBUS
{{ 15 L }}
Chartered 10/31/88
Liquidated 5/31/30
Brown Back <$VALUE
4x5 1-9028 <$400
3x10-20 1-9600 <$400
50-100 1-1278 <$2500
1902 Date Back
4x5 1-18500 <$150
4x10 1-36500 <$150
1902 Plain Back
4x5 18501-55410 <$150
4x10 36501-69543 <$150
Total Issue $4,742,180
Out at close $19,295
****
7431 Jackson
FNB OF COMMERCE
{{ 5 L 6 S }}
Chartered 10/04
1902 Red Seal <$VALUE
4x5 1-1775 <$1500
3x10-20 1-1380 <$1500
1902 Date Back
4x5 1-3600 <$450
3x10-20 1-2820 <$450
1902 Plain Back
4x5 3601-10023 <$450
3x10-20 2821-7028 <$450
1929 Small Size
5 Type 1 1-2004 <$225
10 Type 1 1-1030 <$225
20 Type 1 1-286 <$225
5 Type 2 1-3588 <$250
10 Type 2 1-1993 <$250
20 Type 2 1-684 <$250
Total Issue $864,150
Out in 1935 $50,000
Large out 1935 $2,220
****
11255 Rockdale
FNB OF CONYERS
{{ 1 L }}
Organized 9/3/18
Receivership 5/12/25
1902 Plain Back <$VALUE
4x5 1-3360 <$1250
3x10-20 1-2408 <$1250
Total Issue $187,600
Out at close $27,700
****
9074 Crisp
AMERICAN NB OF CORDELE
{{ 1 L }}
Chartered 3/08
Liquidated 1/27/19
1902 Red Seal <$VALUE
4x5 1-600 <$1500
4x10 1-650 <$1500
1902 Date Back
4x5 1-10250 <$850
4x10 1-9750 <$850
1902 Plain Back
4x5 10251-13939 <$850
4x10 9751-13019 <$850
Total Issue $837,540
Out at close $100,000
****
5975 Crisp
CORDELE NB, CORDELE
{{ 10 L }}
Chartered 9/24/01
Liquidated 2/28/17
Brown Back <$VALUE
4x5 1-2150 <$600
3x10-20 1-1650 <$600
1882 Date Back
4x5 1-4825 <$600
3x10-20 1-3976 <$600
Total Issue $420,800
Out at close $50,000
****
****
14257 Crisp
FNB IN CORDELE
{{ 2 S }}
Chartered 8/34
1929 Small Size <$VALUE
5 Type 2 1-5572 <$600
10 Type 2 1-3144 <$600
Total Issue $59,300
Out in 1935 $50,000
****
4554 Crisp
FNB OF CORDELE
{{ 1 L }}
Chartered 4/16/91
Receivership 3/4/99
Brown Back <$VALUE
4x5 1-1723 <$1500
Total Issue $34,460
Out in 1916 $205
****
9613 Habersham
FNB OF CORNELIA
{{ 4 L 10 S }}
Chartered 12/09
1902 Date Back <$VALUE
4x5 1-2100 <$600
3x10-20 1-1640 <$600
1902 Plain Back
4x5 2101-8414 <$600
3x10-20 1641-5526 <$600
1929 Small Size
5 Type 1 1-1304 <$200
10 Type 1 1-638 <$200
20 Type 1 1-214 <$225
5 Type 2 1-1404 <$250
10 Type 2 1-708 <$250
20 Type 2 1-240 <$275
Total Issue $566,560
Out in 1935 $30,000
Large out 1935 $1,500
****
8945 Newton
FNB OF COVINGTON
{{ 3 L }}
Organized 10/28/07
Receivership 12/8/25
1902 Red Seal <$VALUE
4x5 1-400 <$1500
3x10-20 1-440 <$1500
1902 Date Back
4x5 1-4150 <$650
3x10-20 1-3020 <$650
1902 Plain Back
4x5 4151-9980 <$650
3x10-20 3021-6900 <$650
Total Issue $574,600
Out at close $40,000
****
10279 Randolph
FNB OF CUTHBERT
{{ UNREPORTED }}
Chartered 10/12
Liquidated 12/26/16
1902 Date Back <$VALUE
4x10 1-3400 <$1500
1902 Plain Back
4x10 3401-4248 <$1500
Total Issue $169,920
Out at close $48,300
****
3907 Whitfield
FNB OF DALTON
{{ 8 L 14 S }}
Chartered 7/10/88
Brown Back <$VALUE
4x5 1-3575 <$750
3x10-20 1-1322 <$750
1902 Red Seal
4x10 1-625 <$1250
1902 Date Back
4x10 1-5525 <$300
1902 Plain Back
4x10 5526-31087 <$300
1929 Small Size
10 Type 1 1-5900 <$100
10 Type 2 1-9655 <$110
Total Issue $1,856,630
Out in 1935 $100,000
Large out 1935 $3,670
****
6496 Whitfield
CITY NB OF DAWSON
{{ 17 L 9 S }}
Chartered 11/20/02
Receivership 11/14/32
1902 Red Seal <$VALUE
3x10-20 1-4340 <$1000
1902 Date Back
3x10-20 1-10900 <$175
1902 Plain Back
3x10-20 10901-28341 <$175
1929 Small Size
10 Type 1 1-2085 <$125
20 Type 1 1-559 <$125
Total Issue $1,826,230
Out at close $100,000
Large out at close $21,120
Outstanding includes Ch 4115
****
4115 Terrell
DAWSON NB, DAWSON
{{ 13 L 9 S }}
Chartered 9/10/89
Closed 12/29/31
Brown Back <$VALUE
4x5 1-4175 <$500
3x10-20 1-2810 <$500
1882 Date Back
4x5 1-746 <$500
3x10-20 1-539 <$500
1902 Date Back
3x10-20 1-10200 <$175
1902 Plain Back
3x10-20 10201-26894 <$175
1929 Small Size
10 Type 1 1-1987 <$150
20 Type 1 1-523 <$165
Total Issue $1,785,050
Out at close $100,000
Large out at close $14,590
Ch 6496 assumed circulation
****
8128 Laurens
CITY NB OF DUBLIN
{{ 1 L }}
Chartered 3/06
Liquidated 12/15/16
1902 Red Seal <$VALUE
3x10-20 1-2000 <$1500
1902 Date Back
3x10-20 1-2020 <$1250
Total Issue $201,000
Out at close $25,000
****
6374 Laurens
FNB OF DUBLIN
{{ 17 L }}
Chartered 8/11/02
Receivership 9/24/28
1902 Red Seal <$VALUE
3x10-20 1-1730 <$1250
1902 Date Back
3x10-20 1-17500 <$175
1902 Plain Back
3x10-20 17501-47676 <$175
Total Issue $2,470,300
Out at close $102,110
****
9593 Dodge
FNB OF EASTMAN
{{ UNREPORTED }}
Chartered 11/09
Liquidated 12/31/18
1902 Date Back <$VALUE
3x10-20 1-3923* <$1500
* 3191-3923 not marked
Total Issue $196,150
Out at close $25,000
****
14061 Elbert
FNB IN ELBERTON
{{ 1 S }}
Chartered 3/34
1929 Small Size <$VALUE
5 Type 2 1-3636 <$600
10 Type 2 1-1944 <$600
Total Issue $37,620
Out in 1935 $20,570
****
9252 Elbert
FNB OF ELBERTON
{{ 21 L 29 S }}
Organized 7/27/08
Liquidated 4/25/34
1902 Date Back <$VALUE
4x5 1-3450 <$165
3x10-20 1-2800 <$165
1902 Plain Back
4x5 3451-19451 <$165
3x10-20 2801-12053 <$165
1929 Small Size
5 Type 1 1-3712 <$100
10 Type 1 1-1826 <$85
20 Type 1 1-456 <$110
5 Type 2 1-2396 <$110
10 Type 2 1-1325 <$125
20 Type 2 1-182 <$135
Total Issue $1,296,180
Out at close $80,000
Large out at close $4,490
****

****
8250 Ben Hill
EXCHANGE NB OF FITZGERALD
{{ 14 L 3 S }}
Organized 5/9/06
Receivership 1/31/31
1902 Red Seal <$VALUE
4x5 1-3175 <$1000
3x10-20 1-2745 <$1000
50-100 1-45 <$5000
1902 Date Back
4x5 1-9250 <$250
3x10-20 1-7100 <$250
50-100 1-100 <$850/$1000
1902 Plain Back
4x5 9251-28920 <$250
3x10-20 7101-20094 <$250
1929 Small Size
5 Type 1 1-1914 <$325
10 Type 1 1-951 <$325
20 Type 1 1-255 <$350
Total Issue $1,950,680
Out at close $97,295
Large out at close $15,695
****
6082 Ben Hill
FNB OF FITZGERALD
{{ 17 L 3 S }}
Chartered 1/4/02
Receivership 1/31/31
Brown Back <$VALUE
3x10-20 1-5800 <$500
1882 Date Back
3x10-20 1-13000 <$500
1882 Value Back
3x10-20 13001-16844 <$500
1902 Plain Back
3x10-20 1-11265 <$225
1929 Small Size
10 Type 1 1-1360 <$350
20 Type 1 1-364 <$350
Total Issue $1,820,730
Out at close $97,660
Large out at close $18,870
****
13550 Ben Hill
NB OF FITZGERALD
{{ 4 S }}
Organized 5/18/31
1929 Small Size <$VALUE
5 Type 1 1-1262 <$275
10 Type 1 1-517 <$275
20 Type 1 1-212 <$275
Total Issue $94,320
Out in 1935 $48,350
****
8966 Ben Hill
THIRD NB OF FITZGERALD
{{ 1 L }}
Organized 12/17/07
Receivership 3/6/16
1902 Red Seal <$VALUE
3x10-20 1-760 <$1250
1902 Date Back
3x10-20 1-5040 <$850
1902 Plain Back
4x10 1-517 <$850
Total Issue $310,680
Out in 1916 $20,305
****
5644 Monroe
FNB OF FORSYTH
{{ UNREPORTED }}
Chartered 12/17/00
Liquidated 1/11/16
Brown Back <$VALUE
3x10-20 1-2170 <$1500
1882 Date Back
3x10-20 1-2153 <$1500
Total Issue $216,150
Out in 1916 $9,260
****
6002 Clay
FNB OF FORT GAINES
{{ 5 L 1 S }}
Organized 10/3/01
Receivership 12/19/32
Brown Back <$VALUE
3x10-20 1-920 <$1000
1882 Date Back
3x10-20 1-2096 <$1000
1902 Plain Back
3x10-20 1-1551 <$500
1929 Small Size
10 Type 1 1-272 <$600
20 Type 1 1-86 <$600
Total Issue $254,990
Out at close $9,350
Large out at close $1,760
****

****
7459 Peach
FNB OF FORT VALLEY
{{ 3 L }}
Chartered 10/04
Liquidated 12/15/15
1902 Red Seal <$VALUE
3x10-20 1-625 <$1500
1902 Date Back
3x10-20 1-2540 <$750
1902 Plain Back
3x10-20 2541-2578 <$750
Total Issue $160,150
Out in 1916 $12,120
****
3983 Hall
FNB OF GAINESVILLE
{{ 4 L 2U + 6 S }}
Chartered 3/6/89
Brown Back <$VALUE
3x10-20 1-4565 <$850
1902 Date Back
3x10-20 1-6800 <$400
1902 Plain Back
3x10-20 6801-13983 <$400
1929 Small Size
10 Type 1 1-1538 <$225
20 Type 1 1-406 <$225
10 Type 2 1-2491 <$250
20 Type 2 1-617 <$250
Total Issue $1,105,650
Out in 1935 $50,000
Large out 1935 $3,130
****
7616 Hall
GAINESVILLE NB,
GAINESVILLE
{{ 4 L 6 S }}
Organized 1/3/05
1902 Red Seal <$VALUE
4x5 1-1486 <$1250
3x10-20 1-1188 <$1250
1902 Date Back
4x5 1-3950 <$400
3x10-20 1-3000 <$400
1902 Plain Back
4x5 3951-9150 <$400
3x10-20 3001-10634 <$400
1929 Small Size
10 Type 1 1-1466 <$225
20 Type 1 1-426 <$225
10 Type 2 1-2688 <$250
20 Type 2 1-828 <$250
Total Issue $986,340
Out in 1935 $49,995
Large out 1935 $2,525
****
8452 Greene
COPELAND NB OF GREENSBORO
{{ 7 L }}
Chartered 12/06
Closed 7/30/24
1902 Red Seal <$VALUE
3x10-20 1-1300 <$1250
1902 Date Back
3x10-20 1-4360 <$300
1902 Plain Back
3x10-20 4361-9753 <$300
Total Issue $552,650
Out at close $50,000
Ch 6967 assumed circulation
****
6967 Greene
GREENSBOROUGH NB,
GREENSBOROUGH
{{ 5 L }}
Organized 8/1/03
Receivership 1/9/26
1902 Red Seal <$VALUE
3x10-20 1-1600 <$1250
1902 Date Back
3x10-20 1-4500 <$400
1902 Plain Back
3x10-20 4501-9762 <$400
Total Issue $568,100
Out in 1924 $9,995
Outstanding includes Ch 8452
****
2075 Spalding
CITY NB OF GRIFFIN
Chartered 1/20/73
Liquidated 1/13/31
2nd title:FNB of Griffin
12/31/27
FIRST TITLE {{ 6 L }}
Original Series <$VALUE
3x1-2 1-1500 <$1750/$4500
4x5 1-2625 <$1500
Series 1875
4x5 1-9162 <$1500

Brown Back
3x10-20 1-2780 <$600
1882 Date Back
3x10-20 1-2236 <$600
1902 Date Back
4x10 1-3625 <$350
3x50-100 1-300 <$850/$1000
1902 Plain Back
4x10 3626-16087 <$350
SECOND TITLE {{ 1 L 3 S }}
1902 Plain Back
4x10 1-2008 <$500
1929 Small Size
10 Type 1 1-1907 <$350
Total Issue $1,407,260
Out at close $70,000
Large out at close $9,010
****
FNB of Griffin
SEE Ch 2075
City NB of Griffin
****
11597 Spalding
SECOND NB OF GRIFFIN
{{ 7 L }}
Chartered 2/20
Liquidated 7/17/28
1902 Plain Back <$VALUE
3x10-20 1-14430 <$350
Total Issue $721,500
Out at close $100,000
****
10089 Henry
FNB OF HAMPTON
{{ 1 L }}
Organized 7/13/11
Receivership 1/27/25
1902 Date Back <$VALUE
4x10 1-2225 <$1250
1902 Plain Back
4x10 2226-7255 <$1250
Total Issue $290,200
Out at close $20,000
****
11695 Hart
FNB OF HARTWELL
{{ 11 L 6 S }}
Organized 3/17/20
Receivership 3/8/32
1902 Plain Back <$VALUE
4x5 1-11824 <$275
3x10-20 1-7561 <$275
1929 Small Size
5 Type 1 1-1892 <$225
10 Type 1 1-914 <$225
20 Type 1 1-250 <$250
Total Issue $756,130
Out at close $75,000
Large out at close $5,780
****
7580 Pulaski
FNB OF HAWKINSVILLE
{{ 5 L }}
Chartered 1/05
Liquidated 3/19/24
1902 Red Seal <$VALUE
3x10-20 1-2600 <$1250
1902 Date Back
3x10-20 1-4600 <$450
1902 Plain Back
3x10-20 4601-9885 <$450
Total Issue $624,250
Out at close $50,000
****
5709 Butts
FNB OF JACKSON
{{ UNREPORTED }}
Chartered 2/12/01
Liquidated 8/28/19
Brown Back <$VALUE
4x5 1-950 <$1500
3x10-20 1-660 <$1500
1882 Date Back
4x5 1-2300 <$1500
3x10-20 1-1840 <$1500
1882 Value Back
4x5 2301-3665 <$1500
3x10-20 1841-2827 <$1500
Total Issue $266,650
Out at close $20,000
****
9186 Butts
JACKSON NB, JACKSON
{{ 16 L 6 S }}
Organized 3/19/08
Liquidated 2/20/34
1902 Date Back <$VALUE
4x5 1-8350 <$250
3x10-20 1-6920 <$250
1902 Plain Back
4x5 8351-23616 <$250
3x10-20 6921-16273 <$250

1929 Small Size
5 Type 1 1-2992 <$175
10 Type 1 1-1622 <$175
20 Type 1 1-390 <$185
5 Type 2 1-1632 <$200
10 Type 2 1-956 <$200
20 Type 2 1-132 <$225
Total Issue $1,540,210
Out in 1934 $75,000
Large out 1935 $5,570
Ch 13897 assumed circulation
****
13897 Butts
JACKSON NB, JACKSON
{{ 3U + 1 S }}
Chartered 12/33
1929 Small Size <$VALUE
5 Type 2 1-282 <$350
10 Type 2 1-150 <$350
20 Type 2 1-70 <$350
Total Issue $4,310
Out in 1935 $25,000
Outstanding includes Ch 9186
****
9039 Jackson
FNB OF JEFFERSON
{{ 19 L 20 S }}
Chartered 2/08
1902 Red Seal <$VALUE
3x10-20 1-300 <$1250
1902 Date Back
3x10-20 1-4150 <$200
1902 Plain Back
3x10-20 4151-18526 <$200
1929 Small Size
10 Type 1 1-3072 <$125
20 Type 1 1-854 <$125
10 Type 2 1-4308 <$150
20 Type 2 1-1297 <$150
Total Issue $1,297,120
Out in 1935 $100,000
Large out 1935 $5,020
****
7247 Walker
FNB OF LA FAYETTE
{{ UNREPORTED }}
Organized 5/7/04
Receivership 7/19/13
1902 Red Seal <$VALUE
3x10-20 1-1700 <$2000
1902 Date Back
3x10-20 1-82 <$1750
Total Issue $89,100
Out in 1916 $1,950
****
3093 Troup
FNB OF LA GRANGE
{{ UNREPORTED }}
Chartered 12/20/83
Liquidated 12/1/91
Brown Back <$VALUE
4x5 1-1829 <$2000
Total Issue $36,580
Out in 1910 $245
****
7762 Troup
LA GRANGE NB, LA GRANGE
{{ 14 L 21 S }}
Chartered 5/05
1902 Red Seal <$VALUE
4x5 1-4000 <$1250
3x10-20 1-3200 <$1250
1902 Date Back
4x5 1-14000 <$200
3x10-20 1-10000 <$200
1902 Plain Back
4x5 14001-46548 <$200
3x10-20 10001-29827 <$200
1929 Small Size
5 Type 1 1-6586 <$85
10 Type 1 1-3582 <$85
20 Type 1 1-924 <$100
5 Type 2 1-12132 <$100
10 Type 2 1-6180 <$100
20 Type 2 1-1764 <$100
Total Issue $3,343,430
Out in 1935 $150,000
Large out 1935 $7,385
****
FNB of Lavonia
SEE Ch 8470
Vickery NB of Lavonia
****
8470 Franklin
VICKERY NB OF LAVONIA
Chartered 12/06
2nd title: FNB of Lavonia
1/10/13
FIRST TITLE {{ 1 L }}
1902 Red Seal <$VALUE
3x10-20 1-340 <$1500

1902 Date Back
3x10-20 1-1305 <$850
SECOND TITLE {{ 14 L 14 S }}
1902 Date Back
3x10-20 1-3000 <$200
1902 Plain Back
3x10-20 3001-16813 <$200
1929 Small Size
10 Type 1 1-2086 <$110
20 Type 1 1-598 <$125
10 Type 2 1-1611 <$125
20 Type 2 1-440 <$125
Total Issue $1,144,730
Out in 1935 $50,000
Large out 1935 $4,240
****
11936 Gwinnett
FNB OF LAWRENCEVILLE
{{ 1 S }}
Chartered 2/21
1929 Small Size <$VALUE
5 Type 2 1-3530 <$500
10 Type 2 1-1675 <$500
20 Type 2 1-565 <$500
Total Issue $45,700
Out in 1935 $25,000
****
6207 Jefferson
FNB OF LOUISVILLE
{{ 4 L 5 S }}
Chartered 4/14/02
1902 Red Seal <$VALUE
4x5 1-1275 <$1500
3x10-20 1-1000 <$1500
1902 Date Back
4x5 1-3380 <$500
3x10-20 1-3110 <$500
1902 Plain Back (dated 1922)
4x5 1-3525 <$500
1929 Small Size
5 Type 1 1-1584 <$275
5 Type 2 1-24750 <$275
Total Issue $540,370
Out in 1935 $50,000
Large out 1935 $965
****
7979 Toombs
FNB OF LYONS
{{ 2 L 3 S }}
Organized 8/30/05
Receivership 9/3/31
1902 Red Seal <$VALUE
3x10-20 1-930 <$1500
1902 Date Back
3x10-20 1-2550 <$650
1902 Plain Back
3x10-20 2551-7187 <$650
1929 Small Size
10 Type 1 1-442 <$300
20 Type 1 1-113 <$300
Total Issue $445,930
Out at close $25,000
Large out at close $2,950
****
4547 Bibb
AMERICAN NB OF MACON
{{ 13 L }}
Chartered 1891
Liquidated 12/8/16
Brown Back <$VALUE
4x5 1-11500 <$500
3x10-20 1-5800 <$500
50-100 1-2488 <$2500
1882 Date Back
4x5 1-6890 <$500
3x10-20 1-3977 <$500
50-100 1-64 <$2500
1902 Date Back
4x5 1-26250 <$175
4x10 1-25250 <$175
1902 Plain Back
4x5 26251-31217 <$175
4x10 25251-29564 <$175
Total Issue $3,046,350
Out in 1916 $498,000
Outstanding includes Ch 9212
****
10945 Bibb
BIBB NB OF MACON
{{ 10 L }}
Chartered 1/17
Liquidated 2/10/26
1902 Plain Back <$VALUE
3x10-20 1-24018 <$250
Total Issue $1,200,900
Out at close $200,000
****

****
8990 Bibb
CITIZENS NB OF MACON
{{ U + 5 L }}
Chartered 1/08
Liquidated 11/11/16
1902 Red Seal <$VALUE
4x5 1-4750 <$1250
3x10-20 1-3800 <$1250
1902 Date Back
4x5 1-24000 <$400
3x10-20 1-18100 <$400
1902 Plain Back
4x5 24001-25335 <$400
3x10-20 18101-19092 <$400
Total Issue $1,746,300
Out in 1916 $250,000
****
9212 Bibb
COMMERCIAL NB OF MACON
{{ 2 L }}
Chartered 8/08
Liquidated 9/30/14
1902 Date Back <$VALUE
4x5 1-15026 <$600
4x10 1-13565 <$600
Total Issue $843,120
Out at close $200,000
Ch 4547 assumed circulation
****
1617 Bibb
FNB OF MACON
{{ 3 L }}
Organized 12/9/65
Receivership 5/16/04
Original Series <$VALUE
4x5 1-3500 <$1500
3x10-20 1-1700<$2000/$2500
Series 1875
3x10-20 1-3100<$2000/$2500
Brown Back
3x10-20 1-6122 <$650
50-100 1-1911 <$2500
Total Issue $902,750
Out in 1916 $7,190
****
FNB & TC in Macon
SEE Ch 10270
Macon NB, Macon
****
8365 Bibb
FOURTH NB OF MACON
{{ 17 L }}
Organized 8/2/06
Receivership 11/26/20
1902 Red Seal <$VALUE
3x10-20 1-8500 <$1000
1902 Date Back
3x10-20 1-32500 <$150
1902 Plain Back
3x10-20 32501-63795 <$150
Total Issue $3,614,750
Out at close $33,660
****
10270 Bibb
MACON NB, MACON
Chartered 9/12
2nd title:FNB & TC in Macon
8/30/30
FIRST TITLE {{ 18 L 6 S }}
1902 Date Back <$VALUE
4x5 1-7100 <$165
3x10-20 1-5680 <$165
1902 Plain Back
4x5 7101-34005 <$165
3x10-20 5681-22378 <$165
1929 Small Size
5 Type 1 1-3596 <$125
10 Type 1 1-1706 <$125
20 Type 1 1-572 <$135
SECOND TITLE {{ 24 S }}
1929 Small Size
5 Type 1 1-6386 <$75
10 Type 1 1-2330 <$75
20 Type 1 1-552 <$85
5 Type 2 1-20888 <$85
10 Type 2 1-10098 <$85
20 Type 2 1-2220 <$85
Total Issue $2,725,320
Out in 1935 $200,000
Large out 1935 $1,165
****

<$VALUEs are for notes in FINE condition. Value changes by approximately 25% for a change of one full grade.

****
3740 Bibb
MERCHANTS NB OF MACON
{{ UNREPORTED }}
Chartered 6/29/87
Liquidated 2/14/93
Brown Back <$VALUE
3x10-20 1-1050 <$1500
Total Issue $52,500
Out in 1910 $340
****
7300 Morgan
FNB OF MADISON
{{ 15 L U + 17 S }}
Chartered 6/04
1902 Red Seal <$VALUE
3x10-20 1-3600 <$1250
1902 Date Back
3x10-20 1-9600 <$225
1902 Plain Back
3x10-20 9601-34948 <$225
1929 Small Size
10 Type 1 1-2886 <$125
20 Type 1 1-784 <$150
10 Type 2 1-6104 <$150
20 Type 2 1-1572 <$150
Total Issue $2,287,120
Out in 1935 $100,000
Large out 1935 $6,460
****
3830 Cobb
FNB OF MARIETTA
{{ 6 L 7 S }}
Chartered 12/30/87
Brown Back <$VALUE
4x5 1-5036 <$750
3x10-20 1-2413 <$750
1902 Red Seal
4x5 1-500 <$1250
3x10-20 1-300 <$1250
1902 Date Back
4x5 1-6450 <$400
3x10-20 1-5120 <$400
1902 Plain Back
4x5 6451-22115 <$400
3x10-20 5121-15038 <$400
1929 Small Size
5 Type 1 1-3206 <$200
10 Type 1 1-1782 <$200
20 Type 1 1-466 <$200
5 Type 2 1-4418 <$225
10 Type 2 1-2424 <$225
20 Type 2 1-528 <$225
Total Issue $1,756,600
Out in 1935 $50,000
Large out 1935 $4,225
****
7986 Banks
ATKINS NB OF MAYSVILLE
{{ 2 L }}
Chartered 11/05
Liquidated 12/2/25
1902 Red Seal <$VALUE
3x10-20 1-1200 <$1500
1902 Date Back
3x10-20 1-2360 <$750
1902 Plain Back
3x10-20 2361-5486 <$750
Total Issue $334,300
Out at close $25,000
****
7969 Henry
FNB OF McDONOUGH
{{ 9 L 9 S }}
Organized 10/28/05
1902 Red Seal <$VALUE
3x10-20 1-1405 <$1250
1902 Date Back
3x10-20 1-6150 <$300
1902 Plain Back
3x10-20 6151-19320 <$300
1929 Small Size
10 Type 1 1-1992 <$175
20 Type 1 1-598 <$175
10 Type 2 1-4061 <$200
20 Type 2 1-893 <$200
Total Issue $1,285,750
Out in 1935 $70,000
Large out 1935 $3,710
****
9672 Baldwin
FNB OF MILLEDGEVILLE
{{ 14 L U + 14 S }}
Chartered 2/10
1902 Date Back <$VALUE
3x10-20 1-3520 <$275
1902 Plain Back
3x10-20 3521-16322 <$275
1929 Small Size
10 Type 1 1-2190 <$150
20 Type 1 1-656 <$150
10 Type 2 1-2209 <$150
20 Type 2 1-510 <$160
Total Issue $1,058,510
Out in 1935 $37,500
Large out 1935 $3,730
****
9088 Jenkins
FNB OF MILLEN
{{ 2 L 2 S }}
Organized 3/17/08
Receivership 6/26/34
1902 Red Seal <$VALUE
3x10-20 1-188 <$1500
1902 Date Back
3x10-20 1-2520* <$750
1902 Plain Back
3x10-20 2651-7146* <$750
* 2521-2650 not marked
1929 Small Size
10 Type 1 1-842 <$550
20 Type 1 1-216 <$550
10 Type 2 1-259 <$600
20 Type 2 1-92 <$600
Total Issue $447,570
Out at close $24,650
Large out at close $1,900
****
6576 Macon
FNB OF MONTEZUMA
{{ 1 L }}
Chartered 1/03
Liquidated 4/14/21
1902 Red Seal <$VALUE
3x10-20 1-750 <$2000
1902 Date Back
3x10-20 1-3110 <$1250
1902 Plain Back
3x10-20 3111-4798 <$1250
Total Issue $277,400
Out in 1935 $680
Ch 11939 assumed circulation
****
9329 Jasper
FARMERS NB OF MONTICELLO
{{ 8 L 10 S }}
Chartered 1/09
1902 Date Back <$VALUE
3x10-20 1-3310 <$300
1902 Plain Back
3x10-20 3311-11992 <$300
1929 Small Size
10 Type 1 1-1622 <$160
20 Type 1 1-408 <$160
5 Type 2 1-3017 <$175
10 Type 2 1-1764 <$175
20 Type 2 1-456 <$185
Total Issue $787,725
Out in 1935 $50,000
Large out 1935 $2,275
****
9346 Jasper
FNB OF MONTICELLO
{{ 6 L 17 S }}
Chartered 2/09
1902 Date Back <$VALUE
3x10-20 1-5960 <$350
1902 Plain Back
3x10-20 5961-14470 <$350
1929 Small Size
5 Type 1 1-210 <$150
10 Type 1 1-1428 <$150
20 Type 1 1-390 <$165
5 Type 2 1-3484 <$165
10 Type 2 1-1451 <$165
20 Type 2 1-588 <$175
Total Issue $905,970
Out in 1935 $50,000
Large out 1935 $2,500
****
7565 Colquitt
FNB OF MOULTRIE
{{ 2 L }}
Organized 12/19/04
Liquidated 3/1/28
1902 Red Seal <$VALUE
3x10-20 1-1100 <$1500
1902 Date Back
3x10-20 1-2230* <$750
* 1725-1790 not issued
Total Issue $163,200
Out at close $590
****
13161 Colquitt
MOULTRIE NB, MOULTRIE
{{ 13 S }}
Chartered 1/28
1929 Small Size <$VALUE
5 Type 1 1-2770 <$150
10 Type 1 1-1150 <$150
20 Type 1 1-188 <$165
5 Type 2 1-10682 <$165
10 Type 2 1-6172 <$165
20 Type 2 1-1524 <$165
Total Issue $320,270
Out in 1935 $98,400
****
9106 Berrien
FNB OF NASHVILLE
{{ UNREPORTED }}
Chartered 4/08
Liquidated 3/1/17
1902 Red Seal <$VALUE
4x5 1-156 <$2000
3x10-20 1-125 <$2000
1902 Date Back
4x5 1-2275 <$1250
3x10-20 1-1780 <$1250
1902 Plain Back
4x5 2276-2724 <$1250
3x10-20 1781-2046 <$1250
Total Issue $166,150
Out at close $25,000
****
3116 Glynn
FNB OF NEW BRUNSWICK
{{ UNREPORTED }}
Chartered 2/2/84
Receivership 6/17/93
Brown Back <$VALUE
3x10-20 1-1947 <$2000
Total Issue $97,350
Out in 1916 $590
****
6047 Coweta
COWETA NB OF NEWNAN
{{ UNREPORTED }}
Chartered 12/13/01
Closed 2/19/20
Brown Back <$VALUE
3x10-20 1-1920 <$1500
1882 Date Back
3x10-20 1-3710 <$1500
1882 Value Back
3x10-20 3711-4167 <$1500
Total Issue $304,350
Out at close $30,000
Ch 1861 assumed circulation
****
1861 Coweta
FNB OF NEWNAN
{{ 16 L 16 S }}
Chartered 8/11/71
Original Series <$VALUE
3x1-2 1-2000 <$1500/$4500
4x5 1-2500 <$1250
3x10-20 1-2150<$1500/$2500
Series 1875
3x10-20 1-2716<$1500/$2000
Brown Back
50-100 1-2134 <$2500
1882 Date Back
50-100 1-270 <$2500
1902 Date Back
3x10-20 1-4400 <$150
1902 Plain Back
3x10-20 4401-27463 <$150
1929 Small Size
10 Type 1 1-5668 <$75
20 Type 1 1-1694 <$85
10 Type 2 1-3750 <$100
20 Type 2 1-980 <$100
Total Issue $2,637,510
Out in 1935 $125,000
Large out 1935 $7,780
Outstanding includes Ch 6047
****
8477 Coweta
MANUFACTURERS NB OF NEWNAN
{{ 5 L 3 S }}
Chartered 12/06
1902 Red Seal <$VALUE
4x10 1-725 <$1250
1902 Date Back
4x10 1-2400 <$350
1902 Plain Back
4x10 2401-6203 <$350
1929 Small Size
10 Type 1 1-902 <$300
10 Type 2 1-1634 <$300
Total Issue $347,580
Out in 1935 $15,000
Large out 1935 $720
****
3382 Coweta
NEWNAN NB, NEWNAN
{{ UNREPORTED }}
Chartered 8/22/85
Liquidated 3/10/00
Brown Back <$VALUE
3x10-20 1-2750 <$1500
Total Issue $137,500
Out in 1910 $1,920
****
8580 Irwin
FNB OF OCILLA
{{ 5 L 10 S }}
Chartered 3/07
1902 Red Seal <$VALUE
4x5 1-600 <$1500
3x10-20 1-490 <$1500
1902 Date Back
4x5 1-4350 <$400
3x10-20 1-3640 <$400
1902 Plain Back
4x5 4351-14155 <$400
3x10-20 3641-9761 <$400
1929 Small Size
5 Type 1 1-2026 <$175
10 Type 1 1-1124 <$175
20 Type 1 1-308 <$175
5 Type 2 1-4296 <$200
10 Type 2 1-2400 <$200
20 Type 2 1-468 <$200
Total Issue $1,027,670
Out in 1935 $50,000
Large out 1935 $2,455
****
9870 Mitchell
FNB OF PELHAM
{{ 1 L 5 S }}
Chartered 10/10
1902 Date Back <$VALUE
3x10-20 1-1820 <$1000
1902 Plain Back
3x10-20 1821-5559 <$1000
1929 Small Size
10 Type 1 1-646 <$350
20 Type 1 1-160 <$350
10 Type 2 1-1284 <$375
20 Type 2 1-324 <$375
Total Issue $355,230
Out in 1935 $20,000
Large out 1935 $840
****
8680 Bryan
PEMBROKE NB, PEMBROKE
{{ U + 5 L 2U + 6 S }}
Organized 4/29/07
1902 Red Seal <$VALUE
4x5 1-275 <$1500
3x10-20 1-220 <$1500
1902 Date Back
4x5 1-2275 <$400
3x10-20 1-1740 <$400
1902 Plain Back
4x5 2276-6995 <$400
3x10-20 1741-4684 <$400
1929 Small Size
5 Type 1 1-1050 <$250
10 Type 1 1-476 <$250
20 Type 1 1-140 <$250
5 Type 2 1-1340 <$275
10 Type 2 1-951 <$275
20 Type 2 1-204 <$275
Total Issue $487,750
Out in 1935 $25,000
Large out 1935 $1,310
****
7994 Brooks
FNB OF QUITMAN
Organized 11/20/05
Liquidated 3/15/35
2nd title: Peoples-FNB of
Quitman 4/4/31
FIRST TITLE {{ 17 L 8 S }}
1902 Red Seal <$VALUE
4x5 1-1600 <$1000
3x10-20 1-1290 <$1000
1902 Date Back
4x5 1-9850 <$175
3x10-20 1-7400 <$175
1902 Plain Back
4x5 9851-40603 <$175
3x10-20 7401-25719 <$175
1929 Small Size
5 Type 1 1-3694 <$175
10 Type 1 1-1838 <$175
20 Type 1 1-526 <$175
SECOND TITLE {{ 8 S }}
1929 Small Size
5 Type 1 1-726 <$150
10 Type 1 1-592 <$150
20 Type 1 1-182 <$150
5 Type 2 1-4840 <$150
10 Type 2 1-2490 <$150
20 Type 2 1-705 <$150
Total Issue $2,621,070
Out in 1935 $100,000
Large out 1935 $13,095
Outstanding includes Ch 11290
Ch 14255 assumed circulation
****
11290 Brooks
PEOPLES NB OF QUITMAN
{{ 8 L 2 S }}
Chartered 1/19
Closed 4/4/31
1902 Plain Back <$VALUE
4x5 1-14646 <$250
1929 Small Size
5 Type 1 1-2960 <$350
Total Issue $381,720
Out at close $50,000
Large out at close $7,135
Ch 7994 assumed circulation
****
Peoples-FNB of Quitman
SEE Ch 7994
FNB of Quitman
****
9615 Taylor
FNB OF REYNOLDS
{{ 5 L 4U + 4 S }}
Organized 12/1/09
Receivership 10/20/32
1902 Date Back <$VALUE
3x10-20 1-2860 <$450
1902 Plain Back
3x10-20 2861-7213 <$450
1929 Small Size
5 Type 1 1-780 <$300
10 Type 1 1-405 <$300
20 Type 1 1-107 <$300
Total Issue $421,190
Out at close $24,340
Large out at close $12,840
****
8628 Polk
CITIZENS NB OF ROCKMART
{{ 1 L }}
Chartered 4/07
Liquidated 1/9/17
1902 Red Seal <$VALUE
3x10-20 1-360 <$2000
1902 Date Back
3x10-20 1-1104 <$1250
Total Issue $73,200
Out at close $10,000
****
9636 Floyd
CHEROKEE NB OF ROME
{{ UNREPORTED }}
Chartered 1/10
Liquidated 7/15/16
1902 Date Back <$VALUE
4x5 1-8750 <$1000
3x10-20 1-6800 <$1000
1902 Plain Back
4x5 8751-8990 <$1000
3x10-20 6801-6988 <$1000
Total Issue $529,200
Out in 1916 $79,300
****
10303 Floyd
EXCHANGE NB OF ROME
{{ 10 L }}
Chartered 12/12
Liquidated 7/11/25
1902 Date Back <$VALUE
4x5 1-4000 <$165
3x10-20 1-3400 <$165
1902 Plain Back
4x5 4001-25090 <$165
3x10-20 3401-16458 <$165
Total Issue $1,324,700
Out at close $150,000
****
2368 Floyd
FNB OF ROME
{{ 14 L 16 S }}
Chartered 8/22/77
Series 1875 <$VALUE
4x10 1-8186 <$1500
Brown Back
4x5 1-8500 <$400
3x10-20 1-5300 <$400
50-100 1-778 <$2500
1882 Date Back
4x5 1-13425 <$400
3x10-20 1-11739 <$400
50-100 1-200 <$2500
1902 Date Back
4x5 1-29627 <$150
3x10-20 1-17200 <$150
1929 Small Size
5 Type 1 1-6958 <$65
10 Type 1 1-3812 <$65
20 Type 1 1-936 <$75
5 Type 2 1-11980 <$85
10 Type 2 1-6103 <$85
20 Type 2 1-1723 <$85
Total Issue $3,922,300
Out in 1935 $150,000
Large out 1935 $6,250
****
3670 Floyd
MERCHANTS NB OF ROME
{{ 3 L }}
Chartered 4/14/87
Liquidated 12/15/97
Brown Back <$VALUE
4x5 1-8804 <$600
Total Issue $176,080
Out in 1910 $1,085
****
10302 Floyd
N CITY B OF ROME
{{ 14 L 28 S }}
Chartered 12/12
1902 Date Back <$VALUE
4x5 1-5500 <$150
3x10-20 1-4200 <$150
1902 Plain Back
4x5 5501-40925 <$150
3x10-20 4201-27600 <$150
1929 Small Size
5 Type 1 1-10028 <$60
10 Type 1 1-4650 <$60
20 Type 1 1-1276 <$75
5 Type 2 1-17378 <$75
10 Type 2 1-9150 <$75
20 Type 2 1-1897 <$80
Total Issue $3,147,790
Out in 1935 $200,000
Large out 1935 $6,070
****
4369 Floyd
ROME NB, ROME
{{ UNREPORTED }}
Chartered 7/15/90
Liquidated 2/23/91
Brown Back <$VALUE
4x5 1-1125 <$1500
Total Issue $22,500
Out in 1910 $105
****
9641 Washington
COHEN NB OF SANDERSVILLE
{{ 3 L }}
Chartered 1/10
Liquidated 3/27/17
1902 Date Back <$VALUE
4x5 1-1300* <$1250
3x10-20 1-1024** <$1250
* 1251-1300 not marked
** 1001-1024 not marked
Total Issue $77,200
Out at close $12,000
****
7934 Washington
FNB OF SANDERSVILLE
{{ U + 6 L }}
Organized 8/15/05
Receivership 3/14/29
1902 Red Seal <$VALUE
4x5 1-1500 <$1500
3x10-20 1-1260 <$1500
1902 Date Back
4x5 1-4850 <$400
3x10-20 1-3720 <$400
1902 Plain Back
4x5 4851-11885 <$400
3x10-20 3721-7987 <$400
Total Issue $730,050
Out at close $25,000
****

13725 Washington
GEORGE D WARTHEN NB OF SANDERSVILLE
{{ 7 S }}
Chartered 7/33
1929 Small Size <$VALUE
5 Type 2 1-5184 <$375
10 Type 2 1-3985 <$375
20 Type 2 1-1594 <$375
Total Issue $97,650
Out in 1935 $37,650

13068 Chatham
CITIZENS & SOUTHERN NB, SAVANNAH
{{ 50+ S }}
Chartered 5/2/27
1929 Small Size <$VALUE
5 Type 1 1-44878 <$15
10 Type 1 1-34886 <$20
20 Type 1 1-5280 <$30
5 Type 2 1-170856 <$15
10 Type 2 1-97730 <$20
20 Type 2 1-12738 <$30
Total Issue $6,159,440
Out in 1935 $500,000

13472 Chatham
LIBERTY NB & TC OF SAVANNAH
{{ 12 S }}
Chartered 6/30
1929 Small Size <$VALUE
5 Type 2 1-22820 <$75
10 Type 2 1-12647 <$75
20 Type 2 1-4344 <$85
Total Issue $327,450
Out in 1935 $200,000

1640 Chatham
MERCHANTS NB OF SAVANNAH
{{ 11 L }}
Chartered 1866
Liquidated 1/14/19
Original Series <$VALUE
4x5 1-5900 <$1250
4x10 1-4100 <$1500
2x20-50-100 1-2213
<$2250/$8500/$8500
Series 1875
4x5 1-7085 <$1250
4x10 1-5487 <$1500
2x20-50-100 1-693
<$2000/$8500/$8500
Brown Back
4x5 1-10817 <$450
3x10-20 1-4782 <$450
1902 Red Seal
4x5 1-8800 <$1000
3x10-20 1-6400 <$1000
1902 Date Back
4x5 1-31165 <$175
3x10-20 1-25734 <$175
1902 Plain Back
4x5 31166-42770 <$175
3x10-20 25735-33059 <$175
Total Issue $4,656,110
Out at close $400,000

3406 Chatham
NB OF SAVANNAH
{{ 13 L }}
Chartered 1885
Liquidated 8/25/19
Brown Back <$VALUE
3x10-20 1-13207 <$500
1902 Red Seal
4x5 1-6500 <$1000
3x10-20 1-3400 <$1000
1902 Date Back
4x5 1-28500 <$175
4x10 1-22750 <$175
3x10-20 1-15200 <$175
1902 Plain Back
4x5 28501-43470 <$175
4x10 22751-34480 <$175
Total Issue $3,968,950
Out at close $399,995

1255 Chatham
SAVANNAH NB, SAVANNAH
{{ UNREPORTED }}
Chartered 6/10/65
Liquidated 6/22/69
Original Series <$VALUE
4x5 1-2500 <$2000
3x10-20 1-700 <$2500/$3000
Total Issue $85,000
Out in 1910 $415

8527 Coweta
FNB OF SENOIA
{{ 1 L }}
Chartered 1/07
Liquidated 2/15/16
1902 Red Seal <$VALUE
3x10-20 1-720 <$2000
1902 Date Back
3x10-20 1-2410 <$1000
1902 Plain Back
3x10-20 2411-2499 <$1000
Total Issue $160,950
Out in 1916 $13,880

8417 Randolph
FNB OF SHELLMAN
{{ 3 L 4 S }}
Chartered 10/06
1902 Red Seal <$VALUE
3x10-20 1-585 <$2000
1902 Date Back
3x10-20 1-3640 <$750
1902 Plain Back
3x10-20 3641-6763 <$750
1929 Small Size
10 Type 1 1-924 <$375
20 Type 1 1-238 <$375
10 Type 2 1-768 <$400
20 Type 2 1-204 <$400
Total Issue $463,160
Out in 1935 $25,000
Large out 1935 $830

7067 Hancock
FNB OF SPARTA
{{ 1 L }}
Chartered 12/03
Liquidated 2/27/23
1902 Red Seal <$VALUE
4x5 1-2100 <$1500
3x10-20 1-1610 <$1500
1902 Date Back
4x5 1-4325 <$750
3x10-20 1-3380 <$750
1902 Plain Back
4x5 4326-9039 <$750
3x10-20 3381-6192 <$750
Total Issue $612,880
Out at close $50,000
Ch 12317 assumed circulation

12317 Hancock
HANCOCK NB OF SPARTA
{{ 8 L 1 S }}
Organized 2/2/23
Receivership 5/24/32
1902 Plain Back <$VALUE
4x5 1-6024 <$325
1929 Small Size
5 Type 1 1-2466 <$500
Total Issue $194,460
Out at close $25,000
Large out at close $3,310
Outstanding includes Ch 7067

7468 Bulloch
FNB OF STATESBORO
{{ 12 L 4 S }}
Chartered 11/04
Liquidated 12/19/31
1902 Red Seal <$VALUE
4x5 1-480 <$1250
3x10-20 1-398 <$1250
1902 Date Back
4x5 1-2625 <$250
3x10-20 1-2100 <$250
1902 Plain Back
4x5 2626-19794 <$250
3x10-20 2101-13905 <$250
1929 Small Size
5 Type 1 1-2943 <$350
10 Type 1 1-1391 <$350
20 Type 1 1-368 <$375
Total Issue $1,336,540
Out at close $100,000
Large out at close $8,105

10829 Screven
NB OF SYLVANIA
{{ 1 L 0 S }}
Chartered 3/16
Liquidated 1/20/30
1902 Plain Back <$VALUE
3x10-20 1-4651 <$1500
1929 Small Size
10 Type 1 1-165 <$750
20 Type 1 1-29 <$750
Total Issue $245,930
Out at close $25,000
Large out at close $11,620

6180 Worth
FNB OF SYLVESTER
{{ UNREPORTED }}
Chartered 3/29/02
Receivership 1/15/25
1902 Red Seal <$VALUE
4x5 1-1525 <$2000
3x10-20 1-1240 <$2000
1902 Date Back
4x5 1-3100 <$1250
3x10-20 1-2440 <$1250
1902 Plain Back (dated 1902)
4x5 3101-5346 <$1250
3x10-20 2441-3869 <$1250
1902 Plain Back (dated 1922)
4x5 1-3730 <$1250
Total Issue $467,470
Out at close $29,300

7220 Haralson
FNB OF TALLAPOOSA
{{ UNREPORTED }}
Chartered 4/21/04
Liquidated 9/8/08
1902 Red Seal <$VALUE
4x5 1-635 <$2500
3x10-20 1-761 <$2500
Total Issue $50,750
Out in 1910 $4,915

FNB of Thomasville
SEE Ch 3767
Thomasville NB, Thomasville

3767 Thomas
THOMASVILLE NB, THOMASVILLE
Chartered 7/30/87
Receivership 7/27/32
2nd title: FNB of Thomasville 7/20/07
FIRST TITLE {{ 6 L }}
Brown Back <$VALUE
4x5 1-2663 <$600
3x10-20 1-1876 <$600
50-100 1-94 <$2500
SECOND TITLE {{ 5 L 6 S }}
1902 Red Seal
4x5 1-250 <$1500
3x10-20 1-200 <$1500
1902 Date Back
4x5 1-4400 <$400
3x10-20 1-3380 <$400
1902 Plain Back
4x5 4401-12460 <$400
3x10-20 3381-8764 <$400
1929 Small Size
5 Type 1 1-1753 <$250
10 Type 1 1-805 <$250
20 Type 1 1-223 <$275
Total Issue $986,710
Out at close $48,860
Large out at close $5,040

9302 McDuffie
FNB OF THOMSON
{{ 4 L 5 S }}
Chartered 12/08
1902 Date Back <$VALUE
3x10-20 1-9800 <$500
1902 Plain Back
3x10-20 9801-14141 <$500
1929 Small Size
10 Type 1 1-774 <$275
20 Type 1 1-222 <$275
10 Type 2 1-3969 <$300
20 Type 2 1-1058 <$300
Total Issue $840,980
Out in 1935 $50,000
Large out 1935 $1,190

6542 Tift
FNB OF TIFTON
{{ UNREPORTED }}
Chartered 12/18/02
Liquidated 11/27/12
1902 Red Seal <$VALUE
3x10-20 1-2100 <$1500
1902 Date Back
3x10-20 1-2731 <$1250
Total Issue $241,550
Out in 1913 $20,000

8350 Tift
NB OF TIFTON
{{ 8 L U + 2 S }}
Organized 8/10/06
Receivership 4/12/30
1902 Red Seal <$VALUE
4x5 1-1450 <$1250
3x10-20 1-1240 <$1250
1902 Date Back
4x5 1-4450 <$350
3x10-20 1-3640 <$350
1902 Plain Back
4x5 4451-14411 <$350
3x10-20 3641-10084 <$350
1929 Small Size
5 Type 1 1-653 <$375
10 Type 1 1-250 <$375
20 Type 1 1-40 <$375
Total Issue $922,810
Out at close $49,160
Large out at close $12,560

6687 Stephens
FNB OF TOCCOA
{{ UNREPORTED }}
Organized 3/25/03
Receivership 11/22/15
1902 Red Seal <$VALUE
3x10-20 1-1196 <$2000
1902 Date Back
3x10-20 1-6169 <$1250
Total Issue $368,250
Out in 1916 $35,350

7330 Greene
NB OF UNION POINT
{{ UNREPORTED }}
Chartered 7/04
Liquidated 4/1/11
1902 Red Seal <$VALUE
3x10-20 1-2000 <$1500
1902 Date Back
3x10-20 1-1115 <$1250
Total Issue $155,750
Out in 1911 $21,450

4429 Lowndes
FNB OF VALDOSTA
{{ 12 L 14 S }}
Chartered 1890
Brown Back <$VALUE
4x5 1-3550 <$600
3x10-20 1-3750 <$600
1882 Date Back
4x5 1-1199 <$600
3x10-20 1-354 <$600
1902 Date Back
3x10-20 1-10600 <$275
1902 Plain Back
3x10-20 10601-33277 <$275
1929 Small Size
10 Type 1 1-3808 <$135
20 Type 1 1-1030 <$135
10 Type 2 1-5251 <$150
20 Type 2 1-1800 <$150
Total Issue $2,404,620
Out in 1935 $125,000
Large out 1935 $6,230

9879 Toombs
FNB OF VIDALIA
{{ 6 L 2 S }}
Organized 6/21/10
Receivership 9/3/31
1902 Date Back <$VALUE
3x10-20 1-1020 <$600
1902 Plain Back
3x10-20 1021-6893 <$600
1929 Small Size
10 Type 1 1-628 <$450
20 Type 1 1-185 <$450
Total Issue $404,530
Out at close $35,000
Large out at close $4,230

9618 Dooly
FNB OF VIENNA
{{ 4 L }}
Chartered 12/09
Liquidated 2/21/17
1902 Date Back <$VALUE
3x10-20 1-6700 <$600
1902 Plain Back
3x10-20 6701-7500 <$600
Total Issue $375,000
Out at close $74,995

8894 Wilkes
CITIZENS NB OF WASHINGTON
{{ 4 L }}
Chartered 9/07
Liquidated 1/23/26
1902 Red Seal <$VALUE
4x10 1-1875 <$1250
1902 Date Back
4x10 1-6425 <$400
1902 Plain Back
4x10 6426-16555 <$400
Total Issue $737,200
Out at close $49,995

8848 Wilkes
NB OF WILKES AT WASHINGTON
{{ 15 L 2 S }}
Organized 7/25/07
Receivership 1/12/31
1902 Red Seal <$VALUE
4x10 1-500 <$1250
1902 Date Back
4x10 1-6050 <$225
1902 Plain Back
4x10 6051-19224 <$225
1929 Small Size
10 Type 1 1-1089 <$400
Total Issue $854,300
Out at close $50,000
Large out at close $8,825

4963 Ware
FNB OF WAYCROSS
{{ 3 L 17 S }}
Organized 5/21/94
Liquidated 11/8/34
Brown Back <$VALUE
4x5 1-2675 <$1000
3x10-20 1-2450 <$1000
1882 Date Back
4x5 1-3675 <$1000
3x10-20 1-2495 <$1000
1902 Date Back
4x5 1-3250 <$500
3x10-20 1-2600 <$500
1902 Plain Back
4x5 3251-10865 <$500
3x10-20 2601-7856 <$500
1929 Small Size
5 Type 1 1-5646 <$100
10 Type 1 1-2984 <$100
20 Type 1 1-772 <$110
5 Type 2 1-4996 <$110
10 Type 2 1-2341 <$110
20 Type 2 1-544 <$125
Total Issue $1,484,680
Out in 1935 $150,000
Large out 1935 $3,095

7899 Burke
FNB OF WAYNESBORO
{{ 4 L U + 6 S }}
Chartered 9/05
1902 Red Seal <$VALUE
3x10-20 1-962 <$1250
1902 Date Back
3x10-20 1-2970 <$450
1902 Plain Back
3x10-20 2971-9433 <$450
1929 Small Size
5 Type 1 1-190 <$165
10 Type 1 1-1250 <$165
20 Type 1 1-350 <$175
5 Type 2 1-3666 <$185
10 Type 2 1-1920 <$185
20 Type 2 1-504 <$200
Total Issue $690,060
Out in 1935 $50,000
Large out 1935 $1,230

8046 Troup
FNB OF WEST POINT
{{ 4 L }}
Chartered 1/06
Liquidated 3/23/26
1902 Red Seal <$VALUE
3x10-20 1-1600 <$1500
1902 Date Back
3x10-20 1-4440 <$500
1902 Plain Back
3x10-20 4441-9282 <$500
Total Issue $544,100
Out at close $40,000

9051 Barrow
FNB OF WINDER
{{ UNREPORTED }}
Chartered 3/08
Liquidated 1/8/18
1902 Red Seal <$VALUE
3x10-20 1-1000 <$1500
1902 Date Back
3x10-20 1-5000 <$1250
1902 Plain Back
3x10-20 5001-5888 <$1250
Total Issue $344,400
Out at close $50,000

10805 Barrow
WINDER NB, WINDER
{{ 10 L 8 S }}
Organized 10/16/15
Receivership 12/30/32
1902 Plain Back <$VALUE
4x5 1-25333 <$275
3x10-20 1-16744 <$275
1929 Small Size
5 Type 1 1-3694 <$150
10 Type 1 1-1998 <$150
20 Type 1 1-459 <$165
Total Issue $1,629,640
Out at close $96,580
Large out at close $7,970

8023 Johnson
FNB OF WRIGHTSVILLE
{{ UNREPORTED }}
Chartered 12/05
Liquidated 1/15/14
1902 Red Seal <$VALUE
3x10-20 1-1250 <$2000
1902 Date Back
3x10-20 1-917 <$1250
Total Issue $108,350
Out in 1914 $7,830

CONDITION affects Value. The Values shown are for notes in FINE condition.

HAWAII

****
5550 Honolulu
FNB OF HAWAII, HONOLULU
Chartered 8/23/00
2nd title: Bishop FNB 7/6/29
3rd title: Bishop NB of Hawaii 11/3/33
FIRST TITLE **{{ 50+ L }}**
Brown Back <$VALUE
4x5 1-21665 <$1500
3x10-20 1-15214<$1500/$2500
50-100 1-540 <$7500
1882 Date Back
4x5 1-32750 <$1000
3x10-20 1-24100<$1000/$1750
3x50-100 1-550 <$7500
1882 Value Back
4x5 32751-57455 <$1250
3x10-20 24101-25700 <$1250/$2250
1902 Plain Back
4x5 1-59669 <$650
4x10 1-50990 <$650
3x50-100 1-360 <$2500
SECOND TITLE **{{ 50+ S }}**
1929 Small Size
5 Type 1 1-54864 <$125
10 Type 1 1-31030 <$125
50 Type 1 1-6544 <$250
100 Type 1 1-2294 <$350
5 Type 2 1-91608 <$125
10 Type 2 1-36672 <$125
THIRD TITLE **{{ 28 S }}**
1929 Small Size
5 Type 2 1-90214 <$175
10 Type 2 1-56269 <$175
50 Type 2 1-2323 <$500
100 Type 2 1-682 <$750
Total Issue $16,682,520
Out in 1934 $3,349,997
Large out 1935 $28,770
****
8207 Maui
BALDWIN NB, KAHULUI
{{ 4 L }}
Chartered 5/06
Liquidated 1/3/21
1902 Red Seal <$VALUE
4x5 1-465 <$50,000
3x10-20 1-384 <$50,000
1902 Date Back
4x5 1-1725 <$10,000
3x10-20 1-1260 <$10,000
1902 Plain Back
4x5 1726-2455 <$10,000
3x10-20 1261-1687 <$10,000
Total Issue $161,950
Out in 1921 $25,000
****
8101 Maui
LAHAINA NB OF LAHAINA
{{ 1 L }}
Chartered 2/06
Liquidated 5/1/17
1902 Red Seal <$VALUE
3x10-20 1-240 <$50,000
1902 Date Back
3x10-20 1-203 <$35,000
Total Issue $22,500
Out in 1917 $6,250
****
10451 Maui
FNB OF PAIA
{{ UNREPORTED }}
Chartered 9/26/13
Liquidated 5/1/17
1902 Date Back <$VALUE
3x10-20 1-200 <$35,000
Total Issue $10,000
Out in 1917 $10,000
****
5994 Maui
FNB OF WAILUKU
{{ 2 L }}
Chartered 11/01
Liquidated 5/1/17
Brown Back <$VALUE
4x5 1-750 <$35,000
3x10-20 1-620 <$35,000
1882 Date Back
4x5 1-975 <$30,000
3x10-20 1-646 <$30,000
Total Issue $97,800
Out in 1917 $24,995
****

Nickname: The Aloha State
Motto: Ua Mau Ke Ea O Ka Aina I Ka Pono (The Life of the Land is Perpetuated in Righteousness)
Capital: Honolulu
Number of towns: 5
Number of issuing charters: 5
Number of small size issuers: 1

Veteran national collectors share a common fantasy: to uncover a Red Seal from Hawaii. Only 4356 Series 1902 Red Seals were issued by Hawaiian banks, and none has surfaced.

The census is dominated by the issues of Charter 5550, The First National Bank of Hawaii, Honolulu. Even though the bank issued over 16 million dollars worth of nationals under three titles, there never seem to be enough to go around.

In 1899, before the bank received its charter, a prospectus indicated that the bank would become a "bank of Issue of United States National Gold Notes". The organization of National Gold Banks with note-issuing privileges remained possible, even after Congress passed legislation which authorized existing National Gold Banks to convert to regular national bank status. Imagine the fun collectors would have had collecting Territorial Gold Bank notes - or small size National Gold Bank notes!

The other four note-issuing Hawaiian banks are represented by a total of seven notes: two $5 Brown Backs on the First National Bank of Wailuku, a $20 1902 Date Back on The Lahaina National Bank, and four Series 1902 blue seal notes on the Baldwin National Bank of Kahului. No notes have been reported for the First National Bank of Paia.

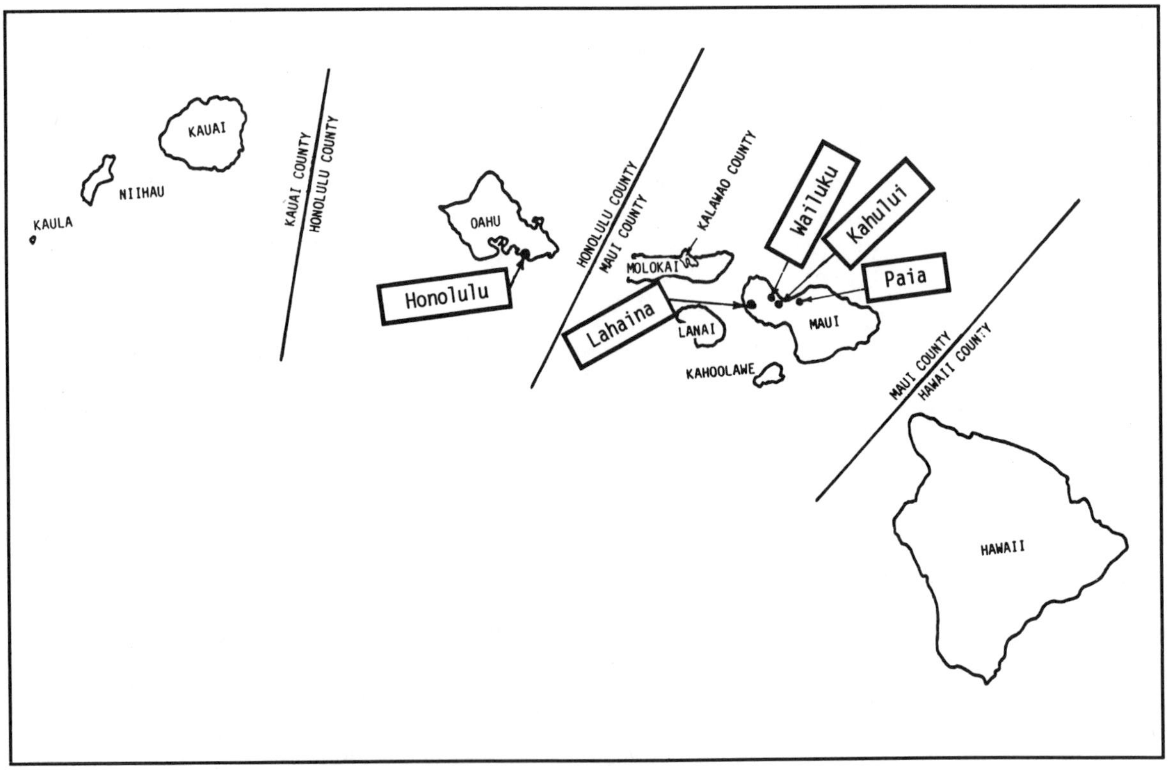

IDAHO

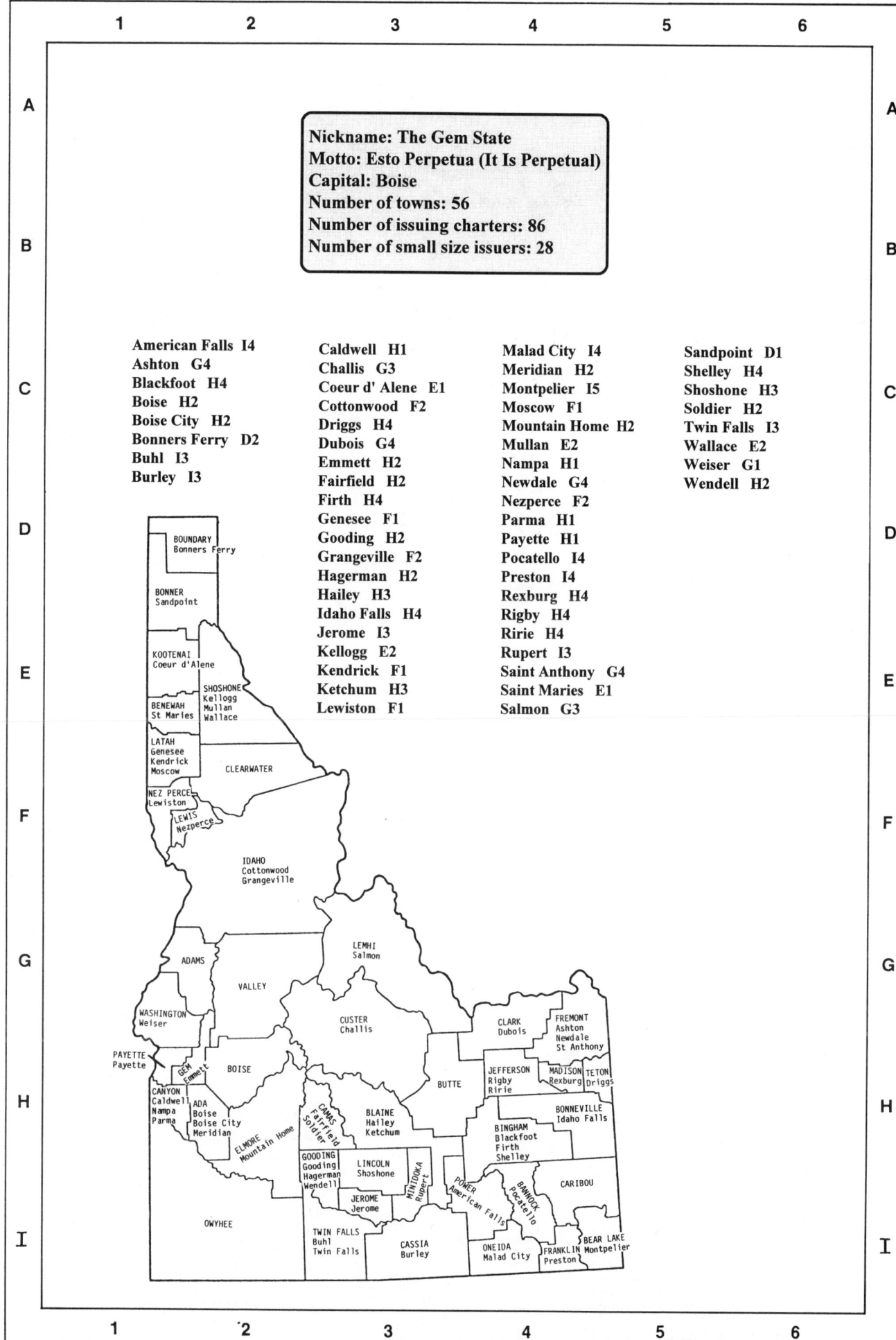

Nickname: The Gem State
Motto: Esto Perpetua (It Is Perpetual)
Capital: Boise
Number of towns: 56
Number of issuing charters: 86
Number of small size issuers: 28

American Falls I4
Ashton G4
Blackfoot H4
Boise H2
Boise City H2
Bonners Ferry D2
Buhl I3
Burley I3
Caldwell H1
Challis G3
Coeur d' Alene E1
Cottonwood F2
Driggs H4
Dubois G4
Emmett H2
Fairfield H2
Firth H4
Genesee F1
Gooding H2
Grangeville F2
Hagerman H2
Hailey H3
Idaho Falls H4
Jerome I3
Kellogg E2
Kendrick F1
Ketchum H3
Lewiston F1
Malad City I4
Meridian H2
Montpelier I5
Moscow F1
Mountain Home H2
Mullan E2
Nampa H1
Newdale G4
Nezperce F2
Parma H1
Payette H1
Pocatello I4
Preston I4
Rexburg H4
Rigby H4
Ririe H4
Rupert I3
Saint Anthony G4
Saint Maries E1
Salmon G3
Sandpoint D1
Shelley H4
Shoshone H3
Soldier H2
Twin Falls I3
Wallace E2
Weiser G1
Wendell H2

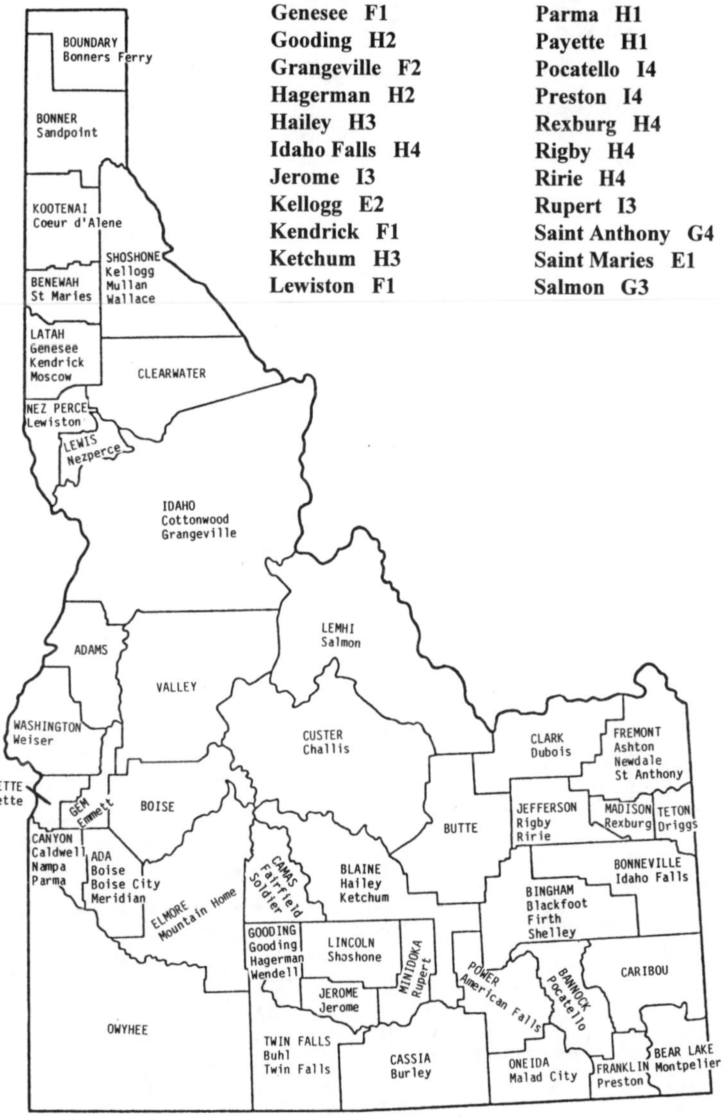

****
8869 Power
FNB OF AMERICAN FALLS
{{ 3 L }}
Organized 8/1/07
Receivership 3/26/23
1902 Red Seal <$VALUE
4x10 1-750 <$4000
1902 Date Back
4x10 1-2450* <$1000
1902 Plain Back
4x10 2551-5277* <$1000
* 2451-2550 not marked
Total Issue $241,080
Out at close $25,000
****
10269 Fremont
FNB OF ASHTON
{{ 3 L }}
Organized 2/3/12
Receivership 3/10/28
1902 Date Back <$VALUE
4x5 1-500* <$850
3x10-20 1-400** <$850
1902 Plain Back
4x5 651-4970* <$850
3x10-20 521-3086** <$850
* 501-650 not marked
** 401-520 not marked
Total Issue $253,700
Out at close $28,950
****
7419 Bingham
FNB OF BLACKFOOT
{{ 6 L 8 S }}
Chartered 10/04
Liquidated 1/2/34
1902 Red Seal <$VALUE
4x5 1-1000 <$4000
3x10-20 1-720 <$4000
1902 Date Back
4x5 1-1825 <$500
3x10-20 1-1350 <$500
1902 Plain Back
4x5 1826-7789 <$500
3x10-20 1351-5213 <$500
1929 Small Size
5 Type 1 1-1858 <$375
10 Type 1 1-1082 <$375
20 Type 1 1-286 <$375
Total Issue $627,410
Out at close $50,000
Large out at close $2,770
Outstanding includes Ch 11198
****
8346 Ada
IDAHO NB OF BOISE
{{ 6 L }}
Organized 7/12/06
Receivership 9/15/21
1902 Red Seal <$VALUE
3x10-20 1-1650 <$4000
1902 Date Back
3x10-20 1-7400 <$350
1902 Plain Back
3x10-20 7401-9472 <$350
Total Issue $556,100
Out in 1918 $100,000
****
10751 Ada
OVERLAND NB OF BOISE
{{ 7 L }}
Organized 6/18/15
Receivership 5/28/21
1902 Date Back <$VALUE
3x10-20 1-7122 <$400
Total Issue $356,100
Out at close $94,400
****
10083 Ada
PACIFIC NB OF BOISE
{{ 14 L }}
Chartered 9/11
Liquidated 1/30/29
1902 Date Back <$VALUE
3x10-20 1-16200 <$200/$225
1902 Plain Back
3x10-20 16201-61305
<$200/$225
Total Issue $3,065,250
Out in 1927 $292,900
****
3471 Ada
BOISE CITY NB, BOISE CITY
Organized 3/9/86
Receivership 8/9/32
2nd Title: Boise City NB,
Boise
TERRITORIAL ISSUES {{ 0 L }}
Brown Back <$VALUE
3x10-20 1-410 <$15,000
STATE ISSUES {{ 1 L }}
Brown Back
3x10-20 411-2524 <$4000
50-100 1-500 <$8500
SECOND TITLE {{ 18 L 20 S }}
1902 Red Seal
4x5 1-2000 <$4000
50-100 1-400 <$8500
1902 Date Back
4x5 1-11750 <$175
3x10-20 1-6800 <$175
50-100 1-1134 <$400/$500
3x50-100 1-820 <$400/$500
1902 Plain Back
4x5 11751-46475 <$175
3x10-20 6801-25341 <$175
3x50-100 821-1091<$400/$500
1929 Small Size
5 Type 1 1-4020 <$125
10 Type 1 1-1962 <$125
20 Type 1 1-636 <$125
50 Type 1 1-273 <$225
100 Type 1 1-94 <$300
Total Issue $3,393,540
Out at close $248,080
Large out at close $31,100
****
1668 Ada
FNB OF IDAHO, BOISE CITY
Organized 3/11/67
2nd Title: FNB of Idaho,
Boise
TERRITORIAL ISSUES {{ 2 L }}
Original Series <$VALUE
3x1-2 1-1800
<$15,000/$20,000
4x5 1-2520 <$15,000
3x10-20 1-2642
<$17,500/$20,000
Series 1875
3x1-2 1-120
<$15,000/$20,000
4x5 1-1790 <$15,000
3x10-20 1-1680
<$17,500/$20,000
Brown Back
3x10-20 1-710 <$15,000
STATE ISSUES {{ 1 L }}
Brown Back
3x10-20 711-5004 <$4000
SECOND TITLE {{ 14 L 23 S }}
1902 Red Seal
50-100 1-1000 <$8500
1902 Date Back
50-100 1-1000 <$400/$450
3x50-100 1-4780 <$400/$450
1902 Plain Back
3x50-100 4781-5839
<$400/$450
1929 Small Size
5 Type 1 1-1036 <$125
10 Type 1 1-408 <$125
20 Type 1 1-204 <$135
50 Type 1 1-952* <$200
100 Type 1 1-326** <$250
5 Type 2 1-19816 <$135
10 Type 2 1-9810 <$135
20 Type 2 1-4119 <$140
*C000004A-F000244A canceled
**E000002A-F000084A canceled
Total Issue $3,041,530
Out in 1935 $500,000
Large out 1935 $30,480
****
10727 Boundary
FNB OF BONNERS FERRY
{{ 3 L U + 6 S }}
Organized 3/25/15
1902 Date Back <$VALUE
4x5 1-400 <$1000
4x10 1-425 <$1000
1902 Plain Back
4x5 401-5690 <$1000
4x10 426-4160 <$1000
1929 Small Size
5 Type 1 1-1382 <$400
10 Type 1 1-684 <$400
5 Type 2 1-2240 <$400
10 Type 2 1-1176 <$400
Total Issue $385,660
Out in 1935 $25,000
Large out 1935 $1,240
****
11065 Twin Falls
FNB OF BUHL
{{ 2 L }}
Organized 8/10/17
Receivership 3/26/25
1902 Plain Back <$VALUE
4x5 1-4095 <$1000
3x10-20 1-3350 <$1000
Total Issue $249,400
Out at close $49,400
****
12256 Cassia
CASSIA NB OF BURLEY
{{ 5 S }}
Chartered 9/22
1929 Small Size <$VALUE
5 Type 2 1-5556 <$350
10 Type 2 1-2772 <$350
20 Type 2 1-900 <$350
Total Issue $73,500
Out in 1935 $50,000
****
10341 Cassia
FNB OF BURLEY
{{ 3 L }}
Organized 2/20/13
Receivership 11/30/21
1902 Date Back <$VALUE
4x5 1-1300 <$850
4x10 1-1300 <$850
1902 Plain Back
4x5 1301-3540 <$850
4x10 1301-3110 <$850
Total Issue $195,200
Out at close $29,600
****
9333 Canyon
AMERICAN NB OF CALDWELL
{{ 1 L }}
Organized 2/2/09
Receivership 12/23/13
1902 Date Back <$VALUE
4x5 1-2685 <$1250
3x10-20 1-2490 <$1250
Total Issue $178,200
Out in 1915 $10,865
****
4690 Canyon
FNB OF CALDWELL
{{ 8 L 11 S }}
Chartered 1892
Brown Back <$VALUE
3x10-20 1-2790 <$4000
1882 Date Back
3x10-20 1-1626 <$2000
1902 Date Back
3x10-20 1-2100 <$275
1902 Plain Back
3x10-20 2101-9404 <$275
1929 Small Size
10 Type 1 1-1316 <$150
20 Type 1 1-362 <$150
10 Type 2 1-1934 <$175
20 Type 2 1-444 <$175
Total Issue $841,620
Out in 1935 $50,000
Large out 1935 $3,570
****
8225 Canyon
WESTERN NB OF CALDWELL
{{ 13 L }}
Chartered 5/06
Liquidated 12/31/24
1902 Red Seal <$VALUE
3x10-20 1-1800 <$4000
1902 Date Back
3x10-20 1-3640 <$200/$250
1902 Plain Back
3x10-20 3641-8400<$200/$250
Total Issue $510,000
Out at close $50,000
****
9477 Custer
FNB OF CHALLIS
{{ UNREPORTED }}
Chartered 7/09
Liquidated 5/28/17
1902 Date Back <$VALUE
3x10-20 1-832 <$2000
Total Issue $41,600
Out at close $8,750
****
7120 Kootenai
EXCHANGE NB OF
COEUR D'ALENE
Organized 1/14/04
Receivership 1/19/29
2nd title: F Exchange NB of
Coeur d'Alene 7/19/15
FIRST TITLE {{ 0 L }}
1902 Red Seal <$VALUE
4x5 1-1320 <$4000
3x10-20 1-1052 <$4000
1902 Date Back
4x5 1-1700 <$1250
3x10-20 1-1298 <$1250
SECOND TITLE {{ 5 L }}
1902 Plain Back
3x10-20 1-13779 <$600
Total Issue $866,850
Out at close $100,000
Outstanding includes Ch 6793
****
F Exchange NB of
Coeur d'Alene
SEE Ch 7120
Exchange NB of Coeur d'Alene
****
6793 Kootenai
FNB OF COEUR D'ALENE
{{ UNREPORTED }}
Chartered 5/03
Liquidated 5/11/15
1902 Red Seal <$VALUE
4x5 1-1865 <$4000
3x10-20 1-1374 <$4000
1902 Date Back
4x5 1-3245 <$1500
3x10-20 1-2348 <$1500
Total Issue $288,300
Out at close $50,000
Ch 7120 assumed circulation
****
13288 Kootenai
FNB OF COEUR D'ALENE
{{ U + 12 S }}
Chartered 3/29
1929 Small Size <$VALUE
5 Type 1 1-3041 <$350
10 Type 1 1-1502 <$325
20 Type 1 1-431 <$350
Total Issue $233,070
Out in 1932 $100,000
****
7923 Idaho
FNB OF COTTONWOOD
{{ 2 L 6 S }}
Chartered 9/05
1902 Red Seal <$VALUE
3x10-20 1-1096 <$4000
1902 Date Back
3x10-20 1-1830 <$1000
1902 Plain Back
3x10-20 1831-5093 <$1000
1929 Small Size
10 Type 1 1-620 <$400
20 Type 1 1-168 <$400
10 Type 2 1-784 <$400
20 Type 2 1-212 <$400
Total Issue $378,890
Out in 1935 $25,000
Large out 1935 $1,440
****
10278 Teton
FNB OF DRIGGS
{{ 3 L }}
Chartered 10/18/12
Liquidated 10/15/29
1902 Date Back <$VALUE
4x5 1-500 <$800
3x10-20 1-500 <$800
1902 Plain Back
4x5 501-4505 <$800
3x10-20 501-2845 <$800
Total Issue $232,350
Out at close $11,595
****
11508 Clark
FNB OF DUBOIS
{{ UNREPORTED }}
Organized 10/27/19
Receivership 5/5/27
1902 Plain Back <$VALUE
4x5 1-2345 <$2000
3x10-20 1-1786 <$2000
Total Issue $136,200
Out at close $25,000
****
6145 Gem
FNB OF EMMETT
{{ 3 L }}
Chartered 3/5/02
Liquidated 4/21/30
1902 Red Seal <$VALUE
3x10-20 1-500 <$4000
1902 Date Back
3x10-20 1-3070* <$750
1902 Plain Back
3x10-20 3311-4607* <$750
* 3071-3310 not marked
Total Issue $255,350
Out at close $1,690
****
FNB of Fairfield
SEE Ch 10162
FNB of Soldier
****
11198 Bingham
FNB OF FIRTH
{{ 1 L }}
Chartered 6/18
Liquidated 1/5/25
1902 Plain Back <$VALUE
4x5 1-1780 <$1500
3x10-20 1-1132 <$1500
Total Issue $82,200
Out at close $25,000
Ch 7419 assumed circulation
****
4808 Latah
FNB OF GENESEE
{{ UNREPORTED }}
Chartered 10/24/92
Liquidated 11/19/93
Brown Back <$VALUE
3x10-20 1-236 <$5000
Total Issue $11,800
Out in 1910 $190
****
9371 Gooding
FNB OF GOODING
{{ 6 L }}
Chartered 3/09
Liquidated 6/26/28
1902 Date Back <$VALUE
4x5 1-2900 <$450
3x10-20 1-2320 <$450
1902 Plain Back
4x5 2901-9120 <$450
3x10-20 2321-6285 <$450
Total Issue $496,650
Out at close $40,000
****
6927 Idaho
FNB OF GRANGEVILLE
{{ 5 L 11 S }}
Organized 4/22/03
1902 Red Seal <$VALUE
3x10-20 1-2140 <$4000
1902 Date Back
3x10-20 1-3300 <$500
1902 Plain Back
3x10-20 3301-10064 <$500
1929 Small Size
10 Type 1 1-1270 <$225
20 Type 1 1-370 <$250
10 Type 2 1-1725 <$250
20 Type 2 1-516 <$250
Total Issue $758,370
Out in 1935 $50,000
Large out 1935 $2,300
****
10294 Gooding
FNB OF HAGERMAN
{{ 1 L }}
Organized 11/23/12
1902 Date Back <$VALUE
3x10-20 1-500 <$1500
1902 Plain Back
3x10-20 501-1237 <$1500
Total Issue $61,850
Out in 1935 $340
****
11053 Blaine
BLAINE COUNTY NB OF
HAILEY
{{ 2 L }}
Chartered 8/17
Liquidated 10/22/25
1902 Plain Back <$VALUE
4x5 1-5615 <$850
3x10-20 1-3716 <$850
Total Issue $298,100
Out at close $50,000
****
3895 Blaine
FNB OF HAILEY
Chartered 6/2/88
Liquidated 5/21/08
TERRITORIAL ISSUES {{ 0 L }}
Brown Back <$VALUE
4x5 1-1525 <$15,000
STATE ISSUES {{ 1 L }}
Brown Back
4x5 1526-3487 <$4000
3x10-20 1-573 <$4000
Total Issue $98,390
Out in 1910 $4,310
****
9145 Blaine
HAILEY NB, HAILEY
{{ 5 L 3 S }}
Chartered 5/08
1902 Date Back <$VALUE
4x5 1-3380 <$500
3x10-20 1-3260 <$500
1902 Plain Back
4x5 3381-10097 <$500
3x10-20 3261-7119 <$500
1929 Small Size
5 Type 1 1-558 <$400
10 Type 1 1-286 <$400
20 Type 1 1-86 <$400
5 Type 2 1-1364 <$400
10 Type 2 1-636 <$400
20 Type 2 1-144 <$400
Total Issue $618,170
Out in 1935 $20,000
Large out 1935 $2,290
****
6982 Bonneville
AMERICAN NB OF
IDAHO FALLS
{{ 3 L U + 17 S }}
Chartered 10/03
1902 Red Seal <$VALUE
4x5 1-625 <$4000
3x10-20 1-490 <$4000
1902 Date Back
4x5 1-2100 <$500
3x10-20 1-1600 <$500
1902 Plain Back
4x5 2101-7050 <$500
3x10-20 1601-4715 <$500
1929 Small Size
5 Type 1 1-3016 <$125
10 Type 1 1-1652 <$125
20 Type 1 1-484 <$135
5 Type 2 1-6998 <$150
10 Type 2 1-4019 <$150
20 Type 2 1-1032 <$160
Total Issue $757,250
Out in 1935 $100,000
Large out 1935 $1,850
****
5820 Bonneville
FNB OF IDAHO FALLS
{{ UNREPORTED }}
Chartered 5/20/01
Liquidated 11/8/01
Brown Back <$VALUE
3x10-20 1-125 <$6000
Total Issue $6,250
Out at close $6,250
All notes reportedly redeemed
****
11278 Bonneville
IDAHO FALLS NB,
IDAHO FALLS
{{ 8 L }}
Chartered 12/18
Liquidated 3/26/27
1902 Plain Back <$VALUE
3x10-20 1-12012 <$400
Total Issue $600,600
Out at close $100,000
****
9680 Jerome
FNB OF JEROME
{{ 7 L }}
Chartered 3/10
Liquidated 6/26/28
1902 Date Back <$VALUE
4x10 1-1225 <$450
1902 Plain Back
4x10 1226-10896 <$450
Total Issue $435,840
Out at close $50,000
****

9566 Shoshone
FNB OF KELLOGG
{{ 1 L 1 S }}
Chartered 10/09
1902 Date Back <$VALUE
4x5 1-625 <$1500
3x10-20 1-500 <$1500
1902 Plain Back
4x5 626-1475 <$1500
3x10-20 501-1006 <$1500
1929 Small Size
5 Type 1 1-311 <$1000
10 Type 1 1-145 <$1000
20 Type 1 1-38 <$1000
Total Issue $102,390
Out in 1935 $6,250
Large out 1935 $390

4790 Latah
FNB OF KENDRICK
{{ UNREPORTED }}
Chartered 8/11/92
Liquidated 5/20/99
Brown Back <$VALUE
50-100 1-177 <$10,000
Total Issue $26,550
Out in 1910 $600

3142 Blaine
FNB OF KETCHUM
{{ 1 L }}
Chartered 3/21/84
Liquidated 4/28/90
TERRITORIAL ISSUES
Brown Back <$VALUE
4x5 1-1469 <$15,000
Total Issue $29,380
Out in 1910 $265

11745 Nez Perce
AMERICAN NB OF LEWISTON
{{ 3 L }}
Chartered 6/20
Liquidated 1/10/25
1902 Plain Back <$VALUE
3x10-20 1-6388 <$600
Total Issue $319,400
Out at close $100,000

10212 Nez Perce
EMPIRE NB OF LEWISTON
{{ 6 L }}
Chartered 6/12
Liquidated 9/1/24
1902 Date Back <$VALUE
3x10-20 1-5300 <$400
1902 Plain Back
3x10-20 5301-13902 <$400
Total Issue $695,100
Out at close $100,000

2972 Nez Perce
FNB OF LEWISTON
Organized 5/29/83
TERRITORIAL ISSUES {{ 1 L }}
Brown Back <$VALUE
3x10-20 1-560 <$15,000
STATE ISSUES {{ 6 L 6 S }}
Brown Back
3x10-20 561-2500 <$4000
1902 Red Seal
50-100 1-700 <$8500
1902 Date Back
50-100 1-440 <$500/$600
3x50-100 1-1720 <$500/$600
1902 Plain Back
3x50-100 1721-2053
<$500/$600
1929 Small Size
50 Type 1 1-252 <$350
100 Type 1 1-84 <$400
5 Type 2 1-564 <$300
10 Type 2 1-50 <$300
20 Type 2 1-110 <$300
Total Issue $940,770
Out in 1935 $100,000
Large out 1935 $12,180

5600 Nez Perce
IDAHO NB OF LEWISTON
{{ 2 L }}
Chartered 10/19/00
Liquidated 8/15/04
Brown Back <$VALUE
3x10-20 1-446 <$4000
Total Issue $22,300
Out in 1910 $640

3023 Nez Perce
LEWISTON NB, LEWISTON
Organized 8/9/83
Liquidated 12/4/33
TERRITORIAL ISSUES {{ 0 L }}
Brown Back <$VALUE
3x10-20 1-605 <$15,000
STATE ISSUES {{ 8 L 10 S }}
Brown Back
3x10-20 606-1375 <$4000
1902 Red Seal
3x10-20 1-1850 <$4000
1902 Date Back
3x10-20 1-7500 <$300/$325
1902 Plain Back
3x10-20 7501-17661
<$300/$325
1929 Small Size
10 Type 1 1-2476 <$200
20 Type 1 1-734 <$200
10 Type 2 1-422 <$250
Total Issue $1,285,160
Out at close $100,000
Large out at close $5,065

13819 Nez Perce
LEWISTON NB, LEWISTON
{{ 10 S }}
Chartered 10/33
1929 Small Size <$VALUE
5 Type 2 1-11514 <$225
10 Type 2 1-6027 <$225
20 Type 2 1-1469 <$225
Total Issue $147,220
Out in 1935 $100,000

8822 Oneida
FNB OF MALAD CITY
{{ 6 L 9 S }}
Organized 6/23/07
1902 Red Seal <$VALUE
4x5 1-187 <$4000
3x10-20 1-188 <$4000
1902 Date Back
4x5 1-2250 <$500
3x10-20 1-2200 <$500
1902 Plain Back
4x5 2251-7992 <$500
3x10-20 2201-6473 <$500
1929 Small Size
5 Type 1 1-1718 <$250
10 Type 1 1-732 <$250
5 Type 2 1-2664 <$275
10 Type 2 1-1404 <$275
Total Issue $552,840
Out in 1935 $30,000
Large out 1935 $1,875

10221 Ada
FNB OF MERIDIAN
{{ 2 L }}
Chartered 7/12
Liquidated 5/13/24
1902 Date Back <$VALUE
3x10-20 1-2100 <$1000
1902 Plain Back
3x10-20 2101-5630 <$1000
Total Issue $281,500
Out at close $40,000

7381 Bear Lake
FNB OF MONTPELIER
{{ 2 L }}
Organized 8/9/04
Receivership 3/13/25
1902 Red Seal <$VALUE
4x5 1-500 <$4000
3x10-20 1-440 <$4000
1902 Date Back
4x5 1-1050* <$1000
3x10-20 1-800** <$1000
1902 Plain Back
4x5 1151-2220* <$1000
3x10-20 881-1481** <$1000
* 1051-1150 not marked
** 801-880 not marked
Total Issue $150,450
Out at close $11,800

3408 Latah
FNB OF MOSCOW
Organized 11/4/85
TERRITORIAL ISSUES {{ 0 L }}
Brown Back <$VALUE
4x5 1-2500 <$15,000
STATE ISSUES {{ 2 L 12 S }}
Brown Back
4x5 2501-4716 <$4000
50-100 1-122 <$8500
1902 Red Seal
3x10-20 1-1150 <$4000
1902 Date Back
3x10-20 1-900* <$700
1902 Plain Back
3x10-20 1061-3557* <$700
* 901-1060 not marked
1929 Small Size
10 Type 1 1-1438 <$175
20 Type 1 1-340 <$175
10 Type 2 1-1272 <$225
20 Type 2 1-325 <$225
Total Issue $494,270
Out in 1935 $50,000
Large out 1935 $1,740

4584 Latah
MOSCOW NB, MOSCOW
{{ UNREPORTED }}
Organized 6/17/91
Receivership 2/4/97
Brown Back <$VALUE
4x5 1-1883 <$5000
Total Issue $37,660
Out in 1915 $195

6521 Elmore
FNB OF MOUNTAIN HOME
{{ 3 L }}
Chartered 12/5/02
Liquidated 12/24/28
1902 Red Seal <$VALUE
3x10-20 1-376 <$5000
1902 Date Back
3x10-20 1-1760 <$850
1902 Plain Back
3x10-20 1761-5381 <$850
Total Issue $287,850
Out at close $25,000

8906 Shoshone
FNB OF MULLAN
{{ 2 L 3 S }}
Chartered 10/07
Liquidated 3/10/33
1902 Red Seal <$VALUE
3x10-20 1-300 <$4000
1902 Date Back
3x10-20 1-1510 <$1000
1902 Plain Back
3x10-20 1511-5703 <$1000
1929 Small Size
10 Type 1 1-591 <$600
20 Type 1 1-160 <$600
Total Issue $354,810
Out at close $25,000
Large out at close $1,530

10693 Canyon
CITIZENS NB OF NAMPA
{{ 1 L }}
Chartered 2/15
Liquidated 12/15/16
1902 Date Back <$VALUE
4x5 1-1000 <$1250
3x10-20 1-900 <$1250
1902 Plain Back
4x5 1001-1420 <$1250
3x10-20 901-1133 <$1250
Total Issue $85,050
Out at close $50,000
Ch 10916 assumed circulation

10916 Canyon
FARMERS & MERCHANTS NB OF NAMPA
{{ 3 L }}
Chartered 10/16
Liquidated 3/16/20
1902 Plain Back <$VALUE
4x5 1-3120 <$650
3x10-20 1-1696 <$650
Total Issue $147,200
Out at close $100,000
Outstanding includes Ch 10693
Ch 8370 assumed circulation

8370 Canyon
FNB OF NAMPA
{{ 3 L }}
Organized 9/15/06
Receivership 6/1/23
1902 Red Seal <$VALUE
4x5 1-600 <$4000
3x10-20 1-480 <$4000
1902 Date Back
4x5 1-1875 <$600
3x10-20 1-1290 <$600
1902 Plain Back
4x5 1876-7297 <$600
3x10-20 1291-4555 <$600
Total Issue $409,690
Out at close $105,000
Outstanding includes Ch 10916

10975 Fremont
FNB OF NEWDALE
{{ 1 L }}
Chartered 4/17
Liquidated 8/1/23
1902 Plain Back <$VALUE
4x5 1-930 <$1500
3x10-20 1-534 <$1500
Total Issue $45,300
Out at close $10,000

6697 Lewis
FNB OF NEZPERCE
{{ UNREPORTED }}
Chartered 3/28/03
Liquidated 11/6/06
1902 Red Seal <$VALUE
3x10-20 1-269 <$5000
Total Issue $13,450
Out in 1910 $1,140

11496 Canyon
FNB OF PARMA
{{ 6 L 4 S }}
Chartered 10/19
1902 Plain Back <$VALUE
4x5 1-14070 <$400
1929 Small Size
5 Type 1 1-3594 <$300
5 Type 2 1-8952 <$325
Total Issue $433,980
Out in 1935 $30,000
Large out 1935 $1,385

5906 Payette
FNB OF PAYETTE
{{ 7 L }}
Chartered 7/17/01
Liquidated 7/6/25
Brown Back <$VALUE
4x5 1-690 <$4000
3x10-20 1-564 <$4000
1882 Date Back
4x5 1-4050 <$2000
3x10-20 1-2940 <$2000
1882 Value Back
4x5 4051-7350 <$2500
3x10-20 2941-5070 <$2500
1902 Plain Back
4x5 1-3330 <$450
3x10-20 1-2110 <$450
Total Issue $614,600
Out in 1925 $60,000

8075 Payette
PAYETTE NB, PAYETTE
{{ 5 L }}
Organized 1/9/06
Receivership 12/13/22
1902 Red Seal <$VALUE
4x5 1-1650 <$4000
3x10-20 1-1300 <$4000
1902 Date Back
4x5 1-5250 <$400
3x10-20 1-3900 <$400
1902 Plain Back
4x5 5251-10475 <$400
3x10-20 3901-7791 <$400
Total Issue $697,050
Out at close $71,700

6347 Bannock
BANNOCK NB OF POCATELLO
{{ 1 L }}
Chartered 7/22/02
Receivership 6/11/21
1902 Red Seal <$VALUE
4x5 1-675 <$4000
3x10-20 1-600 <$4000
1902 Date Back
4x5 1-1300* <$1500
3x10-20 1-840** <$1500
1902 Plain Back
4x5 1401-1720* <$1500
3x10-20 921-1120** <$1500
* 1301-1400 not marked
** 841-920 not marked
Total Issue $133,900
Out at close $11,700

4023 Bannock
FNB OF POCATELLO
Chartered 5/3/89
Liquidated 7/7/28
TERRITORIAL ISSUES {{ 2 L }}
Brown Back <$VALUE
4x5 1-800 <$15,000
STATE ISSUES {{ 2 L }}
Brown Back
4x5 801-2650 <$4000
50-100 1-127 <$8500
1882 Date Back
50-100 1-17 <$8500
1902 Date Back
4x5 1-900 <$1000
50-100 1-160 <$1250/$1500
3x50-100 1-40 <$1250/$1500
1902 Plain Back
4x5 901-3118 <$1000
Total Issue $170,960
Out in 1925 $12,300

4827 Bannock
IDAHO NB OF POCATELLO
{{ UNREPORTED }}
Chartered 12/20/92
Liquidated 8/5/95
Brown Back <$VALUE
4x5 1-919 <$5000
Total Issue $18,380
Out in 1910 $105

7526 Franklin
FNB OF PRESTON
{{ 6 L 2 S }}
Chartered 12/04
Liquidated 3/7/31
1902 Red Seal <$VALUE
3x10-20 1-1000 <$4000
1902 Date Back
3x10-20 1-2110 <$500
1902 Plain Back
3x10-20 2111-6362 <$500
1929 Small Size
10 Type 1 1-341 <$750
20 Type 1 1-94 <$750
Total Issue $399,840
Out at close $25,000
Large out at close $3,830

7133 Madison
FNB OF REXBURG
{{ 2U + 7 L }}
Organized 1/19/04
Receivership 8/11/24
1902 Red Seal <$VALUE
4x5 1-1650 <$4000
3x10-20 1-1200 <$4000
1902 Date Back
4x5 1-3350 <$500
3x10-20 1-2440 <$500
1902 Plain Back
4x5 3351-8935 <$500
3x10-20 2441-5697 <$500
Total Issue $556,550
Out at close $50,000

11458 Jefferson
JEFFERSON COUNTY NB OF RIGBY
{{ 1 L }}
Organized 6/9/19
Receivership 1/17/25
1902 Plain Back <$VALUE
3x10-20 1-1478 <$2000
Total Issue $73,900
Out at close $50,000

10920 Jefferson
FNB OF RIRIE
{{ 1 L }}
Organized 10/9/16
Receivership 8/11/24
1902 Plain Back <$VALUE
3x10-20 1-1617 <$2000
Total Issue $80,850
Out at close $16,250

10429 Minidoka
FNB OF RUPERT
{{ 1 L }}
Chartered 8/5/13
Receivership 2/7/23
1902 Date Back <$VALUE
3x10-20 1-500 <$1250
1902 Plain Back
3x10-20 501-2233 <$1250
Total Issue $111,650
Out at close $25,000

10517 Minidoka
RUPERT NB, RUPERT
{{ 1 L }}
Chartered 4/14
Liquidated 1/31/25
1902 Date Back <$VALUE
3x10-20 1-500 <$1000
1902 Plain Back
3x10-20 501-5193 <$1000
Total Issue $259,650
Out at close $50,000

7230 Fremont
COMMERCIAL NB OF SAINT ANTHONY
{{ 2 L 6 S }}
Chartered 4/04
1902 Red Seal <$VALUE
3x10-20 1-582 <$4000
1902 Date Back
3x10-20 1-1720 <$1000
1902 Plain Back
3x10-20 1721-5812 <$1000
1929 Small Size
10 Type 1 1-716 <$275
20 Type 1 1-200 <$275
10 Type 2 1-864 <$325
20 Type 2 1-282 <$325
Total Issue $400,940
Out in 1935 $25,000
Large out 1935 $1,950

5764 Fremont
FNB OF SAINT ANTHONY
{{ 6 L }}
Chartered 3/30/01
Receivership 3/4/24
Brown Back <$VALUE
4x5 1-1775 <$4000
3x10-20 1-1310 <$4000
1882 Date Back
4x5 1-3800 <$2000
3x10-20 1-2740 <$2000
1882 Value Back
4x5 3801-6340 <$2500
3x10-20 2741-4222 <$2500
1902 Plain Back
3x10-20 1-2200 <$400
Total Issue $548,900
Out at close $47,600

10771 Benewah
FNB OF SAINT MARIES
{{ 3 L 2 S }}
Chartered 8/15
Liquidated 12/22/31
1902 Plain Back <$VALUE
4x5 1-5193 <$600
3x10-20 1-3232 <$600
1929 Small Size
5 Type 1 1-594 <$600
10 Type 1 1-292 <$600
20 Type 1 1-83 <$600
Total Issue $310,760
Out at close $25,000
Large out at close $1,255

9432 Lemhi
CITIZENS NB OF SALMON
{{ 8 L 8 S }}
Organized 4/27/09
Receivership 5/25/32
1902 Date Back <$VALUE
4x5 1-7650 <$400
3x10-20 1-5920 <$400
1902 Plain Back
4x5 7651-22105 <$400
3x10-20 5921-15308 <$400
1929 Small Size
5 Type 1 1-2750 <$325
10 Type 1 1-1355 <$325
20 Type 1 1-288 <$350
Total Issue $1,405,860
Out at close $96,160
Large out at close $9,365

8080 Lemhi
FNB OF SALMON
{{ 3 L }}
Organized 1/13/06
Receivership 8/8/11
1902 Red Seal <$VALUE
4x5 1-725 <$4000
3x10-20 1-650 <$4000
1902 Date Back
4x5 1-1375 <$1250
3x10-20 1-957 <$1250
Total Issue $122,350
Out in 1915 $2,450

****

9263 Bonner
BONNER COUNTY NB OF SANDPOINT
{{ 2 L 7 S }}
Organized 10/27/08

1902 Date Back	<$VALUE
3x10-20 1-1510	<$1250
1902 Plain Back	
3x10-20 1511-3080	<$1250
1929 Small Size	
5 Type 1 1-894	<$500
10 Type 1 1-284	<$500
5 Type 2 1-670	<$525
10 Type 2 1-393	<$525
Total Issue	$205,140
Out in 1935	$12,500
Large out 1935	$650

****

8341 Bonner
FNB OF SANDPOINT
{{ 2 L 5 S }}
Chartered 8/06
Liquidated 5/31/32

1902 Red Seal	<$VALUE
3x10-20 1-300	<$4000
1902 Date Back	
3x10-20 1-1420	<$1250
1902 Plain Back	
3x10-20 1421-2929	<$1250
1929 Small Size	
10 Type 1 1-261	<$450
20 Type 1 1-51	<$450
Total Issue	$183,230
Out at close	$12,500
Large out at close	$1,610

****

11434 Bingham
FNB OF SHELLEY
{{ 3 L }}
Organized 7/15/19
Receivership 2/13/25

1902 Plain Back	<$VALUE
4x5 1-5100	<$850
Total Issue	$102,000
Out at close	$19,600

****

6577 Lincoln
FNB OF SHOSHONE
{{ 2 L }}
Chartered 1/03
Liquidated 6/28/28

1902 Red Seal	<$VALUE
3x10-20 1-400	<$4000
1902 Date Back	
3x10-20 1-700	<$1000
1902 Plain Back	
3x10-20 701-6396	<$1000
Total Issue	$339,800
Out at close	$40,000

****

9272 Lincoln
LINCOLN COUNTY NB OF SHOSHONE
{{ 3 L 7 S }}
Chartered 11/08

1902 Date Back	<$VALUE
3x10-20 1-2820	<$800
1902 Plain Back	
3x10-20 2821-7819	<$800
1929 Small Size	
10 Type 1 1-752	<$325
20 Type 1 1-242	<$325
5 Type 2 1-324	<$350
10 Type 2 1-1494	<$350
20 Type 2 1-240	<$350
Total Issue	$486,470
Out in 1935	$30,000
Large out 1935	$1,545

****

10162 Camas
FNB OF SOLDIER
Organized 3/20/12
Receivership 8/26/20
2nd title: FNB of Fairfield 11/12/15
FIRST TITLE {{ 0 L }}

1902 Date Back	<$VALUE
4x5 1-805	<$3000
3x10-20 1-582	<$3000
SECOND TITLE {{ 0 L }}	
1902 Plain Back	
3x10-20 1-399	<$3000
Total Issue	$65,150
Out at close	$5,850

****

7608 Twin Falls
FNB OF TWIN FALLS
{{ 4 L }}
Organized 1/14/05
Receivership 12/12/31

1902 Red Seal	<$VALUE
4x5 1-330	<$4000
3x10-20 1-984	<$4000
1902 Date Back	
4x5 1-3725	<$600
3x10-20 1-2120	<$600
1902 Plain Back	
4x5 3726-9845	<$600
3x10-20 2121-6034	<$600
Total Issue	$554,400
Out at close	$3,255

****

11274 Twin Falls
TWIN FALLS NB, TWIN FALLS
{{ 2 L 3 S }}
Organized 10/28/18
Receivership 12/2/31

1902 Plain Back	<$VALUE
4x5 1-5105	<$850
3x10-20 1-5957	<$850
1929 Small Size	
5 Type 1 1-1328	<$500
10 Type 1 1-612	<$500
20 Type 1 1-198	<$500
Total Issue	$500,270
Out at close	$49,280
Large out at close	$3,920

****

4773 Shoshone
FNB OF WALLACE
{{ 9 L 18 S }}
Chartered 1892

Brown Back	<$VALUE
4x5 1-7525	<$4000
3x10-20 1-2960	<$4000
1882 Date Back	
4x5 1-3356	<$2000
3x10-20 1-2481	<$2000
1902 Date Back	
4x5 1-3250	<$325
3x10-20 1-2800	<$325
1902 Plain Back	
4x5 3251-18135	<$325
3x10-20 2801-12736	<$325
1929 Small Size	
10 Type 1 1-2184	<$135
20 Type 1 1-636	<$140
10 Type 2 1-3600	<$160
20 Type 2 1-648	<$175
Total Issue	$1,745,490
Out in 1935	$100,000
Large out 1935	$6,480

****

9134 Shoshone
WALLACE NB, WALLACE
{{ UNREPORTED }}
Chartered 5/08
Liquidated 6/10/16

1902 Date Back	<$VALUE
4x5 1-2000	<$1500
3x10-20 1-3879	<$1500
Total Issue	$233,950
Out in 1916	$39,600

****

6754 Washington
FNB OF WEISER
{{ 6 L }}
Chartered 4/03
Liquidated 9/1/23

1902 Red Seal	<$VALUE
4x5 1-550	<$4000
3x10-20 1-1270	<$4000
1902 Date Back	
4x5 1-5950	<$400
3x10-20 1-3940	<$400
1902 Plain Back	
4x5 5951-11565	<$400
3x10-20 3941-7820	<$400
Total Issue	$696,800
Out at close	$74,995

****

8139 Washington
WEISER NB, WEISER
{{ 4 L }}
Chartered 2/19/06
Receivership 6/23/24

1902 Red Seal	<$VALUE
3x10-20 1-1275	<$4000
1902 Date Back	
3x10-20 1-3450	<$450
1902 Plain Back	
3x10-20 3451-9291	<$450
Total Issue	$528,300
Out at close	$64,100

****

9491 Gooding
FNB OF WENDELL
{{ 1 L }}
Organized 6/30/09
Receivership 1/5/22

1902 Date Back	<$VALUE
3x10-20 1-2170	<$1500
1902 Plain Back	
3x10-20 2171-3569	<$1500
Total Issue	$178,450
Out at close	$24,300

****

CONDITION affects Value. The Values shown are for notes in FINE condition.

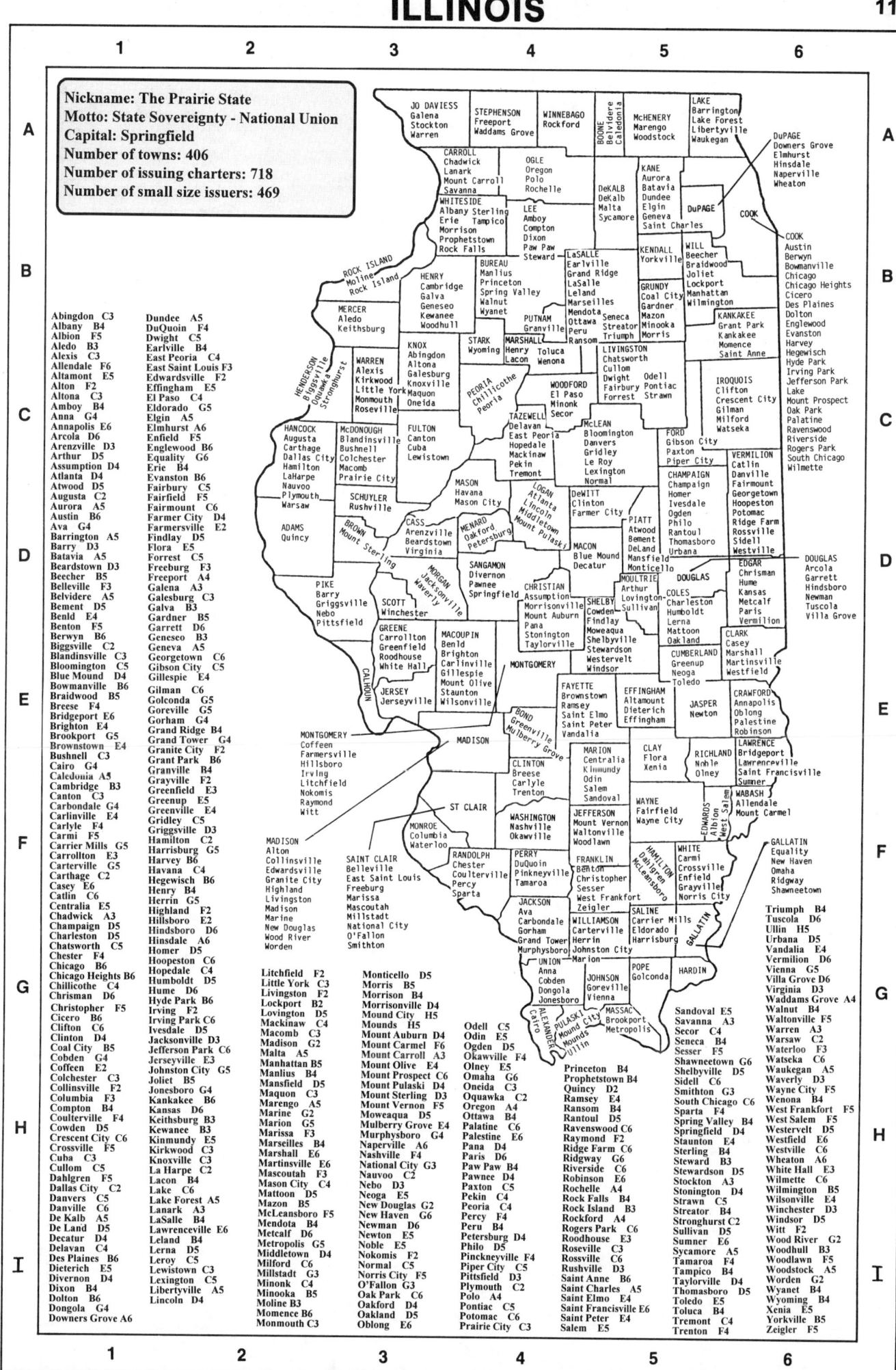

Nickname: The Prairie State
Motto: State Sovereignty - National Union
Capital: Springfield
Number of towns: 406
Number of issuing charters: 718
Number of small size issuers: 469

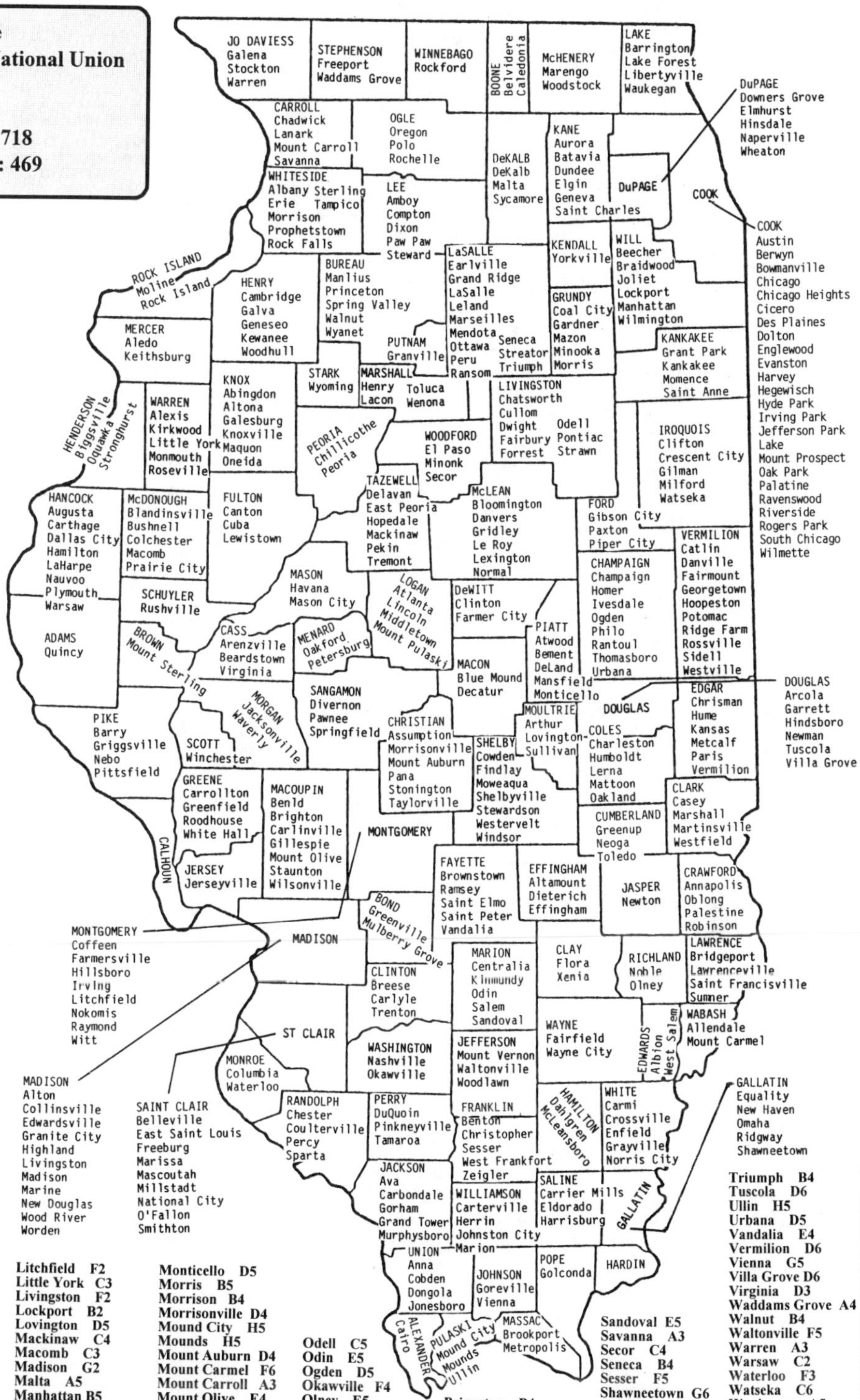

3377 Knox
FNB OF ABINGDON
{{ 8 L }}
Organized 8/5/85
Receivership 12/17/27
Brown Back <$VALUE
4x5 1-3750 <$350
3x10-20 1-1205 <$350
1902 Red Seal
3x10-20 1-2000 <$350
1902 Date Back
3x10-20 1-5300 <$150
1902 Plain Back
3x10-20 5301-14449 <$150
Total Issue $957,700
Out at close $8,200

6089 Whiteside
FNB OF ALBANY
{{ UNREPORTED }}
Chartered 1/11/02
Liquidated 6/7/11
Brown Back <$VALUE
3x10-20 1-400 <$1500
1882 Date Back
3x10-20 1-115 <$1500
Total Issue $25,750
Out in 1911 $4,650

9025 Edwards
ALBION NB, ALBION
{{ 4 L 3 S }}
Organized 9/11/07
Liquidated 11/12/30
1902 Red Seal <$VALUE
3x10-20 1-600 <$600
1902 Date Back
3x10-20 1-1900 <$300
1902 Plain Back
3x10-20 1901-8628 <$300
1929 Small Size
10 Type 1 1-457 <$300
20 Type 1 1-59 <$300
Total Issue $495,900
Out in 1929 $50,000
Large out at close $9,670

8429 Edwards
FNB OF ALBION
{{ 8 L 3 S }}
Organized 10/17/06
Receivership 4/27/32
1902 Red Seal <$VALUE
4x5 1-1050 <$350
3x10-20 1-880 <$350
1902 Date Back
4x5 1-3550 <$175
3x10-20 1-2480 <$175
1902 Plain Back
4x5 3551-13840 <$175
3x10-20 2481-6664 <$175
1929 Small Size
5 Type 1 1-780 <$300
10 Type 1 1-90 <$300
20 Type 1 1-63 <$300
Total Issue $711,360
Out in 1930 $50,000
Large out at close $9,060

9649 Mercer
FARMERS NB OF ALEDO
{{ 5 L 13 S }}
Organized 1/5/10
Receivership 10/30/33
1902 Date Back <$VALUE
4x5 1-3500 <$250
3x10-20 1-2520 <$250
1902 Plain Back
4x5 3501-10214 <$250
3x10-20 2521-6599 <$250
1929 Small Size
5 Type 1 1-1348 <$100
10 Type 1 1-691 <$100
20 Type 1 1-212 <$100
Total Issue $641,570
Out at close $45,000
Large out at close $2,415

7145 Mercer
FNB OF ALEDO
{{ 8 L }}
Organized 1/24/04
Receivership 9/27/28
1902 Red Seal <$VALUE
3x10-20 1-1095 <$300
1902 Date Back
4x5 1-2200 <$150
3x10-20 1-2720 <$150
1902 Plain Back
4x5 2201-7515 <$150
3x10-20 2721-6164 <$150
Total Issue $513,250
Out at close $40,000

4967 Warren
FNB OF ALEXIS
{{ 2 L 2 S }}
Organized 5/18/94
Liquidated 1/16/31
Brown Back <$VALUE
4x5 1-2875 <$750
3x10-20 1-1120 <$750
1882 Date Back
4x5 1-1683 <$750
3x10-20 1-913 <$750
1902 Date Back
3x10-20 1-1000 <$500
1902 Plain Back
3x10-20 1001-4081 <$500
1929 Small Size
10 Type 1 1-361 <$400
20 Type 1 1-42 <$400
Total Issue $423,560
Out at close $25,000
Large out at close $4,390

10318 Wabash
FARMERS NB OF ALLENDALE
{{ UNREPORTED }}
Chartered 1/13
Liquidated 4/10/18
1902 Date Back <$VALUE
3x10-20 1-432 <$1000
Total Issue $21,600
Out at close $6,260

8293 Wabash
FNB OF ALLENDALE
{{ 3 L 6 S }}
Organized 12/4/05
1902 Red Seal <$VALUE
3x10-20 1-288 <$750
1902 Date Back
3x10-20 1-620 <$375
1902 Plain Back
3x10-20 621-4305 <$375
1929 Small Size
10 Type 1 1-548 <$175
20 Type 1 1-158 <$175
10 Type 2 1-831 <$200
20 Type 2 1-125 <$200
Total Issue $292,300
Out in 1935 $25,000
Large out 1935 $1,010

13993 Effingham
FNB IN ALTAMONT
{{ 1 S }}
Chartered 2/34
1929 Small Size <$VALUE
10 Type 2 1-486 <$500
20 Type 2 1-118 <$500
Total Issue $7,220
Out in 1935 $25,000
Outstanding includes Ch 8733

8733 Effingham
FNB OF ALTAMONT
{{ 3 L 5 S }}
Organized 3/8/07
Liquidated 4/12/34
1902 Red Seal <$VALUE
3x10-20 1-700 <$600
1902 Date Back
3x10-20 1-1610 <$300
1902 Plain Back
3x10-20 1611-4770 <$300
1929 Small Size
10 Type 1 1-566 <$200
20 Type 1 1-146 <$200
10 Type 2 1-98 <$250
20 Type 2 1-30 <$250
Total Issue $326,560
Out at close $25,000
Large out at close $1,390
Ch 13993 assumed circulation

1428 Madison
ALTON NB, ALTON
{{ 50+ L 0 S }}
Chartered 1865
Liquidated 5/17/30
Original Series <$VALUE
3x1-2 1-3792 <$200/$750
4x5 1-3210 <$250
Series 1875
4x5 1-4782 <$250
Brown Back
4x5 1-11017 <$150
3x10-20 1-1485 <$150/$200
1902 Red Seal
3x10-20 1-1800 <$150/$200
1902 Date Back
3x10-20 1-2200 <$100
1902 Plain Back
3x10-20 2201-4242 <$100
1929 Small Size
20 Type 1 1-2* <$750
* E000002A, F000002A canceled
Total Issue $775,690
Out at close $10,630
Large out at close $10,430

5188 Madison
CITIZENS NB OF ALTON
{{ 13 L 3 S }}
Chartered 4/24/99
Liquidated 5/17/30
Brown Back <$VALUE
4x5 1-8150 <$175
3x10-20 1-4440 <$175/$225
1882 Date Back
4x5 1-6850* <$150
3x10-20 1-5060** <$150/$200
1882 Value Back
4x5 7251-10361* <$175
3x10-20 5381-6850** <$175/$225
* 6851-7250 not marked
** 5061-5380 not marked
1902 Plain Back
4x10 1-19106 <$100
1929 Small Size
10 Type 1 1-1283 <$150
Total Issue $1,775,940
Out at close $99,535
Large out at close $22,555

1445 Madison
FNB OF ALTON
{{ 3 L }}
Chartered 1865
Liquidated 3/30/82
Original Series <$VALUE
3x1-2 1-5000 <$300/$850
4x5 1-4250 <$400
4x10 1-1300 <$750
Series 1875
4x5 1-2862 <$400
4x10 1-909 <$750
Total Issue $255,600
Out in 1910 $2,416

13625 Knox
ALTONA NB, ALTONA
{{ 5 S }}
Chartered 7/32
1929 Small Size <$VALUE
10 Type 1 1-310 <$175
20 Type 1 1-106 <$175
10 Type 2 1-141 <$200
20 Type 2 1-55 <$200
Total Issue $33,830
Out in 1935 $24,800

11331 Knox
FNB OF ALTONA
{{ 5 L 6 S }}
Chartered 4/19
Liquidated 11/5/32
1902 Plain Back <$VALUE
3x10-20 1-6845 <$225
1929 Small Size
10 Type 1 1-987 <$150
20 Type 1 1-246 <$150
Total Issue $430,990
Out at close $50,000
Large out at close $3,630

5223 Lee
FNB OF AMBOY
{{ 15 L 4 S }}
Chartered 10/13/99
Liquidated 10/2/34
Brown Back <$VALUE
4x5 1-4050 <$225
3x10-20 1-3420 <$225
1882 Date Back
4x5 1-4250 <$200
3x10-20 1-3100 <$200
1882 Value Back
4x5 4251-7700 <$225
3x10-20 3101-4800 <$225
1902 Plain Back
4x5 1-8808 <$100
3x10-20 1-6000 <$100
1929 Small Size
5 Type 1 1-647 <$175
10 Type 1 1-281 <$175
20 Type 1 1-59 <$175
Total Issue $1,165,510
Out in 1929 $50,000
Large out at close $5,390

5525 Union
ANNA NB, ANNA
{{ 2 L 4 S }}
Chartered 8/2/00
Brown Back <$VALUE
50-100 1-440 <$1250/$1500
1882 Date Back
50-100 1-260 <$1250/$1500
3x50-100 1-137 <$1250/$1500
1902 Plain Back
3x50-100 1-270 <$650/$750
1929 Small Size
50 Type 1 1-127 <$250
100 Type 1 1-43 <$300
Total Issue $270,650
Out in 1935 $50,000
Large out 1935 $3,550

4449 Union
FNB OF ANNA
{{ 10 L 6 S }}
Organized 9/13/90
Receivership 1/12/33
Brown Back <$VALUE
3x10-20 1-2316 <$275/$300
1902 Date Back
4x5 1-3230 <$150
4x10 1-3035 <$150
1902 Plain Back
4x5 3231-11464 <$150
4x10 3036-9683 <$150
1929 Small Size
5 Type 1 1-2028 <$135
10 Type 1 1-1051 <$135
Total Issue $856,300
Out at close $48,800
Large out at close $4,490

10257 Crawford
FNB OF ANNAPOLIS
{{ 6 L 7 S }}
Chartered 9/13/12
1902 Date Back <$VALUE
3x10-20 1-1100 <$275
1902 Plain Back
3x10-20 1101-4783 <$275
1929 Small Size
10 Type 1 1-626 <$150
20 Type 1 1-170 <$150
10 Type 2 1-392 <$175
20 Type 2 1-160 <$175
Total Issue $304,230
Out in 1935 $25,000
Large out 1935 $1,200

2204 Douglas
FNB OF ARCOLA
{{ 7 L 11 S }}
Chartered 11/9/74
Original Series <$VALUE
4x5 1-1950 <$500
Series 1875
4x5 1-3259 <$500
Brown Back
50-100 1-1297 <$1250/$1500
1882 Date Back
50-100 1-300 <$1250/$1500
3x50-100 1-98 <$1250/$1500
1902 Date Back
4x10 1-1000 <$175
1902 Plain Back
4x10 1001-9874 <$175
1929 Small Size
10 Type 1 1-2178 <$100
10 Type 2 1-2220 <$125
Total Issue $916,070
Out in 1935 $50,000
Large out 1935 $8,430

9183 Cass
FNB OF ARENZVILLE
{{ 12 L U + 13 S }}
Chartered 7/08
1902 Date Back <$VALUE
3x10-20 1-10000 <$165
1902 Plain Back
3x10-20 10001-25382 <$165
1929 Small Size
5 Type 1 1-2096 <$85
10 Type 1 1-2110 <$85
20 Type 1 1-416 <$100
5 Type 2 1-3282 <$100
10 Type 2 1-1560 <$100
Total Issue $1,540,510
Out in 1935 $50,000
Large out 1935 $7,120

5233 Moultrie
FNB OF ARTHUR
{{ 7 L 8 S }}
Chartered 11/13/99
Receivership 12/13/33
Brown Back <$VALUE
4x5 1-3185 <$375
3x10-20 1-2406 <$375
1882 Date Back
4x5 1-4000 <$375
3x10-20 1-2700 <$375
1882 Value Back
4x5 4001-5750 <$375
3x10-20 2701-3620 <$375
1902 Plain Back
4x5 1-6016 <$200
3x10-20 1-4248 <$200
1929 Small Size
5 Type 1 1-1732 <$150
10 Type 1 1-818 <$150
20 Type 1 1-231 <$150
Total Issue $941,480
Out at close $50,000
Large out at close $3,470

5316 Christian
FNB OF ASSUMPTION
{{ 3 L 6 S }}
Chartered 4/30/00
Brown Back <$VALUE
3x10-20 1-1830 <$500
1882 Date Back
3x10-20 1-1800* <$500
1882 Value Back
3x10-20 1941-2711* <$500
* 1801-1940 not marked
1902 Plain Back
3x10-20 1-2989 <$300
1929 Small Size
10 Type 1 1-622 <$150
20 Type 1 1-212 <$150
10 Type 2 1-178 <$200
20 Type 2 1-45 <$200
Total Issue $441,940
Out in 1935 $25,000
Large out 1935 $1,620

3711 Logan
ATLANTA NB, ATLANTA
{{ 5 L 9 S }}
Chartered 1887
Brown Back <$VALUE
4x5 1-4199 <$375
3x10-20 1-1219 <$375
1902 Red Seal
3x10-20 1-500 <$400
1902 Date Back
3x10-20 1-3700 <$200
1902 Plain Back
3x10-20 3701-10697 <$200
1929 Small Size
10 Type 1 1-1236 <$125
20 Type 1 1-346 <$150
10 Type 2 1-516 <$150
20 Type 2 1-237 <$150
Total Issue $830,360
Out in 1935 $50,000
Large out 1935 $3,140

2283 Logan
FNB OF ATLANTA
{{ U + 0 L }}
Chartered 7/2/75
Liquidated 4/15/79
Series 1875 <$VALUE
3x10-20 1-592 <$1250/$1750
Total Issue $20,600
Out in 1910 $210

6359 Piatt
FNB OF ATWOOD
{{ 4 L 5 S }}
Organized 7/17/02
Receivership 12/5/33
1902 Red Seal <$VALUE
3x10-20 1-1306 <$600
1902 Date Back
3x10-20 1-1780 <$300
1902 Plain Back
3x10-20 1781-5308 <$300
1929 Small Size
10 Type 1 1-566 <$200
20 Type 1 1-148 <$200
Total Issue $382,420
Out at close $25,000
Large out at close $1,810

6751 Hancock
FNB OF AUGUSTA
{{ 4 L 1 S }}
Organized 4/13/03
Receivership 12/23/30
1902 Red Seal <$VALUE
3x10-20 1-1940 <$600
1902 Date Back
3x10-20 1-2350* <$300
1902 Plain Back
3x10-20 2651-6710* <$300
* 2351-2650 not marked
1929 Small Size
5 Type 1 1-1278 <$500
Total Issue $470,840
Out at close $35,000
Large out at close $7,150

American NB of Aurora
SEE Ch 4469
German American NB of Aurora

2945 Kane
AURORA NB, AURORA
{{ 9 L 18 S }}
Organized 4/30/83
Receivership 6/18/34
Brown Back <$VALUE
3x10-20 1-4942 <$200/$250
1902 Red Seal
3x10-20 1-4000 <$250
1902 Date Back
3x10-20 1-6800 <$110
1902 Plain Back
3x10-20 6801-21435 <$110
1929 Small Size
10 Type 1 1-2276 <$40
20 Type 1 1-676 <$50
10 Type 2 1-406 <$50
20 Type 2 1-132 <$60
Total Issue $1,743,230
Out at close $99,150
Large out at close $7,210

13565 Kane
FNB IN AURORA
{{ 4 S }}
Organized 7/28/31
Receivership 7/6/32
1929 Small Size <$VALUE
10 Type 1 1-551 <$250
20 Type 1 1-108 <$250
Total Issue $46,020
Out at close $198,200
Outstanding includes Ch 38

38 Kane
FNB OF AURORA
{{ 8 L 15 S }}
Organized 6/20/63
Liquidated 9/25/31
Original Series <$VALUE
4x5 1-9280 <$750
Series 1875
3x10-20 1-3989 <$1000/$1500
Brown Back
50-100 1-1464 <$1250/$1500
1902 Red Seal
3x10-20 1-2000 <$350
1902 Date Back
3x10-20 1-6200 <$125
1902 Plain Back
3x10-20 6201-20224 <$125
1929 Small Size
10 Type 1 1-3026 <$40
20 Type 1 1-920 <$50
Total Issue $2,007,810
Out at close $200,000
Large out at close $26,590
Outstanding includes Ch 4469
Ch 13565 assumed circulation

4469 Kane
GERMAN AMERICAN NB OF AURORA
Chartered 1890
Closed 12/31/29
2nd title: American NB 6/10/18
FIRST TITLE {{ 3 L }}
Brown Back <$VALUE
3x10-20 1-8240 <$225/$250
1882 Date Back
3x10-20 1-1250 <$225/$250
1902 Date Back
3x10-20 1-5400 <$150
1902 Plain Back
3x10-20 5401-7200 <$150
SECOND TITLE {{ 6 L 3 S }}
1902 Plain Back
3x10-20 1-12377 <$125
1929 Small Size
10 Type 1 1-423 <$250
20 Type 1 1-60 <$250
Total Issue $1,485,930
Out at close $100,000
Large out at close $67,420
Ch 38 assumed circulation

<$VALUEs are for notes in FINE condition. Value changes by approximately 25% for a change of one full grade.

****
3854 Kane
MERCHANTS NB OF AURORA
{{ 28 L 15 S }}
Chartered 1888
Brown Back <$VALUE
4x5 1-5880 <$225
50-100 1-327 <$1250/$1500
1902 Red Seal
50-100 1-84 <$2250/$2500
1902 Date Back
50-100 1-600 <$350/$400
3x50-100 1-2680 <$350/$400
1902 Plain Back
3x50-100 2681-4305 <$350/$400
1929 Small Size
50 Type 1 1-857 <$110
100 Type 1 1-272 <$165
Total Issue $1,765,800
Out in 1935 $300,000
Large out 1935 $26,100
****
4596 Kane
OLD SECOND NB OF AURORA
{{ 28 L 33 S }}
Organized 5/25/91
Brown Back <$VALUE
3x10-20 1-6960 <$200
1882 Date Back
3x10-20 1-1482 <$200
1902 Date Back
3x10-20 1-11500 <$75
1902 Plain Back
3x10-20 11501-42994 <$75
1929 Small Size
10 Type 1 1-5262 <$25
20 Type 1 1-1322 <$35
10 Type 2 1-4159 <$25
20 Type 2 1-583 <$35
Total Issue $3,099,410
Out in 1935 $200,000
Large out 1935 $9,790
****
1909 Kane
SECOND NB OF AURORA
{{ 3 L }}
Chartered 12/27/71
Liquidated 7/13/91
Original Series <$VALUE
3x1-2 1-1868 <$350/$1000
4x5 1-2000 <$450
3x10-20 1-800 <$750/$1250
Series 1875
4x5 1-2735 <$450
3x10-20 1-1336 <$750/$1250
Total Issue $210,840
Out in 1910 $964
****
1792 Kane
UNION NB OF AURORA
{{ 3 L }}
Chartered 2/18/71
Liquidated 4/22/79
Original Series <$VALUE
3x1-2 1-2000 <$350/$1000
4x5 1-4625 <$450
3x10-20 1-1400 <$750/$1250
Series 1875
4x5 1-765 <$450
3x10-20 1-764 <$750/$1250
Total Issue $226,000
Out in 1910 $1,553
****
10337 Cook
AUSTIN NB, AUSTIN
Organized 2/7/13
Receivership 4/6/31
2nd title: Austin NB of Chicago 2/23/21
FIRST TITLE {{ 2 L }}
1902 Date Back <$VALUE
4x5 1-1500 <$300
3x10-20 1-1400 <$300
1902 Plain Back
4x5 1501-2100 <$300
3x10-20 1401-1720 <$300
SECOND TITLE {{ 2U + 3 L 3 S }}
1902 Plain Back
4x5 1-3126 <$165
3x10-20 1-1850 <$165
1929 Small Size
5 Type 1 1-465 <$165
10 Type 1 1-246 <$165
20 Type 1 1-66 <$165
Total Issue $319,650
Out at close $25,000
Large out at close $3,280
****
10911 Jackson
FNB OF AVA
{{ 6 S }}
Chartered 10/16 as FNB of Willisville, under which there was no issue. Issuing title adopted 7/1/27.
1929 Small Size <$VALUE
5 Type 1 1-456 <$165
10 Type 1 1-234 <$165
20 Type 1 1-116 <$165
50 Type 1 1-84 <$350
5 Type 2 1-388 <$175
10 Type 2 1-435 <$175
Total Issue $73,130
Out in 1935 $40,000
****
11283 Lake
FNB OF BARRINGTON
{{ U + 3 L 8 S }}
Chartered 1/19
1902 Plain Back <$VALUE
3x10-20 1-1059 <$300
1929 Small Size
10 Type 1 1-880 <$135
20 Type 1 1-270 <$135
10 Type 2 1-2017 <$150
20 Type 2 1-385 <$150
Total Issue $166,020
Out in 1935 $60,000
Large out 1935 $550
****
5771 Pike
FNB OF BARRY
{{ 13 L 9 S }}
Chartered 1901
Brown Back <$VALUE
3x10-20 1-1750 <$250/$300
1882 Date Back
3x10-20 1-4300 <$250/$300
1882 Value Back
3x10-20 4301-6501 <$250/$300
1902 Plain Back
3x10-20 1-5095 <$135
1929 Small Size
10 Type 1 1-1250 <$90
20 Type 1 1-366 <$100
10 Type 2 1-1278 <$100
20 Type 2 1-255 <$100
Total Issue $804,100
Out in 1935 $60,000
Large out 1935 $3,320
****
9500 Kane
BATAVIA NB, BATAVIA
{{ 8 L 15 S }}
Chartered 8/09
1902 Date Back <$VALUE
4x10 1-5250* <$135
1902 Plain Back
4x10 6051-23944* <$135
* 5251-6050 not marked
1929 Small Size
10 Type 1 1-4602 <$60
10 Type 2 1-780 <$65
Total Issue $1,241,680
Out in 1935 $40,000
Large out 1935 $3,680
****
339 Kane
FNB OF BATAVIA
{{ 6 L }}
Chartered 1864
Liquidated 8/30/79
Original Series <$VALUE
3x1-2 1-2800 <$300/$850
4x5 1-6300 <$400
Series 1875
3x1-2 1-1140 <$300/$850
4x5 1-1590 <$400
Total Issue $177,500
Out in 1910 $1,526
****
4646 Kane
FNB OF BATAVIA
{{ 7 L 11 S }}
Chartered 1891
Brown Back <$VALUE
3x10-20 1-2370 <$300
1882 Date Back
3x10-20 1-263 <$300
1902 Date Back
3x10-20 1-1600 <$150
1902 Plain Back
3x10-20 1601-12684 <$150
1929 Small Size
10 Type 1 1-1882 <$60
20 Type 1 1-566 <$65
10 Type 2 1-1998 <$70
20 Type 2 1-395 <$75
Total Issue $974,570
Out in 1935 $80,000
Large out 1935 $4,010
****
3640 Cass
FNB OF BEARDSTOWN
{{ 9 L 9 S }}
Chartered 1887
Brown Back <$VALUE
3x10-20 1-6866 <$250/$300
1902 Red Seal
3x10-20 1-1600 <$250/$300
1902 Date Back
3x10-20 1-6900 <$135
1902 Plain Back
3x10-20 6901-21384 <$135
1929 Small Size
10 Type 1 1-2516 <$100
20 Type 1 1-674 <$100
10 Type 2 1-264 <$125
20 Type 2 1-81 <$125
Total Issue $1,728,600
Out in 1935 $25,000
Large out 1935 $6,660
****
7726 Will
FNB OF BEECHER
{{ 1 L }}
Chartered 5/05
Liquidated 12/27/16
1902 Red Seal <$VALUE
3x10-20 1-480 <$1250
1902 Date Back
3x10-20 1-2300 <$600
1902 Plain Back
3x10-20 2301-2317 <$600
Total Issue $139,850
Out in 1916 $25,000
****
13236 St Clair
BELLEVILLE NB, BELLEVILLE
{{ 3U + 6 S }}
Chartered 8/28
1929 Small Size <$VALUE
5 Type 1 1-1176 <$100
10 Type 1 1-486 <$100
20 Type 1 1-240 <$100
Total Issue $93,240
Out in 1935 $48,900
****
2154 St Clair
FNB OF BELLEVILLE
{{ 11 L 9 S }}
Chartered 6/15/74
Original Series <$VALUE
3x1-2 1-2000 <$300/$850
4x5 1-1250 <$400
3x10-20 1-500 <$750/$1250
Series 1875
4x5 1 1820 <$400
3x10-20 1-2769 <$750/$1250
Brown Back
4x5 1-3250 <$200
50-100 1-2460 <$1250/$1500
1882 Date Back
4x5 1-6250 <$200
50-100 1-900 <$1250/$1500
3x50-100 1-85 <$1250/$1500
1902 Date Back
4x5 1-2500 <$100
3x50-100 1-920 <$400/$450
1902 Plain Back
4x5 2501-38061 <$100
3x50-100 921-1269<$400/$450
1929 Small Size
5 Type 1 1-7334 <$50
50 Type 1 1-276 <$125
100 Type 1 1-80 <$175
5 Type 2 1-6180 <$60
100 Type 2 1-88 <$300
Total Issue $2,419,090
Out in 1935 $150,000
Large out 1935 $13,350
****
11478 St Clair
SAINT CLAIR NB OF BELLEVILLE
{{ 7 L 15 S }}
Chartered 10/19
1902 Plain Back <$VALUE
3x10-20 1-12134 <$135
1929 Small Size
10 Type 1 1-2836 <$50
20 Type 1 1-868 <$60
10 Type 2 1-2717 <$55
20 Type 2 1-754 <$65
Total Issue $923,270
Out in 1935 $120,000
Large out 1935 $4,820
****
1097 Boone
FNB OF BELVIDERE
{{ 7 L 6 S }}
Chartered 1865
Liquidated 10/22/31
Original Series <$VALUE
3x1-2 1-2400 <$300/$850
4x5 1-4750 <$400
3x10-20 1-1300 <$750/$1250
Series 1875
4x5 1-240 <$400
3x10-20 1-2634 <$750/$1250
Brown Back
4x5 1-9824 <$250
3x10-20 1-1159 <$250
1902 Red Seal
4x5 1-1715 <$275
3x10-20 1-1334 <$275
1902 Date Back
4x5 1-4800 <$135
3x10-20 1-3220 <$135
1902 Plain Back
4x5 4801-16030 <$135
3x10-20 3221-10382 <$135
1929 Small Size
10 Type 1 1-1150 <$125
20 Type 1 1-328 <$135
Total Issue $1,611,990
Out at close $75,000
Large out at close $10,610
****
3190 Boone
SECOND NB OF BELVIDERE
{{ 6 L 13 S }}
Chartered 1884
Brown Back <$VALUE
3x10-20 1-4441 <$300
1902 Red Seal
3x10-20 1-2000 <$300
1902 Date Back
3x10-20 1-3300* <$150
1902 Plain Back
3x10-20 3801-10263* <$150
* 3301-3800 not marked
1929 Small Size
10 Type 1 1-1846 <$65
20 Type 1 1-474 <$75
5 Type 2 1-1478 <$85
10 Type 2 1-634 <$85
20 Type 2 1-130 <$100
Total Issue $1,019,170
Out in 1935 $50,000
Large out 1935 $3,450
****
4829 Piatt
FNB OF BEMENT
{{ 3 L }}
Chartered 1892
Liquidated 6/29/29
Brown Back <$VALUE
3x10-20 1-2670 <$500
1882 Date Back
3x10-20 1-300 <$450
1902 Date Back
3x10-20 1-750 <$350
1902 Plain Back
3x10-20 751-2047 <$350
Total Issue $250,850
Out at close $10,600
****
FNB of Benld
SEE Ch 7728
NB of Benld
****
7728 Macoupin
NB OF BENLD
Organized 5/2/05
2nd title: FNB of Benld 7/3/23
FIRST TITLE {{ 2 L }}
1902 Red Seal <$VALUE
3x10-20 1-1000 <$850
1902 Date Back
3x10-20 1-1660 <$400
1902 Plain Back
3x10-20 1661-3840 <$400
SECOND TITLE {{ 1 L 4 S }}
1902 Plain Back
3x10-20 1-1945 <$500
1929 Small Size
10 Type 1 1-652 <$175
20 Type 1 1-178 <$175
10 Type 2 1-480 <$200
20 Type 2 1-105 <$200
Total Issue $406,630
Out in 1935 $25,000
Large out 1935 $1,540
****
8234 Franklin
COAL BELT NB OF BENTON
{{ UNREPORTED }}
Organized 5/25/06
Receivership 2/9/09
1902 Red Seal <$VALUE
3x10-20 1-330 <$1500
Total Issue $16,500
Out in 1915 $540
****
6136 Franklin
FNB OF BENTON
{{ 8 L 4 S }}
Organized 1/11/02
Receivership 12/2/30
1902 Red Seal <$VALUE
4x5 1-2150 <$250
3x10-20 1-2180 <$250
1902 Date Back
4x5 1-3800 <$125
3x10-20 1-3040 <$125
1902 Plain Back (dated 1902)
3x10-20 3041-9648 <$125
1902 Plain Back (dated 1922)
3x10-20 1-10818 <$125
1929 Small Size
10 Type 1 1-1167 <$150
20 Type 1 1-350 <$150
Total Issue $1,363,320
Out at close $100,000
Large out at close $17,100
****
American NB & TC of Berwyn
SEE Ch 12426
FNB of Berwyn
****
12426 Cook
FNB OF BERWYN
Organized 7/31/23
Receivership 6/21/32
2nd title: F American NB & TC 12/15/30
FIRST TITLE {{ 5 L 3 S }}
1902 Plain Back <$VALUE
4x5 1-20817 <$175
1929 Small Size
5 Type 1 1-6362 <$125
SECOND TITLE {{ 2 S }}
1929 Small Size
5 Type 1 1-2341 <$200
Total Issue $677,430
Out at close $97,660
Large out at close $2,870
****
3003 Henderson
FNB OF BIGGSVILLE
{{ 5 L }}
Organized 4/10/83
Receivership 1/31/27
Brown Back <$VALUE
3x10-20 1-2472 <$400
1902 Red Seal
3x10-20 1-2300 <$400
1902 Date Back
3x10-20 1-3300 <$200
1902 Plain Back
3x10-20 3301-8376 <$200
Total Issue $657,400
Out at close $15,300
****
8908 McDonough
FNB OF BLANDINSVILLE
{{ 4 L 4 S }}
Chartered 10/07
Liquidated 4/19/32
1902 Red Seal <$VALUE
4x10 1-375 <$750
1902 Date Back
4x10 1-2275 <$350
1902 Plain Back
4x10 2276-6427 <$350
1929 Small Size
10 Type 1 1-613 <$250
Total Issue $308,860
Out at close $19,995
Large out at close $965
Ch 13597 assumed circulation
****
13597 McDonough
FNB OF BLANDINSVILLE
{{ 3 S }}
Chartered 2/32
1929 Small Size <$VALUE
10 Type 1 1-328 <$250
5 Type 2 1-202 <$300
10 Type 2 1-55 <$300
Total Issue $21,240
Out in 1935 $20,000
Outstanding includes Ch 8908
****
FNB of Bloomington
SEE Ch 819
NB of Bloomington
****
819 McLean
NB OF BLOOMINGTON
Chartered 1865
Liquidated 1/13/31
2nd title:FNB of Bloomington 1/27/85
FIRST TITLE {{ 2 L }}
Original Series <$VALUE
4x5 1-2185 <$600
3x10-20 1-4640<$1000/$1500
SECOND TITLE {{ 8 L 9 S }}
Brown Back
3x10-20 1-66 <$350
50-100 1-1417 <$1250/$1500
1902 Red Seal
50-100 1-566 <$2250/$2500
1902 Date Back
50-100 1-1140 <$400/$500
3x50-100 1-200 <$400/$500
1902 Plain Back
4x5 1-8740 <$125
3x50-100 201-508<$400/$500
1929 Small Size
5 Type 1 1-3301 <$75
50 Type 1 1-168 <$200
100 Type 1 1-30 <$275
Total Issue $1,216,680
Out at close $150,000
Large out at close $24,710
****
2386 McLean
N STATE B OF BLOOMINGTON
{{ UNREPORTED }}
Chartered 6/5/78
Liquidated 5/3/98
Series 1875 <$VALUE
3x10-20 1-4947<$1500/$2000
Total Issue $247,350
Out in 1910 $2,030
****
5119 McLean
STATE NB OF BLOOMINGTON
{{ 3 L }}
Chartered 1898
Liquidated 4/19/18
Brown Back <$VALUE
3x10-20 1-3900 <$450
1882 Date Back
4x5 1-5730 <$450
3x10-20 1-4340 <$450
1882 Value Back
4x5 5731-5950 <$450
3x10-20 4341-4512 <$450
Total Issue $539,600
Out at close $50,000
****
2676 McLean
THIRD NB OF BLOOMINGTON
{{ 3 L }}
Chartered 1882
Liquidated 3/15/11
Series 1875 <$VALUE
4x5 1-9544 <$600
50-100 1-145 <$4000
1902 Red Seal
3x10-20 1-1660 <$600
1902 Date Back
3x10-20 1-1637 <$350
Total Issue $377,480
Out in 1911 $38,050
****
9530 DeWitt
FNB OF BLUE MOUND
{{ 3 L }}
Organized 8/19/09
Receivership 3/27/26
1902 Date Back <$VALUE
4x5 1-1625 <$500
3x10-20 1-1530 <$500
1902 Plain Back
4x5 1626-3100 <$500
3x10-20 1531-3951 <$500
Total Issue $259,550
Out at close $24,200
****

CONDITION affects Value. The Values shown are for notes in FINE condition.

****
10237 Cook
BOWMANVILLE NB, BOWMANVILLE
Organized 7/25/12
Receivership 6/21/32
2nd title: Bowmanville NB of Chicago 1/24/23
FIRST TITLE {{ 3 L }}
1902 Date Back <$VALUE
3x10-20 1-1900 <$350
1902 Plain Back
3x10-20 1901-4420 <$350
SECOND TITLE {{ 3 L U + 5 S }}
1902 Plain Back
3x10-20 1-2835 <$350
1929 Small Size
10 Type 1 1-673 <$165
20 Type 1 1-202 <$165
Total Issue $427,370
Out at close $35,000
Large out at close $3,010
****
11895 Will
FNB IN BRAIDWOOD
{{ 2 L }}
Organized 12/6/20
Receivership 10/27/33
1902 Plain Back <$VALUE
3x10-20 1-1722 <$500
Total Issue $86,100
Out at close $840
****
1964 Will
MINERS NB OF BRAIDWOOD
Chartered 4/22/72
Receivership 11/1/33
2nd title: Commercial NB of Wilmington 1/31/78
FIRST TITLE {{ 4 L }}
Original Series <$VALUE
3x1-2 1-1500 <$500/$1250
4x5 1-2875 <$600
Series 1875
4x5 1-1105 <$600
SECOND TITLE {{ 6 L 4 S }}
Series 1875
50-100 1-626 <$4000
Brown Back
50-100 1-350 <$1250/$1500
1882 Date Back
50-100 1-57 <$1250/$1500
1902 Date Back
3x50-100 1-640 <$400/$500
1902 Plain Back
3x50-100 641-888<$400/$500
1929 Small Size
50 Type 1 1-145 <$200
100 Type 1 1-32 <$275
Total Issue $526,750
Out at close $50,000
Large out at close $6,200
****
9893 Clinton
FNB OF BREESE
{{ 6 L 9 S }}
Organized 10/14/10
Receivership 5/31/34
1902 Date Back <$VALUE
4x5 1-3100 <$225
3x10-20 1-2340 <$225
1902 Plain Back
4x5 3101-10764 <$225
3x10-20 2341-7532 <$225
1929 Small Size
5 Type 1 1-1978 <$125
10 Type 1 1-926 <$125
20 Type 1 1-254 <$125
5 Type 2 1-306 <$175
10 Type 2 1-80 <$175
20 Type 2 1-50 <$175
Total Issue $740,590
Out at close $50,000
Large out at close $2,920
****
8347 Lawrence
FNB OF BRIDGEPORT
{{ 4 L U + 9 S }}
Organized 7/31/06
1902 Red Seal <$VALUE
4x5 1-500 <$500
4x10 1-650 <$500
1902 Date Back
4x5 1-2375 <$250
4x10 1-2275 <$250
1902 Plain Back
4x5 2376-7385 <$250
4x10 2276-5770 <$250
1929 Small Size
5 Type 1 1-1630 <$125
10 Type 1 1-1062 <$125
5 Type 2 1-4652 <$150
10 Type 2 1-2202 <$150

Total Issue $572,400
Out in 1935 $50,000
Large out 1935 $1,140
****
9397 Macoupin
FNB OF BRIGHTON
{{ 6 L 8 S }}
Organized 3/27/09
1902 Date Back <$VALUE
4x5 1-1975 <$200
3x10-20 1-1520 <$200
1902 Plain Back
4x5 1976-6005 <$200
3x10-20 1521-3962 <$200
1929 Small Size
5 Type 1 1-738 <$100
10 Type 1 1-430 <$100
20 Type 1 1-140 <$100
5 Type 2 1-954 <$110
10 Type 2 1-584 <$110
20 Type 2 1-158 <$125
Total Issue $396,710
Out in 1935 $25,000
Large out 1935 $1,850
****
6713 Massac
BROOKPORT NB, BROOKPORT
{{ 5 L 11 S }}
Chartered 4/03
1902 Red Seal <$VALUE
3x10-20 1-1086 <$500
1902 Date Back
3x10-20 1-2020 <$250
1902 Plain Back
3x10-20 2021-6016 <$250
1929 Small Size
10 Type 1 1-710 <$135
20 Type 1 1-180 <$135
10 Type 2 1-400 <$150
20 Type 2 1-35 <$175
Total Issue $424,000
Out in 1935 $25,000
Large out 1935 $1,440
****
10397 Fayette
FNB OF BROWNSTOWN
{{ 4 L 5 S }}
Chartered 5/13
1902 Date Back <$VALUE
4x5 1-550 <$300
3x10-20 1-480 <$300
1902 Plain Back
4x5 551-4210 <$300
3x10-20 481-2554 <$300
1929 Small Size
5 Type 1 1-746 <$200
10 Type 1 1-440 <$200
20 Type 1 1-130 <$200
5 Type 2 1-864 <$225
10 Type 2 1-571 <$225
20 Type 2 1-145 <$225
Total Issue $289,210
Out in 1935 $25,000
Large out 1935 $1,270
****
1791 McDonough
FARMERS NB OF BUSHNELL
{{ 3 L }}
Chartered 2/18/71
Receivership 12/17/84
Original Series <$VALUE
3x1-2 1-2100 <$500/$1250
4x5 1-2875 <$600
Series 1875
3x1-2 1-560 <$500/$1250
4x5 1-4650 <$600
Total Issue $163,800
Out in 1915 $1,015
****
4709 McDonough
FNB OF BUSHNELL
{{ 13 L 8 S }}
Chartered 1892
Liquidated 12/21/32
Brown Back <$VALUE
4x5 1-4575 <$225
3x10-20 1-2880 <$225
1882 Date Back
4x5 1-2152 <$225
3x10-20 1-1680 <$225
1902 Date Back
4x5 1-2625 <$100
3x10-20 1-2100 <$100
1902 Plain Back
4x5 2626-15111 <$100
3x10-20 2101-8680 <$100
1929 Small Size
5 Type 1 1-2024 <$100
10 Type 1 1-953 <$100
20 Type 1 1-348 <$100
Total Issue $1,258,420
Out at close $75,000
Large out at close $6,820
****

****
3735 Alexander
ALEXANDER COUNTY NB OF CAIRO
{{ 5 L }}
Chartered 1887
Liquidated 4/30/26
Brown Back <$VALUE
4x5 1-800 <$300
50-100 1-804 <$1250/$1500
1902 Red Seal
3x10-20 1-300 <$350
1902 Date Back
3x10-20 1-3500 <$175
1902 Plain Back
3x10-20 3501-7311 <$175
Total Issue $517,150
Out in 1925 $39,300
****
6815 Alexander
CAIRO NB, CAIRO
{{ 9 L }}
Chartered 6/03
Liquidated 7/1/30
1902 Red Seal <$VALUE
3x10-20 1-4300 <$250
1902 Date Back
3x10-20 1-5300 <$125
1902 Plain Back
3x10-20 5301-12530 <$125
Total Issue $841,500
Out at close $11,240
****
785 Alexander
CITY NB OF CAIRO
{{ 4 L }}
Chartered 2/7/65
Liquidated 1/2/07
Original Series <$VALUE
3x1-2 1-4000 <$400/$1000
4x5 1-2750 <$500
3x10-20 1-2100 <$750/$1250
Series 1875
3x10-20 1-1486 <$750/$1250
Brown Back
3x10-20 1-1558 <$300
50-100 1-1099 <$1250/$1500
1902 Red Seal
3x10-20 1-1137 <$300
Total Issue $553,900
Out in 1910 $20,714
****
33 Alexander
FNB OF CAIRO
{{ UNREPORTED }}
Chartered 7/24/63
Liquidated 10/10/74
Original Series <$VALUE
3x1-2 1-800 <$1250/$2000
4x5 1-2850 <$1250
4x10 1-1430 <$1500
Total issue $118,200
Out in 1910 $1,142
****
13804 Alexander
SECURITY NB OF CAIRO
{{ 7 S }}
Chartered 10/33
1929 Small Size <$VALUE
5 Type 2 1-6164 <$100
10 Type 2 1-3175 <$100
20 Type 2 1-1115 <$100
Total Issue $84,870
Out in 1935 $48,450
****
10567 Boone
CALEDONIA NB, CALEDONIA
{{ 2 L 4 S }}
Chartered 6/14
Liquidated 8/14/34
1902 Date Back <$VALUE
3x10-20 1-500 <$600
1902 Plain Back
3x10-20 501-2145 <$600
1929 Small Size
10 Type 1 1-308 <$300
20 Type 1 1-87 <$300
Total Issue $136,170
Out at close $12,500
Large out at close $780
****
2572 Henry
FARMERS NB OF CAMBRIDGE
{{ 8 L 10 S }}
Organized 10/1/81
Liquidated 9/12/34
Series 1875 <$VALUE
4x10 1-3121 <$750
Brown Back
3x10-20 1-3100 <$325
1882 Date Back
3x10-20 1-3100* <$300

1882 Value Back
3x10-20 3301-5730* <$325
* 3101-3300 not marked
1902 Plain Back
3x10-20 1-4748 <$175
1929 Small Size
10 Type 1 1-1072 <$110
20 Type 1 1-310 <$125
Total Issue $905,260
Out at close $50,000
Large out at close $3,800
****
2540 Henry
FNB OF CAMBRIDGE
{{ 7 L 6 S }}
Organized 6/17/81
Liquidated 1/13/31
Series 1875 <$VALUE
3x10-20 1-4285 <$750/$1250
Brown Back
3x10-20 1-2900 <$325
1882 Date Back
3x10-20 1-3340 <$300
1882 Value Back
3x10-20 3341-5474 <$325
1902 Plain Back
3x10-20 1-4736 <$185
1929 Small Size
10 Type 1 1-595 <$165
20 Type 1 1-143 <$175
Total Issue $922,610
Out at close $50,000
Large out at close $8,510
****
3593 Fulton
CANTON NB, CANTON
{{ 9 L 11 S }}
Organized 11/17/86
Receivership 12/13/33
Brown Back <$VALUE
50-100 1-1228 <$1250/$1500
1902 Red Seal
4x5 1-1833 <$275
3x10-20 1-666 <$275
1902 Date Back
4x5 1-7500 <$135
3x10-20 1-5000 <$135
1902 Plain Back
4x5 7501-20487 <$135
3x10-20 5001-14095 <$135
1929 Small Size
5 Type 1 1-3320 <$85
10 Type 1 1-1508 <$85
20 Type 1 1-420 <$100
5 Type 2 1-468 <$125
10 Type 2 1-259 <$125
20 Type 2 1-110 <$125
Total Issue $1,616,260
Out at close $99,995
Large out at close $7,845
****
415 Fulton
FNB OF CANTON
{{ 8 L 8 S }}
Organized 4/2/64
Receivership 12/13/33
Original Series <$VALUE
3x1-2 1-6000 <$400/$1250
4x5 1-6075 <$500
Series 1875
3x10-20 1-1210 <$750/$1250
Brown Back
4x5 1-3590 <$300
50-100 1-255 <$1250/$1500
1902 Red Seal
50-100 1-1420 <$2250/$2500
1902 Date Back
50-100 1-500 <$400/$500
3x50-100 1-1699 <$400/$500
1902 Plain Back
3x50-100 1700-2039 <$400/$500
1929 Small Size
50 Type 1 1-237 <$150
100 Type 1 1-75 <$225
Total Issue $1,235,900
Out at close $99,700
Large out at close $14,500
****
7598 Jackson
CARBONDALE NB, CARBONDALE
{{ 7 L 12 S }}
Chartered 2/05
1902 Red Seal <$VALUE
4x5 1-2850 <$275
3x10-20 1-1860 <$275
1902 Date Back
4x5 1-4250 <$125
3x10-20 1-3220 <$125
1902 Plain Back
4x5 4251-15891 <$125
3x10-20 3221-10317 <$125

1929 Small Size
5 Type 1 1-2544 <$60
10 Type 1 1-1164 <$60
20 Type 1 1-284 <$70
5 Type 2 1-2186 <$70
10 Type 2 1-1222 <$70
20 Type 2 1-377 <$75
Total Issue $1,194,600
Out in 1935 $60,000
Large out 1935 $3,470
****
12596 Jackson
FNB IN CARBONDALE
{{ 5 L 15 S }}
Chartered 11/24
1902 Plain Back <$VALUE
3x10-20 1-6362 <$175
1929 Small Size
10 Type 1 1-2514 <$60
20 Type 1 1-714 <$70
10 Type 2 1-3059 <$60
20 Type 2 1-815 <$70
Total Issue $601,510
Out in 1935 $100,000
Large out 1935 $4,660
Outstanding includes Ch 4904
****
4904 Jackson
FNB OF CARBONDALE
{{ 6 L }}
Chartered 1893
Liquidated 12/9/24
Brown Back <$VALUE
4x5 1-6325 <$300
3x10-20 1-2260 <$300
1882 Date Back
4x5 1-2129 <$275
3x10-20 1-1564 <$275
1902 Date Back
4x5 1-1400 <$150
3x10-20 1-1100 <$150
1902 Plain Back
4x5 1401-6740 <$150
3x10-20 1101-4287 <$150
Total Issue $709,430
Out at close $50,000
Ch 12596 assumed circulation
****
4299 Macoupin
CARLINVILLE NB, CARLINVILLE
{{ 3 L 7 S }}
Chartered 1890
Brown Back <$VALUE
3x10-20 1-1460 <$500
1882 Date Back
3x10-20 1-86 <$500
1902 Date Back
3x10-20 1-1070 <$275
1902 Plain Back
3x10-20 1071-2310 <$275
1929 Small Size
10 Type 1 1-314 <$150
20 Type 1 1-102 <$150
10 Type 2 1-3110 <$150
20 Type 2 1-700 <$150
Total Issue $268,980
Out in 1935 $50,000
Large out 1935 $870
****
2042 Macoupin
FNB OF CARLINVILLE
{{ 2 L }}
Chartered 9/7/72
Liquidated 12/16/84
Original Series <$VALUE
3x1-2 1-2240 <$500/$1250
4x5 1-2815 <$600
Series 1875
3x1-2 1-460 <$500/$1250
4x5 1-3785 <$600
Total Issue $145,500
Out in 1910 $756
****
5548 Clinton
FNB OF CARLYLE
{{ 7 L 8 S }}
Chartered 8/23/00
Liquidated 10/25/34
Brown Back <$VALUE
3x10-20 1-2600 <$325
1882 Date Back
3x10-20 1-4300 <$325
1882 Value Back
3x10-20 4301-5538 <$175
1902 Plain Back
3x10-20 1-4458 <$175
1929 Small Size
10 Type 1 1-1152 <$100
20 Type 1 1-306 <$110
10 Type 2 1-1189 <$135
20 Type 2 1-210 <$135
Total Issue $751,730
Out at close $50,000
Large out at close $3,660
****

****
4934 White
FNB OF CARMI
{{ 13 L 15 S }}
Chartered 1893
Brown Back <$VALUE
3x10-20 1-3570 <$300
1882 Date Back
3x10-20 1-2850 <$275
1902 Date Back
3x10-20 1-1200 <$125
1902 Plain Back
4x5 1-8555 <$125
3x10-20 1201-11466 <$125
1929 Small Size
5 Type 1 1-3720 <$65
10 Type 1 1-1878 <$65
20 Type 1 1-506 <$75
5 Type 2 1-1674 <$75
10 Type 2 1-958 <$75
20 Type 2 1-317 <$80
Total Issue $1,374,690
Out in 1935 $50,000
Large out 1935 $4,350
****
5357 White
NB OF CARMI
{{ 8 L 12 S }}
Chartered 5/18/00
Brown Back <$VALUE
3x10-20 1-1350 <$300
1882 Date Back
3x10-20 1-3030 <$300
1882 Value Back
3x10-20 3031-4436 <$300
1902 Plain Back
3x10-20 1-4637 <$165
1929 Small Size
10 Type 1 1-780 <$85
20 Type 1 1-266 <$85
10 Type 2 1-1477 <$100
20 Type 2 1-240 <$100
Total Issue $619,140
Out in 1935 $40,000
Large out 1935 $1,800
****
8015 Saline
FNB OF CARRIER MILLS
{{ 5 L 3 S }}
Organized 11/11/05
Receivership 9/27/33
1902 Red Seal <$VALUE
4x5 1-312 <$1000
3x10-20 1-250 <$1000
1902 Date Back
4x5 1-2125 <$450
3x10-20 1-1660 <$450
1902 Plain Back
4x5 2126-7144 <$450
3x10-20 1661-4608 <$450
1929 Small Size
5 Type 1 1-776 <$400
10 Type 1 1-436 <$400
20 Type 1 1-127 <$400
Total Issue $456,700
Out at close $25,000
Large out at close $1,360
****
2390 Greene
GREENE COUNTY NB OF CARROLLTON
{{ 32 L }}
Chartered 7/1/78
Liquidated 6/6/18
Series 1875 <$VALUE
4x5 1-25735 <$250
Brown Back
4x5 1-3165 <$225
3x10-20 1-2314 <$225
1882 Date Back
4x5 1-4350 <$200
3x10-20 1-3340 <$200
1882 Value Back
4x5 4351-4525 <$200
3x10-20 3341-3513 <$200
Total Issue $959,850
Out at close $50,000
****
7889 Williamson
FNB OF CARTERVILLE
{{ 5 L 4 S }}
Organized 8/10/05
Receivership 10/10/31
1902 Red Seal <$VALUE
3x10-20 1-1600 <$400
1902 Date Back
3x10-20 1-4500 <$200
1902 Plain Back
3x10-20 4501-13289 <$200
1929 Small Size
10 Type 1 1-844 <$175
20 Type 1 1-219 <$175
Total Issue $821,370
Out at close $50,000
Large out at close $5,650
****

****
1167 Hancock
HANCOCK COUNTY NB OF
CARTHAGE
{{7 L 9 S}}
Organized 2/24/65
Receivership 5/22/34
Original Series <$VALUE
4x5 1-4025 <$500
4x20 1-625 <$1250
Series 1875
4x5 1-1250 <$500
4x20 1-250 <$1250
Brown Back
3x10-20 1-3304 <$250
1902 Red Seal
3x10-20 1-2200 <$300
1902 Date Back
3x10-20 1-5100 <$135
1902 Plain Back
3x10-20 5101-19838 <$135
1929 Small Size
10 Type 1 1-1522 <$85
20 Type 1 1-448 <$90
10 Type 2 1-268 <$125
20 Type 2 1-42 <$125
Total Issue $1,591,800
Out at close $75,000
Large out at close $16,950
****
8043 Clark
CASEY NB, CASEY
{{3 L 4 S}}
Chartered 1/06
1902 Red Seal <$VALUE
3x10-20 1-300 <$750
1902 Date Back
3x10-20 1-2040 <$350
1902 Plain Back
3x10-20 2041-5665 <$350
1929 Small Size
10 Type 1 1-524 <$250
20 Type 1 1-158 <$250
10 Type 2 1-532 <$275
20 Type 2 1-84 <$275
Total Issue $355,650
Out in 1935 $10,000
Large out 1935 $1,330
****
13673 Clark
FNB IN CASEY
{{ UNREPORTED }}
Chartered 3/33
1929 Small Size <$VALUE
5 Type 2 1-120 <$600
10 Type 2 1-165 <$600
Total Issue $2,250
Out in 1935 $25,000
Outstanding includes Ch 6026
****
6026 Clark
FNB OF CASEY
{{5 L 7 S}}
Chartered 11/4/01
Liquidated 5/10/33
Brown Back <$VALUE
3x10-20 1-1270 <$400
1882 Date Back
3x10-20 1-3100 <$400
1882 Value Back
3x10-20 3101-5727 <$400
1902 Plain Back
3x10-20 1-5024 <$200
1929 Small Size
10 Type 1 1-1071 <$125
20 Type 1 1-260 <$125
Total Issue $696,510
Out at close $50,000
Large out at close $3,600
Ch 13673 assumed circulation
****
7276 Vermilion
FNB OF CATLIN
{{3 L 7 S}}
Chartered 5/04
1902 Red Seal <$VALUE
3x10-20 1-1250 <$500
1902 Date Back
3x10-20 1-1860 <$250
1902 Plain Back
3x10-20 1861-5912 <$250
1929 Small Size
10 Type 1 1-586 <$150
20 Type 1 1-160 <$150
10 Type 2 1-741 <$165
20 Type 2 1-157 <$165
Total Issue $423,010
Out in 1935 $25,000
Large out 1935 $1,210
****

****
11904 Marion
CENTRALIA NB, CENTRALIA
{{4 L}}
Chartered 1/21
Liquidated 3/8/24
1902 Plain Back <$VALUE
3x10-20 1-5596 <$200
Total Issue $279,800
Out at close $100,000
****
11923 Marion
CITY NB OF CENTRALIA
{{4 L 13 S}}
Organized 1/24/21
1902 Plain Back <$VALUE
3x10-20 1-8736 <$150
1929 Small Size
10 Type 1 1-2036 <$60
20 Type 1 1-534 <$60
10 Type 2 1-2581 <$70
20 Type 2 1-519 <$70
Total Issue $659,230
Out in 1935 $75,000
Large out 1935 $2,640
****
1001 Marion
FNB OF CENTRALIA
{{3 L}}
Chartered 1865
Liquidated 2/25/85
Original Series <$VALUE
4x5 1-3600 <$600
3x10-20 1-1150 <$750/$1250
Series 1875
4x5 1-2975 <$600
3x10-20 1-1524 <$750/$1250
Total Issue $265,200
Out in 1910 $1,935
****
3303 Marion
OLD NB OF CENTRALIA
{{6 L 12 S}}
Chartered 1885
Brown Back <$VALUE
4x5 1-2900 <$250
3x10-20 1-7022 <$250
1902 Red Seal
3x10-20 1-2600 <$275
1902 Date Back
3x10-20 1-5800 <$135
1902 Plain Back
3x10-20 5801-17483 <$135
1929 Small Size
10 Type 1 1-2024 <$75
20 Type 1 1-517 <$75
Total Issue $1,596,730
Out in 1935 $50,000
Large out 1935 $5,900
****
5619 Carroll
FNB OF CHADWICK
{{6 L 8 S}}
Chartered 11/8/00
Receivership 1/12/34
Brown Back <$VALUE
3x10-20 1-1600 <$325
1882 Date Back
3x10-20 1-3450* <$325
1882 Value Back
3x10-20 3651-5302* <$325
* 3451-3650 not marked
1902 Plain Back
3x10-20 1-5055 <$175
1929 Small Size
10 Type 1 1-976 <$150
20 Type 1 1-330 <$150
10 Type 2 1-158 <$175
Total Issue $697,590
Out at close $49,600
Large out at close $3,460
****
2829 Champaign
CHAMPAIGN NB, CHAMPAIGN
{{3 L 4 S}}
Chartered 1882
Brown Back <$VALUE
4x5 1-3229 <$750
3x10-20 1-451 <$750
1902 Red Seal
3x10-20 1-1420 <$750
1902 Date Back
3x10-20 1-2870 <$375
1902 Plain Back
3x10-20 2871-9466 <$375
1929 Small Size
10 Type 1 1-1114 <$225
20 Type 1 1-292 <$225
10 Type 2 1-1303 <$225
20 Type 2 1-255 <$225
Total Issue $751,440
Out in 1935 $45,000
Large out 1935 $2,470
****

****
913 Champaign
FNB OF CHAMPAIGN
{{7 L 9 S}}
Organized 1/30/65
Receivership 3/4/32
Original Series <$VALUE
4x5 1-2825 <$600
3x10-20 1-900 <$750/$1250
Series 1875
4x5 1-588 <$600
3x10-20 1-779 <$750/$1250
Brown Back
3x10-20 1-3126 <$450
1902 Red Seal
3x10-20 1-2000 <$500
1902 Date Back
3x10-20 1-4700 <$250
1902 Plain Back
3x10-20 4701-17630 <$250
1929 Small Size
10 Type 1 1-1720 <$135
20 Type 1 1-544 <$150
Total Issue $1,458,490
Out at close $94,720
Large out at close $10,150
****
14024 Coles
CHARLESTON NB, CHARLESTON
{{4 S}}
Chartered 2/34
1929 Small Size <$VALUE
5 Type 2 1-3156 <$250
10 Type 2 1-1043 <$250
20 Type 2 1-447 <$250
50 Type 2 1-407 <$450
Total Issue $55,500
Out in 1935 $44,650
****
763 Coles
FNB OF CHARLESTON
{{12 L 2 S}}
Organized 1/10/65
Receivership 11/12/30
Original Series <$VALUE
3x1-2 1-3200 <$400/$1000
4x5 1-6100 <$450
3x10-20 1-2340 <$750/$1250
Series 1875
4x5 1-3540 <$450
3x10-20 1-1834 <$750/$1250
Brown Back
4x5 1-11726 <$225
3x10-20 1-2413 <$225
1902 Red Seal
4x5 1-3250 <$225
3x10-20 1-2400 <$225
1902 Date Back
4x5 1-6450 <$100
3x10-20 1-4960 <$100
1902 Plain Back
4x5 6451-20925 <$100
3x10-20 4961-14926 <$100
1929 Small Size
5 Type 1 1-1232 <$225
10 Type 1 1-509 <$225
20 Type 1 1-49 <$250
Total Issue $2,195,850
Out at close $88,230
Large out at close $14,850
****
11358 Coles
N TRUST B OF CHARLESTON
{{18 L 24 S}}
Organized 5/17/19
Liquidated 6/30/34
1902 Plain Back <$VALUE
4x5 1-31778 <$85
3x10-20 1-19663 <$100
1929 Small Size
5 Type 1 1-6642 <$45
10 Type 1 1-3232 <$45
20 Type 1 1-988 <$50
5 Type 2 1-2454 <$60
10 Type 2 1-1130 <$60
20 Type 2 1-160 <$65
Total Issue $2,157,220
Out at close $200,000
Large out at close $8,310
****
1851 Coles
SECOND NB OF CHARLESTON
{{4 L}}
Chartered 7/26/71
Liquidated 5/23/19
Original Series <$VALUE
3x1-2 1-3220 <$450/$1250
4x5 1-4025 <$500
3x10-20 1-1060 <$750/$1250
Series 1875
4x5 1-2497 <$500
3x10-20 1-1803 <$750/$1250
Brown Back
3x10-20 1-7910 <$300
1882 Date Back
4x5 1-2155 <$300
3x10-20 1-1551 <$300
1902 Date Back
4x5 1-4650 <$175
3x10-20 1-3320 <$175
1902 Plain Back
4x5 4651-7740 <$175
3x10-20 3321-4862 <$175
Total Issue $1,203,740
Out at close $100,000
****
5519 Livingston
COMMERCIAL NB OF
CHATSWORTH
{{4 L 3 S}}
Chartered 7/27/00
Receivership 3/8/30
Brown Back <$VALUE
3x10-20 1-1700 <$350
1882 Date Back
3x10-20 1-2790* <$350
1882 Value Back
3x10-20 2991-4269* <$350
* 2791-2990 not marked
1902 Plain Back
3x10-20 1-4074 <$250
1929 Small Size
10 Type 1 1-325 <$300
20 Type 1 1-26 <$300
Total Issue $524,770
Out at close $39,280
Large out at close $16,680
****
4187 Randolph
FNB OF CHESTER
{{ UNREPORTED }}
Chartered 12/23/89
Liquidated 2/15/97
Brown Back <$VALUE
3x10-20 1-537 <$1500
Total Issue $26,850
Out in 1910 $340
****
13119 Cook
ADDISON NB OF CHICAGO
{{6 L}}
Chartered 9/27
Liquidated 9/3/29
1902 Plain Back <$VALUE
3x10-20 1-7550 <$150
Total Issue $377,500
Out at close $194,200
****
11737 Cook
ALBANY PARK NB OF CHICAGO
Organized 4/13/20
Receivership 5/19/31
2nd title:Albany Park NB
& TC 3/9/28
FIRST TITLE {{8 L}}
1902 Plain Back <$VALUE
3x10-20 1-24243 <$125
SECOND TITLE {{5 L U + 11 S}}
1902 Plain Back
3x10-20 1-3979 <$125
1929 Small Size
10 Type 1 1-2897 <$65
20 Type 1 1-1025 <$75
Total Issue $1,707,920
Out at close $200,000
Large out at close $22,540
****
12001 Cook
ALLIANCE NB OF CHICAGO
{{12 L 50+ S}}
Organized 7/22/21
Receivership 6/15/32
1902 Plain Back <$VALUE
4x5 1-62129 <$75
1929 Small Size
5 Type 1 1-4662 <$50
10 Type 1 1-2135 <$50
20 Type 1 1-557 <$55
Total Issue $1,577,380
Out at close $147,720
Large out at close $8,600
****
3500 Cook
AMERICAN EXCHANGE NB OF
CHICAGO
{{ UNREPORTED }}
Chartered 5/10/86
Liquidated 2/11/98
Brown Back <$VALUE
50-100 1-300 <$1750/$2000
Total Issue $45,000
Out in 1910 $2,200
****
American NB & TC of Chicago
SEE Ch 13216
Straus NB & TC of Chicago
****

****
5111 Cook
AMERICAN NB OF CHICAGO
{{ UNREPORTED }}
Chartered 2/7/98
Liquidated 9/15/00
Brown Back <$VALUE
3x10-20 1-1620 <$1250
50-100 1-360 <$1750/$2000
Total Issue $135,000
All notes reportedly redeemed
****
10763 Cook
ATLAS EXCHANGE NB OF
CHICAGO
{{6 L}}
Chartered 8/15
Liquidated 8/1/30
1902 Plain Back <$VALUE
4x5 1-11865 <$150
3x10-20 1-13046 <$150
Total Issue $889,600
Out at close $9,110
****
3503 Cook
ATLAS NB OF CHICAGO
{{U + 1 L}}
Chartered 5/15/86
Liquidated 2/19/97
Brown Back <$VALUE
4x5 1-2357 <$850
3x10-20 1-937 <$850
Total Issue $93,990
Out in 1910 $1,340
****
Austin NB of Chicago
SEE Ch 10337
Austin NB, Austin
****
4787 Cook
BANKERS NB OF CHICAGO
{{8 L}}
Chartered 8/3/92
Liquidated 8/31/09
Brown Back <$VALUE
4x5 1-41500 <$225
3x10-20 1-44519 <$225
Total Issue $3,055,950
Out in 1910 $51,005
****
Bowmanville NB of Chicago
SEE Ch 10237
Bowmanville NB, Bowmanville
****
Calumet NB of Chicago
SEE Ch 3102
Calumet NB of South Chicago
****
2047 Cook
CENTRAL NB OF CHICAGO
{{2 L}}
Chartered 9/18/72
Receivership 12/1/77
Original Series <$VALUE
3x1-2 1-2000 <$1000/$2000
4x5 1-3650 <$1000
3x10-20 1-858 <$1500/$2000
Total Issue $125,900
Out in 1915 $515
****
4666 Cook
CHEMICAL NB OF CHICAGO
{{ UNREPORTED }}
Organized 12/15/91
Receivership 7/21/93
Brown Back <$VALUE
3x10-20 1-1021 <$1250
Total Issue $51,050
Out in 1915 $240
****
2601 Cook
CHICAGO NB, CHICAGO
{{4 L}}
Chartered 1881
Liquidated 8/15/13
Series 1875 <$VALUE
3x10-20 1-4042 <$850/$1500
Brown Back
3x10-20 1-3565 <$350
Total Issue $380,350
Out in 1913 $42,045
****
818 Cook
CITY NB OF CHICAGO
{{1 L}}
Organized 2/18/65
Receivership 5/17/76
Original Series <$VALUE
3x1-2 1-1600 <$750/$1500
4x5 1-9325 <$750
3x10-20 1-3300<$1000/$1500
Total Issue $359,500
Out in 1915 $2,508
****

****
Columbia NB of Chicago
SEE Ch 3677
United States NB of Chicago
****
713 Cook
COMMERCIAL NB OF CHICAGO
{{14 L}}
Chartered 1865
Liquidated 7/30/10
Original Series <$VALUE
3x1-2 1-10000 <$400/$1000
4x5 1-7250 <$450
3x10-20 1-6600 <$750/$1250
50-100 1-400 <$4000
Series 1875
50-100 1-200 <$4000
Brown Back
3x10-20 1-22782 <$135/$165
1902 Red Seal
4x5 1-20000 <$135
3x10-20 1-71000 <$135/$165
1902 Date Back
4x5 1-52345 <$60
3x10-20 1-37725 <$70
Total Issue $8,637,250
Out in 1910 $3,042,697
****
Continental & Commercial NB
of Chicago
SEE Ch 2894
Continental NB of Chicago
****
2894 Cook
CONTINENTAL NB OF CHICAGO
Chartered 1883
2nd title: Continental &
Commercial NB 8/1/10
FIRST TITLE {{25 L}}
Brown Back <$VALUE
3x10-20 1-24939 <$135/$165
50-100 1-6940 <$1250/$1500
1902 Red Seal
4x5 1-75000 <$125
3x10-20 1-15000 <$125/$165
50-100 1-23300<$1750/$2000
1902 Date Back
4x5 1-39980 <$45
3x10-20 1-35710 <$50
50-100 1-5607 <$300/$350
SECOND TITLE {{50+ L}}
1902 Date Back
4x5 1-518815 <$45
3x10-20 1-389968 <$50
50-100 1-3334 <$300/$350
3x50-100 1-10301<$300/$350
Total Issue $44,409,150
Out in 1935 $118,300
****
1845 Cook
COOK COUNTY NB OF CHICAGO
{{ UNREPORTED }}
Chartered 7/8/71
Receivership 2/1/75
Original Series <$VALUE
4x5 1-6597 <$1500
3x10-20 1-4042<$1500/$2000
Total Issue $334,040
Out in 1915 $1,315
****
1709 Cook
CORN EXCHANGE NB OF
CHICAGO
{{3 L}}
Chartered 1870
Liquidated 1/4/79
Original Series <$VALUE
3x1-2 1-5000 <$450/$1250
4x5 1-14496 <$500
3x10-20 1-4936 <$750/$1250
50-100 1-200 <$4000
Total Issue $591,720
Out in 1910 $4,695
****
5106 Cook
CORN EXCHANGE NB OF
CHICAGO
{{U + 27 L}}
Chartered 1897
Liquidated 9/27/24
Brown Back <$VALUE
4x5 1-20000 <$150
3x10-20 1-9000 <$150/$200
50-100 1-7001 <$1250/$1500
1882 Date Back
4x5 1-58845 <$125
3x10-20 1-32522 <$125/$175
50-100 1-3000 <$1250/$1500
3x50-100 1-6342<$1250/$1500
Total Issue $6,738,650
Out in 1915 $1,199,850
****

14110 Cook
DISTRICT NB OF CHICAGO
{{ 10 S }}
Chartered 4/34
1929 Small Size <$VALUE
10 Type 2 1-12460 <$75
Total Issue $124,600
Out in 1935 $100,000

12227 Cook
DOUGLASS NB OF CHICAGO
{{ 8U + 9 L 10 S }}
Organized 11/4/21
Receivership 5/21/32
1902 Plain Back <$VALUE
4x5 1-79328 <$65
1929 Small Size
5 Type 1 1-8275 <$60
10 Type 1 1-3693 <$60
20 Type 1 1-1115 <$70
Total Issue $2,190,190
Out at close $238,540
Large out at close $9,930

6535 Cook
DROVERS DEPOSIT NB OF CHICAGO
Chartered 12/02
2nd title:Drovers NB 5/22/13
FIRST TITLE {{ 7 L }}
1902 Red Seal <$VALUE
4x5 1-8815 <$250
3x10-20 1-8074 <$250
1902 Date Back
4x5 1-26220 <$150
3x10-20 1-18217 <$150
SECOND TITLE {{ 2 L 50+ S }}
1902 Plain Back
3x50-100 1-2800*<$350/$400
* 908-1000 not issued
1929 Small Size
5 Type 1 1-3088 <$20
10 Type 1 1-6158 <$20
20 Type 1 1-3104 <$30
50 Type 1 1-506 <$85
100 Type 1 1-252 <$135
5 Type 2 1-23926 <$20
10 Type 2 1-11669 <$20
20 Type 2 1-3155 <$30
Total Issue $4,129,020
Out in 1935 $1,000,000
Large out 1935 $5,960

Drovers NB of Chicago
SEE Ch 6535
Drovers Deposit NB of Chicago

7926 Cook
FEDERAL NB OF CHICAGO
{{ 3 L }}
Chartered 9/28/05
Liquidated 11/2/07
1902 Red Seal <$VALUE
3x10-20 1-12617 <$350
Total Issue $630,850
Out in 1910 $100,480

320 Cook
FIFTH NB OF CHICAGO
{{ 3 L }}
Chartered 1864
Liquidated 12/30/82
Original Series <$VALUE
3x1-2 1-16000 <$450/$1250
4x5 1-15500 <$500
3x10-20 1-9180<$1000/$1500
Total Issue $849,000
Out in 1910 $5,414

8 Cook
FNB OF CHICAGO*
{{ 30 L }}
Chartered 6/22/63
Liquidated 4/29/82
*Reorganized as Ch 2670 which retook Ch 8 5/24/11
Original Series <$VALUE
4x5 1-8000 <$750
3x10-20 1-14100<$1000/$1500
50-100 1-1067 <$4000
Series 1875
3x10-20 1-200 <$1000/$1500
50-100 1-209 <$4000
1902 Date Back
4x5 1-68138 <$75
3x10-20 1-92594 <$75
3x50-100 1-2000 <$300/$350
Total Issue $1,066,400
Out in 1935 $50,925
Outstanding includes Ch 2670

2670 Cook
FNB OF CHICAGO
{{ 28 L }}
Organized 4/24/82
RETOOK Ch 8 5/24/11
Brown Back <$VALUE
4x5 1-12500 <$150
3x10-20 1-18141 <$150/$175
50-100 1-400 <$1250/$1500
1902 Red Seal
4x5 1-149050 <$150
3x10-20 1-107980<$150/$175
50-100 1-866 <$1750/$2000
1902 Date Back
4x5 1-111670 <$50
3x10-20 1-76000 <$60
50-100 1-4444 <$350/$450
Total Issue $16,426,950
Out in 1915 $1,077,000

3698 Cook
FORT DEARBORN NB OF CHICAGO
{{ U + 16 L }}
Chartered 1887
Liquidated 1/9/24
Brown Back <$VALUE
4x5 1-40900 <$175
3x10-20 1-12000 <$175/$200
50-100 1-6216 <$1250/$1500
1902 Red Seal
4x5 1-12500 <$200
3x10-20 1-7000<$2000/$2250
1902 Date Back
4x5 1-78379 <$85
3x10-20 1-55240 <$85
Total Issue $7,279,980
Out in 1917 $50,000

276 Cook
FOURTH NB OF CHICAGO
{{ 5 L }}
Organized 2/24/64
Receivership 2/2/76
Original Series <$VALUE
3x1-2 1-2000 <$400/$1250
4x5 1-7185 <$450
3x10-20 1-2600<$1000/$1500
Total Issue $283,700
Out in 1915 $2,400

1734 Cook
GERMAN NB OF CHICAGO
{{ UNREPORTED }}
Organized 11/15/70
Receivership 12/20/78
Original Series <$VALUE
4x5 1-4750 <$1500
3x10-20 1-2300<$1500/$2000
50-50 1-2574 <$4000
Series 1875
50-50 1-54 <$4000
Total Issue $472,800
Out in 1915 $2,760

4489 Cook
GLOBE NB OF CHICAGO
{{ UNREPORTED }}
Chartered 12/20/90
Liquidated 12/6/98
Brown Back <$VALUE
3x10-20 1-2493 <$1250
Total Issue $124,650
Out in 1910 $1,640

12945 Cook
HALSTED EXCHANGE NB OF CHICAGO
{{ 8 S }}
Chartered 6/26
1929 Small Size <$VALUE
5 Type 1 1-6102 <$60
5 Type 2 1-50160 <$60
Total Issue $433,860
Out in 1935 $200,000

6723 Cook
HAMILTON NB OF CHICAGO
{{ 7 L }}
Chartered 4/03
Liquidated 3/30/10
1902 Red Seal <$VALUE
3x10-20 1-23250 <$250
1902 Date Back
4x5 1-3065 <$150
3x10-20 1-3323 <$150
Total Issue $1,389,950
Out in 1910 $116,430

2450 Cook
HIDE & LEATHER NB OF CHICAGO
{{ UNREPORTED }}
Chartered 1/27/80
Liquidated 12/22/97
Series 1875 <$VALUE
4x5 1-5750 <$1250
4x10 1-10916 <$1500
Total Issue $551,640
Out in 1910 $3,040

2048 Cook
HOME NB OF CHICAGO
{{ 4 L }}
Chartered 9/19/72
Liquidated 12/7/97
Original Series <$VALUE
3x1-2 1-100 <$500/$1500
4x5 1-3799 <$600
3x10-20 1-2461<$1000/$1500
Total Issue $199,530
Out in 1910 $719

Inland-Irving NB of Chicago
SEE Ch 10179
Irving Park NB, Irving Park

12391 Cook
JACKSON PARK NB OF CHICAGO
{{ 6 L 6 S }}
Organized 5/25/23
Receivership 6/25/32
1902 Plain Back <$VALUE
4x5 1-34017 <$175
1929 Small Size
5 Type 1 1-15427 <$100
Total Issue $1,143,150
Out at close $194,900
Large out at close $4,830

Jefferson Park NB of Chicago
SEE Ch 10108
Jefferson Park NB, Jefferson Park

11999 Cook
KENWOOD NB OF CHICAGO
{{ 5 L }}
Chartered 8/21
Liquidated 4/20/29
1902 Plain Back <$VALUE
3x10-20 1-22468 <$175
Total Issue $1,123,400
Out at close $200,000

9750 Cook
LaSALLE STREET NB OF CHICAGO
{{ 3 L }}
Chartered 5/10
Liquidated 10/21/12
1902 Date Back <$VALUE
3x10-20 1-24932 <$300
Total Issue $1,246,600
Out at close $646,745

10247 Cook
LAWNDALE NB OF CHICAGO
{{ 8U + 12 L 2U + 18 S }}
Chartered 8/12
1902 Date Back <$VALUE
4x5 1-4850 <$75
3x10-20 1-3840 <$75
1902 Plain Back
4x5 4851-9973 <$75
3x10-20 3841-7442 <$75
1929 Small Size
5 Type 1 1-3628 <$35
10 Type 1 1-1814 <$40
20 Type 1 1-516 <$45
5 Type 2 1-17282 <$35
10 Type 2 1-8470 <$40
20 Type 2 1-1768 <$45
Total Issue $1,057,630
Out in 1935 $250,000
Large out 1935 $4,010

12873 Cook
LAWRENCE AVENUE NB OF CHICAGO
{{ 6 L 7 S }}
Organized 1/11/26
Receivership 1/9/31
1902 Plain Back <$VALUE
4x5 1-29758 <$150
1929 Small Size
5 Type 1 1-11347 <$75
Total Issue $935,570
Out at close $200,000
Large out at close $9,360

14246 Cook
LIBERTY NB OF CHICAGO
{{ 12 S }}
Chartered 8/10/34
1929 Small Size <$VALUE
5 Type 2 1-21002 <$75
10 Type 2 1-16375 <$75
20 Type 2 1-2902 <$75
Total Issue $326,800
Out in 1935 $300,000

3647 Cook
LINCOLN NB OF CHICAGO
{{ 1 L }}
Chartered 3/12/87
Liquidated 7/30/00
Brown Back <$VALUE
4x5 1-5081 <$750
3x10-20 1-2016 <$750
Total Issue $202,420
Out in 1910 $2,595

9010 Cook
LIVE STOCK EXCHANGE NB OF CHICAGO
{{ U + 8 L }}
Chartered 1/08
Liquidated 2/5/24
1902 Red Seal <$VALUE
4x5 1-2500 <$250
4x10 1-2500 <$250
1902 Date Back
4x5 1-20794 <$150
4x10 1-22540 <$150
Total Issue $1,467,480
Out at close $50,000

13674 Cook
LIVE STOCK NB OF CHICAGO
{{ 50+ S }}
Chartered 4/33
1929 Small Size <$VALUE
5 Type 2 1-30762 <$20
10 Type 2 1-21935 <$20
20 Type 2 1-11997 <$30
50 Type 2 1-731 <$200
100 Type 2 1-5856 <$200
Total Issue $1,235,250
Out in 1935 $1,000,000

724 Cook
MANUFACTURERS NB OF CHICAGO
{{ 2 L }}
Chartered 1/18/65
Liquidated 9/25/73
Original Series <$VALUE
3x1-2 1-6300 <$600/$1500
4x5 1-16420 <$750
3x10-20 1-2304<$1000/$1500
50-100 1-500 <$4000
Total Issue $550,100
Out in 1910 $4,726

466 Cook
MECHANICS NB OF CHICAGO
{{ UNREPORTED }}
Chartered 6/28/64
Liquidated 12/30/74
Original Series <$VALUE
4x5 1-4390 <$1500
3x10-20 1-2542<$1500/$2000
Total Issue $214,900
Out in 1910 $1,510

642 Cook
MERCHANTS NB OF CHICAGO
{{ UNREPORTED }}
Chartered 12/24/64
Liquidated 3/29/02
Original Series <$VALUE
4x5 1-14750 <$1000
4x10 1-4250 <$1250
3x20-50 1-3700<$1500/$4000
Series 1875
4x5 1-3820 <$1000
4x10 1-3125 <$1250
3x20-50 1-900 <$1500/$4000
Brown Back
50-100 1-333 <$1500/$1750
Total Issue $1,222,350
Out in 1910 $6,590

3179 Cook
METROPOLITAN NB OF CHICAGO
{{ 2 L }}
Chartered 5/6/84
Liquidated 5/31/02
Brown Back <$VALUE
4x5 1-5893 <$500
3x10-20 1-4375 <$500
50-100 1-9000 <$1500/$1750
Total Issue $1,686,610
Out at close $656,700

13684 Cook
MID-CITY NB OF CHICAGO
{{ U + 18 S }}
Chartered 5/33
1929 Small Size <$VALUE
5 Type 2 1-33090 <$35
10 Type 2 1-12348 <$40
20 Type 2 1-3132 <$50
Total Issue $351,570
Out in 1935 $200,000

14245 Cook
MILWAUKEE AVENUE NB OF CHICAGO
{{ 11 S }}
Chartered 8/34
1929 Small Size <$VALUE
5 Type 2 1-6000 <$85
10 Type 2 1-6025 <$85
20 Type 2 1-3015 <$85
Total Issue $150,550
Out in 1935 $146,500

8121 Cook
MONROE NB OF CHICAGO
{{ 2 L }}
Chartered 3/06
Liquidated 11/21/11
1902 Red Seal <$VALUE
4x5 1-6250 <$400
3x10-20 1-5000 <$400
1902 Date Back
4x5 1-7310 <$300
3x10-20 1-5838 <$300
Total Issue $813,100
Out in 1912 $131,840

11092 Cook
MUTUAL NB OF CHICAGO
{{ 16 L 27 S }}
Chartered 10/17
1902 Plain Back <$VALUE
4x5 1-99512 <$45
1929 Small Size
5 Type 1 1-40752 <$30
5 Type 2 1-70962 <$30
Total Issue $3,567,610
Out in 1935 $300,000
Large out 1935 $6,110

2826 Cook
NB OF AMERICA, CHICAGO
{{ 1 L }}
Chartered 11/24/82
Liquidated 2/11/98
Brown Back <$VALUE
3x10-20 1-7553 <$600
50-100 1-3298 <$1500/$1750
Total Issue $872,350
Out in 1910 $12,300

NB of Commerce in Chicago
SEE Ch 8842
N Produce B of Chicago

1693 Cook
NB OF COMMERCE OF CHICAGO
{{ UNREPORTED }}
Chartered 1869
Liquidated 12/2/76
Original Series <$VALUE
3x1-2 1-1206 <$1000/$2000
4x5 1-4495 <$1000
3x10-20 1-2144<$1250/$2000
Total Issue $203,130
Out in 1910 $820

1867 Cook
NB OF ILLINOIS, CHICAGO
{{ U + 4 L }}
Chartered 8/29/71
Receivership 12/21/96
Original Series <$VALUE
3x1-2 1-3000 <$500/$1500
4x5 1-4500 <$650
3x10-20 1-2600 <$850/$1500
Series 1875
4x5 1-2000 <$650
3x10-20 1-1719 <$850/$1500
Brown Back
3x10-20 1-1370 <$400
Total Issue $429,450
Out in 1915 $2,359

6290 Cook
NB OF NORTH AMERICA, CHICAGO
{{ 4 L }}
Chartered 6/6/02
Liquidated 11/28/04
1902 Red Seal <$VALUE
3x10-20 1-12375 <$300/$350
Total Issue $618,750
Out in 1910 $38,630

4605 Cook
NB OF THE REPUBLIC OF CHICAGO
{{ U + 50+ L 50+ S }}
Chartered 1891
Liquidated 7/25/31
Brown Back <$VALUE
4x5 1-58965 <$175
3x10-20 1-39334 <$175/$200
50-100 1-3620 <$1250/$1500
1882 Date Back
4x5 1-34212 <$175
3x10-20 1-21355 <$175/$200
50-100 1-94 <$1250/$1500
1902 Date Back
4x5 1-70000 <$50
3x10-20 1-56000 <$60
1902 Plain Back
4x5 70001-413037 <$50
3x10-20 56001-346591 <$60
1929 Small Size
5 Type 1 1-156813 <$15
10 Type 1 1-89239 <$20
20 Type 1 1-30503 <$30
Total Issue $44,764,470
Out at close $8,000,000
Large out at close $388,040
Outstanding includes Ch 8532

13146 Cook
N BUILDERS B OF CHICAGO
{{ 12 L 29 S }}
Chartered 11/27
1902 Plain Back <$VALUE
4x5 1-9525 <$110
3x10-20 1-4907 <$110
1929 Small Size
5 Type 1 1-7014 <$40
10 Type 1 1-3952 <$40
20 Type 1 1-1106 <$50
5 Type 2 1-8466 <$40
10 Type 2 1-5258 <$40
20 Type 2 1-1000 <$50
Total Issue $1,131,020
Out in 1935 $200,000
Large out 1935 $2,520

8532 Cook
N CITY B OF CHICAGO
{{ 12 L }}
Organized 2/5/07
Closed 12/20/24
1902 Red Seal <$VALUE
4x5 1-24650 <$200
3x10-20 1-20140 <$200/$225
1902 Date Back
4x5 1-59925 <$100
3x10-20 1-42245 <$100
Total Issue $4,810,750
Out in 1917 $100,000
Ch 4605 assumed circulation

3847 Cook
N LIVESTOCK B OF CHICAGO
{{ 1 L }}
Chartered 2/23/88
Liquidated 2/7/08
Brown Back <$VALUE
4x5 1-1000 <$500
3x10-20 1-810 <$500
50-100 1-1172 <$1500/$1750
Total Issue $236,300
Out in 1910 $19,855

8842 Cook
N PRODUCE B OF CHICAGO
Chartered 8/07
Liquidated 12/31/27
2nd title:NB of Commerce in Chicago 11/23/22
FIRST TITLE {{ 3 L }}
1902 Red Seal <$VALUE
3x10-20 1-2500 <$400
1902 Date Back
3x10-20 1-22500 <$200
1902 Plain Back
3x10-20 22501-31500 <$200
SECOND TITLE {{ 3 L }}
1902 Plain Back
3x10-20 1-9210 <$200
Total Issue $2,160,500
Out at close $140,000

508 Cook
NORTHWESTERN NB OF CHICAGO
{{ 4 L }}
Chartered 8/30/64
Liquidated 9/15/00
Original Series <$VALUE
4x5 1-30025 <$500
3x10-20 1-2000 <$750/$1250
50-100 1-1834 <$4000
Series 1875
4x5 1-4000 <$500
50-100 1-1100 <$4000
Brown Back
4x5 1-6238 <$350
50-100 1-3215 <$1250/$1500
Total Issue $1,827,610
Out in 1910 $19,860

3502 Cook
PARK NB OF CHICAGO
{{ UNREPORTED }}
Organized 5/11/86
Receivership 7/14/90
Brown Back <$VALUE
50-100 1-491 <$1750/$2000
Total Issue $73,650
Out in 1915 $400

12285 Cook
PORTAGE PARK NB OF CHICAGO
{{ 6 L 12 S }}
Chartered 12/22
Closed 2/14/31
1902 Plain Back <$VALUE
3x10-20 1-19096 <$175
1929 Small Size
5 Type 1 1-3164 <$80
10 Type 1 1-2510 <$80
20 Type 1 1-506 <$90
Total Issue $1,261,040
Out at close $200,000
Large out at close $22,210
Ch 10179 assumed circulation

7358 Cook
PRAIRIE NB OF CHICAGO
{{ 3 L }}
Chartered 8/04
Liquidated 9/8/10
1902 Red Seal <$VALUE
3x10-20 1-10750 <$500
1902 Date Back
3x10-20 1-3914 <$300
Total Issue $733,200
Out in 1910 $238,050

3882 Cook
PRAIRIE STATE NB OF CHICAGO
{{ UNREPORTED }}
Chartered 5/8/88
Liquidated 10/15/97
Brown Back <$VALUE
50-100 1-364 <$1750/$2000
Total Issue $54,600
Out in 1910 $250

12605 Cook
ROSELAND NB OF CHICAGO
{{ 3 L 6 S }}
Chartered 12/24
Liquidated 3/4/33
1902 Plain Back <$VALUE
4x5 1-3336 <$375
1929 Small Size
5 Type 1 1-1632 <$250
10 Type 1 1-967 <$250
20 Type 1 1-283 <$275
Total Issue $316,160
Out at close $65,000
Large out at close $2,090

1978 Cook
SCANDINAVIAN NB OF CHICAGO
{{ 1 L }}
Chartered 5/7/72
Receivership 12/12/72
Original Series <$VALUE
3x1-2 1-2000 <$1250/$2000
4x5 1-3750 <$1250
3x10-20 1-1000<$1500/$2000
Total Issue $135,000
Out in 1915 $199

225 Cook
SECOND NB OF CHICAGO
{{ UNREPORTED }}
Organized 2/1/64
Liquidated 9/25/73
Original Series <$VALUE
4x5 1-3475 <$1500
4x10 1-1435 <$1750
Total Issue $126,900
Out in 1910 $1,170

13216 Cook
STRAUS NB & TC OF CHICAGO
Chartered 6/28
2nd title:American NB & TC 1/3/33
FIRST TITLE {{ 23 S }}
1929 Small Size <$VALUE
5 Type 1 1-7008 <$25
10 Type 1 1-3958 <$25
20 Type 1 1-1098 <$35
SECOND TITLE {{ 15 S }}
1929 Small Size
5 Type 1 1-1642 <$30
10 Type 1 1-526 <$35
20 Type 1 1-212 <$50
5 Type 2 1-56728 <$30
10 Type 2 1-36703 <$30
20 Type 2 1-7986 <$40
Total Issue $1,496,130
Out in 1935 $933,400

236 Cook
THIRD NB OF CHICAGO
{{ 5 L }}
Organized 2/5/64
Receivership 11/24/77
Original Series <$VALUE
3x1-2 1-14000 <$450/$1500
4x5 1-23000 <$500
4x10 1-5150 <$850
3x20-50 1-3600<$1500/$4000
Series 1875
3x20-50 1-2468<$1500/$4000
Total Issue $1,403,480
Out in 1915 $9,993

966 Cook
TRADERS NB OF CHICAGO
{{ 1 L }}
Chartered 1865
Liquidated 9/4/78
** Beware of counterfeit $5 notes with an incorrect plate date, May 10, 1865.
Original Series <$VALUE
3x1-2 1-7930 <$1000/$2000
4x5 1-5075 <$1000
3x10-20 1-2122<$1250/$2000
Total Issue $247,250
Out in 1910 $2,410

698 Cook
UNION NB OF CHICAGO
{{ 2 L }}
Chartered 1/11/65
Liquidated 12/29/84
Original Series <$VALUE
4x5 1-8820 <$750
4x10 1-5825 <$1000
3x20-50 1-8210<$1500/$4000
Total Issue $1,312,500
Out in 1910 $8,950

3278 Cook
UNION NB OF CHICAGO
{{ 2 L }}
Chartered 12/27/84
Liquidated 9/1/00
Brown Back <$VALUE
3x10-20 1-3119 <$400
50-100 1-3033 <$1250/$1500
Total Issue $610,900
Out in 1910 $19,280

3677 Cook
UNITED STATES NB OF CHICAGO
Organized 4/23/87
Receivership 5/22/93
2nd title:Columbia NB 1/28/91
FIRST TITLE {{ 0 L }}
Brown Back <$VALUE
4x5 1-1800 <$1000
3x10-20 1-795 <$1000
SECOND TITLE {{ 1 L }}
Brown Back
3x10-20 1-669 <$850
Total Issue $109,200
Out in 1915 $655

Washington Park NB of Chicago
SEE Ch 3916
Oakland NB of Chicago

12004 Cook
WEST ENGLEWOOD NB OF CHICAGO
{{ 1 L }}
Chartered 8/21
Liquidated 8/1/27
1902 Plain Back <$VALUE
4x5 1-4550 <$600
Total Issue $91,000
Out at close $25,000

11009 Cook
WEST SIDE NB OF CHICAGO
Organized 5/5/17
Receivership 10/16/31
2nd title:West Side-Atlas NB of Chicago 8/6/30
FIRST TITLE {{ 9 L 9 S }}
1902 Plain Back <$VALUE
4x5 1-73815 <$125
1929 Small Size
5 Type 1 1-3566 <$65
10 Type 1 1-1684 <$65
20 Type 1 1-574 <$75
SECOND TITLE {{ 5 S }}
1929 Small Size
5 Type 1 1-1592 <$100
10 Type 1 1-702 <$100
20 Type 1 1-221 <$110
Total Issue $1,869,600
Out at close $200,000
Large out at close $10,195

West Side-Atlas NB of Chicago
SEE Ch 11009
West Side NB of Chicago

13373 Cook
CITIZENS NB OF CHICAGO HEIGHTS
{{ 3 S }}
Chartered 9/29
1929 Small Size <$VALUE
5 Type 2 1-6170 <$175
10 Type 2 1-2814 <$175
Total Issue $58,990
Out in 1935 $38,500

5876 Cook
FNB OF CHICAGO HEIGHTS
Organized 6/11/01
Receivership 7/7/32
2nd title:FNB & TC 1/12/29
FIRST TITLE {{ 6 L }}
Brown Back <$VALUE
3x10-20 1-1770 <$300
1882 Date Back
3x10-20 1-3740 <$300
1882 Value Back
3x10-20 3741-6193 <$300
1902 Plain Back
3x10-20 1-5376 <$175
SECOND TITLE {{ 0 L 5 S }}
1902 Plain Back
3x10-20 1-224 <$350
1929 Small Size
10 Type 1 1-966 <$150
20 Type 1 1-258 <$150
Total Issue $767,070
Out at close $50,000
Large out at close $5,500

5584 Peoria
FNB OF CHILLICOTHE
{{ 6 L 7 S }}
Chartered 9/24/00
Brown Back <$VALUE
3x10-20 1-1400 <$300
1882 Date Back
3x10-20 1-1740 <$300
1882 Value Back
3x10-20 1741-2766 <$300
1902 Plain Back
3x10-20 1-2945 <$200
1929 Small Size
10 Type 1 1-592 <$135
20 Type 1 1-160 <$135
10 Type 2 1-847 <$150
20 Type 2 1-187 <$150
Total Issue $422,480
Out in 1935 $25,000
Large out 1935 $1,370

7111 Edgar
FNB OF CHRISMAN
{{ 4 L 5 S }}
Chartered 1/04
1902 Red Seal <$VALUE
3x10-20 1-1026 <$600
1902 Date Back
3x10-20 1-1870 <$300
1902 Plain Back
3x10-20 1871-5646 <$300
1929 Small Size
10 Type 1 1-570 <$200
20 Type 1 1-166 <$200
10 Type 2 1-634 <$200
20 Type 2 1-181 <$200
Total Issue $397,680
Out in 1935 $25,000
Large out 1935 $1,400

8260 Franklin
FNB OF CHRISTOPHER
{{ 2 L 7 S }}
Organized 5/12/06
Receivership 12/7/31
1902 Red Seal <$VALUE
3x10-20 1-300 <$750
1902 Date Back
3x10-20 1-960 <$375
1902 Plain Back
3x10-20 961-4147 <$375
1929 Small Size
10 Type 1 1-1220 <$175
20 Type 1 1-358 <$175
Total Issue $338,510
Out at close $58,200
Large out at close $2,140

11662 Cook
FNB OF CICERO
{{ U + 10 L 6 S }}
Chartered 3/20
1902 Plain Back <$VALUE
4x5 1-10192 <$175
1929 Small Size
5 Type 1 1-1922 <$150
5 Type 2 1-5918 <$150
Total Issue $291,090
Out in 1935 $25,000
Large out 1935 $730

6318 Iroquois
FNB OF CLIFTON
{{ 1 L 6 S }}
Chartered 6/02
1902 Red Seal <$VALUE
3x10-20 1-700 <$1000
1902 Date Back
3x10-20 1-880* <$500
1902 Plain Back
3x10-20 981-2698* <$500
* 881-980 not marked
1929 Small Size
10 Type 1 1-304 <$250
20 Type 1 1-104 <$250
10 Type 2 1-6 <$275
20 Type 2 1-15 <$275
Total Issue $200,980
Out in 1935 $12,500
Large out 1935 $730

1926 De Witt
De WITT COUNTY NB OF CLINTON
{{ 12 L 13 S }}
Chartered 1/20/72
Original Series <$VALUE
3x1-2 1-1500 <$350/$850
4x5 1-1875 <$400
3x10-20 1-1420 <$750/$1250
Series 1875
4x5 1-398 <$400
3x10-20 1-1407 <$750/$1250
Brown Back
3x10-20 1-2170 <$225
1882 Date Back
3x10-20 1-671 <$225
1902 Date Back
3x10-20 1-3400 <$100
1902 Plain Back
3x10-20 3401-18930 <$100
1929 Small Size
10 Type 1 1-2504 <$65
20 Type 1 1-607 <$75
5 Type 2 1-181 <$75
10 Type 2 1-375 <$85
20 Type 2 1-50 <$85
Total Issue $1,519,155
Out in 1935 $70,000
Large out 1935 $5,635

10132 Grundy
FNB OF COAL CITY
{{ 1 L 2 S }}
Chartered 1/22/12
1902 Date Back <$VALUE
4x5 1-515 <$850
3x10-20 1-394 <$850
1902 Plain Back
4x5 516-1260 <$850
3x10-20 395-894 <$850
1929 Small Size
5 Type 1 1-251 <$600
10 Type 1 1-129 <$600
20 Type 1 1-25 <$600
Total Issue $88,170
Out in 1935 $6,250
Large out 1935 $450

5630 Union
FNB OF COBDEN
{{ 5 L 5 S }}
Chartered 11/23/00
Brown Back <$VALUE
3x10-20 1-1500 <$375
1882 Date Back
3x10-20 1-1700 <$375
1882 Value Back
3x10-20 1701-2760 <$375
1902 Plain Back
3x10-20 1-2695 <$250
1929 Small Size
10 Type 1 1-658 <$165
20 Type 1 1-170 <$165
10 Type 2 1-656 <$185
20 Type 2 1-175 <$185
Total Issue $417,690
Out in 1935 $25,000
Large out 1935 $1,090

7579 Montgomery
COFFEEN NB, COFFEEN
{{ 3 L 4 S }}
Chartered 1/05
1902 Red Seal <$VALUE
3x10-20 1-1110 <$600
1902 Date Back
3x10-20 1-1960 <$300
1902 Plain Back
3x10-20 1961-5481 <$300
1929 Small Size
10 Type 1 1-780 <$175
20 Type 1 1-158 <$175
10 Type 2 1-1107 <$200
20 Type 2 1-269 <$200
Total Issue $411,760
Out in 1935 $35,000
Large out 1935 $1,480

8485 McDonough
NB OF COLCHESTER
{{ 6 L 4 S }}
Chartered 12/06
1902 Red Seal <$VALUE
3x10-20 1-820 <$500
1902 Date Back
3x10-20 1-1750 <$250
1902 Plain Back
3x10-20 1751-5157 <$250
1929 Small Size
10 Type 1 1-542 <$200
20 Type 1 1-136 <$200
10 Type 2 1-512 <$225
20 Type 2 1-147 <$225
Total Issue $355,750
Out in 1935 $25,000
Large out 1935 $1,260

6125 Madison
FNB OF COLLINSVILLE
{{ 8 L 14 S }}
Chartered 2/02
1902 Red Seal <$VALUE
4x5 1-3170 <$375
3x10-20 1-2312 <$375
1902 Date Back
4x5 1-3400 <$175
3x10-20 1-2380 <$175
1902 Plain Back (dated 1902)
4x5 3401-7265 <$175
3x10-20 2381-4638 <$175
1902 Plain Back (dated 1922)
4x5 1-8520 <$175
3x10-20 1-6014 <$175
1929 Small Size
5 Type 1 1-3830 <$75
10 Type 1 1-1956 <$75
20 Type 1 1-500 <$85
5 Type 2 1-5318 <$100
10 Type 2 1-2608 <$100
20 Type 2 1-640 <$100
Total Issue $1,385,030
Out in 1935 $100,000
Large out 1935 $3,950

13805 Monroe
FNB IN COLUMBIA
{{ U + 4 S }}
Chartered 10/33
1929 Small Size <$VALUE
5 Type 2 1-2340 <$175
10 Type 2 1-2730 <$175
20 Type 2 1-1545 <$175
Total Issue $69,900
Out in 1935 $43,400

7717 Monroe
FNB OF COLUMBIA
{{ 4 L 6 S }}
Organized 4/17/05
Liquidated 10/21/33
1902 Red Seal <$VALUE
3x10-20 1-940 <$600
1902 Date Back
3x10-20 1-1740 <$275
1902 Plain Back
3x10-20 1741-8469 <$275
1929 Small Size
10 Type 1 1-1197 <$175
20 Type 1 1-318 <$175
Total Issue $580,430
Out at close $50,000
Large out at close $3,950

7031 Lee
FNB OF COMPTON
{{ 2 L 3 S }}
Chartered 11/3/03
Receivership 11/1/33
1902 Red Seal <$VALUE
3x10-20 1-350 <$750
1902 Date Back
3x10-20 1-2210 <$375
1902 Plain Back
3x10-20 2211-5561 <$375
1929 Small Size
10 Type 1 1-476 <$300
20 Type 1 1-99 <$300
Total Issue $335,990
Out at close $25,000
Large out at close $1,480

12000 Randolph
FNB OF COULTERVILLE
{{ 8 L 7 S }}
Chartered 8/20
1902 Plain Back <$VALUE
4x5 1-2419 <$600
3x10-20 1-1749 <$600
1929 Small Size
5 Type 1 1-1106 <$400
10 Type 1 1-494 <$400
20 Type 1 1-134 <$400
5 Type 2 1-1110 <$400
10 Type 2 1-525 <$400
20 Type 2 1-204 <$400
Total Issue $229,610
Out in 1935 $25,000
Large out 1935 $60

9700 Shelby
FNB OF COWDEN
{{ 2 L }}
Chartered 3/10
Liquidated 5/11/26
1902 Date Back <$VALUE
3x10-20 1-1820 <$600
1902 Plain Back
3x10-20 1821-4389 <$600
Total Issue $219,450
Out at close $25,000

6598 Iroquois
FNB OF CRESCENT CITY
{{ 3 L 3 S }}
Organized 11/8/02
Receivership 9/27/33
1902 Red Seal <$VALUE
3x10-20 1-1200 <$1000
1902 Date Back
3x10-20 1-1780 <$500
1902 Plain Back
3x10-20 1781-5231 <$500
1929 Small Size
10 Type 1 1-523 <$400
20 Type 1 1-140 <$400
Total Issue $369,730
Out at close $25,000
Large out at close $2,060

8801 White
FNB OF CROSSVILLE
{{ 2 L 6 S }}
Organized 5/31/07
1902 Red Seal <$VALUE
3x10-20 1-547 <$850
1902 Date Back
3x10-20 1-870* <$400
1902 Plain Back
3x10-20 991-2775* <$400
* 871-990 not marked
1929 Small Size
10 Type 1 1-304 <$200
20 Type 1 1-106 <$200
10 Type 2 1-192 <$225
20 Type 2 1-75 <$225
Total Issue $200,480
Out in 1935 $12,750
Large out 1935 $690

****
11144 Fulton
FNB OF CUBA
{{ 3 L 3 S }}
Chartered 2/18
Liquidated 2/28/31
1902 Plain Back <$VALUE
4x5 1-23052 <$275
1929 Small Size
20 Type 1 1-493 <$275
Total Issue $520,200
Out at close $50,000
Large out at close $4,040
****
8684 Livingston
FNB OF CULLOM
{{ 4 L 11 S }}
Organized 4/27/07
1902 Red Seal <$VALUE
3x10-20 1-700 <$400
1902 Date Back
3x10-20 1-1320 <$200
1902 Plain Back
3x10-20 1321-3890 <$200
1929 Small Size
10 Type 1 1-376 <$110
20 Type 1 1-116 <$110
10 Type 2 1-467 <$125
20 Type 2 1-110 <$125
Total Issue $272,850
Out in 1935 $20,000
Large out 1935 $1,910
****
7750 Hamilton
FNB OF DAHLGREN
{{ 2 L }}
Organized 4/25/05
Receivership 7/22/29
1902 Red Seal <$VALUE
3x10-20 1-1050 <$750
1902 Date Back
3x10-20 1-2300 <$400
1902 Plain Back
3x10-20 2301-6483 <$400
Total Issue $376,650
Out at close $29,250
****
5609 Hancock
FNB OF DALLAS CITY
{{ 12 L 10 S }}
Chartered 10/26/00
Receivership 10/26/33
Brown Back <$VALUE
4x5 1-2500 <$275
3x10-20 1-1860 <$275
1882 Date Back
4x5 1-3500 <$275
3x10-20 1-2220 <$275
1882 Value Back
4x5 3501-6490 <$275
3x10-20 2221-3871 <$275
1902 Plain Back
3x10-20 1-7897 <$150
1929 Small Size
10 Type 1 1-1520 <$100
20 Type 1 1-487 <$100
Total Issue $1,010,840
Out at close $75,000
Large out at close $5,170
****
6740 McLean
FNB OF DANVERS
{{ 1 L 2 S }}
Organized 4/15/03
Receivership 2/2/32
1902 Red Seal <$VALUE
3x10-20 1-400 <$1250
1902 Date Back
3x10-20 1-620 <$600
1902 Plain Back
3x10-20 621-1371 <$600
1929 Small Size
10 Type 1 1-174 <$450
20 Type 1 1-46 <$450
Total Issue $104,510
Out in 1935 $6,500
Large out 1935 $750
****
5812 Vermilion
DANVILLE NB, DANVILLE
{{ 6 L }}
Chartered 5/01
Closed 1/3/20
Brown Back <$VALUE
3x10-20 1-7500 <$275
1882 Date Back
3x10-20 1-11600 <$275
1882 Value Back
3x10-20 11601-15962 <$275
Total Issue $1,173,100
Out at close $150,000
Ch 2584 assumed circulation
****

****
113 Vermilion
FNB OF DANVILLE
{{ 11 L 14 S }}
Chartered 1863
Original Series <$VALUE
4x5 1-5500 <$450
Series 1875
4x5 1-3143 <$450
Brown Back
50-100 1-2317 <$1250/$1500
1902 Red Seal
50-100 1-2300 <$2250/$2500
1902 Date Back
50-100 1-2000 <$350/$400
3x50-100 1-4550 <$350/$400
1902 Plain Back
3x50-100 4551-5672 <$350/$400
1929 Small Size
50 Type 1 1-1170 <$100
100 Type 1 1-372 <$165
5 Type 2 1-2040 <$35
10 Type 2 1-900 <$40
20 Type 2 1-405 <$50
Total Issue $3,184,910
Out in 1935 $300,000
Large out 1935 $33,550
****
4731 Vermilion
PALMER NB OF DANVILLE
Chartered 1892
2nd title:Palmer-American NB 11/28/31
FIRST TITLE {{ 6 L 6 S }}
Brown Back <$VALUE
3x10-20 1-1170 <$250
50-100 1-2617 <$1250/$1500
1882 Date Back
3x10-20 1-3213 <$250
50-100 1-46 <$1250/$1500
1902 Date Back
3x50-100 1-5192 <$400/$500
1902 Plain Back
3x50-100 5193-6442 <$400/$500
1929 Small Size
50 Type 1 1-722 <$110
100 Type 1 1-242 <$175
SECOND TITLE {{ 2 S }}
1929 Small Size
50 Type 1 1-56 <$200
100 Type 1 1-27 <$250
Total Issue $2,623,900
Out in 1935 $100,000
Large out 1935 $26,550
****
Palmer-American NB of Danville
SEE Ch 4731
Palmer NB of Danville
****
2584 Vermilion
SECOND NB OF DANVILLE
{{ 18 L 14 S }}
Chartered 1881
Series 1875 <$VALUE
4x5 1-8750 <$450
50-100 1-1329 <$4000
Brown Back
50-100 1-2100 <$1250/$1500
1882 Date Back
50-100 1-800 <$1250/$1500
3x50-100 1-2934<$1250/$1500
1902 Plain Back
3x50-100 1-4279 <$300/$400
1929 Small Size
50 Type 1 1-1320 <$100
100 Type 1 1-404 <$150
Total Issue $3,251,000
Out in 1935 $500,000
Large out 1935 $7,955
Outstanding includes Ch 5812
****
2702 De Kalb
De KALB NB, De KALB
Chartered 1882
Liquidated 4/24/34
2nd title:FNB of De Kalb 5/13/02
FIRST TITLE {{ 3 L }}
Series 1875 <$VALUE
3x10-20 1-1459<$1000/$1500
SECOND TITLE {{ 4 L 7 S }}
1902 Red Seal
3x10-20 1-900 <$500
1902 Date Back
3x10-20 1-4250 <$275
1902 Plain Back
3x10-20 4251-8225 <$275
1929 Small Size
10 Type 1 1-942 <$150
20 Type 1 1-260 <$150
Total Issue $616,920
Out in 1934 $40,000
Large out 1935 $2,200
****

****
14008 De Kalb
FNB IN De KALB
{{ 15 S }}
Chartered 2/34
1929 Small Size <$VALUE
5 Type 2 1-796 <$400
10 Type 2 1-487 <$400
20 Type 2 1-165 <$400
Total Issue $12,150
Out in 1935 $40,000
Outstanding includes Ch 2702
****
FNB of De Kalb
SEE Ch 2702
DeKalb NB, De Kalb
****
5699 Piatt
FNB OF De LAND
{{ 4 L 6 S }}
Chartered 2/1/01
Brown Back <$VALUE
4x5 1-2200 <$400
3x10-20 1-1700 <$400
1882 Date Back
4x5 1-2200 <$400
3x10-20 1-1560* <$400
1882 Value Back
4x5 2201-3885 <$400
3x10-20 1761-2647* <$400
* 1561-1760 not marked
1902 Plain Back
4x5 1-4335 <$225
3x10-20 1-2353 <$225
1929 Small Size
5 Type 1 1-1162 <$135
10 Type 1 1-554 <$135
20 Type 1 1-170 <$135
5 Type 2 1-1390 <$165
10 Type 2 1-867 <$165
20 Type 2 1-197 <$165
Total Issue $651,460
Out in 1935 $35,000
Large out 1935 $2,165
****
4576 De Witt
CITIZENS NB OF DECATUR
{{ 11 L 20 S }}
Organized 5/8/91
Brown Back <$VALUE
4x5 1-2750 <$175
3x10-20 1-7560 <$175
1882 Date Back
4x5 1-1965 <$175
3x10-20 1-1389 <$175
1902 Date Back
3x10-20 1-11400 <$100
1902 Plain Back
3x10-20 11401-41064 <$100
1929 Small Size
10 Type 1 1-6232 <$25
20 Type 1 1-1696 <$35
10 Type 2 1-4354 <$25
20 Type 2 1-901 <$35
Total Issue $3,233,950
Out in 1935 $100,000
Large out 1935 $10,020
****
2124 De Witt
DECATUR NB, DECATUR
{{ 5 L }}
Chartered 8/12/73
Liquidated 5/31/93
Original Series <$VALUE
3x1-2 1-4900 <$350/$1000
4x5 1-5525 <$400
Series 1875
4x5 1-6404 <$400
Total Issue $263,080
Out in 1910 $1,585
****
477 De Witt
FNB OF DECATUR
{{ UNREPORTED }}
Chartered 7/6/64
Liquidated 1/10/70
Original Series <$VALUE
3x1-2 1-2910 <$1250/$2000
4x5 1-3750 <$1500
Total Issue $89,550
Out in 1910 $996
****
5089 De Witt
MILLIKIN NB OF DECATUR
{{ 28 L 50+ S }}
Chartered 1897
Brown Back <$VALUE
4x5 1-4250 <$175
3x10-20 1-11000 <$175
1882 Date Back
4x5 1-15250 <$175
3x10-20 1-10000 <$175
1882 Value Back
4x5 15251-18657 <$175
3x10-20 10001-12041 <$175
1902 Plain Back
4x5 1-88157 <$75
3x10-20 1-46669 <$85
1929 Small Size
5 Type 1 1-17216 <$25
10 Type 1 1-8642 <$25
20 Type 1 1-2574 <$35
5 Type 2 1-4934 <$25
10 Type 2 1-2695 <$30
20 Type 2 1-785 <$35
Total Issue $7,117,980
Out in 1935 $497,480
Large out 1935 $23,085
****
4920 De Witt
NB OF DECATUR
{{ 18 L 31 S }}
Chartered 1893
Brown Back <$VALUE
4x5 1-11300 <$175
3x10-20 1-7500 <$175
1882 Date Back
4x5 1-7625 <$175
3x10-20 1-5530 <$175
1902 Date Back
3x10-20 1-9500 <$85
1902 Plain Back
3x10-20 9501-51960 <$85
1929 Small Size
10 Type 1 1-7566 <$25
20 Type 1 1-2236 <$35
Total Issue $4,350,280
Out in 1935 $300,000
Large out 1935 $14,760
****
3781 Tazewell
TAZEWELL COUNTY NB OF DELAVAN
{{ 12 L 10 S }}
Chartered 1887
Brown Back <$VALUE
3x10-20 1-1360 <$250
1902 Red Seal
4x10 1-1063 <$250
1902 Date Back
4x5 1-3675 <$125
4x10 1-3250 <$125
1902 Plain Back
4x5 3676-13639 <$125
4x10 3251-9926 <$125
1929 Small Size
5 Type 1 1-2502 <$100
10 Type 1 1-1264 <$100
5 Type 2 1-3568 <$100
10 Type 2 1-1785 <$100
Total Issue $966,930
Out in 1935 $50,000
Large out 1935 $2,720
****
10319 Cook
FNB OF DES PLAINES
{{ 4 L 9 S }}
Chartered 1/27/13
1902 Date Back <$VALUE
3x10-20 1-2200 <$275
1902 Plain Back
3x10-20 2201-10061 <$275
1929 Small Size
10 Type 1 1-1268 <$175
20 Type 1 1-370 <$175
10 Type 2 1-396 <$175
20 Type 2 1-155 <$185
Total Issue $630,590
Out in 1935 $50,000
Large out 1935 $2,630
****
9582 Effingham
FNB OF DIETERICH
{{ 4 L 6 S }}
Chartered 11/09
1902 Date Back <$VALUE
3x10-20 1-2150* <$325
1902 Plain Back
3x10-20 2311-5089* <$325
* 2151-2310 not marked
1929 Small Size
10 Type 1 1-578 <$150
20 Type 1 1-144 <$150
10 Type 2 1-733 <$175
20 Type 2 1-75 <$175
Total Issue $315,240
Out in 1935 $25,000
Large out 1935 $1,260
****
10296 Sangamon
FNB OF DIVERNON
{{ 3 L }}
Chartered 12/12
Liquidated 2/13/20
1902 Date Back <$VALUE
4x10 1-1825* <$500
1902 Plain Back
4x10 2026-3092* <$500
* 1826-2025 not marked
Total Issue $120,600
Out at close $25,000
****

****
13856 Lee
CITY NB IN DIXON
{{ 6 S }}
Chartered 12/33
1929 Small Size <$VALUE
10 Type 2 1-2366 <$150
20 Type 2 1-685 <$150
Total Issue $37,360
Out in 1935 $100,000
Outstanding includes Ch 3294
****
3294 Lee
CITY NB OF DIXON
{{ 3 L 10 S }}
Organized 12/9/84
Liquidated 1/19/34
Brown Back <$VALUE
4x5 1-6297 <$350
50-100 1-210 <$1250/$1500
1902 Red Seal
3x10-20 1-850 <$400
1902 Date Back
3x10-20 1-2440 <$200
1902 Plain Back
3x10-20 2441-4791 <$200
1929 Small Size
10 Type 1 1-1614 <$85
20 Type 1 1-370 <$100
10 Type 2 1-167 <$150
20 Type 2 1-18 <$150
Total Issue $582,760
Out at close $100,000
Large out 1935 $1,980
Ch 13856 assumed circulation
****
1881 Lee
DIXON NB, DIXON
{{ 6 L 6 S }}
Chartered 9/19/71
Original Series <$VALUE
3x1-2 1-1500 <$400/$1250
4x5 1-4125 <$500
3x10-20 1-600 <$750/$1250
Series 1875
4x5 1-4489 <$500
3x10-20 1-1090 <$750/$1250
Brown Back
4x5 1-4250 <$350
3x10-20 1-1320 <$350
1882 Date Back
4x5 1-2957 <$325
3x10-20 1-2461 <$325
1902 Date Back
3x50-100 1-2058 <$350/$450
1902 Plain Back
3x50-100 2059-2410 <$350/$450
1929 Small Size
50 Type 1 1-250 <$175
100 Type 1 1-83 <$225
Total Issue $1,324,770
Out in 1930 $100,000
Large out 1935 $22,490
****
902 Lee
LEE COUNTY NB OF DIXON
{{ 2 L }}
Chartered 1865
Liquidated 1/21/85
Original Series <$VALUE
3x1-2 1-2400 <$500/$1250
4x5 1-4400 <$500
3x10-20 1-1250 <$750/$1250
Series 1875
3x1-2 1-1060 <$500/$1250
4x5 1-3815 <$500
3x10-20 1-166 <$750/$1250
Total Issue $252,400
Out in 1910 $2,319
****
8679 Cook
FNB OF DOLTON
{{ 4 L 10 S }}
Organized 4/17/07
Liquidated 2/23/35
1902 Red Seal <$VALUE
3x10-20 1-650 <$500
1902 Date Back
3x10-20 1-1850 <$250
1902 Plain Back
3x10-20 1851-8085 <$250
1929 Small Size
10 Type 1 1-1202 <$125
20 Type 1 1-368 <$150
10 Type 2 1-1099 <$150
20 Type 2 1-235 <$150
Total Issue $568,720
Out in 1935 $50,000
Large out 1935 $1,710
Ch 14319 assumed circulation
****

****
10086 Union
FNB OF DONGOLA
{{ 1 L }}
Chartered 9/11
Liquidated 6/1/33
1902 Date Back <$VALUE
4x10 1-725 <$750
1902 Plain Back
4x10 726-1723 <$750
Total Issue $68,920
Out at close $520
****
9725 Du Page
FNB OF DOWNERS GROVE
{{ 4 L 3 S }}
Organized 1/31/10
Receivership 6/19/31
1902 Date Back <$VALUE
4x10 1-3800 <$750
1902 Plain Back
4x10 3801-11505 <$750
1929 Small Size
10 Type 1 1-939 <$450
Total Issue $516,540
Out at close $35,000
Large out at close $4,040
****
5638 Kane
FNB OF DUNDEE
{{ 6 L 5 S }}
Chartered 12/13/00
Brown Back <$VALUE
4x5 1-1025 <$300
3x10-20 1-1270 <$300
1882 Date Back
4x5 1-2400 <$300
3x10-20 1-2200 <$300
1882 Value Back
4x5 2401-4880 <$300
3x10-20 2201-3459 <$300
1902 Plain Back
3x10-20 1-5573 <$200
1929 Small Size
10 Type 1 1-1192 <$150
20 Type 1 1-328 <$150
Total Issue $744,080
Out in 1935 $25,000
Large out 1935 $5,760
****
4737 Perry
FNB OF DuQUOIN
{{ 5 L 15 S }}
Organized 4/11/92
Receivership 2/6/35
Brown Back <$VALUE
4x5 1-7250 <$350
50-100 1-740 <$1250/$1500
1882 Date Back
4x5 1-992 <$350
50-100 1-263 <$1250/$1500
1902 Date Back
3x10-20 1-1940 <$200
1902 Plain Back
3x10-20 1941-8580 <$200
1929 Small Size
10 Type 1 1-2222 <$65
20 Type 1 1-542 <$70
10 Type 2 1-2365 <$75
20 Type 2 1-572 <$75
Total Issue $977,740
Out at close $100,000
Large out at close $3,760
****
8044 Livingston
FNB OF DWIGHT
{{ 4 L 8 S }}
Chartered 1/06
1902 Red Seal <$VALUE
3x10-20 1-920 <$500
1902 Date Back
3x10-20 1-3460 <$250
1902 Plain Back
3x10-20 3461-10047 <$250
1929 Small Size
10 Type 1 1-950 <$100
20 Type 1 1-298 <$100
10 Type 2 1-1140 <$110
20 Type 2 1-271 <$110
Total Issue $657,930
Out in 1935 $44,000
Large out 1935 $2,500
****

<$VALUEs are for notes in FINE condition. Value changes by approximately 25% for a change of one full grade.

****
7555 LaSalle
EARLVILLE NB, EARLVILLE
{{ 3 L }}
Organized 12/6/04
Receivership 10/27/33
1902 Red Seal <$VALUE
3x10-20 1-2160 <$500
1902 Date Back
3x10-20 1-3540 <$250
1902 Plain Back
3x10-20 3541-9234 <$250
Total Issue $569,700
Out at close $2,440
****
3323 LaSalle
FNB OF EARLVILLE
{{ 5 L 9 S }}
Organized 3/3/85
Receivership 11/10/33
Brown Back <$VALUE
4x5 1-3338 <$350
3x10-20 1-646 <$350
1902 Red Seal
3x10-20 1-990 <$400
1902 Date Back
3x10-20 1-3600 <$200
1902 Plain Back
3x10-20 3601-10884 <$200
1929 Small Size
10 Type 1 1-1123 <$100
20 Type 1 1-304 <$100
Total Issue $796,620
Out at close $50,000
Large out at close $3,730
****
14010 Tazewell
FNB IN EAST PEORIA
{{ 2 S }}
Chartered 2/34
1929 Small Size <$VALUE
5 Type 2 1-846 <$400
10 Type 2 1-446 <$400
20 Type 2 1-137 <$400
Total Issue $11,430
Out in 1935 $25,000
Outstanding includes Ch 6724
****
6724 Tazewell
FNB OF EAST PEORIA
{{ 5 L 3 S }}
Organized 3/4/03
Liquidated 9/10/34
1902 Red Seal <$VALUE
4x5 1-1095 <$400
3x10-20 1-882 <$400
1902 Date Back
4x5 1-1675 <$200
3x10-20 1-1230 <$200
1902 Plain Back
4x5 1676-6145 <$200
3x10-20 1231-3925 <$200
1929 Small Size
5 Type 1 1-808 <$150
10 Type 1 1-386 <$150
20 Type 1 1-130 <$150
5 Type 2 1-268 <$175
10 Type 2 1-262 <$175
20 Type 2 1-20 <$175
Total Issue $452,510
Out at close $25,000
Large out 1935 $335
Ch 14010 assumed circulation
****
8932 St Clair
CITY NB OF
EAST SAINT LOUIS
{{ 1 L }}
Chartered 10/26/07
Liquidated 1/16/09
1902 Red Seal <$VALUE
3x10-20 1-4582 <$600
Total Issue $229,100
Out in 1910 $57,045
****
10399 St Clair
DROVERS NB OF
EAST SAINT LOUIS
{{ 8 L }}
Organized 4/30/13
Receivership 5/22/24
1902 Date Back <$VALUE
4x5 1-7500 <$125
3x10-20 1-6000 <$125
1902 Plain Back
4x5 7501-29830 <$125
3x10-20 6001-19889 <$125
Total Issue $1,591,050
Out at close $200,000
****
11596 St Clair
FNB IN EAST SAINT LOUIS
{{ 9 L 16 S }}
Organized 2/2/20
Liquidated 5/8/34
1902 Plain Back <$VALUE
3x50-100 1-6467 <$300/$350
1929 Small Size
50 Type 1 1-1051 <$100
100 Type 1 1-346 <$150
Total Issue $2,139,650
Out at close $400,000
Large out at close $43,250
****
4328 St Clair
FNB OF EAST SAINT LOUIS
{{ 4 L }}
Chartered 5/31/90
Liquidated 3/30/07
Brown Back <$VALUE
4x5 1-10150 <$275
3x10-20 1-8109 <$275
Total Issue $608,450
Out in 1910 $27,910
****
12178 St Clair
SECURITY NB OF
EAST SAINT LOUIS
{{ 3 L }}
Chartered 4/22
Liquidated 6/11/24
1902 Plain Back <$VALUE
3x10-20 1-13778 <$200
Total Issue $688,900
Out at close $300,000
****
5070 St Clair
SOUTHERN ILLINOIS NB OF
EAST SAINT LOUIS
{{ 14 L 21 S }}
Chartered 1897
Brown Back <$VALUE
3x10-20 1-7600 <$175/$200
1882 Date Back
3x10-20 1-11000 <$150/$175
1882 Value Back
3x10-20 11001-12090 <$175/$200
1902 Plain Back
3x10-20 1-22296 <$85
1929 Small Size
10 Type 1 1-4130 <$30
20 Type 1 1-1172 <$40
10 Type 2 1-4212 <$30
20 Type 2 1-1150 <$40
Total Issue $2,552,860
Out in 1935 $150,000
Large out 1935 $8,940
****
11039 Madison
EDWARDSVILLE NB,
EDWARDSVILLE
Chartered 7/17
2nd title:Edwardsville NB & TC 8/15/29
FIRST TITLE {{ 8 L }}
1902 Plain Back <$VALUE
4x5 1-15825 <$135
3x10-20 1-10822 <$135
SECOND TITLE {{ 29 S }}
1929 Small Size
5 Type 1 1-6336 <$30
10 Type 1 1-3588 <$35
20 Type 1 1-790 <$40
5 Type 2 1-7958 <$30
10 Type 2 1-4143 <$35
20 Type 2 1-1152 <$40
Total Issue $1,462,020
Out in 1935 $200,000
Large out 1935 $4,195
****
5062 Madison
FNB OF EDWARDSVILLE
{{ 13 L }}
Chartered 1897
Liquidated 7/11/17
Brown Back <$VALUE
4x5 1-5650 <$200
3x10-20 1-3580 <$200
1882 Date Back
4x5 1-6900 <$175
3x10-20 1-4960 <$175
1882 Value Back
4x5 6901-8104 <$200
3x10-20 4961-5596<$200
1902 Plain Back
4x5 1-135 <$150
3x10-20 1-298 <$150
Total Issue $751,480
Out at close $100,000
****
4233 Effingham
FNB OF EFFINGHAM
{{ 6 L 5 S }}
Chartered 1890
Brown Back <$VALUE
4x5 1-900 <$400
3x10-20 1-2200 <$400
1882 Date Back
4x5 1-330 <$400
3x10-20 1-3 <$400
1902 Date Back
3x10-20 1-1800* <$275
1902 Plain Back
3x10-20 2001-5098* <$275
* 1801-2000 not marked
1929 Small Size
10 Type 1 1-506 <$175
20 Type 1 1-176 <$175
10 Type 2 1-574 <$200
20 Type 2 1-163 <$200
Total Issue $450,130
Out in 1935 $25,000
Large out 1935 $2,650
****
FNB of El Paso
SEE Ch 2997
NB of El Paso
****
2997 Woodford
NB OF EL PASO
Organized 7/9/83
Receivership 12/21/31
2nd title: FNB of El Paso 2/13/93
FIRST TITLE {{ 0 L }}
Brown Back <$VALUE
3x10-20 1-575 <$600
SECOND TITLE {{ 6 L }}
Brown Back
3x10-20 1-2117 <$350
1902 Red Seal
3x10-20 1-2300 <$350
1902 Date Back
4x5 1-3450 <$175
3x10-20 1-2140 <$175
1902 Plain Back
4x5 3451-22331 <$175
3x10-20 2141-7246 <$175
Total Issue $1,058,520
Out at close $6,800
****
5510 Woodford
WOODFORD COUNTY NB OF
EL PASO
{{ 7 L }}
Chartered 7/20/00
Brown Back <$VALUE
3x10-20 1-1750 <$325
1882 Date Back
3x10-20 1-3740* <$300
1882 Value Back
3x10-20 3941-5628* <$300
* 3741-3940 not marked
1902 Plain Back
4x5 1-12410 <$175
Total Issue $617,100
Out in 1935 $1,875
****
7539 Saline
FNB OF ELDORADO
{{ 3 L }}
Organized 12/17/04
Receivership 8/6/26
1902 Red Seal <$VALUE
3x10-20 1-1100 <$750
1902 Date Back
3x10-20 1-3070 <$375
1902 Plain Back
3x10-20 3071-9625 <$375
Total Issue $536,250
Out at close $49,100
****
4735 Kane
ELGIN NB, ELGIN
{{ 5 L 5 S }}
Chartered 1892
Brown Back <$VALUE
4x5 1-5400 <$300
50-100 1-1867 <$1250/$1500
1882 Date Back
4x5 1-100 <$300
50-100 1-400 <$1250/$1500
3x50-100 1-26 <$1250/$1500
1902 Date Back
3x10-20 1-3500 <$200
1902 Plain Back
3x10-20 3501-4587 <$200
1929 Small Size
10 Type 1 1-534 <$135
20 Type 1 1-148 <$150
10 Type 2 1-493 <$200
20 Type 2 1-57 <$200
Total Issue $741,770
Out in 1935$74 $25,000
Large out 1935 $3,460
****
1365 Kane
FNB OF ELGIN
{{ 13 L 4 S }}
Chartered 1865
Original Series <$VALUE
4x5 1-4675 <$500
3x10-20 1-1250 <$750/$1250
Series 1875
4x5 1-1340 <$500
3x10-20 1-466 <$750/$1250
Brown Back
4x5 1-4500 <$250
50-100 1-2196 <$1250/$1500
1902 Red Seal
50-100 1-1960 <$2250/$2500
1902 Date Back
50-100 1-1800 <$400/$500
3x50-100 1-640 <$400/$500
1902 Plain Back
3x50-100 641-671<$400/$500
1929 Small Size
50 Type 1 1-148 <$225
100 Type 1 1-26 <$300
Total Issue $1,417,250
Out in 1935 $50,000
Large out 1935 $9,700
****
2016 Kane
HOME NB OF ELGIN
{{ 14 L 3 S }}
Chartered 7/20/72
Receivership 1/20/32
Original Series <$VALUE
3x1-2 1-3000 <$400/$1250
4x5 1-4000 <$500
3x10-20 1-900 <$750/$1250
Series 1875
3x10-20 1-4359 <$750/$1250
Brown Back
4x5 1-3500 <$250
50-100 1-2574 <$1250/$1500
1882 Date Back
4x5 1-2635 <$225
50-100 1-680 <$1250/$1500
1902 Date Back
3x50-100 1-1927 <$400/$500
1902 Plain Back
3x50-100 1928-2354 <$400/$500
1929 Small Size
50 Type 1 1-219 <$200
100 Type 1 1-59 <$275
Total Issue $1,658,350
Out at close $114,100
Large out at close $32,250
****
7236 Kane
UNION NB OF ELGIN
{{ 13 L 12 S }}
Chartered 4/04
1902 Red Seal <$VALUE
3x10-20 1-4800 <$225/$250
1902 Date Back
3x10-20 1-6400 <$110
1902 Plain Back
3x10-20 6401-20465 <$110
1929 Small Size
10 Type 1 1-2484 <$50
20 Type 1 1-658 <$60
10 Type 2 1-936 <$75
20 Type 2 1-289 <$75
Total Issue $1,506,390
Out in 1935 $100,000
Large out 1935 $5,800
****
9836 Du Page
FNB OF ELMHURST
{{ 10 L 6 S }}
Chartered 9/10
Liquidated 2/16/32
1902 Date Back <$VALUE
4x10 1-2444 <$175
1902 Plain Back
4x10 2445-8137 <$175
1929 Small Size
10 Type 1 1-734 <$200
Total Issue $369,520
Out at close $24,995
Large out at close $2,105
****
7948 White
FNB OF ENFIELD
Chartered 10/05
{{ 6 L 6 S }}
1902 Red Seal <$VALUE
3x10-20 1-950 <$500
1902 Date Back
3x10-20 1-2140 <$250
1902 Plain Back
3x10-20 2141-6458 <$250
1929 Small Size
10 Type 1 1-768 <$150
20 Type 1 1-232 <$150
10 Type 2 1-232 <$175
20 Type 2 1-10 <$175
Total Issue $446,840
Out in 1935 $30,000
Large out 1935 $1,770
****
4073 Cook
FNB OF ENGLEWOOD
{{ 3 L }}
Chartered 1889
Brown Back <$VALUE
4x5 1-10070 <$450
50-100 1-1048 <$1500/$1750
1902 Date Back
4x5 1-5367 <$350
4x10 1-5295 <$350
Total Issue $677,740
Out in 1935 $2,765
****
6978 Gallatin
FNB OF EQUALITY
{{ 3 L }}
Chartered 10/03
Liquidated 2/26/29
1902 Red Seal <$VALUE
3x10-20 1-1080 <$750
1902 Date Back
3x10-20 1-1980 <$375
1902 Plain Back
3x10-20 1981-7304 <$375
Total Issue $419,200
Out at close $35,000
****
6951 Whiteside
FNB OF ERIE
{{ 6 L 4 S }}
Organized 7/28/03
Receivership 10/19/31
1902 Red Seal <$VALUE
4x5 1-1500 <$500
3x10-20 1-1160 <$500
1902 Date Back
4x5 1-2675 <$250
3x10-20 1-1940 <$250
1902 Plain Back
4x5 2676-8080 <$250
3x10-20 1941-5778 <$250
1929 Small Size
5 Type 1 1-828 <$200
10 Type 1 1-412 <$200
20 Type 1 1-112 <$200
Total Issue $601,500
Out at close $40,000
Large out at close $4,070
****
5279 Cook
CITY NB OF EVANSTON
Chartered 4/10/00
Liquidated 6/21/33
2nd title:City NB & TC 1/17/27
FIRST TITLE {{ 6 L }}
Brown Back <$VALUE
3x10-20 1-7000 <$300
1882 Date Back
3x10-20 1-6400 <$300
1882 Value Back
3x10-20 6401-9292 <$300
1902 Plain Back
3x10-20 1-8921 <$150
SECOND TITLE {{ 3 L 28 S }}
1902 Plain Back
3x10-20 1-3396 <$175
1929 Small Size
10 Type 1 1-4351 <$40
20 Type 1 1-1321 <$50
Total Issue $1,850,030
Out at close $300,000
Large out 1935 $5,400
Ch 13709 assumed circulation
****
4767 Cook
EVANSTON NB, EVANSTON
{{ UNREPORTED }}
Organized 6/29/92
Receivership 6/7/93
Brown Back <$VALUE
3x10-20 1-473 <$1500
Total Issue $23,650
Out in 1915 $100
****
13709 Cook
FNB & TC OF EVANSTON
{{ UNREPORTED }}
Chartered 6/33
1929 Small Size <$VALUE
5 Type 2 1-542 <$400
10 Type 2 1-73 <$400
20 Type 2 1-12 <$400
Total Issue $3,680
Out in 1935 $150,000
Outstanding includes Ch 5279
****
1987 Livingston
FNB OF FAIRBURY
{{ 2 L }}
Chartered 5/27/72
Liquidated 3/31/10
Original Series <$VALUE
3x1-2 1-1500 <$750/$1500
4x5 1-3375 <$850
Series 1875
4x5 1-4119 <$850
Brown Back
50-100 1-926 <$1250/$1500
1882 Date Back
50-100 1-21 <$1250/$1500
Total Issue $299,430
Out in 1910 $39,440
****
6609 Wayne
FAIRFIELD NB, FAIRFIELD
{{ 13 L 28 S }}
Chartered 2/03
1902 Red Seal <$VALUE
4x5 1-1862 <$300
3x10-20 1-1205 <$300
50-100 1-61 <$2250/$2500
1902 Date Back
4x5 1-4050 <$150
3x10-20 1-2380 <$150
50-100 1-200 <$500/$600
1902 Plain Back
4x5 4051-12833 <$150
3x10-20 2381-7549 <$150
1929 Small Size
5 Type 1 1-2008 <$35
10 Type 1 1-1110 <$35
20 Type 1 1-276 <$45
5 Type 2 1-1268 <$40
10 Type 2 1-855 <$40
20 Type 2 1-195 <$50
Total Issue $949,500
Out in 1935 $60,000
Large out 1935 $4,140
****
5009 Wayne
FNB OF FAIRFIELD
{{ 6 L 3 S }}
Chartered 1895
Liquidated 1/6/32
Brown Back <$VALUE
4x5 1-2075 <$375
3x10-20 1-530 <$375
1882 Date Back
4x5 1-749 <$375
3x10-20 1-543 <$375
1902 Date Back
4x5 1-250 <$250
3x10-20 1-200 <$250
1902 Plain Back
4x5 251-1837 <$250
3x10-20 201-1302 <$250
1929 Small Size
5 Type 1 1-296 <$250
10 Type 1 1-148 <$250
20 Type 1 1-31 <$250
Total Issue $233,450
Out at close $12,500
Large out at close $2,260
****
11443 Vermilion
FNB OF FAIRMOUNT
{{ 2 L 5 S }}
Chartered 8/19
1902 Plain Back <$VALUE
3x10-20 1-2154 <$600
1929 Small Size
10 Type 1 1-526 <$175
20 Type 1 1-160 <$175
10 Type 2 1-961 <$200
20 Type 2 1-109 <$200
Total Issue $170,250
Out in 1935 $29,800
Large out 1935 $570
****

****
2156 De Witt
FNB OF FARMER CITY
{{ 4 L }}
Chartered 7/11/74
Liquidated 5/30/94
Original Series <$VALUE
3x1-2 1-1500 <$400/$1250
4x5 1-2875 <$600
Series 1875
3x1-2 1-720 <$400/$1250
4x5 1-4857 <$600
Total Issue $165,740
Out in 1910 $1,011
****
3407 De Witt
JOHN WEEDMAN NB OF FARMER CITY
{{ 8 L 6 S }}
Organized 10/26/85
Receivership 2/19/32
Brown Back <$VALUE
4x5 1-4331 <$500
3x10-20 1-931 <$500
1902 Red Seal
3x10-20 1-2050 <$500
1902 Date Back
4x5 1-5750 <$225
3x10-20 1-3700 <$225
1902 Plain Back
4x5 5751-17273 <$225
3x10-20 3701-10839 <$225
1929 Small Size
5 Type 1 1-1837 <$165
10 Type 1 1-865 <$165
20 Type 1 1-245 <$165
Total Issue $1,259,490
Out at close $71,280
Large out at close $8,360
****
4958 De Witt
OLD FNB OF FARMER CITY
{{ 2 L 2 S }}
Organized 5/14/94
Receivership 10/25/30
Brown Back <$VALUE
3x10-20 1-1560 <$500
1882 Date Back
3x10-20 1-2603 <$500
1902 Date Back
3x10-20 1-1000 <$350
1902 Plain Back
3x10-20 1001-8320 <$350
1929 Small Size
10 Type 1 1-523 <$300
20 Type 1 1-53 <$300
Total Issue $661,890
Out at close $50,000
Large out at close $13,330
****
10057 Montgomery
FNB OF FARMERSVILLE
{{ 3 L }}
Organized 2/4/11
Receivership 6/29/27
1902 Date Back <$VALUE
3x10-20 1-1660 <$600
1902 Plain Back
3x10-20 1661-4719 <$600
Total Issue $235,950
Out at close $24,990
****
8212 Shelby
FINDLAY NB, FINDLAY
{{ UNREPORTED }}
Chartered 5/9/06
Liquidated 7/17/07
1902 Red Seal <$VALUE
3x10-20 1-137 <$1500
Total Issue $6,850
Out in 1910 $950
****
6861 Shelby
FNB OF FINDLAY
{{ 3 L }}
Chartered 6/03
Liquidated 12/31/27
1902 Red Seal <$VALUE
4x5 1-450 <$650
3x10-20 1-420 <$650
1902 Date Back
4x5 1-1550 <$325
3x10-20 1-1120 <$325
1902 Plain Back
4x5 1551-5005 <$325
3x10-20 1121-3208 <$325
Total Issue $290,500
Out at close $25,000
****

****
1961 Clay
FNB OF FLORA
{{ 8 L 8 S }}
Chartered 4/18/72
Original Series <$VALUE
3x1-2 1-2940 <$500/$1500
4x5 1-1890 <$500
3x10-20 1-1000 <$850/$1250
Series 1875
3x1-2 1-320 <$500/$1500
4x5 1-2535 <$500
3x10-20 1-2063 <$850/$1250
Brown Back
4x5 1-3475 <$350
3x10-20 1-3590 <$350
1882 Date Back
4x5 1-1660 <$350
3x10-20 1-1100 <$350
1902 Date Back
4x5 1-1750 <$225
3x10-20 1-1300 <$225
1902 Plain Back
4x5 1751-8790 <$225
3x10-20 1301-5970 <$225
1929 Small Size
5 Type 1 1-1690* <$125
10 Type 1 1-796 <$125
20 Type 1 1-218 <$125
5 Type 2 1-1731 <$135
10 Type 2 1-945 <$135
20 Type 2 1-274 <$135
* 1660 not issued
Total Issue $1,217,625
Out in 1935 $50,000
Large out 1935 $5,150
****
11509 Clay
FLORA NB, FLORA
{{ 5 L 7 S }}
Chartered 11/19
Liquidated 5/14/31
1902 Plain Back <$VALUE
4x5 1-10500 <$250
3x10-20 1-5840 <$250
1929 Small Size
5 Type 1 1-1256 <$135
10 Type 1 1-651 <$135
20 Type 1 1-182 <$135
Total Issue $600,580
Out at close $65,000
Large out at close $5,960
****
7680 Livingston
FNB OF FORREST
{{ 2 L }}
Chartered 4/05
Liquidated 6/1/14
1902 Red Seal <$VALUE
3x10-20 1-1100 <$1000
1902 Date Back
3x10-20 1-1321 <$500
Total Issue $121,050
Out in 1914 $18,870
****
7941 St Clair
FNB OF FREEBURG
{{ 3 L 5 S }}
Chartered 10/05
1902 Red Seal <$VALUE
3x10-20 1-950 <$500
1902 Date Back
3x10-20 1-1630 <$250
1902 Plain Back
3x10-20 1631-5189 <$250
1929 Small Size
10 Type 1 1-638 <$150
20 Type 1 1-192 <$150
10 Type 2 1-392 <$175
20 Type 2 1-50 <$175
Total Issue $373,190
Out in 1935 $25,000
Large out 1935 $1,710
****
319 Stephenson
FNB OF FREEPORT
{{ UNREPORTED }}
Chartered 1864
Liquidated 2/24/83
Original Series <$VALUE
3x1-2 1-3300 <$1250/$2000
4x5 1-8475 <$1250
Series 1875
4x5 1-4190 <$1250
Total Issue $269,800
Out in 1910 $1,803
****
FNB of Freeport
SEE Ch 2875
Freeport NB, Freeport
****

****
13695 Stephenson
FNB OF FREEPORT
{{ 10 S }}
Chartered 5/33
1929 Small Size <$VALUE
10 Type 2 1-9959 <$75
20 Type 2 1-2942 <$75
Total Issue $158,430
Out in 1935 $107,650
****
2875 Stephenson
FREEPORT NB, FREEPORT
Organized 1/11/83
Receivership 10/9/33
2nd title: FNB of Freeport 6/4/87
FIRST TITLE {{ 0 L }}
Brown Back <$VALUE
4x5 1-2781 <$600
SECOND TITLE {{ 7 L 14 S }}
Brown Back
3x10-20 1-2889 <$350
1902 Red Seal
3x10-20 1-1900 <$350
1902 Date Back
3x10-20 1-7800 <$175
1902 Plain Back
3x10-20 7801-20016 <$175
1929 Small Size
10 Type 1 1-3243 <$60
20 Type 1 1-898 <$70
Total Issue $1,598,210
Out at close $200,000
Large out at close $6,720
****
385 Stephenson
SECOND NB OF FREEPORT
{{ 5 L 1 S }}
Chartered 1864
Liquidated 2/1/30
Original Series <$VALUE
3x1-2 1-6400 <$400/$1250
4x5 1-8385 <$500
Series 1875
4x5 1-5870 <$500
Brown Back
4x5 1-9083 <$350
3x10-20 1-425 <$350
1902 Red Seal
3x10-20 1-1100 <$400
1902 Date Back
3x10-20 1-3300* <$200
1902 Plain Back
3x10-20 3801-8720* <$200
* 3301-3800 not marked
1929 Small Size
10 Type 1 1-271 <$350
20 Type 1 1-68 <$350
Total Issue $1,035,430
Out in Dec 1930 $30,560
Large out Dec 1930 $12,830
****
3279 Jo Daviess
GALENA NB, GALENA
{{ 3 L 3 S }}
Organized 12/23/84
Receivership 10/9/33
Brown Back <$VALUE
4x5 1-650 <$450
3x10-20 1-2254 <$450
1902 Red Seal
3x10-20 1-850 <$500
1902 Date Back
3x10-20 1-2050 <$250
1902 Plain Back
3x10-20 2051-4501 <$250
1929 Small Size
10 Type 1 1-525 <$225
20 Type 1 1-130 <$225
Total Issue $440,350
Out at close $24,820
Large out at close $2,220
****
979 Jo Daviess
MERCHANTS NB OF GALENA
{{ 20 L 2 S }}
Organized 3/7/65
Receivership 10/9/33
Original Series <$VALUE
3x1-2 1-2300 <$300/$1000
4x5 1-7850 <$300
3x10-20 1-800 <$750/$1250
Series 1875
3x1-2 1-620 <$300/$1000
4x5 1-3905 <$300
Brown Back
4x5 1-5562 <$300
3x10-20 1-546 <$300
1902 Red Seal
3x10-20 1-800 <$350
1902 Date Back
3x10-20 1-2040 <$175
1902 Plain Back
3x10-20 2041-3746 <$175
1929 Small Size
10 Type 1 1-426 <$225
20 Type 1 1-111 <$225
Total Issue $694,420
Out at close $25,000
Large out at close $4,890
****
831 Jo Daviess
NB OF GALENA
{{ 2 L }}
Chartered 1865
Liquidated 1/11/85
Original Series <$VALUE
3x1-2 1-4000 <$500/$1250
4x5 1-3700 <$600
4x10 1-1700 <$850
4x20 1-500 <$1500
Series 1875
3x1-2 1-900 <$500/$1250
4x5 1-2030 <$600
4x10 1-779 <$850
4x20 1-108 <$1500
Total Issue $286,900
Out in 1910 $2,037
****
F Galesburg NB & TC of Galesburg
SEE Ch 241
FNB of Galesburg
****
241 Knox
FNB OF GALESBURG
Chartered 1864
2nd title:F Galesburg NB & TC 4/23/28
FIRST TITLE {{ 10 L }}
Original Series <$VALUE
3x1-2 1-2700 <$350/$1000
4x5 1-4375 <$400
3x10-20 1-3500 <$750/$1250
Series 1875
3x10-20 1-1796 <$750/$1250
Brown Back
3x10-20 1-4089 <$225/$250
1902 Red Seal
3x10-20 1-6500 <$225/$250
1902 Date Back
3x10-20 1-10300 <$110
1902 Plain Back
3x10-20 10301-29453 <$110
SECOND TITLE {{ 2 L 28 S }}
1902 Plain Back
3x10-20 1-2514 <$150
1929 Small Size
10 Type 1 1-9470 <$25
20 Type 1 1-2308 <$35
10 Type 2 1-9495 <$25
20 Type 2 1-2221 <$35
Total Issue $3,478,130
Out in 1935 $422,850
Large out 1935 $15,950
Outstanding includes Ch 3138
****
3138 Knox
GALESBURG NB, GALESBURG
{{ 6 L }}
Chartered 1884
Closed 4/23/28
Brown Back <$VALUE
4x5 1-8950 <$275
3x10-20 1-1300 <$275
1902 Red Seal
3x10-20 1-3320 <$300
1902 Date Back
3x10-20 1-7200 <$150
1902 Plain Back
3x10-20 7201-19823 <$150
Total Issue $1,401,150
Out at close $100,000
Ch 241 assumed circulation
****
491 Knox
SECOND NB OF GALESBURG
{{ 2 L }}
Chartered 8/5/64
Liquidated 2/24/03
Original Series <$VALUE
3x1-2 1-1700 <$500/$1250
4x5 1-4050 <$600
3x10-20 1-2340 <$850/$1500
Series 1875
4x5 1-1425 <$600
3x10-20 1-972 <$850/$1500
Brown Back
3x10-20 1-2689 <$400
Total Issue $418,050
Out in 1910 $3,881
****

****
2793 Henry
FARMERS & MERCHANTS NB OF GALVA
Organized 9/9/82
Liquidated 8/15/34
2nd title: Galva FNB 5/21/94
FIRST TITLE {{ 0 L }}
Brown Back <$VALUE
3x10-20 1-784 <$750
SECOND TITLE {{ 4 L 6 S }}
Brown Back
3x10-20 1-498 <$350
1902 Red Seal
3x10-20 1-1550 <$350
1902 Date Back
4x5 1-3935 <$200
3x10-20 1-3050 <$200
1902 Plain Back
4x5 3936-8345 <$200
3x10-20 3051-5684 <$200
1929 Small Size
5 Type 1 1-828 <$150
10 Type 1 1-418 <$150
20 Type 1 1-144 <$150
5 Type 2 1-400 <$175
10 Type 2 1-192 <$175
Total Issue $663,820
Out at close $30,000
Large out at close $2,080
****
827 Henry
FNB OF GALVA
{{ 1 L }}
Chartered 1865
Liquidated 1/2/85
Original Series <$VALUE
3x1-2 1-2300 <$750/$1500
4x5 1-3435 <$750
3x10-20 1-1000<$1000/$1500
Series 1875
3x10-20 1-1142<$1000/$1500
Total Issue $187,300
Out in 1910 $1,326
****
Galva FNB, Galva
SEE Ch 2793
Farmers & Merchants NB of Galva
****
9406 Grundy
FNB OF GARDNER
{{ 4 L 4 S }}
Organized 4/21/09
Receivership 6/28/32
1902 Date Back <$VALUE
3x10-20 1-2130 <$275
1902 Plain Back
3x10-20 2131-5920 <$275
1929 Small Size
10 Type 1 1-447 <$175
20 Type 1 1-116 <$175
Total Issue $336,740
Out at close $24,760
Large out at close $3,310
****
6192 Douglas
FNB OF GARRETT
{{ UNREPORTED }}
Chartered 4/4/02
Liquidated 8/6/03
1902 Red Seal <$VALUE
3x10-20 1-358 <$1500
Total Issue $17,900
Out in 1910 $610
****
2332 Henry
FARMERS NB OF GENESEO
{{ 7 L 5 S }}
Chartered 4/24/76
Series 1875 <$VALUE
4x5 1-9517 <$500
Brown Back
4x5 1-4000 <$325
3x10-20 1-2020 <$325
1882 Date Back
4x5 1-3000 <$325
3x10-20 1-2180 <$325
1882 Value Back
4x5 3001-3097 <$325
3x10-20 2181-2225 <$325
1902 Plain Back
4x5 1-8180 <$200
3x10-20 1-4242 <$200
1929 Small Size
5 Type 1 1-1662 <$135
10 Type 1 1-764 <$135
20 Type 1 1-260 <$135
5 Type 2 1-920 <$165
10 Type 2 1-411 <$165
20 Type 2 1-110 <$165
Total Issue $1,058,040
Out in 1935 $12,500
Large out 1935 $3,515
****

****
534 Henry
FNB OF GENESEO
{{ 10 L 16 S }}
Chartered 1864
Original Series <$VALUE
3x1-2 1-4080 <$400/$1250
4x5 1-4500 <$500
3x10-20 1-1000 <$750/$1250
Series 1875
4x5 1-3405 <$500
3x10-20 1-880 <$750/$1250
Brown Back
3x10-20 1-3509 <$275
1902 Red Seal
3x10-20 1-1600 <$275
1902 Date Back
3x10-20 1-5400 <$125
1902 Plain Back
3x10-20 5401-19341 <$125
1929 Small Size
10 Type 1 1-2204 <$50
20 Type 1 1-618 <$60
10 Type 2 1-2238 <$60
20 Type 2 1-595 <$65
Total Issue $1,735,680
Out in 1935 $100,000
Large out 1935 $7,170
****
8740 Kane
FNB OF GENEVA
{{ 5 L 6 S }}
Chartered 6/07
1902 Red Seal <$VALUE
4x10 1-234 <$750
1902 Date Back
4x10 1-825 <$375
1902 Plain Back
4x10 826-3242 <$375
1929 Small Size
10 Type 1 1-1090 <$150
10 Type 2 1-1523 <$165
Total Issue $219,670
Out in 1935 $25,000
Large out 1935 $690
****
13448 Vermilion
FNB IN GEORGETOWN
{{ 3 S }}
Chartered 4/30
1929 Small Size <$VALUE
10 Type 2 1-1732 <$250
20 Type 2 1-444 <$250
Total Issue $26,200
Out in 1935 $22,850
****
5285 Vermilion
FNB OF GEORGETOWN
{{ 3 L 1 S }}
Chartered 4/12/00
Liquidated 5/24/30
Brown Back <$VALUE
3x10-20 1-2900 <$500
1882 Date Back
3x10-20 1-2230 <$500
1882 Value Back
3x10-20 2231-2236 <$500
1902 Plain Back
3x10-20 1-1809 <$350
1929 Small Size
10 Type 1 1-147 <$450
20 Type 1 1-10 <$450
Total Issue $357,270
Out at close $14,700
Large out at close $4,680
****
7365 Vermilion
GEORGETOWN NB, GEORGETOWN
{{ UNREPORTED }}
Chartered 8/17/04
Liquidated 10/27/05
1902 Red Seal <$VALUE
3x10-20 1-460 <$1500
Total Issue $23,000
Out in 1910 $1,880
****

CONDITION affects Value. The Values shown are for notes in FINE condition.

8174 Ford
FNB OF GIBSON CITY
{{ 8 L 15 S }}
Organized 3/31/06
1902 Red Seal <$VALUE
4x5 1-2050 <$400
3x10-20 1-2000 <$400
1902 Date Back
4x5 1-6400 <$200
3x10-20 1-4440 <$200
1902 Plain Back
4x5 6401-18252 <$200
3x10-20 4441-12190 <$200
1929 Small Size
5 Type 1 1-3222 <$75
10 Type 1 1-1566 <$75
20 Type 1 1-422 <$75
5 Type 2 1-1444 <$85
10 Type 2 1-840 <$85
20 Type 2 1-180 <$85
Total Issue $1,376,020
Out in 1935 $80,000
Large out 1935 $4,380

12314 Macoupin
AMERICAN NB OF GILLESPIE
{{ 4 L 6 S }}
Organized 2/2/23
Liquidated 10/14/30
1902 Plain Back <$VALUE
4x5 1-11731 <$165
1929 Small Size
5 Type 1 1-2195 <$85
10 Type 1 1-228 <$85
Total Issue $314,150
Out at close $50,000
Large out at close $2,700
Ch 7903 assumed circulation

7903 Macoupin
GILLESPIE NB, GILLESPIE
{{ 5 L 9 S }}
Organized 7/24/05
Receivership 12/19/31
1902 Red Seal <$VALUE
3x10-20 1-2000 <$350
1902 Date Back
3x10-20 1-3840 <$175
1902 Plain Back
3x10-20 3841-12077 <$175
1929 Small Size
10 Type 1 1-954 <$85
20 Type 1 1-275 <$85
Total Issue $794,090
Out at close $75,000
Large out at close $7,990
Outstanding includes Ch 12314

5856 Iroquois
FNB OF GILMAN
{{ 7 L 10 S }}
Chartered 6/01
Brown Back <$VALUE
3x10-20 1-1600 <$325
1882 Date Back
3x10-20 1-3540* <$325
1882 Value Back
3x10-20 3981-6020* <$325
* 3541-3980 not marked
1902 Plain Back
3x10-20 1-4904 <$175
1929 Small Size
10 Type 1 1-1116 <$85
20 Type 1 1-337 <$100
Total Issue $733,600
Out in 1935 $25,000
Large out 1935 $3,060

14173 Pope
FNB IN GOLCONDA
{{ 3 S }}
Chartered 5/34
1929 Small Size <$VALUE
10 Type 2 1-1512 <$350
20 Type 2 1-504 <$350
Total Issue $25,200
Out in 1935 $24,700

7385 Pope
FNB OF GOLCONDA
{{ 4 L 7 S }}
Organized 8/16/04
Liquidated 3/25/35
1902 Red Seal <$VALUE
3x10-20 1-1600 <$400
1902 Date Back
3x10-20 1-3640 <$200
1902 Plain Back
3x10-20 3641-10787 <$200
1929 Small Size
10 Type 1 1-1166 <$135
20 Type 1 1-318 <$135
10 Type 2 1-343 <$150
20 Type 2 1-140 <$150
Total Issue $733,700
Out in 1932 $50,000
Large out at close $3,100

7606 Johnson
FNB OF GOREVILLE
{{ 1 L 1 S }}
Organized 1/31/05
Receivership 12/5/30
1902 Red Seal <$VALUE
3x10-20 1-340 <$1250
1902 Date Back
3x10-20 1-780 <$600
1902 Plain Back
3x10-20 781-1846 <$600
1929 Small Size
10 Type 1 1-111 <$400
20 Type 1 1-18 <$400
Total Issue $118,120
Out at close $8,000
Large out at close $1,220

10690 Jackson
FNB OF GORHAM
{{ 3 S }}
Chartered 1/15
1929 Small Size <$VALUE
5 Type 2 1-2752 <$300
10 Type 2 1-1430 <$300
20 Type 2 1-396 <$300
Total Issue $35,980
Out in 1935 $25,000

6684 LaSalle
FNB OF GRAND RIDGE
{{ 2 L 2 S }}
Chartered 3/03
1902 Red Seal <$VALUE
3x10-20 1-600 <$1250
1902 Date Back
3x10-20 1-900 <$600
1902 Plain Back
3x10-20 901-2055 <$600
1929 Small Size
10 Type 1 1-273 <$400
20 Type 1 1-68 <$400
Total Issue $157,290
Out in 1935 $10,000
Large out 1935 $470

7712 Jackson
FNB OF GRAND TOWER
{{ 3 L 6 S }}
Chartered 4/05
1902 Red Seal <$VALUE
3x10-20 1-300 <$1000
1902 Date Back
3x10-20 1-1300* <$500
1902 Plain Back
3x10-20 1461-5212* <$500
* 1301-1460 not marked
1929 Small Size
10 Type 1 1-650 <$225
20 Type 1 1-176 <$225
10 Type 2 1-1167 <$250
20 Type 2 1-223 <$250
Total Issue $351,850
Out in 1935 $25,000
Large out 1935 $1,320

F Granite City NB, Granite City
SEE Ch 6564
Granite City NB, Granite City

5433 Madison
FNB OF GRANITE CITY
{{ 8 L 13 S }}
Chartered 6/16/00
Closed 1/17/31
Brown Back <$VALUE
3x10-20 1-3800 <$200/$250
1882 Date Back
3x10-20 1-5400 <$175/$225
1882 Value Back
3x10-20 5401-8750<$175/$225
1902 Plain Back
3x10-20 1-13289 <$135
1929 Small Size
10 Type 1 1-1301 <$65
20 Type 1 1-407 <$75
Total Issue $1,418,850
Out at close $99,995
Large out at close $16,685
Ch 6564 assumed circulation

6564 Madison
GRANITE CITY NB, GRANITE CITY
Chartered 12/02
2nd title:F Granite City NB 1/17/31
FIRST TITLE {{ 12 L 7 S }}
1902 Red Seal <$VALUE
3x10-20 1-3100 <$250/$275
1902 Date Back
4x5 1-4250 <$110
3x10-20 1-2360 <$110
1902 Plain Back
4x5 4251-29614 <$110
3x10-20 2361-17215 <$110
1929 Small Size
5 Type 1 1-3084 <$75
10 Type 1 1-1502 <$75
20 Type 1 1-496 <$75
SECOND TITLE {{ 4 U + 9 S }}
1929 Small Size
5 Type 1 1-458 <$65
10 Type 1 1-188 <$65
20 Type 1 1-22 <$75
5 Type 2 1-12700 <$65
10 Type 2 1-6110 <$65
20 Type 2 1-1348 <$65
Total Issue $2,029,410
Out in 1935 $100,000
Large out 1935 $11,745
Outstanding includes Ch 5433

11952 Kankakee
FNB OF GRANT PARK
{{ 3 L 14 S }}
Chartered 4/21
1902 Plain Back <$VALUE
4x10 1-3799 <$350
1929 Small Size
10 Type 1 1-1098 <$75
10 Type 2 1-1247 <$75
Total Issue $230,310
Out in 1935 $25,000
Large out 1935 $750

5124 Kankakee
GRANT PARK NB, GRANT PARK
{{ UNREPORTED }}
Chartered 6/6/98
Liquidated 11/20/07
Brown Back <$VALUE
3x10-20 1-807 <$1250
Total Issue $40,350
Out in 1910 $3,350

10458 Putnam
FNB OF GRANVILLE
{{ UNREPORTED }}
Organized 10/17/13
Receivership 3/15/34
1902 Date Back <$VALUE
4x5 1-585 <$850
3x10-20 1-463 <$850
Total Issue $34,850
Out at close $130

14035 Putnam
GRANVILLE NB, GRANVILLE
{{ 5 S }}
Chartered 2/34
1929 Small Size <$VALUE
10 Type 2 1-1684 <$300
20 Type 2 1-558 <$300
Total Issue $28,000
Out in 1935 $25,000

6460 White
FARMERS NB OF GRAYVILLE
{{ 3 L 3 S }}
Organized 10/4/02
1902 Red Seal <$VALUE
3x10-20 1-800 <$750
1902 Date Back
3x10-20 1-1000 <$375
1902 Plain Back
3x10-20 1001-2705 <$375
1929 Small Size
10 Type 1 1-312 <$275
20 Type 1 1-102 <$275
10 Type 2 1-132 <$300
20 Type 2 1-60 <$300
Total Issue $208,730
Out in 1935 $12,500
Large out 1935 $730

4999 White
FNB OF GRAYVILLE
{{ 7 L 11 S }}
Organized 5/8/95
Receivership 11/1/33
Brown Back <$VALUE
3x10-20 1-2770 <$350
1882 Date Back
3x10-20 1-2762 <$350
1902 Date Back
3x10-20 1-1000 <$175
1902 Plain Back
3x10-20 1001-7759 <$175
1929 Small Size
10 Type 1 1-1195 <$85
20 Type 1 1-320 <$85
Total Issue $774,650
Out at close $50,000
Large out at close $3,760

8473 Greene
FNB OF GREENFIELD
{{ 2 L 2 S }}
Organized 11/28/06
Receivership 1/10/33
1902 Red Seal <$VALUE
3x10-20 1-550 <$1000
1902 Date Back
3x10-20 1-1510 <$500
1902 Plain Back
3x10-20 1511-3381 <$500
1929 Small Size
10 Type 1 1-303 <$300
20 Type 1 1-92 <$300
Total Issue $225,770
Out at close $15,000
Large out at close $1,450

6191 Cumberland
FNB OF GREENUP
{{ UNREPORTED }}
Chartered 4/4/02
Liquidated 7/6/09
1902 Red Seal <$VALUE
3x10-20 1-990 <$1250
1902 Date Back
3x10-20 1-161 <$850
Total Issue $57,550
Out in 1910 $10,665

8115 Cumberland
GREENUP NB, GREENUP
{{ 6 L 10 S }}
Chartered 3/06
1902 Red Seal <$VALUE
3x10-20 1-760 <$450
1902 Date Back
3x10-20 1-4750 <$200
1902 Plain Back
3x10-20 4751-12551 <$200
1929 Small Size
10 Type 1 1-1237 <$125
20 Type 1 1-317 <$125
Total Issue $777,810
Out in 1934 $25,000
Large out 1935 $2,900

9734 Bond
BRADFORD NB OF GREENVILLE
{{ 8 L 17 S }}
Chartered 4/10
1902 Date Back <$VALUE
3x10-20 1-8100 <$175
1902 Plain Back
3x10-20 8101-23652 <$175
1929 Small Size
10 Type 1 1-2762 <$65
20 Type 1 1-712 <$75
10 Type 2 1-2131 <$75
20 Type 2 1-521 <$75
Total Issue $1,465,490
Out in 1935 $100,000
Large out 1935 $5,000

1841 Bond
FNB OF GREENVILLE
{{ 1 L }}
Chartered 7/5/71
Liquidated 1/9/83
Original Series <$VALUE
3x1-2 1-3300 <$1000/$2000
4x5 1-2800 <$1000
3x10-20 1-1750<$1250/$2000
Series 1875
3x10-20 1-520 <$1250/$2000
Total Issue $186,000
Out in 1910 $1,146

11208 McLean
FNB OF GRIDLEY
{{ 2 L }}
Chartered 7/18
Liquidated 8/25/23
1902 Plain Back <$VALUE
4x5 1-2220 <$500
4x10 1-1930 <$500
Total Issue $121,600
Out at close $30,000

2116 Pike
GRIGGSVILLE NB, GRIGGSVILLE
{{ 5 L 2 S }}
Chartered 7/8/73
Receivership 1/26/32
Original Series <$VALUE
3x1-2 1-900 <$500/$1250
4x5 1-2775 <$600
Series 1875
4x5 1-5746 <$600
Brown Back
3x10-20 1-1220 <$400
1882 Date Back
3x10-20 1-344 <$400
1902 Date Back
3x10-20 1-720 <$275
1902 Plain Back
3x10-20 721-1786 <$275
1929 Small Size
10 Type 1 1-229 <$350
20 Type 1 1-36 <$350
Total Issue $360,480
Out at close $12,500
Large out at close $2,480

9883 Hancock
FNB OF HAMILTON
{{ 5 L 4 S }}
Organized 10/10
Receivership 3/4/32
1902 Date Back <$VALUE
4x5 1-3050 <$200
3x10-20 1-2220 <$200
1902 Plain Back
4x5 3051-9449 <$200
3x10-20 2221-6449 <$200
1929 Small Size
5 Type 1 1-1053 <$175
10 Type 1 1-499 <$175
20 Type 1 1-145 <$175
Total Issue $590,360
Out at close $49,580
Large out at close $6,090

5153 Saline
CITY NB OF HARRISBURG
{{ 9 L 16 S }}
Chartered 1898
Brown Back <$VALUE
4x5 1-2625 <$200
3x10-20 1-1500 <$200/$250
1882 Date Back
4x5 1-9000 <$200
3x10-20 1-6700 <$200/$250
1882 Value Back
4x5 9001-12585 <$200
3x10-20 6701-8516<$200/$250
1902 Plain Back
4x5 1-14765 <$125
3x10-20 1-11137 <$125
1929 Small Size
5 Type 1 1-4024 <$40
10 Type 1 1-1786 <$50
20 Type 1 1-492 <$60
5 Type 2 1-2496 <$40
10 Type 2 1-877 <$50
20 Type 2 1-320 <$60
Total Issue $1,971,720
Out in 1935 $50,000
Large out 1935 $4,785

4003 Saline
FNB OF HARRISBURG
{{ 9 L 16 S }}
Organized 3/23/89
Brown Back <$VALUE
3x10-20 1-3479 <$200/$250
1902 Date Back
3x10-20 1-5160* <$125
1902 Plain Back
3x10-20 5361-17891* <$125
* 5161-5360 not marked
1929 Small Size
10 Type 1 1-1940 <$40
20 Type 1 1-582 <$50
10 Type 2 1-1831 <$50
20 Type 2 1-400 <$60
Total Issue $1,281,050
Out in 1935 $75,000
Large out 1935 $3,850

8667 Cook
FNB OF HARVEY
{{ 5 L 6 S }}
Organized 3/11/07
Receivership 2/1/32
1902 Red Seal <$VALUE
3x10-20 1-375 <$500
1902 Date Back
3x10-20 1-4700 <$225
1902 Plain Back
3x10-20 4701-12825 <$225
1929 Small Size
10 Type 1 1-890 <$150
20 Type 1 1-252 <$150
Total Issue $743,640
Out at close $48,800
Large out at close $5,370

2242 Mason
HAVANA NB, HAVANA
{{ 4 L 10 S }}
Chartered 3/30/75
Original Series <$VALUE
3x10-20 1-900 <$750/$1250
Series 1875
3x10-20 1-2540 <$750/$1250
Brown Back
3x10-20 1-6150 <$375
1882 Date Back
3x10-20 1-5790 <$375
1902 Plain Back
3x10-20 1-1818 <$225
1929 Small Size
10 Type 1 1-1236 <$85
20 Type 1 1-418 <$100
10 Type 2 1-428 <$100
20 Type 2 1-255 <$100
Total Issue $993,600
Out in 1935 $99,040
Large out 1935 $2,920

8605 Cook
INTER STATE NB OF HEGEWISCH
{{ U + 8 L }}
Chartered 3/07
Liquidated 2/11/27
1902 Red Seal <$VALUE
4x5 1-165 <$500
3x10-20 1-130 <$500
1902 Date Back
4x5 1-550* <$250
3x10-20 1-440** <$250
1902 Plain Back
4x5 651-3860* <$250
3x10-20 521-2471** <$250
* 551-650 not marked
** 441-520 not marked
Total Issue $210,550
Out at close $25,000

1482 Marshall
FNB OF HENRY
{{ 5 L }}
Organized 6/5/65
Receivership 11/7/33
Original Series <$VALUE
4x5 1-3200 <$650
3x10-20 1-510 <$1000/$1500
Series 1875
3x10-20 1-1436<$1000/$1500
Brown Back
3x10-20 1-1930 <$450
1902 Red Seal
50-100 1-160 <$2250/$2500
1902 Date Back
50-100 1-240 <$500/$600
3x50-100 1-200 <$500/$600
1902 Plain Back
3x50-100 1-770 <$500/$600
Total Issue $406,300
Out at close $4,420

7049 Marshall
HENRY NB, HENRY
{{ 6 L U + 4 S }}
Chartered 11/03
Liquidated 1/12/32
1902 Red Seal <$VALUE
3x10-20 1-1380 <$450
1902 Date Back
3x10-20 1-2200 <$200
1902 Plain Back
3x10-20 2201-6488 <$200
1929 Small Size
10 Type 1 1-547 <$165
20 Type 1 1-122 <$175
Total Issue $440,860
Out at close $30,000
Large out at close $3,870

8670 Williamson
CITY NB OF HERRIN
{{ 4 L 5 S }}
Organized 4/24/07
Receivership 10/22/31
1902 Red Seal <$VALUE
3x10-20 1-1575 <$300
1902 Date Back
3x10-20 1-4100* <$150
1902 Plain Back
3x10-20 4301-13282* <$150
* 4101-4300 not marked
1929 Small Size
10 Type 1 1-849 <$100
20 Type 1 1-223 <$110
Total Issue $820,550
Out at close $50,000
Large out at close $6,170

<$VALUEs are for notes in FINE condition. Value changes by approximately 25% for a change of one full grade.

****

5303 Williamson
FNB OF HERRIN
{{ 8 L 2 S }}
Chartered 4/24/00
Receivership 12/31/32
Brown Back <$VALUE
3x10-20 1-3200 <$300
1882 Date Back
3x10-20 1-4140 <$300
1882 Value Back
3x10-20 4141-6336 <$300
1902 Plain Back
3x50-100 1-759 <$400/$500
1929 Small Size
50 Type 1 1-125 <$225
100 Type 1 1-19 <$325
Total Issue $715,450
Out at close $49,695
Large out at close $12,095

****

6653 Madison
FNB OF HIGHLAND
{{ 12 L 14 S }}
Chartered 3/03
1902 Red Seal <$VALUE
4x5 1-1925 <$250
3x10-20 1-1790 <$250
1902 Date Back
4x5 1-7000 <$110
3x10-20 1-5000 <$110
1902 Plain Back
4x5 7001-22000 <$110
3x10-20 5001-14589 <$110
1929 Small Size
5 Type 1 1-3120 <$65
10 Type 1 1-2018 <$65
20 Type 1 1-442 <$65
5 Type 2 1-4704 <$75
10 Type 2 1-2743 <$75
20 Type 2 1-583 <$75
Total Issue $1,627,780
Out in 1935 $100,000
Large out 1935 $3,710

****

2789 Montgomery
HILLSBORO NB, HILLSBORO
{{ 10 L 19 S }}
Chartered 1882
Brown Back <$VALUE
3x10-20 1-2837 <$300
1902 Red Seal
3x10-20 1-4560 <$300
1902 Date Back
3x10-20 1-7300 <$125
1902 Plain Back
3x10-20 7301-22944 <$125
1929 Small Size
10 Type 1 1-3296 <$50
20 Type 1 1-884 <$60
10 Type 2 1-2806 <$50
20 Type 2 1-373 <$60
Total Issue $1,856,410
Out in 1935 $150,000
Large out 1935 $7,120
Outstanding includes Ch 8647

****

8006 Montgomery
PEOPLES NB OF HILLSBORO
{{ 5 L 4 S }}
Chartered 12/05
Liquidated 7/25/31
1902 Red Seal <$VALUE
4x5 1-1400 <$400
3x10-20 1-1320 <$400
1902 Date Back
4x5 1-3800 <$175
3x10-20 1-2420 <$175
1902 Plain Back
4x5 3801-11292 <$175
3x10-20 2421-7336 <$175
1929 Small Size
5 Type 1 1-869 <$125
10 Type 1 1-393 <$125
20 Type 1 1-140 <$125
Total Issue $753,090
Out at close $50,000
Large out at close $5,890

****

5538 Douglas
FNB OF HINDSBORO
{{ 5 L 5 S }}
Chartered 8/14/00
Liquidated 11/22/32
Brown Back <$VALUE
3x10-20 1-2190 <$400
1882 Date Back
3x10-20 1-2540 <$400
1882 Value Back
3x10-20 2541-3809 <$400
1902 Plain Back
3x10-20 1-3935 <$250
1929 Small Size
10 Type 1 1-644 <$165
20 Type 1 1-198 <$165
Total Issue $559,100
Out at close $35,000
Large out at close $3,630

****

11308 Du Page
FNB OF HINSDALE
{{ 15 S }}
Organized 1/11/19
1929 Small Size <$VALUE
5 Type 2 1-9590 <$100
10 Type 2 1-5280 <$100
20 Type 2 1-1535 <$100
Total Issue $131,450
Out in 1935 $100,000

****

2965 Champaign
FNB OF HOMER
{{ UNREPORTED }}
Chartered 6/2/83
Liquidated 6/22/87
Brown Back <$VALUE
4x5 1-802 <$1500
Total Issue $16,040
Out in 1910 $180

****

11882 Champaign
FNB IN HOMER
{{ 0 L 6 S }}
Chartered 11/20
1902 Plain Back <$VALUE
3x10-20 1-654 <$850
1929 Small Size
5 Type 1 1-962 <$175
10 Type 1 1-478 <$175
5 Type 2 1-3630 <$175
10 Type 2 1-1520 <$175
Total Issue $123,590
Out in 1935 $40,000
Large out 1935 $120

****

13744 Vermilion
CITY NB OF HOOPESTON
{{ 4 S }}
Chartered 8/33
1929 Small Size <$VALUE
5 Type 2 1-6100 <$125
10 Type 2 1-2846 <$125
20 Type 2 1-815 <$125
Total Issue $75,260
Out in 1935 $41,800

****

2808 Vermilion
FNB OF HOOPESTON
{{ 7 L 7 S }}
Organized 9/26/82
Receivership 8/15/33
Brown Back <$VALUE
4x5 1-3684 <$300
3x10-20 1-538 <$300
1902 Red Seal
3x10-20 1-2150 <$300
1902 Date Back
3x10-20 1-4300* <$150
1902 Plain Back
3x10-20 4901-14359* <$150
* 4301-4900 not marked
1929 Small Size
5 Type 1 1-494 <$100
10 Type 1 1-840 <$100
20 Type 1 1-238 <$100
Total Issue $1,019,810
Out at close $65,000
Large out at close $10,910
Outstanding includes Ch 9425

****

9425 Vermilion
HOOPESTON NB, HOOPESTON
{{ 7 L 6 S }}
Chartered 6/09
Closed 8/15/31
1902 Date Back <$VALUE
4x5 1-7600 <$135
3x10-20 1-5660 <$135
1902 Plain Back
4x5 7601-24361 <$135
3x10-20 5661-16423 <$135
1929 Small Size
5 Type 1 1-2214 <$85
10 Type 1 1-1029 <$85
20 Type 1 1-279 <$85
Total Issue $1,470,010
Out at close $100,000
Large out at close $10,700
Ch 2808 assumed circulation

****

9398 Tazewell
HOPEDALE NB, HOPEDALE
{{ 3 L 3 S }}
Organized 4/1/09
Receivership 2/2/32
1902 Date Back <$VALUE
3x10-20 1-2350 <$350
1902 Plain Back
3x10-20 2351-5656 <$350
1929 Small Size
5 Type 1 1-674 <$250
10 Type 1 1-277 <$250
20 Type 1 1-71 <$250
Total Issue $328,160
Out at close $23,980
Large out at close $3,650

****

7168 Coles
FNB OF HUMBOLDT
{{ 2 L 4 S }}
Chartered 3/04
1902 Red Seal <$VALUE
4x5 1-300 <$1000
3x10-20 1-240 <$1000
1902 Date Back
4x5 1-600 <$500
3x10-20 1-480 <$500
1902 Plain Back
4x5 601-1384 <$500
3x10-20 481-978 <$500
1929 Small Size
5 Type 1 1-379 <$250
10 Type 1 1-197 <$250
20 Type 1 1-68 <$250
Total Issue $125,930
Out in 1935 $16,250
Large out 1935 $365

****

11108 Edgar
FNB OF HUME
{{ 6 L 7 S }}
Organized 11/23/17
1902 Plain Back <$VALUE
3x10-20 1-4757 <$125/$150
1929 Small Size
10 Type 1 1-754 <$100
20 Type 1 1-230 <$100
10 Type 2 1-474 <$100
20 Type 2 1-132 <$100
Total Issue $318,070
Out in 1935 $30,000
Large out 1935 $1,320

****

3916 Cook
OAKLAND NB, HYDE PARK
Organized 6/21/88
Receivership 6/9/31
2nd title: Oakland NB of Chicago 6/22/08
3rd title:Washington Park NB of Chicago 3/17/10
FIRST TITLE {{ 6 L }}
Brown Back <$VALUE
4x5 1-3764 <$400
50-100 1-383 <$1500/$1750
SECOND TITLE {{ 2 L }}
1902 Red Seal
4x5 1-350 <$500
50-100 1-120 <$2250/$2500
1902 Date Back
4x5 1-598 <$350
50-100 1-30 <$500/$600
THIRD TITLE {{ 13 L 18 S }}
1902 Date Back
4x5 1-8500 <$100
3x10-20 1-6700 <$100
1902 Plain Back
4x5 8501-61678 <$100
3x10-20 6701-45793 <$100
1929 Small Size
5 Type 1 1-12002 <$40
10 Type 1 1-5632 <$40
20 Type 1 1-1697 <$50
Total Issue $4,599,020
Out at close $500,000
Large out at close $47,830

****

8647 Montgomery
IRVING NB, IRVING
{{ 2 L 2 S }}
Chartered 4/07
Liquidated 4/20/31
1902 Red Seal <$VALUE
3x10-20 1-500 <$850
1902 Date Back
3x10-20 1-1510 <$400
1902 Plain Back
3x10-20 1511-4480 <$400
1929 Small Size
10 Type 1 1-271 <$300
20 Type 1 1-78 <$300
Total Issue $274,620
Out at close $20,200
Large out at close $3,160
Ch 2789 assumed circulation

****

10179 Cook
IRVING PARK NB, IRVING PARK
Organized 4/18/12
Receivership 6/9/31
2nd title: Inland-Irving NB of Chicago 2/14/31
FIRST TITLE {{ 8 L 6 S }}
1902 Date Back <$VALUE
3x10-20 1-4200 <$150
1902 Plain Back
3x10-20 4201-19847 <$150
1929 Small Size
10 Type 1 1-1598 <$100
20 Type 1 1-496 <$100
SECOND TITLE {{ 2 S }}
1929 Small Size
10 Type 1 1-389 <$175
20 Type 1 1-50 <$200
Total Issue $1,177,090
Out at close $300,000
Large out at close $30,780
Outstanding includes Ch 12285

****

6133 Champaign
FNB OF IVESDALE
{{ 3 L 6 S }}
Chartered 2/02
1902 Red Seal <$VALUE
3x10-20 1-1200 <$750
1902 Date Back
3x10-20 1-1580 <$375
1902 Plain Back (dated 1902)
3x10-20 1581-2961 <$375
1902 Plain Back (dated 1922)
3x10-20 1-2061 <$375
1929 Small Size
10 Type 1 1-568 <$150
20 Type 1 1-162 <$150
10 Type 2 1-727 <$150
20 Type 2 1-131 <$150
Total Issue $374,510
Out in 1935 $25,000
Large out 1935 $1,140

****

5763 Morgan
AYERS NB OF JACKSONVILLE
{{ 20 L 44 S }}
Organized 3/25/01
Receivership 11/21/32
Brown Back <$VALUE
4x5 1-2000 <$150
3x10-20 1-5500 <$150/$200
1882 Date Back
4x5 1-7750* <$150
3x10-20 1-5400**<$150/$200
1882 Value Back
4x5 9001-19055* <$150
3x10-20 6401-12219** <$150/$200
* 7751-9000 not marked
** 5401-6400 not marked
1902 Plain Back
4x5 1-21277 <$85
3x10-20 1-13703 <$85
1929 Small Size
5 Type 1 1-14887 <$25
10 Type 1 1-7411 <$25
20 Type 1 1-2110 <$35
Total Issue $3,562,210
Out at close $492,740
Large out at close $16,820

****

511 Morgan
FNB OF JACKSONVILLE
{{ U + 7 L }}
Chartered 9/6/64
Liquidated 11/30/98
Original Series <$VALUE
3x1-2 1-6000 <$375/$1000
4x5 1-3000 <$400
3x10-20 1-3800 <$750/$1250
Series 1875
3x10-20 1-3026 <$750/$1250
Brown Back
3x10-20 1-5214 <$300
Total Issue $692,000
Out in 1910 $6,043

****

1719 Morgan
JACKSONVILLE NB, JACKSONVILLE
{{ 6 L }}
Chartered 10/10/70
Liquidated 12/16/14
Original Series <$VALUE
3x1-2 1-1000 <$375/$1000
4x5 1-2500 <$400
3x10-20 1-2100 <$750/$1250
3x20-50 1-820 <$1250/$4000
Series 1875
3x10-20 1-7734 <$750/$1250
Brown Back
3x10-20 1-11200 <$300
1882 Date Back
4x5 1-3335 <$300
3x10-20 1-2143 <$300
1902 Date Back
4x5 1-8500 <$175
3x10-20 1-5340 <$175
Total Issue $1,421,050
Out in 1915 $106,042

****

10108 Cook
JEFFERSON PARK NB, JEFFERSON PARK
Organized 10/5/11
Receivership 6/25/32
2nd title: Jefferson Park NB of Chicago 6/28/21
FIRST TITLE {{ 2 L }}
1902 Date Back <$VALUE
4x5 1-1100 <$300
3x10-20 1-900 <$300
1902 Plain Back
4x5 1101-1750 <$300
3x10-20 901-1240 <$300
SECOND TITLE {{ 4 L 12 S }}
1902 Plain Back
3x10-20 1-8928 <$200
1929 Small Size
10 Type 1 1-1484 <$65
20 Type 1 1-424 <$75
Total Issue $683,320
Out at close $74,400
Large out at close $6,200

****

2328 Jersey
FNB OF JERSEYVILLE
{{ 1 L }}
Chartered 3/30/76
Liquidated 4/28/94
Series 1875 <$VALUE
4x5 1-4261 <$1000
Total Issue $85,220
Out in 1910 $615

****

4952 Jersey
NB OF JERSEYVILLE
{{ 18 L }}
Organized 3/31/94
Receivership 1/15/27
Brown Back <$VALUE
4x5 1-2890 <$250
50-100 1-378 <$1250/$1500
1882 Date Back
4x5 1-977 <$250
50-100 1-160 <$1250/$1500
1902 Date Back
3x10-20 1-625* <$125
1902 Plain Back
3x10-20 826-3627* <$125
* 626-825 not marked
Total Issue $303,120
Out at close $24,400

****

7458 Williamson
FNB OF JOHNSTON CITY
{{ 1 L }}
Organized 10/29/04
Receivership 8/17/14
1902 Red Seal <$VALUE
4x5 1-1650 <$1000
3x10-20 1-1320 <$1000
1902 Date Back
4x5 1-3550 <$600
3x10-20 1-2365 <$600
Total Issue $288,250
Out in 1935 $18,945

****

6423 Will
CITIZENS NB OF JOLIET
{{ UNREPORTED }}
Chartered 9/02
Liquidated 6/26/11
1902 Red Seal <$VALUE
3x10-20 1-4800 <$1000
1902 Date Back
3x10-20 1-2140 <$650
Total Issue $347,000
Out in 1911 $73,050

****

512 Will
FNB OF JOLIET
{{ 13 L }}
Organized 8/1/64
Receivership 11/10/30
Original Series <$VALUE
4x5 1-3000 <$400
3x10-20 1-2700 <$750/$1250
Series 1875
4x5 1-230 <$400
3x10-20 1-2066 <$750/$1250
Brown Back
3x10-20 1-8283 <$200
1902 Red Seal
3x10-20 1-4000 <$200
1902 Date Back
3x10-20 1-16700 <$100
1902 Plain Back
3x10-20 16701-49893 <$100
Total Issue $3,411,700
Out at close $15,990

****

4520 Will
JOLIET NB, JOLIET
{{ 12 L 12 S }}
Organized 10/29/90
Receivership 2/10/32
Brown Back <$VALUE
3x10-20 1-7340 <$200
1882 Date Back
3x10-20 1-2170 <$200
1902 Date Back
3x10-20 1-9200 <$100
1902 Plain Back
3x10-20 9201-29346 <$100
1929 Small Size
10 Type 1 1-1744 <$40
20 Type 1 1-435 <$50
Total Issue $2,099,640
Out at close $97,180
Large out at close $16,200

****

1882 Will
WILL COUNTY NB OF JOLIET
{{ 13 L 13 S }}
Chartered 9/20/71
Receivership 7/15/31
Original Series <$VALUE
3x1-2 1-2000 <$375/$1000
4x5 1-2500 <$400
3x10-20 1-600 <$750/$1250
Series 1875
4x5 1-714 <$400
3x10-20 1-2713 <$750/$1250
Brown Back
3x10-20 1-14405 <$200
1882 Date Back
4x5 1-4311 <$200
3x10-20 1-3134 <$200
1902 Date Back
3x10-20 1-11000 <$100
1902 Plain Back
3x10-20 11001-39501 <$100
1929 Small Size
10 Type 1 1-2875 <$50
20 Type 1 1-821 <$50
Total Issue $3,449,170
Out at close $200,000
Large out at close $28,840

****

12373 Union
FNB OF JONESBORO
{{ 2 L 2 S }}
Chartered 5/23
1902 Plain Back <$VALUE
4x5 1-1785 <$500
1929 Small Size
5 Type 1 1-1024 <$400
5 Type 2 1-1826 <$400
Total Issue $75,550
Out in 1935 $10,000
Large out 1935 $180

****

4342 Kankakee
CITY NB OF KANKAKEE
{{ 12 L 28 S }}
Chartered 1890
Brown Back <$VALUE
4x5 1-10300 <$200
3x10-20 1-3760 <$200
1882 Date Back
4x5 1-1046 <$200
3x10-20 1-806 <$200
1902 Date Back
3x10-20 1-7200 <$100
1902 Plain Back
3x10-20 7201-26955 <$100
1929 Small Size
10 Type 1 1-4692 <$25
20 Type 1 1-1310 <$35
10 Type 2 1-1500 <$25
20 Type 2 1-260 <$35
Total Issue $2,261,890
Out in 1935 $150,000
Large out 1935 $6,245

****

CONDITION affects Value. The Values shown are for notes in FINE condition.

****
1793 Kankakee
FNB OF KANKAKEE
{{ 6 L }}
Organized 2/20/71
Liquidated 6/21/16
Original Series <$VALUE
3x1-2 1-1000 <$400/$1000
4x5 1-3500 <$450
Series 1875
4x5 1-3505 <$450
Brown Back
4x5 1-6400 <$225
3x10-20 1-3190 <$225
1882 Date Back
4x5 1-1585 <$200
3x10-20 1-1514 <$200
1902 Date Back
4x5 1-10750 <$135
3x10-20 1-8400 <$135
1902 Plain Back
4x5 10751-11435 <$135
3x10-20 8401-8846 <$135
Total Issue $1,211,000
Out in 1916 $142,450
****
9293 Edgar
FARMERS NB OF KANSAS
Organized 10/10/08
Receivership 12/17/30
2nd title:Kansas NB 8/3/26
FIRST TITLE {{ 11 L }}
1902 Date Back <$VALUE
4x5 1-3750 <$125
3x10-20 1-2840 <$125
1902 Plain Back
4x5 3751-10489 <$125
3x10-20 2841-7106 <$125
SECOND TITLE {{ 1 L 3 S }}
1902 Plain Back
4x5 1-1813 <$250
3x10-20 1-1474 <$250
1929 Small Size
5 Type 1 1-771 <$175
10 Type 1 1-396 <$175
20 Type 1 1-113 <$175
Total Issue $735,490
Out at close $50,000
Large out at close $8,280
****
2011 Edgar
FNB OF KANSAS
{{ 38 L }}
Chartered 7/12/72
Liquidated 7/1/26
Original Series <$VALUE
3x1-2 1-2900 <$300/$800
4x5 1-3375 <$350
Series 1875
4x5 1-8425 <$350
Brown Back
4x5 1-7900 <$250
3x10-20 1-2400 <$250
1882 Date Back
4x5 1-1594 <$250
3x10-20 1-1056 <$250
1902 Date Back
4x5 1-1700 <$150
3x10-20 1-1280 <$150
1902 Plain Back
4x5 1701-7865 <$150
3x10-20 1281-5134 <$150
Total Issue $1,027,180
Out at close $50,000
****
Kansas NB, Kansas
SEE Ch 9293
Farmers NB of Kansas
****
1805 Mercer
FARMERS NB OF KEITHSBURG
{{ 1 L }}
Chartered 3/24/71
Liquidated 7/3/79
Original Series <$VALUE
4x5 1-2435 <$1250
3x10-20 1-860 <$1500/$2000
Total Issue $91,700
Out in 1910 $450
****
1785 Henry
FNB OF KEWANEE
{{ 10 L 14 S }}
Chartered 2/6/71
Receivership 10/6/31
Original Series <$VALUE
4x5 1-1450 <$450
3x10-20 1-1970 <$750/$1250
Series 1875
4x5 1-249 <$450
3x10-20 1-2223 <$750/$1250
Brown Back
4x5 1-3600 <$250
3x10-20 1-2340 <$250
1882 Date Back
4x5 1-1326 <$250
3x10-20 1-1250 <$250
1902 Date Back
4x5 1-4475 <$135
3x10-20 1-3520 <$135
1902 Plain Back
4x5 4476-16195 <$135
3x10-20 3521-11135 <$135
1929 Small Size
5 Type 1 1-1652 <$60
10 Type 1 1-782 <$60
20 Type 1 1-220 <$70
Total Issue $1,525,180
Out at close $75,000
Large out at close $10,030
****
4854 Henry
KEWANEE NB, KEWANEE
{{ 2 L }}
Chartered 1893
Liquidated 12/12/12
Brown Back <$VALUE
3x10-20 1-4700 <$500
1882 Date Back
3x10-20 1-2710 <$500
Total Issue $370,500
Out in 1913 $35,450
****
2501 Henry
UNION NB OF KEWANEE
{{ 2 L }}
Chartered 1881
Liquidated 9/3/12
Series 1875 <$VALUE
3x10-20 1-3564 <$850/$1500
Brown Back
3x10-20 1-2900 <$500
1882 Date Back
3x10-20 1-2709 <$500
Total Issue $458,650
Out at close $72,700
****
6143 Marion
FNB OF KINMUNDY
{{ 6 L U + 8 S }}
Chartered 3/02
1902 Red Seal <$VALUE
4x5 1-765 <$350
3x10-20 1-614 <$350
1902 Date Back
4x5 1-2850 <$175
3x10-20 1-2140 <$175
1902 Plain Back (dated 1902)
4x5 2851-5220 <$175
3x10-20 2141-3655 <$175
1902 Plain Back (dated 1922)
4x5 1-3152 <$175
3x10-20 1-2325 <$175
1929 Small Size
5 Type 1 1-1476 <$85
10 Type 1 1-628 <$85
20 Type 1 1-186 <$85
5 Type 2 1-1516 <$85
10 Type 2 1-888 <$85
20 Type 2 1-204 <$85
Total Issue $637,260
Out in 1935 $40,000
Large out 1935 $2,190
****
2313 Warren
FNB OF KIRKWOOD
{{ 6 L 6 S }}
Chartered 12/18/75
Liquidated 12/1/32
Series 1875 <$VALUE
3x10-20 1-2132 <$750/$1250
Brown Back
4x5 1-3090 <$300
3x10-20 1-1874 <$300
1882 Date Back
4x5 1-3400 <$300
3x10-20 1-2502 <$300
1882 Value Back
4x5 3401-3429 <$300
1902 Plain Back
3x10-20 1-7073 <$175
1929 Small Size
10 Type 1 1-960 <$150
20 Type 1 1-233 <$150
Total Issue $894,990
Out at close $50,000
Large out at close $5,770
****
3287 Knox
FARMERS NB OF KNOXVILLE
{{ 7 L 10 S }}
Chartered 1885
Brown Back <$VALUE
4x5 1-3850 <$300
3x10-20 1-346 <$300
1902 Red Seal
3x10-20 1-500 <$350
1902 Date Back
3x10-20 1-5300 <$150
1902 Plain Back
3x10-20 5301-13140 <$150
1929 Small Size
10 Type 1 1-1492 <$85
20 Type 1 1-382 <$100
10 Type 2 1-90 <$125
20 Type 2 1-47 <$125
Total Issue $913,500
Out in 1935 $30,000
Large out 1935 $4,210
****
759 Knox
FNB OF KNOXVILLE
{{ UNREPORTED }}
Chartered 1865
Liquidated 1/16/85
Original Series <$VALUE
3x1-2 1-2700 <$1250/$2000
4x5 1-4100 <$1250
3x10-20 1-500 <$1500/$2000
Series 1875
3x1-2 1-1040 <$1250/$2000
4x5 1-3890 <$1250
Total Issue $203,500
Out in 1910 $1,698
****
8468 Hancock
FNB OF La HARPE
{{ 3 L 2 S }}
Organized 11/20/06
Receivership 12/7/33
1902 Red Seal <$VALUE
4x5 1-312 <$750
3x10-20 1-250 <$750
1902 Date Back
4x5 1-1000* <$375
3x10-20 1-800** <$375
1902 Plain Back
4x5 1101-2554* <$375
3x10-20 881-1824** <$375
* 1001-1100 not marked
** 801-880 not marked
1929 Small Size
5 Type 1 1-396 <$350
10 Type 1 1-191 <$350
20 Type 1 1-62 <$350
Total Issue $191,800
Out at close $12,500
Large out at close $720
****
347 Marshall
FNB OF LACON
{{ 4 L 8 S }}
Chartered 1864
Original Series <$VALUE
4x5 1-4750 <$600
Series 1875
4x5 1-2860 <$600
Brown Back
3x10-20 1-2785 <$350
1902 Red Seal
50-100 1-680 <$2250/$2500
1902 Date Back
50-100 1-500 <$400/$500
3x50-100 1-738 <$400/$500
1902 Plain Back
3x50-100 739-866<$400/$500
1929 Small Size
5 Type 1 1-2070 <$85
10 Type 1 1-944 <$85
5 Type 2 1-2846 <$100
10 Type 2 1-1700 <$100
Total Issue $834,920
Out in 1935 $50,000
Large out 1935 $7,440
****
2858 Cook
DROVERS NB OF UNION STOCK YARDS, LAKE
{{ 5 L }}
Chartered 1/12/83
Liquidated 12/13/02
Brown Back <$VALUE
4x5 1-11565 <$400
3x10-20 1-5817 <$400
Total Issue $522,150
Out in 1910 $12,620
****
1678 Cook
UNION STOCK YARDS NB OF CHICAGO, LAKE
{{ 1 L }}
Chartered 3/12/68
Liquidated 2/29/88
Original Series <$VALUE
3x1-2 1-3000 <$850/$2000
4x5 1-3750 <$1000
3x10-20 1-1000<$1250/$2000
Series 1875
4x5 1-1228 <$1000
3x10-20 1-2731<$1250/$2000
Total Issue $301,110
Out in 1910 $1,433
****
8937 Lake
FNB OF LAKE FOREST
{{ 5 L 14 S }}
Chartered 10/07
1902 Red Seal <$VALUE
4x5 1-800 <$450
4x10 1-850 <$450
1902 Date Back
4x5 1-600 <$225
4x10 1-600 <$225
1902 Plain Back
4x5 601-9743 <$225
4x10 601-7844 <$225
1929 Small Size
5 Type 1 1-5856 <$65
10 Type 1 1-2840 <$65
5 Type 2 1-6524 <$65
10 Type 2 1-3700 <$65
Total Issue $974,320
Out in 1935 $100,000
Large out 1935 $2,050
****
1755 Carroll
FNB OF LANARK
{{ 6 L 8 S }}
Chartered 12/19/70
Receivership 11/21/34
Original Series <$VALUE
4x5 1-2750 <$500
3x10-20 1-1100 <$750/$1250
Series 1875
4x5 1-500 <$500
3x10-20 1-2081 <$750/$1250
Brown Back
3x10-20 1-4910 <$300
1882 Date Back
3x10-20 1-555 <$300
1902 Date Back
3x10-20 1-2600 <$175
1902 Plain Back
3x10-20 2601-8803 <$175
1929 Small Size
10 Type 1 1-1198 <$100
20 Type 1 1-318 <$100
10 Type 2 1-309 <$110
20 Type 2 1-88 <$110
Total Issue $1,052,340
Out at close $50,000
Large out at close $4,300
****
14297 Carroll
NB OF LANARK
{{ 3 S }}
Chartered 11/34
1929 Small Size <$VALUE
5 Type 2 1-1568 <$225
10 Type 2 1-996 <$225
20 Type 2 1-240 <$225
50 Type 2 1-48 <$500
Total Issue $25,000
Out in 1935 $24,950
****
2804 LaSalle
CITY NB OF LaSALLE
{{ UNREPORTED }}
Chartered 1882
Liquidated 1/8/84
Brown Back <$VALUE
3x10-20 1-450 <$1250
Total Issue $22,500
Out in 1910 $130
****
114 LaSalle
FNB OF LaSALLE
{{ UNREPORTED }}
Chartered 10/26/63
Liquidated 8/30/69
Original Series <$VALUE
4x5 1-2275 <$1500
Total Issue $45,500
Out in 1910 $430
****
2503 LaSalle
LaSALLE NB, LaSALLE
Chartered 1881
2nd title:LaSalle NB & TC 11/22/29
FIRST TITLE {{ 32 L 2 S }}
Series 1875 <$VALUE
3x10-20 1-2762 <$750/$1250
Brown Back
3x10-20 1-3250 <$200
1882 Date Back
4x5 1-5500* <$135
3x10-20 1-3240**<$135/$175
1882 Value Back
4x5 5901-8720* <$150
3x10-20 3451-5133** <$150/$200
* 5501-5900 not marked
** 3241-3450 not marked
1902 Plain Back
3x10-20 1-3568 <$100
1929 Small Size
5 Type 1 1-4084 <$65
10 Type 1 1-2060 <$65
SECOND TITLE {{ 21 S }}
1929 Small Size
5 Type 1 1-11500 <$30
10 Type 1 1-2162 <$30
5 Type 2 1-14398 <$30
10 Type 2 1-6985 <$30
Total Issue $1,772,730
Out in 1935 $200,000
Large out 1935 $5,145
****
5385 Lawrence
FNB OF LAWRENCEVILLE
{{ 7 L 5 S }}
Chartered 6/1/00
Receivership 8/22/32
Brown Back <$VALUE
3x10-20 1-1390 <$250/$300
1882 Date Back
3x10-20 1-4110 <$225/$275
1882 Value Back
3x10-20 4111-5995<$225/$275
1902 Plain Back
3x10-20 1-6104 <$150
1929 Small Size
10 Type 1 1-1089 <$125
20 Type 1 1-259 <$125
Total Issue $770,870
Out at close $50,000
Large out at close $4,240
****
7864 LaSalle
FNB OF LELAND
{{ 4 L }}
Organized 7/15/05
Receivership 8/1/32
1902 Red Seal <$VALUE
3x10-20 1-1000 <$650
1902 Date Back
3x10-20 1-2110 <$300
1902 Plain Back
3x10-20 2111-5450 <$300
Total Issue $322,500
Out at close $2,090
****
8224 Coles
FNB OF LERNA
{{ 3 L 3 S }}
Chartered 5/06
1902 Red Seal <$VALUE
3x10-20 1-750 <$800
1902 Date Back
3x10-20 1-400 <$400
1902 Plain Back
3x10-20 401-1645 <$400
1929 Small Size
10 Type 1 1-271 <$300
20 Type 1 1-69 <$300
Total Issue $144,290
Out in 1935 $10,000
Large out 1935 $500
****
6586 McLean
FNB OF LeROY
{{ 4 L 6 S }}
Organized 1/10/03
Receivership 2/19/32
1902 Red Seal <$VALUE
3x10-20 1-3013 <$600
1902 Date Back
3x10-20 1-3600 <$300
1902 Plain Back
3x10-20 3601-10864 <$300
1929 Small Size
10 Type 1 1-842 <$165
20 Type 1 1-236 <$175
Total Issue $772,690
Out at close $48,560
Large out at close $5,650
****
1808 Fulton
FNB OF LEWISTOWN
{{ UNREPORTED }}
Chartered 4/1/71
Liquidated 5/12/86
Original Series <$VALUE
4x5 1-1750 <$1250
3x10-20 1-500 <$1500/$2000
Series 1875
3x10-20 1-1915<$1500/$2000
Total Issue $155,750
Out in 1910 $865
****
4941 Fulton
LEWISTOWN NB, LEWISTOWN
{{ 5 L 9 S }}
Chartered 1894
Brown Back <$VALUE
3x10-20 1-2670 <$300
1882 Date Back
3x10-20 1-2489 <$300
1902 Date Back
3x10-20 1-1000 <$200
1902 Plain Back
3x10-20 1001-8134 <$200
1929 Small Size
10 Type 1 1-1176 <$85
20 Type 1 1-294 <$100
10 Type 2 1-1383 <$100
20 Type 2 1-316 <$110
Total Issue $790,640
Out in 1935 $50,000
Large out 1935 $2,770
****
2824 McLean
FNB OF LEXINGTON
{{ UNREPORTED }}
Chartered 11/23/82
Liquidated 4/1/93
Brown Back <$VALUE
3x10-20 1-1367 <$1500
Total Issue $68,350
Out in 1910 $350
****
F Lake County NB of Libertyville
SEE Ch 6514
FNB of Libertyville
****
6514 Lake
FNB OF LIBERTYVILLE
Organized 11/1/02
Receivership 12/5/33
2nd title:F Lake County NB of Libertyville 8/1/32
FIRST TITLE {{ 1 L 2 S }}
1902 Red Seal <$VALUE
50-100 1-130 <$2250/$2500
1902 Date Back
50-100 1-120 <$850/$1500
3x50-100 1-411 <$850/$1500
1929 Small Size
5 Type 1 1-1452 <$250
10 Type 1 1-674 <$250
SECOND TITLE {{ 2 S }}
1929 Small Size
5 Type 1 1-370 <$250
10 Type 1 1-262 <$250
Total Issue $251,070
Out at close $98,440
Large out at close $5,290
Outstanding includes Ch 6670
****
6670 Lake
LAKE COUNTY NB OF LIBERTYVILLE
{{ 4 L 6 S }}
Chartered 3/03
Liquidated 7/30/32
1902 Red Seal <$VALUE
3x10-20 1-1612 <$500
1902 Date Back
3x10-20 1-3680 <$225
1902 Plain Back
3x10-20 3681-11571 <$225
1929 Small Size
10 Type 1 1-944 <$150
20 Type 1 1-268 <$150
Total Issue $747,950
Out at close $50,000
Large out at close $4,740
Ch 6514 assumed circulation
****
American NB of Lincoln
SEE Ch 3613
German American NB of Lincoln
****
14118 Logan
FNB IN LINCOLN
{{ 9 S }}
Chartered 4/34
1929 Small Size <$VALUE
5 Type 2 1-8770 <$75
10 Type 2 1-4180 <$75
20 Type 2 1-1380 <$75
Total Issue $113,250
Out in 1935 $85,250
****

CONDITION affects Value. The Values shown are for notes in FINE condition.

2126 Logan
FNB OF LINCOLN
{{ 50+ L }}
Chartered 8/25/73
Liquidated 1/6/23
Original Series <$VALUE
3x1-2 1-1220 <$275/$800
4x5 1-1875 <$400
Series 1875
4x5 1-3250 <$400
50-100 1-650 <$4000
Brown Back
50-100 1-1927 <$1250/$1500
1882 Date Back
50-100 1-600 <$1250/$1500
3x50-100 1-15 <$1250/$1500
1902 Date Back
3x10-20 1-1600 <$150
1902 Plain Back
3x10-20 1601-5798 <$150
Total Issue $878,800
Out at close $80,000

3613 Logan
GERMAN AMERICAN NB OF LINCOLN
Organized 12/18/86
Liquidated 11/18/31
2nd title:American NB of Lincoln 5/24/18
FIRST TITLE {{ 7 L }}
Brown Back <$VALUE
4x5 1-4609 <$300
3x10-20 1-1809 <$300
1902 Red Seal
3x10-20 1-2500 <$300
1902 Date Back
4x5 1-6915 <$150
3x10-20 1-4200 <$150
1902 Plain Back
4x5 6916-10315 <$150
3x10-20 4201-5820 <$150
SECOND TITLE {{ 5 L 4 S }}
1902 Plain Back
4x5 1-40650 <$150
1929 Small Size
5 Type 1 1-6839 <$100
Total Issue $1,823,100
Out in 1931 $100,000
Large out at close $8,970

3369 Logan
LINCOLN NB, LINCOLN
{{ 12 L 18 S }}
Organized 7/1/85
Receivership 5/10/34
Brown Back <$VALUE
4x5 1-7763 <$200
3x10-20 1-2432 <$200/$250
1902 Red Seal
4x5 1-3400 <$200
3x10-20 1-2060 <$200/$250
1902 Date Back
4x5 1-5800 <$100
3x10-20 1-5000 <$100
1902 Plain Back
4x5 5801-28120 <$100
3x10-20 5001-18053 <$100
1929 Small Sie 100
5 Type 1 1-5742 <$35
10 Type 1 1-2618 <$35
20 Type 1 1-658 <$40
5 Type 2 1-168 <$50
10 Type 2 1-174 <$50
Total Issue $2,323,790
Out at close $150,000
Large out at close $9,550

3962 Montgomery
FNB OF LITCHFIELD
{{ 10 L 12 S }}
Organized 11/24/88
Brown Back <$VALUE
3x10-20 1-6312 <$300
1902 Date Back
3x10-20 1-5400 <$135
1902 Plain Back
3x10-20 5401-15957 <$135
1929 Small Size
10 Type 1 1-1742 <$50
20 Type 1 1-514 <$60
10 Type 2 1-932 <$60
20 Type 2 1-300 <$60
Total Issue $1,294,970
Out in 1935 $50,000
Large out 1935 $5,240

10079 Montgomery
LITCHFIELD NB, LITCHFIELD
{{ 6 L 8 S }}
Organized 9/6/11
1902 Date Back <$VALUE
3x10-20 1-3200 <$175
1902 Plain Back
3x10-20 3201-10551 <$175
1929 Small Size
10 Type 1 1-1184 <$100
20 Type 1 1-346 <$110
10 Type 2 1-1128 <$110
20 Type 2 1-339 <$110
Total Issue $658,170
Out in 1935 $50,000
Large out 1935 $3,730

6065 Warren
FNB OF LITTLE YORK
{{ 1 L }}
Chartered 12/01
Liquidated 11/1/16
Brown Back <$VALUE
3x10-20 1-400 <$2000
1882 Date Back
3x10-20 1-503 <$2000
Total Issue $45,150
Out at close $5,950

11845 Madison
FNB OF LIVINGSTON
{{ 0 L 4 S }}
Organized 9/21/20
Receivership 7/5/34
1902 Plain Back <$VALUE
4x5 1-3415 <$750
3x10-20 1-2038 <$750
1929 Small Size
5 Type 1 1-912 <$150
10 Type 1 1-434 <$150
20 Type 1 1-108 <$150
5 Type 2 1-802 <$175
10 Type 2 1-279 <$175
20 Type 2 1-98 <$175
Total Issue $245,320
Out at close $24,700
Large out at close $630

8933 Will
FNB OF LOCKPORT
{{ 3 L 8 S }}
Chartered 10/07
1902 Red Seal <$VALUE
3x10-20 1-185 <$650
1902 Date Back
3x10-20 1-560 <$325
1902 Plain Back
3x10-20 561-4244 <$325
1929 Small Size
10 Type 1 1-1034 <$85
20 Type 1 1-296 <$100
Total Issue $319,010
Out in 1934 $25,000
Large out 1935 $780

FNB of Lovington
SEE Ch 5494
Shepherd NB of Lovington

5494 Moultrie
SHEPHERD NB OF LOVINGTON
Chartered 7/11/00
Liquidated 11/12/23
2nd title:FNB of Lovington 7/3/20
FIRST TITLE {{ 1 L }}
Brown Back <$VALUE
50-100 1-560 <$1500/$1750
1882 Date Back
50-100 1-160 <$1500/$1750
3x50-100 1-208<$1500/$1750
SECOND TITLE {{ 1 L }}
1902 Plain Back
4x5 1-1827 <$600
Total Issue $196,540
Out at close $25,000

8732 Tazewell
FNB OF MACKINAW
{{ 6 L 7 S }}
Chartered 6/07
1902 Red Seal <$VALUE
4x5 1-250 <$400
3x10-20 1-200 <$400
1902 Date Back
4x5 1-1700 <$200
3x10-20 1-1220 <$200
1902 Plain Back
4x5 1701-9559 <$200
3x10-20 1221-6254 <$200
1929 Small Size
5 Type 1 1-1680 <$125
10 Type 1 1-836 <$125
20 Type 1 1-242 <$125
5 Type 2 1-2120 <$135
10 Type 2 1-1145 <$135
20 Type 2 1-242 <$135
Total Issue $675,370
Out in 1935 $50,000
Large out 1935 $2,080

967 McDonough
FNB OF MACOMB
{{ 4 L }}
Chartered 4/1/65
Liquidated 4/14/86
Original Series <$VALUE
3x1-2 1-4200 <$400/$1250
4x5 1-4375 <$450
3x10-20 1-1100 <$750/$1250
Series 1875
3x1-2 1-2000 <$400/$1250
3x10-20 1-2518 <$750/$1250
Brown Back
3x10-20 1-535 <$350
Total Issue $326,150
Out in 1910 $2,178

9169 McDonough
MACOMB NB, MACOMB
{{ 9 L 15 S }}
Chartered 6/08
Liquidated 12/15/34
1902 Date Back <$VALUE
3x10-20 1-8700 <$100
1902 Plain Back
3x10-20 8701-23399 <$100
1929 Small Size
10 Type 1 1-2228 <$40
20 Type 1 1-640 <$45
10 Type 2 1-1462 <$50
20 Type 2 1-243 <$60
Total Issue $1,399,910
Out at close $100,000
Large out at close $5,390

1872 McDonough
UNION NB OF MACOMB
{{ 8 L 15 S }}
Chartered 9/8/71
Original Series <$VALUE
4x5 1-3450 <$400
3x10-20 1-600 <$750/$1250
Series 1875
4x5 1-1350 <$400
3x10-20 1-1976 <$750/$1250
Brown Back
3x10-20 1-8960 <$250
1882 Date Back
3x10-20 1-2236 <$250
1902 Date Back
3x10-20 1-4600 <$100
1902 Plain Back
3x10-20 4601-18154 <$100
1929 Small Size
10 Type 1 1-2262 <$40
20 Type 1 1-628 <$50
10 Type 2 1-2240 <$50
20 Type 2 1-562 <$60
Total Issue $1,937,020
Out in 1935 $100,000
Large out 1935 $6,990

8457 Madison
FNB OF MADISON
{{ 5 L 8 S }}
Organized 11/26/06
Liquidated 9/6/34
1902 Red Seal <$VALUE
4x5 1-385 <$350
4x10 1-385 <$350
1902 Date Back
4x5 1-3700 <$165
4x10 1-3500 <$165
1902 Plain Back
4x5 3701-14201 <$165
4x10 3501-12149 <$165
1929 Small Size
5 Type 1 1-2878 <$110
10 Type 1 1-1592 <$110
5 Type 2 1-1404 <$125
10 Type 2 1-636 <$125
Total Issue $988,320
Out at close $49,995
Large out at close $2,875

5815 De Kalb
FNB OF MALTA
{{ 3 L 6 S }}
Chartered 5/01
Brown Back <$VALUE
3x10-20 1-500 <$1000
1882 Date Back
3x10-20 1-580 <$1000
1882 Value Back
3x10-20 581-600 <$1000
1902 Plain Back
3x10-20 1-604 <$650
1929 Small Size
10 Type 1 1-312 <$250
20 Type 1 1-106 <$250
10 Type 2 1-522 <$275
20 Type 2 1-94 <$275
Total Issue $123,740
Out in 1935 $25,000
Large out 1935 $320

8713 Will
FNB OF MANHATTAN
{{ 2 L 4 S }}
Chartered 5/07
1902 Red Seal <$VALUE
3x10-20 1-350 <$1000
1902 Date Back
3x10-20 1-1020 <$500
1902 Plain Back
3x10-20 1021-2078 <$500
1929 Small Size
10 Type 1 1-269 <$250
20 Type 1 1-86 <$250
Total Issue $147,860
Out in 1935 $10,000
Large out 1935 $490

8648 Bureau
FNB OF MANLIUS
{{ 3 L 5 S }}
Chartered 4/07
1902 Red Seal <$VALUE
3x10-20 1-800 <$700
1902 Date Back
3x10-20 1-1860 <$350
1902 Plain Back
3x10-20 1861-5372 <$350
1929 Small Size
10 Type 1 1-558 <$150
20 Type 1 1-148 <$150
10 Type 2 1-842 <$175
20 Type 2 1-160 <$175
Total Issue $371,460
Out in 1935 $24,200
Large out 1935 $1,300

6096 Piatt
FNB OF MANSFIELD
{{ 3 L }}
Chartered 1/16/02
Liquidated 8/1/07
Brown Back <$VALUE
3x10-20 1-541 <$600
Total Issue $27,050
Out in 1910 $2,780

8482 Knox
FNB OF MAQUON
{{ 4 L }}
Organized 11/10/06
Receivership 8/14/29
1902 Red Seal <$VALUE
4x5 1-751 <$500
4x10 1-625 <$500
1902 Date Back
4x5 1-1300 <$250
4x10 1-1275 <$250
1902 Plain Back
4x5 1301-5881 <$250
4x10 1276-4678 <$250
Total Issue $344,740
Out at close $23,400

1870 McHenry
FNB OF MARENGO
{{ 3 L 1 S }}
Chartered 9/6/71
Receivership 8/29/32
Original Series <$VALUE
3x1-2 1-1500 <$500/$1250
4x5 1-2875 <$500
Series 1875
3x1-2 1-320 <$500/$1250
4x5 1-4137 <$500
Brown Back
4x5 1-2050 <$400
3x10-20 1-600 <$400
1882 Date Back
4x5 1-581 <$400
3x10-20 1-469 <$400
1902 Date Back
3x10-20 1-1470 <$250
1902 Plain Back
3x10-20 1471-2820 <$250
1929 Small Size
10 Type 1 1-265 <$350
20 Type 1 1-45 <$350
Total Issue $417,710
Out at close $12,500
Large out at close $2,160

10582 Madison
FNB OF MARINE
{{ 7 S }}
Organized 7/7/14
1929 Small Size <$VALUE
5 Type 1 1-1610 <$125
10 Type 1 1-806 <$125
20 Type 1 1-152 <$125
5 Type 2 1-1372 <$150
10 Type 2 1-750 <$150
20 Type 2 1-250 <$150
Total Issue $134,260
Out in 1935 $35,000

4502 Williamson
FNB OF MARION
{{ 8 L 2 S }}
Organized 12/27/90
Receivership 12/5/30
Brown Back <$VALUE
3x10-20 1-3490 <$300
1882 Date Back
3x10-20 1-1236 <$300
1902 Date Back
3x10-20 1-6700 <$150
1902 Plain Back
3x10-20 6701-23620 <$150
1929 Small Size
10 Type 1 1-1203 <$200
20 Type 1 1-315 <$200
Total Issue $1,527,280
Out at close $100,000
Large out at close $16,835

6691 St Clair
FNB OF MARISSA
{{ 8 L 6 S }}
Organized 3/12/03
Liquidated 7/29/33
1902 Red Seal <$VALUE
4x5 1-2250 <$850
3x10-20 1-1350 <$850
1902 Date Back
4x5 1-3100 <$400
3x10-20 1-2560 <$400
1902 Plain Back
4x5 3101-10795 <$400
3x10-20 2561-7587 <$400
1929 Small Size
5 Type 1 1-1503 <$200
10 Type 1 1-915 <$200
20 Type 1 1-247 <$200
Total Issue $862,380
Out at close $49,995
Large out 1935 $3,340
Ch 13735 assumed circulation

13735 St Clair
FNB OF MARISSA
{{ 2U + 1 S }}
Chartered 7/33
1929 Small Size <$VALUE
5 Type 2 1-162 <$300
10 Type 2 1-120 <$300
20 Type 2 1-37 <$300
Total Issue $2,750
Out in 1935 $25,000
Outstanding includes Ch 6691

1852 LaSalle
FNB OF MARSEILLES
{{ 7 L }}
Chartered 7/28/71
Receivership 10/27/33
Original Series <$VALUE
3x1-2 1-3040 <$400/$1250
4x5 1-4325 <$500
Series 1875
4x5 1-4075 <$500
Brown Back
4x5 1-2575 <$300
3x10-20 1-660 <$300
1882 Date Back
4x5 1-286 <$300
3x10-20 1-328 <$300
1902 Date Back
3x10-20 1-3800* <$200
1902 Plain Back
3x10-20 4161-13366* <$200
* 3801-4160 not marked
Total Issue $958,120
Out in 1927 $73,800

4759 Clark
DULANEY NB OF MARSHALL
{{ 5 L 15 S }}
Chartered 1892
Brown Back <$VALUE
3x10-20 1-3370 <$300
1882 Date Back
3x10-20 1-1056 <$300
1902 Date Back
3x10-20 1-1900 <$175
1902 Plain Back
3x10-20 1901-9244 <$175
1929 Small Size
10 Type 1 1-2056 <$50
20 Type 1 1-564 <$60
10 Type 2 1-300 <$75
20 Type 2 1-147 <$75
Total Issue $880,480
Out in 1935 $50,000
Large out 1935 $2,470

6721 Clark
FNB OF MARTINSVILLE
{{ 4 L 2 S }}
Organized 3/17/03
Receivership 10/11/30
1902 Red Seal <$VALUE
4x5 1-850 <$500
3x10-20 1-840 <$500
1902 Date Back
4x5 1-1775 <$250
3x10-20 1-1280 <$250
1902 Plain Back
4x5 1776-6021 <$250
3x10-20 1281-3743 <$250
1929 Small Size
5 Type 1 1-387 <$250
10 Type 1 1-158 <$250
20 Type 1 1-54 <$250
Total Issue $394,140
Out at close $25,000
Large out at close $3,600

13795 St Clair
FNB IN MASCOUTAH
{{ 3 S }}
Chartered 10/33
1929 Small Size <$VALUE
5 Type 2 1-6208 <$175
10 Type 2 1-2855 <$175
20 Type 2 1-800 <$175
Total Issue $75,590
Out in 1935 $42,050

9736 St Clair
FNB OF MASCOUTAH
{{ 6 L 5 S }}
Organized 3/28/10
Receivership 1/12/34
1902 Date Back <$VALUE
4x5 1-3450 <$150
3x10-20 1-2580 <$150
1902 Plain Back
4x5 3451-10634 <$150
3x10-20 2581-7367 <$150
1929 Small Size
5 Type 1 1-1617 <$100
10 Type 1 1-792 <$100
20 Type 1 1-224 <$100
Total Issue $703,940
Out at close $49,995
Large out at close $2,215

1850 Mason
FNB OF MASON CITY
{{ 3 L }}
Chartered 7/26/71
Liquidated 9/15/98
Original Series <$VALUE
4x5 1-2500 <$600
3x10-20 1-420 <$1000/$1500
Series 1875
4x5 1-2560 <$600
3x10-20 1-426 <$1000/$1500
Brown Back
3x10-20 1-2217 <$500
Total Issue $256,150
Out in 1910 $2,395

1024 Coles
FNB OF MATTOON
{{ 2 L }}
Chartered 1865
Liquidated 7/1/11
Original Series <$VALUE
3x1-2 1-2800 <$600/$1500
4x5 1-5350 <$650
3x10-20 1-800 <$1000/$1500
Series 1875
4x5 1-480 <$650
3x10-20 1-914 <$1000/$1500
Brown Back
50-100 1-369 <$1500/$1750
1902 Red Seal
4x5 1-575 <$600
50-100 1-394 <$2250/$2500
Total Issue $342,250
Out in 1911 $25,600

****
2147 Coles
MATTOON NB, MATTOON
{{ UNREPORTED }}
Chartered 5/20/74
Liquidated 7/1/11
Original Series <$VALUE
4x5 1-502 <$1250
4x20 1-312 <$2000
Series 1875
4x5 1-1350 <$1250
4x20 1-1103 <$2000
Brown Back
50-100 1-1295 <$1750/$2000
1882 Date Back
50-100 1-202 <$1750/$2000
Total Issue $374,790
Out in 1911 $3,900
****
10045 Coles
NB OF MATTOON
{{3 L 3 S}}
Chartered 6/11
1902 Date Back <$VALUE
3x10-20 1-2000 <$300
3x50-100 1-560 <$500/$600
1902 Plain Back
3x10-20 2001-4020 <$300
3x50-100 561-587<$500/$600
1929 Small Size
10 Type 1 1-388 <$175
20 Type 1 1-128 <$175
50 Type 1 1-62 <$275
100 Type 1 1-20 <$350
Total Issue $416,999
Out in 1935 $40,000
Large out 1935 $2,050
****
10144 Coles
STATE NB OF MATTOON
{{6 L}}
Chartered 2/12
Liquidated 5/2/21
1902 Date Back <$VALUE
4x5 1-5000 <$200
3x10-20 1-3300 <$200
3x50-100 1-200 <$500/$600
1902 Plain Back
4x5 5001-12500 <$200
3x10-20 3301-7595 <$200
Total Issue $679,750
Out at close $150,000
****
10186 Grundy
FNB OF MAZON
{{6 L 5 S}}
Organized 4/16/12
Receivership 10/8/32
1902 Date Back <$VALUE
4x5 1-1550 <$200
3x10-20 1-1160 <$200
1902 Plain Back
4x5 1551-9350 <$200
3x10-20 1161-6381 <$200
1929 Small Size
5 Type 1 1-1387 <$150
10 Type 1 1-659 <$150
20 Type 1 1-204 <$150
Total Issue $611,680
Out at close $50,000
Large out at close $4,270

6649 Hamilton
FNB OF McLEANSBORO
{{2 L 1 S}}
Chartered 2/03
Receivership 8/4/30
1902 Red Seal <$VALUE
4x5 1-1400 <$750
3x10-20 1-1020 <$750
1902 Date Back
4x5 1-1800 <$375
3x10-20 1-1320 <$375
1902 Plain Back (dated 1902)
4x5 1801-3750 <$375
3x10-20 1321-2450 <$375
1902 Plain Back (dated 1922)
4x5 1-2665 <$375
3x10-20 1-1529 <$375
1929 Small Size
5 Type 1 1-322 <$350
10 Type 1 1-148 <$350
20 Type 1 1-39 <$350
Total Issue $429,470
Out at close $25,000
Large out at close $3,980
****
9408 Hamilton
PEOPLES NB OF McLEANSBORO
{{3 L 5 S}}
Chartered 5/09
1902 Date Back <$VALUE
4x5 1-1900 <$350
3x10-20 1-1480 <$350
1902 Plain Back
4x5 1901-6270 <$350
3x10-20 1481-4113 <$350
1929 Small Size
5 Type 1 1-890 <$150
10 Type 1 1-450 <$150
20 Type 1 1-142 <$150
5 Type 2 1-592 <$175
10 Type 2 1-426 <$175
20 Type 2 1-72 <$175
Total Issue $410,450
Out in 1935 $25,000
Large out 1935 $1,400
****
1177 LaSalle
FNB OF MENDOTA
{{4 L 5 S}}
Organized 2/13/65
Receivership 2/12/32
Original Series <$VALUE
3x1-2 1-2000 <$500/$1250
4x5 1-4550 <$500
3x10-20 1-2140<$1000/$1500
Series 1875
4x5 1-2660 <$500
3x10-20 1-1186<$1000/$1500
Brown Back
4x5 1-6360 <$400
50-100 1-215 <$1250/$1500
1902 Red Seal
3x10-20 1-750 <$500
1902 Date Back
3x10-20 1-3300 <$250
1902 Plain Back
3x10-20 3301-9312 <$250
1929 Small Size
10 Type 1 1-743 <$125
20 Type 1 1-220 <$125
Total Issue $1,054,030
Out at close $48,800
Large out at close $7,990
****
5086 LaSalle
MENDOTA NB, MENDOTA
{{3 L 1 S}}
Organized 7/14/97
Receivership 2/12/32
Brown Back <$VALUE
4x5 1-1200 <$500
3x10-20 1-660 <$500
1882 Date Back
4x5 1-893 <$500
3x10-20 1-704 <$500
1902 Plain Back
4x5 1-1390 <$500
3x10-20 1-879 <$500
1929 Small Size
5 Type 1 1-315 <$400
10 Type 1 1-139 <$400
20 Type 1 1-32 <$400
Total Issue $203,440
Out at close $11,320
Large out at close $1,400
****
13611 LaSalle
NB OF MENDOTA
{{3 S}}
Chartered 4/32
1929 Small Size <$VALUE
5 Type 1 1-622 <$250
10 Type 1 1-314 <$250
5 Type 2 1-1504 <$250
Total Issue $45,020
Out in 1935 $13,800
****
7954 Edgar
FNB OF METCALF
{{3 L 3 S}}
Chartered 10/05
Liquidated 7/15/34
1902 Red Seal <$VALUE
3x10-20 1-470 <$750
1902 Date Back
3x10-20 1-1200* <$375
1902 Plain Back
3x10-20 1321-2787* <$375
* 1201-1320 not marked
1929 Small Size
10 Type 1 1-347 <$250
20 Type 1 1-81 <$250
Total Issue $193,390
Out at close $12,500
Large out at close $660
****
8745 Massac
CITY NB OF METROPOLIS
{{4 L 10 S}}
Chartered 6/07
1902 Red Seal <$VALUE
3x10-20 1-1500 <$500
1902 Date Back
3x10-20 1-3700 <$225
1902 Plain Back
3x10-20 3701-11442 <$225
1929 Small Size
10 Type 1 1-1378 <$125
20 Type 1 1-366 <$125
10 Type 2 1-1523 <$125
20 Type 2 1-248 <$125
Total Issue $793,890
Out in 1935 $50,000
Large out 1935 $2,480
****
3156 Massac
FNB OF METROPOLIS
{{3 L 9 S}}
Chartered 1884
Brown Back <$VALUE
3x10-20 1-2593 <$450
1902 Red Seal
3x10-20 1-2100 <$450
1902 Date Back
3x10-20 1-3400 <$225
1902 Plain Back
3x10-20 3401-11193 <$225
1929 Small Size
10 Type 1 1-1454 <$125
20 Type 1 1-386 <$125
5 Type 2 1-278 <$125
10 Type 2 1-637 <$125
20 Type 2 1-135 <$125
Total Issue $938,320
Out in 1935 $48,050
Large out 1935 $2,655
****
5254 Massac
N STATE B OF METROPOLIS
{{4 L 10 S}}
Chartered 2/8/00
Brown Back <$VALUE
3x10-20 1-3800 <$400
1882 Date Back
3x10-20 1-3200* <$400
1882 Value Back
3x10-20 3401-4938* <$400
* 3201-3400 not marked
1902 Plain Back
3x10-20 1-6003 <$225
1929 Small Size
10 Type 1 1-1338 <$125
20 Type 1 1-360 <$125
10 Type 2 1-1209 <$125
20 Type 2 1-245 <$125
Total Issue $877,520
Out in 1935 $50,000
Large out 1935 $2,640
****
7791 Logan
FNB OF MIDDLETOWN
{{ UNREPORTED }}
Chartered 6/16/05
Liquidated 11/22/06
1902 Red Seal <$VALUE
4x5 1-245 <$1500
3x10-20 1-204 <$1500
Total Issue $15,100
Out in 1910 $1,445
****
5149 Iroquois
FNB OF MILFORD
{{6 L 1 S}}
Organized 10/8/98
Receivership 3/4/30
Brown Back <$VALUE
4x5 1-1550 <$500
3x10-20 1-1410 <$500
1882 Date Back
4x5 1-3050 <$450
3x10-20 1-2160 <$450
1882 Value Back
4x5 3051-4560 <$450
3x10-20 2161-2921 <$450
1902 Plain Back
4x5 1-6665 <$250
3x10-20 1-4587 <$250
1929 Small Size
5 Type 1 1-480 <$350
10 Type 1 1-179 <$350
20 Type 1 1-27 <$350
Total Issue $729,780
Out at close $45,980
Large out at close $17,800
****
8425 St Clair
FNB OF MILLSTADT
{{5 L 10 S}}
Chartered 11/06
1902 Red Seal <$VALUE
4x5 1-750 <$400
3x10-20 1-600 <$400
1902 Date Back
4x5 1-1900 <$200
3x10-20 1-1410 <$200
1902 Plain Back
4x5 1901-10615 <$200
3x10-20 1411-6643 <$200
1929 Small Size
5 Type 1 1-2360 <$85
10 Type 1 1-1020 <$85
20 Type 1 1-278 <$85
5 Type 2 1-1840 <$100
10 Type 2 1-1346 <$100
20 Type 2 1-372 <$100
Total Issue $784,910
Out in 1935 $60,000
Large out 1935 $3,100
****
9601 Woodford
FNB OF MINONK
{{ UNREPORTED }}
Chartered 12/09
Liquidated 9/1/17
1902 Date Back <$VALUE
4x5 1-1550 <$850
3x10-20 1-1670 <$850
1902 Plain Back
4x5 1551-2130 <$850
3x10-20 1671-2007 <$850
Total Issue $142,950
Out at close $50,000
****
9208 Grundy
FARMERS' FNB OF MINOOKA
{{2 L 6 S}}
Chartered 7/08
1902 Date Back <$VALUE
3x10-20 1-2400 <$500
1902 Plain Back
3x10-20 2401-6029 <$500
1929 Small Size
10 Type 1 1-604 <$150
20 Type 1 1-158 <$150
10 Type 2 1-521 <$175
20 Type 2 1-165 <$175
Total Issue $365,160
Out in 1935 $25,000
Large out 1935 $1,540
****
160 Rock Island
FNB OF MOLINE
{{2 L}}
Chartered 12/16/63
Liquidated 2/10/05
Original Series <$VALUE
3x1-2 1-3900 <$750/$1500
4x5 1-7300 <$750
3x10-20 1-1000<$1000/$1500
50-100 1-372 <$4000
Series 1875
4x5 1-3310 <$750
3x10-20 1-382 <$1000/$1500
Brown Back
4x5 1-7020 <$650
3x10-20 1-3344 <$650
1902 Red Seal
4x5 1-1400 <$750
3x10-20 1-1122 <$750
Total Issue $713,200
Out in 1910 $10,908
****
1941 Rock Island
MOLINE NB, MOLINE
{{1 L}}
Chartered 2/28/72
Liquidated 5/2/06
Original Series <$VALUE
4x5 1-2700 <$750
3x10-20 1-1500<$1000/$1500
Series 1875
4x5 1-1750 <$750
3x10-20 1-2485<$1000/$1500
Brown Back
4x5 1-2440 <$650
3x10-20 1-3739 <$650
Total Issue $524,000
Out in 1910 $11,990
****
7079 Kankakee
FNB OF MOMENCE
{{3 L 2 S}}
Organized 12/14/03
Receivership 12/17/31
1902 Red Seal <$VALUE
3x10-20 1-1233 <$700
1902 Date Back
3x10-20 1-1910 <$350
1902 Plain Back
3x10-20 1911-5116 <$350
1929 Small Size
10 Type 1 1-425 <$275
20 Type 1 1-107 <$275
Total Issue $355,790
Out at close $24,760
Large out at close $2,730
****

****
85 Warren
FNB OF MONMOUTH
{{ UNREPORTED }}
Chartered 1863
Liquidated 7/3/82
Original Series <$VALUE
4x5 1-4675 <$1500
Series 1875
4x5 1-2910 <$1500
Total Issue $151,700
Out in 1910 $1,200
****
2751 Warren
FNB OF MONMOUTH
{{ UNREPORTED }}
Organized 7/7/82
Receivership 4/22/84
Brown Back <$VALUE
3x10-20 1-570 <$1250
Total Issue $28,500
Out in 1915 $140
****
1706 Warren
MONMOUTH NB OF MONMOUTH
{{2 L}}
Chartered 9/9/70
Liquidated 8/18/90
Original Series <$VALUE
3x1-2 1-2000 <$500/$1250
4x5 1-3450 <$500
3x10-20 1-1100<$1000/$1500
Series 1875
3x1-2 1-200 <$500/$1250
3x10-20 1-2909<$1000/$1500
Total Issue $280,450
Out in 1910 $1,560
****
4400 Warren
NB OF MONMOUTH
{{16 L 24 S}}
Chartered 1890
Brown Back <$VALUE
3x10-20 1-7140 <$200/$225
1882 Date Back
3x10-20 1-3491 <$200/$225
1902 Date Back
4x5 1-8000 <$100
3x10-20 1-8200 <$100
1902 Plain Back
4x5 8001-26000 <$100
3x10-20 8201-31355 <$100
1929 Small Size
10 Type 1 1-4572 <$40
20 Type 1 1-1276 <$50
10 Type 2 1-4550 <$50
20 Type 2 1-1120 <$60
Total Issue $3,114,640
Out in 1935 $200,000
Large out 1935 $11,040
****
4313 Warren
PEOPLES NB OF MONMOUTH
{{0 L 3 S}}
Organized 5/2/90
Receivership 10/26/33
Brown Back <$VALUE
4x5 1-4075 <$850
50-100 1-295 <$1750/$2000
1882 Date Back
4x5 1-110 <$850
50-100 1-3 <$1750/$2000
1902 Date Back
50-100 1-400 <$750/$850
3x50-100 1-898 <$750/$850
1902 Plain Back
3x50-100 899-1077<$750/$850
1929 Small Size
50 Type 1 1-155 <$225
100 Type 1 1-24 <$300
Total Issue $518,550
Out at close $50,000
Large out at close $6,345
****
2205 Warren
SECOND NB OF MONMOUTH
{{4 L 4 S}}
Chartered 11/9/74
Original Series <$VALUE
4x5 1-2250 <$500
Series 1875
4x5 1-6267 <$500
Brown Back
50-100 1-560 <$1250/$1500
1882 Date Back
50-100 1-800 <$1250/$1500
3x50-100 1-220<$1250/$1500
1902 Date Back
3x50-100 1-1078 <$400/$500
1902 Plain Back
3x50-100 1079-1365 <$400/$500
1929 Small Size
50 Type 1 1-212 <$165
100 Type 1 1-60 <$200
Total Issue $870,190
Out in 1935 $75,000
Large out 1935 $8,450
****
4826 Piatt
FNB OF MONTICELLO
{{12 L 16 S}}
Organized 11/17/92
Receivership 1/12/34
Brown Back <$VALUE
3x10-20 1-6780 <$300
1882 Date Back
3x10-20 1-3522 <$300
1902 Date Back
3x10-20 1-3400 <$135
1902 Plain Back
3x10-20 3401-17078 <$135
1929 Small Size
10 Type 1 1-2210 <$50
20 Type 1 1-656 <$60
10 Type 2 1-73 <$85
Total Issue $1,581,00
Out at close $99,600
Large out at close $7,340
****
13865 Piatt
NB OF MONTICELLO
{{4 S}}
Chartered 12/33
1929 Small Size <$VALUE
5 Type 2 1-6188 <$175
10 Type 2 1-2230 <$175
20 Type 2 1-680 <$175
Total Issue $66,840
Out in 1935 $45,800
****
8163 Grundy
FARMERS & MERCHANTS NB OF MORRIS
{{8 L 5 S}}
Chartered 4/06
Closed 5/16/31
1902 Red Seal <$VALUE
3x10-20 1-1550 <$300
1902 Date Back
3x10-20 1-7500 <$150
1902 Plain Back
3x10-20 7501-22386 <$150
1929 Small Size
10 Type 1 1-1345 <$100
20 Type 1 1-394 <$100
Total Issue $1,324,780
Out at close $100,000
Large out at close $14,805
Ch 531 assumed circulation
****
FNB of Morris
SEE Ch 1773
FNB of Seneca
****
531 Grundy
GRUNDY COUNTY NB OF MORRIS
{{13 L 13 S}}
Organized 9/16/64
Original Series <$VALUE
3x1-2 1-3840 <$400/$1000
4x5 1-7790 <$500
Series 1875
4x5 1-3150 <$500
Brown Back
3x10-20 1-3007 <$250
1902 Red Seal
3x10-20 1-3600 <$250
1902 Date Back
3x10-20 1-6700 <$110
1902 Plain Back
3x10-20 6701-20441 <$110
1929 Small Size
10 Type 1 1-1908 <$50
20 Type 1 1-566 <$60
10 Type 2 1-218 <$85
20 Type 2 1-50 <$85
Total Issue $1,775,980
Out in 1935 $100,000
Large out 1935 $14,206
Outstanding includes Ch 8163
****

<$VALUEs are for notes in **FINE** condition. Value changes by approximately **25%** for a change of one full grade.

***

1033 Whiteside
FNB OF MORRISON
{{ 8 L 7 S }}
Organized 1/28/65
Receivership 12/7/33
Original Series <$VALUE
4x5 1-7125 <$500
3x10-20 1-1640 <$750/$1250
Series 1875
4x5 1-925 <$500
3x10-20 1-1360 <$750/$1250
Brown Back
3x10-20 1-2336 <$300
1902 Red Seal
3x10-20 1-2800 <$300
1902 Date Back
3x10-20 1-5400 <$150
1902 Plain Back
3x10-20 5401-17626 <$150
1929 Small Size
10 Type 1 1-1320 <$85
20 Type 1 1-426 <$100
Total Issue $1,579,420
Out at close $49,700
Large out at close $8,605

***

6745 Christian
FNB OF MORRISONVILLE
{{ 3 L 3 S }}
Organized 3/18/03
Receivership 6/29/31
1902 Red Seal <$VALUE
3x10-20 1-1160 <$700
1902 Date Back
3x10-20 1-1880 <$350
1902 Plain Back
3x10-20 1881-4776 <$350
1929 Small Size
10 Type 1 1-341 <$225
20 Type 1 1-109 <$225
Total Issue $330,340
Out at close $25,000
Large out at close $2,930

***

7443 Pulaski
FNB OF MOUND CITY
{{ 2 L 1 S }}
Organized 9/15/04
Receivership 12/19/31
1902 Red Seal <$VALUE
3x10-20 1-550 <$1000
1902 Date Back
3x10-20 1-800* <$500
1902 Plain Back
3x10-20 901-2325* <$500
* 801-900 not marked
1929 Small Size
10 Type 1 1-192 <$400
20 Type 1 1-41 <$400
Total Issue $160,190
Out at close $10,000
Large out at close $990

***

10445 Pulaski
FNB OF MOUNDS
{{ 2 L 3 S }}
Chartered 9/13
Liquidated 2/10/32
1902 Date Back <$VALUE
4x5 1-475 <$500
4x10 1-475 <$500
1902 Plain Back
4x5 476-2736 <$500
4x10 476-2089 <$500
1929 Small Size
5 Type 1 1-410 <$300
10 Type 1 1-179 <$300
Total Issue $161,320
Out at close $10,000
Large out at close $820

***

9922 Christian
FNB OF MOUNT AUBURN
{{ 4 L 8 S }}
Chartered 1/11
1902 Date Back <$VALUE
3x10-20 1-2500 <$300
1902 Plain Back
3x10-20 2501-8605 <$300
1929 Small Size
10 Type 1 1-980 <$100
20 Type 1 1-252* <$110
10 Type 2 1-1137 <$125
20 Type 2 1-224 <$125
* 228-230 not issued
Total Issue $534,780
Out in 1935 $40,000
Large out 1935 $1,640

***

American-FNB of Mount Carmel
SEE Ch 5782
American NB of Mount Carmel

***

5782 Wabash
AMERICAN NB OF MOUNT CARMEL
Organized 4/5/01
Receivership 5/31/34
2nd title:American-FNB of Mount Carmel 12/14/31
FIRST TITLE {{ 6 L 7 S }}
Brown Back <$VALUE
3x10-20 1-3600 <$300
1882 Date Back
3x10-20 1-5300 <$300
1882 Value Back
3x10-20 5301-9606 <$300
1902 Plain Back
3x10-20 1-10598 <$150
1929 Small Size
10 Type 1 1-1812 <$85
20 Type 1 1-584 <$85
SECOND TITLE {{ 5 S }}
1929 Small Size
10 Type 1 1-312 <$85
20 Type 1 1-106 <$85
10 Type 2 1-1474 <$85
20 Type 2 1-302 <$85
Total Issue $1,421,220
Out at close $98,950
Large out at close $6,570

***

4480 Wabash
FNB OF MOUNT CARMEL
{{ 7 L 7 S }}
Chartered 1890
Liquidated 11/10/31
Brown Back <$VALUE
3x10-20 1-4320 <$300
1882 Date Back
3x10-20 1-1028 <$300
1902 Date Back
3x10-20 1-6000 <$150
1902 Plain Back
3x10-20 6001-20844 <$150
1929 Small Size
5 Type 1 1-788 <$100
10 Type 1 1-1404 <$100
20 Type 1 1-414 <$100
Total Issue $1,467,160
Out at close $100,000
Large out at close $13,030

***

409 Carroll
FNB OF MOUNT CARROLL
{{ 4 L }}
Chartered 1864
Liquidated 6/29/20
Original Series <$VALUE
3x1-2 1-2000 <$600/$1500
4x5 1-7250 <$650
Series 1875
4x5 1-6500 <$650
Brown Back
50-100 1-2667 <$1250/$1500
1902 Red Seal
3x10-20 1-4100 <$600
1902 Date Back
3x10-20 1-1940 <$300
1902 Plain Back
3x10-20 1941-3268 <$300
Total Issue $1,053,450
Out at close $50,000

***

13452 Macoupin
FNB IN MOUNT OLIVE
{{ 3 S }}
Organized 4/2/30
Receivership 1/20/32
1929 Small Size <$VALUE
5 Type 1 1-804 <$225
10 Type 1 1-365 <$225
20 Type 1 1-72 <$225
Total Issue $54,660
Out at close $48,380
Outstanding includes Ch 7350

***

7350 Macoupin
FNB OF MOUNT OLIVE
{{ 4 L 3 S }}
Organized 7/15/04
Receivership 8/12/32
1902 Red Seal <$VALUE
4x5 1-1000 <$500
3x10-20 1-830 <$500
1902 Date Back
4x5 1-1825 <$250
3x10-20 1-1300 <$250
1902 Plain Back
4x5 1826-7463 <$250
3x10-20 1301-4642 <$250
1929 Small Size
5 Type 1 1-625 <$250
10 Type 1 1-319 <$250
20 Type 1 1-45 <$250
Total Issue $486,150
Out at close $55,000
Large out at close $4,395
Ch 13452 assumed circulation

***

14285 Macoupin
MOUNT OLIVE NB, MOUNT OLIVE
{{ 5 S }}
Chartered 10/34
1929 Small Size <$VALUE
100 Type 2 1-250 <$400
Total Issue $25,000
Out in 1935 $25,000

***

10048 Cook
MOUNT PROSPECT NB, MOUNT PROSPECT
{{ 3 L }}
Chartered 7/11
Liquidated 1/2/26
1902 Date Back <$VALUE
3x10-20 1-600 <$500
1902 Plain Back
3x10-20 601-974 <$500
Total Issue $48,700
Out at close $6,250

***

3839 Logan
FNB OF MOUNT PULASKI
{{ 12 L 10 S }}
Chartered 1888
Brown Back <$VALUE
4x5 1-4698 <$250
3x10-20 1-2216 <$250/$300
1902 Red Seal
4x5 1-500 <$250
3x10-20 1-400 <$250/$300
1902 Date Back
4x5 1-3900* <$125
3x10-20 1-2620** <$125
1902 Plain Back
4x5 4301-11935* <$125
3x10-20 2921-7099** <$125
* 3901-4300 not marked
** 2621-2920 not marked
1929 Small Size
5 Type 1 1-840 <$85
10 Type 1 1-1006 <$85
20 Type 1 1-288 <$85
5 Type 2 1-3724 <$85
10 Type 2 1-1982 <$85
20 Type 2 1-609 <$85
Total Issue $999,150
Out in 1935 $75,000
Large out 1935 $3,550

***

2402 Brown
FNB OF MOUNT STERLING
{{ 15 L }}
Chartered 11/18/78
Receivership 12/17/30
Series 1875 <$VALUE
4x5 1-8228 <$400
Brown Back
3x10-20 1-1290 <$250/$300
1882 Date Back
3x10-20 1-5700 <$250/$300
1882 Value Back
3x10-20 5701-6910 <$250/$300
1902 Plain Back
3x10-20 1-9690 <$125
Total Issue $1,059,060
Out at close $17,250

***

5057 Jefferson
HAM NB OF MOUNT VERNON
{{ 10 L 5 S }}
Chartered 1897
Liquidated 11/7/30
Brown Back <$VALUE
4x5 1-5100 <$250
3x10-20 1-2800 <$250
1882 Date Back
4x5 1-7000 <$250
3x10-20 1-5300 <$250
1882 Value Back
4x5 7001-8011 <$250
3x10-20 5301-5890 <$250
1902 Plain Back
4x5 1-15409 <$125
3x10-20 1-10832 <$125
1929 Small Size
5 Type 1 1-985 <$135
10 Type 1 1-715 <$135
20 Type 1 1-166 <$150
Total Issue $1,638,870
Out in 1929 $97,060
Large out at close $14,505

***

1996 Jefferson
MOUNT VERNON NB, MOUNT VERNON
{{ UNREPORTED }}
Chartered 6/10/72
Liquidated 10/11/86
Original Series <$VALUE
3x1-2 1-1500 <$1250/$2000
4x5 1-2625 <$1250
Series 1875
4x5 1-5543 <$1250
Total Issue $170,860
Out in 1910 $974

***

5689 Jefferson
THIRD NB OF MOUNT VERNON
{{ 9 L 11 S }}
Chartered 1/21/01
Receivership 1/3/33
Brown Back <$VALUE
3x10-20 1-4100 <$250
1882 Date Back
3x10-20 1-7000 <$250
1882 Value Back
3x10-20 7001-11391 <$250
1902 Plain Back
3x10-20 1-11347 <$150
1929 Small Size
10 Type 1 1-2146 <$75
20 Type 1 1-566 <$85
Total Issue $1,538,580
Out in 1935 $100,000
Large out 1935 $9,070

***

7739 Shelby
FNB OF MOWEAQUA
{{ 6 L }}
Organized 4/8/05
Receivership 5/23/28
1902 Red Seal <$VALUE
4x5 1-950 <$400
3x10-20 1-760 <$400
1902 Date Back
4x5 1-1675 <$200
3x10-20 1-1200 <$200
1902 Plain Back
4x5 1676-9460 <$200
3x10-20 1201-5842 <$200
Total Issue $538,300
Out at close $49,050

***

7379 Bond
FNB OF MULBERRY GROVE
{{ 6 L 10 S }}
Chartered 8/04
1902 Red Seal <$VALUE
3x10-20 1-1206 <$500
1902 Date Back
3x10-20 1-1910 <$250
1902 Plain Back
3x10-20 1911-7732 <$250
1929 Small Size
10 Type 1 1-976 <$125
20 Type 1 1-286 <$125
10 Type 2 1-1053 <$150
20 Type 2 1-305 <$150
Total Issue $556,400
Out in 1935 $40,000
Large out 1935 $2,120

***

4804 Jackson
CITY NB OF MURPHYSBORO
{{ 8 L 9 S }}
Chartered 1892
Brown Back <$VALUE
4x5 1-4275 <$250
3x10-20 1-2680 <$250
1882 Date Back
4x5 1-1847 <$250
3x10-20 1-1255 <$250
1902 Date Back
3x10-20 1-1900 <$125
1902 Plain Back
3x10-20 1901-9580 <$125
1929 Small Size
10 Type 1 1-1168 <$65
20 Type 1 1-304 <$75
10 Type 2 1-1247 <$85
20 Type 2 1-310 <$85
Total Issue $923,420
Out in 1935 $50,000
Large out 1935 $3,465

***

4019 Jackson
FNB OF MURPHYSBORO
{{ 4 L 3 S }}
Organized 4/19/89
Brown Back <$VALUE
3x10-20 1-4739 <$300
1902 Date Back
50-100 1-500 <$400/$500
3x50-100 1-690 <$400/$500
1902 Plain Back
3x50-100 691-882 <$400/$500
1929 Small Size
5 Type 1 1-420 <$100
50 Type 1 1-113 <$150
100 Type 1 1-20 <$225
5 Type 2 1-2894 <$100
Total Issue $605,420
Out in 1935 $50,000
Large out 1935 $10,910

***

4551 Du Page
FNB OF NAPERVILLE
{{ 4 L }}
Organized 2/26/91
Receivership 4/27/34
Brown Back <$VALUE
4x5 1-2875 <$850
3x10-20 1-720 <$850
1882 Date Back
4x5 1-297 <$850
3x10-20 1-223 <$850
1902 Date Back
4x5 1-1275 <$650
3x10-20 1-1028 <$650
Total Issue $187,490
Out at close $715

***

8221 Washington
FARMERS & MERCHANTS NB OF NASHVILLE
{{ 3 L 9 S }}
Chartered 5/06
1902 Red Seal <$VALUE
3x10-20 1-880 <$400
1902 Date Back
3x10-20 1-1470 <$200
1902 Plain Back
3x10-20 1471-8032 <$200
1929 Small Size
5 Type 1 1-808 <$100
10 Type 1 1-1104 <$100
20 Type 1 1-308 <$100
5 Type 2 1-1558 <$110
10 Type 2 1-776 <$110
20 Type 2 1-264 <$110
Total Issue $593,870
Out in 1935 $50,000
Large out 1935 $2,180

***

6524 Washington
FNB OF NASHVILLE
{{ 8 L 11 S }}
Chartered 12/02
1902 Red Seal <$VALUE
4x5 1-2250 <$250
3x10-20 1-2160 <$250
1902 Date Back
4x5 1-6650 <$125
3x10-20 1-4740 <$125
1902 Plain Back
4x5 6651-15979 <$125
3x10-20 4741-10619 <$125
1929 Small Size
5 Type 1 1-2690 <$75
10 Type 1 1-1438 <$75
20 Type 1 1-392 <$75
5 Type 2 1-2250 <$85
10 Type 2 1-1422 <$85
20 Type 2 1-144 <$85
Total Issue $1,251,900
Out in 1935 $75,000
Large out 1935 $4,290

***

12991 St Clair
N STOCK YARDS NB OF NATIONAL CITY
{{ 50+ S }}
Chartered 9/26
1929 Small Size <$VALUE
5 Type 1 1-10378 <$50
10 Type 1 1-7678 <$50
20 Type 1 1-2142 <$55
5 Type 2 1-44406 <$50
10 Type 2 1-25398 <$50
20 Type 2 1-6435 <$55
Total Issue $1,633,770
Out in 1935 $750,000

***

9118 St Clair
NATIONAL STOCK YARDS NB, NATIONAL CITY
{{ 6 L }}
Chartered 4/08
Liquidated 10/26/26
1902 Date Back <$VALUE
4x5 1-32045 <$175
3x10-20 1-26304 <$175
Total Issue $1,956,100
Out in 1917 $195,800

***

8898 Hancock
FNB OF NAUVOO
{{ 1 L }}
Chartered 9/07
Liquidated 2/28/19
1902 Red Seal <$VALUE
3x10-20 1-650 <$1500
1902 Date Back
3x10-20 1-2330 <$850
1902 Plain Back
3x10-20 2331-3208 <$850
Total Issue $192,900
Out at close $35,000

***

10492 Pike
FNB OF NEBO
{{ 3 L 5 S }}
Organized 1/28/14
Receivership 4/12/32
1902 Plain Back <$VALUE
3x10-20 1-4523 <$350
1929 Small Size
10 Type 1 1-736 <$200
20 Type 1 1-208 <$200
Total Issue $295,270
Out at close $38,980
Large out at close $3,900

***

13892 Cumberland
CUMBERLAND COUNTY NB IN NEOGA
{{ 2 S }}
Chartered 12/33
1929 Small Size <$VALUE
5 Type 2 1-6592 <$275
Total Issue $32,960
Out in 1935 $50,000
Outstanding includes Ch 5426

***

5426 Cumberland
CUMBERLAND COUNTY NB OF NEOGA
{{ 10 L 8 S }}
Chartered 6/15/00
Liquidated 2/10/34
Brown Back <$VALUE
3x10-20 1-1350 <$300
1882 Date Back
4x5 1-4350 <$300
3x10-20 1-2540 <$300
1882 Value Back
4x5 4351-6500 <$300
3x10-20 2541-3860 <$300
1902 Plain Back
4x5 1-18735 <$150
1929 Small Size
5 Type 1 1-6184 <$100
5 Type 2 1-1526 <$100
Total Issue $958,350
Out at close $50,000
Large out at close $1,885
Ch 13892 assumed circulation

***

7841 Cumberland
NEOGA NB, NEOGA
{{ UNREPORTED }}
Organized 7/11/05
Receivership 1/21/25
1902 Red Seal <$VALUE
3x10-20 1-560 <$1250
1902 Date Back
3x10-20 1-2070 <$750
1902 Plain Back
3x10-20 2071-4194 <$750
Total Issue $237,700
Out at close $24,700

***

13696 Madison
PRANGE NB OF NEW DOUGLAS
{{ U + 6 S }}
Chartered 5/33
Liquidated 11/10/34
1929 Small Size <$VALUE
5 Type 2 1-1384 <$200
10 Type 2 1-661 <$200
20 Type 2 1-755 <$200
Total Issue $28,630
Out at close $25,000

***

<$VALUEs are for notes in FINE condition. Value changes by approximately 25% for a change of one full grade.

****
8053 Gallatin
FNB OF NEW HAVEN
{{ UNREPORTED }}
Chartered 1/06
Liquidated 10/7/16
1902 Red Seal <$VALUE
4x5 1-258 <$1500
3x10-20 1-191 <$1500
1902 Date Back
4x5 1-1800 <$850
3x10-20 1-1360 <$850
1902 Plain Back
4x5 1801-1957 <$850
3x10-20 1361-1473 <$850
Total Issue $127,500
Out at close $24,600
****
7575 Douglas
NEWMAN NB, NEWMAN
{{ 3 L 5 S }}
Organized 1/12/05
Receivership 10/2/33
1902 Red Seal <$VALUE
4x5 1-2140 <$400
3x10-20 1-1706 <$400
1902 Date Back
4x5 1-3250 <$200
3x10-20 1-2320 <$200
1902 Plain Back
4x5 3251-11325 <$200
3x10-20 2321-7658 <$200
1929 Small Size
5 Type 1 1-1656 <$125
10 Type 1 1-826 <$125
20 Type 1 1-199 <$125
Total Issue $860,620
Out at close $50,000
Large out at close $3,880
****
5869 Jasper
FNB OF NEWTON
{{ 5 L 6 S }}
Organized 5/24/01
Liquidated 4/25/34
Brown Back <$VALUE
3x10-20 1-1750 <$300
1882 Date Back
3x10-20 1-1640* <$300
1882 Value Back
3x10-20 1841-3966* <$300
* 1641-1840 not marked
1902 Plain Back
3x10-20 1-4270 <$175
1929 Small Size
10 Type 1 1-964 <$85
20 Type 1 1-308 <$85
10 Type 2 1-258 <$100
20 Type 2 1-63 <$100
Total Issue $597,940
Out at close $50,000
Large out at close $3,470
Ch 14074 assumed circulation
****
9527 Richland
FNB OF NOBLE
{{ 3 L 2 S }}
Organized 7/19/09
Receivership 11/14/31
1902 Date Back <$VALUE
4x10 1-2775 <$350
1902 Plain Back
4x10 2776-7448 <$350
1929 Small Size
10 Type 1 1-693 <$300
Total Issue $339,500
Out at close $24,700
Large out at close $2,800
****
7547 Montgomery
FARMERS NB OF NOKOMIS
{{ 5 L }}
Chartered 1/05
Closed 7/2/29
1902 Red Seal <$VALUE
3x10-20 1-2222 <$600
1902 Date Back
3x10-20 1-5700 <$250
1902 Plain Back
3x10-20 5701-16547 <$250
Total Issue $938,450
Out at close $73,950
Ch 1934 assumed circulation
****
1934 Montgomery
NOKOMIS NB, NOKOMIS
{{ 3 L 2 S }}
Chartered 2/9/72
Receivership 2/9/33
Original Series <$VALUE
4x5 1-1700 <$600
3x10-20 1-700 <$1000/$1500
Series 1875
4x5 1-141 <$600
3x10-20 1-2587<$1000/$1500
Brown Back
4x5 1-2000 <$400
50-100 1-2060 <$1250/$1500
1882 Date Back
4x5 1-280 <$400
50-100 1-560 <$1250/$1500
1902 Date Back
4x5 1-2900* <$250
3x50-100 1-1539 <$400/$500
1902 Plain Back
4x5 3651-7650* <$250
3x50-100 1540-1808
<$400/$500
* 2901-3650 not marked
1929 Small Size
50 Type 1 1-127 <$300
100 Type 1 1-29 <$400
Total Issue $1,300,270
Out at close $75,000
Large out at close $27,150
Outstanding includes Ch 7547
****
4930 McLean
FNB OF NORMAL
{{ 2 L 3 S }}
Chartered 1893
Brown Back <$VALUE
3x10-20 1-1240 <$750
1882 Date Back
3x10-20 1-763 <$750
1902 Date Back
3x10-20 1-1000 <$450
1902 Plain Back
3x10-20 1001-3598 <$450
1929 Small Size
5 Type 1 1-2280 <$275
5 Type 2 1-3562 <$275
Total Issue $366,260
Out in 1935 $20,000
Large out 1935 $1,090
****
7971 White
FNB OF NORRIS CITY
{{ 3 L 3 S }}
Organized 9/18/05
Receivership 3/31/30
1902 Red Seal <$VALUE
4x5 1-880 <$600
3x10-20 1-644 <$600
1902 Date Back
4x5 1-1725 <$300
3x10-20 1-1280 <$300
1902 Plain Back
4x5 1726-6115 <$300
3x10-20 1281-3856 <$300
1929 Small Size
5 Type 1 1-289 <$250
10 Type 1 1-135 <$250
20 Type 1 1-10 <$250
Total Issue $382,870
Out at close $25,000
Large out at close $7,190
****
6924 St Clair
FNB OF O'FALLON
{{ 16 L U + 18 S }}
Chartered 8/03
1902 Red Seal <$VALUE
4x5 1-1270 <$250
3x10-20 1-857 <$250
1902 Date Back
4x5 1-2100 <$100
3x10-20 1-1360 <$100
1902 Plain Back
4x5 2101-16835 <$100
3x10-20 1361-10856 <$100
1929 Small Size
5 Type 1 1-3882 <$50
10 Type 1 1-1860 <$50
20 Type 1 1-482 <$65
5 Type 2 1-4152 <$70
10 Type 2 1-3005 <$70
20 Type 2 1-650 <$70
Total Issue $1,297,460
Out in 1935 $100,000
Large out 1935 $4,420
****
11507 Cook
FNB OF OAK PARK
{{ 3 L }}
Organized 10/31/19
Receivership 4/1/31
1902 Plain Back <$VALUE
4x5 1-15415 <$400
Total Issue $308,300
Out at close $1,800
****
8256 Menard
FNB OF OAKFORD
{{ 9 L 3 S }}
Chartered 6/06
Liquidated 4/20/31
1902 Red Seal <$VALUE
3x10-20 1-750 <$350
1902 Date Back
3x10-20 1-1920 <$175
1902 Plain Back
3x10-20 1921-5683 <$175
1929 Small Size
10 Type 1 1-338 <$200
20 Type 1 1-93 <$200
Total Issue $353,090
Out at close $25,000
Large out at close $3,860
****
2212 Coles
OAKLAND NB, OAKLAND
{{ 7 L 10 S }}
Chartered 12/16/74
Original Series <$VALUE
4x5 1-2250 <$500
Series 1875
4x5 1-3629 <$500
Brown Back
3x10-20 1-4160 <$300
1882 Date Back
3x10-20 1-2673 <$300
1902 Date Back
3x10-20 1-1060 <$150
1902 Plain Back
3x10-20 1061-8176 <$150
1929 Small Size
10 Type 1 1-1366 <$85
20 Type 1 1-388 <$85
Total Issue $996,550
Out in 1934 $13,250
Large out 1935 $3,480
****
8607 Crawford
FNB OF OBLONG
{{ 5 L 12 S }}
Chartered 3/07
1902 Red Seal <$VALUE
3x10-20 1-800 <$600
1902 Date Back
3x10-20 1-4140 <$300
1902 Plain Back
3x10-20 4141-11487 <$300
1929 Small Size
10 Type 1 1-1208 <$100
20 Type 1 1-346 <$100
10 Type 2 1-1698 <$110
20 Type 2 1-470 <$110
Total Issue $754,730
Out in 1935 $75,000
Large out 1935 $2,650
Outstanding includes Ch 8696
****
8696 Crawford
OIL BELT NB OF OBLONG
{{ 3 L 5 S }}
Chartered 5/07
Liquidated 12/15/31
1902 Red Seal <$VALUE
3x10-20 1-270 <$1250
1902 Date Back
3x10-20 1-560* <$600
1902 Plain Back
3x10-20 661-8084* <$600
* 561-660 not marked
1929 Small Size
10 Type 1 1-821 <$250
20 Type 1 1-214 <$250
Total Issue $492,640
Out at close $50,000
Large out at close $4,890
Ch 8607 assumed circulation
****
9624 Livingston
FARMERS NB OF ODELL
{{ 3 L }}
Organized 11/29/09
Receivership 9/21/27
1902 Date Back <$VALUE
3x10-20 1-1910 <$400
1902 Plain Back
3x10-20 1911-4453 <$400
Total Issue $222,650
Out at close $22,400
****
9525 Marion
FNB OF ODIN
{{ 2 L 3 S }}
Organized 8/3/09
Receivership 9/27/33
1902 Date Back <$VALUE
4x5 1-1750 <$400
4x10 1-1700 <$400
1902 Plain Back
4x5 1751-5895 <$400
4x10 1701-4577 <$400
1929 Small Size
5 Type 1 1-943 <$250
10 Type 1 1-543 <$250
Total Issue $361,850
Out at close $20,000
Large out at close $900
****
5304 Champaign
FNB OF OGDEN
{{ 3 L 2 S }}
Chartered 4/24/00
Brown Back <$VALUE
3x10-20 1-750 <$500
1882 Date Back
3x10-20 1-900* <$500
1882 Value Back
3x10-20 1001-1080* <$500
* 901-1000 not marked
1902 Plain Back
3x10-20 1-1117 <$350
1929 Small Size
10 Type 1 1-291 <$350
20 Type 1 1-74 <$350
Total Issue $173,690
Out in 1935 $10,000
Large out 1935 $620
****
11754 Washington
FNB OF OKAWVILLE
{{ 3 L 7 S }}
Chartered 6/20
1902 Plain Back <$VALUE
4x5 1-16647 <$250
1929 Small Size
5 Type 1 1-6202 <$135
5 Type 2 1-12964 <$135
Total Issue $583,820
Out in 1935 $50,000
Large out 1935 $1,440
****
11780 Washington
OLD EXCHANGE NB OF
OKAWVILLE
{{ 8 L 10 S }}
Organized 6/15/20
1902 Plain Back <$VALUE
3x10-20 1-5848 <$200
1929 Small Size
10 Type 1 1-1266 <$100
20 Type 1 1-398 <$110
10 Type 2 1-1005 <$135
20 Type 2 1-489 <$135
Total Issue $435,950
Out in 1935 $50,000
Large out 1935 $230
****
1641 Richland
FNB OF OLNEY
{{ 6 L 8 S }}
Organized 12/5/65
Liquidated 8/28/34
Original Series <$VALUE
3x1-2 1-5200 <$400/$1250
4x5 1-4750 <$400
3x10-20 1-720 <$750/$1250
Series 1875
4x5 1-2242 <$400
3x10-20 1-1148 <$750/$1250
Brown Back
3x10-20 1-4875 <$375
1902 Red Seal
3x10-20 1-900 <$400
1902 Date Back
3x10-20 1-3500 <$200
1902 Plain Back
3x10-20 3501-12874 <$200
1929 Small Size
10 Type 1 1-1652 <$100
20 Type 1 1-530 <$100
10 Type 2 1-24 <$150
Total Issue $1,354,650
Out at close $75,000
Large out at close $6,320
****
2629 RICHLAND
OLNEY NB, OLNEY
{{ UNREPORTED }}
Chartered 2/14/82
Liquidated 3/11/87
Series 1875 <$VALUE
4x5 1-2671 <$1500
Total Issue $53,420
Out in 1910 $260
****
10291 Gallatin
FNB OF OMAHA
{{ 2 L }}
Chartered 11/12
Liquidated 5/10/17
1902 Date Back <$VALUE
4x5 1-1016 <$600
4x10 1-1017* <$600
1902 Plain Back
4x5 1017-1463 <$600
4x10 1118-1380* <$600
* 1018-1117 not marked
Total Issue $84,460
Out at close $25,000
****
10752 Knox
FNB OF ONEIDA
{{ 3 L 3 S }}
Organized 6/5/15
Receivership 6/21/32
1902 Plain Back <$VALUE
4x5 1-4565 <$400
3x10-20 1-2839 <$400
1929 Small Size
5 Type 1 1-666 <$250
10 Type 1 1-335 <$250
20 Type 1 1-83 <$250
Total Issue $283,290
Out at close $24,760
Large out at close $1,920
****
6086 Henderson
FNB OF OQUAWKA
{{ 3 L }}
Chartered 1/02
Liquidated 6/15/14
Brown Back <$VALUE
3x10-20 1-1090 <$750
1882 Date Back
3x10-20 1-1296 <$750
Total Issue $119,300
Out in 1914 $17,245
****
1969 Ogle
FNB OF OREGON
{{ 3 L }}
Chartered 4/23/72
Liquidated 7/6/15
Original Series <$VALUE
3x1-2 1-1500 <$750/$1500
4x5 1-2275 <$750
Series 1875
4x5 1-6864 <$750
Brown Back
3x10-20 1-2620 <$650
1882 Date Back
3x10-20 1-715 <$650
1902 Date Back
3x10-20 1-791 <$500
Total Issue $396,580
Out in 1915 $22,000
****
1154 LaSalle
FNB OF OTTAWA
{{ 12 L 21 S }}
Chartered 1865
Original Series <$VALUE
4x5 1-4000 <$500
3x10-20 1-1665 <$750/$1250
Series 1875
4x5 1-2800 <$500
3x10-20 1-1638 <$750/$1250
Brown Back
3x10-20 1-6261 <$250
1902 Red Seal
3x10-20 1-3200 <$250
1902 Date Back
3x10-20 1-9100 <$100
1902 Plain Back
3x10-20 9101-29858 <$100
1929 Small Size
10 Type 1 1-4250* <$40
20 Type 1 1-1246** <$50
10 Type 2 1-1239 <$50
20 Type 2 1-495 <$50
* 2378-2962 not issued
** 719-942 not issued
Total Issue $2,632,930
Out in 1935 $150,000
Large out 1935 $10,760
****
1465 LaSalle
N CITY B OF OTTAWA
{{ 6 L }}
Organized 6/26/65
Receivership 10/6/31
Original Series <$VALUE
4x5 1-4620 <$500
3x10-20 1-1912 <$750/$1250
Series 1875
3x10-20 1-1700 <$750/$1250
Brown Back
4x5 1-8230 <$350
3x10-20 1-3076 <$350
1902 Red Seal
4x5 1-4030 <$350
3x10-20 1-2388 <$350
1902 Date Back
4x5 1-5000 <$150
3x10-20 1-4200 <$150
1902 Plain Back
4x5 5001-18240 <$150
3x10-20 4201-13476 <$150
Total Issue $1,830,000
Out at close $11,705
****
11934 Cook
FNB OF PALATINE
{{ 4 L 3 S }}
Organized 1/25/21
Receivership 2/2/32
1902 Plain Back <$VALUE
4x5 1-4836 <$350
1929 Small Size
5 Type 1 1-1355 <$250
Total Issue $137,370
Out at close $15,000
Large out at close $690
****
8892 Crawford
FNB OF PALESTINE
{{ 2 L 2 S }}
Organized 7/23/07
Receivership 10/20/32
1902 Red Seal <$VALUE
3x10-20 1-200 <$1000
1902 Date Back
3x10-20 1-990* <$500
1902 Plain Back
3x10-20 1111-2974* <$500
* 991-1110 not marked
1929 Small Size
10 Type 1 1-277 <$350
20 Type 1 1-59 <$350
Total Issue $182,400
Out at close $12,500
Large out at close $1,180
****
4038 Christian
FNB OF PANA
{{ UNREPORTED }}
Chartered 5/18/89
Liquidated 3/16/99
Brown Back <$VALUE
4x5 1-1444 <$1250
Total Issue $28,880
Out in 1910 $215
****
6734 Christian
PANA NB, PANA
{{ 9 L 4 S }}
Organized 4/14/03
Receivership 4/1/30
1902 Red Seal <$VALUE
3x10-20 1-2725 <$300
1902 Date Back
3x10-20 1-3200 <$125
1902 Plain Back
3x10-20 3201-19543 <$125
1929 Small Size
10 Type 1 1-804 <$135
20 Type 1 1-171 <$135
Total Issue $1,182,160
Out at close $100,000
Large out at close $31,590
****
6451 Edgar
CITIZENS NB OF PARIS
{{ 7 L 15 S }}
Chartered 10/02
1902 Red Seal <$VALUE
4x5 1-2925 <$250
3x10-20 1-2180 <$250
1902 Date Back
4x5 1-4250 <$125
3x10-20 1-3200 <$125
1902 Plain Back
4x5 4251-19815 <$125
3x10-20 3201-13364 <$125
1929 Small Size
5 Type 1 1-3316 <$50
10 Type 1 1-1842 <$50
20 Type 1 1-458 <$60
5 Type 2 1-1110 <$75
10 Type 2 1-668 <$75
20 Type 2 1-115 <$75
Total Issue $1,511,490
Out in 1935 $50,000
Large out 1935 $4,935
****

CONDITION affects Value. The Values shown are for notes in FINE condition.

****
2100 Edgar
EDGAR COUNTY NB OF PARIS
{{ 13 L 16 S }}
Chartered 4/9/73
Original Series <$VALUE
3x1-2 1-3680 <$375/$1000
4x5 1-3000 <$500
3x10-20 1-600 <$750/$1250
Series 1875
4x5 1-534 <$500
3x10-20 1-3108 <$750/$1250
Brown Back
4x5 1-13350 <$250
50-100 1-1300 <$1250/$1500
1882 Date Back
4x5 1-4018 <$250
50-100 1-646 <$1250/$1500
1902 Date Back
4x5 1-2500 <$100
3x10-20 1-2000 <$100
1902 Plain Back
4x5 2501-17840 <$100
3x10-20 2001-12159 <$100
1929 Small Size
5 Type 1 1-3266 <$50
10 Type 1 1-1816 <$50
20 Type 1 1-476 <$60
5 Type 2 1-1392 <$75
10 Type 2 1-680 <$75
20 Type 2 1-120 <$75
Total Issue $2,158,710
Out in 1935 $60,000
Large out 1935 $6,015
****
1555 Edgar
FNB OF PARIS
{{ 18 L }}
Organized 1865
Liquidated 8/12/85
Original Series <$VALUE
3x1-2 1-1500 <$400/$1250
4x5 1-2525 <$500
3x10-20 1-3040 <$750/$1250
Series 1875
3x10-20 1-3532 <$750/$1250
Total Issue $386,600
Out in 1910 $2,821
****
3376 Edgar
FNB OF PARIS
Organized 7/16/85
Receivership 5/4/31
2nd title:FNB & TC 7/26/28
FIRST TITLE {{ 10 L }}
Brown Back <$VALUE
4x5 1-12873 <$250
3x10-20 1-2787 <$250
1902 Red Seal
4x5 1-4250 <$250
3x10-20 1-2600 <$250
1902 Date Back
4x5 1-7350 <$125
3x10-20 1-6100 <$125
1902 Plain Back
4x5 7351-26409 <$125
3x10-20 6101-18060 <$125
SECOND TITLE {{ 1 L 6 S }}
1902 Plain Back
4x5 1-1414 <$200
3x10-20 1-854 <$200
1929 Small Size
5 Type 1 1-2007 <$75
10 Type 1 1-1008 <$75
20 Type 1 1-305 <$75
Total Issue $2,271,260
Out at close $120,000
Large out at close $17,145
****
6228 Lee
FNB OF PAW PAW
{{ 2 L }}
Chartered 4/24/02
Liquidated 11/10/02
1902 Red Seal <$VALUE
3x10-20 1-150 <$1250
Total Issue $7,500
Out in 1910 $310
****
7440 Sangamon
NB OF PAWNEE
{{ 3 L }}
Chartered 10/04
Liquidated 1/31/24
1902 Red Seal <$VALUE
3x10-20 1-2850 <$700
1902 Date Back
3x10-20 1-3400 <$350
1902 Plain Back
3x10-20 3401-7283 <$350
Total Issue $506,650
Out at close $50,000
****

****
1876 Ford
FNB OF PAXTON
{{ 3 L }}
Chartered 9/13/71
Liquidated 1/28/76
Original Series <$VALUE
3x1-2 1-2500 <$500/$1250
4x5 1-2535 <$500
3x10-20 1-284 <$750/$1250
Total Issue $77,400
Out in 1910 $471
****
2926 Ford
FNB OF PAXTON
{{ 4 L 7 S }}
Organized 3/30/83
Liquidated 10/23/33
Brown Back <$VALUE
3x10-20 1-2180 <$350
1902 Red Seal
3x10-20 1-1250 <$350
1902 Date Back
3x10-20 1-3600 <$175
1902 Plain Back
3x10-20 3601-14039 <$175
1929 Small Size
10 Type 1 1-1487 <$100
20 Type 1 1-476 <$100
Total Issue $1,019,790
Out at close $74,340
Large out at close $6,670
****
American NB of Pekin
SEE Ch 3770
German American NB of Pekin
****
2287 Tazewell
FARMERS NB OF PEKIN
{{ 12 L 6 S }}
Chartered 7/22/75
Receivership 1/26/32
Series 1875 <$VALUE
3x10-20 1-2144 <$750/$1250
Brown Back
4x5 1-3300 <$300
3x10-20 1-3925 <$300
1882 Date Back
4x5 1-6975 <$300
3x10-20 1-4545 <$300
1902 Plain Back
4x5 1-16240 <$150
3x10-20 1-10717 <$150
1929 Small Size
5 Type 1 1-2506 <$100
10 Type 1 1-1194 <$100
20 Type 1 1-310 <$100
Total Issue $1,780,870
Out at close $95,800
Large out at close $10,480
****
1637 Tazewell
FNB OF PEKIN
{{ 1 L }}
Chartered 3/5/66
Liquidated 3/25/75
Original Series <$VALUE
3x1-2 1-1000 <$1000/$2000
4x5 1-2450 <$1000
3x10-20 1-1472<$1250/$2000
Total Issue $127,600
Out in 1910 $1,089
****
3770 Tazewell
GERMAN AMERICAN NB OF PEKIN
Chartered 1887
2nd title:American NB 6/19/18
FIRST TITLE {{ 7 L }}
Brown Back <$VALUE
4x5 1-280 <$300
50-100 1-1693 <$1250/$1500
1902 Red Seal
4x5 1-1825 <$350
3x10-20 1-670 <$350
1902 Date Back
4x5 1-5500 <$175
3x10-20 1-4500 <$175
1902 Plain Back
4x5 5501-7450 <$175
3x10-20 4501-6060 <$175
SECOND TITLE {{ 4 L 14 S }}
1902 Plain Back
4x5 1-12515 <$175
3x10-20 1-8702 <$175
1929 Small Size
5 Type 1 1-3806 <$45
10 Type 1 1-1732 <$45
20 Type 1 1-418 <$50
5 Type 2 1-4510 <$60
10 Type 2 1-2726 <$60
20 Type 2 1-723 <$60
Total Issue $1,799,480
Out in 1935 $100,000
Large out 1935 $4,650
****
9788 Tazewell
HERGET NB OF PEKIN
{{ 13 L U + 17 S }}
Chartered 6/10
1902 Date Back <$VALUE
4x5 1-9000 <$100
3x10-20 1-6800 <$100
1902 Plain Back
4x5 9001-33843 <$100
3x10-20 6801-22073 <$100
1929 Small Size
5 Type 1 1-5466 <$50
10 Type 1 1-2476 <$50
20 Type 1 1-734 <$60
5 Type 2 1-6302 <$65
10 Type 2 1-3720 <$65
20 Type 2 1-1209 <$65
Total Issue $2,274,020
Out in 1935 $150,000
Large out 1935 $2,290
****
3214 Peoria
CENTRAL NB OF PEORIA
Chartered 1884
2nd title:Central NB & TC 8/1/28
FIRST TITLE {{ 13 L }}
Brown Back <$VALUE
3x10-20 1-6081 <$150/$200
1902 Red Seal
4x5 1-5000 <$150
3x10-20 1-6100 <$150/$200
1902 Date Back
4x5 1-11750 <$75
3x10-20 1-8900 <$75
1902 Plain Back
4x5 11751-113963 <$75
3x10-20 8901-11000 <$75
SECOND TITLE {{ 6 L 3U + 36 S }}
1902 Plain Back
4x5 1-6935 <$85
3x10-20 1-1085 <$85
1929 Small Size
5 Type 1 1-10990 <$20
10 Type 1 1-5656 <$20
20 Type 1 1-1982 <$30
5 Type 2 1-8052 <$20
10 Type 2 1-4653 <$20
20 Type 2 1-1068 <$30
Total Issue $4,746,310
Out in 1935 $400,000
Large out 1935 $22,930
****
Commercial German NB of Peoria
SEE Ch 3296
Commercial NB of Peoria
****
Commercial Merchants NB & TC of Peoria
SEE Ch 3296
Commercial NB of Peoria
****
3296 Peoria
COMMERCIAL NB OF PEORIA
Chartered 1885
2nd title:Commercial German NB 1/2/04
3rd title:Commercial NB 5/24/18
4th title:Commercial Merchants NB & TC 2/21/30
FIRST TITLE {{ 2 L }}
Brown Back <$VALUE
4x5 1-4000 <$350
3x10-20 1-8670 <$350
SECOND TITLE {{ 12 L }}
Brown Back
4x5 1-6345 <$200
3x10-20 1-5698 <$200
1902 Red Seal
4x5 1-18500 <$200
3x10-20 1-11800 <$200
1902 Date Back
4x5 1-35000 <$65
3x10-20 1-28200 <$75
1902 Plain Back
4x5 35001-45500 <$65
3x10-20 28201-35200 <$75
THIRD TITLE {{ 16 L 5 S }}
1902 Plain Back
4x5 1-6500 <$65
3x10-20 1-3600 <$75
3x50-100 1-7513 <$300/$350
1929 Small Size
50 Type 1 1-1212 <$100
100 Type 1 1-404 <$150
FOURTH TITLE {{ 22 S }}
1929 Small Size
50 Type 1 1-3440 <$85
100 Type 1 1-1672 <$135
Total Issue $9,384,750
Out in 1935 $1,500,000
Large out 1935 $82,645
Outstanding includes Ch 3254 and Ch 5361
****
176 Peoria
FNB OF PEORIA
{{ 32 L 50+ S }}
Chartered 1863
Original Series <$VALUE
3x1-2 1-2000 <$300/$750
4x10 1-6500 <$750
4x20 1-1033 <$1250
Brown Back
3x10-20 1-2683 <$150/$200
50-100 1-1550 <$1250/$1500
1902 Red Seal
4x5 1-15215 <$125
3x10-20 1-11114 <$125/$175
1902 Date Back
4x5 1-35500 <$50
3x10-20 1-25700 <$60
1902 Plain Back
4x5 35501-117710 <$50
3x10-20 25701-80370 <$60
1929 Small Size
5 Type 1 1-19347 <$20
10 Type 1 1-10338 <$20
20 Type 1 1-2704 <$30
Total Issue $9,477,160
Out in 1935 $420,295
Large out 1935 $29,865
****
3070 Peoria
GERMAN AMERICAN NB OF PEORIA
{{ 3 L }}
Chartered 10/31/83
Liquidated 1/2/04
Brown Back <$VALUE
4x5 1-4920 <$350
3x10-20 1-6452 <$350
50-100 1-1000 <$1250/$1500
1902 Red Seal
4x5 1-467 <$350
50-100 1-20 <$2250/$2500
Total Issue $597,350
Out in 1910 $27,210
****
5361 Peoria
ILLINOIS NB OF PEORIA
{{ 2 L }}
Chartered 5/21/00
Liquidated 6/1/15
Brown Back <$VALUE
4x5 1-5450 <$400
50-100 1-3540 <$1250/$1500
1882 Date Back
4x5 1-10295 <$400
50-100 1-1200 <$1250/$1500
3x50-100 1-478<$1250/$1500
Total Issue $1,145,400
Out at close $200,000
Ch 3254 assumed circulation
****
1117 Peoria
MECHANICS NB OF PEORIA
{{ 1 L }}
Chartered 1865
Liquidated 10/4/84
Original Series <$VALUE
3x1-2 1-2500 <$600/$1250
4x5 1-5375 <$600
3x10-20 1-1180 <$750/$1250
Series 1875
3x10-20 1-1706 <$750/$1250
Total Issue $264,300
Out in 1910 $1,893
****
3254 Peoria
MERCHANTS NB OF PEORIA
Chartered 1884
Closed 2/21/30
2nd title:Merchants & Illinois NB 6/21/15
FIRST TITLE {{ 2 L }}
Brown Back <$VALUE
50-100 1-3149 <$1250/$1500
1902 Red Seal
3x10-20 1-6500 <$300
1902 Date Back
3x10-20 1-11652 <$150
SECOND TITLE {{ 12 L 6 S }}
1902 Plain Back
3x10-20 1-76107 <$75
1929 Small Size
10 Type 1 1-3374 <$80
20 Type 1 1-920 <$90
Total Issue $5,498,140
Out at close $481,580
Large out at close $188,410
Ch 3296 assumed circulation
****

****
Merchants & Illinois NB of Peoria
SEE Ch 3254
Merchants NB of Peoria
****
2878 Peoria
PEORIA NB, PEORIA
{{ 2 L }}
Organized 2/12/83
Receivership 10/7/05
Brown Back <$VALUE
3x10-20 1-8118 <$500
1902 Red Seal
3x10-20 1-4384 <$500
Total Issue $625,100
Out in 1915 $8,180
****
207 Peoria
SECOND NB OF PEORIA
{{ 2 L }}
Chartered 1864
Liquidated 2/24/83
Original Series <$VALUE
4x5 1-5500 <$500
4x10 1-3325 <$750
3x20-50 1-700 <$1250/$4000
Series 1875
4x10 1-499 <$500
3x20-50 1-638 <$1250/$4000
Total Issue $410,140
Out in 1910 $2,810
****
7627 Randolph
FNB OF PERCY
{{ 3 L 6 S }}
Organized 1/24/05
Liquidated 3/30/35
1902 Red Seal <$VALUE
3x10-20 1-300 <$750
1902 Date Back
3x10-20 1-960 <$375
1902 Plain Back
3x10-20 961-3344 <$375
1929 Small Size
10 Type 1 1-478 <$150
20 Type 1 1-116 <$150
10 Type 2 1-301 <$175
Total Issue $227,810
Out in 1934 $16,250
Large out at close $730
****
441 LaSalle
FNB OF PERU
{{ 2 L }}
Chartered 1864
Liquidated 2/24/83
Original Series <$VALUE
3x1-2 1-4200 <$750/$1500
4x5 1-3350 <$750
2x10-20-50 1-956
<$1000/$1500/$4000
Series 1875
4x5 1-250 <$750
2x10-20-50 1-577
<$1000/$1500/$4000
Total Issue $230,970
Out in 1910 $1,577
****
2951 LaSalle
PERU NB, PERU
{{ 6 L 7 S }}
Organized 4/28/83
Receivership 11/21/34
Brown Back <$VALUE
4x5 1-3131 <$400
3x10-20 1-194 <$400
1902 Red Seal
3x10-20 1-595 <$400
1902 Date Back
3x10-20 1-3000* <$175
1902 Plain Back
3x10-20 3201-10367* <$175
* 3001-3200 not marked
1929 Small Size
10 Type 1 1-833 <$85
20 Type 1 1-210 <$100
Total Issue $695,600
Out in 1932 $50,000
Large out at close $6,840
Ch 13577 assumed circulation
****
13577 LaSalle
STATE-NB OF PERU
{{ U + 3 S }}
Organized 11/9/31
Receivership 1/12/34
1929 Small Size <$VALUE
5 Type 1 1-136 <$200
10 Type 1 1-212 <$200
20 Type 1 1-59 <$200
Total Issue $23,880
Out at close $50,000
Outstanding includes Ch 2951
****

****
3043 Menard
FNB OF PETERSBURG
Chartered 1883
2nd title: State NB of Petersburg 1/23/29
FIRST TITLE {{ 12 L }}
Brown Back <$VALUE
3x10-20 1-3348 <$225/$275
1902 Red Seal
3x10-20 1-2850 <$225/$275
1902 Date Back
3x10-20 1-7500* <$135
1902 Plain Back
3x10-20 8001-15318* <$135
* 7501-8000 not marked
SECOND TITLE {{ 6 S }}
1929 Small Size
10 Type 1 1-1512 <$70
20 Type 1 1-398 <$85
10 Type 2 1-504 <$100
20 Type 2 1-145 <$100
Total Issue $1,222,220
Out in 1935 $50,000
Large out 1935 $5,120
****
State NB of Petersburg
SEE Ch 3043
FNB of Petersburg
****
6211 Champaign
FNB OF PHILO
{{ UNREPORTED }}
Chartered 4/02
Liquidated 1/1/10
1902 Red Seal <$VALUE
3x10-20 1-1440 <$1250
1902 Date Back
3x10-20 1-162 <$850
Total Issue $80,100
Out in 1910 $14,910
****
6025 Perry
FNB OF PINCKNEYVILLE
{{ 9 L 11 S }}
Organized 11/9/01
Liquidated 3/8/34
Brown Back <$VALUE
4x5 1-1000 <$300
3x10-20 1-2800 <$300
1882 Date Back
4x5 1-2050 <$300
3x10-20 1-2640 <$300
1882 Value Back
4x5 2051-5305 <$300
3x10-20 2641-4493 <$300
1902 Plain Back
3x10-20 1-4755 <$125
1929 Small Size
10 Type 1 1-1290 <$75
20 Type 1 1-344 <$75
Total Issue $847,180
Out at close $50,000
Large out at close $3,630
Ch 13975 assumed circulation
****
5322 Ford
FNB OF PIPER CITY
{{ 6 L 8 S }}
Chartered 5/2/00
Brown Back <$VALUE
4x5 1-3000 <$350
3x10-20 1-2500 <$350
1882 Date Back
4x5 1-3725 <$350
3x10-20 1-2400 <$350
1882 Value Back
4x5 3726-5775 <$350
3x10-20 2401-3420 <$350
1902 Plain Back
4x5 1-5580 <$175
3x10-20 1-3977 <$175
1929 Small Size
5 Type 1 1-734 <$125
10 Type 1 1-886 <$125
20 Type 1 1-326 <$125
5 Type 2 1-192 <$150
Total Issue $897,210
Out in 1935 $25,000
Large out 1935 $2,845
****

<$VALUEs are for notes in FINE condition. Value changes by approximately 25% for a change of one full grade.

1042 Pike
FNB OF PITTSFIELD
{{6 L 14 S}}
Chartered 1865
Original Series <$VALUE
4x5 1-2900 <$450
3x10-20 1-1260 <$750/$1250
Series 1875
3x10-20 1-1814 <$750/$1250
Brown Back
3x10-20 1-3315 <$350
1902 Red Seal
3x10-20 1-1660 <$350
1902 Date Back
3x10-20 1-3440* <$125
1902 Plain Back
3x10-20 3941-9344* <$125
* 3441-3940 not marked
1929 Small Size
5 Type 1 1-1084 <$60
10 Type 1 1-1562 <$60
20 Type 1 1-474 <$60
5 Type 2 1-2570 <$70
10 Type 2 1-1414 <$70
20 Type 2 1-516 <$70
Total Issue $1,148,980
Out in 1935 $100,000
Large out 1935 $4,630

12658 Hancock
FNB OF PLYMOUTH
{{3 L 2 S}}
Organized 3/7/25
Receivership 11/21/30
1902 Plain Back <$VALUE
4x5 1-3670 <$350
1929 Small Size
5 Type 1 1-1133 <$350
Total Issue $107,390
Out at close $25,000
Large out at close $1,530

1806 Ogle
EXCHANGE NB OF POLO
{{8 L 2 S}}
Chartered 3/31/71
Liquidated 10/20/30
Original Series <$VALUE
4x5 1-3400 <$500
3x10-20 1-980 <$1000/$1500
Series 1875
3x10-20 1-1606<$1000/$1500
Brown Back
50-100 1-980 <$1250/$1500
1882 Date Back
50-100 1-428 <$1250/$1500
1902 Date Back
50-100 1-550 <$400/$500
3x50-100 1-1247 <$400/$500
1902 Plain Back
3x50-100 1248-1479 <$400/$500
1929 Small Size
50 Type 1 1-107 <$300
100 Type 1 1-19 <$400
Total Issue $904,250
Out at close $65,000
Large out at close $20,700

1837 Livingston
LIVINGSTON COUNTY NB OF PONTIAC
{{4 L 1 S}}
Chartered 6/22/71
Liquidated 1/13/31
Original Series <$VALUE
3x1-2 1-3000 <$500/$1250
4x5 1-5650 <$600
Series 1875
4x5 1-4937 <$600
Brown Back
3x10-20 1-2820 <$400
1882 Date Back
3x10-20 1-789 <$400
1902 Date Back
3x50-100 1-960 <$400/$500
1902 Plain Back
3x50-100 961-1158<$400/$500
1929 Small Size
50 Type 1 1-68 <$350
100 Type 1 1-11 <$500
Total Issue $723,690
Out in 1930 $50,000
Large out at close $17,350

2141 Livingston
NB OF PONTIAC
{{8 L 3 S}}
Chartered 4/6/74
Receivership 9/26/34
Original Series <$VALUE
4x5 1-3250 <$4000
Series 1875
4x5 1-4509 <$4000
Brown Back
3x10-20 1-3380 <$300
1882 Date Back
3x10-20 1-2281 <$300
1902 Date Back
3x50-100 1-797 <$400/$500
1902 Plain Back
3x50-100 798-972<$400/$500
1929 Small Size
50 Type 1 1-156 <$250
100 Type 1 1-25 <$350
Total Issue $768,030
Out at close $49,695
Large out at close $7,495

6824 Vermilion
POTOMAC NB, POTOMAC
{{2 L}}
Chartered 6/03
Liquidated 4/23/29
1902 Red Seal <$VALUE
4x5 1-1911 <$750
3x10-20 1-2369 <$750
1902 Date Back
4x5 1-1700 <$375
3x10-20 1-1250 <$375
1902 Plain Back
4x5 1701-6699 <$375
3x10-20 1251-4348 <$375
Total Issue $508,050
Out at close $24,250

2254 McDonough
FNB OF PRAIRIE CITY
{{ UNREPORTED }}
Chartered 5/6/75
Liquidated 12/24/78
Original Series <$VALUE
3x10-20 1-540 <$2500
Series 1875
3x10-20 1-40 <$2500
Total Issue $29,000
Out in 1910 $260

Citizens FNB of Princeton
SEE Ch 2413
Citizens NB of Princeton

2413 Bureau
CITIZENS NB OF PRINCETON
Chartered 2/21/79
2nd title:Citizens FNB
1/2/30
FIRST TITLE {{14 L 6 S}}
Series 1875 <$VALUE
3x10-20 1-2878 <$750/$1250
Brown Back
3x10-20 1-4900 <$250
50-100 1-480 <$1250/$1500
1882 Date Back
3x10-20 1-6100 <$250
50-100 1-24 <$1250/$1500
1882 Value Back
3x10-20 6101-8263 <$250
1902 Plain Back
3x10-20 1-12154 <$135
1929 Small Size
10 Type 1 1-1234 <$75
20 Type 1 1-420 <$75
SECOND TITLE {{15 S}}
1929 Small Size
10 Type 1 1-1500 <$50
20 Type 1 1-400 <$60
5 Type 2 1-324 <$75
10 Type 2 1-3084 <$75
20 Type 2 1-731 <$75
Total Issue $1,794,870
Out in 1935 $150,000
Large out 1935 $14,805
Outstanding includes Ch 903

2165 Bureau
FARMERS NB OF PRINCETON
{{13 L 3 S}}
Chartered 8/8/74
Liquidated 1/14/30
Original Series <$VALUE
3x10-20 1-900 <$750/$1250
Series 1875
3x10-20 1-2674 <$750/$1250
Brown Back
3x10-20 1-5040 <$275
1882 Date Back
3x10-20 1-5623 <$275
1902 Date Back
3x10-20 1-2200 <$135
1902 Plain Back
3x10-20 2201-16955 <$135
1929 Small Size
10 Type 1 1-336 <$200
20 Type 1 1-23 <$200
Total Issue $1,582,520
Out at close $106,260
Large out at close $83,340

---

903 Bureau
FNB OF PRINCETON
{{13 L 7 S}}
Chartered 3/16/65
Closed 1/2/30
Original Series <$VALUE
3x1-2 1-1400 <$375/$1000
4x5 1-3650 <$400
3x10-20 1-2130 <$750/$1250
Series 1875
3x1-2 1-140 <$375/$1000
4x5 1-1925 <$400
3x10-20 1-768 <$750/$1250
Brown Back
4x5 1-6663 <$250
3x10-20 1-1514 <$250
1902 Red Seal
3x10-20 1-3000 <$250
1902 Date Back
3x10-20 1-7500 <$125
1902 Plain Back
3x10-20 7501-21900 <$125
1929 Small Size
10 Type 1 1-595 <$100
20 Type 1 1-59 <$110
Total Issue $1,760,840
Out at close $94,980
Large out at close $52,200
Ch 2413 assumed circulation

6375 Whiteside
FARMERS NB OF PROPHETSTOWN
{{5 L 12 S}}
Chartered 8/02
1902 Red Seal <$VALUE
3x10-20 1-2840 <$450
1902 Date Back
3x10-20 1-3900 <$225
1902 Plain Back
3x10-20 3901-12092 <$225
1929 Small Size
10 Type 1 1-1414 <$65
20 Type 1 1-384 <$75
5 Type 2 1-324 <$85
10 Type 2 1-919 <$85
20 Type 2 1-215 <$85
Total Issue $892,630
Out in 1935 $60,000
Large out 1935 $3,035

1968 Whiteside
FNB OF PROPHETSTOWN
{{ UNREPORTED }}
Chartered 4/23/72
Liquidated 3/19/78
Original Series <$VALUE
3x1-2 1-1500 <$1250/$2000
4x5 1-2775 <$1250
Series 1875
4x5 1-1270 <$1250
Total Issue $88,400
Out in 1910 $315

---

424 Adams
FNB OF QUINCY
{{1 L}}
Chartered 5/16/64
Liquidated 1/16/99
Original Series <$VALUE
3x1-2 1-9200 <$650/$1500
4x5 1-7370 <$750
3x10-20 1-3100<$1250/$2000
Brown Back
4x5 1-10251 <$600
Total Issue $553,420
Out in 1910 $4,706

---

703 Adams
MERCHANTS & FARMERS NB OF QUINCY
{{1 L}}
Chartered 1/11/65
Liquidated 8/8/72
Original Series <$VALUE
4x5 1-4245 <$1250
3x10-20 1-1426<$1500/$2000
Total Issue $156,200
Out in 1910 $1,140

3752 Adams
QUINCY NB, QUINCY
Organized 6/7/87
Receivership 11/10/30
2nd title:Quincy-Ricker NB
& TC 1/26/23
FIRST TITLE {{6 L}}
Brown Back <$VALUE
4x5 1-5889 <$200
3x10-20 1-1232 <$200/$250
1902 Red Seal
4x5 1-1175 <$200
3x10-20 1-930 <$200/$250
1902 Date Back
4x5 1-6150 <$100
3x10-20 1-4220 <$100
1902 Plain Back
4x5 6151-11600 <$100
3x10-20 4221-7680 <$100
SECOND TITLE {{12 L 18 S}}
1902 Plain Back
4x5 1-31140 <$85
3x10-20 1-22816 <$85
1929 Small Size
5 Type 1 1-7102 <$25
10 Type 1 1-3317 <$30
20 Type 1 1-765 <$40
Total Issue $3,132,860
Out at close $500,000
Large out at close $198,150

Quincy-Ricker NB & TC, Quincy
SEE Ch 3752
Quincy NB, Quincy

2519 Adams
RICKER NB OF QUINCY
{{34 L}}
Chartered 1881
Liquidated 6/12/23
Series 1875 <$VALUE
4x5 1-30079 <$325
3x10-20 1-5300 <$750/$1250
Brown Back
4x5 1-21150 <$150
3x10-20 1-16240 <$150/$175
1882 Date Back
4x5 1-31750 <$150
3x10-20 1-21900 <$150/$175
1882 Value Back
4x5 31751-47157 <$150
3x10-20 21901-30660 <$150/$175
1902 Plain Back
4x5 1-8250 <$75
3x10-20 1-5540 <$85
Total Issue $5,019,720
Out in 1922 $445,000
Ch 3752 assumed circulation

9895 Fayette
RAMSEY NB, RAMSEY
{{3 L U+8 S}}
Chartered 11/10
1902 Date Back <$VALUE
3x10-20 1-1760 <$275
1902 Plain Back
3x10-20 1761-5526 <$275
1929 Small Size
10 Type 1 1-642 <$100
20 Type 1 1-168 <$100
10 Type 2 1-423 <$125
20 Type 2 1-60 <$125
Total Issue $340,410
Out in 1935 $25,000
Large out 1935 $1,160

8289 LaSalle
FNB OF RANSOM
{{1 L 3 S}}
Organized 6/27/06
Receivership 11/1/33
1902 Red Seal <$VALUE
3x10-20 1-300 <$1250
1902 Date Back
3x10-20 1-560 <$600
1902 Plain Back
3x10-20 561-1207 <$600
1929 Small Size
10 Type 1 1-164 <$250
20 Type 1 1-29 <$250
Total Issue $88,670
Out at close $6,500
Large out at close $500

5193 Champaign
FNB OF RANTOUL
{{4 L 16 S}}
Chartered 5/20/99
Brown Back <$VALUE
4x5 1-3970 <$350
50-100 1-810 <$1250/$1500
1882 Date Back
4x5 1-3200 <$350
50-100 1-260 <$1250/$1500
3x50-100 1-308<$1250/$1500
1882 Value Back
4x5 3201-3725 <$350
1902 Plain Back
4x5 1-5885 <$250
3x10-20 1-4474 <$250
1929 Small Size
5 Type 1 1-1674 <$60
10 Type 1 1-998 <$70
20 Type 1 1-246 <$75
5 Type 2 1-1768 <$75
10 Type 2 1-1012 <$75
20 Type 2 1-210 <$85
Total Issue $895,580
Out in 1935 $50,000
Large out 1935 $3,140

10215 Cook
RAVENSWOOD NB, RAVENSWOOD
{{3 L}}
Organized 4/30/12
Receivership 6/25/32
1902 Date Back <$VALUE
4x5 1-930 <$500
4x10 1-935 <$500
1902 Plain Back
4x5 931-2126 <$500
4x10 936-1835 <$500
Total Issue $115,920
Out at close $525

6910 Montgomery
FNB OF RAYMOND
{{3 L 3 S}}
Organized 7/16/03
1902 Red Seal <$VALUE
3x10-20 1-1020 <$750
1902 Date Back
3x10-20 1-1910 <$375
1902 Plain Back
3x10-20 1911-5428 <$375
1929 Small Size
10 Type 1 1-580 <$225
20 Type 1 1-182 <$225
10 Type 2 1-389 <$250
20 Type 2 1-135 <$250
Total Issue $385,630
Out in 1935 $25,000
Large out 1935 $1,900

8630 Vermilion
CITY NB OF RIDGE FARM
{{12 L 4 S}}
Organized 2/7/07
Liquidated 5/19/34
1902 Red Seal <$VALUE
4x5 1-625 <$400
3x10-20 1-500 <$400
1902 Date Back
4x5 1-1800 <$150
3x10-20 1-1320 <$150
1902 Plain Back
4x5 1801-5063 <$150
3x10-20 1321-3255 <$150
1929 Small Size
5 Type 1 1-584 <$125
10 Type 1 1-282 <$125
20 Type 1 1-86 <$150
5 Type 2 1-322 <$175
10 Type 2 1-151 <$175
20 Type 2 1-30 <$175
Total Issue $349,990
Out at close $18,000
Large out at close $1,220

5313 Vermilion
FNB OF RIDGE FARM
{{4 L 7 S}}
Chartered 4/28/00
Receivership 10/10/33
Brown Back <$VALUE
3x10-20 1-2900 <$400
1882 Date Back
3x10-20 1-3540 <$400
1882 Value Back
3x10-20 3541-5204 <$400
1902 Plain Back
3x10-20 1-5883 <$250
1929 Small Size
10 Type 1 1-1144 <$110
20 Type 1 1-316 <$125
10 Type 2 1-84 <$150
Total Issue $806,750
Out at close $50,000
Large out at close $3,920

9439 Gallatin
FNB OF RIDGWAY
{{3 L 3 S}}
Organized 5/7/09
Receivership 2/4/33
1902 Date Back <$VALUE
3x10-20 1-2110 <$350
1902 Plain Back
3x10-20 2111-6088 <$350
1929 Small Size
10 Type 1 1-568 <$200
20 Type 1 1-145 <$200
Total Issue $355,880
Out at close $25,000
Large out at close $2,060

12386 Cook
FNB OF RIVERSIDE
{{7 L 40 S}}
Organized 4/6/23
Receivership 7/6/32
1902 Plain Back <$VALUE
4x5 1-16486 <$165
1929 Small Size
5 Type 1 1-5157 <$60
Total Issue $484,430
Out at close $49,280
Large out at close $2,610

5049 Crawford
FNB OF ROBINSON
{{3 L 2 S}}
Organized 7/1/96
Liquidated 3/4/32
Brown Back <$VALUE
4x5 1-1700 <$450
3x10-20 1-820 <$450
1882 Date Back
4x5 1-1378 <$450
3x10-20 1-1029 <$450
1902 Plain Back
4x5 1-2865 <$300
3x10-20 1-1884 <$300
1929 Small Size
5 Type 1 1-507 <$200
10 Type 1 1-240 <$200
20 Type 1 1-68 <$200
Total Issue $343,280
Out at close $18,750
Large out 1935 $830
Ch 13605 assumed circulation

13605 Crawford
SECOND NB OF ROBINSON
{{14 S}}
Chartered 3/32
1929 Small Size <$VALUE
5 Type 1 1-1032 <$60
10 Type 1 1-574 <$60
20 Type 1 1-212 <$60
100 Type 1 1-40 <$250
5 Type 2 1-9878 <$65
10 Type 2 1-4944 <$65
20 Type 2 1-1452 <$65
Total Issue $242,710
Out in 1935 $150,000
Outstanding includes Ch 5049

1922 Ogle
FNB OF ROCHELLE
{{ UNREPORTED }}
Chartered 1/13/72
Liquidated 8/9/81
Original Series <$VALUE
3x1-2 1-1500 <$1250/$2000
4x5 1-2875 <$1250
Series 1875
4x5 1-2510 <$1250
Total Issue $115,200
Out in 1910 $653

1907 Ogle
ROCHELLE NB, ROCHELLE
{{7 L 2 S}}
Chartered 12/26/71
Liquidated 9/1/34
Original Series <$VALUE
3x1-2 1-1993 <$400/$1250
4x5 1-2875 <$450
Series 1875
4x5 1-5724 <$450
Brown Back
4x5 1-4050 <$350
3x10-20 1-980 <$350
1882 Date Back
4x5 1-243 <$350
3x10-20 1-396 <$350
1902 Date Back
3x10-20 1-1260 <$250
1902 Plain Back
3x10-20 1261-3390 <$250
1929 Small Size
10 Type 1 1-288 <$300
20 Type 1 1-67 <$300
Total Issue $531,425
Out in 1930 $20,000
Large out at close $2,425

****
6998 Whiteside
FNB OF ROCK FALLS
{{ 6 L 6 S }}
Organized 9/1/03
Receivership 6/10/32
1902 Red Seal <$VALUE
3x10-20 1-550 <$400
1902 Date Back
3x10-20 1-1760 <$250
1902 Plain Back
3x10-20 1761-6864 <$250
1929 Small Size
5 Type 1 1-748 <$150
10 Type 1 1-304 <$150
20 Type 1 1-64 <$150
Total Issue $419,060
Out at close $24,460
Large out at close $3,270
****
108 Rock Island
FNB OF ROCK ISLAND
{{ 1 L }}
Chartered 10/21/63
Liquidated 4/19/90
Original Series <$VALUE
3x1-2 1-3200 <$750/$1500
4x5 1-5750 <$850
4x10 1-1450 <$1000
Series 1875
4x5 1-2660 <$850
Brown Back
4x5 1-2372 <$750
Total Issue $289,640
Out in 1910 $2,277
****
2155 Rock Island
PEOPLES NB OF ROCK ISLAND
{{ 12 L }}
Chartered 6/22/74
Liquidated 5/15/26
Original Series <$VALUE
3x1-2 1-3000 <$500/$1250
4x5 1-3000 <$500
3x10-20 1-900 <$750/$1250
Series 1875
4x5 1-984 <$500
3x10-20 1-3831 <$750/$1250
Brown Back
4x5 1-3575 <$350
3x10-20 1-1780 <$350
1882 Date Back
4x5 1-1434 <$350
3x10-20 1-997 <$350
1902 Date Back
4x5 1-1000 <$200
3x10-20 1-800 <$200
1902 Plain Back
4x5 1001-4415 <$200
3x10-20 801-3450 <$200
Total Issue $831,060
Out at close $55,000
****
1889 Rock Island
ROCK ISLAND NB, ROCK ISLAND
{{ 4 L }}
Chartered 10/7/71
Liquidated 3/3/15
Original Series <$VALUE
3x1-2 1-3000 <$600/$1500
4x5 1-3500 <$600
3x10-20 1-1100<$1000/$1500
Series 1875
3x10-20 1-3162<$1000/$1500
Brown Back
50-100 1-2486 <$1250/$1500
1882 Date Back
50-100 1-518 <$1250/$1500
1902 Date Back
3x50-100 1-452 <$650/$750
Total Issue $861,700
Out in 1915 $77,500
****
11679 Winnebago
COMMERCIAL NB OF ROCKFORD
{{ 6 L 14 S }}
Chartered 4/20
Liquidated 4/18/32
1902 Plain Back <$VALUE
4x10 1-29778 <$200
1929 Small Size
10 Type 1 1-6882 <$65
Total Issue $1,604,040
Out at close $200,000
Large out at close $9,990
Ch 479 assumed circulation
****

****
429 Winnebago
FNB OF ROCKFORD
{{ UNREPORTED }}
Organized 5/20/64
Receivership 3/15/69
Original Series <$VALUE
4x5 1-2275 <$1500
Total Issue $45,500
Out in 1915 $240
****
4325 Winnebago
FOREST CITY NB OF ROCKFORD
{{ 6 L 14 S }}
Organized 4/8/90
Receivership 4/19/32
Brown Back <$VALUE
3x10-20 1-5920 <$300/$350
1882 Date Back
3x10-20 1-698 <$300/$350
1902 Date Back
3x10-20 1-5900 <$175
1902 Plain Back
3x10-20 5901-20341 <$175
1929 Small Size
10 Type 1 1-4086 <$50
20 Type 1 1-1170 <$60
Total Issue $1,698,610
Out at close $198,620
Large out at close $10,720
****
13652 Winnebago
ILLINOIS NB & TC OF ROCKFORD
{{ 16 S }}
Chartered 12/32
1929 Small Size <$VALUE
10 Type 1 1-1440 <$35
20 Type 1 1-1036 <$45
50 Type 1 1-126 <$135
10 Type 2 1-1223 <$40
20 Type 2 1-320 <$50
50 Type 2 1-72 <$200
Total Issue $270,750
Out in 1935 $200,000
****
3952 Winnebago
MANUFACTURERS NB OF ROCKFORD
Organized 11/20/88
Receivership 6/16/31
2nd title:Manufacturers NB & TC 3/24/28
FIRST TITLE {{ 10 L }}
Brown Back <$VALUE
4x5 1-5840 <$300
3x10-20 1-9358 <$300
1902 Date Back
4x5 1-12050 <$150
3x10-20 1-9680 <$150
1902 Plain Back
4x5 12051-38331 <$150
3x10-20 9681-27959 <$150
SECOND TITLE {{ 2 L 11 S }}
1902 Plain Back
3x10-20 1-3381 <$200
1929 Small Size
10 Type 1 1-3084 <$60
20 Type 1 1-870 <$60
Total Issue $3,207,760
Out at close $200,000
Large out at close $24,320
****
1816 Winnebago
ROCKFORD NB, ROCKFORD
{{ 13 L 12 S }}
Organized 3/8/71
Receivership 2/12/32
Original Series <$VALUE
3x1-2 1-4400 <$400/$1250
4x5 1-2900 <$400
3x10-20 1-1500 <$750/$1250
Series 1875
3x1-2 1-200 <$400/$1250
4x5 1-3633 <$400
3x10-20 1-1592 <$750/$1250
Brown Back
4x5 1-4700 <$250
3x10-20 1-5170 <$250
1882 Date Back
4x5 1-2245 <$250
3x10-20 1-1224 <$250
1902 Date Back
4x5 1-4500 <$125
3x10-20 1-3400 <$125
1902 Plain Back
4x5 4501-26325 <$125
3x10-20 3401-18398 <$125

1929 Small Size
5 Type 1 1-1200 <$50
10 Type 1 1-783 <$50
20 Type 1 1-445 <$60
50 Type 1 1-86 <$150
100 Type 1 1-63 <$200
Total Issue $2,413,240
Out at close $199,980
Large out at close $19,755
****
482 Winnebago
SECOND NB OF ROCKFORD
{{ 2 L }}
Organized 7/13/64
Receivership 11/10/96
Original Series <$VALUE
3x1-2 1-3800 <$500/$1500
4x5 1-6005 <$500
3x10-20 1-1400<$1000/$1500
50-100 1-266 <$4000
Series 1875
4x5 1-1750 <$500
3x10-20 1-1078<$1000/$1500
50-100 1-372 <$4000
Brown Back
3x10-20 1-4709 <$400
Total Issue $629,150
Out in 1915 $4,279
****
11731 Winnebago
SECURITY NB OF ROCKFORD
{{ 5 L 7 S }}
Organized 5/3/20
Receivership 6/18/31
1902 Plain Back <$VALUE
3x10-20 1-22093 <$165
1929 Small Size
10 Type 1 1-3099 <$75
20 Type 1 1-927 <$85
Total Issue $1,401,830
Out at close $200,000
Large out at close $19,660
****
9823 Winnebago
SWEDISH-AMERICAN NB OF ROCKFORD
{{ 8 L 12 S }}
Chartered 8/10
1902 Date Back <$VALUE
4x5 1-9025 <$150
3x10-20 1-6420 <$150
1902 Plain Back
4x5 9026-30845 <$150
3x10-20 6421-19248 <$150
1929 Small Size
5 Type 1 1-4586 <$50
10 Type 1 1-2182 <$50
20 Type 1 1-548 <$60
5 Type 2 1-1008 <$75
10 Type 2 1-395 <$75
20 Type 2 1-125 <$75
Total Issue $1,925,050
Out in 1935 $50,000
Large out 1935 $4,565
****
479 Winnebago
THIRD NB OF ROCKFORD
{{ 9 L 19 S }}
Chartered 1864
Original Series <$VALUE
4x5 1-2250 <$450
3x10-20 1-1600 <$750/$1250
Series 1875
4x5 1-1530 <$450
3x10-20 1-536 <$750/$1250
Brown Back
3x10-20 1-5127 <$250
1902 Red Seal
3x10-20 1-10000 <$250/$300
1902 Date Back
3x10-20 1-16700 <$125
1902 Plain Back
3x10-20 16701-35906 <$125
1929 Small Size
10 Type 1 1-6688 <$40
20 Type 1 1-1666 <$50
Total Issue $3,335,250
Out in 1935 $450,000
Large out 1935 $14,960
Outstanding includes Ch 11679
****
883 Winnebago
WINNEBAGO NB OF ROCKFORD
{{ 4 L }}
Chartered 1865
Liquidated 1/8/20
Original Series <$VALUE
3x1-2 1-1800 <$500/$1500
4x5 1-5825 <$500
3x10-20 1-1800<$1000/$1500
Series 1875
3x1-2 1-300 <$500/$1500
4x5 1-1590 <$500
3x10-20 1-927 <$1000/$1500

Brown Back
3x10-20 1-4803 <$350
1902 Red Seal
4x5 1-7000 <$400
3x10-20 1-6500 <$400
1902 Date Back
4x5 1-9750 <$225
3x10-20 1-6600 <$225
1902 Plain Back
4x5 9751-11572 <$225
3x10-20 6601-7434 <$225
Total Issue $1,603,440
Out in 1919 $10,000
Ch 1816 assumed circulation
****
10305 Cook
ROGERS PARK NB, ROGERS PARK
{{ 5 L 6 S }}
Organized 12/16/12
Receivership 9/24/31
1902 Date Back <$VALUE
3x10-20 1-2300 <$225
1902 Plain Back
3x10-20 2301-10184 <$225
1929 Small Size
10 Type 1 1-853 <$175
20 Type 1 1-217 <$175
Total Issue $586,420
Out at close $50,000
Large out at close $6,380
****
8637 Greene
FNB OF ROODHOUSE
{{ 4 L 7 S }}
Organized 3/27/07
Receivership 2/1/33
1902 Red Seal <$VALUE
3x10-20 1-500 <$350
1902 Date Back
3x10-20 1-3400 <$175
1902 Plain Back
3x10-20 3401-10824 <$175
1929 Small Size
10 Type 1 1-1123 <$100
20 Type 1 1-265 <$100
Total Issue $665,380
Out at close $50,000
Large out at close $4,690
****
5883 Warren
FNB OF ROSEVILLE
{{ 1 L }}
Chartered 7/01
Liquidated 5/3/26
Brown Back <$VALUE
3x10-20 1-640 <$850
1882 Date Back
3x10-20 1-820 <$850
1882 Value Back
3x10-20 821-939 <$850
1902 Plain Back
4x5 1-1440 <$650
Total Issue $107,750
Out in 1925 $8,350
****
9877 Vermilion
FARMERS NB OF ROSSVILLE
{{ 2 L }}
Chartered 10/10
Liquidated 5/31/24
1902 Date Back <$VALUE
3x10-20 1-2900 <$500
1902 Plain Back
3x10-20 2901-6580 <$500
Total Issue $329,000
Out at close $40,000
****
5398 Vermilion
FNB OF ROSSVILLE
{{ 3 L 6 S }}
Chartered 6/4/00
Brown Back <$VALUE
3x10-20 1-2440 <$500
1882 Date Back
3x10-20 1-2500* <$500
1882 Value Back
3x10-20 2701-3880* <$500
* 2501-2700 not marked
1902 Plain Back
3x10-20 1-4260 <$350
1929 Small Size
10 Type 1 1-912 <$135
20 Type 1 1-254 <$135
10 Type 2 1-766 <$165
20 Type 2 1-251 <$165
Total Issue $626,880
Out in 1935 $25,000
Large out 1935 $1,960
****

****
1453 Schuyler
FNB OF RUSHVILLE
{{ 4 L }}
Chartered 1865
Liquidated 9/30/84
Original Series <$VALUE
3x1-2 1-6670 <$450/$1250
4x5 1-3525 <$500
3x10-20 1-1063 <$850/$1250
Series 1875
3x10-20 1-2112 <$850/$1250
Total Issue $262,600
Out in 1910 $1,880
****
5470 Kankakee
FNB OF SAINT ANNE
{{ UNREPORTED }}
Chartered 6/29/00
Liquidated 9/1/19
Brown Back <$VALUE
3x10-20 1-890 <$1250
1882 Date Back
3x10-20 1-2130 <$1250
1882 Value Back
3x10-20 2131-2722 <$1250
Total Issue $180,600
Out at close $25,000
****
2021 Kane
KANE COUNTY NB OF SAINT CHARLES
{{ 1 L }}
Chartered 7/26/72
Liquidated 5/31/78
Original Series <$VALUE
4x5 1-1875 <$1000
3x10-20 1-150 <$1250/$2000
Series 1875
4x5 1-220 <$1000
3x10-20 1-46 <$1250/$2000
Total Issue $51,700
Out in 1910 $275
****
6219 Kane
SAINT CHARLES NB, SAINT CHARLES
{{ 6 L 9 S }}
Chartered 4/02
1902 Red Seal <$VALUE
3x10-20 1-2080 <$400
1902 Date Back
3x10-20 1-3500 <$175
1902 Plain Back (dated 1902)
3x10-20 3501-6342 <$175
1902 Plain Back (dated 1922)
3x10-20 1-4612 <$175
1929 Small Size
10 Type 1 1-1190 <$100
20 Type 1 1-292 <$110
10 Type 2 1-1497 <$110
20 Type 2 1-180 <$125
Total Issue $776,710
Out in 1935 $50,000
Large out 1935 $2,830
****
9388 Fayette
FNB OF SAINT ELMO
{{ 5 L U + 5 S }}
Organized 2/16/09
1902 Date Back <$VALUE
4x5 1-1575 <$350
4x10 1-1575 <$350
1902 Plain Back
4x5 1576-5180 <$350
4x10 1576-4000 <$350
1929 Small Size
5 Type 1 1-818 <$175
10 Type 1 1-488 <$175
5 Type 2 1-2634 <$200
10 Type 2 1-1240 <$200
Total Issue $342,990
Out in 1935 $25,000
Large out 1935 $1,090
****
8846 Lawrence
FNB OF SAINT FRANCISVILLE
Chartered 8/07
2nd title:Peoples NB of Saint Francisville 11/16/20
FIRST TITLE {{ 1 L }}
1902 Red Seal <$VALUE
3x10-20 1-240 <$650
1902 Date Back
3x10-20 1-3210 <$350
1902 Plain Back
3x10-20 3211-5660 <$350
SECOND TITLE {{ 4 L 8 S }}
1902 Plain Back
3x10-20 1-5493 <$250

1929 Small Size
10 Type 1 1-1212 <$100
20 Type 1 1-316 <$100
10 Type 2 1-304 <$125
20 Type 2 1-95 <$125
Total Issue $685,230
Out in 1935 $25,000
Large out 1935 $2,330
****
Peoples NB of Saint Francisville
SEE Ch 8846
FNB of Saint Francisville
****
9896 Fayette
FNB OF SAINT PETER
{{ 4 L 6 S }}
Chartered 12/10
Liquidated 5/25/32
1902 Date Back <$VALUE
4x5 1-715 <$350
3x10-20 1-574 <$350
1902 Plain Back
4x5 716-3685 <$350
3x10-20 575-2331 <$350
1929 Small Size
5 Type 1 1-643 <$175
10 Type 1 1-301 <$175
20 Type 1 1-89 <$200
Total Issue $238,280
Out at close $25,000
Large out at close $2,240
****
1715 Marion
SALEM NB, SALEM
{{ 7 L 10 S }}
Chartered 9/30/70
Original Series <$VALUE
4x5 1-3250 <$500
Series 1875
4x5 1-6059 <$500
Brown Back
4x5 1-5700 <$350
3x10-20 1-2240 <$350
1882 Date Back
4x5 1-602 <$350
3x10-20 1-416 <$350
1902 Date Back
4x5 1-2500 <$200
3x10-20 1-1880 <$200
1902 Plain Back
4x5 2501-9826 <$200
3x10-20 1881-6794 <$200
1929 Small Size
5 Type 1 1-1816 <$100
10 Type 1 1-1112 <$100
20 Type 1 1-306 <$110
5 Type 2 1-3468 <$125
10 Type 2 1-1828 <$125
20 Type 2 1-292 <$125
Total Issue $1,180,620
Out in 1935 $75,000
Large out 1935 $3,590
****
9786 Marion
FNB OF SANDOVAL
{{ 3 L 4 S }}
Chartered 6/10
1902 Date Back <$VALUE
4x5 1-1700 <$350
3x10-20 1-1320 <$350
1902 Plain Back
4x5 1701-5843 <$350
3x10-20 1321-3795 <$350
1929 Small Size
5 Type 1 1-710 <$165
10 Type 1 1-516 <$165
20 Type 1 1-128 <$165
5 Type 2 1-900 <$185
10 Type 2 1-455 <$185
20 Type 2 1-163 <$185
Total Issue $386,540
Out in 1935 $25,000
Large out 1935 $1,380
****
8540 Carroll
FNB OF SAVANNA
{{ 9 L 14 S }}
Organized 1/30/07
Receivership 1/12/34
1902 Red Seal <$VALUE
4x5 1-750 <$275
3x10-20 1-1200 <$275
1902 Date Back
4x5 1-3600 <$125
3x10-20 1-2160 <$125
1902 Plain Back
4x5 3601-15280 <$125
3x10-20 2161-12852 <$125
1929 Small Size
10 Type 1 1-2325 <$50
20 Type 1 1-667 <$60
Total Issue $1,242,740
Out at close $98,860
Large out at close $5,360
****

****
13886 Carroll
NB OF SAVANNA
{{ 6 S }}
Chartered 12/33
1929 Small Size <$VALUE
10 Type 2 1-6421 <$100
Total Issue $64,210
Out in 1935 $41,400
****
6007 Woodford
FNB OF SECOR
{{ 2 L 3 S }}
Organized 10/21/01
Receivership 2/6/33
Brown Back <$VALUE
3x10-20 1-1700 <$500
1882 Date Back
3x10-20 1-1560* <$500
1882 Value Back
3x10-20 1691-2777* <$500
* 1561-1690 not marked
1902 Plain Back
3x10-20 1-2156 <$350
1929 Small Size
10 Type 1 1-483 <$250
20 Type 1 1-122 <$250
Total Issue $375,270
Out at close $25,000
Large out at close $3,460
****
1773 LaSalle
FNB OF SENECA
Chartered 1/19/71
2nd title:FNB of Morris
4/5/72
FIRST TITLE {{ 1 L }}
Original Series <$VALUE
4x5 1-4600 <$850
SECOND TITLE {{ 15 L 9 S }}
Original Series
4x5 1-3250 <$400
Series 1875
4x5 1-3335 <$400
Brown Back
4x5 1-12150 <$225
50-100 1-2572 <$1250/$1500
1882 Date Back
4x5 1-3110 <$225
50-100 1-399 <$1250/$1500
1902 Date Back
4x5 1-9000 <$125
50-100 1-1334 <$400/$500
3x50-100 1-2360 <$400/$500
1902 Plain Back
4x5 9001-80630 <$125
3x50-100 2361-3097
<$400/$500
1929 Small Size
5 Type 1 1-6100 <$75
50 Type 1 1-223 <$125
100 Type 1 1-68 <$175
Total Issue $3,852,200
Out in 1935 $75,000
Large out 1935 $20,710
****
8758 Franklin
FNB OF SESSER
{{ 1 L 2 S }}
Organized 4/25/07
Receivership 12/26/30
1902 Red Seal <$VALUE
4x5 1-175 <$1000
4x10 1-180 <$1000
1902 Date Back
4x5 1-600 <$500
4x10 1-600 <$500
1902 Plain Back
4x5 601-1800 <$500
4x10 601-1368 <$500
1929 Small Size
5 Type 1 1-180 <$400
10 Type 1 1-62 <$400
Total Issue $110,540
Out at close $6,500
Large out at close $660
****
9435 Gallatin
CITY NB OF SHAWNEETOWN
{{ 3 L 1 S }}
Organized 5/24/09
Receivership 5/26/30
1902 Date Back <$VALUE
4x5 1-950* <$350
3x10-20 1-720** <$350
1902 Plain Back
4x5 1201-4100* <$350
3x10-20 861-2489** <$350
* 951-1200 not marked
** 721-860 not marked
1929 Small Size
5 Type 1 1-321 <$350
10 Type 1 1-134 <$350
20 Type 1 1-15 <$350

Total Issue $225,920
Out at close $22,120
Large out at close $4,530
****
915 Gallatin
FNB OF SHAWNEETOWN
{{ 2 L }}
Chartered 3/21/65
Liquidated 3/31/09
Original Series <$VALUE
3x1-2 1-1600 <$750/$1500
4x5 1-4500 <$850
3x10-20 1-4000<$1000/$1500
Series 1875
3x10-20 1-1256<$1000/$1500
Brown Back
4x5 1-2638 <$600
3x10-20 1-348 <$600
1902 Red Seal
3x10-20 1-330 <$700
Total Issue $447,460
Out in 1910 $7,738
****
7752 Gallatin
FNB OF SHAWNEETOWN
{{ 3 L 3 S }}
Organized 4/24/05
Receivership 9/21/34
1902 Red Seal <$VALUE
4x5 1-1060 <$600
3x10-20 1-638 <$600
1902 Date Back
4x5 1-1825 <$300
3x10-20 1-1300 <$300
1902 Plain Back
4x5 1826-5967 <$300
3x10-20 1301-3734 <$300
1929 Small Size
5 Type 1 1-874 <$150
10 Type 1 1-424 <$150
20 Type 1 1-120 <$150
5 Type 2 1-846 <$175
10 Type 2 1-570 <$175
20 Type 2 1-67 <$175
Total Issue $436,470
Out at close $25,000
Large out at close $1,350
****
1775 Gallatin
GALLATIN NB OF
SHAWNEETOWN
{{ 4 L }}
Chartered 1/25/71
Liquidated 5/7/74
Original Series <$VALUE
3x1-2 1-5000 <$500/$1250
4x5 1-5500 <$500
3x10-20 1-1700 <$750/$1250
50-100 1-200 <$4000
Total Issue $250,000
Out in 1910 $1,591
****
7396 Shelby
CITIZENS NB OF
SHELBYVILLE
{{ 5 L }}
Organized 8/1/04
Receivership 2/21/28
1902 Red Seal <$VALUE
4x5 1-1950 <$400
3x10-20 1-1360 <$400
1902 Date Back
4x5 1-3500 <$200
3x10-20 1-2520 <$200
1902 Plain Back
4x5 3501-10055 <$200
3x10-20 2521-6745 <$200
Total Issue $645,350
Out at close $50,000
****
2128 Shelby
FNB OF SHELBYVILLE
{{ U + 15 L 4 S }}
Chartered 10/11/73
Liquidated 12/19/31
Original Series <$VALUE
3x1-2 1-1500 <$375/$1000
4x5 1-7075 <$400
Series 1875
4x5 1-2884 <$400
Brown Back
4x5 1-4075 <$250
50-100 1-1600<$1250/$1500
1882 Date Back
4x5 1-1730 <$225
50-100 1-682 <$1250/$1500
1902 Date Back
4x5 1-1875 <$100
50-100 1-868 <$400/$500
1902 Plain Back
4x5 1876-20607 <$100
3x50-100 869-1098<$400/$500

1929 Small Size
5 Type 1 1-2538 <$100
50 Type 1 1-133 <$175
100 Type 1 1-36 <$225
Total Issue $1,489,360
Out at close $100,000
Large out at close $19,485
****
8374 Vermilion
FNB OF SIDELL
{{ 2 L 3 S }}
Organized 7/23/06
Receivership 9/27/33
1902 Red Seal <$VALUE
4x10 1-860 <$650
1902 Date Back
4x10 1-2825 <$350
1902 Plain Back
4x10 2826-8435 <$350
1929 Small Size
10 Type 1 1-1068 <$200
Total Issue $435,880
Out at close $25,000
Large out at close $1,470
****
13525 St Clair
FNB OF SMITHTON
{{ U + 4 S }}
Chartered 1/31/31
1929 Small Size <$VALUE
5 Type 1 1-570 <$175
10 Type 1 1-276 <$175
20 Type 1 1-94 <$175
5 Type 2 1-1664 <$200
10 Type 2 1-790 <$200
20 Type 2 1-220 <$200
Total Issue $65,560
Out in 1935 $22,750
****
3102 Cook
CALUMET NB OF
SOUTH CHICAGO
Organized 12/20/83
Receivership 10/7/31
2nd title: Calumet NB of
Chicago 12/03
FIRST TITLE {{ 1 L }}
Brown Back <$VALUE
3x10-20 1-2561 <$650
SECOND TITLE {{ 10 L 7 S }}
1902 Red Seal
3x10-20 1-5000 <$250
1902 Date Back
3x10-20 1-12300 <$100
1902 Plain Back
3x10-20 12301-38706 <$100
1929 Small Size
10 Type 1 1-1564 <$85
20 Type 1 1-434 <$85
Total Issue $2,459,270
Out at close $100,000
Large out at close $18,590
****
7015 Randolph
FNB OF SPARTA
{{ 8 L 8 S }}
Chartered 10/03
1902 Red Seal <$VALUE
4x5 1-1725 <$500
3x10-20 1-1320 <$500
1902 Date Back
4x5 1-2400 <$250
3x10-20 1-1820 <$250
1902 Plain Back
4x5 2401-10945 <$250
3x10-20 1821-7448 <$250
1929 Small Size
5 Type 1 1-1878 <$200
10 Type 1 1-940 <$200
20 Type 1 1-260 <$200
5 Type 2 1-2066 <$200
10 Type 2 1-1256 <$200
20 Type 2 1-414 <$200
Total Issue $866,910
Out in 1935 $50,000
Large out 1935 $2,740
****
3465 Bureau
SPRING VALLEY NB,
SPRING VALLEY
{{ UNREPORTED }}
Organized 3/6/86
Receivership 7/5/05
Brown Back <$VALUE
4x5 1-2838 <$1500
3x10-20 1-2073 <$1500
Total Issue $160,410
Out in 1915 $1,770
****

****
2688 Sangamon
FARMERS NB OF SPRINGFIELD
{{ 3 L }}
Organized 5/15/82
Liquidated 2/1/19
Series 1875 <$VALUE
3x10-20 1-4685<$1000/$1500
1902 Red Seal
50-100 1-1334 <$2250/$2500
1902 Date Back
50-100 1-1300 <$500/$600
3x50-100 1-144 <$500/$600
Total Issue $665,350
Out at close $75,000
****
205 Sangamon
FNB OF SPRINGFIELD
{{ 21 L 50+ S }}
Organized 12/12/63
Original Series <$VALUE
3x1-2 1-15000 <$375/$1000
4x5 1-9000 <$400
4x10 1-7125 <$750
Series 1875
4x5 1-4405 <$400
4x10 1-6075 <$750
Brown Back
3x10-20 1-9534 <$200/$250
1902 Red Seal
3x10-20 1-10500 <$200/$250
1902 Date Back
3x10-20 1-16500 <$100
1902 Plain Back
3x10-20 16501-44407 <$100
1929 Small Size
10 Type 1 1-8820 <$25
20 Type 1 1-2256 <$35
10 Type 2 1-9404 <$25
20 Type 2 1-2867 <$35
Total Issue $5,044,450
Out in 1935 $500,000
Large out 1935 $16,330
****
3548 Sangamon
ILLINOIS NB OF
SPRINGFIELD
{{ 16 L 27 S }}
Chartered 1886
Brown Back <$VALUE
3x10-20 1-6794 <$200/$250
1902 Red Seal
3x10-20 1-5300 <$200/$250
1902 Date Back
3x10-20 1-17000* <$100
1902 Plain Back
3x10-20 19001 48224* <$100
* 17001-19000 not marked
1929 Small Size
10 Type 1 1-6445 <$35
20 Type 1 1-1708 <$40
Total Issue $3,607,560
Out in 1935 $150,000
Large out 1935 $13,050
****
1662 Sangamon
RIDGELEY NB OF
SPRINGFIELD
{{ 12 L }}
Chartered 1866
Liquidated 2/1/19
Original Series <$VALUE
4x5 1-8250 <$400
Series 1875
4x5 1-6984 <$400
Brown Back
4x5 1-9733 <$225
3x10-20 1-4743 <$225/$275
1902 Red Seal
3x10-20 1-3500 <$225/$275
1902 Date Back
3x10-20 1-20000 <$125
1902 Plain Back
3x10-20 20001-24859 <$125
Total Issue $2,154,440
Out in 1918 $245,995
****
1733 Sangamon
STATE NB OF SPRINGFIELD
{{ 13 L }}
Chartered 11/70
Liquidated 6/30/17
Original Series <$VALUE
3x1-2 1-4000 <$375/$1000
4x5 1-9000 <$400
3x10-20 1-1800 <$750/$1250
Series 1875
4x5 1-8174 <$400
3x10-20 1-1581 <$750/$1250
Brown Back
4x5 1-17350 <$200
3x10-20 1-9460 <$200/$250

1882 Date Back
4x5 1-2806 <$200
3x10-20 1-2312 <$200/$250
1902 Date Back
4x5 1-12253 <$125
4x10 1-11045 <$125
Total Issue $2,456,170
Out at close $194,600
****
10173 Macoupin
FNB OF STAUNTON
{{ 4 L U + 9 S }}
Chartered 4/12
Liquidated 12/18/34
1902 Date Back <$VALUE
4x5 1-1430 <$200
3x10-20 1-1098 <$200
1902 Plain Back
4x5 1431-10035 <$200
3x10-20 1099-6878 <$200
1929 Small Size
5 Type 1 1-1774 <$100
10 Type 1 1-920 <$100
20 Type 1 1-254 <$100
5 Type 2 1-1382 <$110
10 Type 2 1-690 <$110
20 Type 2 1-165 <$125
Total Issue $700,610
Out at close $50,000
Large out at close $2,570
****
10777 Macoupin
STAUNTON NB, STAUNTON
{{ 6 L 10 S }}
Organized 8/28/15
Liquidated 1/21/35
1902 Plain Back <$VALUE
4x5 1-8325 <$175
3x10-20 1-6675 <$175
1929 Small Size
5 Type 1 1-1646 <$100
10 Type 1 1-1038 <$100
20 Type 1 1-295 <$100
Total Issue $647,310
Out at close $50,000
Large out at close $2,210
****
1717 Whiteside
FNB OF STERLING
Chartered 10/8/70
Receivership 3/29/34
2nd title:F Sterling NB
3/8/30
FIRST TITLE {{ 6 L 3 S }}
Original Series <$VALUE
3x1-2 1-2600 <$400/$1250
4x5 1-4600 <$450
3x10-20 1-1000 <$750/$1250
Series 1875
4x5 1-3631 <$450
3x10-20 1-1600 <$750/$1250
Brown Back
3x10-20 1-5360 <$250/$300
1882 Date Back
3x10-20 1-381 <$250/$300
1902 Date Back
3x10-20 1-2400* <$165
1902 Plain Back
3x10-20 2801-8287* <$165
* 2401-2800 not marked
1929 Small Size
5 Type 1 1-1544 <$125
10 Type 1 1-1378 <$125
20 Type 1 1-470 <$125
SECOND TITLE {{ 9 S }}
1929 Small Size
5 Type 1 1-1968 <$100
10 Type 1 1-894 <$100
20 Type 1 1-304 <$100
5 Type 2 1-2030 <$125
10 Type 2 1-840 <$125
20 Type 2 1-183 <$125
Total Issue $1,365,790
Out at close $149,150
Large out at close $7,755
Outstanding includes Ch 2709
****
F Sterling NB, Sterling
SEE Ch 1717
FNB of Sterling
****
2709 Whiteside
STERLING NB, STERLING
{{ 6 L 2 S }}
Chartered 1882
Closed 3/8/30
Series 1875 <$VALUE
4x5 1-5461 <$450
3x10-20 1-279 <$750/$1250
1902 Red Seal
3x10-20 1-2800 <$350
1902 Date Back
3x10-20 1-3500* <$175

1902 Plain Back (dated 1902)
3x10-20 4001-6400* <$175
* 3501-4000 not marked
1902 Plain Back (dated 1922)
3x10-20 1-3620 <$175
1929 Small Size
10 Type 1 1-396 <$300
20 Type 1 1-66 <$300
Total Issue $795,850
Out at close $49,280
Large out at close $17,650
Ch 1717 assumed circulation
****
6543 Lee
FNB OF STEWARD
{{ 2 L 5 S }}
Organized 11/20/02
Receivership 11/1/33
1902 Red Seal <$VALUE
3x10-20 1-1350 <$650
1902 Date Back
3x10-20 1-1850 <$350
1902 Plain Back
3x10-20 1851-5446 <$350
1929 Small Size
10 Type 1 1-831 <$150
20 Type 1 1-243 <$150
Total Issue $418,820
Out at close $50,000
Large out at close $2,020
****
9438 Shelby
FNB OF STEWARDSON
{{ 1 L }}
Organized 5/14/09
Receivership 5/1/28
1902 Date Back <$VALUE
3x10-20 1-2120 <$750
1902 Plain Back
3x10-20 2121-5013 <$750
Total Issue $250,650
Out at close $25,000
****
13666 Jo Daviess
FNB OF STOCKTON
{{ 4 S }}
Chartered 3/33
1929 Small Size <$VALUE
5 Type 2 1-2450 <$250
10 Type 2 1-1310 <$250
20 Type 2 1-310 <$250
Total Issue $31,550
Out in 1935 $25,000
****
5291 Christian
FNB OF STONINGTON
{{ 3 L 4 S }}
Chartered 4/16/00
Liquidated 2/2/31
Brown Back <$VALUE
3x10-20 1-2800 <$400
1882 Date Back
3x10-20 1-3560 <$400
1882 Value Back
3x10-20 3561-5301 <$400
1902 Plain Back
3x10-20 1-5727 <$250
1929 Small Size
10 Type 1 1-585 <$200
20 Type 1 1-181 <$200
Total Issue $748,220
Out at close $50,000
Large out at close $9,100
****
7151 Livingston
FARMERS NB OF STRAWN
{{ 3 L 2 S }}
Organized 1/12/04
Receivership 6/11/30
1902 Red Seal <$VALUE
3x10-20 1-1302 <$750
1902 Date Back
3x10-20 1-1720 <$375
1902 Plain Back
3x10-20 1721-5084 <$375
1929 Small Size
10 Type 1 1-247 <$350
20 Type 1 1-38 <$350
Total Issue $338,680
Out at close $25,000
Large out at close $6,200
****
4476 LaSalle
CITY NB OF STREATOR
{{ UNREPORTED }}
Chartered 11/28/90
Liquidated 1/13/97
Brown Back <$VALUE
3x10-20 1-1069 <$1250
Total Issue $53,450
Out in 1910 $650
****

****
2170 LaSalle
FNB OF STREATOR
{{ UNREPORTED }}
Chartered 8/21/74
Liquidated 4/24/78
Original Series <$VALUE
4x5 1-2795 <$1250
Total Issue $55,900
Out in 1910 $280
****
2681 LaSalle
STREATOR NB, STREATOR
{{ U + 8 L 5 S }}
Chartered 1882
Series 1875 <$VALUE
3x10-20 1-1820 <$750/$1250
50-100 1-115 <$4000
1902 Red Seal
3x10-20 1-1400 <$300
1902 Date Back
3x10-20 1-2400 <$150
1902 Plain Back (dated 1902)
3x10-20 2401-2673 <$150
1902 Plain Back (dated 1922)
3x10-20 1-1897 <$150
1929 Small Size
10 Type 1 1-530 <$150
20 Type 1 1-138 <$150
10 Type 2 1-604 <$150
20 Type 2 1-119 <$150
Total Issue $463,530
Out in 1935 $25,000
Large out 1935 $1,770
****
2176 LaSalle
UNION NB OF STREATOR
{{ 6 L 3 S }}
Chartered 8/28/74
Original Series <$VALUE
4x10 1-1225 <$750
Series 1875
4x10 1-2600 <$750
Brown Back
4x5 1-2000 <$250
50-100 1-2080 <$1250/$1500
1882 Date Back
4x5 1-20 <$250
50-100 1-700 <$1250/$1500
3x50-100 1-249<$1250/$1500
1902 Date Back
3x50-100 1-1280 <$400/$500
1902 Plain Back
3x50-100 1281-1573
<$400/$500
1929 Small Size
50 Type 1 1-235 <$125
100 Type 1 1-84 <$175
Total Issue $1,186,800
Out in 1935 $100,000
Large out 1935 $12,595
****
5813 Henderson
FNB OF STRONGHURST
{{ 6 L }}
Organized 4/27/01
Receivership 7/17/31
Brown Back <$VALUE
3x10-20 1-1400 <$400
1882 Date Back
3x10-20 1-2250* <$400
1882 Value Back
3x10-20 2411-4488* <$400
* 2251-2410 not marked
1902 Plain Back
3x10-20 1-3452 <$225
Total Issue $467,000
Out in 1927 $50,000
****
7692 Moultrie
FNB OF SULLIVAN
{{ 8 L 9 S }}
Chartered 4/05
1902 Red Seal <$VALUE
3x10-20 1-2150 <$300
1902 Date Back
3x10-20 1-3600* <$150
1902 Plain Back
3x10-20 3851-10465* <$150
* 3601-3850 not marked
1929 Small Size
10 Type 1 1-1198 <$85
20 Type 1 1-324 <$100
10 Type 2 1-1302 <$110
20 Type 2 1-315 <$110
Total Issue $760,830
Out in 1935 $50,000
Large out 1935 $2,590
****

****
6907 Lawrence
FNB OF SUMNER
{{ 2 L U + 5 S }}
Organized 7/29/03
1902 Red Seal <$VALUE
3x10-20 1-1490 <$650
1902 Date Back
3x10-20 1-1820 <$300
1902 Plain Back
3x10-20 1821-5690 <$300
1929 Small Size
10 Type 1 1-566 <$175
20 Type 1 1-160 <$175
10 Type 2 1-656 <$200
20 Type 2 1-174 <$200
Total Issue $422,200
Out in 1935 $25,000
Large out 1935 $1,170
****
9572 De Kalb
CITIZENS NB OF SYCAMORE
{{ 6 L }}
Chartered 10/09
Closed 1/2/26
1902 Date Back <$VALUE
3x10-20 1-4900 <$300
1902 Plain Back
3x10-20 4901-12800 <$300
Total Issue $640,000
Out at close $73,700
Ch 1896 assumed circulation
****
FNB of Sycamore
SEE Ch 1896
Sycamore NB, Sycamore
****
1896 De Kalb
SYCAMORE NB, SYCAMORE
Chartered 11/2/71
Receivership 10/31/31
2nd title:FNB of Sycamore
1/2/26
FIRST TITLE {{ 5 L }}
Original Series <$VALUE
4x5 1-1700 <$600
3x10-20 1-500 <$1000/$1500
Series 1875
4x5 1-1132 <$600
3x10-20 1-1414<$1000/$1500
Brown Back
50-100 1-744 <$1250/$1500
1882 Date Back
50-100 1-789 <$1250/$1500
1902 Date Back
3x50-100 1-1760 <$500/$600
SECOND TITLE {{ 4 L U + 12 S }}
1902 Plain Back
3x10-20 1-6491 <$350
1929 Small Size
10 Type 1 1-2493 <$150
20 Type 1 1-778 <$150
Total Issue $1,389,780
Out at close $175,000
Large out at close $29,040
Outstanding includes Ch 9572
****
8629 Perry
FNB OF TAMAROA
{{ 3 L 4 S }}
Organized 3/9/07
Receivership 12/9/33
1902 Red Seal <$VALUE
4x5 1-600 <$700
4x10 1-600 <$700
1902 Date Back
4x5 1-1900 <$350
4x10 1-1750 <$350
1902 Plain Back
4x5 1901-6677 <$350
4x10 1751-5123 <$350
1929 Small Size
5 Type 1 1-1044 <$175
10 Type 1 1-628 <$175
5 Type 2 1-164 <$200
10 Type 2 1-95 <$200
Total Issue $445,230
Out at close $24,345
Large out at close $1,335
****
9230 Whiteside
FNB OF TAMPICO
{{ 6 L 12 S }}
Chartered 8/08
Liquidated 12/22/31
1902 Date Back <$VALUE
3x10-20 1-1160* <$300
1902 Plain Back
3x10-20 1301-2777* <$300
* 1161-1300 not marked
1929 Small Size
10 Type 1 1-200 <$165
20 Type 1 1-44 <$175
Total Issue $156,130
Out at close $11,960
Large out at close $1,750
****
5410 Christian
FARMERS NB OF TAYLORVILLE
{{ 14 L 14 S }}
Chartered 6/7/00
Receivership 1/19/33
Brown Back <$VALUE
3x10-20 1-4200 <$275
50-100 1-390 <$1250/$1500
1882 Date Back
3x10-20 1-6800 <$250
1882 Value Back
3x10-20 6801-10121 <$250
1902 Plain Back
3x10-20 1-12004 <$100
1929 Small Size
10 Type 1 1-1945 <$60
20 Type 1 1-460 <$70
Total Issue $1,546,650
Out at close $100,000
Large out at close $9,060
****
3579 Christian
FNB OF TAYLORVILLE
{{ 8 L 1 S }}
Organized 10/9/86
Receivership 10/18/29
Brown Back <$VALUE
3x10-20 1-3977 <$300
1902 Red Seal
3x10-20 1-2350 <$300
1902 Date Back
3x10-20 1-6700* <$125
1902 Plain Back
3x10-20 7701-22405* <$125
* 6701-7700 not marked
1929 Small Size
10 Type 1 1-212* <$350
20 Type 1 1-64** <$350
*E000212A-F000212A canceled
**C000064A-F000064A canceled
Total Issue $1,456,900
Out at close $98,550
Large out at close $78,250
****
8940 Christian
TAYLORVILLE NB,
TAYLORVILLE
{{ 29 L 4 S }}
Organized 4/6/07
Liquidated 12/16/31
1902 Red Seal <$VALUE
4x5 1-2550 <$225
3x10-20 1-2040 <$225
1902 Date Back
4x5 1-9500 <$85
3x10-20 1-7300 <$85
1902 Plain Back
4x5 9501-34022 <$85
3x10-20 7301-22143 <$85
1929 Small Size
5 Type 1 1-2300* <$125
10 Type 1 1-1133** <$125
20 Type 1 147-335 <$125
* 368-826 not issued
**D000073A-F00416A canceled
Total Issue $2,065,870
Out at close $75,000
Large out at close $11,670
****
8155 Champaign
FNB OF THOMASBORO
{{ 4 L 5 S }}
Chartered 4/06
1902 Red Seal <$VALUE
3x10-20 1-750 <$600
1902 Date Back
3x10-20 1-1980 <$300
1902 Plain Back
3x10-20 1981-5848 <$300
1929 Small Size
10 Type 1 1-548 <$165
20 Type 1 1-158 <$165
10 Type 2 1-871 <$200
20 Type 2 1-82 <$200
Total Issue $392,090
Out in 1935 $25,000
Large out 1935 $1,890
****
13682 Cumberland
FNB IN TOLEDO
{{ 4 S }}
Chartered 5/33
1929 Small Size <$VALUE
5 Type 2 1-5064 <$165
10 Type 2 1-2076 <$165
Total Issue $46,080
Out in 1935 $21,990
****

****
5273 Cumberland
FNB OF TOLEDO
{{ 6 L 5 S }}
Chartered 4/2/00
Liquidated 6/6/33
Brown Back <$VALUE
3x10-20 1-1880 <$350
1882 Date Back
3x10-20 1-3540 <$350
1882 Value Back
3x10-20 3541-5019 <$350
1902 Plain Back
3x10-20 1-5656 <$175
1929 Small Size
5 Type 1 1-1396 <$150
10 Type 1 1-705 <$150
20 Type 1 1-196 <$150
Total Issue $735,450
Out at close $50,000
Large out at close $4,560
****
11333 Marshall
CITIZENS NB OF TOLUCA
{{ 3 L 2 S }}
Chartered 4/19
1902 Plain Back <$VALUE
4x5 1-2185 <$500
1929 Small Size
5 Type 1 1-686 <$400
Total Issue $64,280
Out in 1935 $5,000
Large out 1935 $250
****
4871 Marshall
FNB OF TOLUCA
{{ 3 L }}
Organized 5/10/93
Receivership 7/5/05
Brown Back <$VALUE
4x5 1-4503 <$650
3x10-20 1-3618 <$650
Total Issue $270,960
Out in 1915 $3,615
****
6421 Tazewell
FNB OF TREMONT
{{ 4 L 4 S }}
Chartered 9/02
Liquidated 1/12/32
1902 Red Seal <$VALUE
3x10-20 1-1160 <$400
1902 Date Back
3x10-20 1-4260 <$200
1902 Plain Back
3x10-20 4261-11591 <$200
1929 Small Size
10 Type 1 1-791 <$165
20 Type 1 1-228 <$165
Total Issue $712,370
Out at close $50,000
Large out at close $5,560
****
9325 Tazewell
TREMONT NB, TREMONT
{{ 2 L }}
Chartered 1/09
Liquidated 1/20/27
1902 Date Back <$VALUE
4x10 1-3100 <$350
1902 Plain Back
4x10 3101-8536 <$350
Total Issue $341,440
Out at close $25,000
****
10125 Clinton
FNB OF TRENTON
{{ 4 L 2 S }}
Organized 12/19/11
Liquidated 5/3/34
1902 Date Back <$VALUE
3x10-20 1-1000 <$250
1902 Plain Back
3x10-20 1001-3373 <$250
1929 Small Size
10 Type 1 1-430 <$250
20 Type 1 1-128 <$250
10 Type 2 1-87 <$300
20 Type 2 1-8 <$300
Total Issue $210,840
Out at close $18,750
Large out at close $1,360
****
7660 LaSalle
FNB OF TRIUMPH
{{ 2 L 7 S }}
Chartered 3/05
1902 Red Seal <$VALUE
3x10-20 1-860 <$1000
1902 Date Back
3x10-20 1-1930 <$500
1902 Plain Back
3x10-20 1931-5277 <$500
1929 Small Size
10 Type 1 1-610 <$175
20 Type 1 1-172 <$175
10 Type 2 1-127 <$200
20 Type 2 1-10 <$200
Total Issue $365,560
Out in 1935 $25,000
Large out 1935 $1,630
****
1723 Douglas
FNB OF TUSCOLA
{{ 2 L 5 S }}
Chartered 10/18/70
Original Series <$VALUE
4x5 1-3300 <$600
3x10-20 1-1834 <$750/$1250
Series 1875
3x10-20 1-3178 <$750/$1250
Brown Back
50-100 1-949 <$1250/$1500
1902 Date Back
3x50-100 1-700 <$500/$600
1902 Plain Back
3x50-100 701-876<$500/$600
1929 Small Size
50 Type 1 1-183 <$200
100 Type 1 1-28 <$300
Total Issue $749,650
Out in 1935 $60,000
Large out 1935 $5,200
****
8180 Pulaski
FNB OF ULLIN
{{ 1 L 1 S }}
Organized 4/3/06
Receivership 12/12/30
1902 Red Seal <$VALUE
3x10-20 1-260 <$1250
1902 Date Back
3x10-20 1-680 <$600
1902 Plain Back
3x10-20 681-1537 <$600
1929 Small Size
10 Type 1 1-79 <$600
20 Type 1 1-14 <$600
Total Issue $96,270
Out at close $6,500
Large out at close $1,500
****
2915 Champaign
FNB OF URBANA
{{ 2 L 3 S }}
Organized 3/29/83
Receivership 3/13/34
Brown Back <$VALUE
4x5 1-3348 <$1000
3x10-20 1-238 <$1000
1902 Red Seal
3x10-20 1-620 <$1000
1902 Date Back
3x10-20 1-3240 <$500
1902 Plain Back
3x10-20 3241-5517 <$500
1929 Small Size
10 Type 1 1-302 <$300
20 Type 1 1-84 <$300
Total Issue $413,910
Out at close $12,500
Large out at close $1,360
****
1779 Fayette
FARMERS & MERCHANTS NB OF
VANDALIA
{{ UNREPORTED }}
Chartered 1/31/71
Liquidated 1/10/91
Original Series <$VALUE
3x10-20 1-3080<$1500/$2000
Series 1875
3x10-20 1-2477<$1500/$2000
Total Issue $277,850
Out in 1910 $1,390
****
4994 Fayette
FNB OF VANDALIA
{{ 5 L 12 S }}
Chartered 1895
Brown Back <$VALUE
3x10-20 1-4200 <$350
1882 Date Back
3x10-20 1-2747 <$350
1902 Date Back
3x10-20 1-1000 <$175
1902 Plain Back
3x10-20 1001-7370 <$175
1929 Small Size
10 Type 1 1-2032 <$60
20 Type 1 1-484 <$65
10 Type 2 1-2513 <$70
20 Type 2 1-423 <$70
Total Issue $929,440
Out in 1935 $100,000
Large out 1935 $3,310
****

****
1517 Fayette
NB OF VANDALIA
{{ UNREPORTED }}
Chartered 1865
Liquidated 1/11/83
Original Series <$VALUE
4x5 1-1300 <$1250
3x10-20 1-2450<$1500/$2000
Series 1875
3x10-20 1-1838<$1500/$2000
Total Issue $240,400
Out in 1910 $1,375
****
10365 Edgar
FNB OF VERMILION
{{ 3 L 4 S }}
Organized 4/15/13
Receivership 1/12/34
1902 Date Back <$VALUE
4x5 1-665 <$350
3x10-20 1-534 <$350
1902 Plain Back
4x5 666-4324 <$350
3x10-20 535-2804 <$350
1929 Small Size
5 Type 1 1-868 <$200
10 Type 1 1-422 <$200
20 Type 1 1-118 <$225
5 Type 2 1-324 <$225
10 Type 2 1-100 <$225
20 Type 2 1-15 <$250
Total Issue $295,120
Out at close $25,000
Large out at close $1,280
****
4433 Johnson
FNB OF VIENNA
{{ 6 L 11 S }}
Chartered 1890
Brown Back <$VALUE
3x10-20 1-4340 <$325
1882 Date Back
3x10-20 1-580 <$325
1902 Date Back
3x10-20 1-2600* <$150
1902 Plain Back
3x10-20 2801-9995* <$150
*2601-2800 not marked
1929 Small Size
10 Type 1 1-1322 <$85
20 Type 1 1-414 <$85
10 Type 2 1-1182 <$100
20 Type 2 1-333 <$100
Total Issue $893,230
Out in 1935 $60,000
Large out 1935 $3,130
****
7088 Douglas
FNB OF VILLA GROVE
{{ 5 L 10 S }}
Chartered 1/04
1902 Red Seal <$VALUE
3x10-20 1-630 <$600
1902 Date Back
3x10-20 1-4580 <$300
1902 Plain Back
3x10-20 4581-12849 <$300
1929 Small Size
10 Type 1 1-1172 <$110
20 Type 1 1-340 <$125
10 Type 2 1-942 <$150
20 Type 2 1-177 <$150
Total Issue $798,030
Out in 1935 $25,000
Large out 1935 $2,450
****
2330 Cass
CENTENNIAL NB OF VIRGINIA
{{ 7 L 3 S }}
Chartered 4/11/76
Liquidated 1/22/31
Series 1875 <$VALUE
4x5 1-7115 <$500
Brown Back
4x5 1-2055 <$400
3x10-20 1-1120 <$400
1882 Date Back
4x5 1-2302 <$400
3x10-20 1-1580 <$400
1902 Plain Back
4x5 1-5215 <$275
3x10-20 1-3237 <$275
1929 Small Size
5 Type 1 1-490 <$250
10 Type 1 1-258 <$250
20 Type 1 1-63 <$250
Total Issue $668,330
Out in 1929 $32,495
Large out at close $6,525
****

****
1471 Cass
FARMERS NB OF VIRGINIA
{{ 3 L }}
Chartered 1865
Liquidated 1/8/18
Original Series <$VALUE
4x5 1-3550 <$750
3x10-20 1-2630<$1000/$1500
4x20 1-200 <$1500
Series 1875
4x5 1-2585 <$750
3x10-20 1-1470<$1000/$1500
Brown Back
3x10-20 1-3093 <$450
1902 Red Seal
4x5 1-2000 <$500
3x10-20 1-1100 <$500
1902 Date Back
4x5 1-2200 <$300
3x10-20 1-2100 <$300
1902 Plain Back
4x5 2201-2890 <$300
3x10-20 2101-2772 <$300
Total Issue $789,750
Out at close $50,000
****
11675 Stephenson
FNB OF WADDAMS GROVE
{{ 1 L }}
Chartered 4/20
Liquidated 11/10/23
1902 Plain Back <$VALUE
4x5 1-2704 <$1000
Total Issue $54,080
Out at close $25,000
****
2684 Bureau
FNB OF WALNUT
{{ 1 L }}
Chartered 1882
Liquidated 1/21/85
Series 1875 <$VALUE
3x10-20 1-878 <$2000/$2500
Total Issue $43,900
Out in 1910 $140
****
11516 Jefferson
FNB OF WALTONVILLE
{{ 1 L }}
Chartered 11/19
Liquidated 1/2/26
1902 Plain Back <$VALUE
4x5 1-2680 <$600
3x10-20 1-1622 <$600
Total Issue $134,700
Out at close $30,000
****
849 Jo Daviess
FARMERS NB OF WARREN
{{ UNREPORTED }}
Chartered 3/1/65
Liquidated 4/28/74
Original Series <$VALUE
3x1-2 1-500 <$1250/$2000
4x5 1-1585 <$1250
3x10-20 1-500 <$1500/$2000
Total Issue $59,200
Out in 1910 $480
****
FNB in Warren
SEE Ch 9096
N Farmers B of Warren
****
9096 Jo Daviess
N FARMERS B OF WARREN
Chartered 4/08
Liquidated 11/5/26
2nd title:FNB in Warren
8/17/20
FIRST TITLE {{ 1 L }}
1902 Red Seal <$VALUE
3x10-20 1-200 <$850
1902 Date Back
3x10-20 1-1950 <$450
1902 Plain Back
3x10-20 1951-3290 <$450
SECOND TITLE {{ 1 L }}
1902 Plain Back
3x10-20 1-2329 <$600
Total Issue $290,950
Out at close $40,000
****
9929 Hancock
FARMERS NB OF WARSAW
{{ 1 L }}
Chartered 2/11
Liquidated 10/10/19
1902 Date Back <$VALUE
4x5 1-1000 <$750
3x10-20 1-800 <$750
1902 Plain Back
4x5 1001-1835 <$750
3x10-20 801-1250 <$750
Total Issue $99,200
Out at close $24,100
****
495 Hancock
FNB OF WARSAW
{{ 1 L }}
Chartered 8/16/64
Liquidated 12/31/86
Original Series <$VALUE
4x5 1-2600 <$1000
3x10-20 1-2700<$1000/$1500
Series 1875
3x10-20 1-676 <$1000/$1500
Brown Back
50-100 1-167 <$1250/$1500
Total Issue $245,850
Out in 1910 $1,655
****
10180 Monroe
FNB OF WATERLOO
{{ 2 L U + 6 S }}
Chartered 4/12
1902 Date Back <$VALUE
4x5 1-1050 <$350
3x10-20 1-840 <$350
1902 Plain Back
4x5 1051-5120 <$350
3x10-20 841-3167 <$350
1929 Small Size
5 Type 1 1-970 <$175
10 Type 1 1-452 <$175
20 Type 1 1-132 <$175
5 Type 2 1-938 <$200
10 Type 2 1-570 <$200
20 Type 2 1-153 <$200
Total Issue $346,260
Out in 1935 $25,000
Large out 1935 $1,530
****
1721 Iroquois
FNB OF WATSEKA
{{ 6 L 4 S }}
Chartered 10/15/70
Receivership 6/29/31
Original Series <$VALUE
4x5 1-3250 <$500
Series 1875
4x5 1-8146 <$500
Brown Back
4x5 1-9450 <$350
3x10-20 1-2180 <$350
1882 Date Back
4x5 1-470 <$350
3x10-20 1-382 <$350
1902 Date Back
4x5 1-2500* <$165
3x10-20 1-1940* <$165
1902 Plain Back
4x5 2751-9745* <$165
3x10-20 2101-6823** <$165
* 2501-2750 not marked
** 1941-2100 not marked
1929 Small Size
5 Type 1 1-994 <$200
10 Type 1 1-444 <$200
20 Type 1 1-132 <$200
Total Issue $1,162,770
Out at close $50,000
Large out at close $3,910
****
945 Lake
FNB OF WAUKEGAN
{{ 5 L 16 S }}
Organized 3/10/65
Original Series <$VALUE
3x1-2 1-1400 <$500/$1250
4x5 1-2150 <$650
3x10-20 1-800 <$1000/$1500
Series 1875
4x5 1-1465 <$650
3x10-20 1-860 <$1000/$1500
Brown Back
4x5 1-4240 <$350
3x10-20 1-579 <$350
1902 Red Seal
4x5 1-650 <$400
3x10-20 1-570 <$400
1902 Date Back
4x5 1-1700* <$200
3x10-20 1-1240** <$200
1902 Plain Back
4x5 1851-11490* <$200
3x10-20 1341-7667** <$200
* 1701-1850 not marked
** 1241-1340 not marked
1929 Small Size
5 Type 1 1-3956 <$65
10 Type 1 1-1918 <$65
20 Type 1 1-460 <$65
5 Type 2 1-3278 <$85
10 Type 2 1-1641 <$85
20 Type 2 1-464 <$85
Total Issue $1,261,740
Out in 1935 $100,000
Large out 1935 $4,065
****

****
10355 Lake
WAUKEGAN NB, WAUKEGAN
{{ 9 L 16 S }}
Organized 3/7/13
Receivership 6/22/31
1902 Date Back <$VALUE
3x10-20 1-2000 <$135
1902 Plain Back
3x10-20 2001-33679 <$135
1929 Small Size
10 Type 1 1-3998 <$60
20 Type 1 1-1153 <$70
Total Issue $2,062,190
Out at close $250,000
Large out at close $26,100
****
6116 Morgan
FNB OF WAVERLY
{{ 16 L 6 S }}
Organized 1/7/02
Receivership 2/7/31
1902 Red Seal <$VALUE
3x10-20 1-2800 <$200
1902 Date Back
3x10-20 1-3400 <$100
1902 Plain Back (dated 1902)
3x10-20 3401-7975 <$100
1902 Plain Back (dated 1922)
3x10-20 1-9498 <$100
1929 Small Size
10 Type 1 1-1255 <$75
20 Type 1 1-356 <$75
Total Issue $1,131,670
Out at close $100,000
Large out at close $15,020
****
10460 Wayne
FNB OF WAYNE CITY
{{ 6 L 6 S }}
Organized 10/30/13
1902 Date Back <$VALUE
3x10-20 1-500 <$300
1902 Plain Back
3x10-20 501-3972 <$300
1929 Small Size
10 Type 1 1-556 <$175
20 Type 1 1-166 <$200
10 Type 2 1-812 <$200
20 Type 2 1-133 <$200
Total Issue $262,660
Out in 1935 $25,000
Large out 1935 $1,660
****
3620 Marshall
FNB OF WENONA
{{ UNREPORTED }}
Chartered 1/18/87
Liquidated 3/1/99
Brown Back <$VALUE
3x10-20 1-811 <$1250
Total Issue $40,550
Out in 1910 $630
****
7673 Franklin
FNB OF WEST FRANKFORT
{{ 2 L 3 S }}
Organized 2/28/05
Receivership 12/7/31
1902 Red Seal <$VALUE
4x5 1-515 <$850
3x10-20 1-420 <$850
1902 Date Back
4x5 1-1075 <$400
3x10-20 1-800 <$400
1902 Plain Back
4x5 1076-6439 <$400
3x10-20 801-3938 <$400
1929 Small Size
5 Type 1 1-657 <$275
10 Type 1 1-323 <$275
20 Type 1 1-95 <$275
Total Issue $407,470
Out at close $24,995
Large out at close $2,855
****
9338 Edwards
FNB OF WEST SALEM
{{ 3 L 3 S }}
Organized 12/12/08
Receivership 11/18/30
1902 Date Back <$VALUE
3x10-20 1-2210 <$450
1902 Plain Back
3x10-20 2211-5644 <$450
1929 Small Size
10 Type 1 1-259 <$250
20 Type 1 1-57 <$250
Total Issue $304,580
Out at close $25,000
Large out at close $6,415
****

****
10641 Shelby
FARMERS NB OF WESTERVELT
{{ 3 L 3 S }}
Chartered 10/14
Liquidated 12/1/31
1902 Date Back <$VALUE
3x10-20 1-500 <$500
1902 Plain Back
3x10-20 501-3801 <$500
1929 Small Size
10 Type 1 1-379 <$300
20 Type 1 1-101 <$300
Total Issue $224,910
Out at close $25,000
Large out at close $2,940
****
8216 Clark
FNB OF WESTFIELD
{{ 15 L 2 S }}
Organized 4/10/06
Receivership 11/28/30
1902 Red Seal <$VALUE
4x5 1-600 <$250
3x10-20 1-480 <$250
1902 Date Back
4x5 1-2850 <$125
3x10-20 1-2220 <$125
1902 Plain Back
4x5 2851-11051 <$125
3x10-20 2221-7377 <$125
1929 Small Size
5 Type 1 1-719 <$175
10 Type 1 1-384 <$175
20 Type 1 1-105 <$175
Total Issue $683,080
Out at close $50,000
Large out at close $7,730
****
7500 Vermilion
FNB OF WESTVILLE
{{ 2 L 5 S }}
Organized 10/13/04
1902 Red Seal <$VALUE
3x10-20 1-1237 <$500
1902 Date Back
3x10-20 1-800* <$250
1902 Plain Back
3x10-20 951-4862* <$250
* 801-950 not marked
1929 Small Size
10 Type 1 1-642 <$135
20 Type 1 1-178 <$135
10 Type 2 1-432 <$150
20 Type 2 1-108 <$150
Total Issue $371,310
Out in 1935 $25,000
Large out 1935 $1,390
****
9368 Du Page
FNB OF WHEATON
{{ 6 L 5 S }}
Organized 3/6/09
Receivership 1/19/33
1902 Date Back <$VALUE
4x10 1-2950 <$500
1902 Plain Back
4x10 2951-8547 <$500
1929 Small Size
10 Type 1 1-979 <$400
Total Issue $400,620
Out at close $24,700
Large out at close $1,860
****
7121 Greene
FNB OF WHITE HALL
Organized 1/4/04
Receivership 3/20/30
2nd title:Peoples-FNB of
White Hall 6/30/22
FIRST TITLE {{ 3 L }}
1902 Red Seal <$VALUE
3x10-20 1-1600 <$500
1902 Date Back
3x10-20 1-2300 <$250
1902 Plain Back
3x10-20 2301-5700 <$250
SECOND TITLE {{ 3 L 3 S }}
1902 Plain Back
3x10-20 1-4023 <$250
1929 Small Size
10 Type 1 1-424 <$250
20 Type 1 1-49 <$250
Total Issue $597,470
Out at close $47,840
Large out at close $16,670
****
Peoples-FNB of White Hall
SEE Ch 7121
FNB of White Hall
****

****
7077 Greene
WHITE HALL NB, WHITE HALL
{{ 7 L 10 S }}
Chartered 12/03
1902 Red Seal <$VALUE
4x5 1-810 <$350
3x10-20 1-648 <$350
1902 Date Back
4x5 1-2800 <$175
3x10-20 1-2360 <$175
1902 Plain Back
4x5 2801-25176 <$175
3x10-20 2361-3260 <$175
1929 Small Size
5 Type 1 1-1824 <$100
10 Type 1 1-1008 <$100
20 Type 1 1-256 <$110
5 Type 2 1-1646 <$110
10 Type 2 1-910 <$110
20 Type 2 1-264 <$125
Total Issue $883,650
Out in 1935 $50,000
Large out 1935 $2,230
****
10828 Cook
FNB OF WILMETTE
{{ 12 S }}
Organized 2/3/16
Receivership 6/25/32
1929 Small Size <$VALUE
5 Type 1 1-3281 <$100
10 Type 1 1-1554 <$100
20 Type 1 1-468 <$110
Total Issue $247,830
Out at close $100,000
****
Commercial NB of Wilmington
SEE Ch 1964
Miners NB of Braidwood
****
177 Will
FNB OF WILMINGTON
{{ 4 L }}
Chartered 1863
Original Series <$VALUE
3x1-2 1-3000 <$400/$1000
4x5 1-9350 <$500
Series 1875
4x5 1-5325 <$500
Brown Back
3x10-20 1-3462 <$350
1902 Red Seal
3x10-20 1-1250 <$400
1902 Date Back
3x10-20 1-4457* <$250
* 4201-4457 not marked
Total Issue $766,950
Out in 1935 $4,080
****
12630 Macoupin
FNB OF WILSONVILLE
{{ 1 L 4 S }}
Organized 1/14/25
Receivership 11/15/33
1902 Plain Back <$VALUE
3x10-20 1-1021 <$750
1929 Small Size
10 Type 1 1-633 <$250
20 Type 1 1-176 <$250
Total Issue $110,150
Out at close $25,000
Large out at close $790
****
1484 Scott
FNB OF WINCHESTER
{{ UNREPORTED }}
Organized 7/25/65
Receivership 3/16/77
Original Series <$VALUE
3x1-2 1-4840 <$1250/$2000
4x5 1-2800 <$1250
3x10-20 1-400 <$1500/$2000
Series 1875
4x5 1-440 <$1250
3x10-20 1-174 <$1500/$2000
Total Issue $117,700
Out in 1915 $698
****
1821 Scott
PEOPLES NB OF WINCHESTER
{{ 6 L }}
Chartered 5/19/71
Liquidated 10/4/75
Original Series <$VALUE
3x1-2 1-1600 <$400/$1000
4x5 1-1800 <$400
3x10-20 1-890 <$750/$1250
Series 1875
4x5 1-240 <$400
Total Issue $93,300
Out in 1910 $503
****

****
7339 Shelby
FNB OF WINDSOR
{{ UNREPORTED }}
Chartered 7/16/04
Liquidated 11/16/05
1902 Red Seal <$VALUE
4x5 1-100 <$1500
3x10-20 1-210 <$1500
Total Issue $12,500
Out in 1910 $1,080
****
13144 Montgomery
NB OF WITT
{{ 3 L 5 S }}
Chartered 11/27
Liquidated 1/10/33
1902 Plain Back <$VALUE
3x10-20 1-1029 <$400
1929 Small Size
5 Type 1 1-2092 <$200
10 Type 1 1-1072 <$200
Total Issue $178,530
Out at close $50,000
Large out 1935 $1,630
Outstanding includes Ch 7538
****
FNB of Witt
SEE Ch 7538
Oland NB of Witt
****
7538 Montgomery
OLAND NB OF WITT
Chartered 12/04
Liquidated 1/10/28
2nd title:FNB of Witt
2/14/22
FIRST TITLE {{ 2 L }}
1902 Red Seal <$VALUE
3x10-20 1-1230 <$750
1902 Date Back
3x10-20 1-3990 <$400
1902 Plain Back
3x10-20 3991-5890 <$400
SECOND TITLE {{ 2 L }}
1902 Plain Back
3x10-20 1-4698 <$400
Total Issue $590,900
Out at close $50,000
Ch 13144 assumed circulation
****
13650 Montgomery
SECURITY NB OF WITT
{{ U + 4 S }}
Chartered 12/32
1929 Small Size <$VALUE
10 Type 1 1-128 <$250
20 Type 1 1-42 <$250
10 Type 2 1-25 <$275
20 Type 2 1-10 <$275
Total Issue $13,170
Out in 1935 $25,000
Outstanding includes Ch 13144
and Ch 7538
****
10264 Montgomery
WITT NB, WITT
{{ 3 L }}
Chartered 9/12
Liquidated 1/11/28
1902 Date Back <$VALUE
3x10-20 1-1700 <$300
1902 Plain Back
3x10-20 1701-5794 <$300
Total Issue $289,700
Out at close $32,500
****
11876 Madison
FNB OF WOOD RIVER
{{ U + 3 L 12 S }}
Chartered 11/20
1902 Plain Back <$VALUE
4x5 1-23531 <$350
1929 Small Size
5 Type 1 1-7238 <$125
5 Type 2 1-17260 <$125
Total Issue $774,060
Out in 1935 $50,000
Large out 1935 $1,530
12525 Henry
FNB IN WOODHULL
{{ UNREPORTED }}
Chartered 4/24
Liquidated 8/31/26
1902 Plain Back <$VALUE
3x10-20 1-624 <$1000
Total Issue $31,200
Out at close $24,700
Outstanding includes Ch 10716
****

10716 Henry
FNB OF WOODHULL
{{ 1 L }}
Chartered 3/15
Liquidated 5/27/24
1902 Date Back <$VALUE
3x10-20 1-700 <$750
1902 Plain Back
3x10-20 701-2742 <$750
Total Issue $137,100
Out at close $25,000
Ch 12525 assumed circulation

11774 Jefferson
FNB OF WOODLAWN
{{ 3 L 6 S }}
Organized 6/22/20
1902 Plain Back <$VALUE
4x5 1-9067 <$400
1929 Small Size
5 Type 1 1-3390 <$150
5 Type 2 1-5568 <$150
Total Issue $310,880
Out in 1935 $25,000
Large out 1935 $670

6811 McHenry
AMERICAN NB OF WOODSTOCK
{{ 2 L 4 S }}
Organized 5/23/03
Liquidated 7/2/34
1902 Red Seal <$VALUE
3x10-20 1-650 <$750
1902 Date Back
3x10-20 1-1220* <$400
1902 Plain Back
3x10-20 1341-4839* <$400
* 1221-1340 not marked
1929 Small Size
10 Type 1 1-586 <$250
20 Type 1 1-156 <$250
10 Type 2 1-197 <$250
20 Type 2 1-73 <$250
Total Issue $331,760
Out at close $25,000
Large out 1935 $1,240
Ch 14137 assumed circulation

372 McHenry
FNB OF WOODSTOCK
{{ UNREPORTED }}
Chartered 1864
Liquidated 4/30/82
Original Series <$VALUE
4x5 1-4500 <$1250
Series 1875
4x5 1-2650 <$1250
Total Issue $143,000
Out in 1910 $1,220

2675 McHenry
FNB OF WOODSTOCK
{{ UNREPORTED }}
Chartered 5/1/82
Liquidated 10/31/89
Brown Back <$VALUE
3x10-20 1-1536 <$1500
Total Issue $76,800
Out in 1910 $440

14137 McHenry
FNB OF WOODSTOCK
{{ 1 S }}
Chartered 5/34
1929 Small Size <$VALUE
5 Type 2 1-550 <$500
10 Type 2 1-277 <$500
20 Type 2 1-55 <$500
Total Issue $6,620
Out in 1935 $25,000
Outstanding includes Ch 6811

FNB of Worden
SEE Ch 10669
Wall NB of Worden

10669 Madison
WALL NB OF WORDEN
Organized 12/4/14
Liquidated 7/18/35
2nd title:FNB of Worden
8/10/20
FIRST TITLE {{ 1 L }}
1902 Date Back <$VALUE
4x5 1-500 <$500
3x10-20 1-400 <$500
1902 Plain Back
4x5 501-1900 <$500
3x10-20 401-1200 <$500
SECOND TITLE {{ 3 L 4 S }}
1902 Plain Back
3x10-20 1-2781 <$400
1929 Small Size
10 Type 1 1-732 <$200
20 Type 1 1-166 <$200
10 Type 2 1-575 <$250
20 Type 2 1-105 <$250
Total Issue $308,740
Out at close $24,995
Large out at close $1,075

9277 Bureau
FNB OF WYANET
{{ 3 L 5 S }}
Organized 10/27/08
1902 Date Back <$VALUE
3x10-20 1-2400 <$400
1902 Plain Back
3x10-20 2401-6043 <$400
1929 Small Size
10 Type 1 1-590 <$200
20 Type 1 1-152 <$200
10 Type 2 1-613 <$225
20 Type 2 1-75 <$225
Total Issue $363,420
Out in 1935 $25,000
Large out 1935 $1,630

2815 Stark
FNB OF WYOMING
{{ 1 L }}
Chartered 1882
Liquidated 1/13/85
Brown Back <$VALUE
3x10-20 1-244 <$1500
Total Issue $12,200
Out in 1910 $130

6629 Stark
NB OF WYOMING
{{ 6 L 8 S }}
Organized 1/14/03
Liquidated 5/25/35
1902 Red Seal <$VALUE
3x10-20 1-1500 <$400
1902 Date Back
3x10-20 1-3150 <$200
1902 Plain Back
4x5 1-4427 <$200
3x10-20 3151-9220 <$200
1929 Small Size
5 Type 1 1-6386* <$150
* 3956-4530 not issued
Total Issue $798,870
Out at close $50,000
Large out at close $3,050

12096 Clay
FNB OF XENIA
{{ 5 L 6 S }}
Chartered 1/22
1902 Plain Back <$VALUE
4x5 1-8272 <$350
1929 Small Size
5 Type 1 1-3220 <$175
5 Type 2 1-5094 <$175
Total Issue $287,510
Out in 1935 $25,000
Large out 1935 $690

6239 Kendall
YORKVILLE NB, YORKVILLE
{{ 3 L 3 S }}
Chartered 5/02
1902 Red Seal <$VALUE
4x5 1-350 <$1000
3x10-20 1-310 <$1000
1902 Date Back
4x5 1-775 <$500
3x10-20 1-620 <$500
1902 Plain Back (dated 1902)
4x5 776-1480 <$500
3x10-20 621-1051 <$500
1902 Plain Back (dated 1922)
4x5 1-1203 <$500
3x10-20 1-735 <$500
1929 Small Size
5 Type 1 1-412 <$350
10 Type 1 1-212 <$350
20 Type 1 1-72 <$350
5 Type 2 1-382 <$350
10 Type 2 1-245 <$350
20 Type 2 1-60 <$350
Total Issue $204,740
Out in 1935 $12,500
Large out 1935 $560

12097 Franklin
FNB OF ZEIGLER
{{ U + 2 L 12 S }}
Chartered 1/22
1902 Plain Back <$VALUE
4x5 1-5983 <$500
1929 Small Size
5 Type 1 1-5196 <$100
5 Type 2 1-10560 <$110
Total Issue $328,340
Out in 1935 $35,000
Large out 1935 $465

<$VALUEs are for notes in **FINE** condition. Value changes by approximately **25%** for a change of one full grade.

INDIAN TERRITORY

The Indian Territory was created May 30, 1854. On May 2, 1890 the western portion of the Indian Territory became the Oklahoma Territory. The two territories were reunited on November 16,1907 to form the State of Oklahoma. National Banks of the Indian Territory are listed with State of Oklahoma banks. The map shows the original territorial divisions and the present-day Oklahoma counties.

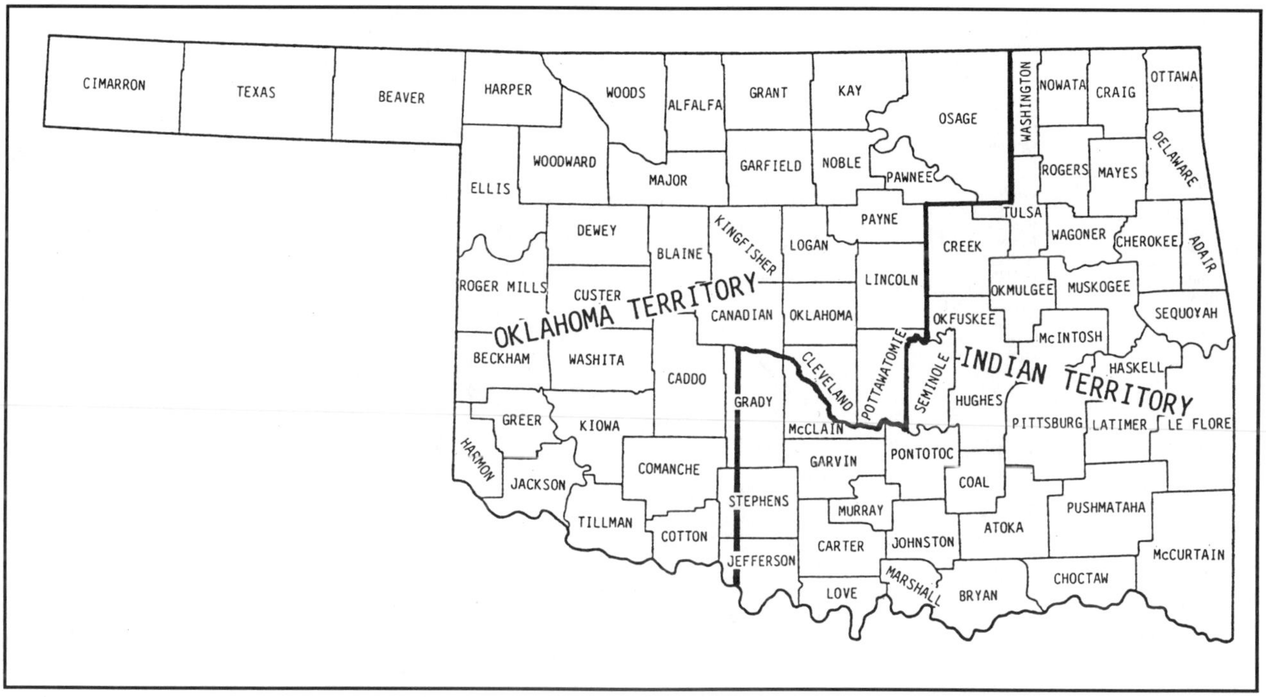

INDIANA

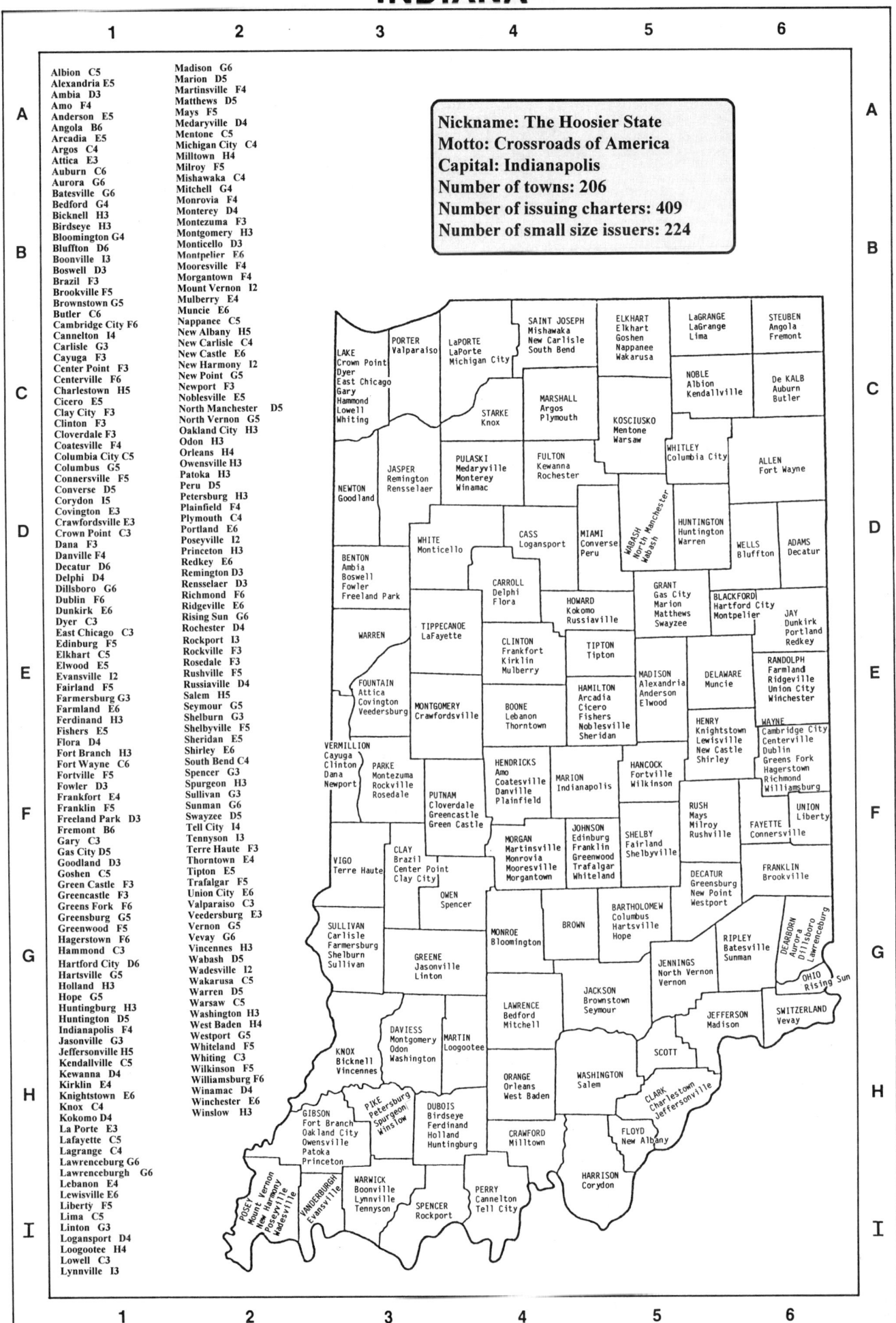

Albion C5
Alexandria E5
Ambia D3
Amo F4
Anderson E5
Angola B6
Arcadia E5
Argos C4
Attica E3
Auburn C6
Aurora G6
Batesville G6
Bedford G4
Bicknell H3
Birdseye H3
Bloomington G4
Bluffton D6
Boonville I3
Boswell D3
Brazil F3
Brookville F5
Brownstown G5
Butler C6
Cambridge City F6
Cannelton I4
Carlisle G3
Cayuga F3
Center Point F3
Centerville F6
Charlestown H5
Cicero E5
Clay City F3
Clinton F3
Cloverdale F3
Coatesville F4
Columbia City C5
Columbus G5
Connersville F5
Converse D5
Corydon I5
Covington E3
Crawfordsville E3
Crown Point C3
Dana F3
Danville F4
Decatur D6
Delphi D4
Dillsboro G6
Dublin F6
Dunkirk E6
Dyer C3
East Chicago C3
Edinburg F5
Elkhart C5
Elwood E5
Evansville I2
Fairland F5
Farmersburg G3
Farmland E6
Ferdinand H3
Fishers E5
Flora D4
Fort Branch H3
Fort Wayne C6
Fortville F5
Fowler D3
Frankfort E4
Franklin F5
Freeland Park D3
Fremont B6
Gary C3
Gas City D5
Goodland D3
Goshen C5
Green Castle F3
Greencastle F3
Greens Fork F6
Greensburg G5
Greenwood F5
Hagerstown F6
Hammond C3
Hartford City D6
Hartsville G5
Holland H3
Hope G5
Huntingburg H3
Huntington D5
Indianapolis F4
Jasonville G3
Jeffersonville H5
Kendallville C5
Kewanna D4
Kirklin E4
Knightstown E6
Knox C4
Kokomo D4
La Porte E3
Lafayette C5
Lagrange C4
Lawrenceburg G6
Lawrenceburgh G6
Lebanon E4
Lewisville E6
Liberty F5
Lima C5
Linton G3
Logansport D4
Loogootee H4
Lowell C3
Lynnville I3
Madison G6
Marion D5
Martinsville F4
Matthews D5
Mays F5
Medaryville D4
Mentone C5
Michigan City C4
Milltown H4
Milroy F5
Mishawaka C4
Mitchell G4
Monrovia F4
Monterey D4
Montezuma F3
Montgomery H3
Monticello D3
Montpelier E6
Mooresville F4
Morgantown F4
Mount Vernon I2
Mulberry E4
Muncie E6
Nappanee C5
New Albany H5
New Carlisle C4
New Castle E6
New Harmony I2
New Point G5
Newport F3
Noblesville E5
North Manchester D5
North Vernon G5
Oakland City H3
Odon H3
Orleans H4
Owensville H3
Patoka H3
Peru D5
Petersburg H3
Plainfield F4
Plymouth C4
Portland E6
Poseyville I2
Princeton H3
Redkey E6
Remington D3
Rensselaer D3
Richmond F6
Ridgeville E6
Rising Sun G6
Rochester D4
Rockport I3
Rockville F3
Rosedale F3
Rushville F5
Russiaville D4
Salem H5
Seymour G5
Shelburn G3
Shelbyville F5
Sheridan E5
Shirley E6
South Bend C4
Spencer G3
Spurgeon H3
Sullivan G3
Sunman G6
Swayzee D5
Tell City I4
Tennyson I3
Terre Haute F3
Thorntown E4
Tipton E5
Trafalgar F5
Union City E6
Valparaiso C3
Veedersburg E3
Vernon G5
Vevay G6
Vincennes H3
Wabash D5
Wadesville I2
Wakarusa C5
Warren D5
Warsaw C5
Washington H3
West Baden H4
Westport G5
Whiteland F5
Whiting C3
Wilkinson F5
Williamsburg F6
Winamac D4
Winchester E6
Winslow H3

Nickname: The Hoosier State
Motto: Crossroads of America
Capital: Indianapolis
Number of towns: 206
Number of issuing charters: 409
Number of small size issuers: 224

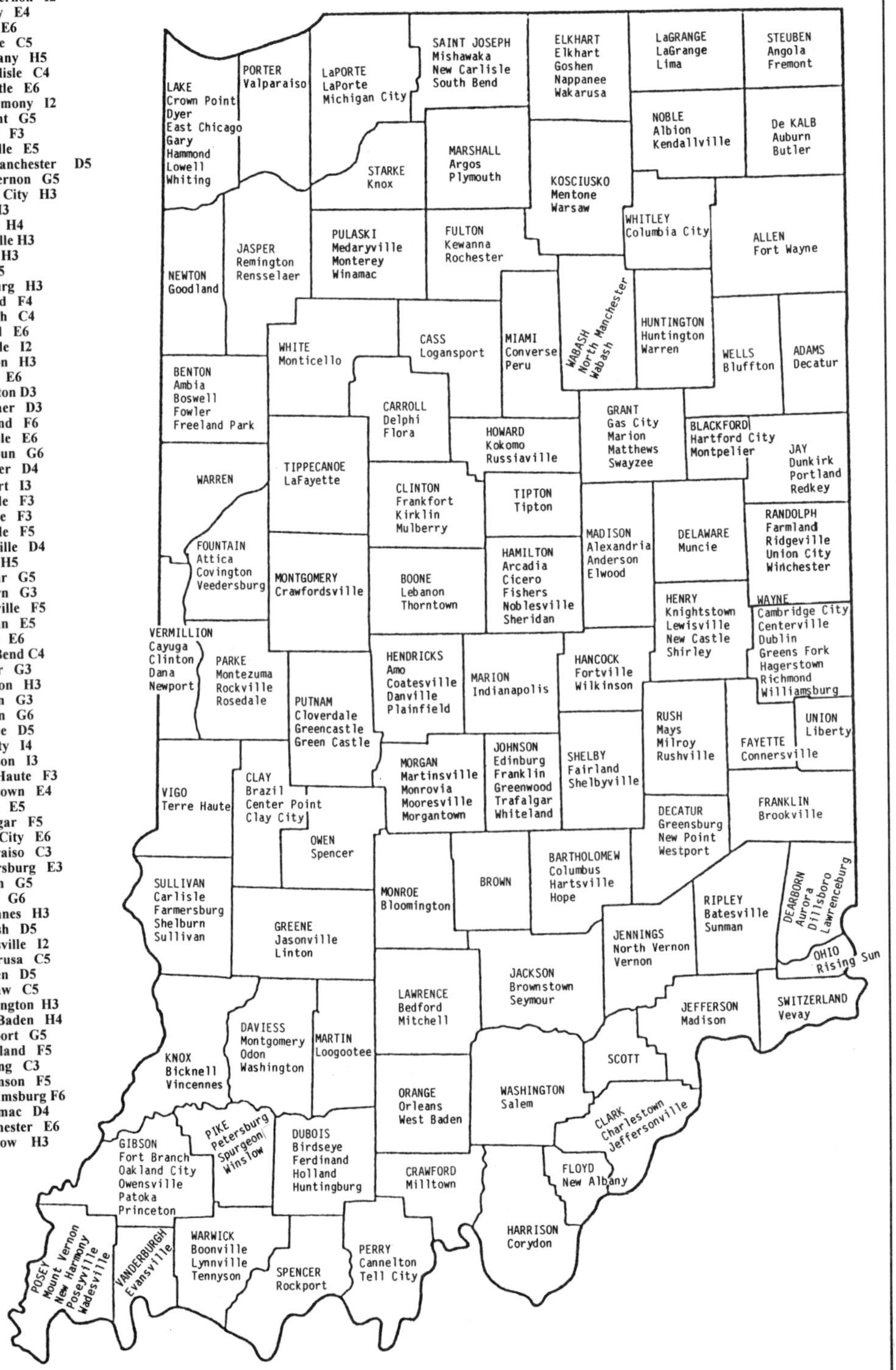

****
8912 Noble
ALBION NB, ALBION
{{ 2 L 3 S }}
Chartered 10/07
1902 Red Seal <$VALUE
4x10 1-375 <$1000
1902 Date Back
4x10 1-950 <$500
1902 Plain Back
4x10 951-2863 <$500
1929 Small Size
10 Type 1 1-484 <$400
10 Type 2 1-309 <$400
Total Issue $161,650
Out in 1935 $10,000
Large out 1935 $490
****
4835 Madison
ALEXANDRIA NB, ALEXANDRIA
{{ 1 L }}
Chartered 1/6/93
Liquidated 1/22/98
Brown Back <$VALUE
3x10-20 1-962 <$1250
Total Issue $48,100
Out in 1910 $680
****
9510 Benton
FNB OF AMBIA
{{ 1 L }}
Organized 7/30/09
Receivership 4/5/21
1902 Date Back <$VALUE
4x10 1-2425* <$850
1902 Plain Back
4x10 2576-4193* <$850
* 2426-2575 not marked
Total Issue $167,720
Out at close $24,600
****
8154 Hendricks
FNB OF AMO
{{ 3 L 2 S }}
Chartered 3/06
Liquidated 1/18/32
1902 Red Seal <$VALUE
3x10-20 1-380 <$1000
1902 Date Back
4x5 1-1250 <$400
3x10-20 1-1680 <$400
1902 Plain Back
4x5 1251-8200 <$400
3x10-20 1681-3413 <$400
1929 Small Size
5 Type 1 1-620 <$400
10 Type 1 1-311 <$400
20 Type 1 1-77 <$400
Total Issue $400,420
Out at close $25,000
Large out at close $2,410
****
44 Madison
FNB OF ANDERSON
{{ UNREPORTED }}
Organized 7/31/63
Receivership 11/23/73
Original Series <$VALUE
3x1-2 1-1900 <$1500/$2000
4x5 1-2600 <$1500
3x10-20 1-170 <$2000/$2500
Total Issue $70,000
Out in 1915 $725
****
2346 Madison
MADISON COUNTY NB OF ANDERSON
{{ 1 L }}
Chartered 1/15/77
Liquidated 3/25/84
Series 1875 <$VALUE
4x5 1-4765 <$1500
Total Issue $95,300
Out in 1910 $565
****
4685 Madison
N EXCHANGE B OF ANDERSON
{{ 9 L 1 S }}
Chartered 1892
Liquidated 10/6/30
Brown Back <$VALUE
4x5 1-4950 <$600
3x10-20 1-1100 <$600
1882 Date Back
4x5 1-1604 <$600
3x10-20 1-1277 <$600
1902 Date Back
4x5 1-4750 <$300
3x10-20 1-3500 <$300
1902 Plain Back
4x5 4751-24787 <$300
3x10-20 3501-14361 <$300
1929 Small Size
5 Type 1 1-114* <$600
10 Type 1 1-27# <$600
20 Type 1 1-35^ <$600
* C000114A-F000114 canceled
# E000027A-F000027A canceled
^ B000035A-F000035A canceled
Total Issue $1,472,820
Out at close $24,855
Large out at close $15,755
****
10290 Madison
PEOPLES STATE NB OF ANDERSON
{{ U + 7 L }}
Chartered 11/26/12
Liquidated 3/16/16
1902 Date Back <$VALUE
4x5 1-3585 <$300
3x10-20 1-2900 <$300
Total Issue $216,700
Out in 1916 $63,680
****
7023 Steuben
FNB OF ANGOLA
{{ 4 L 3 S }}
Chartered 10/03
Liquidated 5/15/31
1902 Red Seal <$VALUE
3x10-20 1-1060 <$600
1902 Date Back
3x10-20 1-3600* <$350
1902 Plain Back
3x10-20 3841-11189* <$350
*3601-3840 not marked
1929 Small Size
10 Type 1 1-705 <$250
20 Type 1 1-188 <$250
Total Issue $677,310
Out at close $50,000
Large out at close $6,150
****
9488 Hamilton
FNB OF ARCADIA
{{ 2 L }}
Organized 7/8/09
Receivership 7/3/28
1902 Date Back <$VALUE
3x10-20 1-2060 <$600
1902 Plain Back
3x10-20 2061-5184 <$600
Total Issue $259,200
Out at close $25,000
****
9726 Marshall
FNB OF ARGOS
{{ 2 L }}
Chartered 4/10
Liquidated 8/26/27
1902 Date Back <$VALUE
3x10-20 1-1770 <$600
1902 Plain Back
3x10-20 1771-4652 <$600
Total Issue $232,600
Out at close $25,000
****
Central NB of Attica
Central NB & TC of Attica
SEE Ch 3755
Citizens NB of Attica
****
3755 Fountain
CITIZENS NB OF ATTICA
Organized 6/7/87
2nd title:Central NB 6/7/07
3rd title:Central NB & TC 1/25/29
FIRST TITLE {{ 2 L }}
Brown Back <$VALUE
3x10-20 1-2434 <$400
1902 Red Seal
3x10-20 1-800 <$500
1902 Date Back
3x10-20 1-3900 <$250
SECOND TITLE {{ 8 L }}
1902 Plain Back
3x10-20 3901-18449 <$150
THIRD TITLE {{ 15 S }}
1929 Small Size
10 Type 1 1-2118 <$100
20 Type 1 1-609 <$100
Total Issue $1,284,310
Out in 1935 $50,000
Large out 1935 $6,470
****
577 Fountain
FNB OF ATTICA
{{ UNREPORTED }}
Chartered 1864
Liquidated 10/28/84
Original Series <$VALUE
3x1-2 1-1920 <$1000/$1500
4x5 1-5850 <$1000
3x10-20 1-500 <$1250/$1500
Series 1875
4x5 1-5580 <$1000
Total Issue $263,200
Out in 1910 $1,716
****
6509 De Kalb
CITY NB OF AUBURN
{{ 5 L 8 S }}
Chartered 11/02
1902 Red Seal <$VALUE
3x10-20 1-720 <$600
1902 Date Back
3x10-20 1-2150 <$300
1902 Plain Back
3x10-20 2151-7736 <$300
1929 Small Size
10 Type 1 1-1311 <$150
20 Type 1 1-367 <$150
Total Issue $545,500
Out in 1935 $30,000
Large out 1935 $1,810
****
2238 De Kalb
FNB OF AUBURN
{{ 2 L }}
Chartered 3/25/75
Liquidated 10/23/99
Original Series <$VALUE
4x5 1-2250 <$750
Series 1875
4x5 1-3783 <$750
Brown Back
3x10-20 1-311 <$750
Total Issue $136,210
Out in 1910 $1,210
****
2963 Dearborn
AURORA NB, AURORA
{{ 1 L }}
Organized 5/26/83
Receivership 11/4/07
Brown Back <$VALUE
4x5 1-2499 <$1000
3x10-20 1-2197 <$1000
1902 Red Seal
4x5 1-790 <$1000
3x10-20 1-572 <$1000
Total Issue $204,230
Out in 1916 $2,185
****
699 Dearborn
FNB OF AURORA
{{ 22 L 18 S }}
Chartered 1865
Original Series <$VALUE
3x1-2 1-12000 <$400/$1000
4x5 1-5000 <$400
3x10-20 1-2420 <$750/$1250
50-100 1-378 <$4000
Series 1875
3x1-2 1-2000 <$400/$1000
4x5 1-3975 <$400
3x10-20 1-2252 <$750/$1250
50-100 1-780 <$4000
Brown Back
4x5 1-20198 <$200
3x10-20 1-8766 <$200/$250
50-100 1-1076 <$1250/$1500
1902 Red Seal
4x5 1-7150 <$200
3x10-20 1-3540 <$200/$250
50-100 1-200 <$2250/$2500
1902 Date Back
4x5 1-5000 <$100
3x10-20 1-4100 <$100
50-100 1-600 <$400/$500
1902 Plain Back
4x5 5001-15210 <$100
3x10-20 4101-10737 <$100
1929 Small Size
5 Type 1 1-3628 <$70
10 Type 1 1-1688 <$70
20 Type 1 1-484 <$80
5 Type 2 1-3460 <$100
10 Type 2 1-1840 <$100
20 Type 2 1-648 <$100
Total Issue $3,258,370
Out in 1935 $100,000
Large out 1935 $13,950
****
7824 Ripley
FNB OF BATESVILLE
{{ 3 L 11 S }}
Chartered 7/05
1902 Red Seal <$VALUE
4x5 1-925 <$750
3x10-20 1-740 <$750
1902 Date Back
4x5 1-2000 <$375
3x10-20 1-1350 <$375
1902 Plain Back
4x5 2001-6796 <$375
3x10-20 1351-4191 <$375
1929 Small Size
5 Type 1 1-988 <$125
10 Type 1 1-806 <$125
20 Type 1 1-226 <$125
5 Type 2 1-1346 <$150
10 Type 2 1-662 <$150
20 Type 2 1-191 <$150
Total Issue $523,260
Out in 1935 $30,000
Large out 1935 $1,820
****
1892 Lawrence
BEDFORD NB, BEDFORD
{{ 1 L }}
Chartered 10/17/71
Liquidated 7/21/79
Original Series <$VALUE
3x1-2 1-3000 <$650/$1250
4x5 1-4500 <$750
3x10-20 1-400 <$1000/$1500
Series 1875
4x5 1-4090 <$750
Total Issue $206,800
Out in 1910 $1,037
****
5187 Lawrence
BEDFORD NB, BEDFORD
{{ 9 L 24 S }}
Chartered 4/21/99
Brown Back <$VALUE
4x5 1-2550 <$300
3x10-20 1-1210 <$300
1882 Date Back
4x5 1-6450* <$275
3x10-20 1-4860** <$275
1882 Value Back
4x5 6851-9146* <$300
3x10-20 5181-6466** <$300
* 6451-6850 not marked
** 4861-5180 not marked
1902 Plain Back
4x5 1-12784 <$150
3x10-20 1-9268 <$150
1929 Small Size
5 Type 1 1-4016 <$65
10 Type 1 1-1862 <$65
20 Type 1 1-528 <$75
5 Type 2 1-4318 <$65
10 Type 2 1-2265 <$65
20 Type 2 1-675 <$85
Total Issue $1,690,100
Out in 1935 $100,000
Large out 1935 $5,375
****
5173 Lawrence
CITIZENS NB OF BEDFORD
{{ 8 L 15 S }}
Chartered 1/25/99
Brown Back <$VALUE
4x5 1-3150 <$300
3x10-20 1-2440 <$300
1882 Date Back
4x5 1-7650 <$300
3x10-20 1-5220 <$300
1882 Value Back
4x5 7651-10310 <$300
3x10-20 5221-6571 <$300
1902 Plain Back
4x5 1-10455 <$150
3x10-20 1-7164 <$150
1929 Small Size
5 Type 1 1-832 <$65
10 Type 1 1-1434 <$65
20 Type 1 1-624 <$75
5 Type 2 1-2870 <$65
10 Type 2 1-1048 <$65
20 Type 2 1-175 <$75
Total Issue $1,501,260
Out in 1935 $100,000
Large out 1935 $4,750
****
3013 Lawrence
INDIANA NB OF BEDFORD
{{ UNREPORTED }}
Chartered 1883
Liquidated 8/25/83
Brown Back <$VALUE
3x10-20 1-225 <$1500
Total Issue $11,250
All notes reportedly redeemed
****
13788 Lawrence
STONE CITY NB OF BEDFORD
{{ 9 S }}
Chartered 9/33
1929 Small Size <$VALUE
5 Type 2 1-9710 <$150
10 Type 2 1-5060 <$150
20 Type 2 1-1575 <$150
Total Issue $130,650
Out in 1935 $85,050
****
7155 Knox
FNB OF BICKNELL
{{ 3 L 8 S }}
Organized 1/7/04
1902 Red Seal <$VALUE
3x10-20 1-1500 <$1000
1902 Date Back
3x10-20 1-2200 <$500
1902 Plain Back
3x10-20 2201-6936 <$500
1929 Small Size
10 Type 1 1-616 <$165
20 Type 1 1-204 <$165
10 Type 2 1-653 <$200
20 Type 2 1-168 <$200
Total Issue $493,130
Out in 1935 $30,000
Large out 1935 $2,740
****
8835 Dubois
BIRDSEYE NB, BIRDSEYE
{{ 4 L 6 S }}
Chartered 8/07
1902 Red Seal <$VALUE
3x10-20 1-300 <$1000
1902 Date Back
3x10-20 1-1870 <$500
1902 Plain Back
3x10-20 1871-5094 <$500
1929 Small Size
10 Type 1 1-536 <$325
20 Type 1 1-160 <$325
10 Type 2 1-737 <$350
20 Type 2 1-124 <$350
Total Issue $330,910
Out in 1935 $25,000
Large out 1935 $1,560
****
8415 Monroe
BLOOMINGTON NB, BLOOMINGTON
{{ 8 L 20 S }}
Organized 10/15/06
1902 Red Seal <$VALUE
4x5 1-1500 <$500
3x10-20 1-1900 <$500
1902 Date Back
4x5 1-3580 <$200
3x10-20 1-7368 <$200
1902 Plain Back
4x5 3581-15357 <$200
3x10-20 7369-18863 <$200
1929 Small Size
5 Type 1 1-3880 <$75
10 Type 1 1-1812 <$75
20 Type 1 1-516 <$75
5 Type 2 1-4360 <$85
10 Type 2 1-2552 <$85
20 Type 2 1-690 <$100
Total Issue $1,723,450
Out in 1935 $100,000
Large out 1935 $4,490
****
1888 Monroe
FNB OF BLOOMINGTON
{{ 9 L 14 S }}
Chartered 10/7/71
Original Series <$VALUE
3x1-2 1-3000 <$500/$1000
4x5 1-4000 <$500
3x10-20 1-1480 <$750/$1250
Series 1875
3x1-2 1-1900 <$500/$1000
4x5 1-7960 <$500
3x10-20 1-1909 <$750/$1250
Brown Back
4x5 1-5475 <$350
3x10-20 1-1320 <$350
1882 Date Back
4x5 1-526 <$350
3x10-20 1-309 <$350
1902 Date Back
4x5 1-1650* <$175
3x10-20 1-1320** <$175
1902 Plain Back
4x5 1901-15585* <$175
3x10-20 1521-10053** <$175
* 1651-1900 not marked
** 1321-1520 not marked
1929 Small Size
5 Type 1 1-4830 <$100
10 Type 1 1-2210 <$100
20 Type 1 1-652 <$100
5 Type 2 1-1762 <$125
10 Type 2 1-1030 <$125
20 Type 2 1-183 <$150
Total Issue $1,827,480
Out in 1935 $30,000
Large out 1935 $6,430
****
13317 Wells
FNB IN BLUFFTON
{{ U + 8 S }}
Chartered 5/9/29
Closed 9/17/31
1929 Small Size <$VALUE
5 Type 1 1-2367 <$150
10 Type 1 1-1127 <$150
20 Type 1 1-346 <$150
Total Issue $180,150
Out at close $100,000
Ch 13305 assumed circulation
****
58 Wells
FNB OF BLUFFTON
{{ UNREPORTED }}
Chartered 8/11/63
Liquidated 12/5/67
Original Series <$VALUE
4x5 1-1250 <$1500
4x10 1-500 <$1750
Total Issue $45,000
Out in 1910 $390
****
Old-FNB in Bluffton
SEE Ch 13305
Old NB of Bluffton
****
13305 Wells
OLD NB OF BLUFFTON
Chartered 3/29
2nd title: Old-FNB in Bluffton 9/17/31
FIRST TITLE {{ 5 S }}
1929 Small Size <$VALUE
5 Type 1 1-2888 <$125
10 Type 1 1-1332 <$125
20 Type 1 1-416 <$125
SECOND TITLE {{ U + 10 S }}
1929 Small Size
5 Type 1 1-368 <$100
10 Type 1 1-180 <$100
20 Type 1 1-54 <$100
5 Type 2 1-2460 <$110
10 Type 2 1-1390 <$110
20 Type 2 1-280 <$125
Total Issue $276,600
Out in 1935 $100,000
Outstanding includes Ch 13317
****
2207 Warrick
BOONVILLE NB, BOONVILLE
{{ 4 L }}
Chartered 11/18/74
Liquidated 9/16/14
Original Series <$VALUE
4x5 1-3250 <$600
Series 1875
4x5 1-10322 <$600
Brown Back
4x5 1-6590 <$500
50-100 1-655 <$1500/$1750
1882 Date Back
4x5 1-2032 <$450
50-100 1-260 <$1250/$1500
3x50-100 1-88 <$1250/$1500
Total Issue $603,130
Out in 1914 $48,300
****
10613 Warrick
CITY NB OF BOONVILLE
Organized 7/28/14
Liquidated 6/25/35
2nd title: FNB of Boonville, 9/29/28
FIRST TITLE {{ 4 L }}
1902 Date Back <$VALUE
3x10-20 1-2500 <$350
1902 Plain Back
3x10-20 2501-13255 <$350
SECOND TITLE {{ 0 L 14 S }}
1902 Plain Back
3x10-20 1-728 <$600
1929 Small Size
10 Type 1 1-2588 <$85
20 Type 1 1-776 <$85
10 Type 2 1-1199 <$100
20 Type 2 1-217 <$125
Total Issue $963,880
Out in 1935 $112,500
Large out 1935 $5,980
Outstanding includes 9266
****

<$VALUEs are for notes in FINE condition. Value changes by approximately 25% for a change of one full grade.

****
9266 Warrick
FARMERS & MERCHANTS NB OF BOONVILLE
{{ 4 L }}
Chartered 11/08
Closed 9/29/28
1902 Date Back <$VALUE
4x5 1-9930 <$350
3x10-20 1-4500* <$350
1902 Plain Back
3x10-20 4741-11864* <$350
* 4501-4740 not marked
Total Issue $791,800
Out at close $75,000
Ch 10613 assumed circulation
****
FNB of Boonville
SEE Ch 10613
City NB of Boonville
****
5476 Benton
FNB OF BOSWELL
{{ 1 L 2 S }}
Chartered 6/30/00
Receivership 10/3/33
Brown Back <$VALUE
3x10-20 1-950 <$1250
1882 Date Back
3x10-20 1-184 <$1250
1902 Plain Back
3x10-20 1-683 <$1000
1929 Small Size
10 Type 1 1-183 <$650
20 Type 1 1-28 <$650
Total Issue $105,190
Out at close $6,250
Large out at close $230
****
8620 Clay
CITIZENS NB OF BRAZIL
{{ 8 L 12 S }}
Organized 3/4/07
Receivership 10/2/33
1902 Red Seal <$VALUE
4x5 1-2085 <$500
3x10-20 1-1666 <$500
1902 Date Back
4x5 1-7500* <$250
3x10-20 1-5720 <$250
1902 Plain Back
4x5 7901-24055* <$250
3x10-20 5721-16465 <$250
* 7501-7900 not marked
1929 Small Size
5 Type 1 1-3296 <$100
10 Type 1 1-1606 <$100
20 Type 1 1-376 <$110
5 Type 2 1-200 <$125
10 Type 2 1-147 <$150
Total Issue $1,672,180
Out at close $100,000
Large out at close $5,940
****
3583 Clay
FNB OF BRAZIL
{{ 8 L 10 S }}
Chartered 1886
Liquidated 6/9/31
Brown Back <$VALUE
4x5 1-3283 <$450
3x10-20 1-2179 <$450
1902 Red Seal
4x5 1-1650 <$500
3x10-20 1-840 <$500
1902 Date Back
4x5 1-7000* <$225
3x10-20 1-5700** <$225
1902 Plain Back
4x5 7401-24006* <$225
3x10-20 6021-17293** <$225
* 7001-7400 not marked
** 5701-6020 not marked
1929 Small Size
5 Type 1 1-2158 <$150
10 Type 1 1-1068 <$150
20 Type 1 1-240 <$150
Total Issue $1,751,520
Out at close $100,000
Large out at close $11,690
****
5267 Clay
RIDDELL NB OF BRAZIL
{{ 7 L U + 6 S }}
Chartered 3/23/00
Brown Back <$VALUE
3x10-20 1-2420 <$350
50-100 1-350 <$1250/$1500
1882 Date Back
3x10-20 1-2700* <$350
50-100 1-100 <$1250/$1500
1882 Value Back
3x10-20 2901-3967* <$350
* 2701-2900 not marked

1902 Plain Back
4x5 1-19061 <$250
1929 Small Size
5 Type 1 1-7730 <$150
5 Type 2 1-10162 <$150
Total Issue $1,050,780
Out in 1935 $50,000
Large out 1935 $2,705
****
1619 Franklin
BROOKVILLE NB, BROOKVILLE
{{ 1 L }}
Chartered 1865
Liquidated 2/18/79
Original Series <$VALUE
4x5 1-4600 <$850
3x10-20 1-1460<$1250/$1500
Series 1875
3x10-20 1-762 <$1250/$1500
Total Issue $203,100
Out in 1910 $1,515
****
5629 Franklin
FRANKLIN COUNTY NB OF BROOKVILLE
{{ 6 L 10 S }}
Chartered 11/22/00
Brown Back <$VALUE
3x10-20 1-2060 <$450
1882 Date Back
3x10-20 1-3300 <$400
1882 Value Back
3x10-20 3301-5020 <$450
1902 Plain Back
3x10-20 1-4838 <$300
1929 Small Size
10 Type 1 1-1162 <$125
20 Type 1 1-334 <$125
10 Type 2 1-717 <$150
20 Type 2 1-215 <$150
Total Issue $717,170
Out in 1935 $50,000
Large out 1935 $3,470
****
7805 Franklin
N BROOKVILLE B, BROOKVILLE
{{ 9 L 18 S }}
Chartered 6/05
1902 Red Seal <$VALUE
3x10-20 1-2100 <$500
1902 Date Back
3x10-20 1-4440 <$250
1902 Plain Back
3x10-20 4441-18282 <$250
1929 Small Size
10 Type 1 1-2490 <$100
20 Type 1 1-620 <$100
10 Type 2 1-1575 <$110
20 Type 2 1-667 <$110
Total Issue $1,271,990
Out in 1935 $100,000
Large out 1935 $5,210
****
9143 Jackson
FNB OF BROWNSTOWN
{{ 5 L 8 S }}
Organized 3/14/08
1902 Date Back <$VALUE
4x5 1-3112* <$300
3x10-20 1-2330** <$300
1902 Plain Back
4x5 3363-10835* <$300
3x10-20 2471-7383** <$300
* 3113-3362 not marked
** 2331-2470 not marked
1929 Small Size
5 Type 1 1-1866 <$150
10 Type 1 1-952 <$150
20 Type 1 1-266 <$175
5 Type 2 1-1918 <$175
10 Type 2 1-907 <$175
20 Type 2 1-255 <$200
Total Issue $754,630
Out in 1935 $50,000
Large out 1935 $2,210
****
9286 De Kalb
FNB OF BUTLER
{{ 2 L 2 S }}
Chartered 12/08
Liquidated 2/28/31
1902 Date Back <$VALUE
3x10-20 1-2160 <$750
1902 Plain Back
3x10-20 2161-5780 <$750
1929 Small Size
10 Type 1 1-287 <$600
20 Type 1 1-93 <$600
Total Issue $317,380
Out at close $25,000
Large out at close $4,170
****

****
70 Wayne
FNB OF CAMBRIDGE CITY*
Chartered 8/63
Liquidated 6/15/82
*Reorganized as Ch 2734 which retook Ch 70 6/12/13
2nd title: FNB & TC 4/21/28
Receivership 10/3/33
FIRST TITLE {{ 3 L }}
Original Series <$VALUE
3x1-2 1-2000 <$750/$1500
4x5 1-3000 <$750
3x10-20 1-2000<$1000/$1500
Series 1875
3x10-20 1-862 <$1000/$1500
1902 Date Back
3x50-100 1-280 <$650/$750
1902 Plain Back
3x50-100 281-337<$650/$750
SECOND TITLE {{ 0 L 3 S }}
1902 Plain Back
3x50-100 1-30 <$650/$750
1929 Small Size
50 Type 1 1-138 <$400
100 Type 1 1-19 <$500
Total Issue $357,100
Out at close $49,990
Large out at close $7,220
Outstanding includes Ch 8804 and Ch 2734
****
2734 Wayne
FNB OF CAMBRIDGE CITY
{{ 1 L }}
Organized 5/11/82
RETOOK Ch 70 6/12/13
Brown Back <$VALUE
50-100 1-876 <$2500
1902 Red Seal
50-100 1-383 <$3500
1902 Date Back
50-100 1-300 <$1000/$1250
Total Issue $233,850
Out in 1913 $50,000
****
8871 Wayne
WAYNE NB OF CAMBRIDGE CITY
{{ 3 L }}
Chartered 9/07
Liquidated 2/3/19
1902 Red Seal <$VALUE
3x10-20 1-1450 <$1000
1902 Date Back
3x10-20 1-3340 <$450
1902 Plain Back
3x10-20 3341-4276 <$450
Total Issue $286,300
Out at close $50,000
****
9682 Perry
CANNELTON NB, CANNELTON
Organized 9/30/09
2nd title:F Cannelton NB 2/8/32
FIRST TITLE {{ 2 L 6 S }}
1902 Date Back <$VALUE
3x10-20 1-1710 <$400
1902 Plain Back
3x10-20 1711-5107 <$400
1929 Small Size
10 Type 1 1-936 <$175
20 Type 1 1-262 <$175
SECOND TITLE {{ 6 S }}
1929 Small Size
10 Type 1 1-326 <$150
20 Type 1 1-104 <$150
10 Type 2 1-1846 <$175
20 Type 2 1-403 <$175
Total Issue $401,510
Out in 1935 $75,000
Large out 1935 $2,890
Outstanding includes Ch 9401
****
F Cannelton NB, Cannelton
SEE Ch 9682
Cannelton NB, Cannelton
****
9401 Perry
FNB OF CANNELTON
{{ 3 L 3 S }}
Chartered 5/09
Liquidated 1/13/32
1902 Date Back <$VALUE
3x10-20 1-2030 <$400
1902 Plain Back
3x10-20 2031-5427 <$400
1929 Small Size
10 Type 1 1-424 <$250
20 Type 1 1-119 <$250
Total Issue $311,070
Out at close $25,000
Large out at close $3,290
Ch 9682 assumed circulation
****

****
8805 Sullivan
FNB OF CARLISLE
{{ 3 L }}
Chartered 7/07
Liquidated 7/11/27
1902 Red Seal <$VALUE
4x5 1-750 <$850
3x10-20 1-600 <$850
1902 Date Back
4x5 1-2450 <$400
3x10-20 1-1900 <$400
1902 Plain Back
4x5 2451-6535 <$400
3x10-20 1901-4204 <$400
Total Issue $385,900
Out in 1924 $35,000
****
9189 Vermillion
FNB OF CAYUGA
{{ 3 L 5 S }}
Organized 6/29/08
Receivership 10/3/33
1902 Date Back <$VALUE
3x10-20 1-2550 <$500
1902 Plain Back
3x10-20 2551-6377 <$500
1929 Small Size
10 Type 1 1-597 <$275
20 Type 1 1-151 <$300
Total Issue $372,790
Out at close $25,000
Large out at close $1,880
****
9250 Clay
FNB OF CENTER POINT
{{ 7 L 8 S }}
Chartered 10/08
1902 Date Back <$VALUE
3x10-20 1-2350 <$300
1902 Plain Back
3x10-20 2351-5981 <$300
1929 Small Size
10 Type 1 1-656 <$175
20 Type 1 1-176 <$175
10 Type 2 1-529 <$200
20 Type 2 1-98 <$200
Total Issue $366,780
Out in 1935 $25,000
Large out 1935 $1,210
****
37 Wayne
FNB OF CENTERVILLE
{{ 7 L }}
Chartered 7/63
Liquidated 5/18/82
Succeeded by Ch 2696
Original Series <$VALUE
3x1-2 1-6500 <$650/$1500
4x5 1-4250 <$750
3x10-20 1-1400<$1000/$1500
Series 1875
4x5 1-1225 <$750
3x10-20 1-868 <$1000/$1500
Total Issue $255,400
Out in 1910 $2,125
****
2696 Wayne
FNB OF CENTERVILLE
{{ UNREPORTED }}
Chartered 5/18/82
Liquidated 10/3/85
Brown Back <$VALUE
50-100 1-356 <$3000
Total Issue $53,400
Out in 1910 $300
****
6952 Clark
FNB OF CHARLESTOWN
{{ 4 L 3 S }}
Chartered 9/03
Liquidated 12/12/33
1902 Red Seal <$VALUE
3x10-20 1-1250 <$750
1902 Date Back
3x10-20 1-1650 <$350
1902 Plain Back
3x10-20 1651-5525 <$350
1929 Small Size
10 Type 1 1-514 <$350
20 Type 1 1-148 <$350
Total Issue $387,350
Out at close $25,000
Large out at close $1,600
****
10720 Hamilton
CITIZENS NB OF CICERO
{{ 8 L 5 S }}
Chartered 4/15
1902 Date Back <$VALUE
3x10-20 1-600 <$225
1902 Plain Back
3x10-20 601-5298 <$225

1929 Small Size
10 Type 1 1-726 <$200
20 Type 1 1-230 <$200
10 Type 2 1-439 <$225
20 Type 2 1-35 <$250
Total Issue $341,150
Out in 1935 $30,000
Large out 1935 $1,630
****
9540 Clay
FNB OF CLAY CITY
{{ 3 L 4 S }}
Chartered 9/09
Liquidated 3/22/34
1902 Date Back <$VALUE
4x5 1-1925 <$450
3x10-20 1-1420 <$450
1902 Plain Back
4x5 1926-6055 <$450
3x10-20 1421-3819 <$450
1929 Small Size
5 Type 1 1-732 <$250
10 Type 1 1-436 <$250
20 Type 1 1-128 <$300
5 Type 2 1-138 <$300
10 Type 2 1-73 <$325
20 Type 2 1-15 <$350
Total Issue $377,250
Out at close $25,000
Large out at close $1,500
****
6480 Vermillion
FNB OF CLINTON
{{ 4 L 7 S }}
Organized 9/25/02
Receivership 10/3/33
1902 Red Seal <$VALUE
4x5 1-450 <$850
3x10-20 1-360 <$850
1902 Date Back
4x5 1-650 <$400
3x10-20 1-540 <$400
1902 Plain Back
4x5 651-5940 <$400
3x10-20 541-3805 <$400
1929 Small Size
5 Type 1 1-1017 <$175
10 Type 1 1-496 <$175
20 Type 1 1-134 <$200
Total Issue $412,400
Out at close $30,000
Large out at close $2,500
****
10465 Putnam
FNB OF CLOVERDALE
{{ 1 L 1 S }}
Chartered 12/13
1902 Date Back <$VALUE
3x10-20 1-400 <$1000
1902 Plain Back
3x10-20 401-1068 <$1000
1929 Small Size
10 Type 1 1-186 <$600
20 Type 1 1-46 <$600
Total Issue $70,080
Out in 1935 $6,250
Large out 1935 $190
****
8447 Hendricks
FNB OF COATESVILLE
{{ 3 L 6 S }}
Chartered 11/06
1902 Red Seal <$VALUE
4x10 1-869 <$850
1902 Date Back
4x10 1-2550* <$400
1902 Plain Back
4x10 2701-7826* <$400
* 2551-2700 not marked
1929 Small Size
10 Type 1 1-1034 <$200
10 Type 2 1-1395 <$200
Total Issue $423,790
Out in 1935 $25,000
Large out 1935 $1,160
****
7175 Whitley
COLUMBIA CITY NB, COLUMBIA CITY
{{ 1 L }}
Chartered 3/04
Liquidated 7/23/10
1902 Red Seal <$VALUE
4x5 1-1775 <$1000
3x10-20 1-1430 <$1000
1902 Date Back
4x5 1-865 <$750
3x10-20 1-258 <$750
Total Issue $137,200
Out in 1910 $43,850
****

****
7132 Whitley
FNB OF COLUMBIA CITY
{{ 6 L }}
Organized 2/2/04
Receivership 3/31/27
1902 Red Seal <$VALUE
4x5 1-1550 <$600
3x10-20 1-1358 <$600
1902 Date Back
4x5 1-6500 <$250
3x10-20 1-4700 <$250
1902 Plain Back
4x5 6501-18105 <$250
3x10-20 4701-12635 <$250
Total Issue $1,092,750
Out at close $94,200
****
1066 Bartholomew
FNB OF COLUMBUS
{{ 4 L 4 S }}
Chartered 1865
Original Series <$VALUE
4x5 1-1000 <$750
3x10-20 1-2550<$1000/$1500
Series 1875
4x5 1-1475 <$750
3x10-20 1-1648<$1000/$1500
Brown Back
50-100 1-1469 <$1750/$2000
1902 Red Seal
50-100 1-534 <$2250/$2500
1902 Date Back
50-100 1-500 <$750/$850
3x50-100 1-1140 <$750/$850
1902 Plain Back
3x50-100 1141-1235 <$750/$850
1929 Small Size
50 Type 1 1-220* <$400
100 Type 1 1-70** <$600
* 122-178 not issued
** 14-64 not issued
Total Issue $1,003,900
Out in 1935 $50,000
Large out 1935 $8,980
****
6265 Fayette
FAYETTE NB OF CONNERSVILLE
{{ 5 L }}
Chartered 5/02
Liquidated 12/31/18
1902 Red Seal <$VALUE
3x10-20 1-1500 <$600
1902 Date Back
3x10-20 1-6800 <$300
1902 Plain Back
3x10-20 6801-8101 <$300
Total Issue $480,050
Out at close $48,100
****
1034 Fayette
FNB OF CONNERSVILLE
{{ 16 L 8 S }}
Organized 2/13/65
Receivership 12/30/30
Original Series <$VALUE
4x5 1-7500 <$500
3x10-20 1-700 <$750/$1250
Series 1875
4x5 1-6530 <$500
3x10-20 1-300 <$750/$1250
Brown Back
4x5 1-6617 <$300
3x10-20 1-826 <$300/$350
1902 Red Seal
3x10-20 1-960 <$350
1902 Date Back
3x10-20 1-7300 <$125
1902 Plain Back
3x10-20 7301-31804 <$125
1929 Small Size
5 Type 1 1-1172 <$150
10 Type 1 1-2458 <$150
20 Type 1 1-638 <$150
Total Issue $2,401,640
Out at close $197,000
Large out at close $29,750
****
11671 Miami
FNB OF CONVERSE
{{ 4 S }}
Chartered 4/20
1929 Small Size <$VALUE
5 Type 1 1-578 <$250
10 Type 1 1-248 <$250
20 Type 1 1-76 <$250
5 Type 2 1-406 <$300
10 Type 2 1-255 <$300
20 Type 2 1-55 <$300
Total Issue $47,020
Out in 1935 $10,000
****

****
7760 Harrison
CORYDON NB, CORYDON
{{ 6 L }}
Organized 5/23/05
Receivership 3/8/22
1902 Red Seal <$VALUE
3x10-20 1-2770 <$600
1902 Date Back
3x10-20 1-9300 <$300
1902 Plain Back
3x10-20 9301-16176 <$300
Total Issue $947,300
Out at close $125,000
****
6625 Harrison
FNB OF CORYDON
{{ 2 L }}
Chartered 2/03
Liquidated 6/30/20
1902 Red Seal <$VALUE
3x10-20 1-1340 <$850
1902 Date Back
3x10-20 1-3340 <$450
1902 Plain Back
3x10-20 3341-4972 <$450
Total Issue $315,600
Out at close $50,000
****
9860 Fountain
FNB OF COVINGTON
{{ 4 L }}
Organized 9/9/10
Liquidated 9/23/27
1902 Date Back <$VALUE
3x10-20 1-3540 <$350
1902 Plain Back
3x10-20 3541-11102 <$350
Total Issue $555,100
Out at close $70,000
****
2533 Montgomery
CITIZENS NB OF
CRAWFORDSVILLE
{{ 14 L 12 S }}
Chartered 1881
Series 1875 <$VALUE
4x5 1-9547 <$500
3x10-20 1-209 <$750/$1250
Brown Back
50-100 1-1566 <$1250/$1500
1882 Date Back
4x5 1-4000 <$225
50-100 1-1000 <$1250/$1500
3x50-100 1-260<$1250/$1500
1882 Value Back
4x5 4001-8423 <$250
1902 Plain Back
4x5 1-7805 <$125
3x10-20 1-6193 <$125
1929 Small Size
5 Type 1 1-3642 <$85
10 Type 1 1-1614 <$85
20 Type 1 1-444 <$100
5 Type 2 1-322 <$110
10 Type 2 1-542 <$110
20 Type 2 1-190 <$125
Total Issue $1,555,710
Out in 1935 $75,000
Large out 1935 $5,800
****
7773 Montgomery
ELSTON NB OF
CRAWFORDSVILLE
{{ 10 L }}
Chartered 6/05
Liquidated 10/1/25
1902 Red Seal <$VALUE
3x10-20 1-3600 <$450
1902 Date Back
3x10-20 1-7900 <$175
1902 Plain Back
3x10-20 7901-18241 <$175
Total Issue $1,092,050
Out at close $100,000
****
571 Montgomery
FNB OF CRAWFORDSVILLE
{{ 12 L U + 16 S }}
Chartered 1864
Original Series <$VALUE
3x1-2 1-3820 <$500/$1000
4x5 1-3000 <$500
3x10-20 1-1900 <$750/$1250
Series 1875
4x5 1-3570 <$500
3x10-20 1-1530 <$750/$1250
Brown Back
4x5 1-6815 <$225
3x10-20 1-2064 <$225/$275
1902 Red Seal
4x5 1-3450 <$250
3x10-20 1-2070 <$250/$300
1902 Date Back
4x5 1-6050 <$100
3x10-20 1-4880 <$100
1902 Plain Back
4x5 6051-21138 <$100
3x10-20 4881-15071 <$100
1929 Small Size
5 Type 1 1-3362 <$75
10 Type 1 1-1832 <$75
20 Type 1 1-484 <$85
5 Type 2 1-2642 <$85
10 Type 2 1-1413 <$85
20 Type 2 1-274 <$90
Total Issue $2,211,990
Out in 1935 $100,000
Large out 1935 $6,985
****
2183 Lake
FNB OF CROWN POINT
{{ 6 L 4 S }}
Chartered 9/11/74
Original Series <$VALUE
4x5 1-2250 <$750
Series 1875
4x5 1-6826 <$750
Brown Back
3x10-20 1-3780 <$500
1882 Date Back
3x10-20 1-2533 <$500
1902 Date Back
3x50-100 1-829 <$650/$750
1902 Plain Back
3x50-100 830-1015
<$650/$750
1929 Small Size
50 Type 1 1-159 <$400
100 Type 1 1-23 <$500
Total Issue $812,420
Out in 1935 $25,000
Large out 1935 $8,180
****
5997 Vermillion
FNB OF DANA
{{ 2 L 6 S }}
Chartered 10/01
Brown Back <$VALUE
3x10-20 1-1400 <$750
1882 Date Back
3x10-20 1-2110 <$750
1882 Value Back
3x10-20 2111-3226 <$750
1902 Plain Back
3x10-20 1-2472 <$500
1929 Small Size
10 Type 1 1-648 <$200
20 Type 1 1-188 <$200
10 Type 2 1-467 <$225
20 Type 2 1-55 <$250
Total Issue $422,110
Out in 1935 $25,000
Large out 1935 $1,130
****
152 Hendricks
FNB OF DANVILLE
{{ 11 L 14 S }}
Chartered 12/63
Original Series <$VALUE
3x1-2 1-1900 <$400/$850
4x5 1-4300 <$400
3x10-20 1-1600 <$750/$1250
Series 1875
3x10-20 1-870 <$750/$1250
Brown Back
3x10-20 1-4636 <$300
1902 Red Seal
4x5 1-3000 <$350
50-100 1-1033 <$2250/$2500
1902 Date Back
4x5 1-4050 <$175
3x10-20 1-3880 <$175
50-100 1-400 <$400/$500
1902 Plain Back
4x5 4051-16970 <$175
3x10-20 3881-12637 <$175
1929 Small Size
5 Type 1 1-3303 <$100
10 Type 1 1-1954 <$100
20 Type 1 1-522 <$110
Total Issue $1,975,970
Out in 1935 $50,000
Large out 1935 $6,545
****
3028 Adams
DECATUR NB, DECATUR
Chartered 1883
Liquidated 11/19/30
2nd title: FNB of Decatur
3/18/03
FIRST TITLE {{ 0 L }}
Brown Back <$VALUE
4x5 1-5776 <$1000
3x10-20 1-259 <$1000
SECOND TITLE {{ 6 L 7 S }}
1902 Red Seal
4x5 1-1300 <$850
3x10-20 1-920 <$850
1902 Date Back
4x5 1-3550 <$350
3x10-20 1-2700 <$350
1902 Plain Back
4x5 3551-15055 <$350
3x10-20 2701-10613 <$350
1929 Small Size
5 Type 1 1-1354 <$225
10 Type 1 1-700 <$225
20 Type 1 1-199 <$225
Total Issue $1,138,720
Out at close $100,000
Large out at close $13,130
****
FNB of Decatur
SEE Ch 3028
Decatur NB, Decatur
****
6986 Carroll
CITIZENS NB OF DELPHI
{{ 5 L 5 S }}
Chartered 10/03
Liquidated 9/15/31
1902 Red Seal <$VALUE
3x10-20 1-5125 <$700
1902 Date Back
3x10-20 1-5200 <$300
1902 Plain Back
3x10-20 5201-15536 <$300
1929 Small Size
10 Type 1 1-1178 <$200
20 Type 1 1-288 <$200
Total Issue $1,138,290
Out at close $75,000
Large out at close $8,980
****
1949 Carroll
FNB OF DELPHI
{{ 2 L }}
Chartered 3/25/72
Receivership 7/20/77
Original Series <$VALUE
3x1-2 1-4680 <$750/$1500
4x5 1-3750 <$750
3x10-20 1-800 <$1000/$1500
Series 1875
4x5 1-235 <$750
3x10-20 1-2 <$1000/$1500
Total Issue $143,200
Out in 1915 $628
****
6882 Dearborn
FNB OF DILLSBORO
{{ 6 L 3 S }}
Chartered 7/03
Liquidated 8/21/31
1902 Red Seal <$VALUE
3x10-20 1-800 <$600
1902 Date Back
3x10-20 1-1450 <$300
1902 Plain Back
3x10-20 1451-4638 <$300
1929 Small Size
10 Type 1 1-353 <$350
20 Type 1 1-97 <$350
Total Issue $304,720
Out at close $25,000
Large out at close $4,040
****
8804 Wayne
FNB OF DUBLIN
{{ 3 L 3 S }}
Chartered 7/07
Liquidated 1/13/31
1902 Red Seal <$VALUE
3x10-20 1-188 <$1000
1902 Date Back
3x10-20 1-1970 <$500
1902 Plain Back
3x10-20 1971-5682 <$500
1929 Small Size
10 Type 1 1-242 <$400
20 Type 1 1-72 <$400
Total Issue $316,660
Out at close $25,000
Large out at close $4,030
Ch 2734 assumed circulation
****
4888 Jay
FNB OF DUNKIRK
{{ 1 L }}
Chartered 4/12/93
Liquidated 1/1/00
Brown Back <$VALUE
4x5 1-1478 <$1250
Total Issue $29,560
Out in 1910 $525
****
****
6909 Lake
FNB OF DYER
{{ 3 L 6 S }}
Chartered 8/03
1902 Red Seal <$VALUE
3x10-20 1-950 <$850
1902 Date Back
3x10-20 1-1890 <$400
1902 Plain Back
3x10-20 1891-5743 <$400
1929 Small Size
10 Type 1 1-572 <$200
20 Type 1 1-168 <$200
10 Type 2 1-753 <$225
20 Type 2 1-125 <$225
Total Issue $399,160
Out in 1935 $25,000
Large out 1935 $1,390
****
13531 Lake
FNB IN EAST CHICAGO
{{ U + 22 S }}
Organized 3/6/31
1929 Small Size <$VALUE
5 Type 1 1-3886 <$60
10 Type 1 1-2376 <$60
20 Type 1 1-662 <$60
5 Type 2 1-9482 <$60
10 Type 2 1-4445 <$60
20 Type 2 1-1115 <$60
Total Issue $452,740
Out in 1935 $171,700
****
7601 Lake
FNB OF EAST CHICAGO
Chartered 2/05
Liquidated 5/15/31
2nd title:FNB & TC of
East Chicago 8/1/28
FIRST TITLE {{ 8 L }}
1902 Red Seal <$VALUE
4x5 1-1960 <$400
3x10-20 1-1476 <$400
1902 Date Back
4x5 1-3900* <$175
3x10-20 1-2740** <$175
1902 Plain Back
4x5 4301-19792* <$175
3x10-20 3061-13820** <$175
* 3901-4300 not marked
** 2741-3060 not marked
SECOND TITLE {{ 3 L 7 S }}
1902 Plain Back
4x5 1-1387 <$200
4x10 1-590 <$200
3x10-20 1-809 <$200
1929 Small Size
5 Type 1 1-2062 <$150
10 Type 1 1-1029 <$150
20 Type 1 1-252 <$150
Total Issue $1,445,470
Out at close $100,000
Large out at close $12,400
****
10171 Lake
INDIANA HARBOR NB OF
EAST CHICAGO
{{ 2 L }}
Chartered 4/12
Liquidated 1/25/32
1902 Date Back <$VALUE
3x10-20 1-3440 <$500
1902 Plain Back
3x10-20 3441-4668 <$500
Total Issue $233,400
Out at close $1,010
****
13532 Lake
UNION NB OF INDIANA
HARBOR AT EAST CHICAGO
{{ U + 20 S }}
Organized 3/6/31
1929 Small Size <$VALUE
5 Type 1 1-2464 <$60
10 Type 1 1-3058 <$60
20 Type 1 1-678 <$70
5 Type 2 1-8932 <$60
10 Type 2 1-3059 <$60
20 Type 2 1-1114 <$75
Total Issue $436,290
Out in 1935 $171,000
****
12058 Lake
UNITED STATES NB OF
INDIANA HARBOR,
EAST CHICAGO
{{ 5 L 6 S }}
Chartered 12/21
Liquidated 5/15/31
1902 Plain Back <$VALUE
4x5 1-12385 <$400
3x10-20 1-9850 <$400
1929 Small Size
5 Type 1 1-2144 <$175
10 Type 1 1-1033 <$175
20 Type 1 1-322 <$175
Total Issue $905,140
Out at close $100,000
Large out at close $8,260
****
6905 Johnson
FARMERS NB OF EDINBURG
{{ 3 L 1 S }}
Chartered 7/03
Liquidated 9/16/30
1902 Red Seal <$VALUE
4x5 1-750 <$850
3x10-20 1-640 <$850
1902 Date Back
4x5 1-1525* <$400
3x10-20 1-1180 <$400
1902 Plain Back
4x5 1626-5830* <$400
3x10-20 1181-3754 <$400
* 1526-1625 not marked
1929 Small Size
5 Type 1 1-332 <$500
10 Type 1 1-153 <$500
20 Type 1 1-27 <$500
Total Issue $373,680
Out at close $25,000
Large out at close $3,710
****
2502 Elkhart
ELKHART NB, ELKHART
{{ 1 L }}
Chartered 1/12/81
Liquidated 9/5/99
Series 1875 <$VALUE
4x5 1-4595 <$1250
Total Issue $91,900
Out in 1910 $640
****
206 Elkhart
FNB OF ELKHART
{{ 10 L 50+ S }}
Chartered 1/64
Original Series <$VALUE
3x1-2 1-630 <$500/$1000
4x5 1-9000* <$500
* 4251-4500 not issued
Series 1875
4x5 1-6498 <$500
Brown Back
4x5 1-12606 <$250
3x10-20 1-769 <$250/$300
1902 Red Seal
50-100 1-1367 <$2250/$2500
1902 Date Back
50-100 1-800 <$400/$600
3x50-100 1-1370 <$400/$500
1902 Plain Back
3x50-100 1371-1778
<$400/$500
1929 Small Size
5 Type 1 1-3256 <$40
10 Type 1 1-1546 <$40
20 Type 1 1-388 <$50
5 Type 2 1-2310 <$40
10 Type 2 1-1383 <$40
20 Type 2 1-466 <$50
Total Issue $1,639,930
Out in 1935 $100,000
Large out 1935 $12,320
****
4841 Elkhart
INDIANA NB OF ELKHART
{{ UNREPORTED }}
Organized 1/7/93
Receivership 11/19/03
Brown Back <$VALUE
4x5 1-3949 <$1250
50-100 1-136 <$2500
Total Issue $99,380
Out in 1915 $1,060
****
4675 Madison
FNB OF ELWOOD
{{ 6 L 10 S }}
Organized 12/29/91
Brown Back <$VALUE
3x10-20 1-3520 <$500
1882 Date Back
3x10-20 1-1200 <$500
1902 Date Back
3x10-20 1-2100 <$300
1902 Plain Back
3x10-20 2101-9198 <$300
1929 Small Size
10 Type 1 1-1186 <$150
20 Type 1 1-314 <$150
10 Type 2 1-1322 <$175
20 Type 2 1-247 <$175
Total Issue $822,900
Out in 1934 $99,600
Large out 1935 $2,970
****
****
8832 Vanderburgh
BANKERS NB OF EVANSVILLE
{{ 3 L }}
Chartered 8/07
Liquidated 8/15/14
1902 Red Seal <$VALUE
4x5 1-4505 <$750
3x10-20 1-4198 <$750
1902 Date Back
4x5 1-13405 <$400
3x10-20 1-8362 <$400
Total Issue $986,200
Out at close $250,000
Ch 2188 assumed circulation
****
2188 Vanderburgh
CITIZENS NB OF EVANSVILLE
{{ 27 L 50+ S }}
Chartered 9/23/74
Original Series <$VALUE
4x5 1-2000 <$450
3x10-20 1-2350 <$750/$1250
Series 1875
4x5 1-250 <$450
3x10-20 1-7566 <$750/$1250
Brown Back
3x10-20 1-15000 <$175/$225
1882 Date Back
3x10-20 1-15641 <$175/$225
1902 Date Back
4x5 1-10000 <$60
3x10-20 1-10000 <$65
1902 Plain Back
4x5 10001-76785 <$60
3x10-20 10001-55720 <$65
1929 Small Size
5 Type 1 1-20704 <$15
10 Type 1 1-8972 <$20
20 Type 1 1-2188 <$30
5 Type 2 1-11792 <$15
10 Type 2 1-5590 <$20
20 Type 2 1-1199 <$30
Total Issue $7,955,390
Out in 1935 $50,000
Large out 1935 $27,805
Outstanding includes Ch 8832
****
6200 Vanderburgh
CITY NB OF EVANSVILLE
{{ 8 L }}
Chartered 4/02
Liquidated 3/7/22
1902 Red Seal <$VALUE
3x10-20 1-14200 <$400
1902 Date Back
3x10-20 1-24500 <$150
1902 Plain Back
3x10-20 24501-43878 <$150
Total Issue $2,903,900
Out at close $350,000
Ch 12132 assumed circulation
****
730 Vanderburgh
EVANSVILLE NB, EVANSVILLE
{{ 3 L }}
Chartered 1865
Liquidated 1/3/85
Original Series <$VALUE
3x1-2 1-10000 <$500/$1250
4x5 1-10525 <$500
3x10-20 1-8000 <$750/$1250
50-100 1-3312 <$4000
Series 1875
4x5 1-500 <$500
3x10-20 1-4000 <$750/$1250
50-100 1-4731 <$4000
Total Issue $2,076,950
Out in 1910 $14,341
****
28 Vanderburgh
FNB OF EVANSVILLE
{{ 2 L }}
Chartered 7/63
Liquidated 5/15/82
Original Series <$VALUE
4x5 1-8800 <$850
3x10-20 1-1240<$1000/$1500
50-100 1-500 <$4000
Series 1875
4x5 1-1500 <$850
3x10-20 1-6322<$1000/$1500
Total Issue $1,217,100
Out in 1910 $9,155
****

2692 Vanderburgh
FNB OF EVANSVILLE
{{ 2 L }}
Chartered 5/15/82
Liquidated 4/16/02
Brown Back <$VALUE
4x5 1-8500 <$600
3x10-20 1-8861 <$600
50-100 1-667 <$1250/$1500
Total Issue $713,100
Out in 1910 $6,125

1772 Vanderburgh
EAST CHESTER NB OF
MOUNT VERNON, NEW YORK
Chartered 1/18/71
Changed name and location
to GERMAN NB of EVANSVILLE,
INDIANA 1/11/73
Liquidated 12/24/90
FIRST TITLE (NY) {{ 4 L }}
Original Series <$VALUE
3x1-2 1-6000 <$500/$1000
4x5 1-3000 <$600
3x10-20 1-1600 <$750/$1250
50-100 1-300 <$3500
SECOND TITLE (IN) {{ 1 L }}
Original Series
4x5 1-3000 <$600
3x10-20 1-1800 <$750/$1250
Series 1875
4x5 1-6221 <$600
3x10-20 1-7581 <$750/$1250
Total Issue $868,470
Out in 1910 $4,011

8492 Vanderburgh
MERCANTILE NB OF
EVANSVILLE
{{ UNREPORTED }}
Chartered 1/07
Liquidated 7/30/10
1902 Red Seal <$VALUE
4x5 1-5000 <$1000
3x10-20 1-4000 <$1000
1902 Date Back
4x5 1-2460 <$650
3x10-20 1-2061 <$650
Total Issue $452,250
Out in 1910 $174,650

989 Vanderburgh
MERCHANTS NB OF
EVANSVILLE
{{ 3 L }}
Chartered 1865
Liquidated 2/6/85
Original Series <$VALUE
3x1-2 1-3380 <$500/$1000
4x5 1-13925 <$600
4x10 1-2750 <$750
3x20-50 1-900 <$1250/$4000
Series 1875
3x1-2 1-2500 <$500/$1000
4x5 1-3250 <$600
4x10 1-3000 <$750
3x20-50 1-910 <$1250/$4000
Total Issue $802,000
Out in 1910 $5,766

12132 Vanderburgh
N CITY B OF EVANSVILLE
{{ 10 L 50+ S }}
Chartered 3/22
1902 Plain Back <$VALUE
4x5 1-14838 <$125
4x5 15001-15072 <$125
3x10-20 1-15196 <$125
1929 Small Size
5 Type 1 1-7318 <$20
10 Type 1 1-5582 <$20
20 Type 1 1-1758 <$30
5 Type 2 1-19306 <$20
10 Type 2 1-10275 <$20
20 Type 2 1-2360 <$30
Total Issue $2,069,900
Out in 1935 $500,000
Large out 1935 $14,680
Outstanding includes Ch 6200

12444 Vanderburgh
OLD NB IN EVANSVILLE
{{ 12 L 50+ S }}
Organized 8/14/23
1902 Plain Back <$VALUE
4x5 1-32405 <$125
3x10-20 1-28435 <$125
1929 Small Size
5 Type 1 1-12576 <$20
10 Type 1 1-10428 <$20
20 Type 1 1-2912 <$30
5 Type 2 1-19328 <$20
10 Type 2 1-11027 <$20
20 Type 2 1-2376 <$30
Total Issue $3,676,680
Out in 1935 $500,000
Large out 1935 $26,290
Outstanding includes Ch 7478

3281 Vanderburgh
OLD NB OF EVANSVILLE
{{ 3 L }}
Chartered 12/31/84
Liquidated 12/22/04
Brown Back <$VALUE
3x10-20 1-29519 <$375
Total Issue $1,475,950
Out in 1910 $40,620

7478 Vanderburgh
OLD STATE NB OF
EVANSVILLE
{{ 6 L }}
Chartered 11/04
Liquidated 9/29/23
1902 Red Seal <$VALUE
4x5 1-10500 <$400
3x10-20 1-15250 <$400
1902 Date Back
4x5 1-38250 <$200
3x10-20 1-28500 <$200
1902 Plain Back
4x5 38251-82680 <$200
3x10-20 28501-53638 <$200
Total Issue $5,308,000
Out at close $500,000
Ch 12444 assumed circulation

8337 Shelby
FAIRLAND NB, FAIRLAND
{{ 3 L 5 S }}
Chartered 8/06
1902 Red Seal <$VALUE
4x5 1-775 <$850
4x10 1-775 <$850
1902 Date Back
4x5 1-2000 <$400
4x10 1-1600 <$400
1902 Plain Back
4x5 2001-6576 <$400
4x10 1601-4806 <$400
1929 Small Size
5 Type 1 1-1392 <$200
10 Type 1 1-592 <$200
5 Type 2 1-1506 <$225
10 Type 2 1-948 <$225
Total Issue $464,550
Out in 1935 $25,000
Large out 1935 $1,130

11035 Sullivan
FNB OF FARMERSBURG
{{ 3 L }}
Chartered 7/17
Liquidated 3/1/25
1902 Plain Back <$VALUE
4x5 1-3225 <$450
4x10 1-2420 <$450
Total Issue $161,300
Out at close $19,200

6504 Randolph
FNB OF FARMLAND
{{ 3 L }}
Organized 10/1/02
Liquidated 12/31/25
1902 Red Seal <$VALUE
4x5 1-375 <$850
3x10-20 1-250 <$850
1902 Date Back
4x5 1-1250 <$400
3x10-20 1-1000 <$400
1902 Plain Back
4x5 1251-3714 <$400
3x10-20 1001-2476 <$400
Total Issue $218,080
Out at close $6,250

7830 Dubois
FERDINAND NB, FERDINAND
{{ UNREPORTED }}
Chartered 7/05
Liquidated 11/27/11
1902 Red Seal <$VALUE
3x10-20 1-956 <$1500
1902 Date Back
3x10-20 1-359 <$1000
Total Issue $65,750
Out in 1912 $12,650

10419 Hamilton
FISHERS NB, FISHERS
{{ 3 L 2 S }}
Chartered 7/13
Liquidated 4/7/30
1902 Date Back <$VALUE
3x10-20 1-1150 <$450
1902 Plain Back
3x10-20 1151-4567 <$450
1929 Small Size
10 Type 1 1-183 <$500
20 Type 1 1-32 <$500
Total Issue $243,170
Out at close $24,420
Large out at close $9,600

8014 Carroll
BRIGHT NB OF FLORA
{{ 2 L 5 S }}
Organized 12/13/05
Receivership 2/13/34
1902 Red Seal <$VALUE
4x5 1-375 <$1000
3x10-20 1-307 <$1000
1902 Date Back
4x5 1-1925 <$500
3x10-20 1-1430 <$500
1902 Plain Back
4x5 1926-5221 <$500
3x10-20 1431-3495 <$500
1929 Small Size
5 Type 1 1-731 <$225
10 Type 1 1-354 <$225
20 Type 1 1-110 <$225
Total Issue $358,390
Out at close $25,000
Large out at close $1,080

7802 Carroll
FNB OF FLORA
{{ 1 L }}
Chartered 6/05
Liquidated 1/9/19
1902 Red Seal <$VALUE
4x5 1-875 <$1250
3x10-20 1-730 <$1250
1902 Date Back
4x5 1-1600 <$750
3x10-20 1-1280 <$750
1902 Plain Back
4x5 1601-2225 <$750
3x10-20 1281-1640 <$750
Total Issue $180,500
Out at close $25,000

9077 Gibson
FARMERS & MERCHANTS NB OF
FORT BRANCH
{{ 3 L 6 S }}
Chartered 3/08
1902 Red Seal <$VALUE
3x10-20 1-300 <$750
1902 Date Back
4x5 1-1805* <$350
3x10-20 1-1340 <$350
1902 Plain Back
4x5 1906-6290* <$350
3x10-20 1341-4072 <$350
* 1806-1905 not marked
1929 Small Size
5 Type 1 1-858 <$175
10 Type 1 1-442 <$175
20 Type 1 1-130 <$175
5 Type 2 1-1008 <$200
10 Type 2 1-598 <$200
20 Type 2 1-135 <$200
Total Issue $425,980
Out in 1935 $25,000
Large out 1935 $770

9073 Gibson
FNB OF FORT BRANCH
{{ 5 L 8 S }}
Organized 1/29/08
1902 Red Seal <$VALUE
4x5 1-250 <$650
3x10-20 1-200 <$650
1902 Date Back
4x5 1-1775 <$275
3x10-20 1-1360 <$275
1902 Plain Back
4x5 1776-5969 <$275
3x10-20 1361-3860 <$275
1929 Small Size
5 Type 1 1-688 <$150
10 Type 1 1-442 <$150
20 Type 1 1-140 <$150
5 Type 2 1-972 <$175
10 Type 2 1-525 <$175
20 Type 2 1-95 <$175
Total Issue $403,350
Out in 1935 $25,000
Large out 1935 $1,750

11 Allen
FNB OF FORT WAYNE*
Chartered 6/63
Liquidated 5/22/82
*Reorganized as Ch 2701
which retook Ch 11 6/10/10
Liquidated 9/29/31
2nd title: F & Hamilton NB
5/10/17
3rd title: FNB 1/19/22
4th title: F & Tri State
NB & TC 12/14/29
FIRST TITLE {{ 8 L }}
Original Series <$VALUE
3x1-2 1-14120 <$500/$1000
4x5 1-15205* <$600
3x10-20 1-2200*<$750/$1250
* 7226-7500 not issued
** 431-1000 not issued
Series 1875
3x10-20 1-156 <$750/$1250
1902 Date Back
4x5 1-22000 <$65
3x10-20 1-14800 <$65
1902 Plain Back (dated 1902)
4x5 22001-26265 <$65
3x10-20 14801-18264 <$65
SECOND TITLE {{ 8 L }}
1902 Plain Back
4x5 1-44750 <$150
3x10-20 1-44000 <$150
THIRD TITLE {{ 21 L 30 S }}
1902 Plain Back (dated 1922)
4x5 1-80793 <$65
3x10-20 1-59646 <$65
1929 Small Size
5 Type 1 1-8808 <$40
10 Type 1 1-4154 <$40
20 Type 1 1-1392 <$50
FOURTH TITLE {{ 14 S }}
1929 Small Size
5 Type 1 1-13588 <$60
10 Type 1 1-6308 <$60
20 Type 1 1-1874 <$70
Total Issue $11,516,080
Out at close $1,000,000
Large out at close $102,370
Outstanding includes Ch 2439
and Ch 2701

F & Hamilton NB of Fort Wayne
F & Tri State NB of
Fort Wayne
SEE Ch 11
FNB of Fort Wayne

2701 Allen
FNB OF FORT WAYNE
{{ 2 L }}
Chartered 5/6/82
RETOOK Ch 11 6/10/10
Brown Back <$VALUE
3x10-20 1-4698 <$600
1902 Red Seal
4x5 1-15000 <$600
3x10-20 1-18100 <$600
50-100 1-1000 <$2250/$2500
1902 Date Back
4x5 1-8750 <$350
3x10-20 1-8000 <$350
50-100 1-398 <$500/$600
Total Issue $1,989,700
Out in 1910 $300,000

865 Allen
FORT WAYNE NB, FORT WAYNE
{{ 2 L }}
Chartered 1865
Liquidated 1/25/85
Original Series <$VALUE
3x1-2 1-10000 <$600/$1250
4x5 1-19250 <$750
3x10-20 1-2300<$1000/$1500
Series 1875
3x10-20 1-9700<$1000/$1500
Total Issue $1,035,000
Out in 1910 $6,470

13818 Allen
FORT WAYNE NB, FORT WAYNE
{{ 21 S }}
Chartered 10/33
1929 Small Size <$VALUE
10 Type 2 1-21903 <$50
20 Type 2 1-6723 <$60
Total Issue $353,490
Out in 1935 $258,550

7725 Allen
GERMAN-AMERICAN NB OF
FORT WAYNE
Chartered 5/05
2nd title:Lincoln NB of
Fort Wayne 5/31/18
3rd title:Lincoln NB & TC
4/21/28
FIRST TITLE {{ 3 L }}
1902 Red Seal <$VALUE
4x5 1-5410 <$500
3x10-20 1-4522 <$500
1902 Date Back
4x5 1-15750 <$250
3x10-20 1-12100 <$250
1902 Plain Back
4x5 15751-23750 <$250
3x10-20 12101-16700 <$250
SECOND TITLE {{ 10 L }}
1902 Plain Back
3x10-20 1-36314 <$150
THIRD TITLE {{ 2 L 50+ S }}
1902 Plain Back
3x10-20 1-3471 <$200
1929 Small Size
10 Type 1 1-30378 <$25
20 Type 1 1-10110 <$35
10 Type 2 1-2121 <$40
20 Type 2 1-430 <$50
Total Issue $6,699,240
Out in 1935 $500,000
Large out 1935 $16,255

2439 Allen
HAMILTON NB OF FORT WAYNE
{{ 9 L }}
Chartered 11/17/79
Liquidated 4/30/17
Series 1875 <$VALUE
4x5 1-5500 <$500
3x10-20 1-16812<$750/$1250
50-100 1-200 <$4000
Brown Back
4x5 1-5000 <$300
3x10-20 1-10300 <$300
1882 Date Back
4x5 1-19000 <$250
3x10-20 1-13700 <$250
1882 Value Back
4x5 19001-22770 <$300
3x10-20 13701-16129 <$300
Total Issue $2,857,450
Out at close $300,000

Lincoln NB of Fort Wayne
Lincoln NB & TC of Fort Wayne
SEE Ch 7725
German-American NB of
Fort Wayne

1100 Allen
MERCHANTS NB OF
FORT WAYNE
{{ UNREPORTED }}
Chartered 5/1/65
Liquidated 11/8/75
Original Series <$VALUE
4x5 1-2840 <$1250
3x10-20 1-1200<$1500/$1750
Total Issue $116,800
Out in 1910 $370

Old-FNB & TC of Fort Wayne
SEE Ch 3285
Old NB of Fort Wayne

3285 Allen
OLD NB OF FORT WAYNE
Organized 12/20/84
Receivership 11/2/33
2nd title: Old-FNB & TC
8/13/31
FIRST TITLE {{ 28 L 12 S }}
Brown Back <$VALUE
3x10-20 1-5740 <$175/$225
1902 Red Seal
3x10-20 1-13100 <$200/$250
1902 Date Back
4x5 1-21000 <$65
3x10-20 1-16200 <$65
1902 Plain Back
4x5 21001-86046 <$65
3x10-20 16201-52236 <$65
1929 Small Size
5 Type 1 1-12460 <$45
10 Type 1 1-5800 <$50
20 Type 1 1-1710 <$55
SECOND TITLE {{ 44 S }}
1929 Small Size
5 Type 1 1-13416 <$20
10 Type 1 1-9942 <$25
20 Type 1 1-3522 <$35
5 Type 2 1-4562 <$20
10 Type 2 1-3326 <$25
20 Type 2 1-1487 <$35
Total Issue $7,709,170
Out at close $1,750,000
Large out at close $81,740
Outstanding includes Ch 2701

4725 Allen
WHITE NB OF FORT WAYNE
{{ 2 L }}
Chartered 4/15/92
Liquidated 8/26/05
Brown Back <$VALUE
3x10-20 1-8285 <$600
Total Issue $414,250
Out in 1910 $20,515

9299 Hancock
FNB OF FORTVILLE
{{ 5 L 7 S }}
Chartered 12/08
1902 Date Back <$VALUE
4x10 1-2950 <$300
1902 Plain Back
4x10 2951-8300 <$300
1929 Small Size
10 Type 1 1-1116 <$175
10 Type 2 1-1145 <$175
Total Issue $410,410
Out in 1935 $25,000
Large out 1935 $1,330

5430 Benton
FNB OF FOWLER
{{ 18 L 2 S }}
Chartered 6/16/00
Receivership 6/2/31
Brown Back <$VALUE
3x10-20 1-870 <$400
1882 Date Back
3x10-20 1-1400* <$400
1882 Value Back
3x10-20 1561-1609* <$400
* 1401-1560 not marked
1902 Plain Back
3x10-20 1-1769 <$150
1929 Small Size
10 Type 1 1-236 <$300
20 Type 1 1-41 <$300
Total Issue $231,480
Out at close $15,000
Large out at close $2,310

6217 Clinton
AMERICAN NB OF FRANKFORT
{{ 6 L }}
Chartered 4/02
Liquidated 3/15/28
1902 Red Seal <$VALUE
3x10-20 1-5400 <$500
1902 Date Back
3x10-20 1-6600 <$200
1902 Plain Back (dated 1902)
3x10-20 6601-12600 <$200
1902 Plain Back (dated 1922)
3x10-20 1-6938 <$200
Total Issue $1,246,900
Out at close $100,000

1854 Clinton
FNB OF FRANKFORT
{{ 16 L 10 S }}
Chartered 7/28/71
Liquidated 1/13/31
Original Series <$VALUE
3x1-2 1-6900 <$500/$1000
4x5 1-7275 <$500
3x10-20 1-1600 <$750/$1250
Series 1875
3x1-2 1-600 <$500/$1000
4x5 1-5950 <$500
3x10-20 1-7994 <$750/$1250
Brown Back
3x10-20 1-20200 <$225
1882 Date Back
3x10-20 1-3604 <$200
1902 Date Back
3x10-20 1-9000 <$100
1902 Plain Back
3x10-20 9001-37859 <$100
1929 Small Size
10 Type 1 1-2375 <$125
20 Type 1 1-659 <$125
Total Issue $4,086,430
Out at close $200,000
Large out at close $32,987

****
3967 Johnson
CITIZENS NB OF FRANKLIN
{{ 8 L 13 S }}
Organized 1/3/89
Receivership 4/10/34
Brown Back <$VALUE
4x5 1-5341 <$225
3x10-20 1-2047 <$225/$275
1902 Date Back
4x5 1-6100 <$125
3x10-20 1-4660 <$125
1902 Plain Back
4x5 6101-20840 <$125
3x10-20 4661-14541 <$125
1929 Small Size
5 Type 1 1-3244 <$85
10 Type 1 1-1504 <$85
20 Type 1 1-442 <$90
5 Type 2 1-1188 <$100
10 Type 2 1-693 <$100
20 Type 2 1-130 <$125
Total Issue $1,609,090
Out at close $100,000
Large out at close $5,775
****
50 Johnson
FNB OF FRANKLIN
{{ UNREPORTED }}
Organized 8/5/63
Receivership 2/13/77
Original Series <$VALUE
4x5 1-2000 <$1250
4x10 1-5446 <$1500
Total Issue $257,840
Out in 1915 $1,750
****
3338 Johnson
FRANKLIN NB, FRANKLIN
{{ 13 L 0 S }}
Chartered 1885
Liquidated 10/24/29
Brown Back <$VALUE
3x10-20 1-6388 <$250
1902 Red Seal
3x10-20 1-3400 <$300
1902 Date Back
3x10-20 1-8300 <$125
1902 Plain Back
3x10-20 8301-26977 <$125
1929 Small Size
10 Type 1 1-228* <$600
*D000228A-F000228A not issued
Total Issue $1,851,900
Out at close $125,000
Large out at close $115,950
****
13378 Johnson
FRANKLIN NB, FRANKLIN
{{ 4 S }}
Chartered 9/29
Liquidated 1/14/31
1929 Small Size <$VALUE
10 Type 1 1-812 <$250
20 Type 1 1-224 <$250
Total Issue $75,600
Out at close $50,000
****
14075 Johnson
JOHNSON COUNTY NB OF FRANKLIN
{{ 3 S }}
Chartered 3/34
1929 Small Size <$VALUE
5 Type 2 1-2320 <$400
10 Type 2 1-1115 <$400
20 Type 2 1-360 <$400
Total Issue $29,950
Out in 1935 $22,100
****
2769 Johnson
NB OF FRANKLIN
{{ UNREPORTED }}
Chartered 8/29/82
Liquidated 1/31/88
Brown Back <$VALUE
4x5 1-1778 <$1500
Total Issue $35,560
Out in 1910 $270
****
78 Johnson
SECOND NB OF FRANKLIN
{{ 1 L }}
Chartered 9/63
Liquidated 6/20/82
Original Series <$VALUE
4x5 1-6350 <$1000
2x10-20-50 1-2050
<$1250/$1500/$4000
Series 1875
2x10-20-50 1-500
<$1250/$1500/$4000
Total Issue $356,500
Out in 1910 $2,565
****

****
7437 Benton
FNB OF FREELAND PARK
{{ 2 L }}
Chartered 10/04
Liquidated 6/25/26
1902 Red Seal <$VALUE
4x5 1-450 <$1000
3x10-20 1-430 <$1000
1902 Date Back
4x5 1-925 <$500
3x10-20 1-740 <$500
1902 Plain Back
4x5 926-2390 <$500
3x10-20 741-1601 <$500
Total Issue $158,350
Out at close $12,500
****
10718 Steuben
FNB OF FREMONT
{{ 2 L 5 S }}
Chartered 3/15
1902 Date Back <$VALUE
3x10-20 1-500 <$600
1902 Plain Back
3x10-20 501-4356 <$600
1929 Small Size
10 Type 1 1-726 <$225
20 Type 1 1-180 <$225
10 Type 2 1-288 <$250
20 Type 2 1-50 <$275
Total Issue $286,840
Out in 1935 $25,000
Large out 1935 $1,010
****
8426 Lake
FNB OF GARY
{{ 10 L 20 S }}
Organized 10/9/06
Receivership 1/27/32
1902 Red Seal <$VALUE
3x10-20 1-840 <$400
50-100 1-424 <$2250/$2500
1902 Date Back
3x10-20 1-5300 <$175
50-100 1-300 <$400/$500
3x50-100 1-1986 <$400/$500
1902 Plain Back
3x10-20 5301-12796 <$175
1929 Small Size
10 Type 1 1-3730 <$100
20 Type 1 1-870 <$100
50 Type 1 1-298 <$175
100 Type 1 1-96 <$200
Total Issue $1,762,100
Out at close $244,240
Large out at close $15,920
****
11094 Lake
NB OF AMERICA AT GARY
{{ 10 L 9 S }}
Organized 12/11/16
Receivership 2/10/32
1902 Plain Back <$VALUE
4x5 1-19528 <$175
3x10-20 1-12562 <$175
1929 Small Size
5 Type 1 1-2640 <$110
10 Type 1 1-1342 <$110
20 Type 1 1-365 <$125
Total Issue $1,222,180
Out at close $99,100
Large out at close $8,810
****
4825 Grant
FNB OF GAS CITY
{{ UNREPORTED }}
Chartered 12/9/92
Liquidated 9/26/06
Brown Back <$VALUE
3x10-20 1-1027 <$1500
Total Issue $51,350
Out in 1910 $2,280
****
7863 Newton
FNB OF GOODLAND
{{ 3 L 5 S }}
Chartered 8/05
Liquidated 7/28/31
1902 Red Seal <$VALUE
3x10-20 1-1400 <$850
1902 Date Back
3x10-20 1-3540 <$450
1902 Plain Back
3x10-20 3541-10908 <$450
1929 Small Size
10 Type 1 1-790 <$200
20 Type 1 1-191 <$200
Total Issue $685,720
Out at close $50,000
Large out at close $6,780
****

****
2067 Elkhart
CITY NB OF GOSHEN
{{ 10 L 50+ S }}
Chartered 12/7/72
Receivership 5/8/34
Original Series <$VALUE
3x1-2 1-1500 <$400/$850
4x5 1-1875 <$500
Series 1875
3x1-2 1-880 <$400/$850
4x5 1-5550 <$500
Brown Back
4x5 1-6000 <$300
3x10-20 1-1860 <$300
1882 Date Back
4x5 1-2399 <$275
3x10-20 1-1899 <$275
1902 Date Back
4x5 1-3250 <$175
3x10-20 1-2400 <$175
1902 Plain Back
4x5 3251-17885 <$175
3x10-20 2401-12360 <$175
1929 Small Size
5 Type 1 1-3006 <$40
10 Type 1 1-1722 <$50
20 Type 1 1-532 <$60
5 Type 2 1-48 <$100
Total Issue $1,749,610
Out at close $98,000
Large out at close $4,025
****
146 Elkhart
FNB OF GOSHEN
{{ 1 L }}
Chartered 12/63
Liquidated 11/7/72
Original Series <$VALUE
3x1-2 1-1204 <$1000/$1500
4x5 1-2999 <$1250
4x10 1-1750 <$1500
Total Issue $136,000
Out in 1910 $1,112
****
14113 Elkhart
FNB OF GOSHEN
{{ 6 S }}
Chartered 4/34
1929 Small Size <$VALUE
5 Type 2 1-2020 <$225
10 Type 2 1-2084 <$225
20 Type 2 1-1035 <$225
Total Issue $51,640
Out in 1935 $50,000
****
2896 Putnam
CENTRAL NB OF GREEN CASTLE
{{ 8 L 18 S }}
Chartered 1883
Brown Back <$VALUE
3x10-20 1-5667 <$400
1902 Red Seal
3x10-20 1-4800 <$500
1902 Date Back
3x10-20 1-6500 <$175
1902 Plain Back
3x10-20 6501-21207 <$175
1929 Small Size
10 Type 1 1-2612 <$75
20 Type 1 1-726 <$75
10 Type 2 1-1602 <$85
20 Type 2 1-396 <$100
Total Issue $1,568,130
Out in 1935 $92,200
Large out 1935 $6,950
****
10409 Putnam
CITIZENS NB OF GREENCASTLE
{{ 1 L }}
Chartered 6/13
Closed 2/27/22
1902 Date Back <$VALUE
4x10 1-2800 <$650
1902 Plain Back
4x10 2801-7261 <$650
Total Issue $290,440
Out at close $50,000
Ch 219 assumed circulation
****
219 Putnam
FNB OF GREENCASTLE
{{ 10 L 18 S }}
Chartered 1/64
Liquidated 9/1/33
Original Series <$VALUE
4x10 1-5500 <$750
Series 1875
4x10 1-3300 <$750
Brown Back
3x10-20 1-4835 <$400

1902 Red Seal
3x10-20 1-3300 <$500
1902 Date Back
3x10-20 1-4700 <$200
1902 Plain Back
3x10-20 4701-17397 <$200
1929 Small Size
10 Type 1 1-2312 <$85
20 Type 1 1-623 <$85
Total Issue $1,842,080
Out at close $100,000
Large out at close $9,490
Outstanding includes Ch 10409
****
7124 Wayne
FNB OF GREENS FORK
{{ 5 L 8 S }}
Chartered 2/04
1902 Red Seal <$VALUE
4x5 1-300 <$1000
3x10-20 1-240 <$1000
1902 Date Back
4x5 1-1850 <$400
3x10-20 1-1450 <$400
1902 Plain Back
4x5 1851-6383 <$400
3x10-20 1451-3951 <$400
1929 Small Size
5 Type 1 1-760 <$250
10 Type 1 1-452 <$250
20 Type 1 1-130 <$275
5 Type 2 1-1092 <$300
10 Type 2 1-539 <$300
20 Type 2 1-159 <$300
Total Issue $422,760
Out in 1935 $25,000
Large out 1935 $1,820
****
1890 Decatur
CITIZENS NB OF GREENSBURG
{{ 8 L 2U + 7 S }}
Chartered 10/14/71
Closed 12/31/30
Original Series <$VALUE
3x1-2 1-1000 <$500/$1000
4x5 1-2750 <$500
3x10-20 1-1600 <$750/$1250
Series 1875
4x5 1-876 <$500
3x10-20 1-5452 <$750/$1250
Brown Back
3x10-20 1-9600 <$300/$350
1882 Date Back
4x5 1-2565 <$300
3x10-20 1-939 <$300/$325
1902 Date Back
4x5 1-4000 <$200
3x10-20 1-3000 <$200
1902 Plain Back
4x5 4001-19050 <$200
3x10-20 3001-12978 <$200
1929 Small Size
5 Type 1 1-1683 <$150
10 Type 1 1-833 <$150
20 Type 1 1-187 <$150
Total Issue $2,161,180
Out at close $100,000
Large out at close $15,840
Ch 2844 assumed circulation
****
Citizens Third NB & TC of Greensburg
SEE Ch 2844
Third NB of Greensburg
****
356 Decatur
FNB OF GREENSBURG
{{ 1 L }}
Chartered 3/31/64
Liquidated 10/26/97
Original Series <$VALUE
4x5 1-7800 <$750
3x10-20 1-2450<$1000/$1500
Series 1875
4x5 1-2000 <$750
3x10-20 1-1292<$1000/$1500
Brown Back
4x5 1-3228 <$650
3x10-20 1-2369 <$650
Total Issue $566,110
Out in 1910 $3,595
****
5435 Decatur
GREENSBURG NB, GREENSBURG
{{ 6 L 6 S }}
Chartered 6/18/00
Liquidated 2/28/33
Brown Back <$VALUE
3x10-20 1-1150 <$400
1882 Date Back
3x10-20 1-4700 <$400
1882 Value Back
3x10-20 4701-7173 <$400
1902 Plain Back
3x10-20 1-8566 <$225

1929 Small Size
10 Type 1 1-1650 <$175
20 Type 1 1-444 <$175
Total Issue $996,730
Out at close $75,000
Large out at close $6,270
****
2844 Decatur
THIRD NB OF GREENSBURG
Organized 12/4/82
Receivership 2/26/34
2nd title: Third NB & TC 5/2/27
3rd title: Citizens Third NB & TC 12/31/30
FIRST TITLE {{ 6 L }}
Brown Back <$VALUE
3x10-20 1-2910 <$300/$350
1902 Red Seal
3x10-20 1-2700 <$300/$350
1902 Date Back
3x10-20 1-5000 <$150
1902 Plain Back
3x10-20 5001-12031 <$150
SECOND TITLE {{ 1 L 4 S }}
1902 Plain Back
3x10-20 1-1546 <$250
1929 Small Size
10 Type 1 1-1222 <$150
20 Type 1 1-418 <$150
THIRD TITLE {{ 10 S }}
1929 Small Size
10 Type 1 1-1109 <$100
20 Type 1 1-302 <$100
Total Issue $1,185,610
Out at close $140,000
Large out at close $11,760
Outstanding includes Ch 1890
****
8461 Johnson
CITIZENS NB OF GREENWOOD
{{ 3 L 6 S }}
Organized 10/31/06
Receivership 10/29/34
1902 Red Seal <$VALUE
3x10-20 1-750 <$850
1902 Date Back
3x10-20 1-1970 <$400
1902 Plain Back
3x10-20 1971-5952 <$400
1929 Small Size
10 Type 1 1-600 <$225
20 Type 1 1-170 <$225
10 Type 2 1-625 <$250
20 Type 2 1-75 <$250
Total Issue $399,250
Out at close $24,700
Large out at close $1,450
****
8422 Johnson
FNB OF GREENWOOD
{{ 2 L 4 S }}
Organized 7/27/06
Liquidated 8/29/34
1902 Red Seal <$VALUE
3x10-20 1-750 <$850
1902 Date Back
3x10-20 1-1770 <$400
1902 Plain Back
3x10-20 1771-5567 <$400
1929 Small Size
10 Type 1 1-638 <$250
20 Type 1 1-160 <$250
10 Type 2 1-295 <$275
20 Type 2 1-68 <$275
Total Issue $377,640
Out at close $24,995
Large out at close $1,895
****
7902 Wayne
FNB OF HAGERSTOWN
{{ 3 L }}
Chartered 9/05
Liquidated 6/30/24
1902 Red Seal <$VALUE
3x10-20 1-635 <$1000
1902 Date Back
3x10-20 1-2950 <$500
1902 Plain Back
3x10-20 2951-6989 <$500
Total Issue $381,200
Out at close $50,000
****
8199 Lake
CITIZENS GERMAN NB OF HAMMOND
Organized 4/2/06
Receivership 1/18/32
2nd title:Citizens NB 12/7/17
3rd title:Hammond NB & TC 1/17/28

FIRST TITLE {{ 4 L }}
1902 Red Seal <$VALUE
4x5 1-1100 <$400
3x10-20 1-910 <$400
1902 Date Back
4x5 1-8000 <$200
3x10-20 1-5560 <$200
1902 Plain Back
4x5 2001-11050 <$200
3x10-20 5561-7320 <$200
SECOND TITLE {{ 4 L }}
1902 Plain Back
4x5 1-11566 <$150
3x10-20 1-8441 <$150
THIRD TITLE {{ 2 L 18 S }}
1902 Plain Back
4x5 1-2004 <$175
3x10-20 1-1714 <$175
1929 Small Size
5 Type 1 1-6821 <$60
10 Type 1 1-3412 <$60
20 Type 1 1-962 <$70
Total Issue $1,958,440
Out at close $384,460
Large out at close $10,510
****
Citizens NB of Hammond
SEE Ch 8199
Citizens German NB of Hammond
****
3478 Lake
FNB OF HAMMOND
{{ 16 L }}
Chartered 1886
Liquidated 2/3/26
Brown Back <$VALUE
4x5 1-5565 <$250
3x10-20 1-2371 <$250/$300
1902 Red Seal
4x5 1-2750 <$300
3x10-20 1-1000 <$300/$350
1902 Date Back
4x5 1-13550 <$100
3x10-20 1-9300 <$100
1902 Plain Back
4x5 13551-45663 <$100
3x10-20 9301-28776 <$100
Total Issue $2,686,910
Out at close $250,000
****
Hammond NB & TC, Hammond
SEE Ch 8199
Citizens German NB of Hammond
****
6959 Blackford
FNB OF HARTFORD CITY
{{ 4 L 8 S }}
Organized 7/10/03
Receivership 5/23/34
1902 Red Seal <$VALUE
3x10-20 1-1082 <$600
1902 Date Back
3x10-20 1-3500 <$300
1902 Plain Back
3x10-20 3501-11174 <$300
1929 Small Size
10 Type 1 1-1130 <$150
20 Type 1 1-342 <$150
10 Type 2 1-652 <$175
20 Type 2 1-196 <$175
Total Issue $730,080
Out at close $50,000
Large out at close $2,890
****
7354 Bartholomew
FNB OF HARTSVILLE
{{ 2 L 0 S }}
Chartered 8/04
Liquidated 1/20/30
1902 Red Seal <$VALUE
4x5 1-606 <$1000
3x10-20 1-485 <$1000
1902 Date Back
4x5 1-1025 <$600
3x10-20 1-720 <$600
1902 Plain Back
4x5 1026-3324 <$600
3x10-20 721-2233 <$600
1929 Small Size
5 Type 1 1-77 <$750
10 Type 1 1-18 <$750
20 Type 1 1-3 <$750
Total Issue $218,250
Out at close $11,515
Large out at close $7,765
****

9090 Dubois
HOLLAND NB, HOLLAND
{{ 3 L 5 S }}
Chartered 4/08
1902 Red Seal <$VALUE
3x10-20 1-200 <$500
1902 Date Back
3x10-20 1-2000 <$225
1902 Plain Back
3x10-20 2001-5113 <$225
1929 Small Size
10 Type 1 1-566 <$200
20 Type 1 1-154 <$200
10 Type 2 1-829 <$225
20 Type 2 1-89 <$225
Total Issue $328,160
Out in 1935 $25,000
Large out 1935 $580

5726 Bartholomew
CITIZENS NB OF HOPE
{{ 2 L }}
Organized 2/7/01
Receivership 2/15/29
Brown Back <$VALUE
3x10-20 1-900 <$600
1882 Date Back
3x10-20 1-2310 <$600
1882 Value Back
3x10-20 2311-3438 <$600
1902 Plain Back
3x10-20 1-2873 <$500
Total Issue $360,550
Out at close $29,450

8929 Dubois
FNB OF HUNTINGBURG
{{ 3 L 9 S }}
Chartered 10/07
1902 Red Seal <$VALUE
3x10-20 1-288 <$700
1902 Date Back
3x10-20 1-1410 <$350
1902 Plain Back
3x10-20 1411-5217 <$350
1929 Small Size
10 Type 1 1-988 <$135
20 Type 1 1-284 <$150
10 Type 2 1-336 <$165
20 Type 2 1-140 <$175
Total Issue $374,770
Out in 1935 $50,000
Large out 1935 $2,290

145 Huntington
FNB OF HUNTINGTON
{{ UNREPORTED }}
Chartered 12/63
Liquidated 1/31/81
Original Series <$VALUE
4x5 1-4000 <$1250
3x10-20 1-1600<$1500/$2000
Series 1875
4x5 1-4030 <$1500
Total Issue $240,600
Out in 1910 $2,205

2508 Huntington
FNB OF HUNTINGTON
{{ 9 L 9 S }}
Chartered 1881
Liquidated 9/14/31
Series 1875 <$VALUE
4x5 1-6948 <$500
3x10-20 1-662 <$750/$1250
Brown Back
4x5 1-3350 <$350
3x10-20 1-2810 <$350
1882 Date Back
4x5 1-5750* <$350
3x10-20 1-4400# <$350
1882 Value Back
4x5 6151-10713* <$350
3x10-20 4721-7300# <$350
* 5751-6150 not marked
# 4401-4720 not marked
1902 Plain Back
4x5 1-8155 <$200
3x10-20 1-5515 <$200
1929 Small Size
5 Type 1 1-2019 <$125
10 Type 1 1-1017 <$125
20 Type 1 1-263 <$150
Total Issue $1,550,820
Out at close $100,000
Large out at close $10,110

13759 Marion
AMERICAN NB AT INDIANAPOLIS
{{ 38 S }}
Chartered 8/33
1929 Small Size <$VALUE
5 Type 2 1-94200* <$25
10 Type 2 1-45670# <$25
20 Type 2 1-17903^ <$35
50 Type 2 1-2441** <$250
100 Type 2 1-816*** <$300
* 59961-73416 not issued
# 30001-36900 not issued
^ 13741-15468 not issued
** 1501-1896 not issued
*** 505-624 not issued
Total Issue $1,286,770
Out in 1935 $836,250

5672 Marion
AMERICAN NB OF INDIANAPOLIS
{{ 10 L }}
Chartered 1/8/01
Liquidated 9/5/10
Brown Back <$VALUE
4x5 1-66320 <$175
3x10-20 1-51572 <$175/$225
1882 Date Back
4x5 1-25025 <$150
3x10-20 1-19569 <$150/$200
Total Issue $5,383,950
Out at close $1,319,540

4158 Marion
CAPITAL NB OF INDIANAPOLIS
{{ 12 L }}
Chartered 1889
Liquidated 7/1/12
Brown Back <$VALUE
4x5 1-16500 <$175
50-100 1-6546 <$1250/$1500
1882 Date Back
4x5 1-5800 <$175
1902 Date Back
4x5 1-28575 <$125
3x10-20 1-17700 <$125
Total Issue $2,884,400
Out at close $1,000,000
Ch 984 assumed circulation

617 Marion
CITIZENS NB OF INDIANAPOLIS
{{ 6 L }}
Chartered 1864
Liquidated 11/11/84
Original Series <$VALUE
3x1-2 1-13865 <$400/$850
4x5 1-16700 <$400
3x10-20 1-11100<$750/$1250
Series 1875
4x5 1-2887 <$400
3x10-20 1-739 <$750/$1250
Total Issue $1,053,015
Out in 1910 $7,219

5845 Marion
COLUMBIA NB OF INDIANAPOLIS
{{ 2 L }}
Chartered 1901
Liquidated 1/2/12
Brown Back <$VALUE
4x5 1-5625 <$400
3x10-20 1-2840 <$400
50-100 1-2653 <$1250/$1500
1882 Date Back
4x5 1-10875 <$375
3x10-20 1-4501 <$375
Total Issue $1,095,000
Out in 1912 $228,100

10671 Marion
COMMERCIAL NB OF INDIANAPOLIS
{{ 4 L }}
Chartered 12/14
Liquidated 6/30/23
1902 Date Back <$VALUE
4x5 1-4500 <$225
3x10-20 1-3700 <$225
1902 Plain Back
4x5 4501-31875 <$225
3x10-20 3701-22647 <$225
Total Issue $1,769,850
Out at close $300,000

9537 Marion
CONTINENTAL NB OF INDIANAPOLIS
{{ 12 L 6 S }}
Organized 7/20/09
Liquidated 1/13/31
1902 Date Back <$VALUE
4x5 1-30000 <$125
3x10-20 1-22600 <$125
1902 Plain Back
4x5 30001-69277 <$125
3x10-20 22601-46428 <$125
1929 Small Size
5 Type 1 1-1858 <$150
10 Type 1 1-878 <$150
20 Type 1 1-235 <$150
Total Issue $3,843,560
Out in 1929 $114,300
Large out at close $14,150

55 Marion
FNB OF INDIANAPOLIS
{{ U + 5 L }}
Chartered 8/63
Liquidated 7/5/81
Original Series <$VALUE
3x1-2 1-6000 <$500/$1000
4x5 1-7500 <$500
3x10-20 1-18500<$850/$1500
50-100 1-1975 <$4000
Series 1875
3x1-2 1-2000 <$500/$1000
4x5 1-4135 <$500
3x10-20 1-830 <$850/$1500
50-100 1-814 <$4000
Total Issue $1,657,550
Out in 1910 $9,626

2556 Marion
FNB OF INDIANAPOLIS
{{ UNREPORTED }}
Organized 9/1/81
Liquidated 11/11/86
Series 1875 <$VALUE
4x5 1-500 <$1000
3x10-20 1-400 <$1250/$1500
50-100 1-400 <$4000
Brown Back
3x10-20 1-4458 <$850
Total Issue $312,900
Out in 1910 $990

9829 Marion
FLETCHER AMERICAN NB OF INDIANAPOLIS
{{ 50+ L 50+ S }}
Organized 8/11/10
Liquidated 1/24/34
1902 Date Back <$VALUE
4x5 1-142000 <$60
3x10-20 1-107000 <$65
1902 Plain Back
4x5 142001-544946 <$60
3x10-20 107001-386372 <$65
1929 Small Size
5 Type 1 1-78855 <$15
10 Type 1 1-42350 <$20
20 Type 1 1-11918 <$30
Total Issue $36,554,330
Out in 1932 $2,419,100
Large out at close $119,020

5116 Marion
FLETCHER NB OF INDIANAPOLIS
{{ 10 L }}
Chartered 3/28/98
Liquidated 9/3/10
Brown Back <$VALUE
4x5 1-23500 <$225
3x10-20 1-24200 <$225/$250
1882 Date Back
4x5 1-16745 <$175
3x10-20 1-6471 <$175/$200
Total Issue $2,338,450
Out at close $1,000,000

783 Marion
FOURTH NB OF INDIANAPOLIS
{{ 1 L }}
Chartered 2/6/65
Liquidated 11/30/65
Original Series <$VALUE
4x5 1-2000 <$1000
3x10-20 1-914 <$1250/$1500
Total Issue $85,700
Out in 1910 $555

984 Marion
INDIANA NB OF INDIANAPOLIS
{{ U + 28 L 50+ S }}
Chartered 1865
Original Series <$VALUE
3x1-2 1-12000 <$350/$850
4x5 1-11740 <$400
4x10 1-10125 <$750
50-100 1-568 <$4000
Series 1875
4x10 1-6345 <$650
Brown Back
3x10-20 1-7842 <$200/$250
1902 Red Seal
3x10-20 1-16100 <$200/$250
50-100 1-3801 <$2250/$2500
1902 Date Back
4x5 1-75000 <$60
3x10-20 1-53200 <$60
50-100 1-1600 <$300/$400
3x50-100 1-2000 <$300/$400
1902 Plain Back
4x5 75001-306715 <$60
3x10-20 53201-192846 <$60
1929 Small Size
5 Type 1 1-27566 <$15
10 Type 1 1-27932 <$20
20 Type 1 1-6580 <$30
5 Type 2 1-183840 <$15
10 Type 2 1-100205 <$20
20 Type 2 1-25402 <$30
Out in 1935 $3,000,000
Large out 1935 $76,155
Outstanding includes Ch 4158

581 Marion
INDIANAPOLIS NB, INDIANAPOLIS
{{ 4 L }}
Organized 11/21/64
Receivership 8/3/93
Original Series <$VALUE
3x1-2 1-7400 <$400/$850
4x5 1-12465 <$400
3x10-20 1-9100 <$750/$1250
50-100 1-1400 <$4000
Series 1875
3x10-20 1-4800 <$750/$1250
50-100 1-84 <$4000
Brown Back
4x5 1-1629 <$350
3x10-20 1-1200 <$350/$400
50-100 1-216 <$1250/$1500
Total Issue $1,332,850
Out in 1915 $7,716

869 Marion
MERCHANTS NB OF INDIANAPOLIS
{{ 50+ L 50+ S }}
Chartered 1865
Original Series <$VALUE
3x1-2 1-10080 <$350/$850
4x5 1-11100 <$400
3x10-20 1-1300 <$750/$1250
Series 1875
4x5 1-4923 <$400
3x10-20 1-2474 <$750/$1250
Brown Back
3x10-20 1-17031 <$175/$225
1902 Red Seal
4x5 1-24000 <$175
3x10-20 1-23600 <$175/$225
1902 Date Back
4x5 1-62830 <$60
3x10-20 1-46068 <$60
1902 Plain Back
4x5 62831-205759 <$60
3x10-20 46069-138791 <$60
1929 Small Size
5 Type 1 1-37134 <$15
10 Type 1 1-18586 <$20
20 Type 1 1-5234 <$30
5 Type 2 1-37350 <$15
10 Type 2 1-20617 <$20
20 Type 2 1-5345 <$30
Total Issue $17,482,920
Out in 1935 $1,000,000
Large out 1935 $33,590

1878 Marion
MERIDIAN NB OF INDIANAPOLIS
{{ 3 L }}
Chartered 9/16/71
Liquidated 10/30/94
Original Series <$VALUE
3x1-2 1-2500 <$350/$850
4x5 1-3000 <$400
3x10-20 1-3050 <$750/$1250
50-100 1-1000 <$4000
Series 1875
4x5 1-2900 <$400
3x10-20 1-2330 <$750/$1250
50-100 1-1278 <$4000
Brown Back
4x5 1-1154 <$350
3x10-20 1-1529 <$350/$400
50-100 1-90 <$1250/$1500
Total Issue $854,230
Out in 1910 $4,784

10121 Marion
N CITY B OF INDIANAPOLIS
{{ 37 L }}
Chartered 1/12
Liquidated 4/30/24
1902 Date Back <$VALUE
4x5 1-47500 <$60
3x10-20 1-31000 <$60
3x50-100 1-2728 <$300/$400
1902 Plain Back
4x5 47501-124812 <$60
3x10-20 31001-79118 <$60
Total Issue $7,134,140
Out at close $1,000,000

6513 Marion
UNION NB OF INDIANAPOLIS
{{ 5 L }}
Chartered 12/02
Liquidated 1/2/12
1902 Red Seal <$VALUE
4x5 1-9605 <$350
3x10-20 1-8658 <$350
1902 Date Back
4x5 1-8965 <$200
3x10-20 1-6239 <$200
Total Issue $1,116,250
Out in 1912 $164,245

7342 Greene
FNB OF JASONVILLE
{{ 3 L 5 S }}
Organized 7/11/04
Receivership 2/5/34
1902 Red Seal <$VALUE
3x10-20 1-1245 <$800
1902 Date Back
3x10-20 1-1920 <$400
1902 Plain Back
3x10-20 1921-9641 <$400
1929 Small Size
10 Type 1 1-1176 <$225
20 Type 1 1-311 <$225
Total Issue $652,180
Out at close $25,000
Large out at close $2,190

1466 Clark
CITIZENS NB OF JEFFERSONVILLE
{{ 4 L }}
Chartered 1865
Liquidated 6/1/14
Original Series <$VALUE
4x5 1-1750 <$500
3x10-20 1-3680 <$750/$1250
Series 1875
3x10-20 1-1014 <$750/$1250
Brown Back
4x5 1-2700 <$350
3x10-20 1-4462 <$350
1902 Red Seal
4x5 1-3150 <$400
3x10-20 1-2440 <$400
1902 Date Back
4x5 1-4117 <$225
3x10-20 1-3297 <$225
Total Issue $978,990
Out at close $64,650

956 Clark
FNB OF JEFFERSONVILLE
{{ 14 L 2U + 18 S }}
Chartered 1865
Liquidated 3/1/32
Original Series <$VALUE
4x5 1-6780 <$400
3x10-20 1-1700 <$750/$1250
Series 1875
4x5 1-5311 <$400
3x10-20 1-400 <$750/$1250
Brown Back
4x5 1-11325 <$175
3x10-20 1-1536 <$175/$225
1902 Red Seal
4x5 1-1750 <$225
3x10-20 1-1200 <$225
1902 Date Back
4x5 1-9000 <$100
3x10-20 1-6900 <$100
1902 Plain Back
4x5 9001-38285 <$100
3x10-20 6901-24193 <$100
1929 Small Size
5 Type 1 1-4167 <$60
10 Type 1 1-2114 <$60
20 Type 1 1-527 <$70
Total Issue $3,035,560
Out at close $150,000
Large out at close $16,540

12532 Noble
CITIZENS NB OF KENDALLVILLE
{{ 5 L 4 S }}
Organized 2/28/24
Receivership 3/16/32
1902 Plain Back <$VALUE
4x5 1-14087 <$350
1929 Small Size
5 Type 1 1-6913 <$250
Total Issue $489,130
Out at close $75,440
Large out at close $2,400

41 Noble
FNB OF KENDALLVILLE
{{ 2 L }}
Chartered 7/63
Liquidated 5/12/82
Succeeded by Ch 2687
Original Series <$VALUE
3x1-2 1-3500 <$600/$1250
4x5 1-5750 <$650
3x10-20 1-1300<$1000/$1500
Series 1875
3x1-2 1-1360 <$600/$1250
4x5 1-1080 <$650
3x10-20 1-1322 <$1000/$1500
Total Issue $292,000
Out in 1910 $1,805

2687 Noble
FNB OF KENDALLVILLE
{{ 1 L }}
Chartered 5/12/82
Liquidated 5/24/94
Brown Back <$VALUE
3x10-20 1-3141 <$850
Total Issue $157,050
Out in 1910 $1,090

10616 Fulton
AMERICAN NB OF KEWANNA
{{ 2 L 1 S }}
Organized 4/21/14
Receivership 2/25/30
1902 Date Back <$VALUE
3x10-20 1-700* <$600
1902 Plain Back
3x10-20 901-4511* <$600
* 701-900 not marked
1929 Small Size
10 Type 1 1-227 <$600
20 Type 1 1-14 <$600
Total Issue $240,850
Out at close $25,000
Large out at close $9,700

8192 Fulton
FNB OF KEWANNA
{{ UNREPORTED }}
Chartered 4/06
Liquidated 2/29/12
1902 Red Seal <$VALUE
3x10-20 1-925 <$1500
1902 Date Back
3x10-20 1-632 <$1000
Total Issue $77,850
Out in 1912 $17,300

9115 Clinton
FNB OF KIRKLIN
{{ 1 L }}
Chartered 4/08
Liquidated 12/16/27
1902 Date Back <$VALUE
3x10-20 1-2890 <$750
1902 Plain Back
3x10-20 2891-5904 <$750
Total Issue $295,200
Out in 1926 $27,600

****
9152 Henry
CITIZENS NB OF KNIGHTSTOWN
{{ 6 L 10 S }}
Chartered 5/08
1902 Date Back <$VALUE
4x5 1-3065 <$250
3x10-20 1-2312 <$250
1902 Plain Back
4x5 3066-11190 <$250
3x10-20 2313-7485 <$250
1929 Small Size
5 Type 1 1-1554 <$125
10 Type 1 1-964 <$125
20 Type 1 1-222 <$125
5 Type 2 1-1564 <$150
10 Type 2 1-645 <$150
20 Type 2 1-146 <$150
Total Issue $746,340
Out in 1935 $50,000
Large out 1935 $2,060
****
872 Henry
FNB OF KNIGHTSTOWN
{{ 4 L U + 9 S }}
Chartered 1865
Original Series <$VALUE
3x1-2 1-1000 <$500/$1000
4x5 1-6750 <$600
3x10-20 1-600 <$750/$1250
Series 1875
3x10-20 1-1030 <$750/$1250
Brown Back
3x10-20 1-1091 <$500
1902 Red Seal
3x10-20 1-950 <$600
1902 Date Back
3x10-20 1-1520 <$300
1902 Plain Back
4x5 1-392 <$300
3x10-20 1521-4159 <$300
1929 Small Size
5 Type 1 1-5266 <$125
5 Type 2 1-11642 <$125
Total Issue $755,530
Out in 1935 $50,000
Large out 1935 $2,295
****
5919 Starke
FNB OF KNOX
{{ UNREPORTED }}
Chartered 7/01
Liquidated 6/17/16
Brown Back <$VALUE
3x10-20 1-1400 <$1250
1882 Date Back
3x10-20 1-1810 <$1250
1882 Value Back
3x10-20 1811-1881 <$1250
Total Issue $164,050
Out in 1916 $21,700
****
4121 Howard
CITIZENS NB OF KOKOMO
{{ 7 L 6 S }}
Organized 2/22/89
Receivership 10/23/31
Brown Back <$VALUE
3x10-20 1-7181 <$350
1902 Date Back
3x10-20 1-13000 <$200
1902 Plain Back
3x10-20 13001-45039 <$200
1929 Small Size
10 Type 1 1-2427 <$150
20 Type 1 1-632 <$150
Total Issue $2,832,460
Out in 1929 $200,000
Large out at close $21,430
****
894 Howard
FNB OF KOKOMO
{{ UNREPORTED }}
Chartered 1865
Liquidated 1/1/85
Original Series <$VALUE
4x5 1-4550 <$1250
Series 1875
4x5 1-4040 <$1250
Total Issue $171,800
Out in 1910 $1,425
****
2375 Howard
HOWARD NB OF KOKOMO
{{ 10 L 6 S }}
Chartered 12/11/77
Liquidated 7/15/30
Series 1875 <$VALUE
4x5 1-12033 <$600
Brown Back
3x10-20 1-6300 <$250/$300
1882 Date Back
4x5 1-10582 <$225
3x10-20 1-9600 <$225
1882 Value Back
4x5 10583-15055 <$225
3x10-20 9601-10640 <$225
1902 Plain Back
3x10-20 1-28431 <$150
1929 Small Size
10 Type 1 1-2045 <$175
20 Type 1 1-346 <$175
Total Issue $2,974,530
Out at close $200,000
Large out at close $39,610
****
6261 Howard
KOKOMO NB, KOKOMO
{{ 1 L }}
Chartered 5/02
Liquidated 2/14/12
1902 Red Seal <$VALUE
3x10-20 1-6200 <$750
1902 Date Back
3x10-20 1-2300 <$450
Total Issue $425,000
Out in 1912 $62,450
****
7415 Tippecanoe
AMERICAN NB OF LAFAYETTE
{{ 2 L }}
Chartered 9/04
Liquidated 2/18/18
1902 Red Seal <$VALUE
3x10-20 1-5000 <$700
1902 Date Back
3x10-20 1-8200 <$350
1902 Plain Back
3x10-20 8201-10441 <$350
Total Issue $772,050
Out at close $125,000
****
5940 Tippecanoe
CITY NB OF LAFAYETTE
{{ 7 L }}
Chartered 8/01
Liquidated 4/30/27
Brown Back <$VALUE
3x10-20 1-3300 <$300
1882 Date Back
4x5 1-7265 <$300
3x10-20 1-5000 <$300
1882 Value Back
4x5 7266-12045 <$300
3x10-20 5001-8210 <$300
1902 Plain Back
4x5 1-6500 <$150
3x10-20 1-4988 <$150
Total Issue $1,195,800
Out at close $100,000
****
11148 Tippecanoe
F-MERCHANTS NB OF LAFAYETTE
{{ 10 L 29 S }}
Chartered 2/18
1902 Plain Back <$VALUE
3x10-20 1-48046 <$100
1929 Small Size
10 Type 1 1-7702 <$30
20 Type 1 1-2026 <$40
10 Type 2 1-3251 <$30
20 Type 2 1-929 <$40
Total Issue $3,158,630
Out in 1935 $325,000
Large out 1935 $10,800
****
23 Tippecanoe
FNB OF LAFAYETTE
{{ 2 L }}
Chartered 7/63
Liquidated 5/31/82
Original Series <$VALUE
3x1-2 1-18000 <$600/$1250
4x5 1-15000 <$650
4x10 1-7000 <$850
2x20-50-100 1-750
<$1250/$4000/$4000
Series 1875
4x5 1-4495 <$650
4x10 1-1500 <$850
Total Issue $962,400
Out in 1910 $6,823
****
2717 Tippecanoe
FNB OF LAFAYETTE
{{ 3 L }}
Chartered 1882
Liquidated 2/18/18
Brown Back <$VALUE
4x5 1-8200 <$400
3x10-20 124980 <$400
1902 Red Seal
3x10-20 1-6900 <$500
1902 Date Back
3x10-20 1-10000 <$250
1902 Plain Back
3x10-20 10001-11871 <$250
Total Issue $1,351,550
Out in 1917 $167,845
****
3280 Tippecanoe
FOWLER NB OF LAFAYETTE
{{ UNREPORTED }}
Chartered 12/30/84
Liquidated 6/29/01
Brown Back <$VALUE
3x10-20 1-3022 <$1000
Total Issue $151,100
Out in 1910 $2,150
****
1967 Tippecanoe
INDIANA NB OF LAFAYETTE
{{ 3 L }}
Chartered 4/22/72
Liquidated 11/13/91
Original Series <$VALUE
3x1-2 1-8000 <$500/$1000
4x5 1-6500 <$600
3x10-20 1-2000 <$750/$1250
Series 1875
3x1-2 1-1000 <$500/$1000
4x5 1-2050 <$600
3x10-20 1-5705 <$750/$1250
Total Issue $601,250
Out in 1910 $3,058
****
2213 Tippecanoe
LAFAYETTE NB, LAFAYETTE
{{ 2 L }}
Chartered 12/24/74
Liquidated 8/29/90
Original Series <$VALUE
3x1-2 1-4000 <$500/$1000
4x5 1-1250 <$600
3x10-20 1-4000 <$750/$1250
50-100 1-167 <$4000
Series 1875
3x1-2 1-860 <$500/$1000
4x5 1-4500 <$600
3x10-20 1-5157 <$750/$1250
50-100 1-1211 <$4000
Total Issue $803,850
Out in 1910 $3,551
****
4468 Tippecanoe
MERCHANTS NB OF LAFAYETTE
{{ 3 L }}
Chartered 1890
Liquidated 2/18/18
Brown Back <$VALUE
3x10-20 1-12390 <$400
1882 Date Back
3x10-20 1-2339 <$400
1902 Date Back
3x10-20 1-10755 <$300
Total Issue $1,274,200
Out at close $100,000
****
5889 Tippecanoe
N FOWLER B OF LAFAYETTE
{{ 7 L 9 S }}
Chartered 7/01
Liquidated 9/1/32
Brown Back <$VALUE
3x10-20 1-6200 <$350
1882 Date Back
3x10-20 1-6200* <$350
1882 Value Back
3x10-20 6701-10400* <$350
* 6201-6700 not marked
1902 Plain Back
3x10-20 1-8844 <$175
1929 Small Size
10 Type 1 1-1949 <$125
20 Type 1 1-494 <$125
Total Issue $1,448,420
Out at close $100,000
Large out at close $9,860
****
930 Tippecanoe
N STATE B OF LAFAYETTE
{{ 10 L }}
Chartered 1865
Liquidated 1/16/85
Original Series <$VALUE
3x1-2 1-20560 <$350/$850
4x5 1-15850 <$400
4x10 1-4450 <$750
3x20-50 1-2776<$1250/$4000
Series 1875
3x1-2 1-2984 <$350/$850
4x5 1-2000 <$400
4x10 1-1534 <$750
3x20-50 1-796 <$1250/$4000
Total Issue $1,107,000
Out in 1910 $7,972
****
4656 Tippecanoe
PERRIN NB OF LAFAYETTE
{{ 1 L }}
Chartered 11/27/91
Liquidated 7/1/02
Brown Back <$VALUE
3x10-20 1-6891 <$750
Total Issue $344,550
Out in 1910 $5,130
****
417 Tippecanoe
SECOND NB OF LAFAYETTE
{{ 3 L }}
Chartered 1864
Liquidated 12/20/77
Original Series <$VALUE
3x1-2 1-7000 <$400/$850
4x5 1-6455 <$400
3x10-20 1-2700 <$750/$1250
50-100 1-200 <$4000
Total Issue $329,100
Out in 1910 $2,570
****
882 Tippecanoe
UNION NB OF LAFAYETTE
{{ 3 L }}
Chartered 3/13/65
Liquidated 12/4/74
Original Series <$VALUE
3x1-2 1-7600 <$400/$850
4x5 1-9300 <$400
3x10-20 1-1500 <$750/$1250
50-100 1-300 <$4000
Total Issue $344,000
Out in 1910 $3,399
****
2184 Lagrange
FNB OF LAGRANGE
{{ 1 L }}
Chartered 9/12/74
Liquidated 7/30/94
Original Series <$VALUE
4x5 1-2250 <$1000
Series 1875
4x5 1-7359 <$1000
Total Issue $192,180
Out in 1910 $1,085
****
4972 Lagrange
NB OF LAGRANGE
{{ 5 L }}
Organized 7/12/94
Receivership 10/24/27
Brown Back <$VALUE
4x5 1-2300 <$400
3x10-20 1-990 <$400
1882 Date Back
4x5 1-2409 <$400
3x10-20 1-1940 <$400
1902 Date Back
4x5 1-830 <$300
3x10-20 1-668 <$300
1902 Plain Back
4x5 831-7125 <$300
3x10-20 669-4752 <$300
Total Issue $620,780
Out at close $49,300
****
377 La Porte
FNB OF La PORTE
Chartered 1864
2nd title:FNB & TC of
La Porte 12/31/28
FIRST TITLE {{ 7 L }}
Original Series <$VALUE
3x1-2 1-4600 <$400/$850
4x5 1-8550 <$500
Series 1875
4x5 1-6000 <$500
Brown Back
4x5 1-6615 <$400
3x10-20 1-1113 <$400
1902 Red Seal
3x10-20 1-2400 <$450
1902 Date Back
4x5 1-6330 <$225
3x10-20 1-4468 <$225
1902 Plain Back
4x5 6331-9758 <$225
3x10-20 4469-7081 <$225
SECOND TITLE {{ 0 L 28 S }}
1902 Plain Back
4x5 1-17 <$350
3x10-20 1-133 <$350
1929 Small Size
5 Type 1 1-2258 <$60
10 Type 1 1-1382 <$60
20 Type 1 1-316 <$65
5 Type 2 1-4728 <$75
10 Type 2 1-2668 <$75
20 Type 2 1-604 <$85
Total Issue $1,429,130
Out in 1935 $100,000
Large out 1935 $5,750
****
4281 Dearborn
CITIZENS NB OF LAWRENCEBURG
{{ 1 L }}
Chartered 4/8/90
Liquidated 10/14/05
Brown Back <$VALUE
4x5 1-2248 <$850
3x10-20 1-1141 <$850
Total Issue $102,010
Out in 1910 $5,370
****
2889 Dearborn
CITY NB OF LAWRENCEBURG
{{ UNREPORTED }}
Organized 2/24/83
Receivership 3/11/84
Brown Back <$VALUE
4x5 1-4050 <$1250
Total Issue $81,000
Out in 1916 $555
****
7909 Dearborn
DEARBORN NB OF LAWRENCEBURG
{{ 7 L 5 S }}
Chartered 9/05
Closed 4/4/31
1902 Red Seal <$VALUE
4x5 1-1750 <$600
3x10-20 1-1410 <$600
1902 Date Back
4x5 1-3500 <$250
3x10-20 1-2300 <$250
1902 Plain Back
4x5 3501-11781 <$250
3x10-20 2301-7658 <$250
1929 Small Size
5 Type 1 1-990 <$200
10 Type 1 1-440 <$200
20 Type 1 1-115 <$200
Total Issue $793,920
Out at close $50,000
Large out at close $7,330
Ch 2612 assumed circulation
****
82 Dearborn
FNB OF LAWRENCEBURG
{{ 1 L }}
Chartered 9/63
Liquidated 2/24/83
Original Series <$VALUE
3x1-2 1-1200 <$750/$1500
4x5 1-9000 <$850
Series 1875
4x5 1-6940 <$850
Total Issue $324,800
Out in 1910 $2,534
****
1418 Dearborn
LAWRENCEBURG NB, LAWRENCEBURG
{{ UNREPORTED }}
Chartered 7/11/65
Liquidated 9/10/72
Original Series <$VALUE
3x1-2 1-2500 <$1000/$2000
4x5 1-5370 <$1000
2x10-20-50 1-1000
<$1250/$2000/$4000
Total Issue $209,900
Out in 1910 $1,775
****
2612 Dearborn
PEOPLES NB OF LAWRENCEBURGH
{{ 21 L 28 S }}
Chartered 1882
Series 1875 <$VALUE
3x10-20 1-4059 <$650/$1250
Brown Back
4x5 1-4000 <$225
4x10 1-1600 <$225
50-100 1-960 <$1250/$1500
1882 Date Back
4x5 1-9250 <$200
4x10 1-5375* <$200
50-100 1-100 <$1250/$1500
1882 Value Back
4x5 9251-16158 <$225
* 5376-11086 not marked
1902 Plain Back
4x10 1-16700 <$100
1929 Small Size
10 Type 1 1-6738 <$40
10 Type 2 1-11546 <$40
Total Issue $2,460,290
Out in 1935 $175,000
Large out 1935 $9,870
Outstanding includes Ch 7909
****
2057 Boone
FNB OF LEBANON
{{ 23 L 12 S }}
Chartered 10/11/72
Receivership 8/29/33
Original Series <$VALUE
3x1-2 1-2000 <$300/$850
4x5 1-4200 <$500
Series 1875
4x5 1-12877 <$500
Brown Back
3x10-20 1-7320 <$300
1882 Date Back
3x10-20 1-2888 <$300
1902 Date Back
3x10-20 1-3400 <$150
1902 Plain Back
3x10-20 3401-17546 <$150
1929 Small Size
10 Type 1 1-2280 <$100
20 Type 1 1-623 <$110
Total Issue $1,950,800
Out at close $100,000
Large out at close $8,760
****
2660 Boone
LEBANON NB, LEBANON
{{ 2 L }}
Chartered 1882
Liquidated 10/26/10
Series 1875 <$VALUE
3x10-20 1-4720 <$850/$1250
1902 Red Seal
3x10-20 1-4200 <$750
1902 Date Back
3x10-20 1-727 <$500
Total Issue $482,350
Out in 1911 $34,430
****
5526 Henry
FNB OF LEWISVILLE
{{ 2 L 2 S }}
Chartered 8/2/00
Receivership 10/8/32
Brown Back <$VALUE
4x5 1-600 <$750
3x10-20 1-490 <$750
1882 Date Back
4x5 1-1200 <$750
3x10-20 1-960 <$750
1882 Value Back
4x5 1201-1950 <$750
3x10-20 961-1385 <$750
1902 Plain Back
3x10-20 1-2286 <$500
1929 Small Size
10 Type 1 1-403 <$400
20 Type 1 1-113 <$400
Total Issue $296,790
Out at close $19,820
Large out at close $1,580
****
1925 Union
FNB OF LIBERTY
{{ UNREPORTED }}
Chartered 1/19/72
Liquidated 7/22/82
Original Series <$VALUE
3x1-2 1-1800 <$1000/$1500
4x5 1-3250 <$1250
Series 1875
4x5 1-4095 <$1250
Total issue $155,900
Out in 1910 $750
****
2007 Union
UNION COUNTY NB OF LIBERTY
{{ 10 L 12 S }}
Chartered 6/29/72
Original Series <$VALUE
4x5 1-2000 <$650
3x10-20 1-500 <$850/$1250
Series 1875
4x5 1-750 <$650
3x10-20 1-2037 <$850/$1250
Brown Back
3x10-20 1-4400 <$400
1882 Date Back
3x10-20 1-1333 <$400
1902 Date Back
3x10-20 1-1700 <$225
1902 Plain Back
3x10-20 1701-9168 <$225
1929 Small Size
10 Type 1 1-1302 <$125
20 Type 1 1-390 <$125
10 Type 2 1-1370 <$150
20 Type 2 1-300 <$150
Total Issue $1,071,520
Out in 1935 $50,000
Large out 1935 $3,140
****

****
1234 Lagrange
N STATE B OF LIMA
{{ UNREPORTED }}
Chartered 1865
Liquidated 3/2/78
Original Series <$VALUE
4x5 1-4763 <$1250
3x10-20 1-960 <$1500/$2000
Series 1875
3x10-20 1-168 <$1500/$2000
Total Issue $151,660
Out in 1910 $850
****
14258 Greene
CITIZENS NB OF LINTON
{{ U + 3 S }}
Chartered 8/34
1929 Small Size <$VALUE
5 Type 2 1-5210 <$400
10 Type 2 1-2760 <$400
Total Issue $53,650
Out in 1935 $50,000
****
7411 Greene
FNB OF LINTON
{{ 7 L 11 S }}
Organized 7/25/04
Receivership 2/1/34
1902 Red Seal <$VALUE
3x10-20 1-630 <$650
1902 Date Back
3x10-20 1-5000 <$250
1902 Plain Back
3x10-20 5001-21746 <$250
1929 Small Size
10 Type 1 1-2386 <$125
20 Type 1 1-690 <$125
10 Type 2 1-18 <$175
Total Issue $1,344,940
Out at close $100,000
Large out at close $6,060
****
City & State NB & TC of Logansport
SEE Ch 5076
City NB of Logansport
****
5076 Cass
CITY NB OF LOGANSPORT
Chartered 1897
Liquidated 10/27/31
2nd title: City & State NB & TC 4/19/30
FIRST TITLE {{ 12 L 16 S }}
Brown Back <$VALUE
3x10-20 1-5600 <$300
1882 Date Back
3x10-20 1-14500 <$300
1882 Value Back
3x10-20 14501-16646 <$300
1902 Plain Back
3x10-20 1-27155 <$125
1929 Small Size
10 Type 1 1-2760 <$75
20 Type 1 1-942 <$75
SECOND TITLE {{ 2 S }}
1929 Small Size
10 Type 1 1-267 <$250
20 Type 1 1-39 <$250
Total Issue $2,769,390
Out at close $200,000
Large out at close $22,800
****
3084 Cass
FNB OF LOGANSPORT
{{ 13 L 16 S }}
Organized 10/3/83
Receivership 11/11/31
Brown Back <$VALUE
3x10-20 1-4795 <$300
1902 Red Seal
3x10-20 1-4900 <$350
1902 Date Back
3x10-20 1-12900 <$125
1902 Plain Back
3x10-20 12901-51391 <$125
1929 Small Size
10 Type 1 1-4169 <$60
20 Type 1 1-1181 <$60
Total Issue $3,446,160
Out at close $246,340
Large out at close $29,390
****
1031 Cass
LOGANSPORT NB, LOGANSPORT
{{ 2 L }}
Chartered 1865
Liquidated 12/1/83
Original Series <$VALUE
4x5 1-3350 <$600
3x10-20 1-1442 <$750/$1250
Series 1875
4x5 1-935 <$600
3x10-20 1-432 <$750/$1250
Total Issue $179,400
Out in 1910 $1,100
****
13580 Cass
NB OF LOGANSPORT
{{ 2U + 24 S }}
Chartered 12/31
1929 Small Size <$VALUE
10 Type 1 1-2376 <$50
20 Type 1 1-706 <$50
10 Type 2 1-4669 <$50
20 Type 2 1-1480 <$50
Total Issue $303,570
Out in 1935 $171,700
****
2596 Cass
STATE NB OF LOGANSPORT
{{ 3 L }}
Organized 12/7/81
Liquidated 1/11/98
Series 1875 <$VALUE
3x10-20 1-3551 <$650/$1250
Total Issue $177,550
Out in 1915 $1,320
****
7241 Martin
FNB OF LOOGOOTEE
{{ 3 L }}
Chartered 5/04
Liquidated 7/13/29
1902 Red Seal <$VALUE
3x10-20 1-330 <$850
1902 Date Back
3x10-20 1-760 <$400
1902 Plain Back
3x10-20 761-2230 <$400
Total Issue $128,000
Out at close $9,250
****
FNB in Lowell
SEE Ch 5931
State NB of Lowell
****
5369 Lake
FNB OF LOWELL
{{ UNREPORTED }}
Chartered 5/25/00
Liquidated 5/29/01
Brown Back <$VALUE
3x10-20 1-200 <$1500
Total Issue $10,000
Out in 1910 $1,100
****
6765 Lake
LOWELL NB, LOWELL
{{ 2 L 2 S }}
Chartered 5/03
1902 Red Seal <$VALUE
50-100 1-420 <$2500
1902 Date Back
50-100 1-520 <$600/$750
3x50-100 1-860 <$600/$750
1902 Plain Back
3x50-100 861-1105 <$600/$750
1929 Small Size
50 Type 1 1-157 <$400
100 Type 1 1-37 <$500
Total Issue $486,550
Out in 1935 $50,000
Large out 1935 $4,000
****
5931 Lake
STATE NB OF LOWELL
Organized 7/11/01
Liquidated 5/21/30
2nd title: FNB in Lowell 2/7/21
FIRST TITLE {{ 2 L }}
Brown Back <$VALUE
3x10-20 1-2400 <$600
1882 Date Back
3x10-20 1-3340 <$600
1882 Value Back
3x10-20 3341-5480 <$600
SECOND TITLE {{ 3 L 2 S }}
1902 Plain Back
3x10-20 1-5346 <$400
1929 Small Size
10 Type 1 1-431 <$400
20 Type 1 1-86 <$400
Total Issue $697,480
Out in 1929 $49,995
Large out at close $13,085
****
8868 Warrick
LYNNVILLE NB, LYNNVILLE
{{ 3 L 5 S }}
Chartered 9/07
1902 Red Seal <$VALUE
3x10-20 1-320 <$750
1902 Date Back
4x5 1-2100 <$375
3x10-20 1-1320 <$375
1902 Plain Back
4x5 2101-6278 <$375
3x10-20 1321-3789 <$375
1929 Small Size
5 Type 1 1-1870 <$225
10 Type 1 1-202 <$225
20 Type 1 1-70 <$250
5 Type 2 1-4526 <$250
Total Issue $430,260
Out in 1935 $25,000
Large out 1935 $1,180
****
111 Jefferson
FNB OF MADISON
{{ 13 L 18 S }}
Chartered 10/63
Original Series <$VALUE
4x10 1-6000 <$750
50-100 1-1900 <$4000
Series 1875
4x10 1-2927 <$750
50-100 1-699 <$4000
Brown Back
3x10-20 1-1458 <$350
50-100 1-661 <$1250/$1500
1902 Red Seal
4x5 1-4450 <$400
3x10-20 1-3120 <$400
1902 Date Back
4x5 1-5400 <$150
3x10-20 1-4360 <$150
1902 Plain Back
4x5 5401-19584 <$150
3x10-20 4361-13623 <$150
1929 Small Size
5 Type 1 1-3592 <$50
10 Type 1 1-1684 <$50
20 Type 1 1-432 <$60
5 Type 2 1-4276 <$50
10 Type 2 1-2037 <$50
20 Type 2 1-405 <$60
Total Issue $2,547,300
Out in 1935 $100,000
Large out 1935 $11,160
****
1457 Jefferson
N BRANCH B OF MADISON
{{ 16 L 27 S }}
Chartered 1865
Original Series <$VALUE
3x1-2 1-3300 <$400/$850
4x5 1-11475 <$500
3x10-20 1-4300 <$750/$1250
Series 1875
4x5 1-820 <$500
3x10-20 1-2554 <$750/$1250
Brown Back
4x5 1-14500 <$300
3x10-20 1-5304 <$300
1902 Red Seal
4x5 1-4500 <$350
3x10-20 1-2700 <$350
1902 Date Back
4x5 1-7000 <$135
3x10-20 1-6800 <$135
1902 Plain Back
4x5 7001-29412 <$135
3x10-20 6801-20724 <$135
1929 Small Size
5 Type 1 1-4940 <$50
10 Type 1 1-2734 <$50
20 Type 1 1-724 <$65
5 Type 2 1-6792 <$60
10 Type 2 1-3892 <$60
20 Type 2 1-786 <$75
Total Issue $3,497,460
Out in 1935 $149,995
Large out 1935 $11,395
****
13717 Grant
FNB IN MARION
{{ U + 5 S }}
Chartered 6/33
1929 Small Size <$VALUE
5 Type 2 1-7096 <$165
10 Type 2 1-3676 <$165
20 Type 2 1-1268 <$175
50 Type 2 1-132 <$300
Total Issue $104,200
Out in 1935 $99,150
****
4189 Grant
FNB OF MARION
{{ 18 L 28 S }}
Organized 12/4/89
Receivership 12/5/33
Brown Back <$VALUE
3x10-20 1-4586 <$250/$300
1902 Date Back
3x10-20 1-13400 <$100
1902 Plain Back
3x10-20 13401-44989 <$100
1929 Small Size
5 Type 1 1-1802 <$35
10 Type 1 1-6691 <$35
20 Type 1 1-1740 <$45
Total Issue $3,143,070
Out at close $350,000
Large out at close $11,050
****
7758 Grant
MARION NB, MARION
{{ 18 L 22 S }}
Organized 5/22/05
Liquidated 11/6/33
1902 Red Seal <$VALUE
4x5 1-3500 <$250
3x10-20 1-5100 <$250
1902 Date Back
4x5 1-12750 <$100
3x10-20 1-9700 <$100
1902 Plain Back
4x5 12751-41754 <$100
3x10-20 9701-28740 <$100
1929 Small Size
5 Type 1 1-8220 <$30
10 Type 1 1-3670 <$35
20 Type 1 1-1064 <$45
5 Type 2 1-1110 <$50
10 Type 2 1-630 <$60
Total Issue $3,203,410
Out at close $250,000
Large out 1935 $9,215
Ch 13729 assumed circulation
****
4964 Morgan
CITIZENS NB OF MARTINSVILLE
{{ 6 L }}
Chartered 1894
Liquidated 2/25/29
Brown Back <$VALUE
4x5 1-1950 <$500
3x10-20 1-940 <$500
1882 Date Back
4x5 1-625 <$500
3x10-20 1-3363 <$500
1902 Date Back
3x10-20 1-3000 <$275
1902 Plain Back
3x10-20 3001-16361 <$275
Total Issue $1,084,700
Out at close $100,000
****
794 Morgan
FNB OF MARTINSVILLE
{{ 10 L 10 S }}
Organized 1/2/65
Receivership 6/27/32
Original Series <$VALUE
3x1-2 1-3640 <$500/$1000
4x5 1-3390 <$500
3x10-20 1-2000 <$750/$1250
Series 1875
3x10-20 1-1046 <$750/$1250
Brown Back
3x10-20 1-2865 <$400
1902 Red Seal
3x10-20 1-1600 <$500
1902 Date Back
3x10-20 1-5400 <$250
1902 Plain Back
3x10-20 5401-19551 <$250
1929 Small Size
10 Type 1 1-1934 <$150
20 Type 1 1-532 <$150
Total Issue $1,618,980
Out at close $99,700
Large out at close $12,350
****
13643 Morgan
NB OF MARTINSVILLE
{{ 5 S }}
Chartered 10/32
1929 Small Size <$VALUE
5 Type 2 1-10272 <$225
10 Type 2 1-4039 <$225
Total Issue $91,750
Out in 1935 $40,050
****
5998 Grant
FNB OF MATTHEWS
{{ UNREPORTED }}
Organized 10/24/01
Receivership 2/13/04
Brown Back <$VALUE
4x5 1-310 <$1500
3x10-20 1-245 <$1500
Total Issue $18,450
Out in 1915 $215
****
8700 Rush
FNB OF MAYS
{{ 4 L 4 S }}
Chartered 5/07
1902 Red Seal <$VALUE
4x5 1-156 <$850
3x10-20 1-125 <$850
1902 Date Back
4x5 1-1390 <$400
3x10-20 1-1094 <$400
1902 Plain Back
4x5 1391-10563 <$400
3x10-20 1095-2214 <$400
1929 Small Size
5 Type 1 1-3148 <$275
5 Type 2 1-4656 <$275
Total Issue $449,050
Out in 1935 $25,000
Large out 1935 $985
****
8537 Pulaski
FNB OF MEDARYVILLE
{{ 1 L }}
Organized 1/23/07
Receivership 6/24/27
1902 Red Seal <$VALUE
3x10-20 1-200 <$1250
1902 Date Back
3x10-20 1-700 <$850
1902 Plain Back
3x10-20 701-1110 <$850
Total Issue $65,500
Out at close $6,100
****
8368 Kosciusko
FNB OF MENTONE
{{ 1 L }}
Chartered 9/06
Liquidated 7/31/11
1902 Red Seal <$VALUE
4x5 1-325 <$1250
3x10-20 1-260 <$1250
1902 Date Back
4x5 1-280 <$850
3x10-20 1-332 <$850
Total Issue $41,700
Out in 1911 $13,400
****
2101 La Porte
FNB OF MICHIGAN CITY
{{ UNREPORTED }}
Chartered 4/11/73
Liquidated 6/30/82
Original Series <$VALUE
3x1-2 1-1500 <$1000/$2000
4x5 1-2875 <$1250
Series 1875
4x5 1-2910 <$1250
Total Issue $123,200
Out in 1910 $649
****
2747 La Porte
FNB OF MICHIGAN CITY
{{ 9 L 9 S }}
Chartered 1882
Brown Back <$VALUE
4x5 1-13570 <$400
50-100 1-224 <$1250/$1500
1902 Red Seal
50-100 1-900 <$2250/$2500
1902 Date Back
3x10-20 1-5400 <$175
50-100 1-600 <$400/$500
3x50-100 1-420 <$400/$500
1902 Plain Back
3x10-20 5401-16320 <$175
3x50-100 421-661 <$400/$500
1929 Small Size
10 Type 1 1-924 <$125
20 Type 1 1-347 <$125
50 Type 1 1-147 <$250
100 Type 1 1-42 <$350
Total Issue $1,677,630
Out in 1935 $62,500
Large out 1935 $11,420
****
9381 La Porte
MERCHANTS NB OF MICHIGAN CITY
{{ 8 L 12 S }}
Chartered 4/09
1902 Date Back <$VALUE
4x5 1-6075 <$225
3x10-20 1-4580 <$225
1902 Plain Back
4x5 6076-22789 <$225
3x10-20 4581-15641 <$225
1929 Small Size
5 Type 1 1-3604 <$110
10 Type 1 1-1762 <$110
20 Type 1 1-486 <$125
5 Type 2 1-440 <$175
10 Type 2 1-125 <$175
20 Type 2 1-75 <$175
Total Issue $1,514,940
Out in 1935 $50,000
Large out 1935 $4,695
****
8650 Crawford
FNB OF MILLTOWN
{{ 3 L 12 S }}
Organized 3/7/07
1902 Red Seal <$VALUE
3x10-20 1-195 <$850
1902 Date Back
3x10-20 1-1030 <$450
1902 Plain Back
3x10-20 1031-3383 <$450
1929 Small Size
10 Type 1 1-482 <$175
20 Type 1 1-130 <$175
10 Type 2 1-95 <$225
20 Type 2 1-15 <$225
Total Issue $224,670
Out in 1935 $16,500
Large out 1935 $1,060
****
11782 Rush
FNB OF MILROY
{{ 5 L 9 S }}
Chartered 7/20
Liquidated 9/20/34
1902 Plain Back <$VALUE
4x5 1-6758 <$275
3x10-20 1-4546 <$275
1929 Small Size
5 Type 1 1-1778 <$125
10 Type 1 1-896 <$125
20 Type 1 1-244 <$125
5 Type 2 1-792 <$150
10 Type 2 1-331 <$150
20 Type 2 1-75 <$150
Total Issue $507,610
Out at close $50,000
Large out at close $1,740
****
5167 Saint Joseph
FNB OF MISHAWAKA
{{ 10 L 15 S }}
Chartered 1/7/99
Brown Back <$VALUE
4x5 1-1540 <$300
3x10-20 1-1426 <$300/$350
1882 Date Back
4x5 1-3200 <$275
3x10-20 1-2280* <$275
1882 Value Back
4x5 3201-6057 <$300
3x10-20 3081-4140* <$300
* 2281-3080 not marked
1902 Plain Back
4x5 1-14531 <$150
3x10-20 1-10208 <$150
1929 Small Size
5 Type 1 1-3908 <$70
10 Type 1 1-1972 <$70
20 Type 1 1-432 <$80
5 Type 2 1-3576 <$100
10 Type 2 1-1930 <$100
20 Type 2 1-550 <$100
Total Issue $1,566,840
Out in 1935 $100,000
Large out 1935 $4,340
****
6433 Lawrence
FNB OF MITCHELL
{{ 3 L 5 S }}
Organized 5/27/02
1902 Red Seal <$VALUE
3x10-20 1-1100 <$750
1902 Date Back
3x10-20 1-1450 <$400
1902 Plain Back
3x10-20 1451-5006 <$400
1929 Small Size
10 Type 1 1-566 <$225
20 Type 1 1-168 <$225
10 Type 2 1-821 <$225
20 Type 2 1-168 <$225
Total Issue $370,990
Out in 1935 $25,000
Large out 1935 $970
****

****
6354 Morgan
FNB OF MONROVIA
{{ 2 L 1 S }}
Organized 4/25/02
Receivership 1/5/33
1902 Red Seal <$VALUE
4x5 1-600 <$1000
3x10-20 1-800 <$1000
1902 Date Back
4x5 1-1775 <$500
3x10-20 1-1330 <$500
1902 Plain Back (dated 1902)
4x5 1776-3350 <$500
3x10-20 1331-2230 <$500
1902 Plain Back (dated 1922)
4x5 1-7440 <$500
1929 Small Size
5 Type 1 1-2744 <$600
Total Issue $461,620
Out at close $24,760
Large out at close $1,690
****
9784 Pulaski
FNB OF MONTEREY
{{ 3 L 6 S }}
Chartered 6/10
1902 Date Back <$VALUE
3x10-20 1-1650 <$400
1902 Plain Back
3x10-20 1651-5197 <$400
1929 Small Size
10 Type 1 1-654 <$200
20 Type 1 1-168 <$200
10 Type 2 1-381 <$225
20 Type 2 1-95 <$250
Total Issue $324,960
Out in 1935 $25,000
Large out 1935 $1,140
****
7463 Parke
FNB OF MONTEZUMA
{{ 5 L 4 S }}
Chartered 11/04
Liquidated 2/29/32
1902 Red Seal <$VALUE
4x5 1-265 <$750
3x10-20 1-230 <$750
1902 Date Back
4x5 1-575 <$350
3x10-20 1-460 <$350
1902 Plain Back
4x5 576-4837 <$350
3x10-20 461-3071 <$350
1929 Small Size
5 Type 1 1-645 <$300
10 Type 1 1-317 <$300
20 Type 1 1-85 <$300
Total Issue $315,660
Out at close $25,000
Large out at close $1,590
****
5734 Daviess
FNB OF MONTGOMERY
{{ 1 L }}
Chartered 3/01
Liquidated 12/6/11
Brown Back <$VALUE
3x10-20 1-680 <$1500
1882 Date Back
3x10-20 1-602 <$1500
Total Issue $64,100
Out in 1912 $2,350
****
2208 White
FNB OF MONTICELLO
{{ 2 L }}
Chartered 12/3/74
Receivership 7/18/79
Original Series <$VALUE
3x1-2 1-1500 <$750/$1500
4x5 1-1875 <$850
Series 1875
3x1-2 1-400 <$750/$1500
4x5 1-600 <$850
Total Issue $59,000
Out in 1915 $376
****
6172 White
MONTICELLO NB, MONTICELLO
{{ 3 L }}
Organized 3/10/02
Receivership 1/7/27
1902 Red Seal <$VALUE
4x5 1-1305 <$750
3x10-20 1-1068 <$750
1902 Date Back
4x5 1-2850 <$350
3x10-20 1-2020 <$350
1902 Plain Back (dated 1902)
4x5 2851-6200 <$350
3x10-20 2021-3900 <$350
1902 Plain Back (dated 1922)
4x5 1-2655 <$350
3x10-20 1-1662 <$350
Total Issue $534,700
Out at close $48,600
****
5278 Blackford
FNB OF MONTPELIER
{{ 6 L 5 S }}
Organized 3/20/00
Receivership 10/3/33
Brown Back <$VALUE
4x5 1-1725 <$400
3x10-20 1-1300 <$400
1882 Date Back
4x5 1-2750* <$400
3x10-20 1-2100** <$400
1882 Value Back
4x5 2901-4705* <$400
3x10-20 2221-3260** <$400
* 2751-2900 not marked
** 2101-2220 not marked
1902 Plain Back
4x5 1-5946 <$250
4x10 1-2488 <$250
3x10-20 1-2300 <$250
1929 Small Size
5 Type 1 1-1518 <$200
10 Type 1 1-895 <$200
20 Type 1 1-218 <$200
Total Issue $815,440
Out at close $50,000
Large out at close $3,150
****
6876 Morgan
FNB OF MOORESVILLE
{{ 4 L }}
Chartered 7/03
Liquidated 8/16/26
1902 Red Seal <$VALUE
3x10-20 1-1056 <$700
1902 Date Back
3x10-20 1-1270 <$350
1902 Plain Back
3x10-20 1271-5668 <$350
Total Issue $336,200
Out at close $35,000
****
7652 Morgan
FNB OF MORGANTOWN
{{ 11 L }}
Chartered 3/05
Liquidated 8/1/29
1902 Red Seal <$VALUE
3x10-20 1-1057 <$500
1902 Date Back
3x10-20 1-1640 <$175
1902 Plain Back
3x10-20 1641-4926 <$175
Total Issue $299,150
Out at close $23,050
****
366 Posey
FNB OF MOUNT VERNON
{{ 9 L }}
Chartered 1864
Liquidated 11/30/23
Original Series <$VALUE
3x1-2 1-5800 <$500/$1000
4x5 1-8300 <$500
Series 1875
3x1-2 1-620 <$500/$1000
4x5 1-6250 <$500
Brown Back
4x5 1-7545 <$350
3x10-20 1-4719 <$350
1902 Red Seal
50-100 1-826 <$2250/$2500
1902 Date Back
50-100 1-600 <$500/$600
3x50-100 1-1213 <$500/$600
Total Issue $1,227,100
Out at close $100,000
****
7786 Posey
MOUNT VERNON NB,
MOUNT VERNON
{{ 2 L }}
Chartered 6/05
Liquidated 6/30/25
1902 Red Seal <$VALUE
3x10-20 1-2050 <$750
1902 Date Back
3x10-20 1-3540 <$375
1902 Plain Back
3x10-20 3541-8627 <$375
Total Issue $533,850
Out at close $49,995
Ch 12780 assumed circulation
****
12780 Posey
MOUNT VERNON NB & TC,
MOUNT VERNON
{{ 3 L 2 S }}
Organized 6/22/25
Liquidated 3/20/30
1902 Plain Back <$VALUE
3x10-20 1-2635 <$500
1929 Small Size
10 Type 1 1-452 <$400
20 Type 1 1-41 <$400
Total Issue $163,790
Out at close $46,885
Large out at close $14,845
Outstanding includes Ch 7786
****
12466 Posey
OLD FNB OF MOUNT VERNON
{{ 2 L 5 S }}
Organized 10/30/23
Liquidated 9/21/31
1902 Plain Back <$VALUE
3x10-20 1-5360 <$450
1929 Small Size
10 Type 1 1-1456 <$225
20 Type 1 1-429 <$225
Total Issue $406,840
Out at close $100,000
Large out at close $18,670
Outstanding includes Ch 366
****
10234 Clinton
CITIZENS NB OF MULBERRY
{{ 6 L 9 S }}
Chartered 7/30/12
Receivership 8/15/33
1902 Date Back <$VALUE
4x5 1-2300 <$300
3x10-20 1-1720* <$300
1902 Plain Back
4x5 2301-10303 <$300
3x10-20 1841-6896* <$300
* 1721-1840 not marked
1929 Small Size
5 Type 1 1-1421 <$150
10 Type 1 1-794 <$150
20 Type 1 1-247 <$165
Total Issue $670,770
Out at close $49,400
Large out at close $2,830
****
4801 Clinton
FARMERS NB OF MULBERRY
{{ 2 L }}
Chartered 1892
Liquidated 7/30/12
Brown Back <$VALUE
3x10-20 1-2843 <$750
Total Issue $142,150
Out in 1912 $10,800
****
2234 Delaware
CITIZENS NB OF MUNCIE
Chartered 3/15/75
2nd title:Union NB 11/26/95
3rd title:Merchants NB
1/26/20
FIRST TITLE {{ 1 L }}
Original Series <$VALUE
4x5 1-2500 <$650
Series 1875
4x5 1-11939 <$650
Brown Back
4x5 1-448 <$500
SECOND TITLE {{ 4 L }}
Brown Back
3x10-20 1-4500 <$250/$300
1882 Date Back
3x10-20 1-2861 <$250/$300
1902 Date Back
3x10-20 1-3500 <$175
1902 Plain Back
3x10-20 3501-8900 <$175
THIRD TITLE {{ 18 L 37 S }}
1902 Plain Back
4x5 1-51111 <$100
3x10-20 1-31301 <$100
1929 Small Size
5 Type 1 1-14634 <$30
10 Type 1 1-7330 <$30
20 Type 1 1-1868 <$40
5 Type 2 1-26306 <$30
10 Type 2 1-11501 <$30
20 Type 2 1-2974 <$40
Total Issue $5,107,060
Out in 1935 $449,995
Large out 1935 $18,685
Outstanding includes Ch 4852
****
4809 Delaware
DELAWARE COUNTY NB OF
MUNCIE
{{ 17 L 50+ S }}
Chartered 1892
Liquidated 5/10/33
Brown Back <$VALUE
4x5 1-8800 <$250
3x10-20 1-4900 <$250/$300
1882 Date Back
4x5 1-5868 <$250
3x10-20 1-4184 <$250/$300
1902 Date Back
4x5 1-5250 <$100
3x10-20 1-4000 <$100
1902 Plain Back
4x5 5251-52375 <$100
3x10-20 4001-36309 <$100
1929 Small Size
5 Type 1 1-9761 <$35
10 Type 1 1-5571 <$35
20 Type 1 1-1206 <$45
Total Issue $4,382,320
Out at close $300,000
Large out at close $16,685
****
4674 Delaware
FARMERS NB OF MUNCIE
{{ 2 L }}
Chartered 1/4/92
Liquidated 1/26/95
Brown Back <$VALUE
4x5 1-2205 <$750
Total Issue $44,100
Out in 1910 $330
****
4852 Delaware
MERCHANTS NB OF MUNCIE
{{ 8 L }}
Chartered 1893
Closed 1/26/20
Brown Back <$VALUE
4x5 1-7300 <$300
3x10-20 1-11200 <$300/$350
1882 Date Back
4x5 1-2490 <$300
3x10-20 1-7426 <$300/$350
1902 Date Back
4x5 1-5500 <$175
3x10-20 1-4400 <$175
1902 Plain Back
4x5 5501-14390 <$175
3x10-20 4401-9402 <$175
Total Issue $1,885,000
Out at close $224,995
Ch 2234 assumed circulation
****
Merchants NB of Muncie
SEE Ch 2234
Citizens NB of Muncie
****
793 Delaware
MUNCIE NB, MUNCIE
{{ 3 L }}
Chartered 1865
Liquidated 1/28/85
Original Series <$VALUE
3x1-2 1-7000 <$400/$850
4x5 1-14500 <$400
3x10-20 1-4200 <$600/$850
Series 1875
4x5 1-6455 <$400
3x10-20 1-2298 <$600/$850
Total Issue $779,000
Out in 1910 $4,940
****
7454 Delaware
PEOPLES NB OF MUNCIE
{{ UNREPORTED }}
Chartered 10/26/04
Liquidated 3/14/08
1902 Red Seal <$VALUE
3x10-20 1-2219 <$1250
Total Issue $110,950
Out in 1910 $15,600
****
Union NB of Muncie
SEE Ch 2234
Citizens NB of Muncie
****
8785 Elkhart
FNB OF NAPPANEE
{{ 3 L 4 S }}
Organized 6/27/07
Receivership 9/26/33
1902 Red Seal <$VALUE
3x10-20 1-900 <$750
1902 Date Back
3x10-20 1-2640 <$375
1902 Plain Back
3x10-20 2641-8503 <$375
1929 Small Size
10 Type 1 1-869 <$275
20 Type 1 1-256 <$275
Total Issue $553,010
Out at close $40,000
Large out at close $2,225
****
701 Floyd
FNB OF NEW ALBANY
{{ 4 L }}
Chartered 1/11/65
Liquidated 10/26/97
Original Series <$VALUE
3x1-2 1-6900 <$350/$750
4x5 1-11000 <$400
3x10-20 1-3200 <$750/$1250
50-100 1-750 <$4000
Series 1875
4x5 1-1300 <$400
3x10-20 1-2442 <$650/$1250
50-100 1-500 <$4000
Brown Back
3x10-20 1-2834 <$350
Total Issue $891,800
Out in 1910 $7,611
****
965 Floyd
MERCHANTS NB OF
NEW ALBANY
{{ 4 L }}
Chartered 1865
Liquidated 12/21/09
Original Series <$VALUE
3x1-2 1-2700 <$350/$750
4x5 1-9400 <$400
3x10-20 1-2900 <$750/$1250
Series 1875
4x5 1-1946 <$400
3x10-20 1-1730 <$750/$1250
Brown Back
3x10-20 1-4433 <$350
1902 Red Seal
4x5 1-3535 <$350
3x10-20 1-2200 <$350
1902 Date Back
3x10-20 1-234 <$250
Total Issue $885,970
Out in 1910 $60,197
****
775 Floyd
NEW ALBANY NB, NEW ALBANY
{{ 10 L 15 S }}
Organized 1/3/65
Receivership 3/23/34
Original Series <$VALUE
3x1-2 1-10000 <$300/$750
4x5 1-21200 <$350
3x20-50 1-1100<$1250/$4000
100-100 1-200 <$4000
Series 1875
4x5 1-6474 <$350
3x20-50 1-1399<$1250/$4000
100-100 1-223 <$4000
Brown Back
50-100 1-1823 <$1250/$1500
1902 Red Seal
3x10-20 1-3500 <$300
1902 Date Back
3x10-20 1-7700 <$125
1902 Plain Back
3x10-20 7701-19900 <$125
1929 Small Size
10 Type 1 1-2622 <$60
20 Type 1 1-672 <$70
10 Type 2 1-368 <$100
20 Type 2 1-100 <$100
Total Issue $2,650,060
Out at close $99,550
Large out at close $13,320
****
2166 Floyd
SECOND NB OF NEW ALBANY
{{ 19 L 40 S }}
Chartered 8/12/74
Receivership 3/23/34
Original Series <$VALUE
4x5 1-6500 <$400
Series 1875
4x5 1-11766 <$400
Brown Back
50-100 1-1975 <$1250/$1500
1882 Date Back
50-100 1-3200 <$1250/$1500
3x50-100 1-533<$1250/$1500
1902 Date Back
4x5 1-5000 <$85
4x10 1-5000 <$85
1902 Plain Back
4x5 5001-62233 <$85
4x10 5001-44070 <$85
1929 Small Size
5 Type 1 1-19334 <$30
10 Type 1 1-7678 <$35
5 Type 2 1-12356 <$30
10 Type 2 1-5080 <$35
Total Issue $5,435,560
Out at close $292,850
Large out at close $16,865
****
5639 Saint Joseph
FNB OF NEW CARLISLE
{{ 5 L 6 S }}
Chartered 12/14/00
Brown Back <$VALUE
3x10-20 1-1500 <$500
1882 Date Back
3x10-20 1-1730 <$500
1882 Value Back
3x10-20 1731-2629 <$500
1902 Plain Back
3x10-20 1-2931 <$275
1929 Small Size
10 Type 1 1-694 <$200
20 Type 1 1-172 <$200
10 Type 2 1-279 <$225
20 Type 2 1-60 <$225
Total Issue $419,270
Out in 1935 $25,000
Large out 1935 $1,940
****
2202 Henry
BUNDY NB OF NEW CASTLE
{{ UNREPORTED }}
Chartered 11/2/74
Liquidated 12/6/80
Original Series <$VALUE
4x5 1-2250 <$1250
Series 1875
4x5 1-1860 <$1250
Total Issue $82,200
Out in 1910 $245
****
Farmers & FNB of New Castle
SEE Ch 9852
Farmers NB of New Castle
****
9852 Henry
FARMERS NB OF NEW CASTLE
Organized 8/11/10
Receivership 12/8/33
2nd title:Farmers & FNB
6/21/22
FIRST TITLE {{ 4 L }}
1902 Date Back <$VALUE
3x10-20 1-6500 <$300
1902 Plain Back
3x10-20 6501-13400 <$300
SECOND TITLE {{ 4 L 12 S }}
1902 Plain Back
3x50-100 1-2131 <$400/$500
1929 Small Size
5 Type 1 1-290 <$150
10 Type 1 1-60 <$150
20 Type 1 1-25 <$150
50 Type 1 1-454 <$175
100 Type 1 1-151 <$200
Total Issue $1,444,850
Out at close $199,400
Large out at close $25,780
Outstanding includes Ch 804
****
804 Henry
FNB OF NEW CASTLE
{{ U + 4 L }}
Chartered 1865
Closed 6/21/22
Original Series <$VALUE
3x1-2 1-1700 <$400/$1000
4x5 1-2650 <$450
3x10-20 1-2800 <$750/$1250
Series 1875
3x1-2 1-300 <$400/$1000
4x5 1-2325 <$450
3x10-20 1-1360 <$750/$1250
Brown Back
3x10-20 1-4877 <$350
1902 Red Seal
3x10-20 1-3300 <$400
1902 Date Back
3x10-20 1-6300 <$275
1902 Plain Back
3x10-20 6301-12308 <$275
Total Issue $1,341,750
Out at close $100,000
Ch 9852 assumed circulation
****

6699 Posey
FNB OF NEW HARMONY
{{ 3 L 3 S }}
Chartered 3/03
Liquidated 4/26/31
1902 Red Seal <$VALUE
3x10-20 1-1180 <$750
1902 Date Back
3x10-20 1-1960 <$400
1902 Plain Back
3x10-20 1961-5475 <$400
1929 Small Size
10 Type 1 1-330 <$400
20 Type 1 1-92 <$400
Total Issue $363,590
Out at close $25,000
Large out at close $4,060

13542 Posey
NEW HARMONY NB, NEW HARMONY
{{ 6 S }}
Chartered 4/31
1929 Small Size <$VALUE
5 Type 1 1-824 <$200
10 Type 1 1-418 <$200
5 Type 2 1-4244 <$200
10 Type 2 1-2148 <$200
Total Issue $92,500
Out in 1935 $39,350

8408 Decatur
FNB OF NEW POINT
{{ 2 L }}
Chartered 10/06
Liquidated 1/1/13
1902 Red Seal <$VALUE
3x10-20 1-400 <$1500
1902 Date Back
3x10-20 1-224 <$1000
Total Issue $31,200
Out in 1913 $5,250

1897 Vermillion
FNB OF NEWPORT
{{ UNREPORTED }}
Chartered 11/6/71
Liquidated 8/7/76
Original Series <$VALUE
4x5 1-1250 <$1250
3x10-20 1-700 <$1500/$2000
Series 1875
3x10-20 1-301 <$1500/$2000
Total Issue $75,050
Out in 1910 $215

9756 Hamilton
AMERICAN NB OF NOBLESVILLE
{{ 8 L 11 S }}
Chartered 5/10
1902 Date Back <$VALUE
3x10-20 1-3790 <$175
1902 Plain Back
3x10-20 3791-11405 <$175
1929 Small Size
10 Type 1 1-1184 <$125
20 Type 1 1-342 <$125
10 Type 2 1-1469 <$125
20 Type 2 1-314 <$125
Total Issue $703,300
Out in 1935 $50,000
Large out 1935 $2,720

4882 Hamilton
FNB OF NOBLESVILLE
{{ 4 L }}
Organized 3/1/93
Receivership 6/3/26
Brown Back <$VALUE
3x10-20 1-2670 <$500
1882 Date Back
3x10-20 1-1609 <$500
1902 Date Back
3x10-20 1-2000* <$300
1902 Plain Back
3x10-20 2401-6876* <$300
* 2001-2400 not marked
Total Issue $557,750
Out at close $49,000

2903 Wabash
FNB OF NORTH MANCHESTER
{{ UNREPORTED }}
Organized 3/17/83
Receivership 10/16/93
Brown Back <$VALUE
4x5 1-3092 <$1500
Total Issue $61,840
Out in 1916 $370

3474 Wabash
LAWRENCE NB OF NORTH MANCHESTER
{{ 6 L }}
Chartered 1886
Liquidated 12/23/29
Brown Back <$VALUE
3x10-20 1-2752 <$500
1902 Red Seal
3x10-20 1-800 <$600
1902 Date Back
3x10-20 1-3600 <$250
1902 Plain Back
3x10-20 3601-16536 <$250
Total Issue $1,004,400
Out at close $63,710

4678 Jennings
FNB OF NORTH VERNON
{{ 5 L 7 S }}
Chartered 1892
Brown Back <$VALUE
4x5 1-3900 <$450
50-100 1-600 <$1500/$1750
1882 Date Back
4x5 1-875 <$450
50-100 1-158 <$1500/$1750
1902 Date Back
4x5 1-1250 <$225
3x50-100 1-559 <$400/$500
1902 Plain Back
4x5 1251-14152 <$225
3x50-100 560-739<$400/$500
1929 Small Size
5 Type 1 1-2580 <$150
50 Type 1 1-118 <$300
100 Type 1 1-36 <$350
5 Type 2 1-3476 <$165
Total Issue $828,770
Out in 1935 $60,000
Large out 1935 $4,270

9122 Jennings
NORTH VERNON NB, NORTH VERNON
{{ 4 L 5 S }}
Chartered 5/08
Liquidated 10/14/32
1902 Date Back <$VALUE
3x10-20 1-2290 <$275
50-100 1-220 <$400/$500
3x50-100 1-80 <$400/$500
1902 Plain Back
3x10-20 2291-8677 <$275
1929 Small Size
10 Type 1 1-1067 <$225
20 Type 1 1-279 <$225
Total Issue $584,350
Out at close $50,000
Large out at close $4,970

9562 Gibson
FNB OF OAKLAND CITY
{{ 5 L 11 S }}
Organized 10/5/09
1902 Date Back <$VALUE
4x5 1-3500 <$275
3x10-20 1-2800 <$275
1902 Plain Back
4x5 3501-11556 <$275
3x10-20 2801-8026 <$275
1929 Small Size
5 Type 1 1-188 <$125
10 Type 1 1-934 <$125
20 Type 1 1-260 <$125
5 Type 2 1-1556 <$150
10 Type 2 1-1160 <$150
20 Type 2 1-264 <$150
Total Issue $800,720
Out in 1935 $50,000
Large out 1935 $2,735

7260 Daviess
FNB OF ODON
{{ 2 L 7 S }}
Chartered 5/04
1902 Red Seal <$VALUE
3x10-20 1-540 <$1000
50-100 1-74 <$3000
1902 Date Back
3x10-20 1-2480 <$500
50-100 1-130 <$750/$850
3x50-100 1-177 <$750/$850
1902 Plain Back
3x10-20 2481-5760 <$500
3x50-100 178-266<$750/$850
1929 Small Size
10 Type 1 1-548 <$175
20 Type 1 1-197 <$175
50 Type 1 1-68 <$350
100 Type 1 1-20 <$450
Total Issue $501,020
Out in 1935 $50,000
Large out 1935 $3,660

5558 Orange
NB OF ORLEANS
{{ 3 L 3 S }}
Chartered 8/27/00
Liquidated 3/22/33
Brown Back <$VALUE
3x10-20 1-970 <$750
1882 Date Back
3x10-20 1-1420 <$750
1882 Value Back
3x10-20 1421-1526 <$750
1902 Plain Back
3x10-20 1-1575 <$600
1929 Small Size
10 Type 1 1-319 <$350
20 Type 1 1-73 <$350
Total Issue $231,450
Out at close $14,000
Large out at close $1,110

5432 Gibson
FNB OF OWENSVILLE
{{ 2 L }}
Chartered 6/16/00
Liquidated 5/16/20
Brown Back <$VALUE
3x10-20 1-1450 <$750
1882 Date Back
3x10-20 1-1930 <$750
1882 Value Back
3x10-20 1931-2807 <$750
Total Issue $212,850
Out at close $25,000

9352 Gibson
PATOKA NB, PATOKA
{{ 2 L 4 S }}
Chartered 3/09
1902 Date Back <$VALUE
4x5 1-1650 <$450
3x10-20 1-1270 <$450
1902 Plain Back
4x5 1651-5008 <$450
3x10-20 1271-3479 <$450
1929 Small Size
5 Type 1 1-766 <$250
10 Type 1 1-368 <$250
20 Type 1 1-118 <$250
5 Type 2 1-560 <$275
10 Type 2 1-461 <$275
20 Type 2 1-140 <$300
Total Issue $343,540
Out in 1935 $20,000
Large out 1935 $770

1879 Miami
CITIZENS NB OF PERU
{{ 10 L 10 S }}
Chartered 9/16/71
Liquidated 10/31/31
Original Series <$VALUE
3x1-2 1-3000 <$400/$1000
4x5 1-3500 <$500
3x10-20 1-1260 <$750/$1250
Series 1875
3x1-2 1-240 <$400/$1000
4x5 1-4603 <$500
3x10-20 1-1100 <$750/$1250
Brown Back
4x5 1-4950 <$300
3x10-20 1-6040 <$300
1882 Date Back
4x5 1-1782 <$300
3x10-20 1-1311 <$300
1902 Date Back
4x5 1-4250 <$175
3x10-20 1-3000 <$175
1902 Plain Back
4x5 4251-19725 <$175
3x10-20 3001-13626 <$175
1929 Small Size
5 Type 1 1-2182 <$125
10 Type 1 1-1113 <$125
20 Type 1 1-336 <$125
Total Issue $2,046,810
Out at close $100,000
Large out at close $12,150

363 Miami
FNB OF PERU
{{ 7 L 9 S }}
Organized 1/1/64
Receivership 9/6/33
Original Series <$VALUE
3x1-2 1-6020 <$400/$1000
4x5 1-4650 <$500
3x10-20 1-1890 <$750/$1250
Series 1875
3x1-2 1-200 <$400/$1000
4x5 1-1675 <$500
3x10-20 1-1159 <$750/$1250
Brown Back
4x5 1-2345 <$400
3x10-20 1-2188 <$400
1902 Red Seal
4x5 1-2150 <$450
3x10-20 1-1590 <$450
1902 Date Back
4x5 1-4700 <$175
3x10-20 1-3580 <$175
1902 Plain Back
4x5 4701-19105 <$175
3x10-20 3581-13468 <$175
1929 Small Size
5 Type 1 1-3125 <$125
10 Type 1 1-1942 <$125
20 Type 1 1-422 <$125
Total Issue $1,905,260
Out at close $100,000
Large out at close $7,185

5300 Pike
FNB OF PETERSBURG
{{ 2 L 6 S }}
Chartered 4/24/00
Brown Back <$VALUE
3x10-20 1-1500 <$600
1882 Date Back
3x10-20 1-1700 <$600
1882 Value Back
3x10-20 1701-2452 <$600
1902 Plain Back
3x10-20 1-3100 <$450
1929 Small Size
10 Type 1 1-736 <$200
20 Type 1 1-170 <$200
10 Type 2 1-435 <$225
20 Type 2 1-76 <$225
Total Issue $423,030
Out in 1935 $25,000
Large out 1935 $1,340

7011 Hendricks
FNB OF PLAINFIELD
Chartered 10/03
2nd title:FNB & TC 1/15/29
FIRST TITLE {{ 3 L }}
1902 Red Seal <$VALUE
3x10-20 1-1156 <$700
1902 Date Back
3x10-20 1-1910 <$350
1902 Plain Back
3x10-20 1911-5767 <$350
SECOND TITLE {{ 0 L 16 S }}
1902 Plain Back
3x10-20 1-40 <$500
1929 Small Size
10 Type 1 1-650 <$90
20 Type 1 1-170 <$90
10 Type 2 1-342 <$100
20 Type 2 1-162 <$100
Total Issue $414,210
Out in 1935 $25,000
Large out 1935 $1,180

2119 Marshall
FNB OF MARSHALL COUNTY AT PLYMOUTH
{{ 27 L 14 S }}
Chartered 7/18/73
Receivership 10/3/33
Original Series <$VALUE
3x1-2 1-800 <$350/$750
4x5 1-2950 <$400
Series 1875
3x1-2 1-400 <$350/$750
4x5 1-6974 <$400
Brown Back
4x5 1-5600 <$850
3x10-20 1-2980<$1500/$1750
1882 Date Back
4x5 1-2039 <$750
3x10-20 1-1448<$1500/$1750
1902 Date Back
4x5 1-1250 <$125
3x10-20 1-1000 <$125
1902 Plain Back
4x5 1251-16041 <$125
3x10-20 1001-10184 <$125
1929 Small Size
5 Type 1 1-4308 <$100
10 Type 1 1-2285 <$100
20 Type 1 1-590 <$100
Total Issue $1,745,820
Out at close $130,000
Large out at close $7,685

7180 Jay
FNB OF PORTLAND
{{ 4 L 10 S }}
Organized 2/29/04
1902 Red Seal <$VALUE
3x10-20 1-2060 <$600
1902 Date Back
3x10-20 1-3300 <$300
1902 Plain Back
3x10-20 3301-10475 <$300
1929 Small Size
10 Type 1 1-1176 <$125
20 Type 1 1-328 <$125
10 Type 2 1-646 <$125
20 Type 2 1-250 <$150
Total Issue $748,130
Out in 1934 $48,200
Out in 1935 $2,630

8149 Posey
BOZEMAN WATERS NB OF POSEYVILLE
{{ 6 L 4 S }}
Organized 3/15/06
Liquidated 11/22/30
1902 Red Seal <$VALUE
4x5 1-1250 <$600
3x10-20 1-1000 <$600
1902 Date Back
4x5 1-3150 <$275
3x10-20 1-2420 <$275
1902 Plain Back
4x5 3151-11290 <$275
3x10-20 2421-7542 <$275
1929 Small Size
5 Type 1 1-739 <$300
10 Type 1 1-345 <$300
20 Type 1 1-108 <$300
Total Issue $733,730
Out at close $50,000
Large out at close $7,510
Ch 13503 assumed circulation

13503 Posey
BOZEMAN WATERS FNB OF POSEYVILLE
{{ U + 10 S }}
Organized 11/7/30
Receivership 1/20/32
1929 Small Size <$VALUE
5 Type 1 1-460 <$150
10 Type 1 1-176 <$150
20 Type 1 1-50 <$175
Total Issue $30,360
Out at close $48,680
Outstanding includes Ch 8149

7036 Posey
FNB OF POSEYVILLE
{{ 3 L 2 S }}
Chartered 11/03
Liquidated 11/22/30
1902 Red Seal <$VALUE
4x5 1-665 <$700
3x10-20 1-534 <$700
1902 Date Back
4x5 1-1775 <$350
3x10-20 1-1360 <$350
1902 Plain Back
4x5 1776-6017 <$350
3x10-20 1361-3822 <$350
1929 Small Size
5 Type 1 1-397 <$400
10 Type 1 1-195 <$400
20 Type 1 1-55 <$400
Total Issue $381,650
Out at close $25,000
Large out at close $3,580

8166 Gibson
AMERICAN NB OF PRINCETON
{{ 1 L }}
Chartered 4/06
Liquidated 5/29/14
1902 Red Seal <$VALUE
4x5 1-2070 <$800
3x10-20 1-1672 <$800
1902 Date Back
4x5 1-5360 <$500
3x10-20 1-3838 <$500
Total Issue $424,100
Out in 1914 $70,960

9463 Gibson
FARMERS NB OF PRINCETON
{{ 10 L 14 S }}
Organized 6/16/09
1902 Date Back <$VALUE
4x5 1-7500 <$175
3x10-20 1-5680 <$175
1902 Plain Back
4x5 7501-24083 <$175
3x10-20 5681-16748 <$175
1929 Small Size
5 Type 1 1-3880 <$100
10 Type 1 1-1914 <$100
20 Type 1 1-514 <$100
5 Type 2 1-3212 <$100
10 Type 2 1-1719 <$100
20 Type 2 1-338 <$110
Total Issue $1,651,990
Out in 1935 $50,000
Large out 1935 $5,210

2066 Gibson
GIBSON COUNTY NB OF PRINCETON
{{ UNREPORTED }}
Chartered 11/30/72
Receivership 11/28/74
Original Series <$VALUE
4x5 1-1250 <$1500
3x10-20 1-400 <$1750/$2000
Total Issue $45,000
Out in 1915 $175

10551 Gibson
PEOPLES AMERICAN NB OF PRINCETON
{{ 6 L 12 S }}
Organized 5/5/14
Receivership 10/2/33
1902 Date Back <$VALUE
3x10-20 1-5000 <$175
1902 Plain Back
3x10-20 5001-22534 <$175
1929 Small Size
10 Type 1 1-2505 <$100
20 Type 1 1-706 <$100
Total Issue $1,361,720
Out at close $100,000
Large out at close $6,250

2180 Gibson
PEOPLES NB OF PRINCETON
{{ 3 L }}
Chartered 9/9/74
Liquidated 5/29/14
Original Series <$VALUE
4x5 1-2250 <$600
Series 1875
4x5 1-7639 <$600
Brown Back
3x10-20 1-5500 <$500
50-100 1-580 <$1250/$1500
1882 Date Back
3x10-20 1-4440 <$500
50-100 1-35 <$1250/$1500
Total Issue $787,030
Out in 1914 $68,545

9670 Jay
FARMERS & MERCHANTS NB OF REDKEY
{{ 1 L }}
Chartered 2/10
Liquidated 10/18/11
1902 Date Back <$VALUE
4x5 1-400 <$1000
3x10-20 1-348 <$1000
Total Issue $25,400
Out in 1912 $5,740

11355 Jasper
FARMERS NB OF REMINGTON
{{ 10 L 9 S }}
Organized 4/14/19
1902 Plain Back <$VALUE
3x10-20 1-4469 <$225
1929 Small Size
10 Type 1 1-782* <$125
20 Type 1 1-252** <$125
10 Type 2 1-455 <$150
20 Type 2 1-205 <$150
* 586-614 not issued
** 163-208 not issued
Total Issue $302,000
Out in 1935 $30,000
Large out 1935 $990

8060 Jasper
FNB OF REMINGTON
{{ UNREPORTED }}
Chartered 1/22/06
Liquidated 11/21/08
1902 Red Seal <$VALUE
4x5 1-215 <$1500
3x10-20 1-148 <$1500
Total Issue $11,700
Out in 1910 $2,140

6651 Jasper
FNB OF RENSSELAER
{{ 1 L }}
Organized 2/16/03
Liquidated 4/12/26
1902 Red Seal <$VALUE
3x10-20 1-585 <$1250
1902 Date Back
3x10-20 1-2090 <$750
1902 Plain Back
3x10-20 2091-4175 <$750
Total Issue $238,000
Out in 1925 $24,600

****
17 Wayne
FNB OF RICHMOND*
{{ 12 L U + 14 S }}
Chartered 6/63
Liquidated 5/5/82
*Reorganized as Ch 2680
which retook Ch 17 5/31/10
Original Series <$VALUE
3x1-2 1-5000 <$500/$1250
4x5 1-5250 <$600
3x10-20 1-4700 <$850/$1250
Series 1875
3x10-20 1-2700 <$850/$1250
1902 Date Back
4x5 1-2850 <$125
3x50-100 1-680 <$400/$500
1902 Plain Back (dated 1902)
4x5 2851-13650 <$125
1902 Plain Back (dated 1922)
4x5 1-35949 <$125
1929 Small Size
5 Type 1 1-18304 <$65
5 Type 2 1-14458 <$65
Total Issue $2,283,390
Out in 1935 $75,000
Large out 1935 $9,830
****
2680 Wayne
FNB OF RICHMOND
{{ 2 L }}
Chartered 5/5/82
RETOOK Ch 17 5/31/10
Brown Back <$VALUE
3x10-20 1-3720 <$600
50-100 1-489 <$1500/$1750
1902 Red Seal
4x5 1-5190 <$750
50-100 1-934 <$2250/$2500
1902 Date Back
4x5 1-1250 <$500
50-100 1-340 <$750/$850
Total Issue $579,250
Out in 1910 $75,000
****
1102 Wayne
RICHMOND NB, RICHMOND
{{ 3 L }}
Chartered 1865
Liquidated 2/28/73
Original Series <$VALUE
3x1-2 1-12400 <$400/$1000
4x5 1-11000 <$500
Total Issue $282,000
Out at close $207,000
Ch 2090 assumed circulation
****
2090 Wayne
RICHMOND NB, RICHMOND
{{ 4 L }}
Chartered 3/5/73
Receivership 7/23/84
Original Series <$VALUE
3x1-2 12401-14400 <$400/$1000
4x5 11001-13000 <$500
3x10-20 1-8148 <$750/$1250
Series 1875
3x1-2 1-2000 <$400/$1000
4x5 1-12450 <$500
3x10-20 1-2712* <$750/$1250
* 1211-1852 not issued
Total Issue $819,900
Out in 1915 $6,469
Outstanding includes Ch 1102
****
1988 Wayne
SECOND NB OF RICHMOND
{{ 13 L 24 S }}
Chartered 5/28/72
Original Series <$VALUE
3x1-2 1-2000 <$375/$850
4x5 1-4000 <$400
3x10-20 1-2000 <$750/$1250
Series 1875
4x5 1-3250 <$400
3x10-20 1-4780 <$750/$1250
Brown Back
4x5 1-9915 <$300
3x10-20 1-7494 <$300
50-100 1-1220 <$1250/$1500
1882 Date Back
4x5 1-1935 <$250
3x10-20 1-6000 <$250
50-100 1-28 <$1250/$1500
1902 Date Back
4x5 1-6000 <$100
3x10-20 1-10000 <$100
1902 Plain Back
4x5 6001-16310 <$100
3x10-20 10001-43592 <$100
1929 Small Size
10 Type 1 1-8024 <$40
20 Type 1 1-2386 <$50
10 Type 2 1-4257 <$40
20 Type 2 1-815 <$50
Total Issue $4,925,330
Out in 1935 $300,000
Large out 1935 $14,260
****
3413 Wayne
UNION NB OF RICHMOND
{{ 7 L }}
Chartered 1885
Liquidated 7/2/28
Brown Back <$VALUE
3x10-20 1-4755 <$400
1902 Red Seal
50-100 1-1000 <$2250/$2500
1902 Date Back
50-100 1-1100 <$500/$600
3x50-100 1-1660 <$500/$600
1902 Plain Back
3x50-100 1661-1959 <$500/$600
Total Issue $1,042,500
Out at close $140,000
****
8351 Randolph
FNB OF RIDGEVILLE
{{ 1 L 0 S }}
Chartered 9/06
Liquidated 1/2/30
1902 Red Seal <$VALUE
4x5 1-334 <$2000
4x10 1-333 <$2000
1902 Date Back
4x5 1-400 <$1000
4x10 1-400 <$1000
1902 Plain Back
4x5 401-1381 <$1000
4x10 401-1042 <$1000
1929 Small Size
5 Type 1 1-22 <$1000
10 Type 1 1-12 <$1000
Total Issue $90,680
Out at close $6,300
Large out at close $5,340
****
1959 Ohio
NB OF RISING SUN
{{ 13 L 12 S }}
Chartered 4/12/72
Liquidated 1/24/33
Original Series <$VALUE
3x1-2 1-1000 <$500/$1250
4x5 1-2000 <$600
3x10-20 1-1500 <$750/$1250
Series 1875
4x5 1-4550 <$600
3x10-20 1-3751 <$750/$1250
Brown Back
4x5 1-9400 <$400
3x10-20 1-5920 <$400
1882 Date Back
4x5 1-2916 <$400
3x10-20 1-1729 <$400
1902 Date Back
4x5 1-3850 <$175
3x10-20 1-2960 <$175
1902 Plain Back
4x5 3851-18100 <$175
3x10-20 2961-12404 <$175
1929 Small Size
5 Type 1 1-3293 <$125
10 Type 1 1-1559 <$125
20 Type 1 1-414 <$125
Total Issue $2,251,530
Out at close $100,000
Large out at close $10,815
****
1952 Fulton
FNB OF ROCHESTER
{{ 3 L }}
Chartered 3/30/72
Liquidated 1/11/76
Original Series <$VALUE
3x1-2 1-1500 <$500/$1000
4x5 1-2915 <$650
Total Issue $65,800
Out in 1910 $283
****
7655 Fulton
FNB OF ROCHESTER
{{ 5 L 9 S }}
Chartered 3/05
1902 Red Seal <$VALUE
3x10-20 1-2212 <$500
1902 Date Back
3x10-20 1-3200 <$250
1902 Plain Back
3x10-20 3201-10790 <$250
1929 Small Size
10 Type 1 1-1204 <$135
20 Type 1 1-326 <$150
10 Type 2 1-1074 <$165
20 Type 2 1-258 <$175
Total Issue $777,360
Out in 1935 $50,000
Large out 1935 $2,400
****
6194 Spencer
FNB OF ROCKPORT
{{ 3 L 4 S }}
Organized 4/3/02
Receivership 3/3/33
1902 Red Seal <$VALUE
3x10-20 1-1300 <$750
1902 Date Back
3x10-20 1-2310 <$375
1902 Plain Back (dated 1902)
3x10-20 2311-4300 <$375
1902 Plain Back (dated 1922)
3x10-20 1-2923 <$375
1929 Small Size
10 Type 1 1-722 <$275
20 Type 1 1-215 <$275
Total Issue $495,270
Out at close $35,000
Large out at close $3,420
****
63 Parke
FNB OF ROCKVILLE
{{ UNREPORTED }}
Chartered 8/63
Liquidated 4/25/77
Original Series <$VALUE
4x5 1-3220 <$1250
4x10 1-7125 <$1500
Series 1875
4x5 1-1617 <$1250
Total Issue $381,740
Out in 1910 $2,170
****
2361 Parke
NB OF ROCKVILLE
{{ 2 L }}
Chartered 6/16/77
Liquidated 5/14/97
Series 1875 <$VALUE
4x5 1-13860 <$650
Total Issue $277,200
Out in 1910 $1,475
****
5067 Parke
ROCKVILLE NB, ROCKVILLE
{{ 9 L 4 S }}
Chartered 1897
Brown Back <$VALUE
4x5 1-1585 <$350
50-100 1-118 <$1500/$1750
1882 Date Back
4x5 1-2338 <$350
50-100 1-160 <$1250/$1500
3x50-100 1-268 <$1250/$1500
1902 Plain Back
4x5 1-9707 <$175
50-100 1-402 <$500/$600
1929 Small Size
5 Type 1 1-1264 <$275
10 Type 1 1-331 <$275
20 Type 1 1-124 <$275
50 Type 1 1-64 <$400
100 Type 1 1-18 <$500
Total Issue $584,460
Out in 1935 $25,000
Large out 1935 $4,160
****
9006 Parke
HARRISON NB OF ROSEDALE
Organized 1/4/08
Receivership 10/3/33
2nd title:Rosedale NB
4/21/10
FIRST TITLE {{ 1 L }}
1902 Red Seal <$VALUE
3x10-20 1-700 <$1000
1902 Date Back
3x10-20 1-190 <$600
SECOND TITLE {{ 2 L 3 S }}
1902 Date Back
3x10-20 1-1730 <$500
1902 Plain Back
3x10-20 1731-5474 <$500
1929 Small Size
10 Type 1 1-559 <$350
20 Type 1 1-170 <$350
Total Issue $372,140
Out at close $25,000
Large out at close $1,580
****
Rosedale NB, Rosedale
SEE Ch 9006
Harrison NB of Rosedale
****
12420 Rush
AMERICAN NB OF RUSHVILLE
{{ 1 L 6 S }}
Organized 7/28/23
Receivership 4/25/33
1902 Plain Back <$VALUE
3x10-20 1-3269 <$600
1929 Small Size
10 Type 1 1-567 <$200
20 Type 1 1-152 <$200
Total Issue $215,710
Out at close $24,820
Large out at close $1,470
****
7374 Rush
PEOPLES NB OF RUSHVILLE
{{ 2 L }}
Chartered 8/04
Liquidated 8/1/23
1902 Red Seal <$VALUE
4x5 1-600 <$850
3x10-20 1-480 <$850
1902 Date Back
4x5 1-1150 <$400
3x10-20 1-780 <$400
1902 Plain Back
4x5 1151-1825 <$400
3x10-20 781-1143 <$400
Total Issue $129,650
Out at close $12,500
****
1869 Rush
RUSH COUNTY NB OF RUSHVILLE
{{ 11 L 14 S }}
Chartered 9/4/71
Original Series <$VALUE
4x5 1-1950 <$600
3x10-20 1-1500 <$750/$1250
50-100 1-150 <$4000
Series 1875
4x5 1-4662 <$400
3x10-20 1-2006 <$750/$1250
50-100 1-44 <$4000
Brown Back
3x10-20 1-2670 <$300/$350
1882 Date Back
3x10-20 1-426 <$300/$350
1902 Date Back
3x10-20 1-1940 <$150
1902 Plain Back
3x10-20 1941-16477 <$150
1929 Small Size
10 Type 1 1-2564 <$100
20 Type 1 1-710 <$100
10 Type 2 1-72 <$100
Total Issue $1,555,050
Out in 1935 $50,000
Large out 1935 $5,980
****
1456 Rush
RUSHVILLE NB, RUSHVILLE
{{ 11 L 18 S }}
Chartered 1865
Original Series <$VALUE
4x5 1-3575 <$500
3x10-20 1-1350 <$750/$1250
Series 1875
4x5 1-1840 <$500
3x10-20 1-1054 <$750/$1250
Brown Back
4x5 1-1321 <$350
3x10-20 1-2130 <$350
1902 Red Seal
4x5 1-700 <$400
3x10-20 1-470 <$400
1902 Date Back
4x5 1-1925 <$150
3x10-20 1-1500 <$150
1902 Plain Back
4x5 1926-13732 <$150
3x10-20 1501-9889 <$150
1929 Small Size
5 Type 1 1-3924 <$75
10 Type 1 1-1834 <$75
20 Type 1 1-466 <$85
5 Type 2 1-2634 <$75
10 Type 2 1-1716 <$75
20 Type 2 1-500 <$100
Total Issue $1,492,020
Out in 1935 $100,000
Large out 1935 $5,025
****
5524 Howard
FNB OF RUSSIAVILLE
{{ 4 L 4 S }}
Chartered 8/1/00
Receivership 12/30/32
Brown Back <$VALUE
3x10-20 1-1800 <$500
1882 Date Back
3x10-20 1-1560 <$500
1882 Value Back
3x10-20 1561-2370 <$500
1902 Plain Back
3x10-20 1-2651 <$350
1929 Small Size
10 Type 1 1-527 <$275
20 Type 1 1-130 <$275
Total Issue $388,270
Out at close $25,000
Large out at close $2,125
****
2173 Washington
NB OF SALEM
{{ 1 L }}
Chartered 8/22/74
Liquidated 7/8/79
Original Series <$VALUE
3x1-2 1-1500 <$750/$1500
4x5 1-1875 <$1000
Series 1875
3x1-2 1-420 <$750/$1500
4x5 1-1655 <$1000
Total Issue $80,200
Out in 1910 $423
****
1032 Jackson
FNB OF SEYMOUR
{{ 8 L 13 S }}
Organized 2/1/65
Liquidated 2/16/32
Original Series <$VALUE
3x1-2 1-2800 <$400/$1000
4x5 1-4625 <$500
3x10-20 1-1200 <$750/$1250
Series 1875
4x5 1-2340 <$500
3x10-20 1-1984 <$750/$1250
Brown Back
4x5 1-3150 <$400
3x10-20 1-3020 <$400
1902 Red Seal
3x10-20 1-3500 <$450
1902 Date Back
3x10-20 1-6000 <$200
1902 Plain Back
3x10-20 6001-19775 <$200
1929 Small Size
5 Type 1 1-1130 <$135
10 Type 1 1-1319 <$135
20 Type 1 1-452 <$135
Total Issue $1,857,930
Out at close $88,500
Large out at close $14,880
****
4652 Jackson
SEYMOUR NB, SEYMOUR
{{ 10 L 14 S }}
Chartered 10/9/91
Brown Back <$VALUE
4x5 1-4550 <$400
3x10-20 1-1120 <$400
1882 Date Back
4x5 1-2719 <$400
3x10-20 1-1716 <$400
1902 Date Back
3x10-20 1-4600 <$200
1902 Plain Back
3x10-20 4601-19246 <$200
1929 Small Size
10 Type 1 1-2492 <$125
20 Type 1 1-668 <$125
10 Type 2 1-2708 <$125
20 Type 2 1-930 <$125
Total Issue $1,524,840
Out in 1935 $100,000
Large out 1935 $5,280
****
7513 Sullivan
FNB OF SHELBURN
{{ 1 L }}
Chartered 12/04
Liquidated 10/21/24
1902 Red Seal <$VALUE
3x10-20 1-300 <$1000
1902 Date Back
3x10-20 1-2090 <$650
1902 Plain Back
3x10-20 2091-4628 <$650
Total Issue $246,400
Out at close $25,000
****
4800 Shelby
FARMERS NB OF SHELBYVILLE
{{ 8 L 5 S }}
Chartered 1892
Brown Back <$VALUE
4x5 1-8378 <$350
50-100 1-950 <$1250/$1500
1882 Date Back
4x5 1-2990 <$350
50-100 1-400 <$1250/$1500
3x50-100 1-3 <$1250/$1500
1902 Date Back
4x5 1-2500 <$200
3x50-100 1-1013 <$350/$450
1902 Plain Back
4x5 2501-21199 <$200
3x50-100 1014-1314 <$350/$450
1929 Small Size
5 Type 1 1-944 <$200
50 Type 1 1-248 <$250
100 Type 1 1-82 <$300
5 Type 2 1-3036 <$200
Total Issue $1,350,190
Out in 1935 $100,000
Large out 1935 $8,470
****
1263 Shelby
FNB OF SHELBYVILLE
{{ U + 6 L 6 S }}
Organized 5/2/65
Receivership 2/10/32
Original Series <$VALUE
4x5 1-4675 <$500
3x10-20 1-900 <$750/$1250
Series 1875
4x5 1-3935 <$500
Brown Back
4x5 1-5730 <$400
3x10-20 1-800 <$400
1902 Red Seal
3x10-20 1-3400 <$450
1902 Date Back
3x10-20 1-6500 <$225
1902 Plain Back
3x10-20 6501-18522 <$225
1929 Small Size
10 Type 1 1-1198 <$175
20 Type 1 1-323 <$175
Total Issue $1,578,540
Out at close $69,280
Large out at close $10,340
****
7946 Shelby
SHELBY NB OF SHELBYVILLE
{{ 8 L 15 S }}
Chartered 10/05
1902 Red Seal <$VALUE
4x5 1-3100 <$400
3x10-20 1-2520 <$400
1902 Date Back
4x5 1-6850 <$150
3x10-20 1-5160 <$150
1902 Plain Back
4x5 6851-23040 <$150
3x10-20 5161-16186 <$150
1929 Small Size
5 Type 1 1-3694 <$75
10 Type 1 1-1730 <$75
20 Type 1 1-432 <$85
5 Type 2 1-3246 <$100
10 Type 2 1-1398 <$100
20 Type 2 1-575 <$100
Total Issue $1,766,270
Out in 1935 $100,000
Large out 1935 $5,755
****
6070 Hamilton
FARMERS NB OF SHERIDAN
{{ 6 L }}
Chartered 12/01
Liquidated 5/9/27
Brown Back <$VALUE
3x10-20 1-1660 <$400
1882 Date Back
3x10-20 1-4000 <$400
1882 Value Back
3x10-20 4001-6992 <$400
1902 Plain Back
3x10-20 1-3737 <$275
Total Issue $619,450
Out at close $60,000
****
FNB of Sheridan
SEE Ch 5296
FN State B of Sheridan
****
5296 Hamilton
FN STATE B OF SHERIDAN
Chartered 4/20/00
Liquidated 5/16/27
2nd title: FNB 1/20/09
FIRST TITLE {{ 0 L }}
Brown Back <$VALUE
3x10-20 1-2820 <$750
SECOND TITLE {{ 3 L }}
1882 Date Back
3x10-20 1-4500 <$600
1882 Value Back
4x5 1-2375 <$600
3x10-20 4501-5864 <$600
1902 Plain Back
4x5 1-20640 <$350
Total Issue $894,500
Out at close $22,400
****

****
9209 Henry
FNB OF SHIRLEY
{{ 1 L }}
Chartered 7/08
Liquidated 9/1/19
1902 Date Back <$VALUE
4x5 1-1100 <$1000
3x10-20 1-880 <$1000
1902 Plain Back
4x5 1101-1855 <$1000
3x10-20 881-1375 <$1000
Total Issue $105,850
Out at close $25,000
****
4764 Saint Joseph
CITIZENS NB OF SOUTH BEND
{{ 17 L 24 S }}
Organized 5/2/92
Receivership 3/23/34
Brown Back <$VALUE
3x10-20 1-8520 <$225/$250
1882 Date Back
3x10-20 1-2171 <$200/$225
1902 Date Back
3x50-100 1-5787 <$350/$400
1902 Plain Back
3x50-100 5788-7619 <$350/$400
1929 Small Size
50 Type 1 1-1980 <$100
100 Type 1 1-627 <$150
Total Issue $3,409,500
Out at close $700,000
Large out at close $49,000
Outstanding includes Ch 1739
****
126 Saint Joseph
FNB OF SOUTH BEND
{{ 18 L 37 S }}
Chartered 11/63
Liquidated 1/12/32
Original Series <$VALUE
4x5 1-8150 <$500
4x10 1-3675 <$750
Series 1875
4x10 1-2816 <$650
Brown Back
4x5 1-5600 <$250
3x10-20 1-3704 <$250/$300
1902 Red Seal
3x10-20 1-4800 <$250/$300
1902 Date Back
3x10-20 1-6300 <$100
1902 Plain Back
3x10-20 6301-36834 <$100
1929 Small Size
20 Type 1 1-10441 <$45
Total Issue $4,054,460
Out at close $900,000
Large out at close $16,290
****
6334 Saint Joseph
MERCHANTS NB OF SOUTH BEND
{{ 10 L 28 S }}
Organized 6/4/02
1902 Red Seal <$VALUE
3x10-20 1-5400 <$300
1902 Date Back
3x10-20 1-7100 <$100
1902 Plain Back
3x10-20 7101-41749 <$100
1929 Small Size
10 Type 1 1-6148 <$40
20 Type 1 1-1782 <$50
10 Type 2 1-2348 <$40
20 Type 2 1-663 <$50
Total Issue $2,976,910
Out in 1935 $100,000
Large out 1935 $10,000
****
1739 Saint Joseph
SOUTH BEND NB, SOUTH BEND
{{ 5 L }}
Chartered 11/29/70
Closed 3/27/19
Original Series <$VALUE
4x5 1-3500 <$450
3x10-20 1-1440 <$750/$1250
Series 1875
4x5 1-7057 <$450
3x10-20 1-2337 <$750/$1250
Brown Back
3x10-20 1-10100 <$350
1882 Date Back
3x10-20 1-1779 <$300
1902 Date Back
3x10-20 1-4900 <$200
1902 Plain Back
3x10-20 4901-7007 <$200
Total Issue $1,344,290
Out at close $100,000
****

****
2178 Owen
FNB OF SPENCER
{{ UNREPORTED }}
Chartered 9/4/74
Liquidated 3/11/76
Original Series <$VALUE
3x1-2 1-2100 <$1000/$2000
4x5 1-2700 <$1250
Total Issue $64,500
Out in 1910 $316
****
9715 Owen
SPENCER NB, SPENCER
{{ 14 L 3 S }}
Organized 3/17/10
Receivership 7/30/32
1902 Date Back <$VALUE
3x10-20 1-2060 <$150
1902 Plain Back
3x10-20 2061-6644 <$150
1929 Small Size
10 Type 1 1-626 <$300
20 Type 1 1-187 <$300
Total Issue $392,200
Out at close $34,280
Large out at close $4,760
****
12028 Pike
FNB OF SPURGEON
{{ 1 L 1 S }}
Organized 9/16/21
1902 Plain Back <$VALUE
4x5 1-3734 <$850
1929 Small Size
5 Type 1 1-1284 <$600
5 Type 2 1-2796 <$600
Total Issue $127,180
Out in 1935 $10,000
Large out 1935 $210
****
2369 Sullivan
FARMERS NB OF SULLIVAN
{{ UNREPORTED }}
Chartered 8/23/77
Liquidated 12/24/83
Series 1875 <$VALUE
3x10-20 1-1750<$1500/$2000
Total Issue $87,500
Out in 1910 $400
****
1932 Sullivan
FNB OF SULLIVAN
{{ UNREPORTED }}
Chartered 2/3/72
Liquidated 1/8/78
Original Series <$VALUE
4x5 1-3165 <$1500
3x10-20 1-500 <$1750/$2000
Total Issue $88,300
Out in 1910 $385
****
5392 Sullivan
NB OF SULLIVAN
Organized 5/21/00
Receivership 7/15/32
2nd title: Peoples NB & TC 11/19/28
FIRST TITLE {{ 6 L }}
Brown Back <$VALUE
3x10-20 1-2900 <$350
1882 Date Back
3x10-20 1-8500 <$350
1882 Value Back
3x10-20 8501-11964 <$350
1902 Plain Back
3x10-20 1-11838 <$200
SECOND TITLE {{ 1 L 10 S }}
1902 Plain Back
3x10-20 1-665 <$275
1929 Small Size
10 Type 1 1-1936 <$110
20 Type 1 1-536 <$125
Total Issue $1,548,830
Out at close $97,660
Large out at close $11,770
****
Peoples NB & TC of Sullivan
SEE Ch 5392
NB of Sullivan
****
8878 Ripley
FARMERS NB OF SUNMAN
{{ 12 L 13 S }}
Chartered 9/07
Liquidated 10/27/31
1902 Red Seal <$VALUE
4x10 1-912 <$500
1902 Date Back
4x10 1-2000 <$175
1902 Plain Back
4x10 2001-6346 <$175

1929 Small Size
10 Type 1 1-653 <$150
Total Issue $329,500
Out at close $25,000
Large out at close $3,550
****
13862 Grant
FNB AT SWAYZEE
{{ 6 S }}
Chartered 12/33
1929 Small Size <$VALUE
5 Type 2 1-3144 <$200
10 Type 2 1-1560 <$200
Total Issue $31,320
Out in 1935 $22,980
****
8820 Grant
FNB OF SWAYZEE
{{ 5 L 8 S }}
Organized 7/22/07
Receivership 12/26/33
1902 Red Seal <$VALUE
4x5 1-356 <$600
4x10 1-356 <$600
1902 Date Back
4x5 1-2400 <$275
4x10 1-2300 <$275
1902 Plain Back
4x5 2401-11360 <$275
4x10 2301-9653 <$275
1929 Small Size
5 Type 1 1-2338 <$150
10 Type 1 1-1274 <$150
5 Type 2 1-950 <$175
10 Type 2 1-372 <$175
Total Issue $789,730
Out at close $49,995
Large out at close $2,265
****
7375 Perry
CITIZENS NB OF TELL CITY
{{ 4 L 7 S }}
Organized 5/9/04
1902 Red Seal <$VALUE
4x5 1-700 <$600
3x10-20 1-500 <$600
1902 Date Back
4x5 1-2650 <$275
3x10-20 1-2000 <$275
1902 Plain Back
4x5 2651-9637 <$275
3x10-20 2001-6764 <$275
1929 Small Size
5 Type 1 1-1782 <$175
10 Type 1 1-846 <$175
20 Type 1 1-258 <$175
5 Type 2 1-500 <$200
10 Type 2 1-336 <$200
20 Type 2 1-25 <$200
Total Issue $711,480
Out in 1935 $25,000
Large out 1935 $3,070
****
2201 Perry
FNB OF TELL CITY
{{ 2 L }}
Chartered 11/2/74
Liquidated 3/4/78
Original Series <$VALUE
4x5 1-2250 <$1500
Series 1875
4x5 1-725 <$1500
Total Issue $59,500
Out in 1910 $285
****
5756 Perry
TELL CITY NB, TELL CITY
{{ 9 L 14 S }}
Organized 3/13/01
Brown Back <$VALUE
4x5 1-1800 <$400
3x10-20 1-1360 <$400
1882 Date Back
4x5 1-3250 <$400
3x10-20 1-2080 <$400
1882 Value Back
4x5 3251-5135 <$400
3x10-20 2081-3188 <$400
1902 Plain Back
4x5 1-9491 <$225
3x10-20 1-6804 <$225
1929 Small Size
5 Type 1 1-3220 <$100
10 Type 1 1-1910 <$100
20 Type 1 1-470 <$100
5 Type 2 1-4462 <$100
10 Type 2 1-2320 <$100
20 Type 2 1-420 <$125
Total Issue $1,217,630
Out in 1935 $100,000
Large out 1935 $5,070
****

****
8956 Warrick
TENNYSON NB, TENNYSON
{{ 2 L 6 S }}
Chartered 11/07
1902 Red Seal <$VALUE
4x5 1-400 <$1000
4x10 1-400 <$1000
1902 Date Back
4x5 1-1650* <$450
4x10 1-1650 <$450
1902 Plain Back
4x5 1751-6190* <$450
4x10 1651-4952 <$450
* 1651-1750 not marked
1929 Small Size
5 Type 1 1-1406 <$175
10 Type 1 1-650 <$175
5 Type 2 1-1572 <$200
10 Type 2 1-744 <$200
Total Issue $442,360
Out in 1935 $25,000
Large out 1935 $1,040
****
F-McKeen NB & TC of Terre Haute
SEE Ch 47
FNB of Terre Haute
****
47 Vigo
FNB OF TERRE HAUTE*
Chartered 8/63
Liquidated 6/29/82
*Reorganized as Ch 2742 which retook Ch 47 5/20/11
2nd title: F-McKeen NB & TC 2/20/28
3rd title: Terre Haute FNB 11/15/32
FIRST TITLE {{ 24 L }}
Original Series <$VALUE
4x5 1-5075 <$500
4x10 1-6225* <$750
2x20-50-100 1-1250** <$1250/$4000/$4000
* 3126-4000 not issued
** 178-500 not issued
Series 1875
4x5 1-350 <$500
4x10 1-899 <$750
2x20-50-100 1-340 <$1250/$4000/$4000
1902 Date Back
3x10-20 1-22000 <$85
1902 Plain Back
3x10-20 22001-88595 <$85
SECOND TITLE {{ 3 L 44 S }}
1902 Plain Back
3x10-20 1-3180 <$150
1929 Small Size
10 Type 1 1-12875 <$40
20 Type 1 1-1752 <$40
THIRD TITLE {{ 6 S }}
1929 Small Size
5 Type 2 1-4570 <$50
10 Type 2 1-3421 <$50
20 Type 2 1-932 <$60
Total Issue $6,246,380
Out in 1935 $500,000
Large out 1935 $67,430
Outstanding includes Ch 2742, Ch 7562, and Ch 7922
****
2742 Vigo
FNB OF TERRE HAUTE
{{ UNREPORTED }}
Chartered 1882
RETOOK Ch 47 5/20/11
Brown Back <$VALUE
3x10-20 1-6121 <$750
1902 Red Seal
3x10-20 1-9500 <$750
1902 Date Back
3x10-20 1-15000 <$600
Total Issue $1,531,050
Out in 1911 $200,000
****
7922 Vigo
McKEEN NB OF TERRE HAUTE
{{ 20 L }}
Chartered 9/05
Closed 2/20/28
1902 Red Seal <$VALUE
4x5 1-14000 <$200
3x10-20 1-12050 <$200/$225
1902 Date Back
4x5 1-22500* <$85
3x10-20 1-11000 <$85
50-100 1-4000 <$350/$400
1902 Plain Back
4x5 23751-43285* <$85
3x10-20 11001-72120 <$85
* 22501-23750 not marked
Total Issue $5,954,200
Out at close $500,000
Ch 2742 assumed circulation
****

****
13938 Vigo
MERCHANTS NB OF TERRE HAUTE
{{ 14 S }}
Chartered 1/34
1929 Small Size <$VALUE
10 Type 2 1-11862 <$85
20 Type 2 1-5754 <$85
Total Issue $233,700
Out in 1935 $176,350
****
1103 Vigo
N STATE B OF TERRE HAUTE
{{ 3 L }}
Chartered 5/65
Liquidated 1/20/05
Original Series <$VALUE
3x1-2 1-4900 <$500/$1000
4x5 1-13575 <$500
3x10-20 1-5660 <$750/$1250
50-100 1-300 <$4000
Series 1875
4x5 1-5750 <$500
3x10-20 1-5300 <$750/$1250
Brown Back
4x5 1-3900 <$400
3x10-20 1-10815 <$400
Total Issue $1,622,750
Out in 1910 $18,746
****
7562 Vigo
TERRE HAUTE NB, TERRE HAUTE
Chartered 1/05
Closed 11/15/32
2nd title: Terre Haute NB & TC 9/7/27
FIRST TITLE {{ 14 L }}
1902 Red Seal <$VALUE
4x5 1-4000 <$200
3x10-20 1-3000 <$200/$250
1902 Date Back
4x5 1-16000 <$85
3x10-20 1-14100 <$85
1902 Plain Back
4x5 16001-62546 <$85
3x10-20 14101-41730 <$85
SECOND TITLE {{ 11 L 24 S }}
1902 Plain Back
4x5 1-15977 <$85
3x10-20 1-15341 <$85
1929 Small Size
5 Type 1 1-18878 <$40
10 Type 1 1-9283 <$40
20 Type 1 1-2576 <$50
Total Issue $6,086,450
Out in 1932 $600,000
Large out at close $31,820
Ch 47 assumed circulation
****
Terre Haute NB, Terre Haute
SEE Ch 47
FNB of Terre Haute
****
3929 Vigo
VIGO COUNTY NB OF TERRE HAUTE
{{ 1 L }}
Organized 10/8/88
Receivership 6/28/05
Brown Back <$VALUE
4x5 1-695 <$850
3x10-20 1-3380 <$850
Total Issue $182,900
Out in 1915 $2,030
****
1046 Boone
FNB OF THORNTOWN
{{ 1 L }}
Chartered 1865
Liquidated 1/13/85
Original Series <$VALUE
4x5 1-2575 <$750
3x10-20 1-1870<$1000/$1500
Series 1875
4x5 1-1650 <$750
3x10-20 1-1140<$1000/$1500
Total Issue $235,000
Out in 1910 $1,355
****
5842 Boone
HOME NB OF THORNTOWN
{{ 2 L 4 S }}
Organized 5/15/01
Brown Back <$VALUE
3x10-20 1-1700 <$600
1882 Date Back
3x10-20 1-2100* <$600
1882 Value Back
3x10-20 2301-3312* <$600
* 2101-2300 not marked
1902 Plain Back
3x10-20 1-2766 <$450

1929 Small Size
10 Type 1 1-770 <$250
20 Type 1 1-230 <$250
10 Type 2 1-275 <$275
20 Type 2 1-50 <$275
Total Issue $466,450
Out in 1935 $30,000
Large out 1935 $1,510
****
7496 Tipton
CITIZENS NB OF TIPTON
{{ 9 L 15 S }}
Chartered 11/04
1902 Red Seal <$VALUE
4x5 1-2050 <$400
3x10-20 1-1550 <$400
1902 Date Back
4x5 1-6500 <$175
3x10-20 1-4700 <$175
1902 Plain Back
4x5 6501-22600 <$175
3x10-20 4701-15117 <$175
1929 Small Size
5 Type 1 1-3202 <$90
10 Type 1 1-1866 <$90
20 Type 1 1-444 <$100
5 Type 2 1-4332 <$100
10 Type 2 1-1748 <$100
20 Type 2 1-410 <$100
Total Issue $1,634,990
Out in 1935 $100,000
Large out 1935 $4,280
****
6251 Tipton
FNB OF TIPTON
{{ 6 L }}
Chartered 5/02
Liquidated 5/5/27
1902 Red Seal <$VALUE
4x5 1-5500 <$500
3x10-20 1-3900 <$500
1902 Date Back
4x5 1-6750 <$300
3x10-20 1-4800 <$300
1902 Plain Back
4x5 6751-19635 <$300
3x10-20 4801-13584 <$300
Total Issue $1,376,900
Out at close $100,000
****
7491 Johnson
FARMERS NB OF TRAFALGAR
{{ 4 L 1 S }}
Organized 9/27/04
Receivership 9/23/31
1902 Red Seal <$VALUE
4x5 1-250 <$1000
3x10-20 1-170 <$1000
1902 Date Back
4x5 1-600 <$500
3x10-20 1-460 <$500
1902 Plain Back
4x5 601-1287 <$500
3x10-20 461-904 <$500
1929 Small Size
5 Type 1 1-128 <$600
10 Type 1 1-66 <$600
20 Type 1 1-18 <$600
Total Issue $94,400
Out at close $6,250
Large out at close $600
****
5094 Randolph
COMMERCIAL NB OF UNION CITY
{{ 3 L }}
Chartered 1897
Liquidated 2/28/30
Brown Back <$VALUE
3x10-20 1-1320 <$650
1882 Date Back
3x10-20 1-1420* <$650
1882 Value Back
3x10-20 1621-1479* <$650
* 1421-1620 not marked
1902 Plain Back
3x10-20 1-2354 <$400
Total Issue $257,650
Out at close $10,935
****
815 Randolph
FNB OF UNION CITY
{{ 1 L }}
Chartered 1865
Liquidated 11/10/77
Original Series <$VALUE
4x5 1-2750 <$1000
3x10-20 1-600 <$1250/$1500
Series 1875
4x5 1-900 <$1000
Total Issue $103,000
Out in 1910 $715
****

2403 Porter
FARMERS NB OF VALPARAISO
{{ 2 L }}
Chartered 12/5/78
Liquidated 11/26/18
Series 1875 <$VALUE
3x10-20 1-2899<$1000/$1500
Brown Back
50-100 1-1120 <$1250/$1500
1882 Date Back
50-100 1-300 <$1250/$1500
3x50-100 1-299<$1250/$1500
Total Issue $432,700
Out at close $48,750

105 Porter
FNB OF VALPARAISO
{{ 1 L }}
Chartered 10/63
Liquidated 4/24/82
Original Series <$VALUE
3x1-2 1-2200 <$850/$1500
4x5 1-4550 <$1000
Series 1875
3x1-2 1-560 <$850/$1500
4x5 1-2430 <$1000
Total Issue $153,400
Out in 1910 $1,203

2704 Porter
FNB OF PORTER COUNTY, VALPARAISO
{{ 5 L }}
Chartered 5/23/82
Liquidated 5/4/02
Series 1875 <$VALUE
3x10-20 1-8726 <$750/$1250
Total Issue $436,300
Out in 1910 $6,265

6215 Porter
VALPARAISO NB, VALPARAISO
{{ 12 L 5 S }}
Organized 3/6/02
Receivership 1/20/32
1902 Red Seal <$VALUE
3x10-20 1-6300 <$400
1902 Date Back
3x10-20 1-6800 <$175
1902 Plain Back (dated 1902)
3x10-20 6801-12390 <$175
1902 Plain Back (dated 1922)
3x10-20 1-9727 <$175
1929 Small Size
10 Type 1 1-1696 <$175
20 Type 1 1-496 <$175
Total Issue $1,582,130
Out at close $98,435
Large out at close $11,715

11044 Fountain
FNB OF VEEDERSBURG
{{ 4 L 3 S }}
Organized 7/3/17
Receivership 3/19/31
1902 Plain Back <$VALUE
3x10-20 1-5007 <$300
1929 Small Size
10 Type 1 1-515 <$300
20 Type 1 1-98 <$300
Total Issue $293,010
Out at close $35,000
Large out at close $5,020

4688 Jennings
FNB OF VERNON
{{ 7 L 3 S }}
Chartered 1892
Liquidated 2/16/31
Brown Back <$VALUE
4x5 1-2875 <$450
3x10-20 1-960 <$450
1882 Date Back
4x5 1-689 <$450
3x10-20 1-501 <$450
1902 Date Back
4x5 1-1150 <$225
3x10-20 1-980 <$225
1902 Plain Back
4x5 1151-9080 <$225
3x10-20 981-6077 <$225
1929 Small Size
5 Type 1 1-257 <$250
10 Type 1 1-599 <$250
20 Type 1 1-147 <$275
Total Issue $691,070
Out at close $50,000
Large out at close $6,770

346 Switzerland
FNB OF VEVAY
{{ 7 L 6 S }}
Chartered 1864
Original Series <$VALUE
4x5 1-3250 <$600
3x10-20 1-2585 <$750/$1250
Series 1875
4x5 1-1475 <$600
3x10-20 1-1013 <$750/$1250
Brown Back
3x10-20 1-4340 <$450
1902 Red Seal
3x10-20 1-2300 <$500
1902 Date Back
3x10-20 1-2840 <$250
1902 Plain Back
3x10-20 2841-9428 <$250
1929 Small Size
10 Type 1 1-1326 <$175
20 Type 1 1-358 <$175
10 Type 2 1-1271 <$175
20 Type 2 1-325 <$200
Total Issue $1,219,530
Out in 1935 $50,000
Large out 1935 $4,800

American NB of Vincennes
SEE Ch 3864
German NB of Vincennes

1873 Knox
FNB OF VINCENNES
{{ 2U + 25 L 3 S }}
Organized 7/15/71
Receivership 10/3/32
Original Series <$VALUE
3x1-2 1-3000 <$400/$1000
4x5 1-3250 <$450
3x10-20 1-1300 <$750/$1250
Series 1875
4x5 1-4657 <$450
3x10-20 1-3238 <$750/$1250
Brown Back
4x5 1-11500 <$200
3x10-20 1-4800 <$200
1882 Date Back
4x5 1-1877 <$200
3x10-20 1-1791 <$200
1902 Date Back
4x5 1-4500 <$100
3x10-20 1-3500 <$100
1902 Plain Back
4x5 4501-18130 <$100
3x10-20 3501-12469 <$100
1929 Small Size
5 Type 1 1-256 <$300
10 Type 1 1-121 <$300
20 Type 1 1-42 <$300
Total Issue $2,003,160
Out at close $19,980
Large out at close $10,655

3864 Knox
GERMAN NB OF VINCENNES
Chartered 1888
2nd title:American NB 1/18/18
FIRST TITLE {{ 4 L }}
Brown Back <$VALUE
4x5 1-19417 <$350
3x10-20 1-5866 <$350/$400
1902 Red Seal
3x10-20 1-2000 <$400
1902 Date Back
4x5 1-14330 <$175
3x10-20 1-9400 <$175
1902 Plain Back
4x5 14331-19830 <$175
3x10-20 9401-12300 <$175
SECOND TITLE {{ 5 L }}
1902 Plain Back
4x5 1-34632 <$150
3x10-20 1-23084 <$150
Total Issue $3,640,080
Out in 1935 $15,645
Outstanding includes Ch 4901

4901 Knox
SECOND NB OF VINCENNES
{{ 2 L }}
Chartered 1893
Closed 10/23/19
Brown Back <$VALUE
4x5 1-13200 <$500
3x10-20 1-4500 <$500
1882 Date Back
4x5 1-4137 <$500
3x10-20 1-2963 <$500
1902 Date Back
3x10-20 1-4100 <$350
1902 Plain Back
3x10-20 4101-6276 <$350
Total Issue $1,033,690
Out at close $100,000

1454 Knox
VINCENNES NB, VINCENNES
{{ 1 L }}
Organized 7/17/65
Receivership 7/22/92
Original Series <$VALUE
4x5 1-6700 <$750
3x10-20 1-4860 <$850/$1250
Series 1875
4x5 1-2005 <$750
3x10-20 1-1866 <$850/$1250
Brown Back
4x5 1-1248 <$650
3x10-20 1-879 <$650
Total Issue $579,310
Out in 1915 $3,610

6309 Wabash
FARMERS & MERCHANTS NB OF WABASH
Organized 6/13/02
Receivership 1/11/34
2nd title: Farmers & Wabash NB of Wabash 12/31/27
FIRST TITLE {{ 11 L }}
1902 Red Seal <$VALUE
4x5 1-3750 <$400
3x10-20 1-3000 <$400
1902 Date Back
4x5 1-8100 <$150
3x10-20 1-5760 <$150
1902 Plain Back
4x5 8101-29681 <$150
3x10-20 5761-18986 <$150
SECOND TITLE {{ 2 L 14 S }}
1902 Plain Back
4x5 1-7996 <$225
1929 Small Size
5 Type 1 1-17526 <$90
5 Type 2 1-7368 <$100
Total Issue $2,499,460
Out at close $157,550
Large out at close $7,330

Farmers & Wabash NB of Wabash
SEE Ch 6309
Farmers & Merchants NB of Wabash

129 Wabash
FNB OF WABASH
{{ 3 L }}
Chartered 11/63
Liquidated 2/15/10
Original Series <$VALUE
3x1-2 1-2600 <$500/$1000
4x5 1-4800 <$600
Series 1875
4x5 1-5400 <$600
Brown Back
4x5 1-11848 <$450
3x10-20 1-1328 <$450
1902 Red Seal
3x10-20 1-3300 <$500
1902 Date Back
3x10-20 1-684 <$350
Total Issue $719,560
Out in 1910 $50,590

3935 Wabash
WABASH NB, WABASH
{{ 14 L }}
Organized 8/15/88
Liquidated 8/25/27
Brown Back <$VALUE
3x10-20 1-7447 <$300
1902 Date Back
3x10-20 1-9200 <$100
1902 Plain Back
3x10-20 9201-34164 <$100
Total Issue $2,080,550
Out at close $200,000

8927 Posey
FARMERS NB OF WADESVILLE
{{ 3 L 5 S }}
Organized 9/28/07
1902 Red Seal <$VALUE
3x10-20 1-240 <$750
1902 Date Back
3x10-20 1-2180 <$350
1902 Plain Back
3x10-20 2181-5890 <$350
1929 Small Size
10 Type 1 1-594 <$225
20 Type 1 1-170 <$225
10 Type 2 1-969 <$250
20 Type 2 1-161 <$250
Total Issue $375,450
Out in 1935 $25,000
Large out 1935 $1,290

11043 Elkhart
FNB OF WAKARUSA
{{ 5 L 14 S }}
Organized 7/14/17
Receivership 10/3/33
1902 Plain Back <$VALUE
4x10 1-5783 <$350
1929 Small Size
10 Type 1 1-1108 <$125
Total Issue $297,800
Out at close $25,000
Large out at close $400

7930 Huntington
FNB OF WARREN
{{ 2 L }}
Organized 5/10/05
Receivership 12/7/28
1902 Red Seal <$VALUE
3x10-20 1-260 <$750
1902 Date Back
3x10-20 1-1650 <$450
1902 Plain Back
3x10-20 1651-4811 <$450
Total Issue $253,550
Out at close $24,995

88 Kosciusko
FNB OF WARSAW
{{ 1 L }}
Chartered 9/63
Liquidated 12/1/81
Original Series <$VALUE
4x5 1-5750 <$1500
Series 1875
4x5 1-2165 <$1500
Total Issue $158,300
Out in 1910 $1,140

3842 Daviess
PEOPLES NB OF WASHINGTON
Chartered 1888
2nd title:Peoples NB & TC 6/1/28
FIRST TITLE {{ 7 L }}
Brown Back <$VALUE
50-100 1-809 <$1500/$1750
1902 Red Seal
3x10-20 1-500 <$500
1902 Date Back
3x10-20 1-7400 <$175
1902 Plain Back
3x10-20 7401-21314 <$175
SECOND TITLE {{ 1 L 12 S }}
1902 Plain Back
3x10-20 1-1000 <$225
1929 Small Size
10 Type 1 1-2460 <$90
20 Type 1 1-658 <$100
10 Type 2 1-1160 <$100
20 Type 2 1-383 <$100
Total Issue $1,507,870
Out in 1935 $75,000
Large out 1935 $5,080

2043 Daviess
WASHINGTON NB, WASHINGTON
{{ 5 L 8 S }}
Chartered 9/9/72
Original Series <$VALUE
4x5 1-1550 <$600
3x10-20 1-480 <$750/$1250
Series 1875
4x5 1-774 <$600
3x10-20 1-1627 <$750/$1250
Brown Back
50-100 1-1230 <$1500/$1750
1882 Date Back
50-100 1-946 <$1250/$1500
1902 Date Back
3x50-100 1-1640 <$500/$600
1902 Plain Back
3x50-100 1641-2061 <$500/$600
1929 Small Size
10 Type 1 1-261 <$150
20 Type 1 1-42 <$150
50 Type 1 1-248 <$250
100 Type 1 1-80 <$300
Total Issue $1,136,580
Out in 1935 $100,000
Large out 1935 $13,750

6388 Orange
WEST BADEN NB, WEST BADEN
{{ 3 L 3 S }}
Chartered 8/02
1902 Red Seal <$VALUE
4x5 1-392 <$750
3x10-20 1-333 <$750
1902 Date Back
4x5 1-575 <$400
3x10-20 1-420 <$400
1902 Plain Back
4x5 576-2453 <$400
3x10-20 421-1485 <$400
1929 Small Size
5 Type 1 1-524* <$325
10 Type 1 1-240** <$325
20 Type 1 1-84*** <$325
5 Type 2 1-252 <$350
10 Type 2 1-204 <$350
20 Type 2 1-105 <$350
* 352-418 not issued
** 175-208 not issued
*** 42-72 not issued
Total Issue $185,630
Out in 1935 $11,000
Large out 1935 $670

9175 Decatur
FNB OF WESTPORT
{{ 1 L }}
Chartered 7/08
Liquidated 7/1/30
1902 Date Back <$VALUE
4x10 1-1150* <$1000
1902 Plain Back
4x10 1251-2302* <$1000
* 1151-1250 not marked
Total Issue $92,080
Out at close $1,250

9492 Johnson
WHITELAND NB, WHITELAND
{{ 2 L }}
Organized 4/14/09
Receivership 10/3/33
1902 Date Back <$VALUE
3x10-20 1-2210 <$750
1902 Plain Back
3x10-20 2211-2934 <$750
Total Issue $146,700
Out at close $535

6526 Lake
FNB OF WHITING
{{ 2U + 2 L }}
Chartered 12/02
Liquidated 2/15/32
1902 Red Seal <$VALUE
3x10-20 1-1512 <$750
1902 Date Back
3x10-20 1-2910 <$350
1902 Plain Back
3x10-20 2911-8888 <$350
Total Issue $520,000
Out at close $3,370

9279 Hancock
FARMERS NB OF WILKINSON
{{ 3 L 2 S }}
Organized 11/2/08
Receivership 9/19/30
1902 Date Back <$VALUE
3x10-20 1-1380 <$400
1902 Plain Back
3x10-20 1381-5338 <$400
1929 Small Size
10 Type 1 1-300 <$400
20 Type 1 1-47 <$400
Total Issue $290,540
Out at close $25,000
Large out at close $4,810

8625 Wayne
FNB OF WILLIAMSBURG
{{ 6 L 3 S }}
Chartered 4/07
Liquidated 5/6/30
1902 Red Seal <$VALUE
4x5 1-450 <$750
4x10 1-450 <$750
1902 Date Back
4x5 1-1775 <$400
4x10 1-1625 <$400
1902 Plain Back
4x5 1776-6673 <$400
4x10 1626-5079 <$400
1929 Small Size
5 Type 1 1-118 <$400
10 Type 1 1-253 <$400
Total Issue $382,340
Out at close $23,055
Large out at close $4,335

8747 Pulaski
CITIZENS NB OF WINAMAC
{{ 3 L }}
Chartered 6/07
Liquidated 12/6/20
1902 Red Seal <$VALUE
3x10-20 1-625 <$850
1902 Date Back
3x10-20 1-4140 <$400
1902 Plain Back
3x10-20 4141-6052 <$400
Total Issue $333,850
Out at close $50,000

7761 Pulaski
FNB OF WINAMAC
{{ 3 L 3 S }}
Chartered 5/05
Liquidated 9/28/31
1902 Red Seal <$VALUE
3x10-20 1-2000 <$750
1902 Date Back
4x5 1-3705 <$350
3x10-20 1-2340* <$350
1902 Plain Back
4x5 3706-11704 <$350
3x10-20 2461-7583* <$350
* 2341-2460 not marked
1929 Small Size
5 Type 1 1-1030 <$300
10 Type 1 1-532 <$300
20 Type 1 1-149 <$300
Total Issue $793,930
Out at close $50,000
Large out at close $6,030

889 Randolph
FNB OF WINCHESTER
{{ 3 L }}
Chartered 1865
Liquidated 8/24/78
Original Series <$VALUE
3x1-2 1-2600 <$500/$1250
4x5 1-2300 <$600
3x10-20 1-1100 <$750/$1250
Series 1875
3x1-2 1-420 <$500/$1250
4x5 1-515 <$600
3x10-20 1-228 <$750/$1250
Total Issue $137,800
Out in 1910 $1,064

9159 Pike
FNB OF WINSLOW
{{ 3 L 5 S }}
Organized 4/25/08
1902 Date Back <$VALUE
4x5 1-2115 <$500
3x10-20 1-1634 <$500
1902 Plain Back
4x5 2116-6471 <$500
3x10-20 1635-4208 <$500
1929 Small Size
5 Type 1 1-1064 <$200
10 Type 1 1-506 <$200
20 Type 1 1-142 <$200
5 Type 2 1-588 <$225
10 Type 2 1-429 <$225
20 Type 2 1-115 <$225
Total Issue $428,670
Out in 1935 $25,000
Large out 1935 $1,120

CONDITION affects Value. The Values shown are for notes in FINE condition.

IOWA

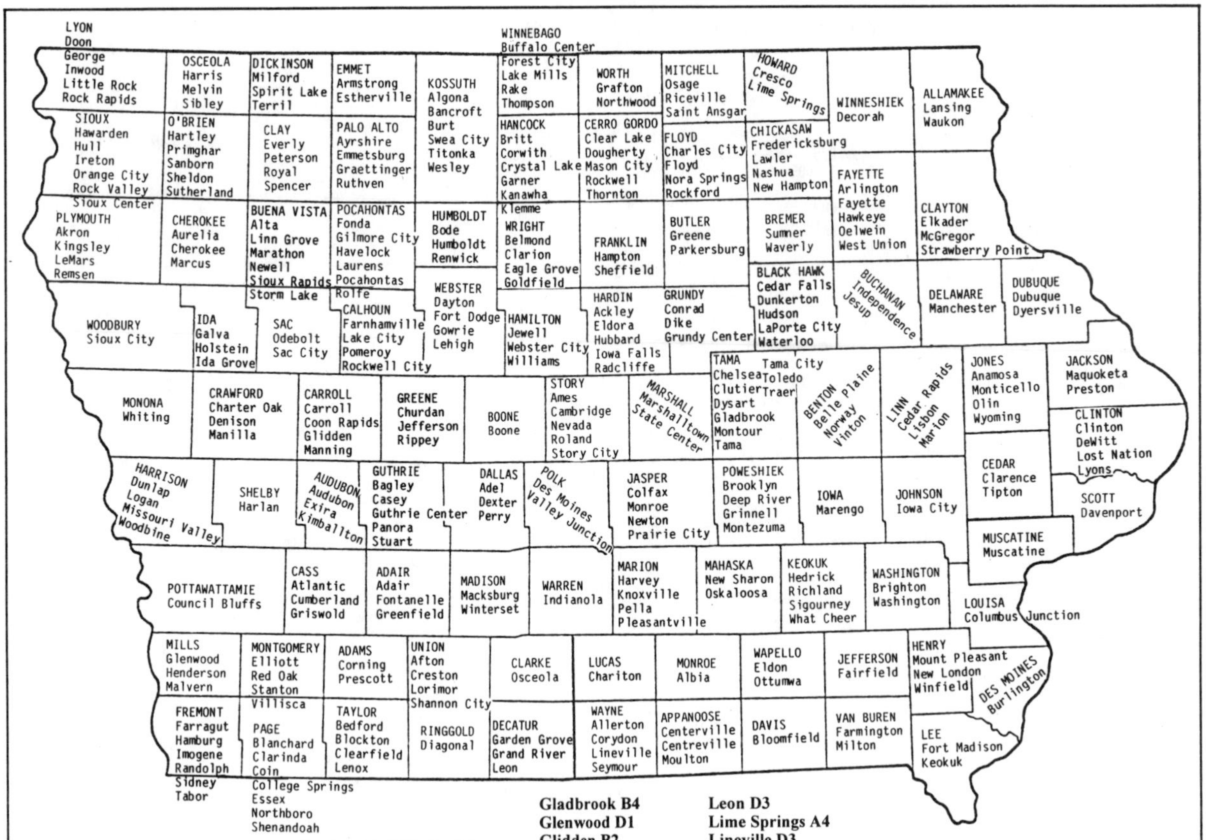

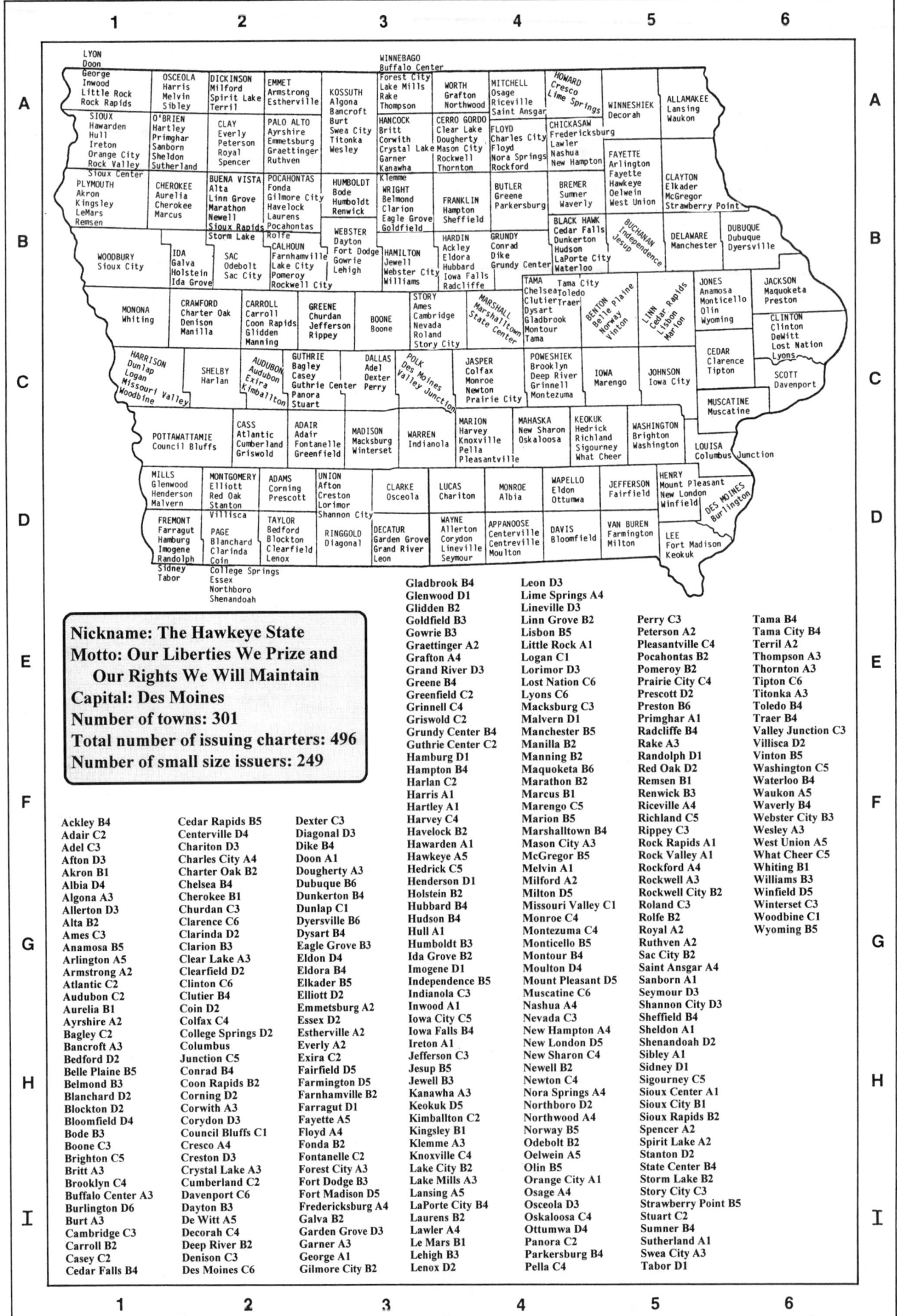

Nickname: The Hawkeye State
Motto: Our Liberties We Prize and Our Rights We Will Maintain
Capital: Des Moines
Number of towns: 301
Total number of issuing charters: 496
Number of small size issuers: 249

Ackley B4
Adair C2
Adel C3
Afton D3
Akron B1
Albia D4
Algona A3
Allerton D3
Alta B2
Ames C3
Anamosa B5
Arlington A5
Armstrong A2
Atlantic C2
Audubon C2
Aurelia B1
Ayrshire A2
Bagley C2
Bancroft A3
Bedford D2
Belle Plaine B5
Belmond B3
Blanchard D2
Blockton D2
Bloomfield D4
Bode B3
Boone C3
Brighton C5
Britt A3
Brooklyn C4
Buffalo Center A3
Burlington D6
Burt A3
Cambridge C3
Carroll B2
Casey C2
Cedar Falls B4
Cedar Rapids B5
Centerville D4
Chariton D3
Charles City A4
Charter Oak B2
Chelsea B4
Cherokee B1
Churdan C3
Clarence C6
Clarinda D2
Clarion B3
Clear Lake A3
Clearfield D2
Clinton C6
Clutier B4
Coin D2
Colfax C4
College Springs D2
Columbus Junction C5
Conrad B4
Coon Rapids B2
Corning D2
Corwith A3
Corydon D3
Council Bluffs C1
Cresco A4
Creston D3
Crystal Lake A3
Cumberland C2
Davenport C6
Dayton B3
De Witt A5
Decorah C4
Deep River B2
Denison C3
Des Moines C6
Dexter C3
Diagonal D3
Dike B4
Doon A1
Dougherty A3
Dubuque B6
Dunkerton B4
Dunlap C1
Dyersville B6
Dysart B4
Eagle Grove B3
Eldon D4
Eldora B4
Elkader B5
Elliott D2
Emmetsburg A2
Essex D2
Estherville A2
Everly A2
Exira C2
Fairfield D5
Farmington D5
Farnhamville B2
Farragut D1
Fayette A5
Floyd A4
Fonda B2
Fontanelle C2
Forest City A3
Fort Dodge B3
Fort Madison D5
Fredericksburg A4
Galva B2
Garden Grove D3
Garner A3
George A1
Gilmore City B2
Gladbrook B4
Glenwood D1
Glidden B2
Goldfield B3
Gowrie B3
Graettinger A2
Grafton A4
Grand River D3
Greene B4
Greenfield C2
Grinnell C4
Griswold C2
Grundy Center B4
Guthrie Center C2
Hamburg D1
Hampton B4
Harlan C2
Harris A1
Hartley A1
Harvey C4
Havelock B2
Hawarden A1
Hawkeye A5
Hedrick C5
Henderson D1
Holstein B2
Hubbard B4
Hudson B4
Hull A1
Humboldt B3
Ida Grove B2
Imogene D1
Independence B5
Indianola C3
Inwood A1
Iowa City C5
Iowa Falls B4
Ireton A1
Jefferson C3
Jesup B5
Jewell B3
Kanawha A3
Keokuk D5
Kimballton C2
Kingsley B1
Klemme A3
Knoxville C4
Lake City B2
Lake Mills A3
Lansing A5
LaPorte City B4
Laurens B2
Lawler A4
Le Mars B1
Lehigh B3
Lenox D2
Leon D3
Lime Springs A4
Lineville D3
Linn Grove B2
Lisbon B5
Little Rock A1
Logan C1
Lorimor D3
Lost Nation C6
Lyons C6
Macksburg C3
Malvern D1
Manchester B5
Manilla B2
Manning B2
Maquoketa B6
Marathon B2
Marcus B1
Marengo C5
Marion B5
Marshalltown B4
Mason City A3
McGregor B5
Melvin A1
Milford A2
Milton D5
Missouri Valley C1
Monroe C4
Montezuma C4
Monticello B5
Montour B4
Moulton D4
Mount Pleasant D5
Muscatine C6
Nashua A4
Nevada C3
New Hampton A4
New London D5
New Sharon C4
Newell B2
Newton C4
Nora Springs A4
Northboro D2
Northwood A4
Norway B5
Odebolt B2
Oelwein A5
Olin B5
Orange City A1
Osage A4
Osceola D3
Oskaloosa C4
Ottumwa D4
Panora C2
Parkersburg B4
Pella C4
Perry C3
Peterson A2
Pleasantville C4
Pocahontas B2
Pomeroy B2
Prairie City C4
Prescott D2
Preston B6
Primghar A1
Radcliffe B4
Rake A3
Randolph D1
Red Oak D2
Remsen B1
Renwick B3
Riceville A4
Richland C5
Rippey C3
Rock Rapids A1
Rock Valley A1
Rockford A4
Rockwell A3
Rockwell City B2
Roland C3
Rolfe B2
Royal A2
Ruthven A2
Sac City B2
Saint Ansgar A4
Sanborn A1
Seymour D3
Shannon City D3
Sheffield B4
Sheldon A1
Shenandoah D2
Sibley A1
Sidney D1
Sigourney C5
Sioux Center A1
Sioux City B1
Sioux Rapids B2
Spencer A2
Spirit Lake A2
Stanton D2
State Center B4
Storm Lake B2
Story City C3
Strawberry Point B5
Stuart C2
Sumner B4
Sutherland A1
Swea City A3
Tabor D1
Tama B4
Tama City B4
Terril A2
Thompson A3
Thornton A3
Tipton C6
Titonka A3
Toledo B4
Traer B4
Valley Junction C3
Villisca D2
Vinton B5
Washington C5
Waterloo B4
Waukon A5
Waverly B4
Webster City B3
Wesley A3
West Union A5
What Cheer C5
Whiting B1
Williams B3
Winfield D5
Winterset C3
Woodbine C1
Wyoming B5

****
8762 Hardin
FNB OF ACKLEY
{{ 12 L 6 S }}
Organized 5/30/07
Receivership 8/10/32
1902 Red Seal <$VALUE
3x10-20 1-360 <$400
1902 Date Back
3x10-20 1-1400* <$165
1902 Plain Back
3x10-20 1601-2908* <$165
* 1401-1600 not marked
1929 Small Size
10 Type 1 1-294 <$200
20 Type 1 1-78 <$200
Total Issue $190,400
Out at close $24,820
Large out at close $8,430
****
8699 Adair
FNB OF ADAIR
{{ UNREPORTED }}
Organized 4/29/07
Receivership 12/27/26
1902 Red Seal <$VALUE
4x5 1-156 <$2000
3x10-20 1-125 <$2000
1902 Date Back
4x5 1-700 <$1250
3x10-20 1-560 <$1250
1902 Plain Back
4x5 701-1249 <$1250
3x10-20 561-907 <$1250
Total Issue $79,700
Out at close $8,750
****
8981 Dallas
FNB OF ADEL
{{ 12 L }}
Chartered 1/08
Liquidated 8/7/28
1902 Red Seal <$VALUE
4x5 1-300 <$500
3x10-20 1-240 <$500
1902 Date Back
4x5 1-3400 <$200
3x10-20 1-2500 <$200
1902 Plain Back
4x5 3401-9395 <$200
3x10-20 2501-6528 <$200
Total Issue $532,300
Out at close $50,000
****
2326 Union
FNB OF AFTON
{{ UNREPORTED }}
Chartered 2/23/76
Liquidated 8/15/79
Series 1875 <$VALUE
4x5 1-1505 <$2000
Total Issue $30,100
Out in 1910 $265
****
7322 Plymouth
FNB, AKRON
{{ 6 L 6 S }}
Organized 1904
1902 Red Seal <$VALUE
3x10-20 1-307 <$750
1902 Date Back
3x10-20 1-2400 <$375
1902 Plain Back
3x10-20 2401-5804 <$375
1929 Small Size
10 Type 1 1-622 <$175
20 Type 1 1-212 <$175
10 Type 2 1-227 <$200
20 Type 2 1-56 <$200
Total Issue $371,700
Out in 1934 $30,000
Large out 1935 $1,760
****
3012 Monroe
ALBIA NB, ALBIA
{{ UNREPORTED }}
Chartered 1883
Liquidated 12/16/84
Brown Back <$VALUE
4x5 1-562 <$2000
Total Issue $11,240
Out in 1910 $105
****
1799 Monroe
FNB OF ALBIA
{{ 6 L 5 S }}
Chartered 3/2/71
Liquidated 6/18/30
Original Series <$VALUE
3x1-2 1-1500 <$500/$1250
4x5 1-1875 <$500
3x10-20 1-1650 <$850/$1500
Series 1875
3x10-20 1-1026 <$850/$1500
Brown Back
50-100 1-1520 <$1250/$1500
1882 Date Back
50-100 1-5 <$1250/$1500
1902 Date Back
3x50-100 1-920 <$500/$600
1902 Plain Back
3x50-100 921-1109 <$500/$600
1929 Small Size
50 Type 1 1-58 <$350
100 Type 1 1-2 <$600
Total Issue $703,400
Out at close $46,350
Large out at close $27,750
****
8603 Monroe
PEOPLES NB OF ALBIA
{{ 6 L 6 S }}
Chartered 3/07
1902 Red Seal <$VALUE
4x5 1-1000 <$400
3x10-20 1-1000 <$400
1902 Date Back
4x5 1-1700 <$175
3x10-20 1-1200 <$175
1902 Plain Back
4x5 1701-9192 <$175
3x10-20 1201-5804 <$175
1929 Small Size
5 Type 1 1-526 <$150
10 Type 1 1-262 <$150
20 Type 1 1-86 <$150
5 Type 2 1-842 <$175
10 Type 2 1-404 <$175
20 Type 2 1-111 <$175
Total Issue $596,330
Out in 1935 $20,000
Large out 1935 $1,920
****
3197 Kossuth
FNB, ALGONA
{{ 6 L }}
Organized 5/15/84
Receivership 11/24/24
Brown Back <$VALUE
4x5 1-4381 <$750
3x10-20 1-1095 <$750
1902 Red Seal
3x10-20 1-1700 <$750
1902 Date Back
3x10-20 1-3460 <$375
1902 Plain Back
3x10-20 3461-6745 <$375
Total Issue $564,620
Out at close $49,600
****
9231 Wayne
FARMERS NB OF ALLERTON
{{ 3 L }}
Chartered 8/08
Liquidated 6/19/26
1902 Date Back <$VALUE
3x10-20 1-2350 <$500
1902 Plain Back
3x10-20 2351-4787 <$500
Total Issue $239,350
Out at close $30,000
****
2191 Wayne
FNB OF ALLERTON
{{ 1 L }}
Chartered 9/29/74
Liquidated 12/6/86
Original Series <$VALUE
4x5 1-3250 <$1250
Series 1875
4x5 1-3057 <$1250
Total Issue $126,140
Out in 1910 $590
****
7126 Buena Vista
FNB, ALTA
{{ 5 L }}
Organized 1/21/04
Receivership 12/3/26
1902 Red Seal <$VALUE
3x10-20 1-630 <$850
1902 Date Back
3x10-20 1-3100* <$400
1902 Plain Back
3x10-20 3341-7757* <$400
* 3101-3340 not marked
Total Issue $419,350
Out at close $48,695
****
10408 Story
AMES NB, AMES
{{ 7 L 7 S }}
Chartered 6/14/13
Liquidated 3/31/33
1902 Date Back <$VALUE
4x10 1-2600 <$200
1902 Plain Back
4x10 2601-12856 <$200
1929 Small Size
10 Type 1 1-1764 <$150
Total Issue $620,080
Out at close $50,000
Large out at close $3,620
****
3017 Story
UNION NB OF AMES
{{ 6 L 7 S }}
Chartered 1883
Liquidated 7/12/32
Brown Back <$VALUE
4x5 1-3762 <$400
3x10-20 1-1200 <$400
1902 Red Seal
3x10-20 1-2000 <$500
1902 Date Back
3x10-20 1-3200* <$200
1902 Plain Back
3x10-20 3541-10021* <$200
* 3301-3540 not marked
1929 Small Size
10 Type 1 1-769 <$150
20 Type 1 1-222 <$150
Total Issue $809,070
Out at close $50,000
Large out 1935 $7,290
****
4696 Jones
ANAMOSA NB, ANAMOSA
{{ 12 L 12 S }}
Organized 2/4/92
Receivership 1/27/32
Brown Back <$VALUE
3x10-20 1-6180 <$400
1882 Date Back
3x10-20 1-2340 <$400
1902 Date Back
3x10-20 1-3800 <$150
1902 Plain Back
3x10-20 3801-16804 <$150
1929 Small Size
10 Type 1 1-1592 <$100
20 Type 1 1-451 <$100
Total Issue $1,415,840
Out at close $98,740
Large out at close $13,000
****
1813 Jones
FNB OF ANAMOSA
{{ UNREPORTED }}
Chartered 4/22/71
Liquidated 12/14/78
Original Series <$VALUE
3x1-2 1-2500 <$1500/$2500
3x10-20 1-1360 <$2000/$2500
Series 1875
3x1-2 1-180 <$1500/$2500
3x10-20 1-236 <$2000/$2500
Total Issue $93,200
Out in 1910 $457
****
American NB of Arlington
SEE Ch 9664
German-American NB of
Arlington
****
9664 Fayette
GERMAN-AMERICAN NB OF
ARLINGTON
Organized 9/28/09
2nd title: American NB of
Arlington 7/18
FIRST TITLE {{ 3 L }}
1902 Date Back <$VALUE
4x5 1-600 <$450
3x10-20 1-480 <$450
1902 Plain Back
4x5 601-1100 <$450
3x10-20 481-880 <$450
SECOND TITLE {{ 6 L 14 S }}
1902 Plain Back
4x5 1-8120 <$300
1929 Small Size
5 Type 1 1-2664 <$100
5 Type 2 1-4596 <$100
Total Issue $331,300
Out in 1935 $24,550
Large out 1935 $3,750
****
5442 Emmet
FNB, ARMSTRONG
{{ 6 L }}
Organized 5/1/00
Receivership 11/17/26
Brown Back <$VALUE
3x10-20 1-1830 <$600
1882 Date Back
3x10-20 1-3440 <$600
1882 Value Back
3x10-20 3441-4740 <$600
1902 Plain Back
3x10-20 1-3444 <$375
Total Issue $500,700
Out at close $49,500
****
2762 Cass
ATLANTIC NB, ATLANTIC
{{ 12 L 9 S }}
Chartered 1882
Liquidated 3/15/33
Series 1875 <$VALUE
3x10-20 1-1285 <$750/$1250
1902 Red Seal
3x10-20 1-925 <$450
1902 Date Back
3x10-20 1-3800* <$175
1902 Plain Back
3x10-20 4301-8897* <$175
* 3801-4300 not marked
1929 Small Size
10 Type 1 1-866 <$125
20 Type 1 1-229 <$125
Total Issue $634,790
Out at close $50,000
Large out at close $5,670
****
1836 Cass
FNB OF ATLANTIC
{{ 2 L }}
Chartered 6/21/71
Liquidated 3/7/76
Original Series <$VALUE
3x1-2 1-2500 <$850/$2000
4x5 1-2625 <$1000
Series 1875
4x5 1-573 <$1000
Total Issue $76,460
Out in 1910 $415
****
4891 Audubon
FNB OF AUDUBON
{{ 6 L 6 S }}
Chartered 1893
Liquidated 1/30/33
Brown Back <$VALUE
4x5 1-3950 <$500
3x10-20 1-1940 <$500
1882 Date Back
4x5 1-2002 <$500
3x10-20 1-1208 <$500
1902 Date Back
3x10-20 1-1400* <$300
1902 Plain Back
3x10-20 1901-4212* <$300
* 1401-1900 not marked
1929 Small Size
10 Type 1 1-487 <$200
20 Type 1 1-103 <$200
Total Issue $528,620
Out at close $25,000
Large out at close $3,680
****
9724 Cherokee
FARMERS NB, AURELIA
{{ 5 L 7 S }}
Chartered 1910
1902 Date Back <$VALUE
3x10-20 1-3500* <$350
1902 Plain Back
3x10-20 3741-9571* <$350
* 3501-3740 not marked
1929 Small Size
10 Type 1 1-1093 <$175
20 Type 1 1-318 <$175
Total Issue $582,290
Out in 1934 $25,000
Large out 1935 $3,070
****
7108 Cherokee
FNB OF AURELIA
{{ 3 L 8 S }}
Chartered 1904
Liquidated 5/11/35
1902 Red Seal <$VALUE
3x10-20 1-300 <$800
1902 Date Back
3x10-20 1-1840 <$400
1902 Plain Back
3x10-20 1841-4782 <$400
1929 Small Size
10 Type 1 1-518 <$150
20 Type 1 1-146 <$150
10 Type 2 1-599 <$150
20 Type 2 1-100 <$165
Total Issue $310,690
Out in 1934 $25,000
Large out 1935 $1,510
****
5479 Palo Alto
FNB, AYRSHIRE
{{ 6 L 2 S }}
Organized 6/11/00
Receivership 8/12/30
Brown Back <$VALUE
3x10-20 1-600 <$600
1882 Date Back
3x10-20 1-680 <$600
1882 Value Back
3x10-20 681-716 <$600
1902 Plain Back
4x5 1-2222 <$350
1929 Small Size
5 Type 1 1-234 <$400
Total Issue $117,260
Out at close $8,000
Large out at close $1,680
****
6995 Guthrie
FNB OF BAGLEY
{{ 6 L 6 S }}
Organized 10/5/03
Receivership 7/3/31
1902 Red Seal <$VALUE
3x10-20 1-350 <$750
1902 Date Back
3x10-20 1-1660 <$350
1902 Plain Back
3x10-20 1661-4126 <$350
1929 Small Size
10 Type 1 1-284 <$225
20 Type 1 1-55 <$225
Total Issue $247,440
Out at close $19,520
Large out at close $3,420
****
5643 Kossuth
FNB, BANCROFT
{{ 7 L }}
Organized 11/10/00
Receivership 10/20/27
Brown Back <$VALUE
3x10-20 1-2650 <$450
1882 Date Back
3x10-20 1-3440 <$450
1882 Value Back
3x10-20 3441-4993 <$450
1902 Plain Back
3x10-20 1-3426 <$250
Total Issue $553,450
Out at close $50,000
****
5165 Taylor
BEDFORD NB, BEDFORD
{{ 13 L 12 S }}
Chartered 12/29/98
Brown Back <$VALUE
4x5 1-3775 <$300
3x10-20 1-1680 <$300
1882 Date Back
4x5 1-2500 <$300
3x10-20 1-1860 <$300
1882 Value Back
4x5 2501-3178 <$300
3x10-20 1861-2324 <$300
1902 Plain Back
4x5 1-4940 <$125
3x10-20 1-3554 <$125
1929 Small Size
5 Type 1 1-1288 <$85
10 Type 1 1-810 <$85
20 Type 1 1-230 <$85
5 Type 2 1-1340 <$100
10 Type 2 1-822 <$100
20 Type 2 1-128 <$100
Total Issue $748,080
Out in 1935 $50,000
Large out 1935 $4,570
****
2298 Taylor
FNB OF BEDFORD
{{ UNREPORTED }}
Chartered 9/18/75
Receivership 2/1/76
Series 1875 <$VALUE
3x10-20 1-540 <$2000/$2500
Total Issue $27,000
Out in 1915 $90
****
4754 Benton
CITIZENS NB OF
BELLE PLAINE
{{ 13 L 10 S }}
Organized 5/18/92
Liquidated 4/23/34
Brown Back <$VALUE
3x10-20 1-4470 <$400
1882 Date Back
3x10-20 1-1296 <$400
1902 Date Back
3x10-20 1-1700 <$200
1902 Plain Back
3x10-20 1701-7695 <$200
1929 Small Size
10 Type 1 1-946 <$150
20 Type 1 1-290 <$150
Total Issue $764,610
Out at close $50,000
Large out at close $4,370
Ch 14069 assumed circulation
****
2012 Benton
FNB OF BELLE PLAINE
{{ 8 L }}
Organized 5/31/72
Receivership 3/3/27
Original Series <$VALUE
3x1-2 1-2152 <$500/$1250
4x5 1-2625 <$600
Series 1875
4x5 1-6232 <$600
Brown Back
3x10-20 1-6090 <$400
1882 Date Back
3x10-20 1-1285 <$400
1902 Date Back
3x10-20 1-2200 <$225
1902 Plain Back
3x10-20 2201-7542 <$225
Total Issue $933,750
Out at close $59,100
****
8748 Wright
FNB OF BELMOND
{{ 2 L }}
Chartered 6/07
Liquidated 4/11/21
1902 Red Seal <$VALUE
4x5 1-250 <$1250
3x10-20 1-200 <$1250
1902 Date Back
4x5 1-775 <$750
3x10-20 1-600 <$750
1902 Plain Back
4x5 776-1075 <$750
3x10-20 601-745 <$750
Total Issue $73,750
Out in 1920 $10,000
****
4902 Page
FNB OF BLANCHARD
{{ 2 L }}
Chartered 1893
Liquidated 6/30/14
Brown Back <$VALUE
3x10-20 1-3220 <$1000
1882 Date Back
3x10-20 1-1568 <$1000
1902 Date Back
3x10-20 1-346 <$750
Total Issue $256,700
Out in 1914 $31,050
****
8211 Taylor
FNB OF BLOCKTON
{{ 3 L 3 S }}
Organized 5/3/06
Receivership 10/22/31
1902 Red Seal <$VALUE
3x10-20 1-200 <$1000
1902 Date Back
3x10-20 1-500* <$500
1902 Plain Back
3x10-20 601-1102* <$500
* 501-600 not marked
1929 Small Size
10 Type 1 1-94 <$400
20 Type 1 1-11 <$400
Total Issue $72,060
Out at close $6,250
Large out at close $1,610
****
1299 Davis
FNB OF BLOOMFIELD
{{ 1 L }}
Chartered 1865
Liquidated 2/5/76
Original Series <$VALUE
4x5 1-4825 <$1500
Series 1875
4x5 1-451 <$1500
Total Issue $105,520
Out in 1910 $850
****
9303 Davis
NB OF BLOOMFIELD
{{ 12 L 3 S }}
Chartered 1/09
Liquidated 2/26/30
1902 Date Back <$VALUE
3x10-20 1-4500 <$250
1902 Plain Back
3x10-20 4501-10920 <$250
1929 Small Size
10 Type 1 1-399 <$400
20 Type 1 1-20 <$400
Total Issue $572,340
Out at close $53,560
Large out at close $27,220
****

****
10371 Humboldt
FNB, BODE
{{ 3 L 3 S }}
Organized 3/29/13
Receivership 10/1/31
1902 Date Back <$VALUE
4x10 1-625 <$600
1902 Plain Back
4x10 626-1450 <$600
1929 Small Size
10 Type 1 1-133 <$400
Total Issue $65,980
Out at close $6,250
Large out at close $970
****
6838 Boone
BOONE NB, BOONE
{{ 7 L }}
Chartered 6/03
Liquidated 3/24/25
1902 Red Seal <$VALUE
3x10-20 1-4550 <$400
1902 Date Back
3x10-20 1-7500 <$200
1902 Plain Back
3x10-20 7501-10458 <$200
Total Issue $750,400
Out in 1924 $48,395
****
13817 Boone
CITIZENS NB OF BOONE
{{ 12 S }}
Chartered 10/33
1929 Small Size <$VALUE
10 Type 2 1-1635 <$125
20 Type 2 1-445 <$125
Total Issue $25,250
Out in 1935 $58,550
Outstanding includes Ch 3273
****
2051 Boone
FNB OF BOONE
{{ 1 L }}
Chartered 9/26/72
Liquidated 1/22/78
Original Series <$VALUE
4x5 1-1600 <$1500
3x10-20 1-700 <$1750/$2000
Series 1875
4x5 1-95 <$1500
Total Issue $68,900
Out in 1910 $350
****
FNB of Boone
SEE Ch 3273
NB of Boone
****
3273 Boone
NB OF BOONE
Organized 11/24/84
Liquidated 1/5/34
2nd title: FNB of Boone 4/88
FIRST TITLE {{ 3 L }}
Brown Back <$VALUE
4x5 1-169 <$500
3x10-20 1-225 <$500
SECOND TITLE {{ 13 L 23 S }}
Brown Back
3x10-20 1-3057 <$350
1902 Red Seal
3x10-20 1-3600 <$350
1902 Date Back
3x10-20 1-7100 <$165
1902 Plain Back
3x10-20 7101-12549 <$165
1929 Small Size
10 Type 1 1-1328 <$50
20 Type 1 1-388 <$60
Total Issue $1,101,170
Out at close $70,000
Large out at close $5,600
Ch 13817 assumed circulation
****
2033 Washington
BRIGHTON NB, BRIGHTON
{{ UNREPORTED }}
Chartered 8/24/72
Liquidated 12/15/81
Original Series <$VALUE
3x1-2 1-1500 <$1500/$2500
4x5 1-2625 <$1500
Series 1875
4x5 1-2615 <$1500
Total Issue $112,300
Out in 1910 $710
****

****
5554 Washington
NB OF BRIGHTON
{{ 1 L }}
Chartered 8/25/00
Liquidated 12/31/06
Brown Back <$VALUE
3x10-20 1-1020 <$1500
Total Issue $51,000
Out in 1910 $3,370
****
5020 Hancock
FNB, BRITT
{{ 5 L }}
Organized 8/13/95
Receivership 2/1/27
Brown Back <$VALUE
4x5 1-4800 <$500
50-100 1-770 <$1250/$1500
1882 Date Back
4x5 1-2503 <$500
50-100 1-300 <$1250/$1500
3x50-100 1-12 <$1250/$1500
1902 Plain Back
4x5 1-4910 <$400
3x10-20 1-3340 <$400
Total Issue $602,760
Out at close $44,300
****
3284 Poweshiek
FNB OF BROOKLYN
{{ 2 L }}
Organized 12/22/84
Receivership 12/4/25
Brown Back <$VALUE
50-100 1-536 <$1500/$1750
1902 Red Seal
3x10-20 1-570 <$1250
1902 Date Back
3x10-20 1-1145 <$600
1902 Plain Back
3x10-20 1146-2168 <$600
Total Issue $217,300
Out at close $14,700
****
5154 Winnebago
FNB, BUFFALO CENTER
{{ 13 L 15 S }}
Organized 10/20/98
Receivership 1/20/33
Brown Back <$VALUE
4x5 1-3850 <$300
3x10-20 1-2520 <$300
1882 Date Back
4x5 1-3250 <$300
3x10-20 1-2340 <$300
1882 Value Back
4x5 3251-4165 <$300
3x10-20 2341-2805 <$300
1902 Plain Back
4x5 1-5237 <$165
4x10 1-850 <$165
3x10-20 1-3097 <$165
1929 Small Size
5 Type 1 1-1255 <$110
10 Type 1 1-579 <$110
20 Type 1 1-173 <$125
Total Issue $813,290
Out at close $49,995
Large out at close $5,915
****
351 Des Moines
THE FNB OF BURLINGTON
Chartered 1864
Liquidated 10/15/23
2nd title:FNB of Burlington 9/25/19
FIRST TITLE {{ 9 L }}
Original Series <$VALUE
4x5 1-3500 <$500
3x10-20 1-2400 <$750/$1250
Series 1875
3x10-20 1-534 <$750/$1250
Brown Back
3x10-20 1-5359 <$300
1902 Red Seal
3x10-20 1-4600 <$300
1902 Date Back
3x10-20 1-6200 <$150
1902 Plain Back
3x10-20 6201-10400 <$150
SECOND TITLE {{ 2 L }}
1902 Plain Back
3x10-20 1-9139 <$175
Total Issue $1,691,600
Out at close $249,995
Outstanding includes Ch 751
****

****
1744 Des Moines
MERCHANTS NB OF BURLINGTON
{{ 27 L 2 S }}
Organized 11/7/70
Liquidated 5/12/30
Original Series <$VALUE
3x1-2 1-1500 <$400/$1250
4x5 1-2375 <$400
3x10-20 1-2500 <$750/$1250
Series 1875
4x5 1-1040 <$400
3x10-20 1-2652 <$750/$1250
Brown Back
50-100 1-2473 <$1250/$1500
1882 Date Back
4x5 1-1825 <$200
1902 Date Back
4x5 1-5000 <$100
3x50-100 1-950 <$350/$400
1902 Plain Back
4x5 5001-26294 <$100
3x50-100 951-1172<$350/$400
1929 Small Size
5 Type 1 1-1506 <$350
50 Type 1 1-29 <$500
100 Type 1 1 <$600
Total Issue $1,614,210
Out at close $92,560
Large out at close $38,080
****
751 Des Moines
N STATE B OF BURLINGTON
{{ 11 L }}
Chartered 1865
Closed 9/25/19
Original Series <$VALUE
3x1-2 1-1000 <$400/$1250
4x5 1-1500 <$450
3x10-20 1-4960 <$750/$1250
Series 1875
3x10-20 1-2250 <$750/$1250
Brown Back
3x10-20 1-7968 <$250
1902 Red Seal
3x10-20 1-5000 <$275
1902 Date Back
3x10-20 1-9800 <$110
1902 Plain Back
3x10-20 9801-12902 <$110
Total Issue $1,689,000
Out at close $143,600
Ch 351 assumed circulation
****
5703 Kossuth
BURT NB, BURT
{{ 4 L }}
Chartered 2/6/01
Liquidated 9/5/27
Brown Back <$VALUE
3x10-20 1-2100 <$500
1882 Date Back
3x10-20 1-2500* <$500
1882 Value Back
3x10-20 2741-3905* <$500
* 2501-2740 not marked
1902 Plain Back
3x10-20 1-2526 <$350
Total Issue $426,550
Out in 1926 $40,000
****
5685 Kossuth
FNB, BURT
{{ 13 L 2 S }}
Organized 1/5/01
Receivership 9/5/30
Brown Back <$VALUE
3x10-20 1-1280 <$400
1882 Date Back
3x10-20 1-1780 <$400
1882 Value Back
3x10-20 1781-2580 <$400
1902 Plain Back
3x10-20 1-1983 <$150
1929 Small Size
10 Type 1 1-235 <$350
20 Type 1 1-29 <$350
Total Issue $309,730
Out at close $25,000
Large out at close $7,760
****
9014 Story
FNB OF CAMBRIDGE
{{ 12 L }}
Organized 10/25/07
Receivership 5/22/26
1902 Red Seal <$VALUE
4x5 1-400 <$400
3x10-20 1-340 <$400
1902 Date Back
4x5 1-2125 <$175
3x10-20 1-1640 <$175
1902 Plain Back
4x5 2126-11890 <$175
3x10-20 1641-7468 <$175
Total Issue $636,200
Out at close $78,700
****
3969 Carroll
FNB OF CARROLL
{{ 3 L }}
Organized 1/25/89
Receivership 10/21/08
Brown Back <$VALUE
3x10-20 1-7028 <$650
Total Issue $351,400
Out in 1915 $6,960
****
8099 Guthrie
ABRAM RUTT NB OF CASEY
{{ 6 L 1 S }}
Chartered 2/06
Liquidated 2/1/30
1902 Red Seal <$VALUE
3x10-20 1-895 <$750
1902 Date Back
3x10-20 1-3450 <$400
1902 Plain Back
3x10-20 3451-9895 <$400
1929 Small Size
10 Type 1 1-67* <$750
*E000067A-F000067A not issued
Total Issue $543,500
Out at close $37,600
Large out at close $33,600
****
3871 Black Hawk
CEDAR FALLS NB, CEDAR FALLS
{{ 14 L 5 S }}
Chartered 4/4/88
Liquidated 6/30/33
Brown Back <$VALUE
4x5 1-7199 <$300
3x10-20 1-3423 <$300
1902 Red Seal
4x5 1-625 <$350
3x10-20 1-500 <$350
1902 Date Back
4x5 1-6850 <$165
3x10-20 1-5300 <$165
1902 Plain Back
4x5 6851-28372 <$165
3x10-20 5301-6020 <$165
1929 Small Size
10 Type 1 1-486 <$200
20 Type 1 1-165 <$200
Total Issue $1,270,030
Out at close $29,995
Large out at close $4,770
****
5507 Black Hawk
CITIZENS NB OF CEDAR FALLS
{{ 1 L }}
Chartered 7/19/00
Liquidated 12/16/05
Brown Back <$VALUE
3x10-20 1-1964 <$1250
Total Issue $98,200
Out in 1910 $6,170
****
2177 Black Hawk
FNB OF CEDAR FALLS
{{ 2 L }}
Chartered 9/1/74
Receivership 6/13/93
Original Series <$VALUE
3x1-2 1-1000 <$750/$1500
4x5 1-1500 <$850
3x10-20 1-200 <$1500/$2000
Series 1875
3x1-2 1-280 <$750/$1500
4x5 1-3520 <$850
3x10-20 1-1219<$1500/$2000
Total Issue $177,750
Out in 1915 $1,112
****
3643 Linn
CEDAR RAPIDS NB, CEDAR RAPIDS
{{ 50+ L 31 S }}
Organized 2/28/87
Liquidated 8/3/32
Brown Back <$VALUE
4x5 1-12975 <$175
3x10-20 1-3941 <$175/$225
1902 Red Seal
3x10-20 1-1000 <$175/$225
1902 Date Back
3x10-20 1-16500 <$85
1902 Plain Back
3x10-20 16501-81276 <$85
1929 Small Size
10 Type 1 1-6938 <$40
20 Type 1 1-2034 <$50
Total Issue $5,230,710
Out at close $499,995
Large out at close $58,710
****
5113 Linn
CITIZENS NB OF CEDAR RAPIDS
{{ 2 L }}
Chartered 3/14/98
Liquidated 6/20/08
Brown Back <$VALUE
3x10-20 1-7526 <$650
Total Issue $376,300
Out in 1910 $48,895
****
483 Linn
CITY NB OF CEDAR RAPIDS
{{ 3 L }}
Chartered 7/19/64
Liquidated 3/28/98
Original Series <$VALUE
3x1-2 1-3000 <$500/$1250
4x5 1-3150 <$650
3x10-20 1-1500<$1000/$1500
Series 1875
3x1-2 1-680 <$500/$1250
4x5 1-1090 <$650
3x10-20 1-1090<$1000/$1500
Brown Back
3x10-20 1-1959 <$500
Total Issue $330,650
Out in 1910 $2,677
****
9168 Linn
COMMERCIAL NB OF CEDAR RAPIDS
{{ 3 L }}
Chartered 6/08
Liquidated 12/15/14
1902 Date Back <$VALUE
4x5 1-6900 <$500
3x10-20 1-4724 <$500
Total Issue $374,200
Out in 1915 $52,645
****
500 Linn
FNB OF CEDAR RAPIDS
{{ 2 L }}
Chartered 8/23/64
Liquidated 5/28/86
Original Series <$VALUE
3x1-2 1-3300 <$750/$1500
4x5 1-9000 <$850
Series 1875
4x5 1-1760 <$850
Brown Back
4x5 1-1128 <$750
Total Issue $254,260
Out in 1910 $2,130
****
2511 Linn
MERCHANTS NB OF CEDAR RAPIDS
{{ 28 L 50+ S }}
Chartered 1881
Series 1875 <$VALUE
4x5 1-10600 <$400
50-100 1-108 <$4000
Brown Back
50-100 1-1200 <$1250/$1500
1882 Date Back
3x10-20 1-10000 <$175/$200
3x50-100 1-2048<$1250/$1500
1882 Value Back
3x10-20 10001-10630 <$175/$200
1902 Plain Back
3x10-20 1-19577 <$75
3x50-100 1-2554 <$75
1929 Small Size
10 Type 1 1-5624 <$25
20 Type 1 1-1796 <$35
50 Type 1 1-700 <$100
100 Type 1 1-164 <$150
10 Type 2 1-96 <$75
Total Issue $3,931,370
Out in 1935 $500,000
Large out 1935 $33,550
****
2841 Appanoose
CENTERVILLE NB, CENTERVILLE
{{ 7 L 6 S }}
Chartered 1882
Brown Back <$VALUE
4x5 1-3324 <$500
3x10-20 1-841 <$500
1902 Red Seal
4x5 1-1000 <$500
50-100 1-600 <$2250/$2500
1902 Date Back
4x5 1-3200 <$250
50-100 1-300 <$500/$600
3x50-100 1-427 <$500/$600
1902 Plain Back
4x5 3201-15099 <$250
3x50-100 428-488<$500/$600
1929 Small Size
5 Type 1 1-1660 <$175
50 Type 1 1-86 <$275
100 Type 1 1-32 <$350
5 Type 2 1-1948 <$175
Total Issue $792,050
Out in 1935 $49,995
Large out 1935 $5,165
****
2197 Appanoose
FARMERS NB OF CENTERVILLE
{{ UNREPORTED }}
Chartered 10/27/74
Liquidated 2/27/79
Original Series <$VALUE
4x5 1-2250 <$1500
Series 1875
4x5 1-1665 <$1500
Total Issue $78,300
Out in 1910 $445
****
337 Appanoose
FNB OF CENTREVILLE, CENTERVILLE
{{ 6 L 12 S }}
Chartered 1864
Original Series <$VALUE
4x5 1-4500 <$750
Series 1875
4x5 1-3295 <$750
Brown Back
4x5 1-2758 <$500
3x10-20 1-192 <$500
1902 Red Seal
4x5 1-1500 <$600
3x10-20 1-2000 <$600
1902 Date Back
4x5 1-2800* <$275
3x10-20 1-2040** <$275
1902 Plain Back
4x5 3051-9420* <$275
3x10-20 2201-6329** <$275
* 2801-3050 not marked
** 2041-2200 not marked
1929 Small Size
5 Type 1 1-1232 <$150
10 Type 1 1-756 <$150
20 Type 1 1-246 <$150
5 Type 2 1-1484 <$175
10 Type 2 1-842 <$175
20 Type 2 1-155 <$175
Total Issue $986,290
Out in 1935 $50,000
Large out 1935 $4,280
****
Chariton & Lucas County NB of Chariton
SEE Ch 9024
Lucas County NB of Chariton
****
6014 Lucas
CHARITON NB, CHARITON
{{ 6 L }}
Chartered 11/01
Closed 10/15/21
Brown Back <$VALUE
3x10-20 1-3300 <$375
1882 Date Back
3x10-20 1-3140 <$375
1882 Value Back
3x10-20 3141-5305 <$375
Total Issue $430,250
Out at close $49,600
Ch 9024 assumed circulation
****
1724 Lucas
FNB OF CHARITON
{{ 3 L }}
Chartered 10/20/70
Receivership 10/31/07
Original Series <$VALUE
3x10-20 1-2000 <$850/$1500
Series 1875
3x10-20 1-925 <$850/$1500
Brown Back
3x10-20 1-2887 <$500
Total Issue $290,600
Out in 1915 $2,840
****

****
9024 Lucas
LUCAS COUNTY NB OF CHARITON
Chartered 2/08
Liquidated 4/19/30
2nd title: Chariton & Lucas County NB of Chariton 10/15/21
FIRST TITLE {{ 12 L }}
1902 Red Seal <$VALUE
3x10-20 1-375 <$300
1902 Date Back
4x5 1-3500 <$125
3x10-20 1-2440 <$125
1902 Plain Back
4x5 3501-6750 <$125
3x10-20 2441-4180 <$125
SECOND TITLE {{ 27 L 5 S }}
1902 Plain Back
4x5 1-7430 <$85
3x10-20 1-5406 <$85
1929 Small Size
5 Type 1 1-1241 <$125
10 Type 1 1-470 <$125
20 Type 1 1-92 <$150
Total Issue $858,120
Out at close $100,000
Large out at close $27,430
Ch 13458 assumed circulation
****
13458 Lucas
NB & TC OF CHARITON
{{ 12 S }}
Chartered 4/30
1929 Small Size <$VALUE
5 Type 1 1-1562 <$70
10 Type 1 1-1018 <$70
20 Type 1 1-256 <$80
5 Type 2 1-2278 <$70
10 Type 2 1-740 <$70
20 Type 2 1-200 <$85
Total Issue $161,450
Out in 1935 $50,000
Large out 1935 $8,520
Outstanding includes Ch 6014 and Ch 9024
****
2579 Floyd
CHARLES CITY NB, CHARLES CITY
{{ 3 L }}
Chartered 10/25/81
Liquidated 10/8/01
Series 1875 <$VALUE
4x5 1-5704 <$650
3x10-20 1-138 <$750/$1250
Total Issue $120,980
Out in 1910 $935
****
4677 Floyd
CITIZENS NB OF CHARLES CITY
{{ 7 L 12 S }}
Organized 1/2/92
Brown Back <$VALUE
3x10-20 1-1900 <$350
1882 Date Back
3x10-20 1-1170 <$350
1902 Date Back
3x10-20 1-1700 <$175
1902 Plain Back
3x10-20 1701-7403 <$175
1929 Small Size
10 Type 1 1-1162 <$75
20 Type 1 1-322 <$85
5 Type 2 1-324 <$100
10 Type 2 1-431 <$100
20 Type 2 1-153 <$100
Total Issue $641,000
Out in 1935 $50,000
Large out 1935 $2,425
****
5979 Floyd
COMMERCIAL NB OF CHARLES CITY
{{ 15 L 17 S }}
Chartered 9/01
Brown Back <$VALUE
3x10-20 1-1650 <$300
1882 Date Back
3x10-20 1-2200 <$300
1882 Value Back
3x10-20 2201-4326 <$300
1902 Plain Back
3x10-20 1-3921 <$125
1929 Small Size
10 Type 1 1-992 <$50
20 Type 1 1-294 <$60
10 Type 2 1-1305 <$60
20 Type 2 1-145 <$60
Total Issue $605,600
Out in 1935 $49,650
Large out 1935 $3,180
****

****
1810 Floyd
FNB OF CHARLES CITY
{{ 28 L }}
Chartered 4/7/71
Liquidated 9/28/29
Original Series <$VALUE
3x1-2 1-1500 <$400/$1250
4x5 1-3875 <$400
Series 1875
4x5 1-3657 <$400
Brown Back
4x5 1-3450 <$250
3x10-20 1-1600 <$250
1882 Date Back
4x5 1-752 <$250
3x10-20 1-598 <$250
1902 Date Back
4x5 1-2400 <$125
3x10-20 1-1880 <$125
1902 Plain Back
4x5 2401-7767 <$125
3x10-20 1881-5243 <$125
Total Issue $769,570
Out at close $43,545
****
4376 Crawford
FNB OF CHARTER OAK
{{ 6 L 6 S }}
Chartered 1890
Brown Back <$VALUE
50-100 1-493 <$1500/$1750
1882 Date Back
50-100 1-114 <$1500/$1750
1902 Date Back
3x10-20 1-2100 <$250
1902 Plain Back
3x10-20 2101-4962 <$250
1929 Small Size
10 Type 1 1-604 <$175
20 Type 1 1-210 <$175
10 Type 2 1-355 <$200
20 Type 2 1-51 <$200
Total Issue $405,160
Out in 1935 $30,000
Large out 1935 $2,140
****
5412 Tama
FNB OF CHELSEA
{{ 6 L 8 S }}
Organized 5/17/00
Receivership 10/30/33
Brown Back <$VALUE
3x10-20 1-1000 <$450
1882 Date Back
3x10-20 1-1620 <$450
1882 Value Back
3x10-20 1621-2277 <$450
1902 Plain Back
3x10-20 1-2097 <$250
1929 Small Size
10 Type 1 1-439 <$150
20 Type 1 1-122 <$150
Total Issue $309,680
Out at close $25,010
Large out at close $2,950
****
3049 Cherokee
FNB, CHEROKEE
{{ 7 L 6 S }}
Organized 8/11/83
Receivership 1/31/31
Brown Back <$VALUE
3x10-20 1-1754 <$450
1902 Red Seal
3x10-20 1-1150 <$500
1902 Date Back
3x10-20 1-1750 <$250
1902 Plain Back
3x10-20 1751-6735 <$250
1929 Small Size
10 Type 1 1-530 <$175
20 Type 1 1-130 <$175
Total Issue $529,350
Out at close $46,280
Large out at close $10,320
****
10711 Cherokee
SECURITY NB, CHEROKEE
{{ 7 L 3 S }}
Organized 2/10/15
Receivership 3/17/30
1902 Date Back <$VALUE
3x10-20 1-1100 <$200
1902 Plain Back
3x10-20 1101-7907 <$200
1929 Small Size
10 Type 1 1-382 <$250
20 Type 1 1-40 <$275
Total Issue $423,070
Out at close $48,920
Large out 1931 $21,400
****

****
6737 Greene
FNB OF CHURDAN
{{ 3 L 6 S }}
Organized 4/7/03
1902 Red Seal <$VALUE
3x10-20 1-1450 <$750
1902 Date Back
3x10-20 1-1680 <$375
1902 Plain Back
3x10-20 1681-4657 <$375
1929 Small Size
10 Type 1 1-588 <$150
20 Type 1 1-138 <$150
10 Type 2 1-348 <$175
20 Type 2 1-33 <$175
Total Issue $361,330
Out in 1935 $25,000
Large out 1935 $1,340
****
7682 Cedar
FNB OF CLARENCE
{{ 7 L 2 S }}
Chartered 4/05
Liquidated 6/19/31
1902 Red Seal <$VALUE
3x10-20 1-1100 <$650
1902 Date Back
3x10-20 1-1610 <$325
1902 Plain Back
3x10-20 1611-4787 <$325
1929 Small Size
10 Type 1 1-315 <$400
20 Type 1 1-81 <$400
Total Issue $322,970
Out at close $25,000
Large out at close $4,920
****
3112 Page
CLARINDA NB, CLARINDA
{{ 5 L }}
Organized 12/26/83
Receivership 11/29/26
Brown Back <$VALUE
3x10-20 1-1830 <$500
1902 Red Seal
3x10-20 1-2000 <$600
1902 Date Back
3x10-20 1-2900 <$300
1902 Plain Back
3x10-20 2901-7691 <$300
Total Issue $576,050
Out at close $49,500
****
2028 Page
FNB OF CLARINDA
{{ 3 L }}
Chartered 8/19/72
Liquidated 3/1/79
Original Series <$VALUE
3x1-2 1-1500 <$600/$1500
4x5 1-4125 <$650
Series 1875
3x1-2 1-240 <$600/$1500
4x5 1-120 <$650
Total Issue $93,600
Out in 1910 $656
****
3796 Wright
FNB, CLARION
{{ 7 L 6 S }}
Organized 8/29/87
Brown Back <$VALUE
50-100 1-1034 <$1500/$1750
1902 Red Seal
50-100 1-334 <$2250/$2500
1902 Date Back
50-100 1-240 <$500/$600
3x50-100 1-958 <$500/$600
1902 Plain Back
3x50-100 959-1087<$500/$600
1929 Small Size
50 Type 1 1-150 <$300
100 Type 1 1-25 <$350
Total Issue $572,950
Out in 1935 $50,000
Large out 1935 $6,200
****
3788 Wright
WRIGHT COUNTY NB, CLARION
{{ UNREPORTED }}
Chartered 9/9/87
Liquidated 6/19/89
Brown Back <$VALUE
3x10-20 1-246 <$2000
Total Issue $12,300
Out in 1910 $100
****

****
7869 Cerro Gordo
FNB OF CLEAR LAKE
{{ 4 L 13 S }}
Organized 7/10/05
Liquidated 5/10/34
1902 Red Seal <$VALUE
3x10-20 1-1400 <$750
1902 Date Back
3x10-20 1-2250 <$375
1902 Plain Back
3x10-20 2251-6631 <$375
1929 Small Size
10 Type 1 1-1063 <$100
20 Type 1 1-310 <$100
Total Issue $502,530
Out at close $60,000
Large out at close $3,510
****
9549 Taylor
FNB OF CLEARFIELD
{{ 6 L 1 S }}
Organized 8/19/09
Receivership 9/5/33
1902 Date Back <$VALUE
3x10-20 1-700 <$350
1902 Plain Back
3x10-20 701-1193 <$350
1929 Small Size
10 Type 1 1-142 <$500
20 Type 1 1-21 <$500
Total Issue $70,690
Out at close $6,250
Large out at close $680
****
2469 Clinton
CITY NB OF CLINTON
{{ 32 L 50+ S }}
Chartered 3/31/80
Series 1875 <$VALUE
3x10-20 1-7080 <$750/$1250
Brown Back
4x5 1-3500 <$200
3x10-20 1-7500 <$200
1882 Date Back
4x5 1-9750 <$200
3x10-20 1-6700 <$200
1882 Value Back
4x5 9751-16195 <$200
3x10-20 6701-9836 <$200
1902 Plain Back
4x5 1-36070 <$85
3x10-20 1-19891 <$85
1929 Small Size
5 Type 1 1-11980 <$30
10 Type 1 1-5600 <$35
20 Type 1 1-1420 <$45
5 Type 2 1-7778 <$30
10 Type 2 1-4930 <$35
20 Type 2 1-1576 <$45
Total Issue $4,316,160
Out in 1935 $396,900
Large out 1935 $20,810
Outstanding includes Ch 3736
****
994 Clinton
CLINTON NB, CLINTON
{{ 14 L U + 14 S }}
Chartered 1865
Original Series <$VALUE
3x1-2 1-1800 <$300/$1000
4x5 1-1100 <$400
3x10-20 1-1560 <$750/$1250
Series 1875
3x10-20 1-1540 <$750/$1250
Brown Back
3x10-20 1-5708 <$225/$250
1902 Red Seal
4x5 1-2150 <$300
3x10-20 1-1360 <$300
1902 Date Back
4x5 1-2650 <$100
3x10-20 1-2520 <$100
1902 Plain Back
4x5 2651-10852 <$100
3x10-20 2521-7429 <$100
1929 Small Size
5 Type 1 1-1882 <$60
10 Type 1 1-936 <$65
20 Type 1 1-272 <$75
5 Type 2 1-1414 <$75
10 Type 2 1-728 <$75
20 Type 2 1-130 <$75
Total Issue $1,333,100
Out in 1935 $60,000
Large out 1935 $4,460
****
FNB of Lyons at Clinton
SEE Ch 66
FNB of Lyons
****

****
3736 Clinton
MERCHANTS NB OF CLINTON
{{ 28 L 7 S }}
Organized 6/7/87
Liquidated 6/4/31
Brown Back <$VALUE
3x10-20 1-2639 <$225
1902 Red Seal
4x5 1-1000 <$250
3x10-20 1-1000 <$250
1902 Date Back
4x5 1-7000 <$85
3x10-20 1-5180 <$85
1902 Plain Back
4x5 7001-20470 <$85
3x10-20 5181-14101 <$85
1929 Small Size
10 Type 1 1-1332 <$75
20 Type 1 1-391 <$85
Total Issue $1,443,240
Out at close $100,000
Large out at close $12,220
Ch 2469 assumed circulation
****
5366 Tama
FNB OF CLUTIER
{{ UNREPORTED }}
Chartered 5/22/00
Liquidated 10/12/08
Brown Back <$VALUE
4x5 1-800 <$1500
3x10-20 1-700 <$1500
1882 Date Back
4x5 1-20 <$1500
3x10-20 1-10 <$1500
Total Issue $51,900
Out in 1910 $6,305
****
7309 Page
FNB OF COIN
{{ 2 L 1 S }}
Organized 6/3/04
Receivership 9/8/31
1902 Red Seal <$VALUE
3x10-20 1-1140 <$3500
1902 Date Back
3x10-20 1-1370 <$2000
1902 Plain Back
3x10-20 1371-2370 <$2000
1929 Small Size
10 Type 1 1-163 <$2000
20 Type 1 1-19 <$2000
Total Issue $187,560
Out at close $10,000
Large out at close $1,600
****
13686 Jasper
FNB IN COLFAX
{{ 6 S }}
Chartered 5/33
1929 Small Size <$VALUE
5 Type 2 1-1564 <$150
10 Type 2 1-635 <$150
20 Type 2 1-180 <$150
Total Issue $17,770
Out in 1935 $24,850
Large out 1935 $1,820
Outstanding includes Ch 7114
****
7114 Jasper
FNB OF COLFAX
{{ 3 L 6 S }}
Organized 1/2/04
Liquidated 6/24/33
1902 Red Seal <$VALUE
4x5 1-875 <$750
3x10-20 1-657 <$750
1902 Date Back
4x5 1-1900 <$375
3x10-20 1-1380 <$375
1902 Plain Back
4x5 1901-5495 <$375
3x10-20 1381-3488 <$375
1929 Small Size
5 Type 1 1-752 <$150
10 Type 1 1-316 <$150
20 Type 1 1-104 <$150
Total Issue $388,650
Out at close $25,000
Large out at close $2,200
Ch 13686 assumed circulation
****
11295 Page
FNB OF COLLEGE SPRINGS
{{ UNREPORTED }}
Chartered 1/19
Liquidated 11/25/29
1902 Plain Back <$VALUE
3x10-20 1-92 <$2500
Total Issue $4,600
Out at close $800
****

****
2032 Louisa
LOUISA COUNTY NB OF COLUMBUS JUNCTION
{{ 13 L 13 S }}
Chartered 8/24/72
Original Series <$VALUE
3x1-2 1-2200 <$400/$1250
4x5 1-2875 <$400
Series 1875
4x5 1-4744 <$400
Brown Back
4x5 1-3756 <$350
3x10-20 1-2200 <$350
1882 Date Back
4x5 1-1509 <$350
3x10-20 1-1129 <$350
1902 Date Back
3x10-20 1-1900 <$150
1902 Plain Back
3x10-20 1901-8048 <$150
1929 Small Size
10 Type 1 1-1042 <$100
20 Type 1 1-294 <$100
10 Type 2 1-509 <$100
20 Type 2 1-105 <$100
Total Issue $942,520
Out in 1935 $50,000
Large out 1935 $4,739
****
9447 Grundy
FNB OF CONRAD
{{ 3 L 3 S }}
Organized 4/24/09
Liquidated 11/5/31
1902 Date Back <$VALUE
3x10-20 1-1930 <$500
1902 Plain Back
3x10-20 1931-4798 <$500
1929 Small Size
10 Type 1 1-332 <$300
20 Type 1 1-83 <$300
Total Issue $269,780
Out at close $25,000
Large out at close $4,620
****
6080 Carroll
COON RAPIDS NB, COON RAPIDS
{{ UNREPORTED }}
Chartered 1/02
Liquidated 12/3/12
Brown Back <$VALUE
3x10-20 1-1120 <$1500
1882 Date Back
3x10-20 1-749 <$1500
Total Issue $93,450
Out in 1913 $13,200
****
5514 Carroll
FNB OF COON RAPIDS
{{ 6 L 4 S }}
Chartered 7/23/00
Liquidated 4/11/33
Brown Back <$VALUE
3x10-20 1-1410 <$400
1882 Date Back
3x10-20 1-1610* <$400
1882 Value Back
3x10-20 1741-2407* <$400
* 1611-1740 not marked
1902 Plain Back
3x10-20 1-2124 <$250
1929 Small Size
10 Type 1 1-438 <$250
20 Type 1 1-104 <$250
Total Issue $335,810
Out at close $25,000
Large out at close $3,010
****
8100 Adams
FARMERS NB OF CORNING
{{ 6 L }}
Chartered 2/06
Liquidated 11/3/25
1902 Red Seal <$VALUE
3x10-20 1-687 <$600
1902 Date Back
3x10-20 1-1610 <$300
1902 Plain Back
3x10-20 1611-3924 <$300
Total Issue $230,550
Out at close $25,000
****

2936 Adams
FNB OF CORNING
{{ 2 L }}
Organized 4/26/83
Receivership 6/22/14
Brown Back <$VALUE
3x10-20 1-1240 <$850
1902 Red Seal
3x10-20 1-3135 <$850
1902 Date Back
3x10-20 1-4227 <$500
Total Issue $430,100
Out in 1915 $26,445

4268 Adams
NB OF CORNING
{{ UNREPORTED }}
Chartered 3/21/90
Liquidated 11/10/96
Brown Back <$VALUE
3x10-20 1-574 <$1500
Total Issue $28,700
Out in 1910 $300

8725 Adams
OKEY-VERNON NB OF CORNING
{{ 14 L 50+ S }}
Chartered 6/07
1902 Red Seal <$VALUE
4x5 1-900 <$400
4x10 1-1100 <$400
1902 Date Back
4x5 1-3500 <$175
4x10 1-3000 <$175
1902 Plain Back
4x5 3501-10246 <$175
4x10 3001-8787 <$175
1929 Small Size
5 Type 1 1-2192 <$60
10 Type 1 1-1162 <$70
5 Type 2 1-2734 <$50
10 Type 2 1-1404 <$60
Total Issue $781,590
Out in 1935 $50,000
Large out 1935 $3,235

5775 Hancock
FNB, CORWITH
{{ 2 L }}
Chartered 4/01
Liquidated 1/12/10
Brown Back <$VALUE
3x10-20 1-1800 <$1500
1882 Date Back
3x10-20 1-30 <$1500
Total Issue $91,500
Out in 1910 $16,160

10146 Wayne
FNB OF CORYDON
{{ 6 L }}
Organized 2/16/12
Receivership 8/18/27
1902 Date Back <$VALUE
3x10-20 1-4000 <$250
1902 Plain Back
3x10-20 4001-11969 <$250
Total Issue $598,450
Out at close $72,900

9306 Pottawattamie
CITY NB OF COUNCIL BLUFFS
{{ 12 L U + 16 S }}
Chartered 12/5/08
1902 Date Back <$VALUE
3x10-20 1-7500 <$125
1902 Plain Back
3x10-20 7501-21002 <$125
1929 Small Size
5 Type 1 1-4736 <$50
10 Type 1 1-2570 <$50
5 Type 2 1-9582 <$50
10 Type 2 1-3536 <$50
Total Issue $1,429,650
Out in 1935 $120,000
Large out 1935 $6,440

5838 Pottawattamie
COMMERCIAL NB OF COUNCIL BLUFFS
{{ 14 L }}
Chartered 5/01
Liquidated 9/10/27
Brown Back <$VALUE
4x5 1-2750 <$300
3x10-20 1-3220 <$300
1882 Date Back
4x5 1-6700 <$300
3x10-20 1-4600 <$300
1882 Value Back
4x5 6701-11610 <$300
3x10-20 4601-7473 <$300
1902 Plain Back
3x10-20 1-6086 <$135
Total Issue $1,126,150
Out in 1925 $100,000

3427 Pottawattamie
COUNCIL BLUFFS NB, COUNCIL BLUFFS
{{ UNREPORTED }}
Chartered 12/30/85
Liquidated 5/5/87
Brown Back <$VALUE
4x5 1-1157 <$1500
Total Issue $23,140
Out in 1910 $195

14028 Pottawattamie
FNB IN COUNCIL BLUFFS
{{ 7 S }}
Chartered 2/34
1929 Small Size <$VALUE
5 Type 2 1-4970 <$125
10 Type 2 1-2480 <$125
20 Type 2 1-840 <$150
Total Issue $66,450
Out in 1935 $50,000

1479 Pottawattamie
FNB OF COUNCIL BLUFFS
{{ 28 L 31 S }}
Organized 6/1/65
Receivership 4/20/34
Original Series <$VALUE
3x1-2 1-2200 <$300/$1000
4x5 1-5500 <$350
Series 1875
4x5 1-4030 <$350
Brown Back
4x5 1-7270 <$200
3x10-20 1-5439 <$200
1902 Red Seal
3x10-20 1-6800 <$200
1902 Date Back
4x5 1-16080 <$75
3x10-20 1-8900 <$85
1902 Plain Back
4x5 16081-69037 <$75
3x10-20 8901-17600 <$85
1929 Small Size
5 Type 1 1-12756 <$25
10 Type 1 1-2278 <$25
20 Type 1 1-584 <$35
5 Type 2 1-2074 <$25
10 Type 2 1-1085 <$25
20 Type 2 1-233 <$35
Total Issue $3,835,010
Out at close $200,000
Large out at close $15,185

1684 Pottawattamie
PACIFIC NB OF COUNCIL BLUFFS
{{ 3 L }}
Chartered 9/68
Liquidated 11/30/78
Original Series <$VALUE
3x1-2 1-4000 <$1000/$2000
4x5 1-7250 <$1500
Series 1875
4x5 1-680 <$1500
Total Issue $178,600
Out in 1910 $1,011

4897 Howard
FNB OF CRESCO
{{ 7 L 10 S }}
Organized 4/7/93
Receivership 10/30/33
Brown Back <$VALUE
3x10-20 1-1870 <$350
1882 Date Back
3x10-20 1-1370 <$350
1902 Date Back
3x10-20 1-1800 <$175
1902 Plain Back
3x10-20 1801-6526 <$175
1929 Small Size
10 Type 1 1-880 <$100
20 Type 1 1-276 <$100
Total Issue $574,220
Out at close $25,000
Large out at close $4,170

2833 Union
CRESTON NB, CRESTON
{{ 6 L 2 S }}
Chartered 1882
Liquidated 1/2/30
Brown Back <$VALUE
3x10-20 1-2510 <$400
1902 Red Seal
3x10-20 1-1130 <$400
1902 Date Back
3x10-20 1-2500 <$200
1902 Plain Back
3x10-20 2501-12548 <$200
1929 Small Size
10 Type 1 1-621 <$400
20 Type 1 1-36 <$400
Total Issue $850,980
Out at close $94,780
Large out 1935 $5,345

12636 Union
FNB IN CRESTON
{{ 25 S }}
Organized 2/2/25
1929 Small Size <$VALUE
5 Type 1 1-2712 <$50
10 Type 1 1-1302 <$50
20 Type 1 1-358 <$55
5 Type 2 1-2658 <$50
10 Type 2 1-1460 <$50
20 Type 2 1-565 <$55
Total Issue $241,630
Out in 1935 $99,400
Outstanding includes Ch 2833

2586 Union
FNB OF CRESTON
{{ 2 L }}
Chartered 10/22/81
Liquidated 3/26/25
Series 1875 <$VALUE
3x10-20 1-235 <$1250/$1750
Brown Back
50-100 1-480 <$1250/$1500
1882 Date Back
50-100 1-300 <$1250/$1500
3x50-100 1-19 <$1250/$1500
1902 Plain Back
3x50-100 1-119 <$750/$850
Total Issue $311,850
Out in 1924 $30,000

9853 Hancock
FARMERS NB OF CRYSTAL LAKE
{{ 3 L 4 S }}
Organized 9/22/10
Receivership 5/23/34
1902 Date Back <$VALUE
3x10-20 1-1660 <$450
1902 Plain Back
3x10-20 1661-4834 <$450
1929 Small Size
10 Type 1 1-548 <$250
20 Type 1 1-138 <$250
10 Type 2 1-146 <$250
20 Type 2 1-35 <$275
Total Issue $293,300
Out at close $25,000
Large out at close $1,690

5305 Hancock
FNB, CRYSTAL LAKE
{{ 3 L }}
Chartered 4/25/00
Liquidated 9/23/10
Brown Back <$VALUE
4x5 1-1465 <$600
3x10-20 1-1274 <$600
1882 Date Back
4x5 1-210 <$600
3x10-20 1-190 <$600
Total Issue $106,700
Out in 1911 $2,095

7326 Cass
FNB OF CUMBERLAND
{{ 1 L }}
Organized 6/7/04
Receivership 7/22/26
1902 Red Seal <$VALUE
3x10-20 1-376 <$2000
1902 Date Back
3x10-20 1-860 <$1000
1902 Plain Back
3x10-20 861-960 <$1000
Total Issue $66,800
Out at close $5,950

1671 Scott
CITIZENS NB OF DAVENPORT
{{ 11 L }}
Chartered 5/4/67
Liquidated 10/15/06
Original Series <$VALUE
3x1-2 1-5600 <$350/$1000
4x5 1-4350 <$400
3x10-20 1-1100 <$750/$1250
Series 1875
3x1-2 1-1000 <$350/$1000
4x5 1-4305 <$400
3x10-20 1-2047 <$750/$1250
Brown Back
50-100 1-5284 <$1250/$1500
Total Issue $1,156,050
Out in 1910 $71,210

---

848 Scott
DAVENPORT NB, DAVENPORT
{{ 5 L }}
Chartered 3/1/65
Liquidated 12/4/01
Original Series <$VALUE
4x5 1-10800 <$500
3x10-20 1-2000 <$850/$1500
Series 1875
4x5 1-4500 <$500
3x10-20 1-2658 <$850/$1500
Brown Back
4x5 1-1595 <$400
50-100 1-1468 <$1250/$1500
Total Issue $791,000
Out in 1910 $8,875

---

15 Scott
FNB OF DAVENPORT*
{{ 50+ L 50+ S }}
Organized 6/22/63
Liquidated 5/9/82
*Reorganized as Ch 2695
which retook Ch 15 5/22/11
Liquidated 4/25/31
Original Series <$VALUE
3x1-2 1-3500 <$350/$1000
4x5 1-3690 <$400
3x10-20 1-2400 <$750/$1250
Series 1875
3x10-20 1-62 <$750/$1250
1902 Date Back
3x10-20 1-8300 <$75
3x50-100 1-1455 <$300/$350
1902 Plain Back
3x10-20 8301-34694 <$75
3x50-100 1456-2011 <$300/$350
1929 Small Size
10 Type 1 1-3573 <$45
20 Type 1 1-1007 <$50
50 Type 1 1-319 <$125
100 Type 1 1-69 <$175
Total Issue $2,924,170
Out at close $395,560
Large out at close $72,720
Outstanding includes Ch 2695

2695 Scott
FNB OF DAVENPORT
{{ 18 L }}
Chartered 1882
RETOOK Ch 15 5/22/11
Brown Back <$VALUE
4x5 1-2300 <$175
3x10-20 1-2025 <$175/$200
50-100 1-1811 <$1250/$1500
1902 Red Seal
3x10-20 1-3300 <$200
50-100 1-2127 <$2250/$2500
1902 Date Back
3x10-20 1-4500 <$100
50-100 1-4 <$350/$400
Total Issue $1,128,550
Out in 1911 $100,000

4022 Scott
IOWA NB OF DAVENPORT
{{ 28 L }}
Chartered 1889
Liquidated 10/31/27
Brown Back <$VALUE
4x5 1-6651 <$175
3x10-20 1-2492 <$150/$175
1882 Date Back
4x5 1-40 <$175
3x10-20 1-20 <$175/$200
1902 Date Back
4x5 1-8750 <$75
3x10-20 1-6300 <$85
1902 Plain Back
4x5 8751-27570 <$75
3x10-20 6301-17726 <$85
Total Issue $1,697,120
Out at close $147,700

5302 Webster
FNB, DAYTON
{{ 7 L 10 S }}
Chartered 4/24/00
Brown Back <$VALUE
3x10-20 1-1880 <$350
1882 Date Back
3x10-20 1-2450* <$350
1882 Value Back
3x10-20 2651-3508* <$350
* 2451-2650 not marked
1902 Plain Back
3x10-20 1-3208 <$175
1929 Small Size
10 Type 1 1-764 <$85
20 Type 1 1-234 <$110
10 Type 2 1-456 <$125
20 Type 2 1-124 <$125
Total Issue $510,760
Out in 1935 $35,000
Large out 1935 $2,230

3182 Clinton
FNB OF De WITT
{{ 27 L 22 S }}
Chartered 1884
Brown Back <$VALUE
3x10-20 1-1220 <$250
1902 Red Seal
3x10-20 1-1750 <$300
1902 Date Back
3x10-20 1-3400 <$100
1902 Plain Back
3x10-20 3401-9796 <$100
1929 Small Size
10 Type 1 1-1152 <$65
20 Type 1 1-290 <$70
10 Type 2 1-1017 <$75
20 Type 2 1-272 <$75
Total Issue $757,830
Out in 1935 $50,000
Large out 1935 $3,140

---

493 Winneshiek
FNB OF DECORAH
{{ 2 L }}
Organized 8/6/64
Receivership 11/24/96
Original Series <$VALUE
4x5 1-7375 <$1000
Series 1875
4x5 1-5040 <$1000
Brown Back
4x5 1-3669 <$850
Total Issue $321,680
Out in 1915 $1,800

5081 Winneshiek
NB OF DECORAH
{{ 6 L 5 S }}
Chartered 1897
Liquidated 1/28/32
Brown Back <$VALUE
3x10-20 1-3450 <$350
1882 Date Back
3x10-20 1-2800 <$350
1882 Value Back
3x10-20 2801-2993 <$350
1902 Plain Back
3x10-20 1-4909 <$200
1929 Small Size
10 Type 1 1-713 <$175
20 Type 1 1-183 <$200
Total Issue $632,340
Out at close $50,000
Large out at close $6,810

6705 Poweshiek
FNB OF DEEP RIVER
{{ 3 L }}
Organized 3/14/03
Receivership 3/25/26
1902 Red Seal <$VALUE
3x10-20 1-1400 <$850
1902 Date Back
3x10-20 1-1560 <$450
1902 Plain Back
3x10-20 1561-3708 <$450
Total Issue $255,400
Out at close $24,600

4784 Crawford
FNB OF DENISON
{{ 14 L 33 S }}
Chartered 1892
Brown Back <$VALUE
4x5 1-11600 <$300
3x10-20 1-5400 <$300
1882 Date Back
4x5 1-2260 <$300
3x10-20 1-1746 <$300
1902 Date Back
4x5 1-3900 <$150
3x10-20 1-3040 <$150
1902 Plain Back
4x5 3901-16025 <$150
3x10-20 3041-10841 <$150
1929 Small Size
5 Type 1 1-3242 <$50
10 Type 1 1-1474 <$55
20 Type 1 1-374 <$60
5 Type 2 1-1421 <$50
10 Type 2 1-1503 <$55
20 Type 2 1-390 <$60
Total Issue $1,757,565
Out in 1935 $100,000
Large out 1935 $8,540

13321 Polk
CENTRAL NB & TC OF DES MOINES
{{ 6U + 50+ S }}
Chartered 5/15/29
1929 Small Size <$VALUE
5 Type 1 1-5434 <$20
10 Type 1 1-2560 <$25
20 Type 1 1-726 <$35
5 Type 2 1-10862 <$20
10 Type 2 1-4980 <$25
20 Type 2 1-1230 <$35
Total Issue $532,450
Out in 1935 $219,100

1970 Polk
CITIZENS NB OF DES MOINES
{{ 6 L }}
Chartered 4/24/72
Liquidated 6/30/17
Original Series <$VALUE
4x5 1-2500 <$450
3x10-20 1-1200 <$750/$1250
Series 1875
4x5 1-3350 <$450
3x10-20 1-1657 <$750/$1250
Brown Back
3x10-20 1-10640 <$300
1882 Date Back
4x5 1-2415 <$300
3x10-20 1-2630 <$300
1902 Date Back
3x10-20 1-7636 <$175
Total Issue $1,353,450
Out in 1916 $140,000
Ch 2307 assumed circulation

2583 Polk
DES MOINES NB, DES MOINES
{{ 50+ L }}
Chartered 1881
Closed 9/20/29
Series 1875 <$VALUE
4x5 1-17381 <$350
50-100 1-596 <$4000
Brown Back
4x5 1-6000 <$175
4x10 1-3000 <$175
50-100 1-2000 <$1250/$1500
1882 Date Back
4x5 1-21750 <$175
4x10 1-20500 <$175
1882 Value Back
4x5 21751-71248 <$175
4x10 20501-52745 <$175
1902 Plain Back
4x5 1-18045 <$50
3x10-20 1-16664 <$60
Total Issue $5,705,880
Out at close $56,390
Ch 2307 assumed circulation

---

389 Polk
FNB OF DES MOINES
{{ UNREPORTED }}
Chartered 4/18/64
Liquidated 3/25/71
Original Series <$VALUE
4x5 1-2500 <$1500
3x10-20 1-996 <$1750/$2000
Total Issue $99,800
Out in 1910 $725

Iowa-Des Moines NB & TC of Des Moines
SEE Ch 2307
Iowa NB of Des Moines

CONDITION affects Value. The Values shown are for notes in FINE condition.

****
2307 Polk
IOWA NB OF DES MOINES
Chartered 10/26/75
2nd title: Iowa-Des Moines NB & TC 9/20/29
FIRST TITLE {{ 28 L }}
Series 1875 <$VALUE
4x5 1-11455 <$350
Brown Back
4x5 1-9600 <$150
3x10-20 1-6500 <$150/$175
1882 Date Back
4x5 1-36160 <$150
3x10-20 1-23054 <$150/$175
1902 Date Back
4x5 1-25195 <$60
3x10-20 1-18257 <$70
SECOND TITLE {{ 50+ S }}
1929 Small Size
5 Type 1 1-11717 <$25
10 Type 1 1-11397 <$25
20 Type 1 1-5783 <$35
50 Type 1 1-416 <$100
100 Type 1 1-314 <$150
Total Issue $6,081,240
Out in 1935 $1,000,000
Large out 1935 $44,695
Outstanding includes Ch 1970 and Ch 2583
****
2631 Polk
MERCHANTS NB OF DES MOINES
{{ 1 L }}
Chartered 2/16/82
Liquidated 3/1/89
Series 1875 <$VALUE
3x10-20 1-1403<$1750/$2000
Total Issue $70,150
Out in 1910 $375
****
950 Polk
N STATE B OF DES MOINES
{{ UNREPORTED }}
Chartered 3/65
Liquidated 6/21/76
Original Series <$VALUE
4x5 1-2800 <$1500
3x10-20 1-1786<$1750/$2000
Total Issue $145,300
Out in 1910 $1,080
****
485 Polk
SECOND NB OF DES MOINES
{{ UNREPORTED }}
Chartered 7/22/64
Liquidated 8/5/68
Original Series <$VALUE
4x5 1-1350 <$1500
3x10-20 1-310 <$1750/$2000
Total Issue $42,500
Out in 1910 $335
****
2886 Polk
VALLEY NB OF DES MOINES
{{ 28 L 18 S }}
Chartered 1883
Brown Back <$VALUE
4x5 1-3375 <$250
3x10-20 1-10539 <$250
1902 Red Seal
4x5 1-8500 <$250
3x10-20 1-7400 <$250
1902 Date Back
4x5 1-17250 <$75
3x10-20 1-13000 <$85
1902 Plain Back
4x5 17251-63862 <$75
3x10-20 13001-41944 <$85
1929 Small Size
5 Type 1 1-4347 <$60
10 Type 1 1-2050 <$60
20 Type 1 1-642 <$70
Total Issue $4,479,340
Out in 1932 $124,040
Large out 1935 $19,850
****
10030 Dallas
FNB OF DEXTER
{{ 3 L }}
Chartered 6/11
Liquidated 5/31/20
1902 Date Back <$VALUE
3x10-20 1-1160 <$500
1902 Plain Back
3x10-20 1161-1654 <$500
Total Issue $82,700
Out at close $18,750
****

****
9125 Ringgold
FNB OF DIAGONAL
{{ 6 L 6 S }}
Chartered 5/08
1902 Date Back <$VALUE
3x10-20 1-2200 <$400
1902 Plain Back
3x10-20 2201-5358 <$400
1929 Small Size
10 Type 1 1-546 <$200
20 Type 1 1-136 <$200
10 Type 2 1-591 <$225
20 Type 2 1-160 <$225
Total Issue $326,090
Out in 1935 $25,000
Large out 1935 $1,710
****
5372 Grundy
FNB OF DIKE
{{ 1 L }}
Chartered 5/25/00
Liquidated 4/5/09
Brown Back <$VALUE
3x10-20 1-1631 <$1500
Total Issue $81,550
Out in 1910 $10,280
****
6764 Lyon
FNB, DOON
{{ 7 L 8 S }}
Organized 4/15/03
Receivership 10/22/31
1902 Red Seal <$VALUE
3x10-20 1-986 <$600
1902 Date Back
3x10-20 1-1730 <$300
1902 Plain Back
3x10-20 1731-7681 <$300
1929 Small Size
10 Type 1 1-769 <$175
20 Type 1 1-186 <$175
Total Issue $501,810
Out at close $49,995
Large out at close $8,035
****
5576 Cerro Gordo
FNB OF DOUGHERTY
{{ 2 L 4 S }}
Organized 7/30/00
Receivership 12/14/31
Brown Back <$VALUE
3x10-20 1-800 <$1000
1882 Date Back
3x10-20 1-740 <$1000
1882 Value Back
3x10-20 741-971 <$1000
1902 Plain Back
3x10-20 1-1091 <$750
1929 Small Size
10 Type 1 1-197 <$500
20 Type 1 1-30 <$500
Total Issue $158,520
Out at close $12,500
Large out at close $2,720
****
1801 Dubuque
COMMERCIAL NB OF DUBUQUE
{{ 2 L }}
Chartered 3/11/71
Receivership 4/2/88
Original Series <$VALUE
3x1-2 1-2400 <$750/$1500
4x5 1-5400 <$750
Series 1875
3x1-2 1-2780 <$750/$1500
4x5 1-10533 <$750
Total Issue $344,560
Out in 1915 $2,081
****
Consolidated NB of Dubuque
SEE Ch 2327
Second NB of Dubuque
****
3140 Dubuque
DUBUQUE NB, DUBUQUE
{{ 6 L }}
Chartered 1884
Closed 1/23/23
Brown Back <$VALUE
4x5 1-2535 <$375
3x10-20 1-1381 <$375
1902 Red Seal
50-100 1-300 <$2250/$2500
1902 Date Back
50-100 1-1000 <$400/$500
3x50-100 1-480 <$400/$500
1902 Plain Back
4x5 1-9096 <$200
Total Issue $616,670
Out at close $99,300
Ch 2327 assumed circulation
****

****
317 Dubuque
FNB OF DUBUQUE
{{ 28 L 33 S }}
Chartered 1864
Original Series <$VALUE
3x1-2 1-9700 <$350/$1000
3x10-20 1-4100 <$750/$1250
3x10-20 5101-6900 <$750/$1250
20 4101-5100 <$1250
Series 1875
3x1-2 1-1370 <$350/$1000
3x10-20 1-2704 <$750/$1250
Brown Back
4x5 1-13677 <$200
50-100 1-883 <$1250/$1500
1902 Red Seal
3x10-20 1-8300 <$200
1902 Date Back
3x10-20 1-11000 <$85
1902 Plain Back
3x10-20 11001-33530 <$85
1929 Small Size
10 Type 1 1-4002 <$25
20 Type 1 1-1240 <$35
10 Type 2 1-10042 <$25
20 Type 2 1-2402 <$35
Total Issue $3,540,000
Out in 1935 $300,000
Large out 1935 $15,830
****
846 Dubuque
MERCHANTS NB OF DUBUQUE
{{ UNREPORTED }}
Chartered 2/27/65
Liquidated 9/30/73
Original Series <$VALUE
3x1-2 1-6000 <$1250/$2000
4x5 1-5275 <$1500
3x10-20 1-2300<$1750/$2000
50-100 1-100 <$5000
Total Issue $265,500
Out in 1910 $3,093
****
1540 Dubuque
N STATE B OF DUBUQUE
{{ UNREPORTED }}
Chartered 8/28/65
Liquidated 3/9/67
Original Series <$VALUE
4x5 1-2500 <$1500
3x10-20 1-902 <$1750/$2000
50-100 1-216 <$5000
Total Issue $127,500
Out in 1910 $1,135
****
2327 Dubuque
SECOND NB OF DUBUQUE
Chartered 3/20/76
Receivership 7/14/32
2nd title:Consolidated NB 1/23/23
FIRST TITLE {{ 7 L }}
Series 1875 <$VALUE
4x5 1-15865 <$450
Brown Back
3x10-20 1-8000 <$250
50-100 1-2476 <$1250/$1500
1882 Date Back
3x10-20 1-11225 <$200
50-100 1-67 <$1250/$1500
1902 Date Back
3x50-100 1-880 <$400/$500
SECOND TITLE {{ 13 L 4 S }}
1902 Plain Back
4x5 1-27239 <$85
1929 Small Size
5 Type 1 1-2995 <$125
Total Issue $2,514,630
Out at close $49,700
Large out at close $25,970
Outstanding includes Ch 3140
****
6722 Black Hawk
FNB OF DUNKERTON
{{ 6 L 7 S }}
Organized 4/1/03
Receivership 10/31/33
1902 Red Seal <$VALUE
3x10-20 1-1468 <$500
1902 Date Back
3x10-20 1-2310 <$250
1902 Plain Back
3x10-20 2311-6031 <$250
1929 Small Size
10 Type 1 1-764 <$150
20 Type 1 1-242 <$150
Total Issue $449,830
Out at close $40,000
Large out at close $2,760
****

****
4139 Harrison
FNB OF DUNLAP
{{ 4 L }}
Chartered 1889
Liquidated 2/23/26
Brown Back <$VALUE
4x5 1-3828 <$600
3x10-20 1-1208 <$600
1902 Date Back
4x5 1-2250 <$350
3x10-20 1-1740 <$350
1902 Plain Back
4x5 2251-5085 <$350
3x10-20 1741-3520 <$350
Total Issue $414,660
Out at close $30,000
****
9555 Dubuque
FNB OF DYERSVILLE
{{ 3 L 3 S }}
Chartered 10/09
Liquidated 5/21/31
1902 Date Back <$VALUE
3x10-20 1-2550 <$450
1902 Plain Back
3x10-20 2551-6577 <$450
1929 Small Size
10 Type 1 1-376 <$350
20 Type 1 1-68 <$350
Total Issue $359,570
Out at close $35,000
Large out at close $6,150
****
5934 Tama
FNB OF DYSART
{{ 6 L }}
Chartered 8/01
Brown Back <$VALUE
3x10-20 1-2600 <$500
1882 Date Back
3x10-20 1-3040 <$500
1882 Value Back
3x10-20 3041-4708 <$500
1902 Plain Back
3x10-20 1-3259 <$250
Total Issue $528,350
Out in 1935 $3,270
****
3439 Wright
FNB, EAGLE GROVE
{{ UNREPORTED }}
Chartered 1/22/86
Liquidated 1/20/90
Brown Back <$VALUE
4x5 1-1021 <$2000
Total Issue $20,420
Out in 1910 $140
****
FNB in Eagle Grove
SEE Ch 4694
Merchants NB of Eagle Grove
****
4694 Wright
MERCHANTS NB OF EAGLE GROVE
Chartered 1892
Liquidated 7/15/24
2nd title: FNB in Eagle Grove 10/26/20
FIRST TITLE {{ 2 L }}
Brown Back <$VALUE
3x10-20 1-1535 <$1000
1882 Date Back
3x10-20 1-306 <$1000
1902 Date Back
3x50-100 1-670 <$850/$1000
SECOND TITLE {{ 0 L }}
1902 Plain Back
3x10-20 1-877 <$1000
Total Issue $303,400
Out at close $39,850
****
5342 Wapello
FNB OF ELDON
{{ 7 L 9 S }}
Chartered 5/8/00
Brown Back <$VALUE
3x10-20 1-1850 <$450
1882 Date Back
3x10-20 1-1600 <$450
1882 Value Back
3x10-20 1601-2324 <$450
1902 Plain Back
3x10-20 1-2640 <$200
1929 Small Size
10 Type 1 1-562 <$125
20 Type 1 1-148 <$125
10 Type 2 1-574 <$150
20 Type 2 1-143 <$150
Total Issue $400,780
Out in 1935 $25,000
Large out 1935 $1,660
****

****
5140 Hardin
FNB OF ELDORA
{{ 6 L 6 S }}
Organized 8/22/98
Receivership 8/10/32
Brown Back <$VALUE
3x10-20 1-1600 <$450
1882 Date Back
3x10-20 1-2500 <$450
1882 Value Back
3x10-20 2501-3017 <$450
1902 Plain Back
3x10-20 1-3954 <$225
1929 Small Size
5 Type 1 1-1022 <$150
10 Type 1 1-426 <$150
20 Type 1 1-65 <$150
Total Issue $492,570
Out at close $35,720
Large out at close $5,735
****
9233 Hardin
HARDIN COUNTY NB OF ELDORA
{{ 7 L 10 S }}
Chartered 9/08
Liquidated 2/14/35
1902 Date Back <$VALUE
4x5 1-2975 <$200
3x10-20 1-2280 <$200
1902 Plain Back
4x5 2976-9094 <$200
3x10-20 2281-6288 <$200
1929 Small Size
5 Type 1 1-1422 <$100
10 Type 1 1-724 <$100
20 Type 1 1-182 <$110
5 Type 2 1-300 <$125
10 Type 2 1-375 <$125
20 Type 2 1-55 <$125
Total Issue $610,570
Out at close $50,000
Large out at close $3,610
Ch 14286 assumed circulation
****
1815 Clayton
FNB OF ELKADER
{{ 15 L 8 S }}
Chartered 1871
Liquidated 11/12/31
Original Series <$VALUE
3x1-2 1-2700 <$500/$1500
4x5 1-2725 <$600
Series 1875
4x5 1-4040 <$600
Brown Back
4x5 1-1632 <$400
3x10-20 1-1380 <$400
1882 Date Back
3x10-20 1-180 <$400
1902 Date Back
3x10-20 1-1150 <$175
1902 Plain Back
3x10-20 1151-2800 <$175
1929 Small Size
10 Type 1 1-298 <$175
20 Type 1 1-68 <$175
Total Issue $425,480
Out at close $22,490
Large out at close $4,382
****
6857 Montgomery
FNB, ELLIOTT
{{ 3 L 4 S }}
Organized 6/15/03
Receivership 7/2/31
1902 Red Seal <$VALUE
3x10-20 1-520 <$750
1902 Date Back
3x10-20 1-2250 <$375
1902 Plain Back
3x10-20 2251-4201 <$375
1929 Small Size
10 Type 1 1-263 <$250
20 Type 1 1-64 <$250
Total Issue $259,510
Out at close $20,000
Large out at close $3,110
****
8035 Palo Alto
EMMETSBURG NB, EMMETSBURG
{{ 3 L }}
Organized 12/23/05
Receivership 3/11/21
1902 Red Seal <$VALUE
3x10-20 1-1100 <$850
1902 Date Back
3x10-20 1-1050* <$400
1902 Plain Back
3x10-20 1251-1870* <$400
* 1051-1250 not marked
Total Issue $148,500
Out at close $22,000
****

****
3337 Palo Alto
FNB OF EMMETSBURG
{{ 7 L }}
Chartered 1885
Liquidated 6/10/27
Brown Back <$VALUE
4x5 1-4675 <$500
3x10-20 1-600 <$500
1902 Red Seal
3x10-20 1-1400 <$500
1902 Date Back
3x10-20 1-4900 <$250
1902 Plain Back
3x10-20 4901-12819 <$250
Total Issue $834,450
Out at close $79,000
****
5803 Page
COMMERCIAL NB OF ESSEX
{{ 7 L 3 S }}
Organized 4/22/01
Receivership 5/5/31
Brown Back <$VALUE
3x10-20 1-3000 <$450
1882 Date Back
3x10-20 1-3300* <$450
1882 Value Back
3x10-20 3551-5142* <$450
* 3301-3550 not marked
1902 Plain Back
3x10-20 1-4050 <$200
1929 Small Size
10 Type 1 1-640 <$200
20 Type 1 1-192 <$200
Total Issue $671,040
Out at close $50,000
Large out at close $8,170
****
5738 Page
FNB OF ESSEX
{{ 8 L 10 S }}
Chartered 3/01
Brown Back <$VALUE
3x10-20 1-1300 <$400
1882 Date Back
3x10-20 1-3490 <$400
1882 Value Back
3x10-20 3491-5297 <$400
1902 Plain Black
3x10-20 1-4352 <$200
1929 Small Size
10 Type 1 1-1212 <$100
20 Type 1 1-312 <$100
10 Type 2 1-36 <$125
Total Issue $657,970
Out in 1935 $25,000
Large out 1935 $2,790
****
4700 Emmet
FNB, ESTHERVILLE
{{ 4 L }}
Organized 1/23/92
Receivership 2/27/26
Brown Back <$VALUE
50-100 1-663 <$2000/$2250
1882 Date Back
50-100 1-898 <$1750/$2000
1902 Date Back
3x50-100 1-1615<$1250/$1500
Total Issue $637,900
Out at close $97,000
****
7828 Clay
FNB, EVERLY
{{ 12 L 4 S }}
Organized 6/17/05
Receivership 8/3/33
1902 Red Seal <$VALUE
3x10-20 1-500 <$500
1902 Date Back
3x10-20 1-1730 <$200
1902 Plain Back
3x10-20 1731-4957 <$200
1929 Small Size
10 Type 1 1-547 <$250
20 Type 1 1-110 <$250
Total Issue $318,870
Out at close $25,000
Large out at close $2,050
****

<$VALUEs are for notes in **FINE** condition. Value changes by approximately **25%** for a change of one full grade.

6870 Audubon
FNB OF EXIRA
{{ 3 L 2 S }}
Organized 6/11/03
Receivership 11/3/33
1902 Red Seal <$VALUE
3x10-20 1-525 <$1000
1902 Date Back
3x10-20 1-800* <$500
1902 Plain Back
3x10-20 861-1634* <$500
* 801-860 not marked
1929 Small Size
10 Type 1 1-215 <$500
20 Type 1 1-41 <$500
Total Issue $125,770
Out at close $9,000
Large out at close $920

8986 Jefferson
FAIRFIELD NB, FAIRFIELD
{{ 3 L }}
Organized 12/24/07
Liquidated 6/1/22
1902 Red Seal <$VALUE
3x10-20 1-1800 <$800
1902 Date Back
3x10-20 1-3540 <$400
1902 Plain Back
3x10-20 3541-6534 <$400
Total Issue $416,700
Out at close $57,100

1475 Jefferson
FNB OF FAIRFIELD
{{ 12 L 25 S }}
Organized 5/9/65
Liquidated 4/26/34
Original Series <$VALUE
3x1-2 1-5603 <$350/$1000
4x5 1-4700 <$400
3x10-20 1-1730 <$750/$1250
Series 1875
4x5 1-2405 <$400
3x10-20 1-1370 <$750/$1250
Brown Back
4x5 1-2344 <$250
3x10-20 1-2634 <$250
1902 Red Seal
3x10-20 1-2000 <$275
1902 Date Back
3x10-20 1-6400 <$135
1902 Plain Back
3x10-20 6401-18454 <$135
1929 Small Size
10 Type 1 1-2208 <$40
20 Type 1 1-570 <$50
10 Type 2 1-869 <$45
20 Type 2 1-135 <$55
Total Issue $1,738,665
Out at close $100,000
Large out at close $7,750

5579 Van Buren
FNB OF FARMINGTON
{{ 6 L }}
Chartered 9/19/00
Liquidated 9/6/26
Brown Back <$VALUE
3x10-20 1-1100 <$500
1882 Date Back
3x10-20 1-1380* <$500
1882 Value Back
3x10-20 1481-2174* <$500
* 1381-1480 not marked
1902 Plain Back
3x10-20 1-990 <$250
Total Issue $213,200
Out at close $25,000

11907 Calhoun
FNB, FARNHAMVILLE
{{ 6 L 4 S }}
Organized 12/6/20
Receivership 7/28/33
1902 Plain Back <$VALUE
3x10-20 1-4051 <$275
1929 Small Size
5 Type 1 1-3144 <$250
10 Type 1 1-156 <$250
20 Type 1 1-34 <$250
Total Issue $312,710
Out at close $40,000
Large out at close $2,210

6700 Fremont
FNB OF FARRAGUT
{{ 3 L 3 S }}
Chartered 3/14/03
1902 Red Seal <$VALUE
3x10-20 1-1200 <$850
1902 Date Back
4x5 1-1850 <$450
3x10-20 1-1120 <$450
1902 Plain Back
4x5 1851-2589 <$450
3x10-20 1121-1608 <$450
1929 Small Size
5 Type 1 1-354 <$350
10 Type 1 1-177 <$350
20 Type 1 1-53 <$350
Total Issue $219,780
Out in 1935 $10,000
Large out 1935 $1,190

9592 Fayette
FNB OF FAYETTE
{{ 3 L }}
Chartered 11/09
Liquidated 6/8/28
1902 Date Back <$VALUE
3x10-20 1-1410* <$500
1902 Plain Back
3x10-20 1541-3198* <$500
* 1411-1540 not marked
Total Issue $159,900
Out at close $5,950

9821 Floyd
FNB OF FLOYD
{{ 3 L 2 S }}
Organized 6/16/10
Receivership 1/9/31
1902 Date Back <$VALUE
3x10-20 1-1740 <$500
1902 Plain Back
3x10-20 1741-4711 <$500
1929 Small Size
10 Type 1 1-280 <$400
20 Type 1 1-69 <$400
Total Issue $260,630
Out at close $24,500
Large out at close $4,830

6550 Pocahontas
FNB, FONDA
{{ 3 L 14 S }}
Chartered 1902
1902 Red Seal <$VALUE
3x10-20 1-356 <$750
1902 Date Back
3x10-20 1-2030 <$400
1902 Plain Back
3x10-20 2031-5111 <$400
1929 Small Size
10 Type 1 1-440 <$85
20 Type 1 1-138 <$85
10 Type 2 1-577 <$100
20 Type 2 1-103 <$100
Total Issue $324,140
Out in 1934 $25,000
Large out 1935 $1,270

7061 Adair
FNB OF FONTANELLE
{{ 6 L 3 S }}
Chartered 12/03
Liquidated 8/12/30
1902 Red Seal <$VALUE
4x5 1-730 <$500
3x10-20 1-544 <$500
1902 Date Back
4x5 1-1500 <$250
3x10-20 1-1160 <$250
1902 Plain Back
4x5 1501-4642 <$250
3x10-20 1161-3112 <$250
1929 Small Size
5 Type 1 1-258 <$300
10 Type 1 1-125 <$300
20 Type 1 1-16 <$300
Total Issue $307,400
Out at close $23,440
Large out at close $6,280

4889 Winnebago
FNB, FOREST CITY
{{ 6 L }}
Organized 2/20/92
Receivership 11/14/25
Brown Back <$VALUE
4x5 1-4055 <$450
3x10-20 1-1668 <$450
1882 Date Back
4x5 1-1778 <$450
3x10-20 1-1207 <$450
1902 Date Back
3x50-100 1-1247 <$400/$500
Total Issue $572,160
Out at close $73,995

5011 Winnebago
FOREST CITY NB,
FOREST CITY
{{ 6 L 10 S }}
Chartered 1895
Brown Back <$VALUE
3x10-20 1-2650 <$450
1882 Date Back
3x10-20 1-3076 <$450
1902 Plain Back
3x10-20 1-5938 <$250
1929 Small Size
10 Type 1 1-954 <$100
20 Type 1 1-298 <$100
10 Type 2 1-1158 <$100
20 Type 2 1-294 <$110
Total Issue $693,660
Out in 1935 $50,000
Large out 1935 $3,640

4566 Webster
COMMERCIAL NB OF
FORT DODGE
{{ 26 L 6 S }}
Chartered 1891
Liquidated 8/5/30
Brown Back <$VALUE
3x10-20 1-3600 <$250
1882 Date Back
3x10-20 1-2113 <$250
1902 Date Back
3x10-20 1-4900 <$100
1902 Plain Back
3x10-20 4901-17626 <$100
1929 Small Size
10 Type 1 1-889 <$125
20 Type 1 1-119 <$125
Total Issue $1,234,570
Out in 1929 $100,000
Large out at close $28,280

1661 Webster
FNB OF FORT DODGE
{{ 29 L 17 S }}
Chartered 1866
Liquidated 2/10/31
Original Series <$VALUE
3x1-2 1-2300 <$350/$1000
4x5 1-3450 <$400
Series 1875
3x1-2 1-200 <$350/$1000
4x5 1-5765 <$400
Brown Back
4x5 1-19275 <$200
3x10-20 1-8528 <$200
1902 Red Seal
4x5 1-4540 <$200
3x10-20 1-3684 <$200
1902 Date Back
4x5 1-16415 <$75
3x10-20 1-13834 <$85
1902 Plain Back
4x5 16416-28915 <$75
3x10-20 13835-42617 <$85
1929 Small Size
10 Type 1 1-3345 <$40
20 Type 1 1-768 <$50
Total Issue $4,285,710
Out at close $300,000
Large out at close $65,780

2763 Webster
FORT DODGE NB, FORT DODGE
{{ 27 L 21 S }}
Organized 7/8/82
Series 1875 <$VALUE
4x5 1-6201 <$400
3x10-20 1-1309 <$750/$1250
1902 Red Seal
3x10-20 1-5200 <$200
1902 Date Back
3x10-20 1-6300 <$85
1902 Plain Back
3x10-20 6301-18992 <$85
1929 Small Size
10 Type 1 1-2204 <$35
20 Type 1 1-614 <$45
10 Type 2 1-1609 <$35
20 Type 2 1-392 <$45
Total Issue $1,628,920
Out in 1935 $99,995
Large out 1935 $7,295

1947 Webster
MERCHANTS NB OF
FORT DODGE
{{ 1 L }}
Chartered 3/20/72
Liquidated 12/31/91
Original Series <$VALUE
3x1-2 1-1500 <$850/$2000
4x5 1-2625 <$1000
Series 1875
4x5 1-7243 <$1000
Total Issue $204,860
Out in 1910 $1,150

11304 Webster
WEBSTER COUNTY NB OF
FORT DODGE
{{ 6 L }}
Chartered 2/19
Liquidated 10/29/23
1902 Plain Back <$VALUE
3x10-20 1-11746 <$175/$200
Total Issue $587,300
Out in 1922 $184,995

3974 Lee
FNB OF FORT MADISON
{{ 1 L }}
Chartered 2/2/89
Liquidated 10/8/95
Brown Back <$VALUE
3x10-20 1-993 <$1500
Total Issue $49,650
Out in 1910 $485

1611 Lee
FORT MADISON NB OF
FORT MADISON
{{ 1 L }}
Chartered 11/20/65
Liquidated 12/26/71
Original Series <$VALUE
4x5 1-1750 <$1250
3x10-20 1-650 <$1500/$2000
Total Issue $67,500
Out in 1910 $430

10541 Chickasaw
FNB OF FREDERICKSBURG
{{ 28 L 1 S }}
Chartered 5/14
Liquidated 1/15/30
1902 Date Back <$VALUE
4x5 1-850 <$125
3x10-20 1-680 <$125
1902 Plain Back
4x5 851-4922 <$125
3x10-20 681-3029 <$125
1929 Small Size
5 Type 1 1-60 <$500
10 Type 1 1-16 <$500
20 Type 1 1-8 <$500
Total Issue $253,610
Out at close $28,700
Large out at close $3,720

10501 Ida
FNB, GALVA
{{ 6 L }}
Organized 3/23/14
Receivership 3/6/28
1902 Date Back <$VALUE
3x10-20 1-860 <$250
1902 Plain Back
3x10-20 861-6250 <$250
Total Issue $312,500
Out at close $41,050

5464 Decatur
FNB OF GARDEN GROVE
{{ UNREPORTED }}
Chartered 6/28/00
Liquidated 6/11/13
Brown Back <$VALUE
4x5 1-1550 <$1500
3x10-20 1-1100 <$1500
1882 Date Back
4x5 1-980 <$1500
3x10-20 1-632 <$1500
Total Issue $137,200
Out in 1913 $20,050

8367 Hancock
FARMERS NB, GARNER
{{ 3 L 3 S }}
Organized 8/22/06
Receivership 3/20/34
1902 Red Seal <$VALUE
3x10-20 1-750 <$850
1902 Date Back
3x10-20 1-1930 <$400
1902 Plain Back
3x10-20 1931-4767 <$400
1929 Small Size
10 Type 1 1-531 <$400
20 Type 1 1-136 <$400
Total Issue $324,030
Out at close $25,000
Large out at close $1,870

4810 Hancock
FNB, GARNER
{{ 6 L }}
Organized 8/24/92
Receivership 12/4/28
Brown Back <$VALUE
3x10-20 1-4100 <$400
1882 Date Back
3x10-20 1-1316 <$400
1902 Date Back
3x10-20 1-2000 <$250
1902 Plain Back
3x10-20 2001-7025 <$250
Total Issue $622,050
Out in 1927 $49,700

9910 Lyon
FNB, GEORGE
{{ 6 L 5 S }}
Organized 12/5/10
Receivership 1/4/33
1902 Date Back <$VALUE
3x10-20 1-1550 <$400
1902 Plain Back
3x10-20 1551-4232 <$400
1929 Small Size
10 Type 1 1-409 <$275
20 Type 1 1-103 <$275
Total Issue $248,500
Out at close $24,640
Large out at close $2,890

6611 Pocahontas
FNB OF GILMORE,
GILMORE CITY
{{ 1 L }}
Organized 12/2/02
Receivership 1/18/26
1902 Red Seal <$VALUE
4x5 1-350 <$1500
3x10-20 1-280 <$1500
1902 Date Back
4x5 1-500 <$850
3x10-20 1-400 <$850
1902 Plain Back
4x5 501-860 <$850
3x10-20 401-654 <$850
Total Issue $70,900
Out at close $6,200

5461 Tama
FNB OF GLADBROOK
{{ 5 L 9 S }}
Chartered 6/00
Brown Back <$VALUE
3x10-20 1-1800 <$500
1882 Date Back
3x10-20 1-3500 <$500
1882 Value Back
3x10-20 3501-4970 <$500
1902 Plain Back
3x10-20 1-4138 <$300
1929 Small Size
10 Type 1 1-956 <$125
20 Type 1 1-253 <$125
Total Issue $633,120
Out in 1935 $45,000
Large out 1935 $2,480

1862 Mills
MILLS COUNTY NB OF
GLENWOOD
{{ 7 L 3 S }}
Organized 8/11/71
Receivership 12/27/32
Original Series <$VALUE
3x1-2 1-1800 <$500/$1250
4x5 1-3975 <$500
Series 1875
4x5 1-5051 <$500
Brown Back
3x10-20 1-3510 <$400
1882 Date Back
3x10-20 1-801 <$400
1902 Date Back
3x50-100 1-750 <$500/$600
1902 Plain Back
3x50-100 751-920 <$500/$600
1929 Small Size
50 Type 1 1-110 <$400
100 Type 1 1-14 <$500
Total Issue $676,470
Out at close $41,250
Large out at close $9,200

4814 Carroll
FNB, GLIDDEN
{{ 13 L 10 S }}
Organized 11/1/92
Liquidated 2/28/35
Brown Back <$VALUE
3x10-20 1-3200 <$400
1882 Date Back
3x10-20 1-1511 <$400
1902 Date Back
3x10-20 1-1700 <$175
1902 Plain Back
3x10-20 1701-7550 <$175
1929 Small Size
10 Type 1 1-1028 <$110
20 Type 1 1-278 <$125
10 Type 2 1-1186 <$135
20 Type 2 1-235 <$150
Total Issue $724,650
Out at close $50,000
Large out at close $3,090

5373 Wright
FNB, GOLDFIELD
{{ UNREPORTED }}
Chartered 5/26/00
Liquidated 9/20/00
Brown Back <$VALUE
3x10-20 1-150 <$2500
Total Issue $7,500
All notes reportedly redeemed

5707 Webster
FNB, GOWRIE
{{ 6 L 7 S }}
Organized 1/15/01
Brown Back <$VALUE
3x10-20 1-1020 <$500
1882 Date Back
3x10-20 1-1730 <$500
1882 Value Back
3x10-20 1731-2691 <$500
1902 Plain Back
3x10-20 1-2126 <$300
1929 Small Size
10 Type 1 1-546 <$175
20 Type 1 1-150 <$175
10 Type 2 1-489 <$175
20 Type 2 1-85 <$200
Total Issue $349,200
Out in 1935 $25,000
Large out 1935 $2,290

5571 Palo Alto
FNB, GRAETTINGER
{{ 3 L 4 S }}
Organized 7/13/00
Receivership 10/30/33
Brown Back <$VALUE
3x10-20 1-500 <$750
1882 Date Back
3x10-20 1-960 <$750
1882 Value Back
3x10-20 961-1225 <$750
1902 Plain Back
3x10-20 1-1028 <$450
1929 Small Size
10 Type 1 1-254 <$300
20 Type 1 1-60 <$300
Total Issue $160,090
Out at close $12,000
Large out at close $1,000

6610 Worth
FNB OF GRAFTON
{{ UNREPORTED }}
Chartered 2/5/03
Liquidated 12/23/04
1902 Red Seal <$VALUE
3x10-20 1-167 <$2000
Total Issue $8,350
Out in 1910 $520

9737 Decatur
FNB OF GRAND RIVER
{{ 3 L 4 S }}
Organized 3/10/10
Receivership 10/30/33
1902 Date Back <$VALUE
3x10-20 1-1730* <$500
1902 Plain Back
3x10-20 1851-4430* <$500
* 1731-1850 not marked
1929 Small Size
10 Type 1 1-496 <$350
20 Type 1 1-121 <$350
Total Issue $265,780
Out at close $25,000
Large out at close $2,300

****
3071 Butler
FNB OF GREENE
{{ UNREPORTED }}
Chartered 11/2/83
Liquidated 12/15/87
Brown Back <$VALUE
3x10-20 1-321 <$1500
Total Issue $16,050
Out in 1910 $70
****
6880 Butler
MERCHANTS NB OF GREENE
{{ 5 L }}
Organized 6/23/03
Receivership 6/4/27
1902 Red Seal <$VALUE
3x10-20 1-2500 <$600
1902 Date Back
3x10-20 1-3200 <$300
1902 Plain Back
3x10-20 3201-7012 <$300
Total Issue $475,600
Out in 1924 $49,500
****
5334 Adair
FNB OF GREENFIELD
{{ 12 L }}
Organized 4/23/00
Receivership 3/21/28
Brown Back <$VALUE
3x10-20 1-800 <$375
1882 Date Back
3x10-20 1-1760 <$375
1882 Value Back
3x10-20 1761-2501 <$375
1902 Plain Back
3x10-20 1-3394 <$175
Total Issue $334,750
Out at close $24,995
****
7439 Poweshiek
CITIZENS NB OF GRINNELL
{{ 3 L 2 S }}
Chartered 9/15/04
Receivership 9/6/30
1902 Red Seal <$VALUE
3x10-20 1-1400 <$800
1902 Date Back
3x10-20 1-700 <$400
1902 Plain Back
3x10-20 701-6891 <$400
1929 Small Size
10 Type 1 1-400 <$400
20 Type 1 1-85 <$400
Total Issue $448,750
Out at close $47,980
Large out at close $13,780
****
1629 Poweshiek
FNB OF GRINNELL
{{ 3 L }}
Organized 1/15/66
Receivership 7/27/04
Original Series <$VALUE
3x1-2 1-3400 <$600/$1500
4x5 1-2250 <$650
3x10-20 1-1460 <$850/$1500
Series 1875
4x5 1-500 <$650
3x10-20 1-1092 <$850/$1500
Brown Back
50-100 1-801 <$1500/$1750
Total Issue $319,750
Out in 1915 $3,661
****
2953 Poweshiek
MERCHANTS NB OF GRINNELL
{{ 5 L }}
Organized 4/28/83
Receivership 11/12/24
Brown Back <$VALUE
50-100 1-866 <$1250/$1500
1902 Red Seal
50-100 1-1067 <$2250/$2500
1902 Date Back
50-100 1-800 <$500/$600
3x50-100 1-1339 <$500/$600
Total Issue $744,700
Out at close $100,000
****
13473 Poweshiek
POWESHIEK COUNTY NB OF
GRINNELL
{{ 3U + 10 S }}
Chartered 6/30
1929 Small Size <$VALUE
5 Type 1 1-734 <$125
10 Type 1 1-376 <$125
20 Type 1 1-122 <$125
Total Issue $59,220
Out in 1935 $26,220
****

****
3048 Cass
FNB OF GRISWOLD
{{ UNREPORTED }}
Organized 9/15/83
Receivership 2/17/97
Brown Back <$VALUE
4x5 1-2472 <$1500
Total Issue $49,440
Out in 1915 $270
****
8915 Cass
GRISWOLD NB, GRISWOLD
{{ 6 L 0 S }}
Organized 9/2/07
Receivership 12/13/29
1902 Red Seal <$VALUE
4x10 1-450 <$750
1902 Date Back
4x10 1-3100 <$350
1902 Plain Back
4x10 3101-8363 <$350
1929 Small Size
10 Type 1 1-101 <$600
Total Issue $358,580
Out at close $30,000
Large out at close $6,060
****
3225 Grundy
FNB OF GRUNDY CENTER
{{ 6 L }}
Chartered 1884
Liquidated 8/27/29
Brown Back <$VALUE
4x5 1-3306 <$450
50-100 1-87 <$1250/$1500
1902 Red Seal
3x10-20 1-1130 <$500
1902 Date Back
3x10-20 1-3300 <$250
1902 Plain Back
3x10-20 3301-9335 <$250
Total Issue $602,420
Out at close $50,000
****
3396 Grundy
GRUNDY COUNTY NB OF
GRUNDY CENTER
{{ 7 L 7 S }}
Organized 9/16/85
Liquidated 4/20/34
Brown Back <$VALUE
4x5 1-5306 <$400
3x10-20 1-1508 <$400
1902 Red Seal
3x10-20 1-1000 <$400
1902 Date Back
3x10-20 1-3200 <$175
1902 Plain Back
3x10-20 3201-9057 <$175
1929 Small Size
10 Type 1 1-956 <$125
20 Type 1 1-278 <$125
10 Type 2 1-157 <$150
20 Type 2 1-14 <$150
Total Issue $776,940
Out at close $49,995
Large out at close $3,575
****
7736 Guthrie
CITIZENS NB OF
GUTHRIE CENTER
{{ UNREPORTED }}
Chartered 5/05
Liquidated 3/23/12
1902 Red Seal <$VALUE
3x10-20 1-760 <$1500
1902 Date Back
3x10-20 1-312 <$1000
Total Issue $53,600
Out at close $20,000
Ch 5424 assumed circulation
****
5424 Guthrie
FNB OF GUTHRIE CENTER
{{ 13 L 4 S }}
Organized 5/4/00
Liquidated 6/23/30
Brown Back <$VALUE
3x10-20 1-1590 <$375
1882 Date Back
3x10-20 1-3050* <$375
1882 Value Back
3x10-20 3551-4507* <$375
* 3051-3550 not marked
1902 Plain Back
3x10-20 1-4672 <$175
1929 Small Size
10 Type 1 1-358 <$250
20 Type 1 1-45 <$250
Total Issue $565,330
Out at close $42,800
Large out at close $15,920
Outstanding includes Ch 7736
****

****
6017 Fremont
FARMERS NB OF HAMBURG
{{ 3 L }}
Chartered 11/01
Liquidated 8/27/10
Brown Back <$VALUE
4x5 1-1480 <$750
3x10-20 1-1188 <$750
1882 Date Back
4x5 1-395 <$750
3x10-20 1-293 <$750
Total Issue $111,550
Out in 1910 $39,100
****
2364 Fremont
FNB OF HAMBURG
{{ UNREPORTED }}
Chartered 6/28/77
Liquidated 12/31/86
Series 1875 <$VALUE
4x5 1-3161 <$1500
Total Issue $63,220
Out in 1910 $345
****
7843 Franklin
CITIZENS NB OF HAMPTON
{{ 13 L 14 S }}
Organized 7/20/05
Liquidated 1/20/34
1902 Red Seal <$VALUE
3x10-20 1-3800 <$300
1902 Date Back
3x10-20 1-6100 <$125
1902 Plain Back
3x10-20 6101-18377 <$125
1929 Small Size
10 Type 1 1-1867 <$70
20 Type 1 1-568 <$75
Total Issue $1,289,030
Out at close $100,000
Large out at close $8,540
****
2573 Franklin
FNB OF HAMPTON
{{ UNREPORTED }}
Chartered 10/13/81
Liquidated 2/1/88
Series 1875 <$VALUE
4x10 1-847 <$1500
Total Issue $33,880
Out in 1910 $180
****
13842 Franklin
FNB OF HAMPTON
{{ 25 S }}
Chartered 11/33
1929 Small Size <$VALUE
10 Type 2 1-3090 <$65
20 Type 2 1-1380 <$70
Total Issue $58,500
Out in 1935 $44,300
****
5207 Shelby
FNB OF HARLAN
{{ UNREPORTED }}
Chartered 7/11/99
Liquidated 3/22/06
Brown Back <$VALUE
3x10-20 1-878 <$1500
Total Issue $43,900
Out in 1910 $3,700
****
10354 Shelby
HARLAN NB, HARLAN
{{ 1 L }}
Chartered 4/13
1902 Date Back <$VALUE
4x5 1-750 <$1000
3x10-20 1-700 <$1000
1902 Plain Back
4x5 751-1165 <$1000
3x10-20 701-1148 <$1000
Total Issue $80,700
Out in 1935 $430
****
6949 Osceola
FNB, HARRIS
{{ UNREPORTED }}
Organized 9/8/03
Liquidated 4/1/06
1902 Red Seal <$VALUE
3x10-20 1-416 <$2000
Total Issue $20,800
Out in 1910 $1,730
****

****
4881 O'Brien
FNB, HARTLEY
{{ 7 L }}
Organized 2/22/93
Receivership 3/22/27
Brown Back <$VALUE
3x10-20 1-1920 <$500
1882 Date Back
3x10-20 1-1730 <$500
1902 Date Back
3x10-20 1-1500 <$250
1902 Plain Back
3x10-20 1501-6414 <$250
Total Issue $503,200
Out at close $49,600
****
6936 Marion
FNB OF HARVEY
{{ 8 L U + 5 S }}
Chartered 8/03
Liquidated 8/23/35
1902 Red Seal <$VALUE
4x5 1-310 <$750
3x10-20 1-246 <$750
1902 Date Back
4x5 1-1925 <$350
3x10-20 1-1410 <$350
1902 Plain Back
4x5 1926-5759 <$350
3x10-20 1411-3671 <$350
1929 Small Size
5 Type 1 1-770 <$250
10 Type 1 1-380 <$250
20 Type 1 1-86 <$250
5 Type 2 1-3228 <$250
Total Issue $389,590
Out in 1935 $25,000
Large out 1935 $1,165
****
7294 Pocahontas
FNB, HAVELOCK
{{ 6 L }}
Organized 4/30/04
Receivership 11/5/27
1902 Red Seal <$VALUE
3x10-20 1-300 <$750
1902 Date Back
3x10-20 1-1610 <$300
1902 Plain Back
3x10-20 1611-4223 <$300
Total Issue $226,150
Out at close $25,000
****
13939 Sioux
FNB IN HAWARDEN
{{ 7 S }}
Chartered 1934
1929 Small Size <$VALUE
5 Type 2 1-748 <$200
10 Type 2 1-417 <$200
Total Issue $7,910
Out in 1935 $25,000
Outstanding includes Ch 4594
****
4594 Sioux
FNB OF HAWARDEN
{{ 3 L 8 S }}
Organized 6/15/91
Liquidated 2/12/34
Brown Back <$VALUE
3x10-20 1-2585 <$600
1882 Date Back
3x10-20 1-496 <$600
1902 Date Back
3x10-20 1-2040 <$350
1902 Plain Back
3x10-20 2041-3806 <$350
1929 Small Size
10 Type 1 1-558 <$110
20 Type 1 1-132 <$125
Total Issue $393,670
Out at close $25,000
Large out 1935 $1,730
Ch 13939 assumed circulation
****
8900 Fayette
FNB OF HAWKEYE
{{ 3 L 5 S }}
Organized 9/16/07
Receivership 11/3/33
1902 Red Seal <$VALUE
4x5 1-525 <$1000
3x10-20 1-510 <$1000
1902 Date Back
4x5 1-1475 <$450
3x10-20 1-990 <$450
1902 Plain Back
4x5 1476-4562 <$450
3x10-20 991-2853 <$450

1929 Small Size
5 Type 1 1-634 <$250
10 Type 1 1-341 <$250
20 Type 1 1-85 <$250
Total issue $319,570
Out at close $25,000
Large out at close $2,120
****
5540 Keokuk
FNB OF HEDRICK
{{ 3 L }}
Organized 8/11/00
Receivership 4/24/25
Brown Back <$VALUE
3x10-20 1-1800 <$650
1882 Date Back
3x10-20 1-1600* <$650
1882 Value Back
3x10-20 1721-2443* <$650
* 1601-1720 not marked
1902 Plain Back
3x10-20 1-1270 <$400
Total Issue $275,650
Out at close $19,800
****
12656 Keokuk
HEDRICK NB, HEDRICK
{{ 6 L 2 S }}
Chartered 3/25
Liquidated 10/14/32
1902 Plain Back <$VALUE
4x5 1-4742 <$300
1929 Small Size
5 Type 1 1-2257 <$400
Total Issue $162,550
Out at close $25,000
Large out at close $860
****
7382 Mills
FARMERS NB OF HENDERSON
{{ 3 L 6 S }}
Organized 3/7/04
Receivership 7/28/33
1902 Red Seal <$VALUE
3x10-20 1-1150 <$800
1902 Date Back
3x10-20 1-1680 <$400
1902 Plain Back
3x10-20 1681-4926 <$400
1929 Small Size
10 Type 1 1-528 <$175
20 Type 1 1-148 <$175
Total Issue $353,240
Out at close $25,000
Large out at close $2,030
****
4553 Ida
FNB, HOLSTEIN
{{ UNREPORTED }}
Chartered 4/15/91
Liquidated 7/1/98
Brown Back <$VALUE
3x10-20 1-565 <$1500
Total Issue $28,250
Out in 1910 $350
****
8970 Hardin
FNB OF HUBBARD
{{ 6 L 4 S }}
Organized 12/3/07
Receivership 10/30/33
1902 Red Seal <$VALUE
3x10-20 1-300 <$600
1902 Date Back
3x10-20 1-1730 <$300
1902 Plain Back
3x10-20 1731-4854 <$300
1929 Small Size
5 Type 1 1-668 <$250
10 Type 1 1-393 <$250
20 Type 1 1-116 <$250
Total Issue $315,240
Out at close $37,500
Large out at close $4,160
Outstanding includes Ch 6435
****
5659 Black Hawk
FNB OF HUDSON
{{ 1 L }}
Chartered 12/29/00
Liquidated 7/1/12
Brown Back <$VALUE
3x10-20 1-1720 <$1000
1882 Date Back
3x10-20 1-728 <$1000
Total Issue $122,400
Out in 1912 $21,200
****

****
6953 Sioux
FNB, HULL
{{ 6 L 4 S }}
Organized 8/14/03
Receivership 12/20/33
1902 Red Seal <$VALUE
3x10-20 1-1990 <$650
1902 Date Back
3x10-20 1-1700 <$300
1902 Plain Back
3x10-20 1701-5824 <$300
1929 Small Size
10 Type 1 1-711 <$250
20 Type 1 1-201 <$250
Total Issue $457,480
Out at close $35,000
Large out at close $2,920
****
13766 Humboldt
FNB IN HUMBOLDT
{{ 7 S }}
Chartered 9/33
1929 Small Size <$VALUE
5 Type 2 1-7162 <$175
10 Type 2 1-3792 <$175
Total Issue $73,730
Out in 1935 $49,300
****
8277 Humboldt
FNB OF HUMBOLDT
{{ 5 L 7 S }}
Organized 5/24/06
Receivership 10/24/33
1902 Red Seal <$VALUE
3x10-20 1-900 <$700
1902 Date Back
3x10-20 1-1620 <$350
1902 Plain Back
3x10-20 1621-5421 <$350
1929 Small Size
5 Type 1 1-1460 <$175
10 Type 1 1-704 <$175
20 Type 1 1-202 <$175
5 Type 2 1-60 <$200
10 Type 2 1-108 <$200
Total Issue $427,710
Out at close $50,000
Large out at close $2,370
****
3930 Ida
FNB, IDA GROVE
{{ 1 L }}
Chartered 10/10/88
Liquidated 5/1/93
Brown Back <$VALUE
3x10-20 1-1192 <$2000
Total Issue $59,600
Out in 1915 $360
****
8295 Fremont
FNB OF IMOGENE
{{ 2 L 4 S }}
Chartered 7/06
1902 Red Seal <$VALUE
3x10-20 1-600 <$1250
1902 Date Back
3x10-20 1-1310* <$750
1902 Plain Back
3x10-20 1471-2442* <$750
* 1311-1470 not marked
1929 Small Size
10 Type 1 1-252 <$300
20 Type 1 1-80 <$300
Total Issue $176,820
Out in 1935 $10,000
Large out 1935 $650
****
1581 Buchanan
FNB OF INDEPENDENCE
{{ UNREPORTED }}
Chartered 1865
Liquidated 10/31/84
Original Series <$VALUE
4x5 1-3525 <$1500
3x10-20 1-1800<$1750/$2000
Series 1875
4x5 1-1000 <$1500
3x10-20 1-2086<$1750/$2000
Total Issue $284,800
Out in 1910 $1,600
****
FNB of Independence
SEE Ch 3263
FNB of the City of
Independence
****

3263 Buchanan
FNB OF THE CITY OF INDEPENDENCE
Organized 10/27/84
Receivership 7/5/28
2nd title: FNB of Independence 12/04
FIRST TITLE {{ 2 L }}
Brown Back <$VALUE
4x5 1-4320 <$500
3x10-20 1-2842 <$500
SECOND TITLE {{ 25 L }}
1902 Red Seal
4x5 1-1340 <$250
3x10-20 1-1074 <$250
1902 Date Back
4x5 1-6350 <$100
3x10-20 1-4660 <$100
1902 Plain Back
4x5 6351-17270 <$100
3x10-20 4661-11983 <$100
Total Issue $1,253,550
Out at close $98,995

2187 Buchanan
PEOPLES NB OF INDEPENDENCE
{{ 30 L }}
Organized 7/30/74
Receivership 7/5/28
Original Series <$VALUE
3x10-20 1-900 <$750/$1250
Series 1875
3x10-20 1-2427 <$750/$1250
Brown Back
3x10-20 1-2600 <$250
1882 Date Back
3x10-20 1-3523 <$250
1902 Date Back
3x10-20 1-1500 <$125
1902 Plain Bak
3x10-20 1501-9019 <$125
Total Issue $923,450
Out at close $65,050

1811 Warren
FNB OF INDIANOLA
{{ 7 L }}
Organized 11/15/70
Receivership 8/20/32
Original Series <$VALUE
3x1-2 1-2820 <$400/$1250
4x5 1-3025 <$500
Series 1875
4x5 1-4669 <$500
Brown Back
4x5 1-3900 <$400
3x10-20 1-2340 <$400
1882 Date Back
4x5 1-686 <$400
3x10-20 1-529 <$400
1902 Date Back
3x10-20 1-2600 <$225
1902 Plain Back
3x10-20 2601-6447 <$225
Total Issue $725,500
Out at close $4,543

8257 Lyon
FARMERS NB, INWOOD
{{ 6 L 4 S }}
Organized 3/19/06
Receivership 12/20/30
1902 Red Seal <$VALUE
3x10-20 1-900 <$500
1902 Date Back
3x10-20 1-2920 <$250
1902 Plain Back
3x10-20 2921-7329 <$250
1929 Small Size
10 Type 1 1-384 <$250
20 Type 1 1-88 <$250
Total Issue $445,050
Out at close $40,000
Large out at close $11,400

7304 Lyon
FNB, INWOOD
{{ 3 L }}
Organized 5/23/04
Receivership 9/6/27
1902 Red Seal <$VALUE
3x10-20 1-1150 <$850
1902 Date Back
3x10-20 1-1610* <$450
1902 Plain Back
3x10-20 1911-4132* <$450
* 1611-1910 not marked
Total Issue $264,100
Out at close $25,000

18 Johnson
FNB OF IOWA CITY*
{{ 13 L 13 S }}
Chartered 7/63
Liquidated 6/24/82
*Rechartered as Ch 2738 which retook Ch 18 12/2/11
Receivership 1/22/32
Original Series <$VALUE
4x5 1-5750 <$650
3x10-20 1-1350<$1000/$1500
Series 1875
4x5 1-1950 <$650
3x10-20 1-602 <$1000/$1500
1902 Date Back
3x10-20 1-1400 <$175
1902 Plain Back
3x10-20 1401-11081 <$175
1929 Small Size
10 Type 1 1-1642 <$125
20 Type 1 1-438 <$125
Total Issue $956,730
Out at close $98,020
Large out at close $14,390
Outstanding includes Ch 2738

2738 Johnson
FNB OF IOWA CITY
{{ 2 L }}
Organized 6/12/82
RETOOK Ch 18 12/2/11
Brown Back <$VALUE
3x10-20 1-3218 <$850
1902 Red Seal
3x10-20 1-3000 <$850
1902 Date Back
3x10-20 1-1700 <$650
Total Issue $395,900
Out in 1911 $100,000

977 Johnson
IOWA CITY NB OF IOWA CITY
{{ UNREPORTED }}
Chartered 4/5/65
Liquidated 4/14/75
Original Series <$VALUE
3x1-2 1-3200 <$1500/$2500
4x5 1-2575 <$1500
3x10-20 1-1600<$2000/$2500
Total Issue $147,500
Out in 1910 $1,426

2821 Johnson
IOWA CITY NB, IOWA CITY
{{ 1 L }}
Chartered 11/14/82
Liquidated 2/7/89
Brown Back <$VALUE
4x5 1-1083 <$1250
3x10-20 1-661 <$1250
50-100 1-215 <$2500
Total Issue $86,960
Out in 1910 $1,425

3252 Hardin
FNB OF IOWA FALLS
{{ 7 L 6 S }}
Organized 8/28/84
Receivership 12/27/32
Brown Back <$VALUE
3x10-20 1-1316 <$500
1902 Red Seal
3x10-20 1-450 <$500
1902 Date Back
3x10-20 1-4100 <$225
1902 Plain Back
3x10-20 4101-10607 <$225
1929 Small Size
10 Type 1 1-925 <$175
20 Type 1 1-223 <$175
Total Issue $700,910
Out at close $49,580
Large out at close $5,350

7521 Hardin
STATE NB OF IOWA FALLS
{{ 6 L 5 S }}
Organized 8/20/04
Receivership 7/7/32
1902 Red Seal <$VALUE
3x10-20 1-1260 <$500
1902 Date Back
3x10-20 1-3300 <$225
1902 Plain Back
3x10-20 3301-9938 <$225
1929 Small Size
10 Type 1 1-823 <$175
20 Type 1 1-214 <$175
Total Issue $634,960
Out at close $49,460
Large out at close $6,840

4794 Sioux
FNB, IRETON
{{ UNREPORTED }}
Organized 8/31/92
Liquidated 9/1/94
Brown Back <$VALUE
3x10-20 1-297 <$2000
Total Issue $14,850
Out in 1910 $180

10123 Greene
FARMERS & MERCHANTS NB OF JEFFERSON
{{ 2 L }}
Organized 12/28/11
Receivership 4/27/23
1902 Date Back <$VALUE
3x10-20 1-2140* <$600
1902 Plain Back
3x10-20 2341-4705* <$600
* 2141-2340 not marked
Total Issue $235,250
Out at close $40,000

8262 Greene
FNB OF JEFFERSON
{{ 3 L }}
Organized 3/26/06
Receivership 12/23/25
1902 Red Seal <$VALUE
3x10-20 1-900 <$850
50-100 1-200 <$2250/$2500
1902 Date Back
3x10-20 1-2540 <$400
50-100 1-100 <$750/$850
1902 Plain Back
3x10-20 2541-3083 <$400
Total Issue $244,150
Out at close $12,100

2856 Buchanan
FNB OF JESUP
{{ UNREPORTED }}
Chartered 1/10/83
Liquidated 4/20/86
Brown Back <$VALUE
4x5 1-2250 <$1500
Total Issue $45,000
Out in 1910 $325

5743 Hamilton
FNB OF JEWELL JUNCTION, JEWELL
{{ 3 L 6 S }}
Organized 2/28/01
Receivership 11/3/33
Brown Back <$VALUE
3x10-20 1-640 <$750
1882 Date Back
3x10-20 1-700 <$750
1882 Value Back
3x10-20 701-775 <$750
1902 Plain Back
3x10-20 1-676 <$450
1929 Small Size
5 Type 1 1-356 <$200
10 Type 1 1-286 <$200
20 Type 1 1-74 <$200
Total Issue $141,270
Out at close $25,000
Large out at close $850

9018 Hancock
FNB, KANAWHA
{{ 3 L 8 S }}
Organized 12/14/07
Receivership 10/7/33
1902 Red Seal <$VALUE
3x10-20 1-700 <$1000
1902 Date Back
3x10-20 1-1870 <$450
1902 Plain Back
3x10-20 1871-4808 <$450
1929 Small Size
10 Type 1 1-548 <$150
20 Type 1 1-116 <$150
Total Issue $322,200
Out at close $25,000
Large out at close $1,570

80 Lee
FNB OF KEOKUK
{{ UNREPORTED }}
Organized 9/9/63
Receivership 3/3/68
Original Series <$VALUE
4x5 1-4600 <$2000
Total Issue $92,000
Out in 1915 $330

1992 Lee
KEOKUK NB, KEOKUK
{{ 14 L 8 S }}
Chartered 6/1/72
Liquidated 1/8/35
Original Series <$VALUE
3x1-2 1-2900 <$350/$1000
4x5 1-2750 <$400
3x10-20 1-400 <$750/$1250
Series 1875
4x5 1-5250 <$400
3x10-20 1-1220 <$750/$1250
Brown Back
3x10-20 1-7840 <$300
1882 Date Back
3x10-20 1-1811 <$300
1902 Date Back
3x10-20 1-2600 <$150
1902 Plain Back
3x10-20 2601-6955 <$150
1929 Small Size
10 Type 1 1-848 <$110
20 Type 1 1-285 <$110
Total Issue $1,170,880
Out at close $44,460
Large out at close $4,570
Ch 14309 assumed circulation

14309 Lee
KEOKUK NB, KEOKUK
{{ UNREPORTED }}
Chartered 12/34
1929 Small Size <$VALUE
10 Type 2 1-30 <$750
20 Type 2 1-105 <$750
Total Issue $2,400
Out in 1935 $39,430
Outstanding includes Ch 1992

1441 Lee
STATE NB OF KEOKUK
{{ 2 L }}
Chartered 1865
Liquidated 5/23/85
Original Series <$VALUE
4x5 1-2100 <$850
3x10-20 1-370 <$1000/$1500
50-100 1-100 <$5000
Series 1875
3x10-20 1-107 <$1000/$1500
Total Issue $295,900
Out in 1910 $1,910

9619 Audubon
LANDMANS NB OF KIMBALLTON
{{ 6 L 5 S }}
Chartered 12/09
1902 Date Back <$VALUE
4x5 1-850* <$250
3x10-20 1-680** <$250
1902 Plain Back
4x5 951-2430* <$250
3x10-20 761-1723** <$250
* 851-950 not marked
** 681-760 not marked
1929 Small Size
5 Type 1 1-414 <$225
10 Type 1 1-206 <$225
20 Type 1 1-64 <$225
5 Type 2 1-36 <$250
10 Type 2 1-881 <$250
20 Type 2 1-219 <$250
Total Issue $180,580
Out in 1935 $25,000
Large out 1935 $1,330

9116 Plymouth
FARMERS NB, KINGSLEY
{{ 2 L 6 S }}
Organized 4/6/08
Receivership 10/30/33
1902 Red Seal <$VALUE
4x5 1-150 <$1250
3x10-20 1-120 <$1250
1902 Date Back
4x5 1-500 <$650
3x10-20 1-380 <$650
1902 Plain Back
4x5 501-1545 <$650
3x10-20 381-1028 <$650
1929 Small Size
5 Type 1 1-694 <$175
10 Type 1 1-410 <$175
20 Type 1 1-128 <$200
5 Type 2 1-42 <$200
Total Issue $152,290
Out at close $25,000
Large out at close $660

6659 Hancock
FNB OF KLEMME
{{ 3 L 8 S }}
Chartered 3/03
1902 Red Seal <$VALUE
3x10-20 1-1006 <$1000
1902 Date Back
3x10-20 1-1610 <$450
1902 Plain Back
3x10-20 1611-4645 <$450
1929 Small Size
10 Type 1 1-540 <$150
20 Type 1 1-140 <$150
5 Type 2 1-312 <$175
10 Type 2 1-380 <$175
20 Type 2 1-151 <$175
Total Issue $340,130
Out in 1935 $25,000
Large out 1935 $1,255

4633 Marion
CITIZENS NB OF KNOXVILLE
{{ 8 L 12 S }}
Chartered 1891
Liquidated 1/21/32
Brown Back <$VALUE
4x5 1-7875 <$350
3x10-20 1-1640 <$350
1882 Date Back
4x5 1-911 <$350
3x10-20 1-690 <$350
1902 Date Back
3x10-20 1-3000 <$175
1902 Plain Back
3x10-20 3001-15170 <$175
1929 Small Size
10 Type 1 1-1525 <$100
20 Type 1 1-462 <$100
Total Issue $1,197,995
Out at close $99,995
Large out at close $12,135

13707 Marion
COMMUNITY NB & TC OF KNOXVILLE
{{ 7 S }}
Chartered 6/33
1929 Small Size <$VALUE
10 Type 2 1-4225 <$150
20 Type 2 1-1314 <$150
Total Issue $68,530
Out in 1935 $48,750

12849 Marion
KNOXVILLE-CITIZENS NB & TC OF KNOXVILLE
{{ 2 S }}
Organized 11/4/25 as Knoxville NB & TC, under which there was no issue. Issuing title adopted 1/21/32.
Receivership 10/10/33
1929 Small Size <$VALUE
10 Type 1 1-586 <$350
20 Type 1 1-125 <$350
Total Issue $50,160
Out at close $100,000
Large out at close $6,580
Outstanding includes Ch 4633

1871 Marion
KNOXVILLE NB, KNOXVILLE
{{ 12 L }}
Chartered 9/7/71
Liquidated 12/17/25
Original Series <$VALUE
3x1-2 1-1000 <$500/$1250
3x10-20 1-2799 <$750/$1250
50-100 1-167 <$5000
Series 1875
3x10-20 1-2733 <$750/$1250
Brown Back
4x5 1-10430 <$275
3x10-20 1-4560 <$275
1882 Date Back
4x5 1-2331 <$275
3x10-20 1-1525 <$275
1902 Date Back
4x5 1-4850 <$150
3x10-20 1-3760 <$150
1902 Plain Back
4x5 4851-13415 <$150
3x10-20 3761-9582 <$150
Total Issue $1,613,520
Out at close $100,000

1986 Marion
MARION COUNTY NB OF KNOXVILLE
{{ 9 L }}
Organized 4/12/72
Receivership 2/1/27
Original Series <$VALUE
3x1-2 1-2000 <$500/$1500
4x5 1-4200 <$500
Series 1875
3x1-2 1-999 <$500/$1500
4x5 1-7286 <$500
Brown Back
4x5 1-5075 <$350
50-100 1-900 <$1250/$1500
1882 Date Back
4x5 1-1390 <$250
50-100 1-259 <$1250/$1500
1902 Date Back
4x5 1-1900 <$175
3x10-20 1-1440 <$175
1902 Plain Back
4x5 1901-8405 <$175
3x10-20 1441-5182 <$175
Total Issue $975,065
Out at close $57,095

4966 Calhoun
FNB, LAKE CITY
{{ 5 L 4 S }}
Organized 6/21/94
Receivership 10/22/31
Brown Back <$VALUE
4x5 1-3825 <$450
3x10-20 1-2580 <$450
1882 Date Back
4x5 1-2558 <$450
3x10-20 1-1752 <$450
1902 Date Back
4x5 1-750 <$250
3x10-20 1-700 <$250
1902 Plain Back
4x5 751-7269 <$250
3x10-20 701-4976 <$250
1929 Small Size
5 Type 1 1-953 <$250
10 Type 1 1-429 <$250
20 Type 1 1-121 <$250
Total Issue $807,290
Out at close $48,800
Large out at close $8,120

5123 Winnebago
FNB, LAKE MILLS
{{ 5 L }}
Organized 2/21/98
Receivership 4/8/27
Brown Back <$VALUE
4x5 1-4325 <$500
3x10-20 1-1960 <$500
1882 Date Back
4x5 1-3200 <$500
3x10-20 1-2180 <$500
1882 Value Back
4x5 3201-3923 <$500
3x10-20 2181-2609 <$500
1902 Plain Back
4x5 1-4575 <$300
3x10-20 1-2799 <$300
Total Issue $624,860
Out at close $49,495

405 Allamakee
FNB OF LANSING
{{ 2 L }}
Chartered 1864
Liquidated 2/25/81
Original Series <$VALUE
3x1-2 1-2940 <$750/$2000
4x5 1-4500 <$850
Series 1875
4x5 1-2040 <$850
Total Issue $145,500
Out in 1910 $1,084

4114 Black Hawk
FNB OF LaPORTE CITY
{{ 7 L }}
Organized 8/12/89
Receivership 2/15/28
Brown Back <$VALUE
3x10-20 1-4892 <$450
1902 Date Back
3x10-20 1-4600 <$225
1902 Plain Back
3x10-20 4601-12748 <$225
Total Issue $882,000
Out at close $75,000

****
4795 Pocahontas
FNB, LAURENS
{{ 6 L 1 S }}
Chartered 1892
Liquidated 6/6/30
Brown Back <$VALUE
3x10-20 1-1310 <$450
1882 Date Back
3x10-20 1-335 <$450
1902 Date Back
3x10-20 1-750 <$275
1902 Plain Back
3x10-20 751-1895 <$275
1929 Small Size
10 Type 1 1-117 <$500
20 Type 1 1-9 <$500
Total Issue $185,100
Out in 1929 $12,500
Large out at close $3,000
****
10599 Chickasaw
FNB OF LAWLER
{{ 13 L }}
Chartered 8/14
Liquidated 4/7/28
1902 Plain Back <$VALUE
3x10-20 1-4262 <$175
Total Issue $213,100
Out at close $49,500
****
2728 Plymouth
FNB, Le MARS
{{ 6 L 12 S }}
Organized 5/23/82
Liquidated 9/27/34
Series 1875 <$VALUE
3x10-20 1-4784 <$750/$1250
1902 Red Seal
3x10-20 1-4900 <$400
1902 Date Back
3x10-20 1-5700 <$175
1902 Plain Back
3x10-20 5701-17207 <$175
1929 Small Size
5 Type 1 1-2334 <$85
10 Type 1 1-1758 <$85
20 Type 1 1-378 <$85
Total Issue $1,565,410
Out in 1935 $57,380
Large out 1935 $6,330
****
2818 Plymouth
Le MARS NB, Le MARS
{{ UNREPORTED }}
Chartered 11/13/82
Receivership 4/17/01
Brown Back <$VALUE
4x5 1-1155 <$1250
50-100 1-654 <$2500
Total Issue $121,200
Out in 1915 $510
****
5868 Webster
FNB, LEHIGH
{{ 3 L 5 S }}
Organized 6/15/01
Receivership 8/17/31
Brown Back <$VALUE
3x10-20 1-1600 <$650
1882 Date Back
3x10-20 1-1130* <$650
1882 Value Back
3x10-20 1331-2064* <$650
* 1131-1330 not marked
1902 Plain Back
3x10-20 1-1770 <$350
1929 Small Size
10 Type 1 1-278 <$175
20 Type 1 1-63 <$175
Total Issue $295,940
Out at close $20,000
Large out at close $3,300
****
14040 Taylor
FNB IN LENOX
{{ 3 S }}
Chartered 3/34
1929 Small Size <$VALUE
5 Type 2 1-934 <$300
10 Type 2 1-390 <$300
20 Type 2 1-185 <$300
Total Issue $12,270
Out in 1935 $37,000
Outstanding includes Ch 5517
****
5517 Taylor
FNB OF LENOX
{{ 13 L 11 S }}
Organized 6/25/00
Liquidated 4/30/34
Brown Back <$VALUE
3x10-20 1-870 <$350
1882 Date Back
4x5 1-2850 <$350
3x10-20 1-1940 <$350
1882 Value Back
4x5 2851-4715 <$350
3x10-20 1941-2995 <$350
1902 Plain Back
4x5 1-4402 <$150
3x10-20 1-2958 <$150
1929 Small Size
5 Type 1 1-1473 <$100
10 Type 1 1-712 <$100
20 Type 1 1-192 <$100
Total Issue $633,440
Out at close $49,995
Large out at close $5,235
Ch 14040 assumed circulation
****
5489 Decatur
EXCHANGE NB OF LEON
{{ 12 L }}
Organized 6/20/00
Receivership 3/9/27
Brown Back <$VALUE
4x5 1-1415 <$400
3x10-20 1-1134 <$400
1882 Date Back
4x5 1-1950 <$400
3x10-20 1-1500 <$400
1882 Value Back
4x5 1951-3251 <$400
3x10-20 1501-2220 <$400
1902 Plain Back
3x10-20 1-2204 <$175
Total Issue $371,220
Out at close $34,500
****
1696 Decatur
FNB OF LEON
{{ 1 L }}
Organized 12/69
Liquidated 7/11/76
Original Series <$VALUE
3x1-2 1-1900 <$1250/$2000
4x5 1-2350 <$1250
50-100 1-200 <$5000
Series 1875
50-100 1-25 <$5000
Total Issue $90,250
Out in 1910 $655
****
6750 Howard
FNB OF LIME SPRINGS
{{ 3 L 10 S }}
Chartered 4/03
Liquidated 6/20/34
1902 Red Seal <$VALUE
3x10-20 1-356 <$1000
1902 Date Back
3x10-20 1-1830 <$450
1902 Plain Back
3x10-20 1831-4563 <$450
1929 Small Size
10 Type 1 1-526 <$150
20 Type 1 1-130 <$150
10 Type 2 1-42 <$175
20 Type 2 1-54 <$175
Total Issue $294,610
Out at close $25,000
Large out at close $1,650
****
7261 Wayne
FNB OF LINEVILLE
{{ 3 L }}
Organized 4/23/04
Receivership 4/9/27
1902 Red Seal <$VALUE
3x10-20 1-300 <$1000
1902 Date Back
3x10-20 1-1780 <$450
1902 Plain Back
3x10-20 1781-4439 <$450
Total Issue $236,950
Out at close $24,300
****
7137 Buena Vista
FNB OF LINN GROVE
{{ 3 L 6 S }}
Chartered 1904
Liquidated 8/25/30
1902 Red Seal <$VALUE
3x10-20 1-732 <$1000
1902 Date Back
3x10-20 1-1090* <$450
1902 Plain Back
3x10-20 1251-3788* <$450
* 1091-1250 not marked
1929 Small Size
10 Type 1 1-180 <$250
20 Type 1 1-13 <$250
Total Issue $238,360
Out in 1929 $19,000
Large out 1931 $5,430
****
2182 Linn
FNB OF LISBON
{{ 1 L }}
Chartered 9/10/74
Liquidated 11/1/81
Original Series <$VALUE
4x5 1-2250 <$1500
Series 1875
4x5 1-2245 <$1500
Total Issue $89,900
Out in 1910 $580
****
8119 Lyon
FNB, LITTLE ROCK
{{ 3 L 3 S }}
Organized 1/24/06
Receivership 10/31/33
1902 Red Seal <$VALUE
3x10-20 1-900 <$1000
1902 Date Back
3x10-20 1-1560 <$450
1902 Plain Back
3x10-20 1561-4531 <$450
1929 Small Size
10 Type 1 1-452 <$350
20 Type 1 1-132 <$350
Total Issue $314,510
Out at close $25,000
Large out at close $2,540
****
6771 Harrison
FNB OF LOGAN
{{ 7 L 7 S }}
Chartered 5/03
1902 Red Seal <$VALUE
4x5 1-1775 <$500
3x10-20 1-2040 <$500
1902 Date Back
4x5 1-3575 <$250
3x10-20 1-2320 <$250
1902 Plain Back
4x5 3576-10320 <$250
3x10-20 2321-6721 <$250
1929 Small Size
5 Type 1 1-1754 <$150
10 Type 1 1-806 <$150
20 Type 1 1-204 <$150
5 Type 2 1-312 <$175
10 Type 2 1-299 <$175
20 Type 2 1-30 <$175
Total Issue $810,560
Out in 1935 $24,995
Large out 1935 $3,395
****
12248 Union
FNB OF LORIMOR
{{ 3 L 10 S }}
Organized 8/7/22
Receivership 9/5/33
1902 Plain Back <$VALUE
3x10-20 1-3178 <$450
1929 Small Size
10 Type 1 1-742 <$110
20 Type 1 1-226 <$110
Total Issue $230,540
Out at close $35,000
Large out at close $1,260
****
5402 Clinton
FNB OF LOST NATION
{{ 4 L 4 S }}
Organized 5/2/00
Receivership 1/11/32
Brown Back <$VALUE
4x5 1-400 <$1250
3x10-20 1-320 <$1250
1882 Date Back
4x5 1-850* <$1250
3x10-20 1-680** <$1250
1882 Value Back
4x5 951-1070* <$1250
3x10-20 761-830** <$1250
* 851-950 not marked
** 681-760 not marked
1902 Plain Back
3x10-20 1-1075 <$750
1929 Small Size
10 Type 1 1-200 <$600
20 Type 1 1-34 <$600
Total Issue $156,730
Out at close $11,010
Large out at close $1,640
****
4536 Clinton
CITIZENS NB OF LYONS
{{ 1 L }}
Chartered 3/23/91
Liquidated 6/11/00
Brown Back <$VALUE
3x10-20 1-1307 <$1500
Total Issue $65,350
Out in 1910 $1,000
****
66 Clinton
FNB OF LYONS*
Chartered 1863
Liquidated 6/15/82
*Rechartered as Ch 2733
which retook Ch 66 8/8/11
Liquidated 10/7/30
2nd title: FNB of Lyons at
Clinton 6/6/22
FIRST TITLE {{ 7 L }}
Original Series <$VALUE
3x1-2 1-2000 <$500/$1500
4x5 1-2250 <$650
4x10 1-1675 <$1000
4x20 1-750 <$1500
Series 1875
4x20 1-758 <$1500
1902 Date Back
4x10 1-1500 <$250
1902 Plain Back (dated 1902)
4x10 1501-8750 <$250
SECOND TITLE {{ 2 L }}
1902 Plain Back (dated 1922)
4x10 1-3418 <$250
Total Issue $729,360
Out at close $8,515
Outstanding includes Ch 2733
****
2733 Clinton
FNB OF LYONS
{{ 3 L }}
Chartered 1882
RETOOK Ch 66 8/8/11
Brown Back <$VALUE
4x5 1-1000 <$600
3x10-20 1-5686 <$600
1902 Red Seal
3x10-20 1-2400 <$650
1902 Date Back
3x10-20 1-2500 <$350
Total Issue $549,300
Out in 1911 $100,000
****
6852 Madison
MACKSBURG NB, MACKSBURG
{{ 1 L 0 S }}
Organized 5/13/03
Liquidated 5/15/30
1902 Red Seal <$VALUE
3x10-20 1-357 <$2000
1902 Date Back
3x10-20 1-660 <$1000
1902 Plain Back
3x10-20 661-1208 <$1000
1929 Small Size
10 Type 1 1-46 <$650
20 Type 1 1-10 <$650
Total Issue $82,210
Out at close $6,010
Large out at close $2,050
****
4834 Mills
FARMERS NB OF MALVERN
{{ UNREPORTED }}
Chartered 1/5/93
Liquidated 8/6/96
Brown Back <$VALUE
50-100 1-120 <$3000
Total Issue $18,000
Out in 1910 $250
****
2247 Mills
FNB OF MALVERN
{{ 5 L }}
Organized 2/9/75
Receivership 12/10/26
Original Series <$VALUE
4x5 1-2500 <$750
Series 1875
4x5 1-3498 <$750
Brown Back
3x10-20 1-1112 <$500
1882 Date Back
4x5 1-580 <$500
3x10-20 1-391 <$500
1902 Date Back
3x10-20 1-500 <$350
1902 Plain Back
3x10-20 501-1281 <$350
Total Issue $170,760
Out at close $12,500
****
8057 Mills
MALVERN NB, MALVERN
{{ 2 L 0 S }}
Chartered 1/06
Liquidated 12/6/29
1902 Red Seal <$VALUE
3x10-20 1-460 <$1500
1902 Date Back
3x10-20 1-1220 <$750
1902 Plain Back
3x10-20 1221-2432 <$750
1929 Small Size
10 Type 1 1-33 <$650
20 Type 1 1-5 <$650
Total Issue $147,180
Out at close $12,500
Large out at close $2,170
****
4221 Delaware
FNB OF MANCHESTER
{{ 7 L }}
Organized 1/17/90
Receivership 2/13/29
Brown Back <$VALUE
4x5 1-2350 <$450
3x10-20 1-620 <$450
1882 Date Back
4x5 1-33 <$450
3x10-20 1-49 <$450
1902 Date Back
3x10-20 1-2750 <$250
1902 Plain Back
3x10-20 2751-7760 <$250
Total Issue $469,110
Out at close $39,445
****
5873 Crawford
FNB OF MANILLA
{{ 6 L 7 S }}
Organized 6/14/01
Receivership 1/30/33
Brown Back <$VALUE
3x10-20 1-400 <$500
1882 Date Back
3x10-20 1-1640 <$500
1882 Value Back
3x10-20 1641-2720 <$500
1902 Plain Back
3x10-20 1-1989 <$300
1929 Small Size
10 Type 1 1-409 <$175
20 Type 1 1-121 <$175
Total Issue $294,510
Out at close $25,000
Large out at close $3,540
****
6041 Crawford
MANILLA NB, MANILLA
{{ 3 L }}
Organized 11/12/01
Receivership 10/20/25
Brown Back <$VALUE
3x10-20 1-400 <$750
1882 Date Back
3x10-20 1-1120 <$750
1882 Value Back
3x10-20 1121-2050 <$750
1902 Plain Back
3x10-20 1-780 <$450
Total Issue $161,500
Out at close $18,450
****
3455 Carroll
FNB OF MANNING
{{ 7 L 13 S }}
Chartered 2/12/86
Brown Back <$VALUE
4x5 1-4270 <$400
50-100 1-550 <$1250/$1500
1902 Red Seal
3x10-20 1-900 <$500
1902 Date Back
3x10-20 1-4740 <$250
1902 Plain Back
3x10-20 4741-12514 <$250
1929 Small Size
10 Type 1 1-1574 <$85
20 Type 1 1-446 <$85
10 Type 2 1-1318 <$100
20 Type 2 1-308 <$100
Total Issue $1,005,900
Out in 1935 $75,000
Large out 1935 $4,580
****
999 Jackson
FNB OF MAQUOKETA
{{ 3 L 4 S }}
Organized 2/20/65
Receivership 6/28/32
Original Series <$VALUE
4x5 1-2450 <$850
3x10-20 1-840 <$1000/$1500
Series 1875
4x5 1-370 <$850
3x10-20 1-1086<$1000/$1500
Brown Back
3x10-20 1-1800 <$650
1902 Red Seal
3x10-20 1-1250 <$750
1902 Date Back
3x10-20 1-700 <$350
1902 Plain Back
3x10-20 701-3556 <$350
1929 Small Size
10 Type 1 1-468 <$250
20 Type 1 1-111 <$250
Total Issue $524,400
Out at close $27,320
Large out at close $3,740
****
4789 Buena Vista
FNB, MARATHON
{{ 2 L 3 S }}
Organized 8/1/92
Receivership 10/31/33
Brown Back <$VALUE
3x10-20 1-1270 <$1000
1882 Date Back
3x10-20 1-333 <$1000
1902 Date Back
3x10-20 1-750 <$750
1902 Plain Back
3x10-20 751-1871 <$750
1929 Small Size
10 Type 1 1-277 <$400
20 Type 1 1-58 <$400
Total Issue $197,280
Out at close $12,500
Large out at close $1,420
****
9819 Cherokee
FNB, MARCUS
{{ 1 L }}
Organized 6/22/10
Receivership 5/18/21
1902 Date Back <$VALUE
3x10-20 1-2350 <$1000
1902 Plain Back
3x10-20 2351-2794 <$1000
Total Issue $139,700
Out at close $21,800
****
2484 Iowa
FNB OF MARENGO
{{ 12 L }}
Organized 5/5/80
Receivership 2/18/27
Series 1875 <$VALUE
4x5 1-2163 <$500
3x10-20 1-1675 <$750/$1250
Brown Back
3x10-20 1-2800 <$300
1882 Date Back
3x10-20 1-2740 <$300
1882 Value Back
3x10-20 2741-3993 <$300
1902 Plain Back
3x10-20 1-2960 <$175
Total Issue $614,660
Out at close $40,600
****
117 Linn
FNB OF MARION*
{{ 6 L 10 S }}
Chartered 1863
Liquidated 7/11/82
*Rechartered as Ch 2753
which retook Ch 117 5/27/11
Original Series <$VALUE
3x1-2 1-1040 <$400/$1250
4x5 1-6350 <$450
Series 1875
4x5 1-3115 <$450
1902 Date Back
3x10-20 1-2100 <$200
1902 Plain Back
3x10-20 2101-8087 <$200
1929 Small Size
10 Type 1 1-1176 <$100
20 Type 1 1-308 <$100
10 Type 2 1-619 <$125
20 Type 2 1-120 <$125
Total Issue $714,960
Out in 1935 $50,000
Large out 1935 $4,790
Outstanding includes Ch 2753
****
2753 Linn
FNB OF MARION
{{ 4 L }}
Chartered 1882
RETOOK Ch 117 5/27/11
Brown Back <$VALUE
4x5 1-4991 <$500
3x10-20 1-183 <$500
1902 Red Seal
3x10-20 1-645 <$500
1902 Date Back
3x10-20 1-700 <$350
Total Issue $176,220
Out in 1911 $50,000
****

4359 Marshall
CITY NB OF MARSHALLTOWN
{{ UNREPORTED }}
Chartered 7/8/90
Liquidated 5/4/08
Brown Back <$VALUE
4x5 1-4478 <$1500
3x10-20 1-980 <$1500
Total Issue $138,560
Out in 1910 $7,020

2971 Marshall
COMMERCIAL NB OF MARSHALLTOWN
{{ UNREPORTED }}
Chartered 6/9/83
Liquidated 10/25/86
Brown Back <$VALUE
3x10-20 1-587 <$1500
Total Issue $29,350
Out in 1910 $150

2115 Marshall
FARMERS NB OF MARSHALLTOWN
{{ 1 L }}
Chartered 6/30/73
Liquidated 9/18/75
Original Series <$VALUE
4x5 1-1590 <$1500
Total Issue $31,800
Out in 1910 $125

411 Marshall
FNB OF MARSHALLTOWN
{{ 3 L }}
Organized 4/25/64
Receivership 6/11/28
Original Series <$VALUE
3x1-2 1-4190 <$650/$1500
4x5 1-10450 <$750
Series 1875
3x1-2 1-500 <$650/$1500
4x5 1-1452 <$750
Brown Back
50-100 1-902 <$1500/$1750
1902 Red Seal
50-100 1-644 <$2250/$2500
1902 Date Back
50-100 1-800 <$700/$850
3x50-100 1-450 <$700/$850
1902 Plain Back
3x50-100 451-507<$700/$850
Total Issue $740,140
Out at close $49,750

4587 Cerro Gordo
CITY NB OF MASON CITY
{{ 5 L }}
Chartered 1891
Liquidated 2/19/21
Brown Back <$VALUE
3x10-20 1-6940 <$450
1882 Date Back
3x10-20 1-1861 <$450
1902 Date Back
3x10-20 1-5600 <$300
1902 Plain Back
3x10-20 5601-13180 <$300
Total Issue $1,099,050
Out at close $197,500

2574 Cerro Gordo
FNB OF MASON CITY
{{ 28 L 34 S }}
Chartered 1881
Series 1875 <$VALUE
3x10-20 1-3643 <$750/$1250
Brown Back
3x10-20 1-7300 <$250
1882 Date Back
3x10-20 1-13900* <$250
1882 Value Back
3x10-20 14901-26138* <$250
* 13901-14900 not marked
1902 Plain Back
3x10-20 1-20492 <$100
1929 Small Size
10 Type 1 1-5426 <$40
20 Type 1 1-1544 <$50
10 Type 2 1-2737 <$40
20 Type 2 1-360 <$50
Total Issue $3,424,060
Out in 1935 $200,000
Large out 1935 $15,290

10428 Cerro Gordo
SECURITY NB OF MASON CITY
{{ 6 L }}
Organized 7/16/13
Receivership 12/29/25
1902 Date Back <$VALUE
4x5 1-3700 <$175
3x10-20 1-2760 <$175
1902 Plain Back
4x5 3701-13395 <$175
3x10-20 2761-9323 <$175
Total Issue $734,050
Out at close $97,900

323 Clayton
FNB OF McGREGOR
{{ 6 L 4 S }}
Chartered 12/19/63
Liquidated 5/29/33
Original Series <$VALUE
3x1-2 1-2600 <$400/$1250
4x5 1-5500 <$500
3x10-20 1-1190 <$750/$1250
Series 1875
3x1-2 1-660 <$400/$1250
4x5 1-2705 <$500
3x10-20 1-1000 <$750/$1250
Brown Back
3x10-20 1-3824 <$450
1902 Red Seal
3x10-20 1-1000 <$500
1902 Date Back
3x10-20 1-1200* <$250
1902 Plain Back
3x10-20 1401-3528* <$250
* 1201-1400 not marked
1929 Small Size
10 Type 1 1-410 <$250
20 Type 1 1-104 <$250
Total Issue $744,580
Out at close $25,000
Large out at close $4,910

5616 Osceola
FNB, MELVIN
{{ 3 L }}
Organized 10/9/00
Receivership 2/12/29
Brown Back <$VALUE
3x10-20 1-920 <$750
1882 Date Back
3x10-20 1-940 <$750
1882 Value Back
3x10-20 941-1183 <$750
1902 Plain Back
4x5 1-3259 <$450
Total Issue $170,330
Out at close $12,500

5539 Dickinson
FNB OF MILFORD
{{ 6 L }}
Organized 8/3/00
Receivership 7/8/26
Brown Back <$VALUE
3x10-20 1-1080 <$500
1882 Date Back
3x10-20 1-2160 <$500
1882 Value Back
3x10-20 2161-2594 <$500
1902 Plain Back
3x10-20 1-1608 <$350
Total Issue $264,100
Out at close $24,000

9298 Dickinson
MILFORD NB, MILFORD
Organized 11/27/08
Receivership 5/11/31
2nd title: Security NB of Milford 10/10/21
FIRST TITLE {{ 3 L }}
1902 Date Back <$VALUE
3x10-20 1-2120 <$450
1902 Plain Back
3x10-20 2121-3360 <$450
SECOND TITLE {{ 3 L 4 S }}
1902 Plain Back
3x10-20 1-1990 <$450
1929 Small Size
10 Type 1 1-318 <$300
20 Type 1 1-84 <$300
Total Issue $296,660
Out at close $25,000
Large out at close $4,380

Security NB of Milford
SEE Ch 9298
Milford NB, Milford

10243 Van Buren
NB OF MILTON
{{ 3 L 3 S }}
Organized 8/9/12
Receivership 6/25/32
1902 Date Back <$VALUE
3x10-20 1-510 <$500
1902 Plain Back
3x10-20 511-1115 <$500
1929 Small Size
10 Type 1 1-120 <$500
20 Type 1 1-15 <$500
Total Issue $64,750
Out at close $7,000
Large out at close $1,550

3189 Harrison
FNB OF MISSOURI VALLEY
{{ 8 L 10 S }}
Chartered 1884
Brown Back <$VALUE
4x5 1-5715 <$400
50-100 1-398 <$1250/$1500
1902 Red Seal
3x10-20 1-1900 <$400
1902 Date Back
3x10-20 1-3040 <$200
1902 Plain Back
3x10-20 3041-9329 <$200
1929 Small Size
10 Type 1 1-1196 <$110
20 Type 1 1-309 <$110
Total Issue $844,290
Out in 1935 $30,000
Large out 1935 $4,170

2215 Jasper
FNB OF MONROE
{{ 2 L }}
Chartered 1/9/75
Liquidated 1/1/77
Original Series <$VALUE
3x1-2 1-1000 <$850/$2000
4x5 1-1000 <$850
3x10-20 1-400 <$1250/$2000
Total Issue $45,000
Out in 1910 $184

7357 Jasper
MONROE NB, MONROE
{{ 1 L 0 S }}
Chartered 8/04
Liquidated 8/7/31
1902 Red Seal <$VALUE
3x10-20 1-400 <$1500
1902 Date Back
3x10-20 1-600 <$850
1902 Plain Back
3x10-20 601-1168 <$850
1929 Small Size
10 Type 1 1-92 <$600
20 Type 1 1-11 <$600
Total Issue $85,240
Out at close $7,000
Large out at close $1,480

2961 Poweshiek
FNB OF MONTEZUMA
{{ 3 L 0 S }}
Organized 5/21/83
Receivership 9/16/29
Brown Back <$VALUE
3x10-20 1-2580 <$850
1902 Red Seal
3x10-20 1-2300 <$850
1902 Date Back
3x10-20 1-2980 <$400
1902 Plain Back
3x10-20 2981-9174 <$400
1929 Small Size
10 Type 1 1-21* <$750
* F000021A not issued
Total Issue $703,950
Out at close $48,850
Large out at close $47,600

2080 Jones
MONTICELLO NB, MONTICELLO
{{ 1 L }}
Chartered 2/3/73
Liquidated 3/30/75
Original Series <$VALUE
3x1-2 1-1500 <$1000/$2000
3x10-20 1-823 <$1500/$2000
Total Issue $48,650
Out in 1910 $121

7469 Tama
FNB OF MONTOUR
{{ 7 L 12 S }}
Organized 10/25/04
Receivership 11/16/33
1902 Red Seal <$VALUE
3x10-20 1-796 <$450
1902 Date Back
3x10-20 1-1910 <$200
1902 Plain Back
3x10-20 1911-5524 <$200
1929 Small Size
10 Type 1 1-578 <$100
20 Type 1 1-178 <$100
Total Issue $372,040
Out at close $30,000
Large out at close $2,390

5319 Appanoose
FNB OF MOULTON
{{ 3 L }}
Organized 4/5/00
Receivership 1/14/27
Brown Back <$VALUE
3x10-20 1-1700 <$750
1882 Date Back
3x10-20 1-2480 <$750
1882 Value Back
3x10-20 2481-3566 <$750
1902 Plain Back
4x10 1-3490 <$450
Total Issue $402,900
Out at close $33,800

299 Henry
FNB OF MOUNT PLEASANT
{{ 14 L 7 S }}
Chartered 1864
Liquidated 1/13/31
Original Series <$VALUE
3x1-2 1-3700 <$400/$1000
4x5 1-2900 <$450
3x10-20 1-1730 <$750/$1250
Series 1875
3x10-20 1-648 <$750/$1250
Brown Back
3x10-20 1-4762 <$300
1902 Red Seal
3x10-20 1-4500 <$300
1902 Date Back
4x5 1-7715 <$135
3x10-20 1-4600 <$135
1902 Plain Back
4x5 7716-18835 <$135
3x10-20 4601-12128 <$135
1929 Small Size
5 Type 1 1-1369 <$150
10 Type 1 1-602 <$150
20 Type 1 1-165 <$150
Total Issue $1,738,590
Out at close $99,995
Large out at close $19,195

922 Henry
N STATE B OF MOUNT PLEASANT
{{ 7 L }}
Chartered 1865
Liquidated 3/10/22
Original Series <$VALUE
3x1-2 1-2910 <$400/$1250
4x5 1-3300 <$500
3x10-20 1-2100 <$750/$1250
Series 1875
4x5 1-483 <$500
3x10-20 1-2187 <$750/$1250
Brown Back
3x10-20 1-6449 <$350
1902 Red Seal
3x10-20 1-3400 <$400
1902 Date Back
3x10-20 1-5800 <$200
1902 Plain Back
3x10-20 5801-10646 <$200
Total Issue $1,329,310
Out at close $88,200

FNB of Muscatine
SEE Ch 1577
Merchants Exchange NB of Muscatine

1577 Muscatine
MERCHANTS EXCHANGE NB OF MUSCATINE
Chartered 1865
Liquidated 7/8/33
2nd title:FNB of Muscatine 6/8/86
FIRST TITLE {{ 1 L }}
Original Series <$VALUE
4x5 1-1825 <$1000
3x10-20 1-820 <$1250/$1500
Series 1875
4x5 1-100 <$1000
3x10-20 1-1070<$1250/$1500
Brown Back
4x5 1-141 <$750
3x10-20 1-46 <$750
50-100 1-13 <$1250/$1500
SECOND TITLE {{ 8 L 28 S }}
Brown Back
4x5 1-2590 <$300
3x10-20 1-1601 <$300
1902 Red Seal
4x5 1-700 <$350
3x10-20 1-390 <$350
1902 Date Back
4x5 1-2015 <$150
3x10-20 1-1614 <$150
1902 Plain Back
4x5 2016-4618 <$150
3x10-20 1615-3123 <$150
1929 Small Size
5 Type 1 1-2119 <$35
10 Type 1 1-1753 <$35
20 Type 1 1-460 <$45
Total Issue $777,880
Out at close $200,000
Large out at close $3,415

692 Muscatine
MUSCATINE NB, MUSCATINE
{{ 1 L }}
Chartered 1865
Liquidated 9/2/78
Original Series <$VALUE
4x5 1-2500 <$1250
3x10-20 1-222 <$1750/$2000
Series 1875
3x10-20 1-144 <$1750/$2000
Total Issue $168,200
Out in 1910 $1,215

2411 Chickasaw
FNB OF NASHUA
{{ 1 L }}
Chartered 2/15/79
Liquidated 11/1/94
Series 1875 <$VALUE
3x10-20 1-2203<$1750/$2000
Total Issue $110,150
Out in 1910 $570

2555 Story
FNB OF NEVADA
{{ 14 L }}
Organized 8/3/81
Receivership 1/10/27
Series 1875 <$VALUE
4x10 1-3332 <$600
Brown Back
50-100 1-827 <$1250/$1500
1882 Date Back
4x5 1-5330 <$250
50-100 1-500 <$1250/$1500
3x50-100 1-504<$1250/$1500
1882 Value Back
4x5 5331-8680 <$250
1902 Plain Back
4x5 1-13194 <$125
Total Issue $895,810
Out at close $73,300

14065 Story
NEVADA NB, NEVADA
{{ 3 S }}
Chartered 3/34
1929 Small Size <$VALUE
5 Type 2 1-2460 <$350
10 Type 2 1-1260 <$350
20 Type 2 1-300 <$350
Total Issue $30,900
Out in 1935 $25,000

2588 Chickasaw
FNB OF NEW HAMPTON
{{ 7 L }}
Organized 5/3/81
Receivership 12/9/26
Series 1875 <$VALUE
4x5 1-4502 <$500
Brown Back
4x5 1-1525 <$300
3x10-20 1-1120 <$300
1882 Date Back
4x5 1-2900 <$300
3x10-20 1-2060 <$300
1882 Value Back
4x5 2901-4398 <$300
3x10-20 2061-2914 <$300
1902 Plain Back
4x5 1-2937 <$150
3x10-20 1-2704 <$150
Total Issue $577,100
Out at close $43,200

7607 Chickasaw
SECOND NB OF NEW HAMPTON
{{ 13 L 6 S }}
Organized 1/3/05
Receivership 7/14/31
1902 Red Seal <$VALUE
3x10-20 1-2100 <$300
1902 Date Back
3x10-20 1-6100 <$125
1902 Plain Back
3x10-20 6101-17422 <$125
1929 Small Size
10 Type 1 1-1138 <$150
20 Type 1 1-313 <$150
Total Issue $1,081,940
Out at close $100,000
Large out at close $19,670

5420 Henry
FNB OF NEW LONDON
{{ 1 L }}
Chartered 6/13/00
Liquidated 12/31/09
Brown Back <$VALUE
3x10-20 1-1800 <$1500
1882 Date Back
3x10-20 1-48 <$1500
Total Issue $92,400
Out in 1910 $14,870

8352 Henry
NEW LONDON NB, NEW LONDON
{{ 3 L 2 S }}
Organized 8/22/06
Receivership 10/30/33
1902 Red Seal <$VALUE
4x10 1-775 <$1000
1902 Date Back
4x10 1-1925 <$450
1902 Plain Back
4x10 1926-5377 <$450
1929 Small Size
10 Type 1 1-686 <$400
Total Issue $287,240
Out at close $20,000
Large out at close $1,570

8950 Mahaska
FNB OF NEW SHARON
{{ 4 L }}
Chartered 11/07
Liquidated 6/1/26
1902 Red Seal <$VALUE
4x5 1-667 <$750
4x10 1-635 <$750
1902 Date Back
4x5 1-3250 <$375
4x10 1-2950 <$375
1902 Plain Back
4x5 3251-8399 <$375
4x10 2951-6885 <$375
Total Issue $482,120
Out at close $50,000

10191 Buena Vista
FNB, NEWELL
{{ 7 L 7 S }}
Organized 4/23/12
Receivership 9/18/33
1902 Date Back <$VALUE
3x10-20 1-1200 <$275
1902 Plain Back
3x10-20 1201-4251 <$275
1929 Small Size
10 Type 1 1-487 <$175
20 Type 1 1-123 <$175
Total Issue $256,530
Out at close $25,000
Large out at close $1,950

650 Jasper
FNB OF NEWTON
{{ 1 L }}
Chartered 1864
Liquidated 12/16/76
Original Series <$VALUE
3x1-2 1-2500 <$1000/$2000
4x5 1-1500 <$1000
3x10-20 1-1028<$1500/$2000
Total Issue $93,900
Out in 1910 $844

<$VALUEs are for notes in **FINE** condition. Value changes by approximately **25%** for a change of one full grade.

2644 Jasper
FNB OF NEWTON
{{ 6 L 5 S }}
Chartered 1882
Liquidated 8/1/32
Series 1875 <$VALUE
50-100 1-1321 <$4000
Brown Back
4x5 1-1450 <$400
50-100 1-523 <$1250/$1500
1882 Date Back
4x5 1-3875 <$400
50-100 1-300 <$1250/$1500
3x50-100 1-328<$1250/$1500
1882 Value Back
4x5 3876-8904 <$400
1902 Plain Back
4x5 1-5860 <$200
3x10-20 1-3322 <$200
1929 Small Size
5 Type 1 1-1273 <$175
10 Type 1 1-627 <$175
20 Type 1 1-174 <$175
Total Issue $924,620
Out at close $65,000
Large out at close $9,550
Ch 13609 assumed circulation

13609 Jasper
NEWTON NB, NEWTON
{{ 8 S }}
Chartered 3/32
1929 Small Size <$VALUE
5 Type 1 1-810 <$125
10 Type 1 1-394 <$125
20 Type 1 1-108 <$135
5 Type 2 1-1394 <$135
10 Type 2 1-1054 <$135
20 Type 2 1-307 <$150
Total Issue $84,550
Out in 1935 $64,400
Large out 1935 $4,310
Outstanding includes Ch 2644

4761 Floyd
FNB OF NORA SPRINGS
{{ 4 L 5 S }}
Chartered 1892
Brown Back <$VALUE
3x10-20 1-1300 <$650
1882 Date Back
3x10-20 1-795 <$650
1902 Date Back
3x10-20 1-1200 <$375
1902 Plain Back
3x10-20 1201-3858 <$375
1929 Small Size
10 Type 1 1-583 <$250
20 Type 1 1-155 <$250
Total Issue $351,230
Out in 1935 $25,000
Large out 1935 $1,730

9015 Page
FNB OF NORTHBORO
{{ 6 L 3 S }}
Organized 1/17/08
Receivership 9/16/32
1902 Red Seal <$VALUE
4x10 1-468 <$500
1902 Date Back
4x10 1-2525 <$250
1902 Plain Back
4x10 2526-7297 <$250
1929 Small Size
5 Type 1 1-338 <$200
10 Type 1 1-707 <$200
Total Issue $363,160
Out at close $25,000
Large out at close $1,970

8373 Worth
FNB OF NORTHWOOD
{{ 4 L 10 S }}
Organized 8/20/06
Receivership 8/8/32
1902 Red Seal <$VALUE
3x10-20 1-1100 <$600
1902 Date Back
3x10-20 1-3200 <$375
1902 Plain Back
3x10-20 3201-9135 <$375
1929 Small Size
10 Type 1 1-837 <$125
20 Type 1 1-217 <$125
Total Issue $588,010
Out at close $49,700
Large out at close $5,840

7287 Benton
FNB OF NORWAY
{{ 3 L }}
Organized 5/23/04
Receivership 3/23/27
1902 Red Seal <$VALUE
3x10-20 1-1320 <$850
1902 Date Back
3x10-20 1-1600 <$450
1902 Plain Back
3x10-20 1601-4264 <$450
Total Issue $279,200
Out at close $25,000

5817 Sac
FARMERS NB OF ODEBOLT
{{ 2 L }}
Chartered 5/16/01
Liquidated 1/7/14
Brown Back <$VALUE
3x10-20 1-2500 <$850
1882 Date Back
3x10-20 1-2218 <$850
Total Issue $235,900
Out at close $50,000
Ch 4511 assumed circulation

4511 Sac
FNB OF ODEBOLT
{{ 14 L 18 S }}
Chartered 1891
Liquidated 6/18/34
Brown Back <$VALUE
3x10-20 1-4090 <$350
1882 Date Back
3x10-20 1-464 <$350
1902 Date Back
3x10-20 1-4100 <$135
1902 Plain Back
3x10-20 4101-15754 <$135
1929 Small Size
5 Type 1 1-4558 <$75
10 Type 1 1-1230 <$75
20 Type 1 1-416 <$85
Total Issue $1,275,860
Out in 1933 $99,160
Large out at close $8,260
Outstanding includes Ch 5817

5778 Fayette
FNB OF OELWEIN
{{ 28 L 10 S }}
Chartered 4/01
Brown Back <$VALUE
3x10-20 1-1600 <$250
1882 Date Back
3x10-20 1-2540 <$250
1882 Value Back
3x10-20 2541-3866 <$250
1902 Plain Back
3x10-20 1-3656 <$100
1929 Small Size
10 Type 1 1-1016 <$100
20 Type 1 1-282 <$100
5 Type 2 1-324 <$100
10 Type 2 1-1343 <$100
20 Type 2 1-181 <$100
Total Issue $569,570
Out in 1935 $50,000
Large out 1935 $3,585

7585 Jones
FNB OF OLIN
{{ 3 L }}
Chartered 1/05
Liquidated 5/21/26
1902 Red Seal <$VALUE
3x10-20 1-1050 <$750
1902 Date Back
3x10-20 1-1560 <$375
1902 Plain Back
3x10-20 1561-3813 <$375
Total Issue $243,150
Out at close $25,000

6132 Sioux
FNB, ORANGE CITY
{{ UNREPORTED }}
Chartered 2/20/02
Liquidated 11/21/05
1902 Red Seal <$VALUE
3x10-20 1-239 <$2500
Total Issue $11,950
Out in 1910 $880

4885 Mitchell
FARMERS NB OF OSAGE
Chartered 1893
2nd title: Osage Farmers NB, Osage 1/5/27
FIRST TITLE {{ 3 L }}
Brown Back <$VALUE
3x10-20 1-1320 <$650
1882 Date Back
3x10-20 1-355 <$650
1902 Date Back
3x10-20 1-700 <$450
1902 Plain Back
3x10-20 701-1277 <$450
SECOND TITLE {{ 10 S }}
1929 Small Size
10 Type 1 1-826 <$125
20 Type 1 1-304 <$125
50 Type 1 1-128 <$275
10 Type 2 1-1499 <$150
20 Type 2 1-305 <$150
Total Issue $293,130
Out in 1935 $100,000
Large out 1935 $540

Osage Farmers NB, Osage
SEE Ch 4885
Farmers NB of Osage

1618 Mitchell
OSAGE NB, OSAGE
{{ 10 L }}
Chartered 1865
Liquidated 4/18/27
Original Series <$VALUE
3x1-2 1-1090 <$400/$1250
4x5 1-2277* <$400
3x10-20 1-800 <$850/$1500
* 2211-2225 not issued
Series 1875
3x10-20 1-964 <$750/$1250
Brown Back
50-100 1-714 <$1250/$1500
1902 Red Seal
50-100 1-253 <$2250/$2500
1902 Date Back
50-100 1-330 <$500/$600
3x50-100 1-273 <$500/$600
Total Issue $401,690
Out at close $25,000

1776 Clarke
FNB OF OSCEOLA
{{ 1 L }}
Chartered 1/26/71
Receivership 2/25/76
Original Series <$VALUE
3x1-2 1-1500 <$1000/$2000
4x5 1-2875 <$1000
Series 1875
4x5 1-340 <$1000
Total Issue $71,800
Out in 1915 $410

6033 Clarke
OSCEOLA NB, OSCEOLA
{{ 3 L }}
Organized 10/8/01
Receivership 4/22/25
Brown Back <$VALUE
4x5 1-950 <$650
3x10-20 1-865 <$650
1882 Date Back
4x5 1-1600 <$650
3x10-20 1-1080 <$650
1882 Value Back
4x5 1601-2875 <$650
3x10-20 1081-1855 <$650
1902 Plain Back
3x10-20 1-878 <$450
Total Issue $256,400
Out at close $25,000

2895 Mahaska
FARMERS & TRADERS NB OF OSKALOOSA
{{ UNREPORTED }}
Chartered 3/5/83
Liquidated 7/30/92
Brown Back <$VALUE
4x5 1-1075 <$1500
3x10-20 1-850 <$1500
Total Issue $64,000
Out in 1910 $380

8076 Mahaska
FARMERS NB OF OSKALOOSA
{{ 7 L }}
Organized 1/24/06
Liquidated 2/21/28
1902 Red Seal <$VALUE
3x10-20 1-890 <$650
1902 Date Back
3x10-20 1-3900 <$275
1902 Plain Back
3x10-20 3901-9112 <$275
Total Issue $500,100
Out at close $50,000

---
147 Mahaska
FNB OF OSKALOOSA
{{ UNREPORTED }}
Chartered 12/10/63
Liquidated 12/17/68
Original Series <$VALUE
3x1-2 1-1000 <$1500/$2500
4x5 1-2525 <$1500
3x10-20 1-270 <$2000/$2500
Total Issue $69,000
Out in 1910 $488

1101 Mahaska
N STATE B OF OSKALOOSA
{{ 1 L }}
Chartered 1865
Liquidated 8/13/81
Original Series <$VALUE
4x5 1-2775 <$1000
4x10 1-2900 <$1500
Series 1875
4x10 1-1447 <$1500
Total Issue $229,380
Out in 1910 $1,505

2417 Mahaska
OSKALOOSA NB, OSKALOOSA
{{ 6 L }}
Organized 3/6/79
Receivership 1/20/32
Series 1875 <$VALUE
3x10-20 1-1892 <$750/$1250
Brown Back
3x10-20 1-4420 <$400
1882 Date Back
3x10-20 1-6500* <$400
1882 Value Back
3x10-20 7001-8540* <$400
* 6501-7000 not marked
1902 Plain Back
3x10-20 1-5964 <$250
Total Issue $1,040,800
Out at close $7,550

---
107 Wapello
FNB OF OTTUMWA
{{ 11 L 10 S }}
Chartered 1863
Liquidated 10/29/31
Original Series <$VALUE
4x5 1-6500 <$400
Series 1875
4x5 1-4330 <$400
Brown Back
3x10-20 1-5000 <$275
50-100 1-944 <$1250/$1500
1902 Red Seal
50-100 1-2166 <$2250/$2500
1902 Date Back
50-100 1-1800 <$350/$400
3x50-100 1-2856 <$350/$400
1902 Plain Back
3x50-100 2857-3558 <$350/$400
1929 Small Size
50 Type 1 1-363 <$125
100 Type 1 1-102 <$150
Total Issue $2,262,700
Out at close $199,500
Large out at close $53,500

1726 Wapello
IOWA NB OF OTTUMWA
{{ 4 L 4 S }}
Chartered 10/70
Liquidated 8/20/31
Original Series <$VALUE
3x1-2 1-2000 <$500/$1000
4x5 1-4410 <$500
Series 1875
4x5 1-6685 <$500
Brown Back
50-100 1-2074 <$1200/$1500
1882 Date Back
50-100 1-287 <$1250/$1500
1902 Date Back
50-100 1-1000 <$500/$600
3x50-100 1-1200 <$500/$600
1902 Plain Back
3x50-100 1201-1579 <$500/$600
1929 Small Size
50 Type 1 1-181 <$175
100 Type 1 1-41 <$225
Total Issue $1,209,700
Out at close $100,000
Large out at close $29,350

2621 Wapello
OTTUMWA NB, OTTUMWA
{{ 13 L 5 S }}
Chartered 1882
Liquidated 10/26/31
Series 1875 <$VALUE
3x10-20 1-3472 <$750/$1250
Brown Back
3x10-20 1-4600 <$300
1882 Date Back
4x5 1-6815 <$300
3x10-20 1-4220 <$300
1882 Value Back
4x5 6816-12100 <$300
3x10-20 4221-7596 <$300
1902 Plain Back
3x50-100 1-1078 <$300/$350
1929 Small Size
50 Type 1 1-182 <$150
100 Type 1 1-39 <$200
Total Issue $1,372,900
Out at close $99,970
Large out at close $31,320

3226 Guthrie
GUTHRIE COUNTY NB OF PANORA
{{ 13 L }}
Organized 7/9/84
Receivership 7/22/26
Brown Back <$VALUE
3x10-20 1-2662 <$500
1902 Red Seal
3x10-20 1-1600 <$500
1902 Date Back
3x10-20 1-3300 <$225
1902 Plain Back
3x10-20 3301-7171 <$225
Total Issue $571,650
Out at close $49,100

9846 Butler
FNB OF PARKERSBURG
{{ 3 L }}
Chartered 9/10
Liquidated 11/14/16
1902 Date Back <$VALUE
4x5 1-3300 <$450
3x10-20 1-2560 <$450
1902 Plain Back
4x5 3301-3785 <$450
3x10-20 2561-2861 <$450
Total Issue $218,750
Out at close $60,000

8047 Marion
CITIZENS NB OF PELLA
{{ 3 L }}
Chartered 1/06
Liquidated 5/4/23
1902 Red Seal <$VALUE
3x10-20 1-300 <$1000
1902 Date Back
3x10-20 1-1750 <$450
1902 Plain Back
3x10-20 1751-2270 <$450
Total Issue $128,500
Out in 1922 $4,900

1891 Marion
FNB OF PELLA
{{ 1 L }}
Chartered 10/14/71
Receivership 6/5/95
Original Series <$VALUE
3x1-2 1-1500 <$1000/$2000
4x5 1-4375 <$1000
Series 1875
4x5 1-3290 <$1000
Brown Back
3x10-20 1-282 <$850
Total Issue $174,900
Out in 1915 $975

2063 Marion
PELLA NB, PELLA
{{ 12 L 12 S }}
Chartered 11/7/72
Original Series <$VALUE
4x5 1-1750 <$500
3x10-20 1-2500 <$750/$1250
Series 1875
3x10-20 1-3410 <$750/$1250
Brown Back
3x10-20 1-3680 <$400
1882 Date Back
3x10-20 1-1564 <$400
1902 Date Back
3x10-20 1-1500 <$175
1902 Plain Back
3x10-20 1501-6944 <$175
1929 Small Size
5 Type 1 1-4242 <$75
5 Type 2 1-8936 <$75
Total Issue $1,111,840
Out in 1935 $47,950
Large out 1935 $4,710

3026 Dallas
FNB OF PERRY
{{ 6 L }}
Chartered 1883
Brown Back <$VALUE
3x10-20 1-2000 <$500
1902 Red Seal
3x10-20 1-2150 <$600
1902 Date Back
3x10-20 1-3000 <$275
1902 Plain Back
3x10-20 3001-7775 <$275
Total Issue $596,250
Out in 1925 $50,000
Out in 1935 $2,940

10130 Dallas
PEOPLES NB OF PERRY
Organized 1/2/12
Receivership 2/5/25
2nd title: Perry NB 2/23/17
FIRST TITLE {{ 3 L }}
1902 Date Back <$VALUE
3x10-20 1-1055* <$400
* 1001-1055 not marked
SECOND TITLE {{ 6 L }}
1902 Plain Back
4x5 1-6270 <$275
3x10-20 1-4480 <$275
Total Issue $402,150
Out at close $72,300

Perry NB, Perry
SEE Ch 10130
Peoples NB of Perry

4601 Clay
FNB, PETERSON
{{ 5 L 7 S }}
Chartered 1891
Brown Back <$VALUE
3x10-20 1-2290 <$450
1882 Date Back
3x10-20 1-481 <$450
1902 Date Back
3x10-20 1-1400 <$300
1902 Plain Back
3x10-20 1401-7128 <$300
1929 Small Size
10 Type 1 1-1024 <$175
20 Type 1 1-286 <$175
10 Type 2 1-478 <$200
20 Type 2 1-178 <$200
Total Issue $599,050
Out in 1934 $25,000
Large out 1935 $2,840

5564 Marion
FNB OF PLEASANTVILLE
{{ 3 L }}
Chartered 8/30/00
Receivership 2/21/25
Brown Back <$VALUE
3x10-20 1-1800 <$650
1882 Date Back
3x10-20 1-1530 <$650
1882 Value Back
3x10-20 1531-2417 <$650
1902 Plain Back
3x10-20 1-1268 <$450
Total Issue $274,250
Out at close $24,700

6303 Pocahontas
FNB OF POCAHONTAS
{{ 4 L }}
Chartered 1902
Liquidated 7/9/24
1902 Red Seal <$VALUE
4x5 1-825 <$1000
3x10-20 1-660 <$1000
1902 Date Back
4x5 1-2125 <$450
3x10-20 1-1600 <$450
1902 Plain Back
4x5 2126-3855 <$450
3x10-20 1601-2542 <$450
Total Issue $253,700
Out in 1922 $24,700
Ch 12544 assumed circulation

****
12544 Pocahontas
FNB IN POCAHONTAS
{{ 3 L }}
Organized 5/12/24
Receivership 1/30/26
1902 Plain Back <$VALUE
4x5 1-155 <$650
3x10-20 1-352 <$650
Total Issue $20,700
Out at close $24,300
Outstanding includes Ch 6303
****
6063 Calhoun
FNB OF POMEROY
{{ 4 L 3 S }}
Organized 12/10/01
Receivership 5/5/31
Brown Back <$VALUE
4x5 1-1055 <$600
3x10-20 1-858 <$600
1882 Date Back
4x5 1-2850 <$600
3x10-20 1-2020 <$600
1882 Value Back
4x5 2851-5015 <$600
3x10-20 2021-3264 <$600
1902 Plain Back
4x5 1-9522 <$375
1929 Small Size
5 Type 1 1-2225 <$350
Total Issue $584,690
Out at close $40,000
Large out at close $4,100
****
6755 Jasper
FNB OF PRAIRIE CITY
{{ 3 L 6 S }}
Organized 4/14/03
1902 Red Seal <$VALUE
3x10-20 1-356 <$1000
1902 Date Back
3x10-20 1-1000 <$450
1902 Plain Back
3x10-20 1001-4219 <$450
1929 Small Size
10 Type 1 1-522 <$175
20 Type 1 1-150 <$175
10 Type 2 1-519 <$200
20 Type 2 1-105 <$200
Total Issue $285,360
Out in 1935 $25,000
Large out 1935 $1,260
****
5912 Adams
FNB OF PRESCOTT
{{ 6 L 10 S }}
Chartered 7/01
Brown Back <$VALUE
4x5 1-1475 <$400
3x10-20 1-1140 <$400
1882 Date Back
4x5 1-1575 <$400
3x10-20 1-1120 <$400
1882 Value Back
4x5 1576-2805 <$400
3x10-20 1121-1815 <$400
1902 Plain Back
4x5 1-2006 <$200
3x10-20 1-1331 <$200
1929 Small Size
5 Type 1 1-776 <$125
10 Type 1 1-386 <$125
20 Type 1 1-130 <$125
5 Type 2 1-260 <$135
10 Type 2 1-341 <$135
20 Type 2 1-65 <$150
Total Issue $408,070
Out in 1935 $24,995
Large out 1935 $1,555
****
8273 Jackson
FNB OF PRESTON
{{ 3 L 3 S }}
Chartered 6/06
Liquidated 8/25/31
1902 Red Seal <$VALUE
4x5 1-200 <$1000
3x10-20 1-160 <$1000
1902 Date Back
4x5 1-1725 <$450
3x10-20 1-1260 <$450
1902 Plain Back
4x5 1726-5202 <$450
3x10-20 1261-3384 <$450
1929 Small Size
5 Type 1 1-457 <$350
10 Type 1 1-209 <$350
20 Type 1 1-57 <$350
Total Issue $318,330
Out at close $25,000
Large out at close $3,350
****

****
6650 O'Brien
FARMERS NB OF PRIMGHAR
{{ UNREPORTED }}
Chartered 2/28/03
Liquidated 11/10/04
1902 Red Seal <$VALUE
3x10-20 1-197 <$2000
Total Issue $9,850
Out in 1910 $600
****
4155 O'Brien
FNB, PRIMGHAR
{{ 7 L 12 S }}
Organized 10/28/89
Brown Back <$VALUE
3x10-20 1-1484 <$400
1902 Date Back
3x10-20 1-1080 <$200
1902 Plain Back
3x10-20 1081-5406 <$200
1929 Small Size
10 Type 1 1-1182 <$100
20 Type 1 1-304 <$100
10 Type 2 1-726 <$110
20 Type 2 1-175 <$110
Total Issue $462,660
Out in 1934 $49,550
Large out 1935 $2,690
****
6435 Hardin
FNB OF RADCLIFFE
{{ 3 L 6 S }}
Organized 9/15/02
Liquidated 12/30/31
1902 Red Seal <$VALUE
3x10-20 1-730 <$1000
1902 Date Back
3x10-20 1-1200 <$450
1902 Plain Back
3x10-20 1201-2294 <$450
1929 Small Size
10 Type 1 1-189 <$200
20 Type 1 1-36 <$200
Total Issue $166,860
Out at close $12,500
Large out at close $2,400
****
11735 Winnebago
FARMERS FNB, RAKE
{{ 12 S }}
Organized 5/12/20
Receivership 10/30/33
1929 Small Size <$VALUE
5 Type 1 1-388 <$150
10 Type 1 1-249 <$150
Total Issue $26,580
Out at close $16,000
****
7833 Fremont
FNB OF RANDOLPH
{{ 3 L 3 S }}
Organized 6/27/05
Receivership 9/8/31
1902 Red Seal <$VALUE
3x10-20 1-860 <$1000
1902 Date Back
3x10-20 1-2030 <$450
1902 Plain Back
3x10-20 2031-5099 <450
1929 Small Size
10 Type 1 1-374 <$350
20 Type 1 1-100 <$350
Total Issue $332,390
Out at close $24,640
Large out at close $3,710
****
6056 Montgomery
FARMERS NB, RED OAK
{{ 7 L 1 S }}
Organized 11/9/01
Receivership 10/14/29
Brown Back <$VALUE
3x10-20 1-2650 <$350
1882 Date Back
3x10-20 1-4200 <$350
1882 Value Back
3x10-20 4201-7106 <$350
1902 Plain Back
3x10-20 1-4958 <$200
1929 Small Size
10 Type 1 1-117* <$500
20 Type 1 1-7** <$500
* E000117A-F000117A not issued
** E000007A-F000007A not issued
Total Issue $743,500
Out at close $58,900
Large out at close $51,100
****

****
2130 Montgomery
FNB OF RED OAK
{{ 12 L 20 S }}
Chartered 11/10/73
Original Series <$VALUE
3x1-2 1-1500 <$400/$1000
4x5 1-2875 <$4000
Series 1875
4x5 1-7092 <$3500
Brown Back
3x10-20 1-6200 <$400
50-100 1-590 <$1250/$1500
1882 Date Back
3x10-20 1-3262 <$400
50-100 1-101 <$1250/$1500
1902 Date Back
3x10-20 1-2000 <$150
1902 Plain Back
3x10-20 2001-15603 <$150
1929 Small Size
10 Type 1 1-2488 <$75
20 Type 1 1-712 <$75
10 Type 2 1-1494 <$85
20 Type 2 1-300 <$85
Total Issue $1,819,400
Out in 1935 $100,000
Large out 1935 $7,180
****
3055 Montgomery
RED OAK NB, RED OAK
{{ 8 L 8 S }}
Organized 8/29/83
Liquidated 1/16/34
Brown Back <$VALUE
3x10-20 1-5380 <$400
1902 Red Seal
3x10-20 1-4400 <$400
1902 Date Back
3x10-20 1-7100 <$200
1902 Plain Back
3x10-20 7101-19009 <$200
1929 Small Size
10 Type 1 1-2086 <$125
20 Type 1 1-545 <$135
Total Issue $1,630,010
Out at close $100,000
Large out at close $8,390
Ch 13785 assumed circulation
****
2230 Montgomery
VALLEY NB, RED OAK
{{ UNREPORTED }}
Chartered 3/3/75
Liquidated 10/20/84
Original Series <$VALUE
3x10-20 1-540 <$2000/$2500
Series 1875
3x10-20 1-634 <$2000/$2500
Total Issue $58,700
Out in 1910 $330
****
6975 Plymouth
FNB, REMSEN
{{ 6 L 12 S }}
Chartered 1903
1902 Red Seal <$VALUE
4x5 1-1450 <$450
3x10-20 1-1000 <$450
1902 Date Back
4x5 1-2050 <$225
3x10-20 1-1540 <$225
1902 Plain Back
4x5 2051-8115 <$225
3x10-20 1541-5621 <$225
1929 Small Size
5 Type 1 1-1334 <$85
10 Type 1 1-776 <$85
20 Type 1 1-226 <$85
5 Type 2 1-1294 <$100
10 Type 2 1-790 <$100
20 Type 2 1-200 <$100
Total Issue $654,300
Out in 1934 $50,000
Large out 1935 $2,660
****
7988 Humboldt
FNB, RENWICK
{{ UNREPORTED }}
Organized 11/24/05
Receivership 1/13/27
1902 Red Seal <$VALUE
3x10-20 1-285 <$2000
1902 Date Back
3x10-20 1-580 <$1000
1902 Plain Back
3x10-20 581-963 <$1000
Total Issue $62,400
Out at close $6,250
****

****
8442 Mitchell
FNB OF RICEVILLE
{{ 3 L 8 S }}
Chartered 11/06
1902 Red Seal <$VALUE
4x10 1-861 <$1000
1902 Date Back
4x10 1-2000 <$450
1902 Plain Back
4x10 2001-6198 <$450
1929 Small Size
10 Type 1 1-997 <$150
5 Type 2 1-120 <$200
Total Issue $342,780
Out at close $24,995
Large out at close $1,645
****
5611 Keokuk
FNB OF RICHLAND
{{ UNREPORTED }}
Chartered 10/29/00
Liquidated 8/31/19
Brown Back <$VALUE
3x10-20 1-720 <$1500
1882 Date Back
3x10-20 1-700 <$1500
1882 Value Back
3x10-20 701-707 <$1500
Total Issue $71,350
Out at close $9,700
****
7609 Greene
FNB OF RIPPEY
{{ 7 L 10 S }}
Chartered 2/05
1902 Red Seal <$VALUE
4x5 1-1045 <$500
3x10-20 1-697 <$500
1902 Date Back
4x5 1-1700 <$250
3x10-20 1-1160 <$250
1902 Plain Back
4x5 1701-5569 <$250
3x10-20 1161-3468 <$250
1929 Small Size
5 Type 1 1-834 <$175
10 Type 1 1-424 <$175
20 Type 1 1-130 <$175
5 Type 2 1-394 <$200
10 Type 2 1-324 <$200
20 Type 2 1-60 <$200
Total Issue $413,000
Out in 1935 $25,000
Large out 1935 $1,560
****
3153 Lyon
FNB, ROCK RAPIDS
{{ 14 L 5 S }}
Organized 3/17/84
Receivership 12/20/30
Brown Back <$VALUE
3x10-20 1-1267 <$300
1902 Red Seal
3x10-20 1-4450 <$300
1902 Date Back
3x10-20 1-6300 <$125
1902 Plain Back
3x10-20 6301-17351 <$125
1929 Small Size
10 Type 1 1-1038 <$165
20 Type 1 1-268 <$165
Total Issue $1,247,840
Out at close $94,100
Large out 1931 $22,160
****
7089 Lyon
LYON COUNTY NB, ROCK RAPIDS
{{ 8 L 6 S }}
Organized 12/15/03
Receivership 10/20/31
1902 Red Seal <$VALUE
3x10-20 1-3200 <$400
1902 Date Back
3x10-20 1-4900 <$175
1902 Plain Back
3x10-20 4901-13649 <$175
1929 Small Size
10 Type 1 1-1027 <$175
20 Type 1 1-276 <$175
Total Issue $937,190
Out at close $74,280
Large out at close $2,110
****
5200 Sioux
FNB, ROCK VALLEY
{{ 12 L 9 S }}
Organized 6/20/99
Receivership 10/31/33
Brown Back <$VALUE
3x10-20 1-3650 <$400
1882 Date Back
3x10-20 1-2900 <$400
1882 Value Back
3x10-20 2901-3900 <$400
1902 Plain Back
3x10-20 1-4766 <$175
1929 Small Size
10 Type 1 1-941 <$150
20 Type 1 1-227 <$150
Total Issue $699,500
Out at close $50,000
Large out at close $6,350
****
3053 Floyd
FNB OF ROCKFORD
{{ 3 L }}
Organized 7/18/83
Receivership 2/23/29
Brown Back <$VALUE
3x10-20 1-1243 <$1000
1902 Red Seal
3x10-20 1-570 <$1000
1902 Date Back
3x10-20 1-1080 <$450
1902 Plain Back
3x10-20 1081-2041 <$450
Total Issue $192,700
Out at close $12,500
****
10217 Cerro Gordo
FNB OF ROCKWELL
{{ 3 L 2 S }}
Organized 6/11/12
Receivership 3/30/31
1902 Date Back <$VALUE
4x5 1-865 <$450
3x10-20 1-694 <$450
1902 Plain Back
4x5 866-8430 <$450
3x10-20 695-914 <$450
1929 Small Size
5 Type 1 1-874 <$400
Total Issue $240,520
Out at close $18,270
Large out at close $2,310
****
5185 Calhoun
FNB OF ROCKWELL CITY
{{ 14 L }}
Chartered 1899
Liquidated 9/26/29
Brown Back <$VALUE
4x5 1-3350 <$350
3x10-20 1-2720 <$350
1882 Date Back
4x5 1-3675 <$350
3x10-20 1-2560 <$350
1882 Value Back
4x5 3676-4740 <$350
3x10-20 2561-3111 <$350
1902 Plain Back
3x10-20 1-5262 <$150
Total Issue $716,450
Out at close $40,800
****
11582 Calhoun
ROCKWELL CITY NB, ROCKWELL CITY
{{ 1 L 5 S }}
Organized 1/13/20
Liquidated 1/29/34
1902 Plain Back <$VALUE
3x10-20 1-1483 <$850
1929 Small Size
10 Type 1 1-283 <$250
20 Type 1 1-62 <$250
Total Issue $98,570
Out in 1932 $12,500
Large out at close $710
****
11249 Story
FNB OF ROLAND
{{ 3 L 44 S }}
Organized 8/17/18
Receivership 11/29/30
1902 Plain Back <$VALUE
4x5 1-4006 <$450
3x10-20 1-2712 <$450
1929 Small Size
5 Type 1 1-470 <$100
10 Type 1 1-227 <$100
20 Type 1 1-30 <$100
Total Issue $247,040
Out at close $30,000
Large out at close $6,740
****
4954 Pocahontas
FNB, ROLFE
{{ 3 L }}
Organized 4/24/94
Receivership 4/3/28
Brown Back <$VALUE
3x10-20 1-1190 <$750
1882 Date Back
3x10-20 1-543 <$750
1902 Date Back
3x10-20 1-600 <$500
1902 Plain Back
3x10-20 601-1458 <$500
Total Issue $159,550
Out at close $12,150
****
10395 Clay
CITIZENS NB, ROYAL
{{ 3 L }}
Organized 4/10/13
Receivership 1/5/27
1902 Date Back <$VALUE
3x10-20 1-400* <$500
1902 Plain Back
3x10-20 521-2643* <$500
* 401-520 not marked
Total Issue $132,150
Out at close $23,700
****
5541 Palo Alto
FNB, RUTHVEN
{{ 3 L }}
Organized 7/7/00
Receivership 5/2/29
Brown Back <$VALUE
3x10-20 1-500 <$750
1882 Date Back
3x10-20 1-580 <$750
1882 Value Back
3x10-20 581-599 <$750
1902 Plain Back
3x10-20 1-539 <$500
Total Issue $81,900
Out at close $7,000
****
4450 Sac
FNB, SAC CITY
{{ 6 L }}
Organized 10/6/90
Receivership 12/2/25
Brown Back <$VALUE
3x10-20 1-2320 <$600
1882 Date Back
3x10-20 1-1174 <$600
1902 Date Back
3x10-20 1-3100 <$350
1902 Plain Back
3x10-20 3101-7260 <$350
Total Issue $537,700
Out at close $47,700
****
10684 Mitchell
FNB OF SAINT ANSGAR
{{ 6 L 6 S }}
Organized 12/9/14
Receivership 10/31/33
1902 Date Back <$VALUE
3x10-20 1-800 <$350
1902 Plain Back
3x10-20 801-3501 <$350
1929 Small Size
10 Type 1 1-512 <$200
20 Type 1 1-126 <$200
Total Issue $220,890
Out at close $25,000
Large out at close $1,670
****
4824 O'Brien
FNB, SANBORN
{{ UNREPORTED }}
Organized 12/6/92
Liquidated 3/1/99
Brown Back <$VALUE
3x10-20 1-521 <$1500
Total Issue $26,050
Out in 1910 $520
****
8247 Wayne
FNB OF SEYMOUR
{{ 5 L 2 S }}
Chartered 6/06
Liquidated 12/17/30
1902 Red Seal <$VALUE
3x10-20 1-1500 <$600
1902 Date Back
3x10-20 1-3100* <$300
1902 Plain Back
3x10-20 3351-9413* <$300
* 3101-3350 not marked
1929 Small Size
10 Type 1 1-459 <$300
20 Type 1 1-132 <$300
Total Issue $589,030
Out at close $50,000
Large out at close $11,010
****

11210 Wayne
SEYMOUR NB, SEYMOUR
{{ 2 L }}
Chartered 7/18
Liquidated 1/2/26
1902 Plain Back <$VALUE
3x10-20 1-4560 <$650
Total Issue $228,000
Out at close $49,995

9723 Union
FNB OF SHANNON CITY
{{ 6 L 5 S }}
Chartered 4/10
1902 Date Back <$VALUE
3x10-20 1-1700 <$300
1902 Plain Back
3x10-20 1701-4962 <$300
1929 Small Size
10 Type 1 1-522 <$175
20 Type 1 1-150 <$175
10 Type 2 1-540 <$200
20 Type 2 1-137 <$200
Total Issue $305,560
Out in 1935 $25,000
Large out 1935 $1,820

12430 Franklin
FNB OF SHEFFIELD
{{ 1 L 6 S }}
Organized 8/7/23
Receivership 6/11/32
1902 Plain Back <$VALUE
3x10-20 1-1847 <$750
1929 Small Size
10 Type 1 1-677 <$175
20 Type 1 1-189 <$175
Total Issue $155,650
Out at close $39,700
Large out at close $2,620

3848 O'Brien
FNB, SHELDON
{{ 8 L }}
Organized 2/8/88
Receivership 3/29/27
Brown Back <$VALUE
3x10-20 1-4135 <$350
1902 Red Seal
3x10-20 1-1000 <$400
1902 Date Back
3x10-20 1-6500* <$175
1902 Plain Back
3x10-20 7001-15887* <$175
* 6501-7000 not marked
Total Issue $1,051,100
Out at close $99,000

7880 O'Brien
SHELDON NB, SHELDON
{{ 6 L 12 S }}
Chartered 1905
1902 Red Seal <$VALUE
3x10-20 1-470 <$450
1902 Date Back
3x10-20 1-3700 <$200
1902 Plain Back
3x10-20 3701-9590 <$200
1929 Small Size
10 Type 1 1-1102 <$100
20 Type 1 1-313 <$100
Total Issue $606,680
Out in 1934 $25,000
Large out 1935 $4,000

8971 Page
COMMERCIAL NB OF SHENANDOAH
{{ UNREPORTED }}
Chartered 12/07
Liquidated 12/20/09
1902 Red Seal <$VALUE
3x10-20 1-675 <$1500
1902 Date Back
3x10-20 1-585 <$1000
Total Issue $63,000
Out in 1910 $29,860

11588 Page
FARMERS NB OF SHENANDOAH
{{ UNREPORTED }}
Chartered 1/20
Liquidated 10/2/24
1902 Plain Back <$VALUE
4x5 1-1955 <$1250
Total Issue $39,100
Out at close $10,000

2363 Page
FNB OF SHENANDOAH
{{ 5 L }}
Organized 5/5/77
Receivership 5/13/26
Series 1875 <$VALUE
3x10-20 1-2769 <$850/$1250
Brown Back
4x5 1-1000 <$500
3x10-20 1-3020 <$500
1882 Date Back
4x5 1-2295 <$500
3x10-20 1-1639 <$500
1902 Plain Back
3x10-20 1-1584 <$300
Total Issue $516,500
Out at close $20,000

2679 Page
SHENANDOAH NB, SHENANDOAH
{{ 8 L }}
Chartered 1882
Liquidated 1/20/27
Series 1875 <$VALUE
3x10-20 1-2475 <$750/$1250
1902 Red Seal
3x10-20 1-3200 <$350
1902 Date Back
3x10-20 1-7000* <$175
1902 Plain Back (dated 1902)
3x10-20 7501-12293* <$175
* 7001-7500 not marked
1902 Plain Back (dated 1922)
3x10-20 1-4364 <$175
Total Issue $1,116,600
Out at close $100,000
Ch 12950 assumed circulation

12950 Page
SHENANDOAH NB, SHENANDOAH
{{ 2 L 18 S }}
Organized 6/21/26
Liquidated 6/1/34
1902 Plain Back <$VALUE
3x10-20 1-3072 <$600
1929 Small Size
10 Type 1 1-2114 <$65
20 Type 1 1-638 <$75
10 Type 2 1-732 <$75
20 Type 2 1-138 <$75
Total Issue $367,080
Out at close $98,980
Large out at close $7,010
Ch 14057 assumed circulation

3320 Osceola
FNB, SIBLEY
{{ 3 L 6 S }}
Organized 2/25/85
Brown Back <$VALUE
4x5 1-3271 <$1000
3x10-20 1-356 <$1000
1902 Red Seal
3x10-20 1-390 <$1000
1902 Date Back
3x10-20 1-1160 <$450
1902 Plain Back
3x10-20 1161-2123 <$450
1929 Small Size
10 Type 1 1-283 <$200
20 Type 1 1-71 <$200
Total Issue $234,370
Out in 1935 $12,500
Large out 1935 $1,480

5145 Fremont
NB OF SIDNEY
{{ 8 L 6 S }}
Organized 9/3/98
Receivership 10/15/31
Brown Back <$VALUE
3x10-20 1-1530 <$325
1882 Date Back
3x10-20 1-3540 <$325
1882 Value Back
3x10-20 3541-4241 <$325
1902 Plain Back
3x10-20 1-6657 <$175
1929 Small Size
5 Type 1 1-664 <$175
10 Type 1 1-724 <$175
20 Type 1 1-192 <$175
Total Issue $707,800
Out at close $60,000
Large out at close $10,055

1786 Keokuk
FNB OF SIGOURNEY
{{ 12 L 2 S }}
Chartered 2/6/71
Liquidated 6/10/30
Original Series <$VALUE
3x1-2 1-2500 <$400/$1000
4x5 1-3625 <$500
Series 1875
4x5 1-3336 <$500
Brown Back
4x5 1-4625 <$300
3x10-20 1-2430 <$300
1882 Date Back
4x5 1-638 <$300
3x10-20 1-495 <$300
1902 Date Back
4x5 1-3375 <$150
3x10-20 1-2600 <$150
1902 Plain Back
4x5 3376-12540 <$150
3x10-20 2601-8178 <$150
1929 Small Size
5 Type 1 1-788 <$350
10 Type 1 1-358 <$350
20 Type 1 1-74 <$350
Total Issue $1,116,930
Out at close $65,000
Large out at close $21,790

7369 Sioux
FNB, SIOUX CENTER
{{ 2 L 4 S }}
Chartered 1904
1902 Red Seal <$VALUE
3x10-20 1-854 <$850
1902 Date Back
3x10-20 1-1590 <$450
1902 Plain Back
3x10-20 1591-4630 <$450
1929 Small Size
10 Type 1 1-546 <$225
20 Type 1 1-126 <$225
10 Type 2 1-341 <$250
20 Type 2 1-113 <$250
Total Issue $327,750
Out in 1934 $24,550
Large out 1935 $1,390

3940 Woodbury
AMERICAN NB, SIOUX CITY
{{ UNREPORTED }}
Chartered 11/14/88
Liquidated 3/12/91
Brown Back <$VALUE
4x5 1-2148 <$1500
Total Issue $42,960
Out in 1910 $300

1976 Woodbury
CITIZENS NB OF SIOUX CITY
{{ UNREPORTED }}
Chartered 5/6/72
Liquidated 4/14/74
Original Series <$VALUE
4x5 1-1500 <$1500
3x10-20 1-300 <$1500/$2000
Total Issue $45,000
Out in 1910 $130

7401 Woodbury
CITY NB OF SIOUX CITY
{{ UNREPORTED }}
Chartered 9/17/04
Liquidated 4/1/05
1902 Red Seal <$VALUE
3x10-20 1-500 <$1500
Total Issue $25,000
Out in 1910 $1,880

4630 Woodbury
COMMERCIAL NB, SIOUX CITY
{{ UNREPORTED }}
Chartered 9/16/91
Liquidated 12/1/92
Brown Back <$VALUE
50-100 1-250 <$2500
Total Issue $37,500
Out in 1910 $250

4235 Woodbury
CORN EXCHANGE NB, SIOUX CITY
{{ 1 L }}
Chartered 9/15/90
Liquidated 4/29/95
Brown Back <$VALUE
3x10-20 1-1032 <$1000
50-100 1-249 <$2500
Total Issue $88,950
Out in 1910 $960

1757 Woodbury
FNB OF SIOUX CITY
{{ 32 L 16 S }}
Chartered 12/28/70
Receivership 12/8/30
Original Series <$VALUE
4x5 1-6750 <$400
3x10-20 1-500 <$750/$1250
Series 1875
3x10-20 1-4383 <$750/$1250
Brown Back
3x10-20 1-7000 <$175/$200
50-100 1-1374 <$1250/$1500
1882 Date Back
4x5 1-3515 <$150
3x10-20 1-1415 <$175/$200
50-100 1-210 <$1250/$1500
1902 Date Back
4x5 1-21500 <$60
3x10-20 1-13200 <$65
1902 Plain Back
4x5 21501-61135 <$60
3x10-20 13201-38101 <$65
1929 Small Size
5 Type 1 1-4712 <$50
10 Type 1 1-2123 <$50
20 Type 1 1-570 <$60
Total Issue $4,574,690
Out at close $1,000,000
Large out at close $65,850

3968 Woodbury
IOWA STATE NB, SIOUX CITY
{{ 6 L }}
Chartered 1889
Liquidated 11/6/09
Brown Back <$VALUE
4x5 1-14280 <$400
3x10-20 1-6222 <$400
1902 Date Back
4x5 1-2845 <$250
3x10-20 1-632 <$250
Total Issue $685,200
Out in 1910 $122,480

5022 Woodbury
LIVE STOCK NB, SIOUX CITY
{{ 28 L 21U + 40 S }}
Chartered 1895
Brown Back <$VALUE
4x5 1-7850 <$175
50-100 1-1140 <$1250/$1500
1882 Date Back
4x5 1-6345 <$175
50-100 1-623 <$1250/$1500
3x50-100 1-254<$1250/$1500
1902 Plain Back
4x5 1-17350 <$60
4x10 1-14966 <$65
1929 Small Size
5 Type 1 1-8544 <$25
10 Type 1 1-4120 <$25
5 Type 2 1-12740 <$25
10 Type 2 1-6454 <$25
Total Issue $2,189,250
Out in 1935 $200,000
Large out 1935 $11,270

4209 Woodbury
MERCHANTS NB OF SIOUX CITY
{{ 2 L }}
Chartered 1890
Liquidated 2/15/11
Brown Back <$VALUE
3x10-20 1-2780 <$650
1882 Date Back
3x10-20 1-173 <$650
1902 Date Back
3x10-20 1-216 <$450
Total Issue $158,450
Out in 1911 $15,850

4431 Woodbury
NB OF SIOUX CITY
{{ UNREPORTED }}
Chartered 10/7/90
Liquidated 12/29/93
Brown Back <$VALUE
50-100 1-554 <$2500
Total Issue $83,100
Out in 1910 $900

10139 Woodbury
NB OF COMMERCE OF SIOUX CITY
Chartered 2/12
2nd title:Toy NB of Sioux City 7/1/20
FIRST TITLE {{ 4 L }}
1902 Date Back <$VALUE
3x10-20 1-6000 <$200
1902 Plain Back
3x10-20 6001-10000 <$200
SECOND TITLE {{ 15 L 41 S }}
1902 Plain Back
3x10-20 1-18200 <$100
1929 Small Size
5 Type 1 1-6728 <$30
10 Type 1 1-2894 <$30
20 Type 1 1-734 <$40
5 Type 2 1-7562 <$30
10 Type 2 1-4235 <$30
20 Type 2 1-1151 <$40
Total Issue $1,976,740
Out in 1935 $200,000
Large out 1935 $12,270

4510 Woodbury
NORTHWESTERN NB OF SIOUX CITY
Organized 8/19/90
Receivership 12/8/30
2nd title:Sioux NB in Sioux City 1/17/20
FIRST TITLE {{ 10 L }}
Brown Back <$VALUE
4x5 1-5000 <$275
3x10-20 1-5040 <$275
1882 Date Back
4x5 1-1355 <$275
3x10-20 1-499 <$275
1902 Date Back
4x5 1-6000 <$125
3x10-20 1-4100 <$125
1902 Plain Back
4x5 6001-9550 <$125
3x10-20 4101-6020 <$125
SECOND TITLE {{ 6 L 7 S }}
1902 Plain Back
4x5 1-9335 <$150
3x10-20 1-7074 <$150
1929 Small Size
5 Type 1 1-1411 <$150
10 Type 1 1-687 <$150
20 Type 1 1-174 <$150
Total Issue $1,541,280
Out at close $100,000
Large out at close $21,020

3124 Woodbury
SECURITY NB, SIOUX CITY
{{ 35 L 23 S }}
Organized 2/1/84
Brown Back <$VALUE
4x5 1-11025 <$175
3x10-20 1-7864 <$175/$200
1902 Red Seal
4x5 1-5500 <$175
3x10-20 1-6600 <$175/$200
1902 Date Back
4x5 1-17500 <$60
3x10-20 1-14100 <$65
1902 Plain Back
4x5 17501-46964 <$60
3x10-20 14101-33043 <$65
1929 Small Size
5 Type 1 1-9048 <$25
10 Type 1 1-3142 <$25
20 Type 1 1-890 <$35
5 Type 2 1-12054 <$25
10 Type 2 1-5013 <$25
20 Type 2 1-1574 <$35
Total Issue $4,353,770
Out in 1935 $248,350
Large out 1935 $19,835

2535 Woodbury
SIOUX NB, SIOUX CITY
{{ 3 L }}
Organized 6/9/81
Receivership 9/9/96
Series 1875 <$VALUE
3x10-20 1-4315 <$850/$1250
Total Issue $215,750
Out in 1915 $1,120

Sioux NB in Sioux City
SEE Ch 4510
Northwestern NB of Sioux City

Toy NB of Sioux City
SEE Ch 10139
NB of Commerce of Sioux City

13400 Buena Vista
FNB IN SIOUX RAPIDS
{{ 6 S }}
Organized 11/8/29
Receivership 8/1/32
1929 Small Size <$VALUE
5 Type 1 1-1109 <$200
10 Type 1 1-491 <$200
20 Type 1 1-182 <$200
Total Issue $84,570
Out at close $49,100
Outstanding includes Ch 9585

9585 Buena Vista
FNB OF SIOUX RAPIDS
{{ 6 L }}
Organized 10/23/09
Liquidated 1/30/30
1902 Date Back <$VALUE
4x5 1-3250 <$250
3x10-20 1-2520 <$250
1902 Plain Back
4x5 3251-9918 <$250
3x10-20 2521-6763 <$250
Total Issue $536,510
Out in 1935 $5,450
Ch 13400 assumed circulation

7189 Buena Vista
FNB, SIOUX RAPIDS
{{ UNREPORTED }}
Organized 3/29/04
Liquidated 7/25/04
1902 Red Seal <$VALUE
3x10-20 1-250 <$2000
Total Issue $12,500
All notes reportedly redeemed

6941 Clay
CITIZENS NB, SPENCER
{{ 13 L }}
Organized 8/11/03
Receivership 11/19/26
1902 Red Seal <$VALUE
3x10-20 1-1120 <$650
1902 Date Back
3x10-20 1-4140 <$275
1902 Plain Back
3x10-20 4141-8803 <$275
Total Issue $496,150
Out at close $49,295

3898 Clay
FNB, SPENCER
{{ 4 L }}
Organized 5/26/88
Receivership 6/25/27
Brown Back <$VALUE
4x5 1-5139 <$850
3x10-20 1-947 <$850
1902 Red Seal
3x10-20 1-250 <$1000
1902 Date Back
3x10-20 1-2200 <$500
1902 Plain Back
3x10-20 2201-4000 <$500
Total Issue $362,630
Out at close $24,300

13020 Dickinson
FNB IN SPIRIT LAKE
{{ 6 L 13 S }}
Organized 12/26
1902 Plain Back <$VALUE
3x10-20 1-1927 <$400
1929 Small Size
10 Type 1 1-1108 <$225
20 Type 1 1-348 <$250
10 Type 2 1-418 <$250
20 Type 2 1-45 <$250
Total Issue $209,670
Out in 1935 $39,400
Large out 1935 $960

4758 Dickinson
FNB OF SPIRIT LAKE
{{ 12 L }}
Organized 6/7/92
Receivership 8/25/27
Brown Back <$VALUE
4x5 1-3475 <$600
50-100 1-514 <$2500
1882 Date Back
4x5 1-1038 <$600
50-100 1-271 <$2500
1902 Date Back
3x10-20 1-1600 <$300
1902 Plain Back
3x10-20 1601-6178 <$300
Total Issue $516,910
Out at close $40,000

<$VALUEs are for notes in FINE condition. Value changes by approximately 25% for a change of one full grade.

***

8032 Dickinson
SPIRIT LAKE NB,
SPIRIT LAKE
{{ 14 L }}
Organized 12/12/05
Receivership 3/23/26
1902 Red Seal <$VALUE
3x10-20 1-1700 <$750
1902 Date Back
3x10-20 1-3640 <$300
1902 Plain Back
3x10-20 3641-7538 <$300
Total Issue $461,900
Out at close $45,200

***

6434 Montgomery
FNB, STANTON
{{ 3 L 3 S }}
Organized 4/23/02
Receivership 10/30/33
1902 Red Seal <$VALUE
3x10-20 1-620 <$1000
1902 Date Back
3x10-20 1-820 <$450
1902 Plain Back (dated 1902)
3x10-20 821-1240 <$450
1902 Plain Back (dated 1922)
3x10-20 1-2046 <$450
1929 Small Size
10 Type 1 1-519 <$350
20 Type 1 1-164 <$350
Total Issue $246,120
Out at close $25,000
Large out at close $1,430

***

8931 Marshall
FNB OF STATE CENTER
{{ 2 L 8 S }}
Chartered 10/07
1902 Red Seal <$VALUE
3x10-20 1-300 <$1250
1902 Date Back
3x10-20 1-760 <$600
1902 Plain Back
3x10-20 761-1790 <$600
1929 Small Size
10 Type 1 1-310 <$200
20 Type 1 1-106 <$200
10 Type 2 1-353 <$200
20 Type 2 1-60 <$200
Total Issue $140,550
Out in 1935 $20,000
Large out 1935 $620

***

Citizens FNB of Storm Lake
SEE Ch 10034
Citizens NB of Storm Lake

***

10034 Buena Vista
CITIZENS NB OF STORM LAKE
Chartered 1911
2nd title:Citizens FNB of
Storm Lake 1/28/20
FIRST TITLE {{ 3 L }}
1902 Date Back <$VALUE
3x10-20 1-1950* <$450
1902 Plain Back
3x10-20 2251-2690* <$450
* 1951-2250 not marked
SECOND TITLE {{ 3 L 6 S }}
1902 Plain Back
3x10-20 1-2914 <$450
1929 Small Size
10 Type 1 1-620 <$225
20 Type 1 1-210 <$225
10 Type 2 1-362 <$225
20 Type 1 1-55 <$225
Total Issue $347,320
Out in 1934 $30,000
Large out 1935 $1,720

***

10223 Buena Vista
COMMERCIAL NB OF
STORM LAKE
{{ UNREPORTED }}
Chartered 1912
Liquidated 7/1/20
1902 Date Back <$VALUE
3x10-20 1-1000 <$1250
1902 Plain Back
3x10-20 1001-1048 <$1250
Total Issue $52,400
Out at close $12,500

***

2595 Buena Vista
FNB, STORM LAKE
{{ 3 L }}
Chartered 12/1/81
Receivership 1/2/04
Series 1875 <$VALUE
4x5 1-3949 <$750
3x10-20 1-874 <$1000/$1500
Brown Back
50-100 1-139 <$2500
Total Issue $143,530
Out in 1915 $1,780

***

9017 Story
FNB OF STORY CITY
{{ 12 L 14 S }}
Organized 1/15/08
Receivership 10/10/32
1902 Red Seal <$VALUE
4x5 1-310 <$450
3x10-20 1-252 <$450
1902 Date Back
4x5 1-4050 <$175
3x10-20 1-2800 <$175
1902 Plain Back
4x5 4051-14130 <$175
3x10-20 2801-8921 <$175
1929 Small Size
5 Type 1 1-1973 <$110
10 Type 1 1-891 <$110
20 Type 1 1-254 <$110
Total Issue $890,580
Out at close $74,995
Large out at close $7,445

***

10222 Story
STORY CITY NB, STORY CITY
{{ 3 L }}
Organized 6/24/12
Receivership 1/3/27
1902 Date Back <$VALUE
3x10-20 1-1500 <$450
1902 Plain Back
3x10-20 1501-4589 <$450
Total Issue $229,450
Out at close $29,600

***

9069 Clayton
FNB OF STRAWBERRY POINT
{{ 4 L }}
Chartered 3/08
Liquidated 12/23/29
1902 Red Seal <$VALUE
4x10 1-250 <$1500
1902 Date Back
4x10 1-700 <$750
1902 Plain Back
4x10 701-4517 <$750
Total Issue $190,680
Out at close $19,260

***

2721 Guthrie
FNB OF STUART
{{ 6 L 4 S }}
Chartered 1882
Brown Back <$VALUE
4x5 1-5629 <$400
3x10-20 1-303 <$400
1902 Red Seal
3x10-20 1-1000 <$450
1902 Date Back
3x10-20 1-2010 <$200
1902 Plain Back
3x10-20 2011-3623 <$200
1929 Small Size
10 Type 1 1-204 <$250
20 Type 1 1-31 <$250
Total Issue $374,840
Out in 1929 $20,000
Large out 1935 $1,940

***

8198 Bremer
FNB OF SUMNER
{{ 14 L 43 S }}
Organized 3/17/06
1902 Red Seal <$VALUE
3x10-20 1-1800 <$350
1902 Date Back
3x10-20 1-2840 <$150
1902 Plain Back
3x10-20 2841-8908 <$150
1929 Small Size
10 Type 1 1-984 <$85
20 Type 1 1-264 <$85
10 Type 2 1-1042 <$85
20 Type 2 1-219 <$85
Total Issue $640,920
Out in 1935 $50,000
Large out 1935 $3,580

***

3618 O'Brien
FNB OF SUTHERLAND
{{ UNREPORTED }}
Chartered 1/14/87
Liquidated 3/15/97
Brown Back <$VALUE
3x10-20 1-751 <$2000
Total Issue $37,550
Out in 1910 $360

***

5637 Kossuth
FNB, SWEA CITY
{{ 4 L }}
Organized 10/24/00
Receivership 10/29/27
Brown Back <$VALUE
3x10-20 1-1270 <$500
1882 Date Back
3x10-20 1-1640 <$500
1882 Value Back
3x10-20 1641-2490 <$500
1902 Plain Back
3x10-20 1-1722 <$375
Total Issue $276,600
Out at close $24,600

***

4609 Fremont
FNB OF TABOR
{{ 3 L }}
Chartered 7/1/91
Receivership 9/14/27
Brown Back <$VALUE
3x10-20 1-1410 <$650
1882 Date Back
3x10-20 1-218 <$650
1902 Date Back
3x10-20 1-1140 <$450
1902 Plain Back
3x10-20 1141-1820 <$450
Total Issue $172,400
Out at close $4,100

***

FNB of Tama
SEE Ch 1880
FNB of Tama City

***

1880 Tama
FNB OF TAMA CITY
Organized 8/5/71
Receivership 1/18/26
2nd title:FNB of Tama
7/11/91
FIRST TITLE {{ 3 L }}
Original Series <$VALUE
3x1-2 1-2700 <$600/$1500
4x5 1-2575 <$600
Series 1875
3x1-2 1-1280 <$600/$1500
4x5 1-4818 <$600
SECOND TITLE {{ 7 L }}
Brown Back
4x5 1-4000 <$350
3x10-20 1-2260 <$350
1882 Date Back
4x5 1-1044 <$350
3x10-20 1-850 <$350
1902 Date Back
3x10-20 1-2140 <$175
1902 Plain Back
3x10-20 2141-6553 <$175
Total Issue $751,790
Out at close $49,297

***

10238 Dickinson
FNB OF TERRIL
{{ 50+ L }}
Organized 7/17/12
Receivership 11/23/26
1902 Date Back <$VALUE
3x10-20 1-1140 <$150
1902 Plain Back
3x10-20 1141-3770 <$150
Total Issue $188,500
Out at close $24,600

***

5054 Winnebago
FNB, THOMPSON
{{ 5 L 9 S }}
Organized 12/21/96
Receivership 6/28/32
Brown Back <$VALUE
4x5 1-1845 <$500
50-100 1-431 <$1250/$1500
1882 Date Back
4x5 1-2320 <$500
50-100 1-360 <$1250/$1500
3x50-100 1-12 <$1250/$1500
1902 Plain Back
4x5 1-13332 <$300
3x50-100 1-200 <$600/$750
1929 Small Size
5 Type 1 1-1196 <$175
10 Type 1 1-571 <$175
20 Type 1 1-162 <$175
Total Issue $638,920
Out at close $50,000
Large out at close $5,890

***

8340 Cerro Gordo
FNB OF THORNTON
{{ 2 L U + 6 S }}
Chartered 8/06
1902 Red Seal <$VALUE
3x10-20 1-300 <$1250
1902 Date Back
3x10-20 1-400* <$650
1902 Plain Back
3x10-20 521-2124* <$650
* 401-520 not marked
1929 Small Size
5 Type 1 1-774 <$200
10 Type 1 1-430 <$200
20 Type 1 1-126 <$200
5 Type 2 1-568 <$225
10 Type 2 1-374 <$225
20 Type 2 1-60 <$225
Total Issue $193,120
Out in 1935 $25,000
Large out 1935 $830

***

6760 Cedar
CITY NB OF TIPTON
{{ 13 L }}
Chartered 5/03
Liquidated 11/10/28
1902 Red Seal <$VALUE
3x10-20 1-1300 <$375
1902 Date Back
3x10-20 1-3240 <$175
1902 Plain Back
3x10-20 3241-9089 <$175
Total Issue $519,450
Out at close $40,450

***

2983 Cedar
FNB OF TIPTON
{{ 3 L }}
Chartered 6/20/83
Liquidated 6/2/03
Brown Back <$VALUE
3x10-20 1-2226 <$650
Total Issue $111,300
Out in 1910 $2,100

***

13232 Cedar
TIPTON NB, TIPTON
{{ U + 5 S }}
Chartered 8/28
Liquidated 6/8/33
1929 Small Size <$VALUE
5 Type 1 1-1684 <$200
Total Issue $50,520
Out at close $49,980

***

5597 Kossuth
FNB, TITONKA
{{ 6 L 1 S }}
Organized 8/20/00
Receivership 12/30/30
Brown Back <$VALUE
3x10-20 1-1800 <$500
1882 Date Back
3x10-20 1-1470 <$500
1882 Value Back
3x10-20 1471-2267 <$500
1902 Plain Back
3x10-20 1-2194 <$300
1929 Small Size
10 Type 1 1-247 <$500
20 Type 1 1-53 <$500
Total Issue $334,230
Out at close $25,000
Large out at close $6,700

***

6432 Tama
FNB OF TOLEDO
{{ 14 L }}
Organized 8/19/02
Receivership 11/3/26
1902 Red Seal <$VALUE
3x10-20 1-2360 <$350
1902 Date Back
3x10-20 1-4800 <$150
1902 Plain Back
3x10-20 4801-10384 <$150
Total Issue $772,200
Out at close $83,800

***

13073 Tama
NB OF TOLEDO
{{ 24 S }}
Chartered 5/27
1929 Small Size <$VALUE
5 Type 1 1-522 <$60
10 Type 1 1-618 <$60
20 Type 1 1-190 <$70
5 Type 2 1-2210 <$60
10 Type 2 1-900 <$60
20 Type 2 1-190 <$70
Total Issue $99,390
Out in 1935 $50,000

***

5135 Tama
FNB OF TRAER
{{ 11 L 16 S }}
Chartered 1898
Liquidated 7/17/34
Brown Back <$VALUE
3x10-20 1-1900 <$350
1882 Date Back
3x10-20 1-2350 <$350
1882 Value Back
3x10-20 2351-3490 <$350
1902 Plain Back
3x10-20 1-11265 <$175
1929 Small Size
10 Type 1 1-2208 <$75
20 Type 1 1-594 <$85
10 Type 2 1-800 <$85
20 Type 2 1-178 <$85
Total Issue $1,048,070
Out at close $99,130
Large out at close $5,430

***

5891 Polk
FNB OF VALLEY JUNCTION
{{ 3 L 10 S }}
Organized 6/24/01
Brown Back <$VALUE
3x10-20 1-900 <$600
1882 Date Back
3x10-20 1-1700* <$600
1882 Value Back
3x10-20 1801-2939* <$600
* 1701-1800 not marked
1902 Plain Back
3x10-20 1-2375 <$400
1929 Small Size
10 Type 1 1-546 <$165
20 Type 1 1-160 <$165
10 Type 2 1-627 <$175
20 Type 2 1-172 <$175
Total Issue $372,370
Out in 1935 $24,600
Large out 1935 $1,750

***

2766 Montgomery
FNB, VILLISCA
{{ 12 L 3 S }}
Organized 5/29/82
Receivership 10/18/30
Series 1875 <$VALUE
4x5 1-3408 <$500
50-100 1-278 <$4000
1902 Red Seal
3x10-20 1-2500 <$400
1902 Date Back
3x10-20 1-2900 <$175
1902 Plain Back
3x10-20 2901-7579 <$175
1929 Small Size
10 Type 1 1-460 <$300
20 Type 1 1-119 <$300
Total Issue $655,690
Out at close $50,000
Large out at close $9,690

***

14041 Montgomery
NODAWAY VALLEY NB
OF VILLISCA
{{ 14 S }}
Chartered 1934
1929 Small Size <$VALUE
5 Type 2 1-714 <$200
10 Type 2 1-345 <$200
20 Type 2 1-115 <$200
Total Issue $9,320
Out in 1935 $30,000
Outstanding includes Ch 7506

***

7506 Montgomery
VILLISCA NB, VILLISCA
{{ 6 L 12 S }}
Organized 11/29/04
Liquidated 3/20/34
1902 Red Seal <$VALUE
3x10-20 1-990 <$600
1902 Date Back
3x10-20 1-1550* <$300
1902 Plain Back
3x10-20 1751-3800* <$300
* 1551-1750 not marked
1929 Small Size
10 Type 1 1-314 <$125
20 Type 1 1-252 <$125
Total Issue $288,580
Out in 1932 $19,760
Large out 1935 $1,000

***

5088 Benton
FARMERS NB OF VINTON
{{ 6 L }}
Chartered 1897
Liquidated 1/10/29
Brown Back <$VALUE
4x5 1-2562 <$500
3x10-20 1-1640 <$500
1882 Date Back
4x5 1-2450 <$500
3x10-20 1-1860 <$500
1882 Value Back
4x5 2451-2735 <$500
3x10-20 1861-1996 <$500
1902 Plain Back
4x10 1-5219 <$300
Total Issue $496,500
Out in 1927 $36,050

***

1593 Benton
FNB OF VINTON
{{ UNREPORTED }}
Chartered 10/18/65
Liquidated 12/13/69
Original Series <$VALUE
4x5 1-1575 <$1500
4x10 1-275 <$2000
Total Issue $42,500
Out in 1910 $175

***

6122 Washington
CITIZENS NB OF WASHINGTON
{{ 1 L }}
Chartered 2/7/02
Liquidated 6/1/08
1902 Red Seal <$VALUE
3x10-20 1-2460 <$1250
Total Issue $123,000
Out in 1910 $13,320

***

398 Washington
FNB OF WASHINGTON
{{ 2 L }}
Chartered 1864
Liquidated 4/11/82
Original Series <$VALUE
3x1-2 1-1698 <$600/$1500
4x5 1-7350 <$650
Series 1875
4x5 1-2500 <$650
4x20 1-318 <$2000
Total Issue $230,930
Out in 1910 $1,650

***

2656 Washington
FNB OF WASHINGTON
{{ 2 L }}
Chartered 4/11/82
Liquidated 3/13/02
Brown Back <$VALUE
3x10-20 1-4243 <$750
Total Issue $212,150
Out in 1910 $3,250

***

1762 Washington
WASHINGTON NB, WASHINGTON
{{ 16 L 12 S }}
Chartered 1/5/71
Liquidated 12/15/33
Original Series <$VALUE
3x1-2 1-1000 <$400/$1000
4x5 1-3750 <$400
4x20 1-375 <$1250
Series 1875
4x5 1-248 <$400
4x20 1-1210 <$1250
Brown Back
3x10-20 1-6190 <$275
1882 Date Back
3x10-20 1-1276 <$275
1902 Date Back
3x10-20 1-4900 <$135
1902 Plain Back
3x10-20 4901-16502 <$135
1929 Small Size
10 Type 1 1-2130 <$85
20 Type 1 1-577 <$100
Total Issue $1,607,200
Out at close $100,000
Large out at close $8,600

***

****
6854 Black Hawk
BLACK HAWK NB OF WATERLOO
{{ 14 L }}
Organized 4/17/03
Receivership 2/13/25
1902 Red Seal <$VALUE
3x10-20 1-7700 <$350
1902 Date Back
3x10-20 1-11600 <$135
1902 Plain Back
3x10-20 11601-26951 <$135
Total Issue $1,732,550
Out at close $189,800
****
2910 Black Hawk
COMMERCIAL NB OF WATERLOO
{{ 13 L }}
Organized 3/16/83
Receivership 7/18/32
Brown Back <$VALUE
4x5 1-3508 <$200
3x10-20 1-2584 <$200
1902 Red Seal
3x10-20 1-8500 <$200
1902 Date Back
3x10-20 1-12900* <$100
1902 Plain Back
3x10-20 14901-27776* <$100
* 12901-14900 not marked
Total Issue $2,013,160
Out at close $14,055
****
792 Black Hawk
FNB OF WATERLOO
{{ 5 L }}
Chartered 1865
Liquidated 1/13/31
Original Series <$VALUE
3x1-2 1-3100 <$350/$1000
4x5 1-1850 <$500
3x10-20 1-900 <$750/$1250
Series 1875
4x5 1-250 <$500
3x10-20 1-1020 <$750/$1250
Brown Back
3x10-20 1-5903 <$350
1902 Red Seal
50-100 1-1900 <$2250/$2500
1902 Date Back
50-100 1-1400 <$400/$500
3x50-100 1-2763 <$400/$500
Total Issue $1,634,400
Out at close $40,580
****
5120 Black Hawk
LEAVITT & JOHNSON NB OF WATERLOO
Organized 4/12/98
Receivership 2/18/32
2nd title:Pioneer NB of Waterloo 5/26/26
FIRST TITLE {{ 26 L }}
Brown Back <$VALUE
3x10-20 1-10800 <$200
1882 Date Back
4x5 1-5000 <$200
3x10-20 1-13800 <$200
1882 Value Back
4x5 5001-6000 <$200
3x10-20 13801-14364 <$200
1902 Plain Back
4x5 1-16129 <$100
3x10-20 1-11107 <$100
SECOND TITLE {{ 6 L 16 S }}
1902 Plain Back
4x5 1-17971 <$150
1929 Small Size
5 Type 1 1-13510 <$65
Total Issue $3,020,850
Out at close $196,940
Large out at close $24,615
****
13702 Black Hawk
NB OF WATERLOO
{{ 12 S }}
Chartered 6/33
1929 Small Size <$VALUE
5 Type 2 1-19040 <$75
10 Type 2 1-10329 <$75
Total Issue $198,490
Out in 1935 $130,950
****
Pioneer NB of Waterloo
SEE Ch 5120
Leavitt & Johnson NB of Waterloo
****

****
5700 Black Hawk
WATERLOO NB, WATERLOO
{{ 3 L }}
Chartered 2/4/01
Liquidated 6/15/04
Brown Back <$VALUE
3x10-20 1-1383 <$650
Total Issue $69,150
Out in 1910 $4,130
****
4921 Allamakee
FNB OF WAUKON
{{ 12 L }}
Organized 4/22/93
Receivership 1/18/26
Brown Back <$VALUE
4x5 1-2140 <$350
3x10-20 1-2294 <$350
1882 Date Back
4x5 1-2115 <$350
3x10-20 1-1267 <$350
1902 Date Back
3x10-20 1-2800 <$150
1902 Plain Back
3x10-20 2801-10287 <$150
Total Issue $777,500
Out at close $93,200
****
10207 Allamakee
PEOPLES NB OF WAUKON
{{ 12 L }}
Organized 5/1/12
Receivership 7/19/27
1902 Date Back <$VALUE
3x10-20 1-1500 <$165
1902 Plain Back
3x10-20 1501-11658 <$165
Total Issue $582,900
Out at close $123,200
****
3105 Bremer
FNB OF WAVERLY
{{ 12 L 18 S }}
Chartered 1884
Brown Back <$VALUE
4x5 1-500 <$300
3x10-20 1-2651 <$300
1902 Red Seal
3x10-20 1-3900 <$300
1902 Date Back
3x10-20 1-5900 <$135
1902 Plain Back
3x10-20 5901-16621 <$135
1929 Small Size
10 Type 1 1-2006 <$65
20 Type 1 1-518 <$75
10 Type 2 1-825 <$75
20 Type 2 1-165 <$75
Total Issue $1,361,470
Out in 1935 $50,000
Large out 1935 $7,140
****
3420 Hamilton
FARMERS NB, WEBSTER CITY
{{ 4 L 8 S }}
Organized 11/23/85
Brown Back <$VALUE
3x10-20 1-3466 <$450
1902 Red Seal
3x10-20 1-1000 <$500
1902 Date Back
3x10-20 1-3400* <$250
1902 Plain Back
3x10-20 3651-9533* <$250
* 3401-3650 not marked
1929 Small Size
10 Type 1 1-956 <$125
20 Type 1 1-302 <$125
10 Type 2 1-1429 <$125
20 Type 2 1-308 <$125
Total Issue $814,000
Out in 1935 $50,000
Large out 1935 $3,110
****
1874 Hamilton
FNB OF WEBSTER CITY
{{ 14 L 9 S }}
Organized 8/10/71
Receivership 11/30/32
Original Series <$VALUE
3x1-2 1-1500 <$350/$1000
4x5 1-3375 <$400
Series 1875
4x5 1-5876 <$400
Brown Back
4x5 1-2400 <$250
3x10-20 1-3630 <$250
1882 Date Back
4x5 1-1985 <$250
3x10-20 1-1657 <$250

1902 Date Back
3x10-20 1-5600 <$100
1902 Plain Back
3x10-20 5601-16557 <$100
1929 Small Size
10 Type 1 1-1810 <$75
20 Type 1 1-492 <$85
Total Issue $1,540,060
Out at close $100,000
Large out at close $13,650
****
2984 Hamilton
HAMILTON COUNTY NB, WEBSTER CITY
{{ UNREPORTED }}
Chartered 6/20/83
Liquidated 6/30/90
Brown Back <$VALUE
4x5 1-1337 <$1500
Total Issue $26,740
Out in 1910 $220
****
5457 Kossuth
FNB, WESLEY
{{ 2 L }}
Organized 6/26/00
Receivership 10/12/28
Brown Back <$VALUE
3x10-20 1-1250 <$750
1882 Date Back
3x10-20 1-1770* <$750
1882 Value Back
3x10-20 1901-2460* <$750
* 1771-1900 not marked
1902 Plain Back
3x10-20 1-2203 <$500
Total Issue $295,650
Out at close $24,600
****
2015 Fayette
FAYETTE COUNTY NB OF WEST UNION
{{ 28 L 8 S }}
Organized 6/26/72
Liquidated 3/14/34
Original Series <$VALUE
3x1-2 1-1500 <$400/$1000
4x5 1-2875 <$400
Series 1875
4x5 1-6249 <$400
Brown Back
4x5 1-6635 <$200
3x10-20 1-2248 <$200
1882 Date Back
4x5 1-1047 <$200
3x10-20 1-792 <$200
1902 Date Back
3x10-20 1-2200 <$85
1902 Plain Back
3x10-20 2201-6708 <$85
1929 Small Size
10 Type 1 1-941 <$100
20 Type 1 1-242 <$100
Total Issue $916,520
Out at close $49,995
Large out at close $5,445
****
3192 Keokuk
FNB OF WHAT CHEER
{{ 8 L 12 S }}
Organized 4/8/84
Receivership 1/18/34
Brown Back <$VALUE
3x10-20 1-2825 <$750
1902 Red Seal
3x10-20 1-1700 <$750
1902 Date Back
3x10-20 1-3300 <$375
1902 Plain Back
3x10-20 3301-9264 <$375
1929 Small Size
10 Type 1 1-976 <$250
20 Type 1 1-278 <$250
Total Issue $781,370
Out at close $50,000
Large out at close $4,070
****
10861 Monona
FNB OF WHITING
{{ 6 L 5 S }}
Organized 5/2/16
Receivership 10/31/33
1902 Plain Back <$VALUE
4x10 1-4827 <$275
1929 Small Size
10 Type 1 1-892 <$225
10 Type 2 1-130 <$225
Total Issue $247,900
Out at close $25,000
Large out at close $2,490
****

****
5585 Hamilton
FNB, WILLIAMS
{{ 3 L 1 S }}
Organized 9/13/00
Receivership 7/1/30
Brown Back <$VALUE
4x5 1-1200 <$750
3x10-20 1-860 <$750
1882 Date Back
4x5 1-1525 <$750
3x10-20 1-1160 <$750
1882 Value Back
4x5 1526-2545 <$750
3x10-20 1161-1762 <$750
1902 Plain Back
4x5 1-2697 <$500
3x10-20 1-1629 <$500
1929 Small Size
5 Type 1 1-315 <$500
10 Type 1 1-140 <$500
20 Type 1 1-9 <$500
Total Issue $360,320
Out at close $24,580
Large out at close $6,510
****
10640 Henry
FARMERS NB OF WINFIELD
{{ 6 L 5 S }}
Organized 5/4/14
1902 Date Back <$VALUE
4x5 1-1250 <$250
3x10-20 1-1000 <$250
1902 Plain Back
4x5 1251-5134 <$250
3x10-20 1001-3291 <$250
1929 Small Size
5 Type 1 1-988 <$175
10 Type 1 1-486 <$175
20 Type 1 1-158 <$175
5 Type 2 1-194 <$200
10 Type 2 1-90 <$200
20 Type 2 1-50 <$200
Total Issue $347,860
Out in 1935 $25,000
Large out 1935 $1,180
****
2002 Madison
CITIZENS NB OF WINTERSET
{{ 10 L 22 S }}
Organized 5/11/72
Receivership 6/4/34
Original Series <$VALUE
3x1-2 1-1700 <$400/$1000
4x5 1-2375 <$400
Series 1875
4x5 1-5908 <$400
Brown Back
50-100 1-390 <$1250/$1500
1882 Date Back
50-100 1-54 <$1250/$1500
1902 Date Back
3x50-100 1-2760 <$350/$400
1902 Plain Back
3x50-100 2761-3672 <$350/$400
1929 Small Size
10 Type 1 1-721 <$65
20 Type 1 1-297 <$75
50 Type 1 1-376 <$110
100 Type 1 1-124 <$165
Total Issue $1,424,860
Out at close $199,100
Large out at close $21,800
****
FNB of Winterset
SEE Ch 1403
NB of Winterset
****
1403 Madison
NB OF WINTERSET
Chartered 1865
Liquidated 2/20/30
2nd title:FNB of Winterset 4/18/83
FIRST TITLE {{ 0 L }}
Original Series <$VALUE
4x5 1-3000 <$850
3x10-20 1-2115 <$1000/$1500
Series 1875
4x5 1-313 <$850
3x10-20 1-468 <$1000/$1500
SECOND TITLE {{ 5 L 2 S }}
Series 1875
4x5 1-865 <$500
Brown Back
4x5 1-1000 <$400
50-100 1-633 <$1250/$1500
1902 Red Seal
4x5 1-1575 <$500
3x10-20 1-1070 <$500

1902 Date Back
4x5 1-2750 <$250
3x10-20 1-2300 <$250
1902 Plain Back
4x5 2751-8745 <$250
3x10-20 2301-6215 <$250
1929 Small Size
10 Type 1 1-260 <$350
20 Type 1 1-40 <$350
Total Issue $918,710
Out at close $37,350
Large out at close $16,950
****
4745 Harrison
FNB OF WOODBINE
{{ 13 L 11 S }}
Chartered 1892
Brown Back <$VALUE
4x5 1-4380 <$300
3x10-20 1-1798 <$300
1882 Date Back
4x5 1-1628 <$300
3x10-20 1-1050 <$300
1902 Date Back
4x5 1-1650 <$125
3x10-20 1-1300 <$125
1902 Plain Back
4x5 1651-7960 <$125
3x10-20 1301-5348 <$125
1929 Small Size
5 Type 1 1-1522 <$85
10 Type 1 1-784 <$85
20 Type 1 1-212 <$85
5 Type 2 1-1684 <$100
10 Type 2 1-1013 <$100
20 Type 2 1-285 <$100
Total Issue $831,550
Out in 1935 $50,000
Large out 1935 $4,590
****
1943 Jones
FNB OF WYOMING
{{ 7 L 3 S }}
Organized 1/27/72
Liquidated 3/3/31
Original Series <$VALUE
4x5 1-1750 <$500
3x10-20 1-900 <$750/$1250
Series 1875
4x5 1-817 <$500
3x10-20 1-805 <$750/$1250
Brown Back
4x5 1-1975 <$400
3x10-20 1-1340 <$400
1882 Date Back
4x5 1-746 <$400
3x10-20 1-404 <$400
1902 Date Back
3x10-20 1-2400 <$200
1902 Plain Back
3x10-20 2401-7982 <$200
1929 Small Size
10 Type 1 1-556 <$275
20 Type 1 1-144 <$275
Total Issue $727,950
Out at close $50,000
Large out at close $10,670
****

CONDITION affects Value. The Values shown are for notes in FINE condition.

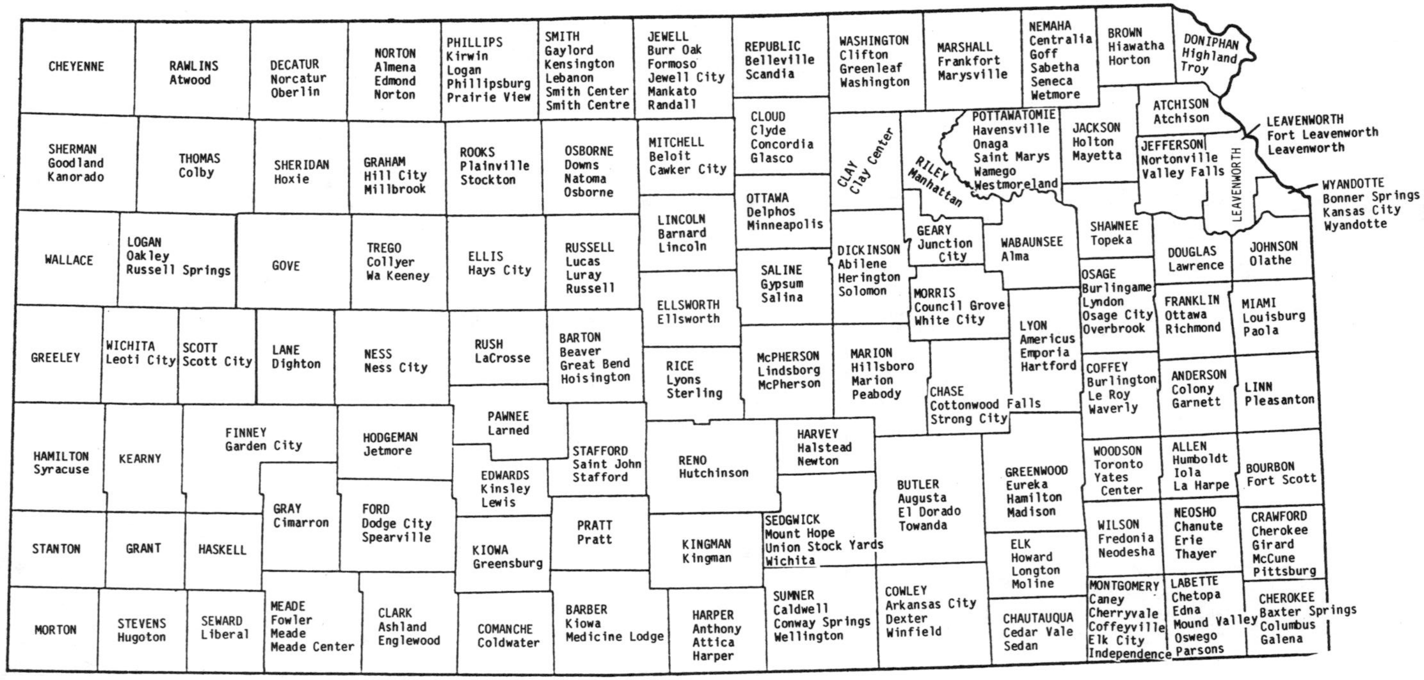

Nickname: The Sunflower State
Motto: Ad Astra Per Aspera (To the Stars Through Difficulties)
Capital: Topeka
Number of towns: 206
Number of issuing charters: 400
Number of small size issuers: 212

Abilene B5
Alma B6
Almena A3
Americus B6
Anthony D4
Arkansas City D5
Ashland D3
Atchison A6
Attica D4
Atwood A2
Augusta C5
Barnard B4
Baxter Springs D7
Beaver B3
Belleville A4
Beloit A4
Bonner Springs B7
Burlingame B6
Burlington B6
Burr Oak A4
Caldwell D5
Caney D6
Cawker City A4
Cedar Vale D6
Centralia A6
Chanute C7
Cherokee C7
Cherryvale D6
Chetopa D7
Cimarron C2
Clay Center A5
Clifton A5
Clyde A4
Coffeyville D6
Colby A2
Coldwater D3
Collyer B3
Colony C6
Columbus D7
Concordia A4
Conway Springs D5
Cottonwood Falls C5
Council Grove B5
Delphos B4
Dexter D5
Dighton B2
Dodge City C3
Downs A3
Edmond A3
Edna D7
El Dorado C5
Elk City D6
Ellsworth B4
Emporia B6
Englewood D3
Erie C7
Eureka C6
Formoso A4
Fort Leavenworth A7
Fort Scott A7
Fowler D2
Frankfort A5
Fredonia C6
Galena D7
Garden City C2
Garnett C6
Gaylord A3
Girard C7
Glasco A4
Goff A6
Goodland A1
Great Bend B3
Greenleaf A5
Greensburg C3
Gypsum B4
Halstead C5
Hamilton C6
Harper D4
Hartford B6
Havensville A6
Hays City B3
Herington B5
Hiawatha A6
Highland A7
Hill City A3
Hillsboro B5
Hoisington B3
Holton A6
Horton A6
Howard C6
Hoxie A2
Hugoton D1
Humboldt C7
Hutchinson C4
Independence D6
Iola C7
Jetmore C3
Jewell City A4
Junction City B5
Kanorado A1
Kansas City B7
Kensington A3
Kingman C4
Kinsley C3
Kiowa D4
Kirwin A3
La Crosse B3
La Harpe C7
Larned C3
Lawrence B6
Le Roy B6
Leavenworth A7
Lebanon A3
Leoti City B1
Lewis C3
Liberal D2
Lincoln B4
Lindsborg B4
Logan A3
Longton C6
Louisburg B7
Lucas B3
Luray B3
Lyndon B6
Lyons B4
Madison C6
Manhattan A5
Mankato A4
Marion B5
Marysville A5
Mayetta A6
McCune C7
McPherson B4
Meade D2
Meade Center D2
Medicine Lodge D4
Millbrook A3
Minneapolis B4
Moline C6
Mound Valley D7
Mount Hope C5
Natoma A3
Neodesha C6
Ness City B3
Newton C5
Norcatur A2
Norton A3
Nortonville A6
Oakley B1
Oberlin A2
Olathe B7
Onaga A6
Osage City B6
Osborne A3
Oswego D7
Ottawa B6
Overbrook B6
Paola B7
Parsons D7
Peabody B5
Phillipsburg A3
Pittsburg C7
Plainville A3
Pleasanton C7
Prairie View A3
Pratt C4
Randall A4
Richmond B6
Russell B3
Russell Springs B1
Sabetha A6
Saint John C4
Saint Marys A6
Salina B4
Scandia A4
Scott City B2
Sedan D6
Seneca A6
Smith Center A3
Smith Centre A3
Solomon B5
Spearville C3
Stafford C4
Sterling B4
Stockton A3
Strong City C5
Syracuse C1
Thayer C7
Topeka B6
Toronto C6
Towanda C5
Troy A7
Union Stock Yards (Wichita) C5
Valley Falls A6
Wakeeney B3
Wamego A6
Washington A5
Waverly B6
Wellington D5
Westmoreland A6
Wetmore A6
White City B5
Wichita C5
Winfield D5
Wyandotte B7
Yates Center C6

****
3777 Dickinson
ABILENE NB, ABILENE
{{ 18 L 12 S }}
Chartered 1887
Brown Back <$VALUE
4x5 1-4900 <$350
50-100 1-654 <$1250/$1500
1902 Red Seal
4x5 1-805 <$400
50-100 1-226 <$2250/$2500
1902 Date Back
4x5 1-1900 <$85
50-100 1-280 <$500/$600
3x50-100 1-310 <$500/$600
1902 Plain Back
4x5 1901-11475 <$85
3x50-100 311-433<$500/$600
1929 Small Size
5 Type 1 1-1470 <$125
50 Type 1 1-100 <$250
100 Type 1 1-34 <$300
5 Type 2 1-1340 <$125
50 Type 2 1-46 <$350
Total Issue $729,350
Out in 1935 $50,000
Large out 1935 $6,860
****
8379 Dickinson
FARMERS NB OF ABILENE
{{ 9 L 12 S }}
Chartered 9/06
1902 Red Seal <$VALUE
4x5 1-1200 <$800
3x10-20 1-1020 <$800
1902 Date Back
4x5 1-3200 <$300
3x10-20 1-2260 <$300
1902 Plain Back
4x5 3201-9845 <$300
3x10-20 2261-6637 <$300
1929 Small Size
5 Type 1 1-1510 <$100
10 Type 1 1-874 <$100
20 Type 1 1-258 <$100
5 Type 2 1-1368 <$100
10 Type 2 1-865 <$100
20 Type 2 1-185 <$100
Total Issue $751,640
Out in 1935 $49,995
Large out 1935 $3,545
****
2427 Dickinson
FNB OF ABILENE
{{ 1 L }}
Chartered 6/23/79
Receivership 1/21/90
Series 1875 <$VALUE
4x5 1-5065 <$2000
Total Issue $101,300
Out in 1915 $655
****
5104 Wabaunsee
ALMA NB, ALMA
{{ 7 L 8 S }}
Chartered 1897
Liquidated 4/20/32
Brown Back <$VALUE
3x10-20 1-1950 <$600
1882 Date Back
3x10-20 1-2100* <$600
1882 Value Back
3x10-20 2401-2614* <$750
* 2101-2400 not marked
1902 Plain Back
3x10-20 1-3613 <$300
1929 Small Size
10 Type 1 1-665 <$150
20 Type 1 1-192 <$150
Total Issue $471,790
Out at close $37,315
Large out at close $4,440
Ch 13601 assumed circulation
****
8357 Wabaunsee
COMMERCIAL NB OF ALMA
{{ 1 L }}
Chartered 9/06
Liquidated 6/17/12
1902 Red Seal <$VALUE
3x10-20 1-1700 <$1500
1902 Date Back
3x10-20 1-1319 <$750
Total Issue $150,950
Out in 1912 $38,790
****
10195 Wabaunsee
FARMERS NB OF ALMA
{{ 4 L 1 S }}
Chartered 5/12
Liquidated 4/21/32
1902 Date Back <$VALUE
3x10-20 1-475 <$750
1902 Plain Back
3x10-20 476-1046 <$750
1929 Small Size
10 Type 1 1-134 <$400
20 Type 1 1-23 <$400
Total Issue $63,100
Out at close $6,250
Large out at close $310
Ch 13601 assumed circulation
****
13601 Wabaunsee
FNB IN ALMA
{{ 7 S }}
Chartered 3/32
1929 Small Size <$VALUE
10 Type 1 1-336 <$175
20 Type 1 1-86 <$175
5 Type 2 1-300 <$175
10 Type 2 1-1100 <$175
20 Type 2 1-254 <$175
Total Issue $48,060
Out in 1934 $43,750
Outstanding includes Ch 5104, and Ch 10195
****
3769 Wabaunsee
FNB OF ALMA
{{ UNREPORTED }}
Organized 8/3/87
Receivership 11/21/90
Brown Back <$VALUE
4x5 1-1228 <$2000
Total Issue $24,560
Out in 1915 $165
****
8255 Norton
FNB OF ALMENA
{{ 13 L 13 S }}
Chartered 6/06
1902 Red Seal <$VALUE
4x5 1-1125 <$600
3x10-20 1-900 <$600
1902 Date Back
4x5 1-3300 <$225
3x10-20 1-2440 <$225
1902 Plain Back
4x5 3301-10739 <$225
3x10-20 2441-6652 <$225
1929 Small Size
5 Type 1 1-1694 <$100
10 Type 1 1-1078 <$100
20 Type 1 1-148 <$100
5 Type 2 1-2604 <$100
10 Type 2 1-1308 <$100
Total Issue $774,240
Out in 1935 $50,000
Large out 1935 $2,870
****
10902 Lyon
FARMERS NB OF AMERICUS
{{ 2 L }}
Chartered 9/16
Liquidated 9/29/24
1902 Plain Back <$VALUE
3x10-20 1-2286 <$850
Total Issue $114,300
Out at close $25,000
****
3394 Harper
ANTHONY NB, ANTHONY
{{ UNREPORTED }}
Chartered 9/16/85
Liquidated 1/13/91
Brown Back <$VALUE
3x10-20 1-416 <$2000
Total Issue $20,800
Out in 1910 $70
****
6752 Harper
CITIZENS NB OF ANTHONY
{{ 8 L 13 S }}
Chartered 4/03
1902 Red Seal <$VALUE
3x10-20 1-2025 <$600
1902 Date Back
3x10-20 1-2800 <$250
1902 Plain Back
3x10-20 2801-8527 <$250
1929 Small Size
5 Type 1 1-668 <$85
10 Type 1 1-1294 <$85
20 Type 1 1-356 <$85
5 Type 2 1-3398 <$85
10 Type 2 1-2371 <$85
20 Type 2 1-504 <$85
Total Issue $718,780
Out in 1935 $70,000
Large out 1935 $2,350
****
3385 Harper
FNB OF ANTHONY
{{ 7 L 12 S }}
Chartered 1885
Brown Back <$VALUE
3x10-20 1-3859 <$600
1902 Red Seal
3x10-20 1-1660 <$750
1902 Date Back
3x10-20 1-2800 <$225
1902 Plain Back
3x10-20 2801-9992 <$225
1929 Small Size
10 Type 1 1-1300 <$85
20 Type 1 1-376 <$85
10 Type 2 1-1810 <$85
20 Type 2 1-252 <$85
Total Issue $921,810
Out in 1935 $50,000
Large out 1935 $3,190
****
3384 Harper
HARPER COUNTY NB OF ANTHONY
{{ UNREPORTED }}
Chartered 8/26/85
Liquidated 12/20/89
Brown Back <$VALUE
3x10-20 1-355 <$2000
Total Issue $17,750
Out in 1910 $90
****
3992 Cowley
AMERICAN NB OF ARKANSAS CITY
{{ UNREPORTED }}
Organized 3/15/89
Receivership 12/26/90
Brown Back <$VALUE
3x10-20 1-932 <$2000
Total Issue $46,600
Out in 1915 $190
****
4640 Cowley
FARMERS NB OF ARKANSAS CITY
{{ 1 L }}
Chartered 9/30/91
Liquidated 3/24/97
Brown Back <$VALUE
4x5 1-2473 <$2000
Total Issue $49,460
Out in 1910 $430
****
3360 Cowley
FNB OF ARKANSAS CITY
{{ UNREPORTED }}
Organized 6/30/85
Liquidated 2/4/97
Brown Back <$VALUE
3x10-20 1-1866 <$2000
Total Issue $93,300
Out in 1915 $570
****
4487 Cowley
HOME NB OF ARKANSAS CITY
{{ 3 L 17 S }}
Chartered 1890
Brown Back <$VALUE
50-100 1-1614 <$1750/$2000
1882 Date Back
50-100 1-154 <$1750/$2000
1902 Date Back
3x10-20 1-2200 <$250
1902 Plain Back
3x10-20 2201-9386 <$250
1929 Small Size
10 Type 1 1-1336 <$75
20 Type 1 1-382 <$85
10 Type 2 1-1562 <$85
20 Type 2 1-513 <$85
Total Issue $886,380
Out in 1935 $50,000
Large out 1935 $2,850
****
10746 Cowley
SECURITY NB OF ARKANSAS CITY
{{ 15 L 15 S }}
Chartered 6/15
1902 Plain Back <$VALUE
4x5 1-16373 <$175
3x10-20 1-11462 <$175
1929 Small Size
5 Type 1 1-3527 <$75
10 Type 1 1-1957 <$75
20 Type 1 1-580 <$75
Total Issue $1,193,390
Out in 1935 $50,000
Large out 1935 $4,570
****
3710 Clark
FNB OF ASHLAND
{{ 1 L }}
Chartered 5/20/87
Liquidated 4/15/91
Brown Back <$VALUE
4x5 1-1028 <$2000
Total Issue $20,560
Out in 1910 $160
****
5386 Clark
STOCKGROWERS NB OF ASHLAND
{{ 2 L 7 S }}
Chartered 6/2/00
Liquidated 11/27/33
Brown Back <$VALUE
3x10-20 1-1700 <$1250
1882 Date Back
3x10-20 1-2130 <$1250
1929 Small Size
5 Type 1 1-1138 <$200
10 Type 1 1-474 <$200
20 Type 1 1-186 <$200
Total Issue $276,400
Out at close $50,000
Large out at close $610
****
2082 Atchison
ATCHISON NB, ATCHISON
{{ 3 L }}
Chartered 2/8/73
Receivership 9/5/99
Original Series <$VALUE
3x1-2 1-1880 <$1250/$2000
4x5 1-3750 <$1250
Series 1875
4x5 1-8480 <$1250
Brown Back
50-100 1-535 <$2000/$2500
Total Issue $334,250
Out in 1915 $2,585
****
11405 Atchison
CITY NB OF ATCHISON
{{ 8 L 25 S }}
Chartered 7/19
1902 Plain Back <$VALUE
4x5 1-13414 <$225
3x10-20 1-9631 <$225
1929 Small Size
5 Type 1 1-3304 <$45
10 Type 1 1-1910 <$45
20 Type 1 1-474 <$55
Total Issue $1,020,430
Out in 1935 $60,000
Large out 1935 $3,750
****
2758 Atchison
EXCHANGE NB OF ATCHISON
{{ 13 L }}
Chartered 1882
Series 1875 <$VALUE
4x5 1-7839 <$1000
50-100 1-142 <$7500
1902 Red Seal
50-100 1-1534 <$2500/$3000
1902 Date Back
50-100 1-800 <$750/$850
3x50-100 1-737 <$750/$850
1902 Plain Back
4x5 1-17285 <$250
Total Issue $1,058,130
Out in 1935 $6,975
****
1672 Atchison
FNB OF ATCHISON
{{ 27 L }}
Chartered 1867
Liquidated 4/24/24
Original Series <$VALUE
3x1-2 1-2900 <$600/$1250
4x5 1-8850 <$600
Series 1875
4x5 1-5275 <$600
Brown Back
3x10-20 1-8722 <$300/$350
1902 Red Seal
4x5 1-3500 <$450
3x10-20 1-1200 <$450/$500
1902 Date Back
4x5 1-5330 <$100
3x10-20 1-4368 <$100
1902 Plain Back
4x5 5331-13555 <$100
3x10-20 4369-8239 <$100
Total Issue $1,546,150
Out at close $100,000
****
3612 Atchison
UNITED STATES NB OF ATCHISON
{{ UNREPORTED }}
Chartered 12/30/86
Liquidated 3/24/91
Brown Back <$VALUE
3x10-20 1-1305 <$2000
Total Issue $65,250
Out in 1910 $450
****
10359 Harper
FNB OF ATTICA
{{ 2 L 3 S }}
Chartered 4/13
1902 Date Back <$VALUE
3x10-20 1-600 <$750
1902 Plain Back
3x10-20 601-1895 <$750
1929 Small Size
10 Type 1 1-306 <$300
20 Type 1 1-100 <$300
Total Issue $125,110
Out in 1935 $10,000
Large out 1935 $570
****
10644 Rawlins
FARMERS NB OF ATWOOD
{{ 10 S }}
Chartered 10/14
1929 Small Size <$VALUE
5 Type 1 1-410 <$175
10 Type 1 1-210 <$175
20 Type 1 1-74 <$175
5 Type 2 1-30 <$200
10 Type 2 1-60 <$200
20 Type 2 1-30 <$200
Total Issue $35,130
Out in 1935 $10,000
****
6643 Butler
FNB OF AUGUSTA
{{ 6 L 21 S }}
Organized 2/9/03
Receivership 7/27/33
1902 Red Seal <$VALUE
3x10-20 1-356 <$1000
1902 Date Back
3x10-20 1-5860 <$300
1902 Plain Back
3x10-20 5861-6581 <$300
1929 Small Size
10 Type 1 1-2061 <$100
20 Type 1 1-565 <$100
Total Issue $538,310
Out at close $75,000
Large out at close $2,250
****
8396 Lincoln
FNB OF BARNARD
{{ 4 L 10 S }}
Chartered 10/06
1902 Red Seal <$VALUE
3x10-20 1-188 <$1000
1902 Date Back
3x10-20 1-1130 <$350
1902 Plain Back
3x10-20 1131-4374 <$350
1929 Small Size
10 Type 1 1-714 <$125
20 Type 1 1-170 <$125
10 Type 2 1-410 <$125
20 Type 2 1-60 <$125
Total Issue $296,640
Out in 1935 $25,000
Large out 1935 $1,850
****
11056 Cherokee
AMERICAN NB OF BAXTER SPRINGS
{{ 6 L 21 S }}
Chartered 8/17
1902 Plain Back <$VALUE
3x10-20 1-8109 <$350
1929 Small Size
10 Type 1 1-1344 <$75
20 Type 1 1-360 <$75
10 Type 2 1-1518 <$75
20 Type 2 1-302 <$75
Total Issue $550,510
Out in 1935 $50,000
Large out 1935 $1,910
****
5952 Cherokee
BAXTER NB OF BAXTER SPRINGS
{{ 7 L 11 S }}
Chartered 8/01
Brown Back <$VALUE
50-100 1-460 <$2000/$2500
1882 Date Back
50-100 1-150 <$2000/$2500
3x50-100 1-200<$2000/$2500
1902 Plain Back
3x10-20 1-2076 <$350
1929 Small Size
10 Type 1 1-694 <$150
20 Type 1 1-178 <$150
10 Type 2 1-444 <$150
20 Type 2 1-132 <$150
Total Issue $315,380
Out in 1935 $25,000
Large out 1935 $2,120
****
1838 Cherokee
FNB OF BAXTER SPRINGS
{{ UNREPORTED }}
Chartered 6/22/71
Liquidated 1/12/75
Original Series <$VALUE
3x1-2 1-1500 <$2000/$3000
4x5 1-1695 <$2000
Total Issue $41,400
Out in 1910 $300
****
11177 Barton
FARMERS NB OF BEAVER
{{ 4 S }}
Chartered 4/18
1929 Small Size <$VALUE
5 Type 2 1-2520 <$400
10 Type 2 1-845 <$400
20 Type 2 1-225 <$400
Total Issue $25,550
Out in 1935 $25,000
****
FNB in Belleville
SEE Ch 3779
FNB of Scandia
****
3386 Republic
FNB OF BELLEVILLE
{{ UNREPORTED }}
Organized 8/28/85
Receivership 12/12/90
Brown Back <$VALUE
4x5 1-1130 <$2000
Total Issue $22,600
Out in 1915 $205
****
NB of Belleville
SEE Ch 3779
FNB of Scandia
****
9559 Republic
PEOPLES NB OF BELLEVILLE
{{ 6 L 15 S }}
Chartered 10/09
1902 Date Back <$VALUE
3x10-20 1-2840 <$250
1902 Plain Back
3x10-20 2841-7388 <$250
1929 Small Size
10 Type 1 1-898 <$125
20 Type 1 1-256 <$125
10 Type 2 1-1245 <$125
20 Type 2 1-231 <$125
Total Issue $471,070
Out in 1935 $40,000
Large out 1935 $3,000
****
3231 Mitchell
FNB OF BELOIT
{{ 19 L 26 S }}
Chartered 1884
Brown Back <$VALUE
4x5 1-4101 <$250
50-100 1-160 <$1250/$1500
1902 Red Seal
4x5 1-600 <$300
50-100 1-264 <$2000/$2500
1902 Date Back
4x5 1-2650 <$100
50-100 1-200 <$400/$500
3x50-100 1-424 <$400/$500
1902 Plain Back
4x5 2651-27005 <$100
1929 Small Size
5 Type 1 1-7920 <$60
5 Type 2 1-16618 <$60
Total Issue $1,154,410
Out in 1935 $75,000
Large out 1935 $4,640
****

<$VALUEs are for notes in **FINE** condition. Value changes by approximately **25%** for a change of one full grade.

***

6701 Mitchell
GERMAN NB OF NORTHERN KANSAS AT BELOIT
Organized 3/24/03
Receivership 11/13/23
2nd title:Union NB of Beloit 12/31/17
FIRST TITLE {{ 8 L }}
1902 Red Seal <$VALUE
4x5 1-2125 <$1000
3x10-20 1-1646 <$1000
1902 Date Back
4x5 1-3350 <$400
3x10-20 1-2340 <$400
1902 Plain Back
4x5 3351-4300 <$400
3x10-20 2341-2900 <$400
SECOND TITLE {{ 2 L }}
1902 Plain Back
4x5 1-2885 <$500
3x10-20 1-1631 <$500
3x50-100 1-20 <$850/$1000
Total Issue $500,050
Out at close $49,300

***

Union NB of Beloit
SEE Ch 6701
German NB of Northern Kansas at Beloit

***

9197 Wyandotte
FNB OF BONNER SPRINGS
{{ 5 L 3 S }}
Chartered 7/08
Liquidated 8/11/31
1902 Date Back <$VALUE
3x10-20 1-2280 <$450
1902 Plain Back
3x10-20 2281-6001 <$450
1929 Small Size
10 Type 1 1-397 <$300
20 Type 1 1-100 <$300
Total Issue $335,870
Out at close $25,000
Large out at close $3,670

***

9157 Osage
BURLINGAME NB, BURLINGAME
{{ 1 L }}
Chartered 6/08
Liquidated 1/19/14
1902 Date Back <$VALUE
3x10-20 1-1299 <$850
Total Issue $64,950
Out in 1914 $11,310

***

4040 Osage
FNB OF BURLINGAME
{{ 5 L 4 S }}
Chartered 1889
Brown Back <$VALUE
3x10-20 1-2303 <$850
1902 Date Back
3x10-20 1-1640* <$350
1902 Plain Back
3x10-20 1941-4736* <$350
* 1641-1940 not marked
1929 Small Size
10 Type 1 1-608 <$150
20 Type 1 1-208 <$150
5 Type 2 1-259 <$150
10 Type 2 1-73 <$150
20 Type 2 1-30 <$150
Total Issue $416,015
Out in 1935 $26,250
Large out 1935 $2,105

***

1979 Coffey
BURLINGTON NB, BURLINGTON
{{ 7 L }}
Chartered 5/10/72
Liquidated 4/26/07
Original Series <$VALUE
3x1-2 1-2300 <$1000/$2000
4x5 1-2425 <$1000
Series 1875
3x1-2 1-580 <$1000/$2000
4x5 1-7762 <$1000
Brown Back
3x10-20 1-3670 <$850
Total Issue $401,640
Out in 1910 $12,474

***

6955 Coffey
FARMERS NB OF BURLINGTON
{{ 7 L }}
Organized 9/10/03
Receivership 5/21/24
1902 Red Seal <$VALUE
3x10-20 1-1400 <$1000
1902 Date Back
3x10-20 1-2510 <$400
1902 Plain Back
3x10-20 2511-6491 <$400
Total Issue $394,550
Out at close $49,300

***

3170 Coffey
PEOPLES NB OF BURLINGTON
{{ 13 L 16 S }}
Chartered 1884
Brown Back <$VALUE
3x10-20 1-4717 <$300
1902 Red Seal
3x10-20 1-1900 <$400
1902 Date Back
3x10-20 1-2900 <$100
1902 Plain Back
3x10-20 2901-8721 <$100
1929 Small Size
10 Type 1 1-1128 <$65
20 Type 1 1-334 <$75
10 Type 2 1-1443 <$75
20 Type 2 1-236 <$75
Total Issue $893,810
Out in 1935 $50,000
Large out 1935 $3,880

***

3880 Jewell
FNB OF BURR OAK
{{ UNREPORTED }}
Chartered 5/5/88
Liquidated 5/15/91
Brown Back <$VALUE
4x5 1-566 <$2000
3x10-20 1-89 <$2000
Total Issue $15,770
Out in 1910 $125

***

7302 Jewell
JEWELL COUNTY NB OF BURR OAK
{{ 5 L 10 S }}
Chartered 6/04
Liquidated 11/14/33
1902 Red Seal <$VALUE
3x10-20 1-3860 <$750
1902 Date Back
3x10-20 1-3400 <$300
1902 Plain Back
3x10-20 3401-8824 <$300
1929 Small Size
10 Type 1 1-1021 <$125
20 Type 1 1-293 <$125
Total Issue $730,620
Out at close $50,000
Large out at close $4,260

***

6333 Sumner
CALDWELL NB, CALDWELL
{{ 5 L }}
Chartered 7/10/02
Liquidated 6/15/09
1902 Red Seal <$VALUE
3x10-20 1-1350 <$2000
1902 Date Back
3x10-20 1 <$1500
Total Issue $67,550
Out in 1910 $11,010

***

3658 Sumner
FNB OF CALDWELL
{{ UNREPORTED }}
Chartered 3/29/87
Liquidated 12/2/93
Brown Back <$VALUE
3x10-20 1-530 <$2000
Total Issue $26,500
Out in 1910 $330

***

5349 Montgomery
CANEY VALLEY NB OF CANEY
{{ 7 L 16 S }}
Chartered 5/14/00
Brown Back <$VALUE
3x10-20 1-2690 <$600
1882 Date Back
3x10-20 1-3400 <$600
1882 Value Back
3x10-20 3401-5192 <$600
1902 Plain Back
3x10-20 1-6082 <$225
1929 Small Size
10 Type 1 1-1297 <$100
20 Type 1 1-374 <$100
Total Issue $820,900
Out in 1935 $25,000
Large out 1935 $3,080

***

5516 Montgomery
HOME NB OF CANEY
{{ 4 L 4 S }}
Chartered 7/23/00
Liquidated 5/4/31
Brown Back <$VALUE
3x10-20 1-1900 <$600
1882 Date Back
3x10-20 1-2740 <$600
1882 Value Back
3x10-20 2741-4232 <$600
1902 Plain Back
3x10-20 1-4334 <$350
1929 Small Size
10 Type 1 1-522 <$250
20 Type 1 1-125 <$250
Total Issue $569,620
Out at close $40,000
Large out at close $6,440

***

4618 Mitchell
FARMERS & MERCHANTS NB OF CAWKER CITY
{{ 1 L }}
Chartered 8/19/91
Liquidated 12/22/96
Brown Back <$VALUE
4x5 1-1913 <$2000
Total Issue $38,260
Out in 1910 $285

***

2640 Mitchell
FNB OF CAWKER CITY
{{ 1 L }}
Chartered 3/1/82
Liquidated 10/9/88
Series 1875 <$VALUE
3x10-20 1-685 <$2500/$3000
Total Issue $34,250
Out in 1910 $120

***

5608 Chautauqua
CEDAR VALE NB, CEDAR VALE
{{ 1 L 3 S }}
Chartered 10/25/00
Brown Back <$VALUE
3x10-20 1-450 <$1500
1882 Date Back
3x10-20 1-614 <$1500
1902 Plain Back
3x10-20 1-619 <$750
1929 Small Size
10 Type 1 1-210 <$500
20 Type 1 1-52 <$500
Total Issue $102,990
Out in 1935 $6,250
Large out 1935 $290

***

Citizens NB of Cedar Vale
SEE Ch 6530
Dosbaugh NB of Cedar Vale

***

6530 Chautauqua
DOSBAUGH NB OF CEDAR VALE
Chartered 12/02
Liquidated 12/29/33
2nd title:Citizens NB of Cedar Vale 3/8/21
FIRST TITLE {{ 2 L }}
1902 Red Seal <$VALUE
3x10-20 1-800 <$1250
1902 Date Back
3x10-20 1-3600 <$500
1902 Plain Back
3x10-20 3601-6150 <$500
SECOND TITLE {{ 6 L 20 S }}
1902 Plain Back
3x10-20 1-4474 <$300
1929 Small Size
10 Type 1 1-1286 <$75
20 Type 1 1-336 <$75
10 Type 2 1-93 <$75
Total Issue $689,610
Out at close $50,000
Large out at close $4,150

***

3824 Nemaha
FNB OF CENTRALIA
{{ 6 L 11 S }}
Chartered 1887
Brown Back <$VALUE
4x5 1-4250 <$500
3x10-20 1-1560 <$500
1902 Red Seal
4x5 1-310 <$600
3x10-20 1-251 <$600
1902 Date Back
4x5 1-2250 <$275
3x10-20 1-1820 <$275
1902 Plain Back
4x5 2251-7680 <$275
3x10-20 1821-5188 <$275
1929 Small Size
5 Type 1 1-1038 <$85
10 Type 1 1-652 <$85
20 Type 1 1-190 <$85
5 Type 2 1-1832 <$100
10 Type 2 1-963 <$100
20 Type 2 1-144 <$100
Total Issue $709,480
Out in 1935 $37,500
Large out 1935 $2,625

***

4036 Neosho
CHANUTE NB, CHANUTE
{{ UNREPORTED }}
Chartered 5/16/89
Liquidated 5/6/97
Brown Back <$VALUE
4x5 1-474 <$2000
3x10-20 1-527 <$2000
Total Issue $35,830
Out in 1910 $250

***

3819 Neosho
FNB OF CHANUTE
{{ 9 L 39 S }}
Chartered 1887
Brown Back <$VALUE
4x5 1-5448 <$400
3x10-20 1-2844 <$400
1902 Red Seal
4x5 1-1000 <$500
3x10-20 1-800 <$500
1902 Date Back
4x5 1-5750 <$225
3x10-20 1-4600 <$225
1902 Plain Back
4x5 5751-20050 <$225
3x10-20 4601-14460 <$225
1929 Small Size
5 Type 1 1-3192 <$40
10 Type 1 1-1798 <$40
20 Type 1 1-478 <$45
5 Type 2 1-4980 <$40
10 Type 2 1-2174 <$40
20 Type 2 1-1039 <$50
Total Issue $1,763,580
Out in 1935 $100,000
Large out 1935 $5,740

***

6072 Neosho
NB OF CHANUTE
{{ UNREPORTED }}
Chartered 12/28/01
Liquidated 10/10/03
Brown Back <$VALUE
4x5 1-290 <$2000
3x10-20 1-222 <$2000
Total Issue $16,900
Out in 1910 $430

***

5447 Crawford
FNB OF CHEROKEE
{{ 2 L 8 S }}
Chartered 6/23/00
Receivership 2/17/32
Brown Back <$VALUE
3x10-20 1-500 <$1000
1882 Date Back
3x10-20 1-580 <$1000
1902 Plain Back
4x10 1-3960 <$500
1929 Small Size
10 Type 1 1-733 <$300
Total Issue $256,380
Out at close $23,980
Large out at close $2,930

***

4288 Montgomery
CHERRYVALE NB, CHERRYVALE
{{ UNREPORTED }}
Organized 4/16/90
Receivership 7/2/92
Brown Back <$VALUE
3x10-20 1-275 <$2000
Total Issue $13,750
Out in 1915 $100

***

3277 Montgomery
FNB OF CHERRYVALE
{{ UNREPORTED }}
Chartered 12/22/84
Liquidated 8/1/95
Brown Back <$VALUE
4x5 1-605 <$2000
3x10-20 1-538 <$2000
Total Issue $39,000
Out in 1910 $310

***

4749 Montgomery
MONTGOMERY COUNTY NB OF CHERRYVALE
{{ 8 L 7 S }}
Organized 5/21/92
Receivership 5/7/31
Brown Back <$VALUE
4x5 1-3525 <$400
3x10-20 1-1440 <$400
1882 Date Back
4x5 1-726 <$400
3x10-20 1-869 <$400
1902 Date Back
3x10-20 1-1560 <$225
1902 Plain Back
3x10-20 1561-7499 <$225
1929 Small Size
10 Type 1 1-707 <$150
20 Type 1 1-195 <$150
Total Issue $641,240
Out at close $50,000
Large out at close $8,000

***

7383 Montgomery
PEOPLES NB OF CHERRYVALE
{{ 1 L }}
Chartered 8/30/04
Liquidated 9/27/09
1902 Red Seal <$VALUE
3x10-20 1-713 <$1500
50-100 1-350 <$3000/$3500
1902 Date Back
3x10-20 1-108 <$750
50-100 1-51 <$1250/$1500
Total Issue $101,200
Out in 1910 $28,760

***

1902 Labette
FNB OF CHETOPA
{{ 3 L }}
Chartered 11/28/71
Liquidated 7/19/75
Original Series <$VALUE
3x1-2 1-1388 <$1000/$2000
4x5 1-2160 <$1000
Total Issue $50,140
Out in 1910 $239

***

11374 Labette
NB OF CHETOPA
{{ 5 L 1 S }}
Chartered 6/19
Liquidated 1/16/32
1902 Plain Back <$VALUE
4x5 1-2345 <$750
3x10-20 1-1392 <$750
1929 Small Size
5 Type 1 1-295 <$500
10 Type 1 1-94 <$500
20 Type 1 1-42 <$500
Total Issue $136,030
Out at close $12,500
Large out at close $2,045

***

13329 Gray
FNB IN CIMARRON
{{ 9 S }}
Chartered 5/21/29
1929 Small Size <$VALUE
5 Type 1 1-1080 <$200
10 Type 1 1-542 <$200
20 Type 1 1-156 <$200
5 Type 2 1-986 <$200
10 Type 2 1-530 <$200
20 Type 2 1-160 <$200
Total Issue $97,070
Out in 1935 $24,400

***

3751 Gray
FNB OF CIMARRON
{{ 1 L }}
Chartered 7/14/87
Liquidated 4/27/89
Brown Back <$VALUE
4x5 1-615 <$2000
Total Issue $12,300
Out in 1910 $85

***

3072 Clay
FNB OF CLAY CENTER
{{ 8 L 10 S }}
Organized 11/1/83
Receivership 9/6/33
Brown Back <$VALUE
4x5 1-4646 <$500
3x10-20 1-1199 <$500
1902 Red Seal
3x10-20 1-1900 <$600
1902 Date Back
3x10-20 1-2900 <$275
1902 Plain Back
3x10-20 2901-8914 <$275
1929 Small Size
10 Type 1 1-1117 <$125
20 Type 1 1-303 <$125
Total Issue $796,950
Out at close $50,000
Large out at close $4,730

***

3345 Clay
PEOPLES NB OF CLAY CENTER
{{ 9 L 16 S }}
Chartered 1885
Brown Back <$VALUE
4x5 1-3725 <$400
3x10-20 1-1695 <$400
1902 Red Seal
3x10-20 1-2350 <$500
1902 Date Back
3x10-20 1-5400 <$250
1902 Plain Back
3x10-20 5401-14209 <$250
1929 Small Size
10 Type 1 1-1746 <$50
20 Type 1 1-484 <$60
10 Type 2 1-2411 <$50
20 Type 2 1-615 <$60
Total Issue $1,186,450
Out in 1935 $75,000
Large out 1935 $5,400

***

7178 Washington
FNB OF CLIFTON
{{ 17U + 9 L 3 S }}
Chartered 3/04
1902 Red Seal <$VALUE
3x10-20 1-1200 <$500
1902 Date Back
3x10-20 1-1330 <$175
1902 Plain Back
3x10-20 1331-3071 <$175
1929 Small Size
10 Type 1 1-394 <$250
20 Type 1 1-118 <$250
10 Type 2 1-97 <$250
20 Type 2 1-40 <$250
Total Issue $253,120
Out in 1935 $17,500
Large out 1935 $2,730

***

11775 Cloud
EXCHANGE NB OF CLYDE
{{ 7 S }}
Chartered 7/20
1929 Small Size <$VALUE
5 Type 1 1-522 <$175
10 Type 1 1-254 <$175
20 Type 1 1-76 <$175
5 Type 2 1-750 <$200
10 Type 2 1-425 <$200
20 Type 2 1-145 <$200
Total Issue $50,920
Out in 1935 $25,000

***

3115 Cloud
FNB OF CLYDE
{{ 1 L }}
Chartered 1/31/84
Liquidated 11/15/92
Brown Back <$VALUE
4x5 1-1772 <$2000
Total Issue $35,440
Out in 1910 $255

***

6797 Montgomery
CONDON NB OF COFFEYVILLE
{{ 18 L U + 21 S }}
Chartered 5/03
1902 Red Seal <$VALUE
3x10-20 1-3150 <$400
1902 Date Back
3x10-20 1-8100 <$100
1902 Plain Back
3x10-20 8101-23547 <$100
1929 Small Size
10 Type 1 1-2494 <$45
20 Type 1 1-712 <$50
10 Type 2 1-2864 <$45
20 Type 2 1-710 <$55
Total Issue $1,612,770
Out in 1935 $100,000
Large out 1935 $6,090

***

3324 Montgomery
FNB OF COFFEYVILLE
{{ 10 L 27 S }}
Chartered 1885
Brown Back <$VALUE
3x10-20 1-2073 <$350
1902 Red Seal
3x10-20 1-1800 <$400
1902 Date Back
3x10-20 1-5400 <$150
1902 Plain Back
3x10-20 5401-17217 <$150
1929 Small Size
10 Type 1 1-2006 <$40
20 Type 1 1-592 <$45
10 Type 2 1-2576 <$45
20 Type 2 1-745 <$50
Total Issue $1,286,560
Out in 1935 $100,000
Large out 1935 $3,760

***

****
11047 Thomas
CITIZENS NB OF COLBY
{{ 1 L }}
Chartered 7/17
Liquidated 10/31/25
1902 Plain Back <$VALUE
4x5 1-750 <$1250
Total Issue $15,000
Out at close $500
****
3512 Thomas
FNB OF COLBY
{{ 1 L }}
Chartered 5/27/86
Liquidated 11/21/88
Brown Back <$VALUE
4x5 1-749 <$2000
Total Issue $14,980
Out in 1910 $65
****
13076 Thomas
THOMAS COUNTY NB OF COLBY
{{ 4U + 5 L 3U + 9 S }}
Chartered 5/12/27
1902 Plain Back <$VALUE
4x5 1-5763 <$250
1929 Small Size
5 Type 1 1-6090 <$125
5 Type 2 1-12876 <$125
Total Issue $362,340
Out in 1935 $50,000
Large out 1935 $810
****
6767 Comanche
COLDWATER NB, COLDWATER
{{ 3 L 3U + 13 S }}
Chartered 5/03
1902 Red Seal <$VALUE
50-100 1-420 <$2500/$3000
1902 Date Back
50-100 1-160 <$1000/$1250
3x50-100 1-400<$1000/$1250
1902 Plain Back
3x50-100 401-491
<$1000/$1250
1929 Small Size
5 Type 1 1-806 <$200
10 Type 1 1-514 <$200
5 Type 2 1-2108 <$200
10 Type 2 1-1140 <$200
Total Issue $286,710
Out in 1935 $25,000
Large out 1935 $3,150
****
3703 Comanche
FNB OF COLDWATER
{{ UNREPORTED }}
Organized 5/9/87
Receivership 10/14/91
Brown Back <$VALUE
4x5 1-1125 <$2000
Total Issue $22,500
Out in 1915 $140
****
11855 Trego
FNB OF COLLYER
{{ 11 S }}
Chartered 10/20
1929 Small Size <$VALUE
20 Type 1 1-91 <$150
50 Type 1 1-84 <$200
100 Type 1 1-82 <$300
Total Issue $61,320
Out in 1935 $50,000
****
11531 Anderson
FNB OF COLONY
{{ 8 L 3 S }}
Organized 11/7/19
Receivership 8/14/31
1902 Plain Back <$VALUE
3x10-20 1-3291 <$300
1929 Small Size
10 Type 1 1-367 <$250
20 Type 1 1-105 <$250
Total Issue $199,170
Out at close $25,000
Large out at close $3,850
****
6103 Cherokee
FNB OF COLUMBUS
{{ 3 L 9 S }}
Chartered 1/02
1902 Red Seal <$VALUE
3x10-20 1-870 <$1000
1902 Date Back
3x10-20 1-2040 <$400
1902 Plain Back (dated 1902)
3x10-20 2041-3299 <$400
1902 Plain Back (dated 1922)
3x10-20 1-2322 <$400
1929 Small Size
10 Type 1 1-676 <$175
20 Type 1 1-158 <$175
10 Type 2 1-484 <$175
20 Type 2 1-171 <$175
Total Issue $392,330
Out in 1935 $25,000
Large out 1935 $1,320
****
3748 Cloud
CITIZENS NB OF CONCORDIA
{{ 1 L }}
Chartered 7/8/87
Liquidated 2/1/98
Brown Back <$VALUE
4x5 1-4405 <$1500
Total Issue $88,100
Out in 1910 $710
****
3090 Cloud
CONCORDIA NB, CONCORDIA
{{ UNREPORTED }}
Chartered 12/15/83
Liquidated 3/12/86
Brown Back <$VALUE
4x5 1-662 <$2000
Total Issue $13,240
Out in 1910 $140
****
3066 Cloud
FNB OF CONCORDIA
{{ 2 L }}
Organized 10/12/83
Brown Back <$VALUE
3x10-20 1-2587 <$1000
1902 Red Seal
50-100 1-1394 <$2500/$3000
1902 Date Back
50-100 1-500 <$1000/$1250
3x50-100 1-927<$1000/$1250
Total Issue $645,200
Out in 1935 $7,290
****
8467 Sumner
FNB OF CONWAY SPRINGS
{{ 8 L 5 S }}
Chartered 12/06
1902 Red Seal <$VALUE
3x10-20 1-900 <$1000
1902 Date Back
3x10-20 1-1100 <$400
1902 Plain Back
3x10-20 1101-4032 <$400
1929 Small Size
10 Type 1 1-506 <$200
20 Type 1 1-138 <$200
10 Type 2 1-914 <$200
20 Type 2 1-144 <$200
Total Issue $305,540
Out in 1935 $20,000
Large out 1935 $1,300
****
2764 Chase
CHASE COUNTY NB OF
COTTONWOOD FALLS
{{ 7 L }}
Organized 6/21/82
Receivership 2/6/28
Series 1875 <$VALUE
4x5 1-1200 <$750
3x10-20 1-1039<$1750/$2000
1902 Red Seal
50-100 1-864 <$2000/$2500
1902 Date Back
3x10-20 1-6600 <$250
1902 Plain Back
3x10-20 6601-14848 <$250
Total Issue $947,950
Out in 1924 $100,000
****
6590 Chase
EXCHANGE NB OF
COTTONWOOD FALLS
{{ 12 L 19 S }}
Chartered 1/03
1902 Red Seal <$VALUE
3x10-20 1-3212 <$500
1902 Date Back
3x10-20 1-5000 <$175
1902 Plain Back
3x10-20 5001-15893 <$175
1929 Small Size
10 Type 1 1-1818 <$60
20 Type 1 1-584 <$60
10 Type 2 1-1949 <$60
20 Type 2 1-470 <$60
Total Issue $1,163,300
Out in 1935 $75,000
Large out 1935 $4,330
****
****
5757 Morris
COUNCIL GROVE NB,
COUNCIL GROVE
{{ 10 L 12 S }}
Chartered 3/01
Brown Back <$VALUE
4x5 1-2000 <$400
3x10-20 1-1600 <$400
1882 Date Back
4x5 1-2850 <$400
3x10-20 1-2100 <$400
1882 Value Back
4x5 2851-5040 <$400
3x10-20 2101-3281 <$400
1902 Plain Back
4x5 1-4869 <$175
3x10-20 1-3119 <$175
1929 Small Size
5 Type 1 1-1698 <$100
10 Type 1 1-952 <$100
20 Type 1 1-266 <$100
5 Type 2 1-18 <$150
10 Type 2 1-25 <$150
Total Issue $778,500
Out in 1935 $25,000
Large out 1935 $3,330
****
2001 Morris
FNB OF COUNCIL GROVE
{{ UNREPORTED }}
Chartered 6/24/72
Liquidated 11/28/76
Original Series <$VALUE
3x1-2 1-1320 <$2000/$3000
4x5 1-1875 <$2000
Series 1875
4x5 1-15 <$2000
Total Issue $44,400
Out in 1915 $290
****
7532 Ottawa
FNB OF DELPHOS
{{ 16 L 7 S }}
Chartered 12/04
1902 Red Seal <$VALUE
3x10-20 1-900 <$350
1902 Date Back
3x10-20 1-1320 <$85
1902 Plain Back
3x10-20 1321-3611 <$85
1929 Small Size
5 Type 1 1-668 <$200
10 Type 1 1-316 <$200
20 Type 1 1-98 <$200
5 Type 2 1-332 <$200
10 Type 2 1-240 <$200
20 Type 2 1-35 <$200
Total Issue $281,070
Out in 1935 $20,000
Large out 1935 $1,730
****
9225 Cowley
FNB OF DEXTER
{{ 6U + 5 L }}
Chartered 8/08
Liquidated 8/1/14
1902 Date Back <$VALUE
3x10-20 1-434 <$300
Total Issue $21,700
Out in 1914 $5,600
****
3888 Lane
FNB OF DIGHTON
{{ UNREPORTED }}
Chartered 5/28/88
Liquidated 10/1/97
Brown Back <$VALUE
4x5 1-2004 <$2000
Total Issue $40,080
Out in 1910 $370
****
9773 Lane
FNB OF DIGHTON
{{ 7 L U + 21 S }}
Chartered 6/10
1902 Date Back <$VALUE
4x5 1-1800 <$400
3x10-20 1-1380 <$400
1902 Plain Back
4x5 1801-5561 <$400
3x10-20 1381-3658 <$400
1929 Small Size
5 Type 1 1-820 <$50
10 Type 1 1-408 <$50
20 Type 1 1-114 <$50
5 Type 2 1-1476 <$55
10 Type 2 1-772 <$55
20 Type 2 1-183 <$65
Total Issue $375,640
Out in 1935 $25,000
Large out 1935 $1,820
****
****
FNB in Dodge City
SEE Ch 7285
NB Of Commerce of Dodge City
****
3596 Ford
FNB OF DODGE CITY
{{ UNREPORTED }}
Chartered 12/4/86
Liquidated 7/27/94
Brown Back <$VALUE
4x5 1-1753 <$2000
Total Issue $35,060
Out in 1910 $400
****
7285 Ford
NB OF COMMERCE OF
DODGE CITY
Chartered 6/04
2nd title:FNB in Dodge City
1/8/21
FIRST TITLE {{ 2 L }}
1902 Red Seal <$VALUE
3x10-20 1-1200 <$1000
1902 Date Back
3x10-20 1-1800 <$400
1902 Plain Back
3x10-20 1801-3580 <$400
SECOND TITLE {{ 4 L 12 S }}
1902 Plain Back
3x10-20 1-4187 <$400
1929 Small Size
10 Type 1 1-1094 <$85
20 Type 1 1-310 <$85
10 Type 2 1-709 <$85
20 Type 2 1-185 <$85
Total Issue $561,980
Out in 1935 $40,000
Large out 1935 $1,600
****
11318 Osborne
DOWNS NB, DOWNS
{{ 2 L 11 S }}
Chartered 3/19
1902 Plain Back <$VALUE
3x10-20 1-3221 <$500
1929 Small Size
10 Type 1 1-544 <$200
20 Type 1 1-142 <$200
10 Type 2 1-883 <$200
20 Type 2 1-139 <$200
Total Issue $222,340
Out in 1935 $25,000
Large out 1935 $2,050
****
3563 Osborne
EXCHANGE NB OF DOWNS
{{ UNREPORTED }}
Chartered 9/30/86
Liquidated 8/1/87
Brown Back <$VALUE
4x5 1-563 <$2000
Total Issue $11,260
Out in 1910 $90
****
3569 Osborne
FNB OF DOWNS
{{ UNREPORTED }}
Organized 10/12/86
Receivership 2/6/92
Brown Back <$VALUE
4x5 1-1258 <$2000
Total Issue $25,160
Out in 1915 $145
****
9160 Norton
FNB OF EDMOND
{{ 5 L }}
Chartered 6/08
Liquidated 3/10/25
1902 Date Back <$VALUE
4x5 1-1784 <$500
4x10 1-1780 <$500
1902 Plain Back
4x5 1785-4290 <$500
4x10 1781-3552 <$500
Total Issue $227,880
Out at close $25,000
****
7590 Labette
FNB OF EDNA
{{ 7 L 16 S }}
Chartered 2/05
1902 Red Seal <$VALUE
3x10-20 1-507 <$750
1902 Date Back
3x10-20 1-1540 <$300
1902 Plain Back
3x10-20 1541-5224 <$300
1929 Small Size
10 Type 1 1-666 <$150
20 Type 1 1-170 <$150
10 Type 2 1-736 <$150
20 Type 2 1-120 <$150
Total Issue $356,670
Out in 1935 $25,000
Large out 1935 $1,470
****
6494 Butler
EL DORADO NB, EL DORADO
{{ 8 L 11 S }}
Chartered 11/02
1902 Red Seal <$VALUE
3x10-20 1-2413 <$600
1902 Date Back
3x10-20 1-3100 <$200
1902 Plain Back
3x10-20 3101-11276 <$200
1929 Small Size
10 Type 1 1-1332 <$100
20 Type 1 1-366 <$100
10 Type 2 1-1642 <$100
20 Type 2 1-492 <$100
Total Issue $834,550
Out in 1935 $50,000
Large out 1935 $2,990
****
3213 Butler
EXCHANGE NB OF EL DORADO
{{ 1 L }}
Chartered 6/26/84
Liquidated 12/17/96
Brown Back <$VALUE
4x5 1-4455 <$1500
Total Issue $89,100
Out in 1910 $660
****
4981 Butler
FARMERS & MERCHANTS NB OF
EL DORADO
{{ 8 L 10 S }}
Chartered 1894
Brown Back <$VALUE
4x5 1-2925 <$500
3x10-20 1-1200 <$500
1882 Date Back
4x5 1-1977 <$500
3x10-20 1-1341 <$500
1902 Date Back
4x5 1-625 <$225
3x10-20 1-500 <$225
1902 Plain Back
4x5 626-6615 <$225
3x10-20 501-4256 <$225
1929 Small Size
5 Type 1 1-1394 <$100
10 Type 1 1-680 <$100
20 Type 1 1-172 <$100
5 Type 2 1-2102 <$100
10 Type 2 1-1066 <$100
20 Type 2 1-396 <$100
Total Issue $702,540
Out in 1935 $37,495
Large out 1935 $2,815
****
1957 Butler
FNB OF EL DORADO
{{ UNREPORTED }}
Chartered 4/11/72
Liquidated 6/30/75
Original Series <$VALUE
3x1-2 1-1680 <$2000/$3000
4x5 1-2575 <$2000
Total Issue $59,900
Out in 1910 $381
****
3833 Butler
MERCHANTS NB OF EL DORADO
{{ UNREPORTED }}
Chartered 1/3/88
Liquidated 2/26/89
Brown Back <$VALUE
4x5 1-1125 <$2000
Total Issue $22,500
Out in 1910 $170
****
3035 Butler
NB OF EL DORADO
{{ UNREPORTED }}
Chartered 8/22/83
Liquidated 2/9/91
Brown Back <$VALUE
3x10-20 1-562 <$2000
Total Issue $28,100
Out in 1910 $200
****
****
8145 Montgomery
FNB OF ELK CITY
{{ 3 L 11 S }}
Chartered 3/06
1902 Red Seal <$VALUE
3x10-20 1-287 <$1250
1902 Date Back
3x10-20 1-1560 <$500
1902 Plain Back
3x10-20 1561-5136 <$500
1929 Small Size
10 Type 1 1-630 <$150
20 Type 1 1-202 <$150
10 Type 2 1-602 <$150
20 Type 2 1-130 <$150
Total Issue $341,810
Out in 1935 $25,000
Large out 1935 $1,880
****
8708 Montgomery
PEOPLES NB OF ELK CITY
{{ UNREPORTED }}
Chartered 5/07
Liquidated 2/16/10
1902 Red Seal <$VALUE
4x5 1-158 <$2000
3x10-20 1-126 <$2000
1902 Date Back
4x5 1-22 <$1500
3x10-20 1-42 <$1500
Total Issue $12,000
Out in 1910 $3,890
****
3447 Ellsworth
CENTRAL NB OF ELLSWORTH
{{ 7 L 4 S }}
Organized 1/13/86
Receivership 3/30/31
Brown Back <$VALUE
3x10-20 1-1987 <$600
1902 Red Seal
3x10-20 1-450 <$750
1902 Date Back
3x10-20 1-1800 <$300
1902 Plain Back
3x10-20 1801-4482 <$300
1929 Small Size
10 Type 1 1-295 <$250
20 Type 1 1-76 <$250
Total Issue $372,770
Out at close $25,000
Large out at close $6,730
****
3249 Ellsworth
FNB OF ELLSWORTH
{{ UNREPORTED }}
Organized 9/11/84
Receivership 2/11/91
Brown Back <$VALUE
4x5 1-517 <$2000
3x10-20 1-321 <$2000
Total Issue $26,390
Out in 1915 $110
****
5498 Lyon
CITIZENS NB OF EMPORIA
{{ 13 L 18 S }}
Chartered 7/14/00
Brown Back <$VALUE
4x5 1-3000 <$300
3x10-20 1-7300 <$300
1882 Date Back
4x5 1-11000 <$300
3x10-20 1-7400 <$300
1882 Value Back
4x5 11001-15750 <$350
3x10-20 7401-10080 <$350
1902 Plain Back
3x10-20 1-15583 <$75
3x50-100 1-901 <$350/$400
1929 Small Size
5 Type 1 1-2790 <$50
10 Type 1 1-2516 <$50
20 Type 1 1-668 <$50
50 Type 1 1-184 <$175
100 Type 1 1-66 <$225
5 Type 2 1-7570 <$60
10 Type 2 1-2599 <$60
20 Type 2 1-700 <$60
Total Issue $2,735,860
Out in 1935 $200,000
Large out 1935 $20,490
Outstanding includes Ch 1983
****

11781 Lyon
COMMERCIAL NB & TC OF EMPORIA
{{ 11 L 16 S }}
Chartered 7/20
1902 Plain Back <$VALUE
4x5 1-10905 <$125
3x10-20 1-7467 <$125
1929 Small Size
5 Type 1 1-3654 <$70
10 Type 1 1-1712 <$70
20 Type 1 1-432 <$75
5 Type 2 1-5624 <$75
10 Type 2 1-2744 <$75
20 Type 2 1-530 <$100
Total Issue $921,790
Out in 1935 $100,000
Large out 1935 $5,480

1983 Lyon
EMPORIA NB, EMPORIA
{{ 20 L }}
Chartered 5/13/72
Liquidated 5/15/20
Original Series <$VALUE
3x1-2 1-2500 <$400/$1000
4x5 1-2375 <$400
Series 1875
3x1-2 1-400 <$400/$1000
4x5 1-8609 <$400
Brown Back
4x5 1-4000 <$300
3x10-20 1-11920 <$300
1882 Date Back
4x5 1-4665 <$300
3x10-20 1-2865 <$300
1902 Date Back
4x5 1-7330 <$100
3x10-20 1-6168 <$100
1902 Plain Back
4x5 7331-14207 <$100
3x10-20 6169-9361 <$100
Total Issue $1,898,920
Out at close $200,000
Ch 5498 assumed circulation

1915 Lyon
FNB OF EMPORIA
{{ 50+ L }}
Chartered 1/2/72
Receivership 11/16/98
Original Series <$VALUE
3x1-2 1-5980 <$300/$800
4x5 1-5255 <$350
Series 1875
3x1-2 1-2000 <$300/$800
4x5 1-11869 <$350
Brown Back
3x10-20 1-915 <$250
Total Issue $428,130
Out in 1915 $3,578

9097 Clark
FNB OF ENGLEWOOD
{{ UNREPORTED }}
Organized 3/21/08
Receivership 1/4/33
1902 Red Seal <$VALUE
4x10 1-250 <$2000
1902 Date Back
4x10 1-741 <$1500
Total Issue $39,640
Out at close $30

3963 Neosho
FNB OF ERIE
{{ 2U + 0 L }}
Organized 1/15/89
Receivership 7/2/92
Brown Back <$VALUE
4x5 1-963 <$1500
Total Issue $19,260
Out in 1915 $210

5655 Greenwood
CITIZENS NB OF EUREKA
{{ 8 L 10 S }}
Chartered 12/26/00
Liquidated 6/1/35
Brown Back <$VALUE
4x5 1-1600 <$400
3x10-20 1-1240 <$400
1882 Date Back
4x5 1-2350 <$400
3x10-20 1-1800 <$400
1882 Value Back
4x5 2351-3750 <$400
3x10-20 1801-2536 <$400
1902 Plain Back
4x5 1-11540 <$225
1929 Small Size
5 Type 1 1-3676 <$150
5 Type 2 1-2006 <$150
Total Issue $646,910
Out at close $35,000
Large out at close $2,470

3148 Greenwood
FNB OF EUREKA
{{ 2 L }}
Chartered 1884
Liquidated 1/8/24
Brown Back <$VALUE
4x5 1-4504 <$750
3x10-20 1-416 <$750
1902 Red Seal
3x10-20 1-650 <$100
1902 Date Back
3x10-20 1-3350 <$400
1902 Plain Back
3x10-20 3351-7411 <$400
Total Issue $513,930
Out at close $50,000

7303 Greenwood
HOME NB OF EUREKA
{{ 1 L 7 S }}
Chartered 6/04
1902 Red Seal <$VALUE
4x5 1-230 <$1500
3x10-20 1-184 <$1500
1902 Date Back
4x5 1-625 <$750
3x10-20 1-480 <$750
1902 Plain Back
4x5 626-1312 <$750
3x10-20 481-940 <$750
1929 Small Size
5 Type 1 1-268 <$300
10 Type 1 1-133 <$300
20 Type 1 1-41 <$300
Total Issue $107,980
Out in 1935 $6,250
Large out 1935 $320

8596 Jewell
FNB OF FORMOSO
{{ 5 L 5 S }}
Chartered 3/07
1902 Red Seal <$VALUE
4x5 1-310 <$1000
3x10-20 1-251 <$1000
1902 Date Back
4x5 1-900 <$450
3x10-20 1-640 <$450
1902 Plain Back
4x5 901-2478 <$450
3x10-20 641-1572 <$450
1929 Small Size
5 Type 1 1-416 <$300
10 Type 1 1-202 <$300
20 Type 1 1-70 <$300
5 Type 2 1-288 <$300
10 Type 2 1-193 <$300
20 Type 2 1-50 <$300
Total Issue $184,280
Out in 1935 $12,500
Large out 1935 $825

8796 Leavenworth
ARMY NB OF FORT LEAVENWORTH
{{ 10 L U + 8 S }}
Chartered 7/07
1902 Red Seal <$VALUE
4x5 1-550 <$2000
4x10 1-550 <$2000
1902 Date Back
4x5 1-1750 <$750
4x10 1-1700 <$750
1902 Plain Back
4x5 1751-6722 <$750
4x10 1701-5381 <$750
1929 Small Size
5 Type 1 1-1264 <$400
10 Type 1 1-726 <$400
5 Type 2 1-1616 <$400
10 Type 2 1-1114 <$400
Total Issue $483,380
Out in 1935 $25,000
Large out 1935 $1,670

3175 Bourbon
CITIZENS NB OF FORT SCOTT
{{ 16 L 44 S }}
Chartered 1884
Brown Back <$VALUE
3x10-20 1-4645 <$250/$300
1902 Red Seal
3x10-20 1-3800 <$300/$350
1902 Date Back
3x10-20 1-5900 <$100
1902 Plain Back
3x10-20 5901-18967 <$100
1929 Small Size
5 Type 1 1-416 <$60
10 Type 1 1-2274 <$50
20 Type 1 1-624 <$60
5 Type 2 1-2340 <$60
10 Type 2 1-1394 <$60
20 Type 2 1-443 <$70
Total Issue $1,628,900
Out in 1935 $100,000
Large out 1935 $6,680

1763 Bourbon
FNB OF FORT SCOTT
{{ 2 L }}
Chartered 1/10/71
Receivership 11/20/08
Original Series <$VALUE
3x1-2 1-2700 <$1500/$2000
4x5 1-2875 <$1500
3x10-20 1-1400<$2000/$2500
Series 1875
3x1-2 1-276 <$1500/$2000
4x5 1-2128 <$1500
3x10-20 1-1254<$2000/$2500
Brown Back
4x5 1-3400 <$1000
50-100 1-1858 <$2000/$2500
Total Issue $594,340
Out in 1915 $17,488

1927 Bourbon
MERCHANTS NB OF FORT SCOTT
{{ UNREPORTED }}
Chartered 1/20/72
Receivership 9/25/78
Original Series <$VALUE
3x1-2 1-2100 <$2000/$3000
4x5 1-3325 <$2000
Series 1875
3x1-2 1-520 <$2000/$3000
4x5 1-1385 <$2000
Total Issue $107,300
Out in 1915 $605

9595 Meade
FNB OF FOWLER
{{ 6 L 4 S }}
Organized 10/26/09
Receivership 1/10/33
1902 Date Back <$VALUE
3x10-20 1-1360 <$350
1902 Plain Back
3x10-20 1361-4944 <$350
1929 Small Size
10 Type 1 1-605 <$200
20 Type 1 1-156 <$200
Total Issue $304,720
Out at close $24,640
Large out at close $2,090

2809 Marshall
FNB OF FRANKFORT
{{ 1 L }}
Chartered 11/3/82
Liquidated 1/8/91
Brown Back <$VALUE
4x5 1-2995 <$1500
Total Issue $59,900
Out in 1910 $510

3835 Wilson
FNB OF FREDONIA
{{ UNREPORTED }}
Chartered 1/14/88
Liquidated 1/2/94
Brown Back <$VALUE
3x10-20 1-503 <$2000
Total Issue $25,150
Out in 1910 $130

7218 Wilson
FREDONIA NB, FREDONIA
{{ UNREPORTED }}
Chartered 4/20/04
Liquidated 10/20/04
1902 Red Seal <$VALUE
4x5 1-105 <$2500
3x10-20 1-88 <$2500
Total Issue $6,500
Out in 1910 $330

4798 Cherokee
GALENA NB, GALENA
{{ 10 L 12 S }}
Chartered 1892
Liquidated 9/10/34
Brown Back <$VALUE
3x10-20 1-1820 <$400
50-100 1-454 <$1500/$1750
1882 Date Back
3x10-20 1-1260 <$400
50-100 1-93 <$1500/$1750
1902 Date Back
3x10-20 1-1440 <$175
3x50-100 1-60 <$500/$600
1902 Plain Back
3x10-20 1441-8442 <$175
1929 Small Size
10 Type 1 1-1382 <$125
20 Type 1 1-370 <$125
10 Type 2 1-591 <$125
20 Type 2 1-134 <$125
Total Issue $809,060
Out at close $50,000
Large out at close $3,810

3900 Finney
FINNEY COUNTY NB OF GARDEN CITY
{{ UNREPORTED }}
Chartered 6/20/88
Liquidated 6/20/93
Brown Back <$VALUE
3x10-20 1-523 <$2000
Total Issue $26,150
Out in 1910 $130

3448 Finney
FNB OF GARDEN CITY
{{ 2 L 7 S }}
Organized 11/16/85
Receivership 7/21/33
Brown Back <$VALUE
4x5 1-3107 <$1000
3x10-20 1-440 <$1000
1902 Red Seal
3x10-20 1-250 <$1250
1902 Date Back
4x5 1-1150 <$600
3x10-20 1-820 <$600
1902 Plain Back
4x5 1151-2375 <$600
3x10-20 821-1684 <$600
1929 Small Size
5 Type 1 1-400 <$175
10 Type 1 1-201 <$175
20 Type 1 1-68 <$175
Total Issue $260,560
Out at close $12,500
Large out at close $1,460

7646 Finney
GARDEN CITY NB, GARDEN CITY
{{ 2 L 4 S }}
Organized 2/1/05
Liquidated 4/4/34
1902 Red Seal <$VALUE
3x10-20 1-800 <$1500
1902 Date Back
3x10-20 1-900 <$750
1902 Plain Back
3x10-20 901-2296 <$750
1929 Small Size
10 Type 1 1-310 <$200
20 Type 1 1-104 <$200
10 Type 2 1-24 <$200
Total Issue $186,120
Out at close $12,500
Large out at close $750

4032 Anderson
ANDERSON COUNTY NB OF GARNETT
{{ UNREPORTED }}
Chartered 5/11/89
Liquidated 5/6/97
Brown Back <$VALUE
50-100 1-198 <$2500/$3000
Total Issue $29,700
Out in 1910 $1,150

2973 Anderson
FNB OF GARNETT
{{ 1 L }}
Organized 6/11/83
Receivership 11/9/96
Brown Back <$VALUE
4x5 1-750 <$1500
3x10-20 1-757 <$1500
Total Issue $52,850
Out in 1915 $385

5292 Anderson
NB OF COMMERCE OF GARNETT
{{ 8 L 5 S }}
Chartered 4/17/00
Receivership 3/25/32
Brown Back <$VALUE
3x10-20 1-1700 <$600
1882 Date Back
3x10-20 1-1650 <$600
1882 Value Back
3x10-20 1651-2398 <$600
1902 Plain Back
3x10-20 1-2728 <$350
1929 Small Size
10 Type 1 1-432 <$225
20 Type 1 1-115 <$225
Total Issue $381,020
Out at close $24,700
Large out at close $3,720

6970 Smith
FNB OF GAYLORD
{{ 3 L 8 S }}
Chartered 9/03
1902 Red Seal <$VALUE
3x10-20 1-300 <$1500
1902 Date Back
3x10-20 1-620 <$750
1902 Plain Back
3x10-20 621-1026 <$750
1929 Small Size
10 Type 1 1-400 <$175
20 Type 1 1-118 <$175
10 Type 2 1-695 <$175
20 Type 2 1-145 <$175
Total Issue $114,310
Out in 1935 $25,000
Large out 1935 $1,190

3216 Crawford
FNB OF GIRARD
{{ 5 L 10 S }}
Chartered 1884
Brown Back <$VALUE
3x10-20 1-2398 <$600
1902 Red Seal
3x10-20 1-2000 <$750
1902 Date Back
3x10-20 1-3140 <$350
1902 Plain Back
3x10-20 3141-4244 <$350
1929 Small Size
10 Type 1 1-302 <$250
20 Type 1 1-102 <$250
5 Type 2 1-96 <$250
Total Issue $462,940
Out in 1935 $12,500
Large out 1935 $1,605

7683 Cloud
FNB OF GLASCO
{{ 21 L 10 S }}
Chartered 4/05
1902 Red Seal <$VALUE
4x5 1-1950 <$700
3x10-20 1-1380 <$700
1902 Date Back
4x5 1-2950 <$250
3x10-20 1-2020 <$250
1902 Plain Back
4x5 2951-9438 <$250
3x10-20 2021-6002 <$250
1929 Small Size
5 Type 1 1-1336 <$100
10 Type 1 1-824 <$100
20 Type 1 1-222 <$100
5 Type 2 1-2576 <$100
10 Type 2 1-1140 <$100
20 Type 2 1-204 <$100
Total Issue $741,380
Out in 1935 $50,000
Large out 1935 $4,675

7416 Nemaha
FNB OF GOFF
{{ 2 L 4 S }}
Chartered 9/04
1902 Red Seal <$VALUE
3x10-20 1-340 <$1500
1902 Date Back
3x10-20 1-780 <$750
1902 Plain Back
3x10-20 781-1486 <$750
1929 Small Size
10 Type 1 1-217 <$250
20 Type 1 1-59 <$250
Total Issue $111,400
Out in 1934 $7,800
Large out 1935 $700

7882 Sherman
FARMERS NB OF GOODLAND
{{ 3 L }}
Chartered 8/05
Liquidated 2/12/27
1902 Red Seal <$VALUE
3x10-20 1-1000 <$1000
1902 Date Back
3x10-20 1-1660 <$500
1902 Plain Back
3x10-20 1661-4343 <$500
Total Issue $267,150
Out at close $25,000

14163 Sherman
FNB IN GOODLAND
{{ 2 S }}
Chartered 5/34
1929 Small Size <$VALUE
5 Type 2 1-1604 <$400
10 Type 2 1-868 <$400
Total Issue $16,700
Out in 1935 $50,000
Outstanding includes Ch 6039 and Ch 11860

6039 Sherman
FNB OF GOODLAND
{{ 4 L 6 S }}
Chartered 12/01
Liquidated 6/4/34
Brown Back <$VALUE
3x10-20 1-1320 <$600
1882 Date Back
3x10-20 1-1610* <$600
1882 Value Back
3x10-20 1731-2846* <$600
* 1611-1730 not marked
1902 Plain Back
3x10-20 1-2138 <$350
1929 Small Size
10 Type 1 1-628 <$175
20 Type 1 1-180 <$175
10 Type 2 1-207 <$175
20 Type 2 1-34 <$175
Total Issue $377,230
Out at close $25,000
Large out at close $1,880
Ch 14163 assumed circulation

5705 Barton
CITIZENS NB OF GREAT BEND
{{ 9 L 7 S }}
Chartered 2/7/01
Receivership 2/20/32
Brown Back <$VALUE
4x5 1-2650 <$350
3x10-20 1-2030 <$350
1882 Date Back
4x5 1-2875 <$350
3x10-20 1-2220 <$350
1882 Value Back
4x5 2876-5190 <$400
3x10-20 2221-3471 <$400
1902 Plain Back
4x5 1-4865 <$175
3x10-20 1-3287 <$175
1929 Small Size
5 Type 1 1-1175 <$150
10 Type 1 1-584 <$150
20 Type 1 1-168 <$150
Total Issue $783,950
Out at close $49,340
Large out at close $5,985

11707 Barton
FARMERS NB OF GREAT BEND
{{ 9 L 26 S }}
Chartered 5/20
1902 Plain Back <$VALUE
4x5 1-12697 <$250
3x10-20 1-8085 <$250
1929 Small Size
5 Type 1 1-3094 <$50
10 Type 1 1-1864 <$50
20 Type 1 1-520 <$60
5 Type 2 1-3820 <$50
10 Type 2 1-1380 <$50
20 Type 2 1-1404 <$65
Total Issue $986,230
Out in 1935 $100,000
Large out 1935 $3,840

3363 Barton
FNB OF GREAT BEND
{{ 13 L 16 S }}
Chartered 1885
Liquidated 1/10/33
Brown Back <$VALUE
3x10-20 1-1629 <$450
1902 Red Seal
3x10-20 1-850 <$600
1902 Date Back
3x10-20 1-5300 <$225
1902 Plain Back
3x10-20 5301-18472 <$225
1929 Small Size
10 Type 1 1-1869 <$75
20 Type 1 1-591 <$75
Total Issue $1,230,610
Out at close $100,000
Large out at close $10,140

3567 Washington
FNB OF GREENLEAF
{{ 1 L }}
Chartered 10/7/86
Liquidated 5/9/88
Brown Back <$VALUE
4x5 1-618 <$2000
Total Issue $12,360
Out in 1910 $105

10557 Kiowa
FARMERS NB OF GREENSBURG
Organized 6/5/14
Receivership 10/12/32
2nd title:FNB in Greensburg 3/12/30
FIRST TITLE {{ 2 L 1 S }}
1902 Date Back <$VALUE
4x5 1-350 <$600
4x10 1-450 <$600
1902 Plain Back
4x5 351-2002 <$600
4x10 451-1597 <$600
1929 Small Size
5 Type 1 1-167 <$500
10 Type 1 1-61 <$500
SECOND TITLE {{ 2 S }}
1929 Small Size
5 Type 1 1-262 <$500
10 Type 1 1-129 <$500
Total Issue $128,190
Out at close $9,820
Large out at close $960

FNB in Greensburg
SEE Ch 10557
Farmers NB of Greensburg

3667 Kiowa
FNB OF GREENSBURG
{{ 1 L }}
Chartered 4/5/87
Liquidated 2/10/88
Brown Back <$VALUE
4x5 1-562 <$2000
Total Issue $11,240
Out in 1910 $150

9695 Saline
GYPSUM VALLEY NB OF GYPSUM
{{ 11 L 17 S }}
Chartered 3/10
1902 Date Back <$VALUE
3x10-20 1-1960 <$200
1902 Plain Back
3x10-20 1961-5413 <$200
1929 Small Size
10 Type 1 1-686 <$100
20 Type 1 1-172 <$100
10 Type 2 1-674 <$100
20 Type 2 1-120 <$100
Total Issue $341,590
Out in 1935 $25,000
Large out 1935 $1,390

3443 Harvey
HALSTEAD NB, HALSTEAD
{{ 1 L }}
Chartered 1/29/86
Liquidated 6/29/89
Brown Back <$VALUE
4x5 1-882 <$2000
Total Issue $17,640
Out in 1910 $170

6932 Greenwood
FNB OF HAMILTON
{{ 4 L 7 S }}
Chartered 8/03
1902 Red Seal <$VALUE
3x10-20 1-980 <$850
1902 Date Back
3x10-20 1-1700 <$400
1902 Plain Back
3x10-20 1701-5274 <$400
1929 Small Size
10 Type 1 1-604 <$150
20 Type 1 1-168 <$150
10 Type 2 1-1091 <$150
20 Type 2 1-169 <$150
Total Issue $383,390
Out in 1935 $25,000
Large out 1935 $1,700

FNB in Harper
SEE Ch 8307
NB of Harper

3265 Harper
FNB OF HARPER
{{ UNREPORTED }}
Chartered 11/17/84
Liquidated 4/30/90
Brown Back <$VALUE
3x10-20 1-452 <$2000
Total Issue $22,600
Out in 1910 $140

3431 Harper
HARPER NB, HARPER
{{ UNREPORTED }}
Organized 1/6/86
Receivership 2/10/90
Brown Back <$VALUE
3x10-20 1-353 <$2000
Total Issue $17,650
Out in 1915 $40

8307 Harper
NB OF HARPER
Chartered 7/06
2nd title:FNB in Harper 6/10/20
FIRST TITLE {{ 1 L }}
1902 Red Seal <$VALUE
3x10-20 1-595 <$1500
1902 Date Back
3x10-20 1-480 <$750
1902 Plain Back
3x10-20 481-980 <$750
SECOND TITLE {{ 1 L 2 S }}
1902 Plain Back
3x10-20 1-1249 <$750
1929 Small Size
10 Type 1 1-314 <$250
20 Type 1 1-106 <$250
10 Type 2 1-1324 <$250
20 Type 2 1-413 <$250
Total Issue $194,260
Out in 1935 $25,000
Large out 1935 $730

8308 Harper
SECURITY NB OF HARPER
{{ UNREPORTED }}
Chartered 7/06
Liquidated 4/15/11
1902 Red Seal <$VALUE
3x10-20 1-595 <$2000
1902 Date Back
3x10-20 1-29 <$1000
Total Issue $31,200
Out in 1911 $9,300

8197 Lyon
HARTFORD NB, HARTFORD
{{ 4 L 2 S }}
Organized 3/27/06
Liquidated 6/23/31
1902 Red Seal <$VALUE
3x10-20 1-700 <$1250
1902 Date Back
3x10-20 1-1650 <$600
1902 Plain Back
3x10-20 1651-5076 <$600
1929 Small Size
10 Type 1 1-255 <$400
20 Type 1 1-56 <$400
Total Issue $310,820
Out at close $25,000
Large out at close $5,410

5506 Pottawatomie
FNB OF HAVENSVILLE
{{ 6 L 6 S }}
Chartered 7/19/00
Receivership 10/11/33
Brown Back <$VALUE
3x10-20 1-900 <$600
1882 Date Back
3x10-20 1-1300* <$600
1882 Value Back
3x10-20 1501-1770* <$600
* 1301-1500 not marked
1902 Plain Back
3x10-20 1-1793 <$300
1929 Small Size
5 Type 1 1-352 <$200
10 Type 1 1-438 <$200
20 Type 1 1-125 <$200
Total Issue $274,990
Out at close $25,000
Large out at close $1,730

3885 Ellis
FNB OF HAYS CITY
{{ 1 L }}
Chartered 1888
Brown Back <$VALUE
4x5 1-2920 <$1500
50-100 1-160 <$2500/$3000
1902 Red Seal
4x5 1-125 <$1500
3x10-20 1-100 <$1500
1902 Date Back
4x5 1-940 <$750
3x10-20 1-768 <$750
Total Issue $147,100
Out in 1935 $390

4058 Dickinson
FNB OF HERINGTON
{{ 2 L 4 S }}
Chartered 1889
Brown Back <$VALUE
4x5 1-500 <$1000
50-100 1-533 <$2000/$2500
1882 Date Back
4x5 1-145 <$1000
50-100 1-4 <$2000/$2500
1902 Date Back
3x10-20 1-1450 <$600
1902 Plain Back
3x10-20 1451-4045 <$600
1929 Small Size
10 Type 1 1-610 <$200
20 Type 1 1-148 <$200
10 Type 2 1-435 <$200
20 Type 2 1-110 <$200
Total Issue $356,610
Out in 1935 $22,000
Large out 1935 $1,340

2589 Brown
FNB OF HIAWATHA
{{ 14 L 5 S }}
Organized 11/12/81
Receivership 1/28/32
Series 1875 <$VALUE
3x10-20 1-2808<$1500/$2000
Brown Back
3x10-20 1-2425 <$500
1882 Date Back
3x10-20 1-3600 <$500
1882 Value Back
3x10-20 3601-6101 <$500
1902 Plain Back
3x10-20 1-4349 <$175
1929 Small Size
10 Type 1 1-933 <$200
20 Type 1 1-238 <$200
Total Issue $868,690
Out at close $54,220
Large out at close $8,240

9136 Doniphan
FNB OF HIGHLAND
{{ 4 L 0 S }}
Organized 4/11/08
Receivership 4/26/32
1902 Date Back <$VALUE
3x10-20 1-760 <$1000
1902 Plain Back
3x10-20 761-1385 <$1000
1929 Small Size
10 Type 1 1-131 <$500
20 Type 1 1-14 <$500
Total Issue $78,790
Out at close $6,250
Large out at close $560

FNB of Hill City
SEE Ch 3758
FNB of Millbrook

6120 Marion
FNB OF HILLSBORO
{{ 3 L 10 S }}
Chartered 2/02
1902 Red Seal <$VALUE
3x10-20 1-500 <$1250
1902 Date Back
3x10-20 1-980 <$500
1902 Plain Back (dated 1902)
3x10-20 981-2219 <$500
1902 Plain Back (dated 1922)
3x10-20 1-1953 <$500
1929 Small Size
10 Type 1 1-584 <$175
20 Type 1 1-172 <$175
10 Type 2 1-978 <$175
20 Type 2 1-137 <$175
Total Issue $301,800
Out in 1935 $25,000
Large out 1935 $1,270

9232 Barton
FNB OF HOISINGTON
{{ 5 L 14 S }}
Chartered 9/08
1902 Date Back <$VALUE
3x10-20 1-1860 <$400
1902 Plain Back
3x10-20 1861-5413 <$400
1929 Small Size
5 Type 1 1-1504 <$85
10 Type 1 1-748 <$85
20 Type 1 1-194 <$85
5 Type 2 1-2852 <$85
10 Type 2 1-1708 <$85
20 Type 2 1-347 <$85
Total Issue $422,210
Out in 1935 $50,000
Large out 1935 $1,470

12694 Barton
HOISINGTON NB, HOISINGTON
{{ 15 S }}
Chartered 4/25
1929 Small Size <$VALUE
5 Type 1 1-1606 <$85
10 Type 1 1-894 <$85
20 Type 1 1-232 <$85
5 Type 2 1-2010 <$85
10 Type 2 1-790 <$85
20 Type 2 1-185 <$85
Total Issue $151,310
Out in 1935 $25,000

3061 Jackson
FNB OF HOLTON
{{ 7 L }}
Organized 9/27/83
Receivership 5/23/31
Brown Back <$VALUE
4x5 1-10223 <$600
3x10-20 1-971 <$600
1902 Red Seal
3x10-20 1-2200 <$700
1902 Date Back
3x10-20 1-2880 <$250
1902 Plain Back
3x10-20 2881-6616 <$250
Total Issue $693,810
Out at close $4,705

5041 Jackson
NB OF HOLTON
{{ 6 L }}
Chartered 5/14/96
Liquidated 7/31/09
Brown Back <$VALUE
4x5 1-3875 <$1000
3x10-20 1-2500 <$1000
1882 Date Back
4x5 1-174 <$1000
Total Issue $205,980
Out in 1910 $24,025

3810 Brown
FNB OF HORTON
{{ 11 L 13 S }}
Chartered 1887
Brown Back <$VALUE
4x5 1-3430 <$400
3x10-20 1-2927 <$400
1902 Red Seal
3x10-20 1-500 <$500
1902 Date Back
3x10-20 1-3300 <$150
1902 Plain Back
3x10-20 3301-10090 <$150
1929 Small Size
5 Type 1 1-5068 <$85
5 Type 2 1-9062 <$85
Total Issue $941,800
Out in 1935 $35,000
Large out 1935 $4,120

3242 Elk
FNB OF HOWARD
{{ 17 L 8 S }}
Chartered 1884
Brown Back <$VALUE
4x5 1-3294 <$300
3x10-20 1-360 <$300/350
1902 Red Seal
4x5 1-875 <$450
3x10-20 1-450 <$450
1902 Date Back
4x5 1-1575 <$125
3x10-20 1-1260 <$125
1902 Plain Back
4x5 1576-3107 <$125
3x10-20 1261-2273 <$125
1929 Small Size
5 Type 1 1-602* <$200
10 Type 1 1-274** <$200
20 Type 1 1-98*** <$200
5 Type 2 1-204 <$200
10 Type 2 1-215 <$200
20 Type 2 1-29 <$200
* 299-412 not issued
** 140-210 not issued
*** 37-74 not issued
Total Issue $337,440
Out in 1935 $12,500
Large out 1935 $1,460

3794 Elk
HOWARD NB, HOWARD
{{ 14 L 8 S }}
Chartered 1887
Brown Back <$VALUE
4x5 1-4200 <$250
50-100 1-472 <$1250/$1500
1902 Red Seal
4x5 1-300 <$350
50-100 1-80 <$2000/$2500
1902 Date Back
4x5 1-2750 <$100
50-100 1-300 <$400/$500
3x50-100 1-383 <$400/$500
1902 Plain Back
4x5 2751-13802 <$100
3x50-100 384-502<$400/$500
1929 Small Size
5 Type 1 1-1786 <$200
50 Type 1 1-106 <$300
100 Type 1 1-42 <$350
Total Issue $729,920
Out in 1935 $50,000
Large out 1935 $4,930

5687 Sheridan
FNB OF HOXIE
{{ 8 L 14 S }}
Chartered 1/19/01
Brown Back <$VALUE
3x10-20 1-2300 <$750
1882 Date Back
3x10-20 1-3300* <$750
1882 Value Back
3x10-20 3541-5144* <$750
* 3301-3540 not marked
1902 Plain Back
3x10-20 1-4311 <$400
1929 Small Size
10 Type 1 1-1108 <$100
20 Type 1 1-348 <$100
10 Type 2 1-907 <$110
20 Type 2 1-250 <$125
Total Issue $710,060
Out in 1935 $50,000
Large out 1935 $2,970

11300 Stevens
FNB OF HUGOTON
{{ 4 S }}
Chartered 2/19
1929 Small Size <$VALUE
5 Type 1 1-630 <$250
10 Type 1 1-262 <$250
5 Type 2 1-2278 <$250
10 Type 2 1-1270 <$250
Total Issue $58,710
Out in 1935 $25,000

3807 Allen
HUMBOLDT FNB, HUMBOLDT
{{ UNREPORTED }}
Organized 11/1/87
Receivership 2/15/96
Brown Back <$VALUE
3x10-20 1-771 <$2000
Total Issue $38,550
Out in 1915 $120

6963 Allen
HUMBOLDT NB, HUMBOLDT
{{ 2 L 8 S }}
Chartered 9/03
1902 Red Seal <$VALUE
3x10-20 1-1500 <$1000
1902 Date Back
3x10-20 1-1900 <$400
1902 Plain Back
3x10-20 1901-5944 <$400
1929 Small Size
10 Type 1 1-766 <$125
20 Type 1 1-222 <$125
10 Type 2 1-531 <$125
20 Type 2 1-125 <$125
Total Issue $452,610
Out in 1935 $30,000
Large out 1935 $2,110

American NB of Hutchinson
SEE Ch 10765
Farmers NB of Hutchinson

8430 Reno
COMMERCIAL NB OF HUTCHINSON
{{ 9 L }}
Chartered 11/06
Liquidated 12/6/23
1902 Red Seal <$VALUE
4x5 1-625 <$500
3x10-20 1-500 <$500
1902 Date Back
4x5 1-6450 <$200
3x10-20 1-4920 <$200
1902 Plain Back
4x5 6451-14835 <$200
3x10-20 4921-10231 <$200
Total Issue $845,750
Out at close $100,000
Ch 10765 assumed circulation

13106 Reno
EXCHANGE NB OF HUTCHINSON
{{ 16 S }}
Chartered 7/25/27
1929 Small Size <$VALUE
10 Type 2 1-8364 <$70
20 Type 2 1-2581 <$70
Total Issue $135,260
Out in 1935 $88,800

10765 Reno
FARMERS NB OF HUTCHINSON
Chartered 8/15
2nd title:American NB of Hutchinson 10/26/17
FIRST TITLE {{ 0 L }}
1902 Plain Back <$VALUE
4x5 1-1095 <$500
3x10-20 1-806 <$500
SECOND TITLE {{ 2 L 23 S }}
1902 Plain Back
3x10-20 1-5160 <$500
1929 Small Size
10 Type 1 1-2274 <$50
20 Type 1 1-686 <$65
10 Type 2 1-1541 <$65
20 Type 2 1-250 <$75
Total Issue $559,370
Out in 1935 $90,000
Large out 1935 $5,155
Outstanding includes Ch 8430

3180 Reno
FNB OF HUTCHINSON
{{ 3U + 27 L }}
Chartered 1884
Brown Back <$VALUE
4x5 1-8002 <$250
3x10-20 1-3938 <$250/$300
1902 Red Seal
3x10-20 1-5300 <$300/$350
1902 Date Back
3x10-20 1-13000 <$100
1902 Plain Back
3x10-20 13001-27779 <$100
Total Issue $2,010,890
Out in 1935 $8,905

3199 Reno
HUTCHINSON NB, HUTCHINSON
{{ UNREPORTED }}
Organized 5/29/84
Receivership 11/6/93
Brown Back <$VALUE
50-100 1-349 <$2500/$3000
Total Issue $52,350
Out in 1915 $50

3861 Reno
NB OF COMMERCE OF HUTCHINSON
{{ UNREPORTED }}
Chartered 3/30/88
Liquidated 6/15/92
Brown Back <$VALUE
50-100 1-266 <$2500/$3000
Total Issue $39,900
Out in 1910 $350

Citizens-FNB of Independence
SEE Ch 4592
Citizens NB of Independence

***

4592 Montgomery
CITIZENS NB OF INDEPENDENCE
Organized 6/10/91
Liquidated 4/9/34
2nd title:Citizens-FNB of Independence 2/14/18
3rd title:FNB in Independence 5/21/31
FIRST TITLE {{ 8 L }}
Brown Back <$VALUE
3x10-20 1-9340 <$300
1882 Date Back
3x10-20 1-3503 <$300
1902 Date Back
3x10-20 1-7200* <$125
1902 Plain Back
3x10-20 7701-9900* <$125
* 7201-7700 not marked
SECOND TITLE {{ 13 L 23 S }}
1902 Plain Back
3x10-20 1-40462 <$125
1929 Small Size
10 Type 1 1-6784 <$30
20 Type 1 1-1640 <$40
THIRD TITLE {{ 7 S }}
1929 Small Size
10 Type 1 1-932 <$75
20 Type 1 1-240 <$75
10 Type 2 1-150 <$75
Total Issue $3,850,310
Out in 1935 $300,000
Large out 1935 $16,980
Ch 13924 assumed circulation
Outstanding includes Ch 3021

***

4499 Montgomery
COMMERCIAL NB OF INDEPENDENCE
{{ 15 L 8 S }}
Organized 1/1/91
Receivership 3/14/30
Brown Back <$VALUE
3x10-20 1-5040 <$250/$300
1882 Date Back
3x10-20 1-1350 <$250
1902 Date Back
3x10-20 1-5400 <$125
1902 Plain Back
3x10-20 5401-27248 <$125
1929 Small Size
10 Type 1 1-624 <$150
20 Type 1 1-168 <$150
Total Issue $1,739,500
Out at close $100,000
Large out at close $42,400

***

FNB in Independence
SEE Ch 4592
Citizens NB of Independence

***

3021 Montgomery
FNB OF INDEPENDENCE
{{ 4 L }}
Chartered 1883
Liquidated 10/15/17
Brown Back <$VALUE
3x10-20 1-2630 <$1000
1902 Red Seal
3x10-20 1-2300 <$1250
1902 Date Back
3x10-20 1-3920 <$500
Total Issue $442,500
Out at close $50,000
Ch 4592 assumed circulation

***

13492 Montgomery
SECURITY NB OF INDEPENDENCE
{{ U + 9 S }}
Chartered 8/30
Liquidated 5/17/32
1929 Small Size <$VALUE
5 Type 1 1-4424 <$100
10 Type 1 1-2129 <$100
Total Issue $260,460
Out at close $100,000

***

FNB of Iola
SEE Ch 5287
Northrup NB of Iola

***

5287 Allen
NORTHRUP NB OF IOLA
Chartered 4/12/00
Liquidated 2/1/30
2nd title:FNB of Iola 1/24/23
FIRST TITLE {{ 9 L }}
Brown Back <$VALUE
4x5 1-3000 <$600
3x10-20 1-2800 <$500
1882 Date Back
4x5 1-2900 <$500
3x10-20 1-2160 <$500
1882 Value Back
4x5 2901-3530 <$500
3x10-20 2161-3506 <$500
1902 Plain Back
3x10-20 1-2000 <$200
SECOND TITLE {{ 10 L }}
1902 Plain Back
3x10-20 1-3389 <$200
Total Issue $715,350
Out at close $22,695

***

3805 Hodgeman
FNB OF JETMORE
{{ UNREPORTED }}
Chartered 10/29/87
Liquidated 4/30/92
Brown Back <$VALUE
4x5 1-1141 <$2000
Total Issue $22,820
Out in 1910 $200

***

3591 Jewell
FNB OF JEWELL CITY
{{ 8 L 6 S }}
Chartered 1886
Brown Back <$VALUE
4x5 1-3550 <$500
50-100 1-499 <$1750/$2000
1902 Red Seal
3x10-20 1-1000 <$600
1902 Date Back
3x10-20 1-2740 <$200
1902 Plain Back
3x10-20 2741-8203 <$200
1929 Small Size
10 Type 1 1-814* <$150
20 Type 1 1-248** <$150
10 Type 2 1-112 <$150
20 Type 2 1-40 <$150
* 573-624 not issued
** 116-204 not issued
Total Issue $672,720
Out in 1935 $25,000
Large out 1935 $3,845

***

4284 Geary
CENTRAL NB OF JUNCTION CITY
{{ 9 L 17 S }}
Chartered 1890
Brown Back <$VALUE
4x5 1-2105 <$400
3x10-20 1-4106 <$400
50-100 1-340 <$1500/$1750
1882 Date Back
50-100 1-128 <$1500/$1750
1902 Date Back
50-100 1-700 <$400/$500
3x50-100 1-1270 <$400/$500
1902 Plain Back
3x50-100 1271-1668 <$400/$500
1929 Small Size
5 Type 1 1-410 <$85
10 Type 1 1-115 <$85
50 Type 1 1-248 <$150
100 Type 1 1-82 <$200
Total Issue $982,400
Out in 1935 $25,000
Large out 1935 $10,200

***

1977 Geary
FNB OF JUNCTION CITY
{{ 1 L }}
Chartered 5/6/72
Liquidated 7/1/75
Original Series <$VALUE
4x5 1-1250 <$2000
3x10-20 1-636 <$2500/$3000
Total Issue $56,800
Out in 1910 $250

***

3543 Geary
FNB OF JUNCTION CITY
{{ 10 L 16 S }}
Organized 7/15/86
Brown Back <$VALUE
4x5 1-5940 <$400
3x10-20 1-2940 <$400
1902 Red Seal
3x10-20 1-1350 <$500
1902 Date Back
3x10-20 1-5100 <$175
1902 Plain Back
3x10-20 5101-15859 <$175
1929 Small Size
10 Type 1 1-2048 <$70
20 Type 1 1-526 <$70
10 Type 2 1-2492 <$70
20 Type 2 1-429 <$75
Total Issue $1,345,750
Out in 1935 $75,000
Large out 1935 $5,080

***

11860 Sherman
FNB OF KANORADO
{{ 5 S }}
Chartered 10/20
Liquidated 6/4/34
1929 Small Size <$VALUE
5 Type 1 1-940 <$275
10 Type 1 1-430 <$275
20 Type 1 1-122 <$275
5 Type 2 1-154 <$300
10 Type 2 1-70 <$300
20 Type 2 1-15 <$300
Total Issue $70,410
Out at close $25,000
Ch 14163 assumed circulation

***

8602 Wyandotte
BANKERS NB OF KANSAS CITY
{{ 1 L }}
Chartered 3/20/07
Liquidated 1/2/09
1902 Red Seal <$VALUE
4x5 1-1490 <$1250
3x10-20 1-1364 <$1250
50-100 1-97 <$3000/$3500
1902 Date Back
4x5 1-605 <$600
3x10-20 1-33 <$600
Total Issue $126,300
Out in 1910 $34,890

***

6311 Wyandotte
COMMERCIAL NB OF KANSAS CITY
{{ 2U + 40 L 50+ S }}
Chartered 6/02
1902 Red Seal <$VALUE
4x5 1-5500 <$200
3x10-20 1-10900 <$200/$250
1902 Date Back
4x5 1-22600* <$40
3x10-20 1-16660** <$50
1902 Plain Back (dated 1902)
4x5 24601-42600* <$40
3x10-20 17661-27260* <$50
* 22601-24600 not marked
** 16661-17660 not marked
1902 Plain Back (dated 1922)
4x5 1-64175 <$40
3x10-20 1-36277 <$50
1929 Small Size
5 Type 1 1-25795 <$15
10 Type 1 1-12741 <$15
20 Type 1 1-3709 <$25
Total Issue $7,950,740
Out in 1935 $300,000
Large out 1935 $27,465

***

3706 Wyandotte
FNB OF KANSAS CITY
{{ UNREPORTED }}
Organized 5/17/87
Receivership 8/17/91
Brown Back <$VALUE
3x10-20 1-959 <$1250
Total Issue $47,950
Out in 1915 $240

***

4381 Wyandotte
INTER-STATE NB OF KANSAS CITY
Chartered 1890
2nd title and location: Inter-State NB of Kansas City, Missouri 1/3/11
FIRST TITLE {{ 16 L }}
Brown Back <$VALUE
4x5 1-13000 <$200
4x10 1-2500 <$200
3x10-20 1-36060 <$200
1882 Date Back
4x5 1-7777 <$200
4x10 1-4711 <$200
3x10-20 1-703 <$200
1902 Date Back
50-100 1-682 <$350/$400
MISSOURI SITE {{ 15 L 9 S }}
1902 Date Back
4x5 1-28830 <$75
3x10-20 1-20568 <$85
1902 Plain Back
4x5 28831-29120 <$75
3x10-20 20569-20916 <$85
1929 Small Size
5 Type 1 1-1498 <$85
10 Type 1 1-710 <$85
20 Type 1 1-204 <$85
5 Type 2 1-928 <$85
10 Type 2 1-525 <$85
20 Type 2 1-45 <$100
Total Issue $4,395,440
Out in 1933 $50,000
Large out 1935 $14,145

***

9309 Wyandotte
PEOPLES NB OF KANSAS CITY
{{ 27 L U + 16 S }}
Chartered 1/09
Liquidated 1/9/34
1902 Date Back <$VALUE
4x5 1-9150 <$75
3x10-20 1-7040 <$75
1902 Plain Back
4x5 9151-39835 <$75
3x10-20 7041-26832 <$75
1929 Small Size
5 Type 1 1-6987 <$50
10 Type 1 1-4054 <$50
20 Type 1 1-970 <$50
Total Issue $2,707,550
Out at close $200,000
Large out at close $12,760

***

13801 Wyandotte
SECURITY NB OF KANSAS CITY
{{ U + 50+ S }}
Chartered 10/33
1929 Small Size <$VALUE
5 Type 2 1-12452 <$20
10 Type 2 1-6217 <$20
20 Type 2 1-1652 <$30
Total Issue $157,470
Out in 1935 $83,000

***

3726 Wyandotte
WYANDOTTE NB OF KANSAS CITY
{{ UNREPORTED }}
Chartered 6/17/87
Liquidated 4/13/97
Brown Back <$VALUE
50-100 1-492 <$2500/$3000
Total Issue $73,800
Out in 1910 $1,650

***

7493 Smith
FNB OF KENSINGTON
{{ 1 L 5 S }}
Chartered 11/04
1902 Red Seal <$VALUE
3x10-20 1-300 <$1500
1902 Date Back
3x10-20 1-520 <$750
1902 Plain Back
3x10-20 521-865 <$750
1929 Small Size
10 Type 1 1-173 <$300
20 Type 1 1-36 <$300
Total Issue $72,950
Out in 1935 $6,250
Large out 1935 $550

***

3737 Kingman
CITIZENS NB OF KINGMAN
{{ UNREPORTED }}
Chartered 6/28/87
Liquidated 12/24/88
Brown Back <$VALUE
3x10-20 1-235 <$2000
Total Issue $11,750
Out in 1910 $60

***

7412 Kingman
FARMERS NB OF KINGMAN
{{ 1 L }}
Chartered 9/26/04
Liquidated 6/30/09
1902 Red Seal <$VALUE
3x10-20 1-1304 <$1500
Total Issue $65,200
Out in 1910 $24,190

***

3509 Kingman
FNB OF KINGMAN
{{ 2 L }}
Chartered 1886
Brown Back <$VALUE
3x10-20 1-3415 <$1000
1902 Red Seal
3x10-20 1-800 <$1250
1902 Date Back
3x10-20 1-3500 <$500
1902 Plain Back
3x10-20 3501-6248 <$500
Total Issue $523,150
Out in 1935 $1,930

***

3559 Kingman
KINGMAN NB, KINGMAN
{{ UNREPORTED }}
Organized 9/16/86
Receivership 10/2/90
Brown Back <$VALUE
4x5 1-2145 <$2000
Total Issue $42,900
Out in 1915 $370

***

3759 Edwards
FNB OF KINSLEY
{{ UNREPORTED }}
Chartered 7/25/87
Liquidated 2/15/94
Brown Back <$VALUE
3x10-20 1-734 <$2000
Total Issue $36,700
Out in 1910 $270

***

5810 Edwards
NB OF KINSLEY
{{ 3 L }}
Chartered 5/01
Liquidated 5/17/28
Brown Back <$VALUE
3x10-20 1-900 <$1000
1882 Date Back
3x10-20 1-1510 <$1000
1882 Value Back
3x10-20 1511-2307 <$1000
1902 Plain Back
3x10-20 1-1475 <$600
Total Issue $234,100
Out at close $25,000

***

8220 Barber
FNB OF KIOWA
{{ 4 L 8 S }}
Chartered 5/06
1902 Red Seal <$VALUE
4x5 1-225 <$1000
3x10-20 1-180 <$1000
1902 Date Back
4x5 1-1000 <$500
3x10-20 1-800 <$500
1902 Plain Back
4x5 1001-5415 <$500
3x10-20 801-3430 <$500
1929 Small Size
5 Type 1 1-298 <$150
10 Type 1 1-602 <$150
20 Type 1 1-184 <$150
5 Type 2 1-896 <$150
10 Type 2 1-334 <$150
20 Type 2 1-62 <$150
Total Issue $369,500
Out in 1935 $25,000
Large out 1935 $1,330

***

3454 Phillips
FNB OF KIRWIN
{{ 1 L }}
Chartered 2/17/86
Liquidated 11/21/95
Brown Back <$VALUE
4x5 1-1954 <$2000
Total Issue $39,080
Out in 1910 $420

***

3970 Rush
FNB OF La CROSSE
{{ UNREPORTED }}
Chartered 1/29/89
Liquidated 2/28/98
Brown Back <$VALUE
4x5 1-1994 <$2000
Total Issue $39,880
Out in 1910 $395

***

7226 Allen
FNB OF La HARPE
{{ 5 L 7 S }}
Organized 4/11/04
Receivership 9/30/33
1902 Red Seal <$VALUE
4x5 1-300 <$800
3x10-20 1-240 <$800
1902 Date Back
4x5 1-1300 <$350
3x10-20 1-980 <$350
1902 Plain Back
4x5 1301-4963 <$350
3x10-20 981-2761 <$350
1929 Small Size
5 Type 1 1-718 <$200
10 Type 1 1-419 <$200
20 Type 1 1-116 <$200
Total Issue $315,910
Out at close $25,000
Large out at close $1,480

***

FNB in Larned
SEE Ch 7125
Moffet Brothers' NB of Larned

***

2666 Pawnee
FNB OF LARNED
{{ 2 L }}
Organized 4/27/82
Receivership 8/26/96
Series 1875 <$VALUE
3x10-20 1-2204<$2500/$3000
Total Issue $110,200
Out in 1915 $510

***

7125 Pawnee
MOFFET BROTHERS' NB OF LARNED
Chartered 2/04
2nd title:FNB in Larned 3/21/22
FIRST TITLE {{ 4 L }}
1902 Red Seal <$VALUE
3x10-20 1-1760 <$1000
1902 Date Back
4x5 1-2600 <$500
3x10-20 1-1380 <$500
1902 Plain Back
4x5 2601-5950 <$500
3x10-20 1381-3140 <$500
SECOND TITLE {{ 3 L 25 S }}
1902 Plain Back
3x10-20 1-3642 <$400
1929 Small Size
5 Type 1 1-2288 <$60
10 Type 1 1-616 <$60
20 Type 1 1-740 <$65
5 Type 2 1-8350 <$65
20 Type 2 1-790 <$75
Total Issue $798,050
Out in 1935 $100,000
Large out 1935 $3,010

***

3849 Douglas
DOUGLAS COUNTY NB OF LAWRENCE
Chartered 2/24/88
2nd title:Lawrence NB 6/3/89
FIRST TITLE {{ 0 L }}
Brown Back <$VALUE
50-100 1-157 <$2500/$3000
SECOND TITLE {{ 17 L 28 S }}
Brown Back
3x10-20 1-3896 <$250/$300
1902 Red Seal
3x10-20 1-1000 <$400
1902 Date Back
3x10-20 1-7100 <$125
1902 Plain Back
3x10-20 7101-20602 <$125
1929 Small Size
10 Type 1 1-2756 <$40
20 Type 1 1-714 <$50
10 Type 2 1-2295 <$45
20 Type 2 1-605 <$60
Total Issue $1,584,540
Out in 1935 $98,950
Large out 1935 $6,410

***

FNB of Lawrence
SEE Ch 3584
Merchants NB of Lawrence

***

Lawrence NB, Lawrence
SEE Ch 3849
Douglas County NB of Lawrence

***

3584 Douglas
MERCHANTS NB OF LAWRENCE
Chartered 11/4/86
2nd title:FNB of Lawrence 5/20/30
FIRST TITLE {{ 20 L 6 S }}
Brown Back <$VALUE
4x5 1-2395 <$200
3x10-20 1-2002 <$200/$250
1902 Red Seal
3x10-20 1-2400 <$250/$300
1902 Date Back
3x10-20 1-7200 <$75
1902 Plain Back
3x10-20 7201-20309 <$75
1929 Small Size
10 Type 1 1-1224 <$75
20 Type 1 1-392 <$75
SECOND TITLE {{ U + 21 S }}
1929 Small Size
10 Type 1 1-1182 <$50
20 Type 1 1-376 <$60
10 Type 2 1-2205 <$50
20 Type 2 1-721 <$65
Total Issue $1,556,440
Out in 1935 $100,000
Large out 1935 $6,110

***

****
1590 Douglas
NB OF LAWRENCE
{{ 2 L }}
Chartered 10/14/65
Liquidated 6/29/89
Original Series <$VALUE
3x1-2 1-4000 <$1500/$2500
4x5 1-3400 <$1500
4x10 1-2075 <$2000
Series 1875
3x1-2 1-600 <$1500/$2500
4x5 1-1700 <$1500
4x10 1-1162 <$2000
Brown Back
3x10-20 1-1067 <$1000
Total Issue $361,180
Out in 1910 $2,428
****
1732 Douglas
SECOND NB OF LAWRENCE
{{ 1 L }}
Chartered 1870
Liquidated 8/23/76
Original Series <$VALUE
4x5 1-2000 <$2000
3x10-20 1-974 <$2500/$3000
Series 1875
4x5 1-330 <$2000
Total Issue $95,300
Out in 1910 $475
****
3881 Douglas
WATKINS NB OF LAWRENCE
{{ 15 L }}
Chartered 5/8/88
Liquidated 12/12/28
Brown Back <$VALUE
3x10-20 1-7789 <$250/$300
1902 Red Seal
3x10-20 1-2000 <$300/$350
1902 Date Back
4x5 1-6350 <$85
3x10-20 1-3160 <$85
1902 Plain Back
4x5 6351-20405 <$85
3x10-20 3161-12339 <$85
Total Issue $1,514,500
Out at close $81,750
****
6149 Coffey
FNB OF Le ROY
{{ 6 L 2U + 10 S }}
Chartered 3/02
1902 Red Seal <$VALUE
3x10-20 1-1400 <$1250
1902 Date Back
3x10-20 1-1620 <$600
1902 Plain Back (dated 1902)
3x10-20 1621-2970 <$600
1902 Plain Back (dated 1922)
3x10-20 1-2012 <$600
1929 Small Size
10 Type 1 1-694 <$125
20 Type 1 1-182 <$125
10 Type 2 1-353 <$125
20 Type 2 1-82 <$125
Total Issue $387,750
Out in 1935 $25,000
Large out 1935 $1,560
****
182 Leavenworth
FNB OF LEAVENWORTH
{{ 22 L 20 S }}
Chartered 1/64
Original Series <$VALUE
3x1-2 1-9600 <$500/$1000
4x5 1-3050 <$500
4x10 1-2200 <$1000
Series 1875
4x10 1-2767 <$1000
Brown Back
3x10-20 1-4823 <$250/$300
1902 Red Seal
3x10-20 1-2500 <$300/$350
1902 Date Back
3x10-20 1-5400 <$100
1902 Plain Back
3x10-20 5401-20950 <$100
1929 Small Size
10 Type 1 1-4228 <$25
20 Type 1 1-1064 <$30
10 Type 2 1-2007 <$25
20 Type 2 1-637 <$30
Total Issue $2,135,500
Out in 1935 $150,000
Large out 1935 $10,970
****

****
3033 Leavenworth
LEAVENWORTH NB, LEAVENWORTH
{{ 28 L 20 S }}
Chartered 1883
Brown Back <$VALUE
3x10-20 1-4582 <$200/$250
1902 Red Seal
3x10-20 1-4370 <$250/$300
1902 Date Back
3x10-20 1-5100 <$60
1902 Plain Back
3x10-20 5101-25873 <$60
1929 Small Size
10 Type 1 1-3568 <$25
20 Type 1 1-1110 <$35
10 Type 2 1-2638 <$25
20 Type 2 1-914 <$35
Total Issue $2,133,190
Out in 1935 $150,000
Large out 1935 $10,600
****
3908 Leavenworth
MANUFACTURERS NB OF LEAVENWORTH
{{ 7 L }}
Chartered 1888
Liquidated 4/23/30
Brown Back <$VALUE
4x5 1-10966 <$400
3x10-20 1-4499 <$400
1902 Date Back
4x5 1-6500 <$200
3x10-20 1-4720 <$200
1902 Plain Back
4x5 6501-14076 <$200
3x10-20 4721-9460 <$200
Total Issue $1,198,790
Out at close $49,470
****
3194 Leavenworth
METROPOLITAN NB OF LEAVENWORTH
{{ UNREPORTED }}
Chartered 5/26/84
Liquidated 3/15/87
Brown Back <$VALUE
3x10-20 1-543 <$1500
Total Issue $27,150
Out in 1910 $100
****
1448 Leavenworth
SECOND NB OF LEAVENWORTH
{{ UNREPORTED }}
Chartered 7/17/65
Liquidated 7/22/74
Original Series <$VALUE
3x1-2 1-3000 <$2000/$3000
4x5 1-2500 <$2000
3x10-20 1-1996<$2500/$3000
Total Issue $164,800
Out in 1910 $1,710
****
5799 Smith
FNB OF LEBANON
{{ 1 L 11 S }}
Chartered 5/01
Brown Back <$VALUE
3x10-20 1-400 <$1500
1882 Date Back
3x10-20 1-594 <$1500
1902 Plain Back
3x10-20 1-435 <$750
1929 Small Size
10 Type 1 1-450 <$250
20 Type 1 1-130 <$250
10 Type 2 1-624 <$250
20 Type 2 1-166 <$250
Total Issue $123,610
Out in 1935 $25,000
Large out 1935 $580
****
3844 Wichita
FNB OF LEOTI CITY
{{ UNREPORTED }}
Chartered 2/7/88
Liquidated 3/4/92
Brown Back <$VALUE
4x5 1-992 <$2000
Total Issue $19,840
Out in 1910 $135
****
10863 Edwards
FNB OF LEWIS
{{ 3 L }}
Chartered 6/16
1902 Plain Back <$VALUE
3x10-20 1-3736 <$500
Total Issue $186,800
Out in 1935 $1,090
****

****
6720 Seward
FNB OF LIBERAL
{{ 3 L 7 S }}
Chartered 4/03
1902 Red Seal <$VALUE
3x10-20 1-1290 <$1000
1902 Date Back
3x10-20 1-1600* <$400
1902 Plain Back
3x10-20 2001-5426* <$400
* 1601-2000 not marked
1929 Small Size
10 Type 1 1-620 <$125
20 Type 1 1-178 <$125
5 Type 2 1-3342 <$125
10 Type 2 1-1836 <$125
20 Type 2 1-576 <$125
Total Issue $440,950
Out in 1935 $50,000
Large out 1935 $3,850
****
13406 Seward
PEOPLES NB OF LIBERAL
{{ 3U + 10 S }}
Chartered 12/29
1929 Small Size <$VALUE
5 Type 1 1-1392 <$100
10 Type 1 1-630 <$100
20 Type 1 1-150 <$125
5 Type 2 1-2922 <$125
10 Type 2 1-1701 <$125
20 Type 2 1-384 <$125
Total Issue $136,860
Out in 1935 $43,950
****
6672 Lincoln
FARMERS NB OF LINCOLN
{{ 5 L 8 S }}
Chartered 3/03
1902 Red Seal <$VALUE
3x10-20 1-820 <$1000
1902 Date Back
3x10-20 1-1690* <$500
1902 Plain Back
3x10-20 1811-4567* <$500
* 1691-1810 not marked
1929 Small Size
10 Type 1 1-580 <$175
20 Type 1 1-148 <$175
10 Type 2 1-688 <$175
20 Type 2 1-157 <$175
Total Issue $331,930
Out in 1935 $25,000
Large out 1935 $1,610
****
3464 Lincoln
FNB OF LINCOLN
{{ 2 L }}
Chartered 3/6/86
Liquidated 9/12/94
Brown Back <$VALUE
4x5 1-1779 <$2000
Total Issue $35,580
Out in 1910 $310
****
3589 McPherson
FNB OF LINDSBORG
{{ 7 L 6 S }}
Organized 11/5/86
Receivership 10/31/30
Brown Back <$VALUE
3x10-20 1-1402 <$650
1902 Red Seal
3x10-20 1-250 <$750
1902 Date Back
3x10-20 1-2700 <$350
1902 Plain Back
3x10-20 2701-9260 <$350
1929 Small Size
10 Type 1 1-470 <$200
20 Type 1 1-78 <$200
Total Issue $583,160
Out at close $38,540
Large out at close $6,910
****
6841 Phillips
FNB OF LOGAN
{{ 3 L 15 S }}
Chartered 6/03
1902 Red Seal <$VALUE
3x10-20 1-650 <$1000
1902 Date Back
3x10-20 1-1940 <$500
1902 Plain Back
3x10-20 1941-5325 <$500
1929 Small Size
10 Type 1 1-622 <$100
20 Type 1 1-210 <$100
10 Type 2 1-881 <$100
20 Type 2 1-211 <$100
Total Issue $374,300
Out in 1935 $30,000
Large out 1935 $1,810
****

****
8525 Elk
FNB OF LONGTON
{{ UNREPORTED }}
Chartered 1/29/07
Liquidated 7/1/09
1902 Red Seal <$VALUE
4x10 1-250 <$2500
1902 Date Back
4x10 1-11 <$1500
Total Issue $10,440
Out in 1910 $2,630
****
9911 Elk
HOME NB OF LONGTON
{{ 2 L 9 S }}
Chartered 12/10
Liquidated 3/25/35
1902 Date Back <$VALUE
3x10-20 1-1600 <$500
1902 Plain Back
3x10-20 1601-5016 <$500
1929 Small Size
10 Type 1 1-600 <$125
20 Type 1 1-160 <$125
10 Type 2 1-787 <$125
20 Type 2 1-175 <$125
Total Issue $317,370
Out in 1935 $25,000
Large out 1935 $1,560
****
11798 Miami
FNB OF LOUISBURG
{{ 2 L 7 S }}
Chartered 7/20
1902 Plain Back <$VALUE
3x10-20 1-2965 <$750
1929 Small Size
10 Type 1 1-674 <$200
20 Type 1 1-170 <$200
10 Type 2 1-1208 <$200
20 Type 2 1-178 <$200
Total Issue $224,730
Out in 1935 $25,000
Large out 1935 $760
****
7561 Russell
FNB OF LUCAS
{{ 3 L 8 S }}
Organized 12/20/04
Liquidated 7/24/34
1902 Red Seal <$VALUE
3x10-20 1-900 <$1000
1902 Date Back
3x10-20 1-2290 <$400
1902 Plain Back
3x10-20 2291-6128 <$400
1929 Small Size
10 Type 1 1-588 <$125
20 Type 1 1-150 <$125
10 Type 2 1-169 <$125
20 Type 2 1-35 <$125
Total Issue $407,070
Out at close $25,000
Large out at close $1,880
****
10065 Russell
FNB OF LURAY
{{ 3 L 6 S }}
Organized 5/22/11
Liquidated 7/31/34
1902 Date Back <$VALUE
3x10-20 1-1850 <$500
1902 Plain Back
3x10-20 1851-5666 <$500
1929 Small Size
10 Type 1 1-751 <$200
20 Type 1 1-223 <$200
Total Issue $355,120
Out at close $30,000
Large out at close $1,530
****
7222 Osage
FNB OF LYNDON
{{ 9 L 9 S }}
Organized 3/26/04
Liquidated 10/19/34
1902 Red Seal <$VALUE
3x10-20 1-540 <$600
1902 Date Back
3x10-20 1-1840 <$200
1902 Plain Back
3x10-20 1841-5136 <$200
1929 Small Size
10 Type 1 1-644 <$125
20 Type 1 1-172 <$125
10 Type 2 1-245 <$125
20 Type 2 1-25 <$125
Total Issue $346,030
Out at close $25,000
Large out at close $1,670
****

****
14048 Rice
CHANDLER NB OF LYONS
{{ 50 S }}
Chartered 3/34
1929 Small Size <$VALUE
5 Type 2 1-6470 <$60
10 Type 2 1-2430 <$60
Total Issue $56,650
Out in 1935 $50,000
****
3577 Rice
FNB OF LYONS
{{ UNREPORTED }}
Chartered 10/22/86
Liquidated 1/18/95
Brown Back <$VALUE
3x10-20 1-612 <$2000
Total Issue $30,600
Out in 1910 $330
****
5353 Rice
LYONS NB, LYONS
{{ 4 L 5 S }}
Chartered 5/15/00
Liquidated 5/16/34
Brown Back <$VALUE
3x10-20 1-950 <$750
1882 Date Back
3x10-20 1-1370* <$750
1882 Value Back
3x10-20 1471-2034* <$750
* 1371-1470 not marked
1902 Plain Back
3x10-20 1-2296 <$400
1929 Small Size
10 Type 1 1-574 <$175
20 Type 1 1-148 <$175
10 Type 2 1-75 <$175
Total Issue $316,950
Out at close $25,000
Large out at close $1,380
****
5529 Greenwood
FNB OF MADISON
{{ 4 L 7 S }}
Chartered 8/3/00
Brown Back <$VALUE
3x10-20 1-1360 <$750
1882 Date Back
3x10-20 1-1710 <$750
1882 Value Back
3x10-20 1711-2507 <$750
1902 Plain Back
3x10-20 1-2882 <$400
1929 Small Size
10 Type 1 1-754 <$175
20 Type 1 1-172 <$175
10 Type 2 1-694 <$175
20 Type 2 1-178 <$175
Total Issue $413,830
Out in 1935 $25,000
Large out 1935 $1,640
****
2094 Riley
FNB OF MANHATTAN
{{ 7 L }}
Chartered 3/19/73
Liquidated 4/13/77
Original Series <$VALUE
3x1-2 1-1900 <$750/$1500
4x5 1-2375 <$750
Series 1875
3x1-2 1-200 <$750/$1500
4x5 1-825 <$750
Total Issue $74,500
Out in 1910 $453
****
3782 Riley
FNB OF MANHATTAN
{{ 10 L 31 S }}
Chartered 1887
Brown Back <$VALUE
4x5 1-4975 <$600
50-100 1-1563 <$1750/$200
1902 Red Seal
50-100 1-333 <$2000/$2500
1902 Date Back
50-100 1-1000 <$400/$500
3x50-100 1-1280 <$400/$500
1902 Plain Back
3x50-100 1281-1640 <$400/$500
1929 Small Size
10 Type 1 1-2174 <$45
20 Type 1 1-618 <$50
10 Type 2 1-2213 <$50
20 Type 2 1-555 <$60
Total Issue $1,181,730
Out in 1935 $100,000
Large out 1935 $11,120
****

****
4008 Riley
UNION NB OF MANHATTAN
{{ 18 L 30 S }}
Chartered 1889
Brown Back <$VALUE
4x5 1-3725 <$200
3x10-20 1-2300 <$200/$250
1882 Date Back
4x5 1-356 <$200
3x10-20 1-166 <$200/$250
1902 Date Back
4x5 1-3350 <$75
3x10-20 1-2540 <$85
1902 Plain Back
4x5 3351-13040 <$75
3x10-20 2541-8813 <$85
1929 Small Size
5 Type 1 1-3878 <$30
10 Type 1 1-1682 <$35
20 Type 1 1-476 <$45
5 Type 2 1-4308 <$35
10 Type 2 1-2601 <$40
20 Type 2 1-670 <$50
Total Issue $1,241,700
Out in 1935 $100,000
Large out 1935 $4,550
****
FNB in Mankato
SEE Ch 6817
Mankato NB, Mankato
****
3745 Jewell
FNB OF MANKATO
{{ UNREPORTED }}
Chartered 7/6/87
Liquidated 9/19/93
Brown Back <$VALUE
3x10-20 1-604 <$2000
Total Issue $30,200
Out in 1910 $240
****
3812 Jewell
JEWELL COUNTY NB OF MANKATO
{{ UNREPORTED }}
Chartered 11/11/87
Liquidated 7/2/90
Brown Back <$VALUE
4x5 1-825 <$2000
Total Issue $16,500
Out in 1910 $90
****
6817 Jewell
MANKATO NB, MANKATO
Chartered 6/03
2nd title:FNB in Mankato 11/6/22
FIRST TITLE {{ 3 L }}
1902 Red Seal <$VALUE
3x10-20 1-1833 <$1250
1902 Date Back
3x10-20 1-3300 <$600
1902 Plain Back
3x10-20 3301-6340 <$600
SECOND TITLE {{ 3 L U + 41 S }}
1902 Plain Back
3x10-20 1-3071 <$600
1929 Small Size
5 Type 1 1-836 <$35
10 Type 1 1-874 <$35
20 Type 1 1-246 <$40
5 Type 2 1-1392 <$40
10 Type 2 1-555 <$45
Total Issue $681,750
Out in 1935 $25,000
Large out 1935 $3,590
****
3928 Marion
COTTONWOOD VALLEY NB OF MARION
{{ UNREPORTED }}
Chartered 10/4/88
Liquidated 9/12/94
Brown Back <$VALUE
50-100 1-166 <$2500/$3000
Total Issue $24,900
Out in 1910 $100
****
10980 Marion
FARMERS & DROVERS NB OF MARION
{{ 4 S }}
Chartered 4/17
1929 Small Size <$VALUE
5 Type 2 1-2000 <$300
10 Type 2 1-925 <$300
20 Type 2 1-309 <$300
Total Issue $25,430
Out in 1935 $25,000
****

3018 Marion
FNB OF MARION
{{ UNREPORTED }}
Organized 7/28/83
Receivership 8/22/93
Brown Back <$VALUE
3x10-20 1-1088 <$2000
Total Issue $54,400
Out in 1915 $280

7911 Marion
MARION NB, MARION
{{3L 11S}}
Organized 9/15/05
1902 Red Seal <$VALUE
4x5 1-625 <$1000
3x10-20 1-520 <$1000
1902 Date Back
4x5 1-1475 <$500
3x10-20 1-1100 <$500
1902 Plain Back
4x5 1476-5020 <$500
3x10-20 1101-3097 <$500
1929 Small Size
5 Type 1 1-696 <$125
10 Type 1 1-432 <$125
20 Type 1 1-124 <$125
5 Type 2 1-1026 <$125
10 Type 2 1-530 <$125
20 Type 2 1-155 <$125
Total Issue $368,960
Out in 1935 $25,000
Large out 1935 $1,490

2791 Marshall
FNB OF MARYSVILLE
{{12L}}
Organized 8/25/82
Receivership 4/15/24
Brown Back <$VALUE
3x10-20 1-3891 <$400
1902 Red Seal
3x10-20 1-3150 <$500
1902 Date Back
3x10-20 1-4400 <$150
1902 Plain Back
3x10-20 4401-9204 <$150
Total Issue $812,250
Out at close $73,500

9934 Jackson
FNB OF MAYETTA
{{1L 3S}}
Chartered 2/18/11
1902 Date Back <$VALUE
3x10-20 1-620 <$1000
1902 Plain Back
3x10-20 621-1361 <$1000
1929 Small Size
10 Type 1 1-215 <$300
20 Type 1 1-47 <$300
Total Issue $86,590
Out in 1935 $6,500
Large out 1935 $390

12191 Crawford
FNB OF McCUNE
{{2L 3S}}
Chartered 5/22
Liquidated 2/1/32
1902 Plain Back <$VALUE
3x10-20 1-1917 <$750
1929 Small Size
10 Type 1 1-459 <$300
20 Type 1 1-112 <$300
Total Issue $136,830
Out at close $25,000
Large out at close $2,030

3521 McPherson
FNB OF McPHERSON
{{ UNREPORTED }}
Organized 6/17/86
Receivership 10/28/99
Brown Back <$VALUE
3x10-20 1-1033 <$2000
Total Issue $51,650
Out in 1915 $330

3803 McPherson
McPHERSON NB, McPHERSON
{{ UNREPORTED }}
Chartered 10/22/87
Liquidated 2/18/95
Brown Back <$VALUE
50-100 1-273 <$2500/$3000
Total Issue $40,950
Out in 1910 $300

3791 McPherson
SECOND NB OF McPHERSON
{{ UNREPORTED }}
Organized 9/16/87
Receivership 3/25/91
Brown Back <$VALUE
3x10-20 1-336 <$2000
Total Issue $16,800
Out in 1915 $40

7192 Meade
FNB OF MEADE
{{4L 10S}}
Chartered 3/04
1902 Red Seal <$VALUE
3x10-20 1-500 <$1000
1902 Date Back
3x10-20 1-1580* <$500
1902 Plain Back
3x10-20 1711-5157* <$500
* 1581-1710 not marked
1929 Small Size
10 Type 1 1-706 <$150
20 Type 1 1-170 <$150
10 Type 2 1-1038 <$150
20 Type 2 1-259 <$150
Total Issue $361,170
Out in 1935 $25,000
Large out 1935 $1,420

3695 Meade
FNB OF MEADE CENTER
{{1L}}
Organized 5/5/87
Receivership 12/24/90
Brown Back <$VALUE
4x5 1-977 <$2000
Total Issue $19,540
Out in 1915 $155

3853 Meade
MEADE COUNTY NB OF MEADE CENTER
{{ UNREPORTED }}
Chartered 3/7/88
Liquidated 10/6/90
Brown Back <$VALUE
3x10-20 1-286 <$2000
Total Issue $14,300
Out in 1910 $120

3594 Barber
CITIZENS NB OF MEDICINE LODGE
{{ UNREPORTED }}
Chartered 11/30/86
Liquidated 2/19/91
Brown Back <$VALUE
4x5 1-1155 <$2000
Total Issue $23,100
Out in 1910 $175

3253 Barber
FNB OF MEDICINE LODGE
{{1L}}
Chartered 9/24/84
Liquidated 3/1/94
Brown Back <$VALUE
4x5 1-2003 <$2000
Total Issue $40,060
Out in 1910 $285

3758 Graham
FNB OF MILLBROOK
{{ UNREPORTED }}
Chartered 7/25/87
Liquidated 12/20/90
2nd title:FNB of Hill City 12/88
FIRST TITLE
Brown Back <$VALUE
4x5 1-587 <$2000
SECOND TITLE
Brown Back
4x5 1-309 <$2000
Total Issue $17,920
Out in 1910 $145

4931 Ottawa
CITIZENS NB OF MINNEAPOLIS
{{9L 11S}}
Chartered 1893
Brown Back <$VALUE
4x5 1-2250 <$450
3x10-20 1-730 <$450
1882 Date Back
4x5 1-869 <$450
3x10-20 1-585 <$450
1902 Date Back
3x10-20 1-1100 <$200
1902 Plain Back
3x10-20 1101-5434 <$200
1929 Small Size
10 Type 1 1-968 <$85
20 Type 1 1-286 <$85
10 Type 2 1-1481 <$100
20 Type 2 1-335 <$100
Total Issue $513,740
Out in 1935 $50,000
Large out 1935 $2,270

3353 Ottawa
FNB OF MINNEAPOLIS
{{1L}}
Chartered 6/17/85
Liquidated 10/9/93
Brown Back <$VALUE
4x5 1-1565 <$1500
Total Issue $31,300
Out in 1910 $230

3731 Ottawa
MINNEAPOLIS NB, MINNEAPOLIS
{{4L}}
Organized 6/14/87
Receivership 2/9/29
Brown Back <$VALUE
4x5 1-3213 <$600
50-100 1-217 <$1750/$2000
1902 Red Seal
50-100 1-360 <$2000/$2500
1902 Date Back
50-100 1-600 <$400/$500
3x50-100 1-774 <$400/$500
1902 Plain Back
3x50-100 775-870<$400/$500
Total Issue $458,310
Out at close $60,000

7318 Elk
FNB OF MOLINE
{{3L 9S}}
Chartered 6/04
Liquidated 12/10/34
1902 Red Seal <$VALUE
3x10-20 1-320 <$1000
1902 Date Back
3x10-20 1-1590 <$500
1902 Plain Back
3x10-20 1591-4817 <$500
1929 Small Size
10 Type 1 1-622 <$125
20 Type 1 1-168 <$125
10 Type 2 1-540 <$125
20 Type 2 1-105 <$125
Total Issue $321,830
Out at close $25,000
Large out at close $1,430

8369 Elk
MOLINE NB, MOLINE
{{3L}}
Organized 8/31/06
Receivership 4/12/26
1902 Red Seal <$VALUE
3x10-20 1-1400 <$1000
1902 Date Back
3x10-20 1-3300 <$500
1902 Plain Back
3x10-20 3301-8573 <$500
Total Issue $498,650
Out at close $50,000

8107 Labette
FNB OF MOUND VALLEY
{{ UNREPORTED }}
Chartered 2/23/06
Liquidated 9/1/09
1902 Red Seal <$VALUE
3x10-20 1-251 <$2500
Total Issue $12,550
Out in 1910 $3,470

5559 Sedgwick
FNB OF MOUNT HOPE
{{7L 6S}}
Chartered 8/27/00
Brown Back <$VALUE
3x10-20 1-500 <$750
1882 Date Back
3x10-20 1-1850 <$750
1882 Value Back
3x10-20 1851-2719 <$750
1902 Plain Back
3x10-20 1-2403 <$350
1929 Small Size
10 Type 1 1-724 <$175
20 Type 1 1-182 <$175
10 Type 2 1-516 <$175
20 Type 2 1-200 <$175
Total Issue $355,540
Out in 1935 $25,000
Large out 1935 $1,200

9384 Osborne
FNB OF NATOMA
{{7L 5S}}
Chartered 4/09
1902 Date Back <$VALUE
3x10-20 1-1720 <$300
1902 Plain Back
3x10-20 1721-4911 <$300
1929 Small Size
10 Type 1 1-706 <$150
20 Type 1 1-140 <$150
10 Type 2 1-586 <$150
20 Type 2 1-178 <$150
Total Issue $314,130
Out in 1935 $25,000
Large out 1935 $1,420

6914 Wilson
FNB OF NEODESHA
{{1L 15S}}
Chartered 8/03
1902 Red Seal <$VALUE
50-100 1-482 <$2500/$3000
1902 Date Back
50-100 1-200 <$1000/$1250
3x50-100 1-700<$1000/$1250
1902 Plain Back
3x50-100 701-897
<$1000/$1250
1929 Small Size
10 Type 1 1-1130 <$100
20 Type 1 1-336 <$100
10 Type 2 1-1150 <$100
20 Type 2 1-185 <$100
Total Issue $449,870
Out in 1935 $50,000
Large out 1935 $4,900

6895 Wilson
NEODESHA NB, NEODESHA
{{10L 8S}}
Chartered 7/03
1902 Red Seal <$VALUE
3x10-20 1-2700 <$600
1902 Date Back
3x10-20 1-3000 <$200
1902 Plain Back
3x10-20 3001-10133 <$200
1929 Small Size
10 Type 1 1-1292 <$125
20 Type 1 1-340 <$125
10 Type 2 1-1759 <$125
20 Type 2 1-451 <$125
Total Issue $786,580
Out in 1935 $50,000
Large out 1935 $2,440

8081 Ness
CITIZENS NB OF NESS CITY
{{4L}}
Organized 2/3/06
Receivership 7/3/24
1902 Red Seal <$VALUE
3x10-20 1-1200 <$1000
1902 Date Back
3x10-20 1-2650 <$500
1902 Plain Back
3x10-20 2651-4915 <$500
Total Issue $305,750
Out in 1921 $44,100

FNB in Ness City
SEE Ch 8142
NB of Ness City

3542 Ness
FNB OF NESS CITY
{{ UNREPORTED }}
Chartered 7/27/86
Liquidated 12/24/96
Brown Back <$VALUE
4x5 1-2154 <$2000
Total Issue $43,080
Out in 1910 $415

8142 Ness
NB OF NESS CITY
Organized 2/17/06
Receivership 2/21/34
2nd title:FNB in Ness City 7/1/30
FIRST TITLE {{5L 2S}}
1902 Red Seal <$VALUE
3x10-20 1-900 <$800
1902 Date Back
3x10-20 1-1560 <$400
1902 Plain Back
3x10-20 1561-4823 <$400
1929 Small Size
10 Type 1 1-316 <$300
20 Type 1 1-104 <$300
SECOND TITLE {{2S}}
1929 Small Size
10 Type 1 1-286 <$300
20 Type 1 1-76 <$300
Total Issue $343,870
Out at close $25,000
Large out at close $2,020

2777 Harvey
FNB OF NEWTON
{{5L 10S}}
Chartered 1882
Brown Back <$VALUE
4x5 1-3399 <$750
50-100 1-66 <$2000/$2500
1902 Red Seal
50-100 1-462 <$2500/$3000
1902 Date Back
50-100 1-380 <$1000/$1250
3x50-100 1-700<$1000/$1250
1902 Plain Back
3x50-100 701-904
<$1000/$1250
1929 Small Size
50 Type 1 1-172 <$225
100 Type 1 1-33 <$350
Total Issue $501,580
Out in 1935 $50,000
Large out 1935 $5,750

3473 Harvey
GERMAN NB OF NEWTON
{{ UNREPORTED }}
Chartered 3/17/86
Liquidated 7/19/89
Brown Back <$VALUE
3x10-20 1-379 <$2000
Total Issue $18,950
Out in 1910 $120

4860 Harvey
MIDLAND NB OF NEWTON
{{4L 10S}}
Chartered 1893
Brown Back <$VALUE
3x10-20 1-1320 <$650
1882 Date Back
3x10-20 1-390 <$650
1902 Date Back
3x10-20 1-820 <$350
1902 Plain Back
3x10-20 821-7707 <$350
1929 Small Size
10 Type 1 1-1378 <$100
20 Type 1 1-392 <$100
10 Type 2 1-1053 <$100
20 Type 2 1-220 <$100
Total Issue $615,500
Out in 1935 $50,000
Large out 1935 $2,290

3297 Harvey
NEWTON NB, NEWTON
{{2L}}
Organized 1/28/85
Receivership 1/16/93
Brown Back <$VALUE
4x5 1-5100* <$1500
* 3682-3975 not issued
Total Issue $96,120
Out in 1915 $770

8290 Decatur
FNB OF NORCATUR
Chartered 7/06
2nd title:Decatur County NB of Oberlin 10/20/34
FIRST TITLE {{4L 9S}}
1902 Red Seal <$VALUE
3x10-20 1-787 <$850
1902 Date Back
3x10-20 1-1560 <$400
1902 Plain Back
3x10-20 1561-4335 <$400
1929 Small Size
10 Type 1 1-568 <$125
20 Type 1 1-168 <$125
10 Type 2 1-492 <$125
20 Type 2 1-120 <$125
SECOND TITLE {{1S}}
1929 Small Size
20 Type 2 1-27 <$350
Total Issue $318,200
Out in 1935 $25,000
Large out 1935 $1,590

3687 Norton
FNB OF NORTON
{{10L 16S}}
Chartered 1887
Brown Back <$VALUE
4x5 1-3575 <$350
50-100 1-462 <$1500/$1750
1902 Red Seal
3x10-20 1-500 <$500
1902 Date Back
3x10-20 1-3640 <$175
1902 Plain Back
3x10-20 3641-9558 <$175
1929 Small Size
10 Type 1 1-1358 <$60
20 Type 1 1-328 <$70
10 Type 2 1-1243 <$70
20 Type 2 1-366 <$70
Total Issue $784,290
Out in 1935 $50,000
Large out 1935 $2,490

8339 Norton
NB OF NORTON
{{1L}}
Chartered 8/06
Liquidated 6/21/10
1902 Red Seal <$VALUE
3x10-20 1-1540 <$1500
1902 Date Back
3x10-20 1-279 <$850
Total Issue $90,950
Out in 1910 $41,950

5359 Jefferson
FNB OF NORTONVILLE
{{6L 5S}}
Chartered 5/19/00
Brown Back <$VALUE
3x10-20 1-1700 <$750
1882 Date Back
3x10-20 1-1610 <$750
1882 Value Back
3x10-20 1611-2360 <$750
1902 Plain Back
3x10-20 1-2475 <$400
1929 Small Size
10 Type 1 1-710 <$200
20 Type 1 1-168 <$200
10 Type 2 1-309 <$200
20 Type 2 1-104 <$200
Total Issue $394,680
Out in 1935 $25,000
Large out 1935 $1,390

10041 Logan
FNB OF OAKLEY
{{1L U+2S}}
Organized 5/25/11
Receivership 8/18/33
1902 Date Back <$VALUE
4x5 1-850 <$750
3x10-20 1-680 <$750
1902 Plain Back
4x5 851-1975 <$750
3x10-20 681-1414 <$750
1929 Small Size
5 Type 1 1-304 <$400
10 Type 1 1-147 <$400
20 Type 1 1-46 <$400
Total Issue $133,660
Out at close $10,000
Large out at close $560

Decatur County NB of Oberlin
SEE Ch 8290
FNB of Norcatur

7298 Decatur
FARMERS NB OF OBERLIN
{{8L 15S}}
Chartered 6/04
1902 Red Seal <$VALUE
3x10-20 1-1390 <$750
50-100 1-300 <$2000/$2500
1902 Date Back
3x10-20 1-2600 <$350
50-100 1-100 <$600/$750
3x50-100 1-100 <$600/$750
1902 Plain Back
3x10-20 2601-7969 <$350
1929 Small Size
5 Type 1 1-1002 <$75
10 Type 1 1-942 <$75
20 Type 1 1-272 <$75
5 Type 2 1-1804 <$75
10 Type 2 1-967 <$75
20 Type 2 1-149 <$85
Total Issue $693,840
Out in 1935 $50,000
Large out 1935 $4,020

3511 Decatur
FNB OF OBERLIN
{{1L}}
Chartered 5/26/86
Liquidated 9/10/97
Brown Back <$VALUE
3x10-20 1-821 <$2000
Total Issue $41,050
Out in 1910 $550

****

4642 Decatur
OBERLIN NB, OBERLIN
{{ 11 L U + 12 S }}
Organized 9/26/91
Liquidated 10/30/34
Brown Back <$VALUE
3x10-20 1-3840 <$400
1882 Date Back
3x10-20 1-1172 <$400
1902 Date Back
3x10-20 1-2100 <$175
1902 Plain Back
3x10-20 2101-8277 <$175
1929 Small Size
10 Type 1 1-1154 <$100
20 Type 1 1-308 <$100
10 Type 2 1-807 <$100
20 Type 2 1-136 <$125
Total Issue $781,440
Out at close $50,000
Large out at close $3,910
****

1828 Johnson
FNB OF OLATHE
{{ 2 L }}
Chartered 5/29/71
Liquidated 11/9/74
Original Series <$VALUE
3x1-2 1-1680 <$1500/$2500
4x5 1-1900 <$1500
Total Issue $46,400
Out in 1910 $290
****

3720 Johnson
FNB OF OLATHE
{{ 8 L 22 S }}
Chartered 1887
Brown Back <$VALUE
4x5 1-3134 <$650
3x10-20 1-413 <$650
1902 Red Seal
4x5 1-200 <$750
3x10-20 1-170 <$750
1902 Date Back
4x5 1-2550 <$300
3x10-20 1-1940 <$300
1902 Plain Back
4x5 2551-10309 <$300
3x10-20 1941-7059 <$300
1929 Small Size
5 Type 1 1-1806 <$75
10 Type 1 1-804 <$75
20 Type 1 1-220 <$75
5 Type 2 1-1810 <$85
10 Type 2 1-1039 <$85
20 Type 2 1-420 <$85
Total Issue $811,620
Out in 1935 $50,000
Large out 1935 $3,075
****

12353 Pottawatomie
FNB OF ONAGA
{{ 4 L 7 S }}
Chartered 4/23
1902 Plain Back <$VALUE
4x5 1-2377 <$1000
1929 Small Size
5 Type 1 1-1136 <$250
5 Type 2 1-1938 <$250
Total Issue $91,310
Out in 1935 $10,000
Large out 1935 $505
****

3813 Osage
FNB OF OSAGE CITY
{{ 2 L }}
Chartered 11/12/87
Liquidated 2/1/98
Brown Back <$VALUE
4x5 1-2052 <$1500
Total Issue $41,040
Out in 1910 $435
****

3472 Osborne
EXCHANGE NB OF OSBORNE
{{ 8 L U + 11 S }}
Chartered 1886
Liquidated 10/15/34
Brown Back <$VALUE
3x10-20 1-1627 <$450
1902 Red Seal
3x10-20 1-270 <$600
1902 Date Back
3x10-20 1-4150 <$200
1902 Plain Back
3x10-20 4151-10241 <$200
1929 Small Size
10 Type 1 1-1186 <$85
20 Type 1 1-298 <$85
10 Type 2 1-544 <$100
20 Type 2 1-75 <$100
Total Issue $720,760
Out at close $50,000
Large out at close $3,790
****

5834 Osborne
FARMERS NB OF OSBORNE
{{ 4 L 9 S }}
Chartered 5/01
Brown Back <$VALUE
3x10-20 1-1300 <$750
1882 Date Back
3x10-20 1-1610 <$750
1882 Value Back
3x10-20 1611-2610 <$750
1902 Plain Back
3x10-20 1-2084 <$400
1929 Small Size
10 Type 1 1-644 <$150
20 Type 1 1-162 <$150
10 Type 2 1-373 <$150
20 Type 2 1-45 <$150
Total Issue $361,410
Out in 1935 $25,000
Large out 1935 $1,990
****

3319 Osborne
FNB OF OSBORNE
{{ 5 L }}
Organized 1/28/85
Receivership 3/30/28
Brown Back <$VALUE
4x5 1-1800 <$600
3x10-20 1-779 <$600
1902 Red Seal
3x10-20 1-2275 <$700
1902 Date Back
3x10-20 1-2900 <$350
1902 Plain Back
3x10-20 2901-8627 <$350
Total Issue $620,050
Out at close $49,450
****

3038 Labette
FNB OF OSWEGO
{{ 2 L }}
Chartered 8/31/83
Liquidated 9/15/94
Brown Back <$VALUE
4x5 1-3031 <$850
Total Issue $60,620
Out in 1910 $435
****

11576 Labette
FNB OF OSWEGO
{{ 6 L 7 S }}
Chartered 1/20
1902 Plain Back <$VALUE
4x5 1-1970 <$600
3x10-20 1-1246 <$600
1929 Small Size
5 Type 1 1-522 <$175
10 Type 1 1-334 <$175
20 Type 1 1-96 <$175
5 Type 2 1-944 <$175
10 Type 2 1-690 <$175
20 Type 2 1-125 <$175
Total Issue $163,040
Out in 1935 $25,000
Large out 1935 $565
****

1718 Franklin
FNB OF OTTAWA
{{ 16 L 22 S }}
Chartered 10/10/70
Original Series <$VALUE
4x5 1-1750 <$500
3x10-20 1-600 <$1500/$2000
Series 1875
3x10-20 1-2027<$1500/$2000
Brown Back
4x5 1-2500 <$300
3x10-20 1-5050 <$300
1882 Date Back
4x5 1-1500 <$200
3x10-20 1-888 <$200
1902 Date Back
3x10-20 1-5300 <$125
1902 Plain Back
3x10-20 5301-18358 <$125
1929 Small Size
10 Type 1 1-2474 <$30
20 Type 1 1-696 <$35
10 Type 2 1-3851 <$30
20 Type 2 1-754 <$35
Total Issue $1,746,700
Out in 1935 $99,995
Large out 1935 $6,975
****

1910 Franklin
PEOPLES NB OF OTTAWA
{{ 13 L 18 S }}
Chartered 12/28/71
Original Series <$VALUE
4x5 1-1700 <$500
3x10-20 1-800 <$1500/$2000
Series 1875
4x5 1-1724 <$500
3x10-20 1-1449<$1500/$2000
Brown Back
3x10-20 1-3900 <$300
1882 Date Back
3x10-20 1-954 <$300
1902 Date Back
3x10-20 1-2100 <$100
1902 Plain Back
3x10-20 2101-15922 <$100
1929 Small Size
10 Type 1 1-2412 <$50
20 Type 1 1-720 <$50
10 Type 2 1-3591 <$50
20 Type 2 1-670 <$50
Total Issue $1,500,160
Out in 1935 $100,000
Large out 1935 $5,650
****

7195 Osage
FNB OF OVERBROOK
{{ 6 L 8 S }}
Chartered 4/04
1902 Red Seal <$VALUE
3x10-20 1-1100 <$750
1902 Date Back
3x10-20 1-1810 <$300
1902 Plain Back
3x10-20 1811-4997 <$300
1929 Small Size
10 Type 1 1-672 <$125
20 Type 1 1-168 <$125
10 Type 2 1-655 <$125
20 Type 2 1-182 <$125
Total Issue $375,520
Out in 1935 $25,000
Large out 1935 $1,290
****

1864 Miami
FNB OF PAOLA
{{ 4 L }}
Chartered 8/16/71
Liquidated 12/1/77
Original Series <$VALUE
3x1-2 1-2000 <$1500/$2500
4x5 1-2750 <$1500
Series 1875
4x5 1-1223 <$1500
Total Issue $89,460
Out in 1910 $577
****

3350 Miami
MIAMI COUNTY NB OF PAOLA
{{ 15 L 22 S }}
Chartered 1885
Brown Back <$VALUE
3x10-20 1-5860 <$300
1902 Red Seal
3x10-20 1-3100 <$400
1902 Date Back
3x10-20 1-6100 <$125
1902 Plain Back
3x10-20 6101-23471 <$125
1929 Small Size
10 Type 1 1-3898 <$40
20 Type 1 1-1098 <$45
5 Type 2 1-1294 <$40
10 Type 2 1-1481 <$40
20 Type 2 1-699 <$45
Total Issue $2,022,450
Out in 1935 $75,000
Large out 1935 $9,660
Outstanding includes Ch 3991
****

3795 Miami
NB OF PAOLA
{{ UNREPORTED }}
Organized 9/30/87
Receivership 2/1/98
Brown Back <$VALUE
3x10-20 1-1435 <$1500
Total Issue $71,750
Out in 1915 $540
****

3991 Miami
PEOPLES NB OF PAOLA
{{ 5 L }}
Chartered 1889
Closed 7/1/24
Brown Back <$VALUE
3x10-20 1-3242 <$600
1902 Date Back
4x5 1-2580 <$300
3x10-20 1-2480 <$300
1902 Plain Back
4x5 2581-7105 <$300
3x10-20 2481-5278 <$300
Total Issue $568,100
Out at close $50,000
Ch 3350 assumed circulation
****

11537 Labette
FARMERS NB OF PARSONS
{{ 8 L }}
Organized 1/18/19
Receivership 3/24/24
1902 Plain Back <$VALUE
3x10-20 1-6574 <$150
Total Issue $328,700
Out at close $100,000
****

1951 Labette
FNB OF PARSONS
{{ U + 16 L 7 S }}
Chartered 3/29/72
Original Series <$VALUE
3x1-2 1-1000 <$400/$1000
4x5 1-2950 <$400
Series 1875
3x1-2 1-520 <$400/$1000
4x5 1-6076 <$400
Brown Back
3x10-20 1-4650 <$300
1882 Date Back
3x10-20 1-1454 <$300
1902 Date Back
3x50-100 1-928 <$350/$400
1902 Plain Back
3x50-100 929-1068<$350/$400
1929 Small Size
50 Type 1 1-180 <$350
100 Type 1 1-32 <$400
Total Issue $833,520
Out in 1935 $50,000
Large out 1935 $6,700
****

3134 Marion
FNB OF PEABODY
{{ 1 L 0 S }}
Chartered 1884
Liquidated 2/16/31
Brown Back <$VALUE
3x10-20 1-1334 <$1500
1902 Red Seal
50-100 1-240 <$3000/$3500
1902 Date Back
50-100 1-150 <$1250/$1500
3x50-100 1-228<$1250/$1500
1902 Plain Back
3x50-100 229-247
<$1250/$1500
1929 Small Size
50 Type 1 1-29 <$650
100 Type 1 1 <$800
Total Issue $196,250
Out at close $12,500
Large out at close $4,000
****

3601 Phillips
FNB OF PHILLIPSBURG
{{ 9 L 9 S }}
Chartered 1886
Brown Back <$VALUE
4x5 1-2857 <$400
3x10-20 1-469 <$400
1902 Red Seal
3x10-20 1-550 <$500
1902 Date Back
3x10-20 1-3480 <$175
1902 Plain Back
3x10-20 3481-9492 <$175
1929 Small Size
10 Type 1 1-1148 <$110
20 Type 1 1-300 <$125
10 Type 2 1-186 <$150
20 Type 2 1-63 <$150
Total Issue $690,690
Out in 1935 $25,000
Large out 1935 $3,660
****

American Exchange NB of Commerce in Pittsburg
SEE Ch 8418
NB of Commerce in Pittsburg
****

3463 Crawford
FNB OF PITTSBURG
{{ U + 11 L 20 S }}
Organized 2/8/86
Receivership 2/7/32
Brown Back <$VALUE
4x5 1-4794 <$300
3x10-20 1-1855 <$300
1902 Red Seal
4x5 1-2550 <$400
3x10-20 1-1680 <$400
1902 Date Back
4x5 1-6700 <$100
3x10-20 1-5240 <$100
1902 Plain Back
4x5 6701-21952 <$100
3x10-20 5241-15651 <$100
1929 Small Size
5 Type 1 1-2349 <$50
10 Type 1 1-1160 <$50
20 Type 1 1-285 <$50
Total Issue $1,719,490
Out at close $96,335
Large out at close $12,175
****

4136 Crawford
MANUFACTURERS NB OF PITTSBURG
{{ 1 L }}
Chartered 10/3/89
Liquidated 3/16/97
Brown Back <$VALUE
3x10-20 1-1150 <$1500
Total Issue $57,500
Out in 1910 $850
****

3475 Crawford
NB OF PITTSBURG
{{ 5 L 15 S }}
Chartered 1886
Brown Back <$VALUE
3x10-20 1-2569 <$500
1902 Red Seal
4x5 1-700 <$600
3x10-20 1-300 <$600
1902 Date Back
4x5 1-2300 <$200
3x10-20 1-1680 <$200
1902 Plain Back
4x5 2301-5634 <$200
3x10-20 1681-3692 <$200
1929 Small Size
5 Type 1 1-692 <$75
10 Type 1 1-428 <$75
20 Type 1 1-118 <$75
5 Type 2 1-988 <$75
10 Type 2 1-466 <$75
20 Type 2 1-170 <$75
Total Issue $528,330
Out in 1935 $25,000
Large out 1935 $1,965
****

8418 Crawford
NB OF COMMERCE IN PITTSBURG
Chartered 10/06
Liquidated 2/20/28
2nd title:American Exchange NB of Commerce in Pittsburg 6/7/26
FIRST TITLE {{ 6 L }}
1902 Red Seal <$VALUE
4x10 1-3750 <$600
1902 Date Back
4x10 1-9500 <$250
1902 Plain Back
4x10 9501-26484 <$250
SECOND TITLE {{ 1 L }}
1902 Plain Back
4x10 1-2456 <$600
Total Issue $1,307,600
Out at close $100,000
****

7313 Rooks
FNB OF PLAINVILLE
{{ 3 L }}
Organized 6/17/04
Receivership 1/23/28
1902 Red Seal <$VALUE
3x10-20 1-1325 <$1250
1902 Date Back
3x10-20 1-1710 <$600
1902 Plain Back
3x10-20 1711-4225 <$600
Total Issue $277,500
Out at close $25,000
****

8803 Linn
FNB OF PLEASANTON
{{ 1 L 3 S }}
Chartered 7/07
1902 Red Seal <$VALUE
3x10-20 1-187 <$1500
1902 Date Back
3x10-20 1-580 <$750
1902 Plain Back
3x10-20 581-1207 <$750
1929 Small Size
10 Type 1 1-272 <$300
20 Type 1 1-78 <$300
Total Issue $95,380
Out in 1935 $12,500
Large out 1935 $330
****

****

9373 Phillips
FNB OF PRAIRIE VIEW
{{ 5 L 5 S }}
Chartered 4/09
1902 Date Back <$VALUE
3x10-20 1-1120 <$400
1902 Plain Back
3x10-20 1121-2108 <$400
1929 Small Size
10 Type 1 1-692 <$200
20 Type 1 1-192 <$200
10 Type 2 1-237 <$225
20 Type 2 1-75 <$225
Total Issue $173,830
Out in 1935 $25,000
Large out 1935 $870
****

FNB in Pratt
SEE Ch 6229
NB of Pratt
****

3649 Pratt
FNB OF PRATT
{{ UNREPORTED }}
Chartered 3/16/87
Liquidated 12/5/95
Brown Back <$VALUE
4x5 1-1885 <$2000
Total Issue $37,700
Out in 1910 $485
****

6229 Pratt
NB OF PRATT
Chartered 4/02
2nd title:FNB in Pratt 2/24/20
FIRST TITLE {{ 3 L }}
1902 Red Seal <$VALUE
3x10-20 1-900 <$1250
1902 Date Back
3x10-20 1-1900 <$600
1902 Plain Back
3x10-20 1901-2820 <$600
SECOND TITLE {{ 6 L 7 S }}
1902 Plain Back (dated 1902)
3x10-20 1-650 <$500
1902 Plain Back (dated 1922)
4x5 1-6371 <$500
1929 Small Size
5 Type 1 1-2872 <$150
5 Type 2 1-6712 <$150
Total Issue $465,640
Out in 1935 $25,000
Large out 1935 $1,380
****

3787 Pratt
PRATT COUNTY NB OF PRATT
{{ UNREPORTED }}
Organized 9/8/87
Receivership 4/7/91
Brown Back <$VALUE
4x5 1-356 <$2000
3x10-20 1-206 <$2000
Total Issue $17,420
Out in 1915 $145
****

11887 Jewell
RANDALL NB, RANDALL
{{ 2 L }}
Chartered 12/20
1902 Plain Back <$VALUE
4x5 1-3255 <$1000
Total Issue $65,100
Out in 1935 $240
****

11728 Franklin
FNB OF RICHMOND
Chartered 5/20
2nd title:Peoples NB of Richmond 3/30/29
FIRST TITLE {{ 5 L }}
1902 Plain Back <$VALUE
4x5 1-6880 <$750
SECOND TITLE {{ 9 S }}
1929 Small Size
5 Type 1 1-2974 <$125
5 Type 2 1-5280 <$125
Total Issue $253,220
Out in 1935 $25,000
Large out 1935 $790
****

Peoples NB of Richmond
SEE Ch 11728
FNB of Richmond
****

3657 Russell
FNB OF RUSSELL
{{ UNREPORTED }}
Chartered 3/25/87
Liquidated 6/19/99
Brown Back <$VALUE
3x10-20 1-1321 <$2000
Total Issue $66,050
Out in 1910 $770

3775 Logan
FNB OF RUSSELL SPRINGS
{{ UNREPORTED }}
Chartered 8/18/87
Liquidated 11/21/88
Brown Back <$VALUE
4x5 1-587 <$2000
Total Issue $11,740
Out in 1910 $105

2990 Nemaha
CITIZENS NB OF SABETHA
{{ 1 L }}
Chartered 1883
Liquidated 1/27/85
Brown Back <$VALUE
4x5 1-587 <$2000
Total Issue $11,740
Out in 1910 $100

2954 Nemaha
FNB OF SABETHA
{{ UNREPORTED }}
Chartered 1883
Liquidated 1/2/85
Brown Back <$VALUE
4x5 1-562 <$2000
Total Issue $11,240
Out in 1910 $65

4626 Nemaha
NB OF SABETHA
{{ 13 L 7 S }}
Organized 8/28/91
Receivership 1/18/32
Brown Back <$VALUE
3x10-20 1-4550 <$300
1882 Date Back
3x10-20 1-1379 <$300
1902 Date Back
3x10-20 1-2400 <$125
1902 Plain Back
3x10-20 2401-9927 <$125
1929 Small Size
10 Type 1 1-1040 <$150
20 Type 1 1-233 <$150
Total Issue $883,160
Out at close $59,280
Large out at close $8,300

3467 Stafford
FNB OF SAINT JOHN
{{ 3 L 9 S }}
Chartered 1886
Brown Back <$VALUE
4x5 1-5127 <$750
3x10-20 1-1306 <$750
1902 Red Seal
3x10-20 1-940 <$850
1902 Date Back
3x10-20 1-2840* <$400
1902 Plain Back
3x10-20 3141-3987* <$400
* 2841-3140 not marked
1929 Small Size
5 Type 1 1-586 <$100
10 Type 1 1-704 <$100
20 Type 1 1-224 <$100
5 Type 2 1-2094 <$100
10 Type 2 1-1022 <$100
20 Type 2 1-324 <$100
Total Issue $528,060
Out in 1935 $50,000
Large out 1935 $1,710

7844 Stafford
SAINT JOHN NB, SAINT JOHN
{{ 7 L 2U + 9 S }}
Chartered 7/05
1902 Red Seal <$VALUE
4x5 1-650 <$1000
3x10-20 1-520 <$1000
1902 Date Back
4x5 1-1825 <$500
3x10-20 1-1260 <$500
1902 Plain Back
4x5 1826-5944 <$500
3x10-20 1261-3726 <$500
1929 Small Size
5 Type 1 1-906 <$125
10 Type 1 1-442 <$125
20 Type 1 1-140 <$125
5 Type 2 1-800 <$125
10 Type 2 1-603 <$125
20 Type 2 1-95 <$125
Total Issue $426,610
Out in 1935 $25,000
Large out 1935 $1,560

3374 Pottawatomie
FNB OF SAINT MARYS
{{ 32 L 9 S }}
Organized 7/29/85
Receivership 1/12/33
Brown Back <$VALUE
3x10-20 1-2931 <$300
1902 Red Seal
3x10-20 1-1600 <$400
1902 Date Back
3x10-20 1-2900 <$100
1902 Plain Back
3x10-20 2901-9684 <$100
1929 Small Size
5 Type 1 1-1182 <$100
10 Type 1 1-737 <$100
20 Type 1 1-218 <$100
Total Issue $816,590
Out at close $50,000
Large out at close $6,790

4619 Pottawatomie
NB OF SAINT MARYS
{{ UNREPORTED }}
Chartered 1891
Liquidated 5/31/10
Brown Back <$VALUE
3x10-20 1-2310 <$1500
1882 Date Back
3x10-20 1-282 <$1500
Total Issue $129,600
Out in 1910 $20,450

4317 Saline
AMERICAN NB OF SALINA
{{ 1 L }}
Chartered 5/20/90
Liquidated 4/30/94
Brown Back <$VALUE
3x10-20 1-780 <$2000
Total Issue $39,000
Out in 1910 $640

4742 Saline
FARMERS NB OF SALINA
{{ 8 L 20 S }}
Chartered 1892
Brown Back <$VALUE
3x10-20 1-7120 <$400
1882 Date Back
3x10-20 1-2865 <$400
1902 Date Back
3x50-100 1-1540 <$400/$500
1902 Plain Back
3x50-100 1541-1914 <$400/$500
1929 Small Size
5 Type 1 1-320 <$100
10 Type 1 1-156 <$100
20 Type 1 1-22 <$100
50 Type 1 1-248 <$175
100 Type 1 1-82 <$225
Total Issue $1,122,950
Out in 1935 $100,000
Large out 1935 $11,230

2538 Saline
FNB OF SALINA
{{ UNREPORTED }}
Chartered 6/27/81
Liquidated 7/5/92
Series 1875 <$VALUE
4x10 1-2581 <$2500
Total Issue $103,240
Out in 1910 $730

4945 Saline
NB OF AMERICA, SALINA
{{ 26 L 22 S }}
Chartered 1894
Brown Back <$VALUE
3x10-20 1-3670 <$250
1882 Date Back
3x10-20 1-5396 <$250
1902 Date Back
3x10-20 1-2000 <$75
1902 Plain Back
3x10-20 2001-13921 <$75
1929 Small Size
10 Type 1 1-2458 <$50
20 Type 1 1-682 <$50
5 Type 2 1-312 <$60
10 Type 2 1-1838 <$60
20 Type 2 1-465 <$60
Total Issue $1,407,910
Out in 1935 $100,000
Large out 1935 $5,355

3531 Saline
SALINA NB, SALINA
{{ UNREPORTED }}
Chartered 7/13/86
Liquidated 4/10/95
Brown Back <$VALUE
3x10-20 1-1343 <$2000
Total Issue $67,150
Out in 1910 $570

3779 Republic
FNB OF SCANDIA
Chartered 1887
2nd title:NB of Belleville 1/15/94
3rd title:FNB in Belleville 6/14/21
FIRST TITLE {{ 0 L }}
Brown Back <$VALUE
4x5 1-1457 <$2000
SECOND TITLE {{ 3 L }}
Brown Back
4x5 1-1488 <$500
3x10-20 1-470 <$500
1902 Red Seal
3x10-20 1-250 <$700
1902 Date Back
3x10-20 1-2940 <$200
1902 Plain Back
3x10-20 2941-4990 <$200
THIRD TITLE {{ 6 L 15 S }}
1902 Plain Back
3x10-20 1-3525 <$300
1929 Small Size
10 Type 1 1-1020 <$100
20 Type 1 1-274 <$100
10 Type 2 1-1495 <$100
20 Type 2 1-365 <$100
Total Issue $636,980
Out in 1935 $50,000
Large out 1935 $5,250

8808 Scott
FNB OF SCOTT CITY
{{ 5 L U + 7 S }}
Chartered 7/07
1902 Red Seal <$VALUE
4x5 1-250 <$1000
3x10-20 1-200 <$1000
1902 Date Back
4x5 1-1525* <$500
3x10-20 1-1180** <$500
1902 Plain Back
4x5 1626-5690* <$500
3x10-20 1261-3675** <$500
* 1526-1625 not marked
** 1181-1260 not marked
1929 Small Size
5 Type 1 1-916 <$150
10 Type 1 1-430 <$150
20 Type 1 1-120 <$150
5 Type 2 1-1352 <$150
10 Type 2 1-648 <$150
20 Type 2 1-204 <$150
Total Issue $397,550
Out in 1935 $25,000
Large out 1935 $1,690

3855 Chautauqua
FNB OF SEDAN
{{ 9 L 9 S }}
Chartered 1888
Brown Back <$VALUE
50-100 1-1148 <$1250/$1500
1902 Red Seal
50-100 1-334 <$2000/$2500
1902 Date Back
50-100 1-640 <$350/$400
3x50-100 1-1298 <$350/$400
1902 Plain Back
3x50-100 1299-1538 <$350/$500
1929 Small Size
50 Type 1 1-212 <$300
100 Type 1 1-72 <$350
5 Type 2 1-200 <$200
10 Type 2 1-150 <$200
Total Issue $812,100
Out in 1935 $75,000
Large out 1935 $9,350

7535 Chautauqua
PEOPLES NB OF SEDAN
{{ UNREPORTED }}
Chartered 12/30/04
Liquidated 9/1/09
1902 Red Seal <$VALUE
3x10-20 1-975 <$2000
1902 Date Back
3x10-20 1-108 <$1500
Total Issue $54,150
Out in 1910 $13,670

4150 Chautauqua
SEDAN NB, SEDAN
{{ UNREPORTED }}
Chartered 11/5/89
Liquidated 2/9/92
Brown Back <$VALUE
4x5 1-713 <$2000
Total Issue $14,260
Out in 1910 $150

2952 Nemaha
FNB OF SENECA
{{ 6 L }}
Chartered 1883
Liquidated 2/4/24
Brown Back <$VALUE
4x5 1-3192 <$600
3x10-20 1-235 <$600
1902 Red Seal
3x10-20 1-2025 <$750
1902 Date Back
3x10-20 1-3300 <$350
1902 Plain Back
3x10-20 3301-6737 <$350
Total Issue $513,690
Out at close $49,995

5101 Nemaha
NB OF SENECA
{{ 8 L 7 S }}
Chartered 1897
Brown Back <$VALUE
50-100 1-1084 <$2000/$2500
1882 Date Back
50-100 1-300 <$1000/$1250
3x50-100 1-180<$1000/$1250
1902 Plain Back
3x50-100 1-555<$1000/$1250
1929 Small Size
50 Type 1 1-161 <$250
100 Type 1 1-32 <$300
Total Issue $458,850
Out in 1935 $25,000
Large out 1935 $5,750

3630 Smith
SMITH COUNTY NB OF SMITH CENTER
{{ UNREPORTED }}
Chartered 2/1/87
Liquidated 6/30/99
Brown Back <$VALUE
4x5 1-3293 <$2000
Total Issue $65,860
Out in 1910 $585

3546 Smith
FNB OF SMITH CENTRE
{{ 6 L 15 S }}
Chartered 1886
Brown Back <$VALUE
4x5 1-4100 <$600
3x10-20 1-1562 <$600
1902 Red Seal
3x10-20 1-1000 <$750
1902 Date Back
3x10-20 1-3000 <$300
1902 Plain Back
3x10-20 3001-8806 <$300
1929 Small Size
10 Type 1 1-1158 <$100
20 Type 1 1-348 <$100
10 Type 2 1-597 <$125
20 Type 2 1-95 <$150
Total Issue $769,510
Out in 1935 $50,000
Large out 1935 $3,820

9794 Dickinson
SOLOMON NB OF SOLOMON
{{ 6 L 9 S }}
Chartered 6/10
1902 Date Back <$VALUE
3x10-20 1-1720 <$450
1902 Plain Back
3x10-20 1721-5195 <$450
1929 Small Size
10 Type 1 1-674 <$125
20 Type 1 1-172 <$125
10 Type 2 1-502 <$125
20 Type 2 1-155 <$125
Total Issue $328,950
Out in 1935 $25,000
Large out 1935 $1,610

10161 Ford
FNB OF SPEARVILLE
{{ 5 L U + 6 S }}
Chartered 3/12
1902 Date Back <$VALUE
3x10-20 1-1700 <$500
1902 Plain Back
3x10-20 1701-5865 <$500
1929 Small Size
10 Type 1 1-788 <$150
20 Type 1 1-242 <$150
10 Type 2 1-565 <$150
20 Type 2 1-95 <$150
Total Issue $377,120
Out in 1935 $30,000
Large out 1935 $1,920

8883 Stafford
FARMERS NB OF STAFFORD
{{ 2 L 6 S }}
Chartered 9/07
1902 Red Seal <$VALUE
3x10-20 1-760 <$1250
1902 Date Back
3x10-20 1-1570 <$600
1902 Plain Back
3x10-20 1571-5021 <$600
1929 Small Size
10 Type 1 1-676 <$200
20 Type 1 1-202 <$200
10 Type 2 1-557 <$200
20 Type 2 1-130 <$200
Total Issue $362,020
Out in 1935 $25,000
Large out 1935 $1,290

3852 Stafford
FNB OF STAFFORD
{{ 1 L }}
Chartered 3/7/88
Liquidated 6/15/92
Brown Back <$VALUE
4x5 1-1141 <$2000
Total Issue $22,820
Out in 1910 $160

3207 Rice
FNB OF STERLING
{{ 4 L 8 S }}
Chartered 1884
Brown Back <$VALUE
4x5 1-3186 <$750
3x10-20 1-299 <$750
1902 Red Seal
3x10-20 1-425 <$850
1902 Date Back
3x10-20 1-1200 <$400
1902 Plain Back
3x10-20 1201-2384 <$400
1929 Small Size
10 Type 1 1-314 <$125
20 Type 1 1-102 <$125
10 Type 2 1-1321 <$125
20 Type 2 1-342 <$125
Total Issue $270,250
Out in 1935 $25,000
Large out 1935 $1,030

3440 Rooks
FNB OF STOCKTON
{{ UNREPORTED }}
Chartered 1/22/86
Liquidated 1/15/90
Brown Back <$VALUE
4x5 1-943 <$2000
Total Issue $18,860
Out in 1910 $175

8274 Rooks
N STATE B OF STOCKTON
{{ 7 L }}
Organized 5/22/06
Receivership 11/14/27
1902 Red Seal <$VALUE
4x5 1-1250 <$750
3x10-20 1-1200 <$750
1902 Date Back
4x5 1-3300 <$350
3x10-20 1-2200 <$350
1902 Plain Back
4x5 3301-9745 <$350
3x10-20 2201-6323 <$350
Total Issue $596,050
Out at close $48,900

7815 Rooks
STOCKTON NB, STOCKTON
{{ 4 L 11 S }}
Chartered 7/05
1902 Red Seal <$VALUE
4x5 1-1000 <$800
3x10-20 1-900 <$800
1902 Date Back
4x5 1-2850 <$350
3x10-20 1-1850 <$350
1902 Plain Back
4x5 2851-5597 <$350
3x10-20 1851-6369 <$350
1929 Small Size
5 Type 1 1-926 <$100
10 Type 1 1-798 <$100
20 Type 1 1-208 <$100
5 Type 2 1-1154 <$100
10 Type 2 1-753 <$100
20 Type 2 1-200 <$100
Total Issue $613,310
Out in 1935 $40,000
Large out 1935 $2,720

3002 Chase
STRONG CITY NB, STRONG CITY
{{ UNREPORTED }}
Chartered 7/13/83
Liquidated 5/26/88
Brown Back <$VALUE
4x5 1-1099 <$2000
Total Issue $21,980
Out in 1910 $155

8114 Hamilton
FNB OF SYRACUSE
{{ 3 L 12 S }}
Chartered 3/06
1902 Red Seal <$VALUE
3x10-20 1-850 <$1250
1902 Date Back
3x10-20 1-1810* <$600
1902 Plain Back
3x10-20 2311-5209* <$600
* 1811-2310 not marked
1929 Small Size
10 Type 1 1-668 <$100
20 Type 1 1-170 <$100
10 Type 2 1-754 <$100
20 Type 2 1-175 <$100
Total Issue $374,470
Out in 1935 $25,000
Large out 1935 $1,800

9465 Neosho
FNB OF THAYER
{{ 5 L 2U + 20 S }}
Chartered 6/09
1902 Date Back <$VALUE
3x10-20 1-1120 <$350
1902 Plain Back
3x10-20 1121-4552 <$350
1929 Small Size
10 Type 1 1-608 <$85
20 Type 1 1-180 <$85
10 Type 2 1-805 <$100
20 Type 2 1-115 <$115
Total Issue $296,030
Out in 1935 $25,000
Large out 1935 $1,250

7907 Shawnee
CAPITAL NB OF TOPEKA
{{ 4 L }}
Chartered 9/05
Liquidated 2/2/10
1902 Red Seal <$VALUE
3x10-20 1-3720 <$1000
1902 Date Back
3x10-20 1-590 <$600
Total Issue $215,500
Out in 1910 $64,470

CONDITION affects Value. The Values shown are for notes in FINE condition.

3078 Shawnee
CENTRAL NB OF TOPEKA
{{ 47 L 50+ S }}
Chartered 1883
Brown Back <$VALUE
3x10-20 1-10839 <$200/$250
1902 Red Seal
3x10-20 1-7000 <$200/$250
1902 Date Back
3x10-20 1-12700 <$65
1902 Plain Back
3x10-20 12701-48288 <$65
1929 Small Size
10 Type 1 1-10502 <$20
20 Type 1 1-2664 <$30
10 Type 2 1-12648 <$20
20 Type 2 1-3393 <$35
Total Issue $4,450,490
Out in 1935 $300,000
Large out 1935 $17,305

10390 Shawnee
FARMERS NB OF TOPEKA
{{ 8 L 8 S }}
Chartered 5/13
Liquidated 9/3/31
1902 Date Back <$VALUE
3x10-20 1-3800 <$175
1902 Plain Back
3x10-20 3801-17347 <$175
1929 Small Size
10 Type 1 1-1513 <$125
20 Type 1 1-396 <$125
Total Issue $1,005,650
Out at close $100,000
Large out at close $12,100

FNB of Topeka
SEE Ch 1660
Kansas Valley NB of Topeka

2646 Shawnee
FNB OF TOPEKA
{{ 13 L }}
Organized 3/13/82
Receivership 7/3/05
Series 1875 <$VALUE
4x5 1-16940 <$400
3x10-20 1-4071<$1500/$2000
Brown Back
50-100 1-2380 <$1750/$2000
Total Issue $899,350
Out in 1915 $24,160

3790 Shawnee
KANSAS NB OF TOPEKA
{{ UNREPORTED }}
Chartered 9/14/87
Liquidated 9/1/94
Brown Back <$VALUE
50-100 1-725 <$2000/$2500
Total Issue $108,750
Out in 1910 $1,400

1660 Shawnee
KANSAS VALLEY NB OF TOPEKA
Organized 8/23/66
Receivership 12/16/73
2nd title:FNB of Topeka 7/73
FIRST TITLE {{ 2 L }}
Original Series <$VALUE
3x1-2 1-3000 <$2000/$3000
4x5 1-1750 <$2000
3x10-20 1-1078<$2500/$3000
SECOND TITLE {{ 0 L }}
Original Series
3x10-20 1-98 <$2500/$3000
Total Issue $108,800
Out in 1915 $24,162

11398 Shawnee
KAW VALLEY NB OF TOPEKA
{{ 16 L U + 8 S }}
Chartered 7/19
Liquidated 11/13/31
1902 Plain Back <$VALUE
4x5 1-11345 <$85
3x10-20 1-7934 <$100
1929 Small Size
5 Type 1 1-1918 <$100
10 Type 1 1-1116 <$100
20 Type 1 1-279 <$100
Total Issue $781,580
Out at close $100,000
Large out at close $9,020

3909 Shawnee
MERCHANTS NB OF TOPEKA
{{ 26 L 25 S }}
Chartered 1888
Brown Back <$VALUE
4x5 1-13616 <$200
3x10-20 1-3996 <$200/$250
1902 Red Seal
4x5 1-500 <$200
4x10 1-1000 <$200
1902 Date Back
4x5 1-5680 <$75
4x10 1-5160 <$75
1902 Plain Back
4x5 5681-21674 <$75
4x10 5161-17706 <$75
1929 Small Size
5 Type 1 1-5294 <$35
10 Type 1 1-4264 <$40
5 Type 2 1-11034 <$35
10 Type 2 1-3986 <$40
Total Issue $2,173,530
Out in 1935 $100,000
Large out 1935 $6,765

12740 Shawnee
NB OF TOPEKA
{{ 50+ S }}
Chartered 5/25
1929 Small Size <$VALUE
5 Type 1 1-3088 <$20
10 Type 1 1-1544 <$20
20 Type 1 1-526 <$30
5 Type 2 1-45356 <$20
10 Type 2 1-26111 <$20
20 Type 2 1-7812 <$30
Total Issue $892,530
Out in 1935 $500,000

2192 Shawnee
STATE NB OF TOPEKA
{{ UNREPORTED }}
Chartered 10/9/74
Liquidated 9/15/75
Original Series <$VALUE
4x5 1-1585 <$2000
Total Issue $31,700
Out in 1910 $85

1945 Shawnee
TOPEKA NB, TOPEKA
{{ 5 L }}
Chartered 3/7/72
Liquidated 8/7/78
Original Series <$VALUE
3x1-2 1-3800 <$850/$2000
4x5 1-2800 <$1000
3x10-20 1-1600<$1500/$2000
Series 1875
3x10-20 1-576 <$1500/$2000
Total Issue $183,800
Out in 1910 $926

6819 Woodson
FNB OF TORONTO
{{ 3 L 24 S }}
Chartered 6/03
1902 Red Seal <$VALUE
4x5 1-625 <$1000
3x10-20 1-470 <$1000
1902 Date Back
4x5 1-1525 <$500
3x10-20 1-1160 <$500
1902 Plain Back
4x5 1526-5402 <$500
3x10-20 1161-3424 <$500
1929 Small Size
5 Type 1 1-730 <$75
10 Type 1 1-424 <$75
20 Type 1 1-118 <$75
5 Type 2 1-1214 <$75
10 Type 2 1-575 <$75
20 Type 2 1-166 <$75
Total Issue $391,880
Out in 1935 $25,000
Large out 1935 $1,170

11154 Butler
FNB OF TOWANDA
{{ 1 L }}
Chartered 3/18
Liquidated 6/5/26
1902 Plain Back <$VALUE
3x10-20 1-1776 <$750
Total Issue $88,800
Out at close $15,000
Ch 12935 assumed circulation

12935 Butler
TOWANDA NB, TOWANDA
{{ 0 L 11 S }}
Chartered 5/26
Liquidated 1/11/35
1902 Plain Back <$VALUE
3x10-20 1-580 <$1000
1929 Small Size
10 Type 1 1-394 <$100
20 Type 1 1-124 <$100
5 Type 2 1-372 <$100
10 Type 2 1-110 <$100
Total Issue $70,480
Out in 1935 $15,000
Large out 1935 $670
Outstanding includes Ch 11154

8162 Doniphan
FNB OF TROY
{{ 7 L 7 S }}
Chartered 4/06
1902 Red Seal <$VALUE
3x10-20 1-750 <$750
1902 Date Back
3x10-20 1-1710 <$300
1902 Plain Back
3x10-20 1711-5217 <$300
1929 Small Size
10 Type 1 1-628 <$125
20 Type 1 1-162 <$125
10 Type 2 1-546 <$125
20 Type 2 1-159 <$125
Total Issue $364,110
Out in 1935 $25,000
Large out 1935 $1,550

9758 Sedgwick
UNION STOCK YARDS NB, UNION STOCK YARDS (WICHITA)
{{ 1 L 11 S }}
Chartered 5/10
1902 Date Back <$VALUE
3x10-20 1-1780 <$500
1902 Plain Back
3x10-20 1781-5312 <$500
1929 Small Size
10 Type 1 1-704 <$175
20 Type 1 1-182 <$175
10 Type 2 1-874 <$175
20 Type 2 1-198 <$175
Total Issue $342,380
Out in 1935 $25,000
Large out 1935 $1,500

11816 Jefferson
FNB OF VALLEY FALLS
{{ 4 L 2 S }}
Chartered 8/20
Liquidated 7/7/31
1902 Plain Back <$VALUE
4x5 1-9782 <$400
1929 Small Size
5 Type 1 1-1402 <$400
Total Issue $237,700
Out at close $25,000
Large out at close $1,110

3776 Trego
FNB OF WaKEENEY
{{ 1 L }}
Chartered 8/18/87
Liquidated 6/30/93
Brown Back <$VALUE
4x5 1-1416 <$2000
Total Issue $28,320
Out in 1910 $190

3434 Pottawatomie
FNB OF WAMEGO
{{ 37 L 28 S }}
Chartered 1886
Brown Back <$VALUE
4x5 1-4394 <$200
3x10-20 1-729 <$200/$250
1902 Red Seal
3x10-20 1-400 <$250/$300
1902 Date Back
3x10-20 1-1820 <$75
1902 Plain Back
3x10-20 1821-3309 <$75
1929 Small Size
10 Type 1 1-424 <$50
20 Type 1 1-126 <$50
10 Type 2 1-98 <$60
20 Type 2 1-15 <$60
Total Issue $351,620
Out in 1935 $20,000
Large out 1935 $3,350

2912 Washington
FNB OF WASHINGTON
{{ 7 L }}
Chartered 1883
Brown Back <$VALUE
4x5 1-3270 <$500
3x10-20 1-235 <$500
1902 Red Seal
3x10-20 1-1325 <$600
1902 Date Back
3x10-20 1-1400 <$225
1902 Plain Back
3x10-20 1401-3241 <$225
Total Issue $305,450
Out in 1935 $1,930

3167 Washington
WASHINGTON NB, WASHINGTON
{{ 7 L }}
Chartered 1884
Brown Back <$VALUE
4x5 1-5258 <$500
3x10-20 1-999 <$500
1902 Red Seal
4x5 1-2250 <$600
3x10-20 1-1800 <$600
1902 Date Back
4x5 1-1100 <$225
3x10-20 1-880 <$225
1902 Plain Back
4x5 1101-3190 <$225
3x10-20 881-2237 <$225
Total Issue $465,760
Out in 1935 $2,420

6101 Coffey
FNB OF WAVERLY
{{ 5 L 7 S }}
Chartered 1/02
1902 Red Seal <$VALUE
4x5 1-1455 <$1000
3x10-20 1-1108 <$1000
1902 Date Back
4x5 1-1475 <$500
3x10-20 1-1090 <$500
1902 Plain Back (dated 1902)
4x5 1476-2885 <$500
3x10-20 1091-1941 <$500
1902 Plain Back (dated 1922)
3x10-20 1-1901 <$500
1929 Small Size
5 Type 1 1-2752 <$150
5 Type 2 1-4422 <$150
Total Issue $438,970
Out in 1935 $25,000
Large out 1935 $1,845

FNB in Wellington
SEE Ch 3091
Wellington NB, Wellington

2879 Sumner
FNB OF WELLINGTON
{{ UNREPORTED }}
Organized 2/13/83
Receivership 10/25/95
Brown Back <$VALUE
3x10-20 1-811 <$2000
Total Issue $40,550
Out in 1915 $320

8399 Sumner
NB OF COMMERCE OF WELLINGTON
{{ 4 L 11 S }}
Chartered 10/06
1902 Red Seal <$VALUE
4x10 1-450 <$850
1902 Date Back
4x10 1-4350 <$300
1902 Plain Back
4x10 4351-15124 <$300
1929 Small Size
10 Type 1 1-2406 <$100
10 Type 2 1-3565 <$100
Total Issue $802,970
Out in 1935 $50,000
Large out 1935 $2,290

3564 Sumner
STATE NB OF WELLINGTON
{{ UNREPORTED }}
Organized 10/1/86
Receivership 9/25/90
Brown Back <$VALUE
3x10-20 1-358 <$2000
Total Issue $17,900
Out in 1915 $50

3865 Sumner
SUMNER NB OF WELLINGTON
{{ 1 L }}
Organized 4/10/88
Receivership 6/26/96
Brown Back <$VALUE
50-100 1-398 <$2500/$3000
Total Issue $59,700
Out in 1915 $700

3091 Sumner
WELLINGTON NB, WELLINGTON
Chartered 1883
2nd title:FNB in Wellington 1/20/21
FIRST TITLE {{ 1 L }}
Brown Back <$VALUE
4x5 1-4075 <$1000
50-100 1-431 <$2000/$2500
1902 Red Seal
3x10-20 1-2260 <$1250
1902 Date Back
3x10-20 1-900* <$600
1902 Plain Back
3x10-20 1101-1530* <$600
* 901-1100 not marked
SECOND TITLE {{ 2 L 3 S }}
1902 Plain Back
3x10-20 1-1912 <$600
1929 Small Size
10 Type 1 1-530 <$200
20 Type 1 1-134 <$200
10 Type 2 1-482 <$200
20 Type 2 1-148 <$200
Total Issue $486,910
Out in 1935 $20,000
Large out 1935 $1,570

3304 Pottawatomie
FNB OF WESTMORELAND
{{ 1 L }}
Chartered 2/17/85
Liquidated 4/15/97
Brown Back <$VALUE
4x5 1-2451 <$2000
Total Issue $49,020
Out in 1910 $425

8974 Nemaha
FNB OF WETMORE
{{ 3 L 0 S }}
Chartered 12/07
1902 Red Seal <$VALUE
3x10-20 1-240 <$1500
1902 Date Back
3x10-20 1-680 <$750
1902 Plain Back
3x10-20 681-1451 <$750
1929 Small Size
10 Type 1 1-210 <$500
20 Type 1 1-62 <$500
Total Issue $104,590
Out in 1935 $8,000
Large out 1935 $260

7970 Morris
FNB OF WHITE CITY
{{ 5 L 7 S }}
Chartered 11/05
1902 Red Seal <$VALUE
3x10-20 1-800 <$800
1902 Date Back
4x5 1-1615 <$350
3x10-20 1-1150 <$350
1902 Plain Back
4x5 1616-5482 <$350
3x10-20 1151-3485 <$350
1929 Small Size
5 Type 1 1-752 <$200
10 Type 1 1-434 <$200
20 Type 1 1-118 <$200
5 Type 2 1-1204 <$200
10 Type 2 1-753 <$200
20 Type 2 1-154 <$200
Total Issue $403,280
Out in 1935 $25,000
Large out 1935 $1,425

FNB in Wichita
SEE Ch 2782
Kansas NB of Wichita

1913 Sedgwick
FNB OF WICHITA
{{ UNREPORTED }}
Chartered 1/2/72
Receivership 9/23/76
Original Series <$VALUE
3x1-2 1-1840 <$2000/$3000
4x5 1-3805 <$2000
Total Issue $85,300
Out in 1915 $499

3683 Sedgwick
FOURTH NB OF WICHITA
{{ 17 L }}
Chartered 1887
Liquidated 3/22/24
Brown Back <$VALUE
4x5 1-6647 <$250
3x10-20 1-5110 <$250/$300
1902 Red Seal
4x5 1-2000 <$250
3x10-20 1-1250 <$250/$300
1902 Date Back
4x5 1-15500 <$75
3x10-20 1-11500 <$75
1902 Plain Back
4x5 15501-21095 <$75
3x10-20 11501-15265 <$75
Total Issue $1,676,090
Out in 1924 $100,000

2782 Sedgwick
KANSAS NB OF WICHITA
Chartered 1882
2nd title:FNB in Wichita 2/24/20
FIRST TITLE {{ 2 L }}
Brown Back <$VALUE
50-100 1-1409 <$2000/$2500
1902 Red Seal
4x5 1-2000 <$850
50-100 1-1201 <$2500/$3000
1902 Date Back
4x5 1-3085 <$400
50-100 1-502 <$850/$1000
3x50-100 1-337 <$850/$1000
SECOND TITLE {{ 50+ S }}
1929 Small Size
5 Type 1 1-46732 <$30
5 Type 2 1-142128 <$30
Total Issue $2,765,350
Out in 1935 $1,000,000
Large out 1935 $4,520
Outstanding includes Ch 5169

6392 Sedgwick
NB OF WICHITA
{{ UNREPORTED }}
Chartered 8/19/02
Liquidated 7/6/08
1902 Red Seal <$VALUE
3x10-20 1-1852 <$1500
Total Issue $92,600
Out in 1910 $15,015

5169 Sedgwick
NB OF COMMERCE OF WICHITA
{{ 6 L }}
Chartered 1/20/99
Closed 2/24/20
Brown Back <$VALUE
3x10-20 1-3100 <$400
1882 Date Back
3x10-20 1-5895 <$400
1902 Plain Back
3x10-20 1-762 <$200
Total Issue $487,850
Out at close $75,000
Ch 2782 assumed circulation

12346 Sedgwick
SOUTHWEST NB OF WICHITA
{{ 22 S }}
Chartered 4/23
1929 Small Size <$VALUE
5 Type 1 1-2782 <$35
10 Type 1 1-1400 <$35
20 Type 1 1-474 <$50
50 Type 1 1-42 <$225
100 Type 1 1-22 <$275
5 Type 2 1-9066 <$50
10 Type 2 1-4931 <$50
20 Type 2 1-1755 <$50
Total Issue $379,880
Out in 1935 $200,000

3524 Sedgwick
STATE NB OF WICHITA
{{ UNREPORTED }}
Organized 6/29/86
Receivership 6/29/94
Brown Back <$VALUE
4x5 1-2999 <$1500
Total Issue $59,980
Out in 1915 $415

****
11010 Sedgwick
UNION NB OF WICHITA
{{ 11 S }}
Chartered 6/17
1929 Small Size <$VALUE
5 Type 2 1-8866 <$100
10 Type 2 1-4260 <$100
20 Type 2 1-2796 <$100
Total Issue $142,850
Out in 1935 $100,000
****
3756 Sedgwick
WEST SIDE NB OF WICHITA
{{ UNREPORTED }}
Chartered 7/19/87
Liquidated 1/13/91
Brown Back <$VALUE
3x10-20 1-652 <$1500
Total Issue $32,600
Out in 1910 $290
****
2786 Sedgwick
WICHITA NB, WICHITA
{{ 1 L }}
Organized 9/20/82
Receivership 9/5/94
Brown Back <$VALUE
4x5 1-8216 <$1000
Total Issue $164,320
Out in 1915 $1,230
****
4556 Cowley
COWLEY COUNTY NB OF
WINFIELD
{{ 7 L }}
Chartered 1891
Closed 12/16/22
Brown Back <$VALUE
4x5 1-3125 <$500
3x10-20 1-2240 <$500
1882 Date Back
4x5 1-1000 <$500
3x10-20 1-700 <$500
1902 Date Back
4x5 1-5500 <$250
3x10-20 1-4100 <$250
1902 Plain Back
4x5 5501-12060 <$250
3x10-20 4101-8313 <$250
Total Issue $886,350
Out at close $100,000
Ch 3218 assumed circulation
****
3218 Cowley
FNB OF WINFIELD
{{ 16 L 46 S }}
Chartered 1884
Brown Back <$VALUE
4x5 1-6964 <$250
3x10-20 1-1164 <$250
1902 Red Seal
3x10-20 1-3800 <$300
1902 Date Back
3x10-20 1-7300 <$100
1902 Plain Back
3x10-20 7301-28487 <$100
1929 Small Size
10 Type 1 1-5110 <$30
20 Type 1 1-1470 <$35
10 Type 2 1-4812 <$30
20 Type 2 1-1610 <$35
Total Issue $2,375,150
Out in 1935 $200,000
Large out 1935 $12,175
Outstanding includes Ch 4556
****
3351 Cowley
WINFIELD NB, WINFIELD
{{ 5 L 13 S }}
Chartered 1885
Brown Back <$VALUE
3x10-20 1-2719 <$500
1902 Red Seal
3x10-20 1-1800 <$600
1902 Date Back
3x10-20 1-2800 <$200
1902 Plain Back
3x10-20 2801-9466 <$200
1929 Small Size
10 Type 1 1-1242 <$125
20 Type 1 1-348 <$125
10 Type 2 1-1395 <$125
20 Type 2 1-390 <$125
Total Issue $837,280
Out in 1935 $50,000
Large out 1935 $3,060
****

****
1840 Wyandotte
FNB OF WYANDOTTE
{{ 3 L }}
Chartered 7/1/71
Liquidated 1/19/78
Original Series <$VALUE
3x1-2 1-2300 <$2000/$3000
4x5 1-3675 <$2000
Series 1875
4x5 1-380 <$2000
Total Issue $92,600
Out in 1910 $587
****
3108 Woodson
WOODSON NB OF
YATES CENTER
{{ UNREPORTED }}
Chartered 1/14/84
Liquidated 12/5/92
Brown Back <$VALUE
3x10-20 1-615 <$2000
Total Issue $30,750
Out in 1910 $120
****
6326 Woodson
YATES CENTER NB,
YATES CENTER
{{ 1 L }}
Organized 7/1/02
Receivership 12/5/13
1902 Red Seal <$VALUE
3x10-20 1-1800 <$1500
1902 Date Back
3x10-20 1-2147 <$750
Total Issue $197,350
Out in 1915 $14,570
****

Nickname: The Bluegrass State
Motto: United We Stand, Divided We Fall
Capital: Frankfort
Number of towns: 111
Number of issuing charters: 238
Number of small size issuers: 141

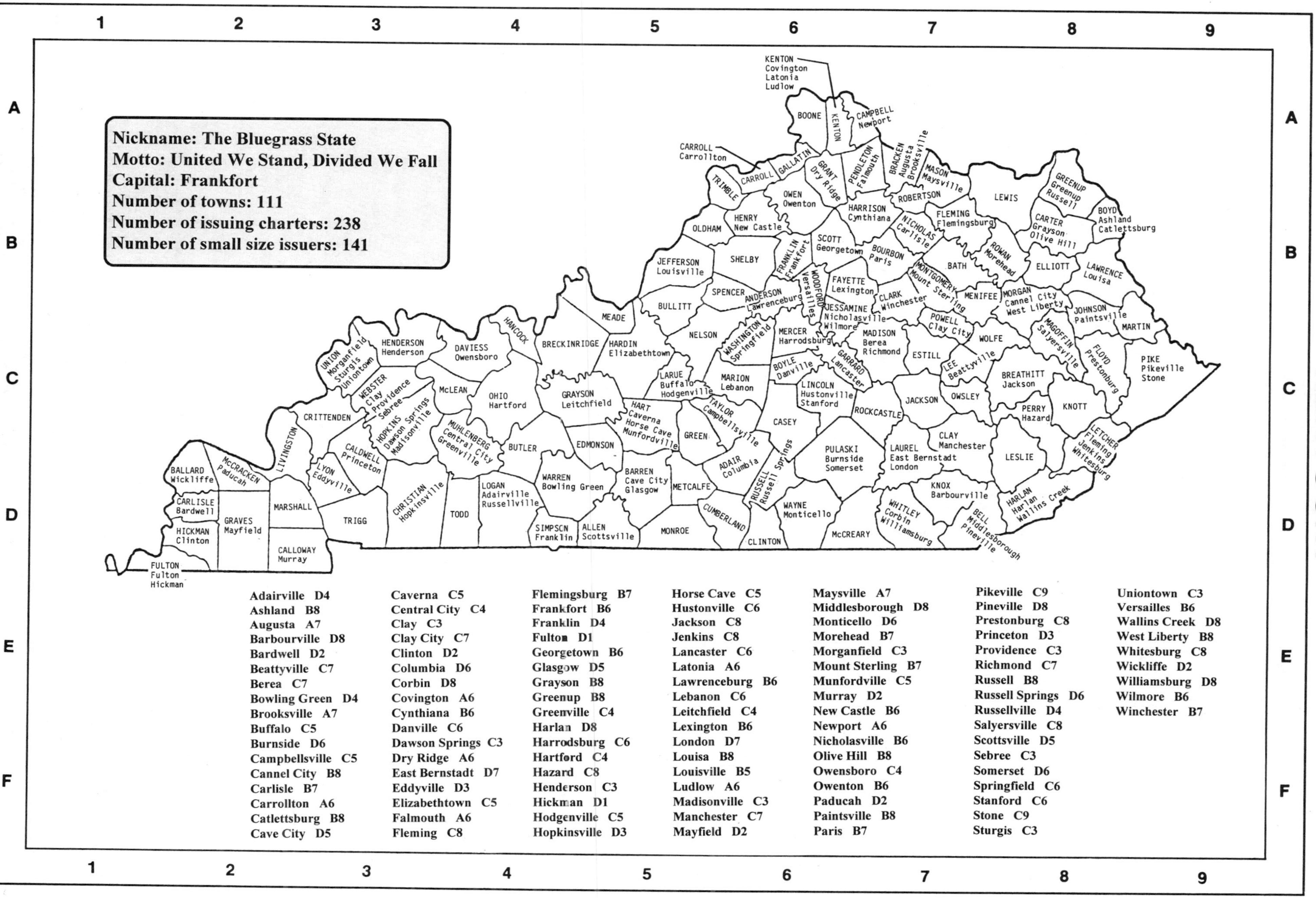

Adairville D4	**Caverna C5**	**Flemingsburg B7**	**Horse Cave C5**	**Maysville A7**	**Pikeville C9**	**Uniontown C3**
Ashland B8	**Central City C4**	**Frankfort B6**	**Hustonville C6**	**Middlesborough D8**	**Pineville D8**	**Versailles B6**
Augusta A7	**Clay C3**	**Franklin D4**	**Jackson C8**	**Monticello D6**	**Prestonburg C8**	**Wallins Creek D8**
Barbourville D8	**Clay City C7**	**Fulton D1**	**Jenkins C8**	**Morehead B7**	**Princeton D3**	**West Liberty B8**
Bardwell D2	**Clinton D2**	**Georgetown B6**	**Lancaster C6**	**Morganfield C3**	**Providence C3**	**Whitesburg C8**
Beattyville C7	**Columbia D6**	**Glasgow D5**	**Latonia A6**	**Mount Sterling B7**	**Richmond C7**	**Wickliffe D2**
Berea C7	**Corbin D8**	**Grayson B8**	**Lawrenceburg B6**	**Munfordville C5**	**Russell B8**	**Williamsburg D8**
Bowling Green D4	**Covington A6**	**Greenup B8**	**Lebanon C6**	**Murray D2**	**Russell Springs D6**	**Wilmore B6**
Brooksville A7	**Cynthiana B6**	**Greenville C4**	**Leitchfield C4**	**New Castle B6**	**Russellville D4**	**Winchester B7**
Buffalo C5	**Danville C6**	**Harlan D8**	**Lexington B6**	**Newport A6**	**Salyersville C8**	
Burnside D6	**Dawson Springs C3**	**Harrodsburg C6**	**London D7**	**Nicholasville B6**	**Scottsville D5**	
Campbellsville C5	**Dry Ridge A6**	**Hartford C4**	**Louisa B8**	**Olive Hill B8**	**Sebree C3**	
Cannel City B8	**East Bernstadt D7**	**Hazard C8**	**Louisville B5**	**Owensboro C4**	**Somerset D6**	
Carlisle B7	**Eddyville D3**	**Henderson C3**	**Ludlow A6**	**Owenton B6**	**Springfield C6**	
Carrollton A6	**Elizabethtown C5**	**Hickman D1**	**Madisonville C3**	**Paducah D2**	**Stanford C6**	
Catlettsburg B8	**Falmouth A6**	**Hodgenville C5**	**Manchester C7**	**Paintsville B8**	**Stone C9**	
Cave City D5	**Fleming C8**	**Hopkinsville D3**	**Mayfield D2**	**Paris B7**	**Sturgis C3**	

8814 Logan
FNB OF ADAIRVILLE
{{3 L U+5 S}}
Chartered 7/07
1902 Red Seal <$VALUE
3x10-20 1-800 <$750
1902 Date Back
3x10-20 1-1770 <$400
1902 Plain Back
3x10-20 1771-5563 <$400
1929 Small Size
10 Type 1 1-626 <$250
20 Type 1 1-160 <$275
10 Type 2 1-566 <$275
20 Type 2 1-201 <$300
Total Issue $384,590
Out in 1935 $25,000
Large out 1935 $1,580

2010 Boyd
ASHLAND NB, ASHLAND
{{25 L 22 S}}
Chartered 7/9/72
Receivership 10/7/31
Original Series <$VALUE
3x1-2 1-4200 <$500/$1000
4x5 1-7500 <$500
3x10-20 1-5380 <$750/$1250
Series 1875
3x1-2 1-11400 <$500/$1000
4x5 1-2966 <$500
3x10-20 1-7472 <$750/$1000
50-100 1-2100 <$5000
Brown Back
3x10-20 1-10200 <$350/$400
1882 Date Back
3x10-20 1-2706 <$300/$350
1902 Date Back
3x10-20 1-4150 <$100
1902 Plain Back
3x10-20 4151-90350 <$100
1929 Small Size
10 Type 1 1-10288 <$65
20 Type 1 1-2869 <$75
Total Issue $7,369,280
Out at close $292,325
Large out at close $67,455

4559 Boyd
MERCHANTS NB OF ASHLAND
{{2 L}}
Chartered 4/19/91
Liquidated 4/30/06
Brown Back <$VALUE
4x5 1-4225 <$750
3x10-20 1-3257 <$750
Total Issue $247,350
Out in 1910 $14,725

3944 Boyd
SECOND NB OF ASHLAND
{{U+4 L 34 S}}
Chartered 12/7/88
Brown Back <$VALUE
4x5 1-2877 <$500
3x10-20 1-506 <$500
1902 Date Back
3x10-20 1-4700 <$275
1902 Plain Back
3x10-20 4701-13115 <$275
1929 Small Size
5 Type 1 1-1040 <$50
10 Type 1 1-7058 <$50
20 Type 1 1-1512 <$60
5 Type 2 1-16838 <$65
10 Type 2 1-15208 <$66
20 Type 2 1-5304 <$75
Total Issue $1,717,060
Out in 1935 $300,000
Large out 1935 $3,340

12293 Boyd
THIRD NB OF ASHLAND
{{6 L 14 S}}
Chartered 1/23
1902 Plain Back <$VALUE
4x10 1-17294 <$225
1929 Small Size
10 Type 1 1-5880 <$125
10 Type 2 1-3727 <$125
Total Issue $1,081,830
Out in 1935 $62,110
Large out 1935 $2,350

4612 Bracken
FARMERS NB OF AUGUSTA
{{6 L}}
Chartered 1891
Liquidated 8/15/26
Brown Back <$VALUE
3x10-20 1-3345 <$600
1882 Date Back
3x10-20 1-929 <$600
1902 Date Back
3x50-100 1-1130 <$600/$750
Total Issue $496,200
Out at close $48,750

4616 Bracken
FNB OF AUGUSTA
{{1 L}}
Chartered 8/18/91
Liquidated 6/20/95
Brown Back <$VALUE
4x5 1-1067 <$1250
Total Issue $21,340
Out in 1910 $190

6262 Knox
FNB OF BARBOURVILLE
{{5 L 3 S}}
Chartered 5/16/02
Liquidated 5/10/34
1902 Red Seal <$VALUE
3x10-20 1-800 <$1250
1902 Date Back
3x10-20 1-1050* <$600
1902 Plain Back
3x10-20 1171-3606* <$600
*1051-1170 not marked
1929 Small Size
10 Type 1 1-397 <$450
20 Type 1 1-114 <$450
Total Issue $257,800
Out at close $15,000
Large out at close $1,280
Ch 13906 assumed circulation

7284 Knox
NB OF JOHN A BLACK OF BARBOURVILLE
{{8 L 2 S}}
Organized 4/18/04
Liquidated 5/10/34
1902 Red Seal <$VALUE
3x10-20 1-908 <$2500
1902 Date Back
3x10-20 1-1700 <$1500
1902 Plain Back
3x10-20 1701-5185 <$1500
1929 Small Size
10 Type 1 1-528 <$850
20 Type 1 1-146 <$850
10 Type 2 1-254 <$850
20 Type 2 1-60 <$850
Total Issue $357,590
Out at close $19,640
Large out at close $1,460
Ch 13906 assumed circulation

13906 Knox
UNION NB OF BARBOURVILLE
{{7 S}}
Chartered 12/33
1929 Small Size <$VALUE
5 Type 2 1-1572 <$250
10 Type 2 1-716 <$250
20 Type 2 1-222 <$250
Total Issue $19,460
Out in 1935 $37,500
Outstanding includes Ch 6262, and Ch 7284

8331 Carlisle
FNB OF BARDWELL
{{4 L 3 S}}
Organized 5/19/06
Receivership 3/4/32
1902 Red Seal <$VALUE
4x5 1-300 <$1500
3x10-20 1-267 <$1500
1902 Date Back
4x5 1-2050 <$600
3x10-20 1-1440 <$600
1902 Plain Back
4x5 2051-6380 <$600
3x10-20 1441-4041 <$600
1929 Small Size
5 Type 1 1-650 <$400
10 Type 1 1-281 <$400
20 Type 1 1-92 <$400
Total Issue $396,400
Out at close $23,440
Large out at close $2,470

7751 Lee
NB OF BEATTYVILLE
{{1 L}}
Organized 5/19/05
Receivership 10/15/10
1902 Red Seal <$VALUE
4x5 1-625 <$2000
3x10-20 1-490 <$2000
1902 Date Back
4x5 1-395 <$1500
3x10-20 1-308 <$1500
Total Issue $60,300
Out in 1916 $1,645

8435 Madison
BEREA NB, BEREA
{{3 L 9 S}}
Chartered 11/06
1902 Red Seal <$VALUE
4x10 1-1000 <$1000
1902 Date Back
4x10 1-2775 <$450
1902 Plain Back
4x10 2776-8748 <$450
1929 Small Size
10 Type 1 1-2140 <$175
10 Type 2 1-3205 <$185
Total Issue $550,370
Out in 1935 $50,000
Large out 1935 $2,000

9365 Warren
AMERICAN NB OF BOWLING GREEN
{{9 L 16 S}}
Organized 2/17/09
1902 Date Back <$VALUE
3x10-20 1-11700 <$175
1902 Plain Back
3x10-20 11701-31612 <$175
1929 Small Size
10 Type 1 1-3504 <$85
20 Type 1 1-998 <$100
10 Type 2 1-5119 <$125
20 Type 2 1-1404 <$125
Total Issue $1,989,870
Out in 1935 $125,000
Large out 1935 $6,900

7804 Warren
BOWLING GREEN NB, BOWLING GREEN
{{3 L}}
Chartered 6/05
Liquidated 5/31/11
1902 Red Seal <$VALUE
3x10-20 1-3800 <$850
1902 Date Back
3x10-20 1-2286 <$400
Total Issue $304,300
Out in 1911 $68,650

5900 Warren
CITIZENS NB OF BOWLING GREEN
{{14 L 24 S}}
Chartered 7/11/01
Brown Back <$VALUE
3x10-20 1-4900 <$350/$400
1882 Date Back
3x10-20 1-8100* <$300/$350
1882 Value Back
3x10-20 8701-13800* <$300/$350
*8101-8700 not marked
1902 Plain Back
3x10-20 1-26923 <$150
1929 Small Size
10 Type 1 1-7102 <$65
20 Type 1 1-1940 <$75
5 Type 2 1-324 <$75
10 Type 2 1-8834 <$75
20 Type 2 1-1740 <$80
Total Issue $3,064,830
Out in 1935 $250,000
Large out 1935 $12,245

11589 Warren
LIBERTY NB OF BOWLING GREEN
{{4 L}}
Chartered 1/20
Liquidated 1/31/24
1902 Plain Back <$VALUE
3x10-20 1-9598 <$375
Total Issue $479,900
Out at close $125,000

2149 Warren
N SOUTHERN KENTUCKY B OF BOWLING GREEN
{{ UNREPORTED }}
Chartered 5/29/74
Liquidated 12/23/76
Original Series <$VALUE
3x1-2 1-900 <$1500/$2500
4x5 1-1125 <$2000
Series 1875
4x5 1-290 <$2000
Total Issue $32,800
Out in 1910 $175

10448 Warren
WARREN NB OF BOWLING GREEN
{{ UNREPORTED }}
Chartered 9/13
Liquidated 4/15/15
1902 Date Back <$VALUE
3x10-20 1-647 <$1500
3x50-100 1-40 <$1750/$2000
Total Issue $42,350
Out in 1911 $16,600

8830 Bracken
FNB OF BROOKSVILLE
{{3 L 5 S}}
Organized 7/8/07
1902 Red Seal <$VALUE
4x5 1-406 <$1000
3x10-20 1-325 <$1000
1902 Date Back
4x5 1-1800 <$500
3x10-20 1-1240 <$500
1902 Plain Back
4x5 1801-6088 <$500
3x10-20 1241-3795 <$500
1929 Small Size
5 Type 1 1-1050 <$225
10 Type 1 1-496 <$225
20 Type 1 1-130 <$225
5 Type 2 1-1320 <$250
10 Type 2 1-708 <$250
20 Type 2 1-192 <$250
Total Issue $430,260
Out in 1935 $25,000
Large out 1935 $1,200

11538 Larue
FNB OF BUFFALO
{{1 L 3 S}}
Chartered 12/19
1902 Plain Back <$VALUE
3x10-20 1-667 <$1500
1929 Small Size
5 Type 1 1-262 <$450
10 Type 1 1-422 <$450
20 Type 1 1-124 <$450
5 Type 2 1-864 <$500
10 Type 2 1-372 <$500
20 Type 2 1-132 <$500
Total Issue $92,090
Out in 1935 $25,000
Large out 1935 $300

8903 Pulaski
FNB OF BURNSIDE
{{2 L 3 S}}
Organized 10/2/07
Receivership 8/8/33
1902 Red Seal <$VALUE
4x5 1-155 <$1250
3x10-20 1-125 <$1250
1902 Date Back
4x5 1-1875 <$600
3x10-20 1-1420 <$600
1902 Plain Back
4x5 1876-6460 <$600
3x10-20 1421-4181 <$600
1929 Small Size
5 Type 1 1-978 <$375
10 Type 1 1-523 <$375
20 Type 1 1-127 <$400
Total Issue $423,560
Out at close $25,000
Large out at close $1,760

6342 Taylor
TAYLOR NB OF CAMPBELLSVILLE
{{3 L 13 S}}
Chartered 7/17/02
1902 Red Seal <$VALUE
4x5 1-885 <$1000
3x10-20 1-998 <$1000
1902 Date Back
4x5 1-1675 <$500
3x10-20 1-1060 <$500
1902 Plain Back
4x5 1676-6077 <$500
3x10-20 1061-3576 <$500
1929 Small Size
5 Type 1 1-2742 <$125
10 Type 1 1-1854 <$125
20 Type 1 1-350 <$125
5 Type 2 1-5338 <$150
10 Type 2 1-3208 <$150
20 Type 2 1-1073 <$150
Total Issue $683,670
Out in 1935 $100,000
Large out 1935 $1,470

7891 Morgan
MORGAN COUNTY NB OF CANNEL CITY
{{4 L 4 S}}
Organized 8/19/05
1902 Red Seal <$VALUE
3x10-20 1-850 <$1250
1902 Date Back
3x10-20 1-1710 <$600
1902 Plain Back
3x10-20 1711-5212 <$600
1929 Small Size
10 Type 1 1-670 <$300
20 Type 1 1-180 <$300
10 Type 2 1-536 <$300
20 Type 2 1-132 <$325
Total Issue $372,900
Out in 1935 $25,000
Large out 1935 $1,550

5959 Nicholas
FNB OF CARLISLE
{{7 L}}
Chartered 9/9/01
Brown Back <$VALUE
4x5 1-1565 <$600
3x10-20 1-1174 <$600
1882 Date Back
4x5 1-1900 <$600
3x10-20 1-1380 <$600
1882 Value Back
4x5 1901-3375 <$600
3x10-20 1381-2232 <$600
Total Issue $269,100
Out in 1935 $820

3074 Carroll
CARROLLTON NB, CARROLLTON
{{5 L 11 S}}
Organized 10/23/83
Receivership 4/25/34
Brown Back <$VALUE
3x10-20 1-3291 <$650
1902 Red Seal
3x10-20 1-2700 <$750
1902 Date Back
3x10-20 1-4540 <$375
1902 Plain Back
3x10-20 4541-13519 <$375
1929 Small Size
10 Type 1 1-1676 <$150
20 Type 1 1-418 <$150
10 Type 2 1-486 <$175
20 Type 2 1-145 <$175
Total Issue $1,133,980
Out at close $60,000
Large out at close $4,910

2592 Carroll
FNB OF CARROLLTON
{{8 L 12 S}}
Organized 10/31/81
Series 1875 <$VALUE
3x10-20 1-5255 <$850/$1250
Brown Back
3x10-20 1-3400 <$600
1882 Date Back
3x10-20 1-4000* <$600
1882 Value Back
3x10-20 4401-6757* <$600
*4001-4400 not marked
1902 Plain Back
3x10-20 1-5633 <$375
1929 Small Size
10 Type 1 1-1600 <$150
20 Type 1 1-478 <$150
10 Type 2 1-1861 <$175
20 Type 2 1-489 <$175
Total Issue $1,234,000
Out in 1935 $60,000
Large out 1935 $4,590

4200 Boyd
BIG SANDY NB OF CATLETTSBURG
{{3 L}}
Chartered 1890
Liquidated 12/7/09
Brown Back <$VALUE
4x5 1-6877 <$750
3x10-20 1-2588 <$750
Total Issue $266,940
Out in 1910 $29,905

2740 Boyd
CATLETTSBURG NB, CATLETTSBURG
{{6 L}}
Chartered 1882
Liquidated 9/16/16
Series 1875 <$VALUE
3x10-20 1-5982 <$850/$1250
1902 Red Seal
4x5 1-2000 <$800
3x10-20 1-4000 <$800
1902 Date Back
4x5 1-7050 <$375
3x10-20 1-5360 <$375
1902 Plain Back
4x5 7051-7615 <$375
3x10-20 5361-5748 <$375
Total Issue $978,800
Out in 1916 $93,950

9602 Boyd
KENTUCKY NB OF CATLETTSBURG
{{8 L 6 S}}
Chartered 12/09
Liquidated 1/24/31
1902 Date Back <$VALUE
4x5 1-5450 <$300
3x10-20 1-4140 <$300
1902 Plain Back
4x5 5451-21328 <$300
3x10-20 4141-13852 <$300
1929 Small Size
5 Type 1 1-1548 <$225
10 Type 1 1-770 <$225
20 Type 1 1-204 <$225
Total Issue $1,236,280
Out at close $75,000
Large out at close $10,440

7919 Barren
H.Y. DAVIS NB OF CAVE CITY
{{2 L}}
Chartered 9/05
Liquidated 1/2/17
1902 Red Seal <$VALUE
3x10-20 1-480 <$2500
1902 Date Back
3x10-20 1-2819 <$2000
Total Issue $164,950
Out at close $28,000

2206 Hart
CAVERNA NB, CAVERNA
{{ UNREPORTED }}
Chartered 11/9/74
Liquidated 5/13/76
Original Series <$VALUE
4x5 1-2250 <$2500
Series 1875
4x5 1-235 <$2500
Total Issue $49,700
Out in 1910 $170

8229 Muhlenberg
FNB OF CENTRAL CITY
{{3 L 7 S}}
Organized 4/21/06
1902 Red Seal <$VALUE
3x10-20 1-900 <$1250
1902 Date Back
3x10-20 1-1990 <$600
1902 Plain Back
3x10-20 1991-9860 <$600
1929 Small Size
10 Type 1 1-1532 <$275
20 Type 1 1-436 <$275
10 Type 2 1-1482 <$300
20 Type 2 1-508 <$300
Total Issue $707,220
Out in 1935 $50,000
Large out 1935 $1,760

8943 Clay
FARMERS NB OF CLAY
{{3 L 8 S}}
Chartered 11/07
1902 Red Seal <$VALUE
3x10-20 1-700 <$1250
1902 Date Back
3x10-20 1-2070 <$600
1902 Plain Back
3x10-20 2071-6135 <$600
1929 Small Size
10 Type 1 1-1086 <$200
20 Type 1 1-326 <$200
10 Type 2 1-1071 <$225
20 Type 2 1-325 <$225
Total Issue $463,240
Out in 1935 $50,000
Large out 1935 $1,220

****
4217 Powell
CLAY CITY NB, CLAY CITY
{{ 3 L 4 S }}
Chartered 1890
Brown Back <$VALUE
4x5 1-1850 <$850
3x10-20 1-2580 <$850
1882 Date Back
4x5 1-205 <$850
3x10-20 1-383 <$850
1902 Date Back
4x5 1-1450 <$500
50-100 1-690 <$600/$750
3x50-100 1-40 <$600/$750
1902 Plain Back
4x5 1451-6199 <$500
1929 Small Size
5 Type 1 1-3192 <$350
5 Type 2 1-6702 <$350
Total Issue $556,000
Out in 1935 $25,000
Large out 1935 $1,790
****
9098 Hickman
FNB OF CLINTON
{{ 6 L 9 S }}
Organized 2/24/08
Receivership 9/26/34
1902 Red Seal <$VALUE
3x10-20 1-675 <$750
1902 Date Back
3x10-20 1-3800 <$375
1902 Plain Back
3x10-20 3801-11468 <$375
1929 Small Size
10 Type 1 1-1340 <$150
20 Type 1 1-390 <$150
10 Type 2 1-465 <$175
20 Type 2 1-233 <$175
Total Issue $743,660
Out at close $49,500
Large out at close $2,170
****
6769 Adair
FNB OF COLUMBIA
Chartered 5/03
2nd title: FNB & TC 5/6/26
FIRST TITLE {{ 1 L }}
1902 Red Seal <$VALUE
3x10-20 1-1200 <$1500
1902 Date Back
3x10-20 1-1450 <$850
1902 Plain Back
3x10-20 1451-3949 <$850
SECOND TITLE {{ 0 L 4 S }}
1902 Plain Back
3x10-20 1-885 <$850
1929 Small Size
10 Type 1 1-694 <$350
20 Type 1 1-182 <$350
10 Type 2 1-693 <$375
20 Type 2 1-210 <$375
Total Issue $376,310
Out in 1935 $25,000
Large out 1935 $1,260
****
7544 Whitley
FNB OF CORBIN
{{ 2 L 5 S }}
Chartered 1/05
1902 Red Seal <$VALUE
3x10-20 1-1050 <$1250
1902 Date Back
3x10-20 1-1940 <$600
1902 Plain Back
3x10-20 1941-5825 <$600
1929 Small Size
10 Type 1 1-708 <$275
20 Type 1 1-176 <$275
10 Type 2 1-692 <$300
20 Type 2 1-212 <$300
Total Issue $418,510
Out in 1935 $24,550
Large out 1935 $1,060
****
9634 Whitley
WHITLEY NB OF CORBIN
{{ 3 L 6 S }}
Chartered 12/22/09
Receivership 7/18/32
1902 Date Back <$VALUE
4x10 1-900* <$500
1902 Plain Back
4x10 1001-6549* <$500
* 901-1000 not marked
1929 Small Size
10 Type 1 1-1148 <$275
Total Issue $330,840
Out at close $24,700
Large out at close $1,480
****

****
4260 Kenton
CITIZENS NB OF COVINGTON
{{ 11 L 11 S }}
Chartered 1890
Brown Back <$VALUE
4x5 1-15450 <$300
3x10-20 1-5500 <$300/$350
1882 Date Back
4x5 1-767 <$300
3x10-20 1-548 <$300/$350
50-100 1-280 <$1250/$1500
1902 Date Back
50-100 1-1700 <$400/$450
3x50-100 1-3375 <$400/$450
1902 Plain Back
3x50-100 3376-4345 <$400/$450
1929 Small Size
50 Type 1 1-562 <$165
100 Type 1 1-186 <$225
50 Type 2 1-246 <$350
100 Type 2 1-56 <$450
Total Issue $2,308,090
Out in 1935 $200,000
Large out 1935 $16,380
****
8564 Kenton
COMMERCIAL NB OF COVINGTON
{{ 3 L }}
Chartered 2/07
Liquidated 7/20/14
1902 Red Seal <$VALUE
4x5 1-2500 <$700
3x10-20 1-2000 <$700
1902 Date Back
4x5 1-5480 <$450
3x10-20 1-3723 <$450
Total Issue $445,750
Out in 1914 $84,150
****
1859 Kenton
COVINGTON CITY NB, COVINGTON
{{ 5 L }}
Chartered 8/10/71
Liquidated 2/1/93
Original Series <$VALUE
3x1-2 1-4000 <$500/$1000
4x5 1-16250 <$500
3x10-20 1-6200 <$750/$1250
50-100 1-300 <$5000
Series 1875
4x5 1-7033 <$500
3x10-20 1-14072<$750/$1000
50-100 1-667 <$5000
Brown Back
4x5 1-529 <$350
3x10-20 1-3816 <$350/$400
Total Issue $1,845,690
Out in 1910 $10,448
****
2722 Kenton
FARMERS & TRADERS NB OF COVINGTON
{{ 3 L }}
Chartered 1882
Liquidated 2/1/10
Brown Back <$VALUE
4x5 1-26207 <$600
50-100 1-3598 <$1250/$1500
1902 Red Seal
4x5 1-14580 <$600
50-100 1-3125 <$2500
1902 Date Back
4x5 1-418 <$400
Total Issue $1,832,550
Out in 1910 $141,145
****
718 Kenton
FNB OF COVINGTON
Organized 11/17/64
2nd title: FNB & TC 1/19/26
FIRST TITLE {{ 18 L }}
Original Series <$VALUE
3x1-2 1-6900 <$400/$1000
4x5 1-15200 <$400
3x10-20 1-6000 <$750/$1250
50-100 1-1160 <$5000
Series 1875
3x1-2 1-1000 <$400/$1000
4x5 1-14335 <$400
3x10-20 1-4900 <$750/$1000
50-100 1-1470 <$5000
Brown Back
4x5 1-13015 <$250
3x10-20 1-9894 <$250/$300
50-100 1-1300 <$1250/$1500
1902 Red Seal
4x5 1-10000 <$250
3x10-20 1-6400 <$250/$300
1902 Date Back
4x5 1-46000 <$85
3x10-20 1-36200 <$85
1902 Plain Back
4x5 46001-103040 <$85
3x10-20 36201-71404 <$85
SECOND TITLE {{ 13 L 39 S }}
1902 Plain Back
4x5 1-25555 <$75
3x10-20 1-18017 <$75
1929 Small Size
5 Type 1 1-19821 <$35
10 Type 1 1-10286 <$35
20 Type 1 1-2561 <$45
Total Issue $11,601,760
Out in 1935 $200,000
Large out 1935 $36,265
****
1847 Kenton
GERMAN NB OF COVINGTON
Chartered 7/13/71
Liquidated 3/31/28
2nd title: Liberty NB of Covington 1/18/18
FIRST TITLE {{ 27 L }}
Original Series <$VALUE
3x1-2 1-5100 <$400/$1000
4x5 1-5495 <$450
3x10-20 1-3200 <$750/$1250
50-100 1-531 <$5000
Series 1875
3x1-2 1-761 <$350/$1000
4x5 1-7702 <$450
3x10-20 1-3415 <$750/$1000
50-100 1-660 <$5000
Brown Back
3x10-20 1-26040 <$300/$350
1882 Date Back
3x10-20 1-5927 <$300/$350
1902 Date Back
3x10-20 1-19000 <$100
1902 Plain Back
3x10-20 19001-25660 <$100
SECOND TITLE {{ 8 L }}
1902 Plain Back
3x10-20 1-43889 <$125
Total Issue $5,878,445
Out at close $326,900
****
Liberty NB of Covington
SEE Ch 1847
German NB of Covington
****
8110 Kenton
MERCHANTS NB OF COVINGTON
{{ UNREPORTED }}
Chartered 2/26/06
Liquidated 7/1/00
1902 Red Seal <$VALUE
4x5 1-1270 <$1500
3x10-20 1-1095 <$1500
Total Issue $80,150
Out in 1910 $10,990
****
2560 Harrison
FARMERS NB OF CYNTHIANA
{{ 13 L 18 S }}
Chartered 9/2/81
Series 1875 <$VALUE
4x5 1-3089 <$500
3x10-20 1-2654 <$750/$1250
Brown Back
3x10-20 1-3100 <$400
1882 Date Back
3x10-20 1-6600 <$400
1882 Value Back
3x10-20 6601-11761 <$400
1902 Plain Back
4x5 1-10481 <$250
3x10-20 1-7275 <$250
1929 Small Size
5 Type 1 1-4114 <$100
10 Type 1 1-2312 <$100
20 Type 1 1-554 <$100
5 Type 2 1-4534 <$110
10 Type 2 1-2947 <$110
20 Type 2 1-765 <$125
Total Issue $1,906,960
Out in 1935 $100,000
Large out 1935 $5,480
****
1900 Harrison
NB OF CYNTHIANA
{{ 6 L 16 S }}
Chartered 11/22/71
Original Series <$VALUE
4x5 1-3250 <$600
3x10-20 1-2600 <$750/$1250
Series 1875
3x10-20 1-3281 <$750/$1000
Brown Back
3x10-20 1-3100 <$400
50-100 1-1627 <$1250/$1500
1882 Date Back
3x10-20 1-2300 <$400
1902 Date Back
3x10-20 1-4200 <$250
1902 Plain Back
3x10-20 4201-19387 <$250
1929 Small Size
10 Type 1 1-2738 <$100
20 Type 1 1-778 <$100
10 Type 2 1-4526 <$110
20 Type 2 1-967 <$125
Total Issue $2,164,690
Out in 1935 $100,000
Large out 1935 $6,260
****
3317 Boyle
BOYLE NB OF DANVILLE
{{ 3 L }}
Chartered 3/2/85
Liquidated 3/31/09
Brown Back <$VALUE
3x10-20 1-9410 <$500
1902 Red Seal
3x10-20 1-3136 <$600
Total Issue $627,300
Out in 1910 $39,890
****
1600 Boyle
CENTRAL NB OF DANVILLE
{{ 2 L }}
Chartered 1865
Liquidated 3/28/85
Original Series <$VALUE
3x1-2 1-1420 <$600/$1250
4x5 1-3500 <$600
3x10-20 1-5558 <$850/$1500
Series 1875
4x5 1-100 <$600
3x10-20 1-5246 <$850/$1250
Total Issue $619,300
Out in 1910 $3,874
****
3381 Boyle
CITIZENS NB OF DANVILLE
{{ 7 L 13 S }}
Chartered 1885
Brown Back <$VALUE
3x10-20 1-9354 <$400
1902 Red Seal
3x10-20 1-3700 <$600
1902 Date Back
3x10-20 1-8300 <$250
1902 Plain Back
3x10-20 8301-18014 <$250
1929 Small Size
10 Type 1 1-2266 <$110
10 Type 2 1-7563 <$125
Total Issue $1,764,990
Out in 1935 $100,000
Large out 1935 $4,800
****
2409 Boyle
FARMERS NB OF DANVILLE
{{ 10 L 16 S }}
Chartered 2/10/79
Series 1875 <$VALUE
3x10-20 1-6578 <$750/$1250
Brown Back
4x5 1-2000 <$400
3x10-20 1-5800 <$400
1882 Date Back
4x5 1-1265 <$400
3x10-20 1-7900 <$400
1882 Value Back
3x10-20 7901-9390 <$400
1902 Plain Back
3x10-20 1-14405 <$250
1929 Small Size
10 Type 1 1-3156 <$100
20 Type 1 1-790 <$100
10 Type 2 1-3999 <$110
20 Type 2 1-1003 <$110
Total Issue $2,218,160
Out in 1935 $100,000
Large out 1935 $6,535
****
1601 Boyle
FNB OF DANVILLE
{{ UNREPORTED }}
Chartered 1865
Liquidated 9/22/85
Original Series <$VALUE
3x1-2 1-3620 <$1500/$2000
4x5 1-2725 <$1500
3x10-20 1-4550<$1750/$2500
50-100 1-55 <$5000
Series 1875
4x5 1-997 <$1500
3x10-20 1-3016<$1500/$2000
50-100 1-100 <$5000
Total Issue $494,090
Out in 1910 $2,895
****

****
11548 Hopkins
FNB OF DAWSON SPRINGS
{{ 3 L 6 S }}
Organized 11/21/19
Receivership 3/14/34
1902 Plain Back <$VALUE
3x10-20 1-3329 <$750
1929 Small Size
10 Type 1 1-1136 <$300
20 Type 1 1-308 <$300
10 Type 2 1-416 <$350
20 Type 2 1-115 <$375
Total Issue $278,030
Out at close $40,000
Large out at close $1,240
****
7012 Grant
FNB OF DRY RIDGE
{{ 4 L 2 S }}
Chartered 10/03
Liquidated 3/29/30
1902 Red Seal <$VALUE
3x10-20 1-2300 <$2000
1902 Date Back
3x10-20 1-3400 <$1000
1902 Plain Back
3x10-20 3401-11738 <$1000
1929 Small Size
10 Type 1 1-334 <$650
20 Type 1 1-131 <$650
Total Issue $737,660
Out at close $50,000
Large out at close $14,770
****
10254 Laurel
FNB OF EAST BERNSTADT
{{ 1 L 5 S }}
Chartered 9/13/12
1902 Date Back <$VALUE
3x10-20 1-1180 <$750
1902 Plain Back
3x10-20 1181-5019 <$750
1929 Small Size
10 Type 1 1-632 <$275
20 Type 1 1-170 <$275
10 Type 2 1-856 <$325
20 Type 2 1-266 <$325
Total Issue $323,150
Out in 1935 $25,000
Large out 1935 $2,260
****
7492 Lyon
FNB OF EDDYVILLE
{{ UNREPORTED }}
Chartered 11/04
Liquidated 4/1/16
1902 Red Seal <$VALUE
3x10-20 1-976 <$2000
1902 Date Back
3x10-20 1-1910 <$1500
1902 Plain Back
3x10-20 1911-1916 <$1500
Total Issue $144,600
Out in 1916 $18,100
****
F Hardin NB of Elizabethtown
SEE Ch 6028
Hardin NB of Elizabethtown
****
3042 Hardin
FNB OF ELIZABETHTOWN
{{ 3 L }}
Chartered 1883
Liquidated 7/29/11
Brown Back <$VALUE
4x5 1-6584 <$600
3x10-20 1-1088 <$600
1902 Red Seal
3x10-20 1-1900 <$750
1902 Date Back
3x10-20 1-1310 <$400
Total Issue $346,580
Out at close $47,600
Ch 6028 assumed circulation
****
6028 Hardin
HARDIN NB OF ELIZABETHTOWN
Chartered 11/22/01
2nd title: F Hardin NB of Elizabethtown 7/29/11
FIRST TITLE {{ 3 L }}
Brown Back <$VALUE
3x10-20 1-3100 <$500
1882 Date Back
3x10-20 1-1270 <$500
SECOND TITLE {{ 17 L 22 S }}
1882 Date Back
3x10-20 1-5400 <$350
1882 Value Back
3x10-20 5401-12782 <$400
1902 Plain Back
3x10-20 1-15377 <$175
1929 Small Size
10 Type 1 1-4228 <$75
20 Type 1 1-1150 <$85
5 Type 2 1-171 <$75
10 Type 2 1-3552 <$85
20 Type 2 1-886 <$90
Total Issue $2,072,225
Out in 1935 $150,000
Large out 1935 $9,355
Outstanding includes Ch 3042
****
11947 Pendleton
FNB OF FALMOUTH
{{ 3 L 12 S }}
Chartered 3/21
1902 Plain Back <$VALUE
4x5 1-4894 <$600
1929 Small Size
5 Type 1 1-1376 <$200
5 Type 2 1-2616 <$200
Total Issue $152,240
Out in 1935 $10,000
Large out 1935 $530
****
11988 Letcher
FNB OF FLEMING
{{ 3 L U + 3 S }}
Organized 6/16/21
Receivership 9/15/33
1902 Plain Back <$VALUE
4x5 1-12794 <$600
1929 Small Size
5 Type 1 1-3776 <$350
5 Type 2 1-952 <$350
Total Issue $373,920
Out at close $25,000
Large out at close $2,665
****
2323 Fleming
FLEMING COUNTY NB OF FLEMINGSBURG
{{ UNREPORTED }}
Chartered 2/11/76
Liquidated 2/09/89
Series 1875 <$VALUE
3x1-2 1-1740 <$1500/$2000
4x5 1-1877 <$1500
3x10-20 1-1451<$2000/$2500
Total Issue $118,790
Out in 1910 $1,325
****
4091 Franklin
FRANKFORT NB, FRANKFORT
{{ UNREPORTED }}
Chartered 8/13/89
Liquidated 9/21/93
Brown Back <$VALUE
3x10-20 1-787 <$1500
Total Issue $39,350
Out in 1910 $370
****
5376 Franklin
N BRANCH B OF KENTUCKY, FRANKFORT
{{ 7 L 14 S }}
Chartered 5/26/00
Brown Back <$VALUE
3x10-20 1-2500 <$600
1882 Date Back
3x10-20 1-7200 <$600
1882 Value Back
3x10-20 7201-10967 <$600
1902 Plain Back
3x10-20 1-13153 <$300
1929 Small Size
10 Type 1 1-2908 <$110
20 Type 1 1-802 <$120
10 Type 2 1-4089 <$135
20 Type 2 1-1035 <$150
Total issue $1,663,310
Out in 1935 $100,000
Large out 1935 $4,960
****

CONDITION affects Value. The Values shown are for notes in FINE condition.

4090 Franklin
STATE NB OF FRANKFORT
{{ 12 L 20 S }}
Chartered 8/12/89
Brown Back <$VALUE
4x5 1-6990 <$500
3x10-20 1-9904 <$500
1902 Date Back
4x5 1-11000 <$150
3x10-20 1-8500 <$150
1902 Plain Back
4x5 11001-38720 <$150
3x10-20 8501-25356 <$150
1929 Small Size
5 Type 1 1-6684 <$100
10 Type 1 1-3100 <$100
20 Type 1 1-788 <$110
5 Type 2 1-10628 <$125
10 Type 2 1-5545 <$125
20 Type 2 1-1377 <$125
Total Issue $3,294,410
Out in 1935 $150,000
Large out 1935 $7,670

7402 Simpson
FARMERS & MERCHANTS NB OF FRANKLIN
{{ UNREPORTED }}
Chartered 9/04
Liquidated 4/1/13
1902 Red Seal <$VALUE
3x10-20 1-700 <$2000
1902 Date Back
3x10-20 1-1017 <$1500
Total Issue $85,850
Out in 1913 $16,200

1760 Simpson
FNB OF FRANKLIN
{{ 1 L }}
Chartered 1/3/71
Liquidated 7/5/79
Original Series <$VALUE
4x5 1-2500 <$1500
3x10-20 1-880 <$1500/$2000
Series 1875
3x10-20 1-726 <$1500/$2000
Total Issue $130,300
Out in 1910 $575

6167 Fulton
CITY NB OF FULTON
{{ 6 L 15 S }}
Chartered 3/19/02
1902 Red Seal <$VALUE
3x10-20 1-2900 <$650
1902 Date Back
3x10-20 1-6800 <$275
1902 Plain Back (dated 1902)
3x10-20 6801-11866 <$275
1902 Plain Back (dated 1922)
3x10-20 1-8473 <$275
1929 Small Size
10 Type 1 1-2452 <$110
20 Type 1 1-566 <$110
10 Type 2 1-4163 <$125
20 Type 2 1-645 <$125
Total Issue $1,431,520
Out in 1935 $80,000
Large out 1935 $4,480

4563 Fulton
FNB OF FULTON
{{ 2 L 2 S }}
Organized 4/24/91
Receivership 12/8/30
Brown Back <$VALUE
50-100 1-1708 <$2000
1882 Date Back
50-100 1-11 <$2000
1902 Date Back
3x10-20 1-2000 <$600
1902 Plain Back
3x10-20 2001-9749 <$600
1929 Small Size
10 Type 1 1-685 <$400
20 Type 1 1-180 <$400
Total Issue $808,000
Out at close $48,380
Large out at close $9,060

2927 Scott
FNB OF GEORGETOWN
{{ 5 L 8 S }}
Chartered 1883
Brown Back <$VALUE
3x10-20 1-3009 <$650
1902 Red Seal
3x10-20 1-2400 <$800
1902 Date Back
3x10-20 1-4440 <$375
1902 Plain Back
3x10-20 4441-12812 <$375
1929 Small Size
10 Type 1 1-1532 <$175
20 Type 1 1-398 <$200
10 Type 2 1-1865 <$200
20 Type 2 1-513 <$225
Total Issue $1,079 640
Out in 1935 $50,000
Large out 1935 $2,330

8579 Scott
GEORGETOWN NB, GEORGETOWN
{{ 7 L 16 S }}
Chartered 3/07
1902 Red Seal <$VALUE
3x10-20 1-2800 <$800
1902 Date Back
4x5 1-7950 <$375
3x10-20 1-4800 <$375
1902 Plain Back
4x5 7951-21455 <$375
3x10-20 4801-12897 <$375
1929 Small Size
10 Type 1 1-2250 <$100
20 Type 1 1-634 <$110
10 Type 2 1-2552 <$125
20 Type 2 1-575 <$135
Total Issue $1,462,050
Out in 1935 $75,000
Large out 1935 $3,520

8439 Barren
CITIZENS NB OF GLASGOW
{{ 4 L 6 S }}
Organized 11/10/06
1902 Red Seal <$VALUE
3x10-20 1-1000 <$850
1902 Date Back
3x10-20 1-3140 <$400
1902 Plain Back
3x10-20 3141-9313 <$400
1929 Small Size
10 Type 1 1-1146 <$250
20 Type 1 1-360 <$250
10 Type 2 1-882 <$275
20 Type 2 1-189 <$275
Total Issue $640,210
Out in 1935 $40,000
Large out 1935 $1,940

9722 Barren
FARMERS NB OF GLASGOW
{{ 4 L 6 S }}
Chartered 4/10
Liquidated 3/15/33
1902 Date Back <$VALUE
3x10-20 1-6600 <$400
1902 Plain Back
3x10-20 6601-17436 <$400
1929 Small Size
10 Type 1 1-1791 <$250
20 Type 1 1-484 <$250
Total Issue $1,037,340
Out at close $75,000
Large out 1935 $610
Ch 13651 assumed circulation

4819 Barren
FNB OF GLASGOW
{{ 4 L 3 S }}
Organized 11/5/92
Receivership 4/15/32
Brown Back <$VALUE
3x10-20 1-5250 <$700
1882 Date Back
3x10-20 1-1543 <$700
1902 Date Back
3x10-20 1-2100 <$400
1902 Plain Back
3x10-20 2101-9518 <$400
1929 Small Size
10 Type 1 1-1122 <$350
20 Type 1 1-265 <$350
Total Issue $914,670
Out at close $50,000
Large out at close $5,600

13651 Barren
NEW FARMERS NB OF GLASGOW
{{ 5 S }}
Chartered 12/32
1929 Small Size <$VALUE
10 Type 1 1-316 <$275
20 Type 1 1-104 <$275
10 Type 2 1-2108 <$275
20 Type 2 1-510 <$275
Total Issue $62,720
Out in 1935 $75,000
Outstanding includes Ch 9722

6872 Barren
THIRD NB OF GLASGOW
{{ 1 L }}
Chartered 7/03
Liquidated 1/27/10
1902 Red Seal <$VALUE
3x10-20 1-1296 <$1500
1902 Date Back
3x10-20 1-68 <$1250
Total Issue $68,200
Out in 1910 $15,300

5486 Barren
TRIGG NB OF GLASGOW
{{ 12 L 5 S }}
Chartered 7/7/00
Receivership 1/28/32
Brown Back <$VALUE
4x5 1-1750 <$600
3x10-20 1-3350 <$600
50-100 1-220 <$2000
1882 Date Back
4x5 1-4850 <$600
3x10-20 1-3320 <$600
50-100 1-100 <$2000
1882 Value Back
4x5 4851-7410 <$600
3x10-20 3321-4630 <$600
1902 Plain Back
3x10-20 1-9383 <$300
1929 Small Size
10 Type 1 1-1342 <$250
20 Type 1 1-423 <$275
Total Issue $1,230,630
Out at close $71,880
Large out at close $9,980

12982 Carter
FNB OF GRAYSON
{{ 5 S }}
Chartered 9/26
1929 Small Size <$VALUE
5 Type 1 1-1224 <$225
10 Type 1 1-572 <$225
5 Type 2 1-4300 <$225
10 Type 2 1-2280 <$225
Total Issue $115,340
Out in 1935 $50,000

7037 Greenup
FNB OF GREENUP
{{ 4 L 4 S }}
Organized 10/31/03
Receivership 2/1/34
1902 Red Seal <$VALUE
3x10-20 1-930 <$1000
1902 Date Back
3x10-20 1-1610 <$500
1902 Plain Back
3x10-20 1611-5647 <$500
1929 Small Size
10 Type 1 1-826 <$350
20 Type 1 1-200 <$350
Total Issue $402,410
Out at close $24,640
Large out at close $1,460

4356 Muhlenberg
FNB OF GREENVILLE
{{ 5 L 4 S }}
Chartered 1890
Brown Back <$VALUE
3x10-20 1-2380 <$1000
1882 Date Back
3x10-20 1-307 <$1000
1902 Date Back
3x10-20 1-2000 <$600
1902 Plain Back
3x10-20 2001-7149 <$600
1929 Small Size
10 Type 1 1-886 <$350
20 Type 1 1-266 <$350
10 Type 2 1-806 <$350
20 Type 2 1-161 <$375
Total Issue $588,160
Out in 1935 $30,000
Large out 1935 $1,970

12243 Harlan
CITIZENS NB OF HARLAN
{{ 5 L 7 S }}
Organized 6/3/22
Receivership 1/19/32
1902 Plain Back <$VALUE
3x10-20 1-12018 <$500
1929 Small Size
10 Type 1 1-2472 <$200
20 Type 1 1-693 <$200
Total Issue $832,380
Out at close $100,000
Large out at close $6,810

9791 Harlan
FNB OF HARLAN
{{ UNREPORTED }}
Chartered 6/10
Liquidated 11/1/16
1902 Date Back <$VALUE
3x10-20 1-3080 <$1500
1902 Plain Back
3x10-20 3080-3322 <$1500
Total Issue $166,100
Out at close $38,700

12295 Harlan
HARLAN NB, HARLAN
{{ 7 L 14 S }}
Chartered 1/23
1902 Plain Back <$VALUE
4x5 1-13030 <$450
3x10-20 1-8498 <$450
1929 Small Size
5 Type 1 1-4922 <$125
10 Type 1 1-2448 <$125
20 Type 1 1-650 <$125
5 Type 2 1-6970 <$150
10 Type 2 1-4530 <$150
20 Type 2 1-1296 <$150
Total Issue $1,164,110
Out in 1935 $100,000
Large out 1935 $2,950

F-Mercer NB of Harrodsburg
SEE Ch 2531
Mercer NB of Harrodsburg

1807 Mercer
FNB OF HARRODSBURG
{{ 4 L }}
Chartered 3/31/71
Closed 3/11/30
Original Series <$VALUE
3x1-2 1-4000 <$600/$1250
4x5 1-1450 <$650
3x10-20 1-1720 <$850/$1250
Series 1875
3x10-20 1-2870 <$850/$1250
Brown Back
3x10-20 1-4890 <$600
1882 Date Back
3x10-20 1-1830 <$600
1902 Date Back
3x10-20 1-4800 <$375
1902 Plain Back
3x10-20 4801-14035 <$375
Total Issue $1,316,250
Out at close $9,535
Ch 2531 assumed circulation

13612 Mercer
MERCER COUNTY NB OF HARRODSBURG
{{ 2U + 7 S }}
Chartered 4/32
1929 Small Size <$VALUE
5 Type 1 1-622 <$175
10 Type 1 1-316 <$175
20 Type 1 1-106 <$175
5 Type 2 1-5792 <$175
10 Type 2 1-3048 <$175
20 Type 2 1-816 <$175
Total Issue $126,100
Out in 1935 $100,000
Outstanding includes Ch 2531

2531 Mercer
MERCER NB OF HARRODSBURG
Chartered 1881
Liquidated 7/20/32
2nd title:F-Mercer NB of Harrodsburg 3/11/30
FIRST TITLE {{ 9 L 3 S }}
Series 1875 <$VALUE
4x10 1-5118 <$750
Brown Back
3x10-20 1-6250 <$600
1882 Date Back
3x10-20 1-7600 <$600
1882 Value Back
3x10-20 7601-11819 <$600
1902 Plain Back
3x10-20 1-11401 <$300
1929 Small Size
10 Type 1 1-1228 <$275
20 Type 1 1-416 <$275
SECOND TITLE {{ 5 S }}
1929 Small Size
10 Type 1 1-907 <$225
20 Type 1 1-190 <$225
Total Issue $1,879,040
Out at close $99,995
Large out 1935 $11,130
Ch 13612 assumed circulation

5792 Ohio
FNB OF HARTFORD
{{ 1 L }}
Chartered 4/26/01
Liquidated 3/5/14
Brown Back <$VALUE
3x10-20 1-1800 <$1500
1882 Date Back
3x10-20 1-1096 <$1500
Total Issue $144,800
Out in 1914 $16,180

8258 Perry
FNB OF HAZARD
{{ 5 L }}
Organized 5/28/06
Liquidated 1/8/29
1902 Red Seal <$VALUE
3x10-20 1-320 <$1250
1902 Date Back
3x10-20 1-1220 <$600
1902 Plain Back
3x10-20 1221-18564 <$600
Total Issue $944,200
Out at close $100,000

13757 Henderson
FNB OF HENDERSON
{{ 6 S }}
Chartered 8/33
1929 Small Size <$VALUE
5 Type 2 1-15384 <$200
10 Type 2 1-5500 <$200
20 Type 2 1-1678 <$200
Total Issue $165,480
Out in 1935 $82,300

1615 Henderson
HENDERSON NB, HENDERSON
{{ 11 L }}
Organized 11/21/65
Receivership 6/11/32
Original Series <$VALUE
3x1-2 1-3600 <$600/$1250
4x5 1-2250 <$600
3x10-20 1-3720 <$850/$1250
50-100 1-330 <$5000
Series 1875
4x5 1-2250 <$600
3x10-20 1-4753 <$850/$1250
50-100 1-71 <$5000
Brown Back
3x10-20 1-6830 <$500
50-100 1-2010 <$2000
1902 Red Seal
3x10-20 1-3050 <$700
50-100 1-450 <$2500
1902 Date Back
3x10-20 1-11400 <$300
50-100 1-800 <$500/$600
1902 Plain Back
3x10-20 11401-28161 <$300
Total Issue $2,982,850
Out at close $16,886

13983 Henderson
OHIO VALLEY NB OF HENDERSON
{{ 6 S }}
Chartered 2/34
1929 Small Size <$VALUE
5 Type 2 1-12526 <$225
10 Type 2 1-4075 <$225
20 Type 2 1-1331 <$225
Total Issue $130,000
Out in 1935 $83,350

2931 Henderson
PLANTERS NB OF HENDERSON
{{ UNREPORTED }}
Chartered 4/20/83
Liquidated 6/30/90
Brown Back <$VALUE
3x10-20 1-1867 <$2000
Total Issue $93,350
Out in 1910 $530

4465 Fulton
FARMERS & MERCHANTS NB OF HICKMAN
{{ UNREPORTED }}
Chartered 11/18/90
Liquidated 12/5/98
Brown Back <$VALUE
4x5 1-1714 <$2000
Total Issue $34,280
Out in 1910 $370

6894 Larue
THE FARMERS NB OF HODGENVILLE
Organized 7/4/03
Liquidated 10/1/30
2nd title: Farmers NB of Hodgenville 11/1/20
FIRST TITLE {{ 3 L }}
1902 Red Seal <$VALUE
3x10-20 1-1660 <$1000
1902 Date Back
3x10-20 1-4000* <$400
1902 Plain Back
3x10-20 4401-6220* <$400
* 4001-4400 not marked
SECOND TITLE {{ 6 L 4 S }}
1902 Plain Back
3x10-20 1-12832 <$400
1929 Small Size
10 Type 1 1-1120 <$300
20 Type 1 1-262 <$325
Total Issue $1,134,240
Out at close $110,000
Large out 1935 $6,395
Outstanding includes Ch 9843
Ch 13479 assumed circulation

9843 Larue
LA RUE NB OF HODGENVILLE
{{ 1 L }}
Chartered 9/10
Closed 11/1/20
1902 Date Back <$VALUE
3x10-20 1-1990 <$1000
1902 Plain Back
3x10-20 1991-3364 <$1000
Total Issue $168,200
Out at close $39,700
Ch 6894 assumed circulation

13479 Larue
LINCOLN NB OF HODGENVILLE
{{ 7 S }}
Chartered 6/30
1929 Small Size <$VALUE
10 Type 1 1-778 <$200
20 Type 1 1-260 <$200
10 Type 2 1-1895 <$225
20 Type 2 1-510 <$225
Total Issue $107,030
Out in 1935 $55,000
Outstanding includes Ch 6894

3856 Christian
FNB OF HOPKINSVILLE
{{ 7 L 2 S }}
Chartered 3/15/88
Liquidated 6/30/30
Brown Back <$VALUE
4x5 1-4929 <$750
3x10-20 1-2106 <$750
1902 Red Seal
4x5 1-630 <$850
50-100 1-166 <$2500
1902 Date Back
4x5 1-5350 <$350
50-100 1-620 <$500/$600
3x50-100 1-760 <$500/$600
1902 Plain Back
4x5 5351-25495 <$350
3x50-100 761-1010<$500/$600
1929 Small Size
5 Type 1 1-1045 <$500
50 Type 1 1-57 <$600
100 Type 1 1-19 <$750
Total Issue $1,156,630
Out at close $75,000
Large out at close $24,120

7602 Hart
FNB OF HORSE CAVE
{{ 5 L 1 S }}
Organized 2/4/05
Receivership 12/9/30
1902 Red Seal <$VALUE
3x10-20 1-1060 <$2500
1902 Date Back
3x10-20 1-1750 <$1500
1902 Plain Back
3x10-20 1751-5209 <$1500
1929 Small Size
10 Type 1 1-290 <$1000
20 Type 1 1-84 <$1000
Total Issue $340,930
Out at close $25,000
Large out at close $4,840

****

2917 Lincoln
NB OF HUSTONVILLE
{{ 5 L 50+ S }}
Chartered 1883
Brown Back <$VALUE
3x10-20 1-1315 <$750
1902 Red Seal
3x10-20 1-555 <$850
1902 Date Back
3x10-20 1-3540 <$450
1902 Plain Back
3x10-20 3541-11270 <$450
1929 Small Size
10 Type 1 1-1294 <$150
20 Type 1 1-378 <$150
10 Type 2 1-1427 <$150
20 Type 2 1-494 <$150
Total Issue $804,150
Out in 1935 $50,000
Large out 1935 $3,470

****

9320 Breathitt
FNB OF JACKSON
{{ 6 L U + 8 S }}
Chartered 1/09
1902 Date Back <$VALUE
4x5 1-5350 <$400
3x10-20 1-4380 <$400
1902 Plain Back
4x5 5351-13780 <$400
3x10-20 4381-10021 <$400
1929 Small Size
5 Type 1 1-1700 <$175
10 Type 1 1-1010 <$175
20 Type 1 1-242 <$175
5 Type 2 1-2232 <$200
10 Type 2 1-1272 <$200
20 Type 2 1-384 <$225
Total Issue $948,850
Out in 1935 $50,000
Large out 1935 $2,935

****

FNB of Jenkins
SEE Ch 10062
Jenkins NB, Jenkins

****

10062 Letcher
JENKINS NB, JENKINS
Organized 6/29/11
Receivership 7/12/32
2nd title:FNB of Jenkins 1/29/12
FIRST TITLE {{ 0 L }}
1902 Date Back <$VALUE
3x10-20 1-564 <$750
SECOND TITLE {{ 5 L 15 S }}
1902 Date Back
3x10-20 1-1600 <$450
1902 Plain Back
3x10-20 1601-14242 <$450
1929 Small Size
10 Type 1 1-1972 <$125
20 Type 1 1-577 <$125
Total Issue $927,860
Out at close $73,800
Large out at close $6,270

****

2888 Garrard
CITIZENS NB OF LANCASTER
{{ 4 L 8 S }}
Chartered 1883
Brown Back <$VALUE
3x10-20 1-3490 <$600
1902 Red Seal
3x10-20 1-2500 <$750
1902 Date Back
3x10-20 1-4200 <$350
1902 Plain Back
3x10-20 4201-11215 <$350
1929 Small Size
10 Type 1 1-1356 <$175
20 Type 1 1-358 <$175
10 Type 2 1-1612 <$200
20 Type 2 1-510 <$200
Total Issue $1,010,890
Out in 1935 $50,000
Large out 1935 $2,940

****

1493 Garrard
NB OF LANCASTER
{{ 4 L 8 S }}
Chartered 1865
Original Series <$VALUE
3x1-2 1-1892 <$600/$1250
4x5 1-1600 <$600
4x10 1-3178 <$850
4x20 1-2387 <$1250
Series 1875
4x5 1-341 <$600
4x10 1-472 <$850
4x20 1-657 <$1250
Brown Back
3x10-20 1-4716 <$500
1902 Red Seal
3x10-20 1-1660 <$650
1902 Date Back
3x10-20 1-3240 <$300
1902 Plain Back
3x10-20 3241-10715 <$300
1929 Small Size
10 Type 1 1-1414 <$175
20 Type 1 1-370 <$175
10 Type 2 1-1920 <$200
20 Type 2 1-539 <$200
Total Issue $1,451,570
Out in 1935 $50,000
Large out 1935 $4,380

****

6248 Kenton
FNB OF LATONIA
{{ 3 L 3 S }}
Chartered 5/9/02
1902 Red Seal <$VALUE
3x10-20 1-1540 <$1000
1902 Date Back
3x10-20 1-1910 <$500
1902 Plain Back (dated 1902)
3x10-20 1911-3489 <$500
1902 Plain Back (dated 1922)
3x10-20 1-2545 <$500
1929 Small Size
10 Type 1 1-746 <$350
20 Type 1 1-190 <$350
10 Type 2 1-780 <$400
20 Type 2 1-273 <$400
Total Issue $459,520
Out in 1935 $25,000
Large out 1935 $1,320

****

2190 Anderson
ANDERSON COUNTY NB OF LAWRENCEBURG
{{ 1 L }}
Chartered 9/25/74
Liquidated 7/29/76
Original Series <$VALUE
4x5 1-2695 <$2000
Total Issue $53,900
Out in 1910 $175

****

8604 Anderson
ANDERSON NB OF LAWRENCEBURG
{{ 6 L 14 S }}
Chartered 3/07
1902 Red Seal <$VALUE
3x10-20 1-3250 <$850
1902 Date Back
3x10-20 1-7700 <$400
1902 Plain Back
3x10-20 7701-22845 <$400
1929 Small Size
10 Type 1 1-2516 <$110
20 Type 1 1-696 <$125
10 Type 2 1-3325 <$135
20 Type 2 1-800 <$150
Total Issue $1,588,480
Out in 1935 $86,250
Large out 1935 $4,690

****

7497 Anderson
LAWRENCEBURG NB, LAWRENCEBURG
{{ 9 L 15 S }}
Chartered 12/04
1902 Red Seal <$VALUE
4x5 1-4150 <$750
3x10-20 1-3060 <$750
1902 Date Back
4x5 1-7750* <$350
3x10-20 1-5300** <$350
1902 Plain Back
4x5 8251-26418* <$350
3x10-20 5701-17282** <$350
* 7751-8250 not marked
** 5301-5700 not marked
1929 Small Size
5 Type 1 1-3788 <$100
10 Type 1 1-2082 <$100
20 Type 1 1-600 <$100
5 Type 2 1-4008 <$110
10 Type 2 1-2397 <$110
20 Type 2 1-888 <$125
Total Issue $2,000,790
Out in 1935 $100,000
Large out 1935 $6,210

****

8862 Anderson
WITHERSPOON NB OF LAWRENCEBURG
{{ 2 L }}
Chartered 9/07
Liquidated 12/15/10
1902 Red Seal <$VALUE
4x5 1-2350 <$1250
4x10 1-2325 <$1250
1902 Date Back
4x5 1-2053 <$750
4x10 1-1339 <$750
Total Issue $234,620
Out in 1911 $50,590

****

3988 Marion
CITIZENS NB OF LEBANON
{{ 21 L 50+ S }}
Chartered 3/11/89
Brown Back <$VALUE
4x5 1-9646 <$375
3x10-20 1-4224 <$375
1902 Date Back
4x5 1-7250 <$150
3x10-20 1-5500 <$150
1902 Plain Back
4x5 7251-24124 <$150
3x10-20 5501-16493 <$150
1929 Small Size
5 Type 1 1-3860 <$50
10 Type 1 1-2270 <$50
20 Type 1 1-570 <$60
5 Type 2 1-4902 <$50
10 Type 2 1-2344 <$50
20 Type 2 1-605 <$65
Total Issue $2,091,700
Out in 1935 $100,000
Large out 1935 $6,385

****

4271 Marion
FARMERS NB OF LEBANON
{{ 5 L 8 S }}
Chartered 1890
Brown Back <$VALUE
4x5 1-4075 <$500
3x10-20 1-1620 <$500
1882 Date Back
4x5 1-400 <$500
3x10-20 1-167 <$500
1902 Date Back
3x10-20 1-3200 <$300
1902 Plain Back
3x10-20 3201-11363 <$300
1929 Small Size
5 Type 1 1-312 <$175
10 Type 1 1-1346 <$175
20 Type 1 1-392 <$185
5 Type 2 1-2024 <$200
10 Type 2 1-1125 <$200
20 Type 2 1-300 <$200
Total Issue $911,530
Out in 1935 $50,000
Large out 1935 $3,260

****

2150 Marion
MARION NB OF LEBANON
{{ 13 L 18 S }}
Chartered 6/3/74
Original Series <$VALUE
4x5 1-1475 <$500
3x20-50 1-650 <$1250/$5000
Series 1875
4x5 1-6750 <$500
3x20-50 1-1305<$1250/$5000
Brown Back
4x5 1-4550 <$350
3x10-20 1-3540 <$350
1882 Date Back
4x5 1-8645 <$300
3x10-20 1-5504 <$300
1902 Date Back
4x5 1-3750 <$150
3x10-20 1-3000 <$150
1902 Plain Back
4x5 3751-29775 <$150
3x10-20 3001-19227 <$150
1929 Small Size
5 Type 1 1-6308 <$60
10 Type 1 1-3126 <$60
20 Type 1 1-852 <$70
5 Type 2 1-8330 <$70
10 Type 2 1-4448 <$70
20 Type 2 1-1301 <$75
Total Issue $3,243,690
Out in 1935 $150,000
Large out 1935 $9,295

****

1694 Marion
NB OF LEBANON
{{ 2 L }}
Chartered 7/24/69
Liquidated 4/7/89
Original Series <$VALUE
3x1-2 1-2110 <$750/$1500
4x5 1-6098 <$850
Series 1875
4x5 1-12028 <$850
Total Issue $373,070
Out in 1910 $2,190

****

5314 Grayson
GRAYSON COUNTY NB OF LEITCHFIELD
{{ 2 L }}
Chartered 4/28/00
Liquidated 2/1/11
Brown Back <$VALUE
3x10-20 1-2200 <$850
1882 Date Back
3x10-20 1-913 <$850
Total Issue $155,650
Out in 1911 $27,300

****

F & City NB of Lexington
SEE Ch 906
Lexington NB, Lexington

****

1720 Fayette
FAYETTE NB OF LEXINGTON
{{ 15 L 6 S }}
Chartered 10/10/70
Liquidated 6/2/31
Original Series <$VALUE
3x1-2 1-4000 <$350/$1000
4x5 1-6000 <$375
3x10-20 1-5900 <$600/$1250
Series 1875
4x5 1-6600 <$375
3x10-20 1-8631 <$600/$1000
Brown Back
4x5 1-9750 <$200
3x10-20 1-24300 <$200/$250
1882 Date Back
4x5 1-6365 <$200
3x10-20 1-3119 <$200/$250
1902 Date Back
4x5 1-16500 <$75
3x10-20 1-12800 <$100
1902 Plain Back
4x5 16501-75625 <$75
3x10-20 12801-47522 <$100
1929 Small Size
5 Type 1 1-6972 <$175
10 Type 1 1-3269 <$175
20 Type 1 1-1045 <$175
Total Issue $7,111,100
Out at close $299,995
Large out at close $40,100

****

760 Fayette
FNB OF LEXINGTON
{{ 5 L }}
Chartered 1/26/65
Liquidated 8/5/13
Original Series <$VALUE
3x1-2 1-11400 <$350/$1000
4x5 1-7420 <$400
3x10-20 1-5860 <$650/$1250
50-50 1-1600 <$5000
Series 1875
3x1-2 1-1000 <$350/$1000
4x5 1-6985 <$400
3x10-20 1-3800 <$600/$1000
50-50 1-2126 <$5000
Brown Back
4x5 1-5765 <$300
50-100 1-2792 <$1250/$1500
1902 Red Seal
3x10-20 1-12000 <$350
1902 Date Back
3x10-20 1-19609 <$175
Total Issue $3,320,250
Out at close $86,450
Ch 906 assumed circulation

****

FNB & TC, Lexington
SEE Ch 906
Lexington NB, Lexington

****

906 Fayette
LEXINGTON CITY NB, LEXINGTON
Chartered 3/17/65
2nd title: F & City NB 8/8/13
3rd title: FNB & TC 3/2/29
FIRST TITLE {{ 8 L }}
Original Series <$VALUE
3x1-2 1-5190 <$350/$1000
4x5 1-5400 <$375
3x10-20 1-2600 <$700/$1000
50-100 1-450 <$5000
Series 1875
4x5 1-250 <$375
3x10-20 1-2461 <$700/$1000
50-100 1-999 <$5000
Brown Back
50-100 1-4948 <$1250/$1500
1902 Red Seal
4x5 1-14150 <$200
3x10-20 1-8940 <$200/$250
50-100 1-667 <$2000
1902 Date Back
4x5 1-19135 <$85
3x10-20 1-15925 <$100
50-100 1-500 <$350/$400
3x50-100 1-172 <$350/$400
SECOND TITLE {{ 16 L }}
1902 Date Back
4x5 1-15000 <$75
3x10-20 1-18000 <$85
3x50-100 1-2900 <$300/$350
1902 Plain Back
4x5 15001-133460 <$75
3x10-20 18001-84939 <$85
3x50-100 2901-3978 <$300/$350
THIRD TITLE {{ 50+ S }}
1929 Small Size
5 Type 1 1-54902 <$15
10 Type 1 1-14978 <$20
20 Type 1 1-4298 <$30
5 Type 2 1-119294 <$15
10 Type 2 1-18733 <$20
20 Type 2 1-5386 <$30
Total Issue $15,342,220
Out in 1935 $1,000,000
Large out 1935 $80,065
Outstanding includes Ch 760, and Ch 3052

****

2393 Fayette
N EXCHANGE B OF LEXINGTON
{{ 3 L }}
Chartered 8/16/78
Liquidated 1/11/06
Series 1875 <$VALUE
4x5 1-12117 <$600
Brown Back
50-100 1-1438 <$1250/$1500
Total Issue $458,040
Out in 1910 $21,985

****

3942 Fayette
PHOENIX NB OF LEXINGTON
{{ 5 L }}
Chartered 11/26/88
Liquidated 3/28/11
Brown Back <$VALUE
3x10-20 1-10618 <$400
1902 Date Back
4x5 1-7005 <$225
3x10-20 1-6161 <$225
Total Issue $979,050
Out in 1911 $184,895

****

Phoenix & Third NB of Lexington
SEE Ch 3052
Third NB of Lexington

****

Phoenix NB & TC of Lexington
SEE Ch 3052
Third NB of Lexington

****

2901 Fayette
SECOND NB OF LEXINGTON
{{ 10 L 12 S }}
Chartered 1883
Brown Back <$VALUE
3x10-20 1-8482 <$350
1902 Red Seal
3x10-20 1-7500 <$400
1902 Date Back
3x10-20 1-10500 <$150
1902 Plain Back
3x10-20 10501-35714 <$150
1929 Small Size
10 Type 1 1-4670 <$75
20 Type 1 1-1152 <$75
5 Type 2 1-324 <$85
10 Type 2 1-5558 <$75
20 Type 2 1-1855 <$85
Total Issue $3,097,540
Out in 1935 $150,000
Large out 1935 $10,095

****

3052 Fayette
THIRD NB OF LEXINGTON
Chartered 1883
Closed 3/2/29
2nd title:Phoenix & Third NB of Lexington 4/27/11
3rd title:Phoenix NB & TC of Lexington 7/17/22
FIRST TITLE {{ 5 L }}
Brown Back <$VALUE
3x10-20 1-4176 <$300
1902 Red Seal
3x10-20 1-2000 <$350
50-100 1-2166 <$2000
1902 Date Back
3x10-20 1-5119 <$100
50-100 1-262 <$300/$350
SECOND TITLE {{ 13 L }}
1902 Date Back
4x5 1-45000 <$60
3x10-20 1-34000 <$75
1902 Plain Back
4x5 45001-110500 <$60
3x10-20 34001-73400 <$75
THIRD TITLE {{ 14 L }}
1902 Plain Back
4x5 1-79805 <$60
3x10-20 1-49913 <$75
Total Issue $10,900,700
Out at close $751,100

****

3943 Laurel
FNB OF LONDON
{{ 3 L }}
Chartered 11/28/88
Receivership 4/9/14
Brown Back <$VALUE
4x5 1-1500 <$750
3x10-20 1-1970 <$750
1902 Date Back
4x5 1-2330 <$500
3x10-20 1-2255 <$500
Total Issue $287,850
Out in 1916 $10,975

****

7890 Laurel
NB OF LONDON
{{ 2 L 4 S }}
Organized 8/26/05
1902 Red Seal <$VALUE
3x10-20 1-1000 <$1250
1902 Date Back
3x10-20 1-1750 <$600
1902 Plain Back
3x10-20 1751-5817 <$600
1929 Small Size
10 Type 1 1-738 <$325
20 Type 1 1-204 <$325
10 Type 2 1-985 <$350
20 Type 2 1-244 <$350
Total Issue $424,340
Out in 1935 $25,000
Large out 1935 $790

****

7110 Lawrence
FNB OF LOUISA
{{ 11 L 19 S }}
Chartered 1/04
1902 Red Seal <$VALUE
4x5 1-375 <$600
3x10-20 1-300 <$600
1902 Date Back
4x5 1-2225 <$225
3x10-20 1-1800 <$225
1902 Plain Back
4x5 2226-7856 <$225
3x10-20 1801-5155 <$225
1929 Small Size
5 Type 1 1-1236 <$125
10 Type 1 1-606 <$125
20 Type 1 1-182 <$135
5 Type 2 1-1496 <$135
10 Type 2 1-983 <$135
20 Type 2 1-276 <$135
Total Issue $555,480
Out in 1935 $30,000
Large out 1935 $1,310

****

<$VALUEs are for notes in FINE condition. Value changes by approximately 25% for a change of one full grade.

****
7122 Lawrence
LOUISA NB, LOUISA
{{ 4 L 9 S }}
Chartered 2/04
1902 Red Seal <$VALUE
3x10-20 1-1690 <$750
1902 Date Back
3x10-20 1-3400 <$375
1902 Plain Back
3x10-20 3401-11460 <$375
1929 Small Size
10 Type 1 1-1444 <$175
20 Type 1 1-410 <$175
10 Type 2 1-1968 <$175
20 Type 2 1-656 <$175
Total Issue $826,140
Out in 1935 $50,000
Large out 1935 $2,600
****
4956 Jefferson
AMERICAN NB OF LOUISVILLE
Chartered 1894
Closed 2/3/19
2nd title: American Southern NB 8/18/15
FIRST TITLE {{ 7 L }}
Brown Back <$VALUE
3x10-20 1-72900 <$225/$275
1882 Date Back
3x10-20 1-44281 <$225/$275
1902 Date Back
3x10-20 1-15831 <$150
SECOND TITLE {{ 2 L }}
1902 Plain Back
4x5 1-10880 <$300
3x10-20 1-16672 <$300
Total Issue $7,701,800
Out at close $800,000
Ch 5312 assumed circulation
****
American Southern NB of Louisville
SEE Ch 4956
American NB of Louisville
****
2164 Jefferson
CITIZENS NB OF LOUISVILLE
Chartered 8/8/74
2nd title: Citizens Union NB of Louisville 1/2/19
FIRST TITLE {{ 14 L }}
Original Series <$VALUE
3x10-20 1-4194 <$650/$1250
50-100 1-666 <$5000
Series 1875
3x10-20 1-9100 <$650/$1000
50-100 1-1719 <$5000
Brown Back
3x10-20 1-32450 <$175/$225
1882 Date Back
4x5 1-24110 <$175
3x10-20 1-17633 <$175/$225
1902 Date Back
4x5 1-11000 <$60
3x10-20 1-13000 <$75
1902 Plain Back
4x5 11001-21500 <$60
3x10-20 13001-17800 <$75
SECOND TITLE {{ 24 L 50+ S }}
1902 Plain Back
4x10 1-199953 <$60
1929 Small Size
10 Type 1 1-53338 <$20
10 Type 2 1-69171 <$20
Total Issue $17,218,910
Out in 1935 $1,000,000
Large out 1935 $56,160
Outstanding includes Ch 4145
****
Citizens Union NB of Louisville
SEE Ch 2164
Citizens NB of Louisville
****
Continental NB of Louisville
SEE Ch
Western NB of Louisville
****
109 Jefferson
FNB OF LOUISVILLE
{{ 31 L 50+ S }}
Chartered 10/63
Original Series <$VALUE
4x5 1-3300 <$350
4x10 1-4415 <$500
3x20-50 1-3436<$1250/$5000
Series 1875
4x10 1-5439 <$350
3x20-50 1-2195<$1000/$5000
Brown Back
4x5 1-4500 <$200
4x10 1-27140 <$200
50-100 1-2867 <$1250/$1500
1902 Red Seal
4x5 1-16000 <$200
3x10-20 1-16600 <$200/$225
1902 Date Back
4x5 1-32165 <$60
3x10-20 1-26934 <$75
1902 Plain Back
4x5 32166-116101 <$60
3x10-20 26935-83658 <$75
1929 Small Size
5 Type 1 1-28782 <$25
10 Type 1 1-20494 <$25
20 Type 1 1-4466 <$30
5 Type 2 1-43176 <$25
10 Type 2 1-20543 <$25
20 Type 2 1-6662 <$35
Total Issue $13,795,110
Out in 1935 $986,100
Large out 1935 $39,880
****
2784 Jefferson
FOURTH NB OF LOUISVILLE
{{ UNREPORTED }}
Chartered 9/26/82
Liquidated 6/2/94
Brown Back <$VALUE
50-100 1-2417 <$2000
Total Issue $362,550
Out in 1910 $2,750
****
2062 Jefferson
GERMAN NB OF LOUISVILLE
{{ 2U + 5 L }}
Chartered 11/5/72
Receivership 1/22/97
Original Series <$VALUE
3x1-2 1-2466 <$500/$1000
4x5 1-3000 <$500
3x10-20 1-800 <$750/$1250
50-100 1-1187 <$5000
Series 1875
3x10-20 1-7076 <$750/$1000
50-100 1-460 <$5000
Brown Back
3x10-20 1-5371 <$400
Total Issue $981,730
Out in 1916 $4,579
****
1908 Jefferson
KENTUCKY NB OF LOUISVILLE
{{ 2 L }}
Chartered 12/27/71
Liquidated 6/2/94
Original Series <$VALUE
3x1-2 1-4000 <$600/$1250
4x5 1-5250 <$600
3x10-20 1-2600 <$750/$1250
50-100 1-2134 <$5000
Series 1875
4x5 1-3263 <$600
3x10-20 1-5669 <$750/$1250
50-100 1-3385 <$5000
Brown Back
50-100 1-4 <$2000
Total Issue $1,432,160
Out in 1910 $7,360
****
14320 Jefferson
LIBERTY NB & TC OF LOUISVILLE
{{ 50+ S }}
Chartered 1/8/35
1929 Small Size <$VALUE
10 Type 2 1-25000 <$150
Total Issue $250,000
Out in 1935 $250,000
****
788 Jefferson
LOUISVILLE CITY NB, LOUISVILLE
{{ 4 L }}
Chartered 2/8/65
Liquidated 10/18/99
Original Series <$VALUE
3x1-2 1-2000 <$400/$1000
4x5 1-1500 <$450
3x10-20 1-4930 <$750/$1250
50-100 1-2300 <$5000
Series 1875
50-100 1-5400 <$5000
Brown Back
50-100 1-1568 <$1250/$1500
Total Issue $1,676,700
Out in 1910 $13,861
****
5161 Jefferson
LOUISVILLE N BANKING C, LOUISVILLE
Chartered 1898
Liquidated 5/15/29
2nd title: Louisville NB 1/11/21
3rd title: Louisville NB & TC 8/15/27
FIRST TITLE {{ 11 L }}
Brown Back <$VALUE
4x5 1-4000 <$225
50-100 1-5267 <$1250/$1500
1882 Date Back
4x5 1-3870 <$175
50-100 1-560 <$1250/$1500
3x50-100 1-468 <$1250/$1500
1902 Plain Back
3x50-100 1-860 <$300/$350
SECOND TITLE {{ 2 L }}
1902 Plain Back
3x50-100 1-1409 <$300/$350
THIRD TITLE {{ 4 L }}
1902 Plain Back
3x50-100 1-2733 <$300/$350
Total Issue $2,398,950
Out at close $500,000
****
2161 Jefferson
MERCHANTS NB OF LOUISVILLE
{{ 2 L }}
Chartered 7/31/74
Liquidated 6/2/94
Original Series <$VALUE
4x5 1-5000 <$600
3x10-20 1-5000 <$750/$1250
50-100 1-1000 <$5000
Series 1875
3x10-20 1-3000 <$750/$1250
50-100 1-2081 <$5000
Total Issue $962,150
Out in 1910 $4,905
****
9241 Jefferson
NB OF COMMERCE OF LOUISVILLE
{{ 6 L }}
Chartered 9/08
Closed 2/3/19
1902 Date Back <$VALUE
4x5 1-33750 <$125
4x10 1-27000 <$125
3x10-20 1-1000 <$125
50-100 1-3000 <$350/$400
3x50-100 1-379 <$350/$400
1902 Plain Back
4x5 33751-38655 <$125
4x10 27001-28235 <$125
Total Issue $2,497,250
Out at close $500,000
Ch 5312 assumed circulation
****
5312 Jefferson
NB OF KENTUCKY OF LOUISVILLE
{{ 50+ L 15 S }}
Chartered 4/28/00
Receivership 11/17/30
Brown Back <$VALUE
4x5 1-94000 <$175
3x10-20 1-50200 <$175/$200
50-100 1-5633 <$1250/$1500
1882 Date Back
4x5 1-115200 <$150
3x10-20 1-64170 <$150/$175
50-100 1-1600 <$1250/$1500
3x50-100 1-2000 <$1250/$1500
1882 Value Back
4x5 115201-187677 <$150
3x10-20 64171-100820 <$150/$200
1902 Plain Back
4x5 1-351933 <$60
3x10-20 1-231982 <$75
1929 Small Size
5 Type 1 1-43491 <$75
10 Type 1 1-21211 <$75
20 Type 1 1-7376 <$85
Total Issue $36,869,760
Out at close $2,500,000
Large out at close $392,760
Outstanding includes Ch 4956, and Ch 9241
****
790 Jefferson
PLANTERS NB OF LOUISVILLE
{{ 3 L }}
Chartered 2/9/65
Liquidated 9/30/75
Original Series <$VALUE
3x1-2 1-1800 <$600/$1250
4x5 1-2000 <$600
3x10-20 1-5016 <$850/$1250
50-100 1-1376 <$5000
Total Issue $506,200
Out in 1910 $2,615
****
777 Jefferson
SECOND NB OF LOUISVILLE
{{ 4 L }}
Chartered 2/2/65
Liquidated 6/2/94
Original Series <$VALUE
3x1-2 1-2000 <$500/$1000
4x5 1-4000 <$500
3x10-20 1-5200 <$750/$1250
50-100 1-900 <$5000
Series 1875
3x10-20 1-2379 <$750/$1250
50-100 1-1933 <$5000
Brown Back
4x5 1-1025 <$400
3x10-20 1-1223 <$400
50-100 1-696 <$1250/$1500
Total Issue $1,079,950
Out in 1910 $6,300
****
5195 Jefferson
SOUTHERN NB OF LOUISVILLE
{{ 9 L }}
Chartered 5/25/99
Liquidated 8/7/15
Brown Back <$VALUE
3x10-20 1-14500 <$250/$300
1882 Date Back
4x5 1-24535 <$250
3x10-20 1-18125 <$250/$300
Total Issue $2,121,950
Out at close $356,250
****
2171 Jefferson
THIRD NB OF LOUISVILLE
{{ 10 L }}
Chartered 8/22/74
Liquidated 8/5/10
Original Series <$VALUE
4x5 1-9000 <$350
Series 1875
4x5 1-31850 <$350
Brown Back
4x5 1-8000 <$225
3x10-20 1-1250 <$225/$250
50-100 1-3638 <$1250/$1500
1882 Date Back
4x5 1-6025 <$225
3x10-20 1-2268 <$225
Total Issue $1,819,000
Out in 1910 $247,195
****
4145 Jefferson
UNION NB OF LOUISVILLE
{{ 12 L }}
Chartered 10/28/89
Closed 1/2/19
Brown Back <$VALUE
4x5 1-25750 <$200
3x10-20 1-29660 <$200/$250
1882 Date Back
4x5 1-3650 <$175
3x10-20 1-2117 <$175/$225
1902 Date Back
4x5 1-29000 <$60
3x10-20 1-20900 <$70
50-100 1-3000 <$300/$350
1902 Plain Back
4x5 29001-34260 <$60
3x10-20 20901-22889 <$70
Total Issue $4,456,500
Out at close $500,000
Ch 2164 assumed circulation
****
7457 Jefferson
WESTERN NB OF LOUISVILLE
Chartered 10/29/04
Liquidated 8/26/09
2nd title: Continental NB of Louisville 9/30/08
FIRST TITLE {{ 1 L }}
1902 Red Seal <$VALUE
4x5 1-4775 <$650
3x10-20 1-6782 <$650
SECOND TITLE {{ 1 L }}
1902 Date Back
4x5 1-1530 <$500
3x10-20 1-792 <$500
Total Issue $504,800
Out in 1910 $91,150
****
5323 Kenton
FNB OF LUDLOW
{{ 3 L 6 S }}
Chartered 5/2/00
Brown Back <$VALUE
3x10-20 1-1850 <$650
1882 Date Back
3x10-20 1-2670 <$650
1882 Value Back
3x10-20 2671-3137 <$650
1902 Plain Back
3x10-20 1-3294 <$400
1929 Small Size
10 Type 1 1-1194 <$200
20 Type 1 1-338 <$200
10 Type 2 1-754 <$225
20 Type 2 1-175 <$225
Total issue $537,290
Out in 1935 $32,150
Large out 1935 $1,450
****
8451 Hopkins
FARMERS NB OF MADISONVILLE
{{ 4 L 8 S }}
Organized 9/8/06
1902 Red Seal <$VALUE
3x10-20 1-375 <$850
1902 Date Back
3x10-20 1-4020 <$450
1902 Plain Back
3x10-20 4021-12630 <$450
1929 Small Size
10 Type 1 1-1362 <$175
20 Type 1 1-382 <$175
10 Type 2 1-1746 <$200
20 Type 2 1-420 <$200
Total Issue $803,670
Out in 1935 $50,000
Large out 1935 $2,460
****
8386 Hopkins
MORTON NB OF MADISONVILLE
{{ 2 L }}
Chartered 10/3/06
Liquidated 9/14/07
1902 Red Seal <$VALUE
3x10-20 1-1054 <$1500
Total Issue $52,700
Out in 1910 $9,610
****
7605 Clay
FNB OF MANCHESTER
{{ 6 L 6 S }}
Chartered 2/05
1902 Red Seal <$VALUE
3x10-20 1-456 <$850
1902 Date Back
3x10-20 1-1900 <$400
1902 Plain Back
3x10-20 1901-6985 <$400
1929 Small Size
10 Type 1 1-1216 <$200
20 Type 1 1-350 <$200
10 Type 2 1-2004 <$225
20 Type 2 1-395 <$225
Total Issue $514,950
Out in 1935 $50,000
Large out 1935 $3,120
****
5033 Graves
CITY NB OF MAYFIELD
{{ 6 L }}
Chartered 1896
Closed 7/2/27
Brown Back <$VALUE
3x10-20 1-6400 <$500
1882 Date Back
3x10-20 1-5413 <$500
1902 Plain Back
3x50-100 1-1280 <$500/$600
Total Issue $910,650
Out at close $80,000
Ch 2245 assumed circulation
****
6834 Graves
FARMERS NB OF MAYFIELD
{{ 2 L }}
Chartered 6/03
Closed 5/13/19
1902 Red Seal <$VALUE
3x10-20 1-1420 <$1000
1902 Date Back
3x10-20 1-2400 <$500
1902 Plain Back
3x10-20 2401-3229 <$500
Total Issue $232,450
Out at close $35,300
Ch 2245 assumed circulation
****
2245 Graves
FNB OF MAYFIELD
{{ 12 L 18 S }}
Chartered 4/8/75
Original Series <$VALUE
3x10-20 1-1800 <$750/$1250
Series 1875
3x10-20 1-3214 <$650/$1000
Brown Back
3x10-20 1-11760 <$375
1882 Date Back
3x10-20 1-8455 <$350
1902 Date Back
3x10-20 1-3000 <$175
1902 Plain Back
3x10-20 3001-27383 <$175
1929 Small Size
10 Type 1 1-6632 <$75
20 Type 1 1-1718 <$85
10 Type 2 1-6410 <$75
20 Type 2 1-1490 <$85
Total Issue $3,328,580
Out in 1935 $230,000
Large out 1935 $18,030
Outstanding includes Ch 6834, and Ch 5033
****
9561 Mason
B OF MAYSVILLE, N BANKING ASSOC.
{{ 4 L }}
Chartered 10/09
Liquidated 7/31/16
1902 Date Back <$VALUE
4x5 1-5050 <$400
3x10-20 1-3900 <$400
1902 Plain Back
4x5 5051-5715 <$400
3x10-20 3901-4236 <$400
Total Issue $326,100
Out in 1916 $82,650
****
2467 Mason
FNB OF MAYSVILLE
{{ 11 L }}
Chartered 3/18/80
Liquidated 11/1/16
Series 1875 <$VALUE
4x5 1-11700 <$500
3x10-20 1-7236 <$850/$1250
Brown Back
4x5 1-3050 <$375
3x10-20 1-2220 <$375
1882 Date Back
4x5 1-4100 <$375
3x10-20 1-3160 <$375
1882 Value Back
4x5 4101-4560 <$375
3x10-20 3161-3390 <$375
Total Issue $1,028,500
Out in 1916 $75,000
****
1702 Mason
NB OF MAYSVILLE
{{ 2 L }}
Chartered 8/24/70
Liquidated 1/4/72
Original Series <$VALUE
3x1-2 1-4000 <$650/$1500
4x5 1-5000 <$750
3x10-20 1-3000<$1000/$1500
Total Issue $270,000
Out in 1910 $720
****

CONDITION affects Value. The Values shown are for notes in FINE condition.

****
2663 Mason
STATE NB OF MAYSVILLE
{{ 15 L 21 S }}
Chartered 1882
Brown Back <$VALUE
3x10-20 1-5300 <$500
1902 Red Seal
3x10-20 1-3600 <$600
1902 Date Back
4x5 1-5915* <$125
3x10-20 1-3800** <$125
1902 Plain Back (dated 1902)
4x5 6416-13965* <$125
3x10-20 4161-7980** <$125
*5916-6415 not marked
**3801-4160 not marked
1902 Plain Back (dated 1922)
4x5 1-11755 <$125
3x10-20 1-8009 <$125
1929 Small Size
5 Type 1 1-5446 <$65
10 Type 1 1-2852 <$65
20 Type 1 1-808 <$75
5 Type 2 1-8032 <$75
10 Type 2 1-4381 <$75
20 Type 2 1-1392 <$85
Total Issue $2,302,120
Out in 1935 $150,000
Large out 1935 $7,050
****
4201 Bell
FNB OF MIDDLESBOROUGH
{{ UNREPORTED }}
Organized 1/8/90
Receivership 8/12/93
Brown Back <$VALUE
3x10-20 1-367 <$2000
Total Issue $18,350
Out in 1916 $100
****
7086 Bell
NB OF MIDDLESBOROUGH
{{ 3 L 13 S }}
Chartered 1/04
1902 Red Seal <$VALUE
3x10-20 1-730 <$850
1902 Date Back
3x10-20 1-2740 <$400
1902 Plain Back
3x10-20 2741-11097 <$400
1929 Small Size
10 Type 1 1-2220 <$110
20 Type 1 1-514 <$125
10 Type 2 1-1011 <$150
Total Issue $806,450
Out in 1935 $61,570
Large out 1935 $1,840
****
6419 Wayne
CITIZENS NB OF MONTICELLO
{{ 6 L 5 S }}
Chartered 9/12/02
Receivership 8/23/33
1902 Red Seal <$VALUE
3x10-20 1-2000 <$850
1902 Date Back
3x10-20 1-2420* <$400
1902 Plain Back
3x10-20 2671-4821* <$400
* 2421-2670 not marked
1929 Small Size
10 Type 1 1-652 <$275
20 Type 1 1-149 <$275
Total Issue $398,050
Out at close $25,000
Large out at close $2,530
****
1931 Wayne
NB OF MONTICELLO
{{ UNREPORTED }}
Chartered 2/2/72
Liquidated 4/23/77
Original Series <$VALUE
4x5 1-1650 <$1500
3x10-20 1-820 <$1500/$2000
Series 1875
3x10-20 1-328 <$1500/$2000
Total Issue $90,400
Out in 1910 $350
****
7593 Rowan
LENORA NB OF MOREHEAD
{{ UNREPORTED }}
Chartered 2/3/05
Liquidated 5/9/06
1902 Red Seal <$VALUE
4x5 1-135 <$2500
3x10-20 1-88 <$2500
Total Issue $7,100
Out in 1910 $710
****

****
7490 Union
MORGANFIELD NB, MORGANFIELD
{{ 5 L 14 S }}
Chartered 11/04
1902 Red Seal <$VALUE
3x10-20 1-2100 <$850
1902 Date Back
3x10-20 1-3900 <$400
1902 Plain Back
3x10-20 3901-19110 <$400
1929 Small Size
10 Type 1 1-2578 <$110
20 Type 1 1-714 <$110
10 Type 2 1-2724 <$125
20 Type 2 1-781 <$125
Total Issue $1,343,720
Out in 1935 $84,060
Large out 1935 $4,700
****
2209 Union
NB OF UNION COUNTY, MORGANFIELD
{{ 2 L }}
Chartered 12/3/74
Liquidated 6/30/91
Original Series <$VALUE
4x5 1-2250 <$750
Series 1875
4x5 1-12911 <$750
50-100 1-586 <$5000
Total Issue $391,120
Out in 1910 $2,930
****
2216 Montgomery
FARMERS NB OF MOUNT STERLING
{{ UNREPORTED }}
Chartered 1/11/75
Liquidated 7/1/89
Original Series <$VALUE
3x10-20 1-5188<$1500/$2000
Series 1875
3x10-20 1-7161<$1500/$2000
Total Issue $617,450
Out in 1910 $3,720
****
6160 Montgomery
MONTGOMERY NB OF MOUNT STERLING
{{ 6 L 8 S }}
Chartered 3/15/02
1902 Red Seal <$VALUE
4x5 1-1450 <$700
3x10-20 1-2620 <$700
1902 Date Back
4x5 1-3700 <$350
3x10-20 1-2540 <$350
1902 Plain Back (dated 1902)
4x5 3701-7515 <$350
3x10-20 2541-4721 <$350
1902 Plain Back (dated 1922)
4x5 1-18041 <$350
1929 Small Size
5 Type 1 1-6946 <$165
5 Type 2 1-14808 <$165
Total Issue $1,189,590
Out in 1935 $50,000
Large out 1935 $820
****
2185 Montgomery
MOUNT STERLING NB, MOUNT STERLING
{{ 6 L 14 S }}
Chartered 9/12/74
Original Series <$VALUE
4x5 1-2250 <$750
Series 1875
4x5 1-8996 <$750
Brown Back
4x5 1-3950 <$500
3x10-20 1-2180 <$500
1882 Date Back
4x5 1-2639 <$500
3x10-20 1-1883 <$500
1902 Date Back
3x10-20 1-1500 <$250
1902 Plain Back
3x10-20 1501-8608 <$250
1929 Small Size
10 Type 1 1-1574 <$100
20 Type 1 1-440 <$100
10 Type 2 1-4957 <$110
20 Type 2 1-1550 <$110
Total Issue $1,218,060
Out in 1935 $100,000
Large out 1935 $4,010
****

****
6129 Montgomery
TRADERS NB OF MOUNT STERLING
{{ 4 L 10 S }}
Chartered 2/17/02
1902 Red Seal <$VALUE
3x10-20 1-2700 <$800
1902 Date Back
3x10-20 1-3500 <$400
1902 Plain Back (dated 1902)
3x10-20 3501-6588 <$400
1902 Plain Back (dated 1922)
3x10-20 1-5021 <$400
1929 Small Size
10 Type 1 1-1356 <$165
20 Type 1 1-392 <$165
10 Type 2 1-1559 <$185
20 Type 2 1-444 <$185
Total Issue $868,320
Out in 1935 $50,000
Large out 1935 $2,250
****
11336 Hart
NB OF MUNFORDVILLE
{{ 4 L }}
Chartered 4/19
1902 Plain Back <$VALUE
3x10-20 1-2382 <$750
Total Issue $119,100
Out in 1935 $740
****
10779 Calloway
FNB OF MURRAY
{{ 3 L 10 S }}
Organized 8/3/15
Receivership 11/23/33
1902 Plain Back <$VALUE
3x10-20 1-9416 <$450
1929 Small Size
10 Type 1 1-2978 <$150
20 Type 1 1-804 <$150
Total Issue $745,960
Out at close $100,000
Large out at close $3,410
****
2196 Henry
NB OF NEW CASTLE
{{ UNREPORTED }}
Chartered 10/22/74
Liquidated 2/4/90
Original Series <$VALUE
3x10-20 1-900 <$2000/$2500
Series 1875
3x10-20 1-1774<$2000/$2500
Total Issue $133,700
Out in 1910 $700
****
American NB of Newport
SEE Ch 2726
German NB of Newport
****
2276 Campbell
FNB OF NEWPORT
{{ 2 L }}
Chartered 6/15/75
Receivership 1/21/97
Original Series <$VALUE
4x5 1-5000 <$750
Series 1875
4x5 1-4646 <$750
3x10-20 1-3965<$1000/$1500
Brown Back
4x5 1-497 <$600
3x10-20 1-198 <$600
Total Issue $411,010
Out in 1916 $2,395
****
2726 Campbell
GERMAN NB OF NEWPORT
Chartered 6/10/82
2nd title:American NB of Newport 1/12/18
FIRST TITLE {{ 4 L }}
Series 1875 <$VALUE
3x10-20 1-2605 <$750/$1250
1902 Red Seal
3x10-20 1-5350 <$500
1902 Date Back
3x10-20 1-7800 <$250
1902 Plain Back
3x10-20 7801-9000 <$250
SECOND TITLE {{ 6 L 15 S }}
1902 Plain Back
3x10-20 1-13914 <$200
1929 Small Size
5 Type 1 1-1854 <$60
10 Type 1 1-2406 <$60
20 Type 1 1-674 <$70
5 Type 2 1-4844 <$65
10 Type 2 1-2598 <$65
20 Type 2 1-888 <$75
Total Issue $1,892,270
Out in 1935 $100,000
Large out 1935 $5,490
****
4765 Campbell
NEWPORT NB, NEWPORT
{{ 8 L 19 S }}
Chartered 1892
Brown Back <$VALUE
3x10-20 1-7020 <$450
1882 Date Back
3x10-20 1-2960 <$450
1902 Date Back
3x10-20 1-7700 <$200
1902 Plain Back
3x10-20 7701-20162 <$200
1929 Small Size
10 Type 1 1-2944 <$60
20 Type 1 1-808 <$70
10 Type 2 1-2717 <$70
20 Type 2 1-916 <$90
Total Issue $1,826,190
Out in 1935 $100,000
Large out 1935 $5,220
****
1831 Jessamine
FNB OF NICHOLASVILLE
{{ 9 L 12 S }}
Chartered 6/2/71
Original Series <$VALUE
3x1-2 1-2100 <$650/$1500
4x5 1-5225 <$650
Series 1875
3x1-2 1-500 <$650/$1500
4x5 1-16139 <$650
Brown Back
4x5 1-5400 <$500
3x10-20 1-1240 <$500
1882 Date Back
4x5 1-268 <$500
3x10-20 1-186 <$500
1902 Date Back
4x5 1-3550 <$225
4x10 1-3550 <$225
1902 Plain Back
4x5 3551-16827 <$225
4x10 3551-13461 <$225
1929 Small Size
5 Type 1 1-4108 <$100
10 Type 1 1-2120 <$100
5 Type 2 1-6452 <$110
10 Type 2 1-3679 <$110
Total Issue $1,819,410
Out in 1935 $74,995
Large out 1935 $3,675
****
7281 Carter
OLIVE HILL NB, OLIVE HILL
{{ UNREPORTED }}
Chartered 5/04
Liquidated 10/15/10
1902 Red Seal <$VALUE
3x10-20 1-1350 <$2500
1902 Date Back
3x10-20 1-246 <$2000
Total Issue $79,800
Out at close $25,000
****
2576 Daviess
FNB OF OWENSBORO
Chartered 1/1/81
Liquidated 3/3/30
2nd title:FNB & TC 12/31/27
FIRST TITLE {{ 12 L }}
Series 1875 <$VALUE
4x5 1-10250 <$750
50-100 1-1999 <$5000
Brown Back
4x5 1-3500 <$450
50-100 1-2000 <$1250/$1500
1882 Date Back
4x5 1-5500 <$450
50-100 1-700 <$1250/$1500
3x50-100 1-660 <$1250/$1500
1882 Value Back
4x5 5501-14500 <$450
1902 Plain Back
4x5 1-22065 <$225
3x50-100 1-603 <$500/$600
SECOND TITLE {{ 1 L 1 S }}
1902 Plain Back
4x5 1-1530 <$250
3x50-100 1-165 <$500/$600
1929 Small Size
10 Type 1 1-300 <$500
20 Type 1 1-46* <$500
*F000046A not issued
Total Issue $2,122,250
Out at close $87,445
Large out at close $66,345
****

****
N Deposit B of Owensboro
SEE Ch 4006
Owensboro NB, Owensboro
****
4006 Daviess
OWENSBORO NB, OWENSBORO
Chartered 4/10/89
Liquidated 11/7/34
2nd title:N Deposit B of Owensboro 1898
FIRST TITLE {{ 0 L }}
Brown Back <$VALUE
3x10-20 1-2034 <$750
SECOND TITLE {{ 14 L 24 S }}
Brown Back
4x5 1-8750 <$500
3x10-20 1-16130 <$500
1902 Date Back
4x5 1-19750 <$200
3x10-20 1-15700 <$200
1902 Plain Back
4x5 19751-76823 <$200
3x10-20 15701-49444 <$200
1929 Small Size
5 Type 1 1-14018 <$50
10 Type 1 1-6348 <$50
20 Type 1 1-1586 <$65
5 Type 2 1-1314 <$75
10 Type 2 1-450 <$75
20 Type 2 1-186 <$85
Total Issue $6,098,390
Out at close $325,000
Large out at close $18,940
Ch 14138 assumed circulation
****
9456 Daviess
UNITED STATES NB OF OWENSBORO
{{ 7 L }}
Chartered 6/09
Liquidated 6/23/21
1902 Date Back <$VALUE
4x5 1-17000 <$300
3x10-20 1-13000 <$300
1902 Plain Back
4x5 17001-30580 <$300
3x10-20 13001-20991 <$300
Total Issue $1,661,150
Out at close $210,300
****
2968 Owen
FARMERS NB OF OWENTON
{{ 6 L 12 S }}
Organized 4/16/83
Brown Back <$VALUE
3x10-20 1-2108 <$600
1902 Red Seal
50-100 1-210 <$2500
1902 Date Back
4x10 1-2000 <$350
50-100 1-800 <$500/$600
1902 Plain Back
4x10 2001-13185 <$350
1929 Small Size
5 Type 1 1-2168 <$125
10 Type 1 1-1722 <$125
20 Type 1 1-170 <$150
5 Type 2 1-3852 <$150
10 Type 2 1-1788 <$150
20 Type 2 1-648 <$165
Total Issue $1,023,160
Out in 1935 $60,000
Large out 1935 $2,490
****
14026 Owen
FNB IN OWENTON
{{ UNREPORTED }}
Chartered 2/34
1929 Small Size <$VALUE
5 Type 2 1-580 <$850
20 Type 2 1-40 <$850
Total Issue $3,700
Out in 1935 $50,000
Outstanding includes Ch 2868
****
2868 Owen
FNB OF OWENTON
{{ 4 L 6 S }}
Organized 1/24/83
Liquidated 4/13/34
Brown Back <$VALUE
50-100 1-1064 <$2000
1902 Red Seal
50-100 1-303 <$2500
1902 Date Back
50-100 1-300 <$500/$600
3x50-100 1-1300 <$500/$600
1902 Plain Back
3x50-100 1301-1606 <$500/$600
1929 Small Size
50 Type 1 1-174 <$350
100 Type 1 1-49 <$450
Total Issue $733,150
Out at close $63,000
Large out 1935 $9,300
Ch 14026 assumed circulation
****
1963 Owen
NB OF OWEN AT OWENTON
{{ 1 L }}
Chartered 4/20/72
Liquidated 3/5/83
Original Series <$VALUE
4x5 1-500 <$1500
3x10-20 1-1928<$1500/$2000
Series 1875
3x10-20 1-318 <$1500/$2000
Total Issue $122,300
Out in 1910 $505
****
2070 McCracken
AMERICAN GERMAN NB OF PADUCAH
{{ 5 L }}
Chartered 12/18/72
Liquidated 5/28/10
Original Series <$VALUE
3x1-2 1-3000 <$500/$1250
4x5 1-3500 <$500
3x10-20 1-700 <$850/$1250
Series 1875
4x5 1-1845 <$500
3x10-20 1-2792 <$750/$1000
Brown Back
3x10-20 1-4900 <$400
1882 Date Back
3x10-20 1-3141 <$400
Total Issue $698,550
Out in 1910 $124,750
****
2093 McCracken
CITY NB OF PADUCAH
{{ 18 L 11 S }}
Chartered 3/18/73
Receivership 10/28/31
Original Series <$VALUE
3x10-20 1-3000 <$750/$1250
50-100 1-400 <$5000
Series 1875
3x10-20 1-5597 <$700/$1000
50-100 1-1895 <$5000
Brown Back
3x10-20 1-2500 <$300
50-100 1-5067 <$1250/$1500
1882 Date Back
3x10-20 1-8432 <$300
50-100 1-799 <$1250/$1500
1902 Date Back
3x10-20 1-10500 <$100
3x50-100 1-1180 <$300/$350
1902 Plain Back
3x10-20 10501-44622 <$100
3x50-100 1181-1722 <$300/$350
1929 Small Size
10 Type 1 1-3415 <$125
20 Type 1 1-667 <$125
50 Type 1 1-314 <$175
100 Type 1 1-85 <$250
Total Issue $5,183,020
Out at close $300,000
Large out at close $60,140
****
1599 McCracken
FNB OF PADUCAH
{{ 6 L 3 S }}
Chartered 1865
Liquidated 3/6/31
Original Series <$VALUE
4x5 1-3300 <$600
3x10-20 1-6720 <$750/$1250
Series 1875
3x10-20 1-2730 <$750/$1250
Brown Back
3x10-20 1-4444 <$450
1902 Red Seal
50-100 1-460 <$2500
1902 Date Back
50-100 1-1334 <$300/$350
3x50-100 1-1678 <$300/$350
1902 Plain Back
3x50-100 1679-2247 <$300/$350
1929 Small Size
10 Type 1 1-1561 <$200
20 Type 1 1-447 <$225
Total Issue $1,738,850
Out at close $150,000
Large out at close $39,630
****

12961 McCracken
PEOPLES NB OF PADUCAH
{{ 3 L 15 S }}
Chartered 7/26
1902 Plain Back <$VALUE
3x10-20 1-6513 <$275
1929 Small Size
10 Type 1 1-3088 <$100
20 Type 1 1-814 <$100
10 Type 2 1-3190 <$100
20 Type 2 1-870 <$100
Total Issue $657,910
Out in 1935 $100,000
Large out 1935 $2,390

7164 Johnson
CITIZENS NB OF PAINTSVILLE
{{ 1 L }}
Chartered 3/10/04
Liquidated 8/2/05
1902 Red Seal <$VALUE
4x5 1-235 <$1500
3x10-20 1-171 <$1500
Total Issue $13,250
Out in 1910 $885

13763 Johnson
FNB OF PAINTSVILLE
{{ 13 S }}
Chartered 9/33
1929 Small Size <$VALUE
5 Type 2 1-12932 <$175
10 Type 2 1-6552 <$175
20 Type 2 1-2064 <$175
Total Issue $171,660
Out in 1935 $89,695

6100 Johnson
PAINTSVILLE NB, PAINTSVILLE
{{ 15 L 23 S }}
Chartered 1/20/02
Liquidated 12/4/33
1902 Red Seal <$VALUE
4x5 1-3945 <$450
3x10-20 1-3162 <$450
1902 Date Back
4x5 1-10500 <$110
3x10-20 1-8200 <$125
1902 Plain Back (dated 1901)
4x5 10501-24450 <$110
3x10-20 8201-16404 <$125
1902 Plain Back (dated 1921)
4x5 1-23650 <$110
3x10-20 1-17128 <$125
1929 Small Size
5 Type 1 1-5638 <$80
10 Type 1 1-4742 <$75
20 Type 1 1-1492 <$80
10 Type 2 1-78 <$125
20 Type 2 1-150 <$125
Total Issue $3,512,080
Out at close $200,000
Large out at close $12,460

13023 Johnson
SECOND NB OF PAINTSVILLE
{{ 5 S }}
Chartered 1/3/27
1929 Small Size <$VALUE
5 Type 2 1-9060 <$200
10 Type 2 1-4930 <$200
20 Type 2 1-1474 <$200
Total Issue $124,080
Out in 1935 $75,000

6323 Bourbon
FNB OF PARIS
{{ 14 L 12 S }}
Chartered 6/26/02
Liquidated 5/9/34
1902 Red Seal <$VALUE
4x5 1-4575 <$500
3x10-20 1-3170 <$500
1902 Date Back
4x5 1-9000 <$175
3x10-20 1-6200 <$175
1902 Plain Back
4x5 9001-29005 <$175
3x10-20 6201-16620 <$175
1929 Small Size
5 Type 1 1-4110 <$100
10 Type 1 1-2182 <$100
20 Type 1 1-622 <$110
5 Type 2 1-688 <$125
10 Type 2 1-520 <$125
20 Type 2 1-219 <$135
Total Issue $2,002,980
Out at close $99,995
Large out 1935 $5,650
Ch 14076 assumed circulation

14076 Bourbon
NB & TC OF PARIS
{{ UNREPORTED }}
Chartered 3/34
1929 Small Size <$VALUE
5 Type 2 1-64 <$850
10 Type 2 1-50 <$850
20 Type 2 1-145 <$850
Total Issue $3,720
Out in 1935 $50,000
Outstanding includes Ch 6323

11944 Pike
DAY & NIGHT NB OF PIKEVILLE
{{ 7 L 2 S }}
Organized 2/28/21
Liquidated 4/7/31
1902 Plain Back <$VALUE
4x5 1-7701 <$2500
3x10-20 1-5135 <$2500
1929 Small Size
5 Type 1 1-990 <$1500
10 Type 1 1-441 <$1500
20 Type 1 1-141 <$1500
Total Issue $483,850
Out at close $50,000
Large out at close $4,860
Ch 7030 assumed circulation

6622 Pike
FNB OF PIKEVILLE
{{ 11 L 26 S }}
Chartered 2/03
1902 Red Seal <$VALUE
3x10-20 1-762 <$750
1902 Date Back
3x10-20 1-4300 <$300
1902 Plain Back
3x10-20 4301-37067 <$300
1929 Small Size
10 Type 1 1-6370 <$65
20 Type 1 1-1758 <$70
10 Type 2 1-8463 <$75
20 Type 2 1-2983 <$85
Total Issue $2,628,900
Out in 1935 $200,000
Large out 1935 $7,760

7030 Pike
PIKEVILLE NB, PIKEVILLE
{{ U + 9 L 3U + 12 S }}
Chartered 11/03
1902 Red Seal <$VALUE
4x5 1-1385 <$750
3x10-20 1-1102 <$750
1902 Date Back
4x5 1-4100 <$375
3x10-20 1-2960 <$375
1902 Plain Back
4x5 4101-13669 <$375
3x10-20 2961-9098 <$375
1929 Small Size
5 Type 1 1-3318 <$110
10 Type 1 1-1790 <$110
20 Type 1 1-440 <$115
5 Type 2 1-6736 <$125
10 Type 2 1-3939 <$125
20 Type 2 1-1152 <$130
Total Issue $1,166,930
Out in 1935 $100,000
Large out 1935 $4,360
Outstanding includes Ch 11944

7215 Bell
BELL NB OF PINEVILLE
{{ 11 L 4 S }}
Organized 3/28/04
Receivership 1/28/32
1902 Red Seal <$VALUE
3x10-20 1-360 <$600
1902 Date Back
3x10-20 1-960* <$200
1902 Plain Back
3x10-20 1081-19386* <$200
* 961-1080 not marked
1929 Small Size
10 Type 1 1-2124 <$300
20 Type 1 1-632 <$300
Total Issue $1,190,580
Out at close $95,980
Large out at close $9,350

4598 Bell
FNB OF PINEVILLE
{{ UNREPORTED }}
Chartered 7/17/91
Liquidated 12/30/98
Brown Back <$VALUE
3x10-20 1-558 <$2000
Total Issue $27,900
Out in 1910 $440

7254 Floyd
FNB OF PRESTONBURG
{{ 2 L 2 S }}
Chartered 5/04
1902 Red Seal <$VALUE
3x10-20 1-383 <$1500
1902 Date Back
3x10-20 1-560 <$750
1902 Plain Back
3x10-20 561-1555 <$750
1929 Small Size
10 Type 1 1-265 <$500
20 Type 1 1-70 <$500
Total Issue $121,200
Out in 1935 $6,500
Large out 1935 $370

5257 Caldwell
FARMERS NB OF PRINCETON
{{ 9 L 12 S }}
Chartered 2/20/00
Brown Back <$VALUE
3x10-20 1-3650 <$500
1882 Date Back
3x10-20 1-3300* <$500
1882 Value Back
3x10-20 3501-5034* <$500
*3301-3500 not marked
1902 Plain Back
3x10-20 1-8391 <$275
1929 Small Size
10 Type 1 1-2132 <$100
20 Type 1 1-622 <$100
5 Type 2 1-324 <$125
10 Type 2 1-1275 <$125
20 Type 2 1-307 <$125
Total Issue $1,076,820
Out in 1935 $30,000
Large out 1935 $3,685

3064 Caldwell
FNB OF PRINCETON
{{ 10 L 15 S }}
Chartered 1883
Brown Back <$VALUE
3x10-20 1-1522 <$500
1902 Red Seal
3x10-20 1-4700 <$500
1902 Date Back
3x10-20 1-11800 <$200
1902 Plain Back
3x10-20 11801-43381 <$200
1929 Small Size
10 Type 1 1-3826 <$100
20 Type 1 1-1038 <$100
10 Type 2 1-1969 <$110
20 Type 2 1-214 <$110
Total Issue $2,858,240
Out in 1935 $100,000
Large out 1935 $8,020

9708 Webster
UNION NB OF PROVIDENCE
{{ 0 L U + 3 S }}
Organized 3/24/10
1902 Date Back <$VALUE
3x10-20 1-2080 <$1250
1902 Plain Back
3x10-20 2081-6131 <$1250
1929 Small Size
10 Type 1 1-838 <$350
20 Type 1 1-158 <$350
10 Type 2 1-785 <$350
20 Type 2 1-185 <$350
Total Issue $387,340
Out in 1935 $25,000
Large out 1935 $990

7653 Madison
CITIZENS NB OF RICHMOND
{{ 5 L 4 S }}
Organized 2/8/05
Receivership 6/26/33
1902 Red Seal <$VALUE
3x10-20 1-2200 <$650
1902 Date Back
3x10-20 1-5400 <$300
1902 Plain Back
3x10-20 5401-17644 <$300
1929 Small Size
10 Type 1 1-1801 <$250
20 Type 1 1-494 <$250
Total Issue $1,159,540
Out at close $67,380
Large out at close $5,980

1309 Madison
FARMERS NB OF RICHMOND
{{ 5 L }}
Chartered 6/20/65
Liquidated 3/20/05
Original Series <$VALUE
3x1-2 1-1900 <$600/$1250
4x5 1-2250 <$600
3x10-20 1-2540 <$850/$1250
50-100 1-390 <$5000
Series 1875
3x1-2 1-580 <$600/$1250
4x5 1-4350 <$600
3x10-20 1-3000 <$750/$1000
Brown Back
4x5 1-4945 <$450
3x10-20 1-5624 <$450
Total Issue $860,000
Out in 1910 $13,666

1728 Madison
FNB OF RICHMOND
{{ 3 L }}
Chartered 10/29/70
Liquidated 10/3/90
Original Series <$VALUE
3x1-2 1-3000 <$600/$1250
4x5 1-2000 <$600
3x10-20 1-6300 <$850/$1250
Series 1875
4x5 1-722 <$600
3x10-20 1-7629 <$750/$1000
Total Issue $765,890
Out in 1910 $4,058

1790 Madison
MADISON NB OF RICHMOND
Chartered 2/15/71
2nd title: Madison NB & TC 9/6/22
3rd title: Madison-Southern NB & TC 6/11/30
FIRST TITLE {{ 5 L }}
Original Series <$VALUE
3x1-2 1-1400 <$500/$1000
4x5 1-2100 <$500
3x10-20 1-2760 <$850/$1250
50-100 1-620 <$5000
Series 1875
3x10-20 1-5415 <$750/$1000
50-100 1-599 <$5000
Brown Back
3x10-20 1-8738 <$350
50-100 1-208 <$1250/$1500
1882 Date Back
3x10-20 1-982 <$350
50-100 1-73 <$1250/$1500
1902 Date Back
4x5 1-4950 <$125
3x10-20 1-3500 <$150
1902 Plain Back
4x5 4951-12300 <$125
3x10-20 3501-8120 <$150
SECOND TITLE {{ 5 L 3 S }}
1902 Plain Back
4x5 1-8109 <$125
3x10-20 1-6091 <$150
1929 Small Size
5 Type 1 1-1544 <$125
10 Type 1 1-768 <$125
20 Type 1 1-260 <$140
THIRD TITLE {{ 18 S }}
1929 Small Size
5 Type 1 1-4756 <$60
10 Type 1 1-2572 <$60
20 Type 1 1-676 <$65
5 Type 2 1-10036 <$65
10 Type 2 1-5833 <$65
20 Type 2 1-1468 <$75
Total Issue $2,927,070
Out in 1935 $200,000
Large out 1935 $15,860
Outstanding includes Ch 9832

4430 Madison
RICHMOND NB, RICHMOND
{{ 1 L }}
Chartered 1890
Liquidated 8/26/10
Brown Back <$VALUE
3x10-20 1-8210 <$750
1882 Date Back
3x10-20 1-926 <$750
Total Issue $456,800
Out in 1910 $70,200

2374 Madison
SECOND NB OF RICHMOND
{{ 1 L }}
Chartered 12/7/77
Liquidated 11/4/97
Series 1875 <$VALUE
3x10-20 1-7275<$1250/$1500
Total Issue $363,750
Out in 1910 $2,790

9832 Madison
SOUTHERN NB OF RICHMOND
{{ 12 L 2 S }}
Chartered 8/10
Closed 6/11/30
1902 Date Back <$VALUE
3x10-20 1-7300 <$175
1902 Plain Back
3x10-20 7301-23981 <$175
1929 Small Size
10 Type 1 1-939 <$300
20 Type 1 1-224 <$300
Total Issue $1,282,270
Out at close $100,000
Large out at close $23,610

8792 Greenup
FNB OF RUSSELL
{{ 1 L 2 S }}
Chartered 7/07
Liquidated 2/27/32
1902 Red Seal <$VALUE
3x10-20 1-300 <$2000
1902 Date Back
3x10-20 1-1150 <$1250
1902 Plain Back
3x10-20 1151-3239 <$1250
1929 Small Size
10 Type 1 1-389* <$500
20 Type 1 1-123** <$500
* 256-316 not issued
** 35-104 not issued
Total Issue $202,990
Out at close $12,500
Large out at close $1,330

11348 Russell
FNB OF RUSSELL SPRINGS
{{ 1 L 3 S }}
Chartered 5/19
1902 Plain Back <$VALUE
3x10-20 1-3207 <$1250
1929 Small Size
10 Type 1 1-714 <$400
20 Type 1 1-180 <$400
10 Type 2 1-660 <$400
20 Type 2 1-140 <$400
Total Issue $234,190
Out in 1935 $25,000
Large out 1935 $1,450

6546 Logan
CITIZENS NB OF RUSSELLVILLE
{{ 3 L 4 S }}
Chartered 12/19/02
1902 Red Seal <$VALUE
3x10-20 1-1290 <$1000
1902 Date Back
3x10-20 1-1610 <$500
1902 Plain Back
3x10-20 1611-5051 <$500
1929 Small Size
10 Type 1 1-714 <$300
20 Type 1 1-180 <$300
10 Type 2 1-988 <$300
20 Type 2 1-290 <$300
Total Issue $397,170
Out in 1935 $25,000
Large out 1935 $1,500

2169 Logan
LOGAN COUNTY NB OF RUSSELLVILLE
{{ UNREPORTED }}
Chartered 8/17/74
Liquidated 1/9/83
Original Series <$VALUE
4x5 1-2250 <$2000
Series 1875
4x5 1-2820 <$2000
Total Issue $101,400
Out in 1910 $570

9842 Logan
N DEPOSIT B OF RUSSELLVILLE
{{ UNREPORTED }}
Chartered 9/10
Liquidated 1/15/16
1902 Date Back <$VALUE
3x10-20 1-750 <$1500
Total Issue $37,500
Out in 1916 $7,830

8905 Magoffin
SALYERSVILLE NB, SALYERSVILLE
{{ 3 L 3 S }}
Chartered 10/07
1902 Red Seal <$VALUE
4x10 1-850 <$1250
1902 Date Back
4x10 1-2250 <$650
1902 Plain Back
4x10 2251-7830 <$650
1929 Small Size
10 Type 1 1-1202 <$400
10 Type 2 1-1890 <$400
Total Issue $438,220
Out in 1935 $25,000
Large out 1935 $1,650

9356 Allen
ALLEN COUNTY NB OF SCOTTSVILLE
{{ UNREPORTED }}
Chartered 3/09
Liquidated 5/12/21
1902 Date Back <$VALUE
3x10-20 1-720 <$1500
1902 Plain Back
3x10-20 721-722 <$1500
Total Issue $36,100
Out at close $5,950

8599 Allen
FNB OF SCOTTSVILLE
{{ 2 L }}
Chartered 3/07
Liquidated 11/8/23
1902 Red Seal <$VALUE
3x10-20 1-190 <$1250
1902 Date Back
3x10-20 1-580 <$750
1902 Plain Back
3x10-20 581-3936 <$750
Total Issue $206,300
Out at close $28,940

7242 Webster
FNB OF SEBREE
{{ 4 L 3 S }}
Chartered 5/04
Liquidated 3/20/33
1902 Red Seal <$VALUE
3x10-20 1-2160 <$1000
1902 Date Back
3x10-20 1-3000 <$450
1902 Plain Back
3x10-20 3001-8914 <$450
1929 Small Size
10 Type 1 1-870 <$350
20 Type 1 1-226 <$350
Total Issue $633,020
Out at close $40,000
Large out at close $3,380

11544 Pulaski
CITIZENS NB OF SOMERSET
{{ 3 L 14 S }}
Chartered 12/19
1902 Plain Back <$VALUE
3x10-20 1-7728 <$450
1929 Small Size
10 Type 1 1-2256 <$100
20 Type 1 1-596 <$100
10 Type 2 1-3851 <$110
20 Type 2 1-793 <$110
Total Issue $647,650
Out in 1935 $100,000
Large out 1935 $1,660

<$VALUEs are for notes in FINE condition. Value changes by approximately 25% for a change of one full grade.

****
5881 Pulaski
FARMERS NB OF SOMERSET
{{ 4 L 12 S }}
Chartered 6/26/01
Brown Back <$VALUE
3x10-20 1-3500 <$600
1882 Date Back
3x10-20 1-3180* <$600
1882 Value Back
3x10-20 3381-7672* <$600
*3181-3380 not marked
1902 Plain Back
3x10-20 1-11952 <$350
1929 Small Size
10 Type 1 1-2852 <$100
20 Type 1 1-748 <$100
10 Type 2 1-4095 <$110
20 Type 2 1-1190 <$110
Total Issue $1,481,830
Out in 1935 $100,000
Large out 1935 $5,310
****
3832 Pulaski
FNB OF SOMERSET
{{ 5 L 17 S }}
Chartered 12/30/87
Brown Back <$VALUE
50-100 1-1754 <$2000
1902 Red Seal
3x10-20 1-2000 <$750
1902 Date Back
3x10-20 1-5500 <$325
1902 Plain Back
3x10-20 5501-21039 <$325
1929 Small Size
10 Type 1 1-2818 <$75
20 Type 1 1-806 <$85
10 Type 2 1-3429 <$100
20 Type 2 1-1185 <$100
Total Issue $1,738,840
Out in 1935 $100,000
Large out 1935 $5,100
****
1748 Pulaski
NB OF SOMERSET
{{ 1 L }}
Chartered 12/8/70
Liquidated 12/31/87
Original Series <$VALUE
4x5 1-1750 <$1000
3x10-20 1-2800<$1250/$1500
Series 1875
3x10-20 1-1849<$1250/$1500
Total Issue $267,450
Out in 1910 $1,545
****
1767 Washington
FNB OF SPRINGFIELD
{{ 3 L 5 S }}
Chartered 1/14/71
Original Series <$VALUE
3x1-2 1-4500 <$600/$1250
4x5 1-1500 <$750
3x10-20 1-2850 <$850/$1250
Series 1875
3x1-2 1-520 <$600/$1250
4x5 1-2595 <$750
3x10-20 1-3116 <$850/$1250
Brown Back
3x10-20 1-5040 <$500
1882 Date Back
3x10-20 1-559 <$500
1902 Date Back
3x10-20 1-2740* <$350
1902 Plain Back
3x10-20 3041-10487* <$350
*2741-3040 not marked
1929 Small Size
10 Type 1 1-1426 <$175
20 Type 1 1-388 <$175
10 Type 2 1-1856 <$200
20 Type 2 1-448 <$200
Total Issue $1,369,240
Out in 1935 $50,000
Large out 1935 $3,790
****
1705 Lincoln
FARMERS NB OF STANFORD
{{ 3 L }}
Chartered 9/14/70
Liquidated 12/31/88
Original Series <$VALUE
3x1-2 1-4500 <$600/$1250
4x5 1-6875 <$600
3x10-20 1-2100 <$850/$1250
Series 1875
3x1-2 1-1200 <$600/$1250
4x5 1-4510 <$600
3x10-20 1-4822 <$850/$1250
Total Issue $602,300
Out in 1910 $2,620
****
2788 Lincoln
FNB OF STANFORD
{{ 4 L 6 S }}
Organized 8/26/82
Liquidated 5/1/34
Brown Back <$VALUE
3x10-20 1-7990 <$500
1902 Red Seal
3x10-20 1-2500 <$650
1902 Date Back
3x10-20 1-3100* <$350
1902 Plain Back
3x10-20 3301-11071* <$350
*3101-3300 not marked
1929 Small Size
10 Type 1 1-1443 <$200
20 Type 1 1-360 <$200
Total Issue $1,207,830
Out at close $50,000
Large out at close $4,400
Ch 14039 assumed circulation
****
14039 Lincoln
FNB OF STANFORD
{{ 1 S }}
Chartered 3/34
1929 Small Size <$VALUE
10 Type 2 1-331 <$600
20 Type 2 1-50 <$600
Total Issue $4,310
Out in 1935 $25,000
Outstanding includes Ch 2788
****
5132 Lincoln
LINCOLN COUNTY NB OF STANFORD
{{ 8 L 10 S }}
Organized 7/30/98
Brown Back <$VALUE
4x5 1-8050 <$500
3x10-20 1-2740 <$500
1882 Date Back
4x5 1-6850 <$500
3x10-20 1-5160 <$500
1882 Value Back
4x5 6851-8697 <$500
3x10-20 5161-6344 <$500
1902 Plain Back
4x5 1-9768 <$250
3x10-20 1-6176 <$250
1929 Small Size
5 Type 1 1-1958 <$150
10 Type 1 1-1008 <$150
20 Type 1 1-296 <$165
5 Type 2 1-2300 <$185
10 Type 2 1-1571 <$185
20 Type 2 1-396 <$200
Total Issue $1,483,170
Out in 1935 $50,000
Large out 1935 $4,360
****
3954 Lincoln
LINCOLN NB OF STANFORD
{{ UNREPORTED }}
Chartered 12/31/88
Liquidated 9/8/90
Brown Back <$VALUE
4x5 1-2549 <$1500
Total Issue $50,980
Out in 1910 $315
****
1204 Lincoln
NB OF STANFORD
{{ 3 L }}
Chartered 1865
Liquidated 10/3/82
Original Series <$VALUE
3x1-2 1-1300 <$600/$1500
4x5 1-2375 <$750
3x10-20 1-2785<$1000/$1500
50-100 1-200 <$5000
Series 1875
3x1-2 1-2000 <$600/$1500
4x5 1-4760 <$750
3x10-20 1-1600<$1000/$1500
Total Issue $408,450
Out in 1910 $2,118
****
11890 Pike
FNB OF STONE
{{ 2 L 0 S }}
Organized 12/3/20
Receivership 3/17/31
1902 Plain Back <$VALUE
4x5 1-5609 <$1000
1929 Small Size
5 Type 1 1-776 <$850
Total Issue $135,460
Out at close $22,180
Large out at close $9,040
****
6244 Union
FNB OF STURGIS
{{ UNREPORTED }}
Chartered 5/7/02
Liquidated 8/10/16
1902 Red Seal <$VALUE
4x5 1-865 <$2000
3x10-20 1-794 <$2000
1902 Date Back
4x5 1-1650 <$1500
3x10-20 1-991 <$1500
Total Issue $139,550
Out in 1916 $15,350
****
8622 Union
FNB OF UNIONTOWN
{{ 2 L }}
Chartered 4/07
Liquidated 5/10/11
1902 Red Seal <$VALUE
3x10-20 1-870 <$1500
1902 Date Back
3x10-20 1-542 <$1000
Total Issue $70,600
Out in 1911 $16,400
****
1835 Woodford
COMMERCIAL NB OF VERSAILLES
{{ UNREPORTED }}
Chartered 6/15/71
Liquidated 8/26/76
Original Series <$VALUE
3x1-2 1-1000 <$1500/$2000
4x5 1-1500 <$1500
3x10-20 1-3409<$1750/$2500
Total Issue $205,450
Out in 1910 $1,062
****
12202 Harlan
WALLINS NB OF WALLINS CREEK
{{ 1 L 1 S }}
Chartered 5/22
Liquidated 2/28/30
1902 Plain Back <$VALUE
4x5 1-4444 <$1500
1929 Small Size
5 Type 1 1-236 <$1000
Total Issue $95,960
Out at close $8,260
Large out at close $2,220
****
7916 Morgan
FNB OF WEST LIBERTY
{{ UNREPORTED }}
Chartered 9/05
Liquidated 4/12/10
1902 Red Seal <$VALUE
3x10-20 1-300 <$2000
1902 Date Back
3x10-20 1-366 <$1500
Total Issue $33,300
Out in 1910 $14,850
****
10433 Letcher
FNB OF WHITESBURG
{{ 3 L 6 S }}
Organized 7/14/13
Receivership 6/17/32
1902 Date Back <$VALUE
4x5 1-850 <$450
3x10-20 1-680 <$450
1902 Plain Back
4x5 851-9930 <$450
3x10-20 681-6696 <$450
1929 Small Size
5 Type 1 1-1619 <$250
10 Type 1 1-790 <$250
20 Type 1 1-221 <$250
Total Issue $655,890
Out at close $50,000
Large out at close $4,260
****
5443 Ballard
FNB OF WICKLIFFE
{{ 1 L }}
Chartered 6/21/00
Liquidated 12/31/17
Brown Back <$VALUE
3x10-20 1-1000 <$1250
1882 Date Back
3x10-20 1-2060* <$1250
1882 Value Back
3x10-20 2221-2420* <$1250
*2061-2220 not marked
Total Issue $171,000
Out at close $25,000
****
7174 Whitley
FNB OF WILLIAMSBURG
{{ 2 L 4 S }}
Chartered 3/04
1902 Red Seal <$VALUE
3x10-20 1-1300 <$1250
1902 Date Back
3x10-20 1-1620 <$600
1902 Plain Back
3x10-20 1621-5790 <$600
1929 Small Size
10 Type 1 1-748 <$300
20 Type 1 1-190 <$300
10 Type 2 1-672 <$300
20 Type 2 1-158 <$300
Total Issue $432,060
Out in 1935 $25,000
Large out 1935 $1,210
****
9880 Jessamine
FNB OF WILMORE
{{ 4 L U + 1 S }}
Chartered 10/10
Liquidated 7/30/30
1902 Date Back <$VALUE
4x5 1-1550 <$450
3x10-20 1-1220 <$450
1902 Plain Back
4x5 1551-6450 <$450
3x10-20 1221-4096 <$450
1929 Small Size
5 Type 1 1-279 <$500
10 Type 1 1-170 <$500
20 Type 1 1-3 <$550
Total Issue $352,730
Out at close $19,050
Large out at close $3,490
****
2148 Clark
CITIZENS NB OF WINCHESTER
{{ 10 L 4 S }}
Chartered 5/29/74
Liquidated 9/30/31
Original Series <$VALUE
3x1-2 1-1302 <$450/$1000
4x5 1-1550 <$500
4x20 1-1025 <$1250
50-100 1-620 <$5000
Series 1875
4x5 1-8233 <$500
4x20 1-868 <$1000
50-100 1-282 <$5000
Brown Back
4x5 1-4650 <$375
3x10-20 1-3030 <$375
1882 Date Back
4x5 1-5770 <$375
3x10-20 1-4126 <$375
1902 Date Back
4x5 1-1650 <$150
3x10-20 1-2340 <$150
1902 Plain Back
4x5 1651-19236 <$150
3x10-20 1341-12765 <$150
1929 Small Size
5 Type 1 1-2522 <$175
10 Type 1 1-1223 <$175
20 Type 1 1-332 <$175
Total Issue $2,266,960
Out at close $100,000
Large out at close $12,130
****
995 Clark
CLARK COUNTY NB OF WINCHESTER
{{ 13 L 22 S }}
Chartered 4/8/65
Original Series <$VALUE
3x1-2 1-8600* <$450/$1000
4x5 1-5100 <$500
3x10-20 1-2750 <$850/$1250
*901-5000 not issued
Series 1875
3x10-20 1-3677 <$750/$1000
Brown Back
3x10-20 1-15374 <$375
1902 Red Seal
3x10-20 1-6500 <$450
1902 Date Back
3x10-20 1-11900 <$150
1902 Plain Back
3x10-20 11901-44576 <$150
1929 Small Size
10 Type 1 1-6296 <$50
20 Type 1 1-1488 <$60
10 Type 2 1-6143 <$60
20 Type 2 1-1754 <$70
Total Issue $4,421,180
Out in 1935 $200,000
Large out 1935 $13,700
****
3290 Clark
WINCHESTER NB OF WINCHESTER
{{ UNREPORTED }}
Chartered 1/16/85
Liquidated 4/29/90
Brown Back <$VALUE
50-100 1-531 <$2500
Total Issue $79,650
Out in 1910 $1,050
****

CONDITION affects Value. The Values shown are for notes in FINE condition.

LOUISIANA

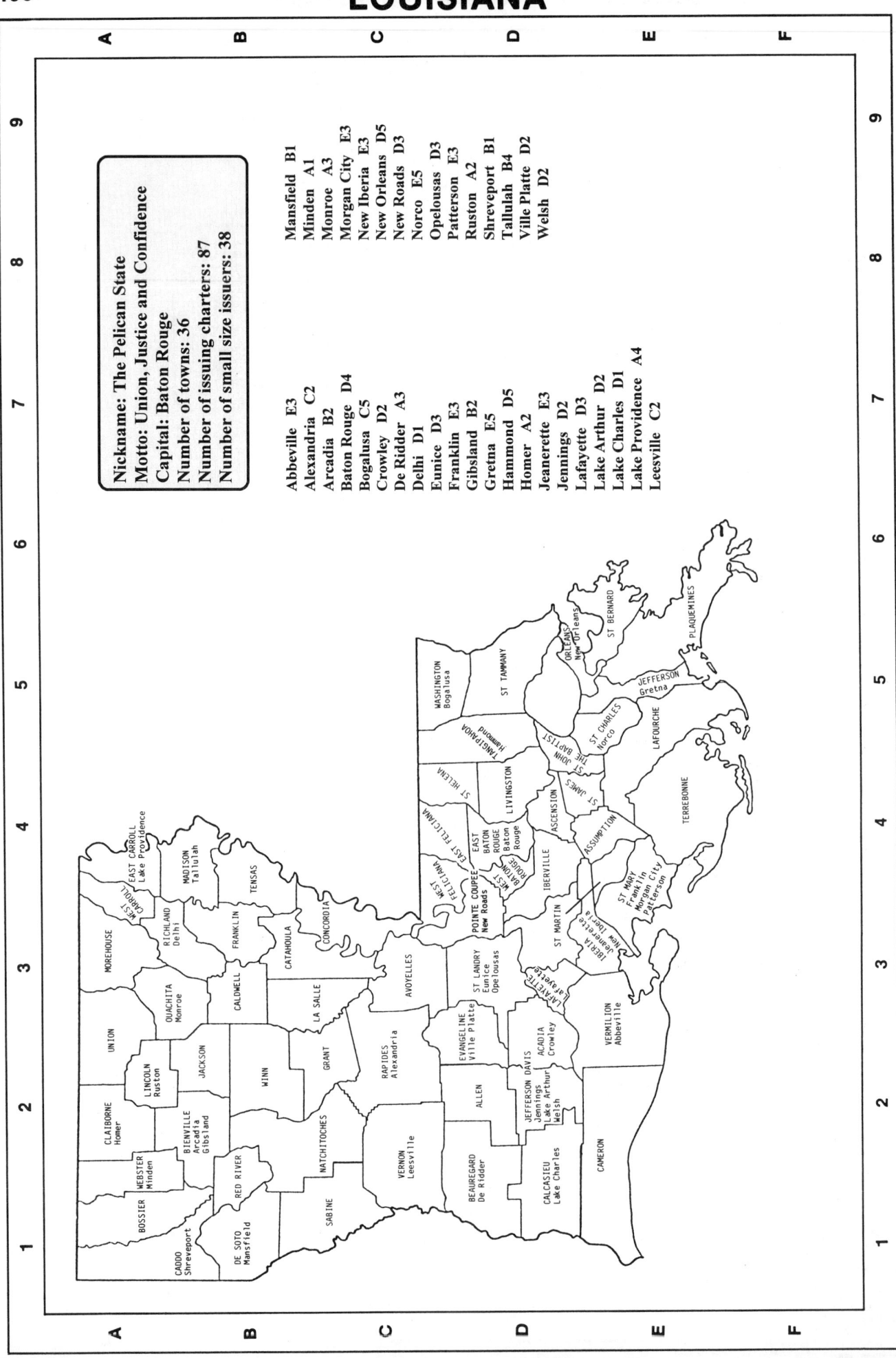

Nickname: The Pelican State
Motto: Union, Justice and Confidence
Capital: Baton Rouge
Number of towns: 36
Number of issuing charters: 87
Number of small size issuers: 38

Abbeville E3
Alexandria C2
Arcadia B2
Baton Rouge D4
Bogalusa C5
Crowley D2
De Ridder A3
Delhi D1
Eunice D3
Franklin E3
Gibsland B2
Gretna E5
Hammond D5
Homer A2
Jeanerette E3
Jennings D2
Lafayette D3
Lake Arthur D2
Lake Charles D1
Lake Providence A4
Leesville C2
Mansfield B1
Minden A1
Monroe A3
Morgan City E3
New Iberia E3
New Orleans D5
New Roads D3
Norco E5
Opelousas D3
Patterson E3
Ruston A2
Shreveport B1
Tallulah B4
Ville Platte D2
Welsh D2

****
5807 Vermilion
FNB OF ABBEVILLE
{{ 4 L 8 S }}
Chartered 5/11/01
Brown Back <$VALUE
3x10-20 1-1600 <$700
1882 Date Back
3x10-20 1-2290 <$600
1882 Value Back
3x10-20 2291-3292 <$600
1902 Plain Back
3x10-20 1-3310 <$400
1929 Small Size
10 Type 1 1-766 <$175
20 Type 1 1-228 <$175
10 Type 2 1-989 <$200
20 Type 2 1-311 <$200
Total Issue $499,530
Out in 1935 $32,730
Large out 1935 $2,250
****
5021 Rapides
FNB OF ALEXANDRIA
{{ 3 L }}
Chartered 1895
Liquidated 3/1/21
Brown Back <$VALUE
3x10-20 1-6250 <$750
1882 Date Back
3x10-20 1-6907 <$700
1902 Plain Back
3x10-20 1-4218 <$500
Total Issue $868,750
Out at close $71,600
****
7476 Bienville
FNB OF ARCADIA
{{ 4 L 13 S }}
Chartered 11/04
Liquidated 8/6/35
1902 Red Seal <$VALUE
3x10-20 1-2300 <$1000
1902 Date Back
3x10-20 1-4500 <$450
1902 Plain Back
3x10-20 4501-12962 <$450
1929 Small Size
10 Type 1 1-1532 <$110
20 Type 1 1-464 <$110
10 Type 2 1-1986 <$135
20 Type 2 1-651 <$150
Total Issue $943,580
Out at close $50,000
Large out at close $3,590
****
13737 East Baton Rouge
CITY NB OF BATON ROUGE
{{ 14 S }}
Chartered 7/33
1929 Small Size <$VALUE
5 Type 2 1-42288 <$85
10 Type 2 1-19157 <$85
20 Type 2 1-5787 <$85
Total Issue $518,750
Out in 1935 $246,150
****
2633 East Baton Rouge
FNB OF BATON ROUGE
{{ 6 L }}
Chartered 2/82
Liquidated 10/1/10
Series 1875 <$VALUE
3x10-20 1-3674<$2500/$3000
Brown Back
4x5 1-2000 <$750
3x10-20 1-4550 <$750
1882 Date Back
4x5 1-1790 <$750
3x10-20 1-817 <$750
Total Issue $527,850
Out at close $85,000
****
9834 East Baton Rouge
LOUISIANA NB OF
BATON ROUGE
{{ 16 L 31 S }}
Chartered 8/10
1902 Date Back <$VALUE
3x10-20 1-13600 <$175
1902 Plain Back
3x10-20 13601-47118 <$175
3x50-100 1-366 <$650/$750
1929 Small Size
10 Type 1 1-8882 <$65
20 Type 1 1-2258 <$70
5 Type 2 1-12300 <$65
10 Type 2 1-5426 <$70
20 Type 2 1-2450 <$75
Total Issue $3,416,040
Out in 1935 $156,500
Large out 1935 $9,870
****
8959 Washington
FNB OF BOGALUSA
{{ UNREPORTED }}
Chartered 12/5/07
Liquidated 4/5/09
1902 Red Seal <$VALUE
4x5 1-129 <$2500
4x10 1-106 <$2500
Total Issue $6,820
Out in 1910 $1,355
****
5520 Acadia
FNB OF CROWLEY
{{ 6 L }}
Chartered 7/28/00
Liquidated 2/10/15
Brown Back <$VALUE
3x10-20 1-5800 <$600
1882 Date Back
3x10-20 1-6626 <$500
Total Issue $621,300
Out at close $75,500
****
12523 Acadia
FNB OF CROWLEY
{{ 16 L 14 S }}
Chartered 4/24
1902 Plain Back <$VALUE
3x10-20 1-5671 <$225
1929 Small Size
10 Type 1 1-2510 <$110
20 Type 1 1-680 <$110
10 Type 2 1-2238 <$135
20 Type 2 1-948 <$135
Total Issue $557,090
Out in 1935 $98,550
Large out 1935 $8,260
Outstanding includes Ch 10700
****
10700 Acadia
FNB OF ACADIA PARISH AT
CROWLEY
{{ 5 L }}
Chartered 2/15
Liquidated 4/5/24
1902 Plain Back <$VALUE
3x10-20 1-13202 <$400
Total Issue $660,100
Out at close $148,300
Ch 12523 assumed circulation
****
14168 Beauregard
FNB IN DE RIDDER
{{ U + 2 S }}
Chartered 5/34
1929 Small Size <$VALUE
5 Type 2 1-5680 <$500
Total Issue $28,400
Out in 1935 $20,200
****
9237 Beauregard
FNB OF DE RIDDER
{{ 6 L 14 S }}
Organized 7/18/08
Liquidated 8/26/35
1902 Date Back <$VALUE
3x10-20 1-1820 <$350
1902 Plain Back
3x10-20 1821-12794 <$350
1929 Small Size
10 Type 1 1-2992 <$100
20 Type 1 1-720 <$110
10 Type 2 1-2043 <$135
20 Type 2 1-392 <$150
Total Issue $933,890
Out at close $57,810
Large out at close $3,360
****
14225 Richland
FNB OF DELHI
{{ UNREPORTED }}
Chartered 7/34
1929 Small Size <$VALUE
10 Type 2 1-1930 <$750
20 Type 2 1-330 <$750
Total Issue $25,900
Out in 1935 $25,000
****
10912 Richland
MACON RIDGE NB OF DELHI
{{ 2 L 3 S }}
Organized 9/11/16
Receivership 2/21/34
1902 Plain Back <$VALUE
4x5 1-7524 <$850
1929 Small Size
5 Type 1 1-2756 <$400
5 Type 2 1-2218 <$450
Total Issue $244,250
Out at close $25,000
Large out at close $560
****
8677 St Landry
FNB OF EUNICE
{{ 1 L }}
Chartered 5/07
Liquidated 2/27/19
1902 Red Seal <$VALUE
3x10-20 1-700 <$2000
1902 Date Back
3x10-20 1-1871 <$1500
Total Issue $128,550
Out at close $11,070
****
4555 St Mary
FNB OF FRANKLIN
{{ 6 L }}
Chartered 4/18/91
Liquidated 12/8/06
Brown Back <$VALUE
4x5 1-2025 <$600
50-100 1-106 <$2500
Total Issue $56,400
Out in 1910 $3,305
****
10049 Bienville
FNB OF GIBSLAND
{{ UNREPORTED }}
Chartered 7/11
Liquidated 3/3/28
1902 Date Back <$VALUE
3x10-20 1-620 <$1500
1902 Plain Back
3x10-20 621-1329 <$1500
Total Issue $66,450
Out at close $5,300
****
13732 Jefferson
FNB OF JEFFERSON PARISH,
GRETNA
{{ 2U + 7 S }}
Chartered 7/33
1929 Small Size <$VALUE
5 Type 2 1-17916 <$200
10 Type 2 1-6912 <$200
Total Issue $158,700
Out in 1935 $74,260
****
11977 Tangipahoa
CITIZENS NB OF HAMMOND
{{ 7 L 15 S }}
Organized 5/28/21
Liquidated 5/18/34
1902 Plain Back <$VALUE
4x5 1-13147 <$200
3x10-20 1-8808 <$200
1929 Small Size
5 Type 1 1-3704 <$100
10 Type 1 1-2010 <$100
20 Type 1 1-492 <$110
5 Type 2 1-336 <$125
10 Type 2 1-220 <$125
20 Type 2 1-90 <$125
Total Issue $999,780
Out at close $49,840
Large out 1935 $4,010
Ch 14086 assumed circulation
****
11638 Claiborne
COMMERCIAL NB OF HOMER
{{ 3 L }}
Chartered 3/20
Liquidated 4/12/24
1902 Plain Back <$VALUE
4x5 1-6360 <$450
3x10-20 1-4640 <$450
Total Issue $359,200
Out at close $48,100
****
4216 Claiborne
HOMER NB, HOMER
{{ 5 L 8 S }}
Chartered 1890
Brown Back <$VALUE
3x10-20 1-2090 <$750
1882 Date Back
3x10-20 1-72 <$750
1902 Date Back
3x10-20 1-3050 <$375
1902 Plain Back
3x10-20 3051-7605 <$375
1929 Small Size
10 Type 1 1-1038 <$175
20 Type 1 1-294 <$175
10 Type 2 1-830 <$200
20 Type 2 1-263 <$200
Total Issue $599,470
Out in 1935 $29,250
Large out 1935 $1,820
****
7768 Iberia
FNB OF JEANERETTE
{{ 6 L 12 S }}
Chartered 6/05
1902 Red Seal <$VALUE
3x10-20 1-2100 <$1000
1902 Date Back
3x10-20 1-3440 <$300
1902 Plain Back
3x10-20 3441-10261 <$300
1929 Small Size
10 Type 1 1-1118 <$135
20 Type 1 1-330 <$135
10 Type 2 1-1972 <$150
20 Type 2 1-383 <$165
Total Issue $752,110
Out in 1935 $48,800
Large out 1935 $3,550
****
5966 Jefferson Davis
FNB OF JENNINGS
{{ 1 L }}
Chartered 9/14/01
Liquidated 1/12/10
Brown Back <$VALUE
4x5 1-975 <$2000
3x10-20 1-648 <$2000
Total Issue $51,900
Out in 1910 $6,345
****
11450 Jefferson Davis
JENNINGS NB, JENNINGS
{{ 6 L }}
Chartered 9/19
Liquidated 6/22/26
1902 Plain Back <$VALUE
3x10-20 1-3826 <$325
Total Issue $191,300
Out at close $21,100
****
7765 Jefferson Davis
STATE NB OF JENNINGS
{{ 2 L }}
Chartered 5/05
Liquidated 4/30/15
1902 Red Seal <$VALUE
3x10-20 1-2800 <$1250
1902 Date Back
4x5 1-4075 <$750
3x10-20 1-2406 <$750
Total Issue $341,800
Out in 1915 $34,400
****
13209 Lafayette
COMMERCIAL NB OF
LAFAYETTE
{{ 2 L 6 S }}
Chartered 5/28
Liquidated 6/30/31
1902 Plain Back <$VALUE
4x5 1-4175 <$500
1929 Small Size
5 Type 1 1-7148 <$175
Total Issue $297,940
Out at close $94,060
Large out at close $1,320
****
5023 Lafayette
FNB OF LAFAYETTE
{{ 8 L 17 S }}
Chartered 1895
Brown Back <$VALUE
4x5 1-6475 <$600
3x10-20 1-4160 <$600
1882 Date Back
4x5 1-6970 <$500
3x10-20 1-4596 <$500
1902 Plain Back
4x5 1-14915 <$250
3x10-20 1-10757 <$250
1929 Small Size
5 Type 1 1-3210 <$75
10 Type 1 1-1816 <$75
20 Type 1 1-466 <$75
5 Type 2 1-5850 <$85
10 Type 2 1-2822 <$85
20 Type 2 1-775 <$85
Total Issue $1,877,000
Out in 1935 $98,750
Large out 1935 $7,200
****
7047 Jefferson Davis
FNB OF LAKE ARTHUR
{{ UNREPORTED }}
Chartered 11/03
Liquidated 1/11/10
1902 Red Seal <$VALUE
3x10-20 1-360 <$2500
1902 Date Back
3x10-20 1-23 <$1500
Total Issue $19,150
Out in 1910 $3,810
****
5157 Calcasieu
CALCASIEU NB OF
LAKE CHARLES
{{ 3 L }}
Chartered 1/1/99
Liquidated 4/3/16
Brown Back <$VALUE
4x5 1-3000 <$850
3x10-20 1-5100 <$850
1882 Date Back
4x5 1-10245 <$750
3x10-20 1-7176 <$750
Total Issue $878,700
Out at close $122,800
Ch 10836 assumed circulation
****
13573 Calcasieu
CALCASIEU NB OF
LAKE CHARLES
{{ 8 S }}
Organized 8/26/31
Liquidated 9/17/34
1929 Small Size <$VALUE
5 Type 1 1-1570 <$125
10 Type 1 1-828 <$125
20 Type 1 1-180 <$135
5 Type 2 1-780 <$175
10 Type 2 1-340 <$165
20 Type 2 1-70 <$200
Total Issue $127,120
Out at close $112,270
Large out at close $9,180
Outstanding includes Ch 10836
and Ch 5157
****
10836 Calcasieu
CALCASIEU NB OF SOUTHWEST
LOUISIANA AT LAKE CHARLES
Chartered 3/16
Closed 12/16/31
2nd title: Calcasieu NB of
Lake Charles 6/28/30
FIRST TITLE {{ 8 L 3 S }}
1902 Plain Back <$VALUE
3x10-20 1-20666 <$275
1929 Small Size
10 Type 1 1-1234 <$225
20 Type 1 1-420 <$250
SECOND TITLE {{ 3 S }}
1929 Small Size
10 Type 1 1-798 <$200
20 Type 1 1-249 <$200
Total Issue $1,235,500
Out at close $121,580
Large out at close $17,230
Ch 13573 assumed circulation
Outstanding includes Ch 5157
****
4154 Calcasieu
FNB OF LAKE CHARLES
{{ 10 L 16 S }}
Chartered 11/8/89
Brown Back <$VALUE
4x5 1-5150 <$600
3x10-20 1-2740 <$600
1882 Date Back
4x5 1-985 <$600
3x10-20 1-707 <$600
1902 Date Back
4x5 1-6600 <$200
4x10 1-6350 <$200
1902 Plain Back
4x5 6601-30120 <$200
4x10 6351-24571 <$200
1929 Small Size
5 Type 1 1-6334 <$85
10 Type 1 1-2568 <$85
5 Type 2 1-9476 <$100
10 Type 2 1-4972 <$100
Total Issue $2,321,490
Out in 1935 $82,595
Large out 1935 $6,635
****
6088 Calcasieu
LAKE CHARLES NB,
LAKE CHARLES
{{ 2 L }}
Chartered 1/10/02
Liquidated 12/31/12
Brown Back <$VALUE
3x10-20 1-5500 <$850
1882 Date Back
4x5 1-4085 <$850
3x10-20 1-2124 <$850
Total Issue $462,900
Out in 1913 $50,500
****
6291 East Carroll
FNB OF LAKE PROVIDENCE
{{ 4 L 3U + 12 S }}
Chartered 6/6/02
1902 Red Seal <$VALUE
3x10-20 1-2550 <$1250
1902 Date Back
3x10-20 1-3940 <$500
1902 Plain Back
3x10-20 3941-12506 <$500
1929 Small Size
10 Type 1 1-1414 <$175
20 Type 1 1-410 <$175
5 Type 2 1-312 <$225
10 Type 2 1-2157 <$175
20 Type 2 1-664 <$185
Total Issue $923,250
Out in 1935 $50,000
Large out 1935 $3,745
****
6264 Vernon
FNB OF LEESVILLE
{{ UNREPORTED }}
Chartered 5/19/02
Liquidated 12/1/10
1902 Red Seal <$VALUE
4x5 1-550 <$2000
3x10-20 1-540 <$2000
1902 Date Back
4x5 1-150 <$1500
3x10-20 1-133 <$1500
Total Issue $47,650
Out in 1911 $5,880
****
11669 De Soto
AMERICAN NB OF MANSFIELD
{{ 8 S }}
Chartered 4/20
1929 Small Size <$VALUE
10 Type 1 1-624 <$150
20 Type 1 1-210 <$150
10 Type 2 1-1930 <$175
20 Type 2 1-400 <$200
Total Issue $89,940
Out in 1935 $42,850
****
7232 De Soto
FNB OF MANSFIELD
{{ 1 L }}
Chartered 4/28/04
Liquidated 3/13/09
1902 Red Seal <$VALUE
3x10-20 1-897 <$2000
Total Issue $44,850
Out in 1910 $9,520
****
10544 Webster
FNB OF MINDEN
{{ 4 L 0 S }}
Chartered 5/14
Liquidated 4/29/30
1902 Date Back <$VALUE
4x5 1-1250 <$500
3x10-20 1-1000 <$500
1902 Plain Back
4x5 1251-11125 <$500
3x10-20 1001-7413 <$500
1929 Small Size
5 Type 1 1-507 <$650
10 Type 1 1-246 <$650
20 Type 1 1-45 <$650
Total Issue $628,520
Out at close $42,740
Large out at close $11,630
****

****
11242 Ouachita
CITIZENS NB OF MONROE
{{ UNREPORTED }}
Chartered 9/18
Closed 2/28/21
1902 Plain Back <$VALUE
3x10-20 1-2364 <$1000
Total Issue $118,200
Out at close $47,600
Ch 8654 assumed circulation
****
4082 Ouachita
MONROE NB, MONROE
{{ UNREPORTED }}
Chartered 7/29/89
Liquidated 4/20/07
Brown Back <$VALUE
3x10-20 1-1606 <$2000
Total Issue $80,300
Out in 1910 $3,050
****
3692 Ouachita
OUACHITA NB OF MONROE
{{ 1 L }}
Chartered 5/2/87
Liquidated 4/20/07
Brown Back <$VALUE
4x5 1-2821 <$2000
3x10-20 1-512 <$2000
Total Issue $82,020
Out in 1910 $2,310
****
8654 Ouachita
OUACHITA NB OF MONROE
{{ 7 L 12 S }}
Chartered 4/07
Liquidated 1/10/33
1902 Red Seal <$VALUE
3x10-20 1-1500 <$1000
1902 Date Back
3x10-20 1-6900 <$275
1902 Plain Back
3x10-20 6901-23207 <$275
1929 Small Size
10 Type 1 1-2996 <$100
20 Type 1 1-867 <$125
Total Issue $1,519,150
Out at close $112,000
Large out at close $6,020
Outstanding includes Ch 11242
Ch 13655 assumed circulation
****
13655 Ouachita
OUACHITA NB OF MONROE
{{ 2U + 7 S }}
Chartered 1/33
1929 Small Size <$VALUE
10 Type 1 1-440 <$200
20 Type 1 1-148 <$200
10 Type 2 1-3285 <$200
20 Type 2 1-773 <$200
Total Issue $92,470
Out in 1935 $96,330
Outstanding includes Ch 8654
and Ch 11242
****
10153 Ouachita
UNION NB OF MONROE
{{ 1 L }}
Organized 3/4/12
Receivership 6/24/15
1902 Date Back <$VALUE
4x5 1-4585 <$750
3x10-20 1-1669 <$750
3x50-100 1-176 <$900/$1000
Total Issue $219,150
Out in 1916 $48,295
****
6801 St Mary
FNB OF MORGAN CITY
{{ U + 2 L }}
Chartered 5/03
Liquidated 5/17/24
1902 Red Seal <$VALUE
3x10-20 1-1200 <$1500
1902 Date Back
3x10-20 1-4350 <$750
1902 Plain Back
3x10-20 4351-7451 <$750
Total Issue $432,550
Out at close $47,500
****
3671 Iberia
NEW IBERIA NB, NEW IBERIA
{{ 4 L 12 S }}
Chartered 4/16/87
Brown Back <$VALUE
4x5 1-3969 <$850
3x10-20 1-1942 <$850
1902 Red Seal
4x10 1-875 <$1250
1902 Date Back
4x5 1-3280 <$350
4x10 1-2900 <$350
1902 Plain Back
4x5 3281-11138 <$350
4x10 2901-9495 <$350
1929 Small Size
5 Type 1 1-3156* <$100
10 Type 1 1-1582 <$100
5 Type 2 1-8434 <$100
10 Type 2 1-4387 <$100
* 3105 not issued
Total Issue $1,089,650
Out in 1935 $78,000
Large out 1935 $3,100
****
4524 Iberia
PEOPLES NB OF NEW IBERIA
{{ 6 L 8 S }}
Chartered 1891
Brown Back <$VALUE
4x5 1-3355 <$650
3x10-20 1-1768 <$650
1882 Date Back
4x5 1-835 <$650
3x10-20 1-652 <$650
1902 Date Back
4x5 1-2500* <$250
3x10-20 1-1920** <$250
1902 Plain Back
4x5 2751-9836* <$250
3x10-20 2121-6912** <$250
* 2501-2750 not marked
** 1921-2120 not marked
1929 Small Size
5 Type 1 1-1908 <$125
10 Type 1 1-914 <$125
20 Type 1 1-240 <$135
5 Type 2 1-2306 <$150
10 Type 2 1-1312 <$150
20 Type 2 1-361 <$165
Total Issue $919,870
Out in 1935 $49,050
Large out 1935 $2,605
****
6858 Iberia
STATE NB OF NEW IBERIA
{{ 7 L 17 S }}
Chartered 6/03
1902 Red Seal <$VALUE
3x10-20 1-4525 <$850
1902 Date Back
3x10-20 1-6800 <$200
1902 Plain Back
3x10-20 6801-21628 <$200
1929 Small Size
5 Type 1 1-3648 <$75
10 Type 1 1-2172 <$75
20 Type 1 1-258 <$85
5 Type 2 1-7596 <$85
10 Type 2 1-4416 <$85
Total Issue $1,660,510
Out in 1935 $98,835
Large out 1935 $6,940
****
3978 Orleans
AMERICAN NB OF
NEW ORLEANS
{{ 1 L }}
Chartered 2/14/89
Receivership 9/10/96
Brown Back <$VALUE
3x10-20 1-2171 <$1000
Total Issue $108,550
Out in 1916 $930
****
Canal-Commercial NB of
New Orleans
SEE Ch 5649
Commercial NB of New Orleans
****
1591 Orleans
CITY NB OF NEW ORLEANS
Chartered 10/14/65
Liquidated 7/3/05
2nd title: Germania NB of
New Orleans 3/1/69
FIRST TITLE {{ 0 L }}
Original Series <$VALUE
4x5 1-6800 <$1500
4x10 1-1800 <$2000
2x20-50-100 1-300
<$3000/$6000/$6000
SECOND TITLE {{ 4 L }}
Original Series
4x10 1-2335 <$2000
2x20-50-100 1-790
<$3000/$6000/$6000
Series 1875
4x10 1-5742 <$2000
2x20-50-100 1-670
<$3000/$6000/$6000
Brown Back
4x5 1-675 <$500
3x10-20 1-4365 <$500
Total Issue $1,097,230
Out in 1910 $11,330
****
5649 Orleans
COMMERCIAL NB OF
NEW ORLEANS
Chartered 12/21/00
Liquidated 12/31/20
2nd title: Canal-Commercial
NB of New Orleans 8/28/19
FIRST TITLE {{ 28 L }}
Brown Back <$VALUE
4x5 1-11500 <$275
3x10-20 1-8000 <$275/$325
1882 Date Back
4x5 1-35000 <$250
3x10-20 1-25200 <$250/$275
SECOND TITLE {{ 6 L }}
1882 Value Back
3x50-100 1-1057
<$45,000/$50,000
1902 Plain Back
3x50-100 1-17 <$900/$1000
Total Issue $2,858,500
Out at close $394,650
****
1937 Orleans
CRESCENT CITY NB OF
NEW ORLEANS
{{ UNREPORTED }}
Chartered 2/15/72
Receivership 3/18/73
Original Series <$VALUE
4x5 1-10005 <$2500
3x10-20 1-3000<$3000/$3500
50-100 1-666 <$6500
Total Issue $450,000
Out in 1916 $1,000
****
162 Orleans
FNB OF NEW ORLEANS
{{ UNREPORTED }}
Organized 12/18/63
Receivership 5/20/67
Original Series <$VALUE
4x5 1-1500 <$1750
4x10 1-2375 <$2250
3x20-50 1-500 <$3000/$6000
Total Issue $180,000
Out in 1916 $1,070
****
7876 Orleans
GERMAN-AMERICAN NB OF
NEW ORLEANS
{{ 8 L }}
Chartered 8/05
Liquidated 12/31/13
1902 Red Seal <$VALUE
4x5 1-28850 <$400
3x10-20 1-15960 <$400
50-100 1-2270 <$1500/$1750
1902 Date Back
4x5 1-32520 <$300
3x10-20 1-19859 <$300
50-100 1-196 <$600/$700
Total Issue $3,388,250
Out in 1914 $387,760
****
Germania NB of New Orleans
SEE Ch 1591
City NB of New Orleans
****
13688 Orleans
HIBERNIA NB IN
NEW ORLEANS
{{ 50+ S }}
Chartered 5/33
1929 Small Size <$VALUE
5 Type 2 1-95360* <$50
10 Type 2 1-49150 <$50
20 Type 2 1-21519 <$50
50 Type 2 1-2319 <$200
100 Type 2 1-1111 <$250
* 75493-75498 not issued
Total Issue $1,625,700
Out in 1935 $849,800
****
2086 Orleans
HIBERNIA NB OF
NEW ORLEANS
{{ 2 L }}
Chartered 2/18/73
Liquidated 7/31/02
Original Series <$VALUE
4x5 1-500 <$1500
3x10-20 1-1200<$2000/$2500
50-100 1-667 <$6000
Series 1875
3x10-20 1-21143<$2000/$2500
50-100 1-267 <$6000
Brown Back
4x5 1-1065 <$650
3x10-20 1-4890 <$650
Total Issue $1,553,050
Out in 1910 $12,725
****
Hibernia NB of New Orleans
SEE Ch 8734
New Hibernia NB of
New Orleans
****
1626 Orleans
LOUISIANA NB OF
NEW ORLEANS
{{ 16 L }}
Chartered 12/30/65
Liquidated 10/2/05
Original Series <$VALUE
3x1-2 1-4000 <$1750/$4500
4x5 1-11550 <$1500
3x10-20 1-10678<$2000/$2500
50-100 1-4203 <$6000
Series 1875
4x5 1-14250 <$1500
3x10-20 1-10400<$2000/$2500
50-100 1-5209 <$6000
Brown Back
4x5 1-13780 <$300
3x10-20 1-11431 <$300/$350
50-100 1-2667 <$1250/$1500
Total Issue $4,248,900
Out in 1910 $62,272
****
7498 Orleans
MERCHANTS NB OF
NEW ORLEANS
Chartered 12/1/04
Liquidated 1/29/09
2nd title: Peoples NB of
New Orleans 4/11/08
FIRST TITLE {{ 1 L }}
1902 Red Seal <$VALUE
4x5 1-3500 <$1000
3x10-20 1-3417 <$1000
SECOND TITLE {{ 0 L }}
1902 Red Seal
3x10-20 1-1307 <$1250
Total Issue $306,200
Out in 1910 $46,775
****
1898 Orleans
MUTUAL NB OF NEW ORLEANS
{{ UNREPORTED }}
Chartered 11/10/71
Receivership 1/27/97
Original Series <$VALUE
4x5 1-10000 <$1500
3x10-20 1-3500<$2000/$2500
50-100 1-300 <$6000
Series 1875
3x10-20 1-2069<$2000/$2500
Brown Back
50-100 1-390 <$2500
Total Issue $581,950
Out in 1916 $2,335
****
13689 Orleans
NB OF COMMERCE IN
NEW ORLEANS
{{ 50+ S }}
Chartered 5/33
1929 Small Size <$VALUE
5 Type 2 1-189566 <$40
10 Type 2 1-68049 <$40
20 Type 2 1-21872 <$45
Total Issue $2,065,760
Out in 1935 $980,800
****
8734 Orleans
NEW HIBERNIA NB OF
NEW ORLEANS
Chartered 6/07
Liquidated 10/22/17
2nd title: Hibernia NB of
New Orleans 1/16/13
FIRST TITLE {{ 2 L }}
1902 Red Seal <$VALUE
4x5 1-5000 <$750
4x10 1-7500 <$750
1902 Date Back
4x5 1-16641 <$350
4x10 1-15055 <$350
SECOND TITLE {{ 4 L }}
1902 Date Back
4x5 1-14302 <$300
3x10-20 1-12207 <$300
Total Issue $2,231,410
Out at close $269,500
****
1778 Orleans
NEW ORLEANS NB,
NEW ORLEANS
{{ 14 L }}
Chartered 1/30/71
Liquidated 7/15/19
Original Series <$VALUE
4x5 1-2750 <$1500
3x10-20 1-4500<$2000/$2500
50-100 1-300 <$6000
Series 1875
4x5 1-250 <$1500
3x10-20 1-2192<$2000/$2500
50-100 1-1301 <$6000
Brown Back
4x10 1-16250 <$350
50-100 1-3967 <$1250/$1500
1882 Date Back
4x10 1-2701 <$275
1902 Date Back
50-100 1-6000 <$400/$500
3x50-100 1-1066 <$400/$500
Total Issue $3,154,340
Out at close $385,000
****
1825 Orleans
NEW ORLEANS N BANKING
ASSOC., NEW ORLEANS
{{ UNREPORTED }}
Chartered 5/27/71
Receivership 10/23/73
Original Series <$VALUE
500 1-720 <$150,000
Total Issue $360,000
Out in 1910 $2,500
****
Peoples NB of New Orleans
SEE Ch 7498
Merchants NB of New Orleans
****
4337 Orleans
SOUTHERN NB OF
NEW ORLEANS
{{ UNREPORTED }}
Chartered 6/6/90
Liquidated 6/5/93
Brown Back <$VALUE
50-100 1-438 <$2500
Total Issue $65,700
Out in 1910 $750
****
1774 Orleans
STATE NB OF NEW ORLEANS
{{ 15 L }}
Chartered 1/20/71
Liquidated 1/30/08
Original Series <$VALUE
3x1-2 1-2200 <$1750/$4500
4x5 1-6950 <$1500
3x10-20 1-5700<$2000/$2500
50-100 1-2100 <$6000
Series 1875
4x5 1-2500 <$1500
3x10-20 1-1500<$2000/$2500
50-100 1-3279 <$6000
Brown Back
50-100 1-5975 <$1250/$1500
Total Issue $2,263,100
Out in 1910 $124,407
****
1747 Orleans
TEUTONIA NB OF
NEW ORLEANS
{{ UNREPORTED }}
Chartered 12/5/70
Liquidated 9/2/74
Original Series <$VALUE
4x5 1-3000 <$2000
3x10-20 1-4260<$2500/$3000
Total Issue $273,000
Out in 1910 $1,255
****
1796 Orleans
UNION NB OF NEW ORLEANS
{{ 7 L }}
Chartered 2/23/71
Liquidated 4/14/02
Original Series <$VALUE
3x1-2 1-4070 <$1750/$4500
4x5 1-7105 <$1500
3x10-20 1-4900<$2000/$2500
50-100 1-1883 <$6000
Series 1875
4x5 1-500 <$1500
3x10-20 1-800 <$2000/$2500
50-100 1-1156 <$6000
Brown Back
4x5 1-9840 <$300
3x10-20 1-2361 <$300/$350
50-100 1-3129 <$1250/$1500
Total Issue $1,697,500
Out in 1910 $41,857
****
3069 Orleans
WHITNEY NB OF NEW ORLEANS
Chartered 1883
2nd title: Whitney-Central
NB, New Orleans 7/3/05
3rd title: Whitney NB of
New Orleans 8/2/29
FIRST TITLE {{ 2 L }}
Brown Back <$VALUE
4x5 1-7745 <$350
50-100 1-9702 <$1250/$1500
1902 Red Seal
4x5 1-1225 <$350
50-100 1-1401 <$1500/$1750
SECOND TITLE {{ 50+ L }}
1902 Red Seal
4x5 1-42665 <$250
3x10-20 1-33334 <$250/$300
50-100 1-3200 <$1500/$1750
1902 Date Back
4x5 1-118500 <$50
3x10-20 1-78600 <$50
50-100 1-4000 <$400/$500
3x50-100 1-6415 <$400/$500
1902 Plain Back
4x5 118501-275375 <$50
3x10-20 78601-165164 <$50
3x50-100 6416-13704
<$400/$500
THIRD TITLE {{ 50+ S }}
1929 Small Size
5 Type 1 1-102442 <$25
10 Type 1 1-47012 <$25
20 Type 1 1-14614 <$35
5 Type 2 1-165302 <$25
10 Type 2 1-79191 <$25
20 Type 2 1-20830 <$35
Total Issue $32,319,230
Out in 1935 $2,399,150
Large out 1935 $148,120
****
7169 Pointe Coupee
FNB OF NEW ROADS
{{ 1 L }}
Organized 3/15/04
Receivership 10/30/12
1902 Red Seal <$VALUE
3x10-20 1-300 <$3000
1902 Date Back
3x10-20 1-197 <$2000
Total Issue $24,850
Out in 1916 $1,110
****

****

13839 St Charles
SAINT CHARLES NB OF NORCO
{{ 4 S }}
Chartered 11/23/33
1929 Small Size <$VALUE
5 Type 2 1-4740 <$275
10 Type 2 1-2675 <$275
20 Type 2 1-660 <$275
Total Issue $63,650
Out in 1935 $42,600

****

4340 St Landry
FNB OF OPELOUSAS
{{ UNREPORTED }}
Chartered 6/10/90
Liquidated 2/3/94
Brown Back <$VALUE
3x10-20 1-358 <$2000
Total Issue $17,900
Out in 1910 $300

****

6920 St Landry
OPELOUSAS NB, OPELOUSAS
{{ UNREPORTED }}
Chartered 8/03
Liquidated 10/22/21
1902 Red Seal <$VALUE
3x10-20 1-2612 <$1500
1902 Date Back
3x10-20 1-3100 <$1000
1902 Plain Back
3x10-20 3101-5266 <$1000
Total Issue $393,900
Out at close $49,600

****

9872 St Landry
PLANTERS NB OF OPELOUSAS
{{ 1 L }}
Chartered 10/10
Liquidated 1/1/18
1902 Date Back <$VALUE
3x10-20 1-1046 <$1250
Total Issue $52,300
Out at close $12,500

****

5843 St Mary
FNB OF PATTERSON
{{ UNREPORTED }}
Chartered 5/31/01
Liquidated 1/11/10
Brown Back <$VALUE
3x10-20 1-455 <$2000
Total Issue $22,750
Out in 1910 $3,450

****

11795 Lincoln
FNB OF RUSTON
{{ 1 L 3 S }}
Chartered 7/20
1902 Plain Back <$VALUE
4x5 1-3355 <$1000
3x10-20 1-2034 <$1000
1929 Small Size
5 Type 1 1-936 <$450
10 Type 1 1-544 <$450
20 Type 1 1-144 <$450
5 Type 2 1-1852 <$500
10 Type 2 1-888 <$500
20 Type 2 1-276 <$500
Total Issue $270,460
Out in 1935 $25,000
Large out 1935 $250

****

8440 Caddo
AMERICAN NB OF SHREVEPORT
{{ 15 L 10 S }}
Organized 1/16/06
Receivership 4/19/35
1902 Red Seal <$VALUE
4x10 1-4500 <$600
1902 Date Back
4x10 1-16500 <$175
1902 Plain Back
4x10 16501-54272 <$175
1929 Small Size
10 Type 1 1-3209 <$125
Total Issue $2,543,420
Out at close $103,640
Large out at close $51,820

****

5752 Caddo
CITIZENS NB OF SHREVEPORT
{{ UNREPORTED }}
Chartered 3/22/01
Liquidated 8/31/03
Brown Back <$VALUE
4x5 1-645 <$1500
3x10-20 1-516 <$1500
Total Issue $38,700
Out in 1910 $945

****

10870 Caddo
CITY NB OF SHREVEPORT
{{ UNREPORTED }}
Chartered 7/16
Closed 1/14/19
1902 Plain Back <$VALUE
4x5 1-1187 <$1000
4x10 1-1085 <$1000
Total Issue $67,140
Out at close $47,600
Ch 3595 assumed circulation

****

13648 Caddo
COMMERCIAL NB IN SHREVEPORT
{{ 10U + 16 S }}
Chartered 12/32
1929 Small Size <$VALUE
5 Type 1 1-6114 <$35
50 Type 1 1-316 <$100
100 Type 1 1-106 <$175
5 Type 2 1-61070 <$35
50 Type 2 1-1622 <$200
100 Type 2 1-751 <$275
Total Issue $803,370
Out in 1935 $943,065
Outstanding includes Ch 3600

****

3600 Caddo
COMMERCIAL NB OF SHREVEPORT
{{ 35 L U + 20 S }}
Chartered 12/9/86
Liquidated 1/10/33
Brown Back <$VALUE
4x5 1-1045 <$300
3x10-20 1-14977 <$300/$350
1902 Red Seal
50-100 1-3000 <$1500/$1750
1902 Date Back
4x5 1-41333 <$50
50-100 1-3000 <$400/$500
3x50-100 1-6735 <$400/$500
1902 Plain Back
4x5 41334-178367 <$50
3x50-100 6736-8741 <$400/$500
1929 Small Size
5 Type 1 1-48331 <$30
50 Type 1 1-1879 <$100
100 Type 1 1-645 <$175
Total Issue $9,822,970
Out at close $992,200
Large out 1935 $48,285
Ch 13648 assumed circulation

****

11521 Caddo
EXCHANGE NB OF SHREVEPORT
{{ 4 L 2 S }}
Chartered 11/19
Liquidated 7/12/30
1902 Plain Back <$VALUE
3x10-20 1-8016 <$250/$300
1929 Small Size
10 Type 1 1-506 <$275
20 Type 1 1-152 <$300
Total Issue $449,400
Out at close $50,810
Large out at close $12,730

****

3595 Caddo
FNB OF SHREVEPORT
{{ 38 L 50+ S }}
Chartered 12/3/86
Brown Back <$VALUE
4x5 1-13375 <$300
3x10-20 1-12250 <$300/$350
50-100 1-1283 <$1250/$1500
1902 Red Seal
4x5 1-9000 <$400
4x10 1-7000 <$400
1902 Date Back
4x5 1-35580 <$50
4x10 1-39085 <$50
1902 Plain Back
4x5 35581-152281 <$50
4x10 39086-132730 <$50
1929 Small Size
5 Type 1 1-44232 <$30
10 Type 1 1-24486 <$30
5 Type 2 1-93922 <$30
10 Type 2 1-48661 <$30
Total Issue $13,639,610
Out in 1935 $672,880
Large out 1935 $27,965
Outstanding includes Ch 10870

****

5844 Caddo
SHREVEPORT NB, SHREVEPORT
{{ UNREPORTED }}
Chartered 5/31/01
Liquidated 5/1/05
Brown Back <$VALUE
50-100 1-355 <$2500
Total Issue $53,250
Out in 1910 $5,650

****

12923 Madison
MADISON NB OF TALLULAH
{{ 4 L 7 S }}
Organized 2/19/26
Receivership 10/4/33
1902 Plain Back <$VALUE
3x10-20 1-2245 <$500
1929 Small Size
10 Type 1 1-1218 <$225
20 Type 1 1-331 <$250
Total Issue $225,050
Out at close $40,000
Large out at close $1,510

****

10588 Evangeline
FNB OF VILLE PLATTE
{{ 0 L 3 S }}
Chartered 7/14
Liquidated 7/14/34
1902 Plain Back <$VALUE
3x10-20 1-3909 <$1250
1929 Small Size
10 Type 1 1-670 <$450
20 Type 1 1-170 <$450
10 Type 1 1-359 <$500
20 Type 1 1-67 <$500
Total Issue $260,980
Out at close $23,650
Large out at close $1,740

****

6360 Jefferson Davis
FNB OF WELSH
{{ 1 L }}
Chartered 7/30/02
Liquidated 1/11/10
1902 Red Seal <$VALUE
4x5 1-305 <$2500
3x10-20 1-298 <$2500
1902 Date Back
4x5 1-35 <$1500
3x10-20 1-51 <$1500
Total Issue $24,250
Out in 1910 $3,730

****

6418 Jefferson Davis
WELSH NB, WELSH
{{ UNREPORTED }}
Chartered 9/11/02
Liquidated 4/17/05
1902 Red Seal <$VALUE
4x5 1-160 <$2500
3x10-20 1-145 <$2500
Total Issue $10,450
Out in 1910 $500

****

CONDITION affects Value. The Values shown are for notes in FINE condition.

MAINE

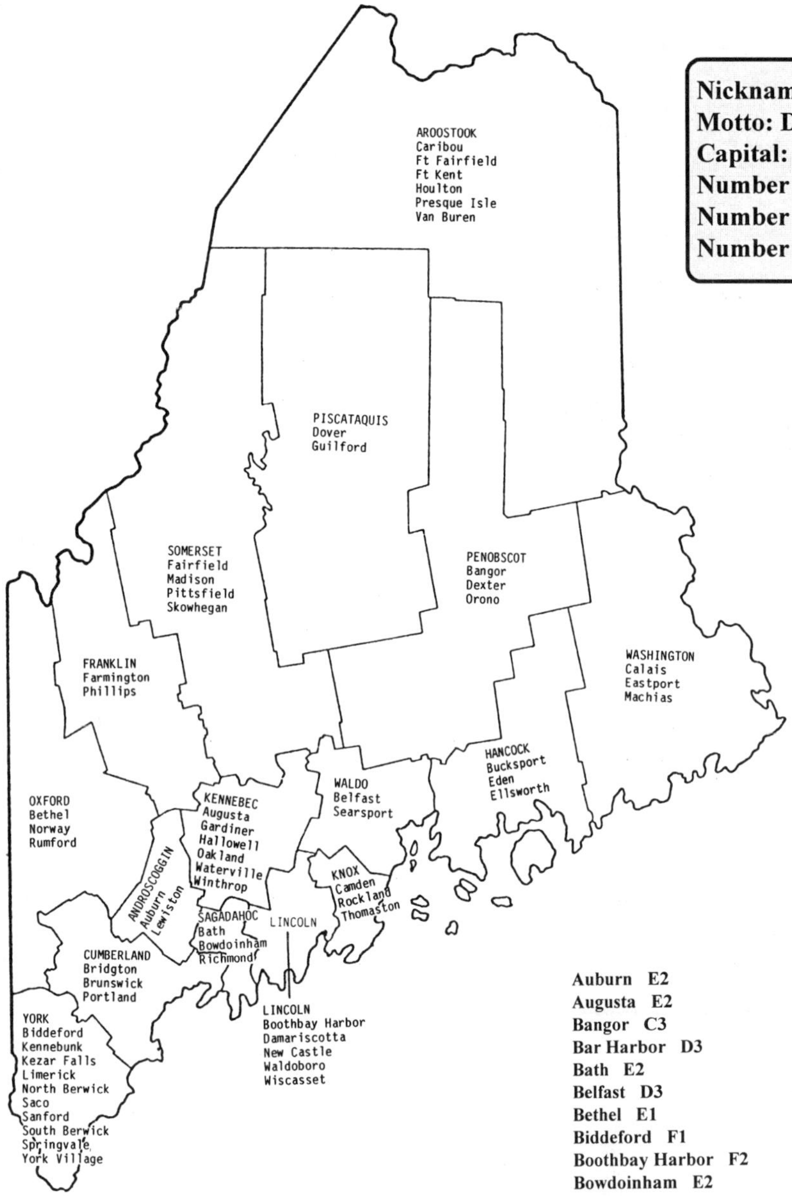

Nickname: The Pine Tree State
Motto: Dirigo (I Direct)
Capital: Augusta
Number of towns: 62
Number of issuing charters: 120
Number of small size issuers: 58

Auburn E2
Augusta E2
Bangor C3
Bar Harbor D3
Bath E2
Belfast D3
Bethel E1
Biddeford F1
Boothbay Harbor F2
Bowdoinham E2
Bridgton E1
Brunswick E1
Bucksport D3
Calais D4
Camden E3
Caribou A3
Damariscotta F2
Dexter C3
Dover C3
Eastport D4
Eden D3
Ellsworth D3
Fairfield C2
Farmington D1
Fort Fairfield A3
Fort Kent A3
Gardiner E2
Guilford C3
Hallowell E2
Houlton A3
Kennebunk F1
Kezar Falls F1
Lewiston E2
Limerick F1
Machias D4
Madison C2
New Castle F2
North Berwick F1
Norway E1
Oakland E2
Orono C3
Phillips D1
Pittsfield C2
Portland E1
Presque Isle A3
Richmond E2
Rockland E3
Rumford E1
Saco F1
Sanford F1
Searsport D3
Skowhegan C2
South Berwick F1
Springvale F1
Thomaston E3
Van Buren A3
Waldoboro F2
Waldoboro' F2
Waterville E2
Winthrop E2
Wiscasset F2
York Village F1

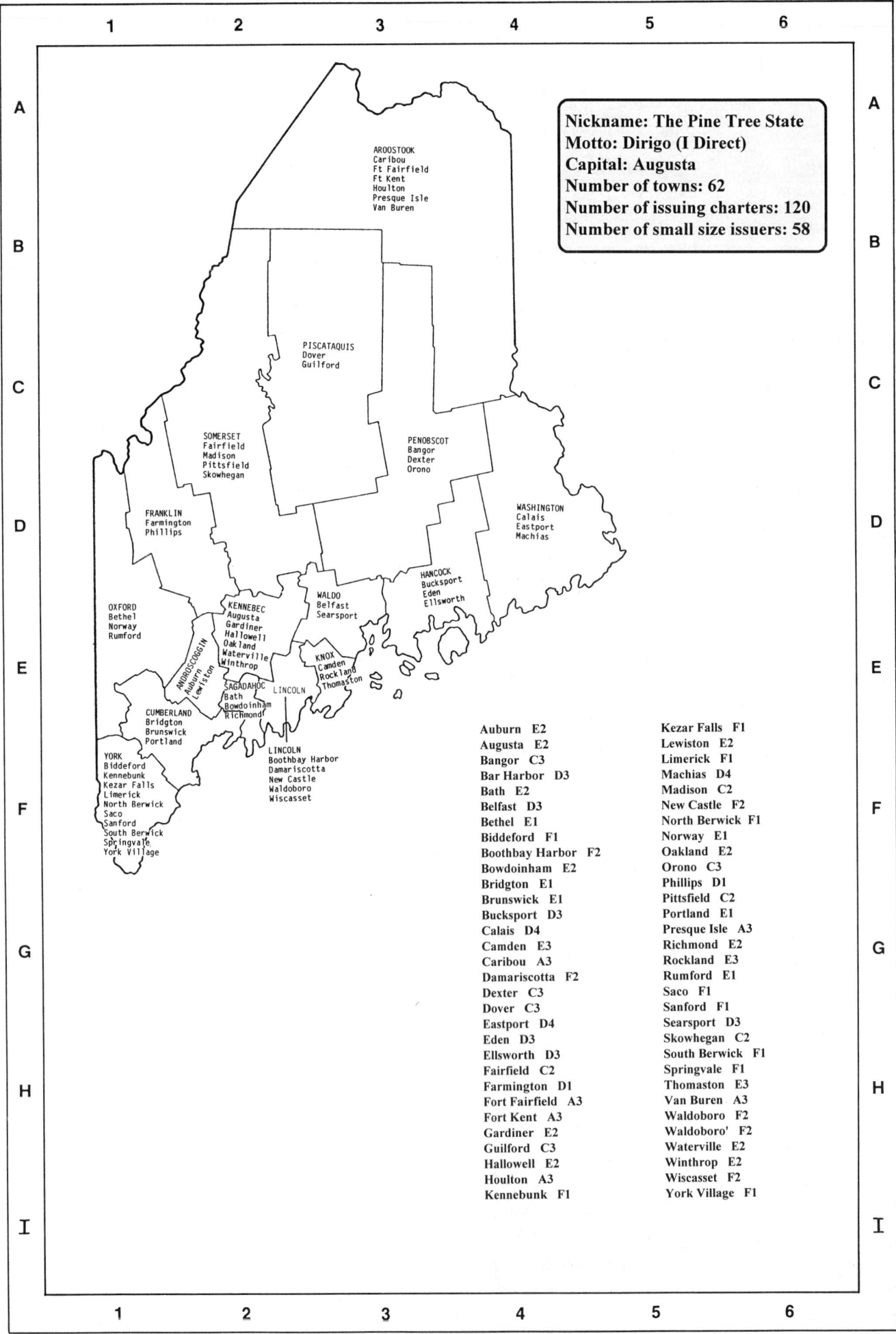

****
154 Androscoggin
FNB OF AUBURN
{{ 6 L }}
Chartered 1863
Liquidated 4/2/17
Original Series <$VALUE
4x5 1-2600 <$600
4x10 1-2250 <$850
2x20-50-100 1-500 & 621-720
<$1250/$5000/$5000
50-100 501-620<$5000/$5000
Series 1875
4x5 1-1000 <$600
4x10 1-1600 <$850
2x20-50-100 1-186
<$1250/$5000/$5000
Brown Back
4x5 1-7930 <$400
3x10-20 1-4506 <$400/$450
1902 Red Seal
4x5 1-5820 <$500
3x10-20 1-4572 <$500
1902 Date Back
4x5 1-8000 <$250
3x10-20 1-5900 <$250
1902 Plain Back
4x5 8001-9595 <$250
3x10-20 5901-6815 <$250
Total Issue $1,654,890
Out at close $86,400
****
2270 Androscoggin
N SHOE & LEATHER B OF
AUBURN
{{ 8 L 16 S }}
Chartered 5/27/75
Receivership 12/19/33
Original Series <$VALUE
3x10-20 1-900 <$850/$1500
Series 1875
3x10-20 1-13899<$850/$1500
Brown Back
4x5 1-26000 <$400
3x10-20 1-5100 <$400/$450
1882 Date Back
4x5 1-7658 <$400
3x10-20 1-5417 <$400/$450
1902 Date Back
3x10-20 1-2000 <$250
1902 Plain Back
3x10-20 2001-4620 <$250
1929 Small Size
10 Type 1 1-3006 <$85
20 Type 1 1-954 <$100
10 Type 2 1-2438 <$110
20 Type 2 1-328 <$150
Total Issue $2,495,740
Out at close $200,000
Large out at close $5,060
****
3271 Kennebec
AUGUSTA NB, AUGUSTA
{{ 2 L }}
Chartered 12/9/84
Liquidated 1/14/02
Brown Back <$VALUE
3x10-20 1-6678 <$1000
Total Issue $333,900
Out in 1910 $4,320
****
367 Kennebec
FNB OF AUGUSTA
{{ 12 L }}
Chartered 1864
Liquidated 3/24/16
Original Series <$VALUE
3x1-2 2001-5000<$400/$1250
4x5 1-9500 <$500
3x10-20 1-3700 <$850/$1500
50-100 1-200 <$5000
Series 1875
4x5 1-4000 <$500
3x10-20 1-4200 <$850/$1500
Brown Back
4x5 1-14455 <$400
3x10-20 1-14218 <$400
1902 Red Seal
4x5 1-7500 <$450
3x10-20 1-10800 <$450
1902 Date Back
4x5 1-11750 <$175
3x10-20 1-7500 <$175
1902 Plain Back
4x5 11751-12286 <$175
3x10-20 7501-7823 <$175
Total Issue $3,036,870
Out at close $100,000
Ch 498 assumed circulation
****
FN Granite B of Augusta
SEE Ch 498
Granite NB of Augusta
****

****
406 Kennebec
FREEMAN'S NB OF AUGUSTA
{{ 1 L }}
Chartered 1864
Liquidated 12/26/84
Original Series <$VALUE
3x1-2 1-2000 <$1250/$2000
4x5 1-2250 <$1250
3x10-20 1-3200<$1500/$2000
Series 1875
3x10-20 1-1130<$1500/$2000
Total Issue $271,500
Out in 1910 $1,631
****
498 Kennebec
GRANITE NB OF AUGUSTA
Organized 7/11/64
2nd title:FN Granite B of
Augusta 3/27/16
FIRST TITLE {{ 4 L }}
Original Series <$VALUE
4x5 1-3500 <$500
3x10-20 1-2600 <$850/$1500
Series 1875
3x10-20 1-2648 <$850/$1500
Brown Back
3x10-20 1-9395 <$500
1902 Red Seal
4x5 1-3000 <$600
3x10-20 1-3300 <$600
1902 Date Back
4x5 1-6700 <$200
3x10-20 1-5300 <$200
1902 Plain Back
4x5 6701-7061 <$200
3x10-20 5301-5512 <$200
SECOND TITLE {{13 L 4U+50+S}}
1902 Plain Back
4x5 1-33702 <$150
3x10-20 1-23040 <$150
1929 Small Size
5 Type 1 1-9456 <$50
10 Type 1 1-4868 <$50
20 Type 1 1-1212 <$60
5 Type 2 1-7806 <$60
10 Type 2 1-5224 <$60
20 Type 2 1-1896 <$65
Total Issue $4,120,400
Out in 1935 $294,395
Large out 1935 $16,435
Outstanding includes Ch 367
****
1687 Penobscot
FARMERS NB OF BANGOR
{{ UNREPORTED }}
Chartered 1868
Liquidated 11/22/78
Original Series <$VALUE
4x5 1-2000 <$2000
3x10-20 1-1400<$2000/$2500
Series 1875
3x10-20 1-1238<$2000/$2500
Total Issue $171,900
Out in 1910 $445
****
112 Penobscot
FNB OF BANGOR
{{ 34 L }}
Chartered 1863
Liquidated 2/28/28
Original Series <$VALUE
3x1-2 1-3400 <$350/$1000
4x5 1-12000 <$400
4x10 1-7000 <$750
3x20-50 1-954*<$1250/$5000
* 301-500 not issued
Series 1875
4x5 1-2051 <$400
4x10 1-737 <$750
3x20-50 1-974 <$1250/$5000
Brown Back
4x5 1-13060 <$250
3x10-20 1-22569 <$250
50-100 1-826 <$2500
1902 Red Seal
4x5 1-10750 <$400
3x10-20 1-12000 <$400
50-100 1-800 <$4000
1902 Date Back
4x5 1-25000 <$75
3x10-20 1-15200 <$85
50-100 1-200 <$750/$850
3x50-100 1-480 <$750/$850
1902 Plain Back
4x5 25001-96436 <$75
3x10-20 15201-54168 <$85
Total Issue $8,033,250
Out at close $338,050
****

****
518 Penobscot
KENDUSKEAG NB OF BANGOR
{{ 4 L }}
Chartered 9/19/64
Liquidated 3/1/06
Original Series <$VALUE
3x1-2 1-700 <$750/$1500
4x5 1-2000 <$850
3x10-20 1-1600<$1000/$1500
Series 1875
3x10-20 1-2386<$1000/$1500
Brown Back
3x10-20 1-4156 <$650
1902 Red Seal
3x10-20 1-574 <$750
Total Issue $479,300
Out in 1910 $5,590
****
1437 Penobscot
MERCHANTS NB OF BANGOR
{{ 13 L 22 S }}
Chartered 1865
Original Series <$VALUE
2x1-2x2 1-1350 <$400/$1000
4x5 1-4150 <$450
3x10-20 1-1660 <$750/$1250
Series 1875
4x5 1-1075 <$450
3x10-20 1-2080 <$750/$1250
Brown Back
3x10-20 1-7284 <$250/$300
1902 Red Seal
3x10-20 1-2100 <$400/$450
1902 Date Back
3x10-20 1-7900 <$125
1902 Plain Back
3x10-20 7901-25339 <$125
1929 Small Size
5 Type 1 1-5234 <$65
10 Type 1 1-2428 <$65
5 Type 2 1-9016 <$70
10 Type 2 1-4995 <$70
Total Issue $2,433,480
Out in 1935 $97,000
Large out 1935 $4,960
****
306 Penobscot
SECOND NB OF BANGOR
{{ 3 L }}
Chartered 1864
Liquidated 1/13/17
Original Series <$VALUE
4x5 1-4575 <$850
3x10-20 1-3420<$1000/$1500
Series 1875
4x5 1-250 <$850
3x10-20 1-2600<$1000/$1500
Brown Back
3x10-20 1-11390 <$650
1902 Red Seal
4x5 1-6500 <$750
3x10-20 1-6200 <$750
1902 Date Back
4x5 1-4977 <$400
3x10-20 1-12100 <$400
1902 Plain Back
3x10-20 12101-14142 <$400
Total Issue $2,213,600
Out at close 150,000
****
1095 Penobscot
TRADERS NB OF BANGOR
{{ UNREPORTED }}
Chartered 1865
Liquidated 1/14/79
Original Series <$VALUE
3x1-2 1-2000 <$1500/$2500
4x5 1-4250 <$1750
3x10-20 1-1500<$2000/$2500
Series 1875
3x10-20 1-702 <$2000/$2500
Total Issue $205,100
Out in 1910 $1,305
****
2089 Penobscot
VEAZIE NB OF BANGOR
{{ 4 L }}
Chartered 3/5/73
Liquidated 4/21/08
Original Series <$VALUE
3x1-2 1-2000 <$600/$1500
4x5 1-3750 <$750
3x10-20 1-1100<$1000/$1500
50-100 1-300 <$5000
Series 1875
4x5 1-5150 <$750
3x10-20 1-1760<$1000/$1500
50-100 1-67 <$5000
Brown Back
4x5 1-8628 <$600
3x10-20 1-2839 <$600
Total Issue $700,560
Out in 1910 $8,537
****

****
FNB of Bar Harbor, Bar Harbor
See Ch 3941
FNB of Bar Harbor, Eden
****
494 Sagadahoc
BATH NB, BATH
{{ 26 L 2U + 23 S }}
Chartered 1864
Original Series <$VALUE
3x1-2 1-2250 <$325/$1000
4x5 1-4000 <$350
3x10-20 1-1300 <$750/$1250
50-100 1-736 <$5000
Series 1875
3x1-2 1-400 <$325/$1000
4x5 1-3080 <$350
3x10-20 1-1135 <$750/$1250
Brown Back
3x10-20 1-12316 <$225/$275
1902 Red Seal
4x5 1-6500 <$350
3x10-20 1-4800 <$350/$400
1902 Date Back
4x5 1-9600 <$85
3x10-20 1-7580 <$85
1902 Plain Back
4x5 9601-41185 <$85
3x10-20 7581-19525 <$85
1929 Small Size
5 Type 1 1-7290 <$50
10 Type 1 1-1980 <$50
20 Type 1 1-528 <$60
5 Type 2 1-4886 <$50
10 Type 2 1-2771 <$50
20 Type 2 1-744 <$60
Total Issue $3,640,630
Out in 1935 $107,445
Large out 1935 $7,975
****
61 Sagadahoc
FNB OF BATH
{{ 3 L }}
Chartered 1863
Liquidated 6/30/82
Original Series <$VALUE
3x1-2 1-3900 <$1000/$1500
4x5 1-2750 <$1000
4x10 1-3250 <$1000
3x20-50 1-1350<$1500/$5000
Series 1875
4x5 1-3239 <$1000
4x10 1-2870 <$1000
Total Issue $532,580
Out in 1910 $3,190
****
2743 Sagadahoc
FNB OF BATH
{{ 37 L 44 S }}
Chartered 1882
Brown Back <$VALUE
4x5 1-13388 <$250
3x10-20 1-6652 <$250/$300
1902 Red Seal
4x5 1-8500 <$350
3x10-20 1-6500 <$350/$400
1902 Date Back
4x5 1-32000 <$75
3x10-20 1-22000 <$85
1902 Plain Back
4x5 32001-95035 <$75
3x10-20 22001-66516 <$85
1929 Small Size
5 Type 1 1-14498 <$30
10 Type 1 1-6368 <$35
20 Type 1 1-1660 <$45
5 Type 2 1-19806 <$30
10 Type 2 1-13230 <$35
20 Type 2 1-3446 <$45
Total Issue $7,638,330
Out in 1935 $338,700
Large out 1935 $13,900
****
761 Sagadahoc
LINCOLN NB OF BATH
{{ 10 L }}
Chartered 1/27/65
Liquidated 6/10/10
Original Series <$VALUE
3x1-2 1-5000 <$375/$1000
4x5 1-4525 <$450
3x10-20 1-2400 <$750/$1250
50-100 1-617 <$5000
Series 1875
4x5 1-6350 <$450
3x10-20 1-1862 <$750/$1250
50-100 1-546 <$5000
Brown Back
4x5 1-9750 <$300
3x10-20 1-9120 <$300
50-100 1-240 <$2500
1902 Red Seal
4x5 1-6000 <$400
3x10-20 1-5800 <$400
1902 Date Back
4x5 1-4442 <$175
3x10-20 1-2108 <$175
Total Issue $1,921,290
Out in 1910 $153,050
****
782 Sagadahoc
MARINE NB OF BATH
{{ 8 L }}
Chartered 2/3/65
Liquidated 4/27/10
Original Series <$VALUE
3x1-2 1-2200 <$400/$1000
4x5 1-3750 <$500
3x10-20 1-1780 <$750/$1250
50-100 1-200 <$5000
Series 1875
3x1-2 1-380 <$400/$1000
4x5 1-1875 <$500
3x10-20 1-1454 <$750/$1250
50-100 1-140 <$5000
Brown Back
4x5 1-12775 <$400
3x10-20 1-6923 <$400
1902 Red Seal
4x5 1-4000 <$450
3x10-20 1-2800 <$450
1902 Date Back
4x5 1-1410 <$200
3x10-20 1-1097 <$200
Total Issue $1,242,800
Out in 1910 $68,000
****
1041 Sagadahoc
SAGADAHOCK NB OF BATH
{{ 2 L }}
Chartered 4/20/65
Liquidated 4/11/94
Original Series <$VALUE
4x5 1-3750 <$1000
3x10-20 1-1800<$1500/$2000
Series 1875
4x5 1-4830 <$1000
3x10-20 1-1190<$1500/$2000
Brown Back
4x5 1-6938 <$850
Total Issue $460,860
Out in 1910 $2,705
****
840 Waldo
BELFAST NB, BELFAST
{{ 19 L }}
Chartered 2/25/65
Liquidated 2/20/05
Original Series <$VALUE
3x1-2 1-9700 <$350/$1000
4x5 1-7175 <$400
3x10-20 1-1720 <$750/$1250
Series 1875
3x1-2 1-960 <$350/$1000
4x5 1-5000 <$400
3x10-20 1-2580 <$750/$1250
Brown Back
4x5 1-11619 <$225
3x10-20 1-7120 <$225/$275
Total Issue $1,100,180
Out in 1910 $10,389
****
7586 Waldo
CITY NB OF BELFAST
{{ 8 L 17 S }}
Organized 1/14/05
Liquidated 10/3/33
1902 Red Seal <$VALUE
4x5 1-3050 <$500
3x10-20 1-2140 <$500
1902 Date Back
4x5 1-4525 <$200
3x10-20 1-3560 <$200
1902 Plain Back
4x5 4526-16107 <$200
3x10-20 3561-10059 <$200
1929 Small Size
5 Type 1 1-6122 <$60
10 Type 1 1-3602 <$60
20 Type 1 1-1190 <$70
5 Type 2 1-2382 <$65
10 Type 2 1-1541 <$65
20 Type 2 1-240 <$75
Total Issue $1,567,790
Out in 1935 $100,710
Large out 1935 $2,750
Ch 13762 assumed circulation
****
4806 Waldo
PEOPLES NB OF BELFAST
{{ UNREPORTED }}
Chartered 10/18/92
Liquidated 10/31/04
Brown Back <$VALUE
4x5 1-1300 <$1500
3x10-20 1-2584 <$1500
Total Issue $155,200
Out in 1910 $2,435
****

****
7613 Oxford
BETHEL NB, BETHEL
{{ 1 L 2 S }}
Chartered 2/05
1902 Red Seal <$VALUE
3x10-20 1-470 <$2000
1902 Date Back
3x10-20 1-1020* <$1000
1902 Plain Back
3x10-20 1221-2595* <$1000
* 1021-1220 not marked
1929 Small Size
10 Type 1 1-296 <$500
20 Type 1 1-95 <$500
Total Issue $182,410
Out in 1935 $9,900
Large out 1935 $280
****
1575 York
BIDDEFORD NB, BIDDEFORD
{{ 10 L }}
Chartered 1865
Closed 8/2/24
Original Series <$VALUE
4x5 1-3955 <$450
3x10-20 1-1540 <$750/$1250
50-100 1-360 <$5000
Series 1875
4x5 1-2700 <$450
3x10-20 1-2522 <$750/$1250
50-100 1-340 <$5000
Brown Back
50-100 1-3507 <$2500
1902 Red Seal
4x5 1-6250 <$450
3x10-20 1-3000 <$450
1902 Date Back
4x5 1-9000 <$175
3x10-20 1-9300 <$175
1902 Plain Back
4x5 9001-17695 <$175
3x10-20 9301-14747 <$175
Total Issue $2,333,500
Out at close $98,700
Ch 1089 assumed circulation
****
1089 York
FNB OF BIDDEFORD
{{ 16 L 26 S }}
Chartered 1865
Original Series <$VALUE
3x1-2 1-1000 <$350/$1000
4x5 1-2875 <$400
3x10-20 1-2050 <$750/$1250
Series 1875
3x10-20 1-3000 <$750/$1250
Brown Back
4x5 1-6988 <$250
3x10-20 1-5195 <$250/$300
50-100 1-1249 <$2500
1902 Red Seal
4x5 1-3300 <$400
3x10-20 1-1700 <$400
50-100 1-160 <$4000
1902 Date Back
4x5 1-7350 <$100
3x10-20 1-5360 <$100
50-100 1-200 <$750/$850
1902 Plain Back
4x5 7351-30740 <$100
3x10-20 5361-21583 <$100
1929 Small Size
5 Type 1 1-7114 <$50
10 Type 1 1-3914 <$50
20 Type 1 1-1020 <$65
5 Type 2 1-8164 <$50
10 Type 2 1-4081 <$50
20 Type 2 1-1035 <$65
Total Issue $3,473,800
Out in 1935 $164,420
Large out 1935 $13,145
Outstanding includes Ch 1575
****
5598 Lincoln
FNB OF BOOTHBAY HARBOR
{{ 2 L }}
Chartered 10/15/00
Liquidated 10/31/28
Brown Back <$VALUE
4x5 1-1850 <$1500
3x10-20 1-1560 <$1500
1882 Date Back
4x5 1-2200 <$1500
3x10-20 1-1530 <$1500
1882 Value Back
4x5 2201-3650 <$1500
3x10-20 1531-2277 <$1500
1902 Plain Back
3x10-20 1-2599 <$1000
Total Issue $431,800
Out at close $19,950
****

****
944 Sagadahoc
N VILLAGE B OF BOWDOINHAM
{{ 2 L }}
Chartered 3/28/65
Liquidated 8/28/90
Original Series <$VALUE
3x1-2 1-1000 <$750/$1500
4x5 1-1600 <$850
3x10-20 1-960 <$1000/$1500
Series 1875
4x5 1-1745 <$850
3x10-20 1-674 <$1000/$1500
Brown Back
4x5 1-520 <$750
3x10-20 1-997 <$750
Total Issue $213,850
Out in 1910 $1,205
****
9181 Cumberland
BRIDGTON NB, BRIDGTON
{{ 5 L }}
Chartered 7/08
Liquidated 9/1/26
1902 Date Back <$VALUE
4x5 1-2900 <$500
3x10-20 1-2920 <$500
1902 Plain Back
4x5 2901-10285 <$500
3x10-20 2921-7541 <$500
Total Issue $582,750
Out at close $48,900
****
Brunswick NB, Brunswick
SEE Ch 1315
Pejepscot NB of Brunswick
****
192 Cumberland
FNB OF BRUNSWICK
{{ 8 L 21 S }}
Organized 12/17/63
Original Series <$VALUE
3x1-2 1-1500 <$500/$1000
4x5 1-2000 <$600
4x10 1-3000 <$750
Series 1875
4x10 1-1250 <$750
50-100 1-280 <$5000
Brown Back
3x10-20 1-4499 <$400/$450
50-100 1-664 <$2500
1902 Red Seal
3x10-20 1-3425 <$500
1902 Date Back
3x10-20 1-3900 <$250
1902 Plain Back
3x10-20 3901-12172 <$250
1929 Small Size
5 Type 1 1-1216 <$100
10 Type 1 1-1342 <$100
20 Type 1 1-354 <$100
5 Type 2 1-10596 <$100
Total Issue $1,576,360
Out in 1935 $71,080
Large out 1935 $3,500
****
1315 Cumberland
PEJEPSCOT NB OF BRUNSWICK
Chartered 1865
Liquidated 11/30/31
2nd title:Brunswick NB
12/31/29
FIRST TITLE {{ 8 L 3 S }}
Original Series <$VALUE
4x5 1-1500 <$650
3x10-20 1-900 <$1000/$1500
Series 1875
4x5 1-500 <$650
3x10-20 1-1258<$1000/$1500
Brown Back
3x10-20 1-5480 <$500
1902 Red Seal
3x10-20 1-1900 <$600
1902 Date Back
3x10-20 1-4000 <$300
1902 Plain Back
3x10-20 4001-12406 <$300
1929 Small Size
10 Type 1 1-618 <$300
20 Type 1 1-212 <$325
SECOND TITLE {{ 4 S }}
1929 Small Size
10 Type 1 1-728 <$275
20 Type 1 1-217 <$275
Total Issue $1,269,440
Out at close $99,995
Large out at close $10,035
Outstanding includes Ch 1118
****

****
1118 Cumberland
UNION NB OF BRUNSWICK
{{ 8 L 2 S }}
Chartered 1865
Closed 12/31/29
Original Series <$VALUE
4x5 1-2250 <$500
3x10-20 1-900 <$850/$1500
50-100 1-400 <$5000
Series 1875
4x5 1-3085 <$500
3x10-20 1-499 <$850/$1500
50-100 1-167 <$5000
Brown Back
4x5 1-12167 <$350
3x10-20 1-1628 <$350/$400
1902 Red Seal
3x10-20 1-1900 <$500
1902 Date Back
3x10-20 1-4080 <$250
1902 Plain Back
3x10-20 4081-12486 <$250
1929 Small Size
10 Type 1 1-433 <$400
20 Type 1 1-10 <$400
Total Issue $1,332,920
Out at close $49,995
Large out at close $22,815
Ch 1315 assumed circulation
****
1079 Hancock
BUCKSPORT NB, BUCKSPORT
{{ 6 L }}
Chartered 1865
Liquidated 1/15/21
Original Series <$VALUE
3x1-2 1-2000 <$750/$1500
4x5 1-2000 <$850
3x10-20 1-2870<$1000/$1500
Series 1875
3x10-20 1-1158<$1000/$1500
Brown Back
3x10-20 1-4926 <$650
1902 Red Seal
3x10-20 1-1900 <$750
1902 Date Back
3x10-20 1-3640 <$400
1902 Plain Back
3x10-20 3641-6052 <$400
Total Issue $895,300
Out at close $45,695
****
1425 Washington
CALAIS NB, CALAIS
{{ 7 L 10 S }}
Organized 5/30/65
Receivership 1/9/34
Original Series <$VALUE
4x5 1-6050 <$650
Series 1875
4x5 1-9425 <$650
Brown Back
3x10-20 1-5363 <$500
1902 Red Seal
3x10-20 1-2100 <$600
1902 Date Back
3x10-20 1-3900 <$300
1902 Plain Back
3x10-20 3901-10751 <$300
1929 Small Size
5 Type 1 1-1762 <$150
10 Type 1 1-958 <$150
20 Type 1 1-250 <$175
Total Issue $1,360,540
Out at close $49,400
Large out at close $4,715
****
2311 Knox
CAMDEN NB, CAMDEN
{{ 11 L 12 S }}
Chartered 12/13/75
Series 1875 <$VALUE
3x10-20 1-3751 <$750/$1250
Brown Back
3x10-20 1-4350 <$350/$400
1882 Date Back
3x10-20 1-3547 <$350/$400
1902 Plain Back
4x10 1-10431 <$200
1929 Small Size
10 Type 1 1-2136 <$150
10 Type 2 1-3774 <$150
Total Issue $1,165,540
Out in 1935 $47,850
Large out 1935 $2,440
****

****
6231 Knox
MEGUNTICOOK NB OF CAMDEN
{{ 3 L }}
Chartered 4/25/02
Liquidated 9/27/21
1902 Red Seal <$VALUE
3x10-20 1-2800 <$1250
1902 Date Back
3x10-20 1-4540 <$650
1902 Plain Back
3x10-20 4541-7240 <$650
Total Issue $502,000
Out at close $47,600
****
6190 Aroostook
CARIBOU NB, CARIBOU
{{ 1 L 3 S }}
Chartered 4/4/02
Receivership 1/15/34
1902 Red Seal <$VALUE
4x5 1-700 <$2000
3x10-20 1-670 <$2000
1902 Date Back
4x5 1-1350 <$1250
3x10-20 1-960 <$1250
1902 Plain Back (dated 1902)
4x5 1351-2050 <$1250
3x10-20 961-1402 <$1250
1902 Plain Back (dated 1922)
3x10-20 1-1262 <$1250
1929 Small Size
10 Type 1 1-312 <$400
20 Type 1 1-106 <$400
10 Type 2 1-37 <$425
Total Issue $253,510
Out at close $12,500
Large out at close $700
****
446 Lincoln
FNB OF DAMARISCOTTA
{{ 6 L 15 S }}
Organized 4/30/64
Original Series <$VALUE
4x5 1-2950 <$650
3x10-20 1-900 <$1000/$1500
Series 1875
3x10-20 1-660 <$1000/$1500
Brown Back
3x10-20 1-1874 <$500
1902 Red Seal
3x10-20 1-940 <$600
1902 Date Back
3x10-20 1-3390 <$300
1902 Plain Back
3x10-20 3391-10992 <$300
1929 Small Size
10 Type 1 1-2064 <$125
20 Type 1 1-588 <$135
10 Type 2 1-2999 <$150
20 Type 2 1-656 <$150
Total Issue $1,064,810
Out in 1935 $79,550
Large out 1935 $3,980
Outstanding includes Ch 953
****
New Castle NB of Damariscotta
SEE Ch 953
New Castle NB, New Castle
****
2259 Penobscot
FNB OF DEXTER
{{ 3 L }}
Chartered 5/17/75
Liquidated 4/29/11
Original Series <$VALUE
4x5 1-2300 <$850
3x10-20 1-880 <$1000/$1500
Series 1875
4x5 1-979 <$850
3x10-20 1-3149<$1000/$1500
Brown Back
3x10-20 1-2400 <$750
1882 Date Back
3x10-20 1-512 <$750
Total Issue $412,630
Out in 1911 $16,395
****
3690 Piscataquis
KINED NB OF DOVER
{{ UNREPORTED }}
Chartered 5/2/87
Liquidated 1/1/06
Brown Back <$VALUE
3x10-20 1-3395 <$1500
Total Issue $169,750
Out in 1910 $4,680
****

****
1495 Washington
FRONTIER NB OF EASTPORT
{{ 6 L 7 S }}
Chartered 1865
Liquidated 7/15/31
Original Series <$VALUE
3x1-2 1-1150 <$650/$1500
4x5 1-3546 <$750
4x10 1-700 <$1000
Series 1875
4x5 1-2318 <$750
4x10 1-1086 <$1000
Brown Back
4x5 1-10537 <$500
3x10-20 1-1399 <$500
1902 Red Seal
3x10-20 1-1600 <$600
1902 Date Back
3x10-20 1-3500 <$275
1902 Plain Back
3x10-20 3501-14313 <$275
1929 Small Size
10 Type 1 1-1469 <$225
20 Type 1 1-428 <$225
Total Issue $1,410,310
Out at close $80,380
Large out at close $10,490
****
3941 Hancock
FNB OF BAR HARBOR, EDEN
Chartered 11/17/88
2nd title: FNB of Bar
Harbor, Bar Harbor
FIRST TITLE {{ 4 L }}
Brown Back <$VALUE
4x5 1-3266 <$1500
50-100 1-171 <$3500
SECOND TITLE {{ 3 L U + 3 S }}
1902 Red Seal
3x10-20 1-120 <$2000
1902 Date Back
3x10-20 1-1300 <$1250
1902 Plain Back
3x10-20 1301-3065 <$1250
1929 Small Size
10 Type 1 1-314 <$600
20 Type 1 1-104 <$600
10 Type 2 1-307 <$650
20 Type 2 1-65 <$650
Total Issue $285,910
Out in 1935 $12,350
Large out 1935 $730
****
3804 Hancock
BURRILL NB OF ELLSWORTH
Chartered 10/24/87
Liquidated 1/8/35
2nd title:Liberty NB of
Ellsworth 11/15/19
FIRST TITLE {{ 3 L }}
Brown Back <$VALUE
4x5 1-3146 <$650
3x10-20 1-646 <$650
1902 Red Seal
4x5 1-200 <$750
3x10-20 1-170 <$750
1902 Date Back
4x5 1-3700* <$250
3x10-20 1-2860** <$250
1902 Plain Back
4x5 3951-6150* <$250
3x10-20 3021-4100** <$250
* 3701-3950 not marked
** 2861-3020 not marked
SECOND TITLE {{ 6 L 14 S }}
1902 Plain Back
4x5 1-6442 <$200
3x10-20 1-4341 <$200
1929 Small Size
5 Type 1 1-1854 <$125
10 Type 1 1-950 <$125
20 Type 1 1-252 <$135
5 Type 2 1-1644 <$150
10 Type 2 1-816 <$150
20 Type 2 1-252 <$165
Total Issue $945,890
Out at close $39,490
Large out at close $2,120
Ch 14303 assumed circulation
****
3814 Hancock
FNB OF ELLSWORTH
{{ UNREPORTED }}
Chartered 11/19/87
Liquidated 9/10/07
Brown Back <$VALUE
4x5 1-3447 <$1500
3x10-20 1-4000 <$1500
Total Issue $268,940
Out in 1910 $8,235
****
Liberty NB of Ellsworth
SEE Ch 3814
Burrill NB of Ellsworth
****

****
2175 Somerset
FNB OF FAIRFIELD
{{ UNREPORTED }}
Chartered 8/24/74
Liquidated 8/1/94
Original Series <$VALUE
50-100 1-600 <$6000
Series 1875
50-100 1-342 <$6000
Total Issue $141,300
Out in 1910 $700
****
4973 Somerset
NB OF FAIRFIELD
{{ 2 L }}
Chartered 1894
Liquidated 4/21/19
Brown Back <$VALUE
3x10-20 1-2900 <$1000
1882 Date Back
3x10-20 1-1469 <$1000
1902 Date Back
3x10-20 1-1210 <$650
Total Issue $278,950
Out at close $24,700
****
4459 Franklin
FNB OF FARMINGTON
{{ 5 L 9 S }}
Organized 10/18/90
Brown Back <$VALUE
3x10-20 1-3270 <$600
1882 Date Back
4x5 1-995 <$600
3x10-20 1-389 <$600
1902 Date Back
4x5 1-2750 <$250
3x10-20 1-2080 <$250
1902 Plain Back
4x5 2751-9730 <$250
3x10-20 2081-6731 <$250
1929 Small Size
5 Type 1 1-1482 <$165
10 Type 1 1-816 <$165
20 Type 1 1-230 <$165
5 Type 2 1-918 <$200
10 Type 2 1-746 <$200
20 Type 2 1-216 <$200
Total Issue $871,390
Out in 1935 $39,450
Large out 1935 $1,680
****
5861 Franklin
PEOPLES NB OF FARMINGTON
{{ 9 L 13 S }}
Chartered 6/14/01
Brown Back <$VALUE
3x10-20 1-2500 <$500
1882 Date Back
3x10-20 1-3250 <$500
1882 Value Back
3x10-20 3251-5742 <$800
1902 Plain Back
3x10-20 1-3998 <$200
1929 Small Size
10 Type 1 1-922 <$150
20 Type 1 1-254 <$150
10 Type 2 1-923 <$165
20 Type 2 1-274 <$165
Total Issue $712,510
Out in 1935 $35,650
Large out 1935 $2,140
****
901 Franklin
SANDY RIVER NB OF
FARMINGTON
{{ UNREPORTED }}
Chartered 3/16/65
Liquidated 11/1/90
Original Series <$VALUE
3x1-2 1-1000 <$1500/$2500
4x5 1-2975 <$2000
3x10-20 1-1400<$2000/$2500
Series 1875
3x10-20 1-2166<$2000/$2500
Brown Back
3x10-20 1-1882 <$1500
Total Issue $336,900
Out in 1910 $1,617
****
13843 Aroostook
FNB OF FORT FAIRFIELD
{{ 1 L }}
Chartered 11/33
1929 Small Size <$VALUE
5 Type 2 1-1686 <$500
10 Type 2 1-890 <$500
Total Issue $17,330
Out in 1935 $9,950
****

****
4781 Aroostook
FORT FAIRFIELD NB,
FORT FAIRFIELD
{{ 1 L 3 S }}
Organized 5/23/92
Receivership 1/8/34
Brown Back <$VALUE
4x5 1-2750 <$1500
3x10-20 1-750 <$1500
1882 Date Back
4x5 1-468 <$1500
3x10-20 1-361 <$1500
1902 Date Back
3x10-20 1-1020 <$850
1902 Plain Back
3x10-20 1021-2964 <$850
1929 Small Size
10 Type 1 1-340 <$400
20 Type 1 1-102 <$400
Total Issue $300,750
Out at close $12,500
Large out at close $740
****
14224 Aroostook
FNB IN FORT KENT
{{ 3 S }}
Chartered 7/34
1929 Small Size <$VALUE
10 Type 2 1-2916 <$450
Total Issue $29,160
Out in 1935 $47,740
Large out 1935 $46,260
Outstanding includes Ch 11403
****
11403 Aroostook
FNB OF FORT KENT
{{ 5 L 6 S }}
Organized 7/7/19
Liquidated 10/31/34
1902 Plain Back <$VALUE
4x5 1-27473 <$500
1929 Small Size
5 Type 1 1-6104 <$200
5 Type 2 1-5408 <$200
Total Issue $759,620
Out at close $37,430
Large out at close $1,230
Ch 14224 assumed circulation
****
939 Kennebec
COBBOSSOE NB OF GARDINER
{{ 1 L }}
Chartered 3/27/65
Liquidated 4/18/84
Original Series <$VALUE
3x1-2 1-1000 <$1500/$2500
4x5 1-2600 <$1500
3x10-20 1-2520<$2000/$2500
Series 1875
4x5 1-2000 <$1500
3x10-20 1-1716<$2000/$2500
Total Issue $308,800
Out in 1910 $1,621
****
1174 Kennebec
GARDINER NB, GARDINER
{{ 4 L }}
Chartered 1865
Liquidated 12/15/09
Original Series <$VALUE
4x5 1-1600 <$850
3x10-20 1-1100<$1000/$1500
Series 1875
4x5 1-450 <$850
3x10-20 1-1133<$1000/$1500
Brown Back
3x10-20 1-4651 <$750
1902 Red Seal
3x10-20 1-375 <$800
Total Issue $403,950
Out in 1910 $6,660
****
3219 Kennebec
MERCHANTS NB OF GARDINER
{{ UNREPORTED }}
Chartered 7/11/84
Liquidated 7/1/03
Brown Back <$VALUE
4x5 1-750 <$1500
3x10-20 1-2227 <$1500
Total Issue $126,350
Out in 1910 $1,415
****

<$VALUEs are for notes in FINE condition. Value changes by approximately 25% for a change of one full grade.

****
9609 Kennebec
NB OF GARDINER
{{ 2 L 4 S }}
Organized 11/5/09
1902 Date Back <$VALUE
4x5 1-2250 <$750
3x10-20 1-2280 <$750
1902 Plain Back
4x5 2251-3300 <$850
3x10-20 2281-2966 <$850
1929 Small Size
5 Type 2 1-5220 <$400
10 Type 2 1-2735 <$400
Total Issue $267,750
Out in 1935 $42,145
Large out 1935 $245
****
740 Kennebec
OAKLAND NB OF GARDINER
{{ 3 L }}
Chartered 1/23/65
Liquidated 12/15/09
Original Series <$VALUE
3x1-2 1-2000 <$750/$1500
4x5 1-2625 <$850
3x10-20 1-2300<$1000/$1500
Series 1875
4x5 1-475 <$850
3x10-20 1-1454<$1000/$1500
Brown Back
4x5 1-6985 <$750
3x10-20 1-883 <$750
1902 Red Seal
3x10-20 1-500 <$850
1902 Date Back
3x10-20 1-15 <$500
Total Issue $469,300
Out in 1910 $6,105
****
4780 Piscataquis
FNB OF GUILFORD
{{ 1 L }}
Chartered 7/19/92
Liquidated 5/1/06
Brown Back <$VALUE
3x10-20 1-1890 <$1500
Total Issue $94,500
Out in 1910 $2,600
****
624 Kennebec
AMERICAN NB OF HALLOWELL
{{ UNREPORTED }}
Chartered 1864
Liquidated 9/10/84
Original Series <$VALUE
4x5 1-2300 <$1750
3x10-20 1-1380<$2000/$2500
Series 1875
4x5 1-965 <$1750
3x10-20 1-1400<$2000/$2500
Total Issue $204,300
Out in 1910 $920
****
310 Kennebec
FNB OF HALLOWELL
{{ UNREPORTED }}
Chartered 3/11/64
Liquidated 4/19/69
Original Series <$VALUE
3x1-2 1-100 <$1750/$2500
4x5 1-1500 <$2000
3x10-20 1-477 <$2000/$2500
Total Issue $54,350
Out in 1910 $378
****
3247 Kennebec
HALLOWELL NB, HALLOWELL
{{ 1 L }}
Chartered 1884
Liquidated 4/4/10
Brown Back <$VALUE
3x10-20 1-2551 <$1500
1902 Red Seal
3x10-20 1-1100 <$1500
1902 Date Back
3x10-20 1-393 <$1000
Total Issue $202,200
Out in 1910 $23,670
****
532 Kennebec
NORTHERN NB OF HALLOWELL
{{ 2 L }}
Chartered 1864
Liquidated 4/4/10
Original Series <$VALUE
3x1-2 1-2000 <$1250/$2000
4x5 1-2000 <$1250
3x10-20 1-2500<$1500/$2000
Series 1875
4x5 1-1250 <$1250
3x10-20 1-2024<$1500/$2000
Brown Back
4x5 1-6697 <$1000
3x10-20 1-9020 <$1000
1902 Red Seal
4x5 1-4250 <$1000
3x10-20 1-2500 <$1000
1902 Date Back
4x5 1-1525 <$600
3x10-20 1-1312 <$600
Total Issue $1,192,240
Out in 1910 $61,020
****
4252 Aroostook
FARMERS NB OF HOULTON
{{ 2 L 3 S }}
Organized 1/27/90
Receivership 1/9/34
Brown Back <$VALUE
4x5 1-2875 <$1250
3x10-20 1-690 <$1250
1882 Date Back
4x5 1-180 <$1250
3x10-20 1-100 <$1250
1902 Date Back
4x5 1-1125 <$750
3x10-20 1-900 <$750
1902 Plain Back
4x5 1126-3915 <$750
3x10-20 901-2639 <$750
1929 Small Size
5 Type 1 1-934 <$350
10 Type 1 1-436 <$350
20 Type 1 1-124 <$350
5 Type 2 1-528 <$400
10 Type 2 1-189 <$400
20 Type 2 1-63 <$400
Total Issue $385,700
Out at close $25,000
Large out at close $730
****
2749 Aroostook
FNB OF HOULTON
{{ 7 L 14 S }}
Chartered 1882
Series 1875 <$VALUE
4x5 1-1850 <$750
3x10-20 1-1617<$1000/$1500
1902 Red Seal
3x10-20 1-1400 <$750
1902 Date Back
3x10-20 1-4600 <$350
1902 Plain Back (dated 1902)
3x10-20 4601-8271 <$350
1902 Plain Back (dated 1921)
3x10-20 1-5402 <$350
1929 Small Size
10 Type 1 1-1422 <$125
20 Type 1 1-346 <$125
10 Type 2 1-8357 <$150
20 Type 2 1-2474 <$150
Total Issue $1,131,390
Out in 1935 $123,630
Large out 1935 $2,100
****
1254 York
OCEAN NB OF KENNEBUNK
{{ 4 L }}
Chartered 1865
Original Series <$VALUE
4x5 1-3550 <$1000
3x10-20 1-1700<$1000/$1500
50-100 1-260 <$5000
Series 1875
4x5 1-1675 <$1000
3x10-20 1-1326<$1000/$1500
50-100 1-148 <$5000
Brown Back
3x10-20 1-3217 <$850
1902 Red Seal
3x10-20 1-900 <$1000
1902 Date Back
4x5 1-2215 <$600
3x10-20 1-1440 <$600
1902 Plain Back
4x5 2216-5630 <$600
3x10-20 1441-3595 <$600
Total Issue $815,200
Out in 1935 $2,520
****
9826 York
KEZAR FALLS NB,
KEZAR FALLS
{{ 2 L 10 S }}
Chartered 8/10
1902 Date Back <$VALUE
3x10-20 1-2130 <$850
1902 Plain Back
3x10-20 2131-7926 <$850
1929 Small Size
10 Type 1 1-1548 <$175
20 Type 1 1-350 <$200
10 Type 2 1-1785 <$225
20 Type 2 1-411 <$225
Total Issue $557,250
Out in 1935 $48,750
Large out in 1935 NONE*
* Census confirms 2 large
****
330 Androscoggin
FNB OF LEWISTON
{{ U + 41 L 50+ S }}
Organized 2/6/64
Original Series <$VALUE
3x1-2 1-10700 <$300/$850
4x5 1-6700 <$350
3x10-20 1-8665 <$750/$1250
50-100 1-1090 <$5000
Series 1875
3x1-2 1-4960 <$300/$850
4x5 1-5430 <$350
3x10-20 1-4381 <$750/$1250
50-100 1-176 <$5000
Brown Back
4x5 1-44910 <$250
3x10-20 1-25494 <$250/$300
1902 Red Seal
4x5 1-19500 <$350
3x10-20 1-14800 <$350
1902 Date Back
4x5 1-34500 <$75
3x10-20 1-21900 <$75
1902 Plain Back
4x5 34501-105659 <$75
3x10-20 21901-69790 <$75
1929 Small Size
5 Type 1 1-16028 <$35
10 Type 1 1-7286 <$40
20 Type 1 1-1946 <$50
5 Type 2 1-28332 <$35
10 Type 2 1-12996 <$40
20 Type 2 1-2532 <$50
Total Issue $11,542,460
Out in 1935 $547,320
Large out 1935 $27,650
****
2260 Androscoggin
MANUFACTURERS NB OF
LEWISTON
{{ 18 L 34 S }}
Chartered 5/17/75
Original Series <$VALUE
4x5 1-1800 <$400
3x10-20 1-1080 <$750/$1250
Series 1875
4x5 1-250 <$400
3x10-20 1-7252 <$750/$1250
Brown Back
3x10-20 1-6360 <$300
1882 Date Back
4x5 1-12000 <$300
3x10-20 1-9077 <$300
1902 Date Back
4x5 1-2500 <$100
3x10-20 1-2000 <$100
1902 Plain Back
4x5 2501-40165 <$100
3x10-20 2001-26428 <$100
1929 Small Size
5 Type 1 1-6942 <$40
10 Type 1 1-3872 <$40
20 Type 1 1-1056 <$50
5 Type 2 1-18262 <$50
10 Type 2 1-3789 <$50
20 Type 2 1-1218 <$60
Total Issue $4,315,010
Out in 1935 $200,000
Large out 1935 $8,195
****
2785 York
LIMERICK NB, LIMERICK
{{ 10 L 6 S }}
Chartered 1882
Liquidated 8/6/31
Brown Back <$VALUE
4x5 1-1891 <$500
3x10-20 1-3250 <$500
1902 Red Seal
3x10-20 1-3000 <$600
1902 Date Back
4x5 1-4280* <$200
3x10-20 1-2660*** <$200
1902 Plain Back
4x5 4531-13520* <$200
3x10-20 2821-8649** <$200
* 4281-4530 not marked
** 2661-2820 not marked
1929 Small Size
5 Type 1 1-938 <$250
10 Type 1 1-477 <$250
20 Type 1 1-137 <$275
Total Issue $1,126,370
Out at close $41,770
Large out at close $4,610
****

****
11462 Washington
MACHIAS NB, MACHIAS
{{ 1 L }}
Chartered 9/19
Liquidated 1/15/21
1902 Plain Back <$VALUE
4x5 1-515 <$1250
3x10-20 1-430 <$1250
Total Issue $31,800
Out at close $19,300
****
4647 Somerset
FNB OF MADISON
{{ 1 L }}
Chartered 10/21/91
Liquidated 2/28/07
Brown Back <$VALUE
3x10-20 1-2097 <$1500
Total Issue $104,850
Out in 1910 $2,940
****
953 Lincoln
NEW CASTLE NB, NEW CASTLE
Chartered 3/30/65
Closed 6/19/33
2nd title:New Castle NB of
Damariscotta 11/16/08
FIRST TITLE {{ 2 L }}
Original Series <$VALUE
3x1-2 1-900 <$1000/$2000
4x5 1-1300 <$1000
3x10-20 1-1500<$1250/$2000
Series 1875
3x10-20 1-898 <$1250/$2000
Brown Back
3x10-20 1-3181 <$850
1902 Red Seal
3x10-20 1-1035 <$1000
SECOND TITLE {{ 3 L 5 S }}
1902 Date Back
3x10-20 1-2700 <$500
1902 Plain Back
3x10-20 2701-7618 <$500
1929 Small Size
10 Type 1 1-778 <$350
20 Type 1 1-210 <$350
Total Issue $813,980
Out at close $32,000
Large out at close $1,720
Ch 446 assumed circulation
****
1523 York
NORTH BERWICK NB,
NORTH BERWICK
{{ 7 L 11 S }}
Organized 7/20/65
Original Series <$VALUE
4x5 1-1600 <$650
3x10-20 1-800 <$1000/$1500
Series 1875
4x5 1-2500 <$650
3x10-20 1-840 <$1000/$1500
Brown Back
4x5 1-3421 <$500
3x10-20 1-1499 <$500
1902 Red Seal
4x5 1-1150 <$600
3x10-20 1-720 <$600
1902 Date Back
4x5 1-3200 <$250
3x10-20 1-2480 <$250
1902 Plain Back
4x5 3201-10367 <$250
3x10-20 2481-7170 <$250
1929 Small Size
5 Type 1 1-1590 <$150
10 Type 1 1-766 <$150
20 Type 1 1-192 <$150
5 Type 2 1-1446 <$165
10 Type 2 1-1106 <$165
20 Type 2 1-292 <$175
Total Issue $1,073,040
Out in 1935 $42,695
Large out 1935 $3,095
****
1956 Oxford
NORWAY NB, NORWAY
{{ 6 L 4 S }}
Chartered 4/10/72
Liquidated 7/25/31
Original Series <$VALUE
3x1-2 1-1000 <$600/$1250
4x5 1-3800 <$650
3x10-20 1-800 <$850/$1500
50-100 1-60 <$5000
Series 1875
3x10-20 1-3431 <$850/$1500
Brown Back
3x10-20 1-3540 <$600
1882 Date Back
4x5 1-1610 <$600
3x10-20 1-815 <$600
1902 Date Back
4x5 1-1775 <$250
3x10-20 1-1360 <$250
1902 Plain Back
4x5 1776-9045 <$250
3x10-20 1361-6132 <$250
1929 Small Size
10 Type 1 1-685 <$275
20 Type 1 1-191 <$275
Total Issue $1,103,020
Out at close $40,700
Large out at close $4,120
****
13750 Oxford
NORWAY NB, NORWAY
{{ 4 S }}
Chartered 8/33
1929 Small Size <$VALUE
5 Type 2 1-3806 <$300
10 Type 2 1-1804 <$300
20 Type 2 1-600 <$300
Total Issue $49,070
Out in 1935 $20,850
****
Messalonskee NB of Oakland
SEE Ch 2231
West Waterville NB of Oakland
****
2231 Kennebec
WEST WATERVILLE NB OF
OAKLAND
Chartered 3/10/75
Liquidated 5/1/24
2nd title:Messalonskee NB
of Oakland 4/15/84
FIRST TITLE {{ 1 L }}
Original Series <$VALUE
3x10-20 1-2150<$1500/$2000
Series 1875
3x10-20 1-724 <$1500/$2000
SECOND TITLE {{ 2 L }}
Series 1875
3x10-20 1-1729<$1500/$2000
Brown Back
3x10-20 1-1960 <$1250
1882 Date Back
3x10-20 1-1611 <$1250
1902 Date Back
3x10-20 1-400* <$600
1902 Plain Back
3x10-20 601-2286* <$600
* 401-600 not marked
Total Issue $523,000
Out at close $19,500
****
1134 Penobscot
ORONO NB, ORONO
{{ 2 L }}
Chartered 5/13/65
Liquidated 7/29/93
Original Series <$VALUE
4x5 1-1900 <$1500
3x10-20 1-800 <$2000/$2500
Series 1875
4x5 1-1900 <$1500
3x10-20 1-600 <$2000/$2500
Brown Back
4x5 1-1947 <$1250
Total Issue $184,940
Out in 1910 $1,120
****
4957 Franklin
PHILLIPS NB, PHILLIPS
{{ 3 L 8 S }}
Chartered 1894
Brown Back <$VALUE
3x10-20 1-5050 <$1250
1882 Date Back
3x10-20 1-3127 <$1250
1902 Date Back
3x10-20 1-1500 <$600
1902 Plain Back
3x10-20 1501-4368 <$600
1929 Small Size
10 Type 1 1-840 <$200
20 Type 1 1-206 <$200
10 Type 2 1-1258 <$225
20 Type 2 1-200 <$225
Total Issue $718,950
Out in 1935 $40,750
Large out 1935 $450
****
2267 Franklin
UNION NB OF PHILLIPS
{{ 2 L }}
Chartered 5/22/75
Liquidated 4/26/95
Original Series <$VALUE
3x1-2 1-360 <$1000/$1500
4x5 1-510 <$1000
3x10-20 1-300 <$1250/$1500
Series 1875
3x1-2 1-400 <$1000/$1500
4x5 1-750 <$1000
3x10-20 1-3104<$1250/$1500
Total Issue $199,200
Out in 1910 $1,222
****
13777 Somerset
FNB OF PITTSFIELD
{{ 6 S }}
Chartered 9/33
1929 Small Size <$VALUE
5 Type 2 1-5736 <$200
10 Type 2 1-2772 <$200
20 Type 2 1-828 <$200
Total Issue $72,960
Out in 1935 $46,210
****
4188 Somerset
PITTSFIELD NB, PITTSFIELD
{{ 6 L 10 S }}
Chartered 12/23/89
Receivership 1/3/34
Brown Back <$VALUE
3x10-20 1-4090 <$500
1882 Date Back
3x10-20 1-375 <$500
1902 Date Back
3x10-20 1-3800 <$300
1902 Plain Back
3x10-20 3801-12140 <$300
1929 Small Size
10 Type 1 1-1294 <$135
20 Type 1 1-356 <$150
Total Issue $950,610
Out at close $50,000
Large out at close $2,770
****
941 Cumberland
CANAL NB OF PORTLAND
{{ 29 L U + 37 S }}
Chartered 3/27/65
Original Series <$VALUE
3x1-2 1-4310 <$350/$1000
4x5 1-6100 <$400
4x10 1-2100 <$750
2x20-50-100 1-3570
<$1250/$5000/$5000
500 1-100 <$150,000
Series 1875
4x5 1-6700 <$400
4x10 1-4900 <$750
2x20-50-100 1-2150
<$1250/$5000/$5000
Brown Back
4x5 1-3860 <$225
3x10-20 1-4624 <$225/$275
50-100 1-1697 <$2500
1902 Red Seal
4x5 1-8650 <$350
3x10-20 1-5940 <$350/$400
50-100 1-200 <$4000
1902 Date Back
4x5 1-23250 <$60
3x10-20 1-15800 <$75
50-100 1-400 <$750/$850
3x50-100 1-760 <$750/$850
1902 Plain Back
4x5 23251-101092 <$60
3x10-20 15801-28700 <$75
1929 Small Size
5 Type 1 1-34268 <$45
5 Type 2 1-132540 <$50
Total Issue $8,154,880
Out in 1935 $268,940
Large out 1935 $16,105
****
1060 Cumberland
CASCO NB, PORTLAND
{{ 4 L }}
Chartered 1865
Liquidated 12/31/15
Original Series <$VALUE
4x5 1-11745 <$650
3x10-20 1-6284 <$850/$1500
50-100 1-1790 <$5000
500 1-290 <$150,000
Brown Back
4x5 1-75420 <$500
3x10-20 1-1388 <$500
1902 Red Seal
4x5 1-1150 <$600
3x10-20 1-1340 <$600
1902 Date Back
4x5 1-6165 <$300
3x10-20 1-4655 <$300
Total Issue $2,986,450
Out in 1916 $52,280
****

4868 Cumberland
CHAPMAN NB OF PORTLAND
{{ 23 L }}
Chartered 1893
Liquidated 5/1/29
Brown Back <$VALUE
4x5 1-11250 <$250
3x10-20 1-4740 <$250/$300
1882 Date Back
4x5 1-5876 <$250
3x10-20 1-4444 <$250/$300
1902 Date Back
4x5 1-2250 <$65
3x10-20 1-2000 <$75
1902 Plain Back
4x5 2251-45151 <$65
3x10-20 2001-28121 <$75
Total Issue $3,110,790
Out at close $390,960

1511 Cumberland
CUMBERLAND NB OF PORTLAND
{{ 5 L }}
Chartered 1865
Liquidated 9/30/12
Original Series <$VALUE
3x1-2 1-3000 <$600/$1250
4x5 1-3500 <$650
3x10-20 1-4100 <$850/$1500
3x50-100 1-300 <$5000
Series 1875
3x1-2 1-2040 <$600/$1250
4x5 1-11000 <$650
3x10-20 1-2744 <$850/$1500
3x50-100 1-100 <$5000
Brown Back
4x5 1-5400 <$500
3x10-20 1-3860 <$500
1902 Red Seal
3x10-20 1-1475 <$650
1902 Date Back
3x10-20 1-1181 <$400
Total Issue $1,191,200
Out at close $35,100

13716 Cumberland
FNB AT PORTLAND
{{ 28 S }}
Chartered 6/33
1929 Small Size <$VALUE
5 Type 2 1-35390 <$50
10 Type 2 1-20327 <$50
20 Type 2 1-6782 <$60
Total Issue $515,860
Out in 1935 $302,300

221 Cumberland
FNB OF PORTLAND
{{ 41 L 50+ S }}
Organized 1/4/64
Receivership 11/6/33
Original Series <$VALUE
3x1-2 1-8046 <$350/$1000
4x5 1-11350 <$350
4x10 1-10575 <$750
2x20-50-100 1-1909
<$1250/$5000/$5000
50-100 1910-3500
<$5000
Series 1875
4x5 1-6255 <$350
4x10 1-6245 <$750
2x20-50-100 1-2069
<$1250/$5000/$5000
Brown Back
4x5 1-11476 <$225
3x10-20 1-8574 <$225/$275
50-100 1-1963 <$2500
1902 Red Seal
4x5 1-2900 <$300
3x10-20 1-2100 <$300/$350
1902 Date Back
4x5 1-21750 <$50
3x10-20 1-16500 <$65
1902 Plain Back
4x5 21751-218308 <$50
3x10-20 16501-45800 <$65
1929 Small Size
5 Type 1 1-52998 <$40
10 Type 1 1-6898 <$40
5 Type 2 1-15206 <$40
10 Type 2 1-3270 <$40
Total Issue $11,943,980
Out at close $596,700
Large out at close $31,770

1023 Cumberland
MERCHANTS NB OF PORTLAND
{{ 10 L }}
Chartered 4/17/65
Liquidated 9/30/05
Original Series <$VALUE
3x1-2 1-6000 <$350/$1000
4x5 1-6750 <$400
3x10-20 1-1900 <$750/$1250
50-100 1-1154 <$5000
500 1-170 <$150,000
Series 1875
3x1-2 1-2000 <$350/$1000
4x5 1-9250 <$400
3x10-20 1-4189 <$750/$1250
50-100 1-653 <$5000
500 1-9 <$150,000
Brown Back
4x5 1-29196 <$300
3x10-20 1-3408 <$300
50-100 1-507 <$2500
1902 Red Seal
4x5 1-190 <$350
3x10-20 1-152 <$350/$400
Total Issue $1,866,770
Out in 1910 $14,936

13710 Cumberland
NB OF COMMERCE OF PORTLAND
{{ 9 S }}
Chartered 6/33
1929 Small Size <$VALUE
5 Type 2 1-11788 <$125
10 Type 2 1-4644 <$125
20 Type 2 1-1776 <$135
Total Issue $140,900
Out in 1935 $98,450

1451 Cumberland
N TRADERS B OF PORTLAND
{{ 10 L }}
Chartered 7/17/65
Liquidated 9/15/08
Original Series <$VALUE
4x5 1-3700 <$500
3x10-20 1-2110 <$750/$1250
50-100 1-1375 <$5000
Series 1875
4x5 1-4850 <$500
3x10-20 1-2499 <$750/$1250
50-100 1-1200 <$5000
Brown Back
4x5 1-4875 <$400
3x10-20 1-3100 <$400
50-100 1-1156 <$2500
1902 Red Seal
3x10-20 1-1507 <$500
Total Issue $1,288,950
Out in 1910 $20,350

4128 Cumberland
PORTLAND NB, PORTLAND
{{ 21 L 2U + 40 S }}
Chartered 9/25/89
Brown Back <$VALUE
4x5 1-12000 <$250
3x10-20 1-27700 <$250/$300
1882 Date Back
4x5 1-2295 <$250
3x10-20 1-1732 <$250/$300
1902 Date Back
4x5 1-20000 <$60
3x10-20 1-16000 <$75
1902 Plain Back
4x5 20001-78985 <$60
3x10-20 16001-52103 <$75
1929 Small Size
5 Type 1 1-12232 <$40
10 Type 1 1-5442 <$40
20 Type 1 1-1410 <$50
5 Type 2 1-13974 <$40
10 Type 2 1-8430 <$40
20 Type 2 1-1835 <$50
Total Issue $6,995,900
Out in 1935 $234,100
Large out 1935 $12,620

878 Cumberland
SECOND NB OF PORTLAND
{{ UNREPORTED }}
Chartered 3/11/65
Liquidated 6/24/72
Original Series <$VALUE
4x5 1-1314 <$2000
4x10 1-500 <$2000
2x20-50-100 1-238
<$2500/$5000/$5000
Total Issue $91,500
Out in 1910 $845

13768 Aroostook
NORTHERN NB OF PRESQUE ISLE
{{ 10 S }}
Chartered 9/33
1929 Small Size <$VALUE
10 Type 2 1-6073 <$200
20 Type 2 1-3015 <$200
Total Issue $121,030
Out in 1935 $97,400

3827 Aroostook
PRESQUE ISLE NB, PRESQUE ISLE
{{ 2 L 4 S }}
Chartered 12/28/87
Receivership 11/7/33
Brown Back <$VALUE
3x10-20 1-1606 <$1250
1902 Red Seal
3x10-20 1-125 <$1500
1902 Date Back
3x10-20 1-1500 <$850
1902 Plain Back
3x10-20 1501-3085 <$850
1929 Small Size
10 Type 1 1-314 <$350
20 Type 1 1-104 <$350
10 Type 2 1-43 <$375
Total Issue $272,550
Out at close $12,500
Large out at close $690

662 Sagadahoc
FNB OF RICHMOND
{{ 3 L }}
Chartered 1864
Liquidated 4/5/16
Original Series <$VALUE
4x5 1-1077 <$850
3x10-20 1-1840<$1000/$1500
Series 1875
4x5 1-400 <$850
3x10-20 1-887 <$1000/$1500
Brown Back
3x10-20 1-5056 <$750
1902 Red Seal
3x10-20 1-2000 <$850
1902 Date Back
3x10-20 1-3540 <$500
1902 Plain Back
3x10-20 3541-3633 <$500
Total Issue $700,340
Out in 1916 $33,690

909 Sagadahoc
RICHMOND NB, RICHMOND
{{ 4 L }}
Chartered 3/18/65
Liquidated 8/1/10
Original Series <$VALUE
3x1-2 1-2000 <$600/$1250
4x5 1-2100 <$750
3x10-20 1-2060 <$850/$1500
50-100 1-325 <$5000
Series 1875
3x1-2 1-1208 <$600/$1250
4x5 1-3418 <$750
3x10-20 1-1180 <$850/$1500
50-100 1-400 <$5000
Brown Back
4x5 1-5595 <$650
50-100 1-594 <$2500
1902 Red Seal
3x10-20 1-1040 <$750
1902 Date Back
3x10-20 1-382 <$400
Total Issue $669,250
Out in 1910 $26,600

2097 Knox
LIME ROCK NB OF ROCKLAND
{{ 4 L }}
Chartered 4/2/73
Liquidated 9/1/03
Original Series <$VALUE
3x1-2 1-2900 <$650/$1250
4x5 1-1000 <$650
3x10-20 1-1610 <$750/$1250
Series 1875
4x5 1-550 <$650
3x10-20 1-3547 <$750/$1250
Brown Back
3x10-20 1-3933 <$500
Total Issue $500,000
Out in 1910 $7,061

2371 Knox
NORTH NB OF ROCKLAND
{{ 19 L 8 S }}
Chartered 9/15/77
Liquidated 5/29/31
Series 1875 <$VALUE
4x5 1-4250 <$450
3x10-20 1-3539 <$750/$1250
Brown Back
3x10-20 1-4320 <$300
1882 Date Back
3x10-20 1-6900 <$300
1882 Value Back
3x10-20 6901-8108 <$750
1902 Plain Back
4x5 1-13924 <$150
4x10 1-10489 <$150
1929 Small Size
5 Type 1 1-2000 <$150
10 Type 1 1-1092 <$165
Total Issue $1,706,910
Out at close $76,060
Large out at close $8,080

1446 Knox
ROCKLAND NB, ROCKLAND
{{ 20 L 20 S }}
Organized 6/24/65
Receivership 8/18/33
Original Series <$VALUE
4x5 1-2500 <$450
3x10-20 1-2000 <$750/$1250
50-100 1-934 <$5000
Series 1875
4x5 1-2895 <$450
3x10-20 1-1566 <$750/$1250
Brown Back
4x5 1-6874 <$250
3x10-20 1-4507 <$250/$300
1902 Red Seal
4x5 1-4815 <$350
3x10-20 1-3574 <$350/$400
1902 Date Back
4x5 1-11000 <$125
3x10-20 1-8000 <$125
1902 Plain Back
4x5 11001-36265 <$125
3x10-20 8001-23269 <$125
1929 Small Size
5 Type 1 1-4943 <$60
10 Type 1 1-2705 <$65
20 Type 1 1-664 <$75
Total Issue $3,343,150
Out at close $149,100
Large out at close $9,890

6287 Oxford
RUMFORD NB, RUMFORD
{{ 5 L 9 S }}
Chartered 6/4/02
1902 Red Seal <$VALUE
4x5 1-2000 <$1000
3x10-20 1-1920 <$1000
1902 Date Back
4x5 1-4050 <$400
3x10-20 1-2820 <$400
1902 Plain Back (dated 1902)
4x5 4051-6900 <$400
3x10-20 2821-4460 <$400
1902 Plain Back (dated 1922)
3x10-20 1-3694 <$400
1929 Small Size
10 Type 1 1-1098 <$175
20 Type 1 1-298 <$175
10 Type 2 1-876 <$225
20 Type 2 1-115 <$225
Total Issue $794,400
Out in 1935 $34,500
Large out 1935 $1,160

1535 York
SACO NB, SACO
{{ 10 L }}
Chartered 1865
Liquidated 3/29/28
Original Series <$VALUE
3x1-2 1-2000 <$500/$1250
4x5 1-3900 <$500
3x10-20 1-1200 <$750/$1250
50-100 1-100 <$5000
Series 1875
4x5 1-480 <$500
3x10-20 1-2910 <$750/$1250
Brown Back
3x10-20 1-8197 <$350/$400
1902 Red Seal
3x10-20 1-4000 <$500
1902 Date Back
3x10-20 1-8300 <$200
1902 Plain Back
3x10-20 8301-19168 <$200
Total Issue $1,886,350
Out at close $45,350

1528 York
YORK NB OF SACO
{{ 16 L 21 S }}
Chartered 1865
Original Series <$VALUE
3x1-2 1-2200 <$500/$1250
4x5 1-5425 <$500
3x10-20 1-1600 <$750/$1250
Series 1875
4x5 1-2565 <$500
3x10-20 1-1800 <$750/$1250
Brown Back
4x5 1-13339 <$300
3x10-20 1-7193 <$300/$350
1902 Red Seal
4x5 1-3600 <$400
3x10-20 1-2060 <$400
1902 Date Back
4x5 1-8130 <$150
3x10-20 1-6168 <$150
1902 Plain Back
4x5 8131-25947 <$150
3x10-20 6169-18015 <$150
1929 Small Size
5 Type 1 1-3936 <$60
10 Type 1 1-1878 <$65
20 Type 1 1-430 <$75
5 Type 2 1-5876 <$85
10 Type 2 1-3036 <$85
20 Type 2 1-888 <$100
Total Issue $2,921,780
Out in 1935 $95,150
Large out 1935 $6,920

5050 York
SANFORD NB, SANFORD
{{ 7 L }}
Chartered 1896
Liquidated 9/5/31
Brown Back <$VALUE
4x5 1-2775 <$750
3x10-20 1-880 <$750
1882 Date Back
4x5 1-4151* <$750
3x10-20 1-3126** <$750
* 3901-4151 not marked
** 2921-3126 not marked
1902 Plain Back
4x5 1-12550 <$400
3x10-20 1-8272 <$400
Total Issue $1,003,420
Out at close $3,495

2642 Waldo
SEARSPORT NB, SEARSPORT
{{ 7 L 5 S }}
Chartered 1882
Liquidated 8/4/31
Series 1875 <$VALUE
4x5 1-7818 <$750
3x10-20 1-1967 <$850/$1500
Brown Back
4x5 1-2400 <$600
3x10-20 1-1640 <$600
1882 Date Back
4x5 1-4600* <$600
3x10-20 1-2960**<$600
1882 Value Back
4x5 4751-8782* <$750
3x10-20 3081-5469** <$750
* 4601-4750 not marked
** 2961-3080 not marked
1902 Plain Back
4x5 1-5200 <$350
3x10-20 1-3471 <$350
1929 Small Size
5 Type 1 1-981 <$250
10 Type 1 1-476 <$250
20 Type 1 1-155 <$250
Total Issue $1,187,940
Out at close $42,975
Large out at close $4,565

239 Somerset
FNB OF SKOWHEGAN
{{ 14 L 26 S }}
Chartered 1864
Original Series <$VALUE
4x5 1-2500 <$450
4x10 1-2650 <$750
3x20-50 1-1300<$1250/$5000
Series 1875
4x5 1-700 <$450
4x10 1-1411 <$750
3x20-50 1-347 <$1250/$5000
Brown Back
3x10-20 1-13728 <$250/$300
1902 Red Seal
3x10-20 1-7500 <$350/$400
1902 Date Back
3x10-20 1-12200 <$150
1902 Plain Back
3x10-20 12201-37041 <$150
1929 Small Size
10 Type 1 1-4372 <$50
20 Type 1 1-1218 <$60
10 Type 2 1-3551 <$50
20 Type 2 1-1086 <$65
Total Issue $3,786,770
Out in 1935 $130,050
Large out 1935 $8,930

298 Somerset
SECOND NB OF SKOWHEGAN
{{ 3 L }}
Chartered 1864
Liquidated 3/15/11
Original Series <$VALUE
3x1-2 1-2000 <$650/$1500
4x5 1-3500 <$750
3x10-20 1-2840<$1000/$1500
Series 1875
4x5 1-900 <$750
3x10-20 1-2400<$1000/$1500
Brown Back
3x10-20 1-11762 <$600
1902 Red Seal
3x10-20 1-6750 <$650
1902 Date Back
3x10-20 1-2478 <$400
Total Issue $1,409,500
Out in 1911 $71,650

959 York
SOUTH BERWICK NB, SOUTH BERWICK
{{ 11 L }}
Chartered 3/31/65
Liquidated 9/11/17
Original Series <$VALUE
3x1-2 1-6200 <$600/$1250
4x5 1-6100 <$600
3x10-20 1-1720 <$850/$1500
Series 1875
4x5 1-2475 <$600
3x10-20 1-1140 <$850/$1500
Brown Back
4x5 1-13632 <$500
3x10-20 1-6694 <$500
1902 Red Seal
4x5 1-3000 <$600
3x10-20 1-2300 <$600
1902 Date Back
4x5 1-7700 <$250
3x10-20 1-5610 <$250
1902 Plain Back
4x5 7701-9745 <$250
3x10-20 5611-6892 <$250
Total Issue $1,667,340
Out at close $98,795

7835 York
SPRINGVALE NB, SPRINGVALE
{{ 3 L 2 S }}
Organized 6/22/05
Receivership 11/6/33
1902 Red Seal <$VALUE
3x10-20 1-356 <$1500
1902 Date Back
3x10-20 1-760 <$600
1902 Plain Back
3x10-20 761-1719 <$600
1929 Small Size
10 Type 1 1-177 <$500
20 Type 1 1-39 <$500
Total Issue $119,050
Out at close $6,250
Large out at close $330

CONDITION affects Value. The Values shown are for notes in FINE condition.

****
1142 Knox
GEORGES NB OF THOMASTON
Organized 2/6/65
2nd title:Thomaston NB
9/16/31
FIRST TITLE {{ 10 L 3 S }}
Original Series <$VALUE
4x5 1-2500 <$600
3x10-20 1-1800 <$850/$1500
Series 1875
4x5 1-2070 <$600
3x10-20 1-2362 <$850/$1500
Brown Back
4x5 1-3776 <$450
3x10-20 1-2807 <$450
1902 Red Seal
4x5 1-1050 <$600
3x10-20 1-720 <$600
1902 Date Back
4x5 1-2650 <$250
3x10-20 1-2100 <$250
1902 Plain Back
4x5 2651-11425 <$250
3x10-20 2101-7735 <$250
1929 Small Size
5 Type 1 1-1352 <$250
10 Type 1 1-666 <$250
20 Type 1 1-178 <$250
SECOND TITLE {{ 11 S }}
1929 Small Size
5 Type 1 1-944 <$125
10 Type 1 1-672 <$125
20 Type 1 1-212 <$135
5 Type 2 1-5130 <$150
10 Type 2 1-1977 <$150
20 Type 2 1-525 <$150
Total Issue $1,439,500
Out in 1935 $98,015
Large out 1935 $7,015
Outstanding includes Ch 890
****
890 Knox
THOMASTON NB, THOMASTON
{{ 10 L 6 S }}
Chartered 3/14/65
Closed 9/16/31
Original Series <$VALUE
3x1-2 1-1000 <$500/$1250
4x5 1-2600 <$500
3x10-20 1-2300 <$850/$1500
Series 1875
4x5 1-2122 <$500
3x10-20 1-1794 <$850/$1500
Brown Back
4x5 1-4947 <$400
3x10-20 1-3267 <$400
1902 Red Seal
4x5 1-1865 <$500
3x10-20 1-1154 <$500
1902 Date Back
4x5 1-3000 <$175
3x10-20 1-2380 <$175
1902 Plain Back
4x5 3001-10615 <$175
3x10-20 2381-7514 <$175
1929 Small Size
5 Type 1 1-1152 <$175
10 Type 1 1-555 <$175
20 Type 1 1-117 <$175
Total Issue $1,331,330
Out at close $50,000
Large out at close $5,080
Ch 1142 assumed circulation
****
Thomaston NB, Thomaston
SEE Ch 1142
Georges NB of Thomaston
****
10628 Aroostook
FNB OF VAN BUREN
{{ 2 L 3 S }}
Organized 6/9/14
Receivership 1/31/34
1902 Date Back <$VALUE
4x10 1-625 <$850
1902 Plain Back
4x10 626-3636 <$850
1929 Small Size
10 Type 1 1-588 <$400
10 Type 2 1-66 <$400
Total Issue $181,380
Out at close $12,500
Large out at close $380
****

****
1108 Lincoln
MEDOMAK NB OF WALDOBORO
{{ 13 L 5 S }}
Organized 3/13/65
Original Series <$VALUE
3x1-2 1-2100 <$450/$1250
4x5 1-1250 <$600
3x10-20 1-880 <$850/$1500
Series 1875
3x1-2 1-900 <$450/$1250
4x5 1-1170 <$600
3x10-20 1-760 <$850/$1500
Brown Back
4x5 1-5747 <$400
3x10-20 1-2634 <$400
1902 Red Seal
4x5 1-1750 <$500
3x10-20 1-1100 <$500
1902 Date Back
4x5 1-2500 <$250
3x10-20 1-2000 <$250
1902 Plain Back
4x5 2501-7767 <$250
3x10-20 2001-5304 <$250
1929 Small Size
5 Type 1 1-706 <$225
10 Type 1 1-346 <$225
20 Type 1 1-108 <$225
5 Type 2 1-1092 <$275
10 Type 2 1-601 <$275
20 Type 2 1-162 <$275
Total Issue $972,190
Out in 1935 $24,110
Large out 1935 $3,085
****
744 Lincoln
WALDOBORO' NB, WALDOBORO'
{{ 2 L }}
Chartered 1/23/65
Liquidated 1/31/84
Original Series <$VALUE
3x1-2 1-2000 <$750/$1500
4x5 1-1000 <$850
3x10-20 1-1100<$1000/$1500
Series 1875
3x1-2 1-100 <$750/$1500
4x5 1-905 <$850
3x10-20 1-628 <$1000/$1500
Total Issue $135,000
Out in 1910 $774
****
2306 Kennebec
MERCHANTS NB OF
WATERVILLE
{{ 2 L }}
Chartered 10/23/75
Liquidated 6/1/05
Series 1875 <$VALUE
3x1-2 1-1880 <$750/$1500
3x10-20 1-4600<$1000/$1500
Brown Back
3x10-20 1-6149 <$750
Total Issue $546,850
Out in 1910 $7,990
****
880 Kennebec
PEOPLES NB OF WATERVILLE
Chartered 3/13/65
Receivership 11/6/33
2nd title:Peoples-Ticonic
NB of Waterville 9/16/31
FIRST TITLE {{ 14 L 6 S }}
Original Series <$VALUE
3x1-2 1-1200 <$350/$1000
4x5 1-2050 <$400
3x10-20 1-5160 <$750/$1250
Series 1875
4x5 1-7500 <$400
3x10-20 1-1864 <$750/$1250
Brown Back
3x10-20 1-15688 <$250/$300
1902 Red Seal
4x5 1-7500 <$400
3x10-20 1-5000 <$400
1902 Date Back
4x5 1-15250 <$125
3x10-20 1-12600 <$125
1902 Plain Back
4x5 15251-51520 <$125
3x10-20 12601-37636 <$125
1929 Small Size
5 Type 1 1-5274 <$100
10 Type 1 1-2584 <$100
20 Type 1 1-636 <$100
SECOND TITLE {{ 14 S }}
1929 Small Size
5 Type 1 1-2943 <$50
10 Type 1 1-2149 <$50
20 Type 1 1-504 <$60
Total Issue $5,312,090
Out at close $304,670
Large out at close $22,630
Outstanding includes Ch 762
****

Peoples-Ticonic NB of
Waterville
SEE Ch 880
Peoples NB of Waterville
****
762 Kennebec
TICONIC NB OF WATERVILLE
{{ 18 L 12 S }}
Chartered 1/28/65
Liquidated 9/8/31
Original Series <$VALUE
4x5 1-4150 <$450
3x10-20 1-1920 <$750/$1250
Series 1875
4x5 1-1970 <$450
3x10-20 1-1972 <$750/$1250
Brown Back
4x5 1-8200 <$300
3x10-20 1-6340 <$300/$350
1902 Red Seal
4x5 1-4300 <$400
3x10-20 1-2680 <$400
1902 Date Back
4x5 1-8250 <$125
3x10-20 1-6580 <$125
1902 Plain Back
4x5 8251-37000 <$125
3x10-20 6581-26219 <$125
1929 Small Size
5 Type 1 1-5001 <$100
10 Type 1 1-2232 <$100
20 Type 1 1-645 <$100
Total Issue $3,430,300
Out at close $166,100
Large out at close $13,770
Ch 880 assumed circulation
****
798 Kennebec
WATERVILLE NB, WATERVILLE
{{ 2 L }}
Chartered 2/14/65
Liquidated 3/3/79
Original Series <$VALUE
3x1-2 1-2400 <$850/$1500
4x5 1-3000 <$850
3x10-20 1-1760<$1000/$1500
50-100 1-532 <$5000
Series 1875
3x1-2 1-1880 <$850/$1500
4x5 1-1075 <$850
3x10-20 1-476 <$1000/$1500
Total Issue $294,500
Out in 1910 $2,020
****
553 Kennebec
NB OF WINTHROP
{{ 2 L }}
Chartered 10/25/64
Liquidated 12/31/97
Original Series <$VALUE
4x5 1-2500 <$1250
3x10-20 1-1201<$1500/$2000
Series 1875
4x5 1-4250 <$1250
3x10-20 1-862 <$1500/$2000
Brown Back
3x10-20 1-1884 <$1000
Total Issue $414,870
Out in 1910 $2,090
****
1549 Lincoln
FNB OF WISCASSET
{{ 9 L }}
Chartered 1865
Liquidated 6/11/17
Original Series <$VALUE
4x5 1-4750 <$650
3x10-20 1-1710 <$850/$1500
Series 1875
4x5 1-3780 <$650
3x10-20 1-1482 <$850/$1500
Brown Back
4x5 1-7350 <$400
3x10-20 1-5700 <$400
1902 Red Seal
4x5 1-2000 <$500
3x10-20 1-1600 <$500
1902 Date Back
4x5 1-2650 <$225
3x10-20 1-2720 <$225
1902 Plain Back
4x5 2651-3325 <$225
3x10-20 2721-3265 <$225
Total Issue $1,111,950
Out at close $45,700
****

****
4844 York
YORK COUNTY NB OF
YORK VILLAGE
{{ 3 L }}
Chartered 1893
Liquidated 10/31/19
Brown Back <$VALUE
4x5 1-5825 <$850
3x10-20 1-2640 <$850
1882 Date Back
4x5 1-2850 <$850
3x10-20 1-2218 <$850
1902 Date Back
4x5 1-1800 <$600
3x10-20 1-1440 <$600
1902 Plain Back
4x5 1801-4645 <$600
3x10-20 1441-3004 <$600
Total Issue $659,500
Out at close $47,100
****

<$VALUEs are for notes in **FINE** condition. Value changes by approximately **25%** for a change of one full grade.

MARYLAND

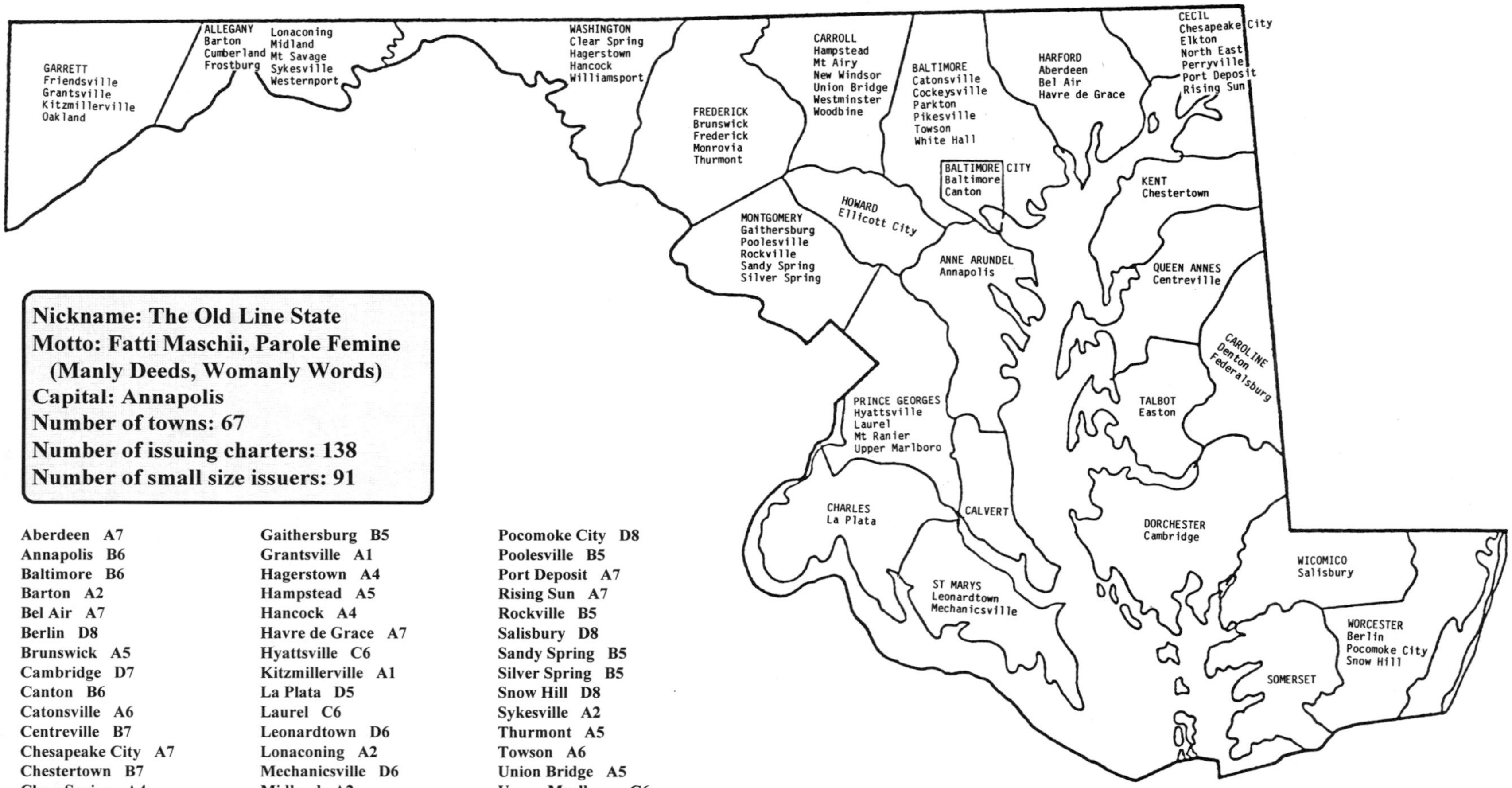

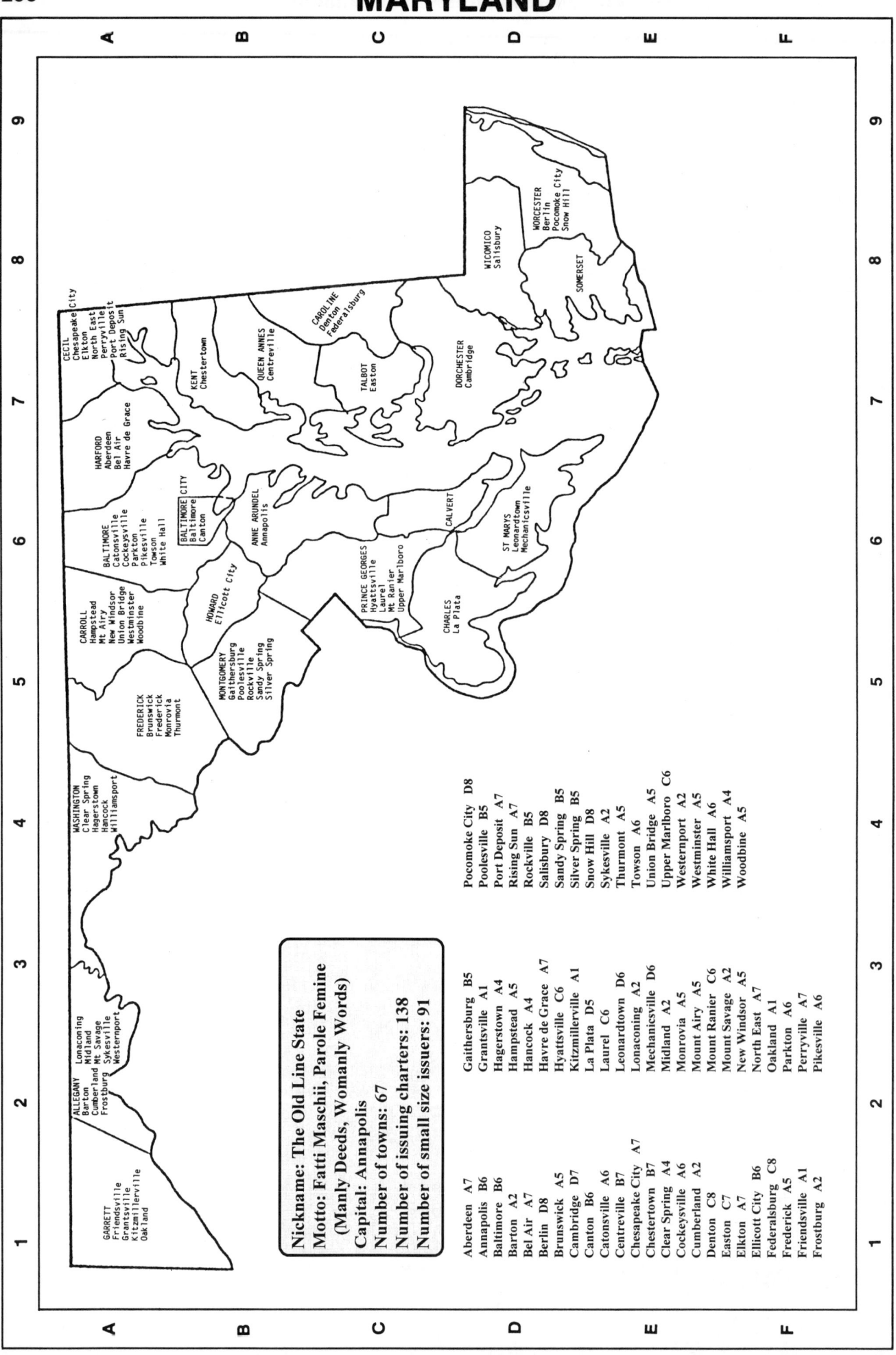

Nickname: The Old Line State
Motto: Fatti Maschii, Parole Femine
(Manly Deeds, Womanly Words)
Capital: Annapolis
Number of towns: 67
Number of issuing charters: 138
Number of small size issuers: 91

Aberdeen A7
Annapolis B6
Baltimore B6
Barton A2
Bel Air A7
Berlin D8
Brunswick A5
Cambridge D7
Canton B6
Catonsville A6
Centreville B7
Chesapeake City A7
Chestertown B7
Clear Spring A4
Cockeysville A6
Cumberland A2
Denton C8
Easton C7
Elkton A7
Ellicott City B6
Federalsburg C8
Frederick A5
Friendsville A1
Frostburg A2
Gaithersburg B5
Grantsville A1
Hagerstown A4
Hampstead A5
Hancock A4
Havre de Grace A7
Hyattsville C6
Kitzmillerville A1
La Plata D5
Laurel C6
Leonardtown D6
Lonaconing A2
Mechanicsville D6
Midland A2
Monrovia A5
Mount Airy A5
Mount Ranier C6
Mount Savage A2
New Windsor A5
North East A7
Oakland A1
Parkton A6
Perryville A7
Pikesville A6
Pocomoke City D8
Poolesville B5
Port Deposit A7
Rising Sun A7
Rockville B5
Salisbury D8
Sandy Spring B5
Silver Spring B5
Snow Hill D8
Sykesville A2
Thurmont A5
Towson A6
Union Bridge A5
Upper Marlboro C6
Westernport A2
Westminster A5
White Hall A6
Williamsport A4
Woodbine A5

4634 Harford
FNB OF ABERDEEN
{{ 4 L 6 S }}
Organized 5/16/91
Brown Back <$VALUE
4x5 1-3425 <$1250
3x10-20 1-680 <$1250
1882 Date Back
4x5 1-526 <$1250
3x10-20 1-301 <$1250
1902 Date Back
4x5 1-1125 <$750
3x10-20 1-860 <$750
1902 Plain Back
4x5 1126-3611 <$750
3x10-20 861-2420 <$750
1929 Small Size
10 Type 1 1-356 <$375
20 Type 1 1-118 <$375
10 Type 2 1-676 <$400
20 Type 2 1-132 <$400
Total Issue $366,210
Out in 1935 $12,500
Large out 1935 $600

1244 Anne Arundel
FARMERS NB OF ANNAPOLIS
{{ 13 L }}
Chartered 1865
Original Series <$VALUE
4x5 1-3500 <$2000
3x10-20 1-1137<$2500/$3000
Series 1875
4x5 1-8250 <$2000
3x10-20 1-3000<$2500/$3000
Brown Back
3x10-20 1-7867 <$1500
1902 Red Seal
3x10-20 1-4050 <$2000
1902 Date Back
3x10-20 1-10100 <$1000
1902 Plain Back
3x10-20 10101-21732 <$1000
Total Issue $2,124,300
Out in 1935 $5,185

826 Anne Arundel
FNB OF ANNAPOLIS
Chartered 2/18/65
Liquidated 11/15/99
2nd title and location:
Traders NB of Baltimore
6/7/72
FIRST TITLE {{ 0 L }}
Original Series <$VALUE
3x1-2 1-140 <$2500/$4000
4x5 1-3500 <$2500
3x10-20 1-1220<$2500/$3000
SECOND TITLE {{ 4 L }}
Original Series
4x5 1-2500 <$500
3x10-20 1-1000 <$750/$1250
Series 1875
4x5 1-3150 <$500
3x10-20 1-5296 <$750/$1250
Brown Back
4x5 1-12373 <$400
Total Issue $806,960
Out in 1910 $3,919

4518 Independent City
AMERICAN NB OF BALTIMORE
{{ UNREPORTED }}
Organized 2/10/91
Receivership 12/21/00
Brown Back <$VALUE
4x5 1-2050 <$1500
3x10-20 1-2811 <$1500
50-100 1-1005 <$2500
Total Issue $332,300
Out in 1915 $2,935

13745 Independent City
BALTIMORE NB, BALTIMORE
{{ 31 S }}
Chartered 8/33
1929 Small Size <$VALUE
5 Type 2 1-86220 <$35
10 Type 2 1-32566 <$35
20 Type 2 1-10024 <$45
Total Issue $957,240
Out in 1935 $367,100

1797 Independent City
CENTRAL NB OF BALTIMORE
{{ 3 L }}
Chartered 2/23/71
Liquidated 7/15/74
Original Series <$VALUE
3x1-2 1-3600 <$650/$2000
4x5 1-6275 <$600
3x10-20 1-1200 <$750/$1250
Total Issue $203,500
Out in 1910 $805

1384 Independent City
CITIZENS NB OF BALTIMORE
{{ 42 L }}
Chartered 1865
Closed 6/30/28
Original Series <$VALUE
4x5 1-8750 <$275
3x10-20 1-5660 <$600/$1000
50-100 1-1448 <$5000
500 1-70 <$150,000
Series 1875
3x10-20 1-8349 <$500/$850
50-100 1-601 <$5000
500 1-50 <$150,000
Brown Back
3x10-20 1-6541 <$150/$200
1902 Red Seal
4x5 1-24665 <$150
3x10-20 1-18334 <$150/$200
1902 Date Back
4x5 1-112000 <$40
3x10-20 1-76500 <$50
3x50-100 1-8003 <$350/$400
1902 Plain Back
4x5 112001-183709 <$40
3x10-20 76501-231681 <$50
3x50-100 8004-10245
<$350/$400
Total Issue $20,799,330
Out at close $2,000,000
Ch 1413 assumed circulation

1303 Independent City
COMMERCIAL & FARMERS NB OF BALTIMORE
{{ 10 L }}
Chartered 1865
Liquidated 4/6/11
Original Series <$VALUE
3x1-2 1-1500 <$750/$2500
4x5 1-17525 <$350
3x10-20 1-5700 <$600/$1000
50-100 1-800 <$5000
500-1000 1-30
<$150,000/$200,000
Series 1875
4x5 1-6500 <$350
3x10-20 1-3358 <$500/$850
50-100 1-334 <$3500
Brown Back
4x5 1-14474 <$200
3x10-20 1-8711 <$200/$250
1902 Red Seal
4x5 1-9500 <$200
4x10 1-9000 <$200/$250
50-100 1-2800 <$2000
1902 Date Back
4x5 1-11730 <$85
4x10 1-13871 <$85
Total Issue $3,640,470
Out in 1911 $316,800

4533 Independent City
CONTINENTAL NB OF BALTIMORE
{{ UNREPORTED }}
Chartered 3/11/91
Liquidated 2/15/02
Brown Back <$VALUE
50-100 1-1349 <$2500
Total Issue $202,350
Out in 1910 $3,700

2499 Independent City
DROVERS & MECHANICS NB OF BALTIMORE
{{ 29 L 10 S }}
Chartered 1/81
Liquidated 9/15/30
Series 1875 <$VALUE
3x10-20 1-10140 <$500/$850
Brown Back
3x10-20 1-37900 <$175/$225
1882 Date Back
3x10-20 1-49000 <$175/$225
1882 Value Back
3x10-20 49001-51400
<$175/$225
1902 Plain Back
3x10-20 1-34243 <$75
1929 Small Size
10 Type 1 1-6086 <$90
20 Type 1 1-1708 <$100
Total Issue $7,209,270
Out in 1929 $613,500
Large out at close $91,800
Outstanding includes Ch 5984

4530 Independent City
EQUITABLE NB OF BALTIMORE
{{ 1 L }}
Chartered 3/5/91
Liquidated 5/17/00
Brown Back <$VALUE
3x10-20 1-3865 <$1500
Total Issue $193,250
Out in 1910 $1,720

1337 Independent City
FARMERS & MERCHANTS NB OF BALTIMORE
{{ 36 L 7 S }}
Chartered 1865
Liquidated 9/3/30
Original Series <$VALUE
4x5 1-10000 <$275
3x10-20 1-8200 <$600/$1000
50-100 1-2508 <$5000
Series 1875
3x10-20 1-7000 <$500/$850
50-100 1-668 <$5000
Brown Back
4x5 1-4582 <$150
3x10-20 1-4106 <$150/$200
1902 Red Seal
4x5 1-7000 <$150
3x10-20 1-7600 <$150/$200
1902 Date Back
4x5 1-54000 <$40
3x10-20 1-38700 <$50
1902 Plain Back
4x5 54001-143115 <$40
3x10-20 38701-82979 <$50
1929 Small Size
5 Type 1 1-6255 <$125
10 Type 1 1-2948 <$125
20 Type 1 1-650 <$125
Total Issue $9,707,120
Out at close $400,000
Large out at close $56,790

204 Independent City
FNB OF BALTIMORE
{{ 17 L }}
Chartered 2/23/64
Liquidated 9/11/16
Original Series <$VALUE
4x5 1-19350 <$300
4x10 1-10450 <$650
2x20-50-100 1-4300
<$1000/$5000/$5000
Series 1875
4x5 1-4500 <$300
4x10 1-1500 <$500
2x20-50-100 1-4000
<$850/$5000/$5000
Brown Back
4x5 1-21155 <$150
3x10-20 1-12380 <$150/200
50-100 1-3000 <$1250/$1500
1902 Red Seal
3x10-20 1-48400 <$150/$200
1902 Date Back
4x5 1-57360 <$60
3x10-20 1-41439 <$75
3x50-100 1-2000 <$400/$500
Total Issue $10,163,250
Out at close $235,600

FNB of Baltimore
SEE Ch 1413
N Mechanics B of Baltimore

2623 Independent City
MANUFACTURERS NB OF BALTIMORE
{{ 6 L }}
Chartered 2/1/82
Liquidated 12/21/03
Series 1875 <$VALUE
4x5 1-4490 <$350
3x10-20 1-6823 <$500/$850
Brown Back
3x10-20 1-1654 <$250/$300
Total Issue $513,650
Out in 1910 7,265

5776 Independent City
MARYLAND NB OF BALTIMORE
{{ 5 L }}
Chartered 4/12/01
Liquidated 6/30/14
Brown Back <$VALUE
4x5 1-4585 <$300
3x10-20 1-3566 <$300/$400
50-100 1-580 <$1250/$1500
1882 Date Back
4x5 1-20720 <$300
3x10-20 1-14358 <$300/$400
50-100 1-223 <$1250/$1500
Total Issue $1,522,750
Out in 1914 $20,950

Merchants Mechanics FNB of Baltimore
SEE Ch 1413
N Mechanics B of Baltimore

Merchants Mechanics NB of Baltimore SEE Ch 1413
N Mechanics B of Baltimore

1336 Independent City
MERCHANTS NB OF BALTIMORE
{{ 18 L }}
Chartered 1865
Liquidated 12/31/12
Original Series <$VALUE
4x5 1-11000 <$275
3x10-20 1-21800<$600/$1000
50-100 1-5675 <$5000
500-1000 1-40
<$150,000/$200,000
Series 1875
4x5 1-1250 <$250
3x10-20 1-6700 <$500/$850
50-100 1-4401 <$5000
Brown Back
4x5 1-26398 <$125
3x10-20 1-20136 <$125/$175
50-100 1-3494 <$1250/$1500
1902 Red Seal
4x5 1-41750 <$125
4x10 1-16250 <$125
3x10-20 1-14400 <$125/$150
1902 Date Back
4x5 1-35277 <$40
4x10 1-33705 <$50
Total Issue $9,559,000
Out at close $650,000
Ch 1413 assumed circulation

Merchants NB of Baltimore
SEE Ch 1413
N Mechanics B of Baltimore

1432 Independent City
NB OF BALTIMORE
{{ 32 L 3 S }}
Chartered 1865
Liquidated 3/31/30
Original Series <$VALUE
4x5 1-19475 <$275
3x10-20 1-12999<$600/$1000
50-100 1-6010 <$5000
Series 1875
4x5 1-4400 <$250
3x10-20 1-5731 <$500/$850
50-100 1-5548 <$5000
Brown Back
4x5 1-5250 <$125
3x10-20 1-6270 <$125/$175
50-100 1-2170 <$1250/$1500
1902 Red Seal
4x5 1-4750 <$150
3x10-20 1-3400 <$150/$200
1902 Date Back
4x5 1-110250 <$40
3x10-20 1-85707 <$40/$50
3x50-100 1-2000 <$350/$400
1902 Plain Back
4x5 110251-133684 <$40
3x10-20 85708-100522
<$40/$50
1929 Small Size
5 Type 1 1-2581 <$225
10 Type 1 1-1866 <$225
20 Type 1 1-159 <$250
Total Issue $12,564,950
Out at close $286,070
Large out at close $77,600

4285 Independent City
NB OF COMMERCE OF BALTIMORE
{{ 18 L }}
Chartered 4/11/90
Liquidated 5/28/21
Brown Back <$VALUE
4x5 1-38000 <$125
3x10-20 1-13040 <$125/$175
50-100 1-4789 <$1250/$1500
1882 Date Back
4x5 1-8446 <$125
3x10-20 1-5156 <$125/$175
50-100 1-199 <$1250/$1500
1902 Date Back
4x5 1-25000 <$50
3x10-20 1-43000 <$60
1902 Plain Back
4x5 25001-56590 <$50
3x10-20 43001-64871 <$60
Total Issue $6,692,270
Out at close $500,000
Ch 1413 assumed circulation

11207 Independent City
N CENTRAL B OF BALTIMORE
{{ 50+ S }}
Chartered 7/18
1929 Small Size <$VALUE
5 Type 1 1-12528 <$25
10 Type 1 1-6126 <$30
5 Type 2 1-57746 <$25
10 Type 2 1-28930 <$30
Total Issue $1,321,430
Out in 1935 $400,000

9639 Independent City
N CITY B OF BALTIMORE
{{ UNREPORTED }}
Chartered 1/10
Liquidated 1/26/14
1902 Date Back <$VALUE
3x10-20 1-4776 <$600
Total Issue $238,800
Out in 1914 $24,230

1109 Independent City
N EXCHANGE B OF BALTIMORE
{{ 38 L }}
Chartered 1865
Liquidated 12/29/23
Original Series <$VALUE
4x5 1-10000 <$275
3x10-20 1-5800 <$600/$1000
50-100 1-2750 <$5000
Series 1875
4x5 1-7700 <$250
3x10-20 1-8934 <$500/$850
50-100 1-712 <$5000
50 713-2469 <$5000
Brown Back
3x10-20 1-43980 <$150/$200
50-100 1-1001 <$1250/$1500
1902 Red Seal
4x5 1-27750 <$150
3x10-20 1-18500 <$150/$200
1902 Date Back
4x5 1-79000 <$40
3x10-20 1-61300 <$50
1902 Plain Back
4x5 79001-110000 <$40
3x10-20 61301-154960 <$50
Total Issue $15,572,950
Out at close $999,995
Outstanding includes Ch 4218

1252 Independent City
N FARMERS & PLANTERS B OF BALTIMORE
{{ 4 L }}
Chartered 6/10/65
Liquidated 5/16/99
Original Series <$VALUE
3x1-2 1-7800 <$600/$2000
4x5 1-13050 <$450
3x10-20 1-9600 <$600/$1000
50-50 1-500 <$5000
50-100 1-1960 <$5000
500 1-62 <$150,000
Series 1875
4x5 1-13750 <$400
3x10-20 1-6000 <$500/$850
50-50 1-600 <$5000
50-100 1-1100 <$5000
Brown Back
4x5 1-5500 <$300
3x10-20 1-9800 <$300/$350
50-100 1-1327 <$1250/$1500
Total Issue $2,754,050
Out in 1910 $20,623

4218 Independent City
N HOWARD B OF BALTIMORE
{{ 2 L }}
Chartered 1890
Liquidated 4/15/15
Brown Back <$VALUE
50-100 1-2640 <$2500
1882 Date Back
50-100 1-953 <$2500
1902 Date Back
4x5 1-8990 <$600
3x10-20 1-6918 <$600
Total Issue $1,064,650
Out at close $134,000
Ch 1109 assumed circulation

2453 Independent City
N MARINE B OF BALTIMORE
{{ 25 L 16 S }}
Chartered 2/9/80
Series 1875 <$VALUE
4x5 1-29012 <$250
3x10-20 1-5149 <$500/$850
50-100 1-877 <$5000
Brown Back
4x5 1-12725 <$125
3x10-20 1-6251 <$125/$175
50-100 1-909 <$1250/$1500
1882 Date Back
4x5 1-20472 <$125
3x10-20 1-16087 <$125/$150
50-100 1-200 <$1250/$1500
3x50-100 1-1300
<$1250/$1500
1902 Plain Back
4x5 1-25585 <$50
3x10-20 1-14104 <$60
3x50-100 1-1021 <$350/$400
1929 Small Size
5 Type 1 1-6964 <$30
10 Type 1 1-3138 <$35
20 Type 1 1-1126 <$45
50 Type 1 1-316 <$175
100 Type 1 1-112 <$225
5 Type 2 1-10432 <$35
10 Type 2 1-5759 <$40
20 Type 2 1-1510 <$50
Total Issue $5,547,850
Out in 1935 $300,000
Large out 1935 $12,565

1413 Independent City
N MECHANICS B OF BALTIMORE
Chartered 1865
2nd title:Merchants-Mechanics NB 12/28/12
3rd title:Merchants-Mechanics FNB 10/13/16
4th title:Merchants NB 1/15/21
5th title:FNB 6/30/28
FIRST TITLE {{ 8 L }}
Original Series <$VALUE
3x1-2 1-5000 <$600/$2000
4x5 1-8500 <$275
3x10-20 1-7124 <$600/$1000
50-100 1-1138 <$5000
500 1-60 <$150,000
Series 1875
3x10-20 1-1100 <$500/$850
50-100 1-400 <$5000
Brown Back
3x10-20 1-11542 <$125
50-100 1-24956<$1250/$1500
1902 Red Seal
4x5 1-32250 <$125
50-100 1-10100<$1750/$2000
1902 Date Back
4x5 1-45474 <$40
50-100 1-8422 <$350/$400
3x50-100 1-2324 <$350/$400
SECOND TITLE {{ 9 L }}
1902 Date Back
4x5 1-89525 <$50
3x10-20 1-70372 <$60
3x50-100 1-3200 <$350/$400
THIRD TITLE {{ 11 L }}
1902 Plain Back
3x10-20 1-35200 <$50
3x50-100 1-3200 <$350/$400
FOURTH TITLE {{ 30 L }}
1902 Plain Back
4x5 1-189662 <$40
3x10-20 1-110727 <$50
3x50-100 1-3200 <$350/$400
FIFTH TITLE {{ 12 L 50+ S }}
1902 Plain Back
4x5 1-10323 <$45
3x10-20 1-8333 <$60
3x50-100 1-220 <$400/$450
1929 Small Size
5 Type 1 1-112312 <$15
10 Type 1 1-54248 <$20
20 Type 1 1-15234 <$30
50 Type 1 1-1902 <$85
100 Type 1 1-622 <$135
5 Type 2 1-103970 <$15
10 Type 2 1-69587 <$20
20 Type 2 1-13450 <$30
Total Issue $47,225,920
Out in 1935 $4,000,000
Large out 1935 $175,970
Outstanding includes Ch 1336, Ch 1384, and Ch 4285

CONDITION affects Value. The Values shown are for notes in FINE condition.

<$VALUEs are for notes in **FINE** condition. Value changes by approximately **25%** for a change of one full grade.

****
1489 Independent City
N UNION B OF MARYLAND AT BALTIMORE
{{ 40 L }}
Chartered 1865
Liquidated 3/12/29
Original Series <$VALUE
4x5 1-4750 <$275
3x10-20 1-4200 <$600/$1000
50-100 1-3674 <$5000
500-1000 1-72
<$150,000/$200,000
Series 1875
4x5 1-30300 <$250
3x10-20 1-3400 <$500/$850
50-100 1-1117 <$5000
Brown Back
4x5 1-42723 <$125
3x10-20 1-24501 <$125/$175
1902 Red Seal
4x5 1-25150 <$125
3x10-20 1-13020 <$125/$175
1902 Date Back
4x5 1-91750 <$40
3x10-20 1-70200 <$50
3x50-100 1-1000 <$350/$400
1902 Plain Back
4x5 91751-151354 <$40
3x10-20 70201-115015 <$50
Total Issue $14,168,990
Out at close $499,995
****
5984 Independent City
OLD TOWN NB OF BALTIMORE
{{ U + 50+ L }}
Chartered 10/3/01
Liquidated 10/31/27
Brown Back <$VALUE
4x5 1-10765 <$150
3x10-20 1-7474 <$150/$200
1882 Date Back
4x5 1-24500 <$125
3x10-20 1-18400 <$125/$175
1882 Value Back
4x5 24501-38240 <$125
3x10-20 18401-27359
<$125/$175
1902 Plain Back
4x5 1-37263 <$40
3x10-20 1-26675 <$40/$50
Total Issue $4,800,760
Out at close $450,800
Ch 2499 assumed circulation
****
414 Independent City
SECOND NB OF BALTIMORE
{{ 35 L }}
Chartered 1864
Liquidated 7/24/22
Original Series <$VALUE
4x5 1-18750 <$275
3x10-20 1-5700 <$600/$1000
50-100 1-500 <$5000
Series 1875
4x5 1-16250 <$250
3x10-20 1-4800 <$500/$850
Brown Back
4x5 1-27767 <$150
3x10-20 1-11075 <$150/$200
50-100 1-1194 <$1250/$1500
1902 Red Seal
4x5 1-34750 <$150
3x10-20 1-18700 <$150/$200
50-100 1-1668 <$2250/$2500
1902 Date Back
4x5 1-68515 <$40
3x10-20 1-50674 <$40/$50
1902 Plain Back
4x5 68516-86678 <$40
3x10-20 50675-62144
<$40/$50
Total Issue $9,309,150
Out at close $500,000
****
814 Independent City
THIRD NB OF BALTIMORE
{{ U + 12 L }}
Chartered 1865
Liquidated 1/31/11
Original Series <$VALUE
4x5 1-11000 <$300
3x10-20 1-3200 <$600/$1000
3x50-100 1-2160 <$5000
Series 1875
4x5 1-22670 <$275
3x10-20 1-3135 <$500/$850
3x50-100 1-467 <$5000
Brown Back
4x5 1-11450 <$150
3x10-20 1-8272 <$150/$200
1902 Red Seal
4x5 1-14500 <$175
3x10-20 1-11200 <$175/$225
1902 Date Back
4x5 1-17804 <$85
3x10-20 1-11921 <$85
Total Issue $4,091,630
Out in 1911 $239,050
****
Traders NB of Baltimore
SEE Ch 826
FNB of Annapolis
****
1325 Independent City
WESTERN NB OF BALTIMORE
{{ 20 L 26 S }}
Chartered 1865
Original Series <$VALUE
3x1-2 1-4000 <$650/$2000
4x5 1-3800 <$400
3x10-20 1-5700 <$650/$1000
50-100 1-2700 <$5000
500 1-526 <$150,000
Series 1875
50-100 1-311 <$5000
Brown Back
4x5 1-5000 <$200
3x10-20 1-3220 <$200/$250
50-100 1-1926 <$1250/$1500
1902 Red Seal
3x10-20 1-12000 <$300/$350
1902 Date Back
4x5 1-24835 <$75
3x10-20 1-22648 <$75
3x50-100 1001-1803
<$400/$500
1929 Small Size
5 Type 1 1-3996 <$35
10 Type 1 1-3992 <$40
20 Type 1 1-1914 <$50
50 Type 1 1-292 <$150
100 Type 1 1-348 <$200
5 Type 2 1-7740 <$40
10 Type 2 1-3465 <$50
20 Type 2 1-410 <$60
Total Issue $5,042,430
Out in 1935 $75,000
Large out 1935 $8,160
****
6399 Allegany
FNB OF BARTON
{{ 2 L 11 S }}
Chartered 8/26/02
1902 Red Seal <$VALUE
3x10-20 1-2056 <$1500
1902 Date Back
3x10-20 1-2370 <$850
1902 Plain Back
3x10-20 2371-7057 <$850
1929 Small Size
10 Type 1 1-830 <$275
20 Type 1 1-234 <$275
10 Type 2 1-594 <$275
20 Type 2 1-132 <$300
Total Issue $542,110
Out in 1935 $25,000
Large out 1935 $910
****
9474 Harford
FARMERS & MERCHANTS NB OF BEL AIR
{{ 2 L 5 S }}
Organized 6/30/09
Receivership 10/11/33
1902 Date Back <$VALUE
4x5 1-2275 <$750
3x10-20 1-1740 <$750
1902 Plain Back
4x5 2276-8238 <$750
3x10-20 1741-5211 <$750
1929 Small Size
5 Type 1 1-966 <$350
10 Type 1 1-592 <$350
20 Type 1 1-156 <$350
Total Issue $508,530
Out at close $25,000
Large out at close $1,310
****
13680 Harford
FNB OF BEL AIR
{{ 4 S }}
Chartered 4/33
1929 Small Size <$VALUE
10 Type 2 1-5583 <$350
20 Type 2 1-1779 <$350
Total Issue $91,410
Out in 1935 $49,300
****
2797 Harford
HARFORD NB OF BEL AIR
{{ 1 L }}
Chartered 1882
Liquidated 8/12/15
Brown Back <$VALUE
4x5 1-550 <$1500
3x10-20 1-1980 <$1500
1902 Red Seal
50-100 1-1160 <$3000
1902 Date Back
50-100 1-640 <$1000
3x50-100 1-265 <$1000
Total Issue $446,250
Out in 1915 $41,650
****
3933 Harford
SECOND NB OF BEL AIR
{{ 7 L 6 S }}
Chartered 10/22/88
Receivership 10/11/33
Brown Back <$VALUE
3x10-20 1-4074 <$600
1902 Date Back
3x10-20 1-6800 <$300
1902 Plain Back
3x10-20 6801-18923 <$300
1929 Small Size
10 Type 1 1-1782 <$150
20 Type 1 1-516 <$165
10 Type 2 1-216 <$165
20 Type 2 1-113 <$185
Total Issue $1,323,110
Out at close $60,000
Large out at close $3,410
****
8319 Worcester
FNB OF BERLIN
{{ 1 L }}
Chartered 8/06
Liquidated 12/17/18
1902 Red Seal <$VALUE
4x5 1-1480 <$2000
3x10-20 1-1188 <$2000
1902 Date Back
4x5 1-2100 <$1000
3x10-20 1-1410 <$1000
1902 Plain Back
4x5 2101-3020 <$1000
3x10-20 1411-1934 <$1000
Total Issue $246,100
Out at close $25,000
****
14044 Frederick
PEOPLES NB IN BRUNSWICK
{{ 26 S }}
Chartered 3/34
1929 Small Size <$VALUE
5 Type 2 1-3986 <$200
10 Type 2 1-2225 <$200
20 Type 2 1-552 <$200
Total Issue $53,220
Out in 1935 $50,000
Outstanding includes Ch 8244
****
8244 Frederick
PEOPLES NB OF BRUNSWICK
{{ 6 L U + 5 S }}
Organized 4/27/06
Liquidated 5/5/34
1902 Red Seal <$VALUE
4x5 1-250 <$1250
3x10-20 1-220 <$1250
1902 Date Back
4x5 1-1475 <$450
3x10-20 1-1080 <$450
1902 Plain Back
4x5 1476-4623 <$450
3x10-20 1081-3087 <$450
1929 Small Size
5 Type 1 1-932 <$250
10 Type 1 1-465 <$250
20 Type 1 1-131 <$275
Total Issue $334,390
Out at close $25,000
Large out 1935 $790
Ch 14044 assumed circulation
****
4085 Dorchester
DORCHESTER NB OF CAMBRIDGE
{{ 1 L }}
Chartered 7/31/89
Liquidated 9/1/15
Brown Back <$VALUE
50-100 1-1767 <$3000
1902 Date Back
3x10-20 1-3496 <$1000
Total Issue $439,850
Out in 1915 $42,750
****
5880 Dorchester
FARMERS & MERCHANTS NB OF CAMBRIDGE
{{ 3 L 10 S }}
Chartered 6/26/01
Brown Back <$VALUE
50-100 1-1520 <$2500
1882 Date Back
50-100 1-560 <$2500
3x50-100 1-1046 <$2500
1902 Plain Back
3x50-100 1-787 <$750/$850
1929 Small Size
50 Type 1 1-186 <$300
100 Type 1 1-64 <$350
50 Type 2 1-89 <$600
100 Type 2 1-35 <$750
Total Issue $872,400
Out in 1935 $60,000
Large out 1935 $7,150
****
2498 Dorchester
NB OF CAMBRIDGE
{{ 12 L 6 S }}
Chartered 12/3/80
Series 1875 <$VALUE
4x5 1-2372 <$650
4x10 1-5698 <$850
Brown Back
3x10-20 1-3500 <$500
1882 Date Back
3x10-20 1-5000 <$500
1882 Value Back
3x10-20 5001-7408 <$500
1902 Plain Back
3x10-20 1-6562 <$250
1929 Small Size
10 Type 1 1-1524 <$125
20 Type 1 1-402 <$160
10 Type 2 1-1511 <$160
20 Type 2 1-413 <$185
Total Issue $1,311,910
Out in 1935 $49,995
Large out 1935 $3,415
****
4799 Baltimore City
CANTON NB, CANTON
{{ 8 L 2 S }}
Chartered 1892
Brown Back <$VALUE
4x5 1-6825 <$500
3x10-20 1-5490 <$500
1882 Date Back
4x5 1-5574 <$500
3x10-20 1-3777 <$500
1902 Date Back
3x50-100 1-2736 <$750/$850
1902 Plain Back
3x50-100 2737-3289
<$750/$850
1929 Small Size
5 Type 1 1-414 <$250
10 Type 1 1-170 <$250
20 Type 1 1-32 <$250
50 Type 1 1-330 <$350
100 Type 1 1-94 <$400
5 Type 2 1-588 <$250
10 Type 2 1-235 <$250
20 Type 2 1-95 <$250
Total Issue $1,722,630
Out in 1935 $100,000
Large out 1935 $9,015
****
5093 Baltimore
FNB OF CATONSVILLE
{{ 10 L }}
Chartered 1897
Liquidated 6/4/21
Brown Back <$VALUE
4x5 1-5025 <$1000
3x10-20 1-2500 <$1000
1882 Date Back
4x5 1-4550 <$850
3x10-20 1-3340 <$850
1882 Value Back
4x5 4551-5778 <$850
3x10-20 3341-4161 <$850
1902 Plain Back
4x5 1-2600 <$400
3x10-20 1-1440 <$400
Total Issue $673,110
Out at close $50,000
****
2341 Queen Annes
CENTREVILLE NB OF MARYLAND, CENTREVILLE
{{ 5 L 4 S }}
Chartered 8/18/76
Series 1875 <$VALUE
3x10-20 1-4382<$1250/$1750
Brown Back
3x10-20 1-1931 <$850
1882 Date Back
3x10-20 1-1647 <$850
1902 Plain Back
4x5 1-3790 <$600
4x10 1-2835 <$600
1929 Small Size
5 Type 1 1-1096 <$350
10 Type 1 1-596 <$350
5 Type 2 1-1722 <$375
10 Type 2 1-984 <$375
Total Issue $674,290
Out in 1935 $20,000
Large out 1935 $1,100
****
3205 Queen Annes
QUEEN ANNE'S NB OF CENTREVILLE
{{ 1 L 1 S }}
Chartered 1884
Liquidated 2/3/31
Brown Back <$VALUE
3x10-20 1-2320 <$3000
1902 Red Seal
3x10-20 1-1040 <$3000
1902 Date Back
3x10-20 1-2320 <$1250
1902 Plain Back
3x10-20 2321-5619 <$1250
1929 Small Size
10 Type 1 1-279 <$600
20 Type 1 1-55 <$600
Total Issue $472,290
Out at close $20,000
Large out at close $2,820
****
6845 Cecil
NB OF CHESAPEAKE CITY
{{ 1 L }}
Chartered 6/03
Liquidated 5/12/22
1902 Red Seal <$VALUE
4x5 1-400 <$2000
3x10-20 1-320 <$2000
1902 Date Back
4x5 1-750 <$1500
3x10-20 1-600 <$1500
1902 Plain Back
4x5 751-1195 <$1500
3x10-20 601-841 <$1500
Total Issue $89,950
Out at close $6,250
****
13798 Kent
FNB OF CHESTERTOWN
{{ UNREPORTED }}
Chartered 10/33
1929 Small Size <$VALUE
20 Type 2 1-162 <$1000
Total Issue $3,240
Out in 1935 $12,500
Outstanding includes Ch 9744
****
1500 Kent
KENT NB OF CHESTERTOWN
{{ UNREPORTED }}
Chartered 1865
Liquidated 2/12/85
Original Series <$VALUE
4x5 1-2250 <$2500
3x10-20 1-1100<$2500/$3000
Series 1875
4x5 1-1150 <$2500
3x10-20 1-622 <$2500/$3000
Total Issue $154,100
Out in 1910 $630
****
4327 Kent
SECOND NB OF CHESTERTOWN
{{ UNREPORTED }}
Chartered 1890
Liquidated 5/5/10
Brown Back <$VALUE
50-100 1-914 <$3000
1882 Date Back
50-100 1-264 <$3000
Total Issue $176,700
Out in 1910 $24,000
****
9744 Kent
THIRD NB OF CHESTERTOWN
{{ 0 L 3 S }}
Organized 4/8/10
Liquidated 3/27/34
1902 Date Back <$VALUE
50-100 1-330 <$2000
3x50-100 1-724 <$2000
1902 Plain Back
3x50-100 725-787 <$2000
1929 Small Size
50 Type 1 1-57 <$1500
100 Type 1 1-4 <$1500
Total Issue $265,750
Out in 1934 $12,500
Large out 1935 $700
Ch 13798 assumed circulation
****
9699 Washington
CLEAR SPRING NB, CLEAR SPRING
{{ 3 L 9 S }}
Organized 12/10/09
1902 Date Back <$VALUE
3x10-20 1-2310 <$750
1902 Plain Back
3x10-20 2311-6870 <$750
1929 Small Size
10 Type 1 1-760 <$250
20 Type 1 1-200 <$275
10 Type 2 1-528 <$275
20 Type 2 1-180 <$275
Total Issue $421,980
Out in 1935 $25,000
Large out 1935 $1,020
****
4496 Baltimore
NB OF COCKEYSVILLE
{{ 5 L 10 S }}
Organized 12/4/90
Brown Back <$VALUE
4x5 1-2235 <$1500
3x10-20 1-1546 <$1500
1882 Date Back
4x5 1-165 <$1250
3x10-20 1-1275 <$1250
1902 Date Back
3x10-20 1-3940 <$650
1902 Plain Back
3x10-20 3941-8226 <$650
1929 Small Size
10 Type 1 1-1226 <$225
20 Type 1 1-342 <$250
10 Type 2 1-1780 <$250
20 Type 2 1-428 <$250
Total Issue $741,310
Out in 1935 $50,000
Large out 1935 $1,590
****
5332 Allegany
CITIZENS NB OF CUMBERLAND
{{ 3 L }}
Chartered 5/5/00
Liquidated 3/8/20
Brown Back <$VALUE
3x10-20 1-6700 <$750
1882 Date Back
3x10-20 1-10400 <$750
1882 Value Back
3x10-20 10401-15098 <$750
Total Issue $1,089,900
Out at close $100,000
****
381 Allegany
FNB OF CUMBERLAND
{{ 16 L 22 S }}
Organized 7/1/64
Original Series <$VALUE
4x5 1-3850 <$500
3x10-20 1-2000 <$750/$1250
Series 1875
4x5 1-1470 <$500
3x10-20 1-1490 <$650/$1250
Brown Back
4x5 1-5000 <$350
3x10-20 1-5866 <$350
1902 Red Seal
3x10-20 1-6400 <$500
1902 Date Back
3x10-20 1-10100 <$125
1902 Plain Back
3x10-20 10101-30046 <$125
1929 Small Size
5 Type 1 1-2948 <$60
10 Type 1 1-3826 <$60
20 Type 1 1-1056 <$65
5 Type 2 1-11004 <$60
10 Type 2 1-5462 <$60
20 Type 2 1-1450 <$65
Total Issue $3,079,860
Out in 1935 $200,000
Large out 1935 $7,095
****
1519 Allegany
SECOND NB OF CUMBERLAND
{{ 28 L 50+ S }}
Chartered 1865
Original Series <$VALUE
3x1-2 1-3000 <$1000/$3000
4x5 1-3750 <$500
3x10-20 1-2600 <$650/$1250
Series 1875
3x10-20 1-2200 <$550/$1000
Brown Back
3x10-20 1-12358 <$350
1902 Red Seal
3x10-20 1-3900 <$400
1902 Date Back
3x10-20 1-19400 <$85
1902 Plain Back
3x10-20 19401-66343 <$85
1929 Small Size
10 Type 1 1-10994 <$40
20 Type 1 1-2882 <$50
10 Type 2 1-12863 <$40
20 Type 2 1-3780 <$50
Total Issue $5,669,760
Out in 1935 $400,000
Large out 1935 $13,610
****

****
2416 Allegany
THIRD NB OF CUMBERLAND
{{ 12 L }}
Chartered 3/6/79
Liquidated 2/17/20
Series 1875 <$VALUE
4x5 1-26865 <$500
Brown Back
3x10-20 1-9275 <$300
1882 Date Back
3x10-20 1-9600* <$275
1882 Value Back
3x10-20 10101-12990* <$300
* 9601-10100 not marked
1902 Plain Back
3x10-20 1-1084 <$250
Total Issue $1,704,750
Out at close $100,000
****
2547 Caroline
DENTON NB, DENTON
{{ 16 L 7 S }}
Chartered 1881
Series 1875 <$VALUE
3x10-20 1-5278 <$750/$1000
Brown Back
3x10-20 1-4000 <$300
50-100 1-360 <$1250/$1500
1882 Date Back
4x5 1-2750 <$300
3x10-20 1-5050 <$300
50-100 1-140 <$1250/$1500
1882 Value Back
4x5 2751-5245 <$300
3x10-20 5051-6713 <$300
1902 Plain Back
4x5 1-19185 <$150
1929 Small Size
5 Type 1 1-6896 <$125
5 Type 2 1-12936 <$125
Total Issue $1,634,710
Out in 1935 $50,000
Large out 1935 $3,860
****
5122 Caroline
PEOPLES NB OF DENTON
{{ 2 L }}
Chartered 1898
Liquidated 6/30/19
Brown Back <$VALUE
3x10-20 1-1220 <$850
1882 Date Back
3x10-20 1-4590* <$850
1882 Value Back
3x10-20 4791-6215* <$850
* 4591-4790 not marked
1902 Plain Back
3x10-20 1-230 <$600
Total Issue $383,250
Out at close $50,000
****
1434 Talbot
EASTON NB OF MARYLAND, EASTON
{{ 18 L 22 S }}
Chartered 1865
Original Series <$VALUE
4x5 1-2000 <$600
3x10-20 1-1900 <$850/$1250
50-100 1-1900 <$5000
Series 1875
4x5 1-435 <$600
3x10-20 1-825 <$750/$1000
50-100 1-1261 <$5000
Brown Back
4x5 1-3635 <$300
3x10-20 1-12078 <$300/$350
50-100 1-836 <$1250/$1500
1902 Red Seal
4x5 1-7750 <$350
3x10-20 1-4600 <$350
1902 Date Back
4x5 1-18250 <$150
3x10-20 1-14300 <$150
1902 Plain Back
4x5 18251-60447 <$150
3x10-20 14301-42374 <$150
1929 Small Size
5 Type 1 1-8254 <$50
10 Type 1 1-4502 <$50
20 Type 1 1-1178 <$60
5 Type 2 1-12244 <$50
10 Type 2 1-6786 <$50
20 Type 2 1-1956 <$60
Total Issue $6,001,040
Out in 1935 $200,000
Large out 1935 $9,605
****

****
4046 Talbot
FARMERS & MERCHANTS NB OF EASTON
{{ UNREPORTED }}
Chartered 5/28/89
Liquidated 12/31/15
Brown Back <$VALUE
4x5 1-1000 <$1250
3x10-20 1-3121 <$1250
50-100 1-656 <$2000
1902 Date Back
4x5 1-4317 <$1000
4x10 1-4164 <$1000
Total Issue $527,350
Out in 1916 $18,440
****
1236 Cecil
NB OF ELKTON
{{ 5 L 3 S }}
Chartered 1865
Liquidated 6/26/30
Original Series <$VALUE
4x5 1-4250 <$850
3x10-20 1-2700<$1250/$1750
Series 1875
4x5 1-1400 <$850
3x10-20 1-122 <$1250/$1750
Brown Back
4x5 1-8555 <$650
3x10-20 1-1140 <$650
1902 Red Seal
3x10-20 1-1270 <$750
1902 Date Back
3x10-20 1-4880 <$375
1902 Plain Back
3x10-20 4881-14498 <$375
1929 Small Size
10 Type 1 1-551 <$375
20 Type 1 1-82 <$400
Total Issue $1,313,500
Out at close $50,000
Large out at close $9,690
****
4162 Cecil
SECOND NB OF ELKTON
{{ 1 L }}
Chartered 11/18/89
Receivership 2/18/22
Brown Back <$VALUE
4x5 1-3750 <$1750
50-100 1-196 <$3000
1882 Date Back
4x5 1-120 <$1750
50-100 1-28 <$3000
1902 Date Back
3x10-20 1-1360* <$1500
1902 Plain Back
3x10-20 1601-2102* <$1500
* 1361-1600 not marked
Total Issue $216,100
Out in 1921 $12,200
****
13773 Howard
PATAPSCO NB IN ELLICOTT CITY
{{ 6 S }}
Chartered 9/33
1929 Small Size <$VALUE
5 Type 2 1-9265 <$275
10 Type 2 1-5220 <$275
20 Type 2 1-1572 <$275
Total Issue $129,965
Out in 1935 $100,000
Outstanding includes Ch 3585
****
3585 Howard
PATAPSCO NB OF ELLICOTT CITY
{{ 10 L 8 S }}
Organized 8/10/86
Liquidated 10/7/33
Brown Back <$VALUE
4x5 1-5152 <$850
3x10-20 1-1315 <$850
1902 Red Seal
4x5 1-2570 <$1000
3x10-20 1-2072 <$1000
1902 Date Back
4x5 1-8950 <$500
3x10-20 1-6600 <$500
1902 Plain Back
4x5 8951-19754 <$500
3x10-20 6601-13617 <$500
1929 Small Size
5 Type 1 1-2223 <$250
10 Type 1 1-1087 <$225
20 Type 1 1-284 <$250
Total Issue $1,565,710
Out at close $50,000
Large out 1935 $2,770
Ch 13773 assumed circulation
****

****
10210 Caroline
FNB OF FEDERALSBURG
{{ 3 L 7 S }}
Organized 5/24/12
Receivership 7/9/31
1902 Date Back <$VALUE
4x5 1-600 <$650
3x10-20 1-580 <$650
1902 Plain Back
4x5 601-5944 <$650
3x10-20 581-3626 <$650
1929 Small Size
5 Type 1 1-593 <$350
10 Type 1 1-291 <$350
20 Type 1 1-79 <$350
Total Issue $344,910
Out at close $25,000
Large out at close $2,570
****
1138 Frederick
CENTRAL NB OF FREDERICK
{{ 4 L }}
Chartered 1865
Liquidated 6/2/13
Original Series <$VALUE
4x5 1-3750 <$750
3x10-20 1-3300<$1000/$1500
50-100 1-567 <$5000
Series 1875
4x5 1-840 <$750
3x10-20 1-4139<$1000/$1500
50-100 1-496 <$5000
Brown Back
3x10-20 1-8992 <$500
50-100 1-392 <$1250/$1500
1902 Red Seal
3x10-20 1-4200 <$600
1902 Date Back
4x5 1-3830 <$350
3x10-20 1-7377 <$350
Total Issue $1,787,050
Out in 1913 $103,600
****
3476 Frederick
CITIZENS NB OF FREDERICK
{{ 9 L 11 S }}
Chartered 1886
Brown Back <$VALUE
3x10-20 1-11010 <$500
1902 Red Seal
3x10-20 1-3000 <$500
1902 Date Back
3x10-20 1-8900 <$150
1902 Plain Back
3x10-20 8901-27134 <$150
1929 Small Size
10 Type 1 1-3014 <$75
20 Type 1 1-774 <$85
10 Type 2 1-3450 <$85
20 Type 2 1-921 <$85
Total Issue $2,383,840
Out in 1935 $100,000
Large out 1935 $5,020
****
1267 Frederick
FARMERS & MECHANICS NB OF FREDERICK
{{ 10 L 12 S }}
Chartered 1865
Original Series <$VALUE
4x5 1-3650 <$600
3x10-20 1-1940 <$850/$1250
50-100 1-184 <$5000
Series 1875
4x5 1-3300 <$600
3x10-20 1-1560 <$850/$1250
50-100 1-290 <$5000
Brown Back
4x5 1-7120 <$450
3x10-20 1-3740 <$450
50-100 1-1573 <$1500/$1750
1902 Red Seal
4x5 1-3665 <$500
3x10-20 1-3434 <$500
50-100 1-200 <$2500
1902 Date Back
4x5 1-3250 <$150
3x10-20 1-9400 <$150
50-100 1-100 <$400/$500
1902 Plain Back
3x10-20 9401-31865 <$150
1929 Small Size
10 Type 1 1-3638 <$75
20 Type 1 1-1042 <$85
10 Type 2 1-4131 <$85
20 Type 2 1-1250 <$85
Total Issue $3,308,330
Out in 1935 $125,000
Large out 1935 $8,170
****

****
1589 Frederick
FNB OF FREDERICK
{{ 3 L }}
Chartered 10/14/65
Liquidated 8/2/09
Original Series <$VALUE
3x1-2 1-3000 <$1000/$3000
4x5 1-3250 <$850
3x10-20 1-2220<$1000/$1500
Series 1875
3x10-20 1-2726<$1000/$1500
Brown Back
3x10-20 1-3095 <$600
1902 Red Seal
3x10-20 1-2135 <$750
Total Issue $588,800
Out in 1910 $18,015
****
1449 Frederick
FREDERICK COUNTY NB OF FREDERICK
{{ 15 L 11 S }}
Organized 6/13/65
Liquidated 9/28/33
Original Series <$VALUE
4x5 1-1700 <$600
4x10 1-4098 <$750
3x20-50 1-450 <$1000/$5000
Series 1875
4x10 1-2150 <$600
3x20-50 1-1113<$1000/$5000
Brown Back
3x10-20 1-14337 <$350
1902 Red Seal
4x5 1-6250 <$400
3x10-20 1-3000 <$400
1902 Date Back
4x5 1-11000 <$125
3x10-20 1-9300 <$125
1902 Plain Back
4x5 11001-39215 <$125
3x10-20 9301-28551 <$125
1929 Small Size
5 Type 1 1-7960 <$85
10 Type 1 1-2386 <$85
20 Type 1 1-773 <$100
Total Issue $4,134,270
Out at close $150,000
Large out 1935 $7,975
Ch 13747 assumed circulation
****
13747 Frederick
FREDERICK COUNTY NB OF FREDERICK
{{ 1 S }}
Chartered 8/33
1929 Small Size <$VALUE
5 Type 2 1-1879 <$500
10 Type 2 1-730 <$500
20 Type 2 1-185 <$500
Total Issue $20,395
Out in 1935 $75,000
Outstanding includes Ch 1449
****
6196 Garrett
FNB OF FRIENDSVILLE
{{ 3 L 7 S }}
Chartered 4/8/02
1902 Red Seal <$VALUE
4x5 1-1525 <$1250
3x10-20 1-1320 <$1250
1902 Date Back
4x5 1-1850 <$750
3x10-20 1-1370 <$750
1902 Plain Back (dated 1902)
4x5 1851-3530 <$750
3x10-20 1371-2403 <$750
1902 Plain Back (dated 1922)
4x5 1-2775 <$750
3x10-20 1-1808 <$750
1929 Small Size
5 Type 1 1-856 <$400
10 Type 1 1-430 <$400
20 Type 1 1-120 <$400
5 Type 2 1-1254 <$400
10 Type 2 1-673 <$400
20 Type 2 1-212 <$400
Total Issue $516,270
Out in 1935 $25,000
Large out 1935 $1,520
****
4926 Allegany
CITIZENS NB OF FROSTBURG
{{ 8 L 9 S }}
Organized 5/24/93
Receivership 6/8/33
Brown Back <$VALUE
4x5 1-6550 <$750
3x10-20 1-2460 <$750
1882 Date Back
4x5 1-3042 <$750
3x10-20 1-2431 <$750

1902 Date Back
4x5 1-1600 <$400
3x10-20 1-1260 <$400
3x50-100 1-44 <$650/$750
1902 Plain Back
4x5 1601-12177 <$400
3x10-20 1261-8187 <$400
1929 Small Size
5 Type 1 1-1961 <$175
10 Type 1 1-1022 <$175
20 Type 1 1-268 <$200
Total Issue $1,252,590
Out at close $49,580
Large out at close $2,520
****
1412 Allegany
FNB OF FROSTBURG
{{ UNREPORTED }}
Chartered 7/10/65
Liquidated 7/30/69
Original Series <$VALUE
4x5 1-1425 <$2000
3x10-20 1-400 <$2000/$2500
Total Issue $48,500
Out in 1910 $210
****
4149 Allegany
FNB OF FROSTBURG
{{ 6 L 8 S }}
Chartered 11/4/89
Receivership 6/4/34
Brown Back <$VALUE
4x5 1-13337 <$750
3x10-20 1-3624 <$750
1902 Date Back
4x5 1-4500 <$400
3x10-20 1-3480 <$400
1902 Plain Back
4x5 4501-15313 <$400
3x10-20 3481-10662 <$400
1929 Small Size
5 Type 1 1-1874 <$135
10 Type 1 1-1138 <$135
20 Type 1 1-328 <$150
5 Type 2 1-886 <$175
10 Type 2 1-421 <$175
20 Type 2 1-153 <$200
Total Issue $1,462,860
Out at close $49,050
Large out at close $3,380
****
13979 Allegany
FROSTBURG NB, FROSTBURG
{{ 7 S }}
Chartered 1/34
1929 Small Size <$VALUE
5 Type 2 1-2030 <$165
10 Type 2 1-2135 <$165
20 Type 2 1-1140 <$165
Total Issue $54,300
Out in 1935 $24,600
****
4608 Montgomery
FNB OF GAITHERSBURG
{{ 7 L 7 S }}
Chartered 1891
Brown Back <$VALUE
3x10-20 1-1730 <$1500
1882 Date Back
3x10-20 1-384 <$1500
1902 Date Back
3x10-20 1-1210 <$650
1902 Plain Back
3x10-20 1211-12682 <$650
1929 Small Size
10 Type 1 1-1936 <$300
20 Type 1 1-464 <$325
10 Type 2 1-2202 <$375
20 Type 2 1-648 <$400
Total Issue $946,620
Out in 1935 $50,000
Large out 1935 $1,210
****
5943 Garrett
FNB OF GRANTSVILLE
{{ 3 L 3 S }}
Organized 8/6/01
Receivership 10/25/33
Brown Back <$VALUE
4x5 1-1815 <$1500
3x10-20 1-1394 <$1500
1882 Date Back
4x5 1-2000* <$1500
3x10-20 1-1500** <$1500
1882 Value Back
4x5 2101-3745* <$1500
3x10-20 1581-2436** <$1500
* 2001-2100 not marked
** 1501-1580 not marked
1902 Plain Back
4x5 1-3377 <$600
3x10-20 1-1949 <$600

1929 Small Size
5 Type 1 1-993 <$400
10 Type 1 1-472 <$400
20 Type 1 1-118 <$400
Total Issue $539,960
Out at close $25,000
Large out at close $1,560
****
1893 Washington
CITIZENS NB OF HAGERSTOWN
Chartered 10/18/71
Liquidated 11/7/04
2nd title and location:
Citizens NB of Washington City, D C 5/1/74
FIRST TITLE (M D) {{ 0 L }}
Original Series <$VALUE
3x1-2 1-1000 <$2000/$4000
4x5 1-530 <$2000
3x10-20 1-620 <$2500/$3500
SECOND TITLE (D C) {{ 7 L }}
Original Series
3x1-2 1-1720 <$2000/$4000
4x5 1-2500 <$1750
3x10-20 1-3000<$2500/$3500
Series 1875
4x5 1-8566 <$1500
3x10-20 1-7661<$2000/$2500
Brown Back
4x5 1-7000 <$500
3x10-20 1-1858 <$500/$600
Total Issue $1,042,470
Out in 1910 $8,041
****
1431 Washington
FNB OF HAGERSTOWN
{{ 13 L 9 S }}
Organized 5/2/65
Receivership 10/5/31
Original Series <$VALUE
3x1-2 1-1100 <$1000/$3000
4x5 1-2250 <$500
3x10-20 1-2700 <$850/$1250
Series 1875
3x10-20 1-2450 <$750/$1000
Brown Back
3x10-20 1-7346 <$400
1902 Red Seal
3x10-20 1-3200 <$500
1902 Date Back
3x10-20 1-7600 <$150
1902 Plain Back
3x10-20 7601-29355 <$150
1929 Small Size
10 Type 1 1-2854 <$125
20 Type 1 1-836 <$125
Total Issue $2,574,610
Out at close $150,000
Large out at close $15,010
****
12590 Washington
NICODEMUS NB OF HAGERSTOWN
{{ 7 L 23 S }}
Chartered 10/24
1902 Plain Back <$VALUE
3x10-20 1-7028 <$250
1929 Small Size
10 Type 1 1-2826 <$60
20 Type 1 1-808 <$65
10 Type 2 1-3510 <$65
20 Type 2 1-1118 <$75
Total Issue $675,380
Out in 1935 $100,000
Large out 1935 $5,080
Outstanding includes Ch 4856
****
4856 Washington
PEOPLES NB OF HAGERSTOWN
{{ 10 L }}
Chartered 1893
Liquidated 11/1/24
Brown Back <$VALUE
3x10-20 1-8160 <$500
1882 Date Back
3x10-20 1-4432 <$500
1902 Date Back
3x10-20 1-3900 <$200
1902 Plain Back
3x10-20 3901-14509 <$200
Total Issue $1,355,050
Out at close $94,200
Ch 12590 assumed circulation
****

<$VALUEs are for notes in FINE condition. Value changes by approximately 25% for a change of one full grade.

4049 Washington
SECOND NB OF HAGERSTOWN
{{ 17 L 17 S }}
Chartered 5/31/89
Brown Back <$VALUE
3x10-20 1-9880 <$400
1902 Date Back
3x10-20 1-9100 <$125
1902 Plain Back
3x10-20 9101-25759 <$125
1929 Small Size
10 Type 1 1-2828 <$55
20 Type 1 1-754 <$65
10 Type 2 1-2538 <$65
20 Type 2 1-1022 <$65
Total Issue $2,087,930
Out in 1935 $100,000
Large out 1935 $5,360

9755 Carroll
FNB OF HAMPSTEAD
{{ 2 L 3 S }}
Organized 4/13/10
Receivership 3/10/33
1902 Date Back <$VALUE
3x10-20 1-2235 <$900
1902 Plain Back
3x10-20 2236-9814 <$900
1929 Small Size
10 Type 1 1-1251 <$400
20 Type 1 1-332 <$425
Total Issue $605,600
Out at close $44,040
Large out at close $2,020

7859 Washington
FNB OF HANCOCK
{{ 1 L 7 S }}
Organized 7/21/05
Receivership 12/28/33
1902 Red Seal <$VALUE
4x5 1-1250 <$2000
3x10-20 1-980 <$2000
1902 Date Back
4x5 1-2550 <$1250
3x10-20 1-1840 <$1250
1902 Plain Back
4x5 2551-8686 <$1250
3x10-20 1841-5553 <$1250
1929 Small Size
5 Type 1 1-1018 <$250
10 Type 1 1-661 <$250
20 Type 1 1-201 <$250
Total Issue $619,690
Out at close $29,700
Large out at close $1,800

13853 Washington
PEOPLES NB OF HANCOCK
{{ 5 S }}
Chartered 12/33
1929 Small Size <$VALUE
5 Type 2 1-3506 <$250
10 Type 2 1-2923 <$250
20 Type 2 1-1281 <$250
Total Issue $72,380
Out in 1935 $39,300

5445 Harford
CITIZENS NB OF
HAVRE de GRACE
{{ 9 L 16 S }}
Chartered 6/22/00
Brown Back <$VALUE
4x5 1-3100 <$600
3x10-20 1-2370 <$600
1882 Date Back
4x5 1-6375* <$550
3x10-20 1-4720** <$550
1882 Value Back
4x5 6776-11025* <$550
3x10-20 5041-7509** <$550
* 6376-6775 not marked
** 4721-5040 not marked
1902 Plain Back
4x5 1-11308 <$300
3x10-20 1-7581 <$300
1929 Small Size
5 Type 1 1-3164 <$100
10 Type 1 1-1458 <$100
20 Type 1 1-404 <$110
10 Type 2 1-3973 <$125
20 Type 2 1-1128 <$125
Total Issue $1,674,830
Out in 1935 $70,000
Large out 1935 $3,030

3010 Harford
FNB OF HAVRE de GRACE
{{ 4 L 2 S }}
Organized 6/23/83
Brown Back <$VALUE
4x5 1-2901 <$1000
3x10-20 1-1613 <$1000
1902 Red Seal
4x5 1-820 <$1000
3x10-20 1-580 <$1000
50-100 1-124 <$2500
1902 Date Back
4x5 1-2675 <$450
3x10-20 1-1960 <$450
50-100 1-100 <$650/$750
1902 Plain Back
4x5 2676-6142 <$450
3x10-20 1961-4193 <$450
1929 Small Size
5 Type 1 1-976 <$400
10 Type 1 1-400 <$400
20 Type 1 1-126 <$400
5 Type 2 1-1310 <$400
10 Type 2 1-551 <$400
20 Type 2 1-151 <$400
Total Issue $633,640
Out in 1935 $20,000
Large out 1935 $1,290

7519 Prince Georges
FNB OF HYATTSVILLE
{{ 7 L 2 S }}
Chartered 12/04
Liquidated 5/31/30
1902 Red Seal <$VALUE
4x5 1-550 <$1500
3x10-20 1-440 <$1500
1902 Date Back
4x5 1-1450 <$850
3x10-20 1-1020 <$850
1902 Plain Back
4x5 1451-12333 <$850
3x10-20 1021-7868 <$850
1929 Small Size
5 Type 1 1-571 <$500
10 Type 1 1-265 <$500
20 Type 1 1-53 <$500
Total Issue $712,450
Out at close $40,000
Large out at close $7,120

8302 Garrett
FNB OF KITZMILLERVILLE
{{ 3 L 8 S }}
Organized 6/25/06
Receivership 5/19/33
1902 Red Seal <$VALUE
4x5 1-506 <$1500
3x10-20 1-405 <$1500
1902 Date Back
4x5 1-2800 <$600
3x10-20 1-1900 <$600
1902 Plain Back
4x5 2801-8760 <$600
3x10-20 1901-5572 <$600
1929 Small Size
5 Type 1 1-998 <$375
10 Type 1 1-472 <$375
20 Type 1 1-145 <$375
Total Issue $559,830
Out at close $24,980
Large out at close $1,490

8456 Charles
SOUTHERN MARYLAND NB OF
LA PLATA
{{ 2 L U + 11 S }}
Organized 8/25/06
1902 Red Seal <$VALUE
4x5 1-200 <$2000
4x10 1-275 <$2000
1902 Date Back
4x5 1-1750 <$1000
4x10 1-1675 <$1000
1902 Plain Back
4x5 1751-6803 <$1000
4x10 1676-5596 <$1000
1929 Small Size
5 Type 1 1-1458 <$300
10 Type 1 1-618 <$300
5 Type 2 1-3102 <$325
10 Type 2 1-1917 <$325
Total Issue $490,400
Out in 1935 $25,000
Large out 1935 $900

4364 Prince Georges
CITIZENS NB OF LAUREL
{{ 2 L 1 S }}
Chartered 1890
Brown Back <$VALUE
4x5 1-2825 <$3000
3x10-20 1-690 <$3000
1882 Date Back
4x5 1-155 <$2500
3x10-20 1-74 <$2500
1902 Date Back
3x10-20 1-1330 <$2000
1902 Plain Back
3x10-20 1331-3504 <$2000
1929 Small Size
10 Type 1 1-448 <$1000
20 Type 1 1-126 <$1000
10 Type 2 1-240 <$1000
20 Type 2 1-65 <$1000
Total Issue $318,700
Out in 1935 $12,500
Large out 1935 $750

6606 St Marys
FNB OF SAINT MARY'S,
LEONARDTOWN
{{ 6 L 4 U + 10 S }}
Organized 1/20/03
1902 Red Seal <$VALUE
3x10-20 1-900 <$1250
1902 Date Back
3x10-20 1-1950 <$600
1902 Plain Back
3x10-20 1951-5779 <$600
1929 Small Size
10 Type 1 1-744 <$165
20 Type 1 1-192 <$185
10 Type 2 1-648 <$185
20 Type 2 1-294 <$200
Total Issue $413,990
Out in 1935 $25,000
Large out 1935 $1,460

7732 Allegany
FNB OF LONACONING
{{ 2 L 6 S }}
Organized 4/27/05
Receivership 4/11/32
1902 Red Seal <$VALUE
4x5 1-1050 <$1500
3x10-20 1-840 <$1500
1902 Date Back
4x5 1-2475 <$850
3x10-20 1-1760 <$850
1902 Plain Back
4x5 2476-8227 <$850
3x10-20 1761-5207 <$850
1929 Small Size
5 Type 1 1-624 <$400
10 Type 1 1-304 <$400
20 Type 1 1-95 <$400
Total Issue $536,250
Out at close $25,000
Large out at close $1,750

9429 St Marys
NB OF MECHANICSVILLE
{{ UNREPORTED }}
Chartered 6/09
Liquidated 5/29/20
1902 Date Back <$VALUE
4x5 1-1975 <$1500
3x10-20 1-1480 <$1500
1902 Plain Back
4x5 1976-3128 <$1500
3x10-20 1481-2098 <$1500
Total Issue $167,460
Out in 1919 $20,260

5331 Allegany
FNB OF MIDLAND
{{ 5 L 4 S }}
Chartered 5/5/00
Receivership 5/9/34
Brown Back <$VALUE
4x5 1-2215 <$1500
3x10-20 1-1714 <$1500
1882 Date Back
4x5 1-2475* <$1500
3x10-20 1-1770** <$1500
1882 Value Back
4x5 2576-4115* <$1500
3x10-20 1851-2696** <$1500
* 2476-2575 not marked
** 1771-1850 not marked
1902 Plain Back
4x5 1-12917 <$600
1929 Small Size
5 Type 1 1-1130 <$400
10 Type 1 1-554 <$400
20 Type 1 1-172 <$400
5 Type 2 1-200 <$450
10 Type 2 1-50 <$450
Total Issue $694,720
Out at close $25,000
Large out at close $1,470

9238 Frederick
FNB OF MONROVIA
{{ 1 L }}
Chartered 9/08
Liquidated 12/30/16
1902 Date Back <$VALUE
3x10-20 1-2710 <$1500
1902 Plain Back
3x10-20 2711-2926 <$1500
Total Issue $146,300
Out at close $18,400

7160 Carroll
FNB OF MOUNT AIRY
{{ 2 L 3 S }}
Organized 2/20/04
1902 Red Seal <$VALUE
3x10-20 1-1456 <$1750
1902 Date Back
3x10-20 1-2430 <$850
1902 Plain Back
3x10-20 2431-7136 <$850
1929 Small Size
10 Type 1 1-818 <$450
20 Type 1 1-222 <$450
10 Type 2 1-675 <$500
20 Type 2 1-215 <$500
Total Issue $516,370
Out in 1935 $25,000
Large out 1935 $1,220

12443 Prince Georges
FNB OF MOUNT RAINIER
{{ 3 L 0 S }}
Chartered 9/23
Liquidated 3/5/30
1902 Plain Back <$VALUE
4x5 1-3570 <$1500
3x10-20 1-2225 <$1500
1929 Small Size
5 Type 1 1-100 <$850
10 Type 1 1-27 <$850
20 Type 1 1-5 <$850
Total Issue $187,870
Out at close $11,970
Large out at close $6,750

6144 Allegany
FNB OF MOUNT SAVAGE
{{ 2 L 8 S }}
Chartered 3/3/02
1902 Red Seal <$VALUE
3x10-20 1-2200 <$2500
1902 Date Back
3x10-20 1-2980 <$1250
1902 Plain Back (dated 1902)
3x10-20 2981-5102 <$1250
1902 Plain Back (dated 1922)
3x10-20 1-3186 <$1250
1929 Small Size
10 Type 1 1-852 <$300
20 Type 1 1-224 <$300
10 Type 2 1-908 <$325
20 Type 2 1-165 <$350
Total Issue $614,780
Out in 1935 $25,000
Large out 1935 $220

747 Carroll
FNB OF NEW WINDSOR
{{ 6 L 3 S }}
Organized 12/24/64
Receivership 10/29/31
Original Series <$VALUE
4x5 1-2100 <$1250
3x10-20 1-1000<$1500/$2000
Series 1875
4x5 1-500 <$1250
3x10-20 1-1518<$1500/$2000
Brown Back
3x10-20 1-5889 <$1000
1902 Red Seal
3x10-20 1-2200 <$1500
1902 Date Back
3x10-20 1-4800 <$500
1902 Plain Back
3x10-20 4801-14865 <$500
1929 Small Size
10 Type 1 1-1119 <$350
20 Type 1 1-278 <$350
Total Issue $1,426,100
Out at close $55,000
Large out at close $5,750

7064 Cecil
FNB OF NORTH EAST
{{ 1 L 2 S }}
Organized 12/3/03
1902 Red Seal <$VALUE
4x5 1-350 <$2500
3x10-20 1-280 <$2500
1902 Date Back
4x5 1-800 <$2000
3x10-20 1-580 <$2000
1902 Plain Back
4x5 801-4473 <$2000
3x10-20 581-2792 <$2000
1929 Small Size
5 Type 1 1-1186 <$400
10 Type 1 1-560 <$400
20 Type 1 1-142 <$400
5 Type 2 1-1440 <$400
10 Type 2 1-638 <$400
20 Type 2 1-165 <$400
Total Issue $353,160
Out in 1935 $25,000
Large out 1935 $390

5623 Garrett
FNB OF OAKLAND
{{ 7 L 11 S }}
Chartered 11/15/00
Brown Back <$VALUE
4x5 1-3650 <$650
3x10-20 1-2870 <$650
1882 Date Back
4x5 1-4150 <$650
3x10-20 1-3240 <$650
1882 Value Back
4x5 4151-7315 <$650
3x10-20 3241-4989 <$650
1902 Plain Back
4x5 1-6814 <$300
3x10-20 1-4674 <$300
1929 Small Size
5 Type 1 1-1842 <$125
10 Type 1 1-960 <$125
20 Type 1 1-314 <$135
5 Type 2 1-2502 <$150
10 Type 2 1-1193 <$150
20 Type 2 1-248 <$150
Total Issue $1,162,170
Out in 1935 $50,000
Large out 1935 $2,880

13776 Garrett
GARRETT NB IN OAKLAND
{{ U + 5 S }}
Chartered 9/33
1929 Small Size <$VALUE
5 Type 2 1-19368 <$175
Total Issue $96,840
Out in 1935 $45,770

6588 Garrett
GARRETT NB OF OAKLAND
{{ 7 L 9 S }}
Organized 1/15/03
Receivership 12/5/33
1902 Red Seal <$VALUE
4x5 1-3240 <$750
3x10-20 1-2474 <$750
1902 Date Back
4x5 1-4250 <$300
3x10-20 1-3080 <$300
1902 Plain Back
4x5 4251-19110 <$300
3x10-20 3081-12939 <$300
1929 Small Size
5 Type 1 1-4374 <$150
10 Type 1 1-2286 <$150
20 Type 1 1-535 <$150
Total Issue $1,550,230
Out at close $98,915
Large out at close $4,655

13867 Baltimore
FNB IN PARKTON
{{ 7 S }}
Chartered 12/33
1929 Small Size <$VALUE
10 Type 2 1-3215 <$175
20 Type 2 1-1020 <$175
Total Issue $52,550
Out in 1935 $50,000
Outstanding includes Ch 9444

9444 Baltimore
FNB OF PARKTON
{{ 3 L 8 S }}
Organized 5/1/09
Liquidated 2/12/34
1902 Date Back <$VALUE
3x10-20 1-2380 <$650
1902 Plain Back
3x10-20 2381-7068 <$650
1929 Small Size
10 Type 1 1-778 <$175
20 Type 1 1-192 <$200
10 Type 2 1-284 <$225
20 Type 2 1-35 <$225
Total Issue $426,660
Out at close $25,000
Large out 1935 $220
Ch 13867 assumed circulation

11193 Cecil
NB OF PERRYVILLE
{{ 3 L 21 S }}
Organized 6/4/18
1902 Plain Back <$VALUE
4x5 1-36061 <$400
1929 Small Size
5 Type 1 1-7552 <$100
5 Type 2 1-17199 <$100
Total Issue $1,033,775
Out in 1935 $50,000
Large out 1935 $1,380

8867 Baltimore
PIKESVILLE NB, PIKESVILLE
{{ 3 L 2 S }}
Organized 7/23/07
Receivership 2/6/32
1902 Red Seal <$VALUE
4x5 1-156 <$2000
3x10-20 1-125 <$2000
1902 Date Back
4x5 1-650* <$1000
3x10-20 1-520** <$1000
1902 Plain Back
4x5 751-2024* <$1000
3x10-20 601-1326** <$1000
* 651-750 not marked
** 521-600 not marked
1929 Small Size
5 Type 1 1-214 <$650
10 Type 1 1-87 <$650
20 Type 1 1-23 <$650
Total Issue $130,550
Out at close $6,250
Large out at close $510

14106 Worcester
CITIZENS NB IN
POCOMOKE CITY
{{ 3 S }}
Chartered 4/34
1929 Small Size <$VALUE
5 Type 2 1-1270 <$400
10 Type 2 1-1800 <$400
20 Type 2 1-1860 <$400
Total Issue $61,550
Out in 1935 $50,000

6202 Worcester
CITIZENS NB OF
POCOMOKE CITY
{{ 1 L 0 S }}
Chartered 4/10/02
Liquidated 7/1/35
1902 Red Seal <$VALUE
3x10-20 1-890 <$3000
1902 Date Back
3x10-20 1-1400 <$1500
1902 Plain Back (dated 1902)
3x10-20 1401-1972 <$1500
1902 Plain Back (dated 1922)
3x10-20 1-1241 <$1500
1929 Small Size
10 Type 1 1-369 <$650
20 Type 1 1-117 <$650
Total Issue $241,330
Out in 1935 $12,500
Large out 1935 $420

4191 Worcester
POCOMOKE CITY NB,
POCOMOKE CITY
{{ 1 L 6 S }}
Organized 8/6/89
Brown Back <$VALUE
3x10-20 1-1611 <$3000
1902 Date Back
3x10-20 1-1300 <$1500
1902 Plain Back
3x10-20 1301-3015 <$1500
1929 Small Size
10 Type 1 1-354 <$350
20 Type 1 1-118 <$350
10 Type 2 1-3316 <$400
20 Type 2 1-1056 <$400
Total Issue $320,980
Out in 1935 $50,000
Large out 1935 $10

8860 Montgomery
POOLESVILLE NB,
POOLESVILLE
{{ 1 L 0 S }}
Chartered 9/07
Liquidated 12/14/29
1902 Red Seal <$VALUE
4x5 1-200 <$2500
3x10-20 1-160 <$2500
1902 Date Back
4x5 1-900 <$1500
3x10-20 1-680 <$1500
1902 Plain Back
4x5 901-2713 <$1500
3x10-20 681-1649 <$1500
1929 Small Size
5 Type 1 1-85* <$1000
* E000085A & F000085A not issued
Total Issue $151,250
Out at close $8,000
Large out at close $6,300

****
13840 Cecil
CECIL NB AT PORT DEPOSIT
{{ 3 S }}
Chartered 11/33
1929 Small Size <$VALUE
5 Type 2 1-2516 <$250
10 Type 2 1-1499 <$250
20 Type 2 1-324 <$250
Total Issue $34,050
Out in 1935 $50,000
Outstanding includes Ch 1211
****
1211 Cecil
CECIL NB OF PORT DEPOSIT
{{ 14 L 7 S }}
Organized 3/6/65
Liquidated 1/8/34
Original Series <$VALUE
3x1-2 1-8074 <$1000/$3000
4x5 1-11000 <$750
4x10 1-4500 <$1000
3x20-50 1-800 <$1500/$5000
Series 1875
4x5 1-4232 <$750
4x10 1-2625 <$1000
3x20-50 1-829 <$1500/$5000
Brown Back
4x5 1-7686 <$600
3x10-20 1-2259 <$600
1902 Red Seal
4x5 1-2100 <$750
3x10-20 1-1360 <$750
1902 Date Back
4x5 1-4400 <$175
3x10-20 1-3420 <$175
1902 Plain Back
4x5 4401-14470 <$175
3x10-20 3421-9999 <$175
1929 Small Size
5 Type 1 1-1760 <$150
10 Type 1 1-990 <$150
20 Type 1 1-288 <$165
5 Type 2 1-1008 <$175
10 Type 2 1-493 <$175
20 Type 2 1-105 <$175
Total Issue $2,134,050
Out at close $50,000
Large out at close $6,280
Ch 13840 assumed circulation
****
5610 Cecil
NB OF PORT DEPOSIT
{{ 1 L }}
Chartered 10/26/00
Liquidated 10/31/13
Brown Back <$VALUE
4x5 1-3500 <$1500
3x10-20 1-2320 <$1500
1882 Date Back
4x5 1-3420 <$1250
3x10-20 1-2450 <$1250
Total Issue $376,900
Out at close $49,995
****
2481 Cecil
NB OF RISING SUN
{{ 8 L 7 U + 15 S }}
Chartered 6/8/80
Series 1875 <$VALUE
3x10-20 1-5083<$1000/$1500
Brown Back
3x10-20 1-3960 <$650
1882 Date Back
3x10-20 1-4200 <$650
1882 Value Back
3x10-20 4201-6680 <$650
1902 Plain Back
3x10-20 1-4701 <$300
1929 Small Size
10 Type 1 1-2152 <$135
20 Type 1 1-560 <$150
10 Type 2 1-4613 <$150
20 Type 2 1-1344 <$150
Total Issue $1,290,530
Out in 1935 $100,000
Large out 1935 $2,370
****
3187 Montgomery
MONTGOMERY COUNTY NB OF ROCKVILLE
{{ 11 L 10 S }}
Organized 11/20/83
Brown Back <$VALUE
3x10-20 1-9751 <$1000
1902 Red Seal
3x10-20 1-5600 <$1000
1902 Date Back
3x10-20 1-8500 <$450
1902 Plain Back
3x10-20 8501-30236 <$450
1929 Small Size
10 Type 1 1-3998 <$300
20 Type 1 1-1050 <$300
10 Type 2 1-4368 <$325
20 Type 2 1-744 <$325
Total Issue $2,703,790
Out in 1935 $100,000
Large out 1935 $5,810
****
6761 Wicomico
PEOPLES NB OF SALISBURY
{{ 2 L }}
Chartered 5/03
Liquidated 7/1/24
1902 Red Seal <$VALUE
4x5 1-1250 <$1500
3x10-20 1-840 <$1500
50-100 1-480 <$3000
1902 Date Back
4x5 1-4300 <$850
3x10-20 1-2830 <$850
50-100 1-100 <$1500
1902 Plain Back
4x5 4301-9850 <$850
3x10-20 2831-6130 <$850
Total Issue $657,500
Out at close $50,000
****
3250 Wicomico
SALISBURY NB, SALISBURY
{{ 4 L 11 S }}
Chartered 1884
Brown Back <$VALUE
50-100 1-1084 <$3000
1902 Red Seal
50-100 1-600 <$3000
1902 Date Back
4x5 1-4700 <$600
50-100 1-240 <$1250
3x50-100 1-662 <$1250
1902 Plain Back
4x5 4701-18635 <$600
3x50-100 663-862 <$1250
1929 Small Size
5 Type 1 1-2074 <$175
50 Type 1 1-118 <$350
100 Type 1 1-146 <$400
5 Type 2 1-800 <$200
50 Type 2 1-65 <$800
100 Type 2 1-45 <$800
Total Issue $1,073,770
Out in 1935 $100,000
Large out 1935 $3,075
****
5561 Montgomery
FNB OF SANDY SPRING
{{ 0 L 5 S }}
Chartered 8/28/00
Brown Back <$VALUE
3x10-20 1-600 <$2500
1882 Date Back
3x10-20 1-740 <$2500
1882 Value Back
3x10-20 741-878 <$2500
1902 Plain Back
3x10-20 1-811 <$2000
1929 Small Size
10 Type 1 1-237 <$850
20 Type 1 1-54 <$850
Total Issue $135,150
Out in 1935 $6,250
Large out 1935 $290
****
9830 Montgomery
SILVER SPRING NB, SILVER SPRING
{{ 4 L 4 S }}
Chartered 8/10
1902 Date Back <$VALUE
3x10-20 1-1835 <$850
1902 Plain Back
3x10-20 1836-7716 <$850
1929 Small Size
10 Type 1 1-970 <$450
20 Type 1 1-234 <$450
10 Type 2 1-1140 <$450
20 Type 2 1-384 <$450
Total Issue $491,160
Out in 1935 $25,000
Large out 1935 $1,620
****
6297 Worcester
COMMERCIAL NB OF SNOW HILL
{{ 11 L 11 S }}
Chartered 6/10/02
1902 Red Seal <$VALUE
4x5 1-2815 <$1000
3x10-20 1-1954 <$1000
1902 Date Back
4x5 1-4000 <$450
3x10-20 1-3010 <$450
1902 Plain Back
4x5 4001-14010 <$450
3x10-20 3011-9342 <$450
1929 Small Size
5 Type 1 1-1786 <$250
10 Type 1 1-990 <$250
20 Type 1 1-284 <$250
5 Type 2 1-3360 <$275
10 Type 2 1-1680 <$275
20 Type 2 1-456 <$275
Total Issue $1,091,080
Out in 1935 $50,000
Large out 1935 $2,070
****
3783 Worcester
FNB OF SNOW HILL
{{ 2 L 6 S }}
Organized 3/1/87
Brown Back <$VALUE
3x10-20 1-1400 <$1250
1902 Red Seal
3x10-20 1-250 <$1500
1902 Date Back
3x10-20 1-1900 <$750
1902 Plain Back
3x10-20 1901-6553 <$750
1929 Small Size
5 Type 1 1-2730 <$325
10 Type 1 1-986 <$300
20 Type 1 1-264 <$325
5 Type 2 1-3352 <$350
10 Type 2 1-1873 <$350
20 Type 2 1-470 <$350
Total Issue $627,780
Out in 1935 $50,000
Large out 1935 $1,215
****
8578 Carroll
FNB OF SYKESVILLE
{{ UNREPORTED }}
Chartered 3/07
Liquidated 1/16/13
1902 Red Seal <$VALUE
4x5 1-160 <$2500
4x10 1-160 <$2500
1902 Date Back
4x5 1-331 <$2000
4x10 1-307 <$2000
Total Issue $28,500
Out at close $6,250
Ch 8587 assumed circulation
****
8587 Carroll
SYKESVILLE NB, SYKESVILLE
{{ 11 L 5 S }}
Chartered 3/07
Liquidated 11/25/30
1902 Red Seal <$VALUE
3x10-20 1-1200 <$1250
1902 Date Back
3x10-20 1-4740 <$400
1902 Plain Back
3x10-20 4741-20263 <$400
1929 Small Size
10 Type 1 1-1065 <$350
20 Type 1 1-250 <$375
Total Issue $1,167,050
Out at close $75,000
Large out at close $9,590
Outstanding includes Ch 8578
****
5829 Frederick
THURMONT NB, THURMONT
{{ 1 L }}
Chartered 5/22/01
Liquidated 5/11/14
Brown Back <$VALUE
4x5 1-275 <$1750
3x10-20 1-1000 <$1750
1882 Date Back
4x5 1-1080 <$1750
3x10-20 1-755 <$1750
Total Issue $134,850
Out in 1914 $9,990
****
8381 Baltimore
SECOND NB OF TOWSON
{{ 3 L 11 S }}
Organized 7/19/06
1902 Red Seal <$VALUE
4x5 1-312 <$1000
3x10-20 1-1370 <$1000
1902 Date Back
4x5 1-1500 <$450
3x10-20 1-4600 <$450
1902 Plain Back
4x5 1501-1900 <$450
3x10-20 4601-15343 <$450
1929 Small Size
10 Type 1 1-1722 <$175
20 Type 1 1-450 <$175
10 Type 2 1-2125 <$175
20 Type 2 1-499 <$175
Total Issue $1,068,440
Out in 1935 $50,000
Large out 1935 $1,810
****
3588 Baltimore
TOWSON NB, TOWSON
{{ 10 L 14 S }}
Organized 11/8/86
Brown Back <$VALUE
4x5 1-6850 <$750
3x10-20 1-1889 <$750
1902 Red Seal
3x10-20 1-1000 <$850
1902 Date Back
3x10-20 1-5000 <$350
1902 Plain Back
3x10-20 5001-21257 <$350
1929 Small Size
10 Type 1 1-3376 <$125
20 Type 1 1-806 <$135
10 Type 2 1-5836 <$135
20 Type 2 1-1271 <$135
Total Issue $1,727,360
Out in 1935 $100,000
Large out 1935 $910
****
9066 Carroll
FNB OF UNION BRIDGE
{{ 4 L }}
Chartered 3/08
Liquidated 8/28/22
1902 Red Seal <$VALUE
4x5 1-650 <$2000
3x10-20 1-530 <$2000
1902 Date Back
4x5 1-2150 <$900
3x10-20 1-1640 <$900
1902 Plain Back
4x5 2151-4515 <$900
3x10-20 1641-2990 <$900
Total Issue $279,300
Out at close $25,000
****
5471 Prince Georges
FNB OF SOUTHERN MARYLAND OF UPPER MARLBORO
{{ 7 L 3 S }}
Chartered 6/29/00
Brown Back <$VALUE
3x10-20 1-1190 <$1000
1882 Date Back
4x5 1-2205 <$1000
3x10-20 1-1660 <$1000
1882 Value Back
4x5 2206-5180 <$1000
3x10-20 1661-3390 <$1000
1902 Plain Back
4x5 1-9870 <$400
3x10-20 1-6561 <$400
1929 Small Size
50 Type 1 1-336 <$450
100 Type 1 1-126 <$650
50 Type 2 1-14 <$750
100 Type 2 1-13 <$1000
Total Issue $1,036,450
Out in 1935 $100,000
Large out 1935 $1,650
****
5831 Allegany
CITIZENS NB OF WESTERNPORT
{{ 6 L 11 S }}
Chartered 5/22/01
Brown Back <$VALUE
3x10-20 1-3350 <$1250
1882 Date Back
3x10-20 1-4000* <$1000
1882 Value Back
3x10-20 4201-6480* <$1000
* 4001-4200 not marked
1902 Plain Back
3x10-20 1-5552 <$500
1929 Small Size
10 Type 1 1-1216 <$250
20 Type 1 1-358 <$250
10 Type 2 1-1456 <$300
20 Type 2 1-226 <$300
Total Issue $904,100
Out in 1935 $40,000
Large out 1935 $1,950
****
1526 Carroll
FARMERS & MECHANICS NB OF WESTMINSTER
{{ 4 L 14 S }}
Chartered 1865
Original Series <$VALUE
4x5 1-1750 <$850
3x10-20 1-2250<$1000/$1500
Series 1875
3x10-20 1-1348<$1000/$1500
Brown Back
50-100 1-1204 <$2000
1902 Red Seal
50-100 1-706 <$2500
1902 Date Back
50-100 1-560 <$500/$600
3x50-100 1-1826 <$500/$600
1902 Plain Back
3x50-100 1827-2425 <$500/$600
1929 Small Size
10 Type 1 1-2804 <$100
20 Type 1 1-788 <$110
10 Type 2 1-3472 <$110
20 Type 2 1-950 <$110
Total Issue $1,508,170
Out in 1935 $100,000
Large out 1935 $6,710
****
742 Carroll
FNB OF WESTMINSTER
{{ 12 L 16 S }}
Organized 12/31/64
Original Series <$VALUE
4x5 1-2750 <$600
3x10-20 1-2750 <$850/$1250
50-100 1-150 <$5000
Series 1875
4x5 1-1930 <$600
3x10-20 1-2154 <$850/$1250
Brown Back
3x10-20 1-10025 <$400
1902 Red Seal
3x10-20 1-4750 <$450
1902 Date Back
3x10-20 1-10800 <$200
1902 Plain Back
3x10-20 10801-30337 <$200
1929 Small Size
10 Type 1 1-3610 <$75
20 Type 1 1-906 <$80
5 Type 2 1-324 <$85
10 Type 2 1-3461 <$85
20 Type 2 1-1080 <$85
Total Issue $3,000,050
Out in 1935 $108,000
Large out 1935 $6,280
****
1596 Carroll
UNION NB OF WESTMINSTER
{{ 11 L 18 S }}
Chartered 1865
Original Series <$VALUE
4x5 1-2100 <$600
3x10-20 1-2545 <$850/$1250
Series 1875
4x5 1-1000 <$600
3x10-20 1-2319 <$850/$1250
Brown Back
3x10-20 1-9487 <$500
1902 Red Seal
3x10-20 1-3400 <$500
1902 Date Back
3x10-20 1-8200 <$175
1902 Plain Back
3x10-20 8201-27151 <$175
1929 Small Size
10 Type 1 1-3132 <$70
20 Type 1 1-796 <$75
10 Type 2 1-4065 <$75
20 Type 2 1-1189 <$75
Total Issue $2,654,970
Out in 1935 $100,000
Large out 1935 $6,370
****
9469 Baltimore
WHITE HALL NB, WHITE HALL
{{ UNREPORTED }}
Chartered 7/09
Liquidated 5/4/23
1902 Date Back <$VALUE
3x10-20 1-2580 <$1250
1902 Plain Back
3x10-20 2581-4871 <$1250
Total Issue $243,550
Out at close $25,000
****
1551 Washington
WASHINGTON COUNTY NB OF WILLIAMSPORT
{{ 10 L }}
Organized 6/65
Liquidated 3/16/33
Original Series <$VALUE
3x1-2 1-2200 <$1000/$3000
4x5 1-4550 <$750
3x10-20 1-2500 <$850/$1250
50-100 1-260 <$5000
Series 1875
4x5 1-1000 <$750
3x10-20 1-3640 <$850/$1250
Brown Back
4x5 1-3034 <$600
3x10-20 1-9203 <$600
1902 Red Seal
3x10-20 1-3400 <$650
1902 Date Back
3x10-20 1-7700 <$225
1902 Plain Back
3x10-20 7701-22658 <$225
Total Issue $2,291,730
Out in 1935 $6,337
****
8799 Carroll
WOODBINE NB, WOODBINE
{{ 1 L 0 S }}
Organized 5/28/07
1902 Red Seal <$VALUE
3x10-20 1-200 <$2500
1902 Date Back
3x10-20 1-860 <$1500
1902 Plain Back
3x10-20 861-4393 <$1500
1929 Small Size
10 Type 1 1-656 <$750
20 Type 1 1-182 <$750
10 Type 2 1-809 <$750
20 Type 2 1-239 <$750
Total Issue $303,720
Out in 1935 $25,000
Large out 1935 $1,560
****

<$VALUEs are for notes in FINE condition. Value changes by approximately 25% for a change of one full grade.

MASSACHUSETTS

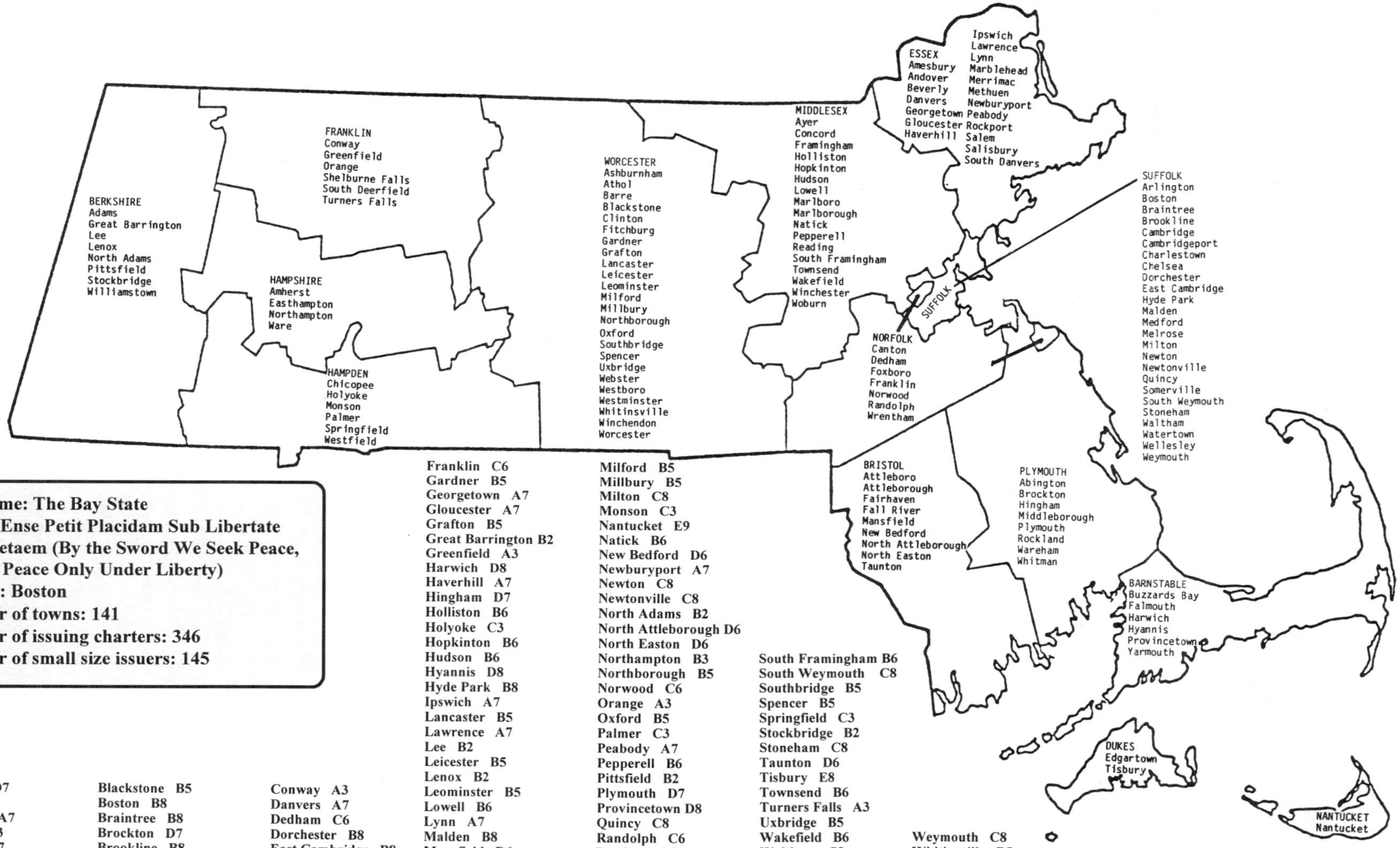

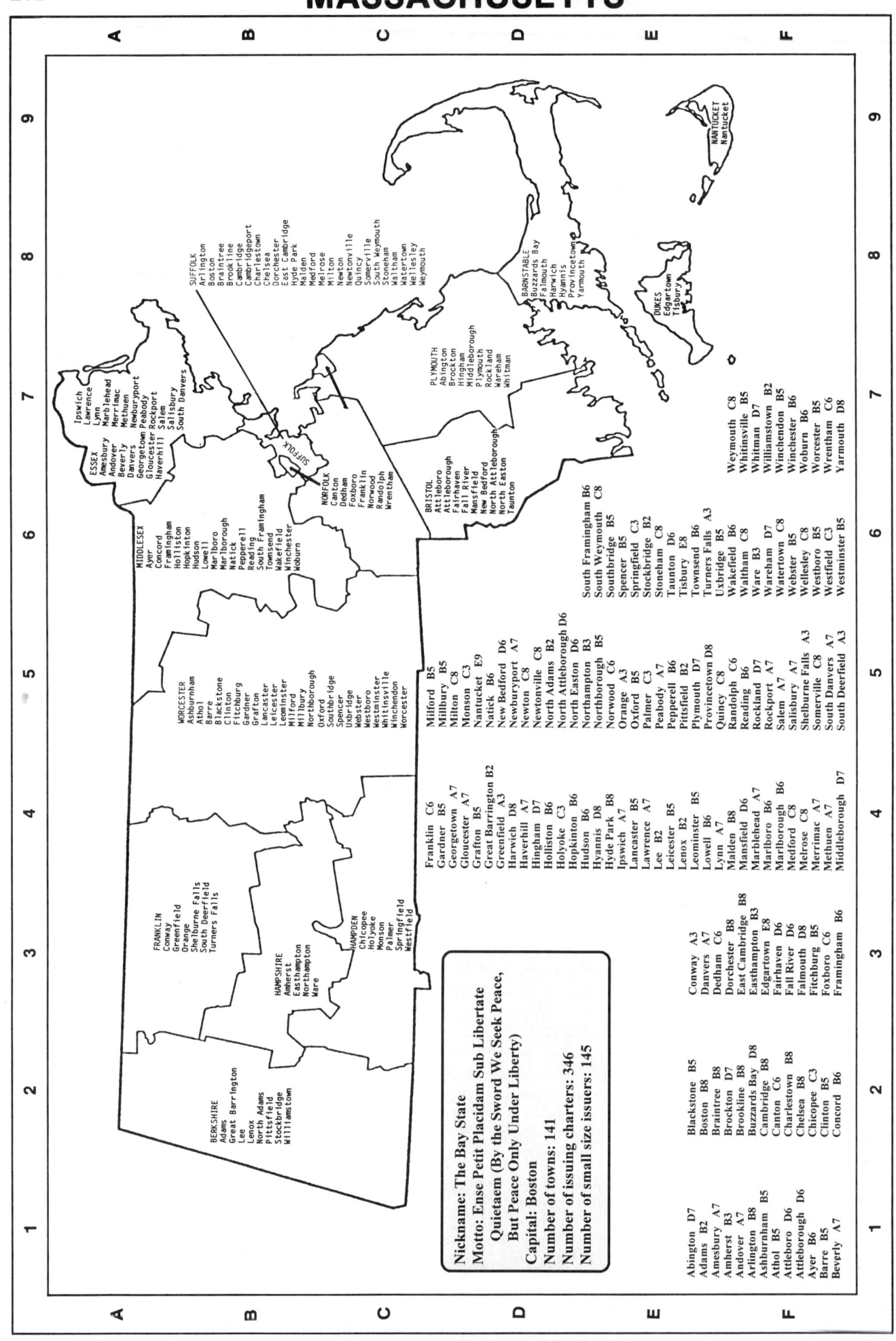

Nickname: The Bay State
Motto: Ense Petit Placidam Sub Libertate Quietaem (By the Sword We Seek Peace, But Peace Only Under Liberty)
Capital: Boston
Number of towns: 141
Number of issuing charters: 346
Number of small size issuers: 145

Abington D7
Adams B2
Amesbury A7
Amherst B3
Andover A7
Arlington B8
Ashburnham B5
Athol B5
Attleboro D6
Attleborough D6
Ayer B6
Barre B5
Beverly A7
Blackstone B5
Boston B8
Braintree B8
Brockton D7
Brookline B8
Buzzards Bay D8
Cambridge B8
Canton C6
Charlestown B8
Chelsea B8
Chicopee C3
Clinton B5
Concord B6
Conway A3
Danvers A7
Dedham C6
Dorchester B8
East Cambridge B8
Easthampton B3
Edgartown E8
Fairhaven D6
Fall River D6
Falmouth D8
Fitchburg B5
Foxboro C6
Framingham B6
Franklin C6
Gardner B5
Georgetown A7
Gloucester A7
Grafton B5
Great Barrington B2
Greenfield A3
Harwich D8
Haverhill A7
Hingham D7
Holliston B6
Holyoke C3
Hopkinton B6
Hudson B6
Hyannis D8
Hyde Park B8
Ipswich A7
Lancaster B5
Lawrence A7
Lee B2
Leicester B5
Lenox B2
Leominster B5
Lowell B6
Lynn A7
Malden B8
Mansfield D6
Marblehead A7
Marlboro B6
Marlborough B6
Medford C8
Melrose C8
Merrimac A7
Methuen A7
Middleborough D7
Milford B5
Millbury B5
Milton C8
Monson C3
Nantucket E9
Natick B6
New Bedford D6
Newburyport A7
Newton C8
Newtonville C8
North Adams B2
North Attleborough D6
North Easton D6
Northampton B3
Northborough B5
Norwood C6
Orange A3
Oxford B5
Palmer C3
Peabody A7
Pepperell B6
Pittsfield B2
Plymouth D7
Provincetown D8
Quincy C8
Randolph C6
Reading B6
Rockland D7
Rockport A7
Salem A7
Salisbury A7
Shelburne Falls A3
Somerville C8
South Danvers A7
South Deerfield A3
South Framingham B6
South Weymouth C8
Southbridge B5
Spencer B5
Springfield C3
Stockbridge B2
Stoneham C8
Taunton D6
Tisbury E8
Townsend B6
Turners Falls A3
Uxbridge B5
Wakefield B6
Waltham C8
Ware B3
Wareham D7
Watertown C8
Webster B5
Wellesley C8
Westboro B5
Westfield C3
Westminster B5
Weymouth C8
Whitinsville B5
Whitman D7
Williamstown B2
Winchendon B5
Winchester B6
Woburn B6
Worcester B5
Wrentham C6
Yarmouth D8

****
1386 Plymouth
ABINGTON NB, ABINGTON
{{ 2 L 3 S }}
Organized 7/1/65
Original Series <$VALUE
4x5 1-2100 <$600
3x10-20 1-1300 <$850/$1500
50-100 1-1480 <$4000
Series 1875
4x5 1-9645 <$600
3x10-20 1-600 <$750/$1250
Brown Back
4x5 1-7736* <$500
3x10-20 1-1593** <$500
* 1931-2500 not issued
** 383-600 not issued
1902 Red Seal
3x10-20 1-940 <$600
1902 Date Back
3x10-20 1-2350* <$350
1902 Plain Back
3x10-20 2591-5631* <$350
* 2351-2590 not marked
1929 Small Size
5 Type 1 1-2800 <$300
5 Type 2 1-5280 <$300
Total Issue $1,202,920
Out in 1935 $23,265
Large out 1935 $2,935
****
462 Berkshire
FNB OF ADAMS
{{ 6 L 5 S }}
Chartered 1864
Original Series <$VALUE
3x1-2 1-7700 <$400/$850
4x5 1-6650 <$400
3x10-20 1-2280 <$750/$1250
Series 1875
3x1-2 1-900 <$400/$850
4x5 1-2650 <$400
3x10-20 1-2200 <$600/$1000
Brown Back
4x5 1-9375 <$350
3x10-20 1-8533 <$350
1902 Red Seal
4x5 1-8300 <$400
3x10-20 1-6255 <$400
1902 Date Back
4x5 1-8250* <$225
3x10-20 1-5900** <$225
1902 Plain Back
4x5 8751-23165* <$225
3x10-20 6261-15480** <$225
* 8251-8750 not marked
** 5901-6260 not marked
1929 Small Size
5 Type 2 1-8760 <$125
10 Type 2 1-4175 <$125
20 Type 2 1-1305 <$125
Total Issue $2,894,850
Out in 1935 $88,482
Large out 1935 $8,582
****
4562 Berkshire
GREYLOCK NB OF ADAMS
{{ 10 L 10 S }}
Chartered 1891
Brown Back <$VALUE
4x5 1-24750 <$250
3x10-20 1-5840 <$250
1882 Date Back
4x5 1-3320 <$250
3x10-20 1-2359 <$250
1902 Date Back
4x5 1-5815 <$150
3x10-20 1-4354 <$150
1902 Plain Back
4x5 5816-24200 <$150
3x10-20 4355-16598 <$150
1929 Small Size
5 Type 1 1-3828 <$85
10 Type 1 1-2032 <$85
20 Type 1 1-460 <$100
5 Type 2 1-5182 <$125
10 Type 2 1-2835 <$125
Total Issue $2,631,470
Out in 1935 $79,700
Large out 1935 $4,470
****
2929 Essex
AMESBURY NB, AMESBURY
{{ 3 L }}
Chartered 1883
Liquidated 11/11/09
Brown Back <$VALUE
4x5 1-17886 <$500
3x10-20 1-3779 <$500
1902 Red Seal
3x10-20 1-1190 <$500
1902 Date Back
3x10-20 1-205 <$350
Total Issue $616,420
Out in 1910 $12,350
****

****
Powow River NB of Amesbury
SEE Ch 1049
Powow River NB of Salisbury
****
393 Hampshire
FNB OF AMHERST
{{ 12 L 9 S }}
Chartered 1864
Original Series <$VALUE
3x1-2 1-2100 <$350/$850
4x5 1-4550 <$400
3x10-20 1-4200 <$750/$1250
Series 1875
4x5 1-1250 <$400
3x10-20 1-2398 <$600/$1000
Brown Back
4x5 1-13784 <$300
3x10-20 1-10912 <$300
50-100 1-240 <$1250/$1500
1902 Red Seal
4x5 1-8000 <$350
3x10-20 1-6000 <$350
1902 Date Back
4x5 1-14750 <$175
3x10-20 1-9100 <$175
1902 Plain Back
4x5 14751-45990 <$175
3x10-20 9101-27786 <$175
1929 Small Size
5 Type 1 1-5726 <$100
10 Type 1 1-3114 <$100
20 Type 1 1-816 <$100
5 Type 2 1-6010 <$125
10 Type 2 1-4491 <$125
20 Type 2 1-1140 <$125
Total Issue $4,637,080
Out in 1935 $147,400
Large out 1935 $9,670
****
1129 Essex
ANDOVER NB, ANDOVER
{{ 6 L }}
Chartered 1865
Original Series <$VALUE
3x1-2 1-3000 <$350/$1000
4x5 1-4000 <$500
3x10-20 1-4610 <$750/$1250
50-100 1-50 <$3500
Series 1875
4x5 1-4500 <$500
3x10-20 1-3720 <$600/$1000
Brown Back
4x5 1-6461 <$300
3x10-20 1-6517 <$300
1902 Red Seal
4x5 1-1900 <$350
3x10-20 1-1240 <$350
1902 Date Back
4x5 1-4550 <$175
3x10-20 1-3440 <$175
1902 Plain Back
4x5 4551-22050 <$175
3x10-20 3441-3960 <$175
Total Issue $1,803,070
Out in 1935 $5,275
****
11868 Suffolk
ARLINGTON NB, ARLINGTON
{{ 2 L 4 S }}
Chartered 11/20
1902 Plain Back <$VALUE
4x5 1-9310 <$400
1929 Small Size
5 Type 1 1-2500 <$225
5 Type 2 1-6116 <$225
Total Issue $291,780
Out in 1935 $20,000
Large out 1935 $130
****
4664 Suffolk
FNB OF ARLINGTON
{{ UNREPORTED }}
Chartered 1891
Liquidated 3/18/13
Brown Back <$VALUE
3x10-20 1-2360 <$1000
1882 Date Back
3x10-20 1-515 <$1000
1902 Date Back
3x10-20 1-223 <$750
Total Issue $154,900
Out in 1913 $5,745
****
2113 Worcester
FNB OF ASHBURNHAM
{{ 4 L }}
Chartered 6/9/73
Liquidated 10/4/98
Original Series <$VALUE
3x1-2 1-1100 <$500/$1250
4x5 1-3500 <$500
Series 1875
4x5 1-10264 <$500
Brown Back
4x5 1-5344 <$400
Total Issue $367,680
Out in 1910 $2,058
****
2172 Worcester
ATHOL NB, ATHOL
{{ 6 L 4 S }}
Chartered 8/22/74
Receivership 8/3/33
Original Series <$VALUE
4x5 1-2500 <$450
Series 1875
4x5 1-18119 <$450
Brown Back
4x5 1-17250 <$300
3x10-20 1-6000 <$300
1882 Date Back
4x5 1-7826 <$300
3x10-20 1-4012 <$300
1902 Date Back
4x5 1-1665 <$175
3x10-20 1-1334 <$175
1902 Plain Back
4x5 1666-20435 <$175
3x10-20 1335-13991 <$175
1929 Small Size
5 Type 1 1-3352 <$150
10 Type 1 1-1878 <$150
20 Type 1 1-482 <$175
5 Type 2 1-12 <$200
Total Issue $2,793,890
Out at close $99,200
Large out at close $6,200
****
13733 Worcester
FNB OF ATHOL
{{ 6 S }}
Chartered 7/33
1929 Small Size <$VALUE
5 Type 2 1-15392 <$100
10 Type 2 1-5732 <$100
20 Type 2 1-1673 <$100
Total Issue $167,740
Out in 1935 $79,050
****
708 Worcester
MILLERS RIVER NB OF ATHOL
{{ 7 L 8 S }}
Organized 12/15/64
Receivership 8/4/33
Original Series <$VALUE
3x1-2 1-3600 <$350/$850
4x5 1-4475 <$375
3x10-20 1-2800 <$750/$1250
50-100 1-150 <$3500
Series 1875
4x5 1-2820 <$375
3x10 20 1-2506 <$600/$1000
Brown Back
4x5 1-3160 <$300
3x10-20 1-10697 <$300
1902 Red Seal
4x5 1-4850 <$350
3x10-20 1-3260 <$350
1902 Date Back
4x5 1-7600 <$175
3x10-20 1-5460 <$175
1902 Plain Back
4x5 7601-20530 <$175
3x10-20 5461-13206 <$175
1929 Small Size
5 Type 1 1-6232 <$100
10 Type 1 1-2928 <$100
20 Type 1 1-743 <$110
Total Issue $2,832,450
Out at close $150,000
Large out at close $4,610
****
2232 Bristol
FNB OF ATTLEBORO
{{ 38 L 20 S }}
Chartered 3/10/75
Original Series <$VALUE
3x1-2 1-1320 <$250/$750
4x5 1-2085 <$300
3x10-20 1-1000 <$750/$1250
Series 1875
4x5 1-1478 <$300
3x10-20 1-548 <$600/$1000
Brown Back
4x5 1-10200 <$175
3x10-20 1-6060 <$175/$225
1882 Date Back
4x5 1-16699 <$175
3x10-20 1-11006 <$175/$225
1902 Date Back
4x5 1-3300 <$75
3x10-20 1-2600 <$75
1902 Plain Back
4x5 3301-61525 <$75
3x10-20 2601-53240 <$75
1929 Small Size
5 Type 1 1-16694 <$50
10 Type 1 1-7766 <$50
20 Type 1 1-2004 <$60
5 Type 2 1-7552 <$50
10 Type 2 1-4612 <$50
20 Type 2 1-540 <$60
Total Issue $7,148,480
Out in 1935 $178,195
Large out 1935 $13,710
****
1604 Bristol
ATTLEBOROUGH NB, ATTLEBOROUGH
{{ 4 L }}
Chartered 1865
Liquidated 7/17/85
Original Series <$VALUE
3x1-2 1-4000 <$400/$850
4x5 1-3250 <$400
3x10-20 1-1300 <$750/$1250
50-100 1-100 <$3500
Series 1875
3x1-2 1-340 <$400/$850
4x5 1-3170 <$400
3x10-20 1-2488 <$600/$1000
50-100 1-16 <$3500
Total Issue $358,900
Out in 1910 $1,705
****
3073 Middlesex
FNB OF AYER
{{ 1 L 2 S }}
Chartered 1883
Brown Back <$VALUE
3x10-20 1-3693 <$850
1902 Red Seal
3x10-20 1-1140 <$850
1902 Date Back
3x10-20 1-2270 <$400
1902 Plain Back
3x10-20 2271-5038 <$400
1929 Small Size
10 Type 1 1-606 <$350
20 Type 1 1-148 <$350
10 Type 2 1-491 <$350
20 Type 2 1-153 <$350
Total Issue $555,640
Out in 1935 $19,350
Large out 1935 $960
****
96 Worcester
FNB OF BARRE
{{ 3 L }}
Chartered 1863
Liquidated 5/9/82
Original Series <$VALUE
3x1-2 1-3100 <$500/$1250
4x5 1-5100 <$600
3x10-20 1-4150 <$750/$1250
Series 1875
3x1-2 1-3340 <$500/$1250
4x5 1-1000 <$600
3x10-20 1-960 <$750/$1000
Total Issue $409,700
Out in 1910 $2,533
****
2685 Worcester
FNB OF BARRE
{{ 4 L }}
Chartered 1882
Liquidated 3/23/12
Brown Back <$VALUE
4x5 1-9987 <$600
3x10-20 1-6022 <$600
1902 Red Seal
4x5 1-5900 <$600
3x10-20 1-3900 <$600
1902 Date Back
4x5 1-2890 <$450
3x10-20 1-2106 <$450
Total Issue $976,940
Out in 1912 $15,580
****
10165 Worcester
SECOND NB OF BARRE
{{ 6 L }}
Chartered 3/12
Closed 10/21/29
1902 Date Back <$VALUE
3x10-20 1-1560* <$250
1902 Plain Back
3x10-20 1681-5537* <$250
* 1561-1689 not marked
Total Issue $276,850
Out at close $8,030
****

****
969 Essex
BEVERLY NB, BEVERLY
{{ 11 L 12 S }}
Chartered 4/1/65
Original Series <$VALUE
3x1-2 1-6700 <$250/$800
4x5 1-5100 <$325
3x10-20 1-2950 <$750/$1250
50-100 1-300 <$3500
Series 1875
3x1-2 1-2500 <$250/$800
4x5 1-5600 <$325
3x10-20 1-2760 <$600/$1000
50-100 1-630 <$3500
Brown Back
4x5 1-13050 <$250
3x10-20 1-4520 <$250
50-100 1-402 <$1250/$1500
1902 Red Seal
4x5 1-4015 <$250
3x10-20 1-2110 <$250
50-100 1-228 <$2250/$2500
1902 Date Back
4x5 1-9750 <$150
3x10-20 1-5900 <$150
50-100 1-600 <$350/$400
3x50-100 1-150 <$350/$400
1902 Plain Back
4x5 9751-23670 <$150
3x10-20 5901-15148 <$150
1929 Small Size
5 Type 1 1-3520 <$100
10 Type 1 1-2026 <$100
20 Type 1 1-478 <$110
5 Type 2 1-2274 <$125
10 Type 2 1-1259 <$125
20 Type 2 1-250 <$125
Total Issue $3,123,980
Out in 1935 $65,880
Large out 1935 $9,450
****
1207 Worcester
WORCESTER COUNTY NB OF BLACKSTONE
Organized 5/3/65
2nd title:Franklin NB, Franklin 2/9/71
FIRST TITLE {{ 2 L }}
Original Series <$VALUE
3x1-2 1-3000 <$500/$1000
4x5 1-2500 <$500
3x10-20 1-500 <$750/$1250
50-100 1-100 <$3500
SECOND TITLE {{ 8 L 8 S }}
Original Series
3x1-2 1-2000 <$350/$850
4x5 1-1750 <$400
3x10-20 1-1100 <$750/$1250
Series 1875
3x1-2 1-880 <$350/$800
4x5 1-7780 <$400
3x10-20 1-4086 <$600/$1000
Brown Back
4x5 1-15291 <$275
3x10-20 1-7001 <$275
1902 Red Seal
4x5 1-1800 <$325
3x10-20 1-1280 <$325
1902 Date Back
4x5 1-5175 <$175
3x10-20 1-3880 <$175
1902 Plain Back
4x5 5176-8050 <$175
3x10-20 3881-5718 <$175
1929 Small Size
5 Type 1 1-744 <$100
10 Type 1 1-356 <$100
20 Type 1 1-90 <$100
5 Type 2 1-390 <$100
10 Type 2 1-292 <$100
20 Type 2 1-45 <$100
Total Issue $1,832,320
Out in 1935 $14,830
Large out 1935 $5,890
****
5840 Suffolk
AMERICAN NB OF BOSTON
{{ 1 L }}
Chartered 5/29/01
Receivership 11/27/05
Brown Back <$VALUE
4x5 1-5185 <$600
3x10-20 1-6791 <$600
Total Issue $443,250
Out in 1916 $2,300
****

****
643 Suffolk
ATLANTIC NB OF BOSTON
Organized 11/28/64
Liquidated 6/25/32
2nd title:Fourth-Atlantic NB 8/30/12
3rd title:Commonwealth Atlantic NB 6/30/23
4th title:Atlantic NB 8/8/24
FIRST TITLE {{ 17 L }}
Original Series <$VALUE
3x1-2 1-3000 <$350/$800
4x5 1-20750 <$375
3x10-20 1-9100 <$750/$1250
50-100 1-567 <$3500
500 1-100 <$150,000
Series 1875
3x1-2 1-2000 <$350/$800
4x5 1-14000 <$375
3x10-20 1-7700 <$600/$1000
50-100 1-1000 <$3500
500 1-100 <$150,000
Brown Back
4x5 1-74487 <$225
3x10-20 1-24718 <$225
50-100 1-500 <$1250/$1500
1902 Red Seal
4x5 1-12000 <$250
3x10-20 1-9800 <$250
1902 Date Back
4x5 1-11135 <$125
3x10-20 1-7796 <$125
SECOND TITLE {{ 11 L }}
1902 Date Back
4x5 1-62500 <$125
3x10-20 1-50000 <$125
3x50-100 1-4200 <$300/$350
1902 Plain Back
4x5 62501-120500 <$125
3x10-20 50001-84000 <$125
THIRD TITLE {{ 8 L }}
1902 Plain Back
4x5 1-40000 <$125
3x10-20 1-23000 <$125
FOURTH TITLE {{ 2 L 14 S }}
1902 Plain Back
4x5 1-9807 <$150
4x10 1-8646 <$150
1929 Small Size
5 Type 1 1-18802 <$35
10 Type 1 1-9170 <$40
Total Issue $17,304,430
Out at close $465,800
Large out at close $81,255
Outstanding includes Ch 2277, and Ch 3923
****
654 Suffolk
ATLAS NB OF BOSTON
{{ 2 L }}
Chartered 12/29/64
Liquidated 4/4/04
Original Series <$VALUE
4x5 1-17000 <$600
3x10-20 1-9100 <$750/$1250
50-100 1-5313 <$3500
500 1-321 <$150,000
1000 1-188 <$200,000
Series 1875
4x5 1-7500 <$600
3x10-20 1-7500 <$600/$1000
50-100 1-400 <$3500
500 1-100 <$150,000
Brown Back
4x5 1-5250 <$500
3x10-20 1-5049 <$500
50-100 1-1362 <$1250/$1500
Total Issue $3,137,200
Out in 1910 $17,655
****
514 Suffolk
BLACKSTONE NB OF BOSTON
{{ 7 L }}
Chartered 9/10/64
Liquidated 4/18/00
Original Series <$VALUE
4x5 1-14500 <$450
3x10-20 1-11400 <$750/$1250
50-100 1-4633 <$3500
500 1-370 <$150,000
Series 1875
4x5 1-11996 <$450
3x10-20 1-11090 <$600/$1000
50-100 1-4810 <$3500
Brown Back
4x5 1-6840 <$325
3x10-20 1-6000 <$325
50-100 1-1000 <$1250/$1500
Total Issue $3,842,670
Out in 1910 $18,350
****

****
684 Suffolk
BLUE HILL NB OF
DORCHESTER (BOSTON)
Chartered 1865
Liquidated 9/30/30
2nd title:Blue Hill NB of
Milton 1/18/81
FIRST TITLE {{ 4 L }}
Original Series <$VALUE
3x1-2 1-4000 <$400/$850
4x5 1-3050 <$400
3x10-20 1-1910 <$750/$1250
50-100 1-1207 <$3500
Series 1875
3x1-2 1-1680 <$400/$850
4x5 1-2815 <$400
3x10-20 1-2004 <$600/$1000
SECOND TITLE {{2U+2 L U+1 S}}
Series 1875
4x5 1-2500 <$350
3x10-20 1-1000 <$600/$1000
50-100 1-200 <$3500
Brown Back
4x5 1-4105 <$275
3x10-20 1-3686 <$275
50-100 1-1103 <$1250/$1500
1902 Red Seal
4x5 1-1990 <$325
3x10-20 1-1001 <$325
50-100 1-141 <$2250/$2500
1902 Date Back
4x5 1-5650 <$125
3x10-20 1-4020 <$125
50-100 1-100 <$350/$400
3x50-100 1-100 <$350/$400
1902 Plain Back
4x5 5651-12290 <$125
3x10-20 4021-8497 <$125
1929 Small Size
5 Type 1 1-709 <$400
10 Type 1 1-350 <$400
20 Type 1 1-74 <$400
Total Issue $1,957,100
Out at close $50,000
Large out at close $9,780
****
Boston-Continental NB, Boston
SEE Ch 11903
Boston NB, Boston
****
408 Suffolk
BOSTON NB IN BOSTON
{{ 13 L }}
Chartered 4/30/64
Liquidated 12/8/98
Original Series <$VALUE
3x1-2 1-26000 <$250/$800
4x5 1-21750 <$350
3x10-20 1-13500<$750/$1250
50-100 1-1600 <$3500
Series 1875
3x1-2 1-5000 <$250/$800
4x5 1-4750 <$350
3x10-20 1-10000<$600/$1000
50-100 1-2804 <$3500
Brown Back
4x5 1-2295 <$200
3x10-20 1-6169 <$200
50-100 1-4390 <$1250/$1500
Total Issue $3,533,450
Out in 1910 $19,416
****
11903 Suffolk
BOSTON NB, BOSTON
Organized 12/21/20
Receivership 12/22/31
2nd title:Boston-Continental
NB 12/26/30
FIRST TITLE {{ U + 8 L 5 S }}
1902 Plain Back <$VALUE
4x5 1-124030 <$125
1929 Small Size
5 Type 1 1-34176 <$125
SECOND TITLE {{ 5 S }}
1929 Small Size
5 Type 1 1-28153 <$125
Total Issue $4,350,470
Out at close $894,520
Large out at close $19,615
Outstanding includes Ch 12540
****
545 Suffolk
BOYLSTON NB OF BOSTON
{{ 20 L }}
Chartered 1864
Liquidated 7/26/23
Original Series <$VALUE
3x1-2 1-11340 <$225/$750
4x5 1-19500 <$250
3x10-20 1-4100 <$750/$1250
50-100 1-2132 <$3500
500 1-150 <$150,000
Series 1875
3x1-2 1-24220 <$225/$750
4x5 1-38500 <$250
3x10-20 1-8464 <$600/$1000
Brown Back
4x5 1-14375 <$150
3x10-20 1-6601 <$150/$200
50-100 1-1344 <$1250/$1500
1902 Red Seal
4x5 1-1300 <$175
3x10-20 1-612 <$175/$200
1902 Date Back
4x5 1-40500 <$60
50-100 1-3740 <$300/$350
3x50-100 1-2787 <$300/$350
1902 Plain Back
4x5 40501-47615 <$60
Total Issue $5,507,800
Out at close $380,000
****
551 Suffolk
BROADWAY NB OF BOSTON
{{ 5 L }}
Organized 10/25/64
Receivership 12/16/99
Original Series <$VALUE
3x1-2 1-2000 <$400/$850
4x5 1-5000 <$400
3x10-20 1-3500 <$750/$1250
50-100 1-500 <$3500
Series 1875
3x1-2 1-2000 <$400/$850
4x5 1-10000 <$400
3x10-20 1-500 <$600/$1000
Brown Back
4x5 1-20985 <$300
Total Issue $1,014,700
Out in 1916 $4,551
****
12540 Suffolk
BROTHERHOOD OF LOCOMOTIVE
ENGINEERS NB OF BOSTON
Chartered 5/24
Closed 12/26/30
2nd title: Engineers NB of
Boston 1/20/27
3rd title: Continental NB
of Boston 8/15/30
FIRST TITLE {{ 5 L }}
1902 Plain Back <$VALUE
4x5 1-30087 <$175
SECOND TITLE {{ 5 L 10 S }}
1902 Plain Back
4x5 1-40345 <$125
1929 Small Size
5 Type 1 1-11712 <$125
THIRD TITLE {{ 2 S }}
1929 Small Size
5 Type 1 1-3709 <$225
Total Issue $1,871,270
Out at close $293,460
Large out at close $11,500
Ch 11903 assumed circulation
****
635 Suffolk
BUNKER HILL NB OF
CHARLESTOWN, BOSTON
{{ 3 L }}
Chartered 12/20/64
Liquidated 4/23/06
Original Series <$VALUE
3x1-2 1-9000 <$400/$850
4x5 1-11350 <$400
3x10-20 1-9760 <$750/$1250
50-100 1-1050 <$3500
Series 1875
4x5 1-12409 <$400
3x10-20 1-7148 <$600/$1000
50-100 1-500 <$3500
Brown Back
4x5 1-15641 <$350
3x10-20 1-6870 <$350
1902 Red Seal
4x5 1-640 <$400
3x10-20 1-530 <$400
Total Issue $2,293,700
Out in 1910 $13,912
****
2103 Suffolk
CENTRAL NB OF BOSTON
{{ 9 L }}
Chartered 4/30/73
Receivership 11/13/02
Original Series <$VALUE
3x1-2 1-3000 <$350/$800
4x5 1-9000 <$400
3x10-20 1-5700 <$750/$1250
50-100 1-300 <$3500
Series 1875
4x5 1-4605 <$400
3x10-20 1-5858 <$600/$1000
50-100 1-398 <$3500
Brown Back
4x5 1-14293 <$300
3x10-20 1-7941 <$300
50-100 1-1300 <$1250/$1500
Total Issue $1,847,610
Out in 1916 $4,257
****
11339 Suffolk
CITIZENS NB OF BOSTON
{{ 7 L }}
Chartered 4/19
Liquidated 5/20/27
1902 Plain Back <$VALUE
4x5 1-59540 <$175
4x10 1-48256 <$175
Total Issue $3,121,040
Out at close $194,825
****
5163 Suffolk
COLONIAL NB OF BOSTON
{{ UNREPORTED }}
Chartered 12/28/92
Liquidated 5/31/04
Brown Back <$VALUE
4x5 1-10437 <$850
3x10-20 1-8746 <$850
Total Issue $646,040
Out in 1910 $8,365
****
1029 Suffolk
COLUMBIAN NB OF BOSTON
{{ 23 L }}
Chartered 4/17/65
Liquidated 12/9/98
Original Series <$VALUE
3x1-2 1-32000 <$225/$750
4x5 1-33250 <$250
3x10-20 1-8220 <$750/$1250
50-100 1-1510 <$3500
500 1-205 <$150,000
Series 1875
3x1-2 1-34200 <$225/$750
4x5 1-66250 <$250
3x10-20 1-8000 <$600/$1000
Brown Back
4x5 1-76169 <$150
3x10-20 1-7600 <$150/$175
Total Issue $5,364,380
Out in 1910 $28,286
****
3923 Suffolk
COMMERCIAL NB OF BOSTON
Chartered 8/27/88
Closed 10/31/28
2nd title:Commercial
Security NB of Boston
1/2/23
FIRST TITLE {{ 7 L }}
Brown Back <$VALUE
4x5 1-14114 <$250
3x10-20 1-2868 <$250
1902 Red Seal
4x5 1-2000 <$250
4x10 1-2000 <$250
1902 Date Back
4x5 1-29600 <$100
4x10 1-28100 <$100
1902 Plain Back
4x5 29601-50700 <$100
4x10 28101-42150 <$100
SECOND TITLE {{ 2 L }}
1902 Plain Back
4x5 1-55670 <$200
Total Issue $4,359,080
Out at close $194,500
Ch 643 assumed circulation
****
Commercial Security NB of
Boston
SEE Ch 3923
Commercial NB of Boston
****
Commonwealth Atlantic NB of
Boston
SEE Ch 643
Atlantic NB of Boston
****
524 Suffolk
CONTINENTAL NB OF BOSTON
{{ 11 L }}
Chartered 10/1/64
Liquidated 1/9/99
Original Series <$VALUE
3x1-2 1-4000 <$250/$750
4x5 1-6750 <$350
3x10-20 1-6900 <$750/$1250
50-100 1-3134 <$3500
500 1-490 <$150,000
Series 1875
3x1-2 1-25000 <$250/$750
4x5 1-31750 <$350
3x10-20 1-11300<$600/$1000
50-100 1-350 <$3500
Brown Back
4x5 1-2256 <$200
3x10-20 1-2983 <$200
Total Issue $2,786,870
Out in 1910 $12,792
****
****
Continental NB of Boston
SEE Ch 12540
Brotherhood of Locomotive
Engineers NB of Boston
****
1993 Suffolk
ELEVENTH WARD NB OF
BOSTON
{{ 1 L }}
Chartered 6/1/72
Liquidated 3/14/78
Original Series <$VALUE
4x5 1-3250 <$750
4x10 1-1142 <$1000
2x20-50-100 1-255
<$1250/$3500/$3500
Series 1875
4x5 1-1149 <$750
4x10 1-319 <$1000
Total Issue $194,870
Out in 1910 $305
****
536 Suffolk
ELIOT NB OF BOSTON
{{ 10 L }}
Chartered 1864
Liquidated 11/29/12
Original Series <$VALUE
4x5 1-23500 <$350
3x10-20 1-6600 <$750/$1250
50-100 1-4101 <$3500
500 1-290 <$150,000
Series 1875
4x5 1-14500 <$350
3x10-20 1-9000 <$600/$1000
50-100 1-3850 <$3500
500 1-100 <$150,000
Brown Back
4x5 1-15155 <$275
3x10-20 1-9983 <$275
50-100 1-6050 <$1250/$1500
1902 Red Seal
4x5 1-36283 <$300
4x10 1-11844 <$300
3x10-20 1-9233 <$300
50-100 1-2715 <$2250/$2500
1902 Date Back
4x5 1-58832 <$150
4x10 1-46756 <$150
Total Issue $9,752,600
Out in 1912 $332,780
****
Engineers NB of Boston
SEE Ch 12540
Brotherhood of Locomotive
Engineers NB of Boston
****
1469 Suffolk
EVERETT NB OF BOSTON
{{ 2 L }}
Chartered 7/19/65
Liquidated 5/19/98
Original Series <$VALUE
4x5 1-4200 <$600
3x10-20 1-6400 <$850/$1250
Series 1875
4x5 1-8650 <$600
3x10-20 1-9040 <$850/$1250
Brown Back
4x5 1-10233 <$500
3x10-20 1-4891 <$500
Total Issue $1,481,210
Out in 1910 $6,480
****
847 Suffolk
FANEUIL HALL NB OF BOSTON
{{ 12 L }}
Chartered 2/27/65
Liquidated 3/16/09
Original Series <$VALUE
3x1-2 1-20000 <$300/$750
4x5 1-15750 <$350
3x10-20 1-7500 <$750/$1250
50-100 1-1250 <$3500
500 1-380 <$150,000
Series 1875
3x1-2 1-10000 <$300/$750
4x5 1-8000 <$350
3x10-20 1-10457<$600/$1000
50-100 1-4766 <$3500
Brown Back
3x10-20 1-3735 <$300
50-100 1-3655 <$1250/$1500
1902 Red Seal
3x10-20 1-644 <$350
50-100 1-339 <$2250/$2500
Total Issue $3,433,300
Out in 1910 $28,233
****
****
12336 Suffolk
FEDERAL NB OF BOSTON
{{ 2U + 37 L 16 S }}
Organized 3/19/23
Receivership 12/15/31
1902 Plain Back <$VALUE
4x5 1-202215 <$60
3x10-20 1-116659 <$60/$70
1929 Small Size
5 Type 1 1-37253 <$50
10 Type 1 1-18854 <$50
20 Type 1 1-5939 <$60
Total Issue $12,838,760
Out at close $1,500,000
Large out at close $75,440
****
2112 Suffolk
FIRST WARD NB OF BOSTON
{{ U + 10 L }}
Chartered 1873
Liquidated 9/11/15
Original Series <$VALUE
3x1-2 1-2000 <$250/$800
4x5 1-3000 <$300
3x10-20 1-1298 <$750/$1250
50-100 1-434 <$3500
Series 1875
3x1-2 1-3998 <$250/$800
4x5 1-10997 <$300
3x10-20 1-2794 <$600/$1000
50-100 1-298 <$3500
Brown Back
4x5 1-21800 <$200
3x10-20 1-9850 <$200
50-100 1-1940 <$1250/$1500
1882 Date Back
4x5 1-14291 <$200
3x10-20 1-8217 <$200
1902 Date Back
4x5 1-9750 <$125
3x10-20 1-5254 <$125
Total Issue $2,998,200
Out at close $164,850
****
200 Suffolk
FNB OF BOSTON
{{ 38 L 50+ S }}
Organized 2/1/64
Original Series <$VALUE
4x5 1-9000 <$250
4x10 1-8625 <$750
2x20-50-100 1-3600
<$1250/$3500/$3500
50-100 3601-6100 <$3500
500 1-659 <$150,000
Series 1875
4x5 1-10500 <$250
4x10 1-10500 <$600
2x20-50-100 1-763
<$1000/$3500/$3500
Brown Back
4x5 1-18769 <$150
3x10-20 1-11555 <$150/$200
50-100 1-2212 <$1250/$1500
1902 Red Seal
4x5 1-61765 <$175
3x10-20 1-49194 <$175/$225
50-100 1-2634 <$2250/$2500
1902 Date Back
4x5 1-21065 <$50
3x10-20 1-146860 <$50
3x50-100 1-7042 <$300/$350
1902 Plain Back
4x5 21066-204252 <$50
1929 Small Size
5 Type 1 1-169738 <$20
10 Type 1 1-59508 <$20
20 Type 1 1-11145 <$30
Total Issue $31,252,020
Out in 1935 $9,961,485
Large out 1935 $36,965
****
Fourth Atlantic NB of Boston
SEE Ch 643
Atlantic NB of Boston
****
2277 Suffolk
FOURTH NB OF BOSTON
{{ 8 L }}
Chartered 6/17/75
Liquidated 8/28/12
Original Series <$VALUE
4x5 1-2250 <$325
Series 1875
4x5 1-42272 <$325
Brown Back
4x5 1-32600 <$250
3x10-20 1-15760 <$250
1882 Date Back
4x5 1-24095 <$250
3x10-20 1-13027 <$250
Total Issue $3,463,690
Out at close $400,000
Ch 643 assumed circulation
****
****
665 Suffolk
FREEMAN'S NB OF BOSTON
{{ 2 L }}
Chartered 12/30/64
Liquidated 2/15/07
Original Series <$VALUE
3x1-2 1-3000 <$600/$1250
4x5 1-7000 <$750
3x10-20 1-6900<$1000/$1250
50-100 1-1160 <$3500
500 1-120 <$150,000
Series 1875
4x5 1-8500 <$750
3x10-20 1-6342<$1000/$1250
50-100 1-140 <$3500
Brown Back
4x5 1-2654 <$600
3x10-20 1-2361 <$600
1902 Red Seal
4x5 1-2805 <$600
3x10-20 1-1032 <$600
50-100 1-419 <$2250/$2500
Total Issue $1,899,500
Out in 1910 $26,818
****
936 Suffolk
GLOBE NB OF BOSTON
{{ 3 L }}
Chartered 3/25/65
Receivership 12/21/99
Original Series <$VALUE
4x5 1-10200 <$500
3x10-20 1-6200 <$750/$1250
50-100 1-900 <$3500
500 1-150 <$150,000
Series 1875
4x5 1-12110 <$500
3x10-20 1-10950<$750/$1250
50-100 1-1810 <$3500
Brown Back
4x5 1-11911 <$450
3x10-20 1-11329 <$450
50-100 1-5140 <$1500
Total Issue $3,360,870
Out in 1916 $17,725
****
778 Suffolk
HAMILTON NB OF BOSTON
{{ UNREPORTED }}
Chartered 2/2/65
Liquidated 1/10/99
Original Series <$VALUE
3x1-2 1-1600 <$850/$1500
4x5 1-2500 <$850
3x10-20 1-2500<$1250/$1500
50-100 1-1600 <$4000
Series 1875
4x5 1-8200 <$850
3x10-20 1-5800<$1250/$1500
Brown Back
4x5 1-7500 <$750
3x10-20 1-2984 <$750
50-100 1-100 <$1750/$2000
Total Issue $1,191,200
Out in 1910 $6,521
****
578 Suffolk
HOWARD NB OF BOSTON
{{ 13 L }}
Chartered 11/19/64
Liquidated 12/17/98
Original Series <$VALUE
3x1-2 1-15000 <$250/$750
4x5 1-17250 <$325
3x10-20 1-5400 <$750/$1250
50-100 1-1565 <$3500
500 1-270 <$150,000
Series 1875
3x1-2 1-3320 <$250/$700
4x5 1-20137 <$325
3x10-20 1-10370<$600/$1000
50-100 1-1400 <$3500
Brown Back
4x5 1-5700 <$225
3x10-20 1-3794 <$225
50-100 1-695 <$1250/$1500
Total Issue $2,615,690
Out in 1910 $13,386
****
1699 Suffolk
KIDDER N GOLD BANK OF
BOSTON
{{ UNREPORTED }}
Chartered 8/15/70
Liquidated 11/8/72
GOLD BANK NOTES
Original Series <$VALUE
50-100 1-50 <$50,000
500-1000 1-75
<$200,000/$300,000
Total Issue $120,000
All notes reportedly redeemed
****

****
2846 Suffolk
LINCOLN NB OF BOSTON
{{ 4 L }}
Chartered 12/23/82
Liquidated 12/12/98
Brown Back <$VALUE
4x5 1-23697 <$400
3x10-20 1-7058 <$400
Total Issue $826,840
Out in 1910 $4,990
****
2111 Suffolk
MANUFACTURERS NB OF BOSTON
{{ 7 L }}
Chartered 5/21/73
Liquidated 1/9/99
Original Series <$VALUE
3x1-2 1-1000 <$350/$800
4x5 1-5750 <$375
3x10-20 1-1500 <$750/$1250
Series 1875
4x5 1-84799 <$350
3x10-20 1-2600 <$600/$1000
Brown Back
4x5 1-32452 <$250
Total Issue $2,670,020
Out at close $271,607
****
505 Suffolk
MARKET NB OF BOSTON
{{ 6 L }}
Chartered 8/26/64
Liquidated 12/17/98
Original Series <$VALUE
3x1-2 1-10000 <$400/$850
4x5 1-10800 <$400
3x10-20 1-7600 <$750/$1250
3x50-100 1-500 <$3500
Series 1875
4x5 1-21690 <$400
3x10-20 1-6700 <$600/$1000
3x50-100 1-500 <$3500
Brown Back
4x5 1-8026 <$350
3x10-20 1-1481 <$350
50-100 1-360 <$1250/$1500
Total Issue $1,953,370
Out in 1910 $10,524
****
974 Suffolk
MASSACHUSETTS NB OF BOSTON
{{ 6 L }}
Chartered 4/4/65
Liquidated 8/5/03
Original Series <$VALUE
3x1-2 1-2800 <$400/$850
4x5 1-6925 <$400
4x10 1-5450 <$750
2x20-50-100 1-2350
<$1250/$3500/$3500
500-1000 1-58
<$150,000/$200,000
Series 1875
4x5 1-17431 <$400
4x10 1-4817 <$600
2x20-50-100 1-400
<$1000/$3500/$3500
Brown Back
4x5 1-13856 <$300
3x10-20 1-2365 <$300
Total Issue $1,916,710
Out in 1910 $11,833
****
11137 Suffolk
MATTAPAN NB OF BOSTON
{{ 3 L }}
Chartered 1/18
Liquidated 3/3/24
1902 Plain Back <$VALUE
4x5 1-28795 <$250
3x10-20 1-12344 <$250
Total Issue $1,193,100
Out at close $161,450
****
677 Suffolk
MAVERICK NB OF BOSTON
{{ 8 L }}
Organized 12/31/64
Receivership 11/2/91
Original Series <$VALUE
3x1-2 1-21350 <$400/$850
4x5 1-14500 <$400
4x10 1-2350 <$750
3x20-50 1-1600<$1250/$3500
100-100 1-200 <$3500
500 1-100 <$150,000
Series 1875
3x1-2 1-7060 <$400/$850
4x5 1-18000 <$400
4x10 1-6121 <$600
Brown Back
4x5 1-13442 <$350
3x10-20 1-2000 <$350
Total Issue $1,765,730
Out in 1916 $8,048
****
932 Suffolk
MECHANICS NB OF BOSTON
{{ 3 L }}
Chartered 3/24/65
Liquidated 7/29/05
Original Series <$VALUE
3x1-2 1-8000 <$400/$850
4x5 1-4900 <$400
3x10-20 1-3440 <$750/$1250
50-100 1-650 <$3500
Series 1875
3x1-2 1-1000 <$400/$850
4x5 1-3550 <$400
3x10-20 1-3736 <$600/$1000
50-100 1-300 <$3500
Brown Back
4x5 1-5646 <$350
3x10-20 1-3768 <$350
50-100 1-514 <$1250/$1500
1902 Red Seal
3x10-20 1-220 <$400
50-100 1-12 <$2250/$2500
Total Issue $1,106,520
Out in 1910 $9,869
****
2304 Suffolk
MERCHANDISE NB OF BOSTON
Chartered 10/13/75
Liquidated 6/7/15
2nd title:Winthrop NB of Boston 2/90
FIRST TITLE {{ 13 L }}
Series 1875 <$VALUE
3x1-2 1-11000 <$300/$750
4x5 1-36374 <$300
3x10-20 1-3799 <$600/$1000
50-100 1-167 <$3500
SECOND TITLE {{ U + 13 L }}
Series 1875
4x5 1-5024 <$325
Brown Back
4x5 1-42500 <$225
3x10-20 1-16900 <$225/$275
1882 Date Back
4x5 1-33461 <$200
3x10-20 1-21072 <$200/$250
Total Issue $4,515,780
Out in 1915 $217,345
****
475 Suffolk
MERCHANTS NB OF BOSTON
{{ 28 L }}
Organized 7/2/64
Original Series <$VALUE
4x5 1-18500 <$250
3x10-20 1-31480<$750/$1250
3x50-100 1-5400 <$3500
500 1-740 <$150,000
1000 1-370 <$200,000
Series 1875
4x5 1-17541 <$250
3x10-20 1-28952<$600/$1000
3x50-100 1-4046 <$3500
500 1-80 <$150,000
Brown Back
4x5 1-25899 <$150
3x10-20 1-42214 <$150/$175
50-100 1-7396 <$1250/$1500
1902 Red Seal
4x5 1-46500 <$150
3x10-20 1-27100 <$150/$175
50-100 1-3800 <$2250/$2500
1902 Date Back
4x5 1-158000 <$40
3x10-20 1-111000 <$60
50-100 1-2000 <$300/$350
3x50-100 1-4000 <$300/$350
1902 Plain Back
4x5 158001-160319 <$40
3x10-20 111001-112155 <$60
Total Issue $23,591,130
Out in 1935 $73,932
Outstanding includes Ch 554
****
2289 Suffolk
METROPOLITAN NB OF BOSTON
{{ 3 L }}
Chartered 7/27/75
Liquidated 9/9/09
Series 1875 <$VALUE
4x5 1-16600 <$400
3x10-20 1-9471 <$600/$1000
Brown Back
3x10-20 1-5550 <$350
1882 Date Back
3x10-20 1-147 <$350
Total Issue $1,090,400
Out in 1910 $22,070
****

****
Monument NB of Boston
SEE Ch 1005
Monument NB of Charlestown
****
716 Suffolk
MOUNT VERNON NB OF BOSTON
{{ 2 L }}
Chartered 1/13/65
Liquidated 10/24/05
Original Series <$VALUE
3x1-2 1-5000 <$500/$1000
4x5 1-5000 <$500
3x10-20 1-2000 <$750/$1250
50-100 1-1050 <$3500
Series 1875
3x1-2 1-3982 <$500/$1000
4x5 1-16384 <$500
Brown Back
4x5 1-21926 <$400
3x10-20 1-3023 <$400
1902 Red Seal
4x5 1-1900 <$450
3x10-20 1-1488 <$450
Total Issue $1,432,160
Out in 1910 $12,399
****
9579 Suffolk
MUTUAL NB OF BOSTON
{{ 1 L }}
Chartered 11/09
Liquidated 9/11/15
1902 Date Back <$VALUE
4x5 1-16240 <$500
3x10-20 1-10720 <$500
50-100 1-300 <$600/$700
3x50-100 1-89 <$600/$700
Total Issue $928,050
Out at close $163,150
****
1099 Suffolk
NB OF BRIGHTON, BOSTON
{{ 3 L }}
Chartered 1865
Liquidated 10/4/81
Original Series <$VALUE
3x1-2 1-5400 <$500/$1000
4x5 1-3900 <$500
3x10-20 1-2900 <$750/$1250
50-100 1-1850 <$3500
Series 1875
3x1-2 1-1800 <$500/$1000
4x5 1-3250 <$500
3x10-20 1-3296 <$750/$1000
Total Issue $766,300
Out in 1910 $3,327
****
554 Suffolk
NB OF COMMERCE, BOSTON
{{ 8 L }}
Organized 10/17/64
Liquidated 5/28/14
Original Series <$VALUE
3x1-2 1-20000 <$250/$750
4x5 1-12500 <$300
3x10-20 1-8800 <$750/$1250
50-100 1-3610 <$3500
500-1000 1-354
<$150,000/$200,000
Series 1875
3x1-2 1-7962 <$250/$750
4x5 1-22000 <$300
3x10-20 1-18500<$600/$1000
50-100 1-2680 <$3500
500-1000 1-100
<$150,000/$200,000
Brown Back
4x5 1-9109 <$150
3x10-20 1-3400 <$150/$200
50-100 1-1594 <$1250/$1500
1902 Red Seal
4x5 1-3460 <$175
3x10-20 1-1282 <$175/$225
50-100 1-198 <$2250/$2500
1902 Date Back
4x5 1-3815 <$100
3x10-20 1-876 <$100/$125
50-100 1-4 <$500/$600
Total Issue $4,694,290
Out at close $50,000
Ch 475 assumed circulation
****
672 Suffolk
NB OF NORTH AMERICA, BOSTON
{{ 23 L }}
Chartered 12/30/64
Liquidated 12/22/98
Original Series <$VALUE
3x1-2 1-11000 <$275/$700
4x5 1-13250 <$300
3x10-20 1-9800 <$750/$1250
50-100 1-2260 <$3500
500 1-260 <$150,000
Series 1875
3x1-2 1-7180 <$275/$700
4x5 1-25960 <$300
3x10-20 1-9920 <$600/$1000
50-100 1-200 <$3500
Brown Back
4x5 1-20460 <$200
3x10-20 1-9025 <$200/$250
50-100 1-626 <$1250/$1500
Total Issue $3,314,450
Out in 1910 $19,046
****
515 Suffolk
NB OF REDEMPTION, BOSTON
{{ 8 L }}
Chartered 9/12/64
Liquidated 5/31/04
Original Series <$VALUE
4x5 1-11250 <$350
3x10-20 1-10500<$750/$1250
3x50-100 1-3280 <$3500
Series 1875
3x10-20 1-3000 <$600/$1000
3x50-100 1-4192 <$3500
Brown Back
4x5 1-15000 <$175
3x10-20 1-19399 <$175/$225
50-100 1-8361 <$1250/$1500
Total Issue $5,504,100
Out in 1910 $48,810
****
1827 Suffolk
NB OF THE COMMONWEALTH, BOSTON
{{ 8 L }}
Chartered 5/27/71
Liquidated 12/24/01
Original Series <$VALUE
4x5 1-4000 <$325
3x10-20 1-11200<$750/$1250
Series 1875
3x10-20 1-10585<$600/$1000
Brown Back
4x5 1-14829 <$200
3x10-20 1-13258 <$200/$250
Total Issue $2,127,730
Out in 1910 $11,060
****
379 Suffolk
NB OF THE REPUBLIC, BOSTON
{{ U + 5 L }}
Chartered 4/13/64
Liquidated 5/7/08
Original Series <$VALUE
4x5 1-30500 <$350
3x10-20 1-16000<$750/$1250
50-100 1-3500 <$3500
500 1-190 <$150,000
Series 1875
4x5 1-28000 <$350
3x10-20 1-15000<$600/$1000
50-100 1-1050 <$3500
Brown Back
4x5 1-55550 <$300
3x10-20 1-19499 <$300
50-100 1-1933 <$1250/$1500
1902 Red Seal
4x5 1-26415 <$350
3x10-20 1-14693 <$350
50-100 1-600 <$2250/$2500
Total Issue $7,226,350
Out in 1910 $109,785
****
609 Suffolk
N CITY B OF BOSTON
{{ 11 L }}
Chartered 12/6/64
Liquidated 2/15/98
Original Series <$VALUE
3x1-2 1-15600 <$250/$750
4x5 1-11000 <$300
3x10-20 1-6400 <$750/$1250
50-100 1-1962 <$3500
500 1-200 <$150,000
Series 1875
3x1-2 1-4610 <$250/$750
4x5 1-18800 <$300
3x10-20 1-7600 <$600/$1000
50-100 1-180 <$3500
Brown Back
3x10-20 1-3377 <$200/$250
Total Issue $1,987,200
Out in 1910 $9,759
****
993 Suffolk
N EAGLE B OF BOSTON
{{ 10 L }}
Chartered 4/7/65
Liquidated 12/13/98
Original Series <$VALUE
3x1-2 1-16500 <$300/$850
4x5 1-9375 <$350
3x10-20 1-4700 <$750/$1250
50-100 1-1500 <$3500
500 1-200 <$150,000
Series 1875
3x1-2 1-7800 <$300/$850
4x5 1-17365 <$350
3x10-20 1-9415 <$600/$1000
50-100 1-840 <$3500
Brown Back
4x5 1-10010 <$250
3x10-20 1-1602 <$250/$300
50-100 1-160 <$1250/$1500
Total Issue $2,129,450
Out in 1910 $10,821
****
529 Suffolk
N EXCHANGE B OF BOSTON
{{ 5 L }}
Chartered 10/10/64
Liquidated 1/31/07
Original Series <$VALUE
4x5 1-10500 <$350
3x10-20 1-10100<$750/$1250
50-100 1-5500 <$3500
500 1-200 <$150,000
Series 1875
4x5 1-26500 <$350
3x10-20 1-20800<$600/$1000
Brown Back
4x5 1-26936 <$300
3x10-20 1-3277 <$300/$350
50-100 1-500 <$1250/$1500
1902 Red Seal
3x10-20 1-1177 <$350
Total Issue $4,046,420
Out in 1910 $23,950
****
5158 Suffolk
N HAMILTON B OF BOSTON
{{ 1 L }}
Chartered 12/7/98
Liquidated 11/30/03
Brown Back <$VALUE
4x5 1-3312 <$850
3x10-20 1-1460 <$850
Total Issue $139,240
Out in 1910 $1,960
****
460 Suffolk
N HIDE & LEATHER B OF BOSTON
{{ 18 L }}
Chartered 6/8/64
Liquidated 1/27/02
Original Series <$VALUE
3x1-2 1-16900 <$250/$750
4x5 1-16350 <$300
3x10-20 1-16380<$750/$1250
50-100 1-3900* <$3500
500 1-278 <$150,000
* 1391-1850 not issued
Series 1875
3x1-2 1-9924 <$250/$750
4x5 1-14665 <$300
3x10-20 1-12207<$600/$1000
50-100 1-3285 <$3500
Brown Back
4x5 1-29847 <$225
3x10-20 1-15050 <$225/$275
50-100 1-3599 <$1500/$1750
Total Issue $5,220,810
Out in 1910 $33,570
****
806 Suffolk
N MARKET B OF BRIGHTON, BOSTON
{{ 7 L }}
Chartered 2/14/65
Liquidated 12/31/12
Original Series <$VALUE
3x1-2 1-2000 <$300/$750
4x5 1-2600 <$350
3x10-20 1-2860 <$750/$1250
50-100 1-1617 <$3500
500 1-50 <$150,000
Series 1875
3x1-2 1-600 <$300/$750
4x5 1-3850 <$350
3x10-20 1-3895 <$600/$1000
50-100 1-740 <$3500
Brown Back
4x5 1-9401 <$250
3x10-20 1-6262 <$250
50-100 1-150 <$1250/$1500
1902 Red Seal
4x5 1-4265 <$300
3x10-20 1-2614 <$300
1902 Date Back
4x5 1-9030 <$150
3x10-20 1-6768 <$150
Total Issue $2,116,920
Out in 1913 $66,800
****

****
1295 Suffolk
N REVERE B OF BOSTON
{{ 12 L }}
Chartered 6/16/65
Liquidated 12/19/98
Original Series <$VALUE
4x5 1-22645 <$300
3x10-20 1-15000<$750/$1250
50-100 1-2660 <$3500
500 1-198 <$150,000
Series 1875
3x1-2 1-2000 <$250/$750
4x5 1-12500 <$300
3x10-20 1-34400<$600/$1000
50-100 1-400 <$3500
Brown Back
4x5 1-21740 <$225
3x10-20 1-6025 <$225/$250
50-100 1-210 <$1250/$1500
Total Issue $4,598,450
Out in 1910 $18,575
****
615 Suffolk
N ROCKLAND B OF ROXBURY, BOSTON
Chartered 1864
2nd title:N Rockland B of Roxbury at Boston 11/21/04
FIRST TITLE {{ 2 L }}
Original Series <$VALUE
3x1-2 1-6000 <$400/$850
4x5 1-10100 <$400
3x10-20 1-3900 <$750/$1250
50-100 1-1000 <$3500
500 1-50 <$150,000
Series 1875
4x5 1-8975 <$400
3x10-20 1-3590 <$600/$1000
50-100 1-400 <$3500
Brown Back
4x5 1-8995 <$350
3x10-20 1-4450 <$350
50-100 1-687 <$1250/$1500
SECOND TITLE {{ U + 6 L }}
1902 Red Seal
4x5 1-4400 <$350
3x10-20 1-1890 <$350
50-100 1-450 <$2250/$2500
1902 Date Back
4x5 1-11000 <$175
3x10-20 1-7500 <$175
50-100 1-300 <$400/$500
3x50-100 1-356 <$400/$500
1902 Plain Back
4x5 11001-25434 <$175
3x10-20 7501-8500 <$175
Total Issue $2,844,130
Out in 1935 $9,052
****
1675 Suffolk
N SECURITY B OF BOSTON
{{ 12 L }}
Chartered 12/10/67
Liquidated 12/31/22
Original Series <$VALUE
3x10-20 1-5000 <$750/$1250
Series 1875
3x10-20 1-9144 <$600/$1000
Brown Back
4x5 1-4840 <$200
3x10-20 1-29236 <$250
1902 Red Seal
3x10-20 1-2500 <$275
1902 Date Back
3x10-20 1-26500 <$135
1902 Plain Back
3x10-20 26501-46020 <$135
Total Issue $4,691,800
Out at close $242,500
****
5155 Suffolk
N SHAWMUT B OF BOSTON
{{ 50+ L }}
Chartered 1898
Brown Back <$VALUE
4x5 1-299580 <$150
4x10 1-41500 <$150
3x10-20 1-133768<$150/$175
1882 Date Back
4x5 1-336465 <$135
4x10 1-309832 <$135
3x10-20 1-8000 <$135/$175
3x50-100 1-10920
<$1250/$1500
1902 Plain Back
4x5 1-6380 <$50
3x10-20 1-3076 <$50/$60
Total Issue $36,873,980
Out in 1935 $62,580
****

****

6104 Suffolk
N SUFFOLK B OF BOSTON
{{ UNREPORTED }}
Chartered 1/25/02
Liquidated 10/30/03
1902 Red Seal <$VALUE
4x5 1-3725 <$1000
3x10-20 1-2970 <$1000
50-100 1-323 <$2250/$2500
Total Issue $271,450
Out in 1910 $5,680

****

985 Suffolk
N UNION B OF BOSTON
{{ 30 L }}
Chartered 4/6/65
Liquidated 10/13/25
Original Series <$VALUE
3x1-2 1-19000 <$225/$750
4x5 1-14200 <$275
3x10-20 1-7420 <$750/$1250
50-100 1-1400 <$3500
500 1-224 <$150,000
Series 1875
3x1-2 1-9240 <$225/$750
4x5 1-22000 <$275
3x10-20 1-10200<$600/$1000
50-100 1-800 <$3500
Brown Back
4x5 1-21572 <$150
3x10-20 1-9842 <$150/$175
50-100 1-1233 <$1250/$1500
1902 Red Seal
4x5 1-5800 <$150
3x10-20 1-4080 <$150/$175
1902 Date Back
4x5 1-62330 <$40
3x10-20 1-46868 <$45
3x50-100 1-1000 <$300/$350
1902 Plain Back
4x5 62331-128805 <$40
3x10-20 46869-48868 <$45
Total Issue $8,886,190
Out at close $347,550

****

1527 Suffolk
N WEBSTER B OF BOSTON
Organized 8/14/65
2nd title: Webster-Atlas NB 4/4/04
FIRST TITLE {{ 4 L }}
Original Series <$VALUE
4x5 1-11000 <$350
3x10-20 1-5600 <$750/$1250
50-100 1-1922 <$3500
500 1-293 <$150,000
Series 1875
4x5 1-23653 <$350
3x10-20 1-16121<$600/$1000
50-100 1-300 <$3500
Brown Back
4x5 1-13005 <$275
3x10-20 1-1374 <$275
SECOND TITLE {{ 16 L U+20 S }}
Brown Back
4x5 1-155 <$200
3x10-20 1-576 <$200
1902 Red Seal
4x5 1-2000 <$175
3x10-20 1-3200 <$175/$225
50-100 1-500 <$2250/$2500
1902 Date Back
4x5 1-43330 <$50
3x10-20 1-26829 <$60
50-100 1-1000 <$300/$350
3x50-100 1-276 <$300/$350
1902 Plain Back
4x5 43331-274307 <$50
1929 Small Size
5 Type 1 1-66256 <$25
10 Type 1 1-3594 <$25
20 Type 1 1-1374 <$35
50 Type 1 1-476 <$150
100 Type 1 1-160 <$200
5 Type 2 1-30834 <$25
Total Issue $12,762,370
Out in 1935 $451,560
Large out 1935 $26,660

****

603 Suffolk
NEW ENGLAND NB OF BOSTON
{{ 18 L }}
Chartered 1864
Liquidated 1/1/14
Original Series <$VALUE
3x1-2 1-12300 <$250/$750
4x5 1-12250 <$300
3x10-20 1-10300<$750/$1250
50-100 1-4383 <$3500
500 1-280 <$150,000
Series 1875
3x1-2 1-14000 <$250/$750
4x5 1-19000 <$300
3x10-20 1-13500<$600/$1000
50-100 1-1900 <$3500
500 1-46 <$150,000
Brown Back
4x5 1-23935 <$150
3x10-20 1-8013 <$150/$175
50-100 1-300 <$1250/$1500
1902 Red Seal
4x5 1-3550 <$150
3x10-20 1-2680 <$150/$200
1902 Date Back
4x5 1-2335 <$65
3x10-20 1-2332 <$75
Total Issue $4,344,600
Out in 1914 $27,550

****

525 Suffolk
NORTH NB OF BOSTON
{{ 16 L }}
Chartered 10/5/64
Liquidated 12/17/98
Original Series <$VALUE
3x1-2 1-9000 <$250/$750
4x5 1-9100 <$325
3x10-20 1-6400 <$750/$1250
3x10-20 7401-10510 <$750/$1250
20 6401-7400 <$1250
2x20-50-100 1-4700 <$1250/$3500/$3500
Series 1875
3x1-2 1-2000 <$250/$750
4x5 1-25000 <$325
3x10-20 1-16000<$600/$1000
2x20-50-100 1-300 <$650/$3500/$3500
Brown Back
4x5 1-12482 <$200
3x10-20 1-6342 <$200/$250
50-100 1-493 <$1250/$1500
Total Issue $3,623,190
Out in 1910 $20,711

****

1015 Suffolk
OLD BOSTON NB OF BOSTON
{{ 4 L }}
Chartered 1865
Liquidated 6/19/16
Original Series <$VALUE
3x1-2 1-1800 <$400/$850
4x5 1-8605 <$400
3x10-20 1-3780 <$750/$1250
50-100 1-1583 <$3500
500 1-393* <$150,000
* 171-200 not issued
Series 1875
4x5 1-7491 <$400
3x10-20 1-1679 <$600/$1000
Brown Back
4x5 1-25792 <$300
3x10-20 1-9539 <$300
50-100 1-340 <$1250/$1500
1902 Red Seal
4x5 1-1950 <$350
3x10-20 1-1320 <$350
1902 Date Back
4x5 1-4135 <$175
3x10-20 1-2853 <$175
Total Issue $2,396,960
Out in 1916 $36,995

****

2373 Suffolk
PACIFIC NB OF BOSTON
{{ 3 L }}
Chartered 11/9/77
Receivership 5/22/82
Series 1875 <$VALUE
3x1-2 1-7860 <$500/$1000
4x5 1-34655 <$500
Total Issue $732,400
Out in 1916 $2,319

****

595 Suffolk
PEOPLES NB OF ROXBURY, BOSTON
Chartered 1864
Liquidated 10/2/22
2nd title:Peoples NB of Roxbury at Boston 11/19/04
FIRST TITLE {{ 3 L }}
Original Series <$VALUE
3x1-2 1-1595 <$400/$1000
4x5 1-5650 <$400
3x10-20 1-3900 <$750/$1250
50-100 1-1886 <$3500
500 1-50 <$150,000
Series 1875
3x1-2 1-10499 <$400/$1000
4x5 1-6524 <$400
3x10-20 1-2991 <$600/$1000
50-100 1-776 <$3500
Brown Back
4x5 1-21500 <$300
3x10-20 1-12548 <$300
50-100 1-200 <$1250/$1500
SECOND TITLE {{ U + 4 L }}
1902 Red Seal
4x5 1-11000 <$350
4x10 1-2375 <$350
3x10-20 1-5700 <$350
1902 Date Back
4x5 1-15543 <$175
4x10 1-9869 <$175
3x50-100 1-140 <$500/$600
Total Issue $3,500,820
Out at close $15,395

****

322 Suffolk
SECOND NB OF BOSTON
{{ 11 L }}
Organized 3/16/64
Original Series <$VALUE
3x1-2 1-20800 <$250/$800
4x5 1-17000 <$300
4x10 1-16191 <$750
3x20-50 1-4300<$1250/$3500
Series 1875
4x5 1-15700 <$300
4x10 1-8250 <$600
Brown Back
4x5 1-18093 <$200
3x10-20 1-8760 <$200
1902 Red Seal
4x5 1-18940 <$200
3x10-20 1-15224 <$200
1902 Date Back
4x5 1-67500 <$85
3x10-20 1-53000 <$85
3x50-100 1-3104 <$300/$350
Total Issue $8,924,500
Out in 1935 $22,095

****

582 Suffolk
SHAWMUT NB OF BOSTON
{{ 14 L }}
Chartered 11/22/64
Liquidated 11/25/98
Original Series <$VALUE
3x1-2 1-4000 <$300/$850
4x5 1-6750 <$350
3x10-20 1-6700 <$750/$1250
50-100 1-3967 <$3500
500 1-290 <$150,000
1000 1-50 <$200,000
Series 1875
3x1-2 1-27000 <$300/$850
4x5 1-10000 <$250
3x10-20 1-39318<$600/$1000
Brown Back
4x5 1-89153 <$175
3x10-20 1-16000 <$175/$225
50-100 1-4372 <$1250/$1500
Total Issue $6,819,810
Out in 1910 $18,348

****

646 Suffolk
SHOE & LEATHER NB OF BOSTON
{{ 13 L }}
Chartered 12/31/64
Liquidated 12/10/01
Original Series <$VALUE
3x1-2 1-10000 <$350/$850
4x5 1-11250 <$400
3x10-20 1-16951<$750/$1250
50-100 1-3609 <$3500
500 1-150 <$150,000
Series 1875
4x5 1-7500 <$400
3x10-20 1-11000<$600/$1000
Brown Back
4x5 1-55418 <$300
3x10-20 1-22516 <$300/$350
Total Issue $4,673,060
Out in 1910 $29,085

****

4202 Suffolk
SOUTH END NB OF BOSTON
{{ 4 L }}
Chartered 1890
Liquidated 1/1/14
Brown Back <$VALUE
4x5 1-10250 <$350
3x10-20 1-10042 <$350
50-100 1-1506 <$1250/$1500
1882 Date Back
4x5 1-4130 <$350
3x10-20 1-2248* <$350
50-100 1-58 <$1250/$1500
* 1937-2200 not issued
1902 Date Back
4x5 1-6185 <$275
3x10-20 1-4632 <$275
Total Issue $1,478,800
Out in 1914 $18,330

****

1028 Suffolk
STATE NB OF BOSTON
{{ 15 L }}
Chartered 4/17/65
Liquidated 11/9/12
Original Series <$VALUE
3x1-2 1-5400 <$250/$800
4x5 1-15565 <$275
4x10 1-10175 <$750
3x20-50 1-6266<$1250/$3500
100-100 1-1486 <$3500
500-1000 1-117 <$150,000/$200,000
Series 1875
3x1-2 1-19564 <$250/$800
4x5 1-29550 <$275
4x10 1-18025 <$600
3x20-50 1-3661<$1000/$3500
Brown Back
4x5 1-43148 <$200
3x10-20 1-14015 <$200
50-100 1-1161 <$1250/$1500
1902 Red Seal
4x5 1-6000* <$225
3x10-20 1-3765 <$225
* 4510-5000 not issued
1902 Date Back
4x5 1-5405 <$100
3x10-20 1-4678 <$100
Total Issue $6,098,260
Out in 1913 $43,690

****

629 Suffolk
SUFFOLK NB OF BOSTON
{{ 3 L }}
Chartered 12/17/64
Liquidated 2/20/02
Original Series <$VALUE
4x5 1-5000 <$450
3x10-20 1-7990 <$750/$1250
3x10-20 10991-16990 <$750/$1250
20 7991-10990 <$1250
50-100 1-3300 <$3500
500 1-450 <$150,000
Series 1875
4x5 1-7635 <$450
3x10-20 1-11960<$600/$1000
50-100 1-1196 <$3500
Brown Back
3x10-20 1-4683 <$400
Total Issue $2,743,750
Out in 1910 $17,990

****

359 Suffolk
THIRD NB OF BOSTON
{{ 15 L }}
Chartered 4/1/64
Liquidated 12/24/01
Original Series <$VALUE
3x1-2 1-9444 <$250/$750
4x5 1-7000 <$300
4x10 1-800 <$750
3x20-50 1-2600<$1250/$3500
Series 1875
4x5 1-10000 <$300
4x10 1-4950 <$600
3x20-50 1-1000<$1000/$3500
Brown Back
4x5 1-143981 <$150
3x10-20 1-21000 <$150/$200
50-100 1-2200 <$1250/$1500
Total Issue $5,272,840
Out in 1910 $31,448

****

1442 Suffolk
TRADERS NB OF BOSTON
{{ 1 L }}
Organized 7/15/65
Receivership 4/4/02
Original Series <$VALUE
4x5 1-4000 <$600
3x10-20 1-2300 <$750/$1250
50-100 1-900 <$3500
Series 1875
4x5 1-7193 <$600
3x10-20 1-5200 <$600/$1000
50-100 1-1212 <$3500
Brown Back
4x5 1-9594 <$450
3x10-20 1-4190 <$450
50-100 1-1001 <$1250/$1500
Total Issue $1,467,190
Out in 1916 $5,860

****

625 Suffolk
TREMONT NB OF BOSTON
{{ 16 L }}
Chartered 12/14/64
Liquidated 12/20/98
Original Series <$VALUE
3x1-2 1-23500 <$250/$800
4x5 1-13440 <$300
3x10-20 1-9380 <$750/$1250
50-100 1-2650 <$3500
500-1000 1-165 <$150,000/$200,000
Series 1875
3x1-2 1-4500 <$250/$800
4x5 1-9500 <$300
3x10-20 1-11437<$600/$1000
50-100 1-695 <$3500
Brown Back
4x5 1-3050 <$200
3x10-20 1-2770 <$200/$250
50-100 1-1509 <$1250/$1500
Total Issue $2,814,750
Out in 1910 $9,695

****

601 Suffolk
WASHINGTON NB OF BOSTON
{{ 10 L }}
Chartered 12/3/64
Liquidated 2/20/02
Original Series <$VALUE
3x1-2 1-8200 <$350/$850
4x5 1-16125 <$400
3x10-20 1-9720 <$750/$1250
50-100 1-2100 <$3500
500 1-200 <$150,000
Series 1875
3x1-2 1-4140 <$350/$850
4x5 1-8045 <$400
3x10-20 1-5400 <$600/$1000
50-100 1-588 <$3500
500 1-40 <$150,000
Brown Back
4x5 1-2086 <$300
3x10-20 1-4136 <$300
50-100 1-260 <$1250/$1500
Total Issue $2,123,820
Out in 1910 $12,189

****

Webster & Atlas NB of Boston
SEE Ch 1527
N Webster B of Boston

****

Winthrop NB of Boston
SEE Ch 2304
Merchandise NB of Boston

****

11347 Suffolk
BRAINTREE NB, BRAINTREE
{{ 7 L 4 S }}
Organized 4/7/19
1902 Plain Back <$VALUE
4x5 1-21015 <$200
1929 Small Size
5 Type 1 1-5372 <$200
5 Type 2 1-8918 <$200
Total Issue $626,050
Out in 1935 $32,600
Large out 1935 $1,130

****

2504 Plymouth
BROCKTON NB, BROCKTON
{{ 6 L }}
Chartered 1881
Series 1875 <$VALUE
4x5 1-11569 <$400
3x10-20 1-173 <$600/$1000
Brown Back
4x5 1-1700 <$300
3x10-20 1-3390 <$300
1882 Date Back
4x5 1-7250 <$300
3x10-20 1-4950 <$300
1882 Value Back
4x5 7251-7930 <$300
3x10-20 4951-5348 <$300
1902 Plain Back
4x5 1-14910 <$175
Total Issue $1,167,730
Out in 1935 $2,220

****

2152 Plymouth
HOME NB OF BROCKTON
{{ 1 L }}
Chartered 6/3/74
Original Series <$VALUE
4x5 1-8500 <$650
Series 1875
4x5 1-650 <$650
3x10-20 1-8933 <$750/$1000
Brown Back
3x10-20 1-3300 <$500
50-100 1-1800 <$1250/$1500
1882 Date Back
3x10-20 1-868 <$500
50-100 1-61 <$1250/$1500
1902 Date Back
3x10-20 1-6000 <$350
1902 Plain Back
3x10-20 6001-7216 <$350
Total Issue $1,478,000
Out in 1935 $2,720

****

3553 Suffolk
BROOKLINE NB, BROOKLINE
{{ 4 L }}
Chartered 8/30/86
Liquidated 10/31/10
Brown Back <$VALUE
4x5 1-15636 <$450
3x10-20 1-2658 <$450
1902 Red Seal
4x5 1-2380 <$500
3x10-20 1-1848 <$500
1902 Date Back
4x5 1-2111 <$275
3x10-20 1-1432 <$275
Total Issue $699,440
Out at close $100,000

****

13222 Barnstable
BUZZARDS BAY NB, BUZZARDS BAY
{{ U + 20 S }}
Chartered 7/28
1929 Small Size <$VALUE
5 Type 1 1-998 <$400
10 Type 1 1-584 <$400
20 Type 1 1-182 <$400
5 Type 2 1-1194 <$400
10 Type 2 1-520 <$400
20 Type 2 1-150 <$400
Total Issue $100,990
Out in 1935 $23,950

****

1228 Suffolk
CAMBRIDGEPORT NB OF CAMBRIDGE
{{ 3 L }}
Chartered 6/6/65
Liquidated 3/30/05
Original Series <$VALUE
4x5 1-3300 <$500
3x10-20 1-1900 <$750/$1250
Series 1875
4x5 1-4940 <$500
3x10-20 1-1332 <$600/$1000
Brown Back
4x5 1-15300 <$450
3x10-20 1-1560 <$450
Total Issue $710,400
Out in 1910 $5,335

****

731 Suffolk
CHARLES RIVER NB OF CAMBRIDGE
{{ 3 L }}
Chartered 1/19/65
Liquidated 9/1/14
Original Series <$VALUE
3x1-2 1-2000 <$450/$1000
4x5 1-2500 <$500
3x10-20 1-1650 <$750/$1250
50-100 1-350 <$3500
Series 1875
4x5 1-2640 <$500
3x10-20 1-1680 <$700/$1000
50-100 1-250 <$3500
Brown Back
4x5 1-2538 <$400
3x10-20 1-1892 <$400
50-100 1-240 <$1250/$1500
1902 Red Seal
4x5 1-2275 <$450
3x10-20 1-1680 <$450
1902 Date Back
4x5 1-415 <$300
3x10-20 1-322 <$300
Total Issue $704,560
Out in 1914 $23,950

****

433 Suffolk
FNB OF CAMBRIDGEPORT, CAMBRIDGE
{{ 2 L }}
Chartered 5/21/64
Liquidated 8/6/04
Original Series <$VALUE
4x5 1-6500 <$600
3x10-20 1-2900 <$750/$1250
50-100 1-1280 <$3500
Series 1875
4x5 1-2915 <$600
3x10-20 1-1260 <$750/$1000
50-100 1-500 <$3500
Brown Back
4x5 1-8264 <$450
3x10-20 1-9822 <$450
50-100 1-400 <$1250/$1500
1902 Red Seal
3x10-20 1-1507 <$500
Total Issue $1,455,030
Out in 1910 $11,040

****

****
Lechmere NB of Cambridge
SEE Ch 614
Lechmere NB of
East Cambridge, Cambridge
****
614 Suffolk
LECHMERE NB OF
EAST CAMBRIDGE, CAMBRIDGE
Chartered 1864
2nd title:Lechmere NB of
Cambridge 1/24/33
FIRST TITLE {{ 10 L 7 S }}
Original Series <$VALUE
3x1-2 1-2500 <$300/$850
4x5 1-3500 <$400
3x10-20 1-1250 <$750/$1250
50-100 1-750 <$3500
Series 1875
3x1-2 1-500 <$300/$850
4x5 1-4475 <$400
3x10-20 1-2524 <$600/$1000
50-100 1-270 <$3500
Brown Back
4x5 1-7232 <$275
3x10-20 1-4040 <$275
1902 Red Seal
4x5 1-2750 <$300
3x10-20 1-3750 <$300
1902 Date Back
4x5 1-10000 <$150
3x10-20 1-6300 <$150
1902 Plain Back
4x5 10001-29145 <$150
3x10-20 6301-18749 <$150
1929 Small Size
5 Type 1 1-3740 <$125
10 Type 1 1-1766 <$125
20 Type 1 1-464 <$125
SECOND TITLE {{ 5 S }}
1929 Small Size
5 Type 1 1-1552 <$100
10 Type 1 1-992 <$100
20 Type 1 1-264 <$110
5 Type 2 1-10290 <$125
10 Type 2 1-5356 <$125
20 Type 2 1-1764 <$125
Total Issue $3,177,580
Out in 1935 $194,050
Large out 1935 $4,420
****
11152 Suffolk
MANUFACTURERS NB OF
CAMBRIDGE
{{ 5 L }}
Chartered 3/18
Liquidated 11/2/25
1902 Plain Back <$VALUE
4x5 1-22559 <$200
4x10 1-15435 <$200
Total Issue $1,068,580
Out at close $175,000
****
770 Suffolk
N CITY B OF CAMBRIDGE
{{ 2 L }}
Chartered 1/31/65
Receivership 2/23/10
Original Series <$VALUE
4x5 1-2750 <$600
3x10-20 1-2400 <$850/$1250
Series 1875
4x5 1-7428 <$600
Brown Back
4x5 1-8241 <$500
3x10-20 1-826 <$500
1902 Red Seal
4x5 1-900 <$500
3x10-20 1-770 <$500
1902 Date Back
4x5 1-522 <$400
3x10-20 1-176 <$400
Total Issue $805,420
Out in 1916 $1,505
****
663 Norfolk
NEPONSET NB OF CANTON
{{ 6 L }}
Chartered 1864
Liquidated 3/25/16
Original Series <$VALUE
3x1-2 1-8700 <$400/$850
4x5 1-7500 <$500
3x10-20 1-3930 <$750/$1250
50-100 1-560 <$3500
Series 1875
3x1-2 1-3480 <$400/$850
4x5 1-8500 <$500
3x10-20 1-3800 <$600/$1000
Brown Back
4x5 1-52996 <$350
3x10-20 1-7663 <$350
1902 Red Seal
4x5 1-4150 <$400
3x10-20 1-2540 <$400
1902 Date Back
4x5 1-8000 <$175
3x10-20 1-5900 <$175
1902 Plain Back
4x5 8001-8577 <$175
3x10-20 5901-6357 <$175
Total Issue $2,993,860
Out in 1916 $59,020
****
1005 Suffolk
MONUMENT NB OF
CHARLESTOWN
Chartered 4/12/65
Liquidated 6/29/05
2nd title:Monument NB of
Boston 3/29/05
FIRST TITLE {{ 5 L }}
Original Series <$VALUE
4x5 1-9600 <$400
4x10 1-1000 <$750
Series 1875
4x5 1-9500 <$400
4x10 1-3999 <$600
Brown Back
4x5 1-3525 <$375
3x10-20 1-5582 <$375
SECOND TITLE {{ 0 L }}
Brown Back
3x10-20 1-198 <$750
Total Issue $941,450
Out in 1910 $7,100
****
9651 Suffolk
BROADWAY NB OF CHELSEA
{{ 3 L 8 S }}
Chartered 2/10
1902 Date Back <$VALUE
4x5 1-4800 <$175
3x10-20 1-3640 <$175
1902 Plain Back
4x5 4801-15285 <$175
3x10-20 3641-10316 <$175
1929 Small Size
5 Type 1 1-2166 <$100
10 Type 1 1-1706 <$100
20 Type 1 1-358 <$110
5 Type 2 1-5260 <$125
10 Type 2 1-3497 <$125
20 Type 2 1-650 <$125
Total Issue $1,106,270
Out in 1935 $79,800
Large out 1935 $1,980
****
533 Suffolk
FNB OF CHELSEA
{{ 1 L }}
Organized 10/14/64
Receivership 8/17/06
Original Series <$VALUE
4x5 1-3500 <$600
3x10-20 1-3150 <$750/$1250
50-100 1-2250 <$3500
Series 1875
4x5 1-1500 <$600
3x10-20 1-2200 <$750/$1000
50-100 1-1996 <$3500
Brown Back
3x10-20 1-4206 <$400
50-100 1-1438 <$1250/$1500
1902 Red Seal
3x10-20 1-649 <$500
50-100 1-108 <$2250/$2500
Total Issue $1,479,050
Out in 1916 $6,225
****
14087 Suffolk
LINCOLN NB OF CHELSEA
{{ 2 S }}
Chartered 3/34
1929 Small Size <$VALUE
5 Type 2 1-7402 <$500
Total Issue $37,010
Out in 1935 $42,100
Large out 1935 $340
Outstanding includes Ch 11270
****
11270 Suffolk
N CITY B OF CHELSEA
{{ 4 L 2 S }}
Organized 11/11/18
Liquidated 10/25/34
1902 Plain Back <$VALUE
4x5 1-2924 <$250
1929 Small Size
5 Type 1 1-6884 <$250
5 Type 2 1-4802 <$250
Total Issue $289,010
Out at close $28,360
Large out 1935 $340
Ch 14087 assumed circulation
****

****
4074 Suffolk
WINNISSIMET NB OF CHELSEA
{{ 1 L }}
Chartered 7/15/89
Liquidated 2/9/07
Brown Back <$VALUE
4x5 1-18350 <$650
3x10-20 1-1235 <$650
Total Issue $552,250
Out in 1910 $12,295
****
1056 Hampden
FNB OF CHICOPEE
{{ 10 L }}
Chartered 4/26/65
Liquidated 4/3/05
Original Series <$VALUE
3x1-2 1-5400 <$325/$750
4x5 1-4500 <$350
3x10-20 1-1800 <$750/$1250
50-100 1-220 <$3500
Series 1875
3x1-2 1-440 <$325/$750
4x5 1-4578 <$350
3x10-20 1-2987 <$600/$1000
50-100 1-110 <$3500
Brown Back
4x5 1-5881 <$275
3x10-20 1-2639 <$275/$325
50-100 1-242 <$1250/$1500
Total Issue $785,480
Out in 1910 $5,991
****
440 Worcester
FNB OF CLINTON
{{ 8 L }}
Chartered 1864
Liquidated 1/10/20
Original Series <$VALUE
3x1-2 1-3600 <$400/$850
4x5 1-4000 <$400
3x10-20 1-3600 <$750/$1250
50-100 1-800 <$3500
Series 1875
3x1-2 1-1000 <$400/$850
4x5 1-4894 <$400
3x10-20 1-1900 <$650/$1000
Brown Back
4x5 1-4400 <$300
3x10-20 1-6133 <$300
1902 Red Seal
4x5 1-1250 <$350
3x10-20 1-2160 <$350
1902 Date Back
4x5 1-4700 <$175
3x10-20 1-3640 <$175
1902 Plain Back
4x5 4701-5394 <$175
3x10-20 3641-4060 <$175
Total Issue $1,434,410
Out at close $45,600
****
Lancaster NB of Clinton
SEE Ch 583
Lancaster NB of Lancaster
****
833 Middlesex
CONCORD NB, CONCORD
{{ 6 L 12 S }}
Chartered 2/23/65
Original Series <$VALUE
3x1-2 1-1300 <$450/$1000
4x5 1-2375 <$500
3x10-20 1-1350 <$750/$1250
50-100 1-360 <$3500
Series 1875
3x1-2 1-380 <$450/$1000
4x5 1-1600 <$500
3x10-20 1-1656 <$650/$1000
50-100 1-130 <$3500
Brown Back
4x5 1-2430 <$350
3x10-20 1-6081 <$350
1902 Red Seal
3x10-20 1-4000 <$400
1902 Date Back
3x10-20 1-8500 <$200
1902 Plain Back
3x10-20 8501-25893 <$200
1929 Small Size
10 Type 1 1-4384 <$85
20 Type 1 1-1124 <$100
10 Type 2 1-7500 <$100
20 Type 2 1-1815 <$110
Total Issue $2,668,220
Out in 1935 $167,400
Large out 1935 $5,360
****

****
895 Franklin
CONWAY NB, CONWAY
{{ 3 L U + 5 S }}
Chartered 3/15/65
Original Series <$VALUE
3x1-2 1-4100 <$400/$1000
4x5 1-4500 <$500
3x10-20 1-1400 <$750/$1250
50-100 1-601 <$3500
Series 1875
3x1-2 1-2480 <$400/$1000
4x5 1-5555 <$500
3x10-20 1-2408 <$600/$1000
Brown Back
4x5 1-21049 <$350
3x10-20 1-743 <$350/$400
1902 Red Seal
4x5 1-800 <$450
3x10-20 1-930 <$450
1902 Date Back
4x5 1-3450 <$225
3x10-20 1-2360 <$225
1902 Plain Back
4x5 3451-9570 <$225
3x10-20 2361-5641 <$225
1929 Small Size
5 Type 1 1-688 <$225
10 Type 1 1-464 <$225
20 Type 1 1-138 <$225
5 Type 2 1-698 <$250
10 Type 2 1-312 <$250
20 Type 2 1-60 <$250
Total Issue $1,581,240
Out in 1935 $24,400
Large out 1935 $5,030
****
7452 Essex
DANVERS NB, DANVERS
{{ U + 3 L 2 S }}
Organized 9/26/04
1902 Red Seal <$VALUE
3x10-20 1-1600 <$350
1902 Date Back
3x10-20 1-3110 <$175
1902 Plain Back
3x10-20 3111-7015 <$175
1929 Small Size
10 Type 1 1-706 <$300
20 Type 1 1-156 <$300
Total Issue $491,830
Out in 1935 $10,330
Large out 1935 $830
****
594 Essex
FNB OF DANVERS
{{ 3 L }}
Chartered 11/30/64
Liquidated 10/25/04
Original Series <$VALUE
3x1-2 1-2900 <$450/$1000
4x5 1-4050 <$500
3x10-20 1-1530 <$750/$1250
50-100 1-811 <$3500
Series 1875
3x1-2 1-1200 <$450/$1000
4x5 1-5545 <$500
3x10-20 1-2221 <$650/$1000
50-100 1-100 <$3500
Brown Back
4x5 1-12418 <$400
3x10-20 1-1348 <$400
Total Issue $852,360
Out in 1910 $4,907
****
669 Norfolk
DEDHAM NB OF DEDHAM
{{ 8 L }}
Chartered 1864
Liquidated 8/27/24
Original Series <$VALUE
3x1-2 1-11400 <$300/$750
4x5 1-7600 <$350
3x10-20 1-4255 <$750/$1250
50-100 1-901 <$3500
Series 1875
3x1-2 1-5000 <$300/$750
4x5 1-8990 <$350
3x10-20 1-3920 <$600/$1000
50-100 1-540 <$3500
Brown Back
4x5 1-6790 <$300
3x10-20 1-5186 <$300
50-100 1-1050 <$1250/$1500
1902 Red Seal
3x10-20 1-1070 <$325
50-100 1-330 <$2250/$2500
1902 Date Back
3x10-20 1-5000 <$150
50-100 1-400 <$400/$500
1902 Plain Back
3x10-20 5001-5648 <$150
Total Issue $2,036,700
Out at close $49,995
Ch 12567 assumed circulation
****

****
12567 Norfolk
DEDHAM NB, DEDHAM
{{ 1 L 6 S }}
Chartered 8/24
Liquidated 12/31/34
1902 Plain Back <$VALUE
4x5 1-9989 <$400
1929 Small Size
5 Type 1 1-10440 <$100
5 Type 2 1-19370 <$100
Total Issue $609,830
Out at close $91,400
Large out at close $8,060
Outstanding includes Ch 669
****
156 Suffolk
FNB OF DORCHESTER
{{ 2 L }}
Chartered 12/14/63
Liquidated 11/23/68
Original Series <$VALUE
3x1-2 1-1660 <$500/$1250
4x5 1-2500 <$600
4x10 1-1325 <$750
3x20-50 1-220 <$1250/$3500
Total Issue $135,500
Out in 1910 $1,722
****
449 Suffolk
CAMBRIDGE NB OF
EAST CAMBRIDGE
{{ 1 L }}
Chartered 6/1/64
Liquidated 3/12/03
Original Series <$VALUE
4x5 1-4700 <$750
3x10-20 1-2100 <$850/$1250
Series 1875
4x5 1-1685 <$750
3x10-20 1-1840 <$850/$1250
Brown Back
3x10-20 1-3507 <$650
Total Issue $500,050
Out in 1910 $3,310
****
428 Hampshire
FNB OF EASTHAMPTON
{{ 6 L 50+ S }}
Chartered 1864
Original Series <$VALUE
3x1-2 1-5400 <$350/$850
4x5 1-6150 <$450
3x10-20 1-2860 <$750/$1250
Series 1875
3x1-2 1-5400 <$350/$850
4x5 1-6371 <$450
3x10-20 1-2613 <$600/$1000
Brown Back
4x5 1-16222 <$400
3x10-20 1-2934 <$400
1902 Red Seal
4x5 1-2900 <$400
3x10-20 1-2120 <$400
1902 Date Back
4x5 1-4400 <$175
3x10-20 1-3280 <$175
1902 Plain Back
4x5 4401-12600 <$175
3x10-20 3281-8343 <$175
1929 Small Size
10 Type 2 1-3141 <$50
20 Type 2 1-1074 <$60
Total Issue $1,935,250
Out in 1935 $33,126
Large out 1935 $6,326
****
7957 Dukes
EDGARTOWN NB, EDGARTOWN
{{ 6 L 3 S }}
Chartered 10/05
1902 Red Seal <$VALUE
4x5 1-1227 <$850
3x10-20 1-869 <$850
1902 Date Back
4x5 1-2000 <$450
3x10-20 1-1440 <$450
1902 Plain Back
4x5 2001-6960 <$450
3x10-20 1441-4364 <$450
1929 Small Size
5 Type 1 1-970 <$350
10 Type 1 1-462 <$350
20 Type 1 1-140 <$350
5 Type 2 1-1120 <$350
10 Type 2 1-648 <$350
20 Type 2 1-172 <$375
Total Issue $514,530
Out in 1935 $24,250
Large out 1935 $980
****

****
1274 Dukes
MARTHA'S VINEYARD NB OF
EDGARTOWN
Chartered 1865
2nd title:Marthas Vineyard
NB of Tisbury 11/15/05
FIRST TITLE {{ U + 0 L }}
Original Series <$VALUE
4x5 1-4000 <$1250
3x10-20 1-1250 <$1500/$2000
Series 1875
4x5 1-6000 <$1250
3x10-20 1-1076 <$1500/$2000
Brown Back
4x5 1-8266 <$1000
3x10-20 1-2734 <$1000
1902 Red Seal
3x10-20 1-10 <$1250
SECOND TITLE {{ U + 6 L 5 S }}
1902 Red Seal
4x5 1-1700 <$1000
3x10-20 1-1240 <$1000
1902 Date Back
4x5 1-3950 <$500
3x10-20 1-2710 <$500
1902 Plain Back
4x5 3951-12975 <$500
3x10-20 2711-8458 <$500
1929 Small Size
5 Type 1 1-1962 <$350
10 Type 1 1-900 <$350
20 Type 1 1-242 <$350
5 Type 2 1-1886 <$400
10 Type 2 1-1521 <$400
20 Type 2 1-396 <$400
Total Issue $1,571,680
Out in 1935 $49,050
Large out 1935 $3,880
****
490 Bristol
NB OF FAIRHAVEN
{{ 16 L 4U + 6 S }}
Chartered 1864
Original Series <$VALUE
3x1-2 1-8000 <$275/$850
4x5 1-7000 <$350
3x10-20 1-4000 <$750/$1250
50-100 1-934 <$3500
Series 1875
3x1-2 1-8586 <$275/$850
4x5 1-3686 <$350
3x10-20 1-2113 <$600/$1000
50-100 1-234 <$3500
Brown Back
4x5 1-9325 <$200
3x10-20 1-6669 <$200/$250
1902 Red Seal
4x5 1-6250 <$225
3x10-20 1-3100 <$225/$275
1902 Date Back
4x5 1-9100 <$85
3x10-20 1-6460 <$85
1902 Plain Back
4x5 9101-28325 <$85
3x10-20 6461-19370 <$85
1929 Small Size
5 Type 1 1-3622 <$125
10 Type 1 1-2104 <$125
20 Type 1 1-550 <$125
5 Type 2 1-5790 <$135
10 Type 2 1-3911 <$135
20 Type 2 1-1092 <$135
Total Issue $3,503,250
Out in 1935 $105,450
Large out 1935 $8,000
****

CONDITION affects Value. The Values shown are for notes in FINE condition.

590 Bristol
FALL RIVER NB, FALL RIVER
{{ 18 L 16 S }}
Chartered 1864
Original Series <$VALUE
3x1-2 1-13100 <$225/$750
4x5 1-5500 <$300
3x10-20 1-10200<$750/$1250
50-100 1-900 <$3500
Series 1875
3x1-2 1-6500 <$225/$750
4x5 1-16400 <$300
3x10-20 1-4100 <$600/$1000
50-100 1-300 <$3500
Brown Back
4x5 1-22553 <$175
3x10-20 1-8600 <$175
50-100 1-1448 <$1250/$1500
1902 Red Seal
4x5 1-12165 <$200
3x10-20 1-6734 <$200
50-100 1-800 <$2250/$2500
1902 Date Back
4x5 1-24580 <$60
3x10-20 1-16968 <$70
50-100 1-300 <$300/$350
3x50-100 1-1080 <$300/$350
1902 Plain Back
4x5 24581-70025 <$60
3x10-20 16969-42591 <$70
3x50-100 1081-1426 <$300/$350
1929 Small Size
5 Type 1 1-9770 <$25
10 Type 1 1-5106 <$25
20 Type 1 1-1282 <$35
50 Type 1 1-280 <$150
100 Type 1 1-110 <$200
5 Type 2 1-14192 <$25
10 Type 2 1-6837 <$30
20 Type 2 1-1915 <$40
Total Issue $8,241,740
Out in 1935 $335,750
Large out 1935 $21,395

256 Bristol
FNB OF FALL RIVER
{{ 38 L }}
Chartered 1864
Liquidated 1/13/25
Original Series <$VALUE
3x1-2 1-26000 <$225/$750
4x5 1-10350 <$300
4x10 1-6475 <$750
3x20-50 1-1600<$1250/$3500
Series 1875
3x1-2 1-2000 <$225/$750
4x5 1-11500 <$300
4x10 1-3375 <$600
3x20-50 1-900 <$1000/$3500
Brown Back
4x5 1-59503 <$150
3x10-20 1-16823 <$150/$175
1902 Red Seal
4x5 1-20150 <$150
3x10-20 1-15900 <$150/$175
1902 Date Back
4x5 1-37300 <$45
3x10-20 1-24068 <$65
1902 Plain Back
4x5 37301-97890 <$45
3x10-20 24069-50817 <$65
Total Issue $8,973,860
Out at close $309,345

612 Bristol
MASSASOIT NB OF
FALL RIVER
{{ 1 L }}
Chartered 12/8/64
Liquidated 6/30/03
Original Series <$VALUE
4x5 1-4280 <$600
4x10 1-3038 <$750
2x20-50-100 1-860
<$1250/$3500/$3500
Series 1875
3x1-2 1-1760 <$500/$1250
4x5 1-6150 <$600
4x10 1-2709 <$750
2x20-50-100 1-300
<$1000/$3500/$3500
Brown Back
4x5 1-24409 <$500
4x10 1-9969 <$500
Total Issue $1,654,310
Out in 1910 $11,829

6821 Bristol
MASSASOIT-POCASSET NB OF
FALL RIVER
{{ 4 L }}
Chartered 6/03
Liquidated 5/28/28
1902 Red Seal <$VALUE
4x5 1-23450 <$350
4x10 1-4500 <$350
3x10-20 1-13620 <$350
1902 Date Back
4x5 1-25669 <$175
4x10 1-15307 <$175
3x10-20 1-1255 <$175
Total Issue $2,518,410
Out at close $5,035

924 Bristol
METACOMET NB OF
FALL RIVER
{{ 19 L }}
Chartered 3/22/65
Liquidated 5/28/28
Original Series <$VALUE
3x1-2 1-7000 <$250/$750
4x5 1-17200 <$300
3x10-20 1-8060 <$750/$1250
50-100 1-775 <$3500
Series 1875
4x5 1-1460 <$300
3x10-20 1-10411<$600/$1000
Brown Back
4x5 1-12070 <$200
3x10-20 1-9667 <$200/$225
1902 Red Seal
4x5 1-7800 <$225
3x10-20 1-4330 <$225/$250
1902 Date Back
4x5 1-41100 <$75
3x10-20 1-28060 <$85
1902 Plain Back
4x5 41101-124645 <$75
3x10-20 28061-70571 <$85
Total Issue $8,566,700
Out at close $492,045

1288 Bristol
N UNION B OF FALL RIVER
{{ 1 L }}
Chartered 6/16/65
Liquidated 6/30/03
Original Series <$VALUE
3x1-2 1-5000 <$450/$1000
4x5 1-4800 <$600
3x10-20 1-4500 <$750/$1250
50-100 1-1000 <$3500
Series 1875
3x1-2 1-1070 <$450/$1000
4x5 1-9000 <$600
3x10-20 1-4326 <$750/$1000
50-100 1-700 <$3500
Brown Back
4x5 1-10937 <$500
3x10-20 1-4465 <$500
50-100 1-1209 <$1250/$1500
Total Issue $1,625,990
Out in 1910 $12,262

679 Bristol
POCASSET NB OF FALL RIVER
{{ 6 L }}
Chartered 12/31/64
Liquidated 6/30/03
Original Series <$VALUE
3x1-2 1-16600 <$300/$850
4x5 1-4400 <$350
3x10-20 1-2300 <$750/$1250
3x10-20 3301-4300
<$750/$1250
20 2301-3300 <$1250
50-100 1-400 <$3500
Series 1875
3x1-2 1-820 <$300/$850
4x5 1-4000 <$350
3x10-20 1-3898 <$600/$1000
50-100 1-80 <$3500
Brown Back
4x5 1-7119 <$250
3x10-20 1-7747 <$250
50-100 1-1701 <$1250/$1500
Total Issue $1,491,880
Out in 1910 $12,956

439 Bristol
SECOND NB OF FALL RIVER
{{ 5 L }}
Chartered 5/26/64
Liquidated 2/24/03
Original Series <$VALUE
3x1-2 1-7000 <$300/$850
4x5 1-2000 <$350
4x10 1-4000 <$750
50-100 1-642 <$3500
Series 1875
3x1-2 1-3990 <$300/$850
4x5 1-2000 <$250
4x10 1-2500 <$600
Brown Back
4x5 1-34208 <$250
3x10-20 1-4829 <$250
Total Issue $1,418,860
Out in 1910 $11,179

1320 Barnstable
FALMOUTH NB, FALMOUTH
{{ 3 L 7 S }}
Chartered 1865
Original Series <$VALUE
3x1-2 1-1400 <$400/$1000
4x5 1-2550 <$500
3x10-20 1-2250 <$750/$1250
Series 1875
3x1-2 1-100 <$400/$1000
4x5 1-3955 <$500
3x10-20 1-1526 <$600/$1000
Brown Back
4x5 1-13906 <$400
3x10-20 1-3154 <$400
1902 Red Seal
4x5 1-1410 <$500
3x10-20 1-1066 <$500
1902 Date Back
4x5 1-1650* <$225
3x10-20 1-1320** <$225
1902 Plain Back
4x5 1851-9230* <$225
3x10-20 1481-2917** <$225
* 1651-1850 not marked
** 1321-1480 not marked
1929 Small Size
5 Type 1 1-2218 <$150
10 Type 1 1-1202 <$150
20 Type 1 1-322 <$150
5 Type 2 1-4808 <$165
10 Type 2 1-3004 <$165
20 Type 2 1-876 <$165
Total Issue $1,423,070
Out in 1935 $97,600
Large out 1935 $3,200

1077 Worcester
FITCHBURG NB OF FITCHBURG
{{ 4 L }}
Chartered 1865
Liquidated 4/15/14
Original Series <$VALUE
4x5 1-5975 <$400
3x10-20 1-2270 <$750/$1250
50-100 1-1000 <$3500
Series 1875
4x5 1-3750 <$400
3x10-20 1-4300 <$600/$1000
50-100 1-700 <$3500
Brown Back
4x5 1-8889 <$300
3x10-20 1-8147 <$300
1902 Red Seal
4x5 1-7750 <$350
3x10-20 1-5200 <$350
1902 Date Back
4x5 1-13942 <$175
3x10-20 1-9737 <$175
Total Issue $2,543,820
Out in 1914 $131,295

702 Worcester
ROLLSTONE NB OF FITCHBURG
{{ 5 L }}
Chartered 1/11/65
Liquidated 2/24/06
Original Series <$VALUE
3x1-2 1-3000 <$300/$850
4x5 1-5250 <$450
3x10-20 1-3257 <$750/$1250
50-100 1-1457 <$3500
Series 1875
4x5 1-2500 <$450
3x10-20 1-4000 <$600/$1000
50-100 1-450 <$3500
Brown Back
4x5 1-30876 <$350
3x10-20 1-11462 <$350
50-100 1-500 <$1250/$1500
1902 Red Seal
4x5 1-3255 <$400
3x10-20 1-1526 <$400
Total Issue $2,225,920
Out in 1910 $22,988

2153 Worcester
SAFETY FUND NB OF
FITCHBURG
{{ 19 L 17 S }}
Chartered 6/9/74
Original Series <$VALUE
4x5 1-2950 <$400
3x20-50 1-2220<$1250/$3500
Series 1875
4x5 1-18492 <$400
3x20-50 1-2000<$1000/$3500
Brown Back
4x5 1-28250 <$175
3x10-20 1-7600 <$175/$225
1882 Date Back
4x5 1-14833 <$300
3x10-20 1-9367 <$225/$275
1902 Date Back
4x5 1-7875 <$100
3x10-20 1-6050 <$100
1902 Plain Back
4x5 7876-45866 <$100
3x10-20 6051-29951 <$100
1929 Small Size
5 Type 1 1-7874 <$50
10 Type 1 1-3742 <$60
20 Type 1 1-1008 <$65
5 Type 2 1-12564 <$65
10 Type 2 1-7279 <$65
20 Type 2 1-1821 <$75
Total Issue $5,771,650
Out in 1935 $194,200
Large out 1935 $10,800

2265 Worcester
WACHUSETT NB OF FITCHBURG
{{ 8 L }}
Chartered 5/20/75
Liquidated 1/2/12
Original Series <$VALUE
3x1-2 1-2000 <$350/$850
4x5 1-3500 <$400
3x10-20 1-2500 <$750/$1250
50-100 1-300 <$3500
Series 1875
3x1-2 1-2000 <$350/$850
4x5 1-7193 <$400
3x10-20 1-5158 <$600/$1000
50-100 1-1052 <$3500
Brown Back
4x5 1-9950 <$350
3x10-20 1-5370 <$350
50-100 1-650 <$1250/$1500
1882 Date Back
4x5 1-3915 <$350
3x10-20 1-2152 <$350
50-100 1-48 <$1250/$1500
Total Issue $1,577,660
Out in 1912 $39,625

9426 Norfolk
FOXBORO NB, FOXBORO
{{ 4 L 6 S }}
Chartered 6/09
1902 Date Back <$VALUE
3x10-20 1-5340 <$350
1902 Plain Back
3x10-20 5341-14430 <$350
1929 Small Size
10 Type 1 1-1284 <$250
20 Type 1 1-402 <$250
10 Type 2 1-1376 <$250
20 Type 2 1-494 <$250
Total Issue $870,420
Out in 1935 $50,000
Large out 1935 $1,250

528 Middlesex
FRAMINGHAM NB, FRAMINGHAM
{{ 5 L 24 S }}
Chartered 1864
Original Series <$VALUE
3x1-2 1-2000 <$400/$850
4x5 1-7000 <$400
3x10-20 1-4000 <$750/$1250
50-100 1-400 <$3500
Series 1875
4x5 1-4000 <$400
3x10-20 1-5064 <$600/$1000
Brown Back
4x5 1-9126 <$300
3x10-20 1-19210 <$300
1902 Red Seal
4x5 1-2900 <$350
3x10-20 1-3440 <$350
1902 Date Back
4x5 1-19000 <$150
3x10-20 1-13600 <$150
1902 Plain Back
4x5 19001-58385 <$150
3x10-20 13601-39356 <$150
1929 Small Size
5 Type 1 1-7988 <$60
10 Type 1 1-5312 <$60
20 Type 1 1-1376 <$70
5 Type 2 1-16598 <$60
10 Type 2 1-7772 <$60
20 Type 2 1-1250 <$70
Total Issue $6,160,910
Out in 1935 $246,750
Large out 1935 $11,710

Franklin NB, Franklin
SEE Ch 1207
Worcester County NB of
Blackstone

884 Worcester
FNB OF GARDNER
{{ 13 L 13 S }}
Chartered 3/13/65
Original Series <$VALUE
3x1-2 1-800 <$350/$1000
4x5 1-2650 <$450
3x10-20 1-1600 <$750/$1250
50-100 1-140 <$3500
Series 1875
4x5 1-3375 <$450
3x10-20 1-2054 <$600/$1000
50-100 1-150 <$3500
Brown Back
3x10-20 1-4450 <$275
1902 Red Seal
4x5 1-4500 <$300
3x10-20 1-4775 <$300
1902 Date Back
4x5 1-13500 <$100
3x10-20 1-9000 <$100
1902 Plain Back
4x5 13501-49075 <$100
3x10-20 9001-26959 <$100
1929 Small Size
5 Type 1 1-9322 <$65
10 Type 1 1-3242 <$65
20 Type 1 1-788 <$85
5 Type 2 1-78 <$125
10 Type 2 1-267 <$125
Total Issue $3,803,200
Out in 1935 $84,940
Large out 1935 $1,410

Westminster NB of Gardner
SEE Ch 2284
Westminster NB of Westminster

2297 Essex
GEORGETOWN NB, GEORGETOWN
{{ 5 L }}
Chartered 9/13/75
Liquidated 1/12/32
Series 1875 <$VALUE
4x5 1-2587 <$600
3x10-20 1-1983 <$650/$1000
Brown Back
4x5 1-5575 <$475
3x10-20 1-1960 <$475
1882 Date Back
4x5 1-3127 <$450
3x10-20 1-2031 <$450
1902 Plain Back
4x5 1-5355 <$375
4x10 1-3480 <$375
Total Issue $770,780
Out at close $2,120

899 Essex
CAPE ANN NB OF GLOUCESTER
{{ 24 L 7 S }}
Chartered 3/16/65
Original Series <$VALUE
3x1-2 1-5300 <$375/$850
4x5 1-2300 <$450
3x10-20 1-2100 <$750/$1250
50-100 1-437 <$3500
Series 1875
3x1-2 1-4660 <$375/$850
4x5 1-4300 <$450
3x10-20 1-1790 <$600/$1000
50-100 1-343 <$3500
Brown Back
4x5 1-22230 <$275
3x10-20 1-7658 <$275
50-100 1-940 <$1250/$1500
1902 Red Seal
4x5 1-7500 <$325
3x10-20 1-4200 <$325
50-100 1-200 <$1500
1902 Date Back
4x5 1-12000 <$100
3x10-20 1-7600 <$100
50-100 1-157 <$400/$500
1902 Plain Back
4x5 12001-93250 <$100
3x10-20 7601-9700 <$100
1929 Small Size
5 Type 1 1-17962 <$100
5 Type 2 1-34078 <$100
Total Issue $4,935,200
Out in 1935 $112,460
Large out 1935 $11,035

2292 Essex
CITY NB OF GLOUCESTER
{{ 9 L }}
Chartered 8/5/75
Liquidated 11/27/12
Series 1875 <$VALUE
4x5 1-42049 <$400
Brown Back
4x5 1-24750 <$300
4x10 1-3000 <$300
3x10-20 1-7040 <$300/$325
50-100 1-1786 <$1250/$1500
1882 Date Back
4x5 1-9227 <$250
4x10 1-4463 <$250
3x10-20 1-490 <$250/$300
Total Issue $2,463,440
Out in 1913 $58,945

549 Essex
FNB OF GLOUCESTER
{{ 5 L }}
Chartered 10/25/64
Liquidated 3/26/08
Original Series <$VALUE
3x1-2 1-7000 <$350/$850
4x5 1-6500 <$400
3x10-20 1-3100 <$750/$1250
Series 1875
3x1-2 1-3000 <$350/$850
4x5 1-7500 <$400
3x10-20 1-2800 <$600/$1000
Brown Back
4x5 1-35193 <$250
3x10-20 1-12536 <$250
1902 Red Seal
4x5 1-7126 <$300
3x10-20 1-4491 <$300
Total Issue $2,322,730
Out in 1910 $41,643

13604 Essex
GLOUCESTER NB OF
GLOUCESTER
{{ 7 S }}
Chartered 3/32
1929 Small Size <$VALUE
5 Type 1 1-1668 <$100
10 Type 1 1-1048 <$100
5 Type 2 1-11738 <$110
10 Type 2 1-5398 <$110
Total Issue $225,590
Out in 1935 $96,150
Large out 1935 $86,000
Outstanding includes Ch 1162

1162 Essex
GLOUCESTER NB, GLOUCESTER
{{ 6 L 5 S }}
Chartered 1865
Liquidated 5/17/32
Original Series <$VALUE
4x5 1-5500 <$400
3x10-20 1-3600 <$750/$1250
50-100 1-900 <$3500
Series 1875
4x5 1-11500 <$400
3x10-20 1-4060 <$600/$1000
50-100 1-300 <$3500
Brown Back
4x5 1-25256 <$250
3x10-20 1-12689 <$250
50-100 1-1603 <$1250/$1500
1902 Red Seal
4x5 1-7800 <$300
3x10-20 1-3140 <$300
50-100 1-580 <$2250/$2500
1902 Date Back
4x5 1-15500 <$150
3x10-20 1-10600 <$150
50-100 1-200 <$400/$500
3x50-100 1-400 <$400/$500
1902 Plain Back
4x5 15501-30277 <$150
3x10-20 10601-13165 <$150
1929 Small Size
5 Type 1 1-3003 <$135
10 Type 1 1-592 <$135
20 Type 1 1-191 <$150
Total Issue $4,225,090
Out at close $58,580
Large out at close $13,570
Ch 13604 assumed circulation

<$VALUEs are for notes in FINE condition. Value changes by approximately 25% for a change of one full grade.

****
188 Worcester
FNB OF GRAFTON
{{ 2 L }}
Chartered 1/7/64
Liquidated 6/21/92
Original Series <$VALUE
3x1-2 1-4000 <$500/$1000
4x5 1-5000 <$500
4x10 1-2500 <$750
Series 1875
3x1-2 1-404 <$500/$1000
4x5 1-3459 <$500
4x10 1-775 <$750
Brown Back
4x5 1-4692 <$500
Total Issue $416,040
Out in 1910 $2,115
****
824 Worcester
GRAFTON NB, GRAFTON
{{ 8 L }}
Chartered 2/18/65
Liquidated 1/26/05
Original Series <$VALUE
3x1-2 1-2800 <$300/$850
4x5 1-5050 <$350
3x10-20 1-1100 <$750/$1250
Series 1875
3x1-2 1-260 <$300/$850
4x5 1-6000 <$350
3x10-20 1-1300 <$600/$1000
Brown Back
4x5 1-8350 <$300
3x10-20 1-870 <$300
Total Issue $566,800
Out in 1910 $3,875
****
1203 Berkshire
N MAHAIWE B OF GREAT BARRINGTON
{{ 10 L 11 S }}
Chartered 1865
Original Series <$VALUE
3x1-2 1-8600 <$350/$1000
4x5 1-7850 <$450
3x10-20 1-2700 <$750/$1250
50-100 1-317 <$3500
Series 1875
3x1-2 1-310 <$350/$1000
4x5 1-4925 <$450
3x10-20 1-1448 <$750/$1250
50-100 1-68 <$3500
Brown Back
4x5 1-15776 <$300
3x10-20 1-3617 <$300
1902 Red Seal
4x5 1-3250 <$350
3x10-20 1-2600 <$350
1902 Date Back
4x5 1-7650 <$175
3x10-20 1-5774 <$175
1929 Small Size
5 Type 1 1-2604 <$85
10 Type 1 1-1392 <$85
20 Type 1 1-426 <$100
5 Type 2 1-9508 <$100
10 Type 2 1-6223 <$100
20 Type 2 1-1776 <$100
Total Issue $2,062,320
Out in 1935 $151,773
Large out 1935 $5,673
****
474 Franklin
FNB OF GREENFIELD
Chartered 1864
2nd title: FNB & TC of Greenfield 10/1/29
FIRST TITLE {{ 13 L 5 S }}
Original Series <$VALUE
3x1-2 1-7250 <$300/$850
4x5 1-4250 <$350
3x10-20 1-4750 <$750/$1250
3x10-20 5251-6250 <$750/$1250
20 4751-5250 <$1250
50-100 1-1196 <$3500
Series 1875
4x5 1-2500 <$350
3x10-20 1-4500 <$600/$1000
Brown Back
3x10-20 1-23073 <$250
1902 Red Seal
3x10-20 1-10000 <$300
1902 Date Back
4x5 1-22500 <$150
3x10-20 1-18000 <$150
1902 Plain Back
4x5 22501-78603 <$150
3x10-20 18001-54704 <$150
1929 Small Size
10 Type 1 1-1220 <$125
20 Type 1 1-406 <$125
SECOND TITLE {{ 12 S }}
1929 Small Size
10 Type 1 1-7178 <$100
20 Type 1 1-1660 <$100
10 Type 2 1-9980 <$100
20 Type 2 1-2553 <$100
Total Issue $7,738,720
Out in 1935 $258,800
Large out 1935 $17,235
****
920 Franklin
FRANKLIN COUNTY NB OF GREENFIELD
{{ 7 L }}
Chartered 3/21/65
Liquidated 10/8/12
Original Series <$VALUE
3x1-2 1-4850 <$325/$750
4x5 1-4500 <$350
3x10-20 1-3530 <$750/$1250
50-100 1-1190 <$3500
Series 1875
3x1-2 1-318 <$325/$750
4x5 1-4323 <$350
3x10-20 1-3586 <$600/$1000
Brown Back
4x5 1-20736 <$275
3x10-20 1-7226 <$275
50-100 1-1278 <$1250/$1500
1902 Red Seal
4x5 1-6500 <$350
3x10-20 1-4500 <$350
1902 Date Back
4x5 1-7777 <$175
3x10-20 1-6646 <$175
Total Issue $2,547,160
Out at close $160,000
****
2264 Franklin
PACKARD NB OF GREENFIELD
{{ 2 L }}
Chartered 5/17/75
Receivership 10/1/03
Original Series <$VALUE
4x5 1-2500 <$600
Series 1875
4x5 1-13808 <$600
Brown Back
4x5 1-7983 <$500
3x10-20 1-1791 <$500
Total Issue $575,370
Out in 1916 $2,165
****
712 Barnstable
CAPE COD NB OF HARWICH
{{ 11 L }}
Chartered 1865
Liquidated 7/31/20
Original Series <$VALUE
3x1-2 1-4000 <$450/$1000
4x5 1-5000 <$500
3x10-20 1-3200 <$750/$1250
50-100 1-1300 <$3500
Series 1875
3x1-2 1-4660 <$450/$1000
4x5 1-5510 <$500
3x10-20 1-4337 <$750/$1000
50-100 1-626 <$3500
Brown Back
4x5 1-21052 <$450
3x10-20 1-16222 <$450
50-100 1-1440 <$1250/$1500
1902 Red Seal
4x5 1-7250 <$450
3x10-20 1-5400 <$450
1902 Date Back
4x5 1-13415 <$225
3x10-20 1-10134 <$225
1902 Plain Back
4x5 13416-23167 <$225
3x10-20 10135-17189 <$225
Total Issue $4,105,180
Out at close $196,800
****
589 Essex
ESSEX NB OF HAVERHILL
{{ 4 L 4 S }}
Organized 11/7/64
Receivership 8/29/33
Original Series <$VALUE
3x1-2 1-2000 <$400/$1000
4x5 1-3250 <$450
3x10-20 1-2450 <$750/$1250
Series 1875
4x5 1-2495 <$450
3x10-20 1-1114 <$600/$1000
Brown Back
3x10-20 1-7871 <$250/$275
50-100 1-234 <$1250/$1500
1902 Red Seal
3x10-20 1-2000 <$400
1902 Date Back
4x5 1-3500 <$200
3x10-20 1-5300 <$200
1902 Plain Back
4x5 3501-61018 <$200
3x10-20 5301-7760 <$200
1929 Small Size
5 Type 1 1-12254 <$100
5 Type 2 1-3532 <$100
Total Issue $2,825,390
Out at close $100,000
Large out at close $6,460
****
481 Essex
FNB OF HAVERHILL
{{ 14 L 25 S }}
Organized 6/23/64
Receivership 8/29/33
Original Series <$VALUE
4x5 1-9000 <$350
3x10-20 1-1200 <$750/$1250
50-100 1-900 <$3500
Series 1875
4x5 1-16750 <$350
3x10-20 1-1200 <$600/$1000
50-100 1-833 <$3500
Brown Back
4x5 1-43264 <$225
3x10-20 1-3891 <$225/$250
1902 Red Seal
4x5 1-5750 <$275
3x10-20 1-4400 <$275/$300
1902 Date Back
4x5 1-9165 <$110
3x10-20 1-6934 <$110
1902 Plain Back
4x5 9166-25067 <$110
3x10-20 6935-17508 <$110
1929 Small Size
5 Type 1 1-4516 <$45
10 Type 1 1-2804 <$45
20 Type 1 1-694 <$50
5 Type 2 1-282 <$60
10 Type 2 1-205 <$60
Total Issue $4,056,980
Out at close $199,995
Large out at close $10,730
****
484 Essex
HAVERHILL NB, HAVERHILL
{{ 9 L 16 S }}
Chartered 1864
Original Series <$VALUE
3x1-2 1-3000 <$275/$800
4x5 1-7050 <$350
3x10-20 1-1680 <$750/$1250
50-100 1-950 <$3500
Series 1875
3x1-2 1-2600 <$275/$800
4x5 1-7550 <$350
3x10-20 1-420 <$600/$1000
50-100 1-1052 <$3500
Brown Back
4x5 1-31940 <$225
3x10-20 1-4815 <$225/$275
50-100 1-2213 <$1250/$1500
1902 Red Seal
4x5 1-7250 <$250
3x10-20 1-5500 <$250/$300
1902 Date Back
4x5 1-20415 <$100
3x10-20 1-15134 <$100
1902 Plain Back
4x5 20416-545935 <$100
3x10-20 15135-37078 <$100
1929 Small Size
5 Type 1 1-7528 <$50
10 Type 1 1-3804 <$50
20 Type 1 1-960 <$60
5 Type 2 1-10832 <$55
10 Type 2 1-4665 <$55
20 Type 2 1-1110 <$60
Total Issue $6,001,690
Out in 1935 $166,050
Large out 1935 $12,165
****
4833 Essex
MERCHANTS NB OF HAVERHILL
{{ 1 L }}
Chartered 1893
Liquidated 9/6/16
Brown Back <$VALUE
3x10-20 1-5120 <$750
1882 Date Back
3x10-20 1-2346 <$700
1902 Date Back
4x10 1-3192 <$450
Total Issue $500,980
Out in 1916 $44,700
****
633 Essex
MERRIMACK NB OF HAVERHILL
{{ 12 L 4 S }}
Chartered 1864
Closed 11/10/34
Original Series <$VALUE
3x1-2 1-1700 <$300/$800
4x5 1-8750 <$300
3x10-20 1-2670 <$750/$1250
50-100 1-830 <$3500
Series 1875
4x5 1-8750 <$300
3x10-20 1-3460 <$600/$1000
50-100 1-200 <$3500
Brown Back
4x5 1-23750 <$175
3x10-20 1-5660 <$175/$225
50-100 1-20 <$1250/$1500
1902 Red Seal
4x5 1-4750 <$225
3x10-20 1-4500 <$225/$250
1902 Date Back
4x5 1-15800 <$100
3x10-20 1-10800 <$100
1902 Plain Back
4x5 15801-44890 <$100
3x10-20 10801-27528 <$100
1929 Small Size
5 Type 1 1-5324 <$75
10 Type 1 1-2836 <$75
20 Type 1 1-778 <$85
5 Type 2 1-5286 <$85
10 Type 2 1-2336 <$85
20 Type 2 1-465 <$100
Total Issue $4,657,030
Out at close $149,695
Large out at close $10,040
Ch 14266 assumed circulation
****
14266 Essex
MERRIMACK NB OF HAVERHILL
{{ 1 L }}
Chartered 9/34 as Northern NB of Haverhill, under which there was no issue. Issuing title adopted 11/10/34.
1929 Small Size <$VALUE
5 Type 2 1-2440 <$600
10 Type 2 1-1488 <$600
20 Type 2 1-570 <$600
Total Issue $38,480
Out in 1935 $149,995
Large out 1935 $10,040
Outstanding includes Ch 633
****
3510 Essex
SECOND NB OF HAVERHILL
{{ 3 L }}
Chartered 5/25/86
Liquidated 2/12/06
Brown Back <$VALUE
4x5 1-29492 <$350
3x10-20 1-3636 <$350/$400
Total Issue $771,640
Out in 1910 $8,480
****
1119 Plymouth
HINGHAM NB, HINGHAM
{{ 3 L }}
Chartered 1865
Liquidated 5/31/16
Original Series <$VALUE
4x5 1-6750 <$600
3x10-20 1-1700 <$750/$1250
Series 1875
4x5 1-4740 <$600
3x10-20 1-2994 <$600/$1000
Brown Back
4x5 1-8760 <$350
3x10-20 1-6053 <$350/$400
1902 Red Seal
4x5 1-3750 <$400
4x10 1-1875 <$400
3x10-20 1-1300 <$400
1902 Date Back
4x5 1-6248 <$275
4x10 1-5718 <$275
3x10-20 1-300 <$275
Total Issue $1,526,030
Out in 1916 $19,480
****
802 Middlesex
HOLLISTON NB, HOLLISTON
{{ 2 L }}
Chartered 2/14/65
Liquidated 1/1/97
Original Series <$VALUE
3x1-2 1-3600 <$500/$1000
4x5 1-4600 <$600
3x10-20 1-1190 <$750/$1250
50-100 1-450 <$3500
Series 1875
3x1-2 1-910 <$500/$1000
4x5 1-3390 <$600
3x10-20 1-1720 <$750/$1000
50-100 1-279 <$3500
Brown Back
4x5 1-4180 <$500
3x10-20 1-1309 <$500
Total Issue $586,250
Out in 1910 $3,105
****
2430 Hampden
CITY NB OF HOLYOKE
{{ 13 L }}
Chartered 8/22/79
Liquidated 12/31/27
Series 1875 <$VALUE
4x5 1-66946 <$300
3x10-20 1-2542<$2000/$2500
Brown Back
4x5 1-8250 <$200
4x10 1-2000 <$200
3x10-20 1-6400 <$200/$250
1882 Date Back
4x5 1-30000 <$175
4x10 1-24750 <$175
3x10-20 1-1000 <$175/$200
1882 Value Back
4x5 30001-46034 <$200
4x10 24751-35020 <$200
1902 Plain Back
4x5 1-42929 <$100
4x10 1-38971 <$100
Total Issue $6,819,920
Out at close $268,000
****
1246 Hampden
HADLEY FALLS NB OF HOLYOKE
{{ 8 L }}
Chartered 1865
Liquidated 12/30/16
Original Series <$VALUE
3x1-2 1-8400 <$350/$850
4x5 1-7400 <$375
3x10-20 1-2000 <$750/$1250
50-100 1-190 <$3500
Series 1875
3x1-2 1-1840 <$350/$850
4x5 1-3915 <$375
3x10-20 1-2924 <$600/$1000
Brown Back
4x5 1-14590 <$250
3x10-20 1-1975 <$250/$300
1902 Red Seal
4x5 1-1750 <$300
3x10-20 1-1300 <$300/$350
1902 Date Back
4x5 1-19500 <$150
3x10-20 1-14200 <$150
1902 Plain Back
4x5 19501-22520 <$150
3x10-20 14201-15847 <$150
Total Issue $2,285,500
Out at close $196,845
****
1939 Hampden
HOLYOKE NB, HOLYOKE
{{ 10 L 12 S }}
Chartered 2/19/72
Original Series <$VALUE
3x1-2 1-2400 <$350/$850
4x5 1-2650 <$400
3x10-20 1-1900 <$750/$1250
50-100 1-100 <$3500
Series 1875
3x1-2 1-5000 <$350/$850
4x5 1-9500 <$400
3x10-20 1-8047 <$600/$1000
Brown Back
4x5 1-1500 <$250
3x10-20 1-10800 <$250/$300
50-100 1-600 <$1250/$1500
1882 Date Back
4x5 1-5115 <$250
3x10-20 1-3107 <$250/$275
50-100 1-200 <$1250/$1500
1902 Date Back
4x5 1-10000 <$100
3x10-20 1-7600 <$100
1902 Plain Back
4x5 10001-49755 <$100
3x10-20 7601-33540 <$100
1929 Small Size
5 Type 1 1-7452 <$60
10 Type 1 1-4062 <$60
20 Type 1 1-1100 <$70
5 Type 2 1-12528 <$70
10 Type 2 1-6204 <$70
20 Type 2 1-1572 <$80
Total Issue $5,167,500
Out in 1935 $188,060
Large out 1935 $9,555
****
3128 Hampden
HOME NB OF HOLYOKE
{{ 4 L }}
Chartered 1884
Liquidated 12/30/16
Brown Back <$VALUE
4x5 1-39570 <$350
50-100 1-1870 <$1250/$1500
1902 Red Seal
4x5 1-6800 <$400
3x10-20 1-8780 <$400
1902 Date Back
4x5 1-23000 <$200
3x10-20 1-14300 <$200
1902 Plain Back
4x5 23001-24342 <$200
3x10-20 14301-14747 <$200
Total Issue $2,871,090
Out at close $193,850
****
4703 Hampden
PARK NB OF HOLYOKE
{{ 3 L 7 S }}
Chartered 1892
Brown Back <$VALUE
50-100 1-4125 <$1250/$1500
1882 Date Back
4x5 1-2250 <$300
3x10-20 1-993 <$300
50-100 1-598 <$1250/$1500
1902 Date Back
4x5 1-4000 <$200
3x10-20 1-2700 <$200
3x50-100 1-438 <$500/$600
1902 Plain Back
4x5 4001-20145 <$200
3x10-20 2701-12362 <$200
3x50-100 439-613<$500/$600
1929 Small Size
5 Type 1 1-1742 <$100
10 Type 1 1-1136 <$100
20 Type 1 1-356 <$110
50 Type 1 1-128 <$200
100 Type 1 1-44 <$300
5 Type 2 1-2552 <$125
10 Type 2 1-1359 <$125
20 Type 2 1-340 <$125
Total Issue $2,238,440
Out in 1935 $86,800
Large out 1935 $5,650
****
626 Middlesex
HOPKINTON NB, HOPKINTON
{{ 10 L 6 S }}
Chartered 1864
Original Series <$VALUE
3x1-2 1-7500 <$400/$1000
4x5 1-6150 <$450
3x10-20 1-1048 <$750/$1250
50-100 1-500 <$3500
Series 1875
3x1-2 1-4500 <$400/$1000
4x5 1-12135 <$450
3x10-20 1-900 <$600/$1000
Brown Back
4x5 1-13510 <$300
3x10-20 1-1351 <$300/$350
1902 Red Seal
4x5 1-1300 <$400
3x10-20 1-805 <$400
1902 Date Back
4x5 1-1550 <$225
3x10-20 1-1440 <$225
1902 Plain Back
4x5 1551-1675 <$225
3x10-20 1441-1535 <$225
1929 Small Size
5 Type 1 1-55 <$300
10 Type 1 1-14 <$350
20 Type 1 1-2 <$400
Total Issue $1,115,080
Out in 1935 $4,950
Large out 1935 $4,190
****
2618 Middlesex
HUDSON NB, HUDSON
{{ 13 L 9 S }}
Chartered 1882
Series 1875 <$VALUE
4x5 1-18280 <$350
3x10-20 1-1616 <$600/$1000
Brown Back
4x5 1-5330 <$275
3x10-20 1-5268 <$275
1882 Date Back
4x5 1-8600 <$250
3x10-20 1-5780 <$250
1882 Value Back
4x5 8601-15905 <$250
3x10-20 5781-10452 <$250
1902 Plain Back
4x5 1-10814 <$125
3x10-20 1-7424 <$125
1929 Small Size
5 Type 1 1-3558 <$100
10 Type 1 1-2000 <$100
20 Type 1 1-478 <$100
5 Type 2 1-5398 <$100
10 Type 2 1-2863 <$100
20 Type 2 1-872 <$100
Total Issue $2,601,740
Out in 1935 $83,430
Large out 1935 $5,080
****

13395 Barnstable
BARNSTABLE COUNTY NB OF HYANNIS
{{ 4 S }}
Chartered 11/29
1929 Small Size <$VALUE
5 Type 1 1-1630 <$200
10 Type 1 1-874 <$200
5 Type 2 1-12494 <$225
10 Type 2 1-7008 <$225
Total Issue $233,890
Out in 1935 $87,050

1107 Barnstable
FNB OF HYANNIS
{{ 14 L }}
Chartered 1865
Liquidated 6/30/16
Original Series <$VALUE
3x1-2 1-2310 <$350/$850
4x5 1-3200 <$400
3x10-20 1-1949 <$750/$1250
Series 1875
3x1-2 1-1300 <$350/$850
4x5 1-2115 <$400
3x10-20 1-1862 <$600/$1000
Brown Back
4x5 1-11910 <$400
3x10-20 1-7260 <$400
1902 Red Seal
4x5 1-3550 <$500
3x10-20 1-2280 <$500
1902 Date Back
4x5 1-7850 <$250
3x10-20 1-5821 <$250
1902 Plain Back
4x5 7851-8352 <$250
Total Issue $1,559,190
Out in 1916 $58,595

7920 Suffolk
HYDE PARK NB, HYDE PARK
{{ 3 L }}
Chartered 9/05
Liquidated 3/8/16
1902 Red Seal <$VALUE
4x5 1-900 <$500
3x10-20 1-805 <$500
1902 Date Back
4x5 1-2295 <$350
3x10-20 1-1806 <$350
Total Issue $194,450
Out in 1916 $13,515

4774 Essex
FNB OF IPSWICH
{{ 3 L 6 S }}
Chartered 1892
Brown Back <$VALUE
4x5 1-8010 <$400
3x10-20 1-596 <$400
1882 Date Back
4x5 1-478 <$400
3x10-20 1-386 <$400
1902 Date Back
4x10 1-3000 <$225
1902 Plain Back
4x10 3001-14961 <$225
1929 Small Size
10 Type 1 1-2342 <$100
10 Type 2 1-1597 <$100
Total Issue $973,790
Out in 1935 $31,160
Large out 1935 $2,050

583 Worcester
LANCASTER NB OF LANCASTER
Organized 11/22/64
Receivership 1/20/86
2nd title:Lancaster NB of Clinton 2/25/82
FIRST TITLE {{ 3 L }}
Original Series <$VALUE
3x1-2 1-5000 <$500/$1000
4x5 1-8250 <$600
3x10-20 1-2900 <$750/$1250
SECOND TITLE {{ 0 L }}
Series 1875
3x10-20 1-1186<$1000/$1500
Brown Back
4x5 1-1260 <$750
Total Issue $523,000
Out in 1916 $3,517

4300 Essex
ARLINGTON NB OF LAWRENCE
{{ 3 L }}
Chartered 1890
Liquidated 10/15/10
Brown Back <$VALUE
4x5 1-26150 <$500
3x10-20 1-5840 <$500
1882 Date Back
4x5 1-2439 <$500
3x10-20 1-782 <$500
Total Issue $902,880
Out at close $100,000

Bay State Lawrence NB of Lawrence
SEE Ch 1014
Bay State NB of Lawrence

1014 Essex
BAY STATE NB OF LAWRENCE
Organized 4/10/65
2nd title:Bay State Merchants NB of Lawrence 7/31/33
FIRST TITLE {{ 21 L U + 29 S }}
Original Series <$VALUE
3x1-2 1-4000 <$250/$750
4x5 1-7350 <$275
3x10-20 1-4931 <$750/$1250
50-100 1-1580 <$3500
Series 1875
4x5 1-12000 <$275
3x10-20 1-6735 <$600/$1000
50-100 1-200 <$3500
Brown Back
4x5 1-11500 <$150
3x10-20 1-11180 <$150/$200
50-100 1-1140 <$1250/$1500
1902 Red Seal
4x5 1-9500 <$175
3x10-20 1-6900 <$175/$225
1902 Date Back
4x5 1-32125 <$50
3x10-20 1-23900 <$60
1902 Plain Back
4x5 32126-110829 <$50
3x10-20 23901-78241 <$60
1929 Small Size
5 Type 1 1-16936 <$30
10 Type 1 1-11370 <$35
20 Type 1 1-2874 <$45
5 Type 2 1-12312 <$35
10 Type 2 1-5592 <$40
20 Type 2 1-636 <$50
SECOND TITLE {{ 6 S }}
1929 Small Size
5 Type 2 1-16118 <$75
10 Type 2 1-8625 <$75
20 Type 2 1-3058 <$85
Total Issue $10,774,290
Out in 1935 $476,510
Large out 1935 $34,310

1962 Essex
LAWRENCE NB, LAWRENCE
{{ 4 L }}
Chartered 4/18/72
Liquidated 3/4/11
Original Series <$VALUE
4x5 1-7500 <$400
3x10-20 1-1000 <$750/$1250
50-100 1-1100 <$3500
Series 1875
4x5 1-6000 <$400
3x10-20 1-9353 <$600/$1000
50-100 1-1804 <$3500
Brown Back
4x5 1-44665 <$250
3x10-20 1-20934 <$250
50-100 1-660 <$1250/$1500
1882 Date Back
4x5 1-9820 <$250
3x10-20 1-4972 <$250
50-100 1-60 <$1250/$1500
Total Issue $3,716,250
Out in 1911 $140,470

3977 Essex
MERCHANTS NB OF LAWRENCE
{{ 4 L }}
Chartered 2/13/89
Liquidated 3/4/11
Brown Back <$VALUE
4x5 1-25933 <$350
3x10-20 1-5763 <$350/$400
1902 Date Back
4x5 1-3150 <$250
3x10-20 1-2592 <$250
Total Issue $999,410
Out in 1911 $46,450

1048 Essex
N PEMBERTON B OF LAWRENCE
{{ 1 L }}
Chartered 4/24/65
Liquidated 1/10/93
Original Series <$VALUE
4x5 1-3500 <$650
3x10-20 1-2000 <$750/$1250
50-100 1-600 <$3500
Series 1875
4x5 1-2000 <$650
3x10-20 1-3900 <$750/$1000
Brown Back
4x5 1-11500 <$600
3x10-20 1-2000 <$600
Total Issue $825,000
Out in 1910 $3,600

2347 Essex
PACIFIC NB OF LAWRENCE
{{ 4 L }}
Chartered 1/30/77
Liquidated 2/15/15
Series 1875 <$VALUE
3x10-20 1-6914 <$650/$1000
Brown Back
3x10-20 1-13700 <$400
1882 Date Back
3x10-20 1-12192 <$350
Total Issue $1,640,300
Out in 1915 $85,600

885 Berkshire
LEE NB, LEE
{{ 11 L 9 S }}
Chartered 3/14/65
Original Series <$VALUE
3x1-2 1-10462 <$350/$850
4x5 1-9050 <$400
3x10-20 1-3600 <$750/$1250
50-100 1-175 <$3500
Series 1875
4x5 1-7000 <$400
3x10-20 1-3282 <$600/$1000
Brown Back
4x5 1-14132 <$250
3x10-20 1-4488 <$250
1902 Red Seal
4x5 1-3500 <$300
3x10-20 1-2500 <$300
1902 Date Back
4x5 1-8950 <$150
3x10-20 1-6840 <$150
1902 Plain Back
4x5 8951-28135 <$150
3x10-20 6841-19360 <$150
1929 Small Size
5 Type 1 1-3654 <$65
10 Type 1 1-2002 <$65
20 Type 1 1-492 <$75
5 Type 2 1-6334 <$85
10 Type 2 1-3684 <$85
20 Type 2 1-900 <$85
Total Issue $3,312,890
Out in 1935 $97,550
Large out 1935 $6,650

918 Worcester
LEICESTER NB, LEICESTER
{{ 4 L }}
Chartered 3/21/65
Liquidated 2/1/04
Original Series <$VALUE
3x1-2 1-6000 <$400/$850
4x5 1-3500 <$450
3x10-20 1-4100 <$750/$1250
50-100 1-303 <$3500
Series 1875
4x5 1-14250 <$450
3x10-20 1-1500 <$600/$1000
Brown Back
4x5 1-13642 <$400
3x10-20 1-645 <$400
Total Issue $1,015,540
Out in 1910 $6,300

4013 Berkshire
LENOX NB, LENOX
{{ U + 12 L 6 S }}
Chartered 4/18/89
Brown Back <$VALUE
4x5 1-9990 <$300
3x10-20 1-3086 <$300
1902 Date Back
4x5 1-4300 <$150
3x10-20 1-3360 <$150
1902 Plain Back
4x5 4301-13695 <$150
3x10-20 3361-9666 <$150
1929 Small Size
5 Type 1 1-1864 <$100
10 Type 1 1-878 <$100
20 Type 1 1-272 <$125
5 Type 2 1-3404 <$125
10 Type 2 1-1687 <$125
20 Type 2 1-372 <$125
Total Issue $1,293,870
Out in 1935 $49,300
Large out 1935 $2,720

513 Worcester
FNB OF LEOMINSTER
{{ 1 L }}
Chartered 1864
Liquidated 7/5/84
Original Series <$VALUE
4x5 1-5200 <$650
3x10-20 1-3900 <$750/$1250
Series 1875
4x5 1-6000 <$650
3x10-20 1-4000 <$750/$1250
Total Issue $619,000
Out in 1910 $2,995

3204 Worcester
LEOMINSTER NB, LEOMINSTER
{{ 7 L 7 S }}
Organized 4/9/84
Receivership 6/11/32
Brown Back <$VALUE
3x10-20 1-4644 <$300
1902 Red Seal
3x10-20 1-8075 <$325
1902 Date Back
3x10-20 1-13500 <$125
1902 Plain Back
3x10-20 13501-41072 <$125
1929 Small Size
10 Type 1 1-3181 <$75
20 Type 1 1-870 <$75
Total Issue $2,984,810
Out at close $144,000
Large out at close $10,410

10059 Worcester
MERCHANTS NB OF LEOMINSTER
{{ 5 L 50+ S }}
Chartered 7/11
1902 Date Back <$VALUE
4x5 1-7350 <$225
3x10-20 1-5460 <$225
1902 Plain Back
4x5 7351-27490 <$225
3x10-20 5461-18738 <$225
1929 Small Size
5 Type 1 1-3974 <$60
10 Type 1 1-2186 <$60
20 Type 1 1-528 <$65
5 Type 2 1-4160 <$75
10 Type 2 1-1977 <$75
20 Type 2 1-565 <$75
Total Issue $1,852,310
Out in 1935 $78,200
Large out 1935 $2,835

986 Middlesex
APPLETON NB OF LOWELL
{{ 14 L 15 S }}
Chartered 4/17/65
Original Series <$VALUE
3x1-2 1-9000 <$300/$850
4x5 1-4000 <$350
3x10-20 1-2600 <$750/$1250
50-100 1-2070 <$3500
500 1-319 <$150,000
Series 1875
3x1-2 1-7000 <$300/$850
4x5 1-3000 <$350
3x10-20 1-3000 <$600/$1000
50-100 1-450 <$3500
Brown Back
4x5 1-40294 <$225
3x10-20 1-21553 <$225/$275
50-100 1-360 <$1250/$1500
1902 Red Seal
4x5 1-10750 <$250
3x10-20 1-6900 <$250/$300
1902 Date Back
4x5 1-21000 <$100
3x10-20 1-19100 <$100
1902 Plain Back
4x5 21001-60743 <$100
3x10-20 19101-54743 <$100
1929 Small Size
5 Type 1 1-12114 <$25
10 Type 1 1-5538 <$30
20 Type 1 1-1432 <$35
5 Type 2 1-13892 <$30
10 Type 2 1-7638 <$35
20 Type 2 1-1899 <$40
Total Issue $8,938,500
Out in 1935 $250,290
Large out 1935 $20,360

331 Middlesex
FNB OF LOWELL
{{ 4 L }}
Chartered 3/22/64
Liquidated 1/4/02
Original Series <$VALUE
3x1-2 1-6000 <$350/$750
4x5 1-7000 <$400
3x10-20 1-4000 <$750/$1250
50-100 1-700 <$3500
Series 1875
3x1-2 1-1320 <$350/$750
4x5 1-2940 <$400
3x10-20 1-2592 <$600/$1000
50-100 1-574 <$3500
Brown Back
4x5 1-5410 <$250
3x10-20 1-3185 <$250
50-100 1-1130 <$1250/$1500
Total Issue $1,193,050
Out in 1910 $7,501

506 Middlesex
MERCHANTS NB OF LOWELL
{{ 2 L }}
Chartered 8/30/64
Liquidated 1/4/02
Original Series <$VALUE
3x1-2 1-140 <$400/$850
4x5 1-5000 <$500
3x10-20 1-7500 <$750/$1250
50-100 1-2134 <$3500
Series 1875
3x1-2 1-1000 <$400/$850
4x5 1-2500 <$500
3x10-20 1-4700 <$600/$1000
50-100 1-1316 <$3500
Brown Back
4x5 1-7278 <$350
3x10-20 1-3503 <$350
50-100 1-1203 <$1250/$1500
Total Issue $1,784,360
Out in 1910 $10,445

12343 Middlesex
MIDDLESEX NB OF LOWELL
{{ 5 S }}
Organized 3/30/23
Receivership 2/3/32
1929 Small Size <$VALUE
5 Type 1 1-4434 <$100
10 Type 1 1-1733 <$100
20 Type 1 1-571 <$100
Total Issue $305,520
Out at close $176,960

1329 Middlesex
OLD LOWELL NB, LOWELL
{{ 8 L 1 S }}
Chartered 1865
Closed 5/31/30
Original Series <$VALUE
3x1-2 1-4000 <$350/$850
4x5 1-6650 <$400
3x10-20 1-1660 <$750/$1250
50-100 1-760 <$3500
Series 1875
3x1-2 1-1200 <$350/$850
4x5 1-5050 <$400
3x10-20 1-2495 <$600/$1000
50-100 1-777 <$3500
Brown Back
4x5 1-4787 <$250
3x10-20 1-4004 <$250
50-100 1-727 <$1250/$1500
1902 Red Seal
4x5 1-1800 <$300
3x10-20 1-1180 <$300
1902 Date Back
4x5 1-13665 <$100
3x10-20 1-11934 <$100
1902 Plain Back
4x5 13666-43110 <$100
3x10-20 11935-38993 <$100
1929 Small Size
5 Type 1 1-2642 <$300
10 Type 1 1-1134 <$300
20 Type 1 1-270 <$300
Total Issue $4,189,840
Out at close $197,235
Large out at close $31,565
Ch 6077 assumed circulation

960 Middlesex
PRESCOTT NB OF LOWELL
{{ 5 L }}
Chartered 3/31/65
Liquidated 3/18/08
Original Series <$VALUE
3x1-2 1-7600 <$400/$850
4x5 1-6250 <$400
3x10-20 1-3000 <$750/$1250
50-100 1-1190* <$3500
* 401-850 not issued
Series 1875
3x1-2 1-3660 <$400/$850
4x5 1-6485 <$400
3x10-20 1-2929 <$600/$1000
50-100 1-657 <$3500
Brown Back
4x5 1-5277 <$300
3x10-20 1-3080 <$300
50-100 1-728 <$1250/$1500
1902 Red Seal
4x5 1-1315 <$350
3x10-20 1-682 <$350
50-100 1-26 <$2250/$2500
Total Issue $1,250,040
Out in 1910 $16,449

753 Middlesex
RAILROAD NB OF LOWELL
{{ 7 L }}
Chartered 1/25/65
Liquidated 1/4/02
Original Series <$VALUE
3x1-2 1-16000 <$350/$750
4x5 1-15200 <$375
4x10 1-9375 <$750
2x20-50-100 1-2550 <$1250/$3500/$3500
Series 1875
3x1-2 1-4000 <$350/$750
4x5 1-12000 <$375
4x10 1-16500 <$600
2x20-50-100 1-600 <$1000/$3500/$3500
Brown Back
4x5 1-2045 <$300
3x10-20 1-5555 <$300
50-100 1-1453 <$1250/$1500
Total Issue $2,814,100
Out in 1910 $16,759

4753 Middlesex
TRADERS NB OF LOWELL
{{ 3 L }}
Organized 6/10/92
Receivership 10/20/13
Brown Back <$VALUE
4x5 1-21300 <$300
3x10-20 1-20240 <$300
50-100 1-847 <$1250/$1500
1882 Date Back
4x5 1-9102 <$300
3x10-20 1-5761 <$300
50-100 1-124 <$1250/$1500
1902 Date Back
4x5 1-2225 <$225
3x10-20 1-2494 <$225
Total Issue $2,222,940
Out in 1916 $28,920

6077 Middlesex
UNION NB OF LOWELL
Chartered 1/2/02
2nd title:Union Old NB, Lowell 5/31/30
FIRST TITLE {{ 22 L 1 S }}
Brown Back <$VALUE
4x5 1-14750 <$150
3x10-20 1-8850 <$150/$200
50-100 1-650 <$1250/$1500
1882 Date Back
4x5 1-28200 <$150
3x10-20 1-19600*<$150/$175
50-100 1-240 <$1250/$1500
3x50-100 1-400<$1250/$1500
1882 Value Back
4x5 28201-54065 <$150
3x10-20 20601-35853* <$150/$200
* 19601-20600 not marked
1902 Plain Back
4x5 1-46900 <$60
4x10 1-35985 <$60
1929 Small Size
5 Type 1 1-7838 <$100
10 Type 1 1-2952 <$100
SECOND TITLE {{ 12 S }}
1929 Small Size
5 Type 1 1-20970 <$50
10 Type 1 1-9534 <$50
5 Type 2 1-20976 <$60
10 Type 2 1-8508 <$60
Total Issue $8,025,710
Out in 1935 $228,600
Large out 1935 $26,330
Outstanding includes Ch 1329

Union Old NB of Lowell
SEE Ch 6077
Union NB of Lowell

****
781 Middlesex
WAMESIT NB OF LOWELL
{{ 4 L }}
Chartered 2/3/65
Liquidated 7/12/27
Original Series <$VALUE
3x1-2 1-11000 <$350/$850
4x5 1-5650 <$400
3x10-20 1-1540 <$750/$1250
50-100 1-700 <$3500
Series 1875
3x1-2 1-1820 <$350/$850
4x5 1-7130 <$400
3x10-20 1-3900 <$600/$1000
50-100 1-150 <$3500
Brown Back
4x5 1-8250 <$250
3x10-20 1-3940 <$250
50-100 1-100 <$1250/$1500
1902 Red Seal
3x10-20 1-2000 <$300
1902 Date Back
3x10-20 1-12700 <$150
1902 Plain Back
3x10-20 12701-33723 <$150
Total Issue $2,882,350
Out at close $148,195
****
1201 Essex
CENTRAL NB OF LYNN
{{ 10 L 5 S }}
Chartered 1865
Original Series <$VALUE
4x5 1-7500 <$400
3x10-20 1-2780 <$750/$1250
3x50-100 1-440 <$3500
Series 1875
4x5 1-17504 <$400
Brown Back
4x5 1-17414 <$250
50-100 1-667 <$1250/$1500
1902 Red Seal
4x5 1-5500 <$300
50-100 1-1000 <$2250/$2500
1902 Date Back
4x5 1-10325 <$150
50-100 1-1240 <$350/$450
3x50-100 1-789 <$350/$450
1902 Plain Back
4x5 10326-20459 <$150
3x50-100 790-804<$350/$450
1929 Small Size
5 Type 1 1-5170 <$150
5 Type 2 1-12876 <$150
Total Issue $2,473,070
Out in 1935 $40,140
Large out 1935 $6,180
****
697 Essex
CITY NB OF LYNN
{{ 5 L 7 S }}
Chartered 1865
Original Series <$VALUE
4x5 1-10250 <$400
3x10-20 1-3700 <$750/$1250
50-100 1-120 <$3500
Series 1875
4x5 1-6090 <$400
3x10-20 1-3552 <$600/$1000
Brown Back
4x5 1-10251 <$225
3x10-20 1-5751 <$225/$250
50-100 1-376 <$1250/$1500
1902 Red Seal
4x5 1-2050 <$250
3x10-20 1-1360 <$250/$300
1902 Date Back
4x5 1-8500 <$150
3x10-20 1-6700 <$150
1902 Plain Back
4x5 8501-26645 <$150
3x10-20 6701-18988 <$150
1929 Small Size
5 Type 1 1-3882 <$75
10 Type 1 1-2054 <$75
20 Type 1 1-508 <$85
5 Type 2 1-3882 <$100
10 Type 2 1-2566 <$100
20 Type 2 1-702 <$100
Total Issue $3,207,440
Out in 1935 $97,450
Large out 1935 $7,540
****
638 Essex
FNB OF LYNN
{{ 9 L }}
Chartered 12/20/64
Liquidated 8/30/04
Original Series <$VALUE
3x1-2 1-10000 <$350/$850
4x5 1-13500 <$400
3x10-20 1-5000 <$750/$1250
50-100 1-900 <$3500
500 1-100 <$150,000
Series 1875
3x1-2 1-7000 <$350/$850
4x5 1-18500 <$400
3x10-20 1-6100 <$600/$1000
50-100 1-800 <$3500
500 1-20 <$150,000
Brown Back
4x5 1-19596 <$250
3x10-20 1-17902 <$250
50-100 1-974 <$1250/$1500
Total Issue $3,028,120
Out in 1910 $25,361
****
3429 Essex
LYNN NB, LYNN
{{ 1 L }}
Chartered 1886
Liquidated 9/7/15
Brown Back <$VALUE
4x5 1-7942 <$750
3x10-20 1-905 <$750
1902 Red Seal
4x5 1-800 <$800
3x10-20 1-410 <$800
1902 Date Back
4x5 1-2215 <$650
3x10-20 1-1726 <$650
Total Issue $371,190
Out at close $19,900
****
4580 Essex
MANUFACTURERS NB OF LYNN
{{ 2 L 5 S }}
Chartered 1891
Brown Back <$VALUE
4x5 1-12925 <$400
3x10-20 1-2920 <$400
1882 Date Back
4x5 1-1004 <$400
3x10-20 1-865 <$400
1902 Date Back
4x5 1-5250 <$200
4x10 1-5425 <$200
1902 Plain Back
4x5 5251-14127 <$200
4x10 5426-12962 <$200
1929 Small Size
5 Type 1 1-2768 <$125
10 Type 1 1-1304 <$125
5 Type 2 1-4562 <$135
10 Type 2 1-2654 <$135
Total Issue $1,479,480
Out in 1935 $44,050
Large out 1935 $2,570
****
2563 Essex
N SECURITY B OF LYNN
{{ 4 L }}
Chartered 9/24/81
Liquidated 1/3/10
Series 1875 <$VALUE
4x5 1-17250 <$400
3x10-20 1-2724 <$600/$1000
Brown Back
4x5 1-8135 <$350
3x10-20 1-4846 <$350
1882 Date Back
4x5 1-1287 <$350
3x10-20 1-725 <$350
Total Issue $948,190
Out in 1910 $42,800
****
12362 Essex
STATE NB IN LYNN
{{ 4 L }}
Organized 4/16/23
Receivership 12/23/31
1902 Plain Back <$VALUE
4x5 1-13340 <$300
Total Issue $266,800
Out at close $1,945
Outstanding includes Ch 11169
****
11169 Essex
STATE NB OF LYNN
{{ 1 L }}
Chartered 4/18
Liquidated 6/8/23
1902 Plain Back <$VALUE
4x5 1-14780 <$500
Total Issue $295,600
Out at close $42,000
Ch 12362 assumed circulation
****
588 Suffolk
FNB OF MALDEN
{{ 12 L 3U + 21 S }}
Chartered 1864
Original Series <$VALUE
4x5 1-5000 <$350
3x10-20 1-2200 <$750/$1250
Series 1875
4x5 1-4090 <$350
3x10-20 1-1246 <$600/$1000
Brown Back
4x5 1-22600 <$200
3x10-20 1-4770 <$200
1902 Red Seal
4x5 1-4750 <$250
4x10 1-2000 <$250
3x10-20 1-2700 <$250
1902 Date Back
4x5 1-7950 <$100
4x10 1-8825 <$100
3x10-20 1-400 <$100
1902 Plain Back
4x5 7951-39214 <$100
4x10 8826-35275 <$100
1929 Small Size
5 Type 1 1-10908 <$40
10 Type 1 1-5474 <$40
5 Type 2 1-18680 <$50
10 Type 2 1-9174 <$50
Total Issue $4,410,640
Out in 1935 $192,010
Large out 1935 $5,650
****
11014 Suffolk
SECOND NB OF MALDEN
{{ 22 S }}
Chartered 6/17
1929 Small Size <$VALUE
5 Type 1 1-18004 <$40
10 Type 1 1-9308 <$40
5 Type 2 1-17374 <$50
10 Type 2 1-8430 <$50
Total Issue $1,269,770
Out in 1935 $163,550
****
5944 Bristol
FNB OF MANSFIELD
{{ 8 L 13 S }}
Chartered 8/23/01
Brown Back <$VALUE
3x10-20 1-3500 <$300
1882 Date Back
3x10-20 1-4440* <$300
1882 Value Back
3x10-20 4641-7673* <$300
* 4441-4640 not marked
1902 Plain Back
3x10-20 1-6573 <$175
1929 Small Size
10 Type 1 1-2554 <$85
20 Type 1 1-794 <$100
10 Type 2 1-4207 <$100
20 Type 2 1-856 <$100
Total Issue $1,195,010
Out in 1935 $84,600
Large out 1935 $2,180
****
767 Essex
MARBLEHEAD NB OF MARBLEHEAD
{{ 3 L }}
Chartered 1/30/65
Liquidated 3/4/04
Original Series <$VALUE
3x1-2 1-5400 <$400/$1000
4x5 1-5585 <$500
3x10-20 1-900 <$750/$1250
Series 1875
3x1-2 1-2000 <$400/$1000
4x5 1-4490 <$500
3x10-20 1-2400 <$600/$1000
Brown Back
4x5 1-16024 <$400
3x10-20 1-1421 <$400
Total Issue $795,030
Out in 1910 $5,267
****
676 Essex
N GRAND B OF MARBLEHEAD
{{ 4 L 5 S }}
Chartered 1864
Original Series <$VALUE
3x1-2 1-5000 <$500/$1000
4x5 1-5000 <$500
3x10-20 1-1700 <$750/$1250
50-100 1-100 <$3500
Series 1875
4x5 1-4495 <$500
3x10-20 1-1733 <$750/$1000
50-100 1-101 <$3500
Brown Back
4x5 1-11185 <$300
3x10-20 1-5589 <$300
1902 Red Seal
4x5 1-4500 <$350
3x10-20 1-2900 <$350
1902 Date Back
4x5 1-8000 <$175
3x10-20 1-5900 <$175
1902 Plain Back
4x5 8001-26830 <$175
3x10-20 5901-18079 <$175
1929 Small Size
5 Type 1 1-3666 <$85
10 Type 1 1-2026 <$85
20 Type 1 1-448 <$100
5 Type 2 1-4004 <$100
10 Type 2 1-2276 <$100
20 Type 2 1-550 <$110
Total Issue $2,934,540
Out in 1935 $82,550
Large out 1935 $7,940
****
158 Middlesex
FNB OF MARLBORO
{{ UNREPORTED }}
Chartered 1863
Liquidated 8/3/82
Original Series <$VALUE
3x1-2 1-4000 <$1000/$2000
4x5 1-6400 <$1000
3x10-20 1-4900<$1500/$2000
Series 1875
3x1-2 1-920 <$1000/$2000
4x5 1-2000 <$1000
3x10-20 1-2652<$1500/$2000
Total Issue $570,200
Out in 1910 $3,206
****
2770 Middlesex
FNB OF MARLBORO
{{ 13 L 14 S }}
Chartered 1882
Brown Back <$VALUE
4x5 1-11017 <$250
3x10-20 1-10008 <$250
50-100 1-1834 <$1250/$1500
1902 Red Seal
4x5 1-10830 <$300
3x10-20 1-9768 <$300
1902 Date Back
4x5 1-7250 <$125
3x10-20 1-11900 <$125
1902 Plain Back
4x5 7251-30009 <$125
3x10-20 11901-32276 <$125
1929 Small Size
10 Type 1 1-3858 <$65
20 Type 1 1-1208 <$65
10 Type 2 1-5503 <$75
20 Type 2 1-1532 <$75
Total Issue $4,376,930
Out in 1935 $144,550
Large out 1935 $7,310
****
2404 Middlesex
PEOPLES NB OF MARLBOROUGH
{{ 14 L 12 S }}
Chartered 12/11/76
Series 1875 <$VALUE
4x5 1-27281 <$350
Brown Back
4x5 1-10750 <$200
3x10-20 1-10300 <$200
1882 Date Back
4x5 1-15750 <$200
3x10-20 1-9400 <$200
1882 Value Back
4x5 15751-21235 <$225
3x10-20 9401-12094 <$225
1902 Plain Back
4x5 1-25105 <$100
3x10-20 1-15277 <$100
1929 Small Size
5 Type 1 1-5328 <$75
10 Type 1 1-2908 <$75
20 Type 1 1-732 <$85
5 Type 2 1-9140 <$100
10 Type 2 1-4222 <$100
20 Type 2 1-837 <$100
Total Issue $4,097,790
Out in 1935 $122,055
Large out 1935 $1,035
****
12979 Suffolk
FNB IN MEDFORD
{{ 0 L 10 S }}
Chartered 8/26
1902 Plain Back <$VALUE
4x5 1-1275 <$750
1929 Small Size
5 Type 1 1-13558 <$100
5 Type 2 1-67040 <$100
Total Issue $767,440
Out in 1935 $200,000
Large out 1935 $70
****
5247 Suffolk
MEDFORD NB, MEDFORD
{{ 2 L }}
Chartered 1/23/00
Liquidated 10/31/08
Brown Back <$VALUE
4x5 1-6365 <$750
3x10-20 1-4268 <$750
Total Issue $340,700
Out in 1910 $13,150
****
4769 Suffolk
MELROSE NB, MELROSE
{{ 3 L }}
Chartered 1892
Liquidated 1/22/16
Brown Back <$VALUE
4x5 1-10750 <$600
4x10 1-2850 <$600
3x10-20 1-1330 <$600
1882 Date Back
4x5 1-4307 <$550
4x10 1-4017 <$550
3x10-20 1-300 <$550
1902 Date Back
4x10 1-9600 <$400
1902 Plain Back
4x10 9601-9696 <$400
Total Issue $1,045,160
Out in 1916 $58,970
****
268 Essex
FNB OF AMESBURY, MERRIMAC
Chartered 1864
2nd title: FNB of Merrimac 3/77
FIRST TITLE {{ 2 L }}
Original Series <$VALUE
3x1-2 1-300 <$500/$1000
4x5 1-5740 <$500
2x10-20-50 1-1930
<$750/$1250/$3500
Series 1875
4x5 1-2000 <$500
SECOND TITLE {{ 4 L 3 S }}
Series 1875
4x5 1-6750 <$500
2x10-20-50 1-1653
<$600/$1000/$3500
Brown Back
4x5 1-13546 <$300
3x10-20 1-6290 <$300
50-100 1-602 <$1250/$1500
1902 Red Seal
4x5 1-2355 <$350
3x10-20 1-1688 <$350
1902 Date Back
4x5 1-4500* <$175
3x10-20 1-3500** <$175
1902 Plain Back
4x5 4751-12825* <$175
3x10-20 3661-8998** <$175
* 4501-4750 not marked
** 3501-3660 not marked
1929 Small Size
5 Type 1 1-1812 <$125
10 Type 1 1-988 <$125
20 Type 1 1-238 <$125
5 Type 2 1-1750 <$150
10 Type 2 1-1215 <$150
20 Type 2 1-340 <$150
Total Issue $2,297,290
Out in 1935 $48,800
Large out 1935 $5,530
****
FNB of Merrimac
SEE Ch 268
FNB of Amesbury, Merrimac
****
12800 Essex
METHUEN NB, METHUEN
{{ 6 L 11 S }}
Organized 6/30/25
1902 Plain Back <$VALUE
4x5 1-5745 <$175
3x10-20 1-3856 <$175
1929 Small Size
5 Type 1 1-3294 <$65
10 Type 1 1-1934 <$65
20 Type 1 1-472 <$75
5 Type 2 1-5744 <$85
10 Type 2 1-2737 <$85
20 Type 2 1-805 <$85
Total Issue $651,390
Out in 1935 $100,000
Large out 1935 $6,070
Outstanding includes Ch 1485
****
1485 Essex
NB OF METHUEN
{{ 8 L }}
Chartered 1865
Liquidated 8/1/25
Original Series <$VALUE
4x5 1-2500 <$400
3x10-20 1-2001 <$750/$1250
Series 1875
4x5 1-1710 <$400
3x10-20 1-2655 <$600/$1000
Brown Back
4x5 1-11250 <$250
3x10-20 1-4020 <$250
1902 Red Seal
4x5 1-2900 <$300
3x10-20 1-1700 <$300
1902 Date Back
4x5 1-7650 <$150
3x10-20 1-5300 <$150
1902 Plain Back
4x5 7651-21275 <$150
3x10-20 5301-13966 <$150
Total Issue $2,009,800
Out at close $100,000
Ch 12800 assumed circulation
****
3994 Plymouth
MIDDLEBOROUGH NB, MIDDLEBOROUGH
{{ 4 L }}
Chartered 3/20/89
Liquidated 6/30/16
Brown Back <$VALUE
4x5 1-6125 <$450
3x10-20 1-2340 <$450
1902 Date Back
4x5 1-4700 <$250
4x10 1-4650 <$250
1902 Plain Back
4x5 4701-4866 <$250
4x10 4651-4838 <$250
Total Issue $530,340
Out in 1916 $27,900
****
2275 Worcester
HOME NB OF MILFORD
{{ 50+ L 10 S }}
Chartered 6/12/75
Original Series <$VALUE
3x10-20 1-800 <$750/$1250
50-100 1-300 <$3500
Series 1875
3x1-2 1-5510 <$275/$850
4x5 1-10132 <$350
3x10-20 1-4432 <$600/$1000
50-100 1-362 <$3500
Brown Back
4x5 1-5800 <$200
3x10-20 1-8179 <$200
50-100 1-867 <$1250/$1500
1882 Date Back
4x5 1-11184 <$200
3x10-20 1-6470 <$200
50-100 1-57 <$1250/$1500
1902 Date Back
4x5 1-2250 <$150
3x10-20 1-1800 <$150
1902 Plain Back
4x5 2251-21200 <$150
3x10-20 1801-14251 <$150
1929 Small Size
5 Type 1 1-3898 <$125
10 Type 1 1-2322 <$125
20 Type 1 1-524 <$125
5 Type 2 1 5162 <$150
10 Type 2 1-2499 <$150
20 Type 2 1-570 <$150
Total Issue $3,319,710
Out in 1935 $97,950
Large out 1935 $6,180
****
866 Worcester
MILFORD NB, MILFORD
Chartered 3/7/65
2nd title:Milford NB & TC 5/16/28
FIRST TITLE {{ 11 L }}
Original Series <$VALUE
3x1-2 1-4810 <$300/$800
4x5 1-7275 <$300
3x10-20 1-3515 <$750/$1250
50-100 1-595 <$3500
Series 1875
4x5 1-4325 <$300
3x10-20 1-4530 <$600/$1000
50-100 1-505 <$3500
Brown Back
4x5 1-3500 <$200
3x10-20 1-26800 <$200
1902 Red Seal
3x10-20 1-11500 <$250
1902 Date Back
3x10-20 1-20500 <$125
1902 Plain Back
3x10-20 20501-42367 <$125
SECOND TITLE {{ 0 L 10 S }}
1902 Plain Back
3x10-20 1-1272 <$350
1929 Small Size
10 Type 1 1-3178 <$100
20 Type 1 1-862 <$100
10 Type 2 1-1390 <$125
20 Type 2 1-541 <$125
Total Issue $5,309,090
Out in 1935 $63,580
Large out 1935 $12,610
****

****
572 Worcester
MILLBURY NB, MILLBURY
{{ 6 L 5 S }}
Organized 10/25/64
Receivership 12/13/33
Original Series <$VALUE
3x1-2 1-6400 <$400/$1000
4x5 1-4900 <$500
3x10-20 1-2360 <$750/$1250
50-100 1-617 <$3500
Series 1875
3x1-2 1-1800 <$400/$1000
4x5 1-9250 <$500
3x10-20 1-3300 <$600/$1000
Brown Back
4x5 1-13883 <$350
3x10-20 1-4083 <$350
1902 Red Seal
4x5 1-3750 <$400
3x10-20 1-2660 <$400
1902 Date Back
4x5 1-3650 <$250
3x10-20 1-3110 <$250
1902 Plain Back
4x5 3651-12872 <$250
3x10-20 3111-9401 <$250
1929 Small Size
5 Type 1 1-1749 <$200
10 Type 1 1-969 <$200
20 Type 1 1-260 <$200
Total Issue $2,258,660
Out at close $50,000
Large out at close $5,600
****
13835 Worcester
MILLBURY NB, MILLBURY
{{ 3 S }}
Chartered 11/33
1929 Small Size <$VALUE
5 Type 2 1-4810 <$250
10 Type 2 1-2175 <$250
20 Type 2 1-740 <$250
Total Issue $60,600
Out in 1935 $37,800
****
Blue Hill NB of Milton
SEE Ch 684
Blue Hill NB of Dorchester, Boston
****
503 Hampden
MONSON NB, MONSON
{{ 4 L 7 S }}
Chartered 1864
Original Series <$VALUE
4x5 1-5500 <$500
3x10-20 1-3100 <$750/$1250
50-100 1-300 <$3500
Series 1875
4x5 1-7000 <$500
3x10-20 1-2430 <$600/$1000
Brown Back
4x5 1-26856 <$400
3x10-20 1-9362 <$400
1902 Red Seal
4x5 1-6700 <$450
3x10-20 1-4620 <$450
1902 Date Back
4x5 1-9850 <$225
3x10-20 1-5260 <$225
1902 Plain Back
4x5 9851-17560 <$225
3x10-20 5261-10412 <$225
1929 Small Size
5 Type 1 1-1720 <$100
10 Type 1 1-796 <$100
20 Type 1 1-222 <$100
5 Type 2 1-2082 <$125
10 Type 2 1-1247 <$125
20 Type 2 1-324 <$125
Total Issue $2,968,880
Out in 1935 $49,200
Large out 1935 $6,760
****
714 Nantucket
PACIFIC NB OF NANTUCKET
{{ 37 L 6 S }}
Chartered 1865
Original Series <$VALUE
3x1-2 1-4300 <$450/$1250
4x5 1-5700 <$500
3x10-20 1-2740 <$750/$1250
50-100 1-400 <$3500
Series 1875
3x1-2 1-702 <$450/$1250
4x5 1-2980 <$500
3x10-20 1-1144 <$600/$1000
50-100 1-12 <$3500
Brown Back
4x5 1-6245 <$400
3x10-20 1-2240 <$400
50-100 1-391 <$1250/$1500
1902 Red Seal
4x5 1-1800 <$500
3x10-20 1-1260 <$500
1902 Date Back
4x5 1-3615 <$250
3x10-20 1-2894 <$250
1902 Plain Back
4x5 3616-10810 <$250
3x10-20 2895-7594 <$250
1929 Small Size
5 Type 1 1-1730 <$175
10 Type 1 1-920 <$175
20 Type 1 1-226 <$175
5 Type 2 1-1540 <$200
10 Type 2 1-1104 <$200
20 Type 2 1-245 <$200
Total Issue $1,602,920
Out at close $48,750
Large out at close $6,245
****
2107 Middlesex
NATICK NB, NATICK
{{ 5 L }}
Chartered 5/14/73
Liquidated 9/2/16
Original Series <$VALUE
4x5 1-3500 <$500
3x10-20 1-740 <$750/$1250
50-100 1-220 <$3500
Series 1875
4x5 1-5791 <$500
3x10-20 1-2360 <$600/$1000
50-100 1-294 <$3500
Brown Back
4x5 1-12130 <$400
3x10-20 1-3032 <$400
1882 Date Back
4x5 1-4800 <$350
3x10-20 1-2826 <$350
50-100 1-25 <$1250/$1500
1902 Date Back
4x5 1-3750 <$225
3x10-20 1-2700 <$225
1902 Plain Back
4x5 3751-4460 <$225
3x10-20 2701-3191 <$225
Total Issue $1,518,220
Out in 1916 $79,550
****
2262 Bristol
CITIZENS NB OF NEW BEDFORD
{{ 3 L }}
Chartered 5/17/75
Liquidated 2/21/99
Original Series <$VALUE
4x5 1-1750 <$500
3x10-20 1-2000 <$750/$1250
Series 1875
3x1-2 1-11460 <$400/$1000
4x5 1-17810 <$500
3x10-20 1-15564<$600/$1000
Brown Back
4x5 1-8101 <$450
Total Issue $1,488,720
Out in 1910 $6,985
****
261 Bristol
FNB OF NEW BEDFORD
{{ 33 L 3U + 21 S }}
Chartered 1864
Original Series <$VALUE
4x5 1-17500 <$350
4x10 1-11300 <$750
2x20-50-100 1-2300
<$1250/$3500/$3500
Series 1875
3x1-2 1-20000 <$275/$750
4x5 1-10700 <$350
4x10 1-5000 <$600
4x20 1-4421 <$1000
2x20-50-100 1-500
<$1000/$3500/$3500
Brown Back
4x5 1-92355 <$175
3x10-20 1-39359 <$175/$225
1902 Red Seal
4x5 1-31808 <$175
3x10-20 1-22676 <$175/$225
1902 Date Back
4x5 1-49830 <$60
3x10-20 1-34668 <$65
1902 Plain Back
4x5 49831-137065 <$60
3x10-20 34669-88779 <$65
1929 Small Size
5 Type 1 1-16886 <$30
10 Type 1 1-9380 <$35
20 Type 1 1-2428 <$45
5 Type 2 1-11982 <$30
10 Type 2 1-4622 <$35
20 Type 2 1-1456 <$45
Total Issue $16,462,930
Out in 1935 $272,950
Large out 1935 $55,160
****
743 Bristol
MECHANICS NB OF NEW BEDFORD
{{ 11 L }}
Chartered 1/23/65
Closed 2/24/19
Original Series <$VALUE
3x1-2 1-7000 <$350/$750
4x5 1-8875 <$375
3x10-20 1-6700 <$750/$1250
3x10-20 7951-13950
<$750/$1250
20 6701-7950 <$1250
50-100 1-950 <$3500
500 1-150 <$150,000
Series 1875
3x1-2 1-5500 <$350/$750
4x5 1-3500 <$375
3x10-20 1-9040 <$600/$1000
50-100 1-670 <$3500
500 1-50 <$150,000
Brown Back
4x5 1-37545 <$250
3x10-20 1-15034 <$250
50-100 1-951 <$1250/$1500
1902 Red Seal
4x5 1-11500 <$300
3x10-20 1-7500 <$300
1902 Date Back
4x5 1-24750 <$100
3x10-20 1-18300 <$100
1902 Plain Back
4x5 24751-32145 <$100
3x10-20 18301-22348 <$100
Total Issue $5,775,450
Out at close $279,995
****
799 Bristol
MERCHANTS NB OF NEW BEDFORD
{{ 18 L 24 S }}
Chartered 2/14/65
Original Series <$VALUE
3x1-2 1-5000 <$275/$750
4x5 1-12537 <$300
3x10-20 1-15400<$750/$1250
50-100 1-2699 <$3500
50 2700 <$3500
500 1-40 <$150,000
Series 1875
3x10-20 1-11900<$600/$1000
4x20 1-3922 <$750
50 1-5565 <$3500
Brown Back
4x5 1-47428 <$225
3x10-20 1-25570 <$225
50-100 1-1650 <$1250/$1500
1902 Red Seal
4x5 1-21050 <$250
3x10-20 1-12970 <$250
50-100 1-360 <$1500
1902 Date Back
4x5 1-53330 <$100
3x10-20 1-34268 <$100
3x50-100 1-1000 <$350/$400
1902 Plain Back
4x5 53331-155099 <$100
3x10-20 34269-96561 <$100
1929 Small Size
5 Type 1 1-25904 <$30
10 Type 1 1-13260 <$35
20 Type 1 1-3664 <$45
5 Type 2 1-6804 <$30
10 Type 2 1-4356 <$35
20 Type 2 1-2160 <$45
Total Issue $16,568,920
Out in 1935 $515,365
Large out 1935 $45,240
****
690 Bristol
NB OF COMMERCE, NEW BEDFORD
{{ U + 6 L }}
Chartered 1/9/65
Liquidated 4/1/98
Original Series <$VALUE
3x1-2 1-7550 <$300/$850
4x5 1-16300 <$350
3x10-20 1-5100 <$750/$1250
3x10-20 7101-15106
<$750/$1250
20 5101-7100 <$1250
50-100 1-1250 <$3500
500-1000 1-30
<$150,000/$200,000
Series 1875
3x1-2 1-5000 <$300/$850
4x5 1-10000 <$350
3x10-20 1-19419<$600/$1000
50-100 1-200 <$3500
Brown Back
4x5 1-16941 <$250
3x10-20 1-6600 <$250/$275
50-100 1-166 <$1250/$1500
Total Issue $3,211,070
Out in 1910 $16,280
****
12405 Bristol
SAFE DEPOSIT NB OF NEW BEDFORD
{{ 7 L 12 S }}
Chartered 7/23
1902 Plain Back <$VALUE
4x5 1-33995 <$175
3x10-20 1-19686 <$175
3x50-100 1-1004 <$500/$600
1929 Small Size
5 Type 1 1-9534 <$60
10 Type 1 1-5284 <$60
20 Type 1 1-1546 <$70
50 Type 1 1-242 <$250
100 Type 1 1-90 <$325
5 Type 2 1-7420 <$75
10 Type 2 1-3951 <$75
20 Type 2 1-700 <$75
Total Issue $2,920,990
Out in 1935 $215,560
Large out 1935 $3,810
****
F & Ocean NB of Newburyport
SEE Ch 1011
Ocean NB of Newburyport
****
279 Essex
FNB OF NEWBURYPORT
{{ 3 L }}
Chartered 1864
Liquidated 6/29/22
Original Series <$VALUE
3x1-2 1-5320 <$450/$1000
4x5 1-10000 <$500
3x10-20 1-4800 <$750/$1250
50-100 1-1200 <$3500
Series 1875
4x5 1-7086 <$500
3x10-20 1-2478 <$600/$1000
Brown Back
3x10-20 1-10746 <$400
1902 Red Seal
3x10-20 1-6600 <$450
1902 Date Back
3x10-20 1-12400 <$200
1902 Plain Back
3x10-20 12401-23336 <$200
Total Issue $2,946,320
Out at close $140,500
****
584 Essex
MECHANICKS NB OF NEWBURYPORT
{{ 4 L }}
Chartered 11/23/64
Liquidated 7/17/00
Original Series <$VALUE
3x1-2 1-3600 <$400/$1000
4x5 1-6250 <$500
3x10-20 1-3690 <$750/$1250
50-100 1-1110 <$3500
Series 1875
3x1-2 1-400 <$400/$1000
4x5 1-3091 <$500
3x10-20 1-3380 <$600/$1000
50-100 1-1069 <$3500
Brown Back
4x5 1-4249 <$400
50-100 1-845 <$1250/$1500
Total Issue $1,098,900
Out in 1910 $6,819
****
1047 Essex
MERCHANTS NB OF NEWBURYPORT
{{ 8 L 9 S }}
Chartered 1865
Original Series <$VALUE
4x5 1-3000 <$375
3x10-20 1-1800 <$750/$1250
50-100 1-300 <$3500
Series 1875
4x5 1-4133 <$375
3x10-20 1-1060 <$600/$1000
50-100 1-400 <$3500
Brown Back
4x5 1-7338 <$250
3x10-20 1-4317 <$250
1902 Red Seal
4x5 1-2580 <$300
3x10-20 1-1868 <$300
1902 Date Back
4x5 1-7500 <$150
3x10-20 1-5800 <$150
1902 Plain Back
4x5 7501-30203 <$150
3x10-20 5801-15437 <$150
1929 Small Size
5 Type 1 1-3884 <$75
10 Type 1 1-2146 <$75
20 Type 1 1-628 <$85
5 Type 2 1-5602 <$85
10 Type 2 1-2861 <$85
20 Type 2 1-925 <$100
Total Issue $2,669,940
Out in 1935 $100,140
Large out 1935 $6,250
****
1011 Essex
OCEAN NB OF NEWBURYPORT
Chartered 4/14/65
2nd title:F & Ocean NB of Newburyport 7/1/22
FIRST TITLE {{ 3 L }}
Original Series <$VALUE
4x5 1-3275 <$500
3x10-20 1-1600 <$750/$1250
50-100 1-670 <$3500
Series 1875
4x5 1-2600 <$500
3x10-20 1-1917 <$600/$1000
50-100 1-699 <$3500
Brown Back
4x5 1-5550 <$400
3x10-20 1-2636 <$400
50-100 1-944 <$1250/$1500
1902 Red Seal
4x5 1-3025 <$500
3x10-20 1-1300 <$500
50-100 1-270 <$2250/$2500
1902 Date Back
4x5 1-6800 <$250
3x10-20 1-4780 <$250
3x50-100 1-240 <$500/$600
1902 Plain Back
4x5 6801-14400 <$250
3x10-20 4781-9120 <$250
SECOND TITLE {{ 1 L 11 S }}
1902 Plain Back
4x5 1-8728 <$300
3x10-20 1-6007 <$300
1929 Small Size
5 Type 1 1-3590 <$75
10 Type 1 1-1836 <$75
20 Type 1 1-528 <$85
5 Type 2 1-2178 <$100
10 Type 2 1-1086 <$100
20 Type 2 1-280 <$100
Total Issue $2,636,580
Out in 1935 $63,020
Large out 1935 $7,160
****
FNB of Newton
SEE Ch 3598
FNB of West Newton, Newton
****
3598 Suffolk
FNB OF WEST NEWTON, NEWTON
Chartered 12/8/86
Liquidated 2/16/31
2nd title:FNB of Newton 7/15/29
FIRST TITLE {{ 4 L }}
Brown Back <$VALUE
4x5 1-12750 <$400
3x10-20 1-7553 <$400
1902 Red Seal
4x5 1-2380 <$450
3x10-20 1-1348 <$450
1902 Date Back
4x5 1-9450 <$250
3x10-20 1-6940 <$250
1902 Plain Back
4x5 9451-29392 <$250
3x10-20 6941-20684 <$250
SECOND TITLE {{ 4 S }}
1929 Small Size
5 Type 1 1-1764 <$165
10 Type 1 1-779 <$165
20 Type 1 1-252 <$165
Total Issue $2,489,990
Out at close $92,400
Large out at close $8,870
****
789 Suffolk
NEWTON NB, NEWTON
{{ 1 L }}
Chartered 2/8/65
Liquidated 5/15/08
Original Series <$VALUE
3x1-2 1-6600 <$750/$1500
4x5 1-4450 <$850
3x10-20 1-2350<$1000/$1250
50-100 1-240 <$3500
Series 1875
3x1-2 1-1000 <$750/$1500
4x5 1-4350 <$850
3x10-20 1-3783<$1000/$1250
50-100 1-379 <$3500
Brown Back
4x5 1-12461 <$650
3x10-20 1-5618 <$650
1902 Red Seal
4x5 1-1665 <$750
3x10-20 1-1210 <$750
Total Issue $1,237,420
Out in 1910 $12,750
****
13252 Suffolk
NEWTON NB, NEWTON
{{ 13 L 23 S }}
Chartered 11/28
1902 Plain Back <$VALUE
4x5 1-5127 <$100
1929 Small Size
5 Type 1 1-8610 <$45
10 Type 1 1-3056 <$45
20 Type 1 1-634 <$50
5 Type 2 1-21648 <$50
10 Type 2 1-5744 <$50
Total Issue $785,960
Out in 1935 $162,050
Large out 1935 $870
****
488 Suffolk
FNB OF NEWTON, NEWTONVILLE
{{ 1 L }}
Chartered 7/27/64
Liquidated 3/11/67
Original Series <$VALUE
3x1-2 1-350 <$1000/$1500
4x5 1-2000 <$1000
3x10-20 1-1765<$1250/$1500
Total Issue $130,000
Out in 1910 $1,058
Ch 1675 assumed circulation
****
1210 Berkshire
ADAMS NB OF NORTH ADAMS
Organized 5/4/65
2nd title:North Adams NB, North Adams 5/4/05
FIRST TITLE {{ 5 L }}
Original Series <$VALUE
3x1-2 1-6000 <$350/$850
4x5 1-7750 <$400
4x10 1-4375 <$750
3x20-50 1-1680<$1250/$3500
50-100 1-334 <$3500
Series 1875
4x5 1-3800 <$400
4x10 1-5548 <$600
3x20-50 1-3808<$1000/$3500
50-100 1-400 <$3500
Brown Back
3x10-20 1-55593 <$300
SECOND TITLE {{ 8 L 13 S }}
1902 Red Seal
4x5 1-20750 <$300
3x10-20 1-11600 <$300
1902 Date Back
4x5 1-25750 <$150
3x10-20 1-19800 <$150
1902 Plain Back
4x5 25751-72555 <$150
3x10-20 19801-53889 <$150
1929 Small Size
5 Type 1 1-11304 <$50
10 Type 1 1-5206 <$50
20 Type 1 1-1610 <$60
5 Type 2 1-16298 <$50
10 Type 2 1-8202 <$50
20 Type 2 1-2748 <$60
Total Issue $10,355,050
Out in 1935 $300,000
Large out 1935 $22,750
****
2396 Berkshire
BERKSHIRE NB OF NORTH ADAMS
{{ 6 L }}
Chartered 8/29/78
Liquidated 11/21/04
Series 1875 <$VALUE
3x1-2 1-3000 <$400/$1000
4x5 1-31336 <$450
Brown Back
4x5 1-3930 <$350
3x10-20 1-3721 <$350
Total Issue $906,370
Out in 1910 $7,862
****
North Adams NB, North Adams
SEE Ch 1210
Adams NB of North Adams
****

****
7675 Bristol
JEWELERS' NB OF
NORTH ATTLEBOROUGH
{{ 1 L }}
Chartered 3/31/05
Receivership 12/20/07
1902 Red Seal <$VALUE
4x5 1-2995 <$1500
3x10-20 1-2268 <$1500
Total Issue $173,300
Out in 1916 $1,370
****
9086 Bristol
MANUFACTURERS NB OF
NORTH ATTLEBOROUGH
{{ 9 L 8 S }}
Chartered 3/08
1902 Red Seal <$VALUE
4x5 1-625 <$350
3x10-20 1-500 <$350
1902 Date Back
4x5 1-11600 <$125
3x10-20 1-8380 <$125
1902 Plain Back
4x5 11601-30767 <$125
3x10-20 8381-21291 <$125
1929 Small Size
5 Type 1 1-4012 <$75
10 Type 1 1-2106 <$75
20 Type 1 1-524 <$85
5 Type 2 1-5570 <$85
10 Type 2 1-3072 <$85
20 Type 2 1-1092 <$85
Total Issue $2,107,400
Out in 1935 $98,050
Large out 1935 $3,200
****
3365 Bristol
NORTH ATTLEBOROUGH NB,
NORTH ATTLEBOROUGH
{{ 1 L }}
Chartered 7/11/85
Liquidated 4/1/05
Brown Back <$VALUE
4x5 1-12808 <$750
3x10-20 1-2537 <$750
Total Issue $383,010
Out in 1910 $4,520
****
416 Bristol
FNB OF EASTON,
NORTH EASTON
{{ 12 L 11 S }}
Chartered 1864
Original Series <$VALUE
3x1-2 1-13300 <$350/$850
4x5 1-7550 <$400
3x10-20 1-4300 <$750/$1250
50-100 1-800 <$3500
Series 1875
3x1-2 1-7980 <$350/$850
4x5 1-5250 <$400
3x10-20 1-4200 <$600/$1000
50-100 1-250 <$3500
Brown Back
4x5 1-23907 <$300
3x10-20 1-12045 <$300
50-100 1-1006 <$1250/$1500
1902 Red Seal
4x5 1-8325 <$350
3x10-20 1-5970 <$350
1902 Date Back
4x5 1-11750 <$175
3x10-20 1-8300 <$175
1902 Plain Back
4x5 11751-29781 <$175
3x10-20 8301-20182 <$175
1929 Small Size
5 Type 1 1-3664 <$75
10 Type 1 1-1766 <$75
20 Type 1 1-476 <$85
5 Type 2 1-3988 <$85
10 Type 2 1-2394 <$85
20 Type 2 1-756 <$85
Total Issue $4,577,910
Out in 1935 $98,095
Large out 1935 $12,085
****
383 Hampshire
FNB OF NORTHAMPTON
{{ 14 L 5 S }}
Chartered 1864
Original Series <$VALUE
3x1-2 1-6200 <$250/$800
4x5 1-11700 <$350
3x10-20 1-9100 <$750/$1250
50-100 1-500 <$3500
Series 1875
3x1-2 1-8032 <$250/$800
4x5 1-582 <$350
3x10-20 1-10604<$600/$1000
Brown Back
4x5 1-11045 <$200
3x10-20 1-9776 <$200
1902 Red Seal
4x5 1-7100 <$250
3x10-20 1-4840 <$250
1902 Date Back
4x5 1-12000 <$125
3x10-20 1-6800 <$125
1902 Plain Back
4x5 12001-29175 <$125
3x10-20 6801-16974 <$125
1929 Small Size
5 Type 1 1-1322 <$125
10 Type 1 1-786 <$125
20 Type 1 1-218 <$150
5 Type 2 1-2044 <$150
10 Type 2 1-940 <$150
20 Type 2 1-185 <$175
Total Issue $4,039,200
Out in 1935 $43,850
Large out 1935 $12,170
****
418 Hampshire
HAMPSHIRE COUNTY NB OF
NORTHAMPTON
{{ 5 L }}
Organized 4/6/64
Liquidated 3/22/20
Original Series <$VALUE
3x1-2 1-1000 <$400/$850
4x5 1-10600 <$400
3x10-20 1-4500 <$750/$1250
Series 1875
3x1-2 1-3000 <$400/$850
4x5 1-3000 <$400
3x10-20 1-4090 <$600/$1000
Brown Back
4x5 1-6000 <$350
3x10-20 1-15541* <$350
* 13634-14800 not issued
1902 Red Seal
3x10-20 1-2900 <$400
1902 Date Back
3x10-20 1-14400 <$200
1902 Plain Back
3x10-20 14401-20785 <$200
Total Issue $2,744,450
Out at close $137,600
****
1018 Hampshire
NORTHAMPTON NB OF
NORTHAMPTON
Chartered 1865
2nd title:Northampton NB &
TC 8/1/30
FIRST TITLE {{ 17 L 6 S }}
Original Series <$VALUE
3x1-2 1-10000 <$250/$750
4x5 1-13650 <$300
3x10-20 1-4450 <$750/$1250
50-100 1-385 <$3500
Series 1875
3x1-2 1-5000 <$250/$750
4x5 1-8880 <$300
3x10-20 1-3633 <$600/$1000
Brown Back
4x5 1-27654 <$200
3x10-20 1-4959 <$200
1902 Red Seal
4x5 1-6850 <$250
3x10-20 1-4960 <$250
1902 Date Back
4x5 1-17250 <$125
3x10-20 1-11600 <$125
1902 Plain Back
4x5 17251-33285 <$125
3x10-20 11601-22536 <$125
1929 Small Size
5 Type 1 1-1538 <$125
10 Type 1 1-778 <$125
20 Type 1 1-260 <$125
SECOND TITLE {{ 5 S }}
1929 Small Size
5 Type 1 1-2130 <$100
10 Type 1 1-976 <$100
20 Type 1 1-244 <$100
5 Type 2 1-5150 <$100
10 Type 2 1-3114 <$100
20 Type 2 1-696 <$100
Total Issue $4,312,320
Out in 1935 $97,550
Large out 1935 $11,740
****
1279 Worcester
NORTHBOROUGH NB,
NORTHBOROUGH
{{ 6 L 5 S }}
Chartered 1865
Original Series <$VALUE
3x1-2 1-3010 <$400/$1000
4x5 1-3550 <$400
3x10-20 1-1305 <$750/$1250
50-100 1-203 <$3500
Series 1875
3x1-2 1-2328 <$400/$1000
4x5 1-4573 <$400
3x10-20 1-600 <$600/$1000
50-100 1-49 <$3500
Brown Back
4x5 1-8599 <$250
3x10-20 1-7396 <$250/$300
1902 Red Seal
4x5 1-4850 <$300
3x10-20 1-3060 <$300
1902 Date Back
4x5 1-7450 <$150
3x10-20 1-5700 <$150
1902 Plain Back
4x5 7451-25894 <$150
3x10-20 5701-18342 <$150
1929 Small Size
5 Type 1 1-3878 <$100
10 Type 1 1-1904 <$100
20 Type 1 1-452 <$100
5 Type 2 1-5168 <$100
10 Type 2 1-3144 <$100
20 Type 2 1-756 <$110
Total Issue $2,906,180
Out in 1935 $98,350
Large out 1935 $5,160
****
8474 Norfolk
NORWOOD NB, NORWOOD
{{ 2 L }}
Chartered 12/06
Liquidated 7/2/17
1902 Red Seal <$VALUE
4x5 1-2950 <$850
3x10-20 1-2260 <$850
1902 Date Back
4x5 1-11250 <$400
3x10-20 1-8200 <$400
1902 Plain Back
4x5 11251-13355 <$400
3x10-20 8201-9318 <$400
Total Issue $905,000
Out at close $98,950
****
2255 Franklin
ORANGE NB, ORANGE
{{ 10 L 6 S }}
Chartered 5/10/75
Original Series <$VALUE
3x1-2 1-2000 <$350/$750
4x5 1-1175 <$375
Series 1875
3x1-2 1-1000 <$350/$750
4x5 1-17659 <$375
Brown Back
4x5 1-11900 <$300
3x10-20 1-5040 <$300/$350
1882 Date Back
4x5 1-8035 <$300
3x10-20 1-5761 <$300/$350
1902 Date Back
4x5 1-1665 <$150
3x10-20 1-1334 <$150
1902 Plain Back
4x5 1666-19020 <$150
3x10-20 1335-12962 <$150
1929 Small Size
5 Type 1 1-3950 <$85
10 Type 1 1-1948 <$85
20 Type 1 1-470 <$100
5 Type 2 1-3868 <$100
10 Type 2 1-2909 <$100
20 Type 2 1-610 <$100
Total Issue $2,711,340
Out in 1935 $83,250
Large out 1935 $5,740
****
764 Worcester
OXFORD NB, OXFORD
{{ 5 L }}
Chartered 1/28/65
Liquidated 1/2/05
Original Series <$VALUE
3x1-2 1-400 <$400/$850
4x5 1-6000 <$400
3x10-20 1-1400 <$750/$1250
Series 1875
3x1-2 1-3240 <$400/$850
4x5 1-5350 <$400
3x10-20 1-912 <$600/$1000
Brown Back
4x5 1-11636 <$350
3x10-20 1-919 <$350/$400
Total Issue $657,470
Out in 1910 $4,192
****
2324 Hampden
PALMER NB, PALMER
{{ 15 L 9 S }}
Chartered 2/14/76
Series 1875 <$VALUE
3x1-2 1-2910 <$300/$750
4x5 1-11566 <$325
3x10-20 1-3809 <$600/$1000
Brown Back
4x5 1-15930 <$200
3x10-20 1-6528 <$200/$225
1882 Date Back
4x5 1-7850 <$200
3x10-20 1-5880 <$200/$225
1882 Value Back
4x5 7851-8277 <$250
3x10-20 5881-6252 <$250
1902 Plain Back
4x5 1-30959 <$125
4x10 1-11725 <$125
1929 Small Size
5 Type 1 1-13156 <$75
5 Type 2 1-29504 <$85
Total Issue $3,189,840
Out in 1935 $98,500
Large out 1935 $5,440
****
958 Essex
SOUTH DANVERS NB OF
PEABODY
{{ 8 L }}
Chartered 3/31/65
Receivership 9/19/00
Original Series <$VALUE
3x1-2 1-6700 <$325/$750
4x5 1-5700 <$350
3x10-20 1-2500 <$750/$1250
50-100 1-360 <$3500
Series 1875
3x1-2 1-2830 <$325/$750
4x5 1-4550 <$350
3x10-20 1-991 <$600/$1000
50-100 1-320 <$3500
Brown Back
4x5 1-8352 <$275
3x10-20 1-1921 <$275/$325
50-100 1-439 <$1250/$1500
Total Issue $858,140
Out in 1916 $3,838
****
Warren NB of Peabody
SEE Ch 616
Warren NB of South Danvers
****
5964 Middlesex
FNB OF PEPPERELL
{{ 2 L 2 S }}
Chartered 9/12/01
Liquidated 3/1/34
Brown Back <$VALUE
3x10-20 1-1700 <$600
1882 Date Back
3x10-20 1-4700 <$600
1882 Value Back
3x10-20 4701-7948 <$600
1902 Plain Back
3x10-20 1-5734 <$450
1929 Small Size
10 Type 1 1-1316 <$350
20 Type 1 1-352 <$350
10 Type 2 1-455 <$375
20 Type 2 1-95 <$375
Total Issue $896,750
Out at close $45,250
Large out at close $2,430
****
1082 Berkshire
AGRICULTURAL NB OF
PITTSFIELD
{{ 14 L }}
Chartered 1865
Original Series <$VALUE
3x1-2 1-7750 <$275/$750
4x5 1-11100 <$300
3x10-20 1-1000 <$750/$1250
3x10-20 1251-200<$750/$1250
20 1001-1250 <$1250
50-100 1-484 <$3500
Series 1875
3x1-2 1-3860 <$275/$750
4x5 1-7660 <$300
3x10-20 1-2101 <$600/$1000
50-100 1-140 <$3500
Brown Back
4x5 1-11678 <$225
3x10-20 1-9416 <$225/$275
50-100 1-990 <$1250/$1500
1902 Red Seal
3x10-20 1-3500 <$300
1902 Date Back
3x10-20 1-8800 <$150
1902 Plain Back
3x10-20 8801-29352 <$150
Total Issue $3,222,360
Out in 1935 $14,484
****
1260 Berkshire
PITTSFIELD NB, PITTSFIELD
Chartered 1865
2nd title:Pittsfield-Third
NB & TC 8/31/29
FIRST TITLE {{ 10 L }}
Original Series <$VALUE
3x1-2 1-14545 <$275/$750
4x5 1-13150 <$300
3x10-20 1-5300 <$750/$1250
50-100 1-1530 <$3500
Series 1875
4x5 1-6950 <$300
3x10-20 1-12158<$600/$1000
Brown Back
4x5 1-8666 <$225
3x10-20 1-8596 <$225/$275
50-100 1-375 <$1250/$1500
1902 Red Seal
3x10-20 1-1900 <$250/$300
1902 Date Back
3x10-20 1-6100 <$150
1902 Plain Back
3x10-20 6101-9481 <$150
SECOND TITLE {{ 11 S }}
1929 Small Size
5 Type 1 1-3816 <$65
10 Type 1 1-2366 <$65
20 Type 1 1-944 <$75
5 Type 2 1-10210 <$65
10 Type 2 1-5376 <$65
20 Type 2 1-1579 <$75
Total Issue $3,271,775
Out in 1935 $196,050
Large out 1935 $15,110
****
Pittsfield-Third NB & TC,
Pittsfield
SEE Ch 1260
Pittsfield NB, Pittsfield
****
2525 Berkshire
THIRD NB OF PITTSFIELD
{{ 7 L }}
Chartered 1881
Closed 8/31/29
Series 1875 <$VALUE
4x5 1-23421 <$400
3x10-20 1-468 <$600/$1000
Brown Back
4x5 1-3150 <$300
3x10-20 1-2820 <$300
1882 Date Back
4x5 1-5350 <$300
3x10-20 1-3660 <$300
1882 Value Back
4x5 5351-8080 <$300
3x10-20 3661-5213 <$300
1902 Plain Back
4x5 1-21812 <$100
Total Issue $1,554,310
Out at close $49,800
Ch 1260 assumed circulation
****
996 Plymouth
OLD COLONY NB OF PLYMOUTH
{{ 12 L 10 S }}
Chartered 4/8/65
Closed 11/10/34
Original Series <$VALUE
3x1-2 1-3000 <$275/$750
4x5 1-7850 <$350
3x10-20 1-3140 <$750/$1250
50-100 1-324 <$3500
Series 1875
4x5 1-4680 <$350
3x10-20 1-6254 <$600/$1000
Brown Back
4x5 1-24831 <$200
3x10-20 1-9980 <$200/$250
1902 Red Seal
4x5 1-8000 <$250
3x10-20 1-9000 <$250/$300
1902 Date Back
4x5 1-20500 <$75
3x10-20 1-14000 <$85
1902 Plain Back
4x5 20501-66735 <$75
3x10-20 14001-44756 <$85
1929 Small Size
5 Type 1 1-5432 <$50
10 Type 1 1-5542 <$50
20 Type 1 1-1552 <$60
5 Type 2 1-9896 <$50
10 Type 2 1-4421 <$50
20 Type 2 1-1292 <$65
Total Issue $6,762,570
Out at close $248,000
Large out at close $14,885
Ch 779 assumed circulation
****
779 Plymouth
PLYMOUTH NB, PLYMOUTH
{{ 11 L 20 S }}
Chartered 2/2/65
Original Series <$VALUE
3x1-2 1-2700 <$275/$750
4x5 1-2750 <$350
3x10-20 1-2050 <$750/$1250
3x10-20 2801-530<$750/$1250
20 2051-2800 <$1250
50-100 1-100 <$3500
Series 1875
3x10-20 1-3948 <$600/$1000
Brown Back
3x10-20 1-19051 <$200/$250
1902 Red Seal
3x10-20 1-6100 <$250/$300
1902 Date Back
4x5 1-3000 <$125
3x10-20 1-14100 <$125
1902 Plain Back
4x5 3001-31530 <$125
3x10-20 14101-32117 <$125
1929 Small Size
5 Type 1 1-5566 <$45
10 Type 1 1-3216 <$50
20 Type 1 1-820 <$55
5 Type 2 1-5444 <$45
10 Type 2 1-2908 <$50
20 Type 2 1-765 <$55
Total Issue $4,547,340
Out in 1935 $280,840
Large out 1935 $22,645
Outstanding includes Ch 996
****
736 Barnstable
FNB OF PROVINCETOWN
{{ 4 L 4 S }}
Chartered 1/21/65
Original Series <$VALUE
3x1-2 1-2990 <$500/$1250
4x5 1-3000 <$600
3x10-20 1-2000 <$750/$1250
50-100 1-1117 <$3500
Series 1875
4x5 1-6500 <$600
3x10-20 1-2800 <$750/$1250
Brown Back
4x5 1-16998 <$500
3x10-20 1-11383 <$500
1902 Red Seal
3x10-20 1-2000 <$500
1902 Date Back
3x10-20 1-3000 <$250
1902 Plain Back
3x10-20 3001-9254 <$250
1929 Small Size
10 Type 1 1-1152 <$175
20 Type 1 1-326 <$200
5 Type 2 1-1928 <$200
10 Type 2 1-922 <$200
20 Type 2 1-240 <$200
Total Issue $2,216,210
Out in 1935 $48,800
Large out 1935 $7,910
****
832 Suffolk
N GRANITE B OF QUINCY
{{ 2 L }}
Chartered 2/23/65
Liquidated 7/1/12
Original Series <$VALUE
3x1-2 1-5100 <$500/$1250
4x5 1-4500 <$600
3x10-20 1-1810 <$750/$1250
50-100 1-510 <$3500
Series 1875
4x5 1-4350 <$600
3x10-20 1-2453 <$750/$1250
50-100 1-200 <$3500
Brown Back
4x5 1-9735 <$500
3x10-20 1-10190 <$500
1902 Red Seal
3x10-20 1-6200 <$500
1902 Date Back
3x10-20 1-7314 <$250
Total Issue $1,902,050
Out in 1912 $99,145
****

CONDITION affects Value. The Values shown are for notes in FINE condition.

<$VALUEs are for notes in **FINE** condition. Value changes by approximately **25%** for a change of one full grade.

****
517 Suffolk
N MOUNT WOLLASTAN B OF QUINCY
{{ 15 L 12 S }}
Chartered 1864
Liquidated 12/31/34
Original Series <$VALUE
3x1-2 1-4920 <$400/$850
4x5 1-3700 <$450
3x10-20 1-2500 <$750/$1250
50-100 1-570 <$3500
Series 1875
4x5 1-3195 <$450
3x10-20 1-1768 <$600/$1000
Brown Back
4x5 1-11804 <$300
3x10-20 1-7885 <$300
50-100 1-630 <$1250/$1500
1902 Red Seal
4x5 1-5900 <$350
3x10-20 1-3880 <$350
50-100 1-180 <$2250/$2500
1902 Date Back
4x5 1-11000 <$175
3x10-20 1-7500 <$175
50-100 1-100 <$500/$600
3x50-100 1-400 <$500/$600
1902 Plain Back
4x5 11001-25353 <$175
3x10-20 7501-16260 <$175
3x50-100 401-591<$500/$600
1929 Small Size
5 Type 1 1-4662 <$90
10 Type 1 1-2342 <$90
20 Type 1 1-706 <$90
50 Type 1 1-250 <$200
100 Type 1 1-94 <$250
5 Type 2 1-5066 <$100
10 Type 2 1-2296 <$100
20 Type 2 1-540 <$100
Total Issue $3,563,630
Out at close $189,005
Large out at close $9,425
****

558 Norfolk
RANDOLPH NB, RANDOLPH
{{ 3 L }}
Chartered 10/29/64
Liquidated 11/27/93
Original Series <$VALUE
4x5 1-7250 <$600
3x10-20 1-3600 <$750/$1250
50-100 1-290 <$3500
Series 1875
4x5 1-7785 <$600
3x10-20 1-2808 <$750/$1000
Brown Back
50-100 1-3280 <$1250/$1500
Total Issue $1,156,600
Out in 1910 $6,810
****

13558 Middlesex
FNB IN READING
{{ 7 S }}
Organized 6/22/31
Liquidated 11/1/33
1929 Small Size <$VALUE
5 Type 1 1-1798 <$150
10 Type 1 1-906 <$150
20 Type 1 1-218 <$150
5 Type 2 1-216 <$175
Total Issue $135,540
Out at close $91,710
Large out at close $88,920
Outstanding includes Ch 4488
****

4488 Middlesex
FNB OF READING
{{ 8 L 4 S }}
Chartered 1890
Liquidated 8/28/31
Brown Back <$VALUE
4x5 1-7590 <$300
3x10-20 1-2934 <$300/$350
1882 Date Back
4x5 1-1367 <$300
3x10-20 1-797 <$300/$350
1902 Date Back
4x5 1-3550 <$150
3x10-20 1-2800 <$150
1902 Plain Back
4x5 3551-13455 <$150
3x10-20 2801-9266 <$150
1929 Small Size
5 Type 1 1-1070 <$175
10 Type 1 1-446 <$175
20 Type 1 1-158 <$175
Total Issue $1,175,910
Out at close $44,840
Large out 1935 $2,790
Ch 13558 assumed circulation
****

****
3868 Plymouth
FNB OF ROCKLAND
{{ 1 L }}
Chartered 4/17/88
Liquidated 9/28/07
Brown Back <$VALUE
4x5 1-3377 <$1250
3x10-20 1-615 <$1250
Total Issue $98,290
Out in 1910 $2,065
****

1194 Essex
ROCKPORT NB, ROCKPORT
{{ 4 L }}
Chartered 1865
Original Series <$VALUE
3x1-2 1-2100 <$500/$1250
4x5 1-3190 <$600
3x10-20 1-2195 <$750/$1250
50-100 1-816 <$3500
Series 1875
4x5 1-3985 <$600
3x10-20 1-920 <$750/$1250
Brown Back
4x5 1-11841 <$400
3x10-20 1-981 <$400
1902 Red Seal
3x10-20 1-1000 <$500
1902 Date Back
3x10-20 1-2220 <$250
1902 Plain Back
3x10-20 2221-3443 <$250
Total Issue $940,170
Out in 1935 $2,528
****

634 Essex
ASIATIC NB OF SALEM
{{ 3 L }}
Chartered 12/20/64
Liquidated 10/12/09
Original Series <$VALUE
3x1-2 1-5200 <$500/$1250
4x5 1-5000 <$600
3x10-20 1-3500 <$750/$1250
50-100 1-1708 <$3500
Series 1875
4x5 1-575 <$600
3x10-20 1-2326 <$750/$1250
50-100 1-1634 <$3500
Brown Back
4x5 1-5605 <$400
3x10-20 1-2862 <$400
50-100 1-1740 <$1250/$1500
1902 Red Seal
4x5 1-6600 <$450
3x10-20 1-2760 <$450
1902 Date Back
4x5 1-2292 <$300
3x10-20 1-1281 <$300
Total Issue $1,826,190
Out in 1910 $58,810
****

407 Essex
FNB OF SALEM
{{ 3 L }}
Chartered 4/30/64
Liquidated 2/24/03
Original Series <$VALUE
4x5 1-12250 <$650
3x10-20 1-5600<$1000/$1250
50-100 1-1300 <$3500
Series 1875
4x5 1-2500 <$650
3x10-20 1-2323<$1000/$1250
50-100 1-387 <$3500
500-1000 1-60
<$150,000/$200,000
Brown Back
4x5 1-10048 <$500
3x10-20 1-5919 <$500
50-100 1-1918 <$1250/$1500
Total Issue $1,818,810
Out in 1910 $9,565
****

691 Essex
MERCANTILE NB OF SALEM
{{ 6 L }}
Chartered 1865
Liquidated 5/21/14
Original Series <$VALUE
3x1-2 1-3950 <$400/$1000
4x5 1-4100 <$500
3x10-20 1-2200 <$750/$1250
50-100 1-792 <$3500
Series 1875
3x1-2 1-1600 <$400/$1000
4x5 1-6250 <$500
3x10-20 1-2998 <$750/$1000
50-100 1-420 <$3500
Brown Back
4x5 1-12425 <$400
3x10-20 1-5869 <$400
50-100 1-1737 <$1250/$1500
1902 Red Seal
4x5 1-6750 <$450
3x10-20 1-2980 <$450
50-100 1-540 <$2250/$2500
1902 Date Back
4x5 1-14760 <$250
3x10-20 1-8469 <$250
50-100 1-212 <$500/$600
3x50-100 1-126 <$500/$600
Total Issue $2,625,900
Out in 1914 $115,185
****

726 Essex
MERCHANTS NB OF SALEM
{{ 6 L }}
Chartered 1865
Original Series <$VALUE
3x1-2 1-3650 <$400/$850
4x5 1-6250 <$400
3x10-20 1-4000 <$750/$1250
50-100 1-525 <$3500
500 1-20 <$150,000
Series 1875
3x1-2 1-2670 <$400/$850
4x5 1-7750 <$400
3x10-20 1-1495 <$600/$1000
50-100 1-70 <$3500
Brown Back
4x5 1-15454 <$350
3x10-20 1-4072 <$350
50-100 1-1601 <$1250/$1500
1902 Red Seal
4x5 1-7830 <$400
3x10-20 1-5168 <$400
1902 Date Back
4x5 1-18415 <$200
3x10-20 1-12934 <$200
1902 Plain Back
4x5 18416-25960 <$200
3x10-20 12935-17879 <$200
Total Issue $3,267,380
Out in 1935 $6,765
****

817 Essex
N EXCHANGE B OF SALEM
{{ UNREPORTED }}
Chartered 2/18/65
Liquidated 6/1/99
Original Series <$VALUE
3x1-2 1-2000 <$1000/$1500
4x5 1-5000 <$1000
3x10-20 1-2553<$1250/$1500
50-100 1-1000 <$3500
Series 1875
4x5 1-5000 <$1000
3x10-20 1-2173<$1250/$1500
50-100 1-600 <$3500
Brown Back
4x5 1-13167 <$850
Total Issue $949,640
Out in 1910 $4,916
****

647 Essex
NAUMKEAG NB OF SALEM
{{ 4 L }}
Chartered 1864
Liquidated 11/16/09
Original Series <$VALUE
3x1-2 1-10970 <$450/$1000
4x5 1-14475 <$500
4x10 1-6175 <$750
3x20-50 1-1850<$1250/$3500
100-100 1-580 <$3500
Series 1875
3x1-2 1-1200 <$450/$1000
4x5 1-15578 <$500
4x10 1-5835 <$750
3x20-50 1-1849<$1000/$3500
100-100 1-290 <$3500
Brown Back
4x5 1-16785 <$350
3x10-20 1-3400 <$350
50-100 1-1819 <$1250/$1500
1902 Red Seal
4x5 1-3850 <$400
3x10-20 1-2400 <$400
50-100 1-114 <$2250/$2500
1902 Date Back
4x5 1-1078 <$250
3x10-20 1-252 <$250
50-100 1-120 <$500/$600
Total Issue $2,618,010
Out in 1910 $46,100
****

704 Essex
SALEM NB, SALEM
{{ 1 L }}
Chartered 1865
Liquidated 11/22/09
Original Series <$VALUE
3x1-2 1-800 <$500/$1000
4x5 1-3500 <$600
3x10-20 1-3000 <$750/$1250
50-100 1-1700 <$3500
Series 1875
4x5 1-5000 <$600
3x10-20 1-4232 <$750/$1000
50-100 1-640 <$3500
Brown Back
4x5 1-17030 <$450
3x10-20 1-2250 <$450
50-100 1-2488 <$1250/$1500
1902 Red Seal
4x5 1-6800 <$500
4x10 1-2000 <$500
3x10-20 1-2680 <$500
1902 Date Back
4x5 1-1638 <$350
4x10 1-1642 <$350
Total Issue $2,161,340
Out in 1910 $50,000
****

1049 Essex
POWOW RIVER NB OF SALISBURY
Chartered 1865
2nd title:Powow River NB of Amesbury 8/28/86
FIRST TITLE {{ 2 L }}
Original Series <$VALUE
4x5 1-3200 <$650
3x10-20 1-1900 <$750/$1250
Series 1875
4x5 1-3340 <$650
3x10-20 1-1908 <$750/$1000
Brown Back
4x5 1-955 <$500
3x10-20 1-485 <$500
SECOND TITLE {{ 9 L 5 S }}
Brown Back
4x5 1-7899 <$400
3x10-20 1-3375 <$400
1902 Red Seal
4x5 1-1650 <$450
4x10 1-500 <$450
3x10-20 1-740 <$450
1902 Date Back
4x5 1-4150 <$150
4x10 1-3900 <$150
3x10-20 1-300 <$150
1902 Plain Back
4x5 4151-13306 <$150
4x10 3901-11718 <$150
1929 Small Size
5 Type 1 1-2858 <$135
10 Type 1 1-1256 <$135
5 Type 2 1-4286 <$150
10 Type 2 1-2042 <$150
Total Issue $1,734,070
Out in 1935 $40,400
Large out 1935 $3,950
****

1144 Franklin
SHELBURNE FALLS NB, SHELBURNE FALLS
{{ 17 L U + 10 S }}
Chartered 1865
Original Series <$VALUE
3x1-2 1-3800 <$300/$800
4x5 1-6500 <$400
3x10-20 1-1720 <$750/$1250
50-100 1-150 <$3500
Series 1875
3x1-2 1-1000 <$300/$800
4x5 1-10765 <$400
3x10-20 1-2578 <$600/$1000
Brown Back
4x5 1-10030 <$300
3x10-20 1-4106 <$300/$350
1902 Red Seal
4x5 1-2665 <$375
3x10-20 1-2134 <$375/$425
1902 Date Back
4x5 1-9850 <$200
3x10-20 1-6960 <$200
1902 Plain Back
4x5 9851-31152 <$200
3x10-20 6961-18157 <$200
1929 Small Size
5 Type 1 1-12120 <$75
5 Type 2 1-25696 <$75
Total Issue $3,195,570
Out in 1935 $100,000
Large out 1935 $7,650
****

4771 Suffolk
SOMERVILLE NB, SOMERVILLE
{{ 9 L 8 S }}
Organized 6/14/92
Brown Back <$VALUE
4x5 1-17350 <$325
3x10-20 1-4360 <$325/$375
1882 Date Back
4x5 1-4555 <$325
3x10-20 1-2841 <$325/$375
1902 Date Back
4x5 1-4600 <$150
3x10-20 1-3360 <$150
1902 Plain Back
4x5 4601-23753 <$150
3x10-20 3361-15920 <$150
1929 Small Size
5 Type 1 1-4046 <$150
10 Type 1 1-2176 <$150
20 Type 1 1-478 <$165
5 Type 2 1-4016 <$175
10 Type 2 1-2030 <$175
20 Type 2 1-731 <$185
Total Issue $2,433,510
Out in 1935 $81,900
Large out 1935 $3,990
****

616 Essex
WARREN NB OF SOUTH DANVERS
Organized 11/18/64
2nd title:Warren NB of Peabody 3/12/72
FIRST TITLE {{ 2 L }}
Original Series <$VALUE
3x1-2 1-3600 <$450/$850
4x5 1-4600 <$500
3x10-20 1-1300*<$750/$1250
50-100 1-840 <$3500
* 831-1000 not issued
SECOND TITLE {{ 8 L 6 S }}
Original Series
3x1-2 1-2000 <$350/$750
4x5 1-2500 <$375
3x10-20 1-1000 <$750/$1250
50-100 1-800 <$3500
Series 1875
4x5 1-7220 <$375
3x10-20 1-2388 <$600/$1000
50-100 1-600 <$3500
Brown Back
4x5 1-8505 <$250
3x10-20 1-6219 <$250/$300
50-100 1-1300 <$1250/$1500
1902 Red Seal
4x5 1-5750 <$300
3x10-20 1-3100 <$300/$350
50-100 1-500 <$2250/$2500
1902 Date Back
4x5 1-13250 <$150
3x10-20 1-8580 <$150
50-100 1-200 <$400/$500
3x50-100 1-560 <$400/$500
1902 Plain Back
4x5 13251-38765 <$150
3x10-20 8581-21739 <$150
3x50-100 561-796<$400/$500
1929 Small Size
5 Type 1 1-3694 <$125
10 Type 1 1-1696 <$125
20 Type 1 1-516 <$125
50 Type 1 1-192 <$225
100 Type 1 1-64 <$275
5 Type 2 1-3166 <$150
10 Type 2 1-2343 <$150
20 Type 2 1-615 <$150
Total Issue $4,410,660
Out in 1935 $146,000
Large out 1935 $13,460
****

8150 Franklin
PRODUCE NB OF SOUTH DEERFIELD
{{ 7 L 5 S }}
Chartered 3/06
1902 Red Seal <$VALUE
3x10-20 1-2400 <$750
1902 Date Back
3x10-20 1-4820 <$350
1902 Plain Back
3x10-20 4821-14566 <$350
1929 Small Size
10 Type 1 1-1442 <$175
20 Type 1 1-392 <$175
10 Type 2 1-1232 <$200
20 Type 2 1-388 <$200
Total Issue $1,001,940
Out in 1935 $43,950
Large out 1935 $1,890
****

2485 Middlesex
SOUTH FRAMINGHAM NB, SOUTH FRAMINGHAM
{{ UNREPORTED }}
Chartered 6/28/80
Liquidated 9/8/88
Series 1875 <$VALUE
4x5 1-3159 <$1250
3x10-20 1-1655<$1500/$2000
Total Issue $145,930
Out in 1910 $595
****

****
618 Suffolk
FNB OF SOUTH WEYMOUTH
{{ 4 L }}
Chartered 1864
Liquidated 6/30/16
Original Series <$VALUE
3x1-2 1-3000 <$450/$1000
4x5 1-2750 <$500
3x10-20 1-2000 <$750/$1250
50-100 1-700 <$3500
Series 1875
4x5 1-7500 <$500
3x10-20 1-2914 <$750/$1000
Brown Back
4x5 1-18099 <$400
3x10-20 1-6625 <$400
1902 Red Seal
4x5 1-4500 <$450
4x10 1-1000 <$450
3x10-20 1-2000 <$450
1902 Date Back
4x5 1-9100 <$200
4x10 1-7700 <$200
3x10-20 1-400 <$200
1902 Plain Back
4x5 9101-10012 <$200
4x10 7701-8617 <$200
Total Issue $2,058,850
Out in 1916 $71,395
****

11388 Worcester
PEOPLES NB OF SOUTHBRIDGE
{{ 4 L 4 S }}
Organized 5/27/19
1902 Plain Back <$VALUE
4x5 1-9616 <$350
4x10 1-8073 <$350
1929 Small Size
5 Type 1 1-2604 <$150
10 Type 1 1-1370 <$150
5 Type 2 1-5326 <$150
10 Type 2 1-2227 <$150
Total Issue $724,460
Out in 1935 $48,750
Large out 1935 $660
****

934 Worcester
SOUTHBRIDGE NB, SOUTHBRIDGE
{{ 13 L 9 S }}
Chartered 3/24/65
Original Series <$VALUE
3x1-2 1-3000 <$350/$750
4x5 1-2850 <$400
3x10-20 1-3500 <$750/$1250
50-100 1-150 <$3500
Series 1875
3x1-2 1-980 <$350/$750
4x5 1-3980 <$400
3x10-20 1-3200 <$600/$1000
Brown Back
4x5 1-11618 <$250
3x10-20 1-6404 <$250/$300
1902 Red Seal
4x5 1-4000 <$300
3x10-20 1-2800 <$300/$350
1902 Date Back
4x5 1-8000 <$125
3x10-20 1-5580 <$125
1902 Plain Back
4x5 8001-26336 <$125
3x10-20 5581-17779 <$125
1929 Small Size
5 Type 1 1-3860 <$90
10 Type 1 1-1946 <$90
20 Type 1 1-4100 <$100
5 Type 2 1-6588 <$100
10 Type 2 1-3168 <$100
20 Type 2 1-840 <$100
Total Issue $3,073,090
Out in 1935 $97,410
Large out 1935 $3,060
****

CONDITION affects Value. The Values shown are for notes in FINE condition.

****
2288 Worcester
SPENCER NB, SPENCER
{{ 6 L 0 S }}
Chartered 7/24/75
Closed 11/22/29
Series 1875 <$VALUE
3x10-20 1-9304 <$650/$1000
Brown Back
4x5 1-18300 <$350
3x10-20 1-6000 <$350
1882 Date Back
4x5 1-7344 <$350
3x10-20 1-5857 <$350
1902 Date Back
4x5 1-1665 <$175
3x10-20 1-1334 <$175
1902 Plain Back
4x5 1666-19460 <$175
3x10-20 1335-12688 <$175
1929 Small Size
5 Type 1 1-284 <$500
10 Type 1 1-289 <$500
20 Type 1 1-10 <$500
Total Issue $2,621,590
Out at close $100,000
Large out at close $72,940
Ch 7595 assumed circulation
****
13394 Worcester
SPENCER NB, SPENCER
{{ 10 S }}
Chartered 11/29
Liquidated 11/10/34
1929 Small Size <$VALUE
5 Type 1 1-4278 <$70
10 Type 1 1-1998 <$70
20 Type 1 1-580 <$80
5 Type 2 1-4504 <$85
10 Type 2 1-2370 <$85
20 Type 2 1-457 <$100
Total Issue $373,180
Out at close $92,300
****
1055 Hampden
AGAWAM NB OF SPRINGFIELD
{{ 8 L }}
Chartered 4/26/65
Liquidated 2/15/05
Original Series <$VALUE
3x1-2 1-19000 <$350/$750
4x5 1-15750 <$400
3x10-20 1-2600 <$750/$1250
50-100 1-300 <$3500
Series 1875
4x5 1-27175 <$400
3x10-20 1-7110 <$600/$1000
50-100 1-168 <$3500
Brown Back
4x5 1-23548 <$300
3x10-20 1-8372 <$300/$350
Total Issue $2,398,760
Out in 1910 $15,239
****
2435 Hampden
CHAPIN NB OF SPRINGFIELD
{{ U + 15 L 4U + 12 S }}
Chartered 9/19/79
Closed 10/11/29
Series 1875 <$VALUE
4x5 1-40998 <$350
3x10-20 1-18368<$600/$1000
50-100 1-2340 <$3500
Brown Back
4x5 1-25750 <$250
3x10-20 1-21200 <$250/$275
1882 Date Back
4x5 1-5680 <$250
3x10-20 1-4176 <$250/$275
1902 Plain Back
4x5 1-85405 <$100
3x10-20 1-43732 <$100
1929 Small Size
5 Type 1 1-855 <$150
10 Type 1 1-309* <$150
20 Type 1 1-14** <$150
*C000309A-F0003309A canceled
**C000014A-F000014A canceled
Total Issue $7,927,210
Out at close $497,650
Large out at close $451,900
Ch 4907 assumed circulation
****
988 Hampden
CHICOPEE NB OF SPRINGFIELD
{{ 8 L }}
Chartered 4/7/65
Closed 1/12/27
Original Series <$VALUE
3x1-2 1-4500 <$325/$750
4x5 1-8500 <$350
3x10-20 1-3100 <$750/$1250
50-100 1-1368 <$3500
Series 1875
3x1-2 1-2520 <$325/$750
4x5 1-12480 <$350
3x10-20 1-5848 <$600/$1000
50-100 1-595 <$3500
Brown Back
3x10-20 1-21655 <$200/$250
1902 Red Seal
3x10-20 1-5500 <$300/$325
1902 Date Back
3x10-20 1-15200 <$125
1902 Plain Back
3x10-20 15201-30002 <$125
Total Issue $4,054,400
Out at close $28,200
Ch 308 assumed circulation
****
2433 Hampden
CITY NB OF SPRINGFIELD
{{ 3 L }}
Chartered 9/9/79
Liquidated 2/8/06
Series 1875 <$VALUE
4x5 1-28970 <$600
3x10-20 1-12400<$750/$1000
Brown Back
4x5 1-3180 <$500
3x10-20 1-2410 <$500
Total Issue $1,383,500
Out in 1910 $10,940
****
14 Hampden
FNB OF SPRINGFIELD
{{ 11 L }}
Chartered 6/24/63
Liquidated 3/5/06
Original Series <$VALUE
3x1-2 1-5000 <$500/$1250
4x5 1-13000 <$600
4x10 1-6875 <$750
2x20-50-100 1-600*
<$1250/$3500/$3500
* 201-500 not issued
Series 1875
4x5 1-8775 <$600
4x10 1-5600 <$750
2x20-50-100 1-200
<$1250/$3500/$3500
Brown Back
4x5 1-30764 <$400
3x10-20 1-2120 <$400/$450
1902 Red Seal
3x10-20 1-3297 <$450/$500
Total Issue $1,940,630
Out in 1910 $15,524
****
982 Hampden
JOHN HANCOCK NB OF SPRINGFIELD
{{ 5 L }}
Chartered 4/5/65
Liquidated 3/28/06
Original Series <$VALUE
3x1-2 1-4000 <$400/$850
4x5 1-5500 <$450
3x10-20 1-1700 <$750/$1250
50-100 1-100 <$3500
Series 1875
3x1-2 1-1440 <$400/$850
4x5 1-6500 <$450
3x10-20 1-6500 <$600/$1000
Brown Back
3x10-20 1-25606 <$250/$300
1902 Red Seal
4x5 1-3740 <$300
3x10-20 1-2738 <$300/$350
Total Issue $2,184,100
Out in 1910 $28,765
****
987 Hampden
PYNCHON NB OF SPRINGFIELD
{{ 7 L }}
Chartered 4/7/65
Receivership 6/24/01
Original Series <$VALUE
3x1-2 1-3000 <$325/$750
4x5 1-6475 <$350
3x10-20 1-1400 <$750/$1250
50-100 1-267 <$3500
Series 1875
4x5 1-2935 <$350
3x10-20 1-2594 <$600/$1000
50-100 1-175 <$3500
Brown Back
4x5 1-25731 <$250
3x10-20 1-1263 <$250/$300
Total Issue $1,046,970
Out in 1916 $5,253
****
181 Hampden
SECOND NB OF SPRINGFIELD
{{ 10 L }}
Chartered 1/2/64
Liquidated 3/30/06
Original Series <$VALUE
3x1-2 1-6816 <$325/$750
4x5 1-10250 <$400
4x10 1-5750 <$750
3x20-50 1-1400<$1250/$3500
Series 1875
4x5 1-7456 <$400
4x10 1-3750 <$600
3x20-50 1-400 <$1000/$3500
Brown Back
4x5 1-11020 <$250
3x10-20 1-3423 <$250/$300
50-100 1-535 <$1250/$1500
1902 Red Seal
4x5 1-520 <$275
3x10-20 1-3405 <$275/$325
Total Issue $1,618,650
Out in 1910 $16,022
****
Springfield Chapin NB & TC, Springfield
SEE Ch 4907
Springfield NB, Springfield
****
4907 Hampden
SPRINGFIELD NB, SPRINGFIELD
Chartered 1893
2nd title:Springfield Chapin NB & TC 10/11/29
3rd title:Springfield NB 7/31/31
FIRST TITLE {{ 14 L }}
Brown Back <$VALUE
4x5 1-37750 <$200
3x10-20 1-11100 <$200/$225
1882 Date Back
4x5 1-14862 <$175
3x10-20 1-12380 <$175/$200
1902 Date Back
4x5 1-35000 <$100
4x10 1-6500 <$100
3x10-20 1-21600 <$100
1902 Plain Back
4x5 35001-45600 <$100
4x10 6501-11350 <$100
3x10-20 21601-26403 <$100
SECOND TITLE {{ U + 5 S }}
1929 Small Size
5 Type 1 1-12538 <$50
10 Type 1 1-6258 <$50
20 Type 1 1-1740 <$50
THIRD TITLE {{ 3U + 19 S }}
1929 Small Size
5 Type 1 1-14294 <$30
10 Type 1 1-10062 <$30
20 Type 1 1-2738 <$35
5 Type 2 1-56732 <$30
10 Type 2 1-26195 <$30
20 Type 2 1-6865 <$35
Total Issue $7,916,820
Out in 1935 $799,910
Large out 1935 $28,500
Outstanding includes Ch 2435
****
308 Hampden
THIRD NB OF SPRINGFIELD
Chartered 1864
2nd title: Third NB & TC 1/12/27
FIRST TITLE {{ 14 L }}
Original Series <$VALUE
4x5 1-12500 <$275
3x10-20 1-9000 <$750/$1250
3x10-20 11501-14500
<$750/$1250
20 9001-11500 <$1250
Series 1875
3x10-20 1-12736<$600/$1000
Brown Back
4x5 1-8499 <$200
3x10-20 1-39001 <$200
1902 Red Seal
4x5 1-22915 <$200
4x10 1-5000 <$200
3x10-20 1-13834 <$200
1902 Date Back
4x5 1-6150 <$100
4x10 1-22575 <$100
3x10-20 1-2000 <$100
1902 Plain Back
4x5 6151-59413 <$100
4x10 22576-25825 <$100
3x10-20 2001-35633 <$100
SECOND TITLE {{ 28 S }}
1929 Small Size
10 Type 1 1-12144 <$25
20 Type 1 1-3600 <$35
50 Type 1 1-1232 <$110
100 Type 1 1-418 <$160
10 Type 2 1-30614 <$25
20 Type 2 1-9625 <$35
Total Issue $11,289,420
Out in 1935 $1,329,921
Large out 1935 $31,421
Outstanding includes Ch 988
****
1170 Berkshire
HOUSATONIC NB OF STOCKBRIDGE
{{ 10 L 4 S }}
Chartered 1865
Original Series <$VALUE
3x1-2 1-8400 <$250/$750
4x5 1-4150 <$350
3x10-20 1-3040 <$750/$1250
50-100 1-620 <$3500
Series 1875
3x1-2 1-3000 <$250/$750
4x5 1-8250 <$350
3x10-20 1-2642 <$600/$1000
50-100 1-200 <$3500
Brown Back
4x5 1-17221 <$200
3x10-20 1-1883 <$200/$250
1902 Red Seal
4x5 1-1500 <$250
3x10-20 1-1500 <$250/$300
1902 Date Back
4x5 1-3600 <$150
3x10-20 1-3100 <$150
1902 Plain Back
4x5 3601-12390 <$150
3x10-20 3101-8728 <$150
1929 Small Size
5 Type 1 1-1792 <$125
10 Type 1 1-864 <$125
20 Type 1 1-224 <$125
5 Type 2 1-2584 <$150
10 Type 2 1-1544 <$150
20 Type 2 1-576 <$150
Total Issue $2,122,230
Out in 1935 $48,850
Large out 1935 $7,020
****
4240 Suffolk
STONEHAM NB, STONEHAM
{{ UNREPORTED }}
Chartered 1890
Liquidated 12/2/16
Brown Back <$VALUE
3x10-20 1-3798 <$1000
1902 Date Back
3x10-20 1-1233 <$750
Total Issue $251,550
Out at close $12,100
****
766 Bristol
BRISTOL COUNTY NB OF TAUNTON
{{ 6 L }}
Chartered 1/30/65
Liquidated 3/25/16
Original Series <$VALUE
3x1-2 1-25700 <$275/$750
4x5 1-11900 <$350
3x10-20 1-5780 <$750/$1250
3x50-100 1-766 <$3500
500 1-234 <$150,000
Series 1875
3x1-2 1-17766 <$275/$750
4x5 1-14264 <$350
3x10-20 1-6807 <$600/$1000
3x50-100 1-380 <$3500
500 1-46 <$150,000
Brown Back
4x5 1-16039 <$175
3x10-20 1-8606 <$175/$225
50-100 1-2180 <$1250/$1500
1902 Red Seal
4x5 1-8350 <$200
3x10-20 1-3740 <$200/$250
50-100 1-640 <$2250/$2500
1902 Date Back
4x5 1-12165 <$125
3x10-20 1-9598 <$125
50-100 1-451 <$400/$500
1902 Plain Back
4x5 12166-13595 <$125
Total Issue $4,143,990
Out in 1916 $129,090
****
947 Bristol
MACHINISTS NB OF TAUNTON
{{ 11 L 11 S }}
Chartered 3/28/65
Original Series <$VALUE
3x1-2 1-6800 <$300/$750
4x5 1-5500 <$300
3x10-20 1-3050 <$750/$1250
50-100 1-650 <$3500
500 1-123 <$150,000
Series 1875
4x5 1-452 <$300
3x10-20 1-2278 <$600/$1000
50-100 1-570 <$3500
500 1-100 <$150,000
Brown Back
4x5 1-1600 <$200
3x10-20 1-18894 <$200/$250
50-100 1-100 <$1250/$1500
1902 Red Seal
4x5 1-5250 <$225
3x10-20 1-3700 <$225/$275
1902 Date Back
4x5 1-11515 <$100
3x10-20 1-9914 <$100
1902 Plain Back
4x5 11516-41030 <$100
3x10-20 9915-27840 <$100
1929 Small Size
5 Type 1 1-5904 <$60
10 Type 1 1-3240 <$60
20 Type 1 1-788 <$75
5 Type 2 1-6224 <$75
10 Type 2 1-3742 <$75
20 Type 2 1-745 <$85
Total Issue $4,757,760
Out in 1935 $123,840
Large out 1935 $8,290
****
957 Bristol
TAUNTON NB, TAUNTON
{{ 8 L }}
Chartered 3/31/65
Liquidated 3/17/17
Original Series <$VALUE
3x1-2 1-12000 <$300/$750
4x5 1-7300 <$350
3x10-20 1-7900 <$750/$1250
50-100 1-1980 <$3500
Series 1875
3x1-2 1-8220 <$300/$750
4x5 1-7843 <$350
3x10-20 1-10100<$600/$1000
50-100 1-334 <$3500
Brown Back
4x5 1-15474 <$200
3x10-20 1-15450 <$200/$225
50-100 1-4305 <$1250/$1500
1902 Red Seal
4x5 1-2550 <$250
3x10-20 1-1290 <$250/$300
1902 Date Back
4x5 1-3835 <$125
3x10-20 1-2492 <$125
Total Issue $3,695,590
Out at close $49,295
****
Martha's Vineyard NB of Tisbury
SEE Ch 1274
Martha's Vineyard NB of Edgartown
****
805 Middlesex
TOWNSEND NB, TOWNSEND
{{ 11 L 7 S }}
Chartered 2/14/65
Original Series <$VALUE
3x1-2 1-1000 <$350/$750
4x5 1-2750 <$375
3x10-20 1-1400 <$750/$1250
3x10-20 1901-3100
<$750/$1250
20 1401-1900 <$1250
50-100 1-400 <$3500
Series 1875
4x5 1-1371 <$375
3x10-20 1-523 <$600/$1000
50-100 1-235 <$3500
Brown Back
4x5 1-3450 <$275
3x10-20 1-6910 <$275/$325
1902 Red Seal
3x10-20 1-2000 <$325/$350
1902 Date Back
3x10-20 1-8600 <$150
1902 Plain Back
3x10-20 8601-25229 <$150
1929 Small Size
10 Type 1 1-2864 <$125
20 Type 1 1-680 <$125
10 Type 2 1-1643 <$125
20 Type 2 1-480 <$125
Total Issue $2,404,240
Out in 1935 $73,750
Large out 1935 $6,130
****
2058 Franklin
CROCKER NB OF TURNERS FALLS
{{ 7 L 4 S }}
Chartered 10/19/72
Liquidated 3/22/35
Original Series <$VALUE
4x5 1-2750 <$400
3x10-20 1-3900 <$750/$1250
50-100 1-800 <$3500
Series 1875
4x5 1-13140 <$400
3x10-20 1-6102 <$600/$1000
50-100 1-410 <$3500
Brown Back
4x5 1-12450 <$300
3x10-20 1-6780 <$300
1882 Date Back
4x5 1-5059 <$300
3x10-20 1-3355 <$300
1902 Date Back
4x5 1-4000 <$150
3x10-20 1-3000 <$150
1902 Plain Back
4x5 4001-22510 <$150
3x10-20 3001-15203 <$150
1929 Small Size
5 Type 1 1-4402* <$100
10 Type 1 1-2180** <$100
20 Type 1 1-628*** <$100
5 Type 2 1-3274 <$125
10 Type 2 1-1507 <$125
20 Type 2 1-370 <$135
* 1158-1510 not issued
** 656-776 not issued
*** 134-258 not issued
Total Issue $3,410,890
Out at close $93,400
Large out at close $7,720
****
1022 Worcester
BLACKSTONE NB OF UXBRIDGE
{{ 9 L 16 S }}
Chartered 1865
Original Series <$VALUE
4x5 1-4250 <$400
3x10-20 1-1600 <$750/$1250
50-100 1-200 <$3500
Series 1875
3x10-20 1-1895 <$600/$1000
50-100 1-233 <$3500
Brown Back
3x10-20 1-6019 <$225/$275
1902 Red Seal
3x10-20 1-4800 <$250/$300
1902 Date Back
3x10-20 1-8600 <$125
1902 Plain Back
3x10-20 8601-27650 <$125
1929 Small Size
10 Type 1 1-2674 <$50
20 Type 1 1-808 <$60
10 Type 2 1-3658 <$60
20 Type 2 1-566 <$60
Total Issue $2,553,450
Out in 1935 $85,050
Large out 1935 $5,440
****
1455 Middlesex
NB OF SOUTH READING, WAKEFIELD
Chartered 1865
Liquidated 7/10/16
2nd title:Wakefield NB, 7/14/02
FIRST TITLE {{ 3 L }}
Original Series <$VALUE
3x1-2 1-3600 <$400/$850
4x5 1-3050 <$400
3x10-20 1-1750 <$750/$1250
Series 1875
3x1-2 1-151 <$400/$850
4x5 1-2800 <$400
3x10-20 1-2171 <$600/$1000
Brown Back
4x5 1-4383 <$350
3x10-20 1-3825 <$350
SECOND TITLE {{ 3 L }}
Brown Back
4x5 1-615 <$350
3x10-20 1-458 <$350
1902 Red Seal
4x5 1-3425 <$400
3x10-20 1-2680 <$400
1902 Date Back
4x5 1-10250 <$200
3x10-20 1-7600 <$200
1902 Plain Back
4x5 10251-10500 <$200
3x10-20 7601-7787 <$200
Total Issue $1,447,765
Out in 1916 $76,300
****

****
Wakefield NB, Wakefield
SEE Ch 1455
NB of South Reading,
Wakefield
****

688 Suffolk
WALTHAM NB, WALTHAM
{{ 12 L 6 S }}
Organized 12/26/64
Original Series <$VALUE
3x1-2 1-6220 <$350/$750
4x5 1-4250 <$375
3x10-20 1-2460 <$750/$1250
50-100 1-200 <$3500
Series 1875
3x1-2 1-240 <$350/$750
4x5 1-3965 <$375
3x10-20 1-1590 <$600/$1000
50-100 1-514 <$3500
Brown Back
4x5 1-6886 <$250
3x10-20 1-2767 <$250
50-100 1-604 <$1250/$1500
1902 Red Seal
4x5 1-2000 <$300
3x10-20 1-860 <$300
50-100 1-160 <$2250/$2500
1902 Date Back
4x5 1-3850 <$150
3x10-20 1-3120 <$150
50-100 1-100 <$400/$500
3x50-100 1-100 <$400/$500
1902 Plain Back
4x5 3851-11254 <$150
3x10-20 3121-7972 <$150
1929 Small Size
5 Type 1 1-2936 <$90
10 Type 1 1-1824 <$90
20 Type 1 1-488 <$90
5 Type 2 1-6586 <$100
10 Type 2 1-3478 <$100
20 Type 2 1-1026 <$100
Total Issue $1,987,860
Out in 1935 $129,300
Large out 1935 $5,620
****

628 Hampshire
WARE NB, WARE
{{ 5 L }}
Chartered 1864
Liquidated 3/1/17
Original Series <$VALUE
4x5 1-6000 <$350
3x10-20 1-7100 <$750/$1250
50-100 1-1500 <$3500
Series 1875
3x10-20 1-8288 <$600/$1000
Brown Back
3x10-20 1-21226 <$250
1902 Red Seal
4x5 1-11250 <$300
3x10-20 1-5500 <$300
1902 Date Back
4x5 1-22000 <$150
3x10-20 1-17400 <$150
1902 Plain Back
4x5 22001-25357 <$150
3x10-20 17401-20088 <$150
Total Issue $4,187,240
Out at close $242,900
****

1440 Plymouth
NB OF WAREHAM
{{ 1 L 6 S }}
Chartered 1865
Original Series <$VALUE
3x1-2 1-3000 <$500/$1000
4x5 1-5000 <$500
3x10-20 1-1200 <$750/$1250
Series 1875
4x5 1-1415 <$500
3x10-20 1-1288 <$600/$1000
Brown Back
4x5 1-4170 <$400
3x10-20 1-2148 <$400
1902 Red Seal
4x5 1-1000 <$500
3x10-20 1-600 <$500
1902 Date Back
4x5 1-2700 <$300
3x10-20 1-2200 <$300
1902 Plain Back
4x5 2721-4100 <$300
3x10-20 2201-3037 <$300
1929 Small Size
5 Type 1 1-2164 <$110
10 Type 1 1-1130 <$110
20 Type 1 1-316 <$110
5 Type 2 1-2870 <$135
10 Type 2 1-1426 <$135
20 Type 2 1-322 <$135
Total Issue $973,040
Out in 1935 $48,564
Large out 1935 $2,414
****

****
2108 Suffolk
UNION MARKET NB OF
WATERTOWN
{{ 6 L 15 S }}
Chartered 5/16/73
Original Series <$VALUE
4x5 1-4100 <$400
3x10-20 1-1000 <$750/$1250
50-100 1-334 <$3500
Series 1875
3x1-2 1-2040 <$350/$800
4x5 1-13675 <$400
3x10-20 1-2143 <$600/$1000
50-100 1-167 <$3500
Brown Back
4x5 1-16000 <$225
3x10-20 1-6330 <$225/$275
1882 Date Back
4x5 1-5749 <$200
3x10-20 1-3900 <$200/$250
1902 Date Back
3x10-20 1-3500 <$100
1902 Plain Back
3x10-20 3501-21122 <$100
1929 Small Size
10 Type 1 1-8662 <$40
20 Type 1 1-2502 <$45
10 Type 2 1-14455 <$40
20 Type 2 1-3901 <$45
Total Issue $3,643,110
Out in 1935 $423,335
Large out 1935 $5,415
****

2312 Worcester
FNB OF WEBSTER
{{ 23 L 0 S }}
Chartered 12/13/75
Closed 12/27/29
Series 1875 <$VALUE
4x5 1-14211 <$350
Brown Back
4x5 1-8350 <$200
3x10-20 1-4800 <$200/$225
1882 Date Back
4x5 1-7850 <$150
3x10-20 1-5160 <$150/$175
1902 Plain Back
4x5 1-20712 <$100
4x10 1-16431 <$100
1929 Small Size
5 Type 1 1-1375 <$500
10 Type 1 1-187 <$500
Total Issue $2,230,170
Out at close $100,000
Large out at close $47,530
Ch 7595 assumed circulation
****

13411 Worcester
FNB OF WEBSTER
{{ 10 S }}
Chartered 12/29
1929 Small Size <$VALUE
5 Type 1 1-4652 <$60
10 Type 1 1-2320 <$60
5 Type 2 1-10104 <$70
10 Type 2 1-4670 <$70
Total Issue $375,980
Out in 1935 $78,400
****

11236 Worcester
WEBSTER NB, WEBSTER
{{ 8 L 6 S }}
Organized 8/15/18
Receivership 11/3/33
1902 Plain Back <$VALUE
4x5 1-60574 <$150
1929 Small Size
5 Type 1 1-12684 <$100
5 Type 2 1-5212 <$100
Total Issue $1,618,060
Out at close $98,050
Large out at close $2,470
****

13780 Worcester
WEBSTER NB, WEBSTER
{{ 4 S }}
Chartered 9/33
1929 Small Size <$VALUE
5 Type 2 1-15466 <$100
10 Type 2 1-8055 <$100
Total Issue $157,880
Out in 1935 $76,200
****

7297 Suffolk
WELLESLEY NB, WELLESLEY
{{ 6 L 17 S }}
Chartered 6/04
1902 Red Seal <$VALUE
4x5 1-2800 <$400
3x10-20 1-2120 <$400/$450
1902 Date Back
4x5 1-5150 <$150
3x10-20 1-3460 <$150
1902 Plain Back
4x5 5151-32674 <$150
3x10-20 3461-19458 <$150
1929 Small Size
5 Type 1 1-7778 <$50
10 Type 1 1-5936 <$50
20 Type 1 1-1050 <$55
5 Type 2 1-17454 <$50
10 Type 2 1-8448 <$50
20 Type 2 1-2865 <$55
Total Issue $2,732,930
Out in 1935 $232,930
Large out 1935 $5,180
****

421 Worcester
FNB OF WESTBORO
{{ 5 L U + 12 S }}
Chartered 1864
Original Series <$VALUE
3x1-2 1-2000 <$400/$850
4x5 1-3000 <$400
3x10-20 1-3200 <$750/$1250
Series 1875
3x1-2 1-1320 <$400/$850
4x5 1-3250 <$400
3x10-20 1-1946 <$600/$1000
Brown Back
3x10-20 1-4890 <$300/$350
1902 Red Seal
4x5 1-1700 <$350
3x10-20 1-1090 <$350/$400
1902 Date Back
4x5 1-4600 <$175
3x10-20 1-3380 <$175
1902 Plain Back
4x5 4601-13841 <$175
3x10-20 3381-9539 <$175
1929 Small Size
5 Type 1 1-3680 <$100
10 Type 1 1-2036 <$100
20 Type 1 1-456 <$100
5 Type 2 1-5002 <$100
10 Type 2 1-3048 <$100
20 Type 2 1-696 <$100
Total Issue $1,842,360
Out in 1935 $97,750
Large out 1935 $3,530
****

190 Hampden
FNB OF WESTFIELD
{{ 18 L 16 S }}
Chartered 1864
Original Series <$VALUE
3x1-2 1-1533 <$275/$750
4x5 1-11500 <$300
4x10 1-2440 <$750
3x20-50 1-750 <$1250/$3500
50-100 1-300 <$3500
Series 1875
4x5 1-6941 <$300
4x10 1-2124 <$600
3x20-50 1-230 <$1000/$3500
50-100 1-65 <$3500
Brown Back
4x5 1-21769 <$200
3x10-20 1-12636 <$200/$225
50-100 1-2510 $1250/$1500
1902 Red Seal
4x5 1-15750 <$200
3x10-20 1-8780 <$200/$225
50-100 1-240 <$2250/$2500
1902 Date Back
4x5 1-20500 <$50
3x10-20 1-13800 <$60
50-100 1-300 <$300/$350
3x50-100 1-400 <$300/$350
1902 Plain Back
4x5 20501-67372 <$50
3x10-20 13801-44170 <$60
3x50-100 401-605<$300/$350
1929 Small Size
5 Type 1 1-8490 <$35
10 Type 1 1-4774 <$35
20 Type 1 1-1308 <$45
5 Type 2 1-15167 <$40
10 Type 2 1-7983 <$40
20 Type 2 1-2424 <$50
Total Issue $7,609,710
Out in 1935 $242,350
Large out 1935 $17,740
****

1367 Hampden
HAMPDEN NB OF WESTFIELD
Chartered 1865
2nd title:Hampden NB & TC
of Westfield 4/2/30
FIRST TITLE {{ 10 L 3 S }}
Original Series <$VALUE
3x1-2 1-4360 <$300/$750
4x5 1-5510 <$350
3x10-20 1-1246 <$750/$1250
50-100 1-357 <$3500
Series 1875
3x1-2 1-2360 <$300/$750
4x5 1-460 <$350
3x10-20 1-4021 <$600/$1000
50-100 1-392 <$3500
Brown Back
4x5 1-9794 <$200
3x10-20 1-3456 <$200/$250
50-100 1-100 <$1250/$1500
1902 Red Seal
4x5 1-1350 <$250
3x10-20 1-1440 <$250/$300
1902 Date Back
4x5 1-5350 <$100
3x10-20 1-3920 <$100
1902 Plain Back
4x5 5351-20087 <$100
3x10-20 3921-14787 <$100
1929 Small Size
5 Type 1 1-1542 <$100
10 Type 1 1-778 <$100
20 Type 1 1-260 <$100
SECOND TITLE {{ 8 S }}
1929 Small Size
5 Type 1 1-2224 <$85
10 Type 1 1-1294 <$85
20 Type 1 1-308 <$85
5 Type 2 1-5930 <$85
10 Type 2 1-2964 <$85
20 Type 2 1-696 <$100
Total Issue $2,530,990
Out in 1935 $96,850
Large out 1935 $5,990
****

2284 Worcester
WESTMINSTER NB OF
WESTMINSTER
Chartered 7/10/75
Liquidated 10/9/16
2nd title:Westminster NB of
Gardner 6/12/94
FIRST TITLE {{ 1 L }}
Series 1875 <$VALUE
4x5 1-16026 <$600
SECOND TITLE {{ 4 L }}
Series 1875
4x5 1-361 <$2000
Brown Back
4x5 1-9100 <$350
3x10-20 1-5300 <$350
1882 Date Back
4x5 1-8026 <$350
3x10-20 1-5336 <$350
1902 Date Back
3x10-20 1-1735 <$250
Total Issue $1,288,810
Out at close $100,000
****

510 Suffolk
UNION NB OF WEYMOUTH
{{ 5 L }}
Chartered 9/6/64
Liquidated 7/26/04
Original Series <$VALUE
3x1-2 1-8000 <$400/$850
4x5 1-9825 <$400
3x10-20 1-3830 <$750/$1250
3x10-20 4331-593<$750/$1250
20 3831-4330 <$1250
Series 1875
3x1-2 1-1000 <$400/$850
4x5 1-14490 <$400
3x10-20 1-6900 <$600/$1000
Brown Back
4x5 1-12900 <$300
3x10-20 1-5120 <$300/$350
50-100 1-520 <$1250/$1500
Total Issue $1,749,800
Out in 1910 $12,397
****

769 Worcester
WHITINSVILLE NB,
WHITINSVILLE
{{ 6 L 12 S }}
Chartered 1/31/65
Original Series <$VALUE
3x1-2 1-3000 <$350/$750
4x5 1-2450 <$375
3x10-20 1-1586 <$750/$1250
50-100 1-290 <$3500
Series 1875
4x5 1-1735 <$375
3x10-20 1-2260 <$600/$1000
Brown Back
4x5 1-2450 <$300
3x10-20 1-4965 <$300/$350
1902 Red Seal
4x5 1-3350 <$300
3x10-20 1-2960 <$300/$350
1902 Date Back
4x5 1-9050 <$150
3x10-20 1-6640 <$150
1902 Plain Back
4x5 9051-28078 <$150
3x10-20 6641-19460 <$150
1929 Small Size
5 Type 1 1-3960 <$60
10 Type 1 1-2206 <$90
20 Type 1 1-484 <$100
5 Type 2 1-5122 <$100
10 Type 2 1-3180 <$100
20 Type 2 1-756 <$100
Total Issue $2,763,080
Out in 1935 $97,250
Large out 1935 $5,620
****

4660 Plymouth
WHITMAN NB, WHITMAN
{{ 2 L 3 S }}
Chartered 1891
Brown Back <$VALUE
4x5 1-3065 <$750
3x10-20 1-744 <$750
1882 Date Back
4x5 1-468 <$700
3x10-20 1-371 <$700
1902 Date Back
4x5 1-975 <$500
3x10-20 1-760 <$500
1902 Plain Back
4x5 976-3050 <$500
3x10-20 761-2016 <$500
1929 Small Size
5 Type 1 1-526 <$300
10 Type 1 1-250 <$300
20 Type 1 1-84 <$300
5 Type 2 1-216 <$350
10 Type 2 1-114 <$350
20 Type 2 1-72 <$350
Total Issue $332,730
Out in 1935 $12,350
Large out 1935 $510
****

3092 Berkshire
WILLIAMSTOWN NB,
WILLIAMSTOWN
{{ 3 L 8 S }}
Chartered 1883
Brown Back <$VALUE
3x10-20 1-3225 <$400
1902 Red Seal
3x10-20 1-3000 <$400
1902 Date Back
3x10-20 1-4360 <$200
1902 Plain Back
3x10-20 4361-13520 <$200
1929 Small Size
10 Type 1 1-1452 <$110
20 Type 1 1-380 <$110
10 Type 2 1-1728 <$125
20 Type 2 1-456 <$125
Total Issue $1,146,370
Out in 1935 $45,340
Large out 1935 $2,080
****

327 Worcester
FNB OF WINCHENDON
{{ 8 L 9 S }}
Chartered 1864
Original Series <$VALUE
4x5 1-5850 <$400
3x10-20 1-3160 <$750/$1250
Series 1875
4x5 1-2375 <$400
3x10-20 1-3600 <$600/$1000
Brown Back
4x5 1-8373 <$300
3x10-20 1-7560 <$300
1902 Red Seal
4x5 1-5630 <$350
3x10-20 1-3948 <$350
1902 Date Back
4x5 1-8850 <$125
3x10-20 1-6160 <$125
1902 Plain Back
4x5 8851-27000 <$125
3x10-20 6161-17938 <$125
1929 Small Size
5 Type 1 1-3938 <$85
10 Type 1 1-1930 <$85
20 Type 1 1-464 <$90
5 Type 2 1-5110 <$100
10 Type 2 1-3108 <$100
20 Type 2 1-792 <$100
Total Issue $3,156,950
Out in 1935 $97,050
Large out 1935 $6,060
****

5071 Middlesex
MIDDLESEX COUNTY NB OF
WINCHESTER
{{ UNREPORTED }}
Chartered 1897
Liquidated 7/1/13
Brown Back <$VALUE
4x5 1-6725 <$850
3x10-20 1-2040 <$850
50-100 1-360 <$1500/$2000
1882 Date Back
4x5 1-3550 <$850
3x10-20 1-1775 <$850
50-100 1-39 <$1500/$2000
Total Issue $456,100
Out in 1913 $28,650
****

11103 Middlesex
WINCHESTER NB, WINCHESTER
{{ 5 L 14 S }}
Chartered 11/17
1902 Plain Back <$VALUE
4x5 1-15025 <$175
3x10-20 1-10853 <$175
1929 Small Size
5 Type 1 1-3912 <$60
10 Type 1 1-2202 <$60
20 Type 1 1-554 <$60
5 Type 2 1-7846 <$70
10 Type 2 1-4065 <$70
20 Type 2 1-1284 <$70
Total Issue $1,264,670
Out in 1935 $125,000
Large out 1935 $2,675
****

746 Middlesex
FNB OF WOBURN
{{ 3 L }}
Chartered 1/24/65
Liquidated 1/18/05
Original Series <$VALUE
3x1-2 1-6000 <$400/$850
4x5 1-3000 <$400
3x10-20 1-8000 <$750/$1250
50-100 1-883 <$3500
Series 1875
4x5 1-2000 <$400
3x10-20 1-3211 <$600/$1000
50-100 1-1070 <$3500
Brown Back
3x10-20 1-12224 <$250/$300
50-100 1-920 <$1250/$1500
Total Issue $1,732,700
Out in 1910 $12,198
****

14033 Middlesex
TANNERS NB IN WOBURN
{{ 1 L }}
Chartered 2/34
1929 Small Size <$VALUE
5 Type 2 1-2516 <$750
Total Issue $12,580
Out in 1935 $31,720
Large out 1935 $1,720
Outstanding includes Ch 11067
****

11067 Middlesex
TANNERS NB OF WOBURN
{{ 3 L 3 S }}
Organized 5/12/17
Liquidated 4/17/34
1902 Plain Back <$VALUE
4x10 1-16472 <$350
1929 Small Size
20 Type 1 1-293 <$300
Total Issue $694,040
Out at close $31,240
Large out at close $1,720
Ch 14033 assumed circulation
****

7550 Middlesex
WOBURN NB, WOBURN
{{ 2 L U + 9 S }}
Chartered 1/05
1902 Red Seal <$VALUE
3x10-20 1-5540 <$500
1902 Date Back
3x10-20 1-9200 <$250
1902 Plain Back
3x10-20 9201-14060 <$250
1929 Small Size
5 Type 1 1-2056 <$100
10 Type 1 1-624 <$100
20 Type 1 1-164 <$125
5 Type 2 1-5398 <$125
10 Type 2 1-2800 <$125
20 Type 2 1-950 <$125
Total Issue $1,172,790
Out in 1935 $78,500
Large out 1935 $1,800
****

<$VALUEs are for notes in FINE condition. Value changes by approximately 25% for a change of one full grade.

****
455 Worcester
CENTRAL NB OF WORCESTER
{{ UNREPORTED }}
Chartered 6/2/64
Liquidated 3/30/03
Original Series <$VALUE
4x5 1-6000 <$850
3x10-20 1-5700<$1000/$1250
50-100 1-1200 <$3500
Series 1875
4x5 1-1625 <$850
3x10-20 1-4672<$1000/$1250
50-100 1-200 <$3500
Brown Back
4x5 1-1500 <$650
3x10-20 1-6131 <$650
50-100 1-1029 <$1250/$1500
1902 Red Seal
3x10-20 1-70 <$850
Total Issue $1,375,500
Out in 1910 $8,395
****
765 Worcester
CITIZENS NB OF WORCESTER
{{ 1 L }}
Chartered 1/30/65
Liquidated 12/12/03
Original Series <$VALUE
3x1-2 1-940 <$500/$1000
4x5 1-3500 <$650
3x10-20 1-1900 <$750/$1250
50-100 1-200 <$3500
Series 1875
4x5 1-2205 <$650
3x10-20 1-2544 <$750/$1000
50-100 1-100 <$3500
Brown Back
4x5 1-2375 <$600
3x10-20 1-6735 <$600
Total Issue $770,250
Out in 1910 $6,493
****
476 Worcester
CITY NB OF WORCESTER
{{ 4 L }}
Chartered 7/2/64
Liquidated 3/30/03
Original Series <$VALUE
3x1-2 1-4300 <$350/$750
4x5 1-6025 <$400
3x10-20 1-1500 <$750/$1250
50-100 1-1990 <$3500
Series 1875
3x1-2 1-600 <$350/$750
4x5 1-1300 <$400
3x10-20 1-2160 <$600/$1000
50 100 1 1160 <$3500
Brown Back
4x5 1-5880 <$300
3x10-20 1-3180 <$300/$350
50-100 1-1256 <$1250/$1500
Total Issue $1,291,500
Out in 1910 $7,910
****
79 Worcester
FNB OF WORCESTER
{{ 6 L }}
Chartered 1863
Liquidated 5/4/82
Original Series <$VALUE
3x1-2 1-4000 <$400/$1000
4x5 1-4950 <$500
3x10-20 1-4010 <$750/$1250
50-100 1-710 <$3500
Series 1875
3x1-2 1-1980 <$400/$1000
4x5 1-5470 <$500
3x10-20 1-2936 <$600/$1000
50-100 1-260 <$3500
Total Issue $731,100
Out in 1910 $3,584
****
2699 Worcester
FNB OF WORCESTER
{{ 3 L }}
Chartered 5/20/82
Liquidated 10/22/03
Brown Back <$VALUE
4x5 1-6673 <$500
3x10-20 1-6474 <$500
50-100 1-804 <$1250/$1500
1902 Red Seal
4x5 1-275 <$600
3x10-20 1-569 <$600
Total Issue $611,710
Out in 1910 $4,110
****

****
1135 Worcester
MECHANICS NB OF WORCESTER
{{ 7 L 12 S }}
Chartered 1865
Original Series <$VALUE
4x5 1-5500 <$350
3x10-20 1-1840 <$750/$1250
50-100 1-720 <$3500
500 1-50 <$150,000
Series 1875
4x5 1-14250 <$350
3x10-20 1-2200 <$600/$1000
50-100 1-1110 <$3500
Brown Back
4x5 1-13508 <$200
3x10-20 1-7355 <$200/$250
50-100 1-890 <$1250/$1500
1902 Red Seal
4x10 1-3000 <$250
3x10-20 1-3000 <$250/$300
1902 Date Back
4x10 1-22125 <$100
3x10-20 1-500 <$100
1902 Plain Back
4x10 22126-72948 <$100
1929 Small Size
5 Type 1 1-21446 <$25
10 Type 1 1-3580 <$25
5 Type 2 1-27808 <$25
10 Type 2 1-13206 <$25
Total Issue $6,010,110
Out in 1935 $228,670
Large out 1935 $11,485
****
7595 Worcester
MERCHANTS NB OF WORCESTER
Chartered 2/05
Liquidated 11/10/34
2nd title:Worcester County NB of Worcester 6/27/27
FIRST TITLE {{ 18 L }}
1902 Red Seal <$VALUE
3x10-20 1-5750 <$150/$200
1902 Date Back
4x5 1-51830 <$50
3x10-20 1-44500 <$60
1902 Plain Back
4x5 51831-553611 <$50
SECOND TITLE {{ 10 L 31 S }}
1902 Plain Back
4x5 1-167528 <$50
1929 Small Size
5 Type 1 1-211318 <$20
5 Type 2 1-291182 <$20
Total Issue $24,730,730
Out at close $1,384,820
Large out at close $45,140
Outstanding includes Ch 2288, Ch 2312, and Ch 10165
****
1073 Worcester
QUINSIGAMOND NB OF WORCESTER
{{ 2 L }}
Chartered 4/28/65
Liquidated 1/15/06
Original Series <$VALUE
3x1-2 1-4000 <$400/$1000
4x5 1-1850 <$500
3x10-20 1-1427 <$750/$1250
50-100 1-700 <$3500
Series 1875
4x5 1-5810 <$500
3x10-20 1-3834 <$600/$1000
50-100 1-505 <$3500
Brown Back
3x10-20 1-10564 <$400/$450
1902 Red Seal
3x10-20 1-693 <$450/$500
Total Issue $1,179,850
Out in 1910 $11,213
****
2273 Worcester
SECURITY NB OF WORCESTER
{{ 3 L }}
Chartered 6/7/75
Liquidated 6/5/78
Original Series <$VALUE
4x5 1-1000 <$1000
3x10-20 1-797 <$1250/$1750
50-100 1-35 <$4000
Total Issue $65,100
Out in 1910 $240
****
Worcester County NB of Worcester
SEE Ch 7595
Merchants NB of Worcester
****

****
442 Worcester
WORCESTER NB, WORCESTER
{{ 6 L }}
Chartered 1864
Liquidated 2/19/17
Original Series <$VALUE
3x1-2 1-15000 <$300/$750
4x5 1-8550 <$350
3x10-20 1-8950 <$750/$1250
50-100 1-2510 <$3500
Series 1875
4x5 1-5250 <$350
3x10-20 1-2582 <$600/$1000
Brown Back
4x5 1-18260 <$200
3x10-20 1-9235 <$200/$250
50-100 1-1100 <$1250/$1500
1902 Red Seal
4x5 1-4825 <$250
3x10-20 1-3320 <$250/$300
1902 Date Back
4x5 1-10750 <$150
3x10-20 1-9442 <$150
Total Issue $3,245,650
Out at close $96,795
****
1085 Norfolk
NB OF WRENTHAM
{{ 5 L 6 S }}
Organized 4/10/65
Original Series <$VALUE
3x1-2 1-3800 <$350/$750
4x5 1-2750 <$375
3x10-20 1-2382 <$750/$1250
50-100 1-100 <$3500
Series 1875
3x1-2 1-380 <$350/$750
4x5 1-1405 <$375
3x10-20 1-747 <$600/$1000
50-100 1-66 <$3500
Brown Back
3x10-20 1-2982 <$250/$300
1902 Red Seal
3x10-20 1-1000 <$300/$350
1902 Date Back
3x10-20 1-3700 <$150
1902 Plain Back
3x10-20 3701-10096 <$150
1929 Small Size
10 Type 1 1-1134 <$135
20 Type 1 1-304 <$150
10 Type 2 1-936 <$175
20 Type 2 1-318 <$175
Total Issue $1,109,490
Out in 1935 $38,750
Large out 1935 $2,960
****
516 Barnstable
FNB OF YARMOUTH
{{ 21 L 9 S }}
Chartered 1864
Original Series <$VALUE
4x5 1-16200 <$350
3x10-20 1-9920 <$750/$1250
50-100 1-1300 <$3500
Series 1875
4x5 1-15650 <$350
3x10-20 1-6268 <$600/$1000
Brown Back
4x5 1-39744 <$200
3x10-20 1-12299 <$200/$250
50-100 1-160 <$1250/$1500
1902 Red Seal
4x5 1-4650 <$300
4x10 1-2175 <$300
3x10-20 1-1600 <$300
1902 Date Back
4x5 1-6000 <$100
4x10 1-5600 <$100
3x10-20 1-400 <$100
1902 Plain Back
4x5 6001-32545 <$100
4x10 5601-13623 <$100
1929 Small Size
5 Type 1 1-5660 <$75
10 Type 1 1-2326 <$75
5 Type 2 1-4338 <$85
10 Type 2 1-2512 <$85
Total Issue $4,907,220
Out in 1935 $86,760
Large out 1935 $15,480
****

MICHIGAN

Nickname: The Wolverine State
Motto: Si Quaeris Peninsulam Circumspice (If You Seek a Pleasant Peninsula, Look About You)
Capital: Lansing
Number of towns: 141
Number of issuing charters: 278
Number of small size issuers: 145

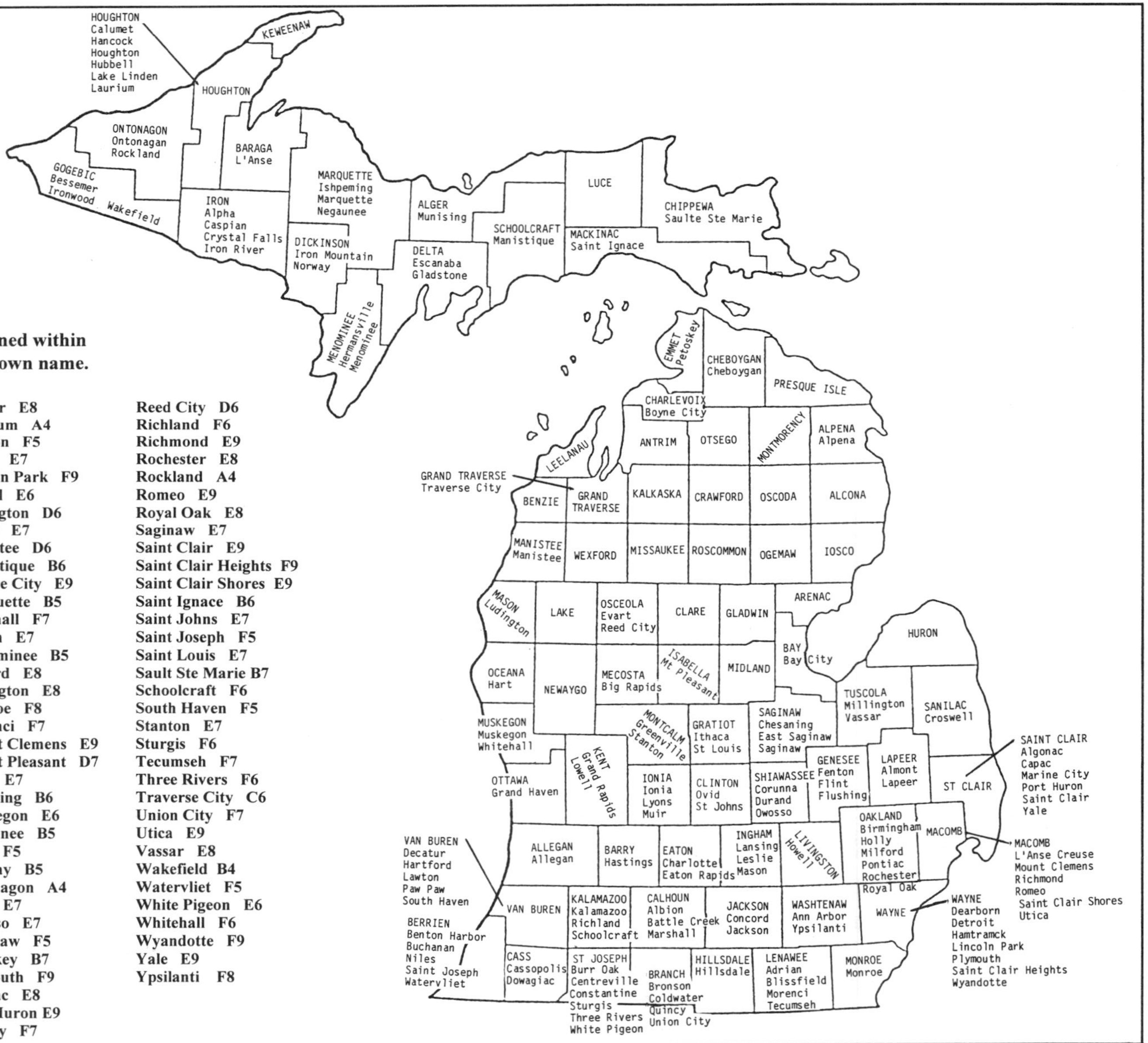

In situations where the town name is not positioned within the county, the alphanumeric index locates the town name.

Adrian F7
Albion F7
Algonac E9
Allegan E6
Almont E8
Alpena C8
Alpha B4
Ann Arbor F8
Battle Creek F7
Bay City D7
Benton Harbor F5
Bessemer B4
Big Rapids D6
Birmingham E8
Blissfield F7
Boyne City C7
Bronson F7
Buchanan F5
Burr Oak F6
Calumet A4
Capac E9
Caspian B4
Cassopolis F6
Centreville F6
Charlotte E7
Cheboygan C7
Chesaning E7
Coldwater F7
Concord F7
Constantine F6
Corunna E7
Croswell E8
Crystal Falls B4
Dearborn F9
Decatur F5
Detroit F9
Dowagiac F6
Durand E7
East Saginaw E7
Eaton Rapids E7
Escanaba B5
Evart D6
Fenton E8
Flint E8
Flushing E8
Gladstone B5
Grand Haven E6
Grand Rapids E6
Greenville E7
Hamtramck F9
Hancock A4
Hart D6
Hartford F5
Hastings E6
Hermansville B5
Hillsdale F7
Holly E8
Houghton A4
Howell E8
Hubbell A4
Ionia E7
Iron Mountain B5
Iron River B4
Ironwood B4
Ishpeming B5
Ithaca E7
Jackson F7
Kalamazoo F6
L'Anse A4
L'Anse Creuse E9
Lake Linden A4
Lansing E7
Lapeer E8
Laurium A4
Lawton F5
Leslie E7
Lincoln Park F9
Lowell E6
Ludington D6
Lyons E7
Manistee D6
Manistique B6
Marine City E9
Marquette B5
Marshall F7
Mason E7
Menominee B5
Milford E8
Millington E8
Monroe F8
Morenci F7
Mount Clemens E9
Mount Pleasant D7
Muir E7
Munising B6
Muskegon E6
Negaunee B5
Niles F5
Norway B5
Ontonagon A4
Ovid E7
Owosso E7
Paw Paw F5
Petoskey B7
Plymouth F9
Pontiac E8
Port Huron E9
Quincy F7
Reed City D6
Richland F6
Richmond E9
Rochester E8
Rockland A4
Romeo E9
Royal Oak E8
Saginaw E7
Saint Clair E9
Saint Clair Heights F9
Saint Clair Shores E9
Saint Ignace B6
Saint Johns E7
Saint Joseph F5
Saint Louis E7
Sault Ste Marie B7
Schoolcraft F6
South Haven F5
Stanton E7
Sturgis F6
Tecumseh F7
Three Rivers F6
Traverse City C6
Union City F7
Utica E9
Vassar E8
Wakefield B4
Watervliet F5
White Pigeon E6
Whitehall F6
Wyandotte F9
Yale E9
Ypsilanti F8

1973 Lenawee
FNB OF ADRIAN
{{ 4 L }}
Chartered 4/26/72
Liquidated 6/11/77
Original Series <$VALUE
3x1-2 1-1000 <$600/$1250
4x5 1-2215 <$650
3x10-20 1-1200 <$850/$1500
Series 1875
3x10-20 1-84 <$850/$1250
Total Issue $113,500
Out in 1910 $448

9421 Lenawee
NB OF COMMERCE, ADRIAN
{{ 7 L 11 S }}
Organized 5/10/09
Receivership 12/5/33
1902 Date Back <$VALUE
4x5 1-7500 <$175
3x10-20 1-5760 <$175
1902 Plain Back
4x5 7501-24988 <$175
3x10-20 5761-17288 <$175
1929 Small Size
5 Type 1 1-3516 <$115
10 Type 1 1-2020 <$115
20 Type 1 1-520 <$125
5 Type 2 1-824 <$150
10 Type 2 1-394 <$150
20 Type 2 1-75 <$150
Total Issue $1,662,800
Out at close $100,000
Large out at close $4,370

7552 Calhoun
ALBION NB, ALBION
{{ UNREPORTED }}
Organized 1/11/05
Receivership 1/4/12
1902 Red Seal <$VALUE
3x10-20 1-800 <$1500
1902 Date Back
3x10-20 1-588 <$1250
Total Issue $69,400
Out in 1915 $1,990

3316 Calhoun
FNB OF ALBION
{{ 2 L }}
Chartered 3/2/85
Liquidated 1/13/05
Brown Back <$VALUE
3x10-20 1-5425 <$1000
Total Issue $271,250
Out in 1910 $6,150

1544 Calhoun
N EXCHANGE B OF ALBION
{{ UNREPORTED }}
Chartered 8/30/65
Liquidated 2/28/85
Original Series <$VALUE
4x5 1-2425 <$1500
3x10-20 1-1000<$1750/$2000
Series 1875
3x10-20 1-550 <$1750/$2000
Total Issue $126,000
Out in 1910 $940

12944 Saint Clair
FNB OF ALGONAC
{{ 1 L 2 S }}
Organized 2/24/26
Receivership 1/17/33
1902 Plain Back <$VALUE
4x5 1-1630 <$850
1929 Small Size
5 Type 1 1-2496 <$500
Total Issue $107,480
Out at close $19,280
Large out at close $230

1829 Allegan
FNB OF ALLEGAN
{{ 8 L }}
Chartered 5/31/71
Receivership 2/18/27
Original Series <$VALUE
3x1-2 1-2900 <$400/$1250
4x5 1-2775 <$500
Series 1875
4x5 1-4160 <$500
Brown Back
4x5 1-1250 <$400
3x10-20 1-2520 <$400
1882 Date Back
4x5 1-960 <$375
3x10-20 1-646 <$375
1902 Date Back
3x10-20 1-2900 <$165
1902 Plain Back
3x10-20 2901-8824 <$165
Total Issue $796,900
Out at close $46,900

12793 Lapeer
FNB OF ALMONT
{{ 1 S }}
Chartered 7/15/25
Receivership 10/9/33
1929 Small Size <$VALUE
5 Type 1 1-820 <$600
10 Type 1 1-452 <$600
20 Type 1 1-118 <$600
Total Issue $65,880
Out at close $20,000

2847 Alpena
ALPENA NB, ALPENA
{{ 5 L 8 S }}
Chartered 12/26/82
Liquidated 6/24/31
Brown Back <$VALUE
4x5 1-1500 <$650
3x10-20 1-4530 <$650
1902 Red Seal
4x5 1-1450 <$650
3x10-20 1-1920 <$650
1902 Date Back
4x5 1-2650 <$350
3x10-20 1-1960 <$350
1902 Plain Back
4x5 2651-9421 <$350
3x10-20 1961-7716 <$350
1929 Small Size
5 Type 1 1-3168 <$175
10 Type 1 1-1408 <$175
20 Type 1 1-467 <$175
Total Issue $1,191,280
Out at close $150,000
Large out at close $4,880

10601 Iron
FNB OF ALPHA
{{ 3 L 5 S }}
Chartered 8/14
1902 Plain Back <$VALUE
3x10-20 1-2714 <$650
1929 Small Size
10 Type 1 1-568 <$350
20 Type 1 1-150 <$350
10 Type 2 1-500 <$350
20 Type 2 1-106 <$375
Total Issue $194,900
Out in 1935 $22,800
Large out 1935 $1,040

22 Washtenaw
FNB OF ANN ARBOR
{{ 4 L }}
Chartered 7/1/63
Liquidated 6/1/82
Original Series <$VALUE
3x1-2 1-3000 <$600/$1500
4x5 1-8400 <$650
3x10-20 1-1860<$1000/$1500
Series 1875
4x5 1-3130 <$650
3x10-20 1-578 <$850/$1250
Total Issue $367,500
Out in 1910 $2,687

2714 Washtenaw
FNB OF ANN ARBOR
Chartered 6/1/82
2nd title:FNB & TC
4/20/29
FIRST TITLE {{ 13 L }}
Brown Back <$VALUE
4x5 1-6850 <$375
3x10-20 1-330 <$400
1902 Red Seal
3x10-20 1-1350 <$400
1902 Date Back
3x10-20 1-10400 <$150
1902 Plain Back
3x10-20 10401-29959 <$150
SECOND TITLE {{ 3U + 31 S }}
1929 Small Size
5 Type 1 1-6190 <$65
10 Type 1 1-5062 <$60
20 Type 1 1-2168 <$65
5 Type 2 1-10054 <$75
10 Type 2 1-4321 <$75
20 Type 2 1-1616 <$85
Total Issue $2,594,330
Out in 1935 $239,480
Large out 1935 $5,810

13858 Calhoun
CENTRAL NB AT
BATTLE CREEK
{{ 4 S }}
Chartered 12/33
1929 Small Size <$VALUE
10 Type 2 1-4618 <$250
20 Type 2 1-1350 <$250
Total Issue $73,180
Out in 1935 $371,380
Outstanding includes Ch 7013

7013 Calhoun
CENTRAL NB OF
BATTLE CREEK
Chartered 10/03
Liquidated 12/4/33
2nd title:Central NB & TC
7/1/31
FIRST TITLE {{ 21 L 16 S }}
1902 Red Seal <$VALUE
4x5 1-3750 <$325
3x10-20 1-7500 <$325
1902 Date Back
4x5 1-19500 <$100
3x10-20 1-13700 <$100
1902 Plain Back
4x5 19501-84820 <$100
3x10-20 13701-54315 <$100
1929 Small Size
5 Type 1 1-7480 <$50
10 Type 1 1-7590 <$50
20 Type 1 1-2710 <$55
SECOND TITLE {{ 12 S }}
1929 Small Size
10 Type 1 1-3858 <$75
20 Type 1 1-1044 <$85
10 Type 2 1-456 <$125
Total Issue $6,228,470
Out at close $360,000
Large out at close $15,440
Ch 13858 assumed circulation

11852 Calhoun
CITY NB OF BATTLE CREEK
Chartered 10/9/20
2nd title:City NB & TC
4/30/28
FIRST TITLE {{ 14 L }}
1902 Plain Back <$VALUE
4x5 1-56670 <$125
3x10-20 1-38206 <$125
SECOND TITLE {{ 6 L 50+ S }}
1902 Plain Back
4x5 1-12063 <$175
3x10-20 1-7554 <$175
1929 Small Size
10 Type 1 1-17976 <$20
20 Type 1 1-5236 <$30
10 Type 2 1-14739* <$25
20 Type 2 1-3655 <$35
* 10087-10092 not issued
Total Issue $5,589,970
Out in 1935 $590,400
Large out 1935 $11,730

1205 Calhoun
FNB OF THE CITY OF
BATTLE CREEK
{{ 1 L }}
Chartered 6/2/65
Liquidated 3/28/85
Original Series <$VALUE
4x5 1-4550 <$1250
3x10-20 1-1750<$1500/$1750
Series 1875
4x5 1-250 <$1250
3x10-20 1-2378<$1500/$1750
Total Issue $302,400
Out in 1910 $1,955

3896 Calhoun
MERCHANTS NB OF
BATTLE CREEK
{{ UNREPORTED }}
Chartered 6/2/88
Liquidated 4/1/95
Brown Back <$VALUE
3x10-20 1-1699 <$1500
Total Issue $84,950
Out in 1910 $720

3314 Calhoun
NB OF BATTLE CREEK
{{ 4 L }}
Chartered 2/26/85
Liquidated 2/13/05
Brown Back <$VALUE
4x5 1-18045 <$500
3x10-20 1-4051 <$500
Total Issue $563,450
Out in 1910 $12,685

Old-Merchants NB & TC of
Battle Creek
SEE Ch 7589
Old NB of Battle Creek

7589 Calhoun
OLD NB OF BATTLE CREEK
Chartered 1/6/05
Liquidated 6/11/34
2nd title:Old NB & TC
1/24/27
3rd title:Old-Merchants NB
& TC 8/31/29
FIRST TITLE {{ 12 L }}
1902 Red Seal <$VALUE
3x10-20 1-7100 <$350
1902 Date Back
3x10-20 1-12800 <$150
1902 Plain Back
3x10-20 12801-59401 <$150
SECOND TITLE {{ 5 L }}
1902 Plain Back
3x10-20 1-20326 <$175
THIRD TITLE {{ 50+ S }}
1929 Small Size
10 Type 1 1-37909 <$20
20 Type 1 1-10245 <$30
Total Issue $7,845,290
Out at close $400,000
Large out 1935 $14,810
Ch 14185 assumed circulation

2853 Bay
BAY NB OF BAY CITY
Chartered 1/6/83
Receivership 12/7/31
2nd title:FNB of Bay City
4/28/91
FIRST TITLE {{ 0 L }}
Brown Back <$VALUE
3x10-20 1-2169 <$1000
SECOND TITLE {{ 10 L 26 S }}
Brown Back
4x5 1-6414 <$400
3x10-20 1-1427 <$400
1902 Red Seal
3x10-20 1-4200 <$450
1902 Date Back
3x10-20 1-14000 <$200
1902 Plain Back
3x10-20 14001-42344 <$200
1929 Small Size
10 Type 1 1-8052 <$50
20 Type 1 1-2071 <$55
Total Issue $3,366,920
Out at close $390,760
Large out at close $17,850

410 Bay
FNB OF BAY CITY
{{ 3 L }}
Chartered 5/2/64
Liquidated 11/8/82
Original Series <$VALUE
3x1-2 1-6700 <$750/$1500
4x5 1-8050 <$850
3x10-20 1-700 <$1250/$1500
Series 1875
3x1-2 1-920 <$750/$1500
4x5 1-825 <$850
3x10-20 1-3700<$1250/$1500
Total Issue $435,600
Out in 1910 $2,557

FNB of Bay City
SEE ALSO Ch 2853
Bay NB of Bay City

13622 Bay
NB OF BAY CITY
{{ 24 S }}
Chartered 6/32
1929 Small Size <$VALUE
5 Type 1 1-5252 <$50
10 Type 1 1-3142 <$50
20 Type 1 1-990 <$55
5 Type 2 1-27046 <$55
10 Type 2 1-12960 <$55
20 Type 2 1-3855 <$60
Total Issue $806,810
Out in 1935 $339,700

4953 Bay
OLD SECOND NB OF BAY CITY
{{ 2 L }}
Chartered 1894
Liquidated 10/29/14
Brown Back <$VALUE
4x5 1-9250 <$650
3x10-20 1-6700 <$650
1882 Date Back
4x5 1-1937 <$600
3x10-20 1-1033 <$600
1902 Date Back
4x5 1-160 <$450
3x10-20 1-150 <$450
Total Issue $621,090
Out at close $50,000

2145 Bay
SECOND NB OF BAY CITY
{{ 6 L }}
Chartered 5/12/74
Liquidated 5/5/94
Original Series <$VALUE
3x1-2 1-1400 <$500/$1250
4x5 1-1000 <$600
4x20 1-225 <$850/$1250
Series 1875
3x1-2 1-520 <$500/$1250
4x5 1-13829 <$600
4x20 1-4353 <$750/$1000
Total Issue $672,420
Out in 1910 $4,071

10143 Berrien
AMERICAN NB OF
BENTON HARBOR
Organized 2/5/12
Receivership 12/29/31
2nd title:American NB & TC
1/16/28
FIRST TITLE {{ 10 L }}
1902 Date Back <$VALUE
4x5 1-4200 <$165
3x10-20 1-3300 <$165
1902 Plain Back
4x5 4201-25710 <$165
3x10-20 3301-17779 <$165
SECOND TITLE {{ 2 L 21 S }}
1902 Plain Back
4x5 1-4561 <$250
3x10-20 1-3110 <$250
1929 Small Size
5 Type 1 1-5307 <$50
10 Type 1 1-2642 <$50
20 Type 1 1-648 <$60
Total Issue $2,045,360
Out at close $197,420
Large out at close $13,950

10529 Berrien
FARMERS & MERCHANTS NB OF
BENTON HARBOR
Organized 4/22/14
Liquidated 1/9/34
2nd title:Farmers &
Merchants NB & TC 5/22/26
FIRST TITLE {{ 6 L }}
1902 Date Back <$VALUE
4x5 1-2750 <$200
3x10-20 1-2300 <$200
1902 Plain Back
4x5 2751-13630 <$200
3x10-20 2301-9346 <$200
SECOND TITLE {{ 3 L 16 S }}
1902 Plain Back
4x5 1-7322 <$225
3x10-20 1-4730 <$225
1929 Small Size
5 Type 1 1-4700 <$75
10 Type 1 1-2756 <$75
20 Type 1 1-780 <$85
Total Issue $1,522,800
Out at close $132,130
Large out at close $5,230

4261 Berrien
FNB OF BENTON HARBOR
{{ 1 L }}
Organized 5/15/90
Receivership 9/21/97
Brown Back <$VALUE
4x5 1-1683 <$1000
Total Issue $33,660
Out in 1915 $120

13607 Gogebic
BESSEMER NB, BESSEMER
{{ 7 S }}
Chartered 3/32
1929 Small Size <$VALUE
10 Type 2 1-3395 <$165
20 Type 2 1-1135 <$175
Total Issue $56,650
Out in 1935 $45,050

3947 Gogebic
FNB OF BESSEMER
{{ 2 L }}
Chartered 1888
Liquidated 5/7/32
Brown Back <$VALUE
4x5 1-2800 <$850
3x10-20 1-572 <$850
1902 Date Back
3x10-20 1-1320 <$600
1902 Plain Back
3x10-20 1321-2804 <$600
Total Issue $224,800
Out at close $1,445

2944 Mecosta
BIG RAPIDS NB, BIG RAPIDS
{{ 1 L }}
Chartered 5/9/83
Liquidated 4/15/95
Brown Back <$VALUE
4x5 1-1113 <$1500
3x10-20 1-1205 <$1500
Total Issue $82,510
Out in 1915 $490

1832 Mecosta
NORTHERN NB OF BIG RAPIDS
{{ 1 L }}
Chartered 6/5/71
Receivership 8/5/93
Original Series <$VALUE
4x5 1-2350 <$1250
3x10-20 1-210 <$1500/$2000
Series 1875
4x5 1-2164 <$1250
3x10-20 1-2161<$1500/$2000
Brown Back
3x10-20 1-556 <$1250
Total Issue $236,630
Out in 1915 $790

13703 Oakland
BIRMINGHAM NB, BIRMINGHAM
{{ 8 S }}
Chartered 6/33
1929 Small Size <$VALUE
5 Type 2 1-4340 <$200
10 Type 2 1-2078 <$200
20 Type 2 1-620 <$225
50 Type 2 1-108 <$500
100 Type 2 1-48 <$650
Total Issue $65,080
Out in 1935 $35,450

9874 Oakland
FNB OF BIRMINGHAM
{{ 3 L 10 S }}
Organized 9/7/10
Receivership 10/14/33
1902 Date Back <$VALUE
4x5 1-550 <$450
3x10-20 1-440 <$450
1902 Plain Back
4x5 551-16252 <$450
3x10-20 441-9549 <$450
3x50-100 1-742 <$750/$850
1929 Small Size
5 Type 1 1-2247 <$165
10 Type 1 1-1027 <$165
20 Type 1 1-316 <$165
50 Type 1 1-158 <$375
100 Type 1 1-56 <$500
Total Issue $1,235,940
Out at close $100,000
Large out at close $6,090

11813 Lenawee
FNB OF BLISSFIELD
{{ 4 L 3 S }}
Organized 8/3/20
Receivership 7/3/31
1902 Plain Back <$VALUE
4x5 1-26414 <$400
1929 Small Size
5 Type 1 1-4212 <$350
Total Issue $654,640
Out at close $58,380
Large out at close $3,100

9020 Charlevoix
FNB OF BOYNE CITY
{{ 6 L 5 S }}
Organized 1/15/08
Receivership 8/7/31
1902 Red Seal <$VALUE
4x5 1-830 <$600
4x10 1-835 <$600
1902 Date Back
4x5 1-3450 <$300
4x10 1-3250 <$300
1902 Plain Back
4x5 3451-12136 <$300
4x10 3251-10272 <$300
1929 Small Size
5 Type 1 1-1543 <$250
10 Type 1 1-750 <$250
Total Issue $794,890
Out at close $50,000
Large out at close $4,700

9704 Branch
PEOPLES NB OF BRONSON
{{ 3 L 7 S }}
Organized 3/7/10
Receivership 5/9/34
1902 Date Back <$VALUE
3x10-20 1-1720 <$450
1902 Plain Back
3x10-20 1721-9444 <$450
1929 Small Size
10 Type 1 1-1234 <$225
20 Type 1 1-302 <$225
10 Type 2 1-518 <$250
20 Type 2 1-75 <$250
Total Issue $589,160
Out at close $50,000
Large out at close $2,250

2046 Berrien
FNB OF BUCHANAN
{{ UNREPORTED }}
Chartered 9/16/72
Liquidated 12/21/78
Original Series <$VALUE
3x1-2 1-1000 <$1500/$2500
4x5 1-2000 <$1500
Series 1875
4x5 1-745 <$1500
Total Issue $59,900
Out in 1910 $262

3925 Berrien
FNB OF BUCHANAN
{{ 5 L 6 S }}
Organized 9/10/88
Receivership 10/30/31
Brown Back <$VALUE
3x10-20 1-1750 <$600
1902 Date Back
3x10-20 1-1960 <$400
1902 Plain Back
3x10-20 1961-7941 <$400
1929 Small Size
10 Type 1 1-876 <$250
20 Type 1 1-263 <$250
Total Issue $568,670
Out at close $48,740
Large out at close $5,000

9497 Saint Joseph
FNB OF BURR OAK
{{ 2 L 7 S }}
Chartered 8/09
1902 Date Back <$VALUE
3x10-20 1-1700 <$500
1902 Plain Back
3x10-20 1701-6847 <$500
1929 Small Size
10 Type 1 1-850 <$225
20 Type 1 1-256 <$250
10 Type 2 1-57 <$300
20 Type 2 1-25 <$300
Total Issue $425,140
Out in 1935 $26,730
Large out 1935 $1,850

3457 Houghton
FNB OF CALUMET
{{ 14 L 20 S }}
Chartered 2/24/86
Liquidated 9/29/34
Brown Back <$VALUE
4x5 1-5758 <$350
3x10-20 1-1061 <$350
1902 Red Seal
4x5 1-1560 <$375
3x10-20 1-1251 <$375
1902 Date Back
4x5 1-11500 <$125
3x10-20 1-9000 <$125
1902 Plain Back
4x5 11501-32671 <$125
3x10-20 9001-22507 <$125
1929 Small Size
5 Type 1 1-5326 <$75
10 Type 1 1-2986 <$70
20 Type 1 1-734 <$75
5 Type 2 1-3418 <$85
10 Type 2 1-1408 <$85
20 Type 2 1-330 <$85
Total Issue $2,505,520
Out at close $193,300
Large out at close $9,680
Ch 14249 assumed circulation

10631 Saint Clair
FNB OF CAPAC
{{ 5 L 2 S }}
Organized 9/17/14
Receivership 12/19/30
1902 Plain Back <$VALUE
4x10 1-2737 <$400
1929 Small Size
10 Type 1 1-220 <$450
Total Issue $122,680
Out at close $9,280
Large out at close $1,130

11802 Iron
CASPIAN NB, CASPIAN
{{ 2 L 10 S }}
Organized 7/17/20
Liquidated 6/16/34
1902 Plain Back <$VALUE
3x10-20 1-2194 <$600
1929 Small Size
10 Type 1 1-566 <$165
20 Type 1 1-166 <$175
10 Type 2 1-30 <$250
20 Type 2 1-20 <$250
Total Issue $164,280
Out at close $19,920
Large out at close $870

1812 Cass
FNB OF CASSOPOLIS
{{ 50+ L 40U + 18 S }}
Chartered 4/18/71
Original Series <$VALUE
3x1-2 1-2900 <$500/$1250
4x5 1-2625 <$500
Series 1875
4x5 1-6150 <$500
Brown Back
4x5 1-2400 <$300
3x10-20 1-700 <$300
1882 Date Back
4x5 1-220 <$300
3x10-20 1-211 <$300
1902 Date Back
3x10-20 1-1300 <$60/$70
1902 Plain Back
3x10-20 1301-3360 <$60/$70
1929 Small Size
5 Type 1 1-432 <$50
10 Type 1 1-246 <$65
20 Type 1 1-71 <$65
Total Issue $495,690
Out in 1935 $19,800
Large out 1935 $5,735

2095 Saint Joseph
FNB OF CENTREVILLE
{{ 3 L }}
Chartered 3/26/73
Liquidated 11/25/93
Original Series <$VALUE
3x1-2 1-2700 <$600/$1250
4x5 1-2325 <$600
Series 1875
3x1-2 1-340 <$600/$1250
4x5 1-5593 <$600
Brown Back
50-100 1-14 <$2250/$2500
Total Issue $175,660
Out in 1910 $1,135

1758 Eaton
FNB OF CHARLOTTE
{{ 6 L 5 S }}
Chartered 12/28/70
Original Series <$VALUE
3x1-2 1-1500 <$500/$1250
4x5 1-3125 <$650
Series 1875
4x5 1-6849 <$650
Brown Back
4x5 1-1750 <$500
3x10-20 1-4490 <$500
1882 Date Back
4x5 1-945 <$500
3x10-20 1-756 <$500
1902 Date Back
50-100 1-800 <$650/$750
3x50-100 1-1220 <$650/$750
1902 Plain Back
3x50-100 1221-1593
<$650/$750
1929 Small Size
50 Type 1 1-314 <$300
100 Type 1 1-75 <$425
Total Issue $1,180,630
Out in 1935 $94,530
Large out 1935 $8,430

3034 Eaton
MERCHANTS NB OF CHARLOTTE
{{ UNREPORTED }}
Chartered 8/18/83
Liquidated 9/30/11
Brown Back <$VALUE
3x10-20 1-2326 <$1500
1902 Red Seal
3x10-20 1-2200 <$1500
1902 Date Back
3x10-20 1-1045 <$1250
Total Issue $278,550
Out in 1911 $48,800

3235 Cheboygan
FNB OF CHEBOYGAN
{{ 5 L 2 S }}
Chartered 8/6/84
Receivership 6/12/30
Brown Back <$VALUE
3x10-20 1-2819 <$650
1902 Red Seal
3x10-20 1-2100 <$650
1902 Date Back
3x10-20 1-3000 <$350
1902 Plain Back
3x10-20 3001-11641 <$350
1929 Small Size
10 Type 1 1-493 <$400
20 Type 1 1-116 <$400
Total Issue $871,500
Out at close $50,000
Large out at close $9,720

11454 Saginaw
FNB OF CHESANING
{{ 2 L }}
Chartered 9/19
Liquidated 9/23/29
1902 Plain Back <$VALUE
4x5 1-16283 <$650
Total Issue $325,860
Out at close $40,060

1235 Branch
COLDWATER NB, COLDWATER
{{ 12 L U + 14 S }}
Chartered 6/6/65
Receivership 5/15/34
Original Series <$VALUE
3x1-2 1-5150 <$500/$1250
4x5 1-4300 <$600
3x10-20 1-900 <$750/$1250
Series 1875
3x1-2 1-1110 <$500/$1250
4x5 1-1780 <$600
3x10-20 1-440 <$750/$1000
Brown Back
4x5 1-5614 <$400
3x10-20 1-765 <$400
1902 Red Seal
3x10-20 1-900 <$450
1902 Date Back
3x10-20 1-1950 <$225
1902 Plain Back
3x10-20 1951-14021 <$225
1929 Small Size
5 Type 1 1-412 <$100
10 Type 1 1-2460 <$85
20 Type 1 1-690 <$100
5 Type 2 1-72 <$150
10 Type 2 1-120 <$150
Total Issue $1,360,800
Out at close $100,000
Large out at close $5,850

1924 Branch
SOUTHERN MICHIGAN NB OF COLDWATER
{{ 20 L 27 S }}
Chartered 1/16/72 1st
Original Series <$VALUE
3x1-2 1-3300 <$400/$1250
4x5 1-4025 <$500
3x10-20 1-1380 <$750/$1250
Series 1875
4x5 1-7416 <$500
3x10-20 1-1934 <$750/$1000
Brown Back
4x5 1-19800 <$375
3x10-20 1-10000 <$375
1882 Date Back
4x5 1-3252 <$350
3x10-20 1-3041 <$350
1902 Date Back
4x5 1-6000 <$150
3x10-20 1-4350 <$150
1902 Plain Back
4x5 6001-33607 <$150
3x10-20 4351-21211 <$150
1929 Small Size
5 Type 1 1-5678 <$65
10 Type 1 1-2576 <$65
20 Type 1 1-990 <$75
5 Type 2 1-5630 <$85
10 Type 2 1-2705 <$85
20 Type 2 1-979 <$85
Total Issue $3,775,280
Out in 1935 $161,800
Large out 1935 $11,770

3251 Jackson
FNB OF CONCORD
{{ 1 L }}
Chartered 9/15/84
Liquidated 11/27/86
Brown Back <$VALUE
4x5 1-677 <$1750
Total Issue $13,540
Out in 1910 $85

2211 Saint Joseph
FARMERS NB OF CONSTANTINE
{{ UNREPORTED }}
Chartered 12/4/74
Liquidated 9/4/93
Original Series <$VALUE
3x10-20 1-900 <$2000/$2500
Series 1875
3x10-20 1-1321<$2000/$2500
Total Issue $111,050
Out in 1910 $560

813 Saint Joseph
FNB OF CONSTANTINE
{{ UNREPORTED }}
Chartered 2/17/65
Liquidated 7/1/94
Original Series <$VALUE
4x5 1-2525 <$2000
3x10-20 1-1270<$2000/$2500
Series 1875
4x5 1-350 <$2000
3x10-20 1-674 <$2000/$2500
Brown Back
3x10-20 1-537 <$1750
Total Issue $181,550
Out in 1910 $970

1256 Shiawassee
FNB OF CORUNNA
{{ 3 L }}
Chartered 6/10/65
Liquidated 3/1/05
Original Series <$VALUE
4x5 1-2050 <$850
3x10-20 1-700 <$1000/$1500
Series 1875
4x5 1-2060 <$850
3x10-20 1-894 <$1000/$1500
Brown Back
3x10-20 1-3679 <$750
Total Issue $345,850
Out in 1910 $6,425

9792 Sanilac
FNB OF CROSWELL
{{ UNREPORTED }}
Chartered 6/10
Liquidated 7/10/17
1902 Date Back <$VALUE
3x10-20 1-1576 <$1500
Total Issue $78,800
Out at close $14,900

11547 Iron
CRYSTAL FALLS NB, CRYSTAL FALLS
{{ 10 L 32 S }}
Organized 11/20/19
Receivership 10/10/34
1902 Plain Back <$VALUE
3x10-20 1-5531 <$200
1929 Small Size
10 Type 1 1-1051 <$60
20 Type 1 1-331 <$65
Total Issue $379,330
Out at close $50,000
Large out at close $2,710

7525 Iron
IRON COUNTY NB OF CRYSTAL FALLS
{{ 6 L 7 S }}
Chartered 12/24/04
Receivership 10/10/34
1902 Red Seal <$VALUE
4x5 1-780 <$600
3x10-20 1-624 <$600
1902 Date Back
4x5 1-1525 <$275
3x10-20 1-1120 <$275
1902 Plain Back
4x5 1526-4540 <$275
3x10-20 1121-2989 <$275
1929 Small Size
5 Type 1 1-736 <$150
10 Type 1 1-356 <$150
20 Type 1 1-108 <$165
5 Type 2 1-512 <$200
10 Type 2 1-243 <$200
20 Type 2 1-35 <$200
Total Issue $349,140
Out at close $24,700
Large out at close $1,640

12989 Wayne
FNB OF DEARBORN
{{ U + 10 S }}
Organized 8/17/26
Receivership 7/3/31
1929 Small Size <$VALUE
5 Type 1 1-1466 <$250
10 Type 1 1-729 <$250
20 Type 1 1-227 <$250
Total Issue $114,960
Out at close $48,200

1722 Van Buren
FNB OF DECATUR
{{ 7 L }}
Chartered 10/15/70
Liquidated 9/20/90
Original Series <$VALUE
3x1-2 1-2300 <$500/$1250
4x5 1-4300 <$500
Series 1875
4x5 1-5751 <$500
Total Issue $212,520
Out in 1910 $1,314

3357 Wayne
AMERICAN EXCHANGE NB OF DETROIT
{{ 3 L }}
Chartered 6/26/85
Liquidated 2/14/11
Brown Back <$VALUE
4x5 1-16552 <$400
3x10-20 1-466 <$400
1902 Red Seal
4x5 1-1960 <$400
3x10-20 1-1542 <$400
Total Issue $470,640
Out in 1911 $29,845

1542 Wayne
AMERICAN NB OF DETROIT
{{ 4 L }}
Chartered 8/29/65
Liquidated 7/24/85
Original Series <$VALUE
4x5 1-12475 <$500
3x10-20 1-5340 <$750/$1250
Series 1875
4x5 1-8725 <$500
3x10-20 1-6952 <$650/$1000
Total Issue $1,038,600
Out in 1910 $5,660

2591 Wayne
COMMERCIAL NB OF DETROIT
{{ 13 L }}
Chartered 11/21/81
Liquidated 6/1/08
Series 1875 <$VALUE
4x5 1-2910 <$400
3x10-20 1-4480 <$600/$1000
Brown Back
4x5 1-10000 <$225
3x10-20 1-37568 <$225
Total Issue $2,360,600
Out in 1910 $189,470

2870 Wayne
DETROIT NB, DETROIT
{{ UNREPORTED }}
Chartered 2/1/83
Liquidated 11/17/02
Brown Back <$VALUE
4x5 1-5826 <$1000
3x10-20 1-3038 <$1000
Total Issue $268,420
Out in 1910 $3,920

10527 Wayne
FIRST & OLD DETROIT NB, DETROIT
Organized 4/22/14
Receivership 5/12/33
2nd title:FNB in Detroit 1/19/22
3rd title:F Wayne NB of Detroit 12/31/31
4th title:FNB, Detroit 10/8/32
FIRST TITLE {{ 23 L }}
1902 Date Back <$VALUE
4x5 1-52750 <$60
3x10-20 1-37000 <$65
3x50-100 1-6000 <$300/$350
1902 Plain Back
4x5 52751-128200 <$60
3x10-20 37001-81300 <$65
SECOND TITLE
{{ 7U + 21 L 10U+ 34 S }}
1902 Plain Back
4x5 1-208931 <$50
3x10-20 1-146601 <$60
3x50-100 1-9302 <$300/$350
1929 Small Size
5 Type 1 1-82286 <$15
10 Type 1 1-41364 <$20
20 Type 1 1-13178 <$30
50 Type 1 1-3652 <$75
100 Type 1 1-1002 <$135
THIRD TITLE {{ 7U + 36 S }}
1929 Small Size
5 Type 1 1-48754 <$15
10 Type 1 1-37514 <$20
20 Type 1 1-17360 <$30
50 Type 1 1-4340 <$75
100 Type 1 1-1654 <$135
FOURTH TITLE {{ 6U + 10 S }}
1929 Small Size
5 Type 1 1-55 <$60
10 Type 1 1-2267 <$50
20 Type 1 1-776 <$60
50 Type 1 1-100 <$125
100 Type 1 1-50 <$200
Total Issue $38,573,600
Out at close $9,351,060
Large out at close $146,130

FNB in Detroit
SEE Ch 10527
F & Old NB, Detroit

97 Wayne
FNB OF DETROIT
{{ 4 L }}
Chartered 10/5/63
Liquidated 6/17/82
Original Series <$VALUE
4x5 1-11140 <$600
4x10 1-9050 <$750
Series 1875
4x5 1-5000 <$600
4x10 1-9047 <$750
Total Issue $1,046,680
Out in 1910 $4,830

2707 Wayne
FNB OF DETROIT
{{ 9 L }}
Chartered 6/19/82
Liquidated 4/30/14
Brown Back <$VALUE
3x10-20 1-19286 <$275/$325
1902 Red Seal
3x10-20 1-25500 <$275/$325
1902 Date Back
4x5 1-43980 <$100
3x10-20 1-27610 <$100
Total Issue $4,499,400
Out in 1914 $566,170

F Wayne NB of Detroit
SEE Ch 10527
F & Old NB, Detroit

FNB, Detroit
SEE Ch 10527
F & Old NB, Detroit

12847 Wayne
GRISWOLD NB OF DETROIT
{{ 6 L }}
Chartered 11/11/25
Liquidated 3/21/27
1902 Plain Back <$VALUE
4x5 1-36740 <$150
3x10-20 1-28918 <$150
Total Issue $2,180,700
Out at close $928,800

Guardian NB of Commerce of Detroit
SEE Ch 8703
NB of Commerce of Detroit

2365 Wayne
MERCHANTS & MANUFACTURERS NB OF DETROIT
{{ 4 L }}
Chartered 7/13/77
Liquidated 4/14/94
Series 1875 <$VALUE
4x5 1-12930 <$500
3x10-20 1-8388 <$650/$1000
Total Issue $678,000
Out in 1910 $2,730

****
10600 Wayne
MERCHANTS NB OF DETROIT
{{ 12 L }}
Chartered 8/14
Liquidated 5/27/29
1902 Plain Back <$VALUE
4x5 1-23990 <$100
3x10-20 1-16730 <$100
3x50-100 1-1282 <$350/$400
Total Issue $1,636,800
Out at close $1,127,450
****
8703 Wayne
NB OF COMMERCE OF DETROIT
Organized 4/24/07
Receivership 5/12/33
2nd title:Guardian NB of Commerce 12/31/31
FIRST TITLE {{ 15 L }}
1902 Red Seal <$VALUE
4x10 1-9050 <$200
1902 Date Back
4x10 1-83000 <$75
3x50-100 1-4455 <$300/$350
1902 Plain Back
4x10 83001-95396 <$75
SECOND TITLE {{ 50+ S }}
1929 Small Size
5 Type 1 1-19176 <$15
10 Type 1 1-11641 <$20
20 Type 1 1-16509 <$30
50 Type 1 1-5687 <$75
100 Type 1 1-433 <$135
Total Issue $10,512,310
Out at close $4,844,240
Large out at close $18,690
****
1433 Wayne
N INSURANCE B OF DETROIT
{{ 1 L }}
Chartered 7/13/65
Liquidated 2/26/69
Original Series <$VALUE
4x5 1-4250 <$1500
Total Issue $85,000
Out in 1910 $495
****
6492 Wayne
OLD DETROIT NB, DETROIT
{{ 6 L }}
Organized 10/28/02
Liquidated 4/30/14
1902 Red Seal <$VALUE
4x5 1-4750 <$400
3x10-20 1-13650 <$400
50-100 1-500 <$3250/$3500
1902 Date Back
4x5 1-41874 <$200
3x10-20 1-23934 <$200
50-100 1-144 <$400/$500
Total Issue $2,908,280
Out in 1914 $537,150
****
3730 Wayne
PRESTON NB OF DETROIT
{{ 5 L }}
Chartered 6/23/87
Liquidated 6/17/02
Brown Back <$VALUE
3x10-20 1-41738 <$400
50-100 1-2000 <$1750/$2000
Total Issue $2,386,900
Out in 1910 $51,180
****
116 Wayne
SECOND NB OF DETROIT
{{ 6 L }}
Chartered 10/7/63
Liquidated 2/24/83
Original Series <$VALUE
3x1-2 1-14380 <$400/$1000
4x5 1-26500 <$450
4x10 1-12700 <$650
3x20-50 1-3784<$1250/$6000
Series 1875
4x5 1-7201 <$450
4x10 1-4926 <$600
Total Issue $1,867,200
Out in 1910 $11,669
****
3514 Wayne
THIRD NB OF DETROIT
{{ 1 L }}
Chartered 6/1/86
Receivership 2/1/94
Brown Back <$VALUE
4x5 1-6377 <$850
Total Issue $127,540
Out in 1915 $680
****

****
3487 Wayne
UNION NB OF DETROIT
{{ UNREPORTED }}
Chartered 4/13/86
Liquidated 3/29/06
Brown Back <$VALUE
3x10-20 1-8418 <$1000
Total Issue $420,900
Out in 1910 $10,365
****
10073 Cass
DOWAGIAC NB, DOWAGIAC
{{ 7 L 11 S }}
Chartered 8/11
1902 Date Back <$VALUE
3x10-20 1-2160 <$250
1902 Plain Back
3x10-20 2161-10317 <$250
1929 Small Size
10 Type 1 1-1248 <$100
20 Type 1 1-308 <$110
10 Type 2 1-1103 <$125
20 Type 2 1-143 <$135
Total Issue $641,580
Out in 1935 $40,250
Large out 1935 $2,300
****
1625 Cass
FNB OF DOWAGIAC
{{ 1 L }}
Chartered 12/29/65
Liquidated 1/3/83
Original Series <$VALUE
4x5 1-5000 <$1250
Series 1875
4x5 1-2750 <$1250
Total Issue $155,000
Out in 1910 $1,095
****
5415 Shiawassee
FNB OF DURAND
{{ 2 L }}
Chartered 6/11/00
Liquidated 4/7/09
Brown Back <$VALUE
4x5 1-1500 <$1250
3x10-20 1-1180 <$1250
Total Issue $89,000
Out in 1910 $10,170
****
3123 Saginaw
EAST SAGINAW NB, EAST SAGINAW
{{ UNREPORTED }}
Chartered 2/13/84
Liquidated 6/23/91
Brown Back <$VALUE
3x10-20 1-1383 <$1500
Total Issue $69,150
Out in 1910 $350
****
637 Saginaw
FNB OF EAST SAGINAW
{{ 1 L }}
Chartered 12/20/64
Receivership 12/10/96
Original Series <$VALUE
3x1-2 1-3200 <$1000/$1750
4x5 1-2700 <$1000
3x10-20 1-2020<$1250/$1750
Series 1875
4x5 1-1000 <$1000
3x10-20 1-1456<$1250/$1750
Brown Back
3x10-20 1-3032 <$1000
Total Issue $415,400
Out in 1915 $2,131
****
2761 Saginaw
HOME NB OF EAST SAGINAW
{{ 2 L }}
Chartered 7/26/82
Liquidated 6/22/96
Series 1875 <$VALUE
4x5 1-8675 <$850
3x10-20 1-4162<$1250/$1500
50-100 1-1333 <$6000
Total Issue $581,550
Out in 1910 $6,285
****
1550 Saginaw
MERCHANTS NB OF EAST SAGINAW
{{ 3 L }}
Chartered 9/5/65
Liquidated 1/9/83
Original Series <$VALUE
3x1-2 1-4000 <$750/$1250
4x5 1-6500 <$750
3x10-20 1-2500<$1000/$1250
3x50-100 1-220 <$6000
Series 1875
4x5 1-500 <$750
3x10-20 1-2352<$1000/$1250
Total Issue $457,600
Out in 1910 $2,767
****
1918 Saginaw
SECOND NB OF EAST SAGINAW
Chartered 1/11/72
2nd title:Second NB of Saginaw 11/12/91
3rd title:Second NB & TC of Saginaw 1/20/30
FIRST TITLE {{ 2 L }}
Original Series <$VALUE
3x1-2 1-1400 <$600/$1250
4x5 1-6750 <$650
3x10-20 1-1200 <$850/$1250
50-100 1-120 <$6000
Series 1875
4x5 1-4197 <$650
3x10-20 1-1258 <$850/$1250
SECOND TITLE {{ 19 L 9 S }}
Brown Back
4x5 1-8250 <$250
3x10-20 1-23940 <$250
1882 Date Back
4x5 1-12515 <$250
3x10-20 1-7137 <$250
1902 Date Back
4x5 1-36500 <$85
3x10-20 1-30000 <$85
1902 Plain Back
4x5 36501-66104 <$85
3x10-20 30001-47319 <$85
1929 Small Size
5 Type 1 1-5650 <$60
10 Type 1 1-2520 <$60
20 Type 1 1-858 <$65
THIRD TITLE {{ 36 S }}
1929 Small Size
5 Type 1 1-15964 <$20
10 Type 1 1-13038 <$25
20 Type 1 1-4436 <$35
5 Type 2 1-46962 <$25
10 Type 2 1-17961 <$30
20 Type 2 1-6875 <$40
Total Issue $8,828,820
Out in 1935 $1,090,050
Large out 1935 $23,370
Outstanding includes Ch 3911
****
2367 Eaton
FNB OF EATON RAPIDS
{{ 4 L 3 S }}
Chartered 8/2/77
Receivership 3/5/34
Series 1875 <$VALUE
3x10-20 1-2483<$1250/$1750
Brown Back
4x5 1-960 <$600
50-100 1-230 <$2500/$2750
1882 Date Back
4x5 1-1090 <$600
50-100 1-147 <$2500/$2750
1902 Plain Back
3x10-20 1-2887 <$400
1929 Small Size
10 Type 1 1-720 <$300
20 Type 1 1-172 <$325
Total Issue $429,890
Out at close $25,000
Large out at close $1,490
****
8496 Delta
ESCANABA NB, ESCANABA
{{ 16 L 14 S }}
Chartered 1/07
1902 Red Seal <$VALUE
4x5 1-1375 <$350
3x10-20 1-1200 <$350
1902 Date Back
4x5 1-6750 <$100
3x10-20 1-5000 <$100
1902 Plain Back
4x5 6751-21073 <$100
3x10-20 5001-14093 <$100
1929 Small Size
5 Type 1 1-3316 <$85
10 Type 1 1-1628 <$85
20 Type 1 1-400 <$100
5 Type 2 1-686 <$150
10 Type 2 1-402 <$150
20 Type 2 1-30 <$150
Total Issue $1,466,820
Out in 1935 $72,695
Large out 1935 $5,380
****
3761 Delta
FNB OF ESCANABA
{{ 18 L 13 S }}
Chartered 1887
Brown Back <$VALUE
3x10-20 1-2720 <$375
1902 Red Seal
3x10-20 1-1300 <$375
1902 Date Back
3x10-20 1-6700 <$85
1902 Plain Back
3x10-20 6701-19359 <$85
1929 Small Size
10 Type 1 1-2170 <$60
20 Type 1 1-598 <$70
10 Type 2 1-2623 <$65
20 Type 2 1-649 <$75
Total Issue $1,410,120
Out in 1935 $100,000
Large out 1935 $5,960
****
12561 Osceola
FNB OF EVART
{{ 3U + 7 S }}
Chartered 6/10/24
1929 Small Size <$VALUE
5 Type 1 1-1004 <$150
10 Type 1 1-508 <$150
20 Type 1 1-138 <$165
5 Type 2 1-1468 <$175
10 Type 2 1-760 <$175
20 Type 2 1-140 <$175
Total Issue $94,900
Out in 1935 $30,250
****
81 Genesee
FNB OF FENTON
{{ UNREPORTED }}
Chartered 9/10/63
Liquidated 5/2/71
Original Series <$VALUE
4x5 1-2750 <$2500
Total Issue $55,000
Out in 1910 $440
****
1780 Genesee
CITIZENS NB OF FLINT
{{ 2 L }}
Chartered 2/1/71
Liquidated 8/5/90
Original Series <$VALUE
3x1-2 1-3000 <$750/$1500
4x5 1-4000 <$750
3x10-20 1-1750<$1000/$1500
Series 1875
4x5 1-241 <$750
3x10-20 1-4445 <$900/$1250
Total Issue $409,570
Out in 1910 $2,295
****
10997 Genesee
FNB AT FLINT
Organized 4/13/17
Receivership 2/27/34
2nd title:FNB & TC at Flint 2/26/30
FIRST TITLE {{ 2 L 3 S }}
1902 Plain Back <$VALUE
3x10-20 1-11710 <$400
1929 Small Size
10 Type 1 1-1232 <$150
20 Type 1 1-412 <$150
SECOND TITLE {{ 11 S }}
1929 Small Size
10 Type 1 1-2646 <$100
20 Type 1 1-868 <$100
10 Type 2 1-2515 <$110
20 Type 2 1-380 <$125
Total Issue $1,004,530
Out at close $200,000
Large out at close $2,420
****
FNB of Flint
SEE ALSO Ch 3361
Flint NB, Flint
****
1588 Genesee
FNB OF FLINT
{{ 3 L }}
Chartered 10/14/65
Liquidated 6/30/85
Original Series <$VALUE
3x1-2 1-5300 <$600/$1500
4x5 1-3700 <$650
3x10-20 1-2380 <$850/$1250
Series 1875
3x10-20 1-6662 <$850/$1250
Total Issue $552,600
Out in 1910 $3,008
****
3361 Genesee
FLINT NB, FLINT
Chartered 6/30/85
Liquidated 4/17/05
2nd title:FNB of Flint 11/8/90
FIRST TITLE {{ 1 L }}
Brown Back <$VALUE
4x5 1-4690 <$850
SECOND TITLE {{ 4 L }}
Brown Back
4x5 1-25995 <$450
3x10-20 1-3950 <$500
Total Issue $811,200
Out in 1910 $14,520
****
7664 Genesee
NB OF FLINT
{{ 4 L }}
Chartered 3/05
Liquidated 6/21/16
1902 Red Seal <$VALUE
3x10-20 1-4100 <$600
1902 Date Back
3x10-20 1-7018 <$350
Total Issue $555,900
Out in 1916 $84,100
****
2708 Genesee
FNB OF FLUSHING
{{ UNREPORTED }}
Chartered 5/26/82
Liquidated 9/21/91
Series 1875 <$VALUE
3x10-20 1-1284 <$2500
Total Issue $64,200
Out in 1910 $220
****
14111 Delta
FNB IN GLADSTONE
{{ 2 S }}
Chartered 4/34
1929 Small Size <$VALUE
5 Type 2 1-1420 <$500
10 Type 2 1-810 <$500
20 Type 2 1-240 <$500
Total Issue $20,000
Out in 1935 $50,000
Outstanding includes Ch 10886
****
10886 Delta
FNB OF GLADSTONE
{{ 4 L 8 S }}
Organized 7/26/16
Liquidated 5/28/34
1902 Plain Back <$VALUE
4x5 1-7160 <$350
3x10-20 1-4847 <$350
1929 Small Size
5 Type 1 1-1494 <$150
10 Type 1 1-714 <$150
20 Type 1 1-222 <$150
5 Type 2 1-510 <$200
10 Type 2 1-293 <$200
20 Type 2 1-40 <$200
Total Issue $506,130
Out at close $20,000
Large out 1935 $2,585
Ch 14111 assumed circulation
****
1849 Ottawa
FNB OF GRAND HAVEN
{{ 2 L }}
Chartered 7/25/71
Liquidated 6/5/91
Original Series <$VALUE
3x1-2 1-2000 <$850/$1750
4x5 1-4000 <$1000
3x10-20 1-1700<$1250/$1750
Series 1875
4x5 1-5400 <$1000
3x10-20 1-3931<$1250/$1750
Total Issue $479,550
Out in 1910 $1,954
****
4578 Ottawa
NB OF GRAND HAVEN
{{ 1 L }}
Chartered 1891
Liquidated 2/19/10
Brown Back <$VALUE
3x10-20 1-5940 <$1000
1882 Date Back
3x10-20 1-636 <$1000
Total Issue $328,800
Out in 1910 $59,520
****
13328 Kent
AMERICAN NB OF GRAND RAPIDS
{{ 20 S }}
Chartered 5/20/29
Liquidated 10/16/31
1929 Small Size <$VALUE
10 Type 1 1-10467 <$50
20 Type 1 1-2801 <$60
Total Issue $964,140
Out at close $467,900
****
812 Kent
CITY NB OF GRAND RAPIDS
{{ 1 L }}
Chartered 2/17/65
Liquidated 1/21/85
Original Series <$VALUE
4x5 1-11250 <$1000
3x10-20 1-1188<$1250/$1500
Series 1875
4x5 1-4270 <$1000
3x10-20 1-1498<$1250/$1500
Total Issue $444,700
Out in 1910 $2,525
****
3488 Kent
FIFTH NB OF GRAND RAPIDS
{{ 4 L }}
Chartered 4/13/86
Liquidated 7/31/08
Brown Back <$VALUE
4x5 1-7838 <$450
3x10-20 1-2732 <$450
1902 Red Seal
3x10-20 1-1429 <$500
Total Issue $364,810
Out in 1910 $31,335
****
294 Kent
FNB OF GRAND RAPIDS
{{ 1 L }}
Chartered 2/29/64
Liquidated 2/24/83
Original Series <$VALUE
4x5 1-12750 <$1000
Series 1875
4x5 1-8540 <$1000
3x10-20 1-1800<$1250/$1750
Total Issue $515,800
Out in 1910 $3,820
****
2611 Kent
FOURTH NB OF GRAND RAPIDS
{{ 6U + 21 L }}
Chartered 1/12/82
Liquidated 4/2/26
Series 1875 <$VALUE
3x10-20 1-8860 <$750/$1000
Brown Back
4x5 1-17000 <$200
3x10-20 1-9600 <$200/$225
1882 Date Back
4x5 1-16750 <$175
3x10-20 1-11800 <$175/$200
1882 Value Back
4x5 16751-32967 <$175
3x10-20 11801-21498 <$175/$225
1902 Plain Back
4x5 1-18965 <$75
3x10-20 1-9726 <$85
Total Issue $3,862,840
Out at close $300,000
****
2460 Kent
GRAND RAPIDS NB, GRAND RAPIDS
{{ 3U + 15 L }}
Chartered 3/1/80
Liquidated 10/1/10
Series 1875 <$VALUE
3x10-20 1-4534 <$750/$1000
Brown Back
4x5 1-12000 <$175
3x10-20 1-15600 <$175/$225
1882 Date Back
4x5 1-7985 <$175
3x10-20 1-2585 <$175/$225
Total Issue $1,535,650
Out in 1910 $393,750
****
Grand Rapids NB, Grand Rapids
SEE Ch 3293
N City B of Grand Rapids
****
Grand Rapids N City B, Grand Rapids
SEE Ch 3293
N City B of Grand Rapids
****
13758 Kent
NB OF GRAND RAPIDS
{{ 50+ S }}
Chartered 8/22/33
1929 Small Size <$VALUE
5 Type 2 1-61133 <$20
10 Type 2 1-23880 <$20
20 Type 2 1-7500 <$30
50 Type 2 1-888 <$350
100 Type 2 1-288 <$450
Total Issue $767,665
Out in 1935 $493,750
****

<$VALUEs are for notes in **FINE** condition. Value changes by approximately **25%** for a change of one full grade.

****
3293 Kent
N CITY B OF GRAND RAPIDS
Chartered 1/22/85
Receivership 9/25/33
2nd title:Grand Rapids N City B 8/24/10
3rd title:Grand Rapids NB 3/13/22
FIRST TITLE {{ 6 L }}
Brown Back <$VALUE
4x5 1-20298 <$250
3x10-20 1-9404 <$250/$300
1902 Red Seal
4x5 1-15750 <$250
3x10-20 1-10200 <$250/$300
1902 Date Back
4x5 1-5077 <$125
3x10-20 1-4062 <$125
SECOND TITLE {{ 12 L }}
1902 Date Back
4x5 1-42000 <$85
3x10-20 1-31800 <$85
1902 Plain Back
4x5 42001-105000 <$85
3x10-20 31801-66200 <$85
THIRD TITLE {{U + 20 L 45 S}}
1902 Plain Back
4x5 1-83875 <$75
3x10-20 1-39882 <$75
3x50-100 1-3051 <$300/$350
1929 Small Size
5 Type 1 1-21968 <$20
10 Type 1 1-10274 <$20
20 Type 1 1-3217 <$35
50 Type 1 1-932 <$100
100 Type 1 1-337 <$175
Total Issue $13,992,470
Out at close $989,900
Large out at close $57,935
****
2890 Kent
OLD NB OF GRAND RAPIDS
{{ 21 L }}
Chartered 2/24/83
Liquidated 4/22/29
Brown Back <$VALUE
4x5 1-20853 <$200
3x10-20 1-6853 <$200/$225
1902 Red Seal
4x5 1-31425 <$200
3x10-20 1-25230 <$200/$225
1902 Date Back
4x5 1-52665 <$50
3x10-20 1-33834 <$60
1902 Plain Back
4x5 52666-179092 <$50
3x10-20 33835-112926 <$60
Total Issue $11,877,850
Out at close $751,950
****
13799 Kent
PEOPLES NB OF GRAND RAPIDS
{{ 24 S }}
Chartered 10/10/33
1929 Small Size <$VALUE
5 Type 2 1-44068 <$35
10 Type 2 1-20712 <$35
20 Type 2 1-6771 <$45
Total Issue $562,880
Out in 1935 $338,400
****
3243 Montcalm
CITY NB OF GREENVILLE
{{ UNREPORTED }}
Chartered 8/28/84
Receivership 6/27/93
Brown Back <$VALUE
3x10-20 1-625 <$1500
Total Issue $31,250
Out in 1915 $70
****
2054 Montcalm
FNB OF GREENVILLE
{{ 4 L }}
Chartered 10/7/72
Liquidated 3/28/92
Original Series <$VALUE
3x1-2 1-3000 <$650/$1500
4x5 1-2875 <$750
3x10-20 1-750 <$1000/$1250
Series 1875
4x5 1-3727 <$750
3x10-20 1-1493<$1000/$1250
Total Issue $259,190
Out in 1910 $912
****

****
11843 Montcalm
GREENVILLE NB, GREENVILLE
{{ 3 L 7 S }}
Organized 9/11/20
Receivership 7/21/31
1902 Plain Back <$VALUE
4x5 1-6942 <$450
3x10-20 1-4322 <$450
1929 Small Size
5 Type 1 1-1053 <$225
10 Type 1 1-555 <$225
20 Type 1 1-174 <$225
Total Issue $440,710
Out at close $50,000
Large out at close $3,990
****
11082 Wayne
PEOPLES NB OF HAMTRAMCK
{{ 2 L }}
Organized 10/1/17
Liquidated 6/21/30
1902 Plain Back <$VALUE
4x5 1-15040 <$500
3x10-20 1-8910 <$500
Total Issue $746,300
Out at close $3,710
****
2143 Houghton
FNB OF HANCOCK
{{ 15 L 8 S }}
Chartered 5/1/74
Liquidated 9/5/34
Original Series <$VALUE
3x1-2 1-3000 <$500/$1250
4x5 1-2750 <$500
4x20 1-250 <$1250
Series 1875
3x1-2 1-1100 <$500/$1250
4x5 1-6593 <$500
4x20 1-1154 <$1000
Brown Back
4x5 1-1500 <$275
3x10-20 1-2350 <$275/$325
50-100 1-340 <$2250/$2500
1882 Date Back
4x5 1-2395 <$250
3x10-20 1-1522 <$250/$300
50-100 1-21 <$2000/$2250
1902 Date Back
4x5 1-1500 <$150
3x10-20 1-1200 <$150
1902 Plain Back
4x5 1501-6185 <$150
3x10-20 1201-4425 <$150
1929 Small Size
5 Type 1 1-1472 <$150
10 Type 1 1-710 <$150
20 Type 1 1-190 <$150
5 Type 2 1-552 <$175
10 Type 2 1-392 <$175
20 Type 2 1-65 <$175
Total Issue $1,107,840
Out at close $48,900
Large out at close $5,060
Ch 14249 assumed circulation
****
14249 Houghton
N METALS B OF HANCOCK
{{ 8 S }}
Chartered 8/34
1929 Small Size <$VALUE
5 Type 2 1-5932 <$275
10 Type 2 1-3640 <$275
20 Type 2 1-940 <$275
Total Issue $84,860
Out in 1935 $350,000
Outstanding includes Ch 2143, Ch 3457, and Ch 12387
****
9087 Houghton
SUPERIOR NB OF HANCOCK
{{ 7 L 14 S }}
Organized 2/1/08
1902 Red Seal <$VALUE
4x5 1-625 <$400
3x10-20 1-500 <$400
1902 Date Back
4x5 1-3500* <$175
3x10-20 1-2560** <$175
1902 Plain Back
4x5 3901-8650* <$175
3x10-20 2801-6025** <$175
* 3501-3900 not marked
** 2561-2800 not marked
1929 Small Size
5 Type 1 1-2236 <$75
10 Type 1 1-1318 <$75
20 Type 1 1-378 <$85
5 Type 2 1-3322 <$100
10 Type 2 1-1815 <$100
20 Type 2 1-371 <$100

Total Issue $745,450
Out in 1935 $98,600
Large out 1935 $2,280
****
6727 Oceana
FNB OF HART
{{ 13 L 13 S }}
Organized 4/14/03
Receivership 9/14/33
1902 Red Seal <$VALUE
4x5 1-550 <$400
3x10-20 1-400 <$400
1902 Date Back
4x5 1-700 <$175
3x10-20 1-560 <$175
1902 Plain Back
4x5 701-5227 <$175
3x10-20 561-3298 <$175
1929 Small Size
5 Type 1 1-2536 <$100
10 Type 1 1-1122 <$100
20 Type 1 1-316 <$110
5 Type 2 1-816 <$135
10 Type 2 1-721 <$135
Total Issue $493,050
Out at close $75,000
Large out at close $2,020
****
9854 Van Buren
OLNEY NB OF HARTFORD
{{ 12 L 4 S }}
Organized 7/20/10
Receivership 9/26/33
1902 Date Back <$VALUE
4x5 1-850 <$165
3x10-20 1-680 <$165
1902 Plain Back
4x5 851-4334 <$165
3x10-20 681-2807 <$165
1929 Small Size
5 Type 1 1-805 <$250
10 Type 1 1-467 <$250
20 Type 1 1-113 <$250
Total Issue $292,760
Out at close $25,000
Large out at close $1,340
****
1745 Barry
HASTINGS NB, HASTINGS
{{ 6 L 6 S }}
Chartered 12/3/70
Receivership 12/27/33
Original Series <$VALUE
3x1-2 1-900 <$600/$1500
4x5 1-3025 <$600
Series 1875
4x5 1-8186 <$600
Brown Back
4x5 1-6150 <$400
3x10-20 1-2190 <$400
1882 Date Back
4x5 1-843 <$400
3x10-20 1-656 <$400
1902 Date Back
4x5 1-2250 <$225
3x10-20 1-1800 <$225
1902 Plain Back
4x5 2251-9750 <$225
3x10-20 1801-6738 <$225
1929 Small Size
5 Type 1 1-1490 <$225
10 Type 1 1-949 <$225
20 Type 1 1-225 <$225
Total Issue $1,171,420
Out at close $50,000
Large out at close $4,680
****
13857 Barry
NB OF HASTINGS
{{ 4 S }}
Chartered 12/33
1929 Small Size <$VALUE
5 Type 2 1-2678 <$275
10 Type 2 1-2844 <$275
20 Type 2 1-1231 <$275
Total Issue $66,450
Out in 1935 $50,000
****
11954 Menominee
FNB OF HERMANSVILLE
{{ 1 L 6 S }}
Organized 3/29/21
1902 Plain Back <$VALUE
4x5 1-3057 <$1250
1929 Small Size
5 Type 1 1-1772 <$300
5 Type 2 1-4856 <$300
Total Issue $138,580
Out in 1935 $22,750
Large out 1935 $230
****

****
168 Hillsdale
FNB OF HILLSDALE
{{ 7 L 11 S }}
Chartered 12/23/63
Receivership 4/3/34
Original Series <$VALUE
4x5 1-5750 <$600
Series 1875
4x5 1-1195 <$600
Brown Back
4x5 1-3915 <$400
3x10-20 1-224 <$400
1902 Red Seal
3x10-20 1-625 <$450
1902 Date Back
3x10-20 1-1120 <$225
1902 Plain Back
3x10-20 1121-8736 <$225
1929 Small Size
10 Type 1 1-2610* <$125
20 Type 1 1-698** <$125
10 Type 2 1-522 <$150
20 Type 2 1-150 <$150
* 728-872 not issued
** 206-262 not issued
Total Issue $932,730
Out at close $99,600
Large out at close $3,760
****
14062 Hillsdale
HILLSDALE COUNTY NB OF HILLSDALE
{{ 4 S }}
Chartered 3/34
1929 Small Size <$VALUE
5 Type 2 1-2888 <$300
10 Type 2 1-5301 <$300
Total Issue $67,450
Out in 1935 $50,000
****
1470 Hillsdale
SECOND NB OF HILLSDALE
{{ 5 L }}
Chartered 7/20/65
Liquidated 12/18/86
Original Series <$VALUE
3x1-2 1-6760 <$600/$1500
4x5 1-4650 <$600
3x10-20 1-1080 <$750/$1250
Series 1875
4x5 1-1480 <$600
3x10-20 1-300 <$750/$1000
Total Issue $225,400
Out in 1910 $1,791
****
1752 Oakland
FNB OF HOLLY
{{ 3 L }}
Chartered 12/14/70
Liquidated 10/31/90
Original Series <$VALUE
4x5 1-3250 <$850
Series 1875
4x5 1-8238 <$850
Total Issue $229,760
Out in 1910 $1,175
****
1965 Oakland
MERCHANTS NB OF HOLLY
{{ 1 L }}
Chartered 4/22/72
Liquidated 12/31/81
Original Series <$VALUE
3x1-2 1-2100 <$1000/$2000
4x5 1-2725 <$1250
Series 1875
4x5 1-2845 <$1250
Total Issue $121,900
Out in 1910 $579
****
5896 Houghton
CITIZENS NB OF HOUGHTON
{{ 13 L 10 S }}
Chartered 7/01
Liquidated 12/1/32
Brown Back <$VALUE
4x5 1-1700 <$250
3x10-20 1-1760 <$250/$300
1882 Date Back
4x5 1-5850 <$250
3x10-20 1-4060 <$250/$300
1882 Value Back
4x5 5851-10650 <$250
3x10-20 4061-6831<$250/$300
1902 Plain Back
4x5 1-8415 <$150
3x10-20 1-5751 <$150
1929 Small Size
5 Type 1 1-2246 <$135
10 Type 1 1-1131 <$135
20 Type 1 1-309 <$135

Total Issue $1,304,720
Out at close $81,760
Large out at close $8,980
****
1247 Houghton
FNB OF HOUGHTON
{{ 5 L }}
Chartered 6/9/65
Liquidated 4/18/85
Original Series <$VALUE
3x1-2 1-6400 <$600/$1500
4x5 1-4250 <$650
3x10-20 1-2840<$1000/$1500
Series 1875
3x1-2 1-1000 <$600/$1500
4x5 1-2205 <$650
3x10-20 1-668 <$850/$1250
Total Issue $341,500
Out in 1910 $3,106
****
7676 Houghton
HOUGHTON NB, HOUGHTON
{{ 16 L 22 S }}
Chartered 4/05
1902 Red Seal <$VALUE
3x10-20 1-4000 <$300
50-100 1-400 <$3250/$3500
1902 Date Back
3x10-20 1-9199 <$85
50-100 1-200 <$400/$500
3x50-100 1-582 <$400/$500
1902 Plain Back
3x10-20 9201-27609 <$85
3x50-100 583-667<$400/$500
1929 Small Size
10 Type 1 1-2624 <$50
20 Type 1 1-779 <$60
50 Type 1 1-232 <$175
100 Type 1 1-84 <$275
Total Issue $2,208,070
Out in 1935 $172,310
Large out 1935 $13,400
****
3334 Houghton
NB OF HOUGHTON
{{ 3 L }}
Chartered 4/18/85
Liquidated 4/7/05
Brown Back <$VALUE
4x5 1-11525 <$600
50-100 1-1083 <$2250/$2500
Total Issue $392,950
Out in 1910 $16,500
****
14144 Livingston
FNB IN HOWELL
{{ 2 S }}
Chartered 5/34
1929 Small Size <$VALUE
5 Type 2 1-2280 <$500
10 Type 2 1-945 <$500
20 Type 2 1-330 <$500
Total Issue $27,450
Out in 1935 $21,250
****
11586 Livingston
FNB OF HOWELL
{{ 3 L 14 S }}
Organized 1/19/20
Receivership 6/18/34
1902 Plain Back <$VALUE
4x5 1-1450 <$400
3x10-20 1-810 <$400
1929 Small Size
5 Type 1 1-4150 <$110
10 Type 1 1-2182 <$110
20 Type 1 1-576 <$125
5 Type 2 1-764 <$150
10 Type 2 1-269 <$150
20 Type 2 1-30 <$175
Total Issue $401,150
Out at close $98,050
Large out at close $460
****
13824 Houghton
FNB AT HUBBELL
{{ 1 S }}
Chartered 11/33
1929 Small Size <$VALUE
5 Type 2 1-3556 <$500
10 Type 2 1-1847 <$500
Total Issue $36,250
Out in 1935 $25,200
****
9359 Houghton
FNB OF HUBBELL
{{ 3 L 10 S }}
Organized 2/19/09
Liquidated 1/6/34
1902 Date Back <$VALUE
3x10-20 1-2050 <$500
1902 Plain Back
3x10-20 2051-8063 <$500

1929 Small Size
10 Type 1 1-1081 <$175
20 Type 1 1-271 <$175
Total Issue $500,530
Out at close $46,100
Large out at close $2,310
****
275 Ionia
FNB OF IONIA
{{ 4 L }}
Chartered 2/24/64
Liquidated 3/2/97
Original Series <$VALUE
3x1-2 1-2300 <$600/$1500
4x5 1-8725 <$650
Series 1875
4x5 1-7675 <$650
Brown Back
50-100 1-916 <$2250/$2500
Total Issue $476,900
Out in 1910 $3,640
****
14187 Ionia
IONIA COUNTY NB OF IONIA
{{ 4 S }}
Chartered 6/34
1929 Small Size <$VALUE
10 Type 2 1-5130 <$350
Total Issue $51,300
Out in 1935 $50,000
****
5789 Ionia
NB OF IONIA
{{ 7 L 14 S }}
Organized 4/9/01
Receivership 6/26/34
Brown Back <$VALUE
50-100 1-600 <$2250/$2500
1882 Date Back
50-100 1-600 <$2000/$2250
3x50-100 1-732<$2000/$2250
1902 Plain Back
4x5 1-12571 <$250
4x10 1-7640 <$250
3x50-100 1-400 <$600/$700
1929 Small Size
5 Type 1 1-5090 <$85
10 Type 1 1-2782 <$85
20 Type 1 1-760 <$100
5 Type 2 1-2472 <$125
10 Type 2 1-885 <$125
20 Type 2 1-225 <$125
Total Issue $1,456,550
Out at close $147,700
Large out at close $7,360
****
Second NB of Ionia
SEE Ch 2008
NB of Lyons
****
3806 Dickinson
FNB OF IRON MOUNTAIN
{{ 8 L 21 S }}
Chartered 10/25/87
Brown Back <$VALUE
4x5 1-4337 <$450
3x10-20 1-1151 <$450
1902 Red Seal
4x5 1-1331 <$600
4x10 1-897 <$600
1902 Date Back
4x5 1-3150 <$250
4x10 1-3300 <$250
1902 Plain Back
4x5 3151-10196 <$250
4x10 3301-9179 <$250
1929 Small Size
5 Type 1 1-1940 <$75
10 Type 1 1-1094 <$75
5 Type 2 1-1728 <$85
10 Type 2 1-997 <$85
20 Type 2 1-2987 <$85
Total Issue $980,060
Out in 1935 $99,595
Large out 1935 $2,585
****
11929 Dickinson
NB OF IRON MOUNTAIN
Organized 1/15/21
Receivership 5/24/32
2nd title:United States NB of Iron Mountain 1/17/22
FIRST TITLE {{ 3 L }}
1902 Plain Back <$VALUE
4x5 1-7000 <$300
SECOND TITLE {{ 4 L 31 S }}
1902 Plain Back
3x10-20 1-9160 <$300
1929 Small Size
10 Type 1 1-1724 <$75
20 Type 1 1-479 <$85
Total Issue $758,920
Out at close $100,000
Large out at close $8,200
****

****
United States NB of
Iron Mountain
SEE Ch 11929
NB of Iron Mountain
****
8545 Iron
FNB OF IRON RIVER
{{ 6 L 18 S }}
Organized 1/25/07
Liquidated 6/16/34
1902 Red Seal <$VALUE
4x5 1-750 <$600
3x10-20 1-750 <$600
1902 Date Back
4x5 1-2700 <$250
3x10-20 1-1860 <$250
1902 Plain Back
4x5 2701-11620 <$250
3x10-20 1861-7927 <$250
1929 Small Size
5 Type 1 1-3390 <$110
10 Type 1 1-1755 <$110
20 Type 1 1-411 <$125
Total Issue $937,570
Out at close $73,085
Large out at close $3,855
****
14102 Iron
IRON RIVER NB, IRON RIVER
{{ 9 S }}
Chartered 4/34
1929 Small Size <$VALUE
5 Type 2 1-15500 <$200
Total Issue $77,500
Out in 1935 $62,500
****
3971 Gogebic
FNB OF IRONWOOD
{{ 1 L }}
Organized 1/31/89
Receivership 6/21/09
Brown Back <$VALUE
4x5 1-2846 <$1250
3x10-20 1-500 <$1250
1902 Date Back
3x10-20 1-250 <$1000
Total Issue $94,420
Out in 1915 $830
****
9517 Gogebic
GOGEBIC NB OF IRONWOOD
{{ 5 L 24 S }}
Chartered 8/09
1902 Date Back <$VALUE
3x10-20 1-2600 <$300
1902 Plain Back
3x10-20 2601-4531 <$300
1929 Small Size
10 Type 1 1-1736 <$75
20 Type 1 1-442 <$75
10 Type 2 1-555 <$125
20 Type 2 1-255 <$135
Total Issue $394,400
Out in 1935 $80,480
Large out 1935 $1,590
****
11469 Gogebic
IRON NB OF IRONWOOD
{{ 6 L 7 S }}
Organized 9/2/19
Receivership 5/26/31
1902 Plain Back <$VALUE
3x10-20 1-11442 <$300
1929 Small Size
10 Type 1 1-1158 <$150
20 Type 1 1-352 <$150
Total Issue $683,820
Out at close $100,000
Large out at close $16,950
****
12387 Gogebic
MERCHANTS & MINERS NB OF
IRONWOOD
{{ 6 L 18 S }}
Chartered 6/1/23
Liquidated 9/28/34
1902 Plain Back <$VALUE
4x5 1-6646 <$300
4x10 1-7282 <$300
1929 Small Size
5 Type 1 1-4488 <$75
10 Type 1 1-2204 <$75
5 Type 2 1-1904 <$85
10 Type 2 1-1129 <$85
Total Issue $711,890
Out at close $96,750
Large out at close $3,500
Ch 14249 assumed circulation
****

****
2084 Marquette
FNB OF ISHPEMING
{{ UNREPORTED }}
Chartered 2/15/73
Liquidated 10/20/75
Original Series <$VALUE
3x1-2 1-1500 <$1500/$2000
4x5 1-2355 <$1500
Total Issue $54,600
Out in 1910 $248
****
3095 Marquette
ISHPEMING NB, ISHPEMING
{{ UNREPORTED }}
Chartered 12/21/83
Liquidated 2/25/01
Brown Back <$VALUE
4x5 1-3099 <$1500
3x10-20 1-68 <$1500
Total Issue $65,380
Out in 1910 $640
****
13931 Marquette
MINERS FNB OF ISHPEMING
{{ 12 S }}
Chartered 1/34
1929 Small Size <$VALUE
5 Type 2 1-9526 <$110
10 Type 2 1-4779 <$100
20 Type 2 1-1584 <$110
Total Issue $127,100
Out in 1935 $99,100
****
5668 Marquette
MINERS NB OF ISHPEMING
{{ 13 L 15 S }}
Chartered 1/5/01
Receivership 1/17/34
Brown Back <$VALUE
3x10-20 1-4900 <$300/$350
1882 Date Back
4x5 1-6165* <$300
3x10-20 1-3600** <$300/$350
1882 Value Back
4x5 6566-10310* <$300
3x10-20 3921-6016**
<$300/$350
* 6166-6565 not marked
** 3601-3920 not marked
1902 Plain Back
3x10-20 1-5848 <$150
1929 Small Size
5 Type 1 1-2702 <$100
10 Type 1 1-1479 <$100
20 Type 1 1-452 <$100
Total Issue $1,439,600
Out at close $100,000
Large out at close $7,060
****
9654 Gratiot
COMMERCIAL NB OF ITHACA
{{ 6 L 6 S }}
Chartered 2/10
1902 Date Back <$VALUE
4x5 1-1950 <$250
3x10-20 1-1560 <$250
1902 Plain Back
4x5 1951-8118 <$250
3x10-20 1561-5353 <$250
1929 Small Size
5 Type 1 1-1230 <$175
10 Type 1 1-600 <$175
20 Type 1 1-156 <$175
5 Type 2 1-1670 <$200
10 Type 2 1-907 <$200
20 Type 2 1-269 <$200
Total Issue $544,430
Out in 1935 $34,600
Large out 1935 $1,440
****
3217 Gratiot
FNB OF ITHACA
{{ 1 L }}
Chartered 7/7/84
Receivership 10/14/96
Brown Back <$VALUE
4x5 1-2268 <$1500
Total Issue $45,360
Out in 1915 $280
****
6485 Gratiot
ITHACA NB, ITHACA
{{ 2 L 2 S }}
Organized 10/10/02
Receivership 12/7/31
1902 Red Seal <$VALUE
4x5 1-845 <$1000
3x10-20 1-688 <$1000
1902 Date Back
4x5 1-1475 <$600
3x10-20 1-1080 <$600
1902 Plain Back
4x5 1476-6176 <$600
3x10-20 1081-3904 <$600
1929 Small Size
5 Type 1 1-607 <$400
10 Type 1 1-281 <$400
20 Type 1 1-82 <$400
Total Issue $414,930
Out at close $25,000
Large out at close $2,090
****
1065 Jackson
FNB OF JACKSON
{{ UNREPORTED }}
Chartered 4/26/65
Liquidated 3/26/78
Original Series <$VALUE
4x5 1-4300 <$1500
3x10-20 1-1800 <$1750/$2000
Series 1875
4x5 1-1100 <$1500
3x10-20 1-130 <$1750/$2000
Total Issue $204,500
Out in 1910 $1,285
****
13741 Jackson
NB OF JACKSON
{{ 10 S }}
Chartered 7/33
1929 Small Size <$VALUE
5 Type 2 1-11274 <$125
10 Type 2 1-5290 <$125
20 Type 2 1-2360 <$125
Total Issue $156,470
Out in 1935 $84,450
****
11289 Jackson
N UNION B OF JACKSON
Chartered 1/19
Closed 3/27/30
2nd title:N Union B & TC
8/19/27
FIRST TITLE {{ 14 L }}
1902 Plain Back <$VALUE
4x5 1-87753 <$100
3x10-20 1-21942 <$100
SECOND TITLE {{ 6 L 4 S }}
1902 Plain Back
4x5 1-11012 <$100
3x10-20 1-9843 <$100
1929 Small Size
5 Type 1 1-3604 <$175
10 Type 1 1-2667 <$165
20 Type 1 1-597 <$175
Total Issue $3,904,330
Out at close $400,000
Large out at close $74,720
Ch 1533 assumed circulation
****
1533 Jackson
PEOPLES NB OF JACKSON
Organized 6/28/65
Receivership 8/24/33
2nd title:Union & Peoples
NB 3/29/30
FIRST TITLE {{ 12 L 4 S }}
Original Series <$VALUE
3x1-2 1-1520 <$500/$1250
4x5 1-5975 <$600
3x10-20 1-700 <$750/$1250
Series 1875
3x10-20 1-2584 <$750/$1000
Brown Back
3x10-20 1-2370 <$350
1902 Red Seal
3x10-20 1-1650 <$350
1902 Date Back
3x10-20 1-9900 <$150
1902 Plain Back
3x10-20 9901-34282 <$150
1929 Small Size
10 Type 1 1-2744 <$110
20 Type 1 1-932 <$125
SECOND TITLE {{ 29 S }}
1929 Small Size
5 Type 1 1-11429 <$45
10 Type 1 1-6758 <$45
20 Type 1 1-3588 <$50
Total Issue $3,661,790
Out at close $700,000
Large out at close $25,295
Outstanding includes Ch 11289
****
Union & Peoples NB of Jackson
SEE Ch 1533
Peoples NB of Jackson
****
3210 Kalamazoo
CITY NB OF KALAMAZOO
{{ 3 L }}
Chartered 6/24/84
Liquidated 1/1/10
Brown Back <$VALUE
4x5 1-9448 <$600
3x10-20 1-1154 <$600
1902 Red Seal
4x5 1-2600 <$600
3x10-20 1-2360 <$600
1902 Date Back
4x5 1-480 <$350
3x10-20 1-382 <$350
Total Issue $445,360
Out in 1910 $56,045
****
191 Kalamazoo
FNB OF KALAMAZOO
Chartered 1/11/64
2nd title: FNB & TC 6/10/27
FIRST TITLE {{ 8 L }}
Original Series <$VALUE
3x1-2 1-17500 <$600/$1250
4x5 1-8200 <$600
Series 1875
4x5 1-5450 <$600
Brown Back
4x5 1-9218 <$300
3x10-20 1-1391 <$300/$350
1902 Red Seal
3x10-20 1-4000 <$350
1902 Date Back
3x10-20 1-8300 <$175
1902 Plain Back
3x10-20 8301-11413 <$175
SECOND TITLE {{ 2 L 37 S }}
1902 Plain Back
3x10-20 1-900 <$250
1929 Small Size
10 Type 1 1-6380 <$35
20 Type 1 1-2034 <$40
50 Type 1 1-500 <$110
10 Type 2 1-5879 <$45
20 Type 2 1-675 <$50
Total Issue $2,229,230
Out in 1935 $453,490
Large out 1935 $10,010
Outstanding includes Ch 1359
****
3211 Kalamazoo
KALAMAZOO NB, KALAMAZOO
Chartered 6/24/84
Liquidated 3/25/30
2nd title:Kalamazoo NB &
TC 6/14/27
FIRST TITLE {{ 10 L }}
Brown Back <$VALUE
4x5 1-11720 <$350
3x10-20 1-1200 <$350
1902 Red Seal
4x5 1-2800 <$350
3x10-20 1-1960 <$350
1902 Date Back
4x5 1-7500 <$165
3x10-20 1-4700 <$165
1902 Plain Back
4x5 7501-17576 <$165
3x10-20 4701-10810 <$165
SECOND TITLE {{ 1 L 3 S }}
1902 Plain Back
4x5 1-693 <$250
1929 Small Size
5 Type 1 1-1187 <$350
Total Issue $1,389,890
Out at close $48,395
Large out at close $13,335
****
1359 Kalamazoo
MICHIGAN NB OF KALAMAZOO
{{ 4 L }}
Chartered 6/29/65
Liquidated 2/23/12
Original Series <$VALUE
3x1-2 1-2000 <$600/$1500
4x5 1-6000 <$650
3x10-20 1-800 <$1000/$1500
Series 1875
3x10-20 1-2058 <$850/$1250
Brown Back
3x10-20 1-4980 <$500
1902 Red Seal
3x10-20 1-2100 <$500
1902 Date Back
3x10-20 1-1296 <$300
Total Issue $691,700
Out at close $10,800
Ch 191 assumed circulation
****
9509 Baraga
BARAGA COUNTY NB OF
L'ANSE
{{ 1 L 3 S }}
Chartered 8/09
Receivership 6/2/32
1902 Date Back <$VALUE
3x10-20 1-720 <$1250
1902 Plain Back
3x10-20 721-1189 <$1250
1929 Small Size
10 Type 1 1-135 <$500
20 Type 1 1-13 <$500
Total Issue $69,110
Out at close $6,250
Large out at close $820
****
12661 Macomb
FNB OF L'ANSE CREUSE
Chartered 2/16/25
Receivership 6/17/31
2nd title:FNB of
Saint Clair Shores 1/24/27
FIRST TITLE {{ 1 L }}
1902 Plain Back <$VALUE
4x5 1-885 <$1250
SECOND TITLE {{ 1 L 1 S }}
1902 Plain Back
4x5 1-5647 <$1250
1929 Small Size
5 Type 1 1-2449 <$650
Total Issue $204,110
Out at close $30,000
Large out at close $1,020
****
3948 Houghton
FNB OF LAKE LINDEN
{{ 9 L 12 S }}
Organized 10/31/88
Brown Back <$VALUE
4x5 1-6200 <$500
50-100 1-784 <$2250/$2500
1902 Date Back
4x5 1-4750 <$175
3x10-20 1-2800 <$175
50-100 1-534 <$500/$600
1902 Plain Back
4x5 4751-17467 <$175
3x10-20 2801-9801 <$175
1929 Small Size
5 Type 1 1-3520 <$125
10 Type 1 1-1274 <$125
20 Type 1 1-374 <$135
5 Type 2 1-54 <$175
10 Type 2 1-60 <$175
20 Type 2 1-15 <$200
Total Issue $1,389,180
Out in 1935 $54,990
Large out 1935 $5,340
****
8148 Ingham
CAPITAL NB OF LANSING
{{ 17 L 38 S }}
Organized 1/16/06
Receivership 3/13/34
1902 Red Seal <$VALUE
3x10-20 1-3600 <$300/$350
1902 Date Back
3x10-20 1-5600* <$125
1902 Plain Back
3x10-20 11401-93023* <$125
* 5601-11400 not marked
1929 Small Size
10 Type 1 1-15754 <$50
20 Type 1 1-4754 <$60
10 Type 2 1-6225 <$60
20 Type 2 1-1590 <$60
Total Issue $6,440,920
Out at close $600,000
Large out at close $20,510
****
3513 Ingham
CITY NB OF LANSING
{{ 14 L 14 S }}
Chartered 6/1/86
Brown Back <$VALUE
4x5 1-3400 <$300
3x10-20 1-7738 <$300/$350
1902 Red Seal
3x10-20 1-2000 <$300/$350
1902 Date Back
3x10-20 1-11500 <$135
1902 Plain Back
3x10-20 11501-52614 <$135
1929 Small Size
5 Type 1 1-47061 <$100
Total Issue $4,682,430
Out in 1935 $45,065
Large out 1935 $11,945
****
1953 Ingham
LANSING NB, LANSING
{{ 1 L }}
Chartered 4/4/72
Liquidated 3/5/92
Original Series <$VALUE
3x10-20 1-2080 <$1500/$2000
Series 1875
3x10-20 1-2776 <$1500/$2000
Total Issue $242,800
Out in 1910 $1,170
****

****
14032 Ingham
LANSING NB, LANSING
{{ 14 S }}
Chartered 2/34
1929 Small Size <$VALUE
10 Type 2 1-14992 <$110
20 Type 2 1-5004 <$110
Total Issue $250,000
Out in 1935 $222,200
****
264 Ingham
SECOND NB OF LANSING
{{ 3 L }}
Chartered 2/18/64
Liquidated 7/31/84
Original Series <$VALUE
3x1-2 1-1600 <$600/$1500
4x5 1-5250 <$650
50-100 1-100 <$6000
Series 1875
3x1-2 1-230 <$600/$1500
4x5 1-500 <$650
50-100 1-250 <$6000
Brown Back
50-100 1-175 <$2250/$2500
Total Issue $202,900
Out in 1910 $1,407
****
1731 Lapeer
FNB OF LAPEER
{{ 11 L 15 S }}
Chartered 11/2/70
Original Series <$VALUE
3x1-2 1-2500 <$450/$1250
4x5 1-2950 <$500
4x10 1-1000 <$850
Series 1875
3x1-2 1-1340 <$450/$1250
4x5 1-2486 <$500
4x10 1-1625 <$850
Brown Back
4x5 1-2550 <$350
3x10-20 1-1680 <$350
1882 Date Back
4x5 1-180 <$350
3x10-20 1-126 <$350
1902 Date Back
4x5 1-1575 <$175
3x10-20 1-1260 <$175
1902 Plain Back
4x5 1576-7050 <$175
3x10-20 1261-5318 <$175
1929 Small Size
5 Type 1 1-5086 <$85
10 Type 1 1-2708 <$85
20 Type 1 1-690 <$100
5 Type 2 1-6230 <$100
10 Type 2 1-3120 <$100
20 Type 2 1-576 <$100
Total Issue $1,256,450
Out in 1935 $92,370
Large out 1935 $2,770
****
8598 Houghton
FNB OF LAURIUM
{{ 8 L 14 S }}
Chartered 3/07
Liquidated 9/5/34
1902 Red Seal <$VALUE
4x5 1-1200 <$450
4x10 1-1200 <$450
1902 Date Back
4x5 1-6650 <$150
4x10 1-6300 <$150
1902 Plain Back
4x5 6651-20168 <$150
4x10 6301-16761 <$150
1929 Small Size
5 Type 1 1-3486 <$100
10 Type 1 1-1766 <$100
5 Type 2 1-4752 <$110
10 Type 2 1-1800 <$110
Total Issue $1,398,100
Out at close $97,600
Large out at close $4,495
****
12084 Van Buren
FNB OF LAWTON
{{ 3 L 3 S }}
Chartered 11/3/21
1902 Plain Back <$VALUE
4x5 1-1525 <$500
3x10-20 1-1025 <$500
1929 Small Size
5 Type 1 1-502 <$325
10 Type 1 1-248 <$325
20 Type 1 1-84 <$325
5 Type 2 1-1168 <$350
10 Type 2 1-693 <$350
20 Type 2 1-233 <$350
Total Issue $139,200
Out in 1935 $21,500
Large out 1935 $60
****

****
2162 Ingham
FNB OF LESLIE
{{ 1 L }}
Chartered 8/1/74
Liquidated 9/25/86
Original Series <$VALUE
4x10 1-1125 <$2000
Series 1875
4x10 1-1470 <$2000
Total Issue $103,800
Out in 1910 $380
****
12999 Wayne
LINCOLN PARK NB, LINCOLN PARK
{{ 17 S }}
Organized 7/3/26
Receivership 2/2/33
1929 Small Size <$VALUE
5 Type 1 1-5108 <$100
10 Type 1 1-2299 <$100
20 Type 1 1-599 <$100
Total Issue $360,060
Out at close $100,000
****
1280 Kent
LOWELL NB, LOWELL
{{ 1 L }}
Chartered 6/14/65
Receivership 9/19/88
Original Series <$VALUE
4x5 1-7125 <$1500
Series 1875
4x5 1-6080 <$1500
Brown Back
4x5 1-1078 <$1250
Total Issue $285,660
Out in 1910 $1,870
****
2773 Mason
FNB OF LUDINGTON
Chartered 9/6/82
Receivership 3/8/34
2nd title:FNB & TC of Ludington 1/24/28
FIRST TITLE {{ 3 L }}
Brown Back <$VALUE
3x10-20 1-3120 <$600
1902 Red Seal
3x10-20 1-1180 <$600
1902 Date Back
3x10-20 1-2340 <$400
1902 Plain Back
3x10-20 2341-9749 <$400
SECOND TITLE {{ 2 L 14 S }}
1902 Plain Back
3x10-20 1-1636 <$400
1929 Small Size
10 Type 1 1-2535 <$100
20 Type 1 1-644 <$110
Total Issue $1,013,630
Out at close $99,160
Large out at close $4,440
****
2008 Ionia
NB OF LYONS
Chartered 7/6/72
Liquidated 1/8/89
2nd title and location: Second NB of Ionia 12/24/72
FIRST TITLE {{ 2 L }}
Original Series <$VALUE
3x1-2 1-1500 <$850/$1500
4x5 1-1875 <$850
SECOND TITLE {{ 1 L }}
Original Series
4x5 1-1475 <$1000
Series 1875
4x5 1-5500 <$1000
50-100 1-220 <$6000
Total Issue $217,500
Out in 1910 $1,502
****
2539 Manistee
FNB OF MANISTEE
{{ 7 L 13 S }}
Chartered 6/30/81
Receivership 12/12/33
Series 1875 <$VALUE
4x5 1-435 <$600
3x10-20 1-2367 <$850/$1250
Brown Back
3x10-20 1-1300 <$450
1882 Date Back
3x10-20 1-2090 <$400
1882 Value Back
3x10-20 2091-2151 <$400
1902 Plain Back
3x10-20 1-3804 <$225
1929 Small Size
10 Type 1 1-2331 <$125
20 Type 1 1-701 <$125
Total Issue $713,780
Out at close $100,000
Large out at close $3,370
****
2606 Manistee
MANISTEE NB, MANISTEE
{{ 1 L }}
Chartered 12/31/81
Liquidated 12/3/01
Series 1875 <$VALUE
50-100 1-1347 <$6000
Total Issue $202,050
Out in 1910 $4,300
****
13513 Schoolcraft
FNB IN MANISTIQUE
{{ 5 S }}
Organized 11/11/30
Liquidated 10/31/34
1929 Small Size <$VALUE
10 Type 1 1-606 <$225
20 Type 1 1-166 <$225
10 Type 2 1-261 <$250
20 Type 2 1-32 <$250
Total Issue $59,530
Out at close $44,320
Outstanding includes Ch 5348
****
5348 Schoolcraft
FNB OF MANISTIQUE
{{ 5 L 2 S }}
Chartered 5/12/00
Liquidated 12/20/30
Brown Back <$VALUE
3x10-20 1-1800 <$500
1882 Date Back
3x10-20 1-3300 <$500
1882 Value Back
3x10-20 3301-5013 <$500
1902 Plain Back
3x10-20 1-6258 <$300
1929 Small Size
10 Type 1 1-695 <$350
20 Type 1 1-159 <$350
Total Issue $714,330
Out at close $45,140
Large out at close $3,900
Ch 13513 assumed circulation
****
11260 Saint Clair
LIBERTY NB OF MARINE CITY
{{ 5 L 4 S }}
Organized 10/7/18
Receivership 1/17/33
1902 Plain Back <$VALUE
4x5 1-22720 <$325
1929 Small Size
5 Type 1 1-1414 <$225
10 Type 1 1-626 <$225
20 Type 1 1-182 <$225
Total Issue $556,220
Out at close $34,100
****
390 Marquette
FNB OF MARQUETTE
Chartered 4/19/64
2nd title:FNB & TC 4/9/25
FIRST TITLE {{ 28 L }}
Original Series <$VALUE
3x1-2 1-6778 <$400/$1000
4x5 1-4665 <$450
3x10-20 1-900 <$750/$1250
3x10-20 1619-1918 <$750/$1250
20 901-1618 <$1250
Series 1875
3x1-2 1-400 <$400/$1000
4x5 1-805 <$450
3x10-20 1-456 <$650/$1000
Brown Back
4x5 1-24089 <$250
3x10-20 1-2363 <$250/$300
1902 Red Seal
4x5 1-6500 <$250
3x10-20 1-4300 <$250/$300
1902 Date Back
4x5 1-9250 <$125
3x10-20 1-6200 <$125
1902 Plain Back
4x5 9251-22500 <$125
3x10-20 6201-14600 <$125
SECOND TITLE {{ 4 L 17 S }}
1902 Plain Back
4x5 1-6962 <$150
3x10-20 1-4313 <$150
1929 Small Size
5 Type 1 1-4434 <$65
10 Type 1 1-2462 <$65
20 Type 1 1-624 <$65
5 Type 2 1-4410 <$75
10 Type 2 1-2057 <$75
20 Type 2 1-465 <$85
Total Issue $3,129,810
Out in 1935 $136,700
Large out 1935 $14,860
****
6003 Marquette
MARQUETTE NB, MARQUETTE
{{ 6 L }}
Chartered 10/01
Liquidated 10/6/21
Brown Back <$VALUE
4x5 1-3000 <$400
3x10-20 1-4200 <$400
1882 Date Back
4x5 1-6250 <$400
3x10-20 1-4500 <$400
1882 Value Back
4x5 6251-11600 <$400
3x10-20 4501-7710 <$400
Total Issue $887,500
Out at close $97,700
Ch 12027 assumed circulation
****
12027 Marquette
UNION NB OF MARQUETTE
{{ 9 L U + 15 S }}
Chartered 10/6/21
1902 Plain Back <$VALUE
4x5 1-19247 <$160
3x10-20 1-5600 <$175
1929 Small Size
5 Type 1 1-14194 <$85
5 Type 2 1-28022 <$100
Total Issue $1,230,870
Out in 1935 $127,000
Large out 1935 $6,815
Outstanding includes Ch 6003
****
1515 Calhoun
FNB OF MARSHALL
{{ 10 L 8 S }}
Chartered 8/9/65
Liquidated 5/1/34
Original Series <$VALUE
4x5 1-6750 <$600
3x10-20 1-2500 <$850/$1250
Series 1875
4x5 1-960 <$600
3x10-20 1-1660 <$750/$1000
Brown Back
3x10-20 1-5823 <$350/$400
1902 Red Seal
3x10-20 1-3200 <$450
1902 Date Back
3x10-20 1-5900 <$175
1902 Plain Back
3x10-20 5901-21198 <$175
1929 Small Size
10 Type 1 1-2560 <$100
20 Type 1 1-678 <$100
10 Type 2 1-606 <$100
20 Type 2 1-192 <$100
Total Issue $2,118,110
Out at close $43,980
Large out 1935 $6,830
Ch 14009 assumed circulation
****
1518 Calhoun
NB OF MICHIGAN AT MARSHALL
{{ 2 L }}
Chartered 8/11/65
Liquidated 5/14/80
Original Series <$VALUE
3x1-2 1-3600 <$750/$1500
4x5 1-8800 <$850
3x10-20 1-1330<$1250/$1500
Series 1875
4x5 1-1955 <$850
3x10-20 1-1200<$1250/$1500
Total Issue $359,600
Out in 1910 $2,131
****
2023 Calhoun
N CITY B OF MARSHALL
{{ 1 L }}
Chartered 7/29/72
Receivership 6/22/91
Original Series <$VALUE
4x5 1-4000 <$1250
3x10-20 1-1200<$1500/$2000
Series 1875
4x5 1-1000 <$1250
3x10-20 1-2637<$1500/$2000
Total Issue $291,850
Out in 1915 $790
****
12697 Ingham
DART NB OF MASON
{{ 3 L 5 S }}
Chartered 4/25
1902 Plain Back <$VALUE
4x5 1-2028 <$500
1929 Small Size
5 Type 1 1-3514 <$275
5 Type 2 1-5904 <$300
Total Issue $175,500
Out in 1935 $25,000
Large out 1935 $170
****
1764 Ingham
FNB OF MASON
{{ 2 L }}
Chartered 1/13/71
Liquidated 10/28/90
Original Series <$VALUE
3x1-2 1-2000 <$1000/$2000
4x5 1-6350 <$1250
Series 1875
4x5 1-6532 <$1250
Total Issue $267,640
Out in 1910 $1,340
****
3256 Menominee
FNB OF MENOMINEE
{{ 15 L 28 S }}
Chartered 10/15/84
Brown Back <$VALUE
3x10-20 1-7168 <$400
1902 Red Seal
4x5 1-4000 <$350
3x10-20 1-5300 <$350
1902 Date Back
4x5 1-12500 <$125
3x10-20 1-8800 <$125
1902 Plain Back
4x5 12501-40042 <$125
3x10-20 8801-26844 <$125
1929 Small Size
5 Type 1 1-6172 <$40
10 Type 1 1-3414 <$40
20 Type 1 1-826 <$45
5 Type 2 1-3900 <$40
10 Type 2 1-2164 <$40
20 Type 2 1-928 <$45
Total Issue $3,395,260
Out in 1935 $188,050
Large out 1935 $9,540
****
4454 Menominee
LUMBERMEN'S NB OF MENOMINEE
{{ 10 L 15 S }}
Chartered 1890
Brown Back <$VALUE
4x5 1-8800 <$400
3x10-20 1-4700 <$400
1882 Date Back
4x5 1-926 <$400
3x10-20 1-31 <$400
1902 Date Back
3x10-20 1-5100 <$175
1902 Plain Back
3x10-20 5101-17918 <$175
1929 Small Size
10 Type 1 1-2132 <$65
20 Type 1 1-620 <$75
10 Type 2 1-1175 <$75
20 Type 2 1-366 <$75
Total Issue $1,548,360
Out in 1935 $80,615
Large out 1935 $6,415
****
2379 Oakland
FNB OF MILFORD
{{ 3 L }}
Chartered 3/14/78
Liquidated 10/21/86
Series 1875 <$VALUE
3x10-20 1-2272 <$850/$1250
Total Issue $113,600
Out in 1910 $510
****
Millington NB, Millington
SEE Ch 8723
Vassar NB, Vassar
****
1587 Monroe
FNB OF MONROE
{{ 10 L 17 S }}
Chartered 10/14/65
Original Series <$VALUE
4x5 1-2575 <$650
3x10-20 1-1492 <$850/$1250
Series 1875
3x10-20 1-1594 <$850/$1250
Brown Back
3x10-20 1-2815 <$450
1902 Red Seal
3x10-20 1-1600 <$450
1902 Date Back
3x10-20 1-3500* <$200
1902 Plain Back
3x10-20 4501-11632* <$200
* 3501-4500 not marked
1929 Small Size
10 Type 1 1-1400 <$100
20 Type 1 1-368 <$100
10 Type 2 1-6304 <$110
20 Type 2 1-1601 <$110
Total Issue $1,231,370
Out in 1935 $92,900
Large out 1935 $4,400
****
5669 Lenawee
FNB OF MORENCI
{{ 2 L }}
Chartered 1/5/01
Liquidated 7/25/27
Brown Back <$VALUE
3x10-20 1-1740 <$850
1882 Date Back
3x10-20 1-1600 <$850
1882 Value Back
3x10-20 1601-2481 <$850
1902 Plain Back
3x10-20 1-2060 <$600
Total Issue $314,050
Out at close $23,850
****
12971 Macomb
FNB IN MOUNT CLEMENS
{{ 3U + 3 L 20 S }}
Chartered 7/26
1902 Plain Back <$VALUE
4x5 1-6568 <$400
1929 Small Size
5 Type 1 1-6722 <$75
10 Type 1 1-2574 <$75
20 Type 1 1-728 <$75
5 Type 2 1-8458 <$85
10 Type 2 1-4620 <$85
20 Type 2 1-1270 <$85
Total Issue $688,710
Out in 1935 $193,150
Large out 1935 $490
****
2214 Macomb
FNB OF MOUNT CLEMENS
{{ UNREPORTED }}
Chartered 12/30/74
Liquidated 5/20/75
Original Series <$VALUE
4x5 1-1350 <$2000
Total Issue $27,000
Out in 1910 $70
****
3215 Isabella
FNB OF MOUNT PLEASANT
{{ 1 L }}
Chartered 6/28/84
Receivership 10/7/96
Brown Back <$VALUE
4x5 1-2436 <$1500
Total Issue $48,720
Out in 1915 $215
****
2017 Ionia
FNB OF MUIR
{{ UNREPORTED }}
Chartered 7/22/72
Liquidated 4/25/78
Original Series <$VALUE
3x1-2 1-1700 <$1500/$2500
4x5 1-2575 <$2000
Series 1875
4x5 1-1735 <$2000
Total Issue $94,700
Out in 1910 $390
****
9000 Alger
FNB OF ALGER COUNTY AT MUNISING
{{ 9 L 6 S }}
Chartered 1/08
1902 Red Seal <$VALUE
4x5 1-1500 <$600
3x10-20 1-1200 <$600
1902 Date Back
4x5 1-3750 <$275
3x10-20 1-2560 <$275
1902 Plain Back
4x5 3751-15691 <$275
3x10-20 2561-10039 <$275
1929 Small Size
5 Type 1 1-1628 <$200
10 Type 1 1-836 <$200
20 Type 1 1-248 <$225
5 Type 2 1-1820 <$250
10 Type 2 1-1185 <$250
20 Type 2 1-321 <$250
Total Issue $1,061,900
Out in 1935 $52,940
Large out 1935 $3,640
****
4398 Muskegon
HACKLEY NB OF MUSKEGON
Chartered 1890
2nd title:Hackley Union NB 9/17/29
FIRST TITLE {{ 13 L }}
Brown Back <$VALUE
3x10-20 1-2640 <$350
1882 Date Back
3x10-20 1-1460 <$350
1902 Date Back
3x10-20 1-3500* <$125
1902 Plain Back
3x10-20 4101-54828* <$125
* 3501-4100 not marked
SECOND TITLE {{ 38 S }}
1929 Small Size
10 Type 1 1-16674 <$25
20 Type 1 1-4726 <$35
10 Type 2 1-9912 <$25
20 Type 2 1-2688 <$35
Total Issue $4,666,840
Out in 1935 $565,410
Large out 1935 $23,260
Outstanding includes Ch 4125
****
Hackley Union NB of Muskegon
SEE Ch 4398
Hackley NB of Muskegon
****
2081 Muskegon
LUMBERMAN'S NB OF MUSKEGON
{{ 1 L }}
Chartered 2/3/73
Liquidated 1/16/93
Original Series <$VALUE
4x5 1-2500 <$1500
Series 1875
4x5 1-7730 <$1500
Total Issue $204,600
Out in 1910 $1,135
****
3088 Muskegon
MERCHANTS NB OF MUSKEGON
{{ 1 L }}
Chartered 12/13/83
Liquidated 3/26/96
Brown Back <$VALUE
4x5 1-4824 <$1250
Total Issue $96,480
Out in 1910 $735
****
1730 Muskegon
MUSKEGON NB, MUSKEGON
{{ 3 L }}
Chartered 11/1/70
Liquidated 8/27/90
Original Series <$VALUE
4x5 1-2250 <$650
4x10 1-2500 <$850
Series 1875
4x5 1-2488 <$650
4x10 1-2513 <$850
Total Issue $295,280
Out in 1910 $1,335
****
4840 Muskegon
N LUMBERMANS B OF MUSKEGON
{{ 12 L 29 S }}
Chartered 1893
Brown Back <$VALUE
3x10-20 1-5280 <$400
1882 Date Back
3x10-20 1-2969 <$400
1902 Date Back
3x10-20 1-3000 <$150
1902 Plain Back
3x10-20 3001-18840 <$150
1929 Small Size
10 Type 1 1-7804 <$45
20 Type 1 1-1728 <$50
10 Type 2 1-6570 <$50
20 Type 2 1-1320 <$50
Total Issue $2,122,150
Out in 1935 $284,150
Large out 1935 $5,540
****

CONDITION affects Value. The Values shown are for notes in FINE condition.

4125 Muskegon
UNION NB OF MUSKEGON
{{ 9 L }}
Chartered 1889
Closed 9/17/29
Brown Back <$VALUE
4x5 1-6690 <$375
3x10-20 1-1887 <$375
1902 Date Back
3x10-20 1-4200 <$150
1902 Plain Back
3x10-20 4201-49677 <$150
Total Issue $2,712,000
Out at close $362,200
Ch 4398 assumed circulation

2085 Marquette
FNB OF NEGAUNEE
{{ 1 L }}
Chartered 2/15/73
Liquidated 11/13/77
Original Series <$VALUE
3x1-2 1-1500 <$1250/$2000
4x5 1-2375 <$1500
Series 1875
4x5 1-1330 <$1500
Total Issue $81,600
Out in 1910 $611

3717 Marquette
FNB OF NEGAUNEE
{{ 7 L 16 S }}
Chartered 1887
Brown Back <$VALUE
4x5 1-3691 <$500
3x10-20 1-1298 <$500
1902 Red Seal
3x10-20 1-1700 <$500
1902 Date Back
3x10-20 1-7200 <$250
1902 Plain Back
3x10-20 7201-19247 <$250
1929 Small Size
10 Type 1 1-2172 <$85
20 Type 1 1-594 <$100
10 Type 2 1-648 <$125
20 Type 2 1-260 <$135
Total Issue $1,399,350
Out in 1935 $93,800
Large out 1935 $7,760

9556 Marquette
NEGAUNEE NB, NEGAUNEE
{{ 10 L 10 S }}
Chartered 10/09
Liquidated 10/24/32
1902 Date Back <$VALUE
3x10-20 1-7500 <$200
1902 Plain Back
3x10-20 7501-20290 <$200
1929 Small Size
10 Type 1 1-1708 <$135
20 Type 1 1-481 <$135
Total Issue $1,174,700
Out at close $93,340
Large out at close $12,190

1886 Berrien
CITIZENS NB OF NILES
{{ 2 L }}
Organized 9/27/71
Receivership 7/8/99
Original Series <$VALUE
3x1-2 1-900 <$750/$1500
4x5 1-3025 <$850
Series 1875
4x5 1-3188 <$850
Brown Back
4x5 1-4819 <$750
Total Issue $225,140
Out in 1915 $1,273

13307 Berrien
CITY NB & TC OF NILES
{{ 2 L U + 17 S }}
Chartered 4/1/29
Receivership 9/18/33
1902 Plain Back <$VALUE
4x10 1-625 <$750
1929 Small Size
10 Type 1 1-6325 <$100
Total Issue $404,500
Out at close $150,000
Large out at close $180

1761 Berrien
FNB OF NILES
{{ 2 L }}
Chartered 1/3/71
Receivership 3/9/01
Original Series <$VALUE
3x1-2 1-4000 <$750/$1500
4x5 1-4400 <$850
3x10-20 1-880 <$1000/$1500
Series 1875
3x1-2 1-100 <$750/$1500
4x5 1-1431 <$850
3x10-20 1-1892 <$1000/$1500
Brown Back
4x5 1-7536 <$750
3x10-20 1-697 <$750
Total Issue $461,290
Out in 1915 $2,943

6863 Dickinson
FNB OF NORWAY
{{ 7 L 50+ S }}
Organized 6/8/03
1902 Red Seal <$VALUE
3x10-20 1-2362 <$600
1902 Date Back
4x5 1-3530 <$275
3x10-20 1-2120 <$275
1902 Plain Back
4x5 3531-13320 <$275
3x10-20 2121-7521 <$275
1929 Small Size
5 Type 1 1-2376 <$60
10 Type 1 1-1110 <$60
20 Type 1 1-304 <$65
Total Issue $934,910
Out in 1935 $53,535
Large out 1935 $4,185

13929 Ontonagon
FNB IN ONTONAGON
{{ 6 S }}
Chartered 1/34
1929 Small Size <$VALUE
5 Type 2 1-654 <$400
10 Type 2 1-251 <$400
20 Type 2 1-117 <$400
Total Issue $8,120
Out in 1935 $25,000
Outstanding includes Ch 6820

6820 Ontonagon
FNB OF ONTONAGON
{{ 3 L 6 S }}
Organized 5/26/03
Liquidated 3/8/34
1902 Red Seal <$VALUE
3x10-20 1-1263 <$1000
1902 Date Back
3x10-20 1-1660 <$500
1902 Plain Back
3x10-20 1661-4850 <$500
1929 Small Size
10 Type 1 1-576 <$200
20 Type 1 1-144 <$200
10 Type 2 1-57 <$250
20 Type 2 1-21 <$250
Total Issue $358,480
Out at close $24,450
Large out at close $1,590
Ch 13929 assumed circulation

3264 Clinton
FNB OF OVID
{{ 2 L }}
Chartered 11/17/84
Liquidated 12/1/97
Brown Back <$VALUE
4x5 1-2641 <$1500
Total Issue $52,820
Out in 1910 $370

1573 Shiawassee
FNB OF OWOSSO
{{ 3 L }}
Chartered 10/2/65
Liquidated 4/14/85
Original Series <$VALUE
3x1-2 1-4800 <$750/$1500
4x5 1-8775 <$850
Series 1875
3x1-2 1-1800 <$750/$1500
4x5 1-4175 <$850
Total Issue $292,000
Out in 1910 $2,103

3410 Shiawassee
SECOND NB OF OWOSSO
{{ UNREPORTED }}
Chartered 11/14/85
Liquidated 1/13/91
Brown Back <$VALUE
4x5 1-1421 <$2000
Total Issue $28,420
Out in 1910 $155

1521 Van Buren
FNB OF PAW PAW
{{ 6 L 4 S }}
Chartered 8/11/65
Receivership 12/8/33
Original Series <$VALUE
4x5 1-4135 <$1000
4x10 1-1350 <$1250
Series 1875
4x5 1-940 <$1000
4x10 1-5 <$1250
Brown Back
4x5 1-5466 <$750
3x10-20 1-701 <$750
1902 Red Seal
3x10-20 1-652 <$850
1902 Date Back
3x10-20 1-2440 <$450
1902 Plain Back
3x10-20 2441-5210 <$450
1929 Small Size
5 Type 1 1-770 <$350
10 Type 1 1-471 <$350
20 Type 1 1-122 <$350
Total Issue $659,170
Out at close $24,760
Large out at close $2,845

5607 Emmet
FNB OF PETOSKEY
{{ 6 L 15 S }}
Chartered 10/24/00
Brown Back <$VALUE
4x5 1-5645 <$500
3x10-20 1-4142 <$500
1882 Date Back
4x5 1-7100 <$500
3x10-20 1-5260 <$500
1882 Value Back
4x5 7101-9205 <$500
3x10-20 5261-6397 <$500
1902 Plain Back
4x5 1-9640 <$250
3x10-20 1-6740 <$250
1929 Small Size
5 Type 1 1-3526 <$85
10 Type 1 1-1704 <$85
20 Type 1 1-434 <$100
5 Type 2 1-3102 <$100
10 Type 2 1-1596 <$100
20 Type 2 1-595 <$110
Total Issue $1,657,220
Out in 1935 $98,600
Large out 1935 $5,220

12953 Wayne
FNB IN PLYMOUTH
{{ 6 L 11 S }}
Chartered 7/26
1902 Plain Back <$VALUE
4x5 1-9902 <$300
1929 Small Size
5 Type 1 1-7566 <$165
5 Type 2 1-13776 <$165
Total Issue $493,900
Out in 1935 $44,790
Large out 1935 $670

1916 Wayne
FNB OF PLYMOUTH
{{ 3 L }}
Chartered 1/5/72
Liquidated 11/14/91
Original Series <$VALUE
3x1-2 1-1500 <$750/$1500
4x5 1-2875 <$750
Series 1875
4x5 1-8643 <$750
Total Issue $237,860
Out in 1910 $1,351

4649 Wayne
FN EXCHANGE B OF PLYMOUTH
{{ 17 L }}
Chartered 11/14/91
Liquidated 8/20/03
Brown Back <$VALUE
4x5 1-1945 <$350
3x10-20 1-239 <$350
Total Issue $50,850
Out in 1910 $1,335

3109 Wayne
PLYMOUTH NB, PLYMOUTH
{{ UNREPORTED }}
Chartered 1/16/84
Liquidated 2/25/90
Brown Back <$VALUE
4x5 1-1993 <$1500
Total Issue $39,860
Out in 1910 $260

12288 Oakland
AMERICAN NB OF PONTIAC
Chartered 12/15/22
Receivership 2/1/28
2nd title:FNB in Pontiac 1/15/24
3rd title:FNB & TC 2/1/28
FIRST TITLE {{ 3 L }}
1902 Plain Back <$VALUE
4x5 1-8750 <$300
3x10-20 1-6600 <$300
SECOND TITLE {{ 10 L }}
1902 Plain Back
4x5 1-34626 <$150
3x10-20 1-24683 <$150
THIRD TITLE {{ 6 L 22 S }}
1902 Plain Back
4x5 1-10837 <$150
3x10-20 1-9024 <$150
1929 Small Size
5 Type 1 1-13618 <$45
10 Type 1 1-6912 <$50
20 Type 1 1-2103 <$55
Total Issue $4,175,230
Out at close $287,370
Large out at close $12,815
Outstanding includes Ch 11549
Ch 13600 assumed circulation

13739 Oakland
COMMUNITY NB OF PONTIAC
{{ 16 S }}
Chartered 7/33
1929 Small Size <$VALUE
5 Type 2 1-38724 <$65
10 Type 2 1-13128 <$65
20 Type 2 1-3972 <$65
Total Issue $404,340
Out in 1935 $182,060

13600 Oakland
FNB AT PONTIAC
{{ 14 S }}
Organized 2/26/32
Receivership 9/13/33
1929 Small Size <$VALUE
10 Type 1 1-4294 <$60
20 Type 1 1-1156 <$65
Total Issue $396,360
Out at close $500,000
Outstanding includes Ch 12288

FNB in Pontiac
FNB & TC in Pontiac
SEE Ch 12288
American NB of Pontiac

434 Oakland
FNB OF PONTIAC
{{ 1 L }}
Chartered 5/21/64
Liquidated 12/31/81
Original Series <$VALUE
3x1-2 1-2200 <$750/$1500
4x5 1-3350 <$850
3x10-20 1-2040 <$1000/$1500
Series 1875
3x10-20 1-1380 <$1000/$1500
Total Issue $249,000
Out in 1910 $2,092

2607 Oakland
FNB OF PONTIAC
{{ 1 L }}
Chartered 1/3/82
Liquidated 12/31/92
Series 1875 <$VALUE
3x10-20 1-2603 <$1500/$2000
Total Issue $130,150
Out in 1910 $2,090

11549 Oakland
NB OF PONTIAC
{{ 1 L }}
Chartered 12/19
Closed 2/16/23
1902 Plain Back <$VALUE
4x5 1-14305 <$750
3x10-20 1-9108 <$750
Total Issue $741,500
Out at close $200,000
Ch 12288 assumed circulation

3388 Oakland
PONTIAC NB, PONTIAC
{{ UNREPORTED }}
Chartered 9/2/85
Liquidated 11/19/98
Brown Back <$VALUE
3x10-20 1-1795 <$1500
Total Issue $89,750
Out in 1910 $1,090

1574 Oakland
SECOND NB OF PONTIAC
{{ UNREPORTED }}
Chartered 10/2/65
Liquidated 9/1/85
Original Series <$VALUE
3x1-2 1-1460 <$1500/$2000
4x5 1-4200 <$1500
4x10 1-2000 <$1750
Series 1875
4x10 1-3245 <$1750
Total Issue $301,100
Out in 1910 $1,720

FNB in Port Huron
SEE Ch 4446
FN Exchange B of Port Huron

FNB & TC of Port Huron
SEE Ch 4446
FN Exchange B of Port Huron

1857 Saint Clair
FNB OF PORT HURON
{{ 1 L }}
Chartered 8/7/71
Liquidated 10/15/90
Original Series <$VALUE
3x1-2 1-3000 <$850/$1750
4x5 1-4250 <$1000
3x10-20 1-2100 <$1250/$1750
Series 1875
3x10-20 1-5268 <$1250/$1750
Total issue $468,400
Out in 1910 $2,593

4446 Saint Clair
FN EXCHANGE B OF PORT HURON
Chartered 1890
2nd title:FNB in Port Huron 1/16/23
3rd title:FNB & TC of Port Huron 1/12/28
4th title:FNT & Savings B 11/22/30
FIRST TITLE {{ 7 L }}
Brown Back <$VALUE
3x10-20 1-13440 <$400
1882 Date Back
3x10-20 1-1608 <$400
1902 Date Back
3x10-20 1-7500* <$150
1902 Plain Back
3x10-20 13501-18300* <$150
* 7501-13500 not marked
SECOND TITLE {{ 2 L }}
1902 Plain Back
3x10-20 1-13940 <$200
THIRD TITLE {{ 4 L 8 S }}
1902 Plain Back
3x10-20 1-4355 <$175
1929 Small Size
10 Type 1 1-2280 <$75
20 Type 1 1-834 <$75
FOURTH TITLE {{ 21 S }}
1929 Small Size
10 Type 1 1-10273 <$40
20 Type 1 1-2310 <$45
5 Type 2 1-61 <$85
Total Issue $3,712,915
Out in 1935 $237,500
Large out 1935 $7,635

FNT & Savings B of Port Huron
SEE Ch 4446
FN Exchange B of Port Huron

2550 Branch
FNB OF QUINCY
{{ 4 L 5 S }}
Chartered 8/6/81
Series 1875 <$VALUE
4x5 1-6847 <$750
3x10-20 1-211 <$1000/$1250
Brown Back
3x10-20 1-1380 <$600
1882 Date Back
3x10-20 1-1650 <$600
1882 Value Back
3x10-20 1651-2657 <$600
1902 Plain Back
3x10-20 1-3936 <$350
1929 Small Size
10 Type 1 1-866 <$200
20 Type 1 1-258 <$200
10 Type 2 1-1052 <$225
20 Type 2 1-162 <$225
Total Issue $642,820
Out in 1935 $34,150
Large out 1935 $2,100

4413 Osceola
FNB OF REED CITY
{{ 3 L 8 S }}
Organized 8/26/90
Receivership 10/5/31
Brown Back <$VALUE
4x5 1-3425 <$750
3x10-20 1-2180 <$750
1882 Date Back
4x5 1-416 <$750
1902 Date Back
3x10-20 1-2600 <$450
1902 Plain Back
3x10-20 2601-9669 <$450
1929 Small Size
10 Type 1 1-805 <$175
20 Type 1 1-244 <$175
Total Issue $746,850
Out at close $50,000
Large out at close $5,430

9099 Kalamazoo
FARMERS NB OF RICHLAND
{{ UNREPORTED }}
Chartered 4/10/08
Liquidated 2/2/14
1902 Red Seal <$VALUE
4x10 1-550 <$2000
1902 Date Back
4x10 1-1640 <$1500
Total Issue $87,600
Out in 1914 $14,445

10742 Macomb
FNB OF RICHMOND
{{ 2 L 6 S }}
Chartered 5/26/15
Receivership 11/6/33
1902 Plain Back <$VALUE
4x10 1-6925 <$650
1929 Small Size
10 Type 1 1-1828 <$225
Total Issue $386,680
Out at close $50,000
Large out at close $650

9218 Oakland
FNB OF ROCHESTER
{{ 4 L 8 S }}
Chartered 8/10/08
Receivership 12/12/33
1902 Date Back <$VALUE
3x10-20 1-4110 <$375
1902 Plain Back
3x10-20 4111-14485 <$375
1929 Small Size
10 Type 1 1-1494 <$175
20 Type 1 1-398 <$175
Total Issue $861,650
Out at close $50,000
Large out at close $2,490

13841 Oakland
ROCHESTER NB, ROCHESTER
{{ UNREPORTED }}
Chartered 11/33
1929 Small Size <$VALUE
5 Type 2 1-4450 <$500
10 Type 2 1-2220 <$500
Total Issue $44,450
Out in 1935 $24,750

FNB of Rockland
SEE Ch 5199
Ontonagon County NB of Rockland

CONDITION affects Value. The Values shown are for notes in FINE condition.

****

5199 Ontonagon
ONTONAGON COUNTY NB OF ROCKLAND
Organized 6/19/99
2nd title:FNB of Rockland 3/04
FIRST TITLE {{ 2 L }}
Brown Back <$VALUE
4x5 1-748 <$750
3x10-20 1-243 <$750
SECOND TITLE {{ 2 L 6 S }}
Brown Back
3x10-20 1-1142 <$750
1882 Date Back
3x10-20 1-1450 <$750
1882 Value Back
3x10-20 1451-1970 <$750
1902 Plain Back
3x10-20 1-2445 <$500
1929 Small Size
10 Type 1 1-638 <$225
20 Type 1 1-156 <$225
10 Type 2 1-246 <$250
20 Type 2 1-41 <$250
Total Issue $365,240
Out in 1935 $25,000
Large out 1935 $1,760

****

2186 Macomb
CITIZENS NB OF ROMEO
{{ 9 L 18 S }}
Chartered 9/16/74
Receivership 10/12/33
Original Series <$VALUE
3x10-20 1-1540<$1000/$1500
Series 1875
3x10-20 1-1315<$1000/$1500
Brown Back
3x10-20 1-2140 <$500
1882 Date Back
3x10-20 1-1971 <$500
1902 Date Back
3x10-20 1-1500 <$200
1902 Plain Back
3x10-20 1501-10834 <$200
1929 Small Size
10 Type 1 1-1489 <$125
20 Type 1 1-423 <$135
Total Issue $1,030,100
Out at close $49,640
Large out at close $1,970

****

354 Macomb
FNB OF ROMEO
{{ 2 L }}
Chartered 3/13/64
Liquidated 5/1/97
Original Series <$VALUE
3x1-2 1-1700 <$750/$1500
4x5 1-2250 <$850
3x10-20 1-1700<$1000/$1500
3x10-20 2201-2600 <$1000/$1500
20 1701-2200 <$1500
Series 1875
3x10-20 1-2048<$1000/$1500
Brown Back
3x10-20 1-2911 <$750
Total Issue $416,450
Out in 1910 $3,172

****

12657 Oakland
FNB OF ROYAL OAK
{{ 6 L 2 S }}
Chartered 2/26/25
Receivership 7/3/31
1902 Plain Back <$VALUE
4x5 1-14578 <$375
1929 Small Size
5 Type 1 1-4226 <$450
Total Issue $418,340
Out at close $47,360
Large out at close $1,915

****

2492 Saginaw
CITIZENS NB OF SAGINAW
{{ UNREPORTED }}
Chartered 9/24/80
Liquidated 6/1/88
Series 1875 <$VALUE
4x5 1-2012 <$1500
3x10-20 1-1315<$1500/$2000
Total Issue $105,990
Out in 1910 $715

****

3911 Saginaw
COMMERCIAL NB OF SAGINAW
{{ 4 L }}
Chartered 1888
Liquidated 12/18/22
Brown Back <$VALUE
3x10-20 1-10297 <$500
1902 Date Back
4x5 1-11405* <$300
3x10-20 1-9500 <$300
* 10416-11045 not marked
Total Issue $1,217,950
Out at close $93,800
Ch 1918 assumed circulation

****

1768 Saginaw
FNB OF SAGINAW
{{ 2 L }}
Chartered 1/16/71
Liquidated 2/6/99
Original Series <$VALUE
3x1-2 1-2500 <$750/$1500
4x5 1-2875 <$850
3x10-20 1-600 <$1000/$1500
Series 1875
4x5 1-1750 <$850
3x10-20 1-2008<$1000/$1500
Brown Back
3x10-20 1-2253 <$750
Total Issue $348,050
Out in 1910 $2,846

****

Second NB of Saginaw
Second NB & TC of Saginaw
SEE Ch 1918
Second NB of East Saginaw

****

1789 Saint Clair
FNB OF SAINT CLAIR
{{ 3 L }}
Chartered 2/14/71
Liquidated 10/20/86
Original Series <$VALUE
3x1-2 1-1600 <$750/$1500
4x5 1-4100 <$850
Series 1875
4x5 1-4836 <$850
Total Issue $186,720
Out in 1910 $1,079

****

10632 Wayne
MICHIGAN NB OF SAINT CLAIR HEIGHTS
{{ 2 L }}
Chartered 10/6/14
Liquidated 1/15/20
1902 Date Back <$VALUE
4x5 1-500 <$850
3x10-20 1-400 <$850
1902 Plain Back
4x5 501-2775 <$850
3x10-20 401-1702 <$850
Total Issue $140,600
Out at close $46,700

****

FNB of Saint Clair Shores
SEE Ch 12661
FNB of L'Anse Creuse

****

3886 Mackinac
FNB OF SAINT IGNACE
{{ 5 L 13 S }}
Chartered 5/14/88
Brown Back <$VALUE
4x5 1-2813 <$600
3x10-20 1-502 <$600
1902 Red Seal
3x10-20 1-125 <$650
1902 Date Back
3x10-20 1-1600 <$300
1902 Plain Back
3x10-20 1601-6653 <$300
1929 Small Size
10 Type 1 1-1210 <$125
20 Type 1 1-418 <$125
10 Type 2 1-462 <$135
20 Type 2 1-78 <$135
Total Issue $549,200
Out in 1935 $49,800
Large out 1935 $2,430

****

1539 Clinton
FNB OF SAINT JOHNS
{{ 1 L }}
Chartered 8/28/65
Liquidated 8/14/85
Original Series <$VALUE
4x5 1-2300 <$1250
3x10-20 1-970 <$1500/$2000
Series 1875
3x10-20 1-764 <$1500/$2000
Total Issue $132,700
Out in 1910 $900

****

3378 Clinton
SAINT JOHNS NB, SAINT JOHNS
{{ 24 L 4 S }}
Chartered 8/15/85
Brown Back <$VALUE
3x10-20 1-2542 <$400
1902 Red Seal
3x10-20 1-500 <$400
1902 Date Back
3x10-20 1-1130 <$100
1902 Plain Back
3x10-20 1131-2834 <$100
1929 Small Size
10 Type 1 1-314 <$300
20 Type 1 1-106 <$300
10 Type 2 1-185 <$300
20 Type 2 1-40 <$300
Total Issue $328,010
Out in 1935 $14,650
Large out 1935 $2,190

****

5594 Berrien
COMMERCIAL NB OF SAINT JOSEPH
Chartered 10/11/00
Receivership 9/28/31
2nd title:Commercial NB & TC 1/19/29
FIRST TITLE {{ 8 L }}
Brown Back <$VALUE
4x5 1-3065 <$400
3x10-20 1-2374 <$400
1882 Date Back
4x5 1-3100 <$400
3x10-20 1-2200 <$400
1882 Value Back
4x5 3101-5200 <$400
3x10-20 2201-3368 <$400
1902 Plain Back
4x5 1-12880 <$175
3x10-20 1-8744 <$175
SECOND TITLE {{ 2 L 10 S }}
1902 Plain Back
4x5 1-870 <$275
3x10-20 1-366 <$275
1929 Small Size
5 Type 1 1-3765 <$135
10 Type 1 1-1755 <$135
20 Type 1 1-518 <$135
Total Issue $1,463,310
Out at close $147,360
Large out at close $11,100

****

1866 Berrien
FNB OF SAINT JOSEPH
{{ 3 L }}
Chartered 8/29/71
Liquidated 6/30/81
Original Series <$VALUE
3x1-2 1-2500 <$600/$1500
4x5 1-3125 <$650
Series 1875
4x5 1-1145 <$650
Total issue $97,900
Out in 1910 $586

****

3239 Gratiot
FNB OF SAINT LOUIS
{{ 1 L }}
Chartered 8/23/84
Liquidated 7/6/97
Brown Back <$VALUE
4x5 1-2659 <$1500
Total Issue $53,180
Out in 1910 $400

****

3547 Chippewa
FNB OF SAULT STE MARIE
{{ 9 L 15 S }}
Chartered 8/86
Brown Back <$VALUE
4x5 1-3600 <$750
3x10-20 1-820 <$750
1902 Red Seal
4x5 1-1200 <$750
3x10-20 1-1020 <$750
1902 Date Back
4x5 1-4750 <$325
3x10-20 1-3580 <$325
1902 Plain Back
4x5 4751-20602 <$325
3x10-20 3581-14326 <$325
1929 Small Size
5 Type 1 1-3596 <$125
10 Type 1 1-1848 <$125
20 Type 1 1-500 <$135
5 Type 2 1-2230 <$135
10 Type 2 1-1246 <$135
20 Type 2 1-345 <$165
Total Issue $1,625,610
Out in 1935 $88,700
Large out 1935 $5,550

****

3747 Chippewa
SAULT STE MARIE NB, SAULT STE MARIE
{{ UNREPORTED }}
Chartered 7/7/87
Receivership 12/10/97
Brown Back <$VALUE
3x10-20 1-1570 <$2000
Total Issue $78,500
Out in 1915 $550

****

1725 Kalamazoo
FNB OF SCHOOLCRAFT
{{ UNREPORTED }}
Chartered 10/22/70
Liquidated 11/17/75
Original Series <$VALUE
4x5 1-3250 <$2500
Series 1875
4x5 1-180 <$2500
Total Issue $68,600
Out in 1910 $405

****

1823 Van Buren
FNB OF SOUTH HAVEN
{{ 3 L }}
Chartered 5/22/71
Liquidated 12/31/89
Original Series <$VALUE
3x1-2 1-1500 <$750/$1500
4x5 1-3125 <$750
Series 1875
4x5 1-3674 <$750
Total Issue $143,480
Out in 1910 $782

****

2914 Montcalm
FNB OF STANTON
{{ UNREPORTED }}
Chartered 4/5/83
Liquidated 4/30/88
Brown Back <$VALUE
3x10-20 1-452 <$2000
Total Issue $22,600
Out in 1910 $150

****

825 Saint Joseph
FNB OF STURGIS
{{ 2 L }}
Chartered 2/18/65
Liquidated 12/31/84
Original Series <$VALUE
3x1-2 1-3300 <$750/$1500
4x5 1-5050 <$850
3x10-20 1-900 <$1000/$1500
Series 1875
4x5 1-4030 <$850
Total Issue $243,100
Out in 1910 $1,619

****

3276 Saint Joseph
NB OF STURGIS
Chartered 12/22/84
Liquidated 7/1/31
2nd title:Sturgis NB 1/22/13
FIRST TITLE {{ 1 L }}
Brown Back <$VALUE
4x5 1-4187 <$850
3x10-20 1-403 <$850
1902 Red Seal
3x10-20 1-530 <$850
1902 Date Back
3x10-20 1-565 <$600
SECOND TITLE {{ 6 L 9 S }}
1902 Date Back
3x10-20 1-1000* <$275
1902 Plain Back
3x10-20 2001-16123* <$275
* 1001-2000 not marked
1929 Small Size
10 Type 1 1-1492 <$175
20 Type 1 1-455 <$175
Total Issue $1,108,910
Out at close $88,180
Large out at close $11,290

****

Sturgis NB, Sturgia
SEE Ch 3276
NB of Sturgis

****

1063 Lenawee
NB OF TECUMSEH
{{ 1 L }}
Chartered 4/26/65
Liquidated 3/3/74
Original Series <$VALUE
4x5 1-2525 <$1500
3x10-20 1-300 <$1750/$2000
Total Issue $65,500
Out in 1910 $610

****

600 Saint Joseph
FNB OF THREE RIVERS
{{ 7 L U + 9 S }}
Chartered 12/3/64
Original Series <$VALUE
3x1-2 1-4400 <$750/$1500
4x5 1-3650 <$850
3x10-20 1-2453<$1000/$1500
Series 1875
3x1-2 1-1240 <$750/$1500
3x10-20 1-273 <$1000/$1500
Brown Back
3x10-20 1-4792 <$750
1902 Red Seal
3x10-20 1-1600 <$750
1902 Date Back
3x10-20 1-2900 <$375
1902 Plain Back
3x10-20 2901-9768 <$375
1929 Small Size
10 Type 1 1-1246 <$175
20 Type 1 1-348 <$175
10 Type 2 1-1165 <$200
20 Type 2 1-183 <$200
Total Issue $1,177,330
Out in 1935 $48,850
Large out 1935 $4,370

****

1919 Saint Joseph
MANUFACTURERS NB OF THREE RIVERS
{{ 2 L }}
Chartered 1/11/72
Liquidated 2/25/81
Original Series <$VALUE
3x1-2 1-1700 <$1000/$2000
4x5 1-2825 <$1000
Series 1875
3x1-2 1-240 <$1000/$2000
4x5 1-2445 <$1000
Total Issue $115,100
Out in 1910 $683

****

3133 Saint Joseph
THREE RIVERS NB, THREE RIVERS
{{ 1 L }}
Chartered 3/5/84
Liquidated 4/27/97
Brown Back <$VALUE
3x10-20 1-1080 <$1500
Total Issue $54,000
Out in 1910 $730

****

3325 Grand Traverse
FNB OF TRAVERSE CITY
{{ 2 L 8 S }}
Chartered 3/24/85
Liquidated 10/31/31
Brown Back <$VALUE
4x5 1-4502 <$850
3x10-20 1-1023 <$850
1902 Red Seal
3x10-20 1-3500 <$850
1902 Date Back
3x10-20 1-6300 <$450
1902 Plain Back
3x10-20 6301-6993 <$450
1929 Small Size
5 Type 1 1-2144 <$200
10 Type 1 1-1009 <$200
20 Type 1 1-367 <$200
Total Issue $834,740
Out at close $99,435
Large out at close $1,355

****

2372 Branch
FARMERS NB OF UNION CITY
{{ 3 L }}
Chartered 10/12/77
Liquidated 4/28/11
Series 1875 <$VALUE
3x10-20 1-4445<$1000/$1500
Brown Back
3x10-20 1-3550 <$700
1882 Date Back
3x10-20 1-671 <$650
Total Issue $433,300
Out in 1911 $35,000

****

1826 Branch
UNION CITY NB, UNION CITY
{{ 5 L 7 S }}
Chartered 5/27/71
Original Series <$VALUE
3x1-2 1-2460 <$650/$1500
4x5 1-3750 <$750
Series 1875
4x5 1-4257 <$750
Brown Back
3x10-20 1-4020 <$600
1882 Date Back
3x10-20 1-705 <$600
1902 Date Back
3x10-20 1-2200* <$325
1902 Plain Back
3x10-20 2451-9444* <$325
* 2201-2450 not marked
1929 Small Size
10 Type 1 1-1300 <$200
20 Type 1 1-374 <$225
10 Type 2 1-320 <$260
20 Type 2 1-15 <$250
Total Issue $1,007,270
Out in 1935 $39,270
Large out 1935 $4,390

****

12826 Macomb
FNB OF UTICA
{{ 3 S }}
Chartered 9/21/25
Liquidated 4/17/34
1929 Small Size <$VALUE
5 Type 1 1-3544 <$350
10 Type 1 1-1600 <$350
5 Type 2 1-814 <$350
10 Type 2 1-528 <$350
Total Issue $211,670
Out at close $46,500

****

2987 Tuscola
FNB OF VASSAR
{{ 1 L }}
Chartered 6/28/83
Liquidated 8/1/01
Brown Back <$VALUE
4x5 1-3496 <$1500
3x10-20 1-171 <$1500
Total Issue $78,470
Out in 1910 $725

****

8723 Tuscola
VASSAR NB, VASSAR
Organized 5/6/07
Receivership 10/25/33
2nd title:Millington NB, Millington 11/27/26
FIRST TITLE {{ 3 L }}
1902 Red Seal <$VALUE
4x5 1-150 <$850
4x10 1-175 <$850
1902 Date Back
4x5 1-550 <$500
4x10 1-550 <$500
1902 Plain Back
4x5 551-1363 <$500
4x10 551-1067 <$500
SECOND TITLE {{ 8 L 2 S }}
1902 Plain Back
4x5 1-765 <$400
1929 Small Size
5 Type 1 1-1290* <$500
* 509-1026 not issued
Total Issue $118,400
Out at close $6,250
Large out at close $520

****

11305 Gogebic
FNB OF WAKEFIELD
{{ 3 L 12 S }}
Organized 2/5/19
1902 Plain Back <$VALUE
3x10-20 1-1910 <$450
1929 Small Size
10 Type 1 1-756 <$100
20 Type 1 1-232 <$100
10 Type 2 1-1524 <$110
20 Type 2 1-215 <$125
Total Issue $188,240
Out in 1935 $49,560
Large out 1935 $810

****

10498 Berrien
FNB OF WATERVLIET
{{ 1 L 12 S }}
Chartered 3/20/14
1902 Date Back <$VALUE
4x5 1-500 <$600
3x10-20 1-400 <$600
1902 Plain Back
4x5 501-2387 <$600
3x10-20 401-1726 <$600
1929 Small Size
5 Type 1 1-1406 <$125
10 Type 1 1-650 <$125
20 Type 1 1-204 <$135
5 Type 2 1-472 <$165
10 Type 2 1-145 <$165
20 Type 2 1-40 <$200
Total Issue $244,310
Out in 1935 $31,635
Large out 1935 $1,480

****

4527 Saint Joseph
FNB OF WHITE PIGEON
{{ 1 L }}
Organized 3/3/91
Receivership 12/27/00
Brown Back <$VALUE
3x10-20 1-2194 <$1500
Total Issue $109,700
Out in 1915 $900

****

****
2429 Muskegon
FNB OF WHITEHALL
{{ UNREPORTED }}
Chartered 8/21/79
Liquidated 9/30/90
Series 1875 <$VALUE
3x10-20 1-1538 <$2500
Total Issue $76,900
Out in 1910 $360
****
12616 Wayne
FNB OF WYANDOTTE
{{ 6 S }}
Chartered 6/14/24
Receivership 12/28/33
1929 Small Size <$VALUE
5 Type 1 1-2790 <$275
10 Type 1 1-1426 <$275
5 Type 2 1-600 <$300
10 Type 2 1-390 <$300
Total Issue $176,160
Out at close $50,000
****
5482 Saint Clair
FNB OF YALE
{{ 4 L 5 S }}
Chartered 7/2/00
Receivership 1/12/33
Brown Back <$VALUE
3x10-20 1-2100 <$750
1882 Date Back
3x10-20 1-2640 <$750
1882 Value Back
3x10-20 2641-3944 <$750
1902 Plain Back
3x10-20 1-5845 <$400
1929 Small Size
10 Type 1 1-1085 <$300
20 Type 1 1-275 <$325
Total Issue $692,550
Out at close $40,000
Large out at close $2,770
****
155 Washtenaw
FNB OF YPSILANTI
{{ 12 L U + 18 S }}
Chartered 12/14/63
Receivership 10/26/33
Original Series <$VALUE
3x1-2 1-3500 <$600/$1500
4x5 1-6950 <$650
Series 1875
4x5 1-4285 <$650
Brown Back
4x5 1-8862 <$500
3x10-20 1-493 <$500
1902 Red Seal
4x5 1-1300 <$500
3x10-20 1-1050 <$500
1902 Date Back
4x5 1-5000* <$225
3x10-20 1-3900** <$225
1902 Plain Back
4x5 10001-34845* <$225
3x10-20 7901-22160** <$225
* 5001-10000 not marked
** 3901-7900 not marked
1929 Small Size
5 Type 1 1-6028 <$75
10 Type 1 1-3188 <$75
20 Type 1 1-856 <$85
5 Type 2 1-312 <$135
10 Type 2 1-225 <$135
20 Type 2 1-30 <$150
Total Issue $2,806,740
Out at close $150,000
Large out at close $7,380
****

MINNESOTA

Nickname: The North Star State
Motto: L'Etoile du Nord (The Star of the North)
Capital: Saint Paul
Number of towns: 270
Number of issuing charters: 434
Number of small size issuers: 248

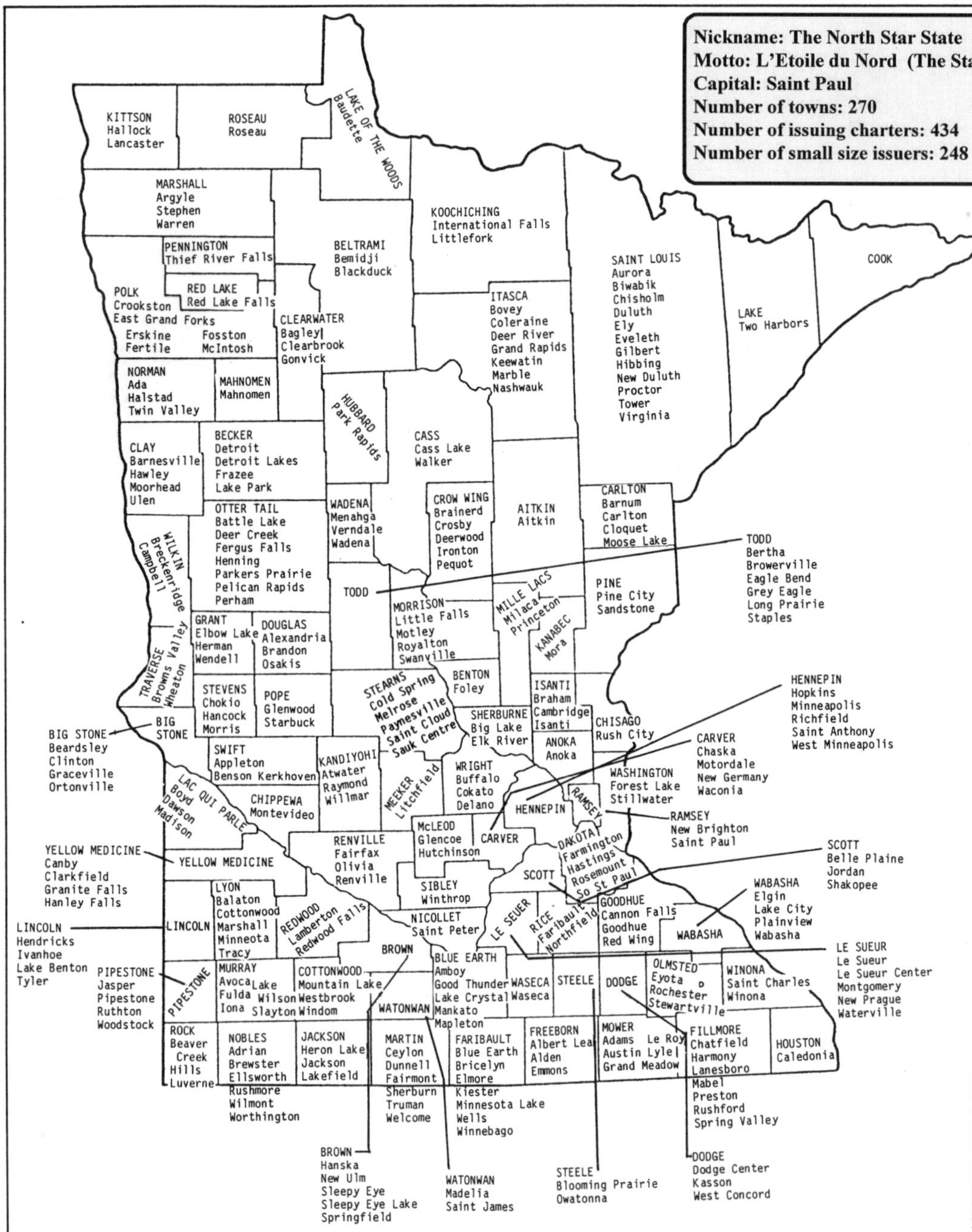

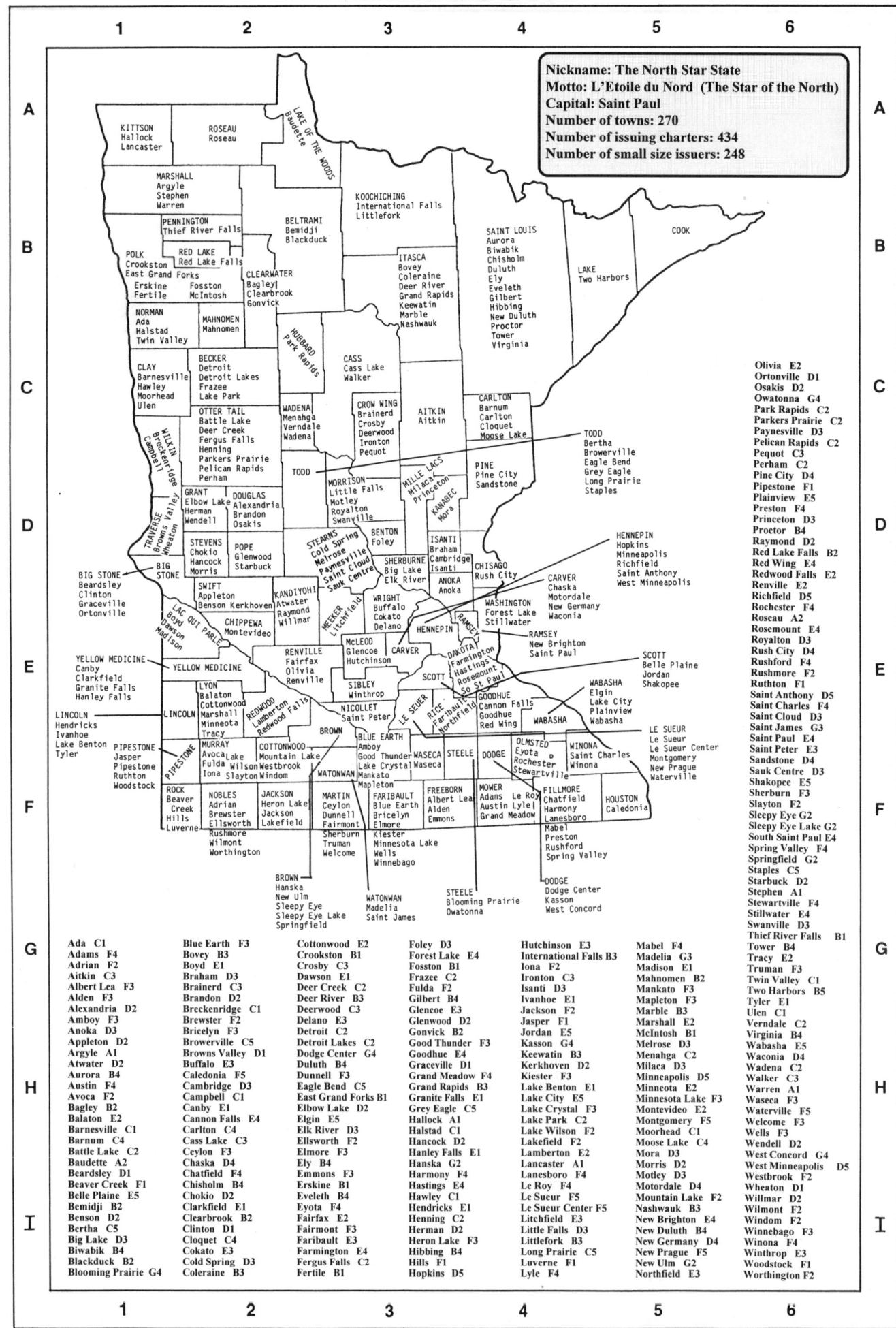

Ada C1
Adams F4
Adrian F2
Aitkin C3
Albert Lea F3
Alden F3
Alexandria D2
Amboy F3
Anoka D3
Appleton D2
Argyle A1
Atwater D2
Aurora B4
Austin F4
Avoca F2
Bagley B2
Balaton E2
Barnesville C1
Barnum C4
Battle Lake C2
Baudette A2
Beardsley D1
Beaver Creek F1
Belle Plaine E5
Bemidji B2
Benson D2
Bertha C5
Big Lake D3
Biwabik B4
Blackduck B2
Blooming Prairie G4
Blue Earth F3
Bovey B3
Boyd E1
Braham D3
Brainerd C3
Brandon D2
Breckenridge C1
Brewster F2
Bricelyn F3
Browerville C5
Browns Valley D1
Buffalo E3
Caledonia F5
Cambridge D3
Campbell C1
Canby E1
Cannon Falls E4
Carlton C4
Cass Lake C3
Ceylon F3
Chaska D4
Chatfield F4
Chisholm B4
Chokio D2
Clarkfield E1
Clearbrook B2
Clinton D1
Cloquet C4
Cokato E3
Cold Spring D3
Coleraine B3
Cottonwood E2
Crookston B1
Crosby C3
Dawson E1
Deer Creek C2
Deer River B3
Deerwood C3
Delano E3
Detroit C2
Detroit Lakes C2
Dodge Center G4
Duluth B4
Dunnell F3
Eagle Bend C5
East Grand Forks B1
Elbow Lake D2
Elgin E5
Elk River D3
Ellsworth F2
Elmore F3
Ely B4
Emmons F3
Erskine B1
Eveleth B4
Eyota F4
Fairfax E2
Fairmont F3
Faribault E3
Farmington E4
Fergus Falls C2
Fertile B1
Foley D3
Forest Lake E4
Fosston B1
Frazee C2
Fulda F2
Gilbert B4
Glencoe E3
Glenwood D2
Gonvick B2
Good Thunder F3
Goodhue E4
Graceville D1
Grand Meadow F4
Grand Rapids B3
Granite Falls E1
Grey Eagle C5
Hallock A1
Halstad C1
Hancock D2
Hanley Falls E1
Hanska G2
Harmony F4
Hastings E4
Hawley C1
Hendricks E1
Henning C2
Herman D2
Heron Lake F3
Hibbing B4
Hills F1
Hopkins D5
Hutchinson E3
International Falls B3
Iona F2
Ironton C3
Isanti D3
Ivanhoe E1
Jackson F2
Jasper F1
Jordan E5
Kasson G4
Keewatin B3
Kerkhoven D2
Kiester F3
Lake Benton E1
Lake City E5
Lake Crystal F3
Lake Park C2
Lake Wilson F2
Lakefield F2
Lamberton E2
Lancaster A1
Lanesboro F4
Le Roy F4
Le Sueur F5
Le Sueur Center F5
Litchfield E3
Little Falls D3
Littlefork B3
Long Prairie C5
Luverne F1
Lyle F4
Mabel F4
Madelia G3
Madison E1
Mahnomen B2
Mankato F3
Mapleton F3
Marble B3
Marshall E2
McIntosh B1
Melrose D3
Menahga C2
Milaca D3
Minneapolis D5
Minneota E2
Minnesota Lake F3
Montevideo E2
Montgomery F5
Moorhead C1
Moose Lake C4
Mora D3
Morris D2
Motley D3
Motordale D4
Mountain Lake F2
Nashwauk B3
New Brighton E4
New Duluth B4
New Germany D4
New Prague F5
New Ulm G2
Northfield E3
Olivia E2
Ortonville D1
Osakis D2
Owatonna G4
Park Rapids C2
Parkers Prairie C2
Paynesville D3
Pelican Rapids C2
Pequot C3
Perham C2
Pine City D4
Pipestone F1
Plainview E5
Preston F4
Princeton D3
Proctor B4
Raymond D2
Red Lake Falls B2
Red Wing E4
Redwood Falls E2
Renville E2
Richfield D5
Rochester F4
Roseau A2
Rosemount E4
Royalton D3
Rush City D4
Rushford F4
Rushmore F2
Ruthton F1
Saint Anthony D5
Saint Charles F4
Saint Cloud D3
Saint James G3
Saint Paul E4
Saint Peter E3
Sandstone D4
Sauk Centre D3
Shakopee E5
Sherburn F3
Slayton F2
Sleepy Eye G2
Sleepy Eye Lake G2
South Saint Paul E4
Spring Valley F4
Springfield G2
Staples C5
Starbuck D2
Stephen A1
Stewartville F4
Stillwater E4
Swanville D3
Thief River Falls B1
Tower B4
Tracy E2
Truman F3
Twin Valley C1
Two Harbors B5
Tyler E1
Ulen C1
Verndale C2
Virginia B4
Wabasha E5
Waconia D4
Wadena C2
Walker C3
Warren A1
Waseca F3
Waterville F5
Welcome F3
Wells F3
Wendell D2
West Concord G4
West Minneapolis D5
Westbrook F2
Wheaton D1
Willmar D2
Wilmont F2
Windom F2
Winnebago F3
Winona F4
Winthrop E3
Woodstock F1
Worthington F2

10665 Norman
ADA NB, ADA
{{6 L 8 S}}
Chartered 12/14
1902 Plain Back <$VALUE
3x10-20 1-1335 <$500
1929 Small Size
10 Type 1 1-536 <$250
20 Type 1 1-160 <$250
10 Type 2 1-324 <$250
20 Type 2 1-81 <$250
Total Issue $122,970
Out in 1935 $25,000
Large out 1935 $1,420

5453 Norman
FNB, ADA
{{5 L}}
Organized 4/13/00
Receivership 2/10/26
Brown Back <$VALUE
3x10-20 1-720 <$850
1882 Date Back
3x10-20 1-1920* <$650
1882 Value Back
3x10-20 2161-2477* <$750
* 1921-2160 not marked
1902 Plain Back
3x10-20 1-1354 <$500
Total Issue $227,550
Out at close $24,500

8059 Mower
FNB OF ADAMS
{{4 L 27 S}}
Organized 1/11/06
Receivership 8/8/32
1902 Red Seal <$VALUE
4x5 1-800 <$1000
3x10-20 1-640 <$1000
1902 Date Back
4x5 1-1450 <$500
3x10-20 1-1020 <$500
1902 Plain Back
4x5 1451-5610 <$500
3x10-20 1021-3477 <$500
1929 Small Size
5 Type 1 1-659 <$85
10 Type 1 1-303 <$85
20 Type 1 1-101 <$85
Total Issue $384,120
Out at close $29,520
Large out at close $3,330

7960 Nobles
FNB OF ADRIAN
{{4 L}}
Organized 10/7/05
Receivership 8/16/26
1902 Red Seal <$VALUE
4x5 1-750 <$1000
3x10-20 1-600 <$1000
1902 Date Back
4x5 1-2200 <$500
3x10-20 1-1830 <$500
1902 Plain Back
4x5 2201-5795 <$500
3x10-20 1831-3921 <$500
Total Issue $356,950
Out at close $34,995

9033 Nobles
NB OF ADRIAN
{{7 L 4 S}}
Chartered 1908
Liquidated 1/13/31
1902 Red Seal <$VALUE
4x5 1-357 <$850
3x10-20 1-586 <$850
1902 Date Back
4x5 1-1825 <$400
3x10-20 1-980 <$400
1902 Plain Back
4x5 1826-4883 <$400
3x10-20 981-2799 <$400
1929 Small Size
5 Type 1 1-343 <$500
10 Type 1 1-160 <$500
20 Type 1 1-36 <$500
Total Issue $298,260
Out at close $25,000
Large out at close $4,640

10783 Aitkin
FARMERS NB, AITKIN
{{3 S}}
Chartered 9/15
1929 Small Size <$VALUE
10 Type 1 1-314 <$500
20 Type 1 1-106 <$500
10 Type 2 1-587 <$500
20 Type 2 1-150 <$500
Total Issue $40,430
Out in 1935 $25,000

6803 Aitkin
FNB OF AITKIN
{{6 L 9 S}}
Chartered 5/03
1902 Red Seal <$VALUE
3x10-20 1-1240 <$850
1902 Date Back
3x10-20 1-1570 <$400
1902 Plain Back
3x10-20 1571-4352 <$400
1929 Small Size
10 Type 1 1-576 <$175
20 Type 1 1-160 <$200
5 Type 2 1-324 <$200
10 Type 2 1-283 <$200
20 Type 2 1-65 <$200
Total Issue $339,110
Out in 1935 $25,000
Large out 1935 $715

4702 Freeborn
ALBERT LEA NB, ALBERT LEA
{{2 L}}
Organized 3/4/92
Liquidated 2/19/02
Brown Back <$VALUE
3x10-20 1-1517 <$1000
Total Issue $75,850
Out in 1910 $2,390

6128 Freeborn
CITIZENS NB, ALBERT LEA
{{8 L}}
Organized 1/22/02
Receivership 2/18/27
1902 Red Seal <$VALUE
4x5 1-1980 <$600
3x10-20 1-1608 <$600
1902 Date Back
4x5 1-3175 <$275
3x10-20 1-2220 <$275
1902 Plain Back (dated 1902)
4x5 3176-5850 <$275
3x10-20 2221-3902 <$275
1902 Plain Back (dated 1922)
4x5 1-2485 <$275
3x10-20 1-1680 <$275
Total Issue $565,800
Out at close $49,395

3560 Freeborn
FNB, ALBERT LEA
{{17 L 32 S}}
Chartered 1886
Brown Back <$VALUE
4x5 1-4025 <$400
3x10-20 1-3938 <$400
1902 Red Seal
3x10-20 1-2000 <$450
1902 Date Back
3x10-20 1-6500* <$150
1902 Plain Back
3x10-20 7001-17803* <$150
* 6501-7000 not marked
1929 Small Size
10 Type 1 1-2107 <$60
20 Type 1 1-572 <$60
Total Issue $1,462,610
Out in 1935 $50,000
Large out 1935 $7,175

6431 Freeborn
SECURITY NB, ALBERT LEA
{{ UNREPORTED }}
Organized 9/20/02
Liquidated 12/9/05
1902 Red Seal <$VALUE
3x10-20 1-456 <$2000
Total Issue $22,800
Out in 1910 $1,380

6631 Freeborn
FNB OF ALDEN
{{6 L 12 S}}
Organized 1/13/03
1902 Red Seal <$VALUE
3x10-20 1-1540 <$850
1902 Date Back
3x10-20 1-2450 <$400
1902 Plain Back
3x10-20 2451-5370 <$400
1929 Small Size
10 Type 1 1-622 <$200
20 Type 1 1-210 <$200
10 Type 2 1-31 <$250
20 Type 2 1-15 <$250
Total Issue $398,630
Out in 1935 $30,000
Large out 1935 $2,090

5859 Douglas
FARMERS NB OF ALEXANDRIA
{{39 L}}
Chartered 6/01
Liquidated 3/1/27
Brown Back <$VALUE
4x5 1-1450 <$350
3x10-20 1-1360 <$350
1882 Date Back
4x5 1-6700 <$300
3x10-20 1-4620 <$300
1882 Value Back
4x5 6701-11300 <$350
3x10-20 4621-7084 <$350
1902 Plain Back
4x5 1-4645 <$150
3x10-20 1-3112 <$150
Total Issue $925,700
Out in 1925 $100,000

2995 Douglas
FNB, ALEXANDRIA
{{8 L}}
Organized 6/9/83
Receivership 1/8/25
Brown Back <$VALUE
3x10-20 1-1402 <$600
1902 Red Seal
3x10-20 1-620 <$600
1902 Date Back
3x10-20 1-3900 <$300
1902 Plain Back
3x10-20 3901-8069 <$300
Total Issue $504,550
Out at close $59,400

9775 Blue Earth
FNB, AMBOY
{{10 L}}
Chartered 1910
Liquidated 8/5/29
1902 Date Back <$VALUE
4x5 1-925* <$350
3x10-20 1-680** <$350
1902 Plain Back
4x5 1076-2575* <$350
3x10-20 801-1856** <$350
* 926-1075 not marked
** 681-800 not marked
Total Issue $144,300
Out at close $12,250

3000 Anoka
ANOKA NB, ANOKA
{{2 L 22 S}}
Organized 5/26/83
Receivership 1/27/31
Brown Back <$VALUE
4x5 1-4474 <$1250
50-100 1-79 <$2250/$2500
1902 Red Seal
3x10-20 1-600 <$1500
1902 Date Back
3x10-20 1-1000 <$750
1902 Plain Back
3x10-20 1001-1984 <$750
1929 Small Size
10 Type 1 1-159 <$300
20 Type 1 1-18 <$300
Total Issue $242,230
Out at close $12,500
Large out at close $3,270

2800 Anoka
FNB, ANOKA
{{ UNREPORTED }}
Organized 9/14/82
Receivership 4/22/89
Brown Back <$VALUE
4x5 1-1321 <$2000
Total Issue $26,420
Out in 1915 $185

13547 Anoka
FNB, ANOKA
{{3 S}}
Chartered 5/31
1929 Small Size <$VALUE
5 Type 1 1-260 <$500
10 Type 1 1-256 <$500
20 Type 1 1-120 <$500
5 Type 2 1-606 <$500
10 Type 2 1-366 <$500
20 Type 2 1-72 <$500
Total Issue $45,690
Out in 1935 $30,000

8813 Swift
FNB OF APPLETON
{{4 L 2U + 13 S}}
Chartered 7/07
1902 Red Seal <$VALUE
3x10-20 1-200 <$1250
1902 Date Back
3x10-20 1-1730 <$600
1902 Plain Back
3x10-20 1731-3959 <$600
1929 Small Size
5 Type 1 1-210 <$200
10 Type 1 1-296 <$200
20 Type 1 1-118 <$200
5 Type 2 1-754 <$200
10 Type 2 1-335 <$200
20 Type 2 1-75 <$200
Total Issue $254,790
Out in 1935 $25,000
Large out 1935 $1,310

4831 Swift
FNB, APPLETON
{{ UNREPORTED }}
Organized 12/27/92
Liquidated 12/1/97
Brown Back <$VALUE
3x10-20 1-429 <$2000
Total Issue $21,450
Out in 1910 $530

5907 Marshall
FNB, ARGYLE
{{6 L}}
Organized 6/18/01
Receivership 1/18/27
Brown Back <$VALUE
4x5 1-1500 <$600
3x10-20 1-1040 <$600
1882 Date Back
4x5 1-1625 <$550
3x10-20 1-1160 <$550
1882 Value Back
4x5 1626-3675 <$600
3x10-20 1161-2700 <$600
1902 Plain Back
4x5 1-2150 <$450
3x10-20 1-1187 <$450
Total Issue $392,850
Out in 1924 $50,000

10570 Kandiyohi
FNB, ATWATER
{{2 L}}
Organized 6/15/14
Receivership 2/14/25
1902 Date Back <$VALUE
3x10-20 1-500 <$1000
1902 Plain Back
3x10-20 501-998 <$1000
Total Issue $49,900
Out at close $10,000

11345 Saint Louis
FNB OF AURORA
{{2 L}}
Chartered 1919
Liquidated 1/9/28
1902 Plain Back <$VALUE
3x10-20 1-1166 <$1000
Total Issue $58,300
Out at close $25,000

4131 Mower
AUSTIN NB, AUSTIN
{{18 L 11 S}}
Chartered 9/28/89
Liquidated 3/24/31
Brown Back <$VALUE
4x5 1-4485 <$400
3x10-20 1-2636 <$400
1902 Date Back
4x5 1-2650* <$125
3x10-20 1-2080** <$125
1902 Plain Back
4x5 2901-8925* <$125
3x10-20 2221-6156** <$125
* 2651-2900 not marked
** 2081-2220 not marked
1929 Small Size
5 Type 1 1-773 <$175
10 Type 1 1-374 <$175
20 Type 1 1-97 <$175
Total Issue $765,070
Out at close $50,000
Large out at close $9,260
Ch 1690 assumed circulation

4847 Mower
CITIZENS NB OF AUSTIN
{{2 L}}
Chartered 1893
Liquidated 12/20/12
Brown Back <$VALUE
4x5 1-4575 <$1000
3x10-20 1-2460 <$1000
1882 Date Back
4x5 1-1260 <$1000
3x10-20 1-1016 <$1000
Total Issue $290,500
Out in 1913 $28,050

1690 Mower
FNB OF AUSTIN
{{11 L 50+ S}}
Organized 1/69
Original Series <$VALUE
3x1-2 1-1300 <$650/$1500
4x5 1-4775 <$750
Series 1875
4x5 1-2675 <$750
Brown Back
4x5 1-5275 <$400
3x10-20 1-3960 <$400
1902 Date Back
4x5 1-5615 <$175
3x10-20 1-4320 <$175
1902 Plain Back
4x5 5616-16725 <$175
3x10-20 4321-11951 <$175
1929 Small Size
5 Type 1 1-3756 <$35
10 Type 1 1-1672 <$35
20 Type 1 1-484 <$40
5 Type 2 1-6642 <$35
10 Type 2 1-3301 <$35
20 Type 2 1-653 <$40
Total Issue $1,741,410
Out in 1935 $131,180
Large out 1935 $11,095
Outstanding includes Ch 4131

11224 Murray
FNB, AVOCA
{{3 L}}
Chartered 7/31/18
Receivership 5/5/28
1902 Plain Back <$VALUE
4x5 1-2227 <$900
Total Issue $44,540
Out at close $6,500

6813 Clearwater
FNB OF BAGLEY
{{4 L 7 S}}
Chartered 6/03
1902 Red Seal <$VALUE
3x10-20 1-820 <$1000
1902 Date Back
3x10-20 1-1570 <$600
1902 Plain Back
3x10-20 1571-4487 <$600
1929 Small Size
10 Type 1 1-530 <$275
20 Type 1 1-140 <$275
10 Type 2 1-492 <$275
20 Type 2 1-166 <$275
Total Issue $322,190
Out in 1935 $25,000
Large out 1935 $1,470

6840 Lyon
FNB OF BALATON
{{4 L}}
Organized 4/30/03
Liquidated 6/28/24
1902 Red Seal <$VALUE
3x10-20 1-626 <$1250
1902 Date Back
3x10-20 1-1610 <$600
1902 Plain Back
3x10-20 1611-3142 <$600
Total Issue $188,400
Out at close $25,000

6098 Clay
BARNESVILLE NB, BARNESVILLE
{{2 L}}
Chartered 1/18/02
Receivership 1/14/14
Brown Back <$VALUE
3x10-20 1-500 <$1000
1882 Date Back
3x10-20 1-522 <$1000
Total Issue $51,100
Out in 1914 $5,610

4959 Clay
FNB, BARNESVILLE
{{18 L 17 S}}
Chartered 1894
Brown Back <$VALUE
3x10-20 1-1190 <$400
1882 Date Back
3x10-20 1-2043 <$350
1902 Date Back
3x10-20 1-1000 <$175
1902 Plain Back
3x10-20 1001-6405 <$175
1929 Small Size
10 Type 1 1-982 <$80
20 Type 1 1-286 <$80
10 Type 2 1-1401 <$100
20 Type 2 1-185 <$100
Total Issue $592,850
Out in 1935 $50,000
Large out 1935 $3,260

11761 Carlton
FNB, BARNUM
{{3 L 5 S}}
Chartered 6/20
1902 Plain Back <$VALUE
3x10-20 1-982 <$750
1929 Small Size
10 Type 1 1-440* <$400
20 Type 1 1-140** <$400
10 Type 2 1-212 <$400
20 Type 2 1-81 <$400
* 131-314 not issued
** 14-106 not issued
Total Issue $73,840
Out in 1935 $10,000
Large out 1935 $360

8756 Otter Tail
FNB OF BATTLE LAKE
{{4 L 7 S}}
Chartered 6/07
1902 Red Seal <$VALUE
3x10-20 1-700 <$1250
1902 Date Back
3x10-20 1-1510 <$600
1902 Plain Back
3x10-20 1511-4020 <$600
1929 Small Size
10 Type 1 1-526 <$325
20 Type 1 1-160 <$325
10 Type 2 1-347 <$350
20 Type 2 1-35 <$350
Total Issue $290,930
Out in 1935 $25,000
Large out 1935 $1,740

10710 Lake of the Woods
FNB, BAUDETTE
{{3 L 14 S}}
Chartered 2/15
1902 Date Back <$VALUE
3x10-20 1-500 <$750
1902 Plain Back
4x5 1-4061 <$750
3x10-20 501-2620 <$750
1929 Small Size
5 Type 1 1-862 <$150
10 Type 1 1-414 <$150
20 Type 1 1-108 <$150
5 Type 2 1-674 <$200
10 Type 2 1-485 <$200
20 Type 2 1-95 <$200
Total Issue $285,200
Out in 1935 $25,000
Large out 1935 $1,170

<$VALUEs are for notes in FINE condition. Value changes by approximately 25% for a change of one full grade.

****
7438 Big Stone
FNB OF BEARDSLEY
{{7 L}}
Organized 7/7/04
Receivership 1/21/27
1902 Red Seal <$VALUE
4x5 1-443 <$800
3x10-20 1-396 <$800
1902 Date Back
4x5 1-1775 <$400
3x10-20 1-1300 <$400
1902 Plain Back
4x5 1776-4182 <$400
3x10-20 1301-2892 <$400
Total Issue $256,900
Out at close $24,995
****
9321 Rock
FNB, BEAVER CREEK
{{4 L}}
Organized 1/4/09
Receivership 9/20/24
1902 Date Back <$VALUE
3x10-20 1-1830 <$750
1902 Plain Back
3x10-20 1831-3799 <$750
Total Issue $189,950
Out at close $25,000
****
7273 Scott
FNB OF BELLE PLAINE
{{1 L 11 S}}
Chartered 5/04
Liquidated 8/19/35
1902 Red Seal <$VALUE
4x5 1-450 <$2000
3x10-20 1-360 <$2000
1902 Date Back
4x5 1-750* <$1250
3x10-20 1-560** <$1250
1902 Plain Back
4x5 851-2770* <$1250
3x10-20 641-1720** <$1250
* 751-850 not marked
** 561-640 not marked
1929 Small Size
5 Type 1 1-794 <$300
10 Type 1 1-392 <$300
20 Type 1 1-110 <$300
5 Type 2 1-446 <$300
10 Type 2 1-254 <$300
20 Type 2 1-75 <$300
Total Issue $235,210
Out at close $25,000
Large out at close $1,090
****
5582 Beltrami
FNB, BEMIDJI
{{7 L 10 S}}
Chartered 9/22/00
Brown Back <$VALUE
3x10-20 1-1350 <$450
1882 Date Back
3x10-20 1-1850 <$400
1882 Value Back
3x10-20 1851-2998 <$450
1902 Plain Back
3x10-20 1-3326 <$250
1929 Small Size
10 Type 1 1-924 <$175
20 Type 1 1-256 <$175
10 Type 2 1-432 <$200
20 Type 2 1-160 <$200
Total Issue $477,380
Out in 1935 $25,000
Large out 1935 $2,050
****
8241 Beltrami
LUMBERMEN'S NB OF BEMIDJI
Organized 4/27/06
2nd title:Northern NB of Bemidji 12/29/09
FIRST TITLE {{0 L}}
1902 Red Seal <$VALUE
3x10-20 1-600 <$1500
1902 Date Back
3x10-20 1-132 <$850
SECOND TITLE {{13 L 10 S}}
1902 Date Back
3x10-20 1-3240 <$200
1902 Plain Back
3x10-20 3241-9330 <$200
1929 Small Size
10 Type 1 1-975 <$150
20 Type 1 1-262 <$150
10 Type 2 1-1188 <$175
20 Type 2 1-185 <$175
Total Issue $608,680
Out in 1935 $50,000
Large out 1935 $3,650
****

****
Northern NB of Bemidji
SEE Ch 8241
Lumbermen's NB of Bemidji
****
6154 Swift
FNB, BENSON
{{6 L}}
Organized 2/24/02
Receivership 7/6/26
1902 Red Seal <$VALUE
4x5 1-1215 <$800
3x10-20 1-934 <$800
1902 Date Back
4x5 1-1450 <$400
3x10-20 1-1080 <$400
1902 Plain Back
4x5 1451-2840 <$400
3x10-20 1081-1936 <$400
3x50-100 1-126 <$850/$1000
Total Issue $256,100
Out in 1924 $25,000
****
7373 Todd
FNB OF BERTHA
{{4 L 8 S}}
Chartered 8/04
1902 Red Seal <$VALUE
3x10-20 1-900 <$1250
1902 Date Back
3x10-20 1-1760* <$600
1902 Plain Back
3x10-20 1881-4302* <$600
* 1761-1880 not marked
1929 Small Size
10 Type 1 1-442 <$250
20 Type 1 1-138 <$250
10 Type 2 1-336 <$250
20 Type 2 1-162 <$250
Total Issue $309,780
Out in 1935 $25,000
Large out 1935 $2,760
****
11611 Sherburne
FNB OF BIG LAKE
{{2 L}}
Chartered 1920
Liquidated 3/26/26
1902 Plain Back <$VALUE
4x5 1-5505 <$1250
Total Issue $110,100
Out at close $25,000
****
8697 Saint Louis
FNB OF BIWABIK
{{5 L}}
Organized 4/2/07
Receivership 5/10/27
1902 Red Seal <$VALUE
4x5 1-300 <$1000
3x10-20 1-250 <$1000
1902 Date Back
4x5 1-1175 <$500
3x10-20 1-920 <$500
1902 Plain Back
4x5 1176-4180 <$500
3x10-20 921-2733 <$500
Total Issue $238,750
Out at close $24,700
****
9147 Beltrami
FNB OF BLACKDUCK
{{4 L}}
Chartered 1908
Liquidated 4/28/25
1902 Date Back <$VALUE
3x10-20 1-760 <$800
1902 Plain Back
3x10-20 761-2617 <$800
Total Issue $130,850
Out at close $25,000
****
6775 Steele
FNB OF BLOOMING PRAIRIE
{{5 L 22 S}}
Chartered 5/03
1902 Red Seal <$VALUE
3x10-20 1-463 <$1250
1902 Date Back
3x10-20 1-1420 <$600
1902 Plain Back
3x10-20 1421-6938 <$600
1929 Small Size
10 Type 1 1-1162 <$175
20 Type 1 1-304 <$175
10 Type 2 1-644 <$200
20 Type 2 1-55 <$200
Total Issue $483,790
Out in 1935 $50,000
Large out 1935 $2,570
****

****
7641 Faribault
FARMERS NB OF BLUE EARTH
{{12 L 6 S}}
Chartered 3/05
Closed 3/29/30
1902 Red Seal <$VALUE
3x10-20 1-1700 <$800
1902 Date Back
3x10-20 1-3140 <$350
1902 Plain Back
3x10-20 3141-8564 <$350
1929 Small Size
10 Type 1 1-344 <$350
20 Type 1 1-42 <$350
Total Issue $538,880
Out at close $50,000
Large out at close $24,320
Ch 5393 assumed circulation
****
F & Farmers NB of Blue Earth
SEE Ch 5393
FNB of Blue Earth
****
5393 Faribault
FNB OF BLUE EARTH
Chartered 6/2/00
2nd title:F & Farmers NB of Blue Earth 3/29/30
FIRST TITLE {{2 L 5 S}}
Brown Back <$VALUE
3x10-20 1-520 <$1250
1882 Date Back
3x10-20 1-880 <$1250
1882 Value Back
3x10-20 881-985 <$1250
1902 Plain Back
3x10-20 1-878 <$850
1929 Small Size
10 Type 1 1-308 <$400
20 Type 1 1-106 <$400
SECOND TITLE {{15 S}}
1929 Small Size
10 Type 1 1-734 <$250
20 Type 1 1-190 <$250
10 Type 2 1-764 <$250
20 Type 2 1-175 <$250
Total Issue $228,330
Out in 1935 $61,250
Large out 1935 $3,730
****
11054 Itasca
FNB, BOVEY
{{2 L 14 S}}
Chartered 8/17
1902 Plain Back <$VALUE
4x5 1-3705 <$850
3x10-20 1-2234 <$850
1929 Small Size
5 Type 1 1-902 <$150
10 Type 1 1-410 <$150
20 Type 1 1-130 <$150
5 Type 2 1-564 <$175
1Q Type 2 1-264 <$175
20 Type 2 1-81 <$175
Total Issue $260,140
Out in 1935 $25,000
Large out 1935 $620
****
6571 Lac Qui Parle
BOYD NB, BOYD
{{ UNREPORTED }}
Chartered 1/03
Liquidated 9/19/21
1902 Red Seal <$VALUE
3x10-20 1-400 <$2000
1902 Date Back
3x10-20 1-553 <$1250
Total Issue $47,650
Out at close $6,250
****
7387 Isanti
FNB OF BRAHAM
{{4 L 15 S}}
Chartered 9/04
1902 Red Seal <$VALUE
4x5 1-900 <$1000
3x10-20 1-772 <$1000
1902 Date Back
4x5 1-1475 <$500
3x10-20 1-1100 <$500
1902 Plain Back
4x5 1476-4655 <$500
3x10-20 1101-3124 <$500
1929 Small Size
5 Type 1 1-688 <$125
10 Type 1 1-370 <$125
20 Type 1 1-86 <$125
5 Type 2 1-1204 <$150
10 Type 2 1-507 <$150
20 Type 2 1-155 <$150

Total Issue $373,250
Out in 1935 $25,000
Large out 1935 $1,305
****
2590 Crow Wing
FNB, BRAINERD
{{8 L 12 S}}
Chartered 1881
Series 1875 <$VALUE
4x5 1-5450 <$750
3x10-20 1-333 <$1000/$1500
Brown Back
3x10-20 1-1900 <$450
1882 Date Back
4x5 1-2665 <$350
3x10-20 1-1860 <$350
1882 Value Back
4x5 2666-4625 <$400
3x10-20 1861-3003 <$400
1902 Plain Back
3x10-20 1-2887 <$200
1929 Small Size
10 Type 1 1-912 <$150
20 Type 1 1-254 <$150
10 Type 2 1-697 <$175
20 Type 2 1-145 <$175
Total Issue $702,720
Out in 1935 $40,000
Large out 1935 $3,100
****
10862 Douglas
FNB OF BRANDON
{{2 L}}
Organized 5/31/16
Receivership 11/11/26
1902 Plain Back <$VALUE
3x10-20 1-2540 <$1000
Total Issue $127,000
Out at close $25,000
****
6335 Wilkin
BRECKENRIDGE NB, BRECKENRIDGE
{{1 L}}
Chartered 7/11/02
Liquidated 2/10/27
1902 Red Seal <$VALUE
3x10-20 1-400 <$2000
1902 Date Back
3x10-20 1-1220 <$1250
1902 Plain Back
3x10-20 1221-3617 <$1250
Total Issue $200,850
Out at close $24,600
****
4644 Wilkin
FNB, BRECKENRIDGE
{{1 L 6 S}}
Chartered 1891
Brown Back <$VALUE
3x10-20 1-1410 <$1500
1882 Date Back
3x10-20 1-206 <$1250
1902 Date Back
3x10-20 1-950 <$1000
1902 Plain Back
3x10-20 951-1932 <$1000
1929 Small Size
10 Type 1 1-302 <$350
20 Type 1 1-85 <$350
Total Issue $207,720
Out in 1935 $12,500
Large out 1935 $1,500
****
10946 Nobles
FNB OF BREWSTER
{{2 L 7 S}}
Chartered 2/17
1902 Plain Back <$VALUE
4x5 1-2960 <$850
1929 Small Size
5 Type 1 1-2724 <$300
5 Type 2 1-4902 <$300
Total Issue $165,430
Out in 1935 $25,000
Large out 1935 $310
****
6478 Faribault
FNB OF BRICELYN
{{5 L}}
Chartered 11/02
Liquidated 10/25/27
1902 Red Seal <$VALUE
3x10-20 1-1356 <$1000
1902 Date Back
3x10-20 1-1650 <$500
1902 Plain Back
3x10-20 1651-3971 <$500
Total Issue $266,350
Out at close $25,000
****

****
7227 Todd
FNB OF BROWERVILLE
{{3 L 7 S}}
Chartered 4/04
Liquidated 2/2/35
1902 Red Seal <$VALUE
3x10-20 1-1207 <$1250
1902 Date Back
3x10-20 1-1500 <$650
1902 Plain Back
3x10-20 1501-4164 <$650
1929 Small Size
10 Type 1 1-498 <$300
20 Type 1 1-158 <$300
10 Type 2 1-260 <$325
20 Type 2 1-45 <$325
Total Issue $320,890
Out at close $25,000
Large out at close $1,470
****
7341 Traverse
FNB OF BROWNS VALLEY
{{4 L}}
Chartered 7/04
Liquidated 10/14/26
1902 Red Seal <$VALUE
3x10-20 1-360 <$1250
1902 Date Back
3x10-20 1-580 <$600
1902 Plain Back
3x10-20 581-1684 <$600
Total Issue $102,200
Out at close $25,000
****
12959 Wright
BUFFALO NB, BUFFALO
{{6 S}}
Chartered 7/26
1929 Small Size <$VALUE
5 Type 2 1-3794 <$400
10 Type 2 1-1843 <$400
20 Type 2 1-165 <$400
Total Issue $40,700
Out in 1935 $25,000
****
11023 Wright
FNB, BUFFALO
{{2 L}}
Organized 6/7/17
Receivership 10/17/25
1902 Plain Back <$VALUE
3x10-20 1-2248 <$1000
Total Issue $112,400
Out at close $34,600
****
7508 Houston
FNB OF CALEDONIA
{{3 L 10 S}}
Chartered 12/04
1902 Red Seal <$VALUE
4x5 1-400 <$1250
3x10-20 1-320 <$1250
1902 Date Back
4x5 1-775 <$650
3x10-20 1-560 <$650
1902 Plain Back
4x5 776-1910 <$650
3x10-20 561-1256 <$650
1929 Small Size
5 Type 1 1-381 <$200
10 Type 1 1-202 <$175
20 Type 1 1-59 <$200
Total Issue $155,630
Out in 1935 $12,500
Large out 1935 $970
****
7428 Isanti
FNB OF CAMBRIDGE
{{5 L 12 S}}
Organized 9/8/04
Receivership 12/8/33
1902 Red Seal <$VALUE
3x10-20 1-1240 <$850
1902 Date Back
3x10-20 1-2000 <$400
1902 Plain Back
3x10-20 2001-7783 <$400
1929 Small Size
10 Type 1 1-1037 <$150
20 Type 1 1-264 <$150
Total Issue $545,060
Out at close $50,000
Large out at close $4,070
****
6259 Wilkin
FNB OF CAMPBELL
{{ UNREPORTED }}
Chartered 5/02
Liquidated 12/14/29
1902 Red Seal <$VALUE
3x10-20 1-400 <$2000

1902 Date Back
3x10-20 1-620 <$1250
1902 Plain Back (dated 1902)
3x10-20 621-720 <$1250
1902 Plain Back (dated 1922)
4x5 1-1225 <$1250
Total Issue $80,500
Out at close $6,250
****
6366 Yellow Medicine
FNB OF CANBY
{{7 L 0 S}}
Chartered 8/2/02
Liquidated 12/31/29
1902 Red Seal <$VALUE
4x5 1-900 <$800
3x10-20 1-540 <$800
1902 Date Back
4x5 1-1575 <$400
3x10-20 1-1260 <$400
1902 Plain Back
4x5 1576-4755 <$400
3x10-20 1261-3084 <$400
1929 Small Size
5 Type 1 1-122 <$850
10 Type 1 1-111 <$850
20 Type 1 1-19 <$850
Total Issue $306,900
Out at close $25,000
Large out at close $12,460
****
7427 Yellow Medicine
N CITIZENS B OF CANBY
{{6 L 14 S}}
Chartered 10/04
1902 Red Seal <$VALUE
3x10-20 1-580 <$750
1902 Date Back
3x10-20 1-3500 <$375
1902 Plain Back
3x10-20 3501-8981 <$375
1929 Small Size
10 Type 1 1-1004 <$125
20 Type 1 1-252 <$125
10 Type 2 1-198 <$150
20 Type 2 1-30 <$150
Total Issue $571,110
Out in 1935 $25,000
Large out 1935 $3,540
****
6704 Goodhue
FARMERS & MERCHANTS NB OF CANNON FALLS
{{3 L}}
Organized 2/14/03
Receivership 12/17/25
1902 Red Seal <$VALUE
3x10-20 1-500 <$1500
1902 Date Back
3x10-20 1-400 <$750
1902 Plain Back
3x10-20 401-807 <$750
Total Issue $65,350
Out at close $9,600
****
13713 Goodhue
FNB IN CANNON FALLS
{{7 S}}
Chartered 6/33
1929 Small Size <$VALUE
5 Type 2 1-4120 <$400
10 Type 2 1-2138 <$400
20 Type 2 1-1047 <$400
Total Issue $62,920
Out in 1935 $60,000
****
2387 Goodhue
FNB, CANNON FALLS
{{ UNREPORTED }}
Chartered 6/10/78
Liquidated 2/21/81
Series 1875 <$VALUE
4x5 1-2540 <$2500
Total Issue $50,800
Out in 1910 $310
****

CONDITION affects Value. The Values shown are for notes in FINE condition.

6973 Carlton
FNB OF CARLTON
{{1 L 7 S}}
Organized 9/29/03
1902 Red Seal <$VALUE
3x10-20 1-620 <$2000
1902 Date Back
3x10-20 1-760 <$1000
1902 Plain Back
3x10-20 761-1762 <$1000
1929 Small Size
10 Type 1 1-486 <$300
20 Type 1 1-140 <$300
10 Type 2 1-229 <$350
20 Type 2 1-40 <$350
Total Issue $168,150
Out in 1935 $25,000
Large out 1935 $710

6352 Cass
FNB OF CASS LAKE
{{5 L 12 S}}
Organized 7/18/02
1902 Red Seal <$VALUE
3x10-20 1-700 <$1250
1902 Date Back
4x5 1-2000 <$600
3x10-20 1-1240 <$600
1902 Plain Back
4x5 2001-5285 <$600
3x10-20 1241-3427 <$600
1929 Small Size
5 Type 1 1-782 <$200
10 Type 1 1-380 <$200
20 Type 1 1-120 <$200
5 Type 2 1-302 <$200
10 Type 2 1-246 <$200
20 Type 2 1-98 <$200
Total Issue $378,640
Out in 1935 $20,410
Large out 1935 $2,000

6029 Martin
FNB, CEYLON
{{7 L 3 S}}
Organized 10/4/01
Receivership 12/8/33
Brown Back <$VALUE
3x10-20 1-1500 <$750
1882 Date Back
3x10-20 1-1670* <$650
1882 Value Back
3x10-20 1801-2660* <$750
* 1671-1800 not marked
1902 Plain Back
3x10-20 1-1619 <$500
1929 Small Size
10 Type 1 1-541 <$500
20 Type 1 1-131 <$500
Total Issue $337,130
Out at close $24,640
Large out at close $1,620

8378 Carver
FNB OF CHASKA
{{10 L 8 S}}
Chartered 9/06
1902 Red Seal <$VALUE
4x5 1-200 <$1200
3x10-20 1-167 <$1200
1902 Date Back
4x5 1-1725 <$500
3x10-20 1-1320 <$500
1902 Plain Back
4x5 1726-5025 <$500
3x10-20 1321-3192 <$500
1929 Small Size
5 Type 1 1-672 <$250
10 Type 1 1-322 <$250
20 Type 1 1-108 <$250
5 Type 2 1-984 <$275
10 Type 2 1-486 <$275
20 Type 2 1-120 <$275
Total Issue $337,070
Out in 1935 $25,000
Large out 1935 $1,490

6608 Fillmore
FNB OF CHATFIELD
{{3 L 19 S}}
Chartered 2/03
1902 Red Seal <$VALUE
3x10-20 1-1056 <$1200
1902 Date Back
3x10-20 1-1600 <$600
1902 Plain Back
3x10-20 1601-7373 <$600
1929 Small Size
10 Type 1 1-1186 <$125
20 Type 1 1-296 <$125
10 Type 2 1-861 <$150
20 Type 2 1-274 <$150
Total Issue $842,220
Out in 1935 $50,000
Large out 1935 $2,800

7647 Saint Louis
FNB OF CHISHOLM
{{14 L 50+ S}}
Organized 2/27/05
1902 Red Seal <$VALUE
4x5 1-425 <$600
3x10-20 1-350 <$600
1902 Date Back
4x5 1-1450 <$300
3x10-20 1-1120 <$300
1902 Plain Back
4x5 1451-5005 <$300
3x10-20 1121-3184 <$300
1929 Small Size
5 Type 1 1-714 <$100
10 Type 1 1-348 <$100
20 Type 1 1-96 <$100
5 Type 2 1-998 <$100
10 Type 2 1-453 <$100
20 Type 2 1-130 <$100
Total Issue $351,240
Out in 1935 $25,000
Large out 1935 $2,200

5969 Stevens
FNB OF CHOKIO
{{ UNREPORTED }}
Chartered 1901
Liquidated 3/16/14
Brown Back <$VALUE
3x10-20 1-910 <$2000
1882 Date Back
3x10-20 1-1082 <$2000
Total Issue $99,600
Out in 1914 $14,770

6448 Yellow Medicine
FNB OF CLARKFIELD
{{ UNREPORTED }}
Organized 10/3/02
Receivership 9/25/17
1902 Red Seal <$VALUE
3x10-20 1-800 <$2000
1902 Date Back
4x5 1-1100 <$1250
3x10-20 1-640 <$1250
1902 Plain Back
4x5 1101-1185 <$1250
3x10-20 641-718 <$1250
Total Issue $99,600
Out at close $14,400

11392 Clearwater
FNB, CLEARBROOK
{{2 L}}
Organized 6/30/19
Receivership 11/2/26
1902 Plain Back <$VALUE
3x10-20 1-2088 <$1000
Total Issue $104,400
Out at close $24,300

7161 Big Stone
FNB OF CLINTON
{{2 L}}
Organized 2/13/04
Receivership 2/10/27
1902 Red Seal <$VALUE
3x10-20 1-470 <$1500
1902 Date Back
3x10-20 1-1140* <$850
1902 Plain Back
3x10-20 1341-2863* <$850
* 1141-1340 not marked
Total Issue $166,650
Out at close $20,000

5405 Carlton
FNB, CLOQUET
{{20 L 42 S}}
Chartered 6/6/00
Brown Back <$VALUE
3x10-20 1-2300 <$400
1882 Date Back
3x10-20 1-7800 <$350
1882 Value Back
3x10-20 7801-10618 <$400
1902 Plain Back
3x10-20 1-9396 <$150
1929 Small Size
10 Type 1 1-2148 <$50
20 Type 1 1-592 <$50
10 Type 2 1-2389 <$60
20 Type 2 1-530 <$60
Total Issue $1,349,910
Out in 1935 $100,000
Large out 1935 $7,040

12395 Wright
FNB, COKATO
{{3 L 7 S}}
Chartered 6/23
1902 Plain Back <$VALUE
4x5 1-1882 <$750
1929 Small Size
5 Type 1 1-848 <$300
10 Type 1 1-252 <$300
20 Type 1 1-76 <$300
Total Issue $87,320
Out in 1935 $15,000
Large out 1935 $320

8051 Stearns
FNB OF COLD SPRING
{{3 L 4 S}}
Chartered 1/06
1902 Red Seal <$VALUE
4x5 1-275 <$1500
3x10-20 1-220 <$1500
1902 Date Back
4x5 1-725 <$850
3x10-20 1-540 <$850
1902 Plain Back
4x5 726-1730 <$850
3x10-20 541-1176 <$850
1929 Small Size
5 Type 1 1-354 <$400
10 Type 1 1-181 <$400
20 Type 1 1-57 <$400
Total Issue $136,220
Out in 1935 $10,000
Large out 1935 $810

8322 Itasca
FNB OF COLERAINE
{{4 L 9 S}}
Chartered 8/06
1902 Red Seal <$VALUE
4x5 1-571 <$1000
3x10-20 1-457 <$1000
1902 Date Back
4x5 1-1975 <$500
3x10-20 1-1520 <$500
1902 Plain Back
4x5 1976-5654 <$500
3x10-20 1521-3508 <$500
1929 Small Size
5 Type 1 1-894 <$200
10 Type 1 1-414 <$200
20 Type 1 1-118 <$200
5 Type 2 1-446 <$225
10 Type 2 1-310 <$225
20 Type 2 1-85 <$225
Total Issue $394,800
Out in 1935 $25,000
Large out 1935 $1,485

6584 Lyon
FNB OF COTTONWOOD
{{6 L 2 S}}
Chartered 1/03
Liquidated 6/9/30
1902 Red Seal <$VALUE
3x10-20 1-1390 <$800
1902 Date Back
3x10-20 1-1600 <$400
1902 Plain Back
3x10-20 1601-4284 <$400
1929 Small Size
10 Type 1 1-183 <$650
20 Type 1 1-25 <$650
Total Issue $297,680
Out at close $25,000
Large out at close $9,820

2567 Polk
FNB, CROOKSTON
{{16 L 14 S}}
Chartered 10/1/81
Series 1875 <$VALUE
4x5 1-6981 <$750
3x10-20 1-255 <$1000/$1500
Brown Back
4x5 1-1750 <$400
3x10-20 1-2800 <$400
1882 Date Back
4x5 1-4600 <$350
3x10-20 1-3000 <$350
1882 Value Back
4x5 4601-7585 <$400
3x10-20 3001-5035 <$400
1902 Plain Back
3x10-20 1-4919 <$175/$200
1929 Small Size
10 Type 1 1-1635 <$100
20 Type 1 1-380 <$100
Total Issue $1,120,470
Out in 1935 $37,500
Large out 1935 $6,360

3262 Polk
MERCHANTS NB, CROOKSTON
{{7 L}}
Organized 10/25/84
Receivership 3/24/24
Brown Back <$VALUE
4x5 1-4710 <$600
3x10-20 1-2814 <$600
1902 Red Seal
3x10-20 1-2900 <$600
1902 Date Back
3x10-20 1-4500 <$300
1902 Plain Back
3x10-20 4501-9182 <$300
Total Issue $839,000
Out at close $74,200

9838 Crow Wing
FNB, CROSBY
{{6 L 13 S}}
Chartered 9/10
1902 Date Back <$VALUE
4x10 1-1850* <$400
1902 Plain Back
4x10 2001-6255* <$400
* 1851-2000 not marked
1929 Small Size
10 Type 1 1-1068 <$150
10 Type 2 1-755 <$150
Total Issue $921,830
Out in 1935 $25,000
Large out 1935 $1,360

6321 Lac Qui Parle
FNB OF DAWSON
{{5 L 2 S}}
Organized 6/6/02
Receivership 5/14/31
1902 Red Seal <$VALUE
4x5 1-1650 <$800
3x10-20 1-1260 <$800
1902 Date Back
4x5 1-1750* <$400
3x10-20 1-1320** <$400
1902 Plain Back
4x5 1901-5360* <$400
3x10-20 1441-3409** <$400
* 1751-1901 not marked
** 1321-1440 not marked
1929 Small Size
5 Type 1 1-536 <$600
10 Type 1 1-219 <$600
20 Type 1 1-54 <$600
Total Issue $409,350
Out at close $30,000
Large out at close $5,450

13564 Lac Qui Parle
NORTHWESTERN NB, DAWSON
{{7 S}}
Chartered 7/31
1929 Small Size <$VALUE
5 Type 1 1-720 <$250
10 Type 1 1-282 <$250
20 Type 1 1-76 <$250
5 Type 2 1-1628 <$250
Total Issue $55,780
Out in 1935 $25,000

13303 Otter Tail
FNB IN DEER CREEK
{{6 S}}
Chartered 3/29
1929 Small Size <$VALUE
5 Type 1 1-524 <$350
10 Type 1 1-160 <$350
20 Type 1 1-54 <$350
5 Type 2 1-692 <$400
10 Type 2 1-435 <$400
20 Type 2 1-100 <$400
Total Issue $41,610
Out in 1935 $25,000

7268 Otter Tail
FNB OF DEER CREEK
{{1 L}}
Organized 5/6/04
Liquidated 8/7/29
1902 Red Seal <$VALUE
3x10-20 1-1140 <$2000
1902 Date Back
3x10-20 1-1510 <$1250
1902 Plain Back
3x10-20 1511-3986 <$1250
Total Issue $256,300
Out at close $20,650

9131 Itasca
FNB, DEER RIVER
{{3 L 4 S}}
Chartered 1908
1902 Date Back <$VALUE
3x10-20 1-860 <$850
1902 Plain Back
3x10-20 861-2782 <$850
1929 Small Size
10 Type 1-314 <$500
20 Type 1-106 <$500
10 Type 1-629 <$500
20 Type 1-162 <$500
Total Issue $180,190
Out in 1935 $24,750
Large out 1935 $620

9703 Crow Wing
FNB, DEERWOOD
{{8 L 10 S}}
Chartered 1910
1902 Date Back <$VALUE
4x5 1-1850 <$400
3x10-20 1-1400 <$400
1902 Plain Back
4x5 1851-6095 <$400
3x10-20 1401-4093 <$400
1929 Small Size
5 Type 1 1-998 <$175
10 Type 1 1-488 <$175
20 Type 1 1-158 <$200
5 Type 2 1-444 <$225
10 Type 2 1-198 <$225
20 Type 2 1-120 <$225
Total Issue $411,330
Out in 1935 $30,000
Large out 1935 $2,120

9903 Wright
FNB, DELANO
{{3 L}}
Organized 11/23/10
Receivership 12/12/25
1902 Date Back <$VALUE
4x5 1-550 <$850
3x10-20 1-440 <$850
1902 Plain Back
4x5 551-850 <$850
3x10-20 441-607 <$850
Total Issue $47,350
Out at close $6,250

3426 Becker
FNB, DETROIT
{{7 L}}
Organized 12/31/85
Receivership 11/23/26
Brown Back <$VALUE
3x10-20 1-1348 <$600
1902 Red Seal
3x10-20 1-250 <$750
1902 Date Back
3x10-20 1-4000 <$300
1902 Plain Back
3x10-20 4001-8328 <$300
Total Issue $496,300
Out at close $37,500

8122 Becker
MERCHANTS NB OF DETROIT
{{7 L}}
Organized 2/9/06
Receivership 6/22/25
1902 Red Seal <$VALUE
3x10-20 1-1600 <$750
1902 Date Back
3x10-20 1-3500 <$350
1902 Plain Back
3x10-20 3501-7970 <$350
Total Issue $478,500
Out at close $56,700

13075 Becker
BECKER COUNTY NB, DETROIT LAKES
{{25 S}}
Chartered 5/27
1929 Small Size <$VALUE
5 Type 1 1-936 <$75
10 Type 1 1-568 <$75
20 Type 1 1-170 <$75
5 Type 2 1-2068 <$85
10 Type 2 1-1200 <$85
20 Type 2 1-280 <$100
Total Issue $110,500
Out in 1935 $50,000

6623 Dodge
FARMERS NB OF DODGE CENTER
{{1 L}}
Organized 2/4/03
Receivership 12/9/24
1902 Red Seal <$VALUE
4x5 1-950 <$2000
3x10-20 1-750 <$2000
1902 Date Back
4x5 1-1400 <$1250
3x10-20 1-960 <$1250
1902 Plain Back
4x5 1401-3175 <$1250
3x10-20 961-2030 <$1250
Total Issue $221,500
Out at close $29,500

6682 Dodge
FNB OF DODGE CENTER
{{4 L}}
Chartered 3/03
Liquidated 3/24/23
1902 Red Seal <$VALUE
3x10-20 1-400 <$1250
1902 Date Back
3x10-20 1-2050 <$600
1902 Plain Back
3x10-20 2051-3283 <$600
Total Issue $184,150
Out at close $25,000

9374 Saint Louis
AMERICAN EXCHANGE NB OF DULUTH
{{33 L}}
Chartered 1909
Closed 4/18/29
1902 Date Back <$VALUE
4x5 1-23500 <$60
3x10-20 1-17600 <$75
1902 Plain Back
4x5 23501-62214 <$60
3x10-20 17601-41464 <$75
Total Issue $3,317,480
Out in 1928 $295,950
Ch 3626 assumed circulation

6520 Saint Louis
CITY NB OF DULUTH
{{40 L 50+ S}}
Chartered 12/02
1902 Red Seal <$VALUE
3x10-20 1-14650 <$250
1902 Date Back
3x10-20 1-22000 <$75
1902 Plain Back
3x10-20 22001-59693 <$75
1929 Small Size
10 Type 1 1-7572 <$20
20 Type 1 1-1822 <$30
10 Type 2 1-7953 <$20
20 Type 2 1-4880 <$30
Total Issue $4,518,440
Out in 1935 $325,000
Large out 1935 $20,320

2768 Saint Louis
DULUTH NB, DULUTH
{{ UNREPORTED }}
Chartered 8/26/82
Liquidated 2/20/88
Brown Back <$VALUE
4x5 1-800 <$1500
3x10-20 1-1127 <$1500
Total Issue $72,350
Out in 1910 $380

12140 Saint Louis
DULUTH NB, DULUTH
{{9 L 19 S}}
Chartered 3/22
1902 Plain Back <$VALUE
3x10-20 1-9078 <$125
1929 Small Size
10 Type 1 1-2100 <$25
20 Type 1 1-644 <$35
10 Type 2 1-2680 <$30
20 Type 2 1-725 <$40
Total Issue $698,480
Out in 1935 $100,000
Large out 1935 $4,080

Duluth Union NB of Duluth
SEE Ch 3626
Union NB of Duluth

F & American NB of Duluth
SEE Ch 3626
Union NB of Duluth

****
1954 Saint Louis
FNB, DULUTH
{{ UNREPORTED }}
Chartered 4/6/72
Receivership 3/13/76
Original Series <$VALUE
3x1-2 1-1500 <$1500/$2000
4x5 1-2085 <$1500
50-100 1-300 <$5000
Total Issue $94,200
Out in 1915 $225
****
FNB of Duluth
SEE Ch 3626
Union NB of Duluth
****
4421 Saint Louis
MARINE NB, DULUTH
{{ 1 L }}
Organized 9/23/90
Receivership 11/11/96
Brown Back <$VALUE
3x10-20 1-2109 <$1000
Total Issue $105,450
Out in 1915 $770
****
3453 Saint Louis
MERCHANTS NB, DULUTH
{{ UNREPORTED }}
Organized 2/10/86
Liquidated 5/20/89
Brown Back <$VALUE
4x5 1-3274 <$1250
Total Issue $65,480
Out in 1910 $435
****
11810 Saint Louis
MINNESOTA NB, DULUTH
{{ 18 L 50+ S }}
Chartered 8/20
1902 Plain Back <$VALUE
4x5 1-25940 <$85
3x10-20 1-25660 <$100
1929 Small Size
5 Type 1 1-16592 <$15
10 Type 1 1-8670 <$20
5 Type 2 1-20768 <$20
10 Type 2 1-12606 <$25
Total Issue $2,757,060
Out in 1935 $450,000
Large out 1935 $8,775
****
4001 Saint Louis
NB OF COMMERCE OF DULUTH
{{ UNREPORTED }}
Organized 3/27/89
Liquidated 3/17/97
Brown Back <$VALUE
3x10-20 1-2267 <$1200
Total Issue $113,350
Out in 1910 $1,310
****
9327 Saint Louis
NORTHERN NB OF DULUTH
{{ 32 L 40 S }}
Chartered 1909
1902 Date Back <$VALUE
3x10-20 1-19500 <$75
1902 Plain Back
3x10-20 19501-65489 <$75
1929 Small Size
50 Type 1 1-1980 <$85
100 Type 1 1-774 <$135
50 Type 2 1-36 <$165
Total Issue $4,334,650
Out in 1935 $750,000
Large out 1935 $18,850
****
13078 Saint Louis
PIONEER NB OF DULUTH
{{ 3 L 19 S }}
Chartered 5/19/27
1902 Plain Back <$VALUE
4x5 1-10925 <$350
1929 Small Size
5 Type 1 1-11108 <$60
5 Type 2 1-21528 <$60
Total Issue $659,380
Out in 1935 $100,000
Large out 1935 $885
****
3626 Saint Louis
UNION NB OF DULUTH
Chartered 1887
2nd title:Duluth Union NB 1/25/88
3rd title:FNB 6/1/89
4th title:F & American NB 4/18/29
FIRST TITLE {{ 0 L }}
Brown Back <$VALUE
50-100 1-306 <$2500
SECOND TITLE {{ 0 L }}
Brown Back
3x10-20 1-429 <$850
THIRD TITLE {{ 39 L }}
Brown Back
3x10-20 1-20997 <$200
1902 Red Seal
4x5 1-11500 <$300
3x10-20 1-5000 <$300
1902 Date Back
4x5 1-21000* <$65
4x10 1-20500** <$70
1902 Plain Back
4x5 23501-55250* <$65
4x10 23001-44650** <$70
3x10-20 1-33733 <$70
* 21001-23500 not marked
** 20501-23000 not marked
FOURTH TITLE {{ 50+ S }}
1929 Small Size
10 Type 1 1-28178 <$20
20 Type 1 1-7296 <$30
10 Type 2 1-8615 <$20
20 Type 2 1-3352 <$30
Total Issue $8,844,240
Out in 1935 $650,000
Large out 1935 $46,680
****
13116 Saint Louis
WESTERN NB, DULUTH
{{ 2 L 24 S }}
Chartered 9/27
1902 Plain Back <$VALUE
3x10-20 1-4427 <$350
1929 Small Size
10 Type 1 1-3614 <$30
20 Type 1 1-1078 <$35
10 Type 2 1-1385 <$35
20 Type 2 1-651 <$40
Total Issue $594,420
Out in 1935 $100,000
Large out 1935 $1,920
****
6738 Martin
FNB OF DUNNELL
{{ 3 L 8 S }}
Chartered 4/03
1902 Red Seal <$VALUE
3x10-20 1-800 <$1250
1902 Date Back
3x10-20 1-910* <$650
1902 Plain Back
3x10-20 1071-2599* <$650
* 911-1070 not marked
1929 Small Size
10 Type 1 1-602 <$300
20 Type 1 1-154 <$300
10 Type 2 1-355 <$350
20 Type 2 1-45 <$350
Total Issue $229,000
Out in 1935 $30,000
Large out 1935 $1,110
****
6266 Todd
FNB OF EAGLE BEND
{{ 6 L 16 S }}
Chartered 5/02
Liquidated 2/02/35
1902 Red Seal <$VALUE
3x10-20 1-1300 <$1250
1902 Date Back
3x10-20 1-1460 <$600
1902 Plain Back
3x10-20 1461-4075 <$600
1929 Small Size
10 Type 1 1-428 <$250
20 Type 1 1-148 <$250
10 Type 2 1-373 <$250
20 Type 2 1-110 <$250
Total Issue $318,120
Out in 1935 $25,000
Large out 1935 $2,650
****
4638 Polk
FNB, EAST GRAND FORKS
{{ 7 L }}
Organized 9/7/91
Receivership 7/28/27
Brown Back <$VALUE
4x5 1-2225 <$750
3x10-20 1-1270 <$750
1882 Date Back
4x5 1-580 <$650
3x10-20 1-474 <$650
1902 Date Back
4x5 1-1725 <$350
3x10-20 1-1260 <$350
1902 Plain Back
4x5 1726-5745 <$350
3x10-20 1261-3632 <$350
Total Issue $439,800
Out at close $37,495
****
4617 Grant
FNB, ELBOW LAKE
{{ 7 L 11 S }}
Chartered 1891
Brown Back <$VALUE
4x5 1-2625 <$850
3x10-20 1-1040 <$850
1882 Date Back
4x5 1-427 <$750
3x10-20 1-126 <$750
1902 Date Back
3x10-20 1-1100* <$400
1902 Plain Back
3x10-20 1301-2860* <$400
* 1101-1300 not marked
1929 Small Size
10 Type 1 1-422 <$275
20 Type 1 1-118 <$275
10 Type 2 1-240 <$300
20 Type 2 1-75 <$300
Total Issue $305,720
Out in 1935 $20,000
Large out 1935 $1,780
****
7184 Wabasha
FNB, ELGIN
{{ 1 L }}
Organized 3/25/04
Liquidated 7/31/09
1902 Red Seal <$VALUE
3x10-20 1-1080 <$2000
1902 Date Back
3x10-20 1-117 <$1250
Total Issue $59,850
Out in 1910 $14,130
****
8757 Sherburne
FNB OF ELK RIVER
{{ 9 L 6 S }}
Chartered 6/07
1902 Red Seal <$VALUE
4x5 1-162 <$1000
4x10 1-162 <$1000
1902 Date Back
4x5 1-1385* <$400
4x10 1-1325** <$400
1902 Plain Back
4x5 1486-4410* <$400
4x10 1426-3701** <$400
* 1386-1485 not marked
** 1326-1425 not marked
1929 Small Size
5 Type 1 1-892 <$350
10 Type 1 1-424 <$350
5 Type 2 1-1298 <$350
10 Type 2 1-779 <$350
Total Issue $312,440
Out in 1935 $20,000
Large out 1935 $1,220
****
5570 Nobles
FNB OF ELLSWORTH
{{ 4 L }}
Chartered 9/5/00
Liquidated 4/15/26
Brown Back <$VALUE
3x10-20 1-740 <$800
1882 Date Back
3x10-20 1-950* <$700
1882 Value Back
3x10-20 1111-1483* <$750
* 951-1110 not marked
1902 Plain Back
3x10-20 1-886 <$600
Total Issue $155,450
Out in 1925 $16,250
****
5377 Faribault
FNB, ELMORE
{{ 11 L 7 S }}
Chartered 5/28/00
Brown Back <$VALUE
4x5 1-665 <$500
3x10-20 1-534 <$500
1882 Date Back
4x5 1-1650 <$400
3x10-20 1-1220 <$400
1882 Value Back
4x5 1651-2495 <$500
3x10-20 1221-1732 <$500
1902 Plain Back
4x5 1-2300 <$300
3x10-20 1-1622 <$300
1929 Small Size
5 Type 1 1-754 <$300
10 Type 1 1-360 <$300
20 Type 1 1-94 <$300
5 Type 2 1-844 <$350
10 Type 2 1-432 <$350
20 Type 2 1-72 <$350
Total Issue $369,080
Out in 1935 $20,000
Large out 1935 $1,940
****
8592 Saint Louis
FNB OF ELY
{{ 3 L 9 S }}
Chartered 3/07
1902 Red Seal <$VALUE
3x10-20 1-1200 <$1500
1902 Date Back
3x10-20 1-700 <$750
1902 Plain Back
3x10-20 701-1582 <$750
1929 Small Size
10 Type 1 1-283 <$250
20 Type 1 1-88 <$250
Total Issue $166,640
Out in 1935 $12,500
Large out 1935 $710
****
6784 Freeborn
FNB OF EMMONS
{{ 5 L 15 S }}
Chartered 5/03
1902 Red Seal <$VALUE
3x10-20 1-1525 <$1000
1902 Date Back
4x5 1-1950 <$500
3x10-20 1-850 <$500
1902 Plain Back
4x5 1951-5055 <$500
3x10-20 851-2902 <$500
1929 Small Size
5 Type 1 1-756 <$150
10 Type 1 1-358 <$150
20 Type 1 1-96 <$150
5 Type 2 1-680 <$150
10 Type 2 1-419 <$150
20 Type 2 1-166 <$150
Total Issue $389,040
Out in 1935 $25,000
Large out 1935 $1,755
****
11173 Polk
FNB, ERSKINE
{{ 4 L }}
Organized 4/22/18
Receivership 3/2/29
1902 Plain Back <$VALUE
4x5 1-2835 <$750
3x10-20 1-1853 <$750
Total Issue $149,350
Out at close $25,000
****
5553 Saint Louis
FNB, EVELETH
{{ 5 L 8 S }}
Chartered 8/25/00
Brown Back <$VALUE
3x10-20 1-1890 <$750
1882 Date Back
3x10-20 1-1700* <$650
1882 Value Back
3x10-20 1901-2411* <$700
* 1701-1900 not marked
1902 Plain Back
3x10-20 1-2259 <$500
1929 Small Size
10 Type 1 1-546 <$250
20 Type 1 1-138 <$250
10 Type 2 1-665 <$250
20 Type 2 1-129 <$250
Total Issue $986,550
Out in 1935 $25,000
Large out 1935 $1,480
****
6991 Saint Louis
MINERS NB OF EVELETH
{{ 4 L 7 S }}
Chartered 10/03
1902 Red Seal <$VALUE
3x10-20 1-700 <$1250
1902 Date Back
3x10-20 1-1320 <$600
1902 Plain Back
3x10-20 1321-4320 <$600
1929 Small Size
10 Type 1 1-544 <$250
20 Type 1 1-150 <$250
10 Type 2 1-536 <$250
20 Type 2 1-130 <$250
Total Issue $309,600
Out in 1935 $25,000
Large out 1935 $1,970
****
5374 Olmsted
FNB OF EYOTA
{{ 4 L }}
Chartered 5/26/00
Liquidated 6/1/16
Brown Back <$VALUE
4x5 1-1125 <$1000
3x10-20 1-860 <$1000
1882 Date Back
4x5 1-1575 <$1000
3x10-20 1-1120 <$1000
1882 Value Back
4x5 1576-1670 <$1000
3x10-20 1121-1127 <$1000
Total Issue $155,250
Out at close $25,000
****
9771 Renville
FNB, FAIRFAX
{{ 6 L 3 S }}
Chartered 1910
1902 Date Back <$VALUE
3x10-20 1-1800 <$450
1902 Plain Back
3x10-20 1801-4242 <$450
1929 Small Size
10 Type 1 1-540 <$500
20 Type 1 1-148 <$500
10 Type 2 1-271 <$500
20 Type 2 1-60 <$500
Total Issue $266,170
Out in 1935 $25,000
Large out 1935 $1,830
****
8551 Martin
FAIRMONT NB, FAIRMONT
{{ 6 L 9 S }}
Chartered 2/07
1902 Red Seal <$VALUE
4x5 1-600 <$700
3x10-20 1-625 <$700
1902 Date Back
4x5 1-1600 <$350
3x10-20 1-1080 <$350
1902 Plain Back
4x5 1601-5888 <$350
3x10-20 1081-3631 <$350
1929 Small Size
5 Type 1 1-828 <$165
10 Type 1 1-546 <$165
20 Type 1 1-180 <$175
5 Type 2 1-100 <$185
10 Type 2 1-80 <$185
20 Type 2 1-54 <$185
Total Issue $424,160
Out in 1935 $20,000
Large out 1935 $1,570
****
4936 Martin
FNB, FAIRMONT
{{ 4 L 20 S }}
Chartered 1894
Brown Back <$VALUE
4x5 1-2875 <$600
50-100 1-447 <$2250/$2500
1882 Date Back
4x5 1-1975 <$600
50-100 1-260 <$1750/$2000
3x50-100 1-40 <$1750/$2000
1902 Date Back
4x10 1-1500 <$500
1902 Plain Back
4x10 1501-9163 <$500
1929 Small Size
10 Type 1 1-1802 <$60
10 Type 2 1-9868 <$65
Total Issue $786,370
Out in 1935 $100,000
Large out 1935 $2,785
****
5423 Martin
MARTIN COUNTY NB, FAIRMONT
{{ 16 L 21 S }}
Chartered 6/14/00
Brown Back <$VALUE
4x5 1-4100 <$300
3x10-20 1-2500 <$300
1882 Date Back
4x5 1-654 <$250
3x10-20 1-4700 <$250
1882 Value Back
3x10-20 4701-6466 <$250
1902 Plain Back
4x5 1-8787 <$135
3x10-20 1-4009 <$150
1929 Small Size
5 Type 1 1-2114 <$60
10 Type 1 1-1116 <$60
20 Type 1 1-340 <$65
5 Type 2 1-1542 <$65
10 Type 2 1-787 <$65
20 Type 2 1-461 <$75
Total Issue $1,120,540
Out in 1935 $75,000
Large out 1935 $5,145
****
1863 Rice
CITIZENS NB OF FARIBAULT
{{ 12 L }}
Organized 7/21/71
Receivership 8/14/34
Original Series <$VALUE
3x1-2 1-5260 <$650/$1500
4x5 1-4500 <$750
Series 1875
4x5 1-8044 <$750
Brown Back
3x10-20 1-4900 <$300
1882 Date Back
3x10-20 1-739 <$250
1902 Date Back
3x10-20 1-2300 <$150
1902 Plain Back
3x10-20 2301-6240 <$150
Total Issue $871,130
Out at close $5,494
****
1686 Rice
FNB OF FARIBAULT
{{ 11 L }}
Organized 12/2/68
Receivership 1/3/05
Original Series <$VALUE
3x1-2 1-1700 <$1250/$2500
4x5 1-4075 <$1500
Series 1875
4x5 1-6275 <$750
Brown Back
3x10-20 1-4041 <$350
Total Issue $417,550
Out in 1915 $3,683
****
11668 Rice
SECURITY NB OF FARIBAULT
Chartered 4/20
2nd title:Security NB & TC 3/22/29
FIRST TITLE {{ 14 L }}
1902 Plain Back <$VALUE
3x10-20 1-8717 <$150
SECOND TITLE {{ 15 S }}
1929 Small Size
5 Type 1 1-4556 <$100
5 Type 2 1-9376 <$100
Total Issue $619,410
Out in 1935 $50,000
Large out 1935 $4,380
****
11687 Dakota
FNB, FARMINGTON
{{ 50+ S }}
Chartered 4/20
1929 Small Size <$VALUE
5 Type 1 1-418 <$75
10 Type 1 1-272 <$75
20 Type 1 1-86 <$75
5 Type 2 1-1020 <$75
10 Type 2 1-636 <$75
20 Type 2 1-125 <$75
Total Issue $53,140
Out in 1935 $25,000
****
2934 Otter Tail
CITIZENS NB OF FERGUS FALLS
{{ UNREPORTED }}
Organized 4/25/83
Liquidated 3/22/97
Brown Back <$VALUE
3x10-20 1-1333 <$2000
Total Issue $66,650
Out in 1910 $380
****

<$VALUEs are for notes in FINE condition. Value changes by approximately 25% for a change of one full grade.

2648 Otter Tail
FERGUS FALLS NB, FERGUS FALLS
Chartered 1882
2nd title:Fergus Falls NB & TC 1/3/31
FIRST TITLE {{ 13 L 12 S }}
Series 1875 <$VALUE
3x10-20 1-2466<$1000/$1500
Brown Back
3x10-20 1-3640 <$400
1882 Date Back
3x10-20 1-3800* <$350
1882 Value Back
3x10-20 4161-8833* <$350
* 3801-4160 not marked
1902 Plain Back
3x10-20 1-6043 <$175
1929 Small Size
10 Type 1 1-1226 <$85
20 Type 1 1-420 <$85
SECOND TITLE {{ 15 S }}
1929 Small Size
10 Type 1 1-806 <$60
20 Type 1 1-232 <$60
10 Type 2 1-1134 <$60
20 Type 2 1-414 <$60
Total Issue $1,268,880
Out in 1935 $100,000
Large out 1935 $7,600

2030 Otter Tail
FNB, FERGUS FALLS
{{ 12 L 28 S }}
Chartered 8/20/72
Original Series <$VALUE
3x1-2 1-1240 <$650/$1500
4x5 1-1875 <$750
Series 1875
4x5 1-4737 <$750
Brown Back
3x10-20 1-5800 <$300
1882 Date Back
3x10-20 1-2390 <$250
1902 Date Back
3x10-20 1-3000 <$175
1902 Plain Back
3x10-20 3001-13483 <$175
1929 Small Size
10 Type 1 1-1812 <$60
20 Type 1 1-600 <$60
10 Type 2 1-2459 <$60
20 Type 2 1-512 <$60
Total Issue $1,437,640
Out in 1935 $100,000
Large out 1935 $7,920

6693 Polk
CITIZENS NB, FERTILE
{{ UNREPORTED }}
Organized 3/26/03
Liquidated 1/18/05
1902 Red Seal <$VALUE
4x5 1-480 <$2500
3x10-20 1-405 <$2500
Total Issue $29,850
Out in 1910 $1,025

5988 Polk
FNB, FERTILE
{{ UNREPORTED }}
Organized 10/9/01
Liquidated 8/31/07
Brown Back <$VALUE
3x10-20 1-525 <$2500
Total Issue $26,250
Out in 1910 $2,390

7933 Benton
FNB OF FOLEY
{{ 4 L 6 S }}
Organized 8/25/05
Receivership 9/20/34
1902 Red Seal <$VALUE
3x10-20 1-850 <$1000
1902 Date Back
3x10-20 1-1620 <$500
1902 Plain Back
3x10-20 1621-4190 <$500
1929 Small Size
10 Type 1 1-531 <$350
20 Type 1 1-144 <$350
Total Issue $301,140
Out at close $25,000
Large out at close $1,510

11652 Washington
FNB, FOREST LAKE
{{ 3 L 1 S }}
Chartered 3/20
Liquidated 2/10/31
1902 Plain Back <$VALUE
3x10-20 1-2624 <$750
1929 Small Size
10 Type 1 1-262 <$400
20 Type 1 1-65 <$400
Total Issue $194,050
Out at close $25,000
Large out at close $4,490

6889 Polk
FNB OF FOSSTON
{{ 10 L 21 S }}
Organized 6/12/03
Receivership 10/16/33
1902 Red Seal <$VALUE
4x5 1-800 <$600
3x10-20 1-700 <$600
1902 Date Back
4x5 1-2000 <$300
3x10-20 1-1330 <$300
1902 Plain Back
4x5 2001-5515 <$300
3x10-20 1331-3458 <$300
1929 Small Size
5 Type 1 1-786 <$100
10 Type 1 1-380 <$100
20 Type 1 1-99 <$100
Total Issue $392,460
Out at close $30,000
Large out at close $3,365

7024 Becker
FNB OF FRAZEE
{{ 5 L 8 S }}
Organized 10/2/03
Receivership 9/26/32
1902 Red Seal <$VALUE
3x10-20 1-812 <$800
1902 Date Back
4x5 1-2250 <$400
3x10-20 1-1480 <$400
1902 Plain Back
4x5 2251-5655 <$400
3x10-20 1481-3659 <$400
1929 Small Size
5 Type 1 1-732 <$300
10 Type 1 1-355 <$300
20 Type 1 1-75 <$300
Total Issue $388,910
Out at close $29,700
Large out at close $2,720

6054 Murray
FNB, FULDA
{{ 3 L }}
Organized 12/14/01
Receivership 10/7/26
Brown Back <$VALUE
3x10-20 1-460 <$1000
1882 Date Back
3x10-20 1-2010 <$900
1882 Value Back
3x10-20 2011-2983 <$900
1902 Plain Back
3x10-20 1-1005 <$700
Total Issue $222,400
Out at close $24,500

9262 Saint Louis
FNB, GILBERT
{{ 10 L 15 S }}
Chartered 1908
1902 Date Back <$VALUE
3x10-20 1-1650 <$300
1902 Plain Back
3x10-20 1651-5140 <$300
1929 Small Size
10 Type 1 1-606 <$150
20 Type 1 1-190 <$150
10 Type 2 1-394 <$175
20 Type 2 1-100 <$175
Total Issue $322,100
Out in 1935 $30,000
Large out 1935 $1,680

2571 McLeod
FNB, GLENCOE
{{ 9 L 11 S }}
Chartered 1881
Series 1875 <$VALUE
4x5 1-5201 <$800
50-100 1-45 <$5000
Brown Back
50-100 1-740 <$2000/$2250
1882 Date Back
50-100 1-300 <$1750/$2000
3x50-100 1-416<$1500/$1750
1902 Plain Back
3x50-100 1-388 <$750/$900
1929 Small Size
50 Type 1 1-163 <$250
100 Type 1 1-27 <$300
Total Issue $532,870
Out in 1935 $50,000
Large out 1935 $5,600

7742 Pope
FNB OF GLENWOOD
{{ 4 L }}
Organized 4/16/05
Receivership 7/14/26
1902 Red Seal <$VALUE
3x10-20 1-400 <$1500
1902 Date Back
3x10-20 1-900 <$750
1902 Plain Back
3x10-20 901-3492 <$750
Total Issue $194,600
Out at close $10,000

10830 Clearwater
FNB, GONVICK
{{ 2 L }}
Organized 2/23
Receivership 11/5/26
1902 Plain Back <$VALUE
4x5 1-3325 <$1000
3x10-20 1-2485 <$1000
Total Issue $165,900
Out at close $24,400

11552 Blue Earth
FNB, GOOD THUNDER
{{ 4 L 16 S }}
Chartered 12/19
1902 Plain Back <$VALUE
4x5 1-6255 <$800
1929 Small Size
5 Type 1 1-2552 <$300
5 Type 2 1-5222 <$300
Total Issue $227,770
Out in 1935 $25,000
Large out 1935 $595

7603 Goodhue
FNB OF GOODHUE
{{ 11 L }}
Organized 12/27/04
Receivership 10/13/33
1902 Red Seal <$VALUE
3x10-20 1-506 <$750
1902 Date Back
3x10-20 1-1550 <$350
1902 Plain Back
3x10-20 1551-3371 <$350
Total Issue $193,850
Out at close $1,400

7213 Big Stone
FNB OF GRACEVILLE
{{ 8 L 13 S }}
Chartered 4/04
1902 Red Seal <$VALUE
3x10-20 1-1110 <$750
1902 Date Back
3x10-20 1-1820 <$400
1902 Plain Back
3x10-20 1821-4604 <$400
1929 Small Size
10 Type 1 1-458 <$200
20 Type 1 1-128 <$200
10 Type 2 1-828 <$200
20 Type 2 1-124 <$200
Total Issue $339,300
Out in 1935 $25,000
Large out 1935 $1,880

6933 Mower
FNB OF GRAND MEADOW
{{ 3 L 0 S }}
Chartered 8/03
Liquidated 1/5/30
1902 Red Seal <$VALUE
3x10-20 1-940 <$2500
1902 Date Back
3x10-20 1-1610 <$1500
1902 Plain Back
3x10-20 1611-4410 <$1500
1929 Small Size
5 Type 1 1-99 <$1250
10 Type 1 1-41 <$1250
20 Type 1 1-4 <$1250
Total Issue $273,410
Out at close $25,000
Large out at close $16,810

6563 Itasca
FNB OF GRAND RAPIDS
{{ 8 L 7 S }}
Chartered 12/30/02
1902 Red Seal <$VALUE
3x10-20 1-1322 <$750
1902 Date Back
3x10-20 1-1680 <$350
1902 Plain Back
3x10-20 1681-6579 <$350
1929 Small Size
5 Type 1 1-990 <$300
10 Type 1 1-308 <$300
20 Type 1 1-106 <$300
5 Type 2 1-2220 <$300
Total Issue $467,030
Out in 1935 $25,000
Large out 1935 $2,020

8416 Yellow Medicine
FNB OF GRANITE FALLS
{{ 4 L }}
Chartered 10/06
Liquidated 3/4/29
1902 Red Seal <$VALUE
4x10 1-900 <$1250
1902 Date Back
4x10 1-2150 <$600
1902 Plain Back
4x10 2151-5853 <$600
Total Issue $270,120
Out at close $25,000

8729 Todd
FNB OF GREY EAGLE
{{ 2 L }}
Organized 5/28/07
Receivership 11/8/23
1902 Red Seal <$VALUE
3x10-20 1-788 <$2000
1902 Date Back
3x10-20 1-1460 <$1000
1902 Plain Back
3x10-20 1461-3036 <$1000
Total Issue $191,200
Out at close $24,000

12607 Todd
NB OF GREY EAGLE
{{ U + 0 L 10 S }}
Chartered 12/24
Liquidated 7/2/34
1902 Plain Back <$VALUE
3x10-20 1-1331 <$1000
1929 Small Size
10 Type 1 1-548 <$300
20 Type 1 1-124 <$300
10 Type 2 1-345 <$300
20 Type 2 1-25 <$300
Total Issue $118,260
Out at close $25,000
Large out at close $1,110

6934 Kittson
FNB OF HALLOCK
{{ 5 L }}
Organized 8/5/03
Receivership 10/16/25
1902 Red Seal <$VALUE
3x10-20 1-356 <$1000
1902 Date Back
3x10-20 1-1870 <$500
1902 Plain Back
3x10-20 1871-3870 <$500
Total Issue $211,300
Out at close $24,600

7196 Norman
FNB OF HALSTAD
{{ 1 L 12 S }}
Chartered 4/04
1902 Red Seal <$VALUE
50-100 1-114 <$5000
1902 Date Back
50-100 1-120 <$1250/$1500
3x50-100 1-80 <$1250/$1500
1929 Small Size
5 Type 1 1-618 <$250
10 Type 1 1-208 <$250
5 Type 2 1-464 <$250
10 Type 2 1-324 <$250
Total Issue $93,180
Out in 1935 $11,500
Large out 1935 $700

6996 Stevens
FNB OF HANCOCK
{{ 24 L 7 S }}
Chartered 10/03
Liquidated 1/9/31
1902 Red Seal <$VALUE
3x10-20 1-1350 <$500
1902 Date Back
3x10-20 1-1460 <$150
1902 Plain Back
3x10-20 1461-4212 <$150
1929 Small Size
10 Type 1 1-242 <$300
20 Type 1 1-48 <$300
Total Issue $298,380
Out at close $25,000
Large out at close $6,170

7033 Stevens
HANCOCK NB, HANCOCK
{{ 20 L 5 S }}
Chartered 11/03
1902 Red Seal <$VALUE
3x10-20 1-1160 <$400
1902 Date Back
3x10-20 1-1610 <$150
1902 Plain Back
3x10-20 1611-4400 <$150
1929 Small Size
10 Type 1 1-526 <$300
20 Type 1 1-150 <$300
10 Type 2 1-286 <$350
20 Type 2 1-51 <$350
Total Issue $331,440
Out in 1935 $25,000
Large out 1935 $1,970

6285 Yellow Medicine
FNB, HANLEY FALLS
{{ UNREPORTED }}
Organized 6/2/02
Liquidated 2/15/09
1902 Red Seal <$VALUE
3x10-20 1-1145 <$2500
Total Issue $57,250
Out in 1910 $7,490

11288 Brown
FNB OF HANSKA
{{ 7 L }}
Chartered 1/19
Liquidated 2/21/27
1902 Plain Back <$VALUE
4x5 1-7210 <$400
Total Issue $144,200
Out at close $24,600

8683 Fillmore
FNB OF HARMONY
{{ 4 L 14 S }}
Chartered 5/07
1902 Red Seal <$VALUE
4x10 1-475 <$1000
1902 Date Back
4x10 1-2150 <$500
1902 Plain Back
4x10 2151-5670 <$500
1929 Small Size
10 Type 1 1-834 <$175
10 Type 2 1-1127 <$200
Total Issue $307,110
Out in 1935 $25,000
Large out 1935 $1,250

---

496 Dakota
FNB, HASTINGS
{{ 5 L 6 S }}
Chartered 1864
Original Series <$VALUE
3x1-2 1-2500 <$750/$1500
4x5 1-1500 <$850
3x10-20 1-2700<$1000/$1500
Series 1875
3x10-20 1-2084<$1000/$1500
Brown Back
3x10-20 1-2510 <$750
1902 Red Seal
3x10-20 1-640 <$850
1902 Date Back
3x10-20 1-1300* <$450
1902 Plain Back
3x10-20 1501-2996* <$450
* 1301-1500 not marked
1929 Small Size
10 Type 1 1-430 <$350
20 Type 1 1-118 <$350
10 Type 2 1-244 <$350
20 Type 2 1-40 <$375
Total Issue $632,200
Out in 1935 $20,000
Large out 1935 $3,130

11212 Dakota
HASTINGS NB, HASTINGS
{{ 15 S }}
Chartered 7/18
1929 Small Size <$VALUE
5 Type 1 1-1000 <$85
10 Type 1 1-620 <$85
20 Type 1 1-182 <$85
5 Type 2 1-1560 <$100
10 Type 2 1-935 <$100
20 Type 2 1-245 <$100
Total Issue $111,090
Out in 1935 $50,000

1538 Dakota
MERCHANTS NB OF HASTINGS
{{ 1 L }}
Chartered 8/26/65
Liquidated 2/7/74
Original Series <$VALUE
3x1-2 1-3800 <$1500/$2000
4x5 1-2375 <$1500
3x10-20 1-1180<$1750/$2000
Total Issue $125,500
Out in 1910 $1,292

7772 Clay
FNB OF HAWLEY
{{ 0 L 5 S }}
Chartered 6/05
1902 Red Seal <$VALUE
3x10-20 1-300 <$2000
1902 Date Back
3x10-20 1-460* <$1250
1902 Plain Back
3x10-20 561-1025* <$1250
* 461-560 not marked
1929 Small Size
10 Type 1 1-412 <$400
20 Type 1 1-128 <$400
10 Type 2 1-196 <$450
20 Type 2 1-30 <$450
Total Issue $108,890
Out in 1935 $25,000
Large out 1935 $730

9457 Lincoln
FARMERS NB, HENDRICKS
{{ 7 L 5 S }}
Organized 5/10/09
Receivership 12/8/33
1902 Date Back <$VALUE
3x10-20 1-1610* <$400
1902 Plain Back
3x10-20 1731-4136* <$400
* 1611-1730 not marked
1929 Small Size
10 Type 1 1-444 <$400
20 Type 1 1-124 <$400
Total Issue $248,320
Out at close $24,700
Large out at close $2,130

6468 Lincoln
FNB OF HENDRICKS
{{ 2 L 6 S }}
Organized 8/6/02
Liquidated 6/25/31
1902 Red Seal <$VALUE
3x10-20 1-600 <$1500
1902 Date Back
3x10-20 1-1810 <$750
1902 Plain Back
3x10-20 1811-4370 <$750
1929 Small Size
10 Type 1 1-286 <$300
20 Type 1 1-46 <$300
Total Issue $271,630
Out at close $25,000
Large out at close $6,310

6906 Otter Tail
FNB OF HENNING
{{ 6 L U + 6 S }}
Organized 7/16/03
1902 Red Seal <$VALUE
3x10-20 1-1000 <$850
1902 Date Back
3x10-20 1-1710 <$400
1902 Plain Back
3x10-20 1711-4234 <$400
1929 Small Size
10 Type 1 1-558 <$300
20 Type 1 1-149 <$300
Total Issue $313,060
Out in 1935 $25,000
Large out 1935 $3,200

****
8049 Grant
FNB OF HERMAN
{{ 7 L 5 S }}
Chartered 1/06
1902 Red Seal <$VALUE
4x5 1-765 <$850
3x10-20 1-634 <$850
1902 Date Back
4x5 1-1550 <$400
3x10-20 1-1140 <$400
1902 Plain Back
4x5 1551-4655 <$400
3x10-20 1141-3053 <$400
1929 Small Size
5 Type 1 1-674 <$400
10 Type 1 1-340 <$400
20 Type 1 1-98 <$400
5 Type 2 1-730 <$400
10 Type 2 1-375 <$400
20 Type 2 1-132 <$400
Total Issue $355,170
Out in 1935 $25,000
Large out 1935 $1,840
****
5383 Jackson
FNB, HERON LAKE
{{ 8 L 12 S }}
Chartered 6/1/00
Brown Back <$VALUE
3x10-20 1-1340 <$850
1882 Date Back
3x10-20 1-2400 <$750
1882 Value Back
3x10-20 2401-3336 <$750
1902 Plain Back
3x10-20 1-2894 <$400
1929 Small Size
10 Type 1 1-624 <$250
20 Type 1 1-212 <$250
10 Type 2 1-711 <$250
20 Type 2 1-55 <$250
Total Issue $449,590
Out in 1935 $35,000
Large out 1935 $2,840
****
5745 Saint Louis
FNB, HIBBING
{{ 9 L 37 S }}
Chartered 3/01
Brown Back <$VALUE
3x10-20 1-2750 <$500
1882 Date Back
3x10-20 1-3540 <$400
1882 Value Back
3x10-20 3541-5323 <$450
1902 Plain Back
3x10-20 1-5013 <$200
1929 Small Size
10 Type 1 1-2330 <$50
20 Type 1 1-642 <$60
10 Type 2 1-1968 <$60
20 Type 2 1-644 <$70
Total Issue $903,700
Out in 1935 $99,650
Large out 1935 $4,290
****
12568 Saint Louis
HIBBING NB, HIBBING
{{ 3 L }}
Chartered 1924
Liquidated 2/14/28
1902 Plain Back <$VALUE
4x5 1-1630 <$650
3x10-20 1-760 <$650
Total Issue $63,000
Out at close $24,600
****
6199 Rock
FNB OF HILLS
{{ 3 L }}
Chartered 4/02
Liquidated 12/7/25
1902 Red Seal <$VALUE
4x5 1-600 <$1500
3x10-20 1-490 <$1500
1902 Date Back
4x5 1-1925 <$750
3x10-20 1-1420 <$750
1902 Plain Back (dated 1902)
4x5 1926-3205 <$750
3x10-20 1421-2095 <$750
1902 Plain Back (dated 1922)
4x5 1-921 <$750
3x10-20 1-600 <$750
Total Issue $253,770
Out at close $25,000
****
FNB of Hopkins
SEE Ch 7958
FNB of West Minneapolis
****
Security NB of Hopkins
SEE Ch 12518
Security NB of
West Minneapolis
****
10147 McLeod
FARMERS NB OF HUTCHINSON
{{ 7 L 11 S }}
Organized 1/24/12
Liquidated 10/15/34
1902 Date Back <$VALUE
3x10-20 1-1310 <$400
1902 Plain Back
3x10-20 1311-4008 <$400
1929 Small Size
10 Type 1 1-1009 <$200
20 Type 1 1-332 <$200
Total Issue $300,780
Out at close $50,000
Large out at close $1,710
****
7380 Koochiching
FNB OF
INTERNATIONAL FALLS
{{ 6 L 9 S }}
Chartered 8/04
1902 Red Seal <$VALUE
3x10-20 1-312 <$1000
1902 Date Back
3x10-20 1-660 <$500
1902 Plain Back
3x10-20 661-7172 <$500
1929 Small Size
10 Type 1 1-1054 <$275
20 Type 1 1-368 <$275
10 Type 2 1-852 <$300
20 Type 2 1-255 <$300
Total Issue $495,220
Out in 1935 $50,000
Large out 1935 $2,940
****
7128 Murray
FNB OF IONA
{{ 4 L }}
Chartered 2/04
Liquidated 2/27/30
1902 Red Seal <$VALUE
3x10-20 1-620 <$1500
1902 Date Back
3x10-20 1-760 <$750
1902 Plain Back
3x10-20 761-1998 <$750
Total Issue $130,900
Out at close $7,450
****
10382 Crow Wing
FNB, IRONTON
{{ 5 L 7 S }}
Organized 3/31/13
Receivership 9/27/33
1902 Date Back <$VALUE
3x10-20 1-1040 <$500
1902 Plain Back
3x10-20 1041-4318 <$500
1929 Small Size
10 Type 1 1-553 <$300
20 Type 1 1-124 <$300
Total Issue $263,960
Out at close $25,000
Large out at close $2,480
****
10554 Isanti
FNB, ISANTI
{{ 2 L 5 S }}
Organized 6/1/14
Receivership 10/16/31
1902 Plain Back <$VALUE
3x10-20 1-2933 <$850
1929 Small Size
10 Type 1 1-355 <$450
20 Type 1 1-88 <$450
Total Issue $167,950
Out at close $25,000
Large out at close $3,830
****
11627 Lincoln
FARMERS & MECHANICS NB OF
IVANHOE
{{ 8 L 6 S }}
Chartered 3/20
Liquidated 7/24/30
1902 Plain Back <$VALUE
3x10-20 1-2629 <$450
1929 Small Size
10 Type 1 1-235 <$350
20 Type 1 1-51 <$350
Total Issue $151,670
Out at close $35,000
Large out at close $12,150
****
6467 Lincoln
FNB OF IVANHOE
{{ 8 L 4 S }}
Organized 9/25/02
Receivership 4/9/31
1902 Red Seal <$VALUE
3x10-20 1-600 <$850
1902 Date Back
3x10-20 1-1700 <$400
1902 Plain Back
3x10-20 1701-4340 <$400
1929 Small Size
10 Type 1 1-243 <$500
20 Type 1 1-58 <$500
Total Issue $268,540
Out at close $25,000
Large out at close $6,410
****
6637 Lincoln
IVANHOE NB, IVANHOE
{{ UNREPORTED }}
Organized 2/21/03
Liquidated 4/25/05
1902 Red Seal <$VALUE
3x10-20 1-196 <$2500
Total Issue $9,800
Out in 1910 $580
****
7797 Jackson
BROWN NB OF JACKSON
{{ 5 L 5 S }}
Organized 5/17/05
Receivership 10/3/32
1902 Red Seal <$VALUE
3x10-20 1-1200 <$1000
1902 Date Back
3x10-20 1-1560 <$500
1902 Plain Back
3x10-20 1561-4115 <$500
1929 Small Size
10 Type 1 1-435 <$375
20 Type 1 1-94 <$400
Total Issue $303,130
Out at close $25,000
Large out at close $3,530
****
5852 Jackson
FNB OF JACKSON
{{ 13 L }}
Chartered 6/01
Liquidated 9/20/28
Brown Back <$VALUE
4x5 1-1350 <$650
3x10-20 1-1080 <$650
1882 Date Back
4x5 1-2200 <$650
3x10-20 1-1600 <$650
1882 Value Back
4x5 2201-3690 <$650
3x10-20 1601-2608 <$650
1902 Plain Back
4x5 1-2695 <$300
3x10-20 1-1326 <$300
Total Issue $405,400
Out in 1926 $35,000
****
6992 Jackson
JACKSON NB, JACKSON
{{ 7 L }}
Organized 8/24/03
Liquidated 7/9/29
1902 Red Seal <$VALUE
3x10-20 1-1450 <$850
1902 Date Back
3x10-20 1-2010 <$400
1902 Plain Back
3x10-20 2011-4569 <$400
Total Issue $300,950
Out at close $12,390
****
6523 Pipestone
FNB OF JASPER
{{ 6 L }}
Organized 10/7/02
Receivership 5/1/25
1902 Red Seal <$VALUE
3x10-20 1-1050 <$1000
1902 Date Back
3x10-20 1-1790 <$500
1902 Plain Back
3x10-20 1791-4256 <$500
Total Issue $265,300
Out at close $29,500
****
11218 Scott
FNB, JORDAN
{{ 15 L 10 S }}
Chartered 8/18
1902 Plain Back <$VALUE
4x5 1-5412 <$300
1929 Small Size
5 Type 1 1-2510 <$200
5 Type 2 1-4600 <$200
Total Issue $206,540
Out in 1935 $25,000
Large out 1935 $720
****
2159 Dodge
FNB OF KASSON
{{ 2 L }}
Chartered 7/25/74
Closed 7/22/94
Original Series <$VALUE
3x1-2 1-1500 <$1250/$2000
4x5 1-1875 <$1500
Series 1875
4x5 1-5000 <$1500
Total Issue $145,000
Out in 1910 $831
****
4969 Dodge
NB OF KASSON
{{ UNREPORTED }}
Chartered 1894
Liquidated 7/10/14
Brown Back <$VALUE
4x5 1-1725 <$1500
3x10-20 1-580 <$1500
1882 Date Back
4x5 1-496 <$1500
3x10-20 1-380 <$1500
Total Issue $92,420
Out at close $11,250
****
10580 Dodge
NB OF DODGE COUNTY,
KASSON
{{ 11 L 19 S }}
Organized 6/29/14
Liquidated 2/4/35
1902 Date Back <$VALUE
4x5 1-750 <$250
3x10-20 1-600 <$250
1902 Plain Back
4x5 751-4725 <$250
3x10-20 601-2937 <$250
1929 Small Size
5 Type 1 1-814 <$60
10 Type 1 1-420 <$60
20 Type 1 1-148 <$60
5 Type 2 1-920 <$75
10 Type 2 1-438 <$75
20 Type 2 1-109 <$75
Total Issue $319,890
Out at close $30,000
Large out at close $2,195
****
11042 Dodge
N FARMERS B OF KASSON
{{ 5 L 18 S }}
Chartered 7/17
Liquidated 2/4/35
1902 Plain Back <$VALUE
4x5 1-2985 <$400
3x10-20 1-2023 <$400
1929 Small Size
5 Type 1 1-1336 <$85
10 Type 1 1-682 <$85
20 Type 1 1-182 <$85
5 Type 2 1-744 <$100
10 Type 2 1-340 <$100
20 Type 2 1-121 <$100
Total Issue $273,230
Out at close $40,000
Large out at close $1,335
****
10903 Itasca
FNB, KEEWATIN
{{ 2 L 8 S }}
Chartered 9/16
1902 Plain Back <$VALUE
4x5 1-3662 <$750
3x10-20 1-2260 <$750
1929 Small Size
5 Type 1 1-694 <$175
10 Type 1 1-426 <$175
20 Type 1 1-102 <$175
5 Type 2 1-1296 <$200
10 Type 2 1-434 <$200
20 Type 2 1-145 <$200
Total Issue $258,880
Out in 1935 $25,000
Large out 1935 $1,350
****
11365 Swift
FNB, KERKHOVEN
{{ 5 L 2 S }}
Organized 5/24/19
Receivership 1/6/31
1902 Plain Back <$VALUE
4x5 1-2000 <$500
3x10-20 1-1827 <$500
1929 Small Size
5 Type 1 1-395 <$600
10 Type 1 1-169 <$600
20 Type 1 1-28 <$600
Total Issue $174,300
Out at close $25,000
Large out at close $4,380
****
10603 Faribault
FNB, KIESTER
{{ 2 L 15 S }}
Chartered 8/14
1902 Date Back <$VALUE
3x10-20 1-600 <$1000
1902 Plain Back
4x5 1-2460 <$1000
3x10-20 601-2288 <$1000
1929 Small Size
5 Type 1 1-994 <$200
10 Type 1 1-484 <$200
20 Type 1 1-160* <$200
5 Type 2 1-1274 <$225
10 Type 2 1-680 <$225
20 Type 2 1-189 <$225
* 146 not issued
Total Issue $255,490
Out in 1935 $35,000
Large out 1935 $1,360
****
4509 Lincoln
FNB, LAKE BENTON
{{ 6 L }}
Organized 12/23/90
Liquidated 10/9/33
Brown Back <$VALUE
3x10-20 1-1410 <$850
1882 Date Back
3x10-20 1-125 <$800
1902 Date Back
3x10-20 1-710 <$500
1902 Plain Back
3x10-20 711-3507 <$500
Total Issue $252,100
Out in 1928 $24,800
****
6696 Lincoln
N CITIZENS B OF
LAKE BENTON
{{ 5 L 4 S }}
Organized 3/16/03
Receivership 10/28/32
1902 Red Seal <$VALUE
4x5 1-350 <$1000
3x10-20 1-260 <$1000
1902 Date Back
4x5 1-500 <$500
3x10-20 1-400 <$500
1902 Plain Back
4x5 501-3355 <$500
3x10-20 401-2213 <$500
1929 Small Size
5 Type 1 1-535 <$500
10 Type 1 1-292 <$500
20 Type 1 1-66 <$500
Total Issue $239,240
Out at close $25,000
Large out at close $3,185
****
1740 Wabasha
FNB OF LAKE CITY
{{ 1 L }}
Chartered 11/29/70
Receivership 1/4/86
Original Series <$VALUE
3x1-2 1-2500 <$2000/$3000
4x5 1-2875 <$2000
Series 1875
3x1-2 1-420 <$2000/$3000
4x5 1-4912 <$2000
Total Issue $170,340
Out in 1915 $1,020
****
11401 Blue Earth
AMERICAN NB OF
LAKE CRYSTAL
{{ 4 L 2 S }}
Chartered 7/19
Liquidated 12/7/31
1902 Plain Back <$VALUE
4x5 1-2882 <$750
1929 Small Size
5 Type 1 1-1665 <$650
Total Issue $107,590
Out at close $25,000
Large out at close $850
Ch 6918 assumed circulation
****
6918 Blue Earth
FNB OF LAKE CRYSTAL
{{ 5 L 8 S }}
Organized 7/18/03
Liquidated 3/9/34
1902 Red Seal <$VALUE
3x10-20 1-720 <$1000
1902 Date Back
3x10-20 1-1150 <$600
1902 Plain Back
3x10-20 1151-2849 <$600
1929 Small Size
5 Type 1 1-684 <$300
10 Type 1 1-687 <$300
20 Type 1 1-176 <$300
Total Issue $261,310
Out at close $60,000
Large out at close $1,780
Ch 13972 assumed circulation
****
7143 Becker
FNB OF LAKE PARK
{{ 2 L }}
Organized 2/10/04
Receivership 8/24/25
1902 Red Seal <$VALUE
3x10-20 1-1200 <$1500
1902 Date Back
3x10-20 1-1490* <$850
1902 Plain Back
3x10-20 1621-3448* <$850
* 1491-1620 not marked
Total Issue $232,400
Out at close $25,000
****
11293 Murray
FNB, LAKE WILSON
{{ 3 L 5 S }}
Chartered 1/19
1902 Plain Back <$VALUE
4x5 1-1410 <$850
1929 Small Size
5 Type 2 1-3754 <$400
10 Type 2 1-1460 <$400
20 Type 2 1-434 <$400
Total Issue $70,250
Out in 1935 $25,000
Large out 1935 $225
****
6537 Jackson
FNB OF LAKEFIELD
{{ 4 L }}
Chartered 12/17/02
Liquidated 6/26/28
1902 Red Seal <$VALUE
4x5 1-995 <$1250
3x10-20 1-817 <$1250
1902 Date Back
4x5 1-1650 <$600
3x10-20 1-1140 <$600
1902 Plain Back
4x5 1651-4240 <$600
3x10-20 1141-2736 <$600
Total Issue $282,350
Out at close $25,000
****
7221 Redwood
FNB OF LAMBERTON
{{ 4 L }}
Organized 4/2/04
Liquidated 6/8/26
1902 Red Seal <$VALUE
3x10-20 1-600 <$1250
1902 Date Back
3x10-20 1-1660 <$600
1902 Plain Back
3x10-20 1661-3631 <$600
Total Issue $211,550
Out at close $24,600
****
11356 Kittson
FNB, LANCASTER
{{ 2 L }}
Organized 5/14/19
Receivership 11/19/23
1902 Plain Back <$VALUE
3x10-20 1-1500 <$1250
Total Issue $75,000
Out at close $24,700
****

<$VALUEs are for notes in FINE condition. Value changes by approximately 25% for a change of one full grade.

10507 Fillmore
FNB OF LANESBORO
{{ 13 L 1 S }}
Chartered 4/14
Liquidated 2/18/30
1902 Date Back <$VALUE
3x10-20 1-500 <$250
1902 Plain Back
4x5 1-5955 <$250
3x10-20 501-4231 <$250
1929 Small Size
5 Type 1 1-318 <$750
Total Issue $340,190
Out at close $30,000
Large out at close $21,960

7109 Mower
FNB OF Le ROY
{{ 2 L 11 S }}
Chartered 1/04
1902 Red Seal <$VALUE
3x10-20 1-1250 <$1500
1902 Date Back
3x10-20 1-1520 <$750
1902 Plain Back
3x10-20 1521-4556 <$750
1929 Small Size
10 Type 1 1-524 <$200
20 Type 1 1-146 <$200
10 Type 2 1-425 <$200
20 Type 2 1-100 <$200
Total Issue $345,510
Out in 1935 $25,000
Large out 1935 $1,780

7199 Le Sueur
FNB OF Le SUEUR
{{ 3 L 1 S }}
Organized 3/9/04
Receivership 2/15/33
1902 Red Seal <$VALUE
4x5 1-200 <$1500
3x10-20 1-202 <$1500
1902 Date Back
4x5 1-550 <$850
3x10-20 1-440 <$850
1902 Plain Back
4x5 551-835 <$850
3x10-20 441-712 <$850
1929 Small Size
5 Type 1 1-186 <$750
10 Type 1 1-82 <$750
20 Type 1 1-15 <$750
Total Issue $78,700
Out at close $6,320
Large out at close $750

6921 Le Sueur
FNB OF Le SUEUR CENTER
{{ 4 L 3 S }}
Chartered 8/03
1902 Red Seal <$VALUE
3x10-20 1-356 <$1500
1902 Date Back
3x10-20 1-540 <$750
1902 Plain Back
3x10-20 541-870 <$750
1929 Small Size
10 Type 1 1-168 <$500
20 Type 1 1-33 <$500
Total Issue $75,340
Out in 1935 $6,250
Large out 1935 $530

6118 Meeker
FNB, LITCHFIELD
{{ 22 L }}
Organized 1/7/02
Receivership 1/14/31
1902 Red Seal <$VALUE
4x5 1-1350 <$300
3x10-20 1-1110 <$300/$350
1902 Date Back
4x5 1-3050 <$125
3x10-20 1-2200 <$125
1902 Plain Back (dated 1902)
4x5 3051-5852 <$125
3x10-20 2201-4045 <$125
1902 Plain Back (dated 1922)
4x5 1-2750 <$125
3x10-20 1-1900 <$125
Total Issue $551,250
Out at close $9,775

13486 Meeker
NORTHWESTERN NB OF LITCHFIELD
{{ U + 28 S }}
Chartered 8/30
1929 Small Size <$VALUE
5 Type 1 1-2086 <$40
10 Type 1 1-1114 <$40
20 Type 1 1-308 <$50
5 Type 2 1-2644 <$50
10 Type 2 1-1160 <$50
20 Type 2 1-310 <$60
Total Issue $197,400
Out in 1935 $75,000

American NB of Little Falls
SEE Ch 4655
German-American NB of Little Falls

13353 Morrison
AMERICAN NB OF LITTLE FALLS
{{ 36 S }}
Chartered 7/29
1929 Small Size <$VALUE
5 Type 1 1-3512 <$40
10 Type 1 1-1332 <$40
20 Type 1 1-462 <$50
5 Type 2 1-4144 <$50
10 Type 2 1-860 <$50
20 Type 2 1-199 <$50
Total Issue $274,020
Out in 1935 $100,000

4034 Morrison
FNB, LITTLE FALLS
{{ 9 L 16 S }}
Chartered 1889
Brown Back <$VALUE
4x5 1-3806 <$500
3x10-20 1-2832 <$500
1902 Date Back
3x10-20 1-3140 <$250
1902 Plain Back
3x10-20 3141-8618 <$250
1929 Small Size
10 Type 1 1-1000 <$60
20 Type 1 1-288 <$60
10 Type 2 1-852 <$70
20 Type 2 1-199 <$75
Total Issue $755,680
Out in 1935 $50,000
Large out 1935 $3,800

4655 Morrison
GERMAN-AMERICAN NB OF LITTLE FALLS
Chartered 1891
Liquidated 8/1/29
2nd title:American NB 5/3/18
FIRST TITLE {{ 7 L }}
Brown Back <$VALUE
3x10-20 1-1910 <$600
1882 Date Back
3x10-20 1-1134 <$500
1902 Date Back
3x10-20 1-2100 <$250
1902 Plain Back
3x10-20 2101-2800 <$250
SECOND TITLE {{ 10 L }}
1902 Plain Back
3x10-20 1-8124 <$250
Total Issue $698,400
Out in 1935 $5,890
Ch 13353 assumed circulation

11863 Koochiching
FNB OF LITTLEFORK
{{ 2 L }}
Chartered 1920
Liquidated 4/25/25
1902 Plain Back <$VALUE
3x10-20 1-1348 <$1000
Total Issue $67,400
Out at close $25,000

6208 Todd
FNB OF LONG PRAIRIE
{{ 1 L }}
Chartered 4/02
Liquidated 7/24/28
1902 Red Seal <$VALUE
3x10-20 1-400 <$1500
1902 Date Back
3x10-20 1-900 <$1000
1902 Plain Back (dated 1902)
3x10-20 901-2157 <$1000
1902 Plain Back (dated 1922)
3x10-20 1-1102 <$1000
Total Issue $182,950
Out at close $24,500

7080 Todd
PEOPLES NB OF LONG PRAIRIE
{{ 5 L U + 10 S }}
Chartered 12/03
1902 Red Seal <$VALUE
3x10-20 1-856 <$1000
1902 Date Back
3x10-20 1-900 <$500
1902 Plain Back
3x10-20 901-3515 <$500
1929 Small Size
10 Type 1 1-502 <$250
20 Type 1 1-142 <$250
10 Type 2 1-503 <$250
20 Type 2 1-156 <$250
Total Issue $273,860
Out in 1935 $25,000
Large out 1935 $2,250

12634 Rock
F & FARMERS NB IN LUVERNE
{{ 6 L 8 S }}
Organized 1/27/25
Receivership 3/23/31
1902 Plain Back <$VALUE
3x10-20 1-2037 <$450
1929 Small Size
10 Type 1 1-588 <$250
20 Type 1 1-148 <$250
Total Issue $144,890
Out at close $55,000
Large out at close $11,810

7770 Rock
FNB OF LUVERNE
{{ 3 L }}
Chartered 6/05
Liquidated 3/25/25
1902 Red Seal <$VALUE
4x5 1-230 <$1250
3x10-20 1-184 <$1250
1902 Date Back
4x5 1-1100 <$650
3x10-20 1-800 <$650
1902 Plain Back
4x5 1001-2170 <$650
3x10-20 801-1552 <$650
Total Issue $134,800
Out at close $15,000
Ch 12634 assumed circulation

3428 Rock
FNB, LUVERNE
{{ 5 L }}
Chartered 1886
Liquidated 3/25/25
Brown Back <$VALUE
4x5 1-3228 <$850
3x10-20 1-516 <$850
1902 Red Seal
3x10-20 1-900 <$1000
1902 Date Back
3x10-20 1-3100 <$500
1902 Plain Back
3x10-20 3101-5566 <$500
Total Issue $413,660
Out at close $39,700
Ch 12634 assumed circulation

8977 Rock
NB OF LUVERNE
{{ 1 L }}
Organized 12/4/07
Receivership 12/31/25
1902 Red Seal <$VALUE
4x5 1-156 <$1500
4x10 1-156 <$1500
1902 Date Back
4x5 1-450* <$1000
4x10 1-550 <$1000
1902 Plain Back
4x5 551-1069* <$1000
4x10 551-838 <$1000
* 451-550 not marked
Total Issue $64,260
Out at close $6,050

5706 Mower
FNB, LYLE
{{ 3 L 18 S }}
Chartered 2/7/01
Brown Back <$VALUE
3x10-20 1-620 <$850
1882 Date Back
3x10-20 1-720 <$850
1882 Value Back
3x10-20 721-879 <$850
1902 Plain Back
4x10 1-1003 <$600
1929 Small Size
10 Type 1 1-524 <$125
10 Type 2 1-229 <$135
Total Issue $148,800
Out in 1935 $15,000
Large out 1935 $1,210

9031 Fillmore
FNB, MABEL
{{ 5 L 13 S }}
Chartered 1908
1902 Red Seal <$VALUE
3x10-20 1-507 <$1000
1902 Date Back
3x10-20 1-1200 <$500
1902 Plain Back
3x10-20 1201-3087 <$500
1929 Small Size
10 Type 1 1-484 <$175
20 Type 1 1-138 <$175
10 Type 2 1-67 <$200
20 Type 2 1-10 <$200
Total Issue $226,170
Out in 1935 $25,000
Large out 1935 $1,770

13784 Watonwan
CITIZENS NB OF MADELIA
{{ 9 S }}
Chartered 9/33
1929 Small Size <$VALUE
5 Type 2 1-5218 <$200
10 Type 2 1-2796 <$200
20 Type 2 1-635 <$200
Total Issue $66,750
Out in 1935 $50,000

7100 Watonwan
FNB OF MADELIA
{{ 4 L }}
Chartered 1/04
Liquidated 7/15/27
1902 Red Seal <$VALUE
4x5 1-250 <$1000
3x10-20 1-214 <$1000
1902 Date Back
4x5 1-1750 <$500
3x10-20 1-1340 <$500
1902 Plain Back
4x5 1751-4330 <$500
3x10-20 1341-2822 <$500
Total Issue $243,400
Out at close $24,300

6795 Lac Qui Parle
FNB OF MADISON
{{ 6 L 1 S }}
Chartered 5/03
Liquidated 4/28/30
1902 Red Seal <$VALUE
3x10-20 1-1225 <$850
1902 Date Back
3x10-20 1-1570 <$450
1902 Plain Back
3x10-20 1571-4070 <$450
1929 Small Size
10 Type 1 1-146 <$650
20 Type 1 1-38 <$650
Total Issue $278,070
Out at close $25,000
Large out at close $11,730

13561 Lac Qui Parle
KLEIN NB OF MADISON
{{ 26 S }}
Chartered 7/31
1929 Small Size <$VALUE
5 Type 1 1-1138 <$100
10 Type 1 1-454 <$100
20 Type 1 1-130 <$125
50 Type 1 1-22 <$200
100 Type 1 1-16 <$300
5 Type 2 1-1202 <$125
10 Type 2 1-778 <$125
20 Type 2 1-190 <$125
Total Issue $110,770
Out in 1935 $50,000

8726 Mahnomen
FNB OF MAHNOMEN
{{ UNREPORTED }}
Chartered 1907
Liquidated 3/1/13
1902 Red Seal <$VALUE
3x10-20 1-360 <$2000
1902 Date Back
3x10-20 1-712 <$1250
Total Issue $53,600
Out in 1913 $14,600

12941 Mahnomen
FNB, MAHNOMEN
{{ 11 S }}
Chartered 6/26
1929 Small Size <$VALUE
5 Type 1 1-462 <$200
10 Type 1 1-276 <$200
20 Type 1 1-116 <$200
5 Type 2 1-840 <$225
10 Type 2 1-450 <$225
20 Type 2 1-185 <$225
Total Issue $56,740
Out in 1935 $25,000

2005 Blue Earth
CITIZENS NB, MANKATO
{{ 2 L }}
Chartered 6/27/72
Closed 4/27/92
Original Series <$VALUE
3x1-2 1-2900 <$1000/$1500
4x5 1-2300 <$1000
3x10-20 1-450 <$1250/$1500
Series 1875
3x1-2 1-600 <$1000/$1500
4x5 1-2155 <$1000
3x10-20 1-681 <$1250/$1500
Total Issue $163,150
Out in 1910 $810

1683 Blue Earth
FNB OF MANKATO
Organized 8/68
2nd title:FNB & TC 12/16/31
3rd title:FNB 1/23/34
FIRST TITLE {{ 21 L 13 S }}
Original Series <$VALUE
3x1-2 1-4300 <$600/$1250
4x5 1-4575 <$600
3x10-20 1-1200 <$850/$1250
Series 1875
4x5 1-1243 <$600
3x10-20 1-540 <$850/$1250
Brown Back
3x10-20 1-3707 <$275
1902 Red Seal
3x10-20 1-750 <$350
1902 Date Back
3x10-20 1-5500 <$125
1902 Plain Back
3x10-20 5501-13036 <$125
1929 Small Size
10 Type 1 1-2320 <$85
20 Type 1 1-586 <$85
SECOND TITLE {{ 7 S }}
1929 Small Size
10 Type 1 1-846 <$100
20 Type 1 1-168 <$100
THIRD TITLE {{ 0 S }}
1929 Small Size
10 Type 2 1-1035 <$200
20 Type 2 1-195 <$200
Total Issue $1,394,200
Out in 1935 $137,500
Large out 1935 $9,730

3562 Blue Earth
MANKATO NB, MANKATO
{{ UNREPORTED }}
Organized 9/23/86
Liquidated 9/26/98
Brown Back <$VALUE
4x5 1-4906 <$1250
Total Issue $98,120
Out in 1910 $770

14220 Blue Earth
NB OF COMMERCE IN MANKATO
{{ 3 S }}
Chartered 7/34
1929 Small Size <$VALUE
5 Type 2 1-2138 <$500
10 Type 2 1-1322 <$500
20 Type 2 1-385 <$500
Total Issue $31,610
Out in 1935 $40,000
Outstanding includes Ch 6519

6519 Blue Earth
NB OF COMMERCE OF MANKATO
{{ 16 L 0 S }}
Organized 9/11/02
Liquidated 8/14/34
1902 Red Seal <$VALUE
3x10-20 1-5525 <$350
1902 Date Back
3x10-20 1-5900 <$150
1902 Plain Back
3x10-20 5901-12645 <$150
1929 Small Size
10 Type 1 1-65 <$650
20 Type 1 1-14 <$650
Total Issue $914,080
Out at close $9,590
Large out at close $5,540

4727 Blue Earth
N CITIZENS B OF MANKATO
{{ 35 L 50+ S }}
Chartered 1892
Brown Back <$VALUE
3x10-20 1-4420 <$250
1882 Date Back
3x10-20 1-690 <$250
1902 Date Back
3x10-20 1-4500 <$75
1902 Plain Back
3x10-20 4501-28914 <$75
1929 Small Size
10 Type 1 1-6279 <$20
20 Type 1 1-1687 <$30
5 Type 2 1-121 <$25
Total Issue $2,281,005
Out in 1935 $100,000
Large out 1935 $15,825

6787 Blue Earth
FNB OF MAPLETON
{{ 8 L 8 S }}
Chartered 5/03
1902 Red Seal <$VALUE
3x10-20 1-880 <$850
1902 Date Back
3x10-20 1-1210 <$400
1902 Plain Back
3x10-20 1211-3525 <$400
1929 Small Size
10 Type 1 1-400 <$300
20 Type 1 1-118 <$300
10 Type 2 1-659 <$300
20 Type 2 1-94 <$300
Total Issue $266,880
Out in 1935 $22,000
Large out 1935 $1,470

11608 Itasca
FNB OF MARBLE
{{ 5 L 11 S }}
Chartered 2/20
Liquidated 10/22/34
1902 Plain Back <$VALUE
4x5 1-7883 <$400
1929 Small Size
5 Type 1 1-3008 <$200
5 Type 2 1-2096 <$200
Total Issue $258,380
Out at close $25,000
Large out at close $890

4614 Lyon
FNB, MARSHALL
{{ 7 L 14 S }}
Chartered 1891
Brown Back <$VALUE
3x10-20 1-1360 <$600
1882 Date Back
3x10-20 1-247 <$500
1902 Date Back
3x10-20 1-900 <$350
1902 Plain Back
3x10-20 901-6450 <$350
1929 Small Size
10 Type 1 1-1042 <$150
20 Type 1 1-284 <$150
10 Type 2 1-288 <$175
20 Type 2 1-77 <$175
Total Issue $503,870
Out in 1935 $25,000
Large out 1935 $3,150

4595 Lyon
LYON COUNTY NB OF MARSHALL
{{ 7 L }}
Chartered 1891
Liquidated 12/1/26
Brown Back <$VALUE
3x10-20 1-1440 <$600
1882 Date Back
3x10-20 1-199 <$500
1902 Date Back
3x10-20 1-900 <$350
1902 Plain Back
3x10-20 901-1614 <$350
Total Issue $162,650
Out at close $12,500

****
6488 Polk
FNB OF McINTOSH
{{ 3 L 3 S }}
Organized 9/9/02
1902 Red Seal <$VALUE
3x10-20 1-1500 <$1250
1902 Date Back
3x10-20 1-1450 <$650
1902 Plain Back
3x10-20 1451-3946 <$650
1929 Small Size
10 Type 1 1-554 <$650
20 Type 1 1-138 <$650
20 Type 2 1-15 <$650
Total Issue $322,400
Out in 1935 $20,000
Large out 1935 $1,980
****
7566 Stearns
FNB OF MELROSE
{{ UNREPORTED }}
Chartered 1905
Liquidated 2/1/12
1902 Red Seal <$VALUE
3x10-20 1-256 <$2500
1902 Date Back
3x10-20 1-151 <$1500
Total Issue $20,350
Out in 1912 $3,650
****
11740 Wadena
FNB, MENAHGA
{{ 3 L 21 S }}
Organized 5/17/20
1902 Plain Back <$VALUE
3x10-20 1-2428 <$650
1929 Small Size
5 Type 1 1-566 <$150
10 Type 1 1-354 <$150
20 Type 1 1-106 <$150
5 Type 2 1-736 <$175
10 Type 2 1-347 <$175
20 Type 2 1-95 <$175
Total Issue $181,390
Out in 1935 $25,000
Large out 1935 $2,135
****
9050 Mille Lacs
FNB, MILACA
{{ 7 L 13 S }}
Chartered 1908
1902 Red Seal <$VALUE
3x10-20 1-700 <$1000
1902 Date Back
3x10-20 1-1560 <$500
1902 Plain Back 500
3x10-20 1561-4322 <$500
1929 Small Size
10 Type 1 1-598 <$250
20 Type 1 1-158 <$250
10 Type 2 1-30 <$275
Total Issue $306,240
Out in 1935 $25,000
Large out 1935 $1,590
****
12972 Hennepin
BLOOMINGTON-LAKE NB, MINNEAPOLIS
{{ 13 L 29 S }}
Chartered 8/26
1902 Plain Back <$VALUE
4x5 1-26396 <$175
1929 Small Size
5 Type 1 1-22858 <$50
5 Type 2 1-41902 <$50
Total Issue $1,428,170
Out in 1935 $200,000
Large out 1935 $2,520
****
13108 Hennepin
CENTRAL NB OF MINNEAPOLIS
{{ 3 L U + 13 S }}
Chartered 7/27/27
1902 Plain Back <$VALUE
4x5 1-5624 <$300
1929 Small Size
5 Type 1 1-7846 <$85
5 Type 2 1-13982 <$85
Total Issue $417,770
Out in 1935 $50,000
Large out 1935 $575
****
6449 Hennepin
CLARKE NB OF MINNEAPOLIS
Chartered 10/02
Liquidated 2/8/11
2nd title:Minnesota NB of Minneapolis 1/6/05
FIRST TITLE {{ 2 L }}
1902 Red Seal <$VALUE
3x10-20 1-1407 <$800
SECOND TITLE {{ 0 L }}
1902 Red Seal
50-100 1-505 <$4000
1902 Date Back
4x5 1-4850 <$600
3x10-20 1-4668 <$600
Total Issue $429,820
Out in 1911 $108,600
****
4739 Hennepin
COLUMBIA NB, MINNEAPOLIS
{{ 1 L }}
Organized 5/13/92
Receivership 1/14/97
Brown Back <$VALUE
4x5 1-2249 <$1250
3x10-20 1-979 <$1250
Total Issue $93,930
Out in 1915 $655
****
10261 Hennepin
COMMERCIAL NB OF MINNEAPOLIS
{{ UNREPORTED }}
Chartered 1912
Liquidated 12/12/14
2nd title:N City B of Minneapolis 5/11/14
FIRST TITLE
1902 Date Back <$VALUE
3x50-100 1-268 <$1500
SECOND TITLE
1902 Date Back
3x10-20 1-115 <$1250
3x10-20 1001-4000* <$1250
* 1001-4000 were issued to the bank, but returned intact to the Comptroller
Total Issue $222,750
Out in 1914 $50,000
Ch 9409 assumed circulation
****
F & Security NB of Minneapolis
SEE Ch 710
FNB of Minneapolis
****
FNB in Minneapolis
SEE Ch 710
FNB of Minneapolis
****
710 Hennepin
FNB OF MINNEAPOLIS
Chartered 1865
2nd title:F & Security NB 5/17/15
3rd title:FNB in Minneapolis 2/21/20
4th title:FNB & TC of Minneapolis 1/31/33
FIRST TITLE {{ 36 L }}
Original Series <$VALUE
4x5 1-7950 <$500
3x10-20 1-800 <$750/$1250
Series 1875
3x10-20 1-4000 <$750/$1250
Brown Back
3x10-20 1-36098 <$200
1902 Red Seal
4x5 1-32500 <$200
3x10-20 1-30600 <$200
1902 Date Back
4x5 1-76303* <$50
3x10-20 1-58276 <$60
* 67666-68665 not issued
SECOND TITLE {{ 25 L }}
1902 Date Back
4x5 1-10000 <$50
3x10-20 1-8000 <$60
1902 Plain Back
4x5 10001-57500 <$50
3x10-20 8001-35000 <$60
THIRD TITLE {{ 50+ L 50+ S }}
1902 Plain Back
4x5 1-166920 <$40
3x10-20 1-109988 <$55
1929 Small Size
5 Type 1 1-54350 <$15
10 Type 1 1-51272 <$20
20 Type 1 1-18442 <$30
FOURTH TITLE {{ 50+ S }}
1929 Small Size
5 Type 1 1-24404 <$15
10 Type 1 1-8124 <$20
20 Type 1 1-2540 <$30
5 Type 2 1-123874 <$15
10 Type 2 1-59907 <$20
20 Type 2 1-15276 <$30
Total Issue $30,509,740
Out in 1935 $3,701,000
Large out 1935 $117,385
****
3784 Hennepin
FLOUR CITY NB, MINNEAPOLIS
{{ UNREPORTED }}
Organized 8/29/87
Liquidated 2/26/01
Brown Back <$VALUE
50-100 1-1318 <$3000
Total Issue $197,700
Out in 1910 $4,850
****
11178 Hennepin
LINCOLN NB OF MINNEAPOLIS
{{ 3 L }}
Chartered 5/18
Liquidated 9/5/22
1902 Plain Back <$VALUE
4x5 1-3460 <$500
3x10-20 1-1685 <$500
Total Issue $153,450
Out in 1921 $50,000
****
3098 Hennepin
MANUFACTURERS NB, MINNEAPOLIS
{{ UNREPORTED }}
Chartered 1883
Liquidated 11/1/84
Brown Back <$VALUE
3x10-20 1-900 <$1250
Total Issue $45,000
Out in 1910 $300
****
11861 Hennepin
MARQUETTE NB OF MINNEAPOLIS
{{ 14 L 21 S }}
Chartered 10/20 as The Payday NB, under which there was no issue. Issuing title adopted 6/26/22.
1902 Plain Back <$VALUE
4x5 1-45912 <$125
1929 Small Size
5 Type 1 1-18814 <$40
5 Type 2 1-54894 <$40
10 Type 2 1-7963 <$50
Total Issue $1,836,760
Out in 1935 $300,000
Large out 1935 $4,080
****
Merchants NB of Minneapolis
SEE Ch 1830
FNB of Saint Anthony
****
9442 Hennepin
METROPOLITAN NB OF MINNEAPOLIS
{{ 37 L 10 S }}
Chartered 1909
Liquidated 3/20/31
1902 Date Back <$VALUE
4x5 1-15500 <$40
3x10-20 1-11100 <$50
1902 Plain Back
4x5 15501-70846 <$40
3x10-20 11101-44607 <$50
1929 Small Size
5 Type 1 1-2893 <$100
10 Type 1 1-1460 <$100
20 Type 1 1-317 <$100
Total Issue $3,859,700
Large out at close $358,230
****
Midland NB of Minneapolis
Midland NB & TC of Minneapolis
SEE Ch 9409
Scandinavian-American NB of Minneapolis
****
11778 Hennepin
MINNEAPOLIS NB, MINNEAPOLIS
{{ 1 L }}
Chartered 7/20
Liquidated 7/9/23
1902 Plain Back <$VALUE
4x5 1-6750 <$600
Total Issue $135,000
Out at close $48,300
****
13096 Hennepin
MINNEHAHA NB, MINNEAPOLIS
{{ 3 L 20 S }}
Chartered 6/27
1902 Plain Back <$VALUE
4x5 1-11631 <$500
1929 Small Size
5 Type 1 1-11374 <$65
5 Type 2 1-21694 <$70
Total Issue $682,310
Out in 1935 $100,000
Large out 1935 $720
****
Minnesota NB of Minneapolis
SEE Ch 6449
Clarke NB of Minneapolis
****
3206 Hennepin
NB OF COMMERCE, MINNEAPOLIS
{{ 2 L }}
Organized 6/11/84
Liquidated 7/15/08
Brown Back <$VALUE
4x5 1-11050 <$650
50-100 1-546 <$2250/$2500
1902 Red Seal
3x10-20 1-875 <$750
50-100 1-5419 <$4000
Total Issue $1,159,500
Out in 1910 $248,610
****
N City B of Minneapolis
SEE Ch 10261
Commercial NB of Minneapolis
****
719 Hennepin
N EXCHANGE B OF MINNEAPOLIS
{{ UNREPORTED }}
Chartered 1/16/65
Receivership 5/24/77
Original Series <$VALUE
4x5 1-2750 <$1500
3x10-20 1-2085<$1750/$2000
Series 1875
3x10-20 1-353 <$1750/$2000
Total Issue $176,900
Out in 1915 $940
****
3145 Hennepin
NICOLLET NB, MINNEAPOLIS
{{ 1 L }}
Organized 3/26/84
Liquidated 1/14/01
Brown Back <$VALUE
4x5 1-11258 <$1000
3x10-20 1-246 <$1000
Total Issue $237,460
Out in 1910 $2,250
****
2006 Hennepin
NORTHWESTERN NB OF MINNEAPOLIS
{{ 50+ L 50+ S }}
Chartered 6/28/72
Original Series <$VALUE
3x1-2 1-5980 <$500/$1000
4x5 1-6000 <$500
3x10-20 1-1700 <$750/$1250
50-100 1-200 <$5000
Series 1875
4x5 1-4698 <$500
3x10-20 1-1741 <$750/$1250
Brown Back
4x5 1-31500 <$175
4x10 1-16250 <$175
3x10-20 1-18400 <$175/$200
1882 Date Back
4x5 1-33074 <$150
4x10 1-27263 <$150
3x10-20 1-802 <$150/$175
1902 Date Back
4x5 1-76225 <$40
4x10 1-45881 <$50
3x10-20 1-16400 <$50
1902 Plain Back
3x10-20 16401-28400 <$50
1929 Small Size
5 Type 1 1-27332 <$15
10 Type 1 1-15626 <$20
5 Type 2 1-21828 <$15
10 Type 2 1-22935 <$20
Total Issue $11,313,760
Out in 1935 $880,660
Large out 1935 $37,445
****
Richfield NB of Minneapolis
SEE Ch 12115
Richfield NB, Richfield
****
9409 Hennepin
SCANDINAVIAN-AMERICAN NB OF MINNEAPOLIS
Chartered 1909
2nd title:Midland NB 12/10/17
3rd title:Midland NB & TC 7/17/25
FIRST TITLE {{ 6 L }}
1902 Date Back <$VALUE
3x10-20 1-9209 <$250
SECOND TITLE {{ 10 L }}
1902 Plain Back
3x10-20 1-19200 <$100
THIRD TITLE {{ 6 L 50+ S }}
1902 Plain Back
3x10-20 1-17843 <$100
1929 Small Size
10 Type 1 1-10388 <$20
20 Type 1 1-2962 <$30
10 Type 2 1-14828 <$20
20 Type 2 1-2998 <$30
Total Issue $3,499,560
Out in 1935 $500,000
Large out 1935 $23,200
Outstanding includes Ch 10261
****
8720 Hennepin
SECURITY NB OF MINNEAPOLIS
{{ 22 L }}
Chartered 6/07
Liquidated 5/4/15
1902 Red Seal <$VALUE
3x10-20 1-15500 <$200
1902 Date Back
4x5 1-29963 <$100
3x10-20 1-14588 <$100
Total Issue $2,603,660
Out at close $450,000
Ch 710 assumed circulation
****
1623 Hennepin
STATE NB, MINNEAPOLIS
{{ 4 L }}
Chartered 1865
Liquidated 12/31/77
Original Series <$VALUE
3x1-2 1-3200 <$750/$1250
4x5 1-6350 <$750
3x10-20 1-800 <$850/$1250
Series 1875
4x5 1-750 <$750
3x10-20 1-320 <$850/$1250
Total Issue $214,000
Out in 1910 $1,557
****
4951 Hennepin
SWEDISH-AMERICAN NB, MINNEAPOLIS
{{ 6 L }}
Organized 4/18/94
Liquidated 12/31/08
Brown Back <$VALUE
3x10-20 1-22938 <$400
Total Issue $1,146,900
Out in 1910 $179,380
****
12282 Hennepin
TRANSPORTATION BROTHERHOODS NB OF MINNEAPOLIS
{{ 10 L 1 S }}
Chartered 12/22
Liquidated 2/4/30
1902 Plain Back <$VALUE
4x5 1-21114 <$300
1929 Small Size
5 Type 1 1-445 <$600
Total Issue $435,630
Out at close $75,000
Large out at close $33,805
****
2795 Hennepin
UNION NB, MINNEAPOLIS
{{ 1 L }}
Organized 10/12/82
Receivership 3/20/97
Brown Back <$VALUE
4x5 1-5000 <$1000
3x10-20 1-2000 <$1000
Total Issue $200,000
Out in 1915 $1,240
****
6917 Lyon
FARMERS & MERCHANTS NB OF MINNEOTA
{{ 9 L 12 S }}
Chartered 8/03
1902 Red Seal <$VALUE
3x10-20 1-856 <$700
1902 Date Back
3x10-20 1-1560 <$300
1902 Plain Back
3x10-20 1561-6230 <$300
1929 Small Size
10 Type 1 1-734 <$150
20 Type 1 1-232 <$150
10 Type 2 1-880 <$150
20 Type 2 1-120 <$150
Total Issue $437,380
Out in 1935 $40,000
Large out 1935 $2,670
****
6413 Lyon
FNB OF MINNEOTA
{{ 6 L 6 S }}
Chartered 9/02
Liquidated 5/20/31
1902 Red Seal <$VALUE
3x10-20 1-620 <$800
1902 Date Back
3x10-20 1-2250 <$400
1902 Plain Back
3x10-20 2251-5462 <$400
1929 Small Size
10 Type 1 1-377 <$350
20 Type 1 1-51 <$350
Total Issue $332,840
Out at close $30,000
Large out at close $5,910
****
6532 Faribault
FARMERS NB OF MINNESOTA LAKE
{{ 4 L 3 S }}
Chartered 12/13/02
1902 Red Seal <$VALUE
3x10-20 1-362 <$1250
1902 Date Back
3x10-20 1-600 <$650
1902 Plain Back
3x10-20 601-990 <$650
1929 Small Size
10 Type 1 1-172 <$600
20 Type 1 1-31 <$600
Total Issue $81,640
Out in 1935 $6,500
Large out 1935 $470
****
6204 Faribault
FNB, MINNESOTA LAKE
{{ 3 L }}
Organized 4/5/02
Receivership 8/6/24
1902 Red Seal <$VALUE
4x5 1-1150 <$1250
3x10-20 1-728 <$1250
50-100 1-44 <$4000
1902 Date Back
4x5 1-1400 <$600
3x10-20 1-930 <$600
50-100 1-44 <$1000/$1200
1902 Plain Back (dated 1902)
4x5 1401-2600 <$600
3x10-20 931-1650 <$600
1902 Plain Back (dated 1922)
4x5 1-445 <$600
3x10-20 1-310 <$600
Total Issue $231,500
Out at close $25,000
****
6860 Chippewa
FNB OF MONTEVIDEO
{{ 6 L }}
Organized 5/25/03
Receivership 2/5/27
1902 Red Seal <$VALUE
3x10-20 1-1020 <$1000
1902 Date Back
3x10-20 1-2170 <$500
1902 Plain Back
3x10-20 2171-4626 <$500
Total Issue $282,300
Out at close $29,495
****

****
11215 Le Sueur
FNB OF MONTGOMERY
{{ 5 L 13 S }}
Chartered 8/18
Liquidated 4/29/35
1902 Plain Back <$VALUE
4x5 1-6252 <$500
1929 Small Size
5 Type 1 1-2592 <$200
5 Type 2 1-4554 <$200
Total Issue $225,520
Out at close $25,000
Large out at close $930
****
F & Moorhead NB of Moorhead
SEE Ch 2569
FNB of Moorhead
****
2569 Clay
FNB OF MOORHEAD
Organized 8/13/81
Receivership 12/24/28
2nd title:F & Moorhead NB
2/26/27
FIRST TITLE {{ 14 L }}
Series 1875 <$VALUE
4x5 1-4774 <$600
50-100 1-41 <$5000
Brown Back
3x10-20 1-670 <$400
1882 Date Back
3x10-20 1-3540 <$350
1882 Value Back
3x10-20 3541-5638 <$350
1902 Plain Back
3x10-20 1-3181 <$175/$200
SECOND TITLE {{ 4 L }}
1902 Plain Back
3x10-20 1-1087 <$400
Total Issue $630,430
Out at close $109,995
****
13297 Clay
FNB, MOORHEAD
{{ 24 S }}
Chartered 3/29
1929 Small Size <$VALUE
10 Type 1 1-1236 <$75
20 Type 1 1-420 <$85
10 Type 2 1-1572 <$75
20 Type 2 1-576 <$85
Total Issue $151,800
Out in 1935 $100,000
****
4713 Clay
MOORHEAD NB, MOORHEAD
{{ 13 L }}
Chartered 1892
Closed 2/26/27
Brown Back <$VALUE
3x10-20 1-3260 <$600
1882 Date Back
3x10-20 1-1949 <$550
1902 Date Back
3x10-20 1-2500 <$250
1902 Plain Back
3x10-20 2501-8230 <$250
Total Issue $671,950
Out at close $59,300
Ch 2569 assumed circulation
****
12947 Carlton
FNB, MOOSE LAKE
{{ 0 L 9 S }}
Chartered 6/26
1902 Plain Back <$VALUE
3x10-20 1-980 <$1250
1929 Small Size
10 Type 1 1-574 <$300
20 Type 1 1-156 <$300
10 Type 2 1-420 <$300
20 Type 2 1-85 <$300
Total Issue $108,060
Out in 1935 $25,000
Large out 1935 $740
****
7292 Kanabec
FNB OF MORA
{{ 9 L 5 S }}
Organized 5/18/04
Receivership 9/14/31
1902 Red Seal <$VALUE
3x10-20 1-1076 <$1000
1902 Date Back
3x10-20 1-1800 <$400
1902 Plain Back
3x10-20 1801-4586 <$400

1929 Small Size
10 Type 1 1-303 <$400
20 Type 1 1-80 <$400
Total Issue $310,800
Out at close $25,000
Large out at close $4,930
****
2933 Stevens
FNB, MORRIS
{{ UNREPORTED }}
Chartered 4/24/83
Liquidated 5/26/96
Brown Back <$VALUE
3x10-20 1-892 <$1500
Total Issue $44,600
Out in 1910 $310
****
6310 Stevens
MORRIS NB, MORRIS
{{ 5 L 5 S }}
Organized 4/15/02
Receivership 1/2/34
1902 Red Seal <$VALUE
3x10-20 1-400 <$850
1902 Date Back
3x10-20 1-1380 <$400
1902 Plain Back
4x5 1-4751 <$400
3x10-20 1381-2780 <$400
1929 Small Size
5 Type 1 1-728 <$325
10 Type 1 1-352 <$325
20 Type 1 1-96 <$325
5 Type 2 1-252 <$350
10 Type 2 1-151 <$350
20 Type 2 1-25 <$350
Total Issue $311,770
Out at close $25,000
Large out at close $1,505
****
7764 Morrison
FNB OF MOTLEY
{{ 9 L 8 S }}
Organized 5/13/05
Receivership 12/16/32
1902 Red Seal <$VALUE
4x5 1-930 <$1000
3x10-20 1-708 <$1000
1902 Date Back
4x5 1-1575 <$400
3x10-20 1-1140 <$400
1902 Plain Back
4x5 1576-4770 <$400
3x10-20 1141-3052 <$400
1929 Small Size
5 Type 1 1-623 <$250
10 Type 1 1-304 <$250
20 Type 1 1-73 <$250
Total Issue $347,690
Out at close $24,700
Large out at close $3,540
****
11550 Carver
FNB OF MOTORDALE
Chartered 12/19
Liquidated 7/31/26
2nd title:FNB of
New Germany 2/3/22
FIRST TITLE {{ 4 L }}
1902 Plain Back <$VALUE
3x10-20 1-900 <$1000
SECOND TITLE {{ 4 L }}
1902 Plain Back
4x5 1-2700 <$850
Total Issue $99,000
Out at close $24,400
****
9267 Cottonwood
FNB, MOUNTAIN LAKE
{{ 5 L 7 S }}
Organized 10/16/08
Receivership 6/12/31
1902 Date Back <$VALUE
3x10-20 1-2020 <$600
1902 Plain Back
3x10-20 2021-4632 <$600
1929 Small Size
10 Type 1 1-282 <$300
20 Type 1 1-73 <$300
Total Issue $257,280
Out at close $25,000
Large out at close $5,160
****
11579 Itasca
AMERICAN NB OF NASHWAUK
{{ 3 L 20 S }}
Chartered 1/20
1902 Plain Back <$VALUE
4x5 1-2165 <$600
3x10-20 1-1396 <$600

1929 Small Size
5 Type 1 1-798 <$65
10 Type 1 1-422 <$65
20 Type 1 1-118 <$65
5 Type 2 1-478 <$75
10 Type 2 1-444 <$75
20 Type 2 1-120 <$75
Total Issue $185,750
Out in 1935 $25,000
Large out 1935 $800
****
10736 Itasca
FNB, NASHWAUK
{{ 4 L 18 S }}
Chartered 5/15
1902 Plain Back <$VALUE
4x5 1-2925 <$500
3x10-20 1-2002 <$500
1929 Small Size
5 Type 1 1-690 <$75
10 Type 1 1-434 <$75
20 Type 1 1-130 <$75
5 Type 2 1-568 <$85
10 Type 2 1-349 <$85
20 Type 2 1-115 <$100
Total Issue $229,570
Out in 1935 $25,000
Large out 1935 $1,300
****
4302 Ramsey
TWIN CITY NB,
NEW BRIGHTON
{{ UNREPORTED }}
Organized 5/7/90
Liquidated 6/23/91
Brown Back <$VALUE
3x10-20 1-235 <$2000
Total Issue $11,750
Out in 1910 $180
****
4750 Saint Louis
NEW DULUTH NB, NEW DULUTH
{{ UNREPORTED }}
Organized 6/9/92
Liquidated 1/31/96
Brown Back <$VALUE
3x10-20 1-413 <$2000
Total Issue $20,650
Out in 1910 $140
****
FNB of New Germany
SEE Ch 11550
FNB of Motordale
****
7092 Le Sueur
FNB OF NEW PRAGUE
{{ 5 L 23 S }}
Chartered 1/04
1902 Red Seal <$VALUE
4x5 1-325 <$1000
3x10-20 1-230 <$1000
1902 Date Back
4x5 1-450 <$500
3x10-20 1-320 <$500
1902 Plain Back
4x5 451-3313 <$500
3x10-20 321-2457 <$500
1929 Small Size
5 Type 1 1-1446 <$100
10 Type 1 1-882 <$100
20 Type 1 1-212 <$100
5 Type 2 1-1118 <$110
10 Type 2 1-665 <$110
20 Type 2 1-155 <$125
Total Issue $344,190
Out in 1935 $50,000
Large out 1935 $1,690
****
2318 Brown
CITIZENS NB, NEW ULM
{{ UNREPORTED }}
Chartered 1/31/76
Liquidated 3/1/83
Series 1875 <$VALUE
3x10-20 1-762 <$2500
Total Issue $38,100
Out in 1910 $230
****
631 Brown
FNB OF NEW ULM
{{ UNREPORTED }}
Chartered 12/17/64
Liquidated 4/18/67
Original Series <$VALUE
4x5 1-550 <$2000
3x10-20 1-860 <$2000
Total Issue $54,000
Out in 1910 $665
****

****
2073 Rice
FNB, NORTHFIELD
{{ 12 L 23 S }}
Chartered 12/30/72
Original Series <$VALUE
3x1-2 1-2500 <$750/$1250
4x5 1-2375 <$750
Series 1875
3x1-2 1-610 <$750/$1250
4x5 1-5557 <$750
Brown Back
4x5 1-3000 <$350
4x10 1-500 <$350
3x10-20 1-3600 <$350
1882 Date Back
4x5 1-2527 <$300
4x10 1-1958 <$300
1902 Date Back
4x5 1-1875 <$175
4x10 1-1875 <$175
1902 Plain Back
4x5 1876-12450 <$175
4x10 1876-10364 <$175
1929 Small Size
5 Type 1 1-3526 <$75
10 Type 1 1-1648 <$75
5 Type 2 1-4372 <$75
10 Type 2 1-2839 <$75
Total Issue $1,481,5230
Out in 1935 $75,000
Large out 1935 $5,930
****
13350 Rice
NORTHFIELD NB & TC,
NORTHFIELD
{{ 19 S }}
Chartered 7/29
1929 Small Size <$VALUE
5 Type 1 1-2790 <$60
10 Type 1 1-1594 <$60
20 Type 1 1-430 <$70
5 Type 2 1-3838 <$70
10 Type 2 1-2120 <$70
20 Type 2 1-456 <$70
Total Issue $280,450
Out in 1935 $100,000
Large out 1935 $6,400
Outstanding includes Ch 5895
****
5895 Rice
NORTHFIELD NB, NORTHFIELD
{{ 17 L }}
Chartered 1901
Liquidated 8/15/29
Brown Back <$VALUE
4x5 1-4775 <$350
3x10-20 1-3070 <$350
1882 Date Back
4x5 1-5750 <$300
3x10-20 1-4100 <$300
1882 Value Back
4x5 5751-10650 <$300
3x10-20 4101-6680 <$300
1902 Plain Back
4x5 1-10265 <$125
3x10-20 1-4828 <$125
Total Issue $1,242,700
Out at close $88,650
Ch 13350 assumed circulation
****
13081 Renville
CITIZENS NB, OLIVIA
{{ U + 23 S }}
Chartered 6/27
1929 Small Size <$VALUE
5 Type 1 1-416 <$150
10 Type 1 1-188 <$150
20 Type 1 1-64 <$150
5 Type 2 1-860 <$125
10 Type 2 1-500 <$150
20 Type 2 1-140 <$150
Total Issue $43,540
Out in 1935 $25,000
****
9063 Renville
PEOPLES NB OF OLIVIA
{{ 2 L }}
Organized 2/25/08
Receivership 2/5/27
1902 Red Seal <$VALUE
3x10-20 1-188 <$1250
1902 Date Back
3x10-20 1-460* <$1000
1902 Plain Back
3x10-20 561-886* <$1000
* 461-560 not marked
Total Issue $53,700
Out at close $6,250

****
6747 Big Stone
CITIZENS NB OF ORTONVILLE
{{ 7 L }}
Organized 4/18/03
Receivership 1/4/27
1902 Red Seal <$VALUE
4x5 1-715 <$800
3x10-20 1-534 <$800
1902 Date Back
4x5 1-680* <$400
3x10-20 1-680** <$400
1902 Plain Back
4x5 1001-2370* <$400
3x10-20 781-1668** <$400
* 681-1000 not marked
** 681-780 not marked
Total Issue $171,800
Out at close $15,400
****
6459 Big Stone
FNB OF ORTONVILLE
{{ 8 L 7 S }}
Organized 10/4/02
Receivership 12/29/32
1902 Red Seal <$VALUE
4x5 1-950 <$600
3x10-20 1-760 <$600
1902 Date Back
4x5 1-1400 <$300
3x10-20 1-1040 <$300
1902 Plain Back
4x5 1401-4485 <$300
3x10-20 1041-2766 <$300
1929 Small Size
5 Type 1 1-538 <$300
10 Type 1 1-287 <$300
20 Type 1 1-77 <$300
Total Issue $327,600
Out at close $25,000
Large out at close $3,475
****
6837 Douglas
FNB OF OSAKIS
{{ 7 L 4 S }}
Chartered 6/03
1902 Red Seal <$VALUE
4x5 1-875 <$850
3x10-20 1-1000 <$850
1902 Date Back
4x5 1-1400 <$400
3x10-20 1-1020 <$400
1902 Plain Back
4x5 1401-4595 <$400
3x10-20 1021-3022 <$400
1929 Small Size
5 Type 1 1-814 <$500
10 Type 1 1-420 <$500
20 Type 1 1-98 <$500
5 Type 2 1-558 <$500
10 Type 2 1-226 <$500
20 Type 2 1-60 <$500
Total Issue $378,130
Out in 1935 $25,000
Large out 1935 $1,500
****
2122 Steele
FARMERS NB, OWATONNA
{{ 8 L }}
Chartered 7/24/73
Original Series <$VALUE
3x1-2 1-1500 <$750/$1250
4x5 1-2375 <$750
Series 1875
3x1-2 1-1020 <$750/$1250
4x5 1-7163 <$750
Total Issue $203,360
Out in 1910 $1,186
****
1911 Steele
FNB, OWATONNA
{{ 12 L 20 S }}
Chartered 12/29/71
Original Series <$VALUE
3x1-2 1-2840 <$750/$1250
4x5 1-4165 <$750
Series 1875
3x1-2 1-540 <$750/$1250
4x5 1-6236 <$750
Brown Back
4x5 1-6725 <$400
3x10-20 1-2600 <$400
1882 Date Back
4x5 1-1598 <$400
3x10-20 1-683 <$400
1902 Date Back
3x10-20 1-2500 <$200
1902 Plain Back
3x10-20 2501-12910 <$200

1929 Small Size
10 Type 1 1-1860 <$85
20 Type 1 1-582 <$85
10 Type 2 1-2242 <$100
20 Type 2 1-525 <$100
Total Issue $1,415,390
Out in 1935 $100,000
Large out 1935 $9,790
****
4928 Steele
N FARMERS B, OWATONNA
{{ 8 L }}
Organized 5/29/93
Receivership 9/10/26
Brown Back <$VALUE
50-100 1-2043 <$1750/$2000
1882 Date Back
50-100 1-341 <$1750/$2000
1902 Date Back
3x10-20 1-1000 <$300
1902 Plain Back
3x10-20 1001-6336 <$300
Total Issue $674,400
Out at close $74,550
****
13692 Hubbard
CITIZENS NB OF
PARK RAPIDS
{{ U + 7 S }}
Chartered 5/33
1929 Small Size <$VALUE
5 Type 2 1-4152 <$300
10 Type 2 1-2004 <$300
Total Issue $41,800
Out in 1935 $25,000
****
5542 Hubbard
FNB, PARK RAPIDS
{{ 12 L 12 S }}
Organized 7/12/00
Receivership 11/8/33
Brown Back <$VALUE
4x5 1-1300 <$500
3x10-20 1-960 <$500
1882 Date Back
4x5 1-3400 <$500
3x10-20 1-2480 <$500
1882 Value Back
4x5 3401-5440 <$500
3x10-20 2481-3586 <$500
1902 Plain Back
4x5 1-15124 <$250
1929 Small Size
5 Type 1 1-4524 <$100
5 Type 2 1-1210 <$125
Total Issue $806,350
Out at close $45,800
Large out at close $2,410
****
6661 Otter Tail
FNB OF PARKERS PRAIRIE
{{ 9 L 9 S }}
Chartered 3/03
1902 Red Seal <$VALUE
4x5 1-1025 <$1250
3x10-20 1-870 <$1250
1902 Date Back
4x5 1-1475 <$500
3x10-20 1-1060 <$500
1902 Plain Back
4x5 1476-4309 <$500
3x10-20 1061-2776 <$500
1929 Small Size
5 Type 1 1-696 <$300
10 Type 1 1-344 <$300
20 Type 1 1-92 <$300
5 Type 2 1-996 <$300
10 Type 2 1-409 <$300
20 Type 2 1-135 <$300
Total Issue $353,310
Out in 1935 $25,000
Large out 1935 $2,140
****
11332 Stearns
FNB OF PAYNESVILLE
{{ 20 L }}
Chartered 4/19
Liquidated 2/10/31
1902 Plain Back <$VALUE
3x10-20 1-1664 <$200
Total Issue $83,200
Out at close $2,150
****

****
6349 Otter Tail
FNB OF PELICAN RAPIDS
{{ 4 L }}
Organized 7/8/02
Liquidated 7/1/26
1902 Red Seal <$VALUE
3x10-20 1-1500 <$1500
1902 Date Back
3x10-20 1-1320 <$800
1902 Plain Back
3x10-20 1321-3189 <$800
Total Issue $234,450
Out in 1925 $24,500
****
11267 Crow Wing
FNB OF PEQUOT
{{ 1 L }}
Chartered 11/18
Liquidated 6/5/29
1902 Plain Back <$VALUE
4x5 1-4159 <$1000
4x10 1-2358 <$1000
Total Issue $177,500
Out at close $25,000
****
6276 Otter Tail
FNB OF PERHAM
{{ 3 L }}
Chartered 5/02
Liquidated 12/28/25
1902 Red Seal <$VALUE
3x10-20 1-590 <$1250
1902 Date Back
4x5 1-1550 <$600
3x10-20 1-1070 <$600
1902 Plain Back
4x5 1551-3755 <$600
3x10-20 1071-2382 <$600
Total Issue $223,700
Out at close $24,300
****
11581 Pine
FNB, PINE CITY
{{ 9 L 6 S }}
Chartered 1/20
1902 Plain Back <$VALUE
3x10-20 1-2614 <$450
1929 Small Size
10 Type 1 1-556 <$350
20 Type 1 1-136 <$350
10 Type 2 1-278 <$400
20 Type 2 1-53 <$400
Total Issue $184,220
Out in 1935 $25,000
Large out 1935 $1,460
****
3982 Pipestone
FNB, PIPESTONE
{{ 11 L 12 S }}
Chartered 1889
Brown Back <$VALUE
4x5 1-2723 <$650
3x10-20 1-576 <$650
1902 Date Back
4x5 1-2125 <$300
3x10-20 1-1640 <$300
1902 Plain Back
4x5 2126-8010 <$300
3x10-20 1641-5263 <$300
1929 Small Size
5 Type 1 1-1484 <$150
10 Type 1 1-684 <$150
20 Type 1 1-202 <$175
5 Type 2 1-1106 <$200
10 Type 2 1-667 <$200
20 Type 2 1-150 <$200
Total Issue $631,610
Out in 1935 $50,000
Large out 1935 $3,540
****
10936 Pipestone
PIPESTONE NB, PIPESTONE
{{ 5 L 0 S }}
Chartered 1/17
Liquidated 12/20/29
1902 Plain Back <$VALUE
3x10-20 1-5575 <$500
1929 Small Size
10 Type 1 1-61 <$1000
20 Type 1 1-10 <$1000
Total Issue $283,610
Out at close $54,860
Large out at close $50,000
****
6293 Wabasha
FNB OF PLAINVIEW
{{ 8 L 20 S }}
Chartered 6/02
1902 Red Seal <$VALUE
4x5 1-1175 <$700
3x10-20 1-860 <$700
1902 Date Back
4x5 1-1500 <$300
3x10-20 1-1080 <$300
1902 Plain Back
4x5 1501-4678 <$300
3x10-20 1081-2988 <$300
1929 Small Size
5 Type 1 1-944 <$100
10 Type 1 1-446 <$100
20 Type 1 1-130 <$100
5 Type 2 1-586 <$125
10 Type 2 1-296 <$125
20 Type 2 1-95 <$125
Total Issue $387,930
Out in 1935 $20,000
Large out 1935 $1,620
****
6279 Fillmore
FNB OF PRESTON
{{ 12 L 11 S }}
Chartered 5/02
1902 Red Seal <$VALUE
3x10-20 1-400 <$600
1902 Date Back
3x10-20 1-1700* <$250
1902 Plain Back
3x10-20 1831-4172* <$250
* 1701-1830 not marked
1929 Small Size
10 Type 1 1-546 <$175
20 Type 1 1-150 <$175
10 Type 2 1-159 <$200
20 Type 2 1-58 <$200
Total Issue $282,110
Out in 1935 $25,000
Large out 1935 $2,080
****
9059 Fillmore
NB OF PRESTON
{{ 1 L }}
Chartered 3/08
Liquidated 3/27/11
1902 Red Seal <$VALUE
3x10-20 1-450 <$1500
1902 Date Back
3x10-20 1-384 <$1000
Total Issue $41,700
Out in 1911 $3,500
****
7708 Mille Lacs
FNB OF PRINCETON
{{ 11 L 9 S }}
Chartered 4/05
Liquidated 11/8/34
1902 Red Seal <$VALUE
3x10-20 1-1300 <$600
1902 Date Back
3x10-20 1-2000 <$250
1902 Plain Back
3x10-20 2001-5203 <$250
1929 Small Size
10 Type 1 1-589 <$250
20 Type 1 1-203 <$250
Total Issue $384,850
Out at close $30,000
Large out at close $2,560
****
4807 Mille Lacs
FNB, PRINCETON
{{ 1 L }}
Organized 10/18/92
Liquidated 12/18/93
Brown Back <$VALUE
4x5 1-598 <$1500
Total Issue $11,960
Out in 1910 $105
****
11125 Saint Louis
FNB, PROCTOR
{{ 7 L 9 S }}
Chartered 1917
1902 Plain Back <$VALUE
4x5 1-12096 <$400
1929 Small Size
5 Type 1 1-4358 <$200
5 Type 2 1-11148 <$200
Total Issue $428,400
Out in 1935 $49,550
Large out 1935 $970
****
11974 Saint Louis
PEOPLES NB OF PROCTOR
{{ 3 L }}
Chartered 5/21
Liquidated 9/30/24
1902 Plain Back <$VALUE
4x5 1-3625 <$800
Total Issue $72,500
Out in 1922 $25,000
****

****
8050 Kandiyohi
FNB OF RAYMOND
{{ 6 L }}
Chartered 1/06
Liquidated 1/14/29
1902 Red Seal <$VALUE
3x10-20 1-300 <$1000
1902 Date Back
3x10-20 1-560 <$500
1902 Plain Back
3x10-20 561-1954 <$500
Total Issue $112,700
Out at close $25,000
****
9837 Red Lake
FARMERS NB OF
RED LAKE FALLS
{{ 3 L }}
Organized 7/19/10
Receivership 1/24/27
1902 Date Back <$VALUE
4x5 1-1350 <$750
3x10-20 1-1080 <$750
1902 Plain Back
4x5 1351-4080 <$750
3x10-20 1081-2668 <$750
Total Issue $215,000
Out at close $24,700
****
3659 Red Lake
FNB, RED LAKE FALLS
{{ UNREPORTED }}
Organized 3/29/87
Liquidated 4/15/95
Brown Back <$VALUE
50-100 1-235 <$3500
Total Issue $35,250
Out in 1910 $350
****
1487 Goodhue
FNB, RED WING
{{ 19 L 29 S }}
Chartered 1865
Original Series <$VALUE
4x5 1-505 <$750
3x10-20 1-1750 <$850/$1250
Series 1875
4x5 1-2850 <$750
3x10-20 1-950 <$850/$1250
Brown Back
4x5 1-5038 <$400
3x10-20 1-823 <$400
1902 Red Seal
4x5 1-3750 <$500
3x10-20 1-2340 <$500
1902 Date Back
4x5 1-5100 <$200
3x10-20 1-3900 <$200
1902 Plain Back
4x5 5101-17283 <$200
3x10-20 3901-12079 <$200
1929 Small Size
5 Type 1 1-3176 <$60
10 Type 1 1-1430 <$60
20 Type 1 1-404 <$60
5 Type 2 1-536 <$70
10 Type 2 1-222 <$70
20 Type 2 1-75 <$70
Total Issue $1,721,580
Out in 1935 $50,000
Large out 1935 $7,220
****
7307 Goodhue
GOODHUE COUNTY NB OF
RED WING
{{ 14 L 11 S }}
Chartered 6/04
1902 Red Seal <$VALUE
4x5 1-5750 <$500
3x10-20 1-4400 <$500
1902 Date Back
4x5 1-7000 <$200
3x10-20 1-3900 <$200
1902 Plain Back
4x5 7001-11281 <$200
3x10-20 3901-7014 <$200
1929 Small Size
5 Type 1 1-1250 <$125
10 Type 1 1-816 <$125
20 Type 1 1-232 <$125
5 Type 2 1-1228 <$150
10 Type 2 1-501 <$150
20 Type 2 1-150 <$150
Total Issue $1,039,720
Out in 1935 $50,000
Large out 1935 $4,100
****

****
13396 Goodhue
RED WING NB & TC,
RED WING
{{ 30 S }}
Chartered 11/29
1929 Small Size <$VALUE
5 Type 1 1-828 <$55
10 Type 1 1-1124 <$50
20 Type 1 1-456 <$60
5 Type 2 1-3944 <$60
10 Type 2 1-2270 <$60
20 Type 2 1-380 <$60
Total Issue $197,020
Out in 1935 $100,000
****
5826 Redwood
FNB, REDWOOD FALLS
{{ 10 L }}
Organized 3/11/01
Receivership 7/29/25
Brown Back <$VALUE
4x5 1-1050 <$650
3x10-20 1-780 <$650
1882 Date Back
4x5 1-1625 <$600
3x10-20 1-1240 <$600
1882 Value Back
4x5 1626-2475 <$600
3x10-20 1241-1698 <$600
1902 Plain Back
4x5 1-3480 <$400
Total Issue $264,000
Out at close $24,400
****
6583 Renville
FNB OF RENVILLE
{{ 4 L }}
Organized 12/19/02
Receivership 2/14/25
1902 Red Seal <$VALUE
3x10-20 1-1220 <$1000
1902 Date Back
3x10-20 1-1390 <$500
1902 Plain Back
3x10-20 1391-2991 <$500
Total Issue $210,550
Out at close $24,600
****
12115 Hennepin
RICHFIELD NB, RICHFIELD
Chartered 2/22
Liquidated 7/28/31
2nd title:Richfield NB of
Minneapolis 9/26/27
FIRST TITLE {{ 5 L }}
1902 Plain Back <$VALUE
4x5 1-5957 <$350
SECOND TITLE {{ 0 L 4 S }}
1902 Plain Back
4x5 1-1565 <$600
1929 Small Size
5 Type 1 1-1434 <$400
Total Issue $193,460
Out at close $25,000
Large out at close $1,670
****
579 Olmsted
FNB, ROCHESTER
{{ U + 11 L U + 38 S }}
Chartered 1864
Original Series <$VALUE
3x1-2 1-800 <$750/$1000
4x5 1-3000 <$750
3x10-20 1-1700 <$850/$1250
Series 1875
3x10-20 1-1512 <$750/$1250
Brown Back
3x10-20 1-2551 <$400
1902 Red Seal
3x10-20 1-900 <$450/$500
1902 Date Back
3x10-20 1-3000 <$200
1902 Plain Back
3x10-20 3001-9844 <$200
1929 Small Size
10 Type 1 1-4822 <$40
20 Type 1 1-1402 <$50
10 Type 2 1-5211 <$50
20 Type 2 1-1078 <$60
Total Issue $1,420,580
Out in 1935 $200,000
Large out 1935 $4,570
****
2316 Olmsted
ROCHESTER NB, ROCHESTER
{{ 3 L }}
Chartered 1/6/76
Liquidated 6/21/24
Series 1875 <$VALUE
4x10 1-2207 <$1500
Brown Back
3x10-20 1-970 <$1250
1882 Date Back
3x10-20 1-573 <$1250
1902 Plain Back
3x10-20 1-740 <$750
Total Issue $202,430
Out in 1922 $11,800
****
2088 Olmsted
UNION NB, ROCHESTER
{{ 11 L 10 S }}
Chartered 3/5/73
Original Series <$VALUE
3x1-2 1-1900 <$750/$1000
4x5 1-2275 <$750
Series 1875
3x1-2 1-400 <$750/$1000
4x5 1-4537 <$750
Brown Back
3x10-20 1-1870 <$400
1882 Date Back
3x10-20 1-681 <$400
1902 Date Back
3x10-20 1-1100 <$200
1902 Plain Back
3x10-20 1101-6626 <$200
1929 Small Size
5 Type 1 1-966 <$100
10 Type 1 1-874 <$100
20 Type 1 1-276 <$100
5 Type 2 1-1010 <$100
10 Type 2 1-505 <$100
20 Type 2 1-157 <$100
Total Issue $734,370
Out in 1935 $50,000
Large out 1935 $3,605
****
6783 Roseau
FNB OF ROSEAU
{{ 3 L 13 S }}
Chartered 5/03
1902 Red Seal <$VALUE
3x10-20 1-620 <$1250
1902 Date Back
3x10-20 1-2020 <$600
1902 Plain Back
3x10-20 2021-4678 <$600
1929 Small Size
10 Type 1 1-522 <$150
20 Type 1 1-124 <$150
10 Type 2 1-337 <$175
20 Type 2 1-155 <$175
Total Issue $317,570
Out in 1935 $25,000
Large out 1935 $1,680
****
11848 Roseau
ROSEAU COUNTY NB OF
ROSEAU
{{ 0 L 2 S }}
Chartered 10/20
Liquidated 12/18/31
1902 Plain Back <$VALUE
3x10-20 1-1427 <$1250
1929 Small Size
10 Type 1 1-508 <$600
20 Type 1 1-69 <$600
Total Issue $110,110
Out at close $30,000
Large out at close $3,100
****
11776 Dakota
FNB OF ROSEMOUNT
{{ 5 L }}
Chartered 7/20
Liquidated 7/1/31
1902 Plain Back <$VALUE
4x5 1-4540 <$650
Total Issue $90,800
Out at close $670
****
6731 Morrison
FNB OF ROYALTON
{{ 1 L }}
Organized 4/9/03
Receivership 7/22/26
1902 Red Seal <$VALUE
3x10-20 1-700 <$1500
1902 Date Back
3x10-20 1-770 <$1000
1902 Plain Back
3x10-20 771-1611 <$1000
Total Issue $115,550
Out at close $11,600
****

****
6954 Chisago
FNB OF RUSH CITY
{{ 5 L }}
Organized 8/1/03
Receivership 2/21/27
1902 Red Seal <$VALUE
3x10-20 1-370 <$1000
1902 Date Back
3x10-20 1-1820 <$500
1902 Plain Back
3x10-20 1821-5677 <$500
Total Issue $302,350
Out at close $48,400
****
6436 Fillmore
FNB OF RUSHFORD
{{ 6 L 14 S }}
Organized 8/29/02
1902 Red Seal <$VALUE
4x5 1-380 <$1000
3x10-20 1-248 <$1000
1902 Date Back
4x5 1-500 <$500
3x10-20 1-440 <$500
1902 Plain Back
4x5 501-3615 <$500
3x10-20 441-2328 <$500
1929 Small Size
5 Type 1 1-998 <$150
10 Type 1 1-518 <$150
20 Type 1 1-158 <$150
5 Type 2 1-974 <$175
10 Type 2 1-658 <$175
20 Type 2 1-192 <$175
Total Issue $340,680
Out in 1935 $35,000
Large out 1935 $970
****
6862 Nobles
FNB OF RUSHMORE
{{ 1 L }}
Chartered 6/03
Liquidated 6/28/26
1902 Red Seal <$VALUE
3x10-20 1-420 <$1500
1902 Date Back
3x10-20 1-560 <$1000
1902 Plain Back
3x10-20 561-873 <$1000
Total Issue $64,650
Out at close $6,250
****
5892 Pipestone
FNB, RUTHTON
{{ UNREPORTED }}
Chartered 7/01
Liquidated 3/12/10
Brown Back <$VALUE
3x10-20 1-400 <$2000
1882 Date Back
3x10-20 1-200 <$2000
Total Issue $30,000
Out in 1910 $8,770
****
1830 Hennepin
FNB OF SAINT ANTHONY
Chartered 5/31/71
Liquidated 1/31/81
2nd title:Merchants NB of
Minneapolis 1/8/74
FIRST TITLE {{ 0 L }}
Original Series <$VALUE
3x1-2 1-1500 <$1500/$2500
4x5 1-1875 <$1500
SECOND TITLE {{ 1 L }}
Original Series
4x5 1-5500 <$5000
Series 1875
4x5 1-4350 <$5000
Total Issue $242,000
Out in 1910 $1,416
****
6237 Winona
FNB OF SAINT CHARLES
{{ 1 L }}
Chartered 5/02
Liquidated 4/17/34
1902 Red Seal <$VALUE
3x10-20 1-900 <$1500
1902 Date Back
3x10-20 1-400 <$1000
1902 Plain Back (dated 1902)
3x10-20 401-780 <$1000
1902 Plain Back (dated 1922)
3x10-20 1-311 <$1000
Total Issue $99,550
Out at close $420
****

****

11818 Stearns
AMERICAN NB OF
SAINT CLOUD
{{ 3 L 22 S }}
Chartered 8/20
1902 Plain Back <$VALUE
3x10-20 1-2183 <$400
1929 Small Size
10 Type 1 1-2184 <$65
20 Type 1 1-572 <$75
5 Type 2 1-241 <$85
10 Type 2 1-309 <$85
20 Type 2 1-75 <$100
Total Issue $314,625
Out in 1935 $40,000
Large out 1935 $6,505
****

2790 Stearns
FNB, SAINT CLOUD
{{ 17 L }}
Organized 9/25/82
Receivership 6/24/25
Brown Back <$VALUE
4x5 1-5804 <$400
3x10-20 1-389 <$400
1902 Red Seal
3x10-20 1-1750 <$400
1902 Date Back
3x10-20 1-2300 <$150
1902 Plain Back
3x10-20 2301-22739 <$150
Total Issue $1,359,980
Out in 1924 $250,000
****

3009 Stearns
GERMAN-AMERICAN NB OF
SAINT CLOUD
{{ UNREPORTED }}
Organized 7/19/83
Liquidated 4/20/97
Brown Back <$VALUE
4x5 1-3805 <$1500
Total Issue $76,100
Out in 1910 $710
****

4797 Stearns
MERCHANTS NB OF
SAINT CLOUD
{{ 16 L }}
Chartered 1892
Liquidated 12/28/26
Brown Back <$VALUE
3x10-20 1-5070 <$350
1882 Date Back
3x10-20 1-708 <$300
1902 Date Back
3x10-20 1-2000 <$150
1902 Plain Back
3x10-20 2001-8110 <$150
Total Issue $694,400
Out at close $100,000
Ch 11818 assumed circulation
****

Citizens & Security NB of
Saint James
SEE Ch 7021
Citizens NB of Saint James
****

7021 Watonwan
CITIZENS NB OF
SAINT JAMES
Organized 9/24/03
Receivership 2/6/33
2nd title:Citizens &
Security NB of Saint James
11/29/20
FIRST TITLE {{ 3 L }}
1902 Red Seal <$VALUE
3x10-20 1-500 <$750
1902 Date Back
3x10-20 1-1660* <$350
1902 Plain Back
3x10-20 1781-2490* <$350
* 1661-1780 not marked
SECOND TITLE {{ 4 L 11 S }}
1902 Plain Back
3x10-20 1-3362 <$350
1929 Small Size
10 Type 1 1-904 <$175
20 Type 1 1-225 <$175
Total Issue $398,840
Out at close $50,000
Large out at close $4,840
****

****

4859 Watonwan
FNB, SAINT JAMES
{{ 9 L }}
Organized 1/30/93
Receivership 11/30/26
Brown Back <$VALUE
4x5 1-2000 <$600
3x10-20 1-590 <$600
1882 Date Back
4x5 1-2162 <$500
3x10-20 1-1432 <$500
1902 Date Back
3x10-20 1-1500 <$300
1902 Plain Back
3x10-20 1501-5678 <$300
Total Issue $468,240
Out at close $50,000
****

6828 Ramsey
AMERICAN NB OF SAINT PAUL
{{ 14 L 2U + 28 S }}
Chartered 6/03
1902 Red Seal <$VALUE
3x10-20 1-2750 <$200/$250
1902 Date Back
3x10-20 1-10500 <$100
1902 Plain Back
3x10-20 10501-1759 <$100
1929 Small Size
10 Type 1 1-2128 <$30
20 Type 1 1-622 <$40
10 Type 2 1-36120 <$30
20 Type 2 1-10152 <$40
Total Issue $1,789,760
Out in 1935 $500,000
Large out 1935 $6,940
****

8108 Ramsey
CAPITAL NB OF SAINT PAUL
{{ 45 L }}
Chartered 2/06
Liquidated 8/30/24
1902 Red Seal <$VALUE
4x5 1-11250 <$175
3x10-20 1-9800 <$175
1902 Date Back
4x5 1-34665 <$40
3x10-20 1-26934 <$50
1902 Plain Back
4x5 34666-93980 <$40
3x10-20 26935-59417 <$50
Total Issue $5,565,450
Out at close $488,600
Outstanding includes Ch 10475
****

3689 Ramsey
COMMERCIAL NB, SAINT PAUL
{{ UNREPORTED }}
Organized 5/2/87
Liquidated 10/27/90
Brown Back <$VALUE
4x5 1-1396 <$1250
3x10-20 1-576 <$1250
50-100 1-94 <$2500
Total Issue $70,820
Out in 1910 $515
****

12922 Ramsey
EMPIRE NB & TC OF
SAINT PAUL
{{ 12 S }}
Chartered 4/26 as The
N Exchange B, under which
there was no issue.
Issuing title adopted 1/2/32.
1929 Small Size <$VALUE
5 Type 1 1-2872 <$85
10 Type 1 1-1660 <$85
20 Type 1 1-366 <$85
50 Type 1 1-64 <$175
100 Type 1 1-12 <$225
5 Type 2 1-6838 <$100
10 Type 2 1-3000 <$100
20 Type 2 1-1005 <$100
Total Issue $340,370
Out in 1935 $200,000
****

203 Ramsey
FNB OF SAINT PAUL
{{ 18 L 50+ S }}
Chartered 1864
Original Series <$VALUE
3x1-2 1-6500 <$400/$1000
4x5 1-15025 <$500
4x10 1-10800 <$750
3x20-100 1-1800<$1250/$5000
Series 1875
4x5 1-3473 <$500
3x10-20 1-5750 <$750/$1250
Brown Back
4x5 1-7017 <$150
3x10-20 1-1853 <$150/$165
1902 Red Seal
3x10-20 1-9900 <$175
1902 Date Back
3x10-20 1-101703 <$60/$70
1929 Small Size
10 Type 1 1-34476 <$20
20 Type 1 1-10522 <$30
10 Type 2 1-248696* <$20
20 Type 2 1-56931 <$30
* 163213-163218 not issued
Total Issue $14,122,220
Out in 1935 $4,307,060
Large out 1935 $70,890
****

2020 Ramsey
MERCHANTS NB OF
SAINT PAUL
{{ 50+ L }}
Chartered 7/24/72
Closed 3/23/29
Original Series <$VALUE
3x1-2 1-2000 <$400/$1000
4x5 1-2000 <$500
3x10-20 1-7100 <$750/$1250
Series 1875
4x5 1-250 <$500
3x10-20 1-1055 <$750/$1250
Brown Back
4x5 1-14250 <$150
3x10-20 1-23800 <$150
50-100 1-2350 <$1250/$1500
1882 Date Back
4x5 1-35020 <$150
3x10-20 1-23223 <$150
50-100 1-262 <$1250/$1500
1902 Date Back
4x5 1-51650 <$40
3x10-20 1-41340 <$50
1902 Plain Back
4x5 51651-84770 <$40
3x10-20 41341-65596 <$50
Total Issue $9,640,200
Out at close $500,000
Ch 203 assumed circulation
****

13131 Ramsey
MIDWAY NB OF SAINT PAUL
{{ 6 L 24 S }}
Chartered 10/10/27
1902 Plain Back <$VALUE
4x5 1-10100 <$250
1929 Small Size
5 Type 1 1-12042 <$50
5 Type 2 1-21794 <$50
Total Issue $672,230
Out in 1935 $100,000
Large out 1935 $1,070
****

10475 Ramsey
NB OF COMMERCE IN
SAINT PAUL
{{ UNREPORTED }}
Chartered 1/14
Closed 10/13/20
1902 Date Back <$VALUE
3x10-20 1-3010 <$1000
Total Issue $150,500
Ch 8108 assumed circulation
****

10940 Ramsey
N EXCHANGE B, SAINT PAUL
{{ 11 L }}
Organized 1/10/17
Liquidated 6/24/26
1902 Plain Back <$VALUE
4x5 1-9775 <$200
3x10-20 1-5062 <$200
Total Issue $448,600
Out in 1924 $210,000
****

2943 Ramsey
N GERMAN-AMERICAN B OF
SAINT PAUL
{{ 5 L }}
Organized 5/2/83
Liquidated 11/27/12
Brown Back <$VALUE
3x10-20 1-4875 <$500
1902 Red Seal
3x10-20 1-11800 <$500
1902 Date Back
4x5 1-10040 <$300
3x10-20 1-4748 <$300
Total Issue $1,271,950
Out at close $100,000
Ch 2020 assumed circulation
****

****

1258 Ramsey
N MARINE B OF SAINT PAUL
{{ 2 L }}
Chartered 6/10/65
Liquidated 12/28/75
Original Series <$VALUE
4x5 1-2885 <$1000
3x10-20 1-1724<$1000/$1500
Total Issue $143,900
Out in 1910 $1,135
****

2959 Ramsey
SAINT PAUL NB, SAINT PAUL
{{ 6 L }}
Organized 5/25/83
Liquidated 9/29/06
Brown Back <$VALUE
4x5 1-20525 <$200
50-100 1-2173 <$1250/$1500
1902 Red Seal
4x5 1-8690 <$200
3x10-20 1-11640 <$200/$250
Total Issue $1,491,950
Out in 1910 $95,780
****

725 Ramsey
SECOND NB OF SAINT PAUL
{{ 12 L }}
Chartered 1865
Liquidated 12/31/12
Original Series <$VALUE
4x5 1-12250 <$500
3x10-20 1-1600 <$750/$1250
50-100 1-100 <$5000
Series 1875
4x5 1-15000 <$500
3x10-20 1-1000 <$750/$1250
Brown Back
4x5 1-12502 <$200
3x10-20 1-1734 <$200
1902 Red Seal
3x10-20 1-11500 <$250
1902 Date Back
4x5 1-12735 <$125
3x10-20 1-6584 <$125
Total Issue $2,185,640
Out at close $343,000
Ch 203 assumed circulation
****

3233 Ramsey
THIRD NB, SAINT PAUL
{{ UNREPORTED }}
Chartered 8/5/84
Liquidated 11/4/87
Brown Back <$VALUE
3x10-20 1-1192 <$1250
Total Issue $59,600
Out in 1910 $365
****

11741 Ramsey
TWIN CITIES NB OF
SAINT PAUL
{{ U + 17 L 25 S }}
Chartered 5/20
Liquidated 2/15/35
1902 Plain Back <$VALUE
3x10-20 1-17104 <$75/$85
1929 Small Size
5 Type 1 1-4734 <$40
10 Type 1 1-1220 <$45
20 Type 1 1-418 <$65
5 Type 2 1-4182 <$45
Total Issue $1,141,490
Out at close $100,000
Large out at close $6,405
****

1794 Nicollet
FNB OF SAINT PETER
{{ 8 L 6 S }}
Chartered 2/23/71
Original Series <$VALUE
3x1-2 1-2000 <$1000/$2000
4x5 1-4875 <$1000
Series 1875
4x5 1-5209 <$1000
Brown Back
3x10-20 1-1510 <$750
1882 Date Back
3x10-20 1-90 <$700
1902 Date Back
3x10-20 1-900 <$400
1902 Plain Back
3x10-20 901-1878 <$400
1929 Small Size
10 Type 1 1-628* <$350
20 Type 1 1-203** <$350
*C000004A-F000314A canceled
**D000003A-F000104A canceled
Total Issue $416,800
Out in 1935 $15,000
Large out 1935 $2,500
****

****

9464 Pine
FNB, SANDSTONE
{{ 5 L 5 S }}
Chartered 1909
1902 Date Back <$VALUE
3x10-20 1-1910 <$500
1902 Plain Back
3x10-20 1911-4745 <$500
1929 Small Size
10 Type 1 1-548 <$400
20 Type 1 1-148 <$400
10 Type 2 1-422 <$400
20 Type 2 1-108 <$400
Total Issue $294,270
Out in 1935 $25,000
Large out 1935 $1,550
****

3155 Stearns
FNB OF SAUK CENTRE
{{ 1 L 0 S }}
Chartered 1884
Liquidated 4/28/30
Brown Back <$VALUE
3x10-20 1-1324 <$1500
1902 Red Seal
50-100 1-140 <$4000
1902 Date Back
50-100 1-700 <$1500
3x50-100 1-820 <$1500
1902 Plain Back
3x50-100 821-959 <$1500
1929 Small Size
50 Type 1 1-6 <$1000
100 Type 1 1 <$1250
Total Issue $434,350
Out at close $50,000
Large out at close $31,800
****

6417 Stearns
MERCHANTS NB OF
SAUK CENTRE
{{ 9 L 4 S }}
Chartered 9/02
1902 Red Seal <$VALUE
3x10-20 1-420 <$750
1902 Date Back
3x10-20 1-1260 <$300
1902 Plain Back
3x10-20 1261-4114 <$300
1929 Small Size
10 Type 1 1-546 <$450
20 Type 1 1-150 <$450
10 Type 2 1-38 <$450
Total Issue $277,840
Out at close $24,820
Out in 1935 $1,960
****

1597 Scott
FNB, SHAKOPEE
{{ UNREPORTED }}
Chartered 1865
Liquidated 8/10/81
Original Series <$VALUE
4x5 1-4575 <$2000
Series 1875
4x5 1-2230 <$2000
Total Issue $136,100
Out in 1910 $920
****

3039 Scott
FNB, SHAKOPEE
{{ 6 L 10 S }}
Chartered 1883
Brown Back <$VALUE
3x10-20 1-2369 <$750
1902 Red Seal
3x10-20 1-745 <$750
1902 Date Back
3x10-20 1-1200* <$375
1902 Plain Back
3x10-20 1401-2276* <$375
* 1201-1400 not marked
1929 Small Size
10 Type 1 1-602 <$225
20 Type 1 1-168 <$225
10 Type 2 1-663 <$250
20 Type 2 1-221 <$250
Total Issue $338,830
Out in 1935 $37,500
Large out 1935 $2,550
****

3127 Scott
MERCHANTS & FARMERS NB OF
SHAKOPEE
{{ UNREPORTED }}
Chartered 1884
Liquidated 5/12/85
Brown Back <$VALUE
4x5 1-562 <$2000
Total Issue $11,240
Out in 1910 $90
****

****

6348 Martin
SHERBURN NB, SHERBURN
{{ 2 L 4 S }}
Chartered 7/22/02
1902 Red Seal <$VALUE
3x10-20 1-1250 <$1250
1902 Date Back
3x10-20 1-1540 <$750
1902 Plain Back
3x10-20 1541-4328 <$750
1929 Small Size
10 Type 1 1-536 <$450
20 Type 1 1-132 <$450
10 Type 2 1-390 <$450
20 Type 2 1-178 <$450
Total Issue $334,360
Out in 1935 $25,000
Large out 1935 $1,430
****

5256 Murray
FNB OF SLAYTON
{{ 5 L }}
Chartered 2/19/00
Liquidated 3/2/27
Brown Back <$VALUE
4x5 1-1375 <$700
3x10-20 1-1540 <$700
1882 Date Back
4x5 1-1350 <$650
3x10-20 1-1060 <$650
1882 Value Back
4x5 1351-1970 <$650
3x10-20 1061-1464 <$650
1902 Plain Back
4x5 1-1419 <$500
4x10 1-755 <$500
3x10-20 1-640 <$500
Total Issue $307,680
Out at close $24,800
****

FNB of Sleepy Eye
SEE Ch 6387
FNB of Sleepy Eye Lake
****

6387 Brown
FNB OF SLEEPY EYE LAKE
Chartered 8/02
2nd title:FNB of Sleepy Eye
4/14/04
FIRST TITLE {{ 1 L }}
1902 Red Seal <$VALUE
3x10-20 1-428 <$3500
SECOND TITLE {{ 21 L 19 S }}
1902 Red Seal
3x10-20 1-800 <$1000
1902 Date Back
3x10-20 1-1540 <$500
1902 Plain Back
3x10-20 1541-6192 <$500
1929 Small Size
10 Type 1 1-1016 <$275
20 Type 1 1-258 <$275
10 Type 2 1-478 <$300
20 Type 2 1-96 <$300
Total Issue $469,620
Out in 1935 $50,000
Large out 1935 $3,470
****

6732 Dakota
STOCKYARDS NB OF
SOUTH SAINT PAUL
{{ 15 L U + 24 S }}
Chartered 4/03
1902 Red Seal <$VALUE
3x10-20 1-1162 <$400
1902 Date Back
3x10-20 1-4200* <$150
1902 Plain Back
3x10-20 4701-13428* <$150
* 4201-4700 not marked
1929 Small Size
10 Type 1 1-3568 <$50
20 Type 1 1-934 <$60
10 Type 2 1-3055 <$60
20 Type 2 1-520 <$70
Total Issue $1,096,610
Out in 1935 $149,350
Large out 1935 $5,960
****

****
6316 Fillmore
FNB OF SPRING VALLEY
{{ 4 L 7 S }}
Chartered 6/23/02
1902 Red Seal <$VALUE
3x10-20 1-1000 <$1250
1902 Date Back
3x10-20 1-3540 <$600
1902 Plain Back
3x10-20 3541-9150 <$600
1929 Small Size
10 Type 1 1-992 <$300
20 Type 1 1-280 <$300
10 Type 2 1-1444 <$300
20 Type 2 1-189 <$300
Total Issue $618,840
Out in 1935 $50,000
Large out 1935 $2,680
****
8269 Brown
FNB OF SPRINGFIELD
{{ 4 L }}
Organized 4/21/06
Liquidated 10/22/29
1902 Red Seal <$VALUE
3x10-20 1-600 <$1200
1902 Date Back
3x10-20 1-1600* <$600
1902 Plain Back
3x10-20 1731-5371* <$600
* 1601-1730 not marked
Total Issue $298,550
Out at close $39,050
****
8523 Todd
CITY NB OF STAPLES
{{ 5 L 10 S }}
Chartered 1/07
Liquidated 5/26/32
1902 Red Seal <$VALUE
3x10-20 1-750 <$750
1902 Date Back
3x10-20 1-1620 <$400
1902 Plain Back
3x10-20 1621-4505 <$400
1929 Small Size
10 Type 1 1-388 <$200
20 Type 1 1-107 <$200
Total Issue $298,310
Out at close $25,000
Large out at close $3,460
****
5568 Todd
FNB, STAPLES
{{ 12 L 10 S }}
Chartered 9/00
Brown Back <$VALUE
4x5 1-1050 <$500
3x10-20 1-1330 <$500
1882 Date Back
4x5 1-1600* <$450
3x10-20 1-1120** <$450
1882 Value Back
4x5 1751-2550* <$450
3x10-20 1201-1713** <$450
* 1601-1750 not marked
** 1121-1200 not marked
1902 Plain Back
4x5 1-7707 <$250
1929 Small Size
5 Type 1 1-2718 <$150
5 Type 2 1-4098 <$165
Total Issue $480,320
Out in 1935 $25,000
Large out 1935 $1,090
****
9596 Pope
FNB, STARBUCK
{{ 50+ L U + 12 S }}
Chartered 1909
1902 Date Back <$VALUE
4x5 1-1600 <$100
3x10-20 1-1220 <$100
1902 Plain Back
4x5 1601-4345 <$100
3x10-20 1221-2811 <$100
1929 Small Size
5 Type 1 1-716 <$150
10 Type 1 1-348 <$150
20 Type 1 1-106 <$150
5 Type 2 1-42 <$175
Total Issue $282,740
Out in 1935 $25,000
Large out 1935 $4,760
****
9064 Marshall
FNB, STEPHEN
{{ 5 L 8 S }}
Chartered 1908
1902 Red Seal <$VALUE
3x10-20 1-750 <$750
1902 Date Back
3x10-20 1-1480 <$400
1902 Plain Back
3x10-20 1481-4127 <$400
1929 Small Size
10 Type 1 1-596 <$225
20 Type 1 1-148 <$225
10 Type 2 1-149 <$250
20 Type 2 1-50 <$250
Total Issue $299,860
Out in 1935 $25,000
Large out 1935 $2,020
****
5330 Olmsted
FNB, STEWARTVILLE
{{ 1 L 4 S }}
Organized 4/11/00
Receivership 10/15/31
Brown Back <$VALUE
3x10-20 1-1200 <$1250
1882 Date Back
3x10-20 1-1500 <$1000
1882 Value Back
3x10-20 1501-2124 <$1000
1902 Plain Back
3x10-20 1-2269 <$750
1929 Small Size
10 Type 1 1-347 <$500
20 Type 1 1-87 <$500
Total Issue $310,910
Out at close $25,000
Large out at close $4,440
****
13615 Olmsted
STEWARTVILLE NB,
STEWARTVILLE
{{ 17 S }}
Chartered 5/32
1929 Small Size <$VALUE
10 Type 1 1-440 <$150
20 Type 1 1-148 <$150
10 Type 2 1-955 <$150
20 Type 2 1-165 <$150
Total Issue $57,010
Out in 1935 $34,750
****
2674 Washington
FNB OF STILLWATER
{{ 15 L 44 S }}
Chartered 1882
Brown Back <$VALUE
4x5 1-13240 <$350
3x10-20 1-643 <$350
1902 Red Seal
3x10-20 1-3500 <$400
1902 Date Back
4x5 1-10415 <$150
3x10-20 1-7200 <$150
1902 Plain Back (dated 1902)
4x5 10416-13415 <$150
3x10-20 7201-9389 <$150
1902 Plain Back (dated 1922)
3x10-20 1-9811 <$150
1929 Small Size
10 Type 1 1-3504 <$50
20 Type 1 1-850 <$60
10 Type 2 1-7120 <$65
20 Type 2 1-1652 <$70
Total Issue $2,116,730
Out in 1935 $200,000
Large out 1935 $14,295
****
1514 Washington
FNB, STILLWATER
{{ 1 L }}
Chartered 1865
Liquidated 4/29/82
Original Series <$VALUE
3x1-2 1-3998 <$1000/$1500
4x5 1-12538 <$1000
Series 1875
4x5 1-2032 <$1000
Total Issue $311,390
Out in 1910 $1,847
****
1783 Washington
LUMBERMEN'S NB OF
STILLWATER
{{ 7 L }}
Chartered 2/3/71
Closed 4/19/19
Original Series <$VALUE
3x1-2 1-2700 <$750/$1500
4x5 1-8250 <$750
3x10-20 1-980 <$1000/$1500
Series 1875
4x5 1-5962 <$750
3x10-20 1-2760<$1000/$1500
Brown Back
4x5 1-4500 <$500
3x10-20 1-3460 <$500
1882 Date Back
4x5 1-573 <$500
3x10-20 1-480 <$500
1902 Date Back
4x5 1-3965 <$300
3x10-20 1-2605 <$300
Total Issue $992,750
Out at close $50,000
Ch 2674 assumed circulation
****
10824 Morrison
FNB, SWANVILLE
{{ 3 L 4 S }}
Organized 1/29/16
Receivership 12/7/33
1902 Plain Back <$VALUE
3x10-20 1-2606 <$850
1929 Small Size
10 Type 1 1-384 <$500
20 Type 1 1-119 <$500
Total Issue $167,620
Out at close $20,000
Large out at close $1,280
****
5894 Pennington
FNB, THIEF RIVER FALLS
{{ 14 L 7 S }}
Organized 6/29/01
Receivership 9/12/33
Brown Back <$VALUE
4x5 1-1105 <$1000
3x10-20 1-788 <$1000
1882 Date Back
4x5 1-1925 <$1000
3x10-20 1-1360 <$1000
1882 Value Back
4x5 1926-4195 <$1000
3x10-20 1361-2910 <$1000
1902 Plain Back
4x5 1-4206 <$600
3x10-20 1-3459 <$600
1929 Small Size
5 Type 1 1-1432 <$400
10 Type 1 1-627 <$400
20 Type 1 1-200 <$400
Total Issue $617,960
Out at close $50,000
Large out at close $3,180
****
3924 Saint Louis
FNB, TOWER
{{ UNREPORTED }}
Organized 8/30/88
Liquidated 10/1/95
Brown Back <$VALUE
3x10-20 1-587 <$2500
Total Issue $29,350
Out in 1910 $200
****
4992 Lyon
FNB, TRACY
{{ 3 L }}
Organized 2/21/95
Receivership 4/29/31
Brown Back <$VALUE
3x10-20 1-1120 <$1250
1882 Date Back
3x10-20 1-644 <$1250
1902 Date Back
3x10-20 1-500 <$750
1902 Plain Back
3x10-20 501-1114 <$750
Total Issue $143,900
Out at close $1,920
****
6364 Martin
TRUMAN NB, TRUMAN
{{ 7 L 9 S }}
Chartered 8/1/02
1902 Red Seal <$VALUE
3x10-20 1-1430 <$1000
1902 Date Back
3x10-20 1-1490 <$400
1902 Plain Back
3x10-20 1491-4219 <$400
1929 Small Size
10 Type 1 1-544 <$250
20 Type 1 1-148 <$250
10 Type 2 1-376 <$300
20 Type 2 1-60 <$300
Total Issue $337,810
Out in 1935 $25,000
Large out 1935 $1,930
****
6401 Norman
FNB OF TWIN VALLEY
{{ 10 L 10 S }}
Chartered 8/02
1902 Red Seal <$VALUE
3x10-20 1-400 <$1000
1902 Date Back
3x10-20 1-1770 <$400
1902 Plain Back
3x10-20 1771-4254 <$400
1929 Small Size
10 Type 1 1-462 <$250
20 Type 1 1-128 <$250
10 Type 2 1-795 <$275
20 Type 2 1-120 <$275
Total Issue $286,130
Out in 1935 $25,000
Large out 1935 $1,610
****
12357 Lake
FNB IN TWO HARBORS
{{ 10 L 19 S }}
Chartered 4/23
1902 Plain Back <$VALUE
4x5 1-3764 <$500
3x10-20 1-2865 <$500
1929 Small Size
5 Type 1 1-1590 <$200
10 Type 1 1-906 <$200
20 Type 1 1-226 <$200
5 Type 2 1-1360 <$200
10 Type 2 1-959 <$200
20 Type 2 1-215 <$200
Total Issue $368,400
Out in 1935 $50,000
Large out 1935 $1,830
****
6304 Lake
FNB OF TWO HARBORS
{{ UNREPORTED }}
Organized 6/14/02
Liquidated 9/22/05
1902 Red Seal <$VALUE
3x10-20 1-474 <$2500
Total Issue $23,700
Out in 1910 $1,120
****
6203 Lincoln
FNB, TYLER
{{ 4 L 4 S }}
Organized 1/24/02
Receivership 12/23/30
1902 Red Seal <$VALUE
3x10-20 1-1190 <$1000
1902 Date Back
3x10-20 1-1560 <$600
1902 Plain Back (dated 1902)
3x10-20 1561-2629 <$600
1902 Plain Back (dated 1922)
3x10-20 1-1548 <$600
1929 Small Size
10 Type 1 1-238 <$450
20 Type 1 1-54 <$450
Total Issue $290,910
Out at close $25,000
Large out at close $5,770
****
7081 Clay
FNB OF ULEN
{{ 2 L }}
Organized 12/12/03
Receivership 10/28/24
1902 Red Seal <$VALUE
3x10-20 1-400 <$1500
1902 Date Back
3x10-20 1-1810* <$750
1902 Plain Back
3x10-20 1941-3585* <$750
* 1811-1940 not marked
Total Issue $199,250
Out at close $24,700
****
6022 Wadena
FNB, VERNDALE
{{ 7 L 6 S }}
Chartered 1901
Brown Back <$VALUE
4x5 1-1525 <$750
3x10-20 1-1090 <$750
1882 Date Back
4x5 1-1575 <$700
3x10-20 1-1180 <$700
1882 Value Back
4x5 1576-2880 <$700
3x10-20 1181-1880 <$700
1902 Plain Back
4x5 1-6047 <$400
1929 Small Size
5 Type 1 1-2760 <$350
5 Type 2 1-3478 <$350
Total Issue $457,730
Out in 1935 $25,000
Large out 1935 $1,670
****
6527 Saint Louis
FNB OF VIRGINIA
{{ 5 L 35 S }}
Chartered 12/11/02
1902 Red Seal <$VALUE
3x10-20 1-676 <$850
1902 Date Back
3x10-20 1-4090 <$400
1902 Plain Back
3x10-20 4091-10361 <$400
1929 Small Size
10 Type 1 1-2094 <$75
20 Type 1 1-646 <$85
10 Type 2 1-2351 <$100
20 Type 2 1-590 <$100
Total Issue $790,320
Out in 1935 $100,000
Large out 1935 $2,940
****
3100 Wabasha
FNB, WABASHA
{{ 10 L 36 S }}
Chartered 1883
Brown Back <$VALUE
4x5 1-3292 <$600
3x10-20 1-1029 <$600
1902 Red Seal
3x10-20 1-2075 <$600
1902 Date Back
3x10-20 1-2800 <$250
1902 Plain Back
3x10-20 2801-7473 <$250
1929 Small Size
10 Type 1 1-982 <$60
20 Type 1 1-274 <$60
10 Type 2 1-738 <$70
20 Type 2 1-303 <$70
Total Issue $699,930
Out in 1935 $49,760
Large out 1935 $3,860
****
11410 Carver
FNB, WACONIA
{{ 4 L 16 S }}
Chartered 8/19
1902 Plain Back <$VALUE
4x5 1-5376 <$450
1929 Small Size
5 Type 1 1-2626 <$125
5 Type 2 1-5018 <$150
Total Issue $103,870
Out in 1935 $25,000
Large out 1935 $500
****
FNB in Wadena
SEE Ch 12507
NB of Wadena
****
4821 Wadena
FNB OF WADENA
{{ 14 L }}
Chartered 1892
Liquidated 5/14/24
Brown Back <$VALUE
4x5 1-3095 <$500
50-100 1-604 <$1250/$1500
1882 Date Back
4x5 1-990 <$450
50-100 1-280 <$1250/$1500
3x50-100 1-15 <$1250/$1500
1902 Date Back
4x5 1-1250 <$200
3x10-20 1-1000 <$200
1902 Plain Back
4x5 1251-4205 <$200
3x10-20 1001-2724 <$200
Total Issue $438,350
Out in 1922 $50,000
Ch 12507 assumed circulation
****
4916 Wadena
MERCHANTS NB, WADENA
{{ 10 L 16 S }}
Organized 5/15/93
Receivership 12/16/32
Brown Back <$VALUE
4x5 1-3725 <$500
3x10-20 1-1860 <$500
1882 Date Back
4x5 1-1604 <$450
3x10-20 1-1205 <$450
1902 Date Back
4x10 1-1750 <$225
1902 Plain Back
4x10 1751-9477 <$225
1929 Small Size
10 Type 1 1-1494 <$100
Total Issue $728,550
Out at close $49,760
Large out at close $6,250
****
12507 Wadena
NB OF WADENA
Chartered 3/24
2nd title:FNB in Wadena
1/8/25
FIRST TITLE {{ 2 L }}
1902 Plain Back <$VALUE
3x10-20 1-1000 <$500
SECOND TITLE {{ 5 L 29 S }}
1902 Plain Back
3x10-20 1-1030 <$350
1929 Small Size
10 Type 1 1-908 <$75
20 Type 1 1-278 <$85
10 Type 2 1-904 <$100
20 Type 2 1-207 <$100
Total Issue $202,520
Out in 1935 $50,000
Large out 1935 $1,630
****
8476 Cass
FNB OF WALKER
{{ 3 L U + 8 S }}
Chartered 12/06
1902 Red Seal <$VALUE
3x10-20 1-240 <$1250
1902 Date Back
3x10-20 1-1500* <$600
1902 Plain Back
3x10-20 1651-3472* <$600
* 1501-1650 not marked
1929 Small Size
10 Type 1 1-390 <$250
20 Type 1 1-116 <$250
10 Type 2 1-984 <$275
20 Type 2 1-222 <$275
Total Issue $237,200
Out in 1935 $25,000
Large out 1935 $1,030
****
5866 Marshall
FNB, WARREN
{{ 9 L }}
Organized 5/18/01
Receivership 10/10/25
Brown Back <$VALUE
3x10-20 1-1380 <$650
1882 Date Back
3x10-20 1-1800 <$600
1882 Value Back
3x10-20 1801-2616 <$600
1902 Plain Back
3x10-20 1-1042 <$350
Total Issue $251,900
Out at close $24,600
****
11286 Marshall
WARREN NB, WARREN
{{ 6 L }}
Organized 12/28/18
Receivership 12/5/25
1902 Plain Back <$VALUE
3x10-20 1-1960 <$400
Total Issue $98,000
Out at close $25,000
****
9253 Waseca
FARMERS NB, WASECA
{{ 5 L 12 S }}
Chartered 1908
1902 Date Back <$VALUE
3x10-20 1-3340* <$350
1902 Plain Back
3x10-20 3591-8930* <$350
* 3341-3590 not marked
1929 Small Size
10 Type 1 1-1148 <$125
20 Type 1 1-312 <$125
10 Type 2 1-512 <$150
20 Type 2 1-60 <$175
Total Issue $559,140
Out in 1935 $50,000
Large out 1935 $4,020
****
6544 Waseca
FNB OF WASECA
{{ 12 L 17 S }}
Chartered 12/18/02
1902 Red Seal <$VALUE
3x10-20 1-2713 <$400
1902 Date Back
3x10-20 1-2840* <$200
1902 Plain Back
3x10-20 3081-8042* <$200
* 2841-3080 not marked
1929 Small Size
10 Type 1 1-2054 <$75
20 Type 1 1-538 <$85
10 Type 2 1-624 <$100
20 Type 2 1-232 <$100
Total Issue $736,430
Out in 1935 $50,000
Large out 1935 $3,470
****

****
7283 Le Sueur
FNB OF WATERVILLE
{{ 8 L 6 S }}
Chartered 6/04
1902 Red Seal <$VALUE
4x5 1-300 <$800
3x10-20 1-220 <$800
1902 Date Back
4x5 1-400* <$400
3x10-20 1-320** <$400
1902 Plain Back
4x5 501-2365* <$400
3x10-20 381-1451** <$400
* 401-500 not marked
** 320-380 not marked
1929 Small Size
5 Type 1 1-730 <$300
10 Type 1 1-348 <$300
20 Type 1 1-98 <$300
5 Type 2 1-1050 <$300
10 Type 2 1-551 <$300
20 Type 2 1-107 <$300
Total Issue $204,290
Out in 1935 $25,000
Large out 1935 $1,320
****
6331 Martin
WELCOME NB, WELCOME
{{ 6 L 8 S }}
Chartered 7/9/02
Liquidated 1/13/31
1902 Red Seal <$VALUE
3x10-20 1-1350 <$850
1902 Date Back
3x10-20 1-2940 <$400
1902 Plain Back
3x10-20 2941-8661 <$400
1929 Small Size
10 Type 1 1-519 <$250
20 Type 1 1-116 <$250
Total Issue $545,610
Out at close $50,000
Large out at close $11,530
****
4669 Faribault
FNB, WELLS
{{ 7 L }}
Organized 12/12/91
Receivership 10/22/23
Brown Back <$VALUE
4x5 1-4525 <$650
3x10-20 1-2500 <$650
1882 Date Back
4x5 1-1105 <$600
3x10-20 1-863 <$600
1902 Date Back
4x5 1-1750* <$400
3x10-20 1-1300* <$400
1902 Plain Back
4x5 1951-8805* <$400
3x10-20 1461-6096** <$400
* 1751-1950 not marked
** 1301-1460 not marked
Total Issue $761,650
Out at close $96,400
****
6788 Faribault
WELLS NB, WELLS
{{ 4 L }}
Organized 4/6/03
Receivership 2/26/24
1902 Red Seal <$VALUE
3x10-20 1-1750 <$850
1902 Date Back
3x10-20 1-1860 <$500
1902 Plain Back
3x10-20 1861-6189 <$500
Total Issue $396,950
Out at close $74,300
****
10898 Grant
FNB, WENDELL
{{ 7 L 3 S }}
Organized 8/19/16
Receivership 9/23/32
1902 Plain Back <$VALUE
4x5 1-3770 <$400
4x10 1-2885 <$400
1929 Small Size
5 Type 1 1-782 <$500
10 Type 1 1-406 <$500
Total Issue $238,620
Out at close $25,000
Large out at close $1,830
****

****
14167 Dodge
FNB IN WEST CONCORD
{{ 5 S }}
Chartered 5/34
1929 Small Size <$VALUE
5 Type 2 1-1080 <$500
10 Type 2 1-575 <$500
Total Issue $11,150
Out in 1935 $10,000
****
5362 Dodge
FNB, WEST CONCORD
{{ 15 L 50+ S }}
Organized 5/7/00
Receivership 6/6/34
Brown Back <$VALUE
4x5 1-2875 <$600
3x10-20 1-1610 <$600
1882 Date Back
4x5 1-2100 <$550
3x10-20 1-1660 <$550
1882 Value Back
4x5 2101-3295 <$550
3x10-20 1661-2353 <$550
1902 Plain Back
4x5 1-4265 <$250
3x10-20 1-3301 <$250
1929 Small Size
5 Type 1 1-1396 <$100
10 Type 1 1-700 <$100
20 Type 1 1-244 <$100
5 Type 2 1-240 <$100
10 Type 2 1-110 <$100
20 Type 2 1-35 <$100
Total Issue $688,010
Out at close $50,000
Large out at close $4,910
****
7958 Hennepin
FNB OF WEST MINNEAPOLIS
Chartered 10/05
2nd title:FNB of Hopkins 7/1/29
FIRST TITLE {{ 10 L }}
1902 Red Seal <$VALUE
4x5 1-600 <$600
3x10-20 1-480 <$600
1902 Date Back
4x5 1-1750 <$250
3x10-20 1-1200 <$250
1902 Plain Back
4x5 1751-6200 <$250
3x10-20 1201-4044 <$250
SECOND TITLE {{ 19 S }}
1929 Small Size
5 Type 1 1-2470* <$75
10 Type 1 413-1150 <$75
20 Type 1 149-364 <$85
5 Type 2 1-2416 <$100
10 Type 2 1-1490 <$100
20 Type 2 1-270 <$100
*C000054A-F000830A canceled
Total Issue $515,580
Out in 1935 $50,000
Large out 1935 $2,240
****
12518 Hennepin
SECURITY NB OF WEST MINNEAPOLIS
Chartered 3/24
2nd title:Security NB of Hopkins 7/1/29
FIRST TITLE {{ 3 L }}
1902 Plain Back <$VALUE
3x10-20 1-3450 <$450
SECOND TITLE {{ 13 S }}
1929 Small Size
10 Type 1 1-1156 <$100
20 Type 1 1-304 <$100
10 Type 2 1-1486 <$100
20 Type 2 1-260 <$100
Total Issue $298,400
Out in 1935 $50,000
Large out 1935 $1,630
****
6412 Cottonwood
FNB OF WESTBROOK
{{ 6 L 7 S }}
Organized 7/15/02
Receivership 9/4/31
1902 Red Seal <$VALUE
3x10-20 1-400 <$1000
1902 Date Back
3x10-20 1-1840 <$500
1902 Plain Back
3x10-20 1841-4415 <$500
1929 Small Size
10 Type 1 1-284 <$275
20 Type 1 1-81 <$275
Total Issue $267,510
Out at close $25,000
Large out at close $5,610
****

****
6035 Traverse
FNB OF WHEATON
{{ 7 L 3 S }}
Chartered 11/01
Liquidated 7/31/31
Brown Back <$VALUE
4x5 1-700 <$1000
3x10-20 1-1360 <$1000
1882 Date Back
4x5 1-1525 <$1000
3x10-20 1-1100 <$1000
1882 Value Back
4x5 1526-2820 <$1000
3x10-20 1101-1805 <$1000
1902 Plain Back
4x5 1-1910 <$600
3x10-20 1-1154 <$600
1929 Small Size
5 Type 1 1-386 <$600
10 Type 1 1-177 <$600
20 Type 1 1-62 <$600
Total Issue $354,190
Out at close $25,000
Large out at close $3,975
****
8993 Traverse
NB OF WHEATON
{{ 3 L }}
Chartered 1/08
Liquidated 8/6/29
1902 Red Seal <$VALUE
3x10-20 1-210 <$1500
1902 Date Back
3x10-20 1-600 <$750
1902 Plain Back
3x10-20 601-1195 <$750
Total Issue $70,260
Out at close $6,550
****
6151 Kandiyohi
FNB OF WILLMAR
{{ 18 L }}
Chartered 3/02
Liquidated 9/7/29
1902 Red Seal <$VALUE
4x5 1-1225 <$400
3x10-20 1-930 <$400
1902 Date Back
4x5 1-2050 <$150
3x10-20 1-1640 <$150
1902 Plain Back (dated 1902)
4x5 2051-5340 <$150
3x10-20 1641-5420 <$150
1902 Plain Back (dated 1922)
4x5 1-6675 <$150
3x10-20 1-4741 <$150
Total Issue $819,350
Out at close $87,250
****
5301 Nobles
FNB, WILMONT
{{ 6 L }}
Chartered 4/24/00
Brown Back <$VALUE
3x10-20 1-1700 <$750
1882 Date Back
3x10-20 1-1630 <$750
1882 Value Back
3x10-20 1631-2276 <$750
1902 Plain Back
3x10-20 1-1698 <$500
Total Issue $283,700
Out in 1935 $1,540
****
5063 Cottonwood
FNB, WINDOM
{{ 5 L 27 S }}
Chartered 1897
Brown Back <$VALUE
4x5 1-2875 <$650
3x10-20 1-1610 <$650
1882 Date Back
4x5 1-2900 <$600
3x10-20 1-2140 <$600
1882 Value Back
4x5 2901-3295 <$600
3x10-20 2141-2353 <$600
1902 Plain Back
3x10-20 1-5752 <$400
1929 Small Size
10 Type 1 1-1638 <$60
20 Type 1 1-412 <$70
10 Type 2 1-1557 <$70
20 Type 2 1-340 <$80
Total Issue $779,240
Out in 1935 $75,000
Large out 1935 $4,710
****

****
6396 Cottonwood
WINDOM NB, WINDOM
{{ 4 L 9 S }}
Chartered 8/02
1902 Red Seal <$VALUE
3x10-20 1-1000 <$850
1902 Date Back
3x10-20 1-2350 <$450
1902 Plain Back
3x10-20 2351-6343 <$450
1929 Small Size
10 Type 1 1-666 <$150
20 Type 1 1-222 <$150
5 Type 2 1-324 <$175
10 Type 2 1-519 <$175
20 Type 2 1-162 <$175
Total Issue $443,800
Out in 1935 $35,000
Large out 1935 $2,435
****
10393 Faribault
BLUE EARTH VALLEY NB, WINNEBAGO
{{ 9 L 10 S }}
Chartered 5/13
1902 Date Back <$VALUE
3x10-20 1-1040 <$400
1902 Plain Back
3x10-20 1041-3908 <$400
1929 Small Size
10 Type 1 1-524 <$250
20 Type 1 1-156 <$250
10 Type 2 1-343 <$275
20 Type 2 1-60 <$300
Total Issue $250,190
Out in 1935 $25,000
Large out 1935 $2,160
****
5406 Faribault
FNB OF WINNEBAGO CITY, WINNEBAGO
{{ 4 L }}
Chartered 6/7/00
Liquidated 2/1/29
Brown Back <$VALUE
4x5 1-775 <$800
3x10-20 1-550 <$800
1882 Date Back
4x5 1-1050 <$800
3x10-20 1-760 <$800
1882 Value Back
4x5 1051-1055 <$800
3x10-20 761-787 <$800
1902 Plain Back
4x5 1 850 <$600
3x10-20 1-546 <$600
Total Issue $147,750
Out in 1927 $12,200
****
550 Winona
FNB, WINONA
{{ 3 L }}
Chartered 1864
Closed 7/21/84
Original Series <$VALUE
3x1-2 1-1900 <$750/$1250
4x5 1-3975 <$750
Series 1875
4x5 1-4206 <$750
Total Issue $173,120
Out in 1910 $1,411
****
2268 Winona
MERCHANTS NB, WINONA
{{ 23 L }}
Chartered 5/22/75
Liquidated 6/16/79
Original Series <$VALUE
3x1-2 1-1640 <$400/$850
4x5 1-2000 <$600
4x10 1-80 <$850
Total Issue $51,400
Out in 1910 $401
****
FNB of Winona
SEE Ch 3224
NB of Winona
****
3224 Winona
NB OF WINONA
Chartered 1884
2nd title:FNB of Winona 2/25/86
FIRST TITLE {{ 1 L }}
Brown Back <$VALUE
4x5 1-2328 <$850
SECOND TITLE {{ 44 L 50+ S }}
Brown Back
4x5 1-8700 <$350
3x10-20 1-8355 <$350
1902 Red Seal
4x5 1-5250 <$350
3x10-20 1-6500 <$350
1902 Date Back
4x5 1-15000 <$60
3x10-20 1-11700 <$70
1902 Plain Back
4x5 15001-37187 <$60
3x10-20 11701-26843 <$70
1929 Small Size
5 Type 1 1-5928 <$30
10 Type 1 1-3446 <$30
20 Type 1 1-956 <$40
5 Type 2 1-4380 <$30
10 Type 2 1-2350 <$30
20 Type 2 1-355 <$40
Total Issue $3,706,020
Out in 1935 $200,000
Large out 1935 $15,635
****
1842 Winona
SECOND NB OF WINONA
{{ 15 L }}
Chartered 7/6/71
Liquidated 1/22/10
Original Series <$VALUE
3x1-2 1-4800 <$500/$1000
4x5 1-3500 <$600
3x10-20 1-900 <$850/$1250
Series 1875
4x5 1-2359 <$600
3x10-20 1-3460 <$850/$1250
Brown Back
4x5 1-9150 <$350
3x10-20 1-8600 <$350
1882 Date Back
4x5 1-2193 <$300
3x10-20 1-734 <$300
Total Issue $1,052,740
Out in 1910 $140,617
****
1643 Winona
UNITED NB OF WINONA
{{ UNREPORTED }}
Chartered 3/10/66
Chartered 2/15/71
Original Series <$VALUE
4x5 1-1805 <$2000
3x10-20 1-200 <$2000
Total Issue $46,100
Out in 1910 $340
****
1782 Winona
WINONA DEPOSIT NB, WINONA
{{ 1 L }}
Chartered 2/3/71
Liquidated 1/28/77
Original Series <$VALUE
3x1-2 1-4000 <$1500/$2000
4x5 1-3750 <$1500
3x10-20 1-1158 <$1500/$2000
Total Issue $152,900
Out in 1910 $938
****
10865 Winona
WINONA N & SAVINGS B, WINONA
{{ 50+ S }}
Chartered 6/16 as Winona NB under which there was no issue. Issuing title adopted 5/8/28.
1929 Small Size <$VALUE
5 Type 2 1-14458 <$25
10 Type 2 1-6944 <$25
20 Type 2 1-3483 <$35
50 Type 2 1-264 <$125
100 Type 2 1-144 <$200
Total Issue $308,430
Out in 1935 $200,000
****
14042 Sibley
FNB IN WINTHROP
{{ 10 S }}
Chartered 3/34
1929 Small Size <$VALUE
5 Type 2 1-4992 <$250
Total Issue $24,960
Out in 1935 $20,000
****
7014 Sibley
FNB OF WINTHROP
{{ 3 L 12 S }}
Organized 9/9/03
Liquidated 4/25/34
1902 Red Seal <$VALUE
3x10-20 1-960 <$1000
1902 Date Back
3x10-20 1-1350* <$600
1902 Plain Back
3x10-20 1551-3886* <$600
* 1351-1550 not marked
1929 Small Size
5 Type 1 1-528 <$175
10 Type 1 1-314 <$175
20 Type 1 1-106 <$200
5 Type 2 1-752 <$200
Total Issue $293,460
Out at close $25,000
Large out at close $1,860
****
7625 Pipestone
FNB OF WOODSTOCK
{{ 7 L 6 S }}
Organized 2/21/05
Receivership 10/26/33
1902 Red Seal <$VALUE
3x10-20 1-520 <$750
1902 Date Back
3x10-20 1-940 <$400
1902 Plain Back
3x10-20 941-2804 <$400
1929 Small Size
10 Type 1 1-467 <$350
20 Type 1 1-130 <$350
Total Issue $209,820
Out at close $25,000
Large out at close $1,820
****
5910 Nobles
CITIZENS NB, WORTHINGTON
{{ 6 L }}
Organized 6/7/01
Receivership 6/19/24
Brown Back <$VALUE
3x10-20 1-1040 <$700
1882 Date Back
3x10-20 1-1250 <$650
1882 Value Back
3x10-20 1251-1868 <$650
1902 Plain Back
4x5 1-610 <$350
3x10-20 1-340 <$350
Total Issue $174,600
Out at close $18,000
****
3550 Nobles
FNB, WORTHINGTON
{{ UNREPORTED }}
Chartered 8/19/86
Liquidated 9/5/88
Brown Back <$VALUE
4x5 1-994 <$2000
Total Issue $19,880
Out in 1910 $120
****
8989 Nobles
WORTHINGTON NB, WORTHINGTON
{{ 7 L U + 17 S }}
Chartered 1/08
1902 Red Seal <$VALUE
4x5 1-275 <$750
3x10-20 1-235 <$750
1902 Date Back
4x5 1-1675* <$300
3x10-20 1-1260** <$300
1902 Plain Back
4x5 1776-5640* <$300
3x10-20 1341-3611** <$300
* 1676-1775 not marked
** 1261-1340 not marked
1929 Small Size
5 Type 1 1-1330 <$85
10 Type 1 1-792 <$85
20 Type 1 1-224 <$100
5 Type 2 1-2094 <$100
10 Type 2 1-1019 <$100
20 Type 2 1-266 <$100
Total Issue $450,880
Out in 1935 $50,000
Large out 1935 $1,850
****

CONDITION affects Value. The Values shown are for notes in FINE condition.

MISSISSIPPI

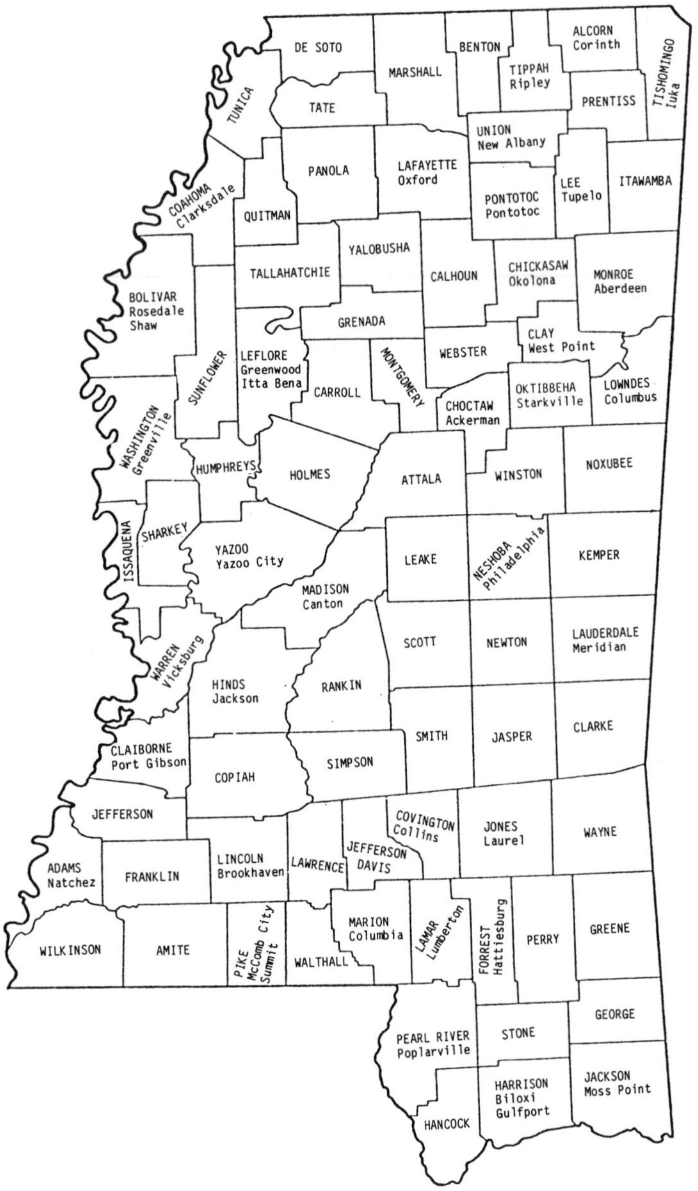

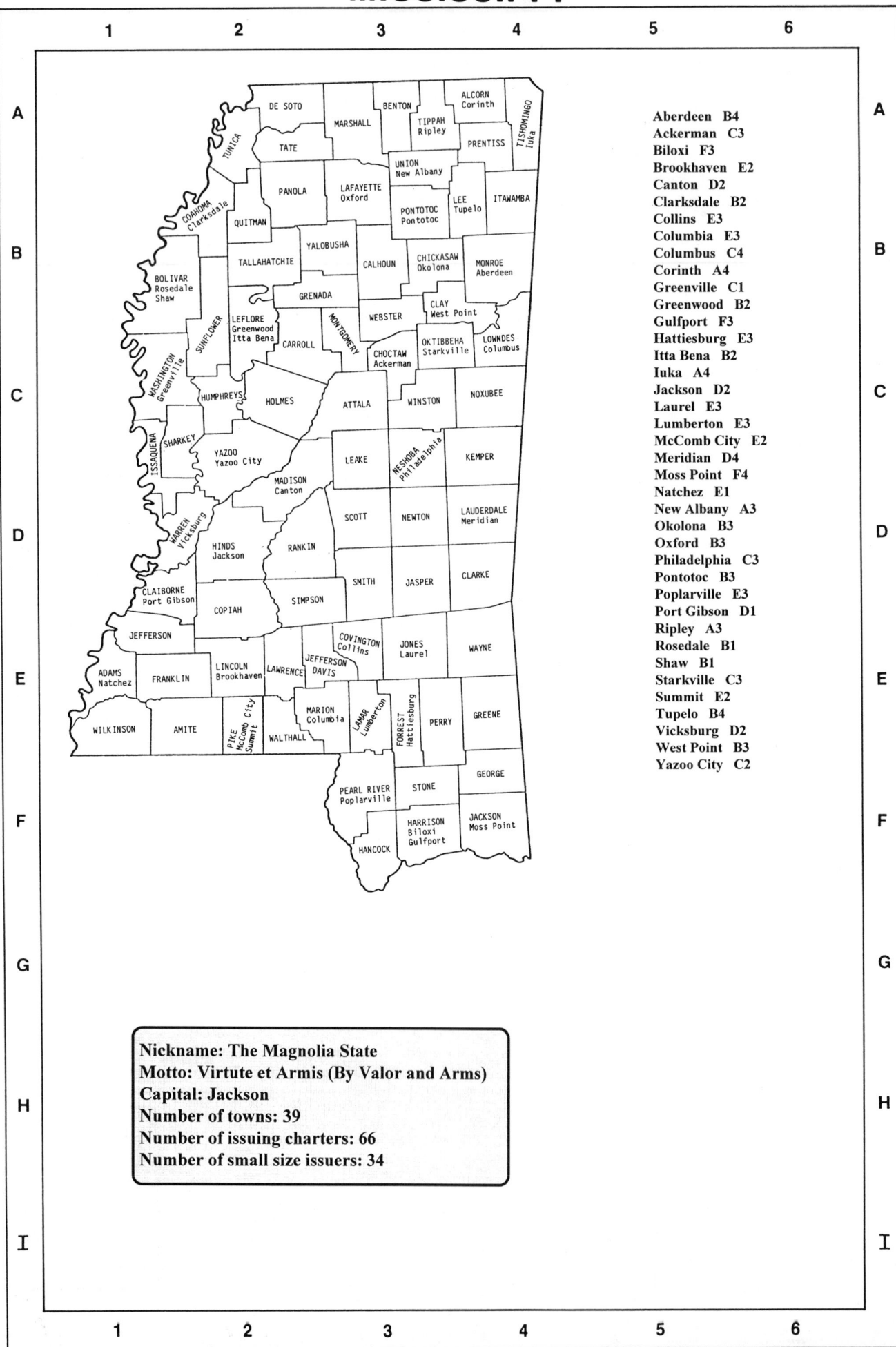

Aberdeen B4
Ackerman C3
Biloxi F3
Brookhaven E2
Canton D2
Clarksdale B2
Collins E3
Columbia E3
Columbus C4
Corinth A4
Greenville C1
Greenwood B2
Gulfport F3
Hattiesburg E3
Itta Bena B2
Iuka A4
Jackson D2
Laurel E3
Lumberton E3
McComb City E2
Meridian D4
Moss Point F4
Natchez E1
New Albany A3
Okolona B3
Oxford B3
Philadelphia C3
Pontotoc B3
Poplarville E3
Port Gibson D1
Ripley A3
Rosedale B1
Shaw B1
Starkville C3
Summit E2
Tupelo B4
Vicksburg D2
West Point B3
Yazoo City C2

Nickname: The Magnolia State
Motto: Virtute et Armis (By Valor and Arms)
Capital: Jackson
Number of towns: 39
Number of issuing charters: 66
Number of small size issuers: 34

3656 Monroe
FNB OF ABERDEEN
{{ 10 L 11 S }}
Chartered 3/23/87
Brown Back <$VALUE
50-100 1-886 <$5000
1902 Red Seal
4x10 1-3438 <$1250
1902 Date Back
4x5 1-8900 <$250
4x10 1-7550 <$250
1902 Plain Back
4x5 8901-26970 <$250
4x10 7551-21829 <$250
1929 Small Size
5 Type 1 1-7368 <$165
10 Type 1 1-2866 <$150
5 Type 2 1-7380 <$185
10 Type 2 1-3580 <$185
Total Issue $2,148,680
Out in 1935 $52,720
Large out 1935 $4,010

9251 Choctaw
FNB OF ACKERMAN
{{ 1 L }}
Organized 8/17/08
Receivership 11/12/26
1902 Date Back <$VALUE
3x10-20 1-820 <$1500
1902 Plain Back
3x10-20 821-956 <$1500
Total Issue $47,800
Out at close $920

10576 Harrison
FNB OF BILOXI
{{ 8 L 13 S }}
Chartered 7/14
1902 Date Back <$VALUE
4x5 1-3150 <$300
3x10-20 1-2340 <$300
1902 Plain Back
4x5 3151-19888 <$300
3x10-20 2341-13787 <$300
1929 Small Size
5 Type 1 1-4586 <$150
10 Type 1 1-2492 <$150
20 Type 1 1-640 <$150
5 Type 2 1-1892 <$175
10 Type 2 1-950 <$175
20 Type 2 1-254 <$175
Total Issue $1,475,050
Out in 1935 $71,780
Large out 1935 $5,410

10494 Lincoln
FNB OF BROOKHAVEN
{{ 5 L 6 S }}
Organized 2/17/14
Receivership 1/13/31
1902 Date Back <$VALUE
4x5 1-1830* <$450
3x10-20 1-1468** <$450
1902 Plain Back
4x5 2331-18388* <$450
3x10-20 1869-11873** <$450
* 1831-2330 not marked
** 1469-11873 not marked
1929 Small Size
5 Type 1 1-1445 <$350
10 Type 1 1-690 <$350
20 Type 1 1-138 <$350
Total Issue $1,062,720
Out in 1935 $74,995
Large out 1935 $12,905

6847 Madison
FNB OF CANTON
{{ 3 L 14 S }}
Organized 5/25/03
1902 Red Seal <$VALUE
3x10-20 1-2325 <$2000
1902 Date Back
3x10-20 1-4440 <$650
1902 Plain Back
3x10-20 4441-11731 <$650
1929 Small Size
10 Type 1 1-1394 <$150
20 Type 1 1-366 <$165
10 Type 2 1-3270 <$175
20 Type 2 1-828 <$185
Total Issue $879,620
Out in 1935 $62,600
Large out 1935 $3,080

6595 Coahoma
FNB OF CLARKSDALE
{{ UNREPORTED }}
Chartered 1/03
Liquidated 6/30/11
1902 Red Seal <$VALUE
4x5 1-1550 <$3000
3x10-20 1-1280 <$3000
1902 Date Back
4x5 1-555 <$2000
3x10-20 1-484 <$2000
Total Issue $130,300
Out in 1911 $20,500

12222 Coahoma
PLANTERS NB OF CLARKSDALE
{{ 2 L 6 S }}
Organized 6/10/22
Receivership 1/26/31
1902 Plain Back <$VALUE
4x5 1-8933 <$1000
1929 Small Size
5 Type 1 1-2096 <$350
10 Type 1 1-1029 <$350
20 Type 1 1-296 <$350
Total Issue $338,800
Out in 1935 $95,500
Large out 1935 $2,650

9728 Covington
FNB OF COLLINS
{{ UNREPORTED }}
Chartered 4/10
Liquidated 12/4/14
1902 Date Back <$VALUE
4x10 1-529 <$2500
Total Issue $21,160
Out in 1915 $2,350

10326 Marion
CITIZENS NB OF COLUMBIA
{{ UNREPORTED }}
Chartered 2/13
Liquidated 9/21/14
1902 Date Back <$VALUE
4x10 1-389 <$2500
Total Issue $15,560
Out in 1914 $7,700

10738 Lowndes
COLUMBUS NB, COLUMBUS
Chartered 5/15
2nd title: F-Columbus NB, Columbus 12/22/30
FIRST TITLE {{ 3 L 3 S }}
1902 Plain Back <$VALUE
4x5 1-7390 <$450
4x10 1-7676 <$450
1929 Small Size
5 Type 1 1-1702 <$150
10 Type 1 1-826 <$150
SECOND TITLE {{ 6U + 50+ S }}
1929 Small Size
5 Type 1 1-5052 <$75
10 Type 1 1-2776 <$75
5 Type 2 1-17948 <$75
10 Type 2 1-9484 <$65
Total Issue $1,058,160
Out in 1935 $129,550
Large out 1935 $1,540

F-Columbus NB, Columbus
SEE Ch 10738
Columbus NB, Columbus

2638 Lowndes
FNB OF COLUMBUS
{{ UNREPORTED }}
Chartered 2/28/82
Liquidated 5/30/94
Series 1875 <$VALUE
50-100 1-1341 <$20,000
Total Issue $201,150
Out in 1910 $2,200

10361 Lowndes
NB OF COMMERCE OF COLUMBUS
{{ 10 L 36 S }}
Chartered 4/13
1902 Date Back <$VALUE
4x10 1-6500 <$200
1902 Plain Back
4x10 6501-32632 <$200
1929 Small Size
10 Type 1 1-5814 <$75
10 Type 2 1-7924 <$75
Total Issue $1,733,360
Out in 1935 $95,200
Large out 1935 $4,060

9751 Alcorn
CITIZENS NB OF CORINTH
{{ 5 L }}
Chartered 5/10
Liquidated 5/25/23
1902 Date Back <$VALUE
4x5 1-2650 <$500
3x10-20 1-2120 <$500
1902 Plain Back
4x5 2651-6940 <$500
3x10-20 2121-4784 <$500
Total Issue $378,000
Out at close $27,700

9094 Alcorn
FNB OF CORINTH
{{ 13 L 4 S }}
Organized 2/27/08
Receivership 11/30/31
1902 Red Seal <$VALUE
4x5 1-1665 <$1250
4x10 1-1730 <$1250
1902 Date Back
4x5 1-1800 <$300
4x10 1-1650 <$300
1902 Plain Back
4x5 1801-9211 <$300
4x10 1651-6990 <$300
1929 Small Size
5 Type 1 1-1292 <$400
10 Type 1 1-726 <$400
Total Issue $648,640
Out at close $33,980
Large out at close $3,480

3765 Washington
FNB OF GREENVILLE
{{ 6 L 12 S }}
Chartered 7/28/87
Brown Back <$VALUE
4x5 1-9850 <$1750
3x10-20 1-4000 <$1750
1902 Red Seal
3x10-20 1-1000 <$1500
1902 Date Back
3x10-20 1-7600 <$350
1902 Plain Back
3x10-20 7601-24956 <$350
1929 Small Size
10 Type 1 1-2846 <$150
20 Type 1 1-848 <$165
10 Type 2 1-3543 <$175
20 Type 2 1-1057 <$200
Total Issue $2,023,890
Out in 1935 $100,000
Large out 1935 $7,850

7216 Leflore
FNB OF GREENWOOD
{{ 19 L 21 S }}
Organized 4/2/04
Receivership 12/27/30
1902 Red Seal <$VALUE
4x5 1-9650 <$1000
3x10-20 1-6890 <$1100
1902 Date Back
4x5 1-20750 <$175
3x10-20 1-14000 <$175
1902 Plain Back
4x5 20751-68059 <$175
3x10-20 14001-44707 <$175
1929 Small Size
5 Type 1 1-4860 <$100
10 Type 1 1-2290 <$100
20 Type 1 1-663 <$100
Total Issue $4,496,790
Out at close $236,380
Large out at close $38,290

13553 Harrison
FNB IN GULFPORT
{{ 3 S }}
Organized 6/5/31
Receivership 12/3/31
1929 Small Size <$VALUE
5 Type 1 1-802 <$450
10 Type 1 1-315 <$425
20 Type 1 1-70 <$450
Total Issue $51,360
Out at close $246,100
Outstanding includes Ch 6188

6188 Harrison
FNB OF GULFPORT
{{ 17 L 24 S }}
Chartered 4/3/02
Liquidated 7/18/31
1902 Red Seal <$VALUE
4x5 1-6000 <$1000
3x10-20 1-9140 <$1000
1902 Date Back
4x5 1-17750 <$175
3x10-20 1-16800 <$175
1902 Plain Back (dated 1902)
4x5 17751-32050 <$175
3x10-20 16801-26606 <$175
1902 Plain Back (dated 1922)
4x5 1-6250 <$175
3x10-20 1-23827 <$175
1929 Small Size
5 Type 1 1-3448 <$100
10 Type 1 1-3137 <$100
20 Type 1 1-906 <$100
Total Issue $4,265,030
Out at close $237,160
Large out 1935 $34,320
Ch 13553 assumed circulation

12478 Forrest
COMMERCIAL NB OF HATTIESBURG
{{ 5 L 8 S }}
Organized 12/26/23
Receivership 6/12/31
1902 Plain Back <$VALUE
4x5 1-11947 <$500
3x10-20 1-6872 <$500
1929 Small Size
5 Type 1 1-2548 <$225
10 Type 1 1-1209 <$200
20 Type 1 1-336 <$225
Total Issue $771,840
Out at close $98,500
Large out at close $10,060

FNB of Commerce, Hattiesburg
SEE Ch 5176
NB of Commerce of Hattiesburg

FNB of Hattiesburg
SEE Ch 5176
NB of Commerce of Hattiesburg

5177 Forrest
FNB OF HATTIESBURG
{{ 2 L }}
Chartered 2/16/99
Liquidated 8/5/08
Brown Back <$VALUE
4x5 1-3070 <$2500
3x10-20 1-1578 <$2500
Total Issue $140,300
Out in 1910 $11,820

5176 Forrest
NB OF COMMERCE OF HATTIESBURG
Chartered 2/7/99
2nd title: FNB of Commerce of Hattiesburg 8/8/08
3rd title: FNB of Hattiesburg 1/18/18
FIRST TITLE {{ 1 L }}
Brown Back <$VALUE
4x5 1-9825 <$1500
3x10-20 1-4749 <$1500
SECOND TITLE {{ 8 L }}
1882 Date Back
4x5 1-35500 <$500
3x10-20 1-23200 <$500
THIRD TITLE {{ 10 L 14 S }}
1882 Value Back
4x5 1-300 <$750
3x10-20 1-120 <$750
1902 Plain Back
4x5 1-23550 <$250
3x10-20 1-13631 <$250
1929 Small Size
5 Type 1 1-5896 <$125
10 Type 1 1-2816 <$125
20 Type 1 1-724 <$125
5 Type 2 1-4180 <$150
10 Type 2 1-1962 <$150
20 Type 2 1-1081 <$150
Total Issue $3,963,360
Out in 1935 $100,000
Large out 1935 $12,380

10688 Leflore
FNB OF ITTA BENA
{{ 6 L 3 S }}
Chartered 1/15
Liquidated 6/14/30
1902 Plain Back <$VALUE
4x5 1-10630 <$500
3x10-20 1-7306 <$500
1929 Small Size
5 Type 1 1-508 <$450
10 Type 1 1-161 <$450
20 Type 1 1-10 <$500
Total Issue $604,000
Out at close $27,800
Large out at close $10,700

10154 Tishomingo
FNB OF IUKA
{{ 1 L }}
Chartered 3/12
Liquidated 3/29/15
1902 Date Back <$VALUE
4x5 1-415 <$2000
3x10-20 1-285 <$2000
Total Issue $22,550
Out in 1915 $5,750

13708 Hinds
CAPITAL NB IN JACKSON
{{ 8 S }}
Chartered 6/33
1929 Small Size <$VALUE
5 Type 2 1-6548 <$225
10 Type 2 1-3056 <$225
20 Type 2 1-1538 <$225
Total Issue $94,060
Out in 1935 $159,530
Outstanding includes Ch 6646

6646 Hinds
CAPITAL NB OF JACKSON
{{ 12 L 18 S }}
Organized 2/21/03
Liquidated 8/15/33
1902 Red Seal <$VALUE
3x10-20 1-6900 <$1250
1902 Date Back
3x10-20 1-17100 <$250
1902 Plain Back
3x10-20 17101-48563 <$250
1929 Small Size
10 Type 1 1-5126 <$125
20 Type 1 1-1418 <$125
Total Issue $3,250,870
Out at close $185,480
Large out 1935 $12,180
Ch 13708 assumed circulation

1610 Hinds
FNB OF JACKSON
{{ UNREPORTED }}
Chartered 11/15/65
Liquidated 12/26/67
Original Series <$VALUE
4x5 1-650 <$6500
3x10-20 1-550 <$7500
Total Issue $40,500
Out in 1910 $125

3332 Hinds
FNB OF JACKSON
{{ 11 L 4 S }}
Organized 3/14/85
Receivership 2/16/31
Brown Back <$VALUE
4x5 1-5844 <$1500
3x10-20 1-3012 <$1500
1902 Red Seal
4x10 1-1500 <$1500
50-100 1-720 <$6500
1902 Date Back
4x10 1-9050 <$250
50-100 1-300 <$1250
3x50-100 1-698 <$1250
1902 Plain Back
4x10 9051-22949 <$250
3x50-100 699-1222 <$1250
1929 Small Size
10 Type 1 1-1969 <$250
50 Type 1 1-124 <$650
100 Type 1 1-11 <$850
Total Issue $1,865,880
Out at close $124,150
Large out at close $38,270

10523 Hinds
JACKSON-STATE NB, JACKSON
{{ 2 L }}
Chartered 4/14 as Jackson NB under which there was no issue. Issuing title adopted 10/12/14.
1902 Date Back <$VALUE
4x5 1-3000 <$1000
3x10-20 1-2400 <$1000
1902 Plain Back
4x5 3001-4840 <$1000
3x10-20 2401-3697 <$1000
Total Issue $281,650
Out in 1935 $1,295
Outstanding includes Ch 10463

10463 Hinds
STATE NB OF JACKSON
{{ UNREPORTED }}
Chartered 11/13
Liquidated 10/3/14
1902 Date Back <$VALUE
4x5 1-1240 <$2000
3x10-20 1-494 <$2000
3x50-100 1-40 <$2500
Total Issue $59,500
Out at close $50,000
Ch 10523 assumed circulation

11898 Jones
COMMERCIAL NB & TC OF LAUREL
{{ 8 L 12 S }}
Chartered 12/20
1902 Plain Back <$VALUE
4x5 1-51975 <$350
1929 Small Size
5 Type 1 1-13898 <$100
5 Type 2 1-29292 <$100
Total Issue $1,602,900
Out in 1935 $91,940
Large out 1935 $2,095

6681 Jones
FNB OF LAUREL
{{ 10 L 6U + 15 S }}
Chartered 3/03
1902 Red Seal <$VALUE
4x5 1-2750 <$1500
3x10-20 1-4225 <$1500
1902 Date Back
4x5 1-7400 <$300
3x10-20 1-5240 <$300
1902 Plain Back
4x5 7401-25120 <$300
3x10-20 5241-17238 <$300
1929 Small Size
5 Type 1 1-3978 <$125
10 Type 1 1-2206 <$125
20 Type 1 1-512 <$125
5 Type 2 1-5544 <$125
10 Type 2 1-2928 <$125
20 Type 2 1-948 <$150
Total Issue $2,019,650
Out in 1935 $99,750
Large out 1935 $4,540

6923 Jones
LAUREL NB, LAUREL
{{ UNREPORTED }}
Chartered 8/13/03
Liquidated 7/24/05
1902 Red Seal <$VALUE
3x10-20 1-741 <$3000
Total Issue $37,050
Out in 1910 $3,230

5613 Lamar
FNB OF LUMBERTON
{{ 5 L 4 S }}
Chartered 11/2/00
Receivership 2/9/33
Brown Back <$VALUE
3x10-20 1-1500 <$1750
1882 Date Back
3x10-20 1-3300 <$850
1882 Value Back
3x10-20 3301-5340 <$1000
1902 Plain Back
3x10-20 1-6559 <$450
1929 Small Size
10 Type 1 1-1212 <$400
20 Type 1 1-324 <$400
Total Issue $781,550
Out at close $49,100
Large out at close $5,700

CONDITION affects Value. The Values shown are for notes in FINE condition.

7461 Pike
FNB OF McCOMB CITY
{{ 3 L 9 S }}
Organized 10/22/04
1902 Red Seal <$VALUE
4x5 1-2400 <$2000
3x10-20 1-1820 <$2000
1902 Date Back
4x5 1-4400 <$850
3x10-20 1-3380 <$850
1902 Plain Back
4x5 4401-12814 <$850
3x10-20 3381-8773 <$850
1929 Small Size
5 Type 1 1-1522 <$200
10 Type 1 1-956 <$200
20 Type 1 1-252 <$200
5 Type 2 1-2386 <$225
10 Type 2 1-1304 <$225
20 Type 2 1-445 <$225
Total Issue $1,001,060
Out in 1935 $49,550
Large out 1935 $3,500

7266 Lauderdale
CITIZENS NB OF MERIDIAN
{{ 14 L 20 S }}
Chartered 5/04
1902 Red Seal <$VALUE
4x5 1-4000 <$1000
3x10-20 1-5400 <$1000
1902 Date Back
4x5 1-11500 <$175
3x10-20 1-7600 <$175
1902 Plain Back
4x5 11501-41235 <$175
3x10-20 7601-25195 <$175
1929 Small Size
5 Type 1 1-5734 <$100
10 Type 1 1-2696 <$85
20 Type 1 1-840 <$100
5 Type 2 1-9796 <$100
10 Type 2 1-4927 <$100
20 Type 2 1-1392 <$100
Total Issue $2,995,120
Out in 1935 $146,695
Large out 1935 $8,215

13551 Lauderdale
FNB IN MERIDIAN
{{ 16 S }}
Chartered 6/31
1929 Small Size <$VALUE
5 Type 2 1-20132 <$100
10 Type 2 1-14204 <$100
20 Type 2 1-4268 <$100
Total Issue $328,060
Out in 1935 $194,650

2957 Lauderdale
FNB OF MERIDIAN
{{ 12 L 4 S }}
Organized 5/3/83
Receivership 1/26/31
Brown Back <$VALUE
4x5 1-9676 <$1250
3x10-20 1-3477 <$1250
1902 Red Seal
3x10-20 1-10100 <$850
1902 Date Back
3x10-20 1-19800 <$200
1902 Plain Back
3x10-20 19801-32577 <$200
1929 Small Size
10 Type 1 1-1298 <$300
20 Type 1 1-362 <$300
Total Issue $2,622,540
Out at close $92,200
Large out at close $21,550

3176 Lauderdale
MERIDIAN NB, MERIDIAN
{{ 2 L }}
Chartered 5/6/84
Liquidated 9/15/03
Brown Back <$VALUE
4x5 1-9110 <$1750
3x10-20 1-2291 <$1750
Total Issue $296,750
Out in 1910 $5,970

8593 Jackson
PASCAGOULA NB OF MOSS POINT
{{ 6 L U + 12 S }}
Organized 2/15/07
1902 Red Seal <$VALUE
4x5 1-725 <$1750
3x10-20 1-630 <$1750
1902 Date Back
4x5 1-7450 <$450
3x10-20 1-5760 <$450
1902 Plain Back
4x5 7451-17574 <$450
3x10-20 5761-12295 <$450
1929 Small Size
5 Type 1 1-2720 <$225
10 Type 1 1-1462 <$225
20 Type 1 1-416 <$225
5 Type 2 1-2336 <$250
10 Type 2 1-1332 <$250
20 Type 2 1-456 <$250
Total Issue $1,265,590
Out in 1935 $45,970
Large out 1935 $5,020

13722 Adams
BRITTON & KOONTZ NB IN NATCHEZ
{{ 9 S }}
Chartered 7/33
1929 Small Size <$VALUE
5 Type 2 1-15828 <$150
10 Type 2 1-8400 <$150
Total Issue $163,140
Out in 1935 $96,590

12537 Adams
BRITTON & KOONTZ NB OF NATCHEZ
{{ 5 L 14 S }}
Organized 4/30/24
Receivership 7/1/33
1902 Plain Back <$VALUE
4x10 1-9244 <$450
1929 Small Size
10 Type 1 1-4729 <$125
Total Issue $653,500
Out at close $100,000
Large out at close $3,740

3701 Adams
FNB OF NATCHEZ
{{ UNREPORTED }}
Chartered 5/9/87
Liquidated 4/15/95
Brown Back <$VALUE
4x5 1-3360 <$3000
Total Issue $67,200
Out in 1910 $605

6305 Adams
NB OF COMMERCE OF NATCHEZ
{{ UNREPORTED }}
Chartered 6/16/02
Liquidated 9/30/05
1902 Red Seal <$VALUE
3x10-20 1-976 <$2500
Total Issue $48,800
Out in 1910 $2,880

8514 Union
FNB OF NEW ALBANY
{{ 3 L }}
Chartered 1/07
Liquidated 11/24/16
1902 Red Seal <$VALUE
3x10-20 1-900 <$2500
1902 Date Back
3x10-20 1-4140 <$1000
1902 Plain Back
3x10-20 4141-4457 <$1000
Total Issue $267,850
Out at close $49,500

9196 Chickasaw
FNB OF OKOLONA
{{ UNREPORTED }}
Chartered 7/08
Liquidated 12/31/19
1902 Date Back <$VALUE
4x5 1-1275 <$2000
3x10-20 1-1020 <$2000
1902 Plain Back
4x5 1276-1315 <$2000
3x10-20 1021-1057 <$2000
Total Issue $79,150
Out at close $10,000

9865 Lafayette
NB OF OXFORD
{{ 6 L 8 S }}
Chartered 10/10
1902 Date Back <$VALUE
4x5 1-3275 <$450
3x10-20 1-2500 <$450
1902 Plain Back
4x5 3276-7729 <$450
3x10-20 2501-5329 <$450
1929 Small Size
5 Type 1 1-2058 <$250
10 Type 1 1-1086 <$250
20 Type 1 1-318 <$250
5 Type 2 1-3276 <$275
10 Type 2 1-1764 <$275
20 Type 2 1-396 <$275
Total Issue $628,030
Out in 1935 $48,150
Large out 1935 $680

9041 Neshoba
FNB OF PHILADELPHIA
{{ 3 L }}
Chartered 2/08
Liquidated 6/19/17
1902 Red Seal <$VALUE
4x5 1-465 <$2000
3x10-20 1-374 <$2000
1902 Date Back
4x5 1-3800 <$1000
3x10-20 1-2800 <$1000
1902 Plain Back
4x5 3801-4355 <$1000
3x10-20 2801-3134 <$1000
Total Issue $271,800
Out at close $49,600

9040 Pontotoc
FNB OF PONTOTOC
{{ 6 L 14 S }}
Chartered 2/08
1902 Red Seal <$VALUE
4x5 1-500 <$1500
3x10-20 1-415 <$1500
1902 Date Back
4x5 1-3700 <$350
3x10-20 1-2800 <$350
1902 Plain Back
4x5 3701-24601 <$350
3x10-20 2801-16612 <$350
1929 Small Size
5 Type 1 1-5416 <$165
10 Type 1 1-2636 <$150
20 Type 1 1-670 <$175
5 Type 2 1-5284 <$185
10 Type 2 1-2643 <$175
20 Type 2 1-785 <$200
Total Issue $1,822,960
Out in 1935 $78,520
Large out 1935 $5,095

8719 Pearl River
NB OF POPLARVILLE
{{ UNREPORTED }}
Chartered 5/07
Liquidated 4/1/10
1902 Red Seal <$VALUE
4x5 1-1136 <$3000
3x10-20 1-920 <$3000
1902 Date Back
4x5 1-314 <$2500
3x10-20 1-312 <$2500
Total Issue $90,600
Out in 1910 $28,550

5715 Claiborne
MISSISSIPPI NB OF PORT GIBSON
{{ UNREPORTED }}
Chartered 2/15/01
Liquidated 8/31/07
Brown Back <$VALUE
4x5 1-1100 <$3000
3x10-20 1-712 <$3000
Total Issue $57,600
Out in 1910 $3,600

9204 Tippah
FNB OF RIPLEY
{{ UNREPORTED }}
Chartered 7/08
Liquidated 1/22/15
1902 Date Back <$VALUE
3x10-20 1-1990 <$2000
Total Issue $99,500
Out in 1915 $15,050

10745 Bolivar
FNB OF ROSEDALE
{{ UNREPORTED }}
Chartered 6/15
Liquidated 3/6/22
1902 Plain Back <$VALUE
4x5 1-2099 <$2000
4x10 1-1785 <$2000
Total Issue $113,380
Out at close $20,400
Ch 12073 assumed circulation

12073 Bolivar
ROSEDALE NB, ROSEDALE
{{ 2 L }}
Organized 11/11/21
Receivership 6/10/29
1902 Plain Back <$VALUE
3x10-20 1-2884 <$1000
Total Issue $144,200
Out at close $25,000
Outstanding includes Ch 10745

7200 Bolivar
FNB OF SHAW
{{ UNREPORTED }}
Chartered 4/5/04
Liquidated 4/25/10
1902 Red Seal <$VALUE
3x10-20 1-560 <$3000
1902 Date Back
3x10-20 1-22 <$2500
Total Issue $29,100
Out in 1910 $5,450

3688 Oktibbeha
FNB OF STARKVILLE
{{ 1 L }}
Chartered 4/30/87
Receivership 8/9/93
Brown Back <$VALUE
4x5 1-1606 <$2500
Total Issue $32,120
Out in 1916 $290

9753 Pike
NB OF SUMMIT
{{ 1 L }}
Chartered 5/10
Liquidated 3/1/13
1902 Date Back <$VALUE
4x5 1-490 <$2000
3x10-20 1-397 <$2000
Total Issue $29,650
Out in 1913 $7,450

10338 Pike
PROGRESSIVE NB OF SUMMIT
{{ UNREPORTED }}
Chartered 3/13
Liquidated 3/15/15
1902 Date Back <$VALUE
3x10-20 1-980 <$2000
Total Issue $49,000
Out in 1915 $16,900

4521 Lee
FNB OF TUPELO
{{ 2 L }}
Chartered 1891
Liquidated 3/10/21
Brown Back <$VALUE
3x10-20 1-2940 <$2000
1882 Date Back
3x10-20 1-823 <$1250
1902 Date Back
3x10-20 1-3600 <$1000
1902 Plain Back
3x10-20 3601-4601 <$1000
Total Issue $418,200
Out at close $11,350

6121 Warren
AMERICAN NB OF VICKSBURG
{{ 2 L }}
Chartered 2/6/02
Liquidated 11/2/10
1902 Red Seal <$VALUE
4x5 1-4500 <$1250
3x10-20 1-4500 <$1250
1902 Date Back
4x5 1-1575 <$650
3x10-20 1-1274 <$650
Total Issue $410,200
Out in 1911 $49,545

7507 Warren
CITIZENS NB OF VICKSBURG
{{ 7 L }}
Chartered 12/04
Liquidated 5/23/29
1902 Red Seal <$VALUE
4x5 1-1575 <$1250
50-100 1-430 <$6500
1902 Date Back
4x5 1-6750 <$300
50-100 1-800 <$1500
3x50-100 1-970 <$1500
1902 Plain Back
4x5 6751-31282 <$300
3x50-100 971-1209 <$1500
Total Issue $1,143,890
Out at close $93,000

3258 Warren
FNB OF VICKSBURG
Chartered 1884
2nd title: FNB & TC of Vicksburg 12/31/29
FIRST TITLE {{ 18 L 3 S }}
Brown Back <$VALUE
3x10-20 1-6338 <$1250
50-100 1-900 <$5000
1902 Red Seal
3x10-20 1-8500 <$1000
1902 Date Back
3x10-20 1-24500 <$150
1902 Plain Back
3x10-20 24501-54447 <$150
1929 Small Size
10 Type 1 1-1226 <$125
20 Type 1 1-418 <$125
SECOND TITLE {{ 22 S }}
1929 Small Size
10 Type 1 1-4618 <$75
20 Type 1 1-1228 <$85
Total Issue $4,147,410
Out in 1935 $184,960
Large out 1935 $14,360

3430 Warren
MERCHANTS NB OF VICKSBURG
Chartered 1886
2nd title: Merchants NB & TC of Vicksburg 1/9/28
FIRST TITLE {{ 3 L }}
Brown Back <$VALUE
4x5 1-7465 <$1750
50-100 1-1060 <$5000
1902 Red Seal
50-100 1-666 <$6500
1902 Date Back
4x5 1-9665 <$400
50-100 1-800 <$1500
3x50-100 1-486 <$1500
1902 Plain Back
4x5 9666-10005 <$400
SECOND TITLE {{ U + 22 S }}
1929 Small Size
5 Type 1 1-4932 <$100
10 Type 1 1-2576 <$85
20 Type 1 1-1104 <$100
5 Type 2 1-15716 <$100
10 Type 2 1-8300 <$100
20 Type 2 1-1875 <$100
Total Issue $1,483,880
Out in 1935 $256,025
Large out 1935 $3,575

803 Warren
NB OF VICKSBURG
{{ UNREPORTED }}
Chartered 2/14/65
Receivership 4/24/68
Original Series <$VALUE
4x5 1-1000 <$6000
3x10-20 1-110 <$7500
Total Issue $25,500
Out in 1916 $55

2891 Clay
FNB OF WEST POINT
{{ 7 L 15 S }}
Chartered 1883
Brown Back <$VALUE
50-100 1-982 <$5000
1902 Red Seal
3x10-20 1-3300 <$1250
1902 Date Back
3x10-20 1-5800 <$300
1902 Plain Back
3x10-20 5801-18282 <$300
1929 Small Size
10 Type 1 1-2046 <$125
20 Type 1 1-544 <$150
10 Type 2 1-4345 <$150
20 Type 2 1-1215 <$150
Total Issue $1,482,190
Out in 1935 $95,900
Large out 1935 $5,240

12587 Yazoo
DELTA NB OF YAZOO CITY
{{ 4 L 50+ S }}
Chartered 10/24
1902 Plain Back <$VALUE
4x5 1-26898 <$450
1929 Small Size
5 Type 1 1-13698 <$85
5 Type 2 1-28884 <$85
Total Issue $1,093,320
Out in 1935 $98,880
Large out 1935 $2,220

3566 Yazoo
FNB OF YAZOO CITY
{{ 1 L }}
Chartered 10/6/86
Liquidated 3/10/11
Brown Back <$VALUE
4x5 1-7711 <$2250
3x10-20 1-3247 <$2250
1902 Red Seal
4x5 1-1650 <$1750
3x10-20 1-1340 <$1750
1902 Date Back
4x5 1-2055 <$1000
3x10-20 1-1235 <$1000
Total Issue $519,420
Out in 1911 $45,750

<$VALUEs are for notes in **FINE** condition. Value changes by approximately **25%** for a change of one full grade.

Nickname: The Show Me State
Motto: Populi Suprema Lex Esto (The Welfare of the People Shall be the Supreme Law)
Capital: Jefferson City
Number of towns: 124
Number of issuing charters: 265
Number of small size issuers: 119

Adrian C2
Albany A2
Appleton City D2
Aurora E2
Bethany A2
Bolivar D3
Boonville C3
Bosworth B3
Braymer B2
Brookfield B3
Brunswick B3
Burlington Junction A1
Butler C2
Cabool D4
Cainesville A2
California C3
Cameron B2
Campbell F6
Canton A4
Cape Girardeau D6
Carondelet C6
Carrollton B3
Carterville E2
Carthage E2
Caruthersville F6
Cassville E2
Centralia C4
Chaffee E6
Chillicothe B3
Clayton C6
Clinton C2
Columbia C4
Cowgill B2
Dexter E6
Edina A4
Eldorado Springs D2
Excelsior Springs C1
Fairview E2
Fulton C4
Gallatin A2
Golden City D2
Grant City A2
Green City A3
Hamilton B2
Hannibal B4
Harrisonville C2
Holden C2
Hopkins A1
Independence C2
Jackson D6
Jamesport A2
Jasper E2
Jefferson City C4
Joplin E2
Kansas City C2
King City A2
Kirksville A3
Knob Noster C2
LaGrange A4
Lamar D2
Lancaster A3
Lathrop B2
Leeds C2
Liberal D2
Liberty C1
Linn Creek D3
Louisiana B5
Ludlow B3
Luxemburg C6
Macon B3
Manchester C6
Maplewood C6
Marceline B3
Marshall B3
Marshfield D3
Maryville A1
Memphis A4
Mexico B4
Milan A3
Moberly B3
Monett E2
Mount Vernon E2
Mountain Grove D3
Neosho E2
Nevada D2
North Kansas City C1
Odessa C2
Palmyra B4
Paris B4
Peirce City E2
Perryville D6
Platte City B1
Plattsburg B2
Pleasant Hill C2
Polo B2
Purdy E2
Ridgeway A2
Rolla D4
Saint Charles C5
Saint Joseph B1
Saint Louis C6
Salem D4
Salisbury B3
Sarcoxie E2
Savannah A1
Sedalia C3
Seneca E2
Seymour D3
Shelbina B4
Springfield E3
Steele F6
Steelville D5
Stewartsville B2
Sweet Springs B3
Tarkio A1
Trenton A3
Unionville A3
Versailles C3
Warrensburg C2
Washington C5
Webb City E2
Wellston C6
West Plains E4
Windsor C2

****
10375 Bates
FNB OF ADRIAN
{{ 1 L }}
Chartered 4/13
Liquidated 8/20/23
1902 Date Back <$VALUE
4x5 1-605 <$1250
3x10-20 1-414 <$1250
1902 Plain Back
4x5 516-850 <$1250
3x10-20 415-747 <$1250
Total Issue $54,350
Out in 1921 $10,000
****
7205 Gentry
FNB OF ALBANY
{{ 6 L 9 S }}
Chartered 4/04
Liquidated 4/1/35
1902 Red Seal <$VALUE
4x5 1-605 <$600
3x10-20 1-485 <$600
1902 Date Back
4x5 1-2050 <$300
3x10-20 1-1560 <$300
1902 Plain Back
4x5 2051-6525 <$300
3x10-20 1561-4407 <$300
1929 Small Size
5 Type 1 1-1034 <$125
10 Type 1 1-482 <$125
20 Type 1 1-170 <$125
5 Type 2 1-170 <$150
10 Type 2 1-78 <$150
20 Type 2 1-20 <$150
Total Issue $469,570
Out at close $29,800
Large out at close $2,440
****
2636 Saint Clair
FNB OF APPLETON CITY
{{ 6 L 2 S }}
Chartered 1882
Liquidated 1/13/32
Series 1875 <$VALUE
3x10-20 1-1905<$1000/$1250
Brown Back
3x10-20 1-760 <$500
1882 Date Back
3x10-20 1-1650* <$450
1882 Value Back
3x10-20 1951-3700* <$450
* 1651-1950 not marked
1902 Plain Back
3x10-20 1-1253 <$300
1929 Small Size
10 Type 1 1-197 <$500
20 Type 1 1-35 <$500
Total Issue $396,920
Out at close $14,000
Large out at close $3,220
****
4409 Lawrence
FNB OF AURORA
{{ UNREPORTED }}
Chartered 9/1/90
Liquidated 7/22/92
Brown Back <$VALUE
4x5 1-688 <$2500
Total Issue $13,760
Out in 1910 $100
****
8009 Harrison
FNB OF BETHANY
{{ 8 L 6 S }}
Chartered 12/05
1902 Red Seal <$VALUE
4x5 1-300 <$500
3x10-20 1-240 <$500
1902 Date Back
4x5 1-900 <$225
3x10-20 1-720 <$225
1902 Plain Back
4x5 901-1830 <$225
3x10-20 721-1282 <$225
1929 Small Size
5 Type 1 1-820 <$175
10 Type 1 1-580 <$175
20 Type 1 1-168 <$175
5 Type 2 1-1910 <$175
10 Type 2 1-1329 <$175
20 Type 2 1-150 <$175
Total Issue $224,100
Out in 1935 $40,000
Large out 1935 $1,110
****
7271 Polk
FNB OF BOLIVAR
{{ 3 L 5 S }}
Chartered 5/04
Liquidated 7/1/33
1902 Red Seal <$VALUE
3x10-20 1-1150 <$1000
1902 Date Back
3x10-20 1-1610 <$500
1902 Plain Back
3x10-20 1611-4792 <$500
1929 Small Size
10 Type 1 1-494 <$350
20 Type 1 1-123 <$350
Total Issue $341,500
Out at close $25,000
Large out at close $2,320
****
10915 Cooper
BOONVILLE NB, BOONVILLE
{{ 13 L 22 S }}
Organized 10/24/16
Receivership 6/21/32
1902 Plain Back <$VALUE
4x5 1-30967 <$100
3x10-20 1-17026 <$100
1929 Small Size
5 Type 1 1-4840 <$50
10 Type 1 1-2346 <$50
20 Type 1 1-676 <$60
Total Issue $1,837,720
Out at close $175,000
Large out at close $16,080
****
1584 Cooper
CENTRAL NB OF BOONVILLE
{{ 17 L }}
Chartered 1865
Liquidated 12/19/16
Original Series <$VALUE
3x1-2 1-6400 <$350/$800
4x5 1-5900 <$400
4x10 1-3750 <$750
Series 1875
4x5 1-2500 <$400
4x10 1-6250 <$650
Brown Back
4x5 1-5987 <$250
3x10-20 1-3586 <$250
1902 Red Seal
4x5 1-3500 <$250
3x10-20 1-2600 <$250
1902 Date Back
4x5 1-2225 <$125
3x10-20 1-1531 <$125
Total Issue $1,220,090
Out in 1916 $59,100
****
7573 Carroll
FNB OF BOSWORTH
{{ 9 L 16 S }}
Chartered 1/05
1902 Red Seal <$VALUE
4x5 1-1500 <$500
3x10-20 1-1240 <$500
1902 Date Back
4x5 1-3150 <$200
3x10-20 1-2300 <$200
1902 Plain Back
4x5 3151-10795 <$200
3x10-20 2301-7239 <$200
1929 Small Size
5 Type 1 1-1582 <$85
10 Type 1 1-902 <$85
20 Type 1 1-234 <$100
5 Type 2 1-2360 <$100
10 Type 2 1-1129 <$100
20 Type 2 1-305 <$100
Total Issue $828,700
Out in 1935 $50,000
Large out 1935 $2,955
****
7351 Caldwell
FNB OF BRAYMER
{{ 8 L 2U + 10 S }}
Chartered 8/04
1902 Red Seal <$VALUE
3x10-20 1-2425 <$500
1902 Date Back
4x5 1-3130 <$200
3x10-20 1-2180 <$200
1902 Plain Back
4x5 3131-14025 <$200
3x10-20 2181-8358 <$200
1929 Small Size
5 Type 1 1-1234 <$100
10 Type 1 1-622 <$100
20 Type 1 1-210 <$100
5 Type 2 1-6040 <$100
Total Issue $949,390
Out in 1935 $60,000
Large out 1935 $3,220
****
12820 Linn
FNB OF BROOKFIELD
{{ 0 L 3 S }}
Organized 9/5/25
Receivership 1/22/31
1902 Plain Back <$VALUE
3x10-20 1-1104 <$1500
1929 Small Size
10 Type 1 1-244 <$400
20 Type 1 1-52 <$400
Total Issue $76,080
Out at close $20,000
Large out at close $3,580
****
4083 Chariton
FNB OF BRUNSWICK
{{ 5 L 4 S }}
Organized 7/8/89
Receivership 10/16/31
Brown Back <$VALUE
4x5 1-2437 <$750
3x10-20 1-526 <$750
1902 Date Back
3x10-20 1-1260 <$450
1902 Plain Back
3x10-20 1261-2024 <$450
1929 Small Size
10 Type 1 1-224 <$350
20 Type 1 1-41 <$350
Total Issue $194,600
Out at close $12,500
Large out at close $2,190
****
6242 Nodaway
FNB OF
BURLINGTON JUNCTION
{{ 2 L 1 S }}
Organized 4/18/02
Receivership 1/22/30
1902 Red Seal <$VALUE
3x10-20 1-500 <$2000
1902 Date Back
3x10-20 1-560 <$1000
1902 Plain Back (dated 1902)
3x10-20 561-720 <$1000
1902 Plain Back (dated 1922)
4x5 1-1340 <$1000
1929 Small Size
5 Type 1 1-113 <$650
Total Issue $91,190
Out at close $6,250
Large out at close $2,860
****
1843 Bates
BATES COUNTY NB OF BUTLER
{{ 6 L }}
Chartered 7/6/71
Liquidated 8/1/94
Original Series <$VALUE
3x1-2 1-3500 <$600/$1000
4x5 1-3125 <$600
Series 1875
3x1-2 1-680 <$600/$1000
4x5 1-4499 <$600
Brown Back
4x5 1-1671 <$500
Total Issue $206,800
Out in 1910 $1,795
****
6405 Bates
BATES NB, BUTLER
{{ UNREPORTED }}
Organized 8/30/02
Receivership 9/20/06
1902 Red Seal <$VALUE
4x5 1-495 <$2500
3x10-20 1-342 <$2500
Total Issue $27,000
Out in 1915 $520
****
2561 Bates
BUTLER NB, BUTLER
{{ 1 L }}
Chartered 9/10/81
Liquidated 8/23/89
Series 1875 <$VALUE
4x5 1-3701 <$2000
Total Issue $74,020
Out in 1910 $555
****
8877 Texas
CABOOL NB, CABOOL
Chartered 9/07
Liquidated 5/5/21
2nd title:FNB of Cabool
4/20/14
FIRST TITLE {{ 0 L }}
1902 Red Seal <$VALUE
4x5 1-156 <$2000
4x10 1-156 <$2000
1902 Date Back
4x5 1-653 <$1000
4x10 1-611 <$1000
SECOND TITLE {{ 4 L }}
1902 Date Back
4x5 1-500 <$500
3x10-20 1-400 <$500
1902 Plain Back
4x5 501-2940 <$500
3x10-20 401-1650 <$500
Total Issue $188,160
Out at close $50,000
****
FNB of Cabool
SEE Ch 8877
Cabool NB, Cabool
****
8407 Harrison
FNB OF CAINESVILLE
{{ 7 L 7 S }}
Chartered 10/06
1902 Red Seal <$VALUE
4x5 1-165 <$600
3x10-20 1-132 <$600
1902 Date Back
4x5 1-1500 <$300
3x10-20 1-1210 <$300
1902 Plain Back
4x5 1501-4875 <$300
3x10-20 1211-3250 <$300
1929 Small Size
5 Type 1 1-752 <$175
10 Type 1 1-350 <$175
20 Type 1 1-98 <$200
5 Type 2 1-550 <$250
10 Type 2 1-448 <$250
20 Type 2 1-106 <$250
Total Issue $334,570
Out in 1935 $25,000
Large out 1935 $1,650
****
1712 Moniteau
MONITEAU NB OF CALIFORNIA
{{ 2U + 50+ L 12 S }}
Chartered 1870
Original Series <$VALUE
3x1-2 1-1900 <$300/$750
4x5 1-3275 <$400
Series 1875
4x5 1-6689 <$400
Brown Back
4x5 1-2721 <$200
3x10-20 1-1120 <$200
1882 Date Back
3x10-20 1-91 <$200
1902 Date Back
3x10-20 1-1100* <$125
1902 Plain Back
3x10-20 1301-3069* <$125
* 1101-1300 not marked
1929 Small Size
10 Type 1 1-420 <$100
20 Type 1 1-128 <$100
10 Type 2 1-379 <$100
20 Type 2 1-121 <$100
Total Issue $523,970
Out in 1935 $19,800
Large out 1935 $3,620
****
4259 Clinton
FNB OF CAMERON
{{ U + 8 L 12 S }}
Chartered 1890
Brown Back <$VALUE
3x10-20 1-4170 <$350
1882 Date Back
3x10-20 1-213 <$350
1902 Date Back
3x10-20 1-2900 <$150
1902 Plain Back
3x10-20 2901-9332 <$150
1929 Small Size
10 Type 1 1-1168 <$75
20 Type 1 1-334 <$85
10 Type 2 1-708 <$85
20 Type 2 1-261 <$85
Total Issue $808,210
Out in 1935 $50,000
Large out 1935 $4,510
****
6885 Dunklin
FNB OF CAMPBELL
{{ 2 L 0 S }}
Organized 4/4/03
Receivership 11/24/30
1902 Red Seal <$VALUE
3x10-20 1-500 <$2000
1902 Date Back
3x10-20 1-760* <$1000
1902 Plain Back
3x10-20 861-1659* <$1000
* 761-860 not marked
1929 Small Size
10 Type 1 1-98 <$750
20 Type 1 1-13 <$750
Total Issue $115,390
Out at close $7,500
Large out at close $1,550
****
7729 Lewis
FNB OF CANTON
{{ 3 L }}
Chartered 5/05
Liquidated 6/26/16
1902 Red Seal <$VALUE
4x5 1-825 <$1000
3x10-20 1-620 <$1000
1902 Date Back
4x5 1-1725 <$500
3x10-20 1-1260 <$500
1902 Plain Back
4x5 1726-1880 <$500
3x10-20 1261-1327 <$500
Total Issue $151,450
Out at close $23,800
****
4611 Cape Girardeau
FNB OF CAPE GIRARDEAU
{{ 8 L 50+ S }}
Chartered 1891
Brown Back <$VALUE
4x5 1-2425 <$500
50-100 1-177 <$1250/$1500
1882 Date Back
4x5 1-515 <$500
50-100 1-102 <$1250/$1500
1902 Date Back
3x50-100 1-947 <$500/$600
1902 Plain Back
4x10 1-7815 <$200
1929 Small Size
10 Type 1 1-4916 <$50
10 Type 2 1-13585 <$50
Total Issue $1,080,810
Out in 1935 $50,000
Large out 1935 $1,940
****
454 Saint Louis
FNB OF CARONDELET
{{ UNREPORTED }}
Chartered 6/2/64
Liquidated 3/15/65
Original Series <$VALUE
4x5 1-1275 <$2500
Total Issue $25,500
Out in 1910 $90
****
4079 Carroll
FNB OF CARROLLTON
{{ 16 L 15 S }}
Chartered 1889
Brown Back <$VALUE
4x5 1-4575 <$300
3x10-20 1-3270 <$300
1882 Date Back
4x5 1-517 <$250
3x10-20 1-599 <$250
1902 Date Back
4x5 1-4600 <$100
3x10-20 1-3560 <$100
1902 Plain Back
4x5 4601-16230 <$100
3x10-20 3561-10538 <$100
1929 Small Size
5 Type 1 1-2366 <$65
10 Type 1 1-1410 <$65
20 Type 1 1-356 <$75
5 Type 2 1-3814 <$75
10 Type 2 1-1503 <$75
20 Type 2 1-440 <$75
Total Issue $1,387,990
Out in 1935 $80,000
Large out 1935 $6,170
****
FNB of Carterville
SEE Ch 4475
FNB of Webb City
****
4815 Jasper
CARTHAGE NB, CARTHAGE
{{ 2 L }}
Chartered 1892
Liquidated 12/4/20
Brown Back <$VALUE
3x10-20 1-6520 <$850
1882 Date Back
3x10-20 1-3821 <$850
1902 Date Back
3x10-20 1-3400 <$600
1902 Plain Back
3x10-20 3401-7249 <$600
Total Issue $879,500
Out at close $100,000
****
4441 Jasper
CENTRAL NB OF CARTHAGE
{{ 13 L 8 S }}
Chartered 1890
Brown Back <$VALUE
3x10-20 1-9080 <$400
1882 Date Back
3x10-20 1-1090 <$400
1902 Date Back
3x10-20 1-5500* <$150
1902 Plain Back
3x10-20 6001-20040* <$150
* 5501-6000 not marked
1929 Small Size
10 Type 1 1-2582 <$125
20 Type 1 1-670 <$150
10 Type 2 1-2778 <$150
20 Type 2 1-724 <$150
Total Issue $1,788,080
Out in 1935 $99,995
Large out 1935 $7,105
****
2013 Jasper
FNB OF CARTHAGE
{{ 1 L }}
Chartered 7/16/72
Liquidated 6/1/78
Original Series <$VALUE
3x1-2 1-1400 <$1500/$2500
4x5 1-2415 <$1500
Series 1875
3x1-2 1-200 <$1500/$2500
4x5 1-1375 <$1500
Total Issue $83,800
Out in 1910 $501
****
3005 Jasper
FNB OF CARTHAGE
{{ 10 L 6 S }}
Chartered 1883
Liquidated 5/12/31
Brown Back <$VALUE
4x5 1-3850 <$400
3x10-20 1-2390 <$400
1902 Red Seal
4x5 1-2400 <$400
3x10-20 1-4120 <$400
1902 Date Back
4x5 1-6700 <$200
3x10-20 1-4720 <$200
1902 Plain Back
4x5 6701-22725 <$200
3x10-20 4721-14995 <$200
1929 Small Size
5 Type 1 1-1904 <$200
10 Type 1 1-905 <$200
20 Type 1 1-273 <$200
Total Issue $1,798,930
Out at close $100,000
Large out at close $12,070
****
10784 Pemiscot
FNB OF CARUTHERSVILLE
{{ 4 L 2 S }}
Organized 9/17/15
Receivership 12/18/30
1902 Plain Back <$VALUE
4x5 1-8388 <$400
3x10-20 1-6368 <$400
1929 Small Size
5 Type 1 1-889 <$500
10 Type 1 1-442 <$500
20 Type 1 1-115 <$500
Total Issue $553,150
Out at close $50,000
Large out at close $11,150
****
14092 Pemiscot
NB OF CARUTHERSVILLE
{{ 6 S }}
Chartered 4/34
1929 Small Size <$VALUE
5 Type 2 1-5580 <$200
10 Type 2 1-2390 <$200
20 Type 2 1-990 <$200
Total Issue $71,600
Out in 1935 $50,000
****

<$VALUEs are for notes in **FINE** condition. Value changes by approximately **25%** for a change of one full grade.

8979 Barry
FNB OF CASSVILLE
{{ 8 L 2 S }}
Chartered 12/07
1902 Red Seal <$VALUE
4x5 1-200 <$600
3x10-20 1-160 <$600
1902 Date Back
4x5 1-1675 <$300
3x10-20 1-1250 <$300
1902 Plain Back
4x5 1676-5601 <$300
3x10-20 1251-3605 <$300
1929 Small Size
5 Type 1 1-832 <$400
10 Type 1 1-470 <$400
20 Type 1 1-146 <$400
5 Type 2 1-732 <$400
10 Type 2 1-410 <$400
20 Type 2 1-154 <$400
Total Issue $385,790
Out in 1935 $25,000
Large out 1935 $1,580

6875 Boone
FNB OF CENTRALIA
{{ 10 L 14 S }}
Chartered 7/03
1902 Red Seal <$VALUE
3x10-20 1-2300 <$500
1902 Date Back
3x10-20 1-3540 <$250
1902 Plain Back
3x10-20 3541-10706 <$250
1929 Small Size
5 Type 1 1-148 <$75
10 Type 1 1-1251 <$75
20 Type 1 1-338 <$75
Total Issue $770,360
Out in 1935 $25,000
Large out 1935 $3,390

9928 Scott
FNB OF CHAFFEE
{{ 3 L 4 S }}
Organized 1/19/11
Receivership 12/11/31
1902 Date Back <$VALUE
4x5 1-1700 <$600
3x10-20 1-1300 <$600
1902 Plain Back
4x5 1701-6467 <$600
3x10-20 1301-3990 <$600
1929 Small Size
5 Type 1 1-844 <$350
10 Type 1 1-412 <$350
20 Type 1 1-112 <$350
Total Issue $392,320
Out at close $39,040
Large out at close $2,660

4111 Livingston
CITIZENS NB OF CHILLICOTHE
{{ 12 L 15 S }}
Chartered 1889
Brown Back <$VALUE
3x10-20 1-6270 <$300
1882 Date Back
3x10-20 1-881 <$300
1902 Date Back
3x10-20 1-6000 <$150
1902 Plain Back
3x10-20 6001-19268 <$150
1929 Small Size
10 Type 1 1-2154 <$85
20 Type 1 1-596 <$85
10 Type 2 1-2481 <$100
20 Type 2 1-656 <$100
Total Issue $1,559,640
Out in 1935 $98,100
Large out 1935 $6,970

3686 Livingston
FNB OF CHILLICOTHE
{{ 11 L 13 S }}
Organized 1/22/87
Receivership 6/22/31
Brown Back <$VALUE
4x5 1-4425 <$300
3x10-20 1-1968 <$300/$350
1902 Red Seal
3x10-20 1-2000 <$350/$400
1902 Date Back
3x10-20 1-6600 <$165
1902 Plain Back
3x10-20 6601-19175 <$165
1929 Small Size
10 Type 1 1-1381 <$100
20 Type 1 1-367 <$100
Total Issue $1,372,550
Out at close $100,000
Large out at close $18,480

12329 Saint Louis
CLAYTON NB, CLAYTON
{{ 4 L 5 S }}
Chartered 3/23
Liquidated 8/29/30
1902 Plain Back <$VALUE
3x10-20 1-4833 <$450
1929 Small Size
10 Type 1 1-607 <$300
20 Type 1 1-167 <$300
Total Issue $298,110
Out at close $60,000
Large out 1935 $860
Ch 13481 assumed circulation

13481 Saint Louis
CLAYTON NB, CLAYTON
{{ 11 S }}
Chartered 7/30
1929 Small Size <$VALUE
10 Type 1 1-1704 <$100
20 Type 1 1-518 <$100
10 Type 2 1-3443 <$125
20 Type 2 1-775 <$125
Total Issue $214,330
Out in 1935 $100,000
outstanding includes Ch 12329

12333 Saint Louis
FNB OF CLAYTON
{{ 5 L 11 S }}
Organized 3/3/23
1902 Plain Back <$VALUE
4x5 1-9080 <$350
3x10-20 1-5926 <$350
1929 Small Size
5 Type 1 1-3930 <$85
10 Type 1 1-1974 <$85
20 Type 1 1-566 <$100
5 Type 2 1-1454 <$125
10 Type 2 1-587 <$125
20 Type 2 1-120 <$125
Total Issue $797,700
Out in 1935 $100,000
Large out 1935 $2,900

7806 Henry
CLINTON NB, CLINTON
{{ U + 8 L 4 S }}
Organized 4/29/05
Receivership 2/10/31
1902 Red Seal <$VALUE
4x5 1-1325 <$400
3x10-20 1-1530 <$400
1902 Date Back
4x5 1-2850 <$200
3x10-20 1-2080 <$200
1902 Plain Back
4x5 2851-9605 <$200
3x10-20 2081-6354 <$200
1929 Small Size
5 Type 1 1-765 <$300
10 Type 1 1-336 <$300
20 Type 1 1-108 <$300
Total Issue $668,870
Out at close $50,000
Large out at close $10,440

1940 Henry
FNB OF CLINTON
{{ 2 L }}
Chartered 2/21/72
Liquidated 2/28/94
Original Series <$VALUE
3x1-2 1-2100 <$1250/$2500
4x5 1-2725 <$1250
Series 1875
4x5 1-6720 <$1250
Brown Back
50-100 1-95 <$1500/$2000
Total Issue $213,650
Out in 1910 $1,819

8509 Henry
PEOPLES NB OF CLINTON
{{ 8 L U + 10 S }}
Organized 12/31/06
Receivership 2/2/32
1902 Red Seal <$VALUE
3x10-20 1-1300 <$400
1902 Date Back
3x10-20 1-3400* <$200
1902 Plain Back
3x10-20 3641-9462* <$200
* 3401-3640 not marked
1929 Small Size
5 Type 1 1-502 <$125
10 Type 1 1-688 <$125
20 Type 1 1-196 <$125
Total Issue $617,960
Out at close $49,280
Large out at close $7,070

1770 Boone
BOONE COUNTY NB OF COLUMBIA
{{ 15 L 17 S }}
Chartered 1/17/71
Original Series <$VALUE
4x5 1-6500 <$500
Series 1875
4x5 1-10993 <$500
Brown Back
4x5 1-6475 <$300
3x10-20 1-2830 <$300
1882 Date Back
4x5 1-1898 <$250
3x10-20 1-1483 <$250
1902 Date Back
4x5 1-4750 <$125
3x10-20 1-3600 <$125
1902 Plain Back
4x5 4751-19360 <$125
3x10-20 3601-13869 <$125
1929 Small Size
5 Type 1 1-3250 <$60
10 Type 1 1-1780 <$60
20 Type 1 1-558 <$70
5 Type 2 1-4392 <$70
10 Type 2 1-2526 <$70
20 Type 2 1-754 <$75
Total Issue $2,147,180
Out in 1935 $99,400
Large out 1935 $7,300

1467 Boone
EXCHANGE NB OF COLUMBIA
{{ 27 L 2U + 21 S }}
Chartered 1865
Original Series <$VALUE
3x1-2 1-2605 <$400/$800
4x5 1-3125 <$400
3x10-20 1-2390 <$750/$1250
Series 1875
3x1-2 1-1000 <$400/$800
4x5 1-2785 <$400
3x10-20 1-798 <$750/$1250
Brown Back
3x10-20 1-6149 <$200/$225
1902 Red Seal
3x10-20 1-3200 <$200/$225
1902 Date Back
3x10-20 1-6300 <$100
1902 Plain Back
3x10-20 6301-21226 <$100
1929 Small Size
10 Type 1 1-2418 <$50
20 Type 1 1-694 <$60
10 Type 2 1-3390 <$65
20 Type 2 1-775 <$65
Total Issue $2,102,135
Out in 1935 $100,000
Large out 1935 $8,940

67 Boone
FNB OF COLUMBIA
{{ UNREPORTED }}
Chartered 8/19/63
Liquidated 9/19/64
Original Series <$VALUE
4x10 1-2250 <$2500
Total Issue $90,000
Out in 1910 $120

6926 Caldwell
FNB OF COWGILL
{{ 7 L 3 S }}
Chartered 8/03
Liquidated 6/15/31
1902 Red Seal <$VALUE
3x10-20 1-900 <$750
1902 Date Back
3x10-20 1-2000 <$400
1902 Plain Back
3x10-20 2001-6295 <$400
1929 Small Size
10 Type 1 1-429 <$400
20 Type 1 1-97 <$400
Total Issue $397,130
Out at close $35,000
Large out at close $5,830

11320 Stoddard
FNB OF DEXTER
{{ 7 L 4 S }}
Organized 3/7/19
Receivership 10/23/31
1902 Plain Back <$VALUE
4x5 1-21805 <$350
1929 Small Size
5 Type 1 1-4128 <$300
Total Issue $559,940
Out at close $50,000
Large out at close $2,150

9490 Knox
FNB OF EDINA
{{ UNREPORTED }}
Chartered 7/09
Liquidated 9/14/14
1902 Date Back <$VALUE
4x5 1-518 <$2000
3x10-20 1-418 <$2000
Total Issue $31,260
Out at close $8,360

10055 Cedar
FNB OF ELDORADO SPRINGS
{{ 8 L }}
Organized 6/30/11
Receivership 9/23/29
1902 Date Back <$VALUE
3x10-20 1-2900 <$300
1902 Plain Back
3x10-20 2901-9655 <$300
Total Issue $482,750
Out at close $49,050

7741 Clay
FNB OF EXCELSIOR SPRINGS
{{ 2 L }}
Organized 5/5/05
Receivership 1/24/25
1902 Red Seal <$VALUE
3x10-20 1-830 <$1500
1902 Date Back
3x10-20 1-1750 <$750
1902 Plain Back
3x10-20 1751-4179 <$750
Total Issue $250,450
Out at close $25,000

8916 Newton
FNB OF FAIRVIEW
{{ 3 L 2 S }}
Organized 10/1/07
Receivership 9/17/30
1902 Red Seal <$VALUE
3x10-20 1-200 <$1000
1902 Date Back
3x10-20 1-1620 <$600
1902 Plain Back
3x10-20 1621-5078 <$600
1929 Small Size
10 Type 1 1-251 <$500
20 Type 1 1-59 <$500
Total Issue $286,040
Out at close $25,000
Large out at close $4,920

8358 Callaway
FARMERS FNB OF FULTON
Organized 8/7/06
Receivership 4/24/26
2nd title:FNB of Fulton
1/23/12
FIRST TITLE {{ 0 L }}
1902 Red Seal <$VALUE
4x5 1-1250 <$1000
3x10-20 1-1010 <$1000
1902 Date Back
4x5 1-3610 <$600
3x10-20 1-2487 <$600
SECOND TITLE {{ 8 L }}
1902 Date Back
3x10-20 1-4100 <$250
1902 Plain Back
3x10-20 4101-14420 <$250
Total Issue $993,050
Out at close $97,700

FNB of Fulton
SEE Ch 8358
Farmers NB of Fulton

5827 Daviess
FNB OF GALLATIN
{{ 4 L 8 S }}
Chartered 5/01
Brown Back <$VALUE
4x5 1-1375 <$600
3x10-20 1-1260 <$600
1882 Date Back
4x5 1-1625 <$600
3x10-20 1-1120 <$600
1882 Value Back
4x5 1626-2925 <$600
3x10-20 1121-1780 <$600
1902 Plain Back
4x10 1-2999 <$400
1929 Small Size
10 Type 1 1-960 <$175
10 Type 2 1-1443 <$175
Total Issue $429,990
Out in 1935 $25,000
Large out 1935 $2,165

10633 Barton
CITIZENS NB OF GOLDEN CITY
{{ 5 L }}
Chartered 10/14
Closed 5/29/28
1902 Date Back <$VALUE
3x10-20 1-800 <$400
1902 Plain Back
3x10-20 801-3681 <$400
Total Issue $184,050
Out at close $25,000

7684 Barton
FNB OF GOLDEN CITY
{{ 3 L 5 S }}
Chartered 4/05
1902 Red Seal <$VALUE
3x10-20 1-256 <$750
1902 Date Back
3x10-20 1-1620 <$400
1902 Plain Back
3x10-20 1621-5392 <$400
1929 Small Size
10 Type 1 1-1190 <$250
20 Type 1 1-328 <$275
10 Type 2 1-1894 <$275
20 Type 2 1-344 <$275
Total Issue $418,980
Out in 1935 $50,000
Large out 1935 $3,920
Outstanding includes Ch 10633

3380 Worth
FNB OF GRANT CITY
{{ 3 L }}
Chartered 1885
Liquidated 7/1/22
Brown Back <$VALUE
3x10-20 1-4070 <$1000
1902 Red Seal
3x10-20 1-700 <$1000
1902 Date Back
3x10-20 1-1460 <$500
1902 Plain Back
3x10-20 1461-2860 <$500
Total Issue $381,500
Out at close $25,000

8570 Sullivan
AMERICAN NB OF GREEN CITY
{{ 5 L }}
Organized 2/13/07
Receivership 3/31/27
1902 Red Seal <$VALUE
4x5 1-200 <$800
3x10-20 1-160 <$800
1902 Date Back
4x5 1-1750 <$400
3x10-20 1-1360 <$400
1902 Plain Back
4x5 1751-4965 <$400
3x10-20 1361-3333 <$400
Total Issue $277,950
Out at close $43,595
Outstanding includes Ch 9029

9029 Sullivan
CITY NB OF GREEN CITY
{{ 2 L }}
Chartered 2/08
Closed 9/24/24
1902 Red Seal <$VALUE
3x10-20 1-500 <$1250
1902 Date Back
3x10-20 1-1630 <$650
1902 Plain Back
3x10-20 1631-3620 <$650
Total Issue $206,000
Out at close $25,000
Outstanding includes Ch 8570

4151 Caldwell
FNB OF HAMILTON
{{ 7 L 1 S }}
Chartered 1889
Liquidated 5/20/30
Brown Back <$VALUE
4x5 1-3275 <$500
3x10-20 1-1930 <$500
1882 Date Back
4x5 1-566 <$450
3x10-20 1-110 <$450
1902 Date Back
3x10-20 1-4200 <$300
1902 Plain Back
3x10-20 4201-14205 <$300
1929 Small Size
10 Type 1 1-648 <$500
20 Type 1 1-130 <$500
Total Issue $943,550
Out at close $75,000
Large out at close $22,210

1571 Marion
FNB OF HANNIBAL
{{ 1 L }}
Chartered 1865
Liquidated 5/15/79
Original Series <$VALUE
3x1-2 1-5340 <$1000/$1500
4x5 1-5140 <$1000
3x10-20 1-2900<$1250/$1500
Series 1875
3x1-2 1-180 <$1000/$1500
4x5 1-1055 <$1000
3x10-20 1-844 <$1250/$1500
Total Issue $338,700
Out in 1910 $2,400

4010 Marion
FNB OF HANNIBAL
{{ 1 L }}
Chartered 4/17/89
Liquidated 8/13/98
Brown Back <$VALUE
4x5 1-3778 <$1500
Total Issue $75,560
Out in 1910 $745

6635 Marion
HANNIBAL NB, HANNIBAL
{{ 13 L 25 S }}
Chartered 2/03
1902 Red Seal <$VALUE
3x10-20 1-5650 <$400
1902 Date Back
3x10-20 1-14500 <$125
1902 Plain Back
3x10-20 14501-42089 <$125
1929 Small Size
10 Type 1 1-5294 <$40
20 Type 1 1-1558 <$50
10 Type 2 1-3750 <$60
20 Type 2 1-505 <$65
Total Issue $2,939,150
Out in 1935 $200,000
Large out 1935 $11,840

6343 Cass
CITIZENS NB OF HARRISONVILLE
{{ 1 L 2 S }}
Chartered 7/02
1902 Red Seal <$VALUE
3x10-20 1-400 <$1500
1902 Date Back
3x10-20 1-660 <$850
1902 Plain Back
3x10-20 661-1285 <$850
1929 Small Size
10 Type 1 1-216 <$500
20 Type 1 1-48 <$500
Total Issue $102,970
Out in 1935 $6,500
Large out 1935 $610

3754 Cass
FNB OF HARRISONVILLE
{{ UNREPORTED }}
Chartered 7/16/87
Liquidated 3/17/94
Brown Back <$VALUE
3x10-20 1-545 <$2500
Total Issue $27,250
Out in 1910 $300

10384 Johnson
FNB OF HOLDEN
{{ 3 L 4 S }}
Chartered 5/13
1902 Date Back <$VALUE
3x10-20 1-1300 <$500
1902 Plain Back
3x10-20 1301-5561 <$500
1929 Small Size
10 Type 1 1-770 <$250
20 Type 1 1-242 <$250
10 Type 2 1-256 <$300
20 Type 2 1-30 <$300
Total Issue $356,450
Out in 1935 $30,000
Large out 1935 $1,870

4174 Nodaway
FNB OF HOPKINS
{{ UNREPORTED }}
Chartered 12/9/89
Liquidated 5/1/94
Brown Back <$VALUE
3x10-20 1-405 <$2500
Total Issue $20,250
Out in 1910 $290

1529 Jackson
FNB OF INDEPENDENCE
{{ UNREPORTED }}
Chartered 1865
Liquidated 3/1/78
Original Series <$VALUE
4x5 1-1750 <$2500
3x10-20 1-1000 <$2500
Series 1875
4x5 1-100 <$2500
3x10-20 1-56 <$2500
Total Issue $89,800
Out in 1910 $1,045

4157 Jackson
FNB OF INDEPENDENCE
{{ 10 L 14 S }}
Chartered 1889
Brown Back <$VALUE
3x10-20 1-8480 <$300/$350
1882 Date Back
3x10-20 1-316 <$275/$325
1902 Date Back
3x10-20 1-6900 <$165
1902 Plain Back
3x10-20 6901-20951 <$165
1929 Small Size
10 Type 1 1-2818 <$75
20 Type 1 1-672 <$85
10 Type 2 1-3070 <$100
20 Type 2 1-690 <$100
Total Issue $1,781,570
Out in 1935 $100,000
Large out 1935 $6,710

7494 Cape Girardeau
PEOPLES NB OF JACKSON
{{ 3 L }}
Chartered 11/04
Liquidated 10/1/28
1902 Red Seal <$VALUE
3x10-20 1-306 <$1250
1902 Date Back
3x10-20 1-1350 <$600
1902 Plain Back
3x10-20 1351-2965 <$600
Total Issue $163,550
Out in 1924 $20,000

7460 Daviess
NB OF JAMESPORT
{{ 1 L }}
Chartered 10/04 as FNB of Jamesport, under which there was no issue. Issuing title adopted 12/2/04.
Liquidated 10/18/11
1902 Red Seal <$VALUE
3x10-20 1-1141 <$2000
1902 Date Back
3x10-20 1-500 <$1250
Total Issue $82,050
Out at close $30,000

6369 Jasper
FNB OF JASPER
{{ 2 L 5 S }}
Chartered 8/02
1902 Red Seal <$VALUE
3x10-20 1-600 <$1250
1902 Date Back
3x10-20 1-1640 <$600
1902 Plain Back
3x10-20 1641-5270 <$600
1929 Small Size
10 Type 1 1-676 <$300
20 Type 1 1-166 <$300
5 Type 2 1-1942 <$300
Total Issue $363,690
Out in 1935 $25,000
Large out 1935 $1,600

13142 Cole
EXCHANGE NB OF JEFFERSON CITY
{{ 4 L 28 S }}
Chartered 11/16/27
1902 Plain Back <$VALUE
4x5 1-4715 <$500
3x10-20 1-2058 <$500
1929 Small Size
5 Type 1 1-5610 <$40
10 Type 1 1-3628 <$40
20 Type 1 1-804 <$50
5 Type 2 1-9880 <$50
10 Type 2 1-5135 <$50
20 Type 2 1-1631 <$50
Total Issue $813,030
Out in 1935 $300,000
Large out 1935 $14,390
Outstanding includes Ch 1809

1809 Cole
FNB OF JEFFERSON CITY
{{ 12 L 12 S }}
Organized 3/16/71
Receivership 8/10/33
Original Series <$VALUE
4x5 1-1625 <$500
3x10-20 1-1100 <$600/$750
Series 1875
4x5 1-2478 <$500
3x10-20 1-1000 <$600/$750
Brown Back
4x5 1-3425 <$300
3x10-20 1-1700 <$300
1882 Date Back
4x5 1-815 <$300
3x10-20 1-602 <$300
1902 Date Back
4x5 1-2850 <$125
3x10-20 1-2240 <$125
1902 Plain Back
4x5 2851-30200 <$125
3x10-20 2241-20418 <$125
1929 Small Size
5 Type 1 1-5214 <$100
10 Type 1 1-2394 <$100
20 Type 1 1-711 <$100
Total Issue $2,397,240
Out at close $200,000
Large out at close $22,860
Ch 13142 assumed circulation

2055 Cole
NB OF JEFFERSON CITY
{{ UNREPORTED }}
Chartered 10/10/72
Liquidated 5/8/79
Original Series <$VALUE
3x1-2 1-2000 <$2000/$2500
4x5 1-2250 <$2000
Series 1875
4x5 2851-1720 <$2000
Total Issue $89,400
Out in 1910 $678

13162 Jasper
CONQUEROR FNB OF JOPLIN
{{ 5 L 18 S }}
Chartered 1/28
1902 Plain Back <$VALUE
4x5 1-4135 <$300
3x10-20 1-2158 <$300
1929 Small Size
5 Type 1 1-3302 <$50
10 Type 1 1-3120 <$60
20 Type 1 1-1583 <$60
50 Type 1 1-316 <$100
100 Type 1 1-128 <$150
Total Issue $838,420
Out in 1935 $150,000
Large out 1935 $1,390

8947 Jasper
CUNNINGHAM NB OF JOPLIN
{{ 6 L }}
Chartered 11/07
Liquidated 1/19/17
1902 Red Seal <$VALUE
4x5 1-4000 <$500
3x10-20 1-3200 <$500
1902 Date Back
4x5 1-12750 <$250
3x10-20 1-9700 <$250
1902 Plain Back
4x5 12751-14590 <$250
3x10-20 9701-11194 <$250
Total Issue $1,091,500
Out at close $200,000

3841 Jasper
FNB OF JOPLIN
{{ 5 L }}
Chartered 1888
Liquidated 2/14/23
Brown Back <$VALUE
4x5 1-7350 <$350
50-100 1-1438 <$1250/$1500
1902 Red Seal
50-100 1-334 <$2250/$2500
1902 Date Back
50-100 1-800 <$600/$700
3x50-100 1-560 <$600/$700
1902 Plain Back
4x5 1-5527 <$250
Total Issue $783,340
Out at close $100,000

4425 Jasper
JOPLIN NB, JOPLIN
Chartered 1890
2nd title:Joplin NB & TC, Joplin 1/17/29
FIRST TITLE {{ 12 L }}
Brown Back <$VALUE
4x5 1-8525 <$300
50-100 1-1530 <$1250/$1500
1882 Date Back
4x5 1-1040 <$300
50-100 1-165 <$1250/$1500
1902 Date Back
50-100 1-1000 <$350/$400
3x50-100 1-2160 <$350/$400
1902 Plain Back
3x50-100 2161-3194 <$350/$400
SECOND TITLE {{ 0 L 12 S }}
1902 Plain Back
3x50-100 1-185 <$400/$500
1929 Small Size
5 Type 1 1-490 <$100
10 Type 1 1-280 <$100
50 Type 1 1-655 <$125
100 Type 1 1-220 <$175
Total Issue $1,800,300
Out in 1935 $200,000
Large out 1935 $23,795

4251 Jackson
AETNA NB OF KANSAS CITY
{{ UNREPORTED }}
Chartered 3/10/90
Liquidated 3/9/93
Brown Back <$VALUE
50-100 1-460 <$1500/$2000
Total Issue $69,000
Out in 1910 $1,400

3544 Jackson
AMERICAN NB OF KANSAS CITY
{{ U + 2 L }}
Chartered 7/29/86
Liquidated 7/27/07
Brown Back <$VALUE
3x10-20 1-13118 <$600
1902 Red Seal
3x10-20 1-1551 <$600
Total Issue $733,450
Out in 1910 $52,350

11491 Jackson
CENTRAL EXCHANGE NB OF KANSAS CITY
{{ 2 L }}
Chartered 10/19
Liquidated 7/16/23
1902 Plain Back <$VALUE
4x5 1-6810 <$400
3x10-20 1-4182 <$400
Total Issue $345,300
Out at close $100,000

8660 Jackson
CENTRAL NB OF KANSAS CITY
{{ 1 L }}
Chartered 4/07
Liquidated 3/15/10
1902 Red Seal <$VALUE
3x10-20 1-1500 <$600
1902 Date Back
3x10-20 1-1298 <$450
Total Issue $139,900
Out in 1910 $57,850

2613 Jackson
CITIZENS NB OF KANSAS CITY
{{ 3 L }}
Chartered 1/11/82
Liquidated 7/28/98
Series 1875 <$VALUE
3x10-20 1-4148 <$600/$750
Total Issue $207,400
Out in 1910 $1,900

5250 Jackson
CITY NB OF KANSAS CITY
{{ 2 L }}
Organized 2/2/00
Receivership 7/20/05
Brown Back <$VALUE
3x10-20 1-8734 <$600
Total Issue $436,700
Out in 1915 $6,420

11472 Jackson
COLUMBIA NB OF KANSAS CITY
{{ 6 S }}
Chartered 10/19
1929 Small Size <$VALUE
5 Type 1 1-8624 <$125
5 Type 2 1-22406 <$125
Total Issue $370,750
Out in 1935 $10,000

1995 Jackson
COMMERCIAL NB OF KANSAS CITY
{{ 1 L }}
Chartered 6/3/72
Receivership 2/11/78
Original Series <$VALUE
3x1-2 1-2940 <$1250/$1500
4x5 1-2500 <$1250
3x10-20 1-500 <$1250/$1500
Series 1875
3x10-20 1-372 <$1250/$1500
Total Issue $108,300
Out in 1915 $797

10039 Jackson
COMMONWEALTH NB OF KANSAS CITY
Chartered 6/11
Liquidated 7/10/30
2nd title:Liberty NB of Kansas City 4/12/23
FIRST TITLE {{ 2 L }}
1902 Date Back <$VALUE
3x10-20 1-9700 <$350
1902 Plain Back
3x10-20 9701-14100 <$350
SECOND TITLE {{ 7 L 3 S }}
1902 Plain Back
3x10-20 1-25469 <$150
1929 Small Size
10 Type 1 1-1910 <$150
20 Type 1 1-553 <$150
Total Issue $2,159,410
Out at close $249,970
Large out at close $55,770

12260 Jackson
CONTINENTAL NB & TC OF KANSAS CITY
{{ 1 L }}
Chartered 10/22
Liquidated 12/17/23
1902 Plain Back <$VALUE
4x5 1-1960 <$650
3x10-20 1-784 <$650
Total Issue $78,400
Out at close $100,000
Outstanding includes Ch 11377

4786 Jackson
CONTINENTAL NB OF KANSAS CITY
{{ UNREPORTED }}
Chartered 8/2/92
Liquidated 11/11/92
Brown Back <$VALUE
3x10-20 1-900 <$1000
Total Issue $45,000
Out in 1910 $400

11377 Jackson
CONTINENTAL NB OF JACKSON COUNTY AT KANSAS CITY
{{ 2 L }}
Chartered 6/19
Liquidated 1/2/23
1902 Plain Back <$VALUE
4x5 1-7780 <$500
3x10-20 1-2554 <$500
Total Issue $283,300
Out at close $100,000
Ch 12260 assumed circulation

12794 Jackson
DROVERS NB IN KANSAS CITY
{{ 16 S }}
Chartered 7/25
Liquidated 3/15/35
1929 Small Size <$VALUE
5 Type 1 1-4680 <$50
10 Type 1 1-2520 <$50
20 Type 1 1-769 <$60
Total Issue $383,880
Out in 1932 $300,000

9560 Jackson
DROVERS NB OF KANSAS CITY
{{ 4 L }}
Chartered 10/09
Liquidated 8/25/25
1902 Date Back <$VALUE
4x5 1-14000 <$250
3x10-20 1-10700 <$250
1902 Plain Back
4x5 14001-17170 <$250
3x10-20 10701-12202 <$250
Total Issue $953,500
Out at close $12,495

11344 Jackson
FIDELITY NB & TC OF KANSAS CITY
{{ 12 L 36 S }}
Organized 4/28/19
Liquidated 11/24/33
1902 Plain Back <$VALUE
4x5 1-138940 <$75
1929 Small Size
10 Type 1 1-9358 <$20
20 Type 1 1-8831 <$25
50 Type 1 1-862 <$65
100 Type 1 1-446 <$120
Total Issue $4,926,200
Out at close $2,000,000
Large out at close $16,185
Outstanding includes Ch 11037

1612 Jackson
FNB OF KANSAS CITY
{{ UNREPORTED }}
Organized 11/23/65
Receivership 2/11/78
Original Series <$VALUE
2x10-20-50 1-3360 <$1500/$2000/$5000
20-50 3361-3439 <$2000/$5000
Total Issue $307,930
Out in 1915 $1,950

3456 Jackson
FNB OF KANSAS CITY
{{ 31 L 18 S }}
Chartered 1886
Brown Back <$VALUE
4x5 1-2039 <$200
3x10-20 1-2655 <$200/$250
1902 Red Seal
4x5 1-7750 <$250
50-100 1-2760 <$2250/$2500
1902 Date Back
4x5 1-57665 <$65
50-100 1-1912 <$300/$350
3x50-100 1-7200 <$300/$350
1902 Plain Back
4x5 57666-127000 <$65
3x50-100 7201-8748 <$300/$350
1929 Small Size
5 Type 1 1-27740 <$35
50 Type 1 1-1070 <$100
100 Type 1 1-356 <$175
5 Type 2 1-13996 <$35
50 Type 2 1-198 <$175
Total Issue $7,203,010
Large out 1935 $42,950

9404 Jackson
GATE CITY NB OF KANSAS CITY
{{ 7 L }}
Chartered 5/09
Closed 2/21/30
1902 Date Back <$VALUE
4x5 1-11500 <$150
3x10-20 1-8900 <$150
1902 Plain Back
4x5 11501-26725 <$150
3x10-20 8901-18394 <$150
Total Issue $1,454,200
Out at close $12,160
Ch 9236 assumed circulation

3793 Jackson
GERMAN AMERICAN NB OF KANSAS CITY
{{ UNREPORTED }}
Chartered 9/24/87
Liquidated 12/5/90
Brown Back <$VALUE
3x10-20 1-1240 <$1250
Total Issue $62,000
Out in 1910 $500

4381 Jackson
INTER-STATE NB OF KANSAS CITY, KANSAS
Chartered 1890
2nd location: Inter-State NB of Kansas City, Missouri 1/3/11
FIRST SITE (KS) {{ 15 L }}
Brown Back <$VALUE
4x5 1-13000 <$200
4x10 1-2500 <$200
3x10-20 1-36060 <$200
1882 Date Back
4x5 1-7777 <$200
4x10 1-4711 <$200
3x10-20 1-703 <$200
1902 Date Back
50-100 1-682 <$350/$400
SECOND SITE (MO) {{15 L 9 S}}
1902 Date Back
4x5 1-28830 <$75
3x10-20 1-20568 <$85
1902 Plain Back
4x5 28831-29120 <$75
3x10-20 20569-20916 <$85
1929 Small Size
5 Type 1 1-1498 <$85
10 Type 1 1-710 <$85
20 Type 1 1-204 <$85
5 Type 2 1-928 <$85
10 Type 2 1-525 <$85
20 Type 2 1-45 <$100
Total Issue $4,395,440
Out in 1935 $50,000
Large out 1935 $14,145

1901 Jackson
KANSAS CITY NB OF KANSAS CITY
{{ 1 L }}
Chartered 11/27/71
Liquidated 11/13/75
Original Series <$VALUE
3x1-2 1-3300 <$750/$1250
4x5 1-3060 <$850
3x10-20 1-700 <$1000/$1250
Total Issue $112,700
Out in 1910 $694

Liberty NB of Kansas City
SEE Ch 10039
Commonwealth NB of Kansas City

2440 Jackson
MERCHANTS NB OF KANSAS CITY
{{ 2 L }}
Chartered 12/2/79
Liquidated 12/22/91
Series 1875 <$VALUE
4x5 1-5000 <$600
3x10-20 1-5250 <$750/$1000
50-100 1-204 <$5000/$6000
Total Issue $393,100
Out in 1910 $1,895

4464 Jackson
METROPOLITAN NB OF KANSAS CITY
{{ 1 L }}
Chartered 11/12/90
Liquidated 6/30/97
Brown Back <$VALUE
3x10-20 1-2000 <$1000
Total Issue $100,000
Out in 1910 $1,140

3904 Jackson
MIDLAND NB OF KANSAS CITY
{{ UNREPORTED }}
Chartered 6/26/88
Liquidated 8/27/97
Brown Back <$VALUE
3x10-20 1-2691 <$1000
Total Issue $134,550
Out in 1910 $1,480

CONDITION affects Value. The Values shown are for notes in FINE condition.

****

10892 Jackson
MIDWEST NB OF KANSAS CITY
Chartered 8/16
Liquidated 10/2/20
2nd title:Midwest NB & TC of Kansas City 6/30/19
FIRST TITLE {{ 3 L }}
1902 Plain Back <$VALUE
4x5 1-7250 <$350
3x10-20 1-2448 <$350
SECOND TITLE {{ 0 L }}
1902 Plain Back
4x5 1-325 <$500
Total Issue $273,900
Out at close $147,000

****

4494 Jackson
MISSOURI NB OF KANSAS CITY
{{ UNREPORTED }}
Organized 12/30/90
Receivership 12/5/96
Brown Back <$VALUE
3x10-20 1-1896 <$1500
Total Issue $94,800
Out in 1915 $710

****

3489 Jackson
NB OF KANSAS CITY
{{ UNREPORTED }}
Organized 4/13/86
Receivership 3/18/95
Brown Back <$VALUE
3x10-20 1-2557 <$1250
Total Issue $127,850
Out in 1915 $770

****

3760 Jackson
NB OF COMMERCE OF KANSAS CITY
{{ 20 L }}
Chartered 1887
Liquidated 9/24/12
Brown Back <$VALUE
4x5 1-10000 <$200
3x10-20 1-28758 <$200
50-100 1-7489 <$1250/$1500
1902 Red Seal
3x10-20 1-10000 <$200
1902 Date Back
4x5 1-44580 <$50
3x10-20 1-54374 <$60
Total Issue $6,871,550
Out at close $1,650,100
Ch 10231 assumed circulation

NB of Commerce of Kansas City
SEE Ch 10231
Southwest NB of Commerce of Kansas City

****

8738 Jackson
NB OF THE REPUBLIC OF KANSAS CITY
{{ 8 L }}
Chartered 6/07
Liquidated 5/16/14
1902 Red Seal <$VALUE
4x5 1-12500 <$200
3x10-20 1-10000 <$200
1902 Date Back
4x5 1-28212 <$100
3x10-20 1-16032 <$100
Total Issue $2,115,840
Out at close $500,000
Ch 9677 assumed circulation

****

11037 Jackson
N CITY B OF KANSAS CITY
{{ 6 L }}
Chartered 7/17
Closed 5/13/19
1902 Plain Back <$VALUE
4x5 1-7560 <$150
3x50-100 1-1520 <$400/$500
Total Issue $531,200
Out in 1918 $358,300
Ch 11344 assumed circulation

****

3863 Jackson
N EXCHANGE B OF KANSAS CITY
{{ UNREPORTED }}
Chartered 4/3/88
Liquidated 1/28/90
Brown Back <$VALUE
3x10-20 1-966 <$1500
Total Issue $48,300
Out in 1910 $410

****

9677 Jackson
N RESERVE B OF KANSAS CITY
{{ 8 L }}
Chartered 2/10
Liquidated 10/2/20
1902 Date Back <$VALUE
4x5 1-27500 <$100
3x10-20 1-21700 <$100
1902 Plain Back
4x5 27501-49005 <$100
3x10-20 21701-32747 <$100
Total Issue $2,617,450
Out at close $616,300
Outstanding includes Ch 8738

****

5138 Jackson
NEW ENGLAND NB OF KANSAS CITY
{{ U + 17 L }}
Chartered 1898
Closed 7/14/25
Brown Back <$VALUE
4x5 1-7250 <$150
3x10-20 1-15300 <$150/$200
1882 Date Back
4x5 1-22995 <$150
3x10-20 1-17214 <$150/$200
1902 Plain Back
4x5 1-42785 <$85
Total Issue $3,086,300
Out at close $1,000,000

****

Park NB of Kansas City
SEE Ch 9383
Leeds NB, Leeds

****

9172 Jackson
SECURITY NB OF KANSAS CITY
{{ 4 L }}
Chartered 6/08
Liquidated 6/1/21
1902 Date Back <$VALUE
3x10-20 1-16900 <$250
1902 Plain Back
3x10-20 16901-23857 <$250
Total Issue $1,192,850
Out at close $175,000

****

9311 Jackson
SOUTHWEST NB OF KANSAS CITY
{{ 3 L }}
Chartered 1/09
Liquidated 10/22/12
1902 Date Back <$VALUE
4x5 1-4430 <$300
3x10-20 1-3230 <$300
Total Issue $250,100
Out at close $71,900

****

10231 Jackson
SOUTHWEST NB OF COMMERCE OF KANSAS CITY
Chartered 7/12
Liquidated 5/2/21
2nd title:NB of Commerce of Kansas City 2/21/19
FIRST TITLE {{ 11 L }}
1902 Date Back <$VALUE
4x5 1-74500 <$50
3x10-20 1-63000 <$60
1902 Plain Back
4x5 74501-130500 <$50
3x10-20 63001-95000 <$60
SECOND TITLE {{ 11 L }}
1902 Plain Back
4x5 1-28500 <$50
3x10-20 1-19000 <$60
3x50-100 1-1640 <$350/$400
Total Issue $9,290,000
Out in 1920 $2,000,000
Outstanding includes Ch 3760

****

10413 Jackson
STOCK YARDS NB OF KANSAS CITY
{{ 6 L 18 S }}
Chartered 6/13
1902 Date Back <$VALUE
4x10 1-8250 <$125
1902 Plain Back
4x10 8251-15342 <$125
1929 Small Size
10 Type 1 1-7014 <$60
Total Issue $1,034,520
Out in 1935 $50,000
Large out 1935 $2,710

****

9236 Jackson
TRADERS NB OF KANSAS CITY
{{ 6 L }}
Chartered 9/08
1902 Date Back <$VALUE
3x10-20 1-13700 <$150
1902 Plain Back
3x10-20 13701-33008 <$150
Total Issue $1,650,400
Large out 1935 $12,040
Outstanding includes Ch 9404

****

3637 Jackson
UNION NB OF KANSAS CITY
{{ 7 L }}
Chartered 2/19/87
Liquidated 1/12/09
Brown Back <$VALUE
3x10-20 1-6803 <$200/$250
50-100 1-6058 <$1000/$1250
1902 Red Seal
4x5 1-12500 <$200
3x10-20 1-4400 <$200/$250
1902 Date Back
4x5 1-3092 <$150
3x10-20 1-2176 <$150
Total Issue $1,889,490
Out at close $600,000

****

6383 Gentry
CITIZENS NB OF KING CITY
{{ 15 L 2U + 6 S }}
Chartered 8/02
Liquidated 6/17/35
1902 Red Seal <$VALUE
4x5 1-2750 <$300
3x10-20 1-2000 <$300
1902 Date Back
4x5 1-3150 <$125
3x10-20 1-2220 <$125
1902 Plain Back
4x5 3151-10200 <$125
3x10-20 2221-6873 <$125
1929 Small Size
5 Type 1 1-1330 <$150
10 Type 1 1-754 <$150
20 Type 1 1-250 <$150
5 Type 2 1-2414 <$175
10 Type 2 1-1064 <$175
20 Type 2 1-210 <$175
Total Issue $844,700
Out at close $50,000
Large out at close $3,730

****

4373 Gentry
FNB OF KING CITY
Chartered 1890
Liquidated 7/14/24
2nd title: FNB & TC of King City 2/7/21
FIRST TITLE {{ 40 L }}
Brown Back <$VALUE
4x5 1-7150 <$150
3x10-20 1-5300 <$150/$200
1882 Date Back
4x5 1-1135 <$150
3x10-20 1-497 <$150/$200
1902 Date Back
3x10-20 1-5200 <$125
1902 Plain Back
3x10-20 5201-9800 <$125
SECOND TITLE {{ 3 L }}
1902 Plain Back
3x10-20 1-2705 <$175
Total Issue $1,080,800
Out at close $100,000

****

5871 Adair
BAIRD NB OF KIRKSVILLE
{{ 2 L }}
Chartered 6/21/01
Liquidated 4/9/06
Brown Back <$VALUE
4x5 1-2710 <$600
3x10-20 1-2107 <$600
Total issue $159,550
Out in 1910 $7,705

****

8276 Adair
CITIZENS NB OF KIRKSVILLE
{{ 6 L 14 S }}
Chartered 6/06
1902 Red Seal <$VALUE
4x5 1-1675 <$400
3x10-20 1-1780 <$400
1902 Date Back
4x5 1-6450 <$200
3x10-20 1-4620 <$200
1902 Plain Back
4x5 6451-21200 <$200
3x10-20 4621-14568 <$200
1929 Small Size
5 Type 1 1-3478 <$85
10 Type 1 1-1650 <$85
20 Type 1 1-468 <$85
5 Type 2 1-3778 <$100
10 Type 2 1-1933 <$100
20 Type 2 1-721 <$100
Total Issue $1,587,040
Out in 1935 $98,995
Large out 1935 $6,465

****

2713 Adair
FNB OF KIRKSVILLE
{{ UNREPORTED }}
Chartered 6/1/82
Liquidated 11/5/94
Series 1875 <$VALUE
4x5 1-2762 <$1500
Total Issue $55,240
Out in 1910 $390

****

5107 Adair
NB OF KIRKSVILLE
{{ 5 L 9 S }}
Chartered 1897
Brown Back <$VALUE
3x10-20 1-4200 <$400
1882 Date Back
3x10-20 1-2940 <$350
1882 Value Back
3x10-20 2941-3629 <$350
1902 Plain Back
3x10-20 1-5821 <$300
1929 Small Size
10 Type 1 1-1152 <$100
20 Type 1 1-324 <$125
10 Type 2 1-1404 <$125
20 Type 2 1-199 <$125
Total Issue $808,520
Out in 1935 $50,000
Large out 1935 $3,620

****

1877 Johnson
FNB OF KNOB NOSTER
{{ 1 L }}
Chartered 9/13/71
Liquidated 5/29/75
Original Series <$VALUE
3x1-2 1-1880 <$2500/$3500
4x5 1-2275 <$2500
Total Issue $54,900
Out in 1910 $282

****

1839 Lewis
FNB OF LaGRANGE
{{ UNREPORTED }}
Chartered 6/30/71
Liquidated 2/24/76
Original Series <$VALUE
3x1-2 1-2040 <$1500/$2500
4x5 1-2375 <$1500
Series 1875
4x5 1-620 <$1500
Total Issue $70,100
Out in 1910 $423

****

4057 Barton
FNB OF LAMAR
{{ 6 L 3 S }}
Organized 1/18/89
Liquidated 7/24/34
Brown Back <$VALUE
3x10-20 1-4269 <$400
1902 Date Back
3x10-20 1-7400 <$250
1902 Plain Back
3x10-20 7401-19842 <$250
1929 Small Size
10 Type 1 1-1079 <$350
20 Type 1 1-276 <$350
Total Issue $1,303,410
Out at close $32,680
Large out at close $6,230

****

2218 Schuyler
FNB OF LANCASTER
{{ 1 L }}
Chartered 1/16/75
Liquidated 11/14/76
Original Series <$VALUE
4x5 1-1425 <$2000
Total Issue $28,500
Out in 1910 $90

****

5544 Clinton
FNB OF LATHROP
{{ 4 L }}
Chartered 8/17/00
Liquidated 5/20/20
Brown Back <$VALUE
3x10-20 1-2200 <$600
1882 Date Back
3x10-20 1-2200* <$500
1882 Value Back
3x10-20 2321-3534* <$500
* 2201-2320 not marked
Total Issue $286,700
Out at close $35,000

****

9383 Jackson
LEEDS NB, LEEDS
Chartered 4/09
2nd title:Park NB of Kansas City 6/11/10
FIRST TITLE {{ 0 L }}
1902 Date Back <$VALUE
50-100 1-63 <$1500
SECOND TITLE {{ 1 L 7 S }}
1902 Date Back
50-100 1-120 <$650/$750
3x50-100 1-289 <$650/$750
1929 Small Size
5 Type 1 1-5806 <$125
5 Type 2 1-11346 <$125
Total Issue $330,610
Out in 1935 $50,000
Large out 1935 $2,050

****

7094 Barton
FNB OF LIBERAL
{{ UNREPORTED }}
Chartered 1/04
Liquidated 5/9/10
1902 Red Seal <$VALUE
4x5 1-525 <$2500
3x10-20 1-490 <$2500
Total Issue $35,000
Out in 1910 $9,600

****

3712 Clay
FNB OF LIBERTY
{{ 4 L 7 S }}
Chartered 1887
Brown Back <$VALUE
3x10-20 1-1430 <$750
1902 Red Seal
3x10-20 1-125 <$750
1902 Date Back
3x10-20 1-1300 <$375
1902 Plain Back
3x10-20 1301-2720 <$375
1929 Small Size
10 Type 1 1-310 <$200
20 Type 1 1-102 <$200
10 Type 2 1-6 <$250
Total Issue $244,650
Out in 1935 $12,500
Large out 1935 $1,140

****

7853 Camden
FNB OF LINN CREEK
{{ 2 L 4 S }}
Chartered 8/05
1902 Red Seal <$VALUE
3x10-20 1-1300 <$2000
1902 Date Back
3x10-20 1-1360 <$1000
1902 Plain Back
3x10-20 1361-4884 <$1000
1929 Small Size
10 Type 1 1-672 <$400
20 Type 1 1-180 <$400
10 Type 2 1-827 <$400
20 Type 2 1-212 <$400
Total Issue $383,630
Out in 1935 $25,000
Large out 1935 $1,740

****

3103 Pike
EXCHANGE NB OF LOUISIANA
{{ UNREPORTED }}
Chartered 1/7/84
Liquidated 7/12/87
Brown Back <$VALUE
4x5 1-783 <$2500
Total Issue $15,660
Out in 1910 $125

****

3111 Pike
MERCANTILE NB OF LOUISIANA
{{ UNREPORTED }}
Chartered 1/19/84
Liquidated 1/27/91
Brown Back <$VALUE
3x10-20 1-495 <$2500
Total Issue $24,750
Out in 1910 $80

****

8657 Livingston
FARMERS NB OF LUDLOW
{{ 8 L }}
Chartered 4/07
Liquidated 4/15/29
1902 Red Seal <$VALUE
3x10-20 1-1300 <$400
1902 Date Back
3x10-20 1-2740 <$175
1902 Plain Back
3x10-20 2741-10167 <$175
Total Issue $573,350
Out at close $60,000
Large out 1935 $4,075
Ch 13293 assumed circulation

****

7900 Livingston
FNB OF LUDLOW
{{ 3 L 3 S }}
Organized 8/7/05
Receivership 1/9/31
1902 Red Seal <$VALUE
4x5 1-830 <$1000
3x10-20 1-664 <$1000
1902 Date Back
4x5 1-1550 <$600
3x10-20 1-1140 <$600
1902 Plain Back
4x5 1551-5389 <$600
3x10-20 1141-3425 <$600
1929 Small Size
10 Type 1 1-289 <$350
20 Type 1 1-84 <$350
Total Issue $356,250
Out at close $25,000
Large out at close $4,530

****

13293 Livingston
LUDLOW NB, LUDLOW
{{ 4 S }}
Chartered 3/29
1929 Small Size <$VALUE
5 Type 1 1-1358 <$250
10 Type 1 1-258 <$250
5 Type 2 1-3344 <$250
Total Issue $72,940
Out in 1935 $20,825

****

13514 Saint Louis
LAFAYETTE NB & TC OF LUXEMBURG
{{ 22 S }}
Chartered 12/30
1929 Small Size <$VALUE
5 Type 2 1-8888 <$85
10 Type 2 1-3780 <$85
Total Issue $82,240
Out in 1935 $48,050

****

2862 Macon
FNB OF MACON
{{ 4 L }}
Chartered 1/23/83
Liquidated 1/14/08
Brown Sack <$VALUE
4x5 1-4368 <$750
3x10-20 1-291 <$750
1902 Red Seal
3x10-20 1-712 <$750
Total Issue $137,510
Out in 1910 $6,025

****

7643 Saint Louis
FNB OF MANCHESTER
{{ 2 L }}
Chartered 3/05
Liquidated 12/19/13
1902 Red Seal <$VALUE
4x5 1-800 <$1250
3x10-20 1-680 <$1250
1902 Date Back
4x5 1-1255 <$750
3x10-20 1-774 <$750
Total Issue $113,800
Out in 1914 $12,300

****

12955 Saint Louis
CITIZENS NB OF MAPLEWOOD
{{ 3 L 13 S }}
Organized 6/16/26
1902 Plain Back <$VALUE
3x10-20 1-4981 <$500
1929 Small Size
10 Type 1 1-2730 <$85
20 Type 1 1-776 <$100
10 Type 2 1-3609 <$100
20 Type 2 1-1009 <$100
Total Issue $562,240
Out in 1935 $94,100
Large out 1935 $2,730

****

****
7066 Linn
FNB OF MARCELINE
{{ 4 L 12 S }}
Organized 11/19/03
Receivership 11/13/31
1902 Red Seal <$VALUE
3x10-20 1-1282 <$1000
1902 Date Back
3x10-20 1-1480 <$500
1902 Plain Back
3x10-20 1481-3485 <$500
1929 Small Size
10 Type 1 1-246 <$200
20 Type 1 1-52 <$200
Total Issue $259,350
Out at close $14,820
Large out at close $2,520
****
2884 Saline
FNB OF MARSHALL
{{ UNREPORTED }}
Chartered 2/14/83
Liquidated 12/6/87
Brown Back <$VALUE
4x5 1-2019 <$2500
Total Issue $40,380
Out in 1910 $265
****
10009 Webster
FNB OF MARSHFIELD
{{ 1 L }}
Chartered 5/11
Liquidated 6/18/23
1902 Date Back <$VALUE
3x10-20 1-1500* <$1000
1902 Plain Back
3x10-20 1621-3232* <$1000
* 1501-1620 not marked
Total Issue $161,600
Out at close $25,000
****
3268 Nodaway
FNB OF MARYVILLE
{{ 9 L 0 S }}
Organized 8/28/84
Receivership 8/10/31
Brown Back <$VALUE
4x5 1-2096 <$300
3x10-20 1-2069 <$300
1902 Red Seal
4x5 1-2175 <$300
3x10-20 1-1650 <$300
1902 Date Back
4x5 1-6100 <$150
3x10-20 1-4700 <$150
1902 Plain Back
4x5 6101-19285 <$150
3x10-20 4701-13651 <$150
1929 Small Size
5 Type 1 1-1791 <$500
10 Type 1 1-857 <$500
20 Type 1 1-262 <$500
Total Issue $1,476,210
Out in 1932 $100,000
Large out 1932 $15,970
****
4243 Nodaway
MARYVILLE NB, MARYVILLE
{{ 2 L }}
Chartered 1890
Liquidated 8/1/13
Brown Back <$VALUE
4x5 1-2745 <$850
3x10-20 1-5460 <$850
1882 Date Back
4x5 1-265 <$850
3x10-20 1-503 <$850
1902 Date Back
4x5 1-2720 <$600
3x10-20 1-1950 <$600
Total Issue $510,250
Out in 1913 $76,245
****
2432 Scotland
SCOTLAND COUNTY NB OF MEMPHIS
{{ 7 L 6 S }}
Chartered 9/2/79
Series 1875 <$VALUE
3x10-20 1-2335 <$850/$1500
Brown Back
3x10-20 1-1120 <$500
1882 Date Back
3x10-20 1-1100 <$400
1882 Value Back
3x10-20 1101-1286 <$400
1902 Plain Back
3x10-20 1-1770 <$250
1929 Small Size
10 Type 1 1-478 <$200
20 Type 1 1-138 <$200
10 Type 2 1-36 <$250
20 Type 2 1-30 <$250
Total Issue $371,750
Out in 1935 $22,000
Large out 1935 $2,180
****
2881 Audrain
FNB OF MEXICO
{{ 10 L 15 S }}
Chartered 1883
Brown Back <$VALUE
4x5 1-3713 <$500
3x10-20 1-1019 <$500
1902 Red Seal
3x10-20 1-2400 <$500
1902 Date Back
3x10-20 1-3300 <$250
1902 Plain Back
3x10-20 3301-10476 <$250
1929 Small Size
10 Type 1 1-1156 <$125
20 Type 1 1-318 <$125
10 Type 2 1-1238 <$150
20 Type 2 1-503 <$150
Total Issue $898,970
Out in 1935 $50,000
Large out 1935 $4,180
****
3110 Sullivan
FNB OF MILAN
{{ 2 L }}
Chartered 1884
Brown Back <$VALUE
4x5 1-5286 <$1250
3x10-20 1-1285 <$1250
1902 Red Seal
3x10-20 1-3300 <$1250
1902 Date Back
3x10-20 1-4800 <$750
1902 Plain Back
3x10-20 4801-5492 <$750
Total Issue $609,570
Large out 1935 $2,275
****
4000 Randolph
FNB OF MOBERLY
{{ UNREPORTED }}
Chartered 3/27/89
Liquidated 5/15/95
Brown Back <$VALUE
4x5 1-2712 <$2500
Total issue $54,240
Out in 1910 $465
****
5973 Barry
FNB OF MONETT
{{ 5 L U + 6 S }}
Chartered 9/01
Brown Back <$VALUE
4x5 1-3180 <$400
3x10-20 1-2168 <$400
1882 Date Back
4x5 1-3250 <$400
3x10-20 1-2420 <$400
1882 Value Back
4x5 3251-6800 <$400
3x10-20 2421-4320 <$400
1902 Plain Back
4x5 1-19318 <$300
1929 Small Size
5 Type 1 1-2074 <$125
10 Type 1 1-1172 <$125
20 Type 1 1-328 <$150
5 Type 2 1-2894 <$150
10 Type 2 1-1372 <$150
20 Type 2 1-362 <$150
Total Issue $1,117,690
Out in 1935 $60,000
Large out 1935 $3,200
****
13504 Lawrence
FNB OF MOUNT VERNON
{{ 3 S }}
Chartered 12/30
1929 Small Size <$VALUE
5 Type 1 1-210 <$350
10 Type 1 1-212 <$350
20 Type 1 1-106 <$350
5 Type 2 1-654 <$400
10 Type 2 1-370 <$400
20 Type 2 1-70 <$400
Total Issue $40,110
Out in 1935 $20,050
****
7282 Wright
FNB OF MOUNTAIN GROVE
{{ 5 L 1 S }}
Organized 3/3/04
Receivership 2/19/34
1902 Red Seal <$VALUE
3x10-20 1-550 <$1000
1902 Date Back
3x10-20 1-960 <$500
1902 Plain Back
3x10-20 961-2589 <$500
1929 Small Size
10 Type 1 1-308 <$650
20 Type 1 1-90 <$650
Total Issue $186,230
Out at close $12,320
Large out at close $1,150
****
6382 Newton
FNB OF NEOSHO
{{ 4 L 7 S }}
Chartered 8/02
1902 Red Seal <$VALUE
3x10-20 1-2288 <$750
1902 Date Back
3x10-20 1-1500 <$350
1902 Plain Back
3x10-20 1501-8680* <$350
* 3138-3215 not issued
1929 Small Size
10 Type 1 1-1292 <$125
20 Type 1 1-368 <$150
5 Type 2 1-300 <$150
10 Type 2 1-1576 <$150
20 Type 2 1-385 <$150
Total Issue $691,140
Out in 1935 $50,000
Large out 1935 $2,765
****
3959 Vernon
FNB OF NEVADA
{{ 6 L 16 S }}
Chartered 1889
Brown Back <$VALUE
3x10-20 1-5700 <$300
50-100 1-634 <$1250/$1500
1902 Date Back
4x5 1-5050 <$150
3x10-20 1-4960 <$150
1902 Plain Back
4x5 5051-17985 <$150
3x10-20 4961-14173 <$150
1929 Small Size
5 Type 1 1-3450 <$75
10 Type 1 1-1722 <$75
20 Type 1 1-454 <$80
5 Type 2 1-2200 <$100
10 Type 2 1-1365 <$100
20 Type 2 1-240 <$100
Total Issue $1,739,200
Out in 1935 $50,000
Large out 1935 $6,375
****
9382 Vernon
THORNTON NB OF NEVADA
{{ 9 L 18 S }}
Chartered 4/09
1902 Date Back <$VALUE
4x5 1-7100 <$125
3x10-20 1-5760 <$125
1902 Plain Back
4x5 7101-21734 <$125
3x10-20 5761-15930 <$125
1929 Small Size
5 Type 1 1-3316 <$50
10 Type 1 1-1524 <$50
20 Type 1 1-432 <$60
5 Type 2 1-5082 <$60
10 Type 2 1-2433 <$60
20 Type 2 1-744 <$65
Total Issue $1,538,560
Out in 1935 $100,000
Large out 1935 $6,790
****
13690 Clay
NB IN NORTH KANSAS CITY
{{ 1 S }}
Chartered 5/33
1929 Small Size <$VALUE
5 Type 2 1-622 <$500
10 Type 2 1-299 <$500
20 Type 2 1-60 <$500
Total Issue $7,300
Out in 1935 $12,500
Outstanding includes Ch 10367
****
10367 Clay
NB OF NORTH KANSAS CITY
Chartered 4/13
Liquidated 1/30/34
2nd title:NB & TC of North Kansas City 1/28/30
FIRST TITLE {{ 2 L 1 S }}
1902 Date Back <$VALUE
3x10-20 1-500 <$650
1902 Plain Back
3x10-20 501-2341 <$650
1929 Small Size
10 Type 1 1-316 <$500
20 Type 1 1-89 <$500
SECOND TITLE {{ 0 S }}
1929 Small Size
10 Type 1 1-17 <$750
Total Issue $147,710
Out at close $670
Large out at close $580
Ch 13690 assumed circulation
****
4141 Lafayette
NB OF ODESSA
{{ 1 L }}
Chartered 10/21/89
Liquidated 1/11/98
Brown Back <$VALUE
3x10-20 1-1275 <$2000
Total Issue $63,750
Out in 1910 $920
****
1735 Marion
FNB OF PALMYRA
{{ 2 L }}
Chartered 11/70
Liquidated 12/12/76
Original Series <$VALUE
3x1-2 1-4700 <$1000/$2000
4x5 1-2900 <$1000
3x10-20 1-1140<$1250/$1500
Total Issue $138,500
Out in 1910 $915
****
2979 Marion
FNB OF PALMYRA
{{ 4 L }}
Chartered 1883
Liquidated 1/15/24
Brown Back <$VALUE
3x10-20 1-2424 <$650
1902 Red Seal
3x10-20 1-620 <$750
1902 Date Back
3x10-20 1-4340 <$350
1902 Plain Back
3x10-20 4341-8942 <$350
Total Issue $599,300
Out at close $60,000
****
1803 Monroe
FNB OF PARIS
{{ 5 L }}
Chartered 3/20/71
Liquidated 3/31/85
Original Series <$VALUE
3x1-2 1-4600 <$750/$1500
4x5 1-1850 <$750
3x10-20 1-1500<$1000/$1250
Series 1875
3x1-2 1-1140 <$750/$1500
4x5 1-1725 <$1000
3x10-20 1-2423<$1000/$1250
Total Issue $296,350
Out in 1910 $1,812
****
3322 Monroe
NB OF PARIS
{{ 1 L }}
Chartered 3/16/85
Liquidated 4/30/01
Brown Back <$VALUE
4x5 1-1100 <$1250
3x10-20 1-2003 <$1250
50-100 1-200 <$2000/$2500
Total Issue $152,150
Out in 1910 $1,945
****
5794 Monroe
PARIS NB, PARIS
{{ 33 L 17 S }}
Chartered 4/01
Brown Back <$VALUE
3x10-20 1-4300 <$150/$200
1882 Date Back
3x10-20 1-4700 <$125/$175
1882 Value Back
3x10-20 4701-7628<$125/$175
1902 Plain Back
3x10-20 1-6219 <$100
1929 Small Size
5 Type 1 1-1868 <$60
10 Type 1 1-1476 <$60
20 Type 1 1-210 <$75
5 Type 2 1-4226 <$75
10 Type 2 1-2305 <$75
Total Issue $1,121,330
Out in 1935 $70,000
Large out 1935 $7,420
****
FNB of Peirce City
SEE Ch 4225
Peirce City NB, Peirce City
****
4225 Lawrence
PEIRCE CITY NB, PEIRCE CITY
Chartered 1890
2nd title: FNB of Peirce City 1/13/10
FIRST TITLE {{ 2 L }}
Brown Back <$VALUE
4x5 1-2625 <$600
3x10-20 1-625 <$600
1882 Date Back
4x5 1-99 <$600
SECOND TITLE {{ 6 L 5U + 9 S }}
1902 Date Back
3x10-20 1-2940 <$150
1902 Plain Back
3x10-20 2941-9897 <$150
1929 Small Size
5 Type 1 1-1550 <$75
10 Type 1 1-952 <$75
20 Type 1 1-212 <$75
5 Type 2 1-2456 <$75
10 Type 2 1-1191 <$75
Total Issue $733,830
Out in 1935 $50,000
Large out 1935 $3,585
****
11402 Perry
FNB OF PERRYVILLE
{{ 6 S }}
Chartered 7/19
1929 Small Size <$VALUE
5 Type 2 1-2556 <$200
10 Type 2 1-1422 <$200
Total Issue $27,000
Out in 1935 $20,000
****
2356 Platte
FARMERS NB OF PLATTE CITY
{{ UNREPORTED }}
Chartered 5/5/77
Receivership 10/1/78
Series 1875 <$VALUE
4x5 1-1350 <$2500
Total Issue $27,000
Out in 1915 $210
****
4329 Platte
FNB OF PLATTE CITY
{{ UNREPORTED }}
Chartered 5/31/90
Liquidated 4/25/92
Brown Back <$VALUE
4x5 1-688 <$2500
Total Issue $13,760
Out in 1910 $90
****
4215 Clinton
FNB OF PLATTSBURG
{{ 7 L 11 S }}
Chartered 1890
Brown Back <$VALUE
4x5 1-3000 <$250
3x10-20 1-4420 <$250/$300
1882 Date Back
4x5 1-630 <$250
3x10-20 1-258 <$250/$300
1902 Date Back
4x5 1-5700 <$135
3x10-20 1-4320 <$135
1902 Plain Back
4x5 5701-15520 <$135
3x10-20 4321-10581 <$135
1929 Small Size
5 Type 1 1-3312 <$60
10 Type 1 1-1490 <$60
20 Type 1 1-412 <$75
5 Type 2 1-4248 <$75
10 Type 2 1-2297 <$75
20 Type 2 1-638 <$75
Total Issue $1,441,120
Out in 1935 $99,995
Large out 1935 $5,475
****
7154 Cass
FARMERS NB OF PLEASANT HILL
{{ UNREPORTED }}
Chartered 3/04
Liquidated 12/27/29
1902 Red Seal <$VALUE
3x10-20 1-480 <$2500
1902 Date Back
3x10-20 1-810 <$1500
1902 Plain Back
3x10-20 811-1471 <$1500
Total Issue $97,550
Out at close $1,260
****
1751 Cass
FNB OF PLEASANT HILL
{{ 2 L }}
Chartered 12/14/70
Liquidated 2/7/78
Original Series <$VALUE
3x1-2 1-1500 <$1000/$2000
4x5 1-4765 <$1250
Total Issue $102,800
Out in 1910 $631
****
7884 Caldwell
FNB OF POLO
{{ 3 L }}
Chartered 8/05
Liquidated 5/31/19
1902 Red Seal <$VALUE
3x10-20 1-400 <$1000
1902 Date Back
3x10-20 1-2500 <$500
1902 Plain Back
3x10-20 2501-3211 <$500
Total Issue $180,550
Out at close $30,000
****
10122 Barry
FNB OF PURDY
{{ 2 L 6 S }}
Chartered 1/12
1902 Date Back <$VALUE
4x5 1-800 <$600
3x10-20 1-590 <$600
1902 Plain Back
4x5 801-4235 <$600
3x10-20 591-2703 <$600
1929 Small Size
5 Type 1 1-888 <$175
10 Type 1 1-408 <$175
20 Type 1 1-124 <$175
5 Type 2 1-1250 <$200
10 Type 2 1-750 <$200
20 Type 2 1-205 <$200
Total Issue $303,700
Out in 1935 $25,000
Large out 1935 $1,330
****
6549 Harrison
FNB OF RIDGEWAY
{{ 13 L }}
Organized 12/12/02
Receivership 12/23/30
1902 Red Seal <$VALUE
3x10-20 1-1360 <$300
1902 Date Back
3x10-20 1-2820 <$150
1902 Plain Back
3x10-20 2821-8233 <$150
Total Issue $479,650
Out at close $10,460
****
1865 Phelps
NB OF ROLLA
{{ 6 L 7 S }}
Organized 8/1/71
Receivership 6/8/32
Original Series <$VALUE
4x5 1-1750 <$750
3x10-20 1-1100<$1000/$1500
Series 1875
4x5 1-1285 <$750
3x10-20 1-85 <$1000/$1500
Brown Back
3x10-20 1-2780 <$400
1882 Date Back
3x10-20 1-1157 <$400
1902 Date Back
3x10-20 1-2300 <$200
1902 Plain Back
3x10-20 2301-9799 <$200
1929 Small Size
10 Type 1 1-982 <$175
20 Type 1 1-270 <$175
Total Issue $898,070
Out at close $49,340
Large out at close $6,100
****

CONDITION affects Value. The Values shown are for notes in FINE condition.

****
260 Saint Charles
FNB OF SAINT CHARLES
{{ 8 L 3 U + 50+ S }}
Chartered 1864
Original Series <$VALUE
4x5 1-5050 <$600
Series 1875
4x5 1-2090 <$600
Brown Back
4x5 1-4764 <$400
3x10-20 1-509 <$400
1902 Red Seal
3x10-20 1-3000 <$400
1902 Date Back
3x10-20 1-7100 <$200
1902 Plain Back
3x10-20 7101-21828 <$200
1929 Small Size
10 Type 1 1-2494 <$40
20 Type 1 1-672 <$50
10 Type 2 1-3322 <$50
20 Type 2 1-929 <$50
Total Issue $1,787,010
Out in 1935 $99,450
Large out 1935 $6,260
****
American NB of Saint Joseph
SEE Ch 9042
German American NB of
Saint Joseph
****
8021 Buchanan
BURNES NB OF SAINT JOSEPH
{{ 18 L 16 S }}
Chartered 12/05
1902 Red Seal <$VALUE
3x10-20 1-3000 <$300
1902 Date Back
4x5 1-11330 <$100
3x10-20 1-9900 <$100
1902 Plain Back
4x5 11331-28170 <$100
3x10-20 9901-20439 <$100
1929 Small Size
5 Type 1 1-4848 <$40
10 Type 1 1-2188 <$40
20 Type 1 1-592 <$50
5 Type 2 1-5502 <$50
10 Type 2 1-3111 <$50
20 Type 2 1-695 <$50
Total Issue $2,155,630
Out in 1935 $137,600
Large out 1935 $8,690
****
1580 Buchanan
FNB OF SAINT JOSEPH
{{ 2 L }}
Chartered 1865
Liquidated 8/13/78
Original Series <$VALUE
4x5 1-1925 <$850
3x10-20 1-2750<$1000/$1500
Series 1875
3x10-20 1-216 <$1000/$1500
Total Issue $186,800
Out in 1910 $1,440
****
FNB of Saint Joseph
SEE Ch 4939
FNB of Buchanan County of
Saint Joseph
****
4939 Buchanan
FNB OF BUCHANAN COUNTY OF
SAINT JOSEPH
Chartered 1894
2nd title:FNB of
Saint Joseph 1/31/14
FIRST TITLE {{ 12 L }}
Brown Back <$VALUE
3x10-20 1-23100 <$125/$175
1882 Date Back
4x5 1-20755 <$100
3x10-20 1-14930 <$100/$150
SECOND TITLE {{ 17 L 3 S }}
1902 Date Back
4x5 1-16000 <$100
3x10-20 1-12800 <$100
1902 Plain Back
4x5 16001-42190 <$100
3x10-20 12801-29504 <$100
1929 Small Size
5 Type 1 1-824 <$250
10 Type 1 1-400 <$250
20 Type 1 1-146 <$250
10 Type 2 1-696 <$250
20 Type 2 1-118 <$250
Total Issue $4,711,160
Out in 1935 $50,000
Large out 1935 $19,720
****

****
9042 Buchanan
GERMAN AMERICAN NB OF
SAINT JOSEPH
Chartered 2/08
2nd title:American NB of
Saint Joseph 1/18/18
FIRST TITLE {{ 5 L }}
1902 Red Seal <$VALUE
4x5 1-1550 <$300
3x10-20 1-1880 <$300
1902 Date Back
4x5 1-11900 <$150
3x10-20 1-8440 <$150
1902 Plain Back
4x5 11901-12900 <$150
3x10-20 8441-8940 <$150
SECOND TITLE {{ 10 L 12 S }}
1902 Plain Back
4x5 1-20580 <$60
4x10 1-16120 <$75
1929 Small Size
5 Type 1 1-7302 <$50
10 Type 1 1-3658 <$50
5 Type 2 1-9732 <$50
10 Type 2 1-5130 <$50
Total Issue $2,424,900
Out in 1935 $150,000
Large out 1935 $8,740
****
2970 Buchanan
NB OF SAINT JOSEPH
{{ 2 L }}
Chartered 6/8/83
Liquidated 12/19/05
Brown Back <$VALUE
3x10-20 1-9118 <$600
1902 Red Seal
3x10-20 1-1743 <$600
Total Issue $543,050
Out in 1910 $15,220
****
2898 Buchanan
SAXTON NB OF SAINT JOSEPH
{{ UNREPORTED }}
Chartered 3/12/83
Liquidated 2/1/94
Brown Back <$VALUE
3x10-20 1-5652 <$1500
Total Issue $282,600
Out in 1910 $1,665
****
4053 Buchanan
SCHUSTER-HAX NB OF
SAINT JOSEPH
{{ UNREPORTED }}
Chartered 6/20/89
Liquidated 2/1/94
Brown Back <$VALUE
4x5 1-1510 <$1500
3x10-20 1-1087 <$1500
Total Issue $84,550
Out in 1910 $680
****
1667 Buchanan
STATE NB OF SAINT JOSEPH
{{ UNREPORTED }}
Chartered 2/12/67
Liquidated 3/31/71
Original Series <$VALUE
3x1-2 1-3500 <$1500/$2000
4x5 1-3835 <$1500
Total Issue $94,200
Out in 1910 $513
****
4228 Buchanan
STATE NB OF SAINT JOSEPH
{{ 3 L }}
Chartered 2/4/90
Liquidated 4/3/97
Brown Back <$VALUE
4x5 1-6260 <$500
Total Issue $125,200
Out in 1910 $1,015
****
Tootle-Lacy NB of
Saint Joseph
SEE Ch 6272
Tootle-Lemon NB of
Saint Joseph
****
6272 Buchanan
TOOTLE-LEMON NB OF
SAINT JOSEPH
Chartered 5/02
2nd title:Tootle-Lacy NB
of Saint Joseph 1/18/18
FIRST TITLE {{ 7 L }}
1902 Red Seal <$VALUE
4x5 1-7830 <$350
3x10-20 1-7468 <$350

1902 Date Back
4x5 1-12415 <$175
3x10-20 1-8934 <$175
1902 Plain Back
4x5 12416-13665 <$175
3x10-20 8935-9434 <$175
SECOND TITLE {{ 8 L }}
1902 Plain Back
4x5 1-47439 <$150
Total Issue $2,223,780
Large out 1935 $9,100
****
13726 Independent City
AMERICAN EXCHANGE NB IN
SAINT LOUIS
{{ 13 S }}
Organized 6/19/33
1929 Small Size <$VALUE
5 Type 2 1-16698 <$75
10 Type 2 1-6189 <$75
20 Type 2 1-1907 <$75
Total Issue $183,520
Out in 1935 $80,000
****
7570 Independent City
AMERICAN EXCHANGE NB OF
SAINT LOUIS
{{ UNREPORTED }}
Chartered 1/21/05
Liquidated 5/23/05
1902 Red Seal <$VALUE
3x10-20 1-1000 <$2000
Total Issue $50,000
Out in 1910 $5,870
****
12506 Independent City
AMERICAN EXCHANGE NB OF
SAINT LOUIS
{{ 13 L 14 S }}
Organized 2/19/24
Receivership 12/5/33
1902 Plain Back <$VALUE
4x5 1-9030 <$100
3x10-20 1-5864 <$100
1929 Small Size
5 Type 1 1-4088 <$75
10 Type 1 1-2032 <$75
20 Type 1 1-503 <$75
Total Issue $778,720
Out at close $79,300
Large out at close $3,960
****
7179 Independent City
BANKERS WORLD'S FAIR NB
OF SAINT LOUIS
{{ UNREPORTED }}
Chartered 5/21/04
Liquidated 12/15/04
1902 Red Seal <$VALUE
50-100 1-334 <$5000
Total Issue $50,100
All notes redeemed
****
12916 Independent City
BOATMEN'S NB OF
SAINT LOUIS
{{ 45U + 23 S }}
Chartered 4/26
1929 Small Size <$VALUE
5 Type 1 1-13044 <$20
10 Type 1 1-9354 <$25
20 Type 1 1-2268 <$35
5 Type 2 1-47572 <$20
10 Type 2 1-30624 <$25
20 Type 2 1-8170 <$35
Total Issue $1,932,220
Out in 1935 $1,016,850
****
9460 Independent City
BROADWAY NB OF
SAINT LOUIS
{{ 1 L }}
Chartered 6/09
Liquidated 2/1/13
1902 Date Back <$VALUE
3x10-20 1-10327 <$850
Total Issue $516,350
Out in 1913 $97,400
****
8455 Independent City
CENTRAL NB OF SAINT LOUIS
{{ 28 L }}
Chartered 12/06
Liquidated 12/31/20
1902 Red Seal <$VALUE
4x5 1-22750 <$100
4x10 1-13900 <$100
50-100 1-2100 <$1750/$2000
1902 Date Back
4x5 1-70000 <$40
4x10 1-61500 <$50
50-100 1-1000 <$300/$400

3x50-100 1-3836 <$300/$400
1902 Plain Back
4x5 70001-90992 <$40
4x10 61501-78702 <$50
Total Issue $7,402,920
Out at close $972,495
****
4575 Independent City
CHEMICAL NB OF
SAINT LOUIS
{{ UNREPORTED }}
Chartered 6/1/91
Liquidated 4/1/97
Brown Back <$VALUE
50-100 1-499 <$2000/$2500
Total Issue $74,850
Out in 1910 $1,500
****
7808 Independent City
CITY NB OF SAINT LOUIS
{{ U + 5 L }}
Chartered 6/05
Liquidated 11/14/10
1902 Red Seal <$VALUE
4x5 1-6670 <$600
3x10-20 1-4732 <$600
1902 Date Back
4x5 1-3840 <$300
3x10-20 1-3640 <$300
Total Issue $628,800
Out in 1911 $98,900
****
4048 Independent City
CONTINENTAL NB OF
SAINT LOUIS
{{ U + 8 L }}
Chartered 5/31/89
Liquidated 7/31/02
Brown Back <$VALUE
4x5 1-26550 <$250
50-100 1-16395<$1250/$1500
Total Issue $1,490,250
Out in 1910 $61,775
****
2835 Independent City
FIFTH NB OF SAINT LOUIS
{{ 1 L }}
Organized 12/6/82
Receivership 11/15/87
Brown Back <$VALUE
4x5 1-1251 <$1000
3x10-20 1-1112 <$1000
50-100 1-367 <$2000/$2500
Total Issue $135,670
Out in 1915 $595
****
FNB in Saint Louis
SEE Ch 170
Third NB of Saint Louis
****
89 Independent City
FNB OF SAINT LOUIS
{{ 2 L }}
Chartered 9/23/63
Liquidated 7/16/70
Original Series <$VALUE
3x1-2 1-2000 <$1000/$2500
4x5 1-2500 <$1250
4x10 1-1100 <$1500
2x20-50-100 1-421
<$2000/$5000/$6000
Total Issue $183,990
Out in 1910 $1,151
****
283 Independent City
FOURTH NB OF SAINT LOUIS
{{ 13 L }}
Chartered 2/26/64
Liquidated 1/15/07
Original Series <$VALUE
4x5 1-7250 <$750
3x10-20 1-3300<$1000/$1500
Series 1875
3x10-20 1-7198<$1000/$1500
3x50-100 1-480<$5000/$6000
Brown Back
4x5 1-8250 <$200
3x10-20 1-7180 <$200
50-100 1-8871 <$1250/$1500
1902 Red Seal
50-100 1-9957 <$1750/$2000
Total Issue $4,138,100
Out in 1910 $335,190
****
Grand Avenue NB of
Saint Louis
SEE Ch 12220
Missouri NB of Saint Louis
****
Grand NB of Saint Louis
SEE Ch 12220
Missouri NB of Saint Louis
****

****
4262 Independent City
LACLEDE NB OF SAINT LOUIS
{{ UNREPORTED }}
Chartered 3/15/90
Liquidated 7/1/95
Brown Back <$VALUE
3x10-20 1-1556 <$1250
Total Issue $77,800
Out in 1910 $870
****
5788 Independent City
MECHANICS NB OF
SAINT LOUIS
{{ U + 10 L }}
Chartered 4/23/01
Liquidated 5/23/05
Brown Back <$VALUE
4x5 1-24575 <$300
3x10-20 1-14604 <$300
50-100 1-4864 <$1250/$1500
Total Issue $1,951,300
Out in 1910 $11,805
****
7715 Independent City
MECHANICS-AMERICAN NB OF
SAINT LOUIS
{{ 46 L }}
Chartered 4/05
Closed 7/7/19
1902 Red Seal <$VALUE
4x5 1-68650 <$100
4x10 1-10000 <$100
3x10-20 1-38540 <$100
1902 Date Back
4x5 1-121217 <$50
4x10 1-113674 <$50
3x10-20 1-5334 <$50
Total Issue $10,938,000
Out at close $800,000
Ch 170 assumed circulation
****
Mercantile-Commerce NB in
Saint Louis
SEE Ch 4178
NB of Commerce in Saint Louis
****
9297 Independent City
MERCANTILE NB OF
SAINT LOUIS
{{ 30 L }}
Chartered 12/08
Liquidated 2/5/18
1902 Date Back <$VALUE
4x5 1-70830 <$50
3x10-20 1-59668 <$60
50-100 1-3000 <$300/$400
3x50-100 1-4160 <$300/$400
1902 Plain Back
4x5 70831-74020 <$50
3x10-20 59669-62668 <$60
Total Issue $6,103,800
Out at close $895,000
****
1501 Independent City
MERCHANTS NB OF
SAINT LOUIS
{{ 4 L }}
Chartered 8/2/65
Liquidated 7/1/95
Original Series <$VALUE
4x5 1-10650 <$1000
3x10-20 1-2360<$1250/$1500
Series 1875
4x5 1-1500 <$1000
3x10-20 1-876 <$1250/$1500
Brown Back
3x10-20 1-2022 <$600
Total Issue $505,900
Out in 1910 $3,830
****
5002 Independent City
MERCHANTS-LACLEDE NB OF
SAINT LOUIS
{{ 50+ L }}
Chartered 1895
Liquidated 6/29/29
Brown Back <$VALUE
4x5 1-39000 <$100
3x10-20 1-100500<$100/$150
50-100 1-833 <$1250/$1500
1882 Date Back
4x5 1-91665 <$100
3x10-20 1-63334 <$100/$135
3x50-100 1-2000<$1000/$1250
3x50-100 3001-3393
<$1000/$1250
1902 Date Back
3x10-20 1-10000 <$50
3x50-100 1-5800 <$300/$350

1902 Plain Back
3x10-20 10001-144796 <$50
3x50-100 5801-6052
<$300/$350
Total Issue $20,281,000
Out at close $604,195
****
12220 Independent City
MISSOURI NB OF
SAINT LOUIS
Organized 6/5/22
Receivership 3/19/34
2nd title:Grand Avenue NB
of Saint Louis 6/8/25
3rd title:Grand NB of
Saint Louis 11/24/25
FIRST TITLE {{ 5 L }}
1902 Plain Back <$VALUE
4x5 1-10500 <$200
3x10-20 1-5300 <$200
SECOND TITLE {{ 11 L }}
1902 Plain Back
4x5 1-8980 <$100
3x10-20 1-4540 <$100
THIRD TITLE {{ 22 L 50+ S }}
1902 Plain Back
4x5 1-27090 <$60
3x10-20 1-18231 <$65/$75
1929 Small Size
5 Type 1 1-20938 <$30
10 Type 1 1-11066 <$40
20 Type 1 1-2716 <$40
5 Type 2 1-6384 <$35
10 Type 2 1-3527 <$40
20 Type 2 1-848 <$40
Total Issue $4,037,120
Out at close $500,000
Large out at close $16,295
****
4178 Independent City
NB OF COMMERCE IN
SAINT LOUIS
Chartered 12/16/89
2nd title:Mercantile
Commerce NB in
Saint Louis 7/15/30
FIRST TITLE {{ 50+ L }}
Brown Back <$VALUE
4x5 1-481250 <$100
4x10 1-117625 <$100
3x10-20 1-256680<$100/$150
50-100 1-260 <$1250/$1500
1882 Date Back
4x5 1-131165 <$100
4x10 1-53471 <$100
3x10-20 1-4995 <$100/$135
1902 Date Back
4x5 1-541670 <$30
4x10 1-511665 <$35
3x50-100 1-8000 <$300/$350
1902 Plain Back
4x5 541671-1000000 <$30
and A1-A550676 <$30
4x10 511666-1000000 <$35
and A1-A171927 <$35
SECOND TITLE {{ 44 S }}
1929 Small Size
5 Type 1 1-6930 <$20
10 Type 1 1-2470 <$20
20 Type 1 1-1246 <$30
5 Type 2 1-21950 <$20
10 Type 2 1-10125 <$20
20 Type 2 1-4130 <$30
Total Issue $112,904,710
Out in 1935 $652,260
Large out 1935 $357,560
****
4232 Independent City
NB OF THE REPUBLIC OF
SAINT LOUIS
{{ UNREPORTED }}
Chartered 2/13/90
Liquidated 5/18/97
Brown Back <$VALUE
50-100 1-769 <$2000/$2500
Total Issue $115,350
Out in 1910 $2,450
****
1665 Independent City
NB OF THE STATE OF
MISSOURI, SAINT LOUIS
{{ 14 L }}
Organized 10/20/66
Receivership 6/23/77
Original Series <$VALUE
3x1-2 1-44572 <$500/$1250
4x5 1-28151 <$500
3x10-20 1-21720<$750/$1250
3x50-100 1-2194<$4000/$5000
Total Issue $2,420,380
Out in 1915 $14,652
****

****
11989 Independent City
N CITY B OF SAINT LOUIS
{{ 43 L 13 S }}
Chartered 7/21
Liquidated 4/14/30
1902 Plain Back <$VALUE
4x5 1-177197 <$40
3x10-20 1-49971 <$50
1929 Small Size
5 Type 1 1-9194 <$50
10 Type 1 1-3858 <$60
20 Type 1 1-874 <$70
Total Issue $6,654,670
Out at close $693,990
Large out at close $151,580
****
11973 Independent City
REPUBLIC NB OF
SAINT LOUIS
{{ 17 L }}
Chartered 5/2/21
Liquidated 9/16/24
1902 Plain Back <$VALUE
4x5 1-50000 <$75
Total Issue $1,000,000
Out at close $419,600
****
1112 Independent City
SAINT LOUIS NB OF
SAINT LOUIS
{{ 15 L }}
Chartered 5/4/65
Liquidated 1/17/99
Original Series <$VALUE
3x1-2 1-10720 <$500/$1500
4x5 1-13750 <$500
3x10-20 1-3900 <$750/$1250
Series 1875
4x5 1-500 <$500
3x10-20 1-8336 <$750/$1250
Brown Back
4x5 1-7875 <$250
50-100 1-150 <$1250/$1500
Total Issue $1,130,400
Out in 1910 $9,172
****
12216 Independent City
SAINT LOUIS NB,
SAINT LOUIS
{{ 11 L 12 S }}
Organized 6/1/22
Receivership 1/13/33
1902 Plain Back <$VALUE
4x5 1-36517 <$85
1929 Small Size
5 Type 1 1-12920 <$60
Total Issue $1,117,940
Out at close $96,520
Large out at close $4,105
****
139 Independent City
SECOND NB OF SAINT LOUIS
{{ 5 L }}
Chartered 1863
Liquidated 1/8/78
Original Series <$VALUE
3x1-2 1-8000 <$750/$1500
4x5 1-8048 <$750
4x10 1-3702 <$1000
2x20-50-100 1-312
<$1250/$4000/$5000
Total Issue $408,320
Out in 1910 $3,418
****
12066 Independent City
SECURITY NB SAVINGS & TC
OF SAINT LOUIS
{{ 11 L 36 S }}
Chartered 12/21
1902 Plain Back <$VALUE
4x5 1-32680 <$75
1929 Small Size
5 Type 1 1-28574 <$30
5 Type 2 1-99024 <$30
Total Issue $2,005,940
Out at close $259,550
Large out at close $2,520
****
13264 Independent City
SOUTH SIDE NB OF
SAINT LOUIS
{{ 5 L 16 S }}
Organized 12/5/28
Receivership 8/19/33
1902 Plain Back <$VALUE
4x5 1-11917 <$300
1929 Small Size
5 Type 1 1-28194 <$75
5 Type 2 1-1722 <$75
Total Issue $1,092,770
Out at close $197,500
Large out at close $1,700
****
5172 Independent City
STATE NB OF SAINT LOUIS
{{ 50+ L }}
Chartered 1/21/99
Liquidated 6/29/29
Brown Back <$VALUE
4x5 1-39000 <$100
3x10-20 1-63600 <$100/$150
1882 Date Back
4x5 1-112327 <$100
3x10-20 1-80042 <$100/$135
3x50-100 1-713<$1000/$1250
1902 Plain Back
4x5 1-147570 <$40
3x10-20 1-129546 <$50
Total Issue $19,815,590
Out at close $1,294,350
****
12389 Independent City
TELEGRAPHERS NB OF
SAINT LOUIS
{{ 20 L 50+ S }}
Chartered 6/23
1902 Plain Back <$VALUE
4x5 1-25146 <$125
3x10-20 1-15241 <$125
1929 Small Size
5 Type 1 1-13302 <$20
10 Type 1 1-8078 <$30
20 Type 1 1-2306 <$40
5 Type 2 1-26638 <$20
10 Type 2 1-14341 <$30
20 Type 2 1-3785 <$40
Total Issue $2,777,730
Out in 1935 $431,750
Large out 1935 $4,280
****
170 Independent City
THIRD NB OF SAINT LOUIS
Chartered 1863
2nd title:FNB in
Saint Louis 7/7/19
FIRST TITLE {{ 50+ L }}
Original Series <$VALUE
3x1-2 1-27000 <$350/$1000
4x5 1-13500 <$400
4x10 1-9500 <$600
3x20-50 1-7400 <$750/$4000
Series 1875
3x20-50 1-3970 <$750/$4000
Brown Back
3x10-20 1-61176 <$100/$150
1902 Red Seal
4x5 1-35000 <$100
4x10 1-10000 <$100
50-100 1-18000<$1750/$2000
1902 Date Back
4x5 1-175165 <$35
4x10 1-143670 <$40
3x50-100 1-2000 <$300/$350
1902 Plain Back
4x5 175166-190165 <$35
4x10 143671-151670 <$40
SECOND TITLE {{ 22 L 50+ S }}
1902 Plain Back
3x10-20 1-101166 <$40
1929 Small Size
10 Type 1 1-45169 <$20
20 Type 1 1-14658 <$30
Total Issue $28,792,000
Out in 1935 $1,000,000
Large out 1935 $125,985
Outstanding includes Ch 7715
****
12491 Independent City
TWELFTH STREET NB OF
SAINT LOUIS
{{ 11 L 18 S }}
Organized 1/12/24
Receivership 1/19/33
1902 Plain Back <$VALUE
4x5 1-26735 <$125
1929 Small Size
5 Type 1 1-20650 <$50
Total Issue $1,154,200
Out at close $300,000
Large out at close $615
****
1381 Independent City
UNION NB OF SAINT LOUIS
{{ 2 L }}
Chartered 7/1/65
Liquidated 10/22/73
Original Series <$VALUE
4x5 1-3665 <$1000
3x10-20 1-2200<$1250/$1500
Total Issue $183,300
Out in 1910 $1,585
****
1858 Independent City
VALLEY NB OF SAINT LOUIS
{{ 11 L }}
Chartered 8/9/71
Liquidated 12/4/85
Original Series <$VALUE
4x5 1-1925 <$1500
3x10-20 1-1860<$1750/$2000
Series 1875
3x10-20 1-1465<$1750/$2000
Total Issue $204,750
Out in 1910 $1,030
****
6773 Independent City
WASHINGTON NB OF
SAINT LOUIS
{{ 8 L }}
Chartered 5/03
Liquidated 3/7/11
1902 Red Seal <$VALUE
3x10-20 1-8000 <$300
1902 Date Back
3x10-20 1-10580 <$150
Total Issue $929,000
Out in 1911 $259,645
****
7921 Dent
FNB OF SALEM
{{ 1 L U + 2 S }}
Chartered 9/05
1902 Red Seal <$VALUE
3x10-20 1-482 <$1500
1902 Date Back
3x10-20 1-970* <$850
1902 Plain Back
3x10-20 1071-2646* <$850
* 971-1070 not marked
1929 Small Size
10 Type 1 1-306 <$450
20 Type 1 1-106 <$450
10 Type 2 1-317 <$450
20 Type 2 1-126 <$450
Total Issue $193,170
Out in 1935 $12,500
Large out 1935 $790
****
8359 Chariton
FARMERS AND MERCHANTS NB
OF SALISBURY
{{ UNREPORTED }}
Chartered 9/06
Liquidated 7/8/13
1902 Red Seal <$VALUE
3x10-20 1-560 <$2500
1902 Date Back
3x10-20 1-1034 <$1500
Total Issue $79,700
Out in 1913 $19,050
****
5515 Jasper
FNB OF SARCOXIE
{{ 1 L 7 S }}
Chartered 7/23/00
Brown Back <$VALUE
3x10-20 1-1850 <$1000
1882 Date Back
3x10-20 1-1690 <$1000
1882 Value Back
3x10-20 1691-2629 <$1000
1902 Plain Back
3x10-20 1-2491 <$750
1929 Small Size
10 Type 1 1-670 <$175
20 Type 1 1-180 <$175
10 Type 2 1-647 <$200
20 Type 2 1-75 <$200
Total Issue $418,270
Out in 1935 $25,000
Large out 1935 $1,640
****
5780 Andrew
FNB OF SAVANNAH
{{ 9 L }}
Chartered 4/01
Liquidated 4/18/25
Brown Back <$VALUE
3x10-20 1-2740 <$500
1882 Date Back
3x10-20 1-3200* <$500
1882 Value Back
3x10-20 3451-5228* <$500
* 3201-3450 not marked
1902 Plain Back
3x10-20 1-2242 <$200
Total Issue $510,500
Out at close $50,000
****
1971 Pettis
CITIZENS NB OF SEDALIA
{{ 11 L 3 S }}
Organized 8/9/72
Receivership 11/6/31
Original Series <$VALUE
3x1-2 1-400 <$400/$1000
4x5 1-5900 <$400
Series 1875
4x5 1-7283 <$400
Brown Back
4x5 1-8300 <$250
3x10-20 1-4600 <$250
1882 Date Back
4x5 1-2551 <$250
3x10-20 1-1947 <$250
1902 Date Back
4x5 1-3550* <$125
4x10 1-3150** <$125
1902 Plain Back
4x5 4051-18591* <$125
4x10 3551-15118** <$125
* 3551-4050 not marked
** 3151-15118 not marked
1929 Small Size
5 Type 1 1-3097 <$175
10 Type 1 1-1479 <$175
Total Issue $1,968,220
Out at close $98,255
Large out at close $14,175
****
1627 Pettis
FNB OF SEDALIA
{{ 2 L }}
Organized 1/2/66
Receivership 5/10/94
Original Series <$VALUE
3x1-2 1-1700 <$750/$1500
4x5 1-3275 <$750
3x10-20 1-2340<$1000/$1250
Series 1875
3x10-20 1-592 <$1000/$1250
Brown Back
3x10-20 1-1572 <$600
Total Issue $299,200
Out in 1915 $2,097
****
4392 Pettis
SEDALIA NB, SEDALIA
{{ 8 L 5 S }}
Organized 7/10/90
Receivership 2/15/32
Brown Back <$VALUE
4x5 1-5250 <$250
3x10-20 1-980 <$250
1882 Date Back
4x5 1-312 <$250
3x10-20 1-232 <$250
1902 Date Back
3x10-20 1-7200 <$125
1902 Plain Back
3x10-20 7201-21116 <$125
1929 Small Size
10 Type 1 1-1813 <$150
20 Type 1 1-462 <$150
Total Issue $1,391,860
Out at close $100,000
Large out at close $13,940
****
2919 Pettis
THIRD NB OF SEDALIA
{{ 9 L 12 S }}
Organized 11/20/82
Brown Back <$VALUE
4x5 1-7785 <$250
3x10-20 1-1629 <$250
1902 Red Seal
4x5 1-4300 <$250
3x10-20 1-3280 <$250
1902 Date Back
4x5 1-5850 <$100
3x10-20 1-4400 <$100
1902 Plain Back
4x5 5851-19059 <$100
3x10-20 4401-13544 <$100
1929 Small Size
5 Type 1 1-3560 <$50
10 Type 1 1-1730 <$50
20 Type 1 1-412 <$60
5 Type 2 1-3406 <$60
10 Type 2 1-2047 <$60
20 Type 2 1-740 <$60
Total Issue $1,857,870
Out in 1935 $100,000
Large out 1935 $7,465
****
7656 Newton
FNB OF SENECA
{{ UNREPORTED }}
Chartered 3/22/05
Liquidated 8/31/06
1902 Red Seal <$VALUE
3x10-20 1-520 <$2500
Total Issue $26,000
Out in 1910 $4,530
****
9932 Webster
PEOPLES NB OF SEYMOUR
{{ 5 L 3 S }}
Organized 1/19/11
Receivership 8/23/33
1902 Date Back <$VALUE
3x10-20 1-1600 <$450
1902 Plain Back
3x10-20 1601-4615 <$450
1929 Small Size
10 Type 1 1-510 <$350
20 Type 1 1-147 <$350
Total Issue $278,990
Out at close $23,000
Large out at close $1,950
****
1711 Shelby
FNB OF SHELBINA
{{ UNREPORTED }}
Chartered 9/21/70
Liquidated 1/1/74
Original Series <$VALUE
3x1-2 1-2000 <$2000/$3000
4x5 1-2650 <$2000
3x10-20 1-634 <$2500/$3000
Total Issue $94,700
Out in 1910 $505
****
9137 Shelby
SHELBINA NB, SHELBINA
{{ 1 L }}
Chartered 5/08
Liquidated 4/28/13
1902 Date Back <$VALUE
3x10-20 1-1332 <$1500
Total Issue $66,600
Out in 1913 $20,200
****
4360 Greene
AMERICAN NB OF
SPRINGFIELD
{{ UNREPORTED }}
Organized 7/9/90
Receivership 2/28/94
Brown Back <$VALUE
3x10-20 1-1375 <$1500
Total Issue $68,750
Out in 1915 $450
****
3718 Greene
CENTRAL NB OF SPRINGFIELD
{{ 2 L }}
Chartered 6/7/87
Liquidated 7/28/99
Brown Back <$VALUE
3x10-20 1-4106 <$750
Total Issue $205,300
Out in 1910 $3,230
****
FNB of Springfield
SEE Ch 1701
NB of Springfield
****
1677 Greene
GREENE COUNTY NB OF
SPRINGFIELD
{{ 3 L }}
Chartered 2/17/68
Liquidated 2/8/88
Original Series <$VALUE
3x1-2 1-4000 <$500/$1250
4x5 1-5750 <$600
3x10-20 1-2000 <$750/$1250
Series 1875
3x10-20 1-1373 <$750/$1250
Total Issue $303,650
Out in 1910 $1,698
****
10074 Greene
McDANIEL NB OF
SPRINGFIELD
{{ 5 L 5 S }}
Organized 8/11/11
Receivership 2/17/33
1902 Date Back <$VALUE
3x10-20 1-4900 <$300
1902 Plain Back
3x10-20 4901-18628 <$300
1929 Small Size
10 Type 1 1-1576 <$200
20 Type 1 1-478 <$200
Total Issue $1,083,320
Out at close $100,000
Large out at close $10,710
****
9315 Greene
MERCHANTS NB OF
SPRINGFIELD
{{ 1 L }}
Chartered 1/09
Liquidated 11/10/13
1902 Date Back <$VALUE
4x5 1-7985 <$600
3x10-20 1-5608 <$600
Total Issue $440,100
Out in 1914 $45,565
****
1701 Greene
NB OF SPRINGFIELD
Chartered 8/18/70
Liquidated 7/6/93
2nd title:FNB of
Springfield 3/3/73
FIRST TITLE {{ 1 L }}
Original Series <$VALUE
3x1-2 1-3000 <$750/$1500
4x5 1-2750 <$750
3x10-20 1-600 <$1000/$1250
SECOND TITLE {{ 2 L }}
Original Series
3x1-2 1-1000 <$750/$1500
4x5 1-3500 <$750
Series 1875
4x5 1-4760 <$750
Brown Back
50-100 1-60 <$2000/$2500
Total Issue $279,200
Out in 1910 $1,938
****
5082 Greene
N EXCHANGE B OF
SPRINGFIELD
{{ 7 L }}
Chartered 7/19/97
Liquidated 3/10/09
Brown Back <$VALUE
4x5 1-7050 <$250
3x10-20 1-5316 <$250
Total Issue $406,800
Out in 1910 $35,705
****
5209 Greene
UNION NB OF SPRINGFIELD
{{ 8 L 14 S }}
Chartered 7/18/99
Brown Back <$VALUE
3x10-20 1-4800 <$200
1882 Date Back
3x10-20 1-6100 <$200
1882 Value Back
3x10-20 6101-8229 <$200
1902 Plain Back
3x10-20 1-11709 <$125
1929 Small Size
10 Type 1 1-5300 <$40
20 Type 1 1-1424 <$40
5 Type 2 1-8070 <$50
10 Type 2 1-4278 <$50
20 Type 2 1-905 <$50
Total Issue $1,827,010
Out in 1935 $300,000
Large out 1935 $6,430
****
12452 Pemiscot
FNB OF STEELE
{{ 0 L 5 S }}
Chartered 10/23
Liquidated 5/8/34
1902 Plain Back <$VALUE
4x5 1-1203 <$1000
1929 Small Size
5 Type 1 1-1028 <$300
10 Type 1 1-178 <$300
20 Type 1 1-48 <$300
5 Type 2 1-1466 <$300
10 Type 2 1-640 <$300
20 Type 2 1-200 <$300
Total Issue $89,070
Out at close $25,000
Large out at close $110
****

****

8914 Crawford
FNB OF STEELVILLE
{{ 4 L 2 S }}
Organized 7/31/07
Receivership 1/30/33
1902 Red Seal <$VALUE
3x10-20 1-200 <$1000
1902 Date Back
3x10-20 1-660* <$500
1902 Plain Back
3x10-20 741-1317* <$500
* 661-740 not marked
1929 Small Size
10 Type 1 1-167 <$500
20 Type 1 1-25 <$500
Total Issue $88,870
Out at close $6,250
Large out at close $570

****

4160 Dekalb
FNB OF STEWARTSVILLE
{{ 7 L 6 S }}
Chartered 1889
Brown Back <$VALUE
3x10-20 1-4200 <$350
1902 Date Back
4x5 1-2700 <$175
3x10-20 1-2300 <$175
1902 Plain Back
4x5 2701-8975 <$175
3x10-20 2301-6771 <$175
1929 Small Size
5 Type 1 1-1750 <$150
10 Type 1 1-826 <$150
20 Type 1 1-232 <$150
5 Type 2 1-1072 <$150
10 Type 2 1-866 <$150
20 Type 2 1-254 <$150
Total Issue $877,050
Out in 1935 $49,200
Large out 1935 $3,500

****

11372 Saline
FNB OF SWEET SPRINGS
{{ 1 L }}
Organized 5/31/19
Receivership 8/24/31
1902 Plain Back <$VALUE
4x5 1-6665 <$1500
Total Issue $133,300
Out at close $735

****

3079 Atchison
FNB OF TARKIO
{{ 5 L 5 S }}
Chartered 1883
Brown Back <$VALUE
4x5 1-3275 <$400
3x10-20 1-613 <$400
1902 Red Seal
3x10-20 1-2190 <$400
1902 Date Back
3x10-20 1-3000 <$150
1902 Plain Back
3x10-20 3001-8846 <$150
1929 Small Size
10 Type 1 1-1108 <$150
20 Type 1 1-326 <$150
10 Type 2 1-6 <$200
20 Type 2 1-15 <$200
Total Issue $753,910
Out in 1935 $25,000
Large out 1935 $4,210

****

1966 Grundy
FNB OF TRENTON
{{ 1 L }}
Chartered 4/22/72
Liquidated 6/22/76
Original Series <$VALUE
4x5 1-2000 <$2500
3x10-20 1-400 <$2750/$3000
Series 1875
4x5 1-400 <$2500
Total Issue $68,000
Out in 1910 $355

****

3957 Grundy
FNB OF TRENTON
{{ UNREPORTED }}
Chartered 1/9/89
Liquidated 12/31/93
Brown Back <$VALUE
4x5 1-1203 <$2500
Total Issue $24,060
Out in 1910 $165

****

3946 Grundy
GRUNDY COUNTY NB OF TRENTON
{{ 2 L }}
Chartered 12/7/88
Liquidated 12/23/93
Brown Back <$VALUE
4x5 1-1199 <$2000
Total Issue $23,980
Out in 1910 $205

****

4933 Grundy
TRENTON NB, TRENTON
{{ 9 L 10 S }}
Chartered 1893
Brown Back <$VALUE
3x10-20 1-5340 <$250
1882 Date Back
3x10-20 1-3225 <$250
1902 Date Back
3x10-20 1-1500 <$150
1902 Plain Back
3x10-20 1501-11272 <$150
1929 Small Size
5 Type 1 1-2342 <$100
10 Type 1 1-1822 <$100
20 Type 1 1-548 <$100
5 Type 2 1-3664 <$125
10 Type 2 1-1366 <$125
20 Type 2 1-250 <$125
Total Issue $1,274,170
Out in 1935 $50,000
Large out 1935 $6,400

****

3068 Putnam
MARSHALL NB OF UNIONVILLE
{{ 11 L 7 S }}
Chartered 1883
Brown Back <$VALUE
4x5 1-4178 <$500
3x10-20 1-527 <$500
1902 Red Seal
3x10-20 1-1950 <$500
1902 Date Back
3x10-20 1-3340 <$250
1902 Plain Back
3x10-20 3341-8891 <$250
1929 Small Size
10 Type 1 1-1128 <$175
20 Type 1 1-293 <$175
Total Issue $754,800
Out in 1935 $25,000
Large out 1935 $4,320

****

3137 Putnam
NB OF UNIONVILLE
{{ 9 L }}
Chartered 1884
Liquidated 1/1/29
Brown Back <$VALUE
4x5 1-3801 <$350
3x10-20 1-956 <$350
1902 Red Seal
3x10-20 1-1560 <$350
1902 Date Back
3x10-20 1-3200 <$175
1902 Plain Back
3x10-20 3201-8797 <$175
Total Issue $641,670
Out at close $38,550

****

13268 Putnam
NB OF UNIONVILLE
{{ 2 L 3 S }}
Organized 12/12/28
Receivership 8/13/32
1902 Plain Back <$VALUE
3x10-20 1-63 <$850
1929 Small Size
10 Type 1 1-578 <$350
20 Type 1 1-161 <$350
Total Issue $57,150
Out at close $39,700
Large out at close $10,920
Outstanding includes Ch 3137

****

13367 Morgan
FNB IN VERSAILLES
{{ 2 S }}
Organized 8/5/29
Receivership 10/16/31
1929 Small Size <$VALUE
5 Type 1 1-523 <$400
10 Type 1 1-260 <$400
20 Type 1 1-105 <$400
Total Issue $43,890
Out at close $30,000
Outstanding includes Ch 7256

****

7256 Morgan
FNB OF VERSAILLES
{{ 13 L }}
Organized 5/5/04
Receivership 11/15/33
1902 Red Seal <$VALUE
3x10-20 1-1380 <$300
1902 Date Back
3x10-20 1-1950 <$125
1902 Plain Back
3x10-20 1951-7325 <$125
Total Issue $435,250
Out at close $27,000
Large out 1935 $6,220
Ch 13367 assumed circulation

****

1856 Johnson
FNB OF WARRENSBURG
{{ 1 L }}
Organized 7/31/71
Receivership 11/1/78
Original Series <$VALUE
3x1-2 1-2200 <$1250/$2000
4x5 1-6700 <$1250
Series 1875
4x5 1-170 <$1250
Total Issue $148,400
Out in 1915 $753

****

5156 Johnson
PEOPLES NB OF WARRENSBURG
{{ 10 L U + 7 S }}
Chartered 11/28/98
Brown Back <$VALUE
4x5 1-1750 <$250
3x10-20 1-3750 <$250
1882 Date Back
4x5 1-4900 <$250
3x10-20 1-3320 <$250
1882 Value Back
4x5 4901-6445 <$250
3x10-20 3321-4007 <$250
1902 Plain Back
4x5 1-19324 <$150
1929 Small Size
5 Type 1 1-2940 <$125
10 Type 1 1-960 <$125
20 Type 1 1-234 <$125
5 Type 2 1-2498 <$125
10 Type 2 1-2295 <$125
20 Type 2 1-462 <$125
Total Issue $1,156,790
Out in 1935 $75,000
Large out 1935 $2,380

****

5388 Franklin
FNB OF WASHINGTON
{{ 7 L }}
Organized 5/12/00
Receivership 11/18/32
Brown Back <$VALUE
4x5 1-1420 <$750
3x10-20 1-1192 <$750
1882 Date Back
4x5 1-1300 <$750
3x10-20 1-1020 <$750
1882 Value Back
4x5 1301-1510 <$750
3x10-20 1021-1144 <$750
Total Issue $175,400
Out at close $795

****

4475 Jasper
FNB OF WEBB CITY
Chartered 1890
Liquidated 6/29/29
2nd title:FNB of Carterville 4/1/97
FIRST TITLE {{ 0 L }}
Brown Back <$VALUE
4x5 1-1550 <$750
SECOND TITLE {{ 15 L }}
Brown Back
3x10-20 1-4350 <$350
1882 Date Back
3x10-20 1-1921 <$350
1902 Date Back
4x5 1-5000 <$100
3x10-20 1-3700 <$100
1902 Plain Back
4x5 5001-16440 <$100
3x10-20 3701-11582 <$100
Total Issue $1,252,450
Out at close $47,400

****

8016 Jasper
NB OF WEBB CITY
{{ 7 L }}
Chartered 12/05
Liquidated 6/6/23
1902 Red Seal <$VALUE
4x5 1-2750 <$450
3x10-20 1-2490 <$450
1902 Date Back
4x5 1-6650 <$250
3x10-20 1-4440 <$250
1902 Plain Back
4x5 6651-14605 <$250
3x10-20 4441-9792 <$250
Total Issue $961,200
Out at close $100,000

****

8011 Saint Louis
FNB OF WELLSTON
{{ 8 L 15 S }}
Chartered 12/05
1902 Red Seal <$VALUE
3x10-20 1-2000 <$350
1902 Date Back
3x10-20 1-3400 <$175
1902 Plain Back
3x10-20 3401-11396 <$175
1929 Small Size
10 Type 1 1-2124 <$50
20 Type 1 1-602 <$60
10 Type 2 1-2337 <$60
20 Type 2 1-816 <$60
Total Issue $909,170
Out in 1935 $98,900
Large out 1935 $2,920

****

5036 Howell
FNB OF WEST PLAINS
{{ 2U + 1 L 2 S }}
Chartered 1896
Brown Back <$VALUE
4x5 1-1725 <$750
3x10-20 1-600 <$750
1882 Date Back
4x5 1-742 <$750
3x10-20 1-478 <$750
1902 Plain Back
3x10-20 1-1605 <$600
1929 Small Size
10 Type 1 1-412 <$400
20 Type 1 1-136 <$400
10 Type 2 1-207 <$400
20 Type 2 1-60 <$400
Total Issue $218,920
Out in 1935 $12,500
Large out 1935 $1,270

****

9519 Henry
FNB OF WINDSOR
{{ 3 L U + 4 S }}
Organized 7/12/09
Receivership 3/28/34
1902 Date Back <$VALUE
3x10-20 1-3300* <$350
1902 Plain Back
3x10-20 3551-10203* <$350
* 3301-3550 not marked
1929 Small Size
10 Type 1 1-1293 <$250
20 Type 1 1-326 <$250
Total Issue $626,850
Out at close $49,520
Large out at close $3,190

****

MONTANA

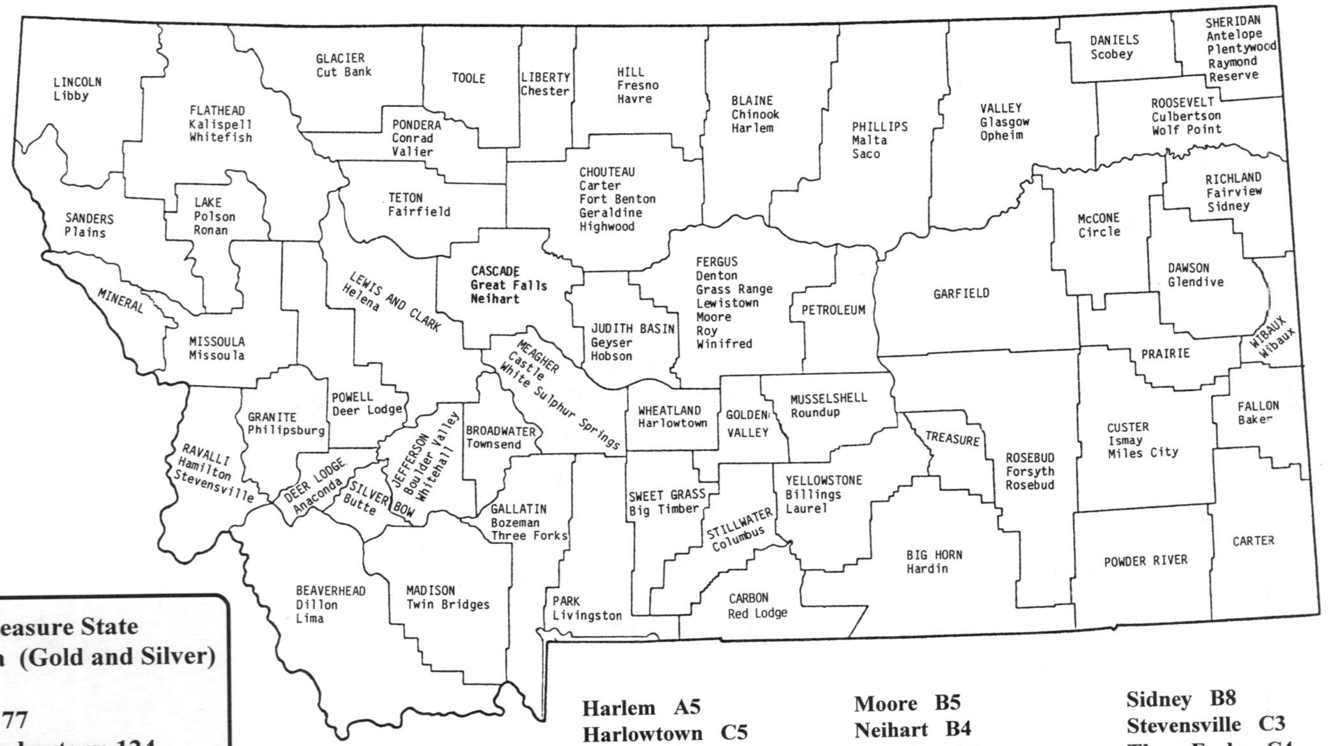

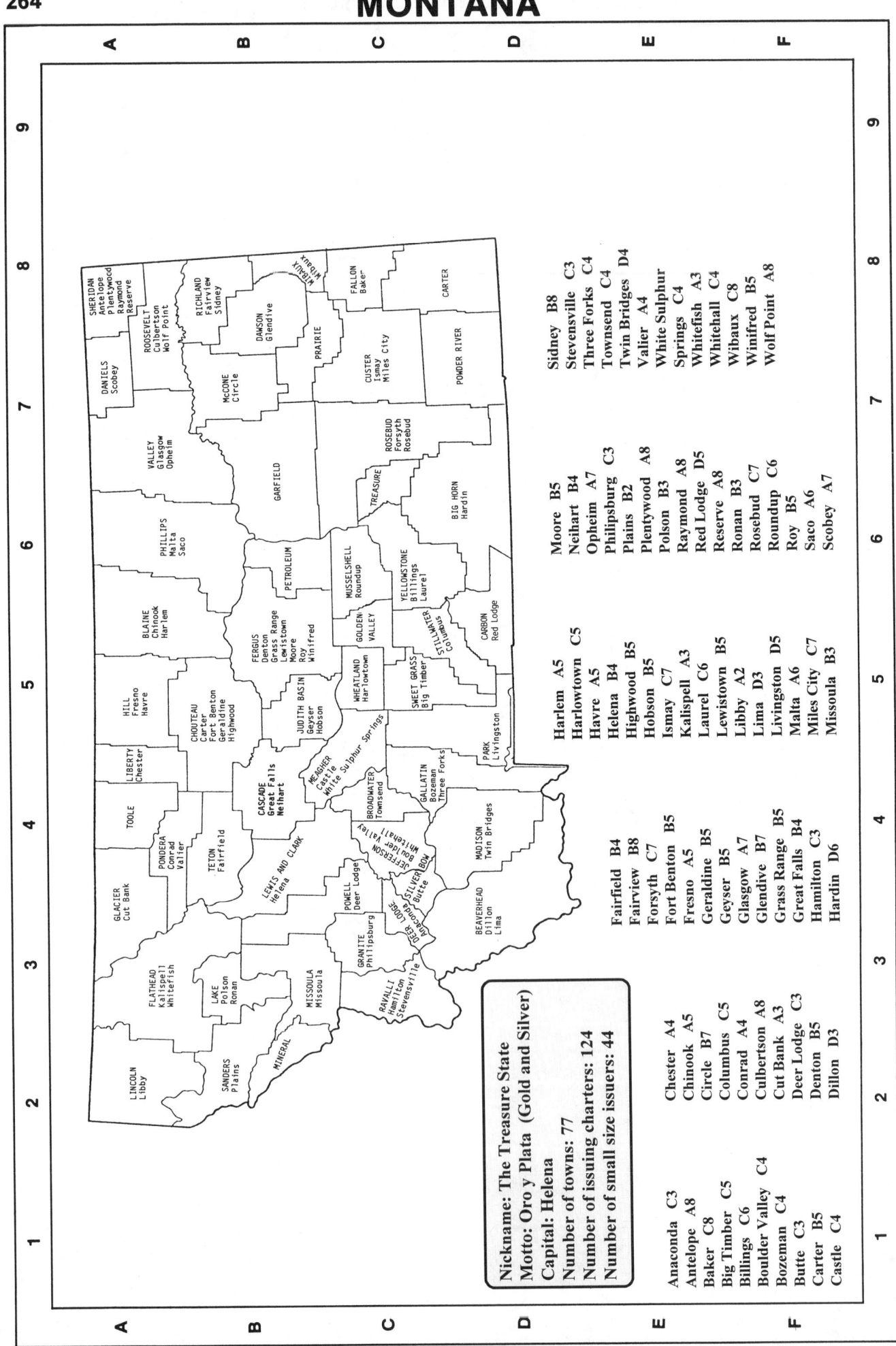

Nickname: The Treasure State
Motto: Oro y Plata (Gold and Silver)
Capital: Helena
Number of towns: 77
Number of issuing charters: 124
Number of small size issuers: 44

Anaconda C3
Antelope A8
Baker C8
Big Timber C5
Billings C6
Boulder Valley C4
Bozeman C4
Butte C3
Carter B5
Castle C4
Chester A4
Chinook A5
Circle B7
Columbus C5
Conrad A4
Culbertson A8
Cut Bank A3
Deer Lodge C3
Denton B5
Dillon D3
Fairfield B4
Fairview B8
Forsyth C7
Fort Benton B5
Fresno A5
Geraldine B5
Geyser B5
Glasgow A7
Glendive B7
Grass Range B5
Great Falls B4
Hamilton C3
Hardin D6
Harlem A5
Harlowtown C5
Havre A5
Helena B4
Highwood B5
Hobson B5
Ismay C7
Kalispell A3
Laurel C6
Lewistown B5
Libby A2
Lima D3
Livingston D5
Malta A6
Miles City C7
Missoula B3
Moore B5
Neihart B4
Opheim A7
Philipsburg C3
Plains B2
Plentywood A8
Polson B3
Raymond A8
Red Lodge D5
Reserve A8
Ronan B3
Rosebud C7
Roundup C6
Roy B5
Saco A6
Scobey A7
Sidney B8
Stevensville C3
Three Forks C4
Townsend C4
Twin Bridges D4
Valier A4
White Sulphur Springs C4
Whitefish A3
Whitehall C4
Wibaux C8
Winifred B5
Wolf Point A8

****
9583 Deer Lodge
ANACONDA NB, ANACONDA
{{ 1 L }}
Chartered 11/09
Liquidated 5/31/24
1902 Date Back <$VALUE
4x5 1-2400 <$1500
3x10-20 1-1920 <$1500
1902 Plain Back
4x5 2401-4295 <$1500
3x10-20 1921-2946 <$1500
Total Issue $233,200
Out at close $25,000
Ch 12542 assumed circulation
****
3965 Deer Lodge
FNB OF ANACONDA
{{ UNREPORTED }}
Chartered 1/17/89
Liquidated 2/1/95
TERRITORIAL ISSUES
Brown Back <$VALUE
50-100 1-167 <$10,000
STATE ISSUES
Brown Back
50-100 168-366 <$6500
Total Issue $54,900
Out in 1910 $600
****
12542 Deer Lodge
NB OF ANACONDA
{{ 4 L 23 S }}
Organized 5/7/24
Receivership 12/5/33
1902 Plain Back <$VALUE
4x5 1-11432 <$500
1929 Small Size
5 Type 1 1-6294 <$150
5 Type 2 1-3690 <$165
Total Issue $435,910
Out at close $49,635
Large out at close $2,005
Outstanding includes Ch 9583
****
11350 Sheridan
FNB OF ANTELOPE
{{ UNREPORTED }}
Chartered 5/19
Liquidated 3/6/22
1902 Plain Back <$VALUE
3x10-20 1-289 <$3500
Total Issue $14,450
Out at close $6,250
****
11074 Fallon
BAKER NB, BAKER
{{ 6 S }}
Chartered 9/17 as FNB of Plevna, under which there was no issue. Issuing title adopted 2/4/25.
1929 Small Size <$VALUE
5 Type 2 1-2364 <$375
10 Type 2 1-1125 <$375
20 Type 2 1-409 <$375
Total Issue $31,250
Out in 1935 $25,000
****
10443 Fallon
FNB OF BAKER
{{ UNREPORTED }}
Organized 8/19/13
Receivership 5/20/24
1902 Date Back <$VALUE
3x10-20 1-960 <$3000
1902 Plain Back
3x10-20 961-2960 <$3000
Total Issue $148,000
Out at close $21,900
****
4932 Sweet Grass
BIG TIMBER NB, BIG TIMBER
{{ 2 L }}
Chartered 1893
Liquidated 12/4/13
Brown Back <$VALUE
3x10-20 1-1970 <$4000
1882 Date Back
3x10-20 1-2809 <$4000
Total Issue $238,950
Out in 1914 $24,425
****
4590 Sweet Grass
FNB OF BIG TIMBER
{{ UNREPORTED }}
Chartered 6/29/91
Liquidated 7/27/93
Brown Back <$VALUE
3x10-20 1-295 <$5000
Total Issue $14,750
Out in 1910 $150
****
3097 Yellowstone
FNB OF BILLINGS
Organized 12/27/83
Receivership 7/2/10
TERRITORIAL ISSUES {{ 4 L }}
Brown Back <$VALUE
4x5 1-2637 <$4000
STATE ISSUES {{ 1 L }}
Brown Back
4x5 2638-5927 <$2500
3x10-20 1-4250 <$2500
1902 Red Seal
50-100 1-523 <$10,000
Total Issue $409,490
Out in 1915 $8,070
****
9355 Yellowstone
MERCHANTS NB OF BILLINGS
{{ 3 L }}
Chartered 3/09
Closed 10/7/21
1902 Date Back <$VALUE
3x10-20 1-6500 <$700
1902 Plain Back
3x10-20 6501-6697 <$700
Total Issue $334,850
Out in 1921 $50,000
Ch 4593 assumed circulation
****
12407 Yellowstone
MIDLAND NB OF BILLINGS
{{ 10 L 43 S }}
Chartered 7/23
1902 Plain Back <$VALUE
3x10-20 1-10734 <$300
1929 Small Size
10 Type 1 1-5080 <$100
20 Type 1 1-1168 <$110
5 Type 2 1-324 <$150
10 Type 2 1-8347 <$125
Total Issue $1,066,750
Out in 1935 $200,000
Large out 1935 $9,645
Outstanding includes Ch 4593
****
Yellowstone Merchants NB of Billings
SEE Ch 4593
Yellowstone NB of Billings
****
4593 Yellowstone
YELLOWSTONE NB OF BILLINGS
Chartered 1891
Liquidated 10/23/23
2nd title: Yellowstone-Merchants NB 10/7/21
FIRST TITLE {{ 4 L }}
Brown Back <$VALUE
3x10-20 1-2790 <$2000
1882 Date Back
3x10-20 1-1166 <$2000
1902 Date Back
3x10-20 1-5100 <$750
1902 Plain Back
3x10-20 5101-10600 <$750
SECOND TITLE {{ 1 L }}
1902 Plain Back
3x10-20 1-2490 <$1250
Total Issue $852,300
Out at close $150,000
Outstanding includes Ch 9355
Ch 12407 assumed circulation
****
4323 Jefferson
FNB OF BOULDER VALLEY
{{ UNREPORTED }}
Chartered 5/28/90
Liquidated 5/1/94
Brown Back <$VALUE
3x10-20 1-402 <$5000
Total Issue $20,100
Out in 1910 $150
****
2803 Gallatin
BOZEMAN NB, BOZEMAN
{{ UNREPORTED }}
Organized 10/23/82
Liquidated 1/1/07
TERRITORIAL ISSUES
Brown Back <$VALUE
4x5 1-1625 <$6000
STATE ISSUES
Brown Back
4x5 1626-3589 <$3500
3x10-20 1-199 <$3500
1902 Red Seal
3x10-20 1-417 <$5000
Total Issue $102,580
Out in 1910 $2,735
****
4968 Gallatin
COMMERCIAL NB OF BOZEMAN
{{ 7 L 16 S }}
Chartered 1894
Brown Back <$VALUE
3x10-20 1-4000 <$1500
1882 Date Back
3x10-20 1-2370 <$1500
1902 Date Back
3x10-20 1-2000 <$300
1902 Plain Back
3x10-20 2001-9587 <$300
1929 Small Size
10 Type 1 1-1260 <$160
20 Type 1 1-438 <$175
10 Type 2 1-1675 <$200
20 Type 2 1-702 <$200
Total Issue $966,800
Out in 1935 $62,500
Large out 1935 $4,230
****
2027 Gallatin
FNB OF BOZEMAN
{{ UNREPORTED }}
Organized 8/14/72
Receivership 9/14/78
TERRITORIAL ISSUES
Original Series <$VALUE
4x5 1-3250 <$6000
Series 1875
4x5 1-1330 <$6000
Total Issue $91,600
Out in 1915 $560
****
3075 Gallatin
GALLATIN VALLEY NB OF BOZEMAN
Chartered 11/14/83
Liquidated 8/18/93
TERRITORIAL ISSUES {{ 1 L }}
Brown Back <$VALUE
3x10-20 1-1040 <$6000
STATE ISSUES {{ 0 L }}
Brown Back
3x10-20 1041-1480 <$4000
Total Issue $74,000
Out in 1910 $520
****
7441 Gallatin
NB OF GALLATIN VALLEY AT BOZEMAN
{{ 2 L }}
Chartered 10/04
Liquidated 3/22/26
1902 Red Seal <$VALUE
3x10-20 1-725 <$4000
1902 Date Back
3x10-20 1-1420 <$1750
1902 Plain Back
3x10-20 1421-2535 <$1750
Total Issue $163,000
Out at close $15,000
****
2566 Silver Bow
FNB OF BUTTE
Chartered 9/24/81
TERRITORIAL ISSUES {{ 5 L }}
Series 1875 <$VALUE
4x5 1-2900 <$5000
3x10-20 1-1180 <$5000
STATE ISSUES {{ 16 L 14 S }}
Series 1875
3x10-20 1181-5797 <$3000
Brown Back
50-100 1-2934 <$2000/$2500
1882 Date Back
50-100 1-1300 <$1250/$1500
3x50-100 1-2908<$1250/$1500
1902 Plain Back
3x50-100 1-1933 <$500/$600
1929 Small Size
50 Type 1 1-268 <$350
100 Type 1 1-164 <$400
Total Issue $2,372,000
Out in 1935 $199,450
Large out 1935 $21,950
****
4283 Silver Bow
SILVER BOW NB OF BUTTE
{{ 6 L }}
Chartered 1890
Liquidated 6/19/22
Brown Back <$VALUE
4x5 1-2500 <$2000
3x10-20 1-2060 <$2000
1882 Date Back
4x5 1-2060 <$2000
3x10-20 1-1398 <$2000
1902 Date Back
3x10-20 1-4380 <$750
50-100 1-1140 <$1250/$1500
1902 Plain Back
3x10-20 4381-7633 <$750
Total Issue $816,750
Out at close $100,000
****
10995 Chouteau
FNB OF CARTER
{{ 1 L }}
Organized 4/25/17
Receivership 11/9/23
1902 Plain Back <$VALUE
3x10-20 1-1420 <$2500
Total Issue $71,000
Out at close $25,000
****
4572 Meagher
FNB OF CASTLE
{{ UNREPORTED }}
Chartered 5/22/91
Liquidated 1/4/93
Brown Back <$VALUE
3x10-20 1-347 <$5000
Total Issue $17,350
Out in 1910 $120
****
11105 Liberty
FNB OF CHESTER
{{ UNREPORTED }}
Organized 11/15/17
Receivership 7/30/23
1902 Plain Back <$VALUE
3x10-20 1-1530 <$3000
Total Issue $76,500
Out at close $24,500
****
13837 Blaine
FARMERS NB IN CHINOOK
{{ 3 S }}
Chartered 11/33
1929 Small Size <$VALUE
10 Type 2 1-2047 <$500
20 Type 2 1-614 <$500
Total Issue $32,750
Out in 1935 $20,450
****
10053 Blaine
FARMERS NB OF CHINOOK
{{ 1 L 5 S }}
Organized 6/3/11
Liquidated 12/18/33
1902 Date Back <$VALUE
3x10-20 1-600 <$1500
1902 Plain Back
3x10-20 601-1269 <$1500
1929 Small Size
10 Type 1 1-513 <$400
20 Type 1 1-138 <$400
Total Issue $110,790
Out at close $25,000
Large out at close $1,880
Ch 6097 assumed circulation
****
6097 Blaine
FNB OF CHINOOK
{{ 4 L 2 S }}
Chartered 1/02
Liquidated 4/30/30
Brown Back <$VALUE
3x10-20 1-980 <$2500
1882 Date Back
3x10-20 1-2000* <$2250
1882 Value Back
3x10-20 2201-2590* <$2500
* 2001-2200 not marked
1902 Plain Back
3x10-20 1-1600 <$600
1929 Small Size
10 Type 1 1-161 <$500
20 Type 1 1-9 <$500
Total Issue $269,240
Out at close $17,620
Large out at close $6,880
Ch 10053 assumed circulation
****
11101 McCone
FNB OF CIRCLE
{{ 8 S }}
Chartered 11/17
1929 Small Size <$VALUE
5 Type 2 1-1754 <$450
10 Type 2 1-1140 <$450
20 Type 2 1-564 <$450
Total Issue $31,450
Out in 1935 $25,000
****
9396 Stillwater
FNB OF COLUMBUS
{{ 5 L 6 S }}
Organized 3/27/09
Receivership 1/29/32
1902 Date Back <$VALUE
3x10-20 1-2110 <$600
1902 Plain Back
3x10-20 2111-5386 <$600
1929 Small Size
10 Type 1 1-379 <$350
20 Type 1 1-102 <$350
Total Issue $304,280
Out at close $24,640
Large out at close $3,505
****
9759 Pondera
FNB OF CONRAD
{{ 4 L U + 13 S }}
Organized 11/23/10
Receivership 10/25/33
1902 Date Back <$VALUE
3x10-20 1-720 <$600
1902 Plain Back
3x10-20 721-7332 <$600
1929 Small Size
10 Type 1 1-1845 <$175
20 Type 1 1-472 <$200
Total Issue $533,940
Out at close $75,000
Large out at close $2,960
****
8168 Roosevelt
FNB OF CULBERTSON
{{ UNREPORTED }}
Chartered 4/06
Liquidated 8/21/11
1902 Red Seal <$VALUE
3x10-20 1-295 <$5000
1902 Date Back
3x10-20 1-568 <$4000
Total Issue $43,150
Out in 1911 $4,950
****
9574 Glacier
FNB OF CUT BANK
{{ UNREPORTED }}
Organized 10/5/09
Receivership 1/29/21
1902 Date Back <$VALUE
3x10-20 1-700 <$4000
1902 Plain Back
3x10-20 701-820 <$4000
Total Issue $41,000
Out at close $5,800
****
1975 Powell
FNB OF DEER LODGE
{{ 1 L }}
Chartered 5/5/72
Liquidated 8/16/79
TERRITORIAL ISSUES
Original Series <$VALUE
4x5 1-3250 <$6000
Series 1875
4x5 1-2098 <$6000
Total Issue $106,960
Out in 1910 $825
****
9899 Powell
UNITED STATES NB OF DEER LODGE
{{ 3 L 3 S }}
Organized 11/9/10
Receivership 10/25/32
1902 Date Back <$VALUE
4x10 1-1750 <$1500
1902 Plain Back
4x10 1751-3882 <$1500
1929 Small Size
10 Type 1 1-482 <$750
Total Issue $184,200
Out at close $12,500
Large out at close $940
****
10819 Fergus
FNB OF DENTON
{{ 3 L }}
Organized 1/8/16
Receivership 3/5/29
1902 Plain Back <$VALUE
3x10-20 1-3154 <$800
Total Issue $157,700
Out at close $24,450
****
3173 Beaverhead
DILLON NB, DILLON
{{ UNREPORTED }}
Chartered 5/2/84
Liquidated 9/20/93
TERRITORIAL ISSUES
Brown Back <$VALUE
3x10-20 1-540 <$6000
STATE ISSUES
Brown Back
3x10-20 541-685 <$4000
Total Issue $34,250
Out in 1910 $260
****
3120 Beaverhead
FNB OF DILLON
Chartered 1884
TERRITORIAL ISSUES {{ 0 L }}
Brown Back <$VALUE
3x10-20 1-520 <$5000
STATE ISSUES {{ 9 L 10 S }}
Brown Back
3x10-20 521-1357 <$1750
1902 Red Seal
4x5 1-1300 <$3500
3x10-20 1-1590 <$3500
1902 Date Back
4x5 1-4700 <$400
3x10-20 1-3560 <$400
1902 Plain Back
4x5 4701-10873 <$400
3x10-20 3561-7821 <$400
1929 Small Size
5 Type 1 1-1696 <$250
10 Type 1 1-470 <$250
20 Type 1 1-250 <$250
5 Type 2 1-2524 <$275
10 Type 2 1-1479 <$275
20 Type 2 1-363 <$275
Total Issue $455,610
Out in 1935 $50,000
Large out 1935 $3,750
****
11307 Teton
FNB OF FAIRFIELD
{{ UNREPORTED }}
Chartered 2/19
1902 Plain Back <$VALUE
3x10-20 1-788 <$3500
Total Issue $39,400
Out in 1935 $140
****
12015 Richland
FNB OF FAIRVIEW
{{ UNREPORTED }}
Organized 8/26/21
Receivership 11/8/23
1902 Plain Back <$VALUE
4x5 1-130 <$4000
4x10 1-30 <$4000
3x10-20 1-68 <$4000
Total Issue $7,200
Out at close $6,200
Outstanding includes Ch 10425
****
7320 Rosebud
FNB OF FORSYTH
{{ 2 L }}
Organized 6/10/04
Receivership 12/18/23
1902 Red Seal <$VALUE
4x5 1-1150 <$4000
3x10-20 1-922 <$4000
1902 Date Back
4x5 1-2950 <$1500
3x10-20 1-2060 <$1500
1902 Plain Back
4x5 2951-5405 <$1500
3x10-20 2061-3540 <$1500
Total Issue $354,200
Out at close $33,700
****

****
2476 Chouteau
FNB OF FORT BENTON
Chartered 5/14/80
Receivership 3/6/97
2nd title: Northwestern NB of Great Falls 4/15/91
FIRST TITLE
TERRITORIAL ISSUES {{ 3 L }}
Series 1875 <$VALUE
4x5 1-3099 <$5000
3x10-20 1-2130 <$5000
STATE ISSUES {{ 0 L }}
Series 1875
3x10-20 2131-2195 <$4000
SECOND TITLE {{ 2 L }}
Series 1875
3x10-20 1-1500 <$3000
Total Issue $246,730
Out in 1915 $1,650
****
4194 Chouteau
STOCKMENS NB OF FORT BENTON
{{ 6 L }}
Organized 12/24/89
Receivership 2/26/24
Brown Back <$VALUE
3x10-20 1-12920 <$1500
1882 Date Back
3x10-20 1-2050 <$1500
1902 Date Back
3x10-20 1-12200 <$400
1902 Plain Back
3x10-20 12201-28090 <$400
Total Issue $2,153,000
Out at close $190,795
****
11096 Hill
FNB OF FRESNO
{{ 1 L }}
Organized 10/3/17
Receivership 10/26/22
1902 Plain Back <$VALUE
3x10-20 1-880 <$2500
Total Issue $44,000
Out at close $14,500
****
10803 Chouteau
FNB OF GERALDINE
{{ 3 L 6 S }}
Chartered 11/15
1902 Plain Back <$VALUE
4x5 1-3920 <$850
3x10-20 1-2393 <$850
1929 Small Size
5 Type 1 1-670 <$350
10 Type 1 1-398 <$350
20 Type 1 1-136 <$350
5 Type 2 1-1608 <$400
10 Type 2 1-627 <$400
20 Type 2 1-144 <$400
Total Issue $275,540
Out in 1935 $24,995
Large out 1935 $1,285
****
10952 Judith Basin
FNB OF GEYSER
{{ 2U + 4 L }}
Chartered 2/17
Liquidated 1/5/35
1902 Plain Back <$VALUE
3x10-20 1-2414 <$1000
Total Issue $120,700
Out in 1925 $25,000
Out at close $470
****
7990 Valley
FNB OF GLASGOW
{{ 11 L U + 18 S }}
Chartered 12/05
1902 Red Seal <$VALUE
4x5 1-250 <$3500
3x10-20 1-400 <$3500
1902 Date Back
4x5 1-3425 <$300
3x10-20 1-2480 <$300
1902 Plain Back
4x5 3426-10860 <$300
3x10-20 2481-7175 <$300
1929 Small Size
5 Type 1 1-1562 <$175
10 Type 1 1-716 <$175
20 Type 1 1-210 <$175
5 Type 2 1-2732 <$175
10 Type 2 1-1433 <$175
20 Type 2 1-336 <$200
Total Issue $750,680
Out in 1935 $50,000
Large out 1935 $3,800
****

****
8655 Valley
GLASGOW NB, GLASGOW
{{ 6 L }}
Organized 2/19/07
Receivership 12/29/25
1902 Red Seal <$VALUE
3x10-20 1-200 <$3500
1902 Date Back
3x10-20 1-500* <$400
1902 Plain Back
3x10-20 601-6852* <$400
* 501-600 not marked
Total Issue $352,600
Out at close $50,000
****
7101 Dawson
FNB OF GLENDIVE
{{ 0 L 11 S }}
Chartered 1/04
1902 Red Seal <$VALUE
3x10-20 1-570 <$4000
1902 Date Back
3x10-20 1-1280 <$2000
1902 Plain Back
3x10-20 1281-2526 <$2000
1929 Small Size
10 Type 1 1-304 <$275
20 Type 1 1-99 <$275
Total Issue $184,920
Out in 1935 $12,500
Large out 1935 $1,090
****
8055 Dawson
MERCHANTS NB OF GLENDIVE
{{ UNREPORTED }}
Chartered 1/06
1902 Red Seal <$VALUE
3x10-20 1-600 <$5000
1902 Date Back
3x10-20 1-2740 <$2000
1902 Plain Back
3x10-20 2741-3318 <$2000
Total Issue $195,900
Large out 1935 $750
****
10939 Fergus
FNB OF GRASS RANGE
{{ 7 L 0 S }}
Organized 12/18/16
Receivership 7/9/30
1902 Plain Back <$VALUE
4x5 1-1850 <$1500
4x10 1-1164 <$1500
1929 Small Size
5 Type 1 1-150 <$1500
10 Type 1 1-63 <$1500
Total Issue $91,840
Out at close $10,000
Large out at close $2,090
****
10530 Cascade
COMMERCIAL NB OF GREAT FALLS
{{ 1 L }}
Organized 4/20/14
Receivership 12/9/22
1902 Plain Back <$VALUE
3x10-20 1-11368 <$1000
Total Issue $568,400
Out at close $177,600
****
3525 Cascade
FNB OF GREAT FALLS
Organized 7/1/86
TERRITORIAL ISSUES {{ 0 L }}
Brown Back <$VALUE
4x5 1-1875 <$4000
STATE ISSUES {{U + 13 L 32 S}}
Brown Back
4x5 1876-7295 <$1500
3x10-20 1-8219 <$1500
1902 Red Seal
3x10-20 1-3500 <$3500
1902 Date Back
3x10-20 1-10500 <$300
1902 Plain Back
3x10-20 10501-28860 <$300
1929 Small Size
10 Type 1 1-3684 <$100
20 Type 1 1-984 <$100
10 Type 2 1-5598 <$125
20 Type 2 1-1229 <$125
Total Issue $2,594,530
Out in 1935 $155,000
Large out 1935 $5,730
****

****
4541 Cascade
GREAT FALLS NB, GREAT FALLS
{{ 10 L 26 S }}
Chartered 1891
Brown Back <$VALUE
3x10-20 1-7640 <$1500
1882 Date Back
3x10-20 1-84 <$1500
1902 Date Back
3x10-20 1-5100 <$300
1902 Plain Back
3x10-20 5101-20724 <$300
1929 Small Size
10 Type 1 1-1228 <$100
20 Type 1 1-1460 <$100
5 Type 2 1-1744 <$125
10 Type 2 1-960 <$125
20 Type 2 1-1129 <$125
Total Issue $1,712,180
Out in 1935 $125,000
Large out 1935 $8,250
****
4434 Cascade
MERCHANTS NB OF GREAT FALLS
{{ UNREPORTED }}
Organized 10/7/90
Receivership 7/29/93
Brown Back <$VALUE
4x5 1-1885 <$3000
Total Issue $37,700
Out in 1915 $330
****
Northwestern NB of Great Falls
SEE Ch 2476
FNB of Fort Benton
****
9486 Ravalli
FNB OF HAMILTON
{{ 5 L U + 2 S }}
Chartered 7/09
Liquidated 5/31/30
1902 Date Back <$VALUE
4x5 1-2100 <$600
3x10-20 1-1660 <$600
1902 Plain Back
4x5 2101-7675 <$600
3x10-20 1661-5093 <$600
1929 Small Size
5 Type 1 1-359 <$500
10 Type 1 1-201 <$500
20 Type 1 1-14 <$500
Total Issue $432,660
Out at close $34,820
Large out at close $10,310
****
9215 Big Horn
FNB OF HARDIN
{{ 3 L 5 S }}
Organized 7/20/08
1902 Date Back <$VALUE
3x10-20 1-2410 <$800
1902 Plain Back
3x10-20 2411-5843 <$800
1929 Small Size
10 Type 1 1-562 <$400
20 Type 1 1-160 <$400
10 Type 2 1-1085 <$450
20 Type 2 1-175 <$450
Total Issue $359,420
Out in 1935 $25,000
Large out 1935 $1,470
****
7644 Blaine
FNB OF HARLEM
{{ 0 L 1 S }}
Organized 2/9/05
Receivership 1/21/32
1902 Red Seal <$VALUE
3x10-20 1-300 <$5000
1902 Date Back
3x10-20 1-660 <$2500
1902 Plain Back
3x10-20 661-1342 <$2500
1929 Small Size
10 Type 1 1-112 <$1250
20 Type 1 1-22 <$1250
Total Issue $91,460
Out at close $6,010
Large out at close $890
****

****
11085 Wheatland
FARMERS NB OF HARLOWTOWN
{{ 4 L 2 S }}
Chartered 10/17
Liquidated 1/22/30
1902 Plain Back <$VALUE
3x10-20 1-2962 <$600
1929 Small Size
10 Type 1 1-150 <$600
20 Type 1 1-9 <$600
Total Issue $158,180
Out at close $20,380
Large out at close $10,300
****
FNB of Harlowtown
SEE Ch 9270
Musselshell Valley NB of Harlowtown
****
9270 Wheatland
MUSSELSHELL VALLEY NB OF HARLOWTOWN
{{ UNREPORTED }}
Organized 10/27/08
Receivership 3/7/23
2nd title: FNB of Harlowtown 6/27/10
FIRST TITLE
1902 Date Back <$VALUE
4x5 1-325 <$3500
3x10-20 1-117 <$3500
50-100 1-27 <$4000
SECOND TITLE
1902 Date Back
4x5 1-925 <$2500
3x10-20 1-830 <$2500
1902 Plain Back
4x5 926-1470 <$2500
3x10-20 831-1193 <$2500
Total Issue $105,450
Out at close $12,100
****
9440 Hill
CITIZENS NB OF HAVRE
{{ UNREPORTED }}
Chartered 6/09
Liquidated 1/2/13
1902 Date Back <$VALUE
3x10-20 1-658 <$2500
Total Issue $32,900
Out in 1913 $6,550
****
5676 Hill
FNB OF HAVRE
{{ 1 L }}
Chartered 1/11/01
Liquidated 2/6/09
Brown Back <$VALUE
4x5 1-330 <$3500
3x10-20 1-307 <$3500
Total Issue $21,950
Out in 1910 $2,325
****
9782 Hill
HAVRE NB, HAVRE
{{ 1 L }}
Organized 5/18/10
Receivership 9/16/21
1902 Date Back <$VALUE
3x10-20 1-1320 <$1500
1902 Plain Back
3x10-20 1321-3566 <$1500
Total Issue $178,300
Out at close $49,600
****
4396 Lewis and Clark
AMERICAN NB OF HELENA
Chartered 1890
2nd title: FNB & TC of Helena 5/23/31
FIRST TITLE {{14 L U + 14 S}}
Brown Back <$VALUE
3x10-20 1-9000 <$1250
1882 Date Back
3x10-20 1-1482 <$1250
1902 Date Back
3x10-20 1-9500 <$300
1902 Plain Back
3x10-20 9501-24379 <$300
1929 Small Size
10 Type 1 1-1570 <$150
20 Type 1 1-466 <$150
SECOND TITLE {{ 30 S }}
1929 Small Size
10 Type 1 1-2068 <$125
20 Type 1 1-530 <$135
10 Type 2 1-4093 <$150
20 Type 2 1-1261 <$150
Total Issue $2,147,000
Out in 1935 $200,000
Large out 1935 $19,610
Outstanding includes Ch 5671
****
1649 Lewis and Clark
FNB OF HELENA
Organized 4/5/66
Receivership 9/11/96
TERRITORIAL ISSUES {{ 7 L }}
Original Series <$VALUE
3x1-2 1-3000<$5000/$10,000
4x5 1-3300 <$5000
3x10-20 1-1120 <$6000
Series 1875
4x5 1-3894 <$5000
3x10-20 1-2539 <$6000
Brown Back
4x5 1 1900 <$3500
3x10-20 1-1030 <$3500
50-100 1-214 <$6500
STATE ISSUES {{ 0 L }}
Brown Back
4x5 1901-2603 <$3000
3x10-20 1031-1730 <$3000
50-100 215-291 <$5000
Total Issue $524,000
Out in 1915 $3,591
****
FNB & TC of Helena
SEE Ch 4396
American NB of Helena
****
4406 Lewis and Clark
HELENA NB, HELENA
{{ UNREPORTED }}
Chartered 8/29/90
Liquidated 1/8/95
Brown Back <$VALUE
3x10-20 1-2067 <$4000
Total Issue $103,350
Out in 1910 $780
****
2732 Lewis and Clark
MERCHANTS NB OF HELENA
Organized 6/14/82
Receivership 6/2/97
TERRITORIAL ISSUES {{ 0 L }}
Series 1875 <$VALUE
3x10-20 1-2700 <$6000
STATE ISSUES {{ 3 L }}
Series 1875
3x10-20 2701-4549 <$3000
Total Issue $227,450
Out in 1915 $1,410
****
1960 Lewis and Clark
MONTANA NB OF HELENA
{{ 1 L }}
Chartered 4/17/72
Liquidated 4/15/73
TERRITORIAL ISSUES
Original Series <$VALUE
4x5 1-1575 <$6000
Total Issue $31,500
Out in 1910 $50
****
2813 Lewis and Clark
MONTANA NB OF HELENA
Organized 11/11/82
Liquidated 2/23/01
TERRITORIAL ISSUES {{ 2 L }}
Brown Back <$VALUE
3x10-20 1-2650 <$4000
STATE ISSUES {{ 0 L }}
Brown Back
3x10-20 2651-5284 <$3000
Total Issue $264,200
Out in 1910 $2,550
****
5671 Lewis and Clark
NB OF MONTANA, HELENA
{{ 24 L 8 S }}
Chartered 1/8/01
Closed 5/23/31
Brown Back <$VALUE
3x10-20 1-10200 <$1250
1882 Date Back
3x10-20 1-11700 <$1000
1882 Value Back
3x10-20 11701-18444 <$1000
1902 Plain Back
3x10-20 1-12365 <$300
1929 Small Size
10 Type 1 1-1188 <$200
20 Type 1 1-343 <$200
Total Issue $2,162,890
Out at close $100,000
Large out at close $22,640
Ch 4396 assumed circulation
****

****
2105 Lewis and Clark
PEOPLES NB OF HELENA
{{ UNREPORTED }}
Chartered 5/13/73
Receivership 9/13/78
TERRITORIAL ISSUES
Original Series <$VALUE
4x5 1-800 <$6000
3x10-20 1-310 <$7000
20 311-1310 <$7000
50-100 1-390 <$15,000
Series 1875
4x5 1-270 <$6000
3x10-20 1-65 <$7000
50-100 1-67 <$15,000
Total Issue $128,700
Out in 1915 $335
****
2757 Lewis and Clark
SECOND NB OF HELENA
{{ UNREPORTED }}
Chartered 7/20/82
Liquidated 9/30/93
TERRITORIAL ISSUES
Brown Back <$VALUE
4x5 1-3125 <$5000
STATE ISSUES
Brown Back
4x5 3126-4253 <$3500
Total Issue $85,060
Out in 1910 $830
****
11131 Chouteau
FNB OF HIGHWOOD
{{ 1 L }}
Organized 12/29/17
Receivership 12/29/22
1902 Plain Back <$VALUE
3x10-20 1-1450 <$2500
Total Issue $72,500
Out at close $25,000
****
10715 Judith Basin
FNB OF HOBSON
{{ 9 L 0 S }}
Organized 1/4/15
Receivership 12/26/30
1902 Plain Back <$VALUE
4x5 1-11691 <$350
1929 Small Size
5 Type 1 1-314 <$1000
10 Type 1 1-81 <$1000
20 Type 1 1-35 <$1000
Total Issue $252,300
Out at close $20,000
Large out at close $1,770
****
9103 Ismay
FNB OF ISMAY
{{ 1 L 6 S }}
Chartered 4/08
1902 Red Seal <$VALUE
3x10-20 1-300 <$4000
1902 Date Back
3x10-20 1-940 <$1500
1902 Plain Back
3x10-20 941-1912 <$1500
1929 Small Size
5 Type 2 1-6856 <$350
Total Issue $144,880
Out in 1935 $20,000
Large out 1935 $560
****

CONDITION affects Value. The Values shown are for notes in FINE condition.

4803 Flathead
CONRAD NB OF KALISPELL
{{ 28 L 50+ S }}
Chartered 1892
Brown Back <$VALUE
4x5 1-7000 <$1250
3x10-20 1-2200 <$1250
1882 Date Back
4x5 1-2723 <$1000
3x10-20 1-1848 <$1000
1902 Date Back
4x5 1-9750 <$200
3x10-20 1-7600 <$200
1902 Plain Back
4x5 9751-48870 <$200
3x10-20 7601-33114 <$200
1929 Small Size
5 Type 1 1-8184 <$100
10 Type 1 1-4388 <$100
20 Type 1 1-1150 <$100
5 Type 2 1-4264 <$125
10 Type 2 1-2506 <$125
20 Type 2 1-623 <$125
Total Issue $3,735,600
Out in 1935 $100,000
Large out 1935 $16,540

4586 Flathead
FNB OF KALISPELL
{{ 13 L 22 S }}
Chartered 1891
Brown Back <$VALUE
3x10-20 1-5070 <$1250
1882 Date Back
3x10-20 1-2765 <$1000
1902 Date Back
3x10-20 1-7700 <$250
1902 Plain Back
3x10-20 7701-32927 <$250
1929 Small Size
10 Type 1 1-2804 <$125
20 Type 1 1-864 <$135
10 Type 2 1-1731 <$150
20 Type 2 1-230 <$175
Total Issue $2,331,930
Out in 1935 $50,000
Large out 1935 $10,225
Outstanding includes Ch 8635

4651 Flathead
GLOBE NB OF KALISPELL
{{ 2 L }}
Chartered 11/21/91
Liquidated 3/2/94
Brown Back <$VALUE
4x5 1-759 <$4000
Total Issue $15,180
Out in 1910 $170

8635 Flathead
KALISPELL NB, KALISPELL
{{ 2 L }}
Chartered 4/07
Liquidated 7/1/15
1902 Red Seal <$VALUE
3x10-20 1-360 <$3500
1902 Date Back
3x10-20 1-3796 <$1250
Total Issue $207,800
Out in 1915 $50,000
Ch 4586 assumed circulation

8716 Yellowstone
CITIZENS NB OF LAUREL
{{ 1 L }}
Organized 5/3/07
Receivership 1/4/23
1902 Red Seal <$VALUE
3x10-20 1-270 <$4000
1902 Date Back
3x10-20 1-960 <$1750
1902 Plain Back
3x10-20 961-2949 <$1750
Total Issue $160,950
Out at close $33,900

8669 Yellowstone
FNB OF LAUREL
{{ UNREPORTED }}
Chartered 5/1/07
Liquidated 9/12/08
1902 Red Seal <$VALUE
4x5 1-130 <$5000
3x10-20 1-103 <$5000
Total Issue $7,750
Out in 1910 $1,535

FNB of Fergus County in Lewistown
SEE Ch 7274
FNB of Lewistown

7274 Fergus
FNB OF LEWISTOWN
Organized 5/9/04
Receivership 4/12/24
2nd title: FNB of Fergus County in Lewistown 1/11/23
FIRST TITLE {{ 17 L }}
1902 Red Seal <$VALUE
4x5 1-5865 <$3500
3x10-20 1-4564 <$3500
1902 Date Back
4x5 1-13000* <$250
3x10-20 1-9400** <$250
1902 Plain Back
4x5 13751-30500* <$250
3x10-20 10001-19600** <$250
* 13001-13750 not marked
** 9401-10000 not marked
SECOND TITLE {{ 1 L }}
1902 Plain Back
4x5 1-185 <$800
3x10-20 1-204 <$800
Total Issue $1,953,900
Out at close $124,500

12608 Fergus
NB OF LEWISTOWN
{{ U + 7 S }}
Chartered 12/24
1929 Small Size <$VALUE
5 Type 2 1-6288 <$250
10 Type 2 1-2874 <$250
20 Type 2 1-867 <$250
Total Issue $77,520
Out in 1935 $50,000

9594 Lincoln
FNB OF LIBBY
{{ 4 L }}
Organized 10/25/09
Liquidated 7/1/29
1902 Date Back <$VALUE
4x5 1-1400 <$500
3x10-20 1-1115 <$500
1902 Plain Back
4x5 1401-5405 <$500
3x10-20 1116-3491 <$500
Total Issue $282,650
Out at close $23,700

FNB of Lima
SEE Ch 11492
Security NB of Lima

11492 Beaverhead
SECURITY NB OF LIMA
Organized 10/3/19
Receivership 7/19/34
2nd title: FNB of Lima 2/23/22
FIRST TITLE {{ 3 L }}
1902 Plain Back <$VALUE
4x5 1-650 <$600
3x10-20 1-650 <$600
SECOND TITLE
{{ U + 16 L U + 10 S }}
1902 Plain Back
3x10-20 1-2301 <$275/$300
1929 Small Size
10 Type 1 1-652 <$175
20 Type 1 1-192 <$175
10 Type 2 1-311 <$200
20 Type 2 1-105 <$200
Total Issue $227,920
Out at close $25,000
Large out at close $1,490

3006 Park
FNB OF LIVINGSTON
{{ UNREPORTED }}
Organized 7/16/83
Receivership 8/25/84
TERRITORIAL ISSUES
Brown Back <$VALUE
4x5 1-562 <$5000
Total Issue $11,240
Out in 1915 $130

4117 Park
LIVINGSTON NB, LIVINGSTON
{{ UNREPORTED }}
Organized 9/11/89
Receivership 7/20/93
TERRITORIAL ISSUES
Brown Back <$VALUE
4x5 1-625 <$5000
STATE ISSUES
Brown Back
4x5 626-1047 <$4000
Total Issue $20,940
Out in 1915 $160

3605 Park
NATIONAL PARK B OF LIVINGSTON
Chartered 1886
Liquidated 12/1/29
TERRITORIAL ISSUES {{ 1 L }}
Brown Back <$VALUE
4x5 1-1000 <$4000
STATE ISSUES {{ 9 L 1 S }}
Brown Back
4x5 1001-5790 <$2000
3x10-20 1-954 <$2000
1902 Red Seal
4x5 1-400 <$3500
3x10-20 1-425 <$3500
1902 Date Back
4x5 1-2350 <$500
3x10-20 1-2200 <$500
1902 Plain Back
4x5 2351-5718 <$500
3x10-20 2201-4585 <$500
1929 Small Size
5 Type 1 1-47* <$750
10 Type 1 1-10 <$750
*E000047A & F000047A not issued
Total Issue $488,260
Out at close $22,790
Large out at close $20,790

9738 Phillips
FNB OF MALTA
{{ 2 L }}
Organized 3/28/10
Receivership 12/28/25
1902 Date Back <$VALUE
3x10-20 1-720 <$1000
1902 Plain Back
3x10-20 721-4708 <$1000
Total Issue $235,400
Out at close $6,495

12536 Custer
FNB IN MILES CITY
{{ 1 L 22 S }}
Chartered 5/24
1902 Plain Back <$VALUE
3x10-20 1-538 <$1500
1929 Small Size
10 Type 2 1-13256 <$135
20 Type 2 1-4015 <$150
Total Issue $239,760
Out in 1935 $150,000
Large out 1935 $6,565
Outstanding includes Ch 2752

2752 Custer
FNB OF MILES CITY
Chartered 7/82
Liquidated 7/1/24
TERRITORIAL ISSUES {{ 0 L }}
Series 1875 <$VALUE
4x5 1-2250 <$6000
STATE ISSUES {{ 12 L }}
Series 1875
4x5 2251-4214 <$3000
3x10-20 1-199 <$3000
1902 Red Seal
3x10-20 1-3975 <$3500
1902 Date Back
3x10-20 1-11800 <$400
1902 Plain Back
3x10-20 11801-24617 <$400
Total Issue $1,523,830
Out at close $150,000
Ch 12536 assumed circulation

Commercial NB of Miles City
SEE Ch 5015
State NB of Miles City

5015 Custer
STATE NB OF MILES CITY
Organized 8/15/95
Receivership 2/15/24
2nd title: Commercial NB of Miles City 1/5/21
FIRST TITLE {{ 5 L }}
Brown Back <$VALUE
4x5 1-5200 <$1500
3x10-20 1-2640 <$1500
1882 Date Back
4x5 1-7574 <$1500
3x10-20 1-4367 <$1500
1902 Date Back
3x10-20 1-5300 <$500
SECOND TITLE {{ 3 L }}
1902 Plain Back
3x10-20 1-3200 <$600
Total Issue $1,030,830
Out at close $98,500

3275 Custer
STOCK GROWERS NB OF MILES CITY
{{ UNREPORTED }}
Organized 12/20/84
Receivership 8/9/93
TERRITORIAL ISSUES
Brown Back <$VALUE
3x10-20 1-890 <$6500
STATE ISSUES
Brown Back
3x10-20 891-1149 <$4000
Total Issue $57,450
Out in 1915 $270

FNB of Missoula
SEE Ch 2106
Missoula NB, Missoula

2106 Missoula
MISSOULA NB, MISSOULA
Chartered 5/14/73
2nd title: FNB of Missoula 1889
TERRITORIAL ISSUES
FIRST TITLE {{ 8 L }}
Original Series <$VALUE
3x1-2 1-700 <$5000/$10,000
4x5 1-2250 <$5000
Series 1875
4x5 1-3293 <$5000
SECOND TITLE {{ 0 L }}
Series 1875
3x10-20 1-440 <$5000
STATE ISSUES {{16 L 6U+50+S}}
Series 1875
3x10-20 441-681 <$3000
Brown Back
3x10-20 1-6750 <$1000
1882 Date Back
3x10-20 1-6576 <$850
1902 Date Back
4x5 1-4700 <$250
3x10-20 1-3500 <$250
1902 Plain Back
4x5 4701-16350 <$250
3x10-20 3501-24859 <$250
1929 Small Size
5 Type 1 1-4846 <$85
10 Type 1 1-3738 <$75
20 Type 1 1-950 <$85
5 Type 2 1-6992 <$100
10 Type 2 1-4421 <$100
20 Type 2 1-645 <$100
Total Issue $2,960,390
Out in 1935 $185,000
Large out 1935 $12,305

3995 Missoula
WESTERN MONTANA NB OF MISSOULA
Chartered 1889
TERRITORIAL ISSUES {{ 0 L }}
Brown Back <$VALUE
4x5 1-1000 <$4000
STATE ISSUES {{ 12 L 30 S }}
Brown Back
4x5 1001-4778 <$1250
3x10-20 1-1330 <$1250
1902 Date Back
4x5 1-6500 <$275
3x10-20 1-5200 <$275
1902 Plain Back
4x5 6501-18710 <$275
3x10-20 5201-13690 <$275
1929 Small Size
5 Type 1 1-3640 <$110
10 Type 1 1-1666 <$100
20 Type 1 1-478 <$110
5 Type 2 1-5016 <$125
10 Type 2 1-2286 <$125
20 Type 2 1-564 <$125
Total Issue $1,546,500
Out in 1935 $100,000
Large out 1935 $6,100

8539 Fergus
FNB OF MOORE
{{ UNREPORTED }}
Organized 1/7/07
Receivership 12/20/23
1902 Red Seal <$VALUE
3x10-20 1-1000 <$5000
1902 Date Back
3x10-20 1-1570 <$2000
1902 Plain Back
3x10-20 1571-3555 <$2000
Total Issue $227,750
Out at close $24,100

4600 Cascade
FNB OF NEIHART
{{ UNREPORTED }}
Chartered 7/22/91
Liquidated 6/11/94
Brown Back <$VALUE
4x5 1-1013 <$4000
Total Issue $20,260
Out at close $10,790

11097 Valley
FNB OF OPHEIM
{{ UNREPORTED }}
Chartered 11/17 as Farmers & Merchants NB of Opheim, under which there was no issue. Issuing title adopted 2/1/18.
Liquidated 2/15/21
1902 Plain Back <$VALUE
4x5 1-15 <$3000
3x10-20 1-56 <$3000
Total Issue $3,100
Out in 1921 $2,500

4658 Granite
FNB OF PHILIPSBURG
{{ 1 L }}
Organized 12/5/91
Liquidated 2/10/97
Brown Back <$VALUE
3x10-20 1-499 <$3500
Total Issue $24,950
Out in 1910 $380

4843 Granite
MERCHANTS & MINERS NB OF PHILIPSBURG
{{ UNREPORTED }}
Chartered 2/1/93
Receivership 7/28/97
Brown Back <$VALUE
3x10-20 1-444 <$4000
Total Issue $22,200
Out in 1915 $130

7172 Sanders
FNB OF PLAINS
{{ 9 L 2U + 5 S }}
Chartered 3/04
1902 Red Seal <$VALUE
3x10-20 1-970 <$3500
1902 Date Back
3x10-20 1-1800 <$400
1902 Plain Back
3x10-20 1801-5323 <$400
1929 Small Size
10 Type 1 1-606 <$400
20 Type 1 1-190 <$400
10 Type 2 1-624 <$400
20 Type 2 1-132 <$400
Total Issue $382,690
Out in 1935 $25,000
Large out 1935 $1,430

10438 Sheridan
FNB OF PLENTYWOOD
{{ UNREPORTED }}
Organized 5/12/13
Receivership 3/31/24
1902 Date Back <$VALUE
3x10-20 1-500 <$3000
1902 Plain Back
3x10-20 501-741 <$3000
Total Issue $37,050
Out at close $6,250

9449 Lake
FNB OF POLSON
{{ 2 L }}
Organized 3/26/09
Receivership 3/22/24
1902 Date Back <$VALUE
3x10-20 1-1950 <$1000
1902 Plain Back
3x10-20 1951-4091 <$1000
Total Issue $204,550
Out at close $24,700

11078 Sheridan
FNB OF RAYMOND
{{ 4 L }}
Chartered 9/17
Liquidated 12/1/27
1902 Plain Back <$VALUE
4x5 1-5005 <$650
Total Issue $100,100
Out at close $15,000

9841 Carbon
UNITED STATES NB OF RED LODGE
{{ 4 L 26 S }}
Chartered 9/10
1902 Date Back <$VALUE
4x10 1-2300* <$650
1902 Plain Back
4x10 2551-11235* <$650
* 2301-2550 not marked
1929 Small Size
10 Type 1 1-2308 <$150
10 Type 2 1-4402 <$150
Total Issue $631,900
Out in 1935 $60,000
Large out 1935 $1,670

10986 Sheridan
FNB OF RESERVE
{{ 1 L 8 S }}
Chartered 5/17
1902 Plain Back <$VALUE
4x5 1-3120 <$2000
3x10-20 1-2069 <$2000
1929 Small Size
5 Type 1 1-544 <$375
10 Type 1 1-370 <$375
20 Type 1 1-96 <$375
5 Type 2 1-1354 <$400
10 Type 2 1-729 <$400
20 Type 2 1-188 <$400
Total Issue $233,710
Out in 1935 $25,000
Large out 1935 $820

9864 Lake
FNB OF RONAN
{{ 1 L }}
Organized 8/31/10
Receivership 2/9/24
1902 Date Back <$VALUE,
3x10-20 1-700 <$2000
1902 Plain Back
3x10-20 701-960 <$2000
Total Issue $48,000
Out at close $5,950

11437 Rosebud
FNB OF ROSEBUD
{{ UNREPORTED }}
Chartered 8/19
Liquidated 12/31/23
1902 Plain Back <$VALUE
3x10-20 1-1212 <$3000
Total Issue $60,600
Out at close $20,000

9165 Musselshell
FNB OF ROUNDUP
{{ 2 L }}
Organized 5/22/08
Receivership 4/5/23
1902 Date Back <$VALUE
3x10-20 1-1290 <$2500
1902 Plain Back
3x10-20 1291-3179 <$2500
Total Issue $158,950
Out at close $24,400

****

10991 Fergus
FNB OF ROY
{{ 4 L }}
Organized 4/11/17
Receivership 2/11/30
1902 Plain Back <$VALUE
4x5 1-2820 <$850
3x10-20 1-1670 <$850
Total Issue $139,900
Out at close $2,410

****

9789 Phillips
FNB OF SACO
{{ 3 L }}
Organized 5/26/10
Receivership 6/4/26
1902 Date Back <$VALUE
3x10-20 1-840 <$1500
1902 Plain Back
3x10-20 841-1442 <$1500
Total Issue $72,100
Out at close $8,000

****

10838 Daniels
FNB OF SCOBEY
{{ 4 L 4 S }}
Organized 3/25/16
Receivership 7/14/31
1902 Plain Back <$VALUE
4x10 1-5839 <$650
1929 Small Size
10 Type 1 1-698 <$400
Total Issue $275,440
Out at close $30,000
Large out at close $3,190

****

11098 Daniels
MERCHANTS NB OF SCOBEY
{{ 1 L }}
Chartered 11/17
Liquidated 12/31/27
1902 Plain Back <$VALUE
3x10-20 1-506 <$2000
Total Issue $25,300
Out at close $13,800

****

10552 Richland
FARMERS NB OF SIDNEY
{{ UNREPORTED }}
Chartered 6/14
Liquidated 10/10/16
1902 Plain Back <$VALUE
3x10-20 1-496 <$2500
Total Issue $24,800
Out at close $20,000

****

9004 Richland
FNB OF SIDNEY
{{ 5 L }}
Organized 12/23/07
Receivership 2/26/24
1902 Red Seal <$VALUE
3x10-20 1-300 <$3500
1902 Date Back
3x10-20 1-2500 <$400
1902 Plain Back
3x10-20 2501-5639 <$400
Total Issue $296,950
Out at close $39,000

****

10709 Ravalli
FNB OF STEVENSVILLE
{{ UNREPORTED }}
Organized 2/14/15
Receivership 3/2/25
1902 Plain Back <$VALUE
3x10-20 1-724 <$3000
Total Issue $36,200
Out at close $10,000

****

9337 Gallatin
FNB OF THREE FORKS
{{ 1 L }}
Chartered 2/09
Liquidated 3/19/23
1902 Date Back <$VALUE
3x10-20 1-820 <$3000
1902 Plain Back
3x10-20 821-989 <$3000
Total Issue $49,450
Out at close $6,250

****

9982 Broadwater
FNB OF TOWNSEND
{{ 1 L }}
Organized 1/31/11
Receivership 1/8/25
1902 Date Back <$VALUE
4x5 1-975 <$1500
4x10 1-975 <$1500
1902 Plain Back
4x5 976-2080 <$1500
4x10 976-1751 <$1500
Total Issue $111,640
Out at close $12,500

****

11008 MADISON
FNB OF TWIN BRIDGES
{{ 5 L }}
Chartered 6/17
1902 Plain Back <$VALUE
3x10-20 1-2348 <$1000
Total Issue $117,400
Out in 1935 $590

****

9520 Pondera
FNB OF VALIER
{{ 1 L 3 S }}
Organized 7/12/09
Receivership 10/25/33
1902 Date Back <$VALUE
3x10-20 1-800 <$1750
1902 Plain Back
3x10-20 801-1447 <$1750
1929 Small Size
10 Type 1 1-184 <$600
20 Type 1 1-32 <$600
Total Issue $87,230
Out at close $6,500
Large out at close $380

****

3375 Meagher
FNB OF
WHITE SULPHUR SPRINGS
Chartered 1885
TERRITORIAL ISSUES **{{ 0 L }}**
Brown Back <$VALUE
3x10-20 1-760* <$4000
* 278 & 279 destroyed in transit
STATE ISSUES **{{ 7 L 20 S }}**
Brown Back
3x10-20 761-3872 <$2000
1902 Red Seal
3x10-20 1-800 <$3500
1902 Date Back
3x10-20 1-2340 <$400
1902 Plain Back
3x10-20 2341-4681 <$400
1929 Small Size
10 Type 1 1-1036 <$200
20 Type 1 1-260 <$200
10 Type 2 1-230 <$225
20 Type 2 1-30 <$250
Total Issue $563,910
Out in 1935 $20,000
Large out 1935 $2,930

****

8589 Flathead
FNB OF WHITEFISH
{{ 3 L 4U + 14 S }}
Chartered 3/07
1902 Red Seal <$VALUE
4x5 1-130 <$4000
3x10-20 1-130 <$4000
1902 Date Back
4x5 1-1350 <$1250
3x10-20 1-1080 <$1250
1902 Plain Back
4x5 1351-5685 <$1250
3x10-20 1081-3706 <$1250
1929 Small Size
5 Type 1 1-946 <$300
10 Type 1 1-454 <$300
20 Type 1 1-120 <$300
5 Type 2 1-1068 <$300
10 Type 2 1-482 <$300
20 Type 2 1-50 <$300
Total Issue $389,280
Out in 1935 $25,000
Large out 1935 $1,135

****

11024 Jefferson
FNB OF WHITEHALL
{{ U + 1 L }}
Chartered 6/17
Liquidated 11/29/22
1902 Plain Back <$VALUE
3x10-20 1-1750 <$2000
Total Issue $87,500
Out at close $25,000

****

8259 Wibaux
FNB OF WIBAUX
{{ 3 L 12 S }}
Chartered 6/06
1902 Red Seal <$VALUE
4x5 1-200 <$3500
3x10-20 1-160 <$3500
1902 Date Back
4x5 1-600 <$1000
3x10-20 1-480 <$1000
1902 Plain Back
4x5 601-1184 <$1000
3x10-20 481-810 <$1000
1929 Small Size
5 Type 1 1-796 <$200
10 Type 1 1-434 <$200
20 Type 1 1-134 <$200
5 Type 2 1-3066 <$225
10 Type 2 1-1420 <$225
20 Type 2 1-434 <$250
Total Issue $180,390
Out in 1935 $50,000
Large out 1935 $330

****

11006 Fergus
FNB OF WINIFRED
{{ 1 L }}
Organized 5/17/17
Receivership 10/15/25
1902 Plain Back <$VALUE
4x5 1-2295 <$2000
3x10-20 1-1434 <$2000
Total Issue $117,600
Out in 1922 $25,000

****

11036 Roosevelt
FNB OF WOLF POINT
{{ 8 S }}
Chartered 7/17
1929 Small Size <$VALUE
5 Type 1 1-1638 <$375
10 Type 1 1-368 <$375
5 Type 2 1-4096 <$400
10 Type 2 1-1344 <$400
Total Issue $105,140
Out in 1935 $25,000

****

<$VALUEs are for notes in **FINE** condition. Value changes by approximately **25%** for a change of one full grade.

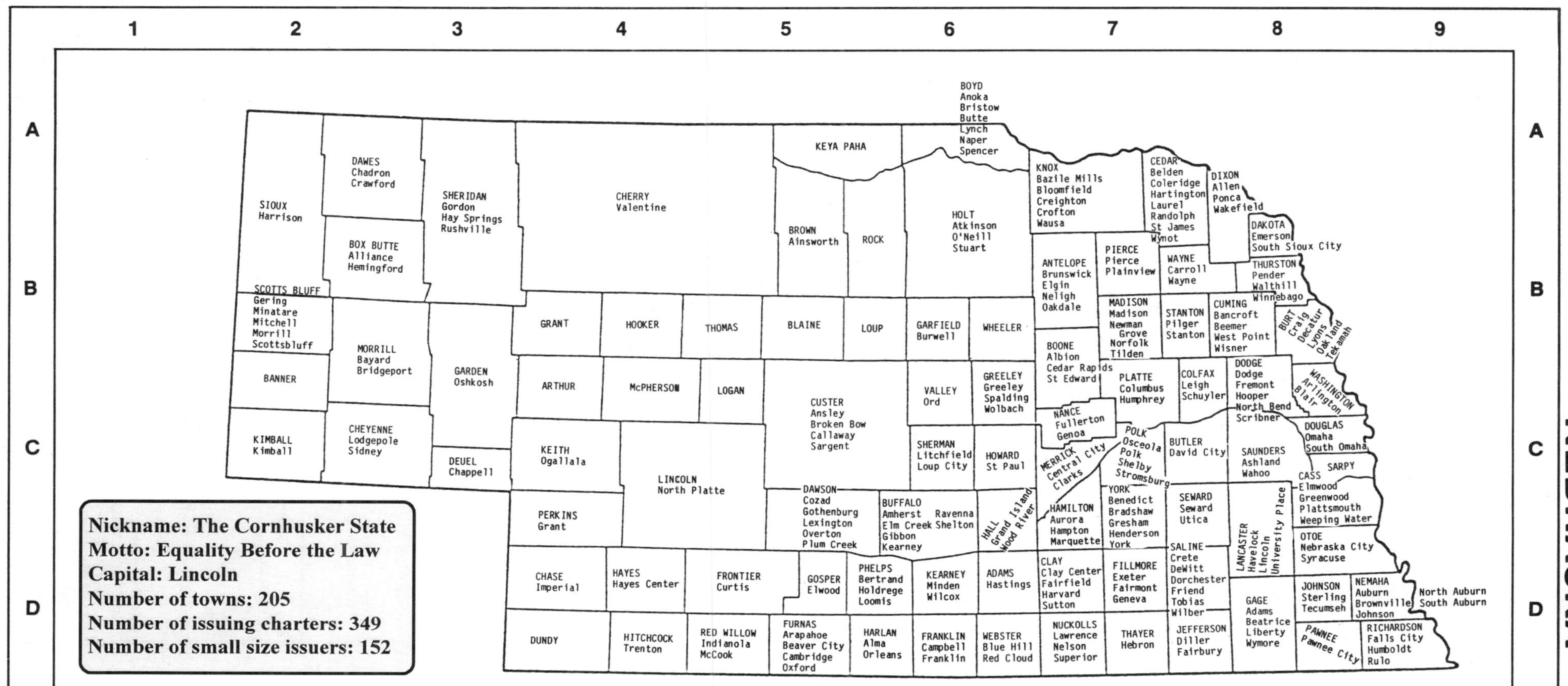

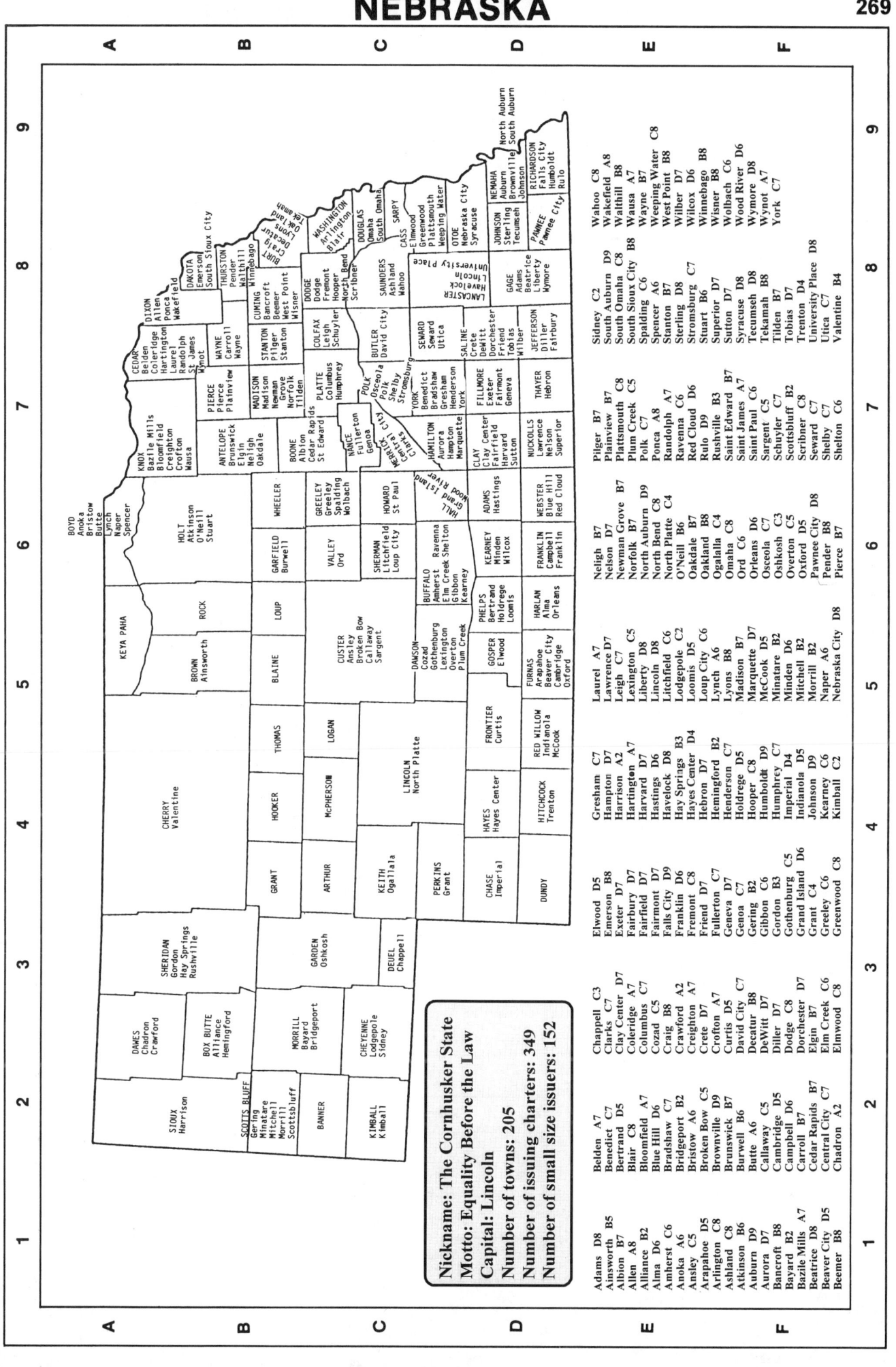

Nickname: The Cornhusker State
Motto: Equality Before the Law
Capital: Lincoln
Number of towns: 205
Number of issuing charters: 349
Number of small size issuers: 152

Adams D8
Ainsworth B5
Albion B7
Allen A8
Alliance B2
Alma D6
Amherst C6
Anoka A6
Ansley C5
Arapahoe D5
Arlington C8
Ashland C8
Atkinson B6
Auburn D9
Aurora D7
Bancroft B8
Bayard B2
Bazile Mills A7
Beatrice D8
Beaver City D5
Beemer B8
Belden A7
Benedict C7
Bertrand D5
Blair C8
Bloomfield A7
Blue Hill D6
Bradshaw C7
Bridgeport B2
Bristow A6
Broken Bow C5
Brownville D9
Brunswick B7
Burwell B6
Butte A6
Callaway C5
Cambridge D5
Campbell D6
Carroll B7
Cedar Rapids B7
Central City C7
Chadron A2
Chappell C3
Clarks C7
Clay Center D7
Coleridge A7
Columbus C7
Cozad C5
Craig B8
Crawford A2
Creighton A7
Crete D7
Crofton A7
Curtis D5
David City C7
Decatur B8
DeWitt D7
Diller D7
Dodge C8
Dorchester D7
Elgin B7
Elm Creek C6
Elmwood C8
Elwood D5
Emerson B8
Exeter D7
Fairbury D7
Fairfield D7
Fairmont D7
Falls City D9
Franklin D6
Fremont C8
Friend D7
Fullerton C7
Geneva D7
Genoa C7
Gering B2
Gibbon C6
Gordon B3
Gothenburg C5
Grand Island D6
Grant C4
Greeley C6
Greenwood C8
Gresham C7
Hampton D7
Harrison A2
Hartington A7
Harvard D7
Hastings D6
Havelock D8
Hay Springs B3
Hayes Center D4
Hebron D7
Hemingford B2
Henderson C7
Holdrege D5
Hooper C8
Humboldt D9
Humphrey C7
Imperial D4
Indianola D5
Johnson D9
Kearney C6
Kimball C2
Laurel A7
Lawrence D7
Leigh C7
Lexington C5
Liberty D8
Lincoln D8
Litchfield C6
Lodgepole C2
Loomis D5
Loup City C6
Lynch A6
Lyons B8
Madison B7
Marquette D7
McCook D5
Minatare B2
Minden D6
Mitchell B2
Morrill B2
Naper A6
Nebraska City D8
Neligh B7
Nelson D7
Newman Grove B7
Norfolk B7
North Auburn D9
North Bend C8
North Platte C4
O'Neill B6
Oakdale B7
Oakland B8
Ogalalla C4
Omaha C8
Ord C6
Orleans D6
Osceola C7
Oshkosh C3
Overton C5
Oxford D5
Pawnee City D8
Pender B8
Pierce B7
Pilger B7
Plainview B7
Plattsmouth C8
Plum Creek C5
Polk C7
Ponca A8
Randolph A7
Ravenna C6
Red Cloud D6
Rulo D9
Rushville B3
Saint Edward B7
Saint James A7
Saint Paul C6
Sargent C5
Schuyler C7
Scottsbluff B2
Scribner C8
Seward C7
Shelby C7
Shelton C6
Sidney C2
South Auburn D9
South Omaha C8
South Sioux City B8
Spalding C6
Spencer A6
Stanton B7
Sterling D8
Stromsburg C7
Stuart B6
Superior D7
Sutton D7
Syracuse D8
Tecumseh D8
Tekamah B8
Tilden B7
Tobias D7
Trenton D4
University Place D8
Utica C7
Valentine B4
Wahoo C8
Wakefield A8
Walthill B8
Wausa A7
Wayne B7
Weeping Water C8
West Point B8
Wilber D7
Wilcox D6
Winnebago B8
Wisner B8
Wolbach C6
Wood River D6
Wymore D8
Wynot A7
York C7

NEBRASKA TERRITORY
Nebraska achieved statehood in 1867. Notes with the territorial imprint were issued by three Nebraska national banks:

FNB of Omaha Ch 209
Omaha NB, Omaha Ch 1633
Otoe County NB of Nebraska City Ch 1417

It has not been possible to identify the serial number ranges for notes issued prior to statehood because these banks continued to issue notes with the territorial imprint for up to 14 years after statehood. Valuations shown below refer to statehood issues.

Any note with the **NEBRASKA TERRITORY** imprint is valued at approximately **$10,000** more than a note with the state imprint.
****

9223 Gage
FNB OF ADAMS
{{ 4 L 2 S }}
Organized 8/14/08
Receivership 9/12/33
1902 Date Back <$VALUE
3x10-20 1-1000 <$400
1902 Plain Back
3x10-20 1001-1986 <$400
1929 Small Size
10 Type 1 1-219 <$400
20 Type 1 1-42 <$400
Total Issue $117,480
Out at close $10,000
Large out at close $1,190
****

4089 Brown
FNB, AINSWORTH
{{ UNREPORTED }}
Chartered 8/12/89
Liquidated 3/3/92
Brown Back <$VALUE
3x10-20 1-295 <$2000
Total Issue $14,750
Out in 1910 $60
****

8992 Brown
NB OF AINSWORTH
{{ 8 L 13 S }}
Organized 1/2/08
Receivership 2/27/29
1902 Red Seal <$VALUE
3x10-20 1-700 <$500
1902 Date Back
3x10-20 1-2090 <$175
1902 Plain Back
3x10-20 2091-6052 <$175
1929 Small Size
10 Type 1 1-624 <$100
20 Type 1 1-210 <$100
10 Type 2 1-910 <$100
20 Type 2 1-243 <$100
Total Issue $414,200
Out in 1935 $35,000
Large out 1935 $3,730
****

4173 Boone
ALBION NB, ALBION
{{ 16 L 50+ S }}
Chartered 1889
Brown Back <$VALUE
3x10-20 1-1820 <$400
1882 Date Back
3x10-20 1-157 <$350
1902 Date Back
3x10-20 1-2000 <$100
1902 Plain Back
3x10-20 2001-7813 <$100
1929 Small Size
10 Type 1 1-1138 <$50
20 Type 1 1-270 <$60
10 Type 2 1-473 <$75
20 Type 2 1-135 <$75
Total Issue $597,610
Out in 1935 $50,000
Large out 1935 $3,280
****

3960 Boone
FNB, ALBION
{{ 32 L 15 S }}
Chartered 1889
Brown Back <$VALUE
4x5 1-1619 <$350
3x10-20 1-1291 <$350/$400
1902 Date Back
4x5 1-3250 <$85
3x10-20 1-2640 <$85
1902 Plain Back
4x5 3251-8685 <$85
3x10-20 2641-6291 <$85
1929 Small Size
5 Type 1 1-1434 <$100
10 Type 1 1-680 <$100
20 Type 1 1-194 <$100
5 Type 2 1-96 <$125
10 Type 2 1-35 <$150
Total Issue $693,110
Out in 1935 $30,000
Large out 1935 $3,880
****

8372 Dixon
FNB OF ALLEN
{{ UNREPORTED }}
Chartered 9/06
Liquidated 3/22/19
1902 Red Seal <$VALUE
3x10-20 1-200 <$2000
1902 Date Back
3x10-20 1-620 <$1250
1902 Plain Back
3x10-20 621-963 <$1250
Total Issue $56,150
Out at close $25,000
****

5657 Box Butte
ALLIANCE NB, ALLIANCE
{{ 9 L 14 S }}
Chartered 12/28/00
Brown Back <$VALUE
3x10-20 1-900 <$450
1882 Date Back
3x10-20 1-4100 <$400
1882 Value Back
3x10-20 4101-6227 <$500
1902 Plain Back
3x10-20 1-4629 <$175
1929 Small Size
10 Type 1 1-1180 <$100
20 Type 1 1-292 <$100
10 Type 2 1-1895 <$100
20 Type 2 1-355 <$100
Total Issue $719,690
Out in 1935 $50,000
Large out 1935 $3,350
****

4226 Box Butte
FNB, ALLIANCE
{{ 6 L 10 S }}
Organized 12/19/89
Receivership 11/3/31
Brown Back <$VALUE
4x5 1-4000 <$600
3x10-20 1-1320 <$600
1882 Date Back
4x5 1-610 <$500
3x10-20 1-369 <$500
1902 Date Back
3x10-20 1-3500 <$300
1902 Plain Back
3x10-20 3501-10517 <$300
1929 Small Size
10 Type 1 1-773 <$150
20 Type 1 1-200 <$150
Total Issue $772,880
Out at close $49,155
Large out at close $7,825
****

13617 Box Butte
NEBRASKA NB OF ALLIANCE
{{ 27 S }}
Chartered 6/32
Liquidated 4/20/35
1929 Small Size <$VALUE
5 Type 2 1-14150 <$85
10 Type 2 1-6264 <$85
20 Type 2 1-1732 <$85
Total Issue $168,030
Out in 1935 $100,000
****

3580 Harlan
FNB, ALMA
{{ UNREPORTED}}
Chartered 10/28/86
Receivership 1/12/97
Brown Back <$VALUE
3x10-20 1-745 <$2000
Total Issue $37,250
Out in 1915 $200
****

9092 Buffalo
FNB OF AMHERST
{{ 2 L 9 S }}
Chartered 4/08
1902 Red Seal <$VALUE
3x10-20 1-240 <$1250
1902 Date Back
3x10-20 1-1740 <$500
1902 Plain Back
3x10-20 1741-4621 <$500
1929 Small Size
10 Type 1 1-562 <$150
20 Type 1 1-148 <$150
5 Type 2 1-222 <$175
10 Type 2 1-397 <$175
20 Type 2 1-80 <$175
Total Issue $301,210
Out in 1935 $25,000
Large out 1935 $1,465
****

6464 Boyd
ANOKA NB, ANOKA
{{ UNREPORTED }}
Organized 10/22/02
Liquidated 7/1/09
1902 Red Seal <$VALUE
4x5 1-495 <$1500
3x10-20 1-474 <$1500
Total Issue $33,600
Out in 1910 $5,650
****

7393 Custer
FNB, ANSLEY
{{ UNREPORTED }}
Chartered 9/04
Liquidated 7/17/16
1902 Red Seal <$VALUE
50-100 1-368 <$3500/$4000
1902 Date Back
50-100 1-160 <$1250/$1500
3x50-100 1-83 <$1250/$1500
Total Issue $99,950
Out at close $24,500
****

3302 Furnas
FNB, ARAPAHOE
{{ 1 L }}
Chartered 2/9/85
Liquidated 12/26/94
Brown Back <$VALUE
4x5 1-2487 <$1500
Total Issue $49,740
Out in 1910 $335
****

4583 Washington
FNB OF ARLINGTON
{{ 4 L 3 S }}
Chartered 5/26/91
Receivership 6/17/32
Brown Back <$VALUE
4x5 1-3350 <$750
3x10-20 1-1000 <$750
1882 Date Back
4x5 1-391 <$650
3x10-20 1-318 <$650
1902 Date Back
4x5 1-1050 <$400
3x10-20 1-810 <$400
1902 Plain Back
4x5 1051-4783 <$400
3x10-20 811-2937 <$400
1929 Small Size
5 Type 1 1-678 <$400
10 Type 1 1-333 <$400
20 Type 1 1-71 <$400
Total Issue $432,270
Out at close $24,995
Large out at close $2,360
****

13435 Saunders
FARMERS & MERCHANTS NB OF ASHLAND
{{ 27 S }}
Chartered 3/7/30
1929 Small Size <$VALUE
10 Type 2 1-1520 <$75
20 Type 2 1-840 <$85
50 Type 2 1-360 <$175
Total Issue $50,000
Out in 1935 $48,750
****

2121 Saunders
FNB OF ASHLAND
{{ 1 L }}
Chartered 7/21/73
Liquidated 1/26/76
Original Series <$VALUE
3x1-2 1-1900 <$2000/$6000
4x5 1-2250 <$2500
Total Issue $54,500
Out in 1910 $304
****

2921 Saunders
NB OF ASHLAND
{{ 10 L 21 S }}
Organized 3/26/83
Receivership 7/16/34
Brown Back <$VALUE
4x5 1-4881 <$450
3x10-20 1-387 <$450
1902 Red Seal
4x5 1-2500 <$450
3x10-20 1-1950 <$450
1902 Date Back
4x5 1-3000 <$175
3x10-20 1-2220 <$175
1902 Plain Back
4x5 3001-11925 <$175
3x10-20 2221-7201 <$175
1929 Small Size
5 Type 1 1-2080 <$60
10 Type 1 1-920 <$60
20 Type 1 1-262 <$70
5 Type 2 1-830 <$75
10 Type 2 1-405 <$75
20 Type 2 1-105 <$75
Total Issue $1,022,360
Out at close $60,000
Large out at close $3,830
****

7881 Holt
ATKINSON NB, ATKINSON
{{ UNREPORTED }}
Chartered 8/05
Liquidated 12/31/13
1902 Red Seal <$VALUE
50-100 1-90 <$3500/$4000
1902 Date Back
50-100 1-66 <$1250/$1500
Total Issue $23,400
Out in 1914 $5,250
****

6489 Holt
FNB, ATKINSON
{{ U + 1 L 6 S }}
Chartered 1902
1902 Red Seal <$VALUE
3x10-20 1-1150 <$1250
1902 Date Back
3x10-20 1-1640 <$600
1902 Plain Back
3x10-20 1641-4225 <$600
1929 Small Size
10 Type 1 1-456 <$175
20 Type 1 1-128 <$175
10 Type 2 1-848 <$200
20 Type 2 1-221 <$200
Total Issue $324,370
Out in 1935 $25,000
Large out 1935 $1,450
****

Carson NB of Auburn
SEE Ch 3628
Carson NB of South Auburn
****

4588 Nemaha
FARMERS AND MERCHANTS NB, AUBURN
{{ UNREPORTED }}
Chartered 6/24/91
Liquidated 8/29/94
Brown Back <$VALUE
4x5 1-1011 <$1500
Total Issue $20,220
Out in 1910 $120
****

FNB of Auburn, Auburn
SEE Ch 3343
FNB of Auburn, North Auburn
****

9056 Hamilton
AURORA NB, AURORA
{{ 2 L }}
Chartered 3/08
Liquidated 8/13/15
1902 Red Seal <$VALUE
3x10-20 1-562 <$1000
1902 Date Back
3x10-20 1-3786 <$500
Total Issue $217,400
Out at close $67,200
****

8246 Hamilton
FIDELITY NB, AURORA
{{ 6 L }}
Chartered 6/06
Liquidated 11/10/20
1902 Red Seal <$VALUE
3x10-20 1-288 <$600
1902 Date Back
3x10-20 1-3060 <$300
1902 Plain Back
3x10-20 3061-4717 <$300
Total Issue $250,250
Out at close $49,100
****

2897 Hamilton
FNB OF AURORA
{{ 3 L 6 S }}
Organized 2/5/83
Liquidated 4/28/34
Brown Back <$VALUE
4x5 1-3385 <$750
3x10-20 1-212 <$750
1902 Red Seal
3x10-20 1-630 <$800
1902 Date Back
3x10-20 1-1150 <$400
1902 Plain Back
3x10-20 1151-2211 <$400
1929 Small Size
10 Type 1 1-259 <$250
20 Type 1 1-78 <$250
Total Issue $245,250
Out at close $15,000
Large out at close $1,430
****

8863 Cuming
FNB OF BANCROFT
{{ 3 L 11 S }}
Chartered 9/07
1902 Red Seal <$VALUE
3x10-20 1-225 <$750
1902 Date Back
3x10-20 1-1470* <$350
1902 Plain Back
3x10-20 1671-4130* <$350
* 1471-1670 not marked
1929 Small Size
10 Type 1 1-506 <$175
20 Type 1 1-144 <$175
10 Type 2 1-37 <$200
Total Issue $265,760
Out in 1935 $20,000
Large out 1935 $1,200
****

9666 Morrill
FNB OF BAYARD
{{ 3 L 11 S }}
Chartered 2/10
1902 Date Back <$VALUE
3x10-20 1-2040 <$350
1902 Plain Back
3x10-20 2041-5497 <$350
1929 Small Size
10 Type 1 1-626 <$150
20 Type 1 1-162 <$150
10 Type 2 1-526 <$175
20 Type 2 1-180 <$175
Total Issue $340,710
Out in 1935 $25,000
Large out 1935 $1,310
****

8469 Knox
FNB OF BAZILE MILLS
{{ 2 L }}
Chartered 12/06
Liquidated 11/14/17
1902 Red Seal <$VALUE
3x10-20 1-300 <$1250
1902 Date Back
3x10-20 1-1240 <$650
1902 Plain Back
3x10-20 1241-1493 <$650
Total Issue $89,650
Out at close $25,000
****

3081 Gage
BEATRICE NB, BEATRICE
{{ 20 L U + 25 S }}
Chartered 1883
Brown Back <$VALUE
4x5 1-3304 <$350
3x10-20 1-386 <$400
1902 Red Seal
3x10-20 1-3500 <$350
1902 Date Back
3x10-20 1-6300 <$85
1902 Plain Back
3x10-20 6301-17742 <$85
1929 Small Size
10 Type 1 1-2144 <$60
20 Type 1 1-596 <$70
10 Type 2 1-2444 <$75
20 Type 2 1-431 <$75
Total Issue $1,390,700
Out in 1935 $99,450
Large out 1935 $7,270
****

2357 Gage
FNB, BEATRICE
{{ 24 L 40 S }}
Chartered 5/12/77
Series 1875 <$VALUE
4x5 1-8240 <$850
Brown Back
3x10-20 1-7340 <$300/$350
1882 Date Back
3x10-20 1-5800 <$250/$300
1882 Value Back
3x10-20 5801-6131 <$350/$400
1902 Plain Back
3x10-20 1-10127 <$100
1929 Small Size
10 Type 1 1-2220 <$35
20 Type 1 1-594 <$40
10 Type 2 1-2214 <$40
20 Type 2 1-298 <$40
Total Issue $1,577,280
Out in 1935 $99,450
Large out 1935 $8,930
****

4148 Gage
GERMAN NB OF BEATRICE
{{ 1 L }}
Chartered 1889
Liquidated 10/16/12
Brown Back <$VALUE
4x5 1-4265 <$1500
50-100 1-185 <$2500/$3000
1902 Date Back
3x10-20 1-262 <$850
Total Issue $126,150
Out in 1912 $12,400
****

4185 Gage
NEBRASKA NB, BEATRICE
{{ 1 L }}
Chartered 12/21/89
Receivership 7/12/93
Brown Back <$VALUE
4x5 1-1882 <$1500
Total Issue $37,640
Out in 1915 $245
****

3619 Furnas
FNB, BEAVER CITY
{{ 1 L }}
Chartered 1/17/87
Liquidated 12/31/98
Brown Back <$VALUE
4x5 1-2592 <$1500
Total Issue $51,840
Out in 1910 $415
****

6818 Cuming
FNB, BEEMER
{{ 8 L 7 S }}
Chartered 6/03
1902 Red Seal <$VALUE
3x10-20 1-1325 <$500
1902 Date Back
3x10-20 1-1730 <$250
1902 Plain Back
3x10-20 1731-4717 <$250
1929 Small Size
10 Type 1 1-646 <$175
20 Type 1 1-140 <$175
10 Type 2 1-262 <$200
20 Type 2 1-75 <$200
Total Issue $361,780
Out in 1935 $24,995
Large out 1935 $2,130
****

10025 Cedar
FNB OF BELDEN
{{ 9 L 4U + 9 S }}
Chartered 5/11
1902 Date Back <$VALUE
3x10-20 1-1520 <$200
1902 Plain Back
3x10-20 1521-4508 <$200
1929 Small Size
5 Type 1 1-966 <$125
10 Type 1 1-314 <$125
20 Type 1 1-106 <$150
5 Type 2 1-2660 <$150
Total Issue $299,240
Out in 1935 $25,000
Large out 1935 $1,370
****

8105 York
FNB, BENEDICT
{{ 3 L U + 18 S }}
Chartered 2/06
1902 Red Seal <$VALUE
3x10-20 1-800 <$750
1902 Date Back
3x10-20 1-1580* <$400
1902 Plain Back
3x10-20 1711-4513* <$400
* 1581-1710 not marked
1929 Small Size
10 Type 1 1-536 <$100
20 Type 1 1-140 <$100
10 Type 2 1-562 <$100
20 Type 2 1-190 <$110
Total Issue $324,030
Out in 1935 $25,000
Large out 1935 $1,650
****

8466 Phelps
FNB OF BERTRAND
{{ 2 L }}
Chartered 12/06
Liquidated 9/26/31
1902 Red Seal <$VALUE
3x10-20 1-225 <$1250
1902 Date Back
3x10-20 1-1430* <$600
* 1431-1630 not marked
Total Issue $85,800
Out in 1916 $20,000
****

8027 Washington
BLAIR NB, BLAIR
{{ UNREPORTED }}
Chartered 12/05
Liquidated 12/31/15
1902 Red Seal <$VALUE
3x10-20 1-1500 <$1500
1902 Date Back
3x10-20 1-3533 <$1000
Total Issue $251,650
Out in 1916 $28,350

2724 Washington
FNB OF BLAIR
{{ UNREPORTED }}
Chartered 7/7/82
Receivership 9/8/86
Series 1875 <$VALUE
4x5 1-2465 <$2500
Total Issue $49,300
Out in 1915 $325

6503 Knox
FNB OF BLOOMFIELD
{{ UNREPORTED }}
Chartered 1902
Liquidated 2/26/14
1902 Red Seal <$VALUE
4x5 1-300 <$1500
3x10-20 1-276 <$1500
1902 Date Back
4x5 1-835 <$1000
3x10-20 1-634 <$1000
Total Issue $68,200
Out in 1914 $14,760

3419 Webster
FNB OF BLUE HILL
{{ 5 L 1 S }}
Chartered 1885
Liquidated 4/29/30
Brown Back <$VALUE
4x5 1-2974 <$750
50-100 1-124 <$2000/$2500
1902 Red Seal
3x10-20 1-320 <$750
1902 Date Back
3x10-20 1-1020 <$400
1902 Plain Back
3x10-20 1021-1861 <$400
1929 Small Size
10 Type 1 1-100 <$500
20 Type 1 1-5 <$500
Total Issue $193,730
Out at close $12,500
Large out at close $4,350

8097 York
FNB, BRADSHAW
{{ 4 L U + 9 S }}
Chartered 2/06
1902 Red Seal <$VALUE
3x10-20 1-700 <$750
1902 Date Back
3x10-20 1-1700 <$400
1902 Plain Back
3x10-20 1701-4508 <$400
1929 Small Size
10 Type 1 1-504 <$150
20 Type 1 1-148 <$150
10 Type 2 1-551 <$150
20 Type 2 1-170 <$150
Total Issue $317,310
Out in 1935 $24,750
Large out 1935 $1,660

9711 Morrill
FNB OF BRIDGEPORT
{{ UNREPORTED }}
Organized 2/23/10
Receivership 5/28/21
1902 Date Back <$VALUE
3x10-20 1-1630 <$1000
1902 Plain Back
3x10-20 1631-2714 <$1000
Total Issue $135,700
Out at close $20,600

9448 Boyd
FNB OF BRISTOW
{{ 5 L }}
Organized 6/5/09
Receivership 3/24/24
1902 Date Back <$VALUE
3x10-20 1-2150 <$300
1902 Plain Back
3x10-20 2151-3662 <$300
Total Issue $183,100
Out at close $25,000

3927 Custer
CENTRAL NEBRASKA NB, BROKEN BOW
{{ UNREPORTED }}
Chartered 9/28/88
Receivership 7/21/91
Brown Back <$VALUE
4x5 1-965 <$2500
Total Issue $19,300
Out in 1915 $110

3445 Custer
CUSTER COUNTY NB, BROKEN BOW
{{ UNREPORTED }}
Chartered 1/30/86
Liquidated 7/2/86
Brown Back <$VALUE
4x5 1-562 <$2500
Total Issue $11,240
All notes reportedly redeemed

5995 Custer
CUSTER NB OF BROKEN BOW
{{ 7 L }}
Chartered 1901
Liquidated 3/1/16
Brown Back <$VALUE
4x5 1-1150 <$1000
3x10-20 1-1060 <$1000
1882 Date Back
4x5 1-1300 <$850
3x10-20 1-1100 <$850
1882 Value Back
3x10-20 1101-1118 <$1000
Total Issue $157,900
Out in 1916 $17,690

3449 Custer
FNB, BROKEN BOW
{{ 11 L }}
Chartered 2/2/86
Liquidated 10/23/99
Brown Back <$VALUE
4x5 1-4394 <$600
Total Issue $87,880
Out in 1910 $795

1846 Nemaha
FNB OF BROWNVILLE
{{ 5 L }}
Chartered 7/12/71
Liquidated 9/16/86
Original Series <$VALUE
3x1-2 1-3600 <$1500/$4000
4x5 1-3000 <$1250
3x10-20 1-1240<$1500/$2000
Series 1875
4x5 1-150 <$1250
3x10-20 1-1489<$1500/$2000
Total Issue $217,450
Out in 1910 $1,295

10033 Antelope
FNB OF BRUNSWICK
{{ 1 L }}
Chartered 6/11
Liquidated 2/15/16
1902 Date Back <$VALUE
3x10-20 1-1503 <$1000
Total Issue $75,150
Out at close $17,450

7340 Garfield
FNB OF BURWELL
{{ 2 L }}
Organized 7/04
Liquidated 3/11/20
1902 Red Seal <$VALUE
3x10-20 1-400 <$1250
1902 Date Back
3x10-20 1-780 <$650
1902 Plain Back
3x10-20 781-881 <$650
Total Issue $64,050
Out at close $10,000

9623 Boyd
FNB OF BUTTE
{{ 14 L 20 S }}
Chartered 1/10
1902 Date Back <$VALUE
4x5 1-3625 <$150
3x10-20 1-2660 <$150
1902 Plain Back
4x5 3626-9135 <$150
3x10-20 2661-6269 <$150
1929 Small Size
5 Type 1 1-824 <$75
10 Type 1 1-412 <$75
20 Type 1 1-148 <$75
5 Type 2 1-978 <$85
10 Type 2 1-405 <$85
20 Type 2 1-25 <$85
Total Issue $572,790
Out in 1935 $25,000
Large out 1935 $3,990

9258 Custer
FNB OF CALLAWAY
{{ 1 L }}
Chartered 10/08
Liquidated 2/7/16
1902 Date Back <$VALUE
4x5 1-1950 <$1000
3x10-20 1-1500 <$1000
1902 Plain Back
4x5 1951-2000 <$1000
3x10-20 1501-1530 <$1000
Total Issue $116,500
Out at close $16,940

6506 Furnas
FNB, CAMBRIDGE
{{ 2 L 3 U + 24 S }}
Chartered 1902
1902 Red Seal <$VALUE
3x10-20 1-800 <$1000
1902 Date Back
3x10-20 1-1700 <$500
1902 Plain Back
3x10-20 1701-4160 <$500
1929 Small Size
10 Type 1 1-504 <$75
20 Type 1 1-150 <$75
10 Type 2 1-590 <$85
20 Type 2 1-150 <$85
Total Issue $305,140
Out in 1935 $24,750
Large out 1935 $1,770

8975 Franklin
FNB OF CAMPBELL
{{ UNREPORTED }}
Chartered 12/07
Liquidated 7/1/14
1902 Red Seal <$VALUE
4x10 1-250 <$1500
1902 Date Back
4x10 1-1431 <$1000
Total Issue $67,240
Out at close $21,830

5957 Wayne
FNB, CARROLL
{{ 3 L }}
Organized 8/21/01
Receivership 8/13/23
Brown Back <$VALUE
3x10-20 1-660 <$750
1882 Date Back
3x10-20 1-1620 <$700
1882 Value Back
3x10-20 1621-2748 <$800
1902 Plain Back
4x5 1-1310 <$450
Total Issue $196,600
Out at close $21,400

8282 Boone
FNB, CEDAR RAPIDS
{{ UNREPORTED }}
Chartered 6/06
Liquidated 7/20/14
1902 Red Seal <$VALUE
3x10-20 1-200 <$1500
1902 Date Back
3x10-20 1-338 <$1000
Total Issue $26,900
Out in 1914 $5,650

8385 Merrick
CENTRAL CITY NB, CENTRAL CITY
{{ 8 L 3 S }}
Organized 9/12/06
Receivership 11/1/33
1902 Red Seal <$VALUE
4x5 1-400 <$500
3x10-20 1-600 <$500
1902 Date Back
4x5 1-1950 <$225
3x10-20 1-1310 <$225
1902 Plain Back
4x5 1951-4960 <$225
3x10-20 1311-2992 <$225
1929 Small Size
5 Type 1 1-502 <$350
10 Type 1 1-254 <$350
20 Type 1 1-81 <$350
Total Issue $326,820
Out at close $19,820
Large out at close $1,720

2871 Merrick
FNB, CENTRAL CITY
{{ 1 L }}
Chartered 2/2/83
Liquidated 2/11/88
Brown Back <$VALUE
4x5 1-1064 <$1500
Total Issue $21,280
Out in 1910 $220

3823 Dawes
FNB, CHADRON
{{ 5 L 15 S }}
Chartered 1887
Brown Back <$VALUE
3x10-20 1-1479 <$600
1902 Red Seal
3x10-20 1-250 <$600
1902 Date Back
3x10-20 1-2650* <$300
1902 Plain Back
3x10-20 2951-7208* <$300
* 2651-2950 not marked
1929 Small Size
10 Type 1 1-900 <$100
20 Type 1 1-254 <$100
10 Type 2 1-425 <$100
20 Type 2 1-160 <$100
Total Issue $538,780
Out in 1935 $37,500
Large out 1935 $2,290

9790 Deuel
FNB OF CHAPPELL
{{ 3 L }}
Chartered 5/10/10
Receivership 1/29/21
1902 Date Back <$VALUE
3x10-20 1-1840 <$450
1902 Plain Back
3x10-20 1841-2873 <$450
Total Issue $143,650
Out at close $23,600

6939 Merrick
FNB OF CLARKS
{{ 2 L }}
Chartered 8/03
Liquidated 11/30/15
1902 Red Seal <$VALUE
4x5 1-1100 <$1000
3x10-20 1-760 <$1000
1902 Date Back
4x5 1-1510 <$500
3x10-20 1-1096 <$500
Total Issue $145,000
Out in 1916 $15,020

3574 Clay
FNB, CLAY CENTER
{{ UNREPORTED }}
Chartered 10/19/86
Liquidated 8/8/89
Brown Back <$VALUE
4x5 1-879 <$2000
Total Issue $17,580
Out in 1910 $140

10023 Cedar
COLERIDGE NB, COLERIDGE
{{ 9 L 23 S }}
Chartered 5/11
1902 Date Back <$VALUE
3x10-20 1-2500 <$175
1902 Plain Back
3x10-20 2501-7267 <$175
1929 Small Size
10 Type 1 1-860 <$65
20 Type 1 1-284 <$75
10 Type 2 1-226 <$85
20 Type 2 1-15 <$100
Total Issue $451,590
Out in 1935 $33,860
Large out 1935 $2,330

9796 Cedar
FNB OF COLERIDGE
{{ 6 L }}
Organized 5/18/10
Receivership 1/12/29
1902 Date Back <$VALUE
3x10-20 1-2800 <$250
1902 Plain Back
3x10-20 2801-7284 <$250
Total Issue $364,200
Out at close $39,350

Central NB of Columbus
SEE Ch 8328
German NB of Columbus

5180 Platte
COMMERCIAL NB, COLUMBUS
{{ 13 L 7 S }}
Organized 1/17/99
Receivership 1/24/33
Brown Back <$VALUE
4x5 1-2050 <$350
3x10-20 1-1460 <$350/$400
1882 Date Back
4x5 1-2800 <$300
3x10-20 1-2110 <$300/$350
1882 Value Back
4x5 2801-3996 <$400
3x10-20 2111-2753 <$400
1902 Plain Back
3x10-20 1-5040 <$175
1929 Small Size
10 Type 1 1-896 <$175
20 Type 1 1-238 <$175
Total Issue $665,890
Out at close $49,640
Large out at close $5,110

2807 Platte
FNB OF COLUMBUS
{{ 9 L 5 S }}
Chartered 1882
Liquidated 6/30/30
Brown Back <$VALUE
4x5 1-4990 <$450
3x10-20 1-390 <$450
1902 Red Seal
3x10-20 1-1710 <$500
1902 Date Back
3x10-20 1-3160 <$150
1902 Plain Back
3x10-20 3161-14509 <$150
1929 Small Size
10 Type 1 1-883 <$200
20 Type 1 1-143 <$200
Total Issue $1,000,390
Out at close $100,000
Large out at close $66,300

8328 Platte
GERMAN NB OF COLUMBUS
Chartered 8/06
2nd title:Central NB of Columbus 4/12/18
FIRST TITLE {{ 2 L }}
1902 Red Seal <$VALUE
4x10 1-575 <$1000
1902 Date Back
4x10 1-4100 <$500
1902 Plain Back
4x10 4101-6900 <$500
SECOND TITLE {{ 21 L 31 S }}
1902 Plain Back
4x10 1-14670 <$65
1929 Small Size
10 Type 1 1-3880 <$50
Total Issue $1,118,600
Out in 1935 $50,000
Large out 1935 $5,130

13426 Dawson
FNB IN COZAD
{{ 12 S }}
Chartered 2/11/30
1929 Small Size <$VALUE
5 Type 1 1-1040 <$100
10 Type 1 1-524 <$100
5 Type 2 1-2863 <$125
10 Type 2 1-1395 <$125
Total Issue $90,905
Out in 1935 $47,150

4165 Dawson
FNB OF COZAD
{{ UNREPORTED }}
Chartered 1889
Liquidated 6/7/15
Brown Back <$VALUE
4x5 1-2905 <$1500
3x10-20 1-478 <$1500
1882 Date Back
4x5 1-103 <$1500
3x10-20 1-89 <$1500
1902 Date Back
3x10-20 1-692 <$1000
Total Issue $123,110
Out in 1915 $10,000

9591 Burt
FNB OF CRAIG
{{ 4 L 4 S }}
Organized 10/25/09
Receivership 1/30/33
1902 Date Back <$VALUE
3x10-20 1-1930* <$350
1902 Plain Back
3x10-20 2061-5129* <$350
* 1931-2060 not marked
1929 Small Size
10 Type 1 1-485 <$350
20 Type 1 1-123 <$350
Total Issue $300,310
Out at close $24,700
Large out at close $2,620

6900 Dawes
FNB OF CRAWFORD
{{ 2 L }}
Chartered 7/03
Liquidated 3/26/27
1902 Red Seal <$VALUE
3x10-20 1-900 <$1000
1902 Date Back
3x10-20 1-1520* <$500
1902 Plain Back
3x10-20 1721-3208* <$500
* 1521-1720 not marked
Total Issue $205,400
Out at close $19,000

8797 Knox
CREIGHTON NB, CREIGHTON
{{ 6 L 0 S }}
Organized 6/27/07
Receivership 1/9/32
1902 Red Seal <$VALUE
3x10-20 1-187 <$600
1902 Date Back
3x10-20 1-580 <$250
1902 Plain Back
3x10-20 581-1089 <$250
1929 Small Size
10 Type 1 1-103 <$750
20 Type 1 1-11 <$750
Total Issue $71,300
Out at close $6,070
Large out at close $1,160

4242 Knox
FNB, CREIGHTON
{{ UNREPORTED }}
Chartered 2/26/90
Liquidated 10/24/95
Brown Back <$VALUE
4x5 1-1381 <$1500
Total Issue $27,620
Out in 1910 $195

9731 Saline
CITY NB OF CRETE
{{ 11 L 17 S }}
Chartered 4/10
1902 Date Back <$VALUE
3x10-20 1-1710 <$175
1902 Plain Back
3x10-20 1711-6526 <$175
1929 Small Size
10 Type 1 1-1081 <$100
20 Type 1 1-292 <$100
Total Issue $426,200
Out in 1935 $25,000
Large out 1935 $2,740

4820 Saline
CRETE NB OF CRETE
{{ UNREPORTED }}
Chartered 12/2/92
Liquidated 1/1/97
Brown Back <$VALUE
4x5 1-1168 <$1500
Total Issue $23,360
Out in 1910 $150

2706 Saline
FNB OF CRETE
{{ 8 L }}
Chartered 1882
Liquidated 3/8/19
Series 1875 <$VALUE
4x5 1-4963 <$850
3x10-20 1-234 <$1250/$1750
1902 Red Seal
3x10-20 1-2700 <$350
1902 Date Back
3x10-20 1-2800 <$175
1902 Plain Back
3x10-20 2801-3739 <$175
Total Issue $432,910
Out in 1919 $50,000

****
8186 Knox
FNB, CROFTON
{{ 6 L 50+ S }}
Organized 2/16/06
Receivership 6/1/32
1902 Red Seal <$VALUE
3x10-20 1-300 <$500
1902 Date Back
3x10-20 1-1250 <$250
1902 Plain Back
3x10-20 1251-4146 <$250
1929 Small Size
10 Type 1 1-346 <$50
20 Type 1 1-103 <$60
Total Issue $255,420
Out at close $25,000
Large out at close $4,420
****
8812 Frontier
FNB OF CURTIS
{{ 2 L }}
Organized 7/07
Liquidated 6/9/14
1902 Red Seal <$VALUE
3x10-20 1-200 <$1000
1902 Date Back
3x10-20 1-1130 <$500
Total Issue $66,500
Out at close $29,400
****
3801 Butler
CENTRAL NEBRASKA NB OF DAVID CITY
{{ 9 L 18 S }}
Organized 9/29/87
Liquidated 10/31/34
Brown Back <$VALUE
3x10-20 1-2787 <$450
1902 Red Seal
3x10-20 1-950 <$450
1902 Date Back
3x10-20 1-3100 <$175
1902 Plain Back
3x10-20 3101-8637 <$175
1929 Small Size
10 Type 1 1-1126 <$100
20 Type 1 1-256 <$100
Total Issue $716,980
Out at close $50,000
Large out at close $3,880
****
3934 Butler
CITY NB OF DAVID CITY
{{ 10 L 13 S }}
Organized 8/31/88
Liquidated 11/4/34
Brown Back <$VALUE
3x10-20 1-3229 <$450
1902 Date Back
3x10-20 1-3400 <$150
1902 Plain Back
3x10-20 3401-8590 <$150
1929 Small Size
10 Type 1 1-958 <$100
20 Type 1 1-252 <$100
10 Type 2 1-161 <$125
20 Type 2 1-65 <$125
Total Issue $681,580
Out at close $50,000
Large out at close $4,610
****
2902 Butler
FNB, DAVID CITY
{{ 9 L 18 S }}
Chartered 1883
Brown Back <$VALUE
4x5 1-3810 <$450
3x10-20 1-340 <$450
1902 Red Seal
3x10-20 1-2640 <$450
1902 Date Back
3x10-20 1-2540 <$175
1902 Plain Back
3x10-20 2541-7732 <$175
1929 Small Size
10 Type 1 1-1046 <$75
20 Type 1 1-260 <$75
10 Type 2 1-242 <$100
20 Type 2 1-85 <$100
Total Issue $709,880
Out in 1935 $37,500
Large out 1935 $3,710
****
8988 Burt
FNB OF DECATUR
{{ 8 L 21 S }}
Chartered 10/30/07
Liquidated 9/11/34
1902 Red Seal <$VALUE
4x5 1-375 <$600
3x10-20 1-300 <$600
1902 Date Back
4x5 1-2175 <$175
3x10-20 1-1660 <$175
1902 Plain Back
4x5 2176-9271 <$175
3x10-20 1661-6407 <$175
1929 Small Size
5 Type 1 1-1600 <$75
10 Type 1 1-768 <$75
20 Type 1 1-240 <$75
5 Type 2 1-530 <$85
10 Type 2 1-155 <$85
20 Type 2 1-70 <$85
Total Issue $656,750
Out at close $50,000
Large out at close $2,960
****
4895 Saline
FNB, DeWITT
{{ UNREPORTED }}
Chartered 4/6/93
Liquidated 3/12/94
Brown Back <$VALUE
4x5 1-576 <$2000
Total Issue $11,520
Out in 1910 $65
****
7355 Jefferson
FNB, DILLER
{{ UNREPORTED }}
Chartered 8/04
Liquidated 7/27/14
1902 Red Seal <$VALUE
3x10-20 1-650 <$1500
1902 Date Back
3x10-20 1-603 <$1000
Total Issue $62,650
Out in 1914 $13,900
****
7333 Dodge
FNB, DODGE
{{ 1 L }}
Organized 6/18/04
Receivership 11/22/24
1902 Red Seal <$VALUE
3x10-20 1-300 <$1500
1902 Date Back
3x10-20 1-580 <$750
1902 Plain Back
3x10-20 581-723 <$750
Total Issue $51,150
Out at close $6,250
****
3390 Saline
FNB, DORCHESTER
{{ 2 L }}
Chartered 9/8/85
Liquidated 7/5/92
Brown Back <$VALUE
4x5 1-1496 <$1000
Total Issue $29,920
Out in 1910 $175
****
5440 Antelope
FNB, ELGIN
{{ 7 L 11 S }}
Chartered 4/19/00
Receivership 11/3/30
Brown Back <$VALUE
3x10-20 1-850 <$450
1882 Date Back
3x10-20 1-1670 <$400
1882 Value Back
3x10-20 1671-2350 <$450
1902 Plain Back
3x10-20 1-4498 <$200
1929 Small Size
10 Type 1 1-446 <$150
20 Type 1 1-98 <$150
Total Issue $423,420
Out at close $50,000
Large out at close $14,150
****
3999 Buffalo
FNB, ELM CREEK
{{ UNREPORTED }}
Chartered 3/26/89
Liquidated 5/15/99
Brown Back <$VALUE
3x10-20 1-781 <$1500
Total Issue $39,050
Out in 1910 $410
****
5787 Cass
FNB OF ELMWOOD
{{ 1 L }}
Chartered 1901
Liquidated 4/20/14
Brown Back <$VALUE
3x10-20 1-1550 <$1250
1882 Date Back
3x10-20 1-1067 <$1250
Total Issue $130,850
Out in 1914 $18,970
****
7204 Gosper
FNB, ELWOOD
{{ 6 L 18 S }}
Chartered 4/04
1902 Red Seal <$VALUE
3x10-20 1-1320 <$650
1902 Date Back
3x10-20 1-1630 <$300
1902 Plain Back
3x10-20 1631-4501 <$300
1929 Small Size
10 Type 1 1-546 <$100
20 Type 1 1-138 <$100
10 Type 2 1-610 <$125
20 Type 2 1-120 <$125
Total Issue $348,870
Out in 1935 $25,000
Large out 1935 $2,050
****
7425 Dakota
FNB, EMERSON
{{ 7 L U + 7 S }}
Chartered 10/04
1902 Red Seal <$VALUE
3x10-20 1-387 <$600
1902 Date Back
3x10-20 1-2100 <$250
1902 Plain Back
3x10-20 2101-6117 <$250
1929 Small Size
10 Type 1 1-610 <$175
20 Type 1 1-206 <$175
10 Type 2 1-723 <$200
20 Type 2 1-85 <$200
Total Issue $395,450
Out in 1935 $30,000
Large out 1935 $2,280
****
3117 Fillmore
EXETER NB OF EXETER
{{ UNREPORTED }}
Organized 2/4/84
Liquidated 4/30/97
Brown Back <$VALUE
4x5 1-2661 <$1500
Total Issue $53,220
Out in 1910 $395
****
3121 Fillmore
FNB OF EXETER
{{ UNREPORTED }}
Organized 2/7/84
Liquidated 4/9/97
Brown Back <$VALUE
3x10-20 1-897 <$1500
Total Issue $44,850
Out in 1910 $310
****
8995 Jefferson
BONHAM NB OF FAIRBURY
{{ 2 L }}
Chartered 1/08
Liquidated 12/2/12
1902 Red Seal <$VALUE
3x10-20 1-1200 <$1250
1902 Date Back
3x10-20 1-870 <$850
Total Issue $103,500
Out at close $50,000
Ch 2994 assumed circulation
****
10340 Jefferson
FARMERS & MERCHANTS NB, FAIRBURY
{{ 9 L }}
Organized 2/8/13
Receivership 3/15/24
1902 Date Back <$VALUE
3x10-20 1-2600 <$175
1902 Plain Back
3x10-20 2601-6596 <$175
Total Issue $329,800
Out at close $59,400
****
2994 Jefferson
FNB OF FAIRBURY
{{ 10 L 43 S }}
Chartered 1883
Brown Back <$VALUE
4x5 1-3487 <$400
50-100 1-410 <$2000/$2500
1902 Red Seal
50-100 1-655 <$3000/$3500
1902 Date Back
50-100 1-300 <$350/$400
3x50-100 1-1430 <$350/$400
1902 Plain Back
3x50-100 1431-1764 <$350/$400
1929 Small Size
10 Type 1 1-1796 <$40
20 Type 1 1-526 <$45
10 Type 2 1-2543 <$45
20 Type 2 1-631 <$50
Total Issue $924,420
Out in 1935 $100,000
Large out 1935 $12,900
Outstanding includes Ch 8995
****
3493 Clay
FNB, FAIRFIELD
{{ UNREPORTED }}
Chartered 4/28/86
Liquidated 4/10/94
Brown Back <$VALUE
4x5 1-1798 <$1500
Total Issue $35,960
Out in 1910 $235
****
3230 Fillmore
FNB OF FAIRMONT
{{ UNREPORTED }}
Organized 7/26/84
Liquidated 5/1/88
Brown Back <$VALUE
4x5 1-927 <$2000
Total Issue $18,540
Out in 1910 $150
****
2746 Richardson
FNB, FALLS CITY
{{ 18 L 15 S }}
Chartered 1882
Series 1875 <$VALUE
3x10-20 1-4150<$1000/$1500
1902 Red Seal
3x10-20 1-2500 <$350
1902 Date Back
3x10-20 1-2840 <$100
1902 Plain Back
3x10-20 2841-9474 <$100
1929 Small Size
10 Type 1 1-1135 <$100
20 Type 1 1-321 <$125
Total Issue $912,820
Out in 1935 $25,000
Large out 1935 $3,770
****
3549 Franklin
FNB, FRANKLIN
{{ UNREPORTED }}
Chartered 8/11/86
Liquidated 3/27/89
Brown Back <$VALUE
4x5 1-933 <$1500
Total Issue $18,660
Out in 1910 $100
****
4504 Dodge
COMMERCIAL NB OF FREMONT
{{ 10 L }}
Chartered 1891
Liquidated 2/16/22
Brown Back <$VALUE
3x10-20 1-7000 <$450
1882 Date Back
3x10-20 1-1215 <$350
1902 Date Back
3x10-20 1-5300 <$150
1902 Plain Back
3x10-20 5301-9744 <$150
Total Issue $897,950
Out at close $98,300
Ch 3188 assumed circulation
****
3188 Dodge
FARMERS AND MERCHANTS NB OF FREMONT
Chartered 5/12/84
Receivership 2/13/33
2nd title:Union NB of Fremont 12/8/21
FIRST TITLE {{ 7 L }}
Brown Back <$VALUE
4x5 1-5831 <$450
3x10-20 1-1367 <$450
1902 Red Seal
3x10-20 1-3000 <$450
1902 Date Back
3x10-20 1-7500 <$200
1902 Plain Back
3x10-20 7501-12800 <$200
SECOND TITLE {{ 32 L 20 S }}
1902 Plain Back
3x10-20 1-19364 <$50/$60
1929 Small Size
10 Type 1 1-2422 <$60
20 Type 1 1-673 <$70
Total Issue $2,169,250
Out at close $149,280
Large out at close $28,810
****
1974 Dodge
FNB OF FREMONT
{{ 18 L }}
Organized 3/16/72
Receivership 11/1/21
Original Series <$VALUE
3x1-2 1-1500 <$1000/$3000
4x5 1-2875 <$850
Series 1875
4x5 1-5969 <$850
Brown Back
4x5 1-3000 <$350
3x10-20 1-7390 <$350
1882 Date Back
4x5 1-4405 <$300
3x10-20 1-2849 <$300
1902 Date Back
4x5 1-7750 <$125
3x10-20 1-6000 <$125
1902 Plain Back
4x5 7751-13985 <$125
3x10-20 6001-9322 <$125
Total Issue $1,590,230
Out at close $150,000
Ch 3188 assumed circulation
****
2848 Dodge
FREMONT NB, FREMONT
{{ 21 L 28 S }}
Chartered 1882
Brown Back <$VALUE
4x5 1-10166 <$375
3x10-20 1-1736 <$375/$400
1902 Red Seal
4x5 1-5000 <$400
3x10-20 1-4900 <$400
1902 Date Back
4x5 1-10250 <$100
3x10-20 1-6500 <$100
1902 Plain Back
4x5 10251-31125 <$100
3x10-20 6501-18870 <$100
1929 Small Size
5 Type 1 1-4690 <$45
10 Type 1 1-2286 <$45
20 Type 1 1-564 <$50
5 Type 2 1-1450 <$50
10 Type 2 1-726 <$50
20 Type 2 1-120 <$60
Total Issue $2,563,570
Out in 1935 $75,000
Large out 1935 $11,105
****
13408 Dodge
STEPHENS NB OF FREMONT
{{ 2U + 27 S }}
Chartered 12/24/29
1929 Small Size <$VALUE
5 Type 1 1-4042 <$60
10 Type 1 1-1346 <$60
20 Type 1 1-282 <$65
5 Type 2 1-1524 <$75
10 Type 2 1-530 <$75
20 Type 2 1-115 <$75
Total Issue $251,080
Out in 1935 $48,350
****
Union NB of Fremont
SEE Ch 3188
Farmers and Merchants NB of Fremont
****
2960 Saline
FNB, FRIEND
{{ 12 L 21 S }}
Organized 5/15/83
Brown Back <$VALUE
4x5 1-3304 <$600
3x10-20 1-638 <$600
1902 Red Seal
3x10-20 1-1450 <$600
1902 Date Back
3x10-20 1-2700 <$250
1902 Plain Back
3x10-20 2701-8475 <$250
1929 Small Size
10 Type 1 1-990 <$125
20 Type 1 1-318 <$125
10 Type 2 1-912 <$125
20 Type 2 1-185 <$125
Total Issue $704,610
Out in 1935 $50,000
Large out 1935 $3,540
****
2964 Nance
FNB, FULLERTON
{{ 8 L 14 S }}
Chartered 1883
Brown Back <$VALUE
4x5 1-3315 <$450
3x10-20 1-193 <$500
1902 Red Seal
3x10-20 1-1150 <$500
1902 Date Back
3x10-20 1-3700 <$175
1902 Plain Back
3x10-20 3701-9488 <$175
1929 Small Size
10 Type 1 1-1106 <$100
20 Type 1 1-288 <$100
10 Type 2 1-521 <$100
20 Type 2 1-305 <$100
Total Issue $720,080
Out in 1935 $50,000
Large out 1935 $4,590
****
5384 Nance
FULLERTON NB, FULLERTON
{{ 11 L 20 S }}
Chartered 6/1/00
Brown Back <$VALUE
3x10-20 1-900 <$400
1882 Date Back
3x10-20 1-2840 <$300/$350
1882 Value Back
3x10-20 2841-4292<$350/$400
1902 Plain Back
3x10-20 1-4433 <$150
1929 Small Size
10 Type 1 1-1076 <$60
20 Type 1 1-296 <$70
10 Type 2 1-807 <$75
20 Type 2 1-183 <$75
Total Issue $593,060
Out in 1935 $50,000
Large out 1935 $3,690
****
4052 Fillmore
FNB OF GENEVA
{{ UNREPORTED }}
Organized 6/19/89
Liquidated 1/30/94
Brown Back <$VALUE
3x10-20 1-410 <$1500
Total Issue $20,500
Out in 1910 $140
****
4484 Fillmore
GENEVA NB, GENEVA
{{ UNREPORTED }}
Organized 12/17/90
Liquidated 3/25/99
Brown Back <$VALUE
3x10-20 1-697 <$1500
Total Issue $34,850
Out in 1910 $480
****
5189 Nance
FNB, GENOA
{{ 10 L 16 S }}
Chartered 4/27/99
Brown Back <$VALUE
3x10-20 1-3150 <$450
1882 Date Back
3x10-20 1-3000 <$400
1882 Value Back
3x10-20 3001-3829 <$450
1902 Plain Back
3x10-20 1-4924 <$175
1929 Small Size
10 Type 1 1-996 <$85
20 Type 1 1-252 <$90
10 Type 2 1-1211 <$100
20 Type 2 1-228 <$100
Total Issue $701,820
Out in 1935 $50,000
Large out 1935 $3,550
****
6805 Nance
GENOA NB, GENOA
{{ 2 L 28 S }}
Chartered 6/03
1902 Red Seal <$VALUE
3x10-20 1-570 <$1250
1902 Date Back
3x10-20 1-1560* <$600
1902 Plain Back
3x10-20 1961-4573* <$600
* 1561-1960 not marked
1929 Small Size
10 Type 1 1-778 <$65
20 Type 1 1-182 <$75
10 Type 2 1-1629 <$80
20 Type 2 1-515 <$80
Total Issue $352,260
Out in 1935 $50,000
Large out 1935 $1,540
****

****
8062 Scotts Bluff
FNB, GERING
{{ UNREPORTED }}
Organized 12/28/05
Receivership 2/26/24
1902 Red Seal <$VALUE
3x10-20 1-495 <$1500
1902 Date Back
3x10-20 1-1200* <$850
1902 Plain Back
3x10-20 1321-1848* <$850
* 1201-1320 not marked
Total Issue $117,150
Out at close $11,500
****
9694 Scotts Bluff
GERING NB, GERING
{{ 2 L 14 S }}
Chartered 3/10
1902 Date Back <$VALUE
3x10-20 1-2000 <$650
1902 Plain Back
3x10-20 2001-5385 <$650
1929 Small Size
10 Type 1 1-692 <$125
20 Type 1 1-166 <$125
10 Type 2 1-531 <$150
20 Type 2 1-88 <$175
Total Issue $337,760
Out in 1935 $25,000
Large out 1935 $1,220
****
3921 Buffalo
FNB, GIBBON
{{ UNREPORTED }}
Chartered 8/17/88
Liquidated 10/10/94
Brown Back <$VALUE
3x10-20 1-527 <$1500
Total Issue $26,350
Out in 1910 $200
****
8521 Sheridan
FNB, GORDON
{{ 3 L 10 S }}
Chartered 1/07
1902 Red Seal <$VALUE
3x10-20 1-1200 <$750
1902 Date Back
3x10-20 1-2900 <$400
1902 Plain Back
3x10-20 2901-8650 <$400
1929 Small Size
10 Type 1 1-1142 <$150
20 Type 1 1-328 <$150
10 Type 2 1-705 <$160
20 Type 2 1-295 <$150
Total Issue $613,330
Out in 1935 $50,000
Large out 1935 $2,310
****
8113 Dawson
CITIZENS NB OF GOTHENBURG
{{ UNREPORTED }}
Chartered 2/06
Liquidated 5/3/15
1902 Red Seal <$VALUE
3x10-20 1-800 <$1500
1902 Date Back
3x10-20 1-2453 <$850
Total Issue $162,650
Out in 1915 $37,800
****
4890 Dawson
FNB OF GOTHENBURG
{{ 1 L }}
Chartered 3/18/93
Liquidated 12/10/96
Brown Back <$VALUE
4x5 1-999 <$1500
Total Issue $19,980
Out in 1910 $130
****
6282 Dawson
GOTHENBURG NB, GOTHENBURG
{{ 3 L }}
Chartered 1902
Liquidated 6/25/15
1902 Red Seal <$VALUE
3x10-20 1-1200 <$750
1902 Date Back
3x10-20 1-3273 <$400
Total Issue $223,650
Out in 1915 $42,600
****

****
3101 Hall
CITIZENS NB, GRAND ISLAND
{{ 1 L }}
Chartered 12/29/83
Receivership 12/14/93
Brown Back <$VALUE
4x5 1-2346 <$1500
Total Issue $46,920
Out in 1915 $380
****
2779 Hall
FNB, GRAND ISLAND
{{ 19 L 45 S }}
Chartered 1882
Brown Back <$VALUE
4x5 1-6405 <$400
3x10-20 1-388 <$400
1902 Red Seal
4x5 1-2250 <$400
3x10-20 1-2400 <$400
1902 Date Back
4x5 1-4225 <$100
3x10-20 1-2940 <$100
1902 Plain Back
4x5 4226-12830 <$100
3x10-20 2941-8209 <$100
1929 Small Size
5 Type 1 1-3746 <$40
10 Type 1 1-2208 <$45
20 Type 1 1-506 <$50
5 Type 2 1-4426 <$50
10 Type 2 1-2449 <$50
20 Type 2 1-670 <$50
Total Issue $1,345,150
Out in 1935 $70,000
Large out 1935 $5,640
****
9395 Hall
GRAND ISLAND NB,
GRAND ISLAND
{{ 35 L 2U + 16 S }}
Chartered 4/09
Liquidated 4/1/30
1902 Date Back <$VALUE
4x5 1-3000 <$65
3x10-20 1-7200 <$75
1902 Plain Back
4x5 3001-14858 <$65
3x10-20 7201-15405 <$75
1929 Small Size
5 Type 1 1-737 <$85
10 Type 1 1-221 <$85
20 Type 1 1-103 <$100
Total Issue $1,115,410
Out at close $100,000
Large out at close $38,690
****
4357 Hall
SECURITY NB OF
GRAND ISLAND
{{ 1 L }}
Chartered 7/3/90
Liquidated 1/12/95
Brown Back <$VALUE
4x5 1-4640 <$1250
Total Issue $92,800
Out in 1910 $600
****
4170 Perkins
FNB, GRANT
{{ UNREPORTED }}
Organized 12/4/89
Receivership 8/14/94
Brown Back <$VALUE
4x5 1-1177 <$1500
Total Issue $23,540
Out in 1915 $90
****
7622 Greeley
FNB OF GREELEY
{{ UNREPORTED }}
Organized 2/3/05
Receivership 12/30/29
1902 Red Seal <$VALUE
3x10-20 1-300 <$1500
1902 Date Back
3x10-20 1-1240 <$850
1902 Plain Back
3x10-20 1241-1789 <$850
1929 Small Size
10 Type 1 1-17 <$750
20 Type 1 1-3 <$750
Total Issue $105,830
Out at close $7,000
Large out at close $5,620
****

****
3403 Cass
FNB OF GREENWOOD
{{ 2 L }}
Chartered 1885
Liquidated 1/1/26
Brown Back <$VALUE
4x5 1-3619 <$1000
3x10-20 1-415 <$1000
1902 Red Seal
3x10-20 1-360 <$1000
1902 Date Back
3x10-20 1-1690* <$500
1902 Plain Back
3x10-20 1851-3733* <$500
* 1691-1850 not marked
Total Issue $297,780
Out at close $25,000
****
8172 York
FNB, GRESHAM
{{ 3 L 17 S }}
Chartered 4/06
Liquidated 6/29/31
1902 Red Seal <$VALUE
3x10-20 1-600 <$750
1902 Date Back
3x10-20 1-1450 <$400
1902 Plain Back
3x10-20 1451-3793 <$400
1929 Small Size
10 Type 1 1-231 <$100
20 Type 1 1-42 <$100
Total Issue $238,550
Out at close $20,000
Large out at close $3,950
****
8285 Hamilton
FNB, HAMPTON
{{ 3 L 9 S }}
Chartered 7/06
1902 Red Seal <$VALUE
3x10-20 1-425 <$750
1902 Dat150e Back
3x10-20 1-1750 <$400
1902 Plain Back
3x10-20 1751-4286 <$400
1929 Small Size
5 Type 1 1-416 <$150
10 Type 1 1-410 <$150
20 Type 1 1-136 <$150
5 Type 2 1-88 <$175
10 Type 2 1-72 <$175
20 Type 2 1-55 <$175
Total Issue $291,210
Out in 1935 $22,500
Large out 1935 $1,200
****
8888 Sioux
FNB OF HARRISON
{{ 2 L }}
Organized 6/28/07
Receivership 2/12/24
1902 Red Seal <$VALUE
3x10-20 1-500 <$1000
1902 Date Back
3x10-20 1-1290 <$500
1902 Plain Back
3x10-20 1291-2087 <$500
Total Issue $129,350
Out at close $15,000
****
12552 Sioux
SIOUX NB OF HARRISON
{{ 2 L 6 S }}
Chartered 6/24
1902 Plain Back <$VALUE
3x10-20 1-866 <$600
1929 Small Size
10 Type 1 1-376 <$175
20 Type 1 1-106 <$175
10 Type 2 1-385 <$200
Total Issue $82,430
Out in 1935 $15,000
Large out 1935 $550
****
4528 Cedar
FNB, HARTINGTON
{{ 10 L 11 S }}
Organized 2/13/91
Receivership 6/1/32
Brown Back <$VALUE
4x5 1-2575 <$450
3x10-20 1-1020 <$450
1882 Date Back
4x5 1-331 <$450
3x10-20 1-268 <$450
1902 Date Back
3x10-20 1-3200 <$175
1902 Plain Back
3x10-20 3201-7635 <$175
1929 Small Size
10 Type 1 1-758 <$150
20 Type 1 1-193 <$150
Total Issue $572,910
Out at close $49,820
Large out at close $8,570
****
5400 Cedar
HARTINGTON NB, HARTINGTON
{{ 7 L }}
Organized 5/21/00
Receivership 11/13/28
Brown Back <$VALUE
3x10-20 1-1200 <$500
1882 Date Back
3x10-20 1-1980 <$400
1882 Value Back
3x10-20 1981-2462 <$500
1902 Plain Back
3x10-20 1-1950 <$200
Total Issue $280,600
Out at close $25,000
****
4129 Clay
FNB, HARVARD
{{ UNREPORTED }}
Chartered 9/25/89
Liquidated 1/10/00
Brown Back <$VALUE
4x5 1-2251 <$1500
Total Issue $45,020
Out in 1910 $405
****
3099 Adams
CITY NB, HASTINGS
{{ UNREPORTED }}
Chartered 12/27/83
Receivership 1/14/91
Brown Back <$VALUE
3x10-20 1-805 <$1500
Total Issue $40,250
Out in 1915 $220
****
3086 Adams
EXCHANGE NB OF HASTINGS
{{ 13 L }}
Chartered 11/21/83
Receivership 1/2/34
Brown Back <$VALUE
4x5 1-6657 <$350
3x10-20 1-507 <$400
1902 Red Seal
3x10-20 1-2350 <$400
1902 Date Back
3x10-20 1-6200 <$125
1902 Plain Back
3x10-20 6201-15047 <$125
Total Issue $1,028,340
Out in 1927 $97,300
****
2528 Adams
FNB, HASTINGS
{{ 34 L 36 S }}
Organized 5/23/81
Receivership 10/13/31
Series 1875 <$VALUE
4x10 1-4516 <$850
Brown Back
3x10-20 1-6300 <$325
1882 Date Back
3x10-20 1-12000 <$275
1882 Value Back
3x10-20 12001-17083 <$325
1902 Plain Back
3x10-20 1-11854 <$50/$60
1929 Small Size
5 Type 1 1-566 <$40
10 Type 1 1-1718 <$40
20 Type 1 1-522 <$50
Total Issue $2,125,190
Out at close $150,000
****
3732 Adams
GERMAN NB OF HASTINGS
Organized 6/7/87
Liquidated 3/9/34
2nd title:Nebraska NB of
Hastings 4/27/17
FIRST TITLE {{ 5 L }}
Brown Back <$VALUE
4x5 1-3496 <$600
3x10-20 1-914 <$600
1902 Red Seal
4x5 1-500 <$600
3x10-20 1-400 <$600
1902 Date Back
4x5 1-2800 <$300
3x10-20 1-2270 <$300
1902 Plain Back
4x5 2801-3415 <$300
3x10-20 2271-2581 <$300
SECOND TITLE {{ 11 L 35 S }}
1902 Plain Back
3x10-20 1-11482 <$150
1929 Small Size
10 Type 1 1-2053 <$50
20 Type 1 1-589 <$60
Total Issue $1,110,930
Out at close $100,000
Large out at close $6,380
Ch 13953 assumed circulation
****
13515 Adams
HASTINGS NB, HASTINGS
{{ 29 S }}
Chartered 12/31/30
1929 Small Size <$VALUE
10 Type 1 1-1234 <$40
20 Type 1 1-420 <$50
10 Type 2 1-182 <$50
20 Type 2 1-70 <$65
Total Issue $127,660
Out in 1935 $63,040
****
Nebraska NB of Hastings
SEE Ch 3732
German NB of Hastings
****
9772 Lancaster
FNB OF HAVELOCK
{{ 0 L 19 S }}
Chartered 6/10
1902 Date Back <$VALUE
3x10-20 1-700 <$1000
1902 Plain Back
3x10-20 701-1247 <$1000
1929 Small Size
10 Type 1 1-185 <$150
20 Type 1 1-33 <$300
Total Issue $77,410
Out in 1935 $6,500
Large out 1935 $770
****
8760 Sheridan
FNB, HAY SPRINGS
{{ 2 L 5 S }}
Chartered 6/07
1902 Red Seal <$VALUE
3x10-20 1-300 <$1000
1902 Date Back
3x10-20 1-850 <$500
1902 Plain Back
3x10-20 851-1855 <$500
1929 Small Size
10 Type 1 1-276 <$300
20 Type 1 1-60 <$300
Total Issue $131,510
Out in 1935 $10,000
Large out 1935 $500
****
8031 Hayes
FNB, HAYES CENTER
{{ 3 L 15 S }}
Chartered 1/06
1902 Red Seal <$VALUE
3x10-20 1-900 <$750
1902 Date Back
3x10-20 1-1600 <$400
1902 Plain Back
3x10-20 1601-4461 <$400
1929 Small Size
10 Type 1 1-586 <$125
20 Type 1 1-140 <$125
10 Type 2 1-468 <$150
20 Type 2 1-165 <$150
Total issue $327,990
Out in 1935 $25,000
Large out 1935 $1,600
****
2756 Thayer
FNB, HEBRON
{{ 2 L }}
Organized 1882
Liquidated 2/8/15
Series 1875 <$VALUE
3x10-20 1-2308<$1500/$2000
1902 Red Seal
3x10-20 1-1000 <$1000
1902 Date Back
3x10-20 1-924 <$500
Total Issue $211,600
Out in 1915 $13,860
****
10242 Box Butte
FNB, HEMINGFORD
{{ 5 L }}
Organized 7/27/12
Receivership 11/10/23
1902 Date Back <$VALUE
3x10-20 1-500 <$400
1902 Plain Back
3x10-20 501-775 <$400
Total Issue $38,750
Out at close $5,950
****

****
8183 York
FNB, HENDERSON
{{ UNREPORTED }}
Chartered 4/06
Liquidated 12/20/13
1902 Red Seal <$VALUE
3x10-20 1-750 <$1500
1902 Date Back
3x10-20 1-875 <$1000
Total Issue $81,250
Out in 1914 $14,860
****
City NB of Holdrege
SEE Ch 4345
United States NB of Holdrege
****
3208 Phelps
FNB, HOLDREGE
{{ 9 L 14 S }}
Chartered 1884
Brown Back <$VALUE
4x5 1-3937 <$450
50-100 1-221 <$2000/$2500
1902 Red Seal
3x10-20 1-1260 <$500
1902 Date Back
3x10-20 1-3400 <$175
1902 Plain Back
3x10-20 3401-8948 <$175
1929 Small Size
10 Type 1 1-1024 <$100
20 Type 1 1-304 <$125
10 Type 2 1-1044 <$125
20 Type 2 1-199 <$125
Total Issue $734,630
Out in 1935 $50,000
Large out 1935 $3,480
****
3875 Phelps
HOLDREGE NB, HOLDREGE
{{ UNREPORTED }}
Chartered 4/26/88
Receivership 3/15/95
Brown Back <$VALUE
4x5 1-2297 <$1500
Total Issue $45,940
Out in 1915 $245
****
4345 Phelps
UNITED STATES NB OF
HOLDREGE
Chartered 1890
Liquidated 7/9/14
2nd title:City NB of
Holdrege 10/04
FIRST TITLE {{ 0 L }}
Brown Back <$VALUE
4x5 1-3505 <$1500
3x10-20 1-524 <$1500
SECOND TITLE {{ 3 L }}
Brown Back
4x5 1-500 <$650
3x10-20 1-400 <$650
1882 Date Back
4x5 1-215 <$650
3x10-20 1-158 <$650
1902 Date Back
3x10-20 1-2860 <$450
Total Issue $281,500
Out at close $52,295
****
5297 Dodge
FNB OF HOOPER
{{ 15 L 4 S }}
Chartered 4/21/00
Brown Back <$VALUE
3x10-20 1-1500 <$400
1882 Date Back
3x10-20 1-1750 <$400
1882 Value Back
3x10-20 1751-2322 <$400
1902 Plain Back
4x5 1-3675 <$150
3x10-20 1-1150 <$150
1929 Small Size
5 Type 1 1-2554 <$300
5 Type 2 1-5544 <$300
Total Issue $426,440
Out in 1935 $25,000
Large out 1935 $995
****

<$VALUEs are for notes in FINE condition. Value changes by approximately 25% for a change of one full grade.

3238 Richardson
FNB, HUMBOLDT
{{ 2 L }}
Chartered 8/22/84
Liquidated 2/28/08
Brown Back <$VALUE
4x5 1-3827 <$1000
3x10-20 1-269 <$1000
1902 Red Seal
3x10-20 1-324 <$1000
Total Issue $106,190
Out in 1910 $4,185

7065 Richardson
NB OF HUMBOLDT
{{ 3 L }}
Chartered 12/03
Liquidated 4/28/27
1902 Red Seal <$VALUE
3x10-20 1-1490 <$750
1902 Date Back
3x10-20 1-1840 <$450
1902 Plain Back
3x10-20 1841-4123 <$450
Total Issue $280,650
Out at close $30,000

5337 Platte
FNB OF HUMPHREY
{{ 2 L 0 S }}
Organized 4/16/00
Receivership 1/30/30
Brown Back <$VALUE
3x10-20 1-740 <$850
1882 Date Back
3x10-20 1-740 <$800
1882 Value Back
3x10-20 741-888 <$850
1902 Plain Back
3x10-20 1-856 <$600
1929 Small Size
10 Type 1 1-37 <$750
20 Type 1 1-12 <$750
Total Issue $127,860
Out at close $9,980
Large out at close $6,320

9762 Chase
FNB OF IMPERIAL
{{ 3 L 5 S }}
Chartered 5/10
1902 Date Back <$VALUE
3x10-20 1-1500 <$400
1902 Plain Back
3x10-20 1501-4446 <$400
1929 Small Size
10 Type 1 1-568 <$300
20 Type 1 1-160 <$300
10 Type 2 1-824 <$300
20 Type 2 1-190 <$300
Total Issue $287,620
Out in 1935 $25,000
Large out 1935 $1,000

3483 Red Willow
FNB, INDIANOLA
{{ 1 L }}
Chartered 4/8/86
Liquidated 8/31/91
Brown Back <$VALUE
4x5 1-1331 <$1500
Total Issue $26,620
Out in 1910 $260

8161 Nemaha
FNB, JOHNSON
{{ 6 L 12 S }}
Chartered 4/06
1902 Red Seal <$VALUE
3x10-20 1-875 <$600
1902 Date Back
3x10-20 1-1560* <$275
1902 Plain Back
3x10-20 1691-4489* <$275
* 1561-1690 not marked
1929 Small Size
10 Type 1 1-498 <$125
20 Type 1 1-146 <$125
10 Type 2 1-775 <$125
20 Type 2 1-145 <$125
Total Issue $326,250
Out in 1935 $25,000
Large out 1935 $1,670

8383 Nemaha
GERMAN NB OF JOHNSON
{{ 1 L }}
Chartered 10/06
Liquidated 4/11/17
1902 Red Seal <$VALUE
3x10-20 1-887 <$1250
1902 Date Back
3x10-20 1-1530 <$750
1902 Plain Back
3x10-20 1531-1657 <$750
Total Issue $127,200
Out in 1916 $25,000

3526 Buffalo
BUFFALO COUNTY NB, KEARNEY
{{ 1 L }}
Chartered 7/3/86
Receivership 11/10/94
Brown Back <$VALUE
3x10-20 1-1310 <$1500
Total Issue $65,500
Out in 1915 $380

6600 Buffalo
CENTRAL NB OF KEARNEY
{{ 4 L }}
Organized 1/26/03
Liquidated 3/30/27
1902 Red Seal <$VALUE
3x10-20 1-2720 <$600
1902 Date Back
3x10-20 1-2900 <$300
1902 Plain Back
3x10-20 2901-7366 <$300
Total Issue $504,300
Out in 1925 $50,000
Ch 13013 assumed circulation

3958 Buffalo
CITY NB OF KEARNEY
{{ 14 L }}
Chartered 12/26/88
Liquidated 3/30/27
Brown Back <$VALUE
4x5 1-6500 <$400
3x10-20 1-1856 <$400
1902 Date Back
4x5 1-3450 <$125
3x10-20 1-2520 <$125
1902 Plain Back
4x5 3451-8520 <$125
3x10-20 2521-5800 <$125
Total Issue $683,200
Out at close $50,000
Ch 13013 assumed circulation

8651 Buffalo
COMMERCIAL NB OF KEARNEY
{{ UNREPORTED }}
Chartered 4/07
Liquidated 5/27/12
1902 Red Seal <$VALUE
3x10-20 1-2250 <$1250
1902 Date Back
3x10-20 1-2340 <$850
Total Issue $229,500
Out in 1912 $68,180

2806 Buffalo
FNB OF KEARNEY
{{ 1 L }}
Chartered 10/25/82
Closed 10/10/94
Brown Back <$VALUE
4x5 1-8170 <$1250
Total Issue $163,400
Out in 1915 $1,295

3201 Buffalo
KEARNEY NB, KEARNEY
{{ UNREPORTED }}
Chartered 6/5/84
Receivership 9/19/95
Brown Back <$VALUE
3x10-20 1-2131 <$1250
Total Issue $106,550
Out in 1915 $480

13420 Kimball
AMERICAN NB OF KIMBALL
{{ 4U + 50+ S }}
Chartered 1/28/30
1929 Small Size <$VALUE
5 Type 1 1-2734 <$20
10 Type 1 1-1678 <$30
20 Type 1 1-430 <$35
5 Type 2 1-6292 <$25
10 Type 2 1-3048 <$35
20 Type 2 1-1032 <$40
Total Issue $316,880
Out in 1935 $100,000

9793 Cedar
FNB OF LAUREL
{{ 7 L }}
Organized 5/19/10
Receivership 2/2/28
1902 Date Back <$VALUE
3x10-20 1-2840 <$250
1902 Plain Back
3x10-20 2841-6074 <$250
Total Issue $303,700
Out at close $40,000

9979 Cedar
LAUREL NB, LAUREL
{{ 9 L }}
Organized 3/21/11
Receivership 5/14/27
1902 Date Back <$VALUE
3x10-20 1-2340* <$175
1902 Plain Back
3x10-20 2541-6288* <$175
* 2341-2540 not marked
Total Issue $314,400
Out at close $40,000

8851 Nuckolls
FNB OF LAWRENCE
{{ 1 L }}
Chartered 8/07
Liquidated 4/28/14
1902 Red Seal <$VALUE
3x10-20 1-750 <$1250
1902 Date Back
3x10-20 1-912 <$850
Total Issue $83,100
Out in 1914 $18,280

9831 Colfax
FNB OF LEIGH
{{ 7 L 2U + 12 S }}
Organized 10/12/10
Receivership 2/2/33
1902 Date Back <$VALUE
4x5 1-2650 <$250
3x10-20 1-2000 <$250
1902 Plain Back
4x5 2651-7700 <$250
3x10-20 2001-4794 <$250
1929 Small Size
5 Type 1 1-819 <$150
10 Type 1 1-474 <$150
20 Type 1 1-140 <$150
Total Issue $463,510
Out at close $37,200
Large out at close $3,380

4161 Dawson
DAWSON COUNTY NB OF LEXINGTON
{{ 6 L }}
Chartered 1889
Liquidated 10/1/16
Brown Back <$VALUE
4x5 1-3510 <$600
3x10-20 1-2806 <$600
1882 Date Back
4x5 1-601 <$600
3x10-20 1-253 <$600
1902 Date Back
3x10-20 1-3180 <$300
1902 Plain Back
3x10-20 3181-3200 <$300
Total Issue $395,170
Out in 1916 $43,900

FNB of Lexington
SEE Ch 3292
FNB of Plum Creek

4080 Gage
FNB, LIBERTY
{{ 1 L }}
Chartered 7/24/89
Liquidated 10/1/97
Brown Back <$VALUE
3x10-20 1-635 <$1500
Total Issue $31,750
Out in 1910 $390

4606 Lancaster
AMERICAN EXCHANGE NB, LINCOLN
{{ UNREPORTED }}
Chartered 7/29/91
Liquidated 6/17/99
Brown Back <$VALUE
3x10-20 1-2515 <$1500
Total Issue $125,750
Out in 1910 $1,870

Capital NB of Lincoln
SEE Ch 2988
Marsh NB of Lincoln

8885 Lancaster
CENTRAL NB OF LINCOLN
{{ 21 L }}
Chartered 9/07
Liquidated 6/21/29
1902 Red Seal <$VALUE
3x10-20 1-2125 <$350
1902 Date Back
3x10-20 1-5600 <$85
1902 Plain Back
3x10-20 5601-18446 <$85
Total Issue $1,028,550
Out at close $115,400

13017 Lancaster
CITY NB IN LINCOLN
{{ 7 L }}
Chartered 12/26
Liquidated 5/3/28
1902 Plain Back <$VALUE
3x10-20 1-3085 <$225
Total Issue $154,250
Out at close $247,900
Outstanding includes Ch 5213

5213 Lancaster
CITY NB OF LINCOLN
{{ 49 L }}
Chartered 8/11/99
Liquidated 1/27/27
Brown Back <$VALUE
3x10-20 1-7800 <$300
1882 Date Back
3x10-20 1-14300 <$275
1882 Value Back
3x10-20 14301-18716 <$300
1902 Plain Back
3x10-20 1-18164 <$60/$70
Total Issue $2,234,000
Out at close $248,300
Ch 13017 assumed circulation

4435 Lancaster
COLUMBIA NB OF LINCOLN
{{ 2 L }}
Chartered 10/7/90
Liquidated 7/20/07
Brown Back <$VALUE
3x10-20 1-6554 <$750
Total Issue $327,700
Out at close $100,000
Ch 1798 assumed circulation

13333 Lancaster
CONTINENTAL NB OF LINCOLN
{{ 48 S }}
Chartered 6/1/29
1929 Small Size <$VALUE
5 Type 1 1-2052 <$30
10 Type 1 1-1224 <$30
20 Type 1 1-830 <$40
50 Type 1 1-42 <$150
5 Type 2 1-7132 <$30
10 Type 2 1-3534 <$30
20 Type 2 1-805 <$40
Total Issue $334,300
Out in 1935 $177,900

1798 Lancaster
FNB, LINCOLN
{{ 35 L 50+ S }}
Chartered 2/24/71
Original Series <$VALUE
3x1-2 1-1500 <$1000/$3000
4x5 1-2625 <$850
Series 1875
3x1-2 1-400 <$1000/$3000
4x5 1-8488 <$850
Brown Back
3x10-20 1-13680 <$300/$350
1882 Date Back
3x10-20 1-1769 <$250/$300
1902 Date Back
3x10-20 1-21500 <$50/$60
1902 Plain Back
3x10-20 21501-21730<$50/$60
1929 Small Size
20 Type 1 1-8642 <$30
20 Type 2 1-8097 <$30
Total Issue $3,289,690
Out in 1935 $847,000
Large out 1935 $9,215
Outstanding includes Ch 4435

3571 Lancaster
GERMAN NB, LINCOLN
{{ 1 L }}
Chartered 10/16/86
Receivership 12/19/95
Brown Back <$VALUE
4x5 1-4135 <$1500
Total Issue $82,700
Out in 1915 $665

2750 Lancaster
LINCOLN NB, LINCOLN
{{ U + 1 L }}
Chartered 7/6/82
Liquidated 7/12/92
Series 1875 <$VALUE
4x5 1-4745 <$1500
50-100 1-55 <$7500/$8000
Total Issue $100,300
Out in 1910 $755

2988 Lancaster
MARSH NB OF LINCOLN
{{ UNREPORTED }}
Chartered 6/29/83
Receivership 2/6/93
2nd title:Capital NB of Lincoln 5/14/84
FIRST TITLE
Brown Back <$VALUE
3x10-20 1-450 <$1500
SECOND TITLE
Brown Back
3x10-20 1-2098 <$1500
Total Issue $127,400
Out in 1915 $650

7239 Lancaster
NB OF COMMERCE, LINCOLN
{{ 31 L 50+ S }}
Chartered 4/04
1902 Red Seal <$VALUE
3x10-20 1-4425 <$300/$350
1902 Date Back
3x10-20 1-13500 <$50/$60
1902 Plain Back
3x10-20 13501-36589<$50/$60
1929 Small Size
10 Type 1 1-5710 <$25
20 Type 1 1-1810 <$35
10 Type 2 1-3288 <$25
20 Type 2 1-1095 <$35
Total Issue $2,665,280
Out in 1935 $298,980
Large out 1935 $14,170

1899 Lancaster
STATE NB OF LINCOLN
{{ 2 L }}
Chartered 11/16/71
Liquidated 12/3/92
Original Series <$VALUE
3x1-2 1-1900 <$2000/$5000
4x5 1-2275 <$1500
Series 1875
4x5 1-8550 <$1500
Brown Back
50-100 1-205 <$2000/$2500
Total Issue $256,750
Out in 1910 $2,015

8093 Sherman
FNB, LITCHFIELD
{{ 4 L 2 S }}
Organized 2/2/06
Receivership 12/29/33
1902 Red Seal <$VALUE
3x10-20 1-400 <$650
1902 Date Back
3x10-20 1-720 <$350
1902 Plain Back
3x10-20 721-1647 <$350
1929 Small Size
10 Type 1 1-192 <$500
20 Type 1 1-42 <$500
Total Issue $118,910
Out at close $10,000
Large out at close $1,050

9741 Cheyenne
FNB OF LODGEPOLE
{{ UNREPORTED }}
Chartered 4/10
Liquidated 9/1/13
1902 Date Back <$VALUE
4x5 1-995 <$1250
3x10-20 1-728 <$1250
Total Issue $56,300
Out in 1913 $18,500

5419 Phelps
FNB, LOOMIS
{{ 6 L 4 S }}
Chartered 6/13/00
Brown Back <$VALUE
3x10-20 1-860 <$600
1882 Date Back
3x10-20 1-1190 <$500
1882 Value Back
3x10-20 1191-1525 <$500
1902 Plain Back
3x10-20 1-1536 <$300
1929 Small Size
10 Type 1 1-384 <$350
20 Type 1 1-116 <$350
10 Type 2 1-184 <$350
20 Type 2 1-30 <$375
Total Issue $235,450
Out in 1935 $17,500
Large out 1935 $1,330

13620 Sherman
FNB IN LOUP CITY
{{ 10 S }}
Organized 6/18/32
1929 Small Size <$VALUE
10 Type 1 1-40 <$150
20 Type 1 1-16 <$150
10 Type 2 1-2112 <$150
20 Type 2 1-415 <$150
Total Issue $33,740
Out in 1935 $25,000
Outstanding includes Ch 7277

3373 Sherman
FNB OF LOUP CITY
{{ UNREPORTED }}
Chartered 8/5/85
Liquidated 6/21/90
Brown Back <$VALUE
4x5 1-1156 <$1500
Total Issue $23,120
Out in 1910 $185

7277 Sherman
FNB OF LOUP CITY
{{ 0 L 1 S }}
Chartered 5/04
Liquidated 6/27/32
1902 Red Seal <$VALUE
3x10-20 1-400 <$1500
1902 Date Back
3x10-20 1-580 <$1000
1902 Plain Back
3x10-20 581-1133 <$1000
1929 Small Size
10 Type 1 1-140 <$650
20 Type 1 1-12 <$650
Total Issue $86,490
Out at close $7,000
Large out at close $970
Ch 13620 assumed circulation

9785 Boyd
FNB OF LYNCH
{{ UNREPORTED }}
Chartered 6/10
Liquidated 2/1/17
1902 Date Back <$VALUE
3x10-20 1-482 <$1500
Total Issue $24,100
Out at close $6,250

6221 Burt
FNB, LYONS
{{ 2 L 7 S }}
Chartered 1902
1902 Red Seal <$VALUE
3x10-20 1-1100 <$750
1902 Date Back
3x10-20 1-1800 <$400
1902 Plain Back (dated 1902)
3x10-20 1801-4330 <$400
1902 Plain Back (dated 1922)
3x10-20 1-2164 <$400
1929 Small Size
10 Type 1 1-530 <$200
20 Type 1 1-148 <$200
10 Type 2 1-418 <$225
20 Type 2 1-193 <$225
Total Issue $437,300
Out in 1935 $25,000
Large out 1935 $1,910

8317 Madison
FARMERS NB, MADISON
{{ 5 L 10 S }}
Chartered 8/06
1902 Red Seal <$VALUE
4x5 1-275 <$650
4x10 1-287 <$650
1902 Date Back
4x5 1-1700 <$300
4x10 1-1750 <$300
1902 Plain Back
4x5 1701-5430 <$300
4x10 1751-4401 <$300
1929 Small Size
5 Type 1 1-896 <$150
10 Type 1 1-548 <$150
5 Type 2 1-1942 <$175
10 Type 2 1-720 <$175
Total Issue $378,290
Out in 1935 $25,000
Large out 1935 $1,360

3773 Madison
FNB OF MADISON
{{ 10 L 17 S }}
Organized 8/1/87
Receivership 1/20/33
Brown Back <$VALUE
4x5 1-3222 <$500
3x10-20 1-400 <$500
1902 Red Seal
3x10-20 1-125 <$500
1902 Date Back
3x10-20 1-3050 <$175
1902 Plain Back
3x10-20 3051-8840 <$175
1929 Small Size
5 Type 1 1-1008 <$90
10 Type 1 1-807 <$90
20 Type 1 1-263 <$90
Total Issue $642,910
Out at close $63,980
Outstanding includes Ch 10021

10021 Madison
MADISON NB, MADISON
{{ 2 L }}
Chartered 5/11
Closed 11/2/26
1902 Date Back <$VALUE
4x5 1-1125 <$500
3x10-20 1-890 <$500
1902 Plain Back
4x5 1126-2030 <$500
3x10-20 891-1577 <$500
Total Issue $119,450
Out at close $15,000
Ch 3773 assumed circulation

8400 Hamilton
FNB, MARQUETTE
{{ 4 L 2 S }}
Organized 10/1/06
1902 Red Seal <$VALUE
4x10 1-250 <$650
1902 Date Back
4x10 1-725 <$350
1902 Plain Back
4x10 726-1580 <$350
1929 Small Size
10 Type 1 1-293 <$500
Total Issue $90,780
Out in 1935 $6,250
Large out 1935 $290

9436 Red Willow
CITIZENS NB OF McCOOK
{{ 1 L }}
Chartered 6/09
Liquidated 7/24/16
1902 Date Back <$VALUE
3x10-20 1-4000 <$500
1902 Plain Back
3x10-20 4001-4244 <$500
Total Issue $212,200
Out at close $45,000

3379 Red Willow
FNB, McCOOK
{{ 4 L 32 S }}
Chartered 1885
Brown Back <$VALUE
4x5 1-3136 <$600
3x10-20 1-394 <$600
1902 Red Seal
3x10-20 1-1930 <$600
1902 Date Back
3x10-20 1-2960 <$250
1902 Plain Back
3x10-20 2961-9077 <$250
1929 Small Size
10 Type 1 1-1588 <$40
20 Type 1 1-444 <$50
10 Type 2 1-2083 <$40
20 Type 2 1-570 <$50
Total Issue $813,560
Out in 1935 $75,000
Large out 1935 $3,170

8823 Red Willow
McCOOK NB, McCOOK
{{ 10 L 2U + 25 S }}
Chartered 8/07
1902 Red Seal <$VALUE
4x5 1-762 <$500
3x10-20 1-610 <$500
1902 Date Back
4x5 1-3350 <$175
3x10-20 1-2570 <$175
1902 Plain Back
4x5 3351-10568 <$175
3x10-20 2571-7270 <$175
1929 Small Size
5 Type 1 1-1738 <$50
10 Type 1 1-818 <$50
20 Type 1 1-220 <$60
5 Type 2 1-2196 <$60
10 Type 2 1-996 <$60
20 Type 2 1-264 <$60
Total Issue $774,440
Out in 1935 $50,000
Large out 1935 $3,390

13316 Scotts Bluff
FNB OF MINATARE
{{ 3 S }}
Chartered 5/29
1929 Small Size <$VALUE
5 Type 2 1-2470 <$400
10 Type 2 1-1172 <$400
20 Type 2 1-444 <$400
Total Issue $32,950
Out in 1935 $24,850

3057 Kearney
FNB, MINDEN
{{ 2 L 1 S }}
Chartered 1883
Brown Back <$VALUE
4x5 1-3112 <$750
3x10-20 1-279 <$750
1902 Red Seal
50-100 1-170 <$3000/$3500
1902 Date Back
50-100 1-240 <$750/$850
3x50-100 1-70 <$750/$850
1902 Plain Back
3x50-100 71-95 <$750/$850
1929 Small Size
50 Type 1 1-47 <$650
100 Type 1 1-2 <$750
Total Issue $176,740
Out in 1935 $12,500
Large out 1935 $1,850

9400 Kearney
MINDEN EXCHANGE NB OF MINDEN
{{ 5 L 23 S }}
Chartered 5/09
1902 Date Back <$VALUE
3x10-20 1-1550 <$300
1902 Plain Back
3x10-20 1551-2739 <$300
1929 Small Size
10 Type 1 1-310 <$60
20 Type 1 1-102 <$65
10 Type 2 1-2583 <$60
20 Type 2 1-670 <$65
Total Issue $207,020
Out in 1935 $50,000
Large out 1935 $810

7026 Scotts Bluff
FNB OF MITCHELL
{{ UNREPORTED }}
Chartered 10/03
Liquidated 3/31/25
1902 Red Seal <$VALUE
3x10-20 1-362 <$1500
1902 Date Back
3x10-20 1-720 <$1000
1902 Plain Back
3x10-20 721-1085 <$1000
Total Issue $72,350
Out at close $6,200

9653 Scotts Bluff
FNB OF MORRILL
{{ UNREPORTED }}
Chartered 2/10
Liquidated 3/31/25
1902 Date Back <$VALUE
3x10-20 1-700 <$1000
1902 Plain Back
3x10-20 701-1073 <$1000
Total Issue $53,650
Out at close $6,500

9665 Boyd
FNB OF NAPER
{{ 2 L 1 S }}
Organized 12/15/09
Receivership 12/12/30
1902 Date Back <$VALUE
4x5 1-800 <$750
4x10 1-800 <$750
1902 Plain Back
4x5 801-1758 <$750
4x10 801-1719 <$750
1929 Small Size
5 Type 1 1-147 <$600
10 Type 1 1-74 <$600
Total Issue $112,770
Out at close $10,000
Large out at close $2,350

2536 Otoe
JAMES SWEET NB OF NEBRASKA CITY
Chartered 1881
Liquidated 6/30/34
2nd title:Merchants NB of Nebraska City 4/12/84
FIRST TITLE {{ 0 L }}
Series 1875 <$VALUE
50-100 1-377 <$7500/$8000
SECOND TITLE {{ 8 L 11 S }}
Series 1875
3x10-20 1-925 <$1250/$1750
Brown Back
50-100 1-940 <$2000/$2500
1882 Date Back
50-100 1-300 <$2000/$2500
3x50-100 1-429<$2000/$2500
1902 Plain Back
3x50-100 1-469 <$450/$500
1929 Small Size
50 Type 1 1-154 <$125
100 Type 1 1-24 <$300
Total Issue $573,900
Out in 1933 $50,000

Merchants NB of Nebraska City
SEE Ch 2536
James Sweet NB of Nebraska City

1855 Otoe
NEBRASKA CITY NB, NEBRASKA CITY
{{ 19 L 32 S }}
Chartered 7/31/71
Original Series <$VALUE
3x1-2 1-4500 <$1000/$3000
4x5 1-5375 <$850
3x10-20 1-600 <$1000/$1500
Series 1875
3x1-2 1-900 <$1000/$3000
4x5 1-655 <$850
3x10-20 1-1815<$1000/$1500
Brown Back
3x10-20 1-8280 <$400
1882 Date Back
3x10-20 1-1528 <$350
1902 Date Back
3x10-20 1-4400 <$100
1902 Plain Back
3x10-20 4401-12676 <$100
1929 Small Size
10 Type 1 1-976 <$40
20 Type 1 1-284 <$50
10 Type 2 1-905 <$50
20 Type 2 1-190 <$60
Total Issue $1,497,920
Out in 1935 $50,000
Large out 1935 $7,439

1417 Otoe
OTOE COUNTY NB OF NEBRASKA CITY
{{ 50+ L 16 S }}
Chartered 1865
** Notes with the NEBRASKA TERRITORY imprint are valued at approximately **$10,000** more than the statehood notes evaluated here.
**Original Series <$VALUE
3x1-2 1-4800 <$1000/$3000
4x5 1-1350 <$850
3x10-20 1-1900<$1000/$1500
Series 1875
3x1-2 1-360 <$1000/$3000
4x5 1-1399 <$850
3x10-20 1-1489<$1000/$1500
Brown Back
50-100 1-1023 <$2000/$2500
1902 Red Seal
3x10-20 1-1600 <$350
1902 Date Back
3x10-20 1-2540 <$100
1902 Plain Back
3x10-20 2541-7796 <$100
1929 Small Size
10 Type 1 1-946 <$125
20 Type 1 1-296 <$125
10 Type 2 1-1049 <$125
20 Type 2 1-240 <$150
Total Issue $981,050
Out in 1935 $50,000
Large out 1935 $6,520

4110 Antelope
FNB, NELIGH
{{ UNREPORTED }}
Chartered 9/7/89
Receivership 11/4/98
Brown Back <$VALUE
4x5 1-1939 <$1500
Total Issue $38,780
Out in 1915 $240

13568 Antelope
NB OF NELIGH
{{ 10 S }}
Chartered 8/12/31
1929 Small Size <$VALUE
5 Type 1 1-310 <$125
10 Type 1 1-260 <$125
20 Type 1 1-314 <$125
5 Type 2 1-1134 <$150
10 Type 2 1-675 <$150
20 Type 2 1-110 <$150
Total Issue $77,200
Out in 1935 $46,000

5690 Antelope
NELIGH NB, NELIGH
{{ 5 L }}
Chartered 1/24/01
Liquidated 2/1/16
Brown Back <$VALUE
3x10-20 1-400 <$600
1882 Date Back
3x10-20 1-2959 <$500
Total Issue $167,950
Out in 1916 $35,580

3495 Nuckolls
FNB, NELSON
{{ 2 L }}
Chartered 1886
Liquidated 4/25/14
Brown Back <$VALUE
4x5 1-4210 <$850
3x10-20 1-687 <$850
1902 Red Seal
4x5 1-1350 <$850
3x10-20 1-740 <$850
1902 Date Back
4x5 1-3545 <$500
3x10-20 1-2822 <$500
Total Issue $394,550
Out at close $54,105

5282 Madison
FNB OF NEWMAN GROVE
{{ 6 L 8 S }}
Chartered 4/10/00
Brown Back <$VALUE
4x5 1-1325 <$600
3x10-20 1-960 <$600
1882 Date Back
4x5 1-1575 <$500
3x10-20 1-1210 <$500
1882 Value Back
4x5 1576-2375 <$500
3x10-20 1211-1717 <$500
1902 Plain Back
4x5 1-2600 <$300
3x10-20 1-1489 <$300
1929 Small Size
5 Type 1 1-788 <$150
10 Type 1 1-368 <$150
20 Type 1 1-86 <$150
5 Type 2 1-1130 <$200
10 Type 2 1-554 <$200
20 Type 2 1-117 <$200
Total Issue $403,870
Out in 1935 $25,000
Large out 1935 $1,640

3741 Madison
CITIZENS NB OF NORFOLK
{{ 10 L }}
Chartered 1887
Liquidated 1/18/29
Brown Back <$VALUE
4x5 1-4050 <$450
3x10-20 1-1319 <$450
1902 Red Seal
3x10-20 1-500 <$500
1902 Date Back
3x10-20 1-3440 <$175
1902 Plain Back
3x10-20 3441-8901 <$175
Total Issue $617,000
Out at close $50,000

2774 Madison
FNB OF NORFOLK
{{ UNREPORTED }}
Chartered 1882
Liquidated 2/3/83
Brown Back <$VALUE
4x5 1-562 <$1500
Total Issue $11,240
Out in 1910 $100

7329 Madison
NEBRASKA NB OF NORFOLK
{{ UNREPORTED }}
Chartered 7/04
Liquidated 8/4/13
1902 Red Seal <$VALUE
3x10-20 1-1000 <$1500
1902 Date Back
3x10-20 1-2073 <$850
Total Issue $153,650
Out in 1913 $22,240

3347 Madison
NORFOLK NB, NORFOLK
{{ 15 L 12 S }}
Organized 5/13/85
Receivership 12/2/31
Brown Back <$VALUE
4x5 1-6075 <$450
50-100 1-580 <$2000/$2500
1902 Red Seal
3x10-20 1-1600 <$500
1902 Date Back
3x10-20 1-6500 <$125
1902 Plain Back
3x10-20 6501-17746 <$125
1929 Small Size
10 Type 1 1-1333 <$100
20 Type 1 1-373 <$110
Total Issue $1,300,540
Out at close $100,000
Large out at close $10,070

3343 Nemaha
FNB OF AUBURN, NORTH AUBURN
Organized 5/12/85
Receivership 10/13/31
2nd title:FNB of Auburn, Auburn 1905
FIRST TITLE {{ 1 L }}
Brown Back <$VALUE
4x5 1-4065 <$750
3x10-20 1-803 <$750
50-100 1-239 <$2000/$2500
SECOND TITLE {{ 12 L 7 S }}
1902 Red Seal
4x5 1-1750 <$450
3x10-20 1-840 <$450
50-100 1-120 <$3000/$3500
1902 Date Back
4x5 1-2150 <$125
3x10-20 1-1720 <$125
50-100 1-100 <$400/$500
1902 Plain Back
4x5 2151-7888 <$125
3x10-20 1721-5434 <$125
1929 Small Size
5 Type 1 1-898 <$175
10 Type 1 1-476 <$175
20 Type 1 1-117 <$175
Total Issue $766,300
Out at close $50,000
Large out at close $8,535

3059 Dodge
FNB, NORTH BEND
{{ 11 L 9 S }}
Chartered 9/8/83
Receivership 2/9/33
Brown Back <$VALUE
4x5 1-3441 <$400
3x50-100 1-92 <$2000/$2500
1902 Red Seal
50-100 1-168 <$3000/$3500
1902 Date Back
50-100 1-700 <$350/$400
3x50-100 1-700 <$350/$400
1902 Plain Back
3x50-100 701-880<$350/$400
1929 Small Size
5 Type 1 1-1519 <$150
10 Type 1 1-861 <$150
Total Issue $530,050
Out at close $49,400
Large out at close $38,765

7449 Dodge
NB OF NORTH BEND
{{ UNREPORTED }}
Chartered 10/04
Liquidated 10/5/14
1902 Red Seal <$VALUE
50-100 1-320 <$3500/$4000
1902 Date Back
50-100 1-260 <$1250/$1500
3x50-100 1-30 <$1250/$1500
Total Issue $94,500
Out at close $17,850

3496 Lincoln
FNB, NORTH PLATTE
{{ 10 L 34 S }}
Chartered 1886
Brown Back <$VALUE
3x10-20 1-2681 <$500
1902 Red Seal
3x10-20 1-800 <$500
1902 Date Back
3x10-20 1-6000 <$175
1902 Plain Back
3x10-20 6001-19935 <$175
1929 Small Size
10 Type 1 1-2356 <$40
20 Type 1 1-694 <$50
10 Type 2 1-1650 <$50
20 Type 2 1-325 <$50
Total Issue $1,418,440
Out in 1935 $100,000
Large out 1935 $6,070

4024 Lincoln
NORTH PLATTE NB, NORTH PLATTE
{{ UNREPORTED }}
Chartered 5/4/89
Receivership 1/14/95
Brown Back <$VALUE
4x5 1-2004 <$1500
Total Issue $40,080
Out in 1915 $315

3424 Holt
FNB OF O'NEILL
{{ 11 L 6 S }}
Chartered 1885
Brown Back <$VALUE
4x5 1-4354 <$450
3x10-20 1-856 <$500
1902 Red Seal
3x10-20 1-900 <$600
1902 Date Back
3x10-20 1-3550 <$250
1902 Plain Back
3x10-20 3551-5829 <$250
1929 Small Size
10 Type 1 1-548 <$200
20 Type 1 1-160 <$200
10 Type 2 1-102 <$225
20 Type 2 1-57 <$225
Total Issue $520,570
Out in 1935 $25,000
Large out 1935 $2,380

5770 Holt
O'NEILL NB, O'NEILL
{{ 21 L 12 S }}
Chartered 4/01
Brown Back <$VALUE
3x10-20 1-2100 <$350
1882 Date Back
3x10-20 1-3000 <$300
1882 Value Back
3x10-20 3001-4890 <$350
1902 Plain Back
3x10-20 1-3745 <$100
1929 Small Size
10 Type 1 1-17* <$100
10 Type 1 619-1714 <$100
20 Type 1 211-506 <$100
10 Type 2 1-657 <$125
20 Type 2 1-105 <$125
* E000017A, F000017A canceled
Total Issue $647,700
Out in 1935 $50,000
Large out 1935 $3,710

CONDITION affects Value. The Values shown are for notes in FINE condition.

****
13339 Antelope
FNB OF OAKDALE
{{ 3U + 5 S }}
Chartered 6/29
1929 Small Size <$VALUE
5 Type 1 1-420 <$200
10 Type 1 1-212 <$200
20 Type 1 1-64 <$200
5 Type 2 1-1024 <$200
10 Type 2 1-465 <$200
20 Type 2 1-140 <$200
Total Issue $45,570
Out in 1935 $22,550
****
10022 Burt
FARMERS AND MERCHANTS NB OF OAKLAND
{{ 8 L 11 S }}
Chartered 5/11
1902 Date Back <$VALUE
3x10-20 1-3300 <$200
1902 Plain Back
3x10-20 3301-8958 <$200
1929 Small Size
10 Type 1 1-974 <$125
20 Type 1 1-274 <$125
10 Type 2 1-1205 <$125
20 Type 2 1-236 <$125
Total Issue $555,990
Out in 1935 $45,600
Large out 1935 $3,470
****
4610 Burt
FNB OF OAKLAND
{{ 10 L U + 10 S }}
Chartered 6/11/91
Receivership 9/18/33
Brown Back <$VALUE
4x5 1-2805 <$450
50-100 1-203 <$2000/$2500
1882 Date Back
4x5 1-375 <$450
50-100 1-100 <$2000/$2500
1902 Date Back
4x5 1-1750 <$175
3x50-100 1-492 <$400/$500
1902 Plain Back
4x5 1751-15821 <$175
1929 Small Size
5 Type 1 1-5256 <$150
Total Issue $706,150
Out at close $50,000
Large out at close $3,540
****
3652 Keith
FNB, OGALALLA
{{ UNREPORTED }}
Organized 3/21/87
Liquidated 1/14/90
Brown Back <$VALUE
3x10-20 1-309 <$2000
Total Issue $15,450
Out in 1910 $80
****
4087 Douglas
AMERICAN NB, OMAHA
{{ 3 L }}
Chartered 8/2/89
Liquidated 2/25/96
Brown Back <$VALUE
4x5 1-2500 <$450
50-100 1-410 <$2000/$2500
Total Issue $111,500
Out in 1910 $2,120
****
9466 Douglas
CITY NB OF OMAHA
{{ 1 L }}
Chartered 6/09
Liquidated 1/11/16
1902 Date Back <$VALUE
4x5 1-15410 <$600
3x10-20 1-11906 <$600
Total Issue $903,500
Out at close $118,785
****
3163 Douglas
COMMERCIAL NB, OMAHA
{{ 1 L }}
Chartered 4/23/84
Liquidated 7/22/05
Brown Back <$VALUE
3x10-20 1-8950 <$750
1902 Red Seal
3x10-20 1-4734 <$750
Total Issue $684,200
Out in 1910 $29,855
****

****
9730 Douglas
CORN EXCHANGE NB OF OMAHA
{{ 6 L }}
Chartered 4/10
Liquidated 12/27/24
1902 Date Back <$VALUE
3x10-20 1-19000 <$175
1902 Plain Back
3x10-20 19001-25817 <$175
Total Issue $1,190,850
Out at close $136,200
****
209 Douglas
FNB OF OMAHA
{{ 14 L }}
Organized 8/26/63
** Notes with the **NEBRASKA TERRITORY** imprint are valued at approximately **$10,000** more than the statehood notes evaluated here.
**Original Series <$VALUE
3x1-2 1-8400 <$1000/$3000
4x5 1-5425 <$850
4x10 1-2050 <$1000
3x20-50 1-1300<$1500/$7500
Series 1875
4x10 1-2090 <$1000
3x20-50 1-1245<$1500/$7500
Brown Back
4x5 1-4439 <$400
3x10-20 1-4892 <$400
50-100 1-718 <$2000/$2500
1902 Red Seal
4x5 1-12250 <$400
3x10-20 1-8000 <$400
1902 Date Back
4x5 1-16665 <$150
3x10-20 1-13235 <$150
Total Issue $2,681,180
Out in 1935 $7,739
****
2775 Douglas
MERCHANTS NB OF OMAHA
{{ 13 L }}
Chartered 1882
Liquidated 5/20/26
Brown Back <$VALUE
3x10-20 1-10754 <$400
1902 Red Seal
3x10-20 1-9000 <$350/$400
1902 Date Back
4x5 1-26825 <$150
3x10-20 1-18451 <$150
Total Issue $2,446,750
Out in 1925 $50,000
****
4270 Douglas
NB OF COMMERCE, OMAHA
{{ UNREPORTED }}
Chartered 3/24/90
Liquidated 12/10/01
Brown Back <$VALUE
50-100 1-1777 <$2000/$2500
Total Issue $266,550
Out in 1910 $10,400
****
2665 Douglas
NEBRASKA NB OF OMAHA
{{ 24 L }}
Chartered 1882
Liquidated 9/21/23
Series 1875 <$VALUE
3x10-20 1-15726<$1000/$1500
1902 Red Seal
3x10-20 1-9000 <$300/$350
1902 Date Back
3x10-20 1-14000 <$50/$60
1902 Plain Back (dated 1902)
3x10-20 14001-24800<$50/$60
1902 Plain Back (dated 1922)
3x10-20 1-1594 <$50/$60
Total Issue $2,556,000
Out in 1922 $200,000
****
1633 Douglas
OMAHA NB, OMAHA
{{ 50+ L 50+ S }}
Chartered 1866
** Notes with the **NEBRASKA TERRITORY** imprint are valued at approximately **$10,000** more than the statehood notes evaluated here.
**Original Series <$VALUE
3x1-2 1-2000 <$1000/$3000
4x5 1-7750 <$850
4x20 1-2250 <$1500
Series 1875
4x5 1-171 <$850
4x20 1-732 <$1500
Brown Back
4x5 1-10585 <$300
3x10-20 1-13230 <$300
50-100 1-4509 <$2000/$2500
1902 Red Seal
4x5 1-16750 <$300
50-100 1-3033 <$3000/$3500
1902 Date Back
4x5 1-43330* <$40
50-100 1-5022 <$300/$350
3x50-100 1-16404<$300/$350
* 43331-53330 not marked
1902 Plain Back
3x50-100 16405-18878 <$300/$350
1929 Small Size
50 Type 1 1-2591 <$85
100 Type 1 1-873 <$135
Total Issue $10,586,980
Out in 1935 $1,000,000
Large out 1935 $94,650
****
3603 Douglas
STATE NB, OMAHA
{{ UNREPORTED }}
Chartered 12/15/86
Liquidated 7/18/88
Brown Back <$VALUE
50-100 1-182 <$2500/$3000
Total Issue $27,300
Out in 1910 $200
****
3516 Douglas
UNION NB, OMAHA
{{ 1 L }}
Chartered 6/8/86
Liquidated 7/22/05
Brown Back <$VALUE
4x5 1-2675 <$750
3x10-20 1-4520 <$750
50-100 1-240 <$2000/$2500
Total Issue $315,500
Out in 1910 $10,055
****
2978 Douglas
UNITED STATES NB, OMAHA
{{ 17 L 2U + 50+ S }}
Chartered 1883
Brown Back <$VALUE
4x5 1-1000 <$400
3x10-20 1-15327 <$400
1902 Red Seal
3x10-20 1-16200 <$350/$400
1902 Date Back
3x10-20 1-32357 <$100
1929 Small Size
10 Type 1 1-12982 <$30
20 Type 1 1-4372 <$40
10 Type 2 1-10884* <$30
20 Type 2 1-4393 <$40
* 6355-6360 not issued
Total Issue $4,714,400
Out in 1935 $1,000,000
Large out 1935 $10,595
****
3339 Valley
FNB OF ORD
{{ 17 L 22 S }}
Chartered 1885
Liquidated 12/8/31
Brown Back <$VALUE
4x5 1-3195 <$400
3x10-20 1-575 <$450
1902 Red Seal
3x10-20 1-600 <$500
1902 Date Back
3x10-20 1-2200* <$100
1902 Plain Back
3x10-20 2441-12216* <$100
* 2201-2440 not marked
1929 Small Size
10 Type 1 1-988 <$65
20 Type 1 1-402 <$75
Total Issue $840,970
Out in 1930 $99,160
Large out 1930 $16,775
****
3481 Valley
ORD NB, ORD
{{ 1 L }}
Chartered 4/7/86
Liquidated 8/22/91
Brown Back <$VALUE
3x10-20 1-470 <$1500
Total Issue $23,500
Out in 1910 $140
****

****
8567 Harlan
CITIZENS NB OF ORLEANS
{{ UNREPORTED }}
Chartered 2/07
Liquidated 3/15/15
1902 Red Seal <$VALUE
4x10 1-250 <$1500
1902 Date Back
4x10 1-2225 <$1000
Total Issue $99,000
Out in 1915 $17,020
****
3342 Harlan
FNB, ORLEANS
{{ UNREPORTED }}
Chartered 5/19/85
Receivership 6/5/97
Brown Back <$VALUE
4x5 1-2489 <$1500
Total Issue $49,780
Out in 1915 $505
****
6493 Polk
FNB, OSCEOLA
{{ 14 L 9 S }}
Chartered 1902
1902 Red Seal <$VALUE
4x5 1-920 <$500
3x10-20 1-738 <$500
1902 Date Back
4x5 1-1650 <$150
3x10-20 1-1140 <$150
1902 Plain Back
4x5 1651-4470 <$150
3x10-20 1141-2962 <$150
1929 Small Size
5 Type 1 1-798 <$175
10 Type 1 1-372 <$175
20 Type 1 1-98 <$175
5 Type 2 1-372 <$200
10 Type 2 1-310 <$200
20 Type 2 1-85 <$200
Total Issue $357,480
Out in 1935 $25,000
Large out 1935 $910
****
10081 Garden
FNB OF OSHKOSH
{{ UNREPORTED }}
Organized 9/11
Liquidated 7/2/15
1902 Date Back <$VALUE
3x10-20 1-372 <$1000
Total Issue $18,600
Out at close $5,450
****
7925 Dawson
FNB, OVERTON
{{ UNREPORTED }}
Chartered 9/05
Liquidated 9/21/14
1902 Red Seal <$VALUE
3x10-20 1-1000 <$1250
1902 Date Back
3x10-20 1-1273 <$1000
Total Issue $113,650
Out at close $24,500
****
13446 Dawson
OVERTON NB, OVERTON
{{ 3U + 7 S }}
Chartered 4/30
1929 Small Size <$VALUE
5 Type 2 1-3536 <$150
10 Type 2 1-1300 <$150
20 Type 2 1-447 <$150
Total Issue $39,620
Out in 1935 $25,000
****
7520 Furnas
FNB, OXFORD
{{ UNREPORTED }}
Chartered 12/04
Liquidated 5/19/14
1902 Red Seal <$VALUE
3x10-20 1-800 <$1500
1902 Date Back
3x10-20 1-1055 <$1000
Total Issue $92,750
Out in 1914 $19,600
****
4078 Pawnee
FARMERS NB OF PAWNEE CITY
{{ 10 L }}
Chartered 1889
Liquidated 4/5/15
Brown Back <$VALUE
3x10-20 1-3897 <$400
1902 Date Back
3x10-20 1-2561 <$250
Total Issue $322,900
Out in 1915 $37,700
****
6541 Pawnee
NB OF PAWNEE CITY
{{ 1 L }}
Chartered 1902
Liquidated 5/14/12
1902 Red Seal <$VALUE
3x10-20 1-732 <$1000
1902 Date Back
3x10-20 1-321 <$750
Total Issue $52,650
Out in 1912 $9,570
****
2825 Pawnee
FNB, PAWNEE CITY
{{ UNREPORTED }}
Chartered 11/24/82
Liquidated 8/1/01
Brown Back <$VALUE
4x5 1-5016 <$1500
50-100 1-62 <$2500/$3000
Total Issue $109,620
Out in 1910 $1,355
****
4791 Thurston
FNB, PENDER
{{ 4 L 8 S }}
Organized 8/2/92
Receivership 7/25/35
Brown Back <$VALUE
50-100 1-934 <$2000/$2500
1882 Date Back
50-100 1-284 <$2000/$2500
1902 Date Back
3x50-100 1-800 <$500/$600
1902 Plain Back
3x50-100 801-963<$500/$600
1929 Small Size
5 Type 1 1-50 <$200
10 Type 1 1-40 <$200
50 Type 1 1-140 <$250
100 Type 1 1-26 <$350
Total Issue $484,950
Out in 1935 $25,000
Large out 1935 $5,400
****
5308 Thurston
PENDER NB, PENDER
{{ 2 L }}
Chartered 4/26/00
Liquidated 7/1/15
Brown Back <$VALUE
3x10-20 1-1270 <$1000
1882 Date Back
3x10-20 1-2386 <$1000
Total Issue $182,800
Out at close $46,400
****
4280 Pierce
FNB OF PIERCE
{{ 1 L }}
Chartered 4/7/90
Liquidated 12/31/96
Brown Back <$VALUE
3x10-20 1-563 <$1500
Total Issue $28,150
Out in 1910 $390
****
13453 Stanton
FARMERS NB IN PILGER
{{ 3U + 15 S }}
Chartered 4/14/30
1929 Small Size <$VALUE
5 Type 1 1-2864 <$110
5 Type 2 1-6246 <$125
Total Issue $117,150
Out in 1935 $25,000
****
5941 Stanton
FARMERS NB OF PILGER
{{ U + 13 L }}
Chartered 1901
Liquidated 4/8/24
Brown Back <$VALUE
4x5 1-1050 <$350
3x10-20 1-870 <$350
1882 Date Back
4x5 1-2975 <$350
3x10-20 1-2260 <$350
1882 Value Back
4x5 2976-5440 <$350
3x10-20 2261-3783 <$350
1902 Plain Back
3x10-20 1-1546 <$200
Total Issue $439,750
Out at close $49,500
****

****
5937 Stanton
FNB, PILGER
{{ 9 L }}
Organized 8/2/01
Receivership 4/22/24
Brown Back <$VALUE
3x10-20 1-1100 <$400
1882 Date Back
3x10-20 1-3840 <$350
1882 Value Back
3x10-20 3841-5966 <$350
1902 Plain Back
3x10-20 1-1496 <$200
Total Issue $428,100
Out at close $48,600
****
9504 Pierce
FNB OF PLAINVIEW
{{ 6 L }}
Organized 7/27/09
Receivership 8/22/28
1902 Date Back <$VALUE
3x10-20 1-2940 <$350
1902 Plain Back
3x10-20 2941-6955 <$350
Total Issue $347,750
Out at close $39,700
****
1914 Cass
FNB, PLATTSMOUTH
{{ 8 L }}
Organized 12/12/71
Receivership 12/21/26
Original Series <$VALUE
3x1-2 1-3240 <$1250/$3500
4x5 1-3125 <$1000
Series 1875
4x5 1-5748 <$1000
Brown Back
4x5 1-4625 <$500
3x10-20 1-1580 <$500
1882 Date Back
4x5 1-1051 <$450
3x10-20 1-812 <$450
1902 Date Back
3x10-20 1-2000 <$250
1902 Plain Back
3x10-20 2001-6406 <$250
Total Issue $747,080
Out at close $48,600
****
3292 Dawson
FNB OF PLUM CREEK
{{ UNREPORTED }}
Chartered 1885
Liquidated 7/10/19
2nd title:FNB of Lexington 7/1/89
FIRST TITLE
Brown Back <$VALUE
4x5 1-1113 <$1500
SECOND TITLE
Brown Back
4x5 1-2050 <$1500
50-100 1-119 <$2500/$3000
1902 Red Seal
50-100 1-141 <$3500/$4000
1902 Date Back
50-100 1-218 <$1250/$1500
Total Issue $134,960
Out in 1919 $12,500
****
8533 Polk
FNB OF POLK
{{ 1 L }}
Chartered 2/07
Liquidated 7/10/14
1902 Red Seal <$VALUE
3x10-20 1-200 <$1250
1902 Date Back
3x10-20 1-350 <$850
Total Issue $27,500
Out in 1914 $6,350
****
3627 Dixon
FNB, PONCA
{{ UNREPORTED }}
Chartered 1/28/87
Receivership 5/13/93
Brown Back <$VALUE
3x10-20 1-489 <$1500
Total Issue $24,450
Out in 1915 $180
****

<$VALUEs are for notes in **FINE** condition. Value changes by approximately **25%** for a change of one full grade.

****
7421 Cedar
FNB OF RANDOLPH
{{ 7 L U + 11 S }}
Chartered 10/04
Liquidated 6/29/35
1902 Red Seal <$VALUE
3x10-20 1-612 <$650
1902 Date Back
3x10-20 1-2600 <$250
1902 Plain Back
3x10-20 2601-6622 <$250
1929 Small Size
10 Type 1 1-746 <$150
20 Type 1 1-232 <$150
10 Type 2 1-152 <$200
20 Type 2 1-65 <$200
Total Issue $437,120
Out at close $34,000
Large out at close $2,430
****
7477 Cedar
SECURITY NB, RANDOLPH
{{ 7 L 13 S }}
Organized 11/2/04
Receivership 2/13/34
1902 Red Seal <$VALUE
4x5 1-535 <$600
3x10-20 1-398 <$600
1902 Date Back
4x5 1-1025 <$250
3x10-20 1-800 <$250
1902 Plain Back
4x5 1026-7176 <$250
3x10-20 801-4833 <$250
1929 Small Size
5 Type 1 1-1436 <$125
10 Type 1 1-794 <$125
20 Type 1 1-199 <$125
Total Issue $530,370
Out at close $50,000
Large out at close $3,040
****
4043 Buffalo
FNB, RAVENNA
{{ UNREPORTED }}
Chartered 5/22/89
Receivership 4/10/95
Brown Back <$VALUE
4x5 1-1358 <$1500
Total Issue $27,160
Out in 1915 $140
****
2811 Webster
FNB, RED CLOUD
{{ UNREPORTED }}
Chartered 11/8/82
Receivership 7/16/91
Brown Back <$VALUE
4x5 1-2600 <$1500
Total Issue $52,000
Out in 1915 $320
****
3181 Webster
RED CLOUD NB, RED CLOUD
{{ 1 L }}
Chartered 5/10/84
Receivership 7/1/91
Brown Back <$VALUE
4x5 1-2067 <$1500
Total Issue $41,340
Out in 1915 $310
****
3674 Richardson
FNB OF RULO
{{ UNREPORTED }}
Chartered 4/19/87
Liquidated 1/20/90
Brown Back <$VALUE
3x10-20 1-735 <$1500
Total Issue $36,750
Out in 1910 $150
****
4176 Sheridan
FNB, RUSHVILLE
{{ UNREPORTED }}
Chartered 12/13/89
Liquidated 1/1/94
Brown Back <$VALUE
3x10-20 1-390 <$1500
Total Issue $19,500
Out in 1910 $180
****
9191 Sheridan
STOCKMEN'S NB OF
RUSHVILLE
{{ 4 L 3 S }}
Chartered 7/08
1902 Date Back <$VALUE
3x10-20 1-1060 <$400
1902 Plain Back
3x10-20 1061-2113 <$400
1929 Small Size
10 Type 1 1-312 <$400
20 Type 1 1-63 <$400
5 Type 2 1-88 <$400
Total Issue $132,370
Out in 1935 $11,000
Large out 1935 $795
****
5346 Boone
FNB, SAINT EDWARD
{{ 3 L }}
Chartered 5/10/00
Liquidated 5/18/16
Brown Back <$VALUE
4x5 1-725 <$750
3x10-20 1-790 <$750
1882 Date Back
4x5 1-1750 <$700
3x10-20 1-1220 <$700
1882 Value Back
4x5 1751-1765 <$700
3x10-20 1221-1303 <$700
Total Issue $154,450
Out at close $23,500
****
5793 Boone
SMITH NB, SAINT EDWARD
{{ 3 L 6 S }}
Organized 4/23/01
Receivership 3/3/33
Brown Back <$VALUE
3x10-20 1-400 <$750
1882 Date Back
3x10-20 1-629 <$750
1902 Plain Back
3x10-20 1-489 <$500
1929 Small Size
10 Type 1 1-322 <$250
20 Type 1 1-87 <$250
Total Issue $105,660
Out at close $25,000
Large out at close $750
****
8335 Cedar
FNB OF SAINT JAMES
Organized 5/11/06
Receivership 12/27/27
2nd title:FNB of Wynot
1/21/08
FIRST TITLE {{ 0 L }}
1902 Red Seal <$VALUE
3x10-20 1-200 <$1500
SECOND TITLE {{ 3 L }}
1902 Red Seal
3x10-20 1-200 <$1000
1902 Date Back
3x10-20 1-720 <$500
1902 Plain Back
3x10-20 721-1520 <$500
Total Issue $96,000
Out at close $10,000
****
3891 Howard
CITIZENS NB OF SAINT PAUL
{{ 2 L }}
Chartered 1888
Liquidated 4/1/11
Brown Back <$VALUE
4x5 1-2898 <$1000
3x10-20 1-532 <$1000
1902 Red Seal
3x10-20 1-250 <$1000
1902 Date Back
3x10-20 1-60 <$650
Total Issue $100,060
Out in 1911 $8,800
****
3126 Howard
FNB, SAINT PAUL
{{ 2 L }}
Chartered 2/20/84
Liquidated 8/1/98
Brown Back <$VALUE
4x5 1-2854 <$1000
Total Issue $57,080
Out in 1910 $475
****
3129 Howard
SAINT PAUL NB, SAINT PAUL
{{ 12U + 13 L }}
Chartered 2/27/84
Liquidated 3/31/97
Brown Back <$VALUE
4x5 1-2628 <$350
Total Issue $52,560
Out in 1910 $840
****

****
7384 Custer
FNB, SARGENT
{{ 2 L }}
Chartered 8/04
Liquidated 10/8/14
1902 Red Seal <$VALUE
4x5 1-500 <$1000
50-100 1-308 <$3000/$3500
1902 Date Back
4x5 1-785 <$500
50-100 1-170 <$750/$850
Total Issue $97,400
Out at close $23,100
****
2778 Colfax
FNB, SCHUYLER
{{ 12 L }}
Organized 9/4/82
Receivership 5/24/24
Brown Back <$VALUE
4x5 1-3492 <$450
3x10-20 1-371 <$450
1902 Red Seal
3x10-20 1-1590 <$400
1902 Date Back
3x10-20 1-3400 <$175
1902 Plain Back
3x10-20 3401-6839 <$175
Total Issue $509,840
Out in 1924 $47,200
****
3152 Colfax
SCHUYLER NB, SCHUYLER
{{ U + 2 L }}
Chartered 1884
Liquidated 6/17/16
Brown Back <$VALUE
4x5 1-3323 <$750
50-100 1-99 <$2000/$2500
1902 Red Seal
4x5 1-850 <$750
50-100 1-215 <$3000/$3500
1902 Date Back
4x5 1-1115 <$500
50-100 1-200 <$750/$850
3x50-100 1-32 <$750/$850
Total Issue $190,860
Out in 1916 $24,695
****
6240 Scotts Bluff
FNB, SCOTTSBLUFF
{{ 5 L }}
Chartered 1902
Liquidated 7/1/25
1902 Red Seal <$VALUE
3x10-20 1-400 <$750
1902 Date Back
3x10-20 1-1920 <$350
1902 Plain Back (dated 1902)
3x10-20 1921-3460 <$350
1902 Plain Back (dated 1922)
4x5 1-1775 <$350
Total Issue $228,500
Out at close $24,400
****
9581 Scotts Bluff
SCOTTSBLUFF NB,
SCOTTSBLUFF
{{ 11 L 2U + 30 S }}
Chartered 11/09
1902 Date Back <$VALUE
4x5 1-2000 <$175
3x10-20 1-2300 <$175
50-100 1-500 <$500/$600
1902 Plain Back
3x10-20 2301-9531 <$175
1929 Small Size
10 Type 1 1-1430 <$60
20 Type 1 1-362 <$75
10 Type 2 1-1673 <$75
20 Type 2 1-476 <$75
Total Issue $747,040
Out in 1935 $60,000
Large out 1935 $3,570
****
6901 Dodge
FNB, SCRIBNER
{{ 3 L 4 S }}
Organized 7/3/03
Receivership 9/20/34
1902 Red Seal <$VALUE
3x10-20 1-400 <$750
1902 Date Back
3x10-20 1-660 <$450
1902 Plain Back
3x10-20 661-1198 <$450
1929 Small Size
10 Type 1 1-193 <$350
20 Type 1 1-44 <$350
Total Issue $96,760
Out at close $8,000
Large out at close $460
****

****
2771 Seward
FNB OF SEWARD
{{ 11 L 1 S }}
Chartered 1882
Liquidated 1/3/30
Brown Back <$VALUE
3x10-20 1-1276 <$500
1902 Red Seal
4x5 1-1050 <$500
3x10-20 1-1600 <$500
1902 Date Back
4x5 1-3050 <$200
3x10-20 1-1920 <$200
1902 Plain Back
4x5 3051-9075 <$200
3x10-20 1921-6052 <$200
1929 Small Size
5 Type 1 1-205 <$600
10 Type 1 1-78 <$600
20 Type 1 1-11 <$600
Total Issue $661,050
Out at close $50,000
Large out at close $42,160
****
3060 Seward
JONES NB OF SEWARD
{{ 6 L 17 S }}
Chartered 1883
Brown Back <$VALUE
3x10-20 1-1293 <$600
1902 Red Seal
3x10-20 1-1475 <$600
1902 Date Back
3x10-20 1-3210* <$275
1902 Plain Back
3x10-20 3511-8554* <$275
* 3211-3510 not marked
1929 Small Size
10 Type 1 1-1146 <$85
20 Type 1 1-288 <$90
10 Type 2 1-510 <$110
20 Type 2 1-164 <$125
Total Issue $677,800
Out in 1935 $49,750
Large out 1935 $3,830
****
7949 Polk
FNB, SHELBY
{{ 22 L 17 S }}
Chartered 10/05
1902 Red Seal <$VALUE
3x10-20 1-985 <$450
1902 Date Back
3x10-20 1-1690 <$60/$70
1902 Plain Back
3x10-20 1691-4261 <$60/$70
1929 Small Size
10 Type 1 1-546 <$60
20 Type 1 1-150 <$75
10 Type 2 1-213 <$75
20 Type 2 1-20 <$80
Total Issue $315,590
Out in 1935 $25,000
Large out 1935 $2,700
****
4042 Buffalo
FNB, SHELTON
{{ 1 L }}
Chartered 5/21/89
Liquidated 5/10/95
Brown Back <$VALUE
4x5 1-1406 <$1500
Total Issue $28,120
Out in 1910 $205
****
9200 Buffalo
SHELTON NB, SHELTON
{{ UNREPORTED }}
Chartered 1908
Liquidated 10/14/12
1902 Date Back <$VALUE
3x10-20 1-474 <$1000
Total Issue $18,960
Out at close $6,680
****
13425 Cheyenne
AMERICAN NB OF SIDNEY
{{ 3U + 18 S }}
Chartered 2/11/30
1929 Small Size <$VALUE
5 Type 1 1-1392 <$65
10 Type 1 1-282 <$85
20 Type 1 1-118 <$85
5 Type 2 1-108 <$110
10 Type 2 1-215 <$110
20 Type 2 1-95 <$125
Total Issue $77,430
Out in 1935 $25,000
****

****
6201 Cheyenne
FNB, SIDNEY
{{ 4 L }}
Organized 3/12/02
Receivership 5/27/21
1902 Red Seal <$VALUE
4x5 1-850 <$600
3x10-20 1-920 <$600
1902 Date Back
4x5 1-1750 <$350
3x10-20 1-1160 <$350
1902 Plain Back
4x5 1751-3215 <$350
3x10-20 1161-1900 <$350
Total Issue $222,300
Out at close $23,200
****
3628 Nemaha
CARSON NB OF SOUTH AUBURN
Chartered 1887
2nd title:Carson NB of
Auburn 8/90
FIRST TITLE {{ 0 L }}
Brown Back <$VALUE
3x10-20 1-429 <$1000
SECOND TITLE {{ 18 L 32 S }}
Brown Back
4x5 1-6330 <$450
3x10-20 1-1848 <$450
1902 Red Seal
3x10-20 1-1200 <$450
1902 Date Back
3x10-20 1-3700 <$100
1902 Plain Back
3x10-20 3701-10846 <$100
1929 Small Size
10 Type 1 1-1226 <$40
20 Type 1 1-328 <$50
10 Type 2 1-1636 <$50
20 Type 2 1-310 <$65
Total Issue $978,230
Out in 1935 $60,000
Large out 1935 $4,870
****
8949 Douglas
LIVE STOCK NB OF
SOUTH OMAHA
{{ 14 L 50+ S }}
Chartered 11/07
1902 Red Seal <$VALUE
3x10-20 1-2550 <$500
1902 Date Back
3x10-20 1-11800 <$100
1902 Plain Back
3x10-20 11801-18784 <$100
1929 Small Size
10 Type 1 1-2072 <$30
20 Type 1 1-1052 <$40
10 Type 2 1-15500 <$30
20 Type 2 1-4277 <$40
Total Issue $1,542,800
Out in 1935 $285,000
Large out 1935 $4,510
****
4589 Douglas
PACKERS NB OF SOUTH OMAHA
{{ 14 L }}
Chartered 1891
Liquidated 3/29/34
Brown Back <$VALUE
4x5 1-7450 <$400
3x10-20 1-2960 <$400
1882 Date Back
4x5 1-4948 <$350
3x10-20 1-2190 <$350
1902 Date Back
4x5 1-11000 <$100
3x10-20 1-8200 <$100
1902 Plain Back
4x5 11001-27835 <$100
3x10-20 8201-18656 <$100
Total Issue $1,994,960
Out in 1924 $200,000
****
3611 Douglas
SOUTH OMAHA NB,
SOUTH OMAHA
{{ 3 L }}
Chartered 1886
Liquidated 1/3/11
Brown Back <$VALUE
4x5 1-10025 <$600
50-100 1-1806 <$2000/$2500
1902 Red Seal
4x5 1-3830 <$500
3x10-20 1-2468 <$500
1902 Date Back
4x5 1-3705 <$350
3x10-20 1-3411 <$350
Total Issue $916,050
Out in 1911 $96,600
****

****
9908 Douglas
STOCK YARDS NB OF
SOUTH OMAHA
{{ 22 L U + 45 S }}
Chartered 12/10
1902 Date Back <$VALUE
4x5 1-30750 <$85
3x10-20 1-23300 <$85
1902 Plain Back
4x5 30751-32484 <$85
3x10-20 23301-24508 <$85
1929 Small Size
5 Type 1 1-5578 <$30
10 Type 1 1-3232 <$30
20 Type 1 1-880 <$40
5 Type 2 1-9356 <$30
10 Type 2 1-5363 <$30
20 Type 2 1-1330 <$40
Total Issue $2,468,950
Out in 1935 $245,260
Large out 1935 $8,035
****
4632 Douglas
UNION STOCK YARDS NB OF
SOUTH OMAHA
{{ 2 L }}
Chartered 1891
Liquidated 1/3/11
Brown Back <$VALUE
4x5 1-4250 <$600
3x10-20 1-6760 <$600
1882 Date Back
4x5 1-2465 <$500
3x10-20 1-1150 <$500
Total Issue $529,800
Out in 1911 $68,895
****
4557 Dakota
FNB, SOUTH SIOUX CITY
{{ UNREPORTED }}
Chartered 4/22/91
Liquidated 10/27/92
Brown Back <$VALUE
4x5 1-613 <$1500
Total Issue $12,260
Out in 1910 $100
****
7574 Greeley
FNB, SPALDING
{{ UNREPORTED }}
Chartered 1/05
Liquidated 7/20/14
1902 Red Seal <$VALUE
4x5 1-925 <$1500
3x10-20 1-730 <$1500
1902 Date Back
4x5 1-1325 <$850
3x10-20 1-904 <$850
Total Issue $126,700
Out in 1914 $22,650
****
7325 Boyd
FNB, SPENCER
{{ 5 L }}
Organized 6/18/04
Receivership 7/14/22
1902 Red Seal <$VALUE
3x10-20 1-3225 <$600
1902 Date Back
3x10-20 1-6500 <$300
1902 Plain Back
3x10-20 6501-11741 <$300
Total Issue $748,300
Out at close $99,995
****
3364 Stanton
FNB, STANTON
{{ 9 L 20 S }}
Chartered 1885
Brown Back <$VALUE
4x5 1-4037 <$500
3x10-20 1-254 <$500
1902 Red Seal
3x10-20 1-750 <$500
1902 Date Back
3x10-20 1-3600 <$150
1902 Plain Back
3x10-20 3601-9320 <$150
1929 Small Size
5 Type 1 1-1244 <$65
10 Type 1 1-792 <$65
20 Type 1 1-244 <$75
5 Type 2 1-1228 <$75
10 Type 2 1-745 <$75
20 Type 2 1-171 <$85
Total Issue $728,070
Out in 1935 $50,000
Large out 1935 $3,210
****

7836 Stanton
STANTON NB, STANTON
{{ 8 L 3U + 21 S }}
Chartered 7/05
1902 Red Seal <$VALUE
4x5 1-461 <$600
3x10-20 1-308 <$600
1902 Date Back
4x5 1-3050 <$200
3x10-20 1-2330 <$200
1902 Plain Back
4x5 3051-9333 <$200
3x10-20 2331-6387 <$200
1929 Small Size
5 Type 1 1-1464 <$65
10 Type 1 1-726 <$65
20 Type 1 1-192 <$75
5 Type 2 1-1928 <$85
10 Type 2 1-902 <$85
20 Type 2 1-245 <$85
Total Issue $664,710
Out in 1935 $50,000
Large out 1935 $3,430

4163 Johnson
FNB, STERLING
{{ UNREPORTED }}
Chartered 11/20/89
Liquidated 6/16/94
Brown Back <$VALUE
4x5 1-1175 <$1500
Total Issue $23,500
Out in 1910 $210

8286 Polk
FNB, STROMSBURG
{{ 10 L 27 S }}
Chartered 7/06
1902 Red Seal <$VALUE
3x10-20 1-375 <$600
1902 Date Back
3x10-20 1-2950 <$175
1902 Plain Back
3x10-20 2951-7963 <$175
1929 Small Size
10 Type 1 1-978 <$50
20 Type 1 1-266 <$60
10 Type 2 1-441 <$60
20 Type 2 1-95 <$70
Total Issue $513,810
Out in 1935 $25,000
Large out 1935 $3,180

6947 Holt
FNB, STUART
{{ 6 L 15 S }}
Chartered 9/03
1902 Red Seal <$VALUE
3x10-20 1-820 <$650
1902 Date Back
3x10-20 1-1750 <$275
1902 Plain Back
3x10-20 1751-4285 <$275
1929 Small Size
10 Type 1 1-470 <$125
20 Type 1 1-124 <$125
10 Type 2 1-698 <$150
20 Type 2 1-120 <$150
Total Issue $307,710
Out in 1935 $25,000
Large out 1935 $2,600

3529 Nuckolls
FNB, SUPERIOR
{{ UNREPORTED }}
Chartered 7/8/86
Receivership 1/12/14
Brown Back <$VALUE
3x10-20 1-2634 <$1250
1902 Red Seal
50-100 1-360 <$3500/$4000
1902 Date Back
50-100 1-400 <$1250/$1500
3x50-100 1-46 <$1250/$1500
Total Issue $257,200
Out in 1915 $27,000

14083 Nuckolls
SECURITY NB OF SUPERIOR
{{ 16 S }}
Chartered 3/28/34
1929 Small Size <$VALUE
5 Type 2 1-2094 <$100
10 Type 2 1-1725 <$100
20 Type 2 1-1389 <$100
Total Issue $55,500
Out in 1935 $50,000

5397 Nuckolls
SUPERIOR NB, SUPERIOR
{{ 3 L }}
Chartered 6/4/00
Liquidated 2/24/14
Brown Back <$VALUE
3x10-20 1-1270 <$850
1882 Date Back
3x10-20 1-953 <$750
Total Issue $111,150
Out in 1914 $17,670

3240 Clay
FNB, SUTTON
{{ 3 L }}
Chartered 8/25/84
Receivership 11/5/13
Brown Back <$VALUE
4x5 1-3514 <$1000
3x10-20 1-222 <$1000
1902 Red Seal
3x10-20 1-515 <$1000
1902 Date Back
4x5 1-470 <$600
3x10-20 1-216 <$600
Total Issue $127,330
Out in 1915 $3,995

3653 Clay
SUTTON NB, SUTTON
{{ 3 L }}
Chartered 1887
Liquidated 1/13/14
Brown Back <$VALUE
4x5 1-4675 <$700
3x10-20 1-1574 <$700
1902 Red Seal
4x5 1-565 <$700
3x10-20 1-454 <$700
1902 Date Back
4x5 1-2126 <$400
3x10-20 1-1575 <$400
Total Issue $327,470
Out in 1914 $32,785

3083 Otoe
FNB, SYRACUSE
{{ 18 L 16 S }}
Chartered 1883
Brown Back <$VALUE
4x5 1-3355 <$500
3x10-20 1-247 <$500
1902 Red Seal
4x5 1-1625 <$500
3x10-20 1-1280 <$500
1902 Date Back
4x5 1-3000 <$125
3x10-20 1-2200 <$125
1902 Plain Back
4x5 3001-8822 <$125
3x10-20 2201-6372 <$125
1929 Small Size
5 Type 1 1-1404 <$80
10 Type 1 1-882 <$80
20 Type 1 1-230 <$90
5 Type 2 1-1198 <$100
10 Type 2 1-685 <$100
20 Type 2 1-215 <$100
Total Issue $810,770
Out in 1935 $50,000
Large out 1935 $3,435

6166 Johnson
CITIZENS NB OF TECUMSEH
{{ 2 L }}
Chartered 1902
Liquidated 3/1/16
1902 Red Seal <$VALUE
3x10-20 1-2100 <$1000
1902 Date Back
3x10-20 1-2969 <$500
Total Issue $253,450
Out in 1916 $35,530

2955 Johnson
FNB, TECUMSEH
{{ UNREPORTED }}
Chartered 5/19/83
Liquidated 11/3/87
Brown Back <$VALUE
4x5 1-1018 <$1500
Total Issue $20,360
Out in 1910 $125

4276 Johnson
TECUMSEH NB, TECUMSEH
{{ 2 L }}
Chartered 1890
Liquidated 8/9/15
Brown Back <$VALUE
3x10-20 1-2520 <$1000
1882 Date Back
3x10-20 1-560 <$850
1902 Date Back
50-100 1-660 <$750/$850
3x50-100 1-96 <$750/$850
Total Issue $277,000
Out at close $46,000

4324 Burt
FNB, TEKAMAH
{{ U + 19 L U + 33 S }}
Chartered 1890
Brown Back <$VALUE
4x5 1-7775 <$400
50-100 1-1000 <$2000/$2500
1882 Date Back
4x5 1-1205 <$350
50-100 1-37 <$2000/$2500
1902 Date Back
3x10-20 1-5200 <$100
1902 Plain Back
3x10-20 5201-17889 <$100
1929 Small Size
10 Type 1 1-2198 <$40
20 Type 1 1-592 <$50
10 Type 2 1-3001 <$50
20 Type 2 1-744 <$50
Total Issue $1,477,410
Out in 1935 $100,000
Large out 1935 $7,130

9217 Madison
FNB OF TILDEN
{{ 6 L U + 9 S }}
Organized 8/3/08
Receivership 11/17/31
1902 Date Back <$VALUE
4x5 1-1425* <$300
3x10-20 1-1100** <$300
1902 Plain Back
4x5 1626-3915* <$300
3x10-20 1261-2668** <$300
* 1426-1625 not marked
** 1101-1260 not marked
1929 Small Size
5 Type 1 1-368 <$225
10 Type 1 1-194 <$225
20 Type 1 1-46 <$225
Total Issue $239,900
Out at close $20,000
Large out at close $3,050

10011 Madison
TILDEN NB, TILDEN
{{ 9 L U + 11 S }}
Chartered 5/11
1902 Date Back <$VALUE
4x5 1-1550 <$200
3x10-20 1-1230 <$200
1902 Plain Back
4x5 1551-4511 <$200
3x10-20 1231-3046 <$200
1929 Small Size
5 Type 1 1-732 <$150
10 Type 1 1-342 <$150
20 Type 1 1-94 <$150
5 Type 2 1-228 <$200
10 Type 2 1-180 <$200
20 Type 2 1-45 <$200
Total Issue $300,120
Out in 1935 $25,000
Large out 1935 $1,650

3725 Saline
FNB, TOBIAS
{{ UNREPORTED }}
Chartered 6/16/87
Liquidated 11/1/97
Brown Back <$VALUE
3x10-20 1-766 <$1500
Total Issue $38,300
Out in 1910 $410

7578 Saline
TOBIAS NB, TOBIAS
{{ UNREPORTED }}
Chartered 1/05
Liquidated 1/2/13
1902 Red Seal <$VALUE
3x10-20 1-256 <$1500
1902 Date Back
3x10-20 1-1034 <$1000
Total Issue $64,500
Out in 1913 $14,650

8218 Hitchcock
FNB, TRENTON
{{ 1 L }}
Chartered 5/06
Liquidated 2/29/16
1902 Red Seal <$VALUE
3x10-20 1-300 <$1250
1902 Date Back
3x10-20 1-1770 <$750
1902 Plain Back
3x10-20 1771-1784 <$750
Total Issue $104,200
Out in 1916 $16,190

7737 Lancaster
FNB, UNIVERSITY PLACE
{{ 3 L }}
Organized 4/17/05
Receivership 12/29/26
1902 Red Seal <$VALUE
3x10-20 1-1300 <$750
1902 Date Back
3x10-20 1-2380 <$400
1902 Plain Back
3x10-20 2381-5628 <$400
Total Issue $346,400
Out at close $40,000

8811 Seward
FNB OF UTICA
{{ 8 L 12 S }}
Organized 7/6/07
Receivership 9/12/33
1902 Red Seal <$VALUE
3x10-20 1-225 <$600
1902 Date Back
3x10-20 1-2290 <$175
1902 Plain Back
3x10-20 2291-5531 <$175
1929 Small Size
10 Type 1 1-561 <$125
20 Type 1 1-144 <$125
10 Type 2 1-723 <$150
20 Type 2 1-215 <$150
Total Issue $350,270
Out in 1935 $30,000
Large out 1935 $2,510

6378 Cherry
FNB, VALENTINE
{{ 8 L 8 S }}
Chartered 1902
1902 Red Seal <$VALUE
4x5 1-366 <$1000
3x10-20 1-290 <$1000
1902 Date Back
4x5 1-2100 <$400
3x10-20 1-1620 <$400
1902 Plain Back
4x5 2101-5373 <$400
3x10-20 1621-3555 <$400
1929 Small Size
10 Type 1 1-628 <$200
20 Type 1 1-162 <$200
10 Type 2 1-359 <$225
20 Type 2 1-88 <$225
Total Issue $369,500
Out in 1935 $25,000
Large out 1935 $1,660

2780 Saunders
FNB, WAHOO
{{ 17 L 50+ S }}
Chartered 1882
Brown Back <$VALUE
4x5 1-5061 <$500
3x10-20 1-318 <$500
1902 Red Seal
3x10-20 1-1800 <$500
1902 Date Back
3x10-20 1-4700 <$125
1902 Plain Back
3x10-20 4701-13765 <$125
1929 Small Size
10 Type 1 1-1698 <$50
20 Type 1 1-442 <$60
10 Type 2 1-1604 <$60
20 Type 2 1-334 <$60
Total Issue $1,073,010
Out in 1935 $80,000
Large out 1935 $5,410

3118 Saunders
SAUNDERS COUNTY NB, WAHOO
{{ 4 L 3 S }}
Chartered 1/3/84
Receivership 4/22/30
Brown Back <$VALUE
4x5 1-6252 <$650
3x10-20 1-485 <$650
1902 Red Seal
3x10-20 1-1000 <$650
1902 Date Back
3x10-20 1-1600 <$350
1902 Plain Back
3x10-20 1601-4128 <$350
1929 Small Size
10 Type 1 1-185 <$400
20 Type 1 1-28 <$400
Total Issue $420,150
Out at close $24,460
Large out at close $10,270

9984 Dixon
FARMERS NB OF WAKEFIELD
{{ 12 L }}
Organized 3/24/11
Receivership 11/21/28
1902 Date Back <$VALUE
3x10-20 1-2500 <$150
1902 Plain Back
3x10-20 2501-7815 <$150
Total Issue $390,750
Out at close $50,000

5368 Dixon
FNB OF WAKEFIELD
{{ 3 L }}
Chartered 5/24/00
Liquidated 11/17/21
Brown Back <$VALUE
3x10-20 1-1400 <$650
1882 Date Back
3x10-20 1-1750 <$600
1882 Value Back
3x10-20 1751-2420 <$600
1902 Plain Back
3x10-20 1-325 <$450
Total Issue $207,250
Out at close $24,600

8685 Thurston
FNB, WALTHILL
{{ 5 L 21 S }}
Chartered 5/07
1902 Red Seal <$VALUE
50-100 1-240 <$3000/$3500
1902 Date Back
50-100 1-150 <$500/$600
3x50-100 1-980 <$500/$600
1902 Plain Back
3x50-100 981-1148<$500/$600
1929 Small Size
5 Type 1 1-1442 <$75
10 Type 1 1-646 <$75
50 Type 1 1-40 <$250
100 Type 1 1-3 <$400
5 Type 2 1-3426 <$75
10 Type 2 1-1795 <$85
Total Issue $476,400
Out in 1935 $50,000
Large out 1935 $3,200

9816 Thurston
WALTHILL NB, WALTHILL
{{ 5 L 1 S }}
Organized 6/25/10
Receivership 7/20/31
1902 Date Back <$VALUE
3x10-20 1-1800 <$350
1902 Plain Back
3x10-20 1801-5360 <$350
1929 Small Size
10 Type 1 1-340 <$450
20 Type 1 1-89 <$500
Total Issue $299,080
Out at close $25,000
Large out at close $4,450

10017 Knox
COMMERCIAL NB OF WAUSA
{{ 1 L }}
Chartered 5/11
Liquidated 11/30/25
1902 Date Back <$VALUE
4x5 1-1300* <$750
3x10-20 1-1080** <$750
1902 Plain Back
4x5 1501-3775* <$750
3x10-20 1241-2559** <$750
* 1301-1500 not marked
** 1081-1240 not marked
Total Issue $203,450
Out at close $25,000

9994 Knox
FNB OF WAUSA
{{ 11 L }}
Organized 5/27/11
Receivership 7/9/25
1902 Date Back <$VALUE
4x5 1-1800 <$175
3x10-20 1-1440 <$175
1902 Plain Back
4x5 1801-6575 <$175
3x10-20 1441-4358 <$175
Total Issue $349,400
Out at close $50,000

9244 Wayne
CITIZENS NB OF WAYNE
{{ 6 L }}
Organized 8/28/08
Receivership 6/2/26
1902 Date Back <$VALUE
3x10-20 1-4200 <$300
1902 Plain Back
3x10-20 4201-9716 <$300
Total Issue $485,800
Out at close $60,000

3392 Wayne
FNB, WAYNE
{{ 1 L 13 S }}
Chartered 1885
Brown Back <$VALUE
4x5 1-4151 <$1000
3x10-20 1-543 <$1000
1902 Red Seal
3x10-20 1-620 <$1000
1902 Date Back
4x5 1-1250* <$650
3x10-20 1-1000** <$650
1902 Plain Back
4x5 1451-3120* <$650
3x10-20 1161-2196** <$650
* 1251-1450 not marked
** 1001-1160 not marked
1929 Small Size
5 Type 1 1-416 <$125
10 Type 1 1-266 <$125
20 Type 1 1-82 <$125
5 Type 2 1-548 <$150
10 Type 2 1-331 <$150
20 Type 2 1-84 <$150
Total Issue $359,380
Out in 1935 $18,750
Large out 1935 $1,670

4354 Wayne
WAYNE NB, WAYNE
{{ UNREPORTED }}
Chartered 7/2/90
Liquidated 5/16/04
Brown Back <$VALUE
3x10-20 1-1036 <$1500
Total Issue $51,800
Out in 1910 $1,080

5281 Cass
CITY NB OF WEEPING WATER
{{ 4 L }}
Chartered 4/10/00
Liquidated 11/22/15
Brown Back <$VALUE
3x10-20 1-1700 <$750
1882 Date Back
3x10-20 1-2721 <$650
Total Issue $221,050
Out at close $46,900

3523 Cass
FNB, WEEPING WATER
{{ 12 L 25 S }}
Chartered 1886
Brown Back <$VALUE
4x5 1-3486 <$650
50-100 1-107 <$2000/$2500
1902 Red Seal
3x10-20 1-1450 <$750
1902 Date Back
3x10-20 1-3200 <$200
1902 Plain Back
3x10-20 3201-9320 <$200
1929 Small Size
10 Type 1 1-1152 <$85
20 Type 1 1-344 <$100
10 Type 2 1-310 <$125
20 Type 2 1-91 <$125
Total Issue $739,590
Out in 1935 $25,000
Large out 1935 $3,335

3370 Cuming
FNB, WEST POINT
{{ 2 L 10 S }}
Chartered 1885
Brown Back <$VALUE
3x10-20 1-1330 <$1000
1902 Red Seal
3x10-20 1-400 <$1000
1902 Date Back
3x10-20 1-1220 <$500
1902 Plain Back
3x10-20 1221-2110 <$500
1929 Small Size
10 Type 1 1-275 <$150
20 Type 1 1-94 <$150
Total Issue $219,780
Out in 1935 $12,500
Large out 1935 $720

3340 Cuming
WEST POINT NB, WEST POINT
{{ 14 L 10 S }}
Organized 5/9/85
Receivership 12/14/31
Brown Back <$VALUE
4x5 1-3231 <$500
3x10-20 1-283 <$500
1902 Red Seal
3x10-20 1-1950 <$500
1902 Date Back
3x10-20 1-3100 <$150
1902 Plain Back
3x10-20 3101-8448 <$150
1929 Small Size
10 Type 1 1-698 <$150
20 Type 1 1-183 <$150
Total Issue $662,510
Out at close $49,995
Large out at close $7,925

2991 Saline
FNB, WILBER
{{ UNREPORTED }}
Organized 7/3/83
Liquidated 3/22/92
Brown Back <$VALUE
4x5 1-2129 <$1500
Total Issue $42,850
Out in 1910 $380

6415 Saline
NB OF WILBER
{{ 1 L }}
Chartered 1902
Liquidated 8/8/16
1902 Red Seal <$VALUE
3x10-20 1-570 <$1500
1902 Date Back
3x10-20 1-549 <$850
Total Issue $55,950
Out in 1916 $9,200

7861 Kearney
FNB, WILCOX
{{ 4 L 17 S }}
Chartered 8/05
1902 Red Seal <$VALUE
3x10-20 1-900 <$650
1902 Date Back
3x10-20 1-1460* <$350
1902 Plain Back
3x10-20 1591-4275* <$350
* 1461-1590 not marked
1929 Small Size
10 Type 1 1-588 <$100
20 Type 1 1-160 <$100
10 Type 2 1-204 <$125
20 Type 2 1-45 <$135
Total Issue $316,170
Out in 1935 $25,000
Large out 1935 $1,900

9671 Thurston
FNB OF WINNEBAGO
{{ 4 L }}
Chartered 2/10
Liquidated 4/1/27
1902 Date Back <$VALUE
3x10-20 1-1060 <$350
1902 Plain Back
3x10-20 1061-3800 <$350
Total Issue $190,000
Out at close $24,600

6866 Cuming
CITIZENS NB, WISNER
{{ 12 L 19 S }}
Chartered 7/03
1902 Red Seal <$VALUE
3x10-20 1-1900 <$500
1902 Date Back
3x10-20 1-3000 <$175
1902 Plain Back
3x10-20 3001-9214 <$175
1929 Small Size
5 Type 1 1-1354 <$75
10 Type 1 1-768 <$75
20 Type 1 1-196 <$80
5 Type 2 1-2466 <$90
10 Type 2 1-1063 <$90
20 Type 2 1-311 <$90
Total Issue $695,100
Out in 1935 $50,000
Large out 1935 $3,030

4029 Cuming
FNB, WISNER
{{ 15 L 17 S }}
Chartered 1889
Brown Back <$VALUE
4x5 1-4030 <$300
50-100 1-479 <$2000/$2500
1902 Date Back
4x5 1-2800 <$125
50-100 1-334 <$400/$500
3x50-100 1-375 <$400/$500
1902 Plain Back
4x5 2801-12940 <$125
3x50-100 376-464<$400/$500
1929 Small Size
5 Type 1 1-1352 <$85
10 Type 1 1-698 <$85
20 Type 1 1-204 <$100
5 Type 2 1-1398 <$100
10 Type 2 1-817 <$100
20 Type 2 1-295 <$100
Total Issue $705,330
Out in 1935 $50,000
Large out 1935 $5,570

8413 Greeley
FNB, WOLBACH
{{ 2 L }}
Chartered 10/06
Liquidated 8/18/14
1902 Red Seal <$VALUE
3x10-20 1-200 <$1250
1902 Date Back
3x10-20 1-332 <$850
Total Issue $26,600
Out at close $6,500

3939 Hall
FNB OF WOOD RIVER
{{ 50+ L 4 S }}
Chartered 1888
Liquidated 11/10/30
Brown Back <$VALUE
4x5 1-3675 <$500
3x10-20 1-1306 <$500
1902 Date Back
4x5 1-2550 <$100
3x10-20 1-2040 <$100
1902 Plain Back
4x5 2551-7025 <$100
3x10-20 2041-5112 <$100
1929 Small Size
5 Type 1 1-456 <$325
10 Type 1 1-200 <$325
20 Type 1 1-26 <$350
Total Issue $563,700
Out at close $40,000
Large out at close $11,110

9138 Gage
CITY NB OF WYMORE
{{ UNREPORTED }}
Chartered 5/08
Liquidated 7/7/10
1902 Date Back <$VALUE
3x10-20 1-1550 <$1000
Total Issue $77,500
Out at close $43,850

4210 Gage
FNB OF WYMORE
{{ 9 L 23 S }}
Organized 1/9/89
Liquidated 12/24/34
Brown Back <$VALUE
3x10-20 1-1520 <$500
1882 Date Back
3x10-20 1-194 <$500
1902 Date Back
3x10-20 1-3100* <$200
1902 Plain Back
3x10-20 3351-9053* <$200
* 3101-3350 not marked
1929 Small Size
10 Type 1 1-982 <$60
20 Type 1 1-296 <$65
10 Type 2 1-823 <$75
20 Type 2 1-94 <$100
Total Issue $642,900
Out at close $50,000
Large out at close $4,870

14282 Gage
WYMORE NB, WYMORE
{{ U + 4 S }}
Chartered 10/34
1929 Small Size <$VALUE
10 Type 2 1-1160 <$350
20 Type 2 1-420 <$350
Total Issue $20,000
Out in 1935 $9,850

FNB of Wynot
SEE Ch 8335
FNB of Saint James

4935 York
CITY NB OF YORK
{{ 16 L 25 S }}
Chartered 1894
Liquidated 9/14/33
Brown Back <$VALUE
3x10-20 1-3970 <$350/$400
1882 Date Back
3x10-20 1-3254 <$350/$400
1902 Date Back
3x10-20 1-2000* <$100
1902 Plain Back
3x10-20 2501-13530* <$100
* 2001-2500 not marked
1929 Small Size
10 Type 1 1-1949 <$50
20 Type 1 1-500 <$60
Total Issue $1,214,640
Out at close $100,000
Large out at close $5,540

7821 York
FARMERS NB OF YORK
{{ 3 L }}
Chartered 7/05
Liquidated 11/19/12
1902 Red Seal <$VALUE
3x10-20 1-1472 <$850
1902 Date Back
3x10-20 1-1654 <$500
Total Issue $156,300
Out at close $50,000
Ch 2683 assumed circulation

2683 York
FNB, YORK
{{ U + 34 L 43 S }}
Chartered 1882
Series 1875 <$VALUE
3x10-20 1-2960<$1000/$1500
1902 Red Seal
4x5 1-2000 <$300
3x10-20 1-4200 <$300
1902 Date Back
4x5 1-7250 <$65
3x10-20 1-5300 <$75
1902 Plain Back (dated 1902)
4x5 7251-15500 <$65
3x10-20 5301-10400 <$75
1902 Plain Back (dated 1922)
3x10-20 1-10332 <$75
1929 Small Size
10 Type 1 1-3094 <$35
20 Type 1 1-814 <$40
10 Type 2 1-4230 <$40
20 Type 2 1-1278 <$50
Total Issue $2,095,780
Out in 1935 $150,000
Large out 1935 $10,095
Outstanding includes Ch 7821

4245 York
NEBRASKA NB, YORK
{{ UNREPORTED }}
Chartered 3/3/90
Liquidated 8/21/97
Brown Back <$VALUE
3x10-20 1-590 <$1500
Total Issue $29,500
Out in 1910 $360

3162 York
YORK NB, YORK
{{ 2 L }}
Chartered 4/23/84
Liquidated 11/6/93
Brown Back <$VALUE
4x5 1-3076 <$1000
Total Issue $61,520
Out in 1910 $440

NEVADA

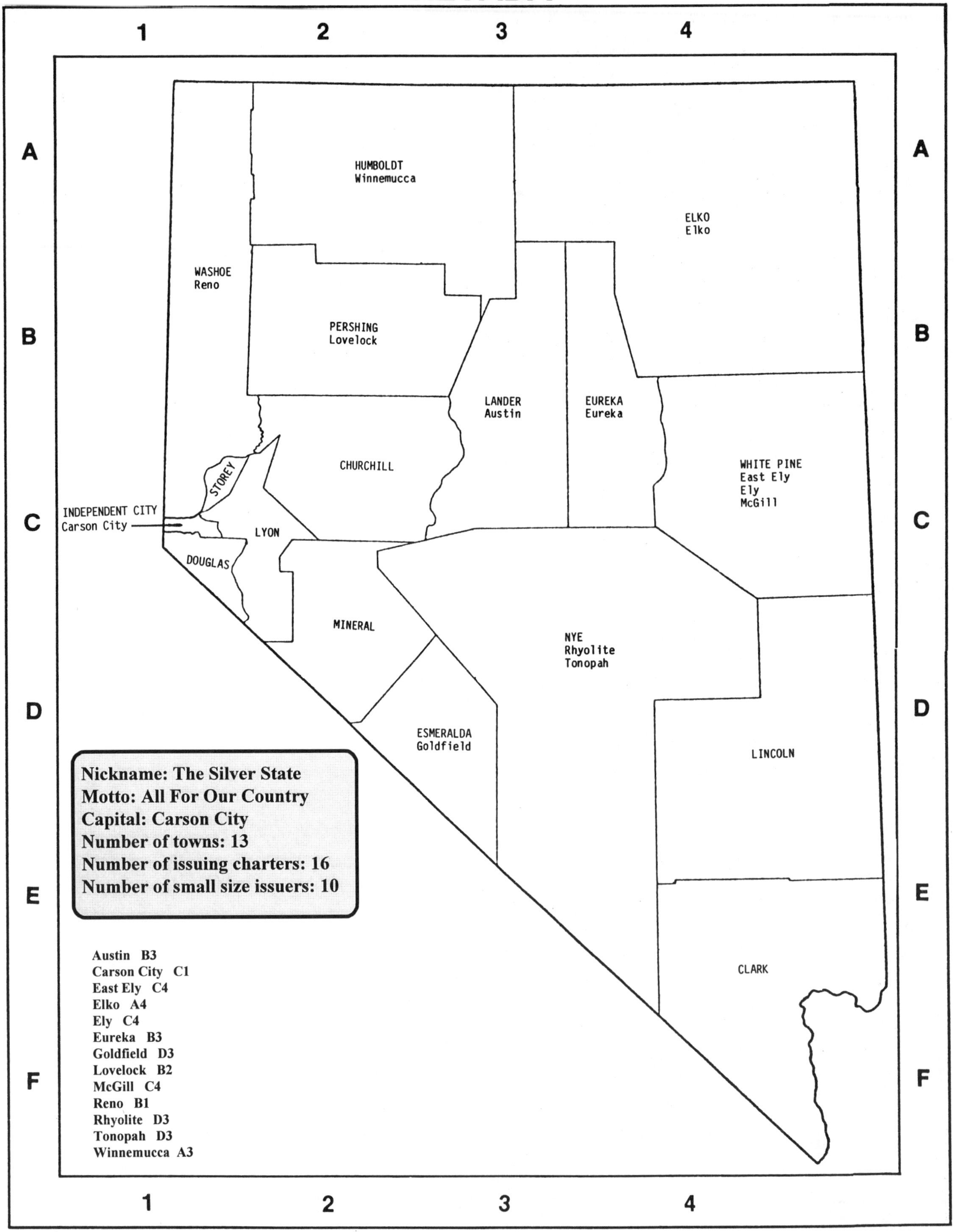

Nickname: The Silver State
Motto: All For Our Country
Capital: Carson City
Number of towns: 13
Number of issuing charters: 16
Number of small size issuers: 10

Austin B3
Carson City C1
East Ely C4
Elko A4
Ely C4
Eureka B3
Goldfield D3
Lovelock B2
McGill C4
Reno B1
Rhyolite D3
Tonopah D3
Winnemucca A3

****
1331 Lander
FNB OF NEVADA, AUSTIN
{{ UNREPORTED }}
Organized 6/23/65
Receivership 10/14/69
Original Series <$VALUE
4x5 1-3585 <$50,000
3x10-20 1-1200 <$50,000
Total Issue $131,700
Out in 1915 $897
****
9242 Independent City
FNB OF CARSON CITY
{{ UNREPORTED }}
Chartered 9/28/08
Receivership 11/15/10
1902 Date Back <$VALUE
4x5 1-305 <$50,000
3x10-20 1-224 <$50,000
Total Issue $17,300
Out in 1911 $3,105
****
9578 White Pine
COPPER NB, EAST ELY
{{ 4 L }}
Chartered 11/5/09
Liquidated 3/5/25
1902 Date Back <$VALUE
3x10-20 1-2950 <$6000
1902 Plain Back
3x10-20 2951-4416 <$6000
Total Issue $220,800
Out at close $23,500
****
7743 Elko
FNB OF ELKO
{{ 23 L 21 S }}
Chartered 5/05
1902 Red Seal <$VALUE
4x5 1-2750 <$6000
3x10-20 1-2205 <$6000
1902 Date Back
4x5 1-7750 <$1000
3x10-20 1-5280 <$1000
1902 Plain Back
4x5 7751-25165 <$1000
3x10-20 5281-16500 <$1000
1929 Small Size
5 Type 1 1-3748 <$700
10 Type 1 1-1980 <$700
20 Type 1 1-514 <$700
5 Type 2 1-1898 <$700
10 Type 2 1-1192 <$700
20 Type 2 1-180 <$800
Total Issue $1,811,480
Out in 1935 $51,762
Large out 1935 $6,262
****
9310 White Pine
ELY NB, ELY
{{ 0 L 2U + 13 S }}
Chartered 1/2/09
1902 Date Back <$VALUE
3x10-20 1-2390 <$8500
1902 Plain Back
3x10-20 2391-6668 <$8500
1929 Small Size
10 Type 1 1-694 <$750
20 Type 1 1-182 <$750
10 Type 2 1-1713 <$750
20 Type 2 1-383 <$750
Total Issue $421,670
Out in 1935 $43,050
Large out 1935 $2,430
Outstanding includes Ch 9452
****
8561 White Pine
FNB OF ELY
{{ 11 L 21 S }}
Organized 1/19/07
1902 Red Seal <$VALUE
4x5 1-1500 <$6000
3x10-20 1-1200 <$6000
1902 Date Back
4x5 1-3625 <$1500
3x10-20 1-2820 <$1500
1902 Plain Back
4x5 3626-13367 <$1500
3x10-20 2821-9112 <$1500
1929 Small Size
5 Type 1 1-1732 <$650
10 Type 1 1-1040 <$650
20 Type 1 1-302 <$700
5 Type 2 1-3622 <$700
10 Type 2 1-2023 <$700
Total Issue $1,001,880
Out in 1935 $49,000
Large out 1935 $3,260
****
11784 Eureka
FARMERS & MERCHANTS NB OF EUREKA
{{ 22 S }}
Chartered 7/20
1929 Small Size <$VALUE
5 Type 1 1-1026 <$750
10 Type 1 1-462 <$750
20 Type 1 1-146 <$750
5 Type 2 1-1472 <$750
10 Type 2 1-620 <$750
20 Type 2 1-90 <$750
Total Issue $91,380
Out in 1935 $27,490
****
9078 Esmeralda
FNB OF GOLDFIELD
{{ 1 L }}
Chartered 3/23/08
Liquidated 6/30/13
1902 Red Seal <$VALUE
4x5 1-750 <$15,000
3x10-20 1-660 <$15,000
1902 Date Back
4x5 1-1050 <$12,500
3x10-20 1-826 <$12,500
Total Issue $110,300
Out in 1913 $20,650
****
7654 Pershing
FNB OF LOVELOCK
{{ 5 L 8 S }}
Chartered 3/05
1902 Red Seal <$VALUE
3x10-20 1-356 <$6500
1902 Date Back
3x10-20 1-1730 <$4000
1902 Plain Back
3x10-20 1731-7155 <$4000
1929 Small Size
10 Type 1 1-854 <$1500
20 Type 1 1-250 <$1500
10 Type 2 1-1481 <$1500
20 Type 2 1-448 <$1500
Total Issue $480,560
Out in 1935 $31,650
Large out 1935 $1,800
****
9452 White Pine
McGILL NB, McGILL
{{ 6 L U + 14 S }}
Chartered 6/17/09
Closed 5/9/34
1902 Date Back <$VALUE
3x10-20 1-2320 <$4000
1902 Plain Back
3x10-20 2321-6383 <$4000
1929 Small Size
10 Type 1 1-768 <$1000
20 Type 1 1-200 <$1000
10 Type 2 1-97 <$1000
20 Type 2 1-15 <$1000
Total Issue $390,500
Out at close $25,000
Large out 1934 $1,210
****
7038 Washoe
FARMERS & MERCHANTS NB OF RENO
Chartered 11/03
2nd title: FNB in Reno 6/24/29
FIRST TITLE {{ 47 L }}
1902 Red Seal <$VALUE
4x5 1-5750 <$5000
3x10-20 1-8800 <$5000
1902 Date Back
4x5 1-14500 <$500
3x10-20 1-10100 <$500
1902 Plain Back
4x5 14501-51013 <$500
3x10-20 10101-32109 <$500
SECOND TITLE {{ 69U + 50+ S }}
1929 Small Size
5 Type 1 1-7932 <$200
10 Type 1 1-3630 <$200
20 Type 1 1-986 <$200
5 Type 2 1-13068 <$175
10 Type 2 1-6528 <$200
20 Type 2 1-1644 <$200
Total Issue $3,918,290
Out in 1935 $186,070
Large out 1935 $11,970
****
FNB in Reno
SEE Ch 7038
Farmers & Merchants NB of Reno
****
2478 Washoe
FNB OF RENO
{{ 1 L }}
Chartered 5/26/80
Liquidated 1/2/96
Series 1875 <$VALUE
4x20 1-2026 <$50,000
Total Issue $162,080
Out in 1910 $1,400
****
8424 Washoe
NIXON NB, RENO
Organized 10/20/06
Receivership 12/9/32
2nd title: Reno NB 8/2/15
FIRST TITLE {{ 14 L }}
1902 Red Seal <$VALUE
3x10-20 1-20000 <$5000
50-100 1-3000 <$20,000
1902 Date Back
3x10-20 1-44849 <$750
50-100 1-2400 <$3500
SECOND TITLE {{50+ L 50+ S}}
1902 Plain Back
4x5 1-42770 <$400
3x10-20 1-61393 <$400
3x50-100 1-3579<$1250/$1500
1929 Small Size
5 Type 1 1-20100 <$175
20 Type 1 1-2345 <$200
50 Type 1 1-588 <$400
100 Type 1 1-354 <$500
Total Issue $10,145,450
Out in 1935 $665,000
Large out 1935 $77,230
****
Reno NB, Reno
SEE Ch 8424
Nixon NB, Reno
****
8686 Nye
FNB OF RHYOLITE
{{ UNREPORTED }}
Organized 5/14/07
Receivership 3/23/10
1902 Red Seal <$VALUE
4x5 1-402 <$35,000
4x10 1-418 <$35,000
1902 Date Back
4x5 1-202 <$30,000
4x10 1-46 <$30,000
Total Issue $30,640
Out in 1915 $295
****
8530 Nye
NEVADA FNB, TONOPAH
{{ 4 L 5 S }}
Chartered 2/07
Liquidated 9/2/32
1902 Red Seal <$VALUE
4x5 1-2500 <$10,000
3x10-20 1-1100 <$10,000
50-100 1-300 <$30,000
1902 Date Back
4x5 1-1250 <$6000
3x10-20 1-700 <$6000
50-100 1-75 <$10,000
1902 Plain Back
4x5 1251-3205 <$6000
3x10-20 701-2047 <$6000
1929 Small Size
5 Type 1 1-594 <$2500
10 Type 1 1-309 <$2500
20 Type 1 1-92 <$2500
Total Issue $375,100
Out at close $21,040
Large out at close $2,180
****
3575 Humboldt
FNB OF WINNEMUCCA
{{ 6 L 31 S }}
Organized 9/27/86
Receivership 12/10/32
Brown Back <$VALUE
4x5 1-4783 <$50,000
3x10-20 1-824 <$50,000
1902 Red Seal
50-100 1-760 <$30,000
1902 Date Back
50-100 1-600 <$5000
3x50-100 1-1098 <$5000
1902 Plain Back
4x5 1-15597 <$2000
3x50-100 1099-1301 <$5000
1929 Small Size
5 Type 1 1-2493 <$600
10 Type 1 1-1404 <$550
20 Type 1 1-260 <$600
Total Issue 1,168,280
Out at close $82,000
Out in 1935 $9,855
****

CONDITION affects Value. The Values shown are for notes in FINE condition.

<$VALUEs are for notes in **FINE** condition. Value changes by approximately **25%** for a change of one full grade.

NEW HAMPSHIRE

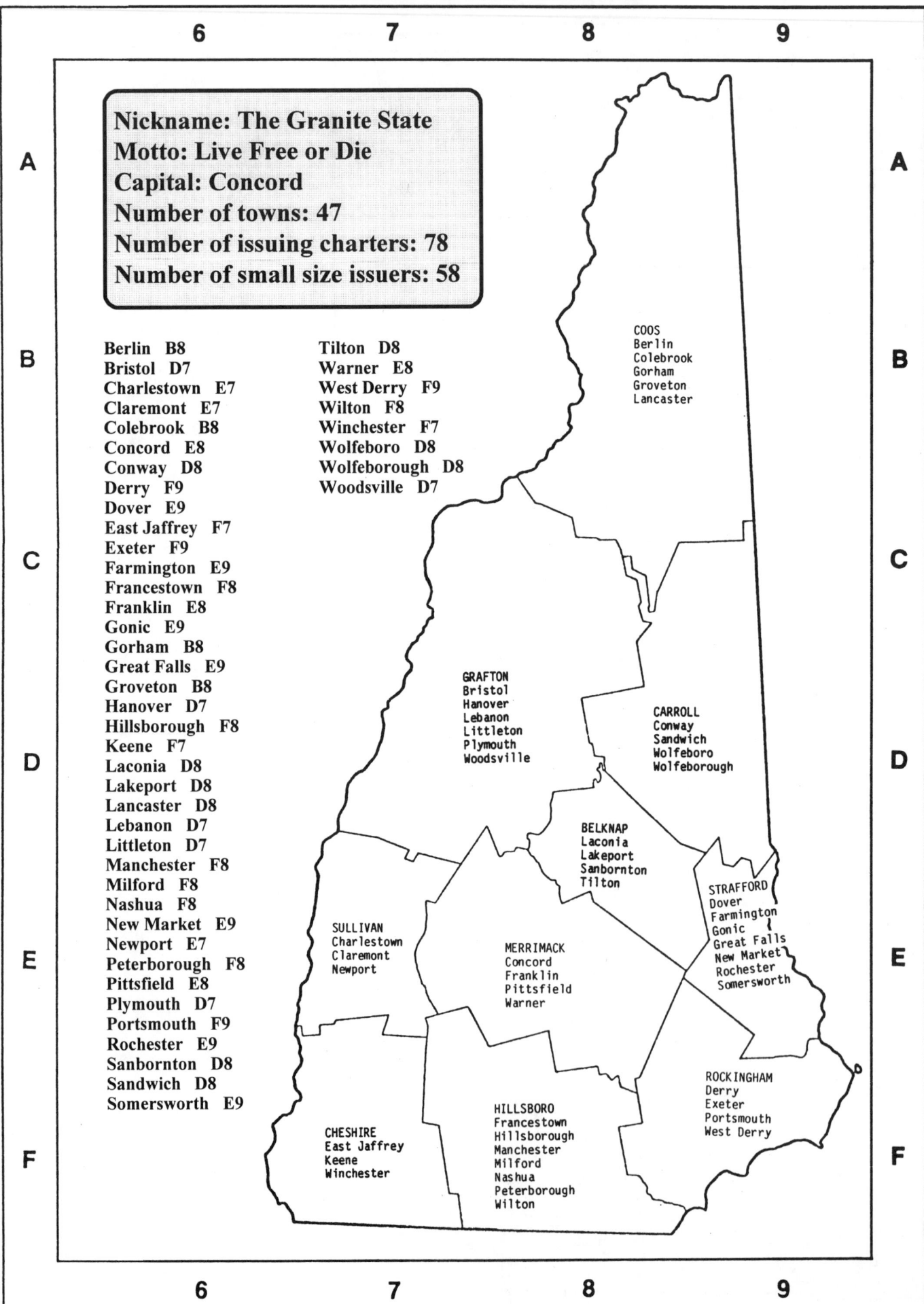

Nickname: The Granite State
Motto: Live Free or Die
Capital: Concord
Number of towns: 47
Number of issuing charters: 78
Number of small size issuers: 58

Berlin B8
Bristol D7
Charlestown E7
Claremont E7
Colebrook B8
Concord E8
Conway D8
Derry F9
Dover E9
East Jaffrey F7
Exeter F9
Farmington E9
Francestown F8
Franklin E8
Gonic E9
Gorham B8
Great Falls E9
Groveton B8
Hanover D7
Hillsborough F8
Keene F7
Laconia D8
Lakeport D8
Lancaster D8
Lebanon D7
Littleton D7
Manchester F8
Milford F8
Nashua F8
New Market E9
Newport E7
Peterborough F8
Pittsfield E8
Plymouth D7
Portsmouth F9
Rochester E9
Sanbornton D8
Sandwich D8
Somersworth E9
Tilton D8
Warner E8
West Derry F9
Wilton F8
Winchester F7
Wolfeboro D8
Wolfeborough D8
Woodsville D7

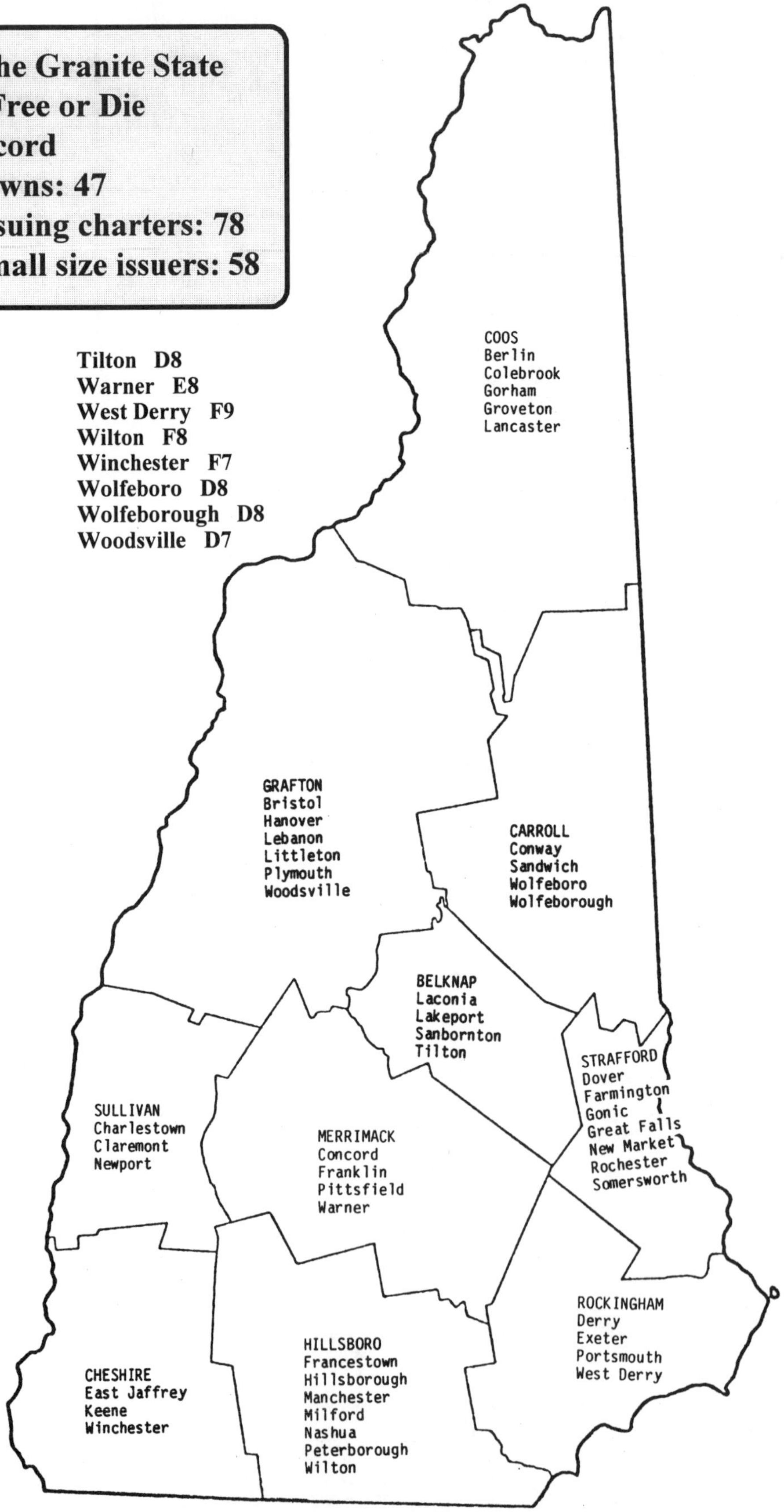

****
14100 Coos
BERLIN CITY NB, BERLIN
{{ U + 6 S }}
Chartered 4/34 as Berlin NB under which there was no issue. Issuing title adopted 5/19/34.
1929 Small Size <$VALUE
10 Type 2 1-6625 <$350
Total Issue $66,250
Out in 1935 $150,000
Outstanding includes Ch 4523 and Ch 5622
****
4523 Coos
BERLIN NB, BERLIN
{{ 8 L 18 S }}
Organized 1/31/91
Liquidated 6/12/34
Brown Back <$VALUE
4x5 1-15338 <$500
3x10-20 1-7400 <$500
1882 Date Back
4x5 1-6161 <$500
3x10-20 1-4096 <$500
1902 Date Back
4x5 1-5000* <$175
4x10 1-5000** <$175
1902 Plain Back
4x5 5401-25214* <$175
4x10 5401-22363** <$175
* 5001-5400 not marked
** 5001-5400 not marked
1929 Small Size
5 Type 1 1-4886 <$100
10 Type 1 1-2820 <$100
5 Type 2 1-2004 <$110
10 Type 2 1-1162 <$110
Total Issue $2,741,000
Out at close $99,200
Large out at close $5,440
Ch 14100 assumed circulation
****
5622 Coos
CITY NB OF BERLIN
{{ 3 L 5 S }}
Chartered 11/12/00
Closed 5/19/34
Brown Back <$VALUE
4x5 1-4000 <$750
3x10-20 1-3500 <$750
1882 Date Back
4x5 1-4750 <$750
3x10-20 1-3380 <$750
1882 Value Back
4x5 4751-7825 <$800
3x10-20 3381-5015 <$800
1902 Plain Back
3x10-20 1-6651 <$450
1929 Small Size
10 Type 1 1-1282 <$300
20 Type 1 1-356 <$300
10 Type 2 1-456 <$300
20 Type 2 1-135 <$325
Total Issue $1,121,700
Out at close $50,000
Large out at close $2,690
****
5151 Grafton
FNB OF BRISTOL
{{ 5 L 7 S }}
Chartered 1898
Brown Back <$VALUE
4x5 1-3675 <$600
3x10-20 1-2930 <$600
1882 Date Back
4x5 1-3975 <$600
3x10-20 1-2760 <$600
1882 Value Back
4x5 3976-5531 <$750
3x10-20 2761-3673 <$750
1902 Plain Back
3x10-20 1-7368 <$300
1929 Small Size
10 Type 1 1-1544 <$200
20 Type 1 1-348 <$200
10 Type 2 1-1128 <$225
20 Type 2 1-296 <$250
Total Issue $1,034,270
Out in 1935 $44,280
Large out 1935 $1,480
****
537 Sullivan
CONNECTICUT RIVER NB OF CHARLESTOWN
{{ 4 L 2 S }}
Chartered 1864
Original Series <$VALUE
4x5 1-5000 <$850
3x10-20 1-1500<$1250/$1500
Series 1875
4x5 1-7744 <$850
Brown Back
4x5 1-19530 <$750
3x10-20 1-855 <$750
1902 Red Seal
3x10-20 1-950 <$850
1902 Date Back
3x10-20 1-1860 <$500
1902 Plain Back
3x10-20 1861-5711 <$500
1929 Small Size
5 Type 1 1-796 <$450
10 Type 1 1-434 <$450
20 Type 1 1-132 <$450
5 Type 2 1-372 <$500
10 Type 2 1-276 <$500
20 Type 2 1-114 <$500
Total Issue $1,168,940
Out in 1935 $21,550
Large out 1935 $4,260
****
596 Sullivan
CLAREMONT NB, CLAREMONT
{{ 10 L 9 S }}
Organized 11/23/64
Liquidated 1/9/34
Original Series <$VALUE
4x5 1-5750 <$600
3x10-20 1-2900 <$850/$1250
50-100 1-500 <$6000
Series 1875
4x5 1-3733 <$600
3x10-20 1-2050 <$850/$1250
Brown Back
4x5 1-7000 <$400
3x10-20 1-5710 <$400
1902 Red Seal
4x5 1-4000 <$500
3x10-20 1-2500 <$500
1902 Date Back
4x5 1-7850 <$175
3x10-20 1-5860 <$175
1902 Plain Back
4x5 7851-26135 <$175
3x10-20 5861-18207 <$175
1929 Small Size
5 Type 1 1-3771 <$125
10 Type 1 1-1866 <$125
20 Type 1 1-486 <$150
Total Issue $2,859,120
Out at close $92,980
Large out at close $7,990
Ch 13829 assumed circulation
****
13829 Sullivan
CLAREMONT NB, CLAREMONT
{{ 4 S }}
Chartered 11/33
1929 Small Size <$VALUE
5 Type 2 1-4456 <$350
10 Type 2 1-2332 <$350
20 Type 2 1-830 <$350
Total Issue $62,200
Out in 1935 $79,990
Outstanding includes Ch 596
****
4793 Sullivan
PEOPLES NB OF CLAREMONT
{{ 6 L 11 S }}
Chartered 1892
Brown Back <$VALUE
4x5 1-12180 <$500
3x10-20 1-4868 <$500
1882 Date Back
4x5 1-3796 <$500
3x10-20 1-2692 <$500
1902 Date Back
4x5 1-3915 <$250
3x10-20 1-2734 <$250
1902 Plain Back
4x5 3916-23355 <$250
3x10-20 2735-15534 <$250
1929 Small Size
5 Type 1 1-4036 <$100
10 Type 1 1-1908 <$100
20 Type 1 1-436 <$125
5 Type 2 1-4756 <$125
10 Type 2 1-2523 <$125
20 Type 2 1-528 <$150
Total Issue $2,288,770
Out in 1935 $82,600
Large out 1935 $5,275
****
4041 Coos
COLEBROOK NB, COLEBROOK
{{ 11 L 10 S }}
Chartered 5/21/89
Brown Back <$VALUE
4x5 1-8004* <$450
3x10-20 1-4632 <$450
* 3310-3340 not issued
1902 Date Back
4x5 1-5500 <$175
4x10 1-5500 <$175
1902 Plain Back
4x5 5501-21737 <$175
4x10 5501-18009 <$175
1929 Small Size
5 Type 1 1-3896 <$150
10 Type 1 1-2040 <$150
5 Type 2 1-6250 <$150
10 Type 2 1-2575 <$150
Total Issue $1,842,440
Out in 1935 $60,600
Large out 1935 $3,750
****
5183 Coos
FARMERS & TRADERS NB OF COLEBROOK
{{ 3 L 7 S }}
Chartered 3/27/99
Brown Back <$VALUE
4x5 1-4400 <$600
3x10-20 1-2820 <$600
1882 Date Back
4x5 1-4550 <$600
3x10-20 1-3300 <$600
1882 Value Back
4x5 4551-6680 <$750
3x10-20 3301-4481 <$750
1902 Plain Back
4x10 1-10640 <$400
1929 Small Size
10 Type 1 1-2388 <$225
10 Type 2 1-3123 <$225
Total Issue $1,184,120
Out in 1935 $40,600
Large out 1935 $2,280
****
318 Merrimack
FNB OF CONCORD
{{ U + 15 L 15 S }}
Chartered 1864
Original Series <$VALUE
3x1-2 1-3100 <$500/$1000
4x5 1-4600 <$500
3x10-20 1-1900 <$850/$1250
50-100 1-821 <$6000
Series 1875
4x5 1-2975 <$500
3x10-20 1-997 <$850/$1250
Brown Back
4x5 1-8120 <$400
3x10-20 1-7419 <$400
50-100 1-1406 <$1750/$2000
1902 Red Seal
4x5 1-7500 <$500
3x10-20 1-3930 <$500
50-100 1-490 <$3000
1902 Date Back
4x5 1-11250* <$125
3x10-20 1-7300 <$125
50-100 1-100 <$500/$600
3x50-100 1-678 <$500/$600
1902 Plain Back
4x5 12251-35665* <$125
3x10-20 7301-19452 <$125
3x50-100 679-953<$500/$600
* 11251-12250 not marked
1929 Small Size
5 Type 1 1-2968 <$100
10 Type 1 1-1436 <$100
20 Type 1 1-512 <$100
50 Type 1 1-208 <$350
100 Type 1 1-64 <$500
5 Type 2 1-4408 <$125
10 Type 2 1-2297 <$125
20 Type 2 1-422 <$125
Total Issue $3,881,270
Out in 1935 $130,995
Large out 1935 $11,255
****
2447 Merrimack
MECHANICS NB OF CONCORD
{{ 27 L 17 S }}
Chartered 1/3/80
Series 1875 <$VALUE
4x5 1-5550 <$450
3x10-20 1-3624 <$750/$1250
50-100 1-58 <$6000
Brown Back
4x5 1-1220 <$350
3x10-20 1-6240 <$350
50-100 1-510 <$1750/$2000
1882 Date Back
4x5 1-15000* <$350
3x10-20 1-9200** <$350
50-100 1-100 <$1750/$2000
1882 Value Back
4x5 15751-24000* <$600
3x10-20 9801-14300** <$600
* 15001-15750 not marked
** 9201-9800 not marked
1902 Plain Back
4x5 1-25406 <$100
3x10-20 1-16013 <$100
3x50-100 1-20 <$500/$600
1929 Small Size
5 Type 1 1-6960 <$70
10 Type 1 1-3246 <$65
20 Type 1 1-878 <$70
5 Type 2 1-12512 <$80
10 Type 2 1-6053 <$80
20 Type 2 1-1605 <$85
Total Issue $4,121,280
Out in 1935 $164,340
Large out 1935 $8,455
****
758 Merrimack
N STATE CAPITAL B OF CONCORD
{{ 16 L 22 S }}
Chartered 1/26/65
Original Series <$VALUE
3x1-2 1-3100 <$600/$1250
4x5 1-5100 <$600
3x10-20 1-2196 <$850/$1250
50-100 1-710 <$6000
Series 1875
4x5 1-5700 <$600
3x10-20 1-2811 <$850/$1250
50-100 1-266 <$6000
Brown Back
4x5 1-13750 <$500
3x10-20 1-7970 <$500
50-100 1-770 <$1750/$2000
1902 Red Seal
4x5 1-8100 <$600
3x10-20 1-4210 <$600
50-100 1-350 <$3000
1902 Date Back
4x5 1-16750 <$150
3x10-20 1-10500 <$150
50-100 1-100 <$500/$600
3x50-100 1-620 <$500/$600
1902 Plain Back
4x5 16751-41230 <$150
3x10-20 10501-25601 <$150
3x50-100 621-748<$500/$600
1929 Small Size
5 Type 1 1-3088 <$100
10 Type 1 1-2228 <$100
20 Type 1 1-676 <$100
50 Type 1 1-186 <$350
100 Type 1 1-70 <$500
5 Type 2 1-9756 <$125
10 Type 2 1-5165 <$125
20 Type 2 1-2046 <$125
Total Issue $4,695,490
Out in 1935 $236,095
Large out 1935 $11,115
****
9476 Carroll
CONWAY NB, CONWAY
{{ 1 L }}
Chartered 7/09
Liquidated 9/17/23
1902 Date Back <$VALUE
3x10-20 1-2580 <$1000
1902 Plain Back
3x10-20 2581-4830 <$1000
Total Issue $241,500
Out at close $24,700
****
499 Rockingham
DERRY NB, DERRY
{{ 5 L 5 S }}
Chartered 1864
Liquidated 9/28/32
Original Series <$VALUE
4x5 1-2500 <$850
3x10-20 1-1300<$1250/$1500
Series 1875
4x5 1-2720 <$850
3x10-20 1-400 <$1250/$1500
Brown Back
4x5 1-7300 <$650
3x10-20 1-1920 <$650
1902 Red Seal
3x10-20 1-2500 <$750
1902 Date Back
3x10-20 1-4440 <$350
1902 Plain Back
3x10-20 4441-13352 <$350
1929 Small Size
10 Type 1 1-893 <$300
20 Type 1 1-243 <$300
Total Issue $1,306,740
Out at close $30,080
Large out at close $4,120
Ch 8038 assumed circulation
****

****
1087 Strafford
COCHECHO NB OF DOVER
{{ 2 L }}
Organized 4/29/65
Receivership 6/6/99
Original Series <$VALUE
4x5 1-2902 <$1250
4x10 1-1450 <$1500
3x20-50 1-1036<$2000/$6000
Series 1875
4x5 1-222 <$1250
4x10 1-250 <$1500
3x20-50 1-1826<$2000/$6000
Brown Back
4x5 1-1173 <$1000
3x10-20 1-2977 <$1000
50-100 1-415 <$1750/$2000
Total Issue $679,860
Out in 1916 $2,800
****
1043 Strafford
DOVER NB, DOVER
{{ 2 L }}
Organized 4/22/65
Receivership 2/7/95
Original Series <$VALUE
3x1-2 1-2000 <$1250/$2000
4x5 1-3750 <$1250
3x10-20 1-1800<$1500/$2000
Series 1875
3x10-20 1-2614<$1500/$2000
Brown Back
3x10-20 1-4959 <$1000
Total Issue $553,650
Out in 1916 $2,665
****
5274 Strafford
MERCHANTS NB OF DOVER
{{ U + 5 L 13 S }}
Chartered 4/2/00
Brown Back <$VALUE
3x10-20 1-6800 <$750
1882 Date Back
3x10-20 1-8800 <$750
1882 Value Back
3x10-20 8801-12991 <$850
1902 Plain Back
3x10-20 1-13174 <$350
1929 Small Size
10 Type 1 1-2782 <$125
20 Type 1 1-758 <$135
10 Type 2 1-3003 <$165
20 Type 2 1-910 <$175
Total Issue $1,954,360
Out in 11935 $98,250
Large out 1935 $3,980
****
1353 Strafford
STRAFFORD NB OF DOVER
{{ 10 L }}
Chartered 1865
Original Series <$VALUE
3x1-2 1-2600 <$600/$1250
4x5 1-4000 <$600
3x10-20 1-3000 <$850/$1250
Series 1875
3x10-20 1-4616 <$850/$1250
Brown Back
3x10-20 1-18959 <$400
1902 Red Seal
4x5 1-3500 <$500
3x10-20 1-2200 <$500
1902 Date Back
4x5 1-6000 <$250
3x10-20 1-5100 <$250
1902 Plain Back
4x5 6001-16122 <$250
3x10-20 5101-11110 <$250
Total Issue $2,479,690
Out in 1935 $5,592
****
1242 Cheshire
MONADNOCK NB OF EAST JAFFREY
{{ 10 L 13 S }}
Chartered 1865
Original Series <$VALUE
3x1-2 1-2200 <$600/$1250
4x5 1-2500 <$600
3x10-20 1-2400 <$850/$1250
50-100 1-100 <$6000
Series 1875
3x1-2 1-1000 <$600/$1250
4x5 1-1045 <$600
3x10-20 1-1828 <$850/$1250
Brown Back
4x5 1-5675 <$400
3x10-20 1-5681 <$400
1902 Red Seal
3x10-20 1-2800 <$500
1902 Date Back
3x10-20 1-6300 <$250
1902 Plain Back
3x10-20 6301-18606 <$250
1929 Small Size
5 Type 1 1-1992 <$150
10 Type 1 1-2034 <$150
20 Type 1 1-200 <$165
5 Type 2 1-5184 <$175
10 Type 2 1-3252 <$175
Total Issue $2,045,390
Out in 1935 $69,900
Large out 1935 $5,390
****
1147 Rockingham
N GRANITE STATE B OF EXETER
{{ 4 L }}
Organized 5/15/65
Receivership 9/23/93
Original Series <$VALUE
3x1-2 1-4110 <$750/$1500
4x5 1-2550 <$850
3x10-20 1-1300<$1000/$1500
50-100 1-270 <$6000
Series 1875
3x1-2 1-870 <$750/$1500
4x5 1-2055 <$850
3x10-20 1-1295<$1000/$1500
50-100 1-269 <$6000
Brown Back
4x5 1-3500 <$750
3x10-20 1-1749 <$750
50-100 1-166 <$1750/$2000
Total Issue $509,950
Out in 1916 $1,077
****
12889 Rockingham
ROCKINGHAM NB OF EXETER
{{ 3 L 15 S }}
Organized 12/30/25
1902 Plain Back <$VALUE
4x5 1-6529 <$750
1929 Small Size
5 Type 1 1-3952 <$100
10 Type 1 1-1134 <$100
20 Type 1 1-306 <$100
5 Type 2 1-6850 <$125
10 Type 2 1-1755 <$125
20 Type 2 1-636 <$150
Total Issue $418,420
Out in 1935 $83,750
Large out 1935 $370
****
2022 Strafford
FARMINGTON NB, FARMINGTON
{{ 6 L 4 S }}
Chartered 7/27/72
Liquidated 11/18/33
Original Series <$VALUE
4x5 1-2170 <$750
3x10-20 1-1632<$1000/$1500
Series 1875
4x5 1-4533 <$750
3x10-20 1-2231<$1000/$1500
Brown Back
4x5 1-3150 <$600
3x10-20 1-2410 <$600
1882 Date Back
4x5 1-415 <$600
3x10-20 1-295 <$600
1902 Date Back
4x10 1-1000* <$350
1902 Plain Back
4x10 1151-2981* <$350
* 1001-1150 not marked
1929 Small Size
10 Type 1 1-1187 <$350
Total Issue $724,220
Out at close $47,120
Large out at close $1,680
Ch 13764 assumed circulation
****
13764 Strafford
FARMINGTON NB, FARMINGTON
{{ 3 S }}
Chartered 9/33
1929 Small Size <$VALUE
5 Type 2 1-3746 <$400
10 Type 2 1-1593 <$400
20 Type 2 1-396 <$400
Total Issue $42,580
Out in 1935 $47,270
Outstanding includes Ch 2022
****

****
576 Hillsborough
FNB OF FRANCESTOWN
{{ 3 L }}
Chartered 11/19/64
Liquidated 10/10/91
Original Series <$VALUE
3x1-2 1-1500 <$750/$1500
4x5 1-3125 <$750
3x10-20 1-2420<$1250/$1750
Series 1875
3x1-2 1-1000 <$750/$1500
4x5 1-1650 <$750
3x10-20 1-1830<$1250/$1750
Brown Back
4x5 1-1650 <$750
3x10-20 1-2430 <$750
Total Issue $475,000
Out in 1910 $2,455
****
2443 Merrimack
FRANKLIN NB, FRANKLIN
{{ 10 L 9 S }}
Chartered 12/20/79
Series 1875 <$VALUE
4x5 1-10000 <$600
3x10-20 1-6518 <$850/$1250
Brown Back
3x10-20 1-8200 <$450
1882 Date Back
3x10-20 1-7800 <$450
1882 Value Back
3x10-20 7801-11507 <$750
1902 Plain Back
3x10-20 1-12778 <$300
1929 Small Size
10 Type 1 1-2784 <$150
20 Type 1 1-730 <$175
10 Type 2 1-2638 <$175
20 Type 2 1-730 <$175
Total Issue $2,445,770
Out in 1935 $87,000
Large out 1935 $5,990
****
838 Strafford
FNB OF GONIC
{{ 2 L }}
Chartered 2/24/65
Liquidated 1/14/79
Original Series <$VALUE
3x1-2 1-2600 <$1250/$2000
4x5 1-3000 <$1250
4x10 1-1100 <$1500
Series 1875
3x1-2 1-693 <$1250/$2000
4x5 1-670 <$1250
4x10 1-255 <$1500
Total Issue $144,065
Out in 1910 $1,003
****
Gorham NB, Gorham
SEE Ch 5258
Groveton NB, Groveton
****
9001 Coos
WHITE MOUNTAIN NB OF GORHAM
{{ 3 L 2U + 6 S }}
Chartered 1/08
1902 Red Seal <$VALUE
4x5 1-175 <$1250
4x10 1-175 <$1250
1902 Date Back
4x5 1-2025 <$600
4x10 1-1900 <$600
1902 Plain Back
4x5 2026-3000 <$600
4x10 1901-7872 <$600
1929 Small Size
5 Type 1 1-1086 <$275
10 Type 1 1-856 <$275
5 Type 2 1-1082 <$300
10 Type 2 1-656 <$300
Total Issue $481,290
Out in 1935 $20,050
Large out 1935 $750
****
1183 Strafford
SOMERSWORTH NB OF GREAT FALLS
Chartered 1865
2nd title: Somersworth NB of Somersworth 9/16/02
FIRST TITLE {{ 2 L }}
Original Series <$VALUE
3x1-2 1-3000 <$750/$1500
4x5 1-2875 <$750
3x10-20 1-1780<$1000/$1500
Series 1875
4x5 1-710 <$750
3x10-20 1-2698<$1000/$1500
Brown Back
4x5 1-9700 <$750
3x10-20 1-6160 <$750
SECOND TITLE {{ 11 L 14 S }}
Brown Back
4x5 9701-10901 <$500
3x10-20 6161-7316 <$500
1902 Red Seal
4x5 1-3590 <$600
3x10-20 1-2564 <$600
1902 Date Back
4x5 1-8150 <$225
3x10-20 1-5820 <$225
1902 Plain Back
4x5 8151-25372 <$225
3x10-20 5821-17445 <$225
1929 Small Size
5 Type 1 1-3474 <$100
10 Type 1 1-1974 <$100
20 Type 1 1-498 <$110
5 Type 2 1-3668 <$125
10 Type 2 1-1980 <$125
20 Type 2 1-636 <$135
Total Issue $2,807,390
Out in 1935 $97,900
Large out 1935 $8,500
****
5317 Coos
COOS COUNTY NB OF GROVETON
{{ 2 L 5 S }}
Chartered 5/1/00
Liquidated 11/28/33
Brown Back <$VALUE
3x10-20 1-2250 <$1000
1882 Date Back
3x10-20 1-2460 <$1000
1882 Value Back
3x10-20 2461-3790 <$1000
1902 Plain Back
3x10-20 1-3996 <$600
1929 Small Size
10 Type 1 1-956 <$350
20 Type 1 1-254 <$350
10 Type 2 1-742 <$350
Total Issue $597,060
Out at close $24,140
Large out at close $1,250
****
5258 Coos
GROVETON NB, GROVETON
Chartered 2/20/00
Liquidated 1/31/11
2nd title:Gorham NB, Gorham 4/30/02
FIRST TITLE {{ 0 L }}
Brown Back <$VALUE
3x10-20 1-753 <$1500
SECOND TITLE {{ 1 L }}
Brown Back
4x5 1-1250 <$1250
3x10-20 1-1900 <$1250
1882 Date Back
4x5 1-50 <$1250
3x10-20 1-49 <$1250
Total Issue $161,100
Out in 1911 $12,750
****
1145 Grafton
DARTMOUTH NB OF HANOVER
{{ 10 L 11 S }}
Chartered 1865
Original Series <$VALUE
4x5 1-2400 <$600
3x10-20 1-950 <$1000/$1500
Series 1875
4x5 1-730 <$600
3x10-20 1-810 <$1000/$1500
Brown Back
3x10-20 1-1633 <$500
1902 Red Seal
4x5 1-800 <$600
3x10-20 1-700 <$600
1902 Date Back
4x5 1-1050 <$275
3x10-20 1-840 <$275
1902 Plain Back
4x5 1051-3185 <$275
3x10-20 841-2177 <$275
1929 Small Size
5 Type 1 1-532 <$175
10 Type 1 1-274 <$175
20 Type 1 1-84 <$200
5 Type 2 1-298 <$200
10 Type 2 1-258 <$200
20 Type 2 1-72 <$225
Total Issue $503,790
Out in 1935 $14,800
Large out 1935 $1,590
****

****
1688 Hillsborough
FNB OF HILLSBOROUGH
{{ 9 L 7 S }}
Chartered 1868
Original Series <$VALUE
3x1-2 1-2300 <$1250/$2000
4x5 1-2775 <$1500
Series 1875
3x1-2 1-840 <$750/$1250
4x5 1-6399 <$750
Brown Back
4x5 1-11039 <$450
3x10-20 1-2493 <$450
1902 Date Back
3x10-20 1-4290 <$275
1902 Plain Back
3x10-20 4291-12297 <$275
1929 Small Size
10 Type 1 1-1328 <$200
20 Type 1 1-328 <$200
10 Type 2 1-1486 <$225
20 Type 2 1-419 <$225
Total Issue $1,301,740
Out in 1935 $42,485
Large out 1935 $3,975
****
Ashuelot Citizens NB of Keene
SEE Ch 946
Ashuelot NB of Keene
****
946 Cheshire
ASHUELOT NB OF KEENE
Chartered 3/28/65
2nd title:Ashuelot Citizens NB of Keene 9/6/24
FIRST TITLE {{ 8 L }}
Original Series <$VALUE
3x1-2 1-2600 <$500/$1000
4x5 1-5050 <$500
3x10-20 1-1298 <$850/$1250
Series 1875
3x1-2 1-2000 <$500/$1000
4x5 1-10000 <$500
3x10-20 1-1700 <$850/$1250
Brown Back
4x5 1-16452 <$350
3x10-20 1-11019 <$350
1902 Red Seal
4x5 1-5000 <$450
3x10-20 1-3400 <$450
1902 Date Back
4x5 1-11500 <$150
3x10-20 1-8200 <$150
1902 Plain Back
4x5 11501-29500 <$150
3x10-20 8201-19000 <$150
SECOND TITLE {{ 8 L U + 22 S }}
1902 Plain Back
4x5 1-10988 <$150
3x10-20 1-7821 <$150
1929 Small Size
5 Type 1 1-7106 <$60
10 Type 1 1-3596 <$60
20 Type 1 1-956 <$70
5 Type 2 1-11570 <$70
10 Type 2 1-5700 <$70
20 Type 2 1-1536 <$75
Total Issue $4,463,930
Out in 1935 $196,245
Large out 1935 $16,195
Outstanding includes Ch 2299
****
559 Cheshire
CHESHIRE NB OF KEENE
{{ 14 L U + 21 S }}
Chartered 1864
Original Series <$VALUE
3x1-2 1-1500 <$500/$1000
4x5 1-6350 <$500
3x10-20 1-3200 <$850/$1250
50-100 1-710 <$6000
Series 1875
3x1-2 1-950 <$500/$1000
4x5 1-4000 <$500
3x10-20 1-3200 <$850/$1250
50-100 1-270 <$6000
Brown Back
4x5 1-18217 <$350
3x10-20 1-10714 <$350
50-100 1-566 <$1750/$2000
1902 Red Seal
4x5 1-8000 <$450
3x10-20 1-4800 <$450
1902 Date Back
4x5 1-16250 <$100
3x10-20 1-11900 <$100
1902 Plain Back
4x5 16251-51080 <$100
3x10-20 11901-35394 <$100
1929 Small Size
5 Type 1 1-7388 <$60
10 Type 1 1-4038 <$60
20 Type 1 1-1008 <$65
5 Type 2 1-9764 <$70
10 Type 2 1-5556 <$70
20 Type 2 1-1584 <$75
Total Issue $5,547,370
Out in 1935 $194,300
Large out 1935 $12,090
****
2299 Cheshire
CITIZENS NB OF KEENE
{{ 12 L }}
Chartered 9/18/75
Closed 9/6/24
Series 1875 <$VALUE
4x5 1-14528 <$600
3x10-20 1-3865 <$850/$1250
Brown Back
4x5 1-14130 <$400
3x10-20 1-5648 <$400
1882 Date Back
4x5 1-13666 <$400
3x10-20 1-8562 <$400
1902 Date Back
4x5 1-16635 <$175
3x10-20 1-10724 <$175
Total Issue $2,619,130
Out at close $149,995
Ch 946 assumed circulation
****
877 Cheshire
KEENE NB, KEENE
{{ 16 L 21 S }}
Chartered 3/11/65
Original Series <$VALUE
3x1-2 1-3400 <$500/$1000
4x5 1-3800 <$500
3x10-20 1-1480 <$750/$1250
Series 1875
3x1-2 1-100 <$500/$1000
4x5 1-2465 <$500
3x10-20 1-2161 <$750/$1250
Brown Back
3x10-20 1-10771 <$325
1902 Red Seal
4x5 1-5500 <$350
3x10-20 1-6000 <$350
1902 Date Back
4x5 1-12100 <$125
3x10-20 1-15500* <$125
1902 Plain Back
4x5 12101-51220 <$125
3x10-20 16751-35412* <$125
* 15501-16750 not marked
1929 Small Size
5 Type 1 1-7512 <$75
10 Type 1 1-3952 <$75
20 Type 1 1-980 <$85
5 Type 2 1-838 <$110
10 Type 2 1-275 <$110
20 Type 2 1-50 <$135
Total Issue $4,656,420
Out in 1935 $186,025
Large out 1935 $9,815
****
1645 Belknap
LACONIA NB, LACONIA
{{ 10 L 12 S }}
Chartered 1866
Original Series <$VALUE
4x5 1-5700 <$600
3x10-20 1-1060 <$850/$1250
Series 1875
3x1-2 1-2000 <$600/$1250
4x5 1-7000 <$600
3x10-20 1-2700 <$850/$1250
Brown Back
4x5 1-8600 <$450
3x10-20 1-4620 <$450
1902 Red Seal
4x5 1-2200 <$600
3x10-20 1-1370 <$600
1902 Date Back
4x5 1-7500 <$275
3x10-20 1-5900 <$275
1902 Plain Back
4x5 7501-24985 <$275
3x10-20 5901-17314 <$275
1929 Small Size
5 Type 1 1-3568 <$150
10 Type 1 1-1994 <$150
20 Type 1 1-504 <$165
5 Type 2 1-3884 <$175
10 Type 2 1-2280 <$175
20 Type 2 1-490 <$185
Total Issue $2,672,080
Out in 1935 $82,300
Large out 1935 $4,865
****

****
Lakeport NB of Laconia
SEE Ch 4740
NB of Lakeport
****
4037 Belknap
PEOPLES NB OF LACONIA
{{ 4 L 6 S }}
Chartered 5/17/89
Brown Back <$VALUE
4x5 1-3005 <$750
3x10-20 1-4089 <$750
1902 Date Back
3x10-20 1-4640 <$400
1902 Plain Back
3x10-20 4641-12713 <$400
1929 Small Size
10 Type 1 1-1364 <$200
20 Type 1 1-380 <$200
10 Type 2 1-1291 <$225
20 Type 2 1-308 <$225
Total Issue $1,046,710
Out in 1935 $43,900
Large out 1935 $2,220
****
4740 Belknap
NB OF LAKEPORT
Organized 4/25/92
2nd title:Lakeport NB of Laconia 4/26/12
FIRST TITLE {{ 3 L }}
Brown Back <$VALUE
4x5 1-4625 <$1000
3x10-20 1-1760 <$1000
1882 Date Back
4x5 1-2020 <$1000
3x10-20 1-1498 <$1000
SECOND TITLE {{ 5 L 8 S }}
1902 Date Back
4x5 1-2200 <$400
3x10-20 1-1760 <$400
1902 Plain Back
4x5 2201-11280 <$400
3x10-20 1761-8075 <$400
1929 Small Size
5 Type 1 1-1614 <$175
10 Type 1 1-1048 <$175
20 Type 1 1-254 <$185
5 Type 2 1-2628 <$200
10 Type 2 1-1020 <$200
20 Type 2 1-324 <$225
Total Issue $1,096,750
Out in 1935 $49,540
Large out 1935 $2,180
****
2600 Coos
LANCASTER NB, LANCASTER
{{ 9 L 12 S }}
Chartered 1881
Series 1875 <$VALUE
3x10-20 1-11589<$850/$1250
Brown Back
3x10-20 1-8000 <$500
1882 Date Back
4x5 1-10080 <$500
3x10-20 1-7200 <$500
1882 Value Back
4x5 10081-20167 <$750
3x10-20 7201-12930 <$750
1902 Plain Back
4x5 1-15245 <$250
3x10-20 1-9144 <$250
1929 Small Size
5 Type 1 1-4528 <$150
10 Type 1 1-2394 <$150
20 Type 1 1-664 <$165
5 Type 2 1-7812 <$175
10 Type 2 1-3660 <$175
20 Type 2 1-876 <$185
Total Issue $3,243,730
Out in 1935 $116,400
Large out 1935 $6,550
****
808 Grafton
NB OF LEBANON
{{ 10 L U + 11 S }}
Chartered 2/16/65
Original Series <$VALUE
3x1-2 1-2000 <$600/$1250
4x5 1-1000 <$600
3x10-20 1-1500 <$850/$1250
50-100 1-600 <$6000
Series 1875
4x5 1-1050 <$600
3x10-20 1-2068 <$850/$1250
Brown Back
3x10-20 1-6745 <$450
50-100 1-685 <$1750/$2000
1902 Red Seal
4x5 1-3125 <$500
3x10-20 1-2350 <$500
1902 Date Back
4x5 1-7950 <$250
3x10-20 1-5920 <$250
1902 Plain Back
4x5 7951-25610 <$250
3x10-20 5921-17634 <$250
1929 Small Size
5 Type 1 1-2254 <$125
10 Type 1 1-1858 <$125
20 Type 1 1-606 <$150
5 Type 2 1-3838 <$150
10 Type 2 1-2869 <$150
20 Type 2 1-1213 <$150
Total Issue $2,657,260
Out in 1935 $97,450
Large out 1935 $7,690
****
1885 Grafton
LITTLETON NB, LITTLETON
{{ 3 L 5 S }}
Chartered 9/25/71
Original Series <$VALUE
3x1-2 1-3000 <$1000/$2000
4x5 1-2750 <$1250
3x10-20 1-2500<$1500/$2000
Series 1875
3x1-2 1-120 <$1000/$2000
4x5 1-2300 <$1250
3x10-20 1-4932<$1500/$2000
Brown Back
3x10-20 1-8946 <$1000
1902 Date Back
4x10 1-2200 <$600
1902 Plain Back
4x10 2201-6549 <$600
1929 Small Size
10 Type 1 1-1138 <$400
10 Type 2 1-1074 <$400
Total Issue $1,276,480
Out in 1935 $21,200
Large out 1935 $2,990
****
574 Hillsborough
AMOSKEAG NB, MANCHESTER
Chartered 11/64
2nd title:Amoskeag NB of Manchester 12/04
FIRST TITLE {{ 2 L }}
Original Series <$VALUE
3x1-2 1-2200 <$600/$1250
4x5 1-3700 <$600
3x10-20 1-4100 <$850/$1250
50-100 1-300 <$6000
Series 1875
3x1-2 1-700 <$600/$1250
4x5 1-5950 <$600
3x10-20 1-2124 <$850/$1250
Brown Back
4x5 1-14000 <$450
3x10-20 1-4974 <$450
SECOND TITLE {{ 10 L 16 S }}
1902 Red Seal
3x10-20 1-8900 <$400
1902 Date Back
3x10-20 1-17300 <$175
1902 Plain Back
3x10-20 17301-47819 <$175
1929 Small Size
5 Type 1 1-2486 <$100
10 Type 1 1-4224 <$100
20 Type 1 1-938 <$125
5 Type 2 1-14680 <$125
10 Type 2 1-6505 <$125
Total Issue $4,507,380
Out in 1935 $141,950
Large out 1935 $9,850
****

CONDITION affects Value. The Values shown are for notes in FINE condition.

1520 Hillsborough
CITY NB OF MANCHESTER
Chartered 1865
2nd title:Merchants NB of Manchester 6/11/80
FIRST TITLE **{{ 0 L }}**
Original Series <$VALUE
2x1-2x2 1-1000 <$850/$2000
4x5 1-4000 <$850
3x10-20 1-2300<$1250/$2000
50-100 1-294 <$6000
Series 1875
4x5 1-500 <$850
3x10-20 1-1297<$1250/$2000
50-100 1-155 <$6000
SECOND TITLE **{{ 11 L 15 S }}**
Series 1875
3x10-20 1-2232 <$850/$1250
50-100 1-140 <$6000
Brown Back
3x10-20 1-10360 <$350
1902 Red Seal
3x10-20 1-3750 <$400
1902 Date Back
3x10-20 1-14700* <$175
1902 Plain Back
3x10-20 15301-40930* <$175
* 14701-15300 not marked
1929 Small Size
10 Type 1 1-3854 <$100
20 Type 1 1-1098 <$100
10 Type 2 1-5613 <$100
20 Type 2 1-1441 <$100
Total Issue $3,675,750
Out in 1935 $130,050
Large out 1935 $8,150

1153 Hillsborough
FNB OF MANCHESTER
{{ 10 L 5 S }}
Chartered 1865
Liquidated 2/14/31
Original Series <$VALUE
4x5 1-4000 <$600
3x10-20 1-2180 <$850/$1250
50-100 1-300 <$6000
Series 1875
4x5 1-3150 <$600
3x10-20 1-2250 <$850/$1250
50-100 1-500 <$6000
Brown Back
4x5 1-7300 <$400
3x10-20 1-7041 <$400
50-100 1-2170 <$1750/$2000
1902 Red Seal
4x5 1-5400 <$450
3x10-20 1-3540 <$450
1902 Date Back
4x5 1-13750 <$200
3x10-20 1-9100 <$200
1902 Plain Back
4x5 13751-42840 <$200
3x10-20 9101-26846 <$200
1929 Small Size
5 Type 1 1-2854 <$250
10 Type 1 1-1277 <$250
20 Type 1 1-300 <$250
Total Issue $3,990,390
Out at close $139,200
Large out at close $16,950

1059 Hillsborough
MANCHESTER NB, MANCHESTER
{{ 12 L 16 S }}
Chartered 1865
Original Series <$VALUE
4x5 1-3750 <$600
3x10-20 1-2600 <$850/$1250
Series 1875
3x1-2 1-3000 <$600/$1250
4x5 1-6750 <$600
3x10-20 1-2466 <$850/$1250
Brown Back
4x5 1-8018 <$350
3x10-20 1-10302 <$350
1902 Red Seal
4x5 1-5900 <$400
3x10-20 1-3560 <$400
1902 Date Back
4x5 1-13350 <$150
3x10-20 1-9660 <$150
1902 Plain Back
4x5 13351-43360 <$150
3x10-20 9661-27733 <$150
1929 Small Size
5 Type 1 1-5426 <$100
10 Type 1 1-3024 <$100
20 Type 1 1-694 <$110
5 Type 2 1-8106 <$110
10 Type 2 1-4191 <$110
20 Type 2 1-1124 <$125
Total Issue $4,236,030
Out in 1935 $146,150
Large out 1935 $9,160

Merchants NB of Manchester
SEE Ch 1520
City NB of Manchester

4693 Hillsborough
NB OF THE COMMONWEALTH OF MANCHESTER
{{ UNREPORTED }}
Organized 2/9/92
Receivership 8/7/93
Brown Back <$VALUE
4x5 1-1233 <$2000
3x10-20 1-1009 <$2000
Total Issue $75,110
Out in 1916 $190

2362 Hillsborough
SECOND NB OF MANCHESTER
{{ 2 L }}
Chartered 6/20/77
Liquidated 2/11/11
Series 1875 <$VALUE
4x5 1-22418 <$1000
3x10-20 1-1300<$1250/$2000
Brown Back
3x10-20 1-9000 <$850
1882 Date Back
3x10-20 1-2324 <$850
Total Issue $1,079,560
Out in 1911 $50,800

1070 Hillsborough
SOUHEGAN NB OF MILFORD
{{ 12 L 17 S }}
Organized 2/17/65
Original Series <$VALUE
3x1-2 1-3000 <$600/$1250
4x5 1-1500 <$600
3x10-20 1-1900 <$850/$1250
50-100 1-255 <$6000
Series 1875
3x1-2 1-1060 <$600/$1250
4x5 1-2350 <$600
3x10-20 1-1349 <$850/$1250
Brown Back
4x5 1-8387 <$400
3x10-20 1-5188 <$400
1902 Red Seal
4x5 1-4050 <$500
3x10-20 1-2680 <$500
1902 Date Back
4x5 1-7800 <$175
3x10-20 1-5700 <$175
1902 Plain Back
4x5 7801-24721 <$175
3x10-20 5701-17015 <$175
1929 Small Size
5 Type 1 1-3434 <$100
10 Type 1 1-1954 <$100
20 Type 1 1-546 <$100
5 Type 2 1-3368 <$125
10 Type 2 1-1886 <$125
20 Type 2 1-467 <$150
Total Issue $2,616,130
Out in 1935 $84,370
Large out 1935 $5,890

84 Hillsborough
FNB OF NASHUA
{{ 1 L }}
Chartered 1863
Liquidated 6/24/82
Original Series <$VALUE
3x1-2 1-2000 <$1500/$2000
4x5 1-4000 <$1500
4x10 1-2200 <$1500
2x20-50-100 1-787 <$2000/$6000/$6000
Series 1875
3x1-2 1-400 <$1500/$2000
4x5 1-1788 <$1500
4x10 1-681 <$1500
Total Issue $393,000
Out in 1910 $2,356

2741 Hillsborough
FNB OF NASHUA
{{ 2 L }}
Chartered 6/26/82
Liquidated 8/10/07
Brown Back <$VALUE
4x5 1-5106 <$1250
3x10-20 1-4588 <$1250
1902 Red Seal
3x10-20 1-2281 <$1250
Total Issue $445,570
Out in 1910 $10,360

1310 Hillsborough
INDIAN HEAD NB OF NASHUA
{{ 15 L 11 S }}
Chartered 1865
Original Series <$VALUE
3x1-2 1-3900 <$600/$1250
4x5 1-2500 <$600
3x10-20 1-1300 <$850/$1250
50-100 1-390 <$6000
Series 1875
3x1-2 1-1940 <$600/$1250
4x5 1-5937 <$600
3x10-20 1-1786 <$850/$1250
Brown Back
4x5 1-13619 <$500
3x10-20 1-5968 <$500
1902 Red Seal
3x10-20 1-3600 <$600
1902 Date Back
4x5 1-9400 <$250
3x10-20 1-5920 <$250
1902 Plain Back
4x5 9401-28110 <$250
3x10-20 5921-17622 <$250
1929 Small Size
5 Type 1 1-3730 <$125
10 Type 1 1-1964 <$125
20 Type 1 1-556 <$135
5 Type 2 1-2980 <$150
10 Type 2 1-1819 <$150
20 Type 2 1-481 <$150
Total Issue $2,943,990
Out in 1935 $82,950
Large out 1935 $6,150

2240 Hillsborough
SECOND NB OF NASHUA
{{ 22 L 3U + 29 S }}
Chartered 3/26/75
Original Series <$VALUE
4x5 1-1500 <$450
3x10-20 1-1500 <$750/$1250
Series 1875
4x5 1-4375 <$450
3x10-20 1-3984 <$750/$1250
Brown Back
4x5 1-3830 <$350
3x10-20 1-9648 <$350
1882 Date Back
4x5 1-12625 <$350
3x10-20 1-8530 <$350
1902 Date Back
4x5 1-2500 <$125
3x10-20 1-2000 <$125
1902 Plain Back
4x5 2501-32725 <$125
3x10-20 2001-19360 <$125
1929 Small Size
5 Type 1 1-9764 <$75
10 Type 1 1-5410 <$75
20 Type 1 1-1436 <$75
5 Type 2 1-14654 <$100
10 Type 2 1-6772 <$100
20 Type 2 1-1635 <$100
Total Issue $4,215,730
Out in 1935 $254,050
Large out 1935 $6 530

1330 Strafford
NEW MARKET NB, NEW MARKET
{{ 5 L 7 S }}
Chartered 1865
Original Series <$VALUE
4x5 1-2500 <$850
3x10-20 1-1040<$1250/$2000
50-100 1-400 <$6000
Series 1875
4x5 1-2245 <$850
3x10-20 1-1030<$1250/$2000
Brown Back
4x5 1-6768 <$650
3x10-20 1-1859 <$650
50-100 1-120 <$1750/$2000
1902 Red Seal
4x5 1-2250 <$750
3x10-20 1-1200 <$750
1902 Date Back
4x5 1-3450 <$375
3x10-20 1-3020 <$375
1902 Plain Back
4x5 3451-12785 <$375
3x10-20 3021-8854 <$375
1929 Small Size
5 Type 1 1-1750 <$250
10 Type 1 1-1952 <$250
20 Type 1 1-236 <$275
5 Type 2 1-2112 <$275
10 Type 2 1-1038 <$275
20 Type 2 1-210 <$300
Total Issue $1,471,190
Out in 1935 $37,310
Large out 1935 $2,160

3404 Sullivan
CITIZENS NB OF NEWPORT
{{ 13 L 6 S }}
Chartered 1885
Brown Back <$VALUE
4x5 1-9463 <$400
3x10-20 1-1609 <$400
1902 Red Seal
4x5 1-1000 <$500
3x10-20 1-800 <$500
1902 Date Back
4x5 1-4950 <$200
3x10-20 1-3620 <$200
1902 Plain Back
4x5 4951-16589 <$200
3x10-20 3621-8196 <$200
1929 Small Size
5 Type 1 1-1704 <$200
10 Type 1 1-976 <$200
20 Type 1 1-224 <$200
5 Type 2 1-2040 <$225
10 Type 2 1-960 <$225
20 Type 2 1-355 <$225
Total Issue $1,234,750
Out in 1935 $49,450
Large out 1935 $5,150

888 Sullivan
FNB OF NEWPORT
{{ 29 L 11 S }}
Chartered 3/14/65
Original Series <$VALUE
3x1-2 1-2600 <$400/$1000
4x5 1-2950 <$450
3x10-20 1-1840 <$750/$1250
50-100 1-100 <$6000
Series 1875
3x1-2 1-400 <$400/$1000
4x5 1-3000 <$450
3x10-20 1-1900 <$750/$1250
Brown Back
4x5 1-12406 <$350
3x10-20 1-6671 <$350
1902 Red Seal
4x5 1-3400 <$450
3x10-20 1-2240 <$450
1902 Date Back
4x5 1-7030 <$175
3x10-20 1-5508 <$175
1902 Plain Back
4x5 7031-23600 <$175
3x10-20 5509-16742 <$175
1929 Small Size
5 Type 1 1-4592 <$150
10 Type 1 1-1522 <$150
20 Type 1 1-304 <$150
5 Type 2 1-5316 <$175
10 Type 2 1-1689 <$175
20 Type 2 1-591 <$175
Total Issue $2,737,220
Out in 1935 $85,100
Large out 1935 $14,200

1179 Hillsborough
FNB OF PETERBOROUGH
{{ 12 L 6U + 50+ S }}
Chartered 1865
Original Series <$VALUE
3x1-2 1-2400 <$600/$1250
4x5 1-2700 <$600
3x10-20 1-1400 <$850/$1250
50-100 1-127 <$6000
Series 1875
4x5 1-3600 <$600
3x10-20 1-1840 <$850/$1250
Brown Back
4x5 1-5584 <$500
3x10-20 1-1955 <$500
1902 Red Seal
4x5 1-1050 <$600
3x10-20 1-740 <$600
1902 Date Back
4x5 1-8700* <$200
3x10-20 1-6600** <$200
1902 Plain Back
4x5 9201-26303* <$200
3x10-20 6961-18610** <$200
* 8701-9200 not marked
** 6601-6960 not marked
1929 Small Size
5 Type 1 1-3924 <$150
10 Type 1 1-1932 <$150
20 Type 1 1-454 <$150
5 Type 2 1-5220 <$150
10 Type 2 1-3060 <$150
20 Type 2 1-684 <$150
Total Issue $2,401,540
Out in 1935 $96,500
Large out 1935 $6,250

1020 Merrimack
PITTSFIELD NB, PITTSFIELD
{{ 2 L }}
Chartered 1865
Original Series <$VALUE
3x1-2 1-800 <$1250/$2000
4x5 1-1700 <$1250
3x10-20 1-1000<$1500/$2000
Series 1875
3x10-20 1-1146<$1250/$2000
Brown Back
3x10-20 1-4627 <$850
1902 Red Seal
3x10-20 1-900 <$1000
1902 Date Back
3x10-20 1-1990* <$600
1902 Plain Back
3x10-20 2121-4982* <$600
* 1991-2120 not marked
Total Issue $670,750
Out in 1935 $1,540

2587 Grafton
PEMIGEWASSET NB OF PLYMOUTH
{{ 6 L 10 S }}
Chartered 1881
Series 1875 <$VALUE
3x10-20 1-6635<$1000/$1500
Brown Back
3x10-20 1-5450 <$600
1882 Date Back
3x10-20 1-6100 <$600
1882 Value Back
3x10-20 6101-10676 <$750
1902 Plain Back
3x10-20 1-8164 <$400
1929 Small Size
10 Type 1 1-2012 <$175
20 Type 1 1-566 <$175
10 Type 2 1-2944 <$200
20 Type 2 1-581 <$200
Total Issue $1,775,950
Out in 1935 $72,800
Large out 1935 $4,250

19 Rockingham
FNB OF PORTSMOUTH*
{{ 19 L 28 S }}
Chartered 1863
Liquidated 4/29/82
*Reorganized as Ch 2672 which retook Ch 19 6/8/10
Original Series <$VALUE
3x1-2 1-18700 <$400/$1000
4x5 1-7000 <$500
4x10 1-6000 <$750
4x20 1-2000 <$1250
Series 1875
4x5 1-1395 <$500
4x10 1-2294 <$750
4x20 1-1250 <$1250
1902 Date Back
3x10-20 1-8900 <$150
1902 Plain Back (dated 1902)
3x10-20 8901-18303 <$150
1902 Plain Back (dated 1922)
3x10-20 1-14748 <$150
1929 Small Size
10 Type 1 1-5172 <$100
20 Type 1 1-1412 <$110
10 Type 2 1-11216 <$125
20 Type 2 1-2975 <$125
Total Issue $3,155,230
Out in 1935 $235,450
Large out 1935 $12,530
Outstanding includes Ch 2672

2672 Rockingham
FNB OF PORTSMOUTH
{{ 5 L }}
Organized 1882
RETOOK Ch 19 6/8/10
Brown Back <$VALUE
3x10-20 1-18757 <$500
50-100 1-667 <$1750/$2000
1902 Red Seal
3x10-20 1-10000 <$600
1902 Date Back
4x5 1-2000 <$400
3x10-20 1-3500 <$400
Total Issue $1,752,900
Out in 1910 $100,000

401 Rockingham
N MECHANICS & TRADERS B OF PORTSMOUTH
{{ 11 L 7 S }}
Chartered 1864
Liquidated 8/1/31
Original Series <$VALUE
3x1-2 1-3200 <$500/$1000
4x5 1-8050 <$500
3x10-20 1-6880 <$750/$1250
Series 1875
4x5 1-2795 <$500
3x10-20 1-5361 <$750/$1250
Brown Back
4x5 1-17136 <$400
3x10-20 1-7796 <$400
1902 Red Seal
4x5 1-5300 <$450
3x10-20 1-4080 <$450
1902 Date Back
4x5 1-7080* <$200
3x10-20 1-5068** <$200
1902 Plain Back
4x5 7581-23612* <$200
3x10-20 5429-15733** <$200
* 7081-7580 not marked
** 5069-5428 not marked
1929 Small Size
5 Type 1 1-1991 <$200
10 Type 1 1-942 <$200
20 Type 1 1-249 <$225
Total Issue $3,292,490
Out at close $94,600
Large out at close $13,260

1052 Rockingham
NEW HAMPSHIRE NB OF PORTSMOUTH
{{ 9 L 10 S }}
Organized 3/22/65
Original Series <$VALUE
3x1-2 1-6200 <$600/$1250
4x5 1-4100 <$600
3x10-20 1-2100 <$850/$1250
50-100 1-100 <$6000
Series 1875
4x5 1-6250 <$600
3x10-20 1-2600 <$850/$1250
Brown Back
4x5 1-8340 <$500
3x10-20 1-6939 <$500
1902 Red Seal
4x5 1-3750 <$600
3x10-20 1-2300 <$600
1902 Date Back
4x5 1-7805 <$250
3x10-20 1-5848 <$250
1902 Plain Back
4x5 7806-25760 <$250
3x10-20 5849-17652 <$250
1929 Small Size
5 Type 1 1-3498 <$125
10 Type 1 1-1934 <$125
20 Type 1 1-514 <$135
5 Type 2 1-3454 <$150
10 Type 2 1-2244 <$150
20 Type 2 1-694 <$150
Total Issue $2,925,800
Out in 1935 $98,599
Large out 1935 $7,024

1025 Rockingham
ROCKINGHAM NB OF PORTSMOUTH
{{ 3 L }}
Chartered 4/17/65
Liquidated 3/31/05
Original Series <$VALUE
3x1-2 1-2400 <$1000/$2000
4x5 1-5950 <$1000
3x10-20 1-3580<$1250/$2000
50-100 1-400 <$6000
Series 1875
4x5 1-4250 <$1000
3x10-20 1-3800<$1250/$2000
Brown Back
4x5 1-11115 <$750
3x10-20 1-15148 <$750
Total Issue $1,624,700
Out in 1910 $15,411

<$VALUEs are for notes in **FINE** condition. Value changes by approximately **25%** for a change of one full grade.

****
13861 Strafford
NEW PUBLIC NB OF ROCHESTER
{{ 4 S }}
Chartered 12/33
1929 Small Size <$VALUE
5 Type 2 1-4990 <$350
10 Type 2 1-2440 <$350
20 Type 2 1-770 <$350
Total Issue $64,750
Out in 1935 $39,250
****
11893 Strafford
PUBLIC NB OF ROCHESTER
{{ 1 L 7 S }}
Organized 10/28/20
Receivership 1/2/34
1902 Plain Back <$VALUE
4x5 1-8570 <$750
3x10-20 1-4683 <$750
1929 Small Size
5 Type 1 1-1544 <$200
10 Type 1 1-780 <$200
20 Type 1 1-256 <$225
5 Type 2 1-114 <$225
10 Type 2 1-150 <$225
20 Type 2 1-75 <$250
Total Issue $532,960
Out at close $101,360
Large out at close $1,360
****
2138 Strafford
ROCHESTER NB, ROCHESTER
{{ 8 L }}
Chartered 3/13/74
Liquidated 4/16/17
Original Series <$VALUE
3x1-2 1-1800 <$600/$1250
4x5 1-2175 <$5000
Series 1875
3x1-2 1-1060 <$600/$1250
4x5 1-6661 <$5000
Brown Back
4x5 1-8225 <$450
3x10-20 1-3030 <$450
1882 Date Back
4x5 1-2759 <$450
3x10-20 1-1956 <$450
1902 Date Back
4x5 1-1250 <$300
3x10-20 1-960 <$300
1902 Plain Back
4x5 1251-1945 <$300
3x10-20 961-1338 <$300
Total Issue $765,800
Out at close $49,695
****
1333 Belknap
CITIZENS NB OF SANBORNTON
Chartered 1865
2nd title:Citizens NB of Tilton 2/19/75
FIRST TITLE {{ 1 L }}
Original Series <$VALUE
4x5 1-2000 <$850
3x10-20 1-1240<$1000/$1500
SECOND TITLE {{ 7 L 9 S }}
Series 1875
4x5 301-3690 <$600
3x10-20 121-1330<$850/$1250
Brown Back
4x5 1-14270 <$450
3x10-20 1-2383 <$450
1902 Red Seal
4x5 1-2350 <$600
3x10-20 1-1560 <$600
1902 Date Back
4x5 1-6000 <$275
3x10-20 1-4200 <$275
1902 Plain Back
4x5 6001-18337 <$275
3x10-20 4201-11332 <$275
1929 Small Size
5 Type 1 1-2620 <$150
10 Type 1 1-1258 <$150
20 Type 1 1-384 <$175
5 Type 2 1-2728 <$175
10 Type 2 1-1424 <$175
20 Type 2 1-325 <$185
Total Issue $1,927,730
Out in 1935 $59,400
Large out 1935 $4,195
****
1071 Carroll
CARROLL COUNTY NB OF SANDWICH
{{ UNREPORTED }}
Chartered 4/28/65
Liquidated 5/24/72
Original Series <$VALUE
4x5 1-1500 <$2000
3x10-20 1-360 <$2000/$2500
Total Issue $48,000
Out in 1910 $485
****
FNB of Somersworth
SEE Ch 1180
Great Falls NB of Somersworth
****
1180 Strafford
GREAT FALLS NB OF SOMERSWORTH
Chartered 1865
2nd title:FNB of Somersworth 9/16/02
FIRST TITLE {{ 1 L }}
Original Series <$VALUE
3x1-2 1-4600 <$750/$1500
4x5 1-7500 <$850
3x10-20 1-1800<$1000/$1500
50-100 1-100 <$6000
Series 1875
4x5 1-11250 <$850
Brown Back
4x5 1-8868 <$650
3x10-20 1-3334 <$650
SECOND TITLE {{ 8 L 9 S }}
Brown Back
4x5 1-2955 <$500
3x10-20 1-1940 <$500
1902 Red Seal
4x5 1-3500 <$600
3x10-20 1-2700 <$600
1902 Date Back
4x5 1-7500 <$275
3x10-20 1-5580 <$275
1902 Plain Back
4x5 7501-25789 <$275
3x10-20 5581-17568 <$275
1929 Small Size
5 Type 1 1-3236 <$175
10 Type 1 1-1884 <$175
20 Type 1 1-500 <$175
5 Type 2 1-4906 <$200
10 Type 2 1-2637 <$200
20 Type 2 1-567 <$200
Total Issue $2,934,700
Out in 1935 $85,150
Large out 1935 $8,030
****
Somersworth NB of Somersworth
SEE Ch 1183
Somersworth NB of Great Falls
****
Citizens NB of Tilton
SEE Ch 1333
Citizens NB of Sanbornton
****
1674 Merrimack
KEARSARGE NB OF WARNER
{{ 2 L }}
Chartered 12/67
Liquidated 6/30/84
Original Series <$VALUE
3x1-2 1-3100 <$1250/$2000
4x5 1-3150 <$1250
Series 1875
4x5 1-3370 <$1250
Total Issue $145,900
Out in 1910 $697
****
8038 Rockingham
FNB OF WEST DERRY
{{ 1 L 7 S }}
Chartered 1/06
1902 Red Seal <$VALUE
3x10-20 1-340 <$1250
1902 Date Back
3x10-20 1-1570 <$600
1902 Plain Back
3x10-20 1571-4238 <$600
1929 Small Size
10 Type 1 1-720 <$300
20 Type 1 1-232 <$300
10 Type 2 1-1931 <$300
20 Type 2 1-607 <$300
Total Issue $331,390
Out in 1935 $60,000
Large out 1935 $3,480
Outstanding includes Ch 499
****
13247 Hillsborough
WILTON NB, WILTON
{{ 14 S }}
Chartered 10/28
1929 Small Size <$VALUE
5 Type 1 1-3790 <$75
10 Type 1 1-2150 <$75
20 Type 1 1-592 <$85
5 Type 2 1-6420 <$100
10 Type 2 1-2845 <$100
20 Type 2 1-680 <$100
Total Issue $387,890
Out in 1935 $78,000
****
887 Cheshire
WINCHESTER NB, WINCHESTER
{{ 13 L U + 12 S }}
Chartered 3/14/65
Original Series <$VALUE
3x1-2 1-3600 <$500/$1000
4x5 1-4500 <$500
3x10-20 1-1400 <$850/$1250
Series 1875
3x1-2 1-800 <$500/$1000
4x5 1-4956 <$500
3x10-20 1-2452 <$850/$1250
Brown Back
4x5 1-12288 <$400
3x10-20 1-5757 <$400
1902 Red Seal
4x5 1-3300 <$500
3x10-20 1-2280 <$500
1902 Date Back
4x5 1-8250 <$175
3x10-20 1-5980 <$175
1902 Plain Back
4x5 8251-24836 <$175
3x10-20 5981-16766 <$175
1929 Small Size
5 Type 1 1-3676 <$125
10 Type 1 1-2000 <$125
20 Type 1 1-458 <$135
5 Type 2 1-4022 <$150
10 Type 2 1-2390 <$150
20 Type 2 1-713 <$150
Total Issue $2,795,860
Out in 1935 $98,045
Large out 1935 $7,215
****
8147 Carroll
WOLFEBORO NB, WOLFEBORO
{{ 7 L 10 S }}
Organized 3/12/06
1902 Red Seal <$VALUE
3x10-20 1-325 <$750
1902 Date Back
3x10-20 1-1750 <$350
1902 Plain Back
3x10-20 1751-10467 <$350
1929 Small Size
10 Type 1 1-1548 <$200
20 Type 1 1-488 <$200
10 Type 2 1-2187 <$225
20 Type 2 1-410 <$225
Total Issue $721,110
Out in 1935 $63,740
Large out 1935 $680
****
1486 Carroll
LAKE NB OF WOLFEBOROUGH
{{ 3 L }}
Chartered 7/26/65
Liquidated 6/29/93
Original Series <$VALUE
4x5 1-4200 <$1000
3x10-20 1-3060<$1500/$2000
Series 1875
4x5 1-5880 <$1000
Brown Back
4x5 1-8825 <$1000
Total Issue $531,100
Out in 1910 $2,310
****
5092 Grafton
WOODSVILLE NB, WOODSVILLE
{{ 4 L 7 S }}
Chartered 1897
Brown Back <$VALUE
4x5 1-4125 <$600
3x10-20 1-2850 <$600
1882 Date Back
4x5 1-4150 <$600
3x10-20 1-3040 <$600
1882 Value Back
4x5 4151-5310 <$750
3x10-20 3041-3675 <$750
1902 Plain Back
4x5 1-8825 <$350
4x10 1-7240 <$350
1929 Small Size
5 Type 1 1-2618 <$225
10 Type 1 1-1392 <$225
5 Type 2 1-3930 <$250
10 Type 2 1-1776 <$250
Total Issue $1,180,520
Out in 1935 $48,950
Large out 1935 $1,330
****

CONDITION affects Value. The Values shown are for notes in FINE condition.

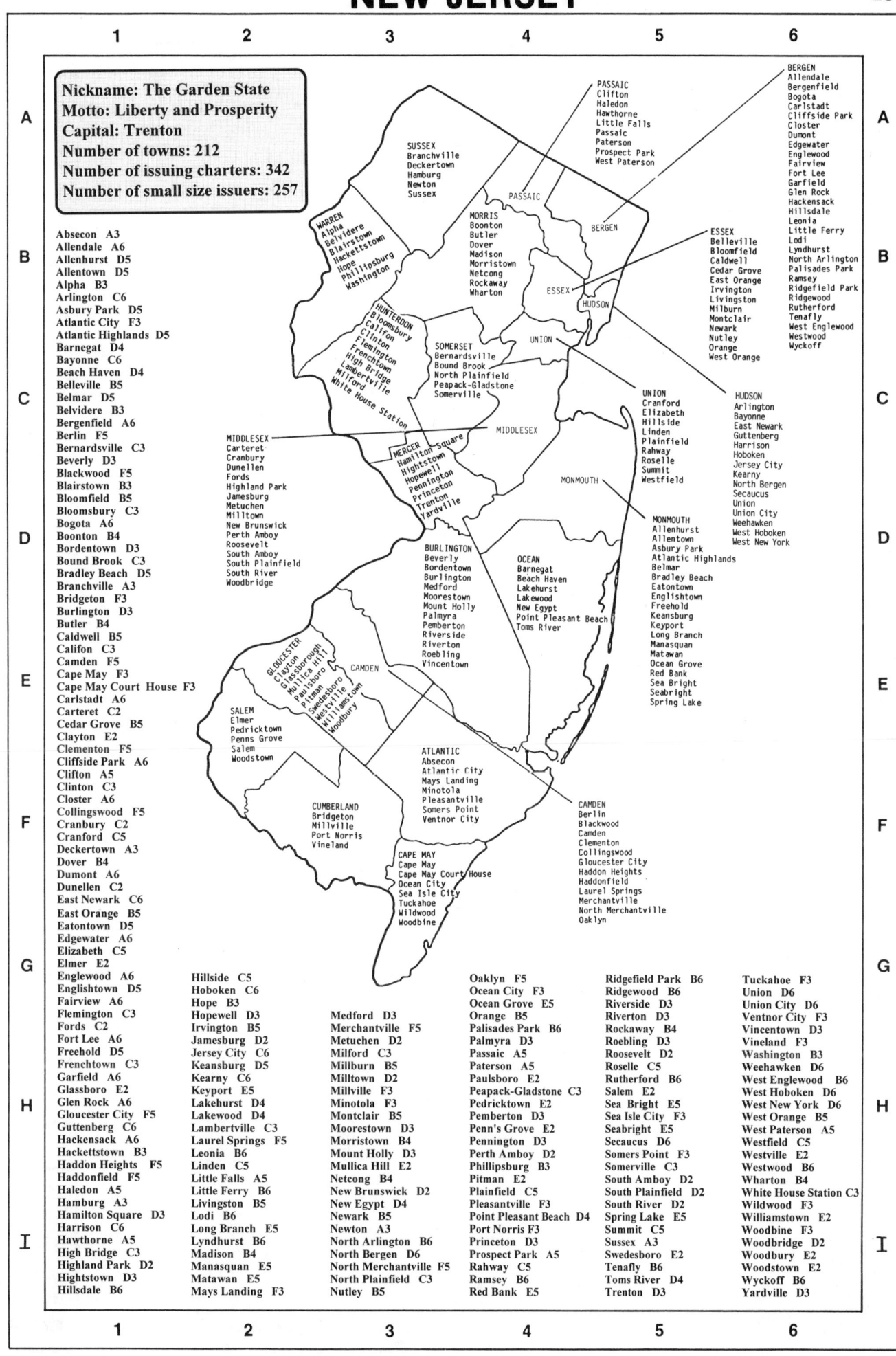

Nickname: The Garden State
Motto: Liberty and Prosperity
Capital: Trenton
Number of towns: 212
Number of issuing charters: 342
Number of small size issuers: 257

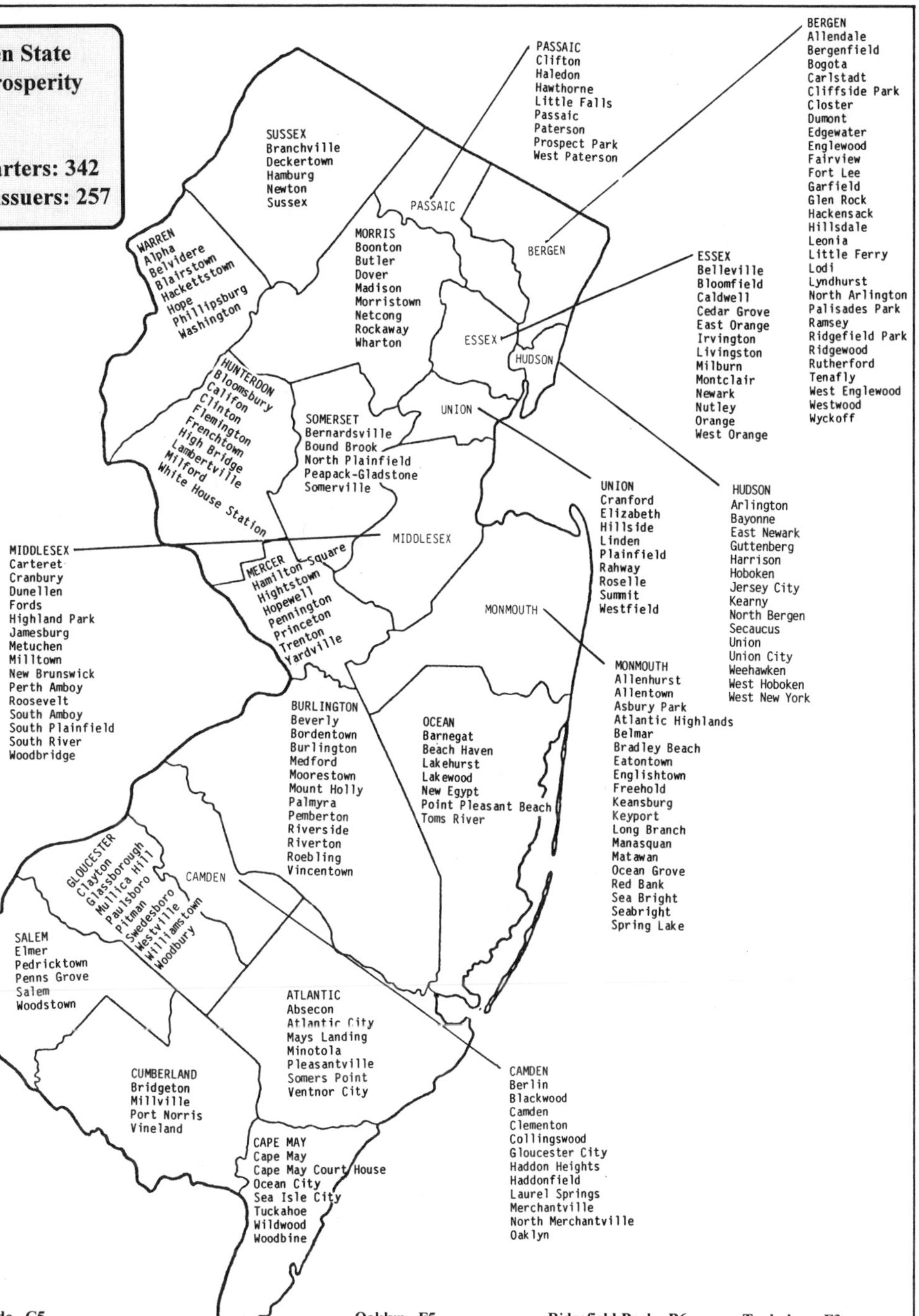

Absecon A3
Allendale A6
Allenhurst D5
Allentown D5
Alpha B3
Arlington C6
Asbury Park D5
Atlantic City F3
Atlantic Highlands D5
Barnegat D4
Bayonne C6
Beach Haven D4
Belleville B5
Belmar D5
Belvidere B3
Bergenfield A6
Berlin F5
Bernardsville C3
Beverly D3
Blackwood F5
Blairstown B3
Bloomfield B5
Bloomsbury C3
Bogota A6
Boonton B4
Bordentown D3
Bound Brook C3
Bradley Beach D5
Branchville A3
Bridgeton F3
Burlington D3
Butler B4
Caldwell B5
Califon C3
Camden F5
Cape May F3
Cape May Court House F3
Carlstadt A6
Carteret C2
Cedar Grove B5
Clayton E2
Clementon F5
Cliffside Park A6
Clifton A5
Clinton C3
Closter A6
Collingswood F5
Cranbury C2
Cranford C5
Deckertown A3
Dover B4
Dumont A6
Dunellen C2
East Newark C6
East Orange B5
Eatontown D5
Edgewater A6
Elizabeth C5
Elmer E2
Englewood A6
Englishtown D5
Fairview A6
Flemington C3
Fords C2
Fort Lee A6
Freehold D5
Frenchtown C3
Garfield A6
Glassboro E2
Glen Rock A6
Gloucester City F5
Guttenberg C6
Hackensack A6
Hackettstown B3
Haddon Heights F5
Haddonfield F5
Haledon A5
Hamburg A3
Hamilton Square D3
Harrison C6
Hawthorne A5
High Bridge C3
Highland Park D2
Hightstown D3
Hillsdale B6
Hillside C5
Hoboken C6
Hope B3
Hopewell D3
Irvington B5
Jamesburg D2
Jersey City C6
Keansburg D5
Kearny C6
Keyport E5
Lakehurst D4
Lakewood D4
Lambertville C3
Laurel Springs F5
Leonia B6
Linden C5
Little Falls A5
Little Ferry B6
Livingston B5
Lodi B6
Long Branch E5
Lyndhurst B6
Madison B4
Manasquan E5
Matawan E5
Mays Landing F3
Medford D3
Merchantville F5
Metuchen D2
Milford C3
Millburn B5
Milltown D2
Millville F3
Minotola F3
Montclair B5
Moorestown D3
Morristown B4
Mount Holly D3
Mullica Hill E2
Netcong B4
New Brunswick D2
New Egypt D4
Newark B5
Newton A3
North Arlington B6
North Bergen D6
North Merchantville F5
North Plainfield C3
Nutley B5
Oaklyn F5
Ocean City F3
Ocean Grove E5
Orange B5
Palisades Park B6
Palmyra D3
Passaic A5
Paterson A5
Paulsboro E2
Peapack-Gladstone C3
Pedricktown E2
Pemberton D3
Penn's Grove E2
Pennington D3
Perth Amboy D2
Phillipsburg B3
Pitman E2
Plainfield C5
Pleasantville F3
Point Pleasant Beach D4
Port Norris F3
Princeton D3
Prospect Park A5
Rahway C5
Ramsey B6
Red Bank E5
Ridgefield Park B6
Ridgewood B6
Riverside D3
Riverton D3
Rockaway B4
Roebling D3
Roosevelt D2
Roselle C5
Rutherford B6
Salem E2
Sea Bright E5
Sea Isle City F3
Seabright E5
Secaucus D6
Somers Point F3
Somerville C3
South Amboy D2
South Plainfield D2
South River D2
Spring Lake E5
Summit C5
Sussex A3
Swedesboro E2
Tenafly B6
Toms River D4
Trenton D3
Tuckahoe F3
Union D6
Union City D6
Ventnor City F3
Vincentown D3
Vineland F3
Washington B3
Weehawken D6
West Englewood B6
West Hoboken D6
West New York D6
West Orange B5
West Paterson A5
Westfield C5
Westville E2
Westwood B6
Wharton B4
White House Station C3
Wildwood F3
Williamstown E2
Woodbine F3
Woodbridge D2
Woodbury E2
Woodstown E2
Wyckoff B6
Yardville D3

****
10823 Atlantic
FNB OF ABSECON
{{ 25 S }}
Chartered 2/16
1929 Small Size <$VALUE
5 Type 1 1-1480 <$85
10 Type 1 1-728 <$85
20 Type 1 1-282 <$100
50 Type 1 1-42 <$350
100 Type 1 1-22 <$450
5 Type 2 1-6370 <$100
10 Type 2 1-2868 <$100
20 Type 2 1-756 <$100
Total Issue $223,370
Out in 1935 $100,000
****
12706 Bergen
FNB OF ALLENDALE
{{ 10 S }}
Chartered 4/25
1929 Small Size <$VALUE
5 Type 1 1-2962 <$125
10 Type 1 1-1586 <$110
20 Type 1 1-356 <$125
5 Type 2 1-7590 <$150
10 Type 2 1-4773 <$150
20 Type 2 1-965 <$150
Total Issue $331,720
Out in 1935 $77,150
****
12891 Monmouth
ALLENHURST NB & TC,
ALLENHURST
{{ 12 S }}
Chartered 2/26 as
Allenhurst NB under which
there was no issue. Issuing
title adopted 5/22/28.
1929 Small Size <$VALUE
5 Type 2 1-11196 <$150
10 Type 2 1-6900 <$150
20 Type 2 1-1404 <$150
50 Type 2 1-132 <$500
100 Type 2 1-132 <$500
Total Issue $172,860
Out in 1935 $95,960
****
3501 Monmouth
FARMERS NB OF ALLENTOWN
{{ 13 L 4 S }}
Chartered 1886
Brown Back <$VALUE
4x5 1-4598 <$350
3x10-20 1-3202 <$350
1902 Red Seal
3x10-20 1-1300 <$400
1902 Date Back
3x10-20 1-4540 <$175
1902 Plain Back
3x10-20 4541-13569 <$175
1929 Small Size
10 Type 1 1-1340 <$200
20 Type 1 1-416 <$200
10 Type 2 1-2487 <$200
20 Type 2 1-618 <$200
Total Issue $1,163,060
Out in 1935 $49,050
Large out 1935 $3,200
****
12823 Warren
ALPHA NB, ALPHA
{{ 4 L 5 S }}
Chartered 9/25
Liquidated 1/10/33
1902 Plain Back <$VALUE
4x5 1-5636 <$400
1929 Small Size
5 Type 1 1-3087 <$225
Total Issue $205,330
Out at close $20,950
Large out at close $665
****
8627 Hudson
FNB OF ARLINGTON
Organized 1/23/07
2nd title:FNB & TC of
Kearny 5/5/24
FIRST TITLE {{ 7 L }}
1902 Red Seal <$VALUE
4x5 1-315 <$400
3x10-20 1-249 <$400
1902 Date Back
4x5 1-1825 <$175
3x10-20 1-1360 <$175
1902 Plain Back
4x5 1826-3145 <$175
3x10-20 1361-2331 <$175
SECOND TITLE {{ 5 L 14 S }}
1902 Plain Back
4x5 1-3000 <$200
3x10-20 1-1554 <$200
1929 Small Size
5 Type 1 1-4332 <$10
10 Type 1 1-2148 <$100
20 Type 1 1-628 <$100
5 Type 2 1-9684 <$100
10 Type 2 1-4782 <$100
20 Type 2 1-1240 <$100
Total Issue $791,140
Out in 1935 $95,700
Large out 1935 $1,170
****
13363 Monmouth
ASBURY PARK NB & TC,
ASBURY PARK
{{ 50+ S }}
Chartered 8/10/29
1929 Small Size <$VALUE
5 Type 1 1-2058 <$85
10 Type 1 1-1034 <$85
20 Type 1 1-524 <$85
5 Type 2 1-13960 <$85
10 Type 2 1-7031 <$85
20 Type 2 1-2700 <$85
Total Issue $380,770
Out in 1935 $87,880
****
3792 Monmouth
ASBURY PARK NB,
ASBURY PARK
{{ UNREPORTED }}
Chartered 9/17/87
Receivership 7/2/91
Brown Back <$VALUE
3x10-20 1-698 <$2000
Total Issue $34,900
Out in 1916 $100
****
3451 Monmouth
FNB OF ASBURY PARK
{{ 1 L }}
Organized 2/4/86
Receivership 2/13/03
Brown Back <$VALUE
4x5 1-4687 <$1500
50-100 1-456 <$3000
Total Issue $162,140
Out in 1916 $720
****
6673 Monmouth
SEACOAST NB OF
ASBURY PARK
{{ UNREPORTED }}
Chartered 3/03
Liquidated 7/1/16
1902 Red Seal <$VALUE
50-100 1-594 <$3500
1902 Date Back
4x5 1-5145 <$1500
50-100 1-600 <$2000
3x50-100 1-361 <$2000
Total Issue $372,250
Out in 1916 $37,800
****
2527 Atlantic
ATLANTIC CITY NB,
ATLANTIC CITY
{{ 14 L 27 S }}
Organized 3/24/81
Receivership 1/30/33
Series 1875 <$VALUE
4x5 1-10154 <$500
3x10-20 1-230 <$750/$1250
Brown Back
4x5 1-2550 <$300
3x10-20 1-2050 <$300
1882 Date Back
4x5 1-5500 <$250
3x10-20 1-3320 <$250/$275
1882 Value Back
4x5 5501-9492 <$250
3x10-20 3321-5505<$250/$275
1902 Plain Back
4x5 1-7662 <$150
4x10 1-6374 <$150
1929 Small Size
5 Type 1 1-5582 <$65
10 Type 1 1-4223 <$65
Total Issue $1,662,210
Out at close $296,100
Large out at close $6,100
Outstanding includes Ch 4420
****
8800 Atlantic
BOARDWALK NB OF
ATLANTIC CITY
{{ 27 L 50+ S }}
Chartered 7/07
1902 Red Seal <$VALUE
4x5 1-985 <$350
3x10-20 1-1126 <$350
1902 Date Back
4x5 1-15750 <$150
3x10-20 1-10900 <$150
1902 Plain Back
4x5 15751-57948 <$150
3x10-20 10901-38611 <$150
1929 Small Size
5 Type 1 1-8792 <$50
10 Type 1 1-4330 <$50
20 Type 1 1-1030 <$60
5 Type 2 1-37618 <$50
10 Type 2 1-22377 <$50
20 Type 2 1-6704 <$60
Total Issue $4,358,610
Out in 1935 $335,150
Large out 1935 $7,600
****
5884 Atlantic
CHELSEA NB OF
ATLANTIC CITY
Chartered 6/27/01
Receivership 1/27/33
2nd title:Chelsea-Second NB
& TC 11/24/31
FIRST TITLE {{ 12 L 8 S }}
Brown Back <$VALUE
3x10-20 1-5400 <$350
1882 Date Back
3x10-20 1-9400 <$350
1882 Value Back
3x10-20 9401-15900 <$350
1902 Plain Back
3x10-20 1-13900 <$175
1929 Small Size
10 Type 1 1-2226 <$100
20 Type 1 1-658 <$110
SECOND TITLE {{ 14 S }}
1929 Small Size
10 Type 1 1-2296 <$85
20 Type 1 1-613 <$100
Total Issue $2,183,840
Out at close $300,000
Large out at close $14,310
Outstanding includes Ch 3621
****
Chelsea-Second NB & TC of
Atlantic City
SEE Ch 5884
Chelsea NB of Atlantic City
****
3621 Atlantic
SECOND NB OF
ATLANTIC CITY
{{ 27 L 6 S }}
Chartered 1/20/87
Closed 11/24/31
Brown Back <$VALUE
4x5 1-11325 <$300
3x10-20 1-5180 <$300
1902 Red Seal
4x5 1-1660 <$350
3x10-20 1-1336 <$350
1902 Date Back
4x5 1-9700 <$100
3x10-20 1-7280 <$100
1902 Plain Back
4x5 9701-30521 <$100
3x10-20 7281-21386 <$100
1929 Small Size
5 Type 1 1-2748 <$175
10 Type 1 1-1320 <$165
20 Type 1 1-314 <$175
Total Issue $2,464,540
Out at close $100,000
Ch 5884 assumed circulation
****
4420 Atlantic
UNION NB OF ATLANTIC CITY
{{ 5 L 7 S }}
Organized 8/14/90
Liquidated 12/15/31
Brown Back <$VALUE
4x5 1-6250 <$450
3x10-20 1-1360 <$450
1882 Date Back
4x5 1-701 <$450
3x10-20 1-541 <$450
1902 Date Back
3x10-20 1-3650 <$300
1902 Plain Back
3x10-20 3651-7678 <$300
1929 Small Size
10 Type 1 1-517 <$175
20 Type 1 1-115 <$175
Total Issue $662,790
Out at close $22,720
Large out at close $2,760
Ch 2527 assumed circulation
****
4119 Monmouth
ATLANTIC HIGHLANDS NB,
ATLANTIC HIGHLANDS
{{ 7 L 6 S }}
Chartered 9/13/89
Brown Back <$VALUE
4x5 1-2125 <$400
3x10-20 1-2320 <$400
1882 Date Back
4x5 1-750 <$400
3x10-20 1-558 <$400
1902 Date Back
4x10 1-7500 <$250
1902 Plain Back
4x10 7501-21974 <$250
1929 Small Size
10 Type 1 1-2454 <$200
5 Type 2 1-9082 <$200
10 Type 2 1-3490 <$200
Total Issue $1,307,910
Out in 1935 $45,820
Large out 1935 $2,020
****
8497 Ocean
FNB OF BARNEGAT
{{ 3 L 14 S }}
Organized 10/10/06
1902 Red Seal <$VALUE
3x10-20 1-850 <$850
1902 Date Back
3x10-20 1-2390 <$400
1902 Plain Back
3x10-20 2391-7208 <$400
1929 Small Size
10 Type 1 1-1474 <$100
20 Type 1 1-422 <$125
10 Type 2 1-5180 <$125
20 Type 2 1-1154 <$125
Total Issue $616,860
Out in 1935 $79,560
Large out 1935 $1,220
****
8454 Hudson
FNB OF BAYONNE
{{ 4 L }}
Organized 12/5/06
Receivership 12/8/13
1902 Red Seal <$VALUE
4x5 1-3000 <$600
3x10-20 1-2400 <$600
1902 Date Back
4x5 1-9050 <$350
3x10-20 1-6554 <$350
Total Issue $688,700
Out in 1916 $9,560
****
11658 Ocean
BEACH HAVEN NB & TC,
BEACH HAVEN
{{ 6U + 14 S }}
Chartered 3/20 as Beach
Haven NB, under which there
was no issue. Issuing title
adopted 3/17/27.
1929 Small Size <$VALUE
5 Type 1 1-2288 <$100
10 Type 1 1-1338 <$100
20 Type 1 1-346 <$100
5 Type 2 1-8260 <$100
10 Type 2 1-4236 <$100
20 Type 2 1-1332 <$100
Total Issue $300,740
Out in 1935 $100,000
****
8382 Essex
FNB OF BELLEVILLE
{{ 3 L 25 S }}
Chartered 10/06
1902 Red Seal <$VALUE
4x5 1-1050 <$500
3x10-20 1-920 <$500
1902 Date Back
4x5 1-6050 <$200
3x10-20 1-4560 <$200
1902 Plain Back
4x5 6051-21095 <$200
3x10-20 4561-13091 <$200
1929 Small Size
5 Type 1 1-2228 <$50
10 Type 1 1-4294 <$50
20 Type 1 1-1338 <$55
5 Type 2 1-19888 <$50
10 Type 2 1-10149 <$50
20 Type 2 1-2615 <$55
Total Issue $1,881,720
Out in 1935 $214,400
Large out 1935 $2,620
****
12019 Essex
PEOPLES NB & TC OF
BELLEVILLE
{{ 12 L 17 S }}
Chartered 9/21 as Peoples
NB, with no issue. Issuing
title adopted 9/24/25.
1902 Plain Back <$VALUE
4x5 1-33107 <$100
1929 Small Size
5 Type 1 1-29852 <$60
5 Type 2 1-59368 <$60
Total Issue $1,854,540
Out in 1935 $102,420
Large out 1935 $2,420
****

****
13848 Monmouth
BELMAR NB, BELMAR
{{ 6 S }}
Chartered 11/33
1929 Small Size <$VALUE
5 Type 2 1-1422 <$250
10 Type 2 1-708 <$250
20 Type 2 1-204 <$250
Total Issue $18,270
Out in 1935 $24,350
Large out 1935 $1,240
Outstanding includes Ch 5363
****
5363 Monmouth
FNB OF BELMAR
{{ 2 L 5 S }}
Chartered 5/21/00
Liquidated 12/1/33
Brown Back <$VALUE
3x10-20 1-1200 <$750
1882 Date Back
3x10-20 1-3000* <$750
1882 Value Back
3x10-20 3161-4383* <$750
* 3001-3160 not marked
1902 Plain Back
3x10-20 1-3613 <$500
1929 Small Size
10 Type 1 1-745 <$275
20 Type 1 1-185 <$275
Total Issue $526,700
Out at close $23,260
Large out 1935 $1,240
Ch 13848 assumed circulation
****
1096 Warren
BELVIDERE NB, BELVIDERE
{{ 25 L }}
Organized 4/10/65
Receivership 10/19/31
Original Series <$VALUE
3x1-2 1-1000 <$300/$850
4x5 1-9650 <$350
3x10-20 1-6000 <$600/$1250
Series 1875
4x5 1-2025 <$350
3x10-20 1-3074 <$600/$1250
Brown Back
4x5 1-3400 <$200
3x10-20 1-7333 <$200/$250
50-100 1-530 <$1250/$1500
1902 Red Seal
4x5 1-4300 <$200
3x10-20 1-2780 <$200/$250
1902 Date Back
4x5 1-4000 <$85
3x10-20 1-3300 <$100
1902 Plain Back
4x5 4001-7725 <$85
3x10-20 3301-5303 <$100
Total Issue $1,851,000
Out at close $8,049
****
13628 Warren
FNB OF BELVIDERE
{{ 20 S }}
Chartered 7/32
1929 Small Size <$VALUE
5 Type 1 1-1234 <$50
10 Type 1 1-624 <$50
20 Type 1 1-212 <$60
50 Type 1 1-84 <$200
5 Type 2 1-6536 <$60
10 Type 2 1-3475 <$60
20 Type 2 1-730 <$65
Total Issue $207,130
Out in 1935 $79,900
****
4980 Warren
WARREN COUNTY NB OF
BELVIDERE
{{ 5 L }}
Chartered 1894
Liquidated 6/1/20
Brown Back <$VALUE
4x5 1-6725 <$400
3x10-20 1-2980 <$400
1882 Date Back
4x5 1-3776 <$400
3x10-20 1-2521 <$400
1902 Date Back
4x5 1-1000 <$225
3x10-20 1-800 <$225
1902 Plain Back
4x5 1001-3055 <$225
3x10-20 801-1910 <$225
Total Issue $641,670
Out at close $26,700
****

****
11368 Bergen
BERGENFIELD NB,
BERGENFIELD
Chartered 6/19
2nd title:Bergenfield NB &
TC 12/10/27
FIRST TITLE {{ 8 L }}
1902 Plain Back <$VALUE
4x5 1-7662 <$225
SECOND TITLE {{ 3 L 4 S }}
1902 Plain Back
4x5 1-1945 <$250
1929 Small Size
5 Type 1 1-3424 <$250
5 Type 2 1-9312 <$250
Total Issue $341,420
Out in 1935 $24,460
Large out 1935 $780
****
9779 Camden
BERLIN NB, BERLIN
{{ 3 L 3U + 20 S }}
Chartered 6/10 as United
Towns NB, under which there
was no issue. Issuing title
adopted 7/15/10.
1902 Date Back <$VALUE
4x10 1-2919* <$500
1902 Plain Back
4x10 3070-3644* <$500
* 2920-3069 not marked
1929 Small Size
5 Type 1 1-1370 <$100
5 Type 2 1-5664 <$100
Total Issue $215,180
Out in 1935 $20,230
Large out 1935 $250
****
6960 Somerset
BERNARDSVILLE NB,
BERNARDSVILLE
{{ 19 L 9 S }}
Chartered 9/03
1902 Red Seal <$VALUE
4x5 1-556 <$500
3x10-20 1-445 <$500
1902 Date Back
4x5 1-3525 <$250
3x10-20 1-2860 <$250
1902 Plain Back
4x5 3526-10174 <$250
3x10-20 2861-6708 <$250
1929 Small Size
5 Type 1 1-2238 <$150
10 Type 1 1-1098 <$150
20 Type 1 1-388 <$150
5 Type 2 1-5976 <$150
10 Type 2 1-3192 <$150
20 Type 2 1-768 <$150
Total Issue $828,990
Out in 1935 $90,450
Large out 1935 $1,390
****
8704 Burlington
FNB OF BEVERLY
Chartered 5/07
2nd title:FNB & TC 11/15/28
FIRST TITLE {{ 6 L }}
1902 Red Seal <$VALUE
3x10-20 1-300 <$600
1902 Date Back
3x10-20 1-1690 <$300
1902 Plain Back
3x10-20 1691-4633 <$300
SECOND TITLE {{ 0 L 8 S }}
1902 Plain Back
3x10-20 1-110 <$400
1929 Small Size
10 Type 1 1-552 <$175
20 Type 1 1-148 <$175
10 Type 2 1-2479 <$200
20 Type 2 1-610 <$200
Total Issue $340,020
Out in 1935 $44,700
Large out 1935 $490
****

CONDITION affects Value. The Values shown are for notes in FINE condition.

9597 Camden
FNB OF BLACKWOOD
Chartered 12/09
2nd title:FNB & TC 10/12/26
FIRST TITLE {{ 2 L }}
1902 Date Back <$VALUE
4x10 1-1075 <$750
1902 Plain Back
4x10 1076-2339 <$750
SECOND TITLE {{ 1 L 1 S }}
1902 Plain Back
4x10 1-297 <$750
1929 Small Size
10 Type 1 1-408 <$600
Total Issue $129,920
Out in 1935 $6,250
Large out 1935 $950

5621 Warren
FNB OF BLAIRSTOWN
{{ 2 L 10 S }}
Chartered 11/10/00
Brown Back <$VALUE
3x10-20 1-2100 <$650
1882 Date Back
3x10-20 1-2580 <$650
1882 Value Back
3x10-20 2581-4015 <$650
1902 Plain Back
3x10-20 1-3463 <$350
1929 Small Size
10 Type 1 1-1376 <$125
20 Type 1 1-410 <$125
10 Type 2 1-272 <$150
20 Type 2 1-85 <$150
Total Issue $615,080
Out in 1935 $88,020
Large out 1935 $920

9833 Warren
PEOPLES NB OF BLAIRSTOWN
{{ 3 L 4 S }}
Organized 7/2/10
Receivership 10/29/31
1902 Date Back <$VALUE
4x5 1-3675 <$275
3x10-20 1-2840 <$275
1902 Plain Back
4x5 3676-14065 <$275
3x10-20 2841-9679 <$275
1929 Small Size
5 Type 1 1-1268 <$250
10 Type 1 1-637 <$250
20 Type 1 1-164 <$250
Total Issue $861,190
Out at close $48,000
Large out at close $1,280

4056 Essex
BLOOMFIELD NB, BLOOMFIELD
{{ 7 L }}
Chartered 6/22/89
Liquidated 4/15/29
Brown Back <$VALUE
4x5 1-2825 <$350
3x10-20 1-5780 <$350
1902 Date Back
3x10-20 1-5700 <$200
1902 Plain Back
3x10-20 5701-14889 <$200
Total Issue $1,089,950
Out at close $43,500

2271 Hunterdon
BLOOMSBURY NB, BLOOMSBURY
{{ 6 L }}
Chartered 5/27/75
Liquidated 4/27/15
Original Series <$VALUE
4x5 1-2400 <$450
Series 1875
4x5 1-12573 <$450
Brown Back
3x10-20 1-5170 <$350
1882 Date Back
3x10-20 1-3562 <$350
Total Issue $736,060
Out in 1915 $30,300

10712 Hunterdon
CITIZENS NB OF BLOOMSBURY
{{ 13 L 9 S }}
Organized 2/20/15
1902 Date Back <$VALUE
4x5 1-1065 <$150
3x10-20 1-874 <$150
1902 Plain Back
4x5 1066-11155 <$150
3x10-20 875-7663 <$150
1929 Small Size
5 Type 1 1-2220 <$125
10 Type 1 1-1106 <$125
20 Type 1 1-338 <$125
5 Type 2 1-2850 <$150
10 Type 2 1-1530 <$150
20 Type 2 1-380 <$150
Total Issue $816,920
Out in 1935 $52,100
Large out 1935 $2,100

11543 Bergen
BOGOTA NB, BOGOTA
{{ 7 L 16 S }}
Chartered 12/19
1902 Plain Back <$VALUE
4x5 1-8197 <$300
1929 Small Size
5 Type 1 1-5786 <$100
10 Type 1 1-3314 <$100
5 Type 2 1-14004 <$110
10 Type 2 1-6624 <$110
Total Issue $672,620
Out in 1935 $91,370
Large out 1935 $730

4274 Morris
BOONTON NB, BOONTON
{{ 3 L 4 S }}
Chartered 1890
Brown Back <$VALUE
4x5 1-4000 <$750
3x10-20 1-1200 <$750
1882 Date Back
4x5 1-520 <$750
3x10-20 1-295 <$750
1902 Date Back
3x10-20 1-2850 <$450
1902 Plain Back
3x10-20 2851-7172 <$450
1929 Small Size
10 Type 1 1-694 <$300
20 Type 1 1-186 <$300
10 Type 2 1-1231 <$300
20 Type 2 1-305 <$300
Total Issue $606,120
Out in 1935 $19,800
Large out 1935 $1,610

9268 Burlington
FNB OF BORDENTOWN
{{ 6 L 9 S }}
Chartered 11/08
1902 Date Back <$VALUE
3x10-20 1-8500 <$250
1902 Plain Back
3x10-20 8501-23399 <$250
1929 Small Size
5 Type 1 1-2746 <$125
10 Type 1 1-1772 <$125
20 Type 1 1-448 <$125
5 Type 2 1-7140 <$125
10 Type 2 1-3696 <$125
20 Type 2 1-1080 <$135
Total Issue $1,506,670
Out in 1935 $99,560
Large out 1935 $2,460

8512 Somerset
BOUND BROOK NB,
BOUND BROOK
{{ 2 L }}
Chartered 1/07
Liquidated 5/31/16
1902 Red Seal <$VALUE
4x5 1-850 <$1250
3x10-20 1-680 <$1250
1902 Date Back
4x5 1-6225 <$500
3x10-20 1-4380 <$500
1902 Plain Back
4x5 6226-6475 <$500
3x10-20 4381-4540 <$500
Total Issue $407,500
Out in 1916 $24,650

3866 Somerset
FNB OF BOUND BROOK
{{ 8 L 13 S }}
Chartered 4/14/88
Brown Back <$VALUE
4x5 1-3976 <$450
3x10-20 1-700 <$450
1902 Red Seal
4x10 1-325 <$500
1902 Date Back
4x10 1-2200 <$250
1902 Plain Back
4x10 2201-5448 <$250
1929 Small Size
10 Type 1 1-4776 <$125
10 Type 2 1-9902 <$125
Total Issue $731,020
Out in 1935 $99,050
Large out 1935 $24,550

10224 Monmouth
FNB OF BRADLEY BEACH
{{ 0 L 8 S }}
Organized 6/1/12
1902 Date Back <$VALUE
3x10-20 1-1285 <$850
1902 Plain Back
3x10-20 1286-5502 <$850
1929 Small Size
5 Type 1 1-524* <$225
10 Type 1 1-420** <$225
20 Type 1 1-138*** <$225
5 Type 2 1-5250 <$225
10 Type 2 1-2924 <$225
20 Type 2 1-840 <$250
* 279-312 not issued
** 300-314 not issued
*** 93-106 not issued
Total Issue $401,270
Out in 1935 $48,220
Large out 1935 $870

13855 Sussex
BRANCHVILLE NB,
BRANCHVILLE
{{ U + 2 S }}
Chartered 12/33
1929 Small Size <$VALUE
5 Type 2 1-2904 <$400
10 Type 2 1-1332 <$400
20 Type 2 1-420 <$400
Total Issue $36,240
Out in 1935 $20,460

7364 Sussex
FNB OF BRANCHVILLE
{{ 5 L 3 S }}
Organized 6/20/04
Receivership 1/6/34
1902 Red Seal <$VALUE
3x10-20 1-1512 <$750
1902 Date Back
3x10-20 1-2480 <$400
1902 Plain Back
3x10-20 2481-7452 <$400
1929 Small Size
10 Type 1 1-724 <$300
20 Type 1 1-180 <$325
10 Type 2 1-283 <$350
20 Type 2 1-35 <$350
Total Issue $516,770
Out at close $25,000
Large out at close $1,260

2999 Cumberland
BRIDGETON NB, BRIDGETON
{{ 18 L 18 S }}
Chartered 1883
Brown Back <$VALUE
4x5 1-4250 <$200
3x10-20 1-4620 <$200/$250
50-100 1-500 <$1250/$1500
1902 Red Seal
4x5 1-6000 <$200
3x10-20 1-1800 <$225/$250
50-100 1-700 <$2250/$2500
1902 Date Back
4x5 1-7550 <$100
3x10-20 1-5200 <$100
50-100 1-100 <$350/$400
3x50-100 1-428 <$350/$400
1902 Plain Back
4x5 7551-23202 <$100
3x10-20 5201-13205 <$100
3x50-100 429-666<$350/$400
1929 Small Size
5 Type 1 1-2010 <$65
10 Type 1 1-1000 <$65
20 Type 1 1-306 <$75
50 Type 1 1-120 <$225
100 Type 1 1-44 <$300
5 Type 2 1-3782 <$85
10 Type 2 1-2208 <$85
20 Type 2 1-384 <$100
Total Issue $2,279,880
Out in 1935 $97,700
Large out 1935 $6,800

1346 Cumberland
CUMBERLAND NB OF
BRIDGETON
{{ 15 L 25 S }}
Chartered 1865
Original Series <$VALUE
4x5 1-2500 <$450
3x10-20 1-3800 <$750/$1250
50-100 1-400 <$4000
Series 1875
3x10-20 1-4000 <$750/$1250
Brown Back
3x10-20 1-6384 <$250
1902 Red Seal
4x5 1-1800 <$275
3x10-20 1-1180 <$275
1902 Date Back
4x5 1-4050 <$125
3x10-20 1-3540 <$125
1902 Plain Back
4x5 4051-4450 <$125
3x10-20 3541-9661 <$125
1929 Small Size
10 Type 1 1-1384 <$60
20 Type 1 1-354 <$70
5 Type 2 1-17466 <$75
10 Type 2 1-6825 <$75
20 Type 2 1-1722 <$75
Total Issue $1,781,790
Out in 1935 $195,750
Large out 1935 $4,510

9498 Cumberland
FARMERS & MERCHANTS NB OF
BRIDGETON
{{ 7 L }}
Chartered 8/09
1902 Date Back <$VALUE
4x5 1-7800 <$200
3x10-20 1-7340 <$200
1902 Plain Back
4x5 7801-24389 <$200
3x10-20 7341-18014 <$200
Total Issue $1,388,480
Out in 1935 $2,830

1222 Burlington
MECHANICS NB OF
BURLINGTON
{{ U + 43 L 33 S }}
Chartered 1865
Original Series <$VALUE
4x5 1-3000 <$350
3x10-20 1-1000 <$600/$1250
50-100 1-100 <$4000
Series 1875
4x5 1-2004 <$350
3x10-20 1-2545 <$600/$1250
Brown Back
4x5 1-11747 <$175
3x10-20 1-8191 <$175/$200
1902 Red Seal
4x5 1-4250 <$200
3x10-20 1-2800 <$200
1902 Date Back
4x5 1-7850 <$50
3x10-20 1-5940 <$70
1902 Plain Back
4x5 7851-45778 <$50
3x10-20 5941-32796 <$70
1929 Small Size
5 Type 1 1-8038 <$35
10 Type 1 1-4172 <$35
20 Type 1 1-1454* <$45
5 Type 2 1-5312 <$35
10 Type 2 1-3311 <$35
20 Type 2 1-500 <$50
* 1447 not issued
Total Issue $4,452,670
Out in 1935 $106,120
Large out 1935 $9,470

6912 Morris
FNB OF BUTLER
{{ 8 L 10 S }}
Chartered 8/03
1902 Red Seal <$VALUE
3x10-20 1-1770 <$400
1902 Date Back
3x10-20 1-5840 <$200
1902 Plain Back
3x10-20 5841-23643 <$200
1929 Small Size
10 Type 1 1-3496 <$125
20 Type 1 1-892 <$125
10 Type 2 1-2861 <$150
20 Type 2 1-576 <$150
Total Issue $1,627,580
Out in 1935 $93,550
Large out 1935 $3,310

7131 Essex
CALDWELL NB, CALDWELL
{{ 3 L 14 S }}
Chartered 2/04
1902 Red Seal <$VALUE
3x10-20 1-846 <$600
1902 Date Back
3x10-20 1-1540 <$300
1902 Plain Back
3x10-20 1541-8070 <$300
1929 Small Size
10 Type 1 1-2622 <$85
20 Type 1 1-718 <$85
10 Type 2 1-4530 <$100
20 Type 2 1-1475 <$100
Total Issue $764,080
Out in 1935 $94,400
Large out 1935 $1,310

9612 Essex
CITIZENS NB OF CALDWELL
Chartered 12/09
2nd title:Citizens NB & TC 5/28/27
FIRST TITLE {{ 4 L }}
1902 Date Back <$VALUE
3x10-20 1-2580 <$300
1902 Plain Back
3x10-20 2581-9678 <$300
SECOND TITLE {{ 1 L 7 S }}
1902 Plain Back
3x10-20 1-1679 <$350
1929 Small Size
10 Type 1 1-1428 <$175
20 Type 1 1-450 <$175
10 Type 2 1-2399 <$175
20 Type 2 1-532 <$175
Total Issue $742,160
Out in 1935 $48,450
Large out 1935 $1,810

9260 Hunterdon
CALIFON NB, CALIFON
{{ 4 L }}
Chartered 10/08
Liquidated 12/15/23
1902 Date Back <$VALUE
3x10-20 1-850* <$500
1902 Plain Back
3x10-20 951-2810* <$500
* 851-950 not marked
Total Issue $140,500
Out at close $24,300

13120 Camden
AMERICAN NB OF CAMDEN
{{ 4 S }}
Organized 9/23/27
1929 Small Size <$VALUE
5 Type 1 1-524 <$200
10 Type 1 1-262 <$200
5 Type 2 1-1370 <$200
10 Type 2 1-994 <$200
Total Issue $48,230
Out in 1935 $17,050

3372 Camden
CAMDEN NB, CAMDEN
{{ 12 L }}
Chartered 1885
Closed 6/30/27
Brown Back <$VALUE
4x5 1-15050 <$250
3x10-20 1-7700 <$250
50-100 1-200 <$1250/$1500
1902 Red Seal
3x10-20 1-3400 <$250
1902 Date Back
3x10-20 1-10100 <$110
1902 Plain Back
3x10-20 10101-26482 <$110
Total Issue $2,210,100
Out at close $98,095
Ch 1209 assumed circulation

F-Camden NB & TC, Camden
SEE Ch 1209
N State B of Camden

431 Camden
FNB OF CAMDEN
{{ 12 L }}
Chartered 5/64
Closed 6/30/22
Original Series <$VALUE
4x5 1-5000 <$375
3x10-20 1-2650 <$600/$1250
50-100 1-667 <$4000
Series 1875
4x5 1-2090 <$375
3x10-20 1-785 <$500/$1000
50-100 1-880 <$4000
Brown Back
4x5 1-2825 <$200
3x10-20 1-1759 <$200
50-100 1-1630 <$1250/$1500
1902 Red Seal
4x5 1-6250 <$250
3x10-20 1-8450 <$225
50-100 1-150 <$2250/$2500
1902 Date Back
4x5 1-19750 <$85
3x10-20 1-12600 <$100
50-100 1-700 <$300/$350
1902 Plain Back
4x5 19751-38592 <$85
3x10-20 12801-23533 <$100
Total Issue $3,558,040
Out at close $195,700
Ch 1209 assumed circulation

FN State B of Camden
SEE Ch 1209
N State B of Camden

1209 Camden
N STATE B OF CAMDEN
Chartered 1865
2nd title:FN State B of Camden 6/30/22
3rd title:F-Camden NB & TC, Camden 6/30/27
FIRST TITLE {{ 10 L }}
Original Series <$VALUE
4x5 1-3500 <$375
3x10-20 1-3400 <$600/$1250
50-100 1-1000 <$4000
Series 1875
3x10-20 1-5500 <$500/$1000
50-100 1-837 <$4000
Brown Back
3x10-20 1-5944 <$250
50-100 1-987 <$1250/$1500
1902 Red Seal
3x10-20 1-2430 <$250
50-100 1-390 <$2250/$2500
1902 Date Back
4x5 1-22000 <$75
3x10-20 1-19900 <$85
50-100 1-600 <$300/$350
3x50-100 1-800 <$300/$350
1902 Plain Back
4x5 22001-62500 <$75
3x10-20 19901-41900 <$85
SECOND TITLE {{ 15 L }}
1902 Plain Back
4x5 1-44066 <$50
4x10 1-17361 <$60
3x10-20 1-14268 <$60
3x50-100 1-1386 <$300/$350
THIRD TITLE {{ 34 L 50+ S }}
1902 Plain Back
4x5 1-58693 <$40
1929 Small Size
5 Type 1 1-102552 <$15
5 Type 2 1-203656 <$15
Total Issue $12,973,160
Out in 1935 $411,000
Large out 1935 $39,555
Outstanding includes Ch 431, Ch 3372, and Ch 13530

13203 Camden
THIRD NB & TC OF CAMDEN
{{ 17 S }}
Chartered 5/28
1929 Small Size <$VALUE
10 Type 1 1-410 <$50
20 Type 1 1-106 <$60
10 Type 2 1-2047 <$50
20 Type 2 1-450 <$60
Total Issue $67,270
Out in 1935 $26,700

5839 Cape May
FNB OF CAPE MAY
{{ UNREPORTED }}
Chartered 5/29/01
Receivership 5/24/04
Brown Back <$VALUE
3x10-20 1-144 <$2500
50-100 1-30 <$3500
Total Issue $11,700
Out in 1916 $270

9285 Cape May
MERCHANTS NB OF CAPE MAY
{{ 7 L 12 S }}
Chartered 12/08
1902 Date Back <$VALUE
3x10-20 1-5700 <$375
1902 Plain Back
3x10-20 5701-15540 <$375
1929 Small Size
10 Type 1 1-1456 <$200
20 Type 1 1-362 <$200
10 Type 2 1-2406 <$225
20 Type 2 1-663 <$225
Total Issue $945,120
Out in 1935 $50,000
Large out 1935 $2,190

<$VALUEs are for notes in FINE condition. Value changes by approximately 25% for a change of one full grade.

7945 Cape May
FNB OF
CAPE MAY COURT HOUSE
{{ 7 L 10 S }}
Chartered 10/05
1902 Red Seal <$VALUE
3x10-20 1-1140 <$1500
1902 Date Back
3x10-20 1-2450 <$650
1902 Plain Back
3x10-20 2451-7424 <$650
1929 Small Size
10 Type 1 1-670 <$500
20 Type 1 1-220 <$500
10 Type 2 1-842 <$500
20 Type 2 1-237 <$500
Total Issue $507,960
Out in 1935 $24,400
Large out 1935 $1,470

5416 Bergen
CARLSTADT NB, CARLSTADT
{{ 10 L 50+ S }}
Chartered 6/12/00
Receivership 4/10/34
Brown Back <$VALUE
4x5 1-1900 <$375
3x10-20 1-1530 <$375
1882 Date Back
4x5 1-3175* <$375
3x10-20 1-2240** <$375
1882 Value Back
4x5 3276-5335* <$375
3x10-20 2321-3478** <$375
* 3176-3275 not marked
** 2241-2320 not marked
1902 Plain Back
4x5 1-5045 <$175
3x10-20 1-2859 <$175
1929 Small Size
5 Type 1 1-4342 <$50
10 Type 1 1-2160 <$50
20 Type 1 1-668 <$60
5 Type 2 1-2014 <$50
10 Type 2 1-1142 <$50
20 Type 2 1-240 <$60
Total Issue $1,005,260
Out at close $100,000
Large out at close $2,000

14153 Middlesex
FNB IN CARTERET
{{ UNREPORTED }}
Chartered 5/34
1929 Small Size <$VALUE
10 Type 2 1-1517 <$750
20 Type 2 1-505 <$750
Total Issue $25,270
Out in 1935 $81,240
Large out 1935 $1,240
Outstanding includes Ch 8437

FNB of Carteret
SEE Ch 8437
FNB of Roosevelt

13136 Essex
FNB OF CEDAR GROVE
{{ 8 S }}
Chartered 10/27
1929 Small Size <$VALUE
10 Type 1 1-622 <$225
20 Type 1 1-212 <$225
10 Type 2 1-2748 <$225
20 Type 2 1-708 <$225
Total Issue $104,400
Out in 1935 $44,980

10471 Gloucester
CLAYTON NB, CLAYTON
{{ 1 L 5 S }}
Chartered 12/13
1902 Date Back <$VALUE
4x10 1-450* <$1000
1902 Plain Back
4x10 551-2163* <$1000
* 451-550 not marked
1929 Small Size
10 Type 1 1-401 <$300
Total Issue $110,580
Out in 1935 $6,250
Large out 1935 $100

14006 Camden
NB OF CLEMENTON
{{ 4 S }}
Chartered 2/34
1929 Small Size <$VALUE
5 Type 2 1-5740 <$300
10 Type 2 1-3443 <$300
20 Type 2 1-816 <$300
Total Issue $79,450
Out in 1935 $50,000

11618 Bergen
CLIFFSIDE PARK NB,
CLIFFSIDE PARK
{{ 11 L 3 S }}
Organized 2/11/20
Liquidated 11/1/34
1902 Plain Back <$VALUE
4x5 1-19050 <$300
1929 Small Size
5 Type 1 1-4452 <$300
5 Type 2 1-2082 <$300
Total Issue $524,970
Out at close $32,270
Large out at close $1,510

14162 Bergen
UNITED NB OF
CLIFFSIDE PARK
{{ 7 S }}
Chartered 5/34
1929 Small Size <$VALUE
5 Type 2 1-33058 <$200
Total Issue $165,290
Out in 1935 $150,000
Outstanding includes Ch 12465

12690 Passaic
CLIFTON NB, CLIFTON
{{ 10 S }}
Chartered 4/25
1929 Small Size <$VALUE
5 Type 1 1-1480 <$100
10 Type 1 1-1208 <$100
20 Type 1 1-512 <$100
5 Type 2 1-7604 <$125
10 Type 2 1-3540 <$125
20 Type 2 1-1255 <$125
Total Issue $276,840
Out in 1935 $79,200

11983 Passaic
FNB OF CLIFTON
{{ 15 L U + 8 S }}
Chartered 6/21
1902 Plain Back <$VALUE
4x5 1-40957 <$110
1929 Small Size
5 Type 1 1-14222 <$110
5 Type 2 1-34718 <$110
Total Issue $1,419,390
Out in 1935 $66,650
Large out 1935 $2,510

1114 Hunterdon
CLINTON NB, CLINTON
{{ 4 L 2 S }}
Organized 7/1/65
Original Series <$VALUE
3x1-2 1-2000 <$400/$1000
4x5 1-3500 <$500
3x10-20 1-1600 <$750/$1250
Series 1875
4x5 1-945 <$500
3x10-20 1-1796 <$750/$1250
Brown Back
3x10-20 1-404 <$500
50-100 1-639 <$1250/$1500
1902 Red Seal
3x10-20 1-395 <$600
1902 Date Back
3x10-20 1-2410 <$300
1902 Plain Back
3x10-20 2411-3951 <$300
1929 Small Size
10 Type 1 1-310 <$400
20 Type 1 1-106 <$400
10 Type 2 1-144 <$400
20 Type 2 1-63 <$400
Total Issue $636,070
Out in 1935 $12,500
Large out 1935 $2,510

2246 Hunterdon
FNB OF CLINTON
{{ 8 L 12 S }}
Chartered 4/8/75
Original Series <$VALUE
4x5 1-4500 <$450
Series 1875
4x5 1-14814 <$450
Brown Back
4x5 1-4400 <$350
3x10-20 1-2600 <$350
1882 Date Back
4x5 1-3273 <$350
3x10-20 1-2157 <$350
1902 Date Back
4x5 1-750 <$165
3x10-20 1-600 <$165
1902 Plain Back
4x5 751-7350 <$165
3x10-20 601-5113 <$165
1929 Small Size
5 Type 1 1-1248 <$125
10 Type 1 1-762 <$125
20 Type 1 1-180 <$125
5 Type 2 1-2412 <$150
10 Type 2 1-1260 <$150
20 Type 2 1-336 <$150
Total Issue $1,316,380
Out in 1935 $38,610
Large out 1935 $3,300

8394 Bergen
CLOSTER NB, CLOSTER
Chartered 10/06
2nd title:Closter NB & TC
7/14/26
FIRST TITLE {{ 5 L }}
1902 Red Seal <$VALUE
3x10-20 1-287 <$750
1902 Date Back
4x5 1-3050 <$350
3x10-20 1-2173 <$350
1902 Plain Back
4x5 3051-9485 <$350
3x10-20 2174-6067 <$350
SECOND TITLE {{ 1 L 12 S }}
1902 Plain Back
4x5 1-2430 <$400
3x10-20 1-1641 <$400
1929 Small Size
5 Type 1 1-2032 <$150
10 Type 1 1-994 <$150
20 Type 1 1-278 <$150
5 Type 2 1-14664 <$150
10 Type 2 1-7680 <$150
20 Type 2 1-2004 <$150
Total Issue $982,210
Out in 1935 $103,850
Large out 1935 $1,875

13969 Camden
CITIZENS NB OF
COLLINGSWOOD
{{ 7 S }}
Chartered 1/34
1929 Small Size <$VALUE
5 Type 2 1-5808 <$175
10 Type 2 1-3288 <$175
20 Type 2 1-828 <$175
Total Issue $78,480
Out in 1935 $53,730

7983 Camden
COLLINGSWOOD NB,
COLLINGSWOOD
{{ 6 L 20 S }}
Organized 11/1/05
Receivership 3/13/34
1902 Red Seal <$VALUE
3x10-20 1-700 <$600
1902 Date Back
4x5 1-2550 <$275
3x10-20 1-2530 <$275
1902 Plain Back
4x5 2551-20797 <$275
3x10-20 2531-13894 <$275
1929 Small Size
5 Type 1 1-4228 <$75
10 Type 1 1-1984 <$75
20 Type 1 1-670 <$75
5 Type 2 1-1696 <$100
10 Type 2 1-866 <$100
20 Type 2 1-444 <$100
Total Issue $1,497,940
Out at close $100,000
Large out at close $3,660

3168 Middlesex
FNB OF CRANBURY
{{ 7 L 20 S }}
Chartered 1884
Brown Back <$VALUE
4x5 1-8275 <$375
3x10-20 1-1500 <$375
1902 Red Seal
4x5 1-2550 <$400
3x10-20 1-1780 <$400
1902 Date Back
4x5 1-5250 <$200
3x10-20 1-3280 <$200
1902 Plain Back
4x5 5251-16350 <$200
3x10-20 3281-10352 <$200
1929 Small Size
5 Type 1 1-3050 <$85
10 Type 1 1-1424 <$85
20 Type 1 1-414 <$85
5 Type 2 1-7476 <$100
10 Type 2 1-4092 <$100
20 Type 2 1-1092 <$100
Total Issue $1,551,860
Out in 1935 $97,445
Large out 1935 $2,815

7171 Middlesex
CRANFORD NB, CRANFORD
{{ UNREPORTED }}
Chartered 3/04
Liquidated 1/15/12
1902 Red Seal <$VALUE
3x10-20 1-1610 <$1500
1902 Date Back
3x10-20 1-1156 <$1000
Total Issue $138,300
Out in 1912 $8,620

12263 Union
FNB OF CRANFORD
{{ 12 L 10 S }}
Organized 10/16/22
1902 Plain Back <$VALUE
4x5 1-15837 <$150
1929 Small Size
5 Type 1 1-14658 <$125
5 Type 2 1-24930 <$125
Total Issue $881,130
Out in 1935 $72,110
Large out 1935 $1,260

1221 Sussex
FARMERS NB OF DECKERTOWN
Chartered 1865
2nd title:Farmers NB of
Sussex 4/9/03
FIRST TITLE {{ 3 L }}
Original Series <$VALUE
3x1-2 1-5000 <$400/$1000
4x5 1-2600 <$500
3x10-20 1-2000 <$750/$1250
Series 1875
4x5 1-2600 <$500
3x10-20 1-2154 <$750/$1250
Brown Back
4x5 1-6150 <$400
3x10-20 1-4260 <$400
SECOND TITLE {{ 13 L 50+ S }}
Brown Back
4x5 1-1185 <$300
3x10-20 1-909 <$300
1902 Red Seal
4x5 1-3500 <$300
3x10-20 1-2200 <$300
1902 Date Back
4x5 1-9900 <$150
3x10-20 1-7320 <$150
1902 Plain Back
4x5 9901-31128 <$150
3x10-20 7321-20781 <$150
1929 Small Size
5 Type 1 1-3400 <$40
10 Type 1 1-1964 <$40
20 Type 1 1-574 <$50
5 Type 2 1-6880 <$40
10 Type 2 1-4034 <$40
20 Type 2 1-1032 <$50
Total Issue $2,967,560
Out in 1935 $97,650
Large out 1935 $6,945

2076 Morris
N UNION B OF DOVER
{{ 17 L 4 S }}
Chartered 1/25/73
Original Series <$VALUE
3x1-2 1-2200 <$300/$850
4x5 1-1475 <$350
3x10-20 1-540 <$600/$1250
Series 1875
3x1-2 1-3880 <$300/$850
4x5 1-9300 <$350
3x10-20 1-3089 <$600/$1250
Brown Back
3x10-20 1-13380 <$250
1882 Date Back
3x10-20 1-7900 <$250
1902 Date Back
3x10-20 1-5550 <$125
1902 Plain Back
3x10-20 5551-2646 <$125
1929 Small Size
10 Type 2 1-2955 <$250
20 Type 2 1-1070 <$250
Total Issue $2,865,300
Out in 1935 $49,092
Large out 1935 $5,842

5136 Morris
PEOPLES NB OF DOVER
{{ UNREPORTED }}
Chartered 8/31/98
Liquidated 12/31/01
Brown Back <$VALUE
4x5 1-744 <$1500
3x10-20 1-200 <$1500
Total Issue $24,880
Out in 1910 $315

11361 Bergen
DUMONT NB, DUMONT
{{ 7 L 6 S }}
Chartered 5/19
1902 Plain Back <$VALUE
4x5 1-5875 <$300
3x10-20 1-3411 <$300
1929 Small Size
5 Type 1 1-1896 <$200
10 Type 1 1-1064 <$200
20 Type 1 1-298 <$200
5 Type 2 1-1854 <$200
10 Type 2 1-740 <$200
20 Type 2 1-195 <$200
Total Issue $465,100
Out in 1935 $22,155
Large out 1935 $1,765

8501 DUNELLEN
FNB OF DUNELLEN
{{ 8 L 2 S }}
Chartered 1/07
1902 Red Seal <$VALUE
3x10-20 1-890 <$500
1902 Date Back
3x10-20 1-2930 <$250
1902 Plain Back
3x10-20 2931-7920 <$250
1929 Small Size
10 Type 1 1-688 <$300
20 Type 1 1-182 <$300
10 Type 2 1-1494 <$300
20 Type 2 1-440 <$300
Total Issue $527,360
Out in 1935 $24,200
Large out 1935 $1,140

9661 Hudson
FNB OF EAST NEWARK
Chartered 2/10
Liquidated 5/19/31
2nd title:Kearny NB 3/1/24
FIRST TITLE {{ 4 L }}
1902 Date Back <$VALUE
4x5 1-2260 <$275
3x10-20 1-1691 <$275
1902 Plain Back
4x5 2261-6485 <$275
3x10-20 1692-3791 <$275
SECOND TITLE {{ 8 L 0 S }}
1902 Plain Back
4x5 1-1440 <$175
3x10-20 1-1024 <$175
1929 Small Size
5 Type 1 1-419 <$500
10 Type 1 1-205 <$500
20 Type 1 1-66 <$500
Total Issue $432,040
Out at close $16,555
Large out 1935 $815
Ch 13537 assumed circulation

4766 Essex
EAST ORANGE NB,
EAST ORANGE
{{ 8 L }}
Chartered 6/29/92
Liquidated 6/30/02
Brown Back <$VALUE
4x5 1-7569 <$250
3x10-20 1-2545 <$250
Total Issue $278,630
Out in 1910 $3,255

10110 Monmouth
FNB OF EATONTOWN
{{ 10 L 2U + 19 S }}
Chartered 12/11
1902 Date Back <$VALUE
4x10 1-1150* <$200
1902 Plain Back
4x10 1301-8720* <$200
* 1151-1300 not marked
1929 Small Size
5 Type 1 1-2344 <$85
10 Type 1 1-1138 <$85
5 Type 2 1-4308 <$100
10 Type 2 1-2340 <$100
Total Issue $532,340
Out in 1935 $34,650
Large out 1935 $930

13893 Bergen
EDGEWATER NB, EDGEWATER
{{ 4 S }}
Chartered 12/33
1929 Small Size <$VALUE
5 Type 2 1-504 <$250
10 Type 2 1-480 <$250
20 Type 2 1-520 <$250
50 Type 2 1-276 <$400
100 Type 2 1-270 <$500
Total Issue $58,520
Out in 1935 $49,000

8401 Bergen
FNB OF EDGEWATER
{{ 5 L 4 S }}
Organized 7/12/06
Receivership 2/5/34
1902 Red Seal <$VALUE
3x10-20 1-700 <$600
1902 Date Back
3x10-20 1-5060 <$300
1902 Plain Back
3x10-20 5061-12934 <$300
1929 Small Size
10 Type 1 1-1086 <$250
20 Type 1 1-298 <$250
10 Type 2 1-1202 <$250
20 Type 2 1-65 <$275
Total Issue $795,940
Out at close $39,050
Large out at close $2,010

487 Union
FNB OF ELIZABETH
{{ 5 L }}
Chartered 7/23/64
Liquidated 3/1/02
Original Series <$VALUE
3x1-2 1-3500 <$400/$1000
4x5 1-8250 <$450
3x10-20 1-4000 <$750/$1250
Series 1875
4x5 1-3475 <$450
3x10-20 1-3570 <$750/$1250
Brown Back
4x5 1-4596 <$350
3x10-20 1-4569 <$350
50-100 1-1014 <$1250/$1500
Total Issue $1,102,970
Out in 1910 $7,213

1436 Union
N STATE B OF ELIZABETH
{{ 16 L 13 S }}
Chartered 1865
Original Series <$VALUE
4x5 1-13050 <$400
4x10 1-8630 <$750
Series 1875
4x5 1-11000 <$400
4x10 1-11487 <$750
Brown Back
3x10-20 1-14707 <$250
1902 Red Seal
3x10-20 1-1900 <$250
1902 Date Back
3x10-20 1-11300 <$110
1902 Plain Back
3x10-20 11301-37599 <$110
1929 Small Size
5 Type 1 1-1232 <$75
10 Type 1 1-3802 <$75
20 Type 1 1-1112 <$75
5 Type 2 1-27050 <$75
Total Issue $4,529,750
Out in 1935 $107,950
Large out 1935 $11,590

11744 Union
PEOPLES NB OF ELIZABETH
{{ U + 15 L 14 S }}
Chartered 6/20
Liquidated 8/4/30
1902 Plain Back <$VALUE
4x5 1-29535 <$110
3x10-20 1-21663 <$110
1929 Small Size
5 Type 1 1-4050 <$100
10 Type 1 1-1831 <$100
20 Type 1 1-464 <$100
Total Issue $1,960,890
Out at close $271,700
Large out at close $34,040

6707 Salem
FNB OF ELMER
{{ 8 L 21 S }}
Chartered 4/03
1902 Red Seal <$VALUE
3x10-20 1-2356 <$500
1902 Date Back
3x10-20 1-4640 <$250
1902 Plain Back
3x10-20 4641-22719 <$250
1929 Small Size
10 Type 1 1-3144 <$85
20 Type 1 1-802 <$100
10 Type 2 1-2995 <$100
20 Type 2 1-780 <$100
Total Issue $1,584,180
Out in 1935 $73,030
Large out 1935 $3,900

4365 Bergen
CITIZENS NB OF ENGLEWOOD
Chartered 1890
2nd title:Citizens NB & TC 4/1/27
FIRST TITLE {{ 5 L }}
Brown Back <$VALUE
4x5 1-2595 <$500
3x10-20 1-742 <$500
1882 Date Back
4x5 1-188 <$500
3x10-20 1-152 <$500
1902 Date Back
4x5 1-1175 <$250
3x10-20 1-940 <$250
1902 Plain Back
4x5 1176-5145 <$250
3x10-20 941-3565 <$250
SECOND TITLE {{ 3 L 18 S }}
1902 Plain Back
4x5 1-1887 <$250
4x10 1-619 <$250
3x10-20 1-600 <$250
1929 Small Size
5 Type 1 1-9098 <$100
10 Type 1 1-3968 <$100
20 Type 1 1-942 <$100
5 Type 2 1-11326 <$100
10 Type 2 1-4147 <$100
20 Type 2 1-1033 <$100
Total Issue $1,216,830
Out in 1935 $89,370
Large out 1935 $690

7223 Monmouth
FNB OF ENGLISHTOWN
{{ 3 L 3 S }}
Chartered 4/04
1902 Red Seal <$VALUE
4x5 1-775 <$1000
3x10-20 1-620 <$1000
1902 Date Back
4x5 1-1325 <$500
3x10-20 1-1000 <$500
1902 Plain Back
4x5 1326-3595 <$500
3x10-20 1001-2337 <$500
1929 Small Size
5 Type 1 1-414 <$400
10 Type 1 1-212 <$400
20 Type 1 1-74 <$400
5 Type 2 1-568 <$400
10 Type 2 1-438 <$400
20 Type 2 1-108 <$400
Total Issue $278,650
Out in 1935 $12,150
Large out 1935 $480

12465 Bergen
FNB OF FAIRVIEW
{{ 21 L 14 S }}
Organized 11/13/23
Liquidated 9/25/34
1902 Plain Back <$VALUE
4x5 1-34477 <$100
1929 Small Size
5 Type 1 1-13708 <$100
5 Type 2 1-15012 <$100
Total Issue $1,175,840
Out at close $63,980
Large out 1935 $2,330
Ch 14162 assumed circulation

2331 Hunterdon
FLEMINGTON NB, FLEMINGTON
Chartered 4/22/76
2nd title:Flemington NB & TC 4/15/30
FIRST TITLE {{ 15 L 2 S }}
Series 1875 <$VALUE
3x10-20 1-8561 <$750/$1250
Brown Back
3x10-20 1-9900 <$350
1882 Date Back
3x10-20 1-8000 <$350
1882 Value Back
3x10-20 8001-8146 <$350
1902 Plain Back
3x10-20 1-17369 <$150
1929 Small Size
10 Type 1 1-1234 <$125
20 Type 1 1-416 <$125
SECOND TITLE {{ 14 S }}
1929 Small Size
10 Type 1 1-1784 <$100
20 Type 1 1-424 <$100
10 Type 2 1-4758 <$100
20 Type 2 1-1403 <$100
Total Issue $2,556,320
Out in 1935 $94,800
Large out 1935 $5,660

892 Hunterdon
HUNTERDON COUNTY NB OF FLEMINGTON
{{ 26 L 43 S }}
Chartered 3/14/65
Original Series <$VALUE
3x1-2 1-4000 <$300/$850
4x5 1-4000 <$350
3x10-20 1-4720 <$750/$1250
Series 1875
4x5 1-1480 <$350
3x10-20 1-5584 <$750/$1250
Brown Back
4x5 1-3000 <$250
3x10-20 1-11931 <$250
1902 Red Seal
3x10-20 1-2100 <$250
1902 Date Back
3x10-20 1-9300 <$100
1902 Plain Back
3x10-20 9301-2673 <$100
1929 Small Size
10 Type 1 1-2888 <$40
20 Type 1 1-758 <$50
10 Type 2 1-4332 <$40
20 Type 2 1-1428 <$50
Total Issue $3,078,320
Out in 1935 $96,750
Large out 1935 $8,150

11428 Middlesex
FORDS NB, FORDS
{{ 2 L 2 S }}
Organized 7/11/19
1902 Plain Back <$VALUE
4x5 1-6654 <$650
1929 Small Size
5 Type 1 1-1408 <$500
5 Type 2 1-8598 <$500
Total Issue $218,310
Out in 1935 $65,450
Large out 1935 $330

8874 Bergen
FNB OF FORT LEE
{{ 6 L 5 S }}
Organized 8/28/07
Liquidated 4/30/35
1902 Red Seal <$VALUE
3x10-20 1-200 <$750
1902 Date Back
3x10-20 1-2910 <$350
1902 Plain Back
3x10-20 2911-10531 <$350
1929 Small Size
10 Type 1 1-1516 <$300
20 Type 1 1-400 <$300
10 Type 2 1-1284 <$300
20 Type 2 1-348 <$300
Total Issue $696,750
Out at close $40,250
Large out at close $2,410

12497 Bergen
PALISADE NB OF FORT LEE
{{ 5 L 3 S }}
Organized 2/11/24
1902 Plain Back <$VALUE
4x5 1-11027 <$500
1929 Small Size
5 Type 1 1-7694* <$300
5 Type 2 1-9906 <$300
* 1360-1994 not issued
Total Issue $481,840
Out in 1935 $11,270
Large out 1935 $780

4182 Monmouth
CENTRAL NB OF FREEHOLD
{{ 2 L 3 S }}
Chartered 12/19/89
Brown Back <$VALUE
3x10-20 1-4310 <$500
1882 Date Back
3x10-20 1-600 <$500
1902 Date Back
3x10-20 1-3340 <$300
1902 Plain Back
3x10-20 3341-10473 <$300
1929 Small Size
10 Type 1 1-1110 <$200
20 Type 1 1-294 <$200
5 Type 2 1-4679 <$225
10 Type 2 1-2353 <$225
20 Type 2 1-654 <$225
Total Issue $931,035
Out in 1935 $38,775
Large out 1935 $1,525

452 Monmouth
FNB OF FREEHOLD
{{ 11 L 6 S }}
Chartered 6/64
Original Series <$VALUE
3x1-2 1-6580 <$350/$1000
4x5 1-6475 <$400
3x10-20 1-1720 <$750/$1250
Series 1875
3x1-2 1-4060 <$350/$1000
4x5 1-6000 <$400
3x10-20 1-300 <$750/$1250
Brown Back
4x5 1-1990 <$275
50-100 1-502 <$1250/$1500
1902 Red Seal
4x5 1-2450 <$300
50-100 1-780 <$2250/$2500
1902 Date Back
4x5 1-3650 <$150
50-100 1-300 <$350/$400
3x50-100 1-159 <$350/$400
1902 Plain Back
4x5 3651-4087 <$150
1929 Small Size
10 Type 1 1-830 <$150
20 Type 1 1-504 <$150
50 Type 1 1-54 <$300
100 Type 1 1-40 <$350
10 Type 2 1-2865 <$175
20 Type 2 1-1020 <$175
Total Issue $1,050,820
Out in 1935 $99,798
Large out 1935 $2,848

951 Monmouth
FREEHOLD N BANKING C, FREEHOLD
{{ 9 L }}
Chartered 3/29/65
Liquidated 12/10/84
Original Series <$VALUE
3x1-2 1-13700 <$350/$1000
4x5 1-9085 <$400
3x10-20 1-2500 <$750/$1250
50-100 1-100 <$4000
Series 1875
4x5 1-6765 <$400
3x10-20 1-2226 <$750/$1250
Total Issue $636,800
Out in 1910 $2,610

7436 Monmouth
N FREEHOLD BANKING C, FREEHOLD
{{ 4 L }}
Chartered 10/04
Liquidated 11/12/31
1902 Red Seal <$VALUE
3x10-20 1-2625 <$500
1902 Date Back
3x10-20 1-5080 <$275
1902 Plain Back
3x10-20 5081-14084 <$275
Total Issue $835,500
Out at close $4,400

1459 Hunterdon
UNION NB OF FRENCHTOWN
{{ 27 L 8 S }}
Chartered 1865
Original Series <$VALUE
4x5 1-4000 <$400
3x10-20 1-2380 <$750/$1250
Series 1875
4x5 1-1815 <$400
3x10-20 1-2676 <$750/$1250
Brown Back
4x5 1-5984 <$225
3x10-20 1-4229 <$225
1902 Red Seal
4x5 1-1975 <$250
3x10-20 1-1270 <$250
1902 Date Back
4x5 1-3550 <$100
3x10-20 1-2620 <$100
1902 Plain Back
4x5 1-12195 <$100
3x10-20 1-8198 <$100
1929 Small Size
5 Type 1 1-1736 <$125
10 Type 1 1-1000 <$125
20 Type 1 1-276 <$125
5 Type 2 1-3266 <$150
10 Type 2 1-1871 <$150
20 Type 2 1-552 <$150
Total Issue $1,648,310
Out in 1935 $48,600
Large out 1935 $4,650

13946 Bergen
FNB IN GARFIELD
{{ 11 S }}
Chartered 1/34
1929 Small Size <$VALUE
5 Type 2 1-5056 <$150
10 Type 2 1-2580 <$150
20 Type 2 1-735 <$150
Total Issue $65,780
Out in 1935 $75,000
Outstanding includes Ch 8462

8462 Bergen
FNB OF GARFIELD
{{ 7 L 12 S }}
Organized 11/5/06
Liquidated 4/17/34
1902 Red Seal <$VALUE
4x5 1-175 <$500
4x10 1-175 <$500
1902 Date Back
4x5 1-5400 <$250
4x10 1-4900 <$250
1902 Plain Back
4x5 5401-21045 <$250
4x10 4901-18018 <$250
1929 Small Size
5 Type 1 1-5186 <$85
10 Type 1 1-2798 <$85
5 Type 2 1-6250 <$100
10 Type 2 1-2928 <$100
Total Issue $1,536,110
Out at close $100,000
Large out 1935 $3,160
Ch 13946 assumed circulation

3843 Gloucester
FNB OF GLASSBORO
{{ 6 L 18 S }}
Chartered 2/4/88
Brown Back <$VALUE
4x5 1-5032 <$400
3x10-20 1-2752 <$400
1902 Red Seal
4x5 1-400 <$450
3x10-20 1-320 <$450
1902 Date Back
4x5 1-5075 <$225
3x10-20 1-3650 <$225
1902 Plain Back
4x5 5076-16450 <$225
3x10-20 3651-10761 <$225
1929 Small Size
5 Type 1 1-2002 <$75
10 Type 1 1-1126 <$70
20 Type 1 1-272 <$75
5 Type 2 1-6784 <$75
10 Type 2 1-3780 <$75
20 Type 2 1-960 <$75
Total Issue $1,380,470
Out in 1935 $99,445
Large out 1935 $885

12609 Bergen
GLEN ROCK NB, GLEN ROCK
{{ 25 S }}
Chartered 12/24 as FNB, under which there was no issue. Issuing title adopted 1/22/29.
1929 Small Size <$VALUE
5 Type 1 1-3810 <$65
10 Type 1 1-1992 <$65
20 Type 1 1-542 <$65
5 Type 2 1-7736 <$75
10 Type 2 1-5165 <$75
20 Type 2 1-1380 <$75
Total Issue $416,790
Out in 1935 $100,000

3936 Camden
GLOUCESTER CITY NB, GLOUCESTER CITY
{{ 1 L }}
Chartered 10/26/88
Receivership 6/12/90
Brown Back <$VALUE
4x5 1-638 <$1500
Total Issue $12,760
Out in 1916 $50

8390 Hudson
FNB OF GUTTENBERG
{{ 14 L }}
Chartered 10/06
Liquidated 6/30/24
1902 Red Seal <$VALUE
4x5 1-1484 <$200
4x10 1-1483 <$200
1902 Date Back
4x5 1-6250 <$100
4x10 1-5625 <$100
1902 Plain Back
4x5 6251-14001 <$100
4x10 5626-11555 <$100
Total Issue $831,220
Out at close $46,750

14014 Hudson
LIBERTY NB IN GUTTENBERG
{{ 3 S }}
Chartered 2/34
1929 Small Size <$VALUE
5 Type 2 1-4584 <$350
10 Type 2 1-2554 <$350
20 Type 2 1-670 <$350
Total Issue $61,860
Out in 1935 $77,300
Large out 1935 $1,250
Outstanding includes Ch 12806

12806 Hudson
LIBERTY NB OF GUTTENBERG
{{ 11 L 10 S }}
Organized 8/4/25
Liquidated 4/24/34
1902 Plain Back <$VALUE
4x5 1-5180 <$150
3x10-20 1-3674 <$150
1929 Small Size
5 Type 1 1-3910 <$110
10 Type 1 1-2176 <$110
20 Type 1 1-520 <$110
5 Type 2 1-3926 <$125
10 Type 2 1-2072 <$125
20 Type 2 1-314 <$125
Total Issue $644,190
Out at close $88,300
Large out 1935 $1,250
Ch 14014 assumed circulation

13364 Bergen
BERGEN COUNTY NB OF HACKENSACK
{{ 18 S }}
Chartered 8/29
1929 Small Size <$VALUE
5 Type 1 1-4824 <$60
10 Type 1 1-2894 <$60
5 Type 2 1-26304 <$60
10 Type 2 1-14868 <$60
Total Issue $598,560
Out in 1935 $186,480

12014 Bergen
CITY NB OF HACKENSACK
Chartered 9/21
2nd title:City NB & TC 5/6/29
FIRST TITLE {{ 24 L }}
1902 Plain Back <$VALUE
4x5 1-45155 <$65
3x10-20 1-1700 <$65
SECOND TITLE {{ 20 S }}
1929 Small Size
5 Type 1 1-28728 <$50
5 Type 2 1-71812 <$50
Total Issue $2,209,000
Out in 1935 $124,500
Large out 1935 $3,280

1905 Bergen
FNB OF HACKENSACK
{{ UNREPORTED }}
Chartered 12/18/71
Liquidated 12/6/79
Original Series <$VALUE
3x1-2 1-3965 <$1000/$2000
4x5 1-3875 <$1000
3x10-20 1-1100<$1250/$2000
Series 1875
4x5 1-1525 <$1000
3x10-20 1-804 <$1250/$2000
Total Issue $223,025
Out in 1910 $1,009

5921 Bergen
HACKENSACK NB, HACKENSACK
{{ 10 L }}
Chartered 7/29/01
Liquidated 3/6/22
Brown Back <$VALUE
4x5 1-6950 <$375
3x10-20 1-5620 <$375
1882 Date Back
4x5 1-10200 <$375
3x10-20 1-6920 <$375
1882 Value Back
4x5 10201-18300 <$375
3x10-20 6921-11420 <$375
1902 Plain Back
4x5 1-4094 <$165
Total Issue $1,438,880
Out at close $96,995

7799 Bergen
PEOPLES NB OF HACKENSACK
{{ 7 L }}
Chartered 6/05
Liquidated 3/15/18
1902 Red Seal <$VALUE
4x5 1-1400 <$450
3x10-20 1-970 <$450
1902 Date Back
4x5 1-4350 <$200
3x10-20 1-3400 <$200
1902 Plain Back
4x5 4351-8725 <$200
3x10-20 3401-6350 <$200
Total Issue $568,500
Out at close $144,400

1259 Warren
HACKETTSTOWN NB, HACKETTSTOWN
{{ 29 L 7 S }}
Organized 5/16/65
Original Series <$VALUE
3x1-2 1-2000 <$300/$850
4x5 1-3500 <$350
3x10-20 1-2200 <$750/$1250
50-100 1-150 <$4000
Series 1875
3x10-20 1-4100 <$750/$1250
Brown Back
3x10-20 1-17307 <$225
1902 Red Seal
3x10-20 1-6000 <$250
1902 Date Back
3x10-20 1-14200 <$75
1902 Plain Back
3x10-20 14201-32873 <$75
1929 Small Size
5 Type 2 1-6900 <$150
10 Type 2 1-3792 <$150
20 Type 2 1-780 <$150
Total Issue $3,314,520
Out in 1935 $51,535
Large out 1935 $9,515

8267 Warren
PEOPLES NB OF HACKETTSTOWN
{{ 7 L 13 S }}
Organized 5/24/06
1902 Red Seal <$VALUE
3x10-20 1-2000 <$350
1902 Date Back
4x5 1-5650 <$175
3x10-20 1-4320 <$175
1902 Plain Back
4x5 5651-18615 <$175
3x10-20 4321-11679 <$175
1929 Small Size
10 Type 1 1-1586 <$100
20 Type 1 1-522 <$100
10 Type 2 1-2215 <$110
20 Type 2 1-650 <$110
Total Issue $1,249,200
Out in 1935 $52,000
Large out 1935 $2,640

13530 Camden
FNB OF HADDON HEIGHTS
{{ 18 S }}
Chartered 2/31
Liquidated 2/14/34
1929 Small Size <$VALUE
5 Type 1 1-8232 <$75
5 Type 2 1-10960 <$75
Total Issue $301,760
Out at close $92,150
Ch 1209 assumed circulation

9413 Camden
HADDON HEIGHTS NB, HADDON HEIGHTS
{{ 4 L }}
Chartered 5/09
Liquidated 7/1/24
1902 Date Back <$VALUE
3x10-20 1-900* <$500
1902 Plain Back
3x10-20 1001-1519* <$500
* 901-1000 not marked
Total Issue $75,950
Out at close $5,600

<$VALUEs are for notes in FINE condition. Value changes by approximately 25% for a change of one full grade.

3996 Camden
HADDONFIELD NB, HADDONFIELD
{{ 11 L }}
Chartered 3/26/89
Brown Back <$VALUE
4x5 1-3716 <$350
3x10-20 1-742 <$350
1902 Date Back
4x5 1-5450 <$350
3x10-20 1-3850 <$350
1902 Plain Back
4x5 5451-14470 <$175
3x10-20 3851-9377 <$175
Total Issue $869,670
Out in 1935 $1,920

12854 Passaic
HALEDON NB, HALEDON
{{ 9 S }}
Chartered 11/25
1929 Small Size <$VALUE
5 Type 1 1-1224 <$125
10 Type 1 1-1042 <$125
20 Type 1 1-318 <$125
5 Type 2 1-3274 <$150
10 Type 2 1-1521 <$150
20 Type 2 1-365 <$150
Total Issue $176,280
Out in 1935 $39,500

8227 Sussex
HARDYSTON NB OF HAMBURG
{{ 3 L 5 S }}
Chartered 5/06
1902 Red Seal <$VALUE
3x10-20 1-1975 <$500
1902 Date Back
3x10-20 1-5440 <$250
1902 Plain Back
3x10-20 5441-14317 <$250
1929 Small Size
5 Type 1 1-1818 <$200
10 Type 1 1-928 <$200
20 Type 1 1-256 <$200
5 Type 2 1-2912* <$225
10 Type 2 1-1596 <$225
20 Type 2 1-414 <$225
* 2583-2820 not issued
Total Issue $993,150
Out in 1935 $50,000
Large out 1935 $2,600

12646 Mercer
FNB OF HAMILTON SQUARE
{{ 6 S }}
Chartered 2/25
1929 Small Size <$VALUE
5 Type 2 1-4000 <$200
10 Type 2 1-2025 <$200
20 Type 2 1-500 <$200
Total Issue $50,250
Out in 1935 $45,150

13034 Hudson
HARRISON NB, HARRISON
{{ 3 L 28 S }}
Chartered 1/27
1902 Plain Back <$VALUE
3x10-20 1-11376 <$300
1929 Small Size
10 Type 1 1-6516 <$50
20 Type 1 1-2014 <$50
10 Type 2 1-2942 <$60
20 Type 2 1-664 <$65
Total Issue $1,244,160
Out in 1935 $103,500
Large out 1935 $2,730

12663 Passaic
FNB OF HAWTHORNE
{{ 10 S }}
Organized 2/24/25
Liquidated 3/15/33
1929 Small Size <$VALUE
5 Type 1 1-1072 <$125
10 Type 1 1-1087 <$125
20 Type 1 1-288 <$125
Total Issue $131,940
Out at close $95,680

5333 Hunterdon
FNB OF HIGH BRIDGE
{{ 20 L 25 S }}
Chartered 5/5/00
Brown Back <$VALUE
4x5 1-2600 <$300
3x10-20 1-1980 <$300
1882 Date Back
4x5 1-2550 <$300
3x10-20 1-1960 <$300
1882 Value Back
4x5 2551-4395 <$300
3x10-20 1961-2880 <$300
1902 Plain Back
4x5 1-4840 <$150
3x10-20 1-2831 <$150
1929 Small Size
5 Type 1 1-422 <$85
10 Type 1 1-972 <$85
20 Type 1 1-292 <$85
5 Type 2 1-3048 <$100
10 Type 2 1-1596 <$100
20 Type 2 1-456 <$100
Total Issue $767,590
Out in 1935 $57,740
Large out 1935 $1,560

12598 Middlesex
FNB OF HIGHLAND PARK
{{ 4 L 14 S }}
Chartered 11/24
1902 Plain Back <$VALUE
3x10-20 1-3024 <$450
1929 Small Size
5 Type 1 1-6128 <$100
10 Type 1 1-3146 <$100
5 Type 2 1-12792 <$100
10 Type 2 1-6324 <$100
Total Issue $651,000
Out in 1935 $95,330
Large out 1935 $730

1759 Mercer
CENTRAL NB OF HIGHTSTOWN
{{ UNREPORTED }}
Chartered 12/70
Liquidated 2/15/79
Original Series <$VALUE
4x5 1-3250 <$1500
Series 1875
4x5 1-750 <$1500
Total Issue $80,000
Out in 1910 $280

1737 Mercer
FNB OF HIGHTSTOWN
{{ 13 L 20 S }}
Chartered 11/70
Original Series <$VALUE
3x1-2 1-6000 <$350/$850
4x5 1-4250 <$350
3x10-20 1-900 <$750/$1250
Series 1875
3x1-2 1-2320 <$350/$850
4x5 1-7804 <$350
3x10-20 1-3406 <$750/$1250
Brown Back
4x5 1-9100 <$275
3x10-20 1-2280 <$275
1882 Date Back
4x5 1-751 <$275
3x10-20 1-439 <$275
1902 Date Back
4x5 1-3150 <$100
3x10-20 1-2500 <$100
1902 Plain Back
4x5 3151-23290 <$100
3x10-20 2501-16451 <$100
1929 Small Size
5 Type 1 1-5234 <$60
10 Type 1 1-2654 <$60
20 Type 1 1-694 <$65
5 Type 2 1-9344 <$60
10 Type 2 1-4891 <$60
20 Type 2 1-1158 <$65
Total Issue $2,637,630
Out in 1935 $117,750
Large out 1935 $4,240

12902 Bergen
HILLSDALE NB, HILLSDALE
{{ 25 L 27 S }}
Chartered 3/26
1902 Plain Back <$VALUE
4x5 1-10547 <$100
1929 Small Size
5 Type 1 1-7264 <$50
5 Type 2 1-16560 <$50
Total Issue $511,660
Out in 1935 $42,200
Large out 1935 $1,055

11727 Union
HILLSIDE NB, HILLSIDE
{{ 6 L 8 S }}
Chartered 5/20
1902 Plain Back <$VALUE
4x5 1-17396 <$150
1929 Small Size
5 Type 1 1-3288 <$125
5 Type 2 1-9084 <$125
Total Issue $491,980
Out in 1935 $24,040
Large out 1935 $1,080

1444 Hudson
FNB OF HOBOKEN
{{ 32 L 46 S }}
Chartered 1865
Liquidated 3/19/35
Original Series <$VALUE
3x1-2 1-2700 <$300/$750
4x5 1-5950 <$300
3x10-20 1-2050 <$750/$1250
Series 1875
4x5 1-2000 <$300
3x10-20 1-2700 <$750/$1250
Brown Back
3x10-20 1-13666 <$250
1902 Red Seal
3x10-20 1-4400 <$250
1902 Date Back
3x10-20 1-26200 <$65
1902 Plain Back
3x10-20 26201-115867 <$65
1929 Small Size
10 Type 1 1-20412 <$20
20 Type 1 1-6322 <$30
10 Type 2 1-10583 <$20
20 Type 2 1-3765 <$30
Total Issue $9,271,140
Out at close $571,290
Large out at close $19,790

3744 Hudson
SECOND NB OF HOBOKEN
{{ 15 L }}
Chartered 7/5/87
Liquidated 9/1/26
Brown Back <$VALUE
4x5 1-1370 <$250
3x10-20 1-7864 <$250
1902 Red Seal
3x10-20 1-1400 <$275
1902 Date Back
3x10-20 1-11400 <$100
1902 Plain Back
3x10-20 11401-58193 <$100
Total Issue $3,400,250
Out at close $635,500

10118 Warren
FNB OF HOPE
{{ 5 L 8 S }}
Chartered 12/11
1902 Date Back <$VALUE
3x10-20 1-1790 <$350
1902 Plain Back
3x10-20 1791-6717 <$350
1929 Small Size
10 Type 1 1-724 <$175
20 Type 1 1-190 <$175
10 Type 2 1-1317 <$175
20 Type 2 1-295 <$175
Total Issue $421,160
Out in 1935 $24,550
Large out 1935 $900

4254 Mercer
HOPEWELL NB, HOPEWELL
{{ 4 L 20 S }}
Chartered 1890
Brown Back <$VALUE
4x5 1-4075 <$450
3x10-20 1-1310 <$450
1882 Date Back
4x5 1-492 <$450
3x10-20 1-368 <$450
1902 Date Back
4x5 1-3950 <$200
3x10-20 1-3200 <$200
1902 Plain Back
4x5 3951-13845 <$200
3x10-20 3201-9601 <$200
1929 Small Size
5 Type 1 1-2524 <$65
10 Type 1 1-1614 <$65
20 Type 1 1-500 <$75
5 Type 2 1-5528 <$75
10 Type 2 1-3189 <$75
20 Type 2 1-975 <$75
Total Issue $1,243,780
Out in 1935 $76,730
Large out 1935 $1,990

7981 Essex
IRVINGTON NB, IRVINGTON
{{ 13 L 12 S }}
Chartered 11/05
1902 Red Seal <$VALUE
4x5 1-2525 <$300
3x10-20 1-1840 <$300
1902 Date Back
4x5 1-12400 <$135
3x10-20 1-8640 <$135
1902 Plain Back
4x5 12401-34060 <$135
3x10-20 8641-23230 <$135
1929 Small Size
5 Type 1 1-3760 <$100
10 Type 1 1-2226 <$100
20 Type 1 1-560 <$100
5 Type 2 1-6224 <$100
10 Type 2 1-3193 <$100
20 Type 2 1-950 <$100
Total Issue $2,380,810
Out in 1935 $76,850
Large out 1935 $4,480

288 Middlesex
FNB OF JAMESBURG
{{ 12 L 3 S }}
Organized 1/29/64
Original Series <$VALUE
3x1-2 1-7000 <$400/$1000
4x5 1-2750 <$400
3x10-20 1-1100* <$750/$1250
* 541-600 not issued
Series 1875
4x5 1-250 <$400
3x10-20 1-1778 <$750/$1250
Brown Back
3x10-20 1-2937 <$350
1902 Red Seal
3x10-20 1-1300 <$375
1902 Date Back
3x10-20 1-1920 <$175
1902 Plain Back
3x10-20 1921-4999 <$175
1929 Small Size
10 Type 1 1-546 <$300
20 Type 1 1-138 <$300
10 Type 2 1-751 <$300
20 Type 2 1-230 <$300
Total Issue $759,130
Out in 1935 $18,600
Large out 1935 $2,530

12255 Hudson
BERGEN NB OF JERSEY CITY
Chartered 9/22
Liquidated 8/15/33
2nd title:Journal Square NB of Jersey City 3/3/26
FIRST TITLE {{ 11 L }}
1902 Plain Back <$VALUE
4x5 1-15520 <$75
3x10-20 1-10415 <$75
SECOND TITLE {{ 20 L 33 S }}
1902 Plain Back
4x5 1-21745 <$50
3x10-20 1-15212 <$65
1929 Small Size
5 Type 1 1-18856 <$20
10 Type 1 1-11146 <$25
20 Type 1 1-3148 <$35
Total Issue $3,638,850
Out at close $444,230
Large out at close $12,490

374 Hudson
FNB OF JERSEY CITY
{{ 5U + 50+ L 50+ S }}
Chartered 4/64
Original Series <$VALUE
3x1-2 1-20000 <$200/$750
4x5 1-9000 <$250
3x10-20 1-2500 <$750/$1250
4x20 1-3000 <$1250
50-100 1-670 <$4000
Series 1875
3x1-2 1-5202 <$200/$750
4x5 1-9750 <$250
3x10-20 1-5500 <$600/$1000
4x20 1-200 <$4000
Brown Back
4x5 1-21104 <$125
3x10-20 1-19621 <$125/$150
50-100 1-700 <$1250/$1500
1902 Red Seal
4x5 1-20750 <$125
3x10-20 1-12180 <$125/$150
50-100 1-2140 <$2250/$2500
1902 Date Back
4x5 1-45750 <$40
3x10-20 1-29100 <$50
50-100 1-400 <$300/$350
1902 Plain Back
4x5 45751-129543 <$40
3x10-20 29101-84000 <$50
1929 Small Size
5 Type 1 1-28194 <$15
10 Type 1 1-17358 <$20
20 Type 1 1-6746 <$30
5 Type 2 1-131318 <$15
10 Type 2 1-78312* <$20
20 Type 2 1-21708 <$30
* 4795-4800, 4807-4812, 4837-4842 not issued
Total Issue $15,532,010
Out in 1935 $1,404,750
Large out 1935 $23,000

12397 Hudson
FRANKLIN NB OF JERSEY CITY
{{ 19 L 26 S }}
Chartered 6/23
1902 Plain Back <$VALUE
4x5 1-25805 <$65
3x10-20 1-17325 <$75
1929 Small Size
5 Type 1 1-15306 <$30
10 Type 1 1-8224 <$30
20 Type 1 1-1962 <$40
5 Type 2 1-28182 <$30
10 Type 2 1-18087 <$30
20 Type 2 1-5196 <$40
Total Issue $2,996,110
Out in 1935 $394,400
Large out 1935 $4,870

1182 Hudson
HUDSON COUNTY NB OF JERSEY CITY
Chartered 1865
2nd title: Union Trust & Hudson County NB, Jersey City 2/21/23
3rd title:Hudson County NB 12/31/27
FIRST TITLE {{ 15 L }}
Original Series <$VALUE
4x5 1-7000 <$350
3x10-20 1-6200 <$750/$1250
Series 1875
3x10-20 1-6621 <$600/$1000
Brown Back
50-100 1-3394 <$1250/$1500
1902 Red Seal
50-100 1-1500 <$2250/$2500
1902 Date Back
4x5 1-22500 <$50
4x10 1-8750 <$60
50-100 1-900 <$300/$350
3x50-100 1-1460 <$300/$350
1902 Plain Back
4x5 22501-54000 <$50
4x10 8751-12750 <$60
SECOND TITLE {{ 38 L }}
1902 Plain Back
4x5 1-69314 <$50
4x10 1-53979 <$60
THIRD TITLE {{ 15 L 50+ S }}
1902 Plain Back
4x5 1-23611 <$50
4x10 1-18341 <$60
1929 Small Size
5 Type 1 1-55006 <$15
10 Type 1 1-30144 <$20
5 Type 2 1-117996 <$15
10 Type 2 1-56868 <$20
Total Issue $12,973,930
Out in 1935 $1,131,310
Large out 1935 $30,845
Outstanding includes Ch 9229

Journal Square NB & TC of Jersey City
SEE Ch 12255
Bergen NB of Jersey City

12939 Hudson
LABOR NB OF JERSEY CITY
{{ U + 10 L 4 S }}
Chartered 6/26
Liquidated 9/18/31
1902 Plain Back <$VALUE
4x5 1-7560 <$135
3x10-20 1-4011 <$135
1929 Small Size
5 Type 1 1-2552 <$200
10 Type 1 1-1178 <$200
20 Type 1 1-301 <$200
Total Issue $535,110
Out at close $85,360
Large out at close $4,430

9229 Hudson
MERCHANTS NB OF JERSEY CITY
{{ 25 L }}
Chartered 8/08
Closed 12/31/27
1902 Date Back <$VALUE
4x5 1-19500 <$60
3x10-20 1-14300 <$65
1902 Plain Back
4x5 19501-51880 <$60
3x10-20 14301-34428 <$65
Total Issue $2,759,000
Out at close $191,400
Ch 1182 assumed circulation

695 Hudson
SECOND NB OF JERSEY CITY
{{ 13 L }}
Chartered 1/9/65
Liquidated 8/1/07
Original Series <$VALUE
4x5 1-9000 <$300
3x10-20 1-17000 <$750/$1250
Series 1875
4x5 1-2290 <$300
3x10-20 1-2808 <$600/$1000
Brown Back
3x10-20 1-7812 <$150/$200
1902 Red Seal
4x5 1-4075 <$225
3x10-20 1-3416 <$225/$250
Total Issue $1,859,100
Out at close $200,000

3680 Hudson
THIRD NB OF JERSEY CITY
{{ 16 L }}
Chartered 4/26/87
Liquidated 1/16/15
Brown Back <$VALUE
4x5 1-24065 <$125
3x10-20 1-15281 <$125/$175
1902 Red Seal
4x5 1-3250 <$175
3x10-20 1-2200 <$175/$225
1902 Date Back
4x5 1-20300 <$65
3x10-20 1-14946 <$75
Total Issue $2,573,650
Out in 1915 $71,745

Union Trust & Hudson County NB of Jersey City
SEE Ch 1182
Hudson County NB of Jersey City

10376 Monmouth
KEANSBURG NB, KEANSBURG
{{ 2 L 4 S }}
Organized 3/24/13
1902 Date Back <$VALUE
4x10 1-725 <$500
1902 Plain Back
4x10 726-2740 <$500
1929 Small Size
10 Type 1 1-738* <$275
10 Type 2 1-6908 <$275
*171-522 not issued
Total Issue $201,840
Out in 1935 $34,050

FNB & TC of Kearny
SEE Ch 8627
FNB of Arlington

Kearny NB, Kearny
SEE Ch 9661
FNB of East Newark

13537 Hudson
KEARNY NB, KEARNY
{{ 2U + 20 S }}
Chartered 4/31
1929 Small Size <$VALUE
5 Type 1 1-2396 <$65
10 Type 1 1-1756 <$65
20 Type 1 1-590 <$65
5 Type 2 1-16880 <$75
10 Type 2 1-7874 <$75
20 Type 2 1-2085 <$75
Total Issue $452,880
Out in 1935 $143,945
Large out 1935 $815
Outstanding includes Ch 9661

3164 Monmouth
FNB OF KEYPORT
{{ UNREPORTED }}
Chartered 4/23/84
Liquidated 7/1/89
Brown Back <$VALUE
4x5 1-1292 <$2000
Total Issue $25,840
Out in 1910 $120

****
4147 Monmouth
PEOPLES NB OF KEYPORT
{{2L 8S}}
Chartered 10/29/89
Brown Back <$VALUE
4x5 1-3425 <$850
3x10-20 1-770 <$850
1882 Date Back
4x5 1-66 <$850
3x10-20 1-124 <$850
1902 Date Back
3x10-20 1-1320 <$500
1902 Plain Back
3x10-20 1321-3524 <$500
1929 Small Size
10 Type 1 1-928 <$175
20 Type 1 1-206 <$175
10 Type 2 1-2471 <$200
20 Type 2 1-651 <$200
Total Issue $408,850
Out in 1935 $39,800
Large out 1935 $650
****
12571 Ocean
FNB OF LAKEHURST
{{5S}}
Chartered 8/24
1929 Small Size <$VALUE
5 Type 1 1-1216 <$250
10 Type 1 1-1009 <$250
Total Issue $97,020
Out in 1935 $25,000
****
5232 Ocean
FNB OF LAKEWOOD
{{6L}}
Chartered 11/11/99
Liquidated 7/3/19
Brown Back <$VALUE
4x5 1-1550 <$500
3x10-20 1-720 <$500
1882 Date Back
4x5 1-3400 <$450
3x10-20 1-2620 <$450
1882 Value Back
4x5 3401-5850 <$450
3x10-20 2621-3840 <$450
Total Issue $376,000
Out at close $42,235
****
7291 Ocean
PEOPLES NB OF LAKEWOOD
{{2L 16S}}
Organized 5/21/04
Receivership 5/14/34
1902 Red Seal <$VALUE
3x10-20 1-832 <$1500
1902 Date Back
3x10-20 1-1660 <$650
1902 Plain Back
3x10-20 1661-3753 <$650
1929 Small Size
5 Type 1 1-3658 <$125
10 Type 1 1-2874 <$125
20 Type 1 1-528 <$125
5 Type 2 1-5928 <$150
10 Type 2 1-3075 <$150
20 Type 2 1-626 <$150
Total Issue $647,700
Out at close $146,000
Large out at close $700
****
2339 Hunterdon
AMWELL NB OF LAMBERTVILLE
{{6L 13S}}
Chartered 7/26/76
Series 1875 <$VALUE
4x5 1-4150 <$400
3x10-20 1-2520 <$750/$1250
Brown Back
3x10-20 1-2620 <$300
1882 Date Back
3x10-20 1-3999 <$300
1902 Plain Back
3x10-20 1-6826 <$200
1929 Small Size
10 Type 1 1-2166 <$100
20 Type 1 1-544 <$100
10 Type 2 1-6017 <$100
20 Type 2 1-1279 <$100
Total Issue $1,162,240
Out in 1935 $79,600
Large out 1935 $1,480
****
1272 Hunterdon
LAMBERTVILLE NB, LAMBERTVILLE
{{14L 28S}}
Chartered 1865
Original Series <$VALUE
4x5 1-4250 <$350
3x10-20 1-1980 <$750/$1250
Series 1875
4x5 1-3850 <$350
3x10-20 1-1740 <$750/$1250
Brown Back
4x5 1-10095 <$200
3x10-20 1-5871 <$200/$250
1902 Red Seal
4x5 1-3000 <$225
3x10-20 1-2080 <$225/$250
1902 Date Back
4x5 1-5000 <$85
3x10-20 1-3800 <$100
1902 Plain Back
4x5 5001-23440 <$85
3x10-20 3801-16066 <$100
1929 Small Size
5 Type 1 1-4432 <$50
10 Type 1 1-2118 <$50
20 Type 1 1-538 <$50
5 Type 2 1-6564 <$60
10 Type 2 1-3961 <$60
20 Type 2 1-1152 <$60
Total Issue $2,699,620
Out in 1935 $96,900
Large out 1935 $6,430
****
12022 Camden
LAUREL SPRINGS NB, LAUREL SPRINGS
{{6S}}
Organized 5/17/21
1929 Small Size <$VALUE
5 Type 1 1-316 <$350
10 Type 1 1-158 <$350
20 Type 1 1-106 <$350
5 Type 2 1-2088 <$350
10 Type 2 1-1119 <$350
20 Type 2 1-290 <$350
Total Issue $59,110
Out in 1935 $22,300
****
11950 Bergen
FNB OF LEONIA
{{5L}}
Chartered 3/21
Liquidated 10/1/26
1902 Plain Back <$VALUE
4x5 1-7615 <$400
Total Issue $152,300
Out at close $6,300
****
11545 Union
LINDEN NB, LINDEN
Chartered 12/19
Liquidated 10/15/31
2nd title: Linden NB & TC 5/23/27
FIRST TITLE {{10L}}
1902 Plain Back <$VALUE
4x5 1-9019 <$150
3x10-20 1-2758 <$150
SECOND TITLE {{4L 7S}}
1902 Plain Back
4x5 1-9862 <$150
3x10-20 1-5724 <$150
1929 Small Size
5 Type 1 1-4613 <$150
10 Type 1 1-1944 <$150
20 Type 1 1-621 <$150
Total Issue $1,131,270
Out at close $111,920
Large out 1935 $8,950
Ch 13540 assumed circulation
****
13540 Union
LINDEN NB, LINDEN
{{5S}}
Chartered 4/31
Liquidated 1/13/32
1929 Small Size <$VALUE
10 Type 1 1-1124 <$225
20 Type 1 1-250 <$225
Total Issue $97,440
Out at close $189,140
Large out at close $8,950
Outstanding includes Ch 11545
****
8829 Passaic
LITTLE FALLS NB, LITTLE FALLS
{{2L 4S}}
Chartered 8/07
1902 Red Seal <$VALUE
4x5 1-156 <$1250
3x10-20 1-125 <$1250
1902 Date Back
4x5 1-850 <$650
3x10-20 1-660 <$650
1902 Plain Back
4x5 851-3224 <$650
3x10-20 661-2021 <$650
1929 Small Size
5 Type 1 1-268 <$400
10 Type 1 1-148 <$400
20 Type 1 1-37 <$400
5 Type 2 1-48 <$400
10 Type 2 1-42 <$400
20 Type 2 1-45 <$400
Total Issue $197,820
Out in 1935 $6,000
Large out 1935 $400
****
12378 Bergen
LITTLE FERRY NB, LITTLE FERRY
{{2L 8S}}
Chartered 5/23
1902 Plain Back <$VALUE
4x5 1-5557 <$650
1929 Small Size
5 Type 1 1-3504 <$300
5 Type 2 1-8988 <$300
Total Issue $261,200
Out in 1935 $21,610
Large out 1935 $360
****
13129 Essex
LIVINGSTON NB, LIVINGSTON
{{12S}}
Chartered 10/27
1929 Small Size <$VALUE
5 Type 1 1-1712 <$100
10 Type 1 1-1322 <$100
5 Type 2 1-6996 <$100
10 Type 2 1-3312 <$100
Total Issue $198,780
Out in 1935 $43,890
****
9420 Bergen
FNB OF LODI
{{6L}}
Chartered 5/09
Liquidated 9/22/17
1902 Date Back <$VALUE
4x5 1-2000 <$350
3x10-20 1-1540 <$350
1902 Plain Back
4x5 2001-2695 <$350
3x10-20 1541-1996 <$350
Total Issue $153,700
Out at close $24,595
****
6038 Monmouth
CITIZENS NB OF LONG BRANCH
{{13L}}
Chartered 11/30/01
Receivership 1/20/32
Brown Back <$VALUE
4x5 1-5850 <$300
3x10-20 1-4960 <$300
1882 Date Back
4x5 1-12250 <$300
3x10-20 1-7300 <$300
1882 Value Back
4x5 12251-22700 <$300
3x10-20 7301-13200 <$300
1902 Plain Back
4x5 1-10160 <$150
4x10 1-8521 <$150
Total Issue $2,023,040
Out at close $6,255
****
4138 Monmouth
FNB OF LONG BRANCH
{{2L}}
Chartered 10/89
Liquidated 4/29/16
Brown Back <$VALUE
4x5 1-7275 <$750
3x10-20 1-2300 <$750
1882 Date Back
4x5 1-495 <$750
3x10-20 1-379 <$750
1902 Date Back
4x5 1-5416 <$500
4x10 1-5486 <$500
Total Issue $617,110
Out in 1916 $27,545
****
10417 Bergen
FNB OF LYNDHURST
{{1L 9S}}
Organized 5/20/13
Receivership 3/5/34
1902 Date Back <$VALUE
4x5 1-875 <$750
3x10-20 1-700 <$750
1902 Plain Back
4x5 876-3445 <$750
3x10-20 701-2206 <$750
1929 Small Size
5 Type 1 1-2612 <$175
10 Type 1 1-1338 <$175
20 Type 1 1-338 <$175
5 Type 2 1-3144 <$200
10 Type 2 1-1688 <$200
20 Type 2 1-381 <$200
Total Issue $418,620
Out at close $99,995
Large out at close $945
****
2551 Morris
FNB OF MADISON
{{22L 10S}}
Chartered 1881
Series 1875 <$VALUE
3x10-20 1-2510 <$600/$1000
Brown Back
3x10-20 1-920 <$250/$300
1882 Date Back
3x10-20 1-1580 <$250/$300
1882 Value Back
3x10-20 1581-5673<$250/$300
1902 Plain Back
4x5 1-43249 <$100
1929 Small Size
5 Type 1 1-13678 <$75
5 Type 2 1-33980 <$75
Total Issue $1,900,370
Out in 1935 $100,000
Large out 1935 $4,430
****
3040 Monmouth
FNB OF MANASQUAN
{{6L}}
Organized 2/3/83
Receivership 5/2/08
Brown Back <$VALUE
4x5 1-7370 <$350
3x10-20 1-1105 <$350
1902 Red Seal
4x5 1-1140 <$400
3x10-20 1-2493 <$400
Total Issue $350,100
Out in 1916 $2,110
****
9213 Monmouth
MANASQUAN NB, MANASQUAN
{{3L 22S}}
Chartered 8/08
1902 Date Back <$VALUE
3x10-20 1-6050 <$225
1902 Plain Back
3x10-20 6051-15785 <$225
1929 Small Size
10 Type 1 1-2242 <$75
20 Type 1 1-646 <$85
10 Type 2 1-4224 <$85
20 Type 2 1-1086 <$85
Total Issue $1,065,250
Out in 1935 $79,950
Large out 1935 $1,840
****
6440 Monmouth
FARMERS & MERCHANTS NB OF MATAWAN
{{8L 8S}}
Chartered 9/02
1902 Red Seal <$VALUE
4x5 1-3550 <$400
3x10-20 1-2860 <$400
1902 Date Back
4x5 1-8100 <$200
3x10-20 1-4780 <$200
1902 Plain Back
4x5 8101-24290 <$200
3x10-20 4781-15249 <$200
1929 Small Size
5 Type 1 1-3184 <$125
10 Type 1 1-1748 <$125
20 Type 1 1-546 <$125
5 Type 2 1-3144 <$150
10 Type 2 1-1668 <$150
20 Type 2 1-420 <$150
Total Issue $1,768,970
Out in 1935 $73,770
Large out 1935 $3,230
****
8582 Atlantic
FNB OF MAYS LANDING
{{2L 5S}}
Organized 1/9/07
1902 Red Seal <$VALUE
3x10-20 1-700 <$1500
1902 Date Back
3x10-20 1-360* <$750
1902 Plain Back
3x10-20 481-5023* <$750
* 361-480 not marked
1929 Small Size
10 Type 1 1-790 <$400
20 Type 1 1-218 <$400
10 Type 2 1-961 <$400
20 Type 2 1-232 <$400
Total Issue $373,960
Out in 1935 $25,000
Large out 1935 $290
****
1191 Burlington
BURLINGTON COUNTY NB OF MEDFORD
{{9L 19S}}
Organized 5/16/65
Original Series <$VALUE
4x5 1-4600 <$450
3x10-20 1-2180 <$750/$1250
Series 1875
4x5 1-2945 <$450
3x10-20 1-1412 <$750/$1250
Brown Back
4x5 1-7133 <$300
3x10-20 1-4392 <$300
1902 Red Seal
4x5 1-2080 <$300
3x10-20 1-1208 <$300
1902 Date Back
4x5 1-4050 <$150
3x10-20 1-3220 <$150
1902 Plain Back
4x5 4051-11880 <$150
3x10-20 3221-8363 <$150
1929 Small Size
5 Type 1 1-1864 <$65
10 Type 1 1-1066 <$65
20 Type 1 1-308 <$75
5 Type 2 1-9206 <$75
Total Issue $1,653,380
Out in 1935 $48,900
Large out 1935 $4,215
****
8323 Camden
FNB OF MERCHANTVILLE
Organized 6/21/06
2nd title:FNB & TC 11/10/24
3rd title:Merchantville NB & TC 6/30/32
FIRST TITLE {{0L}}
1902 Red Seal <$VALUE
4x5 1-525 <$850
3x10-20 1-580 <$850
1902 Date Back
4x5 1-2050 <$400
3x10-20 1-1520 <$400
1902 Plain Back
4x5 2051-5250 <$400
3x10-20 1521-3260 <$400
SECOND TITLE {{3L 1S}}
1902 Plain Back
4x5 1-5007 <$350
1929 Small Size
5 Type 1 1-1703 <$200
THIRD TITLE {{U+6S}}
1929 Small Size
5 Type 1 1-2518 <$175
5 Type 2 1-16522 <$175
Total Issue $616,880
Out in 1935 $35,700
Large out 1935 $1,095
****
Merchantville NB & TC of Merchantville
SEE Ch 8323
FNB of Merchantville
****
7754 Middlesex
METUCHEN NB, METUCHEN
{{13L 12S}}
Organized 4/28/05
Liquidated 4/25/34
1902 Red Seal <$VALUE
4x5 1-1600 <$200
3x10-20 1-1120 <$200/$250
1902 Date Back
4x5 1-3250 <$100
3x10-20 1-2360 <$100
1902 Plain Back
4x5 3251-16185 <$100
3x10-20 2361-9993 <$100
1929 Small Size
5 Type 1 1-4140 <$100
10 Type 1 1-1964 <$100
20 Type 1 1-546 <$100
5 Type 2 1-2520 <$125
10 Type 2 1-1140 <$125
20 Type 2 1-192 <$125
Total Issue $1,246,750
Out at close $88,830
Large out 1935 $2,990
Ch 13916 assumed circulation
****
13916 Middlesex
METUCHEN NB, METUCHEN
{{2S}}
Chartered 12/33
1929 Small Size <$VALUE
5 Type 2 1-5112 <$350
10 Type 2 1-2306 <$350
20 Type 2 1-800 <$350
Total Issue $64,620
Out in 1935 $76,550
Large out 1935 $2,990
Outstanding includes Ch 7754
****
8779 Hunterdon
FNB OF MILFORD
{{11L 6S}}
Chartered 7/07
1902 Red Seal <$VALUE
3x10-20 1-287 <$400
1902 Date Back
4x5 1-1825 <$175
3x10-20 1-1440 <$175
1902 Plain Back
4x5 1826-9670 <$175
3x10-20 1441-6722 <$175
1929 Small Size
5 Type 1 1-1930 <$150
10 Type 1 1-1122 <$150
20 Type 1 1-266 <$150
5 Type 2 1-3480 <$175
10 Type 2 1-1929 <$175
20 Type 2 1-528 <$175
Total Issue $748,240
Out in 1935 $48,950
Large out 1935 $1,650
****
8661 Essex
FNB OF MILLBURN
{{0L 2S}}
Chartered 4/07
1902 Red Seal <$VALUE
3x10-20 1-340 <$1500
1902 Date Back
3x10-20 1-1780 <$750
1902 Plain Back
3x10-20 1781-3916 <$750
1929 Small Size
10 Type 1 1-316 <$400
20 Type 1 1-106 <$400
10 Type 2 1-558 <$400
20 Type 2 1-192 <$400
Total Issue $253,900
Out in 1935 $12,150
Large out 1935 $650
****
10935 Middlesex
FNB OF MILLTOWN
{{12S}}
Chartered 1/17
1929 Small Size <$VALUE
5 Type 1 1-1562 <$100
10 Type 1 1-786 <$100
5 Type 2 1-16836 <$100
10 Type 2 1-7824 <$100
Total Issue $256,440
Out in 1935 $97,790
****
5208 Cumberland
MECHANICS NB OF MILLVILLE
Chartered 7/12/99
Receivership 10/13/33
2nd title:Mechanics NB & TC 5/13/31
FIRST TITLE {{20L 12S}}
Brown Back <$VALUE
4x5 1-6450 <$250
3x10-20 1-3760 <$250
1882 Date Back
4x5 1-8700* <$250
3x10-20 1-6560** <$250
1882 Value Back
4x5 9101-13500* <$250
3x10-20 6881-9140** <$250
* 8701-9100 not marked
** 6561-6880 not marked
1902 Plain Back
4x5 1-16979 <$75
3x10-20 1-11841 <$75
1929 Small Size
5 Type 1 1-2926 <$65
10 Type 1 1-1460 <$65
20 Type 1 1-336 <$65
SECOND TITLE {{6S}}
1929 Small Size
5 Type 1 1-1356 <$75
10 Type 1 1-988 <$75
20 Type 1 1-165 <$75
Total Issue $2,311,090
Out at close $98,560
Large out at close $6,430
****

1270 Cumberland
MILLVILLE NB, MILLVILLE
{{ 10 L 21 S }}
Chartered 1865
Original Series <$VALUE
3x1-2 1-5965 <$350/$1000
4x5 1-3750 <$400
3x10-20 1-2000 <$750/$1250
Series 1875
4x5 1-2706 <$400
3x10-20 1-965 <$750/$1250
Brown Back
3x10-20 1-8149 <$300
1902 Red Seal
3x10-20 1-4000 <$300
1902 Date Back
3x10-20 1-8100 <$125
1902 Plain Back
3x10-20 8101-26835 <$125
1929 Small Size
10 Type 1 1-3216 <$50
20 Type 1 1-772 <$60
10 Type 2 1-3867 <$50
20 Type 2 1-898 <$60
Total Issue $2,598,625
Out in 1935 $96,350
Large out 1935 $6,020

10440 Atlantic
FNB OF MINOTOLA
{{ 1 L 10 S }}
Chartered 9/13
1902 Date Back <$VALUE
4x10 1-500* <$1000
1902 Plain Back
4x10 601-2275* <$1000
* 501-600 not marked
1929 Small Size
10 Type 1 1-518 <$150
10 Type 2 1-5700 <$150
Total Issue $179,080
Out in 1935 $44,710
Large out 1935 $300

9577 Essex
ESSEX NB OF MONTCLAIR
{{ 6 L }}
Chartered 1909
Liquidated 4/8/22
1902 Date Back <$VALUE
4x5 1-9500 <$175
3x10-20 1-10000 <$175
1902 Plain Back
4x5 9501-25025 <$175
3x10-20 10001-19584 <$175
Total Issue $1,479,700
Out at close $145,300

9339 Essex
FNB OF MONTCLAIR
Chartered 2/09
2nd title:FNB & TC 4/11/25
FIRST TITLE {{ 4 L }}
1902 Date Back <$VALUE
4x5 1-12100 <$125
3x10-20 1-8160 <$125
1902 Plain Back
4x5 12101-27800 <$125
3x10-20 8161-17520 <$125
SECOND TITLE {{ 8 L 36 S }}
1902 Plain Back
4x5 1-21659 <$100
1929 Small Size
5 Type 1 1-20220 <$20
10 Type 1 1-8312 <$25
20 Type 1 1-2142 <$35
5 Type 2 1-77544 <$20
10 Type 2 1-12840 <$25
20 Type 2 1-4920* <$35
* 4297-4302 not issued
Total Issue $3,841,940
Out in 1935 $460,560
Large out 1935 $4,280

12268 Essex
MONTCLAIR NB, MONTCLAIR
{{ 5 L 19 S }}
Chartered 11/22
1902 Plain Back <$VALUE
4x5 1-3845 <$225
4x10 1-2506 <$225
1929 Small Size
5 Type 1 1-8108 <$40
10 Type 1 1-4264 <$45
5 Type 2 1-27610 <$40
10 Type 2 1-14470 <$45
Total Issue $958,970
Out in 1935 $150,850
Large out 1935 $850

12675 Essex
PEOPLES NB OF MONTCLAIR
{{ 2 S }}
Chartered 4/25
Liquidated 1/16/34
1929 Small Size <$VALUE
5 Type 1 1-4686 <$300
10 Type 1 1-2120 <$300
20 Type 1 1-598 <$300
5 Type 2 1-306 <$300
10 Type 2 1-360 <$300
20 Type 2 1-160 <$300
Total Issue $347,870
Out at close $71,550

3387 Burlington
MOORESTOWN NB, MOORESTOWN
{{ 6 L }}
Chartered 1885
Liquidated 2/1/27
Brown Back <$VALUE
4x5 1-2898 <$500
3x10-20 1-1494 <$500
1902 Red Seal
4x5 1-1375 <$500
3x10-20 1-1070 <$500
1902 Date Back
4x5 1-4200 <$300
3x10-20 1-3080 <$300
1902 Plain Back
4x5 4201-12084 <$300
3x10-20 3081-7785 <$300
Total Issue $844,590
Out at close $33,900

1188 Morris
FNB OF MORRISTOWN
{{ 13 L 32 S }}
Chartered 1865
Original Series <$VALUE
3x1-2 1-410 <$350/$850
4x5 1-4713 <$400
3x10-20 1-2900 <$750/$1250
Series 1875
4x5 1-8839 <$400
Brown Back
4x5 1-7950 <$300
3x10-20 1-917 <$300
1902 Red Seal
3x10-20 1-1900 <$300
1902 Date Back
3x10-20 1-12800 <$110
1902 Plain Back
3x10-20 12801-42241 <$110
1929 Small Size
10 Type 1 1-5618 <$40
20 Type 1 1-1532 <$50
10 Type 2 1-11555 <$40
20 Type 2 1-3811 <$50
Total Issue $3,542,680
Out in 1935 $191,050
Large out 1935 $9,370

1113 Morris
N IRON B OF MORRISTOWN
{{ 10 L }}
Chartered 1865
Original Series <$VALUE
4x5 1-1750 <$400
3x10-20 1-2000 <$750/$1250
Series 1875
4x5 1-5500 <$400
3x10-20 1-3432 <$750/$1250
Brown Back
4x5 1-7100 <$300
3x10-20 1-3540 <$300
50-100 1-980 <$1250/$1500
1902 Red Seal
4x5 1-4165 <$300
3x10-20 1-2534 <$300
1902 Date Back
4x5 1-10925 <$150
3x10-20 1-7832 <$150
Total Issue $1,702,700
Out in 1935 $3,865

1168 Burlington
FARMERS NB OF NEW JERSEY
AT MOUNT HOLLY
{{ 10 L }}
Chartered 1865
Liquidated 12/30/11
Original Series <$VALUE
3x1-2 1-1150 <$350/$1000
4x5 1-3875 <$400
3x10-20 1-2350 <$750/$1250
50-100 1-1050 <$4000
Series 1875
3x1-2 1-1110 <$350/$1000
3x10-20 1-562 <$750/$1250
50-100 1-1549 <$4000
Brown Back
50-100 1-4181 <$1250/$1500
1902 Red Seal
50-100 1-2467 <$2250/$2500
1902 Date Back
50-100 1-1419 <$400/$500
Total Issue $1,834,300
Out in 1912 $100,586

1356 Burlington
MOUNT HOLLY NB,
MOUNT HOLLY
{{ 12 L 9 S }}
Organized 6/1/65
Receivership 8/4/33
Original Series <$VALUE
3x1-2 1-2000 <$350/$850
4x5 1-3700 <$400
3x10-20 1-1500 <$750/$1250
50-100 1-140 <$4000
Series 1875
3x10-20 1-3488 <$750/$1250
Brown Back
3x10-20 1-6294 <$275
1902 Red Seal
3x10-20 1-4300 <$300
1902 Date Back
3x10-20 1-8500 <$150
1902 Plain Back
3x10-20 8501-27362 <$150
1929 Small Size
10 Type 1 1-2975 <$125
20 Type 1 1-766 <$125
Total Issue $2,522,620
Out at close $100,000
Large out at close $7,920

2343 Burlington
UNION NB AT MOUNT HOLLY
Chartered 9/15/76
2nd title:Union NB & TC
at Mount Holly 2/11/28
FIRST TITLE {{ 5 L }}
Series 1875 <$VALUE
3x10-20 1-6076 <$750/$1250
Brown Back
3x10-20 1-9600 <$400
1882 Date Back
3x10-20 1-8800 <$400
1882 Value Back
3x10-20 8801-9600 <$400
1902 Plain Back
3x10-20 1-17072 <$150
SECOND TITLE {{ 3 L 41 S }}
1902 Plain Back
3x10-20 1-1589 <$150
1929 Small Size
10 Type 1 1-3976 <$30
20 Type 1 1-1318 <$40
10 Type 2 1-9043 <$30
20 Type 2 1-3168 <$40
Total Issue $2,747,360
Out in 1935 $186,900
Large out 1935 $4,590

6728 Gloucester
FARMERS NB OF
MULLICA HILL
{{ 8 L 13 S }}
Chartered 4/03
1902 Red Seal <$VALUE
4x5 1-970 <$450
3x10-20 1-652 <$450
1902 Date Back
4x5 1-4750 <$225
3x10-20 1-3430 <$225
1902 Plain Back
4x5 4751-15564 <$225
3x10-20 3431-10603 <$225
1929 Small Size
5 Type 1 1-1978 <$125
10 Type 1 1-1130 <$125
20 Type 1 1-348 <$125
5 Type 2 1-3442 <$150
10 Type 2 1-1577 <$150
20 Type 2 1-540 <$150
Total Issue $1,106,110
Out in 1935 $48,800
Large out 1935 $1,800

6692 Morris
CITIZENS NB OF NETCONG
{{ 6 L 7 S }}
Chartered 3/03
1902 Red Seal <$VALUE
3x10-20 1-3700 <$600
1902 Date Back
3x10-20 1-5700 <$300
1902 Plain Back
3x10-20 5701-15447 <$300
1929 Small Size
10 Type 1 1-1296 <$200
20 Type 1 1-388 <$200
5 Type 2 1-324 <$225
10 Type 2 1-2738 <$225
20 Type 2 1-768 <$225
Total Issue $1,126,030
Out in 1935 $49,050
Large out 1935 $2,755

208 Middlesex
FNB OF NEW BRUNSWICK
{{ 1 L }}
Chartered 1/19/64
Liquidated 2/26/68
Original Series <$VALUE
3x1-2 1-100 <$1500/$2000
4x5 1-2500 <$1500
4x10 1-1000 <$1750
Total Issue $90,500
Out in 1910 $1,191

587 Middlesex
NB OF NEW JERSEY,
NEW BRUNSWICK
{{ 13 L 3U + 50+ S }}
Chartered 11/64
Original Series <$VALUE
3x1-2 1-6900 <$350/$1000
4x5 1-6000 <$400
3x10-20 1-5200 <$750/$1250
50-100 1-500 <$4000
Series 1875
3x1-2 1-3680 <$350/$1000
4x5 1-15272 <$400
3x10-20 1-2400 <$750/$1250
Brown Back
4x5 1-16511 <$250
3x10-20 1-6345 <$250
1902 Red Seal
4x5 1-3900 <$300
3x10-20 1-2940 <$300
1902 Date Back
4x5 1-9850* <$125
3x10-20 1-6600** <$125
1902 Plain Back
4x5 10601-26449* <$125
3x10-20 7201-17135** <$125
* 9851-10600 not marked
** 6601-7200 not marked
1929 Small Size
5 Type 1 1-18964 <$25
10 Type 1 1-7414 <$25
20 Type 1 1-2362 <$35
5 Type 2 1-37764 <$25
10 Type 2 1-17105 <$25
20 Type 2 1-4432 <$35
Total Issue $4,944,750
Out in 1935 $354,735
Large out 1935 $8,120

3697 Middlesex
PEOPLES NB OF
NEW BRUNSWICK
{{ 7 L 19 S }}
Chartered 5/5/87
Brown Back <$VALUE
3x10-20 1-10278 <$300
1902 Red Seal
3x10-20 1-2000 <$350
1902 Date Back
3x10-20 1-10100 <$150
1902 Plain Back
3x10-20 10101-28823 <$150
1929 Small Size
10 Type 1 1-4174 <$50
20 Type 1 1-1228 <$60
10 Type 2 1-9349 <$50
20 Type 2 1-2480 <$60
Total Issue $2,595,940
Out in 1935 $158,050
Large out 1935 $5,010

13910 Ocean
FNB IN NEW EGYPT
{{ 7 S }}
Chartered 12/33
1929 Small Size <$VALUE
10 Type 2 1-4488 <$300
20 Type 2 1-1392 <$300
Total Issue $72,720
Out in 1935 $48,220

8254 Ocean
FNB OF NEW EGYPT
{{ 1 L }}
Organized 5/7/06
Liquidated 3/15/34
1902 Red Seal <$VALUE
3x10-20 1-350 <$1500
1902 Date Back
3x10-20 1-920 <$750
1902 Plain Back
3x10-20 921-1836 <$750
Total Issue $109,300
Out at close $500

9605 Essex
AMERICAN NB OF NEWARK
{{ 18 L }}
Chartered 12/09
Liquidated 6/29/27
1902 Date Back <$VALUE
4x5 1-25750 <$50
3x10-20 1-19300 <$65
1902 Plain Back
4x5 25751-81932 <$50
3x10-20 19301-52756 <$65
Total Issue $4,276,440
Out at close $250,995

9912 Essex
BROAD & MARKET NB OF
NEWARK
Organized 11/17/10
Receivership 6/11/32
2nd title:Broad & Market NB
& TC 4/22/27
3rd title:New Jersey NB &
TC 9/27/28
FIRST TITLE {{ 16 L }}
1902 Date Back <$VALUE
4x5 1-13850 <$50
3x10-20 1-10600 <$60
1902 Plain Back
4x5 13851-51688 <$50
3x10-20 10601-34509<$60
SECOND TITLE {{ 17 L }}
1902 Plain Back
4x5 1-19400 <$50
3x10-20 1-13358 <$60
3x50-100 1-3174 <$250/$300
THIRD TITLE {{ 6 L 25 S }}
1902 Plain Back
4x5 1-4999 <$100
3x10-20 1-4800 <$100
3x50-100 1-497 <$275/$325
1929 Small Size
5 Type 1 1-22328 <$20
10 Type 1 1-10966 <$25
20 Type 1 1-3091 <$35
50 Type 1 1-1075 <$100
100 Type 1 1-282 <$165
Total Issue $7,263,260
Out at close $1,026,600
Large out at close $68,300
Outstanding includes Ch 12604

1217 Essex
ESSEX COUNTY NB OF NEWARK
{{ 21 L }}
Chartered 1865
Liquidated 12/31/17
Original Series <$VALUE
3x1-2 1-10000 <$250/$750
4x5 1-11700 <$300
3x10-20 1-3200 <$750/$1250
50-100 1-500 <$4000
Series 1875
4x5 1-9500 <$300
3x10-20 1-6062 <$600/$1000
50-100 1-100 <$4000
Brown Back
4x5 1-11017 <$150
1902 Red Seal
4x5 1-12475 <$150
4x10 1-9325 <$175
3x10-20 1-2300 <$175/$225
1902 Date Back
4x5 1-90000 <$75
4x10 1-72925 <$75
3x10-20 1-3327 <$75
1902 Plain Back
4x5 90001-94259 <$75
4x10 72926-75808 <$75
Total Issue $7,623,080
Out at close $198,820
Ch 1316 assumed circulation

52 Essex
FNB OF NEWARK
{{ 10 L }}
Organized 8/7/63
Receivership 6/14/80
Original Series <$VALUE
3x1-2 1-4600 <$300/$850
4x5 1-17450 <$350
4x10 1-5075 <$750
3x20-50 1-3847*<$1250/$4000
* 293-1000 not issued
Series 1875
3x1-2 1-2000 <$300/$850
4x5 1-12257 <$350
4x10 1-2250 <$600
Total Issue $1,265,430
Out in 1916 $6,508

12604 Essex
FOREST HILL NB OF NEWARK
{{ 5 L }}
Chartered 12/24
Closed 9/28/27
1902 Plain Back <$VALUE
4x5 1-8182 <$250
Total Issue $163,640
Out at close $47,700
Ch 9912 assumed circulation

2045 Essex
GERMAN NB OF THE CITY OF
NEWARK
Chartered 9/14/72
Liquidated 12/31/20
2nd title:Union NB 6/14/02
FIRST TITLE {{ 4 L }}
Original Series <$VALUE
3x1-2 1-3000 <$300/$850
4x5 1-3000 <$350
3x10-20 1-2500 <$750/$1250
50-100 1-867 <$4000
Series 1875
4x5 1-4450 <$350
3x10-20 1-4220 <$600/$1000
50-100 1-743 <$4000
Brown Back
3x10-20 1-3048 <$300
50-100 1-94 <$1250/$1500
SECOND TITLE {{ 28 L }}
Brown Back
4x5 1-31500 <$100
3x10-20 1-24900 <$125/$175
50-100 1-2000 <$1250/$1500
1882 Date Back
4x5 1-63147 <$100
3x10-20 1-36084 <$125/$175
50-100 1-2921 <$1250/$1500
1902 Date Back
4x5 1-80000 <$40
4x10 1-66875 <$50
3x50-100 1-477 <$300/$350
1902 Plain Back
4x5 80001-94026 <$40
4x10 66876-82767 <$50
Total Issue $11,898,740
Out at close $173,995

12771 Essex
LABOR NB OF NEWARK
Chartered 6/25 as Labor
Cooperative NB, under
which there was no issue.
Issuing title adopted
1/20/27.
2nd issuing title:Union NB
in Newark 8/2/29
FIRST TITLE {{ 2 L }}
1902 Plain Back <$VALUE
4x5 1-3835 <$450
SECOND TITLE {{ 12 S }}
1929 Small Size
5 Type 1 1-15588 <$75
5 Type 2 1-60402 <$75
Total Issue $846,350
Out in 1935 $95,040
Large out 1935 $315

12570 Essex
LINCOLN NB OF NEWARK
{{ 28 L 32 S }}
Chartered 8/24
1902 Plain Back <$VALUE
3x10-20 1-48941 <$50/$60
1929 Small Size
20 Type 1 1-13056 <$35
20 Type 2 1-14529* <$35
* 5221-5232 not issued
Total Issue $4,304,110
Out in 1935 $600,000
Large out 1935 $4,700

CONDITION affects Value. The Values shown are for notes in FINE condition.

****
2040 Essex
MANUFACTURERS NB OF NEWARK
{{ U + 23 L }}
Chartered 9/5/72
Closed 5/29/20
Original Series <$VALUE
3x1-2 1-9000 <$250/$750
4x5 1-7500 <$250
3x10-20 1-3000 <$600/$1250
50-100 1-400 <$4000
Series 1875
4x5 1-9000 <$250
3x10-20 1-5042 <$500/$1000
50-100 1-1751 <$4000
Brown Back
4x5 1-31600 <$110
4x10 1-4500 <$125
3x10-20 1-9000 <$125/$175
50-100 1-2500 <$1250/$1500
1882 Date Back
4x5 1-21000 <$110
4x10 1-14104 <$125
50-100 1-1595 <$1250/$1500
1902 Date Back
4x5 1-14150 <$65
4x10 1-8925 <$65
3x50-100 1-3320 <$300/$350
1902 Plain Back
4x5 14151-16650 <$65
4x10 8926-10925 <$65
Total Issue $5,560,160
Out at close $342,745
Ch 1818 assumed circulation
****
1251 Essex
MECHANICS NB OF NEWARK
{{ 8 L }}
Organized 6/9/65
Receivership 11/2/81
Original Series <$VALUE
3x1-2 1-19000 <$275/$850
4x5 1-19250 <$300
4x10 1-5800 <$750
50-100 1-1200 <$4000
Series 1875
4x10 1-3000 <$600
50-100 1-2440 <$4000
Total Issue $1,378,000
Out in 1916 $8,138
****
Merchants & Manufacturers NB of Newark
SEE Ch 1818
Merchants NB of Newark
****
1818 Essex
MERCHANTS NB OF NEWARK
Chartered 5/15/71
Liquidated 3/19/27
2nd title:Merchants & Manufacturers NB 5/29/20
FIRST TITLE {{ 29 L }}
Original Series <$VALUE
3x1-2 1-4400 <$250/$750
4x5 1-4400 <$250
3x10-20 1-4600 <$600/$1250
50-50 1-100 <$4000
Series 1875
4x5 1-6700 <$250
3x10-20 1-4271 <$500/$1000
50-50 1-1979 <$4000
Brown Back
4x5 1-22500 <$110
3x10-20 1-18340 <$125/$175
50-100 1-2510 <$1250/$1500
1882 Date Back
4x5 1-21460 <$110
3x10-20 1-14596 <$125/$175
50-100 1-748 <$1250/$1500
1902 Date Back
4x5 1-37500 <$40
4x10 1-36000 <$50
1902 Plain Back
4x5 37501-78000 <$40
4x10 36001-67500 <$50
SECOND TITLE {{ 30 L }}
1902 Plain Back
4x5 1-72760 <$40
3x10-20 1-43044 <$50
3x50-100 1-2504 <$250/$300
Total Issue $12,403,550
Out at close $832,700
Outstanding includes Ch 2040
****
1316 Essex
N NEWARK BANKING C, NEWARK
{{ 14 L }}
Organized 6/24/65
Original Series <$VALUE
3x1-2 1-8000 <$250/$750
4x5 1-21750 <$275
3x10-20 1-4500 <$600/$1250
3x50-100 1-920 <$4000
Series 1875
4x5 1-7473 <$275
3x50-100 1-2563 <$4000
Brown Back
50-100 1-4760 <$1250/$1500
1902 Red Seal
4x5 1-5830 <$250
4x10 1-3750 <$250
3x10-20 1-2000 <$250
50-100 1-3688 <$2250/$2500
1902 Date Back
4x5 1-61230 <$125
4x10 1-48200 <$125
50-100 1-1000 <$300/$350
3x50-100 1-1531 <$300/$350
Total Issue $7,039,360
Out in 1935 $26,500
Outstanding includes Ch 1217
****
1452 Essex
N STATE B OF NEWARK
{{ 28 L 16 S }}
Chartered 1865
Original Series <$VALUE
3x1-2 1-14500 <$250/$750
4x5 1-13850 <$275
3x10-20 1-6720 <$600/$1250
50-100 1-2280 <$4000
Series 1875
3x1-2 1-880 <$250/$750
4x5 1-8250 <$275
3x10-20 1-2200 <$500/$1000
50-100 1-4688 <$4000
Brown Back
50-100 1-4898 <$1250/$1500
1902 Red Seal
50-100 1-706 <$2250/$2500
1902 Date Back
4x5 1-27000 <$40
3x10-20 1-15500 <$50
50-100 1-1700 <$300/$350
3x50-100 1-1738 <$300/$350
1902 Plain Back
4x5 27001-87775 <$40
3x10-20 15501-48172 <$50
3x50-100 1739-2230 <$300/$350
1929 Small Size
5 Type 1 1-8454 <$30
10 Type 1 1-4206 <$35
20 Type 1 1-1174 <$40
50 Type 1 1-500 <$100
100 Type 1 1-134 <$165
5 Type 2 1-13014 <$30
10 Type 2 1-7625 <$35
20 Type 2 1-3152 <$40
Total Issue $8,908,920
Out in 1935 $339,300
Large out 1935 $25,440
****
New Jersey NB & TC of Newark
SEE Ch 9912
Broad & Market NB of Newark
****
1220 Essex
NEWARK CITY NB, NEWARK
{{ 7 L }}
Chartered 6/5/65
Liquidated 6/30/02
Original Series <$VALUE
3x1-2 1-13500 <$275/$750
4x5 1-14750 <$300
3x10-20 1-2400 <$600/$1250
50-100 1-784 <$4000
Series 1875
4x5 1-14303 <$300
3x10-20 1-3300 <$500/$1000
Brown Back
4x5 1-13551 <$200
3x10-20 1-1006 <$200
Total Issue $1,372,480
Out in 1910 $8,572
****
2083 Essex
NORTH WARD NB OF NEWARK
{{ 29 L 2 S }}
Chartered 2/14/73
Liquidated 4/19/30
Original Series <$VALUE
3x1-2 1-3000 <$250/$750
4x5 1-5000 <$250
3x10-20 1-1000 <$600/$1250
4x20 1-1000 <$1250
50-100 1-600 <$4000
Series 1875
3x10-20 1-5812 <$250/$750
50-100 1-734 <$4000
Brown Back
4x5 1-7865 <$125
3x10-20 1-3874 <$125/$175
1882 Date Back
4x5 1-6849 <$125
3x10-20 1-5328 <$125/$165
1902 Date Back
4x5 1-10000 <$40
4x10 1-10000 <$50
1902 Plain Back
4x5 10001-56474 <$40
4x10 10001-48365 <$50
1929 Small Size
5 Type 1 1-1558 <$200
10 Type 1 1-862 <$200
Total Issue $4,652,620
Out at close $125,015
Large out at close $33,925
****
362 Essex
SECOND NB OF NEWARK
{{ 1 L }}
Chartered 4/5/64
Liquidated 6/14/02
Original Series <$VALUE
4x5 1-7500 <$600
3x10-20 1-6000 <$750/$1250
50-100 1-800 <$4000
Series 1875
4x5 1-5900 <$600
3x10-20 1-3540 <$750/$1250
50-100 1-661 <$4000
Brown Back
4x5 1-6225 <$500
3x10-20 1-4310 <$500
50-100 1-1461 <$1250/$1500
Total Issue $1,523,300
Out in 1910 $8,840
****
Union NB in Newark
SEE Ch 12771
Labor NB of Newark
****
Union NB of Newark
SEE Ch 2045
German NB of the City of Newark
****
876 Sussex
MERCHANTS NB OF NEWTON
{{ 12 L }}
Chartered 3/10/65
Closed 1/2/25
Original Series <$VALUE
3x1-2 1-3000 <$300/$850
4x5 1-2150 <$350
3x10-20 1-2620 <$600/$1250
Series 1875
3x1-2 1-1060 <$300/$850
4x5 1-3750 <$350
3x10-20 1-1452 <$600/$1250
Brown Back
4x5 1-22651 <$275
3x10-20 1-3518 <$275
1902 Red Seal
3x10-20 1-4000 <$300
1902 Date Back
3x10-20 1-9400 <$125
1902 Plain Back
3x10-20 9401-20966 <$125
Total Issue $2,219,120
Out at close $100,000
Ch 925 assumed circulation
****
Sussex & Merchants NB of Newton
SEE Ch 925
Sussex NB of Newton
****
925 Sussex
SUSSEX NB OF NEWTON
Chartered 3/22/65
2nd title:Sussex & Merchants NB of Newton 1/2/25
FIRST TITLE {{ 14 L }}
Original Series <$VALUE
4x5 1-4300 <$300
3x10-20 1-3090 <$600/$1250
50-100 1-544 <$4000
Series 1875
4x5 1-2750 <$300
3x10-20 1-5021 <$500/$1000
50-100 1-135 <$4000
Brown Back
4x5 1-15277 <$200
3x10-20 1-19108 <$200
1902 Red Seal
3x10-20 1-7700 <$225/$250
1902 Date Back
3x10-20 1-19690 <$100
1902 Plain Back
3x10-20 19691-42290 <$100
SECOND TITLE {{ 6 L 36 S }}
1902 Plain Back
3x10-20 1-19711 <$125
1929 Small Size
5 Type 1 1-6160 <$20
10 Type 1 1-7828 <$20
20 Type 1 1-2874 <$30
5 Type 2 1-35308 <$20
10 Type 2 1-19191 <$20
20 Type 2 1-624 <$35
Total Issue $6,774,680
Out in 1935 $390,195
Large out 1935 $17,285
****
12033 Bergen
NORTH ARLINGTON NB, NORTH ARLINGTON
{{ 0 L 6 S }}
Organized 7/7/21
1902 Plain Back <$VALUE
4x5 1-815 <$1250
1929 Small Size
5 Type 1 1-2336 <$250
5 Type 2 1-11520 <$250
Total Issue $143,980
Out in 1935 $26,560
Large out 1935 $100
****
12732 Hudson
FNB OF NORTH BERGEN
{{ 9 L 15 S }}
Chartered 5/25
1902 Plain Back <$VALUE
4x5 1-11589 <$150
3x10-20 1-4994 <$150
1929 Small Size
10 Type 1 1-3172 <$75
20 Type 1 1-820 <$75
10 Type 2 1-4552 <$85
20 Type 2 1-1378 <$85
Total Issue $843,280
Out in 1935 $78,050
Large out 1935 $2,100
****
12903 Camden
PENNSAUKEN TOWNSHIP NB OF NORTH MERCHANTVILLE
{{ 2 S }}
Organized 12/30/25
1929 Small Size <$VALUE
5 Type 2 1-3790 <$500
10 Type 2 1-2490 <$500
Total Issue $43,850
Out in 1935 $20,450
****
9391 Somerset
BOROUGH NB OF NORTH PLAINFIELD
{{ UNREPORTED }}
Chartered 4/09
Liquidated 9/15/10
1902 Date Back <$VALUE
4x5 1-445 <$1500
4x10 1-427 <$1500
Total Issue $25,980
Out in 1910 $10,700
****
11409 Essex
FNB OF NUTLEY
{{ 9 S }}
Chartered 7/19
1929 Small Size <$VALUE
5 Type 1 1-9670 <$125
5 Type 2 1-29774 <$125
Total Issue $438,970
Out in 1935 $42,150
****
12750 Essex
FRANKLIN NB OF NUTLEY
{{ 13 S }}
Chartered 5/25
1929 Small Size <$VALUE
5 Type 1 1-1036 <$100
10 Type 1 1-526 <$100
20 Type 1 1-260 <$100
50 Type 1 1-106 <$250
5 Type 2 1-6626 <$100
10 Type 2 1-3095 <$100
20 Type 2 1-750 <$100
Total Issue $204,720
Out in 1935 $75,850
****
12621 Camden
OAKLYN NB, OAKLYN
{{ 11 S }}
Chartered 1/25
1929 Small Size <$VALUE
5 Type 1 1-996 <$125
10 Type 1 1-448 <$125
20 Type 1 1-146 <$125
5 Type 2 1-3338 <$125
10 Type 2 1-1690 <$125
20 Type 2 1-595 <$125
Total Issue $119,770
Out in 1935 $41,250
****
****
6060 Cape May
FNB OF OCEAN CITY
{{ 21 L 32 S }}
Chartered 12/21/01
Receivership 11/18/32
Brown Back <$VALUE
3x10-20 1-1750 <$225
1882 Date Back
3x10-20 1-2010* <$225
1882 Value Back
3x10-20 2611-6368* <$225
* 2011-2610 not marked
1902 Plain Back
3x10-20 1-31336 <$125
1929 Small Size
10 Type 1 1-8294 <$50
20 Type 1 1-2138 <$60
Total Issue $2,726,900
Out at close $300,000
Large out at close $13,500
****
12521 Cape May
OCEAN CITY NB, OCEAN CITY
{{ 1 L 14 S }}
Organized 11/16/23
Receivership 6/18/34
1902 Plain Back <$VALUE
3x10-20 1-5259 <$450
1929 Small Size
10 Type 1 1-2124 <$100
20 Type 1 1-544 <$100
10 Type 2 1-948 <$125
20 Type 2 1-325 <$125
Total Issue $471,650
Out at close $79,500
Large out at close $1,080
****
5403 Monmouth
OCEAN GROVE NB, OCEAN GROVE
{{ 4 L 0 S }}
Chartered 6/6/00
Receivership 1/26/32
Brown Back <$VALUE
3x10-20 1-2220 <$500
1882 Date Back
3x10-20 1-2720 <$500
1882 Value Back
3x10-20 2721-4141 <$500
1902 Plain Back
3x10-20 1-3569 <$350
1929 Small Size
10 Type 1 1-474 <$650
20 Type 1 1-124 <$650
Total Issue $539,820
Out at close $24,040
Large out at close $2,280
****
1317 Essex
ORANGE NB, ORANGE
{{ 4 L }}
Organized 6/13/65
Receivership 12/19/33
Original Series <$VALUE
3x1-2 1-5000 <$400/$1000
4x5 1-8600 <$400
3x10-20 1-3000 <$750/$1250
Series 1875
4x5 1-6250 <$400
3x10-20 1-4700 <$750/$1250
Brown Back
4x5 1-3650 <$350
3x10-20 1-2030 <$350
50-100 1-3365 <$1500/$1750
1902 Red Seal
4x5 1-4500 <$400
3x10-20 1-1800 <$400
50-100 1-1400 <$2250/$2500
1902 Date Back
4x5 1-12270 <$250
3x10-20 1-5912 <$250
50-100 1-195 <$450/$500
Total Issue $2,346,500
Out at close $5,184
****
4724 Essex
SECOND NB OF ORANGE
{{ 14 L 46 S }}
Chartered 1892
Brown Back <$VALUE
4x5 1-3600 <$250
3x10-20 1-3670 <$250
50-100 1-590 <$1250/$1500
1882 Date Back
4x5 1-9195 <$250
3x10-20 1-5562 <$250
50-100 1-200 <$1250/$1500
1902 Date Back
4x5 1-9600 <$100
3x10-20 1-7160 <$100
1902 Plain Back
4x5 9601-43275 <$100
3x10-20 7161-27330 <$100
1929 Small Size
5 Type 1 1-6542 <$30
10 Type 1 1-3270 <$30
20 Type 1 1-748 <$40
5 Type 2 1-14424 <$30
10 Type 2 1-5808 <$30
20 Type 2 1-1128 <$40
Total Issue $3,702,980
Out in 1935 $129,850
Large out 1935 $6,800
****
14088 Bergen
NB OF PALISADES PARK
{{ 1 S }}
Chartered 4/34
1929 Small Size <$VALUE
5 Type 2 1-5300 <$650
Total Issue $26,500
Out in 1935 $37,660
Outstanding includes Ch 11909
****
11909 Bergen
PALISADES PARK NB, PALISADES PARK
Organized 12/22/20
Liquidated 5/17/34
2nd title:Palisades Park NB & TC 5/15/29
FIRST TITLE {{ 18 L }}
1902 Plain Back <$VALUE
4x5 1-26057 <$150
SECOND TITLE {{ 14 S }}
1929 Small Size
5 Type 1 1-14718 <$125
5 Type 2 1-12062 <$125
Total Issue $1,022,990
Out at close $82,790
Large out 1935 $2,060
Ch 14088 assumed circulation
****
11793 Burlington
PALMYRA NB, PALMYRA
{{ 1 L 7 S }}
Organized 7/2/20
Receivership 1/6/34
1902 Plain Back <$VALUE
4x5 1-2125 <$750
3x10-20 1-1449 <$750
1929 Small Size
5 Type 1 1-508 <$225
10 Type 1 1-244 <$225
20 Type 1 1-82 <$225
5 Type 2 1-254 <$250
10 Type 2 1-103 <$250
20 Type 2 1-15 <$275
Total Issue $157,270
Out at close $12,500
Large out at close $390
****
12834 Passaic
AMERICAN NB OF PASSAIC
{{ 2U + 11 L 5 S }}
Chartered 10/25
Liquidated 8/26/31
1902 Plain Back <$VALUE
4x5 1-6075 <$150
3x10-20 1-4791 <$150
1929 Small Size
5 Type 1 1-4563 <$150
10 Type 1 1-2220 <$150
20 Type 1 1-557 <$150
Total Issue $697,980
Out at close $194,180
Large out at close $5,850
****
13123 Passaic
LINCOLN NB OF PASSAIC
{{ 13 L 14 S }}
Chartered 9/27
Liquidated 12/16/31
1902 Plain Back <$VALUE
4x5 1-22670 <$100
3x10-20 1-9390 <$100
1929 Small Size
5 Type 1 1-14306 <$50
10 Type 1 1-6783 <$50
20 Type 1 1-1976 <$60
Total Issue $1,996,180
Out at close $454,100
Large out at close $12,380
****

****
12205 Passaic
PASSAIC NB & TC, PASSAIC
{{ 50+ L 50+ S }}
Chartered 5/22
1902 Plain Back <$VALUE
3x10-20 1-171372 <$50/$60
1929 Small Size
10 Type 1 1-55064* <$20
20 Type 1 1-16442 <$30
10 Type 2 1-58008 <$20
20 Type 2 1-17179 <$30
* 54398 not issued
Total Issue $14,769,080
Out in 1935 $1,300,860
Large out 1935 $39,460
Outstanding includes Ch 3572
****
3572 Passaic
PASSAIC NB, PASSAIC
{{ 8 L }}
Chartered 10/16/86
Closed 6/22/22
Brown Back <$VALUE
4x5 1-5125 <$225
3x10-20 1-8333 <$225/$250
1902 Red Seal
3x10-20 1-2850 <$250/$275
1902 Date Back
3x10-20 1-14300 <$125
1902 Plain Back
3x10-20 14301-24339 <$125
Total Issue $1,878,600
Out at close $123,600
Ch 12205 assumed circulation
****
12726 Passaic
BROADWAY NB OF PATERSON
{{ 12 L }}
Chartered 5/25
Liquidated 7/1/29
1902 Plain Back <$VALUE
3x10-20 1-3701 <$125
Total Issue $185,050
Out at close $48,850
****
329 Passaic
FNB OF PATERSON
{{ 30 L 39 S }}
Organized 3/16/64
Original Series <$VALUE
3x1-2 1-6500 <$225/$750
4x5 1-16575 <$275
3x10-20 1-5822 <$750/$1250
50-100 1-466 <$4000
Series 1875
3x10-20 1-7799 <$600/$1000
Brown Back
3x10-20 1-17820 <$150/$200
50-100 1-1073 <$1250/$1500
1902 Red Seal
4x5 1-12500 <$125
3x10-20 1-20700 <$150/$200
1902 Date Back
4x5 1-44665 <$45
3x10-20 1-33634 <$60
1902 Plain Back
4x5 44666-98972 <$45
3x10-20 33635-65818 <$60
1929 Small Size
5 Type 1 1-15730 <$15
10 Type 1 1-9052 <$20
20 Type 1 1-2078 <$30
5 Type 2 1-39110 <$15
10 Type 2 1-21110 <$20
20 Type 2 1-4199 <$30
Total Issue $10,477,250
Out in 1935 $355,930
Large out 1935 $20,120
****
12560 Passaic
LABOR CO-OPERATIVE NB OF PATERSON
{{ 6 L }}
Organized 5/23/24
Liquidated 3/16/35
1902 Plain Back <$VALUE
4x5 1-3425 <$225
3x10-20 1-2429 <$225
Total Issue $189,950
Out at close $860
****
12383 Passaic
NB OF AMERICA IN PATERSON
{{ 25 L 33 S }}
Organized 4/21/23
1902 Plain Back <$VALUE
4x5 1-50405 <$50
3x10-20 1-41393 <$60
1929 Small Size
5 Type 1 1-12958 <$25
10 Type 1 1-12204 <$25
20 Type 1 1-3232 <$35
5 Type 2 1-34702 <$25
10 Type 2 1-17856 <$25

Total Issue $4,760,080
Out in 1935 $211,920
Large out 1935 $11,915
****
810 Passaic
PASSAIC COUNTY NB OF PATERSON
Chartered 2/17/65
2nd title:Second NB 4/15/74
FIRST TITLE {{ 0 L }}
Original Series <$VALUE
3x1-2 1-2400 <$500/$1000
4x5 1-4087 <$500
3x10-20 1-900 <$750/$1250
SECOND TITLE {{ 15 L 2U+32 S }}
Original Series
4x5 1-2800 <$350
Series 1875
4x5 1 11121 <$350
Brown Back
3x10-20 1-9320 <$175/$225
1902 Red Seal
3x10-20 1-5400 <$200/$250
1902 Date Back
3x10-20 1-10900 <$75
1902 Plain Back
3x10-20 10901-30824 <$75
1929 Small Size
10 Type 1 1-4116 <$25
20 Type 1 1-1189 <$35
100 Type 1 1-920 <$150
Total Issue $3,636,000
Out in 1935 $544,650
Large out 1935 $6,410
****
4072 Passaic
PATERSON NB, PATERSON
{{ 28 L 36 S }}
Chartered 7/8/89
Brown Back <$VALUE
4x5 1-8950 <$150
3x10-20 1-11671 <$150/$200
50-100 1-763 <$1250/$1500
1902 Date Back
3x10-20 1-17000 <$50
50-100 1-500 <$300/$350
3x50-100 1-1400 <$300/$350
1902 Plain Back
3x10-20 17001-60769 <$50
3x50-100 1401-2599 <$300/$350
1929 Small Size
10 Type 1 1-13134 <$25
20 Type 1 1-3503 <$35
50 Type 1 1-1112 <$85
100 Type 1 1-334 <$150
Total Issue $6,382,600
Out in 1935 $617,710
Large out 1935 $17,710
****
Second NB of Paterson
SEE Ch 810
Passaic County NB of Paterson
****
5981 Gloucester
FNB OF PAULSBORO
Chartered 10/1/01
2nd title:FNB & TC 11/1/24
FIRST TITLE {{ 9 L }}
Brown Back <$VALUE
4x5 1-1700 <$300
3x10-20 1-1260 <$300
1882 Date Back
4x5 1-3350 <$300
3x10-20 1-2340 <$300
1882 Value Back
4x5 3351-5735 <$300
3x10-20 2341-3708 <$300
1902 Plain Back
4x5 1-1850 <$175
3x10-20 1-1260 <$175
SECOND TITLE {{ 1 L 12 S }}
1902 Plain Back
4x5 1-2549 <$200
3x10-20 1-1586 <$200
1929 Small Size
5 Type 1 1-1104 <$125
10 Type 1 1-654 <$125
20 Type 1 1-200 <$125
5 Type 2 1-7070 <$150
10 Type 2 1-4164 <$150
20 Type 2 1-976 <$150
Total Issue $820,250
Out in 1935 $81,500
Large out 1935 $1,600
****
12002 Somerset
PEAPACK-GLADSTONE NB, PEAPACK-GLADSTONE
{{ 6 L }}
Chartered 8/21
Liquidated 11/30/25
1902 Plain Back <$VALUE
4x5 1-550 <$300
3x10-20 1-260 <$300

Total Issue $24,000
Out at close $9,900
****
8007 Salem
FNB OF PEDRICKTOWN
{{ 3 L 6 S }}
Organized 11/24/05
1902 Red Seal <$VALUE
3x10-20 1-1250 <$750
1902 Date Back
3x10-20 1-2490 <$375
1902 Plain Back
3x10-20 2491-7416 <$375
1929 Small Size
10 Type 1 1-780 <$225
20 Type 1 1-200 <$225
10 Type 2 1-1392 <$250
20 Type 2 1-336 <$250
Total Issue $524,740
Out in 1935 $22,730
Large out 1935 $980
****
8129 Burlington
PEOPLES NB OF PEMBERTON
Organized 2/3/06
2nd title:Peoples NB & TC 5/1/28
FIRST TITLE {{ 2 L }}
1902 Red Seal <$VALUE
3x10-20 1-900 <$850
1902 Date Back
3x10-20 1-2520 <$500
1902 Plain Back
3x10-20 2521-4139 <$500
SECOND TITLE {{ 0 L 5 S }}
1902 Plain Back
3x10-20 1-191 <$600
1929 Small Size
10 Type 1 1-396 <$250
20 Type 1 1-128 <$250
10 Type 2 1-152 <$275
20 Type 2 1-40 <$275
Total Issue $302,940
Out in 1935 $13,000
Large out 1935 $920
****
5387 Salem
PENN'S GROVE NB, PENN'S GROVE
Chartered 6/2/00
2nd title: Penn's Grove NB & TC 6/5/28
FIRST TITLE {{ 3 L }}
Brown Back <$VALUE
3x10-20 1-1900 <$600
1882 Date Back
3x10-20 1-2440 <$600
1882 Value Back
3x10-20 2441-3797 <$600
1902 Plain Back
3x10-20 1-3428 <$400
SECOND TITLE {{ 0 L 15 S }}
1902 Plain Back
3x10-20 1-325 <$500
1929 Small Size
10 Type 1 1-864 <$100
20 Type 1 1-200 <$100
10 Type 2 1-7390 <$125
20 Type 2 1-1564 <$125
Total Issue $653,520
Out in 1935 $100,000
Large out 1935 $660
****
5718 Mercer
FNB OF PENNINGTON
{{ 5 L 9 S }}
Chartered 2/16/01
Brown Back <$VALUE
4x5 1-1165 <$400
3x10-20 1-874 <$400
1882 Date Back
4x5 1-2375 <$400
3x10-20 1-1760 <$400
1882 Value Back
4x5 2376-4165 <$400
3x10-20 1761-2772 <$400
1902 Plain Back
4x5 1-3855 <$300
3x10-20 1-2310 <$300
1929 Small Size
5 Type 1 1-1004 <$135
10 Type 1 1-472 <$135
20 Type 1 1-148 <$150
5 Type 2 1-5070 <$150
10 Type 2 1-2519 <$150
20 Type 2 1-730 <$150
Total Issue $622,840
Out in 1935 $69,550
Large out 1935 $1,050
****

****
11351 Middlesex
CITY NB OF PERTH AMBOY
{{ 4 L }}
Chartered 5/19
Liquidated 6/30/23
1902 Plain Back <$VALUE
4x5 1-6465 <$300
3x10-20 1-3130 <$300
Total Issue $285,800
Out at close $58,300
****
5215 Middlesex
FNB OF PERTH AMBOY
{{ 18 L 12 S }}
Chartered 8/23/99
Brown Back <$VALUE
4x5 1-3500 <$200
3x10-20 1-4900 <$200/$225
1882 Date Back
4x5 1-12150 <$200
3x10-20 1-8620 <$200/$225
1882 Value Back
4x5 12151-17420 <$200
3x10-20 8621-11368 <$200/$225
1902 Plain Back
4x5 1-15433 <$85
4x10 1-6576 <$100
3x10-20 1-6561 <$100
1929 Small Size
5 Type 1 1-5434 <$50
10 Type 1 1-3546 <$50
20 Type 1 1-800 <$60
5 Type 2 1-14410 <$50
10 Type 2 1-8088 <$50
20 Type 2 1-1535 <$60
Total Issue $2,786,960
Out in 1935 $146,800
Large out 1935 $5,605
****
12524 Middlesex
PERTH AMBOY NB, PERTH AMBOY
{{ 5 L 50+ S }}
Chartered 4/24
1902 Plain Back <$VALUE
3x10-20 1-7053 <$200
1929 Small Size
10 Type 1 1-3232 <$25
20 Type 1 1-774 <$35
5 Type 2 1-22124 <$25
10 Type 2 1-6374 <$25
20 Type 2 1-1575 <$35
Total Issue $845,310
Out in 1935 $113,600
Large out 1935 $2,050
****
1239 Warren
PHILLIPSBURG NB, PHILLIPSBURG
Chartered 1865
2nd title:Phillipsburg NB & TC 1925
FIRST TITLE {{ 27 L }}
Original Series <$VALUE
4x5 1-7100 <$300
3x10-20 1-2300 <$750/$1250
50-100 1-301 <$4000
Series 1875
4x5 1-2500 <$300
3x10-20 1-4480 <$750/$1250
50-100 1-335 <$4000
Brown Back
4x5 1-13517 <$125
3x10-20 1-12215 <$125/$175
50-100 1-1963 <$1250/$1500
1902 Red Seal
4x5 1-6500 <$150
3x10-20 1-3200 <$175/$225
50-100 1-300 <$2250/$2500
1902 Date Back
4x5 1-16000 <$60
3x10-20 1-11300 <$75
50-100 1-300 <$300/$350
1902 Plain Back
4x5 16001-41000 <$60
3x10-20 11301-27000 <$75
SECOND TITLE {{ 4 L 32 S }}
1902 Plain Back
4x5 1-12037 <$75
4x10 1-5839 <$85
3x10-20 1-4701 <$85
1929 Small Size
5 Type 1 1-8350 <$35
10 Type 1 1-4546 <$35
20 Type 1 1-1122 <$55
5 Type 2 1-11100 <$35
10 Type 2 1-5914 <$35
20 Type 2 1-1384 <$60
Total Issue $5,861,510
Out in 1935 $165,800
Large out 1935 $12,310
****

****
5556 Warren
SECOND NB OF PHILLIPSBURG
{{ 27 L 19 S }}
Chartered 8/25/00
Brown Back <$VALUE
4x5 1-2750 <$150
3x10-20 1-7100 <$150/$200
1882 Date Back
4x5 1-9600 <$150
3x10-20 1-5960 <$150/$200
1882 Value Back
4x5 9601-15450 <$150
3x10-20 5961-9296 <$150/$200
1902 Plain Back
4x5 1-13630 <$60
3x10-20 1-9828 <$75
1929 Small Size
5 Type 1 1-3998 <$45
10 Type 1 1-2194 <$50
20 Type 1 1-606 <$60
5 Type 2 1-5652 <$45
10 Type 2 1-3048 <$50
20 Type 2 1-828 <$60
Total Issue $2,347,400
Out in 1935 $98,340
Large out 1935 $4,580
****
8500 Gloucester
PITMAN NB, PITMAN
Chartered 1/07
2nd title:Pitman NB & TC 5/5/26
FIRST TITLE {{ 1 L }}
1902 Red Seal <$VALUE
3x10-20 1-400 <$1000
1902 Date Back
3x10-20 1-1350 <$500
1902 Plain Back
3x10-20 1351-3189 <$500
SECOND TITLE {{ 0 L 16 S }}
1902 Plain Back
4x10 1-735 <$500
1929 Small Size
10 Type 1 1-1820 <$85
10 Type 2 1-6150 <$85
Total Issue $379,550
Out in 1935 $54,810
Large out 1935 $470
****
2243 Union
CITY NB OF PLAINFIELD
{{ 41 L }}
Chartered 4/7/75
Liquidated 6/28/26
Original Series <$VALUE
4x5 1-1000 <$300
3x10-20 1-500 <$750/$1250
Series 1875
4x5 1-7702 <$300
3x10-20 1-4455 <$750/$1250
Brown Back
4x5 1-15250 <$125
3x10-20 1-8580 <$125/$175
1882 Date Back
4x5 1-14692 <$125
3x10-20 1-10201 <$125/$175
1902 Date Back
4x5 1-2500 <$50
3x10-20 1-2000 <$60
1902 Plain Back
4x5 2501-13950 <$50
3x10-20 2001-9589 <$60
Total Issue $2,718,130
Out at close $27,800
****
447 Union
FNB OF PLAINFIELD
{{ 31 L 29 S }}
Chartered 5/64
Closed 10/17/32
Original Series <$VALUE
4x5 1-6450 <$300
3x10-20 1-4000 <$750/$1250
Series 1875
4x5 1-7500 <$300
3x10-20 1-2400 <$600/$1000
Brown Back
4x5 1-16550 <$150
3x10-20 1-8140 <$150/$200
1902 Red Seal
4x5 1-8600 <$150
4x10 1-2250 <$175
3x10-20 1-4360 <$175/$225
1902 Date Back
4x5 1-17250 <$50
4x10 1-13750* <$60
3x10-20 1-500 <$60
1902 Plain Back
4x5 17251-56244 <$50
4x10 14251-46468* <$60
* 13751-14250 not marked

1929 Small Size
5 Type 1 1-16817 <$40
10 Type 1 1-7911 <$40
Total Issue $5,804,770
Out at close $400,000
Large out 1935 $12,085
Ch 13629 assumed circulation
****
13629 Union
FNB OF PLAINFIELD
{{ 18 S }}
Chartered 8/32 as Fourth NB under which there was no issue. Issuing title adopted 10/17/32.
1929 Small Size <$VALUE
5 Type 1 1-1432 <$50
10 Type 1 1-722 <$50
5 Type 2 1-22406 <$50
10 Type 2 1-11655 <$50
Total Issue $314,860
Out in 1935 $162,285
Large out 1935 $12,085
Outstanding includes Ch 447
****
13174 Union
PLAINFIELD NB, PLAINFIELD
{{ U + 27 S }}
Chartered 1/28
1929 Small Size <$VALUE
5 Type 1 1-5860 <$30
10 Type 1 1-2130 <$30
20 Type 1 1-476 <$40
5 Type 2 1-14668 <$30
10 Type 2 1-7155 <$30
20 Type 2 1-1865 <$40
Total Issue $542,910
Out in 1935 $126,150
****
6508 Atlantic
FNB OF PLEASANTVILLE
{{ 4 L 2U + 41 S }}
Chartered 11/26/02
Receivership 11/21/34
1902 Red Seal <$VALUE
3x10-20 1-1356 <$500
1902 Date Back
3x10-20 1-2580 <$275
1902 Plain Back
3x10-20 2581-7555 <$275
1929 Small Size
5 Type 1 1-2050 <$40
10 Type 1 1-1610 <$40
20 Type 1 1-502 <$50
5 Type 2 1-1128 <$40
10 Type 2 1-465 <$40
Total Issue $674,180
Out at close $100,000
Large out at close $820
****
12510 Atlantic
PLEASANTVILLE NB, PLEASANTVILLE
{{ 3 L 12 S }}
Organized 2/20/24
Receivership 2/4/33
1902 Plain Back <$VALUE
4x5 1-8497 <$350
1929 Small Size
5 Type 1 1-7198 <$125
Total Issue $385,880
Out at close $100,000
Large out at close $320
****
5712 Ocean
OCEAN COUNTY NB OF POINT PLEASANT BEACH
{{ 10 L 10 S }}
Chartered 2/13/01
Brown Back <$VALUE
4x5 1-1100 <$600
3x10-20 1-770 <$600
1882 Date Back
4x5 1-2850 <$600
3x10-20 1-2180 <$600
1882 Value Back
4x5 2851-5430 <$600
3x10-20 2181-3797 <$600
1902 Plain Back
4x10 1-7284 <$400
1929 Small Size
10 Type 1 1-1866 <$300
10 Type 2 1-3816 <$300
Total Issue $800,430
Out in 1935 $37,370
Large out 1935 $1,710
****

****
13215 Ocean
POINT PLEASANT BEACH NB & TC, POINT PLEASANT BEACH
{{ 6 S }}
Organized 5/1/28 as Point Pleasant Beach NB, under which there was no issue. Issuing title adopted 8/22/29.
Receivership 2/3/32
1929 Small Size <$VALUE
5 Type 1 1-2233 <$325
10 Type 1 1-1078 <$325
20 Type 1 1-370 <$325
Total Issue $176,070
Out at close $94,900
****
10036 Cumberland
FNB OF PORT NORRIS
{{ 6 L 3 S }}
Organized 10/26/10
Receivership 10/31/33
1902 Date Back <$VALUE
4x5 1-1465 <$350
3x10-20 1-1134 <$350
1902 Plain Back
4x5 1466-6660 <$350
3x10-20 1135-4261 <$350
1929 Small Size
5 Type 1 1-840 <$300
10 Type 1 1-494 <$300
20 Type 1 1-138 <$300
5 Type 2 1-290 <$350
10 Type 2 1-93 <$350
20 Type 2 1-30 <$375
Total Issue $420,630
Out at close $23,950
Large out at close $350
****
4872 Mercer
FNB OF PRINCETON
{{ 23 L 50 S }}
Chartered 1893
Brown Back <$VALUE
4x5 1-8125 <$225
3x10-20 1-3220 <$225/$275
1882 Date Back
4x5 1-3107 <$225
3x10-20 1-2228 <$225/$275
1902 Date Back
4x5 1-1900 <$75
3x10-20 1-1440 <$85
1902 Plain Back
4x5 1901-27555 <$75
3x10-20 1441-18502 <$85
1929 Small Size
5 Type 1 1-9084 <$30
10 Type 1 1-4424 <$35
20 Type 1 1-1154 <$45
5 Type 2 1-15400 <$35
10 Type 2 1-8157 <$35
20 Type 2 1-2553 <$50
Total Issue $2,859,310
Out in 1935 $195,100
Large out 1935 $5,770
****
1681 Mercer
PRINCETON NB, PRINCETON
{{ 2 L }}
Chartered 1866
Liquidated 5/17/84
Original Series <$VALUE
4x5 1-5000 <$850
Series 1875
4x5 1-9182 <$850
Total Issue $283,640
Out in 1910 $1,175
****
12861 Passaic
PROSPECT PARK NB, PROSPECT PARK
{{ 3 L 9 S }}
Chartered 12/25
1902 Plain Back <$VALUE
3x10-20 1-3348 <$450
1929 Small Size
10 Type 1 1-2528 <$150
20 Type 1 1-688 <$150
10 Type 2 1-5497 <$150
20 Type 2 1-1395 <$150
Total Issue $484,510
Out in 1935 $80,350
Large out 1935 $670
****
12828 Union
CITIZENS NB OF RAHWAY
{{ 9 L 5 S }}
Chartered 9/25
Liquidated 8/10/32
1902 Plain Back <$VALUE
4x5 1-18482 <$150
1929 Small Size
5 Type 1 1-11195 <$150
Total Issue $705,490
Out at close $92,860
Large out at close $3,040
****
896 Union
NB OF RAHWAY
{{ 2 L }}
Chartered 3/16/65
Liquidated 3/9/87
Original Series <$VALUE
3x1-2 1-2000 <$600/$1250
4x5 1-2000 <$600
3x10-20 1-800 <$750/$1250
Series 1875
3x10-20 1-1592 <$750/$1250
Brown Back
3x10-20 1-531 <$600
Total Issue $196,150
Out in 1910 $1,276
****
5260 Union
RAHWAY NB, RAHWAY
{{ 12 L 16 S }}
Chartered 3/1/00
Brown Back <$VALUE
3x10-20 1-5000 <$200/$250
1882 Date Back
3x10-20 1-5450 <$200/$250
1882 Value Back
3x10-20 5451-7435<$200/$250
1902 Plain Back
3x10-20 1-15352 <$110
1929 Small Size
10 Type 1 1-2674 <$65
20 Type 1 1-812 <$65
10 Type 2 1-4674 <$65
20 Type 2 1-1318 <$65
Total Issue $1,720,330
Out in 1935 $77,200
Large out 1935 $4,120
****
881 Union
UNION NB OF RAHWAY
{{ 4 L }}
Chartered 3/13/65
Liquidated 9/10/78
Original Series <$VALUE
3x1-2 1-3400 <$400/$1000
4x5 1-5550 <$400
3x10-20 1-1550 <$750/$1250
Series 1875
4x5 1-455 <$400
3x10-20 1-780 <$750/$1250
Total Issue $253,600
Out in 1910 $1,469
****
9367 Bergen
FNB OF RAMSEY
Chartered 3/09
2nd title:FNB & TC 2/1/26
FIRST TITLE {{ 1 L }}
1902 Date Back <$VALUE
3x10-20 1-1030 <$650
1902 Plain Back
3x10-20 1031-2430 <$650
SECOND TITLE {{ 1 L 2U+ 20 S }}
1902 Plain Back
3x10-20 1-297 <$650
1929 Small Size
10 Type 1 1-1750 <$85
20 Type 1 1-524 <$85
10 Type 2 1-2408 <$85
20 Type 2 1-601 <$85
Total Issue $340,330
Out in 1935 $69,750
Large out 1935 $300
****
11553 Monmouth
BROAD STREET NB OF RED BANK
{{ 7 L }}
Organized 11/19/19
Receivership 4/15/33
1902 Plain Back <$VALUE
4x5 1-19150 <$200
Total Issue $383,000
Out at close $1,470
****
445 Monmouth
FNB OF RED BANK
{{ 12 L }}
Chartered 5/64
Liquidated 5/23/14
Original Series <$VALUE
3x1-2 1-3000 <$375/$1000
4x5 1-3645 <$400
3x10-20 1-2200 <$750/$1250
Series 1875
3x10-20 1-2174 <$750/$1250
Brown Back
3x10-20 1-6185 <$350
1902 Red Seal
3x10-20 1-6400 <$350
1902 Date Back
3x10-20 1-6245 <$165
Total Issue $1,248,100
Out in 1914 $75,935
****
4535 Monmouth
NAVESINK NB OF RED BANK
{{ UNREPORTED }}
Organized 3/19/91
Receivership 8/14/03
Brown Back <$VALUE
4x5 1-2911 <$1500
50-100 1-125 <$2500
Total Issue $76,970
Out in 1916 $300
****
2257 Monmouth
SECOND NB OF RED BANK
Chartered 5/12/75
2nd title:Second NB & TC 7/1/24
FIRST TITLE {{ 28 L }}
Original Series <$VALUE
4x5 1-3375 <$300
Series 1875
4x5 1-19657 <$300
Brown Back
4x5 1-14000 <$200
3x10-20 1-5000 <$200/$250
1882 Date Back
4x5 1-6775 <$200
3x10-20 1-4912 <$200/$250
1902 Date Back
4x5 1-1250 <$75
3x10-20 1-1000 <$85
1902 Plain Back
4x5 1251-10700 <$75
3x10-20 1001-6660 <$85
SECOND TITLE {{ 4 L 14 S }}
1902 Plain Back
4x10 1-7972 <$125
1929 Small Size
10 Type 1 1-3788 <$100
10 Type 2 1-6409 <$100
Total Issue $2,528,990
Out in 1935 $74,995
Large out 1935 $5,995
****
9780 Bergen
FNB OF RIDGEFIELD PARK
{{ 4 L }}
Chartered 6/10
Liquidated 12/15/19
1902 Date Back <$VALUE
4x5 1-3150 <$400
3x10-20 1-2360 <$400
1902 Plain Back
4x5 3151-6060 <$400
3x10-20 2361-3908 <$400
Total Issue $316,600
Out at close $45,400
****
11759 Bergen
CITIZENS NB OF RIDGEWOOD
Chartered 6/20
2nd title:Citizens NB & TC 3/27/26
FIRST TITLE {{ 2 L }}
1902 Plain Back <$VALUE
4x5 1-2067 <$400
3x10-20 1-1665 <$400
SECOND TITLE {{ 2 L 38 S }}
1902 Plain Back
4x5 1-2363 <$400
3x10-20 1-1665 <$400
1929 Small Size
5 Type 1 1-3880 <$40
10 Type 1 1-3206 <$40
20 Type 1 1-700 <$50
5 Type 2 1-7674 <$45
10 Type 2 1-2735 <$45
20 Type 2 1-500 <$60
Total Issue $723,580
Out in 1935 $76,955
Large out 1935 $1,305
****
5205 Bergen
FNB OF RIDGEWOOD
Chartered 7/8/99
Liquidated 6/23/34
2nd title:FNB & TC 10/14/29
FIRST TITLE {{ 13 L }}
Brown Back <$VALUE
4x5 1-1530 <$300
3x10-20 1-1168 <$300
1882 Date Back
4x5 1-2625* <$300
3x10-20 1-1900** <$300
1882 Value Back
4x5 2826-3925* <$300
3x10-20 2001-2500** <$300
* 2626-2825 not marked
** 1901-2000 not marked
1902 Plain Back
4x5 1-7103 <$135
3x10-20 1-4515 <$135
SECOND TITLE {{ 15 S }}
1929 Small Size
5 Type 1 1-2196 <$135
10 Type 1 1-1046 <$135
20 Type 1 1-288 <$135
5 Type 2 1-1354 <$150
10 Type 2 1-715 <$150
20 Type 2 1-212 <$150
Total Issue $841,670
Out at close $44,200
Large out at close $720
****
12984 Burlington
FNB OF RIVERSIDE
{{ U + 28 S }}
Chartered 9/26
1929 Small Size <$VALUE
10 Type 1 1-1528 <$65
20 Type 1 1-460 <$65
10 Type 2 1-5081 <$75
20 Type 2 1-1180 <$75
Total Issue $221,290
Out in 1935 $84,550
****
6823 Burlington
RIVERSIDE NB, RIVERSIDE
{{ 1 L }}
Chartered 6/03
Liquidated 12/31/18
1902 Red Seal <$VALUE
3x10-20 1-1600 <$1500
1902 Date Back
3x10-20 1-2370 <$850
1902 Plain Back
3x10-20 2371-3231 <$850
Total Issue $241,550
Out at close $23,100
****
8484 Burlington
CINNAMINSON NB OF RIVERTON
{{ 3 L }}
Chartered 12/06
Liquidated 4/1/25
1902 Red Seal <$VALUE
3x10-20 1-340 <$1000
1902 Date Back
3x10-20 1-2780 <$500
1902 Plain Back
3x10-20 2781-5887 <$500
Total Issue $311,350
Out at close $25,000
****
8566 Morris
FNB OF ROCKAWAY
{{ 1 L }}
Chartered 2/07
Liquidated 12/30/31
1902 Red Seal <$VALUE
3x10-20 1-900 <$1500
1902 Date Back
3x10-20 1-2910 <$750
1902 Plain Back
3x10-20 2911-6145 <$750
Total Issue $352,250
Out at close $1,230
****
11620 Burlington
FNB OF ROEBLING
Chartered 2/20
2nd title:FNB & TC 3/1/30
FIRST TITLE {{ 8 L U + 4 S }}
1902 Plain Back <$VALUE
4x5 1-7966 <$175
3x10-20 1-5757 <$175
1929 Small Size
5 Type 1 1-824 <$75
10 Type 1 1-414 <$75
20 Type 1 1-146 <$75
SECOND TITLE {{ 22 S }}
1929 Small Size
5 Type 1 1-1996 <$50
10 Type 1 1-1464 <$50
20 Type 1 1-372 <$60
5 Type 2 1-8592 <$65
10 Type 2 1-4598 <$65
20 Type 2 1-1344 <$70
Total Issue $822,430
Out in 1935 $100,000
Large out 1935 $1,440
****
8437 Middlesex
FNB OF ROOSEVELT
Organized 7/31/06
Liquidated 1/16/35
2nd title:FNB of Carteret 1/16/23
FIRST TITLE {{ 0 L }}
1902 Red Seal <$VALUE
3x10-20 1-660 <$1250
1902 Date Back
3x10-20 1-3010 <$600
1902 Plain Back
3x10-20 3011-5340 <$600
SECOND TITLE {{ 3 L 5 S }}
1902 Plain Back
3x10-20 1-2335 <$350
1929 Small Size
10 Type 1 1-1546 <$225
20 Type 1 1-478 <$225
10 Type 2 1-2532 <$250
20 Type 2 1-828 <$250
Total Issue $608,750
Out at close $70,170
Large out at close $1,240
Ch 14153 assumed circulation
****
8483 Union
FNB OF ROSELLE
{{ 2 L 5 S }}
Chartered 12/06
1902 Red Seal <$VALUE
3x10-20 1-500 <$1000
1902 Date Back
3x10-20 1-3260 <$500
1902 Plain Back
3x10-20 3261-13420 <$500
1929 Small Size
10 Type 1 1-1520 <$225
20 Type 1 1-368 <$225
10 Type 2 1-2400 <$250
20 Type 2 1-708 <$250
Total Issue $869,520
Out in 1935 $47,310
Large out 1935 $2,120
****
5005 Bergen
RUTHERFORD NB, RUTHERFORD
{{ 26 L 35 S }}
Chartered 1895
Brown Back <$VALUE
4x5 1-7375 <$250
3x10-20 1-3340 <$250/$300
1882 Date Back
4x5 1-8032 <$250
3x10-20 1-5499 <$250/$300
1902 Date Back
4x5 1-1250 <$75
3x10-20 1-1000 <$85
1902 Plain Back
4x5 1251-25235 <$75
3x10-20 1001-15450 <$85
3x50-100 1-565 <$350/$400
1929 Small Size
5 Type 1 1-5168 <$40
10 Type 1 1-2394 <$40
20 Type 1 1-690 <$50
50 Type 1 1-284 <$175
100 Type 1 1-84 <$225
5 Type 2 1-10014 <$40
10 Type 2 1-5904 <$40
20 Type 2 1-1488 <$50
Total Issue $2,824,490
Out in 1935 $195,400
Large out 1935 $7,540
****
3922 Salem
CITY NB OF SALEM
Chartered 8/20/88
2nd title:City NB & TC 5/26/25
FIRST TITLE {{ 9 L }}
Brown Back <$VALUE
4x5 1-7700 <$350
3x10-20 1-7295 <$350
1902 Red Seal
4x5 1-830 <$400
3x10-20 1-668 <$400
1902 Date Back
4x5 1-9650 <$175
3x10-20 1-6160 <$175
1902 Plain Back
4x5 9651-23750 <$175
3x10-20 6161-14800 <$175
SECOND TITLE {{ 6 L 33 S }}
1902 Plain Back
4x5 1-6285 <$175
3x10-20 1-4845 <$175
1929 Small Size
5 Type 1 1-6108 <$40
10 Type 1 1-3854 <$40
20 Type 1 1-952 <$50
5 Type 2 1-14024 <$40
10 Type 2 1-6108 <$40
20 Type 2 1-1990 <$50
Total Issue $2,851,420
Out in 1935 $162,900
Large out 1935 $5,110
****
Salem NB & TC, Salem
SEE Ch 1326
Salem N Banking C, Salem
****
****
1326 Salem
SALEM N BANKING CO, SALEM
Chartered 1865
2nd title:Salem NB & TC 5/26/25
FIRST TITLE {{ 5 L }}
Original Series <$VALUE
4x5 1-4750 <$400
3x10-20 1-3000 <$750/$1250
50-100 1-575 <$4000
Series 1875
4x5 1-2185 <$400
3x10-20 1-1163 <$750/$1250
Brown Back
3x10-20 1-6139 <$350
1902 Red Seal
4x5 1-3000 <$400
3x10-20 1-2500 <$400
1902 Date Back
4x5 1-9350* <$175
3x10-20 1-6760** <$175
1902 Plain Back
4x5 9851-22350* <$175
3x10-20 7121-15260** <$175
* 9351-9850 not marked
** 6761-7120 not marked
SECOND TITLE {{ 9 L 22 S }}
1902 Plain Back
4x5 1-6431 <$175
3x10-20 1-4809 <$175
1929 Small Size
5 Type 1 1-4642 <$50
10 Type 1 1-2270 <$50
20 Type 1 1-560 <$60
5 Type 2 1-6776 <$50
10 Type 2 1-3824 <$50
20 Type 2 1-869 <$60
Total Issue $2,936,280
Out in 1935 $80,350
Large out 1935 $4,930
****
14177 Monmouth
SEA BRIGHT NB, SEA BRIGHT
{{ 2 S }}
Chartered 6/34
1929 Small Size <$VALUE
5 Type 2 1-5900 <$500
Total Issue $29,500
Out in 1935 $14,700
****
5926 Monmouth
FNB OF SEABRIGHT
{{ 4 L 3 S }}
Chartered 7/31/01
Liquidated 7/27/31
Brown Back <$VALUE
3x10-20 1-2300 <$650
1882 Date Back
3x10-20 1-2750* <$650
1882 Value Back
3x10-20 2871-4655* <$650
* 2751-2870 not marked
1902 Plain Back
3x10-20 1-3165 <$450
1929 Small Size
10 Type 1 1-397 <$400
20 Type 1 1-102 <$400
Total Issue $542,060
Out at close $21,710
Large out at close $2,700
****
12279 Cape May
FNB OF SEA ISLE CITY
{{ 5 L 4 S }}
Organized 10/26/22
Receivership 11/11/31
1902 Plain Back <$VALUE
4x5 1-3908 <$500
4x10 1-2441 <$500
1929 Small Size
5 Type 1 1-954 <$400
10 Type 1 1-501 <$400
Total Issue $234,480
Out at close $23,380
Large out at close $1,440
****

<$VALUEs are for notes in **FINE** condition. Value changes by approximately **25%** for a change of one full grade.

****
9380 Hudson
FNB OF SECAUCUS
{{ 5 L U + 8 S }}
Organized 3/17/09
Receivership 6/18/34
1902 Date Back <$VALUE
4x5 1-3050 <$400
3x10-20 1-2170 <$400
1902 Plain Back
4x5 3051-9280 <$400
3x10-20 2171-5860 <$400
1929 Small Size
5 Type 1 1-1024 <$250
10 Type 1 1-672 <$250
20 Type 1 1-135 <$250
Total Issue $565,840
Out at close $25,000
Large out at close $1,060
****
12559 Atlantic
FNB OF SOMERS POINT
{{ 4 S }}
Organized 6/12/24
Receivership 10/13/33
1929 Small Size <$VALUE
5 Type 1 1-950 <$350
10 Type 1 1-660 <$350
20 Type 1 1-192 <$350
5 Type 2 1-292 <$375
10 Type 2 1-285 <$375
20 Type 2 1-50 <$375
Total Issue $96,450
Out at close $49,550
****
395 Somerset
FNB OF SOMERVILLE
{{ 17 L }}
Chartered 4/64
Liquidated 3/1/17
Original Series <$VALUE
3x1-2 1-4000 <$300/$850
4x5 1-8150 <$350
3x10-20 1-3400 <$750/$1250
Series 1875
4x5 1-2480 <$350
3x10-20 1-2202 <$600/$1000
Brown Back
4x5 1-7394 <$200
3x10-20 1-6034 <$200/$250
1902 Red Seal
4x5 1-5500 <$225
4x10 1-1650 <$225
3x10-20 1-2880 <$225/$250
1902 Date Back
4x5 1-11100 <$100
4x10 1-9225 <$100
3x10-20 1-200 <$100
1902 Plain Back
4x5 11101-13225 <$100
4x10 9226-10917 <$100
Total Issue $1,993,460
Out at close $100,000
****
4942 Somerset
SECOND NB OF SOMERVILLE
{{ 8 L 12 S }}
Chartered 1894
Brown Back <$VALUE
4x5 1-3525 <$275
3x10-20 1-1620 <$275
1882 Date Back
4x5 1-1841 <$275
3x10-20 1-1198 <$275
1902 Date Back
4x5 1-725 <$125
3x10-20 1-580 <$125
1902 Plain Back
4x5 726-6230 <$125
3x10-20 581-3855 <$125
1929 Small Size
5 Type 1 1-1762 <$100
10 Type 1 1-2368 <$100
20 Type 1 1-738 <$100
5 Type 2 1-7222 <$100
10 Type 2 1-3541 <$100
20 Type 2 1-885 <$100
Total Issue $938,290
Out in 1935 $115,080
Large out 1935 $1,350
****
3878 Middlesex
FNB OF SOUTH AMBOY
{{ 14 L 7 S }}
Chartered 5/2/88
Brown Back <$VALUE
4x5 1-2290 <$275
3x10-20 1-6365 <$275
1902 Red Seal
4x10 1-625 <$300
1902 Date Back
4x5 1-5680 <$125
4x10 1-5750 <$125
1902 Plain Back
4x5 5681-18176 <$125
4x10 5751-15589 <$125
1929 Small Size
5 Type 1 1-2792 <$125
10 Type 1 1-1508 <$125
5 Type 2 1-5976 <$125
10 Type 2 1-3084 <$125
Total Issue $1,611,090
Out in 1935 $49,340
Large out 1935 $2,670
****
11847 Middlesex
FNB OF SOUTH PLAINFIELD
{{ 1 L }}
Chartered 10/20
1902 Plain Back <$VALUE
3x10-20 1-2524 <$1000
Total Issue $126,200
Out in 1935 $250
****
6179 Middlesex
FNB OF SOUTH RIVER
{{ 0 L 2 S }}
Chartered 3/28/02
1902 Red Seal <$VALUE
4x5 1-1005 <$1250
3x10-20 1-738 <$1250
1902 Date Back
4x5 1-1650 <$600
3x10-20 1-1260 <$600
1902 Plain Back (dated 1902)
4x5 1651-2665 <$600
3x10-20 1261-1852 <$600
1902 Plain Back (dated 1922)
3x10-20 1-1537 <$600
1929 Small Size
10 Type 1 1-400 <$400
20 Type 1 1-118 <$400
10 Type 2 1-204 <$400
20 Type 2 1-105 <$400
Total Issue $322,050
Out in 1935 $12,050
Large out 1935 $510
****
5730 Monmouth
FNB OF SPRING LAKE
{{ 4 L 1 S }}
Chartered 3/2/01
Liquidated 2/24/34
Brown Back <$VALUE
3x10-20 1-1500 <$650
1882 Date Back
3x10-20 1-2560 <$650
1882 Value Back
3x10-20 2561-4151 <$650
1902 Plain Back
3x10-20 1-3377 <$500
1929 Small Size
10 Type 1 1-769 <$500
20 Type 1 1-200 <$500
Total Issue $521,540
Out at close $22,000
Large out 1935 $480
****
5061 Union
FNB OF SUMMIT
Chartered 1897
2nd title:FNB & TC 1/13/27
FIRST TITLE {{ 4 L }}
Brown Back <$VALUE
4x5 1-2375 <$375
3x10-20 1-770 <$375
1882 Date Back
4x5 1-1625 <$375
3x10-20 1-1202 <$375
1902 Plain Back
4x5 1-7090 <$200
3x10-20 1-4170 <$200
SECOND TITLE {{ 3 L 15 S }}
1902 Plain Back
4x5 1-7337 <$200
1929 Small Size
5 Type 1 1-8574 <$85
10 Type 1 1-4318 <$85
20 Type 1 1-1250 <$85
5 Type 2 1-13716 <$100
10 Type 2 1-8409 <$100
20 Type 2 1-2162 <$100
Total Issue $1,537,850
Out in 1935 $167,600
Large out 1935 $1,705
****
Farmers NB of Sussex
SEE Ch 1221
Farmers NB of Deckertown
****
2923 Gloucester
SWEDESBORO NB, SWEDESBORO
{{ 9 L 26 S }}
Chartered 1883
Brown Back <$VALUE
3x10-20 1-2240 <$350
1902 Red Seal
3x10-20 1-4350 <$350
1902 Date Back
3x10-20 1-9100 <$175
1902 Plain Back
3x10-20 9101-29068 <$175
1929 Small Size
10 Type 1 1-3286 <$65
20 Type 1 1-866 <$65
10 Type 2 1-3835 <$75
20 Type 2 1-825 <$75
Total Issue $2,138,830
Out in 1935 $84,550
Large out 1935 $3,870
****
8614 Bergen
FNB OF TENAFLY
{{ U + 3 L }}
Chartered 3/07
Liquidated 6/30/26
1902 Red Seal <$VALUE
4x5 1-221 <$1000
3x10-20 1-195 <$1000
1902 Date Back
4x5 1-2300 <$500
3x10-20 1-1760 <$500
1902 Plain Back
4x5 2301-6729 <$500
3x10-20 1761-4280 <$500
Total Issue $362,750
Out at close $22,400
****
2509 Ocean
FNB OF TOMS RIVER
{{ 28 L 50 S }}
Chartered 1881
Series 1875 <$VALUE
3x10-20 1-5257 <$750/$1250
Brown Back
3x10-20 1-3600 <$300
1882 Date Back
4x5 1-4630 <$300
3x10-20 1-2820 <$300
1882 Value Back
4x5 4631-8285 <$300
3x10-20 2821-4680 <$300
1902 Plain Back
4x5 1-27773 <$100
3x10-20 1-17514 <$100
1929 Small Size
5 Type 1 1-9620 <$60
10 Type 1 1-4368 <$60
20 Type 1 1-1282 <$60
50 Type 1 1-432 <$150
100 Type 1 1-188 <$200
5 Type 2 1-14298 <$60
10 Type 2 1-6966 <$60
20 Type 2 1-1643 <$60
Total Issue $3,394,640
Out in 1935 $300,295
Large out 1935 $6,100
****
1400 Ocean
OCEAN COUNTY NB OF TOMS RIVER
{{ 2 L }}
Chartered 1865
Liquidated 1/11/81
Original Series <$VALUE
4x5 1-4950 <$850
3x10-20 1-3100<$1000/$1500
Series 1875
3x10-20 1-1852<$1000/$1500
Total Issue $346,600
Out in 1910 $1,735
****
3709 Mercer
BROAD STREET NB OF TRENTON
{{ 20 L 25 S }}
Chartered 5/19/87
Brown Back <$VALUE
4x5 1-14549 <$125
3x10-20 1-2416 <$125/$175
1902 Red Seal
4x5 1-800 <$175
3x10-20 1-680 <$200/$225
1902 Date Back
4x5 1-21580 <$50
3x10-20 1-16968 <$50/$60
1902 Plain Back
4x5 21581-76567 <$50
3x10-20 16969-50941<$50/$60
1929 Small Size
5 Type 1 1-30682 <$30
10 Type 1 1-2084 <$30
5 Type 2 1-64678 <$30
Total Issue $5,909,060
Out in 1935 $179,245
Large out 1935 $10,575
****
F-Mechanics NB of Trenton
SEE Ch 1327
Mechanics NB of Trenton
****
281 Mercer
FNB OF TRENTON
{{ 50+ L }}
Chartered 2/64
Closed 7/3/28
Original Series <$VALUE
3x1-2 1-1560 <$225/$750
4x5 1-3650 <$275
4x10 1-6900 <$600
3x20-100 1-4270<$1250/$4000
Series 1875
4x10 1-9354 <$600
Brown Back
4x5 1-8000 <$110
3x10-20 1-28800 <$125/$175
1902 Red Seal
4x5 1-26415 <$125
3x10-20 1-18434 <$150/$175
1902 Date Back
4x5 1-49250 <$40
3x10-20 1-30700 <$50
1902 Plain Back
4x5 49251-140310 <$40
3x10-20 30701-88258 <$50
Total Issue $11,683,260
Out at close $492,550
Ch 1327 assumed circulation
****
1327 Mercer
MECHANICS NB OF TRENTON
Chartered 1865
2nd title:F-Mechanics NB 7/3/28
FIRST TITLE {{ 50+ L }}
Original Series <$VALUE
3x1-2 1-2400 <$225/$750
4x5 1-8250 <$275
3x10-20 1-5680 <$600/$1250
50-100 1-1100 <$4000
Series 1875
3x1-2 1-1186 <$225/$750
4x5 1-14200 <$275
3x10-20 1-7061 <$600/$1000
50-100 1-933 <$4000
Brown Back
4x5 1-36600 <$110
3x10-20 1-20680 <$125/$175
50-100 1-2197 <$1250/$1500
1902 Red Seal
4x5 1-18915 <$125
3x10-20 1-11134 <$150/$200
1902 Date Back
4x5 1-44500 <$40
3x10-20 1-33200 <$50
1902 Plain Back
4x5 44501-214478 <$40
3x10-20 33201-147235 <$50
SECOND TITLE {{ 10 L 50+ S }}
1902 Plain Back
4x5 1-24949 <$40
3x10-20 1-11865 <$50
1929 Small Size
5 Type 1 1-69662 <$15
10 Type 1 1-39666 <$20
20 Type 1 1-13264 <$30
5 Type 2 1-121928 <$15
10 Type 2 1-62362 <$20
20 Type 2 1-15444 <$30
Total Issue $24,786,660
Out in 1935 $1,576,550
Large out 1935 $61,420
Outstanding includes Ch 281
****
12949 Mercer
PROSPECT NB OF TRENTON
{{ 5 S }}
Chartered 6/26
1929 Small Size <$VALUE
5 Type 2 1-7490 <$150
10 Type 2 1-5355 <$150
20 Type 2 1-535 <$150
Total Issue $101,700
Out in 1935 $84,150
****
13039 Mercer
SECURITY NB OF TRENTON
{{ U + 12 S }}
Chartered 2/27
1929 Small Size <$VALUE
5 Type 1 1-4318 <$60
5 Type 2 1-45696 <$60
Total Issue $358,020
Out in 1935 $92,220
****
14189 Cape May
FNB OF TUCKAHOE
{{ 2U + 0 S }}
Chartered 6/34
1929 Small Size <$VALUE
5 Type 2 1-400 <$350
10 Type 2 1-165 <$350
20 Type 2 1-83 <$350
Total Issue $5,310
Out in 1935 $12,500
Large out 1935 $630
Outstanding includes Ch 8681
****
8681 Cape May
TUCKAHOE NB
{{ 1 L 1 S }}
Organized 3/22/07
Liquidated 8/3/34
1902 Red Seal <$VALUE
4x5 1-150 <$1250
3x10-20 1-120 <$1250
1902 Date Back
4x5 1-1375 <$600
3x10-20 1-1010 <$600
1902 Plain Back
4x5 1376-3807 <$600
3x10-20 1011-2527 <$600
1929 Small Size
5 Type 1 1-514 <$500
10 Type 1 1-260 <$500
20 Type 1 1-84 <$500
Total Issue $252,590
Out at close $11,300
Large out at close $660
Ch 14189 assumed circulation
****
9544 Hudson
FNB OF TOWN OF UNION
Chartered 9/09
2nd title:FNB of Union City 8/29/25
FIRST TITLE {{ 5 L }}
1902 Date Back <$VALUE
4x5 1-3625 <$175
3x10-20 1-2770 <$175
1902 Plain Back
4x5 3626-10425 <$175
3x10-20 2771-7260 <$175
SECOND TITLE {{ 12 L 22 S }}
1902 Plain Back
4x5 1-10944 <$100
3x10-20 1-7572 <$100
1929 Small Size
5 Type 1 1-11240 <$40
10 Type 1 1-5126 <$40
20 Type 1 1-1336 <$50
5 Type 2 1-22060 <$40
10 Type 2 1-10607 <$40
20 Type 2 1-2512 <$50
Total Issue $2,240,670
Out in 1935 $189,050
Large out 1935 $3,910
****
FNB of Union City
SEE Ch 9544
FNB of Town of Union
****
NB of North Hudson at Union City
SEE Ch 9867
NB of North Hudson at West Hoboken
****
10248 Atlantic
VENTNOR CITY NB, VENTNOR CITY
{{ 4 L 27 S }}
Chartered 8/12
1902 Date Back <$VALUE
4x5 1-1300 <$350
3x10-20 1-1100* <$350
1902 Plain Back
4x5 1301-7291 <$350
3x10-20 1181-4696* <$350
* 1101-1180 not marked
1929 Small Size
5 Type 1 1-1040 <$75
10 Type 1 1-570 <$75
20 Type 1 1-184 <$75
5 Type 2 1-10388 <$85
10 Type 2 1-5622 <$85
20 Type 2 1-1490 <$85
Total Issue $606,060
Out in 1935 $84,300
Large out 1935 $480
****
370 Burlington
FNB OF VINCENTOWN
{{ 10 L 19 S }}
Chartered 4/64
Original Series <$VALUE
4x5 1-4500 <$400
3x10-20 1-2400 <$750/$1250
Series 1875
3x10-20 1-1572 <$750/$1250
Brown Back
3x10-20 1-3740 <$350
1902 Red Seal
3x10-20 1-1500 <$350
1902 Date Back
4x5 1-6700 <$150
3x10-20 1-8040 <$150
1902 Plain Back
4x5 6701-15975 <$150
3x10-20 8041-14137 <$150
1929 Small Size
5 Type 1 1-2018 <$70
10 Type 1 1-928 <$70
20 Type 1 1-254 <$80
5 Type 2 1-2842 <$75
10 Type 2 1-1682 <$75
20 Type 2 1-456 <$85
Total Issue $1,763,800
Out in 1935 $48,500
Large out 1935 $4,880
****
2399 Cumberland
VINELAND NB, VINELAND
{{ 3 L }}
Chartered 9/25/78
Liquidated 1/11/81
Series 1875 <$VALUE
4x5 1-2535 <$750
Total Issue $50,700
Out in 1910 $280
****
2918 Cumberland
VINELAND NB, VINELAND
{{ 8 L }}
Chartered 1883
Brown Back <$VALUE
4x5 1-6447 <$375
50-100 1-340 <$1250/$1500
1902 Red Seal
4x5 1-2955 <$400
50-100 1-706 <$2250/$2500
1902 Date Back
4x5 1-3850 <$200
50-100 1-400 <$400/$500
3x50-100 1-478 <$400/$500
1902 Plain Back
4x5 3851-21755 <$200
3x50-100 479-611<$400/$500
Total Issue $992,790
Out in 1935 $3,305
****
860 Warren
FNB OF WASHINGTON
{{ 27 L 20 S }}
Chartered 3/6/65
Original Series <$VALUE
3x1-2 1-600 <$300/$850
4x5 1-2950 <$350
3x10-20 1-2200 <$750/$1250
Series 1875
4x5 1-2350 <$350
3x10-20 1-1840 <$600/$1000
Brown Back
3x10-20 1-11173 <$200/$225
1902 Red Seal
4x5 1-3000 <$250
3x10-20 1-3000 <$250
1902 Date Back
4x5 1-8225 <$100
3x10-20 1-6380 <$100
1902 Plain Back
4x5 8226-26135 <$100
3x10-20 6381-18459 <$100
1929 Small Size
5 Type 1 1-3408 <$60
10 Type 1 1-1910 <$60
20 Type 1 1-446 <$65
5 Type 2 1-6572 <$60
10 Type 2 1-3546 <$60
20 Type 2 1-1030 <$65
Total Issue $2,889,980
Out in 1935 $98,150
Large out 1935 $7,420
****
5121 Warren
WASHINGTON NB, WASHINGTON
{{ 5 L }}
Organized 5/16/98
Receivership 11/17/11
Brown Back <$VALUE
4x5 1-2940 <$350
3x10-20 1-1454 <$350
1882 Date Back
4x5 1-820 <$350
3x10-20 1-872 <$350
Total Issue $191,500
Out in 1916 $1,865
****
12829 Hudson
HAMILTON NB OF WEEHAWKEN
{{ 9 L 15 S }}
Chartered 10/25
1902 Plain Back <$VALUE
4x5 1-11017 <$225
1929 Small Size
5 Type 1 1-7188 <$100
5 Type 2 1-16536 <$100
Total Issue $518,660
Out in 1935 $44,500
Large out 1935 $930
****

****

12402 Bergen
WEST ENGLEWOOD NB, WEST ENGLEWOOD
{{ 7 L 14 S }}
Chartered 6/23
1902 Plain Back <$VALUE
4x5 1-16707 <$250
1929 Small Size
5 Type 1 1-7402 <$100
5 Type 2 1-15684 <$100
Total Issue $634,620
Out in 1935 $35,300
Large out 1935 $520

****

9867 Hudson
NB OF NORTH HUDSON AT WEST HOBOKEN
Organized 9/19/10
Receivership 8/6/31
2nd title:NB of North Hudson at Union City 7/14/25
FIRST TITLE {{ 8 L }}
1902 Date Back <$VALUE
4x5 1-9250 <$150
3x10-20 1-6500 <$150
1902 Plain Back
4x5 9251-30950 <$150
3x10-20 6501-18920 <$150
SECOND TITLE {{ 10 L U+13 S }}
1902 Plain Back
4x5 1-8690 <$125
3x10-20 1-5728 <$125
1929 Small Size
5 Type 1 1-3261 <$100
10 Type 1 1-1588 <$100
20 Type 1 1-417 <$100
Total Issue $2,268,350
Out at close $140,000
Large out at close $13,160

****

12064 Hudson
FNB OF WEST NEW YORK
{{ 10 L 14 S }}
Organized 11/14/21
Receivership 12/14/34
1902 Plain Back <$VALUE
4x5 1-11390 <$150
3x10-20 1-7934 <$150
1929 Small Size
5 Type 1 1-4162 <$100
10 Type 1 1-2206 <$100
20 Type 1 1-594 <$100
5 Type 2 1-5108 <$100
10 Type 2 1-3175 <$100
20 Type 2 1-686 <$100
Total Issue $1,024,010
Out at close $97,850
Large out at close $3,240

****

14305 Hudson
NB OF WEST NEW YORK
{{ UNREPORTED }}
Chartered 11/34
1929 Small Size <$VALUE
5 Type 2 1-3760 <$750
10 Type 2 1-1920 <$750
20 Type 2 1-600 <$750
Total Issue $50,000
Out in 1935 $50,000

****

9542 Essex
FNB OF WEST ORANGE
{{ 12 L 16 S }}
Chartered 9/09
1902 Date Back <$VALUE
4x5 1-5750 <$100
3x10-20 1-4500 <$100
1902 Plain Back
4x5 5751-29655 <$100
3x10-20 4501-19490 <$100
1929 Small Size
5 Type 1 1-4062 <$75
10 Type 1 1-2102 <$75
20 Type 1 1-568 <$75
5 Type 2 1-7872 <$75
10 Type 2 1-4116 <$75
20 Type 2 1-1056 <$75
Total Issue $1,985,380
Out in 1935 $93,445
Large out 1935 $3,535

****

12848 Passaic
WESTSIDE NB OF WEST PATERSON
{{ 3 L 4 S }}
Organized 7/17/25
Receivership 9/22/33
1902 Plain Back <$VALUE
4x5 1-5727 <$300
1929 Small Size
5 Type 1 1-3394 <$175
5 Type 2 1-1100 <$175
Total Issue $221,860
Out at close $25,000
Large out at close $620

****

4719 Union
FNB OF WESTFIELD
{{ 1 L }}
Chartered 4/2/92
Liquidated 6/30/03
Brown Back <$VALUE
4x5 1-1200 <$1250
3x10-20 1-978 <$1250
Total Issue $72,900
Out in 1910 $1,045

****

10142 Union
NB OF WESTFIELD
{{ 10 L 12 S }}
Chartered 2/12
1902 Date Back <$VALUE
4x5 1-6100 <$150
3x10-20 1-4480 <$150
1902 Plain Back
4x5 6101-27305 <$150
3x10-20 4481-18669 <$150
1929 Small Size
5 Type 1 1-4072 <$100
10 Type 1 1-2124 <$100
20 Type 1 1-518 <$100
5 Type 2 1-7438 <$100
10 Type 2 1-3698 <$100
20 Type 2 1-1080 <$100
Total Issue $1,887,080
Out in 1935 $98,500
Large out 1935 $3,740

****

8623 Union
PEOPLES NB OF WESTFIELD
{{ 1 L }}
Chartered 4/07
Liquidated 6/30/16
1902 Red Seal <$VALUE
4x5 1-1192 <$1000
4x10 1-1242 <$1000
1902 Date Back
4x5 1-6450 <$500
4x10 1-5625 <$500
1902 Plain Back
4x5 6451-6540 <$500
4x10 5626-5673 <$500
Total Issue $431,240
Out in 1916 $28,895

****

10430 Gloucester
FNB OF WESTVILLE
{{ 2 L 2 S }}
Chartered 8/5/13
1902 Date Back <$VALUE
4x5 1-450 <$650
3x10-20 1-360 <$650
1902 Plain Back
4x5 451-1753 <$650
3x10-20 361-1088 <$650
1929 Small Size
5 Type 1 1-351 <$500
10 Type 1 1-165 <$500
20 Type 1 1-51 <$500
Total Issue $110,010
Out in 1935 $6,250
Large out 1935 $310

****

8777 Bergen
FNB OF WESTWOOD
{{ 5 L 20 S }}
Chartered 7/07
1902 Red Seal <$VALUE
3x10-20 1-237 <$750
1902 Date Back
3x10-20 1-940 <$375
1902 Plain Back
3x10-20 941-17041 <$375
1929 Small Size
5 Type 1 1-942 <$75
10 Type 1 1-2952 <$75
20 Type 1 1-672 <$85
5 Type 2 1-7380 <$100
10 Type 2 1-4332 <$100
Total Issue $1,230,140
Out in 1935 $90,050
Large out 1935 $2,910

****

13047 Morris
FNB OF WHARTON
{{ 2 L 5 S }}
Chartered 3/27
Liquidated 2/17/32
1902 Plain Back <$VALUE
4x5 1-1137 <$600
4x10 1-690 <$600
3x10-20 1-516 <$600
1929 Small Size
5 Type 1 1-762 <$250
10 Type 1 1-380 <$250
20 Type 1 1-97 <$250
Total Issue $133,400
Out at close $25,000
Large out at close $400

****

9061 Hunterdon
FNB OF WHITE HOUSE STATION
{{ 4 L 1 S }}
Organized 12/23/07
Receivership 12/30/31
1902 Red Seal <$VALUE
4x5 1-500 <$2000
3x10-20 1-400 <$2000
1902 Date Back
4x5 1-1400 <$1000
3x10-20 1-1100 <$1000
1902 Plain Back
4x5 1401-4120 <$1000
3x10-20 1101-2879 <$1000
1929 Small Size
5 Type 1 1-390 <$1000
10 Type 1 1-186 <$1000
20 Type 1 1-50 <$1000
Total Issue $285,210
Out at close $14,700
Large out at close $1,190

****

6278 Cape May
MARINE NB OF WILDWOOD
{{ 9 L 5 S }}
Chartered 5/26/02
1902 Red Seal <$VALUE
4x5 1-750 <$750
3x10-20 1-1220 <$750
1902 Date Back
4x5 1-2975 <$325
3x10-20 1-2300 <$325
1902 Plain Back
4x5 2976-14290 <$325
3x10-20 2301-9673 <$325
1929 Small Size
5 Type 1 1-2040 <$200
10 Type 1 1-1078 <$200
20 Type 1 1-272 <$200
5 Type 2 1-2508 <$225
10 Type 2 1-1507 <$225
20 Type 2 1-456 <$225
Total Issue $1,040,700
Out in 1935 $50,000
Large out 1935 $2,070

****

7265 Gloucester
FNB OF WILLIAMSTOWN
{{ 2 L 10 S }}
Organized 5/5/04
1902 Red Seal <$VALUE
3x10-20 1-1377 <$750
1902 Date Back
3x10-20 1-2470 <$375
1902 Plain Back
3x10-20 2471-7000 <$375
1929 Small Size
10 Type 1 1-736 <$165
20 Type 1 1-196 <$165
10 Type 2 1-1259 <$185
20 Type 2 1-260 <$185
Total Issue $504,320
Out in 1935 $24,350
Large out 1935 $1,090

****

12977 Cape May
WOODBINE NB, WOODBINE
{{ 15U + 12 S }}
Organized 7/1/26
1929 Small Size <$VALUE
5 Type 1 1-1888 <$75
10 Type 1 1-836 <$75
5 Type 2 1-3396 <$75
10 Type 2 1-1632 <$75
Total Issue $140,100
Out in 1935 $27,740

****

8299 Cape May
FNB OF WOODBRIDGE
Organized 6/12/06
Receivership 12/2/31
2nd title:FNB & TC 5/24/30
FIRST TITLE {{ U + 9 L 0 S }}
1902 Red Seal <$VALUE
4x5 1-875 <$500
3x10-20 1-740 <$500
1902 Date Back
4x5 1-2850 <$200
3x10-20 1-2020 <$200
1902 Plain Back
4x5 2851-8730 <$200
3x10-20 2021-5633 <$200
1929 Small Size
5 Type 1 1-414 <$150
10 Type 1 1-210 <$150
20 Type 1 1-74 <$150
SECOND TITLE {{ 10 S }}
1929 Small Size
5 Type 1 1-1894 <$125
10 Type 1 1-957 <$125
20 Type 1 1-306 <$125
Total Issue $695,610
Out at close $100,000
Large out at close $2,470

****

3716 Gloucester
FARMERS & MECHANICS NB OF WOODBURY
{{ 12 L 25 S }}
Chartered 6/4/87
Brown Back <$VALUE
4x5 1-4949 <$300
3x10-20 1-4199 <$300
1902 Red Seal
4x5 1-1500 <$350
3x10-20 1-1400 <$350
1902 Date Back
4x5 1-9250 <$150
3x10-20 1-7200 <$150
1902 Plain Back
4x5 9251-30690 <$150
3x10-20 7201-21659 <$150
1929 Small Size
5 Type 1 1-4424 <$50
10 Type 1 1-2156 <$50
20 Type 1 1-494 <$60
5 Type 2 1-13322 <$50
10 Type 2 1-2665 <$50
20 Type 2 1-801 <$60
Total Issue $2,536,320
Out in 1935 $100,000
Large out 1935 $1,260

****

1199 Gloucester
FNB OF WOODBURY
Chartered 1865
2nd title:FNB & TC of Woodbury 2/2/25
FIRST TITLE {{ 6 L }}
Original Series <$VALUE
4x5 1-3750 <$450
3x10-20 1-1600 <$750/$1250
Series 1875
4x5 1-1875 <$450
3x10-20 1-2678 <$750/$1250
Brown Back
4x5 1-6500 <$300
3x10-20 1-4760 <$300
1902 Red Seal
4x5 1-2350 <$350
3x10-20 1-1160 <$350
1902 Date Back
4x5 1-4650 <$150
3x10-20 1-3420 <$150
1902 Plain Back
4x5 4651-11250 <$150
3x10-20 3421-7390 <$150
SECOND TITLE {{ 6 L 25 S }}
1902 Plain Back
3x10-20 1-3481 <$150
1929 Small Size
10 Type 1 1-2292 <$50
20 Type 1 1-550 <$60
10 Type 2 1-14473 <$50
20 Type 2 1-3832 <$60
Total Issue $1,992,840
Out in 1935 $160,680
Large out 1935 $4,250

****

399 Salem
FNB OF WOODSTOWN
{{ 17 L 14 S }}
Chartered 4/64
Original Series <$VALUE
4x5 1-3575 <$400
3x10-20 1-1220 <$750/$1250
Series 1875
4x5 1-2500 <$400
3x10-20 1-800 <$750/$1250
Brown Back
4x5 1-7783 <$275
3x10-20 1-4813 <$275
1902 Red Seal
3x10-20 1-3600 <$300
1902 Date Back
4x5 1-6900* <$150
3x10-20 1-4500** <$150
1902 Plain Back
4x5 7201-22130* <$150
3x10-20 4741-13932** <$150
* 6901-7200 not marked
** 4501-4740 not marked
1929 Small Size
5 Type 1 1-3172 <$100
10 Type 1 1-1564 <$100
20 Type 1 1-400 <$100
5 Type 2 1-4584 <$100
10 Type 2 1-2232 <$100
20 Type 2 1-696 <$100
Total Issue $2,234,170
Out in 1935 $73,080
Large out 1935 $4,450

****

11734 Salem
WOODSTOWN NB, WOODSTOWN
Chartered 5/20
2nd title:Woodstown NB & TC 3/23/25
FIRST TITLE {{ 0 L }}
1902 Plain Back <$VALUE
4x5 1-2560 <$500
3x10-20 1-1590 <$500
SECOND TITLE {{ 2 L 12 S }}
1902 Plain Back
4x5 1-2020 <$500
3x10-20 1-1276 <$500
1929 Small Size
5 Type 1 1-2046 <$100
10 Type 1 1-1086 <$100
20 Type 1 1-336 <$100
5 Type 2 1-4132 <$100
10 Type 2 1-2783 <$100
20 Type 2 1-1128 <$100
Total Issue $474,610
Out in 1935 $75,000
Large out 1935 $740

****

12272 Bergen
FNB OF WYCKOFF
{{ 6 S }}
Chartered 11/22
1929 Small Size <$VALUE
5 Type 1 1-830 <$175
10 Type 1 1-418 <$175
20 Type 1 1-104 <$175
5 Type 2 1-3066 <$200
10 Type 2 1-1975 <$200
20 Type 2 1-435 <$200
Total Issue $106,240
Out in 1935 $39,750

****

12606 Mercer
YARDVILLE NB, YARDVILLE
{{ 6 S }}
Chartered 12/24
1929 Small Size <$VALUE
5 Type 2 1-3556 <$225
10 Type 2 1-1800 <$225
20 Type 2 1-461 <$225
Total Issue $45,000
Out in 1935 $41,850

****

NEW MEXICO

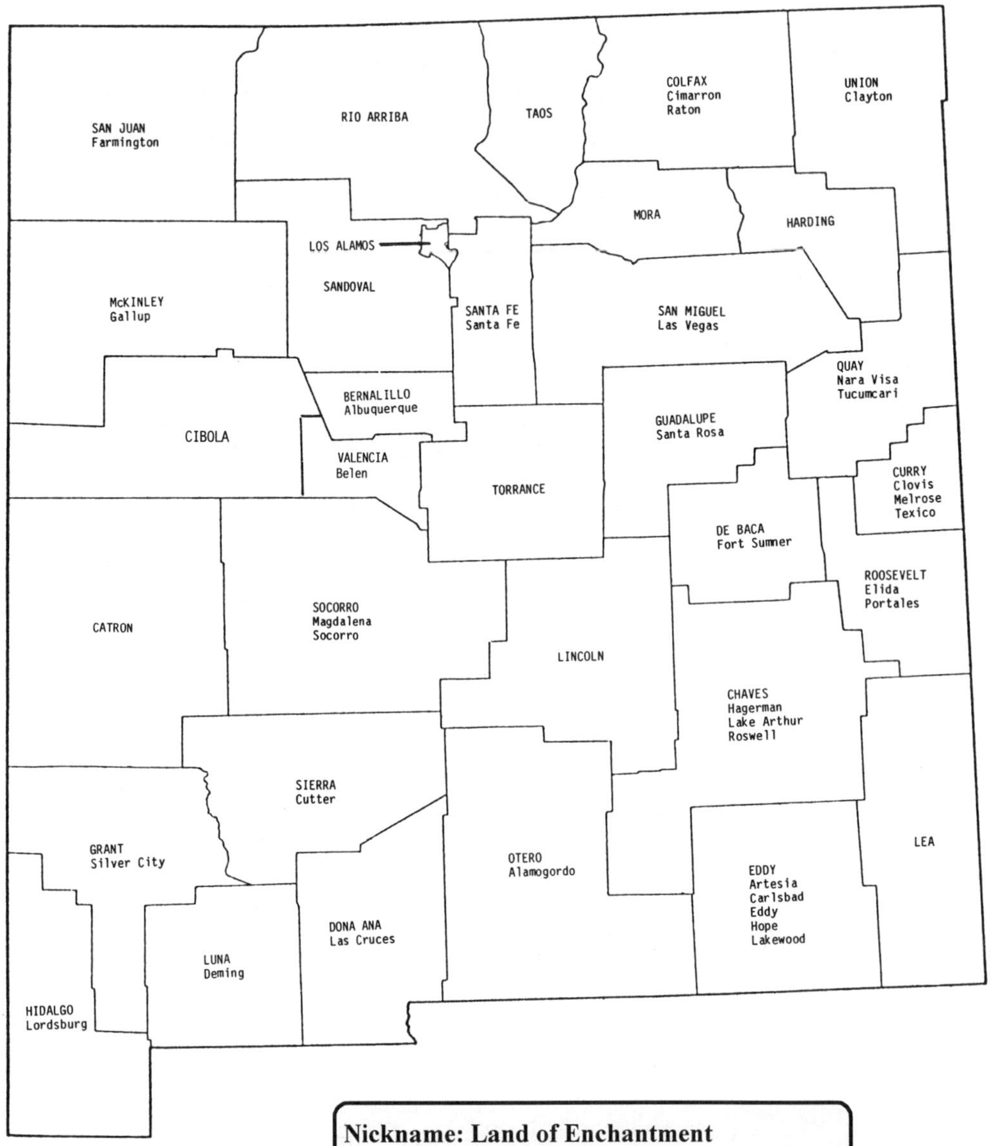

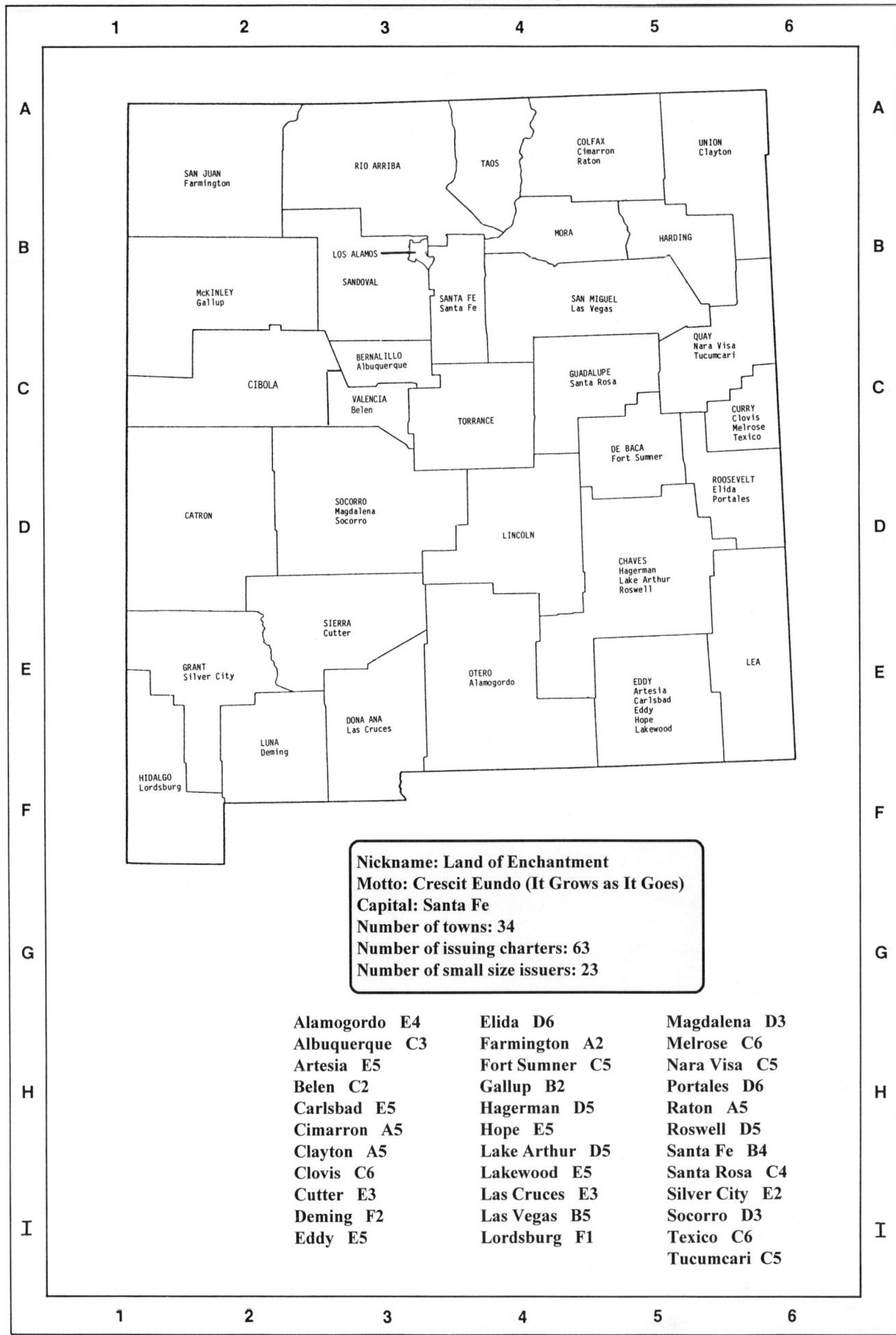

Nickname: Land of Enchantment
Motto: Crescit Eundo (It Grows as It Goes)
Capital: Santa Fe
Number of towns: 34
Number of issuing charters: 63
Number of small size issuers: 23

Alamogordo E4
Albuquerque C3
Artesia E5
Belen C2
Carlsbad E5
Cimarron A5
Clayton A5
Clovis C6
Cutter E3
Deming F2
Eddy E5
Elida D6
Farmington A2
Fort Sumner C5
Gallup B2
Hagerman D5
Hope E5
Lake Arthur D5
Lakewood E5
Las Cruces E3
Las Vegas B5
Lordsburg F1
Magdalena D3
Melrose C6
Nara Visa C5
Portales D6
Raton A5
Roswell D5
Santa Fe B4
Santa Rosa C4
Silver City E2
Socorro D3
Texico C6
Tucumcari C5

****
8315 Otero
CITIZENS NB OF ALAMOGORDO
{{ 3 L }}
Chartered 7/06
Liquidated 1/16/12
TERRITORIAL ISSUES
1902 Red Seal <$VALUE
4x5 1-450 <$5000
3x10-20 1-460 <$5000
1902 Date Back
4x5 1-1675 <$4000
3x10-20 1-1198 <$4000
Total Issue $125,400
Out at close $50,000
****
5244 Otero
FNB OF ALAMOGORDO
Chartered 1/15/00
Liquidated 7/1/15
TERRITORIAL ISSUES {{ 1 L }}
Brown Back <$VALUE
4x5 1-1010 <$5000
3x10-20 1-776 <$5000
1882 Date Back
4x5 1-1100 <$4500
3x10-20 1-780 <$4500
STATE ISSUES {{ 0 L }}
1882 Date Back
4x5 1-105 <$3000
3x10-20 1-46 <$3000
Total Issue $124,400
Out in 1915 $12,750
****
3222 Bernalillo
ALBUQUERQUE NB, ALBUQUERQUE
{{ UNREPORTED }}
Organized 7/14/84
Receivership 8/11/93
TERRITORIAL ISSUES
Brown Back <$VALUE
4x5 1-2125 <$5000
3x10-20 1-1423 <$5000
Total Issue $113,650
Out in 1916 $740
****
Albuquerque N T & Savings B
SEE Ch 12485
Albuquerque NB, Albuquerque
****
12485 Bernalillo
ALBUQUERQUE NB, ALBUQUERQUE
Chartered 1/24
2nd title: Albuquerque N T & Savings B 10/8/28
FIRST TITLE {{ 31 L }}
1902 Plain Back <$VALUE
4x5 1-13809 <$175
3x10-20 1-9581 <$175
SECOND TITLE {{ 16 L 50+ S }}
1902 Plain Back
4x5 1-7373 <$175
1929 Small Size
5 Type 1 1-16408 <$100
10 Type 1 1-4362 <$100
20 Type 1 1-1056 <$110
5 Type 2 1-20464 <$110
10 Type 2 1-10392 <$110
20 Type 2 1-2764 <$125
Total Issue $2,044,890
Out in 1935 $251,900
Large out 1935 $6,810
****
11442 Bernalillo
CITIZENS NB OF ALBUQUERQUE
{{ 4 L }}
Organized 8/8/19
Receivership 4/14/24
1902 Plain Back <$VALUE
4x5 1-22150 <$600
Total Issue $443,000
Out at close $74,500
****
13814 Bernalillo
FNB IN ALBUQUERQUE
{{ 13 S }}
Chartered 10/33
1929 Small Size <$VALUE
5 Type 2 1-5560 <$225
10 Type 2 1-5037 <$225
20 Type 2 1-2520 <$225
Total Issue $128,570
Out in 1935 $274,260
Large out 1935 $245,800
Outstanding includes Ch 2614
****
2614 Bernalillo
FNB OF ALBUQUERQUE
Organized 12/24/81
Liquidated 2/7/34
TERRITORIAL ISSUES {{ 15 L }}
Series 1875 <$VALUE
4x5 1-9957 <$3000
3x10-20 1-7468 <$3500
Brown Back
50-100 1-2960 <$5000
1882 Date Back
4x5 1-2500 <$2500
50-100 1-1400 <$3000
3x50-100 1-300 <$3000
STATE ISSUES {{ 50+ L 50+ S }}
1882 Date Back
4x5 1-11000* <$350
3x50-100 1-2586 <$1500
1882 Value Back
4x5 14501-40530* <$500
* 11001-14500 not marked
1902 Plain Back
4x5 1-33972 <$175
3x10-20 1-23633 <$175/$200
1929 Small Size
5 Type 1 1-14517 <$100
10 Type 1 1-8159 <$100
20 Type 1 1-1971 <$110
Total Issue $5,831,300
Out at close $329,910
Large out 1935 $33,480
Ch 13814 assumed circulation
****
7186 Bernalillo
STATE NB OF ALBUQUERQUE
Organized 3/17/04
Receivership 4/14/24
TERRITORIAL ISSUES {{ 6 L }}
1902 Red Seal <$VALUE
3x10-20 1-5500 <$2500
1902 Date Back
3x10-20 1-4100 <$1500
STATE ISSUES {{ 8 L }}
1902 Date Back
3x10-20 1-4200 <$350
1902 Plain Back
3x10-20 4201-24532 <$350
Total Issue $1,706,600
Out at close $157,400
****
7043 Eddy
FNB OF ARTESIA
Organized 8/15/03
TERRITORIAL ISSUES {{ 0 L }}
1902 Red Seal <$VALUE
3x10-20 1-800 <$5000
1902 Date Back
3x10-20 1-1450 <$4500
STATE ISSUES {{ 10 L 16 S }}
1902 Date Back
3x10-20 1-1150 <$650
1902 Plain Back
3x10-20 1151-9958 <$650
1929 Small Size
10 Type 1 1-1566 <$300
20 Type 1 1-402 <$300
10 Type 2 1-2421 <$325
20 Type 2 1-512 <$325
Total Issue $787,050
Out in 1935 $47,450
Large out 1935 $2,600
Outstanding includes Ch 9468
****
9468 Eddy
STATE NB OF ARTESIA
Chartered 7/09
Liquidated 3/23/14
TERRITORIAL ISSUES {{ 1 L }}
1902 Date Back <$VALUE
3x10-20 1-1700 <$4500
STATE ISSUES {{ 0 L }}
1902 Date Back
3x10-20 1-15 <$3000
Total Issue $85,750
Out at close $25,000
Ch 7043 assumed circulation
****
6597 Valencia
FNB OF BELEN
Chartered 1/03
TERRITORIAL ISSUES {{ 1 L }}
1902 Red Seal <$VALUE
3x10-20 1-400 <$5000
1902 Date Back
3x10-20 1-560 <$4500
STATE ISSUES {{ 12 L 50 S }}
1902 Date Back
3x10-20 1-700 <$600
1902 Plain Back
3x10-20 701-8393 <$600
1929 Small Size
5 Type 1 1-3220 <$250
10 Type 1 1-618 <$250
20 Type 1 1-210 <$250
5 Type 2 1-2648 <$250
Total Issue $639,770
Out in 1935 $29,030
Large out 1935 $3,080
****
12569 Eddy
CARLSBAD NB
{{ 9 S }}
Chartered 8/24
1929 Small Size <$VALUE
20 Type 1 1-518 <$400
20 Type 2 1-500 <$450
Total Issue $72,160
Out in 1935 $31,700
****
5487 Eddy
FNB OF CARLSBAD
Chartered 7/7/00
Receivership 5/14/24
TERRITORIAL ISSUES {{ 0 L }}
Brown Back <$VALUE
4x5 1-500 <$5500
3x10-20 1-840 <$5500
1882 Date Back
4x5 1-725 <$5000
3x10-20 1-580 <$5000
STATE ISSUES {{ 3 L }}
1882 Date Back
4x5 1-700 <$1500
3x10-20 1-520 <$1500
1882 Value Back
4x5 701-1450 <$1500
3x10-20 521-880 <$1500
1902 Plain Back
4x5 1-1650 <$1000
3x10-20 1-967 <$1000
Total Issue $249,850
Out at close $24,595
****
6884 Eddy
NB OF CARLSBAD
Organized 7/8/03
Receivership 2/6/24
TERRITORIAL ISSUES {{ 1 L }}
1902 Red Seal <$VALUE
3x10-20 1-400 <$6000
1902 Date Back
3x10-20 1-650 <$5500
STATE ISSUES {{ 1 L }}
1902 Date Back
3x10-20 1-200 <$2000
1902 Plain Back
3x10-20 201-1193 <$2000
Total Issue $112,150
Out at close $11,800
****
9292 Colfax
FNB OF CIMARRON
Chartered 12/08
Liquidated 1/2/26
TERRITORIAL ISSUES {{ 0 L }}
1902 Date Back <$VALUE
3x10-20 1-900 <$6000
STATE ISSUES {{ 1 L }}
1902 Date Back
3x10-20 1-260* <$2500
1902 Plain Back
3x10-20 381-1601* <$2500
* 261-380 not marked
Total Issue $125,050
Out at close $12,500
****
5713 Union
FNB OF CLAYTON
Chartered 2/14/01
Receivership 3/1/24
TERRITORIAL ISSUES {{ 5 L }}
Brown Back <$VALUE
4x5 1-2875 <$4000
3x10-20 1-2080 <$4000
1882 Date Back
4x5 1-2350 <$3500
3x10-20 1-1480 <$3500
STATE ISSUES {{ 3 L }}
1882 Date Back
4x5 1-1700 <$1250
3x10-20 1-1180 <$1250
1882 Value Back
4x5 1701-3715 <$1250
3x10-20 1181-2323 <$1250
1902 Plain Back
4x5 1-2355 <$750
3x10-20 1-1332 <$750
Total Issue $586,650
Out at close $50,000
****
8767 Curry
CLOVIS NB, CLOVIS
Chartered 6/07
TERRITORIAL ISSUES {{ 1 L }}
1902 Red Seal <$VALUE
4x5 1-150 <$5000
4x10 1-150 <$5000
1902 Date Back
4x5 1-1500 <$4500
4x10 1-1150 <$4500
STATE ISSUES {{ 5 L 8 S }}
1902 Date Back
4x5 1-750 <$850
4x10 1-750 <$850
1902 Plain Back
4x5 751-6260 <$850
4x10 751-4775 <$850
1929 Small Size
5 Type 1 1-1490 <$500
10 Type 1 1-644 <$500
5 Type 2 1-3264 <$550
10 Type 2 1-1572 <$550
Total Issue $516,580
Out in 1935 $22,850
Large out 1935 $1,440
****
8784 Curry
FNB OF CLOVIS
Organized 6/14/07
Receivership 2/20/24
TERRITORIAL ISSUES {{ 0 L }}
1902 Red Seal <$VALUE
3x10-20 1-400 <$5000
1902 Date Back
3x10-20 1-800 <$4500
STATE ISSUES {{ 3 L }}
1902 Date Back
3x10-20 1-320 <$1500
1902 Plain Back
3x10-20 321-5376 <$1500
Total Issue $328,800
Out at close $55,800
****
8662 Sierra
FNB OF CUTTER
{{ UNREPORTED }}
Chartered 4/27/07 as FNB of Engle, under which there was no issue. Issuing title adopted 9/7/07.
Liquidated 7/22/08
TERRITORIAL ISSUES
1902 Red Seal <$VALUE
3x10-20 1-136 <$7500
Total Issue $6,800
Out in 1910 $1,610
****
6974 Luna
DEMING NB, DEMING
Organized 8/5/03
Receivership 3/4/24
2nd title: FNB in Deming 2/15/22
FIRST TITLE
TERRITORIAL ISSUES {{ 2 L }}
1902 Red Seal <$VALUE
3x10-20 1-1200 <$5000
1902 Date Back
3x10-20 1-1000 <$4500
STATE ISSUES {{ 1 L }}
1902 Date Back
3x10-20 1-1570 <$2500
1902 Plain Back
3x10-20 1571-3250 <$2500
SECOND TITLE {{ 1 L }}
1902 Plain Back
3x10-20 1-476 <$2500
Total Issue $296,300
Out at close $21,995
****
FNB in Deming
SEE Ch 6974
Deming NB, Deming
****
3160 Luna
FNB OF DEMING
{{ UNREPORTED }}
Organized 4/22/84
Receivership 2/29/92
TERRITORIAL ISSUES
Brown Back <$VALUE
3x10-20 1-930 <$7500
Total Issue $46,500
Out in 1916 $370
****
4746 Luna
NB OF DEMING
{{ UNREPORTED }}
Chartered 6/1/92
Liquidated 3/26/95
TERRITORIAL ISSUES
Brown Back <$VALUE
3x10-20 1-363 <$7500
Total Issue $18,150
Out in 1910 $120
****
4455 Eddy
FNB OF EDDY
{{ UNREPORTED }}
Organized 10/31/90
Receivership 11/10/96
TERRITORIAL ISSUES
Brown Back <$VALUE
3x10-20 1-579 <$7500
Total Issue $28,950
Out in 1916 $170
****
8348 Roosevelt
FNB OF ELIDA
Chartered 8/06
TERRITORIAL ISSUES {{ 2 L }}
1902 Red Seal <$VALUE
3x10-20 1-800 <$5000
1902 Date Back
3x10-20 1-1160 <$4500
STATE ISSUES {{ 1 L 8 S }}
1902 Date Back
3x10-20 1-870 <$2000
1902 Plain Back
3x10-20 871-5098 <$2000
1929 Small Size
10 Type 1 1-772 <$500
20 Type 1 1-224 <$500
10 Type 2 1-972 <$550
20 Type 2 1-301 <$550
Total Issue $441,840
Out in 1935 $24,450
Large out 1935 $1,890
****
6183 San Juan
FNB OF FARMINGTON
Chartered 3/31/02
TERRITORIAL ISSUES {{ 0 L }}
1902 Red Seal <$VALUE
3x10-20 1-1450 <$5500
1902 Date Back
3x10-20 1-1200 <$4500
STATE ISSUES {{ 1 L 6 S }}
1902 Date Back
3x10-20 1-1770 <$2000
1902 Plain Back (dated 1902)
3x10-20 1771-2666 <$2000
1902 Plain Back (dated 1922)
3x10-20 1-2204 <$2000
1929 Small Size
10 Type 1 1-696 <$500
20 Type 1 1-190 <$500
10 Type 2 1-966 <$550
20 Type 2 1-162 <$550
Total Issue $453,460
Out in 1935 $24,600
Large out 1935 $1,720
****
9151 San Juan
SAN JUAN COUNTY NB OF FARMINGTON
Organized 5/6/08
Receivership 2/12/24
TERRITORIAL ISSUES {{ 0 L }}
1902 Date Back <$VALUE
3x10-20 1-800 <$5500
STATE ISSUES {{ 1 L }}
1902 Date Back
3x10-20 1-320 <$2500
1902 Plain Back
3x10-20 321-1572 <$2500
Total Issue $118,600
Out in 1926 $3,150
Ch 12514 assumed circulation
****
8617 De Baca
FNB OF FORT SUMNER
Organized 2/28/07 as FNB of Sunnyside, under which there was no issue. Issuing title adopted 10/8/07.
Receivership 2/26/24
TERRITORIAL ISSUES {{ 0 L }}
1902 Red Seal <$VALUE
4x10 1-235 <$6500
1902 Date Back
4x10 1-575 <$6000
STATE ISSUES {{ 2 L }}
1902 Date Back
4x10 1-250 <$2500
1902 Plain Back
4x10 251-880 <$2500
Total Issue $67,600
Out at close $5,850
****
FNB in Gallup
SEE Ch 11900
NB of Gallup
****
9988 McKinley
FNB OF GALLUP
Chartered 4/13/11
Liquidated 12/20/13
TERRITORIAL ISSUES {{ 0 L }}
1902 Date Back <$VALUE
3x10-20 1-800 <$6000
STATE ISSUES {{ 1 L }}
1902 Date Back
3x10-20 1-331 <$3500
Total Issue $56,550
Out in 1914 $12,610
****
11900 McKinley
NB OF GALLUP
Chartered 12/20
Receivership 12/19/33
2nd title: FNB in Gallup 10/10/22
FIRST TITLE {{ 1 L }}
1902 Plain Back <$VALUE
4x5 1-1650 <$2000
3x10-20 1-910 <$2000
SECOND TITLE {{ 15 L 8 S }}
1902 Plain Back
4x5 1-15757 <$750
1929 Small Size
5 Type 1 1-6808 <$600
5 Type 2 1-2118 <$650
Total Issue $608,470
Out at close $46,200
Large out at close $2,035
****
FNB of Hagerman
SEE Ch 7503
Hagerman NB, Hagerman
****
7503 Chaves
HAGERMAN NB, HAGERMAN
Chartered 12/04
2nd title: FNB of Hagerman 5/9/07
TERRITORIAL ISSUES
FIRST TITLE {{ 2 L }}
1902 Red Seal <$VALUE
3x10-20 1-611 <$5000
SECOND TITLE {{ 0 L }}
1902 Red Seal
3x10-20 1-450 <$5000
1902 Date Back
3x10-20 1-950 <$4500
STATE ISSUES {{ 4 L 5 S }}
1902 Date Back
3x10-20 1-880 <$1500
1902 Plain Back
3x10-20 881-4988 <$1500
1929 Small Size
10 Type 1 1-792 <$650
20 Type 1 1-210 <$650
10 Type 2 1-1045 <$650
20 Type 2 1-186 <$650
Total Issue $436,840
Out in 1935 $24,350
Large out 1935 $1,380
****
9441 Eddy
FNB OF HOPE
Organized 5/3/09
Receivership 10/30/22
TERRITORIAL ISSUES {{ 0 L }}
1902 Date Back <$VALUE
3x10-20 1-600 <$5000
STATE ISSUES {{ 3 L }}
1902 Date Back
3x10-20 1-920 <$1500
1902 Plain Back
3x10-20 921-2708 <$1500
Total Issue $165,400
Out at close $17,750
****

<$VALUEs are for notes in **FINE** condition. Value changes by approximately **25%** for a change of one full grade.

8584 Chaves
FNB OF LAKE ARTHUR
Chartered 3/07
Liquidated 12/31/13
TERRITORIAL ISSUES {{ 2 L }}
1902 Red Seal <$VALUE
3x10-20 1-188 <$6000
1902 Date Back
3x10-20 1-1400 <$5500
STATE ISSUES {{ 0 L }}
1902 Date Back
3x10-20 1-225 <$3500
Total Issue $90,650
Out in 1914 $13,010

8782 Eddy
LAKEWOOD NB, LAKEWOOD
{{ UNREPORTED }}
Chartered 7/07
Liquidated 12/31/21
TERRITORIAL ISSUES
1902 Red Seal <$VALUE
3x10-20 1-200 <$7500
1902 Date Back
3x10-20 1-460 <$7000
STATE ISSUES
1902 Date Back
3x10-20 1-200 <$3500
1902 Plain Back
3x10-20 201-437 <$3500
Total Issue $54,850
Out at close $6,250

7720 Dona Ana
FNB OF LAS CRUCES
Organized 4/25/05
TERRITORIAL ISSUES {{ 1 L }}
1902 Red Seal <$VALUE
3x10-20 1-660 <$5500
1902 Date Back
3x10-20 1-700 <$4500
STATE ISSUES {{ 5 L 4 S }}
1902 Date Back
3x10-20 1-320 <$1250
1902 Plain Back
3x10-20 321-2563 <$1250
1929 Small Size
10 Type 1 1-459 <$750
20 Type 1 1-123 <$750
Total Issue $238,450
Out in 1935 $12,500
Large out 1935 $850

2436 Dona Ana
FNB OF LAS VEGAS
Chartered 9/22/79
Receivership 5/4/25
TERRITORIAL ISSUES {{ 7 L }}
Series 1875 <$VALUE
4x10 1-7452 <$3000
Brown Back
3x10-20 1-6700 <$2000
1882 Date Back
3x10-20 1-3800 <$1750
STATE ISSUES {{ 22 L }}
1882 Date Back
3x10-20 1-2600 <$650
1882 Value Back
3x10-20 2601-4894 <$750
1902 Plain Back
3x10-20 1-12887 <$300
Total Issue $1,712,130
Out at close $200,000
Outstanding includes Ch 2454

2454 San Miguel
SAN MIGUEL NB OF
LAS VEGAS
Chartered 2/9/80
Liquidated 1/2/20
TERRITORIAL ISSUES {{ 10 L }}
Series 1875 <$VALUE
4x5 1-3100 <$3000
4x10 1-5070 <$3000
Brown Back
3x10-20 1-6400 <$2000
1882 Date Back
3x10-20 1-4400 <$1750
STATE ISSUES {{ 3 L }}
1882 Date Back
3x10-20 1-2600 <$650
1882 Value Back
3x10-20 2601-5345 <$750
Total Issue $1,072,050
Out at close $100,000
Ch 2436 assumed circulation

8880 Hidalgo
FNB OF LORDSBURG
Organized 9/21/07
TERRITORIAL ISSUES {{ 0 L }}
1902 Red Seal <$VALUE
3x10-20 1-762 <$5500
1902 Date Back
3x10-20 1-1000 <$4500
STATE ISSUES {{ 1 L }}
1902 Date Back
3x10-20 1-950 <$2000
1902 Plain Back
3x10-20 951-3820 <$2000
Total Issue $279,100
Out in 1935 $845

10268 Socorro
FNB OF MAGDALENA
{{ 5 L }}
Chartered 9/20/12
Receivership 1/18/23
1902 Date Back <$VALUE
3x10-20 1-2500 <$1000
1902 Plain Back
3x10-20 2501-6443 <$1000
Total Issue $322,150
Out at close $47,200

8397 Curry
FNB OF MELROSE
Chartered 10/06
TERRITORIAL ISSUES {{ 0 L }}
1902 Red Seal <$VALUE
3x10-20 1-860 <$5500
1902 Date Back
3x10-20 1-950 <$4500
STATE ISSUES {{ 6 L 7 S }}
1902 Date Back
3x10-20 1-930 <$1000
1902 Plain Back
3x10-20 931-5062 <$1000
1929 Small Size
10 Type 1 1-798 <$500
20 Type 1 1-192 <$500
10 Type 2 1-1023 <$550
20 Type 2 1-283 <$550
Total Issue $430,410
Out in 1935 $25,000
Large out 1935 $1,690

8663 Quay
FNB OF NARA VISA
Chartered 4/07
TERRITORIAL ISSUES {{ 3 L }}
1902 Red Seal <$VALUE
3x10-20 1-200 <$5000
1902 Date Back
3x10-20 1-580 <$4500
STATE ISSUES {{ 3 L 3 S }}
1902 Date Back
3x10-20 1-100 <$1750
1902 Plain Back
3x10-20 101-841 <$1750
1929 Small Size
10 Type 1 1-217 <$1000
20 Type 1 1-55 <$1000
Total Issue $100,670
Out in 1935 $6,050
Large out 1935 $380

8364 Roosevelt
CITIZENS NB OF PORTALES
{{ 1 L }}
Chartered 9/06
Liquidated 1/5/10
TERRITORIAL ISSUES
1902 Red Seal <$VALUE
4x10 1-2125 <$5000
1902 Date Back
4x10 1-583 <$4500
Total Issue $108,320
Out at close $50,000

6187 Roosevelt
FNB OF PORTALES
Chartered 4/3/02
TERRITORIAL ISSUES {{ 1 L }}
1902 Red Seal <$VALUE
3x10-20 1-1800 <$5000
1902 Date Back
3x10-20 1-1900 <$4500
STATE ISSUES {{ 3 L 14 S }}
1902 Date Back
3x10-20 1-1740 <$850
1902 Plain Back (dated 1902)
3x10-20 1741-5110 <$850
1902 Plain Back (dated 1922)
3x10-20 5111-10133 <$850
1929 Small Size
10 Type 1 1-1570 <$250
20 Type 1 1-394 <$250
10 Type 2 1-1945 <$275
20 Type 2 1-600 <$275
Total Issue $864,580
Out in 1935 $48,450
Large out 1935 $3,430

6363 Colfax
CITIZENS NB OF RATON
{{ UNREPORTED }}
Chartered 7/31/02
Liquidated 7/7/04
TERRITORIAL ISSUES
1902 Red Seal <$VALUE
4x5 1-200 <$6000
3x10-20 1-882 <$6000
Total Issue $48,100
Out in 1910 $1,850

12924 Colfax
FNB IN RATON
{{ 50+ S }}
Chartered 4/26
1929 Small Size <$VALUE
5 Type 1 1-6416 <$150
10 Type 1 1-3318 <$125
20 Type 1 1-908 <$135
5 Type 2 1-8688 <$175
10 Type 2 1-4404 <$175
20 Type 2 1-1080 <$175
Total Issue $609,600
Out in 1935 $149,790

4734 Colfax
FNB OF RATON
Chartered 1892
Liquidated 4/30/26
TERRITORIAL ISSUES {{ 12 L }}
Brown Back <$VALUE
4x5 1-5680 <$4500
3x10-20 1-3868 <$4500
1882 Date Back
4x5 1-3032 <$4000
3x10-20 1-2215 <$4000
STATE ISSUES {{ 17 L }}
1902 Date Back
4x5 1-4150 <$450
3x10-20 1-2920 <$450
1902 Plain Back
4x5 4151-16400 <$450
3x10-20 2921-10819 <$450
Total Issue $1,347,340
Out at close $96,900

8098 Colfax
NB OF NEW MEXICO OF RATON
Chartered 2/06
Liquidated 5/19/30
TERRITORIAL ISSUES {{ 0 L }}
1902 Red Seal <$VALUE
3x10-20 1-600 <$4500
1902 Date Back
3x10-20 1-1200 <$4000
STATE ISSUES {{ 4 L 3 S }}
1902 Date Back
3x10-20 1-320 <$1000
1902 Plain Back
3x10-20 321-8064 <$1000
1929 Small Size
10 Type 1 1-389 <$650
20 Type 1 1-87 <$650
Total Issue $526,980
Out at close $46,640
Large out 1935 $13,840

8120 Colfax
RATON NB, RATON
{{ 3 L }}
Chartered 3/06
Liquidated 9/1/11
TERRITORIAL ISSUES
1902 Red Seal <$VALUE
3x10-20 1-2400 <$4500
1902 Date Back
3x10-20 1-1462 <$4000
Total Issue $193,100
Out in 1911 $61,750

American NB of Roswell
SEE Ch 6714
Roswell NB, Roswell

6777 Chaves
CITIZENS NB OF ROSWELL
Organized 4/20/03
Receivership 11/16/23
TERRITORIAL ISSUES {{ 3 L }}
1902 Red Seal <$VALUE
3x10-20 1-2112 <$4500
1902 Date Back
3x10-20 1-2000 <$4000
STATE ISSUES {{ 8 L }}
1902 Date Back
3x10-20 1-5000 <$700
1902 Plain Back
3x10-20 5001-15988 <$700
Total Issue $1,005,000
Out at close $188,200
Outstanding includes Ch 6714

5220 Chaves
FNB OF ROSWELL
Chartered 9/18/99
TERRITORIAL ISSUES {{ 3 L }}
Brown Back <$VALUE
3x10-20 1-2670 <$4000
1882 Date Back
3x10-20 1-1900 <$3500
STATE ISSUES {{ 23 L 26 S }}
1882 Date Back
3x10-20 1-2300 <$750
1882 Value Back
3x10-20 2301-5500 <$750
1902 Plain Back
3x10-20 1-14572 <$300
1929 Small Size
10 Type 1 1-3044 <$200
20 Type 1 1-896 <$200
10 Type 2 1-3379 <$225
20 Type 2 1-1194 <$225
Total Issue $1,579,930
Out in 1935 $97,850
Large out 1935 $5,320

6714 Chaves
ROSWELL NB, ROSWELL
Chartered 4/03
Liquidated 12/10/21
2nd title: American NB of
Roswell 1/15/06
TERRITORIAL ISSUES
FIRST TITLE {{ 0 L }}
1902 Red Seal <$VALUE
3x10-20 1-1143 <$4500
SECOND TITLE {{ 0 L }}
1902 Red Seal
3x10-20 1-800 <$4500
1902 Date Back
3x10-20 1-1950 <$4000
STATE ISSUES {{ 3 L }}
1902 Date Back
3x10-20 1-1800 <$1000
1902 Plain Back
3x10-20 1801-7089 <$1000
Total Issue $549,300
Out at close $100,000
Ch 6777 assumed circulation

1750 Santa Fe
FNB OF SANTA FE
Chartered 12/13/70
TERRITORIAL ISSUES {{ 23 L }}
Original Series <$VALUE
3x1-2 1-5000 <$3500/$6500
4x5 1-3250 <$3500
2x10-20-50 1-1700
<$5000/$6500/$8500
Series 1875
3x1-2 1-3500 <$3500/$6500
4x5 1-5374 <$3500
2x10-20-50 1-2021
<$5000/$6500/$8500
Brown Back
3x10-20 1-5675 <$3000
1902 Date Back
4x5 1-1900 <$2500
3x10-20 1-1540 <$2500
STATE ISSUES {{ 20 L 50+ S }}
1902 Date Back
4x5 1-850 <$600
3x10-20 1-480 <$600
1902 Plain Back
4x5 851-11865 <$600
3x10-20 481-7885 <$600
1929 Small Size
5 Type 1 1-3058 <$250
10 Type 1 1-918 <$250
20 Type 1 1-312 <$250
5 Type 2 1-2986 <$300
10 Type 2 1-1985 <$300
20 Type 2 1-315 <$300
Total Issue $1,805,510
Out in 1935 $70,908
Large out 1935 $8,108

2024 Santa Fe
SECOND NB OF NEW MEXICO
AT SANTA FE
{{ 10 L }}
Chartered 8/1/72
Liquidated 7/17/92
TERRITORIAL ISSUES
Original Series <$VALUE
3x1-2 1-1000 <$3500/$6500
4x5 1-3500 <$3500
4x10 1-999 <$4500
3x20-50 1-964 <$6500/$8500
Series 1875
4x5 1-441 <$3500
3x20-50 1-2208<$6500/$8500
Total Issue $472,700
Out in 1910 $2,337

6081 Guadalupe
FNB OF SANTA ROSA
Chartered 1/3/02
TERRITORIAL ISSUES {{ 1 L }}
Brown Back <$VALUE
3x10-20 1-920 <$5000
1882 Date Back
3x10-20 1-1200 <$4500
STATE ISSUES {{ 7 L 16 S }}
1882 Date Back
4x5 1-1000 <$1250
3x10-20 1-1300* <$1250
1882 Value Back
4x5 1001-3950 <$1250
3x10-20 1801-3360* <$1250
* 1301-1800 not marked
1902 Plain Back
3x10-20 1-4981 <$750
1929 Small Size
10 Type 1 1-1578 <$400
20 Type 1 1-382 <$425
10 Type 2 1-141 <$500
20 Type 2 1-20 <$500
Total Issue $744,380
Out in 1935 $27,840
Large out 1935 $3,540

8132 Grant
AMERICAN NB OF
SILVER CITY
Chartered 3/06
TERRITORIAL ISSUES {{ 2 L }}
1902 Red Seal <$VALUE
3x10-20 1-2000 <$4500
1902 Date Back
3x10-20 1-1900 <$4000
STATE ISSUES {{ 48 L U+15 S }}
1902 Date Back
3x10-20 1-1800 <$375
1902 Plain Back
3x10-20 1801-9913 <$375
1929 Small Size
10 Type 1 1-1358 <$275
20 Type 1 1-380 <$275
10 Type 2 1-2121 <$325
20 Type 2 1-359 <$325
Total Issue $846,120
Out in 1935 $50,000
Large out 1935 $4,180

3554 Grant
FNB OF SILVER CITY
{{ UNREPORTED }}
Chartered 9/17/86
Receivership 2/29/92
TERRITORIAL ISSUES
Brown Back <$VALUE
3x10-20 1-457 <$6500
Total Issue $22,850
Out in 1916 $120

3539 Grant
SILVER CITY NB,
SILVER CITY
Chartered 7/22/86
Receivership 5/14/24
TERRITORIAL ISSUES {{ 1 L }}
Brown Back <$VALUE
3x10-20 1-2136 <$5000
1902 Red Seal
3x10-20 1-1500 <$5000
1902 Date Back
3x10-20 1-2200 <$4000
STATE ISSUES {{ 4 L }}
1902 Date Back
3x10-20 1-1440 <$850
1902 Plain Back
3x10-20 1441-6355 <$850
Total Issue $609,550
Out at close $41,500

2627 Socorro
FNB OF SOCORRO
{{ UNREPORTED }}
Chartered 2/13/82
Liquidated 7/31/86
TERRITORIAL ISSUES
Series 1875 <$VALUE
3x10-20 1-664 <$7500
Total Issue $33,200
Out in 1910 $190

4485 Socorro
NEW MEXICO NB OF SOCORRO
{{ UNREPORTED }}
Chartered 12/18/90
Liquidated 11/16/95
TERRITORIAL ISSUES
Brown Back <$VALUE
4x5 1-500 <$6500
3x10-20 1-269 <$6500
Total Issue $23,450
Out in 1910 $125

4574 Socorro
SOCORRO NB, SOCORRO
{{ UNREPORTED }}
Chartered 5/26/91
Liquidated 7/16/94
TERRITORIAL ISSUES
Brown Back <$VALUE
4x5 1-664 <$6500
3x10-20 1-140 <$6500
Total Issue $20,280
Out in 1910 $135

8173 Curry
FNB OF TEXICO
{{ 1 L }}
Chartered 4/12/06
Receivership 9/5/11
TERRITORIAL ISSUES
1902 Red Seal <$VALUE
3x10-20 1-420 <$7000
1902 Date Back
3x10-20 1-10 <$6500
Total Issue $21,500
Out in 1916 $320

8391 Curry
TEXICO NB, TEXICO
{{ UNREPORTED }}
Chartered 10/06
Liquidated 3/6/12
TERRITORIAL ISSUES
1902 Red Seal <$VALUE
3x10-20 1-300 <$7000
1902 Date Back
3x10-20 1-221 <$6500
Total Issue $26,050
Out at close $7,200

14081 Quay
F-AMERICAN NB IN
TUCUMCARI
{{ 6 S }}
Chartered 3/34
1929 Small Size <$VALUE
10 Type 2 1-1842 <$650
Total Issue $18,420
Out in 1935 $25,000
Large out 1935 $23,560
Outstanding includes Ch 6288

6288 Quay
FNB OF TUCUMCARI
Chartered 6/4/02
Liquidated 5/8/34
TERRITORIAL ISSUES {{ 0 L }}
1902 Red Seal <$VALUE
4x5 1-1250 <$5000
3x10-20 1-1100 <$5000
1902 Date Back
4x5 1-2400 <$4500
3x10-20 1-1580 <$4500
STATE ISSUES {{ 5 L 3 S }}
1902 Date Back
4x5 1-1850 <$850
3x10-20 1-1320 <$850
1902 Plain Back (dated 1902)
4x5 1851-2305 <$850
3x10-20 1321-1607 <$850
1902 Plain Back (dated 1922)
3x10-20 1-1082 <$850
1929 Small Size
10 Type 1 1-310 <$700
20 Type 1 1-104 <$700
10 Type 2 1-61 <$750
20 Type 2 1-15 <$750
Total Issue $419,540
Out at close $11,710
Large out 1935 $1,440
Ch 14081 assumed circulation

NATIONAL BANK NOTES

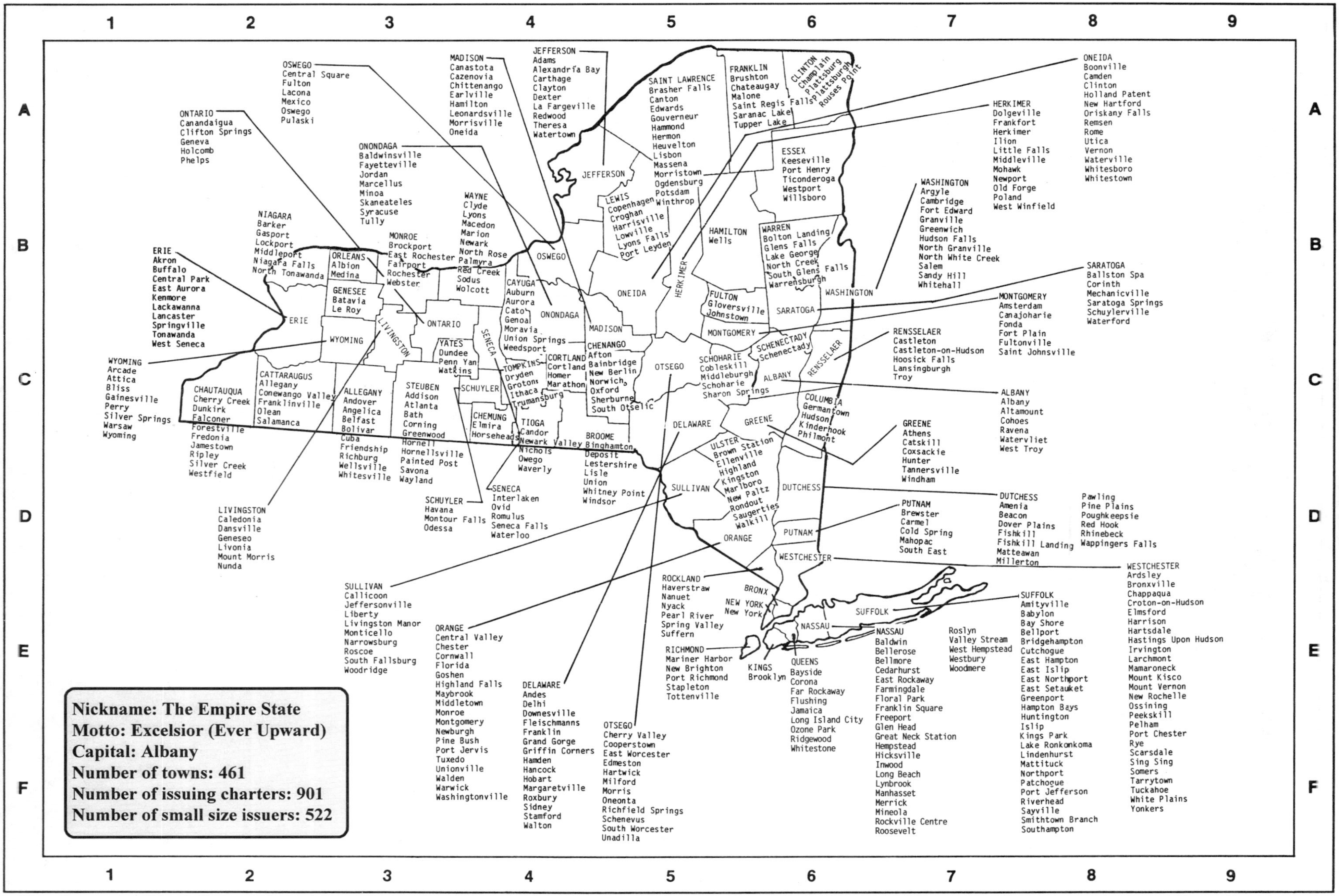

Nickname: The Empire State
Motto: Excelsior (Ever Upward)
Capital: Albany
Number of towns: 461
Number of issuing charters: 901
Number of small size issuers: 522

Adams A4
Addison C3
Afton C5
Akron B1
Albany C7
Albion B3
Alexandria Bay A4
Allegany C2
Altamont C7
Amenia D7
Amityville E8
Amsterdam C7
Andes E4
Andover C3
Angelica C3
Arcade C1
Ardsley E8
Argyle B7
Athens D7
Atlanta C3
Attica C1
Auburn C4
Aurora C4
Babylon E8
Bainbridge C5
Baldwin E7
Baldwinsville A3
Ballston Spa B8
Barker C2
Batavia B3
Bath C3
Bay Shore E8
Bayside E6
Beacon D7
Belfast C3
Bellerose E6
Bellmore E7
Bellport E8
Binghamton D4
Bliss C1
Bolivar C3
Bolton Landing B6
Boonville A8
Brasher Falls A5
Brewster D7
Bridgehampton E8
Brockport B3
Bronxville E8
Brooklyn E6
Brown Station D5
Brushton A6
Buffalo B1
Caledonia D2
Callicoon E3
Cambridge B7
Camden A8
Canajoharie C7
Canandaigua A2
Canastota A3
Candor C4
Canton A5
Carmel D7
Carthage A4
Castleton C7
Castleton On Hudson C7
Cato C4
Catskill D7
Cazenovia A3
Cedarhurst E7
Central Park B1
Central Square A2
Central Valley E3
Champlain A6
Chappaqua E8
Chateaugay A6
Cherry Creek C2
Cherry Valley F5
Chester E3
Chittenango A3
Clayton A4
Clifton Springs A2
Clinton A8
Clyde B4
Cobleskill C5
Cohoes C7
Cold Spring D7
Conewango Valley C2
Cooperstown F5
Copenhagen B5
Corinth B8
Corning C3
Cornwall E3
Corona E6
Cortland C4
Coxsackie D7
Croghan B5
Croton On Hudson E8
Cuba C3
Cutchogue E8
Dansville D2
Delhi E4
Deposit D4
Dexter A4
Dolgeville A7
Dover Plains D7
Downsville F4
Dryden C4
Dundee C3
Dunkirk C2
Earlville A3
East Aurora B1
East Hampton E8
East Islip E8
East Northport E8
East Rochester B3
East Rockaway E7
East Setauket E8
East Worcester F5
Edmeston F5
Edwards A5
Ellenville D5
Elmira C4
Elmsford E8
Fairport B3
Falconer C2
Far Rockaway E6
Farmingdale E7
Fayetteville A3
Fishkill D7
Fishkill Landing D7
Fleischmanns F4
Floral Park E7
Florida E3
Flushing E6
Fonda C7
Forestville C2
Fort Edward B7
Fort Plain C7
Frankfort A7
Franklin F4
Franklin Square E7
Franklinville C2
Fredonia C2
Freeport E7
Friendship C3
Fulton A2
Fultonville C7
Gainesville C1
Gasport C2
Geneseo D2
Geneva A2
Genoa C4
Germantown C6
Glen Head E7
Glens Falls B6
Gloversville B5
Goshen E3
Gouverneur A5
Grand Gorge F4
Granville B7
Great Neck Station F7
Greenport E8
Greenwich B7
Greenwood C3
Griffin Corners F4
Groton C4
Hamden F4
Hamilton A3
Hammond A5
Hampton Bays E8
Hancock F4
Harrison E8
Harrisville B5
Hartsdale E8
Hartwick F5
Hastings Upon Hudson E8
Havana D3
Haverstraw E5
Hempstead F7
Herkimer A7
Hermon A5
Heuvelton A5
Hicksville F7
Highland D5
Highland Falls E3
Hobart F4
Holcomb A2
Holland Patent A8
Homer C4
Hoosick Falls C7
Hornell C3
Hornellsville C3
Horseheads C4
Hudson C5
Hudson Falls B7
Hunter D7
Huntington E8
Ilion A7
Interlaken D4
Inwood E6
Irvington E8
Islip F8
Ithaca C4
Jamaica F6
Jamestown C2
Jeffersonville E3
Johnstown B5
Jordan B3
Keeseville B6
Kenmore B1
Kinderhook C6
Kings Park F8
Kingston D5
La Fargeville A4
Lackawanna C1
Lacona A2
Lake George B6
Lake Ronkonkoma F8
Lancaster C1
Lansingburgh C7
Larchmont E8
Le Roy B3
Leonardsville A3
Lestershire D4
Liberty E3
Lindenhurst F8
Lisbon A5
Lisle D4
Little Falls A7
Livingston Manor E3
Livonia D2
Lockport C2
Long Beach F7
Long Island City F6
Lowville B5
Lynbrook F7
Lyons B4
Lyons Falls B5
Macedon B4
Mahopac D7
Malone A6
Mamaroneck E8
Manhasset F7
Marathon C4
Marcellus B3
Margaretville F4
Mariner Harbor E5
Marion B4
Marlboro D5
Massena A5
Matteawan D7
Mattituck F8
Maybrook E3
Mechanicville B8
Medina B3
Merrick F7
Mexico A2
Middleburgh C5
Middleport C2
Middletown E3
Middleville A7
Milford F5
Millerton D7
Mineola F7
Minoa B3
Mohawk A7
Monroe E3
Montgomery F3
Monticello E3
Montour Falls D3
Moravia C4
Morris F5
Morristown A5
Morrisville A3
Mount Kisco E8
Mount Morris D2
Mount Vernon E8
Nanuet E5
Narrowsburg E3
New Berlin C5
New Brighton E5
New Hartford A8
New Paltz D5
New Rochelle E8
New York E6
Newark B4
Newark Valley C3
Newburgh F3
Newport A7
Niagara Falls C2
Nichols C3
North Creek B6
North Granville B7
North Rose B4
North Tonawanda C2
North White Creek B7
Northport F8
Norwich C5
Nunda D2
Nyack E5
Odessa D3
Ogdensburg A5
Old Forge A7
Olean C2
Oneida A3
Oneonta F5
Oriskany Falls A8
Ossining E8
Oswego A2
Ovid D4
Owego C3
Oxford C5
Ozone Park F6
Painted Post C3
Palmyra B4
Patchogue F8
Pawling D8
Pearl River E5
Peekskill E8
Pelham F8
Penn Yan C3
Perry C1
Phelps A2
Philmont C6
Pine Bush F3
Pine Plains D8
Plattsburg A6
Plattsburgh A6
Poland A7
Port Chester F8
Port Henry B6
Port Jefferson F8
Port Jervis F3
Port Leyden B5
Port Richmond E5
Potsdam A5
Poughkeepsie D8
Pulaski A2
Ravena C7
Red Creek B4
Red Hook D8
Redwood A4
Remsen A8
Rhinebeck D8
Richburg C3
Richfield Springs F5
Ridgewood F6
Ripley C2
Riverhead F8
Rochester B3
Rockville Centre F7
Rome A8
Romulus D4
Rondout D5
Roosevelt F7
Roscoe E3
Roslyn F7
Rouses Point A6
Roxbury F4
Rye F8
Saint Johnsville C7
Saint Regis Falls A6
Salamanca C2
Salem B7
Sandy Hill B7
Saranac Lake A6
Saratoga Springs B8
Saugerties D5
Savona C3
Sayville F8
Scarsdale F8
Schenectady C6
Schenevus F5
Schoharie C5
Schuylerville B8
Seneca Falls D4
Sharon Springs C5
Sherburne C5
Sidney F4
Silver Creek C2
Silver Springs C1
Sing Sing F8
Skaneateles B3
Smithtown Branch F8
Sodus B4
Somers F8
South East D7
South Fallsburg E3
South Glens Falls B6
South Otselic C5
South Worcester F5
Southampton F8
Spring Valley E5
Springville C1
Stamford F4
Stapleton E5
Suffern E5
Syracuse B3
Tannersville D7
Tarrytown F8
Theresa A4
Ticonderoga B6
Tonawanda C1
Tottenville E5
Troy C7
Trumansburg C4
Tuckahoe F8
Tully B3
Tupper Lake A6
Tuxedo F3
Unadilla F5
Union D4
Union Springs C4
Unionville F3
Utica A8
Valley Stream F7
Vernon A8
Walden F3
Walkill D5
Walton F4
Wappingers Falls D8
Warrensburgh B6
Warsaw C1
Warwick F3
Washingtonville F3
Waterford B8
Waterloo D4
Watertown A4
Waterville A8
Watervliet C7
Watkins C3
Waverly C3
Wayland C3
Webster B3
Weedsport C4
Wells B5
Wellsville C3
West Hempstead F7
West Seneca C1
West Troy C7
West Winfield A7
Westbury F7
Westfield C2
Westport B6
White Plains F8
Whitehall B7
Whitesboro A8
Whitestone F6
Whitestown A8
Whitesville C3
Whitney Point D4
Willsboro B6
Windham D7
Windsor D4
Winthrop A5
Wolcott B4
Woodmere F7
Woodridge E3
Wyoming C1
Yonkers F8

****
2845 Jefferson
ADAMS NB, ADAMS
{{ UNREPORTED }}
Chartered 12/23/82
Liquidated 7/10/89
Brown Back <$VALUE
3x10-20 1-984 <$1250
Total Issue $49,200
Out in 1910 $190
****
4103 Jefferson
CITIZENS NB OF ADAMS
{{ 3 L }}
Chartered 8/29/89
Liquidated 7/2/19
Brown Back <$VALUE
4x5 1-3725 <$500
50-100 1-280 <$1250/$1500
1882 Date Back
4x5 1-730 <$500
50-100 1-174 <$1250/$1500
1902 Date Back
3x10-20 1-4180 <$350
1902 Plain Back
3x10-20 4181-5820 <$350
Total Issue $448,200
Out at close $50,000
****
4061 Jefferson
FARMERS NB OF ADAMS
{{ 7 L 9 S }}
Chartered 6/29/89
Liquidated 8/16/32
Brown Back <$VALUE
50-100 1-794 <$1250/$1500
1882 Date Back
50-100 1-70 <$1250/$1500
1902 Date Back
3x10-20 1-3940 <$200
1902 Plain Back
3x10-20 3941-12484 <$200
1929 Small Size
10 Type 1 1-1569 <$150
20 Type 1 1-450 <$150
Total Issue $901,940
Out at close $50,000
Large out at close $2,670
****
71 Jefferson
FNB OF ADAMS
{{ 1 L }}
Chartered 8/27/63
Liquidated 3/7/73
Original Series <$VALUE
3x1-2 1-520 <$1250/$2000
4x5 1-4500 <$1250
Total Issue $92,600
Out in 1910 $792
****
1531 Jefferson
HUNGERFORD NB OF ADAMS
{{ 3 L }}
Chartered 1865
Liquidated 1/27/81
Original Series <$VALUE
3x1-2 1-6000 <$500/$1000
4x5 1-4600 <$600
2x10-20-50 1-1855 <$600/$1250/$3500
Series 1875
3x1-2 1-192 <$500/$1000
4x5 1-759 <$600
2x10-20-50 1-66 <$600/$1250/$3500
Total Issue $311,030
Out in 1910 $1,604
****
5178 Steuben
FNB OF ADDISON
{{ 7 L 9 S }}
Chartered 2/17/99
Brown Back <$VALUE
4x5 1-3100 <$350
3x10-20 1-2160 <$350
1882 Date Back
4x5 1-3500 <$350
3x10-20 1-2480 <$350
1882 Value Back
4x5 3501-4957 <$350
3x10-20 2481-3334 <$350
1902 Plain Back
4x5 1-7200 <$225
3x10-20 1-5060 <$225
1929 Small Size
5 Type 1 1-1926 <$150
10 Type 1 1-904 <$150
20 Type 1 1-242 <$150
5 Type 2 1-3590 <$150
10 Type 2 1-2028 <$150
20 Type 2 1-456 <$175
Total Issue $1,021,250
Out in 1935 $50,000
Large out 1935 $2,320
****

****
11513 Chenango
FNB OF AFTON
{{ 3 L 5 S }}
Chartered 11/19
1902 Plain Back <$VALUE
4x5 1-12602 <$450
1929 Small Size
5 Type 1 1-3238 <$300
5 Type 2 1-8442 <$300
Total Issue $391,390
Out in 1935 $25,000
Large out 1935 $720
****
5631 Erie
WICKWARE NB OF AKRON
{{ 5 L }}
Chartered 11/24/00
Liquidated 1/1/20
Brown Back <$VALUE
4x5 1-1925 <$400
3x10-20 1-1320 <$400
1882 Date Back
4x5 1-1850 <$400
3x10-20 1-1430 <$400
1882 Value Back
4x5 1851-2985 <$400
3x10-20 1431-1945 <$400
Total Issue $261,450
Out at close $25,000
****
1291 Albany
ALBANY CITY NB, ALBANY
{{ 3 L }}
Chartered 6/16/65
Liquidated 2/5/02
Original Series <$VALUE
4x5 1-9050 <$400
3x10-20 1-2808 <$600/$1250
50-100 1-498 <$3500
Series 1875
4x5 1-9125 <$400
3x10-20 1-3554 <$500/$1000
50-100 1-446 <$3500
Brown Back
4x5 1-6018 <$300
3x10-20 1-3214 <$300
50-100 1-486 <$1250/$1500
Total Issue $1,177,160
Out in 1910 $7,750
****
267 Albany
FNB OF ALBANY
{{ U + 20 L }}
Chartered 2/64
Liquidated 11/29/26
Original Series <$VALUE
4x5 1-5550 <$300
3x10-20 1-4900 <$600/$1250
3x20-50 1-850 <$1250/$3500
Series 1875
4x5 1-1185 <$300
3x10-20 1-1854 <$500/$1000
3x20-50 1-615 <$1250/$3500
Brown Back
4x5 1-15158 <$150
3x10-20 1-6160 <$150/$200
1902 Red Seal
4x5 1-6850 <$150
3x10-20 1-5240 <$150/$200
1902 Date Back
4x5 1-65000 <$50
3x10-20 1-48000 <$60
1902 Plain Back
4x5 65001-139720 <$50
3x10-20 48001-95620 <$60
Total Issue $9,219,110
Out at close $500,000
****
1045 Albany
MERCHANTS NB OF ALBANY
{{ 2 L }}
Chartered 4/22/65
Liquidated 1/20/02
Original Series <$VALUE
4x5 1-3000 <$500
3x10-20 1-2800 <$600/$1250
50-100 1-768 <$3500
Series 1875
4x5 1-4931 <$500
3x10-20 1-2524 <$600/$1000
50-100 1-868 <$3500
Brown Back
4x5 1-4088 <$350
3x10-20 1-4747 <$350
50-100 1-1267 <$1250/$1500
Total Issue $1,179,380
Out in 1910 $7,570
****

****
739 Albany
N ALBANY EXCHANGE B, ALBANY
{{ 1 L }}
Chartered 1/23/65
Liquidated 1/10/85
Original Series <$VALUE
4x5 1-10325 <$650
3x10-20 1-4180 <$750/$1250
50-100 1-913 <$3500
Series 1875
4x5 1-6150 <$650
3x10-20 1-6200 <$750/$1250
50-100 1-1165 <$3500
Total Issue $1,160,200
Out in 1910 $5,025
****
1301 Albany
N COMMERCIAL B OF ALBANY
Chartered 1865
2nd title:N Commercial B & TC 4/28/20
FIRST TITLE {{ 16 L }}
Original Series <$VALUE
4x5 1-3600 <$300
3x10-20 1-3300 <$600/$1250
50-100 1-4034 <$3500
Series 1875
4x5 1-500 <$300
3x10-20 1-4700 <$500/$1000
50-100 1-2337 <$3500
Brown Back
3x10-20 1-9260 <$125/$175
50-100 1-5100 <$1250/$1500
1902 Red Seal
4x5 1-29000 <$125
3x10-20 1-15200 <$125/$175
50-100 1-2400 <$2250/$2500
1902 Date Back
4x5 1-104830 <$50
3x10-20 1-68268 <$60
50-100 1-1800 <$300/$350
3x50-100 1-3000 <$300/$350
1902 Plain Back
4x5 104831-132830 <$50
3x10-20 68269-83268 <$60
SECOND TITLE {{ 26 L 50+ S }}
1902 Plain Back
4x5 1-129100 <$50
3x10-20 1-77924 <$60
3x50-100 1-1200 <$300/$350
1929 Small Size
5 Type 1 1-57936 <$15
10 Type 1 1-29710 <$20
20 Type 1 1-5318 <$30
5 Type 2 1-154292 <$15
10 Type 2 1-38248 <$20
20 Type 2 1-11977 <$30
Total Issue $24,536,170
Out in 1935 $1,500,000
Large out 1935 $50,975
****
3282 Albany
N EXCHANGE B OF ALBANY
{{ 3 L }}
Chartered 1/2/85
Liquidated 4/29/07
Brown Back <$VALUE
4x5 1-20310 <$300
3x10-20 1-15444 <$300
50-100 1-1334 <$1250/$1500
1902 Red Seal
4x5 1-460 <$300
3x10-20 1-69 <$300
Total Issue $1,391,150
Out in 1910 $13,850
****
1289 Albany
N MECHANICS & FARMERS B OF ALBANY
{{ 1 L }}
Chartered 6/16/65
Liquidated 8/4/68
Original Series <$VALUE
4x5 1-3000 <$650
3x10-20 1-1000 <$750/$1250
50-100 1-1433 <$3500
Total Issue $324,950
Out in 1910 $1,410
****
1262 Albany
NEW YORK STATE NB OF ALBANY
{{ 29 L 50+ S }}
Chartered 1865
Original Series <$VALUE
3x1-2 1-1460 <$250/$750
4x5 1-3800 <$300
3x10-20 1-7100 <$600/$1250
50-100 1-700 <$3500
Series 1875
4x5 1-6000 <$300
3x10-20 1-5560 <$500/$1000
50-100 1-484 <$3500

Brown Back
4x5 1-27900 <$150
3x10-20 1-9260 <$150/$175
50-100 1-300 <$1250/$1500
1902 Red Seal
4x5 1-15065 <$150
3x10-20 1-10074 <$150/$175
1902 Date Back
4x5 1-57530 <$50
3x10-20 1-40068 <$60
1902 Plain Back
4x5 57531-99424 <$50
3x10-20 40069-67211 <$60
1929 Small Size
5 Type 1 1-74556 <$15
10 Type 1 1-40938 <$20
20 Type 1 1-14496 <$30
5 Type 2 1-151384 <$15
10 Type 2 1-73801 <$20
20 Type 2 1-20785 <$30
Total Issue $16,577,040
Out in 1935 $2,000,000
Large out 1935 $13,950
****
1123 Albany
UNION NB OF ALBANY
{{ 2 L }}
Chartered 1865
Liquidated 3/7/85
Original Series <$VALUE
4x5 1-16300 <$500
3x10-20 1-6480 <$750/$1250
50-100 1-300 <$3500
Series 1875
4x5 1-20350 <$500
Total Issue $1,104,500
Out in 1910 $5,480
****
4998 Orleans
CITIZENS NB OF ALBION
{{ 15 L 3 S }}
Organized 5/2/95
Liquidated 1/21/32
Brown Back <$VALUE
4x5 1-4900 <$200
3x10-20 1-2840 <$200/$250
1882 Date Back
4x5 1-3772 <$200
3x10-20 1-2340 <$200/$250
1902 Date Back
4x5 1-830 <$100
3x10-20 1-668 <$100
1902 Plain Back
4x5 831-9330 <$100
3x10-20 669-5996 <$100
1929 Small Size
5 Type 1 1-1236 <$250
10 Type 1 1-622 <$250
20 Type 1 1-171 <$250
Total Issue $1,013,760
Out at close $49,280
Large out at close $5,090
****
166 Orleans
FNB OF ALBION
{{ 4 L }}
Organized 12/12/63
Receivership 8/26/84
Original Series <$VALUE
3x1-2 1-9400 <$350/$750
4x5 1-4700 <$500
3x10-20 1-1400 <$750/$1250
Series 1875
3x1-2 1-2300 <$350/$850
4x5 1-2960 <$500
3x10-20 1-1248 <$600/$1250
Brown Back
4x5 1-980 <$300
3x10-20 1-374 <$300/$350
Total Issue $382,400
Out in 1916 $2,566
****
1509 Orleans
ORLEANS COUNTY NB OF ALBION
{{ 8 L }}
Chartered 1865
Liquidated 10/2/20
Original Series <$VALUE
3x1-2 1-8000 <$300/$850
4x5 1-4875 <$400
3x10-20 1-1380 <$750/$1250
Series 1875
3x1-2 1-900 <$300/$850
4x5 1-5185 <$400
3x10-20 1-1456 <$600/$1000
Brown Back
4x5 1-4158 <$225
3x10-20 1-1442 <$225/$275
1902 Red Seal
3x10-20 1-870 <$300
1902 Date Back
3x10-20 1-2450 <$150
1902 Plain Back
3x10-20 2451-2600 <$150
Total Issue $716,260
Out at close $24,545
****

****
5284 Jefferson
FNB OF THE THOUSAND ISLANDS, ALEXANDRIA BAY
{{ 3 L 4 S }}
Chartered 4/11/00
Receivership 12/7/33
Brown Back <$VALUE
3x10-20 1-1310 <$2500
1882 Date Back
3x10-20 1-1500 <$2500
1882 Value Back
3x10-20 1501-1990 <$2500
1902 Plain Back
3x10-20 1-2001 <$2000
1929 Small Size
10 Type 1 1-403 <$1250
20 Type 1 1-120 <$1250
Total Issue $303,630
Out at close $14,995
Large out at close $1,055
****
7009 Cattaraugus
FNB OF ALLEGANY
{{ 6 L 6 S }}
Chartered 10/03
1902 Red Seal <$VALUE
3x10-20 1-1640 <$500
1902 Date Back
3x10-20 1-2150 <$250
1902 Plain Back
3x10-20 2151-6523 <$250
1929 Small Size
10 Type 1 1-704 <$200
20 Type 1 1-170 <$200
10 Type 2 1-1188 <$200
20 Type 2 1-368 <$200
Total Issue $490,030
Out in 1935 $25,000
Large out 1935 $970
****
9866 Albany
FNB OF ALTAMONT
{{ 3 L 6 S }}
Organized 9/2/10
1902 Date Back <$VALUE
4x5 1-1850 <$400
3x10-20 1-1410 <$400
1902 Plain Back
4x5 1851-6950 <$400
3x10-20 1411-4429 <$400
1929 Small Size
5 Type 1 1-936 <$200
10 Type 1 1-460 <$200
20 Type 1 1-150 <$200
5 Type 2 1-1746 <$200
10 Type 2 1-1020 <$200
20 Type 2 1-264 <$200
Total Issue $458,340
Out in 1935 $25,000
Large out 1935 $1,090
****
706 Dutchess
FNB OF AMENIA
{{ 15 L 18 S }}
Chartered 1/65
Original Series <$VALUE
3x1-2 1-4000 <$300/$850
4x5 1-3750 <$350
3x10-20 1-2400 <$600/$1250
Series 1875
4x5 1-1250 <$350
3x10-20 1-2292 <$500/$1000
Brown Back
4x5 1-7125 <$200
3x10-20 1-8215 <$200/$250
1902 Red Seal
4x5 1-4250 <$200
3x10-20 1-2800 <$200/$250
1902 Date Back
4x5 1-8500 <$100
3x10-20 1-6240 <$100
1902 Plain Back
4x5 8501-22319 <$100
3x10-20 6241-20227 <$100
1929 Small Size
10 Type 1 1-2808 <$50
20 Type 1 1-784 <$60
10 Type 2 1-4740 <$60
20 Type 2 1-1500 <$60
Total Issue $2,930,540
Out in 1935 $100,000
Large out 1935 $6,180
****
8873 Suffolk
FNB OF AMITYVILLE
Chartered 9/07
2nd title:FNB & TC 3/16/26
FIRST TITLE {{ 0 L }}
1902 Red Seal <$VALUE
3x10-20 1-200 <$3000
1902 Date Back
3x10-20 1-1950 <$2000
1902 Plain Back
3x10-20 1951-6852 <$2000

SECOND TITLE {{ 0 L 5 S }}
1902 Plain Back
3x10-20 1-2059 <$2000
1929 Small Size
10 Type 1 1-1162 <$500
20 Type 1 1-324 <$500
10 Type 2 1-1877 <$500
20 Type 2 1-504 <$500
Total Issue $593,000
Out in 1935 $37,500
Large out 1935 $1,500
****
4211 Montgomery
AMSTERDAM CITY NB, AMSTERDAM
{{ 10 L 22 S }}
Organized 1/20/90
Brown Back <$VALUE
3x10-20 1-2010 <$250
50-100 1-1810 <$1250/$1500
1882 Date Back
3x10-20 1-233 <$250
50-100 1-13 <$1250/$1500
1902 Date Back
4x5 1-7750 <$150
3x10-20 1-4500 <$150
50-100 1-900 <$400/$500
1902 Plain Back
4x5 7751-47060 <$150
3x10-20 4501-30585 <$150
1929 Small Size
5 Type 1 1-7420 <$50
10 Type 1 1-4076 <$50
20 Type 1 1-1012 <$60
5 Type 2 1-16410 <$60
10 Type 2 1-7683 <$60
20 Type 2 1-1991 <$60
Total Issue $3,778,350
Out in 1935 $200,000
Large out 1935 $7,770
****
1335 Montgomery
FARMERS NB OF AMSTERDAM
{{ 10 L 20 S }}
Chartered 1865
Original Series <$VALUE
3x1-2 1-5160 <$350/$850
4x5 1-3875 <$400
3x10-20 1-2250 <$600/$1250
50-100 1-770 <$3500
Series 1875
4x5 1-855 <$400
3x10-20 1-1200 <$600/$1000
50-100 1-687 <$3500
Brown Back
3x10-20 1-14215 <$250
50-100 1-3109 <$1250/$1500
1902 Red Seal
3x10-20 1-6095 <$250/$300
50-100 1-335 <$2250/$2500
1902 Date Back
3x10-20 1-15900 <$150
50-100 1-400 <$400/$500
3x50-100 1-634 <$400/$500
1902 Plain Back
4x5 1-1425 <$150
3x10-20 15901-33809 <$150
1929 Small Size
5 Type 1 1-4932 <$50
10 Type 1 1-2580 <$50
20 Type 1 1-670 <$60
5 Type 2 1-16052 <$60
10 Type 2 1-9936 <$60
20 Type 2 1-2448 <$60
Total Issue $4,592,740
Out in 1935 $200,000
Large out 1935 $2,992
****

CONDITION affects Value. The Values shown are for notes in FINE condition.

****
1307 Montgomery
FNB OF AMSTERDAM
{{ 13 L 21 S }}
Chartered 1865
Original Series <$VALUE
3x1-2 1-1000 <$300/$750
4x5 1-2000 <$350
3x10-20 1-2140 <$600/$1250
50-100 1-503 <$3500
Series 1875
3x1-2 1-1180 <$300/$750
4x5 1-5005 <$350
3x10-20 1-1498 <$500/$1000
50-100 1-31 <$3500
Brown Back
3x10-20 1-12835 <$200
50-100 1-200 <$1250/$1500
1902 Red Seal
4x5 1-5500 <$200
4x10 1-2000 <$200
3x10-20 1-1404 <$200
50-100 1-82 <$2250/$2500
1902 Date Back
4x5 1-8250 <$100
4x10 1-4750 <$100
3x10-20 1-4700 <$400/$500
50-100 1-200 <$400/$500
1902 Plain Back
4x5 8251-25012 <$100
3x10-20 4701-20199 <$100
1929 Small Size
5 Type 1 1-3638 <$45
10 Type 1 1-1839 <$45
20 Type 1 1-603 <$55
50 Type 1 1-276 <$150
100 Type 1 1-106 <$200
Total Issue $3,525,680
Out in 1935 $200,000
Large out 1935 $7,585
****
2239 Montgomery
MANUFACTURERS NB OF AMSTERDAM
{{ 1 L }}
Chartered 3/25/75
Liquidated 8/1/82
Original Series <$VALUE
4x5 1-3750 <$750
Series 1875
4x5 1-1775 <$750
3x10-20 1-638 <$850/$1250
Total Issue $142,400
Out in 1910 $640
****
2920 Montgomery
MERCHANTS NB OF AMSTERDAM
{{ UNREPORTED }}
Chartered 4/9/83
Liquidated 3/15/90
Brown Back <$VALUE
4x5 1-6579 <$1250
Total Issue $131,580
Out in 1910 $640
****
302 Delaware
FNB OF ANDES
{{ 2 L }}
Chartered 3/3/64
Liquidated 7/28/96
Original Series <$VALUE
3x1-2 1-3500 <$750/$1250
4x5 1-6250 <$750
Series 1875
4x5 1-2800 <$750
Brown Back
4x5 1-11950 <$600
Total Issue $437,500
Out in 1910 $2,504
****
11243 Delaware
NB OF ANDES
{{ 2 L 4 S }}
Chartered 9/18
1902 Plain Back <$VALUE
4x5 1-13282 <$600
1929 Small Size
5 Type 1 1-3226 <$300
5 Type 2 1-7140 <$300
Total Issue $398,120
Out in 1935 $25,000
Large out 1935 $1,105
****
13909 Allegany
ANDOVER NB, ANDOVER
{{ 1 S }}
Chartered 12/33
1929 Small Size <$VALUE
10 Type 2 1-634 <$600
20 Type 2 1-143 <$600
Total Issue $9,200
Out in 1935 $25,000
Outstanding includes Ch 8146
****

****
8146 Allegany
BURROWS NB OF ANDOVER
{{ 2 L 4 S }}
Chartered 3/06
Liquidated 12/30/33
1902 Red Seal <$VALUE
3x10-20 1-1040 <$750
1902 Date Back
3x10-20 1-2010 <$400
1902 Plain Back
3x10-20 2011-6277 <$400
1929 Small Size
10 Type 1 1-584 <$300
20 Type 1 1-178 <$300
10 Type 2 1-137 <$300
Total Issue $423,620
Out at close $25,000
Large out 1935 $1,320
Ch 13909 assumed circulation
****
564 Allegany
FNB OF ANGELICA
{{ 2 L }}
Organized 11/3/64
Receivership 4/19/86
Original Series <$VALUE
3x1-2 1-4100 <$750/$1250
4x5 1-3000 <$750
3x10-20 1-2100<$1000/$1250
Series 1875
3x1-2 1-2260 <$750/$1250
4x5 1-6660 <$750
3x10-20 1-538 <$1000/$1250
Brown Back
4x5 1-500 <$600
3x10-20 1-728 <$600
Total Issue $403,300
Out in 1916 $2,041
****
10410 Wyoming
FNB OF ARCADE
{{ 2 L 2U + 6 S }}
Chartered 6/13
Liquidated 11/21/34
1902 Date Back <$VALUE
3x10-20 1-1200 <$500
1902 Plain Back
3x10-20 1201-5731 <$500
1929 Small Size
10 Type 1 1-744 <$250
20 Type 1 1-162 <$250
10 Type 2 1-444 <$250
20 Type 2 1-192 <$250
Total Issue $358,910
Out at close $25,000
Large out at close $690
****
12992 Westchester
FNB OF ARDSLEY
{{ 3 S }}
Chartered 9/26
1929 Small Size <$VALUE
5 Type 2 1-3648 <$600
10 Type 2 1-1704 <$600
20 Type 2 1-528 <$600
Total Issue $45,840
Out in 1935 $25,000
****
8343 Washington
FNB OF ARGYLE
{{ UNREPORTED }}
Organized 7/12/06
Receivership 8/15/30
1902 Red Seal <$VALUE
4x10 1-406 <$1500
1902 Date Back
4x10 1-1125 <$1000
1902 Plain Back
4x10 1126-2871 <$1000
1929 Small Size
10 Type 1 1-119 <$750
Total Issue $138,220
Out at close $7,500
Large out at close $720
****
13521 Washington
NB OF ARGYLE
{{ 2U + 4 S }}
Chartered 1/31
1929 Small Size <$VALUE
5 Type 1 1-624 <$300
10 Type 1 1-314 <$300
20 Type 1 1-106 <$300
5 Type 2 1-2726 <$300
10 Type 2 1-1435 <$300
20 Type 2 1-190 <$300
Total Issue $82,060
Out in 1935 $29,900
****

****
10856 Greene
ATHENS NB, ATHENS
{{ 3 L 8 S }}
Organized 4/26/16
1902 Plain Back <$VALUE
3x10-20 1-4685 <$400
1929 Small Size
10 Type 1 1-1030 <$175
20 Type 1 1-282 <$175
10 Type 2 1-2135 <$200
20 Type 2 1-588 <$200
Total Issue $363,000
Out in 1935 $50,000
Large out 1935 $770
****
12071 Steuben
ATLANTA NB, ATLANTA
{{ 3 L 7 S }}
Organized 12/7/21
1902 Plain Back <$VALUE
4x5 1-3477 <$500
1929 Small Size
5 Type 1 1-1096 <$250
5 Type 2 1-2754 <$250
Total Issue $116,190
Out in 1935 $10,000
Large out 1935 $260
****
2437 Wyoming
ATTICA NB, ATTICA
{{ UNREPORTED }}
Chartered 9/27/79
Liquidated 8/30/81
Series 1875 <$VALUE
3x10-20 1-1000<$1500/$2000
Total Issue $50,000
Out in 1910 $170
****
199 Wyoming
FNB OF ATTICA
{{ 1 L }}
Organized 1/14/64
Receivership 4/14/65
Original Series <$VALUE
4x5 1-2200 <$1250
Total Issue $44,000
Out in 1915 $235
****
Auburn-Cayuga NB & TC of Auburn
SEE Ch 1345
Cayuga County NB of Auburn
****
1285 Cayuga
AUBURN CITY NB OF AUBURN
{{ 1 L }}
Chartered 6/16/65
Liquidated 6/26/75
Original Series <$VALUE
3x1-2 1-3030 <$600/$1250
4x5 1-5725 <$600
4x10 1-1751 <$750
2x20-50-100 1-249
<$1250/$3500/$3500
Total Issue $247,000
Out in 1910 $1,837
****
1345 Cayuga
CAYUGA COUNTY NB OF AUBURN
Chartered 1865
2nd title:Auburn-Cayuga NB & TC 9/26/31
3rd title:NB of Auburn 5/31/33
FIRST TITLE {{ 18 L 3 S }}
Original Series <$VALUE
4x5 1-14250 <$300
3x10-20 1-2500 <$600/$1250
Series 1875
4x5 1-6574 <$300
3x10-20 1-3730 <$500/$1000
Brown Back
4x5 1-12050 <$125
3x10-20 1-13503 <$125/$175
1902 Red Seal
4x5 1-5500 <$125
3x10-20 1-4300 <$125/$175
1902 Date Back
4x5 1-13000 <$60
3x10-20 1-11000 <$75
1902 Plain Back
4x5 13001-49416 <$60
3x10-20 11001-35322 <$75
1929 Small Size
5 Type 1 1-5382 <$100
10 Type 1 1-2434 <$100
20 Type 1 1-678 <$100
SECOND TITLE {{ 8 S }}
1929 Small Size
5 Type 1 1-4964 <$60
10 Type 1 1-3382 <$60
20 Type 1 1-798 <$60

THIRD TITLE {{ 14 S }}
1929 Small Size
5 Type 2 1-22266 <$40
10 Type 2 1-12456 <$40
20 Type 2 1-2880 <$45
Total Issue $5,853,500
Out in 1935 $400,000
Large out 1935 $24,025
Outstanding includes Ch 1350
****
231 Cayuga
FNB OF AUBURN
{{ 2 L }}
Organized 1/13/64
Receivership 2/20/88
Original Series <$VALUE
3x1-2 1-2800 <$500/$1250
4x5 1-4450 <$500
4x10 1-1800 <$750
Series 1875
4x5 1-6250 <$500
4x10 1-3343 <$600
Brown Back
3x10-20 1-1319 <$450
Total Issue $499,670
Out in 1916 $2,943
****
NB of Auburn
SEE Ch 1345
Cayuga County NB of Auburn
****
1350 Cayuga
NB OF AUBURN
{{ 13 L 8 S }}
Chartered 1865
Closed 9/26/31
Original Series <$VALUE
3x1-2 1-6000 <$300/$750
4x5 1-6000 <$300
3x10-20 1-3900 <$600/$1250
Series 1875
4x5 1-2500 <$300
3x10-20 1-4525 <$500/$1000
Brown Back
3x10-20 1-9025 <$200/$250
1902 Red Seal
3x10-20 1-1800 <$200/$250
1902 Date Back
3x10-20 1-17100 <$100
1902 Plain Back
3x10-20 17101-49312 <$100
1929 Small Size
10 Type 1 1-3479 <$75
20 Type 1 1-953 <$85
Total Issue $3,951,200
Out at close $200,000
Large out at close $19,710
Ch 1345 assumed circulation
****
1351 Cayuga
N EXCHANGE B OF AUBURN
{{ 2 L }}
Chartered 6/28/65
Liquidated 11/16/88
Original Series <$VALUE
4x5 1-7250 <$500
3x10-20 1-1600 <$750/$1250
Series 1875
4x5 1-605 <$500
3x10-20 1-4234 <$600/$1000
Brown Back
3x10-20 1-1864 <$450
Total Issue $542,000
Out in 1910 $2,860
****
412 Cayuga
FNB OF AURORA
{{ 7 L 10 S }}
Chartered 5/64
Original Series <$VALUE
3x1-2 1-2932 <$350/$1000
4x5 1-6250 <$400
3x10-20 1-800 <$750/$1250
Series 1875
4x5 1-2662 <$400
3x10-20 1-696 <$600/$1000
Brown Back
4x5 1-14169 <$300
3x10-20 1-1062 <$300
1902 Red Seal
3x10-20 1-3000 <$300
1902 Date Back
3x10-20 1-3940 <$150
1902 Plain Back
3x10-20 3941-11895 <$150
1929 Small Size
10 Type 1 1-1360 <$125
20 Type 1 1-390 <$125
10 Type 2 1-1808 <$150
20 Type 2 1-530 <$150
Total Issue $1,506,010
Out in 1935 $50,000
Large out 1935 $5,040
****

****
4906 Suffolk
BABYLON NB, BABYLON
{{ 2 L }}
Chartered 1893
Liquidated 4/13/13
Brown Back <$VALUE
3x10-20 1-1740 <$2000
1882 Date Back
3x10-20 1-890 <$2000
Total Issue $131,500
Out in 1913 $5,900
****
10358 Suffolk
BABYLON NB, BABYLON
Chartered 4/13
2nd title:Babylon NB & TC 8/24/26
FIRST TITLE {{ 1 L }}
1902 Date Back <$VALUE
3x10-20 1-1067 <$2000
SECOND TITLE {{ U + 9 S }}
1929 Small Size
5 Type 1 1-1876 <$400
10 Type 1 1-934 <$400
20 Type 1 1-282 <$400
5 Type 2 1-7944 <$400
10 Type 2 1-4152 <$400
20 Type 2 1-1200 <$400
Total Issue $304,750
Out in 1935 $100,000
Large out 1935 $100
****
2543 Chenango
FNB OF BAINBRIDGE
{{ 6 L 7 S }}
Chartered 1881
Series 1875 <$VALUE
4x5 1-8916 <$400
3x10-20 1-294 <$600/$1000
Brown Back
3x10-20 1-1900 <$350
1882 Date Back
4x5 1-4050 <$350
3x10-20 1-2820 <$350
1882 Value Back
4x5 4051-7340 <$350
3x10-20 2821-4910 <$350
1902 Plain Back
3x10-20 1-6012 <$225
1929 Small Size
10 Type 1 1-1390 <$175
20 Type 1 1-362 <$175
10 Type 2 1-1759 <$200
20 Type 2 1-403 <$200
Total Issue $1,133,410
Out in 1935 $25,000
Large out 1935 $2,910
****
11474 Nassau
BALDWIN NB, BALDWIN
Chartered 10/19
2nd title:Baldwin NB & TC 4/1/30
FIRST TITLE {{ 10 L 1 S }}
1902 Plain Back <$VALUE
4x5 1-8815 <$350
3x10-20 1-6094 <$350
1929 Small Size
5 Type 1 1-812 <$300
10 Type 1 1-416 <$300
20 Type 1 1-142 <$300
SECOND TITLE {{ 7 S }}
1929 Small Size
5 Type 1 1-1130 <$250
10 Type 1 1-706 <$250
20 Type 1 1-144 <$250
5 Type 2 1-3582 <$250
10 Type 2 1-1990 <$250
20 Type 2 1-564 <$250
Total Issue $689,990
Out in 1935 $50,000
Large out 1935 $1,675
****
292 Onondaga
FNB OF BALDWINSVILLE
Chartered 2/64
2nd title:FNB & TC 8/31/29
FIRST TITLE {{ 3 L 1 S }}
Original Series <$VALUE
4x5 1-3500 <$600
3x10-20 1-3500 <$750/$1250
Series 1875
4x5 1-250 <$600
3x10-20 1-2000 <$750/$1250
Brown Back
4x5 1-4966 <$450
3x10-20 1-2452 <$450
1902 Red Seal
3x10-20 1-1550 <$500
1902 Date Back
3x10-20 1-2700 <$300
1902 Plain Back
3x10-20 2701-5926 <$300

1929 Small Size
10 Type 1 1-314 <$250
20 Type 1 1-106 <$250
SECOND TITLE {{ 4 S }}
1929 Small Size
10 Type 1 1-314 <$250
20 Type 1 1-74 <$250
10 Type 2 1-1548 <$250
20 Type 2 1-132 <$250
Total Issue $1,023,120
Out in 1935 $25,000
Large out 1935 $3,140
****
1253 Saratoga
BALLSTON SPA NB, BALLSTON SPA
{{ 15 L 28 S }}
Chartered 1865
Original Series <$VALUE
4x5 1-4000 <$400
3x10-20 1-2000 <$750/$1250
Series 1875
4x5 1-1500 <$400
3x10-20 1-2826 <$600/$1000
Brown Back
3x10-20 1-12616 <$350
1902 Red Seal
3x10-20 1-3800 <$350
1902 Date Back
3x10-20 1-8200 <$175
1902 Plain Back
3x10-20 8201-38848 <$175
1929 Small Size
10 Type 1 1-6488 <$75
20 Type 1 1-1688 <$75
10 Type 2 1-8754 <$75
20 Type 2 1-2520 <$75
Total Issue $3,844,280
Out in 1935 $200,000
Large out 1935 $8,040
****
954 Saratoga
FNB OF BALLSTON SPA
{{ 11 L 7 S }}
Chartered 3/31/65
Liquidated 11/24/31
Original Series <$VALUE
3x1-2 1-3200 <$400/$1000
4x5 1-4750 <$500
3x10-20 1-2100 <$750/$1250
Series 1875
3x10-20 1-2554 <$600/$1000
Brown Back
3x10-20 1-12280 <$400
1902 Red Seal
3x10-20 1-3800 <$400
1902 Date Back
3x10-20 1-8000* <$175
1902 Plain Back
3x10-20 8501-26026* <$175
* 8001-8500 not marked
1929 Small Size
10 Type 1 1-1713 <$175
20 Type 1 1-477 <$175
Total Issue $2,609,020
Out at close $100,000
Large out at close $11,630
****
10126 Niagara
SOMERSET NB OF BARKER
{{ 2 L 9 S }}
Chartered 1/12
1902 Date Back <$VALUE
3x10-20 1-1600 <$400
1902 Plain Back
3x10-20 1601-6141 <$400
1929 Small Size
10 Type 1 1-662 <$175
20 Type 1 1-170 <$175
10 Type 2 1-1477 <$200
20 Type 2 1-153 <$200
Total Issue $385,000
Out in 1935 $25,000
Large out 1935 $840
****

<$VALUEs are for notes in FINE condition. Value changes by approximately 25% for a change of one full grade.

340 Genesee
FNB OF BATAVIA
{{ U + 12 L 6U + 18 S }}
Chartered 3/64
Original Series <$VALUE
3x1-2 1-2000 <$250/$750
4x5 1-6750 <$300
Series 1875
4x5 1-5000 <$300
Brown Back
3x10-20 1-6543 <$250
1902 Red Seal
4x5 1-3665 <$250
3x10-20 1-3934 <$250
1902 Date Back
4x5 1-8500 <$100
3x10-20 1-6100 <$100
1902 Plain Back
4x5 8501-24420 <$100
3x10-20 6101-16946 <$100
1929 Small Size
5 Type 1 1-3884 <$50
10 Type 1 1-1856 <$50
20 Type 1 1-480 <$60
5 Type 2 1-4704 <$60
10 Type 2 1-2767 <$60
20 Type 2 1-630 <$60
Total Issue $2,527,120
Out in 1935 $100,000
Large out 1935 $6,660

2421 Genesee
GENESEE COUNTY NB OF BATAVIA
{{ 1 L }}
Chartered 4/4/79
Liquidated 10/11/84
Series 1875 <$VALUE
4x5 1-5040 <$850
Total Issue $100,800
Out in 1910 $495

1074 Genesee
NB OF GENESEE, BATAVIA
{{ 2 L }}
Chartered 4/28/65
Liquidated 5/21/88
Original Series <$VALUE
3x1-2 1-4800 <$400/$1000
4x5 1-4550 <$500
3x10-20 1-1500 <$750/$1250
Series 1875
4x5 1-4885 <$500
3x10-20 1-1738 <$600/$1000
Brown Back
4x5 1-675 <$350
3x10-20 1-146 <$350
Total Issue $395,400
Out in 1910 $2,456

10235 Steuben
BATH NB, BATH
{{ 12 L 10 S }}
Chartered 7/12
1902 Date Back <$VALUE
4x5 1-2350 <$175
4x10 1-2300 <$175
1902 Plain Back
4x5 2351-12430 <$175
4x10 2301-10558 <$175
1929 Small Size
5 Type 1 1-2626 <$125
10 Type 1 1-1332 <$125
5 Type 2 1-6010 <$125
10 Type 2 1-2820 <$125
Total Issue $887,870
Out in 1935 $50,000
Large out 1935 $2,310

165 Steuben
FNB OF BATH
{{ 3 L }}
Chartered 12/21/63
Liquidated 1/10/98
Original Series <$VALUE
3x1-2 1-2000 <$500/$1000
4x5 1-3480 <$500
3x10-20 1-2500 <$750/$1250
Series 1875
3x10-20 1-1641 <$600/$1000
Brown Back
3x10-20 1-2411 <$400
Total Issue $407,200
Out in 1910 $3,085

10029 Suffolk
FNB OF BAY SHORE
Chartered 6/11
2nd title:FNB & TC 11/12/27
FIRST TITLE {{ 3 L }}
1902 Date Back <$VALUE
3x10-20 1-2270* <$1250
1902 Plain Back
3x10-20 2471-6646* <$1250
* 2271-2470 not marked
SECOND TITLE {{ 0 L 5 S }}
1902 Plain Back
3x10-20 1-617 <$1500
1929 Small Size
10 Type 1 1-758 <$600
20 Type 1 1-190 <$600
10 Type 2 1-1412 <$600
20 Type 2 1-396 <$600
Total Issue $453,470
Out in 1935 $25,000
Large out 1935 $1,100

7939 Queens
BAYSIDE NB, BAYSIDE
{{ 4 L }}
Chartered 10/05
Liquidated 8/15/28
1902 Red Seal <$VALUE
4x5 1-600 <$1000
3x10-20 1-480 <$1000
1902 Date Back
4x5 1-2925 <$400
3x10-20 1-2100 <$400
1902 Plain Back
4x5 2926-8155 <$400
3x10-20 2101-5298 <$400
Total Issue $464,000
Out at close $25,000

Fishkill NB of Beacon
SEE Ch 35
FNB of Fishkill Landing

Matteawan NB of Beacon
SEE Ch 4914
Matteawan NB, Matteawan

9644 Allegany
FNB OF BELFAST
{{ 2 L 5 S }}
Chartered 1/10
1902 Date Back <$VALUE
3x10-20 1-2210* <$400
1902 Plain Back
3x10-20 2351-6217* <$400
* 2211-2350 not marked
1929 Small Size
10 Type 1 1-652 <$250
20 Type 1 1-152 <$250
10 Type 2 1-1116 <$250
20 Type 2 1-284 <$250
Total Issue $385,050
Out in 1935 $25,000
Large out 1935 $1,100

13234 Nassau
FNB OF BELLEROSE
{{ 3U + 8 S }}
Chartered 8/28
1929 Small Size <$VALUE
5 Type 1 1-1232 <$400
10 Type 1 1-1040 <$400
20 Type 1 1-106 <$400
50 Type 1 1-22 <$600
100 Type 1 1-12 <$750
5 Type 2 1-8459 <$400
10 Type 2 1-4268 <$400
20 Type 2 1-1160 <$400
Total Issue $234,055
Out in 1935 $81,090

11072 Nassau
FNB OF BELLMORE
{{ 2 L 6 S }}
Chartered 8/17
1902 Plain Back <$VALUE
4x5 1-3646 <$1000
1929 Small Size
5 Type 1 1-2818 <$500
10 Type 1 1-402 <$500
5 Type 2 1-5266 <$500
10 Type 2 1-1429 <$500
Total Issue $222,200
Out in 1935 $40,000
Large out 1935 $280

12473 Suffolk
BELLPORT NB, BELLPORT
{{ 3 L 3 S }}
Organized 12/1/23
1902 Plain Back <$VALUE
4x5 1-4085 <$1000
3x10-20 1-707 <$1000
1929 Small Size
5 Type 1 1-3556* <$750
5 Type 2 1-8394 <$750
* 782-950 canceled
Total Issue $260,630
Out in 1935 $25,000
Large out 1935 $540

1189 Broome
CITY NB OF BINGHAMTON
{{ 9 L 18 S }}
Chartered 1865
Original Series <$VALUE
3x1-2 1-4400 <$350/$1000
4x5 1-6500 <$400
3x10-20 1-2500 <$600/$1250
50-100 1-370 <$3500
Series 1875
3x1-2 1-340 <$350/$1000
4x5 1-5290 <$400
3x10-20 1-3100 <$600/$1000
50-100 1-272 <$3500
Brown Back
4x5 1-14947 <$250
3x10-20 1-1843 <$250
1902 Red Seal
4x5 1-1425 <$250
3x10-20 1-1380 <$250
1902 Date Back
4x5 1-6750 <$125
3x10-20 1-5500* <$125
* 3444 canceled
1902 Plain Back
4x5 6751-10053 <$125
1929 Small Size
10 Type 1 1-2460 <$50
20 Type 1 1-828 <$60
10 Type 2 1-10002 <$60
20 Type 2 1-2882 <$60
Total Issue $2,005,020
Out in 1935 $200,000
Large out 1935 $5,913

202 Broome
FNB OF BINGHAMTON
{{ U + 19 L 50+ S }}
Chartered 1/64
Original Series <$VALUE
3x1-2 1-2000 <$250/$850
4x5 1-3650 <$350
4x10 1-2250 <$750
3x20-50 1-1570<$1250/$3500
Series 1875
3x20-50 1-1730<$1000/$3500
Brown Back
4x5 1-9420 <$150
3x10-20 1-9023 <$150
50-100 1-600 <$1250/$1500
1902 Red Seal
4x5 1-14000 <$150
4x10 1-3000 <$150
3x10-20 1-20600 <$150/$200
1902 Date Back
4x5 1-38500 <$60
4x10 1-25000* <$75
3x10-20 1-2600 <$75
1902 Plain Back
4x5 38501-98742 <$60
4x10 27501-69890* <$75
* 25001-27500 not marked
1929 Small Size
5 Type 1 1-13266 <$20
10 Type 1 1-7762 <$20
5 Type 2 1-70302 <$20
10 Type 2 1-41385 <$20
Total Issue $9,225,050
Out in 1935 $600,000
Large out 1935 $26,580

2136 Broome
MERCHANTS NB OF BINGHAMTON
{{ 3 L }}
Chartered 2/24/74
Liquidated 6/25/91
Original Series <$VALUE
3x1-2 1-3000 <$500/$850
4x5 1-3625 <$500
3x20-50 1-250 <$1250/$3500
Series 1875
3x1-2 1-1740 <$500/$850
4x5 1-16475 <$500
3x20-50 1-227 <$1000/$3500
Total Issue $478,170
Out in 1910 $2,186

1513 Broome
N BROOME COUNTY B, BINGHAMTON
{{ 3 L }}
Organized 8/9/65
Receivership 1/28/95
Original Series <$VALUE
3x1-2 1-1000 <$500/$850
4x5 1-3000 <$500
3x10-20 1-2400 <$750/$1250
Series 1875
3x10-20 1-2003 <$600/$1000
Brown Back
3x10-20 1-2196 <$400
Total Issue $394,950
Out in 1916 $1,676

10754 Wyoming
BLISS NB, BLISS
{{ 3 L 6 S }}
Organized 6/25/15
1902 Plain Back <$VALUE
4x10 1-6346 <$400
1929 Small Size
10 Type 1 1-1134 <$250
10 Type 2 1-2265 <$250
Total Issue $344,530
Out in 1935 $25,000
Large out 1935 $690

13246 Allegany
FNB OF BOLIVAR
{{ 2 S }}
Chartered 10/28
1929 Small Size <$VALUE
5 Type 2 1-1980 <$450
10 Type 2 1-1002 <$450
20 Type 2 1-279 <$450
Total Issue $25,500
Out in 1935 $24,000

13089 Warren
BOLTON NB OF BOLTON LANDING
{{ 0 L 2 S }}
Chartered 6/27
1902 Plain Back <$VALUE
3x10-20 1-1223 <$1000
1929 Small Size
10 Type 1 1-776 <$400
20 Type 1 1-190 <$400
10 Type 2 1-1489 <$400
20 Type 2 1-336 <$400
Total Issue $152,120
Out in 1935 $25,000
Large out 1935 $400

2320 Oneida
FNB OF BOONVILLE
{{ 8 L 13 S }}
Chartered 2/3/76
Series 1875 <$VALUE
4x5 1-11467 <$350
Brown Back
3x10-20 1-7300 <$250/$300
1882 Date Back
3x10-20 1-5472 <$250/$300
1902 Plain Back
3x10-20 1-12579 <$150
1929 Small Size
10 Type 1 1-2176 <$75
20 Type 1 1-586 <$85
5 Type 2 1-324 <$100
10 Type 2 1-2763 <$100
20 Type 2 1-793 <$100
Total Issue $1,742,880
Out in 1935 $75,000
Large out 1935 $4,195

8022 Oneida
N EXCHANGE B OF BOONVILLE
{{ 3 L 5 S }}
Chartered 12/05
1902 Red Seal <$VALUE
3x10-20 1-975 <$500
1902 Date Back
3x10-20 1-2390 <$250
1902 Plain Back
3x10-20 2391-6915 <$250
1929 Small Size
10 Type 1 1-704 <$200
20 Type 1 1-194 <$200
10 Type 2 1-945 <$200
20 Type 2 1-264 <$200
Total Issue $474,750
Out in 1935 $25,000
Large out 1935 $840

10943 Saint Lawrence
BRASHER FALLS NB, BRASHER FALLS
{{ 2 L 5 S }}
Organized 10/16/16
Receivership 8/3/33
1902 Plain Back <$VALUE
4x10 1-6399 <$500
1929 Small Size
10 Type 1 1-1116 <$200
Total Issue $322,920
Out at close $25,000
Large out at close $940

2225 Putnam
FNB OF BREWSTER
{{ 7 L 10 S }}
Chartered 2/23/75
Original Series <$VALUE
4x10 1-675 <$750
Series 1875
4x10 1-5476 <$600
Brown Back
3x10-20 1-10900 <$300
1882 Date Back
3x10-20 1-7311 <$300
1902 Date Back
3x10-20 1-1000 <$175
1902 Plain Back
3x10-20 1001-9242 <$175
1929 Small Size
10 Type 1 1-1334 <$125
20 Type 1 1-404 <$125
10 Type 2 1-2740 <$150
20 Type 2 1-756 <$150
Total Issue $1,789,730
Out in 1935 $50,000
Large out 1935 $3,380

9669 Suffolk
BRIDGEHAMPTON NB, BRIDGEHAMPTON
{{ 3 L 5 S }}
Chartered 2/10
1902 Date Back <$VALUE
4x5 1-1270* <$1000
4x10 1-1265** <$1000
1902 Plain Back
4x5 1371-7720* <$1000
4x10 1366-6051** <$1000
* 1271-1370 not marked
** 1266-1365 not marked
1929 Small Size
5 Type 1 1-3272 <$600
10 Type 1 1-1764 <$600
5 Type 2 1-9550 <$600
10 Type 2 1-5304 <$600
Total Issue $701,230
Out in 1935 $100,000
Large out 1935 $1,290

13965 Monroe
BROCKPORT NB, BROCKPORT
{{ U + 4 S }}
Chartered 1/34
1929 Small Size <$VALUE
5 Type 2 1-5092 <$250
10 Type 2 1-2772 <$250
20 Type 2 1-876 <$275
Total Issue $70,700
Out in 1935 $50,000

382 Monroe
FNB OF BROCKPORT
{{ 9 L U + 9 S }}
Organized 4/4/64
Receivership 2/2/34
Original Series <$VALUE
3x1-2 1-2600 <$350/$1000
4x5 1-4375 <$400
Series 1875
4x5 1-3990 <$400
Brown Back
3x10-20 1-2009 <$300
1902 Red Seal
3x10-20 1-640 <$300
1902 Date Back
3x10-20 1-1060 <$150
1902 Plain Back
3x10-20 1061-2945 <$150
1929 Small Size
10 Type 1 1-1398 <$125
20 Type 1 1-376 <$125
10 Type 2 1-66 <$150
20 Type 2 1-45 <$150
Total Issue $590,560
Out at close $50,000
Large out at close $2,880

8240 Westchester
GRAMATAN NB OF BRONXVILLE
Chartered 5/06
2nd title:Gramatan NB & TC 7/7/27
FIRST TITLE {{ 7 L }}
1902 Red Seal <$VALUE
4x5 1-287 <$850
3x10-20 1-230 <$850
1902 Date Back
4x5 1-4715 <$400
3x10-20 1-3634 <$400
1902 Plain Back
4x5 4716-16938 <$400
3x10-20 3635-11649 <$400
SECOND TITLE {{ 2 L 18 S }}
1902 Plain Back
4x5 1-9866 <$400
1929 Small Size
5 Type 1 1-21074 <$150
5 Type 2 1-69408 <$150
Total Issue $2,115,060
Out in 1935 $200,000
Large out 1935 $3,010

1491 Kings
ATLANTIC NB OF BROOKLYN
{{ UNREPORTED }}
Chartered 7/26/65
Liquidated 7/15/72
Original Series <$VALUE
4x5 1-2885 <$1250
3x10-20 1-1800<$1500/$2000
50-100 1-600 <$5000
Total Issue $237,700
Out in 1910 $1,195

1223 Kings
FARMERS AND CITIZENS NB OF BROOKLYN
{{ 1 L }}
Organized 6/5/65
Receivership 9/6/67
Original Series <$VALUE
3x1-2 1-5300 <$1000/$1500
4x5 1-4100 <$1000
3x10-20 1-2228<$1500/$2000
50-100 1-240 <$5000
Total Issue $255,900
Out in 1915 $942

923 Kings
FNB OF THE CITY OF BROOKLYN
Organized 3/21/65
Liquidated 11/22/28
2nd title:FNB of Brooklyn, New York 4/23/26
FIRST TITLE {{ 17 L }}
Original Series <$VALUE
3x1-2 1-27000 <$350/$850
4x5 1-12950 <$400
3x10-20 1-4592 <$750/$1250
50-100 1-850 <$4000
Series 1875
3x1-2 1-5467 <$350/$850
4x5 1-5972 <$400
3x10-20 1-3000 <$750/$1250
50-100 1-1781 <$4000
Brown Back
4x5 1-5575 <$250
3x10-20 1-4702 <$250
50-100 1-1157 <$1250/$1500
1902 Red Seal
4x5 1-12250 <$250
3x10-20 1-4400 <$250
50-100 1-1200 <$2250/$2500
1902 Date Back
4x5 1-34250 <$125
3x10-20 1-24200 <$125
50-100 1-200 <$400/$500
1902 Plain Back
4x5 34251-104759 <$125
3x10-20 24201-66417 <$125
SECOND TITLE {{ 6 L }}
1902 Plain Back
4x5 1-7113 <$150
3x10-20 1-2961 <$150
3x50-100 1-205 <$400/$500
Total Issue $8,267,765
Out at close $200,000

10054 Kings
GREENPOINT NB OF BROOKLYN
{{ 3 L }}
Chartered 7/11
Liquidated 7/10/26
1902 Date Back <$VALUE
4x5 1-4600 <$750
4x10 1-4525 <$750
1902 Plain Back
4x5 4601-12417 <$750
4x10 4526-10560 <$750
Total Issue $670,740
Out at close $50,000

Manufacturers NB of Brooklyn
SEE Ch 1443
Manufacturers NB of New York City

658 Kings
NASSAU NB OF BROOKLYN
{{ 15 L }}
Chartered 1864
Original Series <$VALUE
3x1-2 1-5400 <$350/$850
4x5 1-3350 <$400
3x10-20 1-2820 <$750/$1250
50-100 1-400 <$3500
Series 1875
3x10-20 1-500 <$600/$1000
50-100 1-900 <$3500
Brown Back
50-100 1-2682 <$1250/$1500
1902 Red Seal
50-100 1-2650 <$2250/$2500
1902 Date Back
4x5 1-10000 <$150
3x10-20 1-8000 <$150
50-100 1-675 <$400/$500
3x50-100 1-1100 <$400/$500
1902 Plain Back
3x10-20 8001-23796 <$150
3x50-100 1101-3156 <$400/$500
Total Issue $3,534,850
Out in 1929 $500,000
Ch 13193 assumed circulation

1543 Kings
N CITY B OF BROOKLYN
{{ UNREPORTED }}
Chartered 1865
Liquidated 8/26/19
Original Series <$VALUE
4x5 1-1500 <$1000
3x10-20 1-600 <$1250/$1500
50-100 1-1258 <$4000
Series 1875
3x10-20 1-2000<$1250/$1500
50-100 1-3123 <$4000
Brown Back
50-100 1-6262 <$1500/$1750
1902 Red Seal
50-100 1-1433 <$2250/$2500
1902 Date Back
50-100 1-3000 <$850/$1000
3x50-100 1-595 <$850/$1000
Total Issue $2,570,150
Out at close $120,000

2976 Kings
SPRAGUE NB OF BROOKLYN
Chartered 6/13/83
Liquidated 4/3/05
2nd title:Sprague NB of New York 4/01
FIRST TITLE {{ 6 L }}
Brown Back <$VALUE
4x5 1-10005 <$400
3x10-20 1-11733 <$400
SECOND TITLE {{ 1 L }}
Brown Back
3x10-20 1-1800 <$400
50-100 1-400 <$1250/$1500
1902 Red Seal
50-100 1-566 <$2250/$2500
Total Issue $1,021,650
Out in 1910 $11,460

9482 Ulster
ASHOKAN NB OF BROWN STATION
{{ U + 1 L }}
Chartered 7/09
Liquidated 6/24/16
1902 Date Back <$VALUE
4x5 1-3025 <$600
3x10-20 1-2180 <$600
1902 Plain Back
4x5 3026-3105 <$600
3x10-20 2181-2250 <$600
Total Issue $174,600
Out in 1916 $11,350

9643 Franklin
FNB OF BRUSHTON
{{ 2 L 2 S }}
Organized 10/20/09
Receivership 12/23/31
1902 Date Back <$VALUE
4x5 1-2100 <$500
3x10-20 1-1560 <$500
1902 Plain Back
4x5 2101-7170 <$500
3x10-20 1561-4571 <$500
1929 Small Size
5 Type 1 1-600 <$400
10 Type 1 1-329 <$400
20 Type 1 1-87 <$400
Total Issue $420,130
Out at close $23,620
Large out at close $1,550

11883 Erie
AMHERST NB OF BUFFALO
{{ 2 L }}
Chartered 12/20
Liquidated 1/19/22
1902 Plain Back <$VALUE
4x5 1-1425 <$300
4x10 1-820 <$300
Total Issue $61,300
Out at close $47,600

11319 Erie
BROADWAY NB OF BUFFALO
{{ 5 L }}
Chartered 3/19
Liquidated 1/16/22
1902 Plain Back <$VALUE
4x5 1-8258 <$150
4x10 1-3360 <$150
Total Issue $299,560
Out at close $100,000

7823 Erie
CENTRAL NB OF BUFFALO
{{ 9 L }}
Chartered 7/05
Liquidated 12/2/16
1902 Red Seal <$VALUE
4x5 1-9750 <$150
3x10-20 1-2890 <$150/$200
50-100 1-1170 <$2250/$2500
1902 Date Back
4x5 1-19415 <$75
3x10-20 1-13634 <$75
50-100 1-200 <$400/$500
3x50-100 1-300 <$400/$500
1902 Plain Back
4x5 19416-37195 <$75
3x10-20 13635-27945 <$75
Total Issue $2,761,150
Out at close $983,700

5174 Erie
CITY NB OF BUFFALO
{{ 3 L }}
Organized 1/26/99
Receivership 6/29/01
Brown Back <$VALUE
4x5 1-5250 <$300
3x10-20 1-4300 <$300
50-100 1-141 <$1250/$1500
Total Issue $341,150
Out in 1916 $1,650

4741 Erie
COLUMBIA NB OF BUFFALO
{{ 30 L }}
Chartered 1892
Liquidated 12/6/13
Brown Back <$VALUE
4x5 1-18750 <$125
3x10-20 1-29100 <$125/$175
1882 Date Back
4x5 1-60807 <$100
3x10-20 1-31600 <$100/$150
50-100 1-8494 <$1250/$1500
1902 Date Back
4x5 1-46327 <$50
4x10 1-13750 <$60
3x10-20 1-11275 <$60
3x50-100 1-1112 <$350/$400
Total Issue $8,218,530
Out at close $2,400,000
Ch 6184 assumed circulation

11768 Erie
COMMUNITY NB OF BUFFALO
Chartered 6/20
Liquidated 6/10/29
2nd title:Community South Side NB 3/2/25
3rd title:Community NB 2/1/26
FIRST TITLE {{ 1 L }}
1902 Plain Back <$VALUE
4x5 1-17250 <$100
3x10-20 1-9800 <$100
SECOND TITLE {{ 3 L }}
1902 Plain Back
4x5 1-8500 <$100
3x10-20 1-5782 <$100
THIRD TITLE {{ 16 L }}
1902 Plain Back
4x5 1-49145 <$60
3x10-20 1-34509 <$60
Total Issue $4,002,450
Out at close $839,550
Outstanding includes Ch 12313

Community-South Side NB of Buffalo
SEE Ch 11768
Community NB of Buffalo

13220 Erie
EAST SIDE NB OF BUFFALO
{{ 4 L 22 S }}
Chartered 6/6/28
Liquidated 3/7/35
1902 Plain Back <$VALUE
3x10-20 1-8352 <$150
1929 Small Size
10 Type 1 1-9130 <$35
20 Type 1 1-2402 <$40
10 Type 2 1-1896 <$40
20 Type 2 1-195 <$50
Total Issue $1,276,500
Out in 1935 $300,000
Large out 1935 $2,405

453 Erie
FARMERS & MECHANICS NB OF BUFFALO
{{ 11 L }}
Chartered 6/2/64
Liquidated 4/3/89
Original Series <$VALUE
3x1-2 1-8220 <$250/$850
4x5 1-6000 <$300
3x10-20 1-4200 <$600/$1250
Series 1875
4x5 1-1110 <$300
3x10-20 1-350 <$500/$1000
Brown Back
4x5 1-3597 <$200
Total Issue $482,740
Out in 1910 $3,140

235 Erie
FNB OF BUFFALO
{{ 1 L }}
Organized 2/5/64
Receivership 4/22/82
Original Series <$VALUE
4x5 1-2500 <$750
4x10 1-3500 <$850
Series 1875
4x5 1-479 <$750
4x10 1-2130 <$850
Total Issue $284,780
Out at close $99,500
Out in 1916 $1,725

12337 Erie
GENESEE NB OF BUFFALO
{{ 10 L 6 S }}
Chartered 3/23
Liquidated 9/30/30
1902 Plain Back <$VALUE
3x10-20 1-22635 <$100
1929 Small Size
10 Type 1 1-2952 <$125
20 Type 1 1-845 <$125
Total Issue $1,410,270
Out at close $250,000
Large out at close $27,920

11435 Erie
LAFAYETTE NB OF BUFFALO
{{ 12 L }}
Chartered 8/19
Liquidated 1/30/24
1902 Plain Back <$VALUE
4x5 1-30320 <$100
3x10-20 1-15738 <$100
3x50-100 1-1560 <$400/$500
Total Issue $1,783,300
Out at close $937,150

13219 Erie
LINCOLN NB OF BUFFALO
{{ 3U + 22 S }}
Organized 6/1/28
Liquidated 10/26/34
1929 Small Size <$VALUE
5 Type 1 1-5342 <$30
10 Type 1 1-2942 <$30
20 Type 1 1-754 <$40
5 Type 2 1-2340 <$35
10 Type 2 1-745 <$35
20 Type 2 1-410 <$45
Total Issue $454,610
Out at close $200,000
Ch 13952 assumed circulation

13952 Erie
LINCOLN-EAST SIDE NB OF BUFFALO
{{ 3 S }}
Chartered 1/34
1929 Small Size <$VALUE
5 Type 2 1-2948 <$150
10 Type 2 1-1583 <$150
20 Type 2 1-636 <$150
Total Issue $43,290
Out in 1935 $110,000
Outstanding includes Ch 13219

6186 Erie
MANUFACTURERS & TRADERS NB OF BUFFALO
{{ 28 L }}
Chartered 4/2/02
Liquidated 11/25/25
1902 Red Seal <$VALUE
4x5 1-7250 <$100
3x10-20 1-10720 <$100/$150
50-100 1-160 <$2250/$2500
1902 Date Back
4x5 1-63830 <$50
3x10-20 1-35668 <$60
50-100 1-3000 <$300/$350
3x50-100 1-1400 <$300/$350
1902 Plain Back (dated 1902)
4x5 63831-179330 <$50
3x10-20 35669-93255 <$60
1902 Plain Back (dated 1922)
4x5 1-75655 <$50
3x10-20 1-39806 <$60
3x50-100 1-2320 <$300/$350
Total Issue $13,837,750
Out at close $1,454,600
Outstanding includes Ch 850

6184 Erie
MARINE NB OF BUFFALO
{{ 31 L }}
Chartered 4/1/02
Liquidated 1/4/19
1902 Red Seal <$VALUE
4x5 1-35750 <$100
3x10-20 1-33100 <$100/$150
1902 Date Back
4x5 1-280000 <$50
3x10-20 1-192000 <$60
3x50-100 1-9502 <$300/$350
1902 Plain Back
4x5 280001-296770 <$50
3x10-20 192001-248015 <$60
Total Issue $23,081,650
Out at close $4,178,400
Outstanding includes Ch 4741

11836 Erie
MERCHANTS NB OF BUFFALO
{{ 6 L }}
Chartered 9/20
Liquidated 1/5/24
1902 Plain Back <$VALUE
4x5 1-30250 <$125
4x10 1-18250 <$125
Total Issue $1,335,000
Out at close $370,700

13441 Erie
NIAGARA NB OF BUFFALO
{{ 27 S }}
Chartered 3/30
1929 Small Size <$VALUE
5 Type 1 1-4504 <$40
10 Type 1 1-2988 <$40
20 Type 1 1-782 <$40
5 Type 2 1-12682 <$40
10 Type 2 1-7055 <$40
20 Type 2 1-2060 <$40
Total Issue $583,400
Out in 1935 $202,700

12445 Erie
RIVERSIDE NB OF BUFFALO
{{ 3 L }}
Chartered 9/23
Liquidated 1/22/26
1902 Plain Back <$VALUE
4x5 1-6930 <$200
Total Issue $138,600
Out at close $44,000

12313 Erie
SOUTH SIDE NB OF BUFFALO
{{ 5 L }}
Chartered 2/23
Closed 3/2/25
1902 Plain Back <$VALUE
4x5 1-16085 <$150
3x10-20 1-8574 <$150
Total Issue $750,400
Out at close $293,800

850 Erie
THIRD NB OF BUFFALO
{{ 11 L }}
Chartered 3/1/65
Liquidated 1/10/17
Original Series <$VALUE
3x1-2 1-4500 <$250/$750
4x5 1-6000 <$300
3x10-20 1-3350 <$600/$1250
50-100 1-800 <$3500
Series 1875
4x5 1-2370 <$300
3x10-20 1-1130 <$500/$1000
50-100 1-388 <$3500
Brown Back
50-100 1-4676 <$1250/$1500
1902 Red Seal
4x5 1-9080 <$150
3x10-20 1-3630 <$150/$200
50-100 1-946 <$2250/$2500
1902 Date Back
4x5 1-41415 <$65
3x10-20 1-26900 <$75
50-100 1-1400 <$300/$350
3x50-100 1-310 <$300/$350
1902 Plain Back
4x5 41416-46695 <$65
3x10-20 26901-31007 <$75
Total Issue $4,570,250
Out at close $500,000
Ch 6186 assumed circulation

5648 Livingston
FNB OF CALEDONIA
{{ U + 5 L 7 S }}
Chartered 12/21/00
Brown Back <$VALUE
4x5 1-1100 <$350
3x10-20 1-1730 <$350
1882 Date Back
4x5 1-2150 <$350
3x10-20 1-1440 <$350
1882 Value Back
4x5 2151-3510 <$350
3x10-20 1441-2179 <$350
1902 Plain Back
4x5 1-3037 <$225
3x10-20 1-2191 <$225
1929 Small Size
10 Type 1 1-644 <$150
20 Type 1 1-180 <$150
10 Type 2 1-3072 <$150
20 Type 2 1-827 <$150
Total Issue $565,440
Out in 1935 $50,000
Large out 1935 $1,530

9427 Sullivan
CALLICOON NB, CALLICOON
{{ 2U + 6 L 3 S }}
Chartered 6/09
Liquidated 3/5/32
1902 Date Back <$VALUE
4x5 1-2550 <$350
4x10 1-2375 <$350
1902 Plain Back
4x5 2551-10771 <$350
4x10 2376-9196 <$350
1929 Small Size
5 Type 1 1-1851 <$300
10 Type 1 1-911 <$300
Total Issue $693,410
Out at close $50,000
Large out 1935 $2,240
Ch 13590 assumed circulation

13590 Sullivan
FNB IN CALLICOON
{{ U + 10 S }}
Organized 1/9/32
1929 Small Size <$VALUE
5 Type 1 1-944 <$125
10 Type 1 1-350 <$125
5 Type 2 1-14004 <$125
10 Type 2 1-8148 <$125
Total Issue $200,820
Out in 1935 $100,000
Outstanding includes Ch 9427

Cambridge Valley NB of Cambridge
SEE Ch 1275
Cambridge Valley NB of North White Creek

2448 Oneida
FNB OF CAMDEN
Chartered 1/12/80
2nd title:FNB & TC 6/2/26
FIRST TITLE {{ 13 L }}
Series 1875 <$VALUE
4x5 1-10340 <$400
3x10-20 1-1510 <$600/$1000
Brown Back
4x5 1-3125 <$300
3x10-20 1-2650 <$300
1882 Date Back
4x5 1-4125 <$300
3x10-20 1-2790 <$300
1882 Value Back
4x5 4126-6654 <$350
3x10-20 2791-3983 <$350
1902 Plain Back
4x5 1-15584 <$175
SECOND TITLE {{ 3 L 10 S }}
1902 Plain Back
4x5 1-7152 <$175
1929 Small Size
5 Type 1 1-4722 <$75
10 Type 1 1-1544 <$75
20 Type 1 1-422 <$85
5 Type 2 1-4566 <$85
10 Type 2 1-1254 <$85
20 Type 2 1-367 <$85
Total Issue $1,591,900
Out in 1935 $98,860
Large out 1935 $3,110

1122 Montgomery
CANAJOHARIE NB, CANAJOHARIE
{{ 8 L 9 S }}
Chartered 5/16/65
Original Series <$VALUE
3x1-2 1-3000 <$400/$1000
4x5 1-2750 <$500
4x10 1-3550 <$750
Series 1875
4x10 1-3097 <$600
Brown Back
3x10-20 1-7015 <$350
1902 Red Seal
3x10-20 1-1900 <$350
1902 Date Back
4x5 1-3950 <$175
3x10-20 1-2740 <$175
1902 Plain Back
4x5 3951-13885 <$175
3x10-20 2741-8952 <$175
1929 Small Size
5 Type 1 1-2090 <$125
10 Type 1 1-898 <$125
20 Type 1 1-264 <$125
5 Type 2 1-2062 <$150
10 Type 2 1-1359 <$150
20 Type 2 1-325 <$150
Total Issue $1,685,590
Out in 1935 $50,000
Large out 1935 $4,520

1257 Montgomery
N SPRAKER B OF CANAJOHARIE
{{ 11 L 14 S }}
Organized 5/11/65
Liquidated 2/8/34
Original Series <$VALUE
3x1-2 1-7100 <$400/$1000
4x5 1-4850 <$500
3x10-20 1-1180 <$600/$1250
Series 1875
3x1-2 1-440 <$400/$1000
4x5 1-2260 <$500
3x10-20 1-2252 <$600/$1000
Brown Back
4x5 1-4070 <$350
3x10-20 1-7870 <$350
1902 Red Seal
4x5 1-3665 <$350
3x10-20 1-2334 <$350
1902 Date Back
4x5 1-7100 <$150
3x10-20 1-5760 <$150
1902 Plain Back
4x5 7101-24475 <$150
3x10-20 5761-17448 <$150
1929 Small Size
5 Type 1 1-3232 <$60
10 Type 1 1-1970 <$60
20 Type 1 1-462 <$75
5 Type 2 1-790 <$100
10 Type 2 1-461 <$100
20 Type 2 1-55 <$100
Total Issue $2,658,560
Out at close $100,000
Large out at close $7,610

13876 Montgomery
N SPRAKER B OF CANAJOHARIE
{{ U + 10 S }}
Chartered 12/33
1929 Small Size <$VALUE
5 Type 2 1-8454 <$100
10 Type 2 1-5196 <$100
20 Type 2 1-1656 <$100
Total Issue $127,350
Out in 1935 $75,000

****
3817 Ontario
CANANDAIGUA NB,
CANANDAIGUA
Chartered 11/25/87
2nd title:Canandaigua NB & TC 2/15/27
FIRST TITLE {{ U + 6 L }}
Brown Back <$VALUE
3x10-20 1-6320 <$500
1902 Red Seal
3x10-20 1-1620 <$500
1902 Date Back
3x10-20 1-6600 <$250
1902 Plain Back
3x10-20 6601-18427 <$250
SECOND TITLE {{ 1 L 12 S }}
1902 Plain Back
3x10-20 1-2704 <$250
1929 Small Size
5 Type 1 1-2410 <$85
10 Type 1 1-2234 <$85
20 Type 1 1-252 <$100
5 Type 2 1-6154 <$100
10 Type 2 1-2989 <$100
20 Type 2 1-888 <$100
Total Issue $1,768,550
Out in 1935 $80,000
Large out 1935 $3,490
****
10047 Ontario
COUNTY NB OF CANANDAIGUA
{{ UNREPORTED }}
Chartered 7/11
Liquidated 9/29/17
1902 Date Back <$VALUE
3x10-20 1-2304 <$850
Total Issue $115,200
Out at close $24,100
****
259 Ontario
FNB OF CANANDAIGUA
{{ UNREPORTED }}
Chartered 2/16/64
Liquidated 1/26/89
Original Series <$VALUE
4x5 1-3005 <$1250
4x10 1-1850 <$1250
Series 1875
4x5 1-2338 <$1250
4x10 1-1337 <$1250
Brown Back
3x10-20 1-770 <$1250
Total Issue $272,840
Out in 1910 $1,385
****
2765 Ontario
ONTARIO COUNTY NB OF
CANANDAIGUA
{{ UNREPORTED }}
Chartered 8/11/82
Liquidated 3/23/87
Series 1875 <$VALUE
4x5 1-2610 <$1500
Total Issue $52,200
Out in 1910 $210
****
1525 Madison
CANASTOTA NB, CANASTOTA
{{ 2 L }}
Chartered 8/14/65
Liquidated 9/25/90
Original Series <$VALUE
3x1-2 1-4380 <$600/$1250
4x5 1-1900 <$600
3x10-20 1-1300<$1000/$1250
50-100 1-635 <$3500
Series 1875
4x5 1-2030 <$600
3x10-20 1-1117<$1000/$1250
50-100 1-338 <$3500
Brown Back
50-100 1-367 <$1250/$1500
Total Issue $422,350
Out in 1910 $2,278
****
4419 Madison
FNB OF CANASTOTA
{{ 4 L 4 S }}
Chartered 1890
Brown Back <$VALUE
3x10-20 1-2310 <$500
1882 Date Back
3x10-20 1-222 <$500
1902 Date Back
3x10-20 1-1180* <$350
1902 Plain Back
3x10-20 1301-2389* <$350
* 1181-1300 not marked
1929 Small Size
10 Type 1 1-292 <$350
20 Type 1 1-69 <$350
10 Type 2 1-696 <$350
20 Type 2 1-204 <$350
Total Issue $282,890
Out in 1935 $12,500
Large out 1935 $800
****
353 Tioga
FNB OF CANDOR
{{ 3 L 4U + 12 S }}
Chartered 3/64
Original Series <$VALUE
3x1-2 1-1300 <$500/$1000
4x5 1-4425 <$600
Series 1875
3x1-2 1-380 <$500/$1000
4x5 1-3589 <$600
Brown Back
4x5 1-5409 <$500
3x10-20 1-368 <$500
1902 Red Seal
4x5 1-945 <$500
3x10-20 1-745 <$500
1902 Date Back
4x5 1-1700 <$300
3x10-20 1-1280 <$300
1902 Plain Back
4x5 1701-4360 <$300
3x10-20 1281-2943 <$300
1929 Small Size
5 Type 1 1-728 <$125
10 Type 1 1-338 <$125
20 Type 1 1-98 <$125
5 Type 2 1-740 <$125
10 Type 2 1-465 <$125
20 Type 2 1-238 <$125
Total Issue $652,750
Out in 1935 $20,000
Large out 1935 $2,050
****
3696 Saint Lawrence
FNB OF CANTON
{{ 10 L 17 S }}
Chartered 5/5/87
Brown Back <$VALUE
3x10-20 1-7014 <$250/$300
1902 Red Seal
3x10-20 1-2000 <$300
1902 Date Back
3x10-20 1-7900 <$150
1902 Plain Back
3x10-20 7901-24319 <$150
1929 Small Size
10 Type 1 1-2802 <$60
20 Type 1 1-756 <$75
5 Type 2 1-312 <$85
10 Type 2 1-3840 <$85
20 Type 2 1-936 <$85
Total Issue $1,984,170
Out in 1935 $100,000
Large out 1935 $6,125
****
8531 Saint Lawrence
SAINT LAWRENCE COUNTY NB
OF CANTON
{{ 11 L 18 S }}
Chartered 2/07
1902 Red Seal <$VALUE
4x5 1-475 <$350
3x10-20 1-400 <$350
1902 Date Back
4x5 1-7750 <$150
3x10-20 1-5580 <$150
1902 Plain Back
4x5 7751-27220 <$150
3x10-20 5581-18317 <$150
1929 Small Size
5 Type 1 1-3956 <$60
10 Type 1 1-1932 <$60
20 Type 1 1-478 <$70
5 Type 2 1-5716 <$70
10 Type 2 1-2678 <$70
20 Type 2 1-955 <$70
Total Issue $1,856,170
Out in 1935 $100,000
Large out 1935 $4,380
****
976 Putnam
PUTNAM COUNTY NB OF
CARMEL
{{ 8 L 15 S }}
Chartered 4/4/65
Original Series <$VALUE
4x5 1-6815 <$500
3x10-20 1-1540 <$600/$1250
Series 1875
3x10-20 1-2648 <$750/$1250
Brown Back
3x10-20 1-12717 <$350
1902 Red Seal
3x10-20 1-1700 <$400
1902 Date Back
3x10-20 1-4440 <$225
1902 Plain Back
3x10-20 4441-12861 <$225
1929 Small Size
10 Type 1 1-2098 <$85
20 Type 1 1-526 <$100
5 Type 2 1-324 <$100
10 Type 2 1-5549 <$100
20 Type 2 1-1217 <$100
Total Issue $1,980,050
Out in 1935 $100,000
Large out 1935 $5,015
****
3672 Jefferson
CARTHAGE NB, CARTHAGE
{{ 8 L 13 S }}
Chartered 4/18/87
Liquidated 2/15/32
Brown Back <$VALUE
4x5 1-5515 <$200
3x10-20 1-1812 <$200/$250
1902 Red Seal
3x10-20 1-1000 <$200/$250
1902 Date Back
3x10-20 1-11700 <$125
1902 Plain Back
3x10-20 11701-28943 <$125
1929 Small Size
10 Type 1 1-2794 <$75
20 Type 1 1-926 <$85
Total Issue $1,976,810
Out at close $200,000
Large out 1935 $4,670
Ch 13584 assumed circulation
****
13584 Jefferson
CARTHAGE N EXCHANGE B,
CARTHAGE
{{ 16 S }}
Chartered 12/31
1929 Small Size <$VALUE
5 Type 1 1-1846 <$60
10 Type 1 1-1396 <$60
20 Type 1 1-328 <$60
5 Type 2 1-14808 <$60
10 Type 2 1-8448 <$60
20 Type 2 1-1920 <$60
Total Issue $375,420
Out in 1935 $200,000
Outstanding includes Ch 3672
****
2442 Jefferson
FNB OF CARTHAGE
{{ 1 L }}
Chartered 12/12/79
Receivership 11/4/98
Series 1875 <$VALUE
4x5 1-8673 <$850
Total Issue $173,460
Out in 1916 $670
****
6094 Jefferson
N EXCHANGE B OF CARTHAGE
Chartered 1/14/02
Liquidated 2/15/32
2nd title:N Exchange B & TC 9/3/29
FIRST TITLE {{ 13 L }}
Brown Back <$VALUE
4x5 1-1950 <$175
3x10-20 1-1380 <$175/$225
1882 Date Back
4x5 1-8850* <$175
3x10-20 1-6400**<$175/$225
1882 Value Back
4x5 9351-17200* <$175
3x10-20 6801-11300**
<$175/$225
* 8851-9350 not marked
** 6401-6800 not marked
1902 Plain Back
4x5 1-12029 <$100
3x10-20 1-8668 <$100
SECOND TITLE {{ 6 S }}
1929 Small Size
5 Type 1 1-2777 <$125
10 Type 1 1-1220 <$125
20 Type 1 1-348 <$125
Total Issue $1,889,250
Out at close $83,620
Large out at close $8,100
****
842 Rensselaer
NB OF CASTLETON
Chartered 2/27/65
Liquidated 5/8/01
{{ 5 L }}
Original Series <$VALUE
3x1-2 1-4200 <$500/$1000
4x5 1-4100 <$500
3x10-20 1-1950*<$750/$1250
* 801-950 canceled
Series 1875
4x5 1-2905 <$500
3x10-20 1-1696 <$600/$1000
Brown Back
4x5 1-3864 <$500
3x10-20 1-1478 <$500
Total Issue $487,080
Out in 1910 $3,508
****
5816 Rensselaer
N EXCHANGE B OF CASTLETON
Chartered 5/15/01
2nd title:N Exchange B of Castleton on Hudson 1/25/27
FIRST TITLE {{ 3 L }}
Brown Back <$VALUE
4x5 1-275 <$650
3x10-20 1-220 <$650
1882 Date Back
4x5 1-2350 <$650
3x10-20 1-1720 <$650
1882 Value Back
4x5 2351-4305 <$650
3x10-20 1721-2755 <$650
1902 Plain Back
4x5 1-2136 <$500
3x10-20 1-1445 <$500
SECOND TITLE {{ 3 L 8 S }}
1902 Plain Back
4x5 1-914 <$500
3x10-20 1-544 <$500
1929 Small Size
5 Type 1 1-1134 <$300
10 Type 1 1-608 <$300
20 Type 1 1-214 <$300
5 Type 2 1-3400 <$300
10 Type 2 1-1990 <$300
20 Type 2 1-375 <$300
Total Issue $541,380
Out in 1935 $50,000
Large out 1935 $1,270
****
N Exchange B of
Castleton on Hudson
SEE Ch 5816
N Exchange B of Castleton
****
9857 Cayuga
FNB OF CATO
{{ 2 L 6 S }}
Organized 9/3/10
1902 Date Back <$VALUE
3x10-20 1-2040 <$400
1902 Plain Back
3x10-20 2041-6455 <$400
1929 Small Size
10 Type 1 1-646 <$200
20 Type 1 1-182 <$200
10 Type 2 1-1386 <$200
20 Type 2 1-360 <$200
Total Issue $404,410
Out in 1935 $25,000
Large out 1935 $760
****
1294 Greene
CATSKILL NB, CATSKILL
Chartered 1865
2nd title:Catskill NB & TC 7/1/31
FIRST TITLE {{ 13 L 4 S }}
Original Series <$VALUE
4x5 1-7625 <$400
3x10-20 1-3100 <$750/$1250
Series 1875
4x5 1-1232 <$400
3x10-20 1-1059 <$600/$1000
Brown Back
4x5 1-6788 <$250
3x10-20 1-6056 <$250
1902 Red Seal
3x10-20 1-3100 <$300
1902 Date Back
3x10-20 1-7200 <$150
1902 Plain Back
3x10-20 7201-19776 <$150
1929 Small Size
10 Type 1 1-1242 <$125
20 Type 1 1-418 <$125
SECOND TITLE {{ 8 S }}
1929 Small Size
10 Type 1 1-848 <$125
20 Type 1 1-176 <$125
10 Type 2 1-3444 <$125
20 Type 2 1-840 <$125
Total Issue $2,215,370
Out in 1935 $80,000
Large out 1935 $6,100
****
1198 Greene
TANNERS NB OF CATSKILL
{{ 12 L 19 S }}
Chartered 1865
Original Series <$VALUE
4x5 1-8250 <$400
4x10 1-2375 <$750
Series 1875
4x5 1-5420 <$400
4x10 1-3515 <$600
Brown Back
4x5 1-6135 <$250
3x10-20 1-4556 <$250
1902 Red Seal
4x5 1-1300 <$300
3x10-20 1-1120 <$300
1902 Date Back
4x5 1-3550 <$150
3x10-20 1-2480 <$150
1902 Plain Back
4x5 3551-9605 <$150
3x10-20 2481-5904 <$150
1929 Small Size
5 Type 1 1-4040 <$75
10 Type 1 1-1944 <$75
20 Type 1 1-484 <$75
5 Type 2 1-10908 <$75
10 Type 2 1-5244 <$75
20 Type 2 1-1500 <$85
Total Issue $1,861,700
Out in 1935 $137,500
Large out 1935 $5,430
****
5675 Madison
CAZENOVIA NB, CAZENOVIA
{{ 3 L }}
Chartered 1/10/01
Brown Back <$VALUE
4x5 1-1675 <$600
3x10-20 1-1230 <$600
1882 Date Back
4x5 1-1900 <$600
3x10-20 1-1260 <$600
1882 Value Back
4x5 1901-2855 <$600
3x10-20 1261-2151 <$600
1902 Plain Back
4x5 1-2645 <$400
3x10-20 1-1681 <$400
Total Issue $396,600
Out in 1935 $410
****
1271 Madison
NB OF CAZENOVIA
{{ 3 L }}
Chartered 6/14/65
Liquidated 7/18/73
Original Series <$VALUE
3x1-2 1-8234 <$500/$1000
4x5 1-3235 <$500
3x10-20 1-1020 <$750/$1250
Total Issue $156,870
Out in 1910 $1,240
****
11854 Nassau
PENINSULA NB OF
CEDARHURST
{{ 6 L 8 S }}
Chartered 10/20
1902 Plain Back <$VALUE
4x5 1-11850 <$500
3x10-20 1-6939 <$500
1929 Small Size
5 Type 1 1-3540 <$350
10 Type 1 1-1984 <$350
20 Type 1 1-526 <$350
5 Type 2 1-6066 <$350
10 Type 2 1-2625 <$350
20 Type 2 1-650 <$375
Total Issue $941,890
Out in 1935 $50,090
Large out 1935 $2,360
****
12951 Erie
CENTRAL PARK NB,
CENTRAL PARK
{{ 2 S }}
Organized 6/25/26
Receivership 10/2/33
1929 Small Size <$VALUE
5 Type 1 1-526 <$400
10 Type 1 1-289 <$400
Total Issue $33,120
Out at close $25,000
****
10109 Oswego
FNB OF CENTRAL SQUARE
{{ 0 L 2 S }}
Chartered 12/11
1902 Date Back <$VALUE
3x10-20 1-660 <$1000
1902 Plain Back
3x10-20 661-1648 <$1000
1929 Small Size
10 Type 1 1-251 <$500
20 Type 1 1-52 <$500
Total Issue $103,700
Out in 1935 $6,250
Large out 1935 $40
****
****
9990 Orange
CENTRAL VALLEY NB,
CENTRAL VALLEY
{{ 4 L 13 S }}
Chartered 4/11
1902 Date Back <$VALUE
4x5 1-2075 <$400
3x10-20 1-1630 <$400
1902 Plain Back
4x5 2076-7680 <$400
3x10-20 1631-4877 <$400
1929 Small Size
5 Type 1 1-1590 <$125
10 Type 1 1-1428 <$125
20 Type 1 1-426 <$150
5 Type 2 1-7248 <$150
10 Type 2 1-3372 <$150
20 Type 2 1-888 <$150
Total Issue $669,670
Out in 1935 $100,000
Large out 1935 $260
****
316 Clinton
FNB OF CHAMPLAIN
{{ 9 L 2U + 9 S }}
Organized 2/20/64
Receivership 3/19/31
Original Series <$VALUE
3x1-2 1-4100 <$400/$1000
4x5 1-6100 <$500
3x10-20 1-2000 <$750/$1250
Series 1875
3x1-2 1-4730 <$400/$1000
4x5 1-4055 <$500
3x10-20 1-2082 <$750/$1250
Brown Back
3x10-20 1-6993 <$400
1902 Red Seal
3x10-20 1-6400 <$500
1902 Date Back
3x10-20 1-7400 <$250
1902 Plain Back
3x10-20 7401-15401 <$250
1929 Small Size
10 Type 1 1-462 <$150
20 Type 1 1-49 <$150
Total Issue $1,924,650
Out at close $37,500
Large out at close $8,730
****
12746 Westchester
CHAPPAQUA NB, CHAPPAQUA
{{ 2U + 8 S }}
Chartered 5/25
1929 Small Size <$VALUE
5 Type 1 1-1154 <$500
10 Type 1 1-476 <$500
20 Type 1 1-160 <$500
5 Type 2 1-996 <$500
10 Type 2 1-925 <$500
20 Type 2 1-265 <$500
Total Issue $101,910
Out in 1935 $32,500
****
8893 Franklin
FNB OF CHATEAUGAY
{{ 2 L 11 S }}
Chartered 9/07
1902 Red Seal <$VALUE
4x10 1-680 <$750
1902 Date Back
4x10 1-2825 <$400
1902 Plain Back
4x10 2826-6949 <$400
1929 Small Size
10 Type 1 1-1303 <$150
10 Type 2 1-4889 <$150
Total Issue $432,530
Out in 1935 $50,000
Large out 1935 $860
****
10481 Chautauqua
CHERRY CREEK NB,
CHERRY CREEK
{{ 3U + 14 L 3U + 6 S }}
Organized 1/26/14
Liquidated 5/15/34
1902 Date Back <$VALUE
4x5 1-410 <$200
4x10 1-420 <$200
1902 Plain Back
4x5 411-4531 <$200
4x10 421-3366 <$200
1929 Small Size
5 Type 1 1-1204 <$200
10 Type 1 1-576 <$200
5 Type 2 1-700 <$200
10 Type 2 1-384 <$200
Total Issue $303,280
Out at close $25,000
Large out at close $1,390
****

****
14078 Chautauqua
CHERRY CREEK NB,
CHERRY CREEK
{{ 3 S }}
Chartered 3/34
1929 Small Size <$VALUE
5 Type 2 1-3010 <$400
10 Type 2 1-1565 <$400
Total Issue $30,700
Out in 1935 $20,900
****
1136 Otsego
N CENTRAL B OF
CHERRY VALLEY
{{ 7 L 8 S }}
Organized 4/13/65
Receivership 10/24/33
Original Series <$VALUE
4x5 1-8500 <$500
4x10 1-3000 <$750
3x20-50 1-400 <$1250/$3500
Series 1875
4x5 1-1749 <$500
4x10 1-2108 <$750
Brown Back
4x5 1-10649 <$300
3x10-20 1-1708 <$300/$350
1902 Red Seal
4x5 1-1700 <$350
3x10-20 1-1320 <$350
1902 Date Back
4x5 1-3900 <$175
3x10-20 1-2760 <$175
1902 Plain Back
4x5 3901-12660 <$175
3x10-20 2761-8266 <$175
1929 Small Size
5 Type 1 1-1940 <$150
10 Type 1 1-894 <$150
20 Type 1 1-232 <$150
5 Type 2 1-12 <$200
10 Type 2 1-45 <$200
Total Issue $1,658,370
Out at close $50,000
Large out at close $5,920
****
13748 Otsego
OTSEGO COUNTY NB OF
CHERRY VALLEY
{{ 13 S }}
Chartered 8/33
1929 Small Size <$VALUE
5 Type 2 1-6698 <$125
10 Type 2 1-3148 <$125
20 Type 2 1-845 <$125
Total Issue $81,870
Out in 1935 $36,050
****
1349 Orange
CHESTER NB, CHESTER
{{ 13 L 19 S }}
Chartered 1865
Original Series <$VALUE
4x5 1-4500 <$450
3x10-20 1-3159 <$750/$1250
Series 1875
4x5 1-4859 <$450
3x10-20 1-2578 <$750/$1250
Brown Back
4x5 1-12093 <$250
3x10-20 1-8149 <$250
1902 Red Seal
4x5 1-3750 <$250
3x10-20 1-2400 <$250
1902 Date Back
4x5 1-10150 <$125
3x10-20 1-6780 <$125
1902 Plain Back
4x5 10151-28380 <$125
3x10-20 6781-17965 <$125
1929 Small Size
5 Type 1 1-3768 <$60
10 Type 1 1-1772 <$60
20 Type 1 1-446 <$70
5 Type 2 1-6764 <$70
10 Type 2 1-3768 <$70
20 Type 2 1-993 <$70
Total Issue $3,148,430
Out in 1935 $89,300
Large out 1935 $7,200
****
179 Madison
FNB OF CHITTENANGO
{{ 3 L }}
Chartered 12/63
Liquidated 2/24/83
Original Series <$VALUE
3x1-2 1-3500 <$500/$1250
4x5 1-13300 <$750
Series 1875
4x5 1-12765 <$750
Total Issue $538,800
Out in 1910 $3,007
****

****
3797 Jefferson
FNB OF CLAYTON
{{ 6 L 1 S }}
Chartered 10/1/87
Closed 1/25/30
Brown Back <$VALUE
4x5 1-6568 <$400
3x10-20 1-1758 <$400
1902 Red Seal
4x5 1-305 <$500
3x10-20 1-244 <$500
1902 Date Back
4x5 1-4475* <$250
3x10-20 1-3260** <$250
1902 Plain Back
4x5 4626-14561* <$250
3x10-20 3381-9591** <$250
* 4476-4625 not marked
** 3261-3380 not marked
1929 Small Size
5 Type 1 1-370 <$500
10 Type 1 1-307 <$500
20 Type 1 1-43 <$500
Total Issue $1,043,010
Out at close $50,000
Large out at close $15,320
Ch 5108 assumed circulation
****
FN Exchange B of Clayton
SEE Ch 5108
N Exchange B of Clayton
****
5108 Jefferson
N EXCHANGE B OF CLAYTON
Chartered 1897
2nd title:FN Exchange B of
Clayton 1/25/30
FIRST TITLE {{ 7 L 3 S }}
Brown Back <$VALUE
4x5 1-4025 <$400
3x10-20 1-2800 <$400
1882 Date Back
4x5 1-4000* <$400
3x10-20 1-3040** <$400
1882 Value Back
4x5 4251-5164* <$400
3x10-20 3241-3818** <$400
* 4001-4250 not marked
** 3041-3240 not marked
1902 Plain Back
4x5 1-8355 <$250
3x10-20 1-5673 <$250
1929 Small Size
5 Type 1 1-826 <$125
10 Type 1 1-418 <$125
20 Type 1 1-142 <$125
SECOND TITLE {{ 12 S }}
1929 Small Size
5 Type 1 1-2746 <$125
10 Type 1 1-1248 <$125
20 Type 1 1-378 <$125
5 Type 2 1-7444 <$125
10 Type 2 1-3936 <$125
20 Type 2 1-1152 <$125
Total Issue $1,336,730
Out in 1935 $100,000
Large out 1935 $4,995
Outstanding includes Ch 3797
****
8717 Ontario
ONTARIO NB OF
CLIFTON SPRINGS
{{ 2 L 1 S }}
Organized 5/10/07
1902 Red Seal <$VALUE
3x10-20 1-300 <$1000
1902 Date Back
3x10-20 1-680 <$600
1902 Plain Back
3x10-20 681-1690 <$600
1929 Small Size
10 Type 1 1-231 <$600
20 Type 1 1-62 <$600
Total Issue $120,800
Out in 1935 $7,000
Large out 1935 $380
****
10295 Oneida
HAYES NB OF CLINTON
{{ 2 L 3 S }}
Chartered 12/12
1902 Date Back <$VALUE
4x5 1-515 <$500
3x10-20 1-414 <$500
1902 Plain Back
4x5 516-1600 <$500
3x10-20 415-1019 <$500
1929 Small Size
5 Type 1 1-408 <$300
10 Type 1 1-212 <$300
20 Type 1 1-74 <$300
5 Type 2 1-1158 <$300
10 Type 2 1-621 <$300
20 Type 2 1-169 <$300
Total Issue $132,170
Out in 1935 $25,000
Large out 1935 $310
****
2468 Wayne
BRIGGS NB OF CLYDE
{{ 12 L }}
Chartered 3/29/80
Series 1875 <$VALUE
3x10-20 1-3766 <$600/$1000
Brown Back
3x10-20 1-1800 <$300
1882 Date Back
3x10-20 1-2500 <$300
1882 Value Back
3x10-20 2501-3035 <$300
1902 Plain Back
3x10-20 1-1610 <$200
Total Issue $510,550
Out in 1935 $1,240
****
304 Wayne
FNB OF CLYDE
{{ UNREPORTED }}
Chartered 3/5/64
Liquidated 4/23/69
Original Series <$VALUE
4x5 1-2200 <$1250
Total Issue $44,000
Out in 1910 $665
****
461 Schoharie
FNB OF COBLESKILL
{{ 14 L 3U + 18 S }}
Chartered 6/64
Original Series <$VALUE
4x5 1-3500 <$350
3x10-20 1-2500 <$600/$1250
Series 1875
4x5 1-2499 <$350
3x10-20 1-1146 <$500/$1000
Brown Back
3x10-20 1-7081 <$250
1902 Red Seal
3x10-20 1-3560 <$250
1902 Date Back
4x5 1-7750 <$125
3x10-20 1-5300 <$125
1902 Plain Back
4x5 7751-25010 <$125
3x10-20 5301-15500 <$125
1929 Small Size
5 Type 1 1-3346 <$75
10 Type 1 1-1702 <$75
20 Type 1 1-426 <$75
5 Type 2 1-6792 <$75
10 Type 2 1-2892 <$75
20 Type 2 1-972 <$75
Total Issue $2,445,470
Out in 1935 $100,000
Large out 1935 $6,240
****
1347 Albany
NB OF COHOES
{{ 20 L 36 S }}
Chartered 1865
Original Series <$VALUE
3x1-2 1-2400 <$300/$750
4x5 1-3650 <$300
3x10-20 1-6200 <$600/$1250
Series 1875
3x1-2 1-1444 <$300/$750
4x5 1-4305 <$300
3x10-20 1-6234 <$500/$1000
Brown Back
4x5 1-18227 <$200
3x10-20 1-21501 <$200
1902 Red Seal
4x5 1-8500 <$200
3x10-20 1-6000 <$200
1902 Date Back
4x5 1-25000 <$100
3x10-20 1-17700 <$100
1902 Plain Back
4x5 25001-73425 <$100
3x10-20 17701-47566 <$100
1929 Small Size
5 Type 1 1-9550 <$45
10 Type 1 1-5256 <$45
20 Type 1 1-1230 <$50
5 Type 2 1-17288 <$50
10 Type 2 1-9117 <$50
20 Type 2 1-2736 <$50
Total Issue $7,538,200
Out in 1935 $250,000
Large out 1935 $16,060
****
4416 Putnam
NB OF
COLD SPRING-ON-HUDSON,
COLD SPRING
{{ 3 L 2 S }}
Chartered 1890
Brown Back <$VALUE
4x5 1-3050 <$1000
3x10-20 1-850 <$1000
1882 Date Back
3x10-20 1-292 <$1000
1902 Date Back
3x10-20 1-1310* <$750
1902 Plain Back
3x10-20 1431-3303* <$750
* 1311-1430 not marked
1929 Small Size
10 Type 1 1-314 <$600
20 Type 1 1-106 <$600
10 Type 2 1-708 <$600
20 Type 2 1-144 <$600
Total Issue $324,770
Out in 1935 $12,500
Large out 1935 $580
****
10930 Cattaraugus
CONEWANGO VALLEY NB,
CONEWANGO VALLEY
{{ 4 L 0 S }}
Organized 12/8/15
Liquidated 5/12/34
1902 Plain Back <$VALUE
4x5 1-13254 <$300
1929 Small Size
5 Type 1 1-3018 <$600
5 Type 2 1-66 <$600
Total Issue $355,950
Out at close $25,000
Large out at close $940
****
7305 Otsego
COOPERSTOWN NB,
COOPERSTOWN
{{ 3 L 6 S }}
Organized 3/26/04
Receivership 12/18/33
1902 Red Seal <$VALUE
3x10-20 1-2526 <$500
1902 Date Back
3x10-20 1-4400 <$250
1902 Plain Back
3x10-20 4401-13372 <$250
1929 Small Size
10 Type 1 1-1439 <$175
20 Type 1 1-382 <$175
Total Issue $927,080
Out at close $50,000
Large out at close $2,870
****
280 Otsego
FNB OF COOPERSTOWN
{{ 13 L 50+ S }}
Chartered 2/64
Original Series <$VALUE
3x1-2 1-5440 <$300/$850
4x5 1-7525 <$400
Series 1875
3x1-2 1-790 <$300/$850
4x5 1-12280 <$400
Brown Back
4x5 1-15908 <$250
3x10-20 1-1014 <$250
1902 Red Seal
4x5 1-2380 <$250
3x10-20 1-1868 <$250
1902 Date Back
4x5 1-7100 <$125
3x10-20 1-5150 <$125
1902 Plain Back
4x5 7101-25335 <$125
3x10-20 5151-17359 <$125
1929 Small Size
5 Type 1 1-4338 <$40
10 Type 1 1-3012 <$40
20 Type 1 1-600 <$50
5 Type 2 1-7966 <$40
10 Type 2 1-4535 <$40
20 Type 2 1-1308 <$50
Total Issue $2,805,960
Out in 1935 $150,000
Large out 1935 $7,540
****
223 Otsego
SECOND NB OF COOPERSTOWN
{{ 15 L 5U + 21 S }}
Chartered 1/64
Original Series <$VALUE
3x1-2 1-14300 <$300/$850
4x5 1-10075 <$400
4x10 1-4675 <$750
Series 1875
3x1-2 1-1940 <$300/$850
4x5 1-5000 <$400
4x10 1-3500 <$600
Brown Back
4x5 1-14484 <$250
3x10-20 1-7629 <$250
1902 Red Seal
4x5 1-4550 <$250
3x10-20 1-4140 <$250
1902 Date Back
4x5 1-7000* <$125
3x10-20 1-5500** <$125
1902 Plain Back
4x5 7751-24373* <$125
3x10-20 6101-17338** <$125
* 7001-7750 not marked
** 5501-6100 not marked
1929 Small Size
5 Type 1 1-3872 <$50
10 Type 1 1-1860 <$50
20 Type 1 1-498 <$60
5 Type 2 1-4728 <$60
10 Type 2 1-2551 <$60
20 Type 2 1-686 <$75
Total Issue $3,383,580
Out in 1935 $100,000
Large out 1935 $9,475
****
420 Otsego
WORTHINGTON NB OF
COOPERSTOWN
Organized 5/9/64
Liquidated 12/15/11
2nd title:FNB of Oneonta
2/27/71
FIRST TITLE {{ 0 L }}
Original Series <$VALUE
3x1-2 1-500 <$750/$1500
4x5 1-2420 <$1000
SECOND TITLE {{ 1 L }}
Original Series
3x1-2 1-1000 <$750/$1500
4x5 1-2000 <$1000
Series 1875
4x5 1-4210 <$1000
Brown Back
3x10-20 1-5267 <$750
1902 Red Seal
3x10-20 1-3000 <$750
1902 Date Back
3x10-20 1-2499 <$600
Total Issue $718,400
Out in 1915 $9,741
****
10077 Lewis
COPENHAGEN NB, COPENHAGEN
{{ 2 L 5 S }}
Chartered 9/11
1902 Date Back <$VALUE
3x10-20 1-1740 <$500
1902 Plain Back
3x10-20 1741-6219 <$500
1929 Small Size
10 Type 1 1-766 <$400
20 Type 1 1-210 <$400
10 Type 2 1-1043 <$400
20 Type 2 1-220 <$400
Total Issue $396,940
Out in 1935 $25,000
Large out 1935 $760
****
6479 Saratoga
CORINTH NB, CORINTH
{{ 2 L 2 S }}
Chartered 11/6/02
Receivership 1/20/32
1902 Red Seal <$VALUE
3x10-20 1-830 <$1000
1902 Date Back
3x10-20 1-1920 <$500
1902 Plain Back
3x10-20 1921-5610 <$500
1929 Small Size
10 Type 1 1-352 <$500
20 Type 1 1-109 <$500
Total Issue $356,200
Out at close $19,460
Large out at close $1,410
****
2655 Steuben
FNB OF CORNING
Chartered 1882
2nd title:FNB & TC 8/10/20
FIRST TITLE {{ 8 L }}
Series 1875 <$VALUE
4x5 1-2351 <$400
3x10-20 1-1705 <$600/$1000
Brown Back
3x10-20 1-2770 <$300
1882 Date Back
4x5 1-8100* <$300
3x10-20 1-5960** <$300
1882 Value Back
4x5 8601-15000* <$300
3x10-20 6261-9480** <$300
* 8101-8600 not marked
** 5961-6260 not marked
SECOND TITLE {{ 6 L 12 S }}
1882 Value Back
4x5 1-6250 <$300
1902 Plain Back
4x5 1-36337 <$200
1929 Small Size
5 Type 1 1-15108 <$100
5 Type 2 1-50906 <$100
Total Issue $2,604,280
Out in 1935 $150,000
Large out 1935 $4,180
****

****
10084 Orange
CORNWALL NB, CORNWALL
{{ 4 L 10 S }}
Chartered 9/11
1902 Date Back <$VALUE
4x5 1-1775 <$350
3x10-20 1-1380 <$350
1902 Plain Back
4x5 1776-11320 <$350
3x10-20 1381-7593 <$350
1929 Small Size
5 Type 1 1-1770 <$150
10 Type 1 1-990 <$150
20 Type 1 1-286 <$150
5 Type 2 1-3480 <$150
10 Type 2 1-2088 <$150
20 Type 2 1-576 <$150
Total Issue $802,670
Out in 1935 $50,000
Large out 1935 $1,780
****
7344 Orange
FNB OF CORNWALL
{{ UNREPORTED }}
Organized 7/25/04
Receivership 5/19/05
1902 Red Seal <$VALUE
4x5 1-130 <$2000
3x10-20 1-103 <$2000
Total Issue $7,750
Out in 1916 $30
****
8853 Queens
FNB OF CORONA
{{ UNREPORTED }}
Chartered 8/07
Liquidated 11/18/15
1902 Red Seal <$VALUE
3x10-20 1-1600 <$1500
1902 Date Back
3x10-20 1-5262 <$1000
Total Issue $343,100
Out in 1916 $16,000
****
226 Cortland
FNB OF CORTLAND
{{ 4 L }}
Chartered 2/64
Liquidated 7/15/16
Original Series <$VALUE
3x1-2 1-2400 <$500/$1000
4x5 1-2750 <$600
4x10 1-3517 <$750
Series 1875
4x5 1-750 <$600
4x10 1-3000 <$750
Brown Back
50-100 1-1960 <$1250/$1500
1902 Red Seal
4x5 1-4915 <$500
3x10-20 1-3134 <$500
1902 Date Back
4x5 1-6600 <$250
3x10-20 1-4960 <$250
1902 Plain Back
4x5 6601-6729 <$250
3x10-20 4961-5048 <$250
Total Issue $1,278,660
Out in 1916 $57,800
****
2272 Cortland
NB OF CORTLAND
{{ 16 L 28 S }}
Chartered 6/1/75
Original Series <$VALUE
4x5 1-4500 <$300
Series 1875
4x5 1-8472 <$300
Brown Back
3x10-20 1-10705 <$200/$225
1882 Date Back
3x10-20 1-10380 <$200/$225
1902 Date Back
3x10-20 1-2500 <$100
1902 Plain Back
3x10-20 2501-38824 <$100
1929 Small Size
10 Type 1 1-11326 <$50
20 Type 1 1-2974 <$55
10 Type 2 1-13350 <$55
20 Type 2 1-3771 <$60
Total Issue $4,500,250
Out in 1935 $350,000
Large out 1935 $9,580
****

2827 Cortland
SECOND NB OF CORTLAND
Chartered 1882
2nd title:Second NB & TC 2/23/28
FIRST TITLE {{ 11 L }}
Brown Back <$VALUE
3x10-20 1-3991 <$175/$225
1902 Red Seal
4x5 1-1750 <$200
3x10-20 1-2760 <$200/$250
1902 Date Back
4x5 1-8850 <$100
3x10-20 1-6300 <$100
1902 Plain Back
4x5 8851-24713 <$100
3x10-20 6301-19201 <$100
SECOND TITLE {{ 0 L 21 S }}
1902 Plain Back
3x10-20 1-1856 <$150
1929 Small Size
10 Type 1 1-5564 <$50
20 Type 1 1-1484 <$50
10 Type 2 1-8261 <$50
20 Type 2 1-2639 <$50
Total Issue $2,566,970
Out in 1935 $200,000
Large out 1935 $4,750

1398 Greene
NB OF COXSACKIE
{{ 9 L }}
Chartered 1865
Original Series <$VALUE
4x5 1-3750 <$500
3x10-20 1-2140 <$750/$1250
Series 1875
3x10-20 1-1878 <$600/$1000
Brown Back
3x10-20 1-4424 <$300
1902 Red Seal
3x10-20 1-950 <$350
1902 Date Back
3x10-20 1-2750 <$175
1902 Plain Back
4x5 1-12665 <$175
3x10-20 2751-10750 <$175
Total Issue $1,335,400
Out in 1935 $3,895

10948 Lewis
CROGHAN NB, CROGHAN
{{ 1 L 7 S }}
Chartered 2/17
1902 Plain Back <$VALUE
3x10-20 1-2800 <$600
1929 Small Size
5 Type 1 1-1274 <$225
10 Type 1 1-724 <$225
20 Type 1 1-192 <$225
5 Type 2 1-3230 <$250
10 Type 2 1-2023 <$250
20 Type 2 1-576 <$250
Total Issue $292,600
Out in 1935 $50,000
Large out 1935 $330

9171 Westchester
FNB OF CROTON ON HUDSON
{{ 3 L 4 S }}
Chartered 6/08
1902 Date Back <$VALUE
4x10 1-4785 <$1000
1902 Plain Back
4x10 4786-11585 <$1000
1929 Small Size
10 Type 1 1-1236 <$600
10 Type 2 1-2604 <$600
Total Issue $563,600
Out in 1935 $25,000
Large out 1935 $890

1143 Allegany
CUBA NB, CUBA
{{ 13 L 18 S }}
Chartered 1865
Original Series <$VALUE
3x1-2 1-2400 <$400/$1000
4x5 1-6425 <$500
3x10-20 1-1910 <$750/$1250
Series 1875
3x10-20 1-2064 <$600/$1000
Brown Back
3x10-20 1-9740 <$350
1902 Red Seal
4x5 1-4500 <$400
3x10-20 1-2700 <$400
1902 Date Back
4x5 1-6400 <$200
3x10-20 1-5180 <$200
1902 Plain Back
4x5 6401-23322 <$200
3x10-20 5181-16645 <$200
1929 Small Size
5 Type 1 1-3888 <$100
10 Type 1 1-1832 <$100
20 Type 1 1-454 <$100
5 Type 2 1-6390 <$100
10 Type 2 1-3435 <$100
20 Type 2 1-900 <$100
Total Issue $2,715,230
Out in 1935 $100,000
Large out 1935 $6,730

2451 Allegany
FNB OF CUBA
{{ 12 L 15 S }}
Chartered 1/29/80
Series 1875 <$VALUE
4x5 1-9248 <$500
Brown Back
4x5 1-2660 <$300
3x10-20 1-3580 <$300
1882 Date Back
4x5 1-6400 <$300
3x10-20 1-4270 <$300
1882 Value Back
4x5 6401-7843 <$300
3x10-20 4271-4956 <$300
1902 Plain Back
4x5 1-13079 <$175
4x10 1-10365 <$175
1929 Small Size
5 Type 1 1-3828 <$100
10 Type 1 1-1778 <$100
5 Type 2 1-7096 <$100
10 Type 2 1-4200 <$100
Total Issue $1,797,000
Out in 1935 $75,000
Large out 1935 $3,840

12551 Suffolk
FNB OF CUTCHOGUE
{{ 5 L 3 S }}
Chartered 6/24
1902 Plain Back <$VALUE
4x5 1-7432 <$1000
1929 Small Size
5 Type 1 1-3500 <$750
5 Type 2 1-8148 <$750
Total Issue $294,380
Out in 1935 $20,700
Large out 1935 $650

75 Livingston
FNB OF DANSVILLE
{{ 2 L }}
Organized 9/4/63
Receivership 9/8/87
Original Series <$VALUE
4x5 1-5000 <$850
Series 1875
4x5 1-3000 <$850
Brown Back
4x5 1-1528 <$750
Total Issue $190,560
Out in 1915 $1,225

4482 Livingston
MERCHANTS & FARMERS NB OF DANSVILLE
{{ 3 L 3 S }}
Chartered 1890
Brown Back <$VALUE
4x5 1-3260 <$600
3x10-20 1-580 <$600
1882 Date Back
4x5 1-261 <$600
3x10-20 1-203 <$600
1902 Date Back
4x5 1-975 <$400
3x10-20 1-780 <$400
1902 Plain Back
4x5 976-2790 <$400
3x10-20 781-1894 <$400
1929 Small Size
5 Type 1 1-416 <$350
10 Type 1 1-210 <$350
20 Type 1 1-74 <$350
5 Type 2 1-456 <$375
10 Type 2 1-268 <$400
20 Type 2 1-90 <$400
Total Issue $299,590
Out in 1935 $12,500
Large out 1935 $920

1323 Delaware
DELAWARE NB OF DELHI
{{ 16 L 12 S }}
Chartered 6/22/65
Original Series <$VALUE
3x1-2 1-4200 <$300/$850
4x5 1-8050 <$350
3x10-20 1-3000 <$600/$1250
Series 1875
3x10-20 1-3058 <$500/$1000
Brown Back
3x10-20 1-5942 <$300
1902 Red Seal
3x10-20 1-2900 <$300
1902 Date Back
3x10-20 1-8100 <$150
1902 Plain Back
3x10-20 8101-24735 <$150
1929 Small Size
10 Type 1 1-2766 <$125
20 Type 1 1-686 <$125
10 Type 2 1-2414 <$150
20 Type 2 1-728 <$150
Total Issue $2,450,730
Out in 1935 $40,000
Large out 1935 $8,075

94 Delaware
FNB OF DELHI
Chartered 9/63
2nd title:FNB of Port Jervis 5/5/70
FIRST TITLE {{ 1 L }}
Original Series <$VALUE
4x5 1-2500 <$600
3x10-20 1-877 <$750/$1250
SECOND TITLE {{ 16 L 21 S }}
Original Series
3x1-2 1-2000 <$400/$850
4x5 1-3750 <$400
3x20-50 1-261 <$750/$1250
Series 1875
4x5 1-6137 <$400
Brown Back
4x5 1-18080 <$300
3x10-20 1-3995 <$300
1902 Red Seal
4x5 1-6800 <$300
3x10-20 1-4480 <$300
1902 Date Back
4x5 1-9500 <$125
3x10-20 1-6400 <$125
1902 Plain Back
4x5 9501-38881 <$125
3x10-20 6401-15689 <$125
1929 Small Size
5 Type 1 1-9416 <$75
10 Type 1 1-760 <$75
20 Type 1 1-246 <$75
5 Type 2 1-4588 <$85
10 Type 2 1-2078 <$85
20 Type 2 1-508 <$85
50 Type 2 1-1290 <$200
100 Type 2 1-636 <$300
Total Issue $3,353,300
Out in 1935 $200,000
Large out 1935 $8,175

472 Broome
DEPOSIT NB, DEPOSIT
{{ 4 L }}
Chartered 7/1/64
Liquidated 2/24/03
Original Series <$VALUE
3x1-2 1-4800 <$500/$850
4x5 1-6300 <$500
3x10-20 1-3400 <$750/$1250
Series 1875
4x5 1-1875 <$500
3x10-20 1-1600 <$750/$1250
Brown Back
4x5 1-3110 <$400
3x10-20 1-1943 <$400
Total Issue $596,850
Out in 1910 $4,223

9434 Broome
FARMERS NB OF DEPOSIT
{{ 8 L 10 S }}
Chartered 6/09
1902 Date Back <$VALUE
3x10-20 1-4740 <$225
1902 Plain Back
3x10-20 4741-13387 <$225
1929 Small Size
10 Type 1 1-1288 <$175
20 Type 1 1-388 <$175
10 Type 2 1-2718 <$175
20 Type 2 1-538 <$175
Total Issue $831,130
Out in 1935 $50,000
Large out 1935 $2,630

8463 Jefferson
FNB OF DEXTER
{{ 3 L 6 S }}
Chartered 12/06
1902 Red Seal <$VALUE
3x10-20 1-750 <$750
1902 Date Back
3x10-20 1-2350 <$375
1902 Plain Back
3x10-20 2351-7074 <$375
1929 Small Size
10 Type 1 1-694 <$250
20 Type 1 1-194 <$250
10 Type 2 1-1427 <$250
20 Type 2 1-396 <$250
Total Issue $478,310
Out in 1935 $25,000
Large out 1935 $980

6447 Herkimer
FNB OF DOLGEVILLE
{{ 5 L 14 S }}
Chartered 10/3/02
1902 Red Seal <$VALUE
3x10-20 1-1600 <$400
1902 Date Back
3x10-20 1-3310 <$200
1902 Plain Back
3x10-20 3311-12367 <$200
1929 Small Size
10 Type 1 1-2438 <$85
20 Type 1 1-586 <$100
10 Type 2 1-4522 <$100
20 Type 2 1-1380 <$100
Total Issue $987,770
Out in 1935 $100,000
Large out 1935 $2,630

822 Dutchess
DOVER PLAINS NB, DOVER PLAINS
{{ 8 L 11 S }}
Chartered 2/18/65
Original Series <$VALUE
3x1-2 1-3000 <$350/$850
4x5 1-2500 <$400
3x10-20 1-2400 <$750/$1250
Series 1875
3x10-20 1-2858 <$600/$1000
Brown Back
3x10-20 1-7116 <$350
1902 Red Seal
3x10-20 1-2300 <$350
1902 Date Back
3x10-20 1-4900 <$175
1902 Plain Back
3x10-20 4901-13750 <$175
1929 Small Size
10 Type 1 1-1528 <$100
20 Type 1 1-360 <$100
10 Type 2 1-2232 <$125
20 Type 2 1-669 <$125
Total Issue $1,656,780
Out in 1935 $50,000
Large out 1935 $4,180

7878 Delaware
FNB OF DOWNSVILLE
{{ 2 L 6 S }}
Chartered 8/05
1902 Red Seal <$VALUE
3x10-20 1-760 <$750
1902 Date Back
3x10-20 1-2280 <$375
1902 Plain Back
3x10-20 2281-6720 <$375
1929 Small Size
10 Type 1 1-676 <$250
20 Type 1 1-172 <$250
10 Type 2 1-1380 <$250
20 Type 2 1-384 <$275
Total Issue $456,680
Out in 1935 $25,000
Large out 1935 $1,310

6487 Tompkins
FNB OF DRYDEN
{{ 2 L 5 S }}
Chartered 11/12/02
1902 Red Seal <$VALUE
3x10-20 1-1056 <$750
1902 Date Back
3x10-20 1-2320 <$375
1902 Plain Back
3x10-20 2321-6678 <$375
1929 Small Size
10 Type 1 1-760 <$300
20 Type 1 1-194 <$300
10 Type 2 1-1125 <$300
20 Type 2 1-315 <$300
Total Issue $473,130
Out in 1935 $25,000
Large out 1935 $790

2463 Yates
DUNDEE NB, DUNDEE
{{ 5 L 0 S }}
Chartered 3/8/80
Series 1875 <$VALUE
4x5 1-6231 <$500
Brown Back
4x5 1-625 <$400
3x10-20 1-740 <$400
1882 Date Back
4x5 1-1000* <$400
3x10-20 1-820** <$400
1882 Value Back
4x5 1101-1224* <$400
3x10-20 901-960** <$400
* 1001-1100 not marked
** 821-900 not marked
1902 Plain Back
3x10-20 1-1306 <$300
1929 Small Size
10 Type 1 1-314 <$500
20 Type 1 1-104 <$500
10 Type 2 1-229 <$500
20 Type 2 1-88 <$500
Total Issue $347,270
Out in 1935 $12,500
Large out 1935 $1,080

2916 Chautauqua
LAKE SHORE NB OF DUNKIRK
{{ U + 11 L 21 S }}
Chartered 1883
Brown Back <$VALUE
3x10-20 1-7423 <$350
1902 Red Seal
3x10-20 1-5650 <$350
1902 Date Back
3x10-20 1-7200 <$175
1902 Plain Back
3x10-20 7201-24065 <$175
1929 Small Size
10 Type 1 1-2882 <$55
20 Type 1 1-784 <$65
10 Type 2 1-2906 <$65
20 Type 2 1-785 <$75
Total Issue $2,169,110
Out in 1935 $105,000
Large out 1935 $5,415

2619 Chautauqua
MERCHANTS NB OF DUNKIRK
{{ U + 28 L 37 S }}
Organized 12/20/81
Series 1875 <$VALUE
4x5 1-2900 <$350
3x10-20 1-3818 <$500/$1000
Brown Back
4x5 1-3250 <$175
3x10-20 1-3900 <$175/$225
1882 Date Back
4x5 1-7000* <$175
3x10-20 1-4800** <$175
1882 Value Back
4x5 7401-17825* <$175
3x10-20 5121-12504** <$175
* 7001-7400 not marked
** 4801-5120 not marked
1902 Plain Back
4x5 1-25775 <$85
3x10-20 1-20224 <$85
1929 Small Size
5 Type 1 1-10316 <$30
10 Type 1 1-5860 <$30
20 Type 1 1-1358 <$35
5 Type 2 1-5844 <$30
10 Type 2 1-2305 <$30
20 Type 2 1-800 <$35
Total Issue $3,909,610
Out in 1935 $200,000
Large out 1935 $9,155

4493 Madison
FNB OF EARLVILLE
{{ 5 L 10 S }}
Chartered 1890
Brown Back <$VALUE
4x5 1-10975 <$350
3x10-20 1-3150 <$350
1882 Date Back
4x5 1-1079 <$350
3x10-20 1-959 <$350
1902 Date Back
3x10-20 1-3460 <$225
1902 Plain Back
3x10-20 3461-11955 <$225
1929 Small Size
10 Type 1 1-1440 <$125
20 Type 1 1-418 <$125
10 Type 2 1-1075 <$125
20 Type 2 1-301 <$150
Total Issue $1,197,610
Out in 1935 $50,000
Large out 1935 $11,410

9950 Erie
FNB OF EAST AURORA
{{ 1 L }}
Chartered 3/11
Liquidated 5/13/16
1902 Date Back <$VALUE
3x10-20 1-1591 <$750
Total Issue $79,550
Out in 1916 $18,030

7763 Suffolk
EAST HAMPTON NB, EAST HAMPTON
{{ 1 L 0 S }}
Chartered 5/05
Liquidated 6/1/31
1902 Red Seal <$VALUE
4x5 1-500 <$3000
3x10-20 1-540 <$3000
1902 Date Back
4x5 1-1725 <$1500
3x10-20 1-1300 <$1500
1902 Plain Back
4x5 1726-5137 <$1500
3x10-20 1301-3402 <$1500
1929 Small Size
5 Type 1 1-351 <$1500
10 Type 1 1-165 <$1500
20 Type 1 1-41 <$1500
Total Issue $335,190
Out at close $15,220
Large out at close $1,230

9322 Suffolk
FNB OF EAST ISLIP
{{ 1 L 10 S }}
Chartered 1/09
1902 Date Back <$VALUE
3x10-20 1-2090 <$1500
1902 Plain Back
3x10-20 2091-6912 <$1500
1929 Small Size
10 Type 1 1-1306 <$300
20 Type 1 1-352 <$300
10 Type 2 1-5098 <$300
20 Type 2 1-1265 <$300
Total Issue $542,480
Out in 1935 $55,690
Large out 1935 $1,010

12593 Suffolk
CITIZENS NB OF EAST NORTHPORT
{{ 1 L 4 S }}
Chartered 11/24
1902 Plain Back <$VALUE
4x5 1-3802 <$1500
1929 Small Size
5 Type 1 1-3700 <$750
5 Type 2 1-8690 <$750
Total Issue $230,490
Out in 1935 $25,000
Large out 1935 $310

10141 Monroe
FNB OF EAST ROCHESTER
{{ 4 L 2U + 15 S }}
Organized 12/19/11
Receivership 10/10/34
1902 Date Back <$VALUE
3x10-20 1-600 <$250
1902 Plain Back
3x10-20 601-7960 <$250
1929 Small Size
10 Type 1 1-4352 <$85
20 Type 1 1-1154 <$85
10 Type 2 1-2023 <$85
20 Type 2 1-610 <$85
Total Issue $830,030
Out at close $150,000
Large out at close $1,990

12818 Nassau
EAST ROCKAWAY NB, EAST ROCKAWAY
Chartered 9/25
2nd title:East Rockaway NB & TC 8/30/30
FIRST TITLE {{ 3 L 2 S }}
1902 Plain Back <$VALUE
3x10-20 1-3735 <$750
1929 Small Size
10 Type 1 1-620 <$400
20 Type 1 1-210 <$400
SECOND TITLE {{ 5 S }}
1929 Small Size
10 Type 1 1-1333 <$400
20 Type 1 1-366 <$400
Total Issue $373,050
Out in 1935 $50,000
Large out 1935 $750

11511 Suffolk
TINKER NB OF EAST SETAUKET
{{ 1 L }}
Chartered 11/19
1902 Plain Back <$VALUE
3x10-20 1-1716 <$2000
Total Issue $85,800
Out in 1935 $320

****
9060 Otsego
EAST WORCESTER NB,
EAST WORCESTER
{{1 L}}
Chartered 3/08
Liquidated 12/5/16
1902 Red Seal <$VALUE
4x10 1-680 <$1000
1902 Date Back
4x10 1-2400 <$600
1902 Plain Back
4x10 2401-2575 <$600
Total Issue $130,200
Out at close $19,600
****
3681 Otsego
FNB OF EDMESTON
{{3 L 3 S}}
Chartered 4/26/87
Brown Back <$VALUE
4x5 1-3194 <$650
3x10-20 1-622 <$650
1902 Red Seal
3x10-20 1-245 <$750
1902 Date Back
3x10-20 1-1360* <$400
1902 Plain Back
3x10-20 1481-2982* <$400
* 1361-1480 not marked
1929 Small Size
10 Type 1 1-310 <$400
20 Type 1 1-104 <$400
10 Type 2 1-494 <$400
20 Type 2 1-132 <$400
Total Issue $294,990
Out in 1935 $12,500
Large out 1935 $700
****
10569 Saint Lawrence
EDWARDS NB, EDWARDS
{{2 L 3 S}}
Organized 3/18/14
1902 Date Back <$VALUE
4x5 1-500 <$500
4x10 1-500 <$500
1902 Plain Back
4x5 501-3185 <$500
4x10 501-2860 <$500
1929 Small Size
5 Type 1 1-752 <$350
10 Type 1 1-452 <$350
5 Type 2 1-1476 <$350
10 Type 2 1-720 <$350
Total Issue $242,360
Out in 1935 $16,500
Large out 1935 $250
****
45 Ulster
FNB OF ELLENVILLE
{{6 L}}
Chartered 7/63
Original Series <$VALUE
4x5 1-3500 <$600
4x10 1-4000 <$750
4x20 1-1750 <$1250
Series 1875
4x5 1-8098 <$600
Brown Back
4x5 1-13885 <$500
3x10-20 1-460 <$500
1902 Red Seal
3x10-20 1-1720 <$600
1902 Date Back
3x10-20 1-2160* <$350
1902 Plain Back
3x10-20 2361-5747* <$350
* 2161-2360 not marked
Total Issue $1,206,010
Out in 1935 $4,695
****
2117 Ulster
HOME NB, ELLENVILLE
{{5 L 5 S}}
Chartered 7/8/73
Original Series <$VALUE
3x1-2 1-2000 <$500/$1250
4x5 1-1750 <$600
3x10-20 1-1800 <$750/$1250
Series 18/5
4x5 1-8141 <$600
3x10-20 1-1800 <$750/$1250
Brown Back
4x5 1-4800 <$500
3x10-20 1-1440 <$500
1882 Date Back
4x5 1-1434 <$500
3x10-20 1-1021 <$500
1902 Date Back
3x10-20 1-1000 <$300
1902 Plain Back
3x10-20 1001-5000 <$300
1929 Small Size
10 Type 1 1-642 <$250
20 Type 1 1-170 <$250
10 Type 2 1-1493 <$250
20 Type 2 1-272 <$250
Total Issue $964,840
Out in 1935 $25,000
Large out 1935 $2,365
****
811 Chemung
CHEMUNG CANAL NB OF
ELMIRA
{{3 L}}
Chartered 2/17/65
Liquidated 8/3/70
Original Series <$VALUE
3x1-2 1-3000 <$400/$1000
4x5 1-2500 <$400
3x10-20 1-616 <$750/$1250
Total Issue $95,800
Out in 1910 $797
****
4105 Chemung
ELMIRA NB, ELMIRA
{{ UNREPORTED }}
Chartered 8/30/89
Receivership 5/26/93
Brown Back <$VALUE
3x10-20 1-1650 <$1250
Total Issue $82,500
Out in 1916 $310
****
119 Chemung
FNB OF ELMIRA
{{ UNREPORTED }}
Chartered 11/63
Liquidated 2/24/83
Original Series <$VALUE
4x5 1-5075 <$1000/$1500
4x10 1-3625 <$1250
Series 1875
4x10 1-1317 <$1250
Total Issue $299,180
Out in 1910 $2,150
****
FNB & TC of Elmira
SEE Ch 149
Second NB of Elmira
****
5137 Chemung
MERCHANTS NB OF ELMIRA
{{9 L}}
Chartered 1898
Closed 9/14/29
Brown Back <$VALUE
3x10-20 1-9300 <$200/$250
1882 Date Back
4x5 1-10000* <$200
3x10-20 1-6300** <$200
1882 Value Back
4x5 10751-14930* <$200
3x10-20 6701-9323** <$200
* 10001-10750 not marked
** 6301-6700 not marked
1902 Plain Back
4x5 1-3750 <$100
3x10-20 1-20061 <$100
Total Issue $2,307,800
Out at close $25,000
Ch 149 assumed circulation
****
1391 Chemung
NB OF CHEMUNG, ELMIRA
{{ UNREPORTED }}
Chartered 7/5/65
Liquidated 6/10/70
Original Series <$VALUE
4x5 1-4550 <$1250
Total Issue $91,000
Out in 1910 $465
****
149 Chemung
SECOND NB OF ELMIRA
Chartered 12/63
2nd title:FNB & TC of
Elmira 9/14/29
FIRST TITLE {{14 L 3 S}}
Original Series <$VALUE
4x5 1-10250 <$300
4x10 1-4125 <$750
3x20-50 1-500 <$1250/$3500
Series 1875
4x5 1-6700 <$300
4x10 1-2200 <$600
3x20-50 1-367 <$1000/$3500
Brown Back
4x5 1-3400 <$150
3x10-20 1-5220 <$150/$200
1902 Red Seal
3x10-20 1-4400 <$150/$200
1902 Date Back
3x10-20 1-14400 <$75
1902 Plain Back
3x10-20 14401-45161 <$75
1929 Small Size
10 Type 1 1-1200 <$75
20 Type 1 1-418 <$75
SECOND TITLE {{U + 36 S}}
1929 Small Size
10 Type 1 1-11852 <$20
20 Type 1 1-3004 <$30
10 Type 2 1-40771 <$20
20 Type 2 1-12498 <$30
Total Issue $5,345,850
Out in 1935 $800,000
Large out 1935 $17,700
Outstanding includes Ch 5137
****
12956 Westchester
FNB OF ELMSFORD
{{3 L 4 S}}
Chartered 7/26
1902 Plain Back <$VALUE
4x5 1-4714 <$1000
1929 Small Size
5 Type 1 1-3590 <$600
5 Type 2 1-8268 <$600
Total Issue $243,320
Out in 1935 $25,000
Large out 1935 $50
****
10869 Monroe
FAIRPORT NB, FAIRPORT
Chartered 6/16
2nd title:Fairport NB & TC
5/27/24
FIRST TITLE {{2 L}}
1902 Plain Back <$VALUE
3x10-20 1-6790 <$350
SECOND TITLE {{6 L 14 S}}
1902 Plain Back
3x10-20 1-7402 <$300
1929 Small Size
10 Type 1 1-2828 <$125
20 Type 1 1-794 <$125
10 Type 2 1-4325 <$150
20 Type 2 1-1260 <$150
Total Issue $1,043,010
Out in 1935 $100,000
Large out 1935 $2,260
****
5407 Chautauqua
FNB OF FALCONER
{{U + 4 L 6 S}}
Chartered 6/7/00
Brown Back <$VALUE
3x10-20 1-820 <$400
1882 Date Back
3x10-20 1-1680* <$400
1882 Value Back
3x10-20 1801-2302* <$400
* 1681-1800 not marked
1902 Plain Back
3x10-20 1-2478 <$250
1929 Small Size
10 Type 1 1-610 <$175
20 Type 1 1-172 <$175
10 Type 2 1-353 <$200
20 Type 2 1-125 <$200
Total Issue $343,250
Out in 1935 $20,000
Large out 1935 $1,060
****
9271 Queens
NB OF FAR ROCKAWAY
{{0 L 2U + 18 S}}
Chartered 11/08
1902 Date Back <$VALUE
4x5 1-1850 <$1250
3x10-20 1-1420 <$1250
1902 Plain Back
4x5 1851-6885 <$1250
3x10-20 1421-4174 <$1250
1929 Small Size
5 Type 1 1-3184 <$200
10 Type 1 1-2460 <$200
20 Type 1 1-564 <$200
5 Type 2 1-15420 <$200
10 Type 2 1-7824 <$200
20 Type 2 1-2208 <$200
Total Issue $856,700
Out in 1935 $200,000
Large out 1935 $1,010
****
8882 Nassau
FNB OF FARMINGDALE
{{3 L 8 S}}
Chartered 9/07
1902 Red Seal <$VALUE
4x5 1-250 <$1500
3x10-20 1-200 <$1500
1902 Date Back
4x5 1-2150 <$600
3x10-20 1-1610 <$600
1902 Plain Back
4x5 2151-9770 <$600
3x10-20 1611-6558 <$600
1929 Small Size
5 Type 1 1-2396 <$400
10 Type 1 1-1366 <$400
20 Type 1 1-402 <$400
5 Type 2 1-3212 <$400
10 Type 2 1-1598 <$400
20 Type 2 1-365 <$400
Total Issue $779,720
Out in 1935 $50,000
Large out 1935 $780
****
1110 Onondaga
NB OF FAYETTEVILLE
{{2 L}}
Organized 4/6/65
Liquidated 11/26/94
Original Series <$VALUE
3x1-2 1-2370 <$750/$1250
4x5 1-4550 <$750
3x10-20 1-1890<$1000/$1250
Series 1875
4x5 1-5410 <$750
3x10-20 1-1401<$1000/$1250
Brown Back
4x5 1-3936 <$600
Total Issue $454,320
Out in 1910 $2,666
****
971 Dutchess
NB OF FISHKILL
{{3 L}}
Chartered 4/1/65
Receivership 1/27/77
Original Series <$VALUE
3x1-2 1-4500 <$500/$1000
4x5 1-4150 <$600
3x10-20 1-2800 <$750/$1250
50-100 1-892 <$3500
Series 1875
3x1-2 1-540 <$500/$1000
3x10-20 1-277 <$750/$1250
Total Issue $395,850
Out in 1916 $1,930
****
35 Dutchess
FNB OF FISHKILL LANDING
Chartered 7/63
2nd title:Fishkill NB of
Beacon 5/6/14
FIRST TITLE {{8 L}}
Original Series <$VALUE
3x1-2 1-4200 <$500/$1000
4x5 1-6750 <$600
4x10 1-1700 <$750
Series 1875
3x1-2 1-540 <$500/$1000
4x5 1-2596 <$600
4x10 1-2007 <$750
Brown Back
4x5 1-5416 <$500
3x10-20 1-3050 <$500
1902 Red Seal
4x5 1-1625 <$500
3x10-20 1-1160 <$500
1902 Date Back
4x5 1-1910 <$350
3x10-20 1-1230 <$350
SECOND TITLE {{3 L 4 S}}
1902 Date Back
4x5 1-1250 <$350
3x10-20 1-1000 <$350
1902 Plain Back
4x5 1251-5012 <$350
3x10-20 1001-3278 <$350
1929 Small Size
5 Type 1 1-1012 <$300
10 Type 1 1-502 <$300
20 Type 1 1-122 <$300
5 Type 2 1-1110 <$325
10 Type 2 1-704 <$325
20 Type 2 1-204 <$350
Total Issue $1,165,850
Out in 1935 $25,000
Large out 1935 $3,385
****
FNB of Fleischmanns
SEE Ch 8874
FNB of Griffin Corners
****
12449 Nassau
FNB & TC OF FLORAL PARK
{{U + 27 S}}
Chartered 10/23 as FNB of
Floral Park, under which
there was no issue. Issuing
title adopted 6/24/26.
1929 Small Size <$VALUE
5 Type 1 1-8748 <$75
10 Type 1 1-5800 <$75
5 Type 2 1-19476 <$75
10 Type 2 1-9855 <$75
Total Issue $806,370
Out in 1935 $200,000
****
9956 Orange
FLORIDA NB, FLORIDA
{{1 L 3 S}}
Organized 2/14/11
Liquidated 12/13/33
1902 Date Back <$VALUE
4x5 1-2075 <$850
3x10-20 1-1520 <$850
1902 Plain Back
4x5 2076-7730 <$850
3x10-20 1521-4839 <$850
1929 Small Size
5 Type 1 1-926 <$400
10 Type 1 1-472 <$400
20 Type 1 1-140 <$400
5 Type 2 1-656 <$450
10 Type 2 1-172 <$450
Total Issue $474,450
Out at close $25,000
Large out at close $730
Ch 13825 assumed circulation
****
13825 Orange
NB OF FLORIDA
{{2 S}}
Chartered 11/33
1929 Small Size <$VALUE
5 Type 2 1-1968 <$600
10 Type 2 1-696 <$600
20 Type 2 1-252 <$600
Total Issue $21,840
Out in 1935 $25,000
Outstanding includes Ch 9956
****
9691 Queens
FLUSHING NB, FLUSHING
{{7 L}}
Chartered 3/10
Liquidated 8/15/28
1902 Date Back <$VALUE
3x10-20 1-12600 <$500
1902 Plain Back
3x10-20 12601-40510 <$500
Total Issue $2,025,500
Out at close $200,000
****
1212 Montgomery
N MOHAWK RIVER B OF FONDA
{{14 L 19 S}}
Chartered 1865
Original Series <$VALUE
3x1-2 1-1480 <$300/$850
4x5 1-3600 <$400
3x10-20 1-2110 <$750/$1250
Series 1875
4x5 1-1957 <$400
3x10-20 1-2326 <$750/$1250
Brown Back
4x5 1-5859 <$350
3x10-20 1-8515 <$350
1902 Red Seal
4x5 1-3500 <$350
3x10-20 1-2500 <$350
1902 Date Back
4x5 1-7650 <$150
3x10-20 1-5800 <$150
1902 Plain Back
4x5 7651-26635 <$150
3x10-20 5801-18785 <$150
1929 Small Size
5 Type 1 1-3476 <$65
10 Type 1 1-1942 <$65
20 Type 1 1-548 <$75
5 Type 2 1-7092 <$75
10 Type 2 1-3686 <$75
20 Type 2 1-965 <$85
Total Issue $2,928,400
Out in 1935 $100,000
Large out 1935 $7,255
****
10444 Chautauqua
FNB OF FORESTVILLE
{{U + 10 L 2U + 8 S}}
Chartered 9/13/13
1902 Date Back <$VALUE
4x5 1-800 <$175
3x10-20 1-640 <$175
1902 Plain Back
4x5 801-5601 <$175
3x10-20 641-3416 <$175
1929 Small Size
5 Type 1 1-1094 <$150
10 Type 1 1-588 <$150
20 Type 1 1-160 <$150
5 Type 2 1-2040 <$150
10 Type 2 1-1020 <$150
20 Type 2 1-204 <$150
Total Issue $394,600
Out in 1935 $40,000
Large out 1935 $1,250
****
1348 Washington
FARMERS NB OF FORT EDWARD
Chartered 6/28/65
Liquidated 6/3/05
2nd title:North Granville
NB, North Granville 2/18/71
FIRST TITLE {{1 L}}
Original Series <$VALUE
3x1-2 1-3000 <$750/$1250
4x5 1-2000 <$850
3x10-20 1-893 <$1000/$1250
50-100 1-19 <$3500
SECOND TITLE {{1 L}}
Original Series
4x5 1-3000 <$850
Series 1875
4x5 1-8955 <$850
Brown Back
4x5 1-19812 <$750
3x10-20 1-1799 <$750
Total Issue $827,790
Out in 1910 $6,266
****
3330 Washington
FNB OF FORT EDWARD
{{ UNREPORTED }}
Chartered 4/8/85
Liquidated 3/26/05
Brown Back <$VALUE
50-100 1-1805 <$1750/$2000
Total Issue $270,750
Out in 1910 $4,425
****
7630 Washington
FORT EDWARD NB,
FORT EDWARD
{{0 L 4 S}}
Chartered 3/05
1902 Red Seal <$VALUE
50-100 1-380 <$2250/$2500
1902 Date Back
50-100 1-400 <$850/$1000
3x50-100 1-360 <$850/$1000
1902 Plain Back
3x50-100 361-468<$850/$1000
1929 Small Size
10 Type 1 1-484 <$300
20 Type 1 1-140 <$300
10 Type 2 1-848 <$300
20 Type 2 1-204 <$300
Total Issue $292,400
Out in 1935 $20,000
Large out 1935 $1,950
****
1218 Washington
NB OF FORT EDWARD
{{ UNREPORTED }}
Chartered 1865
Liquidated 4/22/85
Original Series <$VALUE
4x5 1-3000 <$1250
3x10-20 1-2220<$1500/$2000
50-50 1-1363 <$3500
Series 1875
50-50 1-1573 <$3500
Total Issue $464,600
Out in 1910 $2,445
****
2860 Montgomery
FORT PLAIN NB, FORT PLAIN
{{8 L 8 S}}
Chartered 1883
Brown Back <$VALUE
3x10-20 1-6874 <$300/$350
1902 Red Seal
3x10-20 1-2900 <$400
1902 Date Back
3x10-20 1-5700 <$200
1902 Plain Back
3x10-20 5701-12070 <$200
1929 Small Size
10 Type 1 1-1334 <$150
20 Type 1 1-400 <$150
10 Type 2 1-2214 <$150
20 Type 2 1-463 <$150
Total Issue $1,251,640
Out in 1935 $50,000
Large out 1935 $3,170
****
467 Montgomery
N FORT PLAIN B,
FORT PLAIN
{{ UNREPORTED }}
Chartered 6/64
Liquidated 2/24/83
Original Series <$VALUE
4x5 1-4000 <$1250
3x10-20 1-5600<$1500/$2000
Series 1875
3x10-20 1-3904<$1500/$2000
Total Issue $555,200
Out in 1910 $2,615
****

***

10351 Herkimer
CITIZENS NB OF FRANKFORT
Chartered 3/20/13
2nd title:Citizens FNB 11/20/22
FIRST TITLE {{ 2 L }}
1902 Date Back <$VALUE
3x10-20 1-1750 <$350
1902 Plain Back
3x10-20 1751-6440 <$350
SECOND TITLE {{ 4 L 16 S }}
1902 Plain Back
3x10-20 1-10197 <$350
1929 Small Size
10 Type 1 1-2964 <$100
20 Type 1 1-776 <$100
10 Type 2 1-4966 <$100
20 Type 2 1-948 <$100
Total Issue $1,171,430
Out in 1935 $100,000
Large out 1935 $2,710
Outstanding includes Ch 3582

***

Citizens FNB of Frankfort
SEE Ch 10351
Citizens NB of Frankfort

***

3582 Herkimer
FNB OF FRANKFORT
{{ 1 L }}
Chartered 11/2/86
Closed 11/20/22
Brown Back <$VALUE
4x5 1-3747 <$1000
3x10-20 1-560 <$1000
1902 Red Seal
3x10-20 1-250 <$1000
1902 Date Back
3x10-20 1-1420* <$600
1902 Plain Back
3x10-20 1541-2276* <$600
* 1421-1540 not marked
Total Issue $229,240
Out at close $12,100
Ch 10351 assumed circulation

***

282 Delaware
FNB OF FRANKLIN
{{ 7 L 6 S }}
Organized 12/24/63
Receivership 7/21/33
Original Series <$VALUE
3x1-2 1-3000 <$350/$850
4x5 1-6250 <$500
3x10-20 1-700 <$750/$1250
Series 1875
3x1-2 1-1580 <$350/$850
4x5 1-5250 <$500
3x10-20 1-400 <$750/$1250
Brown Back
4x5 1-13815 <$350
3x10-20 1-943 <$400
1902 Red Seal
4x5 1-2862 <$400
3x10-20 1-2135 <$400
1902 Date Back
4x5 1-3725 <$200
3x10-20 1-2820 <$200
1902 Plain Back
4x5 3726-12687 <$200
3x10-20 2821-8578 <$200
1929 Small Size
5 Type 1 1-1859 <$175
10 Type 1 1-929 <$175
20 Type 1 1-229 <$175
Total Issue $1,616,970
Out at close $50,000
Large out at close $5,948

***

12997 Nassau
FRANKLIN SQUARE NB, FRANKLIN SQUARE
{{ 7 S }}
Chartered 10/26
1929 Small Size <$VALUE
5 Type 2 1-2436 <$500
10 Type 2 1-2520 <$500
20 Type 2 1-636 <$500
50 Type 2 1-132 <$1000
100 Type 2 1-72 <$1250
Total Issue $63,900
Out in 1935 $50,000

***

2755 Cattaraugus
FARMERS NB OF FRANKLINVILLE
Chartered 1882
2nd title:Union NB of Franklinville 3/15/00
FIRST TITLE {{ 0 L }}
Brown Back <$VALUE
4x5 1-5520 <$850
SECOND TITLE {{ 6 L 8 S }}
Brown Back
4x5 1-300 <$500
3x10-20 1-619 <$500
1902 Red Seal
4x5 1-2280 <$500
3x10-20 1-1628 <$500
1902 Date Back
4x5 1-5300 <$250
3x10-20 1-4020 <$250
1902 Plain Back
4x5 5301-14425 <$250
3x10-20 4021-9747 <$250
1929 Small Size
5 Type 1 1-1958 <$150
10 Type 1 1-984 <$150
20 Type 1 1-268 <$150
5 Type 2 1-2592 <$150
10 Type 2 1-1487 <$150
20 Type 2 1-456 <$175
Total Issue $1,237,090
Out in 1935 $50,000
Large out 1935 $2,545

***

2345 Cattaraugus
FNB OF FRANKLINVILLE
{{ 2 L }}
Chartered 1/15/77
Liquidated 3/20/00
Series 1875 <$VALUE
4x5 1-8393 <$850
Brown Back
4x5 1-1008 <$750
Total Issue $188,020
Out in 1910 $990

***

8157 Cattaraugus
PEOPLES NB OF FRANKLINVILLE
{{ UNREPORTED }}
Organized 4/3/06
Receivership 1/13/08
1902 Red Seal <$VALUE
3x10-20 1-510 <$1500
Total Issue $25,500
Out in 1916 $440

***

Union NB of Franklinville
SEE Ch 2755
Farmers NB of Franklinville

***

841 Chautauqua
FREDONIA NB, FREDONIA
{{ 4 L }}
Chartered 2/27/65
Receivership 6/19/05
Original Series <$VALUE
4x5 1-2250 <$500
3x10-20 1-800 <$750/$1250
Series 1875
4x5 1-1910 <$500
3x10-20 1-1674 <$600/$1000
Brown Back
4x5 1-5735 <$350
3x10-20 1-2761 <$350
1902 Red Seal
4x5 1-30 <$400
3x10-20 1-88 <$400
Total Issue $464,650
Out in 1916 $2,970

***

9019 Chautauqua
NB OF FREDONIA
{{ U + 10 L 3U + 12 S }}
Chartered 2/08
1902 Red Seal <$VALUE
3x10-20 1-500 <$300
1902 Date Back
3x10-20 1-2100 <$125
1902 Plain Back
3x10-20 2101-13072 <$125
1929 Small Size
5 Type 1 1-8176 <$75
10 Type 1 1-784 <$75
20 Type 1 1-262 <$75
5 Type 2 1-25194 <$75
Total Issue $1,128,330
Out in 1935 $100,000
Large out 1935 $2,520

***

11518 Nassau
CITIZENS NB OF FREEPORT
{{ 1 L 1 S }}
Chartered 11/19
1902 Plain Back <$VALUE
4x5 1-3589 <$1250
1929 Small Size
5 Type 1 1-1456 <$850
5 Type 2 1-3036 <$850
Total Issue $130,640
Out in 1935 $10,000
Large out 1935 $300

***

7703 Nassau
FNB OF FREEPORT
Chartered 4/05
2nd title:FNB & TC 7/8/26
FIRST TITLE {{ U + 8 L }}
1902 Red Seal <$VALUE
4x5 1-300 <$750
3x10-20 1-240 <$750
1902 Date Back
4x5 1-1400 <$350
3x10-20 1-920 <$350
1902 Plain Back
4x5 1401-4768 <$350
3x10-20 921-2862 <$350
SECOND TITLE {{3 L 2U + 10 S}}
1902 Plain Back
4x5 1-3407 <$350
3x10-20 1-2514 <$350
1929 Small Size
5 Type 1 1-4970 <$200
10 Type 1 1-2800 <$200
20 Type 1 1-622 <$200
5 Type 2 1-9064* <$200
10 Type 2 1-4164** <$200
20 Type 2 1-1056***<$200
* 6465-7464 canceled
** 3300-3324 canceled
*** 656-876 canceled
Total Issue $940,450
Out in 1935 $75,000
Large out 1935 $3,190

***

2632 Allegany
CITIZENS NB OF FRIENDSHIP
{{ 6 L }}
Chartered 1882
Liquidated 8/11/17
Series 1875 <$VALUE
4x5 1-12679 <$500
3x10-20 1-761 <$600/$1000
Brown Back
4x5 1-2950 <$400
3x10-20 1-2320 <$400
1882 Date Back
4x5 1-4100 <$400
3x10-20 1-2500 <$400
1882 Value Back
4x5 4101-5088 <$400
3x10-20 2501-2961 <$400
Total Issue $716,440
Out at close $50,000

***

265 Allegany
FNB OF FRIENDSHIP
{{ 5 L }}
Chartered 2/64
Liquidated 8/11/17
Original Series <$VALUE
4x5 1-6500 <$600
Series 1875
4x5 1-6000 <$600
Brown Back
4x5 1-3954 <$500
3x10-20 1-1862 <$500
50-100 1-219 <$1250/$1500
1902 Red Seal
4x5 1-2250 <$500
3x10-20 1-1600 <$500
1902 Date Back
4x5 1-3100 <$250
3x10-20 1-2300 <$250
1902 Plain Back
4x5 3101-3547 <$250
3x10-20 2301-2569 <$250
Total Issue $779,420
Out at close $40,000

***

11055 Allegany
UNION NB OF FRIENDSHIP
{{ 8 L 12 S }}
Chartered 8/17
1902 Plain Back <$VALUE
4x5 1-16351 <$200
3x10-20 1-11023 <$200
1929 Small Size
5 Type 1 1-1986 <$125
10 Type 1 1-1992 <$125
20 Type 1 1-562 <$125
5 Type 2 1-5054 <$125
10 Type 2 1-2983 <$125
20 Type 2 1-756 <$125
Total Issue $1,194,930
Out in 1935 $88,495
Large out 1935 $2,935

***

1178 Oswego
CITIZENS NB OF FULTON
Chartered 1865
2nd title:Citizens NB & TC 7/22/29
FIRST TITLE {{ 14 L }}
Original Series <$VALUE
3x1-2 1-3600 <$300/$750
4x5 1-8500 <$300
3x10-20 1-4000 <$600/$1250
Series 1875
3x10-20 1-3369 <$500/$1000
Brown Back
3x10-20 1-15165 <$200/$250
1902 Red Seal
3x10-20 1-2900 <$250
1902 Date Back
3x10-20 1-7200 <$100
1902 Plain Back
3x10-20 7201-30031 <$100
SECOND TITLE {{ 15 S }}
1929 Small Size
10 Type 1 1-6346 <$60
10 Type 2 1-11940 <$60
Total Issue $3,461,410
Out in 1935 $125,000
Large out 1935 $6,980

***

968 Oswego
FNB OF FULTON
{{ 7 L }}
Chartered 4/1/65
Liquidated 2/15/17
Original Series <$VALUE
3x1-2 1-3000 <$350/$750
4x5 1-4025 <$350
3x10-20 1-1250 <$600/$1250
Series 1875
3x1-2 1-480 <$350/$750
4x5 1-1345 <$350
3x10-20 1-1354 <$500/$1000
Brown Back
4x5 1-17088 <$250
3x10-20 1-1888 <$250
1902 Red Seal
3x10-20 1-2275 <$250
1902 Date Back
3x10-20 1-5400 <$125
1902 Plain Back
3x10-20 5401-6152 <$125
Total Issue $1,112,510
Out at close $57,500

***

2869 Montgomery
FULTONVILLE NB, FULTONVILLE
{{ 2 L 2 S }}
Chartered 1883
Brown Back <$VALUE
4x5 1-3897 <$850
3x10-20 1-253 <$850
1902 Red Seal
3x10-20 1-790 <$850
1902 Date Back
3x10-20 1-1540 <$500
1902 Plain Back
3x10-20 1541-3374 <$500
1929 Small Size
10 Type 1 1-314 <$500
20 Type 1 1-106 <$500
10 Type 2 1-542 <$500
20 Type 2 1-91 <$500
Total Issue $337,590
Out in 1935 $12,500
Large out 1935 $970

***

5867 Wyoming
GAINESVILLE NB, GAINESVILLE
{{ 6 L 3 S }}
Chartered 6/19/01
Brown Back <$VALUE
4x5 1-1675 <$400
3x10-20 1-1290 <$400
1882 Date Back
4x5 1-2250 <$400
3x10-20 1-1520 <$400
1882 Value Back
4x5 2251-3980 <$400
3x10-20 1521-2445 <$400
1902 Plain Back
4x5 1-10197 <$225
1929 Small Size
5 Type 1 1-2670 <$400
5 Type 2 1-7154 <$400
Total Issue $619,660
Out in 1935 $25,000
Large out 1935 $730

***

10623 Niagara
FNB OF GASPORT
{{ 2 L 3 S }}
Organized 9/19/14
Receivership 12/30/31
1902 Date Back <$VALUE
3x10-20 1-800 <$500
1902 Plain Back
3x10-20 801-5417 <$500
1929 Small Size
10 Type 1 1-482 <$350
20 Type 1 1-128 <$350
Total Issue $315,130
Out at close $24,640
Large out at close $1,790

***

886 Livingston
GENESEE VALLEY NB OF GENESEO
Chartered 3/14/65
2nd title:Genesee Valley NB & TC 6/14/30
FIRST TITLE {{18 L U + 4 S }}
Original Series <$VALUE
3x1-2 1-3200 <$250/$750
4x5 1-5350 <$300
3x10-20 1-2470 <$600/$1250
Series 1875
4x5 1-4605 <$300
3x10-20 1-2978 <$500/$1000
Brown Back
4x5 1-15818 <$200
3x10-20 1-12035 <$200
1902 Red Seal
4x5 1-5500 <$200
3x10-20 1-4000 <$200
1902 Date Back
4x5 1-9500 <$100
3x10-20 1-7400 <$100
1902 Plain Back
4x5 9501-36760 <$100
3x10-20 7401-24075 <$100
1929 Small Size
5 Type 1 1-3066 <$75
10 Type 1 1-1550 <$75
20 Type 1 1-520 <$75
SECOND TITLE {{ 16 S }}
1929 Small Size
5 Type 1 1-3566 <$60
10 Type 1 1-1614 <$60
20 Type 1 1-368 <$60
5 Type 2 1-12748 <$75
10 Type 2 1-6651 <$75
20 Type 2 1-1537 <$75
Total Issue $4,310,910
Out in 1935 $200,000
Large out 1935 $10,435

***

167 Ontario
FNB OF GENEVA
{{ 2 L }}
Chartered 12/63
Liquidated 5/20/19
Original Series <$VALUE
3x1-2 1-3020 <$600/$1250
4x5 1-6300 <$650
Series 1875
4x5 1-2985 <$650
Brown Back
4x5 1-8748 <$600
3x10-20 1-469 <$600
1902 Red Seal
50-100 1-490 <$2250/$2500
1902 Date Back
50-100 1-520 <$650/$750
3x50-100 1-174 <$650/$750
Total Issue $594,210
Out at close $25,000

***

949 Ontario
GENEVA NB, GENEVA
{{ 3 L }}
Chartered 3/29/65
Liquidated 11/20/23
Original Series <$VALUE
3x1-2 1-6400 <$500/$850
4x5 1-5560 <$500
3x10-20 1-4340 <$750/$1250
Series 1875
3x10-20 1-4180 <$600/$1000
Brown Back
50-100 1-2151 <$1250/$1500
1902 Red Seal
50-100 1-1190 <$2250/$2500
1902 Date Back
50-100 1-1000 <$650/$750
3x50-100 1-1323 <$650/$750
Total Issue $1,551,100
Out in 1922 $87,500

***

9921 Cayuga
FNB OF GENOA
{{ 1 L 2 S }}
Organized 1/4/11
Receivership 7/2/31
1902 Date Back <$VALUE
3x10-20 1-2020 <$500
1902 Plain Back
3x10-20 2021-6328 <$500
1929 Small Size
10 Type 1 1-396 <$500
20 Type 1 1-106 <$500
Total Issue $352,880
Out at close $25,000
Large out at close $2,350

***

12242 Columbia
GERMANTOWN NB, GERMANTOWN
{{ 3 L 2 S }}
Organized 1/7/22
Receivership 1/22/32
1902 Plain Back <$VALUE
3x10-20 1-1151 <$500
1929 Small Size
10 Type 1 1-191 <$500
20 Type 1 1-49 <$500
Total Issue $74,890
Out at close $9,520
Large out at close $760

***

13126 Nassau
FNB OF GLEN HEAD
{{ 2U + 16 S }}
Chartered 9/27
1929 Small Size <$VALUE
5 Type 1 1-1038 <$200
10 Type 1 1-526 <$200
5 Type 2 1-18204 <$200
Total Issue $153,720
Out in 1935 $40,350

***

980 Warren
FNB OF GLENS FALLS
{{ 14 L 19 S }}
Chartered 4/5/65
Original Series <$VALUE
3x1-2 1-4500 <$300/$750
4x5 1-4800 <$350
3x10-20 1-1320 <$600/$1250
50-100 1-490 <$3500
Series 1875
4x5 1-3420 <$350
3x10-20 1-1232 <$500/$1000
50-100 1-733 <$3500
Brown Back
4x5 1-6390 <$300
3x10-20 1-4455 <$300
50-100 1-1175 <$1250/$1500
1902 Red Seal
4x5 1-3000 <$350
3x10-20 1-1490 <$350
50-100 1-170 <$2250/$2500
1902 Date Back
4x5 1-9250 <$150
3x10-20 1-6500 <$150
50-100 1-180 <$400/$500
3x50-100 1-474 <$400/$500
1902 Plain Back
4x5 9251-31060 <$150
3x10-20 6501-18013 <$150
3x50-100 475-791<$400/$500
1929 Small Size
5 Type 1 1-3710 <$75
10 Type 1 1-1676 <$75
20 Type 1 1-498 <$75
50 Type 1 1-156 <$200
100 Type 1 1-54 <$250
5 Type 2 1-4004 <$85
10 Type 2 1-2172 <$85
20 Type 2 1-700 <$85
Total Issue $3,337,910
Out in 1935 $134,000
Large out 1935 $9,400

***

1293 Warren
GLENS FALLS NB, GLENS FALLS
{{ 2 L }}
Chartered 6/16/65
Liquidated 5/27/05
Original Series <$VALUE
3x1-2 1-3000 <$600/$1250
4x5 1-5000 <$650
3x10-20 1-1700 <$750/$1250
Series 1875
3x10-20 1-3834 <$750/$1250
Brown Back
3x10-20 1-10240 <$600
Total Issue $903,700
Out in 1910 $10,134

***

Glens Falls NB & TC of Glens Falls
SEE Ch 7699
NB of Glens Falls

***

<$VALUEs are for notes in FINE condition. Value changes by approximately 25% for a change of one full grade.

****
4846 Warren
MERCHANTS NB OF
GLENS FALLS
{{ 2 L }}
Chartered 1893
Liquidated 5/27/22
Brown Back <$VALUE
4x5 1-11375 <$600
3x10-20 1-2100 <$600
1882 Date Back
4x5 1-445 <$600
3x10-20 1-632 <$600
1902 Date Back
4x5 1-1250* <$350
3x10-20 1-1000** <$350
1902 Plain Back
4x5 1451-3005* <$350
3x10-20 1161-1994** <$350
* 1251-1450 not marked
** 1001-1160 not marked
Total Issue $532,800
Out at close $25,000
****
7699 Warren
NB OF GLENS FALLS
Chartered 4/05
2nd title:Glens Falls NB & TC 10/3/32
FIRST TITLE {{ 11 L 5 S }}
1902 Red Seal <$VALUE
3x10-20 1-5000 <$400
1902 Date Back
3x10-20 1-8800 <$175
1902 Plain Back
3x10-20 8801-26064 <$175
1929 Small Size
10 Type 1 1-2376 <$125
20 Type 1 1-672 <$125
SECOND TITLE {{ 6 S }}
1929 Small Size
10 Type 1 1-358 <$125
20 Type 1 1-82 <$125
10 Type 2 1-4737 <$125
20 Type 2 1-1413 <$125
Total Issue $1,883,350
Out in 1935 $100,000
Large out 1935 $3,800
****
9305 Fulton
CITY NB OF GLOVERSVILLE
Chartered 1/09
2nd title:City NB & TC 2/5/29
FIRST TITLE {{ 22 L }}
1902 Date Back <$VALUE
4x5 1-10300 <$50
3x10-20 1-7780 <$60
1902 Plain Back
4x5 10301-116193 <$50
3x10-20 7781-64328 <$60
SECOND TITLE {{ 50+ S }}
1929 Small Size
5 Type 1 1-23288 <$25
10 Type 1 1-10098 <$25
20 Type 1 1-2694 <$35
5 Type 2 1-40036 <$25
10 Type 2 1-10660 <$25
20 Type 2 1-5335 <$35
Total Issue $7,581,540
Out in 1935 $500,000
Large out 1935 $14,840
****
3312 Fulton
FULTON COUNTY NB
OF GLOVERSVILLE
Chartered 1885
2nd title:Fulton County NB & TC 6/20/30
FIRST TITLE {{ 15 L }}
Brown Back <$VALUE
4x5 1-4546 <$200
3x10-20 1-4486 <$200/$250
1902 Red Seal
4x5 1-2450 <$200
3x10-20 1-1460 <$200/$250
50-100 1-70 <$2250/$2500
1902 Date Back
4x5 1-9600 <$100
3x10-20 1-6160 <$100
50-100 1-100 <$350/$400
3x50-100 1-200 <$350/$400
1902 Plain Back
4x5 9601-37970 <$100
3x10-20 6161-23423 <$100
SECOND TITLE {{ 33 S }}
1929 Small Size
5 Type 1 1-11908 <$25
10 Type 1 1-7404 <$25
20 Type 1 1-1454 <$35
5 Type 2 1-23718 <$25
10 Type 2 1-14085 <$25
20 Type 2 1-3015 <$35

Total Issue $3,738,970
Out in 1935 $350,000
Large out 1935 $6,460
****
1938 Fulton
NB OF GLOVERSVILLE
{{ 2 L }}
Chartered 2/17/72
Liquidated 2/28/78
Original Series <$VALUE
3x1-2 1-2700 <$500/$1000
4x5 1-3075 <$600
3x10-20 1-600 <$750/$1250
Series 1875
3x10-20 1-557 <$750/$1250
Total Issue $132,850
Out in 1910 $514
****
1474 Fulton
N FULTON B OF
GLOVERSVILLE
{{ UNREPORTED }}
Chartered 1865
Liquidated 2/20/85
Original Series <$VALUE
3x1-2 1-9000 <$750/$1250
4x5 1-8000 <$850
3x10-20 1-3100<$1000/$1500
Series 1875
4x5 1-4705 <$850
3x10-20 1-2462<$1000/$1500
Total Issue $577,200
Out in 1910 $2,707
****
1408 Orange
GOSHEN NB, GOSHEN
{{ 6 L 5 S }}
Chartered 1865
Original Series <$VALUE
3x1-2 1-3000 <$400/$1000
4x5 1-3600 <$500
4x10 1-1700 <$750
3x20-50 1-600 <$1250/$3500
Series 1875
4x5 1-2000 <$500
4x10 1-1965 <$600
3x20-50 1-400 <$1000/$3500
Brown Back
4x5 1-3279 <$350
3x10-20 1-2788 <$350
1902 Red Seal
4x5 1-1100 <$400
3x10-20 1-745 <$400
1902 Date Back
4x5 1-2700 <$200
3x10-20 1-2040 <$200
1902 Plain Back
4x5 2701-7775 <$200
3x10-20 2041-5103 <$200
1929 Small Size
5 Type 1 1-878 <$200
10 Type 1 1-472 <$200
20 Type 1 1-168 <$200
5 Type 2 1-1356 <$200
10 Type 2 1-708 <$200
20 Type 2 1-204 <$200
Total Issue $1,151,240
Out in 1935 $27,500
Large out 1935 $3,420
****
1399 Orange
NB OF ORANGE COUNTY OF
GOSHEN
{{ 12 L 20 S }}
Chartered 1865
Original Series <$VALUE
3x1-2 1-3000 <$300/$850
4x5 1-4050 <$400
4x10 1-1175 <$750
3x20-50 1-600 <$1250/$3500
Series 1875
4x5 1-3199 <$400
4x10 1-2060 <$600
3x20-50 1-432 <$1000/$3500
Brown Back
4x5 1-13054 <$200
3x10-20 1-7160 <$200
50-100 1-1067 <$1250/$1500
1902 Red Seal
4x5 1-4250 <$250
3x10-20 1-2900 <$250
50-100 1-100 <$2250/$2500
1902 Date Back
4x5 1-9000 <$125
3x10-20 1-6500 <$125
50-100 1-250 <$400/$500
1902 Plain Back
4x5 9001-30869 <$125
3x10-20 6501-20974 <$125
1929 Small Size
5 Type 1 1-4398 <$60
10 Type 1 1-2148 <$60
20 Type 1 1-520 <$65

5 Type 2 1-9692 <$65
10 Type 2 1-4505 <$65
20 Type 2 1-1124 <$70
Total Issue $3,568,620
Out in 1935 $108,950
Large out 1935 $8,040
****
13911 Saint Lawrence
FNB IN GOUVERNEUR
{{ 2 S }}
Chartered 12/33
1929 Small Size <$VALUE
5 Type 2 1-1404 <$500
10 Type 2 1-905 <$500
20 Type 2 1-140 <$500
Total Issue $18,870
Out in 1935 $100,000
Outstanding includes Ch 2510
****
2510 Saint Lawrence
FNB OF GOUVERNEUR
{{ 12 L 22 S }}
Organized 2/19/81
Liquidated 5/25/34
Series 1875 <$VALUE
4x5 1-5759 <$400
3x10-20 1-101 <$600/$1000
Brown Back
3x10-20 1-1240 <$300
1882 Date Back
3x10-20 1-2740 <$300
1882 Value Back
3x10-20 2741-12105 <$300
1902 Plain Back
3x10-20 1-25228 <$150
1929 Small Size
10 Type 1 1-5864 <$75
20 Type 1 1-1556 <$85
Total Issue $2,587,440
Out at close $200,000
Large out at close $8,120
Ch 13911 assumed circulation
****
7618 Delaware
FNB OF GRAND GORGE
{{ 2 L 8 S }}
Chartered 2/05
1902 Red Seal <$VALUE
3x10-20 1-631 <$1250
1902 Date Back
3x10-20 1-1980 <$750
1902 Plain Back
3x10-20 1981-6470 <$750
1929 Small Size
10 Type 1 1-1064 <$350
20 Type 1 1-268 <$350
10 Type 2 1-2166 <$350
20 Type 2 1-620 <$350
Total Issue $485,110
Out in 1935 $50,000
Large out 1935 $890
****
3154 Washington
FARMERS NB OF GRANVILLE
{{ 6 L 8 S }}
Organized 3/20/84
Receivership /18/32
Brown Back <$VALUE
3x10-20 1-3481 <$350
1902 Red Seal
3x10-20 1-2400 <$400
1902 Date Back
3x10-20 1-4540 <$200
1902 Plain Back
3x10-20 4541-17620 <$200
1929 Small Size
10 Type 1 1-1845 <$125
20 Type 1 1-541 <$125
Total Issue $1,350,670
Out at close $97,540
Large out at close $7,410
****
4985 Washington
GRANVILLE NB, GRANVILLE
{{ 6 L 4 S }}
Organized 1/30/95
Liquidated 10/19/31
Brown Back <$VALUE
3x10-20 1-5400 <$350
1882 Date Back
3x10-20 1-3874 <$350
1902 Date Back
3x10-20 1-1000 <$250
1902 Plain Back
3x10-20 1001-9721 <$250
1929 Small Size
10 Type 1 1-825 <$200
20 Type 1 1-234 <$200
Total Issue $1,027,330
Out at close $50,000
Large out at close $5,110
****

****
2294 Washington
NB OF GRANVILLE
{{ UNREPORTED }}
Chartered 8/25/75
Liquidated 4/21/95
Series 1875 <$VALUE
3x10-20 1-6226<$1250/$1500
Total Issue $311,300
Out in 1910 $1,245
****
7255 Washington
WASHINGTON COUNTY NB OF
GRANVILLE
{{ 4 L 3U + 12 S }}
Chartered 5/04
1902 Red Seal <$VALUE
3x10-20 1-1472 <$500
1902 Date Back
3x10-20 1-5040 <$250
1902 Plain Back
3x10-20 5041-12523 <$250
1929 Small Size
5 Type 1 1-832 <$100
10 Type 1 1-832 <$100
20 Type 1 1-420 <$100
5 Type 2 1-3462 <$100
10 Type 2 1-1640 <$100
20 Type 2 1-255 <$100
Total Issue $863,840
Out in 1935 $51,190
Large out 1935 $1,640
****
12659 Nassau
FNB OF GREAT NECK AT
GREAT NECK STATION
{{ 8 L 2 S }}
Chartered 3/25
Liquidated 10/31/31
1902 Plain Back <$VALUE
4x5 1-13384 <$500
1929 Small Size
5 Type 1 1-4109 <$850
Total Issue $390,950
Out at close $46,760
Large out at close $2,890
****
334 Suffolk
FNB OF GREENPORT
{{ 6 L 10 S }}
Chartered 3/64
Original Series <$VALUE
3x1-2 1-2880 <$1500/$3500
4x5 1-4750 <$1500
3x10-20 1-1400<$2500/$3500
Series 1875
4x5 1-1000 <$1500
3x10-20 1-466 <$2500/$3500
Brown Back
3x10-20 1-5499 <$1500
1902 Red Seal
3x10-20 1-3260 <$1500
1902 Date Back
3x10-20 1-4400 <$650
1902 Plain Back
3x10-20 4401-13281 <$650
1929 Small Size
10 Type 1 1-1546 <$350
20 Type 1 1-358 <$350
10 Type 2 1-2089 <$350
20 Type 2 1-596 <$350
Total Issue $1,493,230
Out in 1935 $50,000
Large out 1935 $3,850
****
3232 Suffolk
PEOPLES NB OF GREENPORT
{{ 1 L 2 S }}
Chartered 1884
Brown Back <$VALUE
4x5 1-3772 <$2000
3x10-20 1-413 <$2000
1902 Red Seal
3x10-20 1-635 <$2000
1902 Date Back
3x10-20 1-1620 <$1000
1902 Plain Back
3x10-20 1621-3473 <$1000
1929 Small Size
10 Type 1 1-314 <$1000
20 Type 1 1-104 <$1000
10 Type 2 1-385 <$1000
20 Type 2 1-180 <$1000
Total Issue $340,000
Out in 1935 $12,200
Large out 1935 $800
****
2517 Washington
FNB OF GREENWICH
{{ 6 L }}
Chartered 1881
Series 1875 <$VALUE
3x10-20 1-3042 <$750/$1250

Brown Back
4x5 1-700 <$500
3x10-20 1-700 <$500
1882 Date Back
4x5 1-1275 <$500
3x10-20 1-960 <$500
1882 Value Back
4x5 1276-2503 <$500
3x10-20 961-1671 <$500
1902 Plain Back
4x5 1-1987 <$300
3x10-20 1-1320 <$300
Total Issue $440,450
Out in 1935 $1,205
****
1266 Washington
WASHINGTON COUNTY NB OF
GREENWICH
{{ 4 L }}
Organized 6/30/65
Receivership 6/8/78
Original Series <$VALUE
2x1-2x2 1-6420 <$500/$1000
4x5 1-4200 <$500
3x10-20 1-2175 <$750/$1250
Series 1875
4x5 1-1720 <$500
3x10-20 1-861 <$750/$1250
Total Issue $308,720
Out in 1916 $1,654
****
8058 Steuben
FNB OF GREENWOOD
{{ 2 L 4 S }}
Organized 12/5/05
1902 Red Seal <$VALUE
3x10-20 1-1040 <$750
1902 Date Back
3x10-20 1-1880 <$400
1902 Plain Back
3x10-20 1881-6035 <$400
1929 Small Size
10 Type 1 1-654 <$300
20 Type 1 1-190 <$300
10 Type 2 1-717 <$300
20 Type 2 1-148 <$300
Total Issue $425,920
Out in 1935 $25,000
Large out 1935 $1,060
****
8847 Delaware
FNB OF GRIFFIN CORNERS
Organized 4/30/07
Receivership 10/5/31
2nd title:FNB of Fleischmanns 4/8/29
FIRST TITLE {{ 3 L }}
1902 Red Seal <$VALUE
3x10-20 1-200 <$750
1902 Date Back
4x5 1-2250 <$500
3x10-20 1-1940 <$500
1902 Plain Back
4x5 2251-7315 <$500
3x10-20 1941-5048 <$500
SECOND TITLE {{ 4 S }}
1929 Small Size
5 Type 1 1-924* <$300
10 Type 1 1-560** <$300
20 Type 1 1-162*** <$300
5 Type 2 1-1512 <$300
10 Type 2 1-696 <$300
20 Type 2 1-264 <$300
* 546-734 canceled
** 281-358 canceled
*** 79-108 canceled
Total Issue $495,310
Out in 1935 $25,000
Large out 1935 $1,110
****
1083 Tompkins
FNB OF GROTON
{{ 13 L 18 S }}
Chartered 4/65
Original Series <$VALUE
3x1-2 1-3900 <$300/$850
4x5 1-3750 <$400
3x10-20 1-1820 <$750/$1250
Series 1875
4x5 1-285 <$400
3x10-20 1-3352 <$600/$1000
Brown Back
3x10-20 1-11920 <$250/$300
1902 Red Seal
3x10-20 1-3800 <$250/$300
1902 Date Back
3x10-20 1-7900 <$125
1902 Plain Back
3x10-20 7901-25190 <$125
1929 Small Size
10 Type 1 1-3406 <$75
20 Type 1 1-518 <$75
10 Type 2 1-8835 <$75

Total Issue $2,759,170
Out in 1935 $100,000
Large out 1935 $6,170
****
12017 Delaware
FNB OF HAMDEN
{{ 3 L 6 S }}
Chartered 9/21
1902 Plain Back <$VALUE
3x10-20 1-2955 <$500
1929 Small Size
10 Type 1 1-758 <$250
20 Type 1 1-190 <$250
10 Type 2 1-956 <$250
20 Type 2 1-240 <$250
Total Issue $230,390
Out in 1935 $25,000
Large out 1935 $950
****
1334 Madison
N HAMILTON B, HAMILTON
{{ 14 L 19 S }}
Chartered 1865
Original Series <$VALUE
3x1-2 1-3000 <$350/$750
4x5 1-2825 <$350
3x10-20 1-1770 <$600/$1250
Series 1875
3x1-2 1-680 <$350/$750
4x5 1-2136 <$350
3x10-20 1-850 <$500/$1000
Brown Back
4x5 1-8033 <$200
3x10-20 1-8183 <$200/$250
1902 Red Seal
4x5 1-4375 <$200
3x10-20 1-2900 <$200/$250
1902 Date Back
4x5 1-7950 <$100
3x10-20 1-5820 <$100
1902 Plain Back
4x5 7951-27615 <$100
3x10-20 5821-19382 <$100
1929 Small Size
5 Type 1 1-3684 <$50
10 Type 1 1-2112 <$50
20 Type 1 1-522 <$60
5 Type 2 1-8220 <$60
10 Type 2 1-4092 <$60
20 Type 2 1-924 <$70
Total Issue $2,972,710
Out in 1935 $104,250
Large out 1935 $6,110
****
10216 Saint Lawrence
CITIZENS NB OF HAMMOND
{{ 3 L 4 S }}
Organized 6/20/12
Receivership 10/12/33
1902 Date Back <$VALUE
4x10 1-1650 <$500
1902 Plain Back
4x10 1651-7583 <$500
1929 Small Size
10 Type 1 1-1185 <$300
Total Issue $374,420
Out in 1935 $25,000
Large out 1935 $1,170
****
12987 Suffolk
HAMPTON BAYS NB,
HAMPTON BAYS
{{ U + 2 L 12 S }}
Chartered 9/26
1902 Plain Back <$VALUE
3x10-20 1-2929 <$1250
1929 Small Size
10 Type 1 1-1508 <$350
20 Type 1 1-402 <$350
10 Type 2 1-2661 <$350
20 Type 2 1-816 <$350
Total Issue $328,100
Out in 1935 $50,000
Large out 1935 $170
****
8613 Delaware
FNB OF HANCOCK
{{ 6 L 15 S }}
Chartered 3/07
1902 Red Seal <$VALUE
3x10-20 1-1125 <$400
1902 Date Back
3x10-20 1-4200 <$200
1902 Plain Back
3x10-20 4201-12956 <$200
1929 Small Size
10 Type 1 1-1942 <$75
20 Type 1 1-562 <$85
10 Type 2 1-5545 <$85
20 Type 2 1-1535 <$85
Total Issue $974,160
Out in 1935 $100,000
Large out 1935 $2,480
****

****
12601 Westchester
FNB OF HARRISON
{{1L U+5S}}
Chartered 11/24
1902 Plain Back <$VALUE
3x10-20 1-2319 <$1250
1929 Small Size
10 Type 1 1-754 <$500
20 Type 1 1-212 <$500
10 Type 2 1-1230 <$500
20 Type 2 1-328 <$500
Total Issue $205,490
Out in 1935 $25,000
Large out 1935 $640
****
10767 Lewis
FNB OF HARRISVILLE
{{2L 7S}}
Organized 7/22/15
1902 Plain Back <$VALUE
4x5 1-5503 <$450
4x10 1-3854 <$450
1929 Small Size
5 Type 1 1-1276 <$200
10 Type 1 1-678 <$200
5 Type 2 1-3884 <$200
10 Type 2 1-2274 <$200
Total Issue $385,340
Out in 1935 $25,000
Large out 1935 $550
****
12705 Westchester
HARTSDALE NB, HARTSDALE
{{7S}}
Chartered 4/25
1929 Small Size <$VALUE
5 Type 2 1-8592 <$500
10 Type 2 1-1896 <$500
Total Issue $61,920
Out in 1935 $50,000
****
11657 Otsego
HARTWICK NB, HARTWICK
{{1L 6S}}
Chartered 3/20
1902 Plain Back <$VALUE
4x10 1-4925 <$600
1929 Small Size
10 Type 1 1-1124 <$300
10 Type 2 1-2532 <$300
Total Issue $289,760
Out in 1935 $25,000
Large out 1935 $650
****
8586 Westchester
FNB OF HASTINGS-UPON-HUDSON
{{3L 3S}}
Chartered 3/07
1902 Red Seal <$VALUE
4x5 1-200 <$2000
3x10-20 1-220 <$2000
1902 Date Back
4x5 1-2600 <$1000
3x10-20 1-1940 <$1000
1902 Plain Back
4x5 2601-7210 <$1000
3x10-20 1941-4949 <$1000
1929 Small Size
5 Type 1 1-718 <$600
10 Type 1 1-426 <$600
20 Type 1 1-120 <$600
5 Type 2 1-1672 <$600
10 Type 2 1-895 <$600
20 Type 2 1-276 <$600
Total Issue $490,980
Out in 1935 $25,000
Large out 1935 $1,060
****
301 Schuyler
FNB OF HAVANA
{{ UNREPORTED }}
Chartered 3/3/64
Liquidated 6/3/73
Original Series <$VALUE
4x5 1-2270 <$1250
3x10-20 1-368 <$1500/$2000
Total Issue $63,800
Out in 1910 $545
****
Havana NB of Havana
SEE Ch 343
Second NB of Havana
****

****
343 Rockland
SECOND NB OF HAVANA
Chartered 3/64
Liquidated 4/15/82
2nd title:Havana NB 1/9/74
FIRST TITLE {{0L}}
Original Series <$VALUE
3x1-2 1-1400 <$1000/$1500
4x5 1-3430 <$1000
SECOND TITLE {{1L}}
Original Series
4x5 3501-4500 <$1000
Series 1875
4x5 1-3800 <$1000
Total Issue $171,600
Out in 1910 $1,115
****
2229 Rockland
NB OF HAVERSTRAW
Chartered 3/2/75
2nd title:NB of Haverstraw & TC 6/3/26
FIRST TITLE {{11L}}
Original Series <$VALUE
3x1-2 1-3000 <$400/$850
4x5 1-5000 <$500
Series 1875
3x1-2 1-720 <$400/$850
4x5 1-14023 <$500
Brown Back
4x5 1-9150 <$350
3x10-20 1-3340 <$350
1882 Date Back
4x5 1-4641 <$350
3x10-20 1-3034 <$350
1902 Date Back
4x5 1-1000 <$250
3x10-20 1-800 <$250
1902 Plain Back
4x5 1001-6865 <$250
3x10-20 801-4018 <$250
SECOND TITLE {{3L 3S}}
1902 Plain Back
4x5 1-625 <$250
3x10-20 1-506 <$250
1929 Small Size
5 Type 1 1-792 <$300
10 Type 1 1-390 <$300
20 Type 1 1-136 <$300
5 Type 2 1-1562 <$300
10 Type 2 1-972 <$300
20 Type 2 1-204 <$325
Total Issue $1,454,670
Out in 1935 $25,000
Large out 1935 $3,355
****
4880 Nassau
FNB OF HEMPSTEAD
{{13L 8S}}
Organized 3/2/93
Receivership 2/13/34
Brown Back <$VALUE
4x5 1-9780 <$600
50-100 1-1330 <$1500/$1750
1882 Date Back
4x5 1-2698 <$600
50-100 1-420 <$1500/$1750
3x50-100 1-102<$1500/$1750
1902 Date Back
4x5 1-1250 <$350
3x50-100 1-1150 <$750/$850
1902 Plain Back
4x5 1251-36122 <$350
3x50-100 1151-1751 <$750/$850
1929 Small Size
5 Type 1 1-11925 <$250
50 Type 1 1-524 <$350
100 Type 1 1-186 <$400
Total Issue $2,324,300
Out at close $250,000
Large out at close $12,000
****
11375 Nassau
SECOND NB OF HEMPSTEAD
{{3L}}
Chartered 6/19
1902 Plain Back <$VALUE
4x5 1-8600 <$750
3x10-20 1-5260 <$750
Total Issue $435,000
Out in 1935 $1,340
****
3183 Herkimer
FNB OF HERKIMER
{{10L 16S}}
Chartered 1884
Brown Back <$VALUE
4x5 1-5076 <$300
3x10-20 1-659 <$300
1902 Red Seal
3x10-20 1-1360 <$350
1902 Date Back
3x10-20 1-2650* <$175
1902 Plain Back
3x10-20 2891-17065* <$175
* 2651-2890 not marked
1929 Small Size
10 Type 1 1-2934 <$75
20 Type 1 1-742 <$75
10 Type 2 1-4393 <$75
20 Type 2 1-1385 <$75
Total Issue $1,392,430
Out in 1935 $100,000
Large out 1935 $4,760
****
5141 Herkimer
HERKIMER NB, HERKIMER
{{15L 9S}}
Organized 7/30/98
Liquidated 11/18/31
Brown Back <$VALUE
3x10-20 1-9900 <$250
1882 Date Back
3x10-20 1-19700 <$250
1882 Value Back
3x10-20 19701-24673 <$250
1902 Plain Back
3x10-20 1-32863 <$125
1929 Small Size
10 Type 1 1-3427 <$100
20 Type 1 1-977 <$100
Total Issue $3,694,660
Out at close $200,000
Large out at close $17,580
****
5605 Saint Lawrence
FNB OF HERMON
{{ UNREPORTED }}
Chartered 10/23/00
Brown Back <$VALUE
3x10-20 1-1900 <$1250
1882 Date Back
3x10-20 1-2050 <$1250
1882 Value Back
3x10-20 2051-3313 <$1250
1902 Plain Back
3x10-20 1-2260 <$1000
Total Issue $373,650
Out in 1935 $850
****
10446 Saint Lawrence
FNB OF HEUVELTON
{{3L 5S}}
Organized 3/28/13
1902 Date Back <$VALUE
3x10-20 1-940 <$500
1902 Plain Back
3x10-20 941-4595 <$500
1929 Small Size
10 Type 1 1-982 <$300
20 Type 1 1-244 <$300
10 Type 2 1-2568 <$300
20 Type 2 1-768 <$300
Total Issue $358,990
Out in 1935 $50,000
Large out 1935 $690
****
11087 Nassau
LONG ISLAND NB OF HICKSVILLE
{{9L 10S}}
Chartered 10/17
1902 Plain Back <$VALUE
4x5 1-30856 <$600
1929 Small Size
5 Type 1 1-3484 <$300
10 Type 1 1-1022 <$300
20 Type 1 1-330 <$300
5 Type 2 1-5184 <$300
10 Type 2 1-3108 <$300
20 Type 2 1-504 <$300
Total Issue $889,640
Out in 1935 $60,000
Large out 1935 $2,230
****
5336 Ulster
FNB OF HIGHLAND
{{3L 4S}}
Chartered 5/7/00
Brown Back <$VALUE
4x5 1-1500 <$600
3x10-20 1-1200 <$600
1882 Date Back
4x5 1-2325 <$600
3x10-20 1-1530 <$600
1882 Value Back
4x5 2326-4005 <$600
3x10-20 1531-2306 <$600
1902 Plain Back
3x10-20 1-3179 <$450
1929 Small Size
10 Type 1 1-684 <$350
20 Type 1 1-180 <$350
10 Type 2 1-527 <$350
20 Type 2 1-160 <$350
Total Issue $515,460
Out in 1935 $25,000
Large out 1935 $1,160
****
8838 Orange
CITIZENS NB OF HIGHLAND FALLS
{{ UNREPORTED }}
Chartered 8/07
Liquidated 12/20/15
1902 Red Seal <$VALUE
4x5 1-187 <$1500
4x10 1-188 <$1500
1902 Date Back
4x5 1-2925 <$850
4x10 1-2625 <$850
1902 Plain Back
4x5 2926-3097 <$850
4x10 2626-2719 <$850
Total Issue $181,960
Out in 1916 $9,075
****
8850 Orange
FNB OF HIGHLAND FALLS
Chartered 8/07
Liquidated 4/7/32
2nd title:FNB & TC 4/2/30
FIRST TITLE {{4L 3S}}
1902 Red Seal <$VALUE
4x5 1-500 <$500
3x10-20 1-400 <$500
1902 Date Back
4x5 1-2975 <$250
3x10-20 1-2030 <$250
1902 Plain Back
4x5 2976-17162 <$250
3x10-20 2031-11830 <$250
1929 Small Size
5 Type 1 1-1536 <$250
10 Type 1 1-774 <$250
20 Type 1 1-260 <$250
SECOND TITLE {{2S}}
1929 Small Size
5 Type 1 1-700 <$250
10 Type 1 1-244 <$250
20 Type 1 1-93 <$250
Total Issue $1,135,260
Out at close $100,000
Large out at close $7,205
****
193 Delaware
FNB OF HOBART
{{1L}}
Chartered 1/64
Liquidated 8/27/81
Original Series <$VALUE
3x1-2 1-500 <$600/$1250
4x5 1-3500 <$650
3x10-20 1-2175 <$750/$1250
Series 1875
3x10-20 1-1409 <$750/$1250
Total Issue $251,700
Out in 1910 $1,364
****
4497 Delaware
NB OF HOBART
{{5L 14S}}
Chartered 1891
Brown Back <$VALUE
3x10-20 1-5340 <$350
1882 Date Back
3x10-20 1-1068 <$350
1902 Date Back
3x10-20 1-3640 <$150
1902 Plain Back
3x10-20 3641-12248 <$150
1929 Small Size
10 Type 1 1-2202 <$85
20 Type 1 1-604 <$85
10 Type 2 1-4752 <$100
20 Type 2 1-1260 <$100
Total Issue $1,210,120
Out in 1935 $100,000
Large out 1935 $2,090
****
10046 Ontario
HAMLIN NB OF HOLCOMB
{{3L 7S}}
Chartered 6/11
1902 Date Back <$VALUE
3x10-20 1-700 <$450
1902 Plain Back
4x5 1-4420 <$450
3x10-20 701-2133 <$450
1929 Small Size
5 Type 1 1-836 <$200
10 Type 1 1-840 <$200
20 Type 1 1-232 <$200
5 Type 2 1-3092 <$200
10 Type 2 1-1512 <$200
20 Type 2 1-456 <$200
Total Issue $338,070
Out in 1935 $50,000
Large out 1935 $750
****
5299 Oneida
FNB OF HOLLAND PATENT
{{9L 4S}}
Chartered 4/21/00
Brown Back <$VALUE
4x5 1-2450 <$300
3x10-20 1-1780 <$300
1882 Date Back
4x5 1-2550 <$300
3x10-20 1-1920 <$300
1882 Value Back
4x5 2551-3980 <$300
3x10-20 1921-2857 <$300
1902 Plain Back
4x5 1-12973 <$175
1929 Small Size
5 Type 1 1-3652 <$200
5 Type 2 1-9636 <$200
Total Issue $777,650
Out in 1935 $30,000
Large out 1935 $1,550
****
2398 Cortland
FNB OF HOMER
{{6L}}
Chartered 9/20/78
Liquidated 3/16/00
Series 1875 <$VALUE
3x10-20 1-8533 <$600/$1000
Brown Back
3x10-20 1-938 <$400
Total Issue $473,550
Out in 1910 $3,110
****
3186 Cortland
HOMER NB, HOMER
{{5L 12S}}
Chartered 1884
Brown Back <$VALUE
3x10-20 1-10514 <$400
1902 Red Seal
3x10-20 1-5000 <$500
1902 Date Back
3x10-20 1-8500 <$250
1902 Plain Back
3x10-20 8501-16617 <$250
1929 Small Size
10 Type 1 1-2212 <$125
20 Type 1 1-576 <$125
10 Type 2 1-4275 <$125
20 Type 2 1-1227 <$125
Total Issue $1,875,680
Out in 1935 $100,000
Large out 1935 $2,580
****
2471 Rensselaer
FNB OF HOOSICK FALLS
Chartered 4/10/80
2nd title:Peoples-FNB 4/11/31
FIRST TITLE {{12L 14S}}
Series 1875 <$VALUE
4x5 1-7694 <$375
Brown Back
4x5 1-1025 <$200
3x10-20 1-990 <$200/$250
1882 Date Back
4x5 1-3875 <$200
3x10-20 1-1680 <$200/$250
1882 Value Back
4x5 3876-4005 <$200
3x10-20 1681-2790<$200/$250
1902 Plain Back
4x5 1-11885 <$125
3x10-20 1-8430 <$125
1929 Small Size
5 Type 1 1-1958 <$50
10 Type 1 1-1030 <$50
20 Type 1 1-290 <$60
SECOND TITLE {{17S}}
1929 Small Size
5 Type 1 1-4022 <$50
10 Type 1 1-1694 <$50
20 Type 1 1-514 <$60
5 Type 2 1-13992 <$50
10 Type 2 1-7368 <$50
20 Type 2 1-2160 <$60
Total Issue $1,728,840
Out in 1935 $200,000
Large out 1935 $3,780
Outstanding includes Ch 5874
****

****
Peoples-FNB of Hoosick Falls
SEE Ch 2471
FNB of Hoosick Falls
****
5874 Rensselaer
PEOPLES NB OF HOOSICK FALLS
{{20L 8S}}
Chartered 6/22/01
Closed 4/11/31
Brown Back <$VALUE
4x5 1-2600 <$200
3x10-20 1-1860 <$200
1882 Date Back
4x5 1-8950 <$200
3x10-20 1-7520 <$200
1882 Value Back
4x5 8951-14850 <$200
3x10-20 7521-10760 <$200
1902 Plain Back
4x5 1-11975 <$100
3x10-20 1-9002 <$100
1929 Small Size
5 Type 1 1-1734 <$125
10 Type 1 1-904 <$125
20 Type 1 1-253 <$135
Total Issue $1,806,220
Out at close $100,000
Large out at close $50,000
Ch 2471 assumed circulation
****
Citizens NB of Hornell
SEE Ch 2522
Citizens NB of Hornellsville
****
FNB of Hornell
SEE Ch 262
FNB of Hornellsville
****
2522 Steuben
CITIZENS NB OF HORNELLSVILLE
Organized 3/12/81
Receivership 5/10/32
2nd title:Citizens NB of Hornell 3/21/07
3rd title:Citizens NB & TC 6/1/28
FIRST TITLE {{1L}}
Series 1875 <$VALUE
3x10-20 1-4445 <$750/$1250
Brown Back
3x10-20 1-3243 <$600
SECOND TITLE {{3L}}
Brown Back
3x10-20 1-2500 <$500
1882 Date Back
3x10-20 1-7100* <$500
1882 Value Back
3x10-20 7601-12156* <$500
* 7101-7600 not marked
1902 Plain Back
3x10-20 1-10677 <$250
THIRD TITLE {{1L 7S}}
1902 Plain Back
3x10-20 1-1161 <$300
1929 Small Size
10 Type 1 1-1988 <$150
20 Type 1 1-534 <$150
Total Issue $1,892,460
Out at close $98,315
Large out at close $9,415
****
262 Steuben
FNB OF HORNELLSVILLE
Organized 11/21/63
Receivership 2/27/32
2nd title:FNB of Hornell 8/23/06
FIRST TITLE {{3L}}
Original Series <$VALUE
3x1-2 1-3000 <$400/$1000
4x5 1-1750 <$500
3x10-20 1-2200 <$750/$1250
Series 1875
4x5 1-1770 <$500
3x10-20 1-804 <$750/$1250
Brown Back
3x10-20 1-10613 <$400
1902 Red Seal
3x10-20 1-3255 <$400
SECOND TITLE {{9L 10S}}
1902 Red Seal
3x10-20 1-1800 <$350
1902 Date Back
3x10-20 1-8700 <$175
1902 Plain Back
3x10-20 8701-22065 <$175
1929 Small Size
10 Type 1 1-2041 <$150
20 Type 1 1-476 <$150
Total Issue $2,301,830
Out at close $98,080
Large out at close $10,540
****

****
8301 Chemung
FNB OF HORSEHEADS
{{ 5 L U + 9 S }}
Chartered 7/06
1902 Red Seal <$VALUE
3x10-20 1-2000 <$1000
1902 Date Back
3x10-20 1-4340* <$600
1902 Plain Back
3x10-20 4581-13119* <$600
* 4341-4580 not marked
1929 Small Size
10 Type 1 1-1294 <$200
20 Type 1 1-384 <$200
10 Type 2 1-2234 <$200
20 Type 2 1-564 <$200
Total Issue $913,290
Out in 1935 $50,000
Large out 1935 $1,790
****
990 Columbia
FARMERS NB OF HUDSON
{{ 8 L 10 S }}
Chartered 4/7/65
Original Series <$VALUE
3x1-2 1-3000 <$350/$850
4x5 1-6000 <$400
3x10-20 1-9650 <$750/$1250
Series 1875
4x5 1-5250 <$400
3x10-20 1-1900 <$600/$1000
Brown Back
4x5 1-9334 <$300
3x10-20 1-5054 <$300
1902 Red Seal
4x5 1-1750 <$300
3x10-20 1-1180 <$300
1902 Date Back
4x5 1-5050 <$150
3x10-20 1-4000 <$150
1902 Plain Back
4x5 5051-11910 <$150
3x10-20 4001-8622 <$150
1929 Small Size
5 Type 1 1-1714 <$125
10 Type 1 1-860 <$125
20 Type 1 1-230 <$125
5 Type 2 1-2198 <$125
10 Type 2 1-1260 <$125
20 Type 2 1-372 <$125
Total Issue $2,181,830
Out in 1935 $50,000
Large out 1935 $6,480
****
396 Columbia
FNB OF HUDSON
Organized 3/25/64
2nd title:FNB & TC 3/30/28
FIRST TITLE {{ 14 L }}
Original Series <$VALUE
4x5 1-3100 <$300
3x10-20 1-4340 <$600/$1250
3x10-20 4841-6240 <$600/$1250
20 4341-4840 <$1250
Series 1875
4x5 1-1000 <$300
3x10-20 1-3956 <$500/$1000
Brown Back
3x10-20 1-7804 <$225
1902 Red Seal
3x10-20 1-2900 <$225
1902 Date Back
4x5 1-15250 <$100
3x10-20 1-10300 <$100
1902 Plain Back
4x5 15251-41269 <$100
3x10-20 10301-25836 <$100
SECOND TITLE {{ 2 L 15 S }}
1902 Plain Back
4x5 1-5038 <$125
1929 Small Size
5 Type 1 1-18662 <$60
5 Type 2 1-48446 <$60
Total Issue $4,132,030
Out in 1935 $200,000
Large out 1935 $9,320
****
1091 Columbia
N HUDSON RIVER B OF HUDSON
{{ 4 L }}
Chartered 4/65
Liquidated 4/24/12
Original Series <$VALUE
3x1-2 1-4986 <$500/$1000
4x5 1-6800 <$500
3x10-20 1-2350 <$750/$1250
3x10-20 3351-4950 <$750/$1250
20 2351-3350 <$1250
50-100 1-700 <$3500
Series 1875
4x5 1-4250 <$500
3x10-20 1-2900 <$600/$1000
50-100 1-601 <$3500
Brown Back
4x5 1-3977 <$400
3x10-20 1-5218 <$400
1902 Red Seal
3x10-20 1-1900 <$500
1902 Date Back
3x10-20 1-1750 <$325
Total Issue $1,326,520
Out in 1912 $30,374
****
Hudson Falls NB, Hudson Falls
SEE Ch 8297
Commercial NB of Sandy Hill
****
Peoples NB of Hudson Falls
SEE Ch 3244
Peoples NB of Sandy Hill
****
Sandy Hill NB of Hudson Falls
SEE Ch 6470
Sandy Hill NB, Sandy Hill
****
7485 Greene
GREENE COUNTY NB OF HUNTER
{{ UNREPORTED }}
Chartered 11/23/04
Liquidated 9/18/08
1902 Red Seal <$VALUE
3x10-20 1-586 <$1500
Total Issue $29,300
Out in 1910 $1,270
****
6587 Suffolk
FNB OF HUNTINGTON
Chartered 1/03
2nd title:FNB & TC 5/16/29
FIRST TITLE {{ 5 L }}
1902 Red Seal <$VALUE
4x5 1-890 <$1500
3x10-20 1-724 <$1500
1902 Date Back
4x5 1-5475 <$750
3x10-20 1-3940 <$750
1902 Plain Back
4x5 5476-15550 <$750
3x10-20 3941-10354 <$750
SECOND TITLE {{ 4 S }}
1929 Small Size
5 Type 1 1-2036 <$600
10 Type 1 1-1046 <$600
20 Type 1 1-278 <$600
5 Type 2 1-2130 <$600
10 Type 2 1-1546 <$600
20 Type 2 1-384 <$600
Total Issue $1,072,690
Out in 1935 $50,000
Large out 1935 $1,990
****
1670 Herkimer
ILION NB, ILION
Chartered 1867
2nd title:Ilion NB & TC 8/26/27
FIRST TITLE {{ 12 L }}
Original Series <$VALUE
4x5 1-6750 <$250
Series 1875
4x5 1-10205 <$250
Brown Back
4x5 1-15214 <$150
3x10-20 1-7225 <$150/$200
50-100 1-395 <$1250/$1500
1902 Red Seal
4x5 1-1550 <$150
3x10-20 1-880 <$150/$200
1902 Date Back
4x5 1-2250 <$75
3x10-20 1-9500 <$75
1902 Plain Back
3x10-20 9501-23915 <$75
SECOND TITLE {{ 3 L 18 S }}
1902 Plain Back
3x10-20 1-2706 <$75
1929 Small Size
10 Type 1 1-2734 <$50
20 Type 1 1-736 <$50
10 Type 2 1-5235 <$50
20 Type 2 1-1382 <$50
Total Issue $2,847,280
Out in 1935 $100,000
Large out 1935 $6,740
****
9109 Herkimer
MANUFACTURERS NB OF ILION
{{ 7 L 17 S }}
Organized 3/30/08
1902 Red Seal <$VALUE
4x5 1-625 <$250
4x10 1-625 <$250
1902 Date Back
4x5 1-5200 <$125
4x10 1-5025 <$125
1902 Plain Back
4x5 5201-16775 <$125
4x10 5026-13998 <$125
1929 Small Size
5 Type 1 1-3206 <$50
10 Type 1 1-1818 <$50
5 Type 2 1-6438 <$50
10 Type 2 1-4154 <$50
Total Issue $1,211,910
Out in 1935 $75,000
Large out 1935 $2,080
****
13037 Seneca
WHEELER NB OF INTERLAKEN
{{ 0 L 10 S }}
Chartered 2/27
1902 Plain Back <$VALUE
3x10-20 1-2300 <$750
1929 Small Size
10 Type 1 1-1370 <$150
20 Type 1 1-386 <$150
10 Type 2 1-2297 <$150
20 Type 2 1-484 <$150
Total Issue $276,170
Out in 1935 $50,000
Large out 1935 $730
****
12460 Nassau
FNB OF INWOOD
{{ 11 S }}
Chartered 11/23
1929 Small Size <$VALUE
5 Type 1 1-1896 <$250
10 Type 1 1-938 <$250
20 Type 1 1-282 <$250
5 Type 2 1-8218 <$250
10 Type 2 1-3301 <$250
20 Type 2 1-696 <$250
Total Issue $235,020
Out in 1935 $50,000
****
6371 Westchester
IRVINGTON NB, IRVINGTON
Chartered 8/8/02
2nd title:Irvington NB & TC 6/16/30
FIRST TITLE {{ 3 L 2 S }}
1902 Date Back <$VALUE
4x5 1-300 <$750
4x10 1-300 <$750
1902 Plain Back
4x5 301-4249 <$750
4x10 301-3118 <$750
1929 Small Size
5 Type 1 1-504 <$400
5 Type 2 1-258 <$400
SECOND TITLE {{ 7 S }}
1929 Small Size
5 Type 1 1-960 <$350
10 Type 1 1-500 <$350
5 Type 2 1-19552 <$350
10 Type 2 1-9068 <$350
Total Issue $487,540
Out in 1935 $100,000
Large out 1935 $750
****
8794 Suffolk
FNB OF ISLIP
{{ 1 L 18 S }}
Organized 7/12/07
1902 Red Seal <$VALUE
3x10-20 1-250 <$3000
1902 Date Back
3x10-20 1-760* <$2000
1902 Plain Back
3x10-20 861-1498* <$2000
*761-860 not marked
1929 Small Size
5 Type 1 1-2680 <$200
10 Type 1 1-1036 <$200
5 Type 2 1-18576 <$200
10 Type 2 1-8820 <$200
Total Issue $411,040
Out in 1935 $118,580
Large out 1935 $30
****
222 Tompkins
FNB OF ITHACA
{{ 18 L 21 S }}
Chartered 1/64
Original Series <$VALUE
4x5 1-9750 <$400
4x10 1-4850 <$750
Series 1875
4x5 1-10126 <$400
4x10 1-4287 <$600
Brown Back
3x10-20 1-6396 <$250
1902 Red Seal
3x10-20 1-3000 <$250
1902 Date Back
3x10-20 1-12200 <$100
1902 Plain Back
3x10-20 12201-37944 <$100
1929 Small Size
10 Type 1 1-4374 <$50
20 Type 1 1-1246 <$50
5 Type 2 1-12092 <$50
10 Type 2 1-2452 <$50
20 Type 2 1-972 <$60
Total Issue $3,646,380
Out in 1935 $150,000
Large out 1935 $8,610
****
729 Tompkins
MERCHANTS & FARMERS NB OF ITHACA
{{ 2 L }}
Chartered 1/19/65
Liquidated 6/20/73
Original Series <$VALUE
3x1-2 1-2360 <$750/$1500
4x5 1-2170 <$850
3x10-20 1-250 <$1000/$1500
Total Issue $67,700
Out in 1910 $640
****
1561 Tompkins
TOMPKINS COUNTY NB OF ITHACA
{{ 11 L 10 S }}
Chartered 1865
Liquidated 5/28/35
Original Series <$VALUE
3x1-2 1-8520 <$400/$850
4x5 1-8000 <$400
3x10-20 1-3400 <$750/$1250
Series 1875
4x5 1-8390 <$400
3x10-20 1-4452 <$600/$1000
Brown Back
4x5 1-3784 <$250
3x10-20 1-5577 <$250
1902 Red Seal
4x5 1-1875 <$300
3x10-20 1-1400 <$300
1902 Date Back
4x5 1-6550 <$150
3x10-20 1-5080 <$150
1902 Plain Back
4x5 6551-11540 <$150
3x10-20 5081-8297 <$150
1929 Small Size
5 Type 1 1-1038 <$125
10 Type 1 1-936 <$125
20 Type 1 1-314 <$125
5 Type 2 1-3868 <$125
10 Type 2 1-2255 <$125
20 Type 2 1-390 <$150
Total Issue $2,045,350
Out in 1935 $100,000
Large out 1935 $5,835
****
8268 Queens
FNB OF JAMAICA
{{ 7 L }}
Chartered 6/06
Liquidated 6/23/26
1902 Red Seal <$VALUE
4x5 1-1025 <$750
3x10-20 1-500 <$750
50-100 1-110 <$2250/$2500
1902 Date Back
4x5 1-5400 <$400
3x10-20 1-3820 <$400
50-100 1-100 <$750/$850
3x50-100 1-120 <$750/$850
1902 Plain Back
4x5 5401-20175 <$400
3x10-20 3821-13829 <$400
Total Issue $1,201,950
Out at close $200,000
****
American NB of Jamestown
SEE Ch 9748
Swedish American NB of Jamestown
****
1563 Chautauqua
CHAUTAUQUA COUNTY NB OF JAMESTOWN
{{ 2 L }}
Chartered 9/18/65
Liquidated 6/18/96
Original Series <$VALUE
3x1-2 1-2000 <$500/$1250
4x5 1-6150 <$500
3x10-20 1-1400 <$750/$1250
Series 1875
4x5 1-2000 <$500
3x10-20 1-2344 <$750/$1000
Brown Back
4x5 1-3322 <$500
3x10-20 1-2420 <$500
Total Issue $547,640
Out in 1910 $3,289
****
City NB of Jamestown
SEE Ch 938
Second NB of Jamestown
****
548 Chautauqua
FNB OF JAMESTOWN
{{ U + 10 L 12 S }}
Chartered 10/64
Original Series <$VALUE
3x1-2 1-5000 <$350/$750
4x5 1-5250 <$350
3x10-20 1-3000 <$600/$1250
Series 1875
4x5 1-1113 <$350
3x10-20 1-2530 <$500/$1000
Brown Back
4x5 1-4400 <$250
3x10-20 1-5583 <$250
1902 Red Seal
3x10-20 1-2700 <$250
1902 Date Back
3x10-20 1-4000* <$125
1902 Plain Back
3x10-20 4501-10695* <$125
* 4001-4500 not marked
1929 Small Size
10 Type 1 1-1314 <$85
20 Type 1 1-380 <$100
10 Type 2 1-1336 <$100
20 Type 2 1-242 <$100
Total Issue $1,608,300
Out in 1935 $50,000
Large out 1935 $6,020
****
3846 Chautauqua
JAMESTOWN NB, JAMESTOWN
{{ 2 L }}
Chartered 2/23/88
Liquidated 7/3/99
Brown Back <$VALUE
4x5 1-5446 <$750
Total Issue $108,920
Out in 1910 $690
****
11360 Chautauqua
LIBERTY NB OF JAMESTOWN
{{ U + 3 L }}
Chartered 5/19
Closed 4/13/29
1902 Plain Back <$VALUE
3x10-20 1-7591 <$400
Total Issue $379,550
Out at close $50,000
Ch 9748 assumed circulation
****
8453 Chautauqua
N CHAUTAUQUA COUNTY B OF JAMESTOWN
{{ U + 10 L U + 19 S }}
Organized 12/3/06
1902 Red Seal <$VALUE
3x10-20 1-1800 <$350
1902 Date Back
3x10-20 1-5600 <$175
1902 Plain Back
3x10-20 5601-12540 <$175
1929 Small Size
10 Type 1 1-1394 <$65
20 Type 1 1-388 <$75
10 Type 2 1-1599 <$75
20 Type 2 1-489 <$75
Total Issue $872,970
Out in 1935 $50,000
Large out 1935 $2,330
****
938 Chautauqua
SECOND NB OF JAMESTOWN
Chartered 3/27/65
Liquidated 6/18/96
2nd title:City NB of Jamestown 3/3/75
FIRST TITLE {{ 1 L }}
Original Series <$VALUE
3x1-2 1-3000 <$400/$850
4x5 1-3200 <$500
3x10-20 1-1528 <$750/$1250
SECOND TITLE {{ 2 L }}
Original Series
4x5 1-250 <$500
3x10-20 1-500 <$750/$1250
Series 1875
4x5 1-1450 <$500
3x10-20 1-2160 <$600/$1000
Brown Back
4x5 1-2200 <$500
3x10-20 1-1180 <$500
Total Issue $425,400
Out in 1910 $2,431
****
9748 Chautauqua
SWEDISH AMERICAN NB OF JAMESTOWN
Chartered 5/10
Liquidated 6/30/31
2nd title:American NB of Jamestown 9/11/19
FIRST TITLE {{ 2 L }}
1902 Date Back <$VALUE
4x5 1-3680 <$500
3x10-20 1-2908 <$500
1902 Plain Back
4x5 3681-5530 <$500
3x10-20 2909-3888 <$500
SECOND TITLE {{U+6 L U+20 S}}
1902 Plain Back
4x5 1-14993 <$200
3x10-20 1-10573 <$200
1929 Small Size
5 Type 1 1-3434 <$60
10 Type 1 1-1675 <$60
20 Type 1 1-462 <$65
Total Issue $1,392,470
Out at close $150,000
Large out at close $4,280
Outstanding includes Ch 11360
****
10456 Sullivan
FNB OF JEFFERSONVILLE
{{ 1 L 4 S }}
Organized 9/8/13
1902 Date Back <$VALUE
3x10-20 1-620 <$600
1902 Plain Back
3x10-20 621-5307 <$600
1929 Small Size
10 Type 1 1-764 <$300
20 Type 1 1-190 <$300
10 Type 2 1-1045 <$300
20 Type 2 1-384 <$325
Total Issue $352,120
Out in 1935 $25,000
Large out 1935 $780
****
2418 Fulton
FNB OF JOHNSTOWN
{{ UNREPORTED }}
Chartered 3/13/79
Liquidated 1/16/89
Series 1875 <$VALUE
4x5 1-6666 <$1250
4x10 1-3845 <$1500
Total Issue $287,120
Out in 1910 $940
****
12375 Onondaga
JORDAN NB, JORDAN
{{ 4 L 5 S }}
Organized 10/6/22
1902 Plain Back <$VALUE
3x10-20 1-2805 <$400
1929 Small Size
10 Type 1 1-724 <$250
20 Type 1 1-194 <$250
10 Type 2 1-1392 <$250
20 Type 2 1-396 <$250
Total Issue $228,810
Out in 1935 $25,000
Large out 1935 $640
****
1753 Essex
KEESEVILLE NB, KEESEVILLE
{{ 15 L 19 S }}
Chartered 12/70
Original Series <$VALUE
3x1-2 1-2000 <$275/$800
4x5 1-2000 <$300
3x10-20 1-2375 <$600/$1250
Series 1875
4x5 1-3104 <$300
3x10-20 1-3579 <$500/$1000
Brown Back
4x5 1-13850 <$200
3x10-20 1-7460 <$200
1882 Date Back
4x5 1-2307 <$200
3x10-20 1-1860 <$200
1902 Date Back
4x5 1-5500 <$100
3x10-20 1-4160 <$100
1902 Plain Back
4x5 5501-21990 <$100
3x10-20 4161-15356 <$100
1929 Small Size
5 Type 1 1-3622 <$50
10 Type 1 1-1974 <$50
20 Type 1 1-504 <$60
5 Type 2 1-4822 <$60
10 Type 2 1-3169 <$60
20 Type 2 1-805 <$70
Total Issue $2,766,000
Out in 1935 $100,000
Large out 1935 $6,840
****

12208 Erie
FNB OF KENMORE
{{6L 12S}}
Chartered 5/22
1902 Plain Back <$VALUE
4x5 1-22822 <$200
1929 Small Size
5 Type 1 1-13982* <$75
5 Type 2 1-50094 <$75
* 5086-5438 canceled
Total Issue $1,115,780
Out in 1935 $200,000
Large out 1935 $1,370

1026 Columbia
NB OF KINDERHOOK
{{6L}}
Chartered 4/17/65
Liquidated 10/1/89
Original Series <$VALUE
3x1-2 1-16460 <$350/$850
4x5 1-10850 <$400
3x10-20 1-2000 <$750/$1250
3x10-20 2501-4700 <$750/$1250
20 2001-2500 <$1250
50-100 1-300 <$3500
Series 1875
4x5 1-5200 <$350
3x10-20 1-1090 <$500/$1000
Brown Back
4x5 1-2032 <$300
3x10-20 1-743 <$300
Total Issue $800,590
Out in 1910 $5,178

929 Columbia
N UNION B OF KINDERHOOK
{{29L 31S}}
Chartered 3/23/65
Original Series <$VALUE
3x1-2 1-11740 <$250/$750
4x5 1-10375 <$250
3x10-20 1-2300 <$600/$1250
50-100 1-75 <$3500
Series 1875
4x5 1-11250 <$250
3x10-20 1-3050 <$500/$1000
Brown Back
4x5 1-31535 <$150
3x10-20 1-8471 <$150/$200
1902 Red Seal
4x5 1-5625 <$150
3x10-20 1-4000 <$150/$200
1902 Date Back
4x5 1-16250 <$65
3x10-20 1-10700 <$75
1902 Plain Back
4x5 16251-55093 <$65
3x10-20 10701-36022 <$75
1929 Small Size
5 Type 1 1-7940 <$35
10 Type 1 1-4252 <$40
20 Type 1 1-1018 <$45
5 Type 2 1-3896 <$35
10 Type 2 1-2456 <$40
20 Type 2 1-515 <$45
Total Issue $5,709,480
Out in 1935 $100,000
Large out 1935 $10,470

12489 Suffolk
KINGS PARK NB, KINGS PARK
{{3L 3S}}
Organized 1/17/24
Liquidated 4/19/34
1902 Plain Back <$VALUE
4x5 1-4486 <$850
1929 Small Size
5 Type 1 1-4898 <$600
5 Type 2 1-4404 <$600
Total Issue $258,680
Out at close $35,000
Large out 1935 $340
Ch 14019 assumed circulation

14019 Suffolk
NB OF KINGS PARK
{{6S}}
Chartered 2/34
1929 Small Size <$VALUE
5 Type 2 1-6866 <$500
Total Issue $34,330
Out in 1935 $35,000
Outstanding includes Ch 12489

451 Ulster
FNB OF KINGSTON
{{1L}}
Chartered 6/1/64
Liquidated 9/26/67
Original Series <$VALUE
3x1-2 1-200 <$750/$1250
4x5 1-4000 <$850
3x10-20 1-2000<$1000/$1500
Total Issue $181,000
Out in 1910 $1,863

2493 Ulster
FNB OF RONDOUT, KINGSTON
{{32L 18S}}
Chartered 10/18/80
Series 1875 <$VALUE
4x5 1-17099 <$400
4x10 1-19709 <$600
3x20-50 1-5231<$1000/$3500
Brown Back
4x5 1-16900 <$250
3x10-20 1-11295 <$250/$300
50-100 1-715 <$1250/$1500
1882 Date Back
4x5 1-15500 <$250
3x10-20 1-10500 <$250/$300
50-100 1-200 <$1250/$1500
3x50-100 1-395<$1250/$1500
1882 Value Back
4x5 15501-24970 <$250
3x10-20 10501-16245 <$250/$300
1902 Plain Back
4x5 1-21035 <$65
3x10-20 1-12516 <$75
3x50-100 1-740 <$300/$350
1929 Small Size
5 Type 1 1-4344 <$50
10 Type 1 1-2090 <$50
20 Type 1 1-664 <$50
50 Type 1 1-286 <$125
100 Type 1 1-98 <$175
5 Type 2 1-5694 <$60
10 Type 2 1-3140 <$60
20 Type 2 1-1158 <$60
Total Issue $5,950,680
Out in 1935 $200,000
Large out 1935 $15,640

1149 Ulster
KINGSTON NB, KINGSTON
{{4L}}
Chartered 1865
Liquidated 5/10/19
Original Series <$VALUE
3x1-2 1-2000 <$400/$850
4x5 1-4000 <$400
3x10-20 1-3000 <$750/$1250
50-100 1-467 <$3500
Series 1875
3x1-2 1-200 <$400/$850
4x5 1-4625 <$400
3x10-20 1-2310 <$600/$1000
50-100 1-67 <$3500
Brown Back
4x5 1-8918 <$350
3x10-20 1-4153 <$350
1902 Red Seal
4x5 1-1850 <$350
3x10-20 1-1660 <$350
1902 Date Back
4x5 1-4600 <$200
3x10-20 1-3380 <$200
1902 Plain Back
4x5 4601-5185 <$200
3x10-20 3381-3593 <$200
Total Issue $1,318,460
Out at close $50,000

1050 Ulster
N ULSTER COUNTY B OF KINGSTON
Organized 3/28/65
Liquidated 12/15/33
2nd title:N Ulster County B & TC of Kingston 7/2/28
FIRST TITLE {{15L}}
Original Series <$VALUE
3x1-2 1-2700 <$250/$750
4x5 1-4500 <$300
3x10-20 1-3000 <$750/$1250
50-100 1-500 <$3500
Series 1875
4x5 1-3250 <$300
3x10-20 1-1676 <$500/$1000
50-100 1-289 <$3500
Brown Back
4x5 1-11677 <$150
3x10-20 1-7175 <$150/$200
50-100 1-879 <$1250/$1500
1902 Red Seal
4x5 1-6450 <$150
3x10-20 1-4540 <$150/$200
50-100 1-60 <$2250/$2500
1902 Date Back
4x5 1-12600* <$100
3x10-20 1-9060** <$100
50-100 1-100 <$400/$500
3x50-100 1-300 <$400/$500
1902 Plain Back
4x5 13351-39415* <$100
3x10-20 9661-24787** <$100
* 12601-13350 not marked
** 9061-9660 not marked
SECOND TITLE {{2L 8S}}
1902 Plain Back
4x5 1-1606 <$125
4x10 1-1533 <$125
1929 Small Size
5 Type 1 1-7508 <$100
10 Type 1 1-4176 <$100
5 Type 2 1-2852 <$100
10 Type 2 1-2459 <$100
Total Issue $4,335,530
Out at close $150,000
Large out 1935 $7,700
Ch 13822 assumed circulation

13822 Ulster
N ULSTER COUNTY B OF KINGSTON
{{8S}}
Chartered 11/33
1929 Small Size <$VALUE
5 Type 2 1-6656 <$100
10 Type 2 1-3884 <$100
20 Type 2 1-3219 <$100
Total Issue $136,500
Out in 1935 $100,000
Outstanding includes Ch 1050

Rondout NB of Kingston
SEE Ch 1120
NB of Rondout

955 Ulster
STATE OF NEW YORK NB OF KINGSTON
{{10L 9S}}
Chartered 3/31/65
Original Series <$VALUE
3x1-2 1-3700 <$350/$750
4x5 1-4950 <$350
3x10-20 1-3000 <$600/$1250
50-100 1-800 <$3500
Series 1875
3x1-2 1-400 <$300/$750
4x5 1-7380 <$350
3x10-20 1-3600 <$500/$1000
50-100 1-166 <$3500
Brown Back
4x5 1-5700 <$250
3x10-20 1-5620 <$250/$300
1902 Red Seal
4x5 1-1900 <$300
3x10-20 1-1440 <$300
1902 Date Back
4x5 1-4600 <$150
3x10-20 1-3500 <$150
1902 Plain Back
4x5 4601-11050 <$150
3x10-20 3501-8015 <$150
1929 Small Size
5 Type 1 1-1908 <$100
10 Type 1 1-906 <$100
20 Type 1 1-246 <$100
5 Type 2 1-3108 <$100
10 Type 2 1-1536 <$100
20 Type 2 1-456 <$100
Total Issue $2,049,890
Out in 1935 $50,000
Large out 1935 $5,680

13365 Jefferson
FNB OF La FARGEVILLE
{{2S}}
Organized 7/20/29
1929 Small Size <$VALUE
5 Type 1 1-296 <$500
10 Type 1 1-200 <$500
20 Type 1 1-52 <$500
5 Type 2 1-654 <$500
10 Type 2 1-316 <$500
20 Type 2 1-144 <$500
Total Issue $36,430
Out in 1935 $9,650

Lackawanna NB, Lackawanna
SEE Ch 6964
Lackawanna NB of West Seneca

10175 Oswego
FNB OF LACONA
{{1L 8S}}
Chartered 4/12
1902 Date Back <$VALUE
3x10-20 1-500* <$750
1902 Plain Back
3x10-20 621-1715* <$750
* 501-620 not marked
1929 Small Size
10 Type 1 1-988 <$175
20 Type 1 1-254 <$175
10 Type 2 1-2362 <$175
20 Type 2 1-664 <$200
Total Issue $212,410
Out in 1935 $50,000
Large out 1935 $320

8793 Warren
FNB OF LAKE GEORGE
{{3L 14S}}
Chartered 7/07
1902 Red Seal <$VALUE
4x10 1-375 <$1000
1902 Date Back
4x10 1-1575 <$500
1902 Plain Back
4x10 1576-4038 <$500
1929 Small Size
10 Type 1 1-516 <$150
10 Type 2 1-170 <$150
Total Issue $209,180
Out in 1935 $10,000
Large out 1935 $440

13130 Suffolk
NB OF LAKE RONKONKOMA
{{1S}}
Chartered 10/27
1929 Small Size <$VALUE
5 Type 1 1-60 <$3000
10 Type 1 1-68 <$3000
20 Type 1 1-31 <$3000
Total Issue $9,600
Out in 1935 $4,850

11912 Erie
CITIZENS NB OF LANCASTER
{{U+8L 15S}}
Chartered 1/21
1902 Plain Back <$VALUE
4x5 1-11865 <$200
3x10-20 1-6989 <$200
1929 Small Size
5 Type 1 1-3566 <$85
10 Type 1 1-1900 <$85
20 Type 1 1-510 <$85
5 Type 2 1-6604 <$100
10 Type 2 1-3222 <$100
20 Type 2 1-690 <$100
Total Issue $947,970
Out in 1935 $100,000
Large out 1935 $2,195

1426 Rennselaer
NB OF LANSINGBURGH
{{2L}}
Chartered 7/11/65
Liquidated 3/6/69
Original Series <$VALUE
3x1-2 1-4500 <$750/$1250
4x5 1-2975 <$850
3x10-20 1-1100<$1000/$1250
Total Issue $137,000
Out in 1910 $1,122

1534 Rennselaer
N EXCHANGE B OF LANSINGBURGH
{{1L}}
Chartered 4/22/65
Liquidated 12/27/70
Original Series <$VALUE
3x1-2 1-3800 <$750/$1250
4x5 1-2875 <$850
3x10-20 1-600 <$1000/$1250
Total Issue $106,500
Out in 1910 $508

6019 Westchester
LARCHMONT NB, LARCHMONT
Chartered 11/13/01
Receivership 8/5/33
2nd title:Larchmont NB & TC 9/5/24
FIRST TITLE {{7L}}
Brown Back <$VALUE
4x5 1-1150 <$600
3x10-20 1-760 <$600
1882 Date Back
4x5 1-4350 <$600
3x10-20 1-2780 <$600
1882 Value Back
4x5 4351-9230 <$600
3x10-20 2781-5526 <$600
1902 Plain Back
4x5 1-2500 <$250
4x10 1-950 <$250
3x10-20 1-940 <$250
SECOND TITLE {{13L 19S}}
1902 Plain Back
4x5 1-20083 <$200
4x10 1-10288 <$200
1929 Small Size
5 Type 1 1-12031 <$125
10 Type 1 1-5973 <$125
Total Issue $2,189,390
Out at close $200,000
Large out at close $6,720

937 Genesee
FNB OF Le ROY
{{2L}}
Chartered 3/25/65
Liquidated 1/2/85
Original Series <$VALUE
3x1-2 1-3000 <$500/$1000
4x5 1-4850 <$600
3x10-20 1-2900 <$750/$1000
Series 1875
4x5 1-1000 <$600
3x10-20 1-3980 <$750/$1000
Total Issue $476,000
Out in 1910 $3,155

6087 Genesee
Le ROY NB, Le ROY
{{7L 3S}}
Chartered 1/8/02
Liquidated 1/31/31
Brown Back <$VALUE
4x5 1-2600 <$450
3x10-20 1-2640 <$450
1882 Date Back
4x5 1-4200 <$450
3x10-20 1-3070 <$450
1882 Value Back
4x5 4201-7740 <$450
3x10-20 3071-4957 <$450
1902 Plain Back
4x5 1-5460 <$300
3x10-20 1-3691 <$300
1929 Small Size
5 Type 1 1-822 <$350
10 Type 1 1-396 <$350
20 Type 1 1-110 <$350
Total Issue $942,020
Out at close $43,875
Large out at close $5,635

3283 Genesee
NB OF Le ROY
{{ UNREPORTED }}
Chartered 1/3/85
Liquidated 6/29/89
Brown Back <$VALUE
3x10-20 1-736 <$1500
Total Issue $36,800
Out in 1910 $250

217 Madison
FNB OF LEONARDSVILLE
{{ UNREPORTED }}
Chartered 1/27/64
Liquidated 7/11/66
Original Series <$VALUE
4x5 1-2250 <$2000
Total Issue $45,000
Out in 1910 $560

7813 Broome
FNB OF LESTERSHIRE
{{ UNREPORTED }}
Chartered 6/05
Liquidated 12/30/16
1902 Red Seal <$VALUE
3x10-20 1-1900 <$1500
1902 Date Back
3x10-20 1-4500 <$750
1902 Plain Back
3x10-20 4501-4967 <$750
Total Issue $343,350
Out in 1916 $49,100

10037 Sullivan
NB OF LIBERTY
{{7L U+17S}}
Chartered 6/11
1902 Date Back <$VALUE
3x10-20 1-2070* <$200
1902 Plain Back
3x10-20 2271-14399* <$200
* 2071-2270 not marked
1929 Small Size
10 Type 1 1-2780 <$85
20 Type 1 1-798 <$100
10 Type 2 1-5391 <$100
20 Type 2 1-1682 <$100
Total Issue $1,070,060
Out in 1935 $100,000
Large out 1935 $3,470

4925 Sullivan
SULLIVAN COUNTY NB OF LIBERTY
{{6L 14S}}
Chartered 1893
Brown Back <$VALUE
4x5 1-2875 <$400
3x10-20 1-720 <$400
1882 Date Back
4x5 1-1668 <$400
3x10-20 1-1165 <$400
1902 Date Back
4x5 1-1300 <$200
3x10-20 1-1090 <$200
1902 Plain Back
4x5 1301-8645 <$200
3x10-20 1091-5533 <$200
1929 Small Size
5 Type 1 1-1782 <$75
10 Type 1 1-1622 <$75
20 Type 1 1-434 <$100
5 Type 2 1-5944 <$100
10 Type 2 1-3166 <$100
20 Type 2 1-929 <$100
Total Issue $917,480
Out in 1935 $100,000
Large out 1935 $1,720

8833 Suffolk
FNB OF LINDENHURST
{{4L 3S}}
Chartered 8/07
1902 Red Seal <$VALUE
3x10-20 1-200 <$2000
1902 Date Back
3x10-20 1-800* <$850
1902 Plain Back
3x10-20 921-1961* <$850
* 801-920 not marked
1929 Small Size
10 Type 1 1-234 <$600
20 Type 1 1-57 <$600
Total Issue $128,930
Out in 1935 $6,500
Large out 1935 $430

12018 Saint Lawrence
FNB OF LISBON
{{1L 2S}}
Organized 5/15/21
1902 Plain Back <$VALUE
3x10-20 1-1234 <$850
1929 Small Size
10 Type 1 1-312 <$600
20 Type 1 1-104 <$600
10 Type 2 1-150 <$600
20 Type 2 1-99 <$600
Total Issue $96,380
Out in 1935 $10,000
Large out 1935 $210

10816 Broome
FNB OF LISLE
{{3L 4S}}
Organized 12/11/15
1902 Plain Back <$VALUE
3x10-20 1-3930 <$500
1929 Small Size
10 Type 1 1-604 <$350
20 Type 1 1-182 <$350
10 Type 2 1-636 <$350
20 Type 2 1-192 <$375
Total Issue $264,780
Out in 1935 $20,000
Large out 1935 $430

1344 Herkimer
HERKIMER COUNTY NB OF LITTLE FALLS
{{3L}}
Chartered 1865
Liquidated 10/11/78
Original Series <$VALUE
3x1-2 1-3582 <$600/$1000
4x5 1-7000 <$600
3x10-20 1-2800 <$750/$1250
50-100 1-640 <$3500
Series 1875
4x5 1-1422 <$600
3x10-20 1-936 <$750/$1250
Total Issue $469,150
Out in 1910 $2,788

2406 Herkimer
LITTLE FALLS NB,
LITTLE FALLS
{{ 20 L 24 S }}
Chartered 1/10/79
Series 1875 <$VALUE
4x5 1-10734 <$400
3x10-20 1-3423 <$600/$1000
Brown Back
4x5 1-7000 <$300
3x10-20 1-6300 <$300
1882 Date Back
4x5 1-8850* <$300
3x10-20 1-5860** <$300
1882 Value Back
4x5 9251-12233* <$300
3x10-20 6181-7615** <$300
* 8851-9250 not marked
** 5861-6180 not marked
1902 Plain Back
4x5 1-15555 <$150
3x10-20 1-10859 <$150
1929 Small Size
5 Type 1 1-6984 <$55
10 Type 1 1-3880 <$55
20 Type 1 1-940 <$60
5 Type 2 1-16002 <$60
10 Type 2 1-7607 <$60
20 Type 2 1-2268 <$70
Total Issue $3,076,850
Out in 1935 $200,000
Large out 1935 $5,380

2400 Herkimer
N HERKIMER COUNTY B OF
LITTLE FALLS
{{ 13 L }}
Chartered 10/24/78
Liquidated 4/28/17
Series 1875 <$VALUE
4x5 1-10527 <$400
3x10-20 1-6436 <$600/$1000
50-100 1-989 <$3500
Brown Back
4x5 1-14325 <$300
3x10-20 1-9300 <$300
50-100 1-470 <$1250/$1500
1882 Date Back
4x5 1-21000 <$300
3x10-20 1-15000 <$300
50-100 1-100 <$1250/$1500
1882 Value Back
4x5 21001-23682 <$300
3x10-20 15001-17100 <$300
Total Issue $2,846,330
Out at close $249,995

10043 Sullivan
LIVINGSTON MANOR NB,
LIVINGSTON MANOR
{{ 3 L U + 8 S }}
Chartered 6/11
1902 Date Back <$VALUE
4x5 1-1360 <$350
3x10-20 1-1380 <$350
1902 Plain Back
4x5 1361-7395 <$350
3x10-20 1381-4941 <$350
1929 Small Size
5 Type 1 1-2018 <$150
10 Type 1 1-1100 <$150
20 Type 1 1-296 <$165
5 Type 2 1-4012 <$175
10 Type 2 1-1884 <$175
20 Type 2 1-600 <$200
Total Issue $607,910
Out in 1935 $50,000
Large out 1935 $1,270

13006 Livingston
STEWART NB OF LIVONIA
Chartered 11/26
2nd title:Stewart NB & TC 11/23/29
3rd title: Stewart NB 7/12/33
FIRST TITLE {{ 3 L 1 S }}
1902 Plain Back <$VALUE
4x5 1-3827 <$400
1929 Small Size
5 Type 1 1-1030 <$350
SECOND TITLE {{ 1 S }}
1929 Small Size
5 Type 1 1-2078 <$350
THIRD TITLE {{ 1 S }}
1929 Small Size
5 Type 2 1-6180 <$350
Total Issue $200,680
Out in 1935 $25,000
Large out 1935 $380

211 Niagara
FNB OF LOCKPORT
{{ 3 L }}
Chartered 1/21/64
Liquidated 2/28/90
Original Series <$VALUE
3x1-2 1-6600 <$400/$850
4x5 1-5750 <$400
4x10 1-3675 <$750
50-100 1-137 <$3500
Series 1875
3x1-2 1-1410 <$400/$850
4x5 1-994 <$400
4x10 1-608 <$600
Brown Back
4x5 1-1220 <$300
3x10-20 1-495 <$300/$350
Total Issue $415,950
Out in 1910 $3,540

1039 Niagara
N EXCHANGE B OF LOCKPORT
{{ 16 L }}
Chartered 4/65
Liquidated 7/27/26
Original Series <$VALUE
3x1-2 1-6100 <$250/$750
4x5 1-6975 <$300
3x10-20 1-1000 <$600/$1250
Series 1875
3x1-2 1-5240 <$250/$750
4x5 1-14450 <$300
Brown Back
4x5 1-18460 <$150
3x10-20 1-5561 <$150/$200
1902 Red Seal
4x5 1-5250 <$150
3x10-20 1-4000 <$150/$200
1902 Date Back
4x5 1-15500 <$75
3x10-20 1-10300 <$75
1902 Plain Back
4x5 15501-52495 <$75
3x10-20 10301-32646 <$75
Total Issue $4,209,650
Out at close $300,000

639 Niagara
NIAGARA COUNTY NB OF
LOCKPORT
Chartered 12/64
2nd title:Niagara County NB & TC 2/13/28
FIRST TITLE {{ 25 L }}
Original Series <$VALUE
3x1-2 1-2820 <$200/$750
4x5 1-5350 <$250
3x10-20 1-1400 <$600/$1250
50-100 1-200 <$3500
Series 1875
4x5 1-3750 <$250
3x10-20 1-1485 <$500/$1000
50-100 1-60 <$3500
Brown Back
4x5 1-7000 <$150
3x10-20 1-9427 <$150/$200
1902 Red Seal
3x10-20 1-6600 <$150/$200
1902 Date Back
3x10-20 1-14600 <$60
1902 Plain Back
3x10-20 14601-74670 <$60
SECOND TITLE {{ 7 L 50+ S }}
1902 Plain Back
3x10-20 1-11639 <$60
1929 Small Size
10 Type 1 1-22794 <$20
20 Type 1 1-6922 <$30
10 Type 2 1-6869 <$20
20 Type 2 1-1241 <$30
Total Issue $7,927,940
Out in 1935 $500,000
Large out 1935 $17,165

11755 Nassau
NB OF LONG BEACH
{{ 3 L }}
Chartered 6/20
Liquidated 1/19/26
1902 Plain Back <$VALUE
4x5 1-2880 <$650
3x10-20 1-1244 <$650
Total Issue $119,800
Out at close $6,700

13074 Nassau
N CITY B OF LONG BEACH
{{ 2U + 6 L 7 S }}
Chartered 5/27
1902 Plain Back <$VALUE
4x5 1-7327 <$600
1929 Small Size
5 Type 1 1-7452 <$350
5 Type 2 1-17136 <$350
Total Issue $455,780
Out in 1935 $39,540
Large out 1935 $695

10329 Queens
COMMERCIAL NB OF
LONG ISLAND CITY
{{ UNREPORTED }}
Chartered 2/13
Liquidated 2/15/15
1902 Date Back <$VALUE
4x5 1-1249 <$1500
4x10 1-783 <$1500
3x10-20 1-212 <$1500
Total Issue $66,900
Out in 1915 $12,850

2426 Lewis
BLACK RIVER NB OF
LOWVILLE
{{ 8 L 6 S }}
Chartered 6/5/79
Series 1875 <$VALUE
4x5 1-7159 <$600
Brown Back
4x5 1-3325 <$450
50-100 1-720 <$1250/$1500
1882 Date Back
4x5 1-6250 <$400
50-100 1-900 <$1250/$1500
3x50-100 1-575<$1250/$1500
1882 Value Back
4x5 6251-8810 <$400
1902 Plain Back
3x50-100 1-1782 <$500/$600
1929 Small Size
5 Type 1 1-348 <$200
10 Type 1 1-149 <$200
20 Type 1 1-61 <$200
50 Type 1 1-304 <$300
100 Type 1 1-104 <$400
Total Issue $1,398,430
Out in 1935 $100,000
Large out 1935 $8,200

348 Lewis
FNB OF LOWVILLE
{{ 4 L }}
Chartered 3/64
Liquidated 7/31/20
Original Series <$VALUE
3x1-2 1-1170 <$500/$1000
4x5 1-3975 <$600
Series 1875
3x1-2 1-302 <$500/$1000
4x5 1-3437 <$600
Brown Back
4x5 1-13453 <$450
1902 Red Seal
3x10-20 1-3000 <$500
1902 Date Back
4x5 1-3930 <$250
3x10-20 1-2220 <$250
1902 Plain Back
4x5 3931-6390 <$250
3x10-20 2221-3527 <$250
Total Issue $878,810
Out at close $50,000

8923 Nassau
LYNBROOK NB, LYNBROOK
Chartered 10/07
2nd title:Lynbrook NB & TC 5/1/28
FIRST TITLE {{ 0 L }}
1902 Red Seal <$VALUE
3x10-20 1-210 <$2000
1902 Date Back
3x10-20 1-1180 <$1000
1902 Plain Back
3x10-20 1181-2409 <$1000
SECOND TITLE {{ 21U + 12 S }}
1929 Small Size
5 Type 1 1-4920 <$150
10 Type 1 1-1212 <$150
5 Type 2 1-16350 <$150
10 Type 2 1-10125 <$150
Total Issue $534,270
Out in 1935 $80,400
Large out 1935 $300

11603 Nassau
PEOPLES NB OF LYNBROOK
Chartered 2/20
2nd title:Peoples NB & TC 12/21/25
FIRST TITLE {{ 1 L }}
1902 Plain Back <$VALUE
4x5 1-18750 <$450
3x50-100 1-390<$1250/$1500
SECOND TITLE {{ 12 L 12 S }}
1902 Plain Back
4x5 1-21907 <$350
1929 Small Size
5 Type 1 1-20900 <$150
5 Type 2 1-29090 <$150
Total Issue $1,683,090
Out in 1935 $75,000
Large out 1935 $4,130

7479 Wayne
GAVITT NB OF LYONS
{{ 6 L }}
Organized 11/15/04
Liquidated 10/16/33
1902 Red Seal <$VALUE
3x10-20 1-3100 <$400
1902 Date Back
3x10-20 1-5000 <$200
1902 Plain Back
3x10-20 5001-11670 <$200
Total Issue $738,500
Out at close $2,340

1027 Wayne
LYONS NB, LYONS
{{ 7 L 2U + 7 S }}
Organized 3/22/65
Original Series <$VALUE
4x5 1-4900 <$400
3x10-20 1-800 <$750/$1250
Series 1875
4x5 1-7000 <$400
3x10-20 1-710 <$600/$1000
Brown Back
50-100 1-2317 <$1250/$1500
1902 Red Seal
3x10-20 1-2300 <$300
1902 Date Back
3x10-20 1-4600 <$150
1902 Plain Back
3x10-20 4601-13558 <$150
1929 Small Size
5 Type 1 1-1038 <$125
10 Type 1 1-614 <$125
20 Type 1 1-222 <$125
5 Type 2 1-3024 <$125
10 Type 2 1-1550 <$125
20 Type 2 1-380 <$150
Total Issue $1,586,790
Out in 1935 $60,000
Large out 1935 $3,885

12836 Lewis
LYONS FALLS NB,
LYONS FALLS
{{ 3 L 6 S }}
Chartered 10/25
1902 Plain Back <$VALUE
4x5 1-4425 <$500
1929 Small Size
5 Type 1 1-2608 <$200
5 Type 2 1-6048 <$200
Total Issue $196,980
Out in 1935 $20,000
Large out 1935 $310

12494 Wayne
FNB OF MACEDON
{{ 4 L 2 S }}
Organized 12/10/23
Receivership 4/10/31
1902 Plain Back <$VALUE
4x5 1-2590 <$400
4x10 1-1767 <$400
1929 Small Size
5 Type 1 1-710 <$400
10 Type 1 1-336 <$400
Total Issue $163,940
Out at close $25,000
Large out at close $300

13121 Putnam
MAHOPAC NB, MAHOPAC
{{ 6 S }}
Chartered 9/27
1929 Small Size <$VALUE
10 Type 1 1-314 <$250
20 Type 1 1-104 <$250
10 Type 2 1-5201 <$250
20 Type 2 1-1410 <$250
Total Issue $111,530
Out in 1935 $55,150

11897 Franklin
CITIZENS NB OF MALONE
{{ 11 S }}
Chartered 12/20
1929 Small Size <$VALUE
5 Type 2 1-13480 <$125
10 Type 2 1-7518 <$125
20 Type 2 1-2412 <$125
Total Issue $190,820
Out in 1935 $100,000

598 Franklin
FARMERS NB OF MALONE
{{ 5 L 4 S }}
Chartered 12/64
Original Series <$VALUE
3x1-2 1-2200 <$400/$850
4x5 1-3600 <$450
3x10-20 1-2700*<$750/$1250
* 1001-1200 not marked
Series 1875
4x5 1-750 <$450
3x10-20 1-3798 <$600/$1000
Brown Back
3x10-20 1-2000 <$350
50-100 1-957 <$1250/$1500
1902 Red Seal
50-100 1-465 <$2250/$2500
1902 Date Back
50-100 1-800 <$400/$500
3x50-100 1-2612 <$400/$500
1929 Small Size
50 Type 1 1-127 <$250
100 Type 1 1-27 <$350
Total Issue $1,553,500
Out in 1935 $37,500
Large out 1935 $8,049

914 Franklin
NB OF MALONE
{{ 2 L }}
Chartered 3/21/65
Liquidated 3/9/85
Original Series <$VALUE
3x1-2 1-6225 <$500/$1000
4x5 1-2900 <$600
3x10-20 1-1900 <$750/$1250
50-100 1-700 <$3500
Series 1875
3x1-2 1-960 <$500/$1000
4x5 1-1250 <$600
3x10-20 1-1824 <$750/$1250
50-100 1-334 <$3500
Total Issue $460,225
Out in 1910 $2,939

3307 Franklin
PEOPLES NB OF MALONE
{{ 1 L }}
Chartered 1885
Liquidated 1/31/20
Brown Back <$VALUE
4x5 1-2200 <$750
3x10-20 1-2818 <$750
50-100 1-420 <$1250/$1500
1902 Red Seal
3x10-20 1-1395 <$750
1902 Date Back
3x10-20 1-4200 <$400
1902 Plain Back
3x10-20 4201-4945 <$400
Total Issue $564,900
Out at close $37,500

3366 Franklin
THIRD NB OF MALONE
{{ UNREPORTED }}
Organized 7/15/85
Receivership 12/30/89
Brown Back <$VALUE
4x5 1-268 <$1500
3x10-20 1-286 <$1500
Total Issue $19,660
Out in 1916 $45

13592 Westchester
FNB IN MAMARONECK
{{ 3U + 2 S }}
Organized 1/5/32
Receivership 1/16/33
1929 Small Size <$VALUE
5 Type 1 1-498 <$500
10 Type 1 1-261 <$500
Total Issue $30,600
Out at close $50,000
Outstanding includes Ch 5411

5411 Westchester
FNB OF MAMARONECK
Chartered 6/8/00
Liquidated 3/18/32
2nd title:FNB & TC 6/4/26
FIRST TITLE {{ 6 L }}
Brown Back <$VALUE
4x5 1-4825 <$1000
3x10-20 1-3430 <$1000
1882 Date Back
4x5 1-5500 <$1000
3x10-20 1-3940 <$1000
1882 Value Back
4x5 5501-8600 <$1000
3x10-20 3941-5660 <$1000
1902 Plain Back
4x5 1-5825 <$600
4x10 1-4186 <$600
SECOND TITLE {{ 1 L 3 S }}
1902 Plain Back
4x5 1-2610 <$600
4x10 1-2380 <$600
1929 Small Size
5 Type 1 1-1902 <$500
10 Type 1 1-925 <$500
Total Issue $1,266,900
Out at close $50,000
Large out 1935 $4,040
Ch 13592 assumed circulation

11924 Nassau
FNB OF MANHASSET
Chartered 1/21
2nd title:FNB & TC 1/14/2
FIRST TITLE {{ 3 L }}
1902 Plain Back <$VALUE
4x5 1-3062 <$750
SECOND TITLE {{ 10 S }}
1929 Small Size
5 Type 1 1-2056 <$350
10 Type 1 1-1036 <$350
5 Type 2 1-6524 <$350
10 Type 2 1-4080 <$350
Total Issue $258,500
Out in 1935 $62,905
Large out 1935 $355

3193 Cortland
FNB OF MARATHON
{{ 6 L 4 S }}
Chartered 1884
Brown Back <$VALUE
4x5 1-6137 <$750
3x10-20 1-510 <$750
1902 Red Seal
3x10-20 1-1040 <$850
1902 Date Back
3x10-20 1-2010 <$400
1902 Plain Back
3x10-20 2011-6553 <$400
1929 Small Size
10 Type 1 1-502 <$350
20 Type 1 1-148 <$350
10 Type 2 1-1068 <$350
20 Type 2 1-231 <$350
Total Issue $591,070
Out in 1935 $20,000
Large out 1935 $1,710

9869 Onondaga
FNB OF MARCELLUS
{{ 3 L 10 S }}
Organized 9/21/10
1902 Date Back <$VALUE
3x10-20 1-2230 <$400
1902 Plain Back
3x10-20 2231-9532 <$400
1929 Small Size
10 Type 1 1-1510 <$150
20 Type 1 1-408 <$150
10 Type 2 1-2364 <$150
20 Type 2 1-732 <$150
Total Issue $654,440
Out in 1935 $50,000
Large out 1935 $1,430

5924 Delaware
PEOPLES NB OF
MARGARETVILLE
{{ 3 L 5 S }}
Chartered 7/30/01
Brown Back <$VALUE
3x10-20 1-1940 <$600
1882 Date Back
4x5 1-2265 <$600
3x10-20 1-1500 <$600
1882 Value Back
4x5 2266-3855 <$600
3x10-20 1501-2398 <$600
1902 Plain Back
3x10-20 1-2853 <$400
1929 Small Size
10 Type 1 1-714 <$200
20 Type 1 1-188 <$200
10 Type 2 1-868 <$200
20 Type 2 1-227 <$200
Total Issue $515,270
Out in 1935 $25,000
Large out 1935 $1,480

<$VALUEs are for notes in FINE condition. Value changes by approximately 25% for a change of one full grade.

****
8194 Richmond
MARINER HARBOR NB, MARINER HARBOR
{{ 0 L 5 S }}
Chartered 4/06
1902 Red Seal <$VALUE
3x10-20 1-495 <$1500
1902 Date Back
3x10-20 1-2710* <$850
1902 Plain Back
3x10-20 2911-6591* <$850
* 2711-2910 not marked
1929 Small Size
10 Type 1 1-852 <$400
20 Type 1 1-210 <$400
10 Type 2 1-2826 <$400
20 Type 2 1-612 <$400
Total Issue $471,120
Out in 1935 $40,000
Large out 1935 $290
****
10546 Wayne
FNB OF MARION
{{ 2 L 4 S }}
Chartered 5/14
1902 Plain Back <$VALUE
3x10-20 1-4117 <$600
1929 Small Size
10 Type 1 1-732 <$300
20 Type 1 1-160 <$300
10 Type 2 1-1107 <$300
20 Type 2 1-214 <$325
Total Issue $284,320
Out in 1935 $25,000
Large out 1935 $650
****
8834 Ulster
FNB OF MARLBORO
{{ 2 L 10 S }}
Chartered 8/07
1902 Red Seal <$VALUE
3x10-20 1-250 <$1000
1902 Date Back
3x10-20 1-940 <$500
1902 Plain Back
3x10-20 941-4591 <$500
1929 Small Size
10 Type 1 1-1040 <$150
20 Type 1 1-276 <$150
10 Type 2 1-1942 <$150
20 Type 2 1-562 <$150
Total Issue $368,230
Out in 1935 $25,000
Large out 1935 $720
****
6694 Saint Lawrence
FNB OF MASSENA
Chartered 3/03
2nd title:FNB & TC 7/27/26
FIRST TITLE {{ 1 L }}
1902 Red Seal <$VALUE
4x5 1-1200 <$1000
3x10-20 1-960 <$1000
1902 Date Back
4x5 1-2225 <$500
3x10-20 1-1580 <$500
1902 Plain Back
4x5 2226-6439 <$500
3x10-20 1581-4037 <$500
SECOND TITLE {{ 1 L 4 S }}
1902 Plain Back
4x5 1-3378 <$500
1929 Small Size
5 Type 1 1-3118 <$300
5 Type 2 1-7932 <$300
Total Issue $603,390
Out in 1935 $25,000
Large out 1935 $370
****
4914 Dutchess
MATTEAWAN NB, MATTEAWAN
Chartered 1893
2nd title:Matteawan NB of Beacon 4/29/14
FIRST TITLE {{ 2 L }}
Brown Back <$VALUE
4x5 1-5575 <$400
3x10-20 1-3470 <$400
1882 Date Back
4x5 1-4545 <$400
3x10-20 1-3611 <$400
1902 Date Back
4x5 1-1920 <$250
3x10-20 1-1256 <$250
SECOND TITLE {{ 9 L 17 S }}
1902 Date Back
4x5 1-1665 <$150
3x10-20 1-1334 <$150
1902 Plain Back
4x5 1666-21095 <$150
3x10-20 1335-14356 <$150
1929 Small Size
5 Type 1 1-3622 <$50
10 Type 1 1-2062 <$50
20 Type 1 1-526 <$60
5 Type 2 1-8646 <$60
10 Type 2 1-4767 <$60
20 Type 2 1-972 <$65
Total Issue $2,203,190
Out in 1935 $100,000
Large out 1935 $4,215
****
13445 Suffolk
MATTITUCK NB & TC, MATTITUCK
{{ 7 S }}
Chartered 4/2/30
1929 Small Size <$VALUE
5 Type 1 1-3124 <$350
10 Type 1 1-1338 <$350
5 Type 2 1-11088 <$350
10 Type 2 1-5700 <$350
Total Issue $286,440
Out in 1935 $61,920
****
11927 Orange
MAYBROOK NB, MAYBROOK
{{ 3 L 5 S }}
Organized 1/12/21
1902 Plain Back <$VALUE
4x5 1-11839 <$500
1929 Small Size
5 Type 1 1-3362 <$250
5 Type 2 1-15240 <$250
Total Issue $413,840
Out in 1935 $50,000
Large out 1935 $70
****
3171 Saratoga
FNB OF MECHANICVILLE
{{ 4 L 2 S }}
Organized 3/6/84
Receivership 7/9/31
Brown Back <$VALUE
3x10-20 1-2446 <$400
1902 Red Seal
3x10-20 1-2500 <$500
1902 Date Back
4x5 1-4180 <$250
3x10-20 1-3140 <$250
1902 Plain Back
4x5 4181-14190 <$250
3x10-20 3141-9494 <$250
1929 Small Size
5 Type 1 1-972 <$300
10 Type 1 1-544 <$300
20 Type 1 1-145 <$300
Total Issue $1,085,000
Out at close $50,000
Large out at close $5,410
****
5037 Saratoga
MANUFACTURERS NB OF MECHANICVILLE
{{ 8 L 5 S }}
Organized 2/1/96
Receivership 8/10/31
Brown Back <$VALUE
3x10-20 1-4960 <$350
1882 Date Back
4x5 1-5650 <$350
3x10-20 1-3720 <$350
1882 Value Back
4x5 5651-5845 <$350
3x10-20 3721-3832 <$350
1902 Plain Back
4x5 1-20395 <$200
3x10-20 1-14007 <$200
1929 Small Size
5 Type 1 1-2216 <$200
10 Type 1 1-1100 <$200
20 Type 1 1-326 <$200
Total Issue $1,836,350
Out at close $100,000
Large out at close $9,160
****
229 Orleans
FNB OF MEDINA
{{ UNREPORTED }}
Organized 2/3/64
Receivership 3/13/67
Original Series <$VALUE
4x5 1-2000 <$2000
Total Issue $40,000
Out in 1915 $240
****
4986 Orleans
MEDINA NB, MEDINA
{{ 1 L }}
Organized 2/19/95
Receivership 6/22/04
Brown Back <$VALUE
3x10-20 1-883 <$1500
Total Issue $44,150
Out in 1916 $310

****
12503 Nassau
FNB OF MERRICK
{{ 1 L 7 S }}
Chartered 3/24
1902 Plain Back <$VALUE
3x10-20 1-4304 <$850
1929 Small Size
5 Type 1 1-3226 <$350
10 Type 1 1-720 <$350
20 Type 1 1-206 <$350
5 Type 2 1-17160 <$350
Total Issue $465,700
Out in 1935 $50,000
Large out 1935 $1,190
****
5293 Oswego
FNB OF MEXICO
{{ 3 L 7 S }}
Chartered 4/18/00
Brown Back <$VALUE
3x10-20 1-1120 <$500
1882 Date Back
3x10-20 1-1620 <$500
1882 Value Back
3x10-20 1621-3557 <$500
1902 Plain Back
3x10-20 1-6866 <$350
1929 Small Size
10 Type 1 1-1488 <$175
20 Type 1 1-370 <$175
10 Type 2 1-1570 <$200
20 Type 2 1-542 <$200
Total Issue $737,370
Out in 1935 $50,000
Large out 1935 $1,880
****
2487 Schoharie
FNB OF MIDDLEBURGH
{{ 6 L 7 S }}
Chartered 7/12/80
Series 1875 <$VALUE
4x5 1-10446 <$400
Brown Back
3x10-20 1-2350 <$300
1882 Date Back
3x10-20 1-1810* <$300
1882 Value Back
3x10-20 2111-3128* <$300
* 1811-2110 not marked
1902 Plain Back
3x10-20 1-5723 <$200
1929 Small Size
10 Type 1 1-1518 <$150
20 Type 1 1-392 <$150
10 Type 2 1-2109 <$150
20 Type 2 1-440 <$150
Total Issue $936,980
Out in 1935 $50,000
Large out 1935 $2,390
****
9206 Niagara
FNB OF MIDDLEPORT
{{ 3 L 2 S }}
Organized 7/14/08
Receivership 12/30/31
1902 Date Back <$VALUE
3x10-20 1-2895 <$350
1902 Plain Back
3x10-20 2896-6876 <$350
1929 Small Size
10 Type 1 1-413 <$300
20 Type 1 1-129 <$300
Total Issue $384,060
Out at close $24,520
Large out at close $2,100
****
523 Orange
FNB OF MIDDLETOWN
{{ 5 L }}
Chartered 9/64
Liquidated 6/4/31
Original Series <$VALUE
4x5 1-3850 <$400
3x10-20 1-1850 <$750/$1250
50-100 1-250* <$3500
* 101-150 canceled
Series 1875
4x5 1-3040 <$400
3x10-20 1-2190 <$600/$1000
Brown Back
4x5 1-3200 <$300
3x10-20 1-6668 <$300
1902 Red Seal
3x10-20 1-3300 <$350
1902 Date Back
3x10-20 1-5440 <$175
1902 Plain Back
3x10-20 5441-12641 <$175
Total Issue $1,564,250
Out at close $5,495
****
Merchants NB of Middletown
SEE Ch 3333
Merchants & Manufacturers NB of Middletown
****

****
3333 Orange
MERCHANTS & MANUFACTURERS NB OF MIDDLETOWN
Chartered 1885
Liquidated 6/4/31
2nd title:Merchants NB 1/11/98
FIRST TITLE {{ 1 L }}
Brown Back <$VALUE
4x5 1-12462 <$300
SECOND TITLE {{ 12 L 4 S }}
Brown Back
3x10-20 1-3136 <$200/$250
1902 Red Seal
3x10-20 1-3800 <$250
1902 Date Back
4x5 1-5750 <$125
3x10-20 1-8200 <$125
1902 Plain Back
4x5 5751-25410 <$125
3x10-20 8201-21619 <$125
1929 Small Size
5 Type 1 1-1856 <$150
10 Type 1 1-816 <$150
20 Type 1 1-237 <$150
Total Issue $2,317,820
Out at close $100,000
Large out at close $10,210
****
1276 Orange
MIDDLETOWN NB, MIDDLETOWN
{{ 3 L }}
Organized 6/14/65
Receivership 11/29/84
Original Series <$VALUE
3x1-2 1-2200 <$400/$850
4x5 1-9200 <$500
3x10-20 1-3250 <$750/$1250
50-100 1-300 <$3500
Series 1875
4x5 1-7570 <$500
3x10-20 1-2592 <$600/$1000
Total Issue $683,500
Out in 1916 $2,858
****
13956 Orange
NB OF MIDDLETOWN
{{ 6 S }}
Chartered 1/34
1929 Small Size <$VALUE
5 Type 2 1-10400 <$150
10 Type 2 1-4920 <$150
20 Type 2 1-1320 <$150
Total Issue $127,600
Out in 1935 $71,800
****
1473 Orange
WALKILL NB OF MIDDLETOWN
{{ 1 L }}
Organized 7/21/65
Receivership 12/31/72
Original Series <$VALUE
3x1-2 1-4000 <$600/$1250
4x5 1-3000 <$750
3x10-20 1-1000 <$850/$1500
50-100 1-172 <$3500
Total Issue $155,800
Out in 1916 $1,004
****
11656 Herkimer
MIDDLEVILLE NB, MIDDLEVILLE
{{ 5 L 10 S }}
Chartered 3/20
1902 Plain Back <$VALUE
4x10 1-9747 <$250
1929 Small Size
10 Type 1 1-2438 <$125
10 Type 2 1-4831 <$125
Total Issue $584,470
Out in 1935 $50,000
Large out 1935 $1,510
****
5210 Otsego
MILFORD NB, MILFORD
{{ 3 L 4 S }}
Chartered 7/20/99
Brown Back <$VALUE
4x5 1-2525 <$500
3x10-20 1-1400 <$500
1882 Date Back
4x5 1-2525 <$500
3x10-20 1-1580 <$500
1882 Value Back
4x5 2526-3518 <$500
3x10-20 1581-2172 <$500
1902 Plain Back
4x5 1-4065 <$350
3x10-20 1-2512 <$350
1929 Small Size
5 Type 1 1-1006 <$250
10 Type 1 1-474 <$250
20 Type 1 1-140 <$250
5 Type 2 1-996 <$250
10 Type 2 1-576 <$250
20 Type 2 1-204 <$250
Total Issue $596,600
Out in 1935 $25,000
Large out 1935 $700
****
2661 Dutchess
MILLERTON NB, MILLERTON
{{ 7 L U + 15 S }}
Chartered 1882
Series 1875 <$VALUE
3x10-20 1-3709 <$600/$1000
1902 Red Seal
3x10-20 1-2100 <$450
1902 Date Back
3x10-20 1-2890 <$200
1902 Plain Back (dated 1902)
3x10-20 2891-4795 <$200
1902 Plain Back (dated 1922)
3x10-20 1-3116 <$200
1929 Small Size
10 Type 1 1-832 <$100
20 Type 1 1-242 <$100
5 Type 2 1-324 <$100
10 Type 2 1-1038 <$100
20 Type 2 1-240 <$100
Total Issue $781,760
Out in 1935 $30,000
Large out 1935 $1,225
****
13404 Nassau
CENTRAL NB OF MINEOLA
{{ 2U + 10 S }}
Chartered 12/29
1929 Small Size <$VALUE
5 Type 1 1-830 <$300
10 Type 1 1-622 <$300
20 Type 1 1-474 <$300
5 Type 2 1-7076 <$300
10 Type 2 1-3635 <$300
20 Type 2 1-575 <$300
Total Issue $202,330
Out in 1935 $64,300
****
9187 Nassau
FNB OF MINEOLA
{{ 5 L 6 S }}
Chartered 7/08
1902 Date Back <$VALUE
4x5 1-4475* <$500
3x10-20 1-2720** <$500
50-100 1-500 <$850/$1000
1902 Plain Back
4x5 4626-15370* <$500
3x10-20 2841-9926** <$500
* 4476-4625 not marked
** 2721-2840 not marked
1929 Small Size
5 Type 1 1-2054 <$300
10 Type 1 1-1094 <$300
20 Type 1 1-284 <$300
5 Type 2 1-4356 <$300
10 Type 2 1-2160 <$300
20 Type 2 1-528 <$300
Total Issue $1,093,980
Out in 1935 $50,000
Large out 1935 $2,130
****
13476 Onondaga
FNB OF MINOA
{{ 5 S }}
Chartered 6/30
1929 Small Size <$VALUE
5 Type 1 1-832 <$300
10 Type 1 1-622 <$300
5 Type 2 1-6550 <$300
10 Type 2 1-3305 <$300
Total Issue $128,080
Out in 1935 $35,900
****
1130 Herkimer
N MOHAWK VALLEY B OF MOHAWK
{{ 13 L U + 10 S }}
Organized 4/3/65
Receivership 10/12/31
Original Series <$VALUE
3x1-2 1-7668 <$350/$850
4x5 1-6000 <$400
3x10-20 1-1400 <$750/$1250
3x50-100 1-70 <$3500
Series 1875
4x5 1-5313 <$400
3x10-20 1-1388 <$600/$1000
Brown Back
4x5 1-6596 <$300
3x10-20 1-2841 <$300
1902 Red Seal
4x5 1-1250 <$300
3x10-20 1-1040 <$300
1902 Date Back
4x5 1-3450 <$150
3x10-20 1-2580 <$150
1902 Plain Back
4x5 3451-14850 <$150
3x10-20 2581-11896 <$150
1929 Small Size
5 Type 1 1-2500 <$125
10 Type 1 1-1187 <$125
20 Type 1 1-286 <$125
Total Issue $1,844,810
Out at close $100,000
Large out at close $10,080
****
7563 Orange
MONROE NB, MONROE
{{ 4 L }}
Organized 11/19/04
Receivership 7/28/32
1902 Red Seal <$VALUE
4x5 1-1370 <$500
3x10-20 1-867 <$500
50-100 1-17 <$2250/$2500
1902 Date Back
4x5 1-5305 <$250
3x10-20 1-3673 <$250
50-100 1-123 <$650/$750
1902 Plain Back
4x5 5306-12580 <$250
3x10-20 3674-8068 <$250
Total Issue $746,750
Out at close $1,920
****
13559 Orange
FNB IN MONTGOMERY
{{ U + 4 S }}
Chartered 6/27/31
1929 Small Size <$VALUE
5 Type 1 1-1038 <$250
5 Type 2 1-6540 <$250
Total Issue $63,840
Out in 1935 $25,000
Outstanding includes Ch 7982
****
7982 Orange
NB OF MONTGOMERY
{{ 2 L 2 S }}
Chartered 11/05
Liquidated 4/7/32
1902 Red Seal <$VALUE
4x5 1-350 <$750
3x10-20 1-280 <$750
1902 Date Back
4x5 1-2575 <$350
3x10-20 1-1840 <$350
1902 Plain Back
4x5 2576-7805 <$350
3x10-20 1841-4993 <$350
1929 Small Size
5 Type 1 1-508 <$350
10 Type 1 1-237 <$350
20 Type 1 1-77 <$350
Total Issue $465,450
Out at close $25,000
Large out 1935 $1,090
Ch 13559 assumed circulation
****
1503 Sullivan
N UNION B OF MONTICELLO
{{ 13 L 15 S }}
Chartered 1865
Original Series <$VALUE
3x1-2 1-2000 <$350/$750
4x5 1-3800 <$400
3x10-20 1-3030 <$750/$1250
50-50 1-150 <$3500
Series 1875
4x5 1-3210 <$400
3x10-20 1-1614 <$600/$1000
Brown Back
4x5 1-4533 <$300
3x10-20 1-2804 <$300
1902 Red Seal
4x5 1-1675 <$300
3x10-20 1-1210 <$300
1902 Date Back
4x5 1-3200 <$150
3x10-20 1-2300 <$150
1902 Plain Back
4x5 3201-10710 <$150
3x10-20 2301-7421 <$150
1929 Small Size
10 Type 1 1-1088 <$100
20 Type 1 1-296 <$100
10 Type 2 1-9042 <$100
20 Type 2 1-2160 <$100
Total Issue $1,541,930
Out in 1935 $100,000
Large out 1935 $4,100
****

****

13583 Schuyler
MONTOUR NB IN MONTOUR FALLS
{{ 19 S }}
Chartered 12/31
1929 Small Size <$VALUE
5 Type 1 1-128 <$75
10 Type 1 1-216 <$75
20 Type 1 1-44 <$75
5 Type 2 1-1872 <$75
10 Type 2 1-852 <$75
20 Type 2 1-252 <$75
Total Issue $45,000
Out in 1935 $25,000
Outstanding includes Ch 10497

****

10497 Schuyler
MONTOUR NB, MONTOUR FALLS
{{ 3 L 3 S }}
Chartered 3/14
Liquidated 2/9/32
1902 Date Back <$VALUE
4x5 1-760 <$400
3x10-20 1-616 <$400
1902 Plain Back
4x5 761-5160 <$400
3x10-20 617-3285 <$400
1929 Small Size
5 Type 1 1-571 <$250
10 Type 1 1-295 <$250
20 Type 1 1-85 <$250
Total Issue $312,480
Out at close $25,000
Large out at close $1,630
Ch 13583 assumed circulation

****

99 Cayuga
FNB OF MORAVIA
{{ 2U + 16 L 12 S }}
Chartered 10/63
Original Series <$VALUE
3x1-2 1-2000 <$350/$750
4x5 1-4500 <$400
3x10-20 1-1000 <$750/$1250
Series 1875
4x5 1-1810 <$400
3x10-20 1-1333 <$600/$1000
Brown Back
3x10-20 1-3805 <$300
1902 Red Seal
4x5 1-1875 <$300
3x10-20 1-2580 <$300
1902 Date Back
4x5 1-8800 <$125
3x10-20 1-6020 <$125
1902 Plain Back
4x5 8801-32647 <$125
3x10-20 6021-19969 <$125
1929 Small Size
5 Type 1 1-4188 <$85
10 Type 1 1-2490 <$85
20 Type 1 1-704 <$100
5 Type 2 1-4568 <$100
10 Type 2 1-2429 <$100
20 Type 2 1-530 <$100
Total Issue $2,678,240
Out in 1935 $50,000
Large out 1935 $8,320
Outstanding includes Ch 2353

****

2353 Cayuga
MORAVIA NB, MORAVIA
{{ 4 L }}
Chartered 4/26/77
Liquidated 6/4/12
Series 1875 <$VALUE
3x10-20 1-3277 <$600/$1000
Brown Back
3x10-20 1-3800 <$400
1882 Date Back
3x10-20 1-2215 <$400
Total Issue $464,600
Out at close $50,000
Ch 99 assumed circulation

****

4870 Otsego
FNB OF MORRIS
{{ 12 L 10 S }}
Chartered 1893
Brown Back <$VALUE
4x5 1-6200 <$250
3x10-20 1-2440 <$250/$300
1882 Date Back
4x5 1-2674 <$250
3x10-20 1-1848 <$250/$300
1902 Date Back
4x5 1-1650 <$150
3x10-20 1-1300 <$150
1902 Plain Back
4x5 1651-9920 <$150
3x10-20 1301-6671 <$150
1929 Small Size
5 Type 1 1-1932 <$125
10 Type 1 1-901 <$125
20 Type 1 1-256 <$125
5 Type 2 1-3396 <$125
10 Type 2 1-1704 <$125
20 Type 2 1-396 <$150
Total Issue $1,109,050
Out in 1935 $50,000
Large out 1935 $2,240

****

8371 Saint Lawrence
FRONTIER NB OF MORRISTOWN
{{ 3 L 5 S }}
Chartered 9/06
1902 Red Seal <$VALUE
4x5 1-375 <$650
3x10-20 1-300 <$650
1902 Date Back
4x5 1-2475 <$325
3x10-20 1-1740 <$325
1902 Plain Back
4x5 2476-6950 <$325
3x10-20 1741-4504 <$325
1929 Small Size
5 Type 1 1-1024 <$250
10 Type 1 1-476 <$250
20 Type 1 1-130 <$250
5 Type 2 1-1232 <$250
10 Type 2 1-768 <$250
20 Type 2 1-132 <$250
Total Issue $478,060
Out in 1935 $25,000
Large out 1935 $1,640

****

245 Madison
FNB OF MORRISVILLE
{{ 6 L 7 S }}
Chartered 2/64
Original Series <$VALUE
4x5 1-6000 <$400
4x10 1-1625 <$750
Series 1875
4x5 1-2865 <$400
4x10 1-1772 <$600
Brown Back
3x10-20 1-6913 <$350
1902 Red Seal
3x10-20 1-2900 <$350
1902 Date Back
3x10-20 1-3740 <$150
1902 Plain Back
3x10-20 3741-12293 <$150
1929 Small Size
10 Type 1 1-1532 <$125
20 Type 1 1-364 <$125
10 Type 2 1-2371 <$125
20 Type 2 1-588 <$125
Total Issue $1,589,550
Out in 1935 $50,000
Large out 1935 $4,290

****

5026 Westchester
MOUNT KISCO NB, MOUNT KISCO
Chartered 1895
2nd title:Mount Kisco NB & TC 1/15/26
FIRST TITLE {{ 7 L }}
Brown Back <$VALUE
4x5 1-2250 <$750
3x10-20 1-900 <$750
1882 Date Back
4x5 1-1314 <$750
3x10-20 1-915 <$750
1902 Plain Back
4x5 1-6997 <$400
3x10-20 1-4243 <$400
SECOND TITLE {{ 3 L 7 S }}
1902 Plain Back
4x5 1-8248 <$400
1929 Small Size
5 Type 1 1-6812 <$250
5 Type 2 1-17496 <$250
Total Issue $970,920
Out in 1935 $50,000
Large out 1935 $2,080

****

1416 Livingston
GENESEE RIVER NB OF MOUNT MORRIS
Chartered 1865
2nd title:Genesee River NB & TC 11/30/29
3rd title:Genesee River NB 2/19/32
FIRST TITLE {{ 6 L 2 S }}
Original Series <$VALUE
3x1-2 1-4000 <$400/$850
4x5 1-1750 <$500
3x10-20 1-2580 <$750/$1250
Series 1875
4x5 1-980 <$500
3x10-20 1-1146 <$600/$1000
Brown Back
4x5 1-3875 <$350
3x10-20 1-1129 <$350
1902 Red Seal
4x5 1-1575 <$350
3x10-20 1-1320 <$350
1902 Date Back
4x5 1-3650 <$175
3x10-20 1-2520 <$175
1902 Plain Back
4x5 3651-12537 <$175
3x10-20 2521-8359 <$175
1929 Small Size
5 Type 1 1-822 <$200
10 Type 1 1-414 <$200
20 Type 1 1-142 <$200
SECOND TITLE {{ 2 S }}
1929 Small Size
5 Type 1 1-756 <$200
10 Type 1 1-336 <$200
20 Type 1 1-92 <$200
THIRD TITLE {{ 3 S }}
1929 Small Size
5 Type 1 1-232 <$200
10 Type 1 1-116 <$200
20 Type 1 1-32 <$200
5 Type 2 1-2888 <$200
10 Type 2 1-1681 <$200
20 Type 2 1-396 <$200
Total Issue $1,338,390
Out in 1935 $50,000
Large out 1935 $3,530

****

1772 Westchester
EAST CHESTER NB OF MOUNT VERNON
Chartered 1/18/71
Liquidated 12/24/90
2nd title and location: German NB of EVANSVILLE, INDIANA 1/1/73
FIRST TITLE (NY) {{ 4 L }}
Original Series <$VALUE
3x1-2 1-6000 <$500/$1000
4x5 1-3000 <$600
3x10-20 1-1600 <$750/$1250
50-100 1-300 <$3500
SECOND TITLE (IN) {{ 1 L }}
Original Series
4x5 1-3000 <$600
3x10-20 1-1800 <$750/$1250
Series 1875
4x5 1-6221 <$600
3x10-20 1-7581 <$750/$1250
Total Issue $868,470
Out in 1910 $4,011

****

5271 Westchester
FNB OF MOUNT VERNON
{{ 16 L 23 S }}
Chartered 4/2/00
Brown Back <$VALUE
4x5 1-7550 <$500
3x10-20 1-7180 <$500
1882 Date Back
4x5 1-20000 <$500
3x10-20 1-14200 <$500
1882 Value Back
4x5 20001-32050 <$500
3x10-20 14201-21310 <$500
1902 Plain Back
4x5 1-31570 <$200
3x10-20 1-20949 <$200
1929 Small Size
5 Type 1 1-11986 <$100
10 Type 1 1-7286 <$100
20 Type 1 1-2066 <$100
5 Type 2 1-26310 <$100
10 Type 2 1-12024 <$100
20 Type 2 1-3495 <$100
Total Issue $5,261,700
Out in 1935 $200,000
Large out 1935 $8,535

****

8516 Westchester
MOUNT VERNON NB, MOUNT VERNON
{{ 1 L }}
Organized 12/11/06
Receivership 4/19/11
1902 Red Seal <$VALUE
4x5 1-1450 <$1500
4x10 1-1400 <$1500
1902 Date Back
4x5 1-8261 <$1000
4x10 1-7751 <$1000
Total Issue $560,260
Out in 1916 $5,525

****

13314 Rockland
NANUET NB, NANUET
{{ 4 S }}
Chartered 4/29
1929 Small Size <$VALUE
5 Type 1 1-788 <$400
10 Type 1 1-388 <$400
20 Type 1 1-126 <$400
50 Type 1 1-32 <$600
100 Type 1 1-12 <$750
5 Type 2 1-2620 <$400
10 Type 2 1-1644 <$400
20 Type 2 1-396 <$400
Total Issue $116,300
Out in 1935 $49,050

****

12496 Sullivan
FNB OF NARROWSBURG
{{ 5 S }}
Organized 1/8/24
1929 Small Size <$VALUE
5 Type 2 1-4330 <$300
10 Type 2 1-3516 <$300
20 Type 2 1-1464 <$300
Total Issue $86,090
Out in 1935 $50,000

****

151 Chenango
FNB OF NEW BERLIN
{{ 3 L }}
Organized 12/11/63
Receivership 4/15/12
Original Series <$VALUE
3x1-2 1-4200 <$600/$1000
4x5 1-8850 <$600
Series 1875
3x1-2 1-940 <$600/$1000
4x5 1-6945 <$600
Brown Back
4x5 1-13233 <$500
3x10-20 1-6269 <$500
1902 Red Seal
4x5 1-5650 <$500
3x10-20 1-3740 <$500
1902 Date Back
4x5 1-3684 <$350
3x10-20 1-2547 <$350
Total Issue $1,420,740
Out in 1916 $12,330

****

10199 Chenango
NB OF NEW BERLIN
{{ 2 L U + 2 S }}
Chartered 5/12
1902 Date Back <$VALUE
4x5 1-1275 <$500
4x10 1-1275* <$500
1902 Plain Back
4x5 1276-3567 <$500
4x10 1376-3062* <$500
* 1276-1375 not marked
1929 Small Size
5 Type 1 1-622 <$400
10 Type 1 1-322 <$400
5 Type 2 1-1370 <$400
10 Type 2 1-768 <$400
Total Issue $246,330
Out in 1935 $12,500
Large out 1935 $640

****

3444 Richmond
FNB OF STATEN ISLAND, NEW BRIGHTON
{{ 3 L }}
Chartered 1/29/86
Liquidated 2/25/05
Brown Back <$VALUE
4x5 1-8155 <$750
3x10-20 1-909 <$750
Total Issue $208,550
Out in 1910 $2,005

****

11785 Oneida
FNB OF NEW HARTFORD
{{ 2 L 8 S }}
Chartered 7/20
1902 Plain Back <$VALUE
3x10-20 1-7605 <$400
1929 Small Size
10 Type 1 1-1468 <$175
20 Type 1 1-414 <$175
10 Type 2 1-2451 <$175
20 Type 2 1-756 <$175
Total Issue $557,640
Out in 1935 $50,000
Large out 1935 $1,760

****

1186 Ulster
HUGUENOT NB OF NEW PALTZ
{{ 16 L 18 S }}
Chartered 1865
Original Series <$VALUE
3x1-2 1-5440 <$250/$750
4x5 1-4300 <$300
3x10-20 1-1710 <$600/$1250
Series 1875
4x5 1-6000 <$300
3x10-20 1-1594 <$500/$1000
Brown Back
4x5 1-9215 <$150
3x10-20 1-6850 <$150/$200
1902 Red Seal
4x5 1-3100 <$150
3x10-20 1-2500 <$150/$200
1902 Date Back
4x5 1-9100 <$75
3x10-20 1-6660 <$85
1902 Plain Back
4x5 9101-27025 <$75
3x10-20 6661-18678 <$85
1929 Small Size
5 Type 1 1-3954 <$60
10 Type 1 1-1844 <$60
20 Type 1 1-470 <$65
5 Type 2 1-5674 <$65
10 Type 2 1-3500 <$65
20 Type 2 1-1152 <$70
Total Issue $2,958,670
Out in 1935 $100,000
Large out 1935 $7,050

****

6427 Westchester
N CITY B OF NEW ROCHELLE
{{ 13 L }}
Chartered 9/17/02
Receivership 2/1/34
1902 Red Seal <$VALUE
4x5 1-5675 <$600
3x10-20 1-6955 <$600
1902 Date Back
4x5 1-22500 <$300
3x10-20 1-15200 <$300
1902 Plain Back
4x5 22501-49350 <$300
3x10-20 15201-31847 <$300
Total Issue $3,040,600
Out at close $5,610

****

7450 New York
AETNA NB OF NEW YORK
{{ 5 L }}
Chartered 10/04
Liquidated 6/5/13
1902 Red Seal <$VALUE
4x5 1-5415 <$450
3x10-20 1-4384 <$450
1902 Date Back
4x5 1-17830 <$225
3x10-20 1-6104 <$225
50-100 1-571 <$600/$750
Total Issue $1,074,950
Out in 1913 $160,600

****

1394 New York
AMERICAN EXCHANGE NB OF NEW YORK
Chartered 7/6/65
Liquidated 11/8/26
2nd title:American Exchange Pacific NB of New York 8/1/25
FIRST TITLE {{ 50+ L }}
Original Series <$VALUE
4x5 1-34750 <$200
3x10-20 1-10060<$500/$1000
50-100 1-4987 <$3500
500 1-354 <$150,000
Series 1875
50-100 1-2335 <$3500
Brown Back
4x5 1-585000 <$100
3x10-20 1-182600<$100/$150
1902 Red Seal
4x5 1-130000 <$100
3x10-20 1-106000<$100/$150
1902 Date Back
4x5 1-294165 <$35
3x10-20 1-274334 <$50
3x50-100 1-9232 <$300/$350
1902 Plain Back
4x5 294166-793825 <$35
3x10-20 274335-665274 <$50
SECOND TITLE {{ 18 L }}
1902 Plain Back
4x5 1-72465 <$50
3x10-20 1-54715 <$60
Total Issue $86,836,550
Out at close $5,000,000

****

American Exchange Pacific NB of New York
SEE Ch 1394
American Exchange NB of New York

****

750 New York
AMERICAN NB OF NEW YORK
{{ 1 L }}
Chartered 1/25/65
Liquidated 5/10/72
Original Series <$VALUE
4x5 1-21090 <$750
3x10-20 1-1499 <$850/$1250
50-100 1-75 <$3500
Total Issue $508,000
Out in 1910 $5,445

****

5112 New York
ASTOR NB OF NEW YORK
{{ 6 L }}
Chartered 2/9/98
Liquidated 3/16/07
Brown Back <$VALUE
4x5 1-38805 <$350
3x10-20 1-12121 <$350/$400
50-100 1-2525 <$1250/$1500
Total Issue $1,760,900
Out in 1910 $42,400

****

1388 New York
ATLANTIC NB OF NEW YORK
{{ 1 L }}
Organized 7/1/65
Receivership 4/28/73
Original Series <$VALUE
3x1-2 1-7100 <$750/$1250
4x5 1-5000* <$750
3x10-20 1-750 <$1000/$1250
50-100 1-130 <$3500
* 1776-3000 canceled
Total Issue $168,000
Out in 1915 $1,068

****

Atlantic NB of the City of New York
SEE Ch 1080
Merchants Exchange NB of the City of New York

****

9569 New York
AUDUBON NB OF NEW YORK
{{ UNREPORTED }}
Chartered 10/09
Liquidated 10/7/11
1902 Date Back <$VALUE
4x5 1-2170 <$1000
3x10-20 1-1727 <$1000
Total Issue $129,750
Out at close $50,000

****

13193 New York
BANK OF AMERICA N ASSOC, NEW YORK
{{ 22 L 50+ S }}
Chartered 3/26/28
Liquidated 11/28/31
1902 Plain Back <$VALUE
4x5 1-75451 <$50
4x10 1-50572 <$60
3x50-100 1-2445 <$350/$400
1929 Small Size
5 Type 1 1-100616 <$25
10 Type 1 1-49936 <$25
20 Type 1 1-16338 <$35
50 Type 1 1-1380 <$125
100 Type 1 1-412 <$175
Total Issue $12,779,550
Out at close $4,500,000
Large out at close $330,980
Outstanding includes Ch 1105 and Ch 658

****

CONDITION affects Value. The Values shown are for notes in FINE condition.

1393 New York
B OF NEW YORK N BANKING ASSOC OF NEW YORK
{{ 50+ L }}
Chartered 7/7/65
Liquidated 7/27/22
Original Series <$VALUE
3x1-2 1-45780 <$200/$750
4x5 1-25500 <$225
3x10-20 1-7440 <$500/$1000
50-100 1-1700 <$3500
500 1-300 <$150,000
1000 1-110 <$200,000
Series 1875
4x5 1-15965 <$225
3x10-20 1-7682 <$500/$1000
50-100 1-1472 <$3500
Brown Back
4x5 1-73580 <$100
3x10-20 1-53175 <$100/$150
50-100 1-200 <$1250/$1500
1902 Red Seal
4x5 1-62500 <$100
3x10-20 1-38000 <$100/$150
1902 Date Back
4x5 1-80000 <$30
3x10-20 1-141000 <$40
3x50-100 1-4000 <$300/$350
1902 Plain Back
4x5 80001-133090 <$30
3x10-20 141001-179992 <$40
Total Issue $22,521,850
Out in 1921 $1,364,750

7447 New York
BATTERY PARK NB OF NEW YORK
{{ 8 L }}
Chartered 10/04
Liquidated 7/24/23
1902 Red Seal <$VALUE
4x5 1-4125 <$350
3x10-20 1-2270 <$350
50-100 1-210 <$2250/$2500
1902 Date Back
4x5 1-19165 <$175
3x10-20 1-12534 <$175
50-100 1-400 <$400/$500
3x50-100 1-512 <$400/$500
1902 Plain Back
4x5 19166-42385 <$175
3x10-20 12535-25578 <$175
Total Issue $2,542,100
Out at close $200,000

Bayside NB of New York
SEE Ch 13334
NB of Bayside in New York

8634 New York
BEAVER NB OF NEW YORK
{{ UNREPORTED }}
Chartered 4/6/07
Liquidated 1/14/08
1902 Red Seal <$VALUE
4x5 1-965 <$1500
3x10-20 1-768 <$1500
Total Issue $57,700
Out in 1910 $4,240

Bowery & East River NB of New York
SEE Ch 1105
East River NB of the City of New York

1297 New York
BOWERY NB OF NEW YORK
{{ 3 L }}
Chartered 6/16/65
Liquidated 1/2/89
Original Series <$VALUE
4x5 1-11000 <$600
3x10-20 1-2099 <$750/$1000
50-100 1-967 <$3500
Series 1875
4x5 1-9000 <$600
3x10-20 1-3200 <$750/$1000
50-100 1-600 <$3500
Brown Back
4x5 1-6479 <$500
3x10-20 1-2028 <$500
50-100 1-448 <$1250/$1500
Total Issue $1,198,180
Out in 1910 $6,200

8926 New York
BRONX NB OF THE CITY OF NEW YORK
{{ 2U + 12 L }}
Chartered 10/07
Liquidated 3/20/28
1902 Red Seal <$VALUE
4x5 1-2480 <$300
4x10 1-2510 <$300
1902 Date Back
4x5 1-7270 <$150
4x10 1-6390 <$150
1902 Plain Back
4x5 7271-16052 <$150
4x10 6391-13776 <$150
Total Issue $1,022,080
Out at close $50,000

13292 New York
BROOKLYN NB OF NEW YORK
{{ U + 12 L 28 S }}
Chartered 3/29
Liquidated 1/12/32
1902 Plain Back <$VALUE
4x5 1-13040 <$175
3x10-20 1-5026 <$175
1929 Small Size
5 Type 1 1-13424 <$50
10 Type 1 1-5943 <$50
20 Type 1 1-1906 <$55
Total Issue $1,500,120
Out at close $500,000
Large out at close $6,145

12419 New York
BUSHWICK NB OF NEW YORK
{{ 2 L }}
Chartered 7/23
Liquidated 4/1/29
1902 Plain Back <$VALUE
4x5 1-4560 <$600
3x10-20 1-2513 <$600
Total Issue $216,850
Out at close $50,000

---
376 New York
CENTRAL NB OF THE CITY OF NEW YORK
{{ 16 L }}
Chartered 4/11/64
Liquidated 3/12/04
Original Series <$VALUE
3x1-2 1-31600 <$250/$750
4x5 1-29900 <$250
3x10-20 1-17600<$500/$1000
3x10-20 20601-27400 <$500/$1000
20 17601-20600 <$1000
50-100 1-8670 <$3500
50 8671-11670 <$3500
Series 1875
3x1-2 1-10000 <$250/$750
4x5 1-28275 <$250
3x10-20 1-18152<$500/$1000
50 1-3000 <$3500
Brown Back
4x5 1-50816 <$125
3x10-20 1-30906 <$125/$175
1902 Red Seal
4x5 1-7450 <$125
3x10-20 1-6190 <$125/$175
Total Issue $8,179,720
Out in 1910 $73,558

12874 New York
CENTRAL NB OF THE CITY OF NEW YORK
{{ 6 L 4 S }}
Chartered 1/26
Liquidated 5/23/30
1902 Plain Back <$VALUE
4x5 1-14176 <$200
4x10 1-7723 <$200
1929 Small Size
5 Type 1 1-2189 <$200
10 Type 1 1-1151 <$200
Total Issue $727,170
Out at close $150,000
Large out at close $13,240

2370 New York
CHASE NB OF THE CITY OF NEW YORK
{{ 50+ L 50+ S }}
Chartered 9/14/77
Series 1875 <$VALUE
3x1-2 1-8000 <$400/$850
4x5 1-16480 <$500
3x10-20 1-22171<$600/$1000
Brown Back
4x5 1-155865 <$125
3x10-20 1-132654<$125/$175
1882 Date Back
4x5 1-158086 <$100
3x10-20 1-123379<$100/$150
3x50-100 1-24463 <$1250/$1500
3x50-100 25001-29000 <$1250/$1500
1902 Plain Back
4x5 1-514671 <$35
4x10 1-92501 <$40
1929 Small Size
5 Type 1 1-999999 <$15
5 Type 1 A000001B-F057756B <$40
10 Type 1 1-750580 <$20
20 Type 1 1-61626 <$30
5 Type 2 1-577370 <$15
10 Type 2 1-600000 <$20
Total Issue $134,717,450
Out in 1935 $12,400,410
Large out 1935 $471,895
Outstanding includes Ch 2598, Ch 1250, and Ch 891

Chatham & Phenix NB of New York
SEE Ch 1375
Chatham NB of New York

10778 New York
CHATHAM & PHENIX NB OF THE CITY OF NEW YORK
Chartered 9/15 as Century NB of New York, under which there was no issue. Issuing title adopted 9/18/15.
Liquidated 2/9/32
2nd title:Chatham Phenix NB & TC 3/16/25
FIRST TITLE {{ 50+ L }}
1902 Plain Back <$VALUE
4x5 1-798100 <$25
3x10-20 1-496750 <$30/$35
3x50-100 1-2000 <$300/$350
SECOND TITLE {{50+ L 50+ S}}
1902 Plain Back
4x5 1-461400 <$25
3x10-20 1-289010 <$30/$35
1929 Small Size
5 Type 1 1-157308 <$15
10 Type 1 1-80466* <$20
20 Type 1 1-28153 <$30
* 65701 canceled
Total Issue $77,903,560
Out at close $6,199,995
Large out at close $517,320
Outstanding includes Ch 1375

1375 New York
CHATHAM NB OF NEW YORK
Chartered 7/1/65
Liquidated 9/18/15
2nd title:Chatham & Phenix NB of New York 2/23/11
FIRST TITLE {{ 10 L }}
Original Series <$VALUE
4x5 1-8300 <$250
3x10-20 1-5000 <$500/$1000
50-100 1-300 <$3500
500-1000 1-10 <$150,000/$200,000
Series 1875
4x5 1-5870 <$250
3x10-20 1-4770 <$500/$1000
Brown Back
4x5 1-16520 <$150
3x10-20 1-3955 <$150/$200
50-100 1-1045 <$1250/$1500
1902 Red Seal
4x5 1-3325 <$150
3x10-20 1-2470 <$150/$200
1902 Date Back
4x5 1-19000 <$75
3x10-20 1-13100 <$75
SECOND TITLE {{ 6 L }}
1902 Date Back
4x5 1-102965 <$75
3x10-20 1-75280 <$75
Total Issue $8,565,100
Out at close $1,200,000
Ch 10778 assumed circulation

Chatham Phenix NB & TC of New York
SEE Ch 10778
Chatham & Phenix NB of the City of New York

1499 New York
CHEMICAL NB OF NEW YORK
{{ 21 L }}
Chartered 8/1/65
Liquidated 5/2/29
Brown Back <$VALUE
4x5 1-500 <$300
4x10 1-1000 <$300
1902 Red Seal
4x5 1-20000 <$175
4x10 1-20000 <$175
1902 Date Back
4x5 1-108000 <$50
4x10 1-57500 <$60
3x50-100 1-12000<$300/$350
1902 Plain Back
4x5 108001-134556 <$50
4x10 57501-76937 <$60
Total Issue $10,018,600
Out at close $349,995

Citizens Central NB of New York
SEE Ch 1290
N Citizens B of the City of New York

Citizens NB of New York
SEE Ch 1290
N Citizens B of the City of New York

13027 New York
CLAREMONT NB OF NEW YORK
{{ 2 L }}
Chartered 1/27
Closed 8/31/29
1902 Plain Back <$VALUE
4x5 1-5395 <$500
3x10-20 1-3242 <$500
Total Issue $270,000
Out at close $100,000
Out in 1935 $1,130
Ch 13260 assumed circulation

7203 New York
COAL & IRON NB OF THE CITY OF NEW YORK
{{ 14 L }}
Chartered 4/04
Liquidated 2/1/26
1902 Red Seal <$VALUE
4x5 1-11000 <$250
50-100 1-2300 <$2250/$2500
1902 Date Back
4x5 1-40165 <$100
3x10-20 1-23100 <$100
50-100 1-2150 <$350/$400
3x50-100 1-2800 <$350/$400
1902 Plain Back
4x5 40166-81222 <$100
3x10-20 23101-51632 <$100
Total Issue $5,793,540
Out at close $415,000

13105 New York
COLLEGE POINT NB OF NEW YORK
{{ 14 S }}
Chartered 7/27
1929 Small Size <$VALUE
5 Type 1 1-8122 <$125
10 Type 1 1-4162 <$125
5 Type 2 1-16790 <$125
10 Type 2 1-7425 <$125
Total Issue $651,580
Out in 1935 $77,100

4512 New York
COLUMBUS NB OF NEW YORK
{{ UNREPORTED }}
Chartered 1/27/91
Liquidated 10/15/91
Brown Back <$VALUE
50-100 1-323 <$1750/$2000
Total Issue $448,450
Out in 1910 $200

3359 New York
COMMERCIAL NB OF NEW YORK CITY
Chartered 6/26/85
Liquidated 6/10/96
2nd title:Southern NB of New York 5/90
FIRST TITLE {{ 1 L }}
Brown Back <$VALUE
3x10-20 1-1772 <$600
SECOND TITLE {{ 2 L }}
Brown Back
4x5 1-32869 <$400
50-100 1-1427 <$1250/$1500
Total Issue $960,030
Out in 1910 $4,575

6425 New York
CONSOLIDATED NB OF NEW YORK
Chartered 9/02
Liquidated 3/4/14
2nd title:N Reserve B of the City of New York 3/1/09
FIRST TITLE {{ 4 L }}
1902 Red Seal <$VALUE
4x5 1-37151 <$350
3x10-20 1-29163 <$350
SECOND TITLE {{ 2 L }}
1902 Date Back
4x5 1-41980 <$300
3x10-20 1-27228 <$300
Total Issue $4,402,170
Out in 1914 $236,040

1389 New York
CONTINENTAL NB OF NEW YORK
{{ 31 L }}
Chartered 7/5/65
Liquidated 5/25/01
Original Series <$VALUE
3x1-2 1-44000 <$200/$750
4x5 1-26450 <$200
3x10-20 1-8976 <$500/$1000
50-100 1-350 <$3500
500-1000 1-70 <$150,000/$200,000
Series 1875
3x1-2 1-28000 <$200/$750
4x5 1-42575 <$200
3x10-20 1-4796 <$500/$1000
50-100 1-500 <$3500
Brown Back
4x5 1-50011 <$125
3x10-20 1-3964 <$125/$175
Total Issue $3,860,020
Out in 1910 $23,756

1556 New York
CROTON NB OF NEW YORK
{{ 1 L }}
Organized 9/9/65
Receivership 10/1/67
Original Series <$VALUE
3x1-2 1-2000 <$750/$1250
4x5 1-5000 <$750
3x10-20 1-1400<$1000/$1250
Total Issue $180,000
Out in 1915 $273

5237 New York
DOMESTIC EXCHANGE NB OF NEW YORK
Chartered 12/20/99
Liquidated 11/15/01
2nd title:N Commercial B of New York 7/25/01
FIRST TITLE {{ 1 L }}
Brown Back <$VALUE
3x10-20 1-8084 <$600
SECOND TITLE {{ 0 L }}
Brown Back
3x10-20 1-963 <$1000
Total Issue $452,350
Out in 1910 $6,870

13237 New York
DUNBAR NB OF NEW YORK
{{ 17U + 10 L 6U + 26 S }}
Chartered 8/28
1902 Plain Back <$VALUE
4x5 1-3960 <$100
3x10-20 1-754 <$150
1929 Small Size
5 Type 1 1-9524* <$30
10 Type 1 1-5340 <$40
20 Type 1 1-1366 <$45
5 Type 2 1-31622 <$35
10 Type 2 1-15674 <$45
20 Type 2 1-5030 <$50
* 9205 canceled
Total Issue $1,302,360
Out in 1935 $304,900
Large out 1935 $1,780

1105 New York
EAST RIVER NB OF THE CITY OF NEW YORK
Chartered 5/1/65
Closed 4/28/28
2nd title:Bowery and East River NB of New York 12/31/25
FIRST TITLE {{ 10 L }}
Original Series <$VALUE
4x5 1-3000 <$350
3x10-20 1-2400 <$600/$1250
50-100 1-2195 <$3500
Series 1875
4x5 1-4500 <$350
3x10-20 1-1800 <$500/$1000
50-100 1-1773 <$3500
Brown Back
4x5 1-4450 <$200
50-100 1-6627 <$1250/$1500
1902 Red Seal
50-100 1-880 <$2250/$2500
1902 Date Back
50-100 1-1134 <$350/$400
3x50-100 1-1360 <$350/$400
1902 Plain Back
4x5 1-24239 <$125
4x10 1-25910 <$125
SECOND TITLE {{ 28 L }}
1902 Plain Back
4x5 1-89611 <$75
4x10 1-71029 <$75
3x50-100 1-8841 <$300/$350
Total Issue $11,045,160
Out at close $3,000,000
Ch 13193 assumed circulation

---
384 New York
EIGHTH NB OF NEW YORK
{{ 1 L }}
Organized 4/16/64
Receivership 12/15/71
Original Series <$VALUE
3x1-2 1-5262 <$750/$1250
4x5 1-5847 <$750
3x10-20 1-2500<$1000/$1250
50-100 1-280 <$3500
Total Issue $310,250
Out in 1915 $1,948

13035 New York
ELMHURST NB OF NEW YORK
{{ 6 L 8 S }}
Organized 1/5/27
Receivership 2/21/34
1902 Plain Back <$VALUE
4x5 1-5187 <$350
4x10 1-3876 <$350
1929 Small Size
5 Type 1 1-6380* <$175
10 Type 1 1-3394** <$175
5 Type 2 1-3596 <$175
10 Type 2 1-1232 <$175
* 1775-2022 canceled
** 825-1020 canceled
Total Issue $664,920
Out at close $100,000
Large out at close $1,360

6284 New York
EQUITABLE NB OF NEW YORK
{{ 5 L }}
Organized 6/2/02
Receivership 2/10/04
1902 Red Seal <$VALUE
4x5 1-810 <$600
3x10-20 1-1511 <$600
Total Issue $91,750
Out in 1915 $640

13959 New York
FIDELITY NB IN NEW YORK
{{ 7 S }}
Chartered 1/34
1929 Small Size <$VALUE
5 Type 2 1-14648 <$200
10 Type 2 1-8405 <$200
Total Issue $157,290
Out in 1935 $68,250

<$VALUEs are for notes in FINE condition. Value changes by approximately 25% for a change of one full grade.

****
341 New York
FIFTH NB OF THE CITY OF NEW YORK
{{ 21 L }}
Chartered 3/26/64
Liquidated 5/28/25
Original Series <$VALUE
4x5 1-8090 <$250
3x10-20 1-1000 <$500/$1000
Series 1875
4x5 1-13140 <$250
Brown Back
4x5 1-55935 <$150
3x10-20 1-4758 <$150/$200
1902 Red Seal
4x5 1-17400 <$150
4x10 1-1625 <$150
3x10-20 1-10840 <$150/$200
1902 Date Back
4x5 1-37415 <$50
4x10 1-32100 <$60
1902 Plain Back
4x5 37416-81493 <$50
4x10 32101-64340 <$60
3x10-20 1-800 <$60
Total Issue $7,039,660
Out at close $250,000
****
FNB of Brooklyn, New York
SEE Ch 923
The FNB of the City of Brooklyn
****
29 New York
FNB OF THE CITY OF NEW YORK
{{ 50+ L 4U + 50+ S }}
Chartered 7/21/63
Original Series <$VALUE
4x5 1-11750 <$200
2x10-20-50 1-4400 <$500/$1000/$3500
20-50 4401-5000 <$1000/$3500
Series 1875
4x5 1-3980 <$200
2x10-20-50 1-5609 <$500/$1000/$3500
500 1-1498 <$150,000
Brown Back
4x5 1-172850 <$125
3x10-20 1-141286<$125/$150
50-100 1-4700 <$1250/$1500
1902 Red Seal
4x5 1-27320 <$125
3x10-20 1-430720<$125/$150
1902 Date Back
4x5 1-680830 <$35
3x10-20 1-553668 <$45
3x50-100 1-12500<$300/$350
1902 Plain Back
4x5 680831-1000000 <$35
4x5 A1-A1000000 <$35
4x5 B1-B123785 <$35
3x10-20 553669-1000000<$45
3x10-20 A1-A300533 <$45
1929 Small Size
5 Type 1 1-301818 <$15
10 Type 1 1-150954 <$20
20 Type 1 1-67662 <$30
5 Type 2 1-229436 <$15
10 Type 2 1-113315* <$20
20 Type 2 1-56719 <$30
* 26881-26886 canceled
Total Issue $180,505,930
Out in 1935 $4,318,150
Large out 1935 $328,025
****
Flushing NB in New York
SEE Ch 13296
NB of Queens County in New York
****
12825 New York
FORDHAM NB IN NEW YORK
{{ 9 L }}
Chartered 9/25
Liquidated 7/31/29
1902 Plain Back <$VALUE
3x10-20 1-24280 <$150
Total Issue $1,214,000
Out at close $486,750
****
13336 New York
FORT GREENE NB IN NEW YORK
{{ 22 S }}
Chartered 6/29
1929 Small Size <$VALUE
5 Type 1 1-6554 <$100
10 Type 1 1-3714 <$100
20 Type 1 1-932 <$100
5 Type 2 1-8688 <$100
10 Type 2 1-5652 <$100
20 Type 2 1-1848 <$100
Total Issue $668,220
Out in 1935 $193,350
****
290 New York
FOURTH NB OF THE CITY OF NEW YORK
{{ 31 L }}
Chartered 1864
Liquidated 6/18/14
Original Series <$VALUE
3x1-2 1-45999 <$200/$750
4x5 1-44375 <$225
4x10 1-24450 <$500
4x20 1-16975 <$1000
50-100 1-13200 <$3500
500 1-1316 <$150,000
1000 1-500 <$200,000
Series 1875
4x5 1-2500 <$225
4x10 1-1250 <$500
Brown Back
4x5 1-44950 <$150
3x10-20 1-42800 <$150/$200
50-100 1-200 <$1250/$1500
1902 Red Seal
4x5 1-19965 <$150
3x10-20 1-15894 <$150/$200
1902 Date Back
4x5 1-129720 <$40
3x10-20 1-85331 <$50
Total Issue $17,854,145
Out at close $2,000,000
Ch 1250 assumed circulation
****
4855 New York
FRANKLIN NB OF NEW YORK
{{ 2 L }}
Chartered 3/1/93
Liquidated 8/1/99
Brown Back <$VALUE
4x5 1-10310 <$600
3x10-20 1-400 <$600
Total Issue $226,200
Out in 1910 $1,265
****
1497 New York
FULTON NB OF NEW YORK
{{ UNREPORTED }}
Chartered 7/31/65
Liquidated 12/20/87
Original Series <$VALUE
3x1-2 1-6000 <$1500/$2000
4x5 1-5000 <$1500
4x10 1-1250 <$2000
Total Issue $180,000
All notes reportedly redeemed
****
1324 New York
GALLATIN NB OF THE CITY OF NEW YORK
{{ 18 L }}
Chartered 6/65
Liquidated 5/27/12
Original Series <$VALUE
4x5 1-28500 <$250
3x10-20 1-8000 <$500/$1000
50-100 1-1000 <$3500
Series 1875
4x5 1-40865 <$250
3x10-20 1-14800<$500/$1000
50-100 1-1900 <$3500
Brown Back
4x5 1-148389 <$150
3x10-20 1-60463 <$150
50-100 1-700 <$1250/$1500
1902 Red Seal
4x5 1-37750 <$150
4x10 1-17500 <$150
3x10-20 1-12900 <$150
1902 Date Back
4x5 1-29938 <$60
4x10 1-19444 <$70
Total Issue $12,534,750
Out in 1912 $261,555
****
2598 New York
GARFIELD NB OF THE CITY OF NEW YORK
{{ 18 L }}
Chartered 1881
Closed 1/26/29
Series 1875 <$VALUE
4x5 1-8225 <$250
3x10-20 1-7144 <$500/$1000
50-100 1-2715 <$3500
Brown Back
4x5 1-11500 <$150
3x10-20 1-4421 <$150/$200
50-100 1-1713 <$1250/$1500
1882 Date Back
4x5 1-53935 <$150
3x10-20 1-39068 <$150
50-100 1-1000 <$1250/$1500
3x50-100 1-2800 <$1250/$1500
1882 Value Back
3x10-20 39069-41566 <$150/$200
1902 Plain Back
4x5 1-19140 <$60
3x10-20 1-15242 <$75
Total Issue $6,788,850
Out at close $49,550
Ch 2370 assumed circulation
****
9717 New York
GOTHAM NB OF NEW YORK
{{ 19 L }}
Chartered 4/10
Liquidated 5/29/25
1902 Date Back <$VALUE
4x5 1-22600 <$60
3x10-20 1-17300 <$75
1902 Plain Back
4x5 22601-219692 <$60
3x10-20 17301-113442 <$75
Total Issue $10,065,940
Out at close $1,500,000
****
12553 New York
GRACE NB OF NEW YORK
{{ 21 L 50+ S }}
Chartered 6/24
1902 Plain Back <$VALUE
4x5 1-54780 <$50
3x10-20 1-36254 <$60
1929 Small Size
5 Type 1 1-57220 <$15
10 Type 1 1-30794 <$20
20 Type 1 1-9174 <$30
5 Type 2 1-146336* <$15
10 Type 2 1-45470 <$20
20 Type 2 1-14660 <$30
* 74575-74580 canceled
Total Issue $9,052,970
Out in 1935 $1,500,000
Large out 1935 $15,745
****
1371 New York
GROCERS NB OF NEW YORK
{{ UNREPORTED }}
Chartered 7/1/65
Liquidated 6/7/69
Original Series <$VALUE
4x5 1-500 <$1250
3x10-20 1-305 <$1500/$2000
50-100 1-400 <$4000
Total Issue $85,250
Out in 1910 $225
****
12300 New York
HAMILTON NB OF NEW YORK
{{ 21 L }}
Chartered 1/23
Liquidated 1/16/28
1902 Plain Back <$VALUE
4x5 1-74138 <$60
4x10 1-65611 <$70
Total Issue $4,107,200
Out at close $1,200,000
****
1352 New York
HANOVER NB OF THE CITY OF NEW YORK
{{ 50+ L }}
Chartered 6/27/65
Liquidated 4/23/29
Original Series <$VALUE
3x1-2 1-9900 <$200/$750
4x5 1-7500 <$225
3x10-20 1-4000 <$500/$1000
3x50-100 1-1920 <$3500
Series 1875
3x1-2 1-18000 <$200/$750
4x5 1-52500 <$225
3x10-20 1-8000 <$500/$1000
3x50-100 1-794 <$3500
Brown Back
4x5 1-238894 <$125
3x10-20 1-127521<$125/$175
50-100 1-100 <$1250/$1500
1902 Red Seal
4x5 1-85000 <$125
4x10 1-49000 <$125
3x10-20 1-23200 <$125/$150
1902 Date Back
4x5 1-203390 <$40
4x10 1-198025 <$50
3x10-20 1-40000 <$50
3x50-100 1-11000<$300/$350
Total Issue $35,345,730
Out at close $88,964
****
9955 New York
HARRIMAN NB OF THE CITY OF NEW YORK
Organized 3/2/11
Receivership 10/16/33
2nd title:Harriman NB & TC 7/12/28
FIRST TITLE {{ 10 L }}
1902 Date Back <$VALUE
4x10 1-39900 <$100
1902 Plain Back
4x10 39901-123129 <$100
SECOND TITLE {{ 6 L U + 12 S }}
1902 Plain Back
4x5 1-9996 <$100
1929 Small Size
5 Type 1 1-38542 <$65
5 Type 2 1-22984 <$65
Total Issue $6,396,260
Out at close $300,000
Large out at close $16,085
****
4567 New York
HIDE & LEATHER NB OF NEW YORK
Chartered 5/9/91
Liquidated 10/5/03
2nd title:NB of the United States in New York 6/30/02
3rd title:Western NB of the United States in New York 2/2/03
FIRST TITLE {{ 5 L }}
Brown Back <$VALUE
4x5 1-60694 <$200
3x10-20 1-8087 <$200/$250
SECOND TITLE {{ 3 L }}
Brown Back
4x5 1-3680 <$200
3x10-20 1-3044 <$200/$250
THIRD TITLE {{ 3 L }}
Brown Back
4x5 1-22985 <$200
3x10-20 1-15765 <$200/$250
Total Issue $3,091,980
Out in 1910 $35,890
****
1231 New York
IMPORTERS & TRADERS NB OF NEW YORK
{{ 26 L }}
Chartered 6/65
Liquidated 5/9/23
Original Series <$VALUE
4x5 1-13750 <$225
4x10 1-9625 <$500
3x20-50 1-2408<$1250/$3500
Series 1875
3x1-2 1-39498 <$200/$750
4x5 1-90550 <$225
4x10 1-6250 <$500
3x20-50 1-6000<$1000/$3500
Brown Back
4x5 1-68563 <$125
3x10-20 1-1916 <$125/$175
1902 Red Seal
4x5 1-4000 <$125
4x10 1-3150 <$125
3x10-20 1-580 <$125/$175
1902 Date Back
4x5 1-27374 <$40
4x5 28001-30000 <$40
4x10 1-11056 <$50
3x10-20 1-16000 <$50
3x50-100 1-2000 <$300/$350
Total Issue $7,875,150
Out at close $50,000
****
4152 New York
INTER-STATE NB OF NEW YORK
{{ UNREPORTED }}
Chartered 11/7/89
Liquidated 4/15/92
Brown Back <$VALUE
4x5 1-2183 <$1250
3x10-20 1-489 <$1250
Total Issue $68,110
Out in 1910 $260
****
Irving N Exchange B of New York
SEE Ch 345
New York N Exchange B of New York
****
Irving NB of New York
SEE Ch 345
New York N Exchange B of New York
****
1357 New York
IRVING NB OF NEW YORK
{{ 15 L }}
Chartered 6/29/65
Liquidated 3/1/07
Original Series <$VALUE
3x1-2 1-13500 <$200/$750
4x5 1-7200 <$200
3x10-20 1-2700 <$500/$1000
50-100 1-950 <$3500
Series 1875
3x1-2 1-7260 <$200/$750
4x5 1-34755 <$250
3x10-20 1-3010 <$500/$1000
50-100 1-530 <$3500
Brown Back
4x5 1-48755 <$175
3x10-20 1-11498 <$175/$225
1902 Red Seal
4x5 1-2975 <$150
3x10-20 1-1796 <$150
50-100 1-840 <$2250/$2500
Total Issue $3,275,700
Out in 1910 $40,127
****
12550 Queens
JAMAICA NB OF NEW YORK
{{ 2U + 8 L 15 S }}
Organized 6/3/24
1902 Plain Back <$VALUE
4x5 1-2229 <$175
4x10 1-1798 <$175
1929 Small Size
5 Type 1 1-4544* <$100
10 Type 1 1-5196** <$100
5 Type 2 1-11072 <$100
10 Type 2 1-12805 <$100
* C000014A-F000208A canceled
** C000019A-F000406A canceled
Total Issue $718,890
Out in 1935 $25,000
Large out 1935 $1,090
****
13304 New York
KINGSBORO NB OF BROOKLYN IN NEW YORK
{{ 3 L 3 S }}
Chartered 3/27/29
1902 Plain Back <$VALUE
4x5 1-1250 <$450
1929 Small Size
5 Type 1 1-3596 <$350
5 Type 2 1-7452 <$350
Total Issue $170,140
Out in 1935 $21,140
Large out 1935 $470
****
12892 New York
LAFAYETTE NB OF BROOKLYN IN NEW YORK
{{ U + 24 S }}
Chartered 2/26
1929 Small Size <$VALUE
5 Type 1 1-13262 <$50
10 Type 1 1-7910 <$50
20 Type 1 1-2994 <$50
5 Type 2 1-24012 <$50
10 Type 2 1-12636 <$50
20 Type 2 1-4728 <$50
Total Issue $1,572,720
Out in 1935 $400,000
****
1196 New York
LEATHER MANUFACTURERS NB OF NEW YORK
{{ 22 L }}
Chartered 5/30/65
Liquidated 4/16/04
Original Series <$VALUE
3x1-2 1-24000 <$200/$750
4x5 1-12650 <$225
4x10 1-3800 <$500
50-100 1-540 <$3500
Series 1875
4x5 1-6700 <$225
4x10 1-7050 <$500
4x20 1-2900 <$1000
50-100 1-2754 <$3500
Brown Back
4x5 1-64532 <$150
3x10-20 1-25079 <$150/$175
50-100 1-5668 <$1250/$1500
Total Issue $5,061,890
Out in 1910 $38,885
****
12214 New York
LEBANON NB OF NEW YORK
{{ 2U + 9 L 8 S }}
Chartered 6/22
Liquidated 8/18/31
1902 Plain Back <$VALUE
4x5 1-15965 <$150
3x10-20 1-8420 <$150
1929 Small Size
5 Type 1 1-2364 <$125
10 Type 1 1-1194 <$125
20 Type 1 1-275 <$125
Total Issue $915,860
Out at close $100,000
Large out at close $8,430
****
12352 New York
LIBERTY NB IN NEW YORK
Chartered 4/23
Liquidated 5/18/32
2nd title:Liberty NB & TC 1/30/28
FIRST TITLE {{ 16 L }}
1902 Plain Back <$VALUE
4x5 1-11161 <$50
3x10-20 1-62714 <$60
SECOND TITLE {{ 10 L 21 S }}
1902 Plain Back
4x5 1-32464 <$50
3x10-20 1-24667 <$60
1929 Small Size
5 Type 1 1-42276 <$35
10 Type 1 1-22824 <$35
20 Type 1 1-7039 <$40
Total Issue $10,733,950
Out at close $1,500,000
Large out at close $74,935
****
4645 New York
LIBERTY NB OF NEW YORK
{{ 31 L }}
Chartered 1891
Liquidated 3/8/21
Brown Back <$VALUE
4x5 1-102500 <$125
4x10 1-12750 <$125
3x10-20 1-60615 <$125/$175
1882 Date Back
4x5 1-34032 <$125
4x10 1-26435 <$125
1902 Date Back
4x5 1-59230 <$40
3x10-20 1-49700 <$50
3x50-100 1-6930 <$300/$350
1902 Plain Back
4x5 59231-194632 <$40
3x10-20 49701-97266 <$50
Total Issue $17,817,230
Out at close $2,000,000
****
2608 New York
LINCOLN NB OF THE CITY OF NEW YORK
{{ 29 L }}
Chartered 1882
Liquidated 9/30/20
Series 1875 <$VALUE
4x5 1-55400 <$250
3x10-20 1-3633 <$500/$1000
Brown Back
4x5 1-17500 <$150
3x10-20 1-22500 <$150/$200
1882 Date Back
4x5 1-141000 <$135
3x10-20 1-94668 <$135/$175
1882 Value Back
4x5 141001-154408 <$150
3x10-20 94669-102904 <$150/$200
Total Issue $10,998,010
Out at close $200,000
****
12885 New York
LONG ISLAND NB OF NEW YORK
{{ 5 L }}
Chartered 2/26
Liquidated 5/29/31
1902 Plain Back <$VALUE
3x10-20 1-11324 <$350
Total Issue $566,200
Out at close $8,550
****
7107 New York
MAIDEN LANE NB OF NEW YORK
{{ 5 L }}
Chartered 1/22/04
Liquidated 4/29/05
1902 Red Seal <$VALUE
4x5 1-2690 <$600
3x10-20 1-2142 <$600
Total Issue $160,900
Out in 1910 $3,295
****

1443 New York
MANUFACTURERS NB OF NEW YORK CITY
Chartered 1865
Liquidated 8/12/14
2nd title:Manufacturers NB of Brooklyn 2/20/85
FIRST TITLE **{{ 3 L }}**
Original Series <$VALUE
3x1-2 1-3000 <$350/$750
4x5 1-2700 <$400
3x10-20 1-2500 <$600/$1000
Series 1875
3x1-2 1-1580 <$350/$750
4x5 1-8350 <$400
3x10-20 1-6788 <$600/$1000
SECOND TITLE **{{ 8 L }}**
Brown Back
4x5 1-13925 <$200
3x10-20 1-19770 <$200/$250
50-100 1-3071 <$1250/$1500
1902 Red Seal
4x5 1-8875 <$200
3x10-20 1-3550 <$200/$250
50-100 1-1000 <$2250/$2500
1902 Date Back
4x5 1-20427 <$100
3x10-20 1-14319 <$100
50-100 1-400 <$400/$500
3x50-100 1-230 <$400/$500
Total Issue $4,182,940
Out in 1914 $210,650

1215 New York
MARINE NB OF THE CITY OF NEW YORK
{{ 6 L }}
Organized 6/3/65
Receivership 5/13/84
Original Series <$VALUE
3x1-2 1-15000 <$300/$750
4x5 1-23125 <$350
4x10 1-4000 <$600
50-100 1-150 <$3500
Series 1875
3x1-2 1-12000 <$300/$750
4x5 1-32425 <$350
Total Issue $1,428,500
Out in 1915 $7,541

Market & Fulton NB of New York
SEE Ch 964
Market NB of New York

964 New York
MARKET NB OF NEW YORK
Chartered 3/24/65
Liquidated 4/8/18
2nd title:Market & Fulton NB of New York 12/20/87
FIRST TITLE **{{ 7 L }}**
Original Series <$VALUE
3x1-2 1-20000 <$250/$750
4x5 1-17000 <$300
3x10-20 1-4400 <$500/$1000
50-100 1-1000 <$3500
Series 1875
4x5 1-53250 <$300
50-100 1-1340 <$3500
Brown Back
4x5 1-19744 <$150
SECOND TITLE **{{ 6 L }}**
Brown Back
4x5 1-84569 <$150
3x10-20 1-2781 <$150/$200
1902 Red Seal
4x5 1-8800 <$150
3x10-20 1-7780 <$150/$200
1902 Date Back
4x5 1-21830 <$85
3x10-20 1-16668 <$85
3x50-100 1-473 <$350/$400
Total Issue $6,254,560
Out at close $111,190

Mechanics & Metals NB of the City of New York
SEE Ch 1250
Mechanics NB of the City of New York

<$VALUEs are for notes in FINE condition. Value changes by approximately 25% for a change of one full grade.

1624 New York
MECHANICS & TRADERS NB OF NEW YORK
{{ 2 L }}
Chartered 7/65
Liquidated 4/24/84
Original Series <$VALUE
4x5 1-7171 <$500
3x10-20 1-4200 <$750/$1250
50-100 1-300 <$3500
Series 1875
4x5 1-3547 <$500
3x10-20 1-2084 <$750/$1250
Total Issue $573,560
Out in 1910 $3,575

1250 New York
MECHANICS NB OF THE CITY OF NEW YORK
Chartered 6/9/65
Closed 4/10/26
2nd title:Mechanics & Metals NB of the City of New York 1/29/10
FIRST TITLE **{{ 29 L }}**
Original Series <$VALUE
3x1-2 1-43000 <$200/$750
4x5 1-19000 <$225
3x10-20 1-4700 <$500/$1000
50-100 1-900 <$3500
500-1000 1-50 <$150,000/$200,000
Series 1875
3x1-2 1-4000 <$200/$750
4x5 1-4000 <$225
Brown Back
4x5 1-11385 <$125
3x10-20 1-9424 <$125/$175
1902 Red Seal
4x5 1-32000 <$125
4x10 1-17250 <$125
3x10-20 1-9000 <$125/$175
1902 Date Back
4x5 1-50030 <$30
4x10 1-26191 <$40
3x10-20 1-1038 <$40
SECOND TITLE **{{ 50+ L }}**
1902 Date Back
4x5 1-374500 <$30
3x10-20 1-286000 <$40
3x50-100 1-2000 <$300/$350
1902 Plain Back
4x5 374501-584500 <$30
4x5 1-35789 <$30
3x10-20 286001-409000 <$40
Total Issue $39,074,820
Out at close $540,000
Ch 2370 assumed circulation

12900 New York
MELROSE NB OF NEW YORK
Chartered 3/26
2nd title:N Bronx B of New York 3/28/31
FIRST TITLE **{{ 3 L 4 S }}**
1902 Plain Back <$VALUE
4x5 1-5195 <$400
1929 Small Size
5 Type 1 1-1512 <$250
SECOND TITLE **{{ 18 S }}**
1929 Small Size
5 Type 1 1-15896 <$60
5 Type 2 1-68312 <$60
10 Type 2 1-49001 <$65
Total Issue $1,457,710
Out in 1935 $500,000
Large out 1935 $610

1067 New York
MERCANTILE NB OF THE CITY OF NEW YORK
{{ 28 L }}
Chartered 5/65
Liquidated 6/19/12
Original Series <$VALUE
3x1-2 1-10000 <$200/$750
4x5 1-11200 <$225
3x10-20 1-9900 <$500/$1000
50-100 1-700 <$3500
Series 1875
3x1-2 1-5000 <$200/$750
4x5 1-53615 <$225
3x10-20 1-10000<$500/$1000
Brown Back
4x5 1-159500 <$100
3x10-20 1-103700<$100/$150
1902 Red Seal
4x5 1-61500 <$100
3x10-20 1-43400 <$100/$150
1902 Date Back
4x5 1-29548 <$50
3x10-20 1-23520 <$60
Total Issue $16,013,260
Out at close $300,000
Ch 345 assumed circulation

1080 New York
MERCHANTS EXCHANGE NB OF THE CITY OF NEW YORK
Chartered 4/28/65
Liquidated 7/11/22
2nd title:Atlantic NB of the City of New York 7/13/15
FIRST TITLE **{{ U + 14 L }}**
Original Series <$VALUE
3x1-2 1-7500 <$200/$750
4x5 1-18600 <$250
4x10 1-7600 <$500
2x20-50-100 1-1010 <$1000/$3500/$3500
500-1000 1-20 <$150,000/$200,000
Series 1875
3x1-2 1-9000 <$200/$750
4x5 1-25830 <$250
4x10 1-14500 <$400
2x20-50-100 1-1000 <$1000/$3500/$3500
Brown Back
4x5 1-29700 <$150
3x10-20 1-10720 <$150/$200
1902 Red Seal
4x5 1-12250 <$150
3x10-20 1-10500 <$150/$200
1902 Date Back
4x5 1-54000 <$65
4x5 55001-56000 <$75
3x10-20 1-35372 <$75
SECOND TITLE **{{ 4 L }}**
1902 Plain Back
4x5 1-16855 <$150
3x10-20 1-11543 <$150
3x50-100 1-120 <$400/$500
Total Issue $7,954,850
Out at close $250,000

1370 New York
MERCHANTS NB OF THE CITY OF NEW YORK
{{ 31 L }}
Organized 6/17/65
Liquidated 2/29/20
Original Series <$VALUE
4x5 1-22000 <$225
3x10-20 1-12200<$500/$1000
50-100 1-1200 <$3500
500-1000 1-100 <$150,000/$200,000
Series 1875
4x5 1-10735 <$225
3x10-20 1-7026 <$500/$1000
50-100 1-1000 <$3500
500-1000 1-64 <$150,000/$200,000
Brown Back
4x5 1-7028 <$100
3x10-20 1-4984 <$100/$150
1902 Red Seal
4x5 1-54165 <$100
4x10 1-12500 <$100
3x10-20 1-26334 <$100/$150
50-100 1-6000 <$2250/$2500
1902 Date Back
4x5 1-150460 <$40
4x10 1-138000 <$50
50-100 1-1600 <$300/$350
3x50-100 1-3000 <$300/$350
1902 Plain Back
4x5 150461-268270 <$40
4x10 138001-227501 <$50
Total Issue $21,837,200
Out at close 1,750,000

1121 New York
METROPOLITAN NB OF NEW YORK
{{ 5 L }}
Chartered 4/25/65
Liquidated 11/18/84
Original Series <$VALUE
4x5 1-15000 <$300
3x10-20 1-10300<$500/$1000
50-100 1-13450 <$3500
500-1000 1-205 <$150,000/$200,000
Series 1875
3x10-20 1-31000<$500/$1000
50-100 1-19934 <$3500
500-1000 1-481 <$150,000/$200,000
Total Issue $8,401,600
Out in 1910 $29,835

12344 New York
NB OF BAY RIDGE IN NEW YORK
{{ 1 L }}
Chartered 3/23
Liquidated 10/21/25
1902 Plain Back <$VALUE
4x5 1-3270 <$1000
Total Issue $65,400
Out at close $25,000

13334 Queens
NB OF BAYSIDE IN NEW YORK
Chartered 6/29
2nd title: Bayside NB of New York 1/25/33
FIRST TITLE **{{ 7 S }}**
1929 Small Size <$VALUE
5 Type 1 1-4110 <$150
10 Type 1 1-2474 <$150
20 Type 1 1-470 <$150
50 Type 1 1-52 <$350
100 Type 1 1-22 <$500
SECOND TITLE **{{ 6U + 8 S }}**
1929 Small Size
5 Type 1 1-1036 <$150
10 Type 1 1-470 <$150
20 Type 1 1-160 <$150
5 Type 2 1-8072 <$150
10 Type 2 1-3862 <$150
20 Type 2 1-4458 <$150
Total Issue $603,560
Out in 1935 $196,550

733 New York
THE NB OF COMMERCE IN NEW YORK
Chartered 1/19/65
Liquidated 4/5/29
2nd title:NB of Commerce in New York, 1905
FIRST TITLE **{{ 50 L }}**
Original Series <$VALUE
4x5 1-91000 <$200
3x10-20 1-60000<$500/$1000
50-100 1-22000 <$3500
4x500 1-575 <$150,000
4x1000 1-575 <$200,000
Series 1875
4x5 1-5995 <$200
3x10-20 1-6508 <$500/$1000
50-100 1-1089 <$3500
4x500 1-95 <$150,000
4x1000 1-125 <$200,000
Brown Back
4x5 1-679000 <$100
3x10-20 1-396600<$100/$150
50-100 1-12133<$1250/$1500
SECOND TITLE **{{ 24 L }}**
1902 Red Seal
4x5 1-553330 <$100
4x10 1-245000 <$100
3x10-20 1-196000<$100/$150
1902 Date Back
4x5 1-1000000 <$35
4x5 A1-A148210 <$35
4x10 1-882805 <$45
3x10-20 1-126668 <$45
3x50-100 1-50000<$300/$350
Total Issue $155,875,000
Out at close $338,085

3771 New York
NB OF DEPOSIT, NEW YORK
{{ 1 L }}
Organized 8/5/87
Receivership 6/9/93
Brown Back <$VALUE
4x5 1-11349 <$750
Total Issue $226,980
Out in 1915 $735

4581 New York
NB OF NORTH AMERICA IN NEW YORK
{{ 26 L }}
Organized 6/11/91
Receivership 1/27/08
Brown Back <$VALUE
4x5 1-77000 <$150
3x10-20 1-61780 <$150/$200
Total Issue $4,629,000
Out in 1915 $29,085

1373 New York
NB OF NORTH AMERICA OF NEW YORK
{{ 1 L }}
Chartered 7/1/65
Liquidated 4/15/69
Original Series <$VALUE
3x1-2 1-6000 <$750/$1250
4x5 1-3100 <$750
4x10 1-2655 <$1000
2x20-50-100 1-750 <$1250/$3500/$3500
Total Issue $340,700
Out in 1910 $1,825

13296 Queens
NB OF QUEENS COUNTY IN NEW YORK
Chartered 3/29
2nd title: Flushing NB in New York 8/11/33
FIRST TITLE **{{ 10 S }}**
1929 Small Size <$VALUE
5 Type 1 1-5534 <$150
10 Type 1 1-3920 <$150
20 Type 1 1-994 <$150
5 Type 2 1-7404 <$150
10 Type 2 1-3144 <$150
20 Type 2 1-492 <$150
SECOND TITLE **{{ 12 S }}**
1929 Small Size
5 Type 2 1-31788 <$150
10 Type 2 1-10295 <$150
20 Type 2 1-3323 <$150
Total Issue $927,150
Out in 1935 $238,600

12897 Queens
NB OF RIDGEWOOD IN NEW YORK
{{ U + 8 L }}
Chartered 3/26
Liquidated 10/13/31
1902 Plain Back <$VALUE
4x5 1-7479 <$350
Total Issue $149,580
Out at close $1,960

1372 New York
NB OF THE COMMONWEALTH, NEW YORK
{{ 1 L }}
Organized 7/1/65
Receivership 9/22/73
Original Series <$VALUE
3x1-2 1-4400 <$750/$1250
4x5 1-6832 <$750
4x10 1-3119 <$1000
Total Issue $283,400
Out in 1915 $2,807

1000 New York
NB OF THE REPUBLIC OF NEW YORK
{{ 32 L }}
Chartered 4/13/65
Liquidated 9/3/01
Original Series <$VALUE
3x1-2 1-5300 <$200/$750
4x5 1-11005 <$250
3x10-20 1-6801 <$500/$1000
50-100 1-6125 <$3500
500-1000 1-50 <$150,000/$200,000
Series 1875
4x5 1-6970 <$250
3x10-20 1-16282<$500/$1000
50-100 1-6167 <$3500
Brown Back
4x5 1-88178 <$150
3x10-20 1-39783 <$150/$200
50-100 1-2333 <$1250/$1500
Total Issue $7,561,610
Out in 1910 $66,740

1476 New York
NB OF THE STATE OF NEW YORK, NEW YORK
{{ 5 L }}
Chartered 1865
Liquidated 12/6/82
Original Series <$VALUE
4x5 1-10000 <$400
4x10 1-5000 <$600
3x20-50 1-2600<$1250/$3500
100-100 1-250 <$3500
500-1000 1-27 <$150,000/$200,000
Series 1875
4x5 1-14425 <$400
4x10 1-4750 <$600
3x20-50 1-1500<$1000/$3500
100-100 1-200 <$3500
Total Issue $1,460,000
Out in 1910 $6,405

NB of the United States in New York
SEE Ch 4567
Hide & Leather NB of New York

12965 New York
NB OF YORKVILLE IN NEW YORK
{{ 4 L 15 S }}
Chartered 7/26
1902 Plain Back <$VALUE
4x5 1-12950 <$350
1929 Small Size
5 Type 1 1-10724 <$125
5 Type 2 1-32618 <$125
10 Type 2 1-5093 <$125
50 Type 2 1-2250 <$300
Total Issue $907,240
Out in 1935 $250,000
Large out 1935 $1,420

687 New York
N BROADWAY B OF NEW YORK
{{ 4 L }}
Chartered 1/9/65
Liquidated 4/21/03
Original Series <$VALUE
4x5 1-18500 <$400
3x10-20 1-15800<$600/$1000
50-100 1-5390 <$3500
Series 1875
4x5 1-9500 <$400
3x10-20 1-4393 <$600/$1000
50-100 1-7975 <$3500
Brown Back
4x5 1-10000 <$300
50-100 1-7697 <$1250/$1500
Total Issue $4,928,950
Out in 1910 $40,950

N Bronx B of New York
SEE Ch 12900
Melrose NB of New York

1261 New York
N BUTCHERS & DROVERS B OF THE CITY OF NEW YORK
{{ 24 L }}
Chartered 6/10/65
Liquidated 9/18/26
Original Series <$VALUE
3x1-2 1-6800 <$200/$750
4x5 1-3800 <$250
3x10-20 1-2500 <$500/$1000
3x50-100 1-650 <$3500
Series 1875
4x5 1-10150 <$250
3x10-20 1-4360 <$500/$1000
3x50-100 1-880 <$3500
Brown Back
4x5 1-9939 <$125
3x10-20 1-4702 <$125/$175
50-100 1-1400 <$1250/$1500
1902 Red Seal
4x5 1-2000 <$150
3x10-20 1-1100 <$150/$200
50-100 1-100 <$2250/$2500
1902 Date Back
4x5 1-5400 <$75
3x10-20 1-3900 <$75
50-100 1-200 <$350/$400
3x50-100 1-1100 <$350/$400
1902 Plain Back
4x5 5401-55137 <$75
3x10-20 3901-37022 <$75
Total Issue $5,051,220
Out at close $500,000

CONDITION affects Value. The Values shown are for notes in FINE condition.

****
1290 New York
N CITIZENS B OF THE CITY OF NEW YORK
Chartered 6/65
Closed 5/29/20
2nd title:Citizens Central NB of New York 3/12/04
3rd title:Citizens NB of New York 3/1/17
FIRST TITLE {{ 3 L }}
Original Series <$VALUE
4x5 1-4950 <$300
3x10-20 1-1800 <$500/$1000
50-100 1-960 <$3500
Series 1875
4x5 1-11250 <$300
3x10-20 1-3700 <$500/$1000
50-100 1-1500 <$3500
Brown Back
4x5 1-42750 <$200
3x10-20 1-23428 <$200/$250
50-100 1-1060 <$1250/$1500
SECOND TITLE {{ 15 L }}
Brown Back
4x5 1-32340 <$125
3x10-20 1-26737 <$125/$175
1902 Red Seal
4x5 1-73000 <$125
4x10 1-27500 <$125
3x10-20 1-26000 <$125/$175
1902 Date Back
4x5 1-271000 <$35
4x10 1-243500 <$40
1902 Plain Back
4x5 271001-271491 <$35
4x10 243501-243520 <$40
THIRD TITLE {{ 3 L }}
1902 Plain Back
4x5 1-46822 <$60
4x10 1-35585 <$75
Total Issue $26,527,510
Out at close $1,000,000
Ch 1499 assumed circulation
****
1461 New York
N CITY B OF NEW YORK
{{ 50+ L U + 50+ S }}
Chartered 7/17/65
Original Series <$VALUE
4x5 1-3400 <$225
3x10-20 1-500 <$500/$1000
50-100 1-600 <$3500
500-1000 1-100 <$150,000/$200,000
Brown Back
4x5 1-140000 <$100
3x10-20 1-386000<$100/$150
1902 Red Seal
4x5 1-270840 <$100
4x10 1-134165 <$100
3x10-20 1-293332<$100/$150
1902 Date Back
4x5 1-472449 <$35
4x10 1-202000 <$40
3x10-20 1-245337 <$40
3x50-100 1-36000<$300/$350
1929 Small Size
5 Type 1 1-368630* <$15
10 Type 1 1-235258 <$20
20 Type 1 1-86872 <$30
5 Type 2 1-563920 <$15
10 Type 2 1-161532 <$20
20 Type 2 1-80255 <$30
* 324078 canceled
Total Issue $128,317,840
Out in 1935 $25,000,000
Large out 1935 $147,685
Outstanding includes Ch 62
****
N Commercial B of New York
SEE Ch 5237
Domestic Exchange NB of New York
****
8665 New York
N COPPER B OF NEW YORK
{{ 6 L }}
Chartered 4/07
Liquidated 2/1/10
1902 Red Seal <$VALUE
4x5 1-22000 <$350
3x10-20 1-23600 <$350
1902 Date Back
4x5 1-27785 <$175
3x10-20 1-13230 <$175
Total Issue $2,837,200
Out in 1910 $686,535
****
444 New York
N CURRENCY B OF NEW YORK CITY
{{ UNREPORTED }}
Chartered 5/28/64
Liquidated 3/23/76
Original Series <$VALUE
4x5 1-3320 <$1250
2x10-20-50 1-1000 <$1500/$2000/$3500
Total Issue $156,400
Out in 1910 $750
****
1075 New York
N MECHANICS BANKING ASSOCIATION OF NEW YORK
{{ 13 L }}
Chartered 5/1/65
Liquidated 10/15/83
Original Series <$VALUE
3x1-2 1-14000 <$200/$750
4x5 1-17250 <$250
3x10-20 1-5650 <$500/$1000
50-100 1-720 <$3500
Series 1875
3x1-2 1-10420 <$200/$750
4x5 1-11865 <$250
Total Issue $1,094,900
Out in 1910 $5,908
****
9939 New York
N NASSAU B OF NEW YORK
{{ UNREPORTED }}
Chartered 3/11
Liquidated 6/18/14
1902 Date Back <$VALUE
4x5 1-15060 <$650
3x10-20 1-11220 <$650
3x50-100 1-340 <$850/$1000
Total Issue $947,200
Out in 1914 $186,100
****
891 New York
N PARK B OF NEW YORK
{{ 2U + 50+ L 2U + 2 S }}
Chartered 3/14/65
Closed: 8/24/29
Original Series <$VALUE
4x5 1-14200 <$250
4x10 1-8678 <$500
2x20-50-1002 1-4262 <$1000/$3500/$3500
500 1-505 <$150,000
Series 1875
4x5 1-11990 <$250
4x10 1-6250 <$500
2x20-50-100 1-620 <$1000/$3500/$3500
Brown Back
4x5 1-114480 <$100
3x10-20 1-65168 <$100/$150
1902 Red Seal
4x5 1-107500 <$100
4x10 1-54500 <$100
3x10-20 1-42000 <$100/$150
1902 Date Back
4x5 1-310000 <$35
4x10 1-277500 <$40
3x50-100 1-12673<$300/$350
3x50-100 19001-20800 <$300/$350
1902 Plain Back
4x5 310001-1000000 <$30
4x5 A1-A414438 <$35
4x10 277501-1000000 <$40
4x10 A1-A84059 <$40
3x10-20 1-5000 <$40/$50
1929 Small Size
5 Type 1 1-3554* <$250
10 Type 1 1-1314** <$250
20 Type 1 1-855 <$250
* C003554A-F003554A canceled
** C001314A-F001314A canceled
Total Issue $90,086,370
Out at close $5,000,000
Large out 1929 $4,739,000
Ch 2370 assumed circulation
****
N Reserve B of the City of New York
SEE Ch 6425
Consolidated NB of New York
****
13260 New York
N SAFETY B & TC OF NEW YORK
{{ 32 S }}
Chartered 11/28 as Lefcourt Normandie NB, under which there was no issue. Issuing title adopted 9/16/30.
1929 Small Size <$VALUE
5 Type 1 1-20503 <$30
10 Type 1 1-14838 <$30
Total Issue $1,505,370
Out in 1935 $418,130
****
917 New York
N SHOE AND LEATHER B OF THE CITY OF NEW YORK
{{ 16 L }}
Chartered 3/21/65
Liquidated 2/28/06
Original Series <$VALUE
3x1-2 1-69500 <$200/$750
4x5 1-45975 <$275
3x10-20 1-8000 <$500/$1000
50-100 1-500 <$3500
500-1000 1-20 <$150,000/$200,000
Series 1875
3x1-2 1-4000 <$200/$750
4x5 1-45295 <$275
3x10-20 1-5000 <$500/$1000
Brown Back
4x5 1-72987 <$200
3x10-20 1-3015 <$200/$250
1902 Red Seal
4x5 1-3645 <$200
3x10-20 1-2936 <$200/$250
Total Issue $4,778,090
Out in 1910 $34,322
****
4898 New York
N UNION B OF NEW YORK
{{ 5 L }}
Chartered 5/24/93
Liquidated 4/16/00
Brown Back <$VALUE
4x5 1-103122 <$250
Total Issue $2,062,440
Out in 1910 $10,170
****
5783 New York
NEW AMSTERDAM NB OF NEW YORK
{{ 7 L }}
Organized 4/18/01
Receivership 1/30/08
Brown Back <$VALUE
4x5 1-10015 <$300
3x10-20 1-8370 <$300
50-100 1-110 <$1250/$1500
Total Issue $635,300
Out in 1915 $4,675
****
1116 New York
NEW YORK COUNTY NB OF NEW YORK
{{ 11 L }}
Chartered 1865
Liquidated 11/21/21
Original Series <$VALUE
4x5 1-13750 <$300
3x10-20 1-2000 <$500/$1000
Series 1875
4x5 1-24480 <$300
Brown Back
4x5 1-11900 <$200
3x10-20 1-7143 <$200/$250
1902 Red Seal
3x10-20 1-7600 <$200/$250
1902 Date Back
3x10-20 1-30150 <$125
1902 Plain Back
3x10-20 30151-42385 <$125
Total Issue $3,959,000
Out at close $196,400
****
345 New York
NEW YORK N EXCHANGE B OF NEW YORK
Chartered 4/1/64
Liquidated 1/6/23
2nd title:Irving N Exchange B of New York 2/20/07
3rd title:Irving NB of New York 7/20/12
FIRST TITLE {{ 5 L }}
Original Series <$VALUE
3x1-2 1-13000 <$300/$750
4x5 1-11650 <$300
10-20-50-100 1-2150 <$500/$1000/$3500/$3500
Series 1875
4x5 1-11750 <$300
10-20-50-100 1-1419 <$500/$1000/$3500/$3500
Brown Back
4x5 1-28760 <$200
3x10-20 1-4480 <$200/$250
50-100 1-5568 <$1250/$1500
1902 Red Seal
4x5 1-33054 <$200
4x10 1-2320 <$200
3x10-20 1-8831 <$200/$250
50-100 1-4532 <$2250/$2500
SECOND TITLE {{ 8 L }}
1902 Red Seal
4x5 1-44300 <$150
4x10 1-41600 <$150/$200
1902 Date Back
4x5 1-40520 <$60
4x10 1-40524 <$70
THIRD TITLE {{ 18 L }}
1902 Date Back
4x5 1-187500 <$40
4x10 1-185000 <$45
3x50-100 1-4000 <$300/$350
1902 Plain Back
4x5 187501-358619 <$40
4x10 185001-320585 <$45
Total Issue $30,662,190
Out at close $2,536,000
Outstanding includes Ch 1067
****
387 New York
NINTH NB OF THE CITY OF NEW YORK
{{ 5 L }}
Chartered 4/18/64
Liquidated 12/31/01
Original Series <$VALUE
3x1-2 1-10000 <$300/$750
4x5 1-15900 <$350
4x10 1-11500 <$500
2x20-50-100 1-4400 <$1000/$3500/$3500
500-1000 1-100 <$150,000/$200,000
Series 1875
4x10 1-15000 <$500
2x20-50-100 1-3000 <$1000/$3500/$3500
500-1000 1-390 <$150,000/$200,000
Brown Back
4x5 1-747 <$250
3x10-20 1-9199 <$250/$300
50-100 1-125 <$1000/$1250
Total Issue $4,062,640
Out in 1910 $16,249
****
6253 New York
NORTHERN NB OF NEW YORK
{{ 1 L }}
Chartered 5/12/02
Liquidated 3/12/07
1902 Red Seal <$VALUE
4x5 1-375 <$850
3x10-20 1-3635 <$850
Total Issue $189,250
Out in 1910 $5,965
****
1232 New York
OCEAN NB OF THE CITY OF NEW YORK
{{ UNREPORTED }}
Organized 6/6/65
Receivership 12/13/71
Original Series <$VALUE
4x5 1-10955 <$1250
3x10-20 1-8420<$1500/$2000
50-100 1-2426 <$4000
Total Issue $1,004,000
Out in 1915 $5,855
****
12280 Queens
OZONE PARK NB OF NEW YORK
{{ 9 L 10 S }}
Organized 10/30/22
Receivership 10/30/34
1902 Plain Back <$VALUE
4x5 1-4995 <$400
3x10-20 1-3574 <$400
1929 Small Size
5 Type 1 1-1666 <$200
10 Type 1 1-1042 <$200
20 Type 1 1-256 <$200
5 Type 2 1-2784 <$200
10 Type 2 1-1733 <$200
20 Type 2 1-289 <$200
Total Issue $458,860
Out at close $48,800
Large out at close $1,730
****
1224 New York
PACIFIC NB OF NEW YORK CITY
{{ UNREPORTED }}
Chartered 6/5/65
Liquidated 5/10/69
Original Series <$VALUE
4x5 1-4087 <$1250
3x10-20 1-310 <$1500/$2000
50-100 1-265 <$4000
Total Issue $136,990
Out in 1910 $860
****
9219 Kings
PEOPLES NB OF BROOKLYN IN NEW YORK
{{ U + 6 L 24 S }}
Chartered 8/08
1902 Date Back <$VALUE
4x5 1-7100 <$300
3x10-20 1-5280 <$300
1902 Plain Back
4x5 7101-16960 <$300
3x10-20 5281-11674 <$300
1929 Small Size
5 Type 1 1-1932 <$100
10 Type 1 1-946 <$100
20 Type 1 1-266 <$100
5 Type 2 1-64982 <$100
10 Type 2 1-37826 <$100
20 Type 2 1-192 <$100
Total Issue $1,776,550
Out in 1935 $250,000
Large out 1935 $2,120
****
1374 New York
PHENIX NB OF THE CITY OF NEW YORK
{{ 16 L }}
Chartered 6/22/65
Liquidated 3/28/11
Original Series <$VALUE
3x1-2 1-9000 <$250/$750
4x5 1-15500 <$250
3x10-20 1-9200 <$500/$1000
50-100 1-2600 <$3500
Series 1875
4x5 1-10385 <$250
3x10-20 1-6278 <$500/$1000
50-100 1-2000 <$3500
Brown Back
4x5 1-21984 <$100
3x10-20 1-8973 <$100/$150
50-100 1-200 <$1250/$1500
1902 Red Seal
4x5 1-46500 <$100
3x10-20 1-29800 <$100/$150
1902 Date Back
4x5 1-18624 <$50
3x10-20 1-23106 <$60
Total Issue $6,892,710
Out in 1911 $26,750
****
11844 New York
PROGRESS NB OF NEW YORK
Chartered 9/20
Liquidated 12/15/28
2nd title:Seventh Avenue NB of New York 3/1/23
3rd title:Seventh NB of New York 10/10/25
FIRST TITLE {{ 2 L }}
1902 Plain Back <$VALUE
4x5 1-2500 <$200
4x10 1-1250 <$200
SECOND TITLE {{ 3U + 9 L }}
1902 Plain Back
4x5 1-4650 <$100
4x10 1-3700 <$100
THIRD TITLE {{ 8 L }}
1902 Plain Back
4x5 1-95341 <$100
Total Issue $2,247,820
Out at close $500,000
****
11034 New York
PUBLIC NB OF NEW YORK
Chartered 7/17
2nd title:Public NB & TC 5/14/27
FIRST TITLE {{ 22 L }}
1902 Plain Back <$VALUE
4x5 1-558065 <$30
4x10 1-478037 <$40
SECOND TITLE {{50+L U+50+S}}
1902 Plain Back
4x5 1-218549 <$30
4x10 1-160709 <$40
1929 Small Size
5 Type 1 1-255992 <$15
10 Type 1 1-161598 <$20
5 Type 2 1-627778 <$15
10 Type 2 1-287624* <$20
* 124033-124038 canceled
Total Issue $64,472,830
Out in 1935 $5,000,000
Large out 1935 $170,750
****
12398 Queens
QUEENSBORO NB OF THE CITY OF NEW YORK
{{ 6 L 2 S }}
Organized 6/11/23
Receivership 8/26/31
1902 Plain Back <$VALUE
4x5 1-28622 <$300
1929 Small Size
5 Type 1 1-3025 <$450
Total Issue $663,190
Out at close $75,000
Large out at close $5,440
****
11655 Queens
RICHMOND HILL NB OF NEW YORK
Organized 2/17/20
Receivership 11/14/33
2nd title:Richmond NB of New York 6/15/29
FIRST TITLE {{ 3 L }}
1902 Plain Back <$VALUE
4x5 1-23057 <$400
SECOND TITLE {{ 10 S }}
1929 Small Size
5 Type 1 1-20430 <$150
5 Type 2 1-31050 <$150
Total Issue $1,229,290
Out at close $335,480
Large out at close $2,305
****
Richmond NB of New York
SEE Ch 11655
Richmond Hill NB of New York
****
12252 Queens
ROCKAWAY BEACH NB OF NEW YORK
{{ 3 L }}
Organized 6/21/22
Receivership 9/19/31
1902 Plain Back <$VALUE
4x5 1-2700 <$650
3x10-20 1-1512 <$650
Total Issue $129,600
Out at close $1,235
****
972 New York
SAINT NICHOLAS NB OF NEW YORK
{{ 28 L }}
Chartered 4/1/65
Liquidated 12/30/82
Original Series <$VALUE
3x1-2 1-64600 <$250/$850
4x5 1-58975 <$350
4x10 1-11750 <$600
Series 1875
3x1-2 1-9230 <$250/$850
4x5 1-10808 <$350
4x10 1-2985 <$600
2x20-50-100 1-1131 <$1000/$3500/$3500
Total Issue $2,569,100
Out in 1910 $14,388
****
3415 New York
SEABOARD NB OF THE CITY OF NEW YORK
{{ 14 L }}
Chartered 1885
Closed 3/31/22
Brown Back <$VALUE
4x5 1-33896 <$150
3x10-20 1-18424 <$150/$200
1902 Red Seal
4x5 1-17000 <$150
4x10 1-11750 <$150
3x10-20 1-4000 <$150/$200
1902 Date Back
4x5 1-43315 <$75
4x10 1-41905 <$75
4x10 42841-44840 <$75
3x50-100 1-1527 <$400/$500
Total Issue $4,014,250
Out in 1921 $63,245
Ch 12123 assumed circulation
****

12123 New York
SEABOARD NB OF THE CITY OF NEW YORK
{{ 4 L }}
Chartered 2/22 as The Mercantile NB, under which there was no issue. Issuing title adopted 3/31/22.
Liquidated 6/18/29
1902 Plain Back <$VALUE
4x5 1-11345 <$250
3x10-20 1-4213 <$250
Total Issue $437,550
Out at close $299,445
Outstanding includes Ch 3415

62 New York
SECOND NB OF NEW YORK*
{{ 13 L }}
Chartered 8/13/63
Liquidated 4/28/82
*Reorganized as Ch 2668 which retook Ch 62 7/13/11
Liquidated 12/31/21
Original Series <$VALUE
4x5 1-12000 <$350
4x10 1-5000 <$600
4x20 1-1000 <$1000
Series 1875
4x5 1-3000 <$350
4x10 1-6715 <$600
4x20 1-2375 <$1000
1902 Date Back
4x5 1-70000 <$150
3x10-20 1-52200 <$150
1902 Plain Back
4x5 70001-123670 <$150
3x10-20 52201-81370 <$150
Total Issue $8,034,980
Out at close $636,595
Ch 1461 assumed circulation

2668 New York
SECOND NB OF THE CITY OF NEW YORK
{{ 8 L }}
Chartered 1882
Liquidated 12/31/21
RETOOK Ch 62 7/13/11
Brown Back <$VALUE
4x5 1-36663 <$250
3x10-20 1-4800 <$250/$300
1902 Red Seal
4x5 1-24150 <$250
3x10-20 1-17340 <$250/$300
1902 Date Back
4x5 1-48500 <$150
3x10-20 1-35500 <$150
Total Issue $5,068,260
Out in 1911 $1,000,000
Ch 1461 assumed circulation

Seventh Avenue NB of New York
SEE Ch 11844
Progress NB of New York

Seventh NB of New York
SEE Ch 998
Seventh Ward NB of New York

Seventh NB of New York
SEE Ch 11844
Progress NB of New York

998 New York
SEVENTH WARD NB OF NEW YORK
Organized 4/11/65
Liquidated 4/9/03
2nd title:Seventh NB of New York 3/1/88
FIRST TITLE {{ 18 L }}
Original Series <$VALUE
3x1-2 1-18000 <$250/$750
4x5 1-7500 <$250
3x10-20 1-1710 <$500/$1000
50-100 1-300 <$3500
Series 1875
4x5 1-2680 <$250
Brown Back
4x5 1-750 <$200
3x10-20 1-310 <$200/$250
50-100 1-161 <$1250/$1500
SECOND TITLE {{ 4 L }}
Brown Back
4x5 1-21925* <$200
3x10-20 1-10546**<$200/$250
50-100 1-1314^<$1250/$1500
* 7256-10065 canceled
** 4513-4676 canceled
^ 1195-1236 canceled
Total Issue $1,670,960
Out in 1910 $24,492

13045 New York
SEWARD NB OF NEW YORK
Chartered 3/27
Liquidated 5/5/31
2nd title: Seward NB & TC of New York 1/21/29
FIRST TITLE {{ 4 L }}
1902 Plain Back <$VALUE
4x5 1-33430 <$150
SECOND TITLE {{U+10 L 10 S}}
1902 Plain Back
4x5 1-7482 <$150
1929 Small Size
5 Type 1 1-35886 <$125
Total Issue $1,894,820
Out at close $500,000
Large out at close $11,670

8922 New York
SHERMAN NB OF NEW YORK
{{ 5 L }}
Chartered 10/07
Liquidated 6/26/19
1902 Red Seal <$VALUE
4x5 1-2250 <$500
3x10-20 1-3600 <$500
1902 Date Back
4x5 1-21165 <$250
3x10-20 1-13334 <$250
1902 Plain Back
4x5 21166-30760 <$250
3x10-20 13335-17355 <$250
Total Issue $1,707,950
Out at close $165,000

254 New York
SIXTH NB OF NEW YORK CITY
{{ 4 L }}
Chartered 2/13/64
Liquidated 1/6/99
Original Series <$VALUE
4x5 1-14250 <$500
4x10 1-2250 <$600
4x20 1-500 <$1000
Series 1875
4x5 1-18750 <$500
Brown Back
4x5 1-9000 <$350
3x10-20 1-10712 <$350/$400
50-100 1-1047 <$1250/$1500
Total Issue $1,662,650
Out in 1910 $10,605

Southern NB of New York
SEE Ch 3359
Commercial NB of New York City

Sprague NB of New York
SEE Ch 2976
Sprague NB of Brooklyn

13149 Queens
SPRINGFIELD GARDENS NB OF NEW YORK
{{ 3U + 5 S }}
Chartered 12/27
1929 Small Size <$VALUE
5 Type 1 1-627 <$250
10 Type 1 1-419 <$250
20 Type 1 1-277 <$250
50 Type 1 1-40 <$250
Total Issue $89,190
Out in 1935 $40,680

5003 New York
STANDARD NB OF NEW YORK
{{ UNREPORTED }}
Chartered 6/12/95
Liquidated 4/26/98
Brown Back <$VALUE
4x5 1-4920 <$1250
Total Issue $98,400
Out in 1910 $515

Staten Island NB & TC of New York
SEE Ch 6198
Port Richmond NB, Port Richmond

13295 New York
STERLING NB & TC OF NEW YORK
{{ 38 S }}
Chartered 3/29
1929 Small Size <$VALUE
5 Type 1 1-36512 <$25
10 Type 1 1-18308 <$25
5 Type 2 1-259360 <$25
10 Type 2 1-131267 <$25
Total Issue $4,803,310
Out in 1935 $1,094,250

13254 New York
STRAUS NB & TC OF NEW YORK
{{ 17 S }}
Chartered 11/28
Liquidated 9/15/31
1929 Small Size <$VALUE
5 Type 1 1-4219 <$50
10 Type 1 1-2048 <$50
20 Type 1 1-618 <$50
Total Issue $323,610
Out at close $100,000

307 New York
TENTH NB OF NEW YORK
{{ 10 L }}
Chartered 4/64
Liquidated 11/23/77
Original Series <$VALUE
3x1-2 1-35000 <$250/$750
4x5 1-49000* <$300
3x10-20 1-14500<$500/$1000
50-100 1-1756 <$3500
500-1000 1-50 <$150,000/$200,000
* 24751-28000 canceled
Series 1875
3x1-2 1-3140 <$250/$750
4x5 1-60 <$300
Total Issue $2,170,300
Out in 1910 $13,972

87 New York
THIRD NB OF NEW YORK
{{ 15 L }}
Chartered 9/21/63
Liquidated 5/20/97
Original Series <$VALUE
3x1-2 1-14000 <$225/$750
4x5 1-11250 <$250
3x10-20 1-12935<$500/$1000
50-100 1-2310 <$3500
* 9414-9428 canceled
Series 1875
3x1-2 1-10000 <$225/$750
4x5 1-16250 <$250
3x10-20 1-11200<$500/$1000
Brown Back
4x5 1-27854 <$250
50-100 1-346 <$1250/$1500
Total Issue $2,831,480
Out in 1910 $12,920

6441 New York
THIRTY FOURTH STREET NB OF NEW YORK
{{ UNREPORTED }}
Chartered 9/29/02
Liquidated 7/22/07
1902 Red Seal <$VALUE
3x10-20 1-3603 <$1500
Total Issue $180,150
Out in 1910 $6,450

905 New York
TRADESMENS NB OF THE CITY OF NEW YORK
{{ 28 L }}
Chartered 3/17/65
Liquidated 1/13/99
Original Series <$VALUE
3x1-2 1-52000 <$200/$750
4x5 1-26000 <$225
3x10-20 1-8700 <$500/$1000
50-100 1-2618 <$3500
500-1000 1-20 <$150,000/$200,000
Series 1875
3x1-2 1-31000 <$200/$750
4x5 1-39365 <$225
3x10-20 1-10200<$500/$1000
50-100 1-3268 <$3500
500-1000 1-30 <$150,000/$200,000
Brown Back
4x5 1-34748 <$125
3x10-20 1-600 <$125/$175
50-100 1-200 <$1250/$1500
Total Issue $4,380,160
Out in 1910 $21,635

9360 New York
UNION EXCHANGE NB OF NEW YORK
{{ 11 L }}
Chartered 3/09
Liquidated 8/10/22
1902 Date Back <$VALUE
4x5 1-76000 <$100
3x10-20 1-57400 <$100
3x50-100 1-2000 <$300/$350
1902 Plain Back
4x5 76001-88115 <$100
3x10-20 57401-65646 <$100
Total Issue $5,544,600
Out at close $400,000

1278 New York
UNION NB OF NEW YORK
{{ 3 L }}
Chartered 6/65
Liquidated 7/21/85
Original Series <$VALUE
3x1-2 1-11000 <$300/$850
4x5 1-13630 <$400
3x10-20 1-4600 <$600/$1000
50-100 1-1000 <$3500
500-1000 1-170 <$150,000/$200,000
Series 1875
3x10-20 1-518 <$600/$1000
50-100 1-400 <$3500
Total Issue $1,048,500
Out in 1910 $6,669

1691 New York
UNION SQUARE NB OF NEW YORK
{{ 1 L }}
Organized 3/30/69
Receivership 12/15/71
Original Series <$VALUE
3x1-2 1-2520 <$1000/$2000
4x5 1-990 <$1250
3x10-20 1-472 <$1500/$2000
Total Issue $56,000
Out in 1915 $219

12406 New York
UNITED NB IN NEW YORK
{{ 1 L }}
Chartered 7/23
Liquidated 6/5/28
1902 Plain Back <$VALUE
4x5 1-1155 <$500
3x10-20 1-3972 <$500
Total Issue $221,700
Out at close $50,000

5990 New York
UNITED NB OF NEW YORK CITY
{{ 5 L }}
Chartered 10/12/01
Liquidated 7/28/06
Brown Back <$VALUE
4x5 1-10040 <$250
3x10-20 1-9066 <$250/$300
50-100 1-240 <$1250/$1500
Total Issue $690,100
Out in 1910 $19,000

2507 New York
UNITED STATES NB OF NEW YORK
{{ 2 L }}
Chartered 3/2/81
Liquidated 12/23/97
Series 1875 <$VALUE
4x5 1-6704 <$600
50-100 1-10001 <$3500
Total Issue $1,634,230
Out in 1910 $12,290

Washington NB of New York
SEE Ch 13360
Washington Square NB of New York

4335 New York
WASHINGTON NB OF THE CITY OF NEW YORK
{{ UNREPORTED }}
Chartered 6/5/90
Liquidated 4/13/91
Brown Back <$VALUE
4x5 1-965 <$1500
3x10-20 1-540 <$1500
Total Issue $46,300
Out in 1910 $290

13360 New York
WASHINGTON SQUARE NB OF NEW YORK
Organized 5/23/29
Liquidated 3/29/32
2nd title: Washington NB of New York 6/17/30
FIRST TITLE {{ 2 S }}
1929 Small Size <$VALUE
5 Type 1 1-1664 <$400
10 Type 1 1-572 <$400
20 Type 1 1-340 <$400
SECOND TITLE {{ 5 S }}
1929 Small Size
5 Type 1 1-1377 <$250
10 Type 1 1-704 <$250
20 Type 1 1-181 <$250
Total Issue $230,310
Out at close $100,000

3700 New York
WESTERN NB OF NEW YORK
{{ 7 L }}
Chartered 5/9/87
Liquidated 1/31/03
Brown Back <$VALUE
4x5 1-53769 <$200
3x10-20 1-23213 <$200/$250
Total Issue $2,236,030
Out in 1910 $24,985

Western NB of the United States in New York
SEE Ch 4567
Hide & Leather NB of New York

6802 Wayne
ARCADIA NB OF NEWARK
Chartered 5/03
Liquidated 6/15/29
2nd title:Arcadia NB & TC 6/25/25
FIRST TITLE {{ 13 L }}
1902 Red Seal <$VALUE
4x5 1-5330 <$200
3x10-20 1-4018 <$200/$250
1902 Date Bak
4x5 1-9000 <$100
3x10-20 1-8800 <$100
3x50-100 1-790 <$350/$400
1902 Plain Back
4x5 9001-21750 <$100
3x10-20 8801-18300 <$100
SECOND TITLE {{ 4 L }}
1902 Plain Back
4x5 1-5735 <$100
3x10-20 1-6334 <$100
3x50-100 1-189 <$350/$400
Total Issue $2,333,650
Out at close $200,000

349 Wayne
FNB OF NEWARK
{{ 14 L U + 12 S }}
Organized 3/2/64
Receivership 10/23/31
Original Series <$VALUE
4x5 1-5000 <$350
Series 1875
4x5 1-4000 <$350
Brown Back
4x5 1-12059 <$200
3x10-20 1-975 <$200/$250
1902 Red Seal
4x5 1-4500 <$200
3x10-20 1-5300 <$200/$250
1902 Date Back
4x5 1-13500 <$100
3x10-20 1-7600 <$100
1902 Plain Back
4x5 13501-35296 <$100
3x10-20 7601-26499 <$100
1929 Small Size
10 Type 1 1-2585 <$100
20 Type 1 1-779 <$100
Total Issue $3,104,380
Out at close $150,000
Large out at close $13,980

10111 Tioga
FNB OF NEWARK VALLEY
{{ 2 L 5 S }}
Organized 9/11/11
1902 Date Back <$VALUE
3x10-20 1-1670 <$400
1902 Plain Back
3x10-20 1671-5577 <$400
1929 Small Size
10 Type 1 1-738 <$250
20 Type 1 1-180 <$250
10 Type 2 1-1128 <$250
20 Type 2 1-318 <$250
Total Issue $362,370
Out in 1935 $25,000
Large out 1935 $950

1106 Orange
HIGHLAND NB OF NEWBURGH
Chartered 1865
2nd title:Highland NB & TC 1/20/26
3rd title:Highland Quassaick NB & TC 5/21/27
FIRST TITLE {{ 12 L }}
Original Series <$VALUE
3x1-2 1-2800 <$250/$750
4x5 1-13150 <$300
4x10 1-6800 <$600
3x20-50 1-3255<$1250/$3500
Series 1875
4x5 1-15247 <$300
4x10 1-5750 <$500
3x20-50 1-931 <$1000/$3500
Brown Back
4x5 1-12125 <$175
3x10-20 1-5760 <$175/$225
50-100 1-570 <$1250/$1500
1902 Red Seal
4x5 1-4000 <$200
50-100 1-2600 <$2250/$2500
1902 Date Back
4x5 1-19250 <$100
3x10-20 1-14400 <$100
1902 Plain Back
4x5 19251-49000 <$100
3x10-20 14401-32900 <$100
SECOND TITLE {{ 3 L }}
1902 Plain Back
4x5 1-3549 <$125
3x10-20 1-3078 <$125
THIRD TITLE {{ 2 L 24 S }}
1902 Plain Back
4x5 1-5745 <$125
3x10-20 1-3746 <$125
1929 Small Size
5 Type 1 1-7630 <$40
10 Type 1 1-3894 <$40
20 Type 1 1-962 <$50
5 Type 2 1-11114 <$50
10 Type 2 1-5894 <$50
20 Type 2 1-1389 <$55
Total Issue $6,242,750
Out in 1935 $200,000
Large out 1935 $15,500

Highland-Quassaick NB & TC of Newburgh
SEE Ch 1106
Highland NB of Newburgh

468 Orange
NB OF NEWBURGH
{{ 20 L 27 S }}
Chartered 6/64
Original Series <$VALUE
4x5 1-15900 <$300
4x10 1-11000 <$600
3x20-50 1-6970<$1250/$3500
Series 1875
4x5 1-7685 <$300
4x10 1-5795 <$500
3x20-50 1-3621<$1000/$3500
Brown Back
4x5 1-11900 <$175
3x10-20 1-43038 <$175/$225
50-100 1-3670 <$1250/$1500
1902 Red Seal
4x5 1-26800 <$200
3x10-20 1-14680 <$200/$250
50-100 1-260 <$2250/$2500
1902 Date Back
4x5 1-29000 <$75
3x10-20 1-29200 <$75
50-100 1-400 <$300/$350
1902 Plain Back
4x5 29001-33500 <$75
3x10-20 29201-99042 <$75
1929 Small Size
10 Type 1 1-11438 <$25
20 Type 1 1-3062 <$35
5 Type 2 1-21440* <$25
10 Type 2 1-6108 <$25
20 Type 2 1-2606 <$35
* 241-246 canceled
Total Issue $13,514,100
Out in 1935 $400,000
Large out 1935 $30,500

1213 Orange
QUASSAICK NB OF NEWBURGH
{{ 21 L }}
Chartered 1865
Liquidated 5/9/27
Original Series <$VALUE
3x1-2 1-12816 <$200/$750
4x5 1-12050 <$300
3x10-20 1-4800 <$600/$1250
50-100 1-350 <$3500
Series 1875
4x5 1-5950 <$300
3x10-20 1-5288 <$500/$1000
50-100 1-700 <$3500
Brown Back
4x5 1-34422 <$175
3x10-20 1-24969 <$175/$225
50-100 1-1100 <$1250/$1500
1902 Red Seal
4x5 1-11200 <$200
4x10 1-4650 <$200
3x10-20 1-4000 <$200/$250
1902 Date Back
4x5 1-30750 <$75
4x10 1-24250 <$75
3x10-20 1-1800 <$75
1902 Plain Back
4x5 30751-85572 <$75
4x10 24251-51000 <$75
3x10-20 1801-13414 <$75
Total Issue $8,220,010
Out at close $290,595

1655 Herkimer
NB OF NEWPORT
{{ 5 L 8 S }}
Organized 5/8/65
Receivership 10/13/33
Original Series <$VALUE
3x1-2 1-3000 <$400/$1000
4x5 1-3075 <$500
3x10-20 1-410 <$750/$1250
Series 1875
3x1-2 1-400 <$400/$1000
4x5 1-1675 <$500
3x10-20 1-1194 <$750/$1250
Brown Back
4x5 1-6033 <$350
3x10-20 1-2808 <$350
1902 Red Seal
4x5 1-1400 <$400
3x10-20 1-960 <$400
1902 Date Back
4x5 1-2600 <$200
3x10-20 1-2040 <$200
1902 Plain Back
4x5 2601-9740 <$200
3x10-20 2041-6249 <$200
1929 Small Size
5 Type 1 1-1840 <$125
10 Type 1 1-884 <$125
20 Type 1 1-268 <$125
5 Type 2 1-242 <$125
10 Type 2 1-180 <$125
20 Type 2 1-25 <$125
Total Issue $1,180,420
Out at close $49,600
Large out at close $3,360

12284 Niagara
CATARACT NB OF NIAGARA FALLS
Chartered 12/22
Liquidated 8/31/29
2nd title:NB of Niagara & TC of Niagara Falls 9/29/27
FIRST TITLE {{ 6 L }}
1902 Plain Back <$VALUE
4x5 1-16342 <$175
3x10-20 1-11704 <$175
SECOND TITLE {{ 8 L }}
1902 Plain Back
4x5 1-13003 <$125
3x10-20 1-16237 <$125
Total Issue $1,983,950
Out at close $559,250

11489 Niagara
FALLS NB OF NIAGARA FALLS
{{ 3 L 3 S }}
Organized 10/16/19
Receivership 10/26/33
1902 Plain Back <$VALUE
4x5 1-13570 <$300
1929 Small Size
5 Type 1 1-2906 <$225
5 Type 2 1-874 <$225
Total Issue $362,950
Out at close $25,000
Large out at close $940

4899 Niagara
FNB OF NIAGARA FALLS
{{ UNREPORTED }}
Organized 4/18/93
Receivership 12/18/96
Brown Back <$VALUE
4x5 1-2297 <$1500
Total Issue $45,940
Out in 1916 $295

NB of Niagara & TC of Niagara Falls
SEE Ch 12284
Cataract NB of Niagara Falls

9399 Tioga
NICHOLS NB, NICHOLS
{{ 3 L 3 S }}
Chartered 5/09
1902 Date Back <$VALUE
3x10-20 1-2460* <$500
1902 Plain Back
3x10-20 2581-4260* <$500
* 2461-2580 not marked
1929 Small Size
10 Type 1 1-310 <$350
20 Type 1 1-102 <$350
10 Type 2 1-24 <$400
20 Type 2 1-46 <$400
Total Issue $245,000
Out in 1935 $10,000
Large out 1935 $230

9716 Warren
NORTH CREEK NB, NORTH CREEK
{{ 4 L 12 S }}
Chartered 3/10
1902 Date Back <$VALUE
3x10-20 1-3300 <$350
1902 Plain Back
3x10-20 3301-10917 <$350
1929 Small Size
10 Type 1 1-1920 <$125
20 Type 1 1-434 <$125
10 Type 2 1-5543 <$125
20 Type 2 1-1776 <$150
Total Issue $804,080
Out in 1935 $100,000
Large out 1935 $2,340

North Granville NB, North Granville
SEE Ch 1348
Farmers NB of Fort Edward

10016 Wayne
FNB OF NORTH ROSE
{{ 3 L 2 S }}
Organized 4/7/11
Receivership 10/29/31
1902 Date Back <$VALUE
4x5 1-1315 <$500
3x10-20 1-974 <$500
1902 Plain Back
4x5 1316-6110 <$500
3x10-20 975-3861 <$500
1929 Small Size
5 Type 1 1-561 <$400
10 Type 1 1-282 <$400
20 Type 1 1-91 <$400
Total Issue $359,920
Out at close $25,000
Large out at close $2,130

6809 Niagara
STATE NB OF NORTH TONAWANDA
{{ 18 L }}
Chartered 6/03
Liquidated 7/3/26
1902 Red Seal <$VALUE
4x5 1-9465 <$175
3x10-20 1-6924 <$175/$225
1902 Date Back
4x5 1-24250 <$85
3x10-20 1-15200 <$85
1902 Plain Back
4x5 24251-58087 <$85
3x10-20 15201-34641 <$85
Total Issue $3,429,290
Out at close $300,000

1275 Washington
CAMBRIDGE VALLEY NB OF NORTH WHITE CREEK
Chartered 1865
2nd title:Cambridge Valley NB of Cambridge 7/25/75
FIRST TITLE {{ 3 L }}
Original Series <$VALUE
3x1-2 1-3000 <$400/$850
4x5 1-8000 <$500
3x10-20 1-1900 <$750/$1250
Series 1875
4x5 1-1080 <$500
SECOND TITLE {{ 5 L 5 S }}
Series 1875
3x10-20 1-2095 <$750/$1250
Brown Back
3x10-20 1-6120 <$500
1902 Red Seal
3x10-20 1-2100 <$500
1902 Date Back
3x10-20 1-4000* <$250
1902 Plain Back
3x10-20 4251-12259* <$250
* 4001-4250 not marked
1929 Small Size
10 Type 1 1-1432 <$200
20 Type 1 1-344 <$200
10 Type 2 1-1998 <$200
20 Type 2 1-395 <$200
Total Issue $1,575,380
Out in 1935 $50,000
Large out 1935 $4,650

5936 Suffolk
FNB OF NORTHPORT
Chartered 8/8/01
2nd title:FNB & TC 3/29/28
FIRST TITLE {{ 3 L }}
Brown Back <$VALUE
3x10-20 1-890 <$1500
1882 Date Back
3x10-20 1-1900 <$1500
1882 Value Back
3x10-20 1901-3092 <$1500
1902 Plain Back
3x10-20 1-2163 <$1000
SECOND TITLE {{ 0 L 3 S }}
1902 Plain Back
3x10-20 1-133 <$1000
1929 Small Size
10 Type 1 1-314 <$750
20 Type 1 1-104 <$750
10 Type 2 1-587 <$750
20 Type 2 1-115 <$750
Total Issue $331,760
Out in 1935 $12,500
Large out 1935 $790

Chenango County NB & TC of Norwich
SEE Ch 3011
Chenango NB of Norwich

3011 Chenango
CHENANGO NB OF NORWICH
Chartered 1883
2nd title:Chenango County NB & TC of Norwich 1/20/26
FIRST TITLE {{ 10 L }}
Brown Back <$VALUE
4x5 1-3200 <$200
3x10-20 1-8563 <$200/$250
1902 Red Seal
3x10-20 1-5700 <$250/$300
1902 Date Back
3x10-20 1-8200 <$125
1902 Plain Back
3x10-20 8201-20800 <$125
SECOND TITLE {{ 0 L 19 S }}
1902 Plain Back
3x10-20 1-5063 <$150
1929 Small Size
10 Type 1 1-4164 <$50
20 Type 1 1-1220 <$50
10 Type 2 1-9408 <$50
20 Type 2 1-3000 <$50
Total Issue $2,625,120
Out in 1935 $200,000
Large out 1935 $5,690

1354 Chenango
NB OF NORWICH
Chartered 1865
2nd title:NB & TC of Norwich 12/3/25
FIRST TITLE {{ 18 L }}
Original Series <$VALUE
3x1-2 1-9600 <$250/$750
4x5 1-4075 <$250
3x10-20 1-3150 <$600/$1250
Series 1875
3x1-2 1-1000 <$250/$750
4x5 1-4960 <$250
3x10-20 1-2082 <$500/$1000
Brown Back
4x5 1-14497 <$150
3x10-20 1-9858 <$150/$200
1902 Red Seal
4x5 1-10100 <$150
4x10 1-7000 <$150
3x10-20 1-1660 <$150/$200
1902 Date Back
4x5 1-30000 <$75
4x10 1-22750 <$75
3x10-20 1-4000 <$75
1902 Plain Back
4x5 30001-46000 <$75
4x10 22751-27100 <$75
3x10-20 4001-25200 <$75
SECOND TITLE {{ 5 L 28 S }}
1902 Plain Back
4x5 1-5558 <$75
3x10-20 1-12469 <$75
1929 Small Size
5 Type 1 1-3432 <$45
10 Type 1 1-1250 <$45
20 Type 1 1-5538 <$45
5 Type 2 1-16808 <$45
10 Type 2 1-8987 <$45
20 Type 2 1-2151 <$50
Total Issue $6,901,200
Out in 1935 $400,000
Large out 1935 $15,000

2224 Livingston
FNB OF NUNDA
{{ 5 L }}
Chartered 2/18/75
Liquidated 2/5/95
Original Series <$VALUE
3x1-2 1-600 <$500/$1250
3x10-20 1-696 <$750/$1250
Series 1875
3x1-2 1-460 <$500/$1250
3x10-20 1-2168 <$750/$1250
Total Issue $148,500
Out in 1910 $544

2378 Rockland
NYACK NB, NYACK
Chartered 3/8/78
2nd title:Nyack NB & TC 5/31/32
FIRST TITLE {{ 8 L 6 S }}
Series 1875 <$VALUE
4x5 1-10857 <$500
Brown Back
4x5 1-4475 <$400
3x10-20 1-3050 <$400
1882 Date Back
4x5 1-10000 <$400
3x10-20 1-6960 <$400
1882 Value Back
4x5 10001-13304 <$400
3x10-20 6961-8616 <$400
1902 Plain Back
4x5 1-16975 <$250
3x10-20 1-11725 <$250
1929 Small Size
5 Type 1 1-4920 <$100
10 Type 1 1-2450 <$100
20 Type 1 1-596 <$100
SECOND TITLE {{ 16 S }}
1929 Small Size
5 Type 1 1-1244 <$100
10 Type 1 1-1074 <$100
20 Type 1 1-274 <$100
5 Type 2 1-16572 <$100
10 Type 2 1-8376 <$100
20 Type 2 1-2268 <$100
Total Issue $2,794,510
Out in 1935 $199,995
Large out 1935 $6,735

1286 Rockland
ROCKLAND COUNTY NB OF NYACK
{{ UNREPORTED }}
Chartered 1865
Liquidated 1/10/78
Original Series <$VALUE
4x5 1-5630 <$1250
3x10-20 1-1900<$1500/$2000
Series 1875
4x5 1-950 <$1250
3x10-20 1-338 <$1500/$2000
Total Issue $243,500
Out in 1910 $1,125

13493 Schuyler
FNB OF ODESSA
{{ 3U + 7 S }}
Chartered 9/30
1929 Small Size <$VALUE
5 Type 1 1-2104 <$150
10 Type 1 1-348 <$150
20 Type 1 1-108 <$150
5 Type 2 1-9598 <$150
10 Type 2 1-1245 <$150
20 Type 2 1-480 <$175
Total Issue $167,000
Out in 1935 $50,000

2446 Saint Lawrence
NB OF OGDENSBURG
{{ 16 L }}
Chartered 1/2/80
Liquidated 12/31/29
Series 1875 <$VALUE
4x5 1-4000 <$375
4x10 1-7037 <$500
Brown Back
3x10-20 1-7500 <$200/$250
1882 Date Back
4x5 1-7500 <$200
3x10-20 1-4640 <$200/$250
1882 Value Back
4x5 7501-12105 <$200
3x10-20 4641-7084<$200/$250
1902 Plain Back
4x5 1-12990 <$100
3x10-20 1-9091 <$100
Total Issue $2,047,130
Out at close $43,340

10964 Herkimer
FNB OF OLD FORGE
{{ 6 L 6 S }}
Chartered 3/17
1902 Plain Back <$VALUE
4x5 1-11018 <$300
4x10 1-8571 <$300
1929 Small Size
5 Type 1 1-2632 <$250
10 Type 1 1-1364 <$250
5 Type 2 1-6996 <$250
10 Type 2 1-3252 <$250
Total Issue $791,500
Out in 1935 $50,000
Large out 1935 $1,580

7102 Cattaraugus
CITIZENS NB OF OLEAN
{{ UNREPORTED }}
Chartered 1/19/04
Liquidated 8/9/06
1902 Red Seal <$VALUE
4x5 1-1520 <$1000
3x10-20 1-1132 <$1000
Total Issue $87,000
Out in 1910 $4,145

2376 Cattaraugus
EXCHANGE NB OF OLEAN
{{ 28 L 50+ S }}
Chartered 1/2/78
Series 1875 <$VALUE
4x5 1-22325 <$250
Brown Back
3x10-20 1-19550 <$175/$225
1882 Date Back
3x10-20 1-34500 <$175/$225
1882 Value Back
3x10-20 34501-37844 <$175/$225
1902 Plain Back
3x10-20 1-80866 <$75
1929 Small Size
10 Type 1 1-23090 <$20
20 Type 1 1-5790 <$30
10 Type 2 1-427 <$40
20 Type 2 1-300 <$50
Total Issue $9,449,970
Out in 1935 $500,000
Large out 1935 $22,040

1887 Cattaraugus
FNB OF OLEAN
{{ 18 L 30 S }}
Chartered 10/3/71
Original Series <$VALUE
3x1-2 1-1800 <$250/$750
4x5 1-6800 <$300
Series 1875
4x5 1-14902 <$300
Brown Back
4x5 1-12900 <$150
3x10-20 1-4400 <$150/$200
1882 Date Back
4x5 1-2165 <$150
3x10-20 1-1701 <$150/$200
1902 Date Back
4x5 1-5400 <$100
3x10-20 1-4320 <$100
1902 Plain Back
4x5 5401-46432 <$100
3x10-20 4321-30743 <$100
1929 Small Size
5 Type 1 1-8986 <$20
10 Type 1 1-5020 <$20
20 Type 1 1-1278 <$30
5 Type 2 1-16194 <$20
10 Type 2 1-9152 <$20
20 Type 2 1-2399 <$30
Total Issue $4,459,790
Out in 1935 $250,000
Large out 1935 $4,020

9822 Cattaraugus
OLEAN NB, OLEAN
{{ 3 L }}
Chartered 7/10
Liquidated 9/15/14
1902 Date Back <$VALUE
4x5 1-6510 <$300
3x10-20 1-4768 <$300
Total Issue $368,600
Out in 1914 $69,350

519 Madison
FNB OF ONEIDA
{{ 1 L }}
Chartered 9/20/64
Liquidated 1/13/74
Original Series <$VALUE
3x1-2 1-1600 <$600/$1250
4x5 1-2650 <$650
3x10-20 1-1900 <$750/$1250
Total Issue $156,000
Out in 1910 $1,313

2401 Madison
N STATE B OF ONEIDA
{{ 7 L }}
Chartered 11/9/78
Liquidated 9/1/13
Series 1875 <$VALUE
4x5 1-19866 <$400
Brown Back
3x10-20 1-5400 <$300
1882 Date Back
3x10-20 1-3169 <$300
Total Issue $825,770
Out in 1914 $35,150

1090 Madison
ONEIDA VALLEY NB OF ONEIDA
{{ 14 L 21 S }}
Chartered 4/65
Original Series <$VALUE
3x1-2 1-4300 <$300/$850
4x5 1-4475 <$300
3x10-20 1-1370 <$600/$1250
Series 1875
3x1-2 1-1120 <$300/$850
4x5 1-5610 <$300
3x10-20 1-1500 <$600/$1250
Brown Back
4x5 1-8046 <$200
3x10-20 1-3858 <$200/$250
1902 Red Seal
4x5 1-1700 <$200
3x10-20 1-1340 <$200/$250
1902 Date Back
4x5 1-5800 <$100
3x10-20 1-4030 <$100
1902 Plain Back
4x5 5801-31180 <$100
3x10-20 4031-20215 <$100
1929 Small Size
5 Type 1 1-5902 <$40
10 Type 1 1-3244 <$40
20 Type 1 1-794 <$50
5 Type 2 1-14604 <$50
10 Type 2 1-6900 <$50
20 Type 2 1-1836 <$50
Total Issue $3,107,190
Out in 1935 $175,000
Large out 1935 $7,290

8920 Otsego
CITIZENS NB OF ONEONTA
Chartered 10/07
2nd title:Citizens NB & TC 5/1/24
FIRST TITLE {{ 6 L }}
1902 Red Seal <$VALUE
4x5 1-1650 <$250
3x10-20 1-1340 <$250
1902 Date Back
4x5 1-8200 <$125
3x10-20 1-6240 <$125
1902 Plain Back
4x5 8201-20450 <$125
3x10-20 6241-13800 <$125
SECOND TITLE {{ 6 L 18 S }}
1902 Plain Back
4x5 1-8168 <$125
4x10 1-7630 <$125
1929 Small Size
5 Type 1 1-5494 <$50
10 Type 1 1-2850 <$50
5 Type 2 1-13428 <$50
10 Type 2 1-6516 <$50
Total Issue $2,135,680
Out in 1935 $100,000
Large out 1935 $1,940

FNB of Oneonta
SEE Ch 420
Worthington NB of Cooperstown

2151 Otsego
WILBER NB OF ONEONTA
{{ 14 L 27 S }}
Chartered 6/6/74
Original Series <$VALUE
3x1-2 1-1500 <$250/$750
4x5 1-4875 <$300
Series 1875
4x5 1-16650 <$300
3x10-20 1-1774 <$500/$1000
Brown Back
3x10-20 1-11100 <$200
1882 Date Back
3x10-20 1-6689 <$200
1902 Date Back
3x10-20 1-2000* <$100
1902 Plain Back
3x10-20 2501-20777* <$100
* 2001-2500 not marked
1929 Small Size
10 Type 1 1-4652 <$40
20 Type 1 1-1128 <$40
10 Type 2 1-12444 <$40
20 Type 2 1-3036 <$40
Total Issue $3,054,640
Out in 1935 $200,000
Large out 1935 $6,570

****
6630 Oneida
FNB OF ORISKANY FALLS
{{ UNREPORTED }}
Chartered 2/03
Liquidated 3/8/26
1902 Red Seal <$VALUE
3x10-20 1-1775 <$1250
1902 Date Back
3x10-20 1-2360 <$750
1902 Plain Back
3x10-20 2361-5328 <$750
Total Issue $355,150
Out at close $25,000
****
FNB of Ossining
FNB & TC of Ossining
SEE Ch 471
FNB of Sing Sing
****
6552 Westchester
OSSINING NB, OSSINING
{{ 9 L }}
Chartered 12/23/02
Liquidated 9/29/26
1902 Red Seal <$VALUE
4x5 1-4920 <$750
3x10-20 1-3597 <$750
1902 Date Back
4x5 1-11100 <$350
3x10-20 1-7600 <$350
1902 Plain Back
4x5 11101-28355 <$350
3x10-20 7601-18411 <$350
Total Issue $1,765,900
Out at close $100,000
****
F & Second NB & TC of Oswego
SEE Ch 255
FNB of Oswego
****
255 Oswego
FNB OF OSWEGO
Chartered 2/64
2nd title:F & Second NB & TC of Oswego 10/15/29
FIRST TITLE {{ 16 L 3 S }}
Original Series <$VALUE
3x1-2 1-3000 <$250/$750
4x5 1-8100 <$300
4x10 1-4800 <$600
Series 1875
3x1-2 1-640 <$250/$750
4x5 1-4411 <$300
4x10 1-3762 <$500
Brown Back
4x5 1-8458 <$200
3x10-20 1-11986 <$200/$250
1902 Red Seal
4x5 1-6200 <$200
3x10-20 1-4220 <$200/$250
1902 Date Back
4x5 1-12250 <$100
3x10-20 1-8600 <$100
1902 Plain Back
4x5 12251-40710 <$100
3x10-20 8601-25629 <$100
1929 Small Size
5 Type 1 1-1506 <$100
10 Type 1 1-776 <$100
20 Type 1 1-260 <$100
SECOND TITLE {{ 31 S }}
1929 Small Size
5 Type 1 1-13842 <$35
10 Type 1 1-7780 <$35
20 Type 1 1-1906 <$40
5 Type 2 1-25748 <$35
10 Type 2 1-11446 <$35
20 Type 2 1-3980 <$40
Total Issue $5,366,530
Out in 1935 $400,000
Large out 1935 $17,510
Outstanding includes Ch 296
****
1355 Oswego
LAKE ONTARIO NB OF OSWEGO
{{ 1 L }}
Chartered 1865
Liquidated 2/24/77
Original Series <$VALUE
3x1-2 1-9750 <$650/$1500
4x5 1-15950 <$850
3x10-20 1-1400<$1000/$1500
Total Issue $437,750
Out in 1910 $3,634
****
821 Oswego
N MARINE B OF OSWEGO
{{ 3 L }}
Chartered 2/18/65
Liquidated 1/25/79
Original Series <$VALUE
3x1-2 1-3000 <$350/$850
4x5 1-6050 <$400
3x10-20 1-580 <$750/$1250
Series 1875
3x1-2 1-1400 <$350/$850
4x5 1-1445 <$400
3x10-20 1-36 <$750/$1250
Total Issue $202,700
Out in 1910 $1,975
****
296 Oswego
SECOND NB OF OSWEGO
Chartered 3/64
Closed 10/15/29
2nd title:Second NB & TC 4/15/24
FIRST TITLE {{ 8 L }}
Original Series <$VALUE
3x1-2 1-4300 <$250/$750
4x5 1-4425 <$300
3x10-20 1-760 <$600/$1250
3x10-20 1001-2500 <$600/$1250
Series 1875
3x10-20 1-2390 <$500/$1000
Brown Back
50-100 1-915 <$1250/$1500
1902 Red Seal
3x10-20 1-1700 <$200/$250
1902 Date Back
3x10-20 1-10100 <$100
1902 Plain Back
3x10-20 10101-20300 <$100
SECOND TITLE {{ 3 L 6 S }}
1902 Plain Back
3x10-20 1-7196 <$125
1929 Small Size
10 Type 1 1-208* <$250
20 Type 1 1-10 <$250
* D000208A-F000208A canceled
Total Issue $1,953,200
Out at close $99,450
Large out at close $85,800
Ch 255 assumed circulation
****
7840 Seneca
FNB OF OVID
{{ 3 L 3 S }}
Organized 6/26/05
1902 Red Seal <$VALUE
3x10-20 1-450 <$750
1902 Date Back
3x10-20 1-1800 <$350
1902 Plain Back
3x10-20 1801-6116 <$350
1929 Small Size
10 Type 1 1-694 <$350
20 Type 1 1-162 <$350
10 Type 2 1-1482 <$350
20 Type 2 1-310 <$375
Total Issue $410,400
Out in 1935 $25,000
Large out 1935 $1,050
****
1019 Tioga
FNB OF OWEGO
{{ 7 L 7 S }}
Chartered 4/65
Original Series <$VALUE
3x1-2 1-4000 <$350/$850
4x5 1-6500 <$400
3x10-20 1-1200 <$750/$1250
Series 1875
3x1-2 1-1420 <$350/$850
4x5 1-2500 <$400
3x10-20 1-374 <$600/$1000
Brown Back
3x10-20 1-5390 <$300
1902 Red Seal
3x10-20 1-1900 <$300
1902 Date Back
3x10-20 1-3800 <$150
1902 Plain Back
3x10-20 3801-11442 <$150
1929 Small Size
10 Type 1 1-1516 <$100
20 Type 1 1-348 <$100
10 Type 2 1-2195 <$100
20 Type 2 1-479 <$100
Total Issue $1,386,650
Out in 1935 $50,000
Large out 1935 $4,170
****
1311 Tioga
N UNION B OF OWEGO
{{ UNREPORTED }}
Chartered 6/20/65
Liquidated 1/11/70
Original Series <$VALUE
3x1-2 1-2000 <$1250/$2000
4x5 1-2000 <$1250
3x10-20 1-762 <$1500/$2000
Total Issue $88,250
Out in 1910 $817
****
2996 Tioga
OWEGO NB, OWEGO
{{ 9 L 16 S }}
Chartered 1883
Brown Back <$VALUE
4x5 1-5809 <$250
3x10-20 1-629 <$250/$300
1902 Red Seal
4x5 1-2425 <$300
3x10-20 1-2040 <$300
1902 Date Back
4x5 1-3950 <$150
3x10-20 1-2620 <$150
1902 Plain Back
4x5 3951-18374 <$150
3x10-20 2621-12261 <$150
1929 Small Size
5 Type 1 1-3720 <$50
10 Type 1 1-1820 <$50
20 Type 1 1-508 <$60
5 Type 2 1-7894 <$60
10 Type 2 1-3967 <$60
20 Type 2 1-1092 <$60
Total Issue $1,661,400
Out in 1935 $100,000
Large out 1935 $5,030
Outstanding includes Ch 862
****
862 Tioga
TIOGA NB OF OWEGO
{{ 5 L }}
Chartered 3/6/65
Closed 12/31/21
Original Series <$VALUE
3x1-2 1-3200 <$400/$850
4x5 1-7200 <$500
4x10 1-1500 <$750
Series 1875
4x5 1-1755 <$500
4x10 1-690 <$600
Brown Back
3x10-20 1-5702 <$350
1902 Red Seal
4x5 1-1850 <$350
3x10-20 1-1440 <$350
1902 Date Back
4x5 1-3050 <$175
3x10-20 1-2520 <$175
1902 Plain Back
4x5 3051-6315 <$175
3x10-20 2521-4657 <$175
Total Issue $1,035,950
Out at close $46,800
Ch 2996 assumed circulation
****
273 Chenango
FNB OF OXFORD
{{ 13 L 11 S }}
Organized 2/10/64
Receivership 4/25/34
Original Series <$VALUE
3x1-2 1-6000 <$300/$750
4x5 1-8800 <$400
2x10-20-50 1-1300 <$750/$1250/$3500
Series 1875
4x5 1-4820 <$400
2x10-20-50 1-320 <$750/$1250/$3500
Brown Back
3x10-20 1-9700 <$250/$300
1902 Red Seal
4x5 1-3000 <$300
3x10-20 1-4700 <$300
1902 Date Back
4x5 1-7250 <$125
3x10-20 1-5100 <$125
1902 Plain Back
4x5 7251-24130 <$125
3x10-20 5101-16697 <$125
1929 Small Size
5 Type 1 1-3550 <$75
10 Type 1 1-2000 <$75
20 Type 1 1-462 <$75
5 Type 2 1-3362 <$100
10 Type 2 1-1596 <$100
20 Type 2 1-314 <$100
Total Issue $2,866,640
Out at close $99,120
Large out at close $8,585
****
14025 Chenango
NB OF OXFORD
{{ 6 S }}
Chartered 2/34
1929 Small Size <$VALUE
5 Type 2 1-6104 <$200
10 Type 2 1-3408 <$200
20 Type 2 1-960 <$200
Total Issue $83,800
Out in 1935 $75,000
****
8865 Queens
FNB OF OZONE PARK
{{ 2 L }}
Chartered 9/07
Liquidated 7/19/22
1902 Red Seal <$VALUE
4x5 1-600 <$850
3x10-20 1-480 <$850
1902 Date Back
4x5 1-6000 <$400
3x10-20 1-4040 <$400
1902 Plain Back
4x5 6001-10975 <$400
3x10-20 4041-7034 <$400
Total Issue $607,200
Out at close $50,000
****
3800 Steuben
BRONSON NB OF PAINTED POST
{{ UNREPORTED }}
Chartered 10/5/87
Liquidated 2/29/92
Brown Back <$VALUE
4x5 1-1050 <$2000
3x10-20 1-542 <$2000
Total Issue $48,100
Out in 1910 $270
****
13664 Steuben
FNB OF PAINTED POST
{{ U + 12 S }}
Chartered 2/33
1929 Small Size <$VALUE
5 Type 1 1-1036 <$250
10 Type 1 1-524 <$250
5 Type 2 1-5616 <$250
10 Type 2 1-3000 <$250
Total Issue $120,600
Out in 1935 $36,910
****
11956 Steuben
PAINTED POST NB, PAINTED POST
{{ 2 L 2 S }}
Organized 2/17/21
Liquidated 7/11/33
1902 Plain Back <$VALUE
4x5 1-6445 <$650
1929 Small Size
5 Type 1 1-1189 <$650
Total Issue $164,570
Out at close $22,250
Large out at close $790
****
295 Wayne
FNB OF PALMYRA
{{ U + 22 L 0 S }}
Chartered 3/64
Liquidated 10/19/29
Original Series <$VALUE
3x1-2 1-10000 <$250/$750
4x5 1-3500 <$300
4x10 1-4500 <$600
2x20-50-100 1-1200 <$1250/$3500/$3500
Series 1875
3x1-2 1-4800 <$250/$750
4x5 1-4973 <$300
4x10 1-5000 <$600
2x20-50-100 1-2816 <$1250/$3500/$3500
Brown Back
4x5 1-73287 <$150
3x10-20 1-45947 <$150/$200
50-100 1-2800 <$1250/$1500
1902 Red Seal
4x5 1-5000 <$150
3x10-20 1-2800 <$150/$200
50-100 1-300 <$2250/$2500
1902 Date Back
4x5 1-3000 <$60
3x10-20 1-2100 <$75
50-100 1-100 <$350/$400
1902 Plain Back
4x5 3001-11633 <$60
3x10-20 2101-7918 <$75
1929 Small Size
5 Type 1 1-110 <$750
10 Type 1 1-32* <$750
20 Type 1 1-4** <$750
* E000032A-F000032A canceled
** C000004A-F000004A canceled
Total Issue $6,503,750
Out at close $50,000
Large out at close $48,900
****
6785 Suffolk
CITIZENS NB OF PATCHOGUE
{{ UNREPORTED }}
Chartered 5/03
Liquidated 6/7/16
1902 Red Seal <$VALUE
4x5 1-1700 <$3000
3x10-20 1-2350 <$3000
1902 Date Back
4x5 1-5350 <$1500
3x10-20 1-3630 <$1500
1902 Plain Back
4x5 5351-5740 <$1500
3x10-20 3631-3818 <$1500
Total Issue $457,200
Out at close $32,700
****
12788 Suffolk
PEOPLES NB OF PATCHOGUE
{{ 6 S }}
Chartered 7/25
1929 Small Size <$VALUE
5 Type 1 1-1684 <$500
10 Type 1 1-792 <$500
5 Type 2 1-16812 <$500
10 Type 2 1-9684 <$500
Total Issue $278,940
Out in 1935 $100,000
****
1269 Dutchess
NB OF PAWLING
{{ 8 L 12 S }}
Chartered 1865
Original Series <$VALUE
3x1-2 1-3500 <$350/$750
4x5 1-4000 <$400
3x10-20 1-2845 <$600/$1250
3x50-100 1-382 <$3500
Series 1875
3x1-2 1-1110 <$350/$750
4x5 1-945 <$400
3x10-20 1-2399 <$600/$1000
3x50-100 1-430 <$3500
Brown Back
4x5 1-13219 <$250
3x10-20 1-9175 <$250/$300
50-100 1-595 <$1250/$1500
1902 Red Seal
4x5 1-1750 <$300
3x10-20 1-1200 <$300
1902 Date Back
4x5 1-7700 <$150
3x10-20 1-5560 <$150
1902 Plain Back
4x5 7701-20490 <$150
3x10-20 5561-13754 <$150
1929 Small Size
5 Type 1 1-1896 <$85
10 Type 1 1-1230 <$85
20 Type 1 1-344 <$100
5 Type 2 1-9096 <$100
10 Type 2 1-4980 <$100
20 Type 2 1-1272 <$100
Total Issue $2,884,710
Out in 1935 $100,000
Large out 1935 $5,781
****
10526 Rockland
FNB OF PEARL RIVER
Chartered 4/14
2nd title:FNB & TC 9/17/25
FIRST TITLE {{ 3 L }}
1902 Plain Back <$VALUE
4x5 1-4875 <$650
3x10-20 1-2980 <$650
SECOND TITLE {{ 1 L 6 S }}
1902 Plain Back
4x5 1-1550 <$650
3x10-20 1-1007 <$650
1929 Small Size
5 Type 1 1-924 <$350
10 Type 1 1-518 <$350
20 Type 1 1-148 <$350
5 Type 2 1-9502 <$350
10 Type 2 1-4806 <$350
20 Type 2 1-768 <$350
Total Issue $515,340
Out in 1935 $75,000
Large out 1935 $1,010
****
8398 Westchester
PEEKSKILL NB, PEEKSKILL
Organized 9/8/06
2nd title:Peekskill NB & TC 5/8/31
FIRST TITLE {{ 10 L 3 S }}
1902 Red Seal <$VALUE
4x5 1-1500 <$1000
3x10-20 1-1400 <$1000
50-100 1-900 <$2250/$2500
1902 Date Back
4x5 1-10000 <$500
3x10-20 1-5800 <$500
50-100 1-100 <$1000/$1250
1902 Plain Back
4x5 10001-31350 <$500
3x10-20 5801-19459 <$500
1929 Small Size
5 Type 1 1-2066 <$200
10 Type 1 1-988 <$200
20 Type 1 1-334 <$200
SECOND TITLE {{ 10 S }}
1929 Small Size
5 Type 1 1-1952 <$175
10 Type 1 1-852 <$175
20 Type 1 1-264 <$175
5 Type 2 1-7778 <$175
10 Type 2 1-4867 <$175
20 Type 2 1-1344 <$200
Total Issue $2,267,090
Out in 1935 $100,000
Large out 1935 $1,320
****
1422 Westchester
WESTCHESTER COUNTY NB OF PEEKSKILL
{{ 12 L 12 S }}
Organized 6/13/65
Original Series <$VALUE
2x1-2x2 1-9450 <$750/$1250
4x5 1-8250 <$850
3x10-20 1-4010<$1000/$1500
Series 1875
4x5 1-3210 <$850
3x10-20 1-2266<$1000/$1500
Brown Back
4x5 1-13190 <$650
3x10-20 1-9322 <$650
1902 Red Seal
4x5 1-3900 <$750
3x10-20 1-2540 <$750
1902 Date Back
4x5 1-11550 <$350
3x10-20 1-8200 <$350
1902 Plain Back
4x5 11551-31706 <$350
3x10-20 8201-21140 <$350
1929 Small Size
5 Type 1 1-3966 <$200
10 Type 1 1-2164 <$200
20 Type 1 1-486 <$200
5 Type 2 1-7266 <$200
10 Type 2 1-3919 <$200
20 Type 2 1-1167 <$200
Total Issue $3,631,720
Out in 1935 $100,000
Large out 1935 $7,940
****
11951 Westchester
PELHAM NB, PELHAM
{{ 1 L }}
Organized 3/18/21
Receivership 7/21/33
1902 Plain Back <$VALUE
4x5 1-4960 <$1500
Total Issue $99,200
Out at close $395
****
169 Yates
FNB OF PENN YAN
{{ UNREPORTED }}
Chartered 12/63
Liquidated 4/6/64
Original Series <$VALUE
4x5 1-225 <$2000
Total Issue $4,500
All notes reportedly redeemed
****
FNB of Penn Yan
SEE Ch 358
FNB of Watkins
****
2405 Yates
YATES COUNTY NB OF PENN YAN
{{ UNREPORTED }}
Chartered 12/30/78
Receivership 8/17/96
Series 1875 <$VALUE
4x5 1-6632 <$1500
Total Issue $132,640
Out in 1916 $470
****

<$VALUEs are for notes in FINE condition. Value changes by approximately 25% for a change of one full grade.

****
4519 Wyoming
FNB OF PERRY
{{ 9 L 10 S }}
Chartered 1891
Brown Back <$VALUE
3x10-20 1-4600 <$400
1882 Date Back
3x10-20 1-965 <$400
1902 Date Back
3x10-20 1-3600 <$175
1902 Plain Back
3x10-20 3601-14125 <$175
1929 Small Size
5 Type 1 1-2432 <$150
10 Type 1 1-2524 <$150
20 Type 1 1-482 <$150
5 Type 2 1-4510 <$150
10 Type 2 1-729 <$150
20 Type 2 1-200 <$150
Total Issue $1,300,580
Out in 1935 $50,000
Large out 1935 $3,660
****
9839 Ontario
PHELPS NB, PHELPS
{{ 4 L 8 S }}
Organized 8/6/10
Liquidated 4/1/35
1902 Date Back <$VALUE
3x10-20 1-2110 <$250
1902 Plain Back
3x10-20 2111-10410 <$250
1929 Small Size
10 Type 1 1-1374 <$150
20 Type 1 1-366 <$175
10 Type 2 1-755 <$175
20 Type 2 1-200 <$175
Total Issue $658,410
Out in 1935 $50,000
Large out 1935 $1,690
****
7233 Columbia
FNB OF PHILMONT
{{ 3 L 0 S }}
Organized 8/6/03
Liquidated 3/24/34
1902 Red Seal <$VALUE
3x10-20 1-732 <$750
1902 Date Back
3x10-20 1-2420 <$400
1902 Plain Back
3x10-20 2421-6076 <$400
1929 Small Size
10 Type 1 1-524 <$500
20 Type 1 1-138 <$500
10 Type 2 1-295 <$500
20 Type 2 1-55 <$500
Total Issue $392,450
Out at close $20,000
Large out 1935 $920
Ch 13945 assumed circulation
****
13945 Columbia
PHILMONT NB, PHILMONT
{{ 6 S }}
Chartered 1/34
1929 Small Size <$VALUE
10 Type 2 1-768 <$300
20 Type 2 1-217 <$300
Total Issue $12,020
Out in 1935 $20,000
Outstanding includes Ch 7233
****
13960 Orange
NB OF PINE BUSH
{{ 2 S }}
Chartered 1/34
1929 Small Size <$VALUE
5 Type 2 1-2386 <$500
10 Type 2 1-1112 <$500
20 Type 2 1-384 <$500
Total Issue $30,730
Out in 1935 $50,000
Outstanding includes Ch 9940
****
9940 Orange
PINE BUSH NB, PINE BUSH
{{ 5 L U + 9 S }}
Organized 1/30/11
Liquidated 3/20/34
1902 Date Back <$VALUE
4x5 1-1875 <$350
3x10-20 1-1420 <$350
1902 Plain Back
4x5 1876-7695 <$350
3x10-20 1421-4983 <$350
1929 Small Size
5 Type 1 1-1918 <$200
10 Type 1 1-1106 <$200
20 Type 1 1-308 <$200
5 Type 2 1-1530 <$250
10 Type 2 1-581 <$250
20 Type 2 1-187 <$250

Total Issue $581,110
Out at close $50,000
Large out 1935 $1,020
Ch 13960 assumed circulation
****
981 Dutchess
STISSING NB OF
PINE PLAINS
{{ 7 L 8 S }}
Chartered 4/5/65
Original Series <$VALUE
3x1-2 1-4600 <$400/$1000
4x5 1-3650 <$500
3x10-20 1-1200 <$750/$1250
Series 1875
3x1-2 1-600 <$400/$1000
4x5 1-3085 <$500
3x10-20 1-1494 <$750/$1250
Brown Back
4x5 1-6739 <$350
3x10-20 1-1445 <$350
1902 Red Seal
3x10-20 1-2000 <$400
1902 Date Back
3x10-20 1-3800 <$200
1902 Plain Back
3x10-20 3801-11697 <$200
1929 Small Size
10 Type 1 1-1304 <$150
20 Type 1 1-348 <$150
10 Type 2 1-2067 <$150
20 Type 2 1-468 <$150
Total Issue $1,337,310
Out in 1935 $45,000
Large out 1935 $3,500
****
6613 Clinton
CITY NB OF PLATTSBURG
{{ 2 L }}
Chartered 2/03
Closed 12/31/20
1902 Red Seal <$VALUE
3x10-20 1-4800 <$500
1902 Date Back
3x10-20 1-8900 <$250
1902 Plain Back
3x10-20 8901-14158 <$250
Total Issue $947,900
Out at close $99,200
Ch 5785 assumed circulation
****
266 Clinton
FNB OF PLATTSBURGH
{{ 7 L 5 S }}
Chartered 2/64
Liquidated 2/17/31
Original Series <$VALUE
3x1-2 1-5000 <$300/$750
4x5 1-4250 <$350
3x10-20 1-1500 <$600/$1250
Series 1875
3x1-2 1-440 <$300/$750
4x5 1-2390 <$350
3x10-20 1-1626 <$500/$1000
Brown Back
3x10-20 1-6678 <$200/$250
1902 Red Seal
3x10-20 1-5400 <$250/$300
1902 Date Back
3x10-20 1-8300 <$125
1902 Plain Back
3x10-20 8301-26825 <$125
1929 Small Size
10 Type 1 1-1130 <$150
20 Type 1 1-225 <$150
Total Issue $2,356,250
Out at close $100,000
Large out at close $13,760
****
2534 Clinton
IRON NB OF PLATTSBURGH
{{ 3 L }}
Chartered 6/8/81
Liquidated 6/4/01
Series 1875 <$VALUE
4x5 1-6034 <$450
3x10-20 1-6333 <$750/$1250
Total Issue $437,330
Out in 1910 $2,610
****
13548 Clinton
MERCHANTS NB IN
PLATTSBURG
{{ 13 S }}
Chartered 5/31
1929 Small Size <$VALUE
20 Type 1 1-1818 <$60
5 Type 2 1-324 <$75
20 Type 2 1-4044 <$60
Total Issue $300,660
Out in 1935 $200,000
Outstanding includes Ch 3174
****

****
3174 Clinton
MERCHANTS NB OF
PLATTSBURGH
{{ 11 L 11 S }}
Chartered 1884
Liquidated 6/24/31
Brown Back <$VALUE
3x10-20 1-5919 <$200
1902 Red Seal
3x10-20 1-5000 <$200
1902 Date Back
3x10-20 1-8700 <$100
1902 Plain Back
3x10-20 8701-39357 <$100
1929 Small Size
20 Type 1 1-2151 <$75
Total Issue $2,771,920
Out at close $200,000
Large out 1935 $7,880
Ch 13548 assumed circulation
****
5785 Clinton
PLATTSBURG NB, PLATTSBURG
Chartered 4/19/01
2nd title:Plattsburg NB
& TC 5/13/20
FIRST TITLE {{ 6 L }}
Brown Back <$VALUE
4x5 1-7615 <$200
3x10-20 1-5854 <$200/$250
1882 Date Back
4x5 1-8350 <$200
3x10-20 1-5960 <$200/$250
1882 Value Back
4x5 8351-14650 <$200
3x10-20 5961-9540<$200/$250
SECOND TITLE {{ 14 L 29 S }}
1882 Value Back
4x5 1-950 <$200
3x10-20 1-420 <$200/$250
1902 Plain Back
4x5 1-31279 <$75
3x10-20 1-20765 <$75
1929 Small Size
5 Type 1 1-12084 <$25
10 Type 1 1-7988 <$25
20 Type 1 1-2370 <$35
5 Type 2 1-34842 <$25
10 Type 2 1-17848 <$25
20 Type 2 1-5685 <$35
Total Issue $4,511,420
Out in 1935 $499,995
Large out 1935 $10,225
Outstanding includes Ch 6613
****
321 Clinton
SECOND NB OF PLATTSBURGH
{{ UNREPORTED }}
Chartered 3/15/64
Liquidated 2/24/03
2nd title:Vilas NB of
Plattsburgh 3/1/69
FIRST TITLE
Original Series <$VALUE
4x5 1-2025 <$850
3x10-20 1-1000<$1000/$1500
SECOND TITLE
Original Series
3x1-2 1-1000 <$850/$1500
4x5 1-250 <$850
3x10-20 1-2300<$1000/$1500
Series 1875
3x1-2 1-500 <$850/$1500
4x5 1-1500 <$850
3x10-20 1-800 <$1000/$1500
Brown Back
3x10-20 1-4072 <$850
Total Issue $491,600
Out in 1910 $4,167
****
Vilas NB of Plattsburgh
SEE Ch 321
Second NB of Plattsburgh
****
9804 Herkimer
CITIZENS NB OF POLAND
{{ 5 L 11 S }}
Chartered 7/10
1902 Date Back <$VALUE
3x10-20 1-4300 <$300
1902 Plain Back
3x10-20 4301-13642 <$300
1929 Small Size
5 Type 1 1-1604 <$150
10 Type 1 1-1082 <$150
20 Type 1 1-308 <$150
5 Type 2 1-3590 <$150
10 Type 2 1-1878 <$150
20 Type 2 1-588 <$175
Total Issue $880,590
Out in 1935 $50,000
Large out 1935 $1,700
****

****
4223 Herkimer
NB OF POLAND
{{ 3 L }}
Chartered 1890
Liquidated 7/1/10
Brown Back <$VALUE
3x10-20 1-6280 <$500
1882 Date Back
3x10-20 1-396 <$500
1902 Date Back
3x10-20 1-82 <$400
Total Issue $337,900
Out in 1910 $32,300
****
2441 Herkimer
POLAND NB, POLAND
{{ 2 L }}
Chartered 12/11/79
Liquidated 1/14/90
Series 1875 <$VALUE
4x5 1-6410 <$850
Total Issue $128,200
Out in 1910 $550
****
402 Westchester
FNB OF PORT CHESTER
Chartered 4/64
2nd title:FNB & TC 4/10/25
FIRST TITLE {{ 14 L }}
Original Series <$VALUE
3x1-2 1-2000 <$500/$1000
4x5 1-5500 <$600
3x10-20 1-1200 <$750/$1250
Series 1875
4x5 1-2870 <$600
3x10-20 1-1338 <$750/$1250
Brown Back
4x5 1-17052 <$400
3x10-20 1-7068 <$400
1902 Red Seal
4x5 1-5750 <$400
3x10-20 1-4900 <$400
1902 Date Back
4x5 1-10250 <$200
3x10-20 1-6600 <$200
1902 Plain Back
4x5 10251-23800 <$200
3x10-20 6601-14980 <$200
SECOND TITLE {{ 2 L 27 S }}
1902 Plain Back
4x5 1-6149 <$200
3x10-20 1-4019 <$200
1929 Small Size
5 Type 1 1-7322 <$75
10 Type 1 1-5718 <$75
20 Type 1 1-1866 <$75
5 Type 2 1-20952 <$75
10 Type 2 1-8744 <$75
20 Type 2 1-3230 <$75
Total Issue $3,951,130
Out in 1935 $250,000
Large out 1935 $8,295
****
4858 Essex
CITIZENS NB OF PORT HENRY
{{ 6 L 18 S }}
Chartered 2/6/93
Brown Back <$VALUE
3x10-20 1-2400 <$350
1882 Date Back
3x10-20 1-1622 <$350
1902 Date Back
3x10-20 1-1460 <$250
1902 Plain Back
3x10-20 1461-13345 <$250
1929 Small Size
10 Type 1 1-2488 <$60
20 Type 1 1-656 <$70
10 Type 2 1-4433 <$70
20 Type 2 1-795 <$70
Total Issue $1,156,580
Out in 1935 $100,000
Large out 1935 $8,490
Outstanding includes Ch 1697
****
1697 Essex
FNB OF PORT HENRY
{{ 13 L }}
Chartered 5/70
Closed 9/1/21
Original Series <$VALUE
3x1-2 1-1660 <$250/$750
4x5 1-9335 <$350
Series 1875
4x5 1-14712 <$350
Brown Back
3x10-20 1-12600 <$200/$250
1882 Date Back
3x10-20 1-1330 <$200/$250
1902 Date Back
3x10-20 1-7000 <$125
1902 Plain Back
3x10-20 7001-12359 <$125

Total Issue $1,803,690
Out at close $100,000
Ch 4858 assumed circulation
****
5068 Suffolk
FNB OF PORT JEFFERSON
{{ 8 L 14 S }}
Chartered 1897
Brown Back <$VALUE
4x5 1-2525 <$1000
3x10-20 1-1710 <$1000
1882 Date Back
4x5 1-3900 <$1000
3x10-20 1-3020 <$1000
1882 Value Back
4x5 3901-4996 <$1000
3x10-20 3021-3725 <$1000
1902 Plain Back
4x5 1-9694 <$600
4x10 1-8045 <$600
1929 Small Size
5 Type 1 1-4816 <$250
10 Type 1 1-2562 <$250
5 Type 2 1-12120 <$250
10 Type 2 1-5808 <$250
Total Issue $1,354,730
Out in 1935 $100,000
Large out 1935 $2,550
****
FNB of Port Jervis
SEE Ch 94
FNB of Delhi
****
1363 Orange
NB OF PORT JERVIS
Chartered 6/29/65
2nd titie:NB & TC 7/19/26
FIRST TITLE {{ 16 L }}
Original Series <$VALUE
4x5 1-4200 <$300
3x10-20 1-2320 <$600/$1250
50-100 1-423 <$3500
Series 1875
4x5 1-2250 <$300
3x10-20 1-3094 <$600/$1250
50-100 1-101 <$3500
Brown Back
4x5 1-8855* <$200
3x10-20 1-7065**<$200/$250
* 4095-4700 canceled
** 2691-2700 canceled
1902 Red Seal
4x5 1-4250 <$200
3x10-20 1-3600 <$200/$250
1902 Date Back
4x5 1-13000 <$100
3x10-20 1-8400 <$100
1902 Plain Back
4x5 13001-33519 <$100
3x10-20 8401-20589 <$100
SECOND TITLE {{ 6 L 17 S }}
1902 Plain Back
4x5 1-5344 <$100
3x10-20 1-3535 <$100
1929 Small Size
5 Type 1 1-5040 <$60
10 Type 1 1-2638 <$60
20 Type 1 1-700 <$70
5 Type 2 1-9378 <$70
10 Type 2 1-4370 <$70
20 Type 2 1-1380 <$75
Total Issue $3,756,160
Out in 1935 $128,950
Large out 1935 $8,220
****
11742 Lewis
PORT LEYDEN NB,
PORT LEYDEN
{{ 2 L 2 S }}
Organized 5/19/20
1902 Plain Back <$VALUE
4x5 1-2095 <$600
3x10-20 1-1546 <$600
1929 Small Size
5 Type 1 1-862 <$400
10 Type 1 1-414 <$400
20 Type 1 1-120 <$400
5 Type 2 1-1080 <$400
10 Type 2 1-564 <$400
20 Type 2 1-204 <$400
Total Issue $199,420
Out in 1935 $20,000
Large out 1935 $360
****
6198 Richmond
PORT RICHMOND NB,
PORT RICHMOND
Chartered 4/02
2nd title:Staten Island NB
& TC of New York 5/1/26
FIRST TITLE {{ 4 L }}
1902 Red Seal <$VALUE
3x10-20 1-2140 <$750
1902 Date Back
3x10-20 1-3780 <$400

1902 Plain Back (dated 1902)
3x10-20 3781-5141 <$400
1902 Plain Back (dated 1922)
3x10-20 1-1676 <$400
SECOND TITLE {{ 2 L U + 18 S }}
1902 Plain Back
3x10-20 1-1215 <$500
1929 Small Size
10 Type 1 1-4020 <$125
20 Type 1 1-922 <$125
10 Type 2 1-23808 <$125
20 Type 2 1-6818 <$125
Total Issue $1,234,880
Out in 1935 $250,000
Large out 1935 $1,050
****
5228 Saint Lawrence
CITIZENS NB OF POTSDAM
{{ 6 L 8 S }}
Chartered 10/30/99
Brown Back <$VALUE
4x5 1-3875 <$350
3x10-20 1-3740 <$350
1882 Date Back
4x5 1-7850 <$350
3x10-20 1-5440 <$350
1882 Value Back
4x5 7851-9350 <$350
3x10-20 5441-6220 <$350
1902 Plain Back
4x5 1-6788 <$200
3x10-20 1-4736 <$200
1929 Small Size
5 Type 1 1-1952 <$125
10 Type 1 1-948 <$125
20 Type 1 1-246 <$125
5 Type 2 1-2986 <$125
10 Type 2 1-1536 <$125
20 Type 2 1-516 <$150
Total Issue $1,320,630
Out in 1935 $50,000
Large out 1935 $2,890
****
868 Saint Lawrence
NB OF POTSDAM
{{ 4 L }}
Chartered 3/7/65
Receivership 3/2/97
Original Series <$VALUE
3x1-2 1-5000 <$400/$850
4x5 1-6500 <$400
3x10-20 1-3790 <$750/$1250
50-100 1-137 <$3500
Series 1875
3x1-2 1-5000 <$400/$850
4x5 1-10190 <$400
3x10-20 1-2510 <$750/$1250
50-100 1-100 <$3500
Brown Back
3x10-20 1-3884 <$350
Total Issue $928,550
Out in 1916 $4,844
****
1305 Dutchess
CITY NB OF POUGHKEEPSIE
{{ 4 L }}
Chartered 6/19/65
Liquidated 8/9/01
Original Series <$VALUE
4x5 1-7000 <$300
3x10-20 1-1789 <$600/$1250
50-100 1-334 <$3500
Series 1875
4x5 1-2960 <$300
3x10-20 1-1651 <$500/$1000
50-100 1-208 <$3500
Brown Back
3x10-20 1-4832 <$300
Total Issue $694,100
Out in 1910 $5,050
****

CONDITION affects Value. The Values shown are for notes in FINE condition.

****
659 Dutchess
FALLKILL NB OF POUGHKEEPSIE
{{ 16 L }}
Chartered 12/64
Original Series <$VALUE
3x1-2 1-19240 <$225/$750
4x5 1-4500 <$250
3x10-20 1-8200 <$600/$1250
50-100 1-1000 <$3500
Series 1875
4x5 1-12395 <$250
3x10-20 1-6300 <$500/$1000
50-100 1-500 <$3500
Brown Back
4x5 1-17250 <$150
3x10-20 1-8022 <$150/$200
50-100 1-1633 <$1250/$1500
1902 Red Seal
4x5 1-8650 <$150
3x10-20 1-4500 <$150/$200
50-100 1-480 <$2250/$2500
1902 Date Back
4x5 1-14750 <$75
3x10-20 1-9700 <$75
50-100 1-300 <$350/$400
3x50-100 1-300 <$350/$400
1902 Plain Back
4x5 14751-19809 <$75
3x10-20 9701-12355 <$75
Total Issue $3,979,080
Out in 1935 $12,473
****
1312 Dutchess
FARMERS & MANUFACTURERS NB OF POUGHKEEPSIE
{{ 31 L 21 S }}
Chartered 1865
Original Series <$VALUE
4x5 1-6975 <$250
3x10-20 1-7324 <$600/$1250
50-100 1-800 <$3500
Series 1875
4x5 1-9120 <$250
3x10-20 1-256 <$500/$1000
50-100 1-178 <$3500
Brown Back
4x5 1-33888 <$125
3x10-20 1-9102 <$125/$175
50-100 1-1000 <$1250/$1500
1902 Red Seal
4x5 1-7665 <$150
3x10-20 1-4734 <$150/$200
1902 Date Back
4x5 1-17500 <$60
3x10-20 1-12000 <$75
1902 Plain Back
4x5 17501-56297 <$60
3x10-20 12001-36783 <$75
1929 Small Size
5 Type 1 1-7626 <$35
10 Type 1 1-3720 <$35
20 Type 1 1-1008 <$40
5 Type 2 1-16468 <$35
10 Type 2 1-9188 <$35
20 Type 2 1-2448 <$40
Total Issue $6,281,670
Out in 1935 $200,000
Large out 1935 $13,980
****
465 Dutchess
FNB OF POUGHKEEPSIE
{{ 9 L 15 S }}
Chartered 6/64
Original Series <$VALUE
4x5 1-5500 <$300
3x10-20 1-3950 <$600/$1250
Series 1875
4x5 1-3727 <$300
3x10-20 1-1368* <$600/$1250
* 354-700 canceled
Brown Back
3x10-20 1-11186 <$225/$275
1902 Red Seal
3x10-20 1-6000 <$200/$250
1902 Date Back
3x10-20 1-9000 <$100
1902 Plain Back
3x10-20 9001-26579 <$100
1929 Small Size
10 Type 1 1-2776 <$50
20 Type 1 1-782 <$60
10 Type 2 1-4289 <$50
20 Type 2 1-1409 <$60
Total Issue $2,952,810
Out in 1935 $100,000
Large out 1935 $7,010
****

****
1380 Dutchess
MERCHANTS NB OF POUGHKEEPSIE
Chartered 1865
2nd title:Merchants NB & TC 7/1/29
FIRST TITLE {{ 7 L }}
Original Series <$VALUE
3x1-2 1-200 <$300/$750
4x5 1-3500 <$350
3x10-20 1-4800 <$600/$1250
50-100 1-600 <$3500
Series 1875
4x5 1-1095 <$350
3x10-20 1-418 <$500/$1000
50-100 1-130 <$3500
Brown Back
3x10-20 1-7035 <$300
50-100 1-1031 <$1250/$1500
1902 Red Seal
3x10-20 1-1402 <$300
50-100 1-266 <$2250/$2500
1902 Date Back
3x10-20 1-3700 <$100
50-100 1-500 <$350/$400
1902 Plain Back
3x10-20 3701-10311 <$100
SECOND TITLE {{ 22 S }}
1929 Small Size
5 Type 1 1-1038 <$50
10 Type 1 1-1966 <$50
20 Type 1 1-530 <$60
50 Type 1 1-106 <$125
100 Type 1 1-42 <$175
5 Type 2 1-12110 <$60
10 Type 2 1-4725 <$60
20 Type 2 1-1435 <$60
Total Issue $2,076,450
Out in 1935 $175,000
Large out 1935 $4,940
****
1306 Dutchess
POUGHKEEPSIE NB, POUGHKEEPSIE
{{ UNREPORTED }}
Chartered 6/19/65
Liquidated 9/14/01
Original Series <$VALUE
4x5 1-10000 <$850
3x10-20 1-5000<$1000/$1500
Series 1875
4x5 1-4997 <$850
3x10-20 1-2775<$1000/$1500
Brown Back
3x10-20 1-4110 <$750
Total Issue $894,190
Out in 1910 $5,065
****
1496 Oswego
PULASKI NB, PULASKI
{{ 3 L }}
Organized 7/3/65
Receivership 7/11/32
Original Series <$VALUE
3x1-2 1-1500 <$600/$1250
4x5 1-4250 <$650
Series 1875
4x5 1-5560 <$650
Brown Back
4x5 1-4931 <$500
3x10-20 1-1028 <$500
1902 Red Seal
3x10-20 1-900 <$600
1902 Date Back
3x10-20 1-500 <$350
1902 Plain Back
3x10-20 501-2311 <$350
Total Issue $514,270
Out at close $2,111
****
9529 Albany
FNB OF RAVENA
{{ 3 L 5 S }}
Chartered 9/09
1902 Date Back <$VALUE
4x5 1-2500* <$400
4x10 1-2375** <$400
1902 Plain Back
4x5 2651-8411* <$400
4x10 2476-6709** <$400
* 2501-2650 not marked
** 2376-2475 not marked
1929 Small Size
5 Type 1 1-1380 <$250
10 Type 1 1-762 <$250
5 Type 2 1-2568 <$250
10 Type 2 1-1464 <$250
Total Issue $551,180
Out in 1935 $25,000
Large out 1935 $1,000
****

****
10781 Wayne
RED CREEK NB, RED CREEK
{{ 3 L 8 S }}
Organized 3/18/15
1902 Plain Back <$VALUE
3x10-20 1-9037 <$400
1929 Small Size
10 Type 1 1-1460 <$200
20 Type 1 1-392 <$200
10 Type 2 1-2306 <$200
20 Type 2 1-625 <$200
Total Issue $622,050
Out in 1935 $50,000
Large out 1935 $1,940
****
752 Dutchess
FNB OF RED HOOK
{{ 14 L 14 S }}
Chartered 1/25/65
Original Series <$VALUE
3x1-2 1-2600 <$350/$1000
4x5 1-5000 <$500
4x10 1-2900 <$750
3x20-50 1-800 <$1250/$3500
Series 1875
3x1-2 1-118 <$350/$1000
4x5 1-2955 <$500
4x10 1-1934 <$750
3x20-50 1-685 <$1250/$3500
Brown Back
4x5 1-18386 <$250
3x10-20 1-10087 <$250/$300
50-100 1-300 <$1250/$1500
1902 Red Seal
4x5 1-5000 <$350
3x10-20 1-3600 <$350/$400
1902 Date Back
4x5 1-11050 <$150
3x10-20 1-8300 <$150
1902 Plain Back
4x5 11051-25074 <$150
3x10-20 8301-16820 <$150
1929 Small Size
5 Type 1 1-2534 <$125
10 Type 1 1-1436 <$125
20 Type 1 1-386 <$125
5 Type 2 1-4824 <$125
10 Type 2 1-2872 <$125
20 Type 2 1-768 <$150
Total Issue $3,345,650
Out in 1935 $75,000
Large out 1935 $8,525
****
10374 Jefferson
REDWOOD NB, REDWOOD
{{ 2 L 2 S }}
Chartered 4/13
1902 Date Back <$VALUE
3x10-20 1-820 <$600
1902 Plain Back
3x10-20 821-3312 <$600
1929 Small Size
10 Type 1 1-400 <$400
20 Type 1 1-118 <$400
10 Type 2 1-576 <$400
20 Type 2 1-192 <$400
Total Issue $213,360
Out in 1935 $15,000
Large out 1935 $1,120
****
6482 Oneida
FNB OF REMSEN
{{ 2 L U + 7 S }}
Chartered 11/7/02
1902 Red Seal <$VALUE
3x10-20 1-1790 <$600
1902 Date Back
3x10-20 1-2360 <$350
1902 Plain Back
3x10-20 2361-6847 <$350
1929 Small Size
5 Type 1 1-260 <$400
10 Type 1 1-618 <$400
20 Type 1 1-170 <$400
5 Type 2 1-4920 <$400
Total Issue $521,730
Out in 1935 $25,000
Large out 1935 $1,230
****
1157 Dutchess
FNB OF RHINEBECK
{{ 17 L 9 S }}
Chartered 1865
Original Series <$VALUE
3x1-2 1-4400 <$200/$750
4x5 1-4150 <$250
4x10 1-2000 <$600
3x20-50 1-600 <$1250/$3500
Series 1875
3x1-2 1-522 <$200/$750
4x5 1-2566 <$250
4x10 1-1500 <$500
3x20-50 1-618 <$1000/$3500
Brown Back
4x5 1-8871 <$175
3x10-20 1-4989 <$175/$225
1902 Red Seal
4x5 1-3250 <$200
3x10-20 1-1400 <$200/$250
1902 Date Back
4x5 1-4900 <$100
3x10-20 1-3780 <$100
1902 Plain Back
4x5 4901-15185 <$100
3x10-20 3781-9790 <$100
1929 Small Size
5 Type 1 1-2026 <$85
10 Type 1 1-1170 <$85
20 Type 1 1-330 <$100
5 Type 2 1-3108 <$100
10 Type 2 1-1592 <$100
20 Type 2 1-361 <$100
Total Issue $1,997,240
Out in 1935 $60,000
Large out 1935 $5,365
****
2553 Allegany
FNB OF RICHBURG
{{ UNREPORTED }}
Chartered 8/11/81
Liquidated 1/10/88
Series 1875 <$VALUE
4x5 1-4906 <$1500
Total Issue $98,120
Out in 1910 $445
****
2651 Otsego
FNB OF RICHFIELD SPRINGS
{{ 7 L 8 S }}
Chartered 1882
Series 1875 <$VALUE
4x5 1-5574 <$500
3x10-20 1-3437 <$600/$1250
Brown Back
4x5 1-2900 <$350
3x10-20 1-2240 <$350
1882 Date Back
4x5 1-3850 <$350
3x10-20 1-3320 <$350
1882 Value Back
4x5 3851-7300 <$350
3x10-20 3321-5331 <$350
1902 Plain Back
4x5 1-5624 <$200
4x10 1-4923 <$200
1929 Small Size
5 Type 1 1-2778 <$150
10 Type 1 1-1214 <$150
5 Type 2 1-5042 <$150
10 Type 2 1-2595 <$150
Total Issue $1,382,620
Out in 1935 $50,000
Large out 1935 $3,645
****
9414 Queens
RIDGEWOOD NB, RIDGEWOOD
{{ UNREPORTED }}
Chartered 5/09
Liquidated 8/31/21
1902 Date Back <$VALUE
3x10-20 1-10900 <$850
1902 Plain Back
3x10-20 10901-18285 <$850
Total Issue $914,250
Out at close $100,000
****
6386 Chautauqua
FNB OF RIPLEY
{{ 4 L 2 S }}
Organized 8/9/02
Receivership 7/30/31
1902 Red Seal <$VALUE
3x10-20 1-1850 <$600
1902 Date Back
3x10-20 1-1810 <$300
1902 Plain Back
3x10-20 1811-5776 <$300
1929 Small Size
10 Type 1 1-392 <$400
20 Type 1 1-105 <$400
Total Issue $417,420
Out at close $25,000
Large out at close $3,840
****
4230 Suffolk
SUFFOLK COUNTY NB OF RIVERHEAD
{{ 6 L 12 S }}
Chartered 1890
Brown Back <$VALUE
3x10-20 1-1830 <$1500
1882 Date Back
3x10-20 1-157 <$1500
1902 Date Back
3x10-20 1-2950 <$1000
1902 Plain Back
3x10-20 2951-19247 <$1000
1929 Small Size
10 Type 1 1-2682 <$350
20 Type 1 1-798 <$350
10 Type 2 1-5873 <$350
20 Type 2 1-1275 <$350
Total Issue $1,402,610
Out in 1935 $100,000
Large out 1935 $3,430
****
1397 Monroe
CLARKE NB OF ROCHESTER
{{ 3 L }}
Chartered 7/10/65
Liquidated 8/11/71
Original Series <$VALUE
3x1-2 1-5700 <$600/$1000
4x5 1-5850 <$600
3x10-20 1-1100 <$850/$1250
50-100 1-150 <$3500
Total Issue $223,000
Out in 1910 $1,616
****
2383 Monroe
COMMERCIAL NB OF ROCHESTER
{{ 2 L }}
Chartered 5/8/78
Liquidated 1/27/91
Series 1875 <$VALUE
4x5 1-21805 <$750
4x10 1-3283 <$1000
Total Issue $567,420
Out in 1910 $2,130
****
1072 Monroe
FARMERS & MECHANICS NB OF ROCHESTER
{{ 1 L }}
Chartered 4/28/65
Liquidated 4/15/73
Original Series <$VALUE
3x1-2 1-3060 <$1000/$1500
4x5 1-1885 <$1000
3x10-20 1-865 <$1500/$2000
Total Issue $96,250
Out in 1910 $742
****
527 Monroe
FNB OF ROCHESTER
{{ 1 L }}
Chartered 10/8/64
Liquidated 8/9/72
Original Series <$VALUE
3x1-2 1-7000 <$750/$1250
4x5 1-6225 <$750
3x10-20 1-1800<$1000/$1250
Total Issue $249,500
Out in 1910 $2,050
****
13330 Monroe
FNB & TC OF ROCHESTER
{{ 33 S }}
Chartered 5/29
1929 Small Size <$VALUE
5 Type 1 1-9360 <$15
10 Type 1 1-5866 <$20
20 Type 1 1-1706 <$30
5 Type 2 1-69408 <$15
10 Type 2 1-32443 <$20
20 Type 2 1-7776 <$30
Total Issue $1,664,470
Out in 1935 $463,200
****
1362 Monroe
FLOUR CITY NB OF ROCHESTER
{{ 7 L }}
Chartered 6/29/65
Liquidated 12/30/05
** COUNTERFEITS of the $10 Original Series note are abundant.
Original Series <$VALUE
4x5 1-8750 <$400
3x10-20 1-2600 <$750/$1250
50-100 1-2000 <$3500
Series 1875
4x5 1-360 <$400
3x10-20 1-4000 <$600/$1000
50-100 1-500 <$3500
Brown Back
4x5 1-9370 <$250
3x10-20 1-16895 <$250/$300
50-100 1-1463 <$1250/$1500
1902 Red Seal
4x5 1-940 <$300
3x10-20 1-1262 <$300/$350
Total Issue $2,220,700
Out in 1910 $31,840
****
Lincoln NB of Rochester
SEE Ch 8026
NB of Rochester
****

****
8026 Monroe
NB OF ROCHESTER
Chartered 12/05
Liquidated 12/1/20
2nd title:Lincoln NB of Rochester 4/7/09
FIRST TITLE {{ 12 L }}
1902 Red Seal <$VALUE
4x5 1-20000 <$150
4x10 1-4500 <$150
3x10-20 1-12000 <$150/$200
50-100 1-800 <$2250/$2500
1902 Date Back
4x5 1-8440 <$75
4x10 1-1335 <$75
50-100 1-170 <$350/$400
SECOND TITLE {{ U + 14 L }}
1902 Date Back
4x5 1-60000 <$65
3x10-20 1-44400 <$75
50-100 1-500 <$350/$400
3x50-100 1-987 <$350/$400
1902 Plain Back
4x5 60001-91991 <$65
3x10-20 44401-63058 <$75
Total Issue $6,862,170
Out at close $800,000
****
12538 Monroe
NB OF ROCHESTER
{{ 14 L }}
Chartered 5/24
Liquidated 9/29/28
1902 Plain Back <$VALUE
4x5 1-64553 <$125
3x10-20 1-50336 <$125
Total Issue $3,807,860
Out at close $1,135,460
Outstanding includes Ch 1104
****
8111 Monroe
NB OF COMMERCE OF ROCHESTER
{{ 19 L }}
Organized 2/1/06
Receivership 6/21/24
1902 Red Seal <$VALUE
4x5 1-11750 <$150
3x10-20 1-9200 <$150/$200
1902 Date Back
4x5 1-47250 <$65
3x10-20 1-33400 <$75
1902 Plain Back
4x5 47251-98825 <$65
3x10-20 33401-63285 <$75
Total Issue $5,835,750
Out at close $459,895
****
1282 Monroe
N UNION B OF ROCHESTER
{{ UNREPORTED }}
Chartered 6/15/65
Liquidated 4/26/66
Original Series <$VALUE
4x5 1-4000 <$1000
3x10-20 1-1500<$1250/$1500
3x50-100 1-152 <$3500
Total Issue $193,000
Out in 1910 $805
****
1104 Monroe
TRADERS NB OF ROCHESTER
{{ 34 L }}
Organized 3/22/65
Liquidated 10/31/24
Original Series <$VALUE
3x1-2 1-2000 <$250/$750
4x5 1-7000 <$250
3x10-20 1-3100 <$600/$1250
50-100 1-600 <$3500
Series 1875
3x10-20 1-2728 <$500/$1000
50-100 1-720 <$3500
Brown Back
3x10-20 1-25579 <$125/$175
1902 Red Seal
3x10-20 1-20000 <$125/$175
1902 Date Back
3x10-20 1-41800 <$60
1902 Plain Back
3x10-20 41801-90341 <$60
Total Issue $7,435,400
Out at close $500,000
Ch 12538 assumed circulation
****

****
8872 Nassau
FNB OF ROCKVILLE CENTRE
{{ 2 L 0 S }}
Chartered 9/07
Liquidated 2/16/32
1902 Red Seal <$VALUE
3x10-20 1-200 <$2500
1902 Date Back
3x10-20 1-2010 <$1250
1902 Plain Back
3x10-20 2011-7169 <$1250
1929 Small Size
10 Type 1 1-466 <$1000
20 Type 1 1-137 <$1000
Total Issue $412,850
Out at close $25,000
Large out at close $1,500
****
1376 Oneida
CENTRAL NB OF ROME
{{ 3 L }}
Organized 7/1/65
Receivership 1/2/95
Original Series <$VALUE
3x1-2 1-1600 <$400/$850
4x5 1-3000 <$450
3x10-20 1-2504 <$750/$1250
Series 1875
4x5 1-7585 <$450
3x10-20 1-154 <$750/$1250
Brown Back
4x5 1-4858 <$400
Total Issue $449,760
Out in 1916 $2,309
****
2410 Oneida
FARMERS NB OF ROME
Chartered 2/10/79
2nd title:Farmers NB & TC 12/30/25
FIRST TITLE {{ 14 L }}
Series 1875 <$VALUE
4x5 1-28513 <$300
Brown Back
3x10-20 1-8800 <$200/$225
1882 Date Back
4x5 1-9265 <$200
3x10-20 1-6560 <$200/$225
1882 Value Back
4x5 9266-11275 <$225
3x10-20 6561-7522 <$250
1902 Plain Back
4x5 1-9190 <$100
3x10-20 1-5892 <$100
SECOND TITLE {{ 14 S }}
1929 Small Size
10 Type 2 1-9315 <$75
20 Type 2 1-2945 <$75
Total Issue $2,242,310
Out in 1935 $100,000
Large out 1935 $5,010
****
1414 Oneida
FNB OF ROME
{{ 5 L }}
Chartered 1865
Liquidated 6/4/15
Original Series <$VALUE
3x1-2 1-6000 <$350/$850
4x5 1-5950 <$400
3x10-20 1-1310 <$750/$1250
Series 1875
3x1-2 1-480 <$350/$850
4x5 1-5750 <$400
3x10-20 1-1610 <$600/$1000
Brown Back
4x5 1-11760 <$300
3x10-20 1-2916 <$300
1902 Red Seal
4x5 1-3165 <$300
3x10-20 1-2434 <$300
1902 Date Back
4x5 1-8415 <$200
3x10-20 1-5966 <$200
Total Issue $1,445,000
Out in 1915 $62,600
****
1410 Oneida
FORT STANWIX NB OF ROME
{{ 12 L }}
Organized 7/8/65
Receivership 2/8/96
Original Series <$VALUE
3x1-2 1-11660 <$300/$750
4x5 1-10900 <$400
3x10-20 1-2070 <$750/$1250
Series 1875
4x5 1-6360 <$400
3x10-20 1-1806 <$600/$1000
Brown Back
4x5 1-13452 <$250
3x10-20 1-3948 <$250/$300
Total Issue $1,063,740
Out in 1916 $5,106
****

****
11739 Seneca
ROMULUS NB, ROMULUS
{{ 2 L 2 S }}
Organized 5/3/20
Receivership 12/7/33
1902 Plain Back <$VALUE
4x5 1-2162 <$750
1929 Small Size
5 Type 1 1-618 <$600
Total Issue $61,780
Out at close $5,000
Large out at close $170
****
34 Ulster
FNB OF RONDOUT
{{ 7 L }}
Chartered 7/63
Liquidated 10/30/80
Original Series <$VALUE
3x1-2 1-5000 <$350/$850
4x5 1-6725 <$400
4x10 1-7000 <$600
3x20-50 1-1050<$1250/$3500
Series 1875
3x1-2 1-4434 <$350/$850
4x5 1-3499 <$400
4x10 1-2529 <$600
3x20-50 1-730 <$1250/$3500
Total Issue $828,610
Out in 1910 $6,260
****
FNB of Rondout
SEE Ch 2493
FNB of Rondout, Kingston
****
1120 Ulster
NB OF RONDOUT
Chartered 1865
2nd title:Rondout NB of Kingston 3/12/04
FIRST TITLE {{ 1 L }}
Original Series <$VALUE
4x5 1-5600 <$400
3x10-20 1-4400 <$750/$1250
Series 1875
3x10-20 1-5400 <$750/$1250
Brown Back
3x10-20 1-9729 <$500
SECOND TITLE {{ 7 L 20 S }}
Brown Back
3x10-20 1-1574 <$300/$350
1902 Red Seal
3x10-20 1-4500 <$300/$350
1902 Date Back
3x10-20 1-8800 <$125
1902 Plain Back
3x10-20 8801-34468 <$125
1929 Small Size
10 Type 1 1-4174 <$40
20 Type 1 1-1138 <$50
10 Type 2 1-7170 <$50
20 Type 2 1-1596 <$50
Total Issue $3,606,170
Out in 1935 $150,000
Large out 1935 $9,820
****
11953 Nassau
FNB OF ROOSEVELT
{{ 3 L 3 S }}
Chartered 4/21
1902 Plain Back <$VALUE
4x5 1-11880 <$750
1929 Small Size
5 Type 1 1-3334 <$600
5 Type 2 1-8952 <$600
Total Issue $382,380
Out in 1935 $25,000
Large out 1935 $470
****
8191 Sullivan
FNB OF ROSCOE
Chartered 4/06
2nd title:FNB & TC 3/20/29
FIRST TITLE {{ 6 L }}
1902 Red Seal <$VALUE
4x5 1-400 <$500
3x10-20 1-335 <$500
1902 Date Back
4x5 1-4700 <$200
3x10-20 1-3500 <$200
1902 Plain Back
4x5 4701-20365 <$200
3x10-20 3501-14162 <$200
SECOND TITLE {{ 13 S }}
1929 Small Size
5 Type 1 1-3434 <$125
10 Type 1 1-2054 <$125
20 Type 1 1-630 <$125
5 Type 2 1-5024 <$125
10 Type 2 1-3216 <$125
20 Type 2 1-864 <$150
Total Issue $1,516,570
Out in 1935 $100,000
Large out 1935 $3,835
****

****
13326 Nassau
ROSLYN NB & TC, ROSLYN
{{ U + 10 S }}
Chartered 5/20/29
1929 Small Size <$VALUE
10 Type 1 1-316 <$300
20 Type 1 1-106 <$300
5 Type 2 1-11794 <$300
10 Type 2 1-5709 <$300
20 Type 2 1-1933 <$300
Total Issue $186,400
Out in 1935 $70,230
****
11969 Clinton
FNB OF ROUSES POINT
{{ 1 L 1 S }}
Organized 4/14/21
Receivership 3/19/31
1902 Plain Back <$VALUE
3x10-20 1-3937 <$750
1929 Small Size
10 Type 1 1-214 <$600
20 Type 1 1-17 <$600
Total Issue $211,730
Out at close $12,500
Large out at close $1,920
****
7678 Delaware
NB OF ROXBURY
{{ 3 L 9 S }}
Chartered 4/05
1902 Red Seal <$VALUE
3x10-20 1-940 <$600
1902 Date Back
3x10-20 1-2250 <$350
1902 Plain Back
3x10-20 2251-6552 <$350
1929 Small Size
10 Type 1 1-1118 <$175
20 Type 1 1-326 <$175
10 Type 2 1-1437 <$175
20 Type 2 1-194 <$200
Total Issue $499,050
Out in 1935 $50,000
Large out 1935 $1,460
****
5662 Westchester
RYE NB, RYE
{{ 7 L 7 S }}
Chartered 12/31/00
Brown Back <$VALUE
3x10-20 1-2570 <$1000
1882 Date Back
3x10-20 1-5400 <$1000
1882 Value Back
3x10-20 5401-8411 <$1000
1902 Plain Back
3x10-20 1-6503 <$600
1929 Small Size
10 Type 1 1-1490 <$400
20 Type 1 1-392 <$400
10 Type 2 1-2154 <$400
20 Type 2 1-615 <$400
Total Issue $1,044,480
Out in 1935 $50,000
Large out 1935 $2,440
****
375 Montgomery
FNB OF SAINT JOHNSVILLE
{{ 7 L 2U + 10 S }}
Chartered 4/64
Original Series <$VALUE
4x5 1-4500 <$500
4x10 1-1500 <$750
Series 1875
4x5 1-1396 <$500
4x10 1-732 <$750
Brown Back
4x5 1-14104 <$350
3x10-20 1-992 <$350
1902 Red Seal
3x10-20 1-3000 <$400
1902 Date Back
3x10-20 1-4100 <$200
1902 Plain Back
3x10-20 4101-12565 <$200
1929 Small Size
10 Type 1 1-1286 <$150
20 Type 1 1-360 <$150
10 Type 2 1-2071 <$150
20 Type 2 1-399 <$175
Total Issue $1,466,180
Out in 1935 $50,000
Large out 1935 $4,750
****
7733 Franklin
ST REGIS FALLS NB, ST REGIS FALLS
{{ 3 L 5 S }}
Chartered 5/05
1902 Red Seal <$VALUE
4x5 1-1175 <$750
3x10-20 1-955 <$750

1902 Date Back
4x5 1-2400 <$400
3x10-20 1-1490 <$400
1902 Plain Back
4x5 2401-7570 <$400
3x10-20 1491-4678 <$400
1929 Small Size
5 Type 1 1-1050 <$350
10 Type 1 1-508 <$350
20 Type 1 1-150 <$350
5 Type 2 1-1182 <$350
10 Type 2 1-613 <$350
20 Type 2 1-174 <$375
Total Issue $552,050
Out in 1935 $25,000
Large out 1935 $1,290
****
2472 Cattaraugus
FNB OF SALAMANCA
{{ 12 L 12 S }}
Chartered 4/12/80
Series 1875 <$VALUE
4x5 1-16153 <$350
Brown Back
3x10-20 1-4000 <$250
1882 Date Back
4x5 1-3980 <$250
3x10-20 1-2470 <$250
1882 Value Back
4x5 3981-6375 <$250
3x10-20 2471-3768 <$250
1902 Plain Back
4x5 1-21041 <$125
1929 Small Size
5 Type 1 1-12304 <$100
5 Type 2 1-25414 <$100
Total Issue $1,755,970
Out in 1935 $100,000
Large out 1935 $3,405
****
2610 Cattaraugus
SALAMANCA NB, SALAMANCA
{{ 3 L }}
Chartered 1/6/82
Liquidated 2/15/02
Series 1875 <$VALUE
4x5 1-8408 <$400
3x10-20 1-65 <$750/$1250
Brown Back
3x10-20 1-20 <$400
Total Issue $172,410
Out in 1910 $1,025
****
3309 Washington
FNB OF SALEM
{{ 2 L }}
Chartered 2/25/85
Liquidated 2/13/05
Brown Back <$VALUE
4x5 1-13375 <$600
50-100 1-178 <$1500/$1750
Total Issue $294,200
Out in 1910 $2,490
****
1127 Washington
NB OF SALEM
{{ 1 L }}
Chartered 1865
Liquidated 5/4/85
Original Series <$VALUE
3x1-2 1-3000 <$650/$1500
4x5 1-8250 <$850
3x10-20 1-2700<$1000/$1500
Series 1875
3x1-2 1-2300 <$650/$1500
4x5 1-2770 <$850
3x10-20 1-1266<$1000/$1500
Total Issue $445,200
Out in 1910 $2,494
****
3245 Washington
PEOPLES NB OF SALEM
{{ 3 L 2 S }}
Organized 6/21/84
Receivership 9/23/31
Brown Back <$VALUE
4x5 1-5285 <$500
3x10-20 1-547 <$500
1902 Red Seal
3x10-20 1-950 <$600
1902 Date Back
4x5 1-3000 <$300
3x10-20 1-2200 <$300
1902 Plain Back
4x5 3001-10069 <$300
3x10-20 2201-6546 <$300
1929 Small Size
5 Type 1 1-777 <$300
10 Type 1 1-395 <$300
20 Type 1 1-104 <$300
Total Issue $768,720
Out at close $35,000
Large out at close $3,360
****

****
7588 Washington
SALEM NB, SALEM
{{ 3 L U + 3 S }}
Chartered 2/05
1902 Red Seal <$VALUE
4x5 1-1250 <$600
3x10-20 1-1110 <$600
1902 Date Back
4x5 1-3000 <$300
3x10-20 1-2240 <$300
1902 Plain Back
4x5 3001-4640 <$300
3x10-20 2241-3141 <$300
1929 Small Size
5 Type 1 1-416 <$300
10 Type 1 1-204 <$300
20 Type 1 1-72 <$300
5 Type 2 1-110 <$300
10 Type 2 1-132 <$300
Total Issue $365,580
Out in 1935 $10,000
Large out 1935 $700
****
8297 Washington
COMMERCIAL NB OF SANDY HILL
Chartered 7/06
Liquidated 2/24/31
2nd title:Hudson Falls NB, Hudson Falls 8/3/10
FIRST TITLE {{ 1 L }}
1902 Red Seal <$VALUE
4x5 1-830 <$850
3x10-20 1-668 <$850
1902 Date Back
4x5 1-1070 <$400
3x10-20 1-827 <$400
SECOND TITLE {{ 2 L 3 S }}
1902 Date Back
3x10-20 1-3940 <$300
1902 Plain Back
3x10-20 3941-13461 <$300
1929 Small Size
10 Type 1 1-635 <$250
20 Type 1 1-162 <$250
Total Issue $843,340
Out in 1935 $50,000
Large out 1935 $5,280
****
184 Washington
FNB OF SANDY HILL
{{ 1 L }}
Chartered 1/64
Liquidated 12/31/82
Original Series <$VALUE
3x1-2 1-3000 <$600/$1250
4x5 1-5000 <$650
3x10-20 1-1000 <$750/$1250
Series 1875
3x1-2 1-1000 <$600/$1250
4x5 1-1930 <$650
3x10-20 1-322 <$750/$1250
Total Issue $224,700
Out in 1910 $1,463
****
2838 Washington
NB OF SANDY HILL
{{ UNREPORTED }}
Chartered 12/14/82
Liquidated 10/28/02
Brown Back <$VALUE
3x10-20 1-3066 <$1250
Total Issue $153,300
Out in 1910 $1,560
****
3244 Washington
PEOPLES NB OF SANDY HILL
Chartered 1884
2nd title:Peoples NB of Hudson Falls 6/23/10
FIRST TITLE {{ 3 L }}
Brown Back <$VALUE
4x5 1-5358 <$750
3x10-20 1-1163 <$750
1902 Red Seal
4x5 1-1300 <$750
3x10-20 1-1880 <$750
1902 Date Back
4x5 1-1072 <$400
3x10-20 1-682 <$400
SECOND TITLE {{ 1 L }}
1902 Date Back
3x10-20 1-3940 <$400
1902 Plain Back
3x10-20 3941-4094 <$400
Total Issue $545,550
Out in 1935 $470
****

****
6470 Washington
SANDY HILL NB, SANDY HILL
Chartered 10/25/02
2nd title:Sandy Hill NB of Hudson Falls 7/7/10
FIRST TITLE {{ 0 L }}
1902 Red Seal <$VALUE
3x10-20 1-3480 <$750
1902 Date Back
3x10-20 1-893 <$400
SECOND TITLE {{ 7 L U + 12 S }}
1902 Date Back
3x10-20 1-3640 <$200
1902 Plain Back
3x10-20 3641-21525 <$200
1929 Small Size
10 Type 1 1-3140 <$100
20 Type 1 1-922 <$100
10 Type 2 1-5469 <$100
20 Type 2 1-1632 <$100
Total Issue $1,681,270
Out in 1935 $125,000
Large out 1935 $3,310
****
5072 Franklin
ADIRONDACK NB OF SARANAC LAKE
Chartered 1897
2nd title:Adirondack NB & TC 4/18/27
FIRST TITLE {{ 1 L }}
Brown Back <$VALUE
50-100 1-453 <$1750/$2000
1882 Date Back
50-100 1-240 <$1500/$1750
3x50-100 1-12 <$1500/$1750
1902 Plain Back
3x50-100 1-165<$1000/$1250
SECOND TITLE {{ 0 L 14 S }}
1902 Plain Back
3x10-20 1-210 <$600
1929 Small Size
10 Type 1 1-1546 <$175
20 Type 1 1-408 <$175
10 Type 2 1-4884 <$175
20 Type 2 1-1488 <$175
Total Issue $379,020
Out in 1935 $100,000
Large out 1935 $1,070
****
8935 Franklin
SARANAC LAKE NB, SARANAC LAKE
{{ 0 L 2 S }}
Chartered 10/07
1902 Red Seal <$VALUE
4x5 1-350 <$1500
4x10 1-350 <$1500
1902 Date Back
4x5 1-1350 <$1000
4x10 1-1300 <$1000
1902 Plain Back
4x5 1351-3868 <$1000
4x10 1301-3292 <$1000
1929 Small Size
5 Type 1 1-856 <$500
10 Type 1 1-310 <$500
5 Type 2 1-3002 <$500
Total Issue $289,330
Out in 1935 $12,500
Large out 1935 $550
****
2615 Saratoga
CITIZENS NB OF SARATOGA SPRINGS
{{ 6 L }}
Chartered 1882
Liquidated 11/1/15
Series 1875 <$VALUE
4x5 1-7708 <$500
3x10-20 1-5206 <$750/$1250
Brown Back
4x5 1-6000 <$400
3x10-20 1-4800 <$400
1882 Date Back
4x5 1-7795 <$400
3x10-20 1-5614 <$400
Total Issue $1,211,060
Out in 1916 $38,550
****

CONDITION affects Value. The Values shown are for notes in FINE condition.

1227 Saratoga
COMMERCIAL NB OF SARATOGA SPRINGS
{{4 L}}
Organized 6/6/65
Receivership 2/11/79
Original Series <$VALUE
3x1-2 1-7300 <$400/$1000
4x5 1-3250 <$500
3x10-20 1-1100 <$750/$1250
Series 1875
3x1-2 1-2840 <$400/$1000
4x5 1-3750 <$500
Total Issue $245,700
Out in 1916 $1,574

893 Saratoga
FNB OF SARATOGA SPRINGS
Chartered 3/14/65
2nd title:Saratoga NB of Saratoga Springs 11/4/15
FIRST TITLE {{7 L}}
Original Series <$VALUE
3x1-2 1-5920 <$350/$850
4x5 1-7000 <$400
3x10-20 1-2300 <$750/$1250
Series 1875
4x5 1-2925 <$400
3x10-20 1-278 <$750/$1250
Brown Back
3x10-20 1-13465 <$300
1902 Red Seal
3x10-20 1-5100 <$350
1902 Date Back
3x10-20 1-9462 <$175
SECOND TITLE {{1 L 12 S}}
1902 Plain Back
3x10-20 1-9541 <$250
1929 Small Size
10 Type 1 1-1866 <$100
20 Type 1 1-328 <$100
10 Type 2 1-7482 <$100
20 Type 2 1-1864 <$100
Total Issue $2,498,820
Out in 1935 $99,995
Large out 1935 $5,455

Saratoga NB of Saratoga Springs
SEE Ch 893 FNB of Saratoga Springs

1040 Ulster
FNB OF SAUGERTIES
Chartered 4/65
2nd title:FNB & TC 8/13/28
FIRST TITLE {{8 L}}
Original Series <$VALUE
3x1-2 1-4000 <$250/$750
4x5 1-4750 <$300
3x10-20 1-3700 <$600/$1250
Series 1875
3x1-2 1-1500 <$250/$750
4x5 1-6500 <$300
3x10-20 1-2444 <$500/$1000
Brown Back
3x10-20 1-7027 <$200/$250
1902 Red Seal
3x10-20 1-2200 <$200/$250
1902 Date Back
3x10-20 1-5100 <$100
1902 Plain Back
3x10-20 5101-10858 <$100
SECOND TITLE {{1 L 15 S}}
1902 Plain Back
3x10-20 1-461 <$150
1929 Small Size
5 Type 1 1-2054 <$50
10 Type 1 1-2814 <$50
20 Type 1 1-756 <$65
5 Type 2 1-4226 <$65
10 Type 2 1-1795 <$65
20 Type 2 1-705 <$75
Total Issue $1,961,360
Out in 1935 $100,000
Large out 1935 $5,570

1208 Ulster
SAUGERTIES NB, SAUGERTIES
{{9 L}}
Chartered 6/2/65
Liquidated 6/16/88
Original Series <$VALUE
3x1-2 1-4000 <$250/$750
4x5 1-6150 <$300
3x10-20 1-2750 <$600/$1250
Series 1875
4x5 1-3680 <$300
3x10-20 1-1550 <$500/$1000
Brown Back
4x5 1-2477 <$200
3x10-20 1-830 <$200/$250
Total Issue $522,640
Out in 1910 $2,571

11349 Steuben
SAVONA NB, SAVONA
{{3 L 4 S}}
Organized 4/23/19
Receivership 5/6/31
1902 Plain Back <$VALUE
4x5 1-5277 <$450
1929 Small Size
5 Type 1 1-564 <$300
Total Issue $122,460
Out at close $10,000
Large out at close $720

5186 Suffolk
OYSTERMENS NB OF SAYVILLE
{{11 L 7 S}}
Chartered 4/15/99
Liquidated 4/14/34
Brown Back <$VALUE
4x5 1-4415 <$2000
3x10-20 1-3384 <$2000
1882 Date Back
4x5 1-5150 <$2000
3x10-20 1-3340 <$2000
1882 Value Back
4x5 5151-7495 <$2000
3x10-20 3341-4468 <$2000
1902 Plain Back
4x5 1-26539 <$1000
1929 Small Size
5 Type 1 1-6720 <$600
5 Type 2 1-4124 <$600
Total Issue $1,383,800
Out at close $50,000
Large out at close $3,080

11708 Westchester
SCARSDALE NB, SCARSDALE
Chartered 5/20
2nd title:Scarsdale NB & TC 10/22/25
FIRST TITLE {{6 L}}
1902 Plain Back <$VALUE
4x5 1-33000 <$350
SECOND TITLE {{10 L 2U+18 S}}
1902 Plain Back
4x5 1-32529 <$350
1929 Small Size
5 Type 1 1-22190 <$150
5 Type 2 1-69200 <$150
Total Issue $2,322,280
Out in 1935 $200,000
Large out 1935 $4,620

1226 Schenectady
MOHAWK NB OF SCHENECTADY
{{12 L 21 S}}
Chartered 1865
Original Series <$VALUE
3x1-2 1-3000 <$250/$750
4x5 1-2600 <$300
3x10-20 1-2300 <$600/$1250
Series 1875
3x10-20 1-2800 <$500/$1000
Brown Back
4x5 1-6430 <$200
3x10-20 1-10776 <$200/$250
1902 Red Seal
3x10-20 1-3800 <$200/$250
1902 Date Back
3x10-20 1-5700 <$100
1902 Plain Back
3x10-20 5701-39142 <$100
1929 Small Size
10 Type 1 1-11558 <$50
20 Type 1 1-3084 <$55
10 Type 2 1-12162 <$50
20 Type 2 1-3733 <$60
Total Issue $4,396,340
Out in 1935 $200,000
Large out 1935 $9,470

4711 Schenectady
UNION NB OF SCHENECTADY
{{14 L 19 S}}
Chartered 1892
Brown Back <$VALUE
4x5 1-10100 <$200
3x10-20 1-7400 <$200
1882 Date Back
4x5 1-3585 <$200
3x10-20 1-2856 <$200
1902 Date Back
4x5 1-4750 <$100
3x10-20 1-3800 <$100
1902 Plain Back
4x5 4751-24075 <$100
3x10-20 3801-16779 <$100
1929 Small Size
5 Type 1 1-7530 <$40
10 Type 1 1-4826 <$40
20 Type 1 1-1178 <$50
5 Type 2 1-35928 <$50
10 Type 2 1-19975 <$50
20 Type 2 1-4690 <$55
Total Issue $3,236,960
Out in 1935 $400,000
Large out 1935 $5,275

4962 Otsego
SCHENEVUS NB, SCHENEVUS
{{7 L 9 S}}
Chartered 1894
Brown Back <$VALUE
4x5 1-3150 <$300
3x10-20 1-1220 <$300/$350
1882 Date Back
4x5 1-2975 <$300
3x10-20 1-2188 <$300/$350
1902 Date Back
4x5 1-1250 <$200
3x10-20 1-1000 <$200
1902 Plain Back
4x5 1251-10395 <$200
3x10-20 1001-6837 <$200
1929 Small Size
5 Type 1 1-1782 <$150
10 Type 1 1-1024 <$150
20 Type 1 1-282 <$150
5 Type 2 1-3504 <$150
10 Type 2 1-1656 <$150
20 Type 2 1-444 <$175
Total Issue $1,034,350
Out in 1935 $50,000
Large out 1935 $2,170

1510 Schoharie
SCHOHARIE COUNTY NB OF SCHOHARIE
{{ UNREPORTED }}
Organized 8/9/65
Receivership 3/23/85
Original Series <$VALUE
4x5 1-2000 <$1000
3x10-20 1-3000<$1250/$1500
Series 1875
3x10-20 1-1622<$1250/$1500
Total Issue $461,100
Out in 1916 $1,295

1298 Saratoga
NB OF SCHUYLERVILLE
{{3 L 8 S}}
Chartered 1865
Original Series <$VALUE
3x1-2 1-2900 <$500/$1000
4x5 1-4825 <$600
3x10-20 1-2200 <$750/$1250
Series 1875
4x5 1-2800 <$600
3x10-20 1-234 <$750/$1250
Brown Back
4x5 1-5595 <$500
3x10-20 1-442 <$500
1902 Red Seal
3x10-20 1-520 <$600
1902 Date Back
3x10-20 1-1360 <$300
1902 Plain Back
3x10-20 1361-3036 <$300
1929 Small Size
10 Type 1 1-926 <$150
20 Type 1 1-208 <$150
10 Type 2 1-2106 <$150
20 Type 2 1-485 <$175
Total Issue $711,780
Out in 1935 $50,000
Large out 1935 $2,110

3329 Seneca
EXCHANGE NB OF SENECA FALLS
{{18 L}}
Chartered 1885
Liquidated 9/30/24
Brown Back <$VALUE
4x5 1-10917 <$300
3x10-20 1-5406 <$300
1902 Red Seal
4x5 1-3500 <$300
3x10-20 1-2600 <$300
1902 Date Back
4x5 1-1250 <$150
3x10-20 1-5400 <$150
1902 Plain Back
4x5 7251-18564 <$150
3x10-20 5401-12576 <$150
Total Issue $1,688,720
Out at close $100,000

102 Seneca
FNB OF SENECA FALLS
{{1 L}}
Chartered 10/63
Liquidated 11/23/80
Original Series <$VALUE
4x5 1-6500 <$1000
Series 1875
4x5 1-550 <$1000
Total Issue $141,000
Out in 1910 $940

1240 Seneca
N EXCHANGE B OF SENECA FALLS
{{2 L}}
Chartered 1865
Liquidated 5/6/85
Original Series <$VALUE
4x5 1-5100 <$600
3x10-20 1-1200 <$750/$1250
Series 1875
4x5 1-4300 <$600
3x10-20 1-1654 <$750/$1250
Total Issue $330,700
Out in 1910 $1,835

7512 Schoharie
FNB OF SHARON SPRINGS
{{2 L 10 S}}
Organized 12/8/04
1902 Red Seal <$VALUE
3x10-20 1-1200 <$750
1902 Date Back
3x10-20 1-2360 <$375
1902 Plain Back
3x10-20 2361-6837 <$375
1929 Small Size
10 Type 1 1-754 <$175
20 Type 1 1-204 <$175
10 Type 2 1-740 <$200
20 Type 2 1-230 <$200
Total Issue $483,570
Out in 1935 $25,000
Large out 1935 $1,270

1166 Chenango
SHERBURNE NB, SHERBURNE
{{12 L 14 S}}
Chartered 1865
Original Series <$VALUE
4x5 1-2250 <$350
4x10 1-2750 <$650
Series 1875
4x10 1-3800 <$350
Brown Back
3x10-20 1-11290 <$250/$300
1902 Red Seal
4x5 1-4750 <$300
3x10-20 1-2200 <$300
1902 Date Back
4x5 1-10200 <$125
3x10-20 1-7560 <$125
1902 Plain Back
4x5 10201-24760 <$125
3x10-20 7561-17967 <$125
1929 Small Size
5 Type 1 1-3984 <$65
10 Type 1 1-2228 <$65
20 Type 1 1-496 <$75
5 Type 2 1-6584 <$75
10 Type 2 1-3574 <$75
20 Type 2 1-972 <$85
Total Issue $2,870,870
Out in 1935 $100,000
Large out 1935 $5,810

13563 Delaware
FNB IN SIDNEY
{{8 S}}
Chartered 7/31
1929 Small Size <$VALUE
10 Type 1 1-1640 <$150
20 Type 1 1-446 <$150
10 Type 2 1-2401 <$150
20 Type 2 1-735 <$150
Total Issue $190,630
Out in 1935 $50,000
Outstanding includes Ch 3822

8513 Delaware
PEOPLES NB OF SIDNEY
{{3 L}}
Chartered 1/07
Liquidated 12/31/27
1902 Red Seal <$VALUE
3x10-20 1-875 <$600
1902 Date Back
3x10-20 1-3900 <$350
1902 Plain Back
3x10-20 3901-11420 <$350
Total Issue $614,750
Out at close $50,000

3822 Delaware
SIDNEY NB, SIDNEY
{{6 L 3 S}}
Chartered 12/15/87
Liquidated 8/18/31
Brown Back <$VALUE
4x5 1-10654 <$400
3x10-20 1-2549 <$400
1902 Red Seal
3x10-20 1-1000 <$500
1902 Date Back
3x10-20 1-4140 <$250
1902 Plain Back
3x10-20 4141-12973 <$250
1929 Small Size
10 Type 1 1-764 <$250
20 Type 1 1-220 <$250
Total Issue $1,111,420
Out at close $50,000
Large out 1935 $2,940
Ch 13563 assumed circulation

10159 Chautauqua
FNB OF SILVER CREEK
{{3U+6 L 2U+20 S}}
Chartered 3/12
1902 Date Back <$VALUE
4x5 1-2400 <$175
3x10-20 1-1920 <$175
1902 Plain Back
4x5 2401-13323 <$175
3x10-20 1921-8794 <$175
1929 Small Size
5 Type 1 1-3660 <$60
10 Type 1 1-1986 <$60
20 Type 1 1-522 <$60
5 Type 2 1-2190 <$65
10 Type 2 1-1180 <$65
20 Type 2 1-330 <$75
Total Issue $1,027,110
Out in 1935 $50,000
Large out 1935 $2,600

10258 Chautauqua
SILVER CREEK NB, SILVER CREEK
{{U+8 L 28 S}}
Chartered 9/12
1902 Date Back <$VALUE
3x10-20 1-3000 <$150
1902 Plain Back
3x10-20 3001-18208 <$150
1929 Small Size
10 Type 1 1-2890 <$60
20 Type 1 1-762 <$60
10 Type 2 1-3193 <$65
20 Type 2 1-895 <$75
Total Issue $1,225,070
Out in 1935 $100,000
Large out 1935 $3,070

6148 Wyoming
SILVER SPRINGS NB, SILVER SPRINGS
{{7 L U+3 S}}
Chartered 3/8/02
1902 Red Seal <$VALUE
4x5 1-1750 <$600
3x10-20 1-1340 <$600
1902 Date Back
4x5 1-1975 <$300
3x10-20 1-1420 <$300
1902 Plain Back (dated 1902)
4x5 1976-3950 <$300
3x10-20 1421-2608 <$300
1902 Plain Back (dated 1922)
4x5 1-9087 <$300
1929 Small Size
5 Type 1 1-2928 <$350
5 Type 2 1-7270 <$350
Total Issue $617,330
Out in 1935 $25,000
Large out 1935 $1,260

471 Westchester
FNB OF SING SING
Chartered 7/64
2nd title:FNB of Ossining 1/14/03
3rd title:FNB & TC of Ossining 1/18/26
FIRST TITLE {{1 L}}
Original Series <$VALUE
3x1-2 1-2000 <$1500/$2500
4x5 1-3550 <$1500
3x10-20 1-2100<$2000/$2500
Series 1875
4x5 1-2385 <$1500
3x10-20 1-1800<$2000/$2500
Brown Back
4x5 1-3565 <$1500
3x10-20 1-1988 <$1500
SECOND TITLE {{7 L}}
1902 Red Seal
4x5 1-1120 <$600
3x10-20 1-1312 <$600
1902 Date Back
4x5 1-7900 <$250
3x10-20 1-5500 <$250
1902 Plain Back
4x5 7901-23569 <$250
3x10-20 5501-15397 <$250
THIRD TITLE {{6 L 16 S}}
1902 Plain Back
4x5 1-4411 <$250
3x10-20 1-3537 <$250
1929 Small Size
5 Type 1 1-3892 <$85
10 Type 1 1-2144 <$85
20 Type 1 1-516 <$85
5 Type 2 1-13754 <$85
10 Type 2 1-7538 <$85
20 Type 2 1-2160 <$85
Total Issue $2,583,370
Out in 1935 $150,000
Large out 1935 $5,560

303 Onondaga
FNB SKANEATELES
{{ UNREPORTED }}
Chartered 3/4/64
Liquidated 12/21/67
Original Series <$VALUE
3x1-2 1-1000 <$1000/$1500
4x5 1-3375 <$1000
3x10-20 1-1250<$1250/$1500
Total Issue $135,000
Out in 1910 $1,052

5360 Onondaga
NB OF SKANEATELES
Chartered 5/19/00
2nd title:NB & TC 6/5/28
FIRST TITLE {{14 L}}
Brown Back <$VALUE
4x5 1-4200 <$250
3x10-20 1-3140 <$250
1882 Date Back
4x5 1-4800 <$250
3x10-20 1-3760 <$250
1882 Value Back
4x5 4801-8240 <$250
3x10-20 3761-5779 <$250
1902 Plain Back
4x5 1-8161 <$150
3x10-20 1-4771 <$150
SECOND TITLE {{0 L 15 S}}
1902 Plain Back
4x5 1-674 <$200
3x10-20 1-667 <$200
1929 Small Size
5 Type 1 1-3138 <$85
10 Type 1 1-1582 <$85
20 Type 1 1-388 <$100
5 Type 2 1-7386 <$100
10 Type 2 1-3472 <$100
20 Type 2 1-1218 <$100
Total Issue $1,474,980
Out in 1935 $100,000
Large out 1935 $3,630

9820 Suffolk
NB OF SMITHTOWN BRANCH
{{3 L}}
Chartered 7/10
Liquidated 5/5/23
1902 Date Back <$VALUE
4x5 1-1950 <$1250
4x10 1-1800 <$1250
1902 Plain Back
4x5 1951-5197 <$1250
4x10 1801-4095 <$1250
Total Issue $267,740
Out at close $25,000

9418 Wayne
FNB OF SODUS
{{3 L 7 S}}
Organized 4/17/09
Receivership 1/12/33
1902 Date Back <$VALUE
3x10-20 1-2280* <$400
1902 Plain Back
3x10-20 2381-8811* <$400
* 2281-2380 not marked
1929 Small Size
10 Type 1 1-1396 <$150
20 Type 1 1-398 <$165
Total Issue $572,070
Out at close $60,000
Large out at close $2,260

1304 Westchester
FARMERS & DROVERS NB OF SOMERS
{{ 3 L }}
Chartered 6/17/65
Liquidated 1/16/96
Original Series <$VALUE
4x5 1-2750 <$1000
3x10-20 1-2000<$1000/$1500
Series 1875
4x5 1-9080 <$1000
3x10-20 1-3166<$1000/$1500
Brown Back
4x5 1-9888 <$850
3x10-20 1-1854 <$850
Total Issue $785,360
Out in 1910 $3,215

830 Putnam
CROTON RIVER NB OF SOUTH EAST
{{ 3 L }}
Chartered 2/22/65
Liquidated 5/25/74
Original Series <$VALUE
3x1-2 1-7010 <$400/$1000
4x5 1-11860 <$500
Total Issue $272,250
Out in 1910 $2,703

11809 Sullivan
SOUTH FALLSBURG NB, SOUTH FALLSBURG
{{ U + 3 L 8 S }}
Chartered 8/20
1902 Plain Back <$VALUE
4x5 1-10415 <$350
1929 Small Size
10 Type 1 1-1542 <$200
10 Type 2 1-7296 <$200
Total Issue $373,780
Out in 1935 $75,000
Large out 1935 $670

5851 Warren
FNB OF SOUTH GLENS FALLS
{{ 2 L 2 S }}
Chartered 6/6/01
Receivership 5/24/32
Brown Back <$VALUE
4x5 1-825 <$600
3x10-20 1-650 <$600
1882 Date Back
4x5 1-850 <$600
3x10-20 1-660 <$600
1882 Value Back
4x5 851-1545 <$600
3x10-20 661-1032 <$600
1902 Plain Back
4x5 1-3110 <$400
3x10-20 1-1873 <$400
1929 Small Size
5 Type 1 1-696 <$350
10 Type 1 1-352 <$350
20 Type 1 1-105 <$350
Total Issue $341,950
Out at close $25,000
Large out at close $900

7774 Chenango
OTSELIC VALLEY NB OF SOUTH OTSELIC
{{ 7 L 18 S }}
Chartered 6/05
1902 Red Seal <$VALUE
4x5 1-1150 <$350
3x10-20 1-820 <$350
1902 Date Back
4x5 1-2300 <$175
3x10-20 1-1760 <$175
1902 Plain Back
4x5 2301-13155 <$175
3x10-20 1761-9200 <$175
1929 Small Size
5 Type 1 1-4140 <$60
10 Type 1 1-1862 <$60
20 Type 1 1-538 <$75
5 Type 2 1-8160 <$75
10 Type 2 1-4758 <$75
20 Type 2 1-1158 <$80
Total Issue $1,199,120
Out in 1935 $100,000
Large out 1935 $2,370

103 Otsego
FNB OF SOUTH WORCESTER
{{ UNREPORTED }}
Chartered 10/7/63
Liquidated 8/4/68
Original Series <$VALUE
4x5 1-6200 <$1250
3x10-20 1-748 <$1000/$1500
Total Issue $161,400
Out in 1910 $1,480

10185 Suffolk
FNB OF SOUTHAMPTON
{{ 8 L 13 S }}
Chartered 5/12
1902 Date Back <$VALUE
4x5 1-2025 <$600
3x10-20 1-1820 <$600
1902 Plain Back
4x5 2026-20020 <$600
3x10-20 1821-14209 <$600
1929 Small Size
5 Type 1 1-3812 <$300
10 Type 1 1-1988 <$300
20 Type 1 1-606 <$300
5 Type 2 1-8470 <$300
10 Type 2 1-3831 <$300
20 Type 2 1-1174 <$325
Total Issue $1,521,350
Out in 1935 $100,000
Large out 1935 $2,460

5390 Rockland
FNB OF SPRING VALLEY
{{ 1 L 7 S }}
Chartered 6/2/00
Brown Back <$VALUE
3x10-20 1-900 <$1000
1882 Date Back
3x10-20 1-900 <$1000
1882 Value Back
3x10-20 901-1006 <$1000
1902 Plain Back
3x10-20 1-831 <$750
1929 Small Size
10 Type 1 1-181 <$350
20 Type 1 1-30 <$350
5 Type 2 1-13320 <$350
10 Type 2 1-13944 <$350
20 Type 2 1-4236 <$350
Total Issue $446,070
Out in 1935 $156,250
Large out 1935 $300

6330 Erie
CITIZENS NB OF SPRINGVILLE
{{ 7 L 19 S }}
Chartered 7/5/02
1902 Red Seal <$VALUE
4x5 1-440 <$300
3x10-20 1-334 <$300
1902 Date Back
4x5 1-2250 <$150
3x10-20 1-1710 <$150
1902 Plain Back
4x5 2251-11122 <$150
3x10-20 1711-7311 <$150
1929 Small Size
5 Type 1 1-4924 <$75
10 Type 1 1-2758 <$75
20 Type 1 1-760 <$85
5 Type 2 1-11328 <$100
10 Type 2 1-5940 <$100
20 Type 2 1-1404 <$100
Total Issue $1,162,010
Out in 1935 $150,000
Large out 1935 $1,810

2892 Erie
FNB OF SPRINGVILLE
{{ 1 L }}
Organized 2/26/83
Receivership 10/3/96
Brown Back <$VALUE
4x5 1-5468 <$1000
Total Issue $109,360
Out in 1916 $620

2602 Delaware
NB OF STAMFORD
{{ 10 L 16 S }}
Chartered 1881
Series 1875 <$VALUE
3x10-20 1-6903 <$600/$1000
Brown Back
3x10-20 1-4700 <$350
1882 Date Back
3x10-20 1-5300 <$350
1882 Value Back
3x10-20 5301-11092 <$350
1902 Plain Back
3x10-20 1-10732 <$200
1929 Small Size
10 Type 1 1-2608 <$125
20 Type 1 1-734 <$125
10 Type 2 1-5326 <$125
20 Type 2 1-1298 <$125
Total Issue $1,995,380
Out in 1935 $100,000
Large out 1935 $4,670

7290 Richmond
RICHMOND BOROUGH NB OF STAPLETON
{{ 2 L }}
Chartered 6/04
Liquidated 7/14/26
1902 Red Seal <$VALUE
3x10-20 1-1724 <$800
1902 Date Back
3x10-20 1-5100 <$400
1902 Plain Back
3x10-20 5101-10575 <$400
Total Issue $614,950
Out at close $40,000

6562 Richmond
STAPLETON NB, STAPLETON
{{ 8 L }}
Chartered 12/02
Liquidated 4/30/28
1902 Red Seal <$VALUE
4x5 1-5580 <$500
3x10-20 1-4733 <$500
1902 Date Back
4x5 1-10850 <$250
3x10-20 1-7600 <$250
1902 Plain Back
4x5 10851-29295 <$250
3x10-20 7601-19908 <$250
Total Issue $1,929,550
Out at close $100,000

5846 Rockland
SUFFERN NB, SUFFERN
Chartered 5/31/01
2nd title:Suffern NB & TC 1/21/25
FIRST TITLE {{ 12 L }}
Brown Back <$VALUE
4x5 1-950 <$600
3x10-20 1-860 <$600
1882 Date Back
4x5 1-5800* <$600
3x10-20 1-4180** <$600
1882 Value Back
4x5 5951-9630* <$600
3x10-20 4301-6781** <$600
* 5801-5950 not marked
** 4181-4300 not marked
1902 Plain Back
4x5 1-3350 <$350
3x10-20 1-2102 <$350
SECOND TITLE {{ 21 S }}
1929 Small Size
5 Type 1 1-8322 <$125
10 Type 1 1-4450 <$125
20 Type 1 1-1326 <$125
50 Type 1 1-314 <$250
100 Type 1 1-126 <$350
5 Type 2 1-16470 <$125
10 Type 2 1-8995 <$125
20 Type 2 1-2490 <$125
Total Issue $1,833,430
Out in 1935 $350,000
Large out 1935 $1,875

5286 Onondaga
AMERICAN EXCHANGE NB OF SYRACUSE
{{ 1 L }}
Chartered 4/12/00
Receivership 2/11/04
Brown Back <$VALUE
4x5 1-5025 <$650
3x10-20 1-6436 <$650
Total Issue $422,300
Out in 1916 $2,455

6965 Onondaga
COMMERCIAL NB OF SYRACUSE
{{ 5 L }}
Chartered 9/03
Liquidated 10/13/15
1902 Red Seal <$VALUE
4x5 1-5000 <$300
3x10-20 1-30500 <$300
1902 Date Back
4x5 1-19638 <$200
3x10-20 1-13126 <$200
Total Issue $2,674,060
Out at close $272,545

6 Onondaga
FNB OF SYRACUSE
{{ 10 L }}
Chartered 6/63
Liquidated 12/31/18
Original Series <$VALUE
4x5 1-30000 <$500
Series 1875
4x5 1-22500 <$500
Brown Back
4x5 1-27105 <$350
3x10-20 1-3548 <$350/$400
1902 Red Seal
4x5 1-8000 <$400
3x10-20 1-6400 <$400
1902 Date Back
4x5 1-16917 <$200
3x10-20 1-11517 <$200
Total Issue $3,163,690
Out at close $148,200

1569 Onondaga
FOURTH NB OF SYRACUSE
{{ UNREPORTED }}
Chartered 9/27/65
Liquidated 1/9/72
Original Series <$VALUE
3x1-2 1-3000 <$750/$1500
4x5 1-4250 <$850
3x10-20 1-480 <$1000/$1500
Total Issue $124,000
Out in 1910 $715

12122 Onondaga
LIBERTY NB OF SYRACUSE
{{ 1 L }}
Chartered 2/22
Liquidated 4/27/29
1902 Plain Back <$VALUE
4x5 1-2250 <$600
3x10-20 1-1924 <$600
Total Issue $141,200
Out at close $2,290

13393 Onondaga
LINCOLN NB & TC OF SYRACUSE
{{ 2U + 31 S }}
Chartered 11/29 as The Lincoln NB & TC, under which there was no issue. Issuing title adopted 11/27/30.
1929 Small Size <$VALUE
5 Type 1 1-22438 <$20
10 Type 1 1-10784 <$20
20 Type 1 1-3376 <$30
5 Type 2 1-85060 <$20
10 Type 2 1-47997 <$20
20 Type 2 1-13499 <$30
Total Issue $2,900,550
Out in 1935 $858,300

1401 Onondaga
MECHANICS NB OF SYRACUSE
{{ UNREPORTED }}
Chartered 7/7/65
Liquidated 3/11/73
Original Series <$VALUE
4x5 1-2625 <$850
3x10-20 1-1046<$1000/$1500
Total Issue $104,800
Out in 1910 $765

1342 Onondaga
MERCHANTS NB OF SYRACUSE
Chartered 1865
2nd title:Merchants NB & TC 6/14/26
FIRST TITLE {{ 12 L }}
Original Series <$VALUE
3x1-2 1-4600 <$250/$750
4x5 1-8107 <$300
3x10-20 1-3000 <$600/$1250
Series 1875
4x5 1-8020 <$300
3x10-20 1-1593 <$500/$1000
Brown Back
3x10-20 1-8280 <$200/$225
1902 Red Seal
3x10-20 1-6500 <$200/$225
1902 Date Back
3x10-20 1-17600 <$100
1902 Plain Back
3x10-20 17601-42823 <$100
SECOND TITLE {{U + 3 L 19 S}}
1902 Plain Back
3x10-20 1-6964 <$125
1929 Small Size
10 Type 1 1-5386 <$35
20 Type 1 1-1320 <$40
10 Type 2 1-6351 <$40
20 Type 2 1-1859 <$45
Total Issue $4,385,790
Out in 1935 $180,000
Large out 1935 $9,990

5465 Onondaga
NB OF SYRACUSE
{{ 7 L }}
Chartered 6/28/00
Liquidated 12/14/18
Brown Back <$VALUE
4x5 1-11000 <$200
3x10-20 1-11800 <$200/$250
1882 Date Back
4x5 1-3800 <$200
3x10-20 1-2162 <$200/$250
Total Issue $994,100
Out in 1916 $48,100

1287 Onondaga
SALT SPRINGS NB OF SYRACUSE
{{ 7 L }}
Organized 5/20/65
Receivership 1/22/34
Original Series <$VALUE
4x5 1-9100 <$400
3x10-20 1-3850 <$600/$1250
Series 1875
3x10-20 1-1890 <$500/$1000
Brown Back
3x10-20 1-13559 <$250/$300
1902 Red Seal
3x10-20 1-5900 <$350/$400
1902 Date Back
3x10-20 1-13800 <$175
1902 Plain Back
3x10-20 13801-39142 <$175
Total Issue $3,399,050
Out at close $9,455

140 Onondaga
SECOND NB OF SYRACUSE
{{ UNREPORTED }}
Chartered 12/3/63
Liquidated 2/18/73
Original Series <$VALUE
4x5 1-4702 <$1000
4x10 1-714 <$1250
Total Issue $122,600
Out in 1910 $1,055

1341 Onondaga
SYRACUSE NB, SYRACUSE
{{ 2 L }}
Chartered 1865
Liquidated 9/25/76
Original Series <$VALUE
3x1-2 1-7000 <$400/$1000
4x5 1-6225 <$500
3x10-20 1-1800 <$750/$1250
20 1801-3205 <$1250
50-100 1-680 <$3500
Total Issue $379,600
Out in 1910 $2,533

159 Onondaga
THIRD NB OF SYRACUSE
{{ 16 L }}
Chartered 12/63
Liquidated 4/27/29
Original Series <$VALUE
3x1-2 1-2500 <$250/$750
4x5 1-5000 <$300
4x10 1-5850 <$600
2x20-50-100 1-806 <$1250/$3500/$3500
Series 1875
4x5 1-500 <$300
4x10 1-6000 <$500
2x20-50-100 1-300 <$1000/$3500/$3500
Brown Back
3x10-20 1-35336 <$150/$200
1902 Red Seal
3x10-20 1-17500 <$200/$225
1902 Date Back
3x10-20 1-26500 <$100
1902 Plain Back
3x10-20 26501-80930 <$100
Total Issue $7,494,940
Out at close $300,000

11057 Greene
MOUNTAIN NB OF TANNERSVILLE
{{ U + 2 L 6 S }}
Organized 6/30/17
Receivership 12/18/33
1902 Plain Back <$VALUE
3x10-20 1-4528 <$500
1929 Small Size
10 Type 1 1-787 <$250
20 Type 1 1-171 <$275
Total Issue $294,140
Out at close $25,000
Large out at close $1,720

364 Westchester
FNB OF TARRYTOWN
{{ 1 L }}
Organized 4/5/64
Receivership 3/23/78
Original Series <$VALUE
3x1-2 1-2500 <$1250/$2000
4x5 1-5000 <$1500
3x10-20 1-1500<$1750/$2000
Series 1875
4x5 1-1154 <$1500
3x10-20 1-382 <$1750/$2000
Total Issue $229,680
Out in 1915 $1,712

2626 Westchester
TARRYTOWN NB, TARRYTOWN
{{ 7 L }}
Chartered 1882
Series 1875 <$VALUE
4x5 1-13275 <$1000
3x10-20 1-1891<$1000/$1500
Brown Back
3x10-20 1-7800 <$600
1882 Date Back
3x10-20 1-11000 <$600
1882 Value Back
3x10-20 11001-12523 <$600
1902 Plain Back
4x5 1-4452 <$400
Total Issue $1,465,240
Out in 1935 $2,660

8158 Jefferson
FARMERS NB OF THERESA
{{ 2 L U + 5 S }}
Chartered 4/06
1902 Red Seal <$VALUE
3x10-20 1-1100 <$750
1902 Date Back
3x10-20 1-2340 <$375
1902 Plain Back
3x10-20 2341-7376 <$375
1929 Small Size
10 Type 1 1-648 <$250
20 Type 1 1-158 <$250
10 Type 2 1-1588 <$275
20 Type 2 1-220 <$275
Total Issue $501,920
Out in 1935 $25,000
Large out 1935 $1,410

4491 Essex
FNB OF TICONDEROGA
{{ 2 L }}
Chartered 1890
Liquidated 12/16/10
Brown Back <$VALUE
4x5 1-6400 <$750
3x10-20 1-3720 <$750
1882 Date Back
4x5 1-1007 <$750
3x10-20 1-692 <$750
Total Issue $368,740
Out in 1911 $23,150

9900 Essex
TICONDEROGA NB, TICONDEROGA
{{ 3 L 9 S }}
Organized 11/14/10
1902 Date Back <$VALUE
3x10-20 1-3600 <$375
3x50-100 1-96 <$850/$1000
1902 Plain Back
3x10-20 3601-12336 <$375
1929 Small Size
10 Type 1 1-1304 <$150
20 Type 1 1-376 <$175
10 Type 2 1-2272 <$175
20 Type 2 1-768 <$200
Total Issue $802,240
Out in 1935 $50,000
Large out 1935 $1,960

4869 Erie
FNB OF TONAWANDA
{{ 14 L }}
Chartered 1893
Liquidated 7/22/16
Brown Back <$VALUE
4x5 1-14905 <$200
3x10-20 1-11818 <$200/$250
1882 Date Back
4x5 1-14900 <$200
3x10-20 1-10520 <$200/$250
1902 Date Back
4x5 1-13455 <$125
3x10-20 1-10381 <$125
Total Issue $2,501,150
Out in 1916 $248,550

8334 Richmond
TOTTENVILLE NB, TOTTENVILLE
{{ 3 L 1 S }}
Chartered 8/06
1902 Red Seal <$VALUE
4x10 1-510 <$1000
1902 Date Back
4x10 1-1600 <$600
1902 Plain Back
4x10 1601-4370 <$600
1929 Small Size
10 Type 1 1-524 <$600
10 Type 2 1-629 <$600
Total Issue $232,930
Out in 1935 $10,000
Large out 1935 $460

1012 Rensselaer
CENTRAL NB OF TROY
{{ 6 L }}
Chartered 4/14/65
Liquidated 4/4/05
Original Series <$VALUE
3x1-2 1-10900 <$250/$750
4x5 1-13100 <$300
3x10-20 1-4500 <$600/$1250
Series 1875
3x1-2 1-120 <$250/$750
4x5 1-30 <$300
3x10-20 1-518 <$500/$1000
Brown Back
4x5 1-14543 <$200
3x10-20 1-11329 <$200/$250
Total Issue $1,425,910
Out in 1910 $16,212

163 Rensselaer
FNB OF TROY
{{ 3 L }}
Chartered 12/63
Liquidated 2/24/83
Original Series <$VALUE
3x1-2 1-4000 <$300/$750
4x5 1-7500 <$350
4x10 1-9000 <$600
4x20 1-1100 <$1250
Series 1875
4x5 1-2313 <$350
4x10 1-4520 <$500
4x20 1-850 <$1000
Total Issue $913,060
Out in 1910 $4,723

721 Rensselaer
MANUFACTURERS NB OF TROY
{{ 22 L 50+ S }}
Chartered 1/65
Original Series <$VALUE
3x1-2 1-13700 <$200/$750
4x5 1-6500 <$225
3x10-20 1-1300 <$600/$1250
50-100 1-100 <$3500
Series 1875
3x1-2 1-2400 <$200/$750
4x5 1-13603 <$225
3x10-20 1-1004 <$500/$1000
Brown Back
4x5 1-8750 <$125
3x10-20 1-15339 <$125/$175
1902 Red Seal
4x5 1-5000 <$125
3x10-20 1-4000 <$125/$175
1902 Date Back
4x5 1-17000 <$50
3x10-20 1-13500 <$60
1902 Plain Back
4x5 17001-88089 <$50
3x10-20 13501-46655 <$60
1929 Small Size
5 Type 1 1-23384 <$15
10 Type 1 1-15922 <$20
20 Type 1 1-4918 <$30
50 Type 1 1-1038 <$100
100 Type 1 1-320 <$150
5 Type 2 1-20106 <$15
10 Type 2 1-16811 <$20
20 Type 2 1-3732 <$30
Total Issue $9,042,920
Out in 1935 $1,000,000
Large out 1935 $29,268
Outstanding includes Ch 991

904 Rensselaer
MERCHANTS & MECHANICS NB OF TROY
{{ 1 L }}
Chartered 3/17/65
Liquidated 12/31/68
Original Series <$VALUE
3x1-2 1-6500 <$500/$1000
4x5 1-4265 <$650
3x10-20 1-1405 <$750/$1250
Total Issue $188,050
Out in 1910 $1,447

992 Rensselaer
MUTUAL NB OF TROY
{{ 12 L }}
Chartered 4/7/65
Liquidated 3/23/05
Original Series <$VALUE
3x1-2 1-14700 <$225/$750
4x5 1-9050 <$250
3x10-20 1-3150 <$600/$1250
Series 1875
3x1-2 1-964 <$225/$750
4x5 1-12883 <$250
3x10-20 1-900 <$500/$1000
Brown Back
4x5 1-26994 <$150
3x10-20 1-8950 <$150/$200
Total Issue $1,706,860
Out in 1910 $18,667

2873 Rensselaer
NB OF TROY
{{ 2 L }}
Chartered 2/7/83
Liquidated 11/16/96
Brown Back <$VALUE
3x10-20 1-8318 <$600
Total Issue $415,900
Out in 1910 $2,180

7612 Rensselaer
N CITY B OF TROY
{{ 14 L U + 31 S }}
Chartered 2/05
1902 Red Seal <$VALUE
4x5 1-12300 <$125
3x10-20 1-9980 <$125/$175
1902 Date Back
4x5 1-31000 <$50
3x10-20 1-21800 <$60
1902 Plain Back
4x5 31001-91017 <$50
3x10-20 21801-59004 <$60
1929 Small Size
5 Type 1 1-20398 <$20
10 Type 1 1-7978 <$25
20 Type 1 1-1870 <$35
5 Type 2 1-65196 <$20
10 Type 2 1-21240 <$25
Total Issue $7,368,940
Out in 1935 $500,000
Large out 1935 $25,890
Outstanding includes Ch 940

621 Rensselaer
N EXCHANGE B OF TROY
{{ 1 L }}
Chartered 12/64
Liquidated 12/6/77
Original Series <$VALUE
3x1-2 1-7000 <$400/$850
4x5 1-5250 <$500
3x10-20 1-1700 <$600/$1250
Series 1875
4x5 1-870 <$500
3x10-20 1-236 <$600/$1000
Total Issue $254,200
Out in 1910 $1,509

991 Rensselaer
N STATE B OF TROY
{{ 21 L }}
Chartered 4/7/65
Closed 9/17/27
Original Series <$VALUE
3x1-2 1-12000 <$200/$750
4x5 1-8740 <$225
3x10-20 1-3700 <$600/$1250
50-100 1-368 <$3500
Series 1875
3x1-2 1-6840 <$200/$750
4x5 1-6500 <$225
3x10-20 1-4670 <$500/$1000
50-100 1-410 <$3500
Brown Back
4x5 1-10083 <$125
3x10-20 1-5470 <$125/$175
1902 Red Seal
4x5 1-7625 <$125
3x10-20 1-5400 <$125/$175
1902 Date Back
4x5 1-31000 <$50
3x10-20 1-18900 <$60
1902 Plain Back
4x5 31001-65060 <$50
3x10-20 18901-40852 <$60
Total Issue $5,175,660
Out at close $250,000
Ch 721 assumed circulation

640 Rensselaer
TROY CITY NB, TROY
{{ 9 L }}
Chartered 12/24/64
Liquidated 5/29/02
Original Series <$VALUE
3x1-2 1-17800 <$200/$750
4x5 1-20750 <$250
3x10-20 1-7700 <$600/$1250
50-100 1-700 <$3500
Series 1875
3x1-2 1-5340 <$200/$750
4x5 1-8927 <$250
3x10-20 1-4887 <$500/$1000
50-100 1-458 <$3500
Brown Back
4x5 1-10445 <$200
3x10-20 1-5794 <$200/$250
Total Issue $2,010,890
Out in 1910 $11,470

963 Rensselaer
UNION NB OF TROY
{{ 12 L 16 S }}
Chartered 3/31/65
Original Series <$VALUE
3x1-2 1-11800 <$200/$750
4x5 1-10600 <$225
3x10-20 1-2800 <$600/$1250
Series 1875
4x5 1-7583 <$225
3x10-20 1-2800 <$500/$1000
Brown Back
4x5 1-4805 <$125
3x10-20 1-3334 <$125/$175
50-100 1-408 <$1250/$1500
1902 Red Seal
4x5 1-8900 <$125
3x10-20 1-4852 <$125/$175
50-100 1-596 <$2250/$2500
1902 Date Back
4x5 1-27500 <$60
3x10-20 1-16800 <$75
50-100 1-600 <$350/$400
3x50-100 1-400 <$350/$400
1902 Plain Back
4x5 27501-64975 <$60
3x10-20 16801-39782 <$75
1929 Small Size
5 Type 1 1-6784 <$40
10 Type 1 1-4116 <$45
20 Type 1 1-1154 <$50
50 Type 1 1-128 <$135
100 Type 1 1-80 <$185
5 Type 2 1-12076 <$50
10 Type 2 1-4575 <$50
20 Type 2 1-1205 <$65
Total Issue $5,820,850
Out in 1935 $100,000
Large out 1935 $12,294

940 Rensselaer
UNITED NB OF TROY
{{ 16 L 4 S }}
Chartered 3/27/65
Closed 1/18/30
Original Series <$VALUE
3x1-2 1-8500 <$200/$750
4x5 1-7300 <$225
3x10-20 1-2300 <$600/$1250
Series 1875
4x5 1-7500 <$225
3x10-20 1-3400 <$500/$1000
Brown Back
4x5 1-11030 <$125
3x10-20 1-21886 <$125/$175
1902 Red Seal
4x5 1-8000 <$125
3x10-20 1-5000 <$125/$175
1902 Date Back
4x5 1-19250 <$60
3x10-20 1-14100 <$75
1902 Plain Back
4x5 19251-54137 <$60
3x10-20 14101-37837 <$75
1929 Small Size
5 Type 1 1-1932 <$150
10 Type 1 1-761 <$150
20 Type 1 1-249 <$175
Total Issue $5,456,490
Out at close $200,000
Large out at close $66,500
Ch 7612 assumed circulation

7541 Tompkins
FNB OF TRUMANSBURG
{{ 6 L 5 S }}
Organized 12/26/04
1902 Red Seal <$VALUE
3x10-20 1-1080 <$700
1902 Date Back
3x10-20 1-2190 <$350
1902 Plain Back
3x10-20 2191-9221 <$350
1929 Small Size
10 Type 1 1-1438 <$250
20 Type 1 1-402 <$250
10 Type 2 1-563 <$250
20 Type 2 1-224 <$250
Total Issue $659,680
Out in 1935 $31,310
Large out 1935 $1,700

13889 Westchester
CRESTWOOD NB IN TUCKAHOE
{{ 4 S }}
Chartered 12/33
1929 Small Size <$VALUE
5 Type 2 1-5760 <$650
10 Type 2 1-2772 <$650
20 Type 2 1-900 <$650
Total Issue $74,520
Out in 1935 $45,470

10525 Westchester
FNB OF TUCKAHOE
Chartered 4/14
2nd title:FNB & TC 1/16/26
FIRST TITLE {{ 3 L }}
1902 Date Back <$VALUE
3x10-20 1-950* <$650
1902 Plain Back
3x10-20 1081-8235* <$650
* 951-1080 not marked
SECOND TITLE {{ 3 L 15 S }}
1902 Plain Back
3x10-20 1-5800 <$650
1929 Small Size
10 Type 1 1-3164 <$250
20 Type 1 1-828 <$250
10 Type 2 1-4668 <$250
20 Type 2 1-1344 <$275
Total Issue $1,064,510
Out in 1935 $100,000
Large out 1935 $2,970

5746 Onondaga
FNB OF TULLY
{{ 3 L 3 S }}
Chartered 3/19/01
Brown Back <$VALUE
4x5 1-500 <$600
3x10-20 1-420 <$600
1882 Date Back
4x5 1-700 <$600
3x10-20 1-560 <$600
1882 Value Back
4x5 701-2495 <$600
3x10-20 561-1537 <$600
1902 Plain Back
4x5 1-7100 <$350
3x10-20 1-4802 <$350
1929 Small Size
5 Type 1 1-1818 <$350
10 Type 1 1-1030 <$350
20 Type 1 1-276 <$350
5 Type 2 1-2284 <$350
10 Type 2 1-1004 <$350
20 Type 2 1-280 <$375
Total Issue $716,370
Out in 1935 $15,000
Large out 1935 $620

8153 Franklin
TUPPER LAKE NB, TUPPER LAKE
{{ 3 L 8 S }}
Chartered 3/06
1902 Red Seal <$VALUE
3x10-20 1-990 <$750
1902 Date Back
3x10-20 1-2540 <$375
1902 Plain Back
3x10-20 2541-12883 <$375
1929 Small Size
10 Type 1 1-1484 <$250
20 Type 1 1-378 <$250
10 Type 2 1-2159 <$250
20 Type 2 1-624 <$275
Total Issue $862,120
Out in 1935 $50,000
Large out 1935 $1,860

11404 Orange
TUXEDO NB, TUXEDO
{{ 4 L 3 S }}
Chartered 7/19
Liquidated 12/28/33
1902 Plain Back <$VALUE
4x5 1-14600 <$400
1929 Small Size
5 Type 1 1-3240 <$400
5 Type 2 1-1996 <$400
Total Issue $399,180
Out at close $25,000
Large out at close $1,220

1463 Otsego
N UNADILLA B, UNADILLA
{{ UNREPORTED }}
Organized 7/17/65
Receivership 8/29/67
Original Series <$VALUE
4x5 1-3000 <$1000
3x10-20 1-800 <$1250/$1750
Total Issue $100,000
Out in 1916 $170

9516 Otsego
UNADILLA NB, UNADILLA
{{ 28 L 10 S }}
Chartered 8/09
1902 Date Back <$VALUE
3x10-20 1-2330 <$75
1902 Plain Back
3x10-20 2331-10259 <$75
1929 Small Size
10 Type 1 1-1362 <$75
20 Type 1 1-382 <$75
5 Type 2 1-324 <$75
10 Type 2 1-1943 <$75
20 Type 2 1-563 <$75
Total Issue $672,820
Out in 1935 $50,000
Large out 1935 $2,545

9276 Broome
FARMERS NB OF UNION
{{ 3 L }}
Chartered 11/08
Liquidated 1/2/28
1902 Date Back <$VALUE
3x10-20 1-2370 <$400
1902 Plain Back
3x10-20 2371-6204 <$400
Total Issue $310,200
Out at close $25,000

342 Cayuga
FNB OF UNION SPRINGS
{{ 1 L }}
Chartered 3/26/64
Liquidated 3/31/90
Original Series <$VALUE
3x1-2 1-5500 <$750/$1500
4x5 1-3250 <$850
3x10-20 1-2100<$1000/$1500
Series 1875
4x5 1-300 <$850
3x10-20 1-1150<$1000/$1500
Brown Back
4x5 1-3122 <$750
Total Issue $323,440
Out in 1910 $1,899

11448 Orange
FNB OF UNIONVILLE
{{ 2 L 3 S }}
Organized 7/26/19
Receivership 10/5/31
1902 Plain Back <$VALUE
4x5 1-9377 <$600
1929 Small Size
5 Type 1 1-2279 <$350
Total Issue $255,910
Out at close $30,000
Large out at close $1,410

120 Oneida
FNB OF UTICA
{{ UNREPORTED }}
Chartered 11/63
Liquidated 6/9/65
Original Series <$VALUE
4x10 1-500 <$2000
Total Issue $20,000
All notes reportedly redeemed

1395 Oneida
FNB OF UTICA
Chartered 1865
Liquidated 9/8/26
2nd title:FNB & TC 6/6/23
FIRST TITLE {{ 29 L }}
Original Series <$VALUE
3x1-2 1-11660 <$200/$750
4x5 1-10500 <$225
4x10 1-11375 <$600
2x20-50-100 1-500
<$1250/$3500/$3500
Series 1875
3x1-2 1-5000 <$200/$750
4x5 1-14250 <$225
4x10 1-7648 <$500
Brown Back
4x5 1-89730 <$125
3x10-20 1-40258 <$125/$175
1902 Red Seal
4x5 1-41330 <$125
3x10-20 1-20468 <$125/$175
1902 Date Back
4x5 1-102500 <$50
3x10-20 1-79500 <$60
1902 Plain Back
4x5 102501-141500 <$50
3x10-20 79501-103900 <$60
SECOND TITLE {{ 6 L }}
1902 Plain Back
4x5 1-26752 <$50
3x10-20 1-15659 <$60
Total Issue $16,434,710
Out at close $600,000

1392 Oneida
ONEIDA NB OF UTICA
Chartered 1865
2nd title:Oneida NB & TC 8/1/29
FIRST TITLE {{ 30 L }}
Original Series <$VALUE
3x1-2 1-7500 <$200/$750
4x5 1-19700 <$225
3x10-20 1-4650 <$600/$1250
Series 1875
4x5 1-18000 <$225
3x10-20 1-4710 <$500/$1000
Brown Back
4x5 1-44015 <$125
3x10-20 1-24664 <$125/$175
1902 Red Seal
4x5 1-20500 <$125
3x10-20 1-9600 <$125/$175
1902 Date Back
4x5 1-42500 <$50
3x10-20 1-31700 <$60
1902 Plain Back
4x5 42501-141842 <$50
3x10-20 31701-95183 <$60
SECOND TITLE {{ 50+ S }}
1929 Small Size
5 Type 1 1-18988 <$15
10 Type 1 1-9980 <$20
20 Type 1 1-2688 <$30
5 Type 2 1-36118 <$15
10 Type 2 1-20544 <$20
20 Type 2 1-5052 <$30
Total Issue $13,837,060
Out in 1935 $500,000
Large out 1935 $28,610

185 Oneida
SECOND NB OF UTICA
{{ 14 L }}
Chartered 1/64
Liquidated 5/6/16
Original Series <$VALUE
3x1-2 1-18000 <$200/$750
4x5 1-8000 <$225
4x10 1-6250 <$600
4x20 1-1300 <$1250
Series 1875
3x1-2 1-2000 <$200/$750
4x5 1-6557 <$225
4x10 1-3438 <$500
4x20 1-123 <$1000
Brown Back
4x5 1-23610 <$200
3x10-20 1-6554 <$200
1902 Red Seal
4x5 1-16080 <$200
4x10 1-5000 <$200
3x10-20 1-7968 <$200
1902 Date Back
4x5 1-27728 <$100
4x10 1-26421 <$100
3x10-20 1-500 <$100
Total Issue $4,248,800
Out in 1916 $270,440

CONDITION affects Value. The Values shown are for notes in FINE condition.

1308 Oneida
UTICA CITY NB, UTICA
Chartered 1865
Liquidated 5/31/30
2nd title:Utica NB & TC
8/5/25
FIRST TITLE {{ 17 L }}
Original Series <$VALUE
3x1-2 1-4600 <$200/$750
4x5 1-4601* <$225
4x10 1-1875 <$500
* 2001 canceled
Series 1875
4x5 1-1000 <$225
4x10 1-5705 <$500
Brown Back
3x10-20 1-32580 <$150/$200
1902 Red Seal
4x5 1-32250 <$150
3x10-20 1-16300 <$150/$200
1902 Date Back
4x5 1-60500 <$75
3x10-20 1-46200 <$75
1902 Plain Back
4x5 60501-132500 <$75
3x10-20 46201-90700 <$75
SECOND TITLE {{ 8 L 7 S }}
1902 Plain Back
4x5 1-20910 <$75
3x10-20 1-13380 <$75
1929 Small Size
5 Type 1 1-4767 <$125
10 Type 1 1-1848 <$125
20 Type 1 1-354 <$125
Total Issue $12,095,770
Out at close $350,000
Large out at close $74,340

Utica NB & TC, Utica
SEE Ch 1308
Utica City NB, Utica

11881 Nassau
VALLEY STREAM NB, VALLEY STREAM
Chartered 11/20
2nd title:Valley Stream
NB & TC 11/23/27
FIRST TITLE {{ 3 L }}
1902 Plain Back <$VALUE
4x5 1-8665 <$750
SECOND TITLE {{ 1 L 6 S }}
1902 Plain Back
4x5 1-3784 <$750
1929 Small Size
5 Type 1 1-7008 <$350
5 Type 2 1-20412 <$350
Total Issue $561,200
Out in 1935 $50,000
Large out 1935 $1,080

1264 Oneida
NB OF VERNON
{{ 12 L 4 S }}
Organized 5/3/65
Original Series <$VALUE
3x1-2 1-5000 <$250/$750
4x5 1-4150 <$300
3x10-20 1-1245 <$600/$1250
Series 1875
3x1-2 1-820 <$250/$750
4x5 1-7673 <$300
3x10-20 1-1020 <$500/$1000
Brown Back
4x5 1-5673 <$250
3x10-20 1-2805 <$250/$300
1902 Red Seal
4x5 1-2140 <$300
3x10-20 1-1394 <$300
1902 Date Back
4x5 1-6650 <$150
3x10-20 1-4980 <$150
1902 Plain Back
4x5 6651-14835 <$150
3x10-20 4981-9642 <$150
1929 Small Size
5 Type 1 1-734 <$175
10 Type 1 1-430 <$175
20 Type 1 1-106 <$175
5 Type 2 1-1514 <$200
10 Type 2 1-726 <$200
20 Type 2 1-254 <$200
Total Issue $1,604,270
Out in 1935 $25,000
Large out 1935 $4,300

FNB & TC of Walden
SEE Ch 10923
Third NB of Walden

5053 Orange
NB OF WALDEN
{{ 3 L }}
Chartered 1896
Liquidated 11/26/16
Brown Back <$VALUE
4x5 1-3500 <$400
3x10-20 1-1600 <$400
1882 Date Back
4x5 1-5575* <$400
3x10-20 1-3940** <$400
1882 Value Back
4x5 5826-6250* <$400
3x10-20 4141-4351** <$400
* 5576-5825 not marked
** 3941-4140 not marked
Total Issue $492,550
Out at close $48,515

10923 Orange
THIRD NB OF WALDEN
Chartered 11/16
2nd title:FNB & TC 5/1/30
FIRST TITLE {{ 5 L }}
1902 Plain Back <$VALUE
4x5 1-16840 <$250
3x10-20 1-10882 <$250
SECOND TITLE {{ 14 S }}
1929 Small Size
5 Type 1 1-1040 <$150
10 Type 1 1-854 <$150
20 Type 1 1-370 <$150
50 Type 1 1-128 <$250
5 Type 2 1-5754 <$150
10 Type 2 1-2650 <$150
20 Type 2 1-790 <$175
Total Issue $1,117,210
Out in 1935 $100,000
Large out 1935 $2,995

2348 Orange
WALDEN NB, WALDEN
{{ 3 L }}
Chartered 2/7/77
Liquidated 1/25/97
Series 1875 <$VALUE
4x5 1-8244 <$650
Total Issue $164,880
Out in 1910 $785

10155 Ulster
WALLKILL NB, WALLKILL
{{ 1 L 8 S }}
Chartered 3/12
1902 Date Back <$VALUE
3x10-20 1-920 <$600
1902 Plain Back
3x10-20 921-2280 <$600
1929 Small Size
5 Type 1 1-1038 <$250
10 Type 1 1-312 <$250
20 Type 1 1-106 <$250
5 Type 2 1-3920 <$250
10 Type 2 1-2455 <$250
20 Type 2 1-555 <$250
Total Issue $231,830
Out in 1935 $50,000
Large out 1935 $130

4495 Delaware
FNB OF WALTON
Chartered 1891
2nd title:FNB & TC 8/9/29
FIRST TITLE {{ 16 L }}
Brown Back <$VALUE
4x5 1-4625 <$200
3x10-20 1-2465 <$200/$250
1882 Date Back
4x5 1-2450 <$200
3x10-20 1-1982 <$200/$250
1902 Date Back
4x5 1-6650 <$100
3x10-20 1-4620 <$100
1902 Plain Back
4x5 6651-23850 <$100
3x10-20 4621-24700 <$100
SECOND TITLE {{ 19 S }}
1929 Small Size
5 Type 1 1-5436 <$50
10 Type 1 1-2934 <$50
20 Type 1 1-872 <$55
5 Type 2 1-9214 <$50
10 Type 2 1-5353 <$50
20 Type 2 1-1704 <$60
Total Issue $2,653,290
Out in 1935 $150,000
Large out 1935 $6,330

9326 Dutchess
NB OF WAPPINGERS FALLS
{{ 0 L 2 S }}
Organized 10/6/08
1902 Date Back <$VALUE
3x10-20 1-1050 <$850
1902 Plain Back
3x10-20 1051-2027 <$850
1929 Small Size
10 Type 1 1-316 <$400
20 Type 1 1-106 <$400
10 Type 2 1-4219 <$400
20 Type 2 1-1332 <$400
Total Issue $201,860
Out in 1935 $50,000
Large out 1935 $280

9135 Warren
EMERSON NB OF WARRENSBURGH
{{ 3 L 5 S }}
Chartered 5/08
1902 Date Back <$VALUE
4x5 1-2650 <$350
4x10 1-3100 <$350
1902 Plain Back
4x5 2651-8484 <$350
4x10 3101-7730 <$350
1929 Small Size
5 Type 1 1-1490 <$200
10 Type 1 1-772 <$200
5 Type 2 1-3438 <$200
10 Type 2 1-1716 <$200
Total Issue $604,250
Out in 1935 $30,000
Large out 1935 $1,100

737 Wyoming
WYOMING COUNTY NB OF WARSAW
{{ 10 L 8 S }}
Chartered 1/21/65
Original Series <$VALUE
4x5 1-3750 <$400
3x10-20 1-1850 <$750/$1250
Series 1875
4x5 1-2720 <$400
3x10-20 1-2312 <$600/$1000
Brown Back
4x5 1-1750 <$300
3x10-20 1-8080 <$300
1902 Red Seal
3x10-20 1-3800 <$300
1902 Date Back
3x10-20 1-10000 <$150
1902 Plain Back
3x10-20 10001-25590 <$150
1929 Small Size
10 Type 1 1-2850 <$75
20 Type 1 1-748 <$75
10 Type 2 1-3489 <$75
20 Type 2 1-1054 <$85
Total Issue $2,563,130
Out in 1935 $100,000
Large out 1935 $5,410

314 Orange
FNB OF WARWICK
{{ 10 L 15 S }}
Chartered 3/64
Original Series <$VALUE
4x5 1-3600 <$400
3x10-20 1-2400 <$750/$1250
Series 1875
4x5 1-2960 <$400
3x10-20 1-1402 <$600/$1000
Brown Back
3x10-20 1-7217 <$300
1902 Red Seal
3x10-20 1-1240 <$300
1902 Date Back
3x10-20 1-9800 <$150
1902 Plain Back
3x10-20 9801-28308 <$150
1929 Small Size
10 Type 1 1-2854 <$100
20 Type 1 1-774 <$100
10 Type 2 1-5028 <$100
20 Type 2 1-1452 <$100
Total Issue $2,502,990
Out in 1935 $100,000
Large out 1935 $6,360

9065 Orange
FNB OF WASHINGTONVILLE
{{ 1 L 1 S }}
Organized 2/27/08
Liquidated 8/18/31
1902 Red Seal <$VALUE
4x5 1-175 <$1250
3x10-20 1-130 <$1250
1902 Date Back
4x5 1-800* <$750
3x10-20 1-600 <$750
1902 Plain Back
4x5 901-1885* <$750
3x10-20 601-1260 <$750
* 801-900 not marked
1929 Small Size
5 Type 1 1-146 <$600
10 Type 1 1-35 <$600
20 Type 1 1-15 <$650
Total Issue $118,980
Out at close $4,630
Large out at close $660

1229 Saratoga
SARATOGA COUNTY NB OF WATERFORD
{{ UNREPORTED }}
Chartered 6/6/65
Liquidated 3/28/71
Original Series <$VALUE
3x1-2 1-3120 <$850/$1500
4x5 1-3000 <$1000
3x10-20 1-1400<$1000/$1500
Total Issue $145,600
Out in 1910 $858

368 Seneca
FNB OF WATERLOO
{{ 7 L U + 8 S }}
Chartered 4/64
Original Series <$VALUE
3x1-2 1-5500 <$300/$850
4x5 1-7200 <$400
3x10-20 1-1000 <$750/$1250
Series 1875
3x1-2 1-1500 <$300/$850
4x5 1-880 <$400
3x10-20 1-632 <$750/$1250
Brown Back
3x10-20 1-4774 <$250/$300
1902 Red Seal
3x10-20 1-4100 <$300
1902 Date Back
3x10-20 1-3660 <$150
1902 Plain Back
3x10-20 3661-11462 <$150
1929 Small Size
10 Type 1 1-1338 <$100
20 Type 1 1-370 <$100
10 Type 2 1-1885 <$100
20 Type 2 1-506 <$100
Total Issue $1,448,650
Out in 1935 $50,000
Large out 1935 $4,120

4296 Jefferson
CITY NB OF WATERTOWN
{{ 3 L }}
Chartered 1890
Liquidated 10/31/25
Brown Back <$VALUE
3x10-20 1-3580 <$400
1882 Date Back
3x10-20 1-748 <$400
1902 Date Back
3x10-20 1-3600 <$300
1902 Plain Back
3x10-20 3601-11839 <$300
Total Issue $808,350
Out at close $40,000
Ch 1490 assumed circulation

73 Jefferson
FNB OF WATERTOWN
{{ 1 L }}
Chartered 9/63
Liquidated 5/26/81
Original Series <$VALUE
4x5 1-4500 <$750
3x10-20 1-2550 <$850/$1250
50-100 1-572 <$3500
Series 1875
3x10-20 1-1833 <$850/$1250
Total Issue $394,950
Out in 1910 $2,010

1490 Jefferson
JEFFERSON COUNTY NB OF WATERTOWN
{{ 18 L 29 S }}
Chartered 1865
Original Series <$VALUE
3x1-2 1-2530 <$200/$750
4x5 1-4700 <$225
4x10 1-2825 <$600
Series 1875
4x5 1-2299 <$225
4x10 1-4327 <$500
Brown Back
4x5 1-4308 <$150
3x10-20 1-4677 <$150/$200
1902 Red Seal
4x5 1-4330 <$150
3x10-20 1-2868 <$150/$200
1902 Date Back
4x5 1-12350 <$75
3x10-20 1-10260 <$85
1902 Plain Back
4x5 12351-69610 <$75
3x10-20 10261-46573 <$85
1929 Small Size
5 Type 1 1-16000 <$35
10 Type 1 1-8674 <$35
20 Type 1 1-2160 <$45
5 Type 2 1-21410 <$35
10 Type 2 1-10425 <$35
20 Type 2 1-2913 <$50
Total Issue $6,238,770
Out in 1935 $390,000
Large out 1935 $27,645
Outstanding includes Ch 4296

1508 Jefferson
NB & LOAN C OF WATERTOWN
{{ 7 L }}
Chartered 1865
Liquidated 12/15/10
Original Series <$VALUE
3x1-2 1-4860 <$400/$1000
4x5 1-5525 <$500
Series 1875
4x5 1-8255 <$500
Brown Back
4x5 1-13147 <$400
3x10-20 1-2481 <$400
1902 Red Seal
3x10-20 1-2100 <$400
1902 Date Back
3x10-20 1-674 <$250
Total Issue $825,590
Out in 1911 $20,090

1507 Jefferson
N UNION B OF WATERTOWN
{{ 6 L }}
Chartered 1865
Liquidated 12/15/10
Original Series <$VALUE
3x1-2 1-4500 <$250/$750
4x5 1-4000 <$350
3x10-20 1-2050 <$600/$1250
Series 1875
3x10-20 1-2940 <$600/$1000
Brown Back
4x5 1-4700 <$250
3x10-20 1-10066 <$250
1902 Red Seal
3x10-20 1-5800 <$300
1902 Date Back
3x10-20 1-2422 <$175
Total Issue $1,360,400
Out in 1911 $63,320

671 Jefferson
SECOND NB OF WATERTOWN
{{ UNREPORTED }}
Chartered 12/30/64
Liquidated 7/21/68
Original Series <$VALUE
3x10-20 1-1800<$1250/$1500
Total Issue $90,000
Out in 1910 $750

2657 Jefferson
WATERTOWN NB, WATERTOWN
{{ 15 L 22 S }}
Chartered 1882
Series 1875 <$VALUE
3x10-20 1-6307 <$500/$1000
1902 Red Seal
3x10-20 1-7800 <$175/$225
1902 Date Back
4x5 1-10000 <$60
3x10-20 1-10300 <$85
1902 Plain Back (dated 1902)
4x5 10001-25750 <$60
3x10-20 10301-20000 <$85
1902 Plain Back (dated 1922)
4x5 1-28200 <$60
3x10-20 1-13589 <$85
1929 Small Size
5 Type 1 1-7806 <$30
10 Type 1 1-4078 <$35
20 Type 1 1-1396 <$45
5 Type 2 1-15320 <$30
10 Type 2 1-7884 <$35
20 Type 2 1-2759 <$45
Total Issue $4,320,800
Out in 1935 $200,000
Large out 1935 $7,205

1361 Oneida
NB OF WATERVILLE
{{ 4 L 8 S }}
Chartered 1865
Original Series <$VALUE
3x1-2 1-2600 <$400/$850
4x5 1-2650 <$500
3x10-20 1-1480 <$750/$1250
Series 1875
4x5 1-4000 <$500
3x10-20 1-3988 <$750/$1250
Brown Back
3x10-20 1-5870 <$350/$400
1902 Red Seal
3x10-20 1-1500 <$400/$450
1902 Date Back
3x10-20 1-4500 <$200
1902 Plain Back
3x10-20 4501-9830 <$200
1929 Small Size
10 Type 1 1-1390* <$150
20 Type 1 1-410** <$150
10 Type 2 1-1931 <$150
20 Type 2 1-440 <$150
* 473-620 canceled
** 45-210 canceled
Total Issue $1,411,310
Out in 1935 $40,000
Large out 1935 $3,030

NB of Watervliet
SEE Ch 1265
NB of West Troy

358 Yates
FNB OF WATKINS
{{ UNREPORTED }}
Chartered 4/64
Receivership 9/18/99
2nd title and location:
FNB of Penn Yan 2/19/73
FIRST TITLE
Original Series <$VALUE
4x5 1-1855 <$1000
3x10-20 1-344 <$1250/$1750
SECOND TITLE
Original Series
4x5 1-1498 <$1000
3x10-20 1-300 <$1250/$1750
Series 1875
3x10-20 1-1047<$1250/$1500
Brown Back
50-100 1-552 <$1250/$1500
Total Issue $234,410
Out in 1916 $925

3047 Yates
FNB OF WATKINS
{{ UNREPORTED }}
Organized 9/14/83
Receivership 2/26/94
Brown Back <$VALUE
3x10-20 1-938 <$1500
Total Issue $46,900
Out in 1916 $100

9977 Yates
GLEN NB OF WATKINS
{{ 6 L 9 S }}
Chartered 3/11
1902 Date Back <$VALUE
4x5 1-3250 <$250
3x10-20 1-2440 <$250
1902 Plain Back
4x5 3251-12380 <$250
3x10-20 2441-8271 <$250
1929 Small Size
5 Type 1 1-1708 <$125
10 Type 1 1-956 <$125
20 Type 1 1-294 <$135
5 Type 2 1-1912 <$125
10 Type 2 1-1413 <$125
20 Type 2 1-392 <$150
Total Issue $836,560
Out in 1935 $50,000
Large out 1935 $2,060

<$VALUEs are for notes in FINE condition. Value changes by approximately 25% for a change of one full grade.

456 Yates
SECOND NB OF WATKINS
Organized 6/2/64
Receivership 7/12/76
2nd title:Watkins NB 3/3/75
FIRST TITLE {{ 7 L }}
Original Series <$VALUE
3x1-2 1-3500 <$300/$750
4x5 1-3275 <$400
3x10-20 1-1050 <$750/$1250
SECOND TITLE {{ 1 L }}
Original Series
4x5 1-500 <$600
3x10-20 1-300 <$750/$1250
Series 1875
4x5 1-175 <$600
3x10-20 1-140 <$750/$1250
Total Issue $171,000
Out in 1915 $984

Watkins NB, Watkins
SEE Ch 456
Second NB of Watkins

12954 Tioga
CITIZENS NB OF WAVERLY
{{ 3 L 10 S }}
Chartered 7/26
1902 Plain Back <$VALUE
3x10-20 1-4348 <$350
1929 Small Size
10 Type 1 1-3162 <$150
20 Type 1 1-760 <$150
10 Type 2 1-2459 <$150
20 Type 2 1-801 <$150
Total Issue $538,930
Out in 1935 $62,640
Large out 1935 $980

297 Tioga
FNB OF WAVERLY
{{ 8 L 15 S }}
Organized 2/13/64
Receivership 10/24/33
Original Series <$VALUE
4x5 1-5125 <$350
Series 1875
4x5 1-4250 <$350
Brown Back
4x5 1-5725 <$250
3x10-20 1-811 <$250/$300
1902 Red Seal
3x10-20 1-5700 <$250/$300
1902 Date Back
3x10-20 1-9300 <$150
1902 Plain Back
3x10-20 9301-27517 <$150
1929 Small Size
10 Type 1 1-2846 <$65
20 Type 1 1-798 <$75
10 Type 2 1-325 <$125
20 Type 2 1-12 <$125
Total Issue $2,273,410
Out at close $100,000
Large out at close $6,750

1192 Tioga
WAVERLY NB, WAVERLY
{{ 3 L }}
Organized 5/29/65
Receivership 4/23/72
Original Series <$VALUE
3x1-2 1-3500 <$600/$1250
4x5 1-1740 <$750
3x10-20 1-626 <$850/$1250
Total Issue $83,600
Out in 1916 $832

5196 Steuben
FNB OF WAYLAND
{{ 6 L 8 S }}
Chartered 6/2/99
Brown Back <$VALUE
4x5 1-945 <$350
3x10-20 1-742 <$350
1882 Date Back
4x5 1-1700 <$350
3x10-20 1-1300 <$350
1882 Value Back
4x5 1701-3320 <$350
3x10-20 1301-2026 <$350
1902 Plain Back
3x10-20 1-6770 <$200
1929 Small Size
10 Type 1 1-1356 <$150
20 Type 1 1-370 <$150
10 Type 2 1-1680 <$150
20 Type 2 1-429 <$165
Total Issue $713,340
Out in 1935 $50,000
Large out 1935 $1,650

13145 Monroe
WEBSTER NB, WEBSTER
{{ 1 L 4 S }}
Chartered 11/1/27
Receivership 11/15/33
1902 Plain Back <$VALUE
4x5 1-3927 <$750
1929 Small Size
5 Type 1 1-5930 <$250
5 Type 2 1-2986 <$250
Total Issue $271,370
Out at close $50,000
Large out at close $725

11020 Cayuga
FNB OF WEEDSPORT
{{ 3 L 5 S }}
Chartered 6/17
1902 Plain Back <$VALUE
4x5 1-5060 <$400
3x10-20 1-3106 <$400
1929 Small Size
5 Type 1 1-1030 <$250
10 Type 1 1-540 <$250
20 Type 1 1-130 <$250
5 Type 2 1-1392 <$250
10 Type 2 1-696 <$250
20 Type 2 1-204 <$250
Total Issue $353,400
Out in 1935 $25,000
Large out 1935 $660

13289 Hamilton
HAMILTON COUNTY NB OF WELLS
{{ 4 S }}
Chartered 3/29
1929 Small Size <$VALUE
5 Type 1 1-1440 <$300
10 Type 1 1-828 <$300
5 Type 2 1-2976 <$300
10 Type 2 1-1452 <$300
Total Issue $122,280
Out in 1935 $22,690

4988 Allegany
CITIZENS NB OF WELLSVILLE
{{ 10 L 16 S }}
Organized 2/5/95
Brown Back <$VALUE
3x10-20 1-7650 <$250/$300
1882 Date Back
3x10-20 1-6588 <$250/$300
1902 Date Back
3x10-20 1-2000 <$150
1902 Plain Back
3x10-20 2001-18219 <$150
1929 Small Size
10 Type 1 1-2728 <$60
20 Type 1 1-792 <$70
5 Type 2 1-324 <$75
10 Type 2 1-2371 <$75
20 Type 2 1-765 <$75
Total Issue $1,922,200
Out in 1935 $100,000
Large out 1935 $4,735

2850 Allegany
FNB OF WELLSVILLE
{{ 3 L }}
Chartered 1883
Liquidated 7/1/17
Brown Back <$VALUE
4x5 1-3151 <$450
3x10-20 1-2070 <$450
1902 Red Seal
3x10-20 1-6300 <$500
1902 Date Back
3x10-20 1-9406 <$300
Total Issue $951,820
Out at close $100,000

13104 Nassau
WEST HEMPSTEAD NB, WEST HEMPSTEAD
{{ 6 S }}
Chartered 7/27
1929 Small Size <$VALUE
5 Type 1 1-2720 <$400
10 Type 1 1-1262 <$400
5 Type 2 1-5390 <$400
10 Type 2 1-2685 <$400
Total Issue $211,120
Out in 1935 $28,500

6964 Erie
LACKAWANNA NB OF WEST SENECA
Chartered 9/03
Liquidated 12/31/34
2nd title:Lackawanna NB, Lackawanna 8/2/09
FIRST TITLE {{ 0 L }}
1902 Red Seal <$VALUE
4x5 1-2960 <$500
3x10-20 1-2278 <$500
SECOND TITLE {{15 L U + 18 S}}
1902 Red Seal
4x5 1-280 <$350
3x10-20 1-146 <$350
1902 Date Back
4x5 1-3800 <$100
3x10-20 1-2750 <$100
1902 Plain Back
4x5 3801-36239 <$100
3x10-20 2751-24694 <$100
1929 Small Size
5 Type 1 1-7018 <$50
10 Type 1 1-3836 <$50
20 Type 1 1-896 <$55
5 Type 2 1-8886 <$60
10 Type 2 1-4455 <$60
20 Type 2 1-949 <$65
Total Issue $2,801,660
Out at close $200,000
Large out at close $6,060

12925 Erie
SENECA NB OF WEST SENECA
{{ 3 L 3 S }}
Organized 7/27/25
Receivership 2/7/34
1902 Plain Back <$VALUE
4x5 1-3452 <$350
3x10-20 1-1881 <$350
1929 Small Size
5 Type 1 1-689 <$225
10 Type 1 1-418 <$225
20 Type 1 1-146 <$225
Total Issue $226,360
Out at close $3,060
Large out at close $855

1265 Albany
NB OF WEST TROY
Chartered 1865
2nd title:NB of Watervliet 5/24/05
FIRST TITLE {{ 4 L }}
Original Series <$VALUE
3x1-2 1-7100 <$250/$750
4x5 1-4200 <$350
4x10 1-875 <$600
Series 1875
3x1-2 1-3054 <$250/$750
4x5 1-3004 <$350
4x10 1-1905 <$500
Brown Back
50-100 1-1692 <$1250/$1500
SECOND TITLE {{ 6 L 14 S }}
1902 Red Seal
50-100 1-367 <$2250/$2500
1902 Date Back
50-100 1-560 <$400/$500
3x50-100 1-160 <$400/$500
1902 Plain Back
4x5 1-16372 <$125
3x10-20 1-11470 <$125
1929 Small Size
5 Type 1 1-3888 <$60
10 Type 1 1-1988 <$60
20 Type 1 1-490 <$70
5 Type 2 1-6956 <$70
10 Type 2 1-3948 <$70
20 Type 2 1-1152 <$75
Total Issue $2,031,860
Out in 1935 $100,000
Large out 1935 $6,230

801 Herkimer
FNB OF WEST WINFIELD
{{ 6 L }}
Chartered 2/14/65
Liquidated 12/20/04
Original Series <$VALUE
3x1-2 1-3600 <$400/$850
4x5 1-4800 <$500
3x10-20 1-1780 <$600/$1250
Series 1875
3x1-2 1-800 <$400/$850
4x5 1-4110 <$500
3x10-20 1-1128 <$600/$1000
Brown Back
4x5 1-10600 <$350
3x10-20 1-3840 <$350
Total Issue $749,600
Out in 1910 $5,688

7483 Herkimer
WEST WINFIELD NB, WEST WINFIELD
{{ 3 L 4 S }}
Chartered 11/04
1902 Red Seal <$VALUE
3x10-20 1-1400 <$600
1902 Date Back
3x10-20 1-2280 <$300
1902 Plain Back
3x10-20 2281-6461 <$300
1929 Small Size
10 Type 1 1-648 <$250
20 Type 1 1-166 <$250
10 Type 2 1-1314 <$250
20 Type 2 1-270 <$250
Total Issue $470,390
Out in 1935 $25,000
Large out 1935 $1,310

11730 Nassau
WHEATLEY HILLS NB OF WESTBURY
{{ 2 L 4 S }}
Chartered 5/20
1902 Plain Back <$VALUE
4x5 1-4485 <$850
3x10-20 1-2463 <$850
1929 Small Size
5 Type 1 1-1050 <$600
10 Type 1 1-558 <$600
20 Type 1 1-174 <$600
5 Type 2 1-1394 <$600
10 Type 2 1-828 <$600
20 Type 2 1-252 <$600
Total Issue $319,000
Out in 1935 $25,000
Large out 1935 $770

504 Chautauqua
FNB OF WESTFIELD
{{ 1 L }}
Chartered 8/64
Liquidated 6/1/84
Original Series <$VALUE
3x1-2 1-2000 <$750/$1250
4x5 1-3250 <$850
3x10-20 1-1500<$1000/$1500
Series 1875
3x1-2 1-160 <$750/$1250
4x5 1-910 <$850
3x10-20 1-1020<$1000/$1500
Total Issue $220,000
Out in 1910 $1,445

12476 Chautauqua
GRAPE BELT NB OF WESTFIELD
{{ U + 7 L 2 S }}
Chartered 12/23
Liquidated 4/13/31
1902 Plain Back <$VALUE
4x5 1-11839 <$450
3x10-20 1-600 <$450
1929 Small Size
5 Type 1 1-2715 <$500
Total Issue $348,230
Out at close $50,000
Large out at close $1,610

3166 Chautauqua
NB OF WESTFIELD
{{ U + 14 L 12 S }}
Chartered 1884
Brown Back <$VALUE
4x5 1-1500 <$200
3x10-20 1-4703 <$200/$250
1902 Red Seal
4x5 1-1250 <$225
3x10-20 1-2000 <$225/$275
1902 Date Back
4x5 1-4050 <$125
3x10-20 1-3100 <$125
1902 Plain Back
4x5 4051-37285 <$125
3x10-20 3101-6630 <$125
1929 Small Size
5 Type 1 1-18290 <$60
5 Type 2 1-24924 <$60
Total Issue $2,140,670
Out in 1935 $75,000
Large out 1935 $4,875

9405 Essex
LAKE CHAMPLAIN NB OF WESTPORT
{{ 3 L 2 S }}
Chartered 5/09
1902 Date Back <$VALUE
4x5 1-1100 <$600
3x10-20 1-860 <$600
1902 Plain Back
4x5 1101-3393 <$600
3x10-20 861-2305 <$600
1929 Small Size
5 Type 1 1-502 <$500
10 Type 1 1-254 <$500
20 Type 1 1-84 <$500
5 Type 2 1-388 <$500
10 Type 2 1-214 <$500
20 Type 2 1-55 <$500
Total Issue $228,670
Out in 1935 $12,500
Large out 1935 $410

6351 Westchester
FNB OF WHITE PLAINS
{{ 3 L }}
Chartered 7/23/02
Liquidated 2/28/20
1902 Red Seal <$VALUE
4x5 1-7750 <$1500
3x10-20 1-5825 <$1500
1902 Date Back
4x5 1-9950 <$600
3x10-20 1-7160 <$600
1902 Plain Back
4x5 9951-15710 <$600
3x10-20 7161-10491 <$600
Total Issue $1,285,000
Out at close $99,995

12574 Westchester
PEOPLES NB OF WHITE PLAINS
Chartered 9/24
2nd title:Peoples NB & TC 5/11/28
FIRST TITLE {{ 3 L }}
1902 Plain Back <$VALUE
4x5 1-2552 <$600
4x10 1-1620 <$600
SECOND TITLE {{ 3 L 9 S }}
1902 Plain Back
4x5 1-1252 <$600
1929 Small Size
5 Type 1 1-3088 <$400
10 Type 1 1-1518 <$400
20 Type 1 1-758 <$400
5 Type 2 1-3334 <$400
10 Type 2 1-1870 <$400
20 Type 2 1-420 <$400
Total Issue $459,330
Out in 1935 $135,000
Large out 1935 $545

285 Washington
FNB OF WHITEHALL
{{ UNREPORTED }}
Chartered 2/64
Liquidated 1/18/82
Original Series <$VALUE
3x1-2 1-1000 <$750/$1250
4x5 1-4900 <$850
4x10 1-2200 <$1000
Series 1875
4x5 1-1059 <$850
4x10 1-688 <$1000
Total Issue $239,700
Out in 1910 $1,542

2233 Washington
MERCHANTS NB OF WHITEHALL
{{ 10 L 12 S }}
Chartered 3/12/75
Original Series <$VALUE
4x5 1-2250 <$400
3x10-20 1-1800 <$750/$1250
Series 1875
4x5 1-2000 <$400
3x10-20 1-2757 <$600/$1000
Brown Back
4x5 1-7410 <$300
3x10-20 1-2476 <$300/$350
1882 Date Back
4x5 1-3488 <$300
3x10-20 1-2463 <$300/$350
1902 Date Back
4x5 1-1250 <$150
3x10-20 1-1000 <$150
1902 Plain Back
4x5 1251-9805 <$150
3x10-20 1001-6779 <$150
1929 Small Size
5 Type 1 1-1918 <$100
10 Type 1 1-938 <$100
20 Type 1 1-284 <$100
5 Type 2 1-3038 <$100
10 Type 2 1-1584 <$100
20 Type 2 1-456 <$100
Total Issue $1,500,860
Out in 1935 $50,000
Large out 1935 $2,785

8388 Washington
NB OF WHITEHALL
{{ 4 L 1 S }}
Organized 9/29/06
Receivership 1/26/32
1902 Red Seal <$VALUE
3x10-20 1-1800 <$600
1902 Date Back
3x10-20 1-4900 <$300
1902 Plain Back
3x10-20 4901-14218 <$300
1929 Small Size
10 Type 1 1-884 <$500
20 Type 1 1-246 <$500
Total Issue $883,460
Out at close $47,900
Large out at close $4,580

1160 Washington
OLD NB OF WHITEHALL
{{ 3 L }}
Organized 5/17/65
Liquidated 7/1/02
Original Series <$VALUE
3x1-2 1-4000 <$600/$1250
4x5 1-4247 <$600
3x10-20 1-1480 <$750/$1250
Series 1875
4x5 1-2908 <$600
3x10-20 1-2020 <$750/$1250
Brown Back
4x5 1-12684 <$400
3x10-20 1-5576 <$400
Total Issue $870,580
Out in 1910 $7,110

11284 Oneida
WHITESTOWN NB OF WHITESBORO
{{ 3 L }}
Chartered 1/19
1902 Plain Back <$VALUE
4x5 1-9090 <$400
Total Issue $181,800
Out in 1935 $510

8957 Queens
FNB OF WHITESTONE
{{ 3 L }}
Chartered 12/07
Liquidated 8/15/28
1902 Red Seal <$VALUE
3x10-20 1-500 <$1000
1902 Date Back
3x10-20 1-1720 <$600
1902 Plain Back
3x10-20 1721-3589 <$600
Total Issue $204,450
Out at close $12,500

1458 Oneida
NB OF WHITESTOWN
{{ UNREPORTED }}
Chartered 7/17/65
Liquidated 2/14/68
Original Series <$VALUE
4x5 1-1725 <$1250
3x10-20 1-200 <$1500/$2000
Total Issue $44,500
Out in 1910 $220

7850 Allegany
FNB OF WHITESVILLE
{{ 2 L 5 S }}
Chartered 7/05
1902 Red Seal <$VALUE
3x10-20 1-1000 <$600
1902 Date Back
3x10-20 1-2000 <$300
1902 Plain Back
3x10-20 2001-6177 <$300
1929 Small Size
10 Type 1 1-700 <$250
20 Type 1 1-180 <$250
10 Type 2 1-895 <$250
20 Type 2 1-279 <$250
Total Issue $436,980
Out in 1935 $25,000
Large out 1935 $980

****

7679 Broome
FNB OF WHITNEY POINT
{{ 3 L 7 S }}
Chartered 4/05

1902 Red Seal	<$VALUE
4x5 1-950	<$800
3x10-20 1-640	<$800
1902 Date Back	
4x5 1-1775	<$400
3x10-20 1-960	<$400
1902 Plain Back	
4x5 1776-2720	<$400
3x10-20 961-1525	<$400
1929 Small Size	
5 Type 1 1-416	<$250
10 Type 1 1-210	<$250
20 Type 1 1-74	<$250
5 Type 2 1-468	<$250
10 Type 2 1-401	<$250
20 Type 2 1-125	<$275
Total Issue	$224,460
Out in 1935	$25,000
Large out 1935	$560

****

11971 Essex
ESSEX COUNTY NB OF WILLSBORO
{{ 0 L 2 S }}
Chartered 5/21

1902 Plain Back	<$VALUE
4x10 1-1272	<$1000
1929 Small Size	
5 Type 1 1-420	<$400
10 Type 1 1-174	<$400
20 Type 1 1-64	<$400
5 Type 2 1-2062	<$400
10 Type 2 1-1125	<$400
20 Type 2 1-270	<$400
Total Issue	$108,560
Out in 1935	$25,000
Large out 1935	$200

****

12164 Greene
FNB IN WINDHAM
{{ 6 S }}
Organized 1/28/22
Liquidated 3/23/34

1929 Small Size	<$VALUE
5 Type 1 1-518	<$200
5 Type 2 1-624	<$200
Total Issue	$18,660
Out at close	$9,870

Ch 13962 assumed circulation

****

13962 Greene
NB OF WINDHAM
{{ 4U + 4 S }}
Chartered 1/34

1929 Small Size	<$VALUE
5 Type 2 1-1606	<$250
Total Issue	$8,030
Out in 1935	$10,000

Outstanding includes Ch 12164

****

9415 Broome
WINDSOR NB, WINDSOR
{{ 3 L 5 S }}
Chartered 5/09

1902 Date Back	<$VALUE
3x10-20 1-2620	<$350
1902 Plain Back	
3x10-20 2621-7033	<$350
1929 Small Size	
10 Type 1 1-728	<$250
20 Type 1 1-170	<$250
10 Type 2 1-1572	<$250
20 Type 2 1-253	<$250
Total Issue	$436,510
Out in 1935	$25,000
Large out 1935	$1,050

****

10747 Saint Lawrence
FNB OF WINTHROP
{{ 5 L 4 S }}
Chartered 6/15

1902 Plain Back	<$VALUE
4x10 1-6562	<$300
1929 Small Size	
10 Type 1 1-1120	<$250
10 Type 2 1-2568	<$250
Total Issue	$355,360
Out in 1935	$25,000
Large out 1935	$840

****

5928 Wayne
FNB OF WOLCOTT
{{ 4 L 7 S }}
Chartered 7/31/01

Brown Back	<$VALUE
3x10-20 1-2000	<$450
1882 Date Back	
3x10-20 1-1810*	<$450
1882 Value Back	
3x10-20 1911-3346*	<$450
* 1811-1910 not marked	
1902 Plain Back	
3x10-20 1-2838	<$300
1929 Small Size	
10 Type 1 1-1640	<$175
20 Type 1 1-436	<$175
10 Type 2 1-344	<$175
20 Type 2 1-165	<$200
Total Issue	$566,660
Out in 1935	$35,000
Large out 1935	$1,000

****

12294 Nassau
HEWLETT-WOODMERE NB, WOODMERE
{{ UNREPORTED }}
Organized 11/29/22
Receivership 5/9/34

1902 Plain Back	<$VALUE
4x5 1-1655	<$1500
3x10-20 1-992	<$1500
1929 Small Size	
5 Type 1 1-506	<$1000
10 Type 1 1-264	<$1000
20 Type 1 1-82	<$1000
5 Type 2 1-234	<$1000
10 Type 2 1-85	<$1000
20 Type 2 1-40	<$1000
Total Issue	$126,380
Out at close	$12,130
Large out at close	$130

****

11059 Sullivan
FNB OF WOODRIDGE
{{ 3 L 4 S }}
Chartered 8/17

1902 Plain Back	<$VALUE
4x5 1-5455	<$400
3x10-20 1-3400	<$400
1929 Small Size	
5 Type 1 1-1186	<$300
10 Type 1 1-574	<$300
20 Type 1 1-180	<$300
5 Type 2 1-1080	<$300
10 Type 2 1-576	<$300
20 Type 2 1-192	<$300
Total Issue	$385,720
Out in 1935	$25,000
Large out 1935	$660

****

13229 Wyoming
NB OF WYOMING
{{ U + 2 S }}
Chartered 8/28

1929 Small Size	<$VALUE
20 Type 1 1-262	<$400
20 Type 2 1-366	<$400
Total Issue	$38,760
Out in 1935	$22,100

****

13319 Westchester
CENTRAL NB OF YONKERS
{{ 21 S }}
Chartered 5/29

1929 Small Size	<$VALUE
5 Type 1 1-10268	<$100
10 Type 1 1-4808	<$100
20 Type 1 1-1438	<$100
5 Type 2 1-46388	<$100
10 Type 2 1-20399	<$100
Total Issue	$1,205,010
Out in 1935	$244,400

****

2074 Westchester
CITIZENS NB OF YONKERS
{{ 3 L }}
Chartered 1/15/73
Liquidated 8/1/03

Original Series	<$VALUE
3x1-2 1-4000	<$500/$1000
4x5 1-3200	<$600
3x10-20 1-1060	<$750/$1250
Series 1875	
4x5 1-7942	<$600
3x10-20 1-3041	<$750/$1250
Brown Back	
3x10-20 1-5917	<$500
Total Issue	$743,740
Out in 1910	$4,567

****

653 Westchester
FNB OF YONKERS
Organized 12/9/64
Receivership 1/23/34
2nd title:FNB & TC 9/30/29
FIRST TITLE {{ 25 L 2 S }}

Original Series	<$VALUE
3x1-2 1-4380	<$300/$750
4x5 1-6250	<$350
3x10-20 1-3600	<$600/$1250
Series 1875	
4x5 1-1000	<$350
3x10-20 1-592	<$600/$1250
Brown Back	
4x5 1-9912	<$250
3x10-20 1-12758	<$250/$300
1902 Red Seal	
4x5 1-5750	<$250
3x10-20 1-4700	<$250/$300
1902 Date Back	
4x5 1-29500	<$100
3x10-20 1-21000	<$100
1902 Plain Back	
4x5 29501-95027	<$100
3x10-20 21001-60976	<$100
1929 Small Size	
5 Type 1 1-1538	<$100
10 Type 1 1-768	<$100
20 Type 1 1-256	<$100
SECOND TITLE {{ 21 S }}	
1929 Small Size	
5 Type 1 1-10372	<$85
10 Type 1 1-5512	<$85
20 Type 1 1-1316	<$85
5 Type 2 1-6228	<$85
10 Type 2 1-2772	<$85
20 Type 2 1-384	<$100
Total Issue	$7,501,300
Out at close	$295,700
Large out at close	$17,840

****

9825 Westchester
YONKERS NB, YONKERS
Organized 3/29/10
2nd title:Yonkers NB & TC 4/13/23
FIRST TITLE {{ 5 L }}

1902 Date Back	<$VALUE
4x5 1-20450	<$200
3x10-20 1-15160	<$200
1902 Plain Back	
4x5 20451-35250	<$200
3x10-20 15161-24360	<$200
SECOND TITLE {{ 6 L 19 S }}	
1902 Plain Back	
3x10-20 1-23740	<$200
1929 Small Size	
10 Type 1 1-14302	<$100
20 Type 1 1-3968	<$100
10 Type 2 1-1526	<$100
20 Type 2 1-540	<$125
Total Issue	$4,470,340
Out in 1935	$181,900
Large out 1935	$7,470

****

NORTH CAROLINA

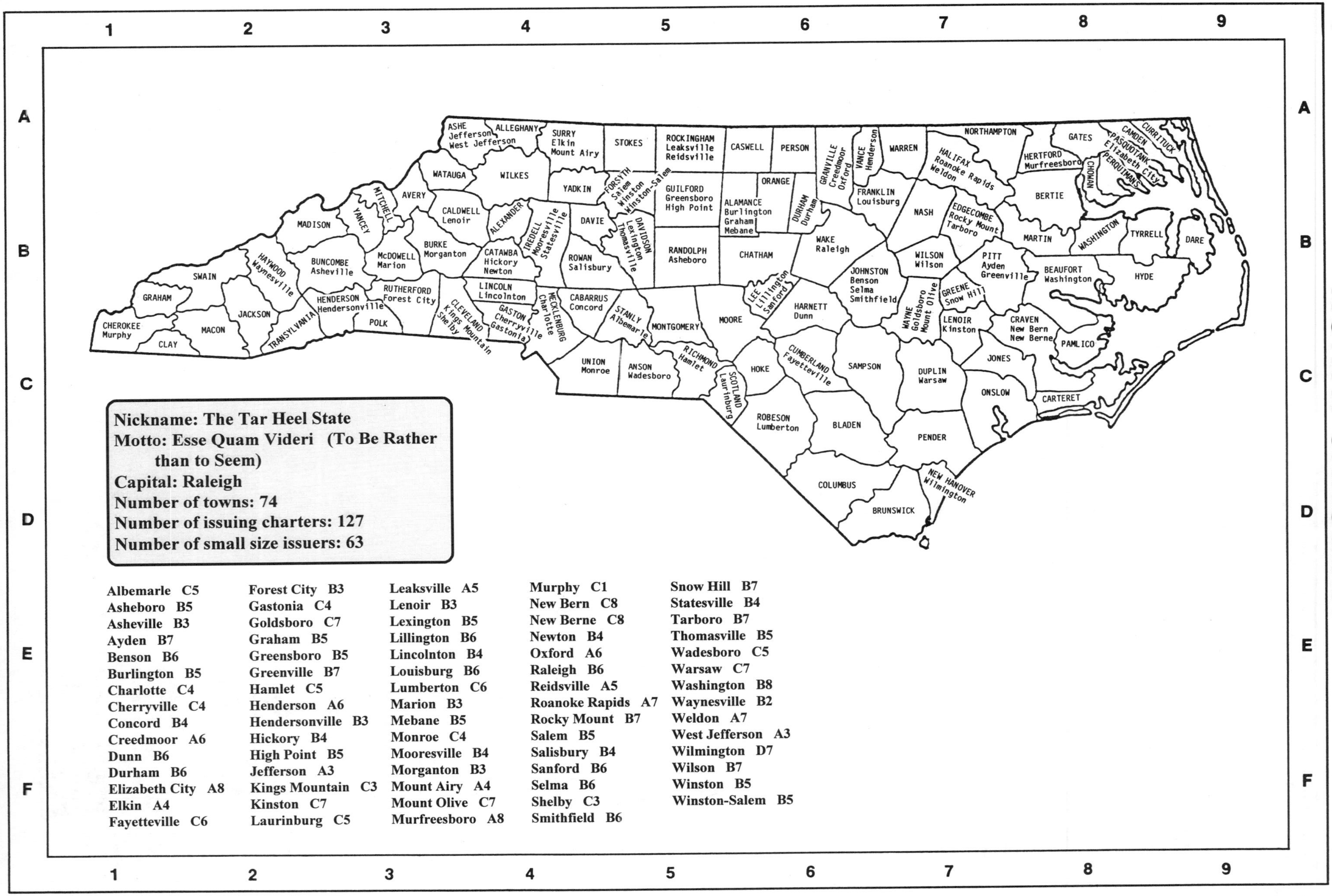

Nickname: The Tar Heel State
Motto: Esse Quam Videri (To Be Rather than to Seem)
Capital: Raleigh
Number of towns: 74
Number of issuing charters: 127
Number of small size issuers: 63

Albemarle C5
Asheboro B5
Asheville B3
Ayden B7
Benson B6
Burlington B5
Charlotte C4
Cherryville C4
Concord B4
Creedmoor A6
Dunn B6
Durham B6
Elizabeth City A8
Elkin A4
Fayetteville C6
Forest City B3
Gastonia C4
Goldsboro C7
Graham B5
Greensboro B5
Greenville B7
Hamlet C5
Henderson A6
Hendersonville B3
Hickory B4
High Point B5
Jefferson A3
Kings Mountain C3
Kinston C7
Laurinburg C5
Leaksville A5
Lenoir B3
Lexington B5
Lillington B6
Lincolnton B4
Louisburg B6
Lumberton C6
Marion B3
Mebane B5
Monroe C4
Mooresville B4
Morganton B3
Mount Airy A4
Mount Olive C7
Murfreesboro A8
Murphy C1
New Bern C8
New Berne C8
Newton B4
Oxford A6
Raleigh B6
Reidsville A5
Roanoke Rapids A7
Rocky Mount B7
Salem B5
Salisbury B4
Sanford B6
Selma B6
Shelby C3
Smithfield B6
Snow Hill B7
Statesville B4
Tarboro B7
Thomasville B5
Wadesboro C5
Warsaw C7
Washington B8
Waynesville B2
Weldon A7
West Jefferson A3
Wilmington D7
Wilson B7
Winston B5
Winston-Salem B5

****
11091 Stanly
FNB OF ALBEMARLE
{{ 0 L 3U + 7 S }}
Chartered 10/17
1902 Plain Back <$VALUE
3x10-20 1-1726 <$1250
1929 Small Size
5 Type 1 1-524 <$200
10 Type 1 1-242 <$200
20 Type 1 1-76 <$200
5 Type 2 1-1910 <$225
10 Type 2 1-960 <$225
20 Type 2 1-270 <$225
Total Issue $150,210
Out in 1935 $27,590
Large out 1935 $6,890
****
8953 Randolph
FNB OF ASHEBORO
{{ 4 L 9 S }}
Chartered 11/07
1902 Red Seal <$VALUE
4x10 1-875 <$1500
1902 Date Back
4x10 1-2500 <$600
1902 Plain Back
4x10 2501-14037 <$600
1929 Small Size
10 Type 1 1-2756 <$225
10 Type 2 1-4535 <$225
Total Issue $807,190
Out in 1935 $50,000
Large out 1935 $1,850
****
8772 Buncombe
AMERICAN NB OF ASHEVILLE
{{ 10 L 9 S }}
Organized 5/15/07
Receivership 11/21/30
1902 Red Seal <$VALUE
4x5 1-3500 <$1250
3x10-20 1-5260 <$1250
50-100 1-660 <$3500
1902 Date Back
4x5 1-20000 <$250
3x10-20 1-12400 <$250
50-100 1-300 <$750/$850
3x50-100 1-755 <$750/$850
1902 Plain Back
4x5 20001-39807 <$250
3x10-20 12401-23781 <$250
3x50-100 756-1104<$750/$850
1929 Small Size
5 Type 1 1-1469 <$200
10 Type 1 1-728 <$200
20 Type 1 1-233 <$200
50 Type 1 1-86 <$450
100 Type 1 1-24 <$600
Total Issue $2,912,100
Out at close $150,000
****
5110 Buncombe
BLUE RIDGE NB OF ASHEVILLE
{{ 3 L }}
Chartered 1/29/98
Liquidated 7/1/07
Brown Back <$VALUE
3x10-20 1-3631 <$1500
50-100 1-1134 <$4000
Total Issue $351,650
Out in 1910 $24,270
****
FNB & TC of Asheville
SEE Ch 12244
NB of Commerce of Asheville
****
3418 Buncombe
FNB OF ASHEVILLE
{{ UNREPORTED }}
Organized 12/4/85
Receivership 8/23/97
Brown Back <$VALUE
4x5 1-3435 <$2000
50-100 1-432 <$4000
Total Issue $133,500
Out in 1916 $495
****
4094 Buncombe
NB OF ASHEVILLE
{{ UNREPORTED }}
Chartered 8/15/89
Liquidated 12/11/97
Brown Back <$VALUE
50-100 1-614 <$4000
Total Issue $92,100
Out in 1910 $1,450
****

****
12244 Buncombe
NB OF COMMERCE OF ASHEVILLE
Chartered 4/24/22
Liquidated 8/10/33
2nd title: FNB & TC of Asheville 3/31/31
FIRST TITLE {{ 4 L 4 S }}
1902 Plain Back <$VALUE
4x5 1-6854 <$400
3x10-20 1-4160 <$400
1929 Small Size
5 Type 1 1-1128 <$175
10 Type 1 1-570 <$175
20 Type 1 1-176 <$175
SECOND TITLE {{ 23 S }}
1929 Small Size
5 Type 1 1-4472 <$100
10 Type 1 1-3243 <$100
20 Type 1 1-774 <$100
Total Issue $855,860
Out at close $239,890
Large out at close $2,140
****
13554 Pitt
FNB IN AYDEN
{{ 6 S }}
Chartered 6/31
1929 Small Size <$VALUE
5 Type 1 1-418 <$350
10 Type 1 1-314 <$350
5 Type 2 1-2136 <$350
10 Type 2 1-1176 <$350
Total Issue $53,820
Out in 1935 $15,070
****
12614 Johnston
FNB OF BENSON
{{ 7 L }}
Organized 12/16/24
Receivership 12/11/28
1902 Plain Back <$VALUE
4x5 1-20232 <$350
Total Issue $404,640
Out at close $50,000
****
8649 Alamance
FNB OF BURLINGTON
{{ 9 L 1 S }}
Organized 4/5/07
Receivership 12/24/31
1902 Red Seal <$VALUE
4x5 1-1312 <$1250
4x10 1-1312 <$1250
1902 Date Back
4x5 1-4200 <$275
4x10 1-4260 <$275
1902 Plain Back
4x5 4201-18908 <$275
4x10 4251-15183 <$275
1929 Small Size
5 Type 1 1-2668 <$500
10 Type 1 1-1244 <$500
Total Issue $1,218,880
Out at close $57,780
Large out at close $3,800
****
13613 Alamance
NB OF BURLINGTON
{{ 16 S }}
Chartered 5/32
1929 Small Size <$VALUE
5 Type 1 1-1590 <$125
10 Type 1 1-740 <$125
20 Type 1 1-460 <$125
5 Type 2 1-10952 <$125
10 Type 2 1-5520 <$125
20 Type 2 1-1560 <$125
Total Issue $288,460
Out in 1935 $99,000
****
5055 Mecklenburg
CHARLOTTE NB, CHARLOTTE
{{ 29 L 50+ S }}
Chartered 1897
Brown Back <$VALUE
3x10-20 1-12145 <$400
1882 Date Back
3x10-20 1-23000 <$400
1882 Value Back
3x10-20 23001-23790 <$400
1902 Plain Back
3x10-20 1-48315 <$85
1929 Small Size
10 Type 1 1-9016 <$40
20 Type 1 1-2462 <$50
5 Type 2 1-101 <$40
10 Type 2 1-20464 <$40
20 Type 2 1-4802 <$50
Total Issue $5,350,085
Out in 1935 $236,300
Large out 1935 $12,235
****

****
2135 Mecklenburg
COMMERCIAL NB OF CHARLOTTE
{{ 50+ L 50+ S }}
Chartered 2/18/74
Original Series <$VALUE
3x1-2 1-1000 <$850/$2500
4x5 1-1450 <$4000
4x20 1-2288 <$2000
Series 1875
4x5 1-3362 <$3500
4x20 1-3238 <$1750
Brown Back
4x5 1-17500 <$400
3x10-20 1-19200 <$400
1882 Date Back
4x5 1-31446 <$400
3x10-20 1-25280 <$400
1902 Date Back
4x5 1-12750 <$75
3x10-20 1-10000 <$75
1902 Plain Back
4x5 12751-116628 <$75
3x10-20 10001-78143 <$75
1929 Small Size
5 Type 1 1-22970 <$35
10 Type 1 1-10946 <$40
20 Type 1 1-2466 <$50
5 Type 2 1-28292 <$35
10 Type 2 1-11734 <$40
20 Type 2 1-3132 <$50
Total Issue $11,949,170
Out in 1935 $250,380
Large out 1935 $38,070
****
1547 Mecklenburg
FNB OF CHARLOTTE
{{ 24 L 12 S }}
Organized 8/26/65
Receivership 12/8/30
Original Series <$VALUE
4x5 1-8535 <$850
3x10-20 1-8096<$1250/$2000
Series 1875
3x10-20 1-5750<$1000/$1750
Brown Back
3x10-20 1-12504 <$400
1902 Red Seal
4x5 1-9250 <$1000
3x10-20 1-6000 <$1000
1902 Date Back
4x5 1-23000 <$85
3x10-20 1-20100 <$85
1902 Plain Back
4x5 23001-86000 <$85
3x10-20 20101-61387 <$85
1929 Small Size
5 Type 1 1-5716 <$200
10 Type 1 1-2642 <$200
20 Type 1 1-744 <$200
Total Issue $7,181,830
Out at close $299,980
Large out at close $42,920
****
1781 Mecklenburg
MERCHANTS & FARMERS NB OF CHARLOTTE
{{ 18 L 17 S }}
Chartered 2/1/71
Receivership 7/24/34
Original Series <$VALUE
3x1-2 1-3000 <$850/$2500
4x5 1-5000 <$850
3x10-20 1-2900<$1250/$2000
Series 1875
4x5 1-4500 <$850
3x10-20 1-6022<$1000/$1750
Brown Back
3x10-20 1-16900 <$450
1882 Date Back
3x10-20 1-5474 <$450
1902 Date Back
4x5 1-5000 <$85
4x10 1-18750 <$85
1902 Plain Back
4x5 5001-47020 <$85
4x10 18751-54615 <$85
1929 Small Size
5 Type 1 1-12378 <$65
10 Type 1 1-6032 <$65
5 Type 2 1-16412 <$85
10 Type 2 1-7848 <$85
Total Issue $5,788,600
Out at close $200,000
Large out at close $11,770
****

****
2314 Mecklenburg
TRADERS NB OF CHARLOTTE
{{ 1 L }}
Chartered 12/21/75
Liquidated 1/16/83
Series 1875 <$VALUE
3x1-2 1-3440 <$1500/$2500
4x5 1-7095 <$1500
Total Issue $159,100
Out in 1910 $695
****
9164 Mecklenburg
UNION NB OF CHARLOTTE
{{ 14 L 26 S }}
Chartered 6/08
1902 Date Back <$VALUE
3x10-20 1-12800 <$125
1902 Plain Back
4x5 1-24267 <$125
3x10-20 12801-46104 <$125
1929 Small Size
5 Type 1 1-9626 <$60
10 Type 1 1-4708 <$60
20 Type 1 1-1188 <$70
5 Type 2 1-24542 <$60
10 Type 2 1-14207 <$60
20 Type 2 1-4369 <$70
Total Issue $3,854,520
Out in 1935 $230,220
Large out 1935 $7,400
****
9548 Gaston
FNB OF CHERRYVILLE
{{ 14 L }}
Chartered 9/09
Liquidated 3/21/27
1902 Date Back <$VALUE
3x10-20 1-4080 <$200
1902 Plain Back
4x5 1-9775 <$200
3x10-20 4081-11068 <$200
Total Issue $748,900
Out at close $17,005
****
3903 Cabarrus
CONCORD NB, CONCORD
{{ 22 L 41 S }}
Chartered 6/26/88
Brown Back <$VALUE
4x5 1-5100 <$650
3x10-20 1-3483 <$650
1902 Date Back
3x10-20 1-8575 <$150
1902 Plain Back
3x10-20 8576-27663 <$150
1929 Small Size
10 Type 1 1-3118 <$75
20 Type 1 1-828 <$85
10 Type 2 1-4543 <$80
20 Type 2 1-987 <$90
Total Issue $2,010,910
Out in 1935 $88,545
Large out 1935 $5,055
****
8902 Granville
FNB OF CREEDMOOR
{{ 3 L }}
Chartered 10/07
Liquidated 1/9/23
1902 Date Back <$VALUE
4x5 1-756 <$600
4x10 1-756 <$600
1902 Plain Back
4x5 757-6015 <$600
4x10 757-4336 <$600
Total Issue $293,740
Out at close $48,000
****
7188 Harnett
FNB OF DUNN
{{ 50+ L }}
Organized 3/24/04
Receivership 11/14/28
1902 Red Seal <$VALUE
3x10-20 1-1250 <$1250
1902 Date Back
3x10-20 1-3850 <$250
1902 Plain Back
3x10-20 3851-10217 <$250
Total Issue $573,350
Out at close $40,000
****
7698 Durham
CITIZENS NB OF DURHAM
{{ 11 L 17 S }}
Chartered 4/05
1902 Red Seal <$VALUE
4x5 1-3645 <$1000
3x10-20 1-2917 <$1000
1902 Date Back
4x5 1-8200 <$175
3x10-20 1-5720 <$175
1902 Plain Back
4x5 8201-29296 <$175
3x10-20 5721-20011 <$175
1929 Small Size
5 Type 1 1-4196 <$60
10 Type 1 1-2244 <$60
20 Type 1 1-720 <$70
5 Type 2 1-7828 <$60
10 Type 2 1-4026 <$60
20 Type 2 1-1440 <$70
Total Issue $2,260,340
Out in 1935 $80,500
Large out 1935 $4,500
****
13657 Durham
DEPOSITORS NB OF DURHAM
{{ 18 S }}
Chartered 1/33
1929 Small Size <$VALUE
5 Type 2 1-22502 <$60
10 Type 2 1-11706 <$60
20 Type 2 1-7398 <$60
Total Issue $377,530
Out in 1935 $193,850
****
3811 Durham
FNB OF DURHAM
{{ 30 L 42 S }}
Chartered 11/9/87
Receivership 1/18/32
Brown Back <$VALUE
4x5 1-13225 <$500
3x10-20 1-4758 <$500
1902 Red Seal
4x5 1-2000 <$1000
4x10 1-2000 <$1000
1902 Date Back
4x5 1-13500 <$85
4x10 1-12750 <$85
1902 Plain Back
4x5 13501-133378 <$85
4x10 12751-98859 <$85
1929 Small Size
5 Type 1 1-29493 <$50
10 Type 1 1-14600 <$50
Total Issue $9,005,110
Out at close $600,000
Large out at close $37,245
****
F & Citizens NB of Elizabeth City
SEE Ch 4628
FNB of Elizabeth City
****
4628 Pasquotank
FNB OF ELIZABETH CITY
Organized 5/26/91
2nd title:F & Citizens NB of Elizabeth City 7/24/18
FIRST TITLE {{ 4 L }}
Brown Back <$VALUE
3x10-20 1-5840 <$600
1882 Date Back
3x10-20 1-2327 <$600
1902 Date Back
3x10-20 1-7400 <$250
1902 Plain Back
3x10-20 7401-8000 <$250
SECOND TITLE {{ 35 L 22 S }}
1902 Plain Back
3x10-20 1-32292 <$200
1929 Small Size
10 Type 1 1-6182 <$90
20 Type 1 1-1702 <$100
10 Type 2 1-4880 <$100
20 Type 2 1-835 <$100
Total Issue $3,063,610
Out in 1935 $116,330
Large out 1935 $13,590
****
5673 Surry
ELKIN NB, ELKIN
{{ 4 L 2 S }}
Chartered 1/9/01
Receivership 1/26/32
Brown Back <$VALUE
3x10-20 1-1840 <$1000
1882 Date Back
3x10-20 1-1780 <$1000
1882 Value Back
3x10-20 1781-2987 <$1000
1902 Plain Back
3x10-20 1-3515 <$500
1929 Small Size
10 Type 1 1-531 <$500
20 Type 1 1-137 <$500
Total Issue $465,400
Out at close $24,700
Large out at close $2,650
****

****
1756 Cumberland
FAYETTEVILLE NB, FAYETTEVILLE
{{ 6 L }}
Chartered 12/21/70
Liquidated 12/31/87
Original Series <$VALUE
3x1-2 1-4500 <$850/$2500
4x5 1-5625 <$850
Series 1875
3x1-2 1-2000 <$850/$2500
4x5 1-7447 <$850
Total Issue $293,940
Out in 1910 $1,420
****
8682 Cumberland
FOURTH NB OF FAYETTEVILLE
{{ 3 L }}
Organized 5/10/07
Receivership 2/14/16
1902 Red Seal <$VALUE
4x10 1-4125 <$1250
1902 Date Back
4x5 1-8395 <$600
4x10 1-7455 <$600
Total Issue $631,100
Out in 1916 $51,325
****
5677 Cumberland
NB OF FAYETTEVILLE
{{ 16 L }}
Chartered 1/12/01
Receivership 8/12/27
Brown Back <$VALUE
4x5 1-2850 <$500
3x10-20 1-2790 <$500
1882 Date Back
4x5 1-8475 <$500
3x10-20 1-6660 <$500
1882 Value Back
4x5 8476-12285 <$500
3x10-20 6661-8727 <$500
1902 Plain Back
3x10-20 1-5106 <$200
Total Issue $1,133,850
Out at close $49,000
****
2003 Cumberland
PEOPLES NB OF FAYETTEVILLE
{{ 4 L }}
Chartered 6/27/72
Receivership 1/20/91
Original Series <$VALUE
3x1-2 1-1960 <$1000/$2500
4x5 1-3635 <$1000
3x10-20 1-600 <$1250/$2000
Series 1875
3x1-2 1-760 <$1000/$2500
4x5 1-3290 <$1000
3x10-20 1-1358<$1250/$2000
Total Issue $250,000
Out in 1916 $1,153
****
9203 Rutherford
FNB OF FOREST CITY
{{ 3 L }}
Chartered 7/08
Liquidated 11/30/15
1902 Date Back <$VALUE
4x5 1-2065 <$600
3x10-20 1-2040 <$600
1902 Plain Back
4x5 2066-2085 <$600
3x10-20 2041-2042 <$600
Total Issue $143,800
Out in 1916 $12,700
****
12461 Rutherford
NB OF FOREST CITY
{{ 3 L }}
Chartered 11/23
Liquidated 7/1/26
1902 Plain Back <$VALUE
4x5 1-1875 <$600
3x10-20 1-1068 <$600
Total Issue $90,900
Out at close $55,000
****

<$VALUEs are for notes in FINE condition. Value changes by approximately 25% for a change of one full grade.

****
7536 Gaston
CITIZENS NB OF GASTONIA
{{ U + 24 L 43 S }}
Organized 12/16/04
Liquidated 11/7/33
1902 Red Seal <$VALUE
4x5 1-1900 <$1000
3x10-20 1-1860 <$1000
1902 Date Back
4x5 1-6600* <$85
3x10-20 1-5230** <$85
1902 Plain Back
4x5 7101-85684* <$85
3x10-20 5531-51767** <$85
* 6601-7100 not marked
** 5231-5530 not marked
1929 Small Size
5 Type 1 1-20768 <$50
10 Type 1 1-11374 <$50
20 Type 1 1-2806 <$60
5 Type 2 1-2280 <$60
10 Type 2 1-581 <$70
20 Type 2 1-540 <$75
Total Issue $6,103,240
Out at close $498,800
Large out at close $65,370
****
4377 Gaston
FNB OF GASTONIA
{{ 20 L 50+ S }}
Organized 7/8/90
Liquidated 1/25/35
Brown Back <$VALUE
4x5 1-3000 <$450
3x10-20 1-6520 <$450
1882 Date Back
4x5 1-2045 <$450
3x10-20 1-667 <$450
1902 Date Back
4x5 1-7750 <$85
3x10-20 1-5600 <$85
1902 Plain Back
4x5 7751-83809 <$85
3x10-20 5601-55678 <$85
1929 Small Size
5 Type 1 1-21734 <$35
10 Type 1 1-11060 <$40
20 Type 1 1-3096 <$50
5 Type 2 1-24964 <$35
10 Type 2 1-12860 <$40
20 Type 2 1-3652 <$50
Total Issue $6,933,930
Out at close $405,570
Large out at close $16,400
****
11477 Gaston
THIRD NB OF GASTONIA
{{ 5 L }}
Chartered 10/19
Liquidated 10/13/26
1902 Plain Back <$VALUE
4x5 1-10401 <$300
4x10 1-6922 <$300
3x10-20 1-2900 <$300
Total Issue $629,900
Out at close $95,900
****
5048 Wayne
NB OF GOLDSBORO
{{ 9 L 5 S }}
Organized 4/28/96
Receivership 12/30/30
Brown Back <$VALUE
4x5 1-4350 <$650
50-100 1-737 <$2000/$2500
1882 Date Back
4x5 1-5495 <$650
50-100 1-400 <$2000/$2500
3x50-100 1-436<$2000/$2500
1902 Plain Back
3x10-20 1-17943 <$325
1929 Small Size
10 Type 1 1-1079 <$300
20 Type 1 1-263 <$300
Total Issue $1,469,900
Out at close $71,590
Large out at close $16,980
****
10614 Wayne
WAYNE NB OF GOLDSBORO
{{ 18 L 21 S }}
Organized 9/11/14
Receivership 2/17/32
1902 Date Back <$VALUE
4x5 1-6000 <$165
3x10-20 1-4800 <$165
1902 Plain Back
4x5 6001-43196 <$165
3x10-20 4801-29219 <$165
1929 Small Size
5 Type 1 1-6038 <$125
10 Type 1 1-2916 <$125
20 Type 1 1-692 <$125
Total Issue $2,764,010
Out at close $177,320
Large out at close $15,855
****
8844 Alamance
NB OF ALAMANCE AT GRAHAM
{{ 8 L 15 S }}
Chartered 8/07
1902 Red Seal <$VALUE
4x5 1-1250 <$1250
3x10-20 1-1000 <$1250
1902 Date Back
4x5 1-3950 <$300
3x10-20 1-3140 <$300
1902 Plain Back
4x5 3951-28589 <$300
3x10-20 3141-18384 <$300
1929 Small Size
5 Type 1 1-4496 <$125
10 Type 1 1-2364 <$125
20 Type 1 1-618 <$135
5 Type 2 1-7718 <$150
10 Type 2 1-5133 <$150
20 Type 2 1-1260 <$150
Total Issue $2,031,980
Out in 1935 $58,000
Large out 1935 $5,270
****
10112 Guilford
THE AMERICAN EXCHANGE NB OF GREENSBORO
Chartered 12/11
Liquidated 9/21/29
2nd title: American Exchange NB 2/21/22
3rd title: American NB & TC 11/1/28
FIRST TITLE {{ 9 L }}
1902 Date Back <$VALUE
4x5 1-24000 <$100
3x10-20 1-19400 <$100
1902 Plain Back
4x5 24001-67000 <$100
3x10-20 19401-46200 <$100
SECOND TITLE {{ 24 L }}
1902 Plain Back
4x5 1-86594 <$85
3x10-20 1-52190 <$85
THIRD TITLE {{ 6 L }}
1902 Plain Back
4x5 1-7510 <$100
3x10-20 1-4354 <$100
Total Issue $8,408,780
Out at close $619,275
Outstanding includes Ch 5031
****
American NB & TC of Greensboro
SEE Ch 10112
The American Exchange NB of Greensboro
****
5168 Guilford
CITY NB OF GREENSBORO
{{ 1 L }}
Organized 1/14/99
Receivership 3/6/08
Brown Back <$VALUE
3x10-20 1-7236 <$1250
Total Issue $361,800
Out in 1916 $4,520
****
9123 Guilford
COMMERCIAL NB OF GREENSBORO
{{ UNREPORTED }}
Chartered 5/08
Liquidated 11/15/11
1902 Date Back <$VALUE
4x5 1-8850 <$850
3x10-20 1-6719 <$850
Total Issue $512,950
Out in 1912 $90,600
****
5031 Guilford
GREENSBORO NB, GREENSBORO
{{ 12 L }}
Chartered 1896
Closed 2/21/22
Brown Back <$VALUE
3x10-20 1-8300 <$500
1882 Date Back
3x10-20 1-8295 <$450
1902 Plain Back
3x10-20 1-8546 <$175
Total Issue $1,257,050
Out at close $98,695
Ch 10112 assumed circulation
****
2322 Guilford
NB OF GREENSBORO
{{ 9 L }}
Chartered 2/7/76
Liquidated 1/18/96
Series 1875 <$VALUE
4x5 1-23833 <$600
Total Issue $476,660
Out in 1910 $2,860
****
13761 Guilford
SECURITY NB OF GREENSBORO
{{ 16 S }}
Chartered 8/33
1929 Small Size <$VALUE
5 Type 2 1-29954 <$65
10 Type 2 1-15565 <$65
20 Type 2 1-6696 <$75
Total Issue $439,340
Out in 1935 $115,950
****
8160 Pitt
NB OF GREENVILLE
{{ 3 L 3 S }}
Organized 2/16/06
Receivership 12/26/30
1902 Red Seal <$VALUE
4x5 1-725 <$1500
3x10-20 1-580 <$1500
1902 Date Back
4x5 1-3175 <$600
3x10-20 1-2600 <$600
1902 Plain Back
4x5 3176-7007 <$600
3x10-20 2601-4927 <$600
1929 Small Size
5 Type 1 1-423 <$400
10 Type 1 1-198 <$400
20 Type 1 1-57 <$400
Total Issue $461,400
Out at close $24,400
Large out at close $5,130
****
10851 Richmond
FNB OF HAMLET
{{ 2 L }}
Chartered 5/16
Liquidated 7/10/23
1902 Plain Back <$VALUE
4x5 1-3180 <$750
4x10 1-2365 <$750
Total Issue $158,200
Out at close $16,750
****
13636 Vance
FNB IN HENDERSON
{{ 2U + 10 S }}
Chartered 10/32
1929 Small Size <$VALUE
5 Type 1 1-1340 <$135
10 Type 1 1-780 <$135
20 Type 1 1-316 <$150
5 Type 2 1-8996 <$160
10 Type 2 1-4071 <$160
20 Type 2 1-1237 <$175
Total Issue $235,350
Out in 1935 $72,400
****
7564 Vance
FNB OF HENDERSON
{{ 21 L 9 S }}
Organized 1/5/05
Liquidated 3/15/33
1902 Red Seal <$VALUE
4x5 1-2050 <$1250
3x10-20 1-1700 <$1250
1902 Date Back
4x5 1-6850 <$200
3x10-20 1-5180 <$200
1902 Plain Back
4x5 6851-41845 <$200
3x10-20 5181-29111 <$200
1929 Small Size
5 Type 1 1-6598 <$175
10 Type 1 1-3396 <$175
20 Type 1 1-765 <$175
Total Issue $2,911,950
Out at close $187,695
Large out at close $12,190
****
10734 Henderson
CITIZENS NB OF HENDERSONVILLE
{{ 7 L 4 S }}
Organized 4/21/15
Receivership 11/28/30
1902 Date Back <$VALUE
4x5 1-650 <$300
3x10-20 1-540 <$300
1902 Plain Back
4x5 651-10890 <$300
3x10-20 541-7238 <$300
1929 Small Size
5 Type 1 1-813 <$300
10 Type 1 1-411 <$300
20 Type 1 1-110 <$325
Total Issue $641,950
Out at close $49,580
Large out at close $7,480
****
8837 Henderson
FNB OF HENDERSONVILLE
{{ 2 L }}
Chartered 8/07
Liquidated 1/1/13
1902 Red Seal <$VALUE
4x10 1-1150 <$1500
1902 Date Back
4x5 1-2217 <$600
4x10 1-2267 <$600
Total Issue $181,020
Out in 1913 $22,245
****
9571 Henderson
PEOPLES NB OF HENDERSONVILLE
{{ UNREPORTED }}
Chartered 10/09
Liquidated 4/30/15
1902 Date Back <$VALUE
4x5 1-2825 <$1000
3x10-20 1-2289 <$1000
Total Issue $170,950
Out in 1915 $14,600
****
4597 Catawba
FNB OF HICKORY
{{ 13 L 37 S }}
Chartered 1891
Brown Back <$VALUE
3x10-20 1-3980 <$500
1882 Date Back
4x5 1-1670 <$500
3x10-20 1-2493 <$500
1902 Date Back
4x5 1-5500 <$125
4x10 1-4750 <$125
1902 Plain Back
4x5 5501-30141 <$125
4x10 4751-24691 <$125
1929 Small Size
5 Type 1 1-16280 <$60
10 Type 1 1-8928 <$60
5 Type 2 1-49288 <$60
10 Type 2 1-24756 <$60
Total Issue $3,465,590
Out in 1935 $335,550
Large out 1935 $5,000
****
4568 Guilford
COMMERCIAL NB OF HIGH POINT
{{ 43 L 33 S }}
Organized 3/23/91
Receivership 2/10/32
Brown Back <$VALUE
4x5 1-10550 <$400
3x10-20 1-4860 <$400
1882 Date Back
4x5 1-3197 <$400
3x10-20 1-2698 <$400
1902 Date Back
4x5 1-9750 <$85
3x10-20 1-8200 <$85
1902 Plain Back
4x5 9751-111400 <$85
3x10-20 8201-72893 <$85
1929 Small Size
5 Type 1 1-17400 <$50
10 Type 1 1-8404 <$50
20 Type 1 1-2233 <$60
Total Issue $7,819,690
Out at close $474,140
Large out at close $22,980
****
FNB of High Point
SEE Ch 3490
NB of High Point
****
3490 Guilford
NB OF HIGH POINT
Chartered 4/21/86
Liquidated 11/28/07
2nd title:FNB of High Point 3/13/06
FIRST TITLE {{ 1 L }}
Brown Back <$VALUE
4x5 1-6148 <$1500
3x10-20 1-3375 <$1500
SECOND TITLE {{ 0 L }}
1902 Red Seal
4x5 1-1105 <$2000
3x10-20 1-883 <$2000
Total Issue $357,960
Out in 1910 $17,975
****
8571 Ashe
FNB OF JEFFERSON
Chartered 2/07
2nd title:FNB of West Jefferson 8/19/15
FIRST TITLE {{ 1 L }}
1902 Red Seal <$VALUE
3x10-20 1-287 <$2000
1902 Date Back
3x10-20 1-378 <$1000
SECOND TITLE {{ 1 L 3 S }}
1902 Plain Back
3x10-20 1-926 <$1000
1929 Small Size
10 Type 1 1-223 <$500
20 Type 1 1-56 <$500
Total Issue $99,650
Out in 1935 $6,250
Large out 1935 $350
****
5451 Cleveland
FNB OF KINGS MOUNTAIN
{{ 8 L 17 S }}
Chartered 6/25/00
Brown Back <$VALUE
3x10-20 1-600 <$750
1882 Date Back
3x10-20 1-2680 <$750
1882 Value Back
3x10-20 2681-4648 <$750
1902 Plain Back
3x10-20 1-7937 <$400
1929 Small Size
10 Type 1 1-1518 <$135
20 Type 1 1-382 <$150
5 Type 2 1-324 <$175
10 Type 2 1-6805 <$160
20 Type 2 1-1440 <$165
Total Issue $894,640
Out in 1935 $80,555
Large out 1935 $2,200
****
9085 Lenoir
FNB OF KINSTON
{{ 6 L 3 S }}
Organized 2/25/08
Receivership 5/1/31
1902 Red Seal <$VALUE
4x5 1-625 <$1250
3x10-20 1-500 <$1250
1902 Date Back
4x5 1-2425 <$400
3x10-20 1-1920 <$400
1902 Plain Back
4x5 2426-7108 <$400
3x10-20 1921-4753 <$400
1929 Small Size
5 Type 1 1-544 <$400
10 Type 1 1-258 <$400
20 Type 1 1-91 <$400
Total Issue $460,030
Out at close $25,400
Large out at close $2,360
****
9044 Lenoir
NB OF KINSTON
{{ 6 L 0 S }}
Organized 2/14/08
Receivership 5/1/31
1902 Red Seal <$VALUE
4x10 1-937 <$1250
1902 Date Back
4x10 1-3300* <$400
1902 Plain Back
4x10 3601-9424* <$400
* 3301-3600 not marked
1929 Small Size
10 Type 1 1-604 <$600
Total Issue $450,680
Out at close $24,340
Large out at close $3,280
****
5651 Scotland
FNB OF LAURINBURG
{{ 2 L 2 S }}
Chartered 12/24/00
Receivership 12/23/30
Brown Back <$VALUE
4x5 1-1265 <$1250
3x10-20 1-954 <$1250
1882 Date Back
4x5 1-1925 <$1250
3x10-20 1-1500 <$1250
1882 Value Back
4x5 1926-3475 <$1250
3x10-20 1501-2429 <$1250
1902 Plain Back
4x10 1-4988 <$750
1929 Small Size
10 Type 1 1-556 <$500
Total Issue $496,830
Out at close $24,680
Large out at close $3,620
****
12259 Rockingham
FNB OF LEAKSVILLE
{{ 6 L 3 S }}
Organized 10/22
1902 Plain Back <$VALUE
4x5 1-3557 <$400
3x10-20 1-2389 <$400
1929 Small Size
5 Type 1 1-1242 <$350
10 Type 1 1-610 <$350
20 Type 1 1-176 <$350
5 Type 2 1-1788 <$350
10 Type 2 1-960 <$350
20 Type 2 1-264 <$375
Total Issue $309,390
Out in 1935 $23,330
Large out 1935 $870
****
8445 Caldwell
FNB OF LENOIR
{{ 3 L 0 S }}
Chartered 11/06
Liquidated 1/28/31
1902 Red Seal <$VALUE
3x10-20 1-460 <$1500
1902 Date Back
3x10-20 1-1920 <$500
1902 Plain Back
3x10-20 1921-3707 <$500
1929 Small Size
10 Type 1 1-177 <$600
20 Type 1 1-29 <$600
Total Issue $222,450
Out at close $11,360
Large out 1935 $940
Ch 13523 assumed circulation
****
13523 Caldwell
UNION NB OF LENOIR
{{ 5 S }}
Chartered 1/31
1929 Small Size <$VALUE
10 Type 1 1-1040 <$300
5 Type 2 1-3132 <$300
10 Type 2 1-1524 <$300
Total Issue $93,300
Out in 1935 $26,610
Small out 1935 $25,670
Outstanding includes Ch 8445
****
FNB of Lexington
SEE Ch 5698
NB of Lexington
****
5698 Davidson
NB OF LEXINGTON
Chartered 1/30/01
Liquidated 10/22/19
2nd title:FNB of Lexington 11/4/11
FIRST TITLE {{ 3 L }}
Brown Back <$VALUE
4x5 1-1140 <$1000
3x10-20 1-974 <$1000
1882 Date Back
4x5 1-435 <$1000
3x10-20 1-336 <$1000
SECOND TITLE {{ 1 L }}
1882 Date Back
4x5 1-1400* <$1000
3x10-20 1-1020** <$1000
1882 Value Back
4x5 1901-2210* <$1000
3x10-20 1421-1534** <$1000
* 1401-1900 not marked
** 1021-1420 not marked
Total Issue $217,900
Out at close $23,400
****
NB of Lillington
SEE Ch 6616
FNB of Sanford
****
8184 Lincoln
COUNTY NB OF LINCOLNTON
{{ 3 L }}
Chartered 4/06
Liquidated 2/8/27
1902 Red Seal <$VALUE
3x10-20 1-1700 <$1500
1902 Date Back
3x10-20 1-3560 <$600
1902 Plain Back
3x10-20 3561-16978 <$600
Total Issue $933,900
Out at close $91,500
****

****
6744 Lincoln
FNB OF LINCOLNTON
{{ 4 L 50+ S }}
Chartered 4/03
1902 Red Seal <$VALUE
4x5 1-1730 <$1500
3x10-20 1-1746 <$1500
1902 Date Back
4x5 1-4300 <$500
3x10-20 1-2770 <$500
1902 Plain Back
4x5 4301-14623 <$500
3x10-20 2771-9678 <$500
1929 Small Size
5 Type 1 1-2032 <$125
10 Type 1 1-926 <$125
20 Type 1 1-296 <$125
5 Type 2 1-4202 <$150
10 Type 2 1-2015 <$150
20 Type 2 1-460 <$165
Total Issue $1,100,660
Out in 1935 $49,995
Large out 1935 $2,175
****
10260 Franklin
FARMERS NB OF LOUISBURG
{{ 5 L }}
Organized 8/1/12
Receivership 5/22/25
1902 Date Back <$VALUE
4x5 1-2575 <$400
3x10-20 1-2100 <$400
1902 Plain Back
4x5 2576-8405 <$400
3x10-20 2101-5393 <$400
Total Issue $437,750
Out at close $23,200
****
7554 Franklin
FNB OF LOUISBURG
{{ 8 L 6 S }}
Organized 1/6/05
Receivership 12/22/31
1902 Red Seal <$VALUE
4x5 1-990 <$1250
3x10-20 1-800 <$1250
1902 Date Back
4x5 1-3575 <$350
3x10-20 1-2700 <$350
1902 Plain Back
4x5 3576-13967 <$350
3x10-20 2701-9318 <$350
1929 Small Size
5 Type 1 1-1457 <$250
10 Type 1 1-714 <$250
20 Type 1 1-185 <$275
Total Issue $913,790
Out at close $49,460
Large out at close $5,570
****
7398 Robeson
FNB OF LUMBERTON
{{ 9 L }}
Organized 7/21/04
Receivership 8/4/25
1902 Red Seal <$VALUE
3x10-20 1-2026 <$1250
1902 Date Back
4x5 1-4380 <$350
3x10-20 1-3020 <$350
1902 Plain Back
4x5 4381-10990 <$350
3x10-20 3021-7117 <$350
Total Issue $676,950
Out at close $46,600
****
10610 Robeson
NB OF LUMBERTON
{{ 1 L }}
Chartered 9/14
1902 Date Back <$VALUE
4x5 1-945 <$1250
4x10 1-445 <$1250
3x10-20 1-349 <$1250
Total Issue $54,150
All notes reportedly redeemed
Census confirms one note.
****
6095 McDowell
FNB OF MARION
{{ 9 L 18 S }}
Chartered 1/15/02
Brown Back <$VALUE
3x10-20 1-2400 <$750
1882 Date Back
3x10-20 1-3800* <$750
1882 Value Back
3x10-20 4041-6816* <$750
* 3801-4040 not marked
1902 Plain Back
3x10-20 1-5771 <$325
1929 Small Size
10 Type 1 1-1394 <$100
20 Type 1 1-390 <$110
5 Type 2 1-312 <$150
10 Type 2 1-2172 <$135
20 Type 2 1-474 <$165
Total Issue $912,550
Out in 1935 $48,400
Large out 1935 $2,725
****
11697 Alamance
FNB OF MEBANE
{{ 4 L 14 S }}
Organized 4/14/20
Receivership 8/16/33
1902 Plain Back <$VALUE
4x5 1-12417 <$450
1929 Small Size
5 Type 1 1-3952 <$150
5 Type 2 1-180 <$185
Total Issue $367,800
Out at close $24,550
Large out at close $830
****
8712 Union
FNB OF MONROE
{{ 9 L U + 3 S }}
Chartered 5/07
Liquidated 6/9/30
1902 Red Seal <$VALUE
4x10 1-3150 <$1250
1902 Date Back
4x10 1-10000 <$300
1902 Plain Back
4x10 10001-39509 <$300
1929 Small Size
10 Type 1 1-1318 <$400
Total Issue $1,785,440
Out at close $89,960
Large out at close $19,850
****
9531 Iredell
FNB OF MOORESVILLE
{{ 15 L 8 S }}
Chartered 9/09
1902 Date Back <$VALUE
4x5 1-3800 <$200
3x10-20 1-3080 <$200
1902 Plain Back
4x5 3801-14564 <$200
3x10-20 3081-10195 <$200
1929 Small Size
5 Type 1 1-2148 <$200
10 Type 1 1-1172 <$200
20 Type 1 1-272 <$200
5 Type 2 1-3420 <$225
10 Type 2 1-1656 <$225
20 Type 2 1-456 <$225
Total Issue $1,011,210
Out in 1935 $45,470
Large out 1935 $2,070
****
5450 Burke
FNB OF MORGANTON
{{ 3 L 10 S }}
Chartered 6/25/00
Brown Back <$VALUE
3x10-20 1-1120 <$1000
1882 Date Back
3x10-20 1-1710 <$1000
1882 Value Back
3x10-20 1711-2221 <$1000
1902 Plain Back
3x10-20 1-1888 <$500
1929 Small Size
10 Type 1 1-1852 <$135
20 Type 1 1-468 <$165
10 Type 2 1-2905 <$200
20 Type 2 1-905 <$200
Total Issue $475,880
Out in 1935 $84,750
Large out 1935 $1,150
****
4896 Surry
FNB OF MOUNT AIRY
{{ 5 L }}
Chartered 1893
Brown Back <$VALUE
3x10-20 1-1590 <$1000
1882 Date Back
3x10-20 1-2947 <$1000
1902 Date Back
3x10-20 1-3450 <$450
1902 Plain Back
3x10-20 3451-10995 <$450
Total Issue $776,600
Out in 1935 $2,030
****
10629 Wayne
FNB OF MOUNT OLIVE
{{ 2 L 5 S }}
Chartered 10/14
1902 Date Back <$VALUE
3x10-20 1-500 <$1000
1902 Plain Back
3x10-20 501-4663 <$1000
1929 Small Size
10 Type 1 1-722 <$400
20 Type 1 1-214 <$400
10 Type 2 1-1920 <$400
20 Type 2 1-396 <$400
Total Issue $329,270
Out in 1935 $23,300
Large out 1935 $970
****
11557 Hertford
FNB OF MURFREESBORO
{{ 5 L }}
Chartered 12/19
Liquidated 3/11/26
1902 Plain Back <$VALUE
4x5 1-9262 <$400
4x10 1-5810 <$400
Total Issue $417,640
Out at close $33,100
****
9458 Cherokee
FNB OF MURPHY
{{ UNREPORTED }}
Chartered 6/09
Liquidated 1/16/11
1902 Date Back <$VALUE
4x5 1-325 <$1500
3x10-20 1-218 <$1500
Total Issue $17,400
Out in 1911 $5,200
****
13298 Craven
FNB OF NEW BERN
{{ 4 S }}
Organized 3/18/29
Receivership 10/26/29
1929 Small Size <$VALUE
5 Type 1 1-184* <$400
* C000184A-F000184A
not issued
Total Issue $5,500
Out at close $23,900
Small out at close $5,500
Outstanding includes Ch 1632
****
1632 Craven
NB OF NEW BERNE
{{ 9 L }}
Chartered 1866
Liquidated 7/17/29
Original Series <$VALUE
4x5 1-5865 <$850
3x10-20 1-1300<$1250/$2000
Series 1875
4x5 1-4482 <$850
3x10-20 1-1429<$1250/$2000
Brown Back
4x5 1-2100 <$750
3x10-20 1-2364 <$750
1902 Red Seal
3x10-20 1-500 <$1250
1902 Date Back
3x10-20 1-3400 <$375
1902 Plain Back
3x10-20 3401-6435 <$375
Total Issue $850,340
Out at close $18,400
Ch 13298 assumed circulation
****
6075 Catawba
SHUFORD NB OF NEWTON
{{ 2 L 7 S }}
Chartered 1/2/02
Brown Back <$VALUE
3x10-20 1-770 <$1250
1882 Date Back
3x10-20 1-1220* <$1250
1882 Value Back
3x10-20 1341-1730* <$1250
* 1221-1340 not marked
1902 Plain Back
3x10-20 1-1374 <$650
1929 Small Size
10 Type 1 1-1228 <$200
20 Type 1 1-328 <$225
10 Type 2 1-2634 <$250
20 Type 2 1-549 <$250
Total Issue $344,060
Out in 1935 $49,800
Large out 1935 $620
****
5885 Granville
FNB OF OXFORD
{{ 6 L }}
Chartered 6/27/01
Liquidated 3/16/34
Brown Back <$VALUE
4x5 1-1565 <$1000
3x10-20 1-1274 <$1000
1882 Date Back
4x5 1-4600 <$850
3x10-20 1-3720 <$850
1882 Value Back
4x5 4601-6700 <$850
3x10-20 3721-4940 <$850
1902 Plain Back
4x5 1-4360 <$450
3x10-20 1-2863 <$450
Total Issue $706,350
Out at close $3,695
Outstanding includes Ch 8996
****
8996 Granville
NB OF GRANVILLE AT OXFORD
{{ 4 L }}
Chartered 1/08
Closed 7/15/29
1902 Red Seal <$VALUE
3x10-20 1-450 <$1500
1902 Date Back
3x10-20 1-3630 <$600
1902 Plain Back
3x10-20 3631-8094 <$600
Total Issue $427,200
Out at close $11,640
Ch 5885 assumed circulation
****
1766 Wake
CITIZENS NB OF RALEIGH
{{ 13 L }}
Chartered 1/13/71
Liquidated 9/21/29
Original Series <$VALUE
3x10-20 1-3100<$1250/$2000
Series 1875
3x10-20 1-3060<$1250/$2000
Brown Back
3x10-20 1-7530 <$500
1882 Date Back
4x5 1-1725 <$450
3x10-20 1-1253 <$450
1902 Date Back
3x10-20 1-17100 <$150
1902 Plain Back
3x10-20 17101-40943 <$150
Total Issue $2,828,800
Out at close $117,550
****
9067 Wake
COMMERCIAL NB OF RALEIGH
{{ 25 L 10 S }}
Organized 2/15/08
Receivership 12/21/31
1902 Red Seal <$VALUE
4x5 1-2000 <$1000
4x10 1-2000 <$1000
1902 Date Back
4x5 1-21750 <$125
4x10 1-20800 <$125
1902 Plain Back
4x5 21751-46628 <$125
4x10 20801-41845 <$125
1929 Small Size
5 Type 1 1-7282 <$125
10 Type 1 1-3069 <$125
Total Issue $3,123,610
Out at close $171,000
Large out at close $13,660
****
9471 Wake
MERCHANTS NB OF RALEIGH
{{ 9 L }}
Chartered 7/09
Liquidated 5/8/23
1902 Date Back <$VALUE
4x5 1-11350 <$175
3x10-20 1-8860 <$175
1902 Plain Back
4x5 11351-20405 <$175
3x10-20 8861-14398 <$175
Total Issue $1,128,000
Out at close $81,500
****
3389 Wake
NB OF RALEIGH
{{ UNREPORTED }}
Chartered 9/7/85
Liquidated 7/15/05
Brown Back <$VALUE
3x10-20 1-3597 <$1500
Total Issue $179,850
Out in 1910 $5,165
****
1557 Wake
RALEIGH NB OF NORTH
CAROLINA, RALEIGH
{{ 5 L }}
Chartered 1865
Liquidated 9/5/85
Original Series <$VALUE
3x1-2 1-2000 <$1000/$2500
4x5 1-10360 <$1000
3x10-20 1-7900<$1500/$2500
50-100 1-1600 <$8500
Series 1875
3x1-2 1-2000 <$1000/$2500
4x5 1-4515 <$1000
3x10-20 1-2330<$1500/$2500
Total Issue $1,069,000
Out in 1910 $4,455
****
1682 Wake
STATE NB OF RALEIGH
{{ UNREPORTED }}
Organized 6/2/68
Receivership 3/31/88
Original Series <$VALUE
4x5 1-2500 <$2000
3x10-20 1-2300<$2000/$2500
Series 1875
4x5 1-110 <$2000
3x10-20 1-1625<$2000/$2500
Total Issue $248,450
Out in 1916 $1,055
****
11229 Rockingham
FNB OF REIDSVILLE
{{ 5 L 11 S }}
Chartered 8/18
1902 Plain Back <$VALUE
4x5 1-10974 <$350
4x10 1-6113 <$350
1929 Small Size
5 Type 1 1-3298 <$175
10 Type 1 1-1772 <$175
5 Type 2 1-11966 <$175
10 Type 2 1-6841 <$175
Total Issue $797,500
Out in 1935 $49,200
Large out 1935 $450
****
FNB of Roanoke Rapids
SEE Ch 5767
FNB of Weldon
****
7362 Edgecombe
FNB OF ROCKY MOUNT
{{ 2 L }}
Chartered 8/04
Closed 12/31/28
1902 Red Seal <$VALUE
3x10-20 1-1200 <$1500
1902 Date Back
3x10-20 1-2850 <$850
1902 Plain Back
3x10-20 2851-7126 <$850
Total Issue $416,300
Out at close $25,010
Ch 10630 assumed circulation
****
FNB of Rocky Mount
SEE Ch 10630
NB of Rocky Mount
****
10630 Edgecombe
NB OF ROCKY MOUNT
Chartered 10/14
Liquidated 9/21/29
2nd title: FNB of
Rocky Mount 12/31/28
FIRST TITLE {{ 1 L }}
1902 Date Back <$VALUE
3x10-20 1-1063 <$1250
SECOND TITLE {{ 0 L }}
1902 Plain Back
4x5 1-514 <$1250
Total Issue $63,430
Out at close $20,930
Outstanding includes Ch 7362
****
10608 Edgecombe
PLANTERS NB OF
ROCKY MOUNT
Chartered 9/14
2nd title: Planters NB & TC
of Rocky Mount 2/1/30
FIRST TITLE {{ 5 L 1 S }}
1902 Date Back <$VALUE
3x10-20 1-2000 <$500
1902 Plain Back
3x10-20 2001-6173 <$500
1929 Small Size
10 Type 1 1-306 <$350
20 Type 1 1-106 <$350
SECOND TITLE {{ 7 S }}
1929 Small Size
5 Type 1 1-1996 <$250
10 Type 1 1-1000 <$250
20 Type 1 1-286 <$275
5 Type 2 1-9080 <$275
10 Type 2 1-4912 <$275
20 Type 2 1-1223 <$275
Total Issue $612,910
Out in 1935 $75,100
Large out 1935 $1,190
****
1659 Forsyth
FNB OF SALEM
{{ UNREPORTED }}
Chartered 1866
Liquidated 1/14/79
Original Series <$VALUE
4x5 1-4280 <$2000
3x10-20 1-2988<$2000/$2500
Series 1875
3x10-20 1-864 <$2000/$2500
Total Issue $278,200
Out in 1910 $1,290
****
2981 Rowan
FNB OF SALISBURY
{{ 15 L 15 S }}
Organized 6/14/83
Brown Back <$VALUE
4x5 1-4895 <$500
50-100 1-80 <$2000/$2500
1902 Red Seal
50-100 1-232 <$3000/$3500
1902 Date Back
4x5 1-500 <$300
3x10-20 1-400 <$300
50-100 1-240 <$750/$850
3x50-100 1-200 <$750/$850
1902 Plain Back
4x5 501-13685 <$300
3x10-20 401-9738 <$300
1929 Small Size
5 Type 1 1-4378 <$150
10 Type 1 1-2040 <$150
20 Type 1 1-520 <$165
5 Type 2 1-7072 <$175
10 Type 2 1-3693 <$175
20 Type 2 1-1002 <$200
Total Issue $1,399,770
Out in 1935 $84,900
Large out 1935 $4,330
****
9076 Rowan
PEOPLES NB OF SALISBURY
{{ 5 L }}
Organized 3/10/08
Receivership 7/3/23
1902 Red Seal <$VALUE
4x5 1-600 <$1250
3x10-20 1-400 <$1250
50-100 1-40 <$3000/$3500
1902 Date Back
4x5 1-8550 <$450
3x10-20 1-5740 <$450
50-100 1-200 <$750/$850
3x50-100 1-100 <$750/$850
1902 Plain Back
4x5 8551-19355 <$450
3x10-20 5741-12542 <$450
Total Issue $1,106,800
Out at close $92,800
****
6616 Lee
FNB OF SANFORD
{{ UNREPORTED }}
Chartered 2/03
Liquidated 1/22/12
2nd title:NB of Lillington
1904
FIRST TITLE
1902 Red Seal <$VALUE
3x10-20 1-532 <$2000
SECOND TITLE
1902 Red Seal
4x5 1-915 <$2000
4x10 1-420 <$2000
50-100 1-178 <$3000/$3500
1902 Date Back
4x5 1-632 <$1250
4x10 1-689 <$1250
Total Issue $128,600
Out in 1912 $9,600
****

****
13791 Lee
NB OF SANFORD
{{ 7 S }}
Chartered 10/33
1929 Small Size <$VALUE
5 Type 2 1-3996 <$250
10 Type 2 1-2040 <$250
20 Type 2 1-600 <$250
Total Issue $52,380
Out in 1935 $23,550
****
10739 Johnston
FNB OF SELMA
{{ 3 L }}
Organized 5/7/15
Receivership 5/16/25
1902 Plain Back <$VALUE
4x5 1-1689 <$750
4x10 1-1288 <$750
Total Issue $85,300
Out at close $8,800
****
6776 Cleveland
FNB OF SHELBY
{{ 18 L 36 S }}
Organized 4/3/03
1902 Red Seal <$VALUE
3x10-20 1-5780 <$1000
1902 Date Back
3x10-20 1-9700 <$125
1902 Plain Back
4x5 1-28232 <$125
3x10-20 9701-36461 <$125
1929 Small Size
5 Type 1 1-9002 <$50
10 Type 1 1-5186 <$50
20 Type 1 1-1354 <$50
5 Type 2 1-18130 <$60
10 Type 2 1-10822 <$60
20 Type 2 1-2445 <$60
Total Issue $3,668,160
Out in 1935 $242,700
Large out 1935 $9,335
****
7959 Cleveland
SHELBY NB, SHELBY
{{ 3 L }}
Chartered 10/05
Liquidated 5/17/22
1902 Red Seal <$VALUE
3x10-20 1-2150 <$1250
1902 Date Back
4x5 1-4030 <$500
3x10-20 1-2860 <$500
1902 Plain Back
4x5 4031-8290 <$500
3x10-20 2861-5457 <$500
Total Issue $546,150
Out at close $48,800
****
11440 Johnston
CITIZENS NB OF SMITHFIELD
{{ UNREPORTED }}
Chartered 8/19
Closed 10/15/21
1902 Plain Back <$VALUE
4x5 1-645 <$1500
Total Issue $12,900
Out at close $6,000
Ch 10502 assumed circulation
****
F & Citizens NB of Smithfield
SEE Ch 10502
FNB of Smithfield
****
10502 Johnston
FNB OF SMITHFIELD
Chartered 4/14
Liquidated 4/25/29
2nd title: F & Citizens NB of Smithfield 10/15/21
FIRST TITLE {{ 4 L }}
1902 Date Back <$VALUE
4x5 1-1000 <$350
4x10 1-1000 <$350
SECOND TITLE {{ 8 L }}
1902 Plain Back
4x5 1-20257 <$225
Total Issue $465,140
Out at close $52,100
Outstanding includes Ch 11440
****
10887 Greene
FNB OF SNOW HILL
{{ 3 L }}
Chartered 8/16
Liquidated 12/27/23
1902 Plain Back <$VALUE
4x5 1-2000 <$750
4x10 1-655 <$750
3x10-20 1-822 <$750
Total Issue $107,300
Out at close $12,100
****
9335 Greene
COMMERCIAL NB OF STATESVILLE
{{ 5 L }}
Organized 12/26/08
Receivership 4/19/28
1902 Date Back <$VALUE
4x5 1-6800 <$400
3x10-20 1-5620 <$400
1902 Plain Back
4x5 6801-23530 <$400
3x10-20 5621-17310 <$400
Total Issue $1,336,100
Out at close $98,200
****
3682 Iredell
FNB OF STATESVILLE
{{ 8 L 8 S }}
Chartered 4/26/87
Receivership 1/27/33
Brown Back <$VALUE
4x5 1-4623 <$750
3x10-20 1-933 <$750
1902 Red Seal
3x10-20 1-2000 <$1250
1902 Date Back
3x10-20 1-9200 <$300
1902 Plain Back
3x10-20 9201-29215 <$300
1929 Small Size
10 Type 1 1-2539 <$250
20 Type 1 1-700 <$250
Total Issue $1,936,200
Out at close $88,200
Large out at close $7,880
****
8356 Edgecombe
FNB OF TARBORO
{{ 6 L }}
Chartered 9/06
Liquidated 5/23/29
1902 Red Seal <$VALUE
4x5 1-1600 <$1500
3x10-20 1-1180 <$1500
1902 Date Back
4x5 1-4000 <$375
3x10-20 1-2900 <$375
1902 Plain Back
4x5 4001-18430 <$375
3x10-20 2901-12253 <$375
Total Issue $1,072,250
Out at close $89,450
****
8788 Davidson
FNB OF THOMASVILLE
{{ 23 L 44 S }}
Chartered 7/07
1902 Red Seal <$VALUE
4x5 1-800 <$1250
4x10 1-800 <$1250
1902 Date Back
4x5 1-1850 <$165
4x10 1-1800 <$165
1902 Plain Back
4x5 1851-22700 <$165
4x10 1801-18728 <$165
1929 Small Size
5 Type 1 1-6864 <$75
10 Type 1 1-3224 <$75
5 Type 2 1-15744 <$75
10 Type 2 1-7584 <$75
Total Issue $1,805,040
Out in 1935 $92,530
Large out 1935 $3,110
****
4947 Anson
FNB OF WADESBORO
{{ 8 L 26 S }}
Chartered 1894
Brown Back <$VALUE
3x10-20 1-1000 <$750
50-100 1-933 <$1750/$2000
1882 Date Back
3x10-20 1-4357 <$750
1902 Date Back
3x10-20 1-3000 <$300
1902 Plain Back
3x10-20 3001-16111 <$300
1929 Small Size
10 Type 1 1-2244 <$75
20 Type 1 1-598 <$85
10 Type 2 1-5510 <$75
20 Type 2 1-1478 <$85
Total Issue $1,504,410
Out in 1935 $84,100
Large out 1935 $4,000
****
11767 Duplin
FNB OF WARSAW
{{ UNREPORTED }}
Organized 6/21/20
Receivership 3/17/27
1902 Plain Back <$VALUE
4x5 1-2315 <$1250
3x10-20 1-1666 <$1250
3x50-100 1-96 <$1750/$2000
Total Issue $153,600
Out at close $2,590
****
4997 Beaufort
FNB OF WASHINGTON
{{ 9 L 12 S }}
Organized 4/11/95
Receivership 12/11/31
Brown Back <$VALUE
3x10-20 1-1100 <$650
1882 Date Back
3x10-20 1-5050* <$650
* 3915-4550 not issued
1902 Date Back
3x10-20 1-1000** <$250
** 959,969,972,978 not issued
1902 Plain Back
3x10-20 1001-17285 <$250
1929 Small Size
10 Type 1 1-1880 <$175
20 Type 1 1-552 <$200
Total Issue $1,318,790
Out at close $97,660
Large out at close $12,240
****
6554 Haywood
FNB OF WAYNESVILLE
{{ 3 L 7 S }}
Chartered 12/26/02
1902 Red Seal <$VALUE
4x5 1-400 <$1500
3x10-20 1-315 <$1500
1902 Date Back
4x5 1-3875 <$500
3x10-20 1-2860 <$500
1902 Plain Back
4x5 3876-13304 <$500
3x10-20 2861-9214 <$500
1929 Small Size
5 Type 1 1-1930 <$200
10 Type 1 1-1064 <$200
20 Type 1 1-276 <$200
5 Type 2 1-3038 <$225
10 Type 2 1-1716 <$225
20 Type 2 1-396 <$250
Total Issue $945,660
Out in 1935 $50,000
Large out 1935 $2,420
****
5767 Halifax
FNB OF WELDON
Chartered 4/3/01
Liquidated 8/30/29
2nd title and location: FNB of Roanoke Rapids 7/1/12
FIRST TITLE {{ 0 L }}
Brown Back <$VALUE
3x10-20 1-1600 <$1500
1882 Date Back
3x10-20 1-946 <$1500
SECOND TITLE {{ 12 L }}
1882 Date Back
3x10-20 1-2060 <$500
50-100 1-196 <$1750/$2000
1882 Value Back
3x10-20 2061-5960 <$500
1902 Plain Back
3x10-20 1-14351 <$200
Total Issue $1,191,850
Out at close $71,750
****
9124 New Hanover
AMERICAN NB OF WILMINGTON
{{ 3 L }}
Chartered 5/08
Liquidated 12/28/15
1902 Red Seal <$VALUE
4x5 1-1250 <$1250
4x10 1-2000 <$1250
1902 Date Back
4x5 1-22342 <$450
4x10 1-20889 <$450
Total Issue $1,387,400
Out in 1916 $117,410
****
4726 New Hanover
ATLANTIC NB OF WILMINGTON
{{ 3 L }}
Chartered 4/18/92
Liquidated 1/18/08
Brown Back <$VALUE
3x10-20 1-9600 <$750
Total Issue $480,000
Out in 1910 $22,950
****
12176 New Hanover
COMMERCIAL NB OF WILMINGTON
{{ 1 L }}
Organized 4/17/22
Receivership 1/31/23
1902 Plain Back <$VALUE
4x5 1-2545 <$1000
3x10-20 1-1034 <$1000
Total Issue $102,600
Out at close $91,500
****
1656 New Hanover
FNB OF WILMINGTON
{{ 1 L }}
Organized 7/25/66
Receivership 12/21/91
Original Series <$VALUE
4x5 1-1510 <$1250
3x10-20 1-4298<$1500/$2000
Series 1875
3x10-20 1-1164<$1500/$2000
Brown Back
3x10-20 1-1368 <$1000
Total Issue $371,700
Out in 1916 $1,515
****
5182 New Hanover
MURCHISON NB OF WILMINGTON
{{ 50+ L }}
Chartered 2/28/99
Liquidated 9/21/29
Brown Back <$VALUE
4x5 1-14750 <$400
50-100 1-6595 <$1750/$2000
1882 Date Back
4x5 1-65100 <$350
3x10-20 1-5000 <$350
50-100 1-4250 <$1500/$1750
3x50-100 1-5374<$1500/$1750
1882 Value Back
4x5 65101-73050 <$350
3x10-20 5001-8041 <$350
1902 Plain Back
3x10-20 1-90469 <$75
Total Issue $9,917,250
Out at close $207,640
Outstanding includes Ch 7913
****
4960 New Hanover
NB OF WILMINGTON
{{ 2 L }}
Chartered 6/16/94
Liquidated 5/27/01
Brown Back <$VALUE
4x5 1-4727 <$1000
50-100 1-568 <$1750/$2000
Total Issue $179,740
Out in 1910 $3,205
****
7913 New Hanover
SOUTHERN NB OF WILMINGTON
{{ 2 L }}
Organized 9/11/05
Liquidated 9/12/13
1902 Red Seal <$VALUE
3x10-20 1-8700 <$1250
1902 Date Back
4x5 1-8395 <$600
3x10-20 1-8798 <$600
Total Issue $1,042,800
Out at close $200,000
Ch 5182 assumed circulation
****
2321 Wilson
FNB OF WILSON
{{ 10 L 1 S }}
Chartered 2/5/76
Liquidated 9/5/32
Series 1875 <$VALUE
3x10-20 1-1813<$1500/$2000
Brown Back
3x10-20 1-5720 <$1000
1882 Date Back
3x10-20 1-8488 <$1000
1902 Plain Back
3x10-20 1-3632 <$500
1929 Small Size
10 Type 1 1-520 <$600
20 Type 1 1-127 <$600
Total Issue $1,029,090
Out at close $17,285
Large out 1935 $2,435
Ch 13626 assumed circulation
****
13626 Wilson
NB OF WILSON
{{ 4 S }}
Chartered 7/32
1929 Small Size <$VALUE
5 Type 1 1-160 <$300
10 Type 1 1-158 <$300
20 Type 1 1-44 <$300
5 Type 2 1-1640 <$350
10 Type 2 1-993 <$350
20 Type 2 1-302 <$350
Total Issue $43,730
Out in 1935 $24,500
Small out 1935 $22,065
Outstanding includes Ch 2321
****
2319 Forsyth
FNB OF WINSTON
{{ 2 L }}
Chartered 2/2/76
Liquidated 2/15/97
Series 1875 <$VALUE
3x10-20 1-5512<$1500/$2000
Brown Back
4x5 1-431 <$1000
3x10-20 1-153 <$1000
Total Issue $291,870
Out in 1910 $2,375
****
9916 Forsyth
MERCHANTS NB OF WINSTON
{{ 4 L }}
Chartered 1/11
Liquidated 5/1/19
1902 Date Back <$VALUE
4x5 1-5750 <$450
3x10-20 1-4480 <$450
1902 Plain Back
4x5 5751-7930 <$450
3x10-20 4481-6076 <$450
Total Issue $462,400
Out at close $66,700
****
4292 Forsyth
PEOPLES NB OF WINSTON
{{ 17 L 7 S }}
Organized 3/24/90
Receivership 6/29/31
Brown Back <$VALUE
3x10-20 1-11620 <$650
1882 Date Back
3x10-20 1-5883 <$600
1902 Date Back
3x10-20 1-24100 <$175
1902 Plain Back
3x10-20 24101-51426 <$175
1929 Small Size
10 Type 1 1-2549 <$200
20 Type 1 1-779 <$200
Total Issue $3,692,870
Out at close $150,000
Large out at close $19,360
****
2425 Forsyth
WACHOVIA NB OF WINSTON
{{ 1 L }}
Chartered 6/3/79
Liquidated 1/3/11
Series 1875 <$VALUE
3x10-20 1-7909<$1500/$2000
Brown Back
3x10-20 1-3800 <$1250
1882 Date Back
3x10-20 1-863 <$1250
Total Issue $628,600
Out in 1911 $25,800
****
FNB of West Jefferson
SEE Ch 8571
FNB of Jefferson
****
12278 Forsyth
FARMERS NB & TC OF WINSTON-SALEM
{{ 15 L 38 S }}
Organized 10/27/22
Liquidated 6/28/34
1902 Plain Back <$VALUE
4x5 1-40667 <$175
3x10-20 1-25824 <$175
1929 Small Size
5 Type 1 1-14372 <$75
10 Type 1 1-7064 <$75
20 Type 1 1-1862 <$75
5 Type 2 1-9208 <$85
10 Type 2 1-4695 <$85
20 Type 2 1-868 <$85
Total Issue $3,293,330
Out at close $235,220
Large out at close $8,600
****

CONDITION affects Value. The Values shown are for notes in FINE condition.

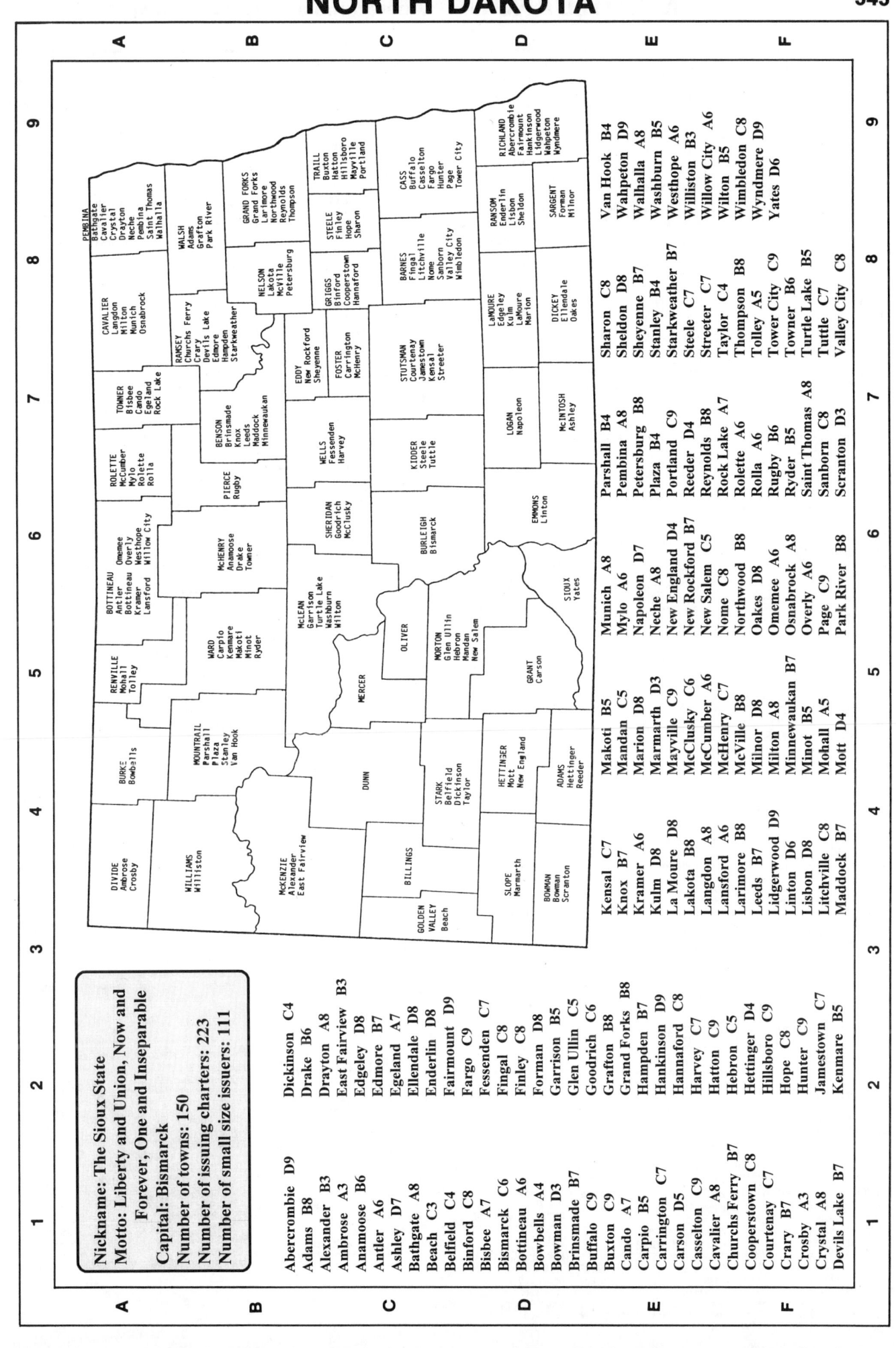

Nickname: The Sioux State
Motto: Liberty and Union, Now and Forever, One and Inseparable
Capital: Bismarck
Number of towns: 150
Number of issuing charters: 223
Number of small size issuers: 111

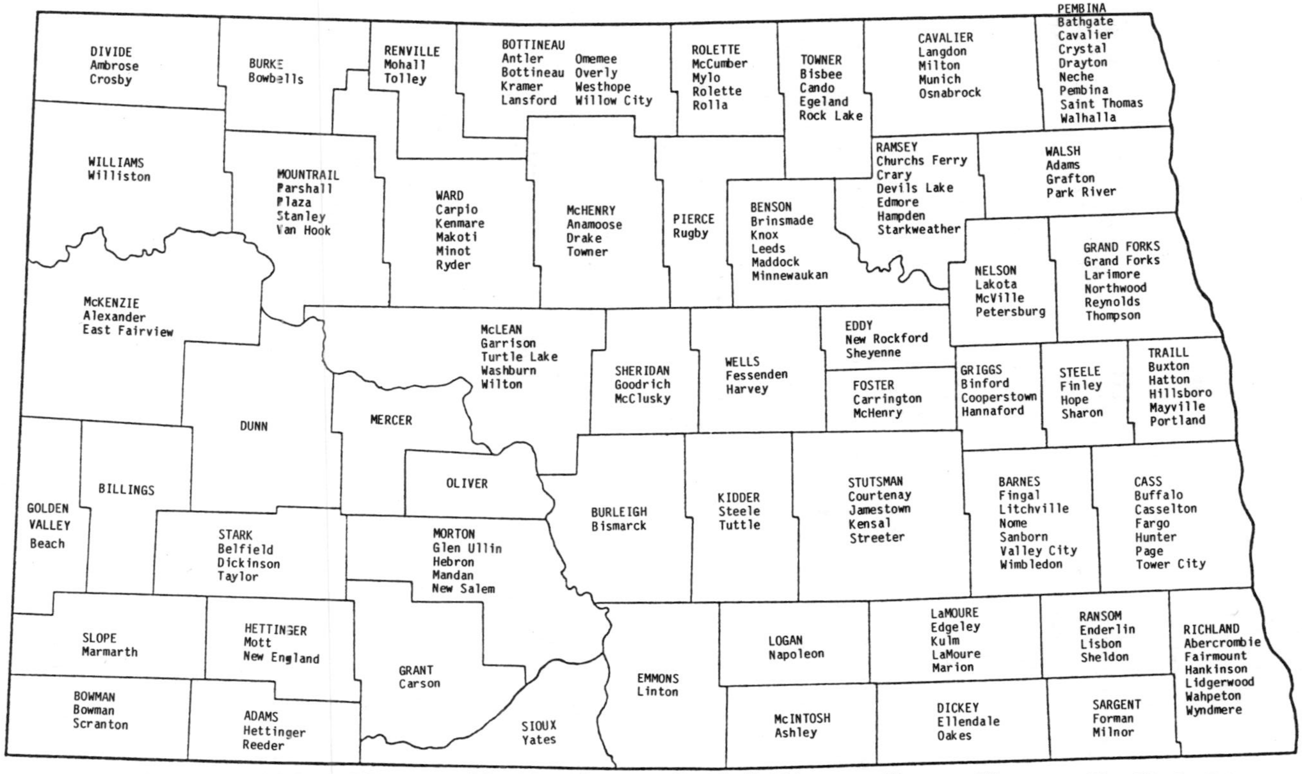

Abercrombie D9
Adams B8
Alexander B3
Ambrose A3
Anamoose B6
Antler A6
Ashley D7
Bathgate A8
Beach C3
Belfield C4
Binford C8
Bisbee A7
Bismarck C6
Bottineau A6
Bowbells A4
Bowman D3
Brinsmade B7
Buffalo C9
Buxton C9
Cando A7
Carpio B5
Carrington C7
Carson D5
Casselton C9
Cavalier A8
Churchs Ferry B7
Cooperstown C8
Courtenay C7
Crary B7
Crosby A3
Crystal A8
Devils Lake B7
Dickinson C4
Drake B6
Drayton A8
East Fairview B3
Edgeley D8
Edmore B7
Egeland A7
Ellendale D8
Enderlin D8
Fairmount D9
Fargo C9
Fessenden C7
Fingal C8
Finley C8
Forman D8
Garrison B5
Glen Ullin C5
Goodrich C6
Grafton B8
Grand Forks B8
Hampden B7
Hankinson D9
Hannaford C8
Harvey C7
Hatton C9
Hebron C5
Hettinger D4
Hillsboro C9
Hope C8
Hunter C9
Jamestown C7
Kenmare B5
Kensal C7
Knox B7
Kramer A6
Kulm D8
La Moure D8
Lakota B8
Langdon A8
Lansford A6
Larimore B8
Leeds B7
Lidgerwood D9
Linton D6
Lisbon D8
Litchville C8
Maddock B7
Makoti B5
Mandan C5
Marion D8
Marmarth D3
Mayville C9
McClusky C6
McCumber A6
McHenry C7
McVille B8
Milnor D8
Milton A8
Minnewaukan B7
Minot B5
Mohall A5
Mott D4
Munich A8
Mylo A6
Napoleon D7
Neche A8
New England D4
New Rockford B7
New Salem C5
Nome C8
Northwood B8
Oakes D8
Omemee A6
Osnabrock A8
Overly A6
Page C9
Park River B8
Parshall B4
Pembina A8
Petersburg B8
Plaza B4
Portland C9
Reeder D4
Reynolds B8
Rock Lake A7
Rolette A6
Rolla A6
Rugby B6
Ryder B5
Saint Thomas A8
Sanborn C8
Scranton D3
Sharon C8
Sheldon D8
Sheyenne B7
Stanley B4
Starkweather B7
Steele C7
Streeter C7
Taylor C4
Thompson B8
Tolley A5
Tower City C9
Towner B6
Turtle Lake B5
Tuttle C7
Valley City C8
Van Hook B4
Wahpeton D9
Walhalla A8
Washburn B5
Westhope A6
Williston B3
Willow City A6
Wilton B5
Wimbledon C8
Wyndmere D9
Yates D6

8419 Richland
FNB, ABERCROMBIE
{{ 2 L }}
Organized 8/25/06
Receivership 6/30/25
1902 Red Seal <$VALUE
3x10-20 1-200 <$2000
1902 Date Back
3x10-20 1-1860 <$600
1902 Plain Back
3x10-20 1861-3766 <$600
Total Issue $198,300
Out at close $24,100

7852 Walsh
FNB OF ADAMS
{{ UNREPORTED }}
Chartered 8/1/05 as FNB of Sarles, under which there was no issue. Issuing title adopted 12/15/05.
Liquidated 11/1/07
1902 Red Seal <$VALUE
3x10-20 1-149 <$2500
Total Issue $7,450
Out in 1910 $1,030

11297 McKenzie
FNB, ALEXANDER
{{ 3 L }}
Organized 1/22/19
Receivership 4/15/24
1902 Plain Back <$VALUE
4x5 1-5350 <$600
Total Issue $107,000
Out at close $24,400

9386 Divide
FNB, AMBROSE
{{ UNREPORTED }}
Organized 11/6/08
Receivership 2/20/30
1902 Date Back <$VALUE
3x10-20 1-720 <$1250
1902 Plain Back
3x10-20 721-1394 <$1250
1929 Small Size
10 Type 1 1-30 <$750
20 Type 1 1-2 <$750
Total Issue $71,740
Out at close $6,500
Large out at close $4,460

9390 McHenry
ANAMOOSE NB, ANAMOOSE
{{ 3 L }}
Organized 3/24/09
Receivership 9/18/26
1902 Date Back <$VALUE
4x5 1-1825* <$500
3x10-20 1-1380** <$500
1902 Plain Back
4x5 1976-4410* <$500
3x10-20 1441-2910** <$500
* 1826-1975 not marked
** 1381-1440 not marked
Total Issue $233,700
Out at close $24,400

9412 McHenry
FNB OF ANAMOOSE
{{ UNREPORTED }}
Chartered 5/09
Liquidated 2/13/14
1902 Date Back <$VALUE
4x10 1-1869 <$1250
Total Issue $74,760
Out in 1914 $13,390

7855 Bottineau
FNB, ANTLER
{{ 1 L }}
Chartered 8/05
Liquidated 3/2/14
1902 Red Seal <$VALUE
3x10-20 1-300 <$2500
1902 Date Back
3x10-20 1-294 <$1500
Total Issue $29,700
Out in 1914 $4,470

10864 McIntosh
FNB OF ASHLEY
{{ 6 L 2 S }}
Chartered 6/16
Liquidated 9/13/30
1902 Plain Back <$VALUE
4x5 1-3365 <$350
3x10-20 1-2226 <$350
1929 Small Size
5 Type 1 1-284 <$450
10 Type 1 1-131 <$450
20 Type 1 1-25 <$400
Total Issue $197,980
Out at close $25,000
Large out at close $5,840

11112 Pembina
BATHGATE NB, BATHGATE
{{ 4 L 2 S }}
Chartered 12/17
Liquidated 1/29/30
1902 Plain Back <$VALUE
4x10 1-3759 <$400
1929 Small Size
10 Type 1 1-227 <$450
Total Issue $163,980
Out at close $22,900
Large out at close $9,280

4537 Pembina
FNB, BATHGATE
{{ UNREPORTED }}
Chartered 3/26/91
Liquidated 3/26/98
Brown Back <$VALUE
3x10-20 1-598 <$2500
Total Issue $29,900
Out in 1910 $380

9484 Golden Valley
FNB, BEACH
{{ 5 L }}
Organized 5/26/09
Receivership 1/24/24
1902 Date Back <$VALUE
4x5 1-1950 <$350
3x10-20 1-1500 <$350
1902 Plain Back
4x5 1951-4015 <$350
3x10-20 1501-2720 <$350
Total Issue $216,300
Out at close $24,300

9539 Stark
FNB, BELFIELD
{{ 7 L 7 S }}
Chartered 9/09
1902 Date Back <$VALUE
4x5 1-1500 <$250
3x10-20 1-1180 <$250
1902 Plain Back
4x5 1501-4955 <$250
3x10-20 1181-3314 <$250
1929 Small Size
5 Type 1 1-930 <$175
10 Type 1 1-408 <$175
20 Type 1 1-130 <$175
5 Type 2 1-180 <$200
10 Type 2 1-230 <$200
20 Type 2 1-95 <$200
Total Issue $337,880
Out at close $25,000
Large out at close $1,620

8265 Griggs
FNB, BINFORD
{{ 3 L 6 S }}
Chartered 6/06
1902 Red Seal <$VALUE
3x10-20 1-475 <$2000
1902 Date Back
3x10-20 1-900 <$600
1902 Plain Back
3x10-20 901-2275 <$600
1929 Small Size
10 Type 1 1-320 <$225
20 Type 1 1-88 <$225
Total Issue $167,260
Out in 1935 $12,500
Large out 1935 $90

6733 Towner
FNB, BISBEE
{{ 3 L }}
Organized 4/1/03
Receivership 1/28/24
1902 Red Seal <$VALUE
3x10-20 1-630 <$1500
1902 Date Back
3x10-20 1-1800 <$500
1902 Plain Back
3x10-20 1801-3609 <$500
Total Issue $211,950
Out at close $22,800

2677 Burleigh
BISMARCK NB, BISMARCK
{{ 1 L }}
Organized 5/3/82
Liquidated 3/1/88
TERRITORIAL ISSUES
Series 1875 <$VALUE
4x5 1-1663 <$10,000
Total Issue $33,260
Out in 1910 $255

2986 Burleigh
CAPITAL NB, BISMARCK
Organized 6/23/83
Liquidated 1/14/96
TERRITORIAL ISSUES {{ 1 L }}
Brown Back <$VALUE
4x5 1-1337 <$8500
STATE ISSUES {{ 0 L }}
Brown Back
4x5 1338-2376 <$3000
Total Issue $47,520
Out in 1910 $490

9622 Burleigh
CITY NB, BISMARCK
{{ 4 L }}
Organized 11/12/09
Receivership 10/18/26
1902 Date Back <$VALUE
4x5 1-3150 <$350
3x10-20 1-2360 <$350
1902 Plain Back
4x5 3151-8525 <$350
3x10-20 2361-5714 <$350
Total Issue $456,200
Out at close $49,400

13398 Burleigh
DAKOTA NB & TC, BISMARCK
{{ 2U + 10 S }}
Chartered 12/29
1929 Small Size <$VALUE
5 Type 1 1-1544 <$100
10 Type 1 1-1048 <$100
20 Type 1 1-368 <$110
5 Type 2 1-3032 <$125
10 Type 2 1-1530 <$125
20 Type 2 1-370 <$125
Total Issue $191,220
Out in 1935 $67,750

2434 Burleigh
FNB, BISMARCK
Chartered 9/12/79
TERRITORIAL ISSUES {{ 0 L }}
Series 1875 <$VALUE
3x10-20 1-2020 <$10,000
STATE ISSUES {{ 15 L 24 S }}
Series 1875
3x10-20 2021-3064 <$2500
Brown Back
3x10-20 1-2010 <$1250
1882 Date Back
3x10-20 1-6900 <$750
1882 Value Back
3x10-20 6901-8336 <$750
1902 Plain Back
3x10-20 1-7763 <$200
1929 Small Size
10 Type 1 1-2176 <$85
20 Type 1 1-620 <$85
10 Type 2 1-2962 <$100
20 Type 2 1-485 <$100
Total Issue $1,303,930
Out in 1935 $100,000
Large out 1935 $6,300

3169 Burleigh
MERCHANTS NB, BISMARCK
{{ UNREPORTED }}
Chartered 1884
Liquidated 10/28/84
TERRITORIAL ISSUES
Brown Back <$VALUE
4x5 1-1125 <$8500
Total Issue $22,500
Out in 1910 $175

7879 Bottineau
BOTTINEAU NB, BOTTINEAU
{{ 1 L 0 S }}
Organized 8/4/05
Receivership 6/23/31
1902 Red Seal <$VALUE
3x10-20 1-300 <$2500
1902 Date Back
3x10-20 1-660 <$1250
1902 Plain Back
3x10-20 661-1234 <$1250
1929 Small Size
10 Type 1 1-92 <$750
20 Type 1 1-17 <$750
Total Issue $84,260
Out at close $7,000
Large out at close $1,330

6085 Bottineau
FNB OF BOTTINEAU
{{ 5 L }}
Organized 12/17/01
Receivership 4/12/23
Brown Back <$VALUE
3x10-20 1-590 <$1250
1882 Date Back
3x10-20 1-2800 <$850
1882 Value Back
3x10-20 2801-4306 <$850
1902 Plain Back
3x10-20 1-492 <$350
Total Issue $269,400
Out at close $35,800

7116 Burke
FNB, BOWBELLS
{{ 0 L 8 S }}
Chartered 1/04
1902 Red Seal <$VALUE
3x10-20 1-300 <$2500
1902 Date Back
3x10-20 1-600 <$1250
1902 Plain Back
3x10-20 601-2346 <$1250
1929 Small Size
10 Type 1 1-540 <$125
20 Type 1 1-136 <$135
10 Type 2 1-850 <$150
20 Type 2 1-113 <$150
Total Issue $191,780
Out at close $25,000
Large out at close $1,070

8976 Bowman
FNB, BOWMAN
{{ 2 L 6 S }}
Chartered 12/07
1902 Red Seal <$VALUE
4x5 1-155 <$2000
3x10-20 1-123 <$2000
1902 Date Back
4x5 1-1700 <$600
3x10-20 1-1280 <$600
1902 Plain Back
4x5 1701-5186 <$600
3x10-20 1281-3397 <$600
1929 Small Size
5 Type 1 1-858 <$175
10 Type 1 1-408 <$175
20 Type 1 1-98 <$175
5 Type 2 1-662 <$200
10 Type 2 1-560 <$200
20 Type 2 1-135 <$200
Total Issue $356,410
Out at close $25,000
Large out at close $1,520

8502 Benson
FNB, BRINSMADE
{{ 1 L }}
Organized 12/11/06
Receivership 2/13/25
1902 Red Seal <$VALUE
4x10 1-750 <$2500
1902 Date Back
4x10 1-2150 <$850
1902 Plain Back
4x10 2151-5056 <$850
Total Issue $232,240
Out at close $24,600

6559 Cass
FNB, BUFFALO
{{ 5 L 6 S }}
Chartered 12/02
1902 Red Seal <$VALUE
3x10-20 1-1200 <$1750
1902 Date Back
3x10-20 1-1700 <$400
1902 Plain Back
3x10-20 1701-4682 <$400
1929 Small Size
10 Type 1 1-526 <$225
20 Type 1 1-156 <$225
10 Type 2 1-432 <$250
20 Type 2 1-162 <$250
Total Issue $351,940
Out in 1935 $25,000
Large out 1935 $1,810

10814 Traill
FNB, BUXTON
{{ 2 L 11 S }}
Chartered 1/16
1902 Plain Back <$VALUE
3x10-20 1-2795 <$600
1929 Small Size
10 Type 1 1-536 <$125
20 Type 1 1-160 <$125
10 Type 2 1-258 <$150
20 Type 2 1-80 <$150
Total Issue $195,290
Out at close $25,000
Large out at close $1,310

7377 Towner
CANDO NB, CANDO
{{ UNREPORTED }}
Organized 7/16/04
Receivership 2/6/26
1902 Red Seal <$VALUE
3x10-20 1-400 <$2500
1902 Date Back
3x10-20 1-560 <$1000
1902 Plain Back
3x10-20 561-968 <$1000
Total Issue $68,400
Out at close $6,500

5798 Towner
FNB, CANDO
{{ 2 L 8 S }}
Chartered 5/01
Brown Back <$VALUE
3x10-20 1-500 <$2000
1882 Date Back
3x10-20 1-680 <$1250
1882 Value Back
3x10-20 681-748 <$1250
1902 Plain Back
3x10-20 1-543 <$600
1929 Small Size
10 Type 1 1-314 <$150
20 Type 1 1-102 <$150
10 Type 2 1-963 <$150
20 Type 2 1-169 <$150
Total Issue $133,640
Out at close $32,000
Large out 1935 $920

7315 Ward
FNB, CARPIO
{{ 2 L 9 S }}
Chartered 6/04
1902 Red Seal <$VALUE
3x10-20 1-300 <$2000
1902 Date Back
3x10-20 1-2050 <$600
1902 Plain Back
3x10-20 2051-5030 <$600
1929 Small Size
10 Type 1 1-568 <$125
20 Type 1 1-178 <$125
10 Type 2 1-42 <$150
20 Type 2 1-15 <$150
Total Issue $322,660
Out in 1935 $25,000
Large out 1935 $1,710

5551 Foster
FNB, CARRINGTON
{{ 4 L }}
Organized 7/6/00
Receivership 3/26/28
Brown Back <$VALUE
3x10-20 1-520 <$1250
1882 Date Back
3x10-20 1-1870 <$850
1882 Value Back
3x10-20 1871-2738 <$850
1902 Plain Back
3x10-20 1-1935 <$400
Total Issue $259,650
Out at close $24,700

13454 Grant
FNB OF CARSON
{{ U + 7 S }}
Chartered 4/15/30
Liquidated 2/25/35
1929 Small Size <$VALUE
5 Type 1 1-566 <$175
10 Type 1 1-332 <$175
20 Type 1 1-106 <$175
5 Type 2 1-616 <$225
10 Type 2 1-215 <$225
20 Type 2 1-50 <$225
Total Issue $55,850
Out in 1935 $25,000

7142 Cass
CASS COUNTY NB, CASSELTON
{{ 4 L }}
Organized 1/11/04
Receivership 12/10/28
1902 Red Seal <$VALUE
3x10-20 1-900 <$1500
1902 Date Back
3x10-20 1-1620 <$400
1902 Plain Back
3x10-20 1621-4513 <$400
Total Issue $270,650
Out at close $25,000

2792 Cass
FNB, CASSELTON
Chartered 1882
Liquidated 3/18/33
TERRITORIAL ISSUES {{ 1 L }}
Brown Back <$VALUE
4x5 1-1175 <$8500
3x10-20 1-640 <$8500
STATE ISSUES {{ 8 L 5 S }}
Brown Back
4x5 1176-2521 <$1250
3x10-20 641-1734 <$1250
1902 Red Seal
4x5 1-1350 <$1500
3x10-20 1-950 <$1500
1902 Date Back
4x5 1-2950 <$250
3x10-20 1-2230 <$250
1902 Plain Back
4x5 2951-9456 <$250
3x10-20 2231-6532 <$250
1929 Small Size
5 Type 1 1-1263 <$200
10 Type 1 1-711 <$200
20 Type 1 1-165 <$200
Total Issue $827,690
Out at close $50,000
Large out at close $5,225

10116 Pembina
FNB, CAVALIER
{{ 1 L }}
Organized 11/24/11
Receivership 2/21/25
1902 Date Back <$VALUE
3x10-20 1-1440 <$850
1902 Plain Back
3x10-20 1441-3342 <$850
Total Issue $167,100
Out at close $25,000

6337 Ramsey
FNB, CHURCHS FERRY
{{ 2 L 11 S }}
Chartered 7/02
1902 Red Seal <$VALUE
3x10-20 1-1500 <$2000
1902 Date Back
3x10-20 1-1610 <$750
1902 Plain Back (dated 1902)
3x10-20 1611-3170 <$750
1902 Plain Back (dated 1922)
3x10-20 1-1539 <$750
1929 Small Size
10 Type 1 1-546 <$250
20 Type 1 1-138 <$250
10 Type 2 1-622 <$275
20 Type 2 1-218 <$275
Total Issue $370,350
Out in 1935 $25,000
Large out 1935 $1,190

5375 Griggs
FNB OF COOPERSTOWN
{{ 7 L }}
Chartered 5/26/00
Liquidated 8/9/29
Brown Back <$VALUE
4x5 1-650 <$1250
3x10-20 1-560 <$1250
1882 Date Back
4x5 1-2575 <$750
3x10-20 1-2040 <$750
1882 Value Back
4x5 2576-4215 <$750
3x10-20 2041-3026 <$750
1902 Plain Back
4x5 1-4320 <$250
3x10-20 1-3064 <$250
Total Issue $516,200
Out in 1935 $3,295
Ch 13362 assumed circulation

13362 Griggs
FNB OF COOPERSTOWN
{{ U + 14 S }}
Chartered 8/29
1929 Small Size <$VALUE
5 Type 1 1-1348 <$100
10 Type 1 1-850 <$100
20 Type 1 1-220 <$100
5 Type 2 1-1046 <$125
10 Type 2 1-670 <$125
20 Type 2 1-195 <$125
Total Issue $133,670
Out in 1935 $41,405
Outstanding includes Ch 5375

****

6210 Stutsman
FNB OF COURTENAY
{{ 0 L 1 S }}
Chartered 4/02
Liquidated 12/21/31
1902 Red Seal <$VALUE
3x10-20 1-400 <$2500
1902 Date Back
3x10-20 1-660 <$1000
1902 Plain Back (dated 1902)
3x10-20 661-830 <$1000
1902 Plain Back (dated 1922)
3x10-20 1-322 <$1000
1929 Small Size
10 Type 1 1-96 <$600
20 Type 1 1-14 <$600
Total Issue $85,040
Out at close $6,500
Large out at close $1,160

****

6407 Ramsey
FNB, CRARY
{{ 5 L 3 S }}
Organized 8/20/02
Receivership 5/18/31
1902 Red Seal <$VALUE
3x10-20 1-900 <$1500
1902 Date Back
4x5 1-1541 <$350
3x10-20 1-1310 <$350
1902 Plain Back
4x5 1542-5130 <$350
3x10-20 1311-3429 <$350
1929 Small Size
5 Type 1 1-390 <$350
10 Type 1 1-173 <$350
20 Type 1 1-65 <$350
Total Issue $348,930
Out at close $25,000
Large out at close $3,430

****

10596 Divide
FNB, CROSBY
{{ 3 L 3 S }}
Organized 4/29/14
Receivership 11/1/32
1902 Plain Back <$VALUE
4x5 1-3287 <$500
1929 Small Size
5 Type 1 1-1577 <$350
Total Issue $113,050
Out at close $25,000
Large out at close $100

****

7918 Pembina
FNB, CRYSTAL
{{ 1 L }}
Organized 9/12/05
Receivership 2/7/25
1902 Red Seal <$VALUE
3x10-20 1-656 <$2000
1902 Date Back
3x10-20 1-1730 <$850
1902 Plain Back
3x10-20 1731-3595 <$850
Total Issue $212,550
Out at close $24,600

****

3397 Ramsey
FNB, DEVIL'S LAKE
Chartered 1885
TERRITORIAL ISSUES {{ 0 L }}
Brown Back <$VALUE
3x10-20 1-415 <$10,000
STATE ISSUES {{ 12 L 9 S }}
Brown Back
3x10-20 416-2943 <$1500
1902 Red Seal
3x10-20 1-1600 <$2000
1902 Date Back
3x10-20 1-3300 <$300
1902 Plain Back
3x10-20 3301-8849 <$300
1929 Small Size
10 Type 1 1-1140 <$175
20 Type 1 1-314 <$175
10 Type 2 1-617 <$175
20 Type 2 1-166 <$175
Total Issue $785,170
Out in 1935 $50,000
Large out 1935 $3,770

****

3714 Ramsey
MERCHANTS NB, DEVILS LAKE
{{ UNREPORTED }}
Organized 5/24/87
Receivership 1/11/97
TERRITORIAL ISSUES
Brown Back <$VALUE
3x10-20 1-620 <$10,000
STATE ISSUES
Brown Back
3x10-20 621-1252 <$3000
Total Issue $62,600
Out in 1915 $355

****

5886 Ramsey
RAMSEY COUNTY NB OF DEVILS LAKE
{{ 5 L 12 S }}
Chartered 1901
Brown Back <$VALUE
3x10-20 1-740 <$1500
1882 Date Back
3x10-20 1-1160 <$1000
1882 Value Back
3x10-20 1161-1272 <$1000
1902 Plain Back
3x10-20 1-4833 <$450
1929 Small Size
10 Type 1 1-1148 <$225
20 Type 1 1-352 <$225
10 Type 2 1-625 <$250
20 Type 2 1-50 <$250
Total Issue $460,620
Out in 1935 $50,000
Large out 1935 $2,580

****

7663 Stark
DAKOTA NB, DICKINSON
{{ 6 L }}
Organized 3/4/05
Receivership 2/7/24
1902 Red Seal <$VALUE
4x5 1-390 <$1500
3x10-20 1-354 <$1500
1902 Date Back
4x5 1-3950 <$250
3x10-20 1-2940 <$250
1902 Plain Back
4x5 3951-8055 <$250
3x10-20 2941-5395 <$250
Total Issue $456,350
Out at close $47,100

****

4384 Stark
FNB, DICKINSON
{{ 7 L 29 S }}
Chartered 7/3/90
Brown Back <$VALUE
4x5 1-3725 <$1250
3x10-20 1-1200 <$1250
1882 Date Back
4x5 1-535 <$750
3x10-20 1-406 <$750
1902 Date Back
3x10-20 1-5900 <$225
1902 Plain Back
3x10-20 5901-17490 <$225
1929 Small Size
10 Type 1 1-2068 <$75
20 Type 1 1-598 <$75
10 Type 2 1-2429 <$75
20 Type 2 1-881 <$85
Total Issue $1,277,750
Out in 1935 $100,000
Large out 1935 $5,765

****

12401 Stark
LIBERTY NB, DICKINSON
{{ 2 L 5 S }}
Organized 6/12/23
1902 Plain Back <$VALUE
3x10-20 1-713 <$600
1929 Small Size
10 Type 1 1-259 <$200
20 Type 1 1-81 <$200
Total Issue $60,910
Out in 1935 $10,000
Large out 1935 $630

****

8201 Stark
MERCHANTS NB OF DICKINSON
{{ 6 L }}
Chartered 5/06
Liquidated 3/1/27
1902 Red Seal <$VALUE
4x5 1-300 <$1500
3x10-20 1-240 <$1500
1902 Date Back
4x5 1-3775 <$250
3x10-20 1-2840 <$250
1902 Plain Back
4x5 3776-9295 <$250
3x10-20 2841-6207 <$250
Total Issue $514,250
Out in 1925 $49,995

****

9524 McHenry
FNB, DRAKE
{{ UNREPORTED }}
Chartered 8/09
Liquidated 3/22/10
1902 Date Back <$VALUE
4x5 1-205 <$1250
3x10-20 1-168 <$1250
Total Issue $12,500
Out in 1910 $9,705

****

12393 McHenry
FNB, DRAKE
{{ 2 L 15 S }}
Chartered 6/23
1902 Plain Back <$VALUE
4x5 1-6247 <$600
1929 Small Size
5 Type 1 1-2582 <$110
5 Type 2 1-5376 <$125
Total Issue $229,280
Out in 1935 $25,000
Large out 1935 $745

****

6225 Pembina
FNB, DRAYTON
{{ 7 L }}
Organized 3/22/02
Receivership 8/12/29
1902 Red Seal <$VALUE
4x5 1-1100 <$1500
3x10-20 1-780 <$1500
1902 Date Back
4x5 1-1500 <$200
3x10-20 1-1120 <$200
1902 Plain Back (dated 1902)
4x5 1501-3585 <$200
3x10-20 1121-2319 <$200
1902 Plain Back (dated 1922)
4x5 1-3480 <$200
3x10-20 1-2195 <$200
Total Issue $428,000
Out at close $49,995

****

10425 McKenzie
FNB OF EAST FAIRVIEW
{{ UNREPORTED }}
Chartered 7/17/13
Liquidated 10/11/21
1902 Date Back <$VALUE
4x5 1-450 <$1250
3x10-20 1-360 <$1250
1902 Plain Back
4x5 451-550 <$1250
3x10-20 361-428 <$1250
Total Issue $32,400
Out at close $6,500

****

7914 La Moure
FNB, EDGELEY
{{ 6 L }}
Organized 8/29/05
Receivership 1/31/27
1902 Red Seal <$VALUE
3x10-20 1-400 <$1500
1902 Date Back
3x10-20 1-2850 <$250
1902 Plain Back
3x10-20 2851-7359 <$250
Total Issue $387,950
Out at close $48,600

****

6601 Ramsey
FNB, EDMORE
{{ 2 L 0 S }}
Organized 1/15/03
Receivership 3/8/30
1902 Red Seal <$VALUE
3x10-20 1-400 <$2000
1902 Date Back
3x10-20 1-560 <$600
1902 Plain Back
3x10-20 561-1146 <$600
1929 Small Size
10 Type 1 1-41 <$750
20 Type 1 1-4 <$750
Total Issue $80,240
Out at close $6,070
Large out at close $3,130

****

7872 Towner
FNB OF EGELAND
{{ 1 L 1 S }}
Chartered 8/05
Liquidated 4/15/30
1902 Red Seal <$VALUE
3x10-20 1-440 <$2500
1902 Date Back
3x10-20 1-1050 <$1000
1902 Plain Back
3x10-20 1051-2369 <$1000
1929 Small Size
10 Type 1 1-20 <$600
20 Type 1 1-5 <$600
Total Issue $142,250
Out at close $9,380
Large out at close $7,580

****

9631 Dickey
ELLENDALE NB, ELLENDALE
{{ 1 L }}
Chartered 1/10
Closed 8/7/25
1902 Date Back <$VALUE
3x10-20 1-1810 <$750
1902 Plain Back
3x10-20 1811-3890 <$750
Total Issue $194,500
Out in 1924 $25,000

****

9521 Dickey
FARMERS NB OF ELLENDALE
{{ 3 L }}
Chartered 8/09
Liquidated 5/15/28
1902 Date Back <$VALUE
4x5 1-615 <$400
3x10-20 1-474 <$400
1902 Plain Back
4x5 616-2640 <$400
3x10-20 475-1669 <$400
Total Issue $136,250
Out in 1927 $6,250

****

6398 Dickey
FNB, ELLENDALE
{{ 7 L 6 S }}
Chartered 8/02
1902 Red Seal <$VALUE
3x10-20 1-1375 <$1500
1902 Date Back
3x10-20 1-1660 <$225
1902 Plain Back
3x10-20 1661-4601 <$225
1929 Small Size
10 Type 1 1-540 <$175
20 Type 1 1-140 <$175
10 Type 2 1-543 <$200
20 Type 2 1-136 <$200
Total Issue $356,150
Out in 1935 $25,000
Large out 1935 $1,430

****

6486 Ransom
FNB OF ENDERLIN
{{ UNREPORTED }}
Chartered 11/11/02
Liquidated 7/1/07
1902 Red Seal <$VALUE
4x5 1-530 <$2500
3x10-20 1-478 <$2500
Total Issue $34,900
Out in 1910 $3,285

****

6255 Richland
FNB OF FAIRMOUNT
{{ 2 L }}
Chartered 5/02
Liquidated 8/28/25
1902 Red Seal <$VALUE
4x5 1-250 <$1500
3x10-20 1-320 <$1500
1902 Date Back
4x5 1-1750 <$600
3x10-20 1-1300 <$600
1902 Plain Back
4x5 1751-4095 <$600
3x10-20 1301-2608 <$600
Total Issue $233,300
Out in 1924 $24,500

****

3602 Cass
CITIZENS NB, FARGO
{{ UNREPORTED }}
Organized 12/14/86
Receivership 1/7/97
TERRITORIAL ISSUES
Brown Back <$VALUE
4x5 1-725 <$8500
3x10-20 1-430 <$8500
STATE ISSUES
Brown Back
4x5 726-1075 <$2500
3x10-20 431-1166 <$2500
Total Issue $79,800
Out in 1915 $565

****

12026 Cass
DAKOTA NB, FARGO
{{ 15 L 17 S }}
Chartered 9/21
1902 Plain Back <$VALUE
4x5 1-19217 <$135
1929 Small Size
5 Type 1 1-16900 <$85
5 Type 2 1-14686 <$85
Total Issue $964,770
Out in 1935 $75,000
Large out 1935 $2,375

****

5087 Cass
FARGO NB, FARGO
{{ 11 L 13 S }}
Chartered 1897
Brown Back <$VALUE
4x5 1-2675 <$1250
3x10-20 1-1460 <$1250
1882 Date Back
4x5 1-3075 <$650
3x10-20 1-2160 <$650
1882 Value Back
4x5 3076-3855 <$650
3x10-20 2161-2605 <$650
1902 Plain Back
4x5 1-5897 <$150
3x10-20 1-3765 <$150
1929 Small Size
5 Type 1 1-1274 <$75
10 Type 1 1-722 <$75
20 Type 1 1-286 <$85
5 Type 2 1-1470 <$100
10 Type 2 1-793 <$100
20 Type 2 1-204 <$100
Total Issue $775,260
Out in 1935 $49,995
Large out 1935 $4,415

****

2377 Cass
FNB OF FARGO
Chartered 2/15/78
2nd title: FNB & TC
12/31/27
FIRST TITLE
TERRITORIAL ISSUES {{ 1 L }}
Series 1875 <$VALUE
4x5 1-2925 <$10,000
3x10-20 1-1200 <$10,000
STATE ISSUES {{ 15 L }}
Series 1875
4x5 2926-4407 <$2500
3x10-20 1201-2128 <$3000
Brown Back
4x5 1-10400 <$1250
3x10-20 1-8140 <$1250
1882 Date Back
4x5 1-12154 <$600
3x10-20 1-8661 <$600
1902 Plain Back
4x5 1-12775 <$125
3x10-20 1-7208 <$125
3x50-100 1-100 <$600/$750
SECOND TITLE {{ 44 S }}
1929 Small Size
5 Type 1 1-3906 <$70
10 Type 1 1-1962 <$70
20 Type 1 1-674 <$75
50 Type 1 1-244 <$200
100 Type 1 1-74 <$250
5 Type 2 1-2174 <$85
10 Type 2 1-1315 <$85
20 Type 2 1-255 <$85
Total Issue $2,589,070
Out in 1935 $150,000
Large out 1935 $11,235

****

8170 Cass
MERCHANTS NB OF FARGO
{{ 18 L }}
Chartered 4/06
Liquidated 7/26/29
1902 Red Seal <$VALUE
4x5 1-2500 <$1500
3x10-20 1-2000 <$1500
1902 Date Back
4x5 1-7000 <$125
3x10-20 1-5120 <$125
1902 Plain Back
4x5 7001-18835 <$125
3x10-20 5121-13314 <$125
Total Issue $1,192,400
Out in 1935 $6,885
Ch 13323 assumed circulation

****

13323 Cass
MERCHANTS NB & TC OF FARGO
{{ 17 S }}
Chartered 5/29
1929 Small Size <$VALUE
5 Type 1 1-3486 <$75
10 Type 1 1-1428 <$75
20 Type 1 1-396 <$85
5 Type 2 1-3566 <$100
10 Type 2 1-1983 <$100
20 Type 2 1-422 <$100
Total Issue $283,880
Out in 1935 $93,115

****

4256 Cass
NB OF NORTH DAKOTA, FARGO
{{ UNREPORTED }}
Organized 3/12/90
Receivership 6/6/93
Brown Back <$VALUE
50-100 1-432 <$5000
Total Issue $64,800
Out in 1915 $150

****

2514 Cass
RED RIVER VALLEY NB, FARGO
Organized 4/5/81
Liquidated 12/30/05
TERRITORIAL ISSUES {{ 0 L }}
Series 1875 <$VALUE
3x10-20 1-2600 <$10,000
STATE ISSUES {{ 3 L }}
Series 1875
3x10-20 2601-2962 <$3500
Brown Back
3x10-20 1-959 <$2500
Total Issue $242,550
Out in 1910 $5,350

****

11555 Cass
SECURITY NB, FARGO
{{ 8 L }}
Organized 11/25/19
Receivership 8/30/28
1902 Plain Back <$VALUE
3x10-20 1-8961 <$225
Total Issue $448,050
Out at close $100,000

****

5408 Wells
FNB, FESSENDEN
{{ 5 L 8 S }}
Chartered 6/7/00
Brown Back <$VALUE
3x10-20 1-400 <$1250
1882 Date Back
3x10-20 1-1990 <$750
1882 Value Back
3x10-20 1991-2703 <$750
1902 Plain Back
3x10-20 1-2176 <$350
1929 Small Size
10 Type 1 1-550 <$150
20 Type 1 1-170 <$150
10 Type 2 1-339 <$200
20 Type 2 1-35 <$200
Total Issue $321,440
Out in 1935 $25,000
Large out 1935 $1,890

****

7295 Barnes
FNB OF FINGAL
{{ 2 L 4 S }}
Chartered 6/04
Liquidated 8/13/32
1902 Red Seal <$VALUE
3x10-20 1-1050 <$1500
1902 Date Back
3x10-20 1-1510 <$600
1902 Plain Back
3x10-20 1511-4280 <$600
1929 Small Size
10 Type 1 1-357 <$300
20 Type 1 1-97 <$300
Total Issue $299,560
Out at close $25,000
Large out at close $3,940

****

7324 Steele
FNB OF FINLEY
{{ 4 L }}
Chartered 6/04
Liquidated 8/14/28
1902 Red Seal <$VALUE
4x5 1-300 <$1500
3x10-20 1-240 <$1500
1902 Date Back
4x5 1-1275 <$375
3x10-20 1-1000 <$375
1902 Plain Back
4x5 1276-4020 <$375
3x10-20 1001-2694 <$375
Total Issue $233,100
Out in 1925 $25,000

****

6474 Sargent
FNB, FORMAN
{{ 1 L 0 S }}
Organized 10/24/02
Receivership 11/24/30
1902 Red Seal <$VALUE
3x10-20 1-500 <$2500
1902 Date Back
3x10-20 1-560 <$1000
1902 Plain Back
3x10-20 561-1141 <$1000
1929 Small Size
10 Type 1 1-67 <$650
20 Type 1 1-9 <$650
Total Issue $87,150
Out at close $7,000
Large out at close $2,360

****

13501 McLean
FNB IN GARRISON
{{ 1 S }}
Chartered 11/30
1929 Small Size <$VALUE
10 Type 1 1-98 <$650
20 Type 1 1-29 <$650
Total Issue $9,360
Out in 1935 $6,500
Large out 1935 $250
Outstanding includes Ch 9778

****

9778 McLean
FNB OF GARRISON
{{ UNREPORTED }}
Chartered 6/10
Liquidated 11/15/30
1902 Date Back <$VALUE
3x10-20 1-720 <$1250
1902 Plain Back
3x10-20 721-1246 <$1250
1929 Small Size
10 Type 1 1-71 <$750
20 Type 1 1-8 <$750
Total Issue $67,520
Out at close $6,500
Large out at close $1,400
Ch 13501 assumed circulation

9016 Morton
FNB OF GLEN ULLIN
{{ UNREPORTED }}
Chartered 2/08
Liquidated 3/10/14
1902 Red Seal <$VALUE
3x10-20 1-187 <$2500
1902 Date Back
3x10-20 1-761 <$1000
Total Issue $47,400
Out in 1914 $18,520

13410 Morton
FNB, GLEN ULLIN
{{ 17 S }}
Chartered 12/29
1929 Small Size <$VALUE
5 Type 1 1-524 <$100
10 Type 1 1-390 <$100
20 Type 1 1-170 <$125
5 Type 2 1-1086 <$150
10 Type 2 1-610 <$150
20 Type 2 1-54 <$150
Total Issue $72,130
Out in 1935 $22,250

8077 Sheridan
FNB, GOODRICH
{{ 1 L 5 S }}
Organized 1/2/06
1902 Red Seal <$VALUE
3x10-20 1-600 <$2500
1902 Date Back
3x10-20 1-1230 <$750
1902 Plain Back
3x10-20 1231-3671 <$750
1929 Small Size
10 Type 1 1-398 <$250
20 Type 1 1-118 <$250
10 Type 2 1-428 <$250
20 Type 2 1-147 <$250
Total Issue $258,810
Out in 1935 $20,000
Large out 1935 $1,180

2840 Walsh
FNB OF GRAFTON
Organized 11/14/82
Receivership 5/25/27
TERRITORIAL ISSUES {{ 0 L }}
Brown Back <$VALUE
3x10-20 1-522 <$8500
STATE ISSUES {{ 6 L }}
Brown Back
3x10-20 523-1238 <$1250
1902 Red Seal
3x10-20 1-545 <$1500
1902 Date Back
3x10-20 1-3900 <$250
1902 Plain Back
3x10-20 3901-8626 <$250
Total Issue $520,450
Out at close $49,600

3096 Walsh
GRAFTON NB, GRAFTON
Chartered 1883
TERRITORIAL ISSUES {{ 0 L }}
Brown Back <$VALUE
3x10-20 1-470 <$8500
STATE ISSUES {{ 11 L 43 S }}
Brown Back
3x10-20 471-1265 <$1250
1902 Red Seal
3x10-20 1-2100 <$1500
1902 Date Back
3x10-20 1-3600 <$150
1902 Plain Back
3x10-20 3601-15621 <$150
1929 Small Size
10 Type 1 1-2098 <$75
20 Type 1 1-531 <$75
Total Issue $1,138,900
Out in 1935 $50,000
Large out 1935 $6,530

2570 Grand Forks
CITIZENS NB OF GRAND FORKS
Organized 9/12/81
Receivership 11/15/33
2nd title: The FNB of Grand Forks 7/90
3rd title: FNB of Grand Forks 6/28/29
FIRST TITLE
TERRITORIAL ISSUES {{ 1 L }}
Series 1875 <$VALUE
4x5 1-1000 <$10,000
3x10-20 1-1129 <$10,000
STATE ISSUES
SECOND TITLE {{ 21 L }}
Series 1875
3x10-20 1-1303 <$3500
Brown Back
50-100 1-1280 <$3000/$3500
1882 Date Back
50-100 1-900 <$2000/$2500
3x50-100 1-1861<$2000/$2500
1902 Plain Back
3x10-20 1-12244 <$150
THIRD TITLE {{ 50+ S }}
1929 Small Size
10 Type 1 1-7716 <$65
20 Type 1 1-2270 <$75
10 Type 2 1-54 <$100
Total Issue $2,270,660
Out at close $399,995
Large out at close $28,865

13790 Grand Forks
FNB IN GRAND FORKS
{{ 11 S }}
Chartered 9/33
1929 Small Size <$VALUE
10 Type 2 1-4250 <$100
20 Type 2 1-1085 <$100
Total Issue $64,200
Out in 1935 $49,100

2564 Grand Forks
FNB, GRAND FORKS
{{ UNREPORTED }}
Chartered 9/24/81
Liquidated 12/2/84
TERRITORIAL ISSUES
Series 1875 <$VALUE
4x5 1-1455 <$10,000
Total Issue $29,100
Out in 1910 $160

The FNB of Grand Forks
FNB of Grand Forks
SEE Ch 2570
Citizens NB of Grand Forks

3301 Grand Forks
GRAND FORKS NB, GRAND FORKS
{{ UNREPORTED }}
Organized 2/6/85
Receivership 4/28/96
TERRITORIAL ISSUES
Brown Back <$VALUE
3x10-20 1-495 <$8500
STATE ISSUES
Brown Back
3x10-20 496-2126 <$3000
Total Issue $106,300
Out in 1915 $710

4812 Grand Forks
MERCHANTS NB, GRAND FORKS
{{ UNREPORTED }}
Organized 11/1/92
Liquidated 2/6/99
Brown Back <$VALUE
4x5 1-1607 <$3000
Total Issue $32,140
Out in 1910 $290

11142 Grand Forks
NORTHWESTERN NB OF GRAND FORKS
{{ 11 L }}
Chartered 2/18
Closed 6/28/29
1902 Plain Back <$VALUE
3x10-20 1-11424 <$165
Total Issue $571,200
Out in 1928 $100,000
Ch 2570 assumed circulation

3504 Grand Forks
SECOND NB, GRAND FORKS
Organized 5/17/86
Receivership 1/7/97
TERRITORIAL ISSUES {{ 0 L }}
Brown Back <$VALUE
4x5 1-600 <$8500
3x10-20 1-200 <$8500
STATE ISSUES {{ 1 L }}
Brown Back
4x5 601-1188 <$2500
3x10-20 201-411 <$2500
Total Issue $44,310
Out in 1915 $270

4372 Grand Forks
UNION NB OF GRAND FORKS
{{ 2 L }}
Chartered 1890
Liquidated 9/9/12
Brown Back <$VALUE
3x10-20 1-2620 <$2000
1882 Date Back
3x10-20 1-337 <$1250
1902 Date Back
3x10-20 1-2628 <$1250
Total Issue $279,750
Out at close $100,000
Ch 2570 assumed circulation

7650 Ramsey
FNB OF HAMPDEN
{{ 2 L 4 S }}
Organized 10/8/04
Liquidated 8/15/34
1902 Red Seal <$VALUE
3x10-20 1-420 <$2000
1902 Date Back
3x10-20 1-840 <$600
1902 Plain Back
3x10-20 841-1799 <$600
1929 Small Size
10 Type 1 1-246 <$300
20 Type 1 1-50 <$300
Total Issue $131,710
Out at close $10,000
Large out at close $560
Ch 7569 assumed circulation

8084 Richland
CITIZENS NB, HANKINSON
{{ 1 L }}
Organized 1/18/06
Receivership 4/30/24
1902 Red Seal <$VALUE
3x10-20 1-250 <$2000
1902 Date Back
3x10-20 1-1600* <$750
1902 Plain Back
3x10-20 1801-3605* <$750
* 1601-1800 not marked
Total Issue $192,750
Out at close $30,000

6218 Richland
FNB, HANKINSON
{{ 6 L 4 S }}
Organized 3/14/02
Receivership 9/28/31
1902 Red Seal <$VALUE
3x10-20 1-1050 <$1500
1902 Date Back
3x10-20 1-1850 <$275
1902 Plain Back (dated 1902)
3x10-20 1851-3231 <$275
1902 Plain Back (dated 1922)
3x10-20 1-1848 <$275
1929 Small Size
10 Type 1 1-435 <$300
20 Type 1 1-65 <$300
Total Issue $340,350
Out at close $30,000
Large out at close $6,460

7727 Griggs
FNB, HANNAFORD
{{ 2 L }}
Organized 4/1/05
Receivership 12/10/26
1902 Red Seal <$VALUE
3x10-20 1-860 <$2000
1902 Date Back
3x10-20 1-1560 <$600
1902 Plain Back
3x10-20 1561-4007 <$600
Total Issue $243,350
Out at close $24,600

5488 Wells
FNB, HARVEY
{{ 4 L 7 S }}
Chartered 7/8/00
Brown Back <$VALUE
3x10-20 1-1160 <$1500
1882 Date Back
3x10-20 1-1710* <$750
1882 Value Back
3x10-20 1841-2385* <$750
* 1711-1840 not marked
1902 Plain Back
3x10-20 1-2110 <$350
1929 Small Size
10 Type 1 1-588 <$175
20 Type 1 1-166 <$175
5 Type 2 1-37 <$225
10 Type 2 1-12 <$225
20 Type 2 1-20 <$225
Total Issue $338,655
Out in 1935 $25,000
Large out 1935 $2,615

7905 Traill
FARMERS & MERCHANTS NB OF HATTON
{{ 3 L 8 S }}
Chartered 9/05
1902 Red Seal <$VALUE
3x10-20 1-200 <$2000
1902 Date Back
3x10-20 1-1410 <$300
1902 Plain Back
3x10-20 1411-4279 <$300
1929 Small Size
10 Type 1 1-560 <$125
20 Type 1 1-160 <$125
10 Type 2 1-415 <$150
20 Type 2 1-75 <$150
Total Issue $282,400
Out in 1935 $25,000
Large out 1935 $1,450

6743 Traill
FNB OF HATTON
{{ 2 L 0 S }}
Organized 4/1/03
Liquidated 6/18/30
1902 Red Seal <$VALUE
3x10-20 1-600 <$2000
1902 Date Back
3x10-20 1-780 <$600
1902 Plain Back
3x10-20 781-1688 <$600
1929 Small Size
10 Type 1 1-34 <$750
20 Type 1 1-11 <$750
Total Issue $117,760
Out at close $7,895
Large out at close $4,535

10741 Morton
FNB, HEBRON
{{ 4 L 7 S }}
Chartered 5/15
1902 Plain Back <$VALUE
3x10-20 1-1825 <$400
1929 Small Size
10 Type 1 1-564 <$175
20 Type 1 1-158 <$175
10 Type 2 1-358 <$200
20 Type 2 1-71 <$200
Total Issue $149,050
Out in 1935 $25,000
Large out 1935 $1,290

8991 Adams
FNB, HETTINGER
{{ 3 L 5 S }}
Chartered 1/08
1902 Red Seal <$VALUE
3x10-20 1-200 <$1500
1902 Date Back
3x10-20 1-2030 <$400
1902 Plain Back
3x10-20 2031-5065 <$400
1929 Small Size
10 Type 1 1-436 <$250
20 Type 1 1-128 <$250
10 Type 2 1-700 <$275
20 Type 2 1-183 <$275
Total Issue $316,630
Out in 1935 $25,000
Large out 1935 $1,820

11677 Adams
LIVESTOCK NB OF HETTINGER
{{ 1 L }}
Chartered 4/20
Liquidated 3/14/27
1902 Plain Back <$VALUE
3x10-20 1-1536 <$1000
Total Issue $76,800
Out in 1924 $25,000

3400 Traill
FNB OF HILLSBORO
Chartered 1885
TERRITORIAL ISSUES {{ 0 L }}
Brown Back <$VALUE
3x10-20 1-410 <$8500
STATE ISSUES {{ 4 L 10 S }}
Brown Back
3x10-20 411-1330 <$1250
1902 Red Seal
3x10-20 1-250 <$1500
1902 Date Back
3x10-20 1-3600 <$300
1902 Plain Back
3x10-20 3601-9164 <$300
1929 Small Size
10 Type 1 1-778 <$125
20 Type 1 1-262 <$125
10 Type 2 1-377 <$150
20 Type 2 1-42 <$150
Total Issue $619,930
Out in 1935 $25,000
Large out 1935 $6,160
Outstanding includes Ch 3411

3411 Traill
HILLSBORO NB, HILLSBORO
Chartered 1885
Closed 11/2/29
TERRITORIAL ISSUES {{ 1 L }}
Brown Back <$VALUE
4x5 1-1125 <$8500
STATE ISSUES {{ 8 L }}
Brown Back
4x5 1126-3174 <$1250
50-100 1-119 <$3000/$3500
1902 Red Seal
3x10-20 1-850 <$1500
1902 Date Back
3x10-20 1-3300 <$175
1902 Plain Back
3x10-20 3301-9013 <$175
Total Issue $574,480
Out at close $49,100
Ch 3400 assumed circulation

5893 Steele
FNB, HOPE
{{ 10 L }}
Organized 5/17/01
Receivership 12/12/27
Brown Back <$VALUE
3x10-20 1-690 <$1250
1882 Date Back
3x10-20 1-4090 <$650
1882 Value Back
3x10-20 4091-5882 <$650
1902 Plain Back
3x10-20 1-3132 <$200
Total Issue $485,200
Out at close $50,000

8395 Steele
HOPE NB, HOPE
{{ 7 L }}
Organized 7/31/06
Liquidated 4/1/27
1902 Red Seal <$VALUE
3x10-20 1-475 <$1500
1902 Date Back
3x10-20 1-3900 <$250
1902 Plain Back
3x10-20 3901-8695 <$250
Total Issue $458,500
Out at close $50,000

6985 Cass
FNB, HUNTER
{{ 2 L 2 S }}
Chartered 10/03
1902 Red Seal <$VALUE
4x5 1-375 <$2000
3x10-20 1-500 <$2000
1902 Date Back
4x5 1-600 <$600
3x10-20 1-480 <$600
1902 Plain Back
4x5 601-1860 <$600
3x10-20 481-1114 <$600
1929 Small Size
5 Type 1 1-349 <$400
10 Type 1 1-195 <$400
20 Type 1 1-58 <$400
Total Issue $154,530
Out in 1935 $10,000
Large out 1935 $730

7820 Stutsman
CITIZENS NB, JAMESTOWN
{{ 2 L }}
Organized 6/16/05
Liquidated 8/23/29
1902 Red Seal <$VALUE
3x10-20 1-480 <$2000
1902 Date Back
3x10-20 1-2150 <$600
1902 Plain Back
3x10-20 1-4894* <$600
* 3754-3940 not issued
Total Issue $259,350
Out at close $19,550

2578 Stutsman
FNB, JAMESTOWN
{{ UNREPORTED }}
Organized 10/25/81
Receivership 9/13/84
TERRITORIAL ISSUES
Series 1875 <$VALUE
4x5 1-1350 <$10,000
Total Issue $27,000
Out in 1915 $215

2580 Stutsman
JAMES RIVER NB OF JAMESTOWN
Chartered 1881
2nd title: James River NB & TC 11/21/29
FIRST TITLE
TERRITORIAL ISSUES {{ 1 L }}
Series 1875 <$VALUE
3x10-20 1-800 <$10,000
STATE ISSUES {{ 1 L 0 S }}
Series 1875
3x10-20 801-1619 <$3500
Brown Back
3x10-20 1-1350 <$2000
1882 Date Back
3x10-20 1-2340 <$1250
1882 Value Back
3x10-20 2341-2655 <$1250
1902 Plain Back
3x10-20 1-1852 <$600
1929 Small Size
10 Type 1 1-314 <$300
20 Type 1 1-106 <$300
SECOND TITLE {{ 5 S }}
1929 Small Size
10 Type 2 1-6229 <$200
20 Type 2 1-1638 <$200
Total Issue $500,410
Out in 1935 $50,000
Large out 1935 $1,850

3331 Stutsman
JAMESTOWN NB, JAMESTOWN
{{ UNREPORTED }}
Chartered 4/10/85
Liquidated 11/29/86
TERRITORIAL ISSUES
Brown Back <$VALUE
3x10-20 1-239 <$10,000
Total Issue $11,950
Out in 1910 $10

4561 Stutsman
LLOYDS NB, JAMESTOWN
{{ UNREPORTED }}
Organized 5/4/91
Receivership 9/14/93
Brown Back <$VALUE
3x10-20 1-587 <$3000
Total Issue $29,350
Out in 1915 $280

F-Kenmare NB, Kenmare
SEE Ch 6555
Kenmare NB, Kenmare

6064 Ward
FNB OF KENMARE
{{ 3 L 0 S }}
Chartered 12/01
Liquidated 1/19/31
Brown Back <$VALUE
3x10-20 1-400 <$1500
1882 Date Back
3x10-20 1-660 <$1000
1882 Value Back
3x10-20 661-740 <$1000
1902 Plain Back
3x10-20 1-474 <$500
1929 Small Size
10 Type 1 1-90 <$750
20 Type 1 1-8 <$750
Total Issue $87,060
Out at close $6,500
Large out at close $1,220

CONDITION affects Value. The Values shown are for notes in FINE condition.

6555 Ward
KENMARE NB, KENMARE
Organized 12/12/02
Receivership 12/8/33
2nd title:F-Kenmare NB 6/9/31
FIRST TITLE {{1 L 3 S}}
1902 Red Seal <$VALUE
3x10-20 1-840 <$2000
1902 Date Back
3x10-20 1-1170 <$750
1902 Plain Back
3x10-20 1171-3078 <$750
1929 Small Size
10 Type 1 1-296 <$350
20 Type 1 1-102 <$350
SECOND TITLE {{0 S}}
1929 Small Size
10 Type 2 1-24 <$500
Total Issue $226,140
Out at close $16,250
Large out at close $1,560

7943 Stutsman
FNB OF KENSAL
{{ UNREPORTED }}
Chartered 10/05
Liquidated 3/25/12
1902 Red Seal <$VALUE
3x10-20 1-300 <$2500
1902 Date Back
3x10-20 1-148 <$1000
Total Issue $22,400
Out in 1912 $4,430

6898 Benson
FNB, KNOX
{{1 L}}
Chartered 7/27/03
Liquidated 12/31/06
1902 Red Seal <$VALUE
3x10-20 1-251 <$2500
Total Issue $12,550
Out in 1910 $870

8029 Bottineau
FNB OF KRAMER
{{3 L 4 S}}
Chartered 1/06
1902 Red Seal <$VALUE
3x10-20 1-300 <$1500
1902 Date Back
3x10-20 1-560 <$600
1902 Plain Back
3x10-20 561-1143 <$600
1929 Small Size
10 Type 1 1-173 <$350
20 Type 1 1-32 <$350
Total Issue $86,370
Out in 1935 $6,500
Large out 1935 $450

11069 La Moure
FNB OF KULM
{{3 L 1 S}}
Chartered 8/17
Liquidated 10/17/31
1902 Plain Back <$VALUE
4x10 1-2069 <$500
1929 Small Size
10 Type 1 1-290 <$600
Total Issue $100,160
Out at close $15,000
Large out at close $3,370

9714 La Moure
FARMERS NB, La MOURE
{{4 L}}
Organized 3/1/10
Receivership 2/25/26
1902 Date Back <$VALUE
3x10-20 1-3340 <$350
1902 Plain Back
3x10-20 3341-7735 <$350
Total Issue $386,750
Out at close $48,700

6690 La Moure
FNB OF La MOURE
{{6 L 5 S}}
Chartered 3/03
Liquidated 8/1/31
1902 Red Seal <$VALUE
4x5 1-750 <$1500
3x10-20 1-775 <$1500
1902 Date Back
4x5 1-1475* <$275
3x10-20 1-1080** <$275
1902 Plain Back
4x5 1626-7527* <$275
3x10-20 1161-4791** <$275
* 1476-1625 not marked
** 1081-1160 not marked
1929 Small Size
5 Type 1 1-756 <$225
10 Type 1 1-351 <$225
20 Type 1 1-82 <$225
Total Issue $497,420
Out at close $50,000
Large out at close $9,725

4143 Nelson
FNB, LAKOTA
{{ UNREPORTED }}
Organized 10/23/89
Receivership 6/13/93
TERRITORIAL ISSUES
Brown Back <$VALUE
3x10-20 1-250 <$8500
STATE ISSUES
Brown Back
3x10-20 251-335 <$3500
Total Issue $16,750
Out in 1915 $90

5455 Nelson
NB OF LAKOTA
{{1 L 2 S}}
Chartered 6/26/00
Brown Back <$VALUE
3x10-20 1-1600 <$2000
1882 Date Back
3x10-20 1-1650 <$1250
1882 Value Back
3x10-20 1651-2354 <$1250
1902 Plain Back
3x10-20 1-2157 <$600
1929 Small Size
10 Type 1 1-488 <$300
20 Type 1 1-164 <$300
10 Type 2 1-585 <$350
20 Type 2 1-74 <$350
Total Issue $361,840
Out in 1935 $25,000
Large out 1935 $1,690

9075 Cavalier
CAVALIER COUNTY NB, LANGDON
{{2 L}}
Organized 1/28/08
Receivership 10/29/23
1902 Red Seal <$VALUE
4x5 1-150 <$2000
3x10-20 1-140 <$2000
1902 Date Back
4x5 1-1250 <$600
3x10-20 1-860 <$600
1902 Plain Back
4x5 1251-3135 <$600
3x10-20 861-1986 <$600
Total Issue $172,000
Out at close $22,900

4802 Cavalier
FNB, LANGDON
{{4 L}}
Organized 9/28/92
Liquidated 7/5/27
Brown Back <$VALUE
3x10-20 1-2150 <$1500
1882 Date Back
3x10-20 1-711 <$850
1902 Date Back
4x10 1-1250 <$300
1902 Plain Back
4x10 1251-4459 <$300
Total Issue $321,410
Out at close $25,000

8187 Bottineau
FNB, LANSFORD
{{ UNREPORTED }}
Organized 3/16/06
Receivership 12/17/23
1902 Red Seal <$VALUE
3x10-20 1-287 <$2500
1902 Date Back
3x10-20 1-560 <$1000
1902 Plain Back
3x10-20 561-853 <$1000
Total Issue $57,000
Out at close $6,500

2854 Grand Forks
FNB, LARIMORE
{{ UNREPORTED }}
Organized 1/9/83
Receivership 2/26/98
TERRITORIAL ISSUES
Brown Back <$VALUE
4x5 1-2250 <$8500
STATE ISSUES
Brown Back
4x5 2251-2973 <$2500
Total Issue $59,460
Out in 1916 $485

6286 Grand Forks
NB OF LARIMORE
{{4 L}}
Organized 5/26/02
Receivership 3/5/29
1902 Red Seal <$VALUE
3x10-20 1-850 <$1500
1902 Date Back
3x10-20 1-1360 <$400
1902 Plain Back
3x10-20 1361-3590 <$400
Total Issue $222,000
Out at close $21,500

6312 Benson
FNB, LEEDS
{{4 L}}
Organized 6/9/02
Receivership 12/1/26
1902 Red Seal <$VALUE
3x10-20 1-1040 <$1500
1902 Date Back
3x10-20 1-1790 <$400
1902 Plain Back
3x10-20 1791-4268 <$400
Total Issue $265,400
Out at close $24,700

Farmers NB of Lidgerwood
SEE Ch 8230
Lidgerwood NB, Lidgerwood

5772 Richland
FNB, LIDGERWOOD
{{7 L}}
Organized 3/29/01
Receivership 6/17/24
Brown Back <$VALUE
3x10-20 1-850 <$1250
1882 Date Back
3x10-20 1-3140* <$600
1882 Value Back
3x10-20 3381-4721* <$600
* 3141-3380 not marked
1902 Plain Back
4x5 1-1185 <$225
3x10-20 1-1102 <$225
Total Issue $357,350
Out at close $49,300

12776 Richland
FNB, LIDGERWOOD
{{1 L 9 S}}
Chartered 6/25
1902 Plain Back <$VALUE
3x10-20 1-1070 <$1000
1929 Small Size
10 Type 1 1-486 <$150
20 Type 1 1-150 <$150
10 Type 2 1-297 <$175
20 Type 2 1-130 <$175
Total Issue $106,230
Out in 1935 $25,000
Large out 1935 $950

8230 Richland
LIDGERWOOD NB, LIDGERWOOD
Organized 3/30/06
Receivership 2/1/27
2nd title: Farmers NB of Lidgerwood 2/6/13
FIRST TITLE {{1 L}}
1902 Red Seal <$VALUE
3x10-20 1-400 <$2000
1902 Date Back
3x10-20 1-562 <$750
SECOND TITLE {{3 L}}
1902 Date Back
3x10-20 1-800 <$400
1902 Plain Back
3x10-20 801-1731 <$400
Total Issue $134,650
Out in 1924 $20,000

9590 Emmons
FNB, LINTON
{{1 L 4 S}}
Chartered 11/09
1902 Date Back <$VALUE
3x10-20 1-660 <$750
1902 Plain Back
3x10-20 1-1162 <$750
1929 Small Size
10 Type 1 1-409 <$300
20 Type 1 1-135 <$300
Total Issue $98,840
Out in 1935 $25,000
Large out 1935 $580

3669 Ransom
FNB, LISBON
Organized 3/30/87
Receivership 1/21/28
TERRITORIAL ISSUES {{0 L}}
Brown Back <$VALUE
3x10-20 1-360 <$8500
STATE ISSUES {{4 L}}
Brown Back
3x10-20 361-2279 <$1500
1902 Red Seal
50-100 1-160 <$5000
1902 Date Back
4x5 1-2930 <$350
50-100 1-500 <$850/$1000
3x50-100 1-647 <$850/$1000
1902 Plain Back
4x5 2931-6330 <$350
Total Issue $501,300
Out at close $49,500

8298 Barnes
FNB, LITCHVILLE
{{11 L 2 S}}
Organized 6/9/06
Receivership 6/30/30
1902 Red Seal <$VALUE
3x10-20 1-687 <$1500
1902 Date Back
3x10-20 1-1680 <$175
1902 Plain Back
3x10-20 1681-4380 <$175
1929 Small Size
10 Type 1 1-205 <$400
20 Type 1 1-23 <$400
Total Issue $268,410
Out at close $25,000
Large out at close $10,140

8226 Benson
FNB, MADDOCK
{{ UNREPORTED }}
Chartered 5/06
Liquidated 10/4/10
1902 Red Seal <$VALUE
4x5 1-175 <$2500
3x10-20 1-230 <$2500
1902 Date Back
4x5 1-165 <$1000
3x10-20 1-137 <$1000
Total Issue $25,150
Out at close $25,000

11184 Ward
FNB OF MAKOTI
{{2 L 2 S}}
Chartered 5/18
Liquidated 1/14/35
1902 Plain Back <$VALUE
4x5 1-8089 <$600
1929 Small Size
5 Type 1 1-2136 <$350
5 Type 2 1-1868 <$350
Total Issue $235,200
Out in 1935 $20,000
Large out 1935 $865

2585 Morton
FNB, MANDAN
Chartered 1881
TERRITORIAL ISSUES {{0 L}}
Series 1875 <$VALUE
4x5 1-2800 <$10,000
STATE ISSUES {{7 L 6 S}}
Series 1875
4x5 2801-5322 <$2000
3x10-20 1-139 <$2500
Brown Back
3x10-20 1-695 <$1250
1882 Date Back
3x10-20 1-1180 <$650
1882 Value Back
3x10-20 1181-2091 <$650
1902 Plain Back
4x10 1-2282 <$250
1929 Small Size
10 Type 1 1-1018 <$150
10 Type 2 1-866 <$150
Total Issue $413,710
Out in 1935 $25,000
Large out 1935 $1,700

10604 Morton
MERCHANTS NB, MANDAN
{{3 L}}
Organized 8/24/14
Receivership 12/26/23
1902 Plain Back <$VALUE
4x5 1-1915 <$400
3x10-20 1-1388 <$400
Total Issue $107,700
Out at close $25,000

9161 La Moure
FNB, MARION
{{1 L}}
Organized 4/30/08
Receivership 3/19/26
1902 Date Back <$VALUE
3x10-20 1-1210 <$750
1902 Plain Back
3x10-20 1211-2088 <$750
Total Issue $104,400
Out at close $12,000

9082 Slope
FNB, MARMARTH
{{5 L 9 S}}
Organized 3/24/08
Receivership 12/8/33
1902 Red Seal <$VALUE
3x10-20 1-200 <$1250
1902 Date Back
3x10-20 1-1990 <$300
1902 Plain Back
3x10-20 1991-4837 <$300
1929 Small Size
10 Type 1 1-519 <$150
20 Type 1 1-148 <$150
Total Issue $300,750
Out at close $25,000
Large out at close $1,720

3673 Traill
FNB, MAYVILLE
{{ UNREPORTED }}
Organized 4/4/87
Receivership 6/25/29
TERRITORIAL ISSUES
Brown Back <$VALUE
4x5 1-900 <$8500
STATE ISSUES
Brown Back
4x5 901-3145 <$2500
3x10-20 1-403 <$2500
1902 Red Seal
3x10-20 1-250 <$2500
1902 Date Back
3x10-20 1-1800* <$1000
* 1757,1758,1775,1776, 1782,1787 not issued
1902 Plain Back
3x10-20 1801-1819 <$1000
Total Issue $186,200
Out at close $4,205

8881 Sheridan
FNB, McCLUSKY
{{1 L 2 S}}
Chartered 9/07
1902 Red Seal <$VALUE
4x10 1-320 <$2000
1902 Date Back
4x10 1-750 <$750
1902 Plain Back
4x10 751-1495 <$750
1929 Small Size
10 Type 1 1-246 <$400
10 Type 2 1-264 <$400
Total Issue $90,000
Out in 1935 $7,000
Large out 1935 $390

7846 Rolette
FNB, McCUMBER
{{ UNREPORTED }}
Chartered 7/26/05
Liquidated 5/10/06
1902 Red Seal <$VALUE
3x10-20 1-136 <$2500
Total Issue $6,800
Out in 1910 $470

8124 Foster
FNB, McHENRY
{{2 L}}
Organized 2/1/06
Receivership 7/3/29
1902 Red Seal <$VALUE
4x5 1-200 <$1500
3x10-20 1-180 <$1500
1902 Date Back
4x5 1-1300 <$600
3x10-20 1-1020 <$600
1902 Plain Back
4x5 1301-4275 <$600
3x10-20 1021-2778 <$600
Total Issue $237,400
Out at close $7,150

10721 Nelson
FNB OF McVILLE
{{4 L 1 S}}
Chartered 4/15
Liquidated 5/12/30
1902 Plain Back <$VALUE
4x5 1-3705 <$350
3x10-20 1-2376 <$350
1929 Small Size
5 Type 1 1-259 <$600
10 Type 1 1-124 <$600
20 Type 1 1-12 <$600
Total Issue $209,550
Out at close $25,000
Large out at close $8,590

8280 Sargent
FNB, MILNOR
{{0 L 10 S}}
Chartered 6/06
1902 Red Seal <$VALUE
3x10-20 1-200 <$2500
1902 Date Back
3x10-20 1-600 <$1000
1902 Plain Back
3x10-20 601-1016 <$1000
1929 Small Size
10 Type 1 1-148 <$125
20 Type 1 1-32 <$125
Total Issue $73,520
Large out 1935 $680

8264 Sargent
MILNOR NB, MILNOR
{{2 L}}
Organized 6/4/06
Liquidated 12/15/28
1902 Red Seal <$VALUE
3x10-20 1-300 <$2000
1902 Date Back
3x10-20 1-770* <$600
1902 Plain Back
3x10-20 871-1545* <$600
* 771-870 not marked
Total Issue $92,250
Out at close $10,000

6518 Cavalier
FNB, MILTON
{{3 L}}
Organized 10/25/02
Receivership 8/11/32
1902 Red Seal <$VALUE
3x10-20 1-420 <$1500
1902 Date Back
3x10-20 1-510 <$500
1902 Plain Back
3x10-20 511-813 <$500
Total Issue $61,650
Out in 1932 $540

5500 Benson
FNB, MINNEWAUKAN
{{2 L}}
Organized 7/9/00
Receivership 1/6/28
Brown Back <$VALUE
3x10-20 1-670 <$2000
1882 Date Back
3x10-20 1-1910 <$1250
1882 Value Back
3x10-20 1911-2705 <$1250
1902 Plain Back
3x10-20 1-1837 <$600
Total Issue $260,600
Out at close $24,745

4009 Ward
FNB, MINOT
{{ UNREPORTED }}
Organized 4/13/89
Receivership 4/12/96
TERRITORIAL ISSUES
Brown Back <$VALUE
3x10-20 1-100 <$8500
50-100 1-50 <$12,500
STATE ISSUES
Brown Back
3x10-20 101-398 <$3000
50-100 51-72 <$5000
Total Issue $30,700
Out in 1915 $145

FNB in Minot
FNB & TC in Minot
SEE Ch 6429
Second NB of Minot

****
6315 Ward
MINOT NB, MINOT
{{ UNREPORTED }}
Organized 6/23/02
Receivership 9/19/05
1902 Red Seal <$VALUE
3x10-20 1-452 <$2500
Total Issue $22,600
Out in 1915 $240
****
6429 Ward
SECOND NB OF MINOT
Chartered 9/02
2nd title:FNB in Minot 7/20/26
3rd title:FNB & TC in Minot 1/29/30
4th title:FNB in Minot 12/5/33
FIRST TITLE {{ 5 L }}
1902 Red Seal <$VALUE
3x10-20 1-740 <$1500
1902 Date Back
3x10-20 1-3700 <$200
50-100 1-450 <$850/$1000
1902 Plain Back
3x10-20 3701-10654 <$200
SECOND TITLE {{ 1 L 2 S }}
1902 Plain Back
3x10-20 1-1498 <$250
1929 Small Size
10 Type 1 1-622 <$100
20 Type 1 1-210 <$100
THIRD TITLE {{ 19 S }}
1929 Small Size
10 Type 1 1-922 <$75
20 Type 1 1-236 <$75
10 Type 2 1-1248 <$100
20 Type 2 1-504 <$100
FOURTH TITLE {{ 0 S }}
1929 Small Size
10 Type 2 1-260 <$150
20 Type 2 1-20 <$150
Total Issue $883,820
Out in 1935 $74,500
Large out 1935 $5,130
****
7689 Ward
UNION NB OF MINOT
{{ 9 L 2 S }}
Chartered 4/05
Liquidated 4/17/30
1902 Red Seal <$VALUE
3x10-20 1-870 <$1500
1902 Date Back
3x10-20 1-2300 <$175
1902 Plain Back
3x10-20 2301-11491 <$175
1929 Small Size
10 Type 1 1-606 <$300
20 Type 1 1-63 <$300
Total Issue $661,970
Out at close $89,770
Large out at close $45,850
****
7008 Renville
FNB, MOHALL
{{ 4 L }}
Organized 8/17/03
Receivership 1/22/25
1902 Red Seal <$VALUE
3x10-20 1-1322 <$1500
1902 Date Back
3x10-20 1-1550 <$350
1902 Plain Back
3x10-20 1551-3438 <$350
Total Issue $238,000
Out at close $24,700
****
9489 Hettinger
FNB, MOTT
{{ 2 L U + 20 S }}
Organized 6/26/09
Receivership 4/23/34
1902 Date Back <$VALUE
3x10-20 1-700 <$600
1902 Plain Back
3x10-20 701-2587 <$600
1929 Small Size
10 Type 1 1-1070 <$75
20 Type 1 1-326 <$80
10 Type 2 1-419 <$100
20 Type 2 1-90 <$100
Total Issue $238,660
Out at close $49,960
Large out at close $780
****
7569 Cavalier
FNB OF MUNICH
{{ 1 L 6 S }}
Organized 12/1/04
1902 Red Seal <$VALUE
3x10-20 1-300 <$2500
1902 Date Back
3x10-20 1-720 <$1000
1902 Plain Back
3x10-20 721-1174 <$1000
1929 Small Size
10 Type 1 1-280 <$225
20 Type 1 1-95 <$250
Total Issue $101,900
Out in 1935 $25,000
Large out 1935 $870
****
7857 Rolette
FNB, MYLO
{{ 2 L }}
Chartered 8/4/05
Liquidated 3/26/08
1902 Red Seal <$VALUE
3x10-20 1-209 <$2000
Total Issue $10,450
Out in 1910 $1,420
****
11378 Logan
FNB, NAPOLEON
{{ 6 S }}
Chartered 6/19
1929 Small Size <$VALUE
5 Type 1 1-516 <$225
10 Type 1 1-318 <$225
20 Type 1 1-106 <$225
5 Type 2 1-528 <$250
10 Type 2 1-245 <$250
20 Type 2 1-85 <$250
Total Issue $54,070
Out in 1935 $25,000
****
11110 Pembina
FNB OF NECHE
{{ 1 L 2 S }}
Chartered 12/17
Liquidated 1/29/30
1902 Plain Back <$VALUE
4x10 1-3841 <$750
1929 Small Size
10 Type 1 1-205 <$400
Total Issue $165,940
Out at close $22,150
Large out at close $9,850
****
9776 Hettinger
FNB OF NEW ENGLAND
{{ 4 L U + 8 S }}
Chartered 6/10
Liquidated 10/1/34
1902 Date Back <$VALUE
4x5 1-900 <$400
3x10-20 1-920 <$400
1902 Plain Back
4x5 901 3613 <$400
3x10-20 921-2620 <$400
1929 Small Size
5 Type 1 1-538 <$175
10 Type 1 1-276 <$175
20 Type 1 1-96 <$175
5 Type 2 1-500 <$200
10 Type 2 1-275 <$200
20 Type 2 1-69 <$200
Total Issue $254,110
Out at close $20,000
Large out at close $1,380
****
6393 Eddy
FNB, NEW ROCKFORD
{{ 6 L 8 S }}
Chartered 8/02
1902 Red Seal <$VALUE
3x10-20 1-620 <$1500
1902 Date Back
3x10-20 1-820 <$300
1902 Plain Back
3x10-20 821-3603 <$300
1929 Small Size
10 Type 1 1-586 <$175
20 Type 1 1-134 <$175
10 Type 2 1-602 <$200
20 Type 2 1-115 <$200
Total Issue $270,710
Out in 1935 $25,000
Large out 1935 $1,110
****
6428 Morton
FNB OF NEW SALEM
{{ 1 L }}
Chartered 9/02
Liquidated 6/11/19
1902 Red Seal <$VALUE
3x10-20 1-540 <$2500
1902 Date Back
3x10-20 1-1580 <$1000
1902 Plain Back
3x10-20 1581-1821 <$1000
Total Issue $118,050
Out in 1918 $20,000
****

****
9287 Barnes
FNB OF NOME
{{ UNREPORTED }}
Chartered 12/08
Liquidated 4/15/12
1902 Date Back <$VALUE
3x10-20 1-857 <$1250
Total Issue $42,850
Out in 1912 $12,600
****
9754 Grand Forks
CITIZENS NB OF NORTHWOOD
{{ 2 L 6 S }}
Chartered 5/10
Liquidated 5/29/31
1902 Date Back <$VALUE
4x5 1-800 <$600
3x10-20 1-640 <$600
1902 Plain Back
4x5 801-3930 <$600
3x10-20 641-2454 <$600
1929 Small Size
5 Type 1 1-362 <$200
10 Type 1 1-187 <$200
20 Type 1 1-48 <$225
Total Issue $229,140
Out at close $25,000
Large out at close $4,970
****
5980 Grand Forks
FNB, NORTHWOOD
{{ 3 L 2 S }}
Organized 8/28/01
Receivership 2/5/30
Brown Back <$VALUE
4x5 1-350 <$1500
3x10-20 1-280 <$1500
1882 Date Back
4x5 1-1625 <$850
3x10-20 1-1180 <$850
1882 Value Back
4x5 1626-2625 <$850
3x10-20 1181-1876 <$850
1902 Plain Back
3x10-20 1-1661 <$500
1929 Small Size
10 Type 1 1-86 <$400
20 Type 1 1-25 <$400
Total Issue $258,570
Out at close $24, 460
Large out at close $16,240
****
6457 Dickey
FNB, OAKES
{{ 3 L 18 S }}
Chartered 10/02
1902 Red Seal <$VALUE
3x10-20 1-1156 <$1500
1902 Date Back
3x10-20 1-1760 <$400
1902 Plain Back
3x10-20 1761-6468 <$400
1929 Small Size
10 Type 1 1-1124 <$100
20 Type 1 1-292 <$100
10 Type 2 1-583 <$125
20 Type 2 1-175 <$125
Total Issue $493,010
Out in 1935 $50,000
Large out 1935 $3,000
****
6988 Dickey
OAKES NB, OAKES
{{ 6 L }}
Organized 3/24/03
Receivership 9/4/26
1902 Red Seal <$VALUE
3x10-20 1-1150 <$1500
1902 Date Back
3x10-20 1-1770* <$300
1902 Plain Back
3x10-20 1901-4082* <$300
* 1771-1900 not marked
Total Issue $261,600
Out at close $24,500
****
6475 Bottineau
FNB, OMEMEE
{{ UNREPORTED }}
Chartered 10/02
Liquidated 11/20/29
1902 Red Seal <$VALUE
3x10-20 1-500 <$2500
1902 Date Back
3x10-20 1-580 <$1000
1902 Plain Back
3x10-20 581-1147 <$1000
1929 Small Size
10 Type 1 1-5 <$1000
Total Issue $82,650
Out at close $6,820
Large out at close $6,520
****

****
7234 Cavalier
FNB, OSNABROCK
{{ 8 L 3 S }}
Organized 4/7/04
Receivership 1/18/32
1902 Red Seal <$VALUE
3x10-20 1-356 <$1500
1902 Date Back
3x10-20 1-1610 <$200
1902 Plain Back
3x10-20 1611-4171 <$200
1929 Small Size
10 Type 1 1-311 <$350
20 Type 1 1-94 <$350
Total Issue $256,290
Out at close $24,815
Large out at close $4,075
****
8096 Bottineau
FNB OF OVERLY
{{ UNREPORTED }}
Chartered 2/06
Liquidated 12/4/11
1902 Red Seal <$VALUE
3x10-20 1-290 <$2500
1902 Date Back
3x10-20 1-45 <$1250
Total Issue $16,750
Out in 1912 $3,150
****
6463 Cass
FNB OF PAGE
{{ 3 L 7 S }}
Chartered 10/02
Liquidated 7/1/32
1902 Red Seal <$VALUE
3x10-20 1-862 <$1500
1902 Date Back
3x10-20 1-1850 <$500
1902 Plain Back
3x10-20 1851-4837 <$500
1929 Small Size
10 Type 1 1-313 <$175
20 Type 1 1-81 <$200
Total Issue $313,450
Out at close $24,580
Large out at close $3,430
****
3436 Walsh
FNB, PARK RIVER
Chartered 1886
TERRITORIAL ISSUES {{ 0 L }}
Brown Back <$VALUE
3x10-20 1-410 <$8500
STATE ISSUES {{ 5 L 4 S }}
Brown Back
3x10-20 411-1357 <$1250
1902 Red Seal
3x10-20 1-250 <$1750
1902 Date Back
3x10-20 1-1020 <$350
1902 Plain Back
3x10-20 1021-2986 <$350
1929 Small Size
10 Type 1 1-414 <$275
20 Type 1 1-140 <$275
10 Type 2 1-572 <$300
20 Type 2 1-142 <$300
Total Issue $279,850
Out in 1935 $25,000
Large out 1935 $1,680
****
11226 Mountrail
FNB, PARSHALL
{{ 1 L 2 S }}
Organized 7/25/18
Receivership 8/8/31
1902 Plain Back <$VALUE
4x5 1-4322 <$1000
1929 Small Size
5 Type 1 1-562 <$400
Total Issue $103,300
Out at close $10,000
Large out at close $930
****
3438 Pembina
FNB, PEMBINA
{{ UNREPORTED }}
Organized 1/20/86
Receivership 1/19/98
TERRITORIAL ISSUES
Brown Back <$VALUE
3x10-20 1-335 <$8500
STATE ISSUES
Brown Back
4x5 1-275 <$3000
3x10-20 336-778 <$3000
Total Issue $44,400
Out in 1915 $240
****

****
11185 Nelson
FNB OF PETERSBURG
{{ 5 L 2 S }}
Chartered 5/18
Liquidated 12/20/30
1902 Plain Back <$VALUE
4x10 1-4243 <$350
1929 Small Size
10 Type 1 1-404 <$400
Total Issue $193,960
Out at close $25,000
Large out at close $4,650
****
9689 Mountrail
FNB, PLAZA
{{ 2 L 5 S }}
Organized 2/11/10
Receivership 8/8/31
1902 Date Back <$VALUE
3x10-20 1-1560 <$600
1902 Plain Back
3x10-20 1561-3852 <$600
1929 Small Size
10 Type 1 1-293 <$275
20 Type 1 1-57 <$275
Total Issue $217,020
Out at close $20,000
Large out at close $3,050
****
13594 Traill
F & FARMERS NB OF PORTLAND
{{ 3 S }}
Organized 1/19/32
1929 Small Size <$VALUE
5 Type 1 1-686 <$350
5 Type 2 1-5028 <$350
Total Issue $45,720
Out in 1935 $25,000
Large out 1935 $500
Outstanding includes Ch 7693
****
7693 Traill
FNB OF PORTLAND
{{ 0 L 1 S }}
Chartered 4/05
Liquidated 4/12/32
1902 Red Seal <$VALUE
3x10-20 1-256 <$2500
1902 Date Back
3x10-20 1-500* <$1250
1902 Plain Back
3x10-20 601-1063* <$1250
* 501-600 not marked
1929 Small Size
10 Type 1 1-113 <$600
20 Type 1 1-13 <$600
Total Issue $74,290
Out at close $6,250
Large out 1935 $500
****
9684 Adams
FNB OF REEDER
{{ 6 L 0 S }}
Chartered 3/10
Liquidated 2/11/30
1902 Date Back <$VALUE
4x5 1-1100 <$300
3x10-20 1-1360 <$300
1902 Plain Back
4x5 1101-4840 <$300
3x10-20 1361-3564 <$300
1929 Small Size
5 Type 1 1-131 <$750
10 Type 1 1-22 <$750
20 Type 1 1-15 <$750
Total Issue $282,050
Out at close $25,000
Large out at close $12,850
****
10496 Grand Forks
FNB OF REYNOLDS
{{ 4 L 5 S }}
Chartered 3/14
Liquidated 3/5/32
1902 Plain Back <$VALUE
3x10-20 1-3137 <$400
1929 Small Size
10 Type 1 1-314 <$250
20 Type 1 1-108 <$250
Total Issue $188,650
Out at close $25,000
Large out at close $4,340
****
8019 Towner
FNB, ROCK LAKE
{{ 3 L 3 S }}
Organized 11/23/05
Receivership 12/8/33
1902 Red Seal <$VALUE
3x10-20 1-295 <$2000
1902 Date Back
3x10-20 1-860 <$500
1902 Plain Back
3x10-20 861-3936 <$500
1929 Small Size
10 Type 1 1-504 <$400
20 Type 1 1-135 <$400
Total Issue $275,990
Out at close $25,000
Large out at close $2,230
****
7866 Rolette
FNB, ROLETTE
{{ 1 L }}
Organized 7/24/05
Receivership 2/19/27
1902 Red Seal <$VALUE
3x10-20 1-520 <$2000
1902 Date Back
3x10-20 1-960 <$750
1902 Plain Back
3x10-20 961-2005 <$750
Total Issue $126,250
Out at close $12,500
****
6157 Rolette
FNB OF ROLLA
{{ 2 L 5 S }}
Chartered 3/02
Liquidated 4/23/35
1902 Red Seal <$VALUE
3x10-20 1-700 <$2000
1902 Date Back
3x10-20 1-1800 <$600
1902 Plain Back (dated 1902)
3x10-20 1801-3061 <$600
1902 Plain Back (dated 1922)
3x10-20 1-1683 <$600
1929 Small Size
10 Type 1 1-542 <$250
20 Type 1 1-136 <$250
10 Type 2 1-718 <$275
20 Type 2 1-88 <$275
Total Issue $329,980
Out in 1935 $25,000
Large out 1935 $1,220
****
6341 Pierce
FNB, RUGBY
{{ 1 L }}
Organized 7/7/02
Receivership 1/4/09
1902 Red Seal <$VALUE
4x5 1-310 <$2500
3x10-20 1-253 <$2500
Total Issue $18,850
Out in 1915 $325
****
9214 Ward
FNB, RYDER
{{ 5 L 6 S }}
Organized 4/22/08
Receivership 8/8/31
1902 Date Back <$VALUE
3x10-20 1-2080 <$350
1902 Plain Back
3x10-20 2081-5154 <$350
1929 Small Size
10 Type 1 1-308 <$200
20 Type 1 1-84 <$200
Total Issue $286,260
Out at close $25,000
Large out at close $3,890
****
4550 Pembina
FNB, SAINT THOMAS
{{ 4 L 3 S }}
Organized 3/7/91
Receivership 11/6/31
Brown Back <$VALUE
3x10-20 1-1550 <$1500
1882 Date Back
3x10-20 1-473 <$1000
1902 Date Back
3x10-20 1-1330 <$350
1902 Plain Back
3x10-20 1331-4178 <$350
1929 Small Size
10 Type 1 1-328 <$350
20 Type 1 1-81 <$350
Total Issue $339,450
Out at close $25,000
Large out at close $4,720
****
8448 Barnes
FNB, SANBORN
{{ 8 L }}
Organized 10/12/06
Receivership 4/10/29
1902 Red Seal <$VALUE
3x10-20 1-320 <$1500
1902 Date Back
3x10-20 1-1790 <$250
1902 Plain Back
3x10-20 1791-4835 <$250
Total Issue $257,750
Out at close $25,000
****

10405 Bowman
FNB OF SCRANTON
{{1L 1S}}
Chartered 6/13
Liquidated 4/24/31
1902 Date Back <$VALUE
4x5 1-500 <$850
3x10-20 1-400 <$850
1902 Plain Back
4x5 501-1675 <$850
3x10-20 401-1099 <$850
1929 Small Size
5 Type 1 1-193 <$500
10 Type 1 1-64 <$500
20 Type 1 1-18 <$500
Total Issue $100,240
Out at close $10,000
Large out at close $1,370

9005 Steele
FNB, SHARON
{{7L 8S}}
Chartered 1/08
1902 Red Seal <$VALUE
3x10-20 1-500 <$1500
1902 Date Back
3x10-20 1-1380 <$275
1902 Plain Back
3x10-20 1381-4339 <$275
1929 Small Size
10 Type 1 1-574 <$150
20 Type 1 1-158 <$150
5 Type 2 1-71 <$200
10 Type 2 1-111 <$200
20 Type 2 1-20 <$225
Total Issue $297,215
Out in 1935 $25,000
Large out 1935 $1,795

6977 Ransom
FNB OF SHELDON
{{4L}}
Chartered 10/03
Liquidated 8/31/23
1902 Red Seal <$VALUE
4x5 1-600 <$1500
3x10-20 1-634 <$1500
50-100 1-47 <$5000
1902 Date Back
4x5 1-1500 <$400
3x10-20 1-1130 <$400
1902 Plain Back
4x5 1501-3370 <$400
3x10-20 1131-2258 <$400
Total Issue $231,050
Out at close $24,995

8886 Eddy
FNB, SHEYENNE
{{7L}}
Organized 8/28/07
Receivership 9/8/25
1902 Red Seal <$VALUE
4x5 1-225 <$1500
3x10-20 1-210 <$1500
1902 Date Back
4x5 1-1725 <$250
3x10-20 1-1290 <$250
1902 Plain Back
4x5 1726-4260 <$250
3x10-20 1291-2712 <$250
Total Issue $235,800
Out at close $24,500

9472 Mountrail
FNB, STANLEY
{{1L}}
Organized 6/15/09
Receivership 12/15/26
1902 Date Back <$VALUE
3x10-20 1-700 <$1000
1902 Plain Back
3x10-20 701-1043 <$1000
Total Issue $52,150
Out at close $6,250

6397 Ramsey
FNB, STARKWEATHER
{{2L 2S}}
Organized 5/19/02
Receivership 12/17/31
1902 Red Seal <$VALUE
3x10-20 1-400 <$2000
1902 Date Back
3x10-20 1-660 <$600
1902 Plain Back
3x10-20 661-1205 <$600
1929 Small Size
10 Type 1 1-114 <$400
20 Type 1 1-12 <$425
Total Issue $88,530
Out at close $6,500
Large out at close $790

8997 Kidder
FNB OF STEELE
{{2L 5S}}
Organized 1/7/08
Liquidated 12/28/32
1902 Red Seal <$VALUE
3x10-20 1-300 <$2000
1902 Date Back
3x10-20 1-1900 <$600
1902 Plain Back
3x10-20 1901-4770* <$600
*3972-4227 not issued
1929 Small Size
10 Type 1 1-409 <$250
20 Type 1 1-136 <$250
Total Issue $281,560
Out at close $25,000
Large out at close $2,630

10724 Stutsman
FNB, STREETER
{{1L}}
Organized 3/27/15
Liquidated 10/2/26
1902 Plain Back <$VALUE
4x10 1-2991 <$1000
Total Issue $119,640
Out at close $24,800

12502 Stark
SECURITY NB OF TAYLOR
{{8S}}
Chartered 3/24
1929 Small Size <$VALUE
5 Type 1 1-792 <$175
10 Type 1 1-372 <$175
20 Type 1 1-114 <$175
5 Type 2 1-452 <$200
10 Type 2 1-240 <$200
20 Type 2 1-131 <$200
Total Issue $67,040
Out in 1935 $25,000

11599 Grand Forks
FNB, THOMPSON
{{13S}}
Chartered 2/20
1929 Small Size <$VALUE
5 Type 1 1-372 <$125
10 Type 1 1-254 <$125
20 Type 1 1-124 <$125
5 Type 2 1-828 <$150
10 Type 2 1-405 <$150
20 Type 2 1-135 <$150
Total Issue $52,170
Out in 1935 $25,000

7810 Renville
FNB, TOLLEY
{{ UNREPORTED }}
Organized 5/17/05
Receivership 11/21/23
1902 Red Seal <$VALUE
3x10-20 1-300 <$2500
1902 Date Back
3x10-20 1-620 <$1250
1902 Plain Back
3x10-20 621-814 <$1250
Total Issue $55,700
Out at close $6,250

6557 Cass
FNB, TOWER CITY
{{7L 0S}}
Organized 12/9/02
Receivership 12/10/29
1902 Red Seal <$VALUE
3x10-20 1-1440 <$1500
1902 Date Back
3x10-20 1-3240 <$275
1902 Plain Back
3x10-20 3241-7563 <$275
1929 Small Size
10 Type 1 1-33 <$750
20 Type 1 1-7 <$750
Total Issue $452,970
Out at close $25,000
Large out at close $22,180

7955 McHenry
FNB, TOWNER
{{1L}}
Organized 9/25/05
Receivership 12/28/20
1902 Red Seal <$VALUE
3x10-20 1-440 <$2000
1902 Date Back
3x10-20 1-1700 <$750
1902 Plain Back
3x10-20 1701-2474 <$750
Total Issue $145,700
Out at close $24,995

8821 McLean
FNB, TURTLE LAKE
{{1L}}
Organized 6/8/07
Receivership 11/21/23
1902 Red Seal <$VALUE
3x10-20 1-300 <$2500
1902 Date Back
3x10-20 1-860 <$1250
1902 Plain Back
3x10-20 861-1349 <$1250
Total Issue $82,450
Out at close $9,700

11338 Kidder
FNB OF TUTTLE
{{2L}}
Chartered 4/19
Liquidated 4/17/24
1902 Plain Back <$VALUE
3x10-20 1-1758 <$650
Total Issue $87,900
Out at close $25,000

5364 Barnes
AMERICAN NB OF VALLEY CITY
{{7L}}
Chartered 5/21/00
Liquidated 2/14/19
Brown Back <$VALUE
3x10-20 1-1150 <$1250
1882 Date Back
3x10-20 1-3500 <$600
1882 Value Back
3x10-20 3501-4368 <$600
Total Issue $275,900
Out in 1918 $50,000

13385 Barnes
AMERICAN NB & TC OF VALLEY CITY
Chartered 10/29
2nd title:American NB of Valley City 7/23/34
FIRST TITLE {{2U + 19S}}
1929 Small Size <$VALUE
5 Type 1 1-832 <$75
10 Type 1 1-556 <$75
20 Type 1 1-158 <$75
5 Type 2 1-2268 <$100
10 Type 2 1-1080 <$100
20 Type 2 1-252 <$100
SECOND TITLE {{1S}}
1929 Small Size
5 Type 2 1-656 <$200
10 Type 2 1-215 <$200
20 Type 2 1 93 <$200
Total Issue $111,750
Out in 1935 $45,200

2650 Barnes
FARMERS & MERCHANTS NB OF VALLEY CITY
{{ UNREPORTED }}
Organized 3/20/82
Liquidated 12/1/89
TERRITORIAL ISSUES
Series 1875 <$VALUE
3x10-20 1-987 <$10,000
Total Issue $49,350
Out in 1910 $190

F & Security NB of Valley City
SEE Ch 11417
Security NB of Valley City

2548 Barnes
FNB OF VALLEY CITY
Chartered 1881
Liquidated 1/12/26
TERRITORIAL ISSUES {{1L}}
Series 1875 <$VALUE
4x5 1-2650 <$10,000
STATE ISSUES {{8L}}
Series 1875
4x5 2651-4388 <$2500
3x10-20 1-121 <$3000
Brown Back
3x10-20 1-1190 <$1000
1882 Date Back
3x10-20 1-1800 <$600
1882 Value Back
3x10-20 1801-2338 <$600
1902 Plain Back
3x10-20 1-1044 <$200
Total Issue $322,410
Out at close $24,600

FNB of Valley City
SEE Ch 13324
NB of Valley City

13324 Barnes
NB OF VALLEY CITY
Chartered 5/29
2nd title:FNB of Valley City 4/11/32
FIRST TITLE {{16S}}
1929 Small Size <$VALUE
10 Type 1 1-998 <$85
20 Type 1 1-320 <$100
SECOND TITLE {{2S}}
1929 Small Size
10 Type 1 1-200 <$200
20 Type 1 1-32 <$200
10 Type 2 1-390 <$200
20 Type 2 1-40 <$225
Total Issue $118,820
Out in 1935 $43,390

11417 Barnes
SECURITY NB OF VALLEY CITY
Chartered 8/19
Liquidated 5/13/29
2nd title:F & Security NB of Valley City 7/16/28
FIRST TITLE {{6L}}
1902 Plain Back <$VALUE
3x10-20 1-5522 <$250
SECOND TITLE {{0L}}
1902 Plain Back
3x10-20 1-19 <$500
Total Issue $277,050
Out in 1935 $2,660
Ch 13324 assumed circulation

10966 Mountrail
FNB, VAN HOOK
{{12L 2S}}
Organized 3/15/17
Receivership 8/8/31
1902 Plain Back <$VALUE
3x10-20 1-2985 <$300
1929 Small Size
10 Type 1 1-305 <$400
20 Type 1 1-92 <$400
Total Issue $178,590
Out at close $25,000
Large out at close $4,450

4552 Richland
CITIZENS NB OF WAHPETON
{{10L 34S}}
Chartered 1891
Brown Back <$VALUE
3x10-20 1-3540 <$1250
1882 Date Back
3x10-20 1-1018 <$600
1902 Date Back
3x10-20 1-2300 <$200
1902 Plain Back
3x10-20 2301-7360 <$200
1929 Small Size
10 Type 1 1-994 <$75
20 Type 1 1-280 <$75
10 Type 2 1-642 <$100
20 Type 2 1-218 <$100
Total Issue $699,920
Out in 1935 $50,000
Large out 1935 $5,810

2624 Richland
FNB, WAHPETON
{{2L}}
Organized 2/2/82
Receivership 4/8/86
TERRITORIAL ISSUES
Series 1875 <$VALUE
4x5 1-610 <$10,000
3x10-20 1-428 <$10,000
Total Issue $33,600
Out in 1915 $230

7695 Richland
GERMAN-AMERICAN NB, WAHPETON
{{ UNREPORTED }}
Chartered 4/17/05
Liquidated 4/22/07
1902 Red Seal <$VALUE
3x10-20 1-362 <$2500
Total Issue $18,100
Out in 1910 $2,200

12875 Richland
NB IN WAHPETON
{{4S}}
Chartered 1/26
1929 Small Size <$VALUE
5 Type 1 1-310 <$250
10 Type 1 1-316 <$250
20 Type 1 1-42 <$250
5 Type 2 1-272 <$250
10 Type 2 1-255 <$250
20 Type 2 1-105 <$250
Total Issue $39,310
Out in 1935 $25,000

4106 Richland
NB OF WAHPETON
Chartered 1889
Liquidated 11/18/26
TERRITORIAL ISSUES {{0L}}
Brown Back <$VALUE
3x10-20 1-250 <$8500
STATE ISSUES {{8L}}
Brown Back
3x10-20 251-4432 <$1250
1902 Date Back
3x10-20 1-2900 <$200
1902 Plain Back
3x10-20 2901-6811 <$200
Total Issue $562,150
Out at close $49,600

9133 Pembina
FNB, WALHALLA
{{6L 2U + 2S}}
Organized 3/14/08
Receivership 12/5/30
1902 Date Back <$VALUE
4x5 1-1407 <$300
3x10-20 1-1085 <$300
1902 Plain Back
4x5 1408-4660 <$300
3x10-20 1086-3105 <$300
1929 Small Size
5 Type 1 1-332 <$400
10 Type 1 1-152 <$400
20 Type 1 1-20 <$400
Total Issue $269,930
Out at close $25,000
Large out at close $5,780

6327 McLean
FNB, WASHBURN
{{6L 5S}}
Organized 6/19/02
Receivership 9/29/30
1902 Red Seal <$VALUE
3x10-20 1-900 <$1500
1902 Date Back
3x10-20 1-1700 <$300
1902 Plain Back
3x10-20 1701-4649 <$300
1929 Small Size
10 Type 1 1-242 <$225
20 Type 1 1-40 <$250
Total Issue $296,770
Out at close $25,000
Large out at close $7,020

7162 Bottineau
FNB, WESTHOPE
{{1L}}
Chartered 3/04
Liquidated 12/12/10
1902 Red Seal <$VALUE
3x10-20 1-490 <$2500
1902 Date Back
3x10-20 1-180 <$1250
Total Issue $33,500
Out in 1911 $5,550

8324 Williams
CITIZENS NB OF WILLISTON
{{ UNREPORTED }}
Chartered 8/06
Liquidated 5/9/13
1902 Red Seal <$VALUE
3x10-20 1-400 <$2500
1902 Date Back
3x10-20 1-520 <$1250
Total Issue $46,000
Out at close $12,500
Ch 5567 assumed circulation

5567 Williams
FNB OF WILLISTON
{{2L 4S}}
Organized 7/10/00
Liquidated 8/19/33
Brown Back <$VALUE
3x10-20 1-500 <$1500
1882 Date Back
3x10-20 1-2760 <$1000
1882 Value Back
3x10-20 2761-3562 <$1000
1902 Plain Back
3x10-20 1-3460 <$500
1929 Small Size
10 Type 1 1-714 <$250
20 Type 1 1-206 <$250
Total Issue $443,660
Out at close $37,495
Large out at close $3,045
Outstanding includes Ch 8324

6766 Bottineau
FNB, WILLOW CITY
{{1L}}
Organized 4/18/03
Receivership 7/12/23
1902 Red Seal <$VALUE
3x10-20 1-400 <$2000
1902 Date Back
3x10-20 1-1280 <$850
1902 Plain Back
3x10-20 1281-2721 <$850
Total Issue $156,050
Out at close $24,300

7332 Bottineau
MERCHANTS NB, WILLOW CITY
{{3L 3S}}
Organized 5/3/04
Receivership 6/27/31
1902 Red Seal <$VALUE
3x10-20 1-500 <$1750
1902 Date Back
3x10-20 1-840 <$600
1902 Plain Back
3x10-20 841-3308 <$600
1929 Small Size
10 Type 1 1-305 <$375
20 Type 1 1-60 <$375
Total Issue $215,900
Out at close $24,400
Large out at close $4,950

11712 McLean
FNB, WILTON
{{5L 3S}}
Chartered 4/28/20
1902 Plain Back <$VALUE
4x5 1-2200 <$450
3x10-20 1-1582 <$450
1929 Small Size
5 Type 1 1-870 <$350
10 Type 1 1-424 <$350
20 Type 1 1-120 <$350
5 Type 2 1-350 <$400
10 Type 2 1-210 <$400
20 Type 2 1-60 <$400
Total Issue $194,090
Out in 1935 $25,000
Large out 1935 $1,380

6712 Barnes
FNB, WIMBLEDON
{{2L}}
Organized 2/7/03
Receivership 4/23/25
1902 Red Seal <$VALUE
3x10-20 1-856 <$1750
1902 Date Back
3x10-20 1-1860 <$600
1902 Plain Back
3x10-20 1861-3810 <$600
Total Issue $233,300
Out at close $25,000

8917 Barnes
MERCHANTS NB, WIMBLEDON
{{1L}}
Organized 9/17/07
Receivership 10/27/22
1902 Red Seal <$VALUE
3x10-20 1-300 <$2000
1902 Date Back
3x10-20 1-770 <$750
1902 Plain Back
3x10-20 771-1172 <$750
Total Issue $73,600
Out at close $10,000

7166 Richland
FNB OF WYNDMERE
{{3L}}
Chartered 3/04
Liquidated 6/10/27
1902 Red Seal <$VALUE
3x10-20 1-516 <$1750
1902 Date Back
3x10-20 1-1060 <$500
1902 Plain Back
3x10-20 1061-2106 <$500
Total Issue $131,100
Out in 1926 $6,250

9698 Sioux
FNB OF YATES
{{ UNREPORTED }}
Chartered 3/10
Liquidated 7/8/15
1902 Date Back <$VALUE
3x10-20 1-456 <$1250
Total Issue $22,800
Out at close $5,510

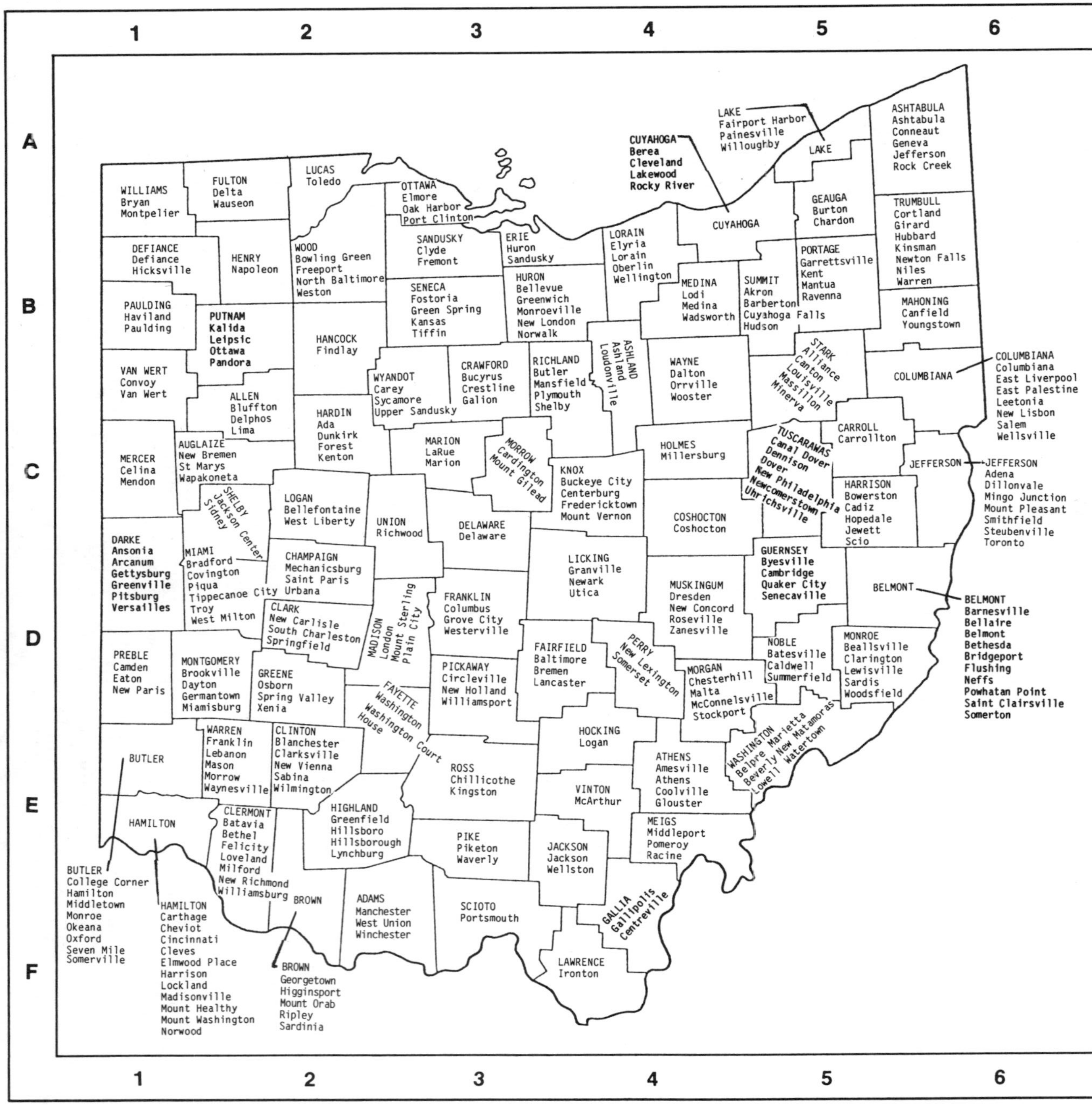

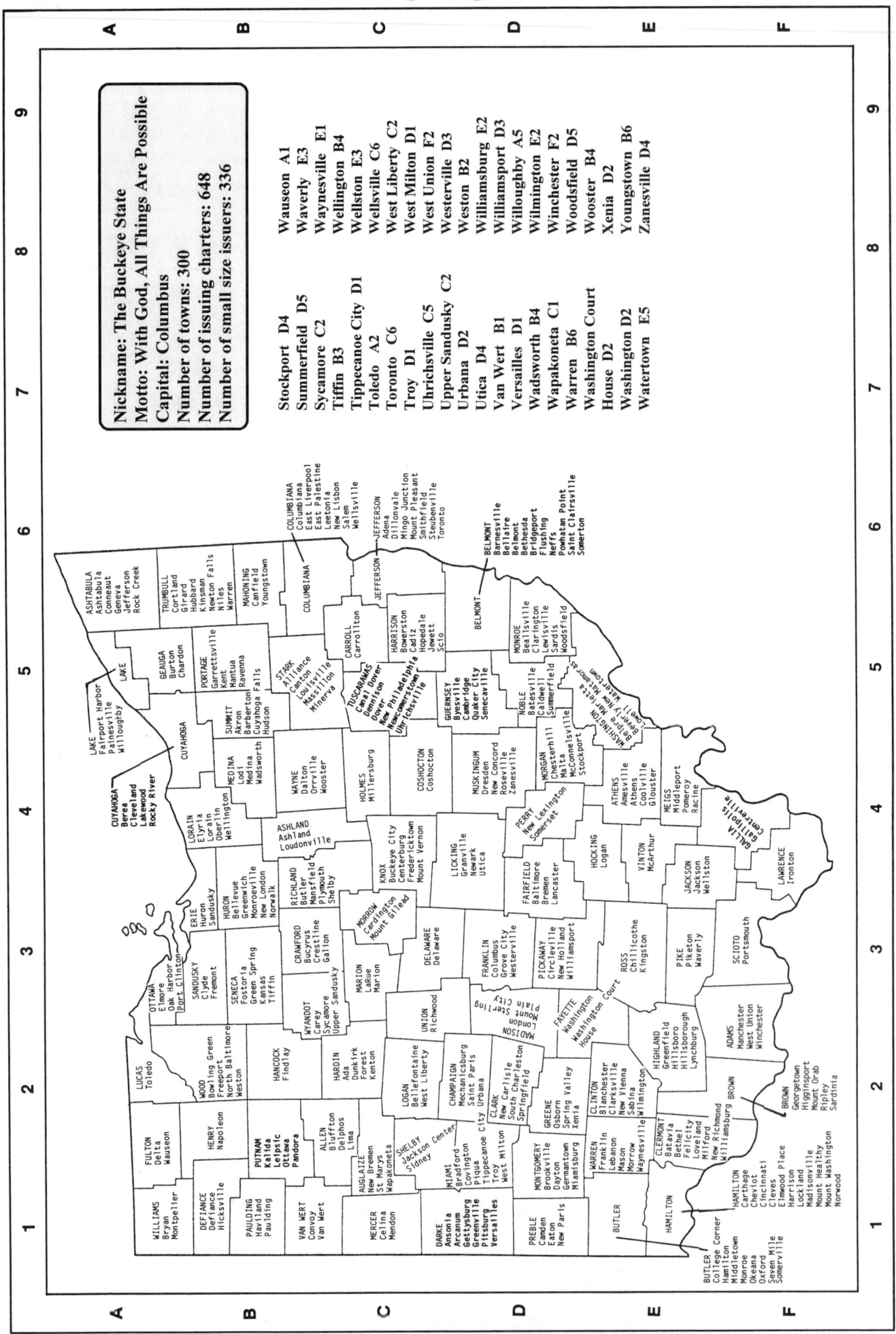

Nickname: The Buckeye State
Motto: With God, All Things Are Possible
Capital: Columbus
Number of towns: 300
Number of issuing charters: 648
Number of small size issuers: 336

Stockport D4
Summerfield D5
Sycamore C2
Tiffin B3
Tippecanoe City D1
Toledo A2
Toronto C6
Troy D1
Uhrichsville C5
Upper Sandusky C2
Urbana D2
Utica D4
Van Wert B1
Versailles D1
Wadsworth B4
Wapakoneta C1
Warren B6
Washington Court House D2
Washington D2
Watertown E5
Wauseon A1
Waverly E3
Waynesville E1
Wellington B4
Wellston E3
Wellsville C6
West Liberty C2
West Milton D1
West Union F2
Westerville D3
Weston B2
Williamsburg E2
Williamsport D3
Willoughby A5
Wilmington E2
Winchester F2
Woodsfield D5
Wooster B4
Xenia D2
Youngstown B6
Zanesville D4

Ada C2
Adena C6
Akron B5
Alliance B5
Amesville E4
Ansonia D1
Arcanum D1
Ashland B4
Ashtabula A6
Athens E4
Baltimore D3
Barberton B5
Barnesville D6
Batavia E2
Batesville D5
Beallsville D5
Bellaire D6
Bellefontaine C2
Bellevue B3
Belmont D6
Belpre E5
Berea A4
Bethel E2
Bethesda D6
Beverly E5
Blanchester E2
Bluffton C2
Bowerston C5
Bowling Green B2
Bradford D1
Bremen D3
Bridgeport D6
Brookville D1
Bryan A1
Buckeye City C4
Bucyrus B3
Burton A5
Butler B3
Byesville D5
Cadiz C5
Caldwell D5
Cambridge D5
Camden D1
Canal Dover C5
Canfield B6
Canton B5
Cardington C3
Carey C2
Carrollton C5
Carthage F1
Celina C1
Centerburg C4
Centreville F4
Chardon A5
Chesterhill D4
Cheviot F1
Chillicothe E3
Cincinnati F1
Circleville D3
Clarington D5
Clarksville E2
Cleveland A4
Cleves F1
Clyde B3
College Corner F1
Columbiana B6
Columbus D3
Conneaut A6
Convoy B1
Coolville E4
Cortland B6
Coshocton C4
Covington D1
Crestline B3
Cuyahoga Falls B5
Dalton B4
Dayton D1
Defiance B1
Delaware C3
Delphos C2
Delta A1
Dennison C5
Dillonvale C6
Dover C5
Dresden D4
Dunkirk C2
East Liverpool B6
East Palestine C6
Eaton D1
Elmore A3
Elmwood Place F1
Elyria B4
Fairport Harbor A5
Felicity E2
Findlay B2
Flushing D6
Forest C2
Fostoria B3
Franklin E1
Fredericktown C4
Freeport B2
Fremont B3
Galion B3
Gallipolis F4
Garrettsville B5
Geneva A6
Georgetown F2
Germantown D1
Gettysburg D1
Girard B6
Glouster E4
Granville D4
Green Spring B3
Greenfield E2
Greenville D1
Greenwich B3
Grove City D3
Hamilton F1
Harrison F1
Haviland B1
Hicksville B1
Higginsport F2
Hillsboro E2
Hillsborough E2
Hopedale C5
Hubbard B6
Hudson B5
Huron B3
Ironton F4
Jackson E3
Jackson Center C1
Jefferson A6
Jewett C5
Kalida B2
Kansas B3
Kent B5
Kenton C2
Kingston E3
Kinsman B6
La Rue C3
Lakewood A4
Lancaster D3
Lebanon E1
Leetonia C6
Leipsic B2
Lewisville D5
Lima C2
Lockland F1
Lodi B4
Logan E4
London D2
Lorain B4
Loudonville B4
Louisville B5
Loveland E2
Lowell E5
Lynchburg E2
Madisonville F1
Malta D4
Manchester F2
Mansfield B3
Mantua B5
Marietta E5
Marion C3
Mason E1
Massillon B5
McArthur E4
McConnelsville D4
Mechanicsburg D2
Medina D1
Mendon E4
Miamisburg F1
Middleport E2
Middletown C4
Milford B5
Millersburg C6
Minerva F1
Mingo Junction B3
Monroe A1
Monroeville E1
Montpelier C3
Morrow F1
Mount Gilead F2
Mount Healthy C6
Mount Orab D2
Mount Pleasant C4
Mount Sterling F1
Mount Vernon B2
Mount Washington F1
Napoleon B2
Neffs D6
New Bremen C1
New Carlisle D2
New Concord D4
New Holland D3
New Lexington D4
New Lisbon C6
New London B3
New Matamoras E5
New Paris D1
New Philadelphia C5
New Richmond E2
New Vienna E2
Newark D4
Newcomerstown C5
Newton Falls B6
Niles B6
North Baltimore B2
Norwalk B3
Norwood F1
Oak Harbor A3
Oberlin B4
Okeana F1
Orrville B4
Osborn D2
Ottawa B2
Oxford F1
Painesville A5
Pandora B2
Paulding B1
Piketon E3
Piqua D1
Pitsburg D1
Plain City D2
Plymouth B3
Pomeroy E4
Port Clinton A3
Portsmouth F2
Powhatan Point D6
Quaker City D5
Racine E4
Ravenna B5
Richwood C2
Ripley F2
Rock Creek A6
Rocky River A4
Roseville D4
Sabina E2
Saint Clairsville D6
Saint Marys C1
Saint Paris D2
Salem C6
Sandusky B3
Sardinia F2
Sardis D5
Scio C5
Senecaville D5
Seven Mile F1
Shelby B3
Sidney C1
Smithfield C6
Somerset D4
Somerton D6
Somerville F1
South Charleston D2
Spring Valley D2
Springfield D2
Steubenville C6

5425 Hardin
FNB OF ADA
{{ 14 L 11 S }}
Chartered 6/14/00
Brown Back <$VALUE
3x10-20 1-650 <$450
1882 Date Back
3x10-20 1-2800* <$450
1882 Value Back
3x10-20 3041-4596* <$450
* 2801-3040 not marked
1902 Plain Back
3x10-20 1-6238 <$275
1929 Small Size
10 Type 1 1-1352 <$150
20 Type 1 1-346 <$150
10 Type 2 1-1130 <$150
20 Type 2 1-171 <$165
Total Issue $711,560
Out in 1935 $50,000
Large out 1935 $2,120

6016 Jefferson
PEOPLES NB OF ADENA
{{ 5 L }}
Chartered 11/9/01
Receivership 4/13/29
Brown Back <$VALUE
3x10-20 1-1070 <$500
1882 Date Back
3x10-20 1-1900 <$500
1882 Value Back
3x10-20 1901-3355 <$500
1902 Plain Back
3x10-20 1-3099 <$350
Total Issue $376,200
Out at close $25,000

4961 Summit
CITIZENS NB OF AKRON
{{ 1 L }}
Chartered 6/19/94
Liquidated 3/5/04
Brown Back <$VALUE
4x5 1-4516 <$1250
3x10-20 1-3563 <$1250
Total Issue $268,470
Out in 1910 $6,395

2946 Summit
CITY NB OF AKRON
{{ 1 L }}
Chartered 5/10/83
Liquidated 5/1/03
Brown Back <$VALUE
3x10-20 1-7080 <$1250
50-100 1-917 <$2500
Total Issue $491,550
Out in 1910 $10,670

27 Summit
FNB OF AKRON
{{ 6 L }}
Chartered 7/63
Liquidated 5/2/82
Original Series <$VALUE
3x1-2 1-6000 <$850/$1750
4x5 1-6500 <$1000
3x10-20 1-5700<$1500/$1750
Series 1875
3x10-20 1-1872<$1500/$1750
Total Issue $538,600
Out in 1910 $3,535

9953 Summit
F-SECOND NB OF AKRON
{{ 17 L }}
Chartered 3/11
Liquidated 4/30/23
1902 Date Back <$VALUE
3x10-20 1-31000* <$250
1902 Plain Back
3x10-20 36001-70482* <$250
* 31001-36000 not marked
Total Issue $3,524,100
Out at close $323,100

2698 Summit
FNB OF AKRON
{{ 8 L }}
Chartered 1882
Liquidated 3/18/11
Brown Back <$VALUE
3x10-20 1-4741 <$850
1902 Red Seal
50-100 1-2713 <$2500/$3000
1902 Date Back
50-100 1-530 <$750/$850
Total Issue $723,500
Out in 1911 $141,750

6763 Summit
N CITY B OF AKRON
{{ 6 L }}
Chartered 5/03
Liquidated 8/31/29
1902 Red Seal <$VALUE
50-100 1-1500 <$2500/$3000
1902 Date Back
50-100 1-800 <$750/$850
3x50-100 1-1940 <$750/$850
1902 Plain Back
3x50-100 1941-2445 <$750/$850
Total Issue $956,250
Out at close $97,500

40 Summit
SECOND NB OF AKRON
{{ 6 L }}
Chartered 7/63
Liquidated 5/31/82
Original Series <$VALUE
3x1-2 1-3000 <$850/$1750
4x5 1-4250 <$1000
3x10-20 1-2100<$1500/$1750
Series 1875
4x5 1-2190 <$1000
3x10-20 1-1100<$1500/$1750
Total Issue $303,800
Out in 1910 $1,995

2716 Summit
SECOND NB OF AKRON
{{ 7 L }}
Chartered 1882
Liquidated 3/18/11
Brown Back <$VALUE
4x5 1-3700 <$750
3x10-20 1-3725 <$750
1902 Red Seal
3x10-20 1-17700 <$1000
1902 Date Back
3x10-20 1-4851 <$500
Total Issue $1,387,800
Out in 1911 $166,150

Alliance FNB of Alliance
SEE Ch 3721
FNB of Alliance

2041 Stark
FNB OF ALLIANCE
{{ 1 L }}
Chartered 9/6/72
Liquidated 1/3/82
Original Series <$VALUE
3x1-2 1-500 <$1000/$1500
4x5 1-1475 <$1000
3x10-20 1-630 <$1500/$1750
Series 1875
4x5 1-875 <$1000
3x10-20 1-526 <$1500/$1750
Total Issue $107,300
Out in 1910 $535

3721 Stark
FNB OF ALLIANCE
Chartered 6/11/87
2nd title: Alliance FNB, Alliance 1/30/22
FIRST TITLE {{ 8 L }}
Brown Back <$VALUE
4x5 1-6225 <$400
50-100 1-269 <$1500/$1750
1902 Red Seal
4x10 1-312 <$500
1902 Date Back
4x10 1-7200 <$175
1902 Plain Back
4x10 7201-17000 <$175
SECOND TITLE {{ 10 L 37 S }}
1902 Plain Back
4x10 1-20286 <$150
1929 Small Size
10 Type 1 1-17048 <$40
10 Type 2 1-16730 <$40
Total Issue $2,858,950
Out in 1935 $300,000
Large out 1935 $5,480

7235 Athens
FNB OF AMESVILLE
{{ 4 L 8 S }}
Chartered 4/04
1902 Red Seal <$VALUE
3x10-20 1-1250 <$1000
1902 Date Back
3x10-20 1-1760 <$500
1902 Plain Back
3x10-20 1761-5301 <$500
1929 Small Size
10 Type 1 1-692 <$250
20 Type 1 1-180 <$250
10 Type 2 1-434 <$300
20 Type 2 1-85 <$300
Total Issue $396,710
Out in 1935 $25,000
Large out 1935 $2,230

9194 Darke
FNB OF ANSONIA
{{ 2 L 4 S }}
Organized 6/16/08
Receivership 8/15/33
1902 Date Back <$VALUE
3x10-20 1-2190 <$750
1902 Plain Back
3x10-20 2191-5898 <$750
1929 Small Size
10 Type 1 1-602 <$400
20 Type 1 1-166 <$400
Total Issue $350,940
Out at close $25,000
Large out at close $1,620

9255 Darke
FARMERS NB OF ARCANUM
{{ U + 2 L }}
Chartered 10/08
Closed 3/24/28
1902 Date Back <$VALUE
4x5 1-1450 <$500
3x10-20 1-1220 <$500
50-100 1-180 <$850/$1000
3x50-100 1-100 <$850/$1000
1902 Plain Back
4x5 1451-7002 <$500
3x10-20 1221-4009 <$500
Total Issue $392,490
Out at close $48,545
Ch 4839 assumed circulation

4839 Darke
FNB OF ARCANUM
Organized 12/10/92
Receivership 6/21/34
2nd title: F-Farmers NB of Arcanum 3/24/28
FIRST TITLE {{ 4 L }}
Brown Back <$VALUE
4x5 1-2315 <$500
50-100 1-154 <$1500/$1750
1882 Date Back
4x5 1-386 <$500
50-100 1-68 <$1500/$1750
1902 Date Back
4x5 1-1775 <$300
3x10-20 1-1420 <$300
1902 Plain Back
4x5 1776-8962 <$300
3x10-20 1421-6143 <$300
SECOND TITLE {{ 6 L 16 S }}
1902 Plain Back
4x5 1-5781 <$200
1929 Small Size
5 Type 1 1-12608 <$75
5 Type 2 1-13144 <$75
Total Issue $1,133,290
Out at close $100,000
Large out at close $4,235
Outstanding includes Ch 9255

183 Ashland
FNB OF ASHLAND
{{ 4 L 12 S }}
Chartered 1/64
Original Series <$VALUE
4x5 1-6450 <$750
Series 1875
4x5 1-2205 <$750
Brown Back
50-100 1-1072 <$1500/$1750
1902 Red Seal
50-100 1-786 <$2250/$2500
1902 Date Back
50-100 1-600 <$650/$750
3x50-100 1-590 <$650/$750
1902 Plain Back
3x50-100 591-847<$650/$750
1929 Small Size
50 Type 1 1-427 <$250
100 Type 1 1-100 <$325
Total Issue $941,650
Out in 1935 $150,000
Large out 1935 $6,650

2031 Ashtabula
ASHTABULA NB, ASHTABULA
{{ 2 L }}
Chartered 8/22/72
Liquidated 7/11/92
Original Series <$VALUE
4x5 1-4700 <$750
Series 1875
4x5 1-14450 <$750
Total Issue $383,000
Out in 1910 $2,280

975 Ashtabula
FARMERS NB OF ASHTABULA
Chartered 4/4/65
2nd title: Farmers NB & TC of Ashtabula 4/1/31
FIRST TITLE {{ 5 L 3 S }}
Original Series <$VALUE
3x1-2 1-500 <$500/$1000
4x5 1-5000 <$500
3x10-20 1-2600 <$850/$1250
Series 1875
4x5 1-2750 <$500
3x10-20 1-3540 <$850/$1250
Brown Back
3x10-20 1-7029 <$450
1902 Red Seal
50-100 1-600 <$2250/$2500
1902 Date Back
50-100 1-600 <$650/$750
3x50-100 1-900 <$650/$750
1902 Plain Back
3x50-100 901-1149<$650/$750
1929 Small Size
5 Type 1 1-1350 <$200
10 Type 1 1-684 <$200
SECOND TITLE {{ 7 S }}
1929 Small Size
5 Type 1 1-1214 <$150
10 Type 1 1-366 <$150
5 Type 2 1-3836 <$150
10 Type 2 1-1995 <$150
Total Issue $1,462,250
Out in 1935 $50,000
Large out 1935 $6,765

4506 Ashtabula
MARINE NB OF SWEDEN OF ASHTABULA
Chartered 1891
Liquidated 3/13/31
2nd title: Marine NB of Ashtabula 3/25/93
FIRST TITLE {{ 0 L }}
Brown Back <$VALUE
4x5 1-738 <$1500
SECOND TITLE {{ 8 L 12 S }}
Brown Back
4x5 1-2825 <$500
3x10-20 1-640 <$500
1882 Date Back
4x5 1-1379 <$450
3x10-20 1-675 <$450
1902 Date Back
3x10-20 1-6300 <$225
1902 Plain Back
3x10-20 6301-24077 <$225
1929 Small Size
10 Type 1 1-1473 <$100
20 Type 1 1-467 <$100
Total Issue $1,512,860
Out at close $93,760
Large out at close $12,120

5075 Ashtabula
NB OF ASHTABULA
{{ 14 L 26 S }}
Organized 3/11/97
Brown Back <$VALUE
4x5 1-3050 <$400
3x10-20 1-1340 <$400
1882 Date Back
4x5 1-10482* <$350
3x10-20 1-7960** <$350
* 9651-10482 not marked
** 7321-7960 not marked
1902 Plain Back
4x5 1-28225 <$175
3x10-20 1-16877 <$175
1929 Small Size
5 Type 1 1-6268 <$75
10 Type 1 1-3156 <$75
20 Type 1 1-722 <$85
5 Type 2 1-6940 <$100
10 Type 2 1-3759 <$100
20 Type 2 1-1351 <$100
Total Issue $2,707,340
Out in 1935 $123,750
Large out 1935 $6,950

7744 Athens
ATHENS NB, ATHENS
{{ 10 L 26 S }}
Chartered 5/05
1902 Red Seal <$VALUE
3x10-20 1-2300 <$650
1902 Date Back
3x10-20 1-4500 <$250
1902 Plain Back
3x10-20 4501-15608 <$250
1929 Small Size
10 Type 1 1-2190 <$75
20 Type 1 1-590 <$85
10 Type 2 1-8279 <$85
20 Type 2 1-1568 <$85
Total Issue $1,211,750
Out in 1935 $125,000
Large out 1935 $6,300
Outstanding includes Ch 233

10479 Athens
B OF ATHENS N BANKING ASSOCIATION, ATHENS
{{ 5 L 13 S }}
Chartered 1/14
1902 Plain Back <$VALUE
3x10-20 1-8699 <$375
1929 Small Size
10 Type 1 1-604 <$125
20 Type 1 1-164 <$140
5 Type 2 1-5490 <$150
10 Type 2 1-7786 <$150
20 Type 2 1-1248 <$150
Total Issue $621,140
Out in 1935 $91,200
Large out 1935 $1,860

233 Athens
FNB OF ATHENS
{{ 4 L }}
Chartered 2/64
Liquidated 5/25/17
Original Series <$VALUE
3x1-2 1-4000 <$500/$1250
4x5 1-3750 <$500
3x10-20 1-800 <$850/$1250
Series 1875
3x1-2 1-440 <$500/$1250
4x5 1-1615 <$600
3x10-20 1-484 <$850/$1250
Brown Back
4x5 1-3585 <$500
3x10-20 1-1232 <$500
1902 Red Seal
3x10-20 1-2300 <$750
1902 Date Back
3x10-20 1-1935 <$375
Total Issue $538,750
Out at close $20,000
Ch 7744 assumed circulation

7639 Fairfield
FNB OF BALTIMORE
{{ UNREPORTED }}
Chartered 3/05
1902 Red Seal <$VALUE
3x10-20 1-300 <$1500
1902 Date Back
3x10-20 1-580 <$1000
1902 Plain Back
3x10-20 581-1142 <$1000
1929 Small Size
10 Type 1 1-229 <$1000
20 Type 1 1-45 <$1000
Total Issue $91,240
Out in 1935 $6,300
Large out 1935 $370

5819 Summit
AMERICAN NB OF BARBERTON
{{ 2 L }}
Chartered 5/1 8/01
Liquidated 8/22/05
Brown Back <$VALUE
3x10-20 1-1192 <$1000
Total Issue $59,600
Out in 1910 $2,610

5230 Summit
FNB OF BARBERTON
{{ 2 L }}
Chartered 11/1/99
Receivership 5/26/05
Brown Back <$VALUE
4x5 1-1558 <$1000
3x10-20 1-1878 <$1000
Total Issue $125,060
Out in 1916 $1,045

911 Belmont
FNB OF BARNESVILLE
{{ 16 L 10 S }}
Chartered 3/18/65
Original Series <$VALUE
3x1-2 1-1600 <$400/$1000
4x5 1-2400 <$500
3x10-20 1-2370 <$750/$1250
Series 1875
3x10-20 1-2286 <$750/$1250
Brown Back
50-100 1-2980 <$1500/$1750
1902 Red Seal
50-100 1-1100 <$2250/$2500
1902 Date Back
50-100 1-500 <$500/$600
3x50-100 1-1700 <$500/$600
1902 Plain Back
3x50-100 1701-2127 <$500/$600
1929 Small Size
50 Type 1 1-252 <$250
100 Type 1 1-80 <$300
5 Type 2 1-480 <$150
10 Type 2 1-120 <$150
20 Type 2 1-120 <$150
Total Issue $1,637,150
Out in 1935 $100,000
Large out 1935 $17,000

6621 Belmont
NB OF BARNESVILLE
{{ 4 L }}
Organized 1/29/03
Receivership 11/14/23
1902 Red Seal <$VALUE
3x10-20 1-6600 <$750
1902 Date Back
3x10-20 1-6600 <$375
1902 Plain Back
3x10-20 6601-14806 <$375
Total Issue $1,070,300
Out at close $98,800

2908 Belmont
PEOPLES NB OF BARNESVILLE
{{ 2 L }}
Chartered 3/24/83
Liquidated 2/26/03
Brown Back <$VALUE
3x10-20 1-7278 <$850
Total Issue $363,900
Out in 1910 $7,225

715 Clermont
FNB OF BATAVIA
{{ 14 L 15 S }}
Organized 1/3/65
Original Series <$VALUE
4x5 1-6000 <$500
3x10-20 1-1552 <$750/$1250
Series 1875
4x5 1-2970 <$500
3x10-20 1-742 <$750/$1250
Brown Back
4x5 1-7765 <$300
3x10-20 1-4973 <$300
1902 Red Seal
3x10-20 1-2600 <$400
1902 Date Back
3x10-20 1-4800 <$175
1902 Plain Back
3x10-20 4801-15772 <$175
1929 Small Size
10 Type 1 1-2704 <$85
20 Type 1 1-416 <$100
10 Type 2 1-4425 <$100
Total Issue $1,873,060
Out in 1935 $80,000
Large out 1935 $7,700

2219 Noble
FNB OF BATESVILLE
{{ UNREPORTED }}
Chartered 1/18/75
Liquidated 12/1/92
Original Series <$VALUE
3x10-20 1-1600<$1750/$2000
Series 1875
3x10-20 1-503 <$1750/$2000
Total Issue $105,150
Out in 1910 $600

7025 Monroe
FNB OF BEALLSVILLE
{{ 2 L 2 S }}
Organized 9/3/03
Receivership 9/26/33
1902 Red Seal <$VALUE
4x5 1-575 <$1250
3x10-20 1-466 <$1250
1902 Date Back
4x5 1-875 <$750
3x10-20 1-680 <$750
1902 Plain Back
4x5 876-2430 <$750
3x10-20 681-1603 <$750
1929 Small Size
5 Type 1 1-376 <$600
10 Type 1 1-185 <$600
20 Type 1 1-49 <$600
Total Issue $191,810
Out at close $12,500
Large out at close $1,020

****
13996 Belmont
FARMERS & MERCHANTS NB IN BELLAIRE
{{ 5 S }}
Chartered 2/34
1929 Small Size <$VALUE
10 Type 2 1-3040 <$250
20 Type 2 1-760 <$275
Total Issue $45,600
Out in 1935 $100,000
Outstanding includes Ch 7327
****
7327 Belmont
FARMERS & MERCHANTS NB OF BELLAIRE
{{ 10 L U + 21 S }}
Chartered 6/25/04
Liquidated 2/13/34
1902 Red Seal <$VALUE
3x10-20 1-5600 <$400
1902 Date Back
3x10-20 1-8000 <$175
1902 Plain Back
3x10-20 8001-26769 <$175
1929 Small Size
10 Type 1 1-2640 <$60
20 Type 1 1-692 <$70
10 Type 2 1-1197 <$85
20 Type 2 1-200 <$100
Total Issue $1,875,860
Out at close $100,000
Large out 1935 $5,100
Ch 13996 assumed circulation
****
13914 Belmont
FNB IN BELLAIRE
{{ 11 S }}
Chartered 12/33
1929 Small Size <$VALUE
10 Type 2 1-8597 <$150
20 Type 2 1-2530 <$150
Total Issue $136,570
Out in 1935 $300,000
Outstanding includes Ch 1944
****
1944 Belmont
FNB OF BELLAIRE
{{ 31 L 50+ S }}
Chartered 3/1/72
Liquidated 1/2/34
Original Series <$VALUE
4x5 1-1150 <$350
4x10 1-2050 <$500
Series 1875
4x10 1-5865 <$500
Brown Back
3x10-20 1-15800 <$250/$300
1882 Date Back
3x10-20 1-7503 <$250/$300
1902 Date Back
3x10-20 1-10800 <$100
1902 Plain Back
3x10-20 10801-47550 <$100
1929 Small Size
10 Type 1 1-8900 <$40
20 Type 1 1-2422 <$50
10 Type 2 1-621 <$60
20 Type 2 1-165 <$75
Total Issue $4,716,400
Out at close $300,000
Large out 1935 $15,660
Ch 13914 assumed circulation
****
1784 Logan
BELLEFONTAINE NB, BELLEFONTAINE
{{ 14 L 16 S }}
Chartered 2/3/71
Receivership 12/26/33
Original Series <$VALUE
3x1-2 1-4000 <$450/$1000
4x5 1-3125 <$500
3x10-20 1-1600 <$750/$1250
Series 1875
3x10-20 1-3588 <$750/$1250
Brown Back
3x10-20 1-4600 <$300/$350
1882 Date Back
3x10-20 1-628 <$300/$350
1902 Date Back
3x10-20 1-5100 <$150
1902 Plain Back
3x10-20 5101-20101 <$150
1929 Small Size
10 Type 1 1-2488 <$75
20 Type 1 1-676 <$85
10 Type 2 1-670 <$100
20 Type 2 1-65 <$125
Total Issue $1,846,750
Out at close $100,000
Large out at close $7,340
****
11726 Logan
PEOPLES NB IN BELLEFONTAINE
{{ 2 L }}
Chartered 5/20
Liquidated 2/1/23
1902 Plain Back <$VALUE
3x10-20 1-2398 <$600
Total Issue $119,900
Out at close $93,595
Outstanding includes Ch 2480
****
2480 Logan
PEOPLES NB OF BELLEFONTAINE
{{ 6 L }}
Chartered 6/2/80
Liquidated 5/21/20
Series 1875 <$VALUE
4x5 1-6972 <$500
3x10-20 1-2363 <$750/$1250
Brown Back
3x10-20 1-1500 <$350/$400
1882 Date Back
3x10-20 1-5350* <$350/$400
1882 Value Back
3x10-20 5851-8669* <$350/$400
* 5351-5850 not marked
Total Issue $766,040
Out at close $100,000
Ch 11726 assumed circulation
****
2302 Huron
FNB OF BELLEVUE
{{ 7 L 9 S }}
Chartered 9/30/75
Series 1875 <$VALUE
4x5 1-4954 <$500
Brown Back
4x5 1-2200 <$375
3x10-20 1-1840 <$375/$425
1882 Date Back
4x5 1-2255 <$350
3x10-20 1-1660 <$350/$400
1902 Plain Back
4x10 1-5824 <$250
1929 Small Size
10 Type 1 1-1462 <$165
Total Issue $683,860
Out in 1935 $27,500
Large out 1935 $2,160
****
6391 Belmont
BELMONT NB OF BELMONT
{{ 3 L 3 S }}
Chartered 8/19/02
Liquidated 2/28/31
1902 Red Seal <$VALUE
3x10-20 1-1280 <$850
1902 Date Back
3x10-20 1-1910 <$500
1902 Plain Back
3x10-20 1911-6059 <$500
1929 Small Size
10 Type 1 1-376 <$400
20 Type 1 1-92 <$425
Total Issue $400,550
Out at close $22,530
Large out at close $2,920
****
4864 Belmont
FNB OF BELMONT
{{ UNREPORTED }}
Organized 3/18/93
Receivership 2/25/02
Brown Back <$VALUE
3x10-20 1-2582 <$1500
Total Issue $129,100
Out in 1916 $1,240
****
8420 Washington
FNB OF BELPRE
{{ 1 L }}
Chartered 10/06
Liquidated 9/14/15
1902 Red Seal <$VALUE
4x5 1-250 <$1500
3x10-20 1-200 <$1500
1902 Date Back
4x5 1-1950 <$1000
3x10-20 1-1436 <$1000
Total Issue $126,000
Out at close $23,100
****
2004 Cuyahoga
FNB OF BEREA
{{ UNREPORTED }}
Chartered 6/27/72
Liquidated 12/1/86
Original Series <$VALUE
3x1-2 1-2600 <$1500/$2500
4x5 1-2975 <$1500
Series 1875
3x1-2 1-40 <$1500/$2500
4x5 1-5818 <$1500
Total Issue $189,060
Out in 1910 $905
****
5627 Clermont
FNB OF BETHEL
{{ 5 L 9 S }}
Chartered 11/19/00
Brown Back <$VALUE
4x5 1-750 <$600
3x10-20 1-452 <$600
50-100 1-76 <$1750/$2000
1882 Date Back
4x5 1-900* <$600
3x10-20 1-660** <$600
50-100 1-40 <$1750/$2000
1882 Value Back
4x5 1001-1865* <$600
3x10-20 741-1125** <$600
* 901-1000 not marked
** 661-740 not marked
1902 Plain Back
4x5 1-2595 <$350
3x10-20 1-1715 <$350
1929 Small Size
5 Type 1 1-1420 <$200
10 Type 1 1-692 <$200
20 Type 1 1-190 <$200
5 Type 2 1-2720 <$225
10 Type 2 1-1308 <$225
20 Type 2 1-413 <$225
Total Issue $428,060
Out in 1935 $42,680
Large out 1935 $450
****
5602 Belmont
FNB OF BETHESDA
{{ 2 L 5 S }}
Chartered 10/22/00
Receivership 9/21/34
Brown Back <$VALUE
3x10-20 1-1900 <$750
1882 Date Back
3x10-20 1-1720 <$750
1882 Value Back
3x10-20 1721-2640 <$750
1902 Plain Back
3x10-20 1-2914 <$500
1929 Small Size
10 Type 1 1-634 <$300
20 Type 1 1-168 <$300
10 Type 2 1-710 <$350
20 Type 2 1-60 <$350
Total Issue $439,200
Out at close $25,000
Large out at close $1,170
****
14261 Belmont
GOSHEN NB OF BETHESDA
{{ 4 S }}
Chartered 9/34
1929 Small Size <$VALUE
5 Type 2 1-1524 <$650
10 Type 2 1-738 <$650
Total Issue $15,000
Out in 1935 $15,000
****
133 Washington
FNB OF BEVERLY
{{ U + 0 L }}
Chartered 11/27/63
Liquidated 11/10/74
Original Series <$VALUE
3x1-2 1-2200 <$1250/$2000
4x5 1-2885 <$1500
4x10 1-1750 <$1750
Total Issue $138,700
Out in 1910 $1,197
****
8588 Clinton
FNB OF BLANCHESTER
{{ 4 L 12 S }}
Chartered 3/07
1902 Red Seal <$VALUE
4x10 1-875 <$750
1902 Date Back
4x10 1-3625 <$350
1902 Plain Back
4x10 3626-10463 <$350
1929 Small Size
10 Type 1 1-1608 <$150
10 Type 2 1-2065 <$160
Total Issue $570,650
Out in 1935 $35,000
Large out 1935 $1,610
****
11573 Allen
CITIZENS NB OF BLUFFTON
{{ 2 L 12 S }}
Chartered 1/20
1902 Plain Back <$VALUE
4x5 1-7197 <$600
1929 Small Size
5 Type 1 1-3014 <$150
5 Type 2 1-6308 <$160
Total Issue $265,900
Out in 1935 $25,000
Large out 1935 $480
****
5626 Allen
FNB OF BLUFFTON
{{ 3 L }}
Chartered 11/19/00
Receivership 11/17/19
Brown Back <$VALUE
3x10-20 1-500 <$600
1882 Date Back
4x5 1-1890 <$600
3x10-20 1-1530 <$600
1882 Value Back
4x5 1891-3075 <$600
3x10-20 1531-2076 <$600
Total Issue $190,300
Out at close $46,700
****
7486 Harrison
FNB OF BOWERSTON
{{ 5 L 2 S }}
Organized 11/15/04
Receivership 6/11/30
1902 Red Seal <$VALUE
3x10-20 1-400 <$1000
1902 Date Back
3x10-20 1-2180 <$400
1902 Plain Back
3x10-20 2181-6209 <$400
1929 Small Size
10 Type 1 1-222 <$750
20 Type 1 1-30 <$750
Total Issue $347,370
Out at close $19,480
Large out at close $4,580
****
4045 Wood
FNB OF BOWLING GREEN
{{ UNREPORTED }}
Chartered 5/23/89
Receivership 1/5/17
Brown Back <$VALUE
4x5 1-1300 <$1500
3x10-20 1-1020 <$1500
1882 Date Back
4x5 1-57 <$1500
3x10-20 1-40 <$1500
1902 Date Back
4x10 1-1163 <$1250
Total Issue $126,660
Out at close $12,500
****
14077 Miami
BRADFORD NB, BRADFORD
{{ 8 S }}
Chartered 3/34
1929 Small Size <$VALUE
10 Type 2 1-3360 <$250
20 Type 2 1-1600 <$250
Total Issue $65,600
Out in 1935 $50,000
****
9163 Miami
FNB OF BRADFORD
{{ 7 L U + 18 S }}
Organized 5/6/08
Receivership 5/1/34
1902 Date Back <$VALUE
3x10-20 1-2330 <$250
1902 Plain Back
3x10-20 2331-16070 <$250
1929 Small Size
10 Type 1 1-3474 <$85
20 Type 1 1-994 <$100
10 Type 2 1-571 <$110
20 Type 2 1-30 <$135
Total Issue $1,137,530
Out at close $123,300
Large out at close $3,620
****
9768 Fairfield
FNB OF BREMEN
{{ 4 L }}
Chartered 6/10
Liquidated 7/1/27
1902 Date Back <$VALUE
3x10-20 1-1515 <$500
1902 Plain Back
3x10-20 1516-4565 <$500
Total Issue $228,250
Out at close $23,500
****
6624 Belmont
BRIDGEPORT NB, BRIDGEPORT
{{ 12 L 18 S }}
Organized 1/13/03
Liquidated 5/11/34
1902 Red Seal <$VALUE
4x5 1-5750 <$450
3x10-20 1-4400 <$450
1902 Date Back
4x5 1-8100 <$175
3x10-20 1-5760 <$175
1902 Plain Back
4x5 8101-27252 <$175
3x10-20 5761-18695 <$175
1929 Small Size
5 Type 1 1-4146 <$85
10 Type 1 1-1986 <$85
20 Type 1 1-512 <$100
5 Type 2 1-746 <$125
10 Type 2 1-439 <$125
20 Type 2 1-150 <$125
Total Issue $2,130,890
Out at close $91,850
Large out 1935 $5,340
Ch 14050 assumed circulation
****
14050 Belmont
BRIDGEPORT NB, BRIDGEPORT
{{ 3 S }}
Chartered 3/34
1929 Small Size <$VALUE
5 Type 2 1-3262 <$500
10 Type 2 1-2574 <$500
20 Type 2 1-650 <$500
Total Issue $55,050
Out in 1935 $100,000
Outstanding includes Ch 6624
****
214 Belmont
FNB OF BRIDGEPORT
{{ 3 L }}
Organized 1/25/64
Liquidated 2/24/03
Original Series <$VALUE
4x5 1-11250 <$600
4x10 1-3250 <$750
Series 1875
4x5 1-2500 <$600
4x10 1-5915 <$750
Brown Back
4x5 1-5612 <$500
3x10-20 1-8329 <$500
Total Issue $1,170,290
Out in 1910 $10,350
****
9553 Montgomery
FNB OF BROOKVILLE
{{ 4 L }}
Chartered 10/09
Liquidated 7/22/29
1902 Date Back <$VALUE
4x5 1-1715 <$400
3x10-20 1-1264 <$400
1902 Plain Back
4x5 1716-6300 <$400
3x10-20 1265-4003 <$400
Total Issue $326,150
Out at close $25,000
****
13740 Williams
CITIZENS NB OF BRYAN
{{ 10 S }}
Chartered 7/33
1929 Small Size <$VALUE
10 Type 2 1-9381 <$165
Total Issue $93,810
Out in 1935 $58,100
****
2474 Williams
FARMERS NB OF BRYAN
{{ 16 L 29 S }}
Chartered 4/16/80
Receivership 2/8/34
Series 1875 <$VALUE
4x10 1-2998 <$650
Brown Back
3x10-20 1-3425 <$300/$350
1882 Date Back
3x10-20 1-3600 <$300/$350
1882 Value Back
3x10-20 3601-4540 <$300/$350
1902 Plain Back
3x10-20 1-27610 <$175
1929 Small Size
10 Type 1 1-4954 <$50
20 Type 1 1-1434 <$60
10 Type 2 1-696 <$85
20 Type 2 1-90 <$110
Total Issue $2,376,750
Out at close $198,500
Large out at close $12,080
****
13899 Williams
FNB IN BRYAN
{{ 9 S }}
Chartered 12/33
1929 Small Size <$VALUE
5 Type 2 1-14886 <$175
Total Issue $74,430
Out in 1935 $40,550
****
237 Williams
FNB OF BRYAN
{{ 14 L 21 S }}
Organized 10/8/63
Receivership 2/7/34
Original Series <$VALUE
3x1-2 1-2200 <$500/$1250
4x5 1-5400 <$500
Series 1875
3x1-2 1-1860 <$500/$1250
4x5 1-3150 <$500
Brown Back
50-100 1-1335 <$1500/$1750
1902 Red Seal
4x5 1-1300 <$350
50-100 1-536 <$2250/$2500
1902 Date Back
4x5 1-3625 <$125
50-100 1-280 <$500/$600
3x50-100 1-1091 <$500/$600
1902 Plain Back
4x5 3626-41550 <$125
3x50-100 1092-1466 <$500/$600
1929 Small Size
5 Type 1 1-5985 <$75
50 Type 1 1-304 <$250
100 Type 1 1-98 <$325
Total Issue $2,067,000
Out at close $149,640
Large out at close $10,855
****
7631 Knox
FNB OF BUCKEYE CITY
{{ UNREPORTED }}
Chartered 3/6/05
Liquidated 4/30/06
1902 Red Seal <$VALUE
3x10-20 1-144 <$2500
Total Issue $7,200
Out in 1910 $700
****
443 Crawford
FNB OF BUCYRUS
{{ 11 L 3U + 9 S }}
Chartered 1864
Original Series <$VALUE
3x1-2 1-1000 <$500/$1000
4x5 1-2750 <$500
3x10-20 1-2300 <$750/$1250
Series 1875
3x10-20 1-1598 <$750/$1250
Brown Back
3x10-20 1-2537 <$400
1902 Red Seal
3x10-20 1-1050 <$400
1902 Date Back
3x10-20 1-2100 <$200
1902 Plain Back
3x10-20 2101-10344 <$200
1929 Small Size
10 Type 1 1-544 <$100
20 Type 1 1-146 <$100
10 Type 2 1-7171 <$100
20 Type 2 1-2122 <$100
Total Issue $1,115,760
Out in 1935 $100,000
Large out 1935 $4,490
****

<$VALUEs are for notes in FINE condition. Value changes by approximately 25% for a change of one full grade.

****

3274 Crawford
SECOND NB OF BUCYRUS
{{ 50+ L 23 S }}
Chartered 1884
Brown Back <$VALUE
4x5 1-4508 <$225
3x10-20 1-1273 <$275/$325
1902 Red Seal
3x10-20 1-1600 <$350
1902 Date Back
3x10-20 1-3700* <$175
1902 Plain Back
3x10-20 4301-17846* <$175
* 3701-4300 not marked
1929 Small Size
10 Type 1 1-2582 <$75
20 Type 1 1-690 <$85
10 Type 2 1-1404 <$90
20 Type 2 1-475 <$100
Total Issue $1,387,370
Out in 1935 $100,000
Large out 1935 $5,570

****

6249 Geauga
FNB OF BURTON
{{ 3 L 10 S }}
Chartered 5/9/02
1902 Red Seal <$VALUE
4x5 1-1100 <$750
3x10-20 1-880 <$750
1902 Date Back
4x5 1-1750 <$375
3x10-20 1-1220 <$375
1902 Plain Back (dated 1902)
4x5 1751-4625 <$375
3x10-20 1221-3015 <$375
1902 Plain Back (dated 1922)
4x5 1-3250 <$375
3x10-20 1-2255 <$375
1929 Small Size
5 Type 1 1-968 <$175
10 Type 1 1-540 <$175
20 Type 1 1-148 <$175
5 Type 2 1-1904 <$200
10 Type 2 1-1065 <$200
20 Type 2 1-300 <$225
Total Issue $592,370
Out in 1935 $35,000
Large out 1935 $1,450

****

6515 Richland
FNB OF BUTLER
{{ UNREPORTED }}
Chartered 12/1/02
Liquidated 6/21/10
1902 Red Seal <$VALUE
3x10-20 1-432 <$2000
Total Issue $21,600
Out in 1910 $5,200

****

5641 Guernsey
FNB OF BYESVILLE
{{ 2 L 4 S }}
Chartered 12/14/00
Brown Back <$VALUE
3x10-20 1-600 <$850
1882 Date Back
3x10-20 1-640 <$850
1882 Value Back
3x10-20 641-704 <$850
1902 Plain Back
3x10-20 1-706 <$600
1929 Small Size
10 Type 1 1-222 <$400
20 Type 1 1-41 <$400
Total Issue $118,740
Out in 1935 $7,000
Large out 1935 $270

****

2444 Harrison
FARMERS & MECHANICS NB OF CADIZ
{{ 6 L }}
Chartered 12/24/79
Liquidated 5/29/11
Series 1875 <$VALUE
4x5 1-14548 <$500
Brown Back
3x10-20 1-3860 <$400
1882 Date Back
3x10-20 1-1106 <$400
Total Issue $539,260
Out in 1911 $33,850

****

100 Harrison
FNB OF CADIZ
Chartered 10/63
2nd title: Union NB & TC of Cadiz 1/12/31
3rd title: Union NB of Cadiz 3/26/32
FIRST TITLE {{ 13 L 5 S }}
Original Series <$VALUE
4x5 1-3750 <$500
3x10-20 1-2750 <$750/$1250
Series 1875
4x5 1-2500 <$500
3x10-20 1-1700 <$750/$1250
Brown Back
4x5 1-9100 <$400
3x10-20 1-5220 <$400
1902 Red Seal
3x10-20 1-4500 <$500
1902 Date Back
3x10-20 1-5500 <$200
1902 Plain Back
3x10-20 5501-17793 <$200
1929 Small Size
10 Type 1 1-1200 <$175
20 Type 1 1-410 <$175
SECOND TITLE {{ 6 S }}
1929 Small Size
10 Type 1 1-1212 <$175
20 Type 1 1-288 <$175
THIRD TITLE {{ 12 S }}
1929 Small Size
10 Type 1 1-1100 <$125
20 Type 1 1-404 <$125
10 Type 2 1-1763 <$125
20 Type 2 1-723 <$125
Total Issue $2,280,200
Out in 1935 $200,000
Large out 1935 $20,040
Outstanding includes Ch 1447, and Ch 4853

****

4853 Harrison
FOURTH NB OF CADIZ
{{ 5 L 8 S }}
Chartered 1893
Closed 1/12/31
Brown Back <$VALUE
3x10-20 1-5360 <$400
50-100 1-1380 <$1500/$1750
1882 Date Back
3x10-20 1-2897 <$400
50-100 1-107 <$1500/$1750
1902 Date Back
3x10-20 1-3600 <$250
1902 Plain Back
3x10-20 3601-21763 <$250
1929 Small Size
10 Type 1 1-1537 <$175
20 Type 1 1-410 <$175
Total Issue $1,865,470
Out at close $110,000
Large out at close $14,720
Ch 100 assumed circulation

****

Union NB of Cadiz and Union NB & TC of Cadiz SEE Ch 100 FNB of Cadiz

****

1447 Harrison
HARRISON NB OF CADIZ
{{ 10 L 9 S }}
Chartered 1865
Closed 1/12/31
Original Series <$VALUE
4x5 1-3000 <$500
3x10-20 1-2260 <$750/$1250
Series 1875
4x5 1-750 <$500
3x10-20 1-2336 <$750/$1250
Brown Back
3x10-20 1-10297 <$300/$350
1902 Red Seal
4x5 1-3000 <$350
3x10-20 1-2100 <$350/$400
1902 Date Back
4x5 1-5150 <$175
3x10-20 1-5220 <$175
1902 Plain Back
4x5 5151-24452 <$175
3x10-20 5221-14668 <$175
1929 Small Size
5 Type 1 1-1974 <$175
10 Type 1 1-842 <$175
20 Type 1 1-323 <$175
Total Issue $2,355,590
Out at close $100,000
Large out at close $13,880
Ch 100 assumed circulation

****

6458 Noble
CITIZENS NB OF CALDWELL
{{ 5 L 13 S }}
Chartered 10/14/02
Receivership 12/21/33
1902 Red Seal <$VALUE
3x10-20 1-3100 <$600
1902 Date Back
3x10-20 1-3600 <$275
1902 Plain Back
3x10-20 3601-12487 <$275
1929 Small Size
10 Type 1 1-1407 <$125
20 Type 1 1-429 <$125
Total Issue $915,250
Out at close $60,000
Large out at close $4,310

****

13844 Noble
FNB OF CALDWELL
{{ 9 S }}
Chartered 11/33
1929 Small Size <$VALUE
10 Type 2 1-5841 <$175
20 Type 2 1-1937 <$175
Total Issue $97,150
Out in 1935 $62,400

****

13154 Noble
NOBLE COUNTY NB IN CALDWELL
{{ 1 L 12 S }}
Organized 12/12/27
Receivership 12/21/33
1902 Plain Back <$VALUE
3x10-20 1-1226 <$600
1929 Small Size
10 Type 1 1-1412 <$125
20 Type 1 1-402 <$125
10 Type 2 1-29 <$200
20 Type 2 1-25 <$200
Total Issue $195,050
Out at close $60,000
Large out at close $5,390
Outstanding includes Ch 2102

****

2102 Noble
NOBLE COUNTY NB OF CALDWELL
{{ 11 L }}
Chartered 4/17/73
Liquidated 4/10/28
Original Series <$VALUE
3x1-2 1-1000 <$500/$1000
4x5 1-2950 <$500
Series 1875
3x10-20 1-11356 <$750/$1250
Brown Back
3x10-20 1-5060 <$350
1882 Date Back
3x10-20 1-1754 <$350
1902 Date Back
3x10-20 1-1800 <$175
1902 Plain Back
3x10-20 1801-8325 <$175
Total Issue $1,048,070
Out at close $43,800
Ch 13154 assumed circulation

****

13905 Guernsey
CENTRAL NB AT CAMBRIDGE
{{ 1 S }}
Chartered 12/33
1929 Small Size <$VALUE
10 Type 2 1-1176 <$600
20 Type 2 1-370 <$600
Total Issue $19,160
Out in 1935 $50,000
Outstanding includes Ch 2872

****

2872 Guernsey
CENTRAL NB OF CAMBRIDGE
{{ 8 L 12 S }}
Organized 12/22/82
Liquidated 7/14/34
Brown Back <$VALUE
3x10-20 1-6039 <$450
1902 Red Seal
3x10-20 1-5100 <$600
1902 Date Back
3x10-20 1-5700 <$250
1902 Plain Back
3x10-20 5701-17020 <$250
1929 Small Size
10 Type 1 1-1205 <$135
20 Type 1 1-325 <$150
Total Issue $1,519,250
Out at close $42,620
Large out 1935 $3,270
Ch 13905 assumed circulation

****

141 Guernsey
FNB OF CAMBRIDGE
{{ 3 L }}
Chartered 12/63
Liquidated 2/24/83
Original Series <$VALUE
3x1-2 1-416 <$500/$1000
4x5 1-1500 <$600
4x10 1-4500 <$750
Series 1875
4x10 1-1170 <$750
Total Issue $258,880
Out in 1910 $1,477

****

1942 Guernsey
GUERNSEY NB OF CAMBRIDGE
{{ 11 L 7 S }}
Chartered 2/29/72
Liquidated 7/29/31
Original Series <$VALUE
3x1-2 1-2000 <$450/$1000
4x5 1-5000 <$450
3x10-20 1-2500 <$750/$1250
Series 1875
4x5 1-3660 <$450
3x10-20 1-1820 <$750/$1250
Brown Back
3x10-20 1-4350 <$350
1882 Date Back
3x10-20 1-1117 <$350
1902 Date Back
3x10-20 1-1900 <$175
1902 Plain Back
3x10-20 1901-8941 <$175
1929 Small Size
10 Type 1 1-860 <$150
20 Type 1 1-194 <$175
Total Issue $1,194,480
Out at close $47,180
Large out at close $7,530

****

6566 Guernsey
NB OF CAMBRIDGE
{{ U + 6 L 2U + 12 S }}
Chartered 12/31/02
1902 Red Seal <$VALUE
3x10-20 1-3000 <$500
1902 Date Back
3x10-20 1-4600 <$250
1902 Plain Back
3x10-20 4601-12962 <$250
1929 Small Size
10 Type 1 1-1674 <$125
20 Type 1 1-466 <$125
10 Type 2 1-912 <$125
20 Type 2 1-240 <$135
Total Issue $968,380
Out in 1935 $58,800
Large out 1935 $3,480

****

2861 Guernsey
OLD NB OF CAMBRIDGE
{{ UNREPORTED }}
Chartered 1/20/83
Liquidated 1/12/03
Brown Back <$VALUE
3x10-20 1-2968 <$1250
Total Issue $148,400
Out in 1910 $2,580

****

8300 Preble
FNB OF CAMDEN
{{ 8 L 12 S }}
Chartered 7/05
Liquidated 2/11/35
1902 Red Seal <$VALUE
4x5 1-725 <$600
3x10-20 1-580 <$600
1902 Date Back
4x5 1-3950 <$250
3x10-20 1-2740 <$250
1902 Plain Back
4x5 3951-11324 <$250
3x10-20 2741-7475 <$250
1929 Small Size
5 Type 1 1-1924 <$125
10 Type 1 1-860 <$125
20 Type 1 1-252 <$125
5 Type 2 1-680 <$150
10 Type 2 1-415 <$150
20 Type 2 1-204 <$150
Total Issue $794,920
Out in 1935 $50,000
Large out 1935 $2,350

****

4293 Tuscarawas
EXCHANGE NB OF CANAL DOVER
Chartered 1890
2nd title: Exchange NB of Dover 6/16/16
FIRST TITLE {{ 2 L }}
Brown Back <$VALUE
3x10-20 1-3320 <$850
1882 Date Back
3x10-20 1-606 <$800
1902 Date Back
3x10-20 1-3000 <$500
1902 Plain Back
3x10-20 3001-3179 <$500
SECOND TITLE {{ 4 L 16 S }}
1902 Plain Back
3x10-20 1-8163 <$325
1929 Small Size
10 Type 1 1-2156 <$100
20 Type 1 1-592 <$115
10 Type 2 1-2120 <$115
20 Type 2 1-669 <$125
Total Issue $998,380
Out in 1935 $100,000
Large out 1935 $2,280

****

4331 Tuscarawas
FNB OF CANAL DOVER
Chartered 1890
2nd title: FNB of Dover 6/8/16
FIRST TITLE {{ 3 L }}
Brown Back <$VALUE
4x5 1-5330 <$650
50-100 1-816 <$1500/$1750
1882 Date Back
4x5 1-750 <$600
50-100 1-89 <$1500/$1750
1902 Date Back
3x10-20 1-3200 <$400
1902 Plain Back
3x10-20 3201-3268 <$400
SECOND TITLE {{ 3 L 11 S }}
1902 Plain Back
3x10-20 1-7316 <$275
1929 Small Size
10 Type 1 1-1142 <$125
20 Type 1 1-340 <$150
10 Type 2 1-1738 <$150
20 Type 2 1-379 <$150
Total Issue $920,830
Out in 1935 $48,850
Large out 1935 $2,970

****

3654 Mahoning
FARMERS' NB OF CANFIELD
{{ 7 L 18 S }}
Organized 2/26/87
Brown Back <$VALUE
4x5 1-3849 <$600
3x10-20 1-1153 <$600
1902 Red Seal
4x5 1-450 <$700
3x10-20 1-360 <$700
1902 Date Back
4x5 1-3400 <$275
3x10-20 1-2620 <$275
1902 Plain Back
4x5 3401-12670 <$275
3x10-20 2621-9077 <$275
1929 Small Size
5 Type 1 1-2730 <$125
10 Type 1 1-1402 <$125
20 Type 1 1-406 <$125
5 Type 2 1-3396 <$125
10 Type 2 1-2084 <$125
20 Type 2 1-516 <$125
Total Issue $1,131,760
Out in 1935 $73,150
Large out 1935 $2,340

****

2489 Stark
CITY NB OF CANTON
{{ 20 L }}
Chartered 1880
Liquidated 4/10/22
Series 1875 <$VALUE
4x5 1-15745 <$500
Brown Back
3x10-20 1-10500 <$400
1882 Date Back
3x10-20 1-13100 <$400
1882 Value Back
3x10-20 13101-20344 <$400
1902 Plain Back
3x10-20 1-5044 <$225
Total Issue $2,109,300
Out at close $197,400

****

76 Stark
FNB OF CANTON
{{ 32 L U + 50+ S }}
Chartered 9/63
Original Series <$VALUE
4x5 1-4600 <$600
3x10-20 1-1860 <$750/$1250
Series 1875
4x5 1-1185 <$600
3x10-20 1-1562 <$750/$1250
Brown Back
3x10-20 1-6917 <$400
1902 Red Seal
3x10-20 1-10500 <$450
1902 Date Back
3x10-20 1-36000 <$100
1902 Plain Back
3x10-20 36001-119145 <$100
1929 Small Size
10 Type 1 1-14964 <$30
20 Type 1 1-4054 <$40
10 Type 2 1-15140 <$40
20 Type 2 1-3480 <$50
Total Issue $8,720,220
Out in 1935 $500,000
Large out 1935 $22,930

****

127 Morrow
FNB OF CARDINGTON
{{ 8 L 10 S }}
Organized 10/15/63
Receivership 10/29/31
Original Series <$VALUE
3x1-2 1-6000 <$500/$1000
4x5 1-8250 <$500
Series 1875
3x1-2 1-660 <$500/$1000
4x5 1-6335 <$500
Brown Back
3x10-20 1-3321 <$400
1902 Red Seal
3x10-20 1-2506 <$500
1902 Date Back
3x10-20 1-3600 <$250
1902 Plain Back
3x10-20 3601-11032 <$250
1929 Small Size
10 Type 1 1-1052 <$175
20 Type 1 1-259 <$175
Total Issue $1,262,150
Out at close $60,000
Large out at close $9,170

****

6119 Wyandot
FNB OF CAREY
{{ 2 L 5 S }}
Chartered 2/6/02
Receivership 10/12/31
1902 Red Seal <$VALUE
4x5 1-1700 <$750
3x10-20 1-1160 <$750
1902 Date Back
4x5 1-1600 <$375
3x10-20 1-1000 <$375
1902 Plain Back (dated 1902)
4x5 1605-3015 <$375
3x10-20 1001-1912 <$375
1902 Plain Back (dated 1922)
3x10-20 1-2551 <$375
1929 Small Size
10 Type 1 1-426 <$325
20 Type 1 1-117 <$325
Total Issue $415,050
Out at close $25,000
Large out at close $2,000

****

13883 Carroll
FNB AT CARROLLTON
{{ 6 S }}
Chartered 12/33
1929 Small Size <$VALUE
5 Type 2 1-5916 <$200
10 Type 2 1-3353 <$200
20 Type 2 1-890 <$200
Total Issue $80,910
Out in 1935 $44,850

****

CONDITION affects Value. The Values shown are for notes in FINE condition.

****
11714 Carroll
FNB IN CARROLLTON
{{ 8 L 17 S }}
Organized 2/26/20
Liquidated 2/21/34
1902 Plain Back <$VALUE
4x5 1-14850 <$250
3x10-20 1-10009 <$250
1929 Small Size
5 Type 1 1-3572 <$100
10 Type 1 1-1936 <$100
20 Type 1 1-532 <$100
5 Type 2 1-198 <$125
10 Type 2 1-170 <$125
20 Type 2 1-65 <$125
Total Issue $1,088,600
Out at close $100,000
Large out at close $3,790
****
5396 Carroll
FNB OF CARROLLTON
{{ UNREPORTED }}
Chartered 6/4/00
Liquidated 5/31/06
Brown Back <$VALUE
3x10-20 1-795 <$1500
Total Issue $39,750
Out in 1910 $2,200
****
8488 Hamilton
FNB OF CARTHAGE
{{ 5 L }}
Chartered 12/06
Liquidated 10/15/27
1902 Red Seal <$VALUE
3x10-20 1-300 <$750
1902 Date Back
3x10-20 1-2160 <$400
1902 Plain Back
3x10-20 2161-5544 <$400
Total Issue $292,200
Out at close $16,910
****
5523 Mercer
FNB OF CELINA
{{ 8 L 15 S }}
Chartered 7/31/00
Brown Back <$VALUE
4x5 1-2325 <$400
3x10-20 1-1780 <$400
1882 Date Back
4x5 1-6000 <$400
3x10-20 1-4520 <$400
1882 Value Back
4x5 6001-9715 <$400
3x10-20 4521-6760 <$400
1902 Plain Back
4x5 1-11147 <$250
3x10-20 1-7992 <$250
1929 Small Size
5 Type 1 1-3734 <$150
10 Type 1 1-1976 <$150
20 Type 1 1-458 <$150
5 Type 2 1-3654 <$175
10 Type 2 1-1996 <$175
20 Type 2 1-620 <$175
Total Issue $1,626,510
Out in 1935 $100,000
Large out 1935 $5,300
****
8182 Knox
FNB OF CENTERBURG
{{ 2 L }}
Chartered 4/06
Liquidated 6/30/30
1902 Red Seal <$VALUE
3x10-20 1-300 <$1000
1902 Date Back
3x10-20 1-1860 <$600
1902 Plain Back
3x10-20 1861-4018 <$600
Total Issue $215,900
Out at close $2,150
****
2181 Gallia
CENTREVILLE NB OF
THURMAN, CENTREVILLE
{{ 6 L }}
Chartered 9/9/74
Liquidated 5/10/01
Original Series <$VALUE
3x1-2 1-1500 <$600/$1500
4x5 1-1875 <$750
Series 1875
3x1-2 1-1100 <$600/$1500
4x5 1-9078 <$750
Brown Back
3x10-20 1-1760 <$600
Total Issue $320,060
Out in 1910 $3,958
****

****
13569 Geauga
THE CENTRAL NB OF CHARDON
Chartered 8/31
2nd title: Central NB of
Chardon 9/10/31
FIRST TITLE {{ 4 S }}
1929 Small Size <$VALUE
5 Type 1 1-666 <$250
10 Type 1 1-332 <$250
20 Type 1 1-84 <$250
SECOND TITLE {{ 5 S }}
1929 Small Size
5 Type 1 1-272 <$225
10 Type 1 1-138 <$225
20 Type 1 1-44 <$225
5 Type 2 1-3610 <$225
10 Type 2 1-1695 <$225
20 Type 2 1-470 <$250
Total Issue $116,100
Out in 1935 $43,150
****
4671 Geauga
FNB OF CHARDON
{{ 7 L 5 S }}
Organized 12/14/91
Liquidated 9/21/31
Brown Back <$VALUE
4x5 1-3100 <$400
50-100 1-397 <$1500/$1750
1882 Date Back
4x5 1-755 <$400
50-100 1-132 <$1500/$1750
1902 Date Back
3x10-20 1-1150 <$300
1902 Plain Back
3x10-20 1151-4869 <$300
1929 Small Size
10 Type 1 1-449 <$300
20 Type 1 1-114 <$300
Total Issue $440,520
Out at close $22,780
Large out at close $2,000
****
5552 Morgan
FNB OF CHESTERHILL
{{ 3 L 6 S }}
Chartered 8/24/00
Brown Back <$VALUE
3x10-20 1-1500 <$650
1882 Date Back
3x10-20 1-1660 <$650
1882 Value Back
3x10-20 1661-2398 <$650
1902 Plain Back
3x10-20 1-2751 <$450
1929 Small Size
10 Type 1 1-750 <$250
20 Type 1 1-172 <$250
10 Type 2 1-506 <$275
20 Type 2 1-170 <$275
Total Issue $406,550
Out in 1935 $25,000
Large out 1935 $1,340
****
8478 Hamilton
FNB OF CHEVIOT
{{ 1 L }}
Chartered 12/06
Liquidated 4/1/20
1902 Red Seal <$VALUE
3x10-20 1-500 <$1250
1902 Date Back
3x10-20 1-1230 <$800
1902 Plain Back
3x10-20 1231-1668 <$800
Total Issue $108,400
Out at close $15,000
****
2993 Ross
CENTRAL NB OF CHILLICOTHE
{{ 6 L 17 S }}
Chartered 1883
Liquidated 5/1/34
Brown Back <$VALUE
3x10-20 1-9580 <$400
1902 Red Seal
3x10-20 1-3900 <$500
1902 Date Back
3x10-20 1-6800 <$200
1902 Plain Back
3x10-20 6801-22240 <$200
1929 Small Size
10 Type 1 1-2805 <$65
20 Type 1 1-667 <$70
Total Issue $2,034,340
Out at close $98,280
Large out at close $8,280
****

****
1277 Ross
CHILLICOTHE NB,
CHILLICOTHE
{{ UNREPORTED }}
Chartered 1865
Liquidated 4/9/77
Original Series <$VALUE
4x5 1-3850 <$1500
3x10-20 1-1220<$1750/$2000
Series 1875
3x10-20 1-316 <$1750/$2000
Total Issue $153,800
Out in 1910 $1,110
****
5634 Ross
CITIZENS NB OF
CHILLICOTHE
{{ 7 L 15 S }}
Chartered 12/7/00
Brown Back <$VALUE
3x10-20 1-7000 <$350
1882 Date Back
3x10-20 1-6400* <$350
1882 Value Back
3x10-20 6901-10294* <$350
* 6481-6900 not marked
1902 Plain Back
3x10-20 1-11565 <$200
1929 Small Size
10 Type 1 1-2882 <$85
20 Type 1 1-742 <$90
10 Type 2 1-2174 <$100
20 Type 2 1-511 <$100
Total Issue $1,736,870
Out in 1935 $100,000
Large out 1935 $5,060
****
128 Ross
FNB OF CHILLICOTHE
{{ 19 L 40 S }}
Chartered 11/63
Original Series <$VALUE
3x1-2 1-2000 <$400/$1000
4x5 1-2500 <$400
4x10 1-5250 <$750
Series 1875
4x10 1-4204 <$650
4x20 1-1458 <$1000
Brown Back
4x5 1-7750 <$300
3x10-20 1-17360 <$300
1902 Red Seal
3x10-20 1-7000 <$350
1902 Date Back
3x10-20 1-10500 <$125
1902 Plain Back
3x10-20 10501-31738 <$125
1929 Small Size
10 Type 1 1-5462 <$35
20 Type 1 1-2098 <$45
10 Type 2 1-13260* <$40
20 Type 2 1-3544** <$50
* 9864-10260 not issued
** 1931-2544 not issued
Total Issue $4,281,410
Out in 1935 $300,000
Large out 1935 $12,720
****
1172 Ross
ROSS COUNTY NB OF
CHILLICOTHE
{{ 12 L 18 S }}
Organized 5/9/65
Receivership 7/14/32
Original Series <$VALUE
4x5 1-3250 <$500
3x10-20 1-3700 <$750/$1250
Series 1875
4x5 1-497 <$500
3x10-20 1-3220 <$750/$1250
Brown Back
4x5 1-5250 <$350
3x10-20 1-13043 <$350
1902 Red Seal
3x10-20 1-5000 <$400
1902 Date Back
3x10-20 1-9600 <$165
1902 Plain Back
3x10-20 9601-31157 <$165
1929 Small Size
10 Type 1 1-3046 <$75
20 Type 1 1-925 <$85
Total Issue $3,279,700
Out at close $149,100
Large out at close $19,320
****

****
8438 Hamilton
AMERICAN NB OF CINCINNATI
{{ 1 L }}
Chartered 11/22/06
Liquidated 11/24/08
1902 Red Seal <$VALUE
4x5 1-1685 <$850
3x10-20 1-857 <$850
Total Issue $76,550
Out in 1910 $13,110
****
3639 Hamilton
ATLAS NB OF CINCINNATI
{{ 10 L 24 S }}
Chartered 2/23/87
Brown Back <$VALUE
4x5 1-2175 <$500
3x10-20 1-12864 <$500
1902 Red Seal
3x10-20 1-900 <$600
1902 Date Back
3x10-20 1-1900 <$250
1902 Plain Back
3x10-20 1901-36811 <$250
1929 Small Size
10 Type 1 1-4248 <$65
20 Type 1 1-1244 <$75
10 Type 2 1-5807 <$70
20 Type 2 1-1335 <$80
Total Issue $3,061,180
Out in 1935 $160,000
Large out 1935 $11,070
****
12446 Hamilton
BROTHERHOOD OF RAILWAY
CLERKS NB OF CINCINNATI
{{ 16 L 5 S }}
Organized 7/16/23
Liquidated 8/22/30
1902 Plain Back <$VALUE
4x5 1-65712 <$200
1929 Small Size
5 Type 1 1-7868 <$350
Total Issue $1,550,280
Out at close $200,000
Large out at close $18,940
****
620 Hamilton
CENTRAL NB OF CINCINNATI
{{ UNREPORTED }}
Chartered 12/12/64
Liquidated 3/31/70
Original Series <$VALUE
4x5 1-3955 <$1250
4x10 1-2400 <$1500
3x20-50 1-1500<$1750/$4000
100-100 1-500 <$4000
Total Issue $440,100
Out in 1910 $2,750
****
2922 Hamilton
CINCINNATI NB, CINCINNATI
{{ UNREPORTED }}
Chartered 4/12/83
Liquidated 8/1/88
Brown Back <$VALUE
3x10-20 1-1664 <$1500
50-100 1-17 <$2250/$2500
Total Issue $85,750
Out in 1910 $500
****
2495 Hamilton
CITIZENS NB OF CINCINNATI
Chartered 11/1/80
Liquidated 1/31/27
2nd title: Citizens NB & TC
12/10/21
FIRST TITLE {{ 50+ L }}
Series 1875 <$VALUE
3x10-20 1-86862<$750/$1250
Brown Back
4x5 1-48300 <$150
3x10-20 1-59680 <$150/$200
1882 Date Back
4x5 1-136665 <$135
3x10-20 1-108334<$135/$185
1882 Value Back
4x5 136666-195165 <$150
3x10-20 108335-137134
<$150/$200
1902 Plain Back
4x5 1-35000 <$65
3x10-20 1-25000 <$65
SECOND TITLE {{ 14 L }}
1902 Plain Back
4x5 1-115334 <$75
3x10-20 1-75686 <$75
Total Issue $27,094,080
Out at close $1,595,400
****

****
1185 Hamilton
COMMERCIAL NB OF
CINCINNATI
{{ 1 L }}
Chartered 5/26/65
Liquidated 4/28/68
Original Series <$VALUE
4x5 1-4000 <$1000
3x10-20 1-5319<$1250/$1500
Total Issue $345,950
Out in 1910 $1,700
****
3707 Hamilton
EQUITABLE NB OF
CINCINNATI
{{ 1 L }}
Chartered 5/17/87
Liquidated 2/14/05
Brown Back <$VALUE
4x5 1-1395 <$750
3x10-20 1-4475 <$750
Total Issue $251,650
Out in 1910 $6,920
****
2616 Hamilton
EXCHANGE NB OF CINCINNATI
{{ 1 L }}
Chartered 1882
Liquidated 8/27/84
Series 1875 <$VALUE
4x5 1-25 <$1250
3x10-20 1-1896<$1500/$1750
Total Issue $95,300
Out in 1910 $395
****
3461 Hamilton
FIDELITY NB OF CINCINNATI
{{ UNREPORTED }}
Organized 2/27/86
Receivership 6/27/87
Brown Back <$VALUE
4x5 1-4698 <$1250
Total Issue $93,960
Out in 1916 $610
****
24 Hamilton
FNB OF CINCINNATI
{{ 50+ L 44 S }}
Chartered 7/63
Original Series <$VALUE
4x5 1-23550 <$450
2x10-20-50 1-9600
<$750/$1250/$4000
2x10-20-50 9851-12250
<$750/$1250/$4000
20-50 9601-9850
<$1250/$4000
100-100 1-3210 <$4000
Series 1875
4x5 1-12200 <$450
2x10-20-50 1-6000
<$750/$1250/$4000
100-100 1-1340 <$4000
Brown Back
4x5 1-43564 <$150
3x10-20 1-29839 <$150/$200
50-100 1-2840 <$1500/$1750
1902 Red Seal
4x5 1-103750 <$150
3x10-20 1-74000 <$150/$200
1902 Date Back
4x5 1-260690 <$50
3x10-20 1-170000 <$50/$60
3x50-100 1-7192 <$350/$400
1902 Plain Back
4x5 260691-423898 <$50
3x10-20 70001-277931
<$50/$60
1929 Small Size
5 Type 1 1-14977 <$40
10 Type 1 1-8844 <$50
20 Type 1 1-4106 <$60
50 Type 1 1-614 <$225
100 Type 1 1-178 <$300
Total Issue $37,757,910
Out in 1935 $680,350
Large out 1935 $100,065
****
93 Hamilton
FOURTH NB OF CINCINNATI
{{ 43 L }}
Chartered 9/63
Liquidated 11/17/23
Original Series <$VALUE
4x5 1-13125 <$500
4x10 1-7880 <$750
3x20-50 1-1330<$1250/$4000
100-100 1-390 <$4000
Series 1875
4x5 1-7391 <$500
4x10 1-5450 <$650
3x20-50 1-705 <$1000/$4000
100-100 1-87 <$4000
Brown Back
4x5 1-7280 <$150
3x10-20 1-28596 <$150/$200
50-100 1-1026 <$1500/$1750
1902 Red Seal
4x5 1-10500 <$150
3x10-20 1-18000 <$150/$200
1902 Date Back
4x5 1-61665 <$50
3x10-20 1-45734 <$50/$60
1902 Plain Back
4x5 61666-80080 <$50
3x10-20 45735-57058
<$50/$60
Total Issue $8,556,570
Out at close $496,295
****
Fifth NB of Cincinnati
SEE Ch 2798
Queen City NB of Cincinnati
****
Fifth-Third NB of Cincinnati
SEE Ch 2798
Queen City NB of Cincinnati
SEE ALSO Ch 20
Third NB of Cincinnati
****
2524 Hamilton
GERMAN NB OF CINCINNATI
Chartered 1881
2nd title: Lincoln NB of
Cincinnati 1/11/18
FIRST TITLE {{ 29 L }}
Series 1875 <$VALUE
3x10-20 1-20315<$750/$1250
Brown Back
4x5 1-10500 <$150
3x10-20 1-19000 <$150/$175
1882 Date Back
4x5 1-51935 <$125
3x10-20 1-36474 <$125/$160
SECOND TITLE {{18 L U+ 50+S}}
1882 Value Back
4x5 1-13455 <$125
3x10-20 1-6786 <$125/$175
1902 Plain Back
4x5 1-61390 <$65
3x10-20 1-39500 <$65
1929 Small Size
5 Type 1 1-19380 <$25
10 Type 1 1-10702 <$25
20 Type 1 1-2752 <$35
5 Type 2 1-26134 <$25
10 Type 2 1-12706 <$25
20 Type 2 1-4630 <$35
Total Issue $10,753,440
Out in 1935 $473,350
Large out 1935 $27,970
****
Lincoln NB of Cincinnati
SEE Ch 2524
German NB of Cincinnati
****
3642 Hamilton
MARKET NB OF CINCINNATI
{{ U + 4 L }}
Chartered 3/8/87
Liquidated 7/2/19
Brown Back <$VALUE
3x10-20 1-6763 <$500
50-100 1-2070 <$1500/$1750
1902 Red Seal
3x10-20 1-3801 <$600
50-100 1-400 <$2250/$2500
1902 Date Back
3x10-20 1-18541 <$350
50-100 1-600 <$500/$600
3x50-100 1-48 <$500/$600
Total Issue $1,927,750
Out at close $158,800
****

<$VALUEs are for notes in **FINE** condition. Value changes by approximately **25%** for a change of one full grade.

844 Hamilton
MERCHANTS NB OF CINCINNATI
{{ 16 L }}
Chartered 2/27/65
Liquidated 1/25/10
Original Series <$VALUE
3x1-2 1-6000 <$750/$2000
4x5 1-9600 <$500
3x10-20 1-14700<$750/$1250
50-100 1-1984 <$4000
Series 1875
3x1-2 1-16 <$750/$2000
3x10-20 1-23996 <$750/$1250
Brown Back
4x5 1-14150 <$175
3x10-20 1-18332 <$175/$225
50-100 1-3400 <$1500/$1750
1902 Red Seal
4x5 1-20500 <$175
3x10-20 1-16000 <$175/$225
1902 Date Back
4x5 1-2686 <$100
3x10-20 1-2374 <$100
Total Issue $5,546,500
Out in 1910 $244,520

2542 Hamilton
METROPOLITAN NB OF CINCINNATI
{{ 3 L }}
Organized 6/23/81
Receivership 2/10/88
Series 1875 <$VALUE
4x5 1-4300 <$600
3x10-20 1-7732 <$750/$1250
100-100 1-456 <$4000
Total Issue $563,800
Out in 1916 $2,500

N Lafayette B of Cincinnati
SEE Ch 2315
NB of Commerce of Cincinnati

2315 Hamilton
NB OF COMMERCE OF CINCINNATI
Chartered 12/21/75
Liquidated 2/1 4/05
2nd title: N Lafayette B of Cincinnati 4/29/79
FIRST TITLE {{ 0 L }}
Series 1875 <$VALUE
4x5 1-10000 <$1250
3x10-20 1-818 <$1500/$1750
SECOND TITLE {{ 6 L }}
Series 1875
3x10-20 1-5278 <$750/$1250
50-100 1-3045 <$4000
Brown Back
50-100 1-5206 <$1500/$1750
Total Issue $1,742,450
Out in 1910 $73,390

630 Hamilton
OHIO NB OF CINCINNATI
{{ 1 L }}
Chartered 12/17/64
Liquidated 7/3/67
Original Series <$VALUE
4x5 1-5000 <$1000
3x10-20 1-4300<$1250/$1500
50-100 1-900 <$4000
Total Issue $450,000
Out in 1910 $5,370

3606 Hamilton
OHIO VALLEY NB OF CINCINNATI
{{ 3 L }}
Chartered 12/20/86
Liquidated 9/12/04
Brown Back <$VALUE
4x5 1-6200 <$600
3x10-20 1-11872 <$600
50-100 1-2888 <$1750/$2000
Total Issue $1,190,800
Out in 1910 $35,795

<$VALUEs are for notes in FINE condition. Value changes by approximately 25% for a change of one full grade.

2798 Hamilton
QUEEN CITY NB OF CINCINNATI
Chartered 1882
Liquidated 2/23/27
2nd title: Fifth NB 1888
3rd title: Fifth-Third NB* 6/2/08
*Took Ch 20 by special act of Congress 3/5/13
FIRST TITLE {{ 0 L }}
Brown Back <$VALUE
4x5 1-5565 <$1250
3x10-20 1-4649 <$1250
50-100 1-1209 <$2250/$2500
SECOND TITLE {{ U + 6 L }}
Brown Back
4x5 1-10000 <$225
3x10-20 1-22665 <$225/$275
1902 Red Seal
4x5 1-16830 <$225
3x10-20 1-27882 <$225/$275
THIRD TITLE {{ 6 L }}
1902 Date Back
4x5 1-110000 <$175
3x10-20 1-84000 <$175
Total Issue $9,989,050
Out in 1927 $1,750,995
Outstanding includes Ch 20

32 Hamilton
SECOND NB OF CINCINNATI*
{{ 18 L 50+ S }}
Chartered 7/63
Liquidated 4/28/82
***Reorganized as Ch 2664 which retook Ch 32 10/31/12**
Original Series <$VALUE
4x5 1-1250 <$600
4x10 1-3325 <$850
3x20-50 1-1355<$1250/$4000
Series 1875
4x10 1-2345 <$750
3x20-50 1-600 <$1250/$4000
1902 Date Back
3x10-20 1-47500 <$125
3x50-100 1-2000 <$500/$600
1902 Plain Back (dated 1902)
3x10-20 47501-52500 <$125
1902 Plain Back (dated 1922)
3x10-20 1-64510 <$125
1929 Small Size
10 Type 1 1-23910 <$30
20 Type 1 1-6334 <$35
10 Type 2 1-18686 <$35
20 Type 2 1-5960 <$45
Total Issue $9,318,270
Out in 1935 $720,700
Large out 1935 $46,850
Outstanding includes Ch 2664

2664 Hamilton
SECOND NB OF CINCINNATI
{{ 6 L }}
Chartered 1882
RETOOK Ch 32 10/31/12
Brown Back <$VALUE
3x10-20 1-7681 <$400
1902 Red Seal
3x10-20 1-19700 <$500
1902 Date Back
3x10-20 1-31000 <$275
50-100 1-4697 <$400/$500
Total Issue $3,623,600
Out in 1912 $200,000

20 Hamilton
THIRD NB OF CINCINNATI
Chartered 7/63
Liquidated 6/14/82
Succeeded by Ch 2730, which consolidated with Ch 2798
By special act of Congress Ch 2798 took Ch 20 3/5/13
2nd title: Fifth-Third NB 6/2/08
Liquidated 2/23/27
FIRST TITLE {{ 1 L }}
Original Series <$VALUE
4x5 1-6050 <$750
3x10-20 1-10120<$850/$1250
3x20-50 1-5300<$1250/$4000
Series 1875
4x5 1-1136 <$750
3x10-20 1-3156 <$850/$1250
3x20-50 1-2752<$1250/$4000
SECOND TITLE {{ 47 L }}
1902 Date Back
4x5 1-79150 <$100
3x10-20 1-63340 <$100
3x50-100 1-4000 <$400/$500
1902 Plain Back
4x5 79151-278994 <$100
3x10-20 63341-211778 <$100
Total Issue $17,168,780
Out at close $1,750,995
Outstanding includes Ch 2798

2730 Hamilton
THIRD NB OF CINCINNATI
{{ 21 L }}
Chartered 6/14/82
Liquidated 6/18/08
Series 1875 <$VALUE
100-100 1-2500 <$4000
Brown Back
4x5 1-2500 <$150
3x10-20 1-82964 <$150/$200
1902 Red Seal
4x5 1-47209 <$175
3x10-20 1-36235 <$175/$225
Total Issue $7,454,130
Out in 1910 $365,345

2549 Hamilton
UNION NB OF CINCINNATI
{{ UNREPORTED }}
Organized 8/6/81
Liquidated 2/14/87
Series 1875 <$VALUE
4x5 1-5500 <$1250
3x10-20 1-5578<$1500/$1750
50-100 1-1336 <$4000
Total Issue $589,300
Out in 1910 $2,700

118 Pickaway
FNB OF CIRCLEVILLE
{{ 9 L 23 S }}
Chartered 11/63
Original Series <$VALUE
4x5 1-6200 <$600
4x10 1-3800 <$850
4x20 1-2025 <$1250
Series 1875
4x5 1-2056 <$600
4x10 1-2875 <$850
4x20 1-1537 <$1250
Brown Back
3x10-20 1-9437 <$500
1902 Red Seal
3x10-20 1-5800 <$600
1902 Date Back
3x10-20 1-8200 <$225
1902 Plain Back
3x10-20 8201-26819 <$225
1929 Small Size
10 Type 1 1-3296 <$100
20 Type 1 1-920 <$100
10 Type 2 1-4466 <$100
20 Type 2 1-990 <$100
Total Issue $3,192,500
Out in 1935 $130,000
Large out 1935 $11,260

172 Pickaway
SECOND NB OF CIRCLEVILLE
{{ 6 L 9 S }}
Chartered 12/63
Original Series <$VALUE
4x5 1-4450 <$600
4x10 1-3550 <$850
Series 1875
4x5 1-1165 <$600
4x10 1-2285 <$850
Brown Back
4x5 1-1677 <$500
3x10-20 1-3712 <$500
1902 Red Seal
3x10-20 1-1822 <$600
1902 Date Back
3x10-20 1-4500 <$300
1902 Plain Back
3x10-20 4501-11409 <$300
1929 Small Size
10 Type 1 1-1440 <$175
20 Type 1 1-382 <$200
10 Type 2 1-1952 <$200
20 Type 2 1-459 <$200
Total Issue $1,387,330
Out in 1935 $54,800
Large out 1935 $5,160

2817 Pickaway
THIRD NB OF CIRCLEVILLE
{{ 3 L 7 S }}
Chartered 1882
Brown Back <$VALUE
3x10-20 1-2384 <$600
1902 Red Seal
3x10-20 1-1290 <$700
1902 Date Back
3x10-20 1-2400 <$400
1902 Plain Back
3x10-20 2401-5455 <$400
1929 Small Size
10 Type 1 1-860 <$225
20 Type 1 1-188 <$225
10 Type 2 1-356 <$250
20 Type 2 1-32 <$275
Total Issue $534,810
Out in 1935 $30,000
Large out 1935 $1,910

5762 Monroe
FNB OF CLARINGTON
{{ 6 L 9 S }}
Chartered 3/30/01
Brown Back <$VALUE
3x10-20 1-1900 <$450
1882 Date Back
4x5 1-2350* <$450
3x10-20 1-1580** <$450
1882 Value Back
4x5 2476-4015* <$450
3x10-20 1681-2594** <$450
* 2351-2475 not marked
** 1581-1680 not marked
1902 Plain Back
4x5 1-3805 <$250
3x10-20 1-2715 <$250
1929 Small Size
5 Type 1 1-964 <$175
10 Type 1 1-578 <$175
20 Type 1 1-212 <$175
5 Type 2 1-1724 <$200
10 Type 2 1-920 <$200
20 Type 2 1-204 <$200
Total Issue $627,790
Out in 1935 $35,000
Large out 1935 $2,050

7370 Clinton
FARMERS NB OF CLARKSVILLE
{{ 3 L 3 S }}
Chartered 8/04
Liquidated 1/12/32
1902 Red Seal <$VALUE
3x10-20 1-1022 <$1000
1902 Date Back
3x10-20 1-1850 <$500
1902 Plain Back
3x10-20 1851-5467 <$500
1929 Small Size
10 Type 1 1-390 <$500
20 Type 1 1-115 <$500
Total Issue $361,650
Out at close $25,000
Large out at close $3,290

5090 Cuyahoga
AMERICAN EXCHANGE NB OF CLEVELAND
{{ 2 L }}
Chartered 10/1/97
Liquidated 1/14/03
Brown Back <$VALUE
4x5 1-6519 <$500
3x10-20 1-4165 <$500
Total Issue $338,630
Out in 1910 $7,820

5194 Cuyahoga
BANK OF COMMERCE NATIONAL ASSOC OF CLEVELAND
{{ 12 L }}
Chartered 5/22/99
Liquidated 2/2/18
Brown Back <$VALUE
3x10-20 1-44700 <$150/$200
50-100 1-1500 <$1500/$1750
1882 Date Back
4x5 1-22020 <$150
3x10-20 1-73000*<$150/$200
50-100 1-3360 <$1500/$1750
1882 Value Back
3x10-20 76001-80495* <$160/$200
* 73001-76000 not marked
Total Issue $7,429,150
Out at close $809,100
Ch 11141 assumed circulation

5805 Cuyahoga
BANKERS NB OF CLEVELAND
{{ 5 L }}
Chartered 5/11/01
Liquidated 2/13/04
Brown Back <$VALUE
4x5 1-13325 <$500
3x10-20 1-10652 <$500
Total Issue $799,100
Out in 1910 $22,045

11862 Cuyahoga
BROTHERHOOD OF LOCOMOTIVE ENGINEERS CO-OPERATIVE NB OF CLEVELAND
Chartered 10/20
Liquidated 9/12/30
2nd title: Engineers NB of Cleveland 2/15/28
FIRST TITLE {{ U + 37 L }}
1902 Plain Back <$VALUE
4x5 1-299874 <$175
SECOND TITLE {{2U+29 L 3 S}}
1902 Plain Back
4x5 1-66166 <$150
1929 Small Size
5 Type 1 1-19163 <$350
Total Issue $7,895,690
Out at close $225,080

4318 Cuyahoga
CENTRAL NB OF CLEVELAND
Chartered 1890
2nd title: Central NB Savings & TC 12/31/20
3rd title: Central NB of Cleveland 1/15/26
4th title: Central United NB of Cleveland 11/16/29
FIRST TITLE {{ 19 L }}
Brown Back <$VALUE
4x5 1-22500 <$175
3x10-20 1-45600 <$175/$225
1882 Date Back
4x5 1-13560 <$150
3x10-20 1-8652 <$150/$200
1902 Date Back
4x5 1-60500 <$50
3x10-20 1-46000 <$50/$60
1902 Plain Back
4x5 60501-109500 <$50
3x10-20 46001-74200<$50/$60
SECOND TITLE {{ 7 L }}
1902 Plain Back
4x5 1-163713 <$100
3x10-20 1-97787 <$100
THIRD TITLE {{ 15 L 22 S }}
1902 Plain Back
4x5 1-106955 <$50
3x10-20 1-66025 <$50/60
1929 Small Size
5 Type 1 1-14880 <$25
10 Type 1 1-11080 <$30
20 Type 1 1-3734 <$40
FOURTH TITLE {{ 50+ S }}
1929 Small Size
5 Type 1 1-113222 <$15
10 Type 1 1-73806 <$20
20 Type 1 1-20414 <$30
5 Type 2 1-273896* <$15
10 Type 2 1-132685 <$20
20 Type 2 1-43277 <$30
* 10015-10020 not issued
Total Issue $38,333,580
Out in 1935 $4,127,500
Large out 1935 $48,520
Large out at close $60,100

5350 Cuyahoga
CENTURY NB OF CLEVELAND
{{ 2 L }}
Chartered 5/15/00
Liquidated 3/20/02
Brown Back <$VALUE
3x10-20 1-4991 <$650
Total Issue $249,550
Out in 1910 $6,360

2956 Cuyahoga
CLEVELAND NB, CLEVELAND
{{ 16 L }}
Chartered 1883
Liquidated 4/19/19
Brown Back <$VALUE
3x10-20 1-12251 <$225/$275
1902 Red Seal
3x10-20 1-25500 <$225/$275
1902 Date Back
3x10-20 1-39360 <$100
1902 Plain Back
3x10-20 39361-48281 <$100
Total Issue $4,301,600
Out at close $476,600

5191 Cuyahoga
COAL & IRON NB OF CLEVELAND
{{ 4 L }}
Chartered 5/13/99
Liquidated 8/15/03
Brown Back <$VALUE
3x10-20 1-13635 <$500
Total Issue $681,750
Out in 1910 $19,440

5152 Cuyahoga
COLONIAL NB OF CLEVELAND
{{ 3 L }}
Chartered 11/2/98
Liquidated 4/2/04
Brown Back <$VALUE
4x5 1-3300 <$500
3x10-20 1-5201 <$500
Total Issue $326,050
Out in 1910 $9,835

807 Cuyahoga
COMMERCIAL NB OF CLEVELAND
{{ 3 L }}
Chartered 2/14/65
Liquidated 12/1/04
Original Series <$VALUE
4x5 1-7650 <$850
3x10-20 1-9320<$1000/$1500
50-100 1-767 <$4000
Series 1875
50-100 1-3583 <$4000
Brown Back
3x10-20 1-10358 <$750
50-100 1-1680 <$1500/$1750
Total Issue $2,041,400
Out in 1910 $33,280

Engineers NB of Cleveland
SEE Ch 11862
Brotherhood of Locomotive Engineers Co-Operative NB of Cleveland

3545 Cuyahoga
EUCLID AVENUE NB OF CLEVELAND
Chartered 7/31/86
Liquidated 4/29/05
2nd title: Euclid-Park NB of Cleveland 7/1/03
FIRST TITLE {{ 6 L }}
Brown Back <$VALUE
4x5 1-32238 <$350
3x10-20 1-10772 <$350/$400
SECOND TITLE {{ 2 L }}
Brown Back
4x5 1-9570 <$400
3x10-20 1-15293 <$400/$450
Total Issue $2,139,410
Out in 1910 $78,790

Euclid-Park NB of Cleveland
SEE Ch 3545
Euclid Avenue NB of Cleveland

7 Cuyahoga
FNB OF CLEVELAND*
{{ 24 L }}
Chartered 6/63
Liquidated 5/13/82
***Reorganized as Ch 2690 which retook Ch 7 5/16/10**
Liquidated 12/30/20
Original Series <$VALUE
3x1-2 1-6900 <$600/$1250
4x5 1-17600 <$600
2x10-20-50 1-2600 <$750/$1250/$4000
Series 1875
2x10-20-50 1-2621 <$750/$1250/$4000
1902 Date Back
4x5 1-47635 <$125
3x10-20 1-55473 <$125
Total Issue $4,582,740
Out at close $457,197
Outstanding includes Ch 2690

2690 Cuyahoga
FNB OF CLEVELAND
{{ 12 L }}
Chartered 1882
RETOOK Ch 7 5/16/10
Brown Back <$VALUE
4x5 1-11305 <$200
3x10-20 1-10532 <$200/$250
1902 Red Seal
4x5 1-65650 <$200
3x10-20 1-47940 <$200/$250
1902 Date Back
4x5 1-40830 <$125
3x10-20 1-32668 <$125
Total Issue $6,912,700
Out in 1910 $300,000

CONDITION affects Value. The Values shown are for notes in FINE condition.

****

5678 Cuyahoga
MARKET NB OF CLEVELAND
{{ 4 L }}
Chartered 1/15/01
Liquidated 11/1/06
Brown Back <$VALUE
3x10-20 1-17522 <$350/$400
Total Issue $876,100
Out in 1910 $35,500
****

3272 Cuyahoga
MERCANTILE NB OF CLEVELAND
{{ 3 L }}
Chartered 12/13/84
Liquidated 12/1/04
Brown Back <$VALUE
3x10-20 1-28220 <$375/$425
Total Issue $1,411,000
Out in 1910 $23,965
****

773 Cuyahoga
MERCHANTS NB OF CLEVELAND
{{ 7 L }}
Chartered 1/31/65
Liquidated 12/27/84
Original Series <$VALUE
3x1-2 1-5000 <$500/$1250
4x5 1-7750 <$500
3x10-20 1-10500<$750/$1250
50-100 1-1400 <$4000
Series 1875
4x5 1-1344 <$500
3x10-20 1-4504 <$750/$1250
50-100 1-2484 <$4000
Total Issue $1,539,680
Out in 1910 $9,329
****

5653 Cuyahoga
METROPOLITAN NB OF CLEVELAND
{{ UNREPORTED }}
Chartered 12/24/00
Liquidated 4/1/02
Brown Back <$VALUE
3x10-20 1-1121 <$1250
Total Issue $56,050
Out in 1910 $1,820
****

2662 Cuyahoga
NB OF COMMERCE OF CLEVELAND
{{ 4 L }}
Chartered 4/17/82
Liquidated 5/29/99
Series 1875 <$VALUE
50-100 1-856 <$4000
Brown Back
4x5 1-16000 <$300
3x10-20 1-12356 <$300/$350
Total Issue $1,066,200
Out in 1910 $10,080
****

786 Cuyahoga
N CITY B OF CLEVELAND
{{ U + 14 L 50+ S }}
Chartered 2/7/65
Original Series <$VALUE
3x1-2 1-1000 <$500/$1250
4x5 1-5500 <$500
3x10-20 1-5050 <$750/$1250
Series 1875
3x10-20 1-4787 <$750/$1250
Brown Back
4x5 1-5990 <$150
50-100 1-2789 <$1500/$1750
1902 Red Seal
4x5 1-6100 <$175
3x10-20 1-4360 <$175/$225
1902 Date Back
4x5 1-20250 <$65
3x10-20 1-16000 <$65
1902 Plain Back
4x5 20251-169098 <$65
3x10-20 16001-111684 <$65
3x50-100 1-6200 <$300/$350
1929 Small Size
5 Type 1 1-62564 <$15
10 Type 1 1-33834 <$20
20 Type 1 1-9260 <$30
5 Type 2 1-83660 <$15
10 Type 2 1-39806 <$20
20 Type 2 1-6459 <$30
Total Issue $17,964,860
Out in 1935 $1,103,675
Large out 1935 $52,810
****

****

7487 Cuyahoga
N COMMERCIAL B OF CLEVELAND
{{ 18 L }}
Chartered 11/04
Liquidated 2/28/21
1902 Red Seal <$VALUE
3x10-20 1-29000 <$200/$225
1902 Date Back
3x10-20 1-86000 <$65
1902 Plain Back
3x10-20 86001-101444 <$65
Total Issue $6,522,200
Out at close $582,000
****

11376 Cuyahoga
NORTHERN NB OF CLEVELAND
{{ 2 L }}
Chartered 6/19
Liquidated 8/1/21
1902 Plain Back <$VALUE
4x5 1-1550 <$750
3x10-20 1-980 <$750
3x50-100 1-100<$1000/$1250
Total Issue $105,000
Out at close $39,700
****

1689 Cuyahoga
OHIO NB OF CLEVELAND
{{ 2 L }}
Chartered 1/14/69
Liquidated 1/1/89
Original Series <$VALUE
4x5 1-17000 <$1000
4x10 1-2000 <$1250
Series 1875
4x5 1-20000 <$1000
4x10 1-6067 <$1250
Total Issue $1,062,680
Out in 1910 $4,735
****

5006 Cuyahoga
PARK NB OF CLEVELAND
{{ 5 L }}
Chartered 6/21/95
Liquidated 7/1/03
Brown Back <$VALUE
3x10-20 1-19824 <$250/$300
Total Issue $991,200
Out in 1910 $27,450
****

13 Cuyahoga
SECOND NB OF CLEVELAND
{{ 4 L }}
Chartered 6/63
Liquidated 5/6/82
Succeeded by Ch 2662
Original Series <$VALUE
4x5 1-7150 <$750
4x10 1-9375 <$850
3x20-50 1-7445<$1250/$4000
Series 1875
4x5 1-4000 <$750
4x10 1-1175 <$850
3x20-50 1-1664<$1250/$4000
Total Issue $1,646,990
Out in 1910 $9,285
****

3950 Cuyahoga
STATE NB OF CLEVELAND
{{ 5 L }}
Chartered 12/22/88
Liquidated 7/1/04
Brown Back <$VALUE
3x10-20 1-21639 <$275/$325
Total Issue $1,081,950
Out in 1910 $34,740
****

11141 Cuyahoga
UNION COMMERCE NB OF CLEVELAND
{{ 8 L }}
Chartered 2/18
Liquidated 12/30/20
1902 Plain Back <$VALUE
4x5 1-44650 <$150
3x10-20 1-25802 <$150
Total Issue $2,183,100
Out at close $1,446,000
Outstanding includes Ch 3202, and Ch 5194
****

3202 Cuyahoga
UNION NB OF CLEVELAND
{{ 12 L }}
Chartered 1884
Liquidated 2/2/18
Brown Back <$VALUE
4x5 1-13023 <$200
3x10-20 1-1268 <$200/$250
1902 Red Seal
4x5 1-18500 <$200
3x10-20 1-25400 <$200/$250
1902 Date Back
4x5 1-71222 <$100
3x10-20 1-55564 <$100
Total Issue $6,166,500
Out at close $850,000
Ch 11141 assumed circulation
****

4782 Cuyahoga
WESTERN RESERVE NB OF CLEVELAND
{{ 2 L }}
Chartered 7/28/92
Liquidated 5/29/99
Brown Back <$VALUE
3x10-20 1-1800 <$650
50-100 1-904 <$1500/$1750
Total Issue $225,600
Out in 1910 $3,700
****

13774 Hamilton
CLEVES NB, CLEVES
{{ 9 S }}
Chartered 9/33
1929 Small Size <$VALUE
5 Type 2 1-6142 <$225
10 Type 2 1-2104 <$225
Total Issue $51,750
Out in 1935 $49,450
****

7456 Hamilton
HAMILTON COUNTY NB OF CLEVES
{{ 4 L 8 S }}
Organized 10/11/04
Receivership 11/6/33
1902 Red Seal <$VALUE
3x10-20 1-1206 <$750
1902 Date Back
3x10-20 1-1960 <$400
1902 Plain Back
3x10-20 1961-5837 <$400
1929 Small Size
10 Type 1 1-1003 <$225
20 Type 1 1-202 <$225
Total Issue $436,570
Out at close $40,380
Large out at close $1,870
****

4197 Sandusky
FNB OF CLYDE
{{ 1 L }}
Chartered 2/7/90
Liquidated 7/2/06
Brown Back <$VALUE
4x5 1-5034 <$1000
3x10-20 1-1612 <$1000
Total Issue $181,280
Out in 1910 $6,375
****

5277 Butler
FNB OF COLLEGE CORNER
{{ UNREPORTED }}
Chartered 4/7/00
Liquidated 7/1/05
Brown Back <$VALUE
3x10-20 1-1107 <$1500
Total Issue $55,350
Out in 1910 $2,980
****

6296 Columbiana
FNB OF COLUMBIANA
{{ 1 L }}
Chartered 6/9/02
Liquidated 12/16/09
1902 Red Seal <$VALUE
3x10-20 1-1190 <$1250
1902 Date Back
3x10-20 1-144 <$850
Total Issue $66,700
Out in 1910 $10,700
****

9282 Franklin
CENTRAL NB OF COLUMBUS
{{ U + 5 L }}
Chartered 11/08
Liquidated 9/3/21
1902 Date Back <$VALUE
4x5 1-15000 <$250
3x10-20 1-11300 <$250
1902 Plain Back
4x5 15001-24425 <$250
3x10-20 11301-17320 <$250
Total Issue $1,354,500
Out at close $194,895
****

City-NB of Commerce, Columbus
and City NB & TC of Columbus
SEE Ch 7621
NB of Commerce, Columbus
****

****

7818 Franklin
CITY NB OF COLUMBUS
{{ 14 L }}
Chartered 7/05
Closed 12/31/26
1902 Red Seal <$VALUE
4x5 1-2750 <$250
3x10-20 1-2000 <$250/$275
1902 Date Back
4x5 1-16750 <$125
3x10-20 1-12700 <$125
1902 Plain Back
4x5 16751-50305 <$125
3x10-20 12701-33004 <$125
Total Issue $2,811,300
Out at close $244,595
Ch 7621 assumed circulation
****

3610 Franklin
CLINTON NB OF COLUMBUS
{{ UNREPORTED }}
Chartered 12/24/86
Liquidated 1/8/00
Brown Back <$VALUE
3x10-20 1-3570 <$1000
Total Issue $178,500
Out in 1910 $2,300
****

2605 Franklin
COMMERCIAL NB OF COLUMBUS
{{ 40 L 7 S }}
Chartered 1882
Closed 11/30/29
Series 1875 <$VALUE
3x10-20 1-4899 <$750/$1250
Brown Back
4x5 1-7000 <$175
3x10-20 1-10000 <$175/$225
1882 Date Back
4x5 1-23000 <$175
3x10-20 1-15200 <$175/$225
1882 Value Back
4x5 23001-38975 <$175
3x10-20 15201-24295 <$175/$225
1902 Plain Back
4x5 1-62939 <$65
4x10 1-28459 <$65
3x10-20 1-24075 <$65
1929 Small Size
5 Type 1 1-3036 <$150
10 Type 1 1-1935 <$150
20 Type 1 1-420 <$150
Total Issue $6,737,670
Out at close $580,995
Large out at close $323,415
Ch 7621 assumed circulation
****

4579 Franklin
DESHLER NB OF COLUMBUS
{{ 7 L }}
Chartered 1891
Liquidated 7/2/10
Brown Back <$VALUE
3x10-20 1-16100 <$225/$275
1882 Date Back
3x10-20 1-4020 <$225/$275
Total Issue $1,006,000
Out in 1910 $259,050
****

FNB of Columbus
SEE Ch 4443
NB of Commerce of Columbus
****

123 Franklin
FNB OF COLUMBUS
{{ 4 L }}
Chartered 11/11/63
Liquidated 10/15/90
Original Series <$VALUE
3x1-2 1-6740 <$600/$1500
4x5 1-10675 <$600
4x10 1-3875 <$850
4x20 1-1200 <$1250
Series 1875
4x5 1-1150 <$600
4x10 1-1000 <$850
4x20 1-2967 <$1250
Brown Back
4x5 1-2000 <$400
3x10-20 1-7711 <$400
Total Issue $1,224,110
Out in 1910 $7,958
****

2423 Franklin
FOURTH NB OF COLUMBUS
{{ 10 L }}
Chartered 4/23/79
Liquidated 6/16/97
Series 1875 <$VALUE
3x10-20 1-5006 <$750/$1250
50-100 1-38 <$4000
Total Issue $256,000
Out in 1910 $2,670
****

599 Franklin
FRANKLIN NB OF COLUMBUS
{{ 2 L }}
Chartered 12/64
Liquidated 1/4/79
Original Series <$VALUE
4x5 1-11000 <$750
4x10 1-1500 <$850
3x20-50 1-470 <$1250/$4000
Series 1875
4x5 1-480 <$750
4x10 1-315 <$850
Total Issue $353,900
Out in 1910 $2,120
****

4697 Franklin
HAYDEN NB OF COLUMBUS
Chartered 1892
Liquidated 5/1/23
2nd title: Hayden-Clinton NB of Columbus 1/9/00
FIRST TITLE {{ 2 L }}
Brown Back <$VALUE
3x10-20 1-2277 <$600
SECOND TITLE {{ 10 L }}
Brown Back
3x10-20 1-17000 <$200/$250
1882 Date Back
3x10-20 1-15979 <$175/$200
1902 Date Back
3x10-20 1-22000 <$125
1902 Plain Back
3x10-20 22001-59606 <$125
Total Issue $4,743,100
Out at close $467,300
****

7745 Franklin
HUNTINGTON NB OF COLUMBUS
{{ 33 L U + 50+ S }}
Chartered 5/05
1902 Red Seal <$VALUE
4x5 1-10750 <$350
3x10-20 1-8150 <$350
1902 Date Back
4x5 1-29830 <$75
3x10-20 1-20368 <$75
1902 Plain Back
4x5 29831-164115 <$75
3x10-20 20369-104760 <$75
1929 Small Size
5 Type 1 1-34214 <$20
10 Type 1 1-19798 <$25
20 Type 1 1-7068 <$30
5 Type 2 1-97792 <$25
20 Type 2 1-27300 <$30
Total Issue $13,240,220
Out in 1935 $1,250,000
Large out 1935 $28,450
****

5029 Franklin
MERCHANTS & MANUFACTURERS NB OF COLUMBUS
{{ 2 L }}
Organized 12/23/95
Liquidated 3/11/05
Brown Back <$VALUE
4x5 1-950 <$600
3x10-20 1-5532 <$600
Total Issue $295,600
Out in 1916 $3,305
****

4443 Franklin
NB OF COMMERCE OF COLUMBUS
Chartered 1890
Liquidated 5/15/28
2nd title: New FNB of Columbus 6/15/97
3rd title: FNB in Columbus 3/5/21
FIRST TITLE {{ 0 L }}
Brown Back <$VALUE
50-100 1-701 <$1750/$2000
SECOND TITLE {{ 6 L }}
Brown Back
50-100 1-8100 <$1500/$1750
1882 Date Back
50-100 1-513 <$1500/$1750
1902 Date Back
50-100 1-5000 <$400/$450
3x50-100 1-4000 <$400/$450
THIRD TITLE {{ 13 L }}
1902 Plain Back
3x50-100 1-4333 <$300/$350
Total Issue $4,230,350
Out at close $489,500
****

****

7621 Franklin
NB OF COMMERCE, COLUMBUS
Chartered 2/05
2nd title: City-NB of Commerce 12/31/26
3rd title: City NB & TC 11/30/29
FIRST TITLE {{ 6 L }}
1902 Red Seal <$VALUE
4x5 1-2000 <$225
3x10-20 1-1650 <$225/$275
1902 Date Back
4x5 1-4015* <$125
3x10-20 1-3134** <$125
1902 Plain Back
4x5 4416-9608* <$125
3x10-20 3435-6769** <$125
* 4016-4415 not marked
** 3135-3434 not marked
SECOND TITLE {{ 10 L 7 S }}
1902 Plain Back
4x5 1-12396 <$100
3x10-20 1-7588 <$100
1929 Small Size
5 Type 1 1-4606 <$125
10 Type 1 1-2150 <$125
20 Type 1 1-724 <$125
THIRD TITLE {{ 50+ S }}
1929 Small Size
5 Type 1 1-29320 <$20
10 Type 1 1-19064 <$20
20 Type 1 1-5200 <$30
5 Type 2 1-61690 <$20
10 Type 2 1-26958 <$20
20 Type 2 1-6727 <$30
Total Issue $4,994,500
Out in 1935 $1,076,150
Large out 1935 $34,610
Outstanding includes Ch 7818, and Ch 2605
****

591 Franklin
N EXCHANGE B OF COLUMBUS
{{ 3 L }}
Chartered 11/30/64
Liquidated 4/1/92
Original Series <$VALUE
4x5 1-7000 <$500
3x10-20 1-4120 <$750/$1250
Series 1875
3x10-20 1-1448 <$750/$1250
Brown Back
3x10-20 1-1742 <$400
Total Issue $505,500
Out in 1910 $3,165
****

New FNB in Columbus
SEE Ch 4443
NB of Commerce in Columbus
****

5065 Franklin
OHIO NB OF COLUMBUS
{{ U + 37 L U + 50+ S }}
Chartered 1897
Brown Back <$VALUE
4x5 1-15200 <$200
3x10-20 1-18420 <$200/$250
1882 Date Back
4x5 1-31317 <$200
3x10-20 1-20841 <$200/$250
1902 Plain Back
4x5 1-118021 <$75
3x10-20 1-78280 <$75
1929 Small Size
5 Type 1 1-28654 <$20
10 Type 1 1-19044 <$25
20 Type 1 1-6076 <$35
5 Type 2 1-90288 <$20
10 Type 2 1-51569 <$25
20 Type 2 1-17115 <$35
Total Issue $13,208,620
Out in 1935 $1,700,000
Large out 1935 $32,205
****

7584 Franklin
UNION NB OF COLUMBUS
{{ UNREPORTED }}
Organized 1/30/05
Receivership 12/7/11
1902 Red Seal <$VALUE
4x5 1-2000 <$1000
50-100 1-1000 <$2250/$2500
1902 Date Back
4x5 1-2860 <$750
50-100 1-569 <$850/$1000
Total Issue $332,550
Out in 1916 $18,690
****

****
3492 Ashtabula
FNB OF CONNEAUT
{{ UNREPORTED }}
Organized 4/27/86
Receivership 12/20/04
Brown Back <$VALUE
4x5 1-2236 <$1500
3x10-20 1-1073 <$1500
Total Issue $98,370
Out in 1916 $580
****
8017 Van Wert
FNB OF CONVOY
{{ 3 L 7 S }}
Chartered 12/05
1902 Red Seal <$VALUE
3x10-20 1-1050 <$1000
1902 Date Back
3x10-20 1-1640 <$500
1902 Plain Back
3x10-20 1641-5389 <$500
1929 Small Size
10 Type 1 1-646 <$225
20 Type 1 1-172 <$250
10 Type 2 1-404 <$250
20 Type 2 1-119 <$275
Total Issue $387,770
Out in 1935 $25,000
Large out 1935 $1,100
****
8175 Athens
COOLVILLE NB, COOLVILLE
{{ 2 L 3 S }}
Organized 3/8/06
Receivership 3/18/31
1902 Red Seal <$VALUE
3x10-20 1-820 <$1500
1902 Date Back
3x10-20 1-1330 <$750
1902 Plain Back
3x10-20 1331-4028 <$750
1929 Small Size
10 Type 1 1-252 <$400
20 Type 1 1-66 <$400
Total Issue $265,440
Out at close $19,000
Large out at close $3,310
****
4772 Trumbull
FNB OF CORTLAND
{{ 1 L }}
Chartered 1892
Liquidated 4/4/11
Brown Back <$VALUE
4x5 1-2975 <$1000
3x10-20 1-1280 <$1000
1882 Date Back
4x5 1-289 <$1000
3x10-20 1-294 <$1000
Total Issue $143,980
Out in 1911 $14,800
****
6892 Coshocton
COMMERCIAL NB OF COSHOCTON
{{ 10 L 15 S }}
Chartered 7/03
1902 Red Seal <$VALUE
4x5 1-2000 <$350
3x10-20 1-3000 <$350
1902 Date Back
4x5 1-6050 <$150
3x10-20 1-4200 <$150
1902 Plain Back
4x5 6051-19120 <$150
3x10-20 4201-12447 <$150
1929 Small Size
5 Type 1 1-1876 <$85
10 Type 1 1-1540 <$85
20 Type 1 1-440 <$100
5 Type 2 1-2736 <$100
10 Type 2 1-1416 <$100
20 Type 2 1-402 <$110
Total Issue $1,432,110
Out in 1935 $100,000
Large out 1935 $3,960
****
5103 Coshocton
COSHOCTON NB, COSHOCTON
{{ 6 L 19 S }}
Chartered 1897
Liquidated 1/12/34
Brown Back <$VALUE
3x10-20 1-3750 <$250/$300
1882 Date Back
3x10-20 1-3500 <$250/$300
1882 Value Back
3x10-20 3501-4118<$250/$300
1902 Plain Back
4x5 1-22268 <$150
1929 Small Size
5 Type 1 1-24408 <$50
5 Type 2 1-8380 <$60
Total Issue $1,612,900
Out at close $168,710
Large out 1935 $2,470
Ch 13923 assumed circulation
****
1920 Coshocton
FNB OF COSHOCTON
{{ 2 L }}
Chartered 1/11/72
Liquidated 2/21/81
Original Series <$VALUE
3x1-2 1-1500 <$600/$1250
4x5 1-6575 <$600
Series 1875
3x1-2 1-120 <$600/$1250
4x5 1-2480 <$600
Total Issue $189,200
Out in 1910 $773
****
5530 Miami
CITIZENS NB OF COVINGTON
{{ 3 L 5 S }}
Chartered 8/6/00
Brown Back <$VALUE
3x10-20 1-1600 <$600
1882 Date Back
3x10-20 1-1700 <$600
1882 Value Back
3x10-20 1701-2448 <$600
1902 Plain Back
3x10-20 1-2932 <$400
1929 Small Size
10 Type 1 1-626 <$250
20 Type 1 1-212 <$250
10 Type 2 1-668 <$300
20 Type 2 1-96 <$300
Total Issue $420,600
Out in 1935 $25,000
Large out 1935 $1,530
****
13273 Crawford
FNB IN CRESTLINE
{{ 15 S }}
Chartered 1/29
1929 Small Size <$VALUE
5 Type 1 1-1036 <$110
10 Type 1 1-524 <$110
5 Type 2 1-2740 <$125
10 Type 2 1-1075 <$125
Total Issue $86,970
Out in 1935 $25,000
****
5099 Crawford
FNB OF CRESTLINE
{{ U + 5 L }}
Organized 11/30/97
Liquidated 1/21/29
Brown Back <$VALUE
4x5 1-4275 <$400
50-100 1-830 <$1500/$1750
1882 Date Back
4x5 1-2800 <$400
50-100 1-300 <$1500/$1750
3x50-100 1-221<$1500/$1750
1882 Value Back
4x5 2801-3250 <$400
1902 Plain Back
3x10-20 1-9002 <$275
Total Issue $825,350
Out at close $71,350
****
378 Summit
FNB OF CUYAHOGA FALLS
{{ UNREPORTED }}
Chartered 4/11/64
Liquidated 3/4/68
Original Series <$VALUE
3x1-2 1-1000 <$1500/$2500
4x5 1-2000 <$1500
Total Issue $45,000
Out in 1910 $503
****
6372 Wayne
FNB OF DALTON
{{ 5 L 8 S }}
Chartered 8/9/02
1902 Red Seal <$VALUE
3x10-20 1-1300 <$1000
1902 Date Back
3x10-20 1-1720 <$500
1902 Plain Back
3x10-20 1721-5882 <$500
1929 Small Size
10 Type 1 1-662 <$275
20 Type 1 1-186 <$300
10 Type 2 1-690 <$350
20 Type 2 1-123 <$350
Total Issue $430,500
Out in 1935 $25,000
Large out 1935 $1,060
****
American NB of Dayton
SEE Ch 4054
Teutonia NB of Dayton
****
2874 Montgomery
CITY NB OF DAYTON
Chartered 1883
Liquidated 3/8/30
2nd title: City NB & TC of Dayton 9/29/28
FIRST TITLE {{ 17 L }}
Brown Back <$VALUE
3x10-20 1-8295 <$300
1902 Red Seal
3x10-20 1-6800 <$300
1902 Date Back
3x10-20 1-12000 <$100
1902 Plain Back
3x10-20 12001-41387 <$100
3x50-100 1-2163 <$350/$400
SECOND TITLE {{ 1 L 11 S }}
1902 Plain Back
3x50-100 1-779 <$450/$500
1929 Small Size
50 Type 1 1-299 <$175
100 Type 1 1-140 <$275
Total Issue $3,733,300
Out at close $444,200
Large out at close $270,700
Outstanding includes Ch 898
****
898 Montgomery
DAYTON NB, DAYTON
{{ 9 L }}
Chartered 3/16/65
Liquidated 7/13/25
Original Series <$VALUE
3x1-2 1-4400 <$400/$1250
4x5 1-8650 <$500
3x10-20 1-5800 <$750/$1250
Series 1875
4x5 1-100 <$500
3x10-20 1-7860 <$750/$1250
Brown Back
4x5 1-4667 <$250
3x10-20 1-5310 <$250/$300
50-100 1-661 <$1500/$1750
1902 Red Seal
4x5 1-2300 <$300
50-100 1-440 <$2250/$2500
1902 Date Back
4x5 1-4400 <$150
50-100 1-800 <$350/$400
3x50-100 1-3668 <$350/$400
1902 Plain Back
4x5 4401-17540 <$150
Total Issue $2,837,790
Out at close $233,200
Ch 2874 assumed circulation
****
9 Montgomery
FNB OF DAYTON
{{ UNREPORTED }}
Chartered 6/22/63
Liquidated 4/9/70
Original Series <$VALUE
3x1-2 1-880 <$1500/$2500
4x5 1-2500 <$1500
3x10-20 1-1836<$1750/$2500
Total Issue $146,200
Out in 1910 $1,009
****
3821 Montgomery
FOURTH NB OF DAYTON
{{ 5 L }}
Chartered 12/8/87
Liquidated 12/21/18
Brown Back <$VALUE
4x5 1-2235 <$300
3x10-20 1-4926 <$250/$300
50-100 1-4508 <$1500/$1750
1902 Red Seal
4x5 1-625 <$350
50-100 1-250 <$2250/$2500
1902 Date Back
4x5 1-10750 <$200
50-100 1-1600 <$450/$500
3x50-100 1-687 <$450/$500
1902 Plain Back
4x5 10751-11505 <$200
Total Issue $1,659,050
Out at close $279,000
****
1788 Montgomery
MERCHANTS NB OF DAYTON
Chartered 2/11/71
2nd title: Merchants NB & TC of Dayton 1/16/22
FIRST TITLE {{ 7 L }}
Original Series <$VALUE
3x1-2 1-6720 <$450/$1000
4x5 1-4000 <$500
3x10-20 1-4300 <$750/$1250
Series 1875
3x10-20 1-5778 <$750/$1250
50-100 1-88 <$4000
Brown Back
3x10-20 1-11220 <$300
50-100 1-1500 <$1500/$1750
1882 Date Back
3x10-20 1-2938 <$300
50-100 1-4 <$1500/$1750
1902 Date Back
3x10-20 1-10000 <$125
1902 Plain Back
3x10-20 10001-21300 <$125
SECOND TITLE {{ 8 L 23 S }}
1902 Plain Back
3x10-20 1-12003 <$125
1929 Small Size
10 Type 1 1-5798 <$35
20 Type 1 1-1592 <$45
10 Type 2 1-381 <$40
20 Type 2 1-185 <$50
Total Issue $3,775,780
Out in 1935 $134,690
Large out 1935 $11,350
****
10 Montgomery
SECOND NB OF DAYTON
{{ 2 L }}
Chartered 6/63
Liquidated 5/26/82
Original Series <$VALUE
3x1-2 1-2310 <$1000/$2000
4x5 1-5630 <$1000
4x10 1-4475 <$2000
50-100 1-1179 <$4000
Series 1875
4x5 1-2800 <$1000
4x10 1-2485 <$2000
50-100 1-592 <$4000
Total Issue $724,200
Out in 1910 $3,784
****
4054 Montgomery
TEUTONIA NB OF DAYTON
Chartered 6/21/89
Liquidated 9/21/23
2nd title: American NB of Dayton 6/1/18
3rd title: American NB & TC of Dayton 2/17/23
FIRST TITLE {{ 6 L }}
Brown Back <$VALUE
3x10-20 1-17300 <$500
1882 Date Back
3x10-20 1-308 <$500
1902 Date Back
3x10-20 1-12600 <$250
1902 Plain Back
3x10-20 12601-17600 <$250
SECOND TITLE {{ 1 L }}
1902 Plain Back
3x10-20 1-10100 <$400
THIRD TITLE {{ 0 L }}
1902 Plain Back
3x10-20 1-884 <$500
Total Issue $2,309,600
Out at close $173,900
****
2678 Montgomery
THIRD NB OF DAYTON
Organized 4/27/82
2nd title: Third NB & TC of Dayton 3/2/25
FIRST TITLE {{ U + 12 L }}
Brown Back <$VALUE
4x5 1-7589 <$200
3x10-20 1-6001 <$200/$250
1902 Red Seal
4x5 1-1250 <$200
3x10-20 1-6400 <$200/$250
1902 Date Back
4x5 1-3500 <$75
3x10-20 1-4000 <$75
1902 Plain Back (dated 1902)
4x5 3501-16750 <$75
3x10-20 4001-10900 <$75
1902 Plain Back (dated 1922)
4x5 1-10250 <$75
3x10-20 1-6100 <$75
SECOND TITLE {{U+ 5 L 36 S}}
1902 Plain Back
4x5 1-14610 <$85
3x10-20 1-9914 <$85
1929 Small Size
5 Type 1 1-15736 <$25
10 Type 1 1-8383 <$25
20 Type 1 1-2028 <$35
Total Issue $4,193,150
Out in 1935 $228,870
Large out 1935 $11,610
****
2604 Montgomery
WINTERS NB OF DAYTON
Chartered 1882
2nd title: Winters NB & TC 2/12/24
FIRST TITLE {{ 37 L }}
Series 1875 <$VALUE
3x10-20 1-29265<$750/$1250
Brown Back
50-100 1-3700 <$1500/$1750
1882 Date Back
4x5 1-16500 <$125
3x10-20 1-18000 <$125/$150
50-100 1-1800 <$1500/$1750
1882 Value Back
4x5 16501-49500 <$150
3x10-20 18001-44000 <$150/$200
3x50-100 1-1800 <$45,000/$50,000
1902 Plain Back
4x5 1-26500 <$50
3x10-20 1-18400 <$50
3x50-100 1-1000 <$300/$350
SECOND TITLE {{ 15 L 50+ S }}
1902 Plain Back
4x5 1-68847 <$50
3x10-20 1-35743 <$50
3x50-100 1-2396 <$300/$350
1929 Small Size
5 Type 1 1-21728 <$25
10 Type 1 1-13012 <$25
20 Type 1 1-3670 <$35
50 Type 1 1-1138 <$110
100 Type 1 1-352 <$175
5 Type 2 1-6426 <$40
10 Type 2 1-2693 <$40
20 Type 2 1-645 <$50
Total Issue $13,888,860
Out in 1935 $699,050
Large out 1935 $46,050
****
1906 Defiance
DEFIANCE NB, DEFIANCE
{{ 3 L }}
Chartered 12/22/71
Liquidated 12/7/91
Original Series <$VALUE
3x1-2 1-6860 <$500/$1250
4x5 1-3750 <$600
3x10-20 1-1400 <$750/$1250
Series 1875
4x5 1-3407 <$600
3x10-20 1-1478 <$750/$1250
Total Issue $321,340
Out in 1910 $1,314
****
4661 Defiance
FNB OF DEFIANCE
{{ 11 L 7 S }}
Organized 11/11/91
Liquidated 2/17/31
Brown Back <$VALUE
3x10-20 1-14500 <$350/$400
1882 Date Back
3x10-20 1-3622 <$350/$400
1902 Date Back
3x10-20 1-3500 <$250
1902 Plain Back
3x10-20 3501-17301 <$250
1929 Small Size
10 Type 1 1-875 <$250
20 Type 1 1-157 <$250
Total Issue $1,842,490
Out at close $51,320
Large out at close $17,020
Ch 13457 assumed circulation
****
2516 Defiance
MERCHANTS NB OF DEFIANCE
{{ 10 L 7 S }}
Organized 4/7/81
Liquidated 2/10/31
Series 1875 <$VALUE
3x10-20 1-4215 <$750/$1250
Brown Back
3x10-20 1-4660 <$400
1882 Date Back
3x10-20 1-6500 <$400
1882 Value Back
3x10-20 6501-10460 <$400
1902 Plain Back
3x10-20 1-10087 <$250
1929 Small Size
10 Type 1 1-881 <$250
20 Type 1 1-170 <$250
Total Issue $1,544,360
Out at close $49,130
Large out at close $15,230
Ch 13457 assumed circulation
****
13457 Defiance
NB OF DEFIANCE
{{ U + 12 S }}
Organized 4/16/30
Receivership 9/10/31
1929 Small Size <$VALUE
10 Type 1 1-1151 <$175
20 Type 1 1-332 <$175
Total Issue $108,900
Out at close $150,000
Outstanding includes Ch 2516 and Ch 4661
****
853 Delaware
DELAWARE COUNTY NB OF DELAWARE
{{ 4 L }}
Chartered 3/1/65
Liquidated 1/6/05
Original Series <$VALUE
4x5 1-4350 <$600
3x10-20 1-1840 <$750/$1250
Series 1875
3x10-20 1-2330 <$750/$1250
Brown Back
4x5 1-18470 <$350
3x10-20 1-2253 <$350/$400
Total Issue $777,550
Out in 1910 $11,485
****
13535 Delaware
DELAWARE COUNTY NB OF DELAWARE
{{ 3U + 13 S }}
Chartered 4/31 as Delaware Co NB, Delaware under which there was no issue. Issuing title adopted 2/27/32.
1929 Small Size <$VALUE
10 Type 1 1-1324 <$75
20 Type 1 1-564 <$85
10 Type 2 1-3705 <$85
20 Type 2 1-865 <$85
Total Issue $201,470
Out in 1935 $87 900
****
7505 Delaware
DELAWARE NB, DELAWARE
{{ 9 L 10 S }}
Chartered 12/04
Liquidated 5/7/31
1902 Red Seal <$VALUE
3x10-20 1-3960 <$600
1902 Date Back
3x10-20 1-6700 <$300
1902 Plain Back
3x10-20 6701-21824 <$300
1929 Small Size
10 Type 1 1-1426 <$175
20 Type 1 1-458 <$175
Total Issue $1,429,720
Out at close $91,970
Large out at close $11,650
****
243 Delaware
FNB OF DELAWARE
{{ 15 L 17 S }}
Chartered 2/64
Original Series <$VALUE
3x1-2 1-300 <$500/$1000
4x5 1-2500 <$500
4x10 1-3225 <$750
Series 1875
4x10 1-2177 <$650
Brown Back
4x5 1-16088 <$275
3x10-20 1-1647 <$275/$325
1902 Red Seal
4x5 1-4650 <$300
3x10-20 1-2640 <$300/$350
1902 Date Back
4x5 1-6700 <$125
3x10-20 1-4840 <$125
1902 Plain Back
4x5 6701-21662 <$125
3x10-20 4841-14523 <$125
1929 Small Size
5 Type 1 1-3352 <$75
10 Type 1 1-1822 <$75
20 Type 1 1-474 <$85
5 Type 2 1-3748 <$90
10 Type 2 1-2200 <$90
20 Type 2 1-640 <$90
Total Issue $2,376,380
Out in 1935 $98,745
Large out 1935 $8,195
****

****
2885 Allen
DELPHOS NB, DELPHOS
{{ 1 L }}
Chartered 2/16/83
Liquidated 5/29/02
Brown Back <$VALUE
4x5 1-4555 <$850
50-100 1-153 <$1500/$1750
Total Issue $114,050
Out in 1910 $1,955
****
274 Allen
FNB OF DELPHOS
{{ 3 L }}
Chartered 2/64
Liquidated 2/24/83
Original Series <$VALUE
3x1-2 1-8000 <$500/$1250
4x5 1-7600 <$600
Series 1875
3x1-2 1-1240 <$500/$1250
4x5 1-4325 <$600
Total Issue $284,700
Out in 1910 $2,378
****
6280 Allen
NB OF DELPHOS
{{ 2 L }}
Chartered 5/29/02
Liquidated 5/14/22
1902 Red Seal <$VALUE
3x10-20 1-2100 <$800
1902 Date Back
3x10-20 1-2350* <$400
1902 Plain Back
3x10-20 2651-4378* <$400
* 2351-2650 not marked
Total Issue $323,900
Out at close $34,400
Ch 12196 assumed circulation
****
12196 Allen
OLD NB OF DELPHOS
{{ 1 L 8 S }}
Organized 3/7/22
1902 Plain Back <$VALUE
3x10-20 1-2986 <$600
1929 Small Size
10 Type 1 1-828 <$175
20 Type 1 1-340 <$175
10 Type 2 1-1683 <$175
20 Type 2 1-395 <$175
Total Issue $264,510
Out in 1935 $50,000
Large out 1935 $1,830
Outstanding includes Ch 6280
****
5577 Fulton
FARMERS NB OF DELTA
{{ 2 L }}
Chartered 9/17/00
Liquidated 7/6/14
Brown Back <$VALUE
3x10-20 1-1700 <$850
1882 Date Back
3x10-20 1-1052 <$850
Total Issue $137,600
Out in 1914 $19,300
****
6843 Tuscarawas
DENNISON NB, DENNISON
{{ 16 L 14 S }}
Organized 6/3/03
Liquidated 11/29/33
1902 Red Seal <$VALUE
4x5 1-1925 <$400
3x10-20 1-1740 <$400
1902 Date Back
4x5 1-3550 <$150
3x10-20 1-2720 <$150
1902 Plain Back
4x5 3551-12550 <$150
3x10-20 2721-8690 <$150
1929 Small Size
5 Type 1 1-1900 <$150
10 Type 1 1-972 <$150
20 Type 1 1-246 <$165
5 Type 2 1-100 <$200
10 Type 2 1-6 <$250
Total Issue $956,400
Out at close $50,000
Large out 1935 $2,940
Ch 13802 assumed circulation
****
13802 Tuscarawas
FNB OF DENNISON
{{ 5 S }}
Chartered 10/33
1929 Small Size <$VALUE
10 Type 2 1-3298 <$225
Total Issue $32,980
Out in 1935 $50,000
Outstanding includes Ch 6843
****
6836 Tuscarawas
TWIN CITY NB OF DENNISON
{{ 1 L }}
Chartered 6/13/03
Liquidated 6/19/05
1902 Red Seal <$VALUE
3x10-20 1-722 <$1500
Total Issue $36,100
Out in 1910 $1,760
****
14011 Jefferson
FNB AT DILLONVALE
{{ 4 S }}
Chartered 2/34
1929 Small Size <$VALUE
10 Type 2 1-1670 <$400
20 Type 2 1-565 <$400
Total Issue $28,000
Out in 1935 $25,000
****
5618 Jefferson
FNB OF DILLONVALE
{{ 6 L 11 S }}
Chartered 11/8/00
Receivership 3/15/34
Brown Back <$VALUE
3x10-20 1-1790 <$400
1882 Date Back
3x10-20 1-2980 <$400
1882 Value Back
3x10-20 2981-4427 <$400
1902 Plain Back
3x10-20 1-12693 <$275
1929 Small Size
10 Type 1 1-2026 <$110
20 Type 1 1-594 <$135
Total Issue $1,138,340
Out at close $50,000
Large out at close $4,660
****
Exchange NB of Dover
SEE Ch 4293
Exchange NB of Canal Dover
****
FNB of Dover SEE Ch 4331
FNB of Canal Dover
****
6529 Muskingum
DRESDEN NB, DRESDEN
{{ UNREPORTED }}
Chartered 12/13/02
Receivership 7/15/15
1902 Red Seal <$VALUE
3x10-20 1-400 <$1500
1902 Date Back
3x10-20 1-1719 <$1000
Total Issue $105,950
Out in 1916 $12,540
****
5144 Muskingum
FNB OF DRESDEN
{{ UNREPORTED }}
Organized 10/7/98
Receivership 10/15/07
Brown Back <$VALUE
4x5 1-2360 <$1250
3x10-20 1-1930 <$1250
Total Issue $143,700
Out in 1916 $1,920
****
6628 Hardin
FNB OF DUNKIRK
{{ 6 L 8 S }}
Organized 2/9/03
Receivership 8/23/33
1902 Red Seal <$VALUE
3x10-20 1-1050 <$750
1902 Date Back
3x10-20 1-1680 <$350
1902 Plain Back
3x10-20 1681-6670 <$350
1929 Small Size
10 Type 1 1-1181 <$200
20 Type 1 1-290 <$200
Total Issue $491,660
Out at close $50,000
Large out at close $3,550
Outstanding includes Ch 6652
****
6652 Hardin
WOODRUFF NB OF DUNKIRK
{{ 4 L }}
Chartered 3/03
Closed 7/15/25
1902 Red Seal <$VALUE
3x10-20 1-1160 <$1000
1902 Date Back
3x10-20 1-1560 <$500
1902 Plain Back
3x10-20 1561-3778 <$500
Total Issue $246,900
Out at close $24,700
Ch 6628 assumed circulation
****
5098 Columbiana
CITIZENS NB OF
EAST LIVERPOOL
{{ 5 L }}
Chartered 1897
Closed 1/5/26
Brown Back <$VALUE
4x5 1-6000 <$350
3x10-20 1-4700 <$350
1882 Date Back
4x5 1-9750 <$350
3x10-20 1-5600 <$350
1882 Value Back
4x5 9751-11860 <$350
3x10-20 5601-6842 <$350
1902 Plain Back
3x10-20 1-10122 <$250
Total Issue $1,440,400
Out at close $100,000
Ch 2146 assumed circulation
****
2146 Columbiana
FNB OF EAST LIVERPOOL
{{ 23 L 47 S }}
Chartered 5/14/74
Original Series <$VALUE
3x1-2 1-1500 <$400/$1000
4x5 1-2875 <$400
Series 1875
4x5 1-10525 <$400
Brown Back
3x10-20 1-14250 <$200/$250
1882 Date Back
3x10-20 1-12084 <$200/$250
1902 Date Back
3x10-20 1-4000 <$100
1902 Plain Back
3x10-20 4001-45384 <$100
1929 Small Size
10 Type 1 1-8950 <$35
20 Type 1 1-2496 <$45
10 Type 2 1-8942 <$35
20 Type 2 1-3132 <$45
Total Issue $4,849,980
Out in 1935 $300,000
Large out 1935 $16,520
Outstanding includes Ch 5098
****
2544 Columbiana
POTTERS NB OF
EAST LIVERPOOL
{{ 32 L 12 S }}
Chartered 1881
Liquidated 10/10/31
Series 1875 <$VALUE
4x5 1-8819 <$400
3x10-20 1-266 <$750/$1250
Brown Back
3x10-20 1-6200 <$175/$225
1882 Date Back
4x5 1-7700* <$150
3x10-20 1-4950**<$150/$200
1882 Value Back
4x5 8101-14350* <$150
3x10-20 5271-8750**
<$150/$200
* 7701-8100 not marked
** 4951-5270 not marked
1902 Plain Back
4x5 1-104286 <$60
1929 Small Size
5 Type 1 1-29596 <$100
Total Issue $4,197,780
Out at close $400,000
Large out at close $18,110
****
13850 Columbiana
FNB AT EAST PALESTINE
{{ 6 S }}
Chartered 11/33
1929 Small Size <$VALUE
10 Type 2 1-3946 <$200
20 Type 2 1-1222 <$200
Total Issue $63,900
Out in 1935 $47,050
****
6593 Columbiana
FNB OF EAST PALESTINE
{{ 4 L 6 S }}
Organized 12/20/02
Receivership 1/3/34
1902 Red Seal <$VALUE
3x10-20 1-1540 <$750
1902 Date Back
3x10-20 1-1750 <$375
1902 Plain Back
3x10-20 1751-6074 <$375
1929 Small Size
10 Type 1 1-709 <$200
20 Type 1 1-168 <$200
Total Issue $443,400
Out at close $25,000
Large out at close $870
****
7557 Preble
EATON NB, EATON
{{ 4 L 8 S }}
Chartered 1/05
1902 Red Seal <$VALUE
3x10-20 1-720 <$750
1902 Date Back
3x10-20 1-4500* <$375
1902 Plain Back
3x10-20 4701-12649* <$375
* 4501-4700 not marked
1929 Small Size
5 Type 1 1-3722 <$175
10 Type 1 1-622 <$175
20 Type 1 1-200 <$185
5 Type 2 1-7614 <$200
Total Issue $879,500
Out in 1935 $60,000
Large out 1935 $2,630
****
530 Preble
FNB OF EATON
{{ UNREPORTED }}
Chartered 10/64
Liquidated 7/4/84
Original Series <$VALUE
4x5 1-4000 <$1250
3x10-20 1-2080<$1500/$1750
Series 1875
4x5 1-1185 <$1250
3x10-20 1-736 <$1500/$1750
Total Issue $244,500
Out in 1910 $1,480
****
3889 Preble
PREBLE COUNTY NB OF EATON
{{ 4 L 9 S }}
Chartered 5/28/88
Brown Back <$VALUE
3x10-20 1-3026 <$600
1902 Red Seal
3x10-20 1-590 <$750
1902 Date Back
3x10-20 1-3240 <$375
1902 Plain Back
3x10-20 3241-7528 <$375
1929 Small Size
10 Type 1 1-782 <$150
20 Type 1 1-266 <$165
10 Type 2 1-1828 <$185
20 Type 2 1-340 <$200
Total Issue $661,120
Out in 1935 $60,000
Large out 1935 $2,130
****
6770 Ottawa
FNB OF ELMORE
{{ 1 L 3 S }}
Organized 4/2/03
Receivership 9/13/33
1902 Red Seal <$VALUE
3x10-20 1-620 <$1250
1902 Date Back
3x10-20 1-700 <$750
1902 Plain Back
3x10-20 701-2080 <$750
1929 Small Size
10 Type 1 1-239 <$500
20 Type 1 1-63 <$500
Total Issue $156,900
Out at close $10,000
Large out at close $360
****
6314 Hamilton
FNB OF ELMWOOD PLACE
{{ 4 L 13 S }}
Chartered 6/23/02
1902 Red Seal <$VALUE
3x10-20 1-920 <$750
1902 Date Back
3x10-20 1-4360 <$375
1902 Plain Back
3x10-20 4361-12814 <$375
1929 Small Size
10 Type 1 1-1494 <$150
20 Type 1 1-446 <$150
10 Type 2 1-1175 <$200
20 Type 2 1-400 <$200
Total Issue $849,610
Out in 1935 $50,000
Large out 1935 $2,080
****
FNB in Elyria
SEE Ch 2863
NB of Elyria
****
438 Lorain
FNB OF ELYRIA
{{ 2 L }}
Chartered 5/64
Liquidated 2/24/83
Original Series <$VALUE
3x1-2 1-6260 <$600/$1250
4x5 1-4750 <$600
3x10-20 1-2200 <$750/$1250
Series 1875
4x5 1-1060 <$600
3x10-20 1-610 <$750/$1250
Total Issue $288,000
Out in 1910 $1,951
****
2863 Lorain
NB OF ELYRIA
Chartered 1883
Liquidated 12/30/22
2nd title: FNB in Elyria
2/5/20
FIRST TITLE {{ 5 L }}
Brown Back <$VALUE
4x5 1-6760 <$400
3x10-20 1-6535 <$400
1902 Red Seal
4x5 1-12145 <$500
3x10-20 1-9438 <$500
1902 Date Back
4x5 1-11000 <$250
3x10-20 1-7900 <$250
1902 Plain Back
4x5 11001-16250 <$250
3x10-20 7901-10600 <$250
SECOND TITLE {{ 0 L }}
1902 Plain Back
4x10 1-8750 <$650
Total Issue $2,381,750
Out at close $137,520
****
6068 Lake
FNB OF FAIRPORT HARBOR
{{ UNREPORTED }}
Chartered 12/27/01
Liquidated 10/30/05
Brown Back <$VALUE
3x10-20 1-1039 <$1500
Total Issue $51,950
Out in 1910 $2,190
****
2882 Clermont
FNB OF FELICITY
{{ UNREPORTED }}
Chartered 2/14/83
Liquidated 1/31/03
Brown Back <$VALUE
3x10-20 1-1212 <$1500
Total Issue $60,600
Out in 1910 $1,410
****
3729 Hancock
AMERICAN NB OF FINDLAY
{{ 8 L }}
Chartered 6/20/87
Closed 1/2/23
Brown Back <$VALUE
4x5 1-8191 <$300
3x10-20 1-1932 <$300
1902 Red Seal
3x10-20 1-1000 <$400
1902 Date Back
3x10-20 1-6900 <$200
1902 Plain Back
3x10-20 6901-13218 <$200
Total Issue $971,320
Out at close $97,600
Ch 36 assumed circulation
****
American-FNB of Findlay
SEE Ch 36
FNB of Findlay
****
Buckeye NB of Findlay
SEE Ch 3477
Farmers NB of Findlay
****
3477 Hancock
FARMERS NB OF FINDLAY
Chartered 1886
Liquidated 6/30/22
2nd title: Buckeye NB of
Findlay 3/04
FIRST TITLE {{ 1 L }}
Brown Back <$VALUE
4x5 1-5329 <$650
3x10-20 1-625 <$650
SECOND TITLE {{ 6 L }}
Brown Back
3x10-20 1-421 <$500
1902 Red Seal
4x5 1-2500 <$600
3x10-20 1-1680 <$600
1902 Date Back
4x5 1-6230 <$300
3x10-20 1-4628 <$300
1902 Plain Back
4x5 6231-11755 <$300
3x10-20 4629-8222 <$300
Total Issue $939,080
Out at close $98,695
****
36 Hancock
FNB OF FINDLAY
Chartered 7/63
2nd title: American-FNB of
Findlay 1/2/23
3rd title: FNB & TC 12/23/30
FIRST TITLE {{ 5 L }}
Original Series <$VALUE
4x5 1-3000 <$500
3x10-20 1-500 <$750/$1250
3x10-20 1001-1200
<$750/$1250
20 501-1000 <$1250
Series 1875
4x5 1-250 <$500
3x10-20 1-900 <$750/$1250
Brown Back
4x5 1-8857 <$400
3x10-20 1-1041 <$400
1902 Red Seal
50-100 1-560 <$2250/$2500
1902 Date Back
3x10-20 1-2200 <$200
50-100 1-800 <$500/$600
3x50-100 1-400 <$500/$600
1902 Plain Back
3x10-20 2201-10300 <$200
SECOND TITLE {{U + 10 L 13 S}}
1902 Plain Back
3x10-20 1-9064 <$200
3x50-100 1-697 <$500/$600
1929 Small Size
10 Type 1 1-2356 <$75
20 Type 1 1-670 <$75
50 Type 1 1-206 <$225
100 Type 1 1-70 <$350
THIRD TITLE {{ 22 S }}
1929 Small Size
10 Type 1 1-1268 <$65
20 Type 1 1-424 <$75
50 Type 1 1-197 <$200
100 Type 1 1-76 <$300
Total Issue $2,387,860
Out in 1935 $259,340
Large out 1935 $16,650
Outstanding includes Ch 3729
****
3177 Belmont
FNB OF FLUSHING
{{ UNREPORTED }}
Organized 5/6/84
Receivership 11/5/98
Brown Back <$VALUE
3x10-20 1-1099 <$1500
Total Issue $54,950
Out in 1916 $280
****
7518 Hardin
FNB OF FOREST
{{ 5 L 6 S }}
Organized 5/18/04
1902 Red Seal <$VALUE
3x10-20 1-800 <$1250
1902 Date Back
3x10-20 1-1470 <$600
1902 Plain Back
3x10-20 1471-5199 <$600
1929 Small Size
10 Type 1 1-684 <$250
20 Type 1 1-170 <$275
10 Type 2 1-623 <$300
20 Type 2 1-115 <$300
Total Issue $369,920
Out in 1935 $25,000
Large out 1935 $1,240
****
2831 Seneca
FNB OF FOSTORIA
{{ 10 L 12 S }}
Organized 7/18/82
Brown Back <$VALUE
4x5 1-3915 <$300
3x10-20 1-972 <$300
1902 Red Seal
4x5 1-2250 <$400
3x10-20 1-1820 <$400
1902 Date Back
4x5 1-3300 <$175
3x10-20 1-2100 <$175
1902 Plain Back
4x5 3301-11222 <$175
3x10-20 2101-7111 <$175
1929 Small Size
5 Type 1 1-1876 <$100
10 Type 1 1-824 <$100
20 Type 1 1-246 <$110
5 Type 2 1-1802 <$125
10 Type 2 1-1043 <$125
20 Type 2 1-240 <$125
Total Issue $1,002,370
Out in 1935 $50,000
Large out 1935 $3,180
****

9192 Seneca
UNION NB OF FOSTORIA
{{ 6 L U + 12 S }}
Organized 6/19/08
Receivership 12/15/33
1902 Date Back <$VALUE
4x5 1-5950 <$200
3x10-20 1-4480 <$200
1902 Plain Back
4x5 5951-18670 <$200
3x10-20 4481-12024 <$200
1929 Small Size
5 Type 1 1-2672 <$100
10 Type 1 1-1274 <$100
20 Type 1 1-338 <$110
5 Type 2 1-550 <$125
10 Type 2 1-266 <$125
20 Type 2 1-90 <$135
Total Issue $1,178,970
Out at close $75,000
Large out at close $3,865

2282 Warren
FARMERS NB OF FRANKLIN
{{ UNREPORTED }}
Chartered 6/28/75
Liquidated 4/1/85
Series 1875 <$VALUE
4x5 1-3614 <$1500
Total Issue $72,280
Out in 1910 $575

738 Warren
FNB OF FRANKLIN
{{ 2 L }}
Chartered 1/23/65
Receivership 2/17/97
Original Series <$VALUE
3x1-2 1-2200 <$600/$1250
4x5 1-2750 <$600
3x10-20 1-2300 <$750/$1250
Series 1875
4x5 1-440 <$600
3x10-20 1-1744 <$750/$1250
Brown Back
4x5 1-4045 <$500
Total Issue $357,900
Out in 1916 $2,146

5100 Warren
FRANKLIN NB, FRANKLIN
{{ 8 L 21 S }}
Chartered 1897
Brown Back <$VALUE
3x10-20 1-3700 <$300
1882 Date Back
3x10-20 1-4340 <$250
1882 Value Back
3x10-20 4341-4512 <$275
1902 Plain Back
4x5 1-45674 <$150
1929 Small Size
5 Type 1 1-4306 <$60
10 Type 1 1-2110 <$60
20 Type 1 1-518 <$65
5 Type 2 1-1894 <$65
10 Type 2 1-818 <$75
20 Type 2 1-227 <$75
Total Issue $1,664,210
Out in 1935 $50,000
Large out 1935 $3,580

8000 Warren
WARREN NB OF FRANKLIN
{{ 1 L }}
Organized 12/12/05
Receivership 3/11/27
1902 Red Seal <$VALUE
3x10-20 1-900 <$1000
1902 Date Back
3x10-20 1-1830 <$500
1902 Plain Back
3x10-20 1831-4827 <$500
Total Issue $286,350
Out at close $23,700

5640 Knox
FNB OF FREDERICKTOWN
{{ 4 L 4 S }}
Chartered 12/14/00
Receivership 12/30/31
Brown Back <$VALUE
3x10-20 1-600 <$750
1882 Date Back
3x10-20 1-970 <$750
1882 Value Back
3x10-20 971-1309 <$750
1902 Plain Back
3x10-20 1-2715 <$500
1929 Small Size
10 Type 1 1-463 <$400
20 Type 1 1-130 <$400
Total Issue $274,580
Out at close $25,000
Large out at close $2,160

11216 Wood
PRAIRIE DEPOT NB OF FREEPORT
{{ 2 L 2 S }}
Organized 7/17/18
Liquidated 1/29/31
1902 Plain Back <$VALUE
3x10-20 1-3610 <$1000
1929 Small Size
10 Type 1 1-309 <$850
20 Type 1 1-84 <$850
Total Issue $209,120
Out at close $16,980
Large out at close $3,220

5 Sandusky
FNB OF FREMONT*
{{ 24 L 27 S }}
Organized 5/23/63
Liquidated 5/22/82
*Reorganized as Ch 2703 which retook Ch 5 2/23/10
Receivership 3/5/34
Original Series <$VALUE
3x1-2 1-4860* <$750/$1500
4x5 1-6000 <$750
3x10-20 1-2500<$1000/$1500
* 2001-4000 not issued
Series 1875
4x5 1-345 <$750
3x10-20 1-428 <$1000/$1500
1902 Date Back
4x5 1-3250 <$150
3x10-20 1-2400 <$150
1902 Plain Back
4x5 3251-14840 <$150
3x10-20 2401-12663 <$150
1929 Small Size
5 Type 1 1-3140 <$100
10 Type 1 1-1744 <$100
20 Type 1 1-510 <$100
5 Type 2 1-888 <$125
10 Type 2 1-343 <$125
20 Type 2 1-65 <$125
Total Issue $1,486,760
Out at close $99,550
Large out at close $5,450
Oustanding includes Ch 2703

2703 Sandusky
FNB OF FREMONT
{{ 6 L }}
Chartered 5/13/82
RETOOK Ch 5 2/23/10
Brown Back <$VALUE
3x10-20 1-4529 <$750
1902 Red Seal
4x5 1-2000 <$850
3x10-20 1-2050 <$850
1902 Date Back
4x5 1-2250 <$400
3x10-20 1-1800 <$400
Total Issue $503,950
Out in 1910 $100,000

1984 Crawford
CITIZENS NB OF GALION
{{ 8 L 3 S }}
Chartered 5/15/72
Receivership 8/4/30
Original Series <$VALUE
3x1-2 1-2000 <$500/$1000
4x5 1-2950 <$500
Series 1875
4x5 1-7400 <$500
Brown Back
4x5 1-6300 <$350
3x10-20 1-2700 <$350
1882 Date Back
4x5 1-1207 <$350
3x10-20 1-1114 <$350
1902 Date Back
4x5 1-2250 <$175
3x10-20 1-1600 <$175
1902 Plain Back
4x5 2251-11175 <$175
3x10-20 1601-7353 <$175
1929 Small Size
5 Type 1 1-719 <$350
10 Type 1 1-386 <$350
20 Type 1 1-94 <$350
Total Issue $1,205,000
Out at close $58,740
Large out at close $12,140

419 Crawford
FNB OF GALION
{{ 10 L 18 S }}
Organized 2/22/64
Original Series <$VALUE
4x5 1-4500 <$450
Series 1875
4x5 1-3730 <$450
Brown Back
4x5 1-11999 <$350
3x10-20 1-918 <$350
1902 Red Seal
3x10-20 1-4100 <$400
1902 Date Back
3x10-20 1-6600 <$200
1902 Plain Back
3x10-20 6601-20429 <$200
1929 Small Size
10 Type 1 1-2570 <$65
20 Type 1 1-660 <$75
10 Type 2 1-2889 <$75
20 Type 2 1-845 <$85
Total Issue $1,956,120
Out in 1935 $100,000
Large out 1935 $7,135

3581 Crawford
GALION NB, GALION
{{ 2 L }}
Chartered 11/2/86
Receivership 2/15/04
Brown Back <$VALUE
4x5 1-3992 <$850
3x10-20 1-1155 <$850
Total Issue $137,590
Out in 1916 $1,715

136 Gallia
FNB OF GALLIPOLIS
{{ 7 L 17 S }}
Chartered 11/63
Original Series <$VALUE
4x5 1-4400 <$600
4x10 1-2625 <$850
Series 1875
4x5 1-130 <$600
4x10 1-2067 <$850
Brown Back
4x5 1-2900 <$500
3x10-20 1-1924 <$500
1902 Red Seal
3x10-20 1-1140 <$600
1902 Date Back
3x10-20 1-4600 <$250
1902 Plain Back
3x10-20 4601-18201 <$250
1929 Small Size
10 Type 1 1-2556 <$135
20 Type 1 1-672 <$135
10 Type 2 1-3618 <$135
20 Type 2 1-957 <$165
Total Issue $1,688,850
Out in 1935 $100,000
Large out 1935 $6,990

2034 Portage
FNB OF GARRETTSVILLE
{{ 8 L 11 S }}
Chartered 8/28/72
Original Series <$VALUE
4x5 1-1200 <$500
3x10-20 1-1820 <$750/$1250
Series 1875
4x5 1-1861 <$500
3x10-20 1-1489 <$750/$1250
Brown Back
4x5 1-6020 <$350
3x10-20 1-2656 <$350
1882 Date Back
4x5 1-1506 <$325
3x10-20 1-974 <$325
1902 Date Back
4x5 1-1650 <$175
3x10-20 1-1240 <$175
1902 Plain Back
4x5 1651-10205 <$175
3x10-20 1241-6996 <$175
1929 Small Size
5 Type 1 1-2004 <$125
10 Type 1 1-942 <$110
20 Type 1 1-294 <$125
5 Type 2 1-2082 <$150
10 Type 2 1-1578 <$150
20 Type 2 1-384 <$150
Total Issue $1,298,380
Out in 1935 $49,995
Large out 1935 $3,925

153 Ashtabula
FNB OF GENEVA*
{{ 3 L 5 S }}
Organized 6/6/63
Liquidated 6/1/82
*Reorganized as Ch 2719 which retook Ch 153 4/11/17
Receivership 12/9/31
Original Series <$VALUE
4x10 1-2000 <$850
3x20-50 1-1000<$1250/$4000
Series 1875
3x20-50 1-614 <$1250/$4000
1902 Plain Back
3x10-20 1-6124 <$400
1929 Small Size
10 Type 1 1-994 <$275
20 Type 1 1-260 <$300
Total Issue $654,580
Out at close $48,680
Large out at close $5,840
Oustanding includes Ch 2719

2719 Ashtabula
FNB OF GENEVA
{{ 1 L }}
Chartered 1882
RETOOK Ch 153 4/11/17
Brown Back <$VALUE
50-100 1-1969 <$1750/$2000
1902 Red Seal
50-100 1-847 <$2250/$2500
1902 Date Back
50-100 1-300 <$850/$1000
3x50-100 1-300 <$850/$1000
Total Issue $542,400
Out in 1917 $50,000

2705 Brown
FNB OF GEORGETOWN
{{ 10 L U + 10 S }}
Chartered 1882
Series 1875 <$VALUE
3x10-20 1-2160 <$750/$1250
1902 Red Seal
3x10-20 1-2500 <$450
1902 Date Back
3x10-20 1-2600 <$200
1902 Plain Back (dated 1902)
3x10-20 2601-4677 <$200
1902 Plain Back (dated 1922)
3x10-20 1-3653 <$200
1929 Small Size
10 Type 1 1-1104 <$125
20 Type 1 1-326 <$125
10 Type 2 1-1635 <$135
20 Type 2 1-400 <$135
Total Issue $779,210
Out in 1935 $50,000
Large out 1935 $2,690

5996 Brown
PEOPLES NB OF GEORGETOWN
{{ 5 L 2U + 14 S }}
Chartered 10/21/01
Brown Back <$VALUE
3x10-20 1-2600 <$450
1882 Date Back
3x10-20 1-3000 <$400
1882 Value Back
3x10-20 3001-4966 <$400
1902 Plain Back
3x10-20 1-4692 <$250
1929 Small Size
10 Type 1 1-1432 <$110
20 Type 1 1-346 <$120
10 Type 2 1-1348 <$125
20 Type 2 1-235 <$125
Total Issue $758,520
Out in 1935 $50,000
Large out 1935 $3,020

86 Montgomery
FNB OF GERMANTOWN
{{ 5 L 9 S }}
Chartered 9/63
Original Series <$VALUE
4x5 1-3000 <$1250
3x10-20 1-1200<$1500/$1750
Series 1875
3x10-20 1-1354<$1500/$1750
Brown Back
3x10-20 1-2137 <$1250
1902 Red Seal
3x10-20 1-600 <$1250
1902 Date Back
3x10-20 1-1200 <$750
1902 Plain Back
3x10-20 1201-2490 <$750
1929 Small Size
10 Type 1 1-314 <$600
20 Type 1 1-104 <$600
10 Type 2 1-147 <$700
20 Type 2 1-6 <$750
Total Issue $481,960
Out in 1935 $12,500
Large out 1935 $1,770

10058 Darke
CITIZENS NB OF GETTYSBURG
{{ 2 L 7 S }}
Chartered 7/11
1902 Date Back <$VALUE
3x10-20 1-1890 <$500
1902 Plain Back
3x10-20 1891-6377 <$500
1929 Small Size
10 Type 1 1-762 <$225
20 Type 1 1-232 <$225
10 Type 2 1-420 <$250
20 Type 2 1-267 <$250
Total Issue $401,950
Out in 1935 $29,050
Large out 1935 $1,070

4884 Trumbull
FNB OF GIRARD
{{ 5 L 9 S }}
Chartered 1893
Brown Back <$VALUE
3x10-20 1-1920 <$400
1882 Date Back
3x10-20 1-1342 <$400
1902 Date Back
3x10-20 1-1000* <$250
1902 Plain Back
3x10-20 1301-6951* <$250
* 1001-1300 not marked
1929 Small Size
10 Type 1 1-1036 <$150
20 Type 1 1-262 <$150
10 Type 2 1-901 <$175
20 Type 2 1-200 <$175
Total Issue $617,260
Out in 1935 $30,000
Large out 1935 $1,130

8423 Athens
FNB OF GLOUSTER
{{ 2 L }}
Chartered 11/06
Liquidated 1/2/30
1902 Red Seal <$VALUE
3x10-20 1-500 <$1250
1902 Date Back
3x10-20 1-460 <$750
1902 Plain Back
3x10-20 461-1241 <$750
Total Issue $87,050
Out at close $3,230

388 Licking
FNB OF GRANVILLE
{{ UNREPORTED }}
Chartered 4/64
Liquidated 1/14/79
Original Series <$VALUE
4x5 1-1500 <$1500
3x10-20 1-1300 <$2000
Series 1875
3x10-20 1-202 <$2000
Total Issue $105,100
Out in 1910 $1,040

2496 Licking
FNB OF GRANVILLE
{{ UNREPORTED }}
Chartered 10/25/80
Liquidated 2/15/86
Series 1875 <$VALUE
4x5 1-1605 <$1500
3x10-20 1-326 <$2000
Total Issue $48,400
Out in 1910 $1,040

2037 Seneca
FNB OF GREEN SPRING
{{ 4 L }}
Chartered 8/30/72
Liquidated 2/18/81
Original Series <$VALUE
3x1-2 1-1600 <$500/$1250
4x5 1-2350 <$600
Series 1875
3x1-2 1-880 <$500/$1250
4x5 1-2510 <$600
Total Issue $109,600
Out in 1910 $564

101 Highland
FNB OF GREENFIELD
{{ UNREPORTED }}
Organized 10/7/63
Receivership 12/12/76
Original Series <$VALUE
3x1-2 1-1000 <$1250/$2000
4x5 1-5187 <$1250
Total Issue $108,740
Out in 1916 $909

10105 Highland
PEOPLES NB OF GREENFIELD
{{ 4 L 2U + 8 S }}
Chartered 11/11
1902 Date Back <$VALUE
4x5 1-2675 <$250
3x10-20 1-1980 <$250
3x50-100 1-36 <$750/$850
1902 Plain Back
4x5 2676-11940 <$250
3x10-20 1981-7483 <$250
1929 Small Size
5 Type 1 1-1788 <$125
10 Type 1 1-984 <$125
20 Type 1 1-230 <$135
5 Type 2 1-2106 <$150
10 Type 2 1-1051 <$150
20 Type 2 1-295 <$165
Total Issue $789,170
Out in 1935 $50,000
Large out 1935 $2,555

1092 Darke
FARMERS NB OF GREENVILLE
{{ 6 L U + 9 S }}
Chartered 4/65
Original Series <$VALUE
4x5 1-2580 <$650
3x10-20 1-1580 <$750/$1250
Series 1875
3x10-20 1-2384 <$750/$1250
Brown Back
3x10-20 1-4097 <$500
1902 Red Seal
3x10-20 1-1700 <$600
1902 Date Back
3x10-20 1-2700* <$225
1902 Plain Back
3x10-20 3201-14618* <$225
* 2701-3200 not marked
1929 Small Size
10 Type 1 1-2720 <$125
20 Type 1 1-736 <$125
10 Type 2 1-2183 <$135
20 Type 2 1-639 <$150
Total Issue $1,556,680
Out in 1935 $100,000
Large out 1935 $4,375

7130 Darke
GREENVILLE NB, GREENVILLE
{{ 9 L 31 S }}
Organized 12/29/03
Liquidated 4/9/34
1902 Red Seal <$VALUE
3x10-20 1-5000 <$500
1902 Date Back
3x10-20 1-6500 <$200
1902 Plain Back
3x10-20 6501-21629 <$200
1929 Small Size
10 Type 1 1-5150 <$50
20 Type 1 1-1208 <$60
10 Type 2 1-852 <$65
20 Type 2 1-150 <$75
Total Issue $1,796,930
Out at close $250,000
Large out 1935 $5,120
Ch 13944 assumed circulation

2992 Darke
SECOND NB OF GREENVILLE
{{ 4 L 16 S }}
Chartered 1883
Brown Back <$VALUE
3x10-20 1-3437 <$600
1902 Red Seal
3x10-20 1-1500 <$700
1902 Date Back
3x10-20 1-4600 <$350
1902 Plain Back
3x10-20 4601-14219 <$350
1929 Small Size
10 Type 1 1-3190 <$80
20 Type 1 1-912 <$85
10 Type 2 1-2906 <$90
20 Type 2 1-867 <$95
Total Issue $1,305,040
Out in 1935 $125,000
Large out 1935 $4,010

7001 Huron
FNB OF GREENWICH
{{ 3 L 8 S }}
Chartered 10/03
1902 Red Seal <$VALUE
3x10-20 1-1350 <$800
1902 Date Back
3x10-20 1-1570 <$400
1902 Plain Back
3x10-20 1571-5335 <$400
1929 Small Size
10 Type 1 1-726 <$175
20 Type 1 1-166 <$200
10 Type 2 1-422 <$225
Total Issue $401,950
Out in 1935 $25,000
Large out 1935 $1,170

6827 Franklin
FNB OF GROVE CITY
{{ 0 L 2 S }}
Chartered 6/03
1902 Red Seal <$VALUE
3x10-20 1-420 <$2000
1902 Date Back
3x10-20 1-560 <$1000
1902 Plain Back
3x10-20 561-1074 <$1000
1929 Small Size
10 Type 1 1-205 <$650
20 Type 1 1-48 <$650
Total Issue $92,760
Out in 1935 $6,300
Large out 1935 $270

56 Butler
FNB OF HAMILTON
Chartered 8/63
2nd title: FNB & TC
of Hamilton 5/5/23
FIRST TITLE {{ 10 L }}
Original Series <$VALUE
4x5 1-2250 <$500
4x10 1-2250 <$750
3x20-50 1-780 <$1250/$4000
Series 1875
4x5 1-369 <$500
4x10 1-299 <$750
3x20-50 1-36 <$1250/$4000
Brown Back
4x5 1-5673 <$350
3x10-20 1-6516 <$350/$400
1902 Red Seal
4x5 1-11000 <$350
3x10-20 1-8000 <$350/$400
1902 Date Back
4x5 1-16750 <$125
3x10-20 1-12400 <$125
1902 Plain Back
4x5 16751-39650 <$125
3x10-20 12401-25500 <$125
SECOND TITLE {{ 11 L 37 S }}
1902 Plain Back
4x5 1-20095 <$125
3x10-20 1-14618 <$125
1929 Small Size
5 Type 1 1-9786 <$40
10 Type 1 1-5656 <$40
20 Type 1 1-3976 <$50
5 Type 2 1-646 <$75
10 Type 2 1-460 <$85
20 Type 2 1-105 <$100
Total Issue $5,624,150
Out in 1935 $200,000
Large out 1935 $14,480

3840 Butler
MIAMI VALLEY NB OF
HAMILTON
{{ 8 L }}
Chartered 1/27/88
Liquidated 9/25/14
Brown Back <$VALUE
4x5 1-17600 <$300
3x10-20 1-6737 <$300/$350
1902 Red Seal
4x5 1-3750 <$400
3x10-20 1-3000 <$400
1902 Date Back
4x5 1-8975 <$250
3x10-20 1-7186 <$250
Total Issue $1,452,650
Out in 1914 $196,500

829 Butler
SECOND NB OF HAMILTON
{{ 13 L 18 S }}
Chartered 2/20/65
Original Series <$VALUE
3x1-2 1-1600 <$500/$1250
4x5 1-2050 <$500
3x10-20 1-2240 <$750/$1250
Series 1875
4x5 1-750 <$500
3x10-20 1-2330 <$750/$1250
Brown Back
4x5 1-12297 <$300
3x10-20 1-5609 <$300/$350
1902 Red Seal
4x5 1-3750 <$350
3x10-20 1-2500 <$350/$400
1902 Date Back
4x5 1-5600 <$150
3x10-20 1-4600 <$150
1902 Plain Back
4x5 5601-20700 <$150
3x10-20 4601-15300 <$150
1929 Small Size
5 Type 1 1-4562 <$60
10 Type 1 1-3286 <$60
20 Type 1 1-796 <$70
5 Type 2 1-5872 <$80
10 Type 2 1-1249 <$80
20 Type 2 1-780 <$85
Total Issue $2,684,880
Out in 1935 $120,000
Large out 1935 $8,100

8228 Hamilton
FNB OF HARRISON
{{ 2 L 7 S }}
Chartered 5/06
1902 Red Seal <$VALUE
3x10-20 1-700 <$1000
1902 Date Back
3x10-20 1-1580 <$500
1902 Plain Back
3x10-20 1581-4950 <$500
1929 Small Size
10 Type 1 1-652 <$225
20 Type 1 1-180 <$225
10 Type 2 1-527 <$250
20 Type 2 1-117 <$250
Total Issue $350,830
Out in 1935 $25,000
Large out 1935 $2,770

10436 Paulding
FARMERS NB OF HAVILAND
{{ 2 L 3 S }}
Organized 8/1/13
Liquidated 8/18/31
1902 Date Back <$VALUE
3x10-20 1-620 <$750
1902 Plain Back
3x10-20 621-2704 <$750
1929 Small Size
10 Type 1 1-274 <$500
20 Type 1 1-50 <$500
Total Issue $157,640
Out at close $14,220
Large out at close $1,530

4867 Defiance
FNB OF HICKSVILLE
{{ 6 L 10 S }}
Organized 2/14/93
Receivership 9/13/33
Brown Back <$VALUE
3x10-20 1-3800 <$400
1882 Date Back
3x10-20 1-1501 <$400
1902 Date Back
3x10-20 1-1500 <$225
1902 Plain Back
3x10-20 1501-7941 <$225
1929 Small Size
10 Type 1 1-1107 <$165
20 Type 1 1-304 <$165
Total Issue $765,000
Out at close $49,640
Large out at close $4,660

5802 Defiance
HICKSVILLE NB, HICKSVILLE
{{ 4 L 5 S }}
Chartered 5/8/01
Brown Back <$VALUE
3x10-20 1-1500 <$500
1882 Date Back
3x10-20 1-1560 <$500
1882 Value Back
3x10-20 1561-2408 <$500
1902 Plain Back
3x10-20 1-2170 <$350
1929 Small Size
10 Type 1 1-600 <$225
20 Type 1 1-180 <$225
10 Type 2 1-634 <$250
20 Type 2 1-210 <$250
Total Issue $372,040
Out in 1935 $25,000
Large out 1935 $600

9394 Brown
FNB OF HIGGINSPORT
Chartered 4/09
Liquidated 4/1/24
2nd title: FNB of
Winchester 10/12/23
FIRST TITLE {{ 2 L }}
1902 Date Back <$VALUE
3x10-20 1-2250 <$750
1902 Plain Back
3x10-20 2251-4040 <$750
SECOND TITLE {{ 0 L }}
1902 Plain Back
3x10-20 1-100 <$1250
Total Issue $207,000
Out at close $25,000

9243 Highland
FARMERS & TRADERS NB OF
HILLSBORO
{{ 5 L 3U + 10 S }}
Chartered 9/08
1902 Date Back <$VALUE
4x5 1-3300 <$275
3x10-20 1-2700 <$275
1902 Plain Back
4x5 3301-10902 <$275
3x10-20 2701-7533 <$275
1929 Small Size
5 Type 1 1-1792 <$150
10 Type 1 1-864 <$150
20 Type 1 1-236 <$150
5 Type 2 1-2100 <$175
10 Type 2 1-1277 <$175
20 Type 2 1-280 <$175
Total Issue $757,480
Out in 1935 $49,995
Large out 1935 $2,125

2449 Highland
MERCHANTS NB OF
HILLSBOROUGH
{{ 5 L 10 S }}
Chartered 1/13/80
Series 1875 <$VALUE
4x10 1-6425 <$750
Brown Back
3x10-20 1-3840 <$400
1882 Date Back
4x5 1-6600 <$400
3x10-20 1-3520 <$400
1882 Value Back
4x5 6601-7725 <$400
3x10-20 3521-4287 <$400
1902 Plain Back
3x10-20 1-5268 <$225
1929 Small Size
10 Type 1 1-1262 <$125
20 Type 1 1-312 <$125
10 Type 2 1-1792 <$135
20 Type 2 1-439 <$150
Total Issue $1,221,110
Out in 1935 $48,850
Large out 1935 $3,200

2039 Highland
CITIZENS NB OF
HILLSBOROUGH
{{ 2 L }}
Chartered 9/4/72
Receivership 6/16/93
Original Series <$VALUE
4x5 1-1250 <$600
3x10-20 1-1700 <$750/$1250
Series 1875
4x5 1-2114 <$600
3x10-20 1-3875 <$750/$1250
Total Issue $346,030
Out in 1916 $1,575

FNB of Hillsborough
SEE Ch 787
Hillsborough NB, Hillsborough

787 Highland
HILLSBOROUGH NB,
HILLSBOROUGH
Chartered 2/7/65
Receivership 7/22/96
2nd title: FNB of
Hillsborough 1/27/85
FIRST TITLE {{ 3 L }}
Original Series <$VALUE
3x1-2 1-1600 <$500/$1250
4x5 1-3775 <$600
3x10-20 1-1830 <$750/$1250
Series 1875
4x5 1-1500 <$600
3x10-20 1-2080 <$750/$1250
SECOND TITLE {{ 0 L }}
Brown Back
3x10-20 1-1688 <$750
Total Issue $393,400
Out at close $2,563

6938 Harrison
FNB OF HOPEDALE
{{ 3 L 11 S }}
Chartered 8/03
1902 Red Seal <$VALUE
4x5 1-2330 <$600
3x10-20 1-1768 <$600
1902 Date Back
4x5 1-3850 <$300
3x10-20 1-2870 <$300
1902 Plain Back
4x5 3851-13735 <$300
3x10-20 2871-9539 <$300
1929 Small Size
5 Type 1 1-2024 <$125
10 Type 1 1-1112 <$125
20 Type 1 1-298 <$135
5 Type 2 1-2018 <$135
10 Type 2 1-1257 <$135
20 Type 2 1-400 <$150
Total Issue $1,080,510
Out in 1935 $50,000
Large out 1935 $2,530

2389 Trumbull
HUBBARD NB, HUBBARD
{{ UNREPORTED }}
Chartered 6/21/78
Liquidated 10/23/86
Series 1875 <$VALUE
4x5 1-6049 <$1250
Total Issue $120,980
Out in 1910 $610

9221 Summit
NB OF HUDSON
{{ 2 L 5 S }}
Organized 8/12/08
1902 Date Back <$VALUE
4x5 1-975* <$500
3x10-20 1-760** <$500
1902 Plain Back
4x5 1076-2702* <$500
3x10-20 821-3089** <$500
* 976-1075 not marked
** 761-820 not marked
1929 Small Size
5 Type 1 1-752 <$250
10 Type 1 1-358 <$250
20 Type 1 1-124 <$250
5 Type 2 1-1254 <$275
10 Type 2 1-537 <$275
20 Type 2 1-119 <$275
Total Issue $281,430
Out in 1935 $20,000
Large out 1935 $765

4778 Erie
FNB OF HURON
{{ 2 L }}
Chartered 1892
Liquidated 6/20/23
Brown Back <$VALUE
3x10-20 1-1590 <$1000
1882 Date Back
3x10-20 1-329 <$1000
1902 Date Back
3x10-20 1-921 <$750
Total Issue $142,000
Out at close $1,600

4336 Lawrence
CITIZENS NB OF IRONTON
{{ 7 L 18 S }}
Chartered 1890
Brown Back <$VALUE
4x5 1-8300 <$300
3x10-20 1-3250 <$300/$350
1882 Date Back
4x5 1-1026 <$300
3x10-20 1-935 <$300/$350
1902 Date Back
4x5 1-5750 <$175
3x10-20 1-4250 <$175
1902 Plain Back
4x5 5751-23165 <$175
3x10-20 4521-16292 <$175
1929 Small Size
5 Type 1 1-4298 <$65
10 Type 1 1-1992 <$65
20 Type 1 1-572 <$75
5 Type 2 1-6180 <$75
10 Type 2 1-2988 <$75
20 Type 2 1-972 <$85
Total Issue $2,070,990
Out in 1935 $100,000
Large out 1935 $6,495

98 Lawrence
FNB OF IRONTON
{{ 43 L U + 50+ S }}
Chartered 10/63
Original Series <$VALUE
3x1-2 1-5900 <$400/$1000
4x5 1-6300 <$400
4x10 1-4175 <$750
4x20 1-2050 <$1250
Series 1875
3x1-2 1-1780 <$400/$1000
4x5 1-6800 <$400
4x10 1-3600 <$650
4x20 1-300 <$1000
Brown Back
4x5 1-21762 <$200
3x10-20 1-12476 <$200/$250
1902 Red Seal
4x5 1-12000 <$200
3x10-20 1-9100 <$200/$250
1902 Date Back
4x5 1-18500 <$75
3x10-20 1-14500 <$85
1902 Plain Back
4x5 18501-66626 <$75
3x10-20 14501-60955 <$85
1929 Small Size
5 Type 1 1-11950 <$25
10 Type 1 1-5374 <$25
20 Type 1 1-2108 <$35
5 Type 2 1-8650* <$30
10 Type 2 1-4250 <$30
20 Type 2 1-1400 <$40
* 3768-3774 not issued
Total Issue $7,981,330
Out in 1935 $234,400
Large out 1935 $38,200
Outstanding includes Ch 242

242 Lawrence
SECOND NB OF IRONTON
{{ 10 L }}
Chartered 2/64
Closed 7/7/21
Original Series <$VALUE
3x1-2 1-6000 <$400/$1000
4x5 1-9150 <$400
3x10-20 1-3640 <$750/$1250
Series 1875
3x1-2 1-2000 <$400/$1000
4x5 1-8000 <$400
3x10-20 1-2616 <$750/$1250
Brown Back
3x10-20 1-10308 <$250
1902 Red Seal
3x10-20 1-5650 <$250
1902 Date Back
3x10-20 1-7900 <$125
1902 Plain Back
3x10-20 7901-13619 <$125
Total Issue $2,174,650
Out in 1920 $123,100
Ch 98 assumed circulation

1903 Jackson
FNB OF JACKSON
{{ 7 L 11 S }}
Chartered 12/7/71
Original Series <$VALUE
4x5 1-4800 <$500
3x10-20 1-580 <$750/$1250
Series 1875
4x5 1-2061 <$500
3x10-20 1-1071 <$750/$1250
Brown Back
4x5 1-2850 <$300
3x10-20 1-3045 <$300/$350
1882 Date Back
4x5 1-990 <$300
3x10-20 1-788 <$300/$350
1902 Date Back
4x5 1-2050 <$175
3x10-20 1-1420 <$175
1902 Plain Back
4x5 2051-9030 <$175
3x10-20 1421-5941 <$175
1929 Small Size
5 Type 1 1-1770 <$125
10 Type 1 1-834 <$125
20 Type 1 1-244 <$135
5 Type 2 1-1680 <$150
10 Type 2 1-1323 <$150
20 Type 2 1-289 <$150
Total Issue $1,125,700
Out in 1935 $50,000
Large out 1935 $3,130

8536 Shelby
FNB OF JACKSON CENTER
{{ 6 L 6 S }}
Organized 1/15/07
1902 Red Seal <$VALUE
3x10-20 1-255 <$850
1902 Date Back
3x10-20 1-2650 <$400
1902 Plain Back
3x10-20 2651-7424 <$400
1929 Small Size
10 Type 1 1-728 <$225
20 Type 1 1-242 <$225
10 Type 2 1-734 <$250
20 Type 2 1-171 <$250
Total Issue $467,430
Out in 1935 $32,700
Large out 1935 $1,710

427 Jefferson
FNB OF JEFFERSON
{{ 5 L }}
Chartered 5/64
Liquidated 3/20/26
Original Series <$VALUE
4x5 1-2000 <$500
3x10-20 1-1400 <$750/$1250
Series 1875
4x5 1-482 <$500
3x10-20 1-1431 <$750/$1250
Brown Back
3x10-20 1-5745 <$400
1902 Red Seal
3x10-20 1-3300 <$500
1902 Date Back
3x10-20 1-4400 <$225
1902 Plain Back
3x10-20 4401-12401 <$225
Total Issue $1,263,490
Out at close $70,000

2026 Jefferson
SECOND NB OF JEFFERSON
{{ UNREPORTED }}
Chartered 8/12/72
Liquidated 12/26/82
Original Series <$VALUE
3x1-2 1-1000 <$1250/$2000
4x5 1-2450 <$1250
3x10-20 1-1200 <$1500/$2000
Series 1875
4x5 1-1700 <$1250
3x10-20 1-1638 <$1500/$2000
Total Issue $229,900
Out in 1910 $940

13150 Harrison
FNB OF JEWETT
{{ 6 S }}
Chartered 12/27
1929 Small Size <$VALUE
5 Type 1 1-1034 <$225
10 Type 1 1-442 <$225
5 Type 2 1-4148 <$250
10 Type 2 1-2184 <$250
Total Issue $100,120
Out in 1935 $33,700

7074 Putnam
FNB OF KALIDA
{{ UNREPORTED }}
Chartered 12/03
Liquidated 2/16/12
1902 Red Seal <$VALUE
3x10-20 1-334 <$1500
1902 Date Back
3x10-20 1-145 <$1000
Total Issue $23,950
Out in 1912 $4,250

11598 Seneca
FNB OF KANSAS
{{ 5 L 8 S }}
Organized 9/11/19
Receivership 9/13/33
1902 Plain Back <$VALUE
4x5 1-8212 <$350
1929 Small Size
5 Type 1 1-2958 <$250
Total Issue $252,980
Out at close $25,000
Large out at close $700

CONDITION affects Value. The Values shown are for notes in FINE condition.

****
652 Portage
KENT NB, KENT
{{ 14 L 50+ S }}
Chartered 12/64
Original Series <$VALUE
3x1-2 1-2400 <$400/$1000
4x5 1-2000 <$450
3x10-20 1-2320 <$750/$1250
Series 1875
3x1-2 1-1360 <$400/$1000
4x5 1-250 <$450
3x10-20 1-2032 <$750/$1250
Brown Back
3x10-20 1-4944 <$300
1902 Red Seal
3x10-20 1-2100 <$350
1902 Date Back
3x10-20 1-4090 <$150
1902 Plain Back
3x10-20 4091-21498 <$150
1929 Small Size
10 Type 1 1-2752 <$40
20 Type 1 1-782 <$60
10 Type 2 1-3634 <$75
20 Type 2 1-949 <$75
Total Issue $2,022,780
Out in 1935 $100,000
Large out 1935 $6,730
****
F Commercial NB of Kenton
SEE Ch 2500
FNB of Kenton
****
2500 Hardin
FNB OF KENTON
Chartered 1881
2nd title: F Commercial NB of Kenton 7/3/31
FIRST TITLE {{ 7 L 8 S }}
Series 1875 <$VALUE
3x10-20 1-2454 <$750/$1250
Brown Back
3x10-20 1-2800 <$500
1882 Date Back
3x10-20 1-3100 <$500
1882 Value Back
3x10-20 3101-4791 <$500
1902 Plain Back
3x10-20 1-5354 <$275
1929 Small Size
10 Type 1 1-874 <$150
20 Type 1 1-250 <$150
SECOND TITLE {{ 12 S }}
1929 Small Size
10 Type 1 1 1246 <$125
20 Type 1 1-398 <$125
10 Type 2 1-3088 <$150
20 Type 2 1-704 <$150
Total Issue $1,019,870
Out in 1935 $100,000
Large out 1935 $2,790
****
3505 Hardin
KENTON NB, KENTON
{{ 7 L 10 S }}
Chartered 1886
Brown Back <$VALUE
4x5 1-350 <$500
3x10-20 1-4529 <$500
1902 Red Seal
3x10-20 1-1600 <$650
1902 Date Back
3x10-20 1-3100* <$250
1902 Plain Back
3x10-20 3301-10545* <$250
* 3101-3300 not marked
1929 Small Size
10 Type 1 1-1384 <$150
20 Type 1 1-328 <$175
10 Type 2 1-1093 <$185
20 Type 2 1-249 <$200
Total Issue $979,010
Out in 1935 $50,000
Large out 1935 $3,110
****
9536 Ross
FNB OF KINGSTON
{{ 3 L 10 S }}
Chartered 9/09
1902 Date Back <$VALUE
4x5 1-1725 <$400
3x10-20 1-1420 <$400
1902 Plain Back
4x5 1726-6775 <$400
3x10-20 1421-4517 <$400
1929 Small Size
5 Type 1 1-1238 <$175
10 Type 1 1-746 <$175
20 Type 1 1-212 <$175
5 Type 2 1-2496 <$200
10 Type 2 1-1160 <$200
20 Type 2 1-496 <$200
Total Issue $502,690
Out in 1935 $50,000
Large out 1935 $1,300
****

****
3077 Trumbull
KINSMAN NB, KINSMAN
{{ 1 L }}
Organized 11/7/83
Liquidated 12/29/33
Brown Back <$VALUE
3x10-20 1-1564 <$1000
1902 Red Seal
3x10-20 1-1075 <$1250
1902 Date Back
3x10-20 1-1900 <$600
1902 Plain Back
3x10-20 1901-4263 <$600
Total Issue $345,100
Out at close $790
****
6675 Marion
CAMPBELL NB OF La RUE
{{ 5 L 9 S }}
Organized 3/2/03
1902 Red Seal <$VALUE
4x5 1-306 <$850
3x10-20 1-305 <$850
1902 Date Back
4x5 1-2450 <$400
3x10-20 1-1720 <$400
1902 Plain Back
4x5 2451-7444 <$400
3x10-20 1721-4742 <$400
1929 Small Size
5 Type 1 1-910 <$200
10 Type 1 1-608 <$200
20 Type 1 1-172 <$225
5 Type 2 1-1122 <$250
10 Type 2 1-318 <$250
20 Type 2 1-132 <$250
Total Issue $503,200
Out in 1935 $30,000
Large out 1935 $1,410
****
13715 Cuyahoga
PEOPLES NB OF LAKEWOOD
{{ 17 S }}
Chartered 6/33
1929 Small Size <$VALUE
5 Type 2 1-25192 <$100
10 Type 2 1-10980 <$100
20 Type 2 1-2607 <$100
50 Type 2 1-132 <$650
Total Issue $294,500
Out in 1935 $137,700
****
7517 Fairfield
FAIRFIELD NB OF LANCASTER
{{ 12 L 26 S }}
Chartered 12/04
1902 Red Seal <$VALUE
3x10-20 1-962 <$350/$400
50-100 1-216 <$2250/$2500
1902 Date Back
3x10-20 1-3000 <$175
50-100 1-100 <$500/$600
3x50-100 1-120 <$500/$600
1902 Plain Back
3x10-20 3001-13047 <$175
1929 Small Size
10 Type 1 1-3942 <$50
20 Type 1 1-1132 <$60
10 Type 2 1-4233 <$65
20 Type 2 1-1014 <$70
Total Issue $1,212,820
Out in 1935 $159,110
Large out 1935 $5,880
****
137 Fairfield
FNB OF LANCASTER
{{ UNREPORTED }}
Chartered 12/63
Liquidated 8/1/77
Original Series <$VALUE
3x1-2 1-2000 <$1250/$1750
4x5 1-5000 <$1250
Series 1875
4x5 1-1485 <$1250
Total Issue $139,700
Out in 1910 $1,174
****
1241 Fairfield
HOCKING VALLEY NB OF LANCASTER
{{ 13 L 10 S }}
Chartered 1865
Original Series <$VALUE
4x5 1-2400 <$600
3x10-20 1-1260 <$750/$1250
Series 1875
3x10-20 1-1566 <$750/$1250
Brown Back
4x5 1-4908 <$275
50-100 1-200 <$1500/$1750
1902 Red Seal
50-100 1-520 <$2250/$2500

1902 Date Back
50-100 1-334 <$500/$600
3x50-100 1-500 <$500/$600
1902 Plain Back
3x50-100 501-707<$500/$600
1929 Small Size
50 Type 1 1-153 <$300
100 Type 1 1-26 <$400
Total Issue $683,810
Out in 1935 $50,000
Large out 1935 $9,250
****
9547 Fairfield
LANCASTER NB, LANCASTER
{{ 6 L U + 40 S }}
Chartered 9/09
1902 Date Back <$VALUE
3x10-20 1-3600 <$225
50-100 1-400 <$500/$600
3x50-100 1-1619 <$500/$600
1902 Plain Back
3x10-20 3601-5181 <$225
3x50-100 1620-1781 <$500/$600
1929 Small Size
5 Type 1 1-1090 <$75
10 Type 1 1-992 <$75
20 Type 1 1-266 <$85
50 Type 1 1-126 <$250
100 Type 1 1-42 <$300
5 Type 2 1-828 <$100
10 Type 2 1-595 <$100
20 Type 2 1-170 <$110
Total Issue $964,930
Out in 1935 $100,000
Large out 1935 $11,030
****
4239 Warren
CITIZENS NB OF LEBANON
Chartered 1890
Closed 12/12/25
2nd title: Citizens NB & TC of Lebanon 2/20/23
FIRST TITLE {{ 4 L }}
Brown Back <$VALUE
3x10-20 1-4300 <$400
1882 Date Back
3x10-20 1-775 <$375
1902 Date Back
3x10-20 1-6200 <$250
1902 Plain Back
3x10-20 6201-11400 <$250
SECOND TITLE {{ 1 L }}
1902 Plain Back
3x10-20 1-2812 <$300
Total Issue $964,350
Out at close $78,500
Ch 2360 assumed circulation
****
8507 Warren
FARMERS & MERCHANTS NB OF LEBANON
{{ UNREPORTED }}
Chartered 1/8/07
Liquidated 1/12/09
1902 Red Seal <$VALUE
4x5 1-520 <$1500
3x10-20 1-557 <$1500
Total Issue $38,250
Out in 1910 $8,075
****
1238 Warren
FNB OF LEBANON
{{ 1 L }}
Chartered 6/7/65
Liquidated 10/24/70
Original Series <$VALUE
4x5 1-2000 <$1250
3x10-20 1-930 <$1500/$1750
Total Issue $86,500
Out in 1910 $515
****
2360 Warren
LEBANON NB, LEBANON
Chartered 5/29/77
2nd title: Lebanon NB & TC 7/5/22
3rd title: Lebanon Citizens NB & TC 12/12/25
FIRST TITLE {{ 4 L }}
Series 1875 <$VALUE
4x5 1-5719 <$500
Brown Back
3x10-20 1-3770 <$350
1882 Date Back
3x10-20 1-8384 <$350
1902 Plain Back
3x10-20 1-7350 <$200
SECOND TITLE {{ 1 L }}
1902 Plain Back
3x10-20 1-4006 <$225
THIRD TITLE {{ 4 L 22 S }}
1902 Plain Back
3x10-20 1-7536 <$175

1929 Small Size
10 Type 1 1-4524 <$50
20 Type 1 1-1248 <$60
10 Type 2 1-3761 <$60
20 Type 2 1-1288 <$65
Total Issue $2,077,750
Out in 1935 $152,795
Large out 1935 $9,215
Outstanding includes Ch 4239
****
3519 Columbiana
FNB OF LEETONIA
{{ 3 L }}
Organized 6/10/86
Receivership 11/04/07
Brown Back <$VALUE
4x5 1-9665 <$500
3x10-20 1-4330 <$500
1902 Red Seal
4x5 1-720 <$650
3x10-20 1-440 <$650
Total Issue $446,200
Out in 1916 $4,670
****
6565 Putnam
FNB OF LEIPSIC
{{ UNREPORTED }}
Chartered 12/30/02
Liquidated 12/8/06
1902 Red Seal <$VALUE
3x10-20 1-270 <$1500
Total Issue $13,500
Out in 1910 $950
****
8978 Monroe
FNB OF LEWISVILLE
{{ 4 L }}
Organized 12/9/07
Receivership 12/19/28
1902 Red Seal <$VALUE
3x10-20 1-700 <$650
1902 Date Back
3x10-20 1-1670 <$350
1902 Plain Back
3x10-20 1671-4830 <$350
Total Issue $276,500
Out at close $24,450
****
5125 Allen
AMERICAN NB OF LIMA
{{ UNREPORTED }}
Chartered 6/11/98
Liquidated 4/8/99
Brown Back <$VALUE
4x5 1-1150 <$1250
Total Issue $23,000
Out in 1910 $295
****
2035 Allen
FNB OF LIMA
{{ 9 L }}
Chartered 8/29/72
Liquidated 12/31/23
Original Series <$VALUE
3x1-2 1-1648 <$500/$1250
4x5 1-4063 <$500
Series 1875
4x5 1-6922 <$500
Brown Back
4x5 1-5550 <$325
3x10-20 1-6400 <$325/$375
1882 Date Back
4x5 1-1620 <$325
3x10-20 1-2328 <$325/$375
1902 Date Back
3x10-20 1-3400 <$150
3x50-100 1-340 <$400/$500
1902 Plain Back
3x10-20 3401-9399 <$150
Total Issue $1,362,690
Out at close $100,000
****
2859 Allen
LIMA NB, LIMA
{{ 1 L }}
Organized 1/16/83
Receivership 3/21/92
Brown Back <$VALUE
4x5 1-7093 <$850
Total Issue $141,860
Out in 1916 $925
****
2497 Allen
MERCHANTS NB OF LIMA
{{ 1 L }}
Chartered 11/17/80
Liquidated 10/22/86
Series 1875 <$VALUE
3x10-20 1-1613<$1000/$1500
Total Issue $80,650
Out in 1910 $390
****

****
13767 Allen
NB OF LIMA
{{ 10 S }}
Chartered 9/33
1929 Small Size <$VALUE
5 Type 2 1-10520 <$100
10 Type 2 1-5345 <$100
20 Type 2 1-1640 <$100
Total Issue $138,850
Out in 1935 $81,600
****
3772 Allen
OHIO NB OF LIMA
{{ 1 L }}
Chartered 8/6/87
Liquidated 6/21/07
Brown Back <$VALUE
4x5 1-7429 <$750
3x10-20 1-1038 <$750
Total Issue $200,480
Out in 1910 $4,450
****
8701 Allen
OLD NB OF LIMA
Organized 3/29/07
Receivership 4/29/31
2nd title: Old N City B of Lima 10/12/25
FIRST TITLE {{ 3 L }}
1902 Red Seal <$VALUE
3x10-20 1-1350 <$600
1902 Date Back
3x10-20 1-4700* <$275
1902 Plain Back
3x10-20 5101-12950* <$275
* 4701-5100 not marked
SECOND TITLE {{ 6 L 7 S }}
1902 Plain Back
4x5 1-25593 <$175
1929 Small Size
5 Type 1 1-9849 <$125
Total Issue $1,522,330
Out at close $150,000
Large out at close $9,480
****
4133 Hamilton
FNB OF LOCKLAND
{{ 4 L 13 S }}
Chartered 10/2/89
Brown Back <$VALUE
3x10-20 1-3383 <$500
1902 Date Back
3x10-20 1-3300 <$350
1902 Plain Back
3x10-20 3301-10764 <$350
1929 Small Size
10 Type 1 1-1544 <$110
20 Type 1 1-412 <$125
10 Type 2 1-1405 <$135
20 Type 2 1-371 <$150
Total Issue $870,900
Out in 1935 $50,000
Large out 1935 $1,940
****
Exchange NB of Lodi
SEE Ch 7017
Lodi NB, Lodi
****
53 Medina
FNB OF LODI
{{ UNREPORTED }}
Chartered 8/63
Liquidated 1/11/76
Original Series <$VALUE
3x1-2 1-1800 <$1500/$2500
4x5 1-1500 <$1500
4x10 1-2952 <$2000
Total Issue $157,080
Out in 1910 $993
****
7017 Medina
LODI NB, LODI
Chartered 10/03
Liquidated 10/8/15
2nd title: Exchange NB of Lodi 1/12/06
FIRST TITLE {{ 0 L }}
1902 Red Seal <$VALUE
3x10-20 1-742 <$1500
SECOND TITLE {{ 1 L }}
1902 Red Seal
3x10-20 1-1300 <$1250
1902 Date Back
3x10-20 1-2453 <$750
Total Issue $224,750
Out at close $38,800
****

****
10677 Medina
PEOPLES NB OF LODI
{{ 6 L 5 S }}
Organized 11/12/14
Receivership 12/8/31
1902 Date Back <$VALUE
3x10-20 1-500 <$350
1902 Plain Back
3x10-20 501-8369 <$350
1929 Small Size
10 Type 1 1-696 <$300
20 Type 1 1-200 <$300
Total Issue $484,210
Out at close $36,600
Large out at close $3,450
****
92 Hocking
FNB OF LOGAN
{{ UNREPORTED }}
Chartered 9/63
Liquidated 7/8/81
Original Series <$VALUE
4x5 1-5500 <$2000
Series 1875
4x5 1-2045 <$2000
Total Issue $150,900
Out in 1910 $1,045
****
7649 Hocking
NB OF LOGAN
Organized 1/24/05
Receivership 4/16/31
2nd title: FNB in Logan 1/16/22
3rd title: F-Rempel NB of Logan 2/3/30
FIRST TITLE {{ 3 L }}
1902 Red Seal <$VALUE
4x5 1-1415 <$1000
3x10-20 1-1134 <$1000
1902 Date Back
4x5 1-3400 <$500
3x10-20 1-2410 <$500
1902 Plain Back
4x5 3401-6500 <$500
3x10-20 2411-4210 <$500
SECOND TITLE {{ 1 L 6 S }}
1902 Plain Back
4x5 1-4791 <$500
3x10-20 1-3522 <$500
1929 Small Size
5 Type 1 1-826 <$400
10 Type 1 1-418 <$400
20 Type 1 1-148 <$400
THIRD TITLE {{ 1 S }}
1929 Small Size
5 Type 1 1-92 <$500
10 Type 1 1-62 <$500
20 Type 1 1-5 <$500
Total Issue $775,120
Out at close $50,000
Large out at close $7,060
****
9284 Hocking
REMPEL NB OF LOGAN
{{ 3 L }}
Chartered 11/08
Liquidated 11/15/29
1902 Date Back <$VALUE
4x10 1-5325 <$400
1902 Plain Back
4x10 5326-16230 <$400
Total Issue $649,200
Out at close $39,100
****
10373 Madison
CENTRAL NB OF LONDON
{{ 5 L U + 12 S }}
Chartered 4/13
1902 Date Back <$VALUE
3x10-20 1-2000 <$250
1902 Plain Back
4x5 1-7460 <$250
3x10-20 2001-11097 <$250
1929 Small Size
5 Type 1 1-3478 <$100
10 Type 1 1-2032 <$100
20 Type 1 1-606 <$100
5 Type 2 1-1474 <$125
10 Type 2 1-357 <$125
20 Type 2 1-135 <$135
Total Issue $1,016,670
Out in 1935 $50,000
Large out 1935 $3,160
****

1064 Madison
MADISON NB OF LONDON
{{ 8 L 10 S }}
Chartered 4/65
Original Series <$VALUE
4x5 1-2300 <$500
3x10-20 1-1520 <$750/$1250
50-100 1-400 <$4000
Series 1875
4x5 1-1250 <$500
3x10-20 1-1324 <$750/$1250
50-100 1-492 <$4000
Brown Back
50-100 1-1063 <$1500/$1750
1902 Red Seal
4x5 1-1825 <$400
3x10-20 1-1230 <$400
1902 Date Back
4x5 1-3350 <$175
3x10-20 1-2780 <$175
1902 Plain Back
4x5 3351-13650 <$175
3x10-20 2781-9058 <$175
1929 Small Size
5 Type 1 1-2396 <$110
10 Type 1 1-1066 <$110
20 Type 1 1-320 <$125
5 Type 2 1-2372 <$125
10 Type 2 1-1262 <$125
20 Type 2 1-444 <$135
Total Issue $1,537,950
Out in 1935 $59,995
Large out 1935 $4,595

2625 Lorain
FNB OF LORAIN
{{ UNREPORTED }}
Chartered 2/6/82
Liquidated 1/10/93
Series 1875 <$VALUE
4x5 1-4690 <$1500
Total Issue $93,800
Out in 1910 $560

5371 Lorain
NB OF COMMERCE OF LORAIN
{{ 7 L 17 S }}
Chartered 5/25/00
Liquidated 12/29/34
Brown Back <$VALUE
4x5 1-5770 <$350
3x10-20 1-4592 <$350
1882 Date Back
4x5 1-7750 <$350
3x10-20 1-5480 <$350
1882 Value Back
4x5 7751-12100 <$350
3x10-20 5481-7499 <$350
1902 Plain Back
3x10-20 1-14373 <$175
1929 Small Size
10 Type 1 1-2642 <$85
20 Type 1 1-824 <$100
10 Type 2 1-1726 <$100
20 Type 2 1-223 <$110
Total Issue $1,959,720
Out at close $100,000
Large out at close $4,740

6657 Ashland
FNB OF LOUDONVILLE
{{ UNREPORTED }}
Chartered 3/03
Liquidated 2/25/18
1902 Red Seal <$VALUE
3x10-20 1-540 <$1500
1902 Date Back
3x10-20 1-1560 <$1000
1902 Plain Back
3x10-20 1561-1739 <$1000
Total Issue $113,950
Out at close $19,600

9630 Stark
FNB OF LOUISVILLE
{{ UNREPORTED }}
Chartered 1/10
Liquidated 1/20/24
1902 Date Back <$VALUE
4x10 1-2525 <$1000
1902 Plain Back
4x10 2526-5681 <$1000
Total Issue $227,240
Out at close $23,350

6816 Clermont
FNB OF LOVELAND
{{ UNREPORTED }}
Chartered 6/03
Liquidated 5/25/11
1902 Red Seal <$VALUE
3x10-20 1-491 <$1500
Total Issue $24,550
Out in 1911 $4,150

6779 Clermont
LOVELAND NB, LOVELAND
{{ 4 L 8 S }}
Chartered 5/03
1902 Red Seal <$VALUE
3x10-20 1-1000 <$1000
1902 Date Back
3x10-20 1-3400 <$500
1902 Plain Back
3x10-20 3401-10490 <$500
1929 Small Size
10 Type 1 1-1056 <$300
20 Type 1 1-328 <$300
10 Type 2 1-1252 <$325
20 Type 2 1-263 <$325
Total Issue $695,000
Out in 1935 $40,000
Large out 1935 $2,180

5329 Washington
FNB OF LOWELL
{{ 6 L 6 S }}
Chartered 5/4/00
Liquidated 10/21/33
Brown Back <$VALUE
3x10-20 1-1400 <$450
1882 Date Back
3x10-20 1-1650 <$450
1882 Value Back
3x10-20 1651-2409 <$450
1902 Plain Back
3x10-20 1-2839* <$300
* 1703-1862 not issued
1929 Small Size
10 Type 1 1-585 <$300
20 Type 1 1-152 <$300
Total Issue $377,740
Out at close $21,080
Large out at close $970

11772 Highland
FNB OF LYNCHBURG
{{ 10 L 4 S }}
Organized 6/11/20
Receivership 9/28/31
1902 Plain Back <$VALUE
4x5 1-12581 <$250
1929 Small Size
5 Type 1 1-3410* <$350
* 1017-2048 not issued
Total Issue $322,960
Out at close $30,000
Large out at close $1,610

8557 Hamilton
FNB OF MADISONVILLE
{{ 1 L }}
Chartered 2/07
Liquidated 3/26/25
1902 Red Seal <$VALUE
4x5 1-725 <$1000
4x10 1-725 <$1000
1902 Date Back
4x5 1-2075 <$500
4x10 1-1725 <$500
1902 Plain Back
4x5 2076-5263 <$500
4x10 1726-3930 <$500
Total Issue $305,960
Out at close $25,000

2052 Morgan
MALTA NB, MALTA
{{ 8 L 11 S }}
Chartered 9/30/72
Original Series <$VALUE
3x1-2 1-1500 <$450/$1250
4x5 1-2850 <$450
3x10-20 1-460 <$750/$1250
Series 1875
3x10-20 1-2320 <$750/$1250
Brown Back
3x10-20 1-4010 <$400
1882 Date Back
3x10-20 1-1174 <$400
1902 Date Back
3x10-20 1-2300 <$225
1902 Plain Back
3x10-20 2301-9373 <$225
1929 Small Size
10 Type 1 1-1336 <$125
20 Type 1 1-378 <$125
10 Type 2 1-1074 <$150
20 Type 2 1-248 <$150
Total Issue $1,072,570
Out in 1935 $50,000
Large out 1935 $3,360

9091 Adams
FARMERS NB OF MANCHESTER
{{ 7 L 9 S }}
Chartered 4/08
1902 Red Seal <$VALUE
3x10-20 1-300 <$650
1902 Date Back
3x10-20 1-2950 <$300
1902 Plain Back
3x10-20 2951-7615 <$300
1929 Small Size
10 Type 1 1-996 <$175
20 Type 1 1-254 <$175
10 Type 2 1-943 <$200
20 Type 2 1-263 <$200
Total Issue $500,680
Out in 1935 $40,000
Large out 1935 $3,860

1982 Adams
MANCHESTER NB, MANCHESTER
{{ 3 L }}
Chartered 5/13/72
Liquidated 1/13/80
Original Series <$VALUE
3x1-2 1-2100 <$500/$1250
4x5 1-2200 <$500
3x10-20 1-1350 <$750/$1250
Series 1875
4x5 1-475 <$500
3x10-20 1-592 <$750/$1250
Total Issue $161,100
Out in 1910 $688

2577 Richland
CITIZENS NB OF MANSFIELD
Chartered 1881
2nd title: Citizens NB & TC of Mansfield 5/20/26
FIRST TITLE {{ 3 L }}
Series 1875 <$VALUE
3x10-20 1-4788 <$750/$1250
Brown Back
50-100 1-1734 <$1500/$1750
1882 Date Back
50-100 1-900 <$1500/$1750
3x50-100 1-838<$1500/$1750
1902 Date Back
3x50-100 1-757 <$500/$600
SECOND TITLE {{ 2 L 14 S }}
1902 Plain Back
3x50-100 1-425 <$500/$600
1929 Small Size
50 Type 1 1-286 <$175
100 Type 1 1-82 <$250
Total Issue $1,274,500
Out in 1935 $100,000
Large out 1935 $9,800

436 Richland
FNB OF MANSFIELD
{{ 7 L }}
Organized 5/24/64
Receivership 10/18/73
Original Series <$VALUE
3x1-2 1-3000 <$500/$1250
4x5 1-2000 <$500
3x10-20 1-1638*<$750/$1250
* 1401-1500 not issued
Total Issue $131,900
Out in 1916 $907

800 Richland
FARMERS NB OF MANSFIELD
{{ 2 L }}
Chartered 2/14/65
Liquidated 3/31/06
Original Series <$VALUE
4x5 1-1925 <$850
3x10-20 1-2430<$1000/$1500
Series 1875
3x10-20 1-2494<$1000/$1500
Brown Back
3x10-20 1-5259 <$650
1902 Red Seal
3x10-20 1-585 <$750
Total Issue $576,900
Out in 1910 $12,285

480 Richland
RICHLAND NB OF MANSFIELD
{{ 4 L }}
Chartered 7/11/64
Liquidated 9/25/75
Original Series <$VALUE
3x1-2 1-4600 <$500/$1250
4x5 1-5500 <$500
3x10-20 1-3073 <$750/$1250
Total Issue $286,650
Out in 1910 $1,822

5370 Portage
FNB OF MANTUA
{{ 4 L 10 S }}
Chartered 5/25/00
Brown Back <$VALUE
3x10-20 1-960 <$500
1882 Date Back
3x10-20 1-3240 <$500
1882 Value Back
3x10-20 3241-4520 <$500
1902 Plain Back
3x10-20 1-6525 <$350
1929 Small Size
5 Type 1 1-1562 <$150
10 Type 1 1-868 <$150
20 Type 1 1-308 <$165
5 Type 2 1-2572 <$175
10 Type 2 1-1624 <$175
20 Type 2 1-336 <$185
Total Issue $771,970
Out in 1935 $50,000
Large out 1935 $1,870

Central NB of Marietta
SEE Ch 5212
German NB of Marietta

4164 Washington
CITIZENS NB OF MARIETTA
{{ 14 L 24 S }}
Chartered 11/23/89
Brown Back <$VALUE
4x5 1-6475 <$225
3x10-20 1-3200 <$225/$275
1882 Date Back
4x5 1-970 <$225
3x10-20 1-227 <$225/$275
1902 Date Back
4x5 1-5650 <$100
3x10-20 1-4220 <$100
1902 Plain Back
4x5 5651-25895 <$100
3x10-20 4221-16547 <$100
1929 Small Size
5 Type 1 1-5928 <$35
10 Type 1 1-2888 <$35
20 Type 1 1-756 <$45
5 Type 2 1-5532 <$45
10 Type 2 1-3076 <$45
20 Type 2 1-795 <$50
Total Issue $2,181,660
Out in 1935 $150,000
Large out 1935 $6,145

142 Washington
FNB OF MARIETTA
{{ 26 L 43 S }}
Organized 11/14/63
Receivership 2/5/34
Original Series <$VALUE
4x5 1-3500 <$400
4x10 1-4125 <$650
Series 1875
4x10 1-3491 <$600
Brown Back
3x10-20 1-10790 <$150/$200
1902 Red Seal
3x10-20 1-7000 <$175/$225
1902 Date Back
3x10-20 1-9700 <$75
1902 Plain Back
3x10-20 9701-74820 <$75
1929 Small Size
10 Type 1 1-13748 <$30
20 Type 1 1-4048 <$40
10 Type 2 1-270 <$50
20 Type 2 1-155 <$60
Total Issue $6,321,580
Out at close $500,000
Large out at close $22,010

5212 Washington
GERMAN NB OF MARIETTA
Organized 5/29/99
Receivership 2/24/27
2nd title: Central NB of Marietta 2/21/18
FIRST TITLE {{ 7 L }}
Brown Back <$VALUE
3x10-20 1-3600 <$400
1882 Date Back
3x10-20 1-6200 <$400
1882 Value Back
3x10-20 6201-10200 <$400
SECOND TITLE {{ 6 L }}
1882 Value Back
3x10-20 1-1190 <$325/$375
1902 Plain Back
3x10-20 1-27874 <$200
Total Issue $2,143,200
Out at close $296,700

859 Washington
MARIETTA NB, MARIETTA
{{ 3 L }}
Chartered 3/6/65
Liquidated 2/16/76
Original Series <$VALUE
3x1-2 1-5500 <$500/$1250
4x5 1-6045 <$600
3x10-20 1-1140 <$750/$1250
Total Issue $205,400
Out in 1910 $1,494

13971 Washington
NEW FNB OF MARIETTA
{{ 3U + 9 S }}
Chartered 1/34
1929 Small Size <$VALUE
5 Type 2 1-5050 <$150
10 Type 2 1-2395 <$150
20 Type 2 1-730 <$175
Total Issue $63,800
Out in 1935 $42,350

5650 Marion
CITY NB OF MARION
{{ 4 L }}
Chartered 12/22/00
Liquidated 9/5/20
Brown Back <$VALUE
4x5 1-2260 <$350
3x10-20 1-1836 <$350
1882 Date Back
4x5 1-6500 <$350
3x10-20 1-4200 <$350
1882 Value Back
4x5 6501-11085 <$350
3x10-20 4201-6950 <$350
Total Issue $706,200
Out at close $95,800
Ch 11831 assumed circulation

287 Marion
FNB OF MARION
{{ 1 L }}
Chartered 2/26/64
Liquidated 1/12/69
Original Series <$VALUE
3x1-2 1-1770 <$850/$1500
4x5 1-1350 <$850
3x10-20 1-1500<$1250/$1500
Total Issue $110,850
Out in 1910 $781

6308 Marion
MARION NB, MARION
{{ U + 13 L 13 S }}
Chartered 6/17/02
Receivership 12/24/31
1902 Red Seal <$VALUE
4x5 1-6000 <$300
3x10-20 1-4800 <$300/$325
1902 Date Back
4x5 1-12750 <$125
3x10-20 1-9500 <$125
1902 Plain Back
4x5 12751-47011 <$125
3x10-20 9501-31409 <$125
1929 Small Size
5 Type 1 1-4700 <$85
10 Type 1 1-2534 <$85
20 Type 1 1-753 <$100
Total Issue $3,254,070
Out at close $196,100
Large out at close $19,280

11831 Marion
N CITY B & TC OF MARION
{{ 2U + 10 L 23 S }}
Chartered 9/20
1902 Plain Back <$VALUE
4x5 1-26404 <$150
3x10-20 1-18822 <$150
1929 Small Size
5 Type 1 1-8650 <$50
10 Type 1 1-3922 <$50
20 Type 1 1-928 <$60
5 Type 2 1-5666 <$60
10 Type 2 1-3260 <$60
20 Type 2 1-878 <$70
Total Issue $2,153,850
Out in 1935 $100,000
Large out 1935 $8,060
Outstanding includes Ch 5650

7403 Warren
FNB OF MASON
{{ 4 L }}
Chartered 9/04
Liquidated 10/19/29
1902 Red Seal <$VALUE
3x10-20 1-1146 <$850
1902 Date Back
3x10-20 1-1760 <$425
1902 Plain Back
3x10-20 1761-5631 <$425
Total Issue $338,850
Out at close $24,100

216 Stark
FNB OF MASSILLON
{{ 14 L 23 S }}
Organized 1/8/64
Receivership 5/23/33
Original Series <$VALUE
4x5 1-7000 <$500
4x10 1-4500 <$750
2x20-50-100 1-405 <$1250/$4000/$4000
Series 1875
4x5 1-4750 <$500
4x10 1-2875 <$750
2x20-50-100 1-220 <$1250/$4000/$4000
Brown Back
3x10-20 1-10780 <$250/$300
1902 Red Seal
3x10-20 1-7000 <$275/$325
1902 Date Back
3x10-20 1-9700 <$125
1902 Plain Back
4x5 1-14000 <$125
3x10-20 9701-51253 <$125
1929 Small Size
10 Type 1 1-7827 <$60
20 Type 1 1-2151 <$70
Total Issue $5,108,140
Out at close $281,460
Large out at close $20,450

4286 Stark
MERCHANTS NB OF MASSILLON
{{ 13 L }}
Chartered 1890
Liquidated 5/1/25
Brown Back <$VALUE
4x5 1-14875 <$350
50-100 1-2820 <$1250/$1500
1882 Date Back
4x5 1-1815 <$300
1902 Date Back
4x5 1-9000 <$125
50-100 1-1500 <$400/$500
3x50-100 1-6745 <$400/$500
1902 Plain Back
4x5 9001-15250 <$125
Total Issue $2,898,050
Out in 1929 $94,255

1318 Stark
UNION NB OF MASSILLON
{{ 15 L 13 S }}
Organized 6/10/65
Liquidated 11/4/31
Original Series <$VALUE
4x5 1-7250 <$400
3x10-20 1-1700 <$750/$1250
Series 1875
3x10-20 1-1746 <$750/$1250
Brown Back
3x10-20 1-10279 <$225/$275
1902 Red Seal
3x10-20 1-5000 <$250/$300
1902 Date Back
3x10-20 1-10000 <$135
1902 Plain Back
3x10-20 10001-35476 <$135
1929 Small Size
10 Type 1 1-2854 <$125
20 Type 1 1-868 <$135
Total Issue $3,130,450
Out at close $150,000
Large out at close $16,640

CONDITION affects Value. The Values shown are for notes in FINE condition.

2036 Vinton
VINTON COUNTY NB OF McARTHUR
{{8 L 8 S}}
Chartered 8/30/72
Original Series <$VALUE
3x1-2 1-1000 <$500/$1250
4x5 1-4250 <$500
3x10-20 1-1600 <$750/$1250
Series 1875
4x5 1-1855 <$500
3x10-20 1-576 <$750/$1250
Brown Back
3x10-20 1-2370 <$350/$400
1882 Date Back
3x10-20 1-528 <$350/$400
1902 Date Back
3x10-20 1-1000 <$225
1902 Plain Back
3x10-20 1001-3178 <$225
1929 Small Size
10 Type 1 1-1058 <$175
20 Type 1 1-292 <$175
10 Type 2 1-1243 <$200
20 Type 2 1-240 <$200
Total Issue $655,450
Out in 1935 $50,000
Large out 1935 $2,270

5259 Morgan
CITIZENS NB OF McCONNELSVILLE
{{7 L 13 S}}
Chartered 2/28/00
Brown Back <$VALUE
3x10-20 1-5400 <$350/$400
1882 Date Back
3x10-20 1-5800 <$350/$400
1882 Value Back
3x10-20 5801-8473 <$350/$400
1902 Plain Back
3x10-20 1-10811 <$200
1929 Small Size
5 Type 1 1-106 <$125
10 Type 1 1-2278 <$125
20 Type 1 1-622 <$125
5 Type 2 1-2038 <$150
10 Type 2 1-2214 <$150
20 Type 2 1-756 <$150
Total Issue $1,496,150
Out in 1935 $100,000
Large out 1935 $4,655

46 Morgan
FNB OF McCONNELSVILLE*
{{9 L 19 S}}
Chartered 7/63
*Liquidated 5/31/83
*Reorganized as Ch 2712
which retook Ch 46 6/8/11
Original Series <$VALUE
3x1-2 1-3500 <$500/$1250
4x5 1-3250 <$600
4x10 1-3875 <$750
Series 1875
4x10 1-1500 <$750
1902 Date Back
3x10-20 1-3000 <$200
1902 Plain Back (dated 1902)
3x10-20 3001-8400 <$200
1902 Plain Back (dated 1922)
3x10-20 1-8160 <$200
1929 Small Size
10 Type 1 1-2518 <$100
20 Type 1 1-708 <$110
10 Type 2 1-1703 <$110
20 Type 2 1-481 <$125
Total Issue $1,388,190
Out in 1935 $100,000
Large out 1935 $6,130
Outstanding includes Ch 2712

2712 Morgan
FNB OF McCONNELSVILLE
{{1 L}}
Chartered 1882
RETOOK Ch 46 6/8/11
Brown Back <$VALUE
3x10-20 1-2861 <$1000
1902 Red Seal
3x10-20 1-5250 <$1250
1902 Date Back
3x10-20 1-2800 <$850
Total Issue $545,550
Out in 1911 $50,000

2325 Champaign
FARMERS NB OF MECHANICSBURG
{{ UNREPORTED }}
Chartered 2/17/76
Liquidated 2/18/81
Series 1875 <$VALUE
4x5 1-2277 <$1500
Total Issue $45,540
Out in 1910 $390

2053 Medina
FNB OF MEDINA
{{2 L}}
Chartered 10/4/72
Liquidated 5/6/74
Original Series <$VALUE
3x1-2 1-800 <$1000/$2000
4x5 1-2050 <$1000
Total Issue $45,000
Out in 1910 $212

5139 Medina
MEDINA COUNTY NB OF MEDINA
{{4 L}}
Chartered 1898
Liquidated 9/15/26
Brown Back <$VALUE
4x5 1-1250 <$500
3x10-20 1-3500 <$500
1882 Date Back
4x5 1-3350 <$500
3x10-20 1-2250 <$500
1882 Value Back
4x5 3351-4465 <$500
3x10-20 2251-2911 <$500
1902 Plain Back
3x10-20 1-5511 <$350
Total Issue $710,400
Out at close $45,345

4842 Medina
OLD PHOENIX NB OF MEDINA
{{6 L 11 S}}
Chartered 1893
Brown Back <$VALUE
3x10-20 1-6575 <$350/$400
1882 Date Back
3x10-20 1-3094 <$350/$400
1902 Date Back
4x5 1-2125 <$200
3x10-20 1-1700 <$200
1902 Plain Back
4x5 2126-13010 <$200
3x10-20 1701-8529 <$200
1929 Small Size
5 Type 1 1-1604 <$125
10 Type 1 1-914 <$125
20 Type 1 1-232 <$135
5 Type 2 1-2982 <$150
10 Type 2 1-1588 <$150
20 Type 2 1-456 <$165
Total Issue $1,340,810
Out in 1935 $50,000
Large out 1935 $3,250

2091 Medina
PHOENIX NB OF MEDINA
{{2 L}}
Chartered 3/10/73
Liquidated 2/10/93
Original Series <$VALUE
3x1-2 1-1500 <$600/$1250
4x5 1-4000 <$600
Series 1875
4x5 1-6289 <$600
Total Issue $213,280
Out in 1910 $1,190

9274 Mercer
FNB OF MENDON
{{5 L 0 S}}
Organized 10/28/08
Receivership 11/29/30
1902 Date Back <$VALUE
3x10-20 1-2110* <$400
1902 Plain Back
3x10-20 2231-5858* <$400
* 2111-2230 not marked
1929 Small Size
10 Type 1 1-317 <$750
20 Type 1 1-74 <$750
Total Issue $320,800
Out at close $25,000
Large out at close $3,710

4822 Montgomery
CITIZENS NB OF MIAMISBURG
{{ UNREPORTED }}
Chartered 12/6/92
Liquidated 7/11/04
Brown Back <$VALUE
3x10-20 1-1745 <$1250
Total Issue $87,250
Out in 1910 $2,670

3876 Montgomery
FNB OF MIAMISBURG
{{9 L 18 S}}
Chartered 4/30/88
Brown Back <$VALUE
3x10-20 1-7747 <$500
1902 Red Seal
3x10-20 1-1000 <$500
1902 Date Back
3x10-20 1-7600 <$225
1902 Plain Back
3x10-20 7601-21908 <$225
1929 Small Size
10 Type 1 1-2662 <$100
20 Type 1 1-698 <$100
10 Type 2 1-2167 <$100
20 Type 2 1-660 <$100
Total Issue $1,811,100
Out in 1935 $100,000
Large out 1935 $6,480

8441 Meigs
CITIZENS NB OF MIDDLEPORT
{{0 L 2 S}}
Chartered 11/06
1902 Red Seal <$VALUE
3x10-20 1-200 <$2000
1902 Date Back
3x10-20 1-700 <$1250
1902 Plain Back
3x10-20 701-1356 <$1250
1929 Small Size
10 Type 1 1-211 <$750
20 Type 1 1-39 <$750
Total Issue $95,140
Out in 1935 $6,500
Large out 1935 $570

2210 Meigs
FNB OF MIDDLEPORT
{{ UNREPORTED }}
Chartered 12/3/74
Liquidated 4/20/78
Original Series <$VALUE
4x5 1-2055 <$2000
Total Issue $41,100
Out in 1910 $230

4472 Meigs
MIDDLEPORT NB, MIDDLEPORT
{{ UNREPORTED }}
Organized 11/22/90
Liquidated 9/5/98
Brown Back <$VALUE
3x10-20 1-584 <$2000
Total Issue $29,200
Out in 1916 $340

F & Merchants NB of Middletown
SEE Ch 2025
Merchants NB of Middletown

1545 Butler
FNB OF MIDDLETOWN
{{7 L}}
Chartered 1865
Closed 9/30/19
Original Series <$VALUE
3x1-2 1-3500 <$500/$1250
4x5 1-5550 <$500
4x10 1-2025 <$750
Series 1875
3x1-2 1-120 <$500/$1250
4x5 1-5250 <$500
4x10 1-2998 <$750
Brown Back
4x5 1-6374 <$350
3x10-20 1-2087 <$350
1902 Red Seal
4x5 1-1300 <$400
3x10-20 1-940 <$400
1902 Date Back
4x5 1-6550 <$225
3x10-20 1-5040 <$225
1902 Plain Back
4x5 6551-10275 <$225
3x10-20 5041-7061 <$225
Total Issue $1,298,400
Out at close $100,000
Ch 2025 assumed circulation

2025 Butler
MERCHANTS NB OF MIDDLETOWN
Chartered 8/1/72
2nd title: F & Merchants
NB of Middletown 9/30/19
FIRST TITLE {{6 L}}
Original Series <$VALUE
3x1-2 1-560 <$500/$1250
4x5 1-3125 <$500
Series 1875
4x5 1-16250 <$500
50-100 1-530 <$4000
Brown Back
3x10-20 1-10750 <$350
1882 Date Back
3x10-20 1-2124 <$350
1902 Date Back
4x5 1-4500 <$125
4x10 1-4500 <$125
1902 Plain Back
4x5 4501-8000 <$125
4x10 4501-6275 <$125
SECOND TITLE {{13 L 50+ S}}
1902 Plain Back
4x5 1-46643 <$100
3x10-20 1-32580 <$100
1929 Small Size
5 Type 1 1-8398 <$25
10 Type 1 1-4892 <$25
20 Type 1 1-1376 <$35
5 Type 2 1-22208 <$30
10 Type 2 1-12048 <$30
20 Type 2 1-3768 <$40
Total Issue $5,103,820
Out in 1935 $400,000
Large out 1935 $16,880
Outstanding includes Ch 1545

8188 Clermont
CITIZENS NB OF MILFORD
{{5 L}}
Chartered 4/06
Liquidated 6/17/13
1902 Red Seal <$VALUE
4x5 1-1415 <$500
3x10-20 1-1184 <$500
1902 Date Back
4x5 1-1940 <$300
3x10-20 1-1238 <$300
Total Issue $188,200
Out in 1913 $33,100

3234 Clermont
MILFORD NB, MILFORD
{{13 L 18 S}}
Organized 6/21/84
Brown Back <$VALUE
4x5 1-7594 <$300
3x10-20 1-2540 <$300/$350
1902 Red Seal
4x5 1-1650 <$350
3x10-20 1-1140 <$350
1902 Date Back
4x5 1-3000 <$150
3x10-20 1-2500 <$150
1902 Plain Back
4x5 3001-17855 <$150
3x10-20 2501-12703 <$150
1929 Small Size
5 Type 1 1-4034 <$65
10 Type 1 1-2110 <$65
20 Type 1 1-646 <$75
5 Type 2 1-3282 <$75
10 Type 2 1-2364 <$75
20 Type 2 1-710 <$90
Total Issue $1,740,520
Out in 1935 $100,000
Large out 1935 $5,305

1923 Holmes
FNB OF MILLERSBURG
{{3 L}}
Chartered 1/13/72
Liquidated 1/12/75
Original Series <$VALUE
3x1-2 1-1400 <$1250/$2000
4x5 1-1925 <$1250
3x10-20 1-600 <$1750/$2000
Total Issue $75,500
Out in 1910 $241

1930 Stark
FNB OF MINERVA
{{2 L}}
Chartered 1/26/72
Liquidated 8/24/77
Original Series <$VALUE
3x1-2 1-1500 <$1250/$2000
4x5 1-3925 <$1500
Total Issue $86,000
Out in 1910 $423

5344 Stark
FNB OF MINERVA
{{1 L}}
Chartered 5/9/00
Liquidated 11/1/05
Brown Back <$VALUE
3x10-20 1-1247 <$1500
Total Issue $62,350
Out in 1910 $2,840

5694 Jefferson
FNB OF MINGO JUNCTION
{{3 L 7 S}}
Chartered 1/26/01
Receivership 6/21/34
Brown Back <$VALUE
4x5 1-825 <$500
3x10-20 1-760 <$500
1882 Date Back
4x5 1-2375 <$500
3x10-20 1-1740 <$500
1882 Value Back
4x5 2376-3781 <$500
3x10-20 1741-2490 <$500
1902 Plain Back
3x10-20 1-3930 <$375
1929 Small Size
10 Type 1 1-798 <$175
20 Type 1 1-212 <$175
10 Type 2 1-122 <$225
20 Type 2 1-70 <$225
Total Issue $527,060
Out at close $25,000
Large out at close $1,480

14183 Jefferson
MINGO JUNCTION NB OF MINGO JUNCTION
{{4 S}}
Chartered 6/34
1929 Small Size <$VALUE
5 Type 2 1-1020 <$400
10 Type 2 1-2404 <$400
20 Type 2 1-1458 <$400
Total Issue $58,300
Out in 1935 $45,800

7947 Butler
MONROE NB, MONROE
{{4 L 12 S}}
Chartered 10/05
1902 Red Seal <$VALUE
3x10-20 1-956 <$600
1902 Date Back
3x10-20 1-1780 <$300
1902 Plain Back
3x10-20 1781-9611 <$300
1929 Small Size
10 Type 1 1-1476 <$100
20 Type 1 1-384 <$125
10 Type 2 1-1398 <$135
20 Type 2 1-434 <$150
Total Issue $685,650
Out in 1935 $50,000
Large out 1935 $1,680

2438 Huron
FNB OF MONROEVILLE
{{3 L}}
Chartered 10/27/79
Liquidated 10/23/06
Series 1875 <$VALUE
4x5 1-14021 <$600
Brown Back
4x5 1-1643 <$500
3x10-20 1-1890 <$500
Total Issue $407,780
Out in 1910 $8,620

5315 Williams
FNB OF MONTPELIER
{{ UNREPORTED }}
Chartered 4/30/00
Liquidated 3/1/16
Brown Back <$VALUE
3x10-20 1-900 <$1250
1882 Date Back
3x10-20 1-757 <$1250
Total Issue $82,850
Out at close $12,500
Ch 5341 assumed circulation

5341 Williams
MONTPELIER NB, MONTPELIER
{{4 L 12 S}}
Chartered 5/8/00
Receivership 1/12/34
Brown Back <$VALUE
4x5 1-1555 <$500
3x10-20 1-1218 <$500
1882 Date Back
4x5 1-1750 <$500
3x10-20 1-1360 <$500
1882 Value Back
4x5 1751-3140 <$500
3x10-20 1361-1998 <$500
1902 Plain Back
4x5 1-5031 <$300
3x10-20 1-3155 <$300
1929 Small Size
5 Type 1 1-1290 <$135
10 Type 1 1-768 <$135
20 Type 1 1-208 <$150
5 Type 2 1-66 <$200
10 Type 2 1-50 <$200
Total Issue $623,540
Out at close $37,500
Large out at close $1,300
Outstanding includes Ch 5315

13912 Williams
NB OF MONTPELIER
{{7 S}}
Chartered 12/33
1929 Small Size <$VALUE
5 Type 2 1-5524 <$175
10 Type 2 1-2748 <$175
20 Type 2 1-840 <$175
Total Issue $71,900
Out in 1935 $44,150

8709 Warren
FNB OF MORROW
{{3 L 4 S}}
Chartered 5/07
1902 Red Seal <$VALUE
4x5 1-150 <$750
3x10-20 1-86 <$750
50-100 1-18 <$2250/$2500
1902 Date Back
4x5 1-1200 <$375
3x10-20 1-800 <$375
50-100 1-60 <$750/$850
1902 Plain Back
4x5 1201-5506 <$375
3x10-20 801-3302 <$375
1929 Small Size
5 Type 1 1-766 <$250
10 Type 1 1-528 <$250
20 Type 1 1-148 <$275
5 Type 2 1-1444 <$300
10 Type 2 1-708 <$300
20 Type 2 1-140 <$300
Total Issue $383,740
Out in 1935 $25,000
Large out 1935 $1,090

8741 Warren
MORROW NB, MORROW
{{2 L 5 S}}
Chartered 6/07
Liquidated 12/31/34
1902 Red Seal <$VALUE
3x10-20 1-600 <$850
1902 Date Back
3x10-20 1-360 <$425
1902 Plain Back
3x10-20 361-3870 <$425
1929 Small Size
10 Type 1 1-660 <$250
20 Type 1 1-212 <$250
10 Type 2 1-535 <$275
20 Type 2 1-75 <$300
Total Issue $295,390
Out at close $25,000
Large out at close $1,210

258 Morrow
FNB OF MOUNT GILEAD
{{ UNREPORTED }}
Chartered 2/16/64
Liquidated 2/24/03
Original Series <$VALUE
4x5 1-6400 <$1250
4x10 1-2500 <$1500
Series 1875
4x5 1-1615 <$1250
4x10 1-750 <$1500
Brown Back
4x5 1-6362 <$1250
3x10-20 1-183 <$1250
Total Issue $426,690
Out in 1910 $3,500

2459 Morrow
MORROW COUNTY NB OF MOUNT GILEAD
{{2 L}}
Chartered 2/25/80
Liquidated 2/5/00
Series 1875 <$VALUE
4x5 1-6465 <$850
Total Issue $129,300
Out in 1910 $850

6620 Morrow
MOUNT GILEAD NB, MOUNT GILEAD
{{8L 7S}}
Organized 1/19/03
Liquidated 8/22/35
1902 Red Seal <$VALUE
3x10-20 1-2600 <$500
1902 Date Back
3x10-20 1-3100 <$225
1902 Plain Back
3x10-20 3101-10625 <$225
1929 Small Size
10 Type 1 1-1394 <$175
20 Type 1 1-390 <$175
5 Type 2 1-155 <$200
10 Type 2 1-757 <$200
Total Issue $800,035
Out at close $38,870
Large out at close $2,375

5251 Morrow
NB OF MORROW COUNTY AT MOUNT GILEAD
{{8L 3S}}
Chartered 2/6/00
Liquidated 11/7/31
Brown Back <$VALUE
4x5 1-3250 <$450
50-100 1-690 <$1500/$1750
1882 Date Back
4x5 1-2950 <$400
50-100 1-280 <$1500/$1750
3x50-100 1-229<$1500/$1750
1882 Value Back
4x5 2951-4177 <$400
1902 Plain Back
4x5 1-17735 <$250
1929 Small Size
5 Type 1 1-3188 <$300
Total Issue $801,630
Out at close $32,355
Large out at close $6,695

7661 Hamilton
FNB OF MOUNT HEALTHY
{{3L 12S}}
Organized 2/24/05
Receivership 6/25/34
1902 Red Seal <$VALUE
3x10-20 1-1500 <$800
1902 Date Back
3x10-20 1-1160 <$400
1902 Plain Back
3x10-20 1161-8995 <$400
1929 Small Size
10 Type 1 1-2216 <$150
20 Type 1 1-630 <$150
10 Type 2 1-938 <$175
20 Type 2 1-196 <$175
Total Issue $746,610
Out at close $74,050
Large out at close $2,540

10692 Brown
BROWN COUNTY NB OF MOUNT ORAB
{{4L 12S}}
Chartered 2/15
1902 Plain Back <$VALUE
4x5 1-4540 <$400
3x10-20 1-2725 <$400
1929 Small Size
5 Type 1 1-862 <$150
10 Type 1 1-486 <$150
20 Type 1 1-132 <$165
5 Type 2 1-1388 <$175
10 Type 2 1-790 <$175
20 Type 2 1-200 <$200
Total Issue $316,750
Out in 1935 $25,000
Large out 1935 $1,150

492 Jefferson
FNB OF MOUNT PLEASANT
{{3L}}
Chartered 8/5/64
Liquidated 2/24/03
Original Series <$VALUE
3x1-2 1-3000 <$600/$1500
4x5 1-3750 <$600
3x10-20 1-4600 <$850/$1500
Series 1875
3x10-20 1-3112 <$850/$1500
Brown Back
3x10-20 1-5217 <$500
Total Issue $736,450
Out in 1910 $6,065

6640 Jefferson
MOUNT PLEASANT NB, MOUNT PLEASANT
{{ UNREPORTED }}
Chartered 2/21/03
Liquidated 1/1/05
1902 Red Seal <$VALUE
3x10-20 1-747 <$1500
Total Issue $37,350
Out in 1910 $1,370

6667 Jefferson
PEOPLES NB OF MOUNT PLEASANT
{{6L 10S}}
Organized 1/3/03
1902 Red Seal <$VALUE
3x10-20 1-2975 <$450
1902 Date Back
3x10-20 1-4100 <$225
1902 Plain Back
3x10-20 4101-13496 <$225
1929 Small Size
10 Type 1 1-1324 <$125
20 Type 1 1-400 <$140
5 Type 2 1-324 <$175
10 Type 2 1-1494 <$175
20 Type 2 1-370 <$175
Total Issue $974,950
Out in 1935 $49,250
Large out 1935 $2,295

9095 Madison
CITIZENS NB OF MOUNT STERLING
{{6L}}
Chartered 4/08
Closed 10/1/26
1902 Red Seal <$VALUE
4x5 1-1125 <$450
3x10-20 1-900 <$450
1902 Date Back
4x5 1-4000 <$225
3x10-20 1-2680 <$225
1902 Plain Back
4x5 4001-12362 <$225
3x10-20 2681-7365 <$225
Total Issue $682,990
Out at close $59,995
Ch 5382 assumed circulation

5382 Madison
FNB OF MOUNT STERLING
Chartered 5/31/00
Receivership 5/19/28
2nd title: F-Citizens NB of Mount Sterling 10/1/26
FIRST TITLE {{12L}}
Brown Back <$VALUE
4x5 1-2325 <$375
3x10-20 1-1700 <$375
1882 Date Back
4x5 1-5700 <$375
3x10-20 1-3840 <$375
1882 Value Back
4x5 5701-8465 <$375
3x10-20 3841-5429 <$375
1902 Plain Back
4x5 1-6980 <$175
3x10-20 1-4015 <$175
SECOND TITLE {{7L}}
1902 Plain Back
3x10-20 1-959 <$250
Total Issue $960,550
Out at close $68,845
Outstanding includes Ch 9095

7248 Knox
FARMERS & MERCHANTS NB OF MOUNT VERNON
{{ UNREPORTED }}
Chartered 5/04
Liquidated 2/17/10
1902 Red Seal <$VALUE
3x10-20 1-2440 <$1250
Total Issue $122,000
Out in 1910 $39,330

908 Knox
FNB OF MOUNT VERNON
{{2L 4S}}
Chartered 3/17/65
Original Series <$VALUE
3x1-2 1-1800 <$750/$1500
4x5 1-1500 <$850
3x10-20 1-1100<$1250/$1500
Series 1875
3x10-20 1-808 <$1250/$1500
Brown Back
50-100 1-89 <$2000/$2500
1902 Red Seal
50-100 1-350 <$2500/$3000
1902 Date Back
50-100 1-300 <$750/$850
3x50-100 1-570 <$750/$850
1902 Plain Back
3x50-100 571-744<$750/$850
1929 Small Size
50 Type 1 1-150 <$500
100 Type 1 1-14 <$650
Total Issue $484,650
Out in 1935 $37,500
Large out 1935 $5,850

1051 Knox
KNOX COUNTY NB OF MOUNT VERNON
{{2L}}
Chartered 4/65
Liquidated 4/1/85
Original Series <$VALUE
3x1-2 1-1200 <$750/$1500
4x5 1-4550 <$750
3x10-20 1-3000<$1000/$1500
Series 1875
4x5 1-1750 <$750
3x10-20 1-1098<$1000/$1500
Total Issue $336,900
Out in 1910 $2,435

Knox NB in Mount Vernon
SEE Ch 7638
New Knox NB of Mount Vernon

3328 Knox
KNOX NB OF MOUNT VERNON
{{ UNREPORTED }}
Chartered 4/1/85
Liquidated 3/10/05
Brown Back <$VALUE
3x10-20 1-2274 <$1250
Total Issue $113,700
Out in 1910 $2,910

7638 Knox
NEW KNOX NB OF MOUNT VERNON
Chartered 3/05
2nd title: Knox NB in Mount Vernon 11/6/22
FIRST TITLE {{2L}}
1902 Red Seal <$VALUE
3x10-20 1-3200 <$750
1902 Date Back
3x10-20 1-4900 <$375
1902 Plain Back
3x10-20 4901-9600 <$375
SECOND TITLE {{3L 11S}}
1902 Plain Back
3x10-20 1-11197 <$250
1929 Small Size
10 Type 1 1-3666 <$150
20 Type 1 1-984 <$150
10 Type 2 1-2647 <$175
20 Type 2 1-705 <$175
Total Issue $1,578,460
Out in 1935 $125,000
Large out 1935 $4,610

9761 Hamilton
FNB OF MOUNT WASHINGTON
{{4L}}
Chartered 5/10
Liquidated 3/28/28
1902 Date Back <$VALUE
3x10-20 1-1870 <$400
1902 Plain Back
3x10-20 1871-5266 <$400
Total Issue $263,300
Out at close $22,650

1917 Henry
FNB OF NAPOLEON
{{3L}}
Chartered 1/9/72
Liquidated 6/30/77
Original Series <$VALUE
3x1-2 1-4000 <$750/$1500
4x5 1-4000 <$850
Series 1875
3x1-2 1-980 <$750/$1500
4x5 1-1035 <$850
Total Issue $125,600
Out in 1910 $691

5218 Henry
FNB OF NAPOLEON
{{7L 8S}}
Chartered 9/2/99
Liquidated 12/15/30
Brown Back <$VALUE
4x5 1-1250 <$750
3x10-20 1-1700 <$750
1882 Date Back
4x5 1-3050 <$700
3x10-20 1-2310 <$700
1882 Value Back
4x5 3051-4270 <$700
3x10-20 2311-2895 <$700
1902 Plain Back
4x5 1-6155 <$350
3x10-20 1-4286 <$350
1929 Small Size
5 Type 1 1-799 <$350
10 Type 1 1-398 <$350
20 Type 1 1-112 <$375
Total Issue $398,090
Out at close $43,700
Large out at close $5,950

9799 Belmont
NEFFS NB, NEFFS
{{2L 2S}}
Chartered 6/10
Liquidated 1/5/31
1902 Date Back <$VALUE
4x5 1-1440 <$750
3x10-20 1-1114 <$750
1902 Plain Back
4x5 1441-5725 <$750
3x10-20 1115-3683 <$750
1929 Small Size
5 Type 1 1-301 <$600
10 Type 1 1-142 <$600
20 Type 1 1-15 <$600
Total Issue $318,000
Out at close $10,070
Large out at close $1,880

7851 Auglaize
FNB OF NEW BREMEN
{{5L 10S}}
Organized 7/22/05
Liquidated 12/7/34
1902 Red Seal <$VALUE
4x5 1-1250 <$600
3x10-20 1-1100 <$600
1902 Date Back
4x5 1-2700 <$300
3x10-20 1-2000 <$300
1902 Plain Back
4x5 2701-9861 <$300
3x10-20 2001-6753 <$300
1929 Small Size
5 Type 1 1-1794 <$150
10 Type 1 1-808 <$150
20 Type 1 1-224 <$175
5 Type 2 1-1032 <$200
10 Type 2 1-591 <$200
20 Type 2 1-140 <$225
Total Issue $757,920
Out at close $50,000
Large out 1935 $2,140

6594 Clark
FNB OF NEW CARLISLE
Chartered 1/03
2nd title: New Carlisle NB 1/25/30
FIRST TITLE {{0L}}
1902 Red Seal <$VALUE
3x10-20 1-500 <$1500
1902 Date Back
3x10-20 1-720* <$850
1902 Plain Back
3x10-20 771-1649* <$850
* 721-770 not marked
SECOND TITLE {{3S}}
1929 Small Size
5 Type 1 1-274 <$500
10 Type 1 1-128 <$500
20 Type 1 1-54 <$500
5 Type 2 1-192 <$500
10 Type 2 1-120 <$500
20 Type 2 1-7 <$500
Total Issue $132,130
Out in 1935 $7,350
Large out 1935 $610

6976 Muskingum
FNB OF NEW CONCORD
{{7L 10S}}
Chartered 10/03
1902 Red Seal <$VALUE
3x10-20 1-1360 <$600
1902 Date Back
3x10-20 1-1730 <$300
1902 Plain Back
3x10-20 1731-5525 <$300
1929 Small Size
10 Type 1 1-710 <$160
20 Type 1 1-212 <$175
10 Type 2 1-2052 <$185
20 Type 2 1-714 <$200
Total Issue $447,090
Out in 1935 $50,000
Large out at close $1,430

7187 Pickaway
FNB OF NEW HOLLAND
{{7L 13S}}
Chartered 3/04
1902 Red Seal <$VALUE
4x5 1-900 <$750
3x10-20 1-665 <$750
1902 Date Back
4x5 1-1700 <$300
3x10-20 1-1270 <$300
1902 Plain Back
4x5 1701-8060 <$300
3x10-20 1271-5820 <$300
1929 Small Size
5 Type 1 1-1772 <$110
10 Type 1 1-890 <$110
20 Type 1 1-276 <$125
5 Type 2 1-2106 <$150
10 Type 2 1-1224 <$160
20 Type 2 1-444 <$175
Total Issue $674,780
Out in 1935 $50,000
Large out 1935 $1,770

6505 Perry
CITIZENS NB OF NEW LEXINGTON
{{8L 12S}}
Chartered 11/24/02
Liquidated 4/5/32
1902 Red Seal <$VALUE
4x5 1-1175 <$450
3x10-20 1-886 <$450
1902 Date Back
4x5 1-1750 <$225
3x10-20 1-1280 <$225
1902 Plain Back
4x5 1751-12258 <$225
3x10-20 1281-7132 <$225
1929 Small Size
5 Type 1 1-1940 <$110
10 Type 1 1-858 <$110
20 Type 1 1-266 <$135
Total Issue $811,160
Out at close $72,480
Large out at close $5,970

2056 Perry
FNB OF NEW LEXINGTON
{{2L}}
Chartered 10/11/72
Liquidated 10/12/75
Original Series <$VALUE
3x1-2 1-1600 <$1000/$1500
4x5 1-2605 <$1000
Total Issue $60,000
Out in 1910 $270

13596 Perry
PEOPLES NB OF NEW LEXINGTON
{{U+13S}}
Chartered 2/32
1929 Small Size <$VALUE
5 Type 1 1-1230 <$110
10 Type 1 1-624 <$110
20 Type 1 1-210 <$110
5 Type 2 1-4060 <$125
10 Type 2 1-2035 <$125
20 Type 2 1-495 <$135
Total Issue $150,090
Out in 1935 $63,000

2203 Columbiana
FNB OF NEW LISBON
{{ UNREPORTED }}
Chartered 11/7/74
Receivership 11/3/98
Original Series <$VALUE
4x5 1-2250 <$1500
Series 1875
4x5 1-4781 <$1500
Brown Back
50-100 1-103 <$2250/$2500
Total Issue $156,070
Out in 1916 $960

1981 Huron
FNB OF NEW LONDON
{{3L}}
Chartered 5/11/72
Liquidated 3/23/92
Original Series <$VALUE
3x1-2 1-2100 <$600/$1250
4x5 1-2675 <$600
Series 1875
4x5 1-6903 <$600
Total Issue $202,060
Out in 1910 $1,135

4712 Huron
NEW LONDON NB, NEW LONDON
{{ UNREPORTED }}
Chartered 1892
Liquidated 11/27/11
Brown Back <$VALUE
4x5 1-2325 <$1250
3x10-20 1-620 <$1250
1882 Date Back
4x5 1-264 <$1250
3x10-20 1-217 <$1250
Total Issue $93,630
Out in 1912 $6,685

10101 Huron
THIRD NB OF NEW LONDON
{{5L 6S}}
Chartered 11/15/11
Receivership 7/20/31
1902 Date Back <$VALUE
4x5 1-1350* <$275
3x10-20 1-1060** <$275
1902 Plain Back
4x5 1551-8030* <$275
3x10-20 1221-5497** <$275
* 1351-1550 not marked
** 1061-1220 not marked
1929 Small Size
5 Type 1 1-1094 <$200
10 Type 1 1-567 <$200
20 Type 1 1-149 <$200
Total Issue $520,170
Out at close $50,000
Large out at close $4,110

5999 Washington
FNB OF NEW MATAMORAS
{{2L 3S}}
Chartered 10/26/01
Receivership 9/26/33
Brown Back <$VALUE
3x10-20 1-760 <$1000
1882 Date Back
3x10-20 1-760 <$1000
1882 Value Back
3x10-20 761-1028 <$1000
1902 Plain Back
3x10-20 1-944 <$600
1929 Small Size
10 Type 1 1-267 <$600
20 Type 1 1-63 <$600
Total Issue $160,180
Out at close $10,000
Large out at close $820

9211 Preble
FNB OF NEW PARIS
{{4L 6S}}
Chartered 7/08
1902 Date Back <$VALUE
3x10-20 1-2260 <$425
1902 Plain Back
3x10-20 2261-6282 <$425
1929 Small Size
10 Type 1 1-696* <$250
20 Type 1 1-202 <$250
10 Type 2 1-210 <$275
20 Type 2 1-15 <$275
* 658 not issued
Total Issue $382,440
Out in 1935 $25,000
Large out 1935 $1,040

1999 Tuscarawas
CITIZENS NB OF NEW PHILADELPHIA
{{12L 23S}}
Chartered 6/20/72
Original Series <$VALUE
3x1-2 1-4680 <$450/$1250
4x5 1-3250 <$400
3x10-20 1-500 <$750/$1250
Series 1875
4x5 1-3595 <$400
3x10-20 1-1399 <$750/$1250
Brown Back
50-100 1-1280 <$1500/$1750
1882 Date Back
50-100 1-278 <$1500/$1750
1902 Date Back
3x50-100 1-1980 <$450/$500
1902 Plain Back
3x50-100 1981-2731 <$450/$500
1929 Small Size
5 Type 1 1-4642 <$60
50 Type 1 1-328 <$175
100 Type 1 1-104 <$275
5 Type 2 1-5622 <$75
Total Issue $1,498,870
Out in 1935 $150,000
Large out 1935 $10,559

1068 Clermont
FNB OF NEW RICHMOND
{{ 2 L }}
Organized 4/27/65
Receivership 11/30/15
Original Series <$VALUE
4x5 1-4300 <$600
3x10-20 1-1630 <$750/$1250
Series 1875
4x5 1-3385 <$600
3x10-20 1-1154 <$750/$1250
Brown Back
3x10-20 1-7273 <$500
1902 Red Seal
3x10-20 1-2600 <$600
1902 Date Back
3x10-20 1-4368 <$350
Total Issue $1,004,950
Out in 1916 $49,715

7542 Clermont
NEW RICHMOND NB, NEW RICHMOND
{{ 4 L 7 S }}
Chartered 1/05
1902 Red Seal <$VALUE
3x10-20 1-500 <$650
1902 Date Back
3x10-20 1-2010 <$325
1902 Plain Back
3x10-20 2011-5530 <$325
1929 Small Size
10 Type 1 1-704 <$225
20 Type 1 1-180 <$225
10 Type 2 1-1261 <$250
20 Type 2 1-192 <$250
Total Issue $381,790
Out in 1935 $25,000
Large out 1935 $1,370

10947 Clinton
FNB OF NEW VIENNA
{{ 1 L }}
Chartered 2/17
Liquidated 5/15/28
1902 Plain Back <$VALUE
4x5 1-3427 <$750
4x10 1-2427 <$750
Total Issue $165,620
Out at close $9,200

858 Licking
FNB OF NEWARK
{{ 50+ L 23 S }}
Chartered 3/3/65
Original Series <$VALUE
3x1-2 1-5000 <$400/$1000
4x5 1-6000 <$400
3x10-20 1-1600 <$750/$1250
Series 1875
4x5 1-500 <$400
3x10-20 1-1086 <$750/$1250
Brown Back
50-100 1-742 <$1500/$1750
1902 Red Seal
50-100 1-360 <$2250/$2500
1902 Date Back
50-100 1-499 <$400/$500
3x50-100 1-80 <$400/$500
1902 Plain Back
3x50-100 81-169 <$400/$500
1929 Small Size
50 Type 1 1-584 <$125
100 Type 1 1-189 <$175
Total Issue $860,300
Out in 1935 $200,000
Large out 1935 $5,450

7787 Licking
FRANKLIN NB OF NEWARK
{{ 16 L }}
Chartered 6/05
Liquidated 10/1/28
1902 Red Seal <$VALUE
3x10-20 1-3000 <$250/$275
1902 Date Back
3x10-20 1-4800 <$125
1902 Plain Back
3x10-20 4801-28605 <$125
Total Issue $1,580,250
Out at close $242,850

9179 Licking
PARK NB, NEWARK
{{ 13 L 13 S }}
Chartered 7/08
1902 Date Back <$VALUE
4x5 1-7500 <$150
3x10-20 1-5700 <$150
1902 Plain Back
4x5 7501-21624 <$160
3x10-20 5701-17241 <$150

1929 Small Size
5 Type 1 1-3716 <$110
10 Type 1 1-1878 <$110
20 Type 1 1-518 <$125
5 Type 2 1-4774 <$125
10 Type 2 1-2378 <$125
20 Type 2 1-600 <$135
Total Issue $1,698,500
Out in 1935 $100,000
Large out 1935 $5,755

3191 Licking
PEOPLES NB OF NEWARK
{{ UNREPORTED }}
Chartered 5/26/84
Liquidated 6/17/05
Brown Back <$VALUE
3x10-20 1-4894 <$1250
1902 Red Seal
3x10-20 1-407 <$1250
Total Issue $265,050
Out in 1910 $16,635

5262 Tuscarawas
FNB OF NEWCOMERSTOWN
{{ 6 L 38 S }}
Chartered 3/8/00
Brown Back <$VALUE
3x10-20 1-970 <$400
1882 Date Back
3x10-20 1-3540 <$375
1882 Value Back
3x10-20 3541-4830 <$375
1902 Plain Back
3x10-20 1-6316 <$225
1929 Small Size
10 Type 1 1-1338 <$45
20 Type 1 1-390 <$50
10 Type 2 1-1024 <$60
20 Type 2 1-285 <$75
Total Issue $748,820
Out in 1935 $50,000
Large out 1935 $2,680

7391 Trumbull
FNB OF NEWTON FALLS
{{ 2 L }}
Chartered 9/04
Liquidated 4/19/24
1902 Red Seal <$VALUE
3x10-20 1-2250 <$1250
1902 Date Back
3x10-20 1-2400 <$600
1902 Plain Back
3x10-20 2401-4698 <$600
Total Issue $347,400
Out at close $22,400

4977 Trumbull
CITY NB OF NILES
{{ 1 L }}
Chartered 9/8/94
Liquidated 1/10/05
Brown Back <$VALUE
3x10-20 1-4177 <$1000
Total Issue $208,850
Out in 1910 $6,830

4190 Trumbull
FNB OF NILES
{{ 3 L }}
Chartered 12/28/89
Receivership 9/3/08
Brown Back <$VALUE
4x5 1-10335 <$400
3x10-20 1-1891 <$400
50-100 1-2441 <$1500/$1750
Total Issue $667,400
Out in 1916 $14,590

4347 Wood
FNB OF NORTH BALTIMORE
{{ 7 L 10 S }}
Chartered 6/12/90
Brown Back <$VALUE
4x5 1-5000 <$400
50-100 1-780 <$1500/$1750
1882 Date Back
4x5 1-770 <$400
50-100 1-65 <$1500/$1750
1902 Date Back
4x10 1-3800 <$200
1902 Plain Back
4x10 3801-14491 <$200
1929 Small Size
10 Type 1 1-2514 <$150
10 Type 2 1-3270 <$165
Total Issue $1,005,330
Out in 1935 $58,700
Large out 1935 $4,090

11275 Huron
CITIZENS NB OF NORWALK
{{ 4 L 50+ S }}
Chartered 12/18
1902 Plain Back <$VALUE
4x5 1-7676 <$300
3x10-20 1-4635 <$300
1929 Small Size
5 Type 1 1-5388 <$75
10 Type 1 1-3434* <$75
20 Type 1 1-984 <$85
5 Type 2 1-7770 <$85
10 Type 2 1-3938 <$85
20 Type 2 1-1109 <$85
* 3074 not issued
Total Issue $971,380
Out in 1935 $200,000
Large out 1935 $1,500

215 Huron
FNB OF NORWALK
{{ 6 L }}
Chartered 1/25/64
Liquidated 2/24/03
Original Series <$VALUE
3x1-2 1-1000 <$400/$1250
4x5 1-5850* <$500
* 2251-3000 not issued
Series 1875
4x5 1-2465 <$500
Brown Back
4x5 1-4895 <$400
3x10-20 1-195 <$400
Total Issue $263,970
Out in 1910 $2,278

931 Huron
NORWALK NB, NORWALK
{{ 3 L }}
Chartered 3/23/65
Liquidated 12/1/18
Original Series <$VALUE
4x5 1-7500 <$600
3x10-20 1-900 <$750/$1250
Series 1875
4x5 1-4585 <$600
Brown Back
4x5 1-11537 <$500
3x10-20 1-1399 <$500
1902 Red Seal
3x10-20 1-1700 <$650
1902 Date Back
3x10-20 1-3300 <$400
1902 Plain Back
3x10-20 3301-3394 <$400
Total Issue $842,090
Out at close $49,495

6322 Hamilton
FNB OF NORWOOD
{{ 9 L 43 S }}
Chartered 6/26/02
1902 Red Seal <$VALUE
3x10-20 1-5400 <$350
1902 Date Back
3x10-20 1-9800 <$175
1902 Plain Back
3x10-20 9801-18989 <$175
1929 Small Size
10 Type 1 1-1760 <$45
20 Type 1 1-4598 <$50
10 Type 2 1-4198 <$50
20 Type 2 1-1361 <$60
Total Issue $1,946,010
Out in 1935 $400,000
Large out 1935 $4,070

8505 Hamilton
NORWOOD NB, NORWOOD
{{ 14 L }}
Chartered 1/07
Liquidated 4/22/29
1902 Red Seal <$VALUE
3x10-20 1-5000 <$300
1902 Date Back
3x10-20 1-13400 <$125
1902 Plain Back
3x10-20 13401-41821 <$125
Total Issue $2,341,050
Out at close $139,450

6632 Ottawa
FNB OF OAK HARBOR
{{ 3 L 9 S }}
Organized 1/15/03
Receivership 10/25/33
1902 Red Seal <$VALUE
3x10-20 1-750 <$1000
1902 Date Back
3x10-20 1-1800 <$500
1902 Plain Back
3x10-20 1801-5325 <$500

1929 Small Size
10 Type 1 1-619 <$250
20 Type 1 1-165 <$275
Total Issue $360,690
Out at close $25,000
Large out at close $1,330

2718 Lorain
CITIZENS NB OF OBERLIN
{{ 2 L }}
Organized 6/2/82
Receivership 11/28/04
Brown Back <$VALUE
3x10-20 1-3403 <$1250
1902 Red Seal
3x10-20 1-869 <$1250
Total Issue $213,600
Out in 1916 $2,120

72 Lorain
FNB OF OBERLIN
{{ UNREPORTED }}
Chartered 8/63
Liquidated 6/1/82
Original Series <$VALUE
3x1-2 1-1700 <$1500/$2500
4x5 1-2000 <$1500
3x10-20 1-2600<$2000/$2500
Series 1875
3x10-20 1-965 <$2000/$2500
Total Issue $226,750
Out in 1910 $1,921

9450 Butler
FNB OF OKEANA
{{ 5 L 3 S }}
Chartered 6/09
1902 Date Back <$VALUE
3x10-20 1-2060 <$400
1902 Plain Back
3x10-20 2061-5777 <$400
1929 Small Size
10 Type 1 1-668 <$300
20 Type 1 1-208 <$300
10 Type 2 1-759 <$325
20 Type 2 1-146 <$325
Total Issue $364,400
Out in 1935 $25,000
Large out 1935 $1,070

6379 Wayne
FNB OF ORRVILLE
{{ UNREPORTED }}
Chartered 8/14/02
Receivership 9/27/05
1902 Red Seal <$VALUE
3x10-20 1-227 <$2000
Total Issue $11,350
Out in 1910 $180

13742 Wayne
NB OF ORRVILLE
{{ 6 S }}
Chartered 8/33
1929 Small Size <$VALUE
5 Type 2 1-2430 <$450
10 Type 2 1-1031 <$450
20 Type 2 1-278 <$450
Total Issue $28,020
Out in 1935 $50,000
Outstanding includes Ch 6362

6362 Wayne
ORRVILLE NB, ORRVILLE
{{ 5 L 12 S }}
Chartered 7/31/02
Liquidated 8/26/33
1902 Red Seal <$VALUE
50-100 1-230 <$2500/$3000
1902 Date Back
50-100 1-360 <$1000/$1250
3x50-100 1-80 <$1000/$1250
1902 Plain Back
3x10-20 1-6745 <$450
1929 Small Size
10 Type 1 1-1389 <$175
20 Type 1 1-377 <$200
Total Issue $574,330
Out at close $50,000
Large out at close $1,990
Ch 13742 assumed circulation

9675 Greene
FNB OF OSBORN
{{ 2 L 9 S }}
Chartered 2/10
1902 Date Back <$VALUE
3x10-20 1-1960 <$500
1902 Plain Back
3x10-20 1961-5986 <$500

1929 Small Size
10 Type 1 1-768 <$175
20 Type 1 1-180 <$175
10 Type 2 1-664 <$200
20 Type 2 1-190 <$200
Total Issue $377,420
Out in 1935 $25,000
Large out 1935 $1,030

7006 Putnam
FNB OF OTTAWA
{{ 2 L 8 S }}
Chartered 10/03
1902 Red Seal <$VALUE
3x10-20 1-420 <$800
1902 Date Back
3x10-20 1-1770 <$400
1902 Plain Back
3x10-20 1771-5462 <$400
1929 Small Size
10 Type 1 1-598 <$200
20 Type 1 1-162 <$200
10 Type 2 1-684 <$225
20 Type 2 1-175 <$225
Total Issue $359,760
Out in 1935 $25,000
Large out 1935 $1,110

4599 Butler
FNB OF OXFORD
{{ 1 L }}
Chartered 7/18/91
Liquidated 2/10/04
Brown Back <$VALUE
4x5 1-6415 <$1250
3x10-20 1-1154 <$1250
Total Issue $186,000
Out in 1910 $3,900

6059 Butler
OXFORD NB, OXFORD
{{ 8 L U + 17 S }}
Chartered 12/21/01
Brown Back <$VALUE
3x10-20 1-3700 <$500
1882 Date Back
3x10-20 1-2160 <$500
1882 Value Back
3x10-20 2161-2190 <$500
1902 Plain Back
3x50-100 1-523 <$600/$750
1929 Small Size
5 Type 1 1-130 <$275
10 Type 1 1-40 <$275
50 Type 1 1-171 <$350
100 Type 1 1-32 <$500
Total Issue $502,050
Out in 1935 $50,000
Large out 1935 $3,380

14232 Lake
FNB IN PAINESVILLE
{{ 7 S }}
Chartered 7/34
1929 Small Size <$VALUE
5 Type 2 1-4000 <$175
10 Type 2 1-1910 <$175
20 Type 2 1-635 <$175
Total Issue $51,800
Out in 1935 $49,100

220 Lake
FNB OF PAINESVILLE
{{ 3 L }}
Chartered 1/64
Liquidated 12/30/82
Original Series <$VALUE
3x1-2 1-10200 <$500/$1250
4x5 1-3750 <$600
4x10 1-2650 <$750
4x20 1-1288 <$1250
Series 1875
3x1-2 1-384 <$500/$1250
4x5 1-2208 <$600
4x10 1-1672 <$750
4x20 1-845 <$1250
Total Issue $515,600
Out in 1910 $3,648

2842 Lake
PAINESVILLE NB, PAINESVILLE
{{ 4 L }}
Organized 7/26/82
Liquidated 9/10/29
Brown Back <$VALUE
3x10-20 1-5520 <$450
1902 Red Seal
3x10-20 1-6800 <$500
1902 Date Back
3x10-20 1-7100 <$250

1902 Plain Back
3x10-20 7101-22936 <$250
Total Issue $1,762,800
Out at close $66,100

13318 Lake
PAINESVILLE NB & TC, PAINESVILLE
{{ 22 S }}
Organized 5/6/29
Liquidated 10/9/34
1929 Small Size <$VALUE
10 Type 1 1-3082 <$60
20 Type 1 1-1036 <$70
10 Type 2 1-2742 <$70
20 Type 2 1-785 <$75
Total Issue $352,360
Out at close $192,350

11343 Putnam
FNB OF PANDORA
{{ 1 L 9 S }}
Organized 4/22/19
1902 Plain Back <$VALUE
3x10-20 1-4533 <$600
1929 Small Size
10 Type 1 1-700 <$200
20 Type 1 1-234 <$200
10 Type 2 1-764 <$225
20 Type 2 1-131 <$225
Total Issue $306,990
Out in 1935 $30,000
Large out 1935 $1,440

5917 Paulding
FNB OF PAULDING
{{ UNREPORTED }}
Chartered 7/25/01
Liquidated 1/12/03
Brown Back <$VALUE
3x10-20 1-240 <$1500
Total Issue $12,000
Out in 1910 $480

5862 Paulding
PAULDING NB, PAULDING
{{ 9 L 15 S }}
Chartered 6/15/01
Liquidated 10/1/35
Brown Back <$VALUE
3x10-20 1-2400 <$400
1882 Date Back
3x10-20 1-5300 <$400
1882 Value Back
3x10-20 5301-8660 <$400
1902 Plain Back
3x10-20 1-7541 <$250
1929 Small Size
5 Type 1 1-1188 <$125
10 Type 1 1-1464 <$125
20 Type 1 1-446 <$125
5 Type 2 1-1724 <$150
10 Type 2 1-841 <$150
20 Type 2 1-105 <$165
Total Issue $1,126,180
Out in 1935 $53,260
Large out 1935 $4,170

7039 Pike
PIKETON NB, PIKETON
{{ 3 L 3 S }}
Chartered 11/03
Liquidated 9/21/31
1902 Red Seal <$VALUE
4x5 1-1136 <$850
3x10-20 1-908 <$850
1902 Date Back
4x5 1-1575 <$400
3x10-20 1-1040 <$400
1902 Plain Back
4x5 1576-5694 <$400
3x10-20 1041-3549 <$400
1929 Small Size
5 Type 1 1-536 <$400
10 Type 1 1-256 <$400
20 Type 1 1-78 <$400
Total Issue $400,250
Out at close $25,000
Large out at close $4,480

<$VALUEs are for notes in FINE condition. Value changes by approximately 25% for a change of one full grade.

****
1061 Miami
CITIZENS NB OF PIQUA
Chartered 4/65
2nd title: Citizens NB & TC of Piqua 1/31/25
FIRST TITLE {{ 7 L }}
Original Series <$VALUE
4x5 1-4200 <$500
3x10-20 1-1710 <$750/$1250
Series 1875
3x10-20 1-2018 <$750/$1250
Brown Back
3x10-20 1-6890 <$325
1902 Red Seal
3x10-20 1-5000 <$350
1902 Date Back
4x5 1-6250 <$150
3x10-20 1-8200 <$150
1902 Plain Back
4x5 6251-21500 <$150
3x10-20 8201-17200 <$150
SECOND TITLE {{ 5 L 28 S }}
1902 Plain Back
4x5 1-9065 <$150
3x10-20 1-5991 <$150
1929 Small Size
5 Type 1 1-6940 <$45
10 Type 1 1-3482 <$45
20 Type 1 1-864 <$50
5 Type 2 1-10570 <$45
10 Type 2 1-4272 <$45
20 Type 2 1-995 <$55
Total Issue $3,272,020
Out in 1935 $200,000
Large out 1935 $9,790
****
1006 Miami
PIQUA NB OF PIQUA
Chartered 4/13/65
2nd title: Piqua NB & TC 2/3/25
FIRST TITLE {{ 12 L }}
Original Series <$VALUE
3x1-2 1-2200 <$400/$1250
4x5 1-7750 <$400
3x10-20 1-1860 <$750/$1250
50-100 1-381 <$4000
Series 1875
3x1-2 1-1000 <$400/$1250
4x5 1-2000 <$400
3x10-20 1-4858 <$750/$1250
50-100 1-121 <$4000
Brown Back
3x10-20 1-7462 <$250/$300
1902 Red Seal
4x5 1-1750 <$300
3x10-20 1-4600 <$300/$350
1902 Date Back
4x5 1-14750 <$150
3x10-20 1-9300 <$150
1902 Plain Back
4x5 14751-35250 <$150
3x10-20 9301-21700 <$150
SECOND TITLE {{ U+3 L 26 S }}
1902 Plain Back
3x10-20 1-12135 <$150
1929 Small Size
10 Type 1 1-5632 <$45
20 Type 1 1-1484 <$55
10 Type 2 1-4343 <$50
20 Type 2 1-1242 <$60
Total Issue $4,241,320
Out in 1935 $200,000
Large out 1935 $14,240
****
3750 Miami
THIRD NB OF PIQUA
{{ 2 L }}
Chartered 7/13/87
Liquidated 2/15/02
Brown Back <$VALUE
4x5 1-6550 <$750
3x10-20 1-429 <$750
Total Issue $152,450
Out in 1910 $1,840
****
9563 Darke
FNB OF PITSBURG
{{ 3 L 3 S }}
Chartered 9/21/09 as the FNB of Arnettsville, under which there was no issue. Issuing title adopted 1/28/10.
Liquidated 5/25/31
1902 Date Back <$VALUE
3x10-20 1-2080 <$500
1902 Plain Back
3x10-20 2081-5999 <$500
1929 Small Size
10 Type 1 1-352 <$400
20 Type 1 1-99 <$400

Total Issue $332,950
Out at close $20,480
Large out at close $2,670
****
5522 Madison
FARMERS NB OF PLAIN CITY
{{ 3 L 10 S }}
Chartered 7/30/00
Brown Back <$VALUE
3x10-20 1-740 <$600
1882 Date Back
3x10-20 1-1900 <$600
1882 Value Back
3x10-20 1901-2876 <$600
1902 Plain Back
3x10-20 1-3021 <$375
1929 Small Size
10 Type 1 1-1082 <$150
20 Type 1 1-270 <$160
10 Type 2 1-1380 <$185
20 Type 2 1-243 <$200
Total Issue $447,830
Out in 1935 $50,000
Large out 1935 $1,710
****
1904 Richland
FNB OF PLYMOUTH
{{ 4 L }}
Chartered 12/15/71
Liquidated 10/1/08
Original Series <$VALUE
3x1-2 1-2100 <$500/$1250
4x5 1-2725 <$500
Series 1875
3x1-2 1-1060 <$500/$1250
4x5 1-8465 <$500
Brown Back
4x5 1-8175 <$400
3x10-20 1-2238 <$400
Total issue $515,000
Out in 1910 $15,268
****
7035 Richland
PEOPLES NB OF PLYMOUTH
{{ 2 L 9 S }}
Chartered 11/03
1902 Red Seal <$VALUE
3x10-20 1-1070 <$650
1902 Date Back
3x10-20 1-1650 <$350
1902 Plain Back
3x10-20 1651-7772 <$350
1929 Small Size
10 Type 1 1-1424 <$175
20 Type 1 1-360 <$175
10 Type 2 1-946 <$200
20 Type 2 1-315 <$225
Total Issue $586,500
Out in 1935 $50,000
Large out 1935 $1,560
****
132 Meigs
FNB OF POMEROY
{{ 1 L }}
Chartered 11/63
Liquidated 3/5/78
Original Series <$VALUE
3x1-2 1-3200 <$1000/$2000
4x5 1-10690 <$1000
4x10 1-1500 <$1250
3x20-50 1-500 <$2000/$4000
Total Issue $344,800
Out in 1910 $3,033
****
1980 Meigs
POMEROY NB, POMEROY
{{ 18 L 21 S }}
Chartered 5/10/72
Original Series <$VALUE
3x1-2 1-1000 <$500/$1250
4x5 1-5500 <$600
2x10-20-50 1-1500 <$750/$1250/$4000
Series 1875
4x5 1-5000 <$600
2x10-20-50 1-192 <$750/$1250/$4000
Brown Back
3x10-20 1-3870 <$300/$350
1882 Date Back
3x10-20 1-1068 <$300/$350
1902 Date Back
3x10-20 1-1500 <$125
1902 Plain Back
3x10-20 1501-7725 <$125
1929 Small Size
10 Type 1 1-1180 <$70
20 Type 1 1-340 <$75
10 Type 2 1-998 <$80
20 Type 2 1-260 <$85
Total Issue $1,127,210
Out in 1935 $50,000
Large out 1935 $5,470
****

****
6227 Ottawa
FNB OF PORT CLINTON
Chartered 4/24/02
Liquidated 9/12/34
2nd title: FN-Magruder B of Port Clinton 1/2/24
3rd title: NB of Port Clinton 6/8/27
FIRST TITLE {{ 1 L }}
1902 Red Seal <$VALUE
3x10-20 1-1190 <$1000
1902 Date Back
3x10-20 1-1370 <$600
1902 Plain Back (dated 1902)
3x10-20 1371-2289 <$600
1902 Plain Back (dated 1922)
3x10-20 1-580 <$600
SECOND TITLE {{ 0 L }}
1902 Plain Back
3x10-20 1-875 <$1000
THIRD TITLE {{ 0 L 9 S }}
1902 Plain Back
4x5 1-1429 <$750
1929 Small Size
5 Type 1 1-7621 <$150
20 Type 1 1-581 <$175
Total Issue $573,630
Out at close $100,000
Large out 1935 $850
Ch 13989 assumed circulation
****
7781 Scioto
CENTRAL NB OF PORTSMOUTH
Chartered 6/05
2nd title: Security Central NB of Portsmouth 2/5/30
FIRST TITLE {{ 10 L 5 S }}
1902 Red Seal <$VALUE
4x5 1-3450 <$325
3x10-20 1-2620 <$325
1902 Date Back
4x5 1-6600 <$150
3x10-20 1-4760 <$150
1902 Plain Back
4x5 6601-24005 <$150
3x10-20 4761-16241 <$150
1929 Small Size
5 Type 1 1-1538 <$125
10 Type 1 1-776 <$125
20 Type 1 1-260 <$125
SECOND TITLE {{ 15 S }}
1929 Small Size
5 Type 1 1-2056 <$100
10 Type 1 1-2531 <$100
20 Type 1 1-312 <$100
Total Issue $1,867,030
Out in 1935 $100,000
Large out 1935 $5,740
****
1088 Scioto
FARMERS NB OF PORTSMOUTH
{{ 3 L }}
Organized 4/29/65
Receivership 2/8/96
Original Series <$VALUE
4x5 1-7750 <$600
3x10-20 1-5100 <$750/$1250
Series 1875
4x5 1-5280 <$600
3x10-20 1-3962 <$750/$1250
Brown Back
4x5 1-2388 <$500
3x10-20 1-1434 <$500
Total Issue $833,160
Out in 1916 $4,750
****
68 Scioto
FNB OF PORTSMOUTH
{{ 50+ L 2U + 50+ S }}
Organized 8/8/63
Receivership 12/19/33
Original Series <$VALUE
3x1-2 1-3400 <$400/$1000
4x5 1-6700 <$400
3x10-20 1-5910 <$750/$1250
Series 1875
3x1-2 1-1180 <$400/$1000
4x5 1-3400 <$400
3x10-20 1-2022 <$750/$1250
Brown Back
4x5 1-1000 <$200
3x10-20 1-5627 <$200/$250
1902 Red Seal
4x5 1-7500 <$225
3x10-20 1-9300 <$225/$275
1902 Date Back
4x5 1-26750 <$65
3x10-20 1-17400 <$65
1902 Plain Back
4x5 26751-89140 <$65
3x10-20 17401-57964 <$65

1929 Small Size
5 Type 1 1-15574 <$30
10 Type 1 1-8470 <$30
20 Type 1 1-2060 <$40
5 Type 2 1-3794 <$35
10 Type 2 1-2743 <$45
Total Issue $7,487,870
Out at close $400,000
Large out at close $27,970
****
1948 Scioto
IRON NB OF PORTSMOUTH
{{ 3 L }}
Chartered 3/25/72
Liquidated 1/19/76
Original Series <$VALUE
4x5 1-3732 <$850
3x10-20 1-1140<$1000/$1500
Total Issue $131,640
Out in 1910 $495
****
1958 Scioto
KINNEY NB OF PORTSMOUTH
{{ 1 L }}
Chartered 4/12/72
Liquidated 8/28/77
Original Series <$VALUE
4x5 1-4250 <$1000
3x10-20 1-800 <$1500/$1750
Series 1875
4x5 1-2080 <$1000
Total Issue $166,600
Out in 1910 $690
****
13832 Scioto
NB OF PORTSMOUTH
{{ U + 22 S }}
Chartered 11/33
1929 Small Size <$VALUE
5 Type 2 1-8368 <$50
10 Type 2 1-10380 <$50
20 Type 2 1-7040 <$50
Total Issue $286,440
Out in 1935 $174,700
****
935 Scioto
PORTSMOUTH NB, PORTSMOUTH
{{ 8 L }}
Chartered 3/24/65
Liquidated 12/7/05
Original Series <$VALUE
4x5 1-10930 <$450
3x10-20 1-4100 <$750/$1250
Series 1875
3x10-20 1-5276 <$750/$1250
Brown Back
4x5 1-10570 <$275
3x10-20 1-1166 <$275/$325
1902 Red Seal
3x10-20 1-293 <$300/$350
Total Issue $971,750
Out in 1910 $12,835
****
Security Central NB of Portsmouth
SEE Ch 7781
Central NB of Portsmouth
****
7759 Belmont
FNB OF POWHATAN POINT
{{ 4 L 6 S }}
Organized 3/9/05
1902 Red Seal <$VALUE
3x10-20 1-500 <$800
1902 Date Back
3x10-20 1-860 <$400
1902 Plain Back
3x10-20 861-2923 <$400
1929 Small Size
5 Type 1 1-1092 <$275
10 Type 1 1-528 <$275
20 Type 1 1-152 <$300
5 Type 2 1-1326 <$325
10 Type 2 1-604 <$325
20 Type 2 1-196 <$350
Total Issue $270,420
Out in 1935 $25,000
Large out 1935 $800
****
1989 Guernsey
QUAKER CITY NB, QUAKER CITY
{{ 15 L 21 S }}
Chartered 5/31/72
Original Series <$VALUE
4x5 1-2000 <$750
3x10-20 1-2100<$1000/$1500
Series 1875
3x10-20 1-1912<$1000/$1500
Brown Back
3x10-20 1-8660 <$500

1882 Date Back
3x10-20 1-2462 <$475
1902 Date Back
3x10-20 1-3900 <$275
1902 Plain Back
3x10-20 3901-17435 <$275
1929 Small Size
10 Type 1 1-2536 <$150
20 Type 1 1-722 <$160
10 Type 2 1-1562 <$175
20 Type 2 1-785 <$185
Total Issue $1,938,570
Out in 1935 $100,000
Large out 1935 $7,070
****
9815 Meigs
FNB OF RACINE
{{ 0 L 4 S }}
Chartered 7/10
1902 Date Back <$VALUE
3x10-20 1-850 <$1000
1902 Plain Back
3x10-20 851-2919 <$1000
1929 Small Size
10 Type 1 1-398 <$425
20 Type 1 1-116 <$425
10 Type 2 1-1181 <$450
20 Type 2 1-302 <$450
Total Issue $201,600
Out in 1935 $25,000
Large out 1935 $900
****
106 Portage
FNB OF RAVENNA
{{ 2 L }}
Chartered 10/17/63
Liquidated 11/10/02
Original Series <$VALUE
4x5 1-2550 <$600
3x10-20 1-1900 <$750/$1250
50-100 1-200 <$4000
Series 1875
3x10-20 1-897 <$750/$1250
50-100 1-341 <$4000
Brown Back
3x10-20 1-2140 <$500
50-100 1-1402 <$1500/$1750
Total Issue $589,300
Out in 1910 $9,155
****
6466 Portage
RAVENNA NB, RAVENNA
{{ 8 L }}
Chartered 10/23/02
Liquidated 10/21/22
1902 Red Seal <$VALUE
4x5 1-2500 <$275
3x10-20 1-5125 <$275/$325
1902 Date Back
4x5 1-6750 <$175
3x10-20 1-4600 <$175
1902 Plain Back
4x5 6751-14765 <$175
3x10-20 4601-9305 <$175
Total Issue $1,066,800
Out at close $86,650
****
350 Portage
SECOND NB OF RAVENNA
{{ 12 L 21 S }}
Chartered 3/64
Original Series <$VALUE
3x1-2 1-9600 <$400/$1000
4x5 1-5000 <$400
3x10-20 1-2550 <$750/$1250
Series 1875
3x1-2 1-2180 <$400/$1000
4x5 1-3505 <$400
3x10-20 1-1482 <$750/$1250
Brown Back
4x5 1-4135 <$250
3x10-20 1-6941 <$250/$300
1902 Red Seal
4x5 1-7000 <$250
3x10-20 1-5200 <$250/$300
1902 Date Back
4x5 1-9250 <$125
3x10-20 1-6400 <$125
1902 Plain Back
4x5 9251-33972 <$125
3x10-20 6401-21788 <$125
1929 Small Size
5 Type 1 1-6312 <$70
10 Type 1 1-2958 <$70
20 Type 1 1-798 <$75
5 Type 2 1-5986 <$80
10 Type 2 1-3834 <$80
20 Type 2 1-963 <$85
Total Issue $3,579,320
Out in 1935 $127,450
Large out 1935 $20,395
****

****
9199 Union
FNB OF RICHWOOD
{{ 4 L 6 S }}
Organized 6/24/08
Receivership 4/17/31
1902 Date Back <$VALUE
3x10-20 1-2655 <$450
1902 Plain Back
3x10-20 2656-8914 <$450
1929 Small Size
10 Type 1 1-565 <$275
20 Type 1 1-169 <$300
Total Issue $499,880
Out at close $40,000
Large out at close $4,690
****
3291 Brown
CITIZENS NB OF RIPLEY
{{ 23 L 20 S }}
Chartered 1885
Brown Back <$VALUE
3x10-20 1-6791 <$300/$350
1902 Red Seal
3x10-20 1-3400 <$300/$350
1902 Date Back
3x10-20 1-6500 <$150
1902 Plain Back
3x10-20 6501-19296 <$150
1929 Small Size
10 Type 1 1-2732 <$75
20 Type 1 1-778 <$80
10 Type 2 1-2634 <$100
20 Type 2 1-785 <$100
Total Issue $1,773,670
Out in 1935 $100,000
Large out 1935 $7,610
****
933 Brown
FARMERS NB OF RIPLEY
{{ 1 L }}
Chartered 3/24/65
Liquidated 1/17/85
Original Series <$VALUE
3x1-2 1-2100 <$850/$2000
4x5 1-4200 <$1000
3x10-20 1-4700<$1250/$2000
Series 1875
4x5 1-3495 <$1000
3x10-20 1-1766<$1250/$2000
Total Issue $487,700
Out in 1910 $2,644
****
289 Brown
FNB OF RIPLEY
{{ 1 L }}
Chartered 2/64
Liquidated 11/10/82
Original Series <$VALUE
3x1-2 1-1200 <$1000/$2000
4x5 1-4775 <$1000
3x10-20 1-3190<$1250/$2000
Series 1875
4x5 1-1015 <$1000
3x10-20 1-900 <$1250/$2000
Total Issue $326,300
Out in 1910 $2,714
****
2837 Brown
RIPLEY NB, RIPLEY
{{ 13 L 17 S }}
Organized 11/29/82
Brown Back <$VALUE
4x5 1-3425 <$300
3x10-20 1-3445 <$300/$350
1902 Red Seal
3x10-20 1-4700 <$300/$350
1902 Date Back
3x10-20 1-5800 <$150
1902 Plain Back
3x10-20 5801-19666 <$150
1929 Small Size
10 Type 1 1-2728 <$80
20 Type 1 1-756 <$85
10 Type 2 1-2803 <$100
20 Type 2 1-874 <$100
Total Issue $1,758,960
Out in 1935 $100,000
Large out 1935 $6,660
****
7790 Ashtabula
FNB OF ROCK CREEK
{{ 3 L }}
Organized 6/15/05
Receivership 7/20/08
1902 Red Seal <$VALUE
3x10-20 1-1450 <$850
Total Issue $72,500
Out in 1916 $1,630
****

****
12347 Cuyahoga
FNB OF ROCKY RIVER
{{ 16 S }}
Chartered 4/23
1929 Small Size <$VALUE
10 Type 1 1-1234 <$150
20 Type 1 1-420 <$150
10 Type 2 1-4253 <$150
20 Type 2 1-1095 <$150
Total Issue $188,870
Out in 1935 $100,000
****
5555 Muskingum
FNB OF ROSEVILLE
{{ 1 L }}
Chartered 8/25/00
Liquidated 12/1/19
Brown Back <$VALUE
3x10-20 1-1000 <$1000
1882 Date Back
3x10-20 1-1020 <$1000
1882 Value Back
3x10-20 1021-1366 <$1000
Total Issue $118,300
Out at close $13,900
****
8411 Clinton
FNB OF SABINA
{{ 2 L 9 S }}
Chartered 10/06
1902 Red Seal <$VALUE
3x10-20 1-520 <$1000
1902 Date Back
3x10-20 1-3560 <$500
1902 Plain Back
3x10-20 3561-11174 <$500
1929 Small Size
10 Type 1 1-1338 <$175
20 Type 1 1-406 <$200
10 Type 2 1-1072 <$225
20 Type 2 1-368 <$225
Total Issue $731,780
Out in 1935 $50,000
Large out 1935 $1,660
****
13922 Belmont
FNB IN ST. CLAIRSVILLE
{{ 2U + 2 S }}
Chartered 1/34
1929 Small Size <$VALUE
5 Type 2 1-2602 <$400
10 Type 2 1-1580 <$400
20 Type 2 1-581 <$400
Total Issue $40,430
Out in 1935 $100,000
Outstanding includes Ch 315
****
315 Belmont
FNB OF ST. CLAIRSVILLE
{{ 16 L U + 22 S }}
Organized 2/15/64
Liquidated 3/10/34
Original Series <$VALUE
3x1-2 1-1600 <$400/$1000
4x5 1-3000 <$400
3x10-20 1-2700 <$750/$1250
Series 1875
3x10-20 1-1648 <$750/$1250
Brown Back
4x5 1-4240 <$225
50-100 1-2432 <$1500/$1750
1902 Red Seal
4x5 1-4750 <$225
3x10-20 1-3200 <$225/$275
1902 Date Back
4x5 1-6850 <$100
3x10-20 1-5180 <$100
1902 Plain Back
4x5 6851-31867 <$100
3x10-20 5181-20379 <$100
1929 Small Size
5 Type 1 1-5620 <$50
10 Type 1 1-2982 <$50
20 Type 1 1-808 <$60
5 Type 2 1-662 <$75
10 Type 2 1-205 <$80
20 Type 2 1-147 <$90
Total Issue $3,099,070
Out at close $150,000
Large out 1935 $8,140
Ch 13922 assumed circulation
****
4993 Belmont
SECOND NB OF
ST. CLAIRSVILLE
{{ 10 L 19 S }}
Chartered 1895
Brown Back <$VALUE
3x10-20 1-4720 <$275/$325
1882 Date Back
3x10 20 1 3310 <$275/$325

1902 Date Back
3x10-20 1-1500 <$150
1902 Plain Back
3x10-20 1501-18406 <$150
1929 Small Size
10 Type 1 1-2798 <$60
20 Type 1 1-774 <$70
10 Type 2 1-3474 <$70
20 Type 2 1-840 <$75
Total Issue $1,636,050
Out in 1935 $100,000
Large out 1935 $5,150
****
4219 Auglaize
FNB OF ST. MARYS
{{ 7 L 10 S }}
Organized 1/16/90
Liquidated 7/23/34
Brown Back <$VALUE
4x5 1-4525 <$500
3x10-20 1-1680 <$500
1882 Date Back
4x5 1-750 <$500
3x10-20 1-442 <$500
1902 Date Back
4x5 1-3500 <$275
3x10-20 1-2540 <$275
1902 Plain Back
4x5 3501-12104 <$275
3x10-20 2541-7635 <$275
1929 Small Size
5 Type 1 1-2002 <$175
10 Type 1 1-1118 <$175
20 Type 1 1-274 <$185
5 Type 2 1-560 <$225
10 Type 2 1-300 <$225
20 Type 2 1-104 <$250
Total Issue $1,003,330
Out at close $57,770
Large out 1935 $2,750
****
8127 Champaign
CENTRAL NB OF SAINT PARIS
{{ 12 L 10 S }}
Chartered 3/06
Closed 6/29/35
1902 Red Seal <$VALUE
3x10-20 1-925 <$450
1902 Date Back
3x10-20 1-3640 <$225
1902 Plain Back
3x10-20 3641-11075 <$225
1929 Small Size
10 Type 1 1-1436 <$165
20 Type 1 1-392 <$175
10 Type 2 1-1250 <$200
20 Type 2 1-256 <$200
Total Issue $750,820
Out in 1935 $50,000
Large out 1935 $2,160
****
2488 Champaign
FNB OF SAINT PARIS
{{ 8 L 10 S }}
Chartered 8/2/80
Series 1875 <$VALUE
4x5 1-7438 <$500
Brown Back
3x10-20 1-830 <$350
1882 Date Back
3x10-20 1-1950* <$350
1882 Value Back
3x10-20 2151-3850* <$350
* 1951-2150 not marked
1902 Plain Back
3x10-20 1-6121 <$175
1929 Small Size
10 Type 1 1-1386 <$150
20 Type 1 1-390 <$150
10 Type 2 1-1743 <$175
20 Type 2 1-423 <$175
Total Issue $844,660
Out in 1935 $50,700
Large out 1935 $3,245
****
973 Columbiana
FARMERS NB OF SALEM
{{ 11 L 18 S }}
Chartered 4/1/65
Original Series <$VALUE
4x5 1-9000 <$500
3x10-20 1-2800 <$750/$1250
Series 1875
4x5 1-5000 <$500
3x10-20 1-3852 <$750/$1250
Brown Back
3x10-20 1-6460 <$350
1902 Red Seal
3x10-20 1-3100 <$375
1902 Date Back
3x10-20 1-6900 <$175
1902 Plain Back
3x10-20 6901-22554 <$175

1929 Small Size
10 Type 1 1-2768 <$75
20 Type 1 1-824 <$85
10 Type 2 1-2380 <$90
20 Type 2 1-569 <$100
Total Issue $2,518,440
Out in 1935 $100,000
Large out 1935 $9,335
****
43 Columbiana
FNB OF SALEM*
{{ 17 L U + 23 S }}
Chartered 7/63
Liquidated 5/15/82
*Reorganized as Ch 2691
which retook Ch 43 9/12/10
Original Series <$VALUE
4x5 1-5750 <$600
3x10-20 1-2090 <$850/$1250
Series 1875
4x5 1-2975 <$600
3x10-20 1-1694 <$850/$1250
1902 Date Back
3x10-20 1-4400 <$150
1902 Plain Back (dated 1902)
3x10-20 4401-11000 <$150
1902 Plain Back (dated 1922)
3x10-20 12365 <$150
1929 Small Size
10 Type 1 1-3536 <$85
20 Type 1 1-1004 <$95
10 Type 2 1-4823 <$100
20 Type 2 1-1348 <$100
Total Issue $1,939,780
Out in 1935 $125,000
Large out 1935 $7,930
Outstanding includes Ch 2691
****
2691 Columbiana
FNB OF SALEM
{{ 1 L }}
Chartered 1882
RETOOK Ch 43 9/12/10
Brown Back <$VALUE
3x10-20 1-6821 <$1000
1902 Red Seal
3x10-20 1-6000 <$1250
1902 Date Back
3x10-20 1-2100 <$850
Total Issue $746,050
Out in 1910 $100,000
****
3141 Erie
CITIZENS NB OF SANDUSKY
{{ UNREPORTED }}
Chartered 3/20/84
Liquidated 10/1/98
Brown Back <$VALUE
3x10-20 1-1795 <$1250
Total Issue $89,750
Out in 1910 $950
****
6455 Erie
COMMERCIAL NB OF SANDUSKY
{{ 2 L }}
Chartered 10/10/02
Liquidated 5/1/22
1902 Red Seal <$VALUE
4x5 1-2250 <$600
3x10-20 1-2200 <$600
1902 Date Back
4x5 1-3850* <$300
3x10-20 1-2960** <$300
1902 Plain Back
4x5 4351-7460* <$300
3x10-20 3361-5083** <$300
* 3851-4350 not marked
** 2961-3360 not marked
Total Issue $558,350
Out at close $55,400
****
16 Erie
FNB OF SANDUSKY
{{ 2 L }}
Chartered 6/63
Liquidated 10/6/82
Original Series <$VALUE
3x1-2 1-2000 <$750/$1500
4x5 1-9750 <$850
4x10 1-3000 <$1250
Series 1875
4x5 1-192 <$850
4x10 1-1619 <$1250
Total Issue $393,600
Out in 1910 $2,432
****
2810 Erie
MOSS NB OF SANDUSKY
{{ 2 L }}
Chartered 11/8/82
Liquidated 10/20/02
Brown Back <$VALUE
4x5 1-7400 <$850
3x10-20 1-7039 <$850
Total Issue $499,960
Out in 1910 $7,685
****

****
210 Erie
SECOND NB OF SANDUSKY
{{ 2 L }}
Chartered 1/20/64
Liquidated 10/15/02
Original Series <$VALUE
3x1-2 1-3600 <$700/$1500
4x5 1-4250 <$750
4x10 1-2625 <$850
Series 1875
4x5 1-1713 <$750
4x10 1-1251 <$850
Brown Back
4x5 1-6478 <$600
3x10-20 1-3171 <$600
Total Issue $580,410
Out in 1910 $5,691
****
2061 Erie
THIRD NB OF SANDUSKY
{{ 4 L }}
Chartered 10/28/72
Liquidated 9/19/92
Original Series <$VALUE
3x1-2 1-3320 <$650/$1500
4x5 1-2550 <$750
3x10-20 1-1200 <$850/$1500
Series 1875
4x5 1-6181 <$750
3x10-20 1-2197 <$850/$1500
Total Issue $361,070
Out in 1910 $1,695
****
4792 Erie
THIRD N EXCHANGE B OF
SANDUSKY
{{ 9 L 18 S }}
Chartered 1892
Brown Back <$VALUE
4x5 1-5275 <$300
3x10-20 1-5150 <$300
1882 Date Back
4x5 1-552 <$300
3x10-20 1-31 <$300
1902 Date Back
4x5 1-3815* <$150
3x10-20 1-2654** <$150
1902 Plain Back
4x5 4566-19788* <$150
3x10-20 3255-13453** <$150
* 3816-4565 not marked
** 2655-3254 not marked
1929 Small Size
5 Type 1 1-2832 <$85
10 Type 1 1-1660 <$85
20 Type 1 1-462 <$100
5 Type 2 1-3846 <$100
10 Type 2 1-2185 <$100
20 Type 2 1-636 <$110
Total Issue $1,737,800
Out in 1935 $100,000
Large out 1935 $4,995
****
7800 Brown
FNB OF SARDINIA
{{ 5 L 9 S }}
Chartered 6/05
1902 Red Seal <$VALUE
3x10-20 1-940 <$850
1902 Date Back
3x10-20 1-1900 <$375
1902 Plain Back
3x10-20 1901-5424 <$375
1929 Small Size
10 Type 1 1-758 <$200
20 Type 1 1-224 <$200
10 Type 2 1-348 <$225
20 Type 2 1-145 <$225
Total Issue $396,940
Out in 1935 $30,000
Large out 1935 $1,520
****
7711 Monroe
FNB OF SARDIS
{{ 1 L }}
Chartered 4/05
Liquidated 11/24/28
1902 Red Seal <$VALUE
3x10-20 1-300 <$1250
1902 Date Back
3x10-20 1-860 <$750
1902 Plain Back
3x10-20 861-2132 <$750
Total Issue $126,600
Out at close $8,000
****

****
5197 Harrison
FARMERS & PRODUCERS NB OF
SCIO
{{ 4 L }}
Chartered 6/9/99
Liquidated 6/1/15
Brown Back <$VALUE
4x5 1-1670 <$600
3x10-20 1-1622 <$600
1882 Date Back
4x5 1-1465 <$550
3x10-20 1-1064 <$550
Total Issue $197,000
Out in 1915 $19,900
****
7399 Guernsey
FNB OF SENECAVILLE
{{ 6 L 5 S }}
Organized 9/1/04
1902 Red Seal <$VALUE
3x10-20 1-460 <$750
1902 Date Back
3x10-20 1-1920 <$350
1902 Plain Back
3x10-20 1921-5408 <$350
1929 Small Size
10 Type 1 1-700 <$300
20 Type 1 1-180 <$300
10 Type 2 1-443 <$325
20 Type 2 1-175 <$325
Total Issue $364,930
Out in 1935 $25,000
Large out 1935 $920
****
9518 Butler
FARMERS NB OF SEVEN MILE
{{ 4 L 6 S }}
Chartered 8/09
1902 Date Back <$VALUE
4x5 1-1850 <$750
3x10-20 1-1480 <$750
1902 Plain Back
4x5 1851-6741 <$750
3x10-20 1481-4356 <$750
1929 Small Size
5 Type 1 1-1048 <$600
10 Type 1 1-508 <$600
20 Type 1 1-152 <$600
5 Type 2 1-966 <$600
10 Type 2 1-664 <$600
20 Type 2 1-204 <$600
Total Issue $448,330
Out in 1935 $25,000
Large out 1935 $940
****
1929 Richland
FNB OF SHELBY
{{ 11 L 7 S }}
Chartered 1/25/72
Original Series <$VALUE
3x1-2 1-2100 <$450/$1250
4x5 1-2725 <$500
Series 1875
4x5 1-5777 <$500
Brown Back
4x5 1-3865 <$300
3x10-20 1-2280 <$300/$350
1882 Date Back
4x5 1-1231 <$300
3x10-20 1-895 <$300/$350
1902 Date Back
4x5 1-1750 <$175
3x10-20 1-1300 <$175
1902 Plain Back
4x5 1751-9570 <$175
3x10-20 1301-6356 <$175
1929 Small Size
5 Type 1 1-1716 <$175
10 Type 1 1-1006 <$175
20 Type 1 1-254 <$200
5 Type 2 1-2034 <$200
10 Type 2 1-1059 <$200
20 Type 2 1-264 <$225
Total Issue $1,118,770
Out in 1935 $50,000
Large out 1935 $3,450
****
7862 Shelby
CITIZENS NB OF SIDNEY
{{ 12 L 19 S }}
Chartered 8/05
1902 Red Seal <$VALUE
4x5 1-1100 <$350
3x10-20 1-580 <$350
1902 Date Back
4x5 1-7750 <$150
3x10-20 1-5600 <$150
1902 Plain Back
4x5 7751-23355 <$150
3x10-20 5601-16144 <$150

1929 Small Size
5 Type 1 1-3160 <$65
10 Type 1 1-1868 <$65
20 Type 1 1-454 <$75
5 Type 2 1-3654 <$75
10 Type 2 1-1865 <$80
20 Type 2 1-624 <$90
Total Issue $1,636,060
Out in 1935 $100,000
Large out 1935 $4,690
****
257 Shelby
FNB OF SIDNEY
{{ 1 L }}
Chartered 2/64
Liquidated 2/26/77
Original Series <$VALUE
4x5 1-2250 <$1000
3x10-20 1-850 <$1250/$1750
Series 1875
4x5 1-555 <$1000
3x10-20 1-44 <$1250/$1750
Total Issue $100,800
Out in 1910 $595
****
5214 Shelby
FNB OF SIDNEY
{{ 9 L 16 S }}
Chartered 8/17/99
Brown Back <$VALUE
4x5 1-5425 <$300
3x10-20 1-3760 <$300
1882 Date Back
4x5 1-6500 <$300
3x10-20 1-4640 <$300
1882 Value Back
4x5 6501-9250 <$300
3x10-20 4641-6180 <$300
1902 Plain Back
4x5 1-12373 <$150
3x10-20 1-8696 <$150
1929 Small Size
5 Type 1 1-3500 <$75
10 Type 1 1-1700 <$75
20 Type 1 1-456 <$85
5 Type 2 1-4104 <$85
10 Type 2 1-2040 <$85
20 Type 2 1-576 <$90
Total Issue $1,786,920
Out in 1935 $100,000
Large out 1935 $6,650
****
13171 Jefferson
FNB AT SMITHFIELD
{{ 1 L 5 S }}
Organized 1/17/28
Receivership 9/10/31
1902 Plain Back <$VALUE
3x10-20 1-602 <$750
1929 Small Size
10 Type 1 1-764 <$350
20 Type 1 1-208 <$350
Total Issue $100,900
Out at close $50,000
Large out at close $12,790
Outstanding includes Ch 501
****
501 Jefferson
FNB OF SMITHFIELD
{{ 8 L }}
Organized 6/24/64
Liquidated 3/13/28
Original Series <$VALUE
3x1-2 1-1700 <$500/$1250
4x5 1-3500 <$500
3x10-20 1-2252 <$750/$1250
Series 1875
3x10-20 1-2580 <$750/$1250
Brown Back
3x10-20 1-9619 <$350
1902 Red Seal
3x10-20 1-3800 <$400
1902 Date Back
3x10-20 1-8100 <$200
1902 Plain Back
3x10-20 8101-23185 <$200
Total Issue $2,150,300
Out at close $88,250
Ch 13171 assumed circulation
****
7237 Perry
FNB OF SOMERSET
{{ UNREPORTED }}
Chartered 4/30/04
Liquidated 3/14/05
1902 Red Seal <$VALUE
3x10-20 1-534 <$1500
Total Issue $26,700
Out in 1910 $1,630
****

****
7984 Belmont
FNB OF SOMERTON
{{ 2 L }}
Chartered 11/05
Liquidated 5/5/30
1902 Red Seal <$VALUE
3x10-20 1-1000 <$1000
1902 Date Back
3x10-20 1-1750 <$500
1902 Plain Back
3x10-20 1751-5462 <$500
Total Issue $323,100
Out at close $5,080
****
9859 Butler
SOMERVILLE NB, SOMERVILLE
{{ 2 L 8 S }}
Chartered 9/10
1902 Date Back <$VALUE
3x10-20 1-1930 <$600
1902 Plain Back
3x10-20 1931-5866 <$600
1929 Small Size
10 Type 1 1-752 <$300
20 Type 1 1-168 <$300
5 Type 2 1-312 <$325
10 Type 2 1-676 <$325
20 Type 2 1-196 <$325
Total Issue $370,820
Out in 1935 $25,000
Large out 1935 $1,195
****
2754 Clark
FARMERS NB OF
SOUTH CHARLESTON
{{ 1 L }}
Chartered 7/12/82
Liquidated 10/15/90
Series 1875 <$VALUE
4x5 1-4277 <$1250
Total Issue $85,540
Out in 1910 $540
****
171 Clark
FNB OF SOUTH CHARLESTON
{{ 3 L }}
Chartered 12/63
Liquidated 2/24/77
Original Series <$VALUE
3x1-2 1-3600 <$600/$1250
4x5 1-5150 <$650
3x10-20 1-1560 <$850/$1250
Series 1875
4x5 1-485 <$650
3x10-20 1-98 <$850/$1250
Total Issue $213,600
Out in 1910 $1,533
****
7896 Greene
SPRING VALLEY NB,
SPRING VALLEY
{{ 1 L 4 S }}
Chartered 9/05
1902 Red Seal <$VALUE
3x10-20 1-450 <$1500
1902 Date Back
3x10-20 1-920 <$750
1902 Plain Back
3x10-20 921-2221 <$750
1929 Small Size
10 Type 1 1-303 <$500
20 Type 1 1-104 <$500
Total Issue $164,210
Out in 1935 $10,000
Large out 1935 $470
****
5160 Clark
CITIZENS NB OF
SPRINGFIELD
{{ 12 L }}
Chartered 1898
Closed 7/27/27
Brown Back <$VALUE
4x5 1-2850 <$275
3x10-20 1-2650 <$275
1882 Date Back
4x5 1-8330 <$275
3x10-20 1-6068 <$275
1882 Value Back
4x5 8331-12630 <$275
3x10-20 6069-8488 <$275
1902 Plain Back
4x5 1-18397 <$150
3x10-20 1-11011 <$150
Total Issue $1,784,990
Out at close $146,995
Ch 2098 assumed circulation
****
9446 Clark
FARMERS NB OF SPRINGFIELD
{{ 6 L }}
Chartered 6/09
Closed 6/2/27
1902 Date Back <$VALUE
3x10-20 1-9100 <$200
1902 Plain Back
3x10-20 9101-33300 <$200
Total Issue $1,665,000
Out at close $199,995
Ch 238 assumed circulation
****
238 Clark
FNB OF SPRINGFIELD
Chartered 2/64
2nd title: FNB & TC 6/2/27
FIRST TITLE {{ 26 L }}
Original Series <$VALUE
4x5 1-6500 <$400
4x10 1-3250 <$750
4x20 1-2010 <$1250
Series 1875
4x5 1-2985 <$400
4x10 1-2907 <$650
4x20 1-2710 <$1000
Brown Back
3x10-20 1-14381 <$175/$225
1902 Red Seal
4x5 1-9830 <$175
3x10-20 1-8768 <$175/$225
1902 Date Back
4x5 1-29330 <$65
3x10-20 1-21368 <$65
1902 Plain Back
4x5 29331-52803 <$65
3x10-20 21369-36777 <$65
SECOND TITLE {{ 10 L 50+ S }}
1902 Plain Back
4x5 1-21472 <$85
3x10-20 1-13774 <$85
1929 Small Size
5 Type 1 1-19170 <$25
10 Type 1 1-12344 <$25
20 Type 1 1-4076 <$35
5 Type 2 1-32786 <$25
10 Type 2 1-17053 <$25
20 Type 2 1-4743 <$35
Total Issue $8,414,860
Out in 1935 $650,000
Large out 1935 $44,115
Outstanding includes Ch 9446,
and Ch 1146
****
2098 Clark
LAGONDA NB OF SPRINGFIELD
Chartered 4/5/73
Liquidated 5/15/34
2nd title: Lagonda-Citizens
NB of Springfield 7/27/27
FIRST TITLE {{ 10 L }}
Original Series <$VALUE
3x1-2 1-2500 <$400/$1000
4x5 1-3000 <$400
3x10-20 1-850 <$750/$1250
Series 1875
3x1-2 1-780 <$400/$1000
4x5 1-2525 <$400
3x10-20 1-4960 <$750/$1250
Brown Back
50-100 1-2640 <$1500/$1750
1882 Date Back
50-100 1-660 <$1500/$1750
1902 Date Back
3x50-100 1-1714 <$400/$500
1902 Plain Back
3x50-100 1715-1918
<$400/$500
SECOND TITLE {{ 3 L 26 S }}
1902 Plain Back
4x5 1-4860 <$200
3x10-20 1-3399 <$200
1929 Small Size
5 Type 1 1-8660 <$50
10 Type 1 1-4766 <$55
20 Type 1 1-1274 <$65
5 Type 2 1-3416 <$65
10 Type 2 1-1614 <$65
20 Type 2 1-225 <$75
Total Issue $2,395,410
Out in 1935 $230,685
Large out 1935 $21,175
Outstanding includes Ch 5160
****
14105 Clark
LAGONDA NB OF SPRINGFIELD
{{ 14 S }}
Chartered 4/34
1929 Small Size <$VALUE
5 Type 2 1-12540 <$110
10 Type 2 1-6070 <$110
20 Type 2 1-3420 <$110
Total Issue $191,800
Out in 1935 $150,000
****
1146 Clark
MAD RIVER NB OF
SPRINGFIELD
{{ 17 L }}
Chartered 1865
Closed 2/1/29
Original Series <$VALUE
3x1-2 1-8200 <$500/$1250
4x5 1-10600 <$600
3x10-20 1-5000 <$750/$1250
Series 1875
4x5 1-8945 <$500
3x10-20 1-4288 <$750/$1250
Brown Back
4x5 1-8425 <$300
3x10-20 1-8405 <$300/$350
1902 Red Seal
4x5 1-4750 <$400
3x10-20 1-2700 <$400
1902 Date Back
4x5 1-8500 <$200
3x10-20 1-6600 <$200
1902 Plain Back
4x5 8501-31010 <$200
3x10-20 6601-20157 <$200
Total Issue $3,343,100
Out at close $143,000
Ch 238 assumed circulation
****
263 Clark
SECOND NB OF SPRINGFIELD
{{ 5 L }}
Chartered 2/18/63
Liquidated 12/20/98
Original Series <$VALUE
4x5 1-5500 <$500
4x10 1-1500 <$750
Series 1875
4x5 1-5680 <$500
4x10 1-2665 <$750
Brown Back
4x5 1-3506 <$350
3x10-20 1-6660 <$350
Total Issue $793,320
Out in 1910 $6,845
****
2620 Clark
SPRINGFIELD NB,
SPRINGFIELD
{{ 10 L }}
Chartered 1/17/82
Receivership 4/5/23
Series 1875 <$VALUE
4x5 1-4900 <$400
4x10 1-3246 <$650
Brown Back
3x10-20 1-4140 <$250/$300
1882 Date Back
3x10-20 1-8500 <$250/$300
1882 Value Back
3x10-20 8501-13936
<$250/$300
1902 Plain Back
3x50-100 1-259 <$400/$500
Total Issue $1,196,390
Out at close $94,750
****
5039 Jefferson
COMMERCIAL NB OF
STEUBENVILLE
{{ 3 L }}
Chartered 1896
Liquidated 11/24/19
Brown Back <$VALUE
4x5 1-5950 <$400
3x10-20 1-4778 <$400
50-100 1-1474 <$1500/$1750
1882 Date Back
4x5 1-9750 <$400
3x10-20 1-6000 <$400
50-100 1-44 <$1500/$1750
1882 Value Back
4x5 9751-10000 <$400
3x10-20 6001-6185 <$400
1902 Plain Back
4x5 1-3155 <$300
4x10 1-1090 <$300
3x10-20 1-1184 <$300
3x50-100 1-92 <$500/$600
Total Issue $1,283,750
Out at close $117,600
****
1164 Jefferson
FNB OF STEUBENVILLE
{{ UNREPORTED }}
Chartered 5/18/65
Liquidated 8/8/68
Original Series <$VALUE
4x5 1-2500 <$1500
3x10-20 1-1700 <$1750/$2000
Total Issue $135,000
Out in 1910 $1,415
****
1062 Jefferson
JEFFERSON NB OF
STEUBENVILLE
{{ UNREPORTED }}
Chartered 4/65
Liquidated 3/21/85
Original Series <$VALUE
4x5 1-6600 <$1250
3x10-20 1-2620 <$1500/$2000
Series 1875
4x5 1-2565 <$1250
3x10-20 1-2770 <$1500/$2000
Total Issue $452,800
Out in 1910 $2,730
****
2160 Jefferson
N EXCHANGE B OF
STEUBENVILLE
Chartered 7/31/74
2nd title: N Exchange B &
TC 7/17/22
FIRST TITLE {{ 14 L }}
Original Series <$VALUE
3x10-20 1-2000 <$750/$1250
Series 1875
3x10-20 1-6140 <$750/$1250
Brown Back
4x5 1-11500 <$250
50-100 1-2000 <$1500/$1750
1882 Date Back
4x5 1-14697 <$250
50-100 1-188 <$1500/$1750
1902 Date Back
3x10-20 1-3000 <$100
1902 Plain Back
3x10-20 3001-32200 <$100
SECOND TITLE {{ 14 L 30 S }}
1902 Plain Back
3x10-20 1-44437 <$100
1929 Small Size
10 Type 1 1-12494 <$35
20 Type 1 1-3498 <$45
10 Type 2 1-4622 <$35
20 Type 2 1-820 <$45
Total Issue $7,108,920
Out in 1935 $200,000
Large out 1935 $18,620
****
7688 Jefferson
PEOPLES NB OF
STEUBENVILLE
{{ 11 L 28 S }}
Chartered 4/05
1902 Red Seal <$VALUE
3x10-20 1-4700 <$300/$350
1902 Date Back
3x10-20 1-8200 <$150
1902 Plain Back
3x10-20 8201-26597 <$150
1929 Small Size
10 Type 1 1-3078 <$60
20 Type 1 1-824 <$70
10 Type 2 1-19262 <$60
20 Type 2 1-6115 <$70
Total Issue $2,163,330
Out in 1935 $300,000
Large out 1935 $5,410
****
3310 Jefferson
STEUBENVILLE NB,
STEUBENVILLE
{{ 2 L }}
Chartered 2/25/85
Liquidated 9/11/02
Brown Back <$VALUE
3x10-20 1-10588 <$650
Total Issue $529,400
Out in 1910 $8,240
****
8042 Morgan
FNB OF STOCKPORT
{{ 2 L 5 S }}
Organized 12/18/05
Receivership 9/11/33
1902 Red Seal <$VALUE
3x10-20 1-700 <$1000
1902 Date Back
3x10-20 1-1610 <$500
1902 Plain Back
3x10-20 1611-4982 <$500
1929 Small Size
10 Type 1 1-552 <$300
20 Type 1 1-172 <$300
Total Issue $337,860
Out in 1935 $25,000
Large out 1935 $1,230
****
6662 Noble
FNB OF SUMMERFIELD
{{ 5 L 7 S }}
Organized 1/27/03
Receivership 12/21/33
1902 Red Seal <$VALUE
3x10-20 1-480 <$850
1902 Date Back
3x10-20 1-1810 <$400
1902 Plain Back
3x10-20 1811-5349 <$400
1929 Small Size
10 Type 1 1-596 <$250
20 Type 1 1-155 <$275
Total Issue $345,810
Out at close $24,700
Large out at close $1,580
****
11383 Wyandot
FNB OF SYCAMORE
{{ 2 L 4 S }}
Organized 4/14/19
1902 Plain Back <$VALUE
4x5 1-10330 <$750
1929 Small Size
5 Type 1 1-2906 <$450
5 Type 2 1-5988 <$450
Total Issue $323,720
Out in 1935 $25,000
Large out 1935 $830
****
5427 Seneca
CITY NB OF TIFFIN
{{ 3 L 10 S }}
Chartered 6/15/00
Brown Back <$VALUE
4x5 1-1615 <$600
3x10-20 1-1194 <$600
1882 Date Back
4x5 1-1840 <$550
3x10-20 1-1522 <$550
1902 Plain Back
4x5 1-4972 <$350
3x10-20 1-3444 <$350
1929 Small Size
5 Type 1 1-1926 <$165
10 Type 1 1-968 <$165
20 Type 1 1-276 <$175
5 Type 2 1-1500 <$225
10 Type 2 1-957 <$225
20 Type 2 1-242 <$250
Total Issue $647,430
Out in 1935 $50,000
Large out 1935 $1,870
****
7795 Seneca
COMMERCIAL NB OF TIFFIN
{{ 30 L 33 S }}
Chartered 6/05
1902 Red Seal <$VALUE
3x10-20 1-6200 <$300/$350
1902 Date Back
3x10-20 1-9300 <$125
1902 Plain Back
3x10-20 9301-44959 <$125
1929 Small Size
10 Type 1 1-6222 <$50
20 Type 1 1-1854 <$60
10 Type 2 1-4626 <$50
20 Type 2 1-1708 <$60
Total Issue $3,234,170
Out in 1935 $250,000
Large out 1935 $11,860
****
900 Seneca
FNB OF TIFFIN
{{ 2 L }}
Chartered 3/16/65
Receivership 10/22/75
Original Series <$VALUE
3x1-2 1-2710 <$750/$1250
4x5 1-2700 <$850
3x10-20 1-540 <$1000/$1500
Series 1875
3x10-20 1-80 <$1000/$1500
Total Issue $98,550
Out in 1910 $784
****
907 Seneca
N EXCHANGE B OF TIFFIN
{{ 6 L }}
Chartered 3/17/65
Liquidated 3/1/85
Original Series <$VALUE
3x1-2 1-4500 <$500/$1250
4x5 1-3100 <$500
3x10-20 1-1340 <$750/$1250
50-100 1-534 <$4000
Series 1875
3x1-2 1-524 <$500/$1250
4x5 1-1300 <$500
3x10-20 1-800 <$650/$1250
50-100 1-322 <$4000
Total Issue $348,520
Out in 1910 $2,260
****
3315 Seneca
TIFFIN NB, TIFFIN
{{ 23 L 30 S }}
Chartered 1885
Brown Back <$VALUE
4x5 1-2620 <$250
3x10-20 1-3317 <$250/$300
50-100 1-508 <$1500/$1750
1902 Red Seal
4x5 1-7125 <$275
3x10-20 1-5100 <$275/$325
1902 Date Back
4x5 1-14250 <$100
3x10-20 1-11500 <$100
1902 Plain Back
4x5 14251-50195 <$100
3x10-20 11501-35711 <$100
1929 Small Size
5 Type 1 1-9662 <$50
10 Type 1 1-4508 <$50
20 Type 1 1-1144 <$55
5 Type 2 1-7208 <$55
10 Type 2 1-4368 <$55
20 Type 2 1-1319 <$60
Total Issue $4,285,120
Out in 1935 $250,000
Large out 1935 $10,700
****
8839 Miami
CITIZENS NB OF
TIPPECANOE CITY
{{ 5 L 14 S }}
Chartered 8/07
Closed 12/1/34
1902 Red Seal <$VALUE
4x5 1-750 <$750
3x10-20 1-600 <$750
1902 Date Back
4x5 1-3500 <$325
3x10-20 1-2680 <$325
1902 Plain Back
4x5 3501-12225 <$325
3x10-20 2681-8253 <$325
1929 Small Size
5 Type 1 1-1890 <$150
10 Type 1 1-928 <$150
20 Type 1 1-276 <$165
5 Type 2 1-1290 <$175
10 Type 2 1-858 <$175
20 Type 2 1-190 <$200
Total Issue $866,480
Out at close $50,000
Large out at close $2,610
Ch 3004 assumed circulation
****
3004 Miami
TIPP NB OF
TIPPECANOE CITY
{{ 4 L 12 S }}
Chartered 1883
Brown Back <$VALUE
4x5 1-3892 <$500
3x10-20 1-252 <$500
1902 Red Seal
3x10-20 1-1150 <$650
1902 Date Back
4x5 1-2300 <$300
3x10-20 1-1760 <$300
1902 Plain Back
4x5 2301-7735 <$300
3x10-20 1761-5110 <$300
1929 Small Size
5 Type 1 1-1582 <$150
10 Type 1 1-796 <$150
20 Type 1 1-236 <$165
5 Type 2 1-2020 <$200
10 Type 2 1-317 <$200
20 Type 2 1-203 <$200
Total Issue $699,010
Out in 1935 $50,000
Large out 1935 $4,615
Outstanding includes Ch 8839
****
2296 Lucas
COMMERCIAL NB OF TOLEDO
{{ UNREPORTED }}
Chartered 9/9/75
Liquidated 7/6/82
Series 1875 <$VALUE
4x5 1-8215 <$1250
Total Issue $164,300
Out in 1910 $1,070
****

91 Lucas
FNB OF TOLEDO
{{ 32 L 3U + 50+ S }}
Organized 6/10/63
Receivership 4/3/34
Original Series <$VALUE
3x1-2 1-10000 <$500/$1250
4x5 1-2000 <$500
4x10 1-11500 <$750
Series 1875
4x10 1-4490 <$750
Brown Back
3x10-20 1-4055 <$300
1902 Red Seal
3x10-20 1-12500 <$350
1902 Date Back
4x5 1-39000 <$65
3x10-20 1-30900 <$65
1902 Plain Back
4x5 39001-90610 <$65
3x10-20 30901-90605 <$65
1929 Small Size
5 Type 1 1-16910 <$25
10 Type 1 1-9426 <$25
20 Type 1 1-2568 <$35
5 Type 2 1-9762 <$25
10 Type 2 1-4089 <$25
20 Type 2 1-625 <$35
Total Issue $9,383,020
Out at close $498,150
Large out at close $20,885

4585 Lucas
HOLCOMB NB OF TOLEDO
Chartered 6/19/91
Liquidated 6/30/07
2nd title: NB of Toledo 8/1/05
FIRST TITLE {{ 1 L }}
Brown Back <$VALUE
50-100 1-3520 <$1500/$1750
SECOND TITLE {{ 0 L }}
Brown Back
50-100 1-1065 <$1500/$1750
Total Issue $687,750
Out in 1910 $75,990

3820 Lucas
KETCHAM NB OF TOLEDO
Chartered 12/5/87
Liquidated 12/31/20
2nd title: NB of Commerce of Toledo 2/25/99
FIRST TITLE {{ 1 L }}
Brown Back <$VALUE
4x5 1-9556 <$850
SECOND TITLE {{ 8 L }}
Brown Back
4x5 1-5000 <$250
3x10-20 1-18731 <$250/$300
1902 Red Seal
3x10-20 1-6500 <$250/$300
1902 Date Back
3x10-20 1-75000 <$150
1902 Plain Back
3x10-20 75001-82563 <$150
Total Issue $5,680,820
Out at close $475,195

1895 Lucas
MERCHANTS NB OF TOLEDO
{{ 6 L }}
Chartered 11/2/71
Liquidated 4/30/07
Original Series <$VALUE
3x1-2 1-4000 <$450/$1000
4x5 1-12250 <$500
3x10-20 1-2000 <$750/$1250
Series 1875
3x10-20 1-6963 <$750/$1250
Brown Back
3x10-20 1-16133 <$300/$350
Total Issue $1,519,800
Out in 1910 $58,667

NB of Commerce of Toledo
SEE Ch 3820
Ketcham NB of Toledo

NB of Toledo
SEE Ch 4585
Holcomb NB of Toledo

14030 Lucas
NB OF TOLEDO
{{ 2U + 14 S }}
Chartered 2/34
1929 Small Size <$VALUE
5 Type 2 1-18528 <$85
10 Type 2 1-9180 <$85
20 Type 2 1-3144 <$85
Total Issue $247,320
Out in 1935 $174,130

809 Lucas
NORTHERN NB OF TOLEDO
{{ 14 L }}
Chartered 2/16/65
Liquidated 4/30/24
Original Series <$VALUE
3x1-2 1-3600 <$400/$1000
4x5 1-5600 <$500
3x10-20 1-1800 <$750/$1250
50-100 1-333 <$4000
Series 1875
3x1-2 1-1000 <$400/$1000
4x5 1-4455 <$500
3x10-20 1-1400 <$750/$1250
Brown Back
4x5 1-7395 <$250
3x10-20 1-12110 <$250/$300
1902 Red Seal
4x5 1-16500 <$250
3x10-20 1-9700 <$250/$300
50-100 1-1366 <$2250/$2500
1902 Date Back
4x5 1-64500 <$150
3x10-20 1-41000 <$150
50-100 1-4000 <$400/$500
1902 Plain Back
4x5 64501-152465 <$150
3x10-20 41001-96443 <$150
Total Issue $10,678,800
Out at close $989,000

248 Lucas
SECOND NB OF TOLEDO
{{ 20 L }}
Chartered 2/64
Liquidated 9/30/24
Original Series <$VALUE
3x1-2 1-12310 <$400/$1000
4x5 1-10150 <$400
4x10 1-6525 <$750
3x20-50 1-2100<$1250/$4000
Series 1875
4x5 1-693 <$400
4x10 1-651 <$650
3x20-50 1-936 <$1000/$4000
Brown Back
4x5 1-3000 <$250
3x10-20 1-18950 <$250/$300
1902 Red Seal
3x10-20 1-32500 <$275/$300
1902 Date Back
4x5 1-35000 <$125
3x10-20 1-67000 <$125
1902 Plain Back
4x5 35001-86490 <$125
3x10-20 67001-133368 <$125
Total Issue $11,930,110
Out at close $886,000

607 Lucas
TOLEDO NB OF TOLEDO
{{ UNREPORTED }}
Chartered 12/6/64
Liquidated 1/21/90
Original Series <$VALUE
4x5 1-6525 <$1250
4x10 1-3750 <$1250
3x20-50 1-1991<$1750/$4000
Series 1875
3x20-50 1-855 <$1750/$4000
Brown Back
4x5 1-1974 <$1000
3x10-20 1-344 <$1000
Total Issue $650,240
Out in 1910 $3,785

8705 Jefferson
FNB OF TORONTO
{{ 1 L }}
Chartered 5/07
Liquidated 2/13/12
1902 Red Seal <$VALUE
4x5 1-1100 <$1000
4x10 1-1100 <$1000
1902 Date Back
4x5 1-1966 <$750
4x10 1-1705 <$750
Total Issue $173,520
Out in 1912 $22,640

8826 Jefferson
NB OF TORONTO
{{ 3 L 10 S }}
Organized 7/30/07
Receivership 2/26/31
1902 Red Seal <$VALUE
3x10-20 1-400 <$750
1902 Date Back
3x10-20 1-5340 <$300
1902 Plain Back
3x10-20 5341-19342 <$300
1929 Small Size
10 Type 1 1-1629 <$175
20 Type 1 1-419 <$175
Total Issue $1,135,120
Out at close $100,000
Large out at close $11,360

59 Miami
FNB OF TROY*
{{ 8 L }}
Chartered 8/63
Liquidated 6/10/82
*Reorganized as Ch 2727 which retook Ch 59 4/30/09
Closed 3/24/23
Original Series <$VALUE
3x1-2 1-3000 <$750/$1500
4x5 1-6000 <$850
4x10 1-5000 <$1000
Series 1875
3x1-2 1-1700 <$750/$1500
4x5 1-4250 <$850
4x10 1-2125 <$1000
1902 Date Back
3x10-20 1-4100* <$250
1902 Plain Back
3x10-20 4601-17103* <$250
* 4100-4600 not marked
Total Issue $1,368,650
Out at close $197,400
Ch 3825 assumed circulation
Outstanding includes Ch 2727

2727 Miami
FNB OF TROY
{{ 3 L }}
Chartered 1882
RETOOK Ch 59 4/30/09
Brown Back <$VALUE
4x5 1-4250 <$600
3x10-20 1-4988 <$600
1902 Red Seal
3x10-20 1-2425 <$750
Total Issue $455,650
Out in 1909 $200,000

F Troy NB & TC, Troy
SEE Ch 3825
Troy NB, Troy

3825 Miami
TROY NB, TROY
Chartered 12/16/87
2nd title: F Troy NB & TC 3/24/23
FIRST TITLE {{ 5 L }}
Brown Back <$VALUE
4x5 1-5420 <$400
3x10-20 1-5280 <$400
1902 Red Seal
3x10-20 1-1000 <$400
1902 Date Back
3x10-20 1-6500* <$175
1902 Plain Back
3x10-20 7301-14300* <$175
* 6501-7300 not marked
SECOND TITLE {{ 8 L 29 S }}
1902 Plain Back
3x10-20 1-24431 <$125
1929 Small Size
10 Type 1 1-7758 <$45
20 Type 1 1-2248 <$50
10 Type 2 1-6910 <$45
20 Type 2 1-2520 <$50
Total Issue $3,213,690
Out in 1935 $300,000
Large out 1935 $19,195
Outstanding includes Ch 2727

2582 Tuscarawas
FARMERS & MERCHANTS NB OF UHRICHSVILLE
{{ UNREPORTED }}
Chartered 1881
Liquidated 11/10/84
Series 1875 <$VALUE
3x10-20 1-952 <$2500
Total Issue $47,600
Out in 1910 $100

5448 Wyandot
COMMERCIAL NB OF UPPER SANDUSKY
{{ 1 L }}
Chartered 6/25/00
Liquidated 6/7/20
Brown Back <$VALUE
3x10-20 1-1200 <$850
1882 Date Back
3x10-20 1-1820* <$850
1882 Value Back
3x10-20 2061-2269* <$850
* 1821-2060 not marked
Total Issue $173,450
Out at close $24,100

90 Wyandot
FNB OF UPPER SANDUSKY
{{ 11 L 6 S }}
Chartered 9/63
Original Series <$VALUE
3x1-2 1-3000 <$850/$1500
4x5 1-3950 <$1000
3x10-20 1-2010<$1250/$1750
Series 1875
4x5 1-1785 <$1000
3x10-20 1-984 <$1250/$1750
Brown Back
3x10-20 1-3234 <$850
1902 Red Seal
3x10-20 1-1240 <$1000
1902 Date Back
3x10-20 1-1990 <$500
1902 Plain Back
3x10-20 1991-4132 <$500
1929 Small Size
10 Type 1 1-622 <$350
20 Type 1 1-210 <$350
10 Type 2 1-285 <$375
20 Type 2 1-27 <$400
Total Issue $775,610
Out in 1935 $22,900
Large out 1935 $3,930

916 Champaign
CHAMPAIGN NB OF URBANA
{{ 12 L 31 S }}
Chartered 3/21/65
Original Series <$VALUE
4x5 1-4300 <$450
3x10-20 1-2000 <$750/$1250
Series 1875
4x5 1-3710 <$450
3x10-20 1-1290 <$750/$1250
Brown Back
4x5 1-2450 <$250
3x10-20 1-7217 <$250/$300
1902 Red Seal
4x5 1-3000 <$250
3x10-20 1-1800 <$250/$300
1902 Date Back
4x5 1-10550 <$150
3x10-20 1-9900 <$150
1902 Plain Back
4x5 10551-43615 <$150
3x10-20 9901-32759 <$150
1929 Small Size
5 Type 1 1-12112 <$45
10 Type 1 1-5934 <$45
20 Type 1 1-1530 <$50
5 Type 2 1-14590 <$45
10 Type 2 1-8012 <$45
20 Type 2 1-2604 <$50
Total Issue $4,502,950
Out in 1935 $300,000
Large out 1935 $20,545
Outstanding includes Ch 4805

863 Champaign
CITIZENS NB OF URBANA
{{ 8 L 16 S }}
Chartered 3/7/65
Original Series <$VALUE
4x5 1-2750 <$500
3x10-20 1-2400 <$750/$1250
Series 1875
4x5 1-585 <$500
3x10-20 1-2192 <$750/$1250
Brown Back
4x5 1-850 <$300
3x10-20 1-9210 <$300
1902 Red Seal
3x10-20 1-3500 <$350
1902 Date Back
4x5 1-7065 <$175
3x10-20 1-4140 <$175
1902 Plain Back
4x5 7066-23000 <$175
3x10-20 4141-14605 <$175
1929 Small Size
5 Type 1 1-4060 <$70
10 Type 1 1-1892 <$75
20 Type 1 1-490 <$85
5 Type 2 1-4098 <$100
10 Type 2 1-2292 <$100
20 Type 2 1-770 <$100
Total Issue $2,491,980
Out in 1935 $100,000
Large out 1935 $8,830

4805 Champaign
NB OF URBANA
{{ 4 L }}
Chartered 1892
Closed 1/17/29
Brown Back <$VALUE
4x5 1-2350 <$500
3x10-20 1-3140 <$500
1882 Date Back
4x5 1-2612 <$500
3x10-20 1-1759 <$500
1902 Date Back
4x5 1-1750* <$275
3x10-20 1-2260** <$275
1902 Plain Back
4x5 2501-17115* <$275
3x10-20 2861-12738** <$275
* 1751-2500 not marked
** 2261-2860 not marked
Total Issue $1,323,390
Out at close $100,000
Ch 916 assumed circulation

2071 Champaign
THIRD NB OF URBANA
{{ 4 L }}
Chartered 12/18/72
Liquidated 10/15/92
Original Series <$VALUE
3x1-2 1-2000 <$750/$1500
4x5 1-2750 <$750
3x10-20 1-1100<$1000/$1500
Series 1875
3x1-2 1-1280 <$750/$1500
4x5 1-2808 <$750
3x10-20 1-2776<$1000/$1500
Total Issue $321,360
Out in 1910 $1,657

7596 Licking
FNB OF UTICA
{{ 2 L 9 S }}
Chartered 2/05
1902 Red Seal <$VALUE
50-100 1-170 <$2500/$3000
1902 Date Back
50-100 1-300 <$1000/$1250
3x50-100 1-206<$1000/$1250
1929 Small Size
50 Type 1 1-126 <$300
100 Type 1 1-36 <$650
Total Issue $181,400
Out in 1935 $50,000
Large out 1935 $1,700

422 Van Wert
FNB OF VAN WERT
{{ 10 L 14 S }}
Chartered 5/64
Original Series <$VALUE
3x1-2 1-3600 <$650/$1500
4x5 1-5725 <$650
Series 1875
3x1-2 1-2260 <$650/$1500
4x5 1-4050 <$650
Brown Back
4x5 1-5943 <$350
3x10-20 1-232 <$350/$400
1902 Red Seal
50-100 1-1260 <$2250/$2500
1902 Date Back
50-100 1-1300 <$650/$750
3x50-100 1-2063 <$650/$750
1902 Plain Back
3x50-100 2064-2702 <$650/$750
1929 Small Size
10 Type 1 1-316 <$125
20 Type 1 1-106 <$125
50 Type 1 1-295 <$225
100 Type 1 1-95 <$325
10 Type 2 1-1117 <$175
20 Type 2 1-295 <$175
Total Issue $1,609,010
Out in 1935 $127,350
Large out 1935 $14,440

2628 Van Wert
VAN WERT NB, VAN WERT
{{ 6 L 15 S }}
Organized 2/8/82
Liquidated 10/22/34
Series 1875 <$VALUE
4x5 1-8773 <$650
3x10-20 1-319 <$850/$1500
Brown Back
4x5 1-2150 <$425
3x10-20 1-1790 <$425
1882 Date Back
4x5 1-1750 <$425
3x10-20 1-1340 <$425
1882 Value Back
4x5 1751-3330 <$425
3x10-20 1341-2212 <$425
1902 Plain Back
3x10-20 1-3131 <$250
1929 Small Size
10 Type 1 1-1888 <$125
20 Type 1 1-494 <$125
10 Type 2 1-1489 <$150
20 Type 2 1-210 <$165
Total Issue $849,310
Out at close $100,000
Large out at close $2,380

9336 Darke
FNB OF VERSAILLES
{{ 0 L 8 S }}
Chartered 2/09
1902 Date Back <$VALUE
3x10-20 1-920 <$1000
1902 Plain Back
3x10-20 921-1737 <$1000
1929 Small Size
10 Type 1 1-308 <$225
20 Type 1 1-104 <$225
10 Type 2 1-3762 <$250
20 Type 2 1-694 <$250
Total Issue $169,310
Out in 1935 $50,000
Large out at close $20

5828 Medina
FNB OF WADSWORTH
{{ 3 L 24 S }}
Chartered 5/22/01
Brown Back <$VALUE
50-100 1-200 <$1750/$2000
1882 Date Back
50-100 1-120 <$1500/$1750
3x50-100 1-417<$1500/$1750
1902 Plain Back
3x10-20 1-9834 <$400
1929 Small Size
10 Type 1 1-3106 <$75
20 Type 1 1-872 <$85
10 Type 2 1-2801 <$100
20 Type 2 1-861 <$100
Total Issue $980,180
Out in 1935 $100,000
Large out 1935 $2,600

5870 Medina
WADSWORTH NB, WADSWORTH
{{ 1 L }}
Chartered 6/21/01
Liquidated 6/30/14
Brown Back <$VALUE
3x10-20 1-1850 <$750
1882 Date Back
4x5 1-3595 <$750
3x10-20 1-2745 <$750
Total Issue $301,650
Out in 1914 $61,600

9961 Auglaize
AUGLAIZE NB OF WAPAKONETA
{{ 5 L 5 S }}
Chartered 3/11
Liquidated 7/25/30
1902 Date Back <$VALUE
3x10-20 1-6300 <$325
1902 Plain Back
3x10-20 6301-21070 <$325
1929 Small Size
10 Type 1 1-787 <$250
20 Type 1 1-277 <$250
Total Issue $1,133,960
Out at close $47,190
Large out at close $11,460

3157 Auglaize
FNB OF WAPAKONETA
{{ 10 L U + 33 S }}
Chartered 1884
Brown Back <$VALUE
3x10-20 1-2593 <$350
1902 Red Seal
3x10-20 1-2000 <$375
1902 Date Back
3x10-20 1-7000 <$175
1902 Plain Back
3x10-20 7001-32109 <$175
1929 Small Size
10 Type 1 1-5194 <$50
20 Type 1 1-1410 <$60
10 Type 2 1-5327 <$50
20 Type 2 1-2000 <$60
Total Issue $2,409,210
Out in 1935 $194,245
Large out 1935 $7,885

<$VALUEs are for notes in FINE condition. Value changes by approximately 25% for a change of one full grade.

3535 Auglaize
PEOPLES NB OF WAPAKONETA
{{ 10 L 19 S }}
Chartered 7/17/86
Brown Back <$VALUE
4x5 1-5948 <$350
3x10-20 1-797 <$350
1902 Red Seal
3x10-20 1-500 <$400
1902 Date Back
3x10-20 1-8000 <$175
1902 Plain Back
3x10-20 8001-22752 <$175
1929 Small Size
10 Type 1 1-2572 <$65
20 Type 1 1-644 <$80
10 Type 2 1-2990 <$70
20 Type 2 1-709 <$85
Total Issue $1,597,090
Out in 1935 $100,000
Large out 1935 $4,020

74 Trumbull
FNB OF WARREN
{{ 5 L }}
Chartered 9/4/63
Liquidated 7/30/02
Original Series <$VALUE
3x1-2 1-3400 <$750/$1500
4x5 1-6250 <$750
3x10-20 1-5660 <$850/$1500
Series 1875
3x10-20 1-3456 <$850/$1500
Brown Back
3x10-20 1-7027 <$600
Total Issue $949,150
Out in 1910 $6,762

6289 Trumbull
NEW NB OF WARREN
{{ UNREPORTED }}
Chartered 6/5/02
Liquidated 2/21/07
1902 Red Seal <$VALUE
3x10-20 1-1949 <$1250
Total Issue $97,450
Out in 1910 $6,760

2479 Trumbull
SECOND NB OF WARREN
{{ 12 L 50+ S }}
Chartered 5/28/80
Series 1875 <$VALUE
4x5 1-12593 <$450
Brown Back
3x10-20 1-3370 <$350
1882 Date Back
3x10-20 1-7700 <$350
1882 Value Back
3x10-20 7701-11440 <$350
1902 Plain Back
3x10-20 1-33217 <$175
1929 Small Size
10 Type 1 1-10746 <$30
20 Type 1 1-2820 <$40
10 Type 2 1-11176 <$30
20 Type 2 1-2631 <$40
Total Issue $3,800,750
Out in 1935 $300,320
Large out 1935 $17,115
Outstanding includes Ch 3362

1578 Trumbull
TRUMBULL NB OF WARREN
{{ UNREPORTED }}
Chartered 1865
Liquidated 7/5/85
Original Series <$VALUE
4x5 1-3625 <$1250
3x10-20 1-2950<$1500/$2000
Series 1875
4x5 1-1500 <$1250
3x10-20 1-3800<$1500/$2000
Total Issue $440,000
Out in 1910 $3,355

6353 Trumbull
UNION NB OF WARREN
{{ 3 L }}
Chartered 7/26/02
Liquidated 12/30/11
1902 Red Seal <$VALUE
4x5 1-6250 <$600
3x10-20 1-7200 <$600
1902 Date Back
4x5 1-2820 <$375
3x10-20 1-4743 <$375
Total Issue $778,550
Out in 1912 $88,350

3362 Trumbull
WESTERN RESERVE NB OF WARREN
{{ 7 L }}
Chartered 1885
Closed 5/24/27
Brown Back <$VALUE
3x10-20 1-5501 <$350/$400
1902 Red Seal
3x10-20 1-5600 <$350/$400
1902 Date Back
3x10-20 1-18300 <$175
1902 Plain Back
3x10-20 18301-44955 <$175
Total Issue $2,802,800
Out at close $196,400
Ch 2479 assumed circulation

1972 Fayette
FAYETTE COUNTY NB OF WASHINGTON
{{ 5 L }}
Chartered 4/25/72
Liquidated 10/26/75
Original Series <$VALUE
3x1-2 1-2000 <$500/$1250
4x5 1-2345 <$500
3x10-20 1-1000 <$750/$1250
Total Issue $106,900
Out in 1910 $427

284 Fayette
FNB OF WASHINGTON
{{ 3 L }}
Chartered 2/64
Liquidated 4/5/78
Original Series <$VALUE
3x1-2 1-4000 <$600/$1250
4x5 1-4750 <$600
4x10 1-3845 <$750
4x20 1-425 <$1250
Total Issue $302,800
Out in 1910 $1,811

13490 Fayette
FNB OF WASHINGTON COURT HOUSE
{{ 6U + 29 S }}
Chartered 8/30
1929 Small Size <$VALUE
5 Type 1 1-1958 <$110
10 Type 1 1-1178 <$110
20 Type 1 1-358 <$110
5 Type 2 1-5296 <$110
10 Type 2 1-2965 <$110
20 Type 2 1-510 <$125
Total Issue $238,710
Out in 1935 $83,350

4763 Fayette
MIDLAND NB OF WASHINGTON C.H. (COURT HOUSE)
{{ 5 L }}
Chartered 1892
Liquidated 3/31/28
Brown Back <$VALUE
4x5 1-3375 <$600
3x10-20 1-1640 <$600
1882 Date Back
4x5 1-1411 <$600
3x10-20 1-1049 <$600
1902 Date Back
4x5 1-1650 <$350
3x10-20 1-1300 <$350
1902 Plain Back
4x5 1651-8120 <$350
3x10-20 1301-5554 <$350
Total Issue $670,270
Out at close $39,955

6943 Washington
FNB OF WATERTOWN
{{ 3 L 5 S }}
Chartered 9/03
Liquidated 8/1/31
1902 Red Seal <$VALUE
3x10-20 1-1400 <$850
1902 Date Back
3x10-20 1-1560 <$400
1902 Plain Back
3x10-20 1561-4920 <$400
1929 Small Size
5 Type 1 1-442 <$325
10 Type 1 1-360 <$325
20 Type 1 1-10 <$350
Total Issue $352,060
Out at close $25,000
Large out at close $1,680

7091 Fulton
FNB OF WAUSEON
{{ 8 L 7 S }}
Organized 10/22/03
Receivership 8/22/31
1902 Red Seal <$VALUE
3x10-20 1-1960 <$850
1902 Date Back
4x5 1-3280 <$375
3x10-20 1-2120 <$375
1902 Plain Back
4x5 3281-10905 <$375
3x10-20 2121-7243 <$375
1929 Small Size
5 Type 1 1-1063 <$300
10 Type 1 1-527 <$300
20 Type 1 1-149 <$300
Total Issue $759,640
Out at close $50,000
Large out at close $4,620

5635 Pike
FNB OF WAVERLY
{{ 8 L 22 S }}
Chartered 12/8/00
Brown Back <$VALUE
3x10-20 1-3400 <$350/$400
1882 Date Back
3x10-20 1-3100 <$350/$400
1882 Value Back
3x10-20 3101-4789<$350/$400
1902 Plain Back
3x10-20 1-12138 <$225
1929 Small Size
10 Type 1 1-2866 <$85
20 Type 1 1-702 <$90
10 Type 2 1-2620 <$95
20 Type 2 1-593 <$100
Total Issue $1,310,610
Out in 1935 $100,000
Large out 1935 $4,570

2220 Warren
WAYNESVILLE NB, WAYNESVILLE
{{ 5 L 10 S }}
Chartered 1/25/75
Original Series <$VALUE
4x5 1-1485 <$500
Series 1875
4x5 1-5279 <$500
Brown Back
4x5 1-5100 <$375
3x10-20 1-2280 <$375
1882 Date Back
4x5 1-2511 <$375
3x10-20 1-1042 <$375
1902 Date Back
3x10-20 1-1000 <$200
1902 Plain Back
3x10-20 1001-7897 <$200
1929 Small Size
10 Type 1 1-1372 <$160
20 Type 1 1-370 <$175
10 Type 2 1-966 <$200
20 Type 2 1-275 <$225
Total Issue $1,030,330
Out in 1935 $50,000
Large out 1935 $4,215

464 Lorain
FNB OF WELLINGTON
{{ 2 L }}
Chartered 6/64
Liquidated 12/12/82
Original Series <$VALUE
4x5 1-8000 <$850
Series 1875
4x5 1-7135 <$850
Total Issue $302,700
Out in 1910 $1,685

2866 Lorain
FNB OF WELLINGTON
{{ 2 L }}
Chartered 1883
Liquidated 12/31/13
Brown Back <$VALUE
3x10-20 1-3858 <$850
1902 Red Seal
3x10-20 1-1300 <$850
1902 Date Back
3x10-20 1-1018 <$600
Total Issue $308,800
Out in 1914 $14,720

3565 Jackson
FNB OF WELLSTON
{{ 14 L 11 S }}
Chartered 10/6/86
Brown Back <$VALUE
4x5 1-6813 <$350
3x10-20 1-1719 <$350/$400
1902 Red Seal
4x5 1-1000 <$375
3x10-20 1-700 <$375/$425
1902 Date Back
4x5 1-3150 <$150
3x10-20 1-2200 <$150
1902 Plain Back
4x5 3151-11610 <$150
3x10-20 2201-7655 <$150
1929 Small Size
5 Type 1 1-2044 <$125
10 Type 1 1-1186 <$125
20 Type 1 1-332 <$135
5 Type 2 1-2060 <$150
10 Type 2 1-962 <$150
20 Type 2 1-235 <$175
Total Issue $1,089,100
Out in 1935 $50,000
Large out 1935 $3,875

1044 Columbiana
FNB OF WELLSVILLE
{{ 3 L }}
Chartered 4/22/65
Liquidated 6/18/03
Original Series <$VALUE
3x1-2 1-1500 <$600/$1250
4x5 1-3825 <$600
3x10-20 1-1604 <$750/$1250
Series 1875
4x5 1-4095 <$600
Brown Back
4x5 1-9442 <$500
3x10-20 1-832 <$500
Total Issue $476,540
Out in 1910 $4,125

6345 Columbiana
PEOPLES NB OF WELLSVILLE
{{ 10 L 10 S }}
Chartered 7/19/02
Receivership 2/6/32
1902 Red Seal <$VALUE
4x5 1-5550 <$300
3x10-20 1-4440 <$300/$350
1902 Date Back
4x5 1-6950* <$150
3x10-20 1-5000** <$150
1902 Plain Back
4x5 7351-26113* <$150
3x10-20 5321-17661** <$150
* 6951-7350 not marked
** 5001-5320 not marked
1929 Small Size
5 Type 1 1-2995 <$150
10 Type 1 1-1496 <$150
20 Type 1 1-326 <$150
Total Issue $1,957,040
Out at close $97,780
Large out at close $10,170

2942 Logan
LOGAN NB OF WEST LIBERTY
{{ UNREPORTED }}
Organized 5/7/83
Receivership 10/18/84
Brown Back <$VALUE
4x5 1-545 <$1500
3x10-20 1-260 <$1500
Total Issue $23,900
Out in 1916 $85

9062 Miami
FNB OF WEST MILTON
{{ 0 L 2 S }}
Organized 2/22/08
Receivership 9/21/34
1902 Red Seal <$VALUE
4x10 1-281 <$2000
1902 Date Back
4x10 1-1250 <$1000
1902 Plain Back
4x10 1251-2264 <$1000
1929 Small Size
10 Type 1 1-382 <$650
Total Issue $124,720
Out at close $7,500
Large out at close $260

9487 Adams
FNB OF WEST UNION
{{ 2 L }}
Chartered 7/09
Liquidated 6/19/28
1902 Date Back <$VALUE
3x10-20 1-2010 <$650
1902 Plain Back
3x10-20 2011-6032 <$650
Total Issue $301,600
Out at close $40,900
Ch 13198 assumed circulation

13198 Adams
NB OF ADAMS COUNTY OF WEST UNION
{{ 1 L 10 S }}
Organized 4/5/28
1902 Plain Back <$VALUE
3x10-20 1-638 <$850
1929 Small Size
10 Type 1 1-1116 <$175
20 Type 1 1-298 <$185
10 Type 2 1-898 <$225
20 Type 2 1-244 <$250
Total Issue $116,580
Out in 1935 $40,000
Large out 1935 $1,730
Outstanding includes Ch 9487

7671 Franklin
FNB OF WESTERVILLE
{{ 1 L }}
Chartered 3/05
Liquidated 3/15/29
1902 Red Seal <$VALUE
3x10-20 1-300 <$2000
1902 Date Back
3x10-20 1-620 <$1250
1902 Plain Back
3x10-20 621-1219 <$1250
Total Issue $75,950
Out at close $1,500

6656 Wood
FNB OF WESTON
{{ 2 L 3 S }}
Chartered 3/03
Liquidated 4/14/31
1902 Red Seal <$VALUE
3x10-20 1-1110 <$1000
1902 Date Back
3x10-20 1-1320 <$500
1902 Plain Back
3x10-20 1321-4089 <$500
1929 Small Size
10 Type 1 1-289 <$500
20 Type 1 1-70 <$500
Total Issue $285,690
Out at close $20,000
Large out at close $2,860

9930 Clermont
FNB OF WILLIAMSBURG
{{ 1 L }}
Chartered 2/11
Liquidated 2/12/17
1902 Date Back <$VALUE
3x10-20 1-1450 <$1000
1902 Plain Back
3x10-20 1451-1620 <$1000
Total Issue $81,000
Out at close $24,300

10267 Pickaway
FARMERS NB OF WILLIAMSPORT
{{ 3 L 7 S }}
Chartered 9/12
1902 Date Back <$VALUE
3x10-20 1-1460 <$400
1902 Plain Back
3x10-20 1461-5773 <$400
1929 Small Size
10 Type 1 1-724 <$225
20 Type 1 1-232 <$225
10 Type 2 1-871 <$250
20 Type 2 1-127 <$250
Total Issue $371,180
Out in 1935 $30,000
Large out 1935 $1,380

11994 Lake
FNB OF WILLOUGHBY
{{ 5 L 6 S }}
Organized 4/26/21
Liquidated 11/16/31
1902 Plain Back <$VALUE
4x10 1-15733 <$350
1929 Small Size
10 Type 1 1-3759 <$250
Total Issue $854,860
Out at close $100,000
Large out at close $5,030

8251 Clinton
CITIZENS NB OF WILMINGTON
{{ 6 L 8 S }}
Organized 5/2/06
Receivership 3/9/31
1902 Red Seal <$VALUE
3x10-20 1-2550 <$600
1902 Date Back
3x10-20 1-6600 <$300
1902 Plain Back
3x10-20 6601-21817 <$300
1929 Small Size
10 Type 1 1-1465 <$175
20 Type 1 1-339 <$175
Total Issue $1,346,930
Out at close $100,000
Large out at close $13,460

FNB of Winchester
SEE Ch 9394
FNB of Higginsport

1997 Clinton
CLINTON COUNTY NB OF WILMINGTON
Chartered 6/11/72
2nd title: Clinton County NB & TC 5/9/22
FIRST TITLE {{ 10 L }}
Original Series <$VALUE
4x5 1-2550 <$450
3x10-20 1-1200 <$750/$1250
Series 1875
4x5 1-1800 <$450
3x10-20 1-3122 <$750/$1250
Brown Back
4x5 1-6525 <$275
3x10-20 1-2374 <$275/$325
1882 Date Back
4x5 1-2940 <$275
3x10-20 1-5060 <$275/$325
1902 Date Back
4x5 1-3500 <$150
3x10-20 1-2600 <$150
1902 Plain Back
4x5 3501-10550 <$150
3x10-20 3601-6820 <$150
SECOND TITLE {{ 7 L 42 S }}
1902 Plain Back
4x5 1-27116 <$150
3x10-20 1-13091 <$150
1929 Small Size
5 Type 1 1-8122 <$50
10 Type 1 1-3694 <$50
20 Type 1 1-984 <$60
5 Type 2 1-10476 <$70
10 Type 2 1-6179 <$70
20 Type 2 1-1555 <$75
Total Issue $3,341,620
Out in 1935 $200,000
Large out 1935 $9,845

CONDITION affects Value. The Values shown are for notes in FINE condition.

****

365 Clinton
FNB OF WILMINGTON
{{ 10 L 18 S }}
Chartered 4/64
Original Series <$VALUE
4x5 1-5475 <$500
3x10-20 1-2000 <$750/$1250
Series 1875
4x5 1-500 <$500
3x10-20 1-1000 <$750/$1250
Brown Back
3x10-20 1-6152 <$300/$325
1902 Red Seal
4x5 1-2000 <$350
3x10-20 1-3800 <$350/$375
1902 Date Back
4x5 1-7100 <$175
3x10-20 1-5600 <$175
1902 Plain Back
4x5 7101-21120 <$175
3x10-20 5601-15166 <$175
1929 Small Size
5 Type 1 1-3154 <$65
10 Type 1 1-1760 <$75
20 Type 1 1-502 <$80
5 Type 2 1-5266 <$90
10 Type 2 1-3147 <$90
20 Type 2 1-650 <$100
Total Issue $2,319,060
Out in 1935 $97,645
Large out 1935 $6,415

****

5414 Monroe
FNB OF WOODSFIELD
{{ 6 L 8 S }}
Chartered 6/9/00
Receivership 1/2/34
Brown Back <$VALUE
4x5 1-2650 <$400
3x10-20 1-2260 <$400
1882 Date Back
4x5 1-3400 <$400
3x10-20 1-2440 <$400
1882 Value Back
4x5 3401-5290 <$400
3x10-20 2441-3610 <$400
1902 Plain Back
4x5 1-5840 <$275
3x10-20 1-4009 <$275
1929 Small Size
5 Type 1 1-1943 <$200
10 Type 1 1-893 <$200
20 Type 1 1-219 <$200
Total Issue $907,700
Out at close $48,980
Large out at close $3,150

****

7670 Wayne
CITIZENS NB OF WOOSTER
{{ 14 L 3U + 19 S }}
Chartered 3/05
1902 Red Seal <$VALUE
3x10-20 1-3000 <$500
1902 Date Back
4x5 1-5650 <$200
3x10-20 1-3300 <$200
50-100 1-200 <$500/$600
3x50-100 1-200 <$500/$600
1902 Plain Back
4x5 5651-19632 <$200
3x10-20 3301-13105 <$200
1929 Small Size
5 Type 1 1-3350 <$70
10 Type 1 1-2038 <$70
20 Type 1 1-542 <$80
5 Type 2 1-4354 <$80
10 Type 2 1-2666 <$80
20 Type 2 1-576 <$100
Total Issue $1,625,670
Out in 1935 $100,000
Large out 1935 $4,385

****

1912 Wayne
NB OF WOOSTER
{{ 2 L }}
Chartered 12/29/71
Liquidated 11/29/91
Original Series <$VALUE
3x1-2 1-3000 <$750/$1500
4x5 1-3500 <$850
3x10-20 1-900 <$1000/$1500
Series 1875
4x5 1-250 <$850
3x10-20 1-2712<$1000/$1500
Total Issue $270,600
Out in 1910 $1,295

****

828 Wayne
WAYNE COUNTY NB OF WOOSTER
{{ 20 L U + 29 S }}
Chartered 2/20/65
Original Series <$VALUE
3x1-2 1-1000 <$600/$1250
4x5 1-2050 <$600
3x10-20 1-1550 <$750/$1250
Series 1875
3x1-2 1-160 <$600/$1250
4x5 1-775 <$600
3x10-20 1-1354 <$750/$1250
Brown Back
3x10-20 1-4512 <$375
1902 Red Seal
3x10-20 1-5700 <$450
1902 Date Back
3x10-20 1-8500 <$150
1902 Plain Back
3x10-20 8501-32179 <$150
1929 Small Size
10 Type 1 1-4684 <$60
20 Type 1 1-1348 <$70
10 Type 2 1-6091 <$70
20 Type 2 1-1969 <$75
Total Issue $2,870,140
Out in 1935 $200,000
Large out 1935 $8,040

****

4657 Wayne
WOOSTER NB, WOOSTER
{{ UNREPORTED }}
Organized 11/30/91
Receivership 11/23/04
Brown Back <$VALUE
3x10-20 1-3786 <$1250
Total Issue $189,300
Out in 1916 $2,180

****

2575 Greene
CITIZENS NB OF XENIA
{{ 14 L 14 S }}
Chartered 1881
Series 1875 <$VALUE
4x5 1-8664 <$500
3x10-20 1-3200 <$750/$1250
Brown Back
3x10-20 1-4500 <$400
1882 Date Back
3x10-20 1-6500 <$400
1882 Value Back
3x10-20 6501-10659 <$400
1902 Plain Back
3x10-20 1-9126 <$200
1929 Small Size
10 Type 1 1-1970 <$110
20 Type 1 1-628 <$125
10 Type 2 1-2557 <$150
20 Type 2 1-570 <$150
Total Issue $1,778,060
Out in 1935 $90,000
Large out 1935 $5,260

****

369 Greene
FNB OF XENIA
{{ 1 L }}
Chartered 4/64
Liquidated 2/24/83
Original Series <$VALUE
4x5 1-3400 <$1000
3x10-20 1-2800<$1250/$1500
Series 1875
4x5 1-2395 <$1000
3x10-20 1-1700<$1250/$1500
Total Issue $340,900
Out in 1910 $2,055

****

277 Greene
SECOND NB OF XENIA
{{ 2 L }}
Organized 1/1/64
Receivership 5/9/88
Original Series <$VALUE
4x5 1-4500 <$1000
3x10-20 1-2500<$1250/$1500
Series 1875
4x5 1-1575 <$1000
3x10-20 1-949 <$1250/$1500
Brown Back
4x5 1-1118 <$650
3x10-20 1-337 <$650
Total Issue $333,160
Out in 1916 $2,185

****

2932 Greene
XENIA NB, XENIA
{{ 9 L U + 22 S }}
Chartered 1883
Brown Back <$VALUE
4x5 1-5006 <$450
3x10-20 1-2724 <$450
1902 Red Seal
4x5 1-1000 <$500
3x10-20 1-1900 <$500
1902 Date Back
4x5 1-5050 <$225
3x10-20 1-3760 <$225
1902 Plain Back
4x5 5051-19391 <$225
3x10-20 3761-13219 <$225
1929 Small Size
5 Type 1 1-3282 <$100
10 Type 1 1-1528 <$100
20 Type 1 1-488 <$100
5 Type 2 1-4082 <$110
10 Type 2 1-2257 <$110
20 Type 2 1-573 <$125
Total Issue $1,703,230
Out in 1935 $90,000
Large out 1935 $5,005

****

2482 Mahoning
COMMERCIAL NB OF YOUNGSTOWN
{{ 20 L 15 S }}
Chartered 6/15/80
Liquidated 3/29/32
Series 1875 <$VALUE
3x10-20 1-5675 <$750/$1250
Brown Back
4x5 1-1500 <$175
3x10-20 1-1400 <$175/$225
50-100 1-4271 <$1500/$1750
1882 Date Back
4x5 1-26750 <$150
3x10-20 1-13300 <$150/$175
50-100 1-200 <$1500/$1750
3x50-100 1-480<$1500/$1750
1882 Value Back
4x5 26751-43250 <$150
3x10-20 13301-21500 <$150/$200
1902 Plain Back
4x5 1-73677 <$65
3x10-20 1-51167 <$65
1929 Small Size
5 Type 1 1-14841 <$90
10 Type 1 1-7434 <$90
20 Type 1 1-2157 <$100
Total Issue $8,296,400
Out at close $500,000
Large out at close $40,610

****

3 Mahoning
FNB OF YOUNGSTOWN*
{{ 50+ L 7U + 50 S }}
Organized 6/2/63
Liquidated 5/15/82
*Reorganized as Ch 2693 which retook Ch 3 4/6/09
Liquidated 2/9/32
Original Series <$VALUE
3x1-2 1-8000 <$600/$1250
4x5 1-7500 <$650
4x10 1-10875 <$850
Series 1875
3x1-2 1-1000 <$600/$1250
4x5 1-2677 <$650
4x10 1-9819 <$850
1902 Date Back
4x5 1-89000 <$75
3x10-20 1-68500 <$75
1902 Plain Back (dated 1909)
4x5 89001-190000 <$75
3x10-20 68501-132100 <$75
1902 Plain Back (dated 1922)
4x5 1-150520 <$75
3x10-20 1-96408 <$75
1929 Small Size
5 Type 1 1-36356 <$50
10 Type 1 1-16596 <$50
20 Type 1 1-5010 <$60
Total Issue $21,999,740
Out at close $931,560
Large out at close $109,195
Ch 13586 assumed circulation

****

2693 Mahoning
FNB OF YOUNGSTOWN
{{ 12 L }}
Chartered 1882
RETOOK Ch 3 4/6/09
Brown Back <$VALUE
4x5 1-5625 <$225
3x10-20 1-10979 <$225/$275
50-100 1-2834 <$1500/$1750
1902 Red Seal
4x5 1-43000 <$225
3x10-20 1-37000 <$225/$275
1902 Date Back
4x5 1-14638 <$150
3x10-20 1-4206* <$150
* 3827-4000 not issued
Total Issue $4,290,910
Out in 1909 $100,000

****

2350 Mahoning
MAHONING NB OF YOUNGSTOWN
{{ 36 L 50+ S }}
Chartered 4/3/77
Series 1875 <$VALUE
4x5 1-11250 <$450
3x10-20 1-7366 <$750/$1250
Brown Back
4x5 1-9000 <$225
50-100 1-5564 <$1500/$1750
1882 Date Back
4x5 1-26500 <$200
3x10-20 1-11400 <$200/$250
50-100 1-2000 <$1500/$1750
3x50-100 1-345<$1500/$1750
1882 Value Back
4x5 26501-27205 <$200
3x10-20 11401-11947 <$200/$250
1902 Plain Back
4x5 1-69910 <$65
3x10-20 1-44478 <$65
3x50-100 1-1039 <$350/$450
1929 Small Size
5 Type 1 1-38704 <$20
10 Type 1 1-18726 <$25
20 Type 1 1-5412 <$35
5 Type 2 1-56822 <$20
10 Type 2 1-16873 <$25
20 Type 2 1-8490 <$35
Total Issue $10,574,210
Out in 1935 $1,000,000
Large out 1935 $23,630

****

12332 Mahoning
SECOND NB IN YOUNGSTOWN
{{ 2 L 3 S }}
Organized 2/28/23
Receivership 11/30/31
1902 Plain Back <$VALUE
4x5 1-17787 <$600
1929 Small Size
5 Type 1 1-4340 <$400
Total Issue $485,940
Out at close $38,720
Large out at close $1,060

****

2217 Mahoning
SECOND NB OF YOUNGSTOWN
{{ 3 L }}
Chartered 1/14/75
Liquidated 5/23/04
Original Series <$VALUE
4x5 1-5000 <$750
Series 1875
4x5 1-1571 <$750
3x10-20 1-4470<$1000/$1500
Brown Back
50-100 1-2630 <$1500/$1750
Total Issue $749,420
Out in 1910 $23,655

****

13586 Mahoning
UNION NB OF YOUNGSTOWN
{{ 50+ S }}
Chartered 12/31
1929 Small Size <$VALUE
5 Type 1 1-17366 <$25
10 Type 1 1-7990 <$30
20 Type 1 1-2586 <$40
5 Type 2 1-50874 <$25
10 Type 2 1-33778 <$30
20 Type 2 1-7926 <$40
Total Issue $2,061,370
Out in 1935 $1,032,410
Outstanding includes Ch 2693

****

4970 Mahoning
WICK NB OF YOUNGSTOWN
{{ UNREPORTED }}
Chartered 7/19/94
Liquidated 10/1/06
Brown Back <$VALUE
4x5 1-1480 <$1250
3x10-20 1-3563 <$1250
Total Issue $207,750
Out in 1910 $6,915

****

2529 Muskingum
CITIZENS NB OF ZANESVILLE
{{ 8 L }}
Chartered 5/28/81
Liquidated 5/11/01
Series 1875 <$VALUE
4x5 1-5656 <$500
3x10-20 1-10704<$750/$1250
50-100 1-1034 <$4000
Total Issue $803,300
Out in 1910 $13,185

****

Citizens NB of Zanesville
SEE Ch 5760
Old Citizens NB of Zanesville

****

5769 Muskingum
COMMERCIAL NB OF ZANESVILLE
{{ UNREPORTED }}
Chartered 4/6/01
Liquidated 6/5/05
Brown Back <$VALUE
4x5 1-2980 <$1250
3x10-20 1-2429 <$1250
Total Issue $181,050
Out in 1910 $7,245

****

164 Muskingum
FNB OF ZANESVILLE
{{ 23 L 40 S }}
Chartered 12/63
Original Series <$VALUE
4x5 1-7250 <$450
4x10 1-3500 <$750
3x20-50 1-875*<$1250/$4000
* 226-500 not issued
Series 1875
4x5 1-986 <$450
4x10 1-2175 <$750
4x20 1-975 <$1250
Brown Back
3x10-20 1-12708 <$225/$275
1902 Red Seal
3x10-20 1-12500 <$225/$275
1902 Date Back
3x10-20 1-20700 <$75
1902 Plain Back
3x10-20 20701-64596 <$75
1929 Small Size
10 Type 1 1-8280 <$35
20 Type 1 1-2132 <$45
10 Type 2 1-9326 <$35
20 Type 2 1-2335 <$45
Total Issue $5,900,520
Out in 1935 $300,000
Large out 1935 $15,620

****

1230 Muskingum
MUSKINGUM NB OF ZANESVILLE
{{ UNREPORTED }}
Chartered 6/6/65
Liquidated 1/7/71
Original Series <$VALUE
4x5 1-1500 <$1250
3x10-20 1-1210<$1500/$2000
Total Issue $90,500
Out in 1910 $590

****

5760 Muskingum
OLD CITIZENS NB OF ZANESVILLE
Chartered 3/28/01
2nd title: Citizens NB in Zanesville 9/20/30
FIRST TITLE {{ 24 L 9 S }}
Brown Back <$VALUE
3x10-20 1-5520 <$350
50-100 1-2160 <$1500/$1750
1882 Date Back
3x10-20 1-11600 <$350
50-100 1-200 <$1500/$1750
1882 Value Back
3x10-20 11601-18113 <$350
1902 Plain Back
3x10-20 1-22254 <$150
1929 Small Size
10 Type 1 1-2756 <$75
20 Type 1 1-936 <$85
SECOND TITLE {{ 44 S }}
1929 Small Size
10 Type 1 1-4454 <$40
20 Type 1 1-1338 <$50
10 Type 2 1-15302 <$40
20 Type 2 1-4110 <$50
Total Issue $3,589,050
Out in 1935 $400,000
Large out 1935 $10,530

****

131 Muskingum
SECOND NB OF ZANESVILLE
{{ UNREPORTED }}
Chartered 11/23/63
Liquidated 11/16/72
Original Series <$VALUE
4x5 1-4317 <$1250
4x10 1-2225 <$1500
Total Issue $175,340
Out in 1910 $1,420

****

4298 Muskingum
UNION NB OF ZANESVILLE
{{ 4 L }}
Chartered 5/3/90
Liquidated 11/8/06
Brown Back <$VALUE
3x10-20 1-7925 <$500
Total Issue $396,250
Out in 1910 $23,430

****

<$VALUEs are for notes in FINE condition. Value changes by approximately 25% for a change of one full grade.

Achille D8
Ada D7
Addington D6
Afton A9
Alex C6
Allen D7
Altus D4
Alva A5
Anadarko C5
Antlers D8
Apache C5
Arapaho B5
Ardmore D6
Atoka D8
Aylesworth D7
Bartlesville A8
Beggs B8
Bennington D8
Berwyn D6
Billings B6
Bixby B8
Blackwell A6
Blair D4
Blanchard C6
Boise City A1
Bokchito D8
Boswell D8
Boynton B8
Braggs B8
Braman A6
Bristow B7
Broken Arrow B8
Broken Bow D9
Buffalo A4
Byars C6
Caddo D8
Calera D8
Calvin C7
Canadian C8
Capitol Hill B6
Carmen A5
Carnegie C5
Cashion B6
Cement C5
Centralia A8
Chandler B7
Checotah C8
Chelsea B8
Cherokee A5
Chickasha C6
Claremore B8
Cleveland B7
Clinton B5
Coalgate D7
Colbert D8
Collinsville B8
Comanche D6
Commerce A9
Cordell C5
Cornish D6
Coweta B8
Coyle B6
Cushing B7
Custer City B5
Davenport B7
Davidson D5
Davis D7
Depew B7
Devol D5
Dewey A8
Duncan D6
Durant D8
Dustin C7
Edmond B6
El Dorado D4
El Reno C6
Elk City C4
Enid B6
Erick C4
Eufaula C8
Fairfax A7
Fairview B5
Foraker A7
Fort Gibson B8
Fort Sill D5
Fort Towson D8
Foss C5
Francis D7
Frederick D5
Gage B4
Geary B5
Gotebo C5
Grandfield D5
Granite C4
Grove B9
Guthrie B6
Guymon A2
Harrah B6
Harrison C5
Hartshorne C8
Haskell B8
Hastings D6
Healdton D6
Heavener C9
Helena A5
Hennessey B6
Henryetta B8
Hobart C5
Holdenville C7
Hollis D4
Hominy A7
Hugo D8
Hydro C5
Idabel D9
Kaw City A6
Kenefic D8
Keota C9
Kiefer B7
Kingfisher B6
Kingston D7
Kiowa C8
Konawa C7
Lahoma B6
Lamont A6
Lawton D5
Leger C4
Lehigh D7
Lenapah A8
Lexington C6
Lindsay D6
Lone Wolf C5
Luther B6
Madill D7
Mangum C4
Mannsville D7
Marietta D6
Marlow D6
Maud C7
Maysville D6
McAlester C8
McLoud C7
Medford A6
Miami A9
Milburn D7
Mill Creek D7
Minco C6
Moore B6
Morris B8
Mounds B7
Mountain View C5
Muldrow C9
Mulhall B6
Muscogee B8
Muskogee B8
Nash A6
New Wilson D6
Newkirk A6
Noble C6
Norman C6
Nowata A8
O'Keene B5
Oakland D7
Okemah C7
Oklahoma City B6
Okmulgee B8
Oktaha B8
Olustee C4
Owasso B8
Pauls Valley D6
Pawhuska A7
Pawnee B7
Perry B6
Pocasset C6
Ponca City A6
Pond Creek A6
Porter B8
Porum B8
Poteau C9
Prague B7
Pryor Creek B8
Purcell C6
Quinton C8
Ralston B7
Ramona A8
Ravia D7
Ringling D6
Roff D7
Rush Springs C6
Ryan D6
Sallisaw C9
Sand Springs B8
Sapulpa B7
Sasakwa C7
Sayre C4
Seiling B5
Seminole C7
Sentinel C5
Shattuck B4
Shawnee C7
Skiatook B8
Snyder C5
Soper D8
South McAlester C8
Spiro C9
Spokogee C7
Sterrett D8
Stigler C9
Stillwater B7
Stilwell B9
Stonewall D7
Stratford D6
Stroud B7
Stuart C7
Sulphur D7
Tahlequah B9
Talihina C9
Taloga B5
Tecumseh C7
Temple D5
Terlton B7
Terral D6
Texhoma A4
Thomas B5
Tipton D5
Tishomingo D7
Tonkawa A6
Tulsa B8
Tupelo D7
Tuttle C6
Tyrone A2
Valliant D9
Verden C6
Vian C9
Vinita A8
Wagoner B8
Wakita A6
Walters D5
Wanette C7
Wapanucka D7
Warner B8
Washington C6
Watonga B5
Waukomis B6
Waurika D6
Waynoka A5
Weatherford B5
Webbers Falls B8
Weleetka C7
Wellston B7
Westville B9
Wetumka C7
Wewoka C7
Wilburton C8
Woodville D7
Woodward B4
Wynnewood D6
Yale B7
Yukon C6

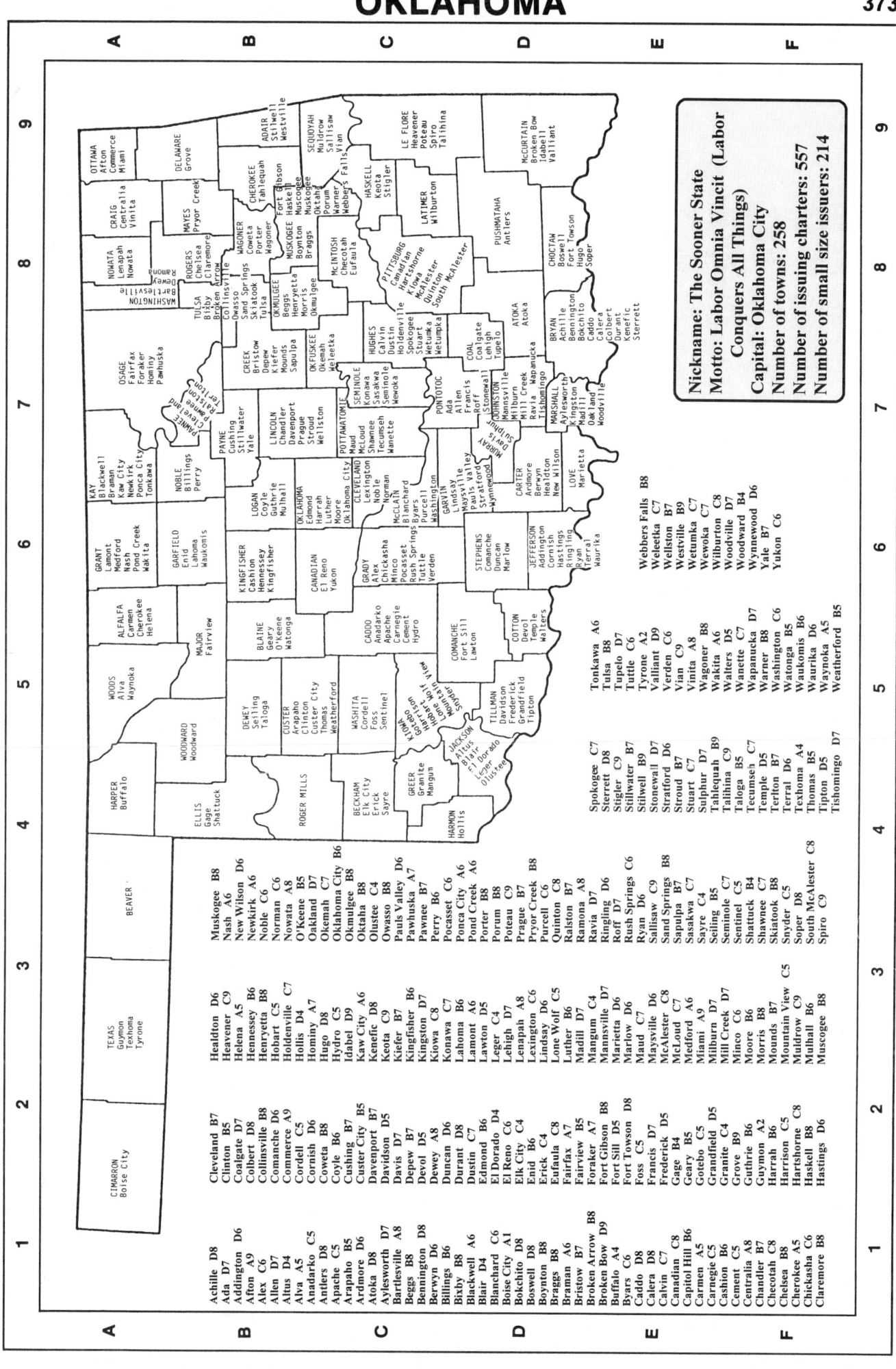

Nickname: The Sooner State
Motto: Labor Omnia Vincit (Labor Conquers All Things)
Capital: Oklahoma City
Number of towns: 258
Number of issuing charters: 557
Number of small size issuers: 214

***

10380 Bryan
FARMERS & MERCHANTS NB OF ACHILLE
{{1L 0S}}
Chartered 5/13
Liquidated 3/4/30
1902 Date Back <$VALUE
3x10-20 1-500 <$1250
1902 Plain Back
3x10-20 501-1431 <$1250
1929 Small Size
10 Type 1 1-45 <$750
20 Type 1 1-5 <$750
Total Issue $74,850
Out at close $5,270
Large out at close $1,970

***

10347 Bryan
FNB OF ACHILLE
{{ UNREPORTED }}
Chartered 3/13
Liquidated 1/11/16
1902 Date Back <$VALUE
3x10-20 1-322 <$1500
Total Issue $16,100
Out in 1916 $3,470

***

5633 Pontotoc
ADA NB, ADA
{{ UNREPORTED }}
Chartered 11/26/00
Liquidated 12/30/12
INDIAN TERRITORY
Brown Back <$VALUE
3x10-20 1-800 <$3500
STATE ISSUES
1882 Date Back
3x10-20 1-588 <$1500
Total Issue $69,400
Out in 1913 $6,750

***

7071 Pontotoc
CITIZENS NB OF ADA
{{ UNREPORTED }}
Chartered 12/24/03
Liquidated 10/10/08
INDIAN TERRITORY
1902 Red Seal <$VALUE
3x10-20 1-610 <$3500
STATE ISSUES
1902 Date Back
3x10-20 1-34 <$1250
Total Issue $32,200
Out in 1910 $3,500

***

12591 Pontotoc
FNB IN ADA
{{11 S}}
Chartered 11/24
1929 Small Size <$VALUE
10 Type 1 1-1226 <$150
20 Type 1 1-408 <$150
10 Type 2 1-1165 <$150
20 Type 2 1-335 <$150
Total Issue $140,870
Out in 1935 $50,000

***

5620 Pontotoc
FNB OF ADA
Chartered 11/10/00
Liquidated 12/22/24
INDIAN TERRITORY {{1L}}
Brown Back <$VALUE
3x10-20 1-1750 <$3000
STATE ISSUES {{8L}}
1882 Date Back
3x10-20 1-2600 <$500
1882 Value Back
3x10-20 2601-6111 <$500
1902 Plain Back
4x5 1-20755 <$300
Total Issue $808,150
Out at close $93,600

***

10513 Pontotoc
MERCHANTS & PLANTERS NB OF ADA
{{ UNREPORTED }}
Organized 4/9/14
Liquidated 12/30/22
1902 Date Back <$VALUE
3x10-20 1-413 <$1500
Total Issue $20,650
Out at close $180

***

10001 Jefferson
FNB OF ADDINGTON
{{ UNREPORTED }}
Chartered 4/11
Liquidated 12/10/28
1902 Date Back <$VALUE
4x5 1-1500 <$1250
3x10-20 1-1240 <$1250
1902 Plain Back
4x5 1501-3185 <$1250
3x10-20 1241-2192 <$1250
Total Issue $173,700
Out in 1920 $24,700

***

8790 Ottawa
FNB OF AFTON
{{ UNREPORTED }}
Chartered 7/9/07
Liquidated 12/16/08
INDIAN TERRITORY
1902 Red Seal <$VALUE
4x5 1-170 <$4000
3x10-20 1-169 <$4000
Total Issue $11,850
Out in 1910 $2,615

***

10339 Ottawa
FNB OF AFTON
{{2L}}
Chartered 3/13
Liquidated 8/5/25
1902 Date Back <$VALUE
3x10-20 1-800 <$750
1902 Plain Back
3x10-20 801-2563 <$750
Total Issue $128,150
Out in 1924 $16,250

***

10193 Grady
FNB OF ALEX
{{3L 7S}}
Chartered 5/12
1902 Date Back <$VALUE
3x10-20 1-1100 <$650
1902 Plain Back
3x10-20 1101-5613 <$650
1929 Small Size
10 Type 1 1-822 <$350
20 Type 1 1-232 <$350
10 Type 2 1-1139 <$350
20 Type 2 1-293 <$350
Total Issue $375,060
Out in 1935 $25,000
Large out 1935 $850

***

9620 Pontotoc
FNB OF ALLEN
{{3L}}
Organized 11/24/09
Receivership 11/14/32
1902 Date Back <$VALUE
3x10-20 1-1220 <$650
1902 Plain Back
3x10-20 1221-4744 <$650
Total Issue $237,200
Out at close $2,110

***

Altus NB, Altus
SEE Ch 7159
Altus NB of Leger

***

12155 Jackson
ALTUS NB, ALTUS
{{2L 11S}}
Chartered 4/22
1902 Plain Back <$VALUE
3x10-20 1-3217 <$750
1929 Small Size
10 Type 1 1-1536 <$135
20 Type 1 1-376 <$150
10 Type 2 1-2616 <$150
20 Type 2 1-756 <$150
Total Issue $339,410
Out in 1935 $50,000
Large out 1935 $2,230
Outstanding includes Ch 8775

***

8775 Jackson
CITY NB OF ALTUS
Chartered 7/07
Closed 3/21/25
OKLAHOMA TERRITORY {{0L}}
1902 Red Seal <$VALUE
3x10-20 1-187 <$3500
STATE ISSUES {{3L}}
1902 Date Back
3x10-20 1-3940 <$600
1902 Plain Back
3x10-20 3941-9399 <$600
Total Issue $479,300
Out at close $50,000
Ch 12155 assumed circulation

***

FNB of Altus
SEE Ch 6113
FNB of Leger

***

13756 Jackson
NB OF COMMERCE IN ALTUS
{{6S}}
Chartered 8/33
1929 Small Size <$VALUE
5 Type 2 1-7926 <$225
10 Type 2 1-4150 <$225
20 Type 2 1-1042 <$225
Total Issue $101,970
Out in 1935 $39,550

***

6490 Woods
ALVA NB, ALVA
Chartered 11/15/02
Liquidated 12/22/08
OKLAHOMA TERRITORY {{1L}}
1902 Red Seal <$VALUE
3x10-20 1-1350 <$3500
STATE ISSUES {{0L}}
1902 Red Seal
3x10-20 1-204 <$3000
Total Issue $77,700
Out in 1910 $12,010

***

5587 Woods
EXCHANGE NB OF ALVA
Chartered 9/26/00
Receivership 3/18/32
2nd title: FNB of Alva 1/22/03
OKLAHOMA TERRITORY
FIRST TITLE {{1L}}
Brown Back <$VALUE
3x10-20 1-184 <$3000
SECOND TITLE {{1L}}
Brown Back
3x10-20 1-1300 <$3000
STATE ISSUES {{3L 5S}}
1882 Date Back
3x10-20 1-1830* <$650
1882 Value Back
3x10-20 1931-2874* <$650
* 1831-1930 not marked
1902 Plain Back
3x10-20 1-2855 <$450
1929 Small Size
10 Type 1 1-509 <$300
20 Type 1 1-124 <$300
Total Issue $406,070
Out at close $24,700
Large out at close $2,830

***

FNB of Alva
SEE Ch 5587
Exchange NB of Alva

***

Anadarko NB, Anadarko
SEE Ch 5923
NB of Anadarko

***

6307 Caddo
CITIZENS NB OF ANADARKO
{{ UNREPORTED }}
Chartered 6/17/02
Liquidated 8/31/08
OKLAHOMA TERRITORY
1902 Red Seal <$VALUE
3x10-20 1-371 <$4000
Total Issue $18,550
Out in 1910 $1,790

***

5905 Caddo
FNB OF ANADARKO
Chartered 7/16/01
OKLAHOMA TERRITORY {{0L}}
Brown Back <$VALUE
4x5 1-700 <$3500
3x10-20 1-1280 <$3500
STATE ISSUES {{3L 7S}}
Brown Back
3x10-20 1-200 <$1500
1882 Date Back
4x5 1-950* <$650
3x10-20 1-1661** <$650
1882 Value Back
4x5 1151-2295* <$650
3x10-20 1821-2494** <$650
* 951-1150 not marked
** 1662-1820 not marked
1902 Plain Back
4x5 1-3155 <$400
3x10-20 1-1806 <$400
1929 Small Size
5 Type 1 1-900 <$175
10 Type 1 1-576 <$175
20 Type 1 1-178 <$175
5 Type 2 1-1386 <$200
10 Type 2 1-778 <$200
20 Type 2 1-305 <$200
Total Issue $515,730
Out in 1935 $25,000
Large out 1935 $620

***

5923 Caddo
NB OF ANADARKO
Chartered 7/30/01
Liquidated 3/1/29
2nd title: Anadarko NB 6/6/21
FIRST TITLE
OKLAHOMA TERRITORY {{1L}}
Brown Back <$VALUE
3x10-20 1-400 <$3000
STATE ISSUES {{0L}}
Brown Back
3x10-20 1-100 <$1500
1882 Date Back
3x10-20 1-560* <$1250
1882 Value Back
3x10-20 621-1074* <$1250
* 561-620 not marked
SECOND TITLE {{1L}}
1902 Plain Back
3x50-100 1-306 <$1250/$1500
Total Issue $155,200
Out at close $25,000

***

7667 Pushmataha
ANTLERS NB, ANTLERS
Chartered 3/05
Liquidated 12/31/30
2nd title: FNB of Antlers 3/15/20
FIRST TITLE
INDIAN TERRITORY {{0L}}
1902 Red Seal <$VALUE
3x10-20 1-400 <$4000
STATE ISSUES {{1L}}
1902 Date Back
3x10-20 1-1860* <$1250
1902 Plain Back
3x10-20 2021-3440* <$1250
* 1861-2020 not marked
SECOND TITLE {{3L 5S}}
1902 Plain Back
3x10-20 1-4997 <$850
1929 Small Size
10 Type 1 1-511 <$400
20 Type 1 1-129 <$400
Total Issue $487,890
Out at close $40,410
Large out at close $8,110
Outstanding includes Ch 8082

***

8082 Pushmataha
CITIZENS NB OF ANTLERS
{{ UNREPORTED }}
Chartered 2/06
Liquidated 3/6/24
INDIAN TERRITORY
1902 Red Seal <$VALUE
3x10-20 1-187 <$4000
STATE ISSUES
1902 Red Seal
3x10-20 1-100 <$4000
1902 Date Back
3x10-20 1-860 <$1500
1902 Plain Back
3x10-20 861-1198 <$1500
Total Issue $74,250
Out at close $6,250
Ch 7667 assumed circulation

***

FNB of Antlers
SEE Ch 7667
Antlers NB, Antlers

***

12120 Caddo
AMERICAN NB OF APACHE
{{6L 7S}}
Chartered 2/22
1902 Plain Back <$VALUE
3x10-20 1-2565 <$600
1929 Small Size
10 Type 1 1-642 <$400
20 Type 1 1-268 <$400
10 Type 2 1-1220 <$400
20 Type 2 1-240 <$400
Total Issue $203,930
Out in 1935 $20,000
Large out 1935 $110

***

7127 Caddo
FNB OF APACHE
Chartered 2/04
OKLAHOMA TERRITORY {{1L}}
1902 Red Seal <$VALUE
3x10-20 1-914 <$4000
STATE ISSUES {{4L 5S}}
1902 Date Back
3x10-20 1-1630 <$750
1902 Plain Back
3x10-20 1631-5231 <$750
1929 Small Size
10 Type 1 1-584 <$450
20 Type 1 1-180 <$450
10 Type 2 1-990 <$450
20 Type 2 1-226 <$450
Total Issue $378,310
Out in 1935 $20,000
Large out 1935 $960

***

6257 Custer
FNB OF ARAPAHO
Chartered 5/14/02
Liquidated 1/5/20
OKLAHOMA TERRITORY {{1L}}
1902 Red Seal <$VALUE
3x10-20 1-1200 <$4000
STATE ISSUES {{1L}}
1902 Date Back
3x10-20 1-1900 <$1000
1902 Plain Back
3x10-20 1901-2720 <$1000
Total Issue $196,000
Out at close $25,000

***

5922 Carter
ARDMORE NB, ARDMORE
Chartered 7/29/01
Liquidated 10/27/17
INDIAN TERRITORY {{1L}}
Brown Back <$VALUE
3x10-20 1-4800 <$3000
STATE ISSUES {{5L}}
1882 Date Back
3x10-20 1-8300 <$500
1882 Value Back
3x10-20 8301-10200 <$500
Total Issue $750,000
Out at close $100,000
Ch 4393 assumed circulation

***

8354 Carter
BANKERS NB OF ARDMORE
{{ UNREPORTED }}
Chartered 9/6/06
Liquidated 7/15/09
INDIAN TERRITORY
1902 Red Seal <$VALUE
3x10-20 1-1500 <$4000
STATE ISSUES
1902 Red Seal
3x10-20 1-500 <$4000
1902 Date Back
3x10-20 1-137 <$1500
Total Issue $106,850
Out in 1910 $23,050

***

4723 Carter
CITY NB OF ARDMORE
{{ UNREPORTED }}
Chartered 1892
Liquidated 3/3/10
INDIAN TERRITORY
Brown Back <$VALUE
3x10-20 1-2120 <$4000
STATE ISSUES
1882 Date Back
3x10-20 1-389 <$1500
Total Issue $125,450
Out in 1910 $16,610

***

11093 Carter
EXCHANGE NB OF ARDMORE
{{7L 16S}}
Chartered 10/17
1902 Plain Back <$VALUE
3x10-20 1-11898 <$275
3x50-100 1-756 <$275
1929 Small Size
10 Type 1 1-1442 <$85
20 Type 1 1-314 <$100
50 Type 1 1-170 <$175
100 Type 1 1-52 <$250
10 Type 2 1-2606 <$100
20 Type 2 1-720 <$100
Total Issue $1,030,760
Out in 1935 $100,000
Large out 1935 $6,490

***

13677 Carter
FNB AT ARDMORE
{{9S}}
Chartered 4/33
1929 Small Size <$VALUE
10 Type 2 1-7510 <$150
20 Type 2 1-2357 <$150
Total Issue $122,240
Out in 1935 $100,000
Outstanding includes Ch 12472

***

12472 Carter
FNB IN ARDMORE
{{6S}}
Organized 12/8/23
Liquidated 4/20/33
1929 Small Size <$VALUE
10 Type 1 1-1017 <$175
20 Type 1 1-335 <$175
Total Issue $101,220
Out at close $100,000

***

4393 Carter
FNB OF ARDMORE
Chartered 1890
Liquidated 2/28/24
INDIAN TERRITORY {{2L}}
Brown Back <$VALUE
4x5 1-2225 <$3000
3x10-20 1-3970 <$3000
STATE ISSUES {{9L}}
Brown Back
4x5 1-450 <$1250
3x10-20 1-320 <$1250
1882 Date Back
4x5 1-965 <$400
3x10-20 1-785 <$400
1902 Date Back
3x10-20 1-5400 <$200
1902 Plain Back
3x10-20 5401-18214 <$200
Total Issue $1,237,250
Out at close $200,000
Outstanding includes Ch 5922

***

10394 Carter
STATE NB OF ARDMORE
{{5L}}
Organized 5/6/13
Receivership 3/4/22
1902 Date Back <$VALUE
3x10-20 1-3300 <$400
3x50-100 1-300 <$750/$850
1902 Plain Back
3x10-20 3301-9345 <$400
Total Issue $542,250
Out at close $99,995

***

8994 Atoka
AMERICAN NB OF ATOKA
{{3L}}
Organized 12/26/07
Receivership 11/1/26
1902 Red Seal <$VALUE
3x10-20 1-187 <$2500
1902 Date Back
3x10-20 1-2070 <$600
1902 Plain Back
3x10-20 2071-5333 <$600
Total Issue $276,000
Out at close $23,600

***

5791 Atoka
ATOKA NB, ATOKA
Chartered 4/24/01
Liquidated 3/31/09
INDIAN TERRITORY {{2L}}
Brown Back <$VALUE
3x10-20 1-2000 <$3000
STATE ISSUES {{1L}}
Brown Back
3x10-20 1-481 <$1500
Total Issue $124,050
Out in 1910 $16,940

***

7666 Atoka
CITIZENS NB OF ATOKA
{{ UNREPORTED }}
Chartered 3/28/05
Liquidated 12/31/06
INDIAN TERRITORY
1902 Red Seal <$VALUE
3x10-20 1-260 <$4000
Total Issue $13,000
Out in 1910 $1,350

***

****
10385 Marshall
FNB OF AYLESWORTH
{{ 1 L }}
Chartered 5/13
Liquidated 1/11/16
1902 Date Back <$VALUE
3x10-20 1-301 <$1250
Total Issue $15,050
Out in 1916 $3,600
****
7032 Washington
AMERICAN NB OF
BARTLESVILLE
Chartered 11/03
Liquidated 4/4/10
INDIAN TERRITORY {{ 3 L }}
1902 Red Seal <$VALUE
3x10-20 1-3862 <$2500
STATE ISSUES {{ 0 L }}
1902 Date Back
4x5 1-290 <$1000
3x10-20 1-896 <$1000
Total Issue $243,700
Out in 1910 $54,350
****
6258 Washington
BARTLESVILLE NB,
BARTLESVILLE
Chartered 5/15/02
2nd title: FNB in
Bartlesville 8/14/20
FIRST TITLE
INDIAN TERRITORY {{ 0 L }}
1902 Red Seal <$VALUE
3x10-20 1-900 <$3000
STATE ISSUES {{ 2 L }}
1902 Date Back
3x10-20 1-4200 <$400
1902 Plain Back
3x10-20 4201-6440 <$400
SECOND TITLE {{ 2 L 22 S }}
1902 Plain Back (dated 1902)
3x10-20 1-2600 <$400
1902 Plain Back (dated 1922)
4x5 1-1855 <$400
3x10-20 1-2563 <$400
1929 Small Size
5 Type 1 1-3084 <$75
10 Type 1 1-1542 <$75
50 Type 1 1-210 <$150
5 Type 2 1-14120 <$85
10 Type 2 1-7171 <$85
20 Type 2 1-210 <$85
50 Type 2 1-635 <$250
Total Issue $1,088,550
Out in 1935 $200,000
Large out 1935 $3,765
Outstanding includes Ch 5310
****
FNB in Bartlesville
SEE Ch 6258
Bartlesville NB, Bartlesville
****
5310 Washington
FNB OF BARTLESVILLE
Chartered 4/27/00
Liquidated 8/9/20
INDIAN TERRITORY {{ 0 L }}
Brown Back <$VALUE
4x5 1-875 <$3000
3x10-20 1-580 <$3000
STATE ISSUES {{ 8 L }}
1882 Date Back
4x5 1-4400 <$400
3x10-20 1-3180 <$400
1882 Value Back
4x5 4401-6650 <$400
3x10-20 3181-4574 <$400
Total Issue $408,200
Out at close $49,995
Ch 6258 assumed circulation
****
9567 Washington
UNION NB OF BARTLESVILLE
{{ 6 L 33 S }}
Chartered 10/09
1902 Date Back <$VALUE
4x5 1-2450 <$275
3x10-20 1-1960 <$275
1902 Plain Back
4x5 2451-6824 <$275
3x10-20 1961-4522 <$275
1929 Small Size
5 Type 1 1-5016 <$60
10 Type 1 1-2478 <$60
20 Type 1 1-752 <$65
5 Type 2 1-9258 <$60
10 Type 2 1-5039 <$60
20 Type 2 1-1235 <$65
Total Issue $873,360
Out in 1935 $200,000
Large out 1935 $1,450
****

****
10482 Okmulgee
FARMERS NB OF BEGGS
{{ 3 L }}
Chartered 1/14
Liquidated 12/30/27
1902 Plain Back <$VALUE
3x10-20 1-5122 <$600
Total Issue $256,100
Out in 1925 $48,400
****
6868 Okmulgee
FNB OF BEGGS
Chartered 6/22/03
Receivership 7/9/31
INDIAN TERRITORY {{ 0 L }}
1902 Red Seal <$VALUE
3x10-20 1-400 <$3500
STATE ISSUES {{ 3 L 3 S }}
1902 Date Back
3x10-20 1-1990 <$600
1902 Plain Back
3x10-20 1991-6632 <$600
1929 Small Size
10 Type 1 1-432 <$350
20 Type 1 1-113 <$350
Total Issue $391,080
Out at close $25,000
Large out at close $3,930
****
10343 Bryan
BENNINGTON NB, BENNINGTON
{{ UNREPORTED }}
Chartered 3/13
Liquidated 1/15/16
1902 Date Back <$VALUE
3x10-20 1-295 <$1500
Total Issue $14,750
Out at close $6,260
Ch 7099 assumed circulation
****
7099 Bryan
FNB OF BENNINGTON
Chartered 1/04
Liquidated 5/27/31
INDIAN TERRITORY {{ 2 L }}
1902 Red Seal <$VALUE
3x10-20 1-576 <$3500
STATE ISSUES {{ 5 L 3 S }}
1902 Red Seal
3x10-20 1-400 <$3500
1902 Date Back
3x10-20 1-2530 <$450
1902 Plain Back
3x10-20 2531-6629 <$450
1929 Small Size
10 Type 1 1-371 <$400
20 Type 1 1-87 <$400
Total Issue $412,950
Out at close $25,000
Large out at close $3,860
Outstanding includes Ch 10343
****
7209 Carter
FNB OF BERWYN
Organized 3/28/04
Receivership 11/6/30
INDIAN TERRITORY {{ 0 L }}
1902 Red Seal <$VALUE
3x10-20 1-900 <$3500
STATE ISSUES {{ 2 L 0 S }}
1902 Date Back
3x10-20 1-460 <$750
1902 Plain Back
3x10-20 461-1241 <$750
1929 Small Size
10 Type 1 1-92 <$750
20 Type 1 1-8 <$750
Total Issue $113,530
Out at close $6,250
Large out at close $1,740
****
5960 Noble
FNB OF BILLINGS
{{ UNREPORTED }}
Chartered 9/10/01
Liquidated 10/25/02
OKLAHOMA TERRITORY
Brown Back <$VALUE
3x10-20 1-136 <$4000
Total Issue $6,800
Out in 1916 $130
****
10467 Tulsa
FNB OF BIXBY
{{ 1 L }}
Organized 12/1/13
Receivership 2/20/29
1902 Date Back <$VALUE
3x10-20 1-500 <$1250
1902 Plain Back
3x10-20 501-1439 <$1250
Total Issue $71,950
Out at close $6,050

****
6916 Kay
BLACKWELL NB, BLACKWELL
{{ UNREPORTED }}
Chartered 8/10/03
Liquidated 3/17/09
OKLAHOMA TERRITORY
1902 Red Seal <$VALUE
3x10-20 1-950 <$3500
STATE ISSUES
1902 Date Back
3x10-20 1-54 <$1250
Total Issue $50,200
Out in 1910 $13,240
****
5460 Kay
FNB OF BLACKWELL
Chartered 6/26/00
Liquidated 11/24/34
OKLAHOMA TERRITORY {{ 1 L }}
Brown Back <$VALUE
3x10-20 1-1490 <$3000
STATE ISSUES {{ 6 L 8 S }}
Brown Back
3x10-20 1-300 <$1500
1882 Date Back
3x10-20 1-1460* <$600
1882 Value Back
3x10-20 1561-2399* <$600
* 1461-1560 not marked
1902 Plain Back
3x10-20 1-2999 <$350
1929 Small Size
10 Type 1 1-698 <$175
20 Type 1 1-192 <$175
10 Type 2 1-222 <$175
20 Type 2 1-48 <$175
Total Issue $427,500
Out at close $25,000
Large out at close $1,750
****
7583 Kay
STATE NB OF BLACKWELL
Chartered 1/30/05
Liquidated 12/4/08
OKLAHOMA TERRITORY {{ 1 L }}
1902 Red Seal <$VALUE
3x10-20 1-476 <$3500
STATE ISSUES {{ 0 L }}
1902 Red Seal
3x10-20 1-294 <$3500
Total Issue $38,500
Out in 1910 $8,930
****
12130 Jackson
FNB IN BLAIR
{{ U + 5 S }}
Chartered 3/22
1929 Small Size <$VALUE
5 Type 1 1-526 <$225
10 Type 1 1-244 <$225
20 Type 1 1-76 <$225
5 Type 2 1-2112 <$225
10 Type 2 1-1092 <$225
20 Type 2 1-276 <$225
Total Issue $66,540
Out in 1935 $25,000
****
10368 Jackson
FNB OF BLAIR
{{ UNREPORTED }}
Chartered 4/13
Liquidated 6/22/16
1902 Date Back <$VALUE
3x10-20 1-337 <$1500
Total Issue $16,850
Out in 1916 $4,950
****
8702 McClain
FNB OF BLANCHARD
Chartered 5/07
INDIAN TERRITORY {{ 0 L }}
1902 Red Seal <$VALUE
3x10-20 1-200 <$3500
STATE ISSUES {{ 3 L 6 S }}
1902 Red Seal
3x10-20 1-400 <$3500
1902 Date Back
3x10-20 1-1910 <$600
1902 Plain Back
3x10-20 1911-5949 <$600
1929 Small Size
10 Type 1 1-708 <$225
20 Type 1 1-200 <$225
10 Type 2 1-1415 <$225
20 Type 2 1-355 <$225
Total Issue $415,180
Out in 1935 $25,000
Large out 1935 $1,220
****

****
11084 Cimarron
FNB OF BOISE CITY
{{ UNREPORTED }}
Organized 8/30/17
Receivership 11/25/24
1902 Plain Back <$VALUE
4x5 1-1145 <$1250
3x10-20 1-452 <$1250
Total Issue $45,500
Out at close $10,000
****
7499 Bryan
BOKCHITO NB, BOKCHITO
{{ UNREPORTED }}
Chartered 12/3/04
Liquidated 12/16/08
INDIAN TERRITORY
1902 Red Seal <$VALUE
3x10-20 1-256 <$4000
STATE ISSUES
1902 Red Seal
3x10-20 1-37 <$4000
Total Issue $14,650
Out in 1910 $1,870
****
6683 Bryan
FNB OF BOKCHITO
Chartered 3/21/03
Liquidated 12/29/08
INDIAN TERRITORY {{ 1 L }}
1902 Red Seal <$VALUE
3x10-20 1-380 <$3500
STATE ISSUES {{ 0 L }}
1902 Date Back
3x10-20 1-21 <$1500
Total Issue $20,050
Out in 1910 $2,090
****
9835 Bryan
FNB OF BOKCHITO
{{ 1 L }}
Chartered 9/10
Liquidated 1/8/16
1902 Date Back <$VALUE
3x10-20 1-2224 <$850
Total Issue $111,200
Out in 1916 $15,840
****
8353 Choctaw
BOSWELL NB, BOSWELL
{{ UNREPORTED }}
Chartered 9/06
Liquidated 1/16/11
INDIAN TERRITORY
1902 Red Seal <$VALUE
3x10-20 1-188 <$4000
STATE ISSUES
1902 Red Seal
3x10-20 1-60 <$4000
1902 Date Back
3x10-20 1-115 <$1500
Total Issue $18,150
Out in 1911 $2,900
****
7651 Choctaw
FNB OF BOSWELL
Organized 2/16/05
Receivership 10/8/26
INDIAN TERRITORY {{ 0 L }}
1902 Red Seal <$VALUE
3x10-20 1-380 <$3500
STATE ISSUES {{ 4 L }}
1902 Date Back
3x10-20 1-3180 <$500
1902 Plain Back
3x10-20 3181-8027 <$500
Total Issue $420,350
Out in 1922 $50,000
Outstanding includes Ch 10363
****
10363 Choctaw
STATE NB OF BOSWELL
{{ 2 L }}
Chartered 4/13
Liquidated 5/31/16
1902 Date Back <$VALUE
3x10-20 1-1390 <$850
Total Issue $69,500
Out at close $25,000
Ch 7651 assumed circulation
****
6511 Muskogee
FNB OF BOYNTON
Chartered 11/29/02
INDIAN TERRITORY {{ 0 L }}
1902 Red Seal <$VALUE
3x10-20 1-400 <$3500
STATE ISSUES {{ 3 L 7 S }}
1902 Date Back
3x10-20 1-1690 <$600
1902 Plain Back
3x10-20 1691-6185 <$600
1929 Small Size
10 Type 1 1-844 <$200
20 Type 1 1-210 <$200
10 Type 2 1-1188 <$225
20 Type 2 1-170 <$225
Total Issue $420,370
Out in 1935 $25,000
Large out 1935 $1,430
****
10437 Muskogee
FNB OF BRAGGS
{{ 12 L }}
Chartered 8/13
Liquidated 12/29/28
1902 Date Back <$VALUE
3x10-20 1-500 <$200
1902 Plain Back
3x10-20 501-4243 <$200
Total Issue $212,150
Out at close $25,000
****
10003 Kay
FNB OF BRAMAN
{{ 1 L 3 S }}
Chartered 4/11
1902 Date Back <$VALUE
3x10-20 1-500* <$1000
1902 Plain Back
3x10-20 601-1425* <$1000
* 501-600 not marked
1929 Small Size
10 Type 1 1-200 <$400
20 Type 1 1-55 <$400
Total Issue $89,850
Out in 1935 $6,250
Large out 1935 $380
****
10115 Creek
BRISTOW NB, BRISTOW
{{ UNREPORTED }}
Organized 11/23/11
Receivership 7/21/24
1902 Date Back <$VALUE
3x10-20 1-475* <$1250
1902 Plain Back
3x10-20 576-1035* <$1250
* 476-575 not marked
Total Issue $51,750
Out at close $3,850
****
6260 Creek
FNB OF BRISTOW
Chartered 5/16/02
Receivership 4/25/28
INDIAN TERRITORY {{ 0 L }}
1902 Red Seal <$VALUE
3x10-20 1-400 <$3500
STATE ISSUES {{ 3 L }}
1902 Date Back
3x10-20 1-2160 <$600
1902 Plain Back (dated 1902)
3x10-20 2161-4260 <$600
1902 Plain Back (dated 1922)
3x10-20 1-2177 <$600
Total Issue $341,850
Out at close $25,000
****
7600 Tulsa
ARKANSAS VALLEY NB OF
BROKEN ARROW
Chartered 2/6/05
Liquidated 2/15/09
INDIAN TERRITORY {{ 1 L }}
1902 Red Seal <$VALUE
4x5 1-800 <$4000
3x10-20 1-560 <$4000
STATE ISSUES {{ 0 L }}
1902 Red Seal
4x5 1-150 <$3500
3x10-20 1-116 <$3500
1902 Date Back
4x5 1-35 <$2000
Total Issue $53,500
Out in 1910 $7,540
****
10255 Tulsa
CITIZENS NB OF
BROKEN ARROW
{{ 1 L }}
Chartered 9/13/12
Liquidated 11/20/22
1902 Date Back <$VALUE
3x10-20 1-1400 <$1500
1902 Plain Back
3x10-20 1401-3452 <$1500
Total Issue $172,600
Out at close $25,000
****

****
7115 Tulsa
FNB OF BROKEN ARROW
Chartered 1/04
INDIAN TERRITORY {{ 0 L }}
1902 Red Seal <$VALUE
3x10-20 1-940 <$4000
STATE ISSUES {{ 4 L 6 S }}
1902 Date Back
3x10-20 1-2120 <$850
1902 Plain Back
3x10-20 2121-6568 <$850
1929 Small Size
10 Type 1 1-828 <$600
20 Type 1 1-198 <$600
10 Type 2 1-791 <$600
20 Type 2 1-243 <$600
Total Issue $461,610
Out in 1935 $24,350
Large out 1935 $1,480
****
10424 McCurtain
FNB OF BROKEN BOW
{{ UNREPORTED }}
Chartered 7/17/13
Receivership 11/2/26
1902 Date Back <$VALUE
3x10-20 1-500 <$2000
1902 Plain Back
3x10-20 501-1224 <$2000
Total Issue $61,200
Out at close $5,950
****
8896 Harper
FNB OF BUFFALO
Organized 9/2/07
Receivership 12/27/24
OKLAHOMA TERRITORY {{ 0 L }}
1902 Red Seal <$VALUE
3x10-20 1-300 <$4000
STATE ISSUES {{ 1 L }}
1902 Date Back
3x10-20 1-870 <$1250
1902 Plain Back
3x10-20 871-1631 <$1250
Total Issue $96,500
Out at close $9,700
****
7389 McClain
FNB OF BYARS
{{ UNREPORTED }}
Chartered 9/04
Liquidated 2/1/11
INDIAN TERRITORY
1902 Red Seal <$VALUE
3x10-20 1-1050 <$4000
STATE ISSUES
1902 Red Seal
3x10-20 1-200 <$4000
1902 Date Back
3x10-20 1-413 <$1500
Total Issue $83,150
Out in 1911 $13,150
****
7368 Bryan
CADDO NB, CADDO
Chartered 8/04
Liquidated 4/2/29
INDIAN TERRITORY {{ 2 L }}
1902 Red Seal <$VALUE
3x10-20 1-1200 <$3000
STATE ISSUES {{ 4 L }}
1902 Date Back
3x10-20 1-4700 <$500
1902 Plain Back
3x10-20 4701-6772 <$500
Total Issue $398,600
Out in 1922 $25,000
****
5246 Bryan
CHOCTAW NB OF CADDO
{{ 3 L }}
Chartered 1/17/00
Liquidated 4/5/08
INDIAN TERRITORY
Brown Back <$VALUE
4x5 1-2287 <$3000
3x10-20 1-1538 <$3000
Total Issue $122,640
Out in 1910 $8,475
****
10010 Bryan
SECURITY NB OF CADDO
{{ 1 L }}
Chartered 5/11
Liquidated 6/9/17
1902 Date Back <$VALUE
4x10 1-764 <$1000
Total Issue $30,560
Out at close $6,260
****

11182 Bryan
CALERA NB, CALERA
{{ 2 L }}
Chartered 5/18
Liquidated 3/22/24
1902 Plain Back <$VALUE
4x5 1-2565 <$850
Total Issue $51,300
Out at close $9,600

10226 Hughes
CALVIN NB, CALVIN
{{ 3 L }}
Chartered 7/12
Liquidated 11/21/23
1902 Date Back <$VALUE
4x10 1-650 <$600
1902 Plain Back
4x10 651-4447 <$600
Total Issue $177,880
Out at close $25,000

7053 Hughes
CITIZENS NB OF CALVIN
{{ 3 L }}
Chartered 12/5/03
Liquidated 5/29/09
INDIAN TERRITORY
1902 Red Seal <$VALUE
3x10-20 1-377 <$3000
Total Issue $18,850
Out in 1912 $2,520

6980 Hughes
FNB OF CALVIN
Chartered 10/03
Liquidated 5/26/34
INDIAN TERRITORY {{ 0 L }}
1902 Red Seal <$VALUE
3x10-20 1-356 <$3500
STATE ISSUES {{ 4 L 5 S }}
1902 Date Back
3x10-20 1-900 <$500
1902 Plain Back
3x10-20 901-5155 <$500
1929 Small Size
10 Type 1 1-764 <$300
20 Type 1 1-204 <$300
10 Type 2 1-361 <$300
20 Type 2 1-30 <$300
Total Issue $350,080
Out at close $25,000
Large out at close $1,300
Ch 5270 assumed circulation

9993 Pittsburg
FNB OF CANADIAN
{{ UNREPORTED }}
Chartered 4/11
Liquidated 6/16/13
1902 Date Back <$VALUE
4x10 1-327 <$2000
Total Issue $13,080
Out in 1913 $4,305

9584 Oklahoma
FNB OF CAPITOL HILL
{{ UNREPORTED }}
Chartered 11/09
Liquidated 7/22/13
1902 Date Back <$VALUE
50-100 1-91 <$2500
Total Issue $13,650
Out in 1913 $5,600

6844 Alfalfa
CARMEN NB, CARMEN
Chartered 6/19/03
Liquidated 4/19/09
OKLAHOMA TERRITORY {{ 1 L }}
1902 Red Seal <$VALUE
3x10-20 1-820 <$3500
STATE ISSUES {{ 0 L }}
1902 Red Seal
3x10-20 1-200 <$3500
1902 Date Back
3x10-20 1-4 <$1500
Total Issue $51,200
Out in 1910 $9,710

10203 Alfalfa
CARMEN NB, CARMEN
{{ 2 L }}
Organized 5/17/12
Receivership 2/19/24
1902 Date Back <$VALUE
3x10-20 1-860 <$750
1902 Plain Back
3x10-20 861-2094 <$750
Total Issue $104,700
Out at close $14,250
Ch 12498 assumed circulation

12498 Alfalfa
FNB IN CARMEN
{{ 3 L 6 S }}
Chartered 2/24
1902 Plain Back <$VALUE
3x10-20 1-1684 <$600
1929 Small Size
10 Type 1 1-680 <$225
20 Type 1 1-170 <$225
10 Type 2 1-1260 <$225
20 Type 2 1-324 <$225
Total Issue $164,480
Out in 1935 $25,000
Large out 1935 $1,230
Outstanding includes Ch 10203

6719 Alfalfa
FNB OF CARMEN
{{ 3 L }}
Chartered 4/13/03
Liquidated 2/4/05
OKLAHOMA TERRITORY
1902 Red Seal <$VALUE
3x10-20 1-286 <$3500
Total Issue $14,300
Out in 1910 $650

11763 Caddo
FNB OF CARNEGIE
{{ 1 L 2 S }}
Organized 6/16/20
Receivership 9/12/33
1902 Plain Back <$VALUE
4x10 1-1184 <$1250
1929 Small Size
10 Type 1 1-330 <$600
Total Issue $67,160
Out at close $6,000
Large out at close $20

6161 Kingfisher
FNB OF CASHION
Chartered 3/15/02
Liquidated 10/24/23
OKLAHOMA TERRITORY {{ 2 L }}
1902 Red Seal <$VALUE
3x10-20 1-1200 <$3000
STATE ISSUES {{ 2 L }}
1902 Date Back
3x10-20 1-1960 <$750
1902 Plain Back (dated 1902)
3x10-20 1961-3470 <$750
1902 Plain Back (dated 1922)
3x10-20 1-486 <$750
Total Issue $257,800
Out at close $25,000

8144 Caddo
FNB OF CEMENT
{{ UNREPORTED }}
Chartered 3/21/06
Liquidated 8/1/08
OKLAHOMA TERRITORY
1902 Red Seal <$VALUE
3x10-20 1-348 <$4000
Total Issue $17,400
Out in 1910 $3,290

7706 Craig
FNB OF CENTRALIA
Chartered 4/05
Liquidated 12/27/19
INDIAN TERRITORY {{ 0 L }}
1902 Red Seal <$VALUE
4x5 1-425 <$4000
3x10-20 1-290 <$4000
STATE ISSUES {{ 2 L }}
1902 Date Back
4x5 1-1400 <$750
3x10-20 1-1060 <$750
1902 Plain Back
4x5 1401-2457 <$750
3x10-20 1061-1609 <$750
Total Issue $152,599
Out at close $25,000

6142 Lincoln
CHANDLER NB, CHANDLER
{{ UNREPORTED }}
Chartered 2/28/02
Liquidated 1/18/09
OKLAHOMA TERRITORY
1902 Red Seal <$VALUE
3x10-20 1-400 <$4000
STATE ISSUES
1902 Red Seal
3x10-20 1-36 <$4000
Total Issue $21,800
Out in 1910 $2,480

5354 Lincoln
FNB OF CHANDLER
Chartered 5/15/00 as
Chandler NB, under which
there was no issue. Issuing
title adopted 5/22/00.
OKLAHOMA TERRITORY {{ 1 L }}
Brown Back <$VALUE
4x5 1-950 <$3000
3x10-20 1-790 <$3000
STATE ISSUES {{ 9 L 15 S }}
Brown Back
4x5 1-500 <$1250
3x10-20 1-780 <$1250
1882 Date Back
4x5 1-3500 <$400
3x10-20 1-2440 <$400
1882 Value Back
4x5 3501-5855 <$400
3x10-20 2441-3588 <$400
1902 Plain Back
3x10-20 1-6870 <$250
1929 Small Size
10 Type 1 1-1540 <$100
20 Type 1 1-430 <$100
10 Type 2 1-2508 <$100
20 Type 2 1-540 <$100
Total Issue $927,380
Out in 1935 $50,000
Large out 1935 $2,790

6269 Lincoln
UNION NB OF CHANDLER
Chartered 5/22/02
OKLAHOMA TERRITORY {{ 1 L }}
1902 Red Seal <$VALUE
3x10-20 1-2400 <$3500
STATE ISSUES {{ 6 L 14 S }}
1902 Date Back
3x10-20 1-3600 <$400
1902 Plain Back
3x10-20 3601-11931 <$400
1929 Small Size
10 Type 1 1-1480 <$150
20 Type 1 1-390 <$150
10 Type 2 1-2392 <$150
20 Type 2 1-611 <$150
Total Issue $888,290
Out in 1935 $50,000
Large out 1935 $1,440

11920 McIntosh
COMMERCIAL NB IN CHECOTAH
{{ 2 L }}
Chartered 1/21
Liquidated 12/22/23
1902 Plain Back <$VALUE
4x5 1-2140 <$750
3x10-20 1-1562 <$750
Total Issue $120,900
Out at close $50,000
Outstanding includes Ch 10063

10063 McIntosh
COMMERCIAL NB OF CHECOTAH
{{ 4 L }}
Chartered 8/11
Liquidated 4/28/21
1902 Date Back <$VALUE
4x5 1-3150 <$450
3x10-20 1-2460 <$450
1902 Plain Back
4x5 3151-6435 <$450
3x10-20 2461-4302 <$450
Total Issue $343,800
Out at close $50,000
Ch 11920 assumed circulation

5128 McIntosh
FNB OF CHECOTAH
Organized 5/23/98
Receivership 12/1/27
INDIAN TERRITORY {{ 2 L }}
Brown Back <$VALUE
4x5 1-1275 <$3000
3x10-20 1-940 <$3000
STATE ISSUES {{ 9 L }}
Brown Back
4x5 1-1500 <$1500
3x10-20 1-1200 <$1500
1882 Date Back
4x5 1-3350 <$400
3x10-20 1-2500 <$400
1882 Value Back
4x5 3351-4750 <$400
3x10-20 2501-3300 <$400
1902 Plain Back
4x5 1-6302 <$250
3x10-20 1-4170 <$250
Total Issue $757,040
Out at close $49,300

10051 McIntosh
PEOPLES NB OF CHECOTAH
{{ 5 L 12 S }}
Chartered 7/11
1902 Date Back <$VALUE
3x10-20 1-835 <$300
1902 Plain Back
3x10-20 836-6807 <$300
1929 Small Size
10 Type 1 1-1488 <$125
20 Type 1 1-388 <$125
10 Type 2 1-2634 <$125
20 Type 2 1-591 <$125
Total Issue $514,350
Out in 1935 $41,750
Large out 1935 $1,580

5955 Rogers
FNB OF CHELSEA
Chartered 8/31/01
INDIAN TERRITORY {{ 0 L }}
Brown Back <$VALUE
3x10-20 1-400 <$4000
STATE ISSUES {{ 1 L 2 S }}
Brown Back
3x10-20 1-100 <$2000
1882 Date Back
3x10-20 1-680 <$1500
1882 Value Back
3x10-20 681-823 <$1500
1902 Plain Back
3x10-20 1-747 <$1000
1929 Small Size
10 Type 1 1-209 <$500
20 Type 1 1-65 <$500
Total Issue $123,840
Out in 1935 $6,250
Large out 1935 $390

9008 Alfalfa
ALFALFA COUNTY NB OF CHEROKEE
{{ 2 L }}
Chartered 1/08
1902 Red Seal <$VALUE
3x10-20 1-200 <$3500
1902 Date Back
3x10-20 1-1420 <$850
1902 Plain Back
3x10-20 1421-3931 <$850
Total Issue $206,550
Out in 1935 $630

9884 Alfalfa
FARMERS NB OF CHEROKEE
{{ 3 L }}
Organized 11/2/10
Receivership 10/5/33
1902 Date Back <$VALUE
3x10-20 1-1940 <$600
1902 Plain Back
3x10-20 1941-4567 <$600
Total Issue $228,350
Out in 1935 $1,010

6677 Alfalfa
FNB OF CHEROKEE
Chartered 3/03
Liquidated 11/2/10
OKLAHOMA TERRITORY {{ 1 L }}
1902 Red Seal <$VALUE
4x5 1-1015 <$3500
3x10-20 1-794 <$3500
STATE ISSUES {{ 0 L }}
1902 Date Back
4x5 1-445 <$1500
3x10-20 1-352 <$1500
Total Issue $86,500
Out in 1911 $12,410

8203 Grady
CHICKASHA NB, CHICKASHA
Chartered 5/06
Closed 2/24/30
INDIAN TERRITORY {{ 0 L }}
1902 Red Seal <$VALUE
3x10-20 1-1500 <$3500
STATE ISSUES {{ 7 L 3 S }}
1902 Date Back
3x10-20 1-4900 <$350
1902 Plain Back
3x10-20 4901-13068 <$350
1929 Small Size
10 Type 1 1-350 <$300
20 Type 1 1-85 <$300
Total Issue $759,600
Out at close $50,000
Large out at close $18,840
Ch 9938 assumed circulation

Citizens-Farmers NB of Chickasha
SEE Ch 5547
Citizens NB of Chickasha

5547 Grady
CITIZENS NB OF CHICKASHA
Chartered 8/21/00
2nd title: Citizens-Farmers NB of Chickasha 12/31/29
FIRST TITLE
INDIAN TERRITORY {{ 1 L }}
Brown Back <$VALUE
50-100 1-1000 <$7500/$8000
STATE ISSUES {{ 4 L }}
1882 Date Back
50-100 1-600 <$2500/$3000
3x50-100 1-389 <$2500/$3000
1902 Plain Back
3x50-100 1-266 <$650/$750
SECOND TITLE {{ 15 S }}
1929 Small Size
5 Type 2 1-12862 <$100
10 Type 2 1-6950 <$100
20 Type 2 1-2334 <$100
Total Issue $584,240
Out in 1935 $100,000
Large out 1935 $3,850

5431 Grady
FNB OF CHICKASHA
Chartered 6/16/00
Liquidated 5/16/35
INDIAN TERRITORY {{ 3 L }}
Brown Back <$VALUE
4x5 1-5000 <$2000
4x10 1-500 <$2000
3x10-20 1-2230 <$2000
50-100 1-390 <$6500/$7500
STATE ISSUES {{ 22 L 15 S }}
Brown Back
4x5 1-750 <$1500
4x10 1-500 <$1500
3x10-20 1-300 <$1500
1882 Date Back
4x5 1-12000 <$400
4x10 1-14050* <$400
50-100 1-200 <$2500/$3000
3x50-100 1-360 <$2500/$3000
* 9701-14050 not marked
1882 Value Back
4x5 12001-20288 <$400
1902 Plain Back
4x5 1-17140 <$125
4x10 1-5670 <$125
3x10-20 1-5801 <$125
3x50-100 1-550 <$400/$500
1929 Small Size
5 Type 1 1-1798 <$85
10 Type 1 1-894 <$85
20 Type 1 1-318 <$85
50 Type 1 1-146 <$150
100 Type 1 1-54 <$225
5 Type 2 1-1332 <$85
10 Type 2 1-556 <$85
20 Type 2 1-185 <$100
Total Issue $2,662,770
Out in 1935 $100,000
Large out 1935 $12,720

9938 Grady
THE OKLAHOMA NB OF CHICKASHA
Chartered 2/11
2nd title: Oklahoma NB of Chickasha 5/16/35
FIRST TITLE {{ 5 L 1 S }}
1902 Date Back <$VALUE
4x5 1-2050* <$400
3x10-20 1-1620** <$400
1902 Plain Back
4x5 2251-6370* <$400
3x10-20 1781-4306** <$400
* 2051-2250 not marked
** 1621-1780 not marked
1929 Small Size
5 Type 1 1-412 <$200
10 Type 1 1-208 <$200
20 Type 1 1-74 <$200
SECOND TITLE {{ 14 S }}
1929 Small Size
5 Type 1 1-2018 <$100
10 Type 1 1-1204 <$100
20 Type 1 1-288 <$100
5 Type 2 1-4732 <$100
10 Type 2 1-3204 <$100
20 Type 2 1-945 <$100
Total Issue $618,360
Out in 1935 $75,000
Large out 1935 $3,250
Outstanding includes Ch 8203

4987 Rogers
FNB OF CLAREMORE
Chartered 1895
Liquidated 3/30/28
INDIAN TERRITORY {{ 0 L }}
Brown Back <$VALUE
3x10-20 1-1240 <$3500
STATE ISSUES {{ 2 L }}
1882 Date Back
3x10-20 1-884 <$850
1902 Date Back
3x10-20 1-500 <$650
1902 Plain Back
3x10-20 501-1802 <$650
Total Issue $196,300
Out in 1925 $13,000

10117 Rogers
NB OF CLAREMORE
{{ 6 L 8 S }}
Chartered 12/11
Liquidated 10/10/31
1902 Date Back <$VALUE
3x10-20 1-3010 <$400
1902 Plain Back
3x10-20 3011-11572 <$400
1929 Small Size
10 Type 1 1-973 <$200
20 Type 1 1-239 <$200
Total Issue $665,660
Out at close $50,000
Large out at close $5,780

7386 Pawnee
CLEVELAND NB, CLEVELAND
Chartered 9/04
OKLAHOMA TERRITORY {{ 0 L }}
1902 Red Seal <$VALUE
4x5 1-250 <$3500
3x10-20 1-200 <$3500
STATE ISSUES {{ 6 L 10 S }}
1902 Red Seal
4x5 1-415 <$3500
3x10-20 1-334 <$3500
1902 Date Back
4x5 1-2000 <$350
3x10-20 1-1400 <$350
1902 Plain Back
4x5 2001-7295 <$350
3x10-20 1401-4483 <$350
1929 Small Size
5 Type 1 1-936 <$175
10 Type 1 1-1012 <$175
20 Type 1 1-172 <$175
5 Type 2 1-3804 <$175
10 Type 2 1-1919 <$175
20 Type 2 1-660 <$175
Total Issue $570,900
Out in 1935 $50,000
Large out 1935 $1,585

5911 Pawnee
FNB OF CLEVELAND
Chartered 7/22/01
OKLAHOMA TERRITORY {{ 1 L }}
Brown Back <$VALUE
4x5 1-600 <$3000
3x10-20 1-540 <$3000
STATE ISSUES {{ 7 L 14 S }}
1882 Date Back
4x5 1-4400 <$500
3x10-20 1-3240 <$500
1882 Value Back
4x5 4401-7850 <$500
3x10-20 3241-5240 <$500
1902 Plain Back
3x10-20 1-5717 <$300
1929 Small Size
10 Type 1 1-1570 <$100
20 Type 1 1-390 <$100
10 Type 2 1-980 <$100
20 Type 2 1-210 <$100
Total Issue $898,850
Out in 1935 $25,000
Large out 1935 $2,000

6851 Pawnee
CLINTON NB, CLINTON
{{ UNREPORTED }}
Chartered 6/23/03
Liquidated 12/19/08
OKLAHOMA TERRITORY
1902 Red Seal <$VALUE
3x10-20 1-800 <$4000
STATE ISSUES
1902 Red Seal
3x10-20 1-112 <$4000
Total Issue $45,600
Out in 1910 $2,080

6940 Custer
FNB OF CLINTON
Chartered 8/03
OKLAHOMA TERRITORY {{ 0 L }}
1902 Red Seal <$VALUE
3x10-20 1-856 <$4000
STATE ISSUES {{ 4 L 6 S }}
1902 Date Back
3x10-20 1-1920 <$500
1902 Plain Back
3x10-20 1921-6098 <$500
1929 Small Size
10 Type 1 1-728 <$200
20 Type 1 1-180 <$200
10 Type 2 1-1156 <$200
20 Type 2 1-329 <$200
Total Issue $431,120
Out in 1935 $25,000
Large out 1935 $1,520

9985 Custer
OKLAHOMA STATE NB OF CLINTON
{{ 3 L }}
Chartered 4/11
1902 Date Back <$VALUE
3x10-20 1-1335 <$600
1902 Plain Back
3x10-20 1336-3782 <$600
Total Issue $189,100
Out in 1935 $730

7321 Coal
COALGATE NB, COALGATE
Chartered 6/28/04
Liquidated 9/12/08
INDIAN TERRITORY {{ 1 L }}
1902 Red Seal <$VALUE
3x10-20 1-2250 <$3500
STATE ISSUES {{ 0 L }}
1902 Red Seal
3x10-20 1-154 <$3500
Total Issue $120,200
Out in 1910 $15,260

5647 Coal
FNB OF COALGATE
Chartered 12/18/00
Receivership 2/27/24
INDIAN TERRITORY {{ 1 L }}
Brown Back <$VALUE
3x10-20 1-1000 <$3500
STATE ISSUES {{ 3 L }}
Brown Back
3x10-20 1-300 <$1500
1882 Date Back
3x10-20 1-2350* <$750
1882 Value Back
3x10-20 2451-3810* <$750
* 2351-2450 not marked
1902 Plain Back
3x10-20 1-1330 <$600
Total Issue $322,000
Out at close $27,300

7962 Bryan
FNB OF COLBERT
{{ UNREPORTED }}
Chartered 10/24/05
Liquidated 3/25/09
INDIAN TERRITORY
1902 Red Seal <$VALUE
3x10-20 1-245 <$5000
Total Issue $12,250
Out in 1910 $2,270

10381 Bryan
FNB OF COLBERT
{{ 1 L 2 S }}
Chartered 5/13
1902 Date Back <$VALUE
3x10-20 1-500 <$1000
1902 Plain Back
3x10-20 501-1350 <$1000
1929 Small Size
10 Type 1 1-252 <$600
20 Type 1 1-67 <$600
Total Issue $90,660
Out in 1935 $6,250
Large out 1935 $400

10280 Tulsa
COLLINSVILLE NB, COLLINSVILLE
{{ 1 L }}
Chartered 10/12
Liquidated 11/10/26
1902 Date Back <$VALUE
3x10-20 1-500 <$1000
1902 Plain Back
3x10-20 501-1056 <$1000
Total Issue $52,800
Out at close $6,250

6138 Tulsa
FNB OF COLLINSVILLE
{{ UNREPORTED }}
Chartered 2/26/02
Liquidated 2/22/09
INDIAN TERRITORY
1902 Red Seal <$VALUE
3x10-20 1-400 <$4000
STATE ISSUES
1902 Red Seal
3x10-20 1-92 <$4000
Total Issue $24,600
Out in 1910 $3,090

9965 Tulsa
FNB OF COLLINSVILLE
{{ 1 L }}
Organized 3/20/11
Receivership 1/5/27
1902 Date Back <$VALUE
3x10-20 1-560* <$1000
1902 Plain Back
3x10-20 661-1288* <$1000
* 561-660 not marked
Total Issue $64,400
Out at close $6,500

8366 Stephens
COMANCHE NB, COMANCHE
{{ UNREPORTED }}
Chartered 9/17/06
Liquidated 1/20/09
INDIAN TERRITORY
1902 Red Seal <$VALUE
3x10-20 1-187 <$4000
STATE ISSUES
1902 Date Back
3x10-20 1-16 <$4000
Total Issue $10,150
Out in 1910 $1,690

6299 Stephens
FNB OF COMANCHE
Chartered 6/12/02
Liquidated 12/16/32
INDIAN TERRITORY {{ 0 L }}
1902 Red Seal <$VALUE
3x10-20 1-550 <$4000
STATE ISSUES {{ 3 L 3 S }}
1902 Date Back
3x10-20 1-1450 <$600
1902 Plain Back
3x10-20 1451-5960 <$600
1929 Small Size
10 Type 1 1-300 <$400
20 Type 1 1-89 <$400
Total Issue $354,180
Out in 1929 $25,000
Large out at close $2,590

10689 Ottawa
FNB OF COMMERCE
{{ 6 L 4 S }}
Chartered 1/15
Liquidated 12/31/31
1902 Plain Back <$VALUE
4x5 1-5879 <$400
4x10 1-4409 <$400
1929 Small Size
5 Type 1 1-970 <$350
10 Type 1 1-465 <$350
Total Issue $350,940
Out at close $25,000
Large out at close $2,350

6647 Washita
CITY NB OF CORDELL
{{ UNREPORTED }}
Chartered 2/26/03
Liquidated 11/10/08
OKLAHOMA TERRITORY
1902 Red Seal <$VALUE
3x10-20 1-382 <$4000
Total Issue $19,100
Out in 1910 $1,950

9971 Washita
CORDELL NB, CORDELL
{{ UNREPORTED }}
Chartered 3/11
Liquidated 8/4/19
1902 Date Back <$VALUE
3x10-20 1-1410 <$1250
1902 Plain Back
3x10-20 1411-1891 <$1250
Total Issue $94,550
Out at close $20,000

9968 Washita
FARMERS NB OF CORDELL
{{ 7 L 7 S }}
Chartered 3/11
1902 Date Back <$VALUE
3x10-20 1-1400 <$400
1902 Plain Back
3x10-20 1401-5451 <$400
1929 Small Size
10 Type 1 1-858 <$250
20 Type 1 1-202 <$250
10 Type 2 1-1080 <$250
20 Type 2 1-372 <$250
Total Issue $366,510
Out in 1935 $25,000
Large out 1935 $2,000

6052 Washita
FNB OF CORDELL
{{ UNREPORTED }}
Chartered 12/6/01
Liquidated 2/5/09
OKLAHOMA TERRITORY
Brown Back <$VALUE
50-100 1-130 <$8500/$9000
STATE ISSUES
Brown Back
50-100 1-9 <$5000
Total Issue $20,850
Out in 1910 $1,450

9972 Washita
STATE NB OF CORDELL
{{ 2 L }}
Chartered 3/11
Liquidated 1/9/20
1902 Date Back <$VALUE
3x10-20 1-1370 <$750
1902 Plain Back
3x10-20 1371-2061 <$750
Total Issue $103,050
Out in 1919 $22,500

7420 Jefferson
FNB OF CORNISH
{{ UNREPORTED }}
Chartered 10/3/04
Liquidated 10/15/05
INDIAN TERRITORY
1902 Red Seal <$VALUE
3x10-20 1-143 <$5000
Total Issue $7,150
Out in 1910 $400

6879 Wagoner
FNB OF COWETA
Chartered 7/03
INDIAN TERRITORY {{ 1 L }}
1902 Red Seal <$VALUE
3x10-20 1-960 <$3500
STATE ISSUES {{ 4 L 6 S }}
1902 Red Seal
3x10-20 1-200 <$3500
1902 Date Back
3x10-20 1-2160 <$500
1902 Plain Back
3x10-20 2161-6473 <$500
1929 Small Size
10 Type 1 1-712 <$225
20 Type 1 1-192 <$225
5 Type 2 1-324 <$225
10 Type 2 1-1067 <$225
20 Type 2 1-219 <$225
Total Issue $464,080
Out in 1935 $25,000
Large out 1935 $1,295

10031 Wagoner
NB OF COMMERCE OF COWETA
{{ 1 L }}
Chartered 6/11
Liquidated 3/22/19
1902 Date Back <$VALUE
3x10-20 1-1295 <$850
1902 Plain Back
3x10-20 1296-2007 <$850
Total Issue $100,350
Out at close $25,000

12148 Logan
FNB OF COYLE
{{ 5 L 6 S }}
Chartered 3/22
1902 Plain Back <$VALUE
3x10-20 1-3009 <$400
1929 Small Size
10 Type 1 1-780 <$250
20 Type 1 1-212 <$250
10 Type 2 1-958 <$250
20 Type 2 1-218 <$250
Total Issue $236,630
Out in 1935 $25,000
Large out 1935 $960

8730 Payne
FARMERS NB OF CUSHING
{{ UNREPORTED }}
Chartered 6/07
Liquidated 1/27/10
OKLAHOMA TERRITORY
1902 Red Seal <$VALUE
3x10-20 1-185 <$4000
STATE ISSUES
1902 Date Back
3x10-20 1-60 <$1500
Total Issue $12,250
Out in 1910 $3,810

10332 Payne
FARMERS NB OF CUSHING
{{ 2 L 3 S }}
Chartered 2/13
1902 Date Back <$VALUE
4x5 1-615 <$850
3x10-20 1-494 <$850
1902 Plain Back
4x5 616-2945 <$850
3x10-20 495-1987 <$850
1929 Small Size
5 Type 1 1-502 <$400
10 Type 1 1-250 <$400
20 Type 1 1-84 <$400
5 Type 2 1-454 <$400
10 Type 2 1-306 <$400
20 Type 2 1-72 <$450
Total Issue $205,160
Out in 1935 $12,500
Large out 1935 $720

6893 Payne
FNB OF CUSHING
Chartered 7/03
OKLAHOMA TERRITORY {{ 0 L }}
1902 Red Seal <$VALUE
3x10-20 1-820 <$3500
STATE ISSUES {{ 10 L 21 S }}
1902 Red Seal
3x10-20 1-200 <$2500
1902 Date Back
3x10-20 1-2040 <$225
1902 Plain Back
3x10-20 2041-9175 <$225
1929 Small Size
10 Type 1 1-2104 <$100
20 Type 1 1-550 <$100
10 Type 2 1-6387 <$100
20 Type 2 1-1535 <$100
Total Issue $796,560
Out in 1935 $100,000
Large out 1935 $2,070

8727 Custer
FNB OF CUSTER CITY
Chartered 6/07
OKLAHOMA TERRITORY {{ 1 L }}
1902 Red Seal <$VALUE
3x10-20 1-500 <$3500
STATE ISSUES {{ 5 L 6 S }}
1902 Date Back
3x10-20 1-1480 <$450
1902 Plain Back
3x10-20 1481-5295 <$450
1929 Small Size
10 Type 1 1-728 <$300
20 Type 1 1-192 <$300
10 Type 2 1-1073 <$300
20 Type 2 1-170 <$350
Total Issue $370,600
Out in 1935 $25,000
Large out 1935 $1,820

9981 Custer
PEOPLES STATE NB OF CUSTER CITY
{{ 2 L }}
Chartered 4/11
Liquidated 4/5/20
1902 Date Back <$VALUE
3x10-20 1-1590 <$850
1902 Plain Back
3x10-20 1591-2444 <$850
Total Issue $122,200
Out at close $25,000

8668 Lincoln
FNB OF DAVENPORT
{{ UNREPORTED }}
Chartered 5/07
Liquidated 10/5/11
OKLAHOMA TERRITORY
1902 Red Seal <$VALUE
3x10-20 1-300 <$4000
STATE ISSUES
1902 Date Back
3x10-20 1-280 <$1750
Total Issue $29,000
Out at close $10,000

11654 Tillman
FNB OF DAVIDSON
{{ UNREPORTED }}
Chartered 3/20
Liquidated 3/30/26
1902 Plain Back <$VALUE
4x10 1-232 <$2000
Total Issue $9,280
Out at close $1,800

5298 Murray
FNB OF DAVIS
Chartered 4/21/00
INDIAN TERRITORY {{ 1 L }}
Brown Back <$VALUE
3x10-20 1-2460 <$3000
STATE ISSUES {{ 5 L 8 S }}
1882 Date Back
3x10-20 1-4000 <$500
1882 Value Back
3x10-20 4001-5713 <$500
1902 Plain Back
3x10-20 1-6770 <$350
1929 Small Size
10 Type 1 1-904 <$175
20 Type 1 1-252 <$175
10 Type 2 1-1309 <$200
20 Type 2 1-312 <$200
Total Issue $850,960
Out in 1935 $30,000
Large out 1935 $2,320

7442 Tillman
MERCHANTS & PLANTERS NB OF DAVIS
{{ UNREPORTED }}
Chartered 10/15/04
Liquidated 5/1/09
INDIAN TERRITORY
1902 Red Seal <$VALUE
3x10-20 1-990 <$4000
STATE ISSUES
1902 Red Seal
3x10-20 1-300 <$3000
1902 Date Back
3x10-20 1-82 <$1750
Total Issue $68,600
Out in 1910 $14,040

12104 Creek
STATE NB OF DEPEW
{{ 6 S }}
Chartered 1/22
1929 Small Size <$VALUE
5 Type 1 1-524 <$225
10 Type 1 1-252 <$225
20 Type 1 1-66 <$225
5 Type 2 1-1884 <$225
10 Type 2 1-1075 <$225
20 Type 2 1-320 <$225
Total Issue $65,330
Out in 1935 $25,000

11535 Cotton
FNB OF DEVOL
{{ 1 L }}
Organized 11/4/19
Receivership 9/17/25
1902 Plain Back <$VALUE
4x5 1-2850 <$1000
Total Issue $57,000
Out at close $9,600

8270 Washington
FNB OF DEWEY
Chartered 6/06
INDIAN TERRITORY {{ 0 L }}
1902 Red Seal <$VALUE
3x10-20 1-700 <$3500
STATE ISSUES {{ 6 L 7 S }}
1902 Date Back
3x10-20 1-2240 <$400
1902 Plain Back
3x10-20 2241-6422 <$400
1929 Small Size
10 Type 1 1-830 <$250
20 Type 1 1-206 <$250
10 Type 2 1-552 <$275
20 Type 2 1-240 <$275
Total Issue $440,940
Out in 1935 $25,000
Large out 1935 $1,420

9986 Washington
SECURITY NB OF DEWEY
{{ 3 L }}
Chartered 4/11
Liquidated 6/2/30
1902 Date Back <$VALUE
3x10-20 1-1960 <$600
1902 Plain Back
3x10-20 1961-4790 <$600
Total Issue $239,500
Out at close $1,940

8616 Stephens
CITY NB OF DUNCAN
Chartered 3/07
Liquidated 2/14/30
INDIAN TERRITORY {{ 0 L }}
1902 Red Seal <$VALUE
3x10-20 1-270 <$3500
STATE ISSUES {{ 1 L 0 S }}
1902 Date Back
3x10-20 1-960* <$1000
1902 Plain Back
3x10-20 1061-2553* <$1000
* 961-1060 not marked
1929 Small Size
10 Type 1 1-86 <$750
20 Type 1 1-4 <$750
Total Issue $146,790
Out at close $7,000
Large out at close $1,360

7289 Stephens
DUNCAN NB, DUNCAN
{{ UNREPORTED }}
Chartered 6/04
Liquidated 10/28/21
INDIAN TERRITORY
1902 Red Seal <$VALUE
4x5 1-430 <$3500
3x10-20 1-398 <$3500
STATE ISSUES
1902 Date Back
4x5 1-900 <$1250
3x10-20 1-660 <$1250
1902 Plain Back
4x5 901-1505 <$1250
3x10-20 661-1041 <$1250
Total Issue $110,650
Out in 1920 $9,700
Ch 10244 assumed circulation

5379 Stephens
FNB OF DUNCAN
Chartered 5/29/00
Liquidated 4/13/09
INDIAN TERRITORY {{ 1 L }}
Brown Back <$VALUE
3x10-20 1-1750 <$3500
STATE ISSUES {{ 0 L }}
1882 Date Back
3x10-20 1-106 <$1250
Total Issue $92,800
Out in 1910 $8,450

10244 Stephens
FNB OF DUNCAN
{{ 1 L }}
Chartered 8/12
Liquidated 9/1/25
1902 Date Back <$VALUE
4x5 1-1100 <$850
3x10-20 1-880 <$850
1902 Plain Back
4x5 1101-3100 <$850
3x10-20 881-2080 <$850
Total Issue $166,000
Out in 1935 $25,000
Large out 1935 $790
Outstanding includes Ch 7289
Ch 12812 assumed circulation

12065 Stephens
SECURITY NB OF DUNCAN
{{ 7 S }}
Chartered 12/21
1929 Small Size <$VALUE
5 Type 1 1-324 <$200
10 Type 1 1-410 <$200
20 Type 1 1-204 <$200
50 Type 1 1-8 <$400
100 Type 1 1-2 <$500
5 Type 2 1-3586 <$200
10 Type 2 1-1956 <$200
20 Type 2 1-576 <$200
Total Issue $111,410
Out in 1935 $50,000

****
6928 Bryan
CHOCTAW-CHICKASAW NB OF DURANT
{{ UNREPORTED }}
Chartered 8/18/03
Liquidated 8/17/09
2nd title: Farmers NB of Durant 9/8/05
FIRST TITLE
INDIAN TERRITORY
1902 Red Seal <$VALUE
4x5 1-385 <$3500
3x10-20 1-282 <$3500
SECOND TITLE
1902 Red Seal
3x10-20 1-700 <$3500
STATE ISSUES
1902 Red Seal
3x10-20 1-72 <$3000
Total Issue $60,400
Out in 1910 $7,665
****
13018 Bryan
DURANT NB IN DURANT
{{ 18 S }}
Chartered 12/26
1929 Small Size <$VALUE
5 Type 1 1-2256 <$85
10 Type 1 1-1392 <$85
20 Type 1 1-366 <$85
5 Type 2 1-7404 <$100
10 Type 2 1-4413 <$100
20 Type 2 1-935 <$100
Total Issue $294,970
Out in 1935 $100,000
****
5590 Bryan
DURANT NB, DURANT
Chartered 10/2/00
Liquidated 2/8/27
INDIAN TERRITORY {{ 0 L }}
Brown Back <$VALUE
3x10-20 1-2600 <$3000
STATE ISSUES {{ 12 L }}
1882 Date Back
3x10-20 1-9900 <$300
1882 Value Back
3x10-20 9901-14220 <$300
1902 Plain Back
3x10-20 1-5592 <$175
Total Issue $1,120,600
Out in 1922 $98,600
****
Farmers NB of Durant
SEE Ch 6928
Choctaw-Chickasaw NB of Durant
****
14005 Bryan
FNB IN DURANT
{{ 4 S }}
Chartered 2/34
1929 Small Size <$VALUE
5 Type 2 1-3410 <$400
10 Type 2 1-1776 <$400
20 Type 2 1-575 <$400
Total Issue $46,310
Out in 1935 $33,710
****
5129 Bryan
FNB OF DURANT
Chartered 1898
Liquidated 4/24/35
INDIAN TERRITORY {{ 4 L }}
Brown Back <$VALUE
4x5 1-2875 <$2500
3x10-20 1-3800 <$2500
STATE ISSUES {{ 16 L 18 S }}
Brown Back
4x5 1-600 <$1000
3x10-20 1-360 <$1000
1882 Date Back
4x5 1-5950* <$300
3x10-20 1-4660** <$300
1882 Value Back
4x5 6351-7923* <$300
3x10-20 4981-6682** <$300
* 5951-6350 not marked
** 4661-4980 not marked
1902 Plain Back
4x5 1-15366 <$150
3x10-20 1-11193 <$150
1929 Small Size
5 Type 1 1-4682 <$75
10 Type 1 1-2248 <$75
20 Type 1 1-528 <$85
5 Type 2 1-2236 <$100
10 Type 2 1-861 <$100
20 Type 2 1-324 <$100
Total Issue $2,002,000
Out at close $47,570
Large out at close $7,170
****
10538 Bryan
STATE NB OF DURANT
{{ 1 L }}
Chartered 5/14
Liquidated 12/28/16
1902 Date Back <$VALUE
3x10-20 1-2000 <$750
1902 Plain Back
3x10-20 2001-2050 <$750
Total Issue $102,500
Out at close $50,000
****
FNB of Dustin
SEE Ch 6804
FNB of Spokogee
****
10151 Oklahoma
CITIZENS NB OF EDMOND
{{ 4 L 6 S }}
Chartered 3/12
1902 Date Back <$VALUE
3x10-20 1-1120 <$600
1902 Plain Back
3x10-20 1121-4374 <$600
1929 Small Size
10 Type 1 1-664 <$350
20 Type 1 1-190 <$350
10 Type 2 1-642 <$350
20 Type 2 1-198 <$350
Total Issue $291,720
Out in 1935 $20,000
Large out 1935 $690
****
6156 Oklahoma
FNB OF EDMOND
Chartered 3/11/02
OKLAHOMA TERRITORY {{ 0 L }}
1902 Red Seal <$VALUE
3x10-20 1-860 <$3500
STATE ISSUES {{ 5 L 7 S }}
1902 Red Seal
3x10-20 1-200 <$3000
1902 Date Back
3x10-20 1-1750 <$500
1902 Plain Back (dated 1902)
3x10-20 1751-3330 <$500
1902 Plain Back (dated 1922)
3x10-20 1-2459 <$500
1929 Small Size
10 Type 1 1-760 <$300
20 Type 1 1-198 <$300
10 Type 2 1-1273 <$300
20 Type 2 1-294 <$300
Total Issue $430,420
Out in 1935 $25,000
Large out 1935 $1,440
****
8944 Jackson
FARMERS & MERCHANTS NB OF EL DORADO
{{ UNREPORTED }}
Chartered 11/12/07
Liquidated 12/30/08
1902 Red Seal <$VALUE
3x10-20 1-154 <$5000
Total Issue $7,700
Out in 1910 $1,750
****
8126 Jackson
FNB OF EL DORADO
{{ UNREPORTED }}
Chartered 3/7/06
Liquidated 12/1/08
OKLAHOMA TERRITORY
1902 Red Seal <$VALUE
3x10-20 1-200 <$4000
STATE ISSUES
1902 Red Seal
3x10-20 1-32 <$4000
Total Issue $11,600
Out in 1910 $1,700
****
9963 Jackson
FNB OF EL DORADO
{{ 0 L 2 S }}
Chartered 3/11
1902 Date Back <$VALUE
3x10-20 1-700 <$1250
1902 Plain Back
3x10-20 701-1841 <$1250
1929 Small Size
10 Type 1 1-286 <$500
20 Type 1 1-75 <$500
Total Issue $118,210
Out in 1935 $7,000
Large out 1935 $20
****
5985 Canadian
CITIZENS NB OF EL RENO
Chartered 10/7/01
OKLAHOMA TERRITORY {{ 1 L }}
Brown Back <$VALUE
3x10-20 1-820 <$3000
STATE ISSUES {{ 6 L U + 31 S }}
1882 Date Back
4x5 1-2100 <$500
3x10-20 1-2160 <$500
1882 Value Back
4x5 2101-5335 <$500
3x10-20 2161-4080 <$500
1902 Plain Back
4x10 1-5819 <$275
1929 Small Size
5 Type 1 1-160 <$100
10 Type 1 1-80 <$100
20 Type 1 1-462 <$100
5 Type 2 1-2764 <$100
10 Type 2 1-1650 <$100
20 Type 2 1-510 <$100
Total Issue $690,020
Out in 1935 $50,930
Large out 1935 $2,280
****
4830 Canadian
FNB OF EL RENO
Chartered 1892
OKLAHOMA TERRITORY {{ 2 L }}
Brown Back <$VALUE
4x5 1-3520 <$3000
50-100 1-490 <$7500/$8000
STATE ISSUES {{ 9 L 13 S }}
1882 Date Back
4x5 1-2237 <$450
50-100 1-260 <$2500/$3000
3x50-100 1-38 <$2500/$3000
1902 Date Back
4x5 1-1250 <$175
3x10-20 1-1000 <$175
1902 Plain Back
4x5 1251-9271 <$175
3x10-20 1001-6318 <$175
1929 Small Size
5 Type 1 1-2088 <$125
10 Type 1 1-1116 <$125
20 Type 1 1-304 <$125
5 Type 2 1-2038 <$150
10 Type 2 1-1360 <$150
20 Type 2 1-465 <$150
Total Issue $937,630
Out in 1935 $50,000
Large out 1935 $3,480
****
6164 Beckham
ELK CITY NB, ELK CITY
{{ UNREPORTED }}
Chartered 3/17/02
Receivership 5/28/04
OKLAHOMA TERRITORY
1902 Red Seal <$VALUE
3x10-20 1-203 <$5000
Total Issue $10,150
Out in 1916 $60
****
5766 Beckham
FNB OF ELK CITY
{{ UNREPORTED }}
Chartered 4/3/01
Liquidated 2/23/09
OKLAHOMA TERRITORY
Brown Back <$VALUE
3x10-20 1-1100 <$4000
STATE ISSUES
1882 Date Back
3x10-20 1-36 <$2000
Total Issue $56,800
Out in 1910 $7,910
****
9952 Beckham
FNB OF ELK CITY
{{ 6 L 11 S }}
Chartered 3/11
1902 Date Back <$VALUE
3x10-20 1-2330 <$500
1902 Plain Back
3x10-20 2331-10642 <$500
1929 Small Size
5 Type 1 1-460 <$175
10 Type 1 1-1286 <$175
20 Type 1 1-346 <$175
5 Type 2 1-4172 <$200
10 Type 2 1-2988 <$200
Total Issue $715,320
Out in 1935 $50,000
Large out 1935 $2,820
****
8231 Garfield
ENID NB, ENID
{{ 2 L }}
Chartered 5/22/06
Liquidated 8/18/08
OKLAHOMA TERRITORY
1902 Red Seal <$VALUE
4x5 1-2550 <$3500
3x10-20 1-2060 <$3500
Total Issue $154,000
Out in 1910 $26,040
****
10202 Garfield
ENID NB, ENID
{{ 6 L }}
Chartered 5/12
Liquidated 4/13/25
1902 Date Back <$VALUE
4x5 1-4350 <$350
3x10-20 1-3060 <$350
1902 Plain Back
4x5 4351-14280 <$350
3x10-20 3061-9344 <$350
Total Issue $752,800
Out at close $100,000
****
5335 Garfield
FNB OF ENID
{{ UNREPORTED }}
Chartered 5/7/00
Liquidated 3/8/09
OKLAHOMA TERRITORY
Brown Back <$VALUE
3x10-20 1-1400 <$3500
STATE ISSUES
Brown Back
3x10-20 1-200 <$2000
Total Issue $80,000
Out in 1910 $9,440
****
9586 Garfield
FNB OF ENID
{{ 14 L 22 S }}
Chartered 11/09
1902 Date Back <$VALUE
3x10-20 1-7700 <$175
1902 Plain Back
3x10-20 7701-22535 <$175
1929 Small Size
10 Type 1 1-3128 <$75
20 Type 1 1-754 <$75
10 Type 2 1-2358 <$85
20 Type 2 1-1005 <$85
Total Issue $1,448,590
Out in 1935 $100,000
Large out 1935 $6,550
****
8010 Beckham
FNB OF ERICK
{{ UNREPORTED }}
Chartered 12/15/05
Liquidated 2/24/09
OKLAHOMA TERRITORY
1902 Red Seal <$VALUE
3x10-20 1-382 <$4000
Total Issue $19,100
Out in 1910 $2,950
****
10875 Beckham
FNB OF ERICK
{{ 1 L 3 S }}
Chartered 7/16
1902 Plain Back <$VALUE
3x10-20 1-1438 <$1250
1929 Small Size
10 Type 1 1-281 <$600
20 Type 1 1-89 <$600
Total Issue $99,440
Out in 1935 $7,500
Large out 1935 $380
****
5967 McIntosh
EUFAULA NB, EUFAULA
Chartered 9/16/01
Liquidated 12/16/22
INDIAN TERRITORY {{ 1 L }}
Brown Back <$VALUE
4x5 1-250 <$3000
3x10-20 1-520 <$3000
STATE ISSUES {{ 8 L }}
1882 Date Back
4x5 1-3575 <$400
3x10-20 1-2700 <$400
1882 Value Back
4x5 3576-7275 <$400
3x10-20 2701-4660 <$400
1902 Plain Back
4x5 1-1275 <$250
4x10 1-410 <$250
3x10-20 1-502 <$250
Total Issue $476,500
Out at close $49,295
Ch 10388 assumed circulation
****
5902 McIntosh
FNB OF EUFAULA
Chartered 7/13/01
Liquidated 5/1/24
INDIAN TERRITORY {{ 5 L }}
Brown Back <$VALUE
4x5 1-2240 <$2500
3x10-20 1-1604 <$2500
STATE ISSUES {{ 12 L }}
Brown Back
4x5 1-415 <$1250
3x10-20 1-334 <$1250
1882 Date Back
4x5 1-4200 <$350
3x10-20 1-2960 <$350
1882 Value Back
4x5 4201-7685 <$350
3x10-20 2961-4855 <$350
1902 Plain Back
3x10-20 1-2182 <$150
Total Issue $655,550
Out at close $50,000
****
10388 McIntosh
STATE NB OF EUFAULA
{{ 5 L 10 S }}
Chartered 5/13
1902 Date Back <$VALUE
3x10-20 1-1280 <$300
1902 Plain Back
3x10-20 1281-7674 <$300
1929 Small Size
10 Type 1 1-1490 <$150
20 Type 1 1-396 <$150
10 Type 2 1-2364 <$175
20 Type 2 1-387 <$175
Total Issue $552,000
Out in 1935 $50,000
Large out 1935 $3,350
Outstanding includes Ch 5967
****
8202 Osage
FAIRFAX NB, FAIRFAX
Chartered 5/06
OKLAHOMA TERRITORY {{ 2 L }}
1902 Red Seal <$VALUE
3x10-20 1-188 <$3000
STATE ISSUES {{ 5 L }}
1902 Red Seal
3x10-20 1-400 <$2500
1902 Date Back
3x10-20 1-1910 <$500
1902 Plain Back
3x10-20 1911-6343 <$500
Total Issue $346,550
Out in 1935 $1,440
****
7972 Osage
FNB OF FAIRFAX
Organized 10/27/05
Receivership 4/12/32
OKLAHOMA TERRITORY {{ 0 L }}
1902 Red Seal <$VALUE
3x10-20 1-187 <$3000
STATE ISSUES {{ 2 L 2 S }}
1902 Red Seal
3x10-20 1-100 <$3000
1902 Date Back
3x10-20 1-1320* <$750
1902 Plain Back
3x10-20 1441-3327* <$750
* 1321-1440 not marked
1929 Small Size
10 Type 1 1-274 <$500
20 Type 1 1-69 <$500
Total Issue $205,420
Out at close $11,960
Large out at close $1,260
****
9767 Major
FARMERS & MERCHANTS NB OF FAIRVIEW
{{ 1 L 2 S }}
Chartered 6/10
1902 Date Back <$VALUE
4x5 1-550 <$1000
4x10 1-550 <$1000
1902 Plain Back
4x5 551-1579 <$1000
4x10 551-1155 <$1000
1929 Small Size
5 Type 1 1-436 <$500
10 Type 1 1-236 <$500
Total Issue $105,020
Out in 1935 $6,250
Large out 1935 $230
****
7117 Major
FNB OF FAIRVIEW
{{ UNREPORTED }}
Chartered 1/04
Liquidated 2/27/05
OKLAHOMA TERRITORY
1902 Red Seal <$VALUE
3x10-20 1-148 <$5000
Total Issue $7,400
Out in 1910 $570
****
10356 Osage
FNB OF FORAKER
{{ 3 L }}
Chartered 4/13
Liquidated 1/19/29
1902 Date Back <$VALUE
4x5 1-410 <$650
4x10 1-420 <$650
1902 Plain Back
4x5 411-1601 <$650
4x10 421-1169 <$650
Total Issue $78,780
Out at close $5,650
****
10561 Muskogee
CITIZENS NB OF FORT GIBSON
{{ 3 L }}
Chartered 6/14
Liquidated 3/31/30
1902 Plain Back <$VALUE
4x10 1-4785 <$650
Total Issue $191,400
Out at close $1,320
****
8079 Muskogee
FARMERS NB OF FORT GIBSON
Chartered 2/06
2nd title: FNB in Fort Gibson 3/19/29
FIRST TITLE
INDIAN TERRITORY {{ 1 L }}
1902 Red Seal <$VALUE
3x10-20 1-500 <$4000
STATE ISSUES {{ 4 L }}
1902 Red Seal
3x10-20 1-300 <$3500
1902 Date Back
3x10-20 1-2110 <$600
1902 Plain Back
3x10-20 2111-8814 <$600
SECOND TITLE {{ 6 S }}
1929 Small Size
10 Type 1 1-734 <$300
20 Type 1 1-194 <$300
10 Type 2 1-910 <$300
20 Type 2 1-230 <$300
Total Issue $561,720
Out in 1935 $25,000
Large out 1935 $1,870
****
FNB in Fort Gibson
SEE Ch 8079
Farmers NB of Fort Gibson
****
6539 Muskogee
FNB OF FORT GIBSON
{{ UNREPORTED }}
Chartered 12/18/02
Liquidated 3/19/09
INDIAN TERRITORY
1902 Red Seal <$VALUE
3x10-20 1-400 <$4000
STATE ISSUES
1902 Red Seal
3x10-20 1 <$5000
Total Issue $20,050
Out in 1910 $2,375
****

CONDITION affects Value. The Values shown are for notes in FINE condition.

****
5753 Comanche
FNB OF FORT SILL
Chartered 3/23/01
2nd title: City NB of Lawton 8/03/01
FIRST TITLE
OKLAHOMA TERRITORY {{ 2 L }}
Brown Back <$VALUE
3x10-20 1-500 <$3000
SECOND TITLE {{ 2 L }}
Brown Back
3x10-20 1-1600 <$3000
STATE ISSUES {{ 10 L 11 S }}
Brown Back
3x10-20 1-400 <$1250
1882 Date Back
3x10-20 1-3800 <$350
1882 Value Back
3x10-20 3801-6242 <$350
1902 Plain Back
3x10-20 1-6107 <$225
1929 Small Size
5 Type 1 1-260 <$175
10 Type 1 1-1324 <$175
20 Type 1 1-444 <$175
5 Type 2 1-6054 <$175
10 Type 2 1-1728 <$175
Total Issue $930,520
Out in 1935 $50,000
Large out 1935 $2,810
****
8078 Choctaw
FNB OF FORT TOWSON
Chartered 2/06
Liquidated 12/31/15
INDIAN TERRITORY {{ 1 L }}
1902 Red Seal <$VALUE
3x10-20 1-187 <$3500
STATE ISSUES {{ 0 L }}
1902 Red Seal
3x10-20 1-100 <$3000
1902 Date Back
3x10-20 1-508 <$1250
Total Issue $39,750
Out in 1916 $5,350
****
6736 Washita
FNB OF FOSS
{{ UNREPORTED }}
Chartered 4/21/03
Liquidated 9/10/08
OKLAHOMA TERRITORY
1902 Red Seal <$VALUE
3x10-20 1-348 <$5000
Total Issue $17,400
Out in 1910 $2,330
****
7185 Pontotoc
FNB OF FRANCIS
{{ UNREPORTED }}
Chartered 3/26/04
Liquidated 10/15/05
INDIAN TERRITORY
1902 Red Seal <$VALUE
3x10-20 1-179 <$5000
Total Issue $8,950
Out in 1910 $490
****
10454 Pontotoc
FRANCIS NB, FRANCIS
{{ UNREPORTED }}
Chartered 10/15/13
Liquidated 4/30/25
1902 Date Back <$VALUE
3x10-20 1-500 <$1500
1902 Plain Back
3x10-20 501-1030 <$1500
Total Issue $51,500
Out at close $6,250
****
8206 Tillman
CITY NB OF FREDERICK
{{ UNREPORTED }}
Chartered 5/4/06
Liquidated 6/15/09
OKLAHOMA TERRITORY
1902 Red Seal <$VALUE
3x10-20 1-187 <$4000
STATE ISSUES
1902 Red Seal
3x10-20 1-72 <$3500
Total Issue $12,950
Out in 1910 $2,830
****

****
13760 Tillman
FNB IN FREDERICK
{{ 3 S }}
Chartered 8/33
1929 Small Size <$VALUE
5 Type 2 1-2220 <$400
10 Type 2 1-1044 <$400
20 Type 2 1-252 <$400
Total Issue $26,580
Out in 1935 $25,000
Outstanding includes Ch 8140
****
8140 Tillman
FNB OF FREDERICK
Chartered 3/7/06 as Frederick NB, under which there was no issue. Issuing title adopted 3/22/06.
Liquidated 9/15/33
OKLAHOMA TERRITORY {{ 0 L }}
1902 Red Seal <$VALUE
4x5 1-565 <$3500
3x10-20 1-461 <$3500
STATE ISSUES {{ 4 L 6 S }}
1902 Date Back
4x5 1-2675 <$600
3x10-20 1-2060 <$600
1902 Plain Back
4x5 2676-7125 <$600
3x10-20 2061-4679 <$600
1929 Small Size
5 Type 1 1-952 <$300
10 Type 1 1-467 <$300
20 Type 1 1-140 <$300
Total Issue $484,180
Out at close $25,000
Large out 1935 $1,320
Ch 13760 assumed circulation
****
10095 Tillman
NB OF COMMERCE OF FREDERICK
{{ 4 L }}
Chartered 10/11
Liquidated 4/26/30
1902 Date Back <$VALUE
4x5 1-3350 <$500
3x10-20 1-2550 <$500
1902 Plain Back
4x5 3351-9060 <$500
3x10-20 2551-6095 <$500
Total Issue $485,950
Out at close $3,540
****
8543 Ellis
FNB OF GAGE
{{ UNREPORTED }}
Chartered 2/13/07
Liquidated 10/2/08
OKLAHOMA TERRITORY
1902 Red Seal <$VALUE
3x10-20 1-178 <$5000
Total Issue $8,900
Out in 1910 $1,420
****
6163 Blaine
FNB OF GEARY
Chartered 3/17/02
Liquidated 8/19/09
OKLAHOMA TERRITORY {{ 1 L }}
1902 Red Seal <$VALUE
3x10-20 1-660 <$3500
STATE ISSUES {{ 0 L }}
1902 Date Back
3x10-20 1-52 <$1500
Total Issue $35,600
Out in 1910 $4,800
****
10020 Blaine
FNB OF GEARY
{{ 1 L 3 S }}
Chartered 5/11
1902 Date Back <$VALUE
3x10-20 1-600 <$1000
1902 Plain Bak
3x10-20 601-1453 <$1000
1929 Small Size
10 Type 1 1-210 <$500
20 Type 1 1-56 <$500
Total Issue $91,970
Out in 1935 $6,250
Large out 1935 $540
****
10389 Kiowa
FNB OF GOTEBO
{{ 3 L }}
Chartered 5/13
Liquidated 12/27/28
1902 Date Back <$VALUE
3x10-20 1-960 <$650
1902 Plain Back
3x10-20 961-4124 <$650
Total Issue $206,200
Out in 1927 $19,500
****

****
10006 Tillman
FNB OF GRANDFIELD
{{ UNREPORTED }}
Organized 4/24/11
Receivership 7/21/23
1902 Date Back <$VALUE
3x10-20 1-620 <$1500
1902 Plain Back
3x10-20 621-1016 <$1500
Total Issue $50,800
Out at close $5,650
****
8342 Greer
FNB OF GRANITE
{{ UNREPORTED }}
Chartered 8/28/06
Liquidated 1/11/09
OKLAHOMA TERRITORY
1902 Red Seal <$VALUE
4x5 1-145 <$5000
3x10-20 1-145 <$5000
Total Issue $10,150
Out in 1910 $1,905
****
10119 Delaware
FNB OF GROVE
{{ 3 L }}
Chartered 12/11
Liquidated 1/1/33
1902 Date Back <$VALUE
4x5 1-750 <$650
4x10 1-750 <$650
1902 Plain Back
4x5 751-3094 <$650
4x10 751-2210 <$650
Total Issue $150,280
Out at close $7,800
****
4705 Logan
CAPITOL NB OF GUTHRIE
{{ 3 L }}
Organized 3/9/92
Receivership 4/4/04
OKLAHOMA TERRITORY
Brown Back <$VALUE
3x10-20 1-3591 <$3000
Total Issue $179,550
Out in 1916 $1,930
****
FNB of Guthrie
SEE Ch 4348
Guthrie NB, Guthrie
****
4348 Logan
GUTHRIE NB, GUTHRIE
Chartered 1890
2nd title: FNB of Guthrie 12/9/12
FIRST TITLE
OKLAHOMA TERRITORY {{ 4 L }}
Brown Back <$VALUE
4x5 1-4000 <$2500
3x10-20 1-1000 <$2500
50-100 1-1688 <$7500/$8500
STATE ISSUES {{ 5 L }}
1882 Date Back
4x5 1-1745 <$500
3x10-20 1-792 <$500
1902 Date Back
4x5 1-3336 <$250
4x10 1-2842 <$250
SECOND TITLE {{ 14 L 20 S }}
1902 Date Back
4x5 1-2750 <$150
3x10-20 1-2600 <$150
1902 Plain Back
4x5 2751-18185 <$150
3x10-20 2601-13172 <$150
1929 Small Size
5 Type 1 1-3802 <$50
10 Type 1 1-2250 <$50
20 Type 1 1-558 <$60
5 Type 2 1-4780 <$75
10 Type 2 1-2447 <$75
20 Type 2 1-698 <$75
Total Issue $2,038,750
Out in 1935 $97,950
Large out 1935 $6,735
****
4383 Logan
NB OF GUTHRIE
{{ UNREPORTED }}
Organized 7/31/90
Receivership 6/22/92
OKLAHOMA TERRITORY
Brown Back <$VALUE
3x10-20 1-515 <$4000
Total Issue $25,750
Out in 1916 $70
****

****
7299 Logan
NB OF COMMERCE OF GUTHRIE
Organized 7/1/04
Liquidated 2/20/12
OKLAHOMA TERRITORY {{ 1 L }}
1902 Red Seal <$VALUE
50-100 1-1266 <$8500/$9000
STATE ISSUES {{ 0 L }}
1902 Red Seal
50-100 1-300 <$6000/$6500
1902 Date Back
3x10-20 1-135 <$850
50-100 1-413 <$1000/$1250
Total Issue $303,600
Out in 1912 $71,420
****
9964 Texas
CITY NB OF GUYMON
{{ 1 L 0 S }}
Chartered 3/11
1902 Date Back <$VALUE
3x10-20 1-600 <$1000
1902 Plain Back
3x10-20 601-1385 <$1000
1929 Small Size
10 Type 1 1-210 <$750
20 Type 1 1-50 <$750
Total Issue $87,850
Out in 1935 $6,500
Large out 1935 $350
****
8138 Texas
FNB OF GUYMON
Chartered 3/06
OKLAHOMA TERRITORY {{ 0 L }}
1902 Red Seal <$VALUE
4x5 1-655 <$3500
3x10-20 1-525 <$3500
STATE ISSUES {{ 7 L 7 S }}
1902 Date Back
4x5 1-1825 <$350
3x10-20 1-1240 <$350
1902 Plain Back
4x5 1826-5962 <$350
3x10-20 1241-3599 <$350
1929 Small Size
5 Type 1 1-1016 <$225
10 Type 1 1-506 <$225
20 Type 1 1-144 <$225
5 Type 2 1-714 <$250
10 Type 2 1-435 <$250
20 Type 2 1-175 <$250
Total Issue $428,080
Out in 1935 $25,000
Large out 1935 $1,580
****
9980 Oklahoma
FNB OF HARRAH
{{ 1 L 2 S }}
Chartered 4/11
1902 Date Back <$VALUE
3x10-20 1-600 <$1250
1902 Plain Back
3x10-20 601-1505 <$1250
1929 Small Size
10 Type 1 1-252 <$600
20 Type 1 1-74 <$600
Total Issue $99,250
Out in 1935 $6,250
Large out 1935 $270
****
6753 Kiowa
FNB OF HARRISON
{{ UNREPORTED }}
Chartered 4/29/03
Liquidated 11/14/03
OKLAHOMA TERRITORY
1902 Red Seal <$VALUE
3x10-20 1-42 <$5000
Total Issue $6,300
Out in 1910 $650
****
7050 Pittsburg
FNB OF HARTSHORNE
Chartered 12/03
Liquidated 10/6/26
INDIAN TERRITORY {{ 2 L }}
1902 Red Seal <$VALUE
4x5 1-730 <$3000
3x10-20 1-584 <$3000
STATE ISSUES {{ 8 L }}
1902 Red Seal
4x5 1-150 <$2500
3x10-20 1-180 <$2500
1902 Date Back
4x5 1-2950 <$300
3x10-20 1-2020 <$300
1902 Plain Back
4x5 2951-10460 <$300
3x10-20 2021-6780 <$300
Total Issue $604,000
Out at close $49,995
****

****
11064 Pittsburg
HARTSHORNE NB, HARSTHORNE
{{ 3 L }}
Chartered 8/17
Liquidated 6/22/21
1902 Plain Back <$VALUE
4x5 1-1210 <$750
3x10-20 1-848 <$750
Total Issue $66,600
Out at close $25,000
****
7822 Muskogee
FNB OF HASKELL
Chartered 7/05
INDIAN TERRITORY {{ 1 L }}
1902 Red Seal <$VALUE
3x10-20 1-800 <$3000
STATE ISSUES {{ 6 L 7 S }}
1902 Red Seal
3x10-20 1-300 <$2500
1902 Date Back
3x10-20 1-2070 <$400
1902 Plain Back
3x10-20 2071-9665 <$400
1929 Small Size
10 Type 1 1-732 <$225
20 Type 1 1-220 <$225
10 Type 2 1-1059 <$250
20 Type 2 1-290 <$250
Total Issue $624,960
Out in 1935 $25,000
Large out 1935 $1,710
****
10160 Muskogee
HASKELL NB, HASKELL
{{ 3 L }}
Chartered 3/12
Liquidated 1/31/28
1902 Date Back <$VALUE
3x10-20 1-1440* <$650
1902 Plain Back
3x10-20 1541-5519* <$650
* 1441-1540 not marked
Total Issue $275,950
Out at close $25,000
****
FNB in Hastings
SEE Ch 10094
NB of Hastings
****
8209 Jefferson
FNB OF HASTINGS
{{ UNREPORTED }}
Chartered 5/7/06
Liquidated 2/27/09
OKLAHOMA TERRITORY
1902 Red Seal <$VALUE
3x10-20 1-200 <$5000
STATE ISSUES
1902 Date Back
3x10-20 1-27 <$2000
Total Issue $11,350
Out in 1910 $1,820
****
8210 Jefferson
NB OF HASTINGS
{{ UNREPORTED }}
Chartered 5/7/06
Liquidated 10/1/08
OKLAHOMA TERRITORY
1902 Red Seal <$VALUE
3x10-20 1-700 <$5000
STATE ISSUES
1902 Red Seal
3x10-20 1-52 <$3500
Total Issue $37,600
Out in 1910 $6,050
****
10094 Jefferson
NB OF HASTINGS
Organized 10/11/11
Liquidated 8/17/23
2nd title:FNB in Hastings 10/30/22
FIRST TITLE {{ 2 L }}
1902 Date Back <$VALUE
4x10 1-1663* <$1000
1902 Plain Back
4x10 1789-4588* <$1000
* 1664-1789 not marked
SECOND TITLE {{ 0 L }}
1902 Plain Back
3x10-20 1-222 <$1250
Total Issue $194,620
Out in 1935 $1,300
Ch 12150 assumed circulation
****

****
11018 Carter
FNB OF HEALDTON
{{ UNREPORTED }}
Chartered 6/17
Liquidated 10/10/31
1902 Plain Back <$VALUE
3x10-20 1-681 <$1500
Total Issue $34,050
Out at close $310
****
9888 Le Flore
FNB OF HEAVENER
{{ 2 L 2 S }}
Chartered 11/10
1902 Date Back <$VALUE
3x10-20 1-700 <$600
1902 Plain Back
3x10-20 701-1602 <$600
1929 Small Size
10 Type 1 1-241 <$400
20 Type 1 1-57 <$400
Total Issue $101,400
Out in 1935 $6,250
Large out 1935 $100
****
10239 Le Flore
STATE NB OF HEAVENER
{{ 1 L 2 S }}
Chartered 8/12
1902 Date Back <$VALUE
3x10-20 1-460* <$850
1902 Plain Back
3x10-20 561-1436* <$850
* 461-560 not marked
1929 Small Size
10 Type 1 1-243 <$600
20 Type 1 1-69 <$600
Total Issue $94,660
Out in 1935 $6,500
Large out 1935 $330
****
8349 Alfalfa
FNB OF HELENA
{{ 1 L }}
Chartered 8/31/06
Liquidated 8/1/07
OKLAHOMA TERRITORY
1902 Red Seal <$VALUE
4x10 1-156 <$5000
Total Issue $6,240
Out in 1910 $930
****
12081 Alfalfa
HELENA NB, HELENA
{{ 3 S }}
Chartered 12/21
1929 Small Size <$VALUE
5 Type 1 1-368 <$400
10 Type 1 1-180 <$400
20 Type 1 1-84 <$400
5 Type 2 1-1408 <$425
10 Type 2 1-900 <$425
20 Type 2 1-264 <$425
Total Issue $53,240
Out in 1935 $25,000
****
10209 Kingfisher
FARMERS & MERCHANTS NB OF HENNESSEY
{{ 4 L U + 11 S }}
Chartered 6/12
1902 Date Back <$VALUE
4x5 1-1075 <$600
3x10-20 1-860 <$600
1902 Plain Back
4x5 1076-3470 <$600
3x10-20 861-2270 <$600
1929 Small Size
5 Type 1 1-420 <$150
10 Type 1 1-306 <$150
20 Type 1 1-50 <$150
5 Type 2 1-1070 <$175
10 Type 2 1-558 <$175
20 Type 2 1-181 <$175
Total Issue $234,410
Out in 1935 $18,100
Large out 1935 $830
****

<$VALUEs are for notes in FINE condition. Value changes by approximately 25% for a change of one full grade.

****
5473 Kingfisher
FNB OF HENNESSEY
Chartered 6/30/00
OKLAHOMA TERRITORY {{ 0 L }}
Brown Back <$VALUE
3x10-20 1-1650 <$3500
STATE ISSUES {{ 4 L 7 S }}
1882 Date Back
3x10-20 1-1650 <$650
1882 Value Back
3x10-20 1651-2394 <$650
1902 Plain Back
3x10-20 1-2668 <$500
1929 Small Size
10 Type 1 1-646 <$225
20 Type 1 1-178 <$225
10 Type 2 1-914 <$225
20 Type 2 1-207 <$225
Total Issue $409,000
Out in 1935 $25,000
Large out 1935 $1,510
****
6111 Kingfisher
HENNESSEY NB, HENNESSEY
{{ UNREPORTED }}
Chartered 1/30/02
Liquidated 12/19/04
OKLAHOMA TERRITORY
1902 Red Seal <$VALUE
3x10-20 1-843 <$4000
Total Issue $42,150
Out in 1910 $1,500
****
6867 Okmulgee
FNB OF HENRYETTA
Organized 6/29/03
Receivership 7/31/23
INDIAN TERRITORY {{ 1 L }}
1902 Red Seal <$VALUE
3x10-20 1-955 <$4000
STATE ISSUES {{ 4 L }}
1902 Red Seal
3x10-20 1-200 <$3000
1902 Date Back
3x10-20 1-2180 <$600
1902 Plain Back
3x10-20 2181-4216 <$600
Total Issue $268,550
Out at close $24,600
****
10349 Okmulgee
MINERS NB OF HENRYETTA
{{ UNREPORTED }}
Organized 2/20/13
Receivership 12/21/23
1902 Date Back <$VALUE
3x10-20 1-1300 <$1250
1902 Plain Back
3x10-20 1301-3740 <$1250
Total Issue $187,000
Out at close $25,000
****
6267 Kiowa
CITY NB OF HOBART
Chartered 5/21/02
Liquidated 9/1/08
OKLAHOMA TERRITORY {{ 1 L }}
1902 Red Seal <$VALUE
3x10-20 1-400 <$4000
STATE ISSUES {{ 0 L }}
1902 Red Seal
3x10-20 1-374 <$3000
Total Issue $38,700
Out in 1910 $6,130
****
10288 Kiowa
CITY NB OF HOBART
{{ 2 L }}
Chartered 11/12
Liquidated 4/1/19
1902 Date Back <$VALUE
3x10-20 1-600 <$750
1902 Plain Back
3x10-20 601-1198 <$750
Total Issue $59,900
Out in 1918 $22,500
****
6358 Kiowa
FARMERS & MERCHANTS NB OF HOBART
Chartered 7/02
OKLAHOMA TERRITORY {{ 0 L }}
1902 Red Seal <$VALUE
3x10-20 1-770 <$4000
STATE ISSUES {{ 1 L }}
1902 Date Back
3x10-20 1-1400* <$850
1902 Plain Back
3x10-20 1561-2328* <$850
* 1401-1560 not marked
Total Issue $154,900
Out in 1935 $590
****

****
5954 Kiowa
FNB OF HOBART
Chartered 8/30/01
Receivership 2/20/19
OKLAHOMA TERRITORY {{ 0 L }}
Brown Back <$VALUE
4x5 1-650 <$3500
3x10-20 1-640 <$3500
STATE ISSUES {{ 2 L }}
Brown Back
3x10-20 1-300 <$1250
1882 Date Back
4x5 1-1875 <$850
3x10-20 1-1410 <$850
1882 Value Back
4x5 1876-2555 <$850
3x10-20 1411-1813 <$850
Total Issue $201,750
Out at close $25,000
****
5915 Kiowa
HOBART NB, HOBART
{{ UNREPORTED }}
Chartered 7/25/01
Liquidated 3/19/09
OKLAHOMA TERRITORY
Brown Back <$VALUE
50-100 1-140 <$8500/$9000
STATE ISSUES
Brown Back
50-100 1-140 <$4000/$4500
1882 Date Back
50-100 1-15 <$3500/$4000
Total Issue $44,250
Out in 1910 $10,700
****
7619 Hughes
AMERICAN NB OF HOLDENVILLE
{{ UNREPORTED }}
Chartered 2/05
Liquidated 9/15/20
INDIAN TERRITORY
1902 Red Seal <$VALUE
3x10-20 1-300 <$4000
STATE ISSUES
1902 Date Back
3x10-20 1-954 <$1500
Total Issue $62,700
Out at close $6,500
****
5270 Hughes
FNB OF HOLDENVILLE
Chartered 3/29/00
INDIAN TERRITORY {{ 0 L }}
Brown Back <$VALUE
3x10-20 1-920 <$3500
STATE ISSUES {{ 6 L 11 S }}
Brown Back
3x10-20 1-360 <$1500
1882 Date Back
3x10-20 1-2810 <$600
1882 Value Back
3x10-20 2811-3776 <$600
1902 Plain Back
3x10-20 1-5338 <$400
1929 Small Size
10 Type 1 1-1240 <$150
20 Type 1 1-306 <$150
10 Type 2 1-2354 <$175
20 Type 2 1-540 <$175
Total Issue $665,160
Out in 1935 $62,500
Large out 1935 $3,080
****
5735 Hughes
NB OF HOLDENVILLE
{{ 1 L }}
Chartered 3/7/01
Receivership 3/23/04
INDIAN TERRITORY
Brown Back <$VALUE
3x10-20 1-1142 <$3500
Total Issue $57,100
Out in 1916 $280
****
6540 Hughes
NB OF COMMERCE, HOLDENVILLE
{{ UNREPORTED }}
Chartered 12/18/02
Liquidated 1/20/09
INDIAN TERRITORY
1902 Red Seal <$VALUE
3x10-20 1-395 <$4000
Total Issue $19,750
Out in 1910 $2,200
****

****
10013 Hughes
STATE NB OF HOLDENVILLE
{{ UNREPORTED }}
Chartered 5/11
Liquidated 12/31/14
1902 Date Back <$VALUE
3x10-20 1-827 <$1500
Total Issue $41,350
Out in 1915 $6,500
****
City NB of Hollis
SEE Ch 8825
Groves NB of Hollis
****
FNB in Hollis
SEE Ch 8825
Groves NB of Hollis
****
8061 Harmon
FNB OF HOLLIS
Chartered 1/23/06
Liquidated 9/27/09
OKLAHOMA TERRITORY {{ 1 L }}
1902 Red Seal <$VALUE
4x5 1-250 <$4000
3x10-20 1-200 <$4000
STATE ISSUES {{ 0 L }}
1902 Red Seal
3x10-20 1-200 <$3500
1902 Date Back
4x5 1-200 <$2000
3x10-20 1-2 <$2000
Total Issue $29,100
Out in 1910 $7,190
****
8825 Harmon
GROVES NB OF HOLLIS
Chartered 8/07
Liquidated 10/26/29
2nd title:City NB of Hollis 6/17/12
3rd title:FNB in Hollis 1/31/21
FIRST TITLE
OKLAHOMA TERRITORY {{ 0 L }}
1902 Red Seal <$VALUE
4x5 1-150 <$4000
3x10-20 1-180 <$4000
STATE ISSUES {{ 0 L }}
1902 Date Back
4x5 1-255 <$1500
3x10-20 1-194 <$1500
SECOND TITLE {{ 0 L }}
1902 Date Back
3x10-20 1-360* <$1000
1902 Plain Back
3x10-20 481-770* <$1000
* 361-480 not marked
THIRD TITLE {{ 3 L }}
1902 Plain Back
3x10-20 1-905 <$650
Total Issue $110,550
Out at close $6,810
****
8056 Harmon
HOLLIS NB, HOLLIS
{{ UNREPORTED }}
Chartered 1/20/06
Liquidated 1/16/08
OKLAHOMA TERRITORY
1902 Red Seal <$VALUE
3x10-20 1-199 <$5000
Total Issue $9,950
Out in 1910 $1,050
****
10240 Harmon
NB OF COMMERCE OF HOLLIS
{{ 3 L 2 S }}
Chartered 8/12
Liquidated 3/21/35
1902 Date Back <$VALUE
4x10 1-750* <$600
1902 Plain Back
4x10 851-2406* <$600
* 751-850 not marked
1929 Small Size
10 Type 1 1-718* <$500
5 Type 2 1-1168 <$500
* 223-526 not issued
Total Issue $126,920
Out at close $7,500
Large out at close $330
****
10249 Harmon
STATE NB OF HOLLIS
{{ UNREPORTED }}
Chartered 8/12
Liquidated 1/4/16
1902 Date Back <$VALUE
3x10-20 1-379 <$1500
Total Issue $18,950
Out in 1916 $4,240
****

****
7927 Osage
FNB OF HOMINY
Chartered 9/05
Liquidated 5/2/35
OKLAHOMA TERRITORY {{ 0 L }}
1902 Red Seal <$VALUE
3x10-20 1-256 <$4000
STATE ISSUES {{ 6 L 7 S }}
1902 Red Seal
3x10-20 1-550 <$3000
1902 Date Back
3x10-20 1-1900 <$450
1902 Plain Back
3x10-20 1901-6582 <$450
1929 Small Size
10 Type 1 1-746 <$200
20 Type 1 1-202 <$200
10 Type 2 1-1181 <$200
20 Type 2 1-278 <$200
Total Issue $455,770
Out in 1935 $25,000
Large out 1935 $1,590
****
10002 Osage
NB OF COMMERCE OF HOMINY
{{ 3 L 8 S }}
Chartered 4/11
1902 Date Back <$VALUE
3x10-20 1-1775 <$500
1902 Plain Back
3x10-20 1776-6589 <$500
1929 Small Size
10 Type 1 1-852 <$175
20 Type 1 1-224 <$175
10 Type 2 1-1053 <$175
20 Type 2 1-190 <$175
Total Issue $421,780
Out in 1935 $25,000
Large out 1935 $1,460
****
6130 Choctaw
FNB OF HUGO
Chartered 2/18/02
Liquidated 9/3/23
INDIAN TERRITORY {{ 0 L }}
1902 Red Seal <$VALUE
3x10-20 1-1840 <$3500
STATE ISSUES {{ 5 L }}
1902 Date Back
3x10-20 1-6100 <$450
1902 Plain Back (dated 1902)
3x10-20 6101-8523 <$450
1902 Plain Back (dated 1922)
4x5 1-1295 <$450
3x10-20 1-766 <$450
Total Issue $582,350
Out at close $60,000
****
7747 Choctaw
HUGO NB, HUGO
Organized 4/11/05
Receivership 5/12/25
INDIAN TERRITORY {{ 1 L }}
1902 Red Seal <$VALUE
3x10-20 1-1280 <$3500
STATE ISSUES {{ 4 L }}
1902 Date Back
3x10-20 1-4050 <$500
1902 Plain Back
3x10-20 4051-5195 <$500
Total Issue $323,750
Out at close $24,200
****
12801 Choctaw
NB OF COMMERCE AT HUGO
{{ 2 S }}
Chartered 8/25
1929 Small Size <$VALUE
5 Type 2 1-1640 <$500
10 Type 2 1-775 <$500
20 Type 2 1-240 <$500
50 Type 2 1-90 <$600
Total Issue $25,250
Out in 1935 $25,000
****
10442 Caddo
FARMERS NB OF HYDRO
{{ 1 L }}
Chartered 9/13
Liquidated 7/17/16
1902 Date Back <$VALUE
3x10-20 1-591 <$1250
Total Issue $29,550
Out in 1916 $10,350
****
9944 Caddo
FNB OF HYDRO
{{ 1 L 3 S }}
Chartered 3/11
1902 Date Back <$VALUE
3x10-20 1-675 <$1250
1902 Plain Back
3x10-20 676-1470 <$1250

1929 Small Size
10 Type 1 1-227 <$400
20 Type 1 1-65 <$400
Total Issue $94,920
Out in 1935 $6,250
Large out 1935 $170
****
8486 McCurtain
FNB OF IDABEL
Organized 12/10/06
Receivership 2/18/25
INDIAN TERRITORY {{ 0 L }}
1902 Red Seal <$VALUE
4x10 1-250 <$4000
STATE ISSUES {{ 1 L }}
1902 Red Seal
4x10 1-315 <$3500
1902 Date Back
4x10 1-2250 <$1500
1902 Plain Back
4x10 2251-3279 <$1500
Total Issue $153,760
Out in 1922 $12,500
****
11913 McCurtain
IDABEL NB, IDABEL
{{ 10 S }}
Chartered 1/21
1929 Small Size <$VALUE
5 Type 1 1-420 <$350
10 Type 1 1-420 <$350
20 Type 1 1-212 <$350
5 Type 2 1-4068 <$350
10 Type 2 1-2148 <$350
20 Type 2 1-528 <$350
Total Issue $115,620
Out in 1935 $50,000
****
10075 Kay
FARMERS NB OF KAW CITY
Chartered 9/11
2nd title:FNB in Kaw City 7/17/20
FIRST TITLE {{ 1 L }}
1902 Date Back <$VALUE
3x10-20 1-1260 <$1000
1902 Plain Back
3x10-20 1261-2380 <$1000
SECOND TITLE {{ 3 L 6 S }}
1902 Plain Back
3x10-20 1-3357 <$600
1929 Small Size
10 Type 1 1-736 <$250
20 Type 1 1-214 <$250
10 Type 2 1-1073 <$250
20 Type 2 1-264 <$250
Total Issue $372,700
Out in 1935 $25,000
Large out 1935 $1,230
****
FNB in Kaw City
SEE Ch 10075
Farmers NB of Kaw City
****
8577 Kay
FNB OF KAW CITY
{{ UNREPORTED }}
Chartered 3/4/07
Liquidated 2/3/09
OKLAHOMA TERRITORY
1902 Red Seal <$VALUE
3x10-20 1-280 <$5000
Total Issue $14,000
Out in 1910 $4,380
****
10402 Kay
NB OF KAW CITY
{{ 3 L 3 S }}
Chartered 6/13
Liquidated 3/12/32
1902 Date Back <$VALUE
3x10-20 1-620* <$600
1902 Plain Back
3x10-20 701-2261* <$600
* 621-700 not marked
1929 Small Size
10 Type 1 1-226 <$450
20 Type 1 1-55 <$450
Total Issue $133,210
Out at close $10,000
Large out at close $650
****
10104 Bryan
FNB OF KENEFIC
{{ UNREPORTED }}
Chartered 11/11
Liquidated 1/18/16
1902 Date Back <$VALUE
3x10-20 1-569 <$2000
Total Issue $28,450
Out in 1916 $5,250
****

****
8177 Haskell
FNB OF KEOTA
Chartered 4/16/06
Liquidated 7/26/09
INDIAN TERRITORY {{ 1 L }}
1902 Red Seal <$VALUE
3x10-20 1-200 <$4000
STATE ISSUES {{ 0 L }}
1902 Date Back
3x10-20 1-65 <$1500
Total Issue $13,250
Out in 1910 $2,380
****
10298 Haskell
KEOTA NB, KEOTA
{{ 1 L }}
Chartered 12/12
Liquidated 12/22/15
1902 Date Back <$VALUE
3x10-20 1-657 <$1500
Total Issue $32,850
Out in 1916 $7,450
****
8553 Creek
FNB OF KIEFER
{{ UNREPORTED }}
Chartered 2/19/07
Liquidated 3/3/08
INDIAN TERRITORY
1902 Red Seal <$VALUE
3x10-20 1-143 <$5000
Total Issue $7,150
Out in 1910 $1,150
****
6702 Kingfisher
FARMERS NB OF KINGFISHER
{{ UNREPORTED }}
Organized 3/30/03
Receivership 11/1/05
OKLAHOMA TERRITORY
1902 Red Seal <$VALUE
3x10-20 1-221 <$5000
Total Issue $11,050
Out in 1916 $170
****
5328 Kingfisher
FNB OF KINGFISHER
Chartered 5/3/00
Receivership 7/27/33
OKLAHOMA TERRITORY {{ 1 L }}
Brown Back <$VALUE
3x10-20 1-2000 <$3500
STATE ISSUES {{ 5 L 7 S }}
Brown Back
3x10-20 1-400 <$2000
1882 Date Back
3x10-20 1-1860 <$750
1882 Value Back
3x10-20 1861-2667 <$750
1902 Plain Back
3x10-20 1-2900 <$500
1929 Small Size
10 Type 1 1-660 <$250
20 Type 1 1-360 <$250
Total Issue $457,390
Out at close $24,520
Large out at close $2,700
****
5740 Kingfisher
KINGFISHER NB, KINGFISHER
{{ UNREPORTED }}
Chartered 3/13/01
Liquidated 9/24/04
OKLAHOMA TERRITORY
Brown Back <$VALUE
3x10-20 1-239 <$5000
Total Issue $11,950
Out in 1910 $350
****
5790 Kingfisher
PEOPLES NB OF KINGFISHER
{{ UNREPORTED }}
Chartered 4/24/01
Liquidated 9/12/08
OKLAHOMA TERRITORY
Brown Back <$VALUE
50-100 1-427 <$8500/$9000
Total Issue $64,050
Out in 1910 $14,650
****

****
9954 Kingfisher
PEOPLES NB OF KINGFISHER
{{ 4 L 11 S }}
Chartered 3/11
1902 Date Back <$VALUE
3x10-20 1-2000 <$600
1902 Plain Back
3x10-20 2001-8346 <$600
1929 Small Size
10 Type 1 1-1126 <$200
20 Type 1 1-310 <$225
5 Type 2 1-324 <$225
10 Type 2 1-1105 <$225
20 Type 2 1-434 <$225
Total Issue $543,410
Out in 1935 $40,000
Large out 1935 $2,195
****
7893 Marshall
FNB OF KINGSTON
{{ UNREPORTED }}
Chartered 8/30/05
Liquidated 6/22/09
INDIAN TERRITORY
1902 Red Seal <$VALUE
3x10-20 1-293 <$5000
Total Issue $14,650
Out in 1910 $2,540
****
9881 Marshall
FNB OF KINGSTON
{{ UNREPORTED }}
Chartered 10/10
Liquidated 4/6/31
1902 Date Back <$VALUE
3x10-20 1-1140 <$1500
1902 Plain Back
3x10-20 1141-2678 <$1500
1929 Small Size
10 Type 1 1-171 <$750
20 Type 1 1-25 <$750
Total Issue $147,160
Out at close $10,000
Large out at close $1,710
Ch 13021 assumed circulation
****
8638 Pittsburg
FNB OF KIOWA
Chartered 4/07
Liquidated 12/31/25
INDIAN TERRITORY {{ 0 L }}
1902 Red Seal <$VALUE
3x10-20 1-200 <$4000
STATE ISSUES {{ 1 L }}
1902 Date Back
3x10-20 1-800* <$1250
1902 Plain Back
3x10-20 1001-1610* <$1250
* 801-1000 not marked
Total Issue $90,500
Out at close $7,100
****
7633 Seminole
FNB OF KONAWA
Chartered 3/05
INDIAN TERRITORY {{ 0 L }}
1902 Red Seal <$VALUE
3x10-20 1-256 <$3500
STATE ISSUES {{ 3 L 8 S }}
1902 Red Seal
3x10-20 1-100 <$3000
1902 Date Back
3x10-20 1-620 <$600
1902 Plain Back
3x10-20 621-4692 <$600
1929 Small Size
10 Type 1 1-888 <$200
20 Type 1 1-234 <$200
10 Type 2 1-1305 <$200
20 Type 2 1-283 <$225
Total Issue $352,470
Out in 1935 $25,000
Large out 1935 $1,290
Outstanding includes Ch 8213
****
8213 Seminole
KONAWA NB, KONAWA
{{ UNREPORTED }}
Chartered 5/06
Liquidated 12/11/15
INDIAN TERRITORY
1902 Red Seal <$VALUE
3x10-20 1-200 <$4000
STATE ISSUES
1902 Red Seal
3x10-20 1-100 <$3500
1902 Date Back
3x10-20 1-1571 <$1500
Total Issue $93,550
Large out 1935 $1,290
Ch 7633 assumed circulation
****

****
9974 Garfield
FNB OF LAHOMA
{{ 5 L }}
Chartered 3/11
Liquidated 8/27/25
1902 Date Back <$VALUE
3x10-20 1-1100* <$750
1902 Plain Back
3x10-20 1231-3432* <$750
* 1101-1230 not marked
Total Issue $171,600
Out at close $25,000
****
7783 Grant
FNB OF LAMONT
{{ UNREPORTED }}
Chartered 6/10/05
Liquidated 8/31/08
OKLAHOMA TERRITORY
1902 Red Seal <$VALUE
3x10-20 1-800 <$4000
STATE ISSUES
1902 Red Seal
3x10-20 1-78 <$3000
Total Issue $43,900
Out in 1910 $7,370
****
12067 Comanche
AMERICAN NB OF LAWTON
{{ 5 L 17 S }}
Chartered 12/21
1902 Plain Back <$VALUE
3x10-20 1-5574 <$350
1929 Small Size
10 Type 1 1-2562 <$75
20 Type 1 1-698 <$75
10 Type 2 1-5400 <$85
20 Type 2 1-1810 <$85
Total Issue $606,380
Out in 1935 $100,000
Large out 1935 $1,720
****
City NB of Lawton
SEE Ch 5753
FNB of Fort Sill
****
5914 Comanche
FNB OF LAWTON
Chartered 7/24/01
Receivership 12/12/21
OKLAHOMA TERRITORY {{ 0 L }}
Brown Back <$VALUE
3x10-20 1-2250 <$3500
STATE ISSUES {{ 14 L }}
Brown Back
3x10-20 1-500 <$1250
1882 Date Back
3x10-20 1-8600 <$450
1882 Value Back
3x10-20 8601-15800 <$450
1902 Plain Back
3x10-20 1-3260 <$165
Total Issue $1,090,500
Out at close $147,500
****
8375 Comanche
LAWTON NB, LAWTON
{{ 1 L }}
Chartered 9/24/06
Liquidated 3/13/09
OKLAHOMA TERRITORY
1902 Red Seal <$VALUE
3x10-20 1-577 <$4000
Total Issue $28,850
Out in 1910 $5,660
****
9962 Comanche
LAWTON NB, LAWTON
{{ 1 L }}
Chartered 3/11
Liquidated 12/9/14
1902 Date Back <$VALUE
3x10-20 1-5149 <$1000
Total Issue $257,450
Out in 1915 $49,000
****
7159 Jackson
ALTUS NB OF LEGER
{{ UNREPORTED }}
Chartered 2/15/04
Liquidated 11/15/08
2nd title: Altus NB, Altus
2/24/05
OKLAHOMA TERRITORY
FIRST TITLE
1902 Red Seal <$VALUE
3x10-20 1-176 <$4000
SECOND TITLE
1902 Red Seal
3x10-20 1-214 <$3500
Total Issue $19,500
Out in 1910 $2,140
****

****
6113 Jackson
FNB OF LEGER
Chartered 1/31/02
Receivership 9/26/30
2nd title: FNB of Altus
8/04
OKLAHOMA TERRITORY
FIRST TITLE {{ 0 L }}
1902 Red Seal <$VALUE
3x10-20 1-209 <$4000
SECOND TITLE {{ 0 L }}
1902 Red Seal
3x10-20 1-225 <$4000
STATE ISSUES {{ 4 L 3 S }}
1902 Date Back
3x10-20 1-1670 <$500
1902 Plain Back (dated 1902)
3x10-20 1671-2605 <$500
1902 Plain Back (dated 1922)
3x10-20 1-2923 <$500
1929 Small Size
10 Type 1 1-310 <$400
20 Type 1 1-73 <$400
Total Issue $325,460
Out at close $25,000
Large out at close $4,120
****
5755 Coal
LEHIGH NB, LEHIGH
Chartered 3/25/01
Receivership 11/8/23
INDIAN TERRITORY {{ 0 L }}
Brown Back <$VALUE
4x5 1-350 <$3500
3x10-20 1-360 <$3500
STATE ISSUES {{ 1 L }}
Brown Back
3x10-20 1-200 <$1750
1882 Date Back
4x5 1-475 <$1250
3x10-20 1-990* <$1250
1882 Value Back
4x5 476-740 <$1250
3x10-20 1091-1441* <$1250
* 991-1090 not marked
1902 Plain Back
3x10-20 1-470 <$1000
Total Issue $145,350
Out at close $11,050
****
8189 Coal
MERCHANTS NB OF LEHIGH
{{ UNREPORTED }}
Chartered 4/06
Liquidated 2/19/20
INDIAN TERRITORY
1902 Red Seal <$VALUE
3x10-20 1-190 <$4000
STATE ISSUES
1902 Red Seal
3x10-20 1-100 <$3500
1902 Date Back
3x10-20 1-695 <$1500
Total Issue $49,250
Out at close $6,250
****
9951 Nowata
LENAPAH NB, LENAPAH
{{ UNREPORTED }}
Chartered 3/11
Liquidated 10/15/17
1902 Date Back <$VALUE
3x10-20 1-1540* <$1500
1902 Plain Back
3x10-20 1671-1918* <$1500
* 1541-1670 not marked
Total Issue $95,900
Out at close $25,000
****
7207 Cleveland
FARMERS NB OF LEXINGTON
Chartered 4/11/04
Liquidated 6/16/09
OKLAHOMA TERRITORY {{ 1 L }}
1902 Red Seal <$VALUE
4x5 1-250 <$4000
3x10-20 1-200 <$4000
STATE ISSUES {{ 0 L }}
1902 Red Seal
4x5 1-100 <$3500
3x10-20 1-80 <$3500
1902 Date Back
4x5 1-295 <$1500
3x10-20 1-208 <$1500
Total Issue $37,300
Out in 1910 $11,990
****
FNB of Lexington
SEE Ch 5462
Lexington NB, Lexington
****

****
5462 Cleveland
LEXINGTON NB, LEXINGTON
Chartered 6/27/00
Receivership 5/24/05
2nd title: FNB of
Lexington 7/04
OKLAHOMA TERRITORY
FIRST TITLE {{ 1 L }}
Brown Back <$VALUE
4x5 1-350 <$3500
3x10-20 1-360 <$3500
SECOND TITLE {{ 0 L }}
Brown Back
4x5 1-145 <$2000
3x10-20 1-66 <$2000
Total Issue $31,200
Out in 1916 $430
****
6171 Garvin
CITIZENS NB OF LINDSAY
Chartered 3/24/02
2nd title: FNB of Lindsay
4/03
INDIAN TERRITORY
FIRST TITLE {{ 0 L }}
1902 Red Seal <$VALUE
3x10-20 1-131 <$4000
SECOND TITLE {{ 0 L }}
1902 Red Seal
3x10-20 1-745 <$4000
STATE ISSUES {{ 4 L 7 S }}
1902 Date Back
3x10-20 1-2110 <$600
1902 Plain Back (dated 1902)
3x10-20 2111-3955 <$600
1902 Plain Back (dated 1922)
3x10-20 1-2712 <$600
1929 Small Size
10 Type 1 1-714 <$300
20 Type 1 1-200 <$300
10 Type 2 1-1622 <$300
20 Type 2 1-267 <$325
Total Issue $465,550
Out in 1935 $25,000
Large out 1935 $1,410
****
FNB of Lindsay
SEE Ch 6171
Citizens NB of Lindsay
****
6710 Garvin
LINDSAY NB, LINDSAY
{{ 1 L }}
Chartered 4/3/03
Liquidated 2/6/08
INDIAN TERRITORY
1902 Red Seal <$VALUE
4x5 1-1410 <$4000
3x10-20 1-975 <$4000
Total Issue $76,950
Out in 1910 $6,925
****
10096 Kiowa
FNB OF LONE WOLF
{{ 6 L 18 S }}
Chartered 10/11
1902 Date Back <$VALUE
4x5 1-1490 <$600
3x10-20 1-1084 <$600
1902 Plain Back
4x5 1491-6473 <$600
3x10-20 1085-4032 <$600
1929 Small Size
5 Type 1 1-1046 <$400
10 Type 1 1-558 <$400
20 Type 1 1-162 <$400
5 Type 2 1-1552 <$400
10 Type 2 1-896 <$400
20 Type 2 1-155 <$400
Total Issue $435,180
Out in 1935 $25,000
Large out 1935 $1,120
****
FNB of Luther
SEE Ch 8563
NB of Luther
****
8563 Oklahoma
NB OF LUTHER
Chartered 2/07
2nd title:FNB of Luther
6/6/08
FIRST TITLE
OKLAHOMA TERRITORY {{ 0 L }}
1902 Red Seal <$VALUE
3x10-20 1-149 <$4000
SECOND TITLE
STATE ISSUES {{ 6 L 6 S }}
1902 Date Back
3x10-20 1-2230 <$400
1902 Plain Back
3x10-20 2231-6706 <$400

1929 Small Size
10 Type 1 1-802 <$250
20 Type 1 1-200 <$250
10 Type 2 1-1253 <$250
20 Type 2 1-264 <$250
Total Issue $432,680
Out in 1935 $25,000
Large out 1935 $1,430
****
7723 Marshall
CITY NB OF MADILL
Chartered 5/05
Liquidated 12/15/17
INDIAN TERRITORY {{ 0 L }}
1902 Red Seal <$VALUE
3x10-20 1-1760 <$3500
STATE ISSUES {{ 3 L }}
1902 Red Seal
3x10-20 1-500 <$2500
1902 Date Back
3x10-20 1-4240 <$600
1902 Plain Back
3x10-20 4241-5142 <$600
Total Issue $370,100
Out at close $49,995
****
13021 Marshall
FNB IN MADILL
{{ 2 L 9 S }}
Chartered 12/26
1902 Plain Back <$VALUE
3x10-20 1-1144 <$750
1929 Small Size
10 Type 1 1-1080 <$150
20 Type 1 1-302 <$150
10 Type 2 1-2222 <$150
20 Type 2 1-503 <$150
Total Issue $190,520
Out in 1935 $38,850
Large out 1935 $2,110
Outstanding includes Ch 5404
and Ch 9881
****
FNB of Madill
SEE Ch 5404
Cotton NB of Oakland
****
6365 Marshall
MADILL NB, MADILL
{{ UNREPORTED }}
Chartered 8/2/02
Liquidated 9/1/08
INDIAN TERRITORY
1902 Red Seal <$VALUE
3x10-20 1-1410 <$4000
STATE ISSUES
1902 Red Seal
3x10-20 1-73 <$3500
Total Issue $74,150
Out in 1910 $8,940
****
10286 Marshall
MADILL NB, MADILL
{{ 2 L 3 S }}
Chartered 11/12
1902 Date Back <$VALUE
3x10-20 1-1010 <$750
1902 Plain Back
3x10-20 1011-3096 <$750
1929 Small Size
10 Type 1 1-396 <$400
20 Type 1 1-118 <$400
10 Type 2 1-504 <$400
20 Type 2 1-114 <$400
Total Issue $200,640
Out in 1934 $12,150
Large out 1935 $620
****
7328 Greer
CITIZENS NB OF MANGUM
{{ UNREPORTED }}
Chartered 7/04
Liquidated 8/18/09
OKLAHOMA TERRITORY
1902 Red Seal <$VALUE
3x10-20 1-356 <$4000
STATE ISSUES
1902 Date Back
3x10-20 1-15 <$1500
Total Issue $18,550
Out in 1910 $2,970
****
5508 Greer
FNB OF MANGUM
Chartered 7/19/00
OKLAHOMA TERRITORY {{ 0 L }}
Brown Back <$VALUE
3x10-20 1-825 <$3500
STATE ISSUES {{ 10 L 16 S }}
Brown Back
3x10-20 1-200 <$1250
1882 Date Back
4x5 1-3755 <$300
3x10-20 1-3040 <$300

1882 Value Back
4x5 3756-6005 <$300
3x10-20 3041-4460 <$300
1902 Plain Back
4x5 1-7402 <$200
3x10-20 1-4459 <$200
1929 Small Size
5 Type 1 1-3032 <$85
10 Type 1 1-1884 <$100
20 Type 1 1-492 <$100
5 Type 2 1-8220 <$100
10 Type 2 1-4296 <$100
20 Type 2 1-1020 <$100
Total Issue $1,132,840
Out in 1935 $100,000
Large out 1935 $2,215
****
5811 Greer
MANGUM NB, MANGUM
Chartered 5/13/01
OKLAHOMA TERRITORY {{ 0 L }}
Brown Back <$VALUE
3x10-20 1-750 <$3500
STATE ISSUES {{ 3 L 0 S }}
Brown Back
3x10-20 1-120 <$1500
1882 Date Back
3x10-20 1-1120 <$750
1882 Value Back
3x10-20 1121-1664 <$750
1902 Plain Back
3x10-20 1-1513 <$500
1929 Small Size
10 Type 1 1-396 <$600
20 Type 1 1-118 <$600
10 Type 2 1-421 <$600
20 Type 2 1-40 <$600
Total Issue $245,280
Out in 1935 $12,500
Large out 1935 $680
****
6578 Johnston
FNB OF MANNSVILLE
{{ UNREPORTED }}
Chartered 1/10/03
Liquidated 12/31/08
INDIAN TERRITORY
1902 Red Seal <$VALUE
4x5 1-245 <$5000
3x10-20 1-315 <$5000
Total Issue $20,650
Out in 1910 $1,490
****
8278 Love
FARMERS NB OF MARIETTA
{{ UNREPORTED }}
Chartered 6/06
Liquidated 12/31/09
INDIAN TERRITORY
1902 Red Seal <$VALUE
3x10-20 1-300 <$4000
STATE ISSUES
1902 Red Seal
3x10-20 1-800 <$3000
1902 Date Back
3x10-20 1-48 <$1500
Total Issue $57,400
Out in 1910 $13,460
****
5345 Love
FNB OF MARIETTA
Chartered 5/9/00
INDIAN TERRITORY {{ 0 L }}
Brown Back <$VALUE
3x10-20 1-500 <$3500
STATE ISSUES {{ 2 L 5 S }}
1882 Date Back
3x10-20 1-1360 <$850
1882 Value Back
3x10-20 1361-1612 <$850
1902 Plain Back
3x10-20 1-1626 <$600
1929 Small Size
10 Type 1 1-578 <$250
20 Type 1 1-170 <$250
10 Type 2 1-1751 <$250
20 Type 2 1-330 <$275
Total Issue $266,090
Out in 1935 $27,500
Large out 1935 $1,240
Outstanding includes Ch 5958
****

<$VALUEs are for notes in **FINE** condition. Value changes by approximately **25%** for a change of one full grade.

5958 Love
MARIETTA NB, MARIETTA
Chartered 9/9/01
Closed 2/3/31
INDIAN TERRITORY {{ 1 L }}
Brown Back <$VALUE
3x10-20 1-700 <$3000
STATE ISSUES {{ 3 L 2 S }}
Brown Back
3x10-20 1-100 <$1500
1882 Date Back
3x10-20 1-2412* <$750
*1621-2412 not marked
1902 Plain Back
3x10-20 1-1799 <$600
1929 Small Size
10 Type 1 1-249 <$500
20 Type 1 1-41 <$500
Total Issue $270,410
Out at close $15,000
Large out at close $2,230
Ch 5345 assumed circulation

12129 Stephens
FNB IN MARLOW
{{ 45 S }}
Chartered 3/22
1929 Small Size <$VALUE
5 Type 1 1-526 <$150
10 Type 1 1-160 <$150
20 Type 1 1-54 <$150
5 Type 2 1-2382 <$175
10 Type 2 1-1208 <$175
20 Type 2 1-348 <$175
Total Issue $62,810
Out in 1935 $25,000

5724 Stephens
FNB OF MARLOW
Chartered 2/25/01
Liquidated 9/14/09
INDIAN TERRITORY {{ U + 0 L }}
Brown Back <$VALUE
4x5 1-480 <$3500
3x10-20 1-388 <$3500
STATE ISSUES {{ 0 L }}
Brown Back
4x5 1-75 <$2000
3x10-20 1-30 <$2000
1882 Date Back
4x5 1-45 <$1500
3x10-20 1-19 <$1500
Total Issue $33,850
Out in 1910 $3,740

10205 Stephens
NB OF MARLOW
{{ 1 L 1 S }}
Chartered 5/29/12
Liquidated 9/3/31
1902 Date Back <$VALUE
4x10 1-775 <$1250
1902 Plain Back
4x10 776-2210 <$1250
1929 Small Size
10 Type 1 1-155 <$600
Total Issue $97,700
Out at close $6,250
Large out at close $440

9946 Stephens
STATE NB OF MARLOW
{{ 4 L 5 S }}
Chartered 3/11
1902 Date Back <$VALUE
4x5 1-625 <$500
3x10-20 1-530 <$500
1902 Plain Back
4x5 626-5179 <$500
3x10-20 531-3192 <$500
1929 Small Size
5 Type 1 1-1014 <$275
10 Type 1 1-592 <$275
20 Type 1 1-162 <$275
5 Type 2 1-1388 <$275
10 Type 2 1-852 <$275
20 Type 2 1-276 <$300
Total Issue $369,540
Out in 1935 $25,000
Large out 1935 $910

8294 Pottawatomie
FNB OF MAUD
Chartered 7/06
OKLAHOMA TERRITORY {{ 0 L }}
1902 Red Seal <$VALUE
3x10-20 1-187 <$4000
STATE ISSUES {{ 1 L 3 S }}
1902 Date Back
3x10-20 1-700* <$1250
1902 Plain Back
3x10-20 801-1644* <$1250
* 701-800 not marked
1929 Small Size
10 Type 1 1-259 <$450
20 Type 1 1-70 <$450
Total Issue $115,490
Out in 1935 $6,250
Large out 1935 $410

10283 Garvin
FARMERS NB OF MAYSVILLE
{{ 1 L }}
Chartered 10/12
Liquidated 4/7/20
1902 Date Back <$VALUE
3x10-20 1-575 <$1250
1902 Plain Back
3x10-20 576-614 <$1250
Total Issue $30,700
Out at close $6,250

8999 Garvin
FNB OF MAYSVILLE
{{ 5 L 8 S }}
Chartered 1/08
1902 Red Seal <$VALUE
3x10-20 1-187 <$3000
1902 Date Back
3x10-20 1-1990 <$400
1902 Plain Back
3x10-20 1991-6500 <$400
1929 Small Size
10 Type 1 1-794 <$175
20 Type 1 1-218 <$175
10 Type 2 1-1258 <$175
20 Type 2 1-345 <$200
Total Issue $427,630
Out in 1935 $25,000
Large out 1935 $1,010

American NB of McAlester
SEE Ch 6230
American NB of
South McAlester

City NB of McAlester
SEE Ch 6406
City NB of South McAlester

FNB of McAlester
SEE Ch 5052
FNB of South McAlester

13770 Pittsburg
NB OF McALESTER
{{ 13 S }}
Chartered 9/33
1929 Small Size <$VALUE
5 Type 2 1-14580 <$125
10 Type 2 1-7464 <$125
20 Type 2 1-2400 <$125
Total Issue $195,540
Out in 1935 $94,890

6660 Pottawatomie
FNB OF McLOUD
Organized 3/2/03
Receivership 11/15/32
OKLAHOMA TERRITORY {{ 0 L }}
1902 Red Seal <$VALUE
3x10-20 1-375 <$4000
STATE ISSUES {{ 1 L 1 S }}
1902 Red Seal
3x10-20 1-100 <$3500
1902 Date Back
3x10-20 1-660 <$1250
1902 Plain Back
3x10-20 661-1591 <$1250
1929 Small Size
10 Type 1 1-210 <$650
20 Type 1 1-35 <$650
Total Issue $120,100
Out at close $7,000
Large out at close $930

5796 Grant
FNB OF MEDFORD
Chartered 5/6/01
OKLAHOMA TERRITORY {{ 0 L }}
Brown Back <$VALUE
3x10-20 1-1590 <$3500
STATE ISSUES {{ 4 L 7 S }}
Brown Back
3x10-20 1-200 <$1500
1882 Date Back
3x10-20 1-1640 <$600
1882 Value Back
3x10-20 1641-2669 <$600
1902 Plain Back
3x10-20 1-2549 <$500
1929 Small Size
10 Type 1 1-758 <$200
20 Type 1 1-196 <$200
10 Type 2 1-596 <$200
20 Type 2 1-105 <$225
Total Issue $427,460
Out in 1935 $25,000
Large out 1935 $1,790

5252 Ottawa
FNB OF MIAMI
Chartered 2/6/00
INDIAN TERRITORY {{ 1 L }}
Brown Back <$VALUE
3x10-20 1-1050 <$3000
STATE ISSUES {{ 22 L 24 S }}
1882 Date Back
3x10-20 1-3700 <$350
1882 Value Back
3x10-20 3701-7127 <$350
1902 Plain Back
3x10-20 1-13005 <$150
1929 Small Size
5 Type 1 1-7864 <$75
10 Type 1 1-3884 <$75
20 Type 1 1-1032 <$85
5 Type 2 1-15994 <$85
Total Issue $1,731,870
Out in 1935 $100,000
Large out 1935 $9,720
Outstanding includes Ch 10019

10019 Ottawa
OTTAWA COUNTY NB OF MIAMI
{{ 14 L }}
Chartered 5/11
Closed 6/22/29
1902 Date Back <$VALUE
4x5 1-1200 <$175
3x10-20 1-920 <$175
1902 Plain Back
4x5 1201-18710 <$175
3x10-20 921-11314 <$175
Total Issue $939,900
Out at close $100,000
Ch 5252 assumed circulation

7842 Johnston
FNB OF MILBURN
{{ UNREPORTED }}
Chartered 7/25/05
Liquidated 1/18/09
INDIAN TERRITORY
1902 Red Seal <$VALUE
3x10-20 1-251 <$4000
Total Issue $12,550
Out in 1910 $1,810

9920 Johnston
FNB OF MILBURN
{{ 3 L }}
Organized 1/3/11
Receivership 10/31/27
1902 Date Back <$VALUE
3x10-20 1-1320* <$650
1902 Plain Back
3x10-20 1561-3420* <$650
* 1321-1560 not marked
Total Issue $171,000
Out at close $16,250

7197 Johnston
FNB OF MILL CREEK
Chartered 4/04
INDIAN TERRITORY {{ 0 L }}
1902 Red Seal <$VALUE
3x10-20 1-1000 <$3500
STATE ISSUES {{ 6 L 8 S }}
1902 Date Back
3x10-20 1-2180 <$450
1902 Plain Back
3x10-20 2181-6394 <$450
1929 Small Size
10 Type 1 1-736 <$250
20 Type 1 1-200 <$250
10 Type 2 1-1047 <$275
20 Type 2 1-344 <$275
Total Issue $455,210
Out in 1935 $25,000
Large out 1935 $1,280

8546 Johnston
MERCHANTS & PLANTERS NB
OF MILL CREEK
{{ UNREPORTED }}
Chartered 2/07
Liquidated 11/30/09
INDIAN TERRITORY
1902 Red Seal <$VALUE
3x10-20 1-240 <$4000
STATE ISSUES
1902 Date Back
3x10-20 1-76 <$1500
Total Issue $15,800
Out in 1910 $4,130

12188 Johnston
MILL CREEK NB, MILL CREEK
{{ 1 L }}
Chartered 5/22
Liquidated 12/27/24
1902 Plain Back <$VALUE
3x10-20 1-1206 <$1250
Total Issue $60,300
Out at close $25,000

8644 Grady
FNB OF MINCO
Chartered 4/07
INDIAN TERRITORY {{ 0 L }}
1902 Red Seal <$VALUE
4x5 1-200 <$4000
4x10 1-200 <$4000
STATE ISSUES {{ 1 L 2 S }}
1902 Date Back
4x5 1-550* <$1250
4x10 1-550** <$1250
1902 Plain Back
4x5 751-1857* <$1250
4x10 651-1426** <$1250
* 551-750 not marked
** 551-650 not marked
1929 Small Size
5 Type 1 1-501 <$500
10 Type 1 1-262 <$500
Total Issue $136,930
Out in 1935 $6,500
Large out 1935 $430

12035 Oklahoma
FNB OF MOORE
{{ 1 L 3 S }}
Chartered 11/21
1902 Plain Back <$VALUE
3x10-20 1-820 <$1250
1929 Small Size
10 Type 1 1-258 <$450
20 Type 1 1-74 <$450
Total Issue $65,360
Out in 1935 $6,250
Large out 1935 $160

8876 Okmulgee
FNB OF MORRIS
Chartered 9/07
Liquidated 5/4/21
INDIAN TERRITORY {{ 0 L }}
1902 Red Seal <$VALUE
3x10-20 1-600 <$4000
STATE ISSUES {{ 2 L }}
1902 Red Seal
3x10-20 1-200 <$3000
1902 Date Back
3x10-20 1-2090 <$750
1902 Plain Back
3x10-20 2091-3483 <$750
Total Issue $214,150
Out at close $25,000
Ch 11932 assumed circulation

11932 Okmulgee
MORRIS NB, MORRIS
{{ 1 L }}
Chartered 2/21
Liquidated 12/30/29
1902 Plain Back <$VALUE
3x10-20 1-1668 <$1000
Total Issue $83,400
Out at close $2,350
Outstanding includes Ch 8876

6263 Creek
FNB OF MOUNDS
Chartered 5/17/02
Liquidated 10/25/28
INDIAN TERRITORY {{ 0 L }}
1902 Red Seal <$VALUE
3x10-20 1-400 <$4000
STATE ISSUES {{ 4 L }}
1902 Red Seal
3x10-20 1-30 <$3000
1902 Date Back
3x10-20 1-2410 <$500
1902 Plain Back
3x10-20 2411-6515 <$500
Total Issue $347,250
Out at close $25,000

5656 Kiowa
FNB OF MOUNTAIN VIEW
Chartered 12/28/00
OKLAHOMA TERRITORY {{ 0 L }}
Brown Back <$VALUE
50-100 1-130 <$8500/$9000
STATE ISSUES {{ 5 L 7 S }}
Brown Back
4x10 1-625 <$1500
1882 Date Back
4x10 1-2150 <$750
1882 Value Back
4x10 2151-3819 <$750
1902 Plain Back
4x10 1-4616 <$500
1929 Small Size
10 Type 1 1-1376 <$300
10 Type 2 1-2455 <$300
Total Issue $489,010
Out in 1935 $25,000
Large out 1935 $1,830

6717 Sequoyah
FNB OF MULDROW
Chartered 4/03
Liquidated 2/27/09
INDIAN TERRITORY {{ 2 L }}
1902 Red Seal <$VALUE
3x10-20 1-840 <$3500
STATE ISSUES {{ 0 L }}
1902 Red Seal
3x10-20 1-132 <$3500
Total Issue $48,600
Out in 1910 $5,470

9975 Sequoyah
FNB OF MULDROW
{{ 4 L }}
Organized 3/25/11
Receivership 10/24/27
1902 Date Back <$VALUE
3x10-20 1-1810 <$500
1902 Plain Back
3x10-20 1811-5410 <$500
Total Issue $270,500
Out at close $24,400

9032 Logan
FNB OF MULHALL
{{ UNREPORTED }}
Chartered 2/14/08
Liquidated 2/15/09
1902 Red Seal <$VALUE
4x10 1-274 <$4000
Total Issue $10,960
Out in 1910 $3,190

4385 Muskogee
FNB OF MUSCOGEE
Chartered 1890
2nd title: FNB of Muskogee
2/14/08
3rd title: FNB & TC 9/30/29
FIRST TITLE
INDIAN TERRITORY {{ 7 L }}
Brown Back <$VALUE
4x5 1-13300 <$2250
3x10-20 1-9948 <$2250
SECOND TITLE
STATE ISSUES {{ 26 L }}
Brown Back
4x5 1-2125 <$1000
3x10-20 1-1700 <$1000
1882 Date Back
4x5 1-3525 <$225
3x10-20 1-2146 <$225
1902 Date Back
4x5 1-13250 <$85
3x10-20 1-8300 <$100
50-100 1-800 <$400/$450
1902 Plain Back
4x5 13251-62750 <$85
3x10-20 8301-38700 <$100
3x50-100 1-4616 <$400/$450
THIRD TITLE {{ 21 S }}
1929 Small Size
50 Type 1 1-1376 <$85
100 Type 1 1-512 <$135
Total Issue $6,252,700
Out in 1935 $300,000
Large out 1935 $45,185

FNB of Muskogee
FNB & TC of Muskogee
SEE Ch 4385
FNB of Muscogee

9701 Muskogee
AMERICAN NB OF MUSKOGEE
{{ 2 L }}
Chartered 3/10
Liquidated 4/24/16
1902 Date Back <$VALUE
3x10-20 1-10700 <$500
1902 Plain Back
3x10-20 10701-11630 <$500
Total Issue $581,500
Out in 1916 $121,350

6911 Muskogee
CITY NB OF MUSKOGEE
{{ 1 L }}
Chartered 8/6/03
Liquidated 3/16/08
INDIAN TERRITORY
1902 Red Seal <$VALUE
3x10-20 1-3858 <$3000
Total Issue $192,900
Out in 1910 $18,880

12890 Muskogee
COMMERCIAL NB IN MUSKOGEE
{{ 16 L U + 33 S }}
Chartered 2/26
1902 Plain Back <$VALUE
3x10-20 1-12118 <$100
1929 Small Size
10 Type 1 1-8638 <$50
20 Type 1 1-2210 <$60
10 Type 2 1-10505 <$50
20 Type 2 1-2876 <$60
Total Issue $1,551,950
Out in 1935 $300,000
Large out 1935 $13,885
Outstanding includes Ch 5236

12918 Muskogee
CITIZENS NB OF MUSKOGEE
{{ 16 S }}
Chartered 4/26
1929 Small Size <$VALUE
5 Type 1 1-1394 <$75
10 Type 1 1-686 <$75
20 Type 1 1-548 <$85
5 Type 2 1-6354 <$85
10 Type 2 1-3415 <$85
20 Type 2 1-1160 <$85
Total Issue $237,860
Out in 1935 $100,000

5236 Muskogee
COMMERCIAL NB OF MUSKOGEE
Chartered 12/13/99
Liquidated 4/2/26
INDIAN TERRITORY {{ 3 L }}
Brown Back <$VALUE
4x5 1-4705 <$2250
3x10-20 1-4802 <$2250
50-100 1-672 <$6500/$7500
STATE ISSUES {{ 16 L }}
Brown Back
4x5 1-1500 <$750
3x10-20 1-1100 <$750
50-100 1 100 <$3000/$3500
1882 Date Back
4x5 1-16250 <$250
3x10-20 1-10200 <$250
50-100 1-200 <$2500/$3000
1882 Value Back
4x5 16251-23250 <$250
3x10-20 10201-14100 <$250
1902 Plain Back
3x10-20 1-23516 <$150
Total Issue $2,910,800
Out at close $250,000

10321 Muskogee
EXCHANGE NB OF MUSKOGEE
{{ 10 L }}
Chartered 1/13
Liquidated 9/23/24
1902 Date Back <$VALUE
4x5 1-5715 <$175
3x10-20 1-4514 <$175
1902 Plain Back
4x5 5716-35215 <$175
3x10-20 4515-23814 <$175
Total Issue $1,895,000
Out at close $300,000

9023 Muskogee
MUSKOGEE NB, MUSKOGEE
{{ 24 L }}
Chartered 2/08
Liquidated 3/29/24
1902 Red Seal <$VALUE
3x10-20 1-750 <$2000
1902 Date Back
3x10-20 1-2700 <$125
1902 Plain Back
3x10-20 2701-11776 <$125
Total Issue $626,300
Out at close $100,000
Ch 12277 assumed circulation

****
12277 Muskogee
MUSKOGEE-SECURITY NB, MUSKOGEE
{{ 1 L }}
Organized 11/8/22 as Security NB of Muskogee, under which there was no issue. Issuing title adopted 4/18/24.
Receivership 11/7/25
1902 Plain Back <$VALUE
3x10-20 1-1178 <$850
Total Issue $58,900
Out at close $100,000
Outstanding includes Ch 9023
****
10113 Muskogee
OKLAHOMA NB OF MUSKOGEE
{{ UNREPORTED }}
Chartered 12/11
Liquidated 5/5/13
1902 Date Back <$VALUE
3x10-20 1-759 <$850
Total Issue $37,950
Out in 1913 $14,450
****
11306 Grant
FNB OF NASH
{{ 6 L 7 S }}
Chartered 2/19
1902 Plain Back <$VALUE
4x5 1-12557 <$350
1929 Small Size
5 Type 1 1-3204 <$225
5 Type 2 1-6952 <$225
Total Issue $382,020
Out in 1935 $25,000
Large out 1935 $1,005
****
10574 Carter
FNB OF NEW WILSON
{{ UNREPORTED }}
Chartered 7/14
Liquidated 11/12/23
1902 Date Back <$VALUE
4x5 1-415* <$1500
3x10-20 1-334** <$1500
1902 Plain Back
4x5 516-855* <$1500
3x10-20 375-605** <$1500
* 416-515 not marked'
** 335-374 not marked
Total Issue $47,350
Out at close $6,250
****
9011 Kay
EASTMAN NB OF NEWKIRK
{{ 7 L 10 S }}
Chartered 1/08
1902 Red Seal <$VALUE
3x10-20 1-1200 <$2000
1902 Date Back
3x10-20 1-2250 <$275
1902 Plain Back
3x10-20 2251-10284 <$275
1929 Small Size
10 Type 1 1-1436 <$175
20 Type 1 1-418 <$175
5 Type 2 1-324 <$200
10 Type 2 1-1261 <$200
20 Type 2 1-415 <$200
Total Issue $733,050
Out in 1935 $48,450
Large out 1935 $2,525
****
8214 Kay
FARMERS NB OF NEWKIRK
{{ UNREPORTED }}
Chartered 5/10/06
Liquidated 1/19/09
OKLAHOMA TERRITORY
1902 Red Seal <$VALUE
3x10-20 1-300 <$4000
STATE ISSUES
1902 Red Seal
3x10-20 1-40 <$3000
Total Issue $17,000
Out in 1910 $3,375
****
5272 Kay
FNB OF NEWKIRK
Chartered 4/2/00
Liquidated 2/9/33
OKLAHOMA TERRITORY {{ 2 L }}
Brown Back <$VALUE
3x10-20 1-450 <$3000
STATE ISSUES {{ 3 L 2 S }}
1882 Date Back
3x10-20 1-800 <$850
1882 Value Back
3x10-20 801-957 <$850
1902 Plain Back
3x10-20 1-1508 <$600
1929 Small Size
10 Type 1 1-280 <$450
20 Type 1 1-79 <$450
Total Issue $172,030
Out at close $11,300
Large out at close $850
****
9937 Cleveland
FNB OF NOBLE
{{ 5 L 4 S }}
Chartered 2/11
Liquidated 7/6/31
1902 Date Back <$VALUE
3x10-20 1-1320 <$500
1902 Plain Back
3x10-20 1321-5389 <$500
1929 Small Size
10 Type 1 1-436 <$350
20 Type 1 1-112 <$350
Total Issue $309,050
Out at close $25,000
Large out at close $3,290
****
12157 Cleveland
CITY NB IN NORMAN
{{ 4 S }}
Chartered 4/22
1929 Small Size <$VALUE
10 Type 2 1-2770 <$300
20 Type 2 1-1370 <$300
Total Issue $55,100
Out in 1935 $50,000
****
6450 Cleveland
CITY NB OF NORMAN
Chartered 10/6/02
Liquidated 10/5/08
OKLAHOMA TERRITORY {{ 1 L }}
1902 Red Seal <$VALUE
3x10-20 1-2300 <$3500
STATE ISSUES {{ 0 L }}
1902 Date Back
3x10-20 1-94 <$1250
Total Issue $119,700
Out in 1910 $16,210
****
5612 Cleveland
CLEVELAND COUNTY NB OF NORMAN
{{ 1 L }}
Chartered 10/30/00
Liquidated 2/28/03
OKLAHOMA TERRITORY
Brown Back <$VALUE
3x10-20 1-280 <$4000
Total Issue $14,000
Out in 1910 $410
****
Farmers NB of Norman
SEE Ch 7293
NB of Norman
****
5248 Cleveland
FNB OF NORMAN
Chartered 1/25/00
OKLAHOMA TERRITORY {{ 3 L }}
Brown Back <$VALUE
3x10-20 1-2750 <$2500
STATE ISSUES {{ 7 L 17 S }}
Brown Back
3x10-20 1-200 <$1500
1882 Date Back
3x10-20 1-4200 <$450
1882 Value Back
3x10-20 4201-5737 <$450
1902 Plain Back
3x10-20 1-7134 <$250
1929 Small Size
10 Type 1 1-1592 <$75
20 Type 1 1-410 <$85
10 Type 2 1-5349 <$100
20 Type 2 1-1412 <$100
Total Issue $1,017,500
Out in 1935 $100,000
Large out 1935 $2,690
****
7293 Cleveland
NB OF NORMAN
Chartered 6/04
Liquidated 8/9/21
2nd title: Farmers NB of Norman 3/18/11
FIRST TITLE
OKLAHOMA TERRITORY {{ 0 L }}
1902 Red Seal <$VALUE
3x10-20 1-300 <$3500
STATE ISSUES {{ 1 L }}
1902 Red Seal
3x10-20 1-100 <$2500
1902 Date Back
3x10-20 1-889 <$750
SECOND TITLE {{ 0 L }}
1902 Date Back
3x10-20 1-1660 <$750
1902 Plain Back
3x10-20 1661-3433 <$750
Total Issue $236,100
Out at close $30,000
****
12036 Cleveland
SECURITY NB OF NORMAN
{{ 7 S }}
Chartered 11/21
1929 Small Size <$VALUE
10 Type 2 1-5686 <$200
20 Type 2 1-1519 <$200
Total Issue $87,240
Out in 1935 $50,000
****
9949 Nowata
COMMERCIAL NB OF NOWATA
{{ 11 L 4 S }}
Chartered 3/11
Liquidated 11/10/30
1902 Date Back <$VALUE
3x10-20 1-3250* <$175
1902 Plain Back
3x10-20 3501-11556* <$175
* 3251-3500 not marked
1929 Small Size
10 Type 1 1-556 <$300
20 Type 1 1-153 <$300
Total Issue $629,520
Out at close $50,000
Large out at close $8,390
****
5401 Nowata
FNB OF NOWATA
Chartered 6/5/00
INDIAN TERRITORY {{ 3 L }}
Brown Back <$VALUE
4x5 1-2250 <$2250
3x10-20 1-1670 <$2250
STATE ISSUES {{ 8 L 11 S }}
1882 Date Back
4x5 1-4000 <$350
3x10-20 1-2780 <$350
1882 Value Back
4x5 4001-6350 <$350
3x10-20 2781-4194 <$350
1902 Plain Back
3x10-20 1-6825 <$200
1929 Small Size
10 Type 1 1-1414 <$100
20 Type 1 1-440 <$110
10 Type 2 1-874 <$125
20 Type 2 1-324 <$125
Total Issue $959,310
Out in 1935 $49,995
Large out 1935 $2,935
****
6367 Nowata
NOWATA NB, NOWATA
Chartered 8/5/02
Receivership 2/19/24
INDIAN TERRITORY {{ 0 L }}
1902 Red Seal <$VALUE
3x10-20 1-820 <$3500
STATE ISSUES {{ 3 L }}
1902 Red Seal
4x5 1-500 <$2500
1902 Date Back
4x5 1-1275 <$500
3x10-20 1-960 <$500
1902 Plain Back
4x5 1276-2970 <$500
3x10-20 961-2021 <$500
Total Issue $211,450
Out at close $16,795
****
9948 Nowata
PRODUCERS NB OF NOWATA
{{ UNREPORTED }}
Chartered 3/11
Liquidated 1/31/14
1902 Date Back <$VALUE
3x10-20 1-2092 <$1250
Total Issue $104,600
Out in 1914 $23,070
****
5887 Blaine
FNB OF O'KEENE
{{ 1 L }}
Chartered 6/28/01
Liquidated 9/7/08
OKLAHOMA TERRITORY
Brown Back <$VALUE
4x5 1-615 <$3500
3x10-20 1-464 <$3500
Total Issue $35,500
Out in 1910 $2,800
****
****
5404 Marshall
COTTON NB OF OAKLAND
Chartered 6/6/00
Liquidated 12/31/26
2nd title:FNB of Madill 1/29/01
INDIAN TERRITORY
FIRST TITLE {{ 0 L }}
Brown Back <$VALUE
50-100 1-85 <$8500/$9000
SECOND TITLE {{ 1 L }}
Brown Back
3x10-20 1-1000 <$3000
50-100 1-167 <$8500/$9000
STATE ISSUES {{ 3 L }}
Brown Back
3x10-20 1-1000 <$1500
50-100 1-167 <$3000/$3500
1882 Date Back
3x10-20 1-1950 <$600
50-100 1-100 <$2500/$3000
1882 Value Back
3x10-20 1951-2886 <$600
1902 Plain Back
3x10-20 1-2859 <$400
Total Issue $390,050
Out at close $29,650
Ch 13021 assumed circulation
****
6477 Okfusee
FNB OF OKEMAH
Chartered 11/4/02
INDIAN TERRITORY {{ 0 L }}
1902 Red Seal <$VALUE
3x10-20 1-370 <$3500
STATE ISSUES {{ 6 L 7 S }}
1902 Red Seal
3x10-20 1-160 <$2500
1902 Date Back
3x10-20 1-2260 <$400
1902 Plain Back
3x10-20 2261-6811 <$400
1929 Small Size
10 Type 1 1-784 <$225
20 Type 1 1-200 <$225
10 Type 2 1-1404 <$225
20 Type 2 1-324 <$225
Total Issue $458,610
Out in 1935 $25,000
Large out 1935 $1,460
****
7677 Okfusee
OKEMAH NB, OKEMAH
Chartered 4/05
INDIAN TERRITORY {{ 0 L }}
1902 Red Seal <$VALUE
3x10-20 1-256 <$3500
STATE ISSUES {{ 10 L 15 S }}
1902 Red Seal
3x10-20 1-500 <$2500
1902 Date Back
3x10-20 1-1880 <$250
1902 Plain Back
3x10-20 1881-13080 <$250
1929 Small Size
10 Type 1 1-2024 <$85
20 Type 1 1-524 <$100
10 Type 2 1-2511 <$100
20 Type 2 1-495 <$100
Total Issue $911,130
Out in 1935 $60,000
Large out 1935 $2,950
****
5716 Oklahoma
AMERICAN NB OF OKLAHOMA CITY
Chartered 2/15/01
Closed 4/22/27
OKLAHOMA TERRITORY {{ 2 L }}
Brown Back <$VALUE
3x10-20 1-5200 <$3000
STATE ISSUES {{ 16 L }}
Brown Back
3x10-20 1-4000 <$1000
1882 Date Back
3x10-20 1-10512 <$350
1902 Plain Back
3x50-100 1-1392 <$350/$400
Total Issue $1,333,600
Out at close $225,000
Outstanding includes Ch 5159
Ch 4862 assumed circulation
****
6981 Oklahoma
COMMERCIAL NB OF OKLAHOMA CITY
{{ 1 L }}
Chartered 10/8/03
Liquidated 10/30/05
OKLAHOMA TERRITORY
1902 Red Seal <$VALUE
4x5 1-575 <$3500
3x10-20 1-2228 <$3500
Total Issue $122,900
Out in 1910 $8,035
****
****
9564 Oklahoma
FARMERS NB OF OKLAHOMA CITY
{{ 9 L }}
Chartered 10/09
1902 Date Back <$VALUE
4x5 1-4100 <$200
3x10-20 1-3100 <$200
1902 Plain Back
4x5 4101-12585 <$200
3x10-20 3101-8358 <$200
Total Issue $669,600
Out in 1935 $2,850
****
4402 Oklahoma
FNB OF OKLAHOMA CITY
{{ UNREPORTED }}
Chartered 8/20/90
Liquidated 12/6/97
OKLAHOMA TERRITORY
Brown Back <$VALUE
4x5 1-1695 <$3500
Total Issue $33,900
Out in 1910 $350
****
FNB & TC of Oklahoma City
FNB in Oklahoma City
SEE Ch 4862
State NB of Oklahoma City
****
11230 Oklahoma
LIBERTY NB OF OKLAHOMA CITY
{{ 50+ S }}
Chartered 8/18
1929 Small Size <$VALUE
5 Type 1 1-10886 <$45
10 Type 1 1-5864 <$50
20 Type 1 1-1882 <$55
5 Type 2 1-58740 <$45
10 Type 2 1-27261 <$50
20 Type 2 1-7875 <$55
Total Issue $1,628,070
Out in 1935 $600,000
****
6678 Oklahoma
OKLAHOMA CITY NB, OKLAHOMA CITY
Chartered 3/03
Liquidated 6/30/11
OKLAHOMA TERRITORY {{ 1 L }}
1902 Red Seal <$VALUE
3x10-20 1-1325 <$3500
50-100 1-500 <$8500/$9000
STATE ISSUES {{ 2 L }}
1902 Red Seal
3x10-20 1-500 <$2000
1902 Date Back
3x10-20 1-1938 <$600
50-100 1-157 <$750/$850
Total Issue $286,700
Out at close $124,000
Ch 4862 assumed circulation
****
4770 Oklahoma
OKLAHOMA NB OF OKLAHOMA CITY
{{ UNREPORTED }}
Chartered 7/1/92
Liquidated 7/15/95
OKLAHOMA TERRITORY
Brown Back <$VALUE
3x10-20 1-368 <$4000
Total Issue $18,400
Out in 1910 $120
****
9856 Oklahoma
OKLAHOMA STOCK YARDS NB OF OKLAHOMA CITY
{{ 9 L }}
Chartered 9/10
Liquidated 5/20/26
1902 Date Back <$VALUE
4x5 1-8935 <$275
3x10-20 1-6610 <$275
Total Issue $509,200
Out in 1917 $100,000
****
8472 Oklahoma
SECURITY NB OF OKLAHOMA CITY
Chartered 12/06
Closed 1/2/30
OKLAHOMA TERRITORY {{ 1 L }}
1902 Red Seal <$VALUE
3x10-20 1-1300 <$3500
STATE ISSUES {{ 15 L 0 S }}
1902 Red Seal
3x10-20 1-2000 <$2000
1902 Date Back
3x10-20 1-8900* <$125
1902 Plain Back
3x10-20 9601-50608* <$125
* 8901-9600 not marked
1929 Small Size
10 Type 1 1-246 <$600
20 Type 1 1-10 <$600
Total Issue $2,711,360
Out at close $72,180
Large out at close $56,220
Ch 4862 assumed circulation
****
4862 Oklahoma
STATE NB OF OKLAHOMA CITY
Chartered 1893
2nd title: FNB in Oklahoma City 10/11/19
3rd title: FNB & TC of Oklahoma City 1/2/30
FIRST TITLE
OKLAHOMA TERRITORY {{ 3 L }}
Brown Back <$VALUE
3x10-20 1-5920 <$2250
STATE ISSUES {{ 8 L }}
Brown Back
3x10-20 1-1500 <$1000
1882 Date Back
4x5 1-3468 <$350
3x10-20 1-6454 <$350
1902 Date Back
3x10-20 1-6000 <$150
1902 Plain Back
3x10-20 6001-9600 <$150
SECOND TITLE {{ 14 L }}
1902 Plain Back
3x50-100 1-3937 <$350/$400
THIRD TITLE {{ 50+ S }}
1929 Small Size
10 Type 1 1-16270 <$25
20 Type 1 1-15898 <$35
50 Type 1 1-2058 <$75
100 Type 1 1-1052 <$125
5 Type 2 1-94070 <$25
10 Type 2 1-84209 <$25
20 Type 2 1-35710 <$35
50 Type 2 1-4636 <$100
Total Issue $8,618,310
Out in 1935 $2,500,000
Large out 1935 $31,750
Outstanding includes Ch 6678, Ch 5716, and Ch 8472
****
5159 Oklahoma
WESTERN NB OF OKLAHOMA CITY
Chartered 1898
Liquidated 11/13/17
OKLAHOMA TERRITORY {{ 1 L }}
Brown Back <$VALUE
50-100 1-1987 <$7500/$8000
STATE ISSUES {{ 3 L }}
1882 Date Back
50-100 1-800 <$2500/$3000
3x50-100 1-533<$2500/$3000
Total Issue $551,300
Out at close $93,000
Ch 5716 assumed circulation
****
12048 Okmulgee
AMERICAN NB OF OKMULGEE
{{ 4 L }}
Chartered 12/21
Liquidated 7/30/29
1902 Plain Back <$VALUE
3x10-20 1-5360 <$450
Total Issue $268,000
Out at close $6,390
****
13751 Okmulgee
CITIZENS NB IN OKMULGEE
{{ 2 S }}
Chartered 8/33
1929 Small Size <$VALUE
20 Type 2 1-874 <$400
Total Issue $17,480
Out in 1935 $25,000
Outstanding includes Ch 6241
****

CONDITION affects Value. The Values shown are for notes in FINE condition.

****

6241 Okmulgee
CITIZENS NB OF OKMULGEE
Chartered 5/5/02
Liquidated 9/30/33
INDIAN TERRITORY {{ 0 L }}
1902 Red Seal <$VALUE
3x10-20 1-850 <$3500
STATE ISSUES {{ 7 L 6 S }}
1902 Red Seal
3x10-20 1-300 <$2000
1902 Date Back
3x10-20 1-2800 <$275
1902 Plain Back (dated 1902)
3x10-20 2801-4010 <$275
1902 Plain Back (dated 1922)
3x10-20 1-2523 <$275
1929 Small Size
10 Type 1 1-743 <$225
20 Type 1 1-197 <$225
Total Issue $452,370
Out at close $25,000
Large out 1935 $1,830
Ch 13751 assumed circulation

****

9947 Okmulgee
EXCHANGE NB OF OKMULGEE
{{ 1 L }}
Chartered 3/11
Liquidated 1/17/12
1902 Date Back <$VALUE
3x10-20 1-332 <$1250
Total Issue $16,600
Out in 1912 $6,300

****

9696 Okmulgee
FARMERS NB OF OKMULGEE
{{ 1 L }}
Chartered 3/10
Liquidated 1/14/11
1902 Date Back <$VALUE
4x5 1-565 <$1250
3x10-20 1-372 <$1250
Total Issue $29,900
Out in 1911 $12,200

****

5418 Okmulgee
FNB OF OKMULGEE
Chartered 6/12/00
Liquidated 5/22/24
INDIAN TERRITORY {{ 0 L }}
Brown Back <$VALUE
3x10-20 1-770 <$3000
STATE ISSUES {{ 5 L }}
Brown Back
3x10-20 1-100 <$1250
1882 Date Back
3x10-20 1-3800 <$450
1882 Value Back
3x10-20 3801-5939 <$450
1902 Plain Back
3x10-20 1-3162 <$350
Total Issue $498,550
Out at close $50,000
Ch 11001 assumed circulation

****

6855 Okmulgee
OKMULGEE NB, OKMULGEE
Chartered 6/25/03
Liquidated 5/17/09
INDIAN TERRITORY {{ 1 L }}
1902 Red Seal <$VALUE
3x10-20 1-2500 <$3500
STATE ISSUES {{ 0 L }}
1902 Red Seal
3x10-20 1-428 <$2500
Total Issue $146,400
Out in 1910 $20,550

****

10015 Muskogee
FNB OF OKTAHA
{{ 1 L }}
Organized 5/13/11
Receivership 5/26/26
1902 Date Back <$VALUE
4x5 1-613 <$1000
3x10-20 1-490 <$1000
1902 Plain Back
4x5 614-1215 <$1000
3x10-20 491-890 <$1000
Total Issue $68,800
Out at close $6,250

****

8754 Jackson
FARMERS NB OF OLUSTEE
{{ UNREPORTED }}
Chartered 6/07
Liquidated 11/8/09
OKLAHOMA TERRITORY
1902 Red Seal <$VALUE
4x10 1-250 <$3500
STATE ISSUES
1902 Red Seal
4x10 1-35 <$3000
Total Issue $11,400
Out in 1910 $2,760

****

8316 Jackson
FNB OF OLUSTEE
Chartered 7/30/06
Liquidated 6/20/09
OKLAHOMA TERRITORY {{ 0 L }}
1902 Red Seal <$VALUE
4x10 1-263 <$3500
STATE ISSUES {{ 1 L }}
1902 Red Seal
4x10 1-85 <$3000
Total Issue $13,920
Out in 1910 $2,360

****

9960 Jackson
FNB OF OLUSTEE
{{ 4 L }}
Chartered 3/11
Liquidated 1/17/29
1902 Date Back <$VALUE
4x10 1-2500 <$450
1902 Plain Back
4x10 2501-6288 <$450
Total Issue $251,520
Out in 1924 $25,000

****

7964 Tulsa
FNB OF OWASSO
Chartered 10/05
Liquidated 8/22/18
INDIAN TERRITORY {{ 0 L }}
1902 Red Seal <$VALUE
3x10-20 1-300 <$3500
STATE ISSUES {{ 1 L }}
1902 Date Back
3x10-20 1-1570 <$850
1902 Plain Back
3x10-20 1571-2249 <$850
Total Issue $127,450
Out at close $25,000

****

5091 Garvin
FNB OF PAULS VALLEY
Chartered 1897
INDIAN TERRITORY {{ 0 L }}
Brown Back <$VALUE
3x10-20 1-1020 <$3500
STATE ISSUES {{ 11 L 20 S }}
Brown Back
3x10-20 1-120 <$1500
1882 Date Back
3x10-20 1-6000 <$450
1902 Plain Back
3x10-20 1-20316 <$200
1929 Small Size
5 Type 1 1-314 <$100
10 Type 1 1-2868 <$100
20 Type 1 1-788 <$100
5 Type 2 1-5472 <$100
10 Type 2 1-3060 <$100
20 Type 2 1-888 <$100
Total Issue $1,724,580
Out in 1935 $100,000
Large out 1935 $4,650

****

6639 Garvin
NB OF COMMERCE OF
PAULS VALLEY
Chartered 2/03
Liquidated 1/10/22
INDIAN TERRITORY {{ 3 L }}
1902 Red Seal <$VALUE
4x5 1-1400 <$3500
3x10-20 1-1120 <$3500
STATE ISSUES {{ 2 L }}
1902 Date Back
4x5 1-400* <$750
3x10-20 1-320** <$750
1902 Plain Back
4x5 501-1030* <$750
3x10-20 401-766** <$750
* 401-500 not marked
** 321-400 not marked
Total Issue $142,900
Out at close $12,500

****

7892 Garvin
PAULS VALLEY NB,
PAULS VALLEY
Chartered 8/05
INDIAN TERRITORY {{ 0 L }}
1902 Red Seal <$VALUE
3x10-20 1-900 <$3500
STATE ISSUES {{ 4 L 9 S }}
1902 Date Back
3x10-20 1-2200 <$500
1902 Plain Back
3x10-20 2201-6702 <$500
1929 Small Size
10 Type 1 1-736 <$175
20 Type 1 1-206 <$175
10 Type 2 1-1691 <$200
20 Type 2 1-276 <$200
Total Issue $471,410
Out in 1935 $25,000
Large out 1935 $1,320

****

8313 Osage
AMERICAN NB OF PAWHUSKA
Chartered 7/06
OKLAHOMA TERRITORY {{ 0 L }}
1902 Red Seal <$VALUE
3x10-20 1-200 <$3500
STATE ISSUES {{ 1 L 1 S }}
1902 Date Back
3x10-20 1-710 <$850
1902 Plain Back
3x10-20 711-1677 <$850
1929 Small Size
10 Type 1 1-241 <$500
20 Type 1 1-62 <$500
Total Issue $115,750
Out in 1935 $6,250
Large out 1935 $240

****

13527 Osage
CITIZENS-FNB OF PAWHUSKA
{{ 16 S }}
Chartered 2/31
Liquidated 1/8/35
1929 Small Size <$VALUE
5 Type 1 1-1902 <$75
10 Type 1 1-1162 <$75
20 Type 1 1-432 <$75
5 Type 2 1-6082 <$85
10 Type 2 1-3165 <$85
20 Type 2 1-925 <$85
Total Issue $259,180
Out in 1935 $100,000
Ch 14304 assumed circulation

****

7883 Osage
CITIZENS NB OF PAWHUSKA
Chartered 8/05
Liquidated 3/24/31
OKLAHOMA TERRITORY {{ 0 L }}
1902 Red Seal <$VALUE
3x10-20 1-762 <$3500
STATE ISSUES {{ 7 L 7 S }}
1902 Date Back
3x10-20 1-4150 <$275
1902 Plain Back
3x10-20 4151-12992 <$275
1929 Small Size
10 Type 1 1-746 <$175
20 Type 1 1-199 <$175
Total Issue $756,340
Out at close $45,450
Large out at close $7,140

****

5961 Osage
FNB OF PAWHUSKA
Chartered 9/10/01
Liquidated 3/4/31
OKLAHOMA TERRITORY {{ 1 L }}
Brown Back <$VALUE
3x10-20 1-1200 <$2500
STATE ISSUES {{ 8 L 4 S }}
1882 Date Back
3x10-20 1-4260 <$350
1882 Value Back
3x10-20 4261-7215 <$350
1902 Plain Back
4x5 1-5547 <$250
4x10 1-2761 <$250
3x10-20 1-2307 <$250
1929 Small Size
5 Type 1 1-874 <$250
10 Type 1 1-496 <$250
20 Type 1 1-136 <$250
Total Issue $829,780
Out at close $50,000
Large out at close $5,790

****

11314 Osage
LIBERTY NB OF PAWHUSKA
{{ 9 L }}
Organized 2/5/19
Liquidated 10/23/28
1902 Plain Back <$VALUE
3x10-20 1-13740 <$200
Total Issue $687,000
Out at close $23,590

****

14304 Osage
NB OF COMMERCE IN
PAWHUSKA
{{ 3 S }}
Chartered 11/34
1929 Small Size <$VALUE
20 Type 2 1-1052 <$350
Total Issue $21,040
Out in 1935 $100,000
Outstanding includes Ch 13527

****

5492 Pawnee
ARKANSAS VALLEY NB OF
PAWNEE
Chartered 7/10/00
Liquidated 9/18/17
OKLAHOMA TERRITORY {{ 1 L }}
Brown Back <$VALUE
4x5 1-1700 <$3000
3x10-20 1-1480 <$3000
STATE ISSUES {{ 2 L }}
1882 Date Back
4x5 1-3800* <$850
3x10-20 1-2320** <$850
1882 Value Back
4x5 3951-4655* <$850
3x10-20 2441-2870** <$850
* 3801-3950 not marked
** 2321-2440 not marked
Total Issue $344,600
Out at close $50,000

****

5224 Pawnee
FNB OF PAWNEE
Chartered 10/20/99
OKLAHOMA TERRITORY {{ 1 L }}
Brown Back <$VALUE
3x10-20 1-920 <$3000
STATE ISSUES {{ 5 L 12 S }}
Brown Back
3x10-20 1-900 <$1250
1882 Date Back
3x10-20 1-3740 <$450
1882 Value Back
3x10-20 3741-5190 <$450
1902 Plain Back
3x10-20 1-6669 <$350
1929 Small Size
10 Type 1 1-1462 <$125
20 Type 1 1-392 <$125
10 Type 2 1-2025 <$150
20 Type 2 1-480 <$150
Total Issue $848,560
Out in 1935 $50,000
Large out 1935 $2,270

****

7611 Pawnee
PAWNEE NB, PAWNEE
Chartered 2/05
OKLAHOMA TERRITORY {{ 1 L }}
1902 Red Seal <$VALUE
3x10-20 1-760 <$3500
STATE ISSUES {{ 7 L 12 S }}
1902 Red Seal
3x10-20 1-200 <$2000
1902 Date Back
3x10-20 1-3540 <$275
1902 Plain Back
3x10-20 3541-11567 <$275
1929 Small Size
10 Type 1 1-1348 <$125
20 Type 1 1-362 <$125
10 Type 2 1-2159 <$150
20 Type 2 1-520 <$150
Total Issue $782,660
Out in 1935 $50,000
Large out 1935 $2,590

****

14020 Noble
FNB IN PERRY
{{ 5 S }}
Chartered 2/34
1929 Small Size <$VALUE
10 Type 2 1-3676 <$400
20 Type 2 1-1272 <$400
Total Issue $62,200
Out in 1935 $50,000

****

6972 Noble
FNB OF PERRY
Organized 9/15/03
Receivership 4/9/34
OKLAHOMA TERRITORY {{ 0 L }}
1902 Red Seal <$VALUE
3x10-20 1-1912 <$3500
STATE ISSUES {{ 4 L 6 S }}
1902 Date Back
3x10-20 1-1540 <$500
1902 Plain Back
3x10-20 1541-5595 <$500
1929 Small Size
10 Type 1 1-746 <$275
20 Type 1 1-201 <$300
Total Issue $444,230
Out at close $25,000
Large out at close $1,880

****

10960 Grady
FNB OF POCASSET
{{ 2 L 4 S }}
Chartered 3/17
1902 Plain Back <$VALUE
4x10 1-3327 <$750
1929 Small Size
10 Type 1 1-698 <$375
10 Type 2 1-1486 <$375
Total Issue $189,820
Out in 1935 $12,600
Large out 1935 $440

****

6061 Kay
FARMERS NB OF PONCA CITY
{{ UNREPORTED }}
Chartered 12/26/01
Liquidated 4/8/09
OKLAHOMA TERRITORY
Brown Back <$VALUE
3x10-20 1-1100 <$3500
STATE ISSUES
Brown Back
3x10-20 1-176 <$2000
Total Issue $63,800
Out in 1910 $10,120

****

9801 Kay
FARMERS NB OF PONCA CITY
Organized 6/28/10
Receivership 1/15/34
2nd title: FNB in
Ponca City 7/11/23
FIRST TITLE {{ 3 L }}
1902 Date Back <$VALUE
3x10-20 1-2100 <$500
1902 Plain Back
3x10-20 2101-6160 <$500
SECOND TITLE {{ 5 L 9 S }}
1902 Plain Back
3x10-20 1-4333 <$400
1929 Small Size
10 Type 1 1-1402 <$150
20 Type 1 1-352 <$165
10 Type 2 1-750 <$175
20 Type 2 1-180 <$175
Total Issue $662,110
Out at close $49,250
Large out at close $2,720

****

13891 Kay
FNB AT PONCA CITY
{{ 6 S }}
Chartered 12/33
1929 Small Size <$VALUE
10 Type 2 1-5046 <$250
20 Type 2 1-1492 <$250
Total Issue $80,300
Out in 1935 $47,400

****

FNB in Ponca City
SEE Ch 9801
Farmers NB of Ponca City

****

5474 Kay
FNB OF PONCA CITY
{{ UNREPORTED }}
Chartered 6/30/00
Liquidated 9/6/09
OKLAHOMA TERRITORY
Brown Back <$VALUE
3x10-20 1-1800 <$3000
STATE ISSUES
1882 Date Back
3x10-20 1-175 <$1500
Total Issue $98,750
Out in 1910 $14,100

****

9616 Kay
GERMANIA NB OF PONCA CITY
{{ 2 L }}
Chartered 12/09
Liquidated 6/4/17
1902 Date Back <$VALUE
3x10-20 1-2000 <$850
1902 Plain Back
3x10-20 2001-2421 <$850
Total Issue $121,050
Out at close $25,000

****

10005 Grant
FARMERS NB OF POND CREEK
Chartered 4/11
Liquidated 12/31/31
2nd title:FNB in Pond Creek
12/19/21
FIRST TITLE {{ 1 L }}
1902 Date Back <$VALUE
3x10-20 1-600 <$850
1902 Plain Back
3x10-20 601-1960 <$850
SECOND TITLE {{ 2 L 3 S }}
1902 Plain Back
3x10-20 1-2174 <$750
1929 Small Size
10 Type 1 1-464 <$400
20 Type 1 1-114 <$400
Total Issue $248,220
Out at close $25,000
Large out at close $2,680

****

FNB in Pond Creek
SEE Ch 10005
Farmers NB of Pond Creek

****

6655 Grant
FNB OF POND CREEK
Chartered 3/4/03
Liquidated 3/20/09
OKLAHOMA TERRITORY {{ 7 L }}
1902 Red Seal <$VALUE
3x10-20 1-620 <$2500
STATE ISSUES {{ 0 L }}
1902 Red Seal
3x10-20 1-300 <$2000
1902 Date Back
3x10-20 1-50 <$1000
Total Issue $48,500
Out in 1910 $10,150

****

7103 Grant
NB OF POND CREEK
{{ UNREPORTED }}
Chartered 1/19/04
Liquidated 5/7/09
OKLAHOMA TERRITORY
1902 Red Seal <$VALUE
3x10-20 1-1050 <$3500
STATE ISSUES
1902 Red Seal
3x10-20 1-188 <$3000
Total Issue $61,900
Out in 1910 $10,570

****

7615 Wagoner
FNB OF PORTER
Chartered 2/05
INDIAN TERRITORY {{ 0 L }}
1902 Red Seal <$VALUE
3x10-20 1-700 <$3500
STATE ISSUES {{ 3 L 6 S }}
1902 Red Seal
3x10-20 1-300 <$3000
1902 Date Back
3x10-20 1-1810 <$650
1902 Plain Back
3x10-20 1811-6402 <$650
1929 Small Size
10 Type 1 1-770 <$250
20 Type 1 1-222 <$250
10 Type 2 1-994 <$275
20 Type 2 1-313 <$275
Total Issue $459,140
Out in 1935 $25,000
Large out 1935 $1,500

****

8676 Wagoner
PORTER NB, PORTER
{{ UNREPORTED }}
Chartered 5/4/07
Liquidated 1/25/08
INDIAN TERRITORY
1902 Red Seal <$VALUE
3x10-20 1-520 <$4000
Total Issue $26,000
Out in 1910 $5,390

****

8479 Muskogee
FNB OF PORUM
Chartered 12/06
Liquidated 12/29/15
INDIAN TERRITORY {{ 0 L }}
1902 Red Seal <$VALUE
4x5 1-150 <$4000
4x10 1-160 <$4000
STATE ISSUES {{ 2 L }}
1902 Date Back
4x5 1-510 <$1000
4x10 1-507 <$1000
Total Issue $39,880
Out in 1916 $2,770

****

10649 Muskogee
NB OF COMMERCE OF PORUM
{{ 1 L }}
Chartered 10/14
Liquidated 4/10/16
1902 Date Back <$VALUE
4x10 1-955 <$1250
Total Issue $38,200
Out at close $16,900

****

****
7118 Le Flore
FNB OF POTEAU
Organized 1/14/04
Receivership 6/19/24
INDIAN TERRITORY {{ 2 L }}
1902 Red Seal <$VALUE
3x10-20 1-700 <$3000
STATE ISSUES {{ 3 L }}
1902 Red Seal
3x10-20 1-300 <$2500
1902 Date Back
3x10-20 1-1880 <$600
1902 Plain Back
3x10-20 1881-4239 <$600
Total Issue $261,950
Out at close $22,700
****
7104 Le Flore
NB OF POTEAU
Chartered 1/04
Liquidated 12/6/19
INDIAN TERRITORY {{ 0 L }}
1902 Red Seal <$VALUE
3x10-20 1-470 <$3500
STATE ISSUES {{ 4 L }}
1902 Red Seal
3x10-20 1-120 <$3000
1902 Date Back
3x10-20 1-4740 <$500
1902 Plain Back
3x10-20 4741-6315 <$500
Total Issue $345,250
Out at close $50,000
****
7177 Lincoln
FNB OF PRAGUE
Chartered 3/04
OKLAHOMA TERRITORY {{ 0 L }}
1902 Red Seal <$VALUE
3x10-20 1-963 <$3500
STATE ISSUES {{ 4 L 8 S }}
1902 Date Back
3x10-20 1-2170 <$500
1902 Plain Back
3x10-20 2171-6553 <$500
1929 Small Size
10 Type 1 1-790 <$175
20 Type 1 1-204 <$175
10 Type 2 1-1049 <$200
20 Type 2 1-324 <$200
Total Issue $464,650
Out in 1935 $25,000
Large out 1935 $1,480
****
8159` Lincoln
PRAGUE NB, PRAGUE
Chartered 4/06
OKLAHOMA TERRITORY {{ 0 L }}
1902 Red Seal <$VALUE
3x10-20 1-200 <$3500
STATE ISSUES {{ 4 L 10 S }}
1902 Red Seal
3x10-20 1-100 <$2500
1902 Date Back
3x10-20 1-1830 <$500
1902 Plain Back
3x10-20 1831-6126 <$500
1929 Small Size
10 Type 1 1-1132 <$175
20 Type 1 1-312 <$175
10 Type 2 1-2472 <$175
20 Type 2 1-828 <$175
Total Issue $467,940
Out in 1935 $50,000
Large out 1935 $730
****
12117 Mayes
AMERICAN NB OF
PRYOR CREEK
{{ 3 S }}
Chartered 2/22
1929 Small Size <$VALUE
5 Type 2 1-1270 <$400
10 Type 2 1-780 <$400
20 Type 2 1-440 <$400
Total Issue $23,050
Out in 1935 $20,000
****
5546 Mayes
FNB OF PRYOR CREEK
Chartered 8/21/00
INDIAN TERRITORY {{ 1 L }}
Brown Back <$VALUE
3x10-20 1-920 <$3500
STATE ISSUES {{ 3 L 6 S }}
Brown Back
3x10-20 1-200 <$1500
1882 Date Back17
3x10-20 1-1800 <$750
1882 Value Back
3x10-20 1801-2424 <$750
1902 Plain Back
3x10-20 1-2483 <$500

1929 Small Size
10 Type 1 1-602 <$250
20 Type 1 1-162 <$250
10 Type 2 1-665 <$300
20 Type 2 1-185 <$300
Total Issue $367,260
Out in 1935 $25,000
Large out 1935 $1,060
****
4756 McClain
CHICKASAW NB OF PURCELL
Chartered 1892
Liquidated 6/21/27
INDIAN TERRITORY {{ 1 L }}
Brown Back <$VALUE
3x10-20 1-5740 <$3000
STATE ISSUES {{ 10 L }}
1882 Date Back
4x5 1-1000 <$300
3x10-20 1-1585 <$300
1902 Date Back
3x10-20 1-2200 <$200
1902 Plain Back
3x10-20 2201-15070 <$200
Total Issue $1,139,750
Out at close $100,000
Outstanding includes Ch 7697
****
12134 McClain
McCLAIN COUNTY NB OF
PURCELL
{{ 14 S }}
Chartered 3/22
1929 Small Size <$VALUE
5 Type 1 1-418 <$125
10 Type 1 1-418 <$125
20 Type 1 1-212 <$125
5 Type 2 1-3750 <$150
10 Type 2 1-2297 <$150
20 Type 2 1-520 <$150
Total Issue $115,180
Out in 1935 $50,000
****
4636 McClain
PURCELL NB, PURCELL
{{ 1 L }}
Chartered 9/22/91
Liquidated 12/30/99
INDIAN TERRITORY
Brown Back <$VALUE
3x10-20 1-704 <$3500
Total Issue $35,200
Out in 1910 $440
****
7697 McClain
UNION NB OF PURCELL
Chartered 4/05
Liquidated 1/14/19
INDIAN TERRITORY {{ 0 L }}
1902 Red Seal <$VALUE
3x10-20 1-950 <$3500
STATE ISSUES {{ 1 L }}
1902 Date Back
3x10-20 1-2040 <$850
1902 Plain Back
3x10-20 2041-2702 <$850
Total Issue $182,600
Out at close $25,000
Ch 4756 assumed circulation
****
6517 Pittsburg
FNB OF QUINTON
Chartered 12/1/02
Liquidated 11/9/29
INDIAN TERRITORY {{ 0 L }}
1902 Red Seal <$VALUE
4x5 1-405 <$3500
3x10-20 1-324 <$3500
STATE ISSUES {{ 5 L 0 S }}
1902 Red Seal
4x5 1-100 <$3000
3x10-20 1-80 <$3000
1902 Date Back
4x5 1-2125 <$400
3x10-20 1-1540 <$400
1902 Plain Back
4x5 2126-7079 <$400
3x10-20 1541-4352 <$400
1929 Small Size
5 Type 1 1-177 <$750
10 Type 1 1-46* <$750
* F000046A not issued
Total Issue $397,540
Out at close $25,000
Large out at close $23,190
****
6232 Pawnee
FNB OF RALSTON
Chartered 4/29/02
Liquidated 12/31/30
OKLAHOMA TERRITORY {{ 0 L }}
1902 Red Seal <$VALUE
3x10-20 1-400 <$4000

STATE ISSUES {{ 3 L 3 S }}
1902 Date Back
3x10-20 1-2320 <$650
1902 Plain Back (dated 1902)
3x10-20 2321-4082 <$650
1902 Plain Back (dated 1922)
3x10-20 1-2659 <$650
1929 Small Size
10 Type 1 1-326 <$500
20 Type 1 1-98 <$500
Total Issue $388,370
Out at close $25,000
Large out at close $3,355
****
7251 Washington
FNB OF RAMONA
{{ 1 L }}
Organized 5/11/04
Receivership 5/2/08
INDIAN TERRITORY
1902 Red Seal <$VALUE
4x5 1-255 <$5000
3x10-20 1-202 <$5000
Total Issue $15,200
Out in 1916 $310
****
7976 Johnston
FNB OF RAVIA
{{ UNREPORTED }}
Chartered 11/13/05
Liquidated 2/1/09
INDIAN TERRITORY
1902 Red Seal <$VALUE
3x10-20 1-245 <$5000
Total Issue $12,250
Out in 1910 $1,590
****
10548 Jefferson
FNB OF RINGLING
{{ 6 L 8 S }}
Chartered 5/14
1902 Plain Back <$VALUE
3x10-20 1-7694 <$400
1929 Small Size
10 Type 1 1-840 <$200
20 Type 1 1-204 <$200
10 Type 2 1-1269 <$200
20 Type 2 1-352 <$225
Total Issue $479,310
Out in 1935 $25,000
Large out 1935 $1,730
****
10172 Pontotoc
FARMERS & MERCHANTS NB OF
ROFF
{{ 2 L }}
Chartered 4/12
Liquidated 12/31/28
1902 Date Back <$VALUE
3x10-20 1-900 <$750
1902 Plain Back
3x10-20 901-2214 <$750
Total Issue $110,700
Out at close $10,000
****
5417 Pontotoc
FNB OF ROFF
Chartered 6/12/00
Receivership 11/21/27
INDIAN TERRITORY {{ 0 L }}
Brown Back <$VALUE
3x10-20 1-920 <$3500
STATE ISSUES {{ 4 L }}
Brown Back
3x10-20 1-300 <$1500
1882 Date Back
3x10-20 1-2600 <$650
1882 Value Back
3x10-20 2601-3800 <$650
1902 Plain Back
3x10-20 1-3075 <$450
Total Issue $404,750
Out at close $30,000
****
8336 Grady
FNB OF RUSH SPRINGS
Chartered 8/06
INDIAN TERRITORY {{ 0 L }}
1902 Red Seal <$VALUE
3x10-20 1-250 <$4000
STATE ISSUES {{ 2 L 4 S }}
1902 Date Back
3x10-20 1-900 <$1000
1902 Plain Back
3x10-20 901-1969 <$1000
1929 Small Size
10 Type 1 1-312 <$400
20 Type 1 1-106 <$400
5 Type 2 1-1952 <$400
10 Type 2 1-644 <$400
20 Type 2 1-51 <$400
Total Issue $159,610
Out in 1935 $20,000
Large out 1935 $260
****

****
5800 Jefferson
FNB OF RYAN
Chartered 5/7/01
Liquidated 7/19/29
INDIAN TERRITORY {{ 1 L }}
Brown Back <$VALUE
3x10-20 1-1420 <$3500
STATE ISSUES {{ 6 L }}
Brown Back
3x10-20 1-400 <$1500
1882 Date Back
3x10-20 1-3660 <$500
1882 Value Back
3x10-20 3661-6446 <$500
1902 Plain Back
3x10-20 1-6296 <$400
Total Issue $728,100
Out at close $46,100
****
10474 Sequoyah
CITIZENS NB OF SALLISAW
{{ 4 L }}
Chartered 1/14
Liquidated 2/1/27
1902 Date Back <$VALUE
3x10-20 1-500 <$500
1902 Plain Back
3x10-20 501-3920 <$500
Total Issue $196,000
Out in 1924 $29,100
****
9973 Sequoyah
FARMERS NB OF SALLISAW
{{ 1 L }}
Chartered 3/11
Liquidated 9/29/13
1902 Date Back <$VALUE
3x10-20 1-997 <$1000
Total Issue $49,850
Out at close $24,300
****
FNB in Sallisaw
SEE Ch 7571
Merchants NB of Sallisaw
****
5596 Sequoyah
FNB OF SALLISAW
Chartered 10/15/00
Liquidated 5/18/09
INDIAN TERRITORY {{ 1 L }}
Brown Back <$VALUE
3x10-20 1-1060 <$3500
STATE ISSUES {{ 0 L }}
1882 Date Back
3x10-20 1-169 <$1500
Total Issue $61,450
Out in 1910 $9,850
****
7571 Sequoyah
MERCHANTS NB OF SALLISAW
Organized 1/3/05
Receivership 10/24/27
2nd title: FNB in
Sallisaw 6/26/20
FIRST TITLE
INDIAN TERRITORY {{ 0 L }}
1902 Red Seal <$VALUE
3x10-20 1-532 <$3500
STATE ISSUES {{ 2 L }}
1902 Date Back
3x10-20 1-1460 <$600
1902 Plain Back
3x10-20 1461-2940 <$600
SECOND TITLE {{ 3 L }}
1902 Plain Back
4x10 1-7120 <$500
Total Issue $458,400
Out at close $48,800
****
12079 Tulsa
FNB OF SAND SPRINGS
{{ 3 L }}
Chartered 12/21
Liquidated 2/6/29
1902 Plain Back <$VALUE
4x5 1-5465 <$750
3x10-20 1-3778 <$750
Total Issue $298,200
Out at close $50,000
****
7788 Creek
AMERICAN NB OF SAPULPA
Chartered 6/05
INDIAN TERRITORY {{ 0 L }}
1902 Red Seal <$VALUE
3x10-20 1-560 <$3500
STATE ISSUES {{ 4 L 10 S }}
1902 Red Seal
3x10-20 1-500 <$2500
1902 Date Back
3x10-20 1-2250 <$500
1902 Plain Back
3x10-20 2251-6600 <$500

1929 Small Size
10 Type 1 1-692 <$175
20 Type 1 1-190 <$175
10 Type 2 1-1561 <$175
20 Type 2 1-312 <$175
Total Issue $469,170
Out in 1935 $25,000
Large out 1935 $1,670
****
5951 Creek
FNB OF SAPULPA
Chartered 8/28/01
Receivership 7/30/23
INDIAN TERRITORY {{ 0 L }}
Brown Back <$VALUE
3x10-20 1-750 <$3500
STATE ISSUES {{ 4 L }}
Brown Back
3x10-20 1-160 <$1500
1882 Date Back
3x10-20 1-3650 <$650
1882 Value Back
3x10-20 3651-6660 <$650
1902 Plain Back
3x10-20 1-1500 <$500
Total Issue $453,500
Out at close $44,900
****
10314 Seminole
FNB OF SASAKWA
{{ UNREPORTED }}
Chartered 1/13
Liquidated 12/28/15
1902 Date Back <$VALUE
3x10-20 1-346 <$1500
Total Issue $17,300
Out in 1916 $3,810
****
9976 Beckham
BECKHAM COUNTY NB OF
SAYRE
{{ 0 L 1 S }}
Chartered 3/11
1902 Date Back <$VALUE
3x10-20 1-675 <$1500
1902 Plain Back
3x10-20 676-1480 <$1500
1929 Small Size
10 Type 1 1-228 <$600
20 Type 1 1-68 <$600
Total Issue $95,840
Out in 1935 $6,250
Large out 1935 $380
****
6058 Beckham
FNB OF SAYRE
Chartered 12/20/01
Liquidated 2/20/09
OKLAHOMA TERRITORY {{ 1 L }}
Brown Back <$VALUE
3x10-20 1-900 <$3500
STATE ISSUES {{ 0 L }}
1882 Date Back
3x10-20 1-91 <$1500
Total Issue $49,550
Out in 1910 $8,150
****
9959 Beckham
FNB OF SAYRE
{{ 6 L 6 S }}
Chartered 3/11
1902 Date Back <$VALUE
3x10-20 1-1275 <$375
1902 Plain Back
3x10-20 1276-5575 <$375
1929 Small Size
10 Type 1 1-858 <$250
20 Type 1 1-202 <$250
10 Type 2 1-936 <$250
20 Type 2 1-384 <$250
Total Issue $371,510
Out in 1935 $25,000
Large out 1935 $1,480
****
8615 Dewey
FNB OF SEILING
Chartered 3/07
OKLAHOMA TERRITORY {{ 1 L }}
1902 Red Seal <$VALUE
3x10-20 1-200 <$3500
STATE ISSUES {{ 1 L 4 S }}
1902 Date Back
3x10-20 1-660 <$1000
1902 Plain Back
3x10-20 661-1372 <$1000
1929 Small Size
10 Type 1 1-316 <$375
20 Type 1 1-106 <$375
10 Type 2 1-1143 <$375
20 Type 2 1-243 <$400
Total Issue $126,510
Out in 1935 $25,000
Large out 1935 $360
****

****
9514 Seminole
FNB OF SEMINOLE
{{ 2 L 2U + 16 S }}
Chartered 8/09
1902 Date Back <$VALUE
3x10-20 1-800 <$1000
1902 Plain Back
3x10-20 801-1722 <$1000
1929 Small Size
10 Type 1 1-584 <$300
20 Type 1 1-162 <$300
10 Type 2 1-1260 <$300
20 Type 2 1-456 <$300
Total Issue $162,300
Out in 1935 $25,000
Large out 1935 $270
****
9995 Washita
FNB OF SENTINEL
{{ 4 L }}
Chartered 4/11
1902 Date Back <$VALUE
4x5 1-1438 <$750
3x10-20 1-1150 <$750
1902 Plain Back
4x5 1439-5410 <$750
3x10-20 1151-3585 <$750
Total Issue $287,450
Out in 1935 $1,045
****
8687 Ellis
FNB OF SHATTUCK
{{ UNREPORTED }}
Chartered 5/15/07
Liquidated 9/11/09
OKLAHOMA TERRITORY
1902 Red Seal <$VALUE
3x10-20 1-187 <$4000
STATE ISSUES
1902 Date Back
3x10-20 1-22 <$1500
Total Issue $10,450
Out in 1910 $3,090
****
9987 Ellis
SHATTUCK NB, SHATTUCK
{{ 2 L 2 S }}
Chartered 4/11
1902 Date Back <$VALUE
3x10-20 1-750 <$850
1902 Plain Back
3x10-20 751-1522 <$850
1929 Small Size
10 Type 1 1-225 <$500
20 Type 1 1-53 <$500
Total Issue $95,960
Out in 1935 $7,500
Large out 1935 $350
****
12339 Pottawatomie
FEDERAL NB OF SHAWNEE
{{ 2 L 18 S }}
Chartered 3/23
1902 Plain Back <$VALUE
4x5 1-1821 <$650
4x10 1-1107 <$650
3x10-20 1-1495 <$650
1929 Small Size
5 Type 1 1-3070 <$100
10 Type 1 1-1770 <$100
20 Type 1 1-418 <$100
5 Type 2 1-7200 <$110
10 Type 2 1-3852 <$110
20 Type 2 1-1344 <$125
Total Issue $505,310
Out in 1935 $100,000
Large out 1935 $370
****
5095 Pottawatomie
FNB OF SHAWNEE
{{ UNREPORTED }}
Chartered 10/28/97
Liquidated 1/16/06
OKLAHOMA TERRITORY
Brown Back <$VALUE
4x5 1-1783 <$3500
3x10-20 1-750 <$3500
Total Issue $73,160
Out in 1910 $2,120
****
12441 Pottawatomie
NB OF COMMERCE IN SHAWNEE
{{ UNREPORTED }}
Organized 8/18/23
Receivership 4/28/24
1902 Plain Back <$VALUE
3x10-20 1-756 <$1250
Total Issue $37,800
Out at close $100,000
Outstanding includes Ch 9998
****

****
9998 Pottawatomie
NB OF COMMERCE OF SHAWNEE
{{ 6 L }}
Chartered 4/11
Liquidated 8/18/23
1902 Date Back <$VALUE
3x10-20 1-6700 <$350
1902 Plain Back
3x10-20 6701-15325 <$350
Total Issue $766,250
Out at close $100,000
Ch 12441 assumed circulation
****
5875 Pottawatomie
OKLAHOMA NB OF SHAWNEE
{{ UNREPORTED }}
Chartered 6/24/01
Liquidated 5/1/09
OKLAHOMA TERRITORY
Brown Back <$VALUE
3x10-20 1-2050 <$3500
STATE ISSUES
1882 Date Back
3x10-20 1-347 <$1250
Total Issue $119,850
Out in 1910 $19,470
****
5115 Pottawatomie
SHAWNEE NB, SHAWNEE
Organized 3/1/98
Receivership 11/15/32
OKLAHOMA TERRITORY {{ 2 L }}
Brown Back <$VALUE
4x5 1-2525 <$3000
3x10-20 1-2880 <$3000
STATE ISSUES {{ 8 L 14 S }}
1882 Date Back
4x5 1-5000 <$400
3x10-20 1-3670 <$400
1882 Value Back
4x5 5001-5700 <$400
3x10-20 3671-4030 <$400
1902 Plain Back
3x10-20 1-8024 <$250
1929 Small Size
10 Type 1 1-1242 <$125
20 Type 1 1-353 <$125
Total Issue $1,028,080
Out at close $50,000
Large out at close $5,930
****
6416 Pottawatomie
STATE NB OF SHAWNEE
Chartered 9/11/02
Receivership 4/9/34
OKLAHOMA TERRITORY {{ 0 L }}
1902 Red Seal <$VALUE
3x10-20 1-1600 <$3000
STATE ISSUES {{ 14 L 26 S }}
1902 Red Seal
3x10-20 1-1500 <$1500
1902 Date Back
3x10-20 1-8200 <$175
1902 Plain Back
3x10-20 8201-25548 <$175
1929 Small Size
10 Type 1 1-3266 <$60
20 Type 1 1-854 <$65
10 Type 2 1-711 <$85
20 Type 2 1-430 <$85
Total Issue $1,746,550
Out at close $100,000
Large out at close $5,940
****
9969 Tulsa
FNB OF SKIATOOK
{{ UNREPORTED }}
Chartered 3/11
Liquidated 8/5/29
1902 Date Back <$VALUE
3x10-20 1-700 <$1250
1902 Plain Back
3x10-20 701-1646 <$1250
Total Issue $82,300
Out at close $4,660
****
10464 Tulsa
OKLAHOMA NB OF SKIATOOK
{{ 1 L }}
Chartered 12/1/13
Liquidated 8/5/29
1902 Date Back <$VALUE
3x10-20 1-475 <$1500
1902 Plain Back
3x10-20 476-1401 <$1500
Total Issue $70,050
Out at close $5,700
****

****
10317 Kiowa
FNB OF SNYDER
{{ 1 L }}
Chartered 1/13
1902 Date Back <$VALUE
3x10-20 1-500 <$1500
1902 Plain Back
3x10-20 501-887 <$1500
Total Issue $44,350
Out in 1935 $150
****
10311 Kiowa
KIOWA NB OF SNYDER
{{ UNREPORTED }}
Chartered 1/13
Liquidated 9/13/13
1902 Date Back <$VALUE
4x5 1-182 <$1500
4x10 1-182 <$1500
Total Issue $10,920
Out at close $9,600
****
10366 Choctaw
FNB OF SOPER
{{ UNREPORTED }}
Organized 4/15/13
Receivership 11/22/23
1902 Date Back <$VALUE
3x10-20 1-1300 <$1500
1902 Plain Back
3x10-20 1301-1344 <$1500
Total Issue $67,200
Out at close $7,500
****
6230 Pittsburg
AMERICAN NB OF
SOUTH McALESTER
Chartered 4/25/02
Liquidated 7/19/26
2nd title: American NB of
McAlester 11/16/07
FIRST TITLE
INDIAN TERRITORY {{ 1 L }}
1902 Red Seal <$VALUE
3x10-20 1-1341 <$3500
SECOND TITLE
STATE ISSUES {{ 9 L }}
1902 Red Seal
3x10-20 1-750 <$2500
1902 Date Back
4x5 1-7350 <$250
3x10-20 1-5660 <$250
1902 Plain Back (dated 1902)
4x5 7351-13565 <$250
3x10-20 5661-9507 <$250
1902 Plain Back (dated 1922)
3x10-20 1-4726 <$250
Total Issue $1,087,500
Out in 1925 $84,995
****
6406 Pittsburg
CITY NB OF
SOUTH McALESTER
Chartered 9/2/02
Liquidated 6/29/25
2nd title: City NB of
McAlester 11/16/07
INDIAN TERRITORY
FIRST TITLE {{ 0 L }}
1902 Red Seal <$VALUE
3x10-20 1-1625 <$3500
SECOND TITLE
STATE ISSUES {{ 8 L }}
1902 Red Seal
3x10-20 1-1500 <$2500
1902 Date Back
4x5 1-1375 <$250
3x10-20 1-2500 <$250
1902 Plain Back
4x5 1376-7975 <$250
3x10-20 2501-6024 <$250
Total Issue $616,950
Out at close $50,000
****
5052 Pittsburg
FNB OF SOUTH McALESTER
Chartered 1896
2nd title: FNB of McAlester
5/24/06
INDIAN TERRITORY
FIRST TITLE {{ 0 L }}
Brown Back <$VALUE
3x10-20 1-1375 <$3000
SECOND TITLE {{ 4 L }}
Brown Back
3x10-20 1-1200 <$2500
STATE ISSUES {{ 15 L 26 S }}
1882 Date Back
4x5 1-4800 <$300
3x10-20 1-6800 <$300

1882 Value Back
4x5 4801-5275 <$300
3x10-20 6801-7139 <$300
1902 Plain Back
4x5 1-15332 <$150
3x10-20 1-10892 <$150
1929 Small Size
5 Type 1 1-3708 <$75
10 Type 1 1-2146 <$75
20 Type 1 1-654 <$75
5 Type 2 1-6614* <$85
10 Type 2 1-3539 <$85
20 Type 2 1-751 <$85
* 1243-1248 not issued
Total Issue $1,844,370
Out in 1935 $100,000
Large out 1935 $6,375
****
5537 Pittsburg
STATE NB OF
SOUTH McALESTER
{{ 1 L }}
Chartered 8/14/00
Liquidated 10/20/02
INDIAN TERRITORY
Brown Back <$VALUE
3x10-20 1-362 <$3500
Total Issue $18,100
Out in 1910 $650
****
9275 Le Flore
FNB OF SPIRO
{{ 6 L }}
Chartered 11/08
Liquidated 8/26/29
1902 Date Back <$VALUE
3x10-20 1-1950 <$400
1902 Plain Back
3x10-20 1951-5281 <$400
Total Issue $264,050
Out at close $18,360
****
6804 Hughes
FNB OF SPOKOGEE
{{ UNREPORTED }}
Chartered 5/03
Liquidated 1/26/11
2nd title: FNB of Dustin
2/18/05
INDIAN TERRITORY
FIRST TITLE
1902 Red Seal <$VALUE
3x10-20 1-173 <$5000
SECOND TITLE
1902 Red Seal
3x10-20 1-185 <$5000
STATE ISSUES
1902 Date Back
3x10-20 1-127 <$2000
Total Issue $24,250
Out in 1911 $3,050
****
7950 Bryan
FNB OF STERRETT
Chartered 10/05
Liquidated 12/10/17
INDIAN TERRITORY {{ 0 L }}
1902 Red Seal <$VALUE
3x10-20 1-600 <$3500
STATE ISSUES {{ 3 L }}
1902 Red Seal
3x10-20 1-200 <$2500
1902 Date Back
3x10-20 1-1930 <$750
1902 Plain Back
3x10-20 1931-2114 <$750
Total Issue $145,700
Out at close $20,000
****
7432 Haskell
AMERICAN NB OF STIGLER
Organized 9/14/04
Receivership 3/1/27
INDIAN TERRITORY {{ 0 L }}
1902 Red Seal <$VALUE
3x10-20 1-400 <$3500
STATE ISSUES {{ 1 L }}
1902 Date Back
3x10-20 1-2260* <$1000
1902 Plain Back
3x10-20 2401-5712* <$1000
* 2261-2400 not marked
Total Issue $305,600
Out at close $24,500
****
7217 Haskell
FNB OF STIGLER
Chartered 4/04
INDIAN TERRITORY {{ 0 L }}
1902 Red Seal <$VALUE
3x10-20 1-1150 <$3500
STATE ISSUES {{ 6 L 4 S }}
1902 Date Back
3x10-20 1-3500 <$400

1902 Plain Back
3x10-20 3501-11919 <$400
1929 Small Size
10 Type 1 1-583 <$350
20 Type 1 1-199 <$350
Total Issue $712,310
Out in 1935 $8,750
Large out 1935 $3,060
****
5206 Payne
FNB OF STILLWATER
Chartered 7/10/99
OKLAHOMA TERRITORY {{ 0 L }}
Brown Back <$VALUE
4x5 1-1225 <$3500
3x10-20 1-550 <$3500
STATE ISSUES {{ 1 L 14 S }}
1882 Date Back
4x5 1-1148 <$1250
3x10-20 1-860 <$1250
1882 Value Back
3x10-20 861-873 <$1250
1929 Small Size
5 Type 1 1-1898 <$125
10 Type 1 1-940 <$125
20 Type 1 1-284 <$125
5 Type 2 1-2014 <$135
10 Type 2 1-1042 <$135
20 Type 2 1-324 <$135
Total Issue $293,000
Out in 1935 $50,000
Large out 1935 $435
****
5436 Payne
NB OF COMMERCE OF
STILLWATER
Chartered 6/18/00
Liquidated 4/1/09
OKLAHOMA TERRITORY {{ 1 L }}
Brown Back <$VALUE
4x5 1-1410 <$3000
3x10-20 1-1286 <$3000
STATE ISSUES {{ 0 L }}
Brown Back
4x5 1-100 <$1500
3x10-20 1-80 <$1500
1882 Date Back
4x5 1-35 <$1500
3x10-20 1-29 <$1500
Total Issue $100,650
Out in 1910 $8,955
****
5347 Payne
STILLWATER NB, STILLWATER
Chartered 5/11/00
OKLAHOMA TERRITORY {{ 6 L }}
Brown Back <$VALUE
4x5 1-1700 <$2250
3x10-20 1-1240 <$2250
STATE ISSUES {{ 5 L 3 S }}
1882 Date Back
4x5 1-1700* <$500
3x10-20 1-1310** <$500
1882 Value Back
4x5 1801-2790* <$500
3x10-20 1391-1981** <$500
* 1701-1800 not marked
** 1311-1390 not marked
1902 Plain Back
4x5 1-10949 <$350
1929 Small Size
5 Type 1 1-3274 <$300
5 Type 2 1-6804 <$300
Total Issue $602,070
Out in 1935 $25,000
Large out 1935 $1,610
****
9970 Adair
FNB OF STILWELL
{{ 5 L 0 S }}
Chartered 3/11
Liquidated 11/18/29
1902 Date Back <$VALUE
3x10-20 1-1600 <$500
1902 Plain Back
3x10-20 1601-5785 <$500
1929 Small Size
10 Type 1 1-42 <$750
20 Type 1 1-8 <$750
Total Issue $292,730
Out at close $12,670
Large out at close $9,400
****
7054 Pontotoc
FNB OF STONEWALL
Chartered 12/03
Liquidated 12/31/28
INDIAN TERRITORY {{ 0 L }}
1902 Red Seal <$VALUE
3x10-20 1-316 <$4000
STATE ISSUES {{ 4 L }}
1902 Date Back
3x10 20 1 1800* <$600

1902 Plain Back
3x10-20 1901-5298* <$600
* 1801-1900 not marked
Total Issue $280,700
Out at close $22,200
****
8524 Garvin
FNB OF STRATFORD
Chartered 1/07
INDIAN TERRITORY {{ 0 L }}
1902 Red Seal <$VALUE
3x10-20 1-200 <$4000
STATE ISSUES {{ 7 L 7 S }}
1902 Date Back
3x10-20 1-2170 <$350
1902 Plain Back
3x10-20 2171-6327 <$350
1929 Small Size
10 Type 1 1-804 <$275
20 Type 1 1-188 <$275
10 Type 2 1-1028 <$300
20 Type 2 1-320 <$300
Total Issue $413,830
Out in 1935 $25,000
Large out 1935 $1,190
****
6306 Lincoln
FNB OF STROUD
Chartered 6/17/02
OKLAHOMA TERRITORY {{ 0 L }}
1902 Red Seal <$VALUE
3x10-20 1-400 <$3500
STATE ISSUES {{ 2 L 5 S }}
1902 Red Seal
3x10-20 1-100 <$2500
1902 Date Back
3x10-20 1-660 <$850
1902 Plain Back
3x10-20 661-1572 <$850
1929 Small Size
10 Type 1 1-518 <$300
20 Type 1 1-166 <$300
10 Type 2 1-838 <$300
20 Type 2 1-204 <$300
Total Issue $167,060
Out in 1935 $25,000
Large out 1935 $370
****
10007 Hughes
FNB OF STUART
{{ UNREPORTED }}
Chartered 5/11
Liquidated 12/15/17
1902 Date Back <$VALUE
4x10 1-825 <$1500
1902 Plain Back
4x10 826-1258 <$1500
Total Issue $50,320
Out at close $24,970
****
11315 Hughes
LIBERTY NB OF STUART
{{ UNREPORTED }}
Chartered 3/19
Liquidated 3/23/21
1902 Plain Back <$VALUE
3x10-20 1-800 <$1500
Total Issue $40,000
Out at close $25,000
****
5748 Murray
FNB OF SULPHUR
Chartered 3/20/01
Liquidated 5/12/09
INDIAN TERRITORY {{ 1 L }}
Brown Back <$VALUE
4x5 1-1000 <$4000
3x10-20 1-1525 <$4000
STATE ISSUES {{ 1 L }}
1882 Date Back
3x10-20 1-165 <$1500
Total Issue $99,550
Out in 1910 $19,075
****
9046 Murray
PARK NB OF SULPHUR
{{ 6 L 6 S }}
Organized 2/3/08
Receivership 11/14/32
1902 Red Seal <$VALUE
3x10-20 1-400 <$2500
1902 Date Back
3x10-20 1-1860 <$450
1902 Plain Back
3x10-20 1861-6038 <$450
1929 Small Size
10 Type 1 1-640 <$350
20 Type 1 1-168 <$350
Total Issue $380,460
Out at close $25,000
Large out at close $2,240
****

****
10468 Cherokee
CENTRAL NB OF TAHLEQUAH
{{ UNREPORTED }}
Chartered 12/13
Liquidated 3/1/20
1902 Date Back <$VALUE
4x5 1-415 <$1250
3x10-20 1-334 <$1250
1902 Plain Back
4x5 416-1340 <$1250
3x10-20 335-714 <$1250
Total Issue $62,500
Out at close $25,000
Ch 11485 assumed circulation
****
6414 Cherokee
CHEROKEE NB OF TAHLEQUAH
{{ UNREPORTED }}
Chartered 9/9/02
Liquidated 11/25/08
INDIAN TERRITORY
1902 Red Seal <$VALUE
3x10-20 1-383 <$4000
Total Issue $19,150
Out in 1910 $1,770
****
5478 Cherokee
FNB OF TAHLEQUAH
Chartered 7/2/00
INDIAN TERRITORY {{ 2 L }}
Brown Back <$VALUE
3x10-20 1-3010 <$2500
STATE ISSUES {{ 6 L 16 S }}
1882 Date Back
3x10-20 1-4100 <$500
1882 Value Back
3x10-20 4101-6000 <$500
1902 Plain Back
3x10-20 1-6430 <$350
1929 Small Sie
10 Type 1 1-1496 <$100
20 Type 1 1-372 <$100
10 Type 2 1-2001 <$110
20 Type 2 1-597 <$110
Total Issue $938,350
Out in 1935 $50,000
Large out 1935 $3,180
****
11485 Cherokee
GUARANTY NB OF TAHLEQUAH
{{ 2 L }}
Chartered 10/19
Liquidated 8/6/25
1902 Plain Back <$VALUE
3x10-20 1-1493 <$750
Total Issue $74,650
Out at close $25,000
Outstanding includes Ch 10468
****
12089 Cherokee
LIBERTY NB OF TAHLEQUAH
{{ 3 L }}
Chartered 1/22
Liquidated 3/28/29
1902 Plain Back <$VALUE
3x10-20 1-3798 <$600
Total Issue $189,900
Out in 1926 $40,000
****
7780 Le Flore
FNB OF TALIHINA
{{ UNREPORTED }}
Chartered 6/10/05
Liquidated 5/14/09
INDIAN TERRITORY
1902 Red Seal <$VALUE
3x10-20 1-200 <$5000
STATE ISSUES
1902 Red Seal
3x10-20 1-100 <$4000
1902 Date Back
3x10-20 1-86 <$2000
Total Issue $19,300
Out in 1910 $4,250
****
7019 Dewey
FNB OF TALOGA
Chartered 10/03
Liquidated 8/12/29
OKLAHOMA TERRITORY {{ 0 L }}
1902 Red Seal <$VALUE
3x10-20 1-676 <$4000
STATE ISSUES {{ 3 L }}
1902 Date Back
3x10-20 1-1810 <$650
1902 Plain Back
3x10-20 1811-5660 <$650
Total Issue $316,800
Out at close $20,395
****

7756 Pottawatomie
FARMERS NB OF TECUMSEH
Chartered 5/05
Liquidated 12/28/22
OKLAHOMA TERRITORY {{ 1 L }}
1902 Red Seal <$VALUE
3x10-20 1-1000 <$3500
STATE ISSUES {{ 2 L }}
1902 Date Back
3x10-20 1-1950 <$750
1902 Plain Back
3x10-20 1951-3992 <$750
Total Issue $249,600
Out at close $25,000
Ch 5378 assumed circulation

5378 Pottawatomie
FNB OF TECUMSEH
Chartered 5/29/00
Liquidated 9/22/25
OKLAHOMA TERRITORY {{ 0 L }}
Brown Back <$VALUE
3x10-20 1-900 <$3500
STATE ISSUES {{ 2 L }}
Brown Back
3x10-20 1-300 <$1500
1882 Date Back
3x10-20 1-840* <$850
1882 Value Back
3x10-20 941-1150* <$850
* 841-940 not marked
1902 Plain Back
3x10-20 1-910 <$750
Total Issue $163,000
Out at close $12,500
Outstanding includes Ch 7756

10304 Pottawatomie
TECUMSEH NB, TECUMSEH
{{ 4 L 6 S }}
Organized 12/14/12
Receivership 11/18/32
1902 Date Back <$VALUE
3x10-20 1-1300 <$500
1902 Plain Back
3x10-20 1301-5646 <$500
1929 Small Size
10 Type 1 1-692 <$275
20 Type 1 1-179 <$275
Total Issue $345,300
Out at close $25,000
Large out at close $2,260

8310 Cotton
FARMERS NB OF TEMPLE
{{ 1 L }}
Chartered 7/25/06
Liquidated 12/15/08
OKLAHOMA TERRITORY
1902 Red Seal <$VALUE
3x10-20 1-677 <$4000
Total Issue $33,850
Out in 1910 $7,240

6570 Cotton
FNB OF TEMPLE
{{ UNREPORTED }}
Chartered 1/03
Liquidated 11/15/09
OKLAHOMA TERRITORY
1902 Red Seal <$VALUE
3x10-20 1-1440 <$3500
STATE ISSUES
1902 Date Back
3x10-20 1-146 <$1500
Total Issue $79,300
Out in 1910 $13,470

9967 Cotton
TEMPLE NB, TEMPLE
{{ UNREPORTED }}
Chartered 3/11
Liquidated 4/10/16
1902 Date Back <$VALUE
3x10-20 1-526 <$1500
Total Issue $26,300
Out in 1916 $4,700

9991 Pawnee
FNB OF TERLTON
{{ UNREPORTED }}
Chartered 4/11
Liquidated 2/3/15
1902 Date Back <$VALUE
3x10-20 1-1294 <$1500
Total Issue $64,700
Out in 1915 $11,550

7996 Jefferson
FNB OF TERRAL
{{ UNREPORTED }}
Chartered 12/5/05
Liquidated 2/12/09
INDIAN TERRITORY
1902 Red Seal <$VALUE
3x10-20 1-600 <$4000
STATE ISSUES
1902 Red Seal
3x10-20 1-150 <$3500
Total Issue $37,500
Out in 1910 $6,920

8852 Texas
FNB OF TEXHOMA
Chartered 8/07
OKLAHOMA TERRITORY {{ 1 L }}
1902 Red Seal <$VALUE
3x10-20 1-200 <$4000
STATE ISSUES {{ 1 L 2 S }}
1902 Date Back
3x10-20 1-660 <$1500
1902 Plain Back
3x10-20 661-1371 <$1500
1929 Small Size
10 Type 1 1-214 <$850
20 Type 1 1-57 <$850
Total Issue $98,230
Out in 1935 $6,250
Large out 1935 $440

7278 Custer
FNB OF THOMAS
Chartered 5/04
OKLAHOMA TERRITORY {{ 0 L }}
1902 Red Seal <$VALUE
3x10-20 1-800 <$3500
STATE ISSUES {{ 4 L 7 S }}
1902 Date Back
3x10-20 1-1950 <$500
1902 Plain Back
3x10-20 1951-5488 <$500
1929 Small Size
10 Type 1 1-654 <$275
20 Type 1 1-170 <$275
10 Type 2 1-1336 <$300
20 Type 2 1-184 <$325
Total Issue $391,080
Out in 1935 $25,000
Large out 1935 $1,970

7771 Custer
THOMAS NB, THOMAS
{{ UNREPORTED }}
Chartered 6/6/05
Liquidated 7/7/08
OKLAHOMA TERRITORY
1902 Red Seal <$VALUE
3x10-20 1-245 <$5000
Total Issue $12,250
Out in 1910 $1,540

11052 Tillman
FNB OF TIPTON
{{ 1 L }}
Chartered 8/17
1902 Plain Back <$VALUE
3x10-20 1-1270 <$1250
Total Issue $63,500
Out in 1935 $240

7042 Johnston
AMERICAN NB OF TISHOMINGO
Chartered 11/24/03
Liquidated 2/28/09
INDIAN TERRITORY {{ 1 L }}
1902 Red Seal <$VALUE
3x10-20 1-320 <$3500
STATE ISSUES {{ 0 L }}
1902 Red Seal
3x10-20 1-75 <$3000
Total Issue $19,750
Out in 1910 $2,230

10431 Johnston
FARMERS NB OF TISHOMINGO
{{ 3 L }}
Chartered 8/6/13
Receivership 12/6/23
1902 Date Back <$VALUE
3x10-20 1-1250 <$500
1902 Plain Back
3x10-20 1251-3820 <$500
Total Issue $191,000
Out at close $24,400

5809 Johnston
FNB OF TISHOMINGO
Chartered 5/13/01
Liquidated 5/12/26
INDIAN TERRITORY {{ 1 L }}
Brown Back <$VALUE
3x10-20 1-1120 <$3000
STATE ISSUES {{ 5 L }}
Brown Back
3x10-20 1-200 <$1250
1882 Date Back
3x10-20 1-2060 <$500
1882 Value Back
3x10-20 2061-3417 <$500
1902 Plain Back
3x10-20 1-1732 <$350
Total Issue $323,450
Out at close $25,000

10012 Johnston
TISHOMINGO NB, TISHOMINGO
{{ 1 L }}
Chartered 5/11
Liquidated 3/15/16
1902 Date Back <$VALUE
3x10-20 1-1655* <$1000
* 1641-1655 not marked
Total Issue $82,750
Out in 1916 $15,410

7444 Kay
FNB OF TONKAWA
Chartered 10/17/04
Liquidated 3/1/09
OKLAHOMA TERRITORY {{ 3 L }}
1902 Red Seal <$VALUE
3x10-20 1-856 <$3000
STATE ISSUES {{ 0 L }}
1902 Red Seal
3x10-20 1-200 <$2000
1902 Date Back
3x10-20 1-13 <$1250
Total Issue $53,450
Out in 1910 $8,280

11397 Kay
FNB OF TONKAWA
{{ UNREPORTED }}
Chartered 7/19 as Farmers NB of Tonkawa, under which there was no issue. Issuing title adopted 4/12/23.
1929 Small Size <$VALUE
5 Type 2 1-5170 <$750
Total Issue $25,850
Out in 1935 $25,000

8595 Kay
TONKAWA NB, TONKAWA
Chartered 3/07
Liquidated 4/7/19
OKLAHOMA TERRITORY {{ 0 L }}
1902 Red Seal <$VALUE
3x10-20 1-750 <$3500
STATE ISSUES {{ 2 L }}
1902 Date Back
3x10-20 1-1930 <$750
1902 Plain Back
3x10-20 1931-2493 <$750
Total Issue $162,150
Out in 1919 $25,000

10342 Tulsa
AMERICAN NB OF TULSA
{{ 5 L }}
Chartered 3/13
Liquidated 1/12/21
1902 Date Back <$VALUE
3x10-20 1-5100 <$350
1902 Plain Back
3x10-20 5101-9800 <$350
Total Issue $490,000
Out at close $100,000

8552 Tulsa
CENTRAL NB OF TULSA
Chartered 2/07
Liquidated 11/1/30
2nd title:Central NB & TC 1/14/29
FIRST TITLE
INDIAN TERRITORY {{ 2 L }}
1902 Red Seal <$VALUE
3x10-20 1-625 <$3000
STATE ISSUES {{ 9 L }}
1902 Red Seal
3x10-20 1-300 <$1500
1902 Date Back
3x10-20 1-7500 <$150
1902 Plain Back
3x10-20 7501-21220 <$150
SECOND TITLE {{ 2 L }}
1902 Plain Back
3x10-20 1-1659 <$200
Total Issue $1,190,200
Out at close $14,080
Ch 9658 assumed circulation

5732 Tulsa
CITY NB OF TULSA
{{ 1 L }}
Chartered 3/5/01
Liquidated 4/11/08
INDIAN TERRITORY
Brown Back <$VALUE
3x10-20 1-1692 <$3000
Total Issue $84,600
Out in 1910 $5,930

9658 Tulsa
EXCHANGE NB OF TULSA
{{ 27 L 44 S }}
Chartered 2/10
Liquidated 6/14/33
1902 Date Back <$VALUE
3x10-20 1-14400 <$75
1902 Plain Back
3x10-20 14401-50873 <$75
1929 Small Size
5 Type 1 1-8078 <$25
10 Type 1 1-14306 <$30
20 Type 1 1-3839 <$40
Total Issue $4,105,030
Out at close $1,000,000
Large out 1935 $14,890
Ch 13679 assumed circulation

6669 Tulsa
FARMERS NB OF TULSA
{{ UNREPORTED }}
Chartered 3/03
Liquidated 1/28/10
INDIAN TERRITORY
1902 Red Seal <$VALUE
3x10-20 1-1140 <$3000
STATE ISSUES
1902 Red Seal
3x10-20 1-300 <$2000
1902 Date Back
3x10-20 1-200 <$1000
Total Issue $82,000
Out in 1910 $17,190

5171 Tulsa
FNB OF TULSA
Chartered 1/21/99
2nd title: FNB & TC 9/29/28
FIRST TITLE
INDIAN TERRITORY {{ 3 L }}
Brown Back <$VALUE
3x10-20 1-3160 <$2250
STATE ISSUES {{ 14 L }}
Brown Back
3x10-20 1-1000 <$1000
1882 Date Back
3x10-20 1-10000* <$300
1882 Value Back
3x10-20 10501-13500* <$300
* 10001-10500 not marked
1902 Plain Back
3x50-100 1-5241 <$350/$400
SECOND TITLE {{ 33 S }}
1929 Small Size
50 Type 1 1-2249 <$85
100 Type 1 1-708 <$135
Total Issue $3,292,750
Out at close $998,800
Large out 1935 $24,535
Outstanding includes Ch 10906 and Ch 12043

10262 Tulsa
LIBERTY NB OF TULSA
{{ 3 L }}
Chartered 9/12
Liquidated 1/8/24
1902 Date Back <$VALUE
3x10-20 1-2200 <$400
1902 Plain Back
3x10-20 2201-4015 <$400
Total Issue $200,750
Out at close $25,000
Ch 12043 assumed circulation

13679 Tulsa
NB OF TULSA
{{ 31 S }}
Chartered 4/33
1929 Small Size <$VALUE
5 Type 2 1-48320 <$50
10 Type 2 1-22854 <$50
20 Type 2 1-4455 <$50
Total Issue $559,240
Out in 1935 $1,000,000
Outstanding includes Ch 9658

9942 Tulsa
NB OF COMMERCE OF TULSA
{{ 6 L 6 S }}
Chartered 3/11
1902 Date Back <$VALUE
3x10-20 1-2590 <$200
1902 Plain Back
3x10-20 2591-6284 <$200
1929 Small Size
10 Type 1 1-780 <$150
20 Type 1 1-210 <$150
10 Type 2 1-673 <$150
20 Type 2 1-287 <$150
Total Issue $398,670
Out in 1935 $25,000
Large out 1935 $650

9943 Tulsa
OKLAHOMA NB OF TULSA
{{ UNREPORTED }}
Chartered 3/11
Liquidated 7/7/11
1902 Date Back <$VALUE
3x10-20 1-500 <$1000
Total Issue $25,000
Out in 1911 $16,750

12042 Tulsa
PRODUCERS NB OF TULSA
{{ 9 L 5 S }}
Chartered 11/14/21
Liquidated 9/3/30
1902 Plain Back <$VALUE
4x5 1-6100 <$175
3x10-20 1-5218 <$175
1929 Small Size
5 Type 1 1-4645 <$150
10 Type 1 1-1997 <$150
20 Type 1 1-616 <$150
Total Issue $715,990
Out at close $250,000
Large out at close $14,710

12043 Tulsa
SECURITY NB OF TULSA
{{ 1 L }}
Chartered 11/21
Closed 6/22/29
1902 Plain Back <$VALUE
3x10-20 1-1866 <$1000
Total Issue $93,300
Out at close $25,000
Ch 5171 assumed circulation
Outstanding includes Ch 10262

10906 Tulsa
UNION NB OF TULSA
{{ 6 L }}
Chartered 9/16
Closed 12/31/20
1902 Plain Back <$VALUE
4x5 1-9000 <$200
3x10-20 1-11062 <$200
Total Issue $733,100
Out at close $500,000
Ch 5171 assumed circulation

10531 Coal
FARMERS NB OF TUPELO
{{ 1 L }}
Chartered 5/14
Liquidated 12/31/25
1902 Date Back <$VALUE
3x10-20 1-1000 <$1000
1902 Plain Back
3x10-20 1001-2377 <$1000
Total Issue $118,850
Out at close $8,900

8609 Coal
FNB OF TUPELO
Chartered 3/07
Liquidated 10/30/11
INDIAN TERRITORY {{ 1 L }}
1902 Red Seal <$VALUE
4x5 1-150 <$3500
3x10-20 1-120 <$3500
STATE ISSUES {{ 0 L }}
1902 Red Seal
3x10-20 1-200 <$3000
1902 Date Back
4x5 1-300 <$1500
3x10-20 1-252 <$1500
Total Issue $37,600
Out in 1912 $7,800

8475 Grady
FNB OF TUTTLE
{{ UNREPORTED }}
Chartered 12/20/06
Liquidated 7/1/09
INDIAN TERRITORY
1902 Red Seal <$VALUE
3x10-20 1-200 <$4000
STATE ISSUES
1902 Date Back
3x10-20 1-39 <$2000
Total Issue $11,950
Out in 1910 $2,540

10032 Texas
FNB OF TYRONE
{{ 3 L 6 S }}
Chartered 6/11
1902 Date Back <$VALUE
3x10-20 1-1200 <$600
1902 Plain Back
3x10-20 1201-4320 <$600
1929 Small Size
10 Type 1 1-606 <$275
20 Type 1 1-150 <$275
10 Type 2 1-611 <$300
20 Type 2 1-150 <$300
Total Issue $279,470
Out in 1935 $20,000
Large out 1935 $1,300

9992 McCurtain
FNB OF VALLIANT
{{ 1 L }}
Chartered 4/11
Liquidated 12/28/15
1902 Date Back <$VALUE
3x10-20 1-703 <$1500
Total Issue $35,150
Out at close $6,250

8759 Grady
FNB OF VERDEN
Chartered 6/07
Liquidated 11/24/19
OKLAHOMA TERRITORY {{ 1 L }}
1902 Red Seal <$VALUE
50-100 1-80 <$8500/$9000
STATE ISSUES {{ 0 L }}
1902 Date Back
50-100 1-120 <$1750/$2000
3x50-100 1-13 <$1750/$2000
Total Issue $33,250
Out at close $6,250

8859 Grady
NB OF VERDEN
Chartered 9/07
OKLAHOMA TERRITORY {{ 0 L }}
1902 Red Seal <$VALUE
4x5 1-150 <$3500
4x10 1-175 <$3500
STATE ISSUES {{ 1 L 1 S }}
1902 Date Back
4x5 1-550* <$1000
4x10 1-550** <$1000
1902 Plain Back
4x5 651-2408* <$1000
4x10 651-1985** <$1000
* 551-650 not marked
** 551-650 not marked
1929 Small Size
5 Type 1 1-524 <$600
10 Type 1 1-262 <$600
Total Issue $169,000
Out in 1935 $6,500
Large out 1935 $440

10573 Sequoyah
FNB OF VIAN
{{ 5 L 4 S }}
Chartered 7/14
Liquidated 12/31/31
1902 Plain Back <$VALUE
4x10 1-6818 <$400
1929 Small Size
10 Type 1 1-786 <$350
Total Issue $319,880
Out at close $25,000
Large out at close $2,640

5860 Craig
CHEROKEE NB OF VINITA
{{ UNREPORTED }}
Chartered 6/13/01
Liquidated 9/15/11
INDIAN TERRITORY
Brown Back <$VALUE
3x10-20 1-420 <$3500
STATE ISSUES
Brown Back
3x10-20 1-100 <$2000
1882 Date Back
3x10-20 1-115 <$1500
Total Issue $31,750
Out at close $6,250

****
6602 Craig
FARMERS NB OF VINITA
{{ UNREPORTED }}
Chartered 2/2/03
Liquidated 2/11/09
INDIAN TERRITORY
1902 Red Seal <$VALUE
3x10-20 1-357 <$4000
STATE ISSUES
1902 Red Seal
3x10-20 1-37 <$3000
Total Issue $19,700
Out in 1910 $2,190
****
4704 Craig
FNB OF VINITA
Chartered 1892
INDIAN TERRITORY {{ 7 L }}
Brown Back <$VALUE
4x5 1-7300 <$2250
3x10-20 1-3840 <$2250
STATE ISSUES {{ 10 L 18 S }}
Brown Back
4x5 1-1250 <$1000
3x10-20 1-500 <$1000
1882 Date Back
4x5 1-2398 <$300
3x10-20 1-1912 <$300
1902 Date Back
4x5 1-3650 <$175
3x10-20 1-3020 <$175
1902 Plain Back
4x5 3651-17260 <$175
3x10-20 3021-11798 <$175
1929 Small Size
5 Type 1 1-2662 <$60
10 Type 1 1-1392 <$60
20 Type 1 1-392 <$70
5 Type 2 1-4276 <$85
10 Type 2 1-2640 <$85
20 Type 2 1-696 <$85
Total Issue $1,738,780
Out in 1935 $80,000
Large out 1935 $8,910
Outstanding includes Ch 5083
****
5083 Craig
VINITA NB, VINITA
Chartered 1897
Closed 8/17/29
INDIAN TERRITORY {{ 1 L }}
Brown Back <$VALUE
4x5 1-3275 <$2500
3x10 20 1 1940 <$2500
STATE ISSUES {{ 13 L }}
Brown Back
4x5 1-500 <$1000
3x10-20 1-300 <$1000
1882 Date Back
4x5 1-3250* <$300
3x10-20 1-2340** <$300
1882 Value Back
4x5 3401-4055* <$300
3x10-20 2461-2869** <$300
* 3251-3400 not marked
** 2341-2460 not marked
1902 Plain Back
4x5 1-7685 <$175
3x10-20 1-5275 <$175
Total Issue $829,500
Out at close $28,400
Ch 4704 assumed circulation
****
7628 Wagoner
CITY NB OF WAGONER
{{ UNREPORTED }}
Chartered 3/2/05
Liquidated 6/1/09
INDIAN TERRITORY
1902 Red Seal <$VALUE
50-100 1-308 <$8500/$9000
STATE ISSUES
1902 Red Seal
50-100 1-50 <$6000/$6500
Total Issue $53,700
Out in 1910 $12,850
****
5016 Wagoner
FNB OF WAGONER
Chartered 1895
INDIAN TERRITORY {{ 1 L }}
Brown Back <$VALUE
3x10-20 1-3050 <$3000
STATE ISSUES {{ 3 L U + 10 S }}
Brown Back
3x10-20 1-500 <$1500
1882 Date Back
3x10-20 1-3453 <$650
1902 Plain Back
3x10-20 1-8337 <$500

1929 Small Size
10 Type 1 1-1500 <$150
20 Type 1 1-370 <$165
10 Type 2 1-1902 <$165
20 Type 2 1-295 <$175
Total Issue $926,320
Out in 1935 $50,000
Large out 1935 $2,940
****
6048 Wagoner
WAGONER NB, WAGONER
{{ UNREPORTED }}
Chartered 12/14/01
Liquidated 10/15/08
INDIAN TERRITORY
Brown Back <$VALUE
50-100 1-210 <$8500/$9000
STATE ISSUES
Brown Back
50-100 1-11 <$3500/$4000
Total Issue $33,150
Out in 1910 $6,550
****
5982 Grant
FNB OF WAKITA
Chartered 10/2/01
Liquidated 6/2/09
OKLAHOMA TERRITORY {{ U + 1 L }}
Brown Back <$VALUE
3x10-20 1-1350 <$3500
STATE ISSUES {{ 0 L }}
1882 Date Back
3x10-20 1-62 <$1500
Total Issue $70,600
Out in 1910 $10,380
****
6612 Cotton
FNB OF WALTERS
Organized 1/10/03
Receivership 8/6/25
OKLAHOMA TERRITORY {{ 0 L }}
1902 Red Seal <$VALUE
4x5 1-650 <$3500
3x10-20 1-880 <$3500
STATE ISSUES {{ 2 L }}
1902 Date Back
4x5 1-2050 <$650
3x10-20 1-1460 <$650
1902 Plain Back
4x5 2051-5085 <$650
3x10-20 1461-3251 <$650
Total Issue $321,250
Out at close $25,000
****
7811 Cotton
WALTERS NB, WALTERS
Organized 6/16/05
Liquidated 4/16/34
OKLAHOMA TERRITORY {{ 0 L }}
1902 Red Seal <$VALUE
3x10-20 1-400 <$3500
STATE ISSUES {{ 3 L 4 S }}
1902 Red Seal
3x10-20 1-400 <$2500
1902 Date Back
3x10-20 1-1350 <$600
1902 Plain Back
3x10-20 1351-5011 <$600
1929 Small Size
10 Type 1 1-606 <$300
20 Type 1 1-162 <$300
10 Type 2 1-281 <$350
20 Type 2 1-60 <$350
Total Issue $350,360
Out at close $20,000
Large out 1935 $1,280
Ch 14108 assumed circulation
****
14108 Cotton
WALTERS NB, WALTERS
{{ 1 S }}
Chartered 4/34
1929 Small Size <$VALUE
5 Type 2 1-934 <$750
10 Type 2 1-558 <$750
20 Type 2 1-120 <$750
Total Issue $12,650
Out in 1935 $20,000
Outstanding includes Ch 7811
****
6641 Pottawatomie
FNB OF WANETTE
{{ UNREPORTED }}
Organized 2/6/03
Receivership 3/24/30
OKLAHOMA TERRITORY
1902 Red Seal <$VALUE
3x10-20 1-400 <$4000
STATE ISSUES
1902 Date Back
3x10-20 1-620* <$1500
1902 Plain Back
3x10-20 681-1465* <$1500
* 621-680 not marked

1929 Small Size
10 Type 1 1-56 <$750
20 Type 1 1-3 <$750
Total Issue $96,970
Out at close $6,300
Large out at close $2,580
****
8304 Pottawatomie
STATE NB OF WANETTE
{{ UNREPORTED }}
Chartered 7/06
Liquidated 1/17/21
OKLAHOMA TERRITORY
1902 Red Seal <$VALUE
3x10-20 1-200 <$4000
STATE ISSUES
1902 Date Back
3x10-20 1-660 <$1500
1902 Plain Back
3x10-20 661-777 <$1500
Total Issue $48,850
Out at close $6,250
****
5950 Johnston
FARMERS NB OF WAPANUCKA
{{ UNREPORTED }}
Chartered 8/27/01
Receivership 3/2/25
2nd title: FNB of Wapanucka 4/03
INDIAN TERRITORY
FIRST TITLE
Brown Back <$VALUE
3x10-20 1-155 <$3500
SECOND TITLE
Brown Back
3x10-20 1-245 <$3500
STATE ISSUES
Brown Back
3x10-20 1-100 <$2000
1882 Date Back
3x10-20 1-680 <$1500
1882 Value Back
3x10-20 681-868 <$1500
1902 Plain Back
3x10-20 1-280 <$1250
Total Issue $82,400
Out at close $5,550
****
FNB of Wapanucka
SEE Ch 5950
Farmers NB of Wapanucka
****
8137 Johnston
PEOPLES NB OF WAPANUCKA
Chartered 3/06
Liquidated 2/25/11
INDIAN TERRITORY {{ 0 L }}
1902 Red Seal <$VALUE
3x10-20 1-188 <$3500
STATE ISSUES {{ 1 L }}
1902 Red Seal
3x10-20 1-100 <$2500
1902 Date Back
3x10-20 1-83 <$1250
Total Issue $18,550
Out in 1911 $3,050
****
8809 Muskogee
FNB OF WARNER
{{ UNREPORTED }}
Chartered 7/07
Liquidated 3/2/13
INDIAN TERRITORY
1902 Red Seal <$VALUE
3x10-20 1-188 <$3500
STATE ISSUES
1902 Red Seal
3x10-20 1-300 <$2500
1902 Date Back
3x10-20 1-665 <$1500
Total Issue $57,650
Out at close $12,110
****
10277 McClain
FNB OF WASHINGTON
{{ 4 L 7 S }}
Chartered 10/12
1902 Date Back <$VALUE
3x10-20 1-1180 <$500
1902 Plain Back
3x10-20 1181-5493 <$500
1929 Small Size
10 Type 1 1-754 <$250
20 Type 1 1-190 <$250
10 Type 2 1-1561 <$250
20 Type 2 1-385 <$250
Total Issue $366,000
Out in 1935 $24,250
Large out 1935 $1,520
****

****
5804 Blaine
FNB OF WATONGA
Chartered 5/10/01
Liquidated 7/21/25
OKLAHOMA TERRITORY {{ 0 L }}
Brown Back <$VALUE
3x10-20 1-1220 <$3500
STATE ISSUES {{ 2 L }}
1882 Date Back
3x10-20 1-1840 <$1000
1882 Value Back
3x10-20 1841-3040 <$1000
1902 Plain Back
3x10-20 1-1380 <$750
Total Issue $282,000
Out at close $25,000
****
7967 Garfield
FNB OF WAUKOMIS
{{ 1 L }}
Chartered 11/1/05
Liquidated 2/10/09
OKLAHOMA TERRITORY
1902 Red Seal <$VALUE
4x5 1-235 <$4000
3x10-20 1-145 <$4000
Total Issue $11,950
Out in 1910 $1,760
****
10227 Garfield
WAUKOMIS NB, WAUKOMIS
{{ 5 L 6 S }}
Chartered 7/12
Liquidated 3/28/32
1902 Date Back <$VALUE
4x10 1-750 <$400
1902 Plain Back
4x10 751-7523 <$400
1929 Small Size
10 Type 1 1-1049 <$200
Total Issue $363,860
Out at close $30,000
Large out at close $2,020
****
8715 Jefferson
CITIZENS NB OF WAURIKA
{{ UNREPORTED }}
Chartered 5/29/07
Liquidated 12/1/08
OKLAHOMA TERRITORY
1902 Red Seal <$VALUE
3x10-20 1-173 <$4000
Total Issue $8,650
Out in 1910 $1,740
****
8744 Jefferson
FNB OF WAURIKA
Chartered 6/07
OKLAHOMA TERRITORY {{ 0 L }}
1902 Red Seal <$VALUE
3x10-20 1-300 <$3500
STATE ISSUES {{ 2 L 4 S }}
1902 Red Seal
3x10-20 1-400 <$2500
1902 Date Back
3x10-20 1-1980 <$600
1902 Plain Back
3x10-20 1981-4654 <$600
1929 Small Size
5 Type 2 1-4520 <$400
10 Type 2 1-2200 <$400
Total Issue $312,300
Out in 1935 $25,000
Large out 1935 $740
****
8861 Jefferson
WAURIKA NB, WAURIKA
Chartered 9/07
OKLAHOMA TERRITORY {{ 0 L }}
1902 Red Seal <$VALUE
3x10-20 1-200 <$3500
STATE ISSUES {{ 1 L 8 S }}
1902 Date Back
3x10-20 1-760* <$1000
1902 Plain Back
3x10-20 821-1742* <$1000
* 761-820 not marked
1929 Small Size
10 Type 1 1-254 <$300
20 Type 1 1-75 <$350
Total Issue $121,340
Out in 1935 $6,600
Large out 1935 $300
****
9709 Woods
FNB OF WAYNOKA
{{ 1 L 1 S }}
Organized 3/7/10
Receivership 9/12/33
1902 Date Back <$VALUE
3x10-20 1-700 <$1000

1902 Plain Back
3x10-20 701-1557 <$1000
1929 Small Size
10 Type 1 1-194 <$750
20 Type 1 1-32 <$750
Total Issue $93,330
Out at close $6,500
Large out at close $550
****
5352 Custer
FNB OF WEATHERFORD
Chartered 5/15/00
Liquidated 4/12/28
OKLAHOMA TERRITORY {{ 0 L }}
Brown Back <$VALUE
3x10-20 1-740 <$3000
STATE ISSUES {{ 4 L }}
1882 Date Back
3x10-20 1-1730 <$600
1882 Value Back
3x10-20 1731-2596 <$600
1902 Plain Back
3x10-20 1-2526 <$450
Total Issue $293,100
Out at close $25,000
****
7238 Custer
GERMAN NB OF WEATHERFORD
Chartered 4/04
2nd title: Liberty NB of Weatherford 6/10/18
FIRST TITLE
OKLAHOMA TERRITORY {{ 1 L }}
1902 Red Seal <$VALUE
3x10-20 1-420 <$3500
STATE ISSUES {{ 0 L }}
1902 Red Seal
3x10-20 1-120 <$2500
1902 Date Back
3x10-20 1-1300 <$1000
SECOND TITLE {{ 2 L 3 S }}
1902 Plain Back
3x10-20 1-1529 <$650
1929 Small Size
10 Type 1 1-386 <$400
20 Type 1 1-120 <$400
10 Type 2 1-385 <$450
20 Type 2 1-55 <$450
Total Issue $210,960
Out in 1935 $12,500
Large out 1935 $670
****
Liberty NB of Weatherford
SEE Ch 7238
German NB of Weatherford
****
5758 Custer
N EXCHANGE B OF WEATHERFORD
{{ UNREPORTED }}
Chartered 3/26/01
Liquidated 6/7/04
OKLAHOMA TERRITORY
Brown Back <$VALUE
3x10-20 1-455 <$3500
Total Issue $22,750
Out in 1910 $570
****
8024 Muskogee
FNB OF WEBBERS FALLS
{{ UNREPORTED }}
Chartered 12/05
Liquidated 12/27/16
INDIAN TERRITORY
1902 Red Seal <$VALUE
3x10-20 1-300 <$4000
STATE ISSUES
1902 Red Seal
3x10-20 1-400 <$3000
1902 Date Back
3x10-20 1-1207* <$1250
* 1081-1207 not marked
Total Issue $95,350
Out at close $14,700
****
6324 Okfuskee
FNB OF WELEETKA
{{ UNREPORTED }}
Chartered 6/28/02
Liquidated 1/8/24
INDIAN TERRITORY
1902 Red Seal <$VALUE
4x5 1-350 <$3500
3x10-20 1-280 <$3500
STATE ISSUES
1902 Date Back
4x5 1-650 <$1250
3x10-20 1-480 <$1250
1902 Plain Back
4x5 651-950 <$1250
3x10-20 481-689 <$1250
Total Issue $74,450
Out in 1921 $5,950
****

****
6689 Okfuskee
WELEETKA NB, WELEETKA
{{ 1 L }}
Chartered 3/25/03
Liquidated 10/1/08
INDIAN TERRITORY
1902 Red Seal <$VALUE
3x10-20 1-359 <$3500
Total Issue $17,950
Out in 1910 $1,800
****
9983 Lincoln
FNB OF WELLSTON
{{ UNREPORTED }}
Chartered 4/11
Liquidated 7/22/29
1902 Date Back <$VALUE
3x10-20 1-620 <$1250
1902 Plain Back
3x10-20 621-1459 <$1250
Total Issue $72,950
Out at close $5,200
Large out 1935 $170
Ch 12078 assumed circulation
****
12078 Lincoln
WELLSTON NB, WELLSTON
{{ 3 S }}
Chartered 12/21
1929 Small Size <$VALUE
10 Type 1 1-246 <$450
20 Type 1 1-69 <$450
Total Issue $23,040
Out in 1935 $6,250
Outstanding includes Ch 9983
****
10158 Adair
FNB OF WESTVILLE
{{ 4 L 2 S }}
Chartered 3/12
Liquidated 9/20/30
1902 Date Back <$VALUE
3x10-20 1-1405 <$500
1902 Plain Back
3x10-20 1406-4830 <$500
1929 Small Size
10 Type 1 1-281 <$600
20 Type 1 1-47 <$600
Total Issue $264,000
Out at close $25,000
Large out at close $4,830
****
7724 Hughes
AMERICAN NB OF WETUMKA
Chartered 5/05
Liquidated 3/1/35
INDIAN TERRITORY {{ 1 L }}
1902 Red Seal <$VALUE
3x10-20 1-263 <$3500
STATE ISSUES {{ 2 L 5 S }}
1902 Red Seal
3x10-20 1-200 <$2500
1902 Date Back
3x10-20 1-960 <$750
1902 Plain Back
3x10-20 961-2845 <$750
1929 Small Size
10 Type 1 1-378 <$300
20 Type 1 1-114 <$300
10 Type 2 1-234 <$350
20 Type 2 1-25 <$350
Total Issue $204,600
Out in 1935 $11,250
Large out 1935 $130
****
5935 Hughes
FNB OF WETUMKA
Chartered 8/7/01
Liquidated 3/11/29
INDIAN TERRITORY {{ 0 L }}
Brown Back <$VALUE
3x10-20 1-570 <$3500
STATE ISSUES {{ 2 L }}
Brown Back
3x10-20 1-200 <$1500
1882 Date Back
3x10-20 1-2420 <$750
1882 Value Back
3x10-20 2421-3632 <$750
1902 Plain Back
3x10-20 1-2693 <$600
Total Issue $354,750
Out at close $13,350
****

****

8052 Seminole
FARMERS NB OF WEWOKA
Chartered 1/10/06
Receivership 7/22/32
INDIAN TERRITORY {{ 0 L }}
1902 Red Seal <$VALUE
3x10-20 1-200 <$3500
STATE ISSUES {{ 1 L 1 S }}
1902 Red Seal
3x10-20 1-100 <$2500
1902 Date Back
3x10-20 1-660 <$1250
1902 Plain Back
3x10-20 661-1649 <$1250
1929 Small Size
10 Type 1 1-177 <$600
20 Type 1 1-34 <$600
Total Issue $112,150
Out at close $6,500
Large out at close $740

****

6254 Seminole
FNB OF WEWOKA
{{ UNREPORTED }}
Chartered 5/13/02
Liquidated 4/13/09
INDIAN TERRITORY
1902 Red Seal <$VALUE
4x5 1-350 <$4000
3x10-20 1-280 <$4000
STATE ISSUES
1902 Red Seal
4x5 1-100 <$3000
3x10-20 1 <$4000
Total Issue $23,050
Out in 1910 $2,020

****

6890 Latimer
FNB OF WILBURTON
{{ UNREPORTED }}
Chartered 7/03
Liquidated 12/14/12
INDIAN TERRITORY
1902 Red Seal <$VALUE
3x10-20 1-320 <$3500
STATE ISSUES
1902 Red Seal
3x10-20 1-100 <$3000
1902 Date Back
3x10-20 1-568 <$1500
Total Issue $49,400
Out in 1913 $4,750

****

10170 Latimer
LATIMER COUNTY NB OF WILBURTON
{{ 2 L }}
Chartered 4/12
Liquidated 2/20/24
1902 Date Back <$VALUE
3x10-20 1-1710 <$750
1902 Plain Back
3x10-20 1711-4031 <$750
Total Issue $201,550
Out at close $25,000

****

7707 Marshall
FNB OF WOODVILLE
Chartered 4/05
Liquidated 4/17/26
INDIAN TERRITORY {{ 1 L }}
1902 Red Seal <$VALUE
3x10-20 1-440 <$3500
STATE ISSUES {{ 2 L }}
1902 Red Seal
3x10-20 1-120 <$2500
1902 Date Back
3x10-20 1-1240* <$850
1902 Plain Back
3x10-20 1341-2692* <$850
* 1241-2692 not marked
Total Issue $162,600
Out at close $12,500

****

5575 Woodward
FNB OF WOODWARD
Chartered 9/12/00
Receivership 1/21/32
OKLAHOMA TERRITORY {{ 0 L }}
Brown Back <$VALUE
3x10-20 1-1420 <$3000
STATE ISSUES {{ 6 L 7 S }}
1882 Date Back
3x10-20 1-3900* <$400
1882 Value Back
3x10-20 4151-5863* <$400
* 3901-4150 not marked
1902 Plain Back
3x10-20 1-5453 <$300
1929 Small Size
10 Type 1 1-936 <$200
20 Type 1 1-201 <$200
Total Issue $717,080
Out at close $49,460
Large out at close $7,360

****

5126 Garvin
FNB OF WYNNEWOOD
Chartered 1898
INDIAN TERRITORY {{ 0 L }}
Brown Back <$VALUE
4x5 1-3160 <$3500
3x10-20 1-2466 <$3500
STATE ISSUES {{ 10 L 14 S }}
Brown Back
4x5 1-400 <$1250
3x10-20 1-320 <$1250
1882 Date Back
4x5 1-3600 <$300
3x10-20 1-2620 <$300
1882 Value Back
4x5 3601-4840 <$300
3x10-20 2621-3363 <$300
1902 Plain Back
4x5 1-7912 <$175
3x10-20 1-5092 <$175
1929 Small Size
5 Type 1 1-1972 <$125
10 Type 1 1-1064 <$125
20 Type 1 1-288 <$125
5 Type 2 1-3198 <$135
10 Type 2 1-2100 <$135
20 Type 2 1-518 <$135
Total Issue $1,093,200
Out in 1935 $49,995
Large out 1935 $4,010

****

5731 Garvin
SOUTHERN NB OF WYNNEWOOD
Chartered 3/2/01
Liquidated 1/8/34
INDIAN TERRITORY {{ 0 L }}
Brown Back <$VALUE
3x10-20 1-960 <$3500
STATE ISSUES {{ 7 L 6 S }}
Brown Back
3x10-20 1-300 <$1250
1882 Date Back
3x10-20 1-2310 <$375
1882 Value Back
3x10-20 2311-3302 <$375
1902 Plain Back
3x10-20 1-3023 <$300
1929 Small Size
10 Type 1 1-732 <$225
20 Type 1 1-184 <$225
10 Type 2 1-280 <$250
20 Type 2 1-72 <$250
Total Issue $449,490
Out at close $25,000
Large out at close $1,860

****

10014 Payne
FNB OF YALE
{{ 3 L 5 S }}
Chartered 5/11
1902 Date Back <$VALUE
3x10-20 1-1195 <$600
1902 Plain Back
3x10-20 1196-4597 <$600
1929 Small Size
10 Type 1 1-576 <$325
20 Type 1 1-182 <$325
10 Type 2 1-561 <$350
20 Type 2 1-145 <$350
Total Issue $294,760
Out in 1935 $18,750
Large out 1935 $970

****

6159 Canadian
FNB OF YUKON
Chartered 3/15/02
OKLAHOMA TERRITORY {{ 0 L }}
1902 Red Seal <$VALUE
3x10-20 1-700 <$3500
STATE ISSUES {{ 3 L 7 S }}
1902 Date Back
3x10-20 1-1830* <$600
1902 Plain Back (dated 1902)
3x10-20 1961-3306* <$600
* 1831-1960 not marked
1902 Plain Back (dated 1922)
3x10-20 1-2396 <$600
1929 Small Size
10 Type 1 1-716 <$300
20 Type 1 1-204 <$300
10 Type 2 1-1444 <$300
20 Type 2 1-293 <$300
Total Issue $407,840
Out in 1935 $25,000
Large out 1935 $1,130

****

10196 Canadian
YUKON NB, YUKON
{{ 5 L 7 S }}
Chartered 5/12
1902 Date Back <$VALUE
3x10-20 1-1400 <$400
1902 Plain Back
3x10-20 1401-5555 <$400
1929 Small Size
10 Type 1 1-772 <$275
20 Type 1 1-212 <$275
10 Type 2 1-917 <$275
20 Type 2 1-222 <$275
Total Issue $363,120
Out in 1935 $25,000
Large out 1935 $1,420

****

OREGON

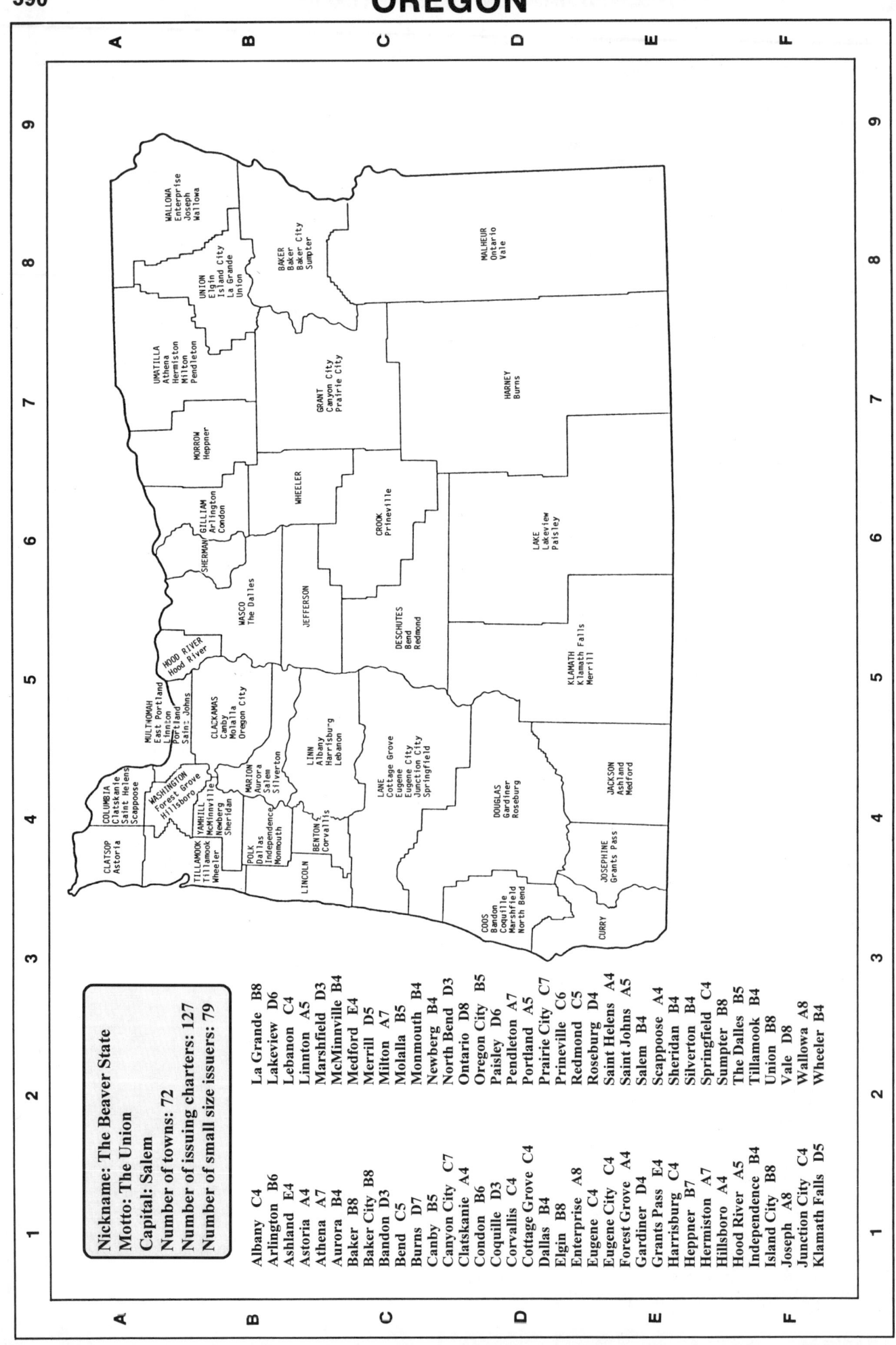

Nickname: The Beaver State
Motto: The Union
Capital: Salem
Number of towns: 72
Number of issuing charters: 127
Number of small size issuers: 79

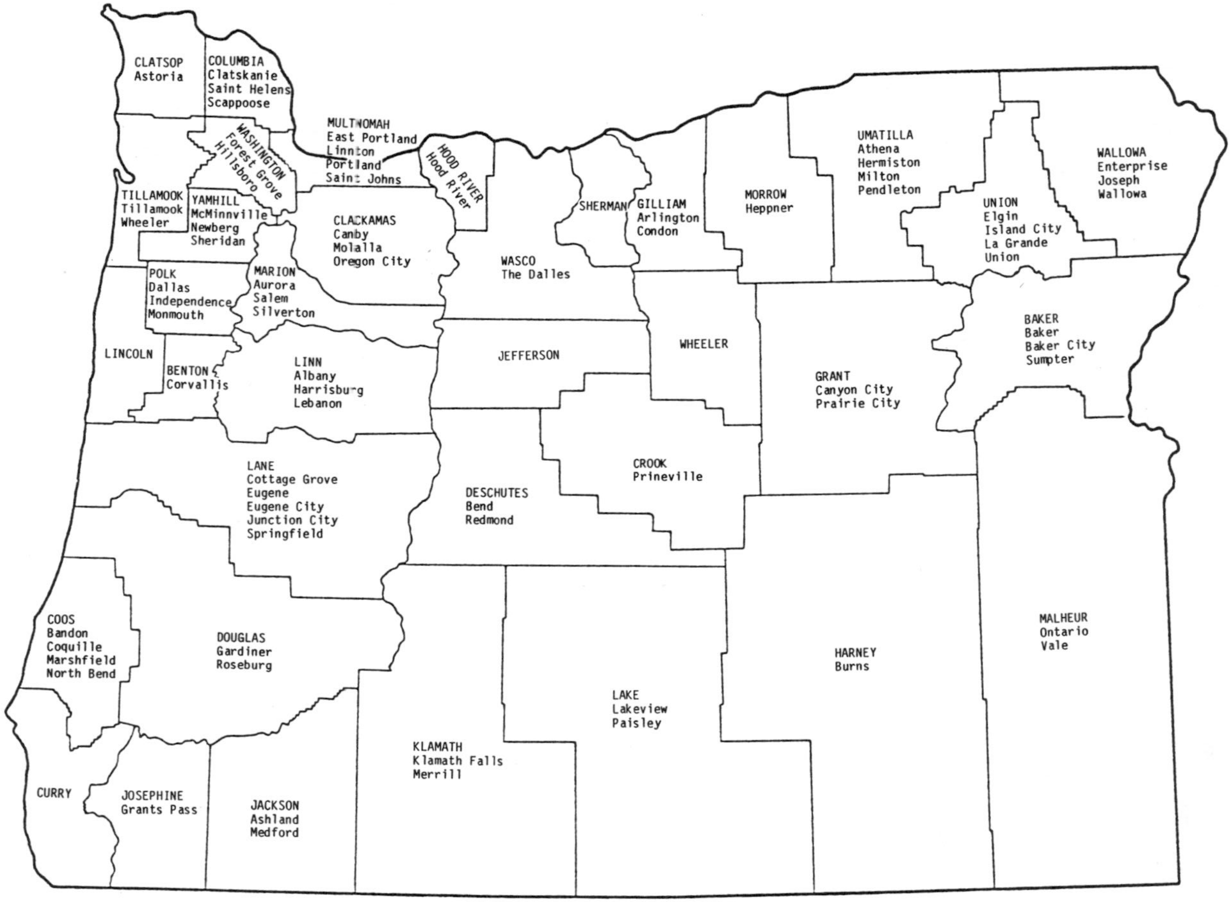

Albany C4	La Grande B8
Arlington B6	Lakeview D6
Ashland E4	Lebanon C4
Astoria A4	Linnton A5
Athena A7	Marshfield D3
Aurora B4	McMinnville B4
Baker B8	Medford E4
Baker City B8	Merrill D5
Bandon D3	Milton A7
Bend C5	Molalla B5
Burns D7	Monmouth B4
Canby B5	Newberg B4
Canyon City C7	North Bend D3
Clatskanie A4	Ontario D8
Condon B6	Oregon City B5
Coquille D3	Paisley D6
Corvallis C4	Pendleton A7
Cottage Grove C4	Portland A5
Dallas B4	Prairie City C7
Elgin B8	Prineville C6
Enterprise A8	Redmond C5
Eugene C4	Roseburg D4
Eugene City C4	Saint Helens A4
Forest Grove A4	Saint Johns A5
Gardiner D4	Salem B4
Grants Pass E4	Scappoose A4
Harrisburg C4	Sheridan B4
Heppner B7	Silverton B4
Hermiston A7	Springfield C4
Hillsboro A4	Sumpter B8
Hood River A5	The Dalles B5
Independence B4	Tillamook B4
Island City B8	Union B8
Joseph A8	Vale D8
Junction City C4	Wallowa A8
Klamath Falls D5	Wheeler B4

2928 Linn
FNB OF ALBANY
{{ 9 L 14 S }}
Organized 4/4/83
Receivership 8/16/33
Brown Back <$VALUE
3x10-20 1-1900 <$1000
1902 Red Seal
3x10-20 1-800 <$1500
1902 Date Back
3x10-20 1-5000 <$200
1902 Plain Back
3x10-20 5001-19292 <$200
1929 Small Size
10 Type 1 1-2432 <$135
20 Type 1 1-665 <$150
Total Issue $1,325,320
Out at close $100,000
Large out at close $6,950

4326 Linn
LINN COUNTY NB OF ALBANY
{{ 1 L }}
Organized 5/31/90
Receivership 7/10/93
Brown Back <$VALUE
3x10-20 1-743 <$2000
Total Issue $37,150
Out in 1910 $230

3918 Gilliam
ARLINGTON NB, ARLINGTON
{{ UNREPORTED }}
Chartered 8/4/88
Receivership 1/19/33
Brown Back <$VALUE
4x5 1-3363 <$2000
3x10-20 1-577 <$2000
1902 Date Back
3x10-20 1-1400 <$1500
1902 Plain Back
3x10-20 1401-2624 <$1500
Total Issue $227,310
Out at close $1,390

3676 Gilliam
FNB OF ARLINGTON
{{ UNREPORTED }}
Chartered 4/21/87
Receivership 8/2/94
Brown Back <$VALUE
4x5 1-1675 <$2500
Total Issue $33,500
Out in 1916 $285

5747 Jackson
FNB OF ASHLAND
{{ 8 L 19 S }}
Chartered 3/20/01
Brown Back <$VALUE
3x10-20 1-1580 <$750
1882 Date Back
3x10-20 1-4400 <$650
1882 Value Back
3x10-20 4401-9200 <$850
1902 Plain Back
3x10-20 1-11674 <$300
1929 Small Size
5 Type 1 1-7356 <$100
10 Type 1 1-1778 <$100
5 Type 2 1-16142 <$110
10 Type 2 1-3984 <$110
Total Issue $1,570,610
Out in 1935 $100,000
Large out 1935 $4,015
Outstanding includes Ch 9431

9431 Jackson
UNITED STATES NB OF ASHLAND
{{ UNREPORTED }}
Chartered 6/09
Liquidated 4/1/14
1902 Date Back <$VALUE
3x10-20 1-1632 <$1750
Total Issue $81,600
Out at close $25,000
Ch 5747 assumed circulation

4403 Clatsop
ASTORIA NB, ASTORIA
{{ 4 L }}
Organized 8/9/90
Receivership 2/24/28
Brown Back <$VALUE
3x10-20 1-2500 <$800
1882 Date Back
3x10-20 1-342 <$600
1902 Date Back
3x10-20 1-2550 <$350
1902 Plain Back
3x10-20 2551-7939 <$350
Total Issue $539,050
Out at close $9,760

3486 Clatsop
FNB OF ASTORIA
{{ 4 L 6 S }}
Chartered 1886
Liquidated 9/28/33
Brown Back <$VALUE
3x10-20 1-1338 <$1000
1902 Red Seal
3x10-20 1-1300 <$1500
1902 Date Back
3x10-20 1-3300 <$400
1902 Plain Back
3x10-20 3301-8863 <$400
1929 Small Size
10 Type 1 1-965 <$250
20 Type 1 1-248 <$275
Total Issue $662,710
Out at close $37,440
Large out at close $3,530

13354 Clatsop
NB OF COMMERCE OF ASTORIA
{{ 14 S }}
Organized 7/23/29
Liquidated 8/9/34
1929 Small Size <$VALUE
5 Type 1 1-2707 <$135
10 Type 1 1-1930 <$135
20 Type 1 1-574 <$150
Total Issue $265,890
Out at close $53,850

4516 Umatilla
FNB OF ATHENA
{{ 2 L 3 S }}
Chartered 1891
Brown Back <$VALUE
3x10-20 1-1540 <$2000
1882 Date Back
3x10-20 1-249 <$1750
1902 Date Back
3x10-20 1-1010* <$1000
1902 Plain Back
3x10-20 1131-2553* <$1000
* 1011-1130 not marked
1929 Small Size
10 Type 1 1-316 <$650
20 Type 1 1-106 <$650
10 Type 2 1-118 <$650
20 Type 2 1-60 <$650
Total Issue $251,160
Out in 1935 $12,500
Large out 1935 $780

FNB in Aurora
SEE Ch 10619
FNB of Canby

FNB of Baker
SEE Ch 2865
FNB of Baker City

4206 Baker
BAKER CITY NB, BAKER CITY
{{ UNREPORTED }}
Organized 1/11/90
Receivership 8/2/94
Brown Back <$VALUE
3x10-20 1-720 <$2500
Total Issue $36,000
Out at close $16,870
Out in 1916 $300

6768 Baker
CITIZENS NB OF BAKER CITY
{{ U + 8 L 8 S }}
Chartered 5/03
Liquidated 5/2/32
1902 Red Seal <$VALUE
4x5 1-1800 <$1500
3x10-20 1-2240 <$1500
1902 Date Back
4x5 1-6050 <$350
3x10-20 1-4420 <$350
1902 Plain Back
4x5 6051-20425 <$350
3x10-20 4421-13613 <$350
1929 Small Size
5 Type 1 1-2230 <$200
10 Type 1 1-1083 <$200
20 Type 1 1-281 <$200
Total Issue $1,402,750
Out at close $81,280
Large out at close $7,850

2865 Baker
FNB OF BAKER CITY
Chartered 1883
2nd title:FNB of Baker 1/24/23
FIRST TITLE {{ 4 L }}
Brown Back <$VALUE
3x10-20 1-3525 <$1250
1902 Red Seal
50-100 1-933 <$3500/$4000
1902 Date Back
50-100 1-600 <$750/$850
3x50-100 1-2750 <$750/$850
SECOND TITLE {{ 3 L 22 S }}
1902 Plain Back
3x50-100 1-256 <$750/$850
1929 Small Size
5 Type 1 1-46510 <$100
10 Type 1 1-2712 <$100
5 Type 2 1-12840 <$125
10 Type 2 1-5256 <$125
Total Issue $1,576,680
Out in 1935 $150,000
Large out 1935 $10,690

9718 Coos
FNB OF BANDON
{{ 1 L }}
Organized 2/25/10
Receivership 4/13/25
1902 Date Back <$VALUE
3x10-20 1-1160* <$1250
1902 Plain Back
3x10-20 1321-2801 <$1250
* 1161-1320 not marked
Total Issue $140,050
Out at close $15,000

9363 Deschutes
FNB OF BEND
{{ 1 L }}
Organized 1/23/09
Receivership 4/29/27
1902 Date Back <$VALUE
3x10-20 1-1220 <$1250
1902 Plain Back
3x10-20 1221-2905 <$1250
Total Issue $145,250
Out at close $12,500

13093 Deschutes
LUMBERMENS NB OF BEND
{{ 5U + 15 S }}
Chartered 6/27
1929 Small Size <$VALUE
5 Type 1 1-1902 <$125
10 Type 1 1-938 <$125
20 Type 1 1-284 <$125
5 Type 2 1-8042 <$135
10 Type 2 1-3804 <$135
20 Type 2 1-1032 <$150
Total Issue $246,310
Out in 1935 $100,000

6295 Harney
FNB OF BURNS
{{ 6 L 7 S }}
Chartered 6/9/02
Receivership 7/7/32
1902 Red Seal <$VALUE
4x5 1-1150 <$1750
3x10-20 1-870 <$1750
1902 Date Back
4x5 1-1725 <$400
3x10-20 1-1820 <$400
1902 Plain Back
4x5 1726-9790 <$400
3x10-20 1821-7410 <$400
1929 Small Size
5 Type 1 1-1454 <$225
10 Type 1 1-739 <$225
20 Type 1 1-204 <$250
Total Issue $745,240
Out at close $50,000
Large out at close $5,400

8691 Harney
HARNEY COUNTY NB OF BURNS
{{ 4 L 9 S }}
Chartered 5/07
1902 Red Seal <$VALUE
4x5 1-460 <$1750
3x10-20 1-371 <$1750
1902 Date Back
4x5 1-1475 <$400
3x10-20 1-1160 <$400
1902 Plain Back
4x5 1476-6570 <$400
3x10-20 1161-4456 <$400
1929 Small Size
5 Type 1 1-1266 <$200
10 Type 1 1-618 <$200
20 Type 1 1-190 <$225
5 Type 2 1-1222 <$225
10 Type 2 1-723 <$225
20 Type 2 1-192 <$250
Total Issue $502,990
Out in 1935 $32,500
Large out 1935 $1,910

10619 Clackamas
FNB OF CANBY
Chartered 9/14
Liquidated 10/15/32
2nd title: FNB in Aurora 5/29/31
FIRST TITLE {{ 2 L 3 S }}
1902 Plain Back <$VALUE
3x10-20 1-3812 <$750
1929 Small Size
10 Type 1 1-462 <$500
20 Type 1 1-124 <$500
SECOND TITLE {{ 1 S }}
1929 Small Size
10 Type 1 1-73 <$750
20 Type 1 1-14 <$750
Total Issue $239,260
Out at close $21,940
Large out at close $1,680

6491 Grant
FNB OF GRANT COUNTY AT CANYON CITY
{{ 1 L }}
Chartered 11/17/02
Liquidated 4/4/28
1902 Red Seal <$VALUE
3x10-20 1-600 <$2500
1902 Date Back
4x5 1-2700 <$1250
3x10-20 1-2320 <$1250
1902 Plain Back
4x5 2701-2820 <$1250
3x10-20 2321-2343 <$1250
Total Issue $203,550
Out at close $1,145

14001 Columbia
FNB OF CLATSKANIE
{{ 1 S }}
Chartered 2/34
1929 Small Size <$VALUE
5 Type 2 1-3296 <$750
10 Type 2 1-1932 <$750
Total Issue $35,800
Out in 1935 $25,000

8261 Gilliam
CONDON NB, CONDON
{{ 1 L }}
Organized 3/24/06
Receivership 12/18/23
1902 Red Seal <$VALUE
3x10-20 1-510 <$2500
1902 Date Back
4x5 1-1200* <$1250
3x10-20 1-780** <$1250
1902 Plain Back
4x5 1301-2210* <$1250
3x10-20 861-1372** <$1250
* 1201-1300 not marked
** 781-860 not marked
Total Issue $138,300
Out at close $11,800

7059 Gilliam
FNB OF CONDON
{{ 1 L 2U + 8 S }}
Chartered 11/21/03
Liquidated 8/4/34
1902 Red Seal <$VALUE
4x5 1-300 <$2500
3x10-20 1-280 <$2500
1902 Date Back
4x5 1-1250* <$1250
3x10-20 1-880** <$1250
1902 Plain Back
4x5 1351-3335* <$1250
3x10-20 961-2184** <$1250
* 1251-1350 not marked
** 881-960 not marked
1929 Small Size
5 Type 1 1-418 <$225
10 Type 1 1-210 <$225
20 Type 1 1-74 <$250
5 Type 2 1-408 <$300
10 Type 2 1-165 <$300
20 Type 2 1-40 <$325
Total Issue $234,410
Out at close $10,410
Large out at close $1,025

6849 Coos
FNB OF COQUILLE
{{ 2 L 3 S }}
Chartered 6/03
1902 Red Seal <$VALUE
3x10-20 1-356 <$2500
1902 Date Back
3x10-20 1-1260 <$1250
1902 Plain Back
3x10-20 1261-2998 <$1250
1929 Small Size
10 Type 1 1-316 <$500
20 Type 1 1-106 <$500
10 Type 2 1-354 <$550
20 Type 2 1-72 <$550
Total Issue $204,360
Out in 1935 $12,500
Large out 1935 $720

8750 Benton
BENTON COUNTY NB OF CORVALLIS
{{ UNREPORTED }}
Chartered 6/07
Liquidated 3/4/16
1902 Red Seal <$VALUE
4x5 1-1115 <$2000
3x10-20 1-1074 <$2000
1902 Date Back
4x5 1-3400 <$1500
3x10-20 1-2480 <$1500
1902 Plain Back
4x5 3401-3510 <$1500
Total Issue $270,200
Out in 1916 $31,010

4301 Benton
FNB OF CORVALLIS
{{ 6 L 13 S }}
Chartered 1890
Brown Back <$VALUE
3x10-20 1-4790 <$1000
1882 Date Back
3x10-20 1-684 <$800
1902 Date Back
4x5 1-2800 <$450
3x10-20 1-2280 <$450
1902 Plain Back
4x5 2801-5750 <$450
3x10-20 2281-9171 <$450
1929 Small Size
10 Type 1 1-3756 <$175
20 Type 1 1-1050 <$175
10 Type 2 1-1023 <$200
20 Type 1 1-290 <$200
Total Issue $1,214,640
Out in 1935 $65,000
Large out 1935 $3,710

5642 Lane
FNB OF COTTAGE GROVE
{{ 2 L 5 S }}
Chartered 12/14/00
Brown Back <$VALUE
3x10-20 1-1050 <$1000
1882 Date Back
3x10-20 1-1080 <$850
1882 Value Back
3x10-20 1081-1176 <$1000
1902 Plain Back
3x10-20 1-1544 <$650
1929 Small Size
10 Type 1 1-654 <$325
20 Type 1 1-190 <$325
10 Type 2 1-1394 <$350
20 Type 2 1-280 <$350
Total Issue $270,080
Out in 1935 $37,500
Large out 1935 $880

7472 Polk
DALLAS NB, DALLAS
{{ 3 L 2U + 7 S }}
Chartered 11/04
Liquidated 6/30/34
1902 Red Seal <$VALUE
4x5 1-775 <$1750
3x10-20 1-626 <$1750
1902 Date Back
4x5 1-1825 <$650
3x10-20 1-1280 <$650
1902 Plain Back
4x5 1826-6540 <$650
3x10-20 1281-4039 <$650
1929 Small Size
5 Type 1 1-916 <$275
10 Type 1 1-414 <$275
20 Type 1 1-116 <$275
5 Type 2 1-474 <$300
10 Type 2 1-297 <$300
20 Type 2 1-70 <$325
Total Issue $452,530
Out at close $22,950
Large out at close $1,710

7072 Polk
FNB OF DALLAS
{{ UNREPORTED }}
Chartered 12/24/03
Liquidated 2/11/04
1902 Red Seal <$VALUE
3x10-20 1-125 <$3500
Total Issue $6,250
All notes reportedly redeemed

FNB of East Portland
See Ch 3025
FNB of East Portland, Portland

6644 Union
FNB OF ELGIN
{{ 1 L 4 S }}
Chartered 2/03
1902 Red Seal <$VALUE
3x10-20 1-676 <$2500
1902 Date Back
3x10-20 1-1200* <$1250
1902 Plain Back
3x10-20 1301-2928* <$1250
* 1201-1300 not marked
1929 Small Size
10 Type 1 1-477 <$400
20 Type 1 1-128 <$400
Total Issue $224,180
Out in 1935 $12,500
Large out 1935 $590

3912 Wallowa
WALLOWA NB OF ENTERPRISE
{{ 1 L 6 S }}
Chartered 7/24/88
Liquidated 10/12/35
Brown Back <$VALUE
3x10-20 1-1733 <$1500
1902 Date Back
3x10-20 1-1440 <$850
1902 Plain Back
3x10-20 1441-2983 <$850
1929 Small Size
10 Type 1 1-372 <$275
20 Type 1 1-158 <$275
10 Type 2 1-3228 <$275
20 Type 2 1-828 <$275
Total Issue $325,920
Out at close $49,550
Large out at close $890

FNB of Eugene
SEE Ch 3458
FNB of Eugene City

10345 Lane
UNITED STATES NB OF EUGENE
{{ 5 L 10 S }}
Chartered 3/13
Liquidated 7/17/35
1902 Date Back <$VALUE
3x10-20 1-2000 <$400
1902 Plain Back
3x10-20 2001-12553 <$400
1929 Small Size
5 Type 1 1-3606 <$185
10 Type 1 1-2122 <$185
20 Type 1 1-498 <$200
5 Type 2 1-3634 <$225
10 Type 2 1-1410 <$225
20 Type 2 1-345 <$235
Total Issue $962,080
Out at close $71,295
Large out at close $2,685

3986 Lane
EUGENE NB OF EUGENE CITY
{{ UNREPORTED }}
Chartered 3/8/89
Liquidated 11/26/92
Brown Back <$VALUE
3x10-20 1-365 <$2500
Total Issue $18,250
Out in 1910 $100

<$VALUEs are for notes in **FINE** condition. Value changes by approximately **25%** for a change of one full grade.

****
3458 Lane
FNB OF EUGENE CITY
Chartered 1886
2nd title: FNB of Eugene 2/16/06
FIRST TITLE {{ 2 L }}
Brown Back <$VALUE
3x10-20 1-2603 <$1500
SECOND TITLE {{ 8 L 11 S }}
1902 Red Seal
3x10-20 1-2900 <$1750
1902 Date Back
4x5 1-7500 <$300
3x10-20 1-5600 <$300
1902 Plain Back
4x5 7501-23105 <$300
3x10-20 5601-16236 <$300
1929 Small Size
5 Type 1 1-3416 <$165
10 Type 1 1-1656 <$165
20 Type 1 1-440 <$165
5 Type 2 1-3764 <$185
10 Type 2 1-2865 <$185
20 Type 2 1-795 <$185
Total Issue $1,867,060
Out in 1935 $100,000
Large out 1935 $5,680
****
8036 Washington
FNB OF FOREST GROVE
{{ 5 L 2U + 8 S }}
Chartered 1/06
1902 Red Seal <$VALUE
3x10-20 1-950 <$1750
1902 Date Back
3x10-20 1-3610 <$500
1902 Plain Back
3x10-20 3611-11903 <$500
1929 Small Size
5 Type 1 1-1988 <$275
10 Type 1 1-964 <$275
20 Type 1 1-210 <$275
5 Type 2 1-1150 <$300
10 Type 2 1-505 <$300
Total Issue $796,130
Out in 1935 $27,830
Large out 1935 $2,830
****
8554 Washington
FOREST GROVE NB, FOREST GROVE
{{ 1 L 6 S }}
Chartered 2/07
1902 Red Seal <$VALUE
3x10-20 1-900 <$2000
1902 Date Back
3x10-20 1-1910 <$1000
1902 Plain Back
3x10-20 1911-4887 <$1000
1929 Small Size
5 Type 1 1-1362 <$300
10 Type 1 1-310 <$300
20 Type 1 1-102 <$325
5 Type 2 1-4318 <$325
Total Issue $382,640
Out in 1935 $25,000
Large out 1935 $930
****
10676 Douglas
FNB OF GARDINER
{{ 3 L 4 S }}
Chartered 1/15
1902 Plain Back <$VALUE
3x10-20 1-2682 <$650
1929 Small Size
5 Type 1 1-212 <$375
10 Type 1 1-196 <$375
20 Type 1 1-104 <$375
5 Type 2 1-1098 <$400
10 Type 2 1-590 <$400
20 Type 2 1-85 <$400
Total Issue $177,790
Out in 1935 $25,000
****
4168 Josephine
FNB OF SOUTHERN OREGON AT GRANT'S PASS
{{ 4 L 10 S }}
Chartered 12/2/89
Brown Back <$VALUE
4x5 1-3175 <$1500
3x10-20 1-520 <$1500
1882 Date Back
4x5 1-33 <$1250
3x10-20 1-89 <$1250
1902 Date Back
3x10-20 1-1250 <$750
1902 Plain Back
3x10-20 1251-8390 <$750

1929 Small Size
10 Type 1 1-1146 <$275
20 Type 1 1-360 <$300
10 Type 2 1-2003 <$325
20 Type 2 1-537 <$325
Total Issue $656,840
Out in 1935 $50,000
Large out 1935 $2,330
****
9146 Linn
FNB OF HARRISBURG
{{ 0 L 2 S }}
Chartered 5/08
1902 Date Back <$VALUE
4x10 1-1000 <$1500
1902 Plain Back
4x10 1001-2145 <$1500
1929 Small Size
10 Type 1 1-366 <$750
Total Issue $107,760
Out in 1935 $6,250
Large out 1935 $310
****
3774 Morrow
FNB OF HEPPNER
{{ 1 L 2 S }}
Chartered 8/15/87
Receivership 2/2/33
Brown Back <$VALUE
4x5 1-1275 <$2000
3x10-20 1-337 <$2000
1902 Red Seal
3x10-20 1-250 <$2500
1902 Date Back
3x10-20 1-2300 <$1250
1902 Plain Back
3x10-20 2301-5457 <$1250
1929 Small Size
10 Type 1 1-573 <$750
20 Type 1 1-150 <$750
Total Issue $413,780
Out at close $25,000
Large out at close $3,240
****
3953 Morrow
NB OF HEPPNER
{{ UNREPORTED }}
Chartered 12/31/88
Liquidated 6/19/97
Brown Back <$VALUE
3x10-20 1-747 <$2500
Total Issue $37,350
Out in 1910 $310
****
9281 Umatilla
FNB OF HERMISTON
{{ 1 L 1 S }}
Chartered 11/08
1902 Date Back <$VALUE
3x10-20 1-800 <$1500
1902 Plain Back
3x10-20 801-1581 <$1500
1929 Small Size
10 Type 1 1-217 <$750
20 Type 1 1-53 <$750
Total Issue $98,430
Out in 1935 $6,250
Large out 1935 $310
****
9923 Washington
AMERICAN NB OF HILLSBORO
{{ 1 L }}
Chartered 1/11
Liquidated 12/30/16
1902 Date Back <$VALUE
3x10-20 1-3640 <$1000
1902 Plain Back
3x10-20 3641-4062 <$1000
Total Issue $203,100
Out at close $50,000
****
Commercial NB of Hillsboro
SEE Ch 9917
Hillsboro NB, Hillsboro
****
3966 Washington
FNB OF HILLSBORO
{{ UNREPORTED }}
Chartered 1/19/89
Liquidated 5/1/97
Brown Back <$VALUE
3x10-20 1-664 <$2500
Total Issue $33,200
Out in 1910 $280
****

****
9917 Washington
HILLSBORO NB, HILLSBORO
Chartered 1/11
2nd title: Commercial NB of Hillsboro 1/3/27
FIRST TITLE {{ 2 L }}
1902 Date Back <$VALUE
3x10-20 1-4500 <$650
1902 Plain Back
3x10-20 4501-10861 <$650
SECOND TITLE {{ 6 S }}
1929 Small Size
5 Type 1 1-1894 <$250
10 Type 1 1-934 <$250
20 Type 1 1-464 <$250
5 Type 2 1-420 <$300
10 Type 2 1-355 <$300
20 Type 2 1-150 <$300
Total Issue $720,240
Out in 1935 $37,500
Large out 1935 $2,020
****
7272 Hood River
FNB OF HOOD RIVER
{{ 3 L 2U + 15 S }}
Chartered 5/04
1902 Red Seal <$VALUE
3x10-20 1-580 <$1750
1902 Date Back
3x10-20 1-6820 <$650
1902 Plain Back
3x10-20 6821-16866 <$650
1929 Small Size
10 Type 1 1-624 <$150
20 Type 1 1-212 <$150
10 Type 2 1-3757 <$165
20 Type 2 1-1273 <$175
Total Issue $998,610
Out in 1935 $25,000
Large out 1935 $3,240
****
3972 Polk
FNB OF INDEPENDENCE
{{ UNREPORTED }}
Chartered 1/31/89
Liquidated 8/4/00
Brown Back <$VALUE
4x5 1-2655 <$2500
50-100 1-18 <$5000
Total Issue $55,800
Out in 1910 $460
****
FNB of Independence
SEE Ch 3979
Independence NB, Independence
****
3979 Polk
INDEPENDENCE NB, INDEPENDENCE
Chartered 2/15/89
2nd title: FNB of Independence 8/1/24
FIRST TITLE {{ 1 L }}
Brown Back <$VALUE
3x10-20 1-1603 <$1500
1902 Date Back
3x10-20 1-1380 <$1000
1902 Plain Back
3x10-20 1381-2260 <$1000
SECOND TITLE {{ 0 L 8 S }}
1902 Plain Back
3x10-20 1-764 <$1250
1929 Small Size
10 Type 1 1-974 <$225
20 Type 1 1-244 <$225
10 Type 2 1-2116 <$250
20 Type 2 1-405 <$250
Total Issue $348,330
Out in 1935 $50,000
Large out 1935 $750
****
3313 Union
FNB OF ISLAND CITY
{{ UNREPORTED }}
Chartered 2/26/85
Liquidated 1/20/00
Brown Back <$VALUE
3x10-20 1-1047 <$3000
Total Issue $52,350
Out in 1910 $610
****
8048 Wallowa
FNB OF JOSEPH
{{ 2 L }}
Organized 12/11/05
Receivership 6/14/23
1902 Red Seal <$VALUE
3x10-20 1-288 <$2000
1902 Date Back
3x10-20 1-1460 <$1250

1902 Plain Back
3x10-20 1461-3496 <$1250
Total Issue $189,200
Out at close $24,300
****
10218 Lane
FNB OF JUNCTION CITY
{{ 3 L U + 2 S }}
Chartered 6/12
1902 Date Back <$VALUE
3x10-20 1-1000 <$850
1902 Plain Back
3x10-20 1001-2778 <$850
1929 Small Size
10 Type 1 1-288 <$600
20 Type 1 1-118 <$600
10 Type 2 1-250 <$650
20 Type 2 1-65 <$650
Total Issue $174,140
Out in 1935 $12,500
Large out 1935 $370
****
11801 Klamath
AMERICAN NB OF KLAMATH FALLS
{{ 3 L 14 S }}
Chartered 7/20
1902 Plain Back <$VALUE
3x10-20 1-15132 <$600
1929 Small Size
10 Type 1 1-2926 <$110
20 Type 1 1-790 <$125
10 Type 2 1-2246 <$150
20 Type 2 1-440 <$165
Total Issue $1,058,220
Out in 1935 $62,500
Large out 1935 $3,100
****
7167 Klamath
FNB OF KLAMATH FALLS
{{ 7 L 18 S }}
Chartered 3/04
1902 Red Seal <$VALUE
3x10-20 1-570 <$1750
1902 Date Back
3x10-20 1-5160 <$300
1902 Plain Back
3x10-20 5161-22910 <$300
1929 Small Size
10 Type 1 1-4076 <$85
20 Type 1 1-1278 <$85
10 Type 2 1-1161 <$100
20 Type 2 1-715 <$100
Total Issue $1,597,830
Out in 1935 $100,000
Large out 1935 $4,540
****
4452 Union
FARMERS & TRADERS NB OF La GRANDE
{{ UNREPORTED }}
Organized 10/29/90
Receivership 10/13/08
Brown Back <$VALUE
3x10-20 1-1882 <$2000
Total Issue $94,100
Out in 1916 $810
****
13602 Union
FNB OF La GRANDE
{{ 3U + 11 S }}
Organized 3/7/32
1929 Small Size <$VALUE
5 Type 1 1-2054 <$135
10 Type 1 1-624 <$135
20 Type 1 1-212 <$150
5 Type 2 1-5488 <$165
10 Type 2 1-3045 <$165
20 Type 2 1-1010 <$175
Total Issue $202,590
Out in 1935 $105,350
****
3655 Union
La GRANDE NB, La GRANDE
{{ 11 L 12 S }}
Chartered 1887
Liquidated 5/29/32
Brown Back <$VALUE
3x10-20 1-2850 <$1000
1902 Red Seal
3x10-20 1-900 <$1500
1902 Date Back
3x10-20 1-8000 <$225
1902 Plain Back
3x10-20 8001-34991 <$225
1929 Small Size
10 Type 1 1-3694 <$125
20 Type 1 1-995 <$135
Total Issue $2,278,090
Out at close $196,795
Large out at close $29,455
****

****
9314 Union
UNITED STATES NB OF La GRANDE
{{ 5 L 10 S }}
Organized 12/9/08
Receivership 5/23/32
1902 Date Back <$VALUE
4x5 1-3625 <$350
3x10-20 1-2840 <$350
1902 Plain Back
4x5 3626-19681 <$350
3x10-20 2841-13424 <$350
1929 Small Size
5 Type 1 1-2716 <$175
10 Type 1 1-1328 <$175
20 Type 1 1-385 <$185
Total Issue $1,272,180
Out at close $86,755
Large out at close $7,805
****
11121 Lake
COMMERCIAL NB OF LAKEVIEW
{{ 1 L 6 S }}
Chartered 12/17
1902 Plain Back <$VALUE
3x10-20 1-1620 <$1250
1929 Small Size
10 Type 1 1-310 <$275
20 Type 1 1-426 <$275
20 Type 2 1-1929 <$275
Total Issue $189,300
Out in 1935 $72,500
Large out 1935 $4,030
Outstanding includes Ch 10432 and Ch 7244
****
7244 Lake
FNB OF LAKEVIEW
{{ 3 L 4 S }}
Chartered 5/04
Liquidated 12/15/31
1902 Red Seal <$VALUE
3x10-20 1-2275 <$1750
1902 Date Back
3x10-20 1-3640 <$600
1902 Plain Back
3x10-20 3641-11867 <$600
1929 Small Size
10 Type 1 1-898 <$400
20 Type 1 1-254 <$400
Total Issue $791,460
Out at close $46,520
Large out at close $5,070
Ch 11121 assumed circulation
****
9127 Linn
FNB OF LEBANON
{{ 4 L 7 S }}
Chartered 5/08
1902 Date Back <$VALUE
4x5 1-1450 <$500
3x10-20 1-1135 <$500
1902 Plain Back
4x5 1451-4150 <$500
3x10-20 1136-8120 <$500
1929 Small Size
10 Type 1 1-1290 <$300
20 Type 1 1-390 <$300
10 Type 2 1-1769 <$325
20 Type 2 1-400 <$325
Total Issue $638,890
Out in 1935 $50,000
Large out 1935 $2,880
****
10164 Linn
LEBANON NB, LEBANON
{{ 1 L 1 S }}
Chartered 3/12
Liquidated 6/18/32
1902 Date Back <$VALUE
3x10-20 1-800 <$850
1902 Plain Back
3x10-20 801-2226 <$850
1929 Small Size
10 Type 1 1-396* <$750
20 Type 1 1-124** <$750
* Sheets 156-316 not issued
** Sheets 24-104 not issued
Total Issue $130,560
Out at close $9,400
Large out at close $700
****
10534 Multnomah
FNB OF LINNTON
{{ 2 L }}
Chartered 5/14
Liquidated 4/1/33
1902 Date Back <$VALUE
4x5 1-500 <$1000
3x10-20 1-400 <$1000
1902 Plain Back
4x5 501-4945 <$1000
3x10-20 401-3089 <$1000

Total Issue $253,350
Out at close $1,440
****
7475 Coos
FNB OF COOS BAY AT MARSHFIELD
{{ 8 L 13 S }}
Chartered 11/04
1902 Red Seal <$VALUE
3x10-20 1-1050 <$1500
1902 Date Back
3x10-20 1-5900 <$325
1902 Plain Back
3x10-20 5901-22952 <$325
1929 Small Size
10 Type 1 1-2622 <$165
20 Type 1 1-734 <$175
5 Type 2 1-221 <$200
10 Type 2 1-818 <$200
20 Type 2 1-290 <$225
Total Issue $1,460,585
Out in 1935 $50,000
Large out 1935 $5,265
****
3399 Yamhill
FNB OF McMINNVILLE
{{ 5 L 9 S }}
Chartered 1885
Brown Back <$VALUE
3x10-20 1-2316 <$1000
1902 Red Seal
3x10-20 1-1350 <$1750
1902 Date Back
3x10-20 1-3440 <$500
1902 Plain Back
3x10-20 3441-10661 <$500
1929 Small Size
10 Type 1 1-1370 <$225
20 Type 1 1-348 <$225
10 Type 2 1-1307 <$250
20 Type 2 1-420 <$250
Total Issue $861,780
Out in 1935 $50,000
Large out 1935 $2,620
****
3857 Yamhill
McMINNVILLE NB, McMINNVILLE
Chartered 3/22/88
Liquidated 12/1/33
2nd title: United States NB of McMinnville 2/19/29
FIRST TITLE {{ 5 L }}
Brown Back <$VALUE
3x10-20 1-4198 <$1000
1902 Red Seal
3x10-20 1-500 <$1750
1902 Date Back
3x10-20 1-4000 <$400
1902 Plain Back
3x10-20 4001-15837 <$400
SECOND TITLE {{ 12 S }}
1929 Small Size
10 Type 1 1-3187 <$175
20 Type 1 1-887 <$175
Total Issue $1,314,810
Out at close $105,930
Large out at close $7,630
Outstanding includes Ch 9806
****
9806 Yamhill
UNITED STATES NB OF McMINNVILLE
{{ 1 L }}
Chartered 7/10
Closed 2/19/29
1902 Date Back <$VALUE
3x10-20 1-3400 <$1000
1902 Plain Back
3x10-20 3401-10870 <$1000
Total Issue $543,500
Out at close $50,000
Ch 3857 assumed circulation
****
United States NB of McMinnville
SEE Ch 3857
McMinnville NB, McMinnville
****

CONDITION affects Value. The Values shown are for notes in FINE condition.

****
7701 Jackson
FNB OF MEDFORD
{{ 10 L 24 S }}
Chartered 4/05
1902 Red Seal <$VALUE
4x5 1-1025 <$1500
3x10-20 1-940 <$1500
1902 Date Back
4x5 1-1500 <$250
3x10-20 1-7200 <$250
1902 Plain Back
4x5 1501-16600 <$250
3x10-20 7201-18267 <$250
1929 Small Size
5 Type 1 1-3618 <$75
10 Type 1 1-1810 <$75
20 Type 1 1-440 <$85
5 Type 2 1-5742 <$100
10 Type 2 1-2943 <$100
20 Type 2 1-907 <$110
Total Issue $1,660,070
Out in 1935 $99,995
Large out 1935 $5,075
****
8236 Jackson
MEDFORD NB, MEDFORD
{{ 3 L 2 S }}
Chartered 5/06
Liquidated 9/19/33
1902 Red Seal <$VALUE
50-100 1-634 <$3500/$4000
1902 Date Back
3x10-20 1-3700 <$450
50-100 1-700 <$750/$850
3x50-100 1-200 <$750/$850
1902 Plain Back
3x10-20 3701-10689 <$450
1929 Small Size
10 Type 1 1-271 <$400
20 Type 1 1-69 <$400
Total Issue $809,090
Out at close $14,750
Large out at close $3,670
****
13771 Jackson
MEDFORD NB, MEDFORD
{{ 5 S }}
Chartered 9/33
1929 Small Size <$VALUE
5 Type 2 1-6003 <$225
10 Type 2 1-2867 <$225
20 Type 2 1-868 <$225
Total Issue $76,045
Out in 1935 $42,000
****
10056 Klamath
FNB OF MERRILL
{{ 2 L 7 S }}
Chartered 7/11
1902 Date Back <$VALUE
4x5 1-515 <$850
3x10-20 1-414 <$850
1902 Plain Back
4x5 516-5219 <$850
3x10-20 415-3014 <$850
1929 Small Size
5 Type 1 1-1042 <$250
10 Type 1 1-564 <$250
20 Type 1 1-164 <$275
5 Type 2 1-1068 <$275
10 Type 2 1-548 <$275
20 Type 2 1-170 <$300
Total Issue $354,080
Out in 1935 $25,000
Large out 1935 $1,185
****
9201 Umatilla
FNB OF MILTON
{{ 2 L }}
Organized 6/6/08
Receivership 2/3/32
1902 Date Back <$VALUE
3x10-20 1-2210 <$850
1902 Plain Back
3x10-20 2211-5151 <$850
Total Issue $257,550
Out at close $1,840
****
11271 Clackamas
FNB OF MOLALLA
{{ 2 S }}
Chartered 12/18
1929 Small Size <$VALUE
20 Type 1 1-258 <$600
20 Type 2 1-336 <$600
Total Issue $37,680
Out in 1935 $25,000
****
10071 Polk
FNB OF MONMOUTH
{{ 1 L 5 S }}
Chartered 8/11
1902 Date Back <$VALUE
3x10-20 1-1120 <$1250
1902 Plain Back
3x10-20 1121-3298 <$1250
1929 Small Size
10 Type 1 1-360 <$375
20 Type 1 1-118 <$375
10 Type 2 1-457 <$400
20 Type 2 1-86 <$425
Total Issue $206,950
Out in 1935 $15,000
Large out 1935 $860
****
7537 Yamhill
FNB OF NEWBERG
{{ 3 L 5 S }}
Chartered 12/04
Liquidated 1/23/35
1902 Red Seal <$VALUE
3x10-20 1-550 <$1750
1902 Date Back
3x10-20 1-3400 <$650
1902 Plain Back
3x10-20 3401-9536 <$650
1929 Small Size
10 Type 1 1-861 <$350
20 Type 1 1-221 <$350
Total Issue $581,480
Out at close $16,680
Large out at close $2,460
****
9358 Yamhill
UNITED STATES NB OF NEWBERG
{{ 5 L U + 8 S }}
Chartered 3/09
1902 Date Back <$VALUE
3x10-20 1-4240 <$500
1902 Plain Back
3x10-20 4241-12319 <$500
1929 Small Size
10 Type 1 1-1376 <$200
20 Type 1 1-320 <$225
10 Type 2 1-1380 <$225
20 Type 2 1-421 <$250
Total Issue $759,130
Out in 1935 $50,000
Large out 1935 $2,670
****
9328 Coos
FNB OF NORTH BEND
{{ 5 L 6 S }}
Organized 1/4/09
Liquidated 4/24/34
1902 Date Back <$VALUE
3x10-20 1-3020 <$500
1902 Plain Back
3x10-20 3021-11678 <$500
1929 Small Size
10 Type 1 1-1313 <$300
20 Type 1 1-344 <$300
Total Issue $703,960
Out at close $39,560
Large out at close $2,210
****
5822 Malheur
FNB OF ONTARIO
{{ 4 L 0 S }}
Chartered 5/21/01
Liquidated 3/12/32
Brown Back <$VALUE
4x5 1-795 <$1250
3x10-20 1-842 <$1250
1882 Date Back
4x5 1-1800 <$1000
3x10-20 1-1430 <$1000
1882 Value Back
4x5 1801-2395 <$1250
3x10-20 1431-1768 <$1250
1902 Plain Back
4x5 1-4509 <$500
1929 Small Size
5 Type 1 1-830 <$850
Total Issue $299,380
Out at close $6,140
Large out at close $1,495
****
9348 Malheur
ONTARIO NB, ONTARIO
{{ 6 L U + 10 S }}
Chartered 2/09
Liquidated 9/18/35
1902 Date Back <$VALUE
4x5 1-4800 <$350
3x10-20 1-3660 <$350
1902 Plain Back
4x5 4801-14832 <$350
3x10-20 3661-9841 <$350
1929 Small Size
5 Type 1 1-1984 <$175
10 Type 1 1-1164 <$175
20 Type 1 1-338 <$175
5 Type 2 1-3262 <$185
10 Type 2 1-1481 <$185
20 Type 2 1-335 <$200
Total Issue $996,430
Out at close $50,440
Large out at close $3,795
****
8556 Clackamas
FNB OF OREGON CITY
{{ 1 L 6 S }}
Chartered 2/07
1902 Red Seal <$VALUE
4x10 1-500 <$2500
1902 Date Back
4x10 1-900 <$1250
1902 Plain Back
4x10 901-3110 <$1250
1929 Small Size
10 Type 1 1-2192 <$300
10 Type 2 1-1784 <$350
Total Issue $93,760
Out in 1935 $26,080
Large out 1935 $900
****
10432 Lake
PAISLEY NB, PAISLEY
{{ 0 L 2 S }}
Chartered 8/13
Liquidated 7/1/31
1902 Date Back <$VALUE
3x10-20 1-740 <$1500
1902 Plain Back
3x10-20 741-2600 <$1500
1929 Small Size
10 Type 1 1-206 <$600
20 Type 1 1-46 <$650
Total Issue $147,880
Out at close $12,500
Large out at close $1,620
Ch 11121 assumed circulation
****
9228 Umatilla
AMERICAN NB OF PENDLETON
{{ 5 L }}
Chartered 8/08
Liquidated 1/16/26
1902 Date Back <$VALUE
4x5 1-20250 <$400
3x10-20 1-15600 <$400
1902 Plain Back
4x5 20251-37890 <$400
3x10-20 15601-40163 <$400
Total Issue $2,765,950
Out at close $120,300
****
7301 Umatilla
COMMERCIAL NB OF PENDLETON
{{ 1 L }}
Chartered 6/14/04
Liquidated 2/5/09
1902 Red Seal <$VALUE
4x5 1-1415 <$1750
3x10-20 1-1369 <$1750
Total Issue $96,750
Out in 1910 $22,265
****
13576 Umatilla
F INLAND NB OF PENDLETON
{{ U + 6 S }}
Organized 10/19/31
Receivership 2/1/34
1929 Small Size <$VALUE
10 Type 1 1-576 <$250
20 Type 1 1-190 <$250
10 Type 2 1-865 <$275
20 Type 2 1-307 <$275
Total Issue $72,150
Out at close $99,995
Outstanding includes Ch 2630
****
2630 Umatilla
FNB OF PENDLETON
{{ 11 L 7 S }}
Chartered 1882
Liquidated 2/1/32
Series 1875 <$VALUE
3x10-20 1-3931<$2500/$3000
Brown Back
3x10-20 1-6300 <$850
1882 Date Back
3x10-20 1-16300 <$750
1882 Value Back
3x10-20 16301-29657 <$850
1902 Plain Back
3x10-20 1-10760 <$275
1929 Small Size
10 Type 1 1-1206 <$250
20 Type 1 1-298 <$275
Total Issue $2,640,520
Out at close $91,955
Large out at close $12,255
Ch 13576 assumed circulation
****
4249 Umatilla
NB OF PENDLETON
{{ UNREPORTED }}
Organized 3/8/90
Receivership 6/8/94
Brown Back <$VALUE
3x10-20 1-923 <$2000
Total Issue $46,150
Out in 1916 $200
****
3665 Umatilla
PENDLETON NB, PENDLETON
{{ UNREPORTED }}
Chartered 4/2/87
Liquidated 2/4/89
Brown Back <$VALUE
3x10-20 1-280 <$2500
Total Issue $14,000
Out in 1916 $80
****
3402 Multnomah
AINSWORTH NB OF PORTLAND
{{ 1 L }}
Chartered 10/27/85
Liquidated 11/3/02
Brown Back <$VALUE
4x5 1-1520 <$1500
50-100 1-698 <$3500
Total Issue $135,100
Out in 1910 $2,010
****
12557 Multnomah
AMERICAN NB OF PORTLAND
{{ 22 S }}
Chartered 7/24 as Portland NB, under which there was no issue. Issuing title adopted 2/28/29.
Liquidated 7/31/34
1929 Small Size <$VALUE
5 Type 1 1-15622 <$60
10 Type 1 1-8812 <$60
20 Type 1 1-2195 <$65
Total Issue $1,260,780
Out at close $174,920
****
12613 Multnomah
BROTHERHOOD CO-OPERATIVE NB OF PORTLAND
Chartered 12/24
Liquidated 7/1/31
2nd title: Brotherhood NB of Portland 6/4/29
3rd title: Columbia NB of Portland 11/22/29
FIRST TITLE {{ 12 L }}
1902 Plain Back <$VALUE
4x5 1-47507 <$150
SECOND TITLE {{ 1 S }}
1929 Small Size
5 Type 1 1-4076 <$400
THIRD TITLE {{ 4 S }}
1929 Small Size
5 Type 1 1-9043 <$225
Total Issue $1,343,710
Out at close $200,000
Large out at close $620
****
Brotherhood NB of Portland
SEE Ch 12613
Brotherhood Co-Operative NB of Portland
****
13294 Multnomah
CENTRAL NB OF PORTLAND
{{ UNREPORTED }}
Chartered 3/29
Liquidated 8/25/31
1929 Small Size <$VALUE
5 Type 1 1-1655 <$650
Total Issue $49,650
Out at close $18,350
****
13299 Multnomah
CITIZENS NB OF PORTLAND
{{ 2U + 15 S }}
Organized 3/19/29
Liquidated 4/1/33
1929 Small Size <$VALUE
5 Type 1 1-4954 <$75
10 Type 1 1-1245 <$75
20 Type 1 1-346 <$85
50 Type 1 1-64 <$275
100 Type 1 1-37 <$350
Total Issue $306,240
Out at close $197,020
****
Columbia NB of Portland
SEE Ch 12613
Brotherhood Co-Operative NB of Portland
****
3422 Multnomah
COMMERCIAL NB OF PORTLAND
{{ UNREPORTED }}
Chartered 12/19/85
Liquidated 5/13/98
Brown Back <$VALUE
50-100 1-1100 <$3500
Total Issue $165,000
Out in 1910 $1,650
****
1553 Multnomah
FNB OF PORTLAND
{{ 32 L 50+ S }}
Chartered 9/8/65
Original Series <$VALUE
4x5 1-1500 <$2000
3x10-20 1-6100<$2500/$3000
Series 1875
3x10-20 1-8100<$2500/$3000
Brown Back
3x10-20 1-16131 <$650
50-100 1-5437 <$2500/$3000
1902 Red Seal
4x5 1-8250 <$1500
3x10-20 1-7100 <$1500
50-100 1-1066 <$3500/$4000
1902 Date Back
4x5 1-27165 <$75
3x10-20 1-64834 <$75
50-100 1-2500 <$500/$600
3x50-100 1-11685<$500/$600
1902 Plain Back
3x10-20 64835-74834 <$75
1929 Small Size
5 Type 1 1-52620 <$20
10 Type 1 1-29046 <$20
20 Type 1 1-8792 <$30
5 Type 2 1-138742 <$20
10 Type 2 1-81276 <$20
20 Type 2 1-26590 <$30
Total Issue $17,037,920
Out in 1935 $2,500,000
Large out 1935 $52,590
****
3025 Multnomah
FNB OF EAST PORTLAND, PORTLAND
{{ UNREPORTED }}
Chartered 8/11/83
Liquidated 10/31/95
Brown Back <$VALUE
3x10-20 1-1288 <$2500
Total Issue $64,400
Out in 1910 $540
****
9180 Multnomah
LUMBERMENS NB OF PORTLAND
{{ 4 L }}
Chartered 7/08
Liquidated 11/3/17
1902 Date Back <$VALUE
4x5 1-24650 <$500
3x10-20 1-18614 <$500
50-100 1-800 <$750/$850
3x50-100 1-400 <$750/$850
Total Issue $1,643,700
Out at close $250,000
Ch 4514 assumed circulation
****
3536 Multnomah
MERCHANTS NB OF PORTLAND
{{ 2 L }}
Chartered 7/19/86
Liquidated 1/11/16
Brown Back <$VALUE
3x10-20 1-14348 <$1000
1902 Red Seal
50-100 1-1300 <$3500/$4000
1902 Date Back
50-100 1-2600 <$750/$850
3x50-100 1-2035 <$750/$850
Total Issue $1,811,150
Out at close $325,000
****
10300 Multnomah
NORTHWESTERN NB OF PORTLAND
{{ 1 L }}
Chartered 12/12
Liquidated 5/3/27
1902 Date Back <$VALUE
3x50-100 1-1387<$900/$1000
Total Issue $346,750
Out at close $21,500
****
3719 Multnomah
OREGON NB OF PORTLAND
{{ UNREPORTED }}
Chartered 6/7/87
Receivership 12/12/93
Brown Back <$VALUE
4x5 1-6225 <$2000
Total Issue $124,500
Out in 1916 $965
****
Peninsula NB of Portland
SEE Ch 10103
Peninsula NB of Saint Johns
****
3184 Multnomah
PORTLAND NB, PORTLAND
{{ 1 L }}
Chartered 5/13/84
Liquidated 6/9/96
Brown Back <$VALUE
4x5 1-4871 <$1750
Total Issue $97,420
Out in 1910 $695
****
4514 Multnomah
UNITED STATES NB OF PORTLAND
{{ 50+ L 50+ S }}
Chartered 1891
Brown Back <$VALUE
3x10-20 1-28140 <$600
1882 Date Back
4x5 1-11200 <$450
3x10-20 1-14524 <$450
1902 Date Back
4x5 1-53500 <$75
3x10-20 1-44000 <$75
1902 Plain Back
4x5 53501-219903 <$75
3x10-20 44001-155558 <$75
1929 Small Size
5 Type 1 1-123762 <$20
10 Type 1 1-62372 <$20
20 Type 1 1-21840 <$30
5 Type 2 1-91860 <$20
10 Type 2 1-59185* <$20
20 Type 2 1-8600 <$30
* 48157-48162 not issued
Total Issue $25,832,230
Out in 1935 $3,000,000
Large out 1935 $58,195
Outstanding includes Ch 9180
****
9763 Grant
FNB OF PRAIRIE CITY
{{ 1 L 2U + 2 S }}
Chartered 5/10
1902 Date Back <$VALUE
4x5 1-615 <$1000
3x10-20 1-494 <$1000
1902 Plain Back
4x5 616-1705 <$1000
3x10-20 495-884 <$1000
1929 Small Size
5 Type 1 1-283 <$600
10 Type 1 1-150 <$600
20 Type 1 1-34 <$600
Total Issue $99,870
Out in 1935 $6,250
Large out 1935 $380
****
3851 Crook
FNB OF PRINEVILLE
{{ UNREPORTED }}
Chartered 3/2/88
Brown Back <$VALUE
3x10-20 1-1322 <$2000
1902 Red Seal
3x10-20 1-200 <$2500
1902 Date Back
3x10-20 1-950 <$1500
1902 Plain Back
3x10-20 951-1319 <$1500
Total Issue $142,050
Out in 1935 $480
****
11294 Deschutes
FNB OF REDMOND
{{ UNREPORTED }}
Organized 12/24/18
Receivership 2/12/31
1902 Plain Back <$VALUE
3x10-20 1-862 <$1750
Total Issue $43,100
Out at close $900
Outstanding includes Ch 11302
****

****

11302 Deschutes
REDMOND NB, REDMOND
{{ UNREPORTED }}
Chartered 2/19
Liquidated 3/3/24
1902 Plain Back <$VALUE
3x10-20 1-382 <$2000
Total Issue $19,100
Out at close $4,700
Ch 11294 assumed circulation
****

9423 Douglas
DOUGLAS NB OF ROSEBURG
{{ 4 L 9 S }}
Chartered 6/09
1902 Date Back <$VALUE
3x10-20 1-2520* <$600
1902 Plain Back
3x10-20 2761-5585* <$600
* 2521-2760 not marked
1929 Small Size
10 Type 1 1-1554 <$250
20 Type 1 1-474 <$250
10 Type 2 1-486 <$275
20 Type 2 1-110 <$300
Total Issue $436,430
Out in 1935 $50,000
Large out 1935 $1,220
****

4624 Douglas
FNB OF ROSEBURG
{{ UNREPORTED }}
Chartered 1891
Liquidated 6/17/11
Brown Back <$VALUE
3x10-20 1-1330 <$2000
1882 Date Back
3x10-20 1-293 <$2000
Total Issue $81,150
Out at close $11,300
****

8955 Douglas
ROSEBURG NB, ROSEBURG
{{ 1 L }}
Chartered 11/07
1902 Red Seal <$VALUE
3x10-20 1-375 <$2500
1902 Date Back
3x10-20 1-1320 <$1250
1902 Plain Back
3x10-20 1321-2707 <$1250
Total Issue $154,100
Out in 1935 $505
****

11200 Columbia
FNB OF SAINT HELENS
{{ 3 L 5 S }}
Chartered 6/18
Liquidated 12/8/33
1902 Plain Back <$VALUE
4x5 1-4780 <$650
3x10-20 1-2741 <$650
1929 Small Size
5 Type 1 1-875 <$325
10 Type 1 1-423 <$325
20 Type 1 1-115 <$350
Total Issue $298,080
Out at close $19,060
Large out 1935 $1,370
****

9047 Multnomah
FNB OF SAINT JOHNS
{{ 1 L }}
Chartered 2/08
Liquidated 3/3/17
1902 Red Seal <$VALUE
4x5 1-600 <$2250
4x10 1-600 <$2250
1902 Date Back
4x5 1-3075 <$1000
4x10 1-2775 <$1000
1902 Plain Back
4x5 3076-3866 <$1000
4x10 2776-3308 <$1000
Total Issue $245,640
Out at close $50,000
Ch 10103 assumed circulation
****

10103 Multnomah
PENINSULA NB OF
SAINT JOHNS
Chartered 11/21/11
Liquidated 4/1/33
2nd title: Peninsula NB of
Portland 9/13/15
FIRST TITLE {{ 1 L }}
1902 Date Back <$VALUE
4x5 1-2675 <$1250
3x10-20 1-2017 <$1250
SECOND TITLE {{ 4 L 10 S }}
1902 Plain Back
3x10-20 1-17338 <$400
1929 Small Size
5 Type 1 1-1960 <$125
10 Type 1 1-1263 <$125
20 Type 1 1-419 <$135
50 Type 1 1-160 <$185
100 Type 1 1-54 <$225
Total Issue $1,286,510
Out at close $204,135
Large out at close $6,215
Outstanding includes Ch 9047
****

3405 Marion
CAPITAL NB OF SALEM
Organized 10/8/85
Receivership 10/24/33
2nd title: FNB in Salem
9/7/23
FIRST TITLE {{ 3 L }}
Brown Back <$VALUE
3x10-20 1-2147 <$2250
1902 Red Seal
3x10-20 1-1750 <$2500
1902 Date Back
3x10-20 1-6700 <$750
1902 Plain Back
3x10-20 6701-14600 <$750
SECOND TITLE {{ 5 L 10 S }}
1902 Plain Back
3x10-20 1-7077 <$600
1929 Small Size
10 Type 1 1-2357 <$250
20 Type 1 1-689 <$275
Total Issue $1,502,800
Out at close $100,000
Large out at close $6,020
****

FNB in Salem
SEE Ch 3405
Capital NB of Salem
****

2816 Marion
FNB OF SALEM
{{ 1 L }}
Chartered 11/11/82
Liquidated 3/1/99
Brown Back <$VALUE
3x10-20 1-1695 <$2000
Total Issue $84,750
Out in 1910 $885
****

9021 Marion
UNITED STATES NB OF SALEM
{{ 2 L 9 S }}
Chartered 2/08
Liquidated 12/15/33
1902 Red Seal <$VALUE
3x10-20 1-750 <$2000
1902 Date Back
3x10-20 1-4300 <$850
1902 Plain Back
3x10-20 4301-4793 <$850
1929 Small Size
10 Type 1 1-1622 <$300
20 Type 1 1-374 <$300
Total Issue $419,350
Out at close $81,540
Large out at close $1,460
****

10992 Columbia
FNB OF SCAPPOOSE
{{ 2 L 3 S }}
Organized 4/17/17
Receivership 10/18/32
1902 Plain Back <$VALUE
4x5 1-4970 <$1250
3x10-20 1-3033 <$1250
1929 Small Size
5 Type 1 1-745 <$500
10 Type 1 1-392 <$500
20 Type 1 1-91 <$550
Total Issue $307,840
Out at close $23,920
Large out at close $1,920
****

8721 Yamhill
FNB OF SHERIDAN
{{ 1 L 4 S }}
Chartered 6/07
1902 Red Seal <$VALUE
4x10 1-310 <$2500
1902 Date Back
4x10 1-925 <$1250
1902 Plain Back
4x10 926-2079 <$1250
1929 Small Size
10 Type 1 1-736 <$375
10 Type 2 1-1365 <$400
Total Issue $153,370
Out in 1935 $25,000
Large out 1935 $550
****

****

11106 Marion
FNB OF SILVERTON
{{ 1 L 3 S }}
Organized 11/21/17
Receivership 8/15/32
1902 Plain Back <$VALUE
3x10-20 1-3760 <$1250
1929 Small Size
10 Type 1 1-464 <$450
20 Type 1 1-135 <$450
Total Issue $232,040
Out at close $24,700
Large out at close $1,950
****

8941 Lane
FNB OF SPRINGFIELD
{{ 1 L 1 S }}
Organized 10/9/07
Receivership 10/22/32
1902 Red Seal <$VALUE
3x10-20 1-187 <$2500
1902 Date Back
3x10-20 1-700 <$1500
1902 Plain Back
3x10-20 701-1378 <$1500
1929 Small Size
5 Type 1 1-280 <$650
10 Type 1 1-116 <$650
Total Issue $93,610
Out at close $6,250
Large out at close $640
****

6547 Baker
FNB OF SUMPTER
{{ UNREPORTED }}
Chartered 12/20/02
Liquidated 2/26/16
1902 Red Seal <$VALUE
3x10-20 1-640 <$2500
1902 Date Back
3x10-20 1-197 <$2000
Total Issue $41,850
Out at close $2,350
****

3441 Wasco
FNB OF THE DALLES
{{ 6 L 12 S }}
Organized 12/28/85
Receivership 3/10/33
Brown Back <$VALUE
3x10-20 1-1490 <$1000
1882 Date Back
3x10-20 1-800 <$850
1902 Date Back
3x10-20 1-5750 <$350
1902 Plain Back
3x10-20 5751-21615 <$350
1929 Small Size
10 Type 1 1-1704 <$165
20 Type 1 1-782 <$175
Total Issue $1,391,330
Out at close $91,660
Large out at close $8,170
****

3534 Wasco
THE DALLES NB, THE DALLES
{{ UNREPORTED }}
Chartered 7/16/86
Receivership 5/7/97
Brown Back <$VALUE
4x5 1-2362 <$2000
Total Issue $47,240
Out in 1916 $255
****

8574 Tillamook
FNB OF TILLAMOOK
{{ 2 L 14 S }}
Chartered 3/07
1902 Red Seal <$VALUE
4x10 1-853 <$2000
1902 Date Back
4x10 1-2550 <$750
1902 Plain Back
4x10 2551-6338 <$750
1929 Small Size
5 Type 1 1-1704 <$120
10 Type 1 1-1244 <$120
20 Type 1 1-274 <$135
50 Type 1 1-62 <$275
5 Type 2 1-3874 <$135
10 Type 2 1-1885 <$135
20 Type 2 1-515 <$150
Total Issue $513,400
Out in 1935 $100,000
Large out 1935 $840
****

****

2947 Union
FNB OF UNION
{{ 5 L 10 S }}
Chartered 1883
Liquidated 9/12/35
Brown Back <$VALUE
4x5 1-3177 <$1500
3x10-20 1-274 <$1500
1902 Red Seal
3x10-20 1-626 <$2000
1902 Date Back
3x10-20 1-3780 <$400
1902 Plain Back
3x10-20 3781-11504 <$400
1929 Small Size
10 Type 1 1-1306 <$200
20 Type 1 1-382 <$200
10 Type 2 1-1571 <$225
20 Type 2 1-280 <$225
Total Issue $829,250
Out at close $49,500
Large out at close $2,850
****

8387 Union
UNION NB, UNION
{{ UNREPORTED }}
Chartered 10/06
Liquidated 12/3/15
1902 Red Seal <$VALUE
3x10-20 1-280 <$2500
1902 Date Back
3x10-20 1-1535 <$1750
Total Issue $90,750
Out in 1916 $12,680
****

8528 Malheur
FNB OF VALE
{{ 1 L }}
Organized 1/14/07
Receivership 11/15/21
1902 Red Seal <$VALUE
3x10-20 1-200 <$2500
1902 Date Back
3x10-20 1-1380 <$1500
1902 Plain Back
3x10-20 1381-1791 <$1500
Total Issue $99,550
Out at close $11,600
****

9496 Malheur
UNITED STATES NB OF VALE
{{ 3 L }}
Organized 7/8/09
Receivership 11/15/21
1902 Date Back <$VALUE
4x5 1-3500 <$650
3x10-20 1-2740 <$650
1902 Plain Back
4x5 3501-7800 <$650
3x10-20 2741-5507 <$650
Total Issue $431,350
Out at close $68,750
****

9002 Wallowa
STOCKGROWERS & FARMERS NB
OF WALLOWA
{{ 2 L 2U + 10 S }}
Chartered 10/26/07
Receivership 3/6/34
1902 Red Seal <$VALUE
4x5 1-300 <$2000
3x10-20 1-240 <$2000
1902 Date Back
4x5 1-2275 <$1000
3x10-20 1-1660 <$1000
1902 Plain Back
4x5 2276-6820 <$1000
3x10-20 1661-4311 <$1000
1929 Small Size
5 Type 1 1-884 <$275
10 Type 1 1-402 <$275
20 Type 1 1-114 <$275
5 Type 2 1-478 <$300
10 Type 2 1-260 <$300
20 Type 2 1-25 <$325
Total Issue $439,760
Out at close $25,000
Large out at close $1,710
****

12427 Tillamook
FNB OF WHEELER
{{ UNREPORTED }}
Chartered 8/23
Liquidated 1/12/26
1902 Plain Back <$VALUE
4x5 1-250 <$2500
Total Issue $5,000
Out at close $4,450
****

NATIONAL BANK NOTES

PENNSYLVANIA

Nickname: The Keystone State
Motto: Virtue, Liberty, and Independence
Capital: Harrisburg
Number of towns: 657
Number of issuing charters: 1196
Number of small size issuers: 899

Adamsburg A4
Addison D3
Akron D7
Albion A1
Alexandria D4
Aliquippa C1
Allegheny D1
Allentown C8
Allenwood C6
Altoona E4
Ambler E8
Ambridge C1
Annville D6
Apollo C2
Ardmore E8
Arendtsville E5
Arnold D2
Ashland E9
Ashley A9
Aspinwall D1
Atglen E8
Athens A6
Auburn E9
Austin A4
Avella E1
Avoca A9
Avondale E8
Avonmore D2
Bainbridge D7
Bakerton E4
Bally E7
Bangor C9
Barnesboro E4
Bath C9
Beaver C1
Beaver Falls C1
Beaver Springs A4
Beaverdale E4
Bedford D4
Beech Creek B5
Belle Vernon E2
Bellefonte C5
Belleville C5
Bellevue D1
Bellwood E4
Bendersville E5
Benson D3
Bentleyville E1
Benton C6
Berlin D3
Bernville E7
Berwick C6
Berwyn E8
Bethlehem C9
Big Run C3
Biglerville E5
Birdsboro E7
Black Lick C3
Blairsville C3
Bloomsburg C6
Bloomsburgh C6
Blossburg A5
Blue Ball D7
Blue Ridge
Summit D5
Bolivar D2
Boswell D3
Boyertown E7
Braddock D1
Bradford A4
Bridgeport E8
Bridgeville D1
Bristol D9
Brockway C3
Brockwayville C3
Brookville C3
Brownstown D7
Brownsville E2
Bruin C2
Bryn Mawr E8
Burgettstown E1
Burnham C5
Burnside C4
Butler C2
Cairnbrook D3
California E1
Cambridge
Springs B2
Camp Hill E5
Canonsburg E1
Canton A6
Carbondale A8
Carlisle E5
Carmichaels E2
Carnegie D1
Carrolltown E4
Cassandra E4
Castle Shannon D1
Catasauqua C8
Catawissa C6
Cecil F1
Central City C5
Centralia D3
Centre Hall C6
Chalfont D9
Chambersburg D5
Chambersburgh D5
Charleroi F1
Chartiers D1
Cheltenham E8
Cherry Tree C3
Chester E8
Christiana D7
Clairton D1
Clarion B3
Clarks Summit A8
Claysburg E4
Claysville F1
Clearfield C4
Clifton Heights E8
Clintonville B2
Clymer C3
Coaldale E9
Coalport C4
Coatesville F8
Cochranton B2
Collegeville E8
Columbia D7
Confluence D3
Conneaut Lake B2
Conneautville B2
Connellsville E2
Conshohocken E8
Conyngham A8
Coopersburg C8
Coplay C8
Coraopolis D1
Corry A1
Coudersport A4
Crafton D1
Cresson E4
Cressona E9
Curwensville C4
Dale F4
Dallas A9
Dallastown E6
Danielsville C9
Danville C6
Darby E8
Dauphin F6
Davidsville D3
Dawson E2
Dayton C2
Delmont D2
Delta E6
Denver D7
Derry D2
Dickson City A8
Dillsburg E6
Donora F1
Dover E6
Downingtown F8
Doylestown D9
Dry Run D5
Dublin D9
DuBois C4
DuBois City C4
Dunbar E2
Duncannon D6
Dunmore A8
Duquesne E1
Dushore B6
East Berlin E5
East Brady B3
East Conemaugh F4
East Greenville E8
East Mauch
Chunk B9
East Smithfield A6
East Stroudsburg C8
Easton C9
Ebensburg F4
Economy C1
Edenburg B3
Edinboro A1
Edwardsville A9
Eldred A4
Elizabeth E1
Elizabethtown D7
Elizabethville F6
Elkins Park D8
Elkland A5
Ellsworth F1
Ellwood City C1
Elverson F8
Elysburg C6
Emaus C8
Emlenton B2
Emporium B4
Ephrata D7
Erie A1
Etna E1
Evans City C2
Everett D4
Exchange C6
Exeter A9
Export D2
Factoryville B7
Fairchance E2
Fairfield E5
Falls Creek C3
Farrell B1
Fawn Grove E6
Fayette City E2
Finleyville F1
Fleetwood E7
Fogelsville C8
Ford City C2
Forest City A7
Frackville E9
Franklin B2
Fredericksburg D6
Fredericktown F1
Fredonia B1
Freedom C1
Freeland A9
Freeport C2
Fryburg B3
Galeton A4
Gallitzin F4
Gap D7
Garrett D3
Genesee A4
Gettysburg E5
Girard A1
Girardville E9
Glassport E1
Glen Campbell C3
Glen Lyon A9
Glen Rock E6
Glenside E8
Goldsboro E6
Grantham E5
Gratz F6
Green Lane E8
Greencastle D5
Greensburg D2
Greenville B1
Grove City B1
Halifax F6
Hallstead A7
Hamburg E7
Hanover E6
Harleysville E8
Harmony C2
Harrisburg F6
Harrisville C2
Hastings F4
Hatboro F8
Hatfield F8
Hawley A8
Hays E1
Hazelhurst A4
Hazleton A9
Hegins E9
Herminie D2
Herndon C6
Hershey F6
Hickory F1
Highland Park F6
Hollidaysburg E4
Homer City C3
Homestead E1
Honesdale A8
Honeybrook F8
Hooversville D3
Hop Bottom A7
Hopewell D4
Houston F1
Houtzdale C4
Howard C5
Hughesville B6
Hummelstown F6
Huntingdon D4
Hyndman D4
Indiana C3
Intercourse D7
Irvona C4
Irwin D2
Jeanette D2
Jefferson E2
Jenkintown F8
Jermyn A8
Jerome D3
Jersey Shore B6
Jessup A8
Johnsonburg B3
Johnstown F4
Juniata E4
Kane A4
Kennett Square F8
Kingston A8
Kittanning C2
Knoxville A5
Koppel C1
Kutztown F7
Laceyville B7
Lake Ariel A8
Lancaster D7
Landisville D7
Langhorne D9
Lansdale F8
Lansdowne E8
Lansford B9
Laporte B6
Latrobe D2
Lawrenceville A5
Lebanon D6
Leechburg C2
Leesport F7
Lehighton B9
Lemasters D5
Lemoyne F5
LeRaysville A6
Lewisburg C6
Lewistown C5
Liberty A5
Ligonier D2
Lilly F4
Lincoln D7
Lititz D7
Littlestown E5
Liverpool D6
Lock Haven B5
Loganton B5
Loysville D6
Luzerne A9
Lykens F6
Lyndora C2
Madera C4
Mahaffey C4
Mahanoy City E9
Malvern F8
Manheim D7
Manor D2
Mansfield A5
Mapleton D4
Marienville B3
Marietta D7
Marion Center C3
Mars C2
Martinsburg E4
Marysville D6
Masontown E2
Mauch Chunk B9
Maytown D7
McAdoo E9
McAlisterville D5
McClure A4
McConnellsburg E4
McDonald F1
McKees Rocks E1
McKeesport E1
McVeytown C5
Meadville B2
Mechanicsburg F5
Media E8
Mercer B1
Mercersburg D5
Meshoppen B7
Meyersdale D3
Middleburgh A4
Middletown F6
Midland C1
Midway F2
Mifflin D5
Mifflinburg C6
Mifflintown D5
Mildred B6
Milford B8
Millersburg F6
Millerstown D6
Millersville D7
Millheim C5
Millsboro F2
Millville C6
Milton C6
Minersville E9
Mocanaqua A9
Mohnton F7
Monaca C1
Monessen E3
Monongahela
City F2
Montgomery B6
Montoursville B6
Montrose A7
Moscow A8
Mount Carmel C6
Mount Holly
Springs F5
Mount Jewett A4
Mount Joy D7
Mount Morris E2
Mount Pleasant E3
Mount Union B4
Mount Wolf E6
Mountville D7
Muncy B6
Munhall E1
Myerstown D6
Nanticoke A9
Natrona E1
Nazareth C9
Neffs D8
Nescopeck B9
Nesquehoning B9
New Albany A6
New Alexandria E3
New Berlin C6
New Bethlehem B3
New Bloomfield D6
New Brighton C1
New Castle C1
New Cumberland F5
New Florence E3
New Freedom E2
New Haven E2
New Holland D7
New Hope D9
New Kensington E3
New Milford A7
New Salem E2
New Tripoli D8
New Wilmington C1
Newfoundland A8
Newport D6
Newtown D9
Newville F5
Nicholson B7
Norristown F8
North Belle
Vernon C9
North East E3
North Girard A1
North Wales A1
Northampton F8
Northumberland C6
Numidia C6
Nuremburg E9
Oakdale E1
Oakmont E1
Oil City B2
Oley F7
Olyphant A8
Orbisonia D4
Orwigsburg E9
Osceola Mills C4
Oxford F8
Palmerton B9
Paoli F8
Parkers Landing C2
Parkesburg F8
Parnassus E3
Patterson D5
Patton F4
Peckville A8
Pen Argyl C9
Penbrook F6
Pennsburg F8
Perkasie D9
Perryopolis E2
Petersburg D4
Philadelphia D8
Philipsburg C5
Phoenixville F8
Picture Rocks B6
Pine Grove F9
Pitcairn E1
Pittsburg E1
Pittsburgh E1
Pittston B9
Pleasant Unity F3
Plumer B2
Plumville C3
Plymouth B9
Point Marion E2
Port Allegany A4
Port Royal D5
Portage F4
Portland C9
Pottstown F8
Pottsville F9
Providence A8
Punxsutawney C3
Quakertown D9
Quarryville D7
Ralston B6
Reading F7
Rebersburg C5
Red Lion E6
Reedsville C5
Renovo B5
Republic E2
Reynoldsville C3
Rices Landing E2
Richland D6
Ridgway B3
Ridley Park E8
Riegelsville D9
Rimersburg B3
Ringtown F9
Roaring Spring F4
Rochester C1
Rockwood D3
Rome A6
Roscoe F2
Royersford F8
Rural Valley C2
Russellton F1
Saegertown B2
Saint Marys B3
Saint Michael F4
Salisbury D3
Saltsburg C3
Saxton D4
Sayre A6
Scenery Hill F2
Schaefferstown D6
Schellburg D4
Schellsburg D4
Schuylkill Haven F9
Schwenksville F8
Scottdale F3
Scranton A8
Selins Grove A4
Selinsgrove A4
Sellersville D9
Seven Valleys E6
Seward F3
Sewickley F1
Shamokin C6
Sharon B1
Sharpsville B1
Sheffield A3
Shenandoah F9
Sheraden F1
Shickshinny B9
Shingle House A4
Shippensburg F5
Shippensburgh F5
Shippenville B3
Shoemakersville F7
Siegfried C9
Sipesville D3
Slatington D8
Sligo B3
Slippery Rock C2
Smethport A4
Smithfield E2
Smithton F3
Somerfield D3
Somerset D3
Souderton F8
South Bethlehem C9
South Fork F4
Spangler F4
Spartansburg B2
Spring City F8
Spring Grove E6
Spring Mills C5
Springdale F1
Springville A7
State College C5
Steelton F6
Stewartstown E6
Stoneboro B1
Stoystown D3
Strasburg D7
Strausstown F7
Stroudsburg C8
Summerville C3
Sunbury C6
Susquehanna A7
Susquehanna
Depot A7
Sutersville F3
Swarthmore E8
Swineford A4
Swissvale F1
Sykesville C3
Tamaqua F9
Tarentum F1
Telford F8
Terre Hill D7
Thompsontown D5
Three Springs D4
Timblin C3
Tioga A5
Tionesta B3
Titusville B2
Topton F7
Towanda A6
Tower City F9
Trafford F3
Trafford City F3
Tremont F9
Trevorton C6
Troy A6
Tunkhannock B7
Turbotville C6
Turtle Creek F1
Tyrone F4
Ulster A6
Ulysses A4
Union City A1
Uniontown E2
Vanderbilt E2
Vandergrift F3
Verona F1
Volant C1
Wampum C1
Warren A3
Washington F2
Waterford A1
Watsontown C6
Wayne E8
Waynesboro D5
Waynesburg E2
Weatherly B9
Webster F3
Wehrum C3
Weissport B9
Wellsborough A5
Wellsville E6
Wernersville F7
West Alexander F2
West Chester F8
West
Conshohocken F8
West Elizabeth F1
West Greenville B1
West Grove F8
West Middlesex B1
West Newton F6
West York E6
Westfield A5
Wilcox B3
Wilkes Barre B9
Wilkinsburg F1
Williamsburg F4
Williamsport B6
Wilmerding F1
Wilson B3
Winburne C4
Windber D3
Windsor E6
Woodlawn C1
Wrightsville E6
Wyalusing A6
Wyoming B9
Yardley D9
York E6
York Springs E5
Youngsville A3
Youngwood F3
Zelienople C2

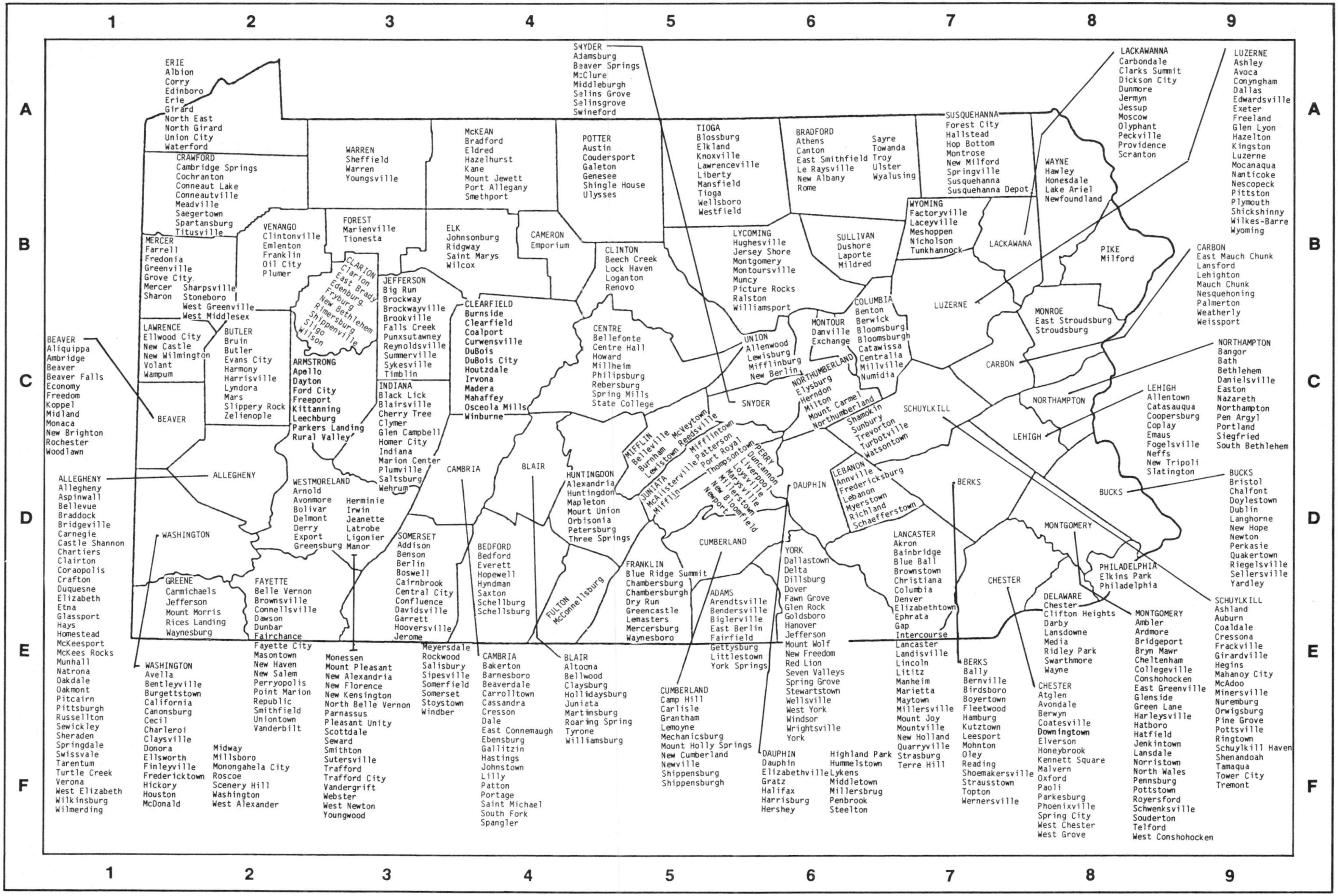
1 2 3 4 5 6 7 8 9
A B C D E F
ERIE
Albion
Corry
Edinboro
Erie
Girard
North East
North Girard
Union City
Waterford
CRAWFORD
Cambridge Springs
Cochranton
Conneaut Lake
Conneautville
Meadville
Saegertown
Spartansburg
Titusville
MERCER
Farrell
Fredonia
Greenville
Grove City
Mercer
Sharon
Sharpsville
Stoneboro
West Greenville
West Middlesex
LAWRENCE
Ellwood City
New Castle
New Wilmington
Volant
Wampum
BEAVER
Aliquippa
Ambridge
Beaver
Beaver Falls
Economy
Freedom
Koppel
Midland
Monaca
New Brighton
Rochester
Woodlawn
BEAVER
ALLEGHENY
Allegheny
Aspinwall
Bellevue
Braddock
Bridgeville
Carnegie
Castle Shannon
Chartiers
Clairton
Coraopolis
Crafton
Duquesne
Elizabeth
Etna
Glassport
Hays
Homestead
McKeesport
McKees Rocks
Munhall
Natrona
Oakdale
Oakmont
Pitcairn
Pittsburgh
Russellton
Sewickley
Sheraden
Springdale
Swissvale
Tarentum
Turtle Creek
Verona
West Elizabeth
Wilkinsburg
Wilmerding
ALLEGHENY
WASHINGTON
WASHINGTON
Avella
Bentleyville
Burgettstown
California
Canonsburg
Cecil
Charleroi
Claysville
Donora
Ellsworth
Finleyville
Fredericktown
Hickory
Houston
McDonald
Midway
Millsboro
Monongahela City
Roscoe
Scenery Hill
Washington
West Alexander
GREENE
Carmichaels
Jefferson
Mount Morris
Rices Landing
Waynesburg
VENANGO
Clintonville
Emlenton
Franklin
Oil City
Plumer
BUTLER
Bruin
Butler
Evans City
Harmony
Harrisville
Lyndora
Mars
Slippery Rock
Zelienople
WARREN
Sheffield
Warren
Youngsville
FOREST
Marienville
Tionesta
CLARION
Clarion
East Brady
Edenburg
Fryburg
New Bethlehem
Rimersburg
Shippenville
Sligo
Wilson
ARMSTRONG
Apollo
Dayton
Ford City
Freeport
Kittanning
Leechburg
Parkers Landing
Rural Valley
WESTMORELAND
Arnold
Avonmore
Bolivar
Delmont
Derry
Export
Greensburg
Herminie
Irwin
Jeanette
Latrobe
Ligonier
Manor
Monessen
Mount Pleasant
New Alexandria
New Florence
New Kensington
North Belle Vernon
Parnassus
Pleasant Unity
Scottdale
Seward
Smithton
Sutersville
Trafford
Trafford City
Vandergrift
Webster
West Newton
Youngwood
FAYETTE
Belle Vernon
Brownsville
Connellsville
Dawson
Dunbar
Fairchance
Fayette City
Masontown
New Haven
New Salem
Perryopolis
Point Marion
Republic
Smithfield
Uniontown
Vanderbilt
McKEAN
Bradford
Eldred
Hazelhurst
Kane
Mount Jewett
Port Allegany
Smethport
ELK
Johnsonburg
Ridgway
Saint Marys
Wilcox
JEFFERSON
Big Run
Brockway
Brockwayville
Brookville
Falls Creek
Punxsutawney
Reynoldsville
Summerville
Sykesville
Timblin
INDIANA
Black Lick
Blairsville
Cherry Tree
Clymer
Glen Campbell
Homer City
Indiana
Marion Center
Plumville
Saltsburg
Wehrum
CLEARFIELD
Burnside
Clearfield
Coalport
Curwensville
DuBois
DuBois City
Houtzdale
Irvona
Madera
Mahaffey
Osceola Mills
Winburne
CAMERON
Emporium
POTTER
Austin
Coudersport
Galeton
Genesee
Shingle House
Ulysses
CLINTON
Beech Creek
Lock Haven
Loganton
Renovo
CENTRE
Bellefonte
Centre Hall
Howard
Millheim
Philipsburg
Rebersburg
Spring Mills
State College
CAMBRIA
BLAIR
SOMERSET
Addison
Benson
Berlin
Boswell
Cairnbrook
Central City
Confluence
Davidsville
Garrett
Hooversville
Jerome
Meyersdale
Rockwood
Salisbury
Sipesville
Somerfield
Somerset
Stoystown
Windber
CAMBRIA
Bakerton
Barnesboro
Beaverdale
Carrolltown
Cassandra
Cresson
Dale
East Conemaugh
Ebensburg
Gallitzin
Hastings
Johnstown
Lilly
Patton
Portage
Saint Michael
South Fork
Spangler
BEDFORD
Bedford
Everett
Hopewell
Hyndman
Saxton
Schellburg
Schellsburg
BLAIR
Altoona
Bellwood
Claysburg
Hollidaysburg
Juniata
Martinsburg
Roaring Spring
Tyrone
Williamsburg
HUNTINGDON
Alexandria
Huntingdon
Mapleton
Mount Union
Orbisonia
Petersburg
Three Springs
FULTON
McConnellsburg
SNYDER
Adamsburg
Beaver Springs
McClure
Middleburgh
Selins Grove
Selinsgrove
Swineford
SNYDER
MIFFLIN
Belleville
Burnham
Lewistown
McVeytown
Reedsville
JUNIATA
McAlisterville
Mifflin
Mifflintown
Patterson
Port Royal
Thompsontown
PERRY
Duncannon
Liverpool
Loysville
Marysville
Millerstown
New Bloomfield
Newport
FRANKLIN
Blue Ridge Summit
Chambersburg
Chambersburgh
Dry Run
Greencastle
Lemasters
Mercersburg
Waynesboro
CUMBERLAND
CUMBERLAND
Camp Hill
Carlisle
Grantham
Lemoyne
Mechanicsburg
Mount Holly Springs
New Cumberland
Newville
Shippensburg
Shippensburgh
ADAMS
Arendtsville
Bendersville
Biglerville
East Berlin
Fairfield
Gettysburg
Littlestown
York Springs
TIOGA
Blossburg
Elkland
Knoxville
Lawrenceville
Liberty
Mansfield
Tioga
Wellsboro
Westfield
LYCOMING
Hughesville
Jersey Shore
Montgomery
Montoursville
Muncy
Picture Rocks
Ralston
Williamsport
UNION
Allenwood
Lewisburg
Mifflinburg
New Berlin
BRADFORD
Athens
Canton
East Smithfield
Le Raysville
New Albany
Rome
Sayre
Towanda
Troy
Ulster
Wyalusing
SULLIVAN
Dushore
Laporte
Mildred
MONTOUR
Danville
Exchange
COLUMBIA
Benton
Berwick
Bloomsburg
Bloomsburgh
Catawissa
Centralia
Millville
Numidia
NORTHUMBERLAND
Elysburg
Herndon
Milton
Mount Carmel
Northumberland
Shamokin
Sunbury
Trevorton
Turbotville
Watsontown
DAUPHIN
DAUPHIN
Dauphin
Elizabethville
Gratz
Halifax
Harrisburg
Hershey
Highland Park
Hummelstown
Lykens
Middletown
Millersbrug
Penbrook
Steelton
YORK
Dallastown
Delta
Dillsburg
Dover
Fawn Grove
Glen Rock
Goldsboro
Hanover
Jefferson
Mount Wolf
New Freedom
Red Lion
Seven Valleys
Spring Grove
Stewartstown
Wellsville
West York
Windsor
Wrightsville
York
LEBANON
Annville
Fredericksburg
Lebanon
Myerstown
Richland
Schaefferstown
LANCASTER
Akron
Bainbridge
Blue Ball
Brownstown
Christiana
Columbia
Denver
Elizabethtown
Ephrata
Gap
Intercourse
Lancaster
Landisville
Lincoln
Lititz
Manheim
Marietta
Maytown
Millersville
Mount Joy
Mountville
New Holland
Quarryville
Strasburg
Terre Hill
SUSQUEHANNA
Forest City
Hallstead
Hop Bottom
Montrose
New Milford
Springville
Susquehanna
Susquehanna Depot
WYOMING
Factoryville
Laceyville
Meshoppen
Nicholson
Tunkhannock
LACKAWANA
LUZERNE
SCHUYLKILL
BERKS
BERKS
Bally
Bernville
Birdsboro
Boyertown
Fleetwood
Hamburg
Kutztown
Leesport
Mohnton
Oley
Reading
Shoemakersville
Strausstown
Topton
Wernersville
CHESTER
CHESTER
Atglen
Avondale
Berwyn
Coatesville
Downingtown
Elverson
Honeybrook
Kennett Square
Malvern
Oxford
Paoli
Parkesburg
Phoenixville
Spring City
West Chester
West Grove
DELAWARE
Chester
Clifton Heights
Darby
Lansdowne
Media
Ridley Park
Swarthmore
Wayne
MONTGOMERY
MONTGOMERY
Ambler
Ardmore
Bridgeport
Bryn Mawr
Cheltenham
Collegeville
Conshohocken
East Greenville
Glenside
Green Lane
Harleysville
Hatboro
Hatfield
Jenkintown
Lansdale
Norristown
North Wales
Pennsburg
Pottstown
Royersford
Schwenksville
Souderton
Telford
West Conshohocken
PHILADELPHIA
Elkins Park
Philadelphia
WAYNE
Hawley
Honesdale
Lake Ariel
Newfoundland
PIKE
Milford
MONROE
East Stroudsburg
Stroudsburg
CARBON
NORTHAMPTON
LEHIGH
BUCKS
LACKAWANNA
Carbondale
Clarks Summit
Dickson City
Dunmore
Jermyn
Jessup
Moscow
Olyphant
Peckville
Providence
Scranton
LUZERNE
Ashley
Avoca
Conyngham
Dallas
Edwardsville
Exeter
Freeland
Glen Lyon
Hazelton
Kingston
Luzerne
Mocanaqua
Nanticoke
Nescopeck
Pittston
Plymouth
Shickshinny
Wilkes-Barre
Wyoming
CARBON
East Mauch Chunk
Lansford
Lehighton
Mauch Chunk
Nesquehoning
Palmerton
Weatherly
Weissport
NORTHAMPTON
Bangor
Bath
Bethlehem
Danielsville
Easton
Nazareth
Northampton
Pen Argyl
Portland
Siegfried
South Bethlehem
LEHIGH
Allentown
Catasauqua
Coopersburg
Coplay
Emaus
Fogelsville
Neffs
New Tripoli
Slatington
BUCKS
Bristol
Chalfont
Doylestown
Dublin
Langhorne
New Hope
Newton
Perkasie
Quakertown
Riegelsville
Sellersville
Yardley
SCHUYLKILL
Ashland
Auburn
Coaldale
Cressona
Frackville
Girardville
Hegins
Mahanoy City
McAdoo
Minersville
Nuremburg
Orwigsburg
Pine Grove
Pottsville
Ringtown
Schuylkill Haven
Shenandoah
Tamaqua
Tower City
Tremont

5777 Snyder
FNB OF BEAVER SPRINGS AT ADAMSBURG
Chartered 4/16/01
2nd title: FNB of Beaver Springs 6/13/12
FIRST TITLE {{ 3 L }}
Brown Back <$VALUE
4x5 1-2050 <$600
3x10-20 1-1540 <$600
1882 Date Back
4x5 1-1005 <$600
3x10-20 1-671 <$600
SECOND TITLE {{ 2 L 5 S }}
1882 Date Back
3x10-20 1-1060* <$600
1882 Value Back
3x10-20 1161-2457* <$600
* 1061-1160 not marked
1902 Plain Back
3x10-20 1-3058 <$350
1929 Small Size
10 Type 1 1-796 <$200
20 Type 1 1-200 <$200
10 Type 2 1-665 <$225
20 Type 2 1-190 <$225
Total Issue $529,610
Out in 1935 $24,495
Large out 1935 $1,095

6709 Somerset
FNB OF ADDISON
{{ 3 L 1 S }}
Chartered 4/03
Receivership 1/28/31
1902 Red Seal <$VALUE
3x10-20 1-1765 <$700
1902 Date Back
3x10-20 1-2270 <$350
1902 Plain Back
3x10-20 2271-6921 <$350
1929 Small Size
10 Type 1 1-267 <$350
20 Type 1 1-73 <$350
Total Issue $459,080
Out at close $20,830
Large out at close $2,610

9364 Lancaster
AKRON NB, AKRON
{{ 3 L 9 S }}
Chartered 3/09
1902 Date Back <$VALUE
3x10-20 1-3800* <$450
1902 Plain Back
3x10-20 3961-9930* <$450
* 3801-3960 not marked
1929 Small Size
5 Type 1 1-594 <$135
10 Type 1 1-864 <$135
20 Type 1 1-208 <$150
5 Type 2 1-4740 <$150
10 Type 2 1-2724 <$150
Total Issue $642,060
Out in 1935 $48,010
Large out 1935 $1,700

13871 Erie
FNB AT ALBION
{{ UNREPORTED }}
Chartered 12/33
1929 Small Size <$VALUE
10 Type 2 1-40 <$750
20 Type 2 1-25 <$750
Total Issue $900
Out in 1935 $25,750
Large out 1935 $1,000
Outstanding includes Ch 9534

9534 Erie
FNB OF ALBION
{{ 4 L 9 S }}
Chartered 9/09
Liquidated 2/6/34
1902 Date Back <$VALUE
3x10-20 1-2380 <$275
1902 Plain Back
3x10-20 2381-6583 <$275
1929 Small Size
10 Type 1 1-1254 <$125
20 Type 1 1-378 <$125
10 Type 2 1-125 <$135
20 Type 2 1-60 <$135
Total Issue $452,200
Out at close $43,800
Large out 1935 $1,000
Ch 13871 assumed circulation

11263 Huntingdon
FNB OF ALEXANDRIA
{{ 2 L 3U + 8 S }}
Chartered 11/18
1902 Plain Back <$VALUE
3x10-20 1-4268 <$400
1929 Small Size
10 Type 1 1-750 <$135
20 Type 1 1-200 <$135
10 Type 2 1-3061 <$135
20 Type 2 1-889 <$135
Total Issue $330,790
Out in 1935 $48,900
Large out 1935 $500

9902 Beaver
ALIQUIPPA NB, ALIQUIPPA
{{ UNREPORTED }}
Chartered 12/10
Liquidated 8/28/14
1902 Date Back <$VALUE
4x5 1-1685 <$850
3x10-20 1-1251 <$850
Total Issue $96,250
Out in 1914 $8,350

Aliquippa NB, Aliquippa
SEE Ch 10951
FNB of Woodlawn

8590 Beaver
FNB OF ALIQUIPPA
{{ 3 L 8 S }}
Chartered 3/07
1902 Red Seal <$VALUE
4x10 1-1500 <$600
1902 Date Back
4x10 1-6900 <$300
1902 Plain Back
4x10 6901-21251 <$300
1929 Small Size
10 Type 1 1-2850 <$125
10 Type 2 1-3792 <$125
Total Issue $1,118,960
Out in 1935 $49,000
Large out 1935 $110

4991 Allegheny
ENTERPRISE NB OF ALLEGHENY
{{ UNREPORTED }}
Organized 4/4/95
Receivership 10/18/05
Brown Back <$VALUE
3x10-20 1-10102 <$1000
Total Issue $505,100
Out in 1916 $4,140

198 Allegheny
FNB OF ALLEGHENY
Organized 1/14/64
Liquidated 1/11/15
2nd title: FNB of Allegheny at Pittsburgh 3/10/09
FIRST TITLE {{ 10 L }}
Original Series <$VALUE
4x5 1-9350 <$450
4x10 1-5725 <$750
4x20 1-2925 <$1250
Series 1875
4x5 1-500 <$450
4x10 1-3200 <$750
4x20 1-3522 <$1250
Brown Back
3x10-20 1-12022 <$250
1902 Red Seal
3x10-20 1-7000 <$250
1902 Date Back
3x10-20 1-4000 <$125
SECOND TITLE {{ 2 L }}
1902 Date Back
4x5 1-30540 <$200
3x10-20 1-16430 <$200
Total Issue $3,653,160
Out at close $349,995
Ch 776 assumed circulation

2261 Allegheny
GERMAN NB OF ALLEGHENY
Chartered 5/17/75
Liquidated 11/19/34
2nd title: NB of America at Pittsburgh 6/1/18
FIRST TITLE {{ 7 L }}
Original Series <$VALUE
4x5 1-1575 <$500
Series 1875
4x5 1-20138 <$500
50-100 1-1458 <$3500
Brown Back
4x5 1-18700 <$300
50-100 1-3480 <$1250/$1500
1882 Date Back
4x5 1-5204 <$275
50-100 1-239 <$1250/$1500
1902 Date Back
3x50-100 1-900 <$400/$500
SECOND TITLE {{ 10 L 23 S }}
1902 Plain Back
4x5 1-95465 <$100
1929 Small Size
5 Type 1 1-27704 <$45
5 Type 2 1-29664 <$45
Total Issue $4,802,630
Out at close $132,735
Large out 1935 $12,205
Ch 14271 assumed circulation

776 Allegheny
SECOND NB OF ALLEGHENY
Chartered 2/2/65
Liquidated 7/24/31
2nd title: Second NB of Allegheny, Pittsburgh 1918
3rd title: Second NB of Pittsburgh 5/12/30
FIRST TITLE {{ 12 L }}
Original Series <$VALUE
3x1-2 1-1050 <$350/$1000
4x5 1-3250 <$400
3x10-20 1-3400 <$750/$1250
50-100 1-100 <$3500
Series 1875
3x10-20 1-3171 <$750/$1250
Brown Back
3x10-20 1-6902 <$250
1902 Red Seal
3x10-20 1-5900 <$250
1902 Date Back
3x10-20 1-14500* <$125
1902 Plain Back
4x5 1-6000 <$125
3x10-20 15501-19500* <$125
* 14501-15500 not marked
SECOND TITLE {{ 8 L 5 S }}
1902 Plain Back
4x5 1-51253 <$100
3x10-20 1-30658 <$100
1929 Small Size
5 Type 1 1-4106 <$100
10 Type 1 1-2623 <$100
20 Type 1 1-642 <$100
THIRD TITLE {{ 3 S }}
1929 Small Size
5 Type 1 1-7180 <$150
Total Issue $5,279,860
Out at close $279,310
Large out at close $39,740
Outstanding includes Ch 198

2235 Allegheny
THIRD NB OF ALLEGHENY
{{ 2 L }}
Chartered 3/18/75
Liquidated 7/1/02
Original Series <$VALUE
3x10-20 1-3600 <$750/$1250
Series 1875
3x10-20 1-5310 <$750/$1250
Brown Back
3x10-20 1-7359 <$600
Total Issue $813,450
Out in 1910 $9,930

1322 Lehigh
ALLENTOWN NB, ALLENTOWN
{{ 21 L 50+ S }}
Chartered 1865
Original Series <$VALUE
4x5 1-14400 <$400
4x10 1-8850 <$750
4x20 1-3375 <$1250
Series 1875
4x5 1-7800 <$400
4x10 1-8425 <$750
4x20 1-3337 <$1250
Brown Back
4x5 1-9670 <$175
3x10-20 1-24809 <$175/$200
1902 Red Seal
3x10-20 1-40000 <$175/$225
1902 Date Back
3x10-20 1-99000 <$85
1902 Plain Back
3x10-20 99001-286302 <$85
1929 Small Size
10 Type 1 1-30838 <$20
20 Type 1 1-7986 <$30
10 Type 2 1-35676 <$20
20 Type 2 1-8071 <$30
Total Issue $22,747,690
Out in 1935 $852,200
Large out 1935 $51,005

161 Lehigh
FNB OF ALLENTOWN
{{ 4 L }}
Organized 12/16/63
Receivership 4/15/78
Original Series <$VALUE
3x1-2 1-6000 <$500/$1250
4x5 1-6750 <$500
4x10 1-6750 <$750
Total Issue $435,000
Out in 1916 $2,291

Merchants-Citizens NB & TC of Allentown
SEE Ch 6645
Merchants NB of Allentown

6645 Lehigh
MERCHANTS NB OF ALLENTOWN
Chartered 2/03
2nd title: Merchants-Citizens NB & TC 1/7/29
3rd title: Merchants NB 1/11/33
FIRST TITLE {{ 8 L }}
1902 Red Seal <$VALUE
4x5 1-7000 <$250
3x10-20 1-11800 <$250
1902 Date Back
4x5 1-12000 <$125
3x10-20 1-16800 <$125
1902 Plain Back
3x10-20 16801-52569 <$125
SECOND TITLE {{ 1 L 18 S }}
1902 Plain Back
3x10-20 1-1500 <$200
1929 Small Size
10 Type 1 1-6040 <$60
20 Type 1 1-1496 <$60
THIRD TITLE {{ 21 S }}
1929 Small Size
10 Type 1 1-416 <$50
20 Type 1 1-158 <$60
10 Type 2 1-7438 <$50
20 Type 2 1-1565 <$60
Total Issue $4,364,970
Out in 1935 $175,250
Large out 1935 $10,490

373 Lehigh
SECOND NB OF ALLENTOWN
{{ 16 L 27 S }}
Chartered 4/64
Original Series <$VALUE
3x1-2 1-6920 <$350/$1000
4x5 1-8000 <$400
3x10-20 1-6698 <$750/$1250
Series 1875
4x5 1-3250 <$400
3x10-20 1-2690 <$750/$1250
Brown Back
4x5 1-3679 <$175
3x10-20 1-4265 <$175/$200
50-100 1-720 <$1250/$1500
1902 Red Seal
4x5 1-5600 <$175
3x10-20 1-4920 <$175/$200
50-100 1-80 <$2250/$2500
1902 Date Back
4x5 1-19000 <$85
3x10-20 1-12100 <$85
50-100 1-200 <$350/$400
3x50-100 1-400 <$350/$400
1902 Plain Back
4x5 19001-47520 <$85
3x10-20 12101-28258 <$85
1929 Small Size
5 Type 1 1-6370 <$25
10 Type 1 1-2950 <$30
20 Type 1 1-778 <$40
5 Type 2 1-10076 <$30
10 Type 2 1-5246 <$30
20 Type 2 1-1085 <$40
Total Issue $4,573,130
Out in 1935 $122,770
Large out 1935 $10,710

11593 Union
ALLENWOOD NB, ALLENWOOD
{{ 2 L 3 S }}
Chartered 2/20
Receivership 12/22/32
1902 Plain Back <$VALUE
4x5 1-12667 <$400
1929 Small Size
5 Type 1 1-2710 <$250
Total Issue $334,640
Out at close $4,900
Large out at close $1,010

247 Blair
FNB OF ALTOONA
{{ 14 L 30 S }}
Chartered 2/64
Original Series <$VALUE
4x5 1-14750 <$400
Series 1875
4x5 1-10680 <$400
Brown Back
3x10-20 1-6548 <$250
1902 Red Seal
3x10-20 1-6500 <$250
1902 Date Back
4x5 1-12500 <$100
3x10-20 1-8200 <$100
1902 Plain Back
4x5 12501-21750 <$100
3x10-20 8201-30866 <$100
1929 Small Size
5 Type 1 1-6020 <$30
10 Type 1 1-2856 <$30
20 Type 1 1-808 <$40
5 Type 2 1-7278 <$30
10 Type 2 1-3578 <$35
20 Type 2 1-742 <$45
Total Issue $3,675,230
Out in 1935 $126,870
Large out 1935 $8,890

2781 Blair
SECOND NB OF ALTOONA
{{ 5 L 4 S }}
Organized 8/19/82
Receivership 4/16/31
Brown Back <$VALUE
4x5 1-3000 <$300
3x10-20 1-3576 <$300
1902 Red Seal
3x10-20 1-3100 <$350
1902 Date Back
3x10-20 1-4500 <$175
1902 Plain Back
3x10-20 4501-13444 <$175
1929 Small Size
10 Type 1 1-793 <$150
20 Type 1 1-205 <$150
Total Issue $1,138,180
Out at close $48,140
Large out at close $6,600

3220 Montgomery
FNB OF AMBLER
{{ 9 L 12 S }}
Organized 5/12/84
Receivership 3/26/34
Brown Back <$VALUE
3x10-20 1-4110 <$600
1902 Red Seal
4x5 1-3166 <$600
4x10 1-1667 <$600
1902 Date Back
4x5 1-9750 <$250
4x10 1-8350 <$250
50-100 1-1080 <$650/$750
3x50-100 1-200 <$650/$750
1902 Plain Back
4x5 9751-15450 <$250
4x10 8351-33064 <$250
1929 Small Size
5 Type 1 1-6214 <$100
10 Type 1 1-3104 <$100
5 Type 2 1-3862 <$110
10 Type 2 1-1569 <$110
Total Issue $2,586,720
Out at close $100,000
Large out at close $5,805

10839 Beaver
AMBRIDGE NB, AMBRIDGE
{{ 4 L 14 S }}
Chartered 4/16
1902 Plain Back <$VALUE
3x10-20 1-10381 <$250
1929 Small Size
10 Type 1 1-1552 <$100
20 Type 1 1-418 <$100
10 Type 2 1-3684 <$110
20 Type 2 1-1159 <$110
Total Issue $722,350
Out in 1935 $64,700
Large out 1935 $2,180

13087 Beaver
ECONOMY NB OF AMBRIDGE
{{ 2 L 12 S }}
Chartered 6/27
Liquidated 4/14/34
1902 Plain Back <$VALUE
3x10-20 1-3299 <$375
1929 Small Size
10 Type 1 1-2050 <$100
20 Type 1 1-578 <$125
10 Type 2 1-602 <$150
20 Type 2 1-149 <$150
Total Issue $366,310
Out at close $43,230
Large out at close $840

8459 Beaver
FNB OF AMBRIDGE
{{ UNREPORTED }}
Chartered 12/8/06
Receivership 6/5/12
1902 Red Seal <$VALUE
4x10 1-500 <$1250
1902 Date Back
4x10 1-1994 <$850
Total Issue $99,760
Out in 1916 $1,150

2384 Lebanon
ANNVILLE NB, ANNVILLE
{{ 8 L 16 S }}
Chartered 5/17/78
Series 1875 <$VALUE
4x5 1-3401 <$500
3x10-20 1-3520 <$750/$1250
Brown Back
4x5 1-4150 <$375
3x10-20 1-2770 <$375
1882 Date Back
4x5 1-3975 <$375
3x10-20 1-3040 <$375
1882 Value Back
4x5 3976-5116 <$375
3x10-20 3041-3714 <$375
1902 Plain Back
4x5 1-11429 <$175
4x10 1-11336 <$175
1929 Small Size
5 Type 1 1-5686 <$70
10 Type 1 1-2902 <$70
5 Type 2 1-9468 <$75
10 Type 2 1-4944 <$75
Total Issue $1,877,040
Out in 1935 $95,780
Large out 1935 $3,780

5723 Armstrong
FNB OF APOLLO
{{ 5 L 10 S }}
Chartered 2/19/01
Brown Back <$VALUE
3x10-20 1-3100 <$500
1882 Date Back
3x10-20 1-3350* <$500
1882 Value Back
3x10-20 3551-5171* <$500
* 3351-3550 not marked
1902 Plain Back
3x10-20 1-5255 <$275
1929 Small Size
10 Type 1 1-1066 <$125
20 Type 1 1-298 <$125
10 Type 2 1-1591 <$135
20 Type 2 1-399 <$135
Total Issue $799,910
Out in 1935 $36,500
Large out 1935 $1,880

9905 Montgomery
ARDMORE NB, ARDMORE
Chartered 12/10
Liquidated 12/11/29
2nd title: Ardmore NB & TC 6/3/25
FIRST TITLE {{ 2 L }}
1902 Date Back <$VALUE
4x5 1-1275 <$350
4x10 1-1275 <$350
1902 Plain Back
4x5 1276-6575 <$350
4x10 1276-5500 <$350
SECOND TITLE {{ 4 L }}
1902 Plain Back
4x5 1-3131 <$300
4x10 1-1622 <$300
3x10-20 1-1282 <$300
Total Issue $543,100
Out at close $10,800

9139 Adams
NB OF ARENDTSVILLE
{{ 4 L 8 S }}
Chartered 5/08
1902 Date Back <$VALUE
3x10-20 1-2590 <$300
1902 Plain Back
3x10-20 2591-6886 <$300
1929 Small Size
5 Type 1 1-918 <$150
10 Type 1 1-504 <$150
20 Type 1 1-150 <$150
5 Type 2 1-1558 <$175
10 Type 2 1-730 <$175
20 Type 2 1-194 <$175
Total Issue $439,050
Out in 1935 $21,450
Large out 1935 $1,440

CONDITION affects Value. The Values shown are for notes in FINE condition.

****
11896 Westmoreland
ARNOLD NB, ARNOLD
Chartered 12/20
2nd title: N Deposit B of Arnold 12/31/26
FIRST TITLE {{ 4 L }}
1902 Plain Back <$VALUE
3x10-20 1-7305 <$225
3x50-100 1-560 <$400/$500
SECOND TITLE {{ 2 L 16 S }}
1902 Plain Back
3x10-20 1-2818 <$275
1929 Small Size
10 Type 1 1-3102 <$65
20 Type 1 1-842 <$75
10 Type 2 1-3553 <$75
20 Type 2 1-930 <$75
Total Issue $987,440
Out in 1935 $96,650
Large out 1935 $3,240
****
N Deposit B of Arnold
SEE Ch 11896
Arnold NB, Arnold
****
5615 Schuylkill
ASHLAND NB, ASHLAND
{{ 16 L 28 S }}
Chartered 11/2/00
Brown Back <$VALUE
4x5 1-3250 <$275
3x10-20 1-6700 <$275
1882 Date Back
4x5 1-10000 <$250
3x10-20 1-6700 <$250
1882 Value Back
4x5 10001-16400 <$250
3x10-20 6701-10120 <$250
1902 Plain Back
3x10-20 1-15033 <$50
1929 Small Size 60
10 Type 1 1-3380 <$50
20 Type 1 1-968 <$60
10 Type 2 1-4968 <$60
20 Type 2 1-1281 <$70
Total Issue $2,379,910
Out in 1935 $122,145
Large out 1935 $4,985
****
2280 Schuylkill
CITIZENS NB OF ASHLAND
{{ 14 L 14 S }}
Chartered 6/24/75
Original Series <$VALUE
4x5 1-1600 <$400
Series 1875
4x5 1-510 <$400
3x10-20 1-2469 <$750/$1250
Brown Back
4x5 1-1950 <$250
3x10-20 1-3750 <$250
1882 Date Back
4x5 1-6100 <$250
3x10-20 1-3573 <$250
1902 Date Back
4x5 1-1000 <$125
3x10-20 1-800 <$125
1902 Plain Back
4x5 1001-13130 <$125
3x10-20 801-7713 <$125
1929 Small Size
5 Type 1 1-2378 <$75
10 Type 1 1-1286 <$75
20 Type 1 1-358 <$85
5 Type 2 1-2430 <$100
10 Type 2 1-1894 <$100
20 Type 2 1-432 <$100
Total Issue $1,572,240
Out in 1935 $60,000
Large out 1935 $3,370
****
403 Schuylkill
FNB OF ASHLAND
{{ UNREPORTED }}
Organized 4/24/64
Receivership 2/28/78
Original Series <$VALUE
3x1-2 1-1000 <$1250/$2000
4x5 1-3000 <$1250
3x10-20 1-5702<$1500/$2000
Total Issue $350,100
Out in 1916 $1,717
****
8656 Luzerne
FNB OF ASHLEY
{{ 5 L 12 S }}
Chartered 4/07
1902 Red Seal <$VALUE
3x10-20 1-675 <$500
1902 Date Back
3x10-20 1-4450 <$250
1902 Plain Back
3x10-20 4451-20637 <$250
1929 Small Size
10 Type 1 1-2966 <$85
20 Type 1 1-784 <$100
5 Type 2 1-324 <$125
10 Type 2 1-4620 <$125
20 Type 2 1-1323 <$125
Total Issue $1,411,920
Out in 1935 $83,450
Large out 1935 $2,325
****
8824 Allegheny
FNB OF ASPINWALL
{{ 2 L }}
Chartered 8/6/07
Receivership 9/7/16
1902 Red Seal <$VALUE
3x10-20 1-900 <$1000
1902 Date Back
3x10-20 1-2400 <$500
1902 Plain Back
3x10-20 2401-2495 <$500
Total Issue $169,750
Out in 1916 $21,900
****
7056 Chester
ATGLEN NB, ATGLEN
{{ 5 L 9 S }}
Chartered 12/03
1902 Red Seal <$VALUE
3x10-20 1-2500 <$750
1902 Date Back
3x10-20 1-3940 <$350
1902 Plain Back
3x10-20 3941-11932 <$350
1929 Small Size
10 Type 1 1-1110 <$150
20 Type 1 1-308 <$165
10 Type 2 1-2152 <$175
20 Type 2 1-470 <$175
Total Issue $856,080
Out in 1935 $39,050
Large out 1935 $1,680
****
5202 Bradford
ATHENS NB, ATHENS
{{ 8 L 12 S }}
Chartered 7/3/99
Brown Back <$VALUE
4x5 1-4675 <$375
3x10-20 1-3040 <$375
1882 Date Back
4x5 1-4550* <$350
3x10-20 1-2960** <$350
1882 Value Back
4x5 4701-6673* <$350
3x10-20 3081-4281** <$350
* 4551-4700 not marked
** 2961-3080 not marked
1902 Plain Back
4x5 1-8360 <$175
3x10-20 1-5419 <$175
1929 Small Size
5 Type 1 1-1960 <$85
10 Type 1 1-988 <$85
20 Type 1 1-296 <$85
5 Type 2 1-3264 <$100
10 Type 2 1-1809 <$100
20 Type 2 1-640 <$100
Total Issue $1,231,970
Out in 1935 $49,200
Large out 1935 $2,420
****
4915 Bradford
FARMERS NB OF ATHENS
{{ 10 L 16 S }}
Chartered 1893
Brown Back <$VALUE
3x10-20 1-6460 <$350
1882 Date Back
3x10-20 1-3974 <$350
1902 Date Back
3x10-20 1-2600 <$175
1902 Plain Back
3x10-20 2601-16421 <$175
1929 Small Size
10 Type 1 1-2148 <$75
20 Type 1 1-646 <$85
10 Type 2 1-3208 <$100
20 Type 2 1-804 <$100
Total Issue $1,597,310
Out in 1935 $73,150
Large out 1935 $3,870
****
1094 Bradford
FNB OF ATHENS
{{ 2 L }}
Chartered 5/1/65
Liquidated 11/30/97
Original Series <$VALUE
3x1-2 1-3700 <$600/$1500
4x5 1-5250 <$650
3x10-20 1-1100 <$850/$1500
Series 1875
4x5 1-3440 <$650
3x10-20 1-1852 <$850/$1500
Brown Back
4x5 1-3900 <$600
3x10-20 1-500 <$600
Total Issue $442,900
Out in 1910 $2,718
****
9240 Schuylkill
FNB OF AUBURN
{{ 5 L }}
Chartered 9/08
Liquidated 10/1/28
1902 Date Back <$VALUE
3x10-20 1-2850 <$450
1902 Plain Back
3x10-20 2851-7059 <$450
Total Issue $352,950
Out at close $16,950
****
12562 Potter
FNB OF AUSTIN
{{ 2 L 10 S }}
Chartered 7/24
1902 Plain Back <$VALUE
3x10-20 1-4368 <$450
1929 Small Size
10 Type 1 1-1582 <$150
20 Type 1 1-380 <$165
10 Type 2 1-1828 <$165
20 Type 2 1-445 <$175
Total Issue $386,100
Out in 1935 $48,800
Large out 1935 $950
****
7854 Washington
LINCOLN NB OF AVELLA
{{ 2 L 2 S }}
Chartered 8/05
Receivership 3/7/31
1902 Red Seal <$VALUE
3x10-20 1-500 <$1000
1902 Date Back
3x10-20 1-2400 <$500
1902 Plain Back
3x10-20 2401-7466 <$500
1929 Small Size
10 Type 1 1-396 <$400
20 Type 1 1-123 <$400
Total Issue $436,820
Out at close $24,700
Large out at close $2,700
****
8494 Luzerne
FNB OF AVOCA
{{ 8 L 19 S }}
Chartered 1/07
1902 Red Seal <$VALUE
4x5 1-1200 <$350
3x10-20 1-1235 <$350
1902 Date Back
4x5 1-5350 <$165
3x10-20 1-3840 <$165
1902 Plain Back
4x5 5351-17187 <$165
3x10-20 3841-12207 <$165
1929 Small Size
5 Type 1 1-5260 <$60
10 Type 1 1-2776 <$60
20 Type 1 1-850 <$70
5 Type 2 1-9072 <$85
10 Type 2 1-5466 <$85
20 Type 2 1-1464 <$85
Total Issue $1,595,500
Out in 1935 $93,070
Large out 1935 $2,300
****
4560 Chester
NB OF AVONDALE
{{ 6 L 18 S }}
Chartered 1891
Brown Back <$VALUE
3x10-20 1-5600 <$600
1882 Date Back
3x10-20 1-1209 <$600
1902 Date Back
3x10-20 1-3600 <$275
1902 Plain Back
3x10-20 3601-13158 <$275
1929 Small Size
10 Type 1 1-2870 <$100
20 Type 1 1-876 <$100
10 Type 2 1-6821 <$125
20 Type 2 1-2128* <$125
* 1741-1746 not issued
Total Issue $1,386,320
Out in 1935 $125,650
Large out 1935 $2,230
****
7594 Westmoreland
FNB OF AVONMORE
{{ 4 L 15 S }}
Chartered 2/05
1902 Red Seal <$VALUE
3x10-20 1-2560 <$500
1902 Date Back
3x10-20 1-1860 <$250
1902 Plain Back
3x10-20 1861-9507 <$250
1929 Small Size
10 Type 1 1-1412 <$100
20 Type 1 1-388 <$125
10 Type 2 1-1892 <$125
20 Type 2 1-434 <$125
Total Issue $762,230
Out in 1935 $50,000
Large out 1935 $880
****
9264 Lancaster
FNB OF BAINBRIDGE
{{ 3 L }}
Chartered 11/08
Liquidated 8/5/29
1902 Date Back <$VALUE
3x10-20 1-3130 <$600
1902 Plain Back
3x10-20 3131-7319 <$600
Total Issue $365,950
Out at close $20,650
****
11757 Cambria
FNB OF BAKERTON
{{ 4 L 12 S }}
Chartered 6/20
1902 Plain Back <$VALUE
3x10-20 1-8862 <$250
1929 Small Size
10 Type 1 1-1516 <$100
20 Type 1 1-454 <$125
10 Type 2 1-2052 <$125
20 Type 2 1-447 <$125
Total Issue $618,000
Out in 1935 $50,000
Large out 1935 $1,910
****
9402 Berks
FNB OF BALLY
{{ 3 L 16 S }}
Chartered 5/09
1902 Date Back <$VALUE
3x10-20 1-2610 <$350
1902 Plain Back
3x10-20 2611-6818 <$350
1929 Small Size
10 Type 1 1-1372 <$100
20 Type 1 1-328 <$100
10 Type 2 1-3647 <$125
20 Type 2 1-957 <$125
Total Issue $518,190
Out in 1935 $75,000
Large out 1935 $1,140
****
14170 Northampton
FNB IN BANGOR
{{ 6 S }}
Chartered 5/34
1929 Small Size <$VALUE
5 Type 2 1-8270 <$175
10 Type 2 1-4705 <$175
20 Type 2 1-1805 <$175
Total Issue $124,500
Out in 1935 $100,000
****
2659 Northampton
FNB OF BANGOR
{{ 14 L 29 S }}
Organized 3/14/82
Liquidated 8/13/34
Series 1875 <$VALUE
3x10-20 1-8223 <$750/$1250
1902 Red Seal
3x10-20 1-11200 <$300
1902 Date Back
3x10-20 1-16300 <$125
1902 Plain Back (dated 1902)
3x10-20 16301-28289 <$125
1902 Plain Back (dated 1922)
3x10-20 1-18000 <$125
1929 Small Size
10 Type 1 1-5606 <$50
20 Type 1 1-1380 <$60
10 Type 2 1-1614 <$60
20 Type 2 1-380 <$60
Total Issue $3,811,300
Out at close $165,055
Large out at close $9,115
****
4513 Northampton
MERCHANTS NB OF BANGOR
{{ 6 L 18 S }}
Chartered 1891
Brown Back <$VALUE
3x10-20 1-8320 <$350
1882 Date Back
3x10-20 1-2281 <$350
1902 Date Back
3x10-20 1-7000 <$150
1902 Plain Back
3x10-20 7001-23751 <$150
1929 Small Size
10 Type 1 1-3526 <$60
20 Type 1 1-906 <$70
10 Type 2 1-4858 <$70
20 Type 2 1-985 <$75
Total Issue $2,106,160
Out in 1935 $123,100
Large out 1935 $5,000
****
5818 Cambria
FNB OF BARNESBORO
{{ 8 L 14 S }}
Chartered 5/16/01
Brown Back <$VALUE
3x10-20 1-3500 <$300
1882 Date Back
3x10-20 1-4940 <$300
1882 Value Back
4x5 4941-7636 <$300
1902 Plain Back
3x10-20 1-10344 <$150
1929 Small Size
10 Type 1 1-1646 <$85
20 Type 1 1-1376 <$85
20 Type 2 1-1081 <$100
Total Issue $1,359,500
Out in 1935 $97,750
Large out 1935 $3,670
****
5444 Northampton
FNB OF BATH
{{ 6 L 19 S }}
Chartered 6/21/00
Brown Back <$VALUE
3x10-20 1-1890 <$350
1882 Date Back
3x10-20 1-4700 <$350
1882 Value Back
3x10-20 4701-6985 <$350
1902 Plain Back
3x10-20 1-7027 <$175
1929 Small Size
10 Type 1 1-2622 <$50
20 Type 1 1-684 <$60
5 Type 2 1-300 <$65
10 Type 2 1-5933 <$65
20 Type 2 1-1861 <$65
Total Issue $1,132,550
Out in 1935 $107,200
Large out 1935 $1,065
****
5042 Beaver
BEAVER NB, BEAVER
{{ 2 L }}
Chartered 5/28/96
Liquidated 6/30/02
Brown Back <$VALUE
4x5 1-2510 <$850
3x10-20 1-437 <$850
Total Issue $72,050
Out in 1910 $1,035
****
3850 Beaver
FNB OF BEAVER
{{ 3 L }}
Chartered 2/29/88
Receivership 3/26/21
Brown Back <$VALUE
4x5 1-5212 <$600
3x10-20 1-2093 <$600
1902 Red Seal
3x10-20 1-500 <$750
1902 Date Back
3x10-20 1-4740 <$350
1902 Plain Back
3x10-20 4741-7449 <$350
Total Issue $606,340
Out at close $47,900
****
8185 Beaver
FORT McINTOSH NB OF BEAVER
{{ 6 L 14 S }}
Chartered 4/06
1902 Red Seal <$VALUE
50-100 1-165 <$2250/$2500
1902 Date Back
4x5 1-4700 <$250
3x10-20 1-2740 <$250
50-100 1-440 <$500/$600
1902 Plain Back
4x5 4701-14610 <$250
3x10-20 2741-9012 <$250
1929 Small Size
5 Type 1 1-1846 <$100
10 Type 1 1-1028 <$100
20 Type 1 1-298 <$125
5 Type 2 1-2338 <$125
10 Type 2 1-1477 <$150
20 Type 2 1-456 <$150
Total Issue $1,021,950
Out in 1935 $50,000
Large out 1935 $1,910
****
4894 Beaver
FARMERS NB OF BEAVER FALLS
{{ 10 L 17 S }}
Chartered 1893
Brown Back <$VALUE
3x10-20 1-3020 <$400
1882 Date Back
3x10-20 1-4814 <$400
1902 Date Back
3x10-20 1-3500 <$175
1902 Plain Back
3x10-20 3501-23344 <$175
1929 Small Size
10 Type 1 1-3172 <$60
20 Type 1 1-866 <$65
5 Type 2 1-324 <$75
10 Type 2 1-2377 <$75
20 Type 2 1-690 <$75
Total Issue $1,892,330
Out in 1935 $100,000
Large out 1935 $4,595
****
14117 Beaver
FNB AT BEAVER FALLS
{{ 9 S }}
Chartered 4/34
1929 Small Size <$VALUE
5 Type 2 1-2230 <$150
10 Type 2 1-4740 <$135
20 Type 2 1-2915 <$150
Total Issue $116,850
Out in 1935 $84,400
****
3356 Beaver
FNB OF BEAVER FALLS
{{ 11 L 26 S }}
Organized 6/2/85
Receivership 5/8/34
Brown Back <$VALUE
4x5 1-8537 <$400
50-100 1-409 <$1250/$1500
1902 Red Seal
3x10-20 1-2135 <$400
1902 Date Back
3x10-20 1-9100 <$175
1902 Plain Back
3x10-20 9101-32818 <$175
1929 Small Size
10 Type 1 1-4522 <$50
20 Type 1 1-1312 <$55
10 Type 2 1-951 <$65
20 Type 2 1-165 <$75
Total Issue $2,421,310
Out at close $148,210
Large out at close $7,090
****
FNB of Beaver Springs
SEE Ch 5777
FNB of Beaver Springs at Adamsburg
****
11317 Cambria
FNB OF BEAVERDALE
{{ 3 L 4 S }}
Chartered 3/19
Receivership 7/28/31
1902 Plain Back <$VALUE
4x5 1-10446 <$275
3x10-20 1-6642 <$275
1929 Small Size
5 Type 1 1-1383 <$200
10 Type 1 1-664 <$200
20 Type 1 1-178 <$200
Total Issue $643,710
Out at close $48,320
Large out at close $4,290
****
Farmers NB of Bedford
Farmers NB & TC of Bedford
SEE Ch 11188
Broad Top NB of Coaldale
****

CONDITION affects Value. The Values shown are for notes in FINE condition.

<$VALUEs are for notes in **FINE** condition. Value changes by approximately **25%** for a change of one full grade.

***

3089 Bedford
FNB OF BEDFORD
Organized 10/31/83
Receivership 10/26/34
2nd title: FNB & TC 7/1/30
FIRST TITLE {{6 L 2 S}}
Brown Back <$VALUE
4x5 1-9310 <$300
3x10-20 1-6469 <$300
1902 Red Seal
4x5 1-4250 <$300
3x10-20 1-3500 <$300
1902 Date Back
4x5 1-6450 <$175
3x10-20 1-4600 <$175
1902 Plain Back
4x5 6451-13475 <$175
3x10-20 4601-9108 <$175
1929 Small Size
5 Type 1 1-818 <$150
10 Type 1 1-418 <$150
20 Type 1 1-146 <$150
SECOND TITLE {{6 S}}
1929 Small Size
5 Type 1 1-986 <$125
10 Type 1 1-440 <$125
20 Type 1 1-88 <$125
5 Type 2 1-2134 <$150
10 Type 2 1-1113 <$150
20 Type 2 1-144 <$150
Total Issue $1,652,910
Out at close $49,750
Large out at close $4,880

***

13205 Clinton
BEECH CREEK NB, BEECH CREEK
{{1 L 3 S}}
Chartered 5/8/28
1902 Plain Back <$VALUE
4x5 1-260 <$750
4x10 1-115 <$750
3x10-20 1-126 <$750
1929 Small Size
5 Type 1 1-416 <$350
10 Type 1 1-208 <$350
20 Type 1 1-74 <$350
5 Type 2 1-510 <$400
10 Type 2 1-311 <$400
20 Type 2 1-125 <$400
Total Issue $58,100
Out in 1935 $10,000
Large out 1935 $130

***

4850 Fayette
FNB OF BELLE VERNON
{{8 L 13 S}}
Chartered 1893
Brown Back <$VALUE
3x10-20 1-5650 <$400
1882 Date Back
3x10-20 1-2749 <$400
1902 Date Back
3x10-20 1-1900 <$175
1902 Plain Back
3x10-20 1901-11263 <$175
1929 Small Size
10 Type 1 1-1372 <$85
20 Type 1 1-372 <$85
10 Type 2 1-1999 <$100
20 Type 2 1-510 <$100
Total Issue $1,140,250
Out in 1935 $48,550
Large out 1935 $2,890

***

459 Centre
FNB OF BELLEFONTE
{{9 L 14 S}}
Chartered 6/64
Original Series <$VALUE
4x5 1-3650 <$450
3x10-20 1-2340 <$750/$1250
Series 1875
3x10-20 1-1708 <$750/$1250
Brown Back
4x5 1-2165 <$300
3x10-20 1-7038 <$300
1902 Red Seal
4x5 1-5300 <$350
3x10-20 1-3980 <$350
1902 Date Back
4x5 1-8050 <$175
3x10-20 1-5580 <$175
1902 Plain Back
4x5 8051-25004 <$175
3x10-20 5581-16944 <$175
1929 Small Size
10 Type 1 1-2854 <$75
20 Type 1 1-748 <$85
10 Type 2 1-3550 <$100
20 Type 2 1-922 <$100
Total Issue $2,640,320
Out in 1935 $96,150
Large out 1935 $7,190

***

5306 Mifflin
BELLEVILLE NB, BELLEVILLE
{{4 L 5 S}}
Chartered 4/26/00
Closed 12/31/34
Brown Back <$VALUE
3x10-20 1-2100 <$400
1882 Date Back
3x10-20 1-2110 <$400
1882 Value Back
3x10-20 2111-3263 <$400
1902 Plain Back
4x5 1-12004 <$225
1929 Small Size
5 Type 1 1-3494 <$200
5 Type 2 1-5928 <$200
Total Issue $642,690
Out at close $24,640
Large out at close $1,450
Ch 10128 assumed circulation

***

10128 Mifflin
FARMERS NB OF BELLEVILLE
Chartered 1/12
2nd title: Kishacoquillas Valley NB 12/31/34
FIRST TITLE {{2 L 5 S}}
1902 Date Back <$VALUE
3x10-20 1-2880 <$300
1902 Plain Back
3x10-20 2881-11932 <$300
1929 Small Size
10 Type 1 1-1534 <$150
20 Type 1 1-412 <$175
10 Type 2 1-2436 <$175
20 Type 2 1-576 <$175
SECOND TITLE {{1 S}}
1929 Small Size
10 Type 2 1-373 <$500
20 Type 2 1-105 <$500
Total Issue $779,790
Out in 1935 $73,500
Large out 1935 $3,220
Outstanding includes Ch 5306

***

Kishacoquillas Valley NB of Belleville
SEE Ch 10128
Farmers NB of Belleville

***

5509 Allegheny
BELLEVUE NB, BELLEVUE
{{1 L}}
Chartered 7/20/00
Liquidated 6/30/02
Brown Back <$VALUE
3x10-20 1-1318 <$1250
Total Issue $65,900
Out in 1910 $1,640

***

8761 Allegheny
CITIZENS NB OF BELLEVUE
{{6 L}}
Chartered 6/07
Liquidated 12/1/27
1902 Red Seal <$VALUE
3x10-20 1-375 <$600
1902 Date Back
3x10-20 1-5000 <$250
1902 Plain Back
3x10-20 5001-20086 <$250
Total Issue $1,023,050
Out at close $93,100

***

7356 Blair
FNB OF BELLWOOD
{{3 L 9 S}}
Chartered 8/04
1902 Red Seal <$VALUE
3x10-20 1-1160 <$600
1902 Date Back
3x10-20 1-1820 <$300
1902 Plain Back
3x10-20 1821-5529 <$300
1929 Small Size
10 Type 1 1-664 <$125
20 Type 1 1-152 <$125
10 Type 2 1-4011 <$125
20 Type 2 1-950 <$125
Total Issue $451,640
Out in 1935 $48,900
Large out 1935 $1,120

***

9114 Adams
BENDERSVILLE NB, BENDERSVILLE
{{2 L 12 S}}
Chartered 4/08
1902 Date Back <$VALUE
3x10-20 1-2090 <$350
1902 Plain Back
3x10-20 2091-6242 <$350
1929 Small Size
10 Type 1 1-1460 <$125
20 Type 1 1-360 <$125
10 Type 2 1-1962 <$125
20 Type 2 1-443 <$150
Total Issue $471,380
Out in 1935 $48,800
Large out 1935 $730

***

7935 Somerset
FNB OF BENSON
{{2 L}}
Chartered 10/05
Receivership 3/28/27
1902 Red Seal <$VALUE
3x10-20 1-360 <$750
1902 Date Back
3x10-20 1-2890 <$375
1902 Plain Back
3x10-20 2891-6912 <$375
Total Issue $363,600
Out at close $24,400

***

8196 Washington
BENTLEYVILLE NB, BENTLEYVILLE
Chartered 4/06
Liquidated 1/9/18
2nd title: FNB of Bentleyville 2/17/15
FIRST TITLE {{0 L}}
1902 Red Seal <$VALUE
3x10-20 1-287 <$1250
1902 Date Back
3x10-20 1-2466 <$750
SECOND TITLE {{1 L}}
1902 Date Back
3x10-20 1-250 <$600
1902 Plain Back
3x10-20 251-678 <$600
Total Issue $171,550
Out at close $20,500

***

13663 Washington
CITIZENS NB OF BENTLEYVILLE
{{3 S}}
Chartered 2/33
1929 Small Size <$VALUE
5 Type 2 1-3288 <$275
10 Type 2 1-1242 <$275
20 Type 2 1-373 <$300
Total Issue $36,320
Out in 1935 $49,200
Large out 1935 $4,220
Outstanding includes Ch 9058

***

9058 Washington
FARMERS & MINERS NB OF BENTLEYVILLE
{{4 L 6 S}}
Chartered 3/08
Liquidated 6/14/33
1902 Red Seal <$VALUE
3x10-20 1-375 <$450
1902 Date Back
3x10-20 1-1420* <$225
1902 Plain Back
3x10-20 1581-16243* <$225
* 1421-1580 not marked
1929 Small Size
10 Type 1 1-1861 <$175
20 Type 1 1-584 <$175
Total Issue $1,102,640
Out at close $25,250
Large out 1935 $4,220
Ch 13663 assumed circulation

***

FNB of Bentleyville
SEE Ch 8196
Bentleyville NB, Bentleyville

***

6328 Columbia
COLUMBIA COUNTY NB OF BENTON
{{2 L 6 S}}
Chartered 7/3/02
1902 Red Seal <$VALUE
4x5 1-500 <$600
3x10-20 1-700 <$600
1902 Date Back
4x5 1-2425 <$300
3x10-20 1-1600 <$300
1902 Plain Back
4x5 2426-7973 <$300
3x10-20 1601-4841 <$300
1929 Small Size
5 Type 1 1-1166 <$175
10 Type 1 1-602 <$175
20 Type 1 1-166 <$175
5 Type 2 1-1166 <$200
10 Type 2 1-768 <$200
20 Type 2 1-204 <$200
Total Issue $555,120
Out in 1935 $24,700
Large out 1935 $585

***

5823 Somerset
FNB OF BERLIN
{{4 L 11 S}}
Chartered 5/21/01
Brown Back <$VALUE
3x10-20 1-1040 <$500
1882 Date Back
3x10-20 1-2750 <$500
1882 Value Back
3x10-20 2751-5420 <$500
1902 Plain Back
3x10-20 1-6181 <$250
1929 Small Size
10 Type 1 1-1352 <$125
20 Type 1 1-400 <$150
10 Type 2 1-1450 <$150
20 Type 2 1-474 <$150
Total Issue $785,150
Out in 1935 $48,600
Large out 1935 $2,490

***

6512 Somerset
PHILSON NB OF BERLIN
{{6 L 13 S}}
Chartered 11/29/02
1902 Red Seal <$VALUE
3x10-20 1-1095 <$450
1902 Date Back
3x10-20 1-2460 <$225
1902 Plain Back
3x10-20 2461-13027 <$225
1929 Small Size
10 Type 1 1-1680 <$100
20 Type 1 1-436 <$125
10 Type 2 1-1220 <$125
20 Type 2 1-320 <$150
Total Issue $877,820
Out in 1935 $51,610
Large out 1935 $2,360

***

8913 Berks
FNB OF BERNVILLE
{{4 L 11 S}}
Chartered 10/07
1902 Red Seal <$VALUE
3x10-20 1-310 <$750
1902 Date Back
3x10-20 1-1140 <$375
1902 Plain Back
3x10-20 1141-4334 <$375
1929 Small Size
10 Type 1 1-1032 <$150
20 Type 1 1-278 <$150
10 Type 2 1-1999 <$150
20 Type 2 1-526 <$150
Total Issue $357,990
Out in 1935 $44,950
Large out 1935 $1,440

***

6162 Columbia
BERWICK NB, BERWICK
{{10 L 21 S}}
Chartered 3/17/02
1902 Red Seal <$VALUE
4x5 1-1200 <$325
3x10-20 1-2160 <$325
1902 Date Back
4x5 1-4900 <$150
3x10-20 1-3500 <$150
1902 Plain Back (dated 1902)
4x5 4901-8950 <$150
3x10-20 3501-6597 <$150
1902 Plain Back (dated 1922)
3x10-20 1-16979 <$150
1929 Small Size
10 Type 1 1-4158 <$50
20 Type 1 1-1178 <$60
20 Type 2 1-3563 <$65
Total Issue $1,951,900
Out in 1935 $110,250
Large out 1935 $3,710

***

568 Columbia
FNB OF BERWICK
{{4 L 6 S}}
Chartered 11/64
Original Series <$VALUE
4x5 1-3675 <$500
3x10-20 1-1200 <$750/$1250
Series 1875
4x5 1-720 <$500
3x10-20 1-498 <$750/$1250
Brown Back
3x10-20 1-5802 <$375
1902 Red Seal
3x10-20 1-1550 <$400
1902 Date Back
3x10-20 1-1900* <$200
1902 Plain Back
3x10-20 2141-6252* <$200
* 1901-2140 not marked
1929 Small Size
10 Type 1 1-834 <$150
20 Type 1 1-212 <$150
10 Type 2 1-727 <$175
20 Type 2 1-85 <$200
Total Issue $937,450
Out in 1935 $24,100
Large out 1935 $2,920

***

3945 Chester
BERWYN NB, BERWYN
{{5 L 10 S}}
Chartered 12/7/88
Liquidated 4/2/34
Brown Back <$VALUE
4x5 1-500 <$750
3x10-20 1-1698 <$750
1902 Date Back
3x10-20 1-4850* <$375
1902 Plain Back
3x10-20 5051-14843* <$375
* 4851-5050 not marked
1929 Small Size
10 Type 1 1-1560 <$150
20 Type 1 1-468 <$175
10 Type 2 1-214 <$200
20 Type 2 1-80 <$200
Total Issue $990,550
Out at close $50,000
Large out 1935 $1,880
Ch 13999 assumed circulation

***

13999 Chester
BERWYN NB, BERWYN
{{3 S}}
Chartered 2/34
1929 Small Size <$VALUE
5 Type 2 1-7912 <$275
Total Issue $39,560
Out in 1935 $136,820
Large out 1935 $1,880
Outstanding includes Ch 3945

***

Bethlehem NB, Bethlehem
SEE Ch 3961
South Bethlehem NB, South Bethlehem

***

138 Northampton
FNB OF BETHLEHEM
Chartered 12/63
2nd title: FNB & TC 1/22/30
FIRST TITLE {{26 L 4 S}}
Original Series <$VALUE
4x5 1-6696 <$400
4x10 1-7250 <$750
3x20-50 1-4138<$1250/$3500
Series 1875
4x5 1-2050 <$400
4x10 1-1780 <$750
3x20-50 1-1207<$1250/$3500
Brown Back
4x5 1-5723 <$200
3x10-20 1-3804 <$200/$250
50-100 1-1100 <$1250/$1500
1902 Red Seal
4x5 1-7750 <$200
3x10-20 1-6800 <$200/$250
1902 Date Back
4x5 1-23250 <$85
3x10-20 1-16000 <$85
1902 Plain Back
4x5 23251-88720 <$85
3x10-20 16001-54626 <$85
1929 Small Size
5 Type 1 1-4628 <$75
10 Type 1 1-2138 <$75
20 Type 1 1-728 <$85
SECOND TITLE {{50+ S}}
1929 Small Size
5 Type 1 1-6770 <$25
10 Type 1 1-5008 <$25
20 Type 1 1-1132 <$35
5 Type 2 1-32938 <$25
10 Type 2 1-18972 <$25
20 Type 2 1-5328 <$35
Total Issue $8,049,300
Out in 1935 $485,500
Large out 1935 $28,135
Outstanding includes Ch 2050

***

2050 Northampton
LEHIGH VALLEY NB OF BETHLEHEM
{{13 L 23 S}}
Chartered 9/26/72
Liquidated 12/19/32
Original Series <$VALUE
3x1-2 1-4600 <$300/$850
4x5 1-5500 <$400
4x10 1-2710 <$750
3x20-50 1-1224<$1250/$3500
Series 1875
4x5 1-3737 <$400
4x10 1-3505 <$750
3x20-50 1-2996<$1250/$3500
Brown Back
4x5 1-2050 <$250
3x10-20 1-1740 <$250
50-100 1-840 <$1250/$1500
1882 Date Back
4x5 1-2145 <$250
3x10-20 1-1423 <$250
50-100 1-14 <$1250/$1500
1902 Date Back
4x5 1-3000* <$125
3x10-20 1-2400** <$125
3x50-100 1-548 <$450/$500
1902 Plain Back
4x5 3501-38252* <$125
3x10-20 2801-23850** <$125
3x50-100 549-718<$450/$500
1929 Small Size
5 Type 1 1-10601 <$50
10 Type 1 1-4899 <$50
20 Type 1 1-1218 <$60
Total Issue $4,185,860
Out at close $217,260
Large out at close $19,865
Ch 138 assumed circulation

***

5667 Jefferson
CITIZENS NB OF BIG RUN
{{4 L 9 S}}
Chartered 1/5/01
Brown Back <$VALUE
3x10-20 1-800 <$500
1882 Date Back
3x10-20 1-860* <$500
1882 Value Back
3x10-20 961-1104* <$500
* 861-960 not marked
1902 Plain Back
3x10-20 1-4090 <$350
1929 Small Size
10 Type 1 1-1036 <$150
20 Type 1 1-274 <$165
10 Type 2 1-1009 <$175
20 Type 2 1-214 <$175
Total Issue $409,110
Out in 1935 $34,150
Large out 1935 $1,120

***

7917 Adams
BIGLERVILLE NB, BIGLERVILLE
{{5 L 12 S}}
Chartered 9/05
1902 Red Seal <$VALUE
3x10-20 1-910 <$500
1902 Date Back
3x10-20 1-4740 <$250
1902 Plain Back
3x10-20 1741-13415 <$250
1929 Small Size
10 Type 1 1-1486 <$100
20 Type 1 1-422 <$125
10 Type 2 1-1773 <$125
20 Type 2 1-430 <$125
Total Issue $882,380
Out in 1935 $48,450
Large out 1935 $2,370

***

3905 Berks
FNB OF BIRDSBORO
{{6 L 11 S}}
Chartered 6/26/88
Receivership 1/19/34
Brown Back <$VALUE
3x10-20 1-3780 <$400
1902 Red Seal
3x10-20 1-400 <$400
1902 Date Back
3x10-20 1-4740 <$175
1902 Plain Back
3x10-20 4741-14016 <$175
1929 Small Size
10 Type 1 1-1570 <$100
20 Type 1 1-392 <$125
Total Issue $1,051,040
Out at close $48,260
Large out at close $3,060

***

8428 Indiana
FNB OF BLACK LICK
{{2 L}}
Chartered 11/06
Liquidated 3/31/19
1902 Red Seal <$VALUE
3x10-20 1-788 <$1500
1902 Date Back
3x10-20 1-2520 <$1000
1902 Plain Back
3x10-20 2521-3564 <$1000
Total Issue $217,600
Out at close $35,400

***

<$VALUEs are for notes in FINE condition. Value changes by approximately 25% for a change of one full grade.

****
4919 Indiana
BLAIRSVILLE NB, BLAIRSVILLE
{{ 7 L 16 S }}
Organized 6/9/93
Liquidated 3/24/34
Brown Back <$VALUE
3x10-20 1-2920 <$300
1882 Date Back
3x10-20 1-3364 <$300
1902 Date Back
3x10-20 1-1700 <$175
1902 Plain Back
3x10-20 1701-15001 <$175
1929 Small Size
10 Type 1 1-2922 <$75
20 Type 1 1-759 <$85
Total Issue $1,330,650
Out at close $82,395
Large out 1935 $3,895
Ch 13868 assumed circulation
****
13868 Indiana
BLAIRSVILLE NB, BLAIRSVILLE
{{ UNREPORTED }}
Chartered 12/33
1929 Small Size <$VALUE
10 Type 2 1-200 <$600
20 Type 2 1-30 <$600
Total Issue $2,600
Out in 1935 $52,835
Large out 1935 $3,995
Outstanding includes Ch 4919
****
867 Indiana
FNB OF BLAIRSVILLE
{{ 10 L }}
Chartered 3/7/65
Liquidated 6/30/28
Original Series <$VALUE
4x5 1-7795 <$450
Series 1875
4x5 1-7200 <$450
Brown Back
3x10-20 1-7691 <$275
1902 Red Seal
3x10-20 1-3200 <$275
1902 Date Back
3x10-20 1-11400 <$125
1902 Plain Back
3x10-20 11401-36737 <$125
Total Issue $2,681,300
Out at close $147,300
****
5211 Columbia
BLOOMSBURG NB, BLOOMSBURG
{{ 10 L }}
Chartered 7/25/99
Liquidated 2/1/26
Brown Back <$VALUE
4x5 1-8735 <$300
3x10-20 1-5006 <$300
1882 Date Back
4x5 1-8600* <$300
3x10-20 1-6000** <$300
1882 Value Back
4x5 9001-13000* <$300
3x10-20 6321-8460** <$300
* 8601-9000 not marked
** 6001-6320 not marked
1902 Plain Back
4x5 1-44192 <$150
Total Issue $1,991,840
Out at close $124,995
****
4543 Columbia
FARMERS NB OF BLOOMSBURG
{{ 8 L 17 S }}
Chartered 1891
Brown Back <$VALUE
4x5 1-10500 <$300
3x10-20 1-3360 <$300
1882 Date Back
4x5 1-1763 <$300
3x10-20 1-1406 <$300
1902 Date Back
3x10-20 1-4940 <$175
1902 Plain Back
3x10-20 4941-16423 <$175
1929 Small Size
10 Type 1 1-2316 <$65
20 Type 1 1-670 <$65
10 Type 2 1-4709 <$75
20 Type 2 1-1373 <$75
Total Issue $1,598,620
Out in 1935 $96,800
Large out 1935 $2,800
****
293 Columbia
FNB OF BLOOMSBURG
{{ 14 L 18 S }}
Chartered 2/64
Original Series <$VALUE
3x1-2 1-3900 <$350/$1000
4x5 1-4050 <$400
Series 1875
3x1-2 1-1080 <$350/$1000
4x5 1-3525 <$400
Brown Back
4x5 1-14288 <$250
3x10-20 1-1045 <$250
1902 Red Seal
3x10-20 1-4700 <$250
1902 Date Back
3x10-20 1-8900 <$125
1902 Plain Back
3x10-20 8901-27621 <$125
1929 Small Size
10 Type 1 1-3214 <$60
20 Type 1 1-790 <$60
10 Type 2 1-4557 <$70
20 Type 2 1-1391 <$70
Total Issue $2,491,490
Out in 1935 $100,000
Large out 1935 $6,630
****
13381 Tioga
CITIZENS NB & TC OF BLOSSBURG
{{ 31 S }}
Chartered 10/29
1929 Small Size <$VALUE
5 Type 1 1-5222 <$45
10 Type 1 1-2706 <$45
20 Type 1 1-786 <$50
5 Type 2 1-6882 <$50
10 Type 2 1-3885 <$50
20 Type 2 1-1380 <$50
Total Issue $514,200
Out in 1935 $125,000
****
5007 Tioga
MINERS NB OF BLOSSBURG
{{ 7 L }}
Organized 6/6/95
Receivership 7/30/29
Brown Back <$VALUE
3x10-20 1-4550 <$325
1882 Date Back
3x10-20 1-3677 <$325
1902 Date Back
3x10-20 1-1000 <$175
1902 Plain Back
3x10-20 1001-8060 <$175
Total Issue $814,350
Out at close $49,000
****
8421 Lancaster
BLUE BALL NB, BLUE BALL
{{ 6 L 15 S }}
Chartered 10/06
1902 Red Seal <$VALUE
3x10-20 1-900 <$850
1902 Date Back
3x10-20 1-4900 <$400
1902 Plain Back
3x10-20 4901-13460 <$400
1929 Small Size
10 Type 1 1-1602 <$275
20 Type 1 1-374 <$275
10 Type 2 1-1651 <$300
20 Type 2 1-302 <$300
Total Issue $881,550
Out in 1935 $48,450
Large out 1935 $2,600
****
12281 Franklin
FNB OF BLUE RIDGE SUMMIT
{{ 1 L 6 S }}
Chartered 12/22
1902 Plain Back <$VALUE
3x10-20 1-2925 <$1000
1929 Small Size
10 Type 1 1-818 <$450
20 Type 1 1-200 <$450
10 Type 2 1-893 <$500
20 Type 2 1-195 <$500
Total Issue $232,160
Out in 1935 $24,300
Large out 1935 $840
****
6135 Westmoreland
BOLIVAR NB, BOLIVAR
{{ 3 L 8 S }}
Chartered 2/24/02
1902 Red Seal <$VALUE
3x10-20 1-540 <$650
1902 Date Back
3x10-20 1-2180 <$300
1902 Plain Back (dated 1901)
3x10-20 2181-4097 <$300
1902 Plain Back (dated 1921)
3x10-20 1-3665 <$300
1929 Small Size
10 Type 1 1-866 <$150
20 Type 1 1-262 <$150
10 Type 2 1-715 <$175
20 Type 2 1-252 <$175
Total Issue $510,690
Out in 1935 $29,500
Large out 1935 $1,890
****
12355 Westmoreland
CITIZENS NB OF BOLIVAR
{{ 0 L 3 S }}
Chartered 4/23
Liquidated 2/26/32
1902 Plain Back <$VALUE
3x10-20 1-3019 <$350
1929 Small Size
10 Type 1 1-594 <$300
20 Type 1 1-135 <$300
Total Issue $202,790
Out at close $21,220
Large out at close $1,540
****
6603 Somerset
FNB OF BOSWELL
{{ 2 L 2 S }}
Chartered 2/03
Receivership 2/9/32
1902 Red Seal <$VALUE
4x5 1-1450 <$700
3x10-20 1-1160 <$700
1902 Date Back
4x5 1-3050 <$350
3x10-20 1-2090 <$350
1902 Plain Back
4x5 3051-9925 <$350
3x10-20 2091-6175 <$350
1929 Small Size
5 Type 1 1-906 <$350
10 Type 1 1-452 <$350
20 Type 1 1-133 <$350
Total Issue $664,510
Out at close $29,395
Large out at close $2,665
****
2900 Berks
FARMERS NB OF BOYERTOWN
Organized 3/14/83
2nd title: Farmers NB & TC 1/12/29
FIRST TITLE {{ 6 L }}
Brown Back <$VALUE
4x5 1-4444 <$500
3x10-20 1-241 <$500
1902 Red Seal
3x10-20 1-2325 <$500
1902 Date Back
3x10-20 1-4240 <$250
1902 Plain Back
3x10-20 4241-24231 <$250
SECOND TITLE {{ 0 L 26 S }}
1902 Plain Back
3x10-20 1-527 <$300
1929 Small Size
10 Type 1 1-4332 <$50
20 Type 1 1-1018 <$60
10 Type 2 1-5795 <$60
20 Type 2 1-1600 <$60
Total Issue $1,927,110
Out in 1935 $131,450
Large out 1935 $4,740
****
2137 Berks
NB OF BOYERTOWN
Chartered 3/3/74
2nd title: NB & TC of Boyertown 12/31/29
FIRST TITLE {{ 10 L 3 S }}
Original Series <$VALUE
4x5 1-2125 <$4000
3x20-50 1-205 <$1250/$3500
Series 1875
4x5 1-7907 <$3500
3x20-50 1-1750<$1250/$3500
Brown Back
3x10-20 1-11200 <$450
1882 Date Back
3x10-20 1-5430 <$450
1902 Date Back
3x10-20 1-2000 <$175
1902 Plain Back
3x10-20 2001-19323 <$175
1929 Small Size
10 Type 1 1-1204 <$100
20 Type 1 1-384 <$100
SECOND TITLE {{ 25 S }}
1929 Small Size
10 Type 1 1-1834 <$60
20 Type 1 1-432 <$60
10 Type 2 1-5894 <$60
20 Type 2 1-1870 <$60
Total Issue $2,589,880
Out in 1935 $127,250
Large out 1935 $6,190
****
2828 Allegheny
BRADDOCK NB, BRADDOCK
{{ 14 L 32 S }}
Chartered 1882
Brown Back <$VALUE
4x5 1-7775 <$200
50-100 1-1178 <$1250/$1500
1902 Red Seal
4x5 1-5000 <$225
3x10-20 1-2910 <$225
50-100 1-430 <$2250/$2500
1902 Date Back
4x5 1-23100 <$100
3x10-20 1-16280 <$100
50-100 1-500 <$350/$400
1902 Plain Back
4x5 23101-47974 <$100
3x10-20 16281-28347 <$100
1929 Small Size
5 Type 1 1-11830 <$25
10 Type 1 1-6044 <$25
20 Type 1 1-1600 <$30
5 Type 2 1-38394 <$30
10 Type 2 1-18084 <$30
20 Type 2 1-5676 <$30
Total Issue $4,489,900
Out in 1935 $483,750
Large out 1935 $7,390
****
2799 Allegheny
FNB OF BRADDOCK
{{ 5 L }}
Organized 10/3/82
Liquidated 4/29/34
Brown Back <$VALUE
4x5 1-5600 <$300
3x10-20 1-2069 <$300
1902 Red Seal
3x10-20 1-6300 <$325
1902 Date Back
3x10-20 1-9100 <$175
1902 Plain Back
3x10-20 9101-20991 <$175
Total Issue $1,580,000
Out at close $3,965
****
13866 Allegheny
FNB OF BRADDOCK
{{ 20 S }}
Chartered 12/33
1929 Small Size <$VALUE
5 Type 2 1-14790 <$50
10 Type 2 1-7600 <$50
20 Type 2 1-2675 <$60
Total Issue $203,450
Out in 1935 $113,900
****
6796 Allegheny
UNION NB OF BRADDOCK
{{ UNREPORTED }}
Chartered 5/23/03
Liquidated 6/3/07
1902 Red Seal <$VALUE
4x5 1-5750 <$1000
3x10-20 1-5602 <$1000
Total Issue $395,100
Out in 1910 $18,985
****
2428 McKean
BRADFORD NB, BRADFORD
{{ 11 L 27 S }}
Chartered 7/25/79
Series 1875 <$VALUE
4x5 1-4150 <$350
3x10-20 1-12098<$600/$1000
Brown Back
3x10-20 1-14900 <$275
1882 Date Back
3x10-20 1-15000* <$275
1882 Value Back
3x10-20 16001-20725* <$275
* 15001-16000 not marked
1902 Plain Back
3x10-20 1-27943 <$110
1929 Small Size
10 Type 1 1-5808 <$35
20 Type 1 1-1460 <$40
10 Type 2 1-8210 <$40
20 Type 2 1-2047 <$40
Total Issue $4,513,020
Out in 1935 $192,700
Large out 1935 $10,050
****
4199 McKean
COMMERCIAL NB OF BRADFORD
{{ 9 L 18 S }}
Organized 1/1/90
Receivership 9/30/35
Brown Back <$VALUE
4x5 1-3000 <$300
3x10-20 1-7800 <$300
1882 Date Back
4x5 1-1530 <$300
3x10-20 1-767 <$300
1902 Date Back
3x10-20 1-7800 <$135
1902 Plain Back
3x10-20 7801-25080 <$135
1929 Small Size
10 Type 1 1-2826 <$60
20 Type 1 1-806 <$60
10 Type 2 1-4116 <$70
20 Type 2 1-915 <$70
Total Issue $2,098,690
Out at close $100,000
Large out at close $5,720
****
2470 McKean
FNB OF BRADFORD
{{ 2 L }}
Chartered 4/9/80
Liquidated 3/2/18
Series 1875 <$VALUE
3x10-20 1-4636 <$850/$1500
Brown Back
3x10-20 1-7760 <$600
1882 Date Back
4x5 1-16855 <$600
3x10-20 1-10322 <$600
Total Issue $1,473,000
Out at close $135,750
****
8329 Montgomery
BRIDGEPORT NB, BRIDGEPORT
{{ 6 L 16 S }}
Chartered 8/06
1902 Red Seal <$VALUE
3x10-20 1-1890 <$500
1902 Date Back
3x10-20 1-7600 <$250
1902 Plain Back
3x10-20 7601-22475 <$250
1929 Small Size
5 Type 1 1-2168 <$85
10 Type 1 1-3360 <$85
20 Type 1 1-866 <$85
5 Type 2 1-10852 <$100
10 Type 2 1-5411 <$100
20 Type 2 1-1590 <$100
Total Issue $1,728,980
Out in 1935 $150,000
Large out 1935 $3,240
****
6636 Allegheny
FNB OF BRIDGEVILLE
{{ 6 L 8 S }}
Chartered 2/03
Receivership 9/20/34
1902 Red Seal <$VALUE
4x5 1-3060 <$450
3x10-20 1-2298 <$450
1902 Date Back
4x5 1-4750 <$225
3x10-20 1-3300 <$225
1902 Plain Back
4x5 4751-15661 <$225
3x10-20 3301-10305 <$225
1929 Small Size
5 Type 1 1-1958 <$150
10 Type 1 1-1114 <$150
20 Type 1 1-284 <$150
5 Type 2 1-2316 <$175
10 Type 2 1-1175 <$175
20 Type 2 1-182 <$175
Total Issue $1,191,200
Out at close $50,000
Large out at close $2,720
****
717 Bucks
FARMERS NB OF BUCKS COUNTY, BRISTOL
{{ 12 L 9 S }}
Chartered 1/65
Original Series <$VALUE
4x5 1-3600 <$500
3x10-20 1-1600 <$750/$1250
Series 1875
4x5 1-1547 <$500
3x10-20 1-2028 <$750/$1250
Brown Back
4x5 1-5353 <$350
3x10-20 1-2797 <$350
1902 Red Seal
4x5 1-1900 <$400
3x10-20 1-960 <$400
1902 Date Back
4x5 1-3650 <$175
3x10-20 1-2900 <$175
1902 Plain Back
4x5 3651-9966 <$175
3x10-20 2901-7004 <$175
1929 Small Size
5 Type 1 1-1528 <$125
10 Type 1 1-888 <$125
20 Type 1 1-230 <$135
5 Type 2 1-2780 <$175
10 Type 2 1-1405 <$175
20 Type 2 1-262 <$175
Total Issue $1,326,680
Out in 1935 $38,850
Large out 1935 $3,710
****
FNB of Brockway
SEE Ch 5497
FNB of Brockwayville
****
5497 Jefferson
FNB OF BROCKWAYVILLE
Chartered 7/12/00
Liquidated 9/14/31
2nd title: FNB of Brockway 4/24/29
FIRST TITLE {{ 5 L }}
Brown Back <$VALUE
4x5 1-1845 <$400
3x10-20 1-1552 <$400
1882 Date Back
4x5 1-3050 <$400
3x10-20 1-2160 <$400
1882 Value Back
4x5 3051-4750 <$400
3x10-20 2161-3060 <$400
1902 Plain Back
4x5 1-4738 <$200
3x10-20 1-3666 <$200
SECOND TITLE {{ 3 S }}
1929 Small Size
5 Type 1 1-1035 <$225
10 Type 1 1-537 <$225
Total Issue $667,170
Out at close $28,720
Large out at close $2,630
****
897 Jefferson
FNB OF BROOKVILLE
{{ UNREPORTED }}
Chartered 3/16/65
Liquidated 3/20/74
Original Series <$VALUE
4x5 1-1500 <$1250
3x10-20 1-1500<$1500/$2000
Total Issue $105,000
Out in 1910 $1,010
****
2392 Jefferson
JEFFERSON COUNTY NB OF BROOKVILLE
{{ 7 L 7 S }}
Chartered 8/15/78
Receivership 11/9/33
Series 1875 <$VALUE
4x5 1-14282 <$450
Brown Back
4x5 1-4375 <$325
3x10-20 1-2980 <$325
1882 Date Back
4x5 1-3600* <$325
3x10-20 1-2540** <$325
1882 Value Back
4x5 3751-4733* <$325
3x10-20 2661-3329** <$325
* 3601-3750 not marked
** 2541-2660 not marked
1902 Plain Back
3x10-20 1-7133 <$175
1929 Small Size
10 Type 1 1-1378 <$150
20 Type 1 1-328 <$175
Total Issue $1,261,940
Out at close $50,000
Large out at close $4,370
****
3051 Jefferson
NB OF BROOKVILLE
{{ 8 L 11 S }}
Chartered 1883
Brown Back <$VALUE
4x5 1-6180 <$300
50-100 1-568 <$1250/$1500
1902 Red Seal
4x5 1-2300 <$325
50-100 1-580 <$2250/$2500
1902 Date Back
4x5 1-6250 <$150
50-100 1-534 <$400/$500
3x50-100 1-1092 <$400/$500
1902 Plain Back
4x5 6251-29928 <$150
3x50-100 1093-1382 <$400/$500
1929 Small Size
5 Type 1 1-3436 <$75
50 Type 1 1-244 <$150
100 Type 1 1-64 <$225
5 Type 2 1-2064 <$85
50 Type 2 1-128 <$225
Total Issue $1,597,360
Out in 1935 $98,500
Large out 1935 $8,655
****

<$VALUEs are for notes in FINE condition. Value changes by approximately 25% for a change of one full grade.

9026 Lancaster
BROWNSTOWN NB, BROWNSTOWN
{{ 4 L 5 S }}
Chartered 2/08
1902 Red Seal <$VALUE
3x10-20 1-660 <$750
1902 Date Back
3x10-20 1-2060 <$400
1902 Plain Back
3x10-20 2061-6520 <$400
1929 Small Size
10 Type 1 1-778 <$175
20 Type 1 1-212 <$175
10 Type 2 1-860 <$200
20 Type 2 1-251 <$200
Total Issue $444,740
Out in 1935 $24,450
Large out 1935 $440

135 Fayette
FNB OF BROWNSVILLE
{{ 1 L }}
Chartered 11/63
Liquidated 5/2/82
Original Series <$VALUE
4x5 1-5160 <$1000
3x10-20 1-800 <$1250/$1750
Series 1875
3x10-20 1-970 <$1250/$1750
Total Issue $191,700
Out in 1910 $1,515

648 Fayette
MONONGAHELA NB OF BROWNSVILLE
{{ 10 L 5 S }}
Chartered 12/64
Receivership 4/16/31
Original Series <$VALUE
4x5 1-3500 <$400
3x10-20 1-5345 <$750/$1250
Series 1875
3x10-20 1-5100 <$750/$1250
Brown Back
3x10-20 1-11305 <$250
1902 Red Seal
4x5 1-3000 <$250
3x10-20 1-2800 <$250
1902 Date Back
4x5 1-8700 <$110
3x10-20 1-7040* <$110
* 998 & 1250 not issued
1902 Plain Back
4x5 8701-26760 <$110
3x10-20 7041-18838 <$110
1929 Small Size
5 Type 1 1-2210 <$150
10 Type 1 1-1066 <$150
20 Type 1 1-260 <$150
Total Issue $2,995,960
Out at close $99,140
Large out at close $14,900

2457 Fayette
N DEPOSIT B OF BROWNSVILLE
{{ 6 L 13 S }}
Chartered 2/24/80
Series 1875 <$VALUE
3x10-20 1-4804 <$750/$1250
Brown Back
3x10-20 1-4150 <$325
1882 Date Back
3x10-20 1-4400 <$325
1882 Value Back
3x10-20 4401-6171 <$325
1902 Plain Back
3x10-20 1-7358 <$175
1929 Small Size
10 Type 1 1-1418 <$75
20 Type 1 1-344 <$85
10 Type 2 1-2201 <$85
20 Type 2 1-480 <$85
Total Issue $1,282,120
Out in 1935 $48,650
Large out 1935 $2,670

2673 Fayette
SECOND NB OF BROWNSVILLE
{{ 7 L 3 S }}
Organized 4/11/82
Liquidated 9/30/30
Brown Back <$VALUE
4x5 1-2735 <$275
3x10-20 1-3317 <$275
1902 Red Seal
4x5 1-2900 <$275
3x10-20 1-2130 <$275
1902 Date Back
4x5 1-10200 <$125
3x10-20 1-6860 <$125
1902 Plain Back (dated 1902)
4x5 10201-18500 <$125
3x10-20 6861-11420 <$125
1902 Plain Back (dated 1922)
4x5 1-11859 <$125
3x10-20 1-8465 <$125
1929 Small Size
5 Type 1 1-1671 <$250
10 Type 1 1-763 <$250
20 Type 1 1-203 <$250
Total Issue $2,106,750
Out at close $87,520
Large out at close $14,140

8919 Butler
FNB OF BRUIN
{{ 3 L 3 S }}
Chartered 10/07
Receivership 9/25/33
1902 Red Seal <$VALUE
4x5 1-150 <$850
3x10-20 1-127 <$850
1902 Date Back
4x5 1-2200 <$400
3x10-20 1-1680 <$400
1902 Plain Back
4x5 2201-7584 <$400
3x10-20 1681-4850 <$400
1929 Small Size
5 Type 1 1-784 <$300
10 Type 1 1-372 <$300
20 Type 1 1-101 <$300
Total Issue $461,490
Out at close $9,525
Large out at close $1,265

3766 Montgomery
BRYN MAWR NB, BRYN MAWR
{{ 4 L 12 S }}
Chartered 7/30/87
Brown Back <$VALUE
4x5 1-3820 <$800
3x10-20 1-684 <$800
1902 Red Seal
3x10-20 1-245 <$850
1902 Date Back
3x10-20 1-1420* <$400
1902 Plain Back
3x10-20 1521-3044* <$400
* 1421-1520 not marked
1929 Small Size
5 Type 2 1-5712 <$175
10 Type 2 1-2640 <$175
20 Type 2 1-900 <$175
Total Issue $348,010
Out in 1935 $42,880
Large out 1935 $620

2408 Washington
BURGETTSTOWN NB, BURGETTSTOWN
{{ 6 L }}
Chartered 2/4/79
Receivership 5/14/25
Series 1875 <$VALUE
3x10-20 1-5653 <$750/$1250
Brown Back
3x10-20 1-5750 <$375
1882 Date Back
3x10-20 1-8500 <$375
1882 Value Back
3x10-20 8501-10928 <$375
1902 Plain Back
3x10-20 1-10138 <$175
Total Issue $1,623,450
Out at close $98,400

6944 Washington
WASHINGTON NB OF BURGETTSTOWN
{{ 6 L 12 S }}
Chartered 9/03
1902 Red Seal <$VALUE
3x10-20 1-3160 <$350
1902 Date Back
3x10-20 1-4600 <$175
1902 Plain Back
3x10-20 4601-14537 <$175
1929 Small Size
10 Type 1 1-1402 <$85
20 Type 1 1-426 <$85
10 Type 2 1-1687 <$100
20 Type 2 1-445 <$100
Total Issue $1,045,860
Out in 1935 $49,400
Large out 1935 $2,920

11257 Mifflin
FNB OF BURNHAM
{{ 2 L 4 S }}
Chartered 10/18
Receivership 1/10/34
1902 Plain Back <$VALUE
4x5 1-3963 <$350
4x10 1-1877 <$350
3x10-20 1-2087 <$350
1929 Small Size
5 Type 1 1-1130 <$225
10 Type 1 1-552 <$225
20 Type 1 1-160 <$225
5 Type 2 1-184 <$300
10 Type 2 1-130 <$300
20 Type 2 1-10 <$300
Total Issue $347,330
Out at close $25,000
Large out at close $950

11902 Clearfield
BURNSIDE NB, BURNSIDE
{{ 3 L 10 S }}
Organized 12/11/20
Receivership 6/26/34
1902 Plain Back <$VALUE
4x5 1-5570 <$300
3x10-20 1-4029 <$300
1929 Small Size
5 Type 1 1-1732 <$135
10 Type 1 1-1000 <$135
20 Type 1 1-302 <$135
5 Type 2 1-1678 <$165
10 Type 2 1-966 <$165
20 Type 2 1-72 <$175
Total Issue $480,540
Out at close $49,350
Large out at close $890

4374 Butler
BUTLER COUNTY NB OF BUTLER
Chartered 1890
2nd title: Butler County NB & TC 6/3/30
FIRST TITLE {{ 12 L 4 S }}
Brown Back <$VALUE
3x10-20 1-16150 <$300
1882 Date Back
3x10-20 1-4599 <$300
1902 Date Back
50-100 1-3000 <$300/$400
3x50-100 1-5580 <$300/$400
1902 Plain Back
3x50-100 5581-7156 <$300/$400
1929 Small Size
50 Type 1 1-716 <$135
100 Type 1 1-240 <$185
SECOND TITLE {{ 6 S }}
1929 Small Size
50 Type 1 1-517 <$135
100 Type 1 1-204 <$185
Total Issue $3,912,750
Out in 1935 $445,750
Large out 1935 $29,800

5391 Butler
FARMERS NB OF BUTLER
{{ 3 L }}
Chartered 6/2/00
Liquidated 7/15/27
Brown Back <$VALUE
50-100 1-2526 <$1500/$1750
1882 Date Back
50-100 1-800 <$1250/$1500
3x50-100 1-991 <$1250/$1500
1902 Plain Back
3x50-100 1-1039 <$500/$650
Total Issue $1,006,400
Out at close $96,250

309 Butler
FNB OF BUTLER
{{ UNREPORTED }}
Organized 3/11/64
Receivership 7/23/79
Original Series <$VALUE
4x5 1-3000 <$1250
3x10-20 1-1100 <$1500/$2000
50-100 1-400 <$4000
Series 1875
3x10-20 1-226 <$1500/$2000
50-100 1-197 <$4000
Total Issue $215,850
Out in 1916 $1,525

9814 Butler
MERCHANTS NB OF BUTLER
{{ 3 L }}
Chartered 7/10
Liquidated 8/18/27
1902 Date Back <$VALUE
50-100 1-1167 <$500/$650
3x50-100 1-2036 <$500/$650
1902 Plain Back
3x50-100 2037-2163 <$500/$650
Total Issue $715,800
Out at close $87,750

10704 Somerset
FNB OF CAIRNBROOK
{{ 2 L 3 S }}
Chartered 2/15
Receivership 9/23/32
1902 Plain Back <$VALUE
3x10-20 1-5669 <$650
1929 Small Size
10 Type 1 1-676 <$300
20 Type 1 1-159 <$300
Total Issue $343,090
Out at close $24,460
Large out at close $1,440

4622 Washington
FNB OF CALIFORNIA
{{ 8 L 9 S }}
Organized 8/6/91
Brown Back <$VALUE
3x10-20 1-6270 <$400
1882 Date Back
3x10-20 1-987 <$400
1902 Date Back
4x5 1-3500 <$175
3x50-100 1-410 <$175
1902 Plain Back
4x5 3501-30280 <$175
1929 Small Size
5 Type 1 1-7302 <$125
5 Type 2 1-14076 <$125
Total Issue $1,360,390
Out in 1935 $47,540
Large out 1935 $2,840

6533 Crawford
FNB OF CAMBRIDGE SPRINGS
{{ 3 L }}
Chartered 12/15/02
Closed 12/15/28
1902 Red Seal <$VALUE
3x10-20 1-3100 <$500
1902 Date Back
4x5 1-3200 <$250
3x10-20 1-2860 <$250
1902 Plain Back
4x5 3201-16032 <$250
3x10-20 2861-10399 <$250
Total Issue $995,590
Out at close $70,850
Ch 9430 assumed circulation

Springs-FNB of Cambridge Springs
SEE Ch 9430
Springs NB of Cambridge Springs

9430 Crawford
SPRINGS NB OF CAMBRIDGE SPRINGS
Chartered 6/09
Liquidated 4/27/34
2nd title: Springs-FNB of Cambridge Springs 12/15/28
FIRST TITLE {{ 4 L }}
1902 Date Back <$VALUE
4x5 1-4200 <$250
3x10-20 1-3140 <$250
1902 Plain Back
4x5 4201-12902 <$250
3x10-20 3141-8735 <$250
SECOND TITLE {{ 2 L 10 S }}
1902 Plain Back
4x5 1-512 <$300
3x10-20 1-198 <$300
3x50-100 1-58 <$500/$600
1929 Small Size
5 Type 1 1-2256 <$125
10 Type 1 1-1003 <$125
20 Type 1 1-301 <$150
50 Type 1 1-142 <$200
100 Type 1 1-44 <$300
Total Issue $962,410
Out in 1935 $63,850
Large out 1935 $4,710
Outstanding includes Ch 6533
Ch 14029 assumed circulation

12380 Cumberland
CAMP HILL NB, CAMP HILL
{{ 4 L 10 S }}
Chartered 5/23
1902 Plain Back <$VALUE
4x5 1-6482 <$275
3x10-20 1-3517 <$275
1929 Small Size
5 Type 1 1-1826 <$125
10 Type 1 1-1016 <$125
20 Type 1 1-304 <$125
5 Type 2 1-2864 <$150
10 Type 2 1-1585 <$150
20 Type 2 1-628 <$150
Total Issue $500,440
Out in 1935 $49,650
Large out 1935 $1,150

13813 Washington
FNB AT CANONSBURG
{{ 2 U + 7 S }}
Chartered 10/33
1929 Small Size <$VALUE
10 Type 2 1-7368 <$150
20 Type 2 1-2508 <$150
Total Issue $123,840
Out in 1935 $94,490

4570 Washington
FNB OF CANONSBURG
{{ 6 L 12 S }}
Organized 4/1/91
Receivership 12/19/33
Brown Back <$VALUE
3x10-20 1-6590 <$375
1882 Date Back
3x10-20 1-2626 <$375
1902 Date Back
3x10-20 1-7000 <$175
1902 Plain Back
3x10-20 7001-24945 <$175
1929 Small Size
10 Type 1 1-2838 <$85
20 Type 1 1-838 <$90
10 Type 2 1-595 <$125
20 Type 2 1-95 <$150
Total Issue $1,986,740
Out at close $100,000
Large out at close $5,490

9317 Bradford
FARMERS NB OF CANTON
{{ 4 L 5 S }}
Chartered 1/09
Liquidated 11/1/32
1902 Date Back <$VALUE
4x5 1-4925 <$225
3x10-20 1-3720 <$225
1902 Plain Back
4x5 4926-14049 <$225
3x10-20 3721-9581 <$225
1929 Small Size
5 Type 1 1-1579 <$175
10 Type 1 1-750 <$175
20 Type 1 1-186 <$175
Total Issue $874,720
Out at close $39,920
Large out at close $3,360
Ch 2505 assumed circulation

2505 Bradford
FNB OF CANTON
{{ 10 L 19 S }}
Chartered 2/16/81
Series 1875 <$VALUE
4x5 1-13382 <$450
50-100 1-274 <$3500
Brown Back
4x5 1-1700 <$275
50-100 1-630 <$1250/$1500
1882 Date Back
3x10-20 1-9000 <$250
50-100 1-172 <$1250/$1500
1882 Value Back
3x10-20 9001-13287 <$250
1902 Plain Back
3x10-20 1-12474 <$135
1929 Small Size
10 Type 1 1-3442 <$60
20 Type 1 1-884 <$70
10 Type 2 1-6703 <$70
20 Type 2 1-1859 <$70
Total Issue $2,218,900
Out in 1935 $144,500
Large out 1935 $5,880
Outstanding includes Ch 9317

664 Lackawanna
FNB OF CARBONDALE
{{ 10 L 16 S }}
Organized 12/14/64
Original Series <$VALUE
4x5 1-4250 <$375
3x10-20 1-2100 <$750/$1250
Series 1875
4x5 1-4850 <$375
3x10-20 1-1914 <$750/$1250
Brown Back
4x5 1-10500 <$225
3x10-20 1-6804 <$225/$250
1902 Red Seal
3x10-20 1-3500 <$275
1902 Date Back
3x10-20 1-14800 <$135
1902 Plain Back
3x10-20 14801-18661 <$135
1929 Small Size
10 Type 2 1-17993 <$60
20 Type 2 1-1836 <$65
Total Issue $2,257,600
Out in 1935 $110,010
Large out 1935 $4,910

21 Cumberland
FNB OF CARLISLE
{{ UNREPORTED }}
Organized 7/7/63
Receivership 10/24/73
Original Series <$VALUE
4x5 1-1420 <$1500
4x10 1-955 <$1750
Total Issue $66,600
Out in 1910 $415

4444 Cumberland
MERCHANTS NB OF CARLISLE
{{ 2 L }}
Chartered 1890
Liquidated 2/1/12
Brown Back <$VALUE
4x5 1-11015 <$600
3x10-20 1-7294 <$600
1882 Date Back
4x5 1-1406 <$600
3x10-20 1-1185 <$600
1902 Date Back
4x5 1-1395 <$375
3x10-20 1-1142 <$375
Total Issue $757,370
Out in 1912 $44,435

5784 Greene
FNB OF CARMICHAELS
{{ 5 L 9 S }}
Chartered 4/19/01
Brown Back <$VALUE
3x10-20 1-920 <$400
1882 Date Back
3x10-20 1-1100* <$400
1882 Value Back
3x10-20 1511-3210* <$400
* 1101-1510 not marked
1902 Plain Back
3x10-20 1-7468 <$225
1929 Small Size
10 Type 1 1-1550 <$110
20 Type 1 1-426 <$125
10 Type 2 1-1512 <$150
20 Type 2 1-345 <$150
Total Issue $746,040
Out in 1935 $43,100
Large out 1935 $2,110

6174 Allegheny
CARNEGIE NB, CARNEGIE
{{ 8 L 16 S }}
Chartered 3/27/02
1902 Red Seal <$VALUE
3x10-20 1-3140 <$350
1902 Date Back
3x10-20 1-10200 <$165
1902 Plain Back (dated 1902)
3x10-20 10201-17900 <$165
1902 Plain Back (dated 1922)
3x10-20 1-11224 <$165
1929 Small Size
10 Type 1 1-3146 <$60
20 Type 1 1-824 <$65
10 Type 2 1-2394 <$75
20 Type 2 1-715 <$75
Total Issue $1,939,080
Out in 1935 $85,550
Large out 1935 $5,910

FNB of Carnegie
SEE Ch 4762
FNB of Chartiers

12934 Allegheny
UNION NB OF CARNEGIE
{{ 4 L 15 S }}
Chartered 5/26
1902 Plain Back <$VALUE
4x5 1-18924 <$225
1929 Small Size
5 Type 1 1-14674 <$65
5 Type 2 1-13328 <$75
Total Issue $885,340
Out in 1935 $51,170
Large out 1935 $1,170

CONDITION affects Value. The Values shown are for notes in FINE condition.

****
5855 Cambria
FNB OF CARROLLTOWN
{{ 6 L 10 S }}
Chartered 6/10/01
Brown Back <$VALUE
4x5 1-3905 <$375
3x10-20 1-3018 <$375
1882 Date Back
4x5 1-4725 <$350
3x10-20 1-3060 <$350
1882 Value Back
4x5 4726-7980 <$350
3x10-20 3061-5011 <$350
1902 Plain Back
4x5 1-6528 <$225
3x10-20 1-4790 <$225
1929 Small Size
5 Type 1 1-2046 <$100
10 Type 1 1-982 <$100
20 Type 1 1-276 <$100
5 Type 2 1-1926 <$125
10 Type 2 1-1243 <$125
20 Type 2 1-413 <$125
Total Issue $1,192,950
Out in 1935 $48,950
Large out 1935 $2,930
****
12720 Cambria
FNB OF CASSANDRA
{{ 2 L 6 S }}
Chartered 5/25
Liquidated 6/10/32
1902 Plain Back <$VALUE
3x10-20 1-4641 <$400
1929 Small Size
10 Type 1 1-1191 <$165
20 Type 1 1-319 <$175
Total Issue $341,790
Out at close $44,730
Large out at close $3,050
****
9128 Allegheny
FNB OF CASTLE SHANNON
{{ 2 L 2 S }}
Chartered 5/08
1902 Date Back <$VALUE
4x5 1-770 <$1500
3x10-20 1-617 <$1500
1902 Plain Back
4x5 771-1505 <$1500
3x10-20 618-1047 <$1500
1929 Small Size
5 Type 1 1-324 <$1000
10 Type 1 1-171 <$1000
20 Type 1 1-51 <$1000
Total Issue $108,550
Out in 1935 $6,400
Large out 1935 $250
****
8283 Lehigh
LEHIGH NB OF CATASAUQUA
{{ 3 L 14 S }}
Chartered 6/06
1902 Red Seal <$VALUE
3x10-20 1-3900 <$400
1902 Date Back
3x10-20 1-1800 <$200
1902 Plain Back
3x10-20 1801-7694 <$200
1929 Small Size
5 Type 1 1-2696 <$85
10 Type 1 1-414 <$85
20 Type 1 1-148 <$100
5 Type 2 1-19465 <$85
10 Type 2 1-3883 <$85
20 Type 2 1-1305 <$100
Total Issue $865,435
Out in 1935 $100,850
Large out 1935 $1,560
****
1411 Lehigh
NB OF CATASAQUA
{{ 18 L 27 S }}
Chartered 1865
Original Series <$VALUE
3x1-2 1-1000 <$350/$1000
4x5 1-7250 <$375
3x10-20 1-10695<$750/$1250
Series 1875
4x5 1-3750 <$375
3x10-20 1-13241<$750/$1250
Brown Back
4x5 1-10500 <$200
3x10-20 1-33812 <$200/$225
1902 Red Seal
4x5 1-12250 <$225
3x10-20 1-10600 <$225
1902 Date Back
4x5 1-26500 <$110
3x10-20 1-21600 <$110
1902 Plain Back
4x5 26501-59990 <$110
3x10-20 21601-41856 <$110

1929 Small Size
5 Type 1 1-1328 <$60
10 Type 1 1-630 <$60
20 Type 1 1-190 <$65
5 Type 2 1-8998 <$50
10 Type 2 1-4354 <$40
20 Type 2 1-12590 <$40
Total Issue $7,830,770
Out in 1935 $214,600
Large out 1935 $15,785
****
7448 Columbia
CATAWISSA NB, CATAWISSA
{{ 5 L 6 S }}
Chartered 10/04
1902 Red Seal <$VALUE
4x5 1-1580 <$350
3x10-20 1-1208 <$350
1902 Date Back
4x5 1-4800 <$175
3x10-20 1-3260 <$175
1902 Plain Back
4x5 4801-11250 <$175
3x10-20 3261-7008 <$175
1929 Small Size
5 Type 2 1-5370 <$150
10 Type 2 1-2695 <$150
20 Type 2 1-1370 <$150
Total Issue $748,600
Out in 1935 $13,120
Large out 1935 $1,910
****
4548 Columbia
FNB OF CATAWISSA
{{ 7 L 11 S }}
Chartered 1891
Brown Back <$VALUE
4x5 1-12465 <$250
3x10-20 1-2574 <$250
1882 Date Back
4x5 1-1350 <$250
3x10-20 1-1049 <$250
1902 Date Back
4x5 1-2650 <$150
3x10-20 1-2120 <$150
1902 Plain Back
4x5 2651-12370 <$150
3x10-20 2121-8677 <$150
1929 Small Size
5 Type 1 1-2004 <$100
10 Type 1 1-974 <$100
20 Type 1 1-284 <$100
5 Type 2 1-3540 <$100
10 Type 2 1-1596 <$100
20 Type 2 1-396 <$100
Total Issue $1,332,920
Out in 1935 $48,560
Large out 1935 $3,415
****
14094 Washington
FNB IN CECIL
{{ U + 8 S }}
Chartered 4/34
1929 Small Size <$VALUE
10 Type 2 1-690 <$250
20 Type 2 1-192 <$250
Total Issue $10,740
Out in 1935 $25,000
Large out 1935 $1,140
Outstanding includes Ch 7076
****
7076 Washington
FNB OF CECIL
{{ 3 L U + 5 S }}
Chartered 12/03
Liquidated 5/19/34
1902 Red Seal <$VALUE
3x10-20 1-1557 <$750
1902 Date Back
3x10-20 1-2410 <$375
1902 Plain Back
3x10-20 2411-7435 <$375
1929 Small Size
10 Type 1 1-834 <$175
20 Type 1 1-200 <$175
10 Type 2 1-48 <$225
20 Type 2 1-15 <$225
Total Issue $524,420
Out at close $25,000
Large out 1935 $1,140
Ch 14094 assumed circulation
****
11967 Somerset
CENTRAL CITY NB,
CENTRAL CITY
{{ 3 L 10 S }}
Organized 4/21
1902 Plain Back <$VALUE
3x10-20 1-8113 <$275
1929 Small Sie
10 Type 1 1-1702 <$100
20 Type 1 1-410 <$110
10 Type 2 1-1758 <$125
20 Type 2 1-396 <$125
Total Issue $582,470
Out in 1935 $50,000
Large out 1935 $1,120
****

****
9568 Columbia
FNB OF CENTRALIA
{{ 3 L 5 S }}
Chartered 10/09
1902 Date Back <$VALUE
3x10-20 1-2760 <$275
1902 Plain Back
3x10-20 2761-8068 <$275
1929 Small Size
10 Type 1 1-836 <$165
20 Type 1 1-214 <$175
10 Type 2 1-1184 <$200
20 Type 2 1-313 <$200
Total Issue $497,340
Out in 1935 $22,000
Large out 1935 $1,220
****
12192 Centre
FNB OF CENTRE HALL
{{ 2 L 5 S }}
Chartered 5/22
1902 Plain Back <$VALUE
4x5 1-3320 <$350
3x10-20 1-2111 <$350
1929 Small Size
5 Type 1 1-1104 <$175
10 Type 1 1-528 <$175
20 Type 1 1-138 <$175
5 Type 2 1-1280 <$200
10 Type 2 1-805 <$200
20 Type 2 1-262 <$200
Total Issue $273,000
Out in 1935 $24,800
Large out 1935 $680
****
12582 Bucks
CHALFONT NB, CHALFONT
{{ 10 S }}
Chartered 9/24
1929 Small Size <$VALUE
5 Type 2 1-6766 <$125
10 Type 2 1-3792 <$125
Total Issue $71,750
Out in 1935 $50,000
****
4272 Franklin
VALLEY NB OF CHAMBERSBURG
{{ 12 L 24 S }}
Chartered 1890
Brown Back <$VALUE
4x5 1-9100 <$275
3x10-20 1-5320 <$275
1882 Date Back
4x5 1-1246 <$275
3x10-20 1-505 <$275
1902 Date Back
4x5 1-6100 <$110
3x10-20 1-4720 <$110
1902 Plain Back
4x5 6101-23973 <$110
3x10-20 4721-16275 <$110
1929 Small Size
5 Type 1 1-8872 <$40
10 Type 1 1-4218 <$40
20 Type 1 1-1080 <$50
5 Type 2 1-9954 <$45
10 Type 2 1-5628 <$45
20 Type 2 1-1545 <$50
Total Issue $2,577,170
Out in 1935 $197,450
Large out 1935 $5,025
****
593 Franklin
NB OF CHAMBERSBURGH
{{ 13 L 27 S }}
Chartered 11/64
Original Series <$VALUE
4x5 1-9250 <$375
3x10-20 1-6100 <$750/$1250
Series 1875
4x5 1-2500 <$375
3x10-20 1-5700 <$750/$1250
Brown Back
4x5 1-1243 <$250
3x10-20 1-7015 <$250
1902 Red Seal
3x10-20 1-3400 <$275
1902 Date Back
3x10-20 1-4900 <$110
1902 Plain Back
3x10-20 4901-29830 <$110
1929 Small Size
5 Type 1 1-8850 <$25
10 Type 1 1-7168 <$25
20 Type 1 1-1846 <$35
5 Type 2 1-21264 <$25
10 Type 2 1-12238 <$25
20 Type 2 1-3702 <$35
Total Issue $4,082,550
Out in 1935 $344,200
Large out 1935 $4,225
****

****
14123 Washington
FNB IN CHARLEROI
{{ 4 S }}
Chartered 4/34
1929 Small Size <$VALUE
5 Type 2 1-4980 <$250
10 Type 2 1-2256 <$250
20 Type 2 1-768 <$250
Total Issue $62,820
Out in 1935 $45,270
****
4534 Washington
FNB OF CHARLEROI
{{ 6 L 11 S }}
Organized 3/12/91
Receivership 5/22/34
Brown Back <$VALUE
3x10-20 1-1870 <$400
1882 Date Back
3x10-20 1-494 <$400
1902 Date Back
3x10-20 1-3400 <$200
1902 Plain Back
3x10-20 3401-11464 <$200
1929 Small Size
10 Type 1 1-1376 <$100
20 Type 1 1-388 <$125
10 Type 2 1-130 <$150
20 Type 2 1-55 <$150
Total Issue $822,920
Out at close $50,000
Large out at close $2,630
****
13585 Washington
NB OF CHARLEROI & TC
{{ 3U + 14 S }}
Chartered 12/31 as NB of Charleroi, under which there was no issue. Issuing title adopted 4/8/32.
1929 Small Size <$VALUE
5 Type 1 1-2474 <$75
10 Type 1 1-1208 <$75
20 Type 1 1-444 <$75
5 Type 2 1-11626 <$85
10 Type 2 1-6370 <$85
20 Type 2 1-1285 <$85
Total Issue $347,510
Out in 1935 $121,700
****
4762 Allegheny
FNB OF CHARTIERS
Organized 5/16/92
Receivership 5/12/25
2nd title: FNB of Carnegie 4/94
FIRST TITLE {{ 1 L }}
Brown Back <$VALUE
4x5 1-775 <$1000
SECOND TITLE {{ 5 L }}
Brown Back
4x5 1-1925 <$450
3x10-20 1-760 <$450
1882 Date Back
4x5 1-509 <$450
3x10-20 1-395 <$450
1902 Date Back
4x5 1-4475 <$200
3x10-20 1-3380 <$200
1902 Plain Back
4x5 4476-17940 <$200
3x10-20 3381-11644 <$200
Total Issue $1,062,930
Out at close $95,000
****
12526 Montgomery
CHELTENHAM NB, CHELTENHAM
{{ 3 L 10 S }}
Chartered 4/24
1902 Plain Back <$VALUE
4x5 1-13947 <$400
1929 Small Size
5 Type 1 1-7434 <$150
5 Type 2 1-15888 <$150
Total Issue $581,400
Out in 1935 $44,740
Large out 1935 $820
****
7000 Indiana
FNB OF CHERRY TREE
{{ 4 L 2U + 20 S }}
Chartered 10/03
Receivership 10/13/33
1902 Red Seal <$VALUE
4x5 1-2530 <$650
3x10-20 1-2094 <$650
1902 Date Back
4x5 1-4750 <$325
3x10-20 1-3340 <$325
1902 Plain Back
4x5 4751-15824 <$325
3x10-20 3341-10421 <$325

1929 Small Size
5 Type 1 1-3834 <$100
10 Type 1 1-1970 <$100
20 Type 1 1-548 <$100
5 Type 2 1-192 <$125
10 Type 2 1-90 <$135
20 Type 2 1-90 <$135
Total Issue $1,295,470
Out at close $98,020
Large out at close $3,210
****
2904 Delaware
CHESTER NB, CHESTER
{{ 11 L 6 S }}
Chartered 1883
Liquidated 10/4/30
Brown Back <$VALUE
4x5 1-4695 <$350
3x10-20 1-2053 <$350
50-100 1-2714 <$1750/$2000
1902 Red Seal
4x5 1-19750 <$350
3x10-20 1-12300 <$350
50-100 1-100 <$2250/$2500
1902 Date Back
4x5 1-28250 <$150
3x10-20 1-18900 <$150
50-100 1-200 <$500/$600
3x50-100 1-400 <$500/$600
1902 Plain Back
4x5 28251-97345 <$150
3x10-20 18901-61465 <$150
1929 Small Size
5 Type 1 1-4903 <$150
10 Type 1 1-2528 <$150
20 Type 1 1-730 <$150
Total Issue $7,165,170
Out at close $279,780
Large out at close $29,580
****
355 Delaware
DELAWARE COUNTY NB OF CHESTER
{{ 23 L 50+ S }}
Chartered 3/64
Original Series <$VALUE
4x5 1-2600 <$400
3x10-20 1-2100 <$750/$1250
50-100 1-1770 <$3500
Series 1875
50-100 1-1766 <$3500
Brown Back
3x10-20 1-13933 <$275
50-100 1-3267 <$1250/$1500
1902 Red Seal
4x5 1-9000 <$275
3x10-20 1-15000 <$275
1902 Date Back
4x5 1-27000* <$100
3x10-20 1-18000** <$100
1902 Plain Back
4x5 28001-132703* <$100
3x10-20 18801-82103**<$100
* 27001-28000 not marked
** 18001-18800 not marked
1929 Small Size
5 Type 1 1-37534 <$20
10 Type 1 1-18318 <$25
20 Type 1 1-5140 <$35
5 Type 2 1-42382 <$25
10 Type 2 1-26916 <$25
20 Type 2 1-9044 <$35
Total Issue $13,067,160
Out in 1935 $726,900
Large out 1935 $18,175
Outstanding includes Ch 6654
****
332 Delaware
FNB OF CHESTER
{{ 16 L U + 23 S }}
Chartered 3/64
Original Series <$VALUE
4x5 1-3000 <$500
3x10-20 1-2720 <$750/$1250
Series 1875
3x10-20 1-1943 <$750/$1250
Brown Back
50-100 1-2219 <$1250/$1500
1902 Red Seal
3x10-20 1-4765 <$150
50-100 1-2795 <$2250/$2500
1902 Date Back
3x10-20 1-15000 <$150
50-100 1-700 <$500/$600
1902 Plain Back
3x10-20 15001-55205 <$150
1929 Small Size
10 Type 1 1-6664 <$40
20 Type 1 1-1890 <$50
10 Type 2 1-8146 <$40
20 Type 2 1-2108 <$50
Total Issue $4,899,010
Out in 1935 $164,870
Large out 1935 $9,950
****

****
6654 Delaware
PENNSYLVANIA NB OF CHESTER
{{ 9 L }}
Chartered 3/03
Closed 7/24/28
1902 Red Seal <$VALUE
4x5 1-5750 <$400
3x10-20 1-5400 <$400
1902 Date Back
4x5 1-9100 <$200
3x10-20 1-6860 <$200
1902 Plain Back
4x5 9101-34925 <$200
3x10-20 6861-22738 <$200
Total Issue $2,220,400
Out at close $145,195
Ch 355 assumed circulation
****
7078 Lancaster
CHRISTIANA NB, CHRISTIANA
{{ 6 L 14 S }}
Chartered 12/03
1902 Red Seal <$VALUE
3x10-20 1-3975 <$750
1902 Date Back
3x10-20 1-5400 <$350
1902 Plain Back
3x10-20 5401-16973 <$350
1929 Small Size
10 Type 1 1-1776 <$135
20 Type 1 1-502 <$150
10 Type 2 1-2821 <$175
20 Type 2 1-694 <$175
Total Issue $1,256,290
Out in 1935 $58,150
Large out 1935 $2,450
****
2849 Lancaster
NB OF CHRISTIANA
{{ UNREPORTED }}
Organized 12/28/82
Liquidated 1/12/04
Brown Back <$VALUE
3x10-20 1-3261 <$1500
1902 Red Seal
3x10-20 1-98 <$1500
Total Issue $167,950
Out in 1910 $1,580
****
6495 Allegheny
CLAIRTON NB, CLAIRTON
{{ 4 L }}
Chartered 11/19/02
Liquidated 2/17/10
1902 Red Seal <$VALUE
4x5 1-1100 <$500
3x10-20 1-870 <$500
1902 Date Back
4x5 1-290 <$350
3x10-20 1-196 <$350
Total Issue $81,100
Out in 1910 $11,980
****
FNB of Clairton
SEE Ch 6794
FNB of Wilson
****
774 Clarion
FNB OF CLARION
{{ 10 L 12 S }}
Chartered 2/1/65
Receivership 4/16/34
Original Series <$VALUE
3x1-2 1-1800 <$350/$1000
4x5 1-3000 <$400
3x10-20 1-2120 <$750/$1250
Series 1875
3x1-2 1-220 <$350/$1000
4x5 1-1430 <$400
3x10-20 1-1650 <$750/$1250
Brown Back
4x5 1-1700 <$275
3x10-20 1-2160 <$275
50-100 1-2112 <$1250/$1500
1902 Red Seal
3x10-20 1-3000 <$300
50-100 1-300 <$2250/$2500
1902 Date Back
3x10-20 1-6700 <$125
50-100 1-200 <$400/$500
1902 Plain Back
3x10-20 6701-21502 <$125
1929 Small Size
10 Type 1 1-2428 <$75
20 Type 1 1-732 <$85
10 Type 2 1-1180 <$110
20 Type 2 1-200 <$125
Total Issue $2,295,420
Out at close $100,000
Large out at close $8,680
****

****
3044 Clarion
SECOND NB OF CLARION
{{ UNREPORTED }}
Organized 9/12/83
Receivership 6/21/12
Brown Back <$VALUE
4x5 1-1135 <$1000
3x10-20 1-2106 <$1000
50-100 1-702 <$1250/$1500
1902 Red Seal
3x10-20 1-641 <$1000
50-100 1-570 <$2250/$2500
1902 Date Back
50-100 1-240 <$850
3x50-100 1-95 <$850
Total Issue $410,600
Out in 1916 $11,015
****
10383 Lackawanna
ABINGTON NB OF
CLARKS SUMMIT
{{ 4 L 10 S }}
Chartered 5/13
1902 Date Back <$VALUE
3x10-20 1-1300 <$375
1902 Plain Back
3x10-20 1301-9728 <$375
1929 Small Size
10 Type 1 1-1678 <$150
20 Type 1 1-508 <$150
10 Type 2 1-2929 <$175
20 Type 2 1-840 <$175
Total Issue $694,130
Out in 1935 $48,800
Large out 1935 $1,320
****
10232 Blair
FNB OF CLAYSBURG
{{ 2 L 11 S }}
Chartered 7/12
1902 Date Back <$VALUE
3x10-20 1-1500 <$300
1902 Plain Back
3x10-20 1501-6417 <$300
1929 Small Size
10 Type 1 1-1432 <$100
20 Type 1 1-412 <$125
10 Type 2 1-2094 <$125
20 Type 2 1-737 <$125
Total Issue $491,890
Out in 1935 $58,750
Large out 1935 $970
****
9307 Washington
FARMERS NB OF CLAYSVILLE
{{ 6 L 11 S }}
Chartered 1/09
1902 Date Back <$VALUE
3x10-20 1-4900 <$175
1902 Plain Back
3x10-20 4901-13751 <$175
1929 Small Size
10 Type 1 1-1448 <$110
20 Type 1 1-396 <$125
10 Type 2 1-345 <$175
20 Type 2 1-89 <$175
Total Issue $827,180
Out in 1935 $29,710
Large out 1935 $2,160
****
4273 Washington
FNB OF CLAYSVILLE
{{ 1 L }}
Organized 3/27/90
Receivership 10/11/04
Brown Back <$VALUE
3x10-20 1-2821 <$850
Total Issue $141,050
Out in 1916 $1,030
****
4255 Washington
NB OF CLAYSVILLE
{{ 7 L 12 S }}
Chartered 1890
Brown Back <$VALUE
4x5 1-1085 <$350
3x10-20 1-1379 <$350
1902 Date Back
4x5 1-3050 <$175
3x10-20 1-2380 <$175
1902 Plain Back
4x5 3051-12640 <$175
3x10-20 2381-8399 <$175
1929 Small Size
5 Type 1 1-2016 <$100
10 Type 1 1-938 <$100
20 Type 1 1-264 <$100
5 Type 2 1-1684 <$100
10 Type 2 1-1069 <$100
20 Type 2 1-307 <$110
Total Issue $937,090
Out in 1935 $49,300
Large out 1935 $2,640
****

****
4836 Clearfield
CLEARFIELD NB, CLEARFIELD
{{ 9 L 13 S }}
Organized 12/20/92
Receivership 7/18/32
Brown Back <$VALUE
4x5 1-10750 <$275
3x10-20 1-9900 <$275
1882 Date Back
4x5 1-5634 <$275
3x10-20 1-8717 <$275
1902 Date Back
4x5 1-5000 <$125
3x10-20 1-7000 <$125
1902 Plain Back
3x10-20 7001-42612 <$125
1929 Small Size
10 Type 1 1-4420 <$60
20 Type 1 1-1378 <$65
Total Issue $3,919,690
Out at close $197,600
Large out at close $17,900
****
13998 Clearfield
COUNTY NB AT CLEARFIELD
{{ 2U + 16 S }}
Chartered 2/34
1929 Small Size <$VALUE
5 Type 2 1-4712 <$50
10 Type 2 1-4696 <$50
20 Type 2 1-4709 <$50
Total Issue $164,700
Out in 1935 $131,000
****
855 Clearfield
COUNTY NB OF CLEARFIELD
{{ 26 L 50+ S }}
Chartered 3/2/65
Receivership 2/26/34
Original Series <$VALUE
4x5 1-2500 <$350
3x10-20 1-1500 <$750/$1250
Series 1875
4x5 1-1248 <$350
3x10-20 1-1458 <$750/$1250
50-100 1-189 <$3500
Brown Back
4x5 1-8070 <$200
50-100 1-3850 <$1250/$1500
1902 Red Seal
4x5 1-12750 <$200
3x10-20 1-7700 <$200
1902 Date Back
4x5 1-35000 <$85
3x10-20 1-29500 <$85
1902 Plain Back
4x5 35001-56000 <$85
3x10-20 29501-117750 <$85
1929 Small Size
10 Type 1 1-14340 <$25
20 Type 1 1-4018 <$35
10 Type 2 1-6848 <$25
20 Type 2 1-1089 <$35
Total Issue $10,070,430
Out at close $495,235
Large out at close $30,585
****
8464 Clearfield
FARMERS & TRADERS NB OF
CLEARFIELD
{{ 1 L }}
Chartered 12/06
Liquidated 11/11/12
1902 Red Seal <$VALUE
4x5 1-2980 <$850
4x10 1-3010 <$850
1902 Date Back
4x5 1-5146 <$600
4x10 1-5074 <$600
Total Issue $485,880
Out in 1913 $32,310
****
768 Clearfield
FNB OF CLEARFIELD
{{ 6 L }}
Chartered 1/30/65
Receivership 10/7/91
Original Series <$VALUE
3x1-2 1-6766 <$400/$1000
4x5 1-3400 <$450
3x10-20 1-1740 <$750/$1250
Series 1875
4x5 1-2315 <$450
3x10-20 1-2076 <$750/$1250
Brown Back
4x5 1-2792 <$350
3x10-20 1-2361 <$350
Total Issue $512,820
Out in 1916 $2,666
****

****
14122 Delaware
CLIFTON HEIGHTS NB,
CLIFTON HEIGHTS
{{ 4 S }}
1929 Small Size <$VALUE
5 Type 2 1-14520 <$350
Total Issue $72,600
Out in 1935 $48,750
****
6275 Delaware
FNB OF CLIFTON HEIGHTS
{{ 6 L 9 S }}
Chartered 5/26/02
Receivership 5/22/34
1902 Red Seal <$VALUE
3x10-20 1-3900 <$450
1902 Date Back
3x10-20 1-5000 <$225
1902 Plain Back (dated 1902)
3x10-20 5001-9260 <$225
1902 Plain Back (dated 1922)
3x10-20 1-3720 <$225
1929 Small Size
10 Type 1 1-1296 <$125
20 Type 1 1-308 <$135
10 Type 2 1-811 <$150
20 Type 2 1-265 <$150
Total Issue $972,130
Out at close $49,150
Large out at close $2,210
****
6948 Venango
FNB OF CLINTONVILLE
{{ 1 L }}
Chartered 9/03
Receivership 4/24/08
1902 Red Seal <$VALUE
3x10-20 1-836 <$1250
Total Issue $41,800
Out in 1916 $410
****
9154 Venango
PEOPLES NB OF
CLINTONVILLE
{{ 2 L 6 S }}
Chartered 6/08
1902 Date Back <$VALUE
3x10-20 1-2280 <$400
1902 Plain Back
3x10-20 2281-6709 <$400
1929 Small Size
10 Type 1 1-738 <$165
20 Type 1 1-182 <$165
10 Type 2 1-963 <$175
20 Type 2 1-256 <$175
Total Issue $416,320
Out in 1935 $24,350
Large out 1935 $700
****
9898 Indiana
CLYMER NB, CLYMER
{{ 3 L 2 S }}
Chartered 12/10
Receivership 8/22/30
1902 Date Back <$VALUE
3x10-20 1-2055* <$350
1902 Plain Back
3x10-20 2156-13052* <$350
* 2056-2155 not marked
1929 Small Size
10 Type 1 1-906 <$350
20 Type 1 1-188 <$350
Total Issue $729,520
Out at close $75,000
Large out at close $10,630
****
11188 Schuylkill
BROAD TOP NB OF COALDALE
Chartered 6/18
Receivership 10/26/34
2nd title: Farmers NB
of Bedford 10/21/25
3rd title: Farmers NB & TC
of Bedford 7/25/27
FIRST TITLE {{ 2 L }}
1902 Plain Back <$VALUE
3x10-20 1-3040 <$500
SECOND TITLE {{ 3 L }}
1902 Plain Back
3x10-20 1-2979 <$225
THIRD TITLE {{ 4 L 16 S }}
1902 Plain Back
3x10-20 1-4850 <$200
1929 Small Size
10 Type 1 1-4614 <$60
20 Type 1 1-1256 <$65
10 Type 2 1-3332 <$65
20 Type 2 1-1060 <$70
Total Issue $1,025,530
Out at close $150,000
Large out at close $2,930
****

****
9739 Schuylkill
FNB OF COALDALE
{{ 4 L 12 S }}
Chartered 4/10
1902 Date Back <$VALUE
3x10-20 1-2460 <$350
1902 Plain Back
3x10-20 2461-7791 <$350
1929 Small Size
10 Type 1 1-774 <$135
20 Type 1 1-220 <$150
10 Type 2 1-2465 <$175
20 Type 2 1-760 <$175
Total Issue $502,240
Out in 1935 $36,850
Large out 1935 $1,000
****
6887 Clearfield
FNB OF COALPORT
{{ 10 L 4 S }}
Chartered 7/03
1902 Red Seal <$VALUE
3x10-20 1-2640 <$350
1902 Date Back
3x10-20 1-600 <$175
1902 Plain Back
3x10-20 601-3969 <$175
1929 Small Size
10 Type 1 1-584 <$175
20 Type 1 1-150 <$175
10 Type 2 1-473 <$200
20 Type 2 1-132 <$200
Total Issue $390,860
Out in 1935 $20,000
Large out 1935 $1,870
****
3990 Chester
NB OF COATESVILLE
{{ 4 L 3 S }}
Chartered 3/13/89
Brown Back <$VALUE
50-100 1-3535 <$1750/$2000
1902 Date Back
50-100 1-1000 <$750/$850
3x50-100 1-2200 <$750/$850
1902 Plain Back
3x50-100 2201-2758 <$750/$850
1929 Small Size
50 Type 1 1-312 <$400
100 Type 1 1-104 <$600
50 Type 2 1-67 <$750
100 Type 2 1-24 <$1000
Total Issue $1,531,500
Out in 1935 $99,200
Large out 1935 $8,700
****
575 Chester
NB OF CHESTER VALLEY,
COATESVILLE
{{ 8 L }}
Chartered 11/64
Original Series <$VALUE
4x5 1-4000 <$750
3x10-20 1-5150 <$1000/$1500
Series 1875
3x10-20 1-2968 <$1000/$1500
Brown Back
3x10-20 1-5771 <$500
1902 Red Seal
3x10-20 1-5300 <$600
1902 Date Back
3x10-20 1-21100 <$300
1902 Plain Back
3x10-20 21101-46512 <$300
Total Issue $3,365,050
Out in 1935 $9,265
****
4971 Crawford
FNB OF COCHRANTON
{{ 5 L 12 S }}
Chartered 1894
Brown Back <$VALUE
3x10-20 1-2650 <$375
1882 Date Back
3x10-20 1-2573 <$375
1902 Date Back
3x10-20 1-1000 <$200
1902 Plain Back
3x10-20 1001-8775 <$200
1929 Small Size
10 Type 1 1-1446 <$100
20 Type 1 1-370 <$110
10 Type 2 1-1687 <$125
20 Type 2 1-475 <$125
Total Issue $857,430
Out in 1935 $48,450
Large out 1935 $2,750
****

****
8404 Montgomery
COLLEGEVILLE NB,
COLLEGEVILLE
{{ 5 L 17 S }}
Chartered 10/06
1902 Red Seal <$VALUE
3x10-20 1-1200 <$600
1902 Date Back
3x10-20 1-5100 <$275
1902 Plain Back
3x10-20 5101-15211 <$275
1929 Small Size
10 Type 1 1-1588 <$100
20 Type 1 1-422 <$100
10 Type 2 1-1739 <$100
20 Type 2 1-525 <$100
Total Issue $994,360
Out in 1935 $48,050
Large out 1935 $2,010
****
3873 Lancaster
CENTRAL NB OF COLUMBIA
{{ 10 L 27 S }}
Chartered 4/21/88
Brown Back <$VALUE
3x10-20 1-4508 <$350
1902 Red Seal
3x10-20 1-800 <$350
1902 Date Back
3x10-20 1-4200 <$175
1902 Plain Back
3x10-20 4201-18350 <$175
1929 Small Size
5 Type 1 1-6910 <$60
10 Type 1 1-3632 <$60
20 Type 1 1-414 <$65
5 Type 2 1-19330 <$75
10 Type 2 1-11287 <$75
Total Issue $1,867,320
Out in 1935 $198,700
Large out 1935 $3,630
****
641 Lancaster
COLUMBIA NB, COLUMBIA
{{ 3 L }}
Chartered 12/64
Liquidated 4/14/17
Original Series <$VALUE
4x5 1-7900 <$600
3x10-20 1-12700 <$1000/$1500
50-100 1-467 <$4000
Series 1875
4x5 1-750 <$600
3x10-20 1-10680 <$1000/$1500
50-100 1-334 <$4000
Brown Back
3x10-20 1-7519 <$500
1902 Red Seal
3x10-20 1-2000 <$600
1902 Date Back
4x5 1-3755 <$400
3x10-20 1-2939 <$400
Total Issue $2,160,150
Out at close $49,500
Ch 371 assumed circulation
****
F-Columbia NB, Columbia
SEE Ch 371
FNB of Columbia
****
371 Lancaster
FNB OF COLUMBIA
Chartered 4/64
2nd title: F-Columbia NB
4/12/17
FIRST TITLE {{ 5 L }}
Original Series <$VALUE
3x1-2 1-1000 <$500/$1250
4x5 1-2996 <$600
3x10-20 1-5700 <$850/$1500
Series 1875
3x1-2 1-920 <$500/$1250
3x10-20 1-2800 <$850/$1500
Brown Back
3x10-20 1-6576 <$350
1902 Red Seal
3x10-20 1-4000 <$350
1902 Date Back
3x10-20 1-6581 <$150
SECOND TITLE {{ 8 L 16 S }}
1902 Plain Back
4x5 1-18915 <$150
3x10-20 1-11630 <$150
1929 Small Size
5 Type 1 1-4778 <$85
10 Type 1 1-2302 <$85
20 Type 1 1-596 <$85
5 Type 2 1-5314 <$85
10 Type 2 1-3417 <$85
20 Type 2 1-708 <$100
Total Issue $2,740,050
Out in 1935 $118,300
Large out 1935 $14,050
Outstanding includes Ch 641
****

****
5307 Somerset
FNB OF CONFLUENCE
{{ 7 L 6 S }}
Chartered 4/26/00
Brown Back <$VALUE
4x5 1-1425 <$500
3x10-20 1-1150 <$500
1882 Date Back
4x5 1-2250 <$500
3x10-20 1-1590 <$500
1882 Value Back
4x5 2251-3425 <$500
3x10-20 1591-2203 <$500
1902 Plain Back
4x5 1-150 <$350
3x10-20 1-3467 <$350
1929 Small Size
10 Type 1 1-648 <$200
20 Type 1 1-180 <$200
10 Type 2 1-937 <$200
20 Type 2 1-220 <$225
Total Issue $515,250
Out in 1935 $25,000
Large out 1935 $1,410
****
13980 Crawford
FNB AT CONNEAUT LAKE
{{ 2 S }}
Chartered 2/34
1929 Small Size <$VALUE
5 Type 2 1-91 <$400
10 Type 2 1-739 <$400
20 Type 2 1-242 <$400
Total Issue $12,685
Out in 1935 $24,500
Large out 1935 $1,185
Outstanding includes Ch 6891
****
6891 Crawford
FNB OF CONNEAUT LAKE
{{ 3 L 5 S }}
Chartered 7/03
Liquidated 3/13/34
1902 Red Seal <$VALUE
3x10-20 1-1655 <$600
1902 Date Back
3x10-20 1-1830 <$300
1902 Plain Back
3x10-20 1831-6171 <$300
1929 Small Size
10 Type 1 1-772 <$185
20 Type 1 1-168 <$185
10 Type 2 1-156 <$225
20 Type 2 1-45 <$225
Total Issue $460,240
Out at close $23,125
Large out 1935 $1,185
Ch 13980 assumed circulation
****
13942 Crawford
FARMERS NB OF
CONNEAUTVILLE
{{ 1 S }}
Chartered 1/34
1929 Small Size <$VALUE
5 Type 2 1-1620 <$400
10 Type 2 1-888 <$400
Total Issue $16,980
Out in 1935 $24,970
Large out 1935 $770
Outstanding includes Ch 12189
****
143 Crawford
FNB OF CONNEAUTVILLE
{{ 6 L }}
Chartered 12/7/63
Liquidated 2/24/03
Original Series <$VALUE
3x1-2 1-2659 <$350/$1000
4x5 1-4650 <$400
3x10-20 1-1788 <$750/$1250
Series 1875
4x5 1-2900 <$400
3x10-20 1-1080 <$750/$1250
Brown Back
3x10-20 1-2009 <$300
Total Issue $408,145
Out in 1910 $2,743
****

<$VALUEs are for notes in FINE condition. Value changes by approximately 25% for a change of one full grade.

12189 Crawford
FNB OF CONNEAUTVILLE
{{2L 5S}}
Chartered 5/22
Liquidated 3/7/34
1902 Plain Back <$VALUE
4x5 1-2925 <$400
3x10-20 1-1951 <$400
1929 Small Size
5 Type 1 1-896 <$175
10 Type 1 1-430 <$175
20 Type 1 1-136 <$200
5 Type 2 1-1192 <$200
Total Issue $231,010
Out at close $22,500
Large out 1935 $770
Ch 13942 assumed circulation

6452 Fayette
CITIZENS NB OF CONNELLSVILLE
{{4L 4S}}
Chartered 10/7/02
Receivership 7/31/30
1902 Red Seal <$VALUE
3x10-20 1-7025 <$400
1902 Date Back
3x10-20 1-9300 <$200
1902 Plain Back
3x10-20 9301-27459 <$200
1929 Small Size
10 Type 1 1-1081 <$175
20 Type 1 1-256 <$175
Total Issue $1,819,780
Out at close $100,000
Large out at close $16,740

7445 Fayette
COLONIAL NB OF CONNELLSVILLE
{{5L}}
Chartered 10/04
Liquidated 4/30/27
1902 Red Seal <$VALUE
3x10-20 1-4700 <$400
1902 Date Back
3x10-20 1-9300 <$200
1902 Plain Back
3x10-20 9301-24016 <$200
Total Issue $1,435,800
Out at close $89,900

2329 Fayette
FNB OF CONNELLSVILLE
{{11L}}
Chartered 4/8/76
Liquidated 6/22/28
Series 1875 <$VALUE
3x10-20 1-1948 <$750/$1250
Brown Back
3x10-20 1-6930 <$275
1882 Date Back
3x10-20 1-9000 <$275
1882 Value Back
3x10-20 9001-9193 <$275
1902 Plain Back
3x10-20 1-24393 <$135
Total Issue $2,123,200
Out at close $119,100
Outstanding includes Ch 4861

13491 Fayette
NB & TC OF CONNELLSVILLE
{{U+10S}}
Chartered 8/30
1929 Small Size <$VALUE
10 Type 1 1-1858 <$50
20 Type 1 1-600 <$60
10 Type 2 1-3864 <$60
20 Type 2 1-1785 <$60
Total Issue $257,820
Out in 1935 $125,000

4481 Fayette
SECOND NB OF CONNELLSVILLE
{{7L 12S}}
Organized 10/28/90
Brown Back <$VALUE
3x10-20 1-3970 <$300
1882 Date Back
3x10-20 1-1072 <$300
1902 Date Back
3x10-20 1-3540 <$150
1902 Plain Back
3x10-20 3541-12766 <$150
1929 Small Size
10 Type 1 1-1432 <$100
20 Type 1 1-378 <$100
10 Type 2 1-888 <$100
20 Type 2 1-456 <$100
Total Issue $1,039,680
Out in 1935 $49,100
Large out 1935 $3,180

Union NB of Connellsville
SEE Ch 6408
New Haven NB, New Haven

4861 Fayette
YOUGH NB OF CONNELLSVILLE
{{1L}}
Chartered 1893
Liquidated 3/3/13
Brown Back <$VALUE
3x10-20 1-7155 <$750
1882 Date Back
3x10-20 1-3838 <$750
Total Issue $549,650
Out at close $62,450

2078 Montgomery
FNB OF CONSHOHOCKEN
{{14L 18S}}
Chartered 1/30/73
Original Series <$VALUE
4x5 1-4120 <$400
3x10-20 1-1800 <$750/$1250
Series 1875
4x5 1-4550 <$400
3x10-20 1-4527 <$750/$1250
Brown Back
4x5 1-11100 <$250
3x10-20 1-6660 <$250
1882 Date Back
4x5 1-7558 <$250
3x10-20 1-4539 <$250
1902 Date Back
4x5 1-4330 <$150
3x10-20 1-3468 <$150
1902 Plain Back
4x5 4331-33285 <$150
3x10-20 3469-21478 <$150
1929 Small Size
5 Type 1 1-5552 <$65
10 Type 1 1-2896 <$65
20 Type 1 1-780 <$75
5 Type 2 1-8012 <$80
10 Type 2 1-4266 <$80
20 Type 2 1-1011 <$80
Total Issue $3,699,320
Total Issue $102,850
Large out 1935 $6,705

2671 Montgomery
TRADESMEN'S NB OF CONSHOHOCKEN
{{5L}}
Chartered 1882
Series 1875 <$VALUE
4x5 1-4961 <$600
3x10-20 1-2552 <$850/$1500
1902 Red Seal
4x5 1-3430 <$500
3x10-20 1-2668 <$500
1902 Date Back
4x5 1-5000 <$250
3x10-20 1-3480 <$250
1902 Plain Back
4x5 5001-6710 <$250
3x10-20 3481-4526 <$250
Total Issue $789,320
Out in 1935 $1,460

13392 Luzerne
CONYNGHAM NB, CONYNGHAM
{{5S}}
Chartered 11/29
1929 Small Size <$VALUE
5 Type 1 1-520 <$175
10 Type 1 1-254 <$175
20 Type 1 1-76 <$175
5 Type 2 1-1918 <$200
10 Type 2 1-945 <$200
20 Type 2 1-240 <$200
Total Issue $63,800
Out in 1935 $20,800

9034 Lehigh
FNB OF COOPERSBURG
{{3L 10S}}
Chartered 2/08
1902 Red Seal <$VALUE
3x10-20 1-240 <$600
1902 Date Back
3x10-20 1-2800 <$300
1902 Plain Back
3x10-20 2801-7436 <$300
1929 Small Size
10 Type 1 1-1220 <$100
20 Type 1 1-300 <$110
10 Type 2 1-2391 <$125
20 Type 2 1-455 <$125
Total Issue $526,010
Out in 1935 $46,800
Large out 1935 $980

9113 Lehigh
COPLAY NB, COPLAY
{{5L U+11S}}
Chartered 4/08
1902 Date Back <$VALUE
4x5 1-2200 <$175
3x10-20 1-2240 <$175
1902 Plain Back
4x5 2201-12083 <$175
3x10-20 2241-8663 <$175
1929 Small Size
5 Type 1 1-1836 <$100
10 Type 1 1-1028 <$100
20 Type 1 1-268 <$100
5 Type 2 1-3748 <$100
10 Type 2 1-1952 <$100
20 Type 2 1-391 <$100
Total Issue $869,810
Out in 1935 $41,850
Large out 1935 $2,210

5069 Allegheny
CORAOPOLIS NB, CORAOPOLIS
{{6L 14S}}
Chartered 1897
Brown Back <$VALUE
3x10-20 1-4470 <$400
1882 Date Back
3x10-20 1-4440 <$400
1882 Value Back
3x10-20 4441-5032 <$400
1902 Plain Back
3x10-20 1-8567 <$175
1929 Small Size
10 Type 1 1-1552 <$85
20 Type 1 1-412 <$100
10 Type 2 1-1421 <$100
20 Type 2 1-419 <$100
Total Issue $1,073,100
Out in 1935 $43,350
Large out 1935 $2,810

4479 Erie
CITIZENS NB OF CORRY
{{7L 15S}}
Chartered 1890
Brown Back <$VALUE
4x5 1-7386 <$375
50-100 1-383 <$1250/$1500
1902 Date Back
3x10-20 1-4400 <$175
1902 Plain Back
3x10-20 4401-13792 <$175
1929 Small Size
10 Type 1 1-1700 <$85
20 Type 1 1-438 <$100
10 Type 2 1-1615 <$125
20 Type 2 1-449 <$125
Total Issue $1,074,460
Out in 1935 $59,050
Large out 1935 $3,530

---

569 Erie
CORRY NB, CORRY
{{2L}}
Organized 11/12/64
Receivership 11/21/91
Original Series <$VALUE
3x1-2 1-1500 <$750/$1500
4x5 1-3500 <$850
3x10-20 1-1700<$1000/$1500
Series 1875
3x10-20 1-2800<$1000/$1500
Brown Back
4x5 1-10025 <$600
Total Issue $503,000
Out in 1916 $2,766

---

605 Erie
FNB OF CORRY
{{2L}}
Organized 12/6/64
Receivership 10/11/87
Original Series <$VALUE
3x1-2 1-4000 <$750/$1500
4x5 1-4000 <$850
3x10-20 1-2000<$1000/$1500
Series 1875
3x1-2 1-1718 <$750/$1500
4x5 1-3221 <$850
3x10-20 1-1542<$1000/$1500
Brown Back
3x10-20 1-1097 <$600
Total Issue $404,960
Out in 1916 $2,285

4823 Erie
NB OF CORRY
{{4L 11S}}
Chartered 1892
Brown Back <$VALUE
3x10-20 1-1540 <$400
1882 Date Back
3x10-20 1-460 <$400
1902 Date Back
3x10-20 1-750* <$275
1902 Plain Back
3x10-20 851-7306* <$275
* 751-850 not marked
1929 Small Size
10 Type 1 1-1418 <$125
20 Type 1 1-356 <$125
10 Type 2 1-1731 <$150
20 Type 2 1-458 <$150
Total Issue $619,570
Out in 1935 $48,650
Large out 1935 $2,130

4948 Potter
FNB OF COUDERSPORT
{{5L 9S}}
Chartered 1894
Brown Back <$VALUE
4x5 1-4325 <$400
3x10-20 1-2540 <$400
1882 Date Back
4x5 1-2986 <$400
3x10-20 1-1937 <$400
1902 Date Back
3x10-20 1-1500 <$225
1902 Plain Back
3x10-20 1501-7596 <$225
1929 Small Size
10 Type 1 1-964 <$125
20 Type 1 1-304 <$125
10 Type 2 1-774 <$150
20 Type 2 1-372 <$150
Total Issue $859,370
Out in 1935 $48,800
Large out 1935 $2,020

6010 Allegheny
FNB OF CRAFTON
{{5L U+6S}}
Chartered 11/5/01
Receivership 1/8/34
Brown Back <$VALUE
4x5 1-975 <$350
3x10-20 1-780 <$350
1882 Date Back
4x5 1-1450 <$350
3x10-20 1-1060 <$350
1882 Value Back
4x5 1451-1755 <$350
3x10-20 1061-1267 <$350
1902 Plain Back
4x5 1-19579 <$200
1929 Small Size
5 Type 1 1-6928 <$125
5 Type 2 1-4016 <$125
Total Issue $776,450
Out at close $50,000
Large out at close $1,970

5768 Cambria
FNB OF CRESSON
{{3L 9S}}
Chartered 4/4/01
Brown Back <$VALUE
3x10-20 1-2400 <$500
1882 Date Back
3x10-20 1-4740 <$500
1882 Value Back
3x10-20 4741-7530 <$500
1902 Plain Back
3x10-20 1-7144 <$275
1929 Small Size
10 Type 1 1-1434 <$100
20 Type 1 1-414 <$100
10 Type 2 1-1330 <$125
20 Type 2 1-542 <$125
Total Issue $1,013,560
Out in 1935 $50,000
Large out 1935 $2,520

9318 Schuylkill
FNB OF CRESSONA
{{6L 22S}}
Chartered 1/09
1902 Date Back <$VALUE
3x10-20 1-2710 <$225
1902 Plain Back
3x10-20 2711-8946 <$225
1929 Small Size
10 Type 1 1-1574 <$75
20 Type 1 1-414 <$85
5 Type 2 1-1608 <$100
10 Type 2 1-3955 <$100
20 Type 2 1-2460 <$100
Total Issue $688,210
Out in 1935 $97,800
Large out 1935 $1,550

6969 Clearfield
CITIZENS NB OF CURWENSVILLE
{{2L}}
Chartered 9/03
Liquidated 3/15/09
1902 Red Seal <$VALUE
4x5 1-4750 <$600
3x10-20 1-3400 <$600
1902 Date Back
4x5 1-145 <$350
3x10-20 1-32 <$350
Total Issue $269,500
Out in 1910 $25,100

7430 Clearfield
CURWENSVILLE NB, CURWENSVILLE
{{8L 16S}}
Chartered 10/04
1902 Red Seal <$VALUE
3x10-20 1-4500 <$275
1902 Date Back
3x10-20 1-9300 <$135
1902 Plain Back
3x10-20 9301-26706 <$135
1929 Small Size
10 Type 1 1-2816 <$60
20 Type 1 1-772 <$65
10 Type 2 1-3886 <$75
20 Type 2 1-1026 <$75
Total Issue $1,881,280
Out in 1935 $98,700
Large out 1935 $4,700

---

300 Clearfield
FNB OF CURWENSVILLE
{{1L}}
Chartered 3/3/64
Liquidated 12/17/75
Original Series <$VALUE
4x5 1-4200 <$1000
3x10-20 1-1686<$1250/$1750
Total Issue $168,300
Out in 1910 $890

12967 Cambria
DALE NB, DALE
{{2L 10S}}
Chartered 7/26
1902 Plain Back <$VALUE
3x10-20 1-3274 <$400
1929 Small Size
10 Type 1 1-1536 <$135
20 Type 1 1-400 <$150
10 Type 2 1-1364 <$150
20 Type 2 1-329 <$150
Total Issue $324,080
Out in 1935 $43,850
Large out 1935 $1,590

8164 Luzerne
FNB OF DALLAS
{{1L 8S}}
Chartered 4/06
1902 Red Seal <$VALUE
3x10-20 1-280 <$1000
1902 Date Back
3x10-20 1-780* <$500
1902 Plain Back
3x10-20 841-1931* <$500
* 781-840 not marked
1929 Small Size
10 Type 1 1-316 <$175
20 Type 1 1-106 <$175
5 Type 2 1-10908 <$175
10 Type 2 1-3228 <$175
20 Type 2 1-936 <$175
Total Issue $247,770
Out in 1935 $69,980
Large out 1935 $150

6648 York
FNB OF DALLASTOWN
Chartered 2/03
2nd title: FNB & TC 1/20/30
FIRST TITLE {{9L 2S}}
1902 Red Seal <$VALUE
4x5 1-1250 <$400
3x10-20 1-2775 <$400
1902 Date Back
4x5 1-4150 <$175
3x10-20 1-3340 <$175
1902 Plain Back
4x5 4151-24102 <$175
3x10-20 3341-14096 <$175
1929 Small Size
5 Type 1 1-1546 <$150
10 Type 1 1-778 <$150
20 Type 1 1-262 <$150
SECOND TITLE {{18S}}
1929 Small Size
5 Type 1 1-4072 <$85
10 Type 1 1-2036 <$85
20 Type 1 1-464 <$85
5 Type 2 1-8830 <$100
10 Type 2 1-4803 <$100
20 Type 2 1-1344 <$100
Total Issue $1,894,150
Out in 1935 $123,300
Large out 1935 $4,055

7931 Northampton
DANIELSVILLE NB, DANIELSVILLE
{{3L 5S}}
Chartered 10/05
1902 Red Seal <$VALUE
4x5 1-765 <$600
3x10-20 1-618 <$600
1902 Date Back
4x5 1-2125 <$300
3x10-20 1-1520 <$300
1902 Plain Back
4x5 2126-5770 <$300
3x10-20 1521-3840 <$300
1929 Small Size
5 Type 1 1-690 <$175
10 Type 1 1-398 <$175
20 Type 1 1-120 <$175
5 Type 2 1-1224 <$200
10 Type 2 1-567 <$200
20 Type 2 1-144 <$200
Total Issue $427,250
Out in 1935 $19,500
Large out 1935 $970

1078 Montour
DANVILLE NB, DANVILLE
{{18L 28S}}
Chartered 4/65
Original Series <$VALUE
3x1-2 1-4100 <$300/$850
4x5 1-5900 <$350
3x10-20 1-2760 <$750/$1250
50-100 1-290 <$3500
Series 1875
4x5 1-1600 <$350
3x10-20 1-5068 <$750/$1250
50-100 1-50 <$3500
Brown Back
4x5 1-9950 <$225
3x10-20 1-12366 <$225
1902 Red Seal
4x5 1-8000 <$250
3x10-20 1-4100 <$250
50-100 1-234 <$2250/$2500
1902 Date Back
4x5 1-16150 <$85
3x10-20 1-10700 <$85
50-100 1-320 <$300/$350
3x50-100 1-400 <$300/$350
1902 Plain Back
4x5 16151-49005 <$85
3x10-20 10701-32511 <$85
3x50-100 401-604<$300/$350
1929 Small Size
5 Type 1 1-7942 <$30
10 Type 1 1-4294 <$30
20 Type 1 1-1086 <$40
5 Type 2 1-14882 <$30
10 Type 2 1-7572 <$30
20 Type 2 1-1944 <$40
Total Issue $5,450,180
Out in 1935 $194,300
Large out 1935 $14,460

---

325 Montour
FNB OF DANVILLE
{{15L 21S}}
Chartered 3/64
Original Series <$VALUE
3x1-2 1-3000 <$300/$850
4x5 1-3400 <$350
3x10-20 1-3720 <$750/$1250
Series 1875
4x5 1-800 <$350
3x10-20 1-2400 <$750/$1250
Brown Back
4x5 1-6145 <$225
3x10-20 1-9942 <$225
1902 Red Seal
4x5 1-5500 <$250
3x10-20 1-7400 <$250
1902 Date Back
4x5 1-15350 <$100
3x10-20 1-10280 <$100
1902 Plain Back
4x5 15351-47305 <$100
3x10-20 10281-28604 <$100
1929 Small Size
5 Type 1 1-6954 <$40
10 Type 1 1-3108* <$40
20 Type 1 1-786 <$50
5 Type 2 1-8570 <$50
10 Type 2 1-5447 <$50
20 Type 2 1-1610 <$55
* 3094 not issued
Total Issue $4,500,180
Out in 1935 $145,700
Large out 1935 $10,725

****
4428 Delaware
FNB OF DARBY
{{ 8 L 17 S }}
Chartered 7/15/90
Receivership 1/23/34
Brown Back <$VALUE
4x5 1-6325 <$350
3x10-20 1-2020 <$350
1882 Date Back
4x5 1-1399 <$350
3x10-20 1-778 <$350
1902 Date Back
4x5 1-7000 <$175
3x10-20 1-5300 <$175
1902 Plain Back
4x5 7001-28850 <$175
3x10-20 5301-19754 <$175
1929 Small Size
5 Type 1 1-4410 <$85
10 Type 1 1-2360 <$85
20 Type 1 1-582 <$85
5 Type 2 1-1908 <$100
10 Type 2 1-420 <$100
20 Type 2 1-50 <$100
Total Issue $2,217,560
Out at close $100,000
Large out at close $5,500
****
11512 Dauphin
DAUPHIN NB, DAUPHIN
{{ 2 L 7 S }}
Chartered 11/19
1902 Plain Back <$VALUE
3x10-20 1-3741 <$375
1929 Small Size
10 Type 1 1-786 <$165
20 Type 1 1-234 <$175
10 Type 2 1-572 <$200
20 Type 2 1-132 <$200
Total Issue $270,650
Out in 1935 $25,000
Large out 1935 $940
****
11407 Somerset
FNB OF DAVIDSVILLE
{{ 2 L 4 S }}
Chartered 7/19
Receivership 7/6/32
1902 Plain Back <$VALUE
3x10-20 1-4389 <$375
1929 Small Size
10 Type 1 1-604 <$250
20 Type 1 1-187 <$250
Total Issue $278,130
Out at close $25,000
Large out at close $1,600
****
4673 Fayette
FNB OF DAWSON
{{ 6 L 11 S }}
Chartered 1891
Brown Back <$VALUE
4x5 1-1500 <$375
3x10-20 1-4460 <$375
1882 Date Back
4x5 1-1650 <$375
3x10-20 1-1420 <$375
1902 Date Back
3x10-20 1-2750 <$175
1902 Plain Back
3x10-20 2751-11856 <$175
1929 Small Size
10 Type 1 1-1360 <$100
20 Type 1 1-370 <$100
10 Type 2 1-1754 <$110
20 Type 2 1-498 <$125
Total Issue $1,103,300
Out in 1935 $41,950
Large out 1935 $2,930
****
5742 Armstrong
FNB OF DAYTON
{{ 3 L 6 S }}
Chartered 3/15/01
Brown Back <$VALUE
3x10-20 1-1290 <$500
1882 Date Back
3x10-20 1-2030 <$500
1882 Value Back
3x10-20 2031-3167 <$500
1902 Plain Back
3x10-20 1-2987 <$250
1929 Small Size
10 Type 1 1-740 <$150
20 Type 1 1-200 <$150
10 Type 2 1-566 <$175
20 Type 2 1-192 <$175
Total Issue $450,100
Out in 1935 $23,400
Large out 1935 $1,120
****

****
9996 Westmoreland
PEOPLES NB OF DELMONT
{{ 1 L 3 S }}
Chartered 4/11
Receivership 6/18/31
1902 Date Back <$VALUE
3x10-20 1-870* <$600
1902 Plain Back
3x10-20 971-2681* <$600
* 871-970 not marked
1929 Small Size
10 Type 1 1-198 <$350
20 Type 1 1-31 <$350
Total Issue $149,650
Out at close $9,760
Large out at close $1,120
****
14201 York
DELTA NB, DELTA
{{ 2 S }}
Chartered 6/34
1929 Small Size <$VALUE
5 Type 2 1-5160 <$450
Total Issue $25,800
Out in 1935 $20,150
****
4205 York
FNB OF DELTA
{{ 5 L 4 S }}
Chartered 1890
Liquidated 6/18/32
Brown Back <$VALUE
4x5 1-1755 <$400
50-100 1-1943 <$1250/$1500
1902 Date Back
4x5 1-2850 <$250
50-100 1-260 <$500/$600
3x50-100 1-612 <$500/$600
1902 Plain Back
4x5 2851-16390 <$250
3x50-100 613-853<$500/$600
1929 Small Size
5 Type 1 1-1618 <$200
50 Type 1 1-94 <$275
100 Type 1 1-28 <$350
Total Issue $1,000,140
Out at close $47,760
Large out at close $6,430
****
4367 York
MILES NB OF DELTA
{{ UNREPORTED }}
Chartered 7/14/90
Liquidated 10/2/99
Brown Back <$VALUE
3x10-20 1-747 <$1500
Total Issue $37,350
Out in 1910 $420
****
5198 York
PEOPLES NB OF DELTA
{{ 5 L 9 S }}
Chartered 6/13/99
Liquidated 12/12/34
Brown Back <$VALUE
3x10-20 1-3500 <$400
1882 Date Back
3x10-20 1-4360 <$400
1882 Value Back
3x10-20 4361-5759 <$400
1902 Plain Back
3x10-20 1-7694 <$225
1929 Small Size
10 Type 1 1-1513 <$150
20 Type 1 1-375 <$175
Total Issue $983,430
Out at close $50,000
Large out at close $2,440
****
6037 Lancaster
DENVER NB, DENVER
{{ 5 L 50+ S }}
Chartered 11/30/01
Brown Back <$VALUE
3x10-20 1-3500 <$500
1882 Date Back
3x10-20 1-4140 <$500
1882 Value Back
3x10-20 4141-7310 <$500
1902 Plain Back
3x10-20 1-5511 <$275
1929 Small Size
10 Type 1 1-1508 <$85
20 Type 1 1-414 <$85
10 Type 2 1-1601 <$85
20 Type 2 1-325 <$100
Total Issue $978,720
Out in 1935 $48,700
Large out 1935 $2,250
****

****
13794 Westmoreland
FNB AT DERRY
{{ 6 S }}
Chartered 10/33
1929 Small Size <$VALUE
5 Type 2 1-6598 <$175
10 Type 2 1-2395 <$175
20 Type 2 1-723 <$175
Total Issue $71,400
Out in 1935 $37,650
****
12912 Westmoreland
FNB IN DERRY
{{ 6 S }}
Chartered 4/26
Receivership 11/3/33
1929 Small Size <$VALUE
5 Type 1 1-408 <$200
10 Type 1 1-554 <$200
20 Type 1 1-254 <$200
Total Issue $75,960
Out at close $50,000
****
6756 Westmoreland
FNB OF DERRY
{{ 2 L }}
Chartered 4/03
Liquidated 12/31/17
1902 Red Seal <$VALUE
3x10-20 1-920 <$750
1902 Date Back
3x10-20 1-1310* <$375
1902 Plain Back
3x10-20 1511-2289* <$375
* 1311-1510 not marked
Total Issue $160,450
Out at close $50,000
****
9851 Lackawanna
DICKSON CITY NB,
DICKSON CITY
{{ 5 L 9 S }}
Chartered 9/10
Liquidated 2/19/34
1902 Date Back <$VALUE
3x10-20 1-4800 <$225
1902 Plain Back
3x10-20 4801-16265 <$225
1929 Small Size
10 Type 1 1-1852 <$125
20 Type 1 1-460 <$125
10 Type 2 1-888 <$150
20 Type 2 1-192 <$150
Total Issue $992,290
Out at close $44,400
Large out at close $2,340
****
12459 Lackawanna
LIBERTY NB OF
DICKSON CITY
{{ 2 L 3 S }}
Chartered 11/23
Receivership 10/6/32
1902 Plain Back <$VALUE
4x5 1-7537 <$500
1929 Small Size
5 Type 1 1-3454 <$300
Total Issue $254,360
Out at close $24,160
Large out at close $640
****
2397 York
DILLSBURG NB, DILLSBURG
{{ 7 L 15 S }}
Chartered 9/17/78
Series 1875 <$VALUE
3x10-20 1-3845 <$750/$1250
Brown Back
3x10-20 1-5100 <$375
1882 Date Back
3x10-20 1-4400* <$375
1882 Value Back
3x10-20 4701-5870* <$375
* 4401-4700 not marked
1902 Plain Back
3x10-20 1-8526 <$175
1929 Small Size
10 Type 1 1-1850 <$75
20 Type 1 1-454 <$85
10 Type 2 1-2129 <$100
20 Type 2 1-558 <$100
Total Issue $1,364,980
Out in 1935 $57,750
Large out 1935 $2,860
****
5835 Washington
FNB OF DONORA
{{ 7 L 9 S }}
Chartered 5/25/01
Liquidated 12/12/32
Brown Back <$VALUE
4x5 1-2000 <$400
3x10-20 1-4500 <$400
1882 Date Back
4x5 1-7550 <$400
3x10-20 1-5180 <$400
1882 Value Back
4x5 7551-11480 <$400
3x10-20 5181-7792 <$400
1902 Plain Back
4x5 1-11310 <$175
3x10-20 1-7518 <$175
1929 Small Size
5 Type 1 1-2689 <$125
10 Type 1 1-1278 <$125
20 Type 1 1-377 <$135
Total Issue $1,688,890
Out at close $73,500
Large out 1935 $3,660
Ch 13644 assumed circulation
****
13644 Washington
UNION NB OF DONORA
{{ 4U + 11 S }}
Chartered 10/32
1929 Small Size <$VALUE
5 Type 1 1-4207 <$125
10 Type 1 1-210 <$125
20 Type 1 1-104 <$125
5 Type 2 1-13956 <$125
10 Type 2 1-7032 <$125
20 Type 2 1-2136 <$125
Total Issue $220,500
Out in 1935 $142,170
Large out 1935 $3,660
Outstanding includes Ch 5835
****
9362 York
DOVER NB, DOVER
{{ 2 L 5 S }}
Chartered 3/09
Liquidated 5/2/34
1902 Date Back <$VALUE
3x10-20 1-2620 <$450
1902 Plain Back
3x10-20 2621-6643 <$450
1929 Small Size
10 Type 1 1-734 <$200
20 Type 1 1-180 <$200
10 Type 2 1-95 <$225
20 Type 2 1-35 <$225
Total Issue $399,440
Out at close $24,490
Large out 1935 $1,410
Ch 14049 assumed circulation
****
14049 York
DOVER NB, DOVER
{{ UNREPORTED }}
Chartered 3/34
1929 Small Size <$VALUE
10 Type 2 1-638 <$750
20 Type 2 1-201 <$750
Total Issue $10,400
Out in 1935 $25,000
Large out 1935 $1,410
Outstanding includes Ch 9362
****
661 Chester
DOWNINGTOWN NB,
DOWNINGTOWN
{{ 9 L 16 S }}
Chartered 12/64
Original Series <$VALUE
3x10-20 1-2500<$1000/$1500
50-100 1-350 <$4000
Series 1875
3x10-20 1-1900<$1000/$1500
50-100 1-217 <$4000
Brown Back
4x5 1-4290 <$500
3x10-20 1-1201 <$500
50-100 1-276 <$1500/$1750
1902 Red Seal
4x5 1-2850 <$500
3x10-20 1-1861 <$500
50-100 1-163 <$2250/$2500
1902 Date Back
4x5 1-9850 <$200
3x10-20 1-5860 <$200
50-100 1-200 <$500/$600
1902 Plain Back
4x5 9851-39789 <$200
3x10-20 5861-17272 <$200
1929 Small Size
5 Type 1 1-6124 <$125
10 Type 1 1-1810 <$125
20 Type 1 1-462 <$125
5 Type 2 1-2518 <$150
10 Type 2 1-1575 <$150
20 Type 2 1-495 <$150
Total Issue $2,742,180
Out in 1935 $101,670
Large out 1935 $9,045
Outstanding includes Ch 8646
****

****
338 Chester
FNB OF DOWNINGTOWN
{{ UNREPORTED }}
Chartered 3/25/64
Liquidated 1/14/68
Original Series <$VALUE
3x1-2 1-100 <$1250/$2000
4x5 1-2475 <$1250
4x10 1-1000 <$2000
Total Issue $100,000
Out in 1910 $889
****
8646 Chester
GRANGE NB OF CHESTER
COUNTY AT DOWNINGTOWN
{{ 5 L 8 S }}
Chartered 4/07
Closed 11/5/32
1902 Red Seal <$VALUE
3x10-20 1-1500 <$1000
1902 Date Back
3x10-20 1-10600 <$500
1902 Plain Back
3x10-20 10601-30821 <$500
1929 Small Size
10 Type 1 1-2666 <$300
20 Type 1 1-697 <$300
Total Issue $1,859,650
Out at close $99,995
Large out at close $6,055
Ch 661 assumed circulation
****
573 Bucks
DOYLESTOWN NB, DOYLESTOWN
Chartered 11/64
2nd title: Doylestown NB &
TC 11/9/26
FIRST TITLE {{ 10 L }}
Original Series <$VALUE
4x5 1-3250 <$450
3x10-20 1-2400 <$750/$1250
Series 1875
4x5 1-2495 <$450
3x10-20 1-1904 <$750/$1250
Brown Back
4x5 1-6307 <$275
3x10-20 1-3820 <$275
1902 Red Seal
3x10-20 1-4100 <$300
1902 Date Back
3x10-20 1-8900 <$150
1902 Plain Back
3x10-20 8901-22431 <$150
SECOND TITLE {{ 2 L 18 S }}
1902 Plain Back
3x10 20 1-4019 <$175
1929 Small Size
10 Type 1 1-3328 <$65
20 Type 1 1-748 <$75
10 Type 2 1-4135 <$75
20 Type 2 1-1416 <$75
Total Issue $2,533,850
Out in 1935 $102,700
Large out 1935 $6,950
****
10811 Franklin
CITIZENS NB OF DRY RUN
Chartered 1/16
2nd title: Path Valley NB
of Dry Run 3/18/32
FIRST TITLE {{ 3 S }}
1929 Small Size <$VALUE
5 Type 1 1-858 <$300
10 Type 1 1-418 <$300
20 Type 1 1-150 <$300
SECOND TITLE {{ 3 S }}
1929 Small Size
5 Type 1 1-274 <$350
10 Type 1 1-110 <$350
20 Type 1 1-34 <$375
5 Type 2 1-982 <$400
10 Type 2 1-576 <$400
20 Type 2 1-192 <$400
Total Issue $102,230
Out in 1935 $25,000
****
Path Valley NB of Dry Run
SEE Ch 10811
Citizens NB of Dry Run
****
13133 Bucks
DUBLIN NB, DUBLIN
{{ 6 S }}
Chartered 10/27
1929 Small Size <$VALUE
5 Type 2 1-8140 <$250
10 Type 2 1-3915 <$250
20 Type 2 1-434 <$250
Total Issue $88,530
Out in 1935 $38,700
****

****
5019 Clearfield
DEPOSIT NB OF DuBOIS
{{ 18 L 29 S }}
Chartered 1895
Brown Back <$VALUE
4x5 1-7800 <$275
3x10-20 1-6920 <$275
1882 Date Back
4x5 1-9358 <$250
3x10-20 1-5740 <$250
1902 Plain Back
3x10-20 1-37100 <$100
1929 Small Size
10 Type 1 1-5962 <$40
20 Type 1 1-1750 <$50
10 Type 2 1-6465 <$50
20 Type 2 1-2100 <$50
Total Issue $3,505,530
Out in 1935 $194,400
Large out 1935 $9,150
****
7453 Clearfield
DuBOIS NB, DuBOIS
{{ 10 L 22 S }}
Chartered 10/04
1902 Red Seal <$VALUE
3x10-20 1-4200 <$250
1902 Date Back
3x10-20 1-9600 <$125
1902 Plain Back
3x10-20 9601-28130 <$125
1929 Small Size
10 Type 1 1-5210 <$40
20 Type 1 1-1260 <$50
5 Type 2 1-324 <$50
10 Type 2 1-6867 <$50
20 Type 2 1-2441 <$50
Total Issue $2,199,410
Out in 1935 $199,805
Large out 1935 $5,395
****
2969 Clearfield
FNB OF DuBOIS CITY
{{ 1 L }}
Chartered 6/6/83
Liquidated 4/8/89
Brown Back <$VALUE
4x5 1-2628 <$1000
Total Issue $52,560
Out in 1910 $280
****
7576 Fayette
FNB OF DUNBAR
{{ 4 L }}
Chartered 1/20/05
Receivership 3/7/27
1902 Red Seal <$VALUE
3x10-20 1-2613 <$600
1902 Date Back
3x10-20 1-4840 <$275
1902 Plain Back
3x10-20 4841-12345 <$275
Total Issue $747,900
Out at close $48,100
****
4142 Perry
DUNCANNON NB, DUNCANNON
{{ 7 L 16 S }}
Chartered 10/22/89
Brown Back <$VALUE
3x10-20 1-5140 <$300
1882 Date Back
3x10-20 1-198 <$300
1902 Date Back
3x10-20 1-5400 <$175
1902 Plain Back
3x10-20 5401-15705 <$175
1929 Small Size
10 Type 1 1-1754 <$75
20 Type 1 1-498 <$85
10 Type 2 1-1783 <$100
20 Type 2 1-455 <$100
Total Issue $1,244,080
Out in 1935 $54,250
Large out 1935 $3,810
****

CONDITION affects Value. The Values shown are for notes in FINE condition.

8778 Perry
PEOPLES NB OF DUNCANNON
{{ 3 L 6 S }}
Chartered 7/07
1902 Red Seal <$VALUE
4x5 1-550 <$500
4x10 1-650 <$500
1902 Date Back
4x5 1-2200 <$250
4x10 1-2025 <$250
1902 Plain Back
4x5 2201-7970 <$250
4x10 2026-6290 <$250
1929 Small Size
5 Type 1 1-1504 <$150
10 Type 1 1-768 <$150
5 Type 2 1-2520 <$165
10 Type 2 1-1452 <$165
Total Issue $566,320
Out in 1935 $24,320
Large out 1935 $1,060

9868 Lackawanna
FNB OF DUNMORE
{{ 10 L 27 S }}
Chartered 10/10
1902 Date Back <$VALUE
4x5 1-5900 <$135
3x10-20 1-4400 <$135
1902 Plain Back
4x5 5901-23231 <$135
3x10-20 4401-14776 <$135
1929 Small Size
5 Type 1 1-10130 <$40
10 Type 1 1-4884 <$40
20 Type 1 1-1162 <$45
5 Type 2 1-22572 <$40
10 Type 2 1-11436 <$40
20 Type 2 1-2904 <$45
Total Issue $2,221,500
Out in 1935 $215,660
Large out 1935 $2,230

4730 Allegheny
FNB OF DUQUESNE
{{ 8 L 18 S }}
Chartered 1892
Brown Back <$VALUE
4x5 1-4700 <$300
3x10-20 1-1830 <$300
1882 Date Back
4x5 1-1811 <$300
3x10-20 1-1783 <$300
1902 Date Back
4x5 1-2425 <$125
3x10-20 1-1680 <$125
3x50-100 1-30 <$400/$500
1902 Plain Back
4x5 2426-12089 <$125
3x10-20 1681-8000 <$125
1929 Small Size
5 Type 1 1-3088 <$60
10 Type 1 1-1462 <$60
20 Type 1 1-410 <$65
5 Type 2 1-5712 <$75
10 Type 2 1-3360 <$75
20 Type 2 1-1197 <$75
Total Issue $1,275,810
Out in 1935 $98,700
Large out 1935 $2,670

4505 Sullivan
FNB OF DUSHORE
{{ 8 L 12 S }}
Chartered 1891
Brown Back <$VALUE
4x5 1-5625 <$300
3x10-20 1-2440 <$300
1882 Date Back
4x5 1-1287 <$300
3x10-20 1-900 <$300
1902 Date Back
4x5 1-2600 <$150
3x10-20 1-2060 <$150
1902 Plain Back
4x5 2601-11820 <$150
3x10-20 2061-7925 <$150
1929 Small Size
5 Type 1 1-1944 <$100
10 Type 1 1-1080 <$100
20 Type 1 1-278 <$100
5 Type 2 1-2954 <$100
10 Type 2 1-1656 <$100
20 Type 2 1-384 <$110
Total Issue $1,133,380
Out in 1935 $49,500
Large out 1935 $3,130

6878 Adams
EAST BERLIN NB,
EAST BERLIN
{{ 2 L 6 S }}
Chartered 7/03
Receivership 4/26/34
1902 Red Seal <$VALUE
3x10-20 1-456 <$700
1902 Date Back
3x10-20 1-1200* <$350
1902 Plain Back
3x10-20 1321-3362* <$350
* 1201-1320 not marked
1929 Small Size
10 Type 1 1-764 <$175
20 Type 1 1-200 <$175
10 Type 2 1-324 <$200
20 Type 2 1-65 <$200
Total Issue $265,280
Out at close $25,000
Large out at close $520

14091 Adams
EAST BERLIN NB,
EAST BERLIN
{{ U + 3 S }}
Chartered 4/34
1929 Small Size <$VALUE
5 Type 2 1-11770 <$300
Total Issue $58,850
Out in 1935 $50,000

5321 Clarion
FNB OF EAST BRADY
{{ 1 L }}
Chartered 5/2/00
Receivership 5/1/08
Brown Back <$VALUE
4x5 1-1810 <$1000
3x10-20 1-1192 <$1000
Total Issue $95,800
Out in 1916 $995

5356 Clarion
PEOPLES NB OF EAST BRADY
{{ 6 L 12 S }}
Chartered 5/16/00
Brown Back <$VALUE
3x10-20 1-3500 <$350
1882 Date Back
3x10-20 1-5400 <$350
1882 Value Back
3x10-20 5401-7923 <$350
1902 Plain Back
3x10-20 1-9129 <$165
1929 Small Size
10 Type 1 1-1928 <$75
20 Type 1 1-510 <$85
10 Type 2 1-2662 <$85
20 Type 2 1-597 <$85
Total Issue $1,243,040
Out in 1935 $65,000
Large out 1935 $3,480

6979 Cambria
FNB OF EAST CONEMAUGH
{{ 4 L }}
Chartered 10/03
Liquidated 1/24/25
1902 Red Seal <$VALUE
4x5 1-3260 <$450
3x10-20 1-2356 <$450
1902 Date Back
4x5 1-4950 <$225
3x10-20 1-3360 <$225
1902 Plain Back
4x5 4951-12240 <$225
3x10-20 3361-7670 <$225
Total Issue $811,300
Out at close $29,100

5166 Montgomery
PERKIOMEN NB OF
EAST GREENVILLE
{{ 7 L 18 S }}
Chartered 1/3/99
Brown Back <$VALUE
3x10-20 1-3190 <$400
1882 Date Back
3x10-20 1-3940* <$400
1882 Value Back
3x10-20 4141-5457* <$400
* 3941-4140 not marked
1902 Plain Back
3x10-20 1-7497 <$175
1929 Small Size
10 Type 1 1-1430 <$85
20 Type 1 1-382 <$100
10 Type 2 1-2260 <$100
20 Type 2 1-342 <$100
Total Issue $968,280
Out in 1935 $50,000
Large out 1935 $1,960

8446 Carbon
CITIZENS NB OF
EAST MAUCH CHUNK
{{ 6 L 12 S }}
Chartered 11/06
1902 Red Seal <$VALUE
4x5 1-1485 <$350
3x10-20 1-1196 <$350
1902 Date Back
4x5 1-4750 <$175
3x10-20 1-3400 <$175
1902 Plain Back
4x5 4751-14530 <$175
3x10-20 3401-9680 <$175
1929 Small Size
5 Type 1 1-1882 <$100
10 Type 1 1-916 <$100
20 Type 1 1-272 <$100
5 Type 2 1-2834 <$125
10 Type 2 1-1629 <$125
20 Type 2 1-364 <$125
Total Issue $1,045,900
Out in 1935 $39,130
Large out 1935 $2,360

10042 Bradford
FNB OF EAST SMITHFIELD
{{ 3 L 6 S }}
Chartered 6/11
1902 Date Back <$VALUE
4x5 1-1615 <$350
3x10-20 1-1254 <$350
1902 Plain Back
4x5 1616-6865 <$350
3x10-20 1255-4325 <$350
1929 Small Size
5 Type 1 1-900 <$175
10 Type 1 1-516 <$175
20 Type 1 1-152 <$175
5 Type 2 1-1956 <$200
10 Type 2 1-888 <$200
20 Type 2 1-264 <$200
Total Issue $453,690
Out in 1935 $23,700
Large out 1935 $870

4011 Monroe
EAST STROUDSBURG NB,
EAST STROUDSBURG
{{ 7 L 12 S }}
Chartered 4/17/89
Brown Back <$VALUE
4x5 1-4440 <$250
50-100 1-396 <$1250/$1500
1902 Date Back
4x5 1-3625 <$150
3x10-20 1-3420 <$150
1902 Plain Back
4x5 3626-14038 <$150
3x10-20 3421-10425 <$150
1929 Small Size
5 Type 1 1-2202 <$100
10 Type 1 1-1138 <$100
20 Type 1 1-326 <$100
5 Type 2 1-3660 <$100
10 Type 2 1-1584 <$100
20 Type 2 1-336 <$100
Total Issue $1,164,530
Out in 1935 $48,310
Large out 1935 $2,100

5578 Monroe
MONROE COUNTY NB OF
EAST STROUDSBURG
Chartered 9/17/00
2nd title: Monroe County NB
& TC 2/15/29
3rd title: Monroe County NB
1/14/33
FIRST TITLE {{ 4 L }}
Brown Back <$VALUE
4x5 1-3600 <$300
3x10-20 1-2690 <$300
1882 Date Back
4x5 1-4500 <$300
3x10-20 1-3420 <$300
1882 Value Back
4x5 4501-7900 <$300
3x10-20 3421-5320 <$300
1902 Plain Back
4x5 1-10145 <$150
3x10-20 1-5749 <$150
3x50-100 1-208 <$400/$500
SECOND TITLE {{ 8 S }}
1929 Small Size
5 Type 1 1-6390 <$65
10 Type 1 1-3346 <$65
20 Type 1 1-932 <$75
THIRD TITLE {{ 16 S }}
1929 Small Size
5 Type 1 1-1040 <$60
10 Type 1 1-308 <$60
20 Type 1 1-106 <$60
5 Type 2 1-15092 <$65
10 Type 2 1-7568 <$65
20 Type 2 1-2148 <$65
Total Issue $1,933,650
Out in 1935 $200,055
Large out 1935 $2,905

1233 Northampton
EASTON NB, EASTON
{{ 21 L U + 28 S }}
Chartered 1865
Original Series <$VALUE
4x5 1-5000 <$375
3x10-20 1-6250 <$750/$1250
50-50 1-3500 <$3500
Series 1875
3x10-20 1-750 <$750/$1250
50-50 1-6200 <$3500
Brown Back
50-100 1-3130 <$1250/$1500
1902 Red Seal
3x10-20 1-5500 <$175/$200
50-100 1-1134 <$2250/$2500
1902 Date Back
3x10-20 1-18000 <$85
50-100 1-1500* <$300/$350
* 1454,55,66,77,79,98,
and 1499 not issued
1902 Plain Back
3x10-20 18001-59181 <$85
1929 Small Size
5 Type 1 1-4920 <$30
10 Type 1 1-8658 <$30
20 Type 1 1-2532 <$40
5 Type 2 1-18532 <$30
10 Type 2 1-8040 <$30
20 Type 2 1-2010 <$40
Total Issue $6,701,780
Out in 1935 $215,850
Large out 1935 $15,760

1171 Northampton
FNB OF EASTON
Chartered 1865
2nd title: FNB & TC of
Easton 7/1/29
FIRST TITLE {{ 24 L }}
Original Series <$VALUE
4x5 1-9000 <$375
3x10-20 1-4400 <$750/$1250
50-100 1-2040 <$3500
Series 1875
4x5 1-3750 <$375
3x10-20 1-4748 <$750/$1250
50-100 1-2322 <$3500
Brown Back
4x5 1-4291 <$225
3x10-20 1-3735 <$225
50-100 1-1376 <$1250/$1500
1902 Red Seal
4x5 1-11250 <$225
3x10-20 1-9300 <$225
1902 Date Back
4x5 1-6750 <$85
3x10-20 1-35400 <$85
1902 Plain Back
4x5 6751-81144 <$85
3x10-20 35401-72707<$85
SECOND TITLE {{ U + 22 S }}
1929 Small Size
5 Type 1 1-17362 <$40
10 Type 1 1-6396 <$40
20 Type 1 1-1790 <$40
5 Type 2 1-21606 <$40
10 Type 2 1-5675 <$40
20 Type 2 1-2276 <$45
Total Issue $9,123,620
Out in 1935 $229,800
Large out 1935 $20,070

2385 Northampton
NORTHAMPTON COUNTY
NB OF EASTON
{{ 2 L }}
Chartered 5/22/78
Liquidated 5/1/98
Series 1875 <$VALUE
3x10-20 1-8204 <$750/$1250
Total Issue $410,200
Out in 1910 $3,100

5118 Northampton
NORTHAMPTON NB OF EASTON
{{ 8 L 7 S }}
Chartered 1898
Brown Back <$VALUE
3x10-20 1-9400 <$275
1882 Date Back
3x10-20 1-8900 <$275
1882 Value Back
3x10-20 8901-11149 <$275
1902 Plain Back
3x50-100 1-1910 <$400/$500
1929 Small Size
50 Type 1 1-322 <$200
100 Type 1 1-90 <$250
50 Type 2 1-108 <$350
100 Type 2 1-36 <$400
Total Issue $1,664,550
Out in 1935 $97,250
Large out 1935 $6,950

6209 Cambria
AMERICAN NB OF EBENSBURG
{{ 11 L 21 S }}
Chartered 4/16/02
1902 Red Seal <$VALUE
4x5 1-4850 <$350
3x10-20 1-4020 <$350
1902 Date Back
4x5 1-8750 <$175
3x10-20 1-6100 <$175
1902 Plain Back (dated 1902)
4x5 8751-17345 <$175
3x10-20 6101-10981 <$175
1902 Plain Back (dated 1922)
4x5 1-11554 <$175
3x10-20 1-8378 <$175
1929 Small Size
5 Type 1 1-4378 <$65
10 Type 1 1-2070 <$65
20 Type 1 1-548 <$75
5 Type 2 1-5812 <$85
10 Type 2 1-2796 <$85
20 Type 2 1-1056 <$85
Total Issue $2,243,370
Out in 1935 $100,000
Large out 1935 $4,640

5084 Cambria
FNB OF EBENSBURG
{{ 10 L 19 S }}
Chartered 1897
Brown Back <$VALUE
4x5 1-3625 <$275
3x10-20 1-3450 <$275
1882 Date Back
4x5 1-4300* <$275
3x10-20 1-3020** <$275
1882 Value Back
4x5 4501-5386* <$275
3x10-20 3181-3628** <$275
* 4301-4500 not marked
** 3021-3180 not marked
1902 Plain Back
4x5 1-18020 <$150
3x10-20 1-11162 <$150
1929 Small Size
5 Type 1 1-6500 <$50
10 Type 1 1-3210 <$50
20 Type 1 1-808 <$60
5 Type 2 1-6866 <$65
10 Type 2 1-4378 <$65
20 Type 2 1-1404 <$65
Total Issue $2,043,370
Out in 1935 $145,050
Large out 1935 $4,560

7528 Beaver
PEOPLES NB OF ECONOMY
{{ UNREPORTED }}
Chartered 12/27/04
Liquidated 2/1/09
1902 Red Seal <$VALUE
50-100 1-238 <$3000
Total Issue $35,700
Out in 1910 $4,250

6182 Clarion
CLARION COUNTY NB OF
EDENBURG
{{ 5 L 2U + 11 S }}
Chartered 3/31/02
1902 Red Seal <$VALUE
3x10-20 1-3150 <$350
1902 Date Back
3x10-20 1-3600 <$175
1902 Plain Back (dated 1902)
3x10-20 3601-6802 <$175
1902 Plain Back (dated 1922)
3x10-20 1-4857 <$175
1929 Small Size
10 Type 1 1-1334 <$100
20 Type 1 1-352 <$110
10 Type 2 1-1243 <$135
20 Type 2 1-254 <$135
Total Issue $880,240
Out in 1935 $50,000
Large out 1935 $2,130

7312 Erie
FNB OF EDINBORO
{{ 3 L 6 S }}
Chartered 6/04
1902 Red Seal <$VALUE
3x10-20 1-1100 <$600
1902 Date Back
3x10-20 1-2170 <$275
1902 Plain Back
3x10-20 2171-5831 <$275
1929 Small Size
10 Type 1 1-652 <$175
20 Type 1 1-170 <$175
10 Type 2 1-866 <$200
20 Type 2 1-194 <$200
Total Issue $418,610
Out in 1935 $24,700
Large out 1935 $1,260

8633 Luzerne
FNB OF EDWARDSVILLE
{{ 1 L }}
Chartered 4/07
Liquidated 1/3/10
1902 Red Seal <$VALUE
4x5 1-1300 <$1000
3x10-20 1-1140 <$1000
1902 Date Back
4x5 1-520 <$650
3x10-20 1-202 <$650
Total Issue $103,500
Out in 1910 $14,085

9862 Luzerne
PEOPLES NB OF
EDWARDSVILLE
{{ 7 L 18 S }}
Chartered 10/10
1902 Date Back <$VALUE
3x10-20 1-8400 <$175
1902 Plain Back
3x10-20 8401-30018 <$175
1929 Small Size
10 Type 1 1-3760 <$65
20 Type 1 1-1054 <$65
10 Type 2 1-6391 <$75
20 Type 2 1-1628 <$75
Total Issue $1,949,450
Out in 1935 $100,600
Large out 1935 $3,340

9416 McKean
FNB OF ELDRED
{{ 3 L 6 S }}
Chartered 5/09
1902 Date Back <$VALUE
4x5 1-2491 <$250
4x10 1-2242* <$250
1902 Plain Back
4x5 2492-8107 <$250
4x10 2343-6304* <$250
* 2243-2342 not marked
1929 Small Size
5 Type 1 1-1302 <$165
10 Type 1 1-726 <$165
5 Type 2 1-2802 <$185
10 Type 2 1-1478 <$185
Total Issue $525,710
Out in 1935 $25,000
Large out 1935 $1,150

5114 Allegheny
FNB OF ELIZABETH
{{ UNREPORTED }}
Organized 3/19/98
Receivership 12/19/13
Brown Back <$VALUE
4x5 1-2250 <$1000
50-100 1-437 <$1750/$2000
1882 Date Back
4x5 1-3072 <$1000
50-100 1-300 <$1750/$2000
3x50-100 1-122<$1750/$2000
Total Issue $247,490
Out in 1916 $14,750

3335 Lancaster
ELIZABETHTOWN NB,
ELIZABETHTOWN
Chartered 1885
2nd title: FNB & TC of
Elizabethtown 3/30/27
FIRST TITLE {{ 5 L }}
Brown Back <$VALUE
3x10-20 1-6728 <$450
1902 Red Seal
3x10-20 1-3500 <$450
1902 Date Back
3x10-20 1-8500 <$225
1902 Plain Back
3x10-20 8501-21616 <$225
SECOND TITLE {{ 2 L 16 S }}
1902 Plain Back
3x10-20 1-3304 <$250
1929 Small Size
10 Type 1 1-3580 <$75
20 Type 1 1-1064 <$75
10 Type 2 1-3940 <$85
20 Type 2 1-1195 <$85
Total Issue $2,163,180
Out in 1935 $121,150
Large out 1935 $5,180

FNB & TC of Elizabethtown
SEE Ch 3335
Elizabethtown NB,
Elizabethtown

<$VALUEs are for notes in **FINE** condition. Value changes by approximately **25%** for a change of one full grade.

****

5563 Dauphin
FNB OF ELIZABETHVILLE
{{ 5 L 6 S }}
Chartered 8/29/00
Brown Back <$VALUE
3x10-20 1-1800 <$400
1882 Date Back
3x10-20 1-2250 <$400
1882 Value Back
3x10-20 2251-3312 <$400
1902 Plain Back
3x10-20 1-3042 <$250
1929 Small Size
10 Type 1 1-782 <$175
20 Type 1 1-192 <$175
10 Type 2 1-855 <$200
20 Type 2 1-148 <$200
Total Issue $489,170
Out in 1935 $24,700
Large out 1935 $330

****

13030 Philadelphia
ELKINS PARK NB,
ELKINS PARK
{{ 8 S }}
Chartered 1/27
1929 Small Size <$VALUE
5 Type 1 1-2474 <$135
5 Type 2 1-19260 <$135
Total Issue $170,520
Out in 1935 $33,000

****

5043 Tioga
PATTISON NB OF ELKLAND
{{ 7 L 13 S }}
Chartered 1896
Brown Back <$VALUE
4x5 1-3925 <$300
3x10-20 1-2680 <$300
1882 Date Back
4x5 1-3750 <$300
3x10-20 1-2650 <$300
1882 Value Back
4x5 3751-4115 <$300
3x10-20 2651-2863 <$300
1902 Plain Back
3x10-20 1-8179 <$165
1929 Small Size
10 Type 1 1-1540 <$100
20 Type 1 1-330 <$110
10 Type 2 1-1820 <$125
20 Type 2 1-435 <$125
Total Issue $1,005,800
Out in 1935 $46,800
Large out 1935 $2,270

****

6929 Washington
NB OF ELLSWORTH
{{ 6 L 2 S }}
Chartered 8/03
Liquidated 4/17/34
1902 Red Seal <$VALUE
4x5 1-400 <$500
3x10-20 1-380 <$500
1902 Date Back
4x5 1-950* <$250
3x10-20 1-740** <$250
1902 Plain Back
4x5 1051-3020* <$250
3x10-20 801-1998** <$250
* 951-1050 not marked
** 741-800 not marked
1929 Small Size
5 Type 1 1-402 <$350
10 Type 1 1-203 <$350
20 Type 1 1-65 <$350
Total Issue $219,340
Out at close $10,000
Large out at close $760

****

11570 Lawrence
CITIZENS NB OF
ELLWOOD CITY
{{ 6 L 10 S }}
Chartered 12/19
Receivership 12/8/31
1902 Plain Back <$VALUE
3x10-20 1-16023 <$175
1929 Small Size
10 Type 1 1-2074 <$110
20 Type 1 1-589 <$120
Total Issue $996,270
Out at close $93,160
Large out at close $7,310

****

5899 Lawrence
ELLWOOD CITY NB,
ELLWOOD CITY
{{ UNREPORTED }}
Chartered 7/10/01
Liquidated 10/24/03
Brown Back <$VALUE
4x5 1-470 <$1500
3x10-20 1-354 <$1500
50-100 1-20 <$2500
Total Issue $30,100
Out in 1910 $605

****

4818 Lawrence
FNB OF ELLWOOD CITY
{{ 9 L 6 S }}
Organized 10/22/92
Receivership 1/10/33
Brown Back <$VALUE
4x5 1-1550 <$275
50-100 1-1126 <$1250/$1500
1882 Date Back
4x5 1-3010 <$275
50-100 1-580 <$1250/$1500
3x50-100 1-24 <$1250/$1500
1902 Date Back
4x5 1-2500 <$150
3x50-100 1-1098 <$400/$500
1902 Plain Back
4x5 2501-33362 <$150
3x50-100 1099-1441 <$400/$500
1929 Small Size
5 Type 1 1-3342 <$125
50 Type 1 1-194 <$200
100 Type 1 1-63 <$250
Total Issue $1,576,850
Out at close $100,000
Large out at close $12,660

****

8678 Lawrence
PEOPLES NB OF
ELLWOOD CITY
{{ 6 L 3 U + 16 S }}
Chartered 5/07
1902 Red Seal <$VALUE
4x5 1-410 <$350
3x10-20 1-328 <$350
1902 Date Back
4x5 1-2575 <$175
3x10-20 1-1880 <$175
1902 Plain Back
4x5 2576-13330 <$175
3x10-20 1881-8950 <$175
1929 Small Size
5 Type 1 1-2656 <$75
10 Type 1 1-1272 <$75
20 Type 1 1-350 <$85
5 Type 2 1-7556 <$100
10 Type 2 1-4704 <$100
20 Type 2 1-1380 <$100
Total Issue $1,049,120
Out in 1935 $96,350
Large out 1935 $2,010

****

10775 Chester
ELVERSON NB, ELVERSON
{{ 2 L 6 S }}
Chartered 9/15
1902 Plain Back <$VALUE
3x10-20 1-5161 <$600
1929 Small Size
10 Type 1 1-800 <$200
20 Type 1 1-200 <$200
10 Type 2 1-798 <$225
20 Type 2 1-244 <$225
Total Issue $342,910
Out in 1935 $25,000
Large out 1935 $1,010

****

10837 Northumberland
FNB OF ELYSBURG
{{ 2 L 6 S }}
Chartered 4/16
1902 Plain Back <$VALUE
3x10-20 1-4924 <$400
1929 Small Size
10 Type 1 1-864 <$175
20 Type 1 1-220 <$175
10 Type 2 1-936 <$200
20 Type 2 1-225 <$200
Total Issue $338,300
Out in 1935 $25,000
Large out 1935 $910

****

7139 Lehigh
EMAUS NB, EMAUS
{{ 8 L 18 S }}
Chartered 2/04
1902 Red Seal <$VALUE
4x5 1-3075 <$500
3x10-20 1-2350 <$500
1902 Date Back
4x5 1-6700 <$250
3x10-20 1-4720 <$250
1902 Plain Back
4x5 6701-22693 <$250
3x10-20 4721-14547 <$250
1929 Small Size
5 Type 1 1-3118 <$125
10 Type 1 1-1624 <$125
20 Type 1 1-446 <$125
5 Type 2 1-11412 <$150
10 Type 2 1-6016 <$150
20 Type 2 1-1880 <$150
Total Issue $1,759,530
Out in 1935 $123,150
Large out 1935 $3,230

****

5481 Venango
FARMERS NB OF EMLENTON
{{ 5 L 12 S }}
Chartered 7/2/00
Brown Back <$VALUE
3x10-20 1-3500 <$400
1882 Date Back
3x10-20 1-3840* <$400
1882 Value Back
3x10-20 4041-5803* <$400
* 3841-4040 not marked
1902 Plain Back
3x10-20 1-6487 <$200
1929 Small Size
10 Type 1 1-1432 <$110
20 Type 1 1-346 <$110
10 Type 2 1-2395 <$125
20 Type 2 1-548 <$125
Total Issue $951,850
Out in 1935 $48,900
Large out 1935 $2,270

****

4615 Venango
FNB OF EMLENTON
{{ 10 L 19 S }}
Chartered 1891
Brown Back <$VALUE
3x10-20 1-7810 <$350
1882 Date Back
3x10-20 1-2553 <$350
1902 Date Back
3x10-20 1-5100 <$150
1902 Plain Back
3x10-20 5101-22305 <$150
1929 Small Size
10 Type 1 1-2914 <$75
20 Type 1 1-740 <$85
10 Type 2 1-3983 <$85
20 Type 2 1-825 <$85
Total Issue $1,953,370
Out in 1935 $95,900
Large out 1935 $4,780

****

3255 Cameron
FNB OF EMPORIUM
{{ 10 L 13 S }}
Organized 9/23/84
Receivership 9/24/32
Brown Back <$VALUE
4x5 1-5100 <$300
3x10-20 1-1525 <$300
1902 Red Seal
4x5 1-4350 <$300
3x10-20 1-2900 <$300
50-100 1-240 <$2250/$2500
1902 Date Back
4x5 1-8250 <$150
3x10-20 1-5200 <$150
3x50-100 1-100 <$400/$500
1902 Plain Back
4x5 8251-44175 <$150
3x10-20 5201-28929 <$150
1929 Small Size
5 Type 1 1-6760 <$100
10 Type 1 1-3258 <$100
20 Type 1 1-873 <$110
Total Issue $3,304,240
Out at close $197,115
Large out at close $15,235

****

2515 Lancaster
EPHRATA NB, EPHRATA
{{ 8 L 22 S }}
Chartered 1881
Series 1875 <$VALUE
3x10-20 1-5697 <$850/$1500
Brown Back
4x5 1-2500 <$400
3x10-20 1-4500 <$400
1882 Date Back
4x5 1-11250 <$400
3x10-20 1-7600 <$400
1882 Value Back
4x5 11251-18475 <$400
3x10-20 7601-11879 <$400
1902 Plain Back
3x10-20 1-15153 <$200
1929 Small Size
10 Type 1 1-3730 <$100
20 Type 1 1-952 <$100
10 Type 2 1-5510 <$110
20 Type 2 1-1358 <$110
Total Issue $2,701,250
Out in 1935 $121,450
Large out 1935 $4,760

****

4923 Lancaster
FARMERS NB OF EPHRATA
{{ 10 L 17 S }}
Chartered 1893
Brown Back <$VALUE
4x5 1-9590 <$400
3x10-20 1-3124 <$400
1882 Date Back
4x5 1-4015 <$400
3x10-20 1-3024 <$400
1902 Date Back
4x5 1-2175 <$200
3x10-20 1-1740 <$200
1902 Plain Back
4x5 2176-16640 <$200
3x10-20 1741-10796 <$200
1929 Small Size
5 Type 1 1-3194 <$125
10 Type 1 1-1540 <$125
20 Type 1 1-474 <$135
5 Type 2 1-4048 <$150
10 Type 2 1-2363 <$150
20 Type 2 1-554 <$150
Total Issue $1,752,150
Out in 1935 $72,995
Large out 1935 $3,005

****

12 Erie
FNB OF ERIE
{{ 21 L 36 S }}
Organized 3/30/63
Original Series <$VALUE
4x5 1-3800 <$500
4x10 1-3250 <$750
4x20 1-1250 <$1250
Series 1875
4x5 1-998 <$500
4x10 1-923 <$750
4x20 1-789 <$1250
Brown Back
3x10-20 1-3898 <$250
1902 Red Seal
3x10-20 1-5360 <$250
1902 Date Back
4x5 1-12500 <$110
3x10-20 1-18800 <$110
1902 Plain Back
3x10-20 18801-67674 <$110
1929 Small Size
10 Type 1 1-8460 <$40
20 Type 1 1-2222 <$50
10 Type 2 1-11076 <$40
20 Type 2 1-2571 <$50
Total Issue $5,459,020
Out in 1935 $267,900
Large out 1935 $14,820

****

535 Erie
KEYSTONE NB OF ERIE
{{ 3 L }}
Chartered 10/64
Receivership 7/26/97
Original Series <$VALUE
3x1-2 1-9100 <$500/$1250
4x5 1-9850 <$600
3x10-20 1-3300 <$750/$1250
Series 1875
4x5 1-1230 <$600
3x10-20 1-4300 <$750/$1250
Brown Back
4x5 1-1150 <$500
3x10-20 1-2800 <$500
Total Issue $810,100
Out in 1910 $4,806

****

870 Erie
MARINE NB OF ERIE
{{ 18 L 33 S }}
Chartered 3/9/65
Original Series <$VALUE
3x1-2 1-3400 <$350/$1000
4x5 1-2250 <$375
3x10-20 1-1520 <$750/$1250
50-100 1-760 <$3500
Series 1875
4x5 1-990 <$375
3x10-20 1-3640 <$750/$1250
Brown Back
3x10-20 1-15730 <$225
1902 Red Seal
3x10-20 1-5300 <$250
1902 Date Back
3x10-20 1-10700 <$100
1902 Plain Back
3x10-20 10701-61208 <$100
1929 Small Size
10 Type 1 1-9234 <$25
20 Type 1 1-2220 <$35
10 Type 2 1-7561 <$25
20 Type 2 1-2421 <$35
Total Issue $5,510,170
Out in 1935 $293,400
Large out 1935 $11,520

****

14219 Erie
NB & TC OF ERIE
{{ 13 S }}
Chartered 7/34
1929 Small Size <$VALUE
10 Type 2 1-4415 <$65
20 Type 2 1-3060 <$85
50 Type 2 1-2033 <$185
100 Type 2 1-1017 <$250
Total Issue $308,700
Out in 1935 $300,000

****

606 Erie
SECOND NB OF ERIE
{{ 22 L 46 S }}
Organized 11/14/64
Receivership 8/13/34
Original Series <$VALUE
3x1-2 1-10000 <$350/$1000
4x5 1-10250 <$375
3x10-20 1-7100 <$750/$1250
Series 1875
3x10-20 1-6988 <$750/$1250
Brown Back
3x10-20 1-9418 <$225
1902 Red Seal
4x5 1-2500 <$250
3x10-20 1-4900 <$250
1902 Date Back
4x5 1-25000 <$100
3x10-20 1-17700 <$100
1902 Plain Back
3x10-20 17701-60416 <$100
1929 Small Size
10 Type 1 1-6830 <$25
20 Type 1 1-2072 <$35
10 Type 2 1-1978 <$35
20 Type 2 1-655 <$45
Total Issue $5,937,420
Out at close $250,000
Large out at close $18,680

****

6453 Allegheny
FNB OF ETNA
{{ 8 L 16 S }}
Chartered 10/10/02
1902 Red Seal <$VALUE
4x5 1-830 <$300
3x10-20 1-670 <$300
1902 Date Back
4x5 1-1275 <$150
3x10-20 1-1000 <$150
1902 Plain Back
4x5 1276-26556 <$150
3x10-20 1001-6750 <$150
1929 Small Size
5 Type 1 1-13918 <$85
5 Type 2 1-28968 <$85
Total Issue $1,481,100
Out in 1935 $98,400
Large out 1935 $2,760

****

8854 Butler
CITIZENS NB OF EVANS CITY
{{ 3 L 6 S }}
Chartered 9/07
1902 Red Seal <$VALUE
3x10-20 1-700 <$600
1902 Date Back
3x10-20 1-2400* <$325
1902 Plain Back
3x10-20 2601-6931* <$325
* 2401-2600 not marked
1929 Small Size
10 Type 1 1-696 <$200
20 Type 1 1-194 <$200
10 Type 2 1-793 <$225
20 Type 2 1-276 <$225
Total Issue $460,040
Out in 1935 $23,950
Large out 1935 $1,050

****

6220 Bedford
FNB OF EVERETT
{{ 4 L 10 S }}
Chartered 4/22/02
1902 Red Seal <$VALUE
4x5 1-450 <$450
3x10-20 1-360 <$450
1902 Date Back
4x5 1-1850 <$200
3x10-20 1-1380 <$200
1902 Plain Back (dated 1902)
4x5 1851-3580 <$200
3x10-20 1381-2462 <$200
1902 Plain Back (dated 1922)
4x5 1-3790 <$200
3x10-20 1-2323 <$200
1929 Small Size
5 Type 1 1-2510 <$135
10 Type 1 1-1130 <$135
20 Type 1 1-352 <$135
5 Type 2 1-2876 <$150
10 Type 2 1-1797 <$150
20 Type 2 1-504 <$150
Total Issue $641,420
Out in 1935 $60,000
Large out 1935 $1,810

****

8410 Montour
FARMERS NB OF EXCHANGE
{{ 4 L 6 S }}
Chartered 10/06
Liquidated 3/25/33
1902 Red Seal <$VALUE
4x5 1-500 <$500
3x10-20 1-440 <$500
1902 Date Back
4x5 1-1950 <$250
3x10-20 1-1530 <$250
1902 Plain Back
4x5 1951-7141 <$250
3x10-20 1531-4546 <$250
1929 Small Size
5 Type 1 1-830 <$200
10 Type 1 1-451 <$200
20 Type 1 1-134 <$200
Total Issue $470,160
Out at close $22,960
Large out at close $1,520

****

13177 Luzerne
FNB OF EXETER
{{ 12 S }}
Organized 7/8/27
1929 Small Size <$VALUE
5 Type 1 1-2402 <$125
10 Type 1 1-1304 <$125
20 Type 1 1-370 <$125
5 Type 2 1-5002 <$135
10 Type 2 1-2399 <$135
20 Type 2 1-737 <$135
Total Issue $258,440
Out in 1935 $39,200

****

7624 Westmoreland
FNB OF EXPORT
{{ 2 L 4 S }}
Chartered 2/05
Liquidated 4/30/34
1902 Red Seal <$VALUE
3x10-20 1-700 <$750
1902 Date Back
3x10-20 1-1430 <$375
1902 Plain Back
3x10-20 1431-4275 <$375
1929 Small Size
10 Type 1 1-440 <$250
20 Type 1 1-135 <$250
Total Issue $291,350
Out at close $15,000
Large out 1935 $780
Ch 14051 assumed circulation

****

14051 Westmoreland
FNB OF EXPORT
{{ 1 S }}
Chartered 3/34
1929 Small Size <$VALUE
10 Type 2 1-395 <$650
20 Type 2 1-96 <$650
Total Issue $5,870
Out in 1935 $15,000
Large out 1935 $780
Outstanding includes Ch 7624

****

9130 Wyoming
FNB OF FACTORYVILLE
{{ 3 L 7 S }}
Chartered 5/08
1902 Date Back <$VALUE
3x10-20 1-3950 <$500
1902 Plain Back
3x10-20 3951-10333 <$500
1929 Small Size
10 Type 1 1-960 <$175
20 Type 1 1-288 <$175
10 Type 2 1-893 <$200
20 Type 2 1-155 <$200
Total Issue $620,840
Out in 1935 $24,150
Large out 1935 $180

****

8245 Fayette
FNB OF FAIRCHANCE
{{ 4 L 4 S }}
Chartered 6/06
Receivership 2/26/31
1902 Red Seal <$VALUE
3x10-20 1-300 <$750
1902 Date Back
3x10-20 1-700 <$375
1902 Plain Back
3x10-20 701-4045 <$375
1929 Small Size
10 Type 1 1-377 <$275
20 Type 1 1-108 <$275
Total Issue $252,830
Out at close $24,700
Large out at close $2,990

****

9256 Adams
FNB OF FAIRFIELD
{{ 3 L 9 S }}
Chartered 10/08
1902 Date Back <$VALUE
3x10-20 1-2460 <$350
1902 Plain Back
3x10-20 2461-6339 <$350
1929 Small Size
5 Type 1 1-758 <$135
10 Type 1 1-730 <$135
20 Type 1 1-238 <$135
5 Type 2 1-1584 <$150
10 Type 2 1-876 <$150
20 Type 2 1-204 <$150
Total Issue $432,810
Out in 1935 $34,380
Large out 1935 $2,410

6384 Jefferson
FNB OF FALLS CREEK
{{ 5 L 12 S }}
Chartered 8/16/02
1902 Red Seal <$VALUE
3x10-20 1-2000 <$450
1902 Date Back
3x10-20 1-4540 <$225
1902 Plain Back
3x10-20 4541-13702 <$225
1929 Small Size
10 Type 1 1-1514 <$125
20 Type 1 1-420 <$125
10 Type 2 1-1876 <$150
20 Type 2 1-599 <$150
Total Issue $957,080
Out in 1935 $48,950
Large out 1935 $2,450

10415 Mercer
FNB OF FARRELL
{{ 4 L }}
Chartered 6/13
Liquidated 11/20/23
1902 Date Back <$VALUE
3x10-20 1-4000 <$300
1902 Plain Back
3x10-20 4001-13477 <$300
Total Issue $673,850
Out at close $84,900

9385 York
FNB OF FAWN GROVE
{{ 3 L 14 S }}
Chartered 4/09
1902 Date Back <$VALUE
3x10-20 1-2660 <$650
1902 Plain Back
3x10-20 2661-7016 <$650
1929 Small Size
10 Type 1 1-776 <$400
20 Type 1 1-210 <$400
10 Type 2 1-876 <$400
20 Type 2 1-245 <$400
Total Issue $436,220
Out in 1935 $24,350
Large out 1935 $850

6800 Fayette
FAYETTE CITY NB
{{ 6 L }}
Chartered 5/03
Receivership 7/28/27
1902 Red Seal <$VALUE
4x5 1-1500 <$350
3x10-20 1-750 <$350
50-100 1-1250 <$2250/$2500
1902 Date Back
4x5 1-6100 <$175
3x10-20 1-3860 <$175
50-100 1-200 <$400/$500
1902 Plain Back
4x5 6101-18566 <$175
3x10-20 3861-11352 <$175
Total Issue $1,223,920
Out at close $69,400

5646 Fayette
FNB OF FAYETTE CITY
{{ UNREPORTED }}
Chartered 12/18/00
Liquidated 8/1/03
Brown Back <$VALUE
3x10-20 1-842 <$1250
Total Issue $42,100
Out in 1910 $1,030

6420 Washington
FNB OF FINLEYVILLE
{{ 3 L 6 S }}
Chartered 9/12/02
Receivership 1/4/34
1902 Red Seal <$VALUE
4x5 1-1525 <$650
3x10-20 1-1080 <$650
1902 Date Back
4x5 1-2325 <$325
3x10-20 1-1600 <$325
1902 Plain Back
4x5 2326-7626 <$325
3x10-20 1601-4733 <$325
1929 Small Size
5 Type 1 1-820 <$200
10 Type 1 1-516 <$200
20 Type 1 1-146 <$200
5 Type 2 1-244 <$225
10 Type 2 1-115 <$225
20 Type 2 1-54 <$225
Total Issue $550,200
Out at close $25,000
Large out at close $1,140

8939 Berks
FNB OF FLEETWOOD
Chartered 11/07
Receivership 2/27/34
2nd title: FNB & TC 2/1/30
FIRST TITLE {{ 4 L 4 S }}
1902 Red Seal <$VALUE
3x10-20 1-590 <$500
1902 Date Back
3x10-20 1-2140* <$250
1902 Plain Back
3x10-20 2341-17079* <$250
* 2141-2340 not marked
1929 Small Size
10 Type 1 1-1076 <$125
20 Type 1 1-366 <$125
SECOND TITLE {{ 16 S }}
1929 Small Size
10 Type 1 1-2668 <$85
20 Type 1 1-756 <$100
10 Type 2 1-1395 <$100
20 Type 2 1-370 <$100
Total Issue $1,264,080
Out at close $125,000
Large out at close $3,860

12975 Lehigh
FOGELSVILLE NB, FOGELSVILLE
{{ 5 S }}
Chartered 8/26
1929 Small Size <$VALUE
10 Type 1 1-316 <$225
20 Type 1 1-106 <$225
10 Type 2 1-1189 <$225
20 Type 2 1-330 <$225
Total Issue $50,170
Out in 1935 $23,950

5130 Armstrong
FNB OF FORD CITY
Organized 6/24/98
Receivership 6/4/34
2nd title: FNB & TC of Ford City 2/7/23
FIRST TITLE {{ 4 L }}
Brown Back <$VALUE
3x10-20 1-2990 <$450
1882 Date Back
3x10-20 1-4400 <$450
1882 Value Back
3x10-20 4401-5494 <$450
1902 Plain Back
3x10-20 1-3300 <$250
SECOND TITLE {{ 1 L 5 S }}
1902 Plain Back
3x50-100 1-1591 <$500/$600
1929 Small Size
50 Type 1 1-353 <$225
100 Type 1 1-113 <$275
Total Issue $1,160,650
Out at close $124,100
Large out at close $11,400

9248 Susquehanna
FARMERS & MINERS NB OF FOREST CITY
{{ 5 L 12 S }}
Chartered 10/08
Receivership 8/10/34
1902 Date Back <$VALUE
3x10-20 1-5200 <$250
1902 Plain Back
3x10-20 5201-15665 <$250
1929 Small Size
10 Type 1 1-1632 <$125
20 Type 1 1-446 <$125
10 Type 2 1-1367 <$135
20 Type 2 1-536 <$135
Total Issue $959,080
Out at close $50,000
Large out at close $1,990

14205 Susquehanna
F & FARMERS NB OF FOREST CITY
{{ 6 S }}
Chartered 6/34
1929 Small Size <$VALUE
10 Type 2 1-4355 <$250
20 Type 2 1-1305 <$250
Total Issue $69,650
Out in 1935 $49,750

5518 Susquehanna
FNB OF FOREST CITY
{{ 4 L 13 S }}
Chartered 7/26/00
Receivership 8/10/34
Brown Back <$VALUE
3x10-20 1-1800 <$500
1882 Date Back
3x10-20 1-5700* <$500
1882 Value Back
3x10-20 5951-8300* <$500
* 5701-5950 not marked
1902 Plain Back
3x10-20 1-6807 <$275
1929 Small Size
10 Type 1 1-1688 <$100
20 Type 1 1-426 <$110
5 Type 2 1-211 <$150
10 Type 2 1-736 <$150
20 Type 2 1-274 <$150
Total Issue $1,011,645
Out at close $50,000
Large out at close $1,985

7860 Schuylkill
FNB OF FRACKVILLE
Chartered 8/05
Receivership 4/23/34
2nd title: FNB & TC of Frackville 2/20/24
FIRST TITLE {{ 5 L }}
1902 Red Seal <$VALUE
3x10-20 1-2460 <$600
1902 Date Back
3x10-20 1-5140 <$250
1902 Plain Back
3x10-20 5141-10890 <$250
SECOND TITLE {{ 3 L 10 S }}
1902 Plain Back
4x5 1-15547 <$250
1929 Small Size
5 Type 1 1-7136 <$125
5 Type 2 1-8068 <$125
Total Issue $1,232,860
Out at close $50,000
Large out at close $2,570

189 Venango
FNB OF FRANKLIN
{{ 14 L }}
Chartered 1/64
Liquidated 12/15/23
Original Series <$VALUE
3x1-2 1-2000 <$350/$850
4x5 1-7000 <$375
3x10-20 1-1500 <$750/$1250
Series 1875
3x1-2 1-480 <$350/$850
4x5 1-990 <$375
3x10-20 1-1054 <$750/$1250
Brown Back
3x10-20 1-6896 <$225/$250
1902 Red Seal
3x10-20 1-7350 <$250/$275
1902 Date Back
3x10-20 1-12900 <$125
1902 Plain Back
3x10-20 12901-30353 <$125
Total Issue $2,529,850
Out at close $195,295

5221 Venango
LAMBERTON NB OF FRANKLIN
{{ 12 L 38 S }}
Chartered 10/9/99
Brown Back <$VALUE
3x10-20 1-8100 <$250
1882 Date Back
4x5 1-7265 <$250
3x10-20 1-4780 <$250
1882 Value Back
4x5 7266-11135 <$250
3x10-20 4781-6677 <$250
1902 Plain Back
3x10-20 1-18382 <$135
1929 Small Size
10 Type 1 1-6202 <$30
20 Type 1 1-1672 <$35
10 Type 2 1-11745 <$30
20 Type 2 1-2998 <$35
Total Issue $2,630,820
Out in 1935 $212,295
Large out 1935 $5,155

1176 Venango
VENANGO NB OF FRANKLIN
{{ UNREPORTED }}
Organized 5/20/65
Receivership 5/1/66
Original Series <$VALUE
4x5 1-4000 <$1500
3x10-20 1-100 <$1500/$2000
Total Issue $85,000
Out in 1916 $195

8783 Lebanon
FNB OF FREDERICKSBURG
{{ 1 L 8 S }}
Chartered 7/07
1902 Red Seal <$VALUE
3x10-20 1-240 <$800
1902 Date Back
3x10-20 1-840* <$400
1902 Plain Back
3x10-20 961-2990* <$400
* 841-960 not marked
1929 Small Size
10 Type 1 1-604 <$165
20 Type 1 1-186 <$165
10 Type 2 1-3198 <$175
20 Type 2 1-680 <$175
Total Issue $265,640
Out in 1935 $48,300
Large out 1935 $450

5920 Washington
FNB OF FREDERICKTOWN
{{ 2 L 6 S }}
Chartered 7/27/01
Brown Back <$VALUE
3x10-20 1-1200 <$600
1882 Date Back
3x10-20 1-2450 <$600
1882 Value Back
3x10-20 2451-3767 <$600
1902 Plain Back
3x10-20 1-3134 <$350
1929 Small Size
10 Type 1 1-730 <$175
20 Type 1 1-190 <$175
10 Type 2 1-984 <$225
20 Type 2 1-306 <$225
Total Issue $487,610
Out in 1935 $25,000
Large out 1935 $1,110

7471 Mercer
FREDONIA NB, FREDONIA
{{ 3 L 6 S }}
Chartered 11/04
Liquidated 3/20/34
1902 Red Seal <$VALUE
3x10-20 1-1325 <$600
1902 Date Back
3x10-20 1-2300 <$300
1902 Plain Back
3x10-20 2301-6967 <$300
1929 Small Size
10 Type 1 1-804 <$200
20 Type 1 1-165 <$200
Total Issue $482,640
Out at close $25,000
Large out at close $1,330
Ch 13884 assumed circulation

13884 Mercer
FREDONIA NB, FREDONIA
{{ 4 S }}
Chartered 12/33
1929 Small Size <$VALUE
10 Type 2 1-761 <$300
20 Type 2 1-179 <$300
Total Issue $11,190
Out in 1935 $24,250
Large out 1935 $1,330
Outstanding includes Ch 7471

5454 Beaver
FREEDOM NB, FREEDOM
{{ 12 L 18 S }}
Chartered 6/26/00
Brown Back <$VALUE
4x5 1-5700 <$300
3x10-20 1-5650 <$300
1882 Date Back
4x5 1-390 <$300
3x10-20 1-9200 <$300
1882 Value Back
3x10-20 9201-13646 <$300
1902 Plain Back
3x10-20 1-14195 <$150
1929 Small Size
10 Type 1 1-2738 <$60
20 Type 1 1-840 <$65
10 Type 2 1-3814 <$65
20 Type 2 1-921 <$75
Total Issue $2,117,990
Out in 1935 $86,000
Large out 1935 $6,440
Outstanding includes Ch 9543

9543 Beaver
SAINT CLAIR NB OF FREEDOM
{{ 2 L }}
Chartered 9/09
Liquidated 1/8/18
1902 Date Back <$VALUE
4x5 1-7150 <$350
3x10-20 1-5060 <$350
1902 Plain Back
4x5 7151-8865 <$350
3x10-20 5061-6135 <$350
Total Issue $484,050
Out at close $71,300
Ch 5454 assumed circulation

6175 Luzerne
FNB OF FREELAND
{{ 7 L 10 S }}
Chartered 3/27/02
Receivership 2/28/34
1902 Red Seal <$VALUE
4x5 1-2730 <$350
3x10-20 1-2148 <$350
1902 Date Back
4x5 1-6600 <$175
3x10-20 1-4880 <$175
1902 Plain Back (dated 1902)
4x5 6601-13420 <$175
3x10-20 4881-8965 <$175
1902 Plain Back (dated 1922)
4x5 1-9621 <$175
3x10-20 1-6441 <$175
1929 Small Size
5 Type 1 1-3122 <$100
10 Type 1 1-1618 <$100
20 Type 1 1-478 <$110
5 Type 2 1-1482 <$135
10 Type 2 1-518 <$135
20 Type 2 1-240 <$135
Total Issue $1,658,610
Out at close $75,000
Large out at close $3,250

7366 Armstrong
FARMERS NB OF FREEPORT
{{ 4 L 7 S }}
Chartered 8/04
Receivership 12/13/33
1902 Red Seal <$VALUE
3x10-20 1-2650 <$450
1902 Date Back
3x10-20 1-4840 <$225
1902 Plain Back
3x10-20 4841-14425 <$225
1929 Small Size
10 Type 1 1-1384 <$135
20 Type 1 1-354 <$135
10 Type 2 1-217 <$175
20 Type 2 1-40 <$175
Total Issue $982,240
Out at close $50,000
Large out at close $3,620

2286 Armstrong
FNB OF FREEPORT
{{ 2 L }}
Chartered 7/21/75
Liquidated 10/10/84
Series 1875 <$VALUE
3x10-20 1-1700<$1000/$1500
Total Issue $85,000
Out in 1910 $430

13826 Armstrong
FNB OF FREEPORT
{{ 2U + 3 S }}
Chartered 11/33
1929 Small Size <$VALUE
5 Type 2 1-3282 <$250
10 Type 2 1-1512 <$250
20 Type 2 1-456 <$250
Total Issue $40,650
Out in 1935 $24,350

9480 Clarion
FNB OF FRYBURG
{{ 3 L 5 S }}
Chartered 7/09
1902 Date Back <$VALUE
3x10-20 1-2220 <$300
1902 Plain Back
3x10-20 2221-6111 <$300
1929 Small Size
10 Type 1 1-694 <$165
20 Type 1 1-190 <$165
10 Type 2 1-656 <$175
20 Type 2 1-180 <$175
Total Issue $380,150
Out in 1935 $22,950
Large out 1935 $1,160

7280 Potter
FNB OF GALETON
{{ 5 L 11 S }}
Chartered 5/04
1902 Red Seal <$VALUE
3x10-20 1-2873 <$350
1902 Date Back
3x10-20 1-4600 <$175
1902 Plain Back
3x10-20 4601-12891 <$175
1929 Small Size
10 Type 1 1-1298 <$100
20 Type 1 1-392 <$100
10 Type 2 1-1626 <$100
20 Type 2 1-329 <$100
Total Issue $935,960
Out in 1935 $48,350
Large out 1935 $2,240

14181 Cambria
FNB AT GALLITZIN
{{ UNREPORTED }}
Chartered 6/34
1929 Small Size <$VALUE
5 Type 2 1-940 <$750
10 Type 2 1-432 <$750
20 Type 2 1-143 <$750
Total Issue $11,880
Out in 1935 $24,290
Outstanding includes Ch 13533

13533 Cambria
FNB IN GALLITZIN
{{ 5 S }}
Chartered 3/31
Liquidated 7/16/34
1929 Small Size <$VALUE
5 Type 1 1-356 <$200
10 Type 1 1-296 <$200
20 Type 1 1-56 <$200
5 Type 2 1-842 <$225
10 Type 2 1-430 <$225
20 Type 2 1-70 <$225
Total Issue $45,070
Out at close $23,250
Large out at close $790
Outstanding includes Ch 6442

6442 Cambria
FNB OF GALLITZIN
{{ 1 L 2 S }}
Chartered 9/29/02
Liquidated 7/29/31
1902 Red Seal <$VALUE
3x10-20 1-560 <$750
1902 Date Back
3x10-20 1-1830 <$375
1902 Plain Back
3x10-20 1831-6894 <$375
1929 Small Size
10 Type 1 1-414 <$300
20 Type 1 1-107 <$300
Total Issue $410,380
Out at close $19,260
Large out 1935 $710
Ch 13533 assumed circulation

2864 Lancaster
GAP NB, GAP
Chartered 1883
2nd title: Gap NB & TC 3/15/30
3rd title: Gap NB 2/1/35
FIRST TITLE {{ 4 L 2 S }}
Brown Back <$VALUE
3x10-20 1-3658 <$500
1902 Red Seal
3x10-20 1-3150 <$500
1902 Date Back
3x10-20 1-4480 <$250
1902 Plain Back
3x10-20 4481-13507 <$250
1929 Small Size
10 Type 1 1-624 <$100
20 Type 1 1-210 <$100
SECOND TITLE {{ 50+ S }}
1929 Small Size
10 Type 1 1-734 <$40
20 Type 1 1-232 <$50
5 Type 2 1-324 <$65
10 Type 2 1-1548 <$65
20 Type 2 1-465 <$65
THIRD TITLE {{ 1 S }}
1929 Small Size
10 Type 2 1-130 <$150
Total Issue $1,177,970
Out in 1935 $48,750
Large out 1935 $2,405

****
6741 Somerset
FNB OF GARRETT
{{ 3 L 5 S }}
Chartered 4/03
1902 Red Seal <$VALUE
3x10-20 1-680 <$600
1902 Date Back
3x10-20 1-2190* <$300
1902 Plain Back
3x10-20 2311-6399* <$300
1929 Small Size
10 Type 1 1-650 <$175
20 Type 1 1-178 <$175
10 Type 2 1-669 <$200
20 Type 2 1-120 <$200
Total Issue $423,400
Out in 1935 $20,600
Large out 1935 $850
****
9783 Potter
FNB OF GENESEE
{{ 3 L 6 S }}
Chartered 6/10
1902 Date Back <$VALUE
3x10-20 1-2020 <$300
1902 Plain Back
3x10-20 2021-6440 <$300
1929 Small Size
10 Type 1 1-736 <$175
20 Type 1 1-210 <$175
5 Type 2 1-840 <$175
10 Type 2 1-624 <$175
20 Type 2 1-204 <$175
Total Issue $405,880
Out in 1935 $25,000
Large out 1935 $1,240
****
311 Adams
FNB OF GETTYSBURG
{{ 10 L 26 S }}
Chartered 3/64
Original Series <$VALUE
4x5 1-4400 <$500
3x10-20 1-1640 <$750/$1250
Series 1875
3x10-20 1-2046 <$750/$1250
Brown Back
3x10-20 1-2688 <$300
1902 Red Seal
3x10-20 1-3240 <$325
1902 Date Back
3x10-20 1-8800 <$150
1902 Plain Back
3x10-20 8801-28559 <$150
1929 Small Size
5 Type 1 1-6896 <$50
10 Type 1 1-3740 <$50
20 Type 1 1-1092 <$60
5 Type 2 1-9214 <$65
10 Type 2 1-5734 <$65
20 Type 2 1-1656 <$65
Total Issue $2,695,500
Out in 1935 $153,470
Large out 1935 $6,520
****
611 Adams
GETTYSBURG NB, GETTYSBURG
{{ 14 L 19 S }}
Chartered 12/64
Original Series <$VALUE
4x5 1-4500 <$400
3x10-20 1-2600 <$750/$1250
50-100 1-250 <$3500
Series 1875
4x5 1-3070 <$400
3x10-20 1-1888 <$750/$1250
50-100 1-131 <$3500
Brown Back
4x5 1-7757 <$250
3x10-20 1-8606 <$250
50-100 1-530 <$1250/$1500
1902 Red Seal
4x5 1-4750 <$275
3x10-20 1-3500 <$275
1902 Date Back
4x5 1-10750 <$135
3x10-20 1-8200 <$135
1902 Plain Back
4x5 10751-41872 <$135
3x10-20 8201-26927 <$135
1929 Small Size
5 Type 1 1-10242 <$50
10 Type 1 1-5542 <$50
20 Type 1 1-1388 <$60
5 Type 2 1-10330 <$65
10 Type 2 1-4820 <$65
20 Type 2 1-1026 <$65
Total Issue $4,478,390
Out in 1935 $137,990
Large out 1935 $9,530
****

****
54 Erie
FNB OF GIRARD
{{ 2 L }}
Chartered 8/63
Liquidated 6/1/82
Original Series <$VALUE
4x5 1-4000 <$750
4x10 1-3225 <$1000
Series 1875
4x10 1-1153 <$1000
Total Issue $255,120
Out in 1910 $1,935
****
7343 Erie
NB OF GIRARD
{{ 7 L 14 S }}
Chartered 7/04
Liquidated 8/1/34
1902 Red Seal <$VALUE
3x10-20 1-2300 <$325
1902 Date Back
3x10-20 1-3800 <$175
1902 Plain Back
3x10-20 3801-22758 <$175
1929 Small Size
10 Type 1 1-3448 <$70
20 Type 1 1-1014 <$75
10 Type 2 1-156 <$85
Total Issue $1,583,020
Out in 1935 $55,360
Large out 1935 $4,500
****
4422 Schuylkill
FNB OF GIRARDVILLE
{{ 4 L 14 S }}
Chartered 1890
Brown Back <$VALUE
3x10-20 1-1810 <$500
1882 Date Back
3x10-20 1-1659 <$500
1902 Date Back
3x10-20 1-3940 <$300
1902 Plain Back
3x10-20 3941-14319 <$300
1929 Small Size
10 Type 1 1-1614 <$150
20 Type 1 1-442 <$150
10 Type 2 1-1863 <$175
20 Type 2 1-427 <$175
Total Issue $1,066,450
Out in 1935 $43,500
Large out 1935 $3,020
****
5708 Allegheny
GLASSPORT NB, GLASSPORT
{{ 1 L }}
Chartered 2/11/01
Liquidated 3/24/06
Brown Back <$VALUE
3x10-20 1-2823 <$1000
Total Issue $141,150
Out in 1910 $4,725
****
5204 Indiana
FNB OF GLEN CAMPBELL
{{ 10 L 50+ S }}
Chartered 7/8/99
Receivership 12/7/31
Brown Back <$VALUE
4x5 1-2225 <$350
3x10-20 1-1670 <$350
50-100 1-295 <$1250/$1500
1882 Date Back
4x5 1-7600 <$350
3x10-20 1-4420 <$350
50-100 1-100 <$1250/$1500
3x50-100 1-142<$1250/$1500
1882 Value Back
4x5 7601-10285 <$350
3x10-20 4421-5855 <$350
1902 Plain Back
4x5 1-15395 <$175
3x10-20 1-10792 <$175
1929 Small Size
5 Type 1 1-2712 <$65
10 Type 1 1-1310 <$65
20 Type 1 1-329 <$75
Total Issue $1,768,140
Out at close $98,620
Large out at close $10,920
****
13160 Luzerne
GLEN LYON NB, GLEN LYON
{{ 2 L 16 S }}
Chartered 1/3/28
1902 Plain Back <$VALUE
4x5 1-3145 <$450
3x10-20 1-2199 <$450
1929 Small Size
5 Type 1 1-4096 <$100
10 Type 1 1-1994 <$100
20 Type 1 1-514 <$110
5 Type 2 1-8284 <$125
10 Type 2 1-4260 <$125
20 Type 2 1-1152 <$125

Total Issue $584,110
Out in 1935 $73,550
Large out 1935 $690
****
435 York
FNB OF GLEN ROCK
{{ 3 L }}
Chartered 5/64
Liquidated 3/15/19
Original Series <$VALUE
4x5 1-6750 <$850
Series 1875
4x5 1-4770 <$850
Brown Back
4x5 1-9878 <$750
3x10-20 1-1105 <$750
1902 Red Seal
4x5 1-2750 <$750
3x10-20 1-1920 <$750
1902 Date Back
4x5 1-3600 <$375
3x10-20 1-2540 <$375
1902 Plain Back
4x5 3601-5203 <$375
3x10-20 2541-3476 <$375
Total Issue $912,070
Out at close $50,000
****
9668 Montgomery
GLENSIDE NB, GLENSIDE
{{ 3 L }}
Chartered 2/10
Liquidated 6/30/25
1902 Date Back <$VALUE
3x10-20 1-1100* <$500
1902 Plain Back
3x10-20 1341-6820* <$500
3x50-100 1-769 <$750/$850
* 1101-1340 not marked
Total Issue $533,250
Out at close $116,850
****
9072 York
FNB OF GOLDSBORO
{{ 2 L 5 S }}
Chartered 3/08
Receivership 11/3/33
1902 Red Seal <$VALUE
3x10-20 1-300 <$1000
1902 Date Back
3x10-20 1-2120 <$450
1902 Plain Back
3x10-20 2121-6411 <$450
1929 Small Size
10 Type 1 1-722 <$275
20 Type 1 1-200 <$275
10 Type 2 1-42 <$300
Total Issue $403,290
Out at close $25,000
Large out at close $1,340
****
9727 Cumberland
GRANTHAM NB, GRANTHAM
{{ 1 L }}
Chartered 4/10
Liquidated 6/14/21
1902 Date Back <$VALUE
3x10-20 1-2360 <$650
1902 Plain Back
3x10-20 2361-3910 <$650
Total Issue $195,500
Out at close $24,100
****
9473 Dauphin
FNB OF GRATZ
{{ 2 L 9 S }}
Chartered 7/09
Receivership 11/16/34
1902 Date Back <$VALUE
4x5 1-2250 <$375
3x10-20 1-1740 <$375
1902 Plain Back
4x5 2251-7451 <$375
3x10-20 1741-4833 <$375
1929 Small Size
5 Type 1 1-2082 <$135
10 Type 1 1-1114 <$135
20 Type 1 1-320 <$150
5 Type 2 1-2202 <$175
10 Type 2 1-1100 <$175
20 Type 2 1-329 <$175
Total Issue $586,960
Out at close $50,020
Large out at close $1,295
****
14214 Montgomery
FNB OF GREEN LANE
{{ 10 S }}
Chartered 7/34
1929 Small Size <$VALUE
5 Type 2 1-2190 <$175
10 Type 2 1-1170 <$175
20 Type 2 1-310 <$175
Total Issue $28,850
Out in 1935 $25,000
****

****
2131 Montgomery
GREEN LANE NB, GREEN LANE
{{ 1 L }}
Chartered 12/15/73
Liquidated 9/9/75
Original Series <$VALUE
3x1-2 1-1500 <$1000/$2000
4x5 1-4500 <$4000
Total Issue $97,500
Out in 1910 $168
****
9084 Montgomery
VALLEY NB OF GREEN LANE
{{ 4 L 11 S }}
Chartered 3/08
Receivership 8/15/34
1902 Red Seal <$VALUE
3x10-20 1-700 <$750
1902 Date Back
3x10-20 1-4880 <$350
1902 Plain Back
3x10-20 4881-13845 <$350
1929 Small Size
10 Type 1 1-1524 <$135
20 Type 1 1-398 <$135
10 Type 2 1-874 <$175
20 Type 2 1-251 <$175
Total Issue $880,210
Out at close $50,000
Large out at close $1,820
****
5857 Franklin
CITIZENS NB OF GREENCASTLE
{{ 2 L 9 S }}
Chartered 6/11/01
Brown Back <$VALUE
3x10-20 1-820 <$600
1882 Date Back
3x10-20 1-1260 <$600
1882 Value Back
3x10-20 1261-1809 <$600
1902 Plain Back
4x10 1-2112 <$350
1929 Small Size
10 Type 1 1-1932 <$100
10 Type 2 1-3697 <$100
Total Issue $368,820
Out in 1935 $41,100
Large out 1935 $1,490
****
1081 Franklin
FNB OF GREENCASTLE
{{ 10 L 17 S }}
Chartered 4/65
Original Series <$VALUE
4x5 1-2200 <$400
3x10-20 1-2120 <$750/$1250
Series 1875
4x5 1-1100 <$400
3x10-20 1-2428 <$750/$1250
Brown Back
3x10-20 1-2888 <$300
1902 Red Seal
3x10-20 1-950 <$350
1902 Date Back
3x10-20 1-5400 <$165
1902 Plain Back
3x10-20 5401-22808 <$165
1929 Small Size
10 Type 1 1-3168 <$75
20 Type 1 1-798 <$85
10 Type 2 1-2776 <$85
20 Type 2 1-883 <$85
Total Issue $1,956,960
Out in 1935 $98,050
Large out 1935 $5,690
****
1894 Westmoreland
FARMERS NB OF GREENSBURG
Chartered 10/27/71
Liquidated 11/1/04
2nd title and location:
Fifth NB of Pittsburgh
6/23/74
FIRST TITLE {{ 1 L }}
Original Series <$VALUE
3x1-2 1-2600 <$600/$1500
4x5 1-4850 <$850
SECOND TITLE {{ 2 L }}
Original Series
3x1-2 1-2000 <$500/$1250
4x5 1-2500 <$650
Series 1875
4x5 1-11956 <$650
Brown Back
4x5 1-4623 <$500
3x10-20 1-668 <$500
Total Issue $534,980
Out in 1910 $3,934
****

****
14055 Westmoreland
FNB IN GREENSBURG
{{ 10 S }}
Chartered 3/34
1929 Small Size <$VALUE
5 Type 2 1-6730 <$110
10 Type 2 1-3921 <$110
20 Type 2 1-1392 <$110
Total Issue $100,700
Out in 1935 $185,120
Large out 1935 $6,740
Outstanding includes Ch 2558
****
2558 Westmoreland
FNB OF GREENSBURG
Organized 8/31/81
Liquidated 5/9/34
2nd title: FNB & TC
of Greensburg 12/31/31
FIRST TITLE {{ 12 L 5 S }}
Series 1875 <$VALUE
4x5 1-10000 <$400
3x10-20 1-3060 <$750/$1250
Brown Back
3x10-20 1-7000 <$275
1882 Date Back
4x5 1-7165* <$275
3x10-20 1-5600** <$275
1882 Value Back
4x5 7666-14200* <$275
3x10-20 6001-9430** <$275
* 7166-7665 not marked
** 5601-6000 not marked
1902 Plain Back
4x5 1-11282 <$135
3x10-20 1-8390 <$135
1929 Small Size
5 Type 1 1-4094 <$75
10 Type 1 1-1852 <$75
20 Type 1 1-514 <$75
SECOND TITLE {{ 18 S }}
1929 Small Size
5 Type 1 1-2798 <$60
10 Type 1 1-2194 <$60
20 Type 1 1-518 <$60
5 Type 2 1-408 <$75
10 Type 2 1-315 <$75
Total Issue $2,682,190
Out at close $229,360
Large out at close $6,740
****
2562 Westmoreland
MERCHANTS & FARMERS NB OF GREENSBURG
{{ 9 L 0 S }}
Chartered 9/19/81
Liquidated 11/26/29
Series 1875 <$VALUE
4x5 1-3000 <$400
3x10-20 1-7366 <$750/$1250
Brown Back
3x10-20 1-6800 <$300
1882 Date Back
3x10-20 1-7900 <$300
1882 Value Back
3x10-20 7901-13008 <$300
1902 Plain Back
3x10-20 1-11733 <$150
1929 Small Size
10 Type 1 1-191 <$500
20 Type 1 1-15 <$500
Total Issue $2,018,600
Out at close $99,150
Large out at close $85,900
****
4974 Westmoreland
WESTMORELAND NB OF GREENSBURG
{{ 3 L }}
Chartered 1894
Liquidated 12/31/24
Brown Back <$VALUE
4x5 1-3925 <$500
3x10-20 1-920 <$500
1882 Date Back
4x5 1-1494 <$500
3x10-20 1-1045 <$500
1902 Date Back
4x5 1-1250 <$300
3x10-20 1-1000 <$300
1902 Plain Back
4x5 1251-1890 <$300
3x10-20 1001-1446 <$300
Total Issue $316,730
Out at close $24,695
****
FNB of Greenville
SEE Ch 249
FNB of West Greenville
****

****
2251 Mercer
GREENVILLE NB, GREENVILLE
{{ 13 L U + 22 S }}
Chartered 4/23/75
Original Series <$VALUE
4x5 1-2000 <$400
4x10 1-875 <$750
Series 1875
4x5 1-750 <$400
4x10 1-3103 <$750
Brown Back
3x10-20 1-8150 <$275
1882 Date Back
3x10-20 1-5815 <$275
1902 Date Back
3x10-20 1-1800 <$135
1902 Plain Back
3x10-20 1801-16502 <$135
1929 Small Size
10 Type 1 1-2586 <$50
20 Type 1 1-758 <$60
10 Type 2 1-2145 <$60
20 Type 2 1-624 <$60
Total Issue $2,017,520
Out in 1935 $88,700
Large out 1935 $5,230
****
5044 Mercer
FNB OF GROVE CITY
{{ 12 L 21 S }}
Chartered 1896
Brown Back <$VALUE
3x10-20 1-4450 <$275
1882 Date Back
3x10-20 1-9500 <$275
1882 Value Back
3x10-20 9501-9720 <$275
1902 Plain Back
3x10-20 1-25658 <$135
1929 Small Size
10 Type 1 1-4620 <$40
20 Type 1 1-1242 <$45
10 Type 2 1-2902 <$50
20 Type 2 1-842 <$50
Total Issue $2,463,500
Out in 1935 $112,600
Large out 1935 $6,720
****
Grove City NB, Grove City
SEE Ch 5501
Peoples NB of Grove City
****
5501 Mercer
PEOPLES NB OF GROVE CITY
Chartered 7/17/00
2nd title: Grove City NB
8/1/08
FIRST TITLE {{ 1 L }}
Brown Back <$VALUE
4x5 1-2605 <$500
3x10-20 1-1955 <$500
SECOND TITLE {{ 9 L 27 S }}
1882 Date Back
3x10-20 1-9400 <$300
1882 Value Back
3x10-20 9401-13552 <$300
1902 Plain Back
3x10-20 1-17892 <$150
1929 Small Size
10 Type 1 1-3454 <$40
20 Type 1 1-1040 <$45
10 Type 2 1-4724 <$45
20 Type 2 1-1586 <$45
Total Issue $2,133,050
Out in 1935 $123,050
Large out 1935 $7,340
****
5601 Dauphin
HALIFAX NB, HALIFAX
{{ 8 L 7 S }}
Chartered 10/20/00
Brown Back <$VALUE
3x10-20 1-2200 <$300
1882 Date Back
3x10-20 1-1990 <$300
1882 Value Back
3x10-20 1991-3032 <$300
1902 Plain Back
3x10-20 1-2720 <$200
1929 Small Size
10 Type 1 1-674 <$165
20 Type 1 1-160 <$165
10 Type 2 1-1330 <$175
20 Type 2 1-192 <$175
Total Issue $474,380
Out in 1935 $24,500
Large out 1935 $1,840
****

****
7702 Susquehanna
FNB OF HALLSTEAD
{{ 3 L 6 S }}
Chartered 4/05
1902 Red Seal <$VALUE
3x10-20 1-1400 <$600
1902 Date Back
3x10-20 1-2090 <$300
1902 Plain Back
3x10-20 2091-6864 <$300
1929 Small Size
10 Type 1 1-824 <$165
20 Type 1 1-190 <$165
10 Type 2 1-1045 <$175
20 Type 2 1-324 <$175
Total Issue $502,370
Out in 1935 $24,350
Large out 1935 $1,050
****
9028 Berks
FNB OF HAMBURG
Chartered 2/08
Receivership 10/30/34
2nd title: FNB & TC 1/16/26
FIRST TITLE {{ 7 L }}
1902 Red Seal <$VALUE
3x10-20 1-700 <$400
1902 Date Back
3x10-20 1-4400 <$175
1902 Plain Back
3x10-20 4401-10550 <$175
SECOND TITLE {{ 1 L 12 S }}
1902 Plain Back
3x10-20 1-2755 <$225
1929 Small Size
10 Type 1 1-3632 <$85
20 Type 1 1-910 <$100
10 Type 2 1-3062 <$100
20 Type 2 1-1085 <$100
Total Issue $1,079,690
Out at close $122,250
Large out at close $3,610
****
14250 Berks
NB OF HAMBURG
{{ 7 S }}
Chartered 8/34
1929 Small Size <$VALUE
5 Type 2 1-13110 <$175
10 Type 2 1-3825 <$175
Total Issue $103,800
Out in 1935 $100,000
****
187 York
FNB OF HANOVER
{{ 16 L 31 S }}
Chartered 1/64
Original Series <$VALUE
4x5 1-5230 <$450
3x10-20 1-4200 <$750/$1250
Series 1875
3x10-20 1-5522 <$750/$1250
Brown Back
4x5 1-4000 <$300
3x10-20 1-15198 <$300
1902 Red Seal
4x5 1-7250 <$350
3x10-20 1-8200 <$350
1902 Date Back
4x5 1-6500 <$135
3x10-20 1-16100 <$135
1902 Plain Back
4x5 6501-7750 <$135
3x10-20 16101-49868 <$135
1929 Small Size
10 Type 1 1-5852 <$45
20 Type 1 1-1562 <$50
10 Type 2 1-8574 <$50
20 Type 2 1-2611 <$50
Total Issue $5,310,520
Out in 1935 $196,000
Large out 1935 $12,060
****
9541 Montgomery
HARLEYSVILLE NB, HARLEYSVILLE
{{ 3 L 18 S }}
Chartered 9/09
1902 Date Back <$VALUE
3x10-20 1-2530 <$375
1902 Plain Back
3x10-20 2531-7271 <$375
1929 Small Size
10 Type 1 1-2758 <$75
20 Type 1 1-758 <$85
10 Type 2 1-5473 <$100
20 Type 2 1-1790 <$100
Total Issue $710,520
Out in 1935 $123,800
Large out 1935 $830
****
2335 Butler
HARMONY NB, HARMONY
{{ UNREPORTED }}
Chartered 6/16/76
Liquidated 7/7/82
Series 1875 <$VALUE
3x10-20 1-1306<$1500/$2000
Total Issue $65,300
Out in 1910 $380
****
201 Dauphin
FNB OF HARRISBURG
{{ 12 L }}
Chartered 1/64
Liquidated 3/29/22
Original Series <$VALUE
4x5 1-4500 <$500
4x10 1-2250 <$750
Series 1875
4x5 1-3064 <$500
4x10 1-1498 <$750
Brown Back
4x5 1-2750 <$350
3x10-20 1-3615 <$350
1902 Red Seal
3x10-20 1-6600 <$350
1902 Date Back
3x10-20 1-8700 <$165
1902 Plain Back
3x10-20 8701-16800 <$165
Total Issue $1,706,950
Out at close $113,800
****
580 Dauphin
HARRISBURG NB, HARRISBURG
{{ 29 L 50+ S }}
Chartered 11/64
Original Series <$VALUE
4x5 1-7650 <$500
3x10-20 1-4500 <$750/$1250
50-100 1-1215* <$3500
* 301-500 not issued
Series 1875
4x5 1-4225 <$500
3x10-20 1-4299 <$750/$1250
50-100 1-1008 <$3500
Brown Back
4x5 1-11836 <$275
3x10-20 1-14494 <$275
50-100 1-3697 <$1250/$1500
1902 Red Seal
4x5 1-12500 <$300
3x10-20 1-7600 <$300
1902 Date Back
4x5 1-20750 <$125
3x10-20 1-18400 <$125
1902 Plain Back
4x5 20751-55460 <$125
3x10-20 18401-41885 <$125
1929 Small Size
5 Type 1 1-9932 <$25
10 Type 1 1-4776 <$25
20 Type 1 1-1084 <$35
5 Type 2 1-18252 <$20
10 Type 2 1-9960 <$25
20 Type 2 1-2791 <$35
Total Issue $7,291,600
Out in 1935 $293,100
Large out 1935 $16,580
****
3713 Dauphin
MERCHANTS NB OF HARRISBURG
{{ 4 L }}
Chartered 5/24/87
Liquidated 12/31/24
Brown Back <$VALUE
3x10-20 1-4394 <$450
1902 Red Seal
3x10-20 1-1000 <$500
1902 Date Back
3x10-20 1-10000* <$275
1902 Plain Back
3x10-20 10501-21241* <$275
* 10001-10500 not marked
Total Issue $1,331,750
Out at close $75,300
****
13812 Butler
FNB IN HARRISVILLE
{{ 4 S }}
Chartered 10/33
1929 Small Size <$VALUE
10 Type 2 1-2537 <$225
20 Type 2 1-680 <$225
Total Issue $38,970
Out in 1935 $42,550
Large out 1935 $1,720
Outstanding includes Ch 6859
****
6859 Butler
FNB OF HARRISVILLE
{{ 4 L 7 S }}
Chartered 6/03
Liquidated 1/9/34
1902 Red Seal <$VALUE
3x10-20 1-540 <$600
1902 Date Back
3x10-20 1-1930 <$275
1902 Plain Back
3x10-20 1931-9198 <$275
1929 Small Size
10 Type 1 1-1148 <$175
20 Type 1 1-309 <$175
Total Issue $592,560
Out at close $35,500
Large out 1935 $1,720
Ch 13812 assumed circulation
****
11227 Cambria
FNB OF HASTINGS
{{ 3 L 12 S }}
Chartered 8/18
1902 Plain Back <$VALUE
3x10-20 1-9110 <$350
1929 Small Size
10 Type 1 1-1378 <$100
20 Type 1 1-372 <$100
10 Type 2 1-2102 <$100
20 Type 2 1-390 <$100
Total Issue $611,640
Out in 1935 $50,000
Large out 1935 $2,040
****
2253 Montgomery
HATBORO NB, HATBORO
{{ 3 L 5 S }}
Chartered 5/4/75
Original Series <$VALUE
4x5 1-1800 <$1250
Series 1875
4x5 1-6121 <$1250
Brown Back
4x5 1-2500 <$1000
3x10-20 1-860 <$1000
1882 Date Back
4x5 1-1248 <$1000
3x10-20 1-921 <$1000
1902 Date Back
3x10-20 1-820 <$750
1902 Plain Back
3x10-20 821-2788 <$750
1929 Small Size
10 Type 1 1-480 <$400
20 Type 1 1-130 <$400
10 Type 2 1-281 <$450
20 Type 2 1-85 <$450
Total Issue $510,740
Out in 1935 $14,650
Large out 1935 $1,290
****
13026 Montgomery
HATFIELD NB, HATFIELD
{{ 14 S }}
Chartered 1/27
1929 Small Size <$VALUE
5 Type 1 1-2060 <$85
10 Type 1 1-622 <$85
20 Type 1 1-212 <$85
5 Type 2 1-8836 <$85
10 Type 2 1-5564 <$85
20 Type 2 1-1313 <$85
Total Issue $250,640
Out in 1935 $97,150
****
6445 Wayne
FNB OF HAWLEY
{{ 5 L 10 S }}
Chartered 10/2/02
1902 Red Seal <$VALUE
3x10-20 1-3300 <$450
1902 Date Back
3x10-20 1-4800 <$200
1902 Plain Back
3x10-20 4801-14589 <$200
1929 Small Size
10 Type 1 1-1572 <$150
20 Type 1 1-400 <$150
10 Type 2 1-2193 <$135
20 Type 2 1-601 <$135
Total Issue $1,070,720
Out in 1935 $50,000
Large out 1935 $2,050
****
6507 Allegheny
HAYS NB, HAYS
{{ 2 L 5 S }}
Chartered 11/26/02
1902 Red Seal <$VALUE
4x5 1-1225 <$650
3x10-20 1-976 <$650
1902 Date Back
4x5 1-2300 <$300
3x10-20 1-1610 <$300
1902 Plain Back
4x5 2301-7794 <$300
3x10-20 1611-4909 <$300
1929 Small Size
5 Type 1 1-1040 <$200
10 Type 1 1-500 <$200
20 Type 1 1-152 <$200
5 Type 2 1-960 <$225
10 Type 2 1-550 <$225
20 Type 2 1-189 <$225
Total Issue $568,150
Out in 1935 $24,695
Large out 1935 $1,055
****
8380 McKean
HAZELHURST NB, HAZELHURST
{{ UNREPORTED }}
Chartered 9/27/06
Liquidated 5/26/08
1902 Red Seal <$VALUE
4x5 1-605 <$1500
3x10-20 1-493 <$1500
Total Issue $36,750
Out in 1910 $3,890
****
3893 Luzerne
FNB OF HAZLETON
{{ 4 L 37 S }}
Chartered 5/31/88
Brown Back <$VALUE
4x5 1-5550 <$350
3x10-20 1-4820 <$350
1902 Red Seal
3x10-20 1-375 <$400
1902 Date Back
3x10-20 1-3448 <$200
1929 Small Size
5 Type 1 1-8194 <$20
10 Type 1 1-6708 <$25
20 Type 1 1-846 <$35
5 Type 2 1-69988 <$20
10 Type 2 1-30444 <$25
Total Issue $1,909,120
Out in 1935 $497,150
Large out 1935 $1,300
****
4204 Luzerne
HAZLETON NB, HAZLETON
{{ 7 L 21 S }}
Chartered 1890
Brown Back <$VALUE
4x5 1-2125 <$250
3x10-20 1-8140 <$250
1882 Date Back
4x5 1-535 <$250
3x10-20 1-235 <$250
1902 Date Back
4x5 1-4950 <$150
3x10-20 1-3960 <$150
1902 Plain Back
4x5 4951-14106 <$150
3x10-20 3961-9871 <$150
1929 Small Size
5 Type 1 1-12066 <$30
10 Type 1 1-7668 <$30
20 Type 1 1-1916 <$40
5 Type 2 1-42580 <$30
10 Type 2 1-22672 <$30
20 Type 2 1-5120 <$40
Total Issue $2,841,620
Out in 1935 $392,010
Large out 1935 $3,080
****
9107 Schuylkill
FNB OF HEGINS
{{ 3 L 11 S }}
Chartered 4/08
Liquidated 3/19/34
1902 Red Seal <$VALUE
3x10-20 1-1150 <$750
1902 Date Back
3x10-20 1-4840 <$375
1902 Plain Back
3x10-20 4841-14470 <$375
1929 Small Size
10 Type 1 1-1514 <$135
20 Type 1 1-354 <$135
10 Type 2 1-905 <$165
20 Type 2 1-158 <$165
Total Issue $926,530
Out at close $50,000
Large out 1935 $1,320
Ch 13994 assumed circulation
****
13994 Schuylkill
FNB OF HEGINS
{{ 3 S }}
Chartered 2/34
1929 Small Size <$VALUE
10 Type 2 1-1299 <$350
20 Type 2 1-456 <$350
Total Issue $22,110
Out in 1935 $44,000
Large out 1935 $1,320
Outstanding includes Ch 9107
****
10188 Westmoreland
FNB OF HERMINIE
{{ 1 L 4 S }}
Chartered 5/12
1902 Date Back <$VALUE
3x10-20 1-1660 <$500
1902 Plain Back
3x10-20 1661-6479 <$500
1929 Small Size
10 Type 1 1-758 <$225
20 Type 1 1-190 <$225
10 Type 2 1-624 <$250
20 Type 2 1-200 <$250
Total Issue $402,470
Out in 1935 $24,700
Large out 1935 $980
****
6049 Northumberland
FNB OF HERNDON
{{ 2 L 4 S }}
Chartered 12/16/01
Liquidated 3/9/34
Brown Back <$VALUE
3x10-20 1-1760 <$600
1882 Date Back
3x10-20 1-2000* <$600
1882 Value Back
3x10-20 2101-3644* <$600
* 2001-2100 not marked
1902 Plain Back
3x10-20 1-2740 <$375
1929 Small Size
10 Type 1 1-792 <$225
20 Type 1 1-192 <$225
10 Type 2 1-249 <$275
20 Type 2 1-29 <$275
Total Issue $480,830
Out at close $24,800
Large out 1935 $1,090
Ch 13982 assumed circulation
****
13982 Northumberland
HERNDON NB, HERNDON
{{ 3 S }}
Chartered 2/34
1929 Small Size <$VALUE
5 Type 2 1-2730 <$350
Total Issue $13,650
Out in 1935 $25,000
Large out 1935 $1,090
Outstanding includes Ch 6049
****
12688 Dauphin
HERSHEY NB, HERSHEY
{{ 24 S }}
Chartered 4/25
1929 Small Size <$VALUE
5 Type 1 1-2052 <$60
10 Type 1 1-624 <$60
20 Type 1 1-208 <$70
5 Type 2 1-21838 <$60
10 Type 2 1-9696 <$60
20 Type 2 1-3156 <$70
Total Issue $393,230
Out in 1935 $177,900
****
7405 Washington
FARMERS NB OF HICKORY
{{ 2 L 2 S }}
Chartered 9/04
Receivership 5/6/31
1902 Red Seal <$VALUE
3x10-20 1-1200 <$700
1902 Date Back
3x10-20 1-2760 <$350
1902 Plain Back
3x10-20 2761-7279 <$350
1929 Small Size
10 Type 1 1-415 <$350
20 Type 1 1-110 <$350
Total Issue $462,050
Out at close $24,635
Large out at close $3,195
****
13196 Cumberland
STATE ROAD NB OF HIGHLAND PARK
{{ 7 S }}
Chartered 4/28
1929 Small Size <$VALUE
5 Type 2 1-7522 <$200
10 Type 2 1-3507 <$200
20 Type 2 1-1094 <$200
Total Issue $94,560
Out in 1935 $39,450
****
6874 Blair
CITIZENS NB OF HOLLIDAYSBURG
{{ 3 L 14 S }}
Chartered 7/03
1902 Red Seal <$VALUE
3x10-20 1-2073 <$600
1902 Date Back
3x10-20 1-2950 <$300
1902 Plain Back
3x10-20 2951-8422 <$300
1929 Small Size
10 Type 1 1-874 <$125
20 Type 1 1-264 <$125
5 Type 2 1-2002 <$135
10 Type 2 1-2232 <$135
20 Type 2 1-499 <$135
Total Issue $651,180
Out in 1935 $50,000
Large out 1935 $1,710
****
57 Blair
FNB OF HOLLIDAYSBURG
{{ UNREPORTED }}
Chartered 8/63
Liquidated 6/30/82
Original Series <$VALUE
4x5 1-2200 <$1500
4x10 1-1200 <$1500
Series 1875
4x5 1-988 <$1500
4x10 1-416 <$1500
Total Issue $128,400
Out in 1910 $800
****
2744 Blair
FNB OF HOLLIDAYSBURG
{{ 2 L }}
Chartered 1882
Liquidated 3/1/17
Brown Back <$VALUE
4x5 1-2341 <$750
3x10-20 1-2571 <$750
1902 Red Seal
4x5 1-2650 <$750
3x10-20 1-2100 <$750
1902 Date Back
4x5 1-8900 <$375
3x10-20 1-6640 <$375
1902 Plain Back
4x5 8901-10486 <$375
3x10-20 6641-7511 <$375
Total Issue $918,640
Out at close $98,595
****
8855 Indiana
HOMER CITY NB, HOMER CITY
{{ 5 L 8 S }}
Chartered 9/07
Receivership 10/18/32
1902 Red Seal <$VALUE
3x10-20 1-1000 <$500
1902 Date Back
3x10-20 1-4580 <$250
1902 Plain Back
3x10-20 4581-13947 <$250
1929 Small Size
10 Type 1 1-1202 <$125
20 Type 1 1-331 <$150
Total Issue $859,190
Out at close $48,920
Large out at close $4,080
****
3829 Allegheny
FNB OF HOMESTEAD
{{ 10 L 24 S }}
Chartered 12/30/87
Brown Back <$VALUE
4x5 1-6350 <$300
3x10-20 1-3000 <$300
1902 Red Seal
4x5 1-750 <$300
4x10 1-875 <$300
1902 Date Back
4x5 1-9850 <$150
4x10 1-9425 <$150
1902 Plain Back
4x5 9851-33051 <$150
4x10 9426-27843 <$150
1929 Small Size
5 Type 1 1-9472 <$45
10 Type 1 1-4688 <$45
5 Type 2 1-22444 <$45
10 Type 2 1-12572 <$45
Total Issue $2,905,120
Out in 1935 $198,150
Large out 1935 $4,500
****
5365 Allegheny
HOMESTEAD NB, HOMESTEAD
{{ 3 L }}
Chartered 5/22/00
Liquidated 1/17/16
Brown Back <$VALUE
4x5 1-4500 <$500
3x10-20 1-3400 <$500
1882 Date Back
4x5 1-8480 <$500
3x10-20 1-6761 <$500
Total Issue $767,300
Out in 1916 $54,225
****

****
644 Wayne
HONESDALE NB, HONESDALE
{{ 12 L 21 S }}
Chartered 12/64
Original Series <$VALUE
3x1-2 1-9000 <$350/$1000
4x5 1-7650 <$400
3x10-20 1-4170 <$750/$1250
50-100 1-1004 <$3500
Series 1875
3x1-2 1-460 <$350/$1000
4x5 1-3600 <$400
3x10-20 1-4100 <$750/$1250
50-100 1-1774 <$3500
Brown Back
4x5 1-7351 <$250
3x10-20 1-4075 <$250
50-100 1-644 <$1250/$1500
1902 Red Seal
4x5 1-2300 <$275
3x10-20 1-1560 <$275
1902 Date Back
4x5 1-9200 <$135
3x10-20 1-7280 <$135
1902 Plain Back
4x5 9201-39508 <$135
3x10-20 7281-25381 <$135
1929 Small Size
5 Type 1 1-5902 <$40
10 Type 1 1-3290 <$40
20 Type 1 1-766 <$50
5 Type 2 1-10200 <$40
10 Type 2 1-5883 <$40
20 Type 2 1-1760 <$50
Total Issue $4,344,490
Out in 1935 $146,750
Large out 1935 $11,760
****

1676 Chester
FNB OF HONEYBROOK
{{ 10 L 24 S }}
Chartered 1868
Original Series <$VALUE
4x10 1-1375 <$600
50-100 1-420 <$4000
Series 1875
4x10 1-2305 <$600
50-100 1-483 <$4000
Brown Back
3x10-20 1-3058 <$450
1902 Red Seal
3x10-20 1-200 <$500
1902 Date Back
3x10-20 1-3810 <$225
1902 Plain Back
3x10-20 3811-26231 <$225
1929 Small Size
10 Type 1 1-3916 <$65
20 Type 1 1-1014 <$75
10 Type 2 1-5213 <$85
20 Type 2 1-1406 <$85
Total Issue $2,193,990
Out in 1935 $121,350
Large out 1935 $5,080
****

11413 Somerset
CITIZENS NB OF HOOVERSVILLE
{{ 1 L 4 S }}
Chartered 8/19
Receivership 7/12/34
1902 Plain Back <$VALUE
4x5 1-5340 <$500
3x10-20 1-2968 <$500
1929 Small Size
5 Type 1 1-1028 <$225
10 Type 1 1-590 <$225
20 Type 1 1-168 <$225
5 Type 2 1-336 <$250
10 Type 2 1-248 <$250
20 Type 2 1-75 <$250
Total Issue $347,260
Out at close $25,000
Large out at close $540
****

6250 Somerset
FNB OF HOOVERSVILLE
{{ 2 L 2U + 4 S }}
Chartered 5/9/02
Receivership 7/12/34
1902 Red Seal <$VALUE
4x5 1-1340 <$600
3x10-20 1-1054 <$600
1902 Date Back
4x5 1-2650 <$300
3x10-20 1-1900 <$300
1902 Plain Back (dated 1902)
4x5 2651-4930 <$300
3x10-20 1901-3199 <$300
1902 Plain Back (dated 1922)
4x5 1-3384 <$300
3x10-20 1-2235 <$300
1929 Small Size
5 Type 1 1-966 <$200
10 Type 1 1-536 <$200
20 Type 1 1-160 <$200
5 Type 2 1-702 <$250
10 Type 2 1-268 <$250
20 Type 2 1-106 <$250
Total Issue $606,130
Out at close $25,000
Large out at close $1,580
****

14156 Somerset
HOOVERSVILLE NB, HOOVERSVILLE
{{ 2U + 2 S }}
Chartered 5/34
1929 Small Size <$VALUE
5 Type 2 1-4016 <$350
10 Type 2 1-2320 <$350
20 Type 2 1-636 <$350
Total Issue $56,000
Out in 1935 $49,000
****

9647 Susquehanna
HOP BOTTOM NB, HOP BOTTOM
{{ 3 L 7 S }}
Chartered 1/10
1902 Date Back <$VALUE
3x10-20 1-2270 <$650
1902 Plain Back
3x10-20 2271-7332 <$650
1929 Small Size
10 Type 1 1-790 <$375
20 Type 1 1-192 <$375
10 Type 2 1-956 <$375
20 Type 2 1-260 <$375
Total Issue $451,800
Out in 1935 $24,050
Large out 1935 $990
****

9638 Bedford
HOPEWELL NB, HOPEWELL
{{ 3 L 3 S }}
Chartered 1/10
Receivership 12/3/31
1902 Date Back <$VALUE
3x10-20 1-1580* <$375
1902 Plain Back
3x10-20 1681-4593* <$375
* 1581-1680 not marked
1929 Small Size
10 Type 1 1-347 <$275
20 Type 1 1-95 <$275
Total Issue $261,870
Out at close $17,500
Large out at close $1,780
****

5908 Washington
FNB OF HOUSTON
{{ 3 L U + 5 S }}
Chartered 7/20/01
Brown Back <$VALUE
3x10-20 1-1600 <$600
1882 Date Back
3x10-20 1-2230 <$600
1882 Value Back
3x10-20 2231-3718 <$600
1902 Plain Back
3x10-20 1-3269 <$350
1929 Small Size
10 Type 1 1-660 <$200
20 Type 1 1-188 <$200
10 Type 2 1-1180 <$225
20 Type 2 1-195 <$225
Total Issue $507,210
Out in 1935 $24,600
Large out 1935 $1,250
****

6695 Clearfield
FNB OF HOUTZDALE
{{ 1 L 2 S }}
Chartered 3/03
Receivership 11/31/31
1902 Red Seal <$VALUE
3x10-20 1-1425 <$850
1902 Date Back
3x10-20 1-1560 <$450
1902 Plain Back
3x10-20 1561-3289 <$450
1929 Small Size
10 Type 1 1-268 <$350
20 Type 1 1-50 <$350
Total Issue $257,780
Out at close $12,700
Large out at close $1,430
****

9249 Centre
FNB OF HOWARD
{{ 2 L 5 S }}
Chartered 10/08
1902 Date Back <$VALUE
4x5 1-2425 <$400
3x10-20 1-1820 <$400
1902 Plain Back
4x5 2426-7090 <$400
3x10-20 1821-4562 <$400
1929 Small Size
5 Type 1 1-926 <$200
10 Type 1 1-454 <$200
20 Type 1 1-142 <$200
5 Type 2 1-1248 <$225
10 Type 2 1-714 <$225
20 Type 2 1-160 <$225
Total Issue $458,540
Out in 1935 $25,000
Large out 1935 $1,030
****

3902 Lycoming
FNB OF HUGHESVILLE
{{ 5 L 10 S }}
Chartered 6/23/88
Brown Back <$VALUE
3x10-20 1-2979 <$400
1902 Red Seal
3x10-20 1-500 <$450
1902 Date Back
3x10-20 1-4400 <$175
1902 Plain Back
3x10-20 4401-12746 <$175
1929 Small Size
10 Type 1 1-1402 <$100
20 Type 1 1-392 <$100
10 Type 2 1-1979 <$100
20 Type 2 1-479 <$100
Total Issue $971,780
Out in 1935 $49,450
Large out 1935 $2,120
****

8924 Lycoming
GRANGE NB OF LYCOMING COUNTY, HUGHESVILLE
{{ 4 L 5 S }}
Chartered 10/07
1902 Red Seal <$VALUE
4x5 1-500 <$850
3x10-20 1-400 <$850
1902 Date Back
4x5 1-2725 <$400
3x10-20 1-2080 <$400
1902 Plain Back
4x5 2726-10575 <$400
3x10-20 2081-7258 <$400
1929 Small Size
5 Type 1 1-986 <$275
10 Type 1 1-568 <$275
20 Type 1 1-170 <$275
5 Type 2 1-2136 <$300
10 Type 2 1-1119 <$300
20 Type 2 1-220 <$300
Total Issue $714,730
Out in 1935 $30,095
Large out 1935 $1,065
****

2822 Dauphin
HUMMELSTOWN NB, HUMMELSTOWN
{{ 3 L 6 S }}
Chartered 1882
Brown Back <$VALUE
3x10-20 1-2285 <$600
1902 Red Seal
3x10-20 1-1700 <$700
1902 Date Back
3x10-20 1-2950 <$350
1902 Plain Back
3x10-20 2951-8100 <$350
1929 Small Size
10 Type 1 1-874 <$175
20 Type 1 1-264 <$175
10 Type 2 1-675 <$200
20 Type 2 1-89 <$200
Total Issue $696,900
Out in 1935 $29,050
Large out 1935 $1,560
****

31 Huntingdon
FNB OF HUNTINGDON
{{ 17 L 50+ S }}
Chartered 7/63
Original Series <$VALUE
4x5 1-8250 <$450
3x10-20 1-2300 <$750/$1250
Series 1875
4x5 1-1175 <$450
3x10-20 1-4000 <$750/$1250
Brown Back
4x5 1-8585 <$275
3x10-20 1-5418 <$275
1902 Red Seal
4x5 1-5250 <$300
3x10-20 1-4000 <$300
1902 Date Back
4x5 1-7975 <$135
3x10-20 1-5400 <$135
1902 Plain Back
4x5 7976-35184 <$135
3x10-20 5401-20882 <$135
1929 Small Size
5 Type 1 1-5884 <$40
10 Type 1 1-3132 <$40
20 Type 1 1-752 <$50
5 Type 2 1-7588 <$40
10 Type 2 1-3828 <$40
20 Type 2 1-1212 <$50
Total Issue $3,554,020
Out in 1935 $147,500
Large out 1935 $8,520
****

6090 Huntingdon
STANDING STONE NB OF HUNTINGDON
{{ 4 L }}
Chartered 1/11/02
Closed 1/2/23
Brown Back <$VALUE
4x5 1-3185 <$500
3x10-20 1-2506 <$500
1882 Date Back
4x5 1-3600 <$500
3x10-20 1-2960 <$500
1882 Value Back
4x5 3601-7585 <$500
3x10-20 2961-5281 <$500
1902 Plain Back
4x5 1-995 <$325
3x10-20 1-474 <$325
Total Issue $648,350
Out at close $50,000
Ch 4965 assumed circulation
****

4965 Huntingdon
UNION NB OF HUNTINGDON
Chartered 1894
2nd title: Union NB & TC 2/1/30
FIRST TITLE {{ 8 L 2 S }}
Brown Back <$VALUE
3x10-20 1-5560 <$300
1882 Date Back
3x10-20 1-2680 <$300
1902 Date Back
3x10-20 1-1000 <$150
1902 Plain Back
3x10-20 1001-29506 <$150
1929 Small Size
10 Type 1 1-1224 <$75
20 Type 1 1-414 <$85
SECOND TITLE {{ 19 S }}
1929 Small Size
10 Type 1 1-3972 <$40
20 Type 1 1-1056 <$40
10 Type 2 1-5355 <$50
20 Type 2 1-1450 <$50
Total Issue $2,458,010
Out in 1935 $171,300
Large out 1935 $8,210
Outstanding includes Ch 6090
****

6615 Bedford
HOBLITZELL NB OF HYNDMAN
{{ 2 L 4 S }}
Chartered 2/03
1902 Red Seal <$VALUE
4x5 1-1081 <$750
3x10-20 1-924 <$750
1902 Date Back
4x5 1-1475 <$375
3x10-20 1-1120 <$375
1902 Plain Back
4x5 1476-4851 <$375
3x10-20 1121-2700 <$375
1929 Small Size
5 Type 1 1-628 <$250
10 Type 1 1-310 <$250
20 Type 1 1-98 <$250
5 Type 2 1-488 <$275
10 Type 2 1-358 <$275
20 Type 2 1-100 <$275
Total Issue $357,060
Out in 1935 $16,100
Large out 1935 $845
****

4063 Bedford
NB OF SOUTH PENNSYLVANIA AT HYNDMAN
{{ 1 L }}
Chartered 7/2/89
Receivership 12/16/02
Brown Back <$VALUE
4x5 1-2698 <$1000
3x10-20 1-257 <$1000
Total Issue $66,810
Out in 1916 $355
****

7993 Indiana
CITIZENS NB OF INDIANA
{{ 4 L 8 S }}
Chartered 12/05
Receivership 9/12/32
1902 Red Seal <$VALUE
4x5 1-800 <$600
3x10-20 1-780 <$600
1902 Date Back
4x5 1-2275 <$275
3x10-20 1-1680 <$275
1902 Plain Back
4x5 2276-3925 <$275
3x10-20 1681-10165 <$275
1929 Small Size
10 Type 1 1-1162 <$150
20 Type 1 1-345 <$165
Total Issue $752,870
Out at close $50,000
Large out at close $4,100
****

14098 Indiana
FNB IN INDIANA
{{ 16 S }}
Chartered 4/34
1929 Small Size <$VALUE
5 Type 2 1-14328 <$100
10 Type 2 1-7728 <$100
20 Type 2 1-3456 <$100
Total Issue $218,040
Out in 1935 $148,900
****

313 Indiana
FNB OF INDIANA
{{ 9 L 21 S }}
Organized 12/10/63
Receivership 5/2/34
Original Series <$VALUE
4x5 1-10450 <$500
3x10-20 1-3300 <$750/$1250
Series 1875
3x10-20 1-4000 <$750/$1250
Brown Back
3x10-20 1-6573 <$300
1902 Red Seal
3x10-20 1-2800 <$300
1902 Date Back
3x10-20 1-16500 <$135
1902 Plain Back
3x10-20 16501-52112 <$135
1929 Small Size
10 Type 1 1-5968 <$50
20 Type 1 1-1694 <$60
10 Type 2 1-132 <$75
20 Type 2 1-70 <$75
Total Issue $4,212,330
Out at close $198,500
Large out at close $9,720
****

9216 Lancaster
FNB OF INTERCOURSE
{{ 8 L U + 15 S }}
Chartered 8/08
1902 Date Back <$VALUE
4x5 1-2905 <$500
3x10-20 1-2605 <$500
1902 Plain Back
4x5 2906-10610 <$500
3x10-20 2606-6504 <$500
1929 Small Size
5 Type 1 1-1210 <$350
10 Type 1 1-712 <$350
20 Type 1 1-202 <$350
5 Type 2 1-2488 <$350
10 Type 2 1-815 <$350
20 Type 2 1-330 <$350
Total Issue $667,850
Out in 1935 $35,000
Large out 1935 $1,770
****

11115 Clearfield
FNB OF IRVONA
{{ 1 L 1 S }}
Chartered 12/17
Receivership 6/2/31
1902 Plain Back <$VALUE
3x10-20 1-1201 <$850
1929 Small Size
10 Type 1 1-130 <$600
20 Type 1 1-15 <$600
Total Issue $69,650
Out at close $5,960
Large out at close $770
****

5255 Westmoreland
CITIZENS NB OF IRWIN
{{ 7 L 11 S }}
Chartered 2/15/00
Receivership 2/10/33
Brown Back <$VALUE
4x5 1-2525 <$300
3x10-20 1-2080 <$300
1882 Date Back
4x5 1-5000 <$300
3x10-20 1-3460 <$300
1882 Value Back
4x5 5001-8485 <$300
3x10-20 3461-5228 <$300
1902 Plain Back
4x5 1-16507 <$175
3x10-20 1-11272 <$175
1929 Small Size
5 Type 1 1-2054 <$135
10 Type 1 1-1126 <$135
20 Type 1 1-305 <$135
Total Issue $1,645,120
Out at close $88,350
Large out at close $9,610
****

****
4698 Westmoreland
FNB OF IRWIN
{{ 5 L 12 S }}
Organized 2/15/92
Brown Back <$VALUE
4x5 1-4100 <$350
3x10-20 1-2520 <$350
50-100 1-480 <$1250/$1500
1882 Date Back
4x5 1-1675 <$350
3x10-20 1-976 <$350
50-100 1-79 <$1250/$1500
1902 Date Back
4x5 1-2480 <$225
3x10-20 1-1688 <$225
1902 Plain Back
4x5 2481-12565 <$225
3x10-20 1689-8466 <$225
1929 Small Size
5 Type 1 1-1876 <$100
10 Type 1 1-1048 <$100
20 Type 1 1-274 <$110
5 Type 2 1-2990 <$135
10 Type 2 1-1656 <$135
20 Type 2 1-396 <$135
Total Issue $1,240,220
Out in 1935 $49,200
Large out 1935 $3,190
****

4092 Westmoreland
FNB OF JEANETTE
{{ 3 L 4 S }}
Chartered 8/13/89
Liquidated 2/11/31
Brown Back <$VALUE
4x5 1-4075 <$600
50-100 1-687 <$1500/$1750
1902 Date Back
3x10-20 1-3840 <$350
1902 Plain Back
3x10-20 3841-12969 <$350
1929 Small Size
10 Type 1 1-791 <$250
20 Type 1 1-196 <$250
Total Issue $903,980
Out at close $50,000
Large out at close $6,960
****

5527 Westmoreland
JEANETTE NB, JEANETTE
{{ UNREPORTED }}
Chartered 8/2/00
Liquidated 7/23/07
Brown Back <$VALUE
3x10-20 1-2838 <$1250
Total Issue $141,900
Out in 1910 $6,130
****

7792 Westmoreland
PEOPLES NB OF JEANETTE
{{ 2 L }}
Chartered 6/05
Liquidated 8/1/27
1902 Red Seal <$VALUE
3x10-20 1-600 <$750
1902 Date Back
3x10-20 1-2450* <$375
1902 Plain Back
3x10-20 2691-6352* <$375
* 2451-2690 not marked
Total Issue $347,600
Out at close $22,400
****

14071 York
CODORUS NB IN JEFFERSON
{{ 3 S }}
Chartered 3/34
1929 Small Size <$VALUE
5 Type 2 1-119 <$400
10 Type 2 1-371 <$400
20 Type 2 1-157 <$400
Total Issue $7,445
Out in 1935 $25,000
Large out 1935 $1,175
Outstanding includes Ch 9660
****

9660 York
CODORUS NB OF JEFFERSON
{{ 2 L 8 S }}
Chartered 2/10
Liquidated 12/1/34
1902 Date Back <$VALUE
3x10-20 1-2390 <$500
1902 Plain Back
3x10-20 2391-6975 <$500
1929 Small Size
10 Type 1 1-750 <$200
20 Type 1 1-192 <$200
10 Type 2 1-516 <$225
20 Type 2 1-72 <$225
Total Issue $423,390
Out at close $21,615
Large out 1935 $1,175
Ch 14071 assumed circulation
****

11370 Greene
FNB OF JEFFERSON
{{ 3 L 5 S }}
Chartered 6/19
1902 Plain Back <$VALUE
4x5 1-5020 <$350
3x10-20 1-3123 <$350
1929 Small Size
5 Type 1 1-1066 <$200
10 Type 1 1-498 <$200
20 Type 1 1-160 <$200
5 Type 2 1-1108 <$225
10 Type 2 1-726 <$225
20 Type 2 1-166 <$225
Total Issue $353,730
Out in 1935 $24,250
Large out 1935 $1,390

12530 Montgomery
CITIZENS NB OF JENKINTOWN
{{ 8 L 5 S }}
Chartered 4/24
Receivership 6/27/31
1902 Plain Back <$VALUE
4x5 1-10650 <$300
3x10-20 1-7480 <$300
1929 Small Size
5 Type 1 1-2385 <$200
10 Type 1 1-1240 <$200
20 Type 1 1-377 <$200
Total Issue $778,190
Out at close $94,120
Large out at close $6,180

2249 Montgomery
JENKINTOWN NB, JENKINTOWN
{{ 10 L }}
Chartered 4/17/75
Liquidated 7/1/22
Original Series <$VALUE
4x5 1-750 <$600
3x10-20 1-600 <$850/$1500
Series 1875
4x5 1-5767 <$600
3x10-20 1-2267 <$850/$1500
Brown Back
4x5 1-8450 <$400
3x10-20 1-5530 <$400
1882 Date Back
4x5 1-8433 <$400
3x10-20 1-5717 <$400
1902 Date Back
4x5 1-1665 <$175
3x10-20 1-1334 <$175
1902 Plain Back
4x5 1666-12375 <$175
3x10-20 1335-4870 <$175
Total Issue $1,664,700
Out at close $90,400

6158 Lackawanna
FNB OF JERMYN
{{ 4 L 14 S }}
Chartered 3/14/02
1902 Red Seal <$VALUE
3x10-20 1-1790 <$500
1902 Date Back
3x10-20 1-2910 <$250
1902 Plain Back (dated 1902)
3x10-20 2911-4959 <$250
1902 Plain Back (dated 1922)
3x10-20 1-3379 <$250
1929 Small Size
10 Type 1 1-2058 <$75
20 Type 1 1-580 <$85
5 Type 2 1-324 <$85
10 Type 2 1-7415 <$85
20 Type 2 1-2111 <$85
Total Issue $817,470
Out in 1935 $96,950
Large out 1935 $965

12029 Somerset
FNB OF JEROME
{{ 1 L 4 S }}
Chartered 10/21
Liquidated 4/15/35
1902 Plain Back <$VALUE
4x5 1-9943 <$400
1929 Small Size
5 Type 1 1-4044 <$200
5 Type 2 1-6942 <$200
Total Issue $354,890
Out at close $21,300
Large out at close $520

<$VALUEs are for notes in FINE condition. Value changes by approximately 25% for a change of one full grade.

1464 Lycoming
JERSEY SHORE NB, JERSEY SHORE
Chartered 1865
2nd title: The Williamsport NB, Williamsport 12/22/70
3rd title: Williamsport NB 1/25/30
FIRST TITLE {{ 1 L }}
Original Series <$VALUE
4x5 1-2275 <$850
3x10-20 1-445 <$1000/$1500
SECOND TITLE {{ 6 L 2 S }}
Original Series
4x5 1-4250 <$450
Series 1875
4x5 1-6000 <$450
50-100 1-530 <$3500
Brown Back
50-100 1-1357 <$1250/$1500
1902 Red Seal
50-100 1-320 <$2250/$2500
1902 Date Back
50-100 1-540 <$350/$450
3x50-100 1-4150 <$350/$450
1902 Plain Back
3x50-100 4151-5600 <$350/$450
1929 Small Size
50 Type 1 1-250 <$125
100 Type 1 1-84 <$175
THIRD TITLE {{ 7 S }}
1929 Small Size
50 Type 1 1-519 <$125
100 Type 1 1-181 <$175
Total Issue $2,474,500
Out in 1935 $238,150
Large out 1935 $19,700

6155 Lycoming
NB OF JERSEY SHORE
{{ 4 L }}
Chartered 3/10/02
Liquidated 6/1/27
1902 Red Seal <$VALUE
3x10-20 1-3900 <$500
1902 Date Back
3x10-20 1-4340 <$275
1902 Plain Back (dated 1901)
3x10-20 4341-7673 <$275
1902 Plain Back (dated 1921)
3x10-20 1-3646 <$275
Total Issue $760,950
Out at close $48,900

13197 Lycoming
UNION NB OF JERSEY SHORE
{{ U + 12 S }}
Chartered 4/28
1929 Small Size <$VALUE
5 Type 1 1-3012 <$100
10 Type 1 1-1366 <$100
20 Type 1 1-618 <$100
50 Type 1 1-90 <$200
100 Type 1 1-52 <$250
5 Type 2 1-4996 <$125
10 Type 2 1-2755 <$125
20 Type 2 1-775 <$125
Total Issue $372,710
Out in 1935 $123,550

9600 Lackawanna
FNB OF JESSUP
{{ 4 L 13 S }}
Chartered 12/09
1902 Date Back <$VALUE
4x5 1-4500 <$225
3x10-20 1-3230 <$225
1902 Plain Back
4x5 4501-17088 <$225
3x10-20 3231-11601 <$225
1929 Small Size
5 Type 1 1-2678 <$100
10 Type 1 1-1586 <$100
20 Type 1 1-494 <$100
5 Type 2 1-9640 <$110
10 Type 2 1-5402 <$110
20 Type 2 1-1165 <$110
Total Issue $1,282,110
Out in 1935 $75,150
Large out 1935 $975

4544 Elk
JOHNSONBURG NB, JOHNSONBURG
{{ 3 L 6 S }}
Chartered 1891
Brown Back <$VALUE
4x5 1-5275 <$500
3x10-20 1-2080 <$500
1882 Date Back
4x5 1-708 <$500
3x10-20 1-579 <$500
1902 Date Back
4x5 1-2000 <$500
3x10-20 1-1600 <$500
1902 Plain Back
4x5 2001-7787 <$275
3x10-20 1601-5062 <$275
1929 Small Size
5 Type 1 1-1016 <$150
10 Type 1 1-652 <$150
20 Type 1 1-176 <$150
5 Type 2 1-1846 <$175
10 Type 2 1-733 <$175
20 Type 2 1-204 <$175
Total Issue $772,810
Out in 1935 $32,095
Large out 1935 $1,835

5059 Cambria
CAMBRIA NB OF JOHNSTOWN
{{ 1 L }}
Chartered 3/1/97
Liquidated 4/1/02
Brown Back <$VALUE
3x10-20 1-4119 <$850
Total Issue $205,950
Out in 1910 $3,755

4212 Cambria
CITIZENS NB OF JOHNSTOWN
{{ 2 L }}
Chartered 1890
Liquidated 12/14/09
Brown Back <$VALUE
3x10-20 1-11520 <$600
1882 Date Back
3x10-20 1-955 <$600
Total Issue $623,750
Out in 1910 $52,280

51 Cambria
FNB OF JOHNSTOWN*
{{ 16 L 28 S }}
Chartered 8/63
Liquidated 6/24/82
*Rechartered as Ch 2739 which retook Ch 51 6/21/11
Receivership 2/5/34
Original Series <$VALUE
4x5 1-2000 <$500
4x10 1-2000 <$750
Series 1875
4x10 1-957 <$750
1902 Date Back
3x10-20 1-11000 <$110
1902 Plain Back
3x10-20 11001-85690 <$110
1929 Small Size
10 Type 1 1-12288 <$30
20 Type 1 1-3368 <$40
10 Type 2 1-222 <$60
20 Type 2 1-126 <$60
Total Issue $5,588,960
Out at close $397,650
Large out at close $21,050
Outstanding includes Ch 2739

2739 Cambria
FNB OF JOHNSTOWN
{{ 4 L }}
Organized 6/15/82
Receivership 2/5/34
RETOOK Ch 51 6/2/11
Brown Back <$VALUE
3x10-20 1-12275 <$350
1902 Red Seal
4x5 1-5500 <$400
3x10-20 1-10500 <$400
1902 Date Back
4x5 1-11750 <$200
3x10-20 1-7100 <$200
Total Issue $1,838,750
Out in 1911 $54,000

12098 Cambria
MOXHAM NB OF JOHNSTOWN
{{ 6 L 19 S }}
Chartered 1/22
1902 Plain Back <$VALUE
4x5 1-28780 <$175
3x10-20 1-19482 <$175
1929 Small Size
5 Type 1 1-8406 <$50
10 Type 1 1-4038 <$50
20 Type 1 1-1082 <$50
5 Type 2 1-9360 <$60
10 Type 2 1-6312 <$60
20 Type 2 1-1596 <$60
Total Issue $2,315,840
Out in 1935 $172,600
Large out 1935 $5,170

10590 Cambria
NB OF JOHNSTOWN
{{ 2 L }}
Chartered 7/14
Closed 01/27/23
1902 Date Back <$VALUE
3x10-20 1-6500 <$350
1902 Plain Back
3x10-20 6501-28061 <$350
Total Issue $1,403,050
Out at close $196,600
Ch 5913 assumed circulation

7465 Cambria
UNION NB OF JOHNSTOWN
{{ 6 L }}
Chartered 11/04
Liquidated 7/31/28
1902 Red Seal <$VALUE
4x5 1-1600 <$300
3x10-20 1-9992 <$300
1902 Date Back
4x5 1-17000 <$150
3x10-20 1-15200 <$150
1902 Plain Back
4x5 17001-18250 <$150
3x10-20 15201-51834 <$150
Total Issue $3,488,300
Out at close $194,700

13781 Cambria
UNITED STATES NB IN JOHNSTOWN
{{ 23 S }}
Chartered 9/33
1929 Small Size <$VALUE
10 Type 2 1-23113 <$85
Total Issue $231,130
Out in 1935 $790,950
Large out 1935 $35,650
Outstanding includes Ch 5913

5913 Cambria
UNITED STATES NB OF JOHNSTOWN
{{ 26 L 44 S }}
Chartered 7/23/01
Liquidated 6/25/34
Brown Back <$VALUE
3x10-20 1-12800 <$275
50-100 1-600 <$1250/$1500
1882 Date Back
4x5 1-10577 <$275
3x10-20 1-14700 <$275
50-100 1-300 <$1250/$1500
3x50-100 1-100<$1250/$1500
1882 Value Back
3x10-20 14701-24881 <$275
1902 Plain Back
4x5 1-41795 <$135
3x10-20 1-53503 <$135
3x50-100 1-2876 <$300/$400
1929 Small Size
5 Type 1 1-22690 <$40
10 Type 1 1-9468 <$40
20 Type 1 1-3140 <$50
50 Type 1 1-920 <$125
100 Type 1 1-350 <$185
Total Issue $8,597,220
Out at close $769,950
Large out 1935 $35,650
Ch 13781 assumed circulation

8238 Blair
FNB OF JUNIATA
{{ 2 L 3 S }}
Chartered 5/06
Liquidated 5/25/31
1902 Red Seal <$VALUE
4x5 1-675 <$600
3x10-20 1-545 <$600
1902 Date Back
4x5 1-2400 <$300
3x10-20 1-1660 <$300
1902 Plain Back
4x5 2401-7919 <$300
3x10-20 1661-4833 <$300
1929 Small Size
5 Type 1 1-727 <$300
10 Type 1 1-267 <$300
20 Type 1 1-82 <$300
Total Issue $482,450
Out at close $22,480
Large out at close $2,530

5025 McKean
FNB OF KANE
{{ 6 L 15 S }}
Organized 11/9/95
Brown Back <$VALUE
3x10-20 1-5900 <$350
1882 Date Back
3x10-20 1-4935 <$350
1902 Plain Back
3x10-20 1-14064 <$165
1929 Small Size
10 Type 1 1-3618 <$65
20 Type 1 1-960 <$75
10 Type 2 1-3095 <$75
20 Type 2 1-788 <$75
Total Issue $1,623,940
Out in 1935 $107,550
Large out 1935 $4,450

2526 Chester
NB OF KENNETT SQUARE, KENNETT SQUARE
Chartered 1881
2nd title: NB & TC of Kennett Square 6/30/30
FIRST TITLE {{ 12 L 3 S }}
Series 1875 <$VALUE
4x5 1-17804 <$600
50-100 1-178 <$3500
Brown Back
3x10-20 1-1500 <$350
50-100 1-1767 <$1500/$1750
1882 Date Back
3x10-20 1-8100 <$350
50-100 1-200 <$1500/$1750
1882 Value Back
3x10-20 8101-13207 <$350
1902 Plain Back
3x10-20 1-13056 <$175
1929 Small Size
10 Type 1 1-1232 <$125
20 Type 1 1-420 <$125
SECOND TITLE {{ 14 S }}
1929 Small Size
10 Type 1 1-3932 <$65
20 Type 1 1-1168 <$75
10 Type 2 1-8307 <$80
20 Type 2 1-2175 <$80
Total Issue $2,692,950
Out in 1935 $211,240
Large out 1935 $5,710

12921 Luzerne
FNB OF KINGSTON
{{ 9 S }}
Chartered 4/26
1929 Small Size <$VALUE
5 Type 1 1-2060 <$135
10 Type 1 1-624 <$135
20 Type 1 1-210 <$135
5 Type 2 1-892 <$150
10 Type 2 1-1207 <$150
20 Type 2 1-324 <$150
Total Issue $147,450
Out in 1935 $48,950

14023 Luzerne
KINGSTON NB, KINGSTON
{{ 16 S }}
Chartered 2/23/34
1929 Small Size <$VALUE
5 Type 2 1-80022 <$85
10 Type 2 1-30456 <$85
20 Type 2 1-8124 <$85
Total Issue $867,150
Out in 1935 $500,000

3104 Armstrong
FARMERS NB OF KITTANNING
{{ 12 L 21 S }}
Chartered 1884
Brown Back <$VALUE
3x10-20 1-8180 <$300
1902 Red Seal
3x10-20 1-4600 <$300
1902 Date Back
3x10-20 1-8700 <$150
1902 Plain Back
3x10-20 8701-26128 <$150
1929 Small Size
10 Type 1 1-2714 <$75
20 Type 1 1-836 <$85
10 Type 2 1-2979 <$85
20 Type 2 1-1242 <$85
Total Issue $2,263,190
Out in 1935 $96,950
Large out 1935 $4,130

69 Armstrong
FNB OF KITTANNING
{{ 2 L }}
Chartered 8/63
Liquidated 7/2/82
Original Series <$VALUE
4x5 1-6750 <$850
3x10-20 1-5400<$1000/$1500
Series 1875
4x5 1-2175 <$850
3x10-20 1-3140<$1000/$1500
Total Issue $605,500
Out in 1910 $3,315

5073 Armstrong
MERCHANTS NB OF KITTANNING
{{ 10 L 16 S }}
Chartered 1897
Brown Back <$VALUE
3x10-20 1-7200 <$300
1882 Date Back
3x10-20 1-8000 <$300
1882 Value Back
3x10-20 8001-9251 <$300
1902 Plain Back
4x10 1-24482 <$165
1929 Small Size
5 Type 1 1-2052 <$75
10 Type 1 1-4772 <$80
10 Type 2 1-6460 <$85
Total Issue $2,214,310
Out in 1935 $96,500
Large out 1935 $4,985

2654 Armstrong
NB OF KITTANNING
{{ 4 L }}
Chartered 4/4/82
Liquidated 3/10/02
Series 1875 <$VALUE
4x5 1-1250 <$500
3x10-20 1-7453 <$750/$1250
Total Issue $397,650
Out in 1910 $4,910

6127 Armstrong
N KITTANNING B, KITTANNING
{{ 12 L 16 S }}
Chartered 2/15/02
1902 Red Seal <$VALUE
3x10-20 1-7000 <$300
1902 Date Back
3x10-20 1-12200 <$150
1902 Plain Back (dated 1902)
3x10-20 12201-17319 <$150
1902 Plain Back (dated 1922)
3x10-20 1-11538 <$150
1929 Small Size
10 Type 1 1-2952 <$75
20 Type 1 1-744 <$85
5 Type 2 1-324 <$90
10 Type 2 1-2960 <$90
20 Type 2 1-968 <$100
Total Issue $2,109,830
Out in 1935 $98,050
Large out 1935 $5,105

9978 Tioga
FNB OF KNOXVILLE
{{ 3 L 6 S }}
Chartered 4/11
1902 Date Back <$VALUE
4x10 1-2268 <$275
1902 Plain Back
4x10 2269-8108 <$275
1929 Small Size
10 Type 1 1-1208 <$175
10 Type 2 1-1776 <$175
Total Issue $414,560
Out in 1935 $24,600
Large out 1935 $1,080

14070 Beaver
FNB AT KOPPEL
{{ 2 S }}
Chartered 3/34
1929 Small Size <$VALUE
5 Type 2 1-3110 <$350
Total Issue $15,550
Out in 1935 $49,840
Large out 1935 $1,290
Outstanding includes Ch 11938

11938 Beaver
FNB OF KOPPEL
{{ 2 L 8 S }}
Organized 2/14/21
Liquidated 11/16/34
1902 Plain Back <$VALUE
4x5 1-14559 <$350
1929 Small Size
5 Type 1 1-7196 <$150
5 Type 2 1-1854 <$150
Total Issue $516,330
Out at close $17,670
Large out 1935 $1,290
Ch 14070 assumed circulation

CONDITION affects Value. The Values shown are for notes in FINE condition.

5102 Berks
KUTZTOWN NB, KUTZTOWN
{{ 12 L 27 S }}
Chartered 1897
Brown Back <$VALUE
4x5 1-4275 <$300
3x10-20 1-3140 <$300
1882 Date Back
4x5 1-4050* <$300
3x10-20 1-2700** <$300
1882 Value Back
4x5 4201-5375* <$300
3x10-20 2821-3512** <$300
* 4051-4200 not marked
** 2701-2820 not marked
1902 Plain Back
4x5 1-23997 <$150
3x10-20 1-14069 <$150
1929 Small Size
10 Type 1 1-4432 <$45
20 Type 1 1-1290 <$50
10 Type 2 1-5518 <$50
20 Type 2 1-1751 <$50
Total Issue $2,219,910
Out in 1935 $148,350
Large out 1935 $5,820

1875 Berks
NB OF KUTZTOWN
Chartered 9/11/71
Closed 1/2/26
2nd title: Keystone NB of Reading 6/27/82
FIRST TITLE {{ 1 L }}
Original Series <$VALUE
4x5 1-1685 <$750
3x10-20 1-800 <$1000/$1500
Series 1875
4x5 1-2750 <$750
3x10-20 1-420 <$1000/$1500
SECOND TITLE {{ 9 L }}
Series 1875
4x5 1-1745 <$450
3x10-20 1-974 <$750/$1250
Brown Back
4x5 1-2100 <$300
3x10-20 1-6850 <$300
1882 Date Back
4x5 1-3280 <$300
3x10-20 1-1575 <$300
1902 Date Back
3x10-20 1-4300 <$150
1902 Plain Back
3x10-20 4301-14549 <$150
Total Issue $1,489,600
Out at close $98,100
Ch 696 assumed circulation

8845 Wyoming
GRANGE NB OF WYOMING COUNTY AT LACEYVILLE
{{ 2 L 5 S }}
Chartered 8/07
1902 Red Seal <$VALUE
4x5 1-600 <$1000
3x10-20 1-460 <$1000
1902 Date Back
4x5 1-2250 <$500
3x10-20 1-1780 <$500
1902 Plain Back
4x5 2251-10750 <$500
3x10-20 1781-3702 <$500
1929 Small Size
5 Type 1 1-1280 <$250
10 Type 1 1-474 <$250
20 Type 1 1-142 <$275
5 Type 2 1-1968 <$300
10 Type 2 1-614 <$300
20 Type 2 1-216 <$300
Total Issue $539,280
Out in 1935 $24,250
Large out 1935 $1,600

9886 Wayne
FNB OF LAKE ARIEL
{{ 5 L 10 S }}
Chartered 11/10
1902 Date Back <$VALUE
4x5 1-4200 <$275
3x10-20 1-3200 <$275
1902 Plain Back
4x5 4201-15314 <$275
3x10-20 3201-10490 <$275
1929 Small Size
5 Type 1 1-2136 <$135
10 Type 1 1-1170 <$135
20 Type 1 1-366 <$135
5 Type 2 1-3682 <$150
10 Type 2 1-1893 <$150
20 Type 2 1-592 <$150
Total Issue $1,058,160
Out in 1935 $48,950
Large out 1935 $1,040

3987 Lancaster
CONESTOGA NB OF LANCASTER
{{ 14 L 37 S }}
Chartered 3/9/89
Brown Back <$VALUE
4x5 1-2463 <$350
3x10-20 1-8106 <$350
1902 Date Back
3x10-20 1-14100 <$150
1902 Plain Back
3x10-20 14101-38356 <$150
1929 Small Size
10 Type 1 1-5054 <$40
20 Type 1 1-1492 <$50
10 Type 2 1-6949 <$40
20 Type 2 1-1804 <$50
Total Issue $2,960,210
Out in 1935 $197,650
Large out 1935 $6,380

597 Lancaster
FARMERS NB OF LANCASTER
{{ 6 L }}
Chartered 12/1/64
Liquidated 11/22/04
Original Series <$VALUE
4x5 1-7700 <$600
3x10-20 1-8250 <$750/$1250
3x50-100 1-1112 <$4000
500 1-64 <$150,000
Series 1875
4x5 1-3270 <$600
3x10-20 1-5240 <$750/$1250
3x50-100 1-1334 <$4000
Brown Back
4x5 1-7050 <$400
3x10-20 1-7908 <$400
50-100 1-1097 <$1250/$1500
Total Issue $2,238,350
Out in 1910 $18,520

333 Lancaster
FNB OF LANCASTER
{{ 12 L }}
Chartered 3/64
Liquidated 6/25/23
Original Series <$VALUE
4x5 1-4000 <$500
3x10-20 1-4700 <$750/$1250
Series 1875
4x5 1-1000 <$500
3x10-20 1-3608 <$750/$1250
Brown Back
3x10-20 1-21077 <$325
1902 Red Seal
3x10-20 1-10900 <$350
1902 Date Back
3x10-20 1-16500 <$150
1902 Plain Back
3x10-20 16501-33544 <$150
Total Issue $3,791,450
Out at close $196,195

2634 Lancaster
FULTON NB OF LANCASTER
{{ U + 12 L 50+ S }}
Chartered 1882
Series 1875 <$VALUE
4x5 1-500 <$500
3x10-20 1-5790 <$750/$1250
50-100 1-200 <$4000
Brown Back
3x10-20 1-8400 <$325
1882 Date Back
3x10-20 1-11400* <$325
1882 Value Back
3x10-20 12901-20634* <$325
* 11401-12900 not marked
1902 Plain Back
3x10-20 1-12387 <$150
1929 Small Size
10 Type 1 1-3588 <$30
20 Type 1 1-964 <$40
10 Type 2 1-31655 <$30
20 Type 2 1-8056 <$40
Total Issue $3,209,180
Out in 1935 $316,770
Large out 1935 $6,080

683 Lancaster
LANCASTER COUNTY NB OF LANCASTER
{{ 9 L 2U + 21 S }}
Chartered 1/65
Original Series <$VALUE
4x5 1-7375 <$500
3x10-20 1-5150 <$750/$1250
50-100 1-651 <$4000
Series 1875
4x5 1-4235 <$500
3x10-20 1-4442 <$750/$1250
50-100 1-879 <$4000
Brown Back
4x5 1-2000 <$350
3x10-20 1-4073 <$350
50-100 1-770 <$1250/$1500
1902 Red Seal
3x10-20 1-1580 <$350
50-100 1-400 <$2250/$2500
1902 Date Back
3x10-20 1-5600 <$175
50-100 1-500* <$500/$600
* 457 and 484 not issued
1902 Plain Back
3x10-20 5601-11791 <$175
1929 Small Size
5 Type 1 1-420 <$50
10 Type 1 1-622 <$50
20 Type 1 1-620 <$60
50 Type 1 1-420 <$150
100 Type 1 1-212 <$200
5 Type 2 1-2592 <$50
10 Type 2 1-1320 <$60
20 Type 2 1-363 <$70
Total Issue $2,514,640
Out in 1935 $284,955
Large out 1935 $8,085

3367 Lancaster
NORTHERN NB OF LANCASTER
{{ 6 L }}
Chartered 1885
Liquidated 2/10/23
Brown Back <$VALUE
3x10-20 1-12760 <$400
1902 Red Seal
50-100 1-1400 <$2250/$2500
1902 Date Back
4x5 1-8500 <$200
50-100 1-700 <$500/$600
3x50-100 1-1371 <$500/$600
1902 Plain Back
4x5 8501-16255 <$200
Total Issue $1,620,850
Out at close $118,950

3650 Lancaster
PEOPLES NB OF LANCASTER
{{ 6 L }}
Chartered 3/16/87
Liquidated 2/28/25
Brown Back <$VALUE
4x5 1-5050 <$400
3x10-20 1-2640 <$400
50-100 1-1806 <$1500/$1750
1902 Red Seal
50-100 1-740 <$2250/$2500
1902 Date Back
50-100 1-1500 <$500/$600
3x50-100 1-1292 <$500/$600
Total Issue $1,162,900
Out at close $99,000

9312 Lancaster
FNB OF LANDISVILLE
{{ 3 L 8 S }}
Chartered 1/09
1902 Date Back <$VALUE
3x10-20 1-3500 <$400
1902 Plain Back
3x10-20 3501-9382 <$400
1929 Small Size
10 Type 1 1-942 <$175
20 Type 1 1-252 <$175
10 Type 2 1-1572 <$200
20 Type 2 1-405 <$200
Total Issue $579,680
Out in 1935 $35,000
Large out 1935 $1,070

3063 Bucks
PEOPLES NB OF LANGHORNE
Chartered 1883
2nd title: Peoples NB & TC 6/11/25
FIRST TITLE {{ 2 L }}
Brown Back <$VALUE
3x10-20 1-1406 <$800
1902 Red Seal
3x10-20 1-740 <$800
1902 Date Back
3x10-20 1-1570 <$400
1902 Plain Back
3x10-20 1571-2850 <$400
SECOND TITLE {{ 0 L 3 S }}
1902 Plain Back
3x10-20 1-729 <$400
1929 Small Size
10 Type 1 1-410* <$300
20 Type 1 1-128** <$300
10 Type 2 1-924 <$300
20 Type 2 1-168 <$300
* 303-316 not issued
** 69-104 not issued
Total Issue $333,650
Out in 1935 $12,000
Large out 1935 $940

7735 Montgomery
CITIZENS NB OF LANSDALE
{{ 3 L }}
Chartered 5/05
Closed 11/16/29
1902 Red Seal <$VALUE
3x10-20 1-2513 <$600
1902 Date Back
3x10-20 1-4940 <$300
1902 Plain Back
3x10-20 4941-14932 <$300
Total Issue $872,250
Out at close $40,900
Ch 430 assumed circulation

430 Montgomery
FNB OF LANSDALE
Chartered 5/64
2nd title: The FNB of Lansdale 11/16/29
FIRST TITLE {{ 9 L }}
Original Series <$VALUE
4x5 1-3310 <$500
3x10-20 1-2100 <$750/$1250
Series 1875
3x10-20 1-1772 <$750/$1250
Brown Back
50-100 1-1053 <$1250/$1500
1902 Red Seal
3x10-20 1-6300 <$300
1902 Date Back
3x10-20 1-9300 <$150
1902 Plain Back
3x10-20 9301-28270 <$150
SECOND TITLE {{ 32 S }}
1929 Small Size
5 Type 1 1-8430 <$40
10 Type 1 1-4282 <$45
20 Type 1 1-1150 <$50
5 Type 2 1-17112 <$50
10 Type 2 1-8862 <$50
20 Type 2 1-2605 <$50
Total Issue $3,020,350
Out in 1935 $225,255
Large out 1935 $7,055
Outstanding includes Ch 7735

13151 Delaware
NB OF LANSDOWNE
{{ 14 S }}
Chartered 12/27
1929 Small Size <$VALUE
5 Type 1 1-1442 <$125
10 Type 1 1-630 <$125
20 Type 1 1-98 <$125
5 Type 2 1-11172 <$125
10 Type 2 1-5988 <$125
20 Type 2 1-1908 <$125
Total Issue $246,720
Out in 1935 $96,180

7051 Carbon
CITIZENS NB OF LANSFORD
{{ 6 L 11 S }}
Chartered 12/03
1902 Red Seal <$VALUE
3x10-20 1-3060 <$350
1902 Date Back
3x10-20 1-4900 <$175
1902 Plain Back
3x10-20 4901-15012 <$175
1929 Small Size
10 Type 1 1-1552 <$100
20 Type 1 1-432 <$100
10 Type 2 1-2087 <$100
20 Type 2 1-489 <$100
Total Issue $1,079,210
Out in 1935 $48,650
Large out 1935 $2,300

5234 Carbon
FNB OF LANSFORD
{{ 9 L 18 S }}
Chartered 11/29/99
Brown Back <$VALUE
3x10-20 1-4050 <$300
1882 Date Back
3x10-20 1-10700 <$300
1882 Value Back
3x10-20 10701-14772 <$300
1902 Plain Back
3x10-20 1-16530 <$135
1929 Small Size
10 Type 1 1-3356 <$50
20 Type 1 1-834 <$60
10 Type 2 1-4383 <$70
20 Type 2 1-1103 <$70
Total Issue $2,134,930
Out in 1935 $93,250
Large out 1935 $5,560

9528 Sullivan
FNB OF LaPORTE
{{ 2 L 26 S }}
Chartered 9/09
1902 Date Back <$VALUE
4x5 1-1925 <$350
3x10-20 1-1630 <$350
1902 Plain Back
4x5 1926-7142 <$350
3x10-20 1631-4726 <$350
1929 Small Size
5 Type 1 1-990 <$75
10 Type 1 1-582 <$75
20 Type 1 1-148 <$75
5 Type 2 1-1544 <$75
10 Type 2 1-736 <$75
20 Type 2 1-264 <$85
Total Issue $481,880
Out in 1935 $25,000
Large out 1935 $1,300

3910 Westmoreland
CITIZENS NB OF LATROBE
{{ 4 L }}
Chartered 7/17/88
Liquidated 7/31/28
Brown Back <$VALUE
3x10-20 1-4051 <$400
1902 Red Seal
3x10-20 1-500 <$450
1902 Date Back
3x10-20 1-4200 <$225
1902 Plain Back
3x10-20 4201-12148 <$225
Total Issue $834,950
Out at close $48,645

14133 Westmoreland
COMMERCIAL NB OF LATROBE
{{ 6 S }}
Chartered 5/34
1929 Small Size <$VALUE
5 Type 2 1-7416 <$175
10 Type 2 1-3744 <$175
20 Type 2 1-1272 <$175
Total Issue $99,960
Out in 1935 $66,660

13700 Westmoreland
FNB IN LATROBE
{{ 5 S }}
Chartered 6/33
1929 Small Size <$VALUE
5 Type 2 1-26544 <$150
Total Issue $132,720
Out in 1935 $147,190
Large out 1935 $5,635
Outstanding includes Ch 3831

3831 Westmoreland
FNB OF LATROBE
{{ 8 L 16 S }}
Chartered 12/30/87
Liquidated 7/21/33
Brown Back <$VALUE
3x10-20 1-11810 <$300
1902 Red Seal
3x10-20 1-1000 <$350
1902 Date Back
3x10-20 1-8700 <$175
1902 Plain Back
3x10-20 8701-25699 <$175
1929 Small Size
5 Type 1 1-2916 <$75
10 Type 1 1-2538 <$75
20 Type 1 1-669 <$85
Total Issue $2,245,490
Out at close $150,000
Large out 1935 $5,635
Ch 13700 assumed circulation

5744 Westmoreland
PEOPLES NB OF LATROBE
{{ 5 L 8 S }}
Chartered 3/16/01
Receivership 8/24/31
Brown Back <$VALUE
3x10-20 1-2250 <$400
1882 Date Back
3x10-20 1-3156 <$400
1902 Plain Back
3x10-20 1-14641 <$200
1929 Small Size
10 Type 1 1-1787 <$135
20 Type 1 1-527 <$135
Total Issue $1,172,810
Out at close $98,495
Large out at close $9,385

9702 Tioga
FNB OF LAWRENCEVILLE
{{ 2 L 5 S }}
Chartered 3/10
1902 Date Back <$VALUE
3x10-20 1-2280 <$350
1902 Plain Back
3x10-20 2281-6187 <$350
1929 Small Size
10 Type 1 1-772 <$175
20 Type 1 1-180 <$175
10 Type 2 1-840 <$200
20 Type 2 1-173 <$200
Total Issue $389,130
Out in 1935 $20,100
Large out 1935 $790

4979 Lebanon
FARMERS NB OF LEBANON
{{ UNREPORTED }}
Chartered 9/20/94
Liquidated 9/1/05
Brown Back <$VALUE
4x5 1-2216 <$1250
3x10-20 1-1229 <$1250
Total Issue $105,770
Out in 1910 $2,010

240 Lebanon
FNB OF LEBANON
{{ 9 L U + 12 S }}
Chartered 2/64
Original Series <$VALUE
4x5 1-3560 <$450
50-50 1-200 <$3500
Series 1875
4x5 1-485 <$450
50-50 1-408 <$3500
Brown Back
4x5 1-5773 <$250
3x10-20 1-3279 <$250
1902 Red Seal
4x5 1-2350 <$300
3x10-20 1-1820 <$300
1902 Date Back
4x5 1-7350 <$135
3x10-20 1-5960 <$135
1902 Plain Back
4x5 7351-10800 <$135
3x10-20 5961-8730 <$135
1929 Small Size
5 Type 1 1-2830 <$65
10 Type 1 1-2224 <$65
20 Type 1 1-526 <$75
5 Type 2 1-9822 <$65
10 Type 2 1-4399 <$65
20 Type 2 1-1677 <$75
Total Issue $1,619,710
Out in 1935 $139,150
Large out 1935 $3,870

4955 Lebanon
PEOPLES NB OF LEBANON
{{ 10 L 21 S }}
Chartered 1894
Brown Back <$VALUE
4x5 1-5400 <$300
3x10-20 1-5080 <$300
1882 Date Back
4x5 1-6551 <$300
3x10-20 1-4638 <$300
1902 Date Back
4x5 1-1650 <$135
3x10-20 1-1320 <$135
1902 Plain Back
4x5 1651-19707 <$135
3x10-20 1321-13045 <$135
1929 Small Size
5 Type 1 1-4656 <$50
10 Type 1 1-2220 <$50
20 Type 1 1-578 <$60
5 Type 2 1-6842 <$50
10 Type 2 1-3657 <$50
20 Type 2 1-1152 <$60
Total Issue $2,207,370
Out in 1935 $121,600
Large out 1935 $4,660

<$VALUEs are for notes in FINE condition. Value changes by approximately **25%** for a change of one full grade.

***

680 Lebanon
THE LEBANON NB, LEBANON
Chartered 12/64
2nd title: Lebanon NB 1/16/30
FIRST TITLE {{ 10 L 2 S }}
Original Series <$VALUE
4x5 1-5250 <$450
3x10-20 1-4790 <$750/$1250
Series 1875
4x5 1-465 <$450
3x10-20 1-4564 <$750/$1250
Brown Back
3x10-20 1-3165 <$275
50-100 1-945 <$1250/$1500
1902 Red Seal
3x10-20 1-3400 <$300
1902 Date Back
3x10-20 1-8600 <$150
1902 Plain Back
3x10-20 8601-23650 <$150
1929 Small Size
10 Type 1 1-1226 <$110
20 Type 1 1-418 <$110
SECOND TITLE {{ 14 S }}
1929 Small Size
10 Type 1 1-1914 <$75
20 Type 1 1-440 <$80
10 Type 2 1-1248 <$75
20 Type 2 1-340 <$85
Total Issue $2,545,140
Out in 1935 $98,100
Large out 1935 $6,740

***

655 Lebanon
VALLEY NB OF LEBANON
{{ 5 L }}
Chartered 12/64
Liquidated 12/1/20
Original Series <$VALUE
3x1-2 1-2000 <$450/$1250
4x5 1-3125 <$500
3x10-20 1-2100 <$750/$1250
Series 1875
4x5 1-2750 <$500
3x10-20 1-1484 <$750/$1250
Brown Back
3x10-20 1-943 <$450
50-100 1-732 <$1250/$1500
1902 Red Seal
4x5 1-950 <$500
3x10-20 1-570 <$500
1902 Date Back
4x5 1-1750 <$250
3x10-20 1-1660 <$250
1902 Plain Back
4x5 1751-8195 <$250
3x10-20 1661-5668 <$250
Total Issue $958,450
Out at close $97,295

***

9290 Armstrong
FARMERS NB OF LEECHBURG
{{ 5 L 7 S }}
Chartered 12/08
Receivership 10/12/31
1902 Date Back <$VALUE
3x10-20 1-5540 <$225
1902 Plain Back
3x10-20 5541-15161 <$225
1929 Small Size
10 Type 1 1-1022 <$150
20 Type 1 1-308 <$150
Total Issue $856,330
Out at close $48,800
Large out at close $4,130

***

5502 Armstrong
FNB OF LEECHBURG
{{ 8 L 18 S }}
Chartered 7/17/00
Brown Back <$VALUE
3x10-20 1-3800 <$325
1882 Date Back
3x10-20 1-4780 <$325
1882 Value Back
3x10-20 4781-6860 <$325
1902 Plain Back
3x10-20 1-17979 <$165
1929 Small Size
5 Type 1 1-2958 <$65
10 Type 1 1-3106 <$65
20 Type 1 1-828 <$75
5 Type 2 1-5704 <$75
10 Type 2 1-3857 <$75
20 Type 2 1-1020 <$75
Total Issue $1,893,900
Out in 1935 $123,300
Large out 1935 $3,570

***

9495 Berks
FNB OF LEESPORT
{{ 4 L 12 S }}
Chartered 8/09
1902 Date Back <$VALUE
3x10-20 1-2460 <$275
1902 Plain Back
3x10-20 2461-9548 <$275
1929 Small Size
10 Type 1 1-1512 <$100
20 Type 1 1-434 <$125
10 Type 2 1-1745 <$125
20 Type 2 1-292 <$135
Total Issue $643,490
Out in 1935 $49,200
Large out 1935 $1,670

***

6531 Carbon
CITIZENS NB OF LEHIGHTON
Chartered 12/13/02
2nd title: Citizens NB & TC 2/1/29
FIRST TITLE {{ 9 L }}
1902 Red Seal <$VALUE
4x5 1-5250 <$300
3x10-20 1-3800 <$300
1902 Date Back
4x5 1-9950 <$135
3x10-20 1-6320 <$135
1902 Plain Back
4x5 9951-28584 <$135
3x10-20 6321-18558 <$135
SECOND TITLE {{ 0 L 16 S }}
1902 Plain Back
4x5 1-1008 <$200
3x10-20 1-480 <$200
1929 Small Size
5 Type 1 1-4090 <$60
10 Type 1 1-2212 <$60
20 Type 1 1-574 <$65
5 Type 2 1-4500 <$65
10 Type 2 1-2805 <$65
20 Type 2 1-635 <$65
Total Issue $2,226,290
Out in 1935 $84,845
Large out 1935 $5,335

***

2308 Carbon
FNB OF LEHIGHTON
{{ 6 L 14 S }}
Chartered 11/3/75
Series 1875 <$VALUE
4x5 1-14784 <$450
Brown Back
4x5 1-4365 <$300
3x10-20 1-2154 <$300
1882 Date Back
4x5 1-4281 <$300
3x10-20 1-2889 <$300
1902 Date Back
4x5 1-8945 <$175
3x10-20 1-6107 <$175
1929 Small Size
5 Type 1 1-2748 <$60
10 Type 1 1-1714 <$60
20 Type 1 1-442 <$65
5 Type 2 1-5996 <$65
10 Type 2 1-3366 <$65
20 Type 2 1-758 <$65
Total Issue $1,522,120
Out in 1935 $81,350
Large out 1935 $4,940

***

8405 Franklin
LEMASTERS NB, LEMASTERS
{{ 1 L }}
Chartered 10/06
Receivership 12/16/16
1902 Red Seal <$VALUE
3x10-20 1-200 <$1000
1902 Date Back
3x10-20 1-2130 <$500
1902 Plain Back
3x10-20 2131-2412 <$500
Total Issue $130,600
Out at close $24,200

***

10950 Franklin
PEOPLES NB OF LEMASTERS
{{ 3 L 5 S }}
Chartered 2/17
1902 Plain Back <$VALUE
3x10-20 1-4638 <$350
1929 Small Size
10 Type 1 1-756 <$200
20 Type 1 1-212 <$200
10 Type 2 1-521 <$200
20 Type 2 1-170 <$200
Total Issue $311,310
Out in 1935 $22,250
Large out 1935 $1,010

***

13494 Cumberland
WEST SHORE NB OF LEMOYNE
{{ 14 S }}
Chartered 9/30
1929 Small Size <$VALUE
5 Type 1 1-3512 <$70
10 Type 1 1-1946 <$70
20 Type 1 1-498 <$75
5 Type 2 1-6048 <$75
10 Type 2 1-3240 <$75
20 Type 2 1-900 <$75
Total Issue $362,520
Out in 1935 $98,810

***

6350 Bradford
FNB OF LeRAYSVILLE
{{ 3 L 4 S }}
Chartered 7/22/02
1902 Red Seal <$VALUE
4x5 1-450 <$1000
3x10-20 1-360 <$1000
1902 Date Back
4x5 1-1900 <$400
3x10-20 1-1390 <$400
1902 Plain Back (dated 1902)
4x5 1901-3785 <$400
3x10-20 1391-2442 <$400
1902 Plain Back (dated 1922)
4x5 1-2925 <$400
3x10-20 1-1789 <$400
1929 Small Size
5 Type 1 1-1010 <$300
10 Type 1 1-636 <$300
20 Type 1 1-138 <$300
5 Type 2 1-1404 <$325
10 Type 2 1-648 <$325
20 Type 2 1-204 <$325
Total Issue $475,350
Out in 1935 $23,380
Large out 1935 $990

***

745 Union
LEWISBURG NB, LEWISBURG
{{ 7 L 17 S }}
Chartered 1/24/65
Original Series <$VALUE
3x1-2 1-3000 <$400/$1000
4x5 1-1600 <$450
3x10-20 1-2140 <$750/$1250
Series 1875
4x5 1-1480 <$450
3x10-20 1-2200 <$750/$1250
Brown Back
3x10-20 1-2945 <$300
1902 Red Seal
3x10-20 1-1650 <$350
1902 Date Back
3x10-20 1-4800 <$175
1902 Plain Back
3x10-20 4801-12347 <$175
1929 Small Size
10 Type 1 1-2864 <$50
20 Type 1 1-880 <$60
10 Type 2 1-4885 <$50
20 Type 2 1-1468 <$60
Total Issue $1,496,350
Out in 1935 $120,600
Large out 1935 $3,450

***

784 Union
UNION NB OF LEWISBURG
{{ 7 L 11 S }}
Chartered 2/7/65
Original Series <$VALUE
3x1-2 1-600 <$400/$1000
4x5 1-1900 <$450
3x10-20 1-2240 <$750/$1250
Series 1875
4x5 1-1305 <$450
3x10-20 1-1876 <$750/$1250
Brown Back
3x10-20 1-6656 <$275
1902 Red Seal
3x10-20 1-2300 <$350
1902 Date Back
3x10-20 1-4900 <$175
1902 Plain Back
3x10-20 4901-14232 <$175
1929 Small Size
10 Type 1 1-1708 <$75
20 Type 1 1-440 <$85
10 Type 2 1-2329 <$85
20 Type 2 1-634 <$85
Total Issue $1,623,550
Out in 1935 $58,450
Large out 1935 $4,180

***

5289 Mifflin
CITIZENS NB OF LEWISTOWN
{{ 4 L 17 S }}
Chartered 4/13/00
Brown Back <$VALUE
3x10-20 1-3600 <$350
1882 Date Back
3x10-20 1-4300 <$350
1882 Value Back
3x10-20 4301-6499 <$350
1902 Plain Back
3x10-20 1-7998 <$250
1929 Small Size
10 Type 1 1-4096 <$50
20 Type 1 1-1108 <$60
10 Type 2 1-5594 <$60
20 Type 2 1-2088 <$60
Total Issue $1,381,270
Out in 1935 $122,800
Large out 1935 $2,260

***

1579 Mifflin
MIFFLIN COUNTY NB OF LEWISTOWN
{{ U + 10 L 4U + 14 S }}
Chartered 1865
Original Series <$VALUE
3x1-2 1-2000 <$350/$850
4x5 1-3200 <$400
3x10-20 1-1660 <$750/$1250
Series 1875
4x5 1-1000 <$400
3x10-20 1-2804 <$750/$1250
Brown Back
3x10-20 1-7619 <$300
1902 Red Seal
3x10-20 1-2200 <$300
1902 Date Back
3x10-20 1-5900 <$135
1902 Plain Back
4x5 1-7280 <$135
3x10-20 5901-15473 <$135
1929 Small Size
5 Type 1 1-3260 <$60
10 Type 1 1-2018 <$60
20 Type 1 1-606 <$70
5 Type 2 1-8242 <$70
10 Type 2 1-4144 <$70
20 Type 2 1-996 <$75
Total Issue $2,121,570
Out in 1935 $102,830
Large out 1935 $5,040

***

10506 Mifflin
RUSSELL NB OF LEWISTOWN
{{ 10 L 18 S }}
Chartered 4/14
1902 Date Back <$VALUE
4x5 1-2900 <$150
3x10-20 1-2330 <$150
1902 Plain Back
4x5 2901-37735 <$150
3x10-20 2331-25248 <$150
1929 Small Size
5 Type 1 1-9324 <$40
10 Type 1 1-4818 <$40
20 Type 1 1-1192 <$50
5 Type 2 1-14692 <$45
10 Type 2 1-7440 <$45
20 Type 2 1-2400 <$55
Total Issue $2,924,800
Out in 1935 $196,950
Large out 1935 $6,385

***

11127 Tioga
FARMERS NB OF LIBERTY
{{ 2 L 2 S }}
Chartered 1/18
1902 Plain Back <$VALUE
4x5 1-5007 <$500
1929 Small Size
5 Type 1 1-1330 <$300
5 Type 2 1-2652 <$300
Total Issue $153,300
Out in 1935 $9,400
Large out 1935 $400

***

13658 Westmoreland
FNB IN LIGONIER
{{ 8 S }}
Chartered 1/33
1929 Small Size <$VALUE
5 Type 1 1-526 <$125
10 Type 1 1-260 <$125
5 Type 2 1-5172 <$125
10 Type 2 1-3521 <$125
Total Issue $92,450
Out in 1935 $103,900
Large out 1935 $5,100
Outstanding includes Ch 13432

***

6281 Westmoreland
FNB OF LIGONIER
{{ 3 L 1 S }}
Chartered 5/29/02
Liquidated 3/3/30
1902 Red Seal <$VALUE
3x10-20 1-860 <$750
1902 Date Back
3x10-20 1-2180 <$375
1902 Plain Back
3x10-20 2181-6046 <$375
1929 Small Size
10 Type 1 1-213 <$400
20 Type 1 1-29 <$400
Total Issue $361,560
Out at close $25,000
Large out at close $8,740
Ch 13432 assumed circulation

***

13432 Westmoreland
LIGONIER NB, LIGONIER
{{ 14 S }}
Chartered 2/30
Liquidated 2/24/33
1929 Small Size <$VALUE
5 Type 1 1-3260 <$75
10 Type 1 1-1650 <$75
20 Type 1 1-560 <$85
Total Issue $264,000
Out at close $114,400
Large out 1935 $5,100
Ch 13658 assumed circulation
Outstanding includes Ch 6281 and Ch 6832

***

6832 Westmoreland
NB OF LIGONIER
{{ 3 L 2 S }}
Chartered 6/03
Liquidated 3/3/30
1902 Red Seal <$VALUE
3x10-20 1-2520 <$500
1902 Date Back
3x10-20 1-4400 <$250
1902 Plain Back
3x10-20 4401-12799 <$250
1929 Small Size
10 Type 1 1-458 <$250
20 Type 1 1-55 <$250
Total Issue $800,030
Out at close $49,280
Large out at close $15,300
Ch 13432 assumed circulation

***

8450 Cambria
FNB OF LILLY
{{ 5 L 8 S }}
Chartered 12/06
1902 Red Seal <$VALUE
4x10 1-250 <$500
1902 Date Back
4x10 1-3500* <$225
1902 Plain Back
4x10 3626-10617* <$225
* 3501-3625 not marked
1929 Small Size
10 Type 1 1-1256 <$135
10 Type 2 1-5916 <$135
Total Issue $569,200
Out in 1935 $44,940
Large out 1935 $1,200

***

3198 Lancaster
LINCOLN NB, LINCOLN
{{ 5 L 12 S }}
Organized 4/28/84
Brown Back <$VALUE
3x10-20 1-4844 <$600
1902 Red Seal
4x5 1-1750 <$600
3x10-20 1-2100 <$600
1902 Date Back
4x5 1-5000 <$300
3x10-20 1-3400 <$300
1902 Plain Back
4x5 5001-16168 <$300
3x10-20 3401-9954 <$300
1929 Small Size
5 Type 1 1-2654 <$150
10 Type 1 1-1184 <$150
20 Type 1 1-346 <$150
5 Type 2 1-3100 <$150
10 Type 2 1-2081 <$150
20 Type 2 1-492 <$150
Total Issue $1,441,590
Out in 1935 $58,200
Large out 1935 $2,860

***

5773 Lancaster
FARMERS NB OF LITITZ
{{ 5 L 14 S }}
Chartered 4/10/01
Brown Back <$VALUE
4x5 1-1500 <$500
3x10-20 1-4380 <$500
1882 Date Back
4x5 1-4800* <$500
3x10-20 1-3460** <$500
1882 Value Back
4x5 5001-8735* <$500
3x10-20 3621-5549** <$500
* 4801-5000 not marked
** 3461-3620 not marked
1902 Plain Back
4x5 1-8400 <$350
3x10-20 1-4793 <$350
1929 Small Size
5 Type 1 1-3256 <$135
10 Type 1 1-1906 <$135
20 Type 1 1-478 <$150
5 Type 2 1-8656 <$150
10 Type 2 1-4701 <$150
20 Type 2 1-1252 <$150
Total Issue $1,493,530
Out in 1935 $120,800
Large out 1935 $2,730

***

2452 Lancaster
LITITZ NB, LITITZ
{{ 2 L }}
Chartered 2/2/80
Receivership 4/19/09
Series 1875 <$VALUE
3x10-20 1-4385<$1000/$1500
Brown Back
4x5 1-3550 <$750
3x10-20 1-3231 <$750
1882 Date Back
4x5 1-23 <$750
Total Issue $452,260
Out in 1916 $3,565

***

9422 Lancaster
LITITZ SPRINGS NB OF LITITZ
{{ 3 L 9 S }}
Chartered 5/09
1902 Date Back <$VALUE
3x10-20 1-1920 <$400
1902 Plain Back
3x10-20 1921-10381 <$400
1929 Small Size
10 Type 1 1-1540 <$175
20 Type 1 1-386 <$175
10 Type 2 1-1678 <$175
20 Type 2 1-516 <$175
Total Issue $684,870
Out in 1935 $50,000
Large out 1935 $1,630

***

9207 Adams
LITTLESTOWN NB, LITTLESTOWN
{{ 2 L 14 S }}
Chartered 7/08
1902 Date Back <$VALUE
4x5 1-1675 <$400
3x10-20 1-1930 <$400
1902 Plain Back
3x10-20 1931-6830 <$400
1929 Small Size
10 Type 1 1-2368 <$85
20 Type 1 1-634 <$100
10 Type 2 1-9141 <$100
20 Type 2 1-2555 <$100
Total Issue $735,670
Out in 1935 $150,000
Large out 1935 $1,100

***

8326 Perry
FNB OF LIVERPOOL
{{ 3 L 5 S }}
Chartered 8/06
1902 Red Seal <$VALUE
4x5 1-450 <$750
3x10-20 1-360 <$750
1902 Date Back
4x5 1-2350 <$375
3x10-20 1-1760 <$375
1902 Plain Back
4x5 2351-7060 <$375
3x10-20 1761-4473 <$375
1929 Small Size
5 Type 1 1-1050 <$175
10 Type 1 1-464 <$175
20 Type 1 1-138 <$175
5 Type 2 1-1080 <$200
10 Type 2 1-652 <$200
20 Type 2 1-150 <$200
Total Issue $482,670
Out in 1935 $25,000
Large out 1935 $1,320

***

11692 Clinton
COUNTY NB OF LOCK HAVEN
{{ UNREPORTED }}
Chartered 4/20
Liquidated 12/31/21
1902 Plain Back <$VALUE
3x10-20 1-11430 <$850
Total Issue $228,600
Out at close $103,500

***

507 Clinton
FNB OF LOCK HAVEN
{{10 L U+23 S}}
Chartered 8/64
Original Series <$VALUE
3x1-2 1-2800 <$350/$1000
4x5 1-3150 <$400
3x10-20 1-4160 <$750/$1250
Series 1875
4x5 1-900 <$400
3x10-20 1-3000 <$750/$1250
Brown Back
3x10-20 1-11006 <$250
1902 Red Seal
4x5 1-2500 <$300
3x10-20 1-3100 <$300
1902 Date Back
4x5 1-7350 <$135
3x10-20 1-5460 <$135
1902 Plain Back
4x5 7351-23465 <$135
3x10-20 5461-16343 <$135
1929 Small Size
5 Type 1 1-4034 <$40
10 Type 1 1-2146 <$40
20 Type 1 1-514 <$50
5 Type 2 1-18086 <$40
10 Type 2 1-10846 <$40
20 Type 2 1-2724 <$50
Total Issue $3,059,580
Out in 1935 $189,750
Large out 1935 $7,030

1273 Clinton
LOCK HAVEN NB, LOCK HAVEN
{{1 L}}
Organized 1/14/65
Receivership 8/20/77
Original Series <$VALUE
4x5 1-2750 <$1000
3x10-20 1-1300<$1000/$1500
Series 1875
4x5 1-155 <$1000
3x10-20 1-450 <$1000/$1500
Total Issue $145,600
Out in 1916 $875

9345 Clinton
LOGANTON NB, LOGANTON
{{3 L 5 S}}
Chartered 2/09
1902 Date Back <$VALUE
3x10-20 1-2440 <$275
1902 Plain Back
3x10-20 2441-6474 <$275
1929 Small Size
10 Type 1 1-756 <$175
20 Type 1 1-198 <$175
10 Type 2 1-839 <$175
20 Type 2 1-205 <$175
Total Issue $405,310
Out in 1935 $24,500
Large out 1935 $1,320

11524 Perry
FNB OF LOYSVILLE
{{2 L 5 S}}
Chartered 11/19
1902 Plain Back <$VALUE
4x5 1-4055 <$375
3x10-20 1-2260 <$375
1929 Small Size
5 Type 1 1-982 <$175
10 Type 1 1-464 <$175
20 Type 1 1-142 <$175
5 Type 2 1-1194 <$200
10 Type 2 1-768 <$200
20 Type 2 1-192 <$200
Total Issue $285,930
Out in 1935 $25,000
Large out 1935 $1,090

8921 Luzerne
LUZERNE NB, LUZERNE
{{7 L 24 S}}
Chartered 10/07
1902 Red Seal <$VALUE
3x10-20 1-1100 <$350
1902 Date Back
3x10-20 1-5740 <$175
1902 Plain Back
3x10-20 5741-24207 <$175
1929 Small Size
10 Type 1 1-5590 <$40
20 Type 1 1-1556 <$40
10 Type 2 1-9096 <$40
20 Type 2 1-3305 <$40
Total Issue $1,944,530
Out in 1935 $165,450
Large out 1935 $3,680

11062 Dauphin
FNB OF LYKENS
{{U+4 L 7 S}}
Chartered 8/17
Receivership 12/29/33
1902 Plain Back <$VALUE
4x5 1-10194 <$275
3x10-20 1-6631 <$275
1929 Small Size
5 Type 1 1-2334 <$150
10 Type 1 1-1084 <$150
20 Type 1 1-264 <$150
5 Type 2 1-500 <$150
10 Type 2 1-178 <$150
20 Type 2 1-45 <$150
Total Issue $707,350
Out at close $50,000
Large out at close $1,370

8576 Butler
LYNDORA NB, LYNDORA
{{2 L 3 S}}
Chartered 3/07
1902 Red Seal <$VALUE
50-100 1-62 <$2250/$2500
1902 Date Back
50-100 1-340 <$750/$850
3x50-100 1-902 <$750/$850
1902 Plain Back
3x50-100 903-1178<$750/$850
1929 Small Size
50 Type 1 1-167 <$300
100 Type 1 1-43 <$350
Total Issue $430,700
Out in 1935 $50,000
Large out 1935 $4,550

7400 Clearfield
MADERA NB, MADERA
{{3 L 4 S}}
Chartered 9/04
1902 Red Seal <$VALUE
3x10-20 1-880 <$600
1902 Date Back
3x10-20 1-1950 <$300
1902 Plain Back
3x10-20 1951-3874 <$300
1929 Small Size
10 Type 1 1-428 <$200
20 Type 1 1-128 <$200
10 Type 2 1-427 <$225
20 Type 2 1-10 <$250
Total Issue $283,210
Out in 1935 $14,750
Large out 1935 $750

7610 Clearfield
MAHAFFEY NB, MAHAFFEY
{{5 L 8 S}}
Chartered 2/05
Receivership 6/16/31
1902 Red Seal <$VALUE
4x5 1-2000 <$400
3x10-20 1-1720 <$400
1902 Date Back
4x5 1-4650 <$200
3x10-20 1-3120 <$200
1902 Plain Back
4x5 4651-14639 <$200
3x10-20 3121-9663 <$200
1929 Small Size
5 Type 1 1-1069 <$150
10 Type 1 1-537 <$150
20 Type 1 1-160 <$150
Total Issue $985,420
Out at close $47,420
Large out at close $4,010

567 Schuylkill
FNB OF MAHANOY CITY
{{10 L U+15 S}}
Organized 9/26/64
Original Series <$VALUE
4x5 1-3600 <$500
3x10-20 1-1100 <$750/$1250
Series 1875
4x5 1-1100 <$500
3x10-20 1-1704 <$750/$1250
Brown Back
3x10-20 1-9981 <$300
1902 Red Seal
3x10-20 1-4800 <$350
1902 Date Back
3x10-20 1-9400 <$175
1902 Plain Back
3x10-20 9401-32747 <$175
1929 Small Size
10 Type 1 1-3924 <$65
20 Type 1 1-1098 <$75
5 Type 2 1-180 <$80
10 Type 2 1-4756 <$80
20 Type 2 1-1314 <$80
Total Issue $3,052,540
Out in 1935 $110,100
Large out 1935 $7,485

3997 Schuylkill
UNION NB OF MAHANOY CITY
{{11 L 24 S}}
Chartered 3/26/89
Brown Back <$VALUE
3x10-20 1-13269 <$300
50-100 1-1244 <$1250/$1500
1902 Date Back
3x10-20 1-13100 <$150
1902 Plain Back
3x10-20 13101-37299 <$150
1929 Small Size
10 Type 1 1-3870 <$50
20 Type 1 1-1058 <$60
10 Type 2 1-4224 <$60
20 Type 2 1-1145 <$60
Total Issue $3,139,300
Out in 1935 $121,150
Large out 1935 $7,010

3147 Chester
NB OF MALVERN
{{4 L 16 S}}
Chartered 1884
Brown Back <$VALUE
50-100 1-1240 <$2250/$2500
1902 Red Seal
4x5 1-2825 <$1000
50-100 1-570 <$2750/$3000
1902 Date Back
4x5 1-3400 <$500
50-100 1-300 <$750/$850
3x50-100 1-511 <$750/$850
1902 Plain Back
4x5 3401-21591 <$500
3x50-100 512-1159<$750/$850
1929 Small Size
5 Type 1 1-18246 <$150
10 Type 1 1-1136 <$150
5 Type 2 1-23594 <$150
10 Type 2 1-6391 <$150
Total Issue $1,891,990
Out in 1935 $114,020
Large out 1935 $5,200

3635 Lancaster
KEYSTONE NB OF MANHEIM
{{9 L 17 S}}
Chartered 2/14/87
Brown Back <$VALUE
3x10-20 1-6136 <$500
1902 Red Seal
4x5 1-1450 <$500
3x10-20 1-720 <$500
1902 Date Back
4x5 1-4950 <$225
3x10-20 1-4000 <$225
1902 Plain Back
4x5 4951-28595 <$225
3x10-20 4001-19189 <$225
1929 Small Size
5 Type 1 1-5216 <$75
10 Type 1 1-2444 <$75
20 Type 1 1-700 <$85
5 Type 2 1-8058 <$85
10 Type 2 1-4056 <$85
20 Type 2 1-1464 <$85
Total Issue $2,400,400
Out in 1935 $122,250
Large out 1935 $5,205

912 Lancaster
MANHEIM NB, MANHEIM
{{14 L 20 S}}
Chartered 3/18/65
Original Series <$VALUE
3x1-2 1-3500 <$350/$1000
4x5 1-3525 <$500
3x10-20 1-1750 <$750/$1250
Series 1875
4x5 1-3000 <$500
3x10-20 1-2250 <$750/$1250
Brown Back
3x10-20 1-6017 <$400
1902 Red Seal
4x5 1-4000 <$400
3x10-20 1-2920 <$400
1902 Date Back
4x5 1-10500 <$175
3x10-20 1-8100 <$175
1902 Plain Back
4x5 10501-37540 <$175
3x10-20 8101-23910 <$175
1929 Small Size
5 Type 1 1-6320* <$100
10 Type 1 1-2850 <$100
20 Type 1 1-788 <$100
5 Type 2 1-8238** <$100
10 Type 2 1-4966 <$100
20 Type 2 1-1428 <$100
* 5816 not issued
** 6229-6234 not issued
Total Issue $3,395,660
Out in 1935 $136,700
Large out 1935 $6,020

6456 Westmoreland
MANOR NB, MANOR
{{7 L 10 S}}
Chartered 10/11/02
1902 Red Seal <$VALUE
3x10-20 1-2840 <$400
1902 Date Back
3x10-20 1-4440 <$175
1902 Plain Back
3x10-20 4441-13897 <$175
1929 Small Size
10 Type 1 1-1452 <$100
20 Type 1 1-414 <$110
10 Type 2 1-1235 <$125
20 Type 2 1-385 <$125
Total Issue $993,700
Out in 1935 $50,000
Large out 1935 $2,740

13618 Tioga
FNB IN MANSFIELD
{{5 S}}
Chartered 6/32
1929 Small Size <$VALUE
5 Type 1 1-350 <$175
10 Type 1 1-118 <$175
5 Type 2 1-6720 <$175
10 Type 2 1-3204 <$175
Total Issue $83,220
Out in 1935 $47,780
Large out 1935 $1,350
Outstanding includes Ch 8810

8810 Tioga
FNB OF MANSFIELD
{{2 L 3 S}}
Chartered 7/07
Liquidated 8/15/32
1902 Red Seal <$VALUE
3x10-20 1-1000 <$600
1902 Date Back
4x5 1-2550 <$300
3x10-20 1-1460 <$300
1902 Plain Back
4x5 2551-7155 <$300
3x10-20 11461-4114 <$300
1929 Small Size
5 Type 1 1-713 <$250
10 Type 1 1-351 <$250
20 Type 1 1-99 <$250
Total Issue $453,130
Out at close $22,000
Large out 1935 $1,350
Ch 13618 assumed circulation

8831 Tioga
GRANGE NB OF MANSFIELD
{{2 L}}
Chartered 8/07
Liquidated 7/13/18
1902 Red Seal <$VALUE
4x5 1-1100 <$1500
3x10-20 1-980 <$1500
1902 Date Back
4x5 1-4450 <$650
3x10-20 1-3140 <$650
1902 Plain Back
4x5 4451-5995 <$650
3x10-20 3141-4066 <$650
Total Issue $394,200
Out at close $46,800

11244 Huntingdon
FNB OF MAPLETON
{{2 L 5 S}}
Chartered 9/18
1902 Plain Back <$VALUE
3x10-20 1-4627 <$450
1929 Small Size
5 Type 1 1-794 <$175
10 Type 1 1-610 <$175
20 Type 1 1-168 <$175
5 Type 2 1-1514 <$200
10 Type 2 1-576 <$200
20 Type 2 1-204 <$200
Total Issue $329,340
Out in 1935 $25,000
Large out 1935 $870

5727 Forest
GOLD STANDARD NB OF MARIENVILLE
{{6 L 11 S}}
Chartered 2/25/01
Brown Back <$VALUE
3x10-20 1-2908 <$500
50-100 1-334 <$1750/$2000
1882 Date Back
3x10-20 1-3500 <$500
50-100 1-100 <$1750/$2000
3x50-100 1-49 <$1750/$2000
1882 Value Back
3x10-20 3501-5331 <$500
1902 Plain Back
3x10-20 1-5831 <$350
1929 Small Size
10 Type 1 1-1354 <$175
20 Type 1 1-404 <$175
10 Type 2 1-2174 <$200
20 Type 2 1-414 <$200
Total Issue $940,590
Out in 1935 $48,750
Large out 1935 $2,390

10707 Lancaster
EXCHANGE NB OF MARIETTA
{{2 L 8 S}}
Chartered 2/15
Liquidated 11/28/34
1902 Plain Back <$VALUE
4x10 1-5679 <$500
1929 Small Size
10 Type 1 1-2615 <$150
Total Issue $384,060
Out at close $50,000
Large out at close $1,360

25 Lancaster
FNB OF MARIETTA*
{{12 L U+24 S}}
Chartered 7/63
Liquidated 5/27/82
*Reorganized as Ch 2710
which retook Ch 25 6/2/11
Original Series <$VALUE
4x5 1-3550 <$500
3x10-20 1-2560 <$750/$1250
Series 1875
4x5 1-1043 <$500
3x10-20 1-1688 <$750/$1250
1902 Date Back
4x5 1-4350 <$150
4x10 1-4350 <$150
1902 Plain Back
4x5 4351-26845 <$150
4x10 4351-18553 <$150
1929 Small Size
5 Type 1 1-5726 <$65
10 Type 1 1-2912 <$65
5 Type 2 1-8100 <$75
10 Type 2 1-4032 <$75
Total Issue $2,010,600
Out in 1935 $98,240
Large out 1935 $7,040
Outstanding includes Ch 2710

2710 Lancaster
FNB OF MARIETTA
{{2 L}}
Chartered 1882
RETOOK Ch 25 6/2/11
Brown Back <$VALUE
3x10-20 1-7748 <$750
1902 Red Seal
4x5 1-4250 <$750
3x10-20 1-4800 <$750
1902 Date Back
4x5 1-3750 <$400
3x10-20 1-3049 <$400
Total Issue $939,850
Out in 1911 $90,000

7819 Indiana
MARION CENTER NB, MARION CENTER
{{4 L 10 S}}
Chartered 5/05
1902 Red Seal <$VALUE
3x10-20 1-1800 <$500
1902 Date Back
3x10-20 1-4700 <$250
1902 Plain Back
3x10-20 4701-13951 <$250
1929 Small Size
10 Type 1 1-1484 <$110
20 Type 1 1-382 <$125
10 Type 2 1-2100 <$125
20 Type 2 1-260 <$125
Total Issue $948,630
Out in 1935 $50,000
Large out 1935 $2,300

5599 Butler
MARS NB, MARS
{{6 L 14 S}}
Chartered 10/16/00
Brown Back <$VALUE
3x10-20 1-2640 <$600
1882 Date Back
3x10-20 1-3800 <$600
1882 Value Back
3x10-20 3801-5553 <$600
1902 Plain Back
3x10-20 1-5343 <$300
1929 Small Size
10 Type 1 1-1142 <$200
20 Type 1 1-296 <$200
10 Type 2 1-1404 <$200
20 Type 2 1-333 <$200
Total Issue $801,540
Out in 1935 $30,000
Large out 1935 $1,870

7974 Blair
FNB OF MARTINSBURG
{{3 L 6 S}}
Chartered 11/05
1902 Red Seal <$VALUE
3x10-20 1-700 <$500
1902 Date Back
3x10-20 1-1660 <$250
1902 Plain Back
3x10-20 1661-6225 <$250
1929 Small Size
10 Type 1 1-736 <$150
20 Type 1 1-200 <$150
10 Type 2 1-1094 <$165
20 Type 2 1-236 <$175
Total Issue $430,070
Out in 1935 $24,050
Large out 1935 $960

7353 Perry
FNB OF MARYSVILLE
{{3 L 6 S}}
Chartered 8/04
1902 Red Seal <$VALUE
3x10-20 1-856 <$500
1902 Date Back
3x10-20 1-2530 <$250
1902 Plain Back
3x10-20 2531-7311 <$250
1929 Small Size
10 Type 1 1-764 <$150
20 Type 1 1-212 <$150
10 Type 2 1-666 <$175
20 Type 2 1-210 <$175
Total Issue $490,490
Out in 1935 $24,650
Large out 1935 $990

5441 Fayette
FNB OF MASONTOWN
{{7 L 7 S}}
Chartered 6/19/00
Receivership 4/18/31
Brown Back <$VALUE
3x10-20 1-2150 <$350
1882 Date Back
3x10-20 1-2450 <$350
1882 Value Back
3x10-20 2451-3244 <$350
1902 Plain Back
4x5 1-14792 <$175
3x10-20 1-10248 <$175
1929 Small Size
10 Type 1 1-1664 <$150
20 Type 1 1-478 <$150
Total Issue $1,235,140
Out at close $98,800
Large out at close $8,720

6528 Fayette
MASONTOWN NB, MASONTOWN
{{5 L 3 S}}
Chartered 12/13/02
Liquidated 1/22/31
1902 Red Seal <$VALUE
4x5 1-1330 <$400
3x10-20 1-1004 <$400
1902 Date Back
4x5 1-2350 <$200
3x10-20 1-1680 <$200
1902 Plain Back
4x5 2351-3750 <$200
3x10-20 1681-18855 <$200
1929 Small Size
10 Type 1 1-1384 <$175
20 Type 1 1-382 <$175
Total Issue $1,223,430
Out at close $85,720
Large out at close $10,910

437 Carbon
FNB OF MAUCH CHUNK
{{5 L}}
Chartered 5/25/64
Liquidated 2/24/03
Original Series <$VALUE
4x5 1-7500 <$500
3x10-20 1-9700 <$750/$1250
Series 1875
3x10-20 1-7500 <$750/$1250
Brown Back
3x10-20 1-10514 <$300
50-100 1-2791 <$1250/$1500
Total Issue $1,954,350
Out in 1910 $13,110

<$VALUEs are for notes in FINE condition. Value changes by approximately 25% for a change of one full grade.

****
2852 Carbon
LINDERMAN NB OF MAUCH CHUNK
{{ 1 L }}
Chartered 1/3/83
Liquidated 12/30/02
Brown Back <$VALUE
3x10-20 1-2648 <$1000
Total Issue $132,400
Out in 1910 $2,220
****
6534 Carbon
MAUCH CHUNK NB, MAUCH CHUNK
{{ 14 L 31 S }}
Chartered 12/15/02
1902 Red Seal <$VALUE
4x5 1-7500 <$275
3x10-20 1-15400 <$275
1902 Date Back
4x5 1-23250 <$135
3x10-20 1-15600 <$135
1902 Plain Back
4x5 23251-73875 <$135
3x10-20 15601-49498 <$135
1929 Small Size
5 Type 1 1-10004 <$40
10 Type 1 1-5350 <$40
20 Type 1 1-1232 <$50
5 Type 2 1-15924 <$40
10 Type 2 1-7638 <$40
20 Type 2 1-2115 <$50
Total Issue $5,839,660
Out in 1935 $210,250
Large out 1935 $12,785
****
469 Carbon
SECOND NB OF MAUCH CHUNK
{{ 4 L }}
Chartered 6/30/64
Liquidated 12/31/02
Original Series <$VALUE
3x1-2 1-2610 <$400/$1000
4x5 1-3065 <$500
3x10-20 1-3920 <$750/$1250
Series 1875
3x10-20 1-2835 <$750/$1250
Brown Back
3x10-20 1-14973 <$400
Total Issue $1,160,750
Out in 1910 $10,779
****
9461 Lancaster
MAYTOWN NB, MAYTOWN
{{ 3 L 7 S }}
Chartered 6/09
1902 Date Back <$VALUE
4x5 1-2275 <$600
3x10-20 1-1970 <$600
1902 Plain Back
4x5 2276-7440 <$600
3x10-20 1971-5008 <$600
1929 Small Size
5 Type 1 1-1014 <$200
10 Type 1 1-496 <$200
20 Type 1 1-142 <$200
5 Type 2 1-2086 <$225
10 Type 2 1-1482 <$225
20 Type 2 1-404 <$225
Total Issue $509,750
Out in 1935 $40,000
Large out 1935 $1,150
****
8619 Schuylkill
FNB OF McADOO
{{ 3 L 12 S }}
Chartered 3/07
1902 Red Seal <$VALUE
3x10-20 1-288 <$600
1902 Date Back
3x10-20 1-2860 <$300
1902 Plain Back
3x10-20 2861-8171 <$300
1929 Small Size
10 Type 1 1-1474 <$150
20 Type 1 1-392 <$165
10 Type 2 1-6638 <$175
20 Type 2 1-1807 <$175
Total Issue $660,950
Out in 1935 $77,700
Large out 1935 $800
****
9526 Juniata
FARMERS NB OF McALISTERVILLE
{{ 3 L 6U + 8 S }}
Chartered 8/09
1902 Date Back <$VALUE
3x10-20 1-2440 <$350
1902 Plain Back
3x10-20 2441-6938 <$350
1929 Small Size
10 Type 1 1-760 <$150
20 Type 1 1-202 <$165
10 Type 2 1-1902 <$165
20 Type 2 1-568 <$165
Total Issue $447,120
Out in 1935 $40,000
Large out 1935 $990
****
7769 Snyder
FNB OF McCLURE
{{ 3 L 6 S }}
Chartered 6/05
1902 Red Seal <$VALUE
4x5 1-1015 <$600
3x10-20 1-814 <$600
1902 Date Back
4x5 1-2350 <$300
3x10-20 1-1680 <$300
1902 Plain Back
4x5 2351-7971 <$300
3x10-20 1681-4973 <$300
1929 Small Size
5 Type 1 1-1062 <$165
10 Type 1 1-528 <$165
20 Type 1 1-162 <$165
5 Type 2 1-1244 <$175
10 Type 2 1-717 <$175
20 Type 2 1-251 <$175
Total Issue $570,460
Out in 1935 $24,550
Large out 1935 $950
****
8083 Fulton
FNB OF McCONNELLSBURG
{{ 1 L 5 S }}
Chartered 2/06
1902 Red Seal <$VALUE
3x10-20 1-287 <$750
1902 Date Back
3x10-20 1-2050 <$350
1902 Plain Back
3x10-20 2051-5808 <$350
1929 Small Size
10 Type 1 1-660 <$185
20 Type 1 1-212 <$185
10 Type 2 1-596 <$200
20 Type 2 1-120 <$200
Total Issue $378,150
Out in 1935 $24,700
Large out 1935 $1,290
****
13765 Fulton
FULTON COUNTY NB OF McCONNELLSBURG
{{ 3 S }}
Chartered 9/33
1929 Small Size <$VALUE
5 Type 2 1-2010 <$250
10 Type 2 1-2653 <$250
20 Type 2 1-1410 <$250
Total Issue $64,780
Out in 1935 $45,600
****
4752 Washington
FNB OF McDONALD
{{ 1 L 5 S }}
Organized 3/23/92
Brown Back <$VALUE
3x10-20 1-1610 <$750
1882 Date Back
3x10-20 1-575 <$750
1902 Date Back
3x50-100 1-280 <$750/$850
1902 Plain Back
3x50-100 281-338<$750/$850
1929 Small Size
50 Type 1 1-48 <$225
100 Type 1 1-2 <$400
Total Issue $209,350
Out in 1935 $12,400
Large out 1935 $2,050
****
5058 Washington
PEOPLES NB OF McDONALD
{{ UNREPORTED }}
Chartered 2/20/97
Liquidated 2/1/07
Brown Back <$VALUE
4x5 1-475 <$1250
3x10-20 1-1130 <$1250
Total Issue $66,000
Out in 1910 $870
****
5142 Allegheny
FNB OF McKEES ROCKS
{{ 12 L 24 S }}
Organized 9/6/98
Liquidated 8/2/34
Brown Back <$VALUE
4x5 1-6800 <$300
3x10-20 1-5400 <$300
1882 Date Back
4x5 1-9250 <$300
3x10-20 1-6240 <$300
1882 Value Back
4x5 9251-12312 <$300
3x10-20 6241-8096 <$300
1902 Plain Back
4x5 1-17094 <$135
4x10 1-7029 <$135
3x10-20 1-9529 <$135
1929 Small Size
5 Type 1 1-7978 <$40
10 Type 1 1-4754 <$40
20 Type 1 1-1238 <$50
5 Type 2 1-2826 <$60
10 Type 2 1-1934 <$60
20 Type 2 1-460 <$60
Total Issue $2,872,340
Out in 1935 $99,940
Large out 1935 $5,800
Ch 14107 assumed circulation
****
4876 Allegheny
CITIZENS NB OF McKEESPORT
{{ UNREPORTED }}
Chartered 3/17/93
Liquidated 1/15/03
Brown Back <$VALUE
4x5 1-1571 <$1250
3x10-20 1-1310 <$1250
Total Issue $96,920
Out in 1910 $1,285
****
2222 Allegheny
FNB OF McKEESPORT
{{ 21 L 34 S }}
Chartered 2/10/75
Original Series <$VALUE
4x5 1-450 <$450
3x10-20 1-360 <$750/$1250
Series 1875
4x5 1-3913 <$450
3x10-20 1-1713 <$750/$1250
Brown Back
4x5 1-14875 <$250
4x10 1-4500 <$250
3x10-20 1-7022 <$250
50-100 1-826 <$1250/$1500
1882 Date Back
4x5 1-23358 <$250
4x10 1-20665 <$250
3x10-20 1-500 <$250
50-100 1-100 <$1250/$1500
3x50-100 1-256<$1250/$1500
1902 Date Back
4x5 1-5000 <$100
3x10-20 1-4000 <$100
3x50-100 1-1167 <$400/$500
1902 Plain Back
4x5 5001-53464 <$100
3x10-20 4001-31181 <$100
3x50-100 1168-1737 <$400/$500
1929 Small Size
5 Type 1 1-8234 <$40
10 Type 1 1-3996 <$40
20 Type 1 1-1100 <$50
50 Type 1 1-356 <$125
100 Type 1 1-116 <$175
5 Type 2 1-4476 <$40
10 Type 2 1-3828 <$40
20 Type 2 1-1653 <$50
Total Issue $6,492,650
Out in 1935 $297,550
Large out 1935 $19,630
****
4625 Allegheny
NB OF McKEESPORT
{{ U + 11 L 2U + 12 S }}
Chartered 1891
Brown Back <$VALUE
4x5 1-9375 <$275
3x10-20 1-11600 <$275
1882 Date Back
4x5 1-6530 <$275
3x10-20 1-4732 <$275
1902 Date Back
4x5 1-10500 <$135
3x10-20 1-9600 <$135
1902 Plain Back
4x5 10501-51374 <$135
3x10-20 9601-35343 <$135
1929 Small Size
5 Type 1 1-7890 <$50
10 Type 1 1-4232 <$50
20 Type 1 1-1114 <$60
5 Type 2 1-10724 <$60
10 Type 2 1-5006 <$60
20 Type 2 1-1413 <$60
Total Issue $4,685,570
Out in 1935 $156,600
Large out 1935 $9,315
****
13967 Allegheny
UNION NB AT McKEESPORT
{{ 4 S }}
Chartered 1/34
1929 Small Size <$VALUE
5 Type 2 1-6540 <$150
10 Type 2 1-3245 <$150
20 Type 2 1-1024 <$150
Total Issue $85,630
Out in 1935 $126,550
Large out 1935 $8,420
Outstanding includes Ch 7559
****

****
7559 Allegheny
UNION NB OF McKEESPORT
{{ 6 L 12 S }}
Chartered 1/05
Liquidated 5/9/34
1902 Red Seal <$VALUE
4x5 1-7750 <$325
3x10-20 1-4800 <$325
1902 Date Back
4x5 1-15500 <$135
3x10-20 1-9300 <$135
1902 Plain Back
4x5 15501-48160 <$135
3x10-20 9301-28967 <$135
1929 Small Size
5 Type 1 1-6334 <$60
10 Type 1 1-2922 <$60
20 Type 1 1-782 <$70
5 Type 2 1-2450 <$75
10 Type 2 1-1170 <$75
20 Type 2 1-140 <$75
Total Issue $3,292,480
Out at close $130,200
Large out 1935 $8,420
Ch 13967 assumed circulation
****
8773 Mifflin
McVEYTOWN NB, McVEYTOWN
{{ 3 L 5 S }}
Chartered 6/07
1902 Red Seal <$VALUE
4x5 1-665 <$750
3x10-20 1-484 <$750
1902 Date Back
4x5 1-2075 <$375
3x10-20 1-1380 <$375
1902 Plain Back
4x5 2076-6581 <$375
3x10-20 1381-4049 <$375
1929 Small Size
5 Type 1 1-1040 <$175
10 Type 1 1-476 <$175
20 Type 1 1-132 <$175
5 Type 2 1-908 <$200
10 Type 2 1-763 <$200
20 Type 2 1-203 <$200
Total Issue $463,400
Out in 1935 $24,500
Large out 1935 $860
****
115 Crawford
FNB OF MEADVILLE
{{ 2 L }}
Organized 10/28/63
Receivership 6/9/80
Original Series <$VALUE
3x1-2 1-2460 <$600/$1250
4x5 1-7750 <$650
3x10-20 1-2500 <$850/$1500
Series 1875
4x5 1-1235 <$650
3x10-20 1-462 <$850/$1500
Total Issue $340,100
Out in 1916 $2,308
****
FNB of Meadville
SEE Ch 4938
New FNB of Meadville
****
871 Crawford
MERCHANTS NB OF MEADVILLE
Chartered 3/9/65
2nd title: Merchants NB & TC 7/1/30
FIRST TITLE {{ 8 L 2 S }}
Original Series <$VALUE
3x1-2 1-2200 <$350/$1000
4x5 1-6000 <$400
3x10-20 1-1400 <$750/$1250
Series 1875
3x10-20 1-2354 <$750/$1250
Brown Back
3x10-20 1-2859 <$300
1902 Red Seal
3x10-20 1-900 <$350
1902 Date Back
3x10-20 1-2400 <$165
1902 Plain Back
3x10-20 2401-17309 <$165
1929 Small Size
10 Type 1 1-2158 <$100
20 Type 1 1-724 <$100
SECOND TITLE {{ 12 S }}
1929 Small Size
10 Type 1 1-1750 <$70
20 Type 1 1-472 <$80
10 Type 2 1-5047 <$80
20 Type 2 1-1162 <$80
Total Issue $1,823,810
Out in 1935 $130,450
Large out 1935 $6,460
****

****
4938 Crawford
NEW FNB OF MEADVILLE
Chartered 1894
2nd title: FNB of Meadville 8/25/30
FIRST TITLE {{ 14 L 3 S }}
Brown Back <$VALUE
3x10-20 1-4120 <$275
50-100 1-1807 <$1250/$1500
1882 Date Back
3x10-20 1-4456 <$275
50-100 1-116 <$1250/$1500
1902 Date Back
3x10-20 1-5000 <$135
1902 Plain Back
3x10-20 5001-37945 <$135
1929 Small Size
10 Type 1 1-3070 <$125
20 Type 1 1-1022 <$125
SECOND TITLE {{ 26 S }}
1929 Small Size
10 Type 1 1-3688 <$50
20 Type 1 1-998 <$60
10 Type 2 1-10118 <$50
20 Type 2 1-2561 <$60
Total Issue $3,414,780
Out in 1935 $214,650
Large out 1935 $8,480
****
380 Cumberland
FNB OF MECHANICSBURG
{{ 8 L }}
Chartered 4/64
Liquidated 3/8/24
Original Series <$VALUE
4x5 1-5000 <$400
3x10-20 1-1800 <$750/$1250
Series 1875
4x5 1-2800 <$400
3x10-20 1-1662 <$750/$1250
Brown Back
4x5 1-4390 <$300
3x10-20 1-5327 <$300
1902 Red Seal
3x10-20 1-5800 <$350
1902 Date Back
4x5 1-6600 <$165
3x10-20 1-6160 <$165
1902 Plain Back
4x5 6601-18065 <$165
3x10-20 6161-13133 <$165
Total Issue $1,991,200
Out at close $120,900
****
8969 Cumberland
MECHANICSBURG NB, MECHANICSBURG
{{ 3 L }}
Chartered 12/07
Liquidated 11/5/23
1902 Red Seal <$VALUE
3x10-20 1-1090 <$600
1902 Date Back
3x10-20 1-5100 <$300
1902 Plain Back
3x10-20 5101-9947 <$300
Total Issue $551,850
Out at close $42,040
****
326 Cumberland
SECOND NB OF MECHANICSBURG
{{ 10 L 3U + 12 S }}
Chartered 3/64
Original Series <$VALUE
4x5 1-3250 <$400
3x10-20 1-1100 <$750/$1250
Series 1875
4x5 1-840 <$400
3x10-20 1-668 <$750/$1250
Brown Back
3x10-20 1-3022 <$275
1902 Red Seal
3x10-20 1-3300 <$325
1902 Date Back
3x10-20 1-4340 <$165
1902 Plain Back
4x5 1-4600 <$165
3x10-20 4341-11481 <$165
1929 Small Size
5 Type 1 1-2348 <$100
10 Type 1 1-856 <$100
20 Type 1 1-254 <$110
5 Type 2 1-3840 <$125
10 Type 2 1-1073 <$125
20 Type 2 1-494 <$125
Total Issue $1,344,440
Out in 1935 $49,300
Large out 1935 $3,290
****

****
3666 Delaware
CHARTER NB OF MEDIA
{{ 4 L }}
Chartered 4/2/87
Liquidated 1/31/28
Brown Back <$VALUE
4x5 1-9436 <$750
3x10-20 1-2187 <$750
1902 Red Seal
4x5 1-2125 <$750
3x10-20 1-1350 <$750
1902 Date Back
4x5 1-6800 <$400
3x10-20 1-5040 <$400
1902 Plain Back
4x5 6801-16295 <$400
3x10-20 5041-11220 <$400
Total Issue $1,294,970
Out at close $47,650
****
312 Delaware
FNB OF MEDIA
{{ 14 L 21 S }}
Chartered 3/64
Original Series <$VALUE
4x5 1-4500 <$500
3x10-20 1-1900 <$750/$1250
Series 1875
3x10-20 1-6430 <$750/$1250
Brown Back
4x5 1-22652 <$400
3x10-20 1-2050 <$400
1902 Red Seal
4x5 1-5325 <$450
3x10-20 1-3970 <$450
1902 Date Back
4x5 1-9350 <$200
3x10-20 1-6180 <$200
1902 Plain Back
4x5 9351-35995 <$200
3x10-20 6181-24012 <$200
1929 Small Size
5 Type 1 1-9342 <$75
10 Type 1 1-4658 <$80
20 Type 1 1-1082 <$100
5 Type 2 1-12540 <$100
10 Type 2 1-6168 <$100
20 Type 2 1-1716 <$100
Total Issue $3,942,920
Out in 1935 $190,720
Large out 1935 $9,710
****
2256 Mercer
FARMERS & MECHANICS NB OF MERCER
{{ 7 L 10 S }}
Chartered 5/11/75
Liquidated 2/8/34
Original Series <$VALUE
4x5 1-4000 <$450
Series 1875
4x5 1-2991 <$450
Brown Back
3x10-20 1-2780 <$300
1882 Date Back
3x10-20 1-2370 <$300
1902 Date Back
3x10-20 1-1400 <$175
1902 Plain Back
3x10-20 1401-10127 <$175
1929 Small Size
10 Type 1 1-2386 <$125
20 Type 1 1-619 <$135
Total Issue $1,121,110
Out at close $71,030
Large out 1935 $3,360
Ch 13846 assumed circulation
****
13846 Mercer
FARMERS NB OF MERCER
{{ 2 S }}
Chartered 11/33
1929 Small Size <$VALUE
5 Type 2 1-1504 <$375
10 Type 2 1-696 <$375
Total Issue $14,480
Out in 1935 $53,360
Large out 1935 $3,460
Outstanding includes Ch 2256
****

<$VALUEs are for notes in **FINE** condition. Value changes by approximately **25%** for a change of one full grade.

***

392 Mercer
FNB OF MERCER
{{6L U+16S}}
Chartered 4/64
Original Series <$VALUE
4x5 1-9000 <$500
Series 1875
4x5 1-4820 <$500
50-100 1-125 <$3500
Brown Back
50-100 1-2305 <$1250/$1500
1902 Red Seal
50-100 1-2314 <$2250/$2500
1902 Date Back
50-100 1-800 <$500/$600
3x50-100 1-2260 <$500/$600
1902 Plain Back
3x50-100 2261-2840 <$500/$600
1929 Small Size
10 Type 1 1-3114 <$75
20 Type 1 1-798 <$85
10 Type 2 1-2557 <$100
20 Type 2 1-825 <$100
Total Issue $2,148,920
Out in 1935 $108,195
Large out 1935 $13,325

***

4909 Mercer
MERCER COUNTY NB OF MERCER
{{ UNREPORTED }}
Chartered 5/13/93
Liquidated 8/11/02
Brown Back <$VALUE
4x5 1-3695 <$1250
3x10-20 1-931 <$1250
Total Issue $120,450
Out in 1910 $1,685

***

9330 Franklin
FNB OF MERCERSBURG
{{5L 10S}}
Chartered 1/09
1902 Date Back <$VALUE
4x5 1-2075 <$300
3x10-20 1-1600 <$300
1902 Plain Back
4x5 2076-9438 <$300
3x10-20 1601-6535 <$300
1929 Small Size
5 Type 1 1-1894 <$125
10 Type 1 1-1008 <$135
20 Type 1 1-274 <$150
5 Type 2 1-2596 <$150
10 Type 2 1-1487 <$150
20 Type 2 1-392 <$150
Total Issue $701,380
Out in 1935 $45,350
Large out 1935 $1,150

***

5429 Wyoming
FNB OF MESHOPPEN
{{4L 14S}}
Chartered 6/15/00
Brown Back <$VALUE
3x10-20 1-2400 <$500
1882 Date Back
4x5 1-2600 <$450
3x10-20 1-2140 <$450
1882 Value Back
4x5 2601-4717 <$450
3x10-20 2141-3293 <$450
1902 Plain Back
4x5 1-5535 <$275
3x10-20 1-3946 <$275
1929 Small Size
5 Type 1 1-2350 <$100
10 Type 1 1-1226 <$100
20 Type 1 1-340 <$100
5 Type 2 1-6632 <$100
10 Type 2 1-4280 <$100
20 Type 2 1-1392 <$100
Total Issue $975,650
Out in 1935 $88,150
Large out 1935 $1,560

***

5833 Somerset
CITIZENS NB OF MEYERSDALE
{{4L 16S}}
Chartered 5/23/01
Brown Back <$VALUE
3x10-20 1-3660 <$400
1882 Date Back
3x10-20 1-5900 <$400
1882 Value Back
3x10-20 5901-9303 <$400
1902 Plain Back
3x10-20 1-8294 <$200
1929 Small Size
10 Type 1 1-2522 <$100
20 Type 1 1-672 <$100
5 Type 2 1-180 <$125
10 Type 2 1-1712 <$125
20 Type 2 1-490 <$125
Total Issue $1,322,630
Out in 1935 $96,500
Large out 1935 $3,155

***

2258 Somerset
FNB OF MEYERSDALE
{{1L}}
Chartered 5/14/75
Liquidated 3/5/80
Original Series <$VALUE
4x5 1-2250 <$1250
Series 1875
4x5 1-560 <$1250
Total Issue $56,200
Out in 1910 $240

***

5801 Somerset
SECOND NB OF MEYERSDALE
{{4L 11S}}
Chartered 5/7/01
Brown Back <$VALUE
3x10-20 1-1530 <$400
1882 Date Back
3x10-20 1-6800 <$400
1882 Value Back
3x10-20 6801-10418 <$400
1902 Plain Back
3x10-20 1-8153 <$200
1929 Small Size
5 Type 1 1-1608 <$125
10 Type 1 1-1264 <$125
20 Type 1 1-384 <$135
5 Type 2 1-3948 <$150
10 Type 2 1-1896 <$150
20 Type 2 1-504 <$150
Total Issue $1,223,990
Out in 1935 $63,550
Large out 1935 $4,965

***

4156 Snyder
FNB OF MIDDLEBURGH
{{6L 30S}}
Chartered 11/12/89
Brown Back <$VALUE
4x5 1-4700 <$350
3x10-20 1-3154 <$350
1902 Date Back
3x10-20 1-3000 <$200
1902 Plain Back
3x10-20 3001-11388 <$200
1929 Small Size
10 Type 1 1-1488 <$65
20 Type 1 1-374 <$75
10 Type 2 1-1738 <$75
20 Type 2 1-507 <$75
Total Issue $982,780
Out in 1935 $49,350
Large out 1935 $2,370

***

7826 Dauphin
CITIZENS NB OF MIDDLETOWN
{{3L}}
Chartered 7/05
Liquidated 12/31/23
1902 Red Seal <$VALUE
4x5 1-1900 <$750
3x10-20 1-1570 <$750
1902 Date Back
4x5 1-4300 <$375
3x10-20 1-3240 <$375
1902 Plain Back
4x5 4301-10020 <$375
3x10-20 3241-6661 <$375
Total Issue $649,950
Out at close $50,000

***

585 Dauphin
NB OF MIDDLETOWN
{{2L}}
Organized 11/23/64
Receivership 9/24/94
Original Series <$VALUE
4x5 1-3500 <$750
3x10-20 1-1800<$1000/$1500
Series 1875
4x5 1-1385 <$750
3x10-20 1-1656<$1000/$1500
Brown Back
3x10-20 1-3917 <$650
Total Issue $466,350
Out in 1916 $1,925

***

8311 Beaver
FNB OF MIDLAND
{{4L 13S}}
Chartered 7/06
1902 Red Seal <$VALUE
4x10 1-650 <$600
1902 Date Back
4x10 1-7050* <$275
1902 Plain Back
4x10 7301-21729* <$275
* 7051-7300 not marked
1929 Small Size
10 Type 1 1-2778 <$100
10 Type 2 1-3780 <$100
Total Issue $1,099,640
Out in 1935 $48,270
Large out 1935 $2,170

***

6626 Washington
MIDWAY NB, MIDWAY
{{4L 11S}}
Chartered 2/03
Receivership 9/15/33
1902 Red Seal <$VALUE
3x10-20 1-3070 <$600
1902 Date Back
3x10-20 1-4700 <$275
1902 Plain Back
3x10-20 4701-14147 <$275
1929 Small Size
10 Type 1 1-1396 <$150
20 Type 1 1-370 <$165
Total Issue $989,010
Out at close $50,000
Large out at close $2,710

***

Peoples NB of Mifflin
SEE Ch 9678
Peoples NB of Patterson

***

174 Union
FNB OF MIFFLINBURG
{{ UNREPORTED }}
Chartered 12/63
Liquidated 3/8/80
Original Series <$VALUE
4x5 1-3250 <$1250
3x10-20 1-2000<$1250/$1750
Series 1875
3x10-20 1-1362<$1250/$1750
Total Issue $233,100
Out in 1910 $1,455

***

4039 Juniata
FNB OF MIFFLINTOWN
{{5L 11S}}
Chartered 5/18/89
Brown Back <$VALUE
4x5 1-10700 <$400
3x10-20 1-2620 <$400
1882 Date Back
4x5 1-495 <$400
3x10-20 1-258 <$400
1902 Date Back
4x10 1-5300 <$200
1902 Plain Back
4x10 5301-17675 <$200
1929 Small Size
10 Type 1 1-2554 <$100
10 Type 2 1-3337 <$100
Total Issue $1,261,410
Out in 1935 $49,050
Large out 1935 $3,610

***

5147 Juniata
JUNIATA VALLEY NB OF MIFFLINTOWN
{{7L 14S}}
Chartered 8/3/98
Brown Back <$VALUE
4x5 1-1000 <$400
3x10-20 1-4600 <$400
1882 Date Back
4x5 1-4700 <$400
3x10-20 1-3040 <$400
1882 Value Back
4x5 4701-6400 <$400
3x10-20 3041-4020 <$400
1902 Plain Back
4x5 1-10570 <$200
3x10-20 1-6113 <$200
1929 Small Size
5 Type 1 1-2420 <$100
10 Type 1 1-1364 <$100
20 Type 1 1-308* <$100
5 Type 2 1-2354 <$125
10 Type 2 1-1315 <$125
20 Type 2 1-372 <$125
* 286 not issued
Total Issue $1,319,690
Out in 1935 $59,700
Large out 1935 $3,080

***

9552 Sullivan
FNB OF MILDRED
{{2L 6S}}
Chartered 10/09
Liquidated 1/9/34
1902 Date Back <$VALUE
4x5 1-2200 <$375
3x10-20 1-1740 <$375
1902 Plain Back
4x5 2201-7667 <$375
3x10-20 1741-4902 <$375
1929 Small Size
5 Type 1 1-912 <$200
10 Type 1 1-486 <$200
20 Type 1 1-122 <$200
Total Issue $469,600
Out at close $13,960
Large out at close $930

***

5496 Pike
FNB OF MILFORD
{{8L 5S}}
Chartered 7/12/00
Brown Back <$VALUE
4x5 1-2120 <$300
3x10-20 1-1572 <$300
1882 Date Back
4x5 1-2150 <$300
3x10-20 1-1520 <$300
1882 Value Back
4x5 2151-3555 <$300
3x10-20 1521-2281 <$300
1902 Plain Back
4x5 1-3792 <$175
3x10-20 1-2094 <$175
1929 Small Size
5 Type 1 1-990 <$175
10 Type 1 1-506 <$175
20 Type 1 1-120 <$175
5 Type 2 1-1366 <$175
10 Type 2 1-796 <$175
20 Type 2 1-272 <$200
Total Issue $581,380
Out in 1935 $24,600
Large out 1935 $1,785

***

2252 Dauphin
FNB OF MILLERSBURG
{{6L 10S}}
Chartered 4/23/75
Original Series <$VALUE
4x5 1-600 <$500
3x10-20 1-460 <$750/$1250
Series 1875
4x5 1-2150 <$500
3x10-20 1-6013 <$750/$1250
Brown Back
3x10-20 1-4560 <$400
1882 Date Back
3x10-20 1-3717 <$400
1902 Date Back
3x10-20 1-1000 <$250
1902 Plain Back
3x10-20 1001-8723 <$250
1929 Small Size
10 Type 1 1-1496 <$135
20 Type 1 1-402 <$135
10 Type 2 1-1565 <$165
20 Type 2 1-362 <$165
Total Issue $1,389,540
Out in 1935 $49,350
Large out 1935 $3,590

***

7156 Perry
FNB OF MILLERSTOWN
{{3L 6S}}
Chartered 3/04
1902 Red Seal <$VALUE
4x5 1-950 <$750
3x10-20 1-760 <$750
1902 Date Back
4x5 1-1925 <$375
3x10-20 1-1390 <$375
1902 Plain Back
4x5 1926-6468 <$375
3x10-20 1391-4000 <$375
1929 Small Size
5 Type 1 1-920 <$175
10 Type 1 1-430 <$175
20 Type 1 1-118 <$175
5 Type 2 1-1174 <$200
10 Type 2 1-636 <$200
20 Type 2 1-204 <$200
Total Issue $470,230
Out in 1935 $24,650
Large out 1935 $1,220

***

2241 Perry
GERMAN NB OF MILLERSTOWN
{{1L}}
Chartered 3/27/75
Liquidated 8/12/84
Original Series <$VALUE
3x10-20 1-900 <$1500/$2000
Series 1875
3x10-20 1-1070<$1500/$2000
Total Issue $98,500
Out in 1910 $435

***

9259 Lancaster
MILLERSVILLE NB, MILLERSVILLE
{{2L 4S}}
Chartered 10/08
Receivership 8/15/33
1902 Date Back <$VALUE
3x10-20 1-2230 <$600
1902 Plain Back
3x10-20 2231-6538 <$600
1929 Small Size
10 Type 1 1-722 <$300
20 Type 1 1-182 <$300
10 Type 2 1-30 <$350
Total Issue $392,360
Out at close $25,000
Large out at close $1,230

***

9511 Centre
FARMERS NB OF MILLHEIM
Chartered 8/09
2nd title: Farmers NB & TC 11/1/26
FIRST TITLE {{2L}}
1902 Date Back <$VALUE
4x5 1-2075 <$300
3x10-20 1-1660 <$300
1902 Plain Back
4x5 2076-5462 <$300
3x10-20 1661-3616 <$300
SECOND TITLE {{1L 13S}}
1902 Plain Back
4x5 1-1020 <$300
3x10-20 1-495 <$300
1929 Small Size
5 Type 1 1-3176 <$100
10 Type 1 1-1868 <$100
20 Type 1 1-566 <$100
5 Type 2 1-7134 <$125
10 Type 2 1-3788 <$125
20 Type 2 1-1068 <$125
Total Issue $705,380
Out in 1935 $107,700
Large out 1935 $920

***

7310 Washington
FNB OF MILLSBORO
{{3L 3S}}
Chartered 6/04
Receivership 4/28/31
1902 Red Seal <$VALUE
3x10-20 1-1100 <$600
1902 Date Back
3x10-20 1-2150 <$300
1902 Plain Back
3x10-20 2151-7196 <$300
1929 Small Size
10 Type 1 1-408 <$250
20 Type 1 1-123 <$250
Total Issue $454,040
Out at close $25,000
Large out at close $2,680

***

5389 Columbia
FNB OF MILLVILLE
{{2L 6S}}
Chartered 6/2/00
Brown Back <$VALUE
3x10-20 1-2000 <$600
1882 Date Back
3x10-20 1-2230 <$600
1882 Value Back
3x10-20 2231-3192 <$600
1902 Plain Back
3x10-20 1-3336 <$350
1929 Small Size
10 Type 1 1-778 <$175
20 Type 1 1-192 <$175
10 Type 2 1-813 <$200
20 Type 2 1-149 <$200
Total Issue $507,230
Out in 1935 $25,000
Large out 1935 $990

***

F Milton NB of Milton
SEE Ch 253
FNB of Milton

***

253 Northumberland
FNB OF MILTON
Chartered 2/64
2nd title: F Milton NB 2/2/29
FIRST TITLE {{6L}}
Original Series <$VALUE
4x5 1-2150 <$450
3x10-20 1-2500 <$750/$1250
50-100 1-100 <$3500
Series 1875
3x10-20 1-1434 <$750/$1250
Brown Back
3x10-20 1-5081 <$300
1902 Red Seal
3x10-20 1-5000 <$350
1902 Date Back
3x10-20 1-7700 <$175
1902 Plain Back
3x10-20 7701-25117 <$175
SECOND TITLE {{0L 18S}}
1902 Plain Back
3x10-20 1-236 <$350
1929 Small Size
10 Type 1 1-6080 <$50
20 Type 1 1-1662 <$60
10 Type 2 1-7434 <$65
20 Type 2 1-2365 <$65
Total Issue $2,712,280
Out in 1935 $194,650
Large out 1935 $11,330
Outstanding includes Ch 711

***

711 Northumberland
MILTON NB, MILTON
{{9L}}
Chartered 1/65
Closed 2/2/29
Original Series <$VALUE
3x1-2 1-3000 <$350/$850
4x5 1-1875 <$400
3x10-20 1-2930 <$750/$1250
Series 1875
3x10-20 1-2100 <$750/$1250
Brown Back
3x10-20 1-6210 <$275
1902 Red Seal
3x10-20 1-3900 <$350
1902 Date Back
3x10-20 1-8000 <$175
1902 Plain Back
3x10-20 8001-25069 <$175
Total Issue $2,062,950
Out at close $98,800
Ch 253 assumed circulation

***

423 Schuylkill
FNB OF MINERSVILLE
{{3L 3S}}
Chartered 5/64
Original Series <$VALUE
3x1-2 1-500 <$500/$1500
4x5 1-2600 <$600
3x10-20 1-2760 <$850/$1500
Series 1875
4x5 1-380 <$600
3x10-20 1-922 <$850/$1500
Brown Back
4x5 1-875 <$650
3x10-20 1-582 <$650
50-100 1-1099 <$1500/$1750
1902 Red Seal
4x5 1-425 <$750
3x10-20 1-350 <$750
1902 Date Back
4x5 1-975 <$375
3x10-20 1-800 <$375
1902 Plain Back
4x5 976-2240 <$375
3x10-20 801-1492 <$375
1929 Small Size
5 Type 1 1-400 <$350
10 Type 1 1-206 <$350
20 Type 1 1-71 <$350
Total Issue $635,930
Out in 1935 $12,300
Large out 1935 $1,590

***

6131 Schuylkill
UNION NB OF MINERSVILLE
{{5L 9S}}
Chartered 2/19/02
1902 Red Seal <$VALUE
4x5 1-1900 <$500
3x10-20 1-2140 <$500
1902 Date Back
4x5 1-4950 <$225
3x10-20 1-3600 <$225
1902 Plain Back (dated 1902)
4x5 4951-9375 <$225
3x10-20 3601-6148 <$225
1902 Plain Back (dated 1922)
4x5 1-6110 <$225
3x10-20 1-4186 <$225
1929 Small Size
5 Type 1 1-2186 <$100
10 Type 1 1-1036 <$100
20 Type 1 1-304 <$125
5 Type 2 1-2964 <$135
10 Type 2 1-1482 <$135
20 Type 2 1-396 <$135
Total Issue $1,173,180
Out in 1935 $50,000
Large out 1935 $2,330

***

12349 Luzerne
FNB OF MOCANAQUA
{{2L 8S}}
Chartered 4/23
1902 Plain Back <$VALUE
4x5 1-11384 <$500
1929 Small Size
5 Type 1 1-5578 <$150
5 Type 2 1-14762 <$150
Total Issue $468,830
Out in 1935 $25,605
Large out 1935 $605

***

8968 Berks
MOHNTON NB, MOHNTON
{{ UNREPORTED }}
Chartered 12/07
Liquidated 6/1/21
1902 Red Seal <$VALUE
3x10-20 1-540 <$1500
1902 Date Back
3x10-20 1-1790 <$850
1902 Plain Back
3x10-20 1791-2786 <$850
Total Issue $166,300
Out at close $14,400

5879 Beaver
CITIZENS NB OF MONACA
{{ 8 L 11 S }}
Chartered 6/01
Brown Back <$VALUE
4x5 1-950 <$400
3x10-20 1-760 <$400
1882 Date Back
4x5 1-4700 <$400
3x10-20 1-3300 <$400
1882 Value Back
4x5 4701-8225 <$400
3x10-20 3301-5355 <$400
1902 Plain Back
4x5 1-6960 <$175
3x10-20 1-4810 <$175
1929 Small Size
5 Type 1 1-2202 <$100
10 Type 1 1-1028 <$100
20 Type 1 1-304 <$110
5 Type 2 1-2430 <$135
10 Type 2 1-1374 <$135
20 Type 2 1-516 <$135
Total Issue $1,069,380
Out in 1935 $48,550
Large out 1935 $1,510

5878 Beaver
MONACA NB, MONACA
{{ 4 L 6 S }}
Chartered 6/25/01
Brown Back <$VALUE
3x10-20 1-1050 <$450
1882 Date Back
3x10-20 1-2460 <$450
1882 Value Back
3x10-20 2461-3856 <$450
1902 Plain Back
3x10-20 1-3418 <$275
1929 Small Size
10 Type 1 1-830 <$165
20 Type 1 1-220 <$165
10 Type 2 1-570 <$175
20 Type 2 1-276 <$175
Total Issue $503,620
Out in 1935 $24,250
Large out 1935 $1,280

11487 Westmoreland
CITIZENS NB OF MONESSEN
{{ 4 L 7 S }}
Chartered 10/19
Liquidated 1/2/31
1902 Plain Back <$VALUE
3x10-20 1-18936 <$275
1929 Small Size
10 Type 1 1-1405 <$165
20 Type 1 1-394 <$165
Total Issue $1,078,380
Out at close $79,600
Large out at close $10,080
Ch 5253 assumed circulation

FNB of Monessen
FNB & TC of Monessen
SEE Ch 5253
Monessen NB, Monessen

5253 Westmoreland
MONESSEN NB, MONESSEN
Organized 12/14/99
Receivership 11/6/31
2nd title: FNB of Monessen 10/02
3rd title: FNB & TC 11/9/26
FIRST TITLE {{ 0 L }}
Brown Back <$VALUE
3x10-20 1-391 <$1000
SECOND TITLE {{ 3 L }}
Brown Back
3x10-20 1-2610 <$500
1882 Date Back
4x5 1-5130 <$500
3x10-20 1-3320 <$500
1882 Value Back
4x5 5131-7730 <$500
3x10-20 3321-4524 <$500
1902 Plain Back
4x5 1-5400 <$250
3x10-20 1-4490 <$250
THIRD TITLE {{ 1 L 6 S }}
1902 Plain Back
3x10-20 1-1924 <$300
1929 Small Size
10 Type 1 1-1655 <$150
20 Type 1 1-446 <$165
Total Issue $1,243,950
Out at close $143,760
Large out at close $12,590
Outstanding includes Ch 11487

5956 Westmoreland
PEOPLES NB OF MONESSEN
Chartered 8/31/01
2nd title: Peoples NB & TC 1/20/28
FIRST TITLE {{ 5 L }}
Brown Back <$VALUE
3x10-20 1-3100 <$400
1882 Date Back
3x10-20 1-5240 <$400
1882 Value Back
3x10-20 5241-8038 <$400
1902 Plain Back
3x10-20 1-6185 <$200
SECOND TITLE {{ 0 L 12 S }}
1902 Plain Back
3x10-20 1-1123 <$200
1929 Small Size
10 Type 1 1-1468 <$100
20 Type 1 1-396 <$100
10 Type 2 1-2141 <$100
20 Type 2 1-600 <$100
Total Issue $1,091,310
Out in 1935 $48,800
Large out 1935 $1,590

5968 Washington
FNB OF MONONGAHELA CITY
{{ 5 L 26 S }}
Chartered 9/6/01
Brown Back <$VALUE
3x10-20 1-1060 <$400
1882 Date Back
3x10-20 1-4400 <$400
1882 Value Back
3x10-20 4401-6966 <$400
1902 Plain Back
3x10-20 1-7104 <$250
1929 Small Size
10 Type 1 1-2432 <$60
20 Type 1 1-646 <$60
10 Type 2 1-4157 <$60
20 Type 2 1-1152 <$65
Total Issue $1,044,550
Out in 1935 $96,850
Large out 1935 $2,400

8866 Lycoming
FARMERS & MERCHANTS NB OF MONTGOMERY
{{ 4 L 10 S }}
Chartered 9/07
1902 Red Seal <$VALUE
3x10-20 1-800 <$600
1902 Date Back
3x10-20 1-3450 <$300
1902 Plain Back
3x10-20 3451-9971 <$300
1929 Small Size
10 Type 1 1-1110 <$110
20 Type 1 1-306 <$125
10 Type 2 1-1727 <$125
20 Type 2 1-666 <$125
Total Issue $672,460
Out in 1935 $43,600
Large out 1935 $1,720

5574 Lycoming
FNB OF MONTGOMERY
{{ 7 L 16 S }}
Chartered 9/11/00
Brown Back <$VALUE
3x10-20 1-2700 <$300
1882 Date Back
3x10-20 1-4940 <$300
1882 Value Back
3x10-20 4941-7275 <$300
1902 Plain Back
3x10-20 1-13933 <$175
1929 Small Size
10 Type 1 1-3250 <$60
20 Type 1 1-816 <$70
10 Type 2 1-3991 <$70
20 Type 2 1-942 <$75
Total Issue $1,547,070
Out in 1935 $98,400
Large out 1935 $4,530

6997 Lycoming
FNB OF MONTOURSVILLE
{{ 8 L 18 S }}
Chartered 10/03
1902 Red Seal <$VALUE
4x5 1-1345 <$350
3x10-20 1-1002 <$350
1902 Date Back
4x5 1-2250 <$175
3x10-20 1-1700 <$175
1902 Plain Back
4x5 2251-17279 <$175
3x10-20 1701-12103 <$175
1929 Small Size
5 Type 1 1-3748 <$65
10 Type 1 1-2186 <$65
20 Type 1 1-562 <$75
5 Type 2 1-8400 <$75
10 Type 2 1-3984 <$75
20 Type 2 1-1032 <$75
Total Issue $1,441,250
Out in 1935 $122,080
Large out 1935 $2,950

6746 Susquehanna
FARMERS NB OF MONTROSE
{{ 3 L }}
Chartered 4/03
Closed 9/1/23
1902 Red Seal <$VALUE
4x5 1-1500 <$750
3x10-20 1-2542 <$750
1902 Date Back
4x5 1-4400 <$375
3x10-20 1-2920 <$375
1902 Plain Back
4x5 4401-9730 <$375
3x10-20 2921-6083 <$375
Total Issue $655,850
Out at close $48,500
Ch 2223 assumed circulation

F & Farmers NB & TC of Montrose
SEE Ch 2223
FNB of Montrose

2223 Susquehanna
FNB OF MONTROSE
Chartered 2/13/75
2nd title: F & Farmers NB & TC of Montrose 12/11/23
FIRST TITLE {{ 5 L }}
Original Series <$VALUE
4x5 1-7500 <$450
Series 1875
4x5 1-2371 <$450
Brown Back
4x5 1-3650 <$300
3x10-20 1-1730 <$300
1882 Date Back
4x5 1-4070 <$300
3x10-20 1-2497 <$300
1902 Date Back
4x5 1-1250 <$150
3x10-20 1-1000 <$150
1902 Plain Back
4x5 1251-6150 <$150
3x10-20 1001-3500 <$150
SECOND TITLE {{ 7 L 17 S }}
1902 Plain Back
4x5 1-16110 <$150
3x10-20 1-9699 <$150
1929 Small Size
5 Type 1 1-6394 <$65
10 Type 1 1-3156 <$65
20 Type 1 1-862 <$75
5 Type 2 1-14348 <$75
10 Type 2 1-7014 <$75
20 Type 2 1-1802 <$75
Total Issue $2,330,860
Out in 1935 $137,150
Large out 1935 $4,925
Outstanding includes Ch 6746 and Ch 11393

9340 Lackawanna
FNB OF MOSCOW
{{ 3 L 15 S }}
Chartered 2/09
1902 Date Back <$VALUE
4x5 1-2950* <$350
3x10-20 1-2220** <$350
1902 Plain Back
4x5 3101-6320* <$350
3x10-20 2301-4197** <$350
* 2951-3100 not marked
** 2221-2300 not marked
1929 Small Size
5 Type 1 1-526 <$175
10 Type 1 1-506 <$175
20 Type 1 1-170 <$175
5 Type 2 1-5024 <$200
10 Type 2 1-2545 <$200
20 Type 2 1-700 <$200
Total Issue $467,360
Out in 1935 $40,350
Large out 1935 $650

3980 Northumberland
FNB OF MOUNT CARMEL
{{ 8 L 15 S }}
Chartered 2/19/89
Brown Back <$VALUE
3x10-20 1-5705 <$300
1882 Date Back
3x10-20 1-250 <$300
1902 Date Back
3x10-20 1-3900 <$175
1902 Plain Back
4x5 1-11520 <$175
3x10-20 3901-12502 <$175
1929 Small Size
5 Type 1 1-2788 <$75
10 Type 1 1-1534 <$75
20 Type 1 1-506 <$85
5 Type 2 1-8124 <$85
10 Type 2 1-3259 <$85
20 Type 2 1-1912 <$85
Total Issue $1,501,100
Out in 1935 $103,400
Large out 1935 $2,780

8393 Northumberland
UNION NB OF MOUNT CARMEL
{{ 10 L 23 S }}
Chartered 10/06
1902 Red Seal <$VALUE
4x5 1-2400 <$300
3x10-20 1-1960 <$300
1902 Date Back
4x5 1-11350 <$150
3x10-20 1-8760 <$150
1902 Plain Back
4x5 11351-38549 <$150
3x10-20 8761-25054 <$150
1929 Small Size
5 Type 1 1-5210 <$60
10 Type 1 1-2726 <$60
20 Type 1 1-794 <$60
5 Type 2 1-9432 <$60
10 Type 2 1-4627 <$60
20 Type 2 1-1245 <$65
Total Issue $2,753,150
Out in 1935 $125,000
Large out 1935 $4,995

8493 Cumberland
FNB OF MOUNT HOLLY SPRINGS
{{ 3 L 2U + 6 S }}
Chartered 1/07
1902 Red Seal <$VALUE
4x5 1-625 <$600
4x10 1-625 <$600
1902 Date Back
4x5 1-1950 <$300
4x10 1-1900 <$300
1902 Plain Back
4x5 1951-6982 <$300
4x10 1901-5655 <$300
1929 Small Size
5 Type 1 1-1656 <$175
10 Type 1 1-786 <$175
5 Type 2 1-1298 <$175
10 Type 2 1-1016 <$175
Total Issue $516,830
Out in 1935 $24,250
Large out 1935 $1,030

7473 McKean
MOUNT JEWETT NB, MOUNT JEWETT
{{ 5 L 8 S }}
Chartered 11/04
1902 Red Seal <$VALUE
4x5 1-3118 <$500
3x10-20 1-2230 <$500
1902 Date Back
4x5 1-5300 <$250
3x10-20 1-3640 <$250
1902 Plain Back
4x5 5301-9807 <$250
3x10-20 3641-6460 <$250
1929 Small Size
5 Type 1 1-1168 <$150
10 Type 1 1-558 <$150
20 Type 1 1-182 <$150
5 Type 2 1-3356 <$175
10 Type 2 1-1996 <$175
20 Type 2 1-472 <$175
Total Issue $829,540
Out in 1935 $41,600
Large out 1935 $1,390

667 Lancaster
FNB OF MOUNT JOY
Chartered 12/64
2nd title: FNB & TC of Mount Joy 4/23/29
FIRST TITLE {{ 12 L }}
Original Series <$VALUE
3x1-2 1-3000 <$400/$1000
4x5 1-2500 <$500
3x10-20 1-1539 <$750/$1250
20 1540-2539 <$1250
Series 1875
4x5 1-455 <$500
3x10-20 1-3329 <$750/$1250
Brown Back
3x10-20 1-8254 <$375
1902 Red Seal
4x5 1-3250 <$375
3x10-20 1-3100 <$375
1902 Date Back
4x5 1-7250 <$150
3x10-20 1-5800 <$150
1902 Plain Back
4x5 7251-30545 <$150
3x10-20 5801-20340 <$150
SECOND TITLE {{ 18 S }}
1929 Small Size
5 Type 1 1-4632 <$60
10 Type 1 1-2516 <$60
20 Type 1 1-712 <$70
5 Type 2 1-6784 <$75
10 Type 2 1-3619 <$75
20 Type 2 1-1124 <$75
Total Issue $3,066,050
Out in 1935 $122,050
Large out 1935 $6,770

1516 Lancaster
UNION N MOUNT JOY B, MOUNT JOY
{{ 11 L 17 S }}
Chartered 1865
Original Series <$VALUE
4x5 1-3250 <$500
3x10-20 1-1700 <$750/$1250
Series 1875
3x10-20 1-3886 <$750/$1250
Brown Back
3x10-20 1-8903 <$350
1902 Red Seal
3x10-20 1-3600 <$375
1902 Date Back
4x5 1-6000 <$165
3x10-20 1-6100 <$165
1902 Plain Back
4x5 6001-44122 <$165
3x10-20 6101-12290 <$165
1929 Small Size
5 Type 1 1-5676 <$60
10 Type 1 1-2264 <$60
20 Type 1 1-648 <$70
5 Type 2 1-8834 <$75
10 Type 2 1-4265 <$75
20 Type 2 1-1332 <$75
Total Issue $2,963,730
Out in 1935 $123,450
Large out 1935 $7,130

6983 Greene
FARMERS & MERCHANTS NB OF MOUNT MORRIS
{{ 4 L }}
Chartered 10/8/03
Receivership 2/21/27
1902 Red Seal <$VALUE
3x10-20 1-956 <$600
1902 Date Back
3x10-20 1-1460 <$300
1902 Plain Back
3x10-20 1461-4468 <$300
Total Issue $271,200
Out at close $24,250

4875 Westmoreland
CITIZENS NB OF MOUNT PLEASANT
{{ 1 L }}
Chartered 2/27/93
Liquidated 4/1/06
Brown Back <$VALUE
3x10-20 1-3192 <$1250
Total Issue $159,600
Out in 1910 $6,530

4892 Westmoreland
FARMERS & MERCHANTS NB OF MOUNT PLEASANT
{{ UNREPORTED }}
Organized 3/27/93
Receivership 10/29/07
Brown Back <$VALUE
4x5 1-4575 <$1250
3x10-20 1-1098 <$1250
Total Issue $146,400
Out in 1916 $1,310

386 Westmoreland
FNB OF MOUNT PLEASANT
{{ 13 L 16 S }}
Chartered 4/64
Liquidated 3/2/32
Original Series <$VALUE
3x1-2 1-400 <$350/$850
4x5 1-5475 <$400
4x10 1-3188 <$750
Series 1875
4x5 1-1911 <$400
4x10 1-2444 <$750
Brown Back
3x10-20 1-6284 <$250
1902 Red Seal
3x10-20 1-4900 <$275
1902 Date Back
3x10-20 1-7900 <$125
1902 Plain Back
3x10-20 7901-24268 <$125
1929 Small Size
10 Type 1 1-2117 <$100
20 Type 1 1-507 <$100
Total Issue $2,335,460
Out at close $95,560
Large out at close $11,240

9198 Westmoreland
PEOPLES NB OF MOUNT PLEASANT
{{ 4 L 8 S }}
Chartered 7/08
Liquidated 3/2/32
1902 Date Back <$VALUE
3x10-20 1-5090 <$250
1902 Plain Back
3x10-20 5091-13598 <$250
1929 Small Size
10 Type 1 1-966 <$150
20 Type 1 1-255 <$150
Total Issue $768,460
Out at close $47,720
Large out at close $4,180

10206 Huntingdon
CENTRAL NB OF MOUNT UNION
{{ 4 L 8 S }}
Chartered 5/12
Receivership 1/21/32
1902 Date Back <$VALUE
4x5 1-3200 <$250
3x10-20 1-2480 <$250
1902 Plain Back
4x5 3201-17784 <$250
3x10-20 2481-11043 <$250
1929 Small Size
5 Type 1 1-2520 <$100
10 Type 1 1-1350 <$100
20 Type 1 1-378 <$125
5 Type 2 1-3614 <$125
10 Type 2 1-1906 <$125
20 Type 2 1-516 <$150
Total Issue $1,157,240
Out in 1935 $59,100
Large out 1935 $2,090

6411 Huntingdon
FNB OF MOUNT UNION
{{ 4 L 9 S }}
Chartered 9/6/02
1902 Red Seal <$VALUE
4x5 1-1000 <$500
3x10-20 1-960 <$500
1902 Date Back
4x5 1-3075 <$250
3x10-20 1-2390 <$250
1902 Plain Back
4x5 3076-14025 <$250
3x10-20 2391-9380 <$250
1929 Small Size
5 Type 1 1-2168 <$125
10 Type 1 1-1134 <$125
20 Type 1 1-308 <$125
5 Type 2 1-2418 <$135
10 Type 2 1-1684 <$135
20 Type 2 1-444 <$135
Total Issue $1,025,350
Out in 1935 $45,300
Large out 1935 $2,080

14121 York
UNION NB IN MOUNT WOLF
{{ 2 S }}
Chartered 4/34
1929 Small Size <$VALUE
10 Type 2 1-73 <$600
Total Issue $730
Out in 1935 $26,030
Large out 1935 $1,030
Outstanding includes Ch 9361

9361 York
UNION NB OF MOUNT WOLF
{{ 2 L 9 S }}
Chartered 3/09
Liquidated 6/30/34
1902 Date Back <$VALUE
3x10-20 1-2710 <$450
1902 Plain Back
3x10-20 2711-7254 <$450
1929 Small Size
10 Type 1 1-1228 <$150
20 Type 1 1-328 <$150
10 Type 2 1-42 <$200
20 Type 2 1-35 <$200
Total Issue $476,860
Out at close $41,300
Large out 1935 $1,030
Ch 14121 assumed circulation

3808 Lancaster
MOUNTVILLE NB, MOUNTVILLE
{{ 6 L 11 S }}
Chartered 11/4/87
Brown Back <$VALUE
4x5 1-6223 <$450
3x10-20 1-2473 <$450
1902 Red Seal
4x5 1-400 <$500
3x10-20 1-340 <$500
1902 Date Back
4x5 1-4550 <$250
3x10-20 1-3200 <$250
1902 Plain Back
4x5 4551-14085 <$250
3x10-20 3201-9089 <$250
1929 Small Size
5 Type 1 1-1514 <$100
10 Type 1 1-1092 <$100
20 Type 1 1-288 <$110
5 Type 2 1-6900 <$110
Total Issue $1,189,260
Out in 1935 $41,850
Large out 1935 $2,680

3480 Lycoming
CITIZENS NB OF MUNCY
{{ 5 L 14 S }}
Chartered 1886
Brown Back <$VALUE
4x5 1-2321 <$450
3x10-20 1-819 <$450
1902 Red Seal
4x5 1-260 <$500
3x10-20 1-206 <$500
1902 Date Back
4x5 1-3550 <$250
3x10-20 1-2640 <$250
1902 Plain Back
4x5 3551-10347 <$250
3x10-20 2641-6934 <$250
1929 Small Size
5 Type 1 1-1432 <$100
10 Type 1 1-868 <$100
20 Type 1 1-264 <$100
10 Type 2 1-3979 <$110
20 Type 2 1-3459 <$110
Total Issue $892,200
Out in 1935 $95,500
Large out 1935 $1,890

837 Lycoming
FNB OF MUNCY
{{ 2 L }}
Chartered 2/23/65
Receivership 2/9/92
Original Series <$VALUE
3x1-2 1-1200 <$600/$1500
4x5 1-3500 <$650
3x10-20 1-1900 <$850/$1500
Series 1875
4x5 1-500 <$650
3x10-20 1-2067 <$850/$1500
Brown Back
3x10-20 1-3062 <$600
Total Issue $437,450
Out in 1916 $2,575

8795 Allegheny
FNB OF MUNHALL
{{ 2 L }}
Chartered 7/07
Liquidated 1/17/16
1902 Red Seal <$VALUE
4x5 1-300 <$850
3x10-20 1-240 <$850
1902 Date Back
4x5 1-4625 <$400
3x10-20 1-3450 <$400
1902 Plain Back
4x5 4626-4685 <$400
3x10-20 3451-3474 <$400
Total Issue $285,400
Out in 1916 $19,005

9752 Lebanon
FARMERS NB OF MYERSTOWN
{{ 1 L }}
Chartered 5/10
Liquidated 5/26/14
1902 Date Back <$VALUE
4x5 1-2905 <$650
3x10-20 1-2252 <$650
Total Issue $170,700
Out in 1914 $37,915

5241 Lebanon
MYERSTOWN NB, MYERSTOWN
{{ 6 L 8 S }}
Chartered 1/5/00
Brown Back <$VALUE
4x5 1-2650 <$400
3x10-20 1-2670 <$400
1882 Date Back
4x5 1-3650* <$400
3x10-20 1-2540** <$400
1882 Value Back
4x5 3801-5920* <$400
3x10-20 2661-3770** <$400
* 3651-3800 not marked
** 2541-2660 not marked
1902 Plain Back
4x5 1-20583 <$225
1929 Small Size
5 Type 1 1-6724 <$135
5 Type 2 1-12672 <$150
Total Issue $1,170,140
Out in 1935 $49,995
Large out 1935 $2,975

3955 Luzerne
FNB OF NANTICOKE
{{ 13 L 31 S }}
Chartered 1/7/89
Brown Back <$VALUE
4x5 1-9050 <$275
3x10-20 1-6838 <$275
1902 Date Back
4x5 1-9900 <$135
3x10-20 1-7900 <$135
1902 Plain Back
4x5 9901-36827 <$135
3x10-20 7901-25488 <$135
1929 Small Size
5 Type 1 1-7924 <$35
10 Type 1 1-3670 <$35
20 Type 1 1-884 <$45
5 Type 2 1-33692 <$45
10 Type 2 1-19344 <$45
20 Type 2 1-5664 <$45
Total Issue $3,573,020
Out in 1935 $296,200
Large out 1935 $5,210

13524 Luzerne
MINERS NB OF NANTICOKE
{{ 26 S }}
Chartered 1/30/31
1929 Small Size <$VALUE
5 Type 1 1-7416 <$40
10 Type 1 1-4860 <$40
20 Type 1 1-1498 <$50
5 Type 2 1-28404 <$50
10 Type 2 1-15125 <$50
20 Type 2 1-4267 <$50
Total Issue $1,072,450
Out in 1935 $251,900

7406 Luzerne
NANTICOKE NB, NANTICOKE
{{ 9 L 19 S }}
Chartered 9/04
1902 Red Seal <$VALUE
3x10-20 1-5500 <$275
1902 Date Back
3x10-20 1-11100 <$135
1902 Plain Bak
3x10-20 11101-33366 <$135
1929 Small Size
5 Type 1 1-18520 <$60
10 Type 1 1-1230 <$60
20 Type 1 1-414 <$70
5 Type 2 1-68124 <$60
Total Issue $2,963,000
Out in 1935 $179,580
Large out 1935 $4,220

5729 Allegheny
FNB OF NATRONA
{{ 4 L 12 S }}
Chartered 2/27/01
Brown Back <$VALUE
3x10-20 1-2840 <$450
1882 Date Back
3x10-20 1-4600 <$450
1882 Value Back
3x10-20 4601-7167 <$450
1902 Plain Back
3x10-20 1-6601 <$275
1929 Small Size
10 Type 1 1-1524 <$125
20 Type 1 1-412 <$135
10 Type 2 1-1882 <$150
20 Type 2 1-520 <$150
Total Issue $1,000,500
Out in 1935 $48,600
Large out 1935 $2,130

5077 Northampton
NAZARETH NB, NAZARETH
Chartered 1897
2nd title: Nazareth NB & TC 10/23/29
FIRST TITLE {{ 11 L }}
Brown Back <$VALUE
3x10-20 1-8150 <$275
1882 Date Back
3x10-20 1-9000* <$275
1882 Value Back
3x10-20 9401-10708* <$275
* 9001-9400 not marked
1902 Plain Back
3x10-20 1-29342 <$165
SECOND TITLE {{ 27 S }}
1929 Small Size
10 Type 1 1-5890 <$60
20 Type 1 1-1598 <$65
10 Type 2 1-10096 <$65
20 Type 2 1-2856 <$65
Total Issue $3,113,240
Out in 1935 $193,700
Large out 1935 $6,730

5686 Northampton
SECOND NB OF NAZARETH
{{ 6 L 10 S }}
Chartered 1/18/01
Brown Back <$VALUE
3x10-20 1-3500 <$375
1882 Date Back
3x10-20 1-4400* <$375
1882 Value Back
3x10-20 4601-6946* <$375
* 4401-4600 not marked
1902 Plain Back
3x10-20 1-6595 <$275
1929 Small Size
10 Type 1 1-1508 <$110
20 Type 1 1-390 <$125
10 Type 2 1-2055 <$135
20 Type 2 1-470 <$135
Total Issue $1,019,280
Out in 1935 $44,950
Large out 1935 $2,940

12471 Lehigh
NEFFS NB, NEFFS
{{ 4 L 11 S }}
Chartered 12/23
1902 Plain Back <$VALUE
3x10-20 1-3961 <$350
1929 Small Size
10 Type 1 1-1688 <$150
20 Type 1 1-454 <$150
10 Type 2 1-2168 <$165
20 Type 2 1-468 <$165
Total Issue $384,850
Out in 1935 $50,000
Large out 1935 $680

12159 Luzerne
NESCOPECK NB, NESCOPECK
{{ 4 S }}
Chartered 4/22
1929 Small Size <$VALUE
5 Type 1 1-524 <$250
10 Type 1 1-254 <$250
20 Type 1 1-76 <$250
5 Type 2 1-1510 <$250
10 Type 2 1-864 <$250
20 Type 2 1-336 <$250
Total Issue $62,990
Out in 1935 $25,000

10251 Carbon
FNB OF NESQUEHONING
{{ 5 L 14 S }}
Chartered 9/12
1902 Date Back <$VALUE
3x10-20 1-1610 <$250
1902 Plain Back
3x10-20 1611-12084 <$250
1929 Small Size
5 Type 1 1-5950 <$100
10 Type 1 1-1348 <$100
20 Type 1 1-552 <$100
5 Type 2 1-6510 <$100
10 Type 2 1-3343 <$100
20 Type 2 1-1131 <$100
Total Issue $1,018,420
Out in 1935 $81,950
Large out 1935 $2,170

8973 Bradford
FNB OF NEW ALBANY
{{ 3 L 5 S }}
Chartered 12/07
1902 Red Seal <$VALUE
4x5 1-625 <$650
3x10-20 1-500 <$650
1902 Date Back
4x5 1-2025 <$325
3x10-20 1-1470 <$325
1902 Plain Back
4x5 2026-7050 <$325
3x10-20 1471-4362 <$325
1929 Small Size
5 Type 1 1-996 <$200
10 Type 1 1-432 <$200
20 Type 1 1-150 <$200
5 Type 2 1-1852 <$225
10 Type 2 1-996 <$225
20 Type 2 1-207 <$225
Total Issue $493,760
Out in 1935 $20,450
Large out 1935 $840

6580 Westmoreland
NEW ALEXANDRIA NB, NEW ALEXANDRIA
{{ 3 L 18 S }}
Chartered 1/03
1902 Red Seal <$VALUE
3x10-20 1-476 <$650
1902 Date Back
3x10-20 1-2610 <$325
1902 Plain Back
3x10-20 2611-7254 <$325
1929 Small Size
10 Type 1 1-686 <$135
20 Type 1 1-194 <$135
10 Type 2 1-389 <$150
20 Type 2 1-60 <$150
Total Issue $456,030
Out in 1935 $22,100
Large out 1935 $1,180

7897 Union
FNB OF NEW BERLIN
{{ 3 L 3 S }}
Chartered 9/05
Receivership 11/3/33
1902 Red Seal <$VALUE
4x5 1-400 <$750
3x10-20 1-300 <$750
1902 Date Back
4x5 1-1600 <$350
3x10-20 1-1380 <$350
1902 Plain Back
4x5 1601-4670 <$350
3x10-20 1381-3488 <$350
1929 Small Size
5 Type 1 1-711 <$300
10 Type 1 1-329 <$300
20 Type 1 1-106 <$300
Total Issue $344,590
Out at close $19,640
Large out at close $1,320

5051 Clarion
CITIZENS NB OF NEW BETHLEHEM
{{ 1 L }}
Chartered 8/27/96
Liquidated 8/10/05
Brown Back <$VALUE
3x10-20 1-3698 <$1000
Total Issue $184,900
Out in 1910 $6,400

4978 Clarion
FNB OF NEW BETHLEHEM
{{ 7 L 22 S }}
Chartered 1894
Brown Back <$VALUE
4x5 1-3050 <$300
3x10-20 1-1850 <$300
1882 Date Back
4x5 1-3664 <$300
3x10-20 1-2751 <$300
1902 Date Back
3x10-20 1-800* <$175
1902 Plain Back
3x10-20 1051-9916* <$175
* 801-1050 not marked
1929 Small Size
10 Type 1 1-4148 <$65
20 Type 1 1-1170 <$65
10 Type 2 1-7433 <$65
20 Type 2 1-1645 <$65
Total Issue $1,356,640
Out in 1935 $194,250
Large out 1935 $2,700

5133 Perry
FNB OF NEW BLOOMFIELD
{{ 18 L 28 S }}
Chartered 1898
Brown Back <$VALUE
4x5 1-3200 <$275
3x10-20 1-2280 <$275
1882 Date Back
4x5 1-3600 <$250
3x10-20 1-2540 <$250
1882 Value Back
4x5 3601-4627 <$250
3x10-20 2541-3210 <$250
1902 Plain Back
3x10-20 1-6626 <$165
1929 Small Size
5 Type 1 1-1658 <$85
10 Type 1 1-874 <$85
20 Type 1 1-294 <$85
5 Type 2 1-2404 <$100
10 Type 2 1-1512 <$100
20 Type 2 1-324 <$100
Total Issue $933,420
Out in 1935 $50,000
Large out 1935 $2,105

3259 Beaver
NB OF NEW BRIGHTON
{{ 2 L }}
Chartered 10/27/84
Liquidated 9/15/04
Brown Back <$VALUE
4x5 1-6975 <$650
50-100 1-250 <$1500/$1750
Total Issue $177,000
Out in 1910 $2,985

632 Beaver
NB OF BEAVER COUNTY, NEW BRIGHTON
{{ 3 L }}
Chartered 12/64
Liquidated 11/12/84
Original Series <$VALUE
3x1-2 1-2000 <$450/$1250
4x5 1-4750 <$600
3x10-20 1-2100 <$750/$1250
50-100 1-150 <$3500
Series 1875
4x5 1-2499 <$600
3x10-20 1-1733 <$750/$1250
Total Issue $369,130
Out in 1910 $2,194

7395 Beaver
OLD NB OF NEW BRIGHTON
{{ 7 L 7 S }}
Chartered 9/04
1902 Red Seal <$VALUE
50-100 1-970 <$2250/$2500
1902 Date Back
4x5 1-4250 <$175
50-100 1-400 <$400/$500
3x50-100 1-632 <$400/$500
1902 Plain Back
4x5 4251-25720 <$175
3x50-100 633-1022<$400/$500
1929 Small Size
5 Type 1 1-4182 <$100
50 Type 1 1-246 <$175
100 Type 1 1-72 <$250
5 Type 2 1-2964 <$100
Total Issue $1,232,680
Out in 1935 $100,000
Large out 1935 $5,645

4549 Beaver
UNION NB OF NEW BRIGHTON
{{ 12 L 21 S }}
Chartered 1891
Brown Back <$VALUE
4x5 1-3000 <$275
50-100 1-1674 <$275
1882 Date Back
4x5 1-3110 <$275
50-100 1-371 <$275
1902 Date Back
3x10-20 1-5900 <$135
1902 Plain Back
3x10-20 5901-24397 <$135
1929 Small Size
10 Type 1 1-3354 <$60
20 Type 1 1-978 <$65
10 Type 2 1-4475 <$65
20 Type 2 1-818 <$70
Total Issue $2,028,510
Out in 1935 $108,200
Large out 1935 $5,010

4676 Lawrence
CITIZENS NB OF NEW CASTLE
{{ 8 L 13 S }}
Chartered 1892
Brown Back <$VALUE
3x10-20 1-7880 <$300
50-100 1-4113 <$1250/$1500
1882 Date Back
3x10-20 1-12 <$300
50-100 1-1507 <$1250/$1500
1902 Date Back
3x50-100 1-4089 <$375/$450
1902 Plain Back
3x50-100 4090-5058 <$375/$450
1929 Small Size
50 Type 1 1-564 <$100
100 Type 1 1-190 <$165
5 Type 2 1-1140 <$100
10 Type 2 1-330 <$100
20 Type 2 1-210 <$100
Total Issue $2,798,500
Out in 1935 $199,000
Large out 1935 $23,920

FNB of Lawrence County at New Castle
SEE Ch 562
FNB of New Castle

562 Lawrence
FNB OF NEW CASTLE
Chartered 11/64
2nd title: FNB of Lawrence County at New Castle 12/31/26
FIRST TITLE {{ 12 L }}
Original Series <$VALUE
4x5 1-3500 <$450
3x10-20 1-4400 <$750/$1250
Series 1875
4x5 1-1500 <$450
3x10-20 1-1668 <$750/$1250
Brown Back
4x5 1-7350 <$300
50-100 1-3196 <$1250/$1500
1902 Red Seal
3x10-20 1-5600 <$300
50-100 1-840 <$2250/$2500
1902 Date Back
3x10-20 1-17500 <$100
50-100 1-500* <$375/$450
* 466,475,482 not issued
1902 Plain Back
3x10-20 17501-42744 <$100
SECOND TITLE {{ 6 L 50+ S }}
1902 Plain Back
3x10-20 1-13339 <$100
1929 Small Size
10 Type 1 1-12574 <$30
20 Type 1 1-3796 <$40
10 Type 2 1-17075 <$30
20 Type 2 1-3585 <$40
Total Issue $5,766,910
Out in 1935 $422,105
Large out 1935 $24,215
Outstanding includes Ch 1156

1156 Lawrence
NB OF LAWRENCE COUNTY AT NEW CASTLE
{{ 12 L }}
Chartered 1865
Closed 12/31/26
Original Series <$VALUE
4x5 1-3250 <$500
3x10-20 1-3000 <$750/$1250
Series 1875
3x10-20 1-4482 <$750/$1250
Brown Back
3x10-20 1-6415 <$300
50-100 1-3282 <$1250/$1500
1902 Red Seal
4x5 1-3750 <$300
3x10-20 1-2600 <$300
50-100 1-700 <$2250/$2500
1902 Date Back
4x5 1-4250 <$150
3x10-20 1-8200 <$150
50-100 1-200 <$500/$600
1902 Plain Back
3x10-20 8201-28621 <$150
Total Issue $3,108,200
Out at close $149,995
Ch 562 assumed circulation

****

8503 Lawrence
UNION NB OF NEW CASTLE
{{ 4 L 2 S }}
Chartered 1/07
Liquidated 11/28/31
1902 Red Seal <$VALUE
4x5 1-500 <$600
3x10-20 1-600 <$600
1902 Date Back
4x5 1-2800 <$275
3x10-20 1-2140 <$275
1902 Plain Back
4x5 2801-7355 <$275
3x10-20 2141-4926 <$275
1929 Small Size
5 Type 1 1-652 <$350
10 Type 1 1-291 <$350
20 Type 1 1-91 <$350
Total Issue $481,340
Out at close $20,955
Large out at close $2,415

****

7349 Cumberland
NEW CUMBERLAND NB,
NEW CUMBERLAND
{{ 5 L 8 S }}
Chartered 8/04
1902 Red Seal <$VALUE
4x5 1-1330 <$500
3x10-20 1-988 <$500
1902 Date Back
4x5 1-2025 <$250
3x10-20 1-1480 <$250
1902 Plain Back
4x5 2026-6545 <$250
3x10-20 1481-4198 <$250
1929 Small Size
5 Type 1 1-848 <$175
10 Type 1 1-490 <$175
20 Type 1 1-140 <$175
5 Type 2 1-1384 <$200
10 Type 2 1-807 <$200
20 Type 2 1-150 <$200
Total Issue $506,430
Out in 1935 $24,700
Large out 1935 $1,640

****

10353 Westmoreland
NEW FLORENCE NB,
NEW FLORENCE
{{ 4 L 6 S }}
Chartered 3/13
Liquidated 2/15/34
1902 Date Back <$VALUE
4x5 1-1065 <$300
3x10-20 1-834 <$300
1902 Plain Back
4x5 1066-6815 <$300
3x10-20 835-4308 <$300
1929 Small Size
5 Type 1 1-908 <$175
10 Type 1 1-560 <$175
20 Type 1 1-152 <$175
5 Type 2 1-494 <$225
10 Type 2 1-225 <$225
20 Type 2 1-20 <$225
Total Issue $435,900
Out at close $23,120
Large out at close $1,480
Ch 13907 assumed circulation

****

13907 Westmoreland
NEW FLORENCE NB,
NEW FLORENCE
{{ 2 S }}
Chartered 12/33
1929 Small Size <$VALUE
5 Type 2 1-1370 <$350
10 Type 2 1-707 <$350
20 Type 2 1-185 <$350
Total Issue $17,620
Out in 1935 $36,530
Large out 1935 $1,480
Outstanding includes Ch 10353

****

13887 York
FNB IN NEW FREEDOM
{{ 3 S }}
Chartered 12/33
1929 Small Size <$VALUE
5 Type 2 1-11854 <$300
Total Issue $59,270
Out in 1935 $50,580
Large out 1935 $580
Outstanding includes Ch 6715

****

6715 York
FNB OF NEW FREEDOM
{{ 8 L 5 S }}
Chartered 4/03
Liquidated 2/13/34
1902 Red Seal <$VALUE
3x10-20 1-3140 <$400
1902 Date Back
4x5 1-3830 <$200
3x10-20 1-2780 <$200
1902 Plain Back
4x5 3831-27846 <$200
3x10-20 2781-4460 <$200
1929 Small Size
5 Type 1 1-6796 <$200
5 Type 2 1-3372 <$200
Total Issue $1,157,660
Out at close $39,250
Large out at close $580
Ch 13887 assumed circulation

****

6408 Fayette
NEW HAVEN NB, NEW HAVEN
Chartered 9/4/02
Receivership 7/3/30
2nd title: Union NB of
Connellsville 10/16/09
FIRST TITLE {{ 0 L }}
1902 Red Seal <$VALUE
3x10-20 1-3162 <$1250
1902 Date Back
3x10-20 1-500 <$750
SECOND TITLE {{ 2 L 2 S }}
1902 Date Back
3x10-20 1-4040 <$400
1902 Plain Back
3x10-20 4041-13120 <$400
1929 Small Size
10 Type 1 1-533 <$300
20 Type 1 1-211 <$300
Total Issue $883,440
Out at close $50,000
Large out at close $10,030

****

8499 Lancaster
FARMERS NB OF NEW HOLLAND
Chartered 1/07
2nd title: Farmers NB & TC
of New Holland 5/10/30
FIRST TITLE {{ 6 L 2 S }}
1902 Red Seal <$VALUE
4x5 1-1000 <$600
3x10-20 1-875 <$600
1902 Date Back
4x5 1-5000 <$300
3x10-20 1-3540 <$300
1902 Plain Back
4x5 5001-14267 <$300
3x10-20 3541-9797 <$300
1929 Small Size
5 Type 1 1-828 <$165
10 Type 1 1-420 <$165
20 Type 1 1-148 <$165
SECOND TITLE {{ 14 S }}
1929 Small Size
5 Type 1 1-2602 <$125
10 Type 1 1-1212 <$125
20 Type 1 1-358 <$125
5 Type 2 1-8726 <$135
10 Type 2 1-5278 <$135
20 Type 2 1-1356 <$135
Total Issue $1,224,010
Out in 1935 $119,150
Large out 1935 $2,230

****

2530 Lancaster
NEW HOLLAND NB,
NEW HOLLAND
{{ 6 L 9 S }}
Chartered 1881
Liquidated 2/13/32
Series 1875 <$VALUE
3x10-20 1-5008 <$750/$1250
Brown Back
3x10-20 1-2390 <$500
1882 Date Back
4x5 1-3250 <$500
3x10-20 1-2300 <$500
1882 Value Back
4x5 3251-10610 <$500
3x10-20 2301-6063 <$500
1902 Plain Back
4x5 1-6950 <$300
4x10 1-16985 <$300
1929 Small Size
10 Type 1 1-4236 <$165
Total Issue $1,957,810
Out at close $101,010
Large out at close $9,400

****

11015 Bucks
SOLEBURY NB OF NEW HOPE
{{ 6 S }}
Chartered 6/17
1929 Small Size <$VALUE
5 Type 1 1-210 <$175
10 Type 1 1-396 <$175
20 Type 1 1-76 <$175
5 Type 2 1-2040 <$200
10 Type 2 1-1152 <$200
20 Type 2 1-336 <$200
Total Issue $67,620
Out in 1935 $29,220

****

4913 Westmoreland
FNB OF NEW KENSINGTON
{{ 8 L 16 S }}
Chartered 1893
Brown Back <$VALUE
3x10-20 1-5140 <$300
1882 Date Back
3x10-20 1-2791 <$300
1902 Date Back
3x10-20 1-1700 <$150
1902 Plain Back
3x10-20 1701-25465 <$150
1929 Small Size
10 Type 1 1-3854 <$60
20 Type 1 1-1026 <$70
10 Type 2 1-4475 <$70
20 Type 2 1-1034 <$70
Total Issue $2,089,590
Out in 1935 $106,000
Large out 1935 $5,000

****

13571 Westmoreland
LOGAN NB & TC OF
NEW KENSINGTON
{{ 28 S }}
Chartered 8/31
1929 Small Size <$VALUE
5 Type 1 1-6047* <$40
5 Type 2 1-31416 <$40
10 Type 2 1-15576 <$50
20 Type 2 1-6468 <$60
* 6048-12214 not issued
Total Issue $623,610
Out in 1935 $266,990

****

Parnassus NB, New Kensington
SEE Ch 7363
Parnassus NB, Parnassus

****

13084 Westmoreland
UNION NB OF
NEW KENSINGTON
{{ 6 L 3 S }}
Chartered 6/3/27
Liquidated 8/7/30
1902 Plain Back <$VALUE
3x10-20 1-4726 <$275
1929 Small Size
10 Type 1 1-1189 <$250
20 Type 1 1-334 <$250
Total Issue $347,720
Out at close $98,200
Large out at close $9,080

****

8960 Susquehanna
GRANGE NB OF SUSQUEHANNA
COUNTY AT NEW MILFORD
{{ 2 L 3 S }}
Chartered 12/07
1902 Red Seal <$VALUE
4x5 1-585 <$1000
3x10-20 1-471 <$1000
1902 Date Back
4x5 1-2475 <$500
3x10-20 1-1580 <$500
1902 Plain Back
4x5 2476-13243 <$500
3x10-20 1581-3210 <$500
1929 Small Size
5 Type 1 1-3448 <$400
5 Type 2 1-9258 <$400
Total Issue $610,340
Out in 1935 $25,000
Large out 1935 $830

****

5837 Fayette
DELMONT NB OF NEW SALEM
{{ UNREPORTED }}
Chartered 5/28/01
Receivership 5/2/06
Brown Back <$VALUE
3x10-20 1-347 <$1500
Total Issue $17,350
Out in 1916 $230

****

6599 Fayette
FNB OF NEW SALEM
{{ 3 L }}
Chartered 1/03
1902 Red Seal <$VALUE
3x10-20 1-1750 <$850
1902 Date Back
3x10-20 1-2330 <$400
1902 Plain Back
3x10-20 2331-5761 <$400
Total Issue $375,550
Out in 1935 $1,090

****

9656 Lehigh
NEW TRIPOLI NB,
NEW TRIPOLI
{{ 2 L 6 S }}
Chartered 2/10
1902 Date Back <$VALUE
3x10-20 1-1760 <$450
1902 Plain Back
3x10-20 1761-5206 <$450
1929 Small Size
10 Type 1 1-586 <$175
20 Type 1 1-168 <$175
10 Type 2 1-527 <$200
20 Type 2 1-168 <$200
Total Issue $324,250
Out in 1935 $19,400
Large out 1935 $770

****

9554 Lawrence
FNB OF NEW WILMINGTON
{{ 5 L 10 S }}
Chartered 10/09
Receivership 12/19/33
1902 Date Back <$VALUE
3x10-20 1-4600 <$225
1902 Plain Back
3x10-20 4601-14073 <$225
1929 Small Size
10 Type 1 1-1438 <$85
20 Type 1 1-372 <$100
10 Type 2 1-246 <$125
20 Type 2 1-60 <$125
Total Issue $838,230
Out at close $50,000
Large out at close $3,610

****

12911 Wayne
FNB OF NEWFOUNDLAND
{{ 7 S }}
Chartered 4/26
1929 Small Size <$VALUE
5 Type 1 1-450 <$150
10 Type 1 1-232 <$150
20 Type 1 1-108 <$150
5 Type 2 1-5556 <$150
10 Type 2 1-3048 <$150
20 Type 2 1-720 <$150
Total Issue $113,040
Out in 1935 $48,880

****

7716 Perry
CITIZENS NB OF NEWPORT
{{ 3 L 7 S }}
Chartered 4/05
1902 Red Seal <$VALUE
3x10-20 1-1350 <$600
1902 Date Back
3x10-20 1-2400 <$275
1902 Plain Back
3x10-20 2401-6785 <$275
1929 Small Size
10 Type 1 1-766 <$165
20 Type 1 1-194 <$165
10 Type 2 1-1002 <$200
20 Type 2 1-215 <$200
Total Issue $490,310
Out in 1935 $24,250
Large out 1935 $1,280

****

4917 Perry
FNB OF NEWPORT
{{ 5 L 9 S }}
Chartered 1893
Brown Back <$VALUE
4x5 1-4825 <$400
3x10-20 1-1580 <$400
1882 Date Back
4x5 1-1904 <$400
3x10-20 1-1541 <$400
1902 Date Back
3x10-20 1-1400 <$250
1902 Plain Back
3x10-20 1401-8082 <$250
1929 Small Size
5 Type 1 1-1490 <$100
10 Type 1 1-978 <$100
20 Type 1 1-276 <$100
5 Type 2 1-2738 <$125
10 Type 2 1-1409 <$125
20 Type 2 1-298 <$125
Total Issue $864,970
Out in 1935 $42,135
Large out 1935 $2,405

****

5245 Perry
PERRY COUNTY NB OF
NEWPORT
{{ 1 L }}
Chartered 1/16/00
Liquidated 3/1/05
Brown Back <$VALUE
4x5 1-1167 <$1000
3x10-20 1-1044 <$1000
Total Issue $75,540
Out in 1910 $1,975

****

324 Bucks
FNB OF NEWTOWN
Chartered 3/64
2nd title: FNB & TC of
Newtown 1/17/28
FIRST TITLE {{ 12 L }}
Original Series <$VALUE
3x1-2 1-2000 <$400/$1250
4x5 1-2350 <$450
3x10-20 1-2750 <$750/$1250
Series 1875
4x5 1-1200 <$450
3x10-20 1-1422 <$750/$1250
Brown Back
4x5 1-4265 <$300
3x10-20 1-2939 <$300
1902 Red Seal
4x5 1-5005 <$350
3x10-20 1-3048 <$350
1902 Date Back
4x5 1-10000 <$165
3x10-20 1-6500 <$165
1902 Plain Back
4x5 10001-28187 <$165
3x10-20 6501-18399 <$165
SECOND TITLE {{ 0 L 14 S }}
1902 Plain Back
4x5 1-1828 <$250
3x10-20 1-1393 <$250
1929 Small Size
5 Type 1 1-4152 <$85
10 Type 1 1-2400 <$85
20 Type 1 1-574 <$100
5 Type 2 1-6218 <$100
10 Type 2 1-3893 <$100
20 Type 2 1-1140 <$100
Total Issue $2,794,510
Out in 1935 $98,350
Large out 1935 $5,060

****

9588 Cumberland
FARMERS NB OF NEWVILLE
{{ 1 L 3 S }}
Chartered 11/09
1902 Date Back <$VALUE
3x10-20 1-1190 <$650
1902 Plain Back
3x10-20 1191-2872 <$650
1929 Small Size
10 Type 1 1-310 <$250
20 Type 1 1-106 <$250
10 Type 2 1-346 <$275
20 Type 2 1-51 <$275
Total Issue $179,400
Out in 1935 $11,000
Large out 1935 $440

****

60 Cumberland
FNB OF NEWVILLE
{{ 14 L 19 S }}
Chartered 8/63
Original Series <$VALUE
3x1-2 1-1200 <$400/$1250
4x5 1-2850 <$500
4x10 1-2950 <$750
Series 1875
4x10 1-1828 <$750
Brown Back
3x10-20 1-5481 <$375
1902 Red Seal
3x10-20 1-4200 <$400
1902 Date Back
3x10-20 1-7800 <$175
1902 Plain Back
3x10-20 7801-24326 <$175
1929 Small Size
5 Type 1 1-5262 <$85
10 Type 1 1-3034 <$85
20 Type 1 1-418 <$100
5 Type 2 1-12686 <$100
10 Type 2 1-6033 <$100
Total Issue $2,468,290
Out in 1935 $121,200
Large out 1935 $7,400

****

7910 Wyoming
FNB OF NICHOLSON
{{ 5 L 9 S }}
Chartered 9/05
1902 Red Seal <$VALUE
3x10-20 1-2373 <$450
1902 Date Back
3x10-20 1-4960 <$225
1902 Plain Back
3x10-20 4961-14935 <$225
1929 Small Size
10 Type 1 1-1718 <$135
20 Type 1 1-426 <$135
10 Type 2 1-2540 <$150
20 Type 2 1-604 <$150
Total Issue $1,057,080
Out in 1935 $40,650
Large out 1935 $2,440

****

272 Montgomery
FNB OF NORRISTOWN
{{ 9 L }}
Chartered 2/64
Liquidated 8/1/25
Original Series <$VALUE
4x5 1-3900 <$500
3x10-20 1-2200 <$750/$1250
50-100 1-530 <$3500
Series 1875
3x10-20 1-500 <$750/$1250
50-100 1-761 <$3500
Brown Back
50-100 1-1810 <$1250/$1500
1902 Red Seal
3x10-20 1-4075 <$250
1902 Date Back
3x10-20 1-19700 <$135
1902 Plain Back
3x10-20 19701-45242 <$135
Total Issue $3,144,000
Out at close $178,250

****

1148 Montgomery
MONTGOMERY NB OF
NORRISTOWN
{{ 11 L 18 S }}
Chartered 1865
Original Series <$VALUE
4x5 1-5000 <$500
3x10-20 1-4000 <$750/$1250
50-100 1-2000 <$3500
Series 1875
3x10-20 1-1127 <$750/$1250
50-100 1-1853 <$3500
Brown Back
3x10-20 1-13092 <$350
50-100 1-2300 <$1250/$1500
1902 Red Seal
3x10-20 1-7000 <$350
1902 Date Back
3x10-20 1-17500 <$150
1902 Plain Back
3x10-20 17501-55206 <$150
1929 Small Size
10 Type 1 1-6184 <$35
20 Type 1 1-1620 <$45
5 Type 2 1-324 <$35
10 Type 2 1-6179 <$40
20 Type 2 1-1657 <$50
Total Issue $5,706,190
Out in 1935 $171,950
Large out 1935 $14,305

****

2581 Montgomery
PEOPLES NB OF NORRISTOWN
{{ 10 L 24 S }}
Chartered 1881
Series 1875 <$VALUE
3x10-20 1-8462 <$750/$1250
Brown Back
3x10-20 1-10000 <$350
1882 Date Back
3x10-20 1-12900 <$350
1882 Value Back
3x10-20 12901-23600 <$350
1902 Plain Back
3x10-20 1-19168 <$135
1929 Small Size
10 Type 1 1-4670 <$35
20 Type 1 1-1318 <$45
5 Type 2 1-324 <$35
10 Type 2 1-5909 <$40
20 Type 2 1-1525 <$50
Total Issue $3,591,070
Out in 1935 $145,850
Large out 1935 $7,955

****

11995 Westmoreland
PEOPLES NB OF
NORTH BELLE VERNON
{{ 3 L 3 S }}
Chartered 7/21
Liquidated 7/22/30
1902 Plain Back <$VALUE
4x5 1-3943 <$450
3x10-20 1-2452 <$450
1929 Small Size
5 Type 1 1-379 <$300
10 Type 1 1-173 <$300
20 Type 1 1-51 <$300
Total Issue $229,330
Out at close $22,420
Large out at close $2,870

****

<$VALUEs are for notes in **FINE** condition. Value changes by approximately **25%** for a change of one full grade.

741 Erie
FNB OF NORTH EAST
{{ 1 L }}
Chartered 1/23/65
Liquidated 12/23/84
Original Series <$VALUE
3x1-2 1-1800 <$1000/$2000
4x5 1-4650 <$1000
Series 1875
4x5 1-3715 <$1000
Total Issue $176,300
Out in 1910 $1,205

4927 Erie
FNB OF NORTH EAST
{{ 2 L 5 S }}
Chartered 1893
Brown Back <$VALUE
4x5 1-3100 <$600
3x10-20 1-1130 <$600
1882 Date Back
4x5 1-1117 <$600
3x10-20 1-901 <$600
1902 Date Back
4x5 1-800 <$400
3x10-20 1-640 <$400
1902 Plain Back
4x5 801-5615 <$400
3x10-20 641-3556 <$400
1929 Small Size
5 Type 1 1-996 <$165
10 Type 1 1-482 <$165
20 Type 1 1-156 <$165
5 Type 2 1-684 <$175
10 Type 2 1-419 <$175
20 Type 2 1-119 <$175
Total Issue $563,500
Out in 1935 $21,380
Large out 1935 $1,330

9149 Erie
NB OF NORTH EAST
{{ 3 L 8 S }}
Chartered 5/08
1902 Date Back <$VALUE
3x10-20 1-3675 <$350
1902 Plain Back
3x10-20 3676-9453 <$350
1929 Small Size
10 Type 1 1-910 <$125
20 Type 1 1-254 <$125
10 Type 2 1-1135 <$150
20 Type 2 1-140 <$150
Total Issue $571,880
Out in 1935 $34,300
Large out 1935 $1,380

12363 Erie
FNB OF NORTH GIRARD
{{ 0 L 2 S }}
Chartered 4/23
Liquidated 8/1/34
1902 Plain Back <$VALUE
3x10-20 1-1090 <$750
1929 Small Size
10 Type 1 1-290 <$350
20 Type 1 1-85 <$350
Total Issue $82,100
Out at close $8,350
Large out at close $330

4330 Montgomery
NORTH WALES NB, NORTH WALES
{{ 6 L 11 S }}
Chartered 1890
Brown Back <$VALUE
3x10-20 1-4290 <$400
1882 Date Back
3x10-20 1-771 <$400
1902 Date Back
3x10-20 1-3900 <$250
1902 Plain Back
3x10-20 3901-13490 <$250
1929 Small Size
10 Type 1 1-1600 <$125
20 Type 1 1-400 <$125
10 Type 2 1-2206 <$150
20 Type 2 1-540 <$150
Total Issue $1,104,410
Out in 1935 $48,950
Large out 1935 $3,060

Cement NB of Siegfried at Northampton
SEE Ch 5227
Cement NB of Siegfried

566 Northumberland
FNB OF NORTHUMBERLAND
{{ 3 L }}
Chartered 11/64
Liquidated 10/6/76
Original Series <$VALUE
3x1-2 1-2000 <$450/$1250
4x5 1-4750 <$600
3x10-20 1-1300 <$750/$1250
Series 1875
4x5 1-65 <$600
Total Issue $171,300
Out in 1910 $1,258

7005 Northumberland
NORTHUMBERLAND NB, NORTHUMBERLAND
{{ 6 L 15 S }}
Chartered 10/03
1902 Red Seal <$VALUE
3x10-20 1-560 <$400
1902 Date Back
3x10-20 1-4250 <$200
1902 Plain Back
3x10-20 4251-17002 <$200
1929 Small Size
5 Type 1 1-1252 <$50
10 Type 1 1-4056 <$50
20 Type 1 1-996 <$65
5 Type 2 1-5596 <$75
10 Type 2 1-3065 <$75
20 Type 2 1-985 <$75
Total Issue $1,356,870
Out in 1935 $105,330
Large out 1935 $3,080

11981 Columbia
VALLEY NB OF NUMIDIA
{{ 4 S }}
Chartered 6/21
1929 Small Size <$VALUE
5 Type 2 1-2710 <$250
10 Type 2 1-1335 <$250
20 Type 2 1-415 <$250
Total Issue $35,200
Out in 1935 $25,000

12563 Schuylkill
FNB OF NUREMBURG
{{ 6 L 5 S }}
Chartered 7/24
1902 Plain Back <$VALUE
4x5 1-8621 <$450
1929 Small Size
5 Type 1 1-3872 <$250
5 Type 2 1-9036 <$250
Total Issue $333,760
Out in 1935 $21,010
Large out 1935 $560

5327 Allegheny
FNB OF OAKDALE
{{ 8 L 10 S }}
Chartered 5/3/00
Brown Back <$VALUE
4x5 1-1950 <$325
3x10-20 1-4148 <$325
50-100 1-324 <$1250/$1500
1882 Date Back
4x5 1-7100 <$300
3x10-20 1-4980 <$300
1882 Value Back
4x5 7101-10900 <$300
3x10-20 4981-7195 <$300
1902 Plain Back
4x5 1-36543 <$150
1929 Small Size
5 Type 1 1-10478 <$85
5 Type 2 1-21636 <$100
Total Issue $2,026,130
Out in 1935 $75,000
Large out 1935 $4,220

7642 Allegheny
FNB OF OAKMONT
{{ 5 L 13 S }}
Chartered 3/05
1902 Red Seal <$VALUE
3x10-20 1-2262 <$500
1902 Date Back
3x10-20 1-4540 <$250
1902 Plain Back
3x10-20 4541-14763 <$250
1929 Small Size
10 Type 1 1-1570 <$100
20 Type 1 1-422 <$100
10 Type 2 1-1554 <$125
20 Type 2 1-504 <$125
Total Issue $1,021,710
Out in 1935 $50,000
Large out 1935 $2,470

173 Venango
FNB OF OIL CITY
{{ 7 L 14 S }}
Chartered 12/63
Original Series <$VALUE
4x5 1-7000 <$500
4x10 1-2750 <$750
3x20-50 1-1000<$1250/$3500
Series 1875
4x5 1-2499 <$500
3x20-50 1-697 <$1250/$3500
Brown Back
3x10-20 1-3854 <$300
1902 Red Seal
3x10-20 1-2700 <$300
1902 Date Back
4x5 1-4488 <$150
3x10-20 1-2560 <$150
1902 Plain Back
4x5 4489-7430 <$150
3x10-20 2561-8712 <$150
1929 Small Size
10 Type 1 1-1372 <$60
20 Type 1 1-406 <$65
5 Type 2 1-13020 <$75
10 Type 2 1-6156 <$75
20 Type 2 1-696 <$75
Total Issue $1,670,170
Out in 1935 $117,320
Large out 1935 $6,470

5565 Venango
LAMBERTON NB OF OIL CITY
{{ 7 L }}
Chartered 8/31/00
Closed 5/24/19
Brown Back <$VALUE
4x5 1-5300 <$300
3x10-20 1-2820 <$300
50-100 1-620 <$1250/$1500
1882 Date Back
4x5 1-8800 <$300
3x10-20 1-4680 <$300
50-100 1-100 <$1250/$1500
1882 Value Back
4x5 8801-12047 <$300
3x10-20 4681-6210 <$300
Total Issue $906,440
Out at close $97,695
Ch 5240 assumed circulation

5240 Venango
OIL CITY NB, OIL CITY
{{ 14 L 29 S }}
Chartered 12/28/99
Liquidated 11/24/34
Brown Back <$VALUE
50-100 1-640 <$1250/$1500
1882 Date Back
3x10-20 1-2000 <$275
50-100 1-560 <$1250/$1500
3x50-100 1-50 <$1250/$1500
1882 Value Back
3x10-20 2001-5400 <$275
1902 Plain Back
4x5 1-42341 <$125
3x10-20 1-26986 <$125
1929 Small Size
5 Type 1 1-13172 <$35
10 Type 1 1-6108 <$35
20 Type 1 1-1494 <$40
5 Type 2 1-9976 <$35
10 Type 2 1-5963 <$35
20 Type 2 1-1510 <$45
Total Issue $3,739,250
Out at close $272,580
Large out 1935 $11,420
Outstanding includes Ch 5565
Ch 14274 assumed circulation

14274 Venango
OIL CITY NB, OIL CITY
{{ 6 S }}
Chartered 9/34
1929 Small Size <$VALUE
5 Type 2 1-6930 <$165
10 Type 2 1-3510 <$165
20 Type 2 1-1020 <$165
Total Issue $90,150
Out in 1935 $300,000
Large out 1935 $11,420
Outstanding includes Ch 5240

8858 Berks
FNB OF OLEY
{{ 2 L 28 S }}
Chartered 9/07
1902 Red Seal <$VALUE
3x10-20 1-600 <$750
1902 Date Back
3x10-20 1-2350 <$375
1902 Plain Back
3x10-20 2351-6548 <$375
1929 Small Size
10 Type 1 1-1750 <$65
20 Type 1 1-418 <$65
10 Type 2 1-2350 <$65
20 Type 2 1-529 <$65
Total Issue $546,640
Out in 1935 $85,750
Large out 1935 $840

8806 Lackawanna
FNB OF OLYPHANT
{{ 3 L }}
Chartered 7/07
Liquidated 2/4/29
1902 Red Seal <$VALUE
4x5 1-625 <$600
3x10-20 1-500 <$600
1902 Date Back
4x5 1-3175 <$300
3x10-20 1-2400 <$300
1902 Plain Back
4x5 3176-7880 <$300
3x10-20 2401-5068 <$300
Total Issue $448,500
Out at close $25,000

14079 Lackawanna
NB OF OLYPHANT
{{ 5 S }}
Chartered 3/34
1929 Small Size <$VALUE
5 Type 2 1-7290 <$225
10 Type 2 1-3465 <$225
Total Issue $71,100
Out in 1935 $46,950

8985 Huntingdon
FNB OF ORBISONIA
{{ 1 L }}
Chartered 1/08
Receivership 10/5/31
1902 Red Seal <$VALUE
3x10-20 1-187 <$1000
1902 Date Back
3x10-20 1-2040 <$500
1902 Plain Back
3x10-20 2041-6514 <$500
Total Issue $335,050
Out at close $1,750

10335 Huntingdon
ORBISONIA NB, ORBISONIA
{{ 2 L }}
Chartered 2/13
Liquidated 3/3/32
1902 Date Back <$VALUE
4x5 1-1165 <$500
3x10-20 1-934 <$500
1902 Plain Back
4x5 1166-5395 <$500
3x10-20 935-3458 <$500
Total Issue $280,800
All notes reportedly redeemed
Census confirms 2 notes

4408 Schuylkill
FNB OF ORWIGSBURG
Chartered 1890
2nd title: FNB & TC 7/1/26
FIRST TITLE {{ 7 L }}
Brown Back <$VALUE
4x5 1-7100 <$400
3x10-20 1-2640 <$400
1882 Date Back
4x5 1-1210 <$400
3x10-20 1-788 <$400
1902 Date Back
4x5 1-3050 <$200
3x10-20 1-2300 <$200
1902 Plain Back
4x5 3051-9888 <$200
3x10-20 2301-6666 <$200
SECOND TITLE {{ 5 L 13 S }}
1902 Plain Back
3x10-20 1-2233 <$200
1929 Small Size
10 Type 1 1-3040 <$65
20 Type 1 1-770 <$75
10 Type 2 1-5368 <$85
20 Type 2 1-1395 <$85
Total Issue $1,336,690
Out in 1935 $108,800
Large out 1935 $3,770

6501 Clearfield
FNB OF OSCEOLA, OSCEOLA MILLS
{{ 5 L 8 S }}
Chartered 11/24/02
1902 Red Seal <$VALUE
4x5 1-3500 <$500
3x10-20 1-2650 <$500
1902 Date Back
4x5 1-4450 <$250
3x10-20 1-3200 <$250
1902 Plain Back
4x5 4451-12680 <$250
3x10-20 3201-8587 <$250
1929 Small Size
5 Type 1 1-1504 <$135
10 Type 1 1-834 <$135
20 Type 1 1-234 <$135
5 Type 2 1-2108 <$150
10 Type 2 1-1606 <$150
20 Type 2 1-3248 <$150
Total Issue $1,100,250
Out in 1935 $90,550
Large out 1935 $2,290

11966 Clearfield
PEOPLES NB OF OSCEOLA MILLS
{{ 2 L 0 S }}
Organized 3/23/21
Receivership 2/10/31
1902 Plain Back <$VALUE
4x5 1-14384 <$500
1929 Small Size
5 Type 1 1-1955 <$600
Total Issue $346,330
Out at close $29,340
Large out at close $2,060

2906 Chester
FARMERS NB OF OXFORD
{{ 5 L 12 S }}
Organized 2/27/83
Receivership 2/27/34
Brown Back <$VALUE
3x10-20 1-3900 <$500
1902 Red Seal
3x10-20 1-3988 <$600
1902 Date Back
3x10-20 1-7200 <$250
1902 Plain Back
3x10-20 7201-21120 <$250
1929 Small Size
10 Type 1 1-2226 <$75
20 Type 1 1-626 <$85
10 Type 2 1-765 <$100
20 Type 2 1-125 <$100
Total Issue $1,669,230
Out at close $73,800
Large out at close $3,740

728 Chester
NB OF OXFORD
{{ 13 L 20 S }}
Chartered 1/19/65
Original Series <$VALUE
3x1-2 1-500 <$400/$1000
4x5 1-2250 <$450
3x10-20 1-1940 <$750/$1250
50-100 1-471 <$3500
Series 1875
4x5 1-847 <$450
3x10-20 1-1157 <$750/$1250
50-100 1-730 <$3500
Brown Back
4x5 1-4380 <$300
50-100 1-3074 <$1250/$1500
1902 Red Seal
4x5 1-5016 <$300
3x10-20 1-3193 <$300
1902 Date Back
4x5 1-4100* <$150
3x10-20 1-3400** <$150
1902 Plain Back
4x5 4501-28316* <$150
3x10-20 3721-18468** <$150
* 4101-4500 not marked
** 3401-3720 not marked
1929 Small Size
5 Type 1 1-4970 <$60
10 Type 1 1-2710 <$60
20 Type 1 1-692 <$70
5 Type 2 1-7432 <$75
10 Type 2 1-3913 <$75
20 Type 2 1-1296 <$75
Total Issue $3,194,780
Out in 1935 $122,100
Large out 1935 $7,250

8930 Carbon
FNB OF PALMERTON
{{ 8 L 14 S }}
Chartered 10/07
1902 Red Seal <$VALUE
3x10-20 1-250 <$300
1902 Date Back
4x5 1-1850 <$150
3x10-20 1-1040 <$150
1902 Plain Back
4x5 1851-11333 <$150
3x10-20 1041-7460 <$150
1929 Small Size
5 Type 1 1-5872 <$60
10 Type 1 1-3202 <$60
20 Type 1 1-1000 <$65
5 Type 2 1-8886 <$75
10 Type 2 1-4704 <$75
20 Type 2 1-1235 <$75
Total Issue $1,216,610
Out in 1935 $125,350
Large out 1935 $2,090

12358 Chester
PAOLI NB, PAOLI
{{ 2 L }}
Chartered 4/23
Liquidated 1/31/27
1902 Plain Back <$VALUE
4x10 1-2582 <$750
Total Issue $103,280
Out at close $22,000

6045 Armstrong
FNB OF PARKERS LANDING
{{ 1 L 7 S }}
Chartered 12/11/01
Brown Back <$VALUE
50-100 1-560 <$1750/$2000
1882 Date Back
50-100 1-220 <$1750/$2000
3x50-100 1-519<$1750/$2000
1902 Plain Back
3x50-100 1-578 <$750/$850
1929 Small Size
50 Type 1 1-203 <$165
100 Type 1 1-36 <$250
Total Issue $473,750
Out in 1935 $49,600
Large out 1935 $7,250

2464 Chester
PARKESBURG NB, PARKESBURG
{{ 4 L }}
Chartered 3/15/80
Receivership 12/6/26
Series 1875 <$VALUE
3x10-20 1-4286 <$750/$1250
Brown Back
4x5 1-1250 <$600
50-100 1-967 <$1750/$2000
1882 Date Back
4x5 1-4000 <$600
50-100 1-400 <$1750/$2000
3x50-100 1-353<$1750/$2000
1882 Value Back
4x5 4001-6592 <$600
1902 Plain Back
3x10-20 1-3420 <$400
Total Issue $835,440
Out at close $42,600

7363 Westmoreland
PARNASSUS NB, PARNASSUS
Chartered 8/04
2nd title: Parnassus NB, New Kensington 1/28/32
FIRST TITLE {{ 2 L 2 S }}
1902 Red Seal <$VALUE
3x10-20 1-1400 <$800
1902 Date Back
3x10-20 1-2380 <$400
1902 Plain Back
3x10-20 2381-7145 <$400
1929 Small Size
10 Type 1 1-476 <$275
20 Type 1 1-138 <$275
SECOND TITLE {{ 3 S }}
1929 Small Size
10 Type 1 1-126 <$225
20 Type 1 1-42 <$225
10 Type 2 1-973 <$225
20 Type 2 1-205 <$225
Total Issue $498,800
Out in 1935 $24,650
Large out 1935 $1,140

9678 Juniata
PEOPLES NB OF PATTERSON
Chartered 2/10
2nd title: Peoples NB of Mifflin 8/28/23
FIRST TITLE {{ 2 L }}
1902 Date Back <$VALUE
4x5 1-1990 <$400
3x10-20 1-1534 <$400
1902 Plain Back
4x5 1991-4915 <$400
3x10-20 1535-3254 <$400
SECOND TITLE {{ 1 L 5 S }}
1902 Plain Back
4x5 1-2548 <$400
3x10-20 1-1959 <$400
1929 Small Size
5 Type 1 1-1634 <$175
10 Type 1 1-732 <$175
5 Type 2 1-1812 <$200
10 Type 2 1-1175 <$200
Total Issue $504,070
Out in 1935 $24,650
Large out 1935 $1,180

4857 Cambria
FNB OF PATTON
{{ 12 L 18 S }}
Organized 9/13/93
Receivership 9/21/34
Brown Back <$VALUE
3x10-20 1-10020 <$300
1882 Date Back
3x10-20 1-5903 <$300
1902 Date Back
3x10-20 1-3000 <$165
1902 Plain Back
3x10-20 3001-22257 <$165
1929 Small Size
10 Type 1 1-5408 <$50
20 Type 1 1-1582 <$50
5 Type 2 1-312 <$60
10 Type 2 1-4159 <$60
20 Type 2 1-1280 <$60
Total Issue $2,492,070
Out at close $200,000
Large out at close $11,165
Outstanding includes Ch 8233

8233 Cambria
GRANGE NB OF PATTON
{{ 4 L }}
Chartered 5/06
Closed 9/11/28
1902 Red Seal <$VALUE
3x10-20 1-800 <$750
1902 Date Back
3x10-20 1-5240 <$375
1902 Plain Back
3x10-20 5241-15364 <$375
Total Issue $808,200
Out at close $60,000
Ch 4857 assumed circulation

7785 Lackawanna
PECKVILLE NB, PECKVILLE
{{ 3 L 7 S }}
Chartered 6/05
Receivership 10/25/33
1902 Red Seal <$VALUE
3x10-20 1-1112 <$700
1902 Date Back
3x10-20 1-2850 <$350
1902 Plain Back
3x10-20 2851-14101 <$350
1929 Small Size
10 Type 1 1-1654 <$150
20 Type 1 1-502 <$150
10 Type 2 1-296 <$175
20 Type 2 1-35 <$175
Total Issue $923,790
Out at close $49,250
Large out at close $1,230

4352 Northampton
FNB OF PEN ARGYL
{{ 8 L 13 S }}
Chartered 1890
Brown Back <$VALUE
3x10-20 1-7580 <$350
1882 Date Back
3x10-20 1-1468 <$350
1902 Date Back
4x5 1-7500 <$165
3x10-20 1-5300 <$165
1902 Plain Back
4x5 7501-27021 <$165
3x10-20 5301-17988 <$165
1929 Small Size
5 Type 1 1-4244 <$100
10 Type 1 1-1986 <$100
20 Type 1 1-564 <$100
5 Type 2 1-6030 <$100
10 Type 2 1-3111 <$100
20 Type 2 1-805 <$100
Total Issue $2,283,740
Out in 1935 $84,250
Large out 1935 $4,190

7710 Northampton
PEN ARGYL NB, PEN ARGYL
{{ 5 L 9 S }}
Chartered 4/05
1902 Red Seal <$VALUE
3x10-20 1-2520 <$500
1902 Date Back
3x10-20 1-4830 <$250
1902 Plain Back
3x10-20 4831-14049 <$250
1929 Small Size
10 Type 1 1-1448 <$125
20 Type 1 1-376 <$125
10 Type 2 1-2328 <$135
20 Type 2 1-590 <$135
Total Issue $995,530
Out in 1935 $48,750
Large out 1935 $1,830

12197 Dauphin
NB OF PENBROOK
{{ 0 L 5 S }}
Chartered 5/22
1902 Plain Back <$VALUE
4x10 1-846 <$850
1929 Small Size
10 Type 1 1-782 <$250
10 Type 2 1-2370 <$250
Total Issue $104,460
Out in 1935 $25,000
Large out 1935 $150

9344 Dauphin
PENBROOK NB, PENBROOK
{{ 2 L }}
Chartered 2/09
Liquidated 7/12/20
1902 Date Back <$VALUE
4x10 1-3725 <$450
1902 Plain Back
4x10 3726-5435 <$450
Total Issue $217,400
Out at close $16,600

2334 Montgomery
FARMERS NB OF PENNSBURG
{{ 9 L 21 S }}
Chartered 5/31/76
Series 1875 <$VALUE
3x10-20 1-5658 <$750/$1250
Brown Back
3x10-20 1-6800 <$300
1882 Date Back
3x10-20 1-6634 <$300
1902 Plain Back
4x10 1-17491 <$150
1929 Small Size
10 Type 1 1-3850 <$75
10 Type 2 1-5535 <$75
Total Issue $1,944,040
Out in 1935 $72,850
Large out 1935 $3,360

2301 Montgomery
PERKIOMEN NB OF PENNSBURG
{{ 3 L }}
Chartered 9/27/75
Liquidated 9/10/95
Series 1875 <$VALUE
3x10-20 1-6198 <$750/$1250
Total Issue $309,900
Out in 1910 $1,440

5736 Bucks
FNB OF PERKASIE
{{ 11 L 13 S }}
Chartered 3/7/01
Brown Back <$VALUE
3x10-20 1-3100 <$325
1882 Date Back
3x10-20 1-5800 <$325
1882 Value Back
3x10-20 5801-8953 <$325
1902 Plain Back
3x10-20 1-8301 <$175
1929 Small Size
10 Type 1 1-1724 <$100
20 Type 1 1-520 <$135
10 Type 2 1-2690 <$135
20 Type 2 1-798 <$135
Total Issue $1,226,400
Out in 1935 $58,750
Large out 1935 $2,690

6344 Fayette
FNB OF PERRYOPOLIS
{{ 5 L 12 S }}
Chartered 7/19/02
1902 Red Seal <$VALUE
3x10-20 1-1600 <$500
1902 Date Back
3x10-20 1-4840 <$250
1902 Plain Back
3x10-20 4841-14489 <$250
1929 Small Size
10 Type 1 1-1444 <$125
20 Type 1 1-360 <$125
10 Type 2 1-1429 <$125
20 Type 2 1-492 <$125
Total Issue $958,420
Out in 1935 $48,800
Large out 1935 $2,480

10313 Huntingdon
FNB OF PETERSBURG
{{ 2 L 8 S }}
Chartered 1/13
1902 Date Back <$VALUE
3x10-20 1-500 <$450
1902 Plain Back
3x10-20 501-3603 <$450
1929 Small Size
10 Type 1 1-586 <$175
20 Type 1 1-150 <$175
10 Type 2 1-501 <$175
20 Type 2 1-175 <$175
Total Issue $241,820
Out in 1935 $18,400
Large out 1935 $580

602 Philadelphia
B OF NORTH AMERICA, PHILADELPHIA
{{ 44 L }}
Chartered 12/64
Liquidated 2/28/23
Original Series <$VALUE
4x5 1-27350 <$500
3x10-20 1-12580<$750/$1250
50-100 1-2300 <$3500
Series 1875
4x5 1-25050 <$500
3x10-20 1-9900 <$750/$1250
50-100 1-2360 <$3500
Brown Back
4x5 1-35298 <$250
3x10-20 1-17240 <$250
50-100 1-2194 <$1250/$1500
1902 Red Seal
4x5 1-23815 <$275
3x10-20 1-17074 <$275
1902 Date Back
4x5 1-72330 <$125
3x10-20 1-53168 <$125
3x50-100 1-1180 <$400/$500
1902 Plain Back
4x5 72331-87330 <$125
3x10-20 53169-61868 <$125
Total Issue $11,233,060
Out at close $488,615
Outstanding includes Ch 541

11539 Philadelphia
BROAD STREET NB OF PHILADELPHIA
{{ 14 L }}
Chartered 12/19
Liquidated 10/6/28
1902 Plain Back <$VALUE
4x5 1-73420 <$125
3x10-20 1-45904 <$125
Total Issue $3,763,600
Out at close $500,000

2317 Philadelphia
CENTENNIAL NB OF PHILADELPHIA
{{ 10 L }}
Chartered 1/19/76
Closed 10/3/25
Series 1875 <$VALUE
4x10 1-18527 <$750
Brown Back
3x10-20 1-13320 <$350
1882 Date Back
3x10-20 1-16114 <$350
1902 Plain Back
3x10-20 1-28261 <$200
Total Issue $3,625,830
Out at close $200,000
Ch 2731 assumed circulation

723 Philadelphia
CENTRAL NB OF PHILADELPHIA
{{ 5 L }}
Chartered 1/17/65
Original Series <$VALUE
3x1-2 1-6000 <$400/$1000
4x5 1-9750 <$450
4x10 1-7500 <$750
3x20-50 1-1900<$1250/$3500
100-100 1-1950 <$3500
Series 1875
4x5 1-3750 <$450
4x10 1-4250 <$750
3x20-50 1-4300<$1250/$3500
100-100 1-1367 <$3500
Brown Back
50-100 1-3440 <$1250/$1500
1902 Red Seal
4x5 1-4220 <$400
3x10-20 1-1387 <$400
50-100 1-3128 <$2250/$2500
1902 Date Back
4x5 1-9435 <$200
3x10-20 1-5606 <$200
50-100 1-3100 <$500/$600
3x50-100 1-2900 <$500/$600
Total Issue $4,913,350
Out in 1935 $26,861
Outstanding includes Ch 540

3723 Philadelphia
CHESTNUT STREET NB OF PHILADELPHIA
{{ UNREPORTED }}
Chartered 6/14/87
Receivership 1/29/98
Brown Back <$VALUE
4x5 1-1770 <$1250
3x10-20 1-535 <$1250
50-100 1-794 <$2000
Total Issue $181,250
Out in 1916 $1,060

543 Philadelphia
CITY NB OF PHILADELPHIA
{{ 1 L }}
Chartered 10/64
Liquidated 6/26/00
Original Series <$VALUE
4x5 1-13400 <$750
3x10-20 1-5000 <$850/$1500
3x50-100 1-1000 <$3500
Series 1875
4x5 1-16324 <$750
3x10-20 1-3758 <$850/$1500
3x50-100 1-400 <$3500
Brown Back
4x5 1-6337 <$650
3x10-20 1-2559 <$650
50-100 1-563<$1250/$1500
Total Issue $1,721,520
Out in 1910 $9,910

13180 Philadelphia
CITY NB OF PHILADELPHIA
{{ 30 S }}
Chartered 2/28 as City NB TC under which there was no issue. Issuing title adopted 1/16/32.
1929 Small Size <$VALUE
5 Type 1 1-12102 <$30
10 Type 1 1-8630 <$30
20 Type 1 1-2104 <$40
5 Type 2 1-45206 <$30
10 Type 2 1-21964 <$30
20 Type 2 1-5765 <$40
Total Issue $1,694,310
Out in 1935 $477,500

556 Philadelphia
COMMERCIAL NB OF PENNSYLVANIA OF PHILADELPHIA
{{ 6 L }}
Chartered 10/27/64
Liquidated 5/31/98
Original Series <$VALUE
4x5 1-9150 <$500
3x10-20 1-6200 <$750/$1250
50-100 1-6300 <$3500
Series 1875
4x5 1-3876 <$500
3x10-20 1-1926 <$750/$1250
50-100 1-1765 <$3500
Brown Back
4x5 1-2900 <$275
3x10-20 1-1124 <$275
50-100 1-655 <$1250/$1500
Total Issue $2,089,020
Out in 1910 $13,560

Commercial NB of Philadelphia
Commercial NB & TC of Philadelphia
SEE Ch 3604
Manayunk NB of Philadelphia

623 Philadelphia
COMMONWEALTH NB OF PHILADELPHIA
{{ 4 L }}
Chartered 12/14/64
Liquidated 12/31/91
Original Series <$VALUE
4x5 1-2000 <$500
3x10-20 1-1300 <$750/$1250
50-100 1-2193 <$3500
Series 1875
4x5 1-1240 <$500
3x10-20 1-822 <$750/$1250
50-100 1-1579 <$3500
Brown Back
4x5 1-250 <$350
3x10-20 1-200 <$350
50-100 1-748 <$1250/$1500
Total Issue $863,900
Out in 1910 $5,320

561 Philadelphia
CONSOLIDATION NB OF PHILADELPHIA
{{ 5 L }}
Chartered 10/29/64
Liquidated 6/8/08
Original Series <$VALUE
4x5 1-19750 <$500
3x10-20 1-1000 <$750/$1250
50-100 1-500 <$3500
500-1000 1-33 <$150,000/$200,000
Series 1875
4x5 1-30237 <$500
Brown Back
4x5 1-5750 <$300
3x10-20 1-33300 <$300
1902 Red Seal
4x5 1-10497 <$350
3x10-20 1-7058 <$350
Total Issue $3,517,080
Out in 1910 $70,950

542 Philadelphia
CORN EXCHANGE NB OF PHILADELPHIA
Chartered 10/64
2nd title: Corn Exchange NB & TC 6/18/28
FIRST TITLE {{ 25 L }}
Original Series <$VALUE
3x1-2 1-4000 <$350/$1000
4x5 1-7250 <$400
3x10-20 1-5326 <$750/$1250
50-100 1-2772 <$3500
Series 1875
4x5 1-9550 <$400
3x10-20 1-7800 <$750/$1250
50-100 1-900 <$3500
Brown Back
4x5 1-11375 <$150
3x10-20 1-15974 <$150/$200
50-100 1-10609<$1250/$1500
1902 Red Seal
4x5 1-15000 <$200
3x10-20 1-11800 <$200
50-100 1-1400 <$2250/$2500
1902 Date Back
4x5 1-62750 <$100
3x10-20 1-44100 <$100
50-100 1-1744 <$350/$450
3x50-100 1-3000 <$350/$450
SECOND TITLE {{ 3 L 50+ S }}
1902 Plain Back
3x10-20 1-1059 <$175
1929 Small Size
5 Type 1 1-26040 <$20
10 Type 1 1-27746 <$25
20 Type 1 1-10508 <$36
5 Type 2 1-155824 <$20
10 Type 2 1-87502 <$25
20 Type 2 1-16790 <$35
Total Issue $15,502,060
Out in 1935 $1,549,770
Large out 1935 $38,575
Outstanding includes Ch 234

522 Philadelphia
EIGHTH NB OF PHILADELPHIA
{{ 30 L 2 S }}
Chartered 9/64
Closed 4/30/30
Original Series <$VALUE
4x5 1-2500 <$400
3x10-20 1-2300 <$750/$1250
50-100 1-2080 <$3500
Series 1875
4x5 1-6250 <$400
3x10-20 1-4020 <$750/$1250
50-100 1-346 <$3500
Brown Back
4x5 1-1500 <$175
3x10-20 1-6882 <$175
50-100 1-2416 <$1250/$1500
1902 Red Seal
4x5 1-6000 <$225
3x10-20 1-2700 <$225
1902 Date Back
4x5 1-9250 <$100
3x10-20 1-7000 <$100
50-100 1-2000 <$400/$500
3x50-100 1-2480 <$400/$500
1902 Plain Back
4x5 9251-141444 <$100
3x10-20 7001-7700 <$100
1929 Small Size
5 Type 1 1-8771 <$400
10 Type 1 1-168 <$400
20 Type 1 1-20 <$400
50 Type 1 1-22 <$500
100 Type 1 1 <$650
Total Issue $6,608,090
Out at close $274,995
Large out at close $43,765
Ch 1 assumed circulation

13032 Philadelphia
ERIE NB OF PHILADELPHIA
{{ U + 20 S }}
Chartered 1/27
1929 Small Size <$VALUE
5 Type 1 1-5550 <$30
10 Type 1 1-3236 <$30
20 Type 1 1-938 <$40
50 Type 1 1-170 <$135
100 Type 1 1-54 <$225
5 Type 2 1-12080 <$40
10 Type 2 1-5155 <$40
20 Type 2 1-2170 <$50
Total Issue $711,970
Out in 1935 $247,200

538 Philadelphia
FARMERS & MECHANICS NB OF PHILADELPHIA
{{ 40 L }}
Chartered 10/64
Liquidated 8/31/18
Original Series <$VALUE
4x5 1-25500 <$400
3x10-20 1-10900<$750/$1250
50-100 1-7000 <$3500
Series 1875
4x5 1-13344 <$400
3x10-20 1-18951<$750/$1250
50-100 1-2500 <$3500
Brown Back
4x5 1-143750 <$150
3x10-20 1-59850 <$150/$175
50-100 1-8050 <$1250/$1500
1902 Red Seal
4x5 1-67500 <$150
4x10 1-34250 <$150
3x10-20 1-21944 <$150/$200
1902 Date Back
4x5 1-196500 <$60
4x10 1-165000 <$60
1902 Plain Back
4x5 196501-238294 <$60
4x10 165001-183580 <$60
Total Issue $26,695,710
Out at close $1,081,745

1 Philadelphia
FNB OF PHILADELPHIA*
{{ 6U + 28 L 4U + 50 S }}
Chartered 6/30/63
Liquidated 6/10/82
*Rechartered as Ch 2731 which retook Ch 1 6/1/02
Original Series <$VALUE
4x5 1-500 <$600
4x10 1-15255 <$850
2x20-50-100 1-6040 <$1500/$3500/$3500
Series 1875
4x5 1-5000 <$600
4x10 1-2500 <$850
2x20-50-100 1-2700 <$1500/$3500/$3500
1902 Red Seal
4x5 1-30000 <$250
4x10 1-10000 <$250
3x10-20 1-41500 <$250
1902 Date Back
4x5 1-114016 <$125
4x10 1-67835 <$125
3x10-20 1-35901 <$125
1902 Plain Back
4x10 67836-69535 <$125
1929 Small Size
5 Type 1 1-26832 <$50
10 Type 1 1-13068 <$50
20 Type 1 1-3054 <$60
5 Type 2 1-57344 <$50
10 Type 2 1-26156 <$50
20 Type 2 1-6510 <$60
Total Issue $15,046,570
Out in 1935 $532,030
Large out 1935 $50,175
Outstanding includes Ch 2317, Ch 2731, and Ch 522

2731 Philadelphia
FNB OF PHILADELPHIA
{{ 2 L }}
Chartered 1882
RETOOK Ch 1 6/1/02
Brown Back <$VALUE
3x10-20 1-16861 <$600
50-100 1-4000 <$1250/$1500
Total Issue $1,443,050
Out at close $800,000

****

286 Philadelphia
FOURTH NB OF PHILADELPHIA
{{ UNREPORTED }}
Organized 2/26/64
Receivership 12/20/71
Original Series <$VALUE
4x5 1-2310 <$1250
3x10-20 1-2998<$1500/$2000
Total Issue $196,100
Out in 1916 $950

****

3557 Philadelphia
FOURTH STREET NB OF PHILADELPHIA
{{ 47 L }}
Chartered 9/15/86
Closed 4/1/26
Brown Back <$VALUE
4x5 1-139405 <$135
3x10-20 1-85102 <$135/$175
50-100 1-14354<$1250/$1500
1902 Red Seal
4x5 1-55250 <$135
3x10-20 1-36400 <$135/$175
50-100 1-500 <$2250/$2500
1902 Date Back
4x5 1-179370 <$60
3x10-20 1-132192 <$60
3x50-100 1-4000 <$350/$400
Total Issue $23,393,300
Out at close $84,480
Ch 5459 assumed circulation

****

5459 Philadelphia
FRANKLIN NB OF PHILADELPHIA
{{ 11 L }}
Chartered 6/26/00
Closed 4/7/28
Brown Back <$VALUE
4x5 1-59330 <$175
3x10-20 1-43868 <$175/$200
1882 Date Back
4x5 1-59980* <$175
3x10-20 1-40989 <$175/$200
* 57559-58980 not issued
Total Issue $6,600,610
Out at close $84,635
Outstanding includes Ch 3557

****

592 Philadelphia
GIRARD NB OF PHILADELPHIA
{{ U + 27 L }}
Organized 11/30/64
Closed 3/31/26
Original Series <$VALUE
4x5 1-8000 <$400
3x10-20 1-14140<$750/$1250
50-100 1-1900 <$3500
Series 1875
3x10-20 1-13727<$750/$1250
Brown Back
4x5 1-29195 <$150
3x10-20 1-49919 <$150/$200
1902 Red Seal
4x5 1-59300 <$150
3x10-20 1-38480 <$150/$200
1902 Date Back
4x5 1-132500 <$75
3x10-20 1-105800 <$75
3x50-100 1-7726 <$350/$400
1902 Plain Back
4x5 132501-213867 <$75
3x10-20 105801-154251 <$75
Total Issue $21,949,590
Out at close $1,071,495

****

3085 Philadelphia
INDEPENDENCE NB OF PHILADELPHIA
{{ 2 L }}
Chartered 12/1/83
Liquidated 5/3/01
Brown Back <$VALUE
4x5 1-24897 <$650
3x10-20 1-4456 <$650
Total Issue $720,740
Out in 1910 $5,455

****

544 Philadelphia
KENSINGTON NB OF PHILADELPHIA
{{ 14 L U + 19 S }}
Organized 10/20/64
Original Series <$VALUE
3x1-2 1-7500 <$400/$1250
4x5 1-7000 <$500
3x10-20 1-2700 <$750/$1250
10-2x50-100 1-250 <$750/$3500/$3500
10-2x50-100 551-693 <$750/$3500/$3500
2x50-100 251-550 <$3500
Series 1875
4x5 1-6250 <$500
3x10-20 1-3500 <$750/$1250
10-2x50-100 1-262 <$750/$3500/$3500
Brown Back
4x5 1-16124 <$150
3x10-20 1-6076 <$150/$175
50-100 1-1336 <$1250/$1500
1902 Red Seal
4x5 1-6300 <$165
3x10-20 1-3720 <$165/$200
50-100 1-120 <$2250/$2500
1902 Date Back
4x5 1-22200 <$65
3x10-20 1-15100 <$65
1902 Plain Back
4x5 22201-46975 <$65
3x10-20 15101-30593 <$65
1929 Small Size
5 Type 1 1-9470 <$30
10 Type 1 1-6486 <$35
20 Type 1 1-1442 <$40
5 Type 2 1-24522 <$30
10 Type 2 1-13005 <$35
20 Type 2 1-3684 <$40
Total Issue $5,608,520
Out in 1935 $338,850
Large out 1935 $8,340

****

2291 Philadelphia
KEYSTONE NB OF PHILADELPHIA
{{ 3 L }}
Chartered 7/30/75
Receivership 5/9/91
Series 1875 <$VALUE
4x5 1-21333 <$650
Total Issue $426,660
Out in 1916 $1,760

****

3604 Philadelphia
MANAYUNK NB OF PHILADELPHIA
Chartered 12/17/86
Receivership 5/22/34
2nd title: Manayunk-Quaker City NB 4/14/28
3rd title: Commercial NB & TC 7/13/29
4th title: Commercial NB 1/14/32
FIRST TITLE {{ 11 L }}
Brown Back <$VALUE
4x5 1-14860 <$200
3x10-20 1-12780 <$200
1902 Red Seal
4x5 1-4250 <$200
3x10-20 1-2000 <$200
1902 Date Back
4x5 1-31415 <$100
3x10-20 1-22434 <$100
1902 Plain Back
4x5 31416-61286 <$100
3x10-20 22435-41558 <$100
SECOND TITLE {{ 6 L }}
1902 Plain Back
3x10-20 1-14034 <$100
THIRD TITLE {{ 19 S }}
1929 Small Size
10 Type 1 1-22706 <$40
20 Type 1 1-6366 <$40
FOURTH TITLE {{ 20 S }}
1929 Small Size
10 Type 1 1-8576 <$30
20 Type 1 1-1982 <$35
10 Type 2 1-8784 <$30
20 Type 2 1-2204 <$35
Total Issue $8,197,120
Out at close $950,000
Large out at close $58,630
Outstanding includes Ch 560 and Ch 4050

****

Manayunk-Quaker City NB of Philadelphia
SEE Ch 3604
Manayunk NB of Philadelphia

****

557 Philadelphia
MANUFACTURERS NB OF PHILADELPHIA
{{ 4 L }}
Organized 10/28/64
Liquidated 2/1/16
Original Series <$VALUE
3x1-2 1-11000 <$400/$1000
4x5 1-11271 <$500
3x10-20 1-5390 <$750/$1250
50-100 1-3144 <$3500
500-1000 1-120* <$150,000/$200,000
* 53-100 not issued
Series 1875
4x5 1-12600 <$500
3x10-20 1-9000 <$750/$1250
50-100 1-2466 <$3500
Brown Back
4x5 1-6826 <$300
3x10-20 1-2979 <$300
50-100 1-1797 <$1250/$1500
1902 Red Seal
4x5 1-2435 <$300
50-100 1-502 <$2250/$2500
1902 Date Back
4x5 1-14384 <$150
50-100 1-2704 <$400/$500
3x50-100 1-26 <$400/$500
Total Issue $3,580,220
Out at close $48,500

****

3684 Philadelphia
MARKET STREET NB OF PHILADELPHIA
{{ 29 L 7 S }}
Chartered 4/28/87
Brown Back <$VALUE
4x5 1-37480 <$150
3x10-20 1-22414 <$150/$175
50-100 1-2400 <$1250/$1500
1902 Red Seal
4x5 1-13300 <$150
3x10-20 1-7080 <$150/$175
50-100 1-1200 <$2250/$2500
1902 Date Back
4x5 1-79500 <$75
3x10-20 1-47000 <$75
50-100 1-1800 <$350/$400
3x50-100 1-14600<$350/$400
1902 Plain Back
3x50-100 14601-17386 <$350/$400
1929 Small Size
50 Type 1 1-1646 <$150
100 Type 1 1-552 <$200
5 Type 2 1-120 <$150
Total Issue $12,412,400
Out in 1935 $471,670
Large out 1935 $43,720

****

610 Philadelphia
MECHANICS NB OF PHILADELPHIA
{{ 18 L }}
Chartered 12/7/64
Liquidated 2/16/03
Original Series <$VALUE
4x5 1-19150 <$400
3x10-20 1-7155 <$750/$1250
20 7156-8405 <$1250
3x10-20 8406-10405 <$750/$1250
50-100 1-1534 <$3500
Series 1875
3x1-2 1-11000 <$400/$1000
4x5 1-20250 <$400
3x10-20 1-6000 <$750/$1250
50-100 1-234 <$3500
Brown Back
4x5 1-24756 <$150
3x10-20 1-11489 <$150/$175
50-100 1-1557 <$1250/$1500
Total Issue $3,194,070
Out in 1910 $27,556

****

2462 Philadelphia
MERCHANTS NB OF PHILADELPHIA
{{ 22 L }}
Chartered 3/6/80
Liquidated 8/3/10
Series 1875 <$VALUE
4x5 1-25100 <$400
3x10-20 1-10852<$750/$1250
50-100 1-9157 <$3500
Brown Back
4x5 1-30000 <$150
3x10-20 1-24000 <$150/$175
50-100 1-9203 $1250/$1500
1882 Date Back
4x5 1-2243 <$150
3x10-20 1-1136 <$150/$175
Total Issue $5,700,260
Out in 1910 $306,350

****

Mount Airy NB in Philadelphia
Mount Airy NB & TC in Philadelphia
SEE Ch 13113
NB of Mount Airy in Philadelphia

****

547 Philadelphia
NB OF COMMERCE, PHILADELPHIA
{{ 2 L }}
Organized 10/25/64
Liquidated 11/28/99
Original Series <$VALUE
4x5 1-7500 <$650
3x10-20 1-4170 <$850/$1500
50-100 1-600* <$3500
* 366-500 not issued
Series 1875
4x5 1-12728 <$650
Brown Back
4x5 1-12578 <$600
Total Issue $934,370
Out in 1910 $5,290

****

546 Philadelphia
NB OF GERMANTOWN, PHILADELPHIA
Organized 10/25/64
2nd title: NB of Germantown & TC 3/21/29
FIRST TITLE {{ 26 L }}
Original Series <$VALUE
3x1-2 1-15000 <$400/$1250
4x5 1-7500 <$400
3x10-20 1-2900 <$750/$1250
Series 1875
3x1-2 1-4040 <$400/$1250
4x5 1-14241 <$400
3x10-20 1-1521 <$750/$1250
Brown Back
4x5 1-24845 <$175
3x10-20 1-8871 <$175/$200
1902 Red Seal
4x5 1-8500 <$200
3x10-20 1-6000 <$200/$225
1902 Date Back
4x5 1-28165 <$100
3x10-20 1-20734 <$100
1902 Plain Back
4x5 28166-59350 <$100
3x10-20 20735-42930 <$100
SECOND TITLE {{ 31 S }}
1929 Small Size
5 Type 1 1-13650 <$25
10 Type 1 1-7414 <$30
20 Type 1 1-1912 <$40
5 Type 2 1-33834 <$25
10 Type 2 1-17349 <$30
20 Type 2 1-4634 <$40
Total Issue $7,014,140
Out in 1935 $388,200
Large out 1935 $14,245

****

13113 Philadelphia
NB OF MOUNT AIRY IN PHILADELPHIA
Chartered 8/27
Receivership 1/15/34
2nd title: Mount Airy NB & TC in Philadelphia 5/21/28
3rd title: Mount Airy NB in Philadelphia 1/19/32
FIRST TITLE {{ 4 L }}
1902 Plain Back <$VALUE
4x5 1-7519 <$300
SECOND TITLE {{ 1 L 9 S }}
1902 Plain Back
4x5 1-7021 <$300
1929 Small Size
5 Type 1 1-10508 <$75
THIRD TITLE {{ 4 S }}
1929 Small Size
5 Type 1 1-4766 <$125
5 Type 2 1-8260 <$125
Total Issue $790,320
Out at close $100,000
Large out at close $1,150

****

11908 Philadelphia
NB OF NORTH PHILADELPHIA, PHILADELPHIA
{{ UNREPORTED }}
Chartered 1/21
Liquidated 10/5/28
1902 Plain Back <$VALUE
4x5 1-5610 <$750
3x10-20 1-3486 <$750
Total Issue $286,550
Out at close $22,950

****

541 Philadelphia
NB OF NORTHERN LIBERTIES, PHILADELPHIA
{{ 5 L }}
Chartered 10/64
Liquidated 3/6/16
Original Series <$VALUE
4x5 1-6400 <$500
3x10-20 1-7760 <$750/$1250
50-100 1-1800 <$3500
Series 1875
4x5 1-4000 <$500
3x10-20 1-11800<$750/$1250
50-100 1-79 <$3500
Brown Back
50-100 1-2600 <$1250/$1500
1902 Red Seal
50-100 1-660 <$2250/$2500
1902 Date Back
4x5 1-19400 <$200
3x10-20 1-13631 <$200
50-100 1-601 <$400/$500
Total Issue $3,142,000
Out at close $175,000
Ch 602 assumed circulation

****

12931 Philadelphia
NB OF OLNEY IN PHILADELPHIA
{{ 2 L 18 S }}
Chartered 5/26
Liquidated 7/16/34
1902 Plain Back <$VALUE
3x10-20 1-12391 <$400
1929 Small Size
10 Type 1 1-7984 <$30
20 Type 1 1-2130 <$40
10 Type 2 1-1368 <$40
20 Type 2 1-150 <$50
Total Issue $1,370,870
Out at close $178,700
Large out 1935 $2,360
Ch 14120 assumed circulation

****

1647 Philadelphia
NB OF THE REPUBLIC OF PHILADELPHIA
{{ 14 L }}
Chartered 3/30/66
Liquidated 1/11/98
Original Series <$VALUE
3x1-2 1-8344 <$400/$1000
4x10 1-4925 <$750
3x20-50 1-10373<$1250/$3500
Series 1875
3x1-2 1-353 <$400/$1000
4x10 1-549 <$750
3x20-50 1-5256<$1250/$3500
Brown Back
3x10-20 1-11270 <$200
Total Issue $2,545,135
Out in 1910 $15,283

****

7929 Philadelphia
N DEPOSIT B OF PHILADELPHIA
{{ U + 1 L }}
Chartered 9/29/05
Receivership 7/14/08
1902 Red Seal <$VALUE
4x5 1-5535 <$750
3x10-20 1-2466 <$750
50-100 1-880 <$2250/$2500
Total Issue $366,000
Out in 1916 $5,505

****

755 Philadelphia
N EXCHANGE B OF PHILADELPHIA
{{ UNREPORTED }}
Chartered 1/25/65
Liquidated 1/8/70
Original Series <$VALUE
3x1-2 1-3020 <$1000/$2000
4x5 1-4420 <$1000
3x10-20 1-1000<$1250/$2000
50-100 1-193 <$3500
Total Issue $182,450
Out in 1910 $1,560

****

1743 Philadelphia
N SECURITY B OF PHILADELPHIA
Chartered 12/70
Liquidated 6/30/30
2nd title: N Security B & TC 6/22/29
FIRST TITLE {{ 30 L }}
Original Series <$VALUE
4x5 1-4000 <$400
3x10-20 1-1601 <$750/$1250
50-100 1-1033 <$3500
Series 1875
4x5 1-6265 <$400
3x10-20 1-3077 <$750/$1250
Brown Back
4x5 1-16000 <$125
3x10-20 1-17090 <$125/$175
1882 Date Back
4x5 1-8565 <$125
3x10-20 1-4486 <$125/$175
1902 Date Back
4x5 1-27500 <$65
3x10-20 1-20900 <$65
1902 Plain Back
4x5 27501-68592 <$65
3x10-20 20901-47731 <$65
SECOND TITLE {{ 2 S }}
1929 Small Size
5 Type 1 1-3753 <$300
10 Type 1 1-1743 <$300
20 Type 1 1-430 <$300
Total Issue $6,260,410
Out at close $250,000
Large out at close $42,730

****

3371 Philadelphia
NINTH NB OF PHILADELPHIA
{{ 7 L }}
Chartered 1885
Liquidated 10/1/23
Brown Back <$VALUE
4x5 1-1650 <$300
3x10-20 1-9215 <$300
1902 Red Seal
3x10-20 1-3900 <$300
1902 Date Back
3x10-20 1-23400 <$150
1902 Plain Back
3x10-20 23401-43888 <$150
Total Issue $2,883,150
Out at close $244,105

****

13325 Philadelphia
NORTH BROAD NB OF PHILADELPHIA
{{ 2U + 14 S }}
Chartered 5/29
1929 Small Size <$VALUE
5 Type 1 1-1030 <$50
10 Type 1 1-312 <$50
20 Type 1 1-100 <$60
5 Type 2 1-33354 <$40
10 Type 2 1-17282 <$40
20 Type 2 1-5544 <$50
Total Issue $512,090
Out in 1935 $246,050

****

13175 Philadelphia
NORTHEAST NB OF PHILADELPHIA
{{ 31 S }}
Chartered 2/28 as Northeast NB of Holmesburg in Philadelphia, under which there was no issue. Issuing title adopted 1/13/32.
1929 Small Size <$VALUE
5 Type 1 1-3708 <$35
10 Type 1 1-1798 <$40
20 Type 1 1-564 <$50
5 Type 2 1-16360 <$35
10 Type 2 1-9173 <$40
20 Type 2 1-2065 <$50
Total Issue $501,630
Out in 1935 $153,850

****

4192 Philadelphia
NORTHERN NB OF PHILADELPHIA
{{ 11 L }}
Chartered 1890
Liquidated 3/4/29
Brown Back <$VALUE
4x5 1-18325 <$200
3x10-20 1-8532 <$200/$225
50-100 1-2366 <$1250/$1500
1882 Date Back
4x5 1-3401 <$200
3x10-20 1-1000 <$200/$225
50-100 1-89 <$2250/$2500
1902 Date Back
4x5 1-18250 <$125
3x10-20 1-14370 <$125
50-100 1-400 <$350/$400
3x50-100 1-1000 <$350/$400
1902 Plain Back
4x5 18251-44017 <$125
3x10-20 14371-31595 <$125
Total Issue $4,049,460
Out at close $171,590

****

3491 Philadelphia
NORTHWESTERN NB OF PHILADELPHIA
Organized 4/3/86
Receivership 6/25/34
2nd title: Northwestern NB & TC 8/3/29
FIRST TITLE {{ 8 L }}
Brown Back <$VALUE
4x5 1-3250 <$250
3x10-20 1-16589 <$250
1902 Red Seal
3x10-20 1-4500 <$250
1902 Date Back
3x10-20 1-28100 <$150
1902 Plain Back
3x10-20 28101-62252 <$150
SECOND TITLE {{ 8 S }}
1929 Small Size
10 Type 1 1-6366 <$75
20 Type 1 1-1590 <$75
10 Type 2 1-5623 <$75
20 Type 2 1-1542 <$75
Total Issue $4,891,880
Out at close $197,400
Large out at close $6,670

****

12573 Philadelphia
OVERBROOK NB OF PHILADELPHIA
{{ 5 L 6 S }}
Chartered 9/24
Receivership 5/15/31
1902 Plain Back <$VALUE
4x5 1-15897 <$200
3x10-20 1-10481 <$200
1929 Small Size
5 Type 1 1-3786 <$150
10 Type 1 1-1972 <$150
20 Type 1 1-506 <$150
Total Issue $1,134,610
Out at close $150,000
Large out at close $7,730

540 Philadelphia
PENN NB OF PHILADELPHIA
{{ 10 L 2 S }}
Chartered 10/64
Closed 7/12/30
Original Series <$VALUE
4x5 1-10000 <$500
3x10-20 1-2000 <$750/$1250
50-100 1-800 <$3500
Series 1875
4x5 1-3500 <$500
3x10-20 1-3100 <$750/$1250
50-100 1-1200 <$3500
Brown Back
50-100 1-1727 <$1250/$1500
1902 Red Seal
4x5 1-3800 <$250
50-100 1-1147 <$2250/$2500
1902 Date Back
4x5 1-38080 <$125
50-100 1-2107 <$350/$400
3x50-100 1-3130 <$350/$400
1902 Plain Back
4x5 38081-45090 <$125
3x50-100 3131-3380 <$350/$400
1929 Small Size
5 Type 1 1-1160 <$400
50 Type 1 1-211 <$450
100 Type 1 1-58 <$500
Total Issue $3,527,850
Out at close $147,900
Large out at close $34,450
Ch 723 assumed circulation

539 Philadelphia
PHILADELPHIA NB, PHILADELPHIA
{{ U + 50 L 3U + 50 S }}
Chartered 10/64
Original Series <$VALUE
4x5 1-11500 <$375
4x10 1-2500 <$750
3x20-50 1-1800 <$1250/$3500
100-100 1-6430 <$3500
500 1-400 <$150,000
Series 1875
4x5 1-24000 <$375
4x10 1-14875 <$750
100-100 1-2639 <$3500
Brown Back
4x5 1-102000 <$125
3x10-20 1-33200 <$125/$175
50-100 1-1634 <$1250/$1500
1902 Red Seal
4x5 1-57500 <$125
3x10-20 1-37000 <$125/$175
1902 Date Back
4x5 1-122000 <$50
3x10-20 1-88800 <$60
1902 Plain Back
4x5 1-13005 <$50
3x10-20 1-9525 <$60
1929 Small Size
5 Type 1 1-150337 <$15
10 Type 1 1-94996 <$20
20 Type 1 1-25424 <$30
Total Issue $31,439,000
Out in 1935 $2,859,730
Large out 1935 $131,275

3507 Philadelphia
PRODUCE NB OF PHILADELPHIA
{{ UNREPORTED }}
Chartered 5/19/86
Liquidated 12/8/91
Brown Back <$VALUE
4x5 1-2983 <$1250
3x10-20 1-965 <$1250
Total Issue $107,910
Out in 1910 $500

4050 Philadelphia
QUAKER CITY NB OF PHILADELPHIA
{{ 18 L }}
Chartered 6/1/89
Closed 4/14/28
Brown Back <$VALUE
3x10-20 1-48460 <$150/$185
1882 Date Back
3x10-20 1-5090 <$150/$185
1902 Date Back
3x10-20 1-50000 <$75
1902 Plain Back
3x10-20 50001-135513 <$75
Total Issue $9,453,150
Out at close $499,995

12860 Philadelphia
QUEEN LANE NB IN GERMANTOWN AT PHILADELPHIA
{{ 8 L }}
Chartered 12/25
Liquidated 10/6/28
1902 Plain Back <$VALUE
4x5 1-9548 <$250
3x10-20 1-4816 <$250
Total Issue $431,760
Out at close $171,710

213 Philadelphia
SECOND NB OF PHILADELPHIA
{{ 10 L 2U + 25 S }}
Chartered 1/64
Original Series <$VALUE
4x5 1-8000 <$450
4x10 1-8250 <$750
Series 1875
4x5 1-8500 <$450
4x10 1-4583 <$750
Brown Back
4x5 1-14700 <$200
3x10-20 1-7780 <$200
1902 Red Seal
4x5 1-8250 <$250
4x10 1-2000 <$250
3x10-20 1-3800 <$250
1902 Date Back
4x5 1-21000 <$125
4x10 1-19000 <$125
1902 Plain Back
4x5 21001-47546 <$125
4x10 19001-34168 <$125
3x10-20 1-6129 <$125
1929 Small Size
5 Type 1 1-5990 <$30
10 Type 1 1-3294 <$35
20 Type 1 1-910 <$45
10 Type 2 1-8208 <$35
20 Type 2 1-2089 <$45
Total Issue $5,195,810
Out in 1935 $145,345
Large out 1935 $11,915

413 Philadelphia
SEVENTH NB OF PHILADELPHIA
{{ U + 0 L }}
Chartered 5/4/64
Liquidated 4/13/98
Original Series <$VALUE
4x5 1-16500 <$1250
3x10-20 1-2345 <$1500/$2000
Series 1875
4x5 1-5000 <$1250
3x10-20 1-4800 <$1500/$2000
Brown Back
3x10-20 1-4467 <$1000
Total Issue $1,010,600
Out in 1910 $6,000

352 Philadelphia
SIXTH NB OF PHILADELPHIA
{{ 10 L 11 S }}
Chartered 3/29/64
Receivership 9/29/34
Original Series <$VALUE
3x1-2 1-3000 <$400/$1250
4x5 1-5250 <$450
3x10-20 1-2900 <$750/$1250
Series 1875
4x5 1-4416 <$450
3x10-20 1-1848 <$750/$1250
Brown Back
4x5 1-5245 <$200
3x10-20 1-2099 <$200
50-100 1-387 <$1250/$1500
1902 Red Seal
3x10-20 1-5275 <$250
1902 Date Back
3x10-20 1-17700 <$125
1902 Plain Back
3x10-20 17701-46606 <$125
1929 Small Size
10 Type 1 1-4506 <$80
20 Type 1 1-1300 <$90
10 Type 2 1-5481 <$80
20 Type 2 1-1208 <$90
Total Issue $3,813,000
Out at close $149,995
Large out at close $8,325

560 Philadelphia
SOUTHWARK NB OF PHILADELPHIA
{{ 17 L }}
Organized 10/29/64
Closed 7/13/29
Original Series <$VALUE
4x5 1-16000 <$400
3x10-20 1-1669 <$750/$1250
Series 1875
4x5 1-12000 <$400
Brown Back
4x5 1-16032 <$175
3x10-20 1-2717 <$175/$225
1902 Red Seal
4x5 1-7950 <$175
3x10-20 1-6120 <$175/$225
1902 Date Back
4x5 1-36100 <$85
3x10-20 1-25960 <$85
1902 Plain Back
4x5 36101-49600 <$85
3x10-20 25961-34560 <$85
3x50-100 1-3192 <$350/$400
Total Issue $5,082,940
Out at close $250,000
Ch 3604 assumed circulation

3498 Philadelphia
SOUTHWESTERN NB OF PHILADELPHIA
{{ 3 L 7 S }}
Organized 4/13/86
Receivership 8/17/34
Brown Back <$VALUE
4x5 1-9267 <$500
3x10-20 1-4049 <$500
1902 Red Seal
4x5 1-1300 <$500
3x10-20 1-680 <$500
1902 Date Back
4x5 1-12310 <$250
3x10-20 1-11860 <$250
1929 Small Size
5 Type 1 1-2398 <$125
10 Type 1 1-1180 <$125
20 Type 1 1-278 <$125
5 Type 2 1-2236 <$135
10 Type 2 1-996 <$135
20 Type 2 1-264 <$135
Total Issue $1,409,510
Out at close $49,995
Large out at close $3,255

3468 Philadelphia
SPRING GARDEN NB OF PHILADELPHIA
{{ UNREPORTED }}
Organized 3/13/86
Receivership 5/21/91
Brown Back <$VALUE
4x5 1-2045 <$1250
3x10-20 1-1098 <$1250
Total Issue $95,800
Out in 1916 $450

3423 Philadelphia
TENTH NB OF PHILADELPHIA
{{ 15 L }}
Chartered 1885
Liquidated 7/1/29
Brown Back <$VALUE
4x5 1-7649 <$200
3x10-20 1-9021 <$200
1902 Red Seal
4x5 1-3500 <$225
3x10-20 1-1600 <$225
1902 Date Back
4x5 1-20150 <$100
3x10-20 1-16434 <$100
1902 Plain Back
4x5 20151-60967 <$100
3x10-20 16435-42040 <$100
Total Issue $4,075,370
Out at close $197,000

7522 Philadelphia
TEXTILE NB OF PHILADELPHIA
{{ 13 L U + 2 S }}
Chartered 12/04
Liquidated 1/1/30
1902 Red Seal <$VALUE
4x5 1-7700 <$300
3x10-20 1-3720 <$300
50-100 1-500 <$2250/$2500
1902 Date Back
4x5 1-29915 <$100
3x10-20 1-18234 <$100
50-100 1-200 <$350/$400
3x50-100 1-1618 <$350/$400
1902 Plain Back
4x5 29916-48873 <$100
3x10-20 18235-29583 <$100
3x50-100 1619-2177 <$350/$400
1929 Small Size
5 Type 1 1-993 <$250
10 Type 1 1-290 <$250
20 Type 1 1-120 <$250
50 Type 1 1-31 <$350
100 Type 1 1-5 <$450
Total Issue $3,519,750
Out at close $200,000
Large out at close $126,110

234 Philadelphia
THIRD NB OF PHILADELPHIA
{{ U + 11 L }}
Organized 2/4/64
Closed 7/29/26
Original Series <$VALUE
3x1-2 1-5000 <$350/$1000
4x5 1-8250 <$400
4x10 1-3750 <$750
3x20-50 1-1900 <$1250/$3500
Series 1875
4x5 1-1542 <$400
4x10 1-2270 <$750
3x20-50 1-1395 <$1250/$3500
Brown Back
4x5 1-2250 <$200
3x10-20 1-8361 <$200
1902 Red Seal
3x10-20 1-13400 <$225
1902 Date Back
4x5 1-45840 <$100
3x10-20 1-33175 <$100
Total Issue $4,532,690
Out at close $149,495
Ch 542 assumed circulation

13003 Philadelphia
TIOGA NB & TC OF PHILADELPHIA
{{ 22 S }}
Chartered 11/26 as Tioga NB, under which there was no issue. Issuing title adopted 8/20/29.
1929 Small Size <$VALUE
5 Type 1 1-4334 <$30
10 Type 1 1-2052 <$35
20 Type 1 1-616 <$45
5 Type 2 1-32980 <$30
10 Type 2 1-16945 <$35
20 Type 2 1-4992 <$45
Total Issue $761,250
Out in 1935 $294,150

570 Philadelphia
TRADESMENS NB OF PHILADELPHIA
Organized 11/9/64
2nd title: Tradesmens NB & TC 9/17/28
FIRST TITLE {{ 19 L }}
Original Series <$VALUE
4x5 1-12000 <$375
4x10 1-1500 <$750
50-100 1-350 <$3500
Series 1875
4x5 1-13998 <$375
4x10 1-500 <$750
50-100 1-266 <$3500
Brown Back
4x5 1-24762 <$125
3x10-20 1-14101 <$125/$175
50-100 1-5000 <$1250/$1500
1902 Red Seal
4x5 1-19200 <$150
3x10-20 1-9320 <$150/$175
50-100 1-1500 <$2250/$2500
1902 Date Back
4x5 1-50165 <$75
3x10-20 1-40134 <$75
50-100 1-800 <$350/$400
3x50-100 1-3456 <$350/$400
1902 Plain Back
4x5 50166-106647 <$75
3x10-20 40135-75257 <$75
3x50-100 3457-4104 <$350/$400
SECOND TITLE {{ U + 7 L 33 S }}
1902 Plain Back
4x5 1-3998 <$65
4x10 1-1500 <$65
3x10-20 1-908 <$65
3x50-100 1-143 <$350/$400
1929 Small Size
5 Type 1 1-23143 <$20
10 Type 1 1-9833 <$20
20 Type 1 1-2986 <$30
50 Type 1 1-480 <$110
100 Type 1 1-186 <$165
Total Issue $12,878,740
Out in 1935 $462,490
Large out 1935 $30,940

563 Philadelphia
UNION NB OF PHILADELPHIA
{{ 20 L }}
Chartered 11/3/64
Liquidated 12/3/27
Original Series <$VALUE
4x5 1-5000* <$375
3x10-20 1-1800 <$750/$1250
50-100 1-2700 <$3500
500-1000 1-80 <$150,000/$200,000
* 3251-3750 not issued
Series 1875
4x5 1-6085 <$375
3x10-20 1-5458 <$750/$1250
50-100 1-2400 <$3500
500-1000 1-11 <$150,000/$200,000
Brown Back
4x5 1-8250 <$150
50-100 1-6605 <$1250/$1500
1902 Red Seal
4x5 1-13000 <$175
4x10 1-4500 <$175
50-100 1-3134 <$2250/$2500
1902 Date Back
4x5 1-52750 <$60
4x10 1-49875 <$60
1902 Plain Back
4x5 52751-147033 <$60
4x10 49876-123256 <$60
Total Issue $11,412,850
Out at close $376,095

656 Philadelphia
WESTERN NB OF PHILADELPHIA
{{ 5 L }}
Chartered 12/29/64
Liquidated 3/28/12
Original Series <$VALUE
4x5 1-6600 <$500
3x10-20 1-2300 <$750/$1250
3x50-100 1-800 <$3500
3x500-1000 1-12 <$150,000/$200,000
Series 1875
4x5 1-7900 <$500
3x10-20 1-200 <$750/$1250
3x50-100 1-789 <$3500
Brown Back
4x5 1-5000 <$225
3x10-20 1-500 <$225
50-100 1-8312 <$1250/$1500
1902 Red Seal
4x5 1-15500 <$300
3x10-20 1-7400 <$300
50-100 1-1000 <$2250/$2500
1902 Date Back
4x5 1-2307 <$150
3x10-20 1-2782 <$150
50-100 1-3700 <$400/$500
3x50-100 1-196 <$400/$500
Total Issue $3,858,290
Out in 1912 $244,210

FNB of Philipsburg
SEE Ch 4832
Philipsburg NB of Philipsburg

5066 Centre
MOSHANNON NB OF PHILIPSBURG
{{ 10 L 14 S }}
Organized 5/3/97
Receivership 10/12/31
Brown Back <$VALUE
3x10-20 1-7600 <$275
1882 Date Back
3x10-20 1-9400 <$275
1882 Value Back
3x10-20 9401-10043 <$275
1902 Plain Back
4x5 1-22580 <$165
3x10-20 1-17720 <$165
1929 Small Size
5 Type 1 1-3818 <$85
10 Type 1 1-1828 <$85
20 Type 1 1-568 <$100
Total Issue $2,512,130
Out at close $148,320
Large out at close $15,900

4832 Centre
PHILIPSBURG NB OF PHILIPSBURG
Chartered 1892
2nd title: FNB of Philipsburg 3/25/93
FIRST TITLE {{ 1 L }}
Brown Back <$VALUE
4x5 1-625 <$600
SECOND TITLE {{ 9 L 15 S }}
Brown Back
4x5 626-10925 <$275
3x10-20 1-7490 <$275
1882 Date Back
4x5 1-4650 <$275
3x10-20 1-3490 <$275
1902 Date Back
4x5 1-3250 <$135
3x10-20 1-2600 <$135
1902 Plain Back
4x5 3251-22066 <$135
3x10-20 2601-14706 <$135
1929 Small Size
5 Type 1 1-4296 <$65
10 Type 1 1-1810 <$65
20 Type 1 1-514 <$75
5 Type 2 1-4118 <$85
10 Type 2 1-2028 <$85
20 Type 2 1-636 <$85
Total Issue $2,389,870
Out in 1935 $98,500
Large out 1935 $6,365

1936 Chester
THE FARMERS & MECHANICS NB OF PHOENIXVILLE
Chartered 2/15/72
2nd title: Farmers & Mechanics-NB of Phoenixville 3/24/32
FIRST TITLE {{ 4 L 2 S }}
Original Series <$VALUE
4x5 1-3100 <$750
3x10-20 1-1400 <$850/$1500
4x20 1-1725 <$1500
Series 1875
4x5 1-3657 <$750
3x10-20 1-1294 <$850/$1500
4x20 1-1365 <$1500
Brown Back
3x10-20 1-4000 <$500
1882 Date Back
3x10-20 1-755 <$500
1902 Date Back
3x10-20 1-1900 <$300
1902 Plain Back
3x10-20 1901-5644 <$300
1929 Small Size
10 Type 1 1-520 <$150
20 Type 1 1-148 <$150
SECOND TITLE {{ 19 S }}
1929 Small Size
10 Type 1 1-4074 <$100
20 Type 1 1-1052 <$100
10 Type 2 1-13895 <$100
20 Type 2 1-3834 <$100
Total Issue $1,672,260
Out in 1935 $270,495
Large out 1935 $8,735
Outstanding includes Ch 674

674 Chester
NB OF PHOENIXVILLE
{{ 5 L 5 S }}
Chartered 12/64
Closed 3/24/32
Original Series <$VALUE
4x5 1-4550 <$750
3x10-20 1-3451 <$850/$1500
50-100 1-477 <$4000
Series 1875
4x5 1-3710 <$750
3x10-20 1-3805 <$850/$1500
50-100 1-395 <$4000
Brown Back
4x5 1-7530 <$600
3x10-20 1-5412 <$600
50-100 1-314 <$1500/$1750
1902 Red Seal
4x5 1-1950 <$700
3x10-20 1-1340 <$700
1902 Date Back
4x5 1-5100 <$350
3x10-20 1-4000 <$350
1902 Plain Back
4x5 5101-12905 <$350
3x10-20 4001-9113 <$350
1929 Small Size
5 Type 1 1-1429 <$250
10 Type 1 1-680 <$250
20 Type 1 1-206 <$250
Total Issue $2,055,240
Out at close $49,575
Large out at close $7,695
Ch 1936 assumed circulation

11643 Lycoming
PICTURE ROCKS NB, PICTURE ROCKS
{{ 4 L U + 2 S }}
Chartered 3/20
Liquidated 4/8/32
1902 Plain Back <$VALUE
4x5 1-11377 <$450
1929 Small Size
5 Type 1 1-2413 <$375
Total Issue $299,930
Out at close $19,960
Large out at close $1,100

8151 Schuylkill
PINE GROVE NB, PINE GROVE
Chartered 3/06
2nd title: Pine Grove NB & TC 1/28/31
FIRST TITLE {{ 3 L 2 S }}
1902 Red Seal <$VALUE
3x10-20 1-340 <$800
1902 Date Back
3x10-20 1-1560 <$400
1902 Plain Back
3x10-20 1561-6264 <$400
1929 Small Size
10 Type 1 1-474 <$225
20 Type 1 1-160 <$225
SECOND TITLE {{ 6 S }}
1929 Small Size
10 Type 1 1-274 <$175
20 Type 1 1-66 <$175
10 Type 2 1-865 <$175
20 Type 2 1-215 <$175
Total Issue $415,150
Out in 1935 $25,000
Large out 1935 $1,050

5848 Allegheny
FNB OF PITCAIRN
{{ 3 L 3 S }}
Chartered 5/31/01
Receivership 3/2/32
Brown Back <$VALUE
4x5 1-1175 <$500
3x10-20 1-1070 <$500
1882 Date Back
4x5 1-2450 <$500
3x10-20 1-1820 <$500
1882 Value Back
4x5 2451-4005 <$500
3x10-20 1821-2780 <$500
1902 Plain Back
4x5 1-3749 <$300
3x10-20 1-2212 <$300
1929 Small Size
5 Type 1 1-702 <$275
10 Type 1 1-344 <$275
20 Type 1 1-109 <$275
Total Issue $536,460
Out at close $23,860
Large out at close $2,310

11892 Allegheny
PEOPLES NB OF PITCAIRN
{{ 2 L 2 S }}
Organized 12/1/20
Receivership 3/2/32
1902 Plain Back <$VALUE
3x10-20 1-4133 <$650
1929 Small Size
10 Type 1 1-622 <$350
20 Type 1 1-137 <$350
Total Issue $260,410
Out at close $23,800
Large out at close $1,940

722 Allegheny
ALLEGHENY NB OF PITTSBURGH
{{ 4 L }}
Organized 1/16/65
Receivership 5/18/08
Original Series <$VALUE
3x1-2 1-9000 <$400/$1000
4x5 1-7250 <$450
3x10-20 1-6400 <$750/$1250
50-100 1-2836 <$3500
Series 1875
4x5 1-5515 <$450
3x10-20 1-2996 <$750/$1250
50-100 1-1304 <$3500
Brown Back
4x5 1-3300 <$275
3x10-20 1-3528 <$275
50-100 1-2625 <$1250/$1500
1902 Red Seal
50-100 1-1410 <$2250/$2500
Total Issue $2,238,750
Out in 1916 $23,178

7581 Allegheny
AMERICAN NB OF PITTSBURG
{{ 1 L }}
Chartered 1/28/05
Liquidated 11/23/08
1902 Red Seal <$VALUE
4x5 1-13995 <$750
3x10-20 1-8733 <$750
Total Issue $716,550
Out in 1910 $36,195

5225 Allegheny
B OF PITTSBURGH N ASSOC, PITTSBURGH
{{ 33 L }}
Chartered 10/23/99
Receivership 9/21/31
Brown Back <$VALUE
4x5 1-98770 <$125
3x10-20 1-55005 <$135/$175
50-100 1-11563<$1250/$1500
1882 Date Back
4x5 1-202500 <$125
3x10-20 1-117500<$125/$175
50-100 1-2900 <$1250/$1500
3x50-100 1-3434<$1250/$1500
1882 Value Back
4x5 202501-269625 <$135
3x10-20 117501-157323 <$135/$185
1902 Plain Back
4x5 1-187040 <$60
3x10-20 1-111528 <$65
Total Issue $30,329,450
Out at close $131,245
Outstanding includes Ch 4910

619 Allegheny
CITIZENS NB OF PITTSBURGH
{{ 3 L }}
Chartered 12/10/64
Liquidated 7/22/02
Original Series <$VALUE
3x1-2 1-10000 <$400/$1000
4x5 1-16775 <$400
3x10-20 1-8490 <$750/$1250
3x50-100 1-450 <$3500
500 1-100 <$150,000
Series 1875
3x10-20 1-5000 <$750/$1250
50-100 1-1751 <$3500
Brown Back
50-100 1-3718 <$1250/$1500
Total Issue $2,217,950
Out in 1910 $21,599

2195 Allegheny
CITY NB OF PITTSBURGH
{{ UNREPORTED }}
Chartered 10/13/74
Liquidated 5/25/76
Original Series <$VALUE
3x1-2 1-1000 <$1250/$2000
4x5 1-1000 <$1250
3x10-20 1-1344<$1500/$2000
Total Issue $92,200
Out in 1910 $331

6567 Allegheny
COLONIAL NB OF PITTSBURG
{{ 1 L }}
Chartered 1/2/03
Liquidated 3/23/04
1902 Red Seal <$VALUE
3x10-20 1-1244 <$1000
Total Issue $62,200
Out in 1910 $1,850

4910 Allegheny
COLUMBIA NB OF PITTSBURGH
{{ 6 L }}
Chartered 1893
Closed 3/5/27
Brown Back <$VALUE
3x10-20 1-15800 <$300
1882 Date Back
4x5 1-9775 <$300
3x10-20 1-4796 <$300
1902 Date Back
4x5 1-16000 <$150
4x10 1-13665 <$150
3x10-20 1-2000 <$150
3x50-100 1-800 <$400/$500
1902 Plain Back
4x5 16001-28912 <$150
Total Issue $2,650,140
Out at close $98,200
Ch 5225 assumed circulation

2711 Allegheny
COMMERCIAL NB OF PITTSBURGH
{{ 8 L }}
Chartered 1882
Liquidated 11/6/15
Series 1875 <$VALUE
4x5 1-2986 <$450
3x10-20 1-4330 <$750/$1250
1902 Red Seal
4x5 1-10400 <$300
3x10-20 1-10800 <$300
50-100 1-2180 <$2250/$2500
1902 Date Back
4x5 1-25000 <$150
3x10-20 1-14200 <$150
50-100 1-44 <$400/$500
1902 Plain Back
4x5 25001-25205 <$150
3x10-20 14201-14308 <$150
Total Issue $2,577,320
Out in 1916 $158,330

6216 Allegheny
COSMOPOLITAN NB OF PITTSBURGH
{{ 2 L }}
Chartered 4/21/02
Receivership 9/5/08
1902 Red Seal <$VALUE
4x5 1-16695 <$600
3x10-20 1-8399 <$600
50-100 1-2949 <$2250/$2500
Total Issue $1,196,200
Out in 1916 $19,730

2236 Allegheny
DIAMOND NB OF PITTSBURGH
{{ 9 L 23 S }}
Chartered 3/23/75
Receivership 11/14/32
Original Series <$VALUE
3x10-20 1-900 <$750/$1250
Series 1875
3x10-20 1-3306 <$750/$1250
Brown Back
4x5 1-10000 <$250
3x10-20 1-5200 <$250
50-100 1-4310 <$1250/$1500
1882 Date Back
4x5 1-23500 <$250
3x10-20 1-17086 <$250
50-100 1-244 <$1250/$1500
1902 Date Back
4x5 1-5000 <$125
3x10-20 1-4000 <$125
1902 Plain Back
4x5 5001-62386 <$125
3x10-20 4001-39049 <$125
1929 Small Size
5 Type 1 1-10244 <$30
10 Type 1 1-5489 <$30
20 Type 1 1-1410 <$40
Total Issue $6,683,730
Out at close $295,320
Large out at close $23,220

2278 Allegheny
DUQUESNE NB OF PITTSBURGH
{{ 28 L 22 S }}
Chartered 6/19/75
Receivership 11/15/32
Original Series <$VALUE
3x10-20 1-900 <$750/$1250
Series 1875
3x10-20 1-4924 <$750/$1250
Brown Back
3x10-20 1-25900 <$150/$200
1882 Date Back
4x5 1-22755 <$125
3x10-20 1-33577 <$125/$175
1902 Date Back
4x5 1-7500 <$75
3x10-20 1-6000 <$75
1902 Plain Back
4x5 7501-105535 <$75
3x10-20 6001-69707 <$75
1929 Small Size
5 Type 1 1-17893 <$25
10 Type 1 1-9384 <$30
20 Type 1 1-2294 <$35
Total Issue $10,691,310
Out at close $493,335
Large out at close $43,090

1057 Allegheny
EXCHANGE NB OF PITTSBURGH
{{ 36 L 31 S }}
Organized 4/8/65
Receivership 10/23/31
Original Series <$VALUE
4x5 1-17000 <$400
3x10-20 1-11950<$750/$1250
50-100 1-2750 <$3500
Series 1875
4x5 1-22500 <$400
3x10-20 1-6352 <$750/$1250
50-100 1-3710 <$3500
Brown Back
4x5 1-16115 <$125
3x10-20 1-14001 <$125/$175
50-100 1-10955<$1250/$1500
1902 Red Seal
4x5 1-26500 <$100
4x10 1-7500 <$100
3x10-20 1-6900 <$100/$150
50-100 1-1500 <$2250/$2500
1902 Date Back
4x5 1-42000 <$50
4x10 1-30250 <$60
3x10-20 1-31500 <$60
50-100 1-1000 <$300/$350
3x50-100 1-1000 <$300/$350
1902 Plain Back
4x5 42001-141401 <$50
3x10-20 31501-114545 <$60
1929 Small Size
5 Type 1 1-18114 <$20
10 Type 1 1-8995 <$20
20 Type 1 1-2835 <$30
Total Issue $18,328,290
Out at close $742,980
Large out at close $93,500

F-Second NB of Pittsburgh
SEE Ch 252
Second NB of Pittsburgh

685 Allegheny
FARMERS DEPOSIT NB OF PITTSBURGH
{{ 50+ L 2U + 50 S }}
Chartered 1/65
Original Series <$VALUE
3x1-2 1-3000 <$350/$1000
4x5 1-8000 <$375
3x10-20 1-4300 <$750/$1250
50-100 1-1000 <$3500
Series 1875
50-100 1-586 <$3500
Brown Back
50-100 1-12844<$1250/$1500
1902 Red Seal
50-100 1-9600 <$2250/$2500
1902 Date Back
4x5 1-35000 <$50
3x10-20 1-10900 <$60
50-100 1-6000 <$300/$350
3x50-100 1-8000 <$300/$350
1902 Plain Back
4x5 35001-527715 <$50
3x10-20 10901-314002 <$60
3x50-100 8001-11928 <$300/$350
1929 Small Size
5 Type 1 1-184014 <$20
10 Type 1 1-57170 <$20
20 Type 1 1-18404 <$30
50 Type 1 1-3216 <$100
100 Type 1 1-1166 <$150
5 Type 2 1-34072 <$20
10 Type 2 1-11700 <$20
Total Issue $47,286,160
Out in 1935 $2,946,030
Large out 1935 $140,030

6023 Allegheny
FEDERAL NB OF PITTSBURGH
{{ 8 L }}
Chartered 11/16/01
Liquidated 1/20/14
Brown Back <$VALUE
4x5 1-20000 <$175
3x10-20 1-43400 <$175/$225
1882 Date Back
4x5 1-64545 <$150
3x10-20 1-44195 <$150/$200
Total Issue $6,070,650
Out in 1914 $384,415

Fifth NB of Pittsburgh
SEE Ch 1894
Farmers NB of Greensburg

FNB at Pittsburgh
SEE Ch 252
Second NB of Pittsburgh

48 Allegheny
FNB OF PITTSBURGH*
{{ 7 L }}
Chartered 8/63
Liquidated 6/29/82
*Rechartered as Ch 2745 which retook Ch 48 6/17/02
Liquidated 4/19/13
Original Series <$VALUE
4x5 1-8000 <$600
4x10 1-4000 <$850
4x20 1-2625 <$1500
Series 1875
4x5 1-15406 <$600
4x10 1-4791 <$850
4x20 1-3345 <$1500
1902 Red Seal
4x5 1-17500 <$350
3x10-20 1-22900 <$350
50-100 1-2200 <$2250/$2500
1902 Date Back
4x5 1-60930 <$200
3x10-20 1-36863 <$200
50-100 1-198 <$400/$500
Total Issue $6,213,810
Out at close $912,895
Ch 252 assumed circulation

2745 Allegheny
FNB OF PITTSBURGH
{{ 4 L }}
Chartered 1882
RETOOK Ch 48 6/17/02
Brown Back <$VALUE
4x5 1-7250 <$275
3x10-20 1-10913 <$275/$325
50-100 1-952 <$1250/$1500
Total Issue $833,450
Out in 1902 $500,000

FNB of Allegheny at Pittsburgh
SEE Ch 198
FNB of Allegheny

926 Allegheny
FNB OF BIRMINGHAM, PITTSBURGH
{{ 4 L 3 S }}
Chartered 3/22/65
Liquidated 1/19/31
Original Series <$VALUE
3x1-2 1-3300 <$500/$1250
4x5 1-3700 <$600
3x10-20 1-1800 <$850/$1500
Series 1875
3x1-2 1-1000 <$500/$1250
4x5 1-4890 <$600
3x10-20 1-1164 <$850/$1500
Brown Back
3x10-20 1-6584 <$400
1902 Red Seal
3x10-20 1-3700 <$500
1902 Date Back
3x10-20 1-8800 <$250
1902 Plain Back
3x10-20 8801-26885 <$250
1929 Small Size
10 Type 1 1-1474 <$250
20 Type 1 1-450 <$250
Total Issue $2,342,390
Out at close $95,980
Large out at close $13,590

13153 Allegheny
FORBES NB OF PITTSBURGH
{{ 16 S }}
Chartered 12/27
1929 Small Size <$VALUE
5 Type 1 1-12142 <$50
5 Type 2 1-59904 <$50
Total Issue $663,780
Out in 1935 $270,000

2415 Allegheny
FORT PITT NB OF PITTSBURGH
{{ 7 L }}
Chartered 3/6/79
Receivership 12/7/07
Series 1875 <$VALUE
4x5 1-4650 <$500
3x10-20 1-8678 <$750/$1250
Brown Back
4x5 1-17965 <$200
3x10-20 1-13242 <$200
50-100 1-878 <$1250/$1500
Total Issue $1,680,000
Out in 1916 $15,535

432 Allegheny
FOURTH NB OF PITTSBURGH
{{ 4 L }}
Chartered 5/64
Liquidated 2/14/10
Original Series <$VALUE
4x5 1-16750 <$500
3x10-20 1-4050 <$750/$1250
Series 1875
4x5 1-250 <$500
3x10-20 1-5800 <$750/$1250
Brown Back
4x5 1-6112 <$300
3x10-20 1-8561 <$300
1902 Red Seal
4x5 1-6000 <$350
3x10-20 1-4900 <$350
1902 Date Back
4x5 1-6050 <$200
3x10-20 1-3751 <$200
Total Issue $2,056,340
Out in 1910 $169,480

757 Allegheny
GERMAN NB OF PITTSBURGH
{{ 10 L }}
Chartered 1/26/65
Receivership 3/4/15
Original Series <$VALUE
3x1-2 1-2000 <$400/$1250
4x5 1-7300 <$450
3x10-20 1-4100 <$750/$1250
50-100 1-370 <$3500
Series 1875
4x5 1-5375 <$450
3x10-20 1-3504 <$750/$1250
50-100 1-550 <$3500
Brown Back
4x5 1-14608 <$200
3x10-20 1-9028 <$200
50-100 1-3885 <$1250/$1500
1902 Red Seal
4x5 1-20250 <$250
3x10-20 1-12700 <$250
50-100 1-400 <$2250/$2500
1902 Date Back
4x5 1-39775 <$100
3x10-20 1-26580 <$100
50-100 1-500 <$350/$400
3x50-100 1-200 <$350/$400
Total Issue $5,457,510
Out in 1916 $244,415

12414 Allegheny
HIGHLAND NB OF PITTSBURGH
{{ 5 L 10 S }}
Chartered 7/23
Closed 1932
1902 Plain Back <$VALUE
4x5 1-23786 <$200
3x10-20 1-16156 <$200
1929 Small Size
5 Type 1 1-5737 <$90
10 Type 1 1-2693 <$90
20 Type 1 1-739 <$100
Total Issue $1,705,890
Out at close $196,820
Large out at close $9,510

6806 Allegheny
INDUSTRIAL NB OF PITTSBURG
{{ UNREPORTED }}
Chartered 6/1/03
Liquidated 3/12/06
1902 Red Seal <$VALUE
4x5 1-2240 <$1000
3x10-20 1-2505 <$1000
50-100 1-340 <$2250/$2500
Total Issue $221,050
Out in 1910 $7,925

675 Allegheny
IRON CITY NB OF PITTSBURGH
{{ 7 L }}
Chartered 12/31/64
Liquidated 2/1/04
Original Series <$VALUE
3x1-2 1-14000 <$450/$1250
4x5 1-18750 <$500
3x10-20 1-3500 <$750/$1250
50-100 1-1038 <$3500
Series 1875
4x5 1-6177 <$500
3x10-20 1-4001 <$750/$1250
50-100 1-100 <$3500
Brown Back
4x5 1-4715 <$350
3x10-20 1-2585 <$350
50-100 1-1046 <$1250/$1500
Total Issue $1,494,740
Out in 1910 $14,530

7560 Allegheny
KEYSTONE NB OF PITTSBURG
{{ 5 L }}
Chartered 1/05
Liquidated 10/24/34
1902 Red Seal <$VALUE
4x5 1-16250 <$400
3x10-20 1-12250 <$400
1902 Date Back
4x5 1-48665 <$200
3x10-20 1-36334 <$200
1902 Plain Back
4x5 48666-48900 <$200
3x10-20 36335-37564 <$200
Total Issue $3,793,700
Out at close $6,380

****
4339 Allegheny
LIBERTY NB OF PITTSBURGH
{{ 8 L }}
Chartered 1890
Liquidated 6/20/23
Brown Back <$VALUE
4x5 1-13300 <$200
3x10-20 1-8440 <$200/$250
1882 Date Back
4x5 1-5165 <$200
3x10-20 1-2431 <$200/$250
1902 Date Back
4x5 1-13500 <$150
3x10-20 1-10100 <$150
1902 Plain Back
4x5 13501-30545 <$150
3x10-20 10101-23496 <$150
Total Issue $2,698,550
Out at close $188,645
****
4883 Allegheny
LINCOLN NB OF PITTSBURGH
{{ U + 4 L }}
Chartered 1893
Liquidated 4/30/15
Brown Back <$VALUE
3x10-20 1-15630 <$250/$300
50-100 1-2816 <$1250/$1500
1882 Date Back
3x10-20 1-13980 <$250/$300
50-100 1-360 <$1250/$1500
1902 Date Back
3x10-20 1-16747 <$250
3x50-100 1-866 <$400/$500
Total Issue $3,010,750
Out in 1915 $448,350
****
2237 Allegheny
MARINE NB OF PITTSBURGH
{{ 20 L }}
Chartered 3/23/75
Liquidated 2/26/29
Original Series <$VALUE
3x1-2 1-1000 <$350/$1000
4x5 1-1000 <$375
3x10-20 1-400 <$750/$1250
Series 1875
3x1-2 1-1520 <$350/$1000
4x5 1-13964 <$375
3x10-20 1-688 <$750/$1250
Brown Back
4x5 1-5750 <$125
3x10-20 1-12950 <$125/$175
1882 Date Back
4x5 1-27170 <$125
3x10-20 1-15808 <$125/$175
1902 Date Back
4x5 1-5000 <$50
3x10-20 1-4000 <$60
1902 Plain Back
4x5 5001-61640 <$50
3x10-20 4001-41269 <$60
Total Issue $5,758,830
Out at close $259,345
****
700 Allegheny
MECHANICS NB OF PITTSBURGH
{{ 2 L }}
Chartered 1/11/65
Liquidated 8/5/02
Original Series <$VALUE
3x1-2 1-14950 <$500/$1250
4x5 1-13500 <$600
3x10-20 1-1100 <$750/$1250
Series 1875
3x10-20 1-1334 <$750/$1250
Brown Back
3x10-20 1-14183 <$500
Total Issue $2,270,900
Out in 1910 $16,981
****
6301 Allegheny
MELLON NB OF PITTSBURGH
{{ U + 50 L 4U + 50 S }}
Chartered 6/13/02
1902 Red Seal <$VALUE
4x5 1-116200 <$100
3x10-20 1-109670 <$100/$135
50-100 1-3070 <$2250/$2500
1902 Date Back
4x5 1-374995 <$40
3x10-20 1-249000 <$50
50-100 1-4000 <$350/$400
3x50-100 1-7600 <$350/$400
1902 Plain Back
4x5 374996-1000000 <$40
4x5 A1-A363739 <$50
3x10-20 249001-696905 <$50
1929 Small Size
5 Type 1 1-514598 <$15
5 Type 2 1-689042* <$15
10 Type 2 1-109968 <$20
20 Type 2 1-21048 <$30
* 660523-660528 not issued

Total Issue $93,291,790
Out in 1935 $1,431,080
Large out 1935 $187,555
****
613 Allegheny
MERCHANTS & MANUFACTURERS NB OF PITTSBURGH
{{ 14 L }}
Chartered 12/8/64
Liquidated 2/1/04
Original Series <$VALUE
3x1-2 1-5000 <$350/$1000
4x5 1-13685 <$375
3x10-20 1-11100 <$750/$1250
50-100 1-2826 <$3500
500 1-100 <$150,000
Series 1875
4x5 1-5915 <$375
3x10-20 1-10522 <$750/$1250
50-100 1-3334 <$3500
500 1-169 <$150,000
Brown Back
4x5 1-16250 <$150
3x10-20 1-45000 <$150/$200
50-100 1-4650 <$1250/$1500
Total Issue $5,829,100
Out in 1910 $64,866
****
2279 Allegheny
METROPOLITAN NB OF PITTSBURGH
{{ 14 L }}
Chartered 6/21/75
Liquidated 7/25/24
Series 1875 <$VALUE
3x10-20 1-10655 <$750/$1250
Brown Back
4x5 1-11500 <$200
3x10-20 1-26550 <$200
1882 Date Back
4x5 1-35680 <$200
3x10-20 1-20753 <$200
1902 Date Back
3x10-20 1-4000 <$100
1902 Plain Back
3x10-20 4001-22134 <$100
Total Issue $4,948,200
Out at close $186,900
****
3874 Allegheny
MONONGAHELA NB OF PITTSBURGH
{{ 18 L 21 S }}
Chartered 4/25/88
Receivership 10/29/31
Brown Back <$VALUE
4x5 1-16390 <$200
3x10-20 1-11585 <$200
50-100 1-925 <$1250/$1500
1902 Red Seal
4x5 1-2000 <$225
3x10-20 1-1200 <$225
1902 Date Back
4x5 1-42330 <$50
3x10-20 1-34668 <$60
1902 Plain Back
4x5 42331-111265 <$50
3x10-20 34669-81724 <$60
1929 Small Size
5 Type 1 1-11451 <$35
10 Type 1 1-5660 <$40
20 Type 1 1-1383 <$50
Total Issue $8,306,390
Out at close $386,860
Large out at close $36,200
****
NB of America at Pittsburgh
SEE Ch 2261
German NB of Allegheny
****
14271 Allegheny
NB OF AMERICA IN PITTSBURGH
{{ U + 4 S }}
Chartered 9/34
1929 Small Size <$VALUE
5 Type 2 1-6934 <$250
Total Issue $34,670
Out in 1935 $113,705
Large out 1935 $12,205
Outstanding includes Ch 2261
****
4918 Allegheny
NB OF WESTERN PENNSYLVANIA AT PITTSBURGH
Chartered 1893
Liquidated 12/27/23
2nd title: Western NB of Pittsburgh 5/17/13
FIRST TITLE {{ 6 L }}
Brown Back <$VALUE
3x10-20 1-45000 <$300
1882 Date Back
3x10-20 1-45504 <$300

SECOND TITLE {{ 7 L }}
1902 Date Back
3x50-100 1-11059 <$350/$400
Total Issue $7,289,950
Out at close $433,500
****
4222 Allegheny
PENNSYLVANIA NB OF PITTSBURGH
{{ 8 L 4 S }}
Chartered 1890
Liquidated 7/1/30
Brown Back <$VALUE
4x5 1-21650 <$300
3x10-20 1-5400 <$300
1882 Date Back
4x5 1-2370 <$300
3x10-20 1-1077 <$300
1902 Date Back
4x5 1-8580 <$135
3x10-20 1-6868 <$135
1902 Plain Back
4x5 8581-38147 <$135
3x10-20 6869-24047 <$135
1929 Small Size
5 Type 1 1-1902 <$125
10 Type 1 1-919 <$125
20 Type 1 1-180 <$125
Total Issue $2,903,340
Out at close $130,450
Large out at close $24,200
****
727 Allegheny
PEOPLES NB OF PITTSBURGH
{{ 17 L }}
Chartered 1/65
Liquidated 9/3/21
Original Series <$VALUE
4x5 1-21500 <$375
3x10-20 1-11900 <$750/$1250
50-100 1-2300 <$3500
500-1000 1-40 <$150,000/$200,000
Series 1875
4x5 1-11145 <$375
3x10-20 1-16000 <$750/$1250
50-100 1-2167 <$3500
Brown Back
4x5 1-4250 <$125
3x10-20 1-61999 <$125/$175
50-100 1-6435 <$1250/$1500
1902 Red Seal
4x5 1-31500 <$100
3x10-20 1-23400 <$100/$135
1902 Date Back
4x5 1-74330 <$50
3x10-20 1-63668 <$60
1902 Plain Back
4x5 74331-135579 <$50
3x10-20 63669-102217 <$60
Total Issue $16,550,580
Out at close $956,895
Ch 252 assumed circulation
****
13701 Allegheny
PITT NB OF PITTSBURGH
{{ 36 S }}
Chartered 6/33
1929 Small Size <$VALUE
5 Type 2 1-122110 <$20
10 Type 2 1-44973 <$20
20 Type 2 1-7795 <$30
Total Issue $1,216,180
Out in 1935 $485,400
****
668 Allegheny
PITTSBURGH NB OF COMMERCE
{{ 14 L }}
Chartered 12/30/64
Liquidated 5/2/03
Original Series <$VALUE
3x1-2 1-5000 <$350/$1000
4x5 1-12500 <$375
3x10-20 1-5300 <$750/$1250
50-100 1-2235 <$3500
500 1-200 <$150,000
Series 1875
3x1-2 1-5880 <$350/$1000
4x5 1-4750 <$375
3x10-20 1-11000 <$750/$1250
50-100 1-282 <$3500
50 283-2429 <$3500
500 1-50 <$150,000
Brown Back
4x5 1-3350 <$125
3x10-20 1-2800 <$125/$150
50-100 1-6605 <$1250/$1500
Total Issue $3,022,050
Out in 1910 $45,893
****

****
6153 Allegheny
REPUBLIC NB OF PITTSBURG
{{ UNREPORTED }}
Chartered 3/10/02
Liquidated 10/30/03
1902 Red Seal <$VALUE
3x10-20 1-1449 <$1250
Total Issue $72,450
Out in 1910 $1,870
****
252 Allegheny
SECOND NB OF PITTSBURGH
Organized 2/13/64
2nd title: F-Second NB of Pittsburgh 4/21/13
3rd title: FNB at Pittsburgh 1/18/18
FIRST TITLE {{ 8 L }}
Original Series <$VALUE
4x5 1-4400 <$400
4x10 1-6125 <$750
50-100 1-1630 <$3500
Series 1875
4x5 1-1435 <$400
4x10 1-3505 <$750
50-100 1-2132 <$3500
Brown Back
3x10-20 1-4662 <$150/$200
50-100 1-7178 <$1250/$1500
1902 Red Seal
4x5 1-20000 <$150
3x10-20 1-30000 <$150/$200
50-100 1-6300 <$2250/$2500
1902 Date Back
4x5 1-47990 <$65
3x10-20 1-31000 <$75
50-100 1-1095 <$350/$400
SECOND TITLE {{ U + 6 L }}
1902 Date Back
4x5 1-78000 <$85
3x10-20 1-55000 <$100
3x50-100 1-3000 <$350/$400
1902 Plain Back
4x5 78001-178000 <$85
3x10-20 55001-117000 <$100
THIRD TITLE {{ 38 L 50+ S }}
1902 Plain Back
4x5 1-1000000 <$40
4x5 A1-A251598 <$40
3x10-20 1-499431 <$50
1929 Small Size
5 Type 1 1-419400 <$15
10 Type 1 1-86666 <$20
20 Type 1 1-29752 <$30
5 Type 2 1-668964 <$15
10 Type 2 1-83439 <$20
20 Type 2 1-41113 <$30
Total Issue $94,412,230
Out in 1935 $4,754,120
Large out 1935 $249,850
Outstanding includes Ch 2745 and Ch 727
****
Second NB of Pittsburgh
Second NB of Allegheny, Pittsburgh
SEE Ch 776
Second NB of Allegheny
****
2281 Allegheny
SMITHFIELD NB OF PITTSBURGH
{{ UNREPORTED }}
Chartered 6/26/75
Liquidated 12/16/78
Original Series <$VALUE
50-100 1-650 <$4000
Total Issue $97,500
Out in 1910 $600
****
291 Allegheny
THIRD NB OF PITTSBURGH
{{ 24 L 18 S }}
Organized 12/30/63
Receivership 1/28/32
Original Series <$VALUE
3x1-2 1-1000 <$350/$1000
4x5 1-4750 <$375
3x10-20 1-8900 <$750/$1250
50-100 1-1134 <$3500
Series 1875
3x10-20 1-2901 <$750/$1250
50-100 1-1300 <$3500
Brown Back
3x10-20 1-22610 <$125/$175
50-100 1-700 <$1250/$1500
1902 Red Seal
3x10-20 1-26000 <$125/$175
1902 Date Back
3x10-20 1-50000 <$60
1902 Plain Back
3x10-20 50001-138362 <$60

1929 Small Size
10 Type 1 1-10463 <$30
20 Type 1 1-2700 <$40
Total Issue $11,460,530
Out at close $415,220
Large out at close $53,410
****
678 Allegheny
TRADESMEN'S NB OF PITTSBURGH
{{ 7 L }}
Chartered 12/31/64
Liquidated 3/29/04
Original Series <$VALUE
3x1-2 1-3000 <$350/$1000
4x5 1-17940 <$400
4x10 1-5425 <$750
3x20-50 1-1050 <$1250/$3500
100-100 1-100 <$3500
500 1-50 <$150,000
Series 1875
4x5 1-7525 <$400
4x10 1-4475 <$750
3x20-50 1-2296 <$1250/$3500
Brown Back
4x5 1-3000 <$225
3x10-20 1-11881 <$225
50-100 1-334 <$1250/$1500
Total Issue $2,037,510
Out in 1910 $19,753
****
705 Allegheny
UNION NB OF PITTSBURGH
{{ 21 L 50+ S }}
Chartered 1/65
Original Series <$VALUE
3x1-2 1-4000 <$350/$1000
4x5 1-6000 <$375
3x10-20 1-3850 <$750/$1250
50-100 1-1400 <$3500
Series 1875
4x5 1-1790 <$375
3x10-20 1-1760 <$750/$1250
50-100 1-800 <$3500
Brown Back
4x5 1-7107 <$110
3x10-20 1-9174 <$125/$175
50-100 1-4420 <$1250/$1500
1902 Red Seal
4x5 1-20500 <$110
3x10-20 1-10700 <$125/$175
50-100 1-990 <$2250/$2500
1902 Date Back
4x5 1-64500 <$50
3x10-20 1-40600 <$65
50-100 1-400 <$350/$400
3x50-100 1-1000 <$350/$400
1902 Plain Back
4x5 64501-186810 <$50
3x10-20 40601-125016 <$60
1929 Small Size
5 Type 1 1-31918 <$15
10 Type 1 1-19412 <$20
20 Type 1 1-4656 <$30
Total Issue $16,108,120
Out in 1935 $439,500
Large out 1935 $38,570
****
Western NB of Pittsburgh
SEE Ch 4918
NB of Western Pennsylvania at Pittsburgh
****
5017 Allegheny
UNITED STATES NB OF PITTSBURGH
{{ 8 L }}
Chartered 1895
Liquidated 10/19/14
Brown Back <$VALUE
4x5 1-7270 <$250
3x10-20 1-10192 <$250
1882 Date Back
4x5 1-13500 <$250
3x10-20 1-7730 <$250
Total Issue $1,311,500
Out at close $140,900
****
6725 Allegheny
WASHINGTON NB OF PITTSBURG
{{ 4 L }}
Chartered 4/03
Liquidated 5/23/10
1902 Red Seal <$VALUE
4x5 1-12455 <$500
50-100 1-2940 <$2250/$2500
1902 Date Back
4x5 1-5765 <$275
50-100 1-215 <$500/$600
Total Issue $837,650
Out in 1910 $152,050
****

****
478 Luzerne
FNB OF PITTSTON
{{ 16 L 26 S }}
Chartered 7/64
Original Series <$VALUE
3x1-2 1-8000 <$350/$1000
4x5 1-18750 <$375
3x10-20 1-10400 <$750/$1250
Series 1875
4x5 1-6250 <$375
3x10-20 1-10856 <$750/$1250
Brown Back
3x10-20 1-11169 <$200/$250
1902 Red Seal
4x5 1-9000 <$200
3x10-20 1-9500 <$200/$250
1902 Date Back
4x5 1-15250 <$75
3x10-20 1-22800 <$85
1902 Plain Back
4x5 15251-20137 <$75
3x10-20 22801-52500 <$85
1929 Small Size
5 Type 1 1-39076 <$30
5 Type 2 1-217512 <$30
Total Issue $8,103,830
Out in 1935 $626,745
Large out 1935 $16,160
****
11865 Luzerne
LIBERTY NB OF PITTSTON
{{ 4 L 15 S }}
Chartered 11/20
1902 Plain Back <$VALUE
4x5 1-12900 <$250
3x10-20 1-8654 <$250
1929 Small Size
5 Type 1 1-4992 <$60
10 Type 1 1-3714 <$60
20 Type 1 1-968 <$60
5 Type 2 1-21716 <$60
10 Type 2 1-9489 <$60
20 Type 2 1-2944 <$60
Total Issue $1,441,810
Out in 1935 $196,950
Large out 1935 $2,060
****
6581 Westmoreland
PLEASANT UNITY NB, PLEASANT UNITY
{{ 3 L 5 S }}
Chartered 1/03
Receivership 10/27/33
1902 Red Seal <$VALUE
4x5 1-1245 <$1000
3x10-20 1-958 <$1000
1902 Date Back
4x5 1-2375 <$500
3x10-20 1-1500 <$500
1902 Plain Back
4x5 2376-7700 <$500
3x10-20 1501-4496 <$500
1929 Small Size
5 Type 1 1-844 <$350
10 Type 1 1-516 <$350
20 Type 1 1-149 <$350
Total Issue $525,760
Out at close $24,700
Large out at close $2,130
****
854 Venango
FNB OF PLUMER
{{ UNREPORTED }}
Chartered 3/1/65
Liquidated 8/25/68
Original Series <$VALUE
4x5 1-1250 <$1250
3x10-20 1-1250 <$1500/$2000
Total Issue $87,500
Out in 1910 $1,055
****
7887 Indiana
FNB OF PLUMVILLE
{{ 1 L 2 S }}
Chartered 8/05
Receivership 10/13/33
1902 Red Seal <$VALUE
3x10-20 1-560 <$1250
1902 Date Back
3x10-20 1-920* <$650
1902 Plain Back
3x10-20 1121-2657* <$650
* 921-1120 not marked
1929 Small Size
10 Type 1 1-282 <$400
20 Type 1 1-76 <$400
Total Issue $186,890
Out at close $10,000
Large out at close $290
****

****
707 Luzerne
FNB OF PLYMOUTH
{{ 10 L 18 S }}
Chartered 1/65
Original Series <$VALUE
3x1-2 1-2000 <$400/$1000
4x5 1-3500 <$450
3x10-20 1-2010 <$750/$1250
Series 1875
4x5 1-2410 <$450
3x10-20 1-1664 <$750/$1250
Brown Back
3x10-20 1-6644 <$275
1902 Red Seal
3x10-20 1-2950 <$300
1902 Date Back
3x10-20 1-8200 <$150
1902 Plain Back
3x10-20 8201-29360 <$150
1929 Small Size
10 Type 1 1-4774 <$60
20 Type 1 1-1318 <$70
10 Type 2 1-9785 <$65
20 Type 2 1-2738 <$75
Total Issue $2,856,810
Out in 1935 $158,460
Large out 1935 $5,100
****
6881 Luzerne
PLYMOUTH NB, PLYMOUTH
{{ 7 L 13 S }}
Chartered 7/03
1902 Red Seal <$VALUE
3x10-20 1-6400 <$400
1902 Date Back
3x10-20 1-10400 <$200
1902 Plain Back
3x10-20 10401-32191 <$200
1929 Small Size
10 Type 1 1-3400 <$75
20 Type 1 1-906 <$85
10 Type 2 1-6080 <$75
20 Type 2 1-1632 <$85
Total Issue $2,335,710
Out in 1935 $96,100
Large out 1935 $4,200
****
6114 Fayette
FNB OF POINT MARION
{{ 2 L 7 S }}
Chartered 1/31/02
1902 Red Seal <$VALUE
3x10-20 1-1800 <$700
1902 Date Back
3x10-20 1-2160 <$350
1902 Plain Back (dated 1901)
3x10-20 2161-3562 <$350
1902 Plain Back (dated 1921)
3x10-20 1-3138 <$350
1929 Small Size
10 Type 1 1-1028 <$135
20 Type 1 1-294 <$135
10 Type 2 1-2224 <$150
20 Type 2 1-696 <$150
Total Issue $558,120
Out in 1935 $48,400
Large out 1935 $1,300
****
9503 Fayette
PEOPLES NB OF POINT MARION
{{ 3 L 6 S }}
Chartered 8/09
Receivership 10/8/31
1902 Date Back <$VALUE
3x10-20 1-4940 <$350
1902 Plain Back
3x10-20 4941-14065 <$350
1929 Small Size
10 Type 1 1-957 <$175
20 Type 1 1-255 <$175
Total Issue $791,270
Out at close $49,400
Large out at close $4,440
****
6066 McKean
CITIZENS NB OF PORT ALLEGANY
{{ 1 L }}
Chartered 12/26/01
Liquidated 5/4/12
Brown Back <$VALUE
4x5 1-1125 <$850
3x10-20 1-840 <$850
1882 Date Back
4x5 1-570 <$850
3x10-20 1-433 <$850
Total Issue $97,550
Out in 1912 $10,105
****
3877 McKean
FNB OF PORT ALLEGANY
{{ 3 L 10 S }}
Chartered 5/2/88
Brown Back <$VALUE
4x5 1-8491 <$500
3x10-20 1-430 <$500
1902 Red Seal
3x10-20 1-200 <$600
1902 Date Back
3x10-20 1-1420 <$300
1902 Plain Back
3x10-20 1421-5464 <$300
1929 Small Size
10 Type 1 1-1396 <$125
20 Type 1 1-320 <$135
10 Type 2 1-3565 <$150
20 Type 2 1-926 <$150
Total Issue $650,850
Out in 1935 $71,700
Large out 1935 $1,050
****
11369 Juniata
FNB OF PORT ROYAL
{{ 2 L 6 S }}
Chartered 6/19
1902 Plain Back <$VALUE
3x10-20 1-4659 <$500
1929 Small Size
10 Type 1 1-812 <$175
20 Type 1 1-274 <$200
10 Type 2 1-1271 <$200
20 Type 2 1-343 <$200
Total Issue $334,120
Out in 1935 $28,900
Large out 1935 $1,000
****
11373 Juniata
PORT ROYAL NB, PORT ROYAL
{{ 3 L 8 S }}
Chartered 6/19
1902 Plain Back <$VALUE
4x5 1-11782 <$350
1929 Small Size
5 Type 1 1-3440 <$125
10 Type 1 1-1114 <$125
20 Type 1 1-324 <$135
5 Type 2 1-3112 <$150
10 Type 2 1-1713 <$150
20 Type 2 1-513 <$150
Total Issue $607,510
Out in 1935 $58,550
Large out 1935 $820
****
7367 Cambria
FNB OF PORTAGE
{{ 4 L 2 S }}
Chartered 8/04
Receivership 3/25/31
1902 Red Seal <$VALUE
3x10-20 1-456 <$600
1902 Date Back
3x10-20 1-2950 <$275
1902 Plain Back
3x10-20 2951-7873 <$275
1929 Small Size
10 Type 1 1-421 <$350
20 Type 1 1-116 <$350
Total Issue $455,360
Out at close $25,000
Large out at close $2,820
****
6665 Northampton
PORTLAND NB, PORTLAND
{{ 4 L 6 S }}
Chartered 3/03
Liquidated 6/23/32
1902 Red Seal <$VALUE
3x10-20 1-1800 <$450
1902 Date Back
3x10-20 1-2520 <$225
1902 Plain Back
3x10-20 2521-11851 <$225
1929 Small Size
10 Type 1 1-882 <$165
20 Type 1 1-247 <$165
Total Issue $765,110
Out at close $39,980
Large out 1935 $2,890
Ch 13606 assumed circulation
****
13606 Northampton
PORTLAND NB, PORTLAND
{{ U + 9 S }}
Chartered 3/32
1929 Small Size <$VALUE
5 Type 1 1-774 <$100
10 Type 1 1-894 <$100
20 Type 1 1-288 <$100
5 Type 2 1-5688 <$125
10 Type 2 1-2808 <$125
20 Type 2 1-888 <$125
Total Issue $185,700
Out in 1935 $86,790
Large out 1935 $2,890
Outstanding includes Ch 6665
****
4714 Montgomery
CITIZENS NB OF POTTSTOWN
Chartered 1892
2nd title: Citizens NB & TC 8/15/28
FIRST TITLE {{ 8 L }}
Brown Back <$VALUE
4x5 1-8750 <$300
3x10-20 1-7300 <$300
1882 Date Back
4x5 1-4445 <$300
3x10-20 1-2718 <$300
1902 Date Back
3x10-20 1-5200 <$135
1902 Plain Back
3x10-20 5201-22851 <$135
SECOND TITLE {{ 3 L 12 S }}
1902 Plain Back
3x10-20 1-928 <$150
1929 Small Size
10 Type 1 1-4160 <$60
20 Type 1 1-986 <$80
10 Type 2 1-4897 <$85
20 Type 2 1-1276 <$90
Total Issue $2,396,160
Out in 1935 $129,645
Large out 1935 $5,445
****
608 Montgomery
NB OF POTTSTOWN
{{ 15 L 23 S }}
Chartered 12/64
Original Series <$VALUE
3x1-2 1-400 <$350/$850
4x5 1-6800 <$400
3x10-20 1-5850 <$750/$1250
50-100 1-350 <$3500
Series 1875
4x5 1-5400 <$400
3x10-20 1-6540 <$750/$1250
Brown Back
4x5 1-5635 <$200
3x10-20 1-8743 <$200
50-100 1-1197 <$1250/$1500
1902 Red Seal
3x10-20 1-13500 <$200/$225
1902 Date Back
3x10-20 1-27400 <$100
1902 Plain Back
3x10-20 27401-81949 <$100
1929 Small Size
10 Type 1 1-8916 <$35
20 Type 1 1-2478 <$45
10 Type 2 1-11091 <$35
20 Type 2 1-1597 <$45
Total Issue $7,395,020
Out in 1935 $257,110
Large out 1935 $17,710
****
3494 Montgomery
N IRON B OF POTTSTOWN
{{ 16 L 21 S }}
Chartered 1886
Brown Back <$VALUE
4x5 1-6695 <$250
3x10-20 1-13411 <$250
1902 Red Seal
3x10-20 1-5000 <$275
1902 Date Back
3x10-20 1-18500 <$125
1902 Plain Back
3x10-20 18501-56529 <$125
1929 Small Size
10 Type 1 1-8064 <$40
20 Type 1 1-2178 <$40
10 Type 2 1-10452 <$40
20 Type 2 1-3087 <$50
Total Issue $4,792,360
Out in 1935 $260,540
Large out 1935 $9,420
****
1152 Schuylkill
GOVERNMENT NB OF POTTSVILLE
{{ 4 L }}
Chartered 5/15/65
Liquidated 11/8/97
Original Series <$VALUE
3x1-2 1-6000 <$400/$1000
4x5 1-6500 <$500
3x10-20 1-4200 <$750/$1250
50-100 1-2306 <$3500
Series 1875
4x5 1-3255 <$500
3x10-20 1-1801 <$750/$1250
50-100 1-167 <$3500
Brown Back
4x5 1-4435 <$350
3x10-20 1-2995 <$350
Total Issue $1,134,550
Out in 1910 $5,732
****
8964 Schuylkill
MERCHANTS NB OF POTTSVILLE
{{ 5 L 16 S }}
Chartered 12/07
Receivership 10/12/34
1902 Red Seal <$VALUE
3x10-20 1-2500 <$350
1902 Date Back
3x10-20 1-7500 <$150
1902 Plain Back
3x10-20 7501-22258 <$150
1929 Small Size
10 Type 1 1-2962 <$60
20 Type 1 1-966 <$70
10 Type 2 1-3903 <$60
20 Type 2 1-666 <$70
Total Issue $1,583,890
Out at close $125,000
Large out at close $3,330
****
649 Schuylkill
MINERS NB OF POTTSVILLE
{{ 15 L 25 S }}
Chartered 12/64
Original Series <$VALUE
4x5 1-7500 <$400
3x10-20 1-7000 <$750/$1250
50-100 1-1000 <$3500
Series 1875
4x5 1-3000 <$400
3x10-20 1-7384 <$750/$1250
50-100 1-1000 <$3500
Brown Back
4x5 1-5500 <$175
3x10-20 1-30827 <$175/$200
50-100 1-3167 <$1250/$1500
1902 Red Seal
3x10-20 1-20000 <$200/$250
1902 Date Back
3x10-20 1-46500 <$100
1902 Plain Back
3x10-20 46501-83296 <$100
1929 Small Size
5 Type 1 1-4100 <$30
10 Type 1 1-5976 <$30
20 Type 1 1-1704 <$40
5 Type 2 1-504 <$30
10 Type 2 1-16864 <$30
20 Type 2 1-4731 <$40
Total Issue $9,620,900
Out in 1935 $440,125
Large out 1935 $18,775
****
1663 Schuylkill
PENNSYLVANIA NB OF POTTSVILLE
Chartered 1866
2nd title: Pennsylvania NB & TC 8/27/28
FIRST TITLE {{ 10 L }}
Original Series <$VALUE
3x1-2 1-3000 <$350/$1000
4x5 1-3600 <$400
3x10-20 1-1660 <$750/$1250
Series 1875
3x10-20 1-7981 <$750/$1250
Brown Back
3x10-20 1-8616 <$200/$250
1902 Red Seal
3x10-20 1-2000 <$250/$275
1902 Date Back
3x10-20 1-10500 <$125
1902 Plain Back
3x10-20 10501-26210 <$125
SECOND TITLE {{ 1 L 15 S }}
1902 Plain Back
3x10-20 1-1118 <$150
1929 Small Size
10 Type 1 1-3102 <$60
20 Type 1 1-914 <$70
10 Type 2 1-2888 <$60
20 Type 2 1-837 <$70
Total Issue $2,807,670
Out in 1935 $100,000
Large out 1935 $5,300
****
521 Lackawanna
FNB OF PROVIDENCE
{{ UNREPORTED }}
Chartered 9/27/64
Liquidated 3/1/67
Original Series <$VALUE
4x5 1-2500 <$1500
3x10-20 1-800 <$1500/$2000
Total Issue $90,000
Out in 1910 $1,110
****
9863 Jefferson
COUNTY NB OF PUNXSUTAWNEY
{{ 6 L 12 S }}
Chartered 10/10
1902 Date Back <$VALUE
3x10-20 1-6700 <$225
1902 Plain Back
3x10-20 6701-25132 <$225
1929 Small Size
10 Type 1 1-2880 <$100
20 Type 1 1-762 <$100
10 Type 2 1-3854 <$125
20 Type 2 1-975 <$125
Total Issue $1,578,880
Out in 1935 $97,300
Large out 1935 $4,600
****
5965 Jefferson
FARMERS NB OF PUNXSUTAWNEY
{{ UNREPORTED }}
Chartered 9/14/01
Liquidated 4/1/08
Brown Back <$VALUE
3x10-20 1-3121 <$1500
Total Issue $156,050
Out in 1910 $8,980
****
3030 Jefferson
FNB OF PUNXSUTAWNEY
{{ 1 L }}
Chartered 8/15/83
Liquidated 8/17/09
Brown Back <$VALUE
3x10-20 1-5264 <$1000
1902 Red Seal
50-100 1-1606 <$2250/$2500
1902 Date Back
50-100 1-138 <$1000/$1250
Total Issue $524,800
Out in 1910 $52,010
****
5702 Jefferson
PUNXSUTAWNEY NB, PUNXSUTAWNEY
{{ 5 L 15 S }}
Chartered 2/6/01
Brown Back <$VALUE
3x10-20 1-2140 <$400
1882 Date Back
3x10-20 1-12200* <$400
1882 Value Back
3x10-20 13001-18028* <$400
* 12201-13000 not marked
1902 Plain Back
3x10-20 1-15518 <$225
1929 Small Size
10 Type 1 1-3420 <$75
20 Type 1 1-1000 <$85
5 Type 2 1-324 <$85
10 Type 2 1-4522 <$85
20 Type 2 1-1075 <$85
Total Issue $2,177,840
Out in 1935 $121,800
Large out 1935 $6,325
****
6465 Bucks
MERCHANTS NB OF QUAKERTOWN
{{ 7 L 10 S }}
Chartered 10/22/02
1902 Red Seal <$VALUE
3x10-20 1-3775 <$350
1902 Date Back
3x10-20 1-4500 <$175
1902 Plain Back
3x10-20 4501-14034 <$175
1929 Small Size
10 Type 1 1-1536 <$100
20 Type 1 1-436 <$125
10 Type 2 1-3477 <$125
20 Type 2 1-988 <$125
Total Issue $1,089,460
Out in 1935 $68,800
Large out 1935 $2,120
****
2366 Bucks
QUAKERTOWN NB, QUAKERTOWN
{{ 18 L 15 S }}
Chartered 7/21/77
Series 1875 <$VALUE
4x5 1-3050 <$450
3x10-20 1-8507 <$750/$1250
Brown Back
3x10-20 1-9500 <$275
1882 Date Back
3x10-20 1-7500* <$275
1882 Value Back
3x10-20 8001-9157* <$275
* 7501-8000 not marked
1902 Plain Back
4x10 1-22921 <$150
1929 Small Size
10 Type 1 1-5290 <$60
10 Type 2 1-13624 <$65
Total Issue $2,789,680
Out in 1935 $138,900
Large out 1935 $4,390
****
8045 Lancaster
FARMERS NB OF QUARRYVILLE
{{ 3 L 2 S }}
Chartered 1/06
1902 Red Seal <$VALUE
3x10-20 1-595 <$1000
1902 Date Back
3x10-20 1-1550 <$450
1902 Plain Back
3x10-20 1551-3374 <$450
1929 Small Size
10 Type 1 1-312 <$400
20 Type 1 1-106 <$400
10 Type 2 1-455 <$400
20 Type 2 1-122 <$400
Total Issue $236,880
Out in 1935 $12,500
Large out 1935 $650
****
3067 Lancaster
QUARRYVILLE NB, QUARRYVILLE
{{ 5 L 12 S }}
Chartered 1883
Brown Back <$VALUE
3x10-20 1-3622 <$500
1902 Red Seal
3x10-20 1-2650 <$500
1902 Date Back
3x10-20 1-5200 <$250
1902 Plain Back
3x10-20 5201-14767 <$250
1929 Small Size
10 Type 1 1-1864 <$125
20 Type 1 1-460 <$150
5 Type 2 1-312 <$150
10 Type 2 1-1767 <$150
20 Type 2 1-549 <$150
Total Issue $1,249,200
Out in 1935 $58,150
Large out 1935 $2,735
****
9508 Lycoming
FNB OF RALSTON
{{ 2 L 5 S }}
Chartered 8/09
1902 Date Back <$VALUE
3x10-20 1-2730 <$375
1902 Plain Back
3x10-20 2731-7198 <$375
1929 Small Size
10 Type 1 1-766 <$175
20 Type 1 1-204 <$175
10 Type 2 1-787 <$175
20 Type 2 1-350 <$175
Total Issue $445,210
Out in 1935 $25,000
Large out 1935 $440
****
2473 Berks
COMMERCIAL NB OF READING
{{ UNREPORTED }}
Chartered 4/14/80
Liquidated 10/23/83
Series 1875 <$VALUE
3x10-20 1-3278 <$1250/$2000
Total Issue $163,900
Out in 1910 $470
****
696 Berks
FARMERS NB OF READING
Organized 12/31/64
Receivership 11/8/34
2nd title: Farmers NB & TC 6/18/28
FIRST TITLE {{ 21 L }}
Original Series <$VALUE
3x1-2 1-12000 <$350/$1000
4x5 1-17275 <$375
3x10-20 1-3700 <$750/$1250
50-100 1-430 <$3500
Series 1875
4x5 1-12750 <$375
3x10-20 1-6197 <$750/$1250
50-100 1-667 <$3500
Brown Back
3x10-20 1-11343 <$175/$200
1902 Red Seal
3x10-20 1-15000 <$200/$225
1902 Date Back
4x5 1-10250 <$85
3x10-20 1-33600 <$85
1902 Plain Back
4x5 10251-66914 <$85
3x10-20 33601-85145 <$85
SECOND TITLE {{ 4 L 50+ S }}
1902 Plain Back
4x5 1-7116 <$100
3x10-20 1-3976 <$100
1929 Small Size
5 Type 1 1-20080 <$15
10 Type 1 1-14219 <$20
20 Type 1 1-4122 <$30
Total Issue $10,523,880
Out at close $575,000
Large out at close $23,565
Outstanding includes Ch 1875
****

***

125 Berks
FNB OF READING
{{ 10 L }}
Chartered 11/63
Liquidated 4/12/21
Original Series <$VALUE
4x5 1-1365 <$400
4x10 1-1730 <$750
2x20-50-100 1-350
<$1250/$3500/$3500
Series 1875
4x5 1-2213 <$400
4x10 1-2117 <$750
2x20-50-100 1-645
<$1250/$3500/$3500
Brown Back
3x10-20 1-2872 <$200
50-100 1-1340 <$1250/$1500
1902 Red Seal
4x5 1-5590 <$200
4x10 1-3000 <$200
3x10-20 1-1979 <$200
50-100 1-490 <$2250/$2500
1902 Date Back
4x5 1-17750 <$75
4x10 1-14500 <$85
3x10-20 1-1000 <$85
50-100 1-300 <$350/$400
1902 Plain Back
4x5 17751-30172 <$75
4x10 14501-22940 <$85
Total Issue $2,779,380
Out at close $187,600

***

Keystone NB of Reading
SEE Ch 1875
NB of Kutztown

***

693 Berks
N UNION B OF READING
{{ 18 L }}
Chartered 1/65
Liquidated 11/30/29
Original Series <$VALUE
4x5 1-3150 <$375
3x10-20 1-3000 <$750/$1250
50-100 1-300 <$3500
Series 1875
4x5 1-1500 <$375
3x10-20 1-2475 <$750/$1250
50-100 1-910 <$3500
Brown Back
4x5 1-7305 <$200
3x10-20 1-5954 <$200
50-100 1-1555 <$1250/$1500
1902 Red Seal
4x5 1-6400 <$200
3x10-20 1-2200 <$200
50-100 1-480 <$2250/$2500
1902 Date Back
4x5 1-10750* <$75
3x10-20 1-7600 <$85
50-100 1-200 <$350/$400
1902 Plain Back
4x5 11501-38132* <$75
3x10-20 7601-23664 <$85
* 10751-11500 not marked
Total Issue $3,511,140
Out at close $83,540

***

2899 Berks
PENN NB OF READING
Organized 3/3/83
Receivership 11/26/34
2nd title: Penn NB & TC
1/12/29
FIRST TITLE {{ 9 L }}
Brown Back <$VALUE
3x10-20 1-4400 <$250/$300
1902 Red Seal
3x10-20 1-6650 <$275/$325
1902 Date Back
3x10-20 1-7700 <$135
1902 Plain Back
3x10-20 7701-25329 <$135
SECOND TITLE {{ 16 S }}
1929 Small Size
10 Type 1 1-3150 <$60
20 Type 1 1-926 <$70
5 Type 2 1-324 <$85
10 Type 2 1-1722 <$85
20 Type 2 1-360 <$85
Total Issue $2,145,110
Out at close $100,000
Large out at close $4,395

***

4887 Berks
READING NB, READING
Organized 1/27/93
Receivership 10/27/34
2nd title: Reading NB & TC
10/9/28
FIRST TITLE {{ 24 L }}
Brown Back <$VALUE
4x5 1-10900 <$150
3x10-20 1-11500 <$150/$200
1882 Date Back
4x5 1-9840 <$150
3x10-20 1-7328 <$150/$175
1902 Date Back
4x5 1-6000 <$50
3x10-20 1-4800 <$60
1902 Plain Back
4x5 6001-44025 <$50
3x10-20 4801-30186 <$60
SECOND TITLE {{ 50+ S }}
1929 Small Size
5 Type 1 1-15614 <$20
10 Type 1 1-9046 <$20
20 Type 1 1-2528 <$30
5 Type 2 1-28960 <$20
10 Type 2 1-15657 <$20
20 Type 2 1-3155 <$30
Total Issue $5,425,010
Out at close $599,585
Large out at close $8,685

***

2552 Berks
SECOND NB OF READING
{{ 28 L }}
Chartered 1881
Liquidated 4/30/27
Series 1875 <$VALUE
4x5 1-6305 <$375
4x10 1-5495 <$750
2x20-50-100 1-600
<$1250/$3500/$3500
Brown Back
4x5 1-11665 <$150
3x10-20 1-7834 <$150/$200
1882 Date Back
4x5 1-25000 <$150
3x10-20 1-17600 <$150/$175
1882 Value Back
4x5 25001-44898 <$150
3x10-20 17601-29956
<$150/$200
1902 Plain Back
4x5 1-28740 <$75
3x10-20 1-17196 <$85
Total Issue $4,915,260
Out at close $287,200

***

11789 Centre
REBERSBURG NB, REBERSBURG
{{ 2 L 4 S }}
Chartered 7/20
1902 Plain Back <$VALUE
4x5 1-4120 <$400
3x10-20 1-2211 <$400
1929 Small Size
5 Type 1 1-1028 <$200
10 Type 1 1-498 <$200
20 Type 1 1-142 <$200
5 Type 2 1-1260 <$225
10 Type 2 1-696 <$225
20 Type 2 1-204 <$225
Total Issue $288,050
Out in 1935 $23,710
Large out 1935 $425

***

6708 York
FARMERS & MERCHANTS NB OF
RED LION
{{ 9 L 15 S }}
Chartered 4/03
1902 Red Seal <$VALUE
4x5 1-3290 <$500
3x10-20 1-2014 <$500
1902 Date Back
4x5 1-4450 <$250
3x10-20 1-3300 <$250
1902 Plain Back
4x5 4451-16733 <$250
3x10-20 3301-10583 <$250
1929 Small Size
5 Type 1 1-3830 <$125
10 Type 1 1-1750 <$125
20 Type 1 1-590 <$125
5 Type 2 1-7898 <$150
10 Type 2 1-4715 <$150
20 Type 2 1-1344 <$150
Total Issue $1,434,530
Out in 1935 $121,550
Large out 1935 $2,340

***

FNB & TC of Red Lion
SEE Ch 5184
Red Lion FNB, Red Lion

***

5184 York
RED LION FNB, RED LION
Chartered 4/7/99
2nd title: FNB & TC of
Red Lion 8/5/30
FIRST TITLE {{ 9 L 1 S }}
Brown Back <$VALUE
4x5 1-3475 <$400
3x10-20 1-2885 <$400
1882 Date Back
4x5 1-4350 <$400
3x10-20 1-3020 <$400
1882 Value Back
4x5 4351-6051 <$400
3x10-20 3021-4008 <$400
1902 Plain Back
4x5 1-20270 <$250
3x10-20 1-8060 <$250
1929 Small Size
5 Type 1 1-1544 <$175
10 Type 1 1-778 <$175
20 Type 1 1-262 <$175
SECOND TITLE {{ 16 S }}
1929 Small Size
5 Type 1 1-3406 <$100
10 Type 1 1-2334 <$100
20 Type 1 1-634 <$100
5 Type 2 1-15218 <$110
10 Type 2 1-7097 <$115
20 Type 2 1-2237 <$125
Total Issue $1,978,110
Out in 1935 $200,000
Large out 1935 $3,370

***

4538 Mifflin
REEDSVILLE NB, REEDSVILLE
{{ 5 L 9 S }}
Chartered 1891
Brown Back <$VALUE
4x5 1-4225 <$400
3x10-20 1-2840 <$400
1882 Date Back
4x5 1-1206 <$400
3x10-20 1-876 <$400
1902 Date Back
4x5 1-3225 <$225
3x10-20 1-2550 <$225
1902 Plain Back
4x5 3226-13285 <$225
3x10-20 2551-9121 <$225
1929 Small Size
5 Type 1 1-2138 <$135
10 Type 1 1-1106 <$135
20 Type 1 1-250 <$135
5 Type 2 1-3756 <$150
10 Type 2 1-1968 <$150
20 Type 2 1-588 <$150
Total Issue $1,226,890
Out in 1935 $49,120
Large out 1935 $3,240

***

3763 Clinton
FNB OF RENOVO
{{ 0 L 2 S }}
Chartered 7/28/87
Receivership 2/26/32
Brown Back <$VALUE
4x5 1-3283 <$1250
50-100 1-221 <$1750/$2000
1902 Red Seal
50-100 1-40 <$2250/$2500
1902 Date Back
50-100 1-300 <$850/$1000
3x50-100 1-160 <$850/$1000
1902 Plain Back
3x50-100 161-194
<$850/$1000
1929 Small Size
50 Type 1 1-32 <$500
100 Type 1 1-3 <$600
Total Issue $209,710
Out at close $12,200
Large out at close $2,500

***

10466 Fayette
FNB OF REPUBLIC
{{ 2 L 3 S }}
Chartered 12/13
Receivership 2/13/31
1902 Date Back <$VALUE
3x10-20 1-380* <$450
1902 Plain Back
3x10-20 481-5500* <$450
* 381-480 not marked
1929 Small Size
10 Type 1 1-360 <$300
20 Type 1 1-104 <$300
Total Issue $309,080
Out at close $25,000
Large out at close $3,110

***

8263 Jefferson
CITIZENS NB OF
REYNOLDSVILLE
{{ 1 L }}
Chartered 6/06
Liquidated 2/18/19
1902 Red Seal <$VALUE
4x5 1-765 <$750
3x10-20 1-594 <$750
1902 Date Back
4x5 1-3900 <$400
3x10-20 1-2800 <$400
1902 Plain Back
4x5 3901-4950 <$400
3x10-20 2801-3460 <$400
Total Issue $317,000
Out at close $39,300

***

4908 Jefferson
FNB OF REYNOLDSVILLE
{{ 7 L 16 S }}
Chartered 1893
Brown Back <$VALUE
3x10-20 1-4020 <$350
1882 Date Back
3x10-20 1-4383 <$350
1902 Date Back
3x10-20 1-2500 <$175
1902 Plain Back
3x10-20 2501-15654 <$175
1929 Small Size
10 Type 1 1-1958 <$60
20 Type 1 1-612 <$70
10 Type 2 1-3414 <$70
20 Type 2 1-805 <$70
Total Issue $1,444,010
Out in 1935 $73,100
Large out 1935 $3,920

***

7620 Jefferson
PEOPLES NB OF
REYNOLDSVILLE
{{ 6 L 13 S }}
Chartered 2/05
Liquidated 9/7/34
1902 Red Seal <$VALUE
4x5 1-2165 <$350
3x10-20 1-1534 <$350
1902 Date Back
4x5 1-3750 <$175
3x10-20 1-8600 <$175
1902 Plain Back
3x10-20 8601-25859 <$175
1929 Small Size
10 Type 1 1-2772 <$80
20 Type 1 1-774 <$90
Total Issue $1,747,150
Out at close $50,770
Large out at close $3,670
Ch 13957 assumed circulation

***

7090 Greene
RICES LANDING NB,
RICES LANDING
{{ 2 L 12 S }}
Chartered 1/04
1902 Red Seal <$VALUE
3x10-20 1-780 <$750
1902 Date Back
3x10-20 1-1310 <$375
1902 Plain Back
3x10-20 1311-5339 <$375
1929 Small Size
5 Type 1 1-3872 <$125
10 Type 1 1-1438 <$125
5 Type 2 1-4410 <$135
10 Type 2 1-2386 <$135
Total Issue $554,300
Out in 1935 $48,750
Large out 1935 $860

***

8344 Lebanon
RICHLAND NB, RICHLAND
{{ 2 L 4 S }}
Chartered 8/06
1902 Red Seal <$VALUE
3x10-20 1-500 <$750
1902 Date Back
3x10-20 1-2370 <$375
1902 Plain Back
3x10-20 2371-6416 <$375
1929 Small Size
10 Type 1 1-652 <$225
20 Type 1 1-180 <$225
10 Type 2 1-1130 <$250
20 Type 2 1-210 <$250
Total Issue $422,020
Out in 1935 $24,600
Large out 1935 $950

***

5014 Elk
ELK COUNTY NB OF RIDGWAY
{{ 11 L 16 S }}
Chartered 1895
Brown Back <$VALUE
4x5 1-4215 <$350
3x10-20 1-3614 <$350
1882 Date Back
4x5 1-8661 <$350
3x10-20 1-6064 <$350
1902 Plain Back
4x5 1-17739 <$165
3x10-20 1-12031 <$165
1929 Small Size
5 Type 1 1-3982 <$75
10 Type 1 1-1850 <$75
20 Type 1 1-516 <$85
5 Type 2 1-5808 <$85
10 Type 2 1-2976 <$85
20 Type 2 1-1008 <$85
Total Issue $2,069,090
Out in 1935 $98,495
Large out 1935 $3,995

***

5945 Elk
RIDGWAY NB, RIDGWAY
{{ 16 L 23 S }}
Chartered 8/26/01
Brown Back <$VALUE
4x5 1-2750 <$250
3x10-20 1-4200 <$250
1882 Date Back
4x5 1-7000 <$250
3x10-20 1-6600 <$250
1882 Value Back
4x5 7001-20490 <$250
3x10-20 6601-13645 <$250
1902 Plain Back
4x5 1-23690 <$100
3x10-20 1-16655 <$100
1929 Small Size
5 Type 1 1-8744 <$45
10 Type 1 1-3910 <$50
20 Type 1 1-946 <$60
5 Type 2 1-9844 <$60
10 Type 2 1-4707 <$60
20 Type 2 1-1545 <$60
Total Issue $3,401,230
Out in 1935 $167,450
Large out 1935 $9,180

***

10847 Delaware
RIDLEY PARK NB,
RIDLEY PARK
{{ 10 L 12 S }}
Chartered 5/16
1902 Plain Back <$VALUE
4x10 1-14716 <$200
1929 Small Size
10 Type 1 1-2860 <$150
10 Type 2 1-4739 <$150
Total Issue $807,630
Out in 1935 $50,000
Large out 1935 $1,320

***

9202 Bucks
FNB OF RIEGELSVILLE
{{ 8 L 9 S }}
Chartered 7/08
1902 Date Back <$VALUE
3x10-20 1-2970 <$250
1902 Plain Back
3x10-20 2971-7533 <$250
1929 Small Size
10 Type 1 1-734 <$150
20 Type 1 1-192 <$150
5 Type 2 1-312 <$175
10 Type 2 1-993 <$175
20 Type 2 1-303 <$175
Total Issue $461,280
Out in 1935 $25,000
Large out 1935 $1,485

***

6676 Clarion
FNB OF RIMERSBURG
{{ 4 L 3U + 8 S }}
Chartered 3/03
1902 Red Seal <$VALUE
4x5 1-4076 <$450
3x10-20 1-3266 <$450
1902 Date Back
4x5 1-4550 <$225
3x10-20 1-3480 <$225
1902 Plain Back
4x5 4551-13581 <$225
3x10-20 3481-9468 <$225
1929 Small Size
5 Type 1 1-1918 <$110
10 Type 1 1-946 <$110
20 Type 1 1-268 <$125
5 Type 2 1-3064 <$125
10 Type 2 1-1633 <$125
20 Type 2 1-396 <$150
Total Issue $1,175,870
Out in 1935 $49,200
Large out 1935 $3,010

***

6569 Clarion
RIMERSBURG NB, RIMERSBURG
{{ UNREPORTED }}
Chartered 1/3/03
Liquidated 2/11/05
1902 Red Seal <$VALUE
3x10-20 1-760 <$1500
Total Issue $38,000
Out in 1910 $1,380

***

6950 Schuylkill
FNB OF RINGTOWN
{{ 2 L 8 S }}
Chartered 9/03
1902 Red Seal <$VALUE
3x10-20 1-1557 <$1000
1902 Date Back
3x10-20 1-2510 <$500
1902 Plain Back
3x10-20 2510-7249 <$500
1929 Small Size
10 Type 1 1-736 <$175
20 Type 1 1-206 <$175
10 Type 2 1-1252 <$200
20 Type 2 1-368 <$200
Total Issue $529,060
Out in 1935 $24,700
Large out 1935 $760

***

12304 Blair
FNB OF ROARING SPRING
{{ 9 S }}
Chartered 1/23
1929 Small Size <$VALUE
10 Type 1 1-1232 <$200
20 Type 1 1-362 <$225
10 Type 2 1-2042 <$225
20 Type 2 1-520 <$225
Total Issue $148,180
Out in 1935 $44,200

***

2977 Beaver
FNB OF ROCHESTER
{{ 11 L 19 S }}
Chartered 1883
Brown Back <$VALUE
4x5 1-4414 <$275
3x10-20 1-951 <$275
1902 Red Seal
3x10-20 1-2340 <$300
1902 Date Back
3x10-20 1-14000 <$135
1902 Plain Back
3x10-20 14001-42722 <$135
1929 Small Size
10 Type 1 1-4590 <$60
20 Type 1 1-1260 <$60
10 Type 2 1-3823 <$60
20 Type 2 1-1500 <$65
Total Issue $2,883,760
Out in 1935 $145,550
Large out 1935 $7,000

***

7749 Beaver
PEOPLES NB OF ROCHESTER
{{ 4 L 5 S }}
Chartered 5/05
Liquidated 2/18/35
1902 Red Seal <$VALUE
4x5 1-1165 <$600
3x10-20 1-839 <$600
1902 Date Back
4x5 1-2300 <$300
3x10-20 1-1670 <$300
1902 Plain Back
4x5 2301-5974 <$300
3x10-20 1671-3837 <$300
1929 Small Size
5 Type 1 1-996 <$175
10 Type 1 1-486 <$175
20 Type 1 1-138 <$200
5 Type 2 1-740 <$200
10 Type 2 1-411 <$200
20 Type 2 1-64 <$200
Total Issue $461,270
Out at close $23,030
Large out at close $990

***

5170 Beaver
ROCHESTER NB, ROCHESTER
{{ UNREPORTED }}
Chartered 1/20/99
Liquidated 1/6/03
Brown Back <$VALUE
50-100 1-161 <$3000
Total Issue $24,150
Out in 1910 $1,100

***

9769 Somerset
FARMERS & MERCHANTS NB OF
ROCKWOOD
{{ 1 L 4 S }}
Organized 5/4/10
Receivership 4/20/34
1902 Date Back <$VALUE
3x10-20 1-2210 <$600
1902 Plain Back
3x10-20 2211-6810 <$600
1929 Small Size
10 Type 1 1-744 <$250
20 Type 1 1-184 <$250
10 Type 2 1-265 <$275
20 Type 2 1-91 <$275
Total Issue $411,690
Out at close $25,000
Large out at close $1,170

***

<$VALUEs are for notes in FINE condition. Value changes by approximately 25% for a change of one full grade.

5340 Somerset
FNB OF ROCKWOOD
{{ 1 L 4 S }}
Chartered 5/8/00
Receivership 4/20/34
Brown Back <$VALUE
3x10-20 1-2040 <$650
1882 Date Back
3x10-20 1-2230 <$650
1882 Value Back
3x10-20 2231-3147 <$650
1902 Plain Back
3x10-20 1-3666 <$450
1929 Small Size
10 Type 1 1-736 <$250
20 Type 1 1-180 <$250
10 Type 2 1-242 <$275
20 Type 2 1-82 <$300
Total Issue $512,470
Out at close $25,000
Large out at close $1,620

10246 Bradford
FARMERS NB OF ROME
{{ 3 L 5 S }}
Chartered 8/12
1902 Date Back <$VALUE
3x10-20 1-1420 <$400
1902 Plain Back
3x10-20 1421-5817 <$400
1929 Small Size
10 Type 1 1-696 <$200
20 Type 1 1-182 <$200
10 Type 2 1-1561 <$200
20 Type 2 1-235 <$200
Total Issue $374,760
Out in 1935 $24,450
Large out 1935 $780

5495 Washington
FNB OF ROSCOE
{{ 5 L 11 S }}
Chartered 7/11/00
Brown Back <$VALUE
3x10-20 1-4300 <$400
1882 Date Back
3x10-20 1-4800 <$400
1882 Value Back
3x10-20 4801-6844 <$400
1902 Plain Back
3x10-20 1-8056 <$250
1929 Small Size
5 Type 1 1-170 <$125
10 Type 1 1-1446 <$125
20 Type 1 1-386 <$125
5 Type 2 1-2564 <$150
10 Type 2 1-1375 <$150
20 Type 2 1-370 <$150
Total Issue $1,132,150
Out in 1935 $49,100
Large out 1935 $1,550

4751 Montgomery
HOME NB OF ROYERSFORD
{{ 1 L }}
Chartered 6/9/92
Liquidated 1/12/03
Brown Back <$VALUE
4x5 1-3039 <$1250
3x10-20 1-529 <$1250
Total Issue $87,230
Out in 1910 $1,135

3551 Montgomery
NB OF ROYERSFORD
{{ U + 6 L 14 S }}
Chartered 8/23/86
Brown Back <$VALUE
4x5 1-2130 <$500
3x10-20 1-4522 <$500
1902 Red Seal
4x5 1-1300 <$600
3x10-20 1-640 <$600
1902 Date Back
4x5 1-5350 <$300
3x10-20 1-3960 <$300
1902 Plain Back
4x5 5351-13980 <$300
3x10-20 3961-9931 <$300
1929 Small Size
5 Type 1 1-1960 <$125
10 Type 1 1-1050 <$125
20 Type 1 1-280 <$150
5 Type 2 1-3235 <$150
10 Type 2 1-1057 <$150
20 Type 2 1-435 <$150
Total Issue $1,293,695
Out in 1935 $46,850
Large out 1935 $1,005

13908 Armstrong
PEOPLES NB OF
RURAL VALLEY
{{ 2 S }}
Chartered 12/33
1929 Small Size <$VALUE
10 Type 2 1-1064 <$400
Total Issue $10,640
Out in 1935 $19,640
Large out 1935 $610
Outstanding includes Ch 6083

6083 Armstrong
RURAL VALLEY NB,
RURAL VALLEY
{{ 2 L 5 S }}
Chartered 1/04/02
Liquidated 1/15/34
Brown Back <$VALUE
3x10-20 1-820 <$650
1882 Date Back
3x10-20 1-1860 <$650
1882 Value Back
3x10-20 1861-3015 <$650
1902 Plain Back
3x10-20 I-2318 <$500
1929 Small Size
10 Type 1 1-590 <$275
20 Type 1 1-168 <$275
10 Type 2 1-6 <$300
20 Type 2 1-15 <$300
Total Issue $363,570
Out at close $20,000
Large out 1935 $610

10493 Allegheny
FNB OF RUSSELLTON
{{ 2 L 3 S }}
Chartered 3/14
Receivership 12/28/33
1902 Date Back <$VALUE
3x10-20 1-900 <$450
1902 Plain Back
3x10-20 901-6123 <$450
1929 Small Size
10 Type 1 1-716 <$225
20 Type 1 1-195 <$225
Total Issue $372,510
Out at close $25,000
Large out at close $1,140

11910 Crawford
FNB OF SAEGERTOWN
{{ 1 L 2 S }}
Organized 12/31/20
Liquidated 6/5/31
1902 Plain Back <$VALUE
3x10-20 1-2804 <$650
1929 Small Size
10 Type 1 1-408 <$350
20 Type 1 1-111 <$350
Total Issue $178,000
Out at close $23,200
Large out at close $2,340

6589 Elk
SAINT MARYS NB,
SAINT MARYS
{{ U + 7 L 21 S }}
Chartered 1/03
1902 Red Seal <$VALUE
4x5 1-5880 <$300
3x10-20 1-4648 <$300
1902 Date Back
4x5 1-10650 <$150
3x10-20 1-8100 <$150
1902 Plain Back
4x5 10651-45510 <$150
3x10-20 8101-29762 <$150
1929 Small Size
5 Type 1 1-7828 <$50
10 Type 1 1-4040 <$50
20 Type 1 1-946 <$60
5 Type 2 1-12582 <$60
10 Type 2 1-6133 <$60
20 Type 2 1-1622 <$60
Total Issue $3,495,740
Out in 1935 $197,400
Large out 1935 $7,760

12588 Cambria
SAINT MICHAEL NB,
SAINT MICHAEL
{{ 7 S }}
Chartered 10/24
1929 Small Size <$VALUE
5 Type 1 1-1184 <$135
10 Type 1 1-580 <$135
20 Type 1 1-228 <$165
5 Type 2 1-1520 <$165
10 Type 2 1-756 <$165
20 Type 2 1-264 <$175
Total Issue $118,120
Out in 1935 $24,750

6106 Somerset
FNB OF SALISBURY
{{ 4 L 9 S }}
Chartered 1/27/02
1902 Red Seal <$VALUE
3x10-20 1-3650 <$500
1902 Date Back
3x10-20 1-4500 <$225
1902 Plain Back (dated 1901)
3x10-20 4501-7988 <$225
1902 Plain Back (dated 1921)
3x10-20 1-6114 <$225
1929 Small Size
10 Type 1 1-1352 <$125
20 Type 1 1-410 <$125
10 Type 2 1-1908 <$125
20 Type 2 1-372 <$125
Total Issue $1,044,440
Out in 1935 $50,000
Large out 1935 $2,640

2609 Indiana
FNB OF SALTSBURG
{{ 7 L 12 S }}
Chartered 1882
Series 1875 <$VALUE
4x5 1-7471 <$400
3x10-20 1-382 <$750/$1250
Brown Back
3x10-20 1-3200 <$350
1882 Date Back
3x10-20 1-4600 <$350
1882 Value Back
3x10-20 4601-6944 <$350
1902 Plain Back
3x10-20 1-5801 <$225
1929 Small Size
10 Type 1 1-1422 <$125
20 Type 1 1-402 <$125
10 Type 2 1-1660 <$150
20 Type 2 1-477 <$150
Total Issue $1,125,470
Out in 1935 $48,200
Large out 1935 $3,270

7229 Bedford
FNB OF SAXTON
{{ 2 L 7 S }}
Chartered 4/04
1902 Red Seal <$VALUE
4x5 1-825 <$750
3x10-20 1-660 <$750
1902 Date Back
4x5 1-1625 <$350
3x10-20 1-1260 <$350
1902 Plain Back
4x5 1616-5466 <$350
3x10-20 1261-3719 <$350
1929 Small Size
5 Type 1 1-1036 <$150
10 Type 1 1-472 <$150
20 Type 1 1-152 <$150
5 Type 2 1-2176 <$175
10 Type 2 1-1164 <$175
20 Type 2 1-348 <$175
Total Issue $451,890
Out in 1935 $29,450
Large out 1935 $1,100

5666 Bradford
FNB OF SAYRE
{{ 6 L 18 S }}
Chartered 1/4/01
Brown Back <$VALUE
3x10-20 1-2850 <$350
1882 Date Back
3x10-20 1-4840 <$350
1882 Value Back
3x10-20 4841-7570 <$350
1902 Plain Back
3x10-20 1-8969 <$175
1929 Small Size
10 Type 1 1-3812 <$60
20 Type 1 1-1082 <$65
10 Type 2 1-5987 <$65
20 Type 2 1-1464 <$65
Total Issue $1,417,160
Out in 1935 $123,000
Large out 1935 $4,060

Merchants and Mechanics
NB of Sayre
SEE Ch 5684
NB of Sayre

5684 Bradford
NB OF SAYRE
Chartered 1/18/01
2nd title: Merchants &
Mechanics NB of Sayre
12/6/23
FIRST TITLE {{ 3 L }}
Brown Back <$VALUE
3x10-20 1-4400 <$400
1882 Date Back
3x10-20 1-4740 <$400
1882 Value Back
3x10-20 4741-7589 <$400
1902 Plain Back
3x10-20 1-2650 <$300
SECOND TITLE {{ 2 L 11 S }}
1902 Plain Back
3x10-20 1-4299 <$300
1929 Small Size
10 Type 1 1-1616 <$75
20 Type 1 1-408 <$100
10 Type 2 1-2155 <$100
20 Type 2 1-528 <$100
Total Issue $1,124,930
Out in 1935 $50,000
Large out 1935 $1,630

7262 Washington
FNB OF SCENERY HILL
{{ 6 L U + 10 S }}
Chartered 5/04
1902 Red Seal <$VALUE
3x10-20 1-1190 <$1500
1902 Date Back
3x10-20 1-2290 <$650
1902 Plain Back
3x10-20 2291-6851 <$650
1929 Small Size
10 Type 1 1-750 <$350
20 Type 1 1-168 <$350
10 Type 2 1-923 <$350
20 Type 2 1-265 <$350
Total Issue $481,740
Out in 1935 $24,400
Large out 1935 $1,300

8962 Lebanon
FNB OF SCHAEFFERSTOWN
{{ 3 L 5 S }}
Chartered 12/07
1902 Red Seal <$VALUE
3x10-20 1-440 <$750
1902 Date Back
3x10-20 1-2040 <$350
1902 Plain Back
3x10-20 2041-6424 <$350
1929 Small Size
10 Type 1 1-710 <$200
20 Type 1 1-180 <$225
10 Type 2 1-1057 <$225
20 Type 2 1-234 <$225
Total Issue $422,650
Out in 1935 $25,000
Large out 1935 $1,190

10666 Bedford
FNB OF SCHELLBURG
Chartered 12/14
2nd title: FNB of
Schellsburg 1/27/33
FIRST TITLE {{ 8 L 6 S }}
1902 Date Back <$VALUE
3x10-20 1-300 <$325
1902 Plain Back
3x10-20 301-4726 <$325
1929 Small Size
10 Type 1 1-652 <$200
20 Type 1 1-170 <$200
SECOND TITLE {{ 2 S }}
1929 Small Size
10 Type 1 1-106 <$300
20 Type 1 1-32 <$300
10 Type 2 1-538 <$300
20 Type 2 1-115 <$300
Total Issue $313,700
Out in 1935 $24,450
Large out 1935 $1,570

FNB of Schellsburg
SEE Ch 10666
FNB of Schellburg

5216 Schuylkill
FNB OF SCHUYLKILL HAVEN
Chartered 8/28/99
2nd title: FNB & TC 1/19/29
FIRST TITLE {{ U + 3 L }}
Brown Back <$VALUE
3x10-20 1-4460 <$500
1882 Date Back
3x10-20 1-4240 <$500
1882 Value Back
3x10-20 4241-5868 <$500
1902 Plain Back
4x10 1-10025 <$300
SECOND TITLE {{ 0 L 16 S }}
1902 Plain Back
4x10 1-539 <$350
1929 Small Size
10 Type 1 1-4154 <$60
10 Type 2 1-10813 <$70
Total Issue $1,296,330
Out in 1935 $99,610
Large out 1935 $2,460

2142 Montgomery
NB OF SCHWENKSVILLE
Chartered 4/17/74
2nd title: NB & TC of
Schwenksville 3/2/31
FIRST TITLE {{ 5 L 1 S }}
Original Series <$VALUE
4x5 1-1750 <$4000
4x20 1-1375 <$1250
Series 1875
4x5 1-1300 <$4000
4x20 1-2080 <$1250
Brown Back
3x10-20 1-3960 <$400
1882 Date Back
4x5 1-2335 <$400
3x10-20 1-1588 <$400
1902 Date Back
3x10-20 1-1200 <$300
1902 Plain Back
3x10-20 1201-7631 <$300
1929 Small Size
10 Type 1 1-614 <$175
20 Type 1 1-212 <$175
SECOND TITLE {{ 13 S }}
1929 Small Size
10 Type 1 1-454 <$150
20 Type 1 1-126 <$150
10 Type 2 1-2003 <$175
20 Type 2 1-257 <$175
Total Issue $1,172,860
Out in 1935 $38,850
Large out 1935 $2,450

5974 Westmoreland
BROADWAY NB OF SCOTTDALE
{{ 4 L 5 S }}
Chartered 9/20/01
Liquidated 3/18/31
Brown Back <$VALUE
3x10-20 1-1850 <$400
1882 Date Back
3x10-20 1-4240 <$400
1882 Value Back
3x10-20 4241-6790 <$400
1902 Plain Back
3x10-20 1-6585 <$275
1929 Small Size
10 Type 1 1-819 <$200
20 Type 1 1-183 <$200
Total Issue $832,350
Out at close $46,150
Large out at close $6,800

4098 Westmoreland
FNB OF SCOTTDALE
{{ 3 L 7 S }}
Chartered 8/26/89
Liquidated 11/10/33
Brown Back <$VALUE
3x10-20 1-3390 <$400
1882 Date Back
3x10-20 1-293 <$400
1902 Date Back
3x10-20 1-4200 <$225
1902 Plain Back
3x10-20 4201-13391 <$225
1929 Small Size
10 Type 1 1-1294 <$135
20 Type 1 1-385 <$135
Total Issue $977,540
Out at close $50,000
Large out 1935 $1,560
Ch 13772 assumed circulation

13772 Westmoreland
FNB OF SCOTTDALE
{{ 6 S }}
Chartered 9/33
1929 Small Size <$VALUE
10 Type 2 1-4919 <$200
20 Type 2 1-1149 <$200
Total Issue $72,170
Out in 1935 $91,290
Large out 1935 $1,560
Outstanding includes Ch 4098

77 Lackawanna
FNB OF SCRANTON*
{{ 28 L 50+ S }}
Chartered 9/63
Liquidated 5/18/82
*Rechartered as Ch 2697
which retook Ch 77 10/19/11
Original Series <$VALUE
4x5 1-5450 <$400
3x10-20 1-7084 <$750/$1250
Series 1875
3x10-20 1-474 <$750/$1250
1902 Date Back
3x10-20 1-61000 <$60
1902 Plain Back
3x10-20 61001-295346 <$60
1929 Small Size
10 Type 1 1-95400 <$20
20 Type 1 1-27452 <$30
10 Type 2 1-326396 <$20
20 Type 2 1-78378 <$30
Total Issue $29,103,960
Out in 1935 $3,866,020
Large out 1935 $64,805
Outstanding includes Ch 2697
and Ch 4183

2697 Lackawanna
FNB OF SCRANTON
{{ 8 L }}
Chartered 1882
RETOOK Ch 77 10/19/11
Brown Back <$VALUE
3x10-20 1-10522 <$250
1902 Red Seal
3x10-20 1-33500 <$250/$275
1902 Date Back
3x10-20 1-58000 <$125
Total Issue $5,101,100
Out in 1911 $1,000,000

8235 Lackawanna
PEOPLES NB OF SCRANTON
{{ 6 L }}
Chartered 5/06
Liquidated 6/30/17
1902 Red Seal <$VALUE
4x5 1-6250 <$350
3x10-20 1-5000 <$350
1902 Date Back
4x5 1-18745 <$175
3x10-20 1-54334 <$175
1902 Plain Back
3x10-20 54335-64531 <$175
Total Issue $3,976,450
Out at close $458,900

13947 Lackawanna
SCRANTON NB, SCRANTON
{{ 12 S }}
Chartered 1/34
1929 Small Size <$VALUE
5 Type 2 1-24210 <$50
10 Type 2 1-12225 <$50
20 Type 2 1-4085 <$60
Total Issue $325,000
Out in 1935 $148,750

49 Lackawanna
SECOND NB OF SCRANTON
{{ 2 L }}
Chartered 8/5/63
Receivership 3/15/79
Original Series <$VALUE
4x5 1-8949 <$750
4x10 1-9577 <$850
Total Issue $562,060
Out in 1916 $2,680

1946 Lackawanna
THIRD NB OF SCRANTON
Chartered 3/11/72
2nd title: Third NB & TC
of Scranton 9/16/29
FIRST TITLE {{ 23 L 2 S }}
Original Series <$VALUE
4x5 1-2750 <$375
3x10-20 1-1900 <$750/$1250
Series 1875
4x5 1-4460 <$375
3x10-20 1-3462 <$750/$1250
Brown Back
4x5 1-9750 <$150
3x10-20 1-17400 <$150/$200
1882 Date Back
4x5 1-9140 <$150
3x10-20 1-6746 <$150/$200
1902 Date Back
4x5 1-24550 <$50
3x10-20 1-19080 <$60
1902 Plain Back
4x5 24551-56546 <$50
3x10-20 19081-87614 <$60
1929 Small Size
5 Type 1 1-1950 <$75
10 Type 1 1-984 <$75
20 Type 1 1-334 <$75
SECOND TITLE {{ 50+ S }}
1929 Small Size
5 Type 1 1-17666 <$15
10 Type 1 1-19420 <$20
20 Type 1 1-6052 <$30
5 Type 2 1-63776 <$15
10 Type 2 1-40278 <$20
20 Type 2 1-18610 <$30
Total Issue $11,181,920
Out in 1935 $758,850
Large out 1935 $15,465

4183 Lackawanna
TRADERS NB OF SCRANTON
{{ 18 L 2 S }}
Chartered 12/20/89
Closed 11/30/29
Brown Back <$VALUE
4x5 1-43100 <$150
3x10-20 1-15520 <$150/$200
1882 Date Back
4x5 1-4577 <$150
3x10-20 1-2863 <$150/$200
1902 Date Back
4x5 1-25750 <$75
3x10-20 1-36600 <$85
1902 Plain Back
4x5 25751-132220 <$75
3x10-20 36601-115758 <$85
1929 Small Size
5 Type 1 1-2531 <$250
10 Type 1 1-1384 <$250
20 Type 1 1-157 <$250
Total Issue $10,482,800
Out at close $500,000
Large out at close $322,190
Ch 2697 assumed circulation

8737 Lackawanna
UNION NB OF SCRANTON
{{ 21 L 27 S }}
Chartered 6/07
Receivership 2/21/34
1902 Red Seal <$VALUE
4x5 1-6000 <$200
3x10-20 1-4800 <$200
1902 Date Back
4x5 1-36500 <$75
3x10-20 1-27000 <$85
1902 Plain Back
4x5 36501-152202 <$75
3x10-20 27001-99989 <$85
1929 Small Size
5 Type 1 1-21246 <$20
10 Type 1 1-12154 <$20
20 Type 1 1-3032 <$30
5 Type 2 1-15686 <$20
10 Type 2 1-8846 <$20
20 Type 2 1-1790 <$30
Total Issue $10,337,140
Out at close $500,000
Large out at close $20,700

357 Snyder
FNB OF SELINS GROVE
{{ 9 L 17 S }}
Chartered 3/64
Original Series <$VALUE
3x1-2 1-1000 <$400/$1250
4x5 1-3000 <$500
3x10-20 1-2160 <$750/$1250
Series 1875
3x1-2 1-400 <$400/$1250
4x5 1-1650 <$500
3x10-20 1-1424 <$750/$1250
Brown Back
4x5 1-4500 <$275
3x10-20 1-4842 <$275
1902 Red Seal
4x5 1-2575 <$300
3x10-20 1-1870 <$300
1902 Date Back
4x5 1-3900 <$150
3x10-20 1-2790 <$150
1902 Plain Back
4x5 3901-12572 <$150
3x10-20 2791-8502 <$150
1929 Small Size
5 Type 1 1-4446 <$60
10 Type 1 1-2394 <$60
20 Type 1 1-618 <$70
5 Type 2 1-6264 <$75
10 Type 2 1-3374 <$75
20 Type 2 1-1040 <$75
Total Issue $1,869,790
Out in 1935 $105,200
Large out 1935 $4,350

8653 Snyder
FARMERS NB OF SELINSGROVE
{{ 4 L 10 S }}
Chartered 4/07
1902 Red Seal <$VALUE
3x10-20 1-850 <$500
1902 Date Back
3x10-20 1-2430 <$250
1902 Plain Back
3x10-20 2431-12037 <$250
1929 Small Size
10 Type 1 1-1408 <$135
20 Type 1 1-404 <$150
10 Type 2 1-2290 <$150
20 Type 2 1-525 <$150
Total Issue $810,710
Out in 1935 $48,250
Large out 1935 $1,500

2667 Bucks
SELLERSVILLE NB, SELLERSVILLE
{{ 13 L 23 S }}
Chartered 1882
Series 1875 <$VALUE
3x10-20 1-5310 <$750/$1250
1902 Red Seal
3x10-20 1-4650 <$275
1902 Date Back
4x5 1-6250 <$125
3x10-20 1-4600 <$125
1902 Plain Back (dated 1902)
4x5 6251-12510 <$125
3x10-20 4601-8634 <$125
1902 Plain Back (dated 1922)
4x5 1-9110 <$125
3x10-20 1-5901 <$125
1929 Small Size
5 Type 1 1-3226 <$60
10 Type 1 1-1536 <$60
20 Type 1 1-422 <$70
5 Type 2 1-4416 <$70
10 Type 2 1-2724 <$70
20 Type 2 1-624 <$75
Total Issue $1,958,530
Out in 1935 $70,160
Large out 1935 $3,920

9507 York
SEVEN VALLEYS NB, SEVEN VALLEYS
{{ 2 L 7 S }}
Chartered 8/09
Receivership 1/23/34
1902 Date Back <$VALUE
3x10-20 1-2530 <$1250
1902 Plain Back
3x10-20 2531-6836 <$1250
1929 Small Size
10 Type 1 1-710 <$500
20 Type 1 1-192 <$500
10 Type 2 1-180 <$500
20 Type 2 1-51 <$500
Total Issue $410,260
Out at close $25,000
Large out at close $920

11899 Westmoreland
FNB OF SEWARD
{{ 1 L }}
Organized 12/21/20
Receivership 1/10/30
1902 Plain Back <$VALUE
4x5 1-4989 <$650
3x10-20 1-2712 <$650
Total Issue $235,380
Out at close $8,320

13699 Allegheny
FNB IN SEWICKLEY
{{ 6 S }}
Chartered 6/33
1929 Small Size <$VALUE
5 Type 2 1-12054 <$175
10 Type 2 1-6935 <$175
Total Issue $129,620
Out in 1935 $97,850
Large out 1935 $4,580
Outstanding includes Ch 4462

4462 Allegheny
FNB OF SEWICKLEY
{{ 9 L 16 S }}
Chartered 1890
Liquidated 7/14/33
Brown Back <$VALUE
4x5 1-9475 <$350
3x10-20 1-3540 <$350
1882 Date Back
4x5 1-2394 <$350
3x10-20 1-1702 <$350
1902 Date Back
4x5 1-6500 <$175
4x10 1-6500 <$175
1902 Plain Back
4x5 6501-28136 <$175
4x10 16501-23395 <$175
1929 Small Size
5 Type 1 1-5739 <$85
10 Type 1 1-2744 <$85
Total Issue $2,334,810
Out at close $75,640
Large out 1935 $4,580
Ch 13699 assumed circulation

3045 Northumberland
FNB OF SHAMOKIN
{{ 2 L }}
Chartered 9/12/83
Liquidated 9/4/03
Brown Back <$VALUE
4x5 1-3465 <$650
3x10-20 1-7732 <$650
Total Issue $455,900
Out in 1910 $5,525

5625 Northumberland
MARKET STREET NB OF SHAMOKIN
{{ 7 L 13 S }}
Chartered 11/17/00
Brown Back <$VALUE
3x10-20 1-9100 <$300
1882 Date Back
3x10-20 1-9300* <$300
1882 Value Back
3x10-20 9801-14227* <$300
* 9301-9800 not marked
1902 Plain Back
3x10-20 1-14439 <$150
1929 Small Size
10 Type 1 1-4180 <$65
20 Type 1 1-1040 <$75
10 Type 2 1-5421 <$75
20 Type 2 1-934 <$85
Total Issue $2,336,790
Out in 1935 $101,080
Large out 1935 $4,450

N-Dime B of Shamokin
SEE Ch 6942
NB of Shamokin

6942 Northumberland
NB OF SHAMOKIN
Chartered 9/03
2nd title: N-Dime B of Shamokin 12/13/32
FIRST TITLE **{{ 5 L 6 S }}**
1902 Red Seal <$VALUE
4x5 1-3575 <$350
3x10-20 1-3620 <$350
1902 Date Back
4x5 1-7300 <$175
3x10-20 1-5180 <$175
1902 Plain Back
4x5 7301-23979 <$175
3x10-20 5181-15543 <$175
1929 Small Size
5 Type 1 1-8764 <$100
10 Type 1 1-3862 <$100
20 Type 1 1-1074 <$100
SECOND TITLE **{{ 16 S }}**
1929 Small Size
5 Type 1 1-624 <$75
10 Type 1 1-526 <$75
20 Type 1 1-106 <$75
5 Type 2 1-30874 <$75
10 Type 2 1-16396 <$75
20 Type 2 1-5344 <$75
Total Issue $2,620,960
Out in 1935 $320,700
Large out 1935 $3,915

689 Northumberland
NORTHUMBERLAND COUNTY NB OF SHAMOKIN
{{ UNREPORTED }}
Organized 1/9/65
Receivership 3/12/77
Original Series <$VALUE
4x5 1-3000 <$1250
3x10-20 1-1252<$1250/$1750
Total Issue $122,600
Out in 1916 $815

12805 Northumberland
WEST END NB OF SHAMOKIN
{{ 1 L 17 S }}
Chartered 8/25
1902 Plain Back <$VALUE
3x10-20 1-3817 <$600
1929 Small Size
5 Type 1 1-2908 <$60
10 Type 1 1-2404 <$60
20 Type 1 1-662 <$70
5 Type 2 1-10762 <$70
10 Type 2 1-6316 <$70
20 Type 2 1-1715 <$70
Total Issue $653,040
Out in 1935 $125,250
Large out 1935 $890

13803 Mercer
FNB IN SHARON
{{ 11 S }}
Chartered 10/33
1929 Small Size <$VALUE
10 Type 2 1-7940 <$100
20 Type 2 1-2076 <$100
Total Issue $120,920
Out in 1935 $245,920
Large out 1935 $7,765
Outstanding includes Ch 1685

1685 Mercer
FNB OF SHARON
{{ 11 L 18 S }}
Organized 8/31/68
Liquidated 3/28/34
Original Series <$VALUE
4x5 1-5000 <$400
Series 1875
4x5 1-14730 <$400
Brown Back
3x10-20 1-12290 <$275
1902 Date Back
3x10-20 1-10500 <$150
1902 Plain Back
3x10-20 10501-33877 <$150
1929 Small Size
10 Type 1 1-7194 <$50
20 Type 1 1-1935 <$60
Total Issue $3,366,790
Out at close $247,940
Large out 1935 $7,765
Ch 13803 assumed circulation

8764 Mercer
McDOWELL NB OF SHARON
{{ 14 L 20 S }}
Chartered 6/07
1902 Red Seal <$VALUE
3x10-20 1-1500 <$275
1902 Date Back
4x5 1-7000 <$125
3x10-20 1-9500 <$125
1902 Plain Back
4x5 7001-62653 <$125
3x10-20 9501-42594 <$125
1929 Small Size
5 Type 1 1-12596 <$50
10 Type 1 1-6892 <$50
20 Type 1 1-1806 <$60
5 Type 2 1-12522 <$60
10 Type 2 1-6461 <$60
20 Type 2 1-2104 <$60
Total Issue $4,635,180
Out in 1935 $244,200
Large out 1935 $11,130

6560 Mercer
MERCHANTS & MANUFACTURERS NB OF SHARON
{{ 4 L 12 S }}
Chartered 12/29/02
1902 Red Seal <$VALUE
3x10-20 1-3700 <$400
1902 Date Back
3x10-20 1-5100 <$200
1902 Plain Back
3x10-20 5101-13952 <$200
1929 Small Size
10 Type 1 1-1570 <$85
20 Type 1 1-412 <$100
5 Type 2 1-324 <$100
10 Type 2 1-4698 <$100
20 Type 2 1-1466 <$100
Total Issue $1,104,160
Out in 1935 $82,100
Large out 1935 $1,505

2244 Mercer
SHARON NB, SHARON
{{ 2 L }}
Chartered 4/7/75
Liquidated 8/20/02
Original Series <$VALUE
4x5 1-5000 <$750
3x10-20 1-2000 <$850/$1500
Series 1875
4x5 1-50 <$750
3x10-20 1-5459 <$850/$1500
Brown Back
3x10-20 1-1427 <$600
Total Issue $545,300
Out in 1910 $4,365

6829 Mercer
FNB OF SHARPSVILLE
{{ 5 L 15 S }}
Chartered 6/03
1902 Red Seal <$VALUE
4x5 1-1100 <$350
3x10-20 1-1785 <$350
1902 Date Back
4x5 1-4850 <$175
3x10-20 1-3380 <$175
1902 Plain Back
4x5 4851-14839 <$175
3x10-20 3381-9827 <$175
1929 Small Size
5 Type 1 1-2054 <$85
10 Type 1 1-1070 <$85
20 Type 1 1-294 <$100
5 Type 2 1-9144 <$100
10 Type 2 1-4392 <$100
20 Type 2 1-1488 <$100
Total Issue $1,179,880
Out in 1935 $96,680
Large out 1935 $1,740

7873 Mercer
SHARPSVILLE NB, SHARPSVILLE
{{ UNREPORTED }}
Chartered 8/05
Liquidated 3/15/11
1902 Red Seal <$VALUE
3x10-20 1-2400 <$1250
1902 Date Back
3x10-20 1-962 <$850
Total Issue $168,100
Out in 1911 $24,750

6193 Warren
SHEFFIELD NB, SHEFFIELD
{{ 5 L 11 S }}
Chartered 4/4/02
1902 Red Seal <$VALUE
4x5 1-1500 <$500
3x10-20 1-2450 <$500
1902 Date Back
4x5 1-4250 <$250
3x10-20 1-3120 <$250
1902 Plain Back (dated 1902)
4x5 4251-7990 <$250
3x10-20 3121-5282 <$250
1902 Plain Back (dated 1922)
4x5 1-5062 <$250
3x10-20 1-3609 <$250
1929 Small Size
5 Type 1 1-1864 <$125
10 Type 1 1-902 <$125
20 Type 1 1-282 <$135
5 Type 2 1-2568 <$135
10 Type 2 1-1481 <$135
20 Type 2 1-378 <$135
Total Issue $1,037,180
Out in 1935 $49,200
Large out 1935 $2,270

9247 Schuylkill
CITIZENS NB OF SHENANDOAH
{{ 11 L 18 S }}
Chartered 10/08
Receivership 12/19/34
1902 Date Back <$VALUE
3x10-20 1-10400 <$200
1902 Plain Back
3x10-20 10401-31410 <$200
1929 Small Size
10 Type 1 1-3172 <$65
20 Type 1 1-888 <$75
10 Type 2 1-2589 <$75
20 Type 2 1-901 <$75
Total Issue $1,911,290
Out at close $100,000
Large out at close $4,180

3143 Schuylkill
FNB OF SHENANDOAH
{{ 6 L 12 S }}
Organized 3/14/84
Receivership 11/7/34
Brown Back <$VALUE
3x10-20 1-11907 <$400
1902 Red Seal
3x10-20 1-5000 <$400
1902 Date Back
3x10-20 1-9900 <$200
1902 Plain Back
3x10-20 9901-29431 <$200
1929 Small Size
5 Type 1 1-14458 <$100
5 Type 2 1-21000 <$100
Total Issue $2,855,640
Out at close $100,000
Large out at close $5,550

4546 Schuylkill
MERCHANTS NB OF SHENANDOAH
{{ U + 14 L 13 S }}
Chartered 1891
Brown Back <$VALUE
3x10-20 1-10480 <$250
1882 Date Back
3x10-20 1-2885 <$250
1902 Date Back
3x10-20 1-6900 <$125
1902 Plain Back
3x10-20 6901-26968 <$125
1929 Small Size
10 Type 1 1-3240 <$75
20 Type 1 1-880 <$85
10 Type 2 1-4195 <$85
20 Type 2 1-1154 <$85
Total Issue $2,381,680
Out in 1935 $98,300
Large out 1935 $5,470

13619 Schuylkill
MINERS NB OF SHENANDOAH
{{ 35 S }}
Chartered 6/15/32
1929 Small Size <$VALUE
5 Type 1 1-830 <$60
10 Type 1 1-1428 <$60
20 Type 1 1-406 <$70
5 Type 2 1-8678 <$60
10 Type 2 1-4707 <$60
20 Type 2 1-1344 <$70
Total Issue $276,640
Out in 1935 $122,650

5977 Allegheny
FNB OF SHERADEN
{{ 2 L }}
Chartered 9/25/01
Liquidated 12/30/16
Brown Back <$VALUE
3x10-20 1-3750 <$750
1882 Date Back
3x10-20 1-4740 <$750
1882 Value Back
3x10-20 4741-5058 <$750
Total Issue $440,400
Out at close $41,800

5573 Luzerne
FNB OF SHICKSHINNY
{{ 7 L 16 S }}
Chartered 9/11/00
Brown Back <$VALUE
3x10-20 1-1200 <$500
1882 Date Back
3x10-20 1-4810 <$500
1882 Value Back
3x10-20 4811-7490 <$500
1902 Plain Back
3x10-20 1-19368 <$275
1929 Small Size
10 Type 1 1-3702 <$125
20 Type 1 1-1056 <$125
10 Type 2 1-4739 <$150
20 Type 2 1-1578 <$150
Total Issue $1,830,690
Out in 1935 $102,050
Large out 1935 $3,100

6799 Potter
FNB OF SHINGLE HOUSE
{{ 1 L 5 S }}
Chartered 5/03
1902 Red Seal <$VALUE
3x10-20 1-1650 <$1250
1902 Date Back
3x10-20 1-2300 <$850
1902 Plain Back
3x10-20 2301-6699 <$850
1929 Small Size
5 Type 1 1-170 <$300
10 Type 1 1-722 <$300
20 Type 1 1-190 <$300
5 Type 2 1-1440 <$300
10 Type 2 1-828 <$300
Total Issue $504,150
Out in 1935 $24,300
Large out 1935 $1,110

6946 Cumberland
PEOPLES NB OF SHIPPENSBURG
{{ U + 4 L 13 S }}
Chartered 9/03
1902 Red Seal <$VALUE
3x10-20 1-2560 <$500
1902 Date Back
3x10-20 1-4000 <$250
1902 Plain Back
3x10-20 4001-13695 <$250
1929 Small Size
10 Type 1 1-4268 <$65
20 Type 1 1-1076 <$75
10 Type 2 1-4012 <$75
20 Type 2 1-1209 <$75
Total Issue $1,262,250
Out in 1935 $123,450
Large out 1935 $2,650

CONDITION affects Value. The Values shown are for notes in FINE condition.

834 Cumberland
FNB OF SHIPPENSBURGH
{{7 L 15 S}}
Chartered 2/23/65
Original Series <$VALUE
4x5 1-1900 <$450
3x10-20 1-1740 <$750/$1250
Series 1875
4x5 1-1485 <$450
3x10-20 1-1602 <$750/$1250
Brown Back
3x10-20 1-3299 <$275
1902 Red Seal
3x10-20 1-1610 <$300
1902 Date Back
4x5 1-3365 <$150
3x10-20 1-1960 <$150
1902 Plain Back
4x5 3366-9995 <$150
3x10-20 1961-6512 <$150
1929 Small Size
5 Type 1 1-7344 <$60
10 Type 1 1-3314 <$60
20 Type 1 1-954 <$65
5 Type 2 1-12408 <$65
10 Type 2 1-6706 <$65
20 Type 2 1-1795 <$65
Total Issue $1,704,390
Out in 1935 $171,250
Large out 1935 $2,915

7874 Clarion
FNB OF SHIPPENVILLE
{{2 L 5 S}}
Chartered 8/05
1902 Red Seal <$VALUE
3x10-20 1-900 <$650
1902 Date Back
3x10-20 1-2110 <$325
1902 Plain Back
3x10-20 2111-6240 <$325
1929 Small Size
10 Type 1 1-650 <$200
20 Type 1 1-150 <$200
10 Type 2 1-851 <$225
20 Type 2 1-222 <$225
Total Issue $426,950
Out in 1935 $25,000
Large out 1935 $1,000

11841 Berks
FNB OF SHOEMAKERSVILLE
{{3 L 10 S}}
Chartered 9/20
1902 Plain Back <$VALUE
3x10-20 1-7845 <$500
1929 Small Size
10 Type 1 1-1568 <$150
20 Type 1 1-404 <$175
10 Type 2 1-1970 <$175
20 Type 2 1-469 <$200
Total Issue $563,890
Out in 1935 $50,000
Large out 1935 $1,320

5227 Northampton
CEMENT NB OF SIEGFRIED
Chartered 10/30/99
2nd title: Cement NB of Siegfried at Northampton 9/22/19
FIRST TITLE {{2 L}}
Brown Back <$VALUE
4x5 1-2985 <$450
3x10-20 1-1846 <$450
1882 Date Back
4x5 1-4850 <$450
3x10-20 1-3260 <$450
1882 Value Back
4x5 4851-7173 <$450
3x10-20 3261-4465 <$450
SECOND TITLE {{5 L 8 S}}
1902 Plain Back
4x5 1-14585 <$275
3x10-20 1-9710 <$275
1929 Small Size
5 Type 1 1-1768 <$150
10 Type 1 1-920 <$150
20 Type 1 1-286 <$150
5 Type 2 1-2972 <$150
10 Type 2 1-1584 <$150
20 Type 2 1-456 <$150
Total Issue $1,478,290
Out in 1935 $49,000
Large out 1935 $3,660

11849 Somerset
FNB OF SIPESVILLE
{{0 L 3 S}}
Chartered 10/20
1902 Plain Back <$VALUE
3x10-20 1-2052 <$850
1929 Small Size
10 Type 1 1-386 <$350
20 Type 1 1-126 <$350
10 Type 2 1-54 <$400
20 Type 2 1-9 <$400
Total Issue $141,600
Out in 1935 $12,500
Large out 1935 $250

6051 Lehigh
CITIZENS NB OF SLATINGTON
{{8 L 14 S}}
Chartered 12/16/01
Brown Back <$VALUE
3x10-20 1-3360 <$325
1882 Date Back
3x10-20 1-4440 <$325
1882 Value Back
3x10-20 4441-7416 <$325
1902 Plain Back
3x10-20 1-5095 <$175
1929 Small Size
5 Type 1 1-1398 <$75
10 Type 1 1-1846 <$75
20 Type 1 1-414 <$85
5 Type 2 1-4524 <$85
10 Type 2 1-2138 <$85
20 Type 2 1-680 <$85
Total Issue $1,053,530
Out in 1935 $84,350
Large out 1935 $2,830

2293 Lehigh
NB OF SLATINGTON
{{16 L 20 S}}
Chartered 8/11/75
Series 1875 <$VALUE
4x5 1-10493 <$400
Brown Back
4x5 1-12600 <$225
3x10-20 1-5900 <$225
1882 Date Back
4x5 1-8595 <$225
3x10-20 1-5687 <$225
1902 Plain Back
4x5 1-18995 <$100
3x10-20 1-12593 <$100
1929 Small Size
5 Type 1 1-4320 <$50
10 Type 1 1-2032 <$50
20 Type 1 1-524 <$60
5 Type 2 1-6230 <$60
10 Type 2 1-2754 <$60
20 Type 2 1-1320 <$60
Total Issue $2,622,150
Out in 1935 $99,100
Large out 1935 $6,415

8946 Clarion
GRANGE NB OF CLARION COUNTY AT SLIGO
Chartered 11/07
2nd title: Sligo NB 2/21/13
FIRST TITLE {{0 L}}
1902 Red Seal <$VALUE
4x5 1-250 <$1500
3x10-20 1-200 <$1500
1902 Date Back
4x5 1-280 <$1000
3x10-20 1-231 <$1000
SECOND TITLE {{2 L 4 S}}
1902 Date Back
3x10-20 1-1200 <$450
1902 Plain Back
3x10-20 1201-5616 <$450
1929 Small Size
10 Type 1 1-684 <$250
20 Type 1 1-170 <$250
10 Type 2 1-1240 <$250
20 Type 2 1-351 <$250
Total Issue $393,810
Out in 1935 $25,000
Large out 1935 $840

Sligo NB, Sligo
SEE Ch 8946
Grange NB of Clarion County at Sligo

8724 Butler
CITIZENS NB OF SLIPPERY ROCK
{{3 L}}
Chartered 6/07
Liquidated 11/30/29
1902 Red Seal <$VALUE
3x10-20 1-400 <$1250
1902 Date Back
3x10-20 1-2560 <$600
1902 Plain Back
3x10-20 2561-6785 <$600
Total Issue $359,250
Out at close $16,800

6483 Butler
FNB OF SLIPPERY ROCK
{{3 L 5 S}}
Chartered 11/7/02
1902 Red Seal <$VALUE
3x10-20 1-775 <$1250
1902 Date Back
3x10-20 1-1680 <$600
1902 Plain Back
3x10-20 1681-5155 <$600
1929 Small Size
10 Type 1 1-644 <$400
20 Type 1 1-164 <$400
10 Type 2 1-765 <$400
20 Type 2 1-222 <$400
Total Issue $366,910
Out in 1935 $25,000
Large out 1935 $1,420

8591 McKean
GRANGE NB OF McKEAN COUNTY AT SMETHPORT
{{5 L 12 S}}
Chartered 3/07
1902 Red Seal <$VALUE
4x5 1-2500 <$650
3x10-20 1-2000 <$650
1902 Date Back
4x5 1-8450 <$300
3x10-20 1-6100 <$300
1902 Plain Back
4x5 8451-26578 <$300
3x10-20 6101-18151 <$300
1929 Small Size
5 Type 1 1-3964 <$150
10 Type 1 1-1864 <$150
20 Type 1 1-506 <$175
5 Type 2 1-6312 <$200
10 Type 2 1-3478 <$200
20 Type 2 1-1152 <$200
Total Issue $1,969,970
Out in 1935 $99,995
Large out 1935 $4,375

6642 Fayette
FNB OF SMITHFIELD
{{3 L 6 S}}
Chartered 2/03
Receivership 5/27/31
1902 Red Seal <$VALUE
3x10-20 1-1116 <$750
1902 Date Back
3x10-20 1-2360 <$375
1902 Plain Back
3x10-20 2361-9161 <$375
1929 Small Size
10 Type 1 1-855 <$175
20 Type 1 1-231 <$175
Total Issue $592,870
Out at close $50,000
Large out at close $5,700

5311 Westmoreland
FNB OF SMITHTON
{{3 L 3 S}}
Chartered 4/27/00
Brown Back <$VALUE
3x10-20 1-1190 <$600
1882 Date Back
3x10-20 1-1170* <$600
1882 Value Back
3x10-20 1311-1632* <$600
* 1171-1310 not marked
1902 Plain Back
3x10-20 1-1796 <$400
1929 Small Size
10 Type 1 1-376 <$300
20 Type 1 1-114 <$300
10 Type 2 1-138 <$300
20 Type 2 1-45 <$325
Total Issue $269,420
Out in 1935 $10,850
Large out 1935 $870

8901 Somerset
FNB OF SOMERFIELD
{{2 L 3 S}}
Chartered 10/07
Receivership 11/5/31
1902 Red Seal <$VALUE
3x10-20 1-450 <$1000
1902 Date Back
3x10-20 1-2380 <$450
1902 Plain Back
3x10-20 2381-6827 <$450
1929 Small Size
10 Type 1 1-512 <$350
20 Type 1 1-114 <$350
Total Issue $408,250
Out at close $24,160
Large out at close $2,520

5452 Somerset
FARMERS NB OF SOMERSET
{{4 L 8 S}}
Chartered 6/26/00
Liquidated 2/20/34
Brown Back <$VALUE
4x5 1-3275 <$450
3x10-20 1-2390 <$450
1882 Date Back
4x5 1-4150 <$450
3x10-20 1-3050 <$450
1882 Value Back
4x5 4151-6900 <$450
3x10-20 3051-4430 <$450
1902 Plain Back
4x5 1-7195 <$275
3x10-20 1-5154 <$275
1929 Small Size
5 Type 1 1-1732 <$125
10 Type 1 1-970 <$125
20 Type 1 1-278 <$135
5 Type 2 1-734 <$150
10 Type 2 1-310 <$150
20 Type 2 1-58 <$150
Total Issue $1,097,550
Out at close $45,950
Large out at close $2,270
Ch 13900 assumed circulation

4100 Somerset
FNB OF SOMERSET
{{7 L 14 S}}
Chartered 8/26/89
Brown Back <$VALUE
4x5 1-4652 <$400
3x10-20 1-1644 <$400
1902 Date Back
4x5 1-2050 <$250
3x10-20 1-1640 <$250
1902 Plain Back
4x5 2051-10847 <$250
3x10-20 1641-7558 <$250
1929 Small Size
5 Type 1 1-2826 <$85
10 Type 1 1-1672 <$85
20 Type 1 1-442 <$100
5 Type 2 1-5782 <$125
10 Type 2 1-2961 <$125
20 Type 2 1-734 <$150
Total Issue $1,081,420
Out in 1935 $100,000
Large out 1935 $1,215

13900 Somerset
PEOPLES NB OF SOMERSET
{{2 S}}
Chartered 12/33
1929 Small Size <$VALUE
5 Type 2 1-2414 <$400
10 Type 2 1-1200 <$400
20 Type 2 1-191 <$400
Total Issue $27,890
Out in 1935 $42,850
Large out 1935 $2,170
Outstanding includes Ch 5452

4227 Somerset
SOMERSET COUNTY NB OF SOMERSET
{{2 L}}
Chartered 1890
Liquidated 1/20/10
Brown Back <$VALUE
4x5 1-2425 <$750
3x10-20 1-4500 <$750
1882 Date Back
4x5 1-30 <$750
3x10-20 1-702 <$750
Total Issue $309,200
Out in 1910 $30,395

13251 Montgomery
PEOPLES NB OF SOUDERTON
{{28 S}}
Chartered 11/28
1929 Small Size <$VALUE
5 Type 1 1-460 <$100
10 Type 1 1-232 <$100
20 Type 1 1-84 <$100
5 Type 2 1-6136 <$100
10 Type 2 1-3691 <$100
20 Type 2 1-920 <$100
Total Issue $123,790
Out in 1935 $65,000

2333 Montgomery
UNION NB OF SOUDERTON
Chartered 5/11/76
2nd title: Union NB & TC 2/1/28
FIRST TITLE {{6 L}}
Series 1875 <$VALUE
4x5 1-3628 <$600
3x10-20 1-3638 <$850/$1500
Brown Back
3x10-20 1-8440 <$300
1882 Date Back
3x10-20 1-8500 <$300
1882 Value Back
3x10-20 8501-8675 <$300
1902 Plain Back
3x10-20 1-15920 <$150
SECOND TITLE {{4 L 14 S}}
1902 Plain Back
3x10-20 1-2176 <$175
1929 Small Size
10 Type 1 1-3226 <$100
20 Type 1 1-802 <$100
10 Type 2 1-3056 <$100
20 Type 2 1-710 <$100
Total Issue $2,349,570
Out in 1935 $84,500
Large out 1935 $4,530

3961 Northampton
SOUTH BETHLEHEM NB, SOUTH BETHLEHEM
Chartered 1/14/89
Receivership 3/26/34
2nd title: Bethlehem NB, Bethlehem 8/25/19
FIRST TITLE {{2 L}}
Brown Back <$VALUE
4x5 1-4319 <$650
3x10-20 1-1299 <$650
1902 Date Back
4x5 1-4600 <$375
3x10-20 1-3640 <$375
1902 Plain Back
4x5 4601-7400 <$375
3x10-20 3641-5140 <$375
SECOND TITLE {{3 L 7 S}}
1902 Plain Back
4x5 1-7755 <$300
3x10-20 1-5258 <$300
1929 Small Size
5 Type 1 1-2144 <$125
10 Type 1 1-1006 <$125
20 Type 1 1-286 <$150
5 Type 2 1-564 <$150
10 Type 2 1-162 <$150
20 Type 2 1-117 <$150
Total Issue $1,140,110
Out at close $50,000
Large out at close $2,970

6573 Cambria
FNB OF SOUTH FORK
{{4 L 10 S}}
Chartered 1/03
1902 Red Seal <$VALUE
4x5 1-1950 <$700
3x10-20 1-1450 <$700
1902 Date Back
4x5 1-3350 <$350
3x10-20 1-2560 <$350
1902 Plain Back
4x5 3351-11925 <$350
3x10-20 2561-8253 <$350
1929 Small Size
5 Type 1 1-2022 <$150
10 Type 1 1-1068 <$150
20 Type 1 1-248 <$150
5 Type 2 1-1874 <$175
10 Type 2 1-1103 <$175
20 Type 2 1-396 <$175
Total Issue $945,470
Out in 1935 $49,400
Large out 1935 $2,030

7181 Cambria
FNB OF SPANGLER
{{4 L 9 S}}
Chartered 3/04
1902 Red Seal <$VALUE
4x5 1-1650 <$450
3x10-20 1-2440 <$450
1902 Date Back
4x5 1-5225 <$225
3x10-20 1-3520 <$225
1902 Plain Back
4x5 5226-15622 <$225
3x10-20 3521-10439 <$225
1929 Small Size
5 Type 1 1-1852 <$125
10 Type 1 1-964 <$125
20 Type 1 1-308 <$125
5 Type 2 1-3110 <$150
10 Type 2 1-1559 <$150
20 Type 2 1-396 <$150
Total Issue $1,178,810
Out in 1935 $49,350
Large out 1935 $2,850

9110 Crawford
GRANGE NB OF SPARTANSBURG
{{2 L 4 S}}
Chartered 4/08
Liquidated 11/13/34
1902 Red Seal <$VALUE
3x10-20 1-700 <$1250
1902 Date Back
3x10-20 1-1510 <$650
1902 Plain Back
3x10-20 1511-5498 <$650
1929 Small Size
10 Type 1 1-652 <$275
20 Type 1 1-182 <$275
10 Type 2 1-187 <$300
20 Type 2 1-68 <$300
Total Issue $374,090
Out at close $22,680
Large out at close $1,030

2018 Chester
NB OF SPRING CITY
Chartered 7/23/72
2nd title: NB & TC of Spring City 6/30/28
FIRST TITLE {{6 L}}
Original Series <$VALUE
4x5 1-2650 <$650
3x10-20 1-1740 <$850/$1500
Series 1875
3x10-20 1-5560 <$850/$1500
Brown Back
3x10-20 1-6000 <$450
1882 Date Back
3x10-20 1-6648 <$450
1902 Date Back
3x10-20 1-7800* <$250
1902 Plain Back
3x10-20 8601-33516* <$250
* 7801-8600 not marked
SECOND TITLE {{1 L 18 S}}
1902 Plain Back
3x10-20 1-2472 <$300
1929 Small Size
10 Type 1 1-6128 <$75
20 Type 1 1-1738 <$80
10 Type 2 1-13648 <$80
20 Type 2 1-3890 <$80
Total Issue $3,663,320
Out in 1935 $249,540
Large out 1935 $7,090

6536 York
FNB OF SPRING GROVE
Chartered 12/17/02
2nd title: Spring Grove NB 5/28/32
FIRST TITLE {{3 L 3 S}}
1902 Red Seal <$VALUE
4x5 1-2900 <$750
3x10-20 1-2520 <$750
1902 Date Back
4x5 1-4225 <$350
3x10-20 1-3120 <$350
1902 Plain Back
4x5 4226-13856 <$350
3x10-20 3121-9389 <$350
1929 Small Size
5 Type 1 1-1650 <$175
10 Type 1 1-808 <$175
20 Type 1 1-202 <$175
SECOND TITLE {{8 S}}
1929 Small Size
5 Type 1 1-232 <$150
10 Type 1 1-476 <$150
20 Type 1 1-96 <$150
5 Type 2 1-7548 <$150
10 Type 2 1-3780 <$150
20 Type 2 1-1020 <$150
Total Issue $1,195,770
Out in 1935 $97,670
Large out 1935 $3,760
Outstanding includes Ch 8141

8141 York
PEOPLES NB OF SPRING GROVE
{{5 L 6 S}}
Chartered 3/06
Closed 5/28/32
1902 Red Seal <$VALUE
4x5 1-1662 <$750
3x10-20 1-1510 <$750
1902 Date Back
4x5 1-4100 <$350
3x10-20 1-2940 <$350
1902 Plain Back
4x5 4101-13353 <$350
3x10-20 2941-8953 <$350
1929 Small Size
5 Type 1 1-1481 <$200
10 Type 1 1-764 <$200
20 Type 1 1-189 <$200
Total Issue $936,400
Out at close $50,000
Large out at close $3,150
Ch 6536 assumed circulation

Spring Grove NB, Spring Grove
SEE Ch 6536
FNB of Spring Grove

11213 Centre
FNB OF SPRING MILLS
{{2L 6S}}
Chartered 7/18
1902 Plain Back <$VALUE
4x5 1-14014 <$600
1929 Small Size
5 Type 1 1-3272 <$175
5 Type 2 1-6936 <$175
Total Issue $413,120
Out in 1935 $22,760
Large out 1935 $210

NB of Springdale
SEE Ch 8320
Springdale NB, Springdale

8320 Allegheny
SPRINGDALE NB, SPRINGDALE
Chartered 8/06
2nd title: NB of Springdale 1/9/32
FIRST TITLE {{4L 9S}}
1902 Red Seal <$VALUE
4x10 1-937 <$500
1902 Date Back
4x10 1-3450 <$250
1902 Plain Back
4x10 3451-15961 <$250
1929 Small Size
5 Type 1 1-2444 <$100
10 Type 1 1-1026 <$100
SECOND TITLE {{6S}}
1929 Small Size
5 Type 1 1-1980 <$100
5 Type 2 1-15434 <$100
Total Issue $947,370
Out in 1935 $49,950
Large out 1935 $1,890

11393 Susquehanna
FNB OF SPRINGVILLE
{{1L 3S}}
Chartered 7/19
Liquidated 9/14/33
1902 Plain Back <$VALUE
3x10-20 1-4276 <$650
1929 Small Size
10 Type 1 1-695 <$300
20 Type 1 1-222 <$300
Total Issue $282,140
Out at close $21,880
Large out at close $820
Ch 2223 assumed circulation

7511 Centre
FNB OF STATE COLLEGE
{{5L 9S}}
Chartered 12/04
1902 Red Seal <$VALUE
4x5 1-1921 <$500
3x10-20 1-1457 <$500
1902 Date Back
4x5 1-4400 <$250
3x10-20 1-3200 <$250
1902 Plain Back
4x5 4401-14782 <$250
3x10-20 3201-9828 <$250
1929 Small Size
5 Type 1 1-2134 <$125
10 Type 1 1-1098 <$125
20 Type 1 1-290 <$150
5 Type 2 1-3000 <$150
10 Type 2 1-1704 <$150
20 Type 2 1-396 <$150
Total Issue $1,102,970
Out in 1935 $50,000
Large out 1935 $1,720

12261 Centre
PEOPLES NB OF STATE COLLEGE
{{2L 16S}}
Chartered 10/22
1902 Plain Back <$VALUE
4x5 1-5167 <$450
3x10-20 1-3820 <$450
1929 Small Size
5 Type 1 1-4266* <$85
10 Type 1 1-2346 <$85
20 Type 1 1-438 <$100
5 Type 2 1-8914 <$100
10 Type 2 1-4240 <$100
20 Type 2 1-1249 <$100
* 3921 not issued
Total Issue $727,560
Out in 1935 $104,100
Large out 1935 $1,210

3599 Dauphin
STEELTON NB, STEELTON
{{3L}}
Chartered 12/9/86
Liquidated 6/30/28
Brown Back <$VALUE
3x10-20 1-5695 <$500
1902 Red Seal
3x10-20 1-3750 <$500
1902 Date Back
3x10-20 1-15500 <$275
1902 Plain Back
3x10-20 15501-16971 <$275
Total Issue $1,320,800
Out at close $4,230

4665 York
FNB OF STEWARTSTOWN
{{5L 9S}}
Organized 10/31/91
Brown Back <$VALUE
4x5 1-5325 <$400
3x10-20 1-2980 <$400
1882 Date Back
4x5 1-1537 <$400
3x10-20 1-1243 <$400
1902 Date Back
3x10-20 1-2700 <$250
1902 Plain Back
3x10-20 2701-11482 <$250
1929 Small Size
10 Type 1 1-1574 <$150
20 Type 1 1-380 <$150
10 Type 2 1-1722 <$150
20 Type 2 1-431 <$150
Total Issue $1,088,370
Out in 1935 $41,700
Large out 1935 $3,100

6444 York
PEOPLES NB OF STEWARTSTOWN
{{5L 11S}}
Chartered 10/2/02
1902 Red Seal <$VALUE
3x10-20 1-3700 <$600
1902 Date Back
3x10-20 1-4300 <$275
1902 Plain Back
3x10-20 4301-13003 <$275
1929 Small Size
10 Type 1 1-1444 <$125
20 Type 1 1-348 <$125
10 Type 2 1-2414 <$125
20 Type 2 1-624 <$150
Total Issue $1,000,170
Out in 1935 $50,000
Large out 1935 $2,560

6638 Mercer
FNB OF STONEBORO
{{8L 5S}}
Chartered 2/03
1902 Red Seal <$VALUE
3x10-20 1-765 <$650
1902 Date Back
3x10-20 1-1000* <$300
1902 Plain Back
3x10-20 1121-3074* <$300
* 1001-1120 not marked
1929 Small Size
10 Type 1 1-312 <$225
20 Type 1 1-104 <$225
10 Type 2 1-220 <$250
20 Type 2 1-58 <$250
Total Issue $226,510
Out in 1935 $12,500
Large out 1935 $1,060

14089 Somerset
FNB AT STOYSTOWN
{{1S}}
Chartered 4/34
1929 Small Size <$VALUE
5 Type 2 1-818 <$600
10 Type 2 1-272 <$600
20 Type 2 1-125 <$600
Total Issue $9,310
Out in 1935 $50,000
Large out 1935 $4,330
Outstanding includes Ch 5682

5682 Somerset
FNB OF STOYSTOWN
{{4L 6S}}
Chartered 1/16/01
Liquidated 5/18/34
Brown Back <$VALUE
4x5 1-1600 <$400
3x10-20 1-1150 <$400
1882 Date Back
4x5 1-3375 <$400
3x10-20 1-2440 <$400
1882 Value Back
4x5 3376-6605 <$400
3x10-20 2441-4218 <$400
1902 Plain Back
3x10-20 1-3923 <$275
3x50-100 1-362 <$500/$600
1929 Small Size
10 Type 1 1-480 <$175
20 Type 1 1-171 <$175
50 Type 1 1-86 <$275
100 Type 1 1-34 <$350
Total Issue $814,670
Out at close $50,000
Large out 1935 $4,330
Ch 14089 assumed circulation

42 Lancaster
FNB OF STRASBURG*
{{3L 5S}}
Chartered 7/63
Liquidated 5/22/82
*Rechartered as Ch 2700 which retook Ch 42 5/20/11
Original Series <$VALUE
4x5 1-5150 <$850
3x10-20 1-2220<$1000/$1500
Series 1875
3x10-20 1-1464<$1000/$1500
1902 Date Back
3x10-20 1-1240 <$500
1902 Plain Back
3x10-20 1241-4530 <$500
1929 Small Size
10 Type 1 1-654 <$225
20 Type 1 1-172 <$225
10 Type 2 1-1061 <$250
20 Type 2 1-253 <$250
Total Issue $589,250
Out in 1935 $24,350
Large out 1935 $2,780
Outstanding includes Ch 2700

2700 Lancaster
FNB OF STRASBURG
{{1L}}
Chartered 1882
RETOOK Ch 42 5/20/11
Brown Back <$VALUE
3x10-20 1-3945 <$750
1902 Red Seal
3x10-20 1-1650 <$750
1902 Date Back
3x10-20 1-1450 <$600
Total Issue $352,250
Out in 1911 $80,000

10452 Berks
STRAUSSTOWN NB, STRAUSSTOWN
{{1L 3S}}
Chartered 10/13
Liquidated 10/1/34
1902 Date Back <$VALUE
3x10-20 1-660 <$650
1902 Plain Back
3x10-20 661-2327 <$650
1929 Small Size
10 Type 1 1-476 <$300
20 Type 1 1-124 <$300
10 Type 2 1-511 <$300
20 Type 2 1-173 <$300
Total Issue $168,360
Out at close $25,000
Large out 1935 $510
Ch 13863 assumed circulation

13863 Berks
STRAUSSTOWN NB, STRAUSSTOWN
{{5S}}
Chartered 12/33
1929 Small Size <$VALUE
5 Type 2 1-3200 <$250
10 Type 2 1-1609 <$250
20 Type 2 1-515 <$250
Total Issue $42,390
Out in 1935 $49,700
Large out 1935 $510
Outstanding includes Ch 10452

F-Stroudsburg NB of Stroudsburg
SEE Ch 3632
Stroudsburg NB, Stroudsburg

2787 Monroe
FNB OF STROUDSBURG
{{4L 8S}}
Chartered 1882
Closed 9/12/32
Brown Back <$VALUE
4x5 1-7027 <$450
3x10-20 1-910 <$450
1902 Red Seal
3x10-20 1-2600 <$500
1902 Date Back
3x10-20 1-4100* <$250
1902 Plain Back
4x5 1-5970 <$250
3x10-20 4351-11919* <$250
* 4101-4350 not marked
1929 Small Size
5 Type 1 1-1656 <$150
10 Type 1 1-878 <$150
20 Type 1 1-234 <$150
Total Issue $1,161,830
Out at close $50,000
Large out at close $3,730
Ch 3632 assumed circulation

3632 Monroe
STROUDSBURG NB, STROUDSBURG
Chartered 2/4/87
2nd title: F-Stroudsburg NB 9/12/32
FIRST TITLE {{12L 12S}}
Brown Back <$VALUE
4x5 1-6288 <$225
3x10-20 1-5292 <$225
1902 Red Seal
4x5 1-1850 <$225
3x10-20 1-1000 <$225
50-100 1-60 <$2250/$2500
1902 Date Back
4x5 1-8050 <$100
3x10-20 1-5840 <$100
3x50-100 1-300 <$350/$450
1902 Plain Back
4x5 8051-26721 <$100
3x10-20 5841-18722 <$100
1929 Small Size
5 Type 1 1-5412 <$60
10 Type 1 1-2566 <$60
20 Type 1 1-694 <$70
SECOND TITLE {{16S}}
1929 Small Size
5 Type 1 1-2576 <$45
10 Type 1 1-2012 <$50
20 Type 1 1-450 <$60
5 Type 2 1-35646 <$45
10 Type 2 1-19544 <$50
20 Type 2 1-4759 <$60
Total Issue $3,152,330
Out in 1935 $345,240
Large out 1935 $7,670
Outstanding includes Ch 2787

6739 Jefferson
UNION NB OF SUMMERVILLE
{{4L 6S}}
Chartered 4/23/03
1902 Red Seal <$VALUE
3x10-20 1-1430 <$600
50-100 1-190 <$2250/$2500
1902 Date Back
3x10-20 1-2160 <$300
50-100 1-200 <$650/$750
1902 Plain Back
3x10-20 2161-4160 <$300
3x50-100 1-687 <$650/$750
1929 Small Size
10 Type 1 1-468 <$175
20 Type 1 1-185 <$175
50 Type 1 1-110 <$350
100 Type 1 1-37 <$400
Total Issue $615,230
Out in 1935 $49,550
Large out 1935 $4,150

1237 Northumberland
FNB OF SUNBURY
{{24L 31S}}
Chartered 1865
Original Series <$VALUE
3x1-2 1-2000 <$350/$1000
4x5 1-5000 <$400
3x10-20 1-4400 <$750/$1250
Series 1875
3x10-20 1-3070 <$750/$1250
Brown Back
4x5 1-4260 <$250
3x10-20 1-3274 <$250
50-100 1-673 <$1250/$1500
1902 Red Seal
4x5 1-7000 <$250
3x10-20 1-4700 <$250
1902 Date Back
4x5 1-16500 <$100
3x10-20 1-13000 <$100
1902 Plain Back
4x5 16501-56220 <$100
3x10-20 13001-38872 <$100
1929 Small Size
5 Type 1 1-10782 <$50
10 Type 1 1-6316 <$50
20 Type 1 1-1958 <$60
5 Type 2 1-24680 <$50
10 Type 2 1-13281 <$50
20 Type 2 1-3566 <$60
Total Issue $5,541,260
Out in 1935 $330,540
Large out 1935 $11,255
Outstanding includes Ch 6877

6877 Northumberland
SUNBURY NB, SUNBURY
{{2L}}
Chartered 7/03
Liquidated 10/26/23
1902 Red Seal <$VALUE
3x10-20 1-1700 <$850
1902 Date Back
3x10-20 1-3270 <$500
1902 Plain Back
3x10-20 3271-4665 <$500
Total Issue $318,250
Out at close $19,000
Ch 1237 assumed circulation

3144 Susquehanna
CITY NB OF SUSQUEHANNA
{{5L 10S}}
Chartered 1884
Brown Back <$VALUE
3x10-20 1-3275 <$350
1902 Red Seal
3x10-20 1-620 <$400
1902 Date Back
3x10-20 1-3640 <$200
1902 Plain Back
4x5 1-5955 <$200
3x10-20 3641-11061 <$200
1929 Small Size
5 Type 1 1-2296 <$135
10 Type 1 1-1078 <$135
20 Type 1 1-296 <$135
5 Type 2 1-3408 <$150
10 Type 2 1-1761 <$150
20 Type 2 1-588 <$150
Total Issue $1,082,390
Out in 1935 $48,450
Large out 1935 $1,510

FNB of Susquehanna
SEE Ch 1053
FNB of Susquehanna Depot

1053 Susquehanna
FNB OF SUSQUEHANNA DEPOT
Chartered 4/65
2nd title: FNB of Susquehanna 3/22/05
FIRST TITLE {{3L}}
Original Series <$VALUE
3x1-2 1-840 <$400/$1250
4x5 1-5750 <$500
3x10-20 1-1600 <$750/$1250
Series 1875
4x5 1-2520 <$500
3x10-20 1-1626 <$750/$1250
Brown Back
4x5 1-22244 <$450
3x10-20 1-3442 <$450
SECOND TITLE {{7L 15S}}
1902 Red Seal
3x10-20 1-3800 <$350
1902 Date Back
4x5 1-8815 <$175
3x10-20 1-5700 <$175
1902 Plain Back
4x5 8816-24165 <$175
3x10-20 5701-15638 <$175
1929 Small Size
5 Type 1 1-1532 <$85
10 Type 1 1-2614 <$85
20 Type 1 1-734 <$100
10 Type 2 1-5431 <$100
20 Type 2 1-1099 <$100
Total Issue $2,770,250
Out in 1935 $79,280
Large out 1935 $6,580

6270 Westmoreland
FNB OF SUTERSVILLE
{{2L 2S}}
Chartered 5/23/02
Receivership 6/10/32
1902 Red Seal <$VALUE
4x5 1-1715 <$700
3x10-20 1-1174 <$700
1902 Date Back
4x5 1-2475 <$350
3x10-20 1-1720 <$350
1902 Plain Back (dated 1902)
4x5 2476-4650 <$350
3x10-20 1721-2984 <$350
1902 Plain Back (dated 1922)
4x5 1-3475 <$350
3x10-20 1-2005 <$350
1929 Small Size
5 Type 1 1-757 <$350
10 Type 1 1-344 <$350
20 Type 1 1-112 <$350
Total Issue $561,740
Out at close $25,000
Large out at close $1,915

7193 Delaware
SWARTHMORE NB, SWARTHMORE
Chartered 3/04
2nd title: Swarthmore NB & TC 1/13/28
FIRST TITLE {{4L}}
1902 Red Seal <$VALUE
3x10-20 1-2900 <$750
1902 Date Back
3x10-20 1-4880 <$350
1902 Plain Back
3x10-20 4881-14144 <$350
SECOND TITLE {{1L 8S}}
1902 Plain Back
3x10-20 1-1021 <$400
1929 Small Size
10 Type 1 1-1652 <$175
20 Type 1 1-422 <$200
10 Type 2 1-2329 <$200
20 Type 2 1-451 <$200
Total Issue $1,085,320
Out in 1935 $48,700
Large out 1935 $2,530

7003 Snyder
FNB OF SWINEFORD
{{2L 7S}}
Chartered 10/03
1902 Red Seal <$VALUE
3x10-20 1-1540 <$650
1902 Date Back
3x10-20 1-2370 <$300
1902 Plain Back
3x10-20 2371-6773 <$300
1929 Small Size
10 Type 1 1-810 <$165
20 Type 1 1-202 <$165
10 Type 2 1-751 <$175
20 Type 2 1-219 <$175
Total Issue $500,380
Out in 1935 $24,350
Large out 1935 $930

6109 Allegheny
FNB OF SWISSVALE
{{7L 12S}}
Chartered 1/28/02
1902 Red Seal <$VALUE
3x10-20 1-1070 <$400
1902 Date Back
3x10-20 1-1470 <$175
1902 Plain Back (dated 1901)
4x5 1-2800 <$175
3x10-20 1471-2600 <$175
1902 Plain Back (dated 1921)
4x5 1-47723 <$175
1929 Small Size
5 Type 1 1-15092 <$85
5 Type 2 1-30356 <$85
Total Issue $1,798,500
Out in 1935 $100,000
Large out 1935 $3,120

14169 Jefferson
FNB IN SYKESVILLE
{{1L}}
Chartered 5/34
1929 Small Size <$VALUE
10 Type 2 1-308 <$650
20 Type 2 1-105 <$650
Total Issue $5,180
Out in 1935 $25,000
Large out 1935 $1,050
Outstanding includes Ch 7488

7488 Jefferson
FNB OF SYKESVILLE
{{2L 7S}}
Chartered 11/04
Liquidated 10/23/34
1902 Red Seal <$VALUE
3x10-20 1-730 <$700
1902 Date Back
3x10-20 1-2290 <$350
1902 Plain Back
3x10-20 2291-7112 <$350
1929 Small Size
10 Type 1 1-746 <$175
20 Type 1 1-212 <$175
10 Type 2 1-411 <$200
20 Type 2 1-186 <$200
Total Issue $470,130
Out at close $25,000
Large out 1935 $1,050
Ch 14169 assumed circulation

<$VALUEs are for notes in **FINE** condition. Value changes by approximately **25%** for a change of one full grade.

****
1219 Schuylkill
FNB OF TAMAQUA
{{ 11 L 16 S }}
Chartered 1865
Original Series <$VALUE
4x5 1-4647 <$500
3x10-20 1-3700 <$750/$1250
50-100 1-300 <$3500
Series 1875
3x10-20 1-2856 <$750/$1250
50-100 1-512 <$3500
Brown Back
3x10-20 1-12109 <$250
1902 Red Seal
3x10-20 1-3600 <$275
1902 Date Back
3x10-20 1-9700 <$135
1902 Plain Back
3x10-20 9701-29529 <$135
1929 Small Size
10 Type 1 1-4162 <$60
20 Type 1 1-1034 <$65
10 Type 2 1-9741 <$60
20 Type 2 1-2391 <$65
Total Issue $3,323,470
Out in 1935 $155,850
Large out 1935 $7,740
****
7286 Schuylkill
TAMAQUA NB, TAMAQUA
{{ 7 L 16 S }}
Chartered 6/04
1902 Red Seal <$VALUE
3x10-20 1-5100 <$300
1902 Date Back
3x10-20 1-10100 <$150
1902 Plain Back
3x10-20 10101-33120 <$150
1929 Small Size
10 Type 1 1-3874 <$60
20 Type 1 1-1036 <$65
10 Type 2 1-5604 <$60
20 Type 2 1-1420 <$70
Total Issue $2,352,200
Out in 1935 $121,350
Large out 1935 $4,110
****
13940 Allegheny
FNB IN TARENTUM
{{ 13 S }}
Chartered 1/34
1929 Small Size <$VALUE
5 Type 2 1-9656 <$75
10 Type 2 1-5478 <$75
20 Type 2 1-1752 <$85
Total Issue $138,100
Out in 1935 $125,000
Large out 1935 $2,700
Outstanding includes Ch 4453
****
2285 Allegheny
FNB OF TARENTUM
{{ 1 L }}
Chartered 7/17/75
Liquidated 1/13/85
Series 1875 <$VALUE
4x5 1-2885 <$850
3x10-20 1-1004<$1000/$1500
Total Issue $107,900
Out in 1910 $520
****
FNB & TC of Tarentum
SEE Ch 4453
NB of Tarentum
****
4453 Allegheny
NB OF TARENTUM
Organized 10/4/90
Liquidated 4/18/34
2nd title: FNB & TC 6/9/27
FIRST TITLE {{ 3 L }}
Brown Back <$VALUE
3x10-20 1-5330 <$350
1882 Date Back
3x10-20 1-1077 <$350
1902 Date Back
3x10-20 1-3500 <$175
1902 Plain Back
3x10-20 3501-11343 <$175
SECOND TITLE {{ 0 L 7 S }}
1902 Plain Back
3x10-20 1-1334 <$250
1929 Small Size
5 Type 1 1-334 <$150
10 Type 1 1-1409 <$150
20 Type 1 1-389 <$150
Total Issue $1,095,440
Out at close $49,100
Large out 1935 $2,700
Ch 13940 assumed circulation
****

****
5351 Allegheny
PEOPLES NB OF TARENTUM
{{ 7 L 17 S }}
Chartered 5/15/00
Brown Back <$VALUE
4x5 1-3295 <$275
3x10-20 1-3042 <$275
1882 Date Back
4x5 1-4500 <$275
3x10-20 1-3180 <$275
1882 Value Back
4x5 4501-6970 <$275
3x10-20 3181-4578 <$275
1902 Plain Back
4x5 1-11105 <$175
3x10-20 1-7404 <$175
1929 Small Size
10 Type 1 1-2822 <$70
20 Type 1 1-786 <$80
10 Type 2 1-4019 <$80
20 Type 2 1-1022 <$80
Total Issue $1,502,870
Out in 1935 $98,800
Large out 1935 $3,460
****
9257 Montgomery
TELFORD NB, TELFORD
{{ 5 L 18 S }}
Chartered 10/08
1902 Date Back <$VALUE
3x10-20 1-5500 <$250
1902 Plain Back
3x10-20 5501-14473 <$250
1929 Small Size
5 Type 1 1-1966 <$85
10 Type 1 1-1070 <$85
20 Type 1 1-294 <$100
5 Type 2 1-6092 <$100
10 Type 2 1-3163 <$100
20 Type 2 1-988 <$100
Total Issue $963,960
Out in 1935 $75,000
Large out 1935 $1,800
****
9316 Lancaster
TERRE HILL NB, TERRE HILL
{{ 4 L 3 S }}
Chartered 1/09
Liquidated 3/7/30
1902 Date Back <$VALUE
3x10-20 1-3350 <$500
1902 Plain Back
3x10-20 3351-8099 <$500
1929 Small Size
10 Type 1 1-232 <$350
20 Type 1 1-42 <$350
Total Issue $423,910
Out at close $27,540
Large out at close $8,620
****
10211 Juniata
FARMERS NB OF
THOMPSONTOWN
{{ 2 L 4 S }}
Chartered 6/12
1902 Date Back <$VALUE
4x5 1-665 <$500
3x10-20 1-534 <$500
1902 Plain Back
4x5 666-4963 <$500
3x10-20 535-3197 <$500
1929 Small Size
5 Type 1 1-1004 <$200
10 Type 1 1-498 <$200
20 Type 1 1-150 <$200
5 Type 2 1-1062 <$225
10 Type 2 1-685 <$225
20 Type 2 1-158 <$225
Total Issue $352,430
Out in 1935 $24,650
Large out 1935 $880
****
10183 Huntingdon
FNB OF THREE SPRINGS
{{ UNREPORTED }}
Chartered 4/12
1902 Date Back <$VALUE
3x10-20 1-1000 <$1500
1902 Plain Back
3x10-20 1001-4760 <$1500
Total Issue $238,000
Out in 1935 $1,110
****
11204 Jefferson
FNB OF TIMBLIN
{{ 2 L 14 S }}
Chartered 7/18
Liquidated 9/18/34
1902 Plain Back <$VALUE
3x10-20 1-4565 <$500
1929 Small Size
10 Type 1 1-738 <$150
20 Type 1 1-180 <$175
10 Type 2 1-358 <$200
20 Type 2 1-105 <$200
Total Issue $299,810
Out at close $22,310
Large out at close $840
****
8092 Tioga
GRANGE NB OF TIOGA
{{ 2 L 4 S }}
Chartered 2/06
1902 Red Seal <$VALUE
3x10-20 1-960 <$1000
1902 Date Back
3x10-20 1-2360 <$450
1902 Plain Back
3x10-20 2361-6796 <$450
1929 Small Size
10 Type 1 1-648 <$275
20 Type 1 1-180 <$275
10 Type 2 1-1207 <$300
20 Type 2 1-260 <$300
Total Issue $465,550
Out in 1935 $21,350
Large out 1935 $1,010
****
5040 Forest
CITIZENS NB OF TIONESTA
{{ 5 L 10 S }}
Organized 5/2/96
Brown Back <$VALUE
4x5 1-2090 <$375
3x10-20 1-944 <$375
1882 Date Back
4x5 1-4200 <$375
3x10-20 1-3200 <$375
1882 Value Back
4x5 4201-4415 <$375
3x10-20 3201-3330 <$375
1902 Plain Back
4x5 1-8475 <$225
3x10-20 1-5856 <$225
1929 Small Size
10 Type 1 1-1364 <$100
20 Type 1 1-368 <$125
10 Type 2 1-1685 <$125
20 Type 2 1-384 <$125
Total Issue $956,630
Out in 1935 $48,350
Large out 1935 $2,010
****
5038 Forest
FOREST COUNTY NB OF
TIONESTA
{{ 4 L 3 S }}
Chartered 1896
Brown Back <$VALUE
4x5 1-4525 <$400
50-100 1-830 <$1250/$1500
1882 Date Back
4x5 1-3150 <$400
50-100 1-300 <$1250/$1500
3x50-100 1-208<$1250/$1500
1882 Value Back
4x5 3151-3319 <$400
1902 Plain Back
3x50-100 1-953 <$500/$600
1929 Small Size
50 Type 1 1-166 <$350
100 Type 1 1-38 <$400
Total Issue $689,230
Out in 1935 $47,290
Large out 1935 $5,490
****
622 Crawford
FNB OF TITUSVILLE
{{ 1 L }}
Chartered 12/14/64
Liquidated 1/15/68
Original Series <$VALUE
3x1-2 1-50 <$1000/$2000
4x5 1-2000 <$1250
3x10-20 1-930 <$1500/$2000
Total Issue $86,750
Out in 1910 $783
****
2466 Crawford
HYDE NB OF TITUSVILLE
{{ 1 L }}
Chartered 3/16/80
Liquidated 6/21/88
Series 1875 <$VALUE
4x5 1-4500 <$850
3x10-20 1-5600<$1000/$1500
50-100 1-1760 <$4000
Total Issue $634,000
Out in 1910 $2,060
****
2834 Crawford
ROBERTS NB OF TITUSVILLE
{{ UNREPORTED }}
Chartered 12/12/82
Liquidated 2/28/87
Brown Back <$VALUE
4x5 1-1772 <$1250
3x10-20 1-1036 <$1250
50-100 1-303 <$2500
Total Issue $132,690
Out in 1910 $845
****

****
879 Crawford
SECOND NB OF TITUSVILLE
{{ 21 L 27 S }}
Chartered 3/11/65
Original Series <$VALUE
3x1-2 1-7253 <$300/$850
4x5 1-6450 <$375
3x10-20 1-2770 <$750/$1250
50-100 1-618 <$3500
Series 1875
3x1-2 1-1326 <$300/$850
4x5 1-7000 <$375
3x10-20 1-4350 <$750/$1250
50-100 1-308 <$3500
Brown Back
3x10-20 1-16240 <$225
1902 Red Seal
4x5 1-11750 <$225
3x10-20 1-7000 <$225
1902 Date Back
4x5 1-19500 <$100
3x10-20 1-16000 <$100
1902 Plain Back
4x5 19501-67719 <$100
3x10-20 16001-45552 <$100
1929 Small Size
5 Type 1 1-10892 <$30
10 Type 1 1-5600 <$35
20 Type 1 1-1494 <$45
5 Type 2 1-18800 <$30
10 Type 2 1-10203 <$35
20 Type 2 1-2334 <$45
Total Issue $6,920,525
Out in 1935 $290,150
Large out 1935 $16,780
****
8223 Berks
NB OF TOPTON
{{ 11 L 3U + 24 S }}
Chartered 5/06
1902 Red Seal <$VALUE
3x10-20 1-800 <$400
1902 Date Back
3x10-20 1-2280 <$175
1902 Plain Back
3x10-20 2281-6562 <$175
1929 Small Size
10 Type 1 1-970 <$70
20 Type 1 1-284 <$85
10 Type 2 1-2249 <$85
20 Type 2 1-470 <$85
Total Issue $492,270
Out in 1935 $50,000
Large out 1935 $1,460
****
3358 Berks
TOPTON NB, TOPTON
{{ 1 L }}
Chartered 6/26/85
Liquidated 12/28/86
Brown Back <$VALUE
3x10-20 1-367 <$1250
Total Issue $18,350
Out in 1910 $80
****
2337 Bradford
CITIZENS NB OF TOWANDA
{{ 13 L 19 S }}
Chartered 6/29/76
Series 1875 <$VALUE
4x5 1-20449 <$350
Brown Back
4x5 1-15000 <$175
3x10-20 1-9000 <$175
1882 Date Back
4x5 1-11750 <$150
3x10-20 1-9000 <$150
1882 Value Back
4x5 11751-12374 <$150
3x10-20 9001-9468 <$175
1902 Plain Back
4x5 1-26175 <$85
3x10-20 1-16721 <$100
1929 Small Size
5 Type 1 1-6068 <$35
10 Type 1 1-3238 <$40
20 Type 1 1-788 <$50
5 Type 2 1-9700 <$35
10 Type 2 1-5783 <$40
20 Type 2 1-1716 <$50
Total Issue $3,850,940
Out in 1935 $144,700
Large out 1935 $8,040
****
39 Bradford
FNB OF TOWANDA
{{ 15 L 22 S }}
Chartered 7/63
Original Series <$VALUE
4x5 1-4600 <$400
3x10-20 1-1600 <$750/$1250
3x10-20 3601-440<$750/$1250
20 1601-3600 <$1250
Series 1875
4x5 1-1900 <$225
3x10-20 1-1926 <$225
Brown Back
4x5 1-10850 <$225
3x10-20 1-6112 <$225
1902 Red Seal
4x5 1-7250 <$225
3x10-20 1-5200 <$225
1902 Date Back
4x5 1-9400 <$100
3x10-20 1-7620 <$100
1902 Plain Back
4x5 9401-31638 <$100
3x10-20 7621-21808 <$100
1929 Small Size
5 Type 1 1-5140 <$50
10 Type 1 1-2474 <$50
20 Type 1 1-708 <$60
5 Type 2 1-8194 <$50
10 Type 2 1-4457 <$50
20 Type 2 1-1300 <$60
Total Issue $3,536,200
Out in 1935 $120,800
Large out 1935 $5,860
****
6117 Schuylkill
TOWER CITY NB, TOWER CITY
{{ 2 L 12 S }}
Chartered 2/6/02
Receivership 4/20/34
1902 Red Seal <$VALUE
3x10-20 1-1900 <$750
1902 Date Back
3x10-20 1-2260 <$350
1902 Plain Back (dated 1902)
3x10-20 2261-5709 <$350
1902 Plain Back (dated 1922)
3x10-20 1-5696 <$350
1929 Small Size
10 Type 1 1-1592 <$125
20 Type 1 1-364 <$125
10 Type 2 1-1120 <$150
20 Type 2 1-192 <$150
Total Issue $819,490
Out at close $50,000
Large out at close $2,290
****
14031 Schuylkill
TOWER CITY NB, TOWER CITY
{{ 5 S }}
Chartered 2/34
1929 Small Size <$VALUE
20 Type 2 1-3140 <$300
Total Issue $62,800
Out in 1935 $50,000
****
FNB of Trafford
SEE Ch 6962
FNB of Trafford City
****
6962 Westmoreland
FNB OF TRAFFORD CITY
Chartered 9/03
Receivership 3/2/32
2nd title: FNB of Trafford
4/10/30
FIRST TITLE {{ 3 L 5 S }}
1902 Red Seal <$VALUE
3x10-20 1-1912 <$750
1902 Date Back
3x10-20 1-2700 <$375
1902 Plain Back
3x10-20 2701-8621 <$375
1929 Small Size
10 Type 1 1-618 <$250
20 Type 1 1-186 <$250
SECOND TITLE {{ 1 S }}
1929 Small Size
10 Type 1 1-12 <$400
Total Issue $586,770
Out at close $28,860
Large out at close $2,760
****
797 Schuylkill
FNB OF TREMONT
{{ 4 L }}
Chartered 2/14/65
Liquidated 3/4/79
Original Series <$VALUE
3x1-2 1-1000 <$650/$1500
4x5 1-2750 <$750
3x10-20 1-2930<$1000/$1500
Total Issue $206,500
Out in 1910 $1,320
****
6165 Schuylkill
TREMONT NB, TREMONT
{{ 1 L 7 S }}
Chartered 3/18/02
1902 Red Seal <$VALUE
3x10-20 1-1250 <$750
1902 Date Back
3x10-20 1-2520 <$375
1902 Plain Back (dated 1902)
3x10-20 2521-4421 <$375
1902 Plain Back (dated 1922)
3x10-20 1-2859 <$375
1929 Small Size
10 Type 1 1-800 <$175
20 Type 1 1-214 <$175
10 Type 2 1-674 <$200
20 Type 2 1-215 <$200
Total Issue $511,220
Out in 1935 $24,650
Large out 1935 $1,330
****
7722 Northumberland
FNB OF TREVORTON
{{ 2 L 5 S }}
Chartered 5/05
1902 Red Seal <$VALUE
3x10-20 1-1300 <$650
1902 Date Back
3x10-20 1-2470 <$325
1902 Plain Back
3x10-20 2471-7219 <$325
1929 Small Size
10 Type 1 1-872* <$200
20 Type 1 1-246 <$200
10 Type 2 1-944 <$225
20 Type 2 1-188 <$225
* 426-472 not issued
Total Issue $514,690
Out in 1935 $24,350
Large out 1935 $1,320
****
4984 Bradford
FNB OF TROY
{{ 6 L 15 S }}
Chartered 1895
Brown Back <$VALUE
4x5 1-6875 <$300
3x10-20 1-4420 <$300
1882 Date Back
4x5 1-5337 <$300
3x10-20 1-3843 <$300
1902 Date Back
4x5 1-1250 <$175
3x10-20 1-1000 <$175
1902 Plain Back
4x5 1251-14954 <$175
3x10-20 1001-9829 <$175
1929 Small Size
5 Type 1 1-4216 <$85
10 Type 1 1-1824 <$85
20 Type 1 1-524 <$100
5 Type 2 1-8348 <$100
10 Type 2 1-4649 <$100
20 Type 2 1-933 <$100
Total Issue $1,853,610
Out in 1935 $136,725
Large out 1935 $5,935
Outstanding includes Ch 8849
****
8849 Bradford
GRANGE NB OF BRADFORD
COUNTY AT TROY
{{ 3 L 5 S }}
Chartered 8/07
Closed 4/30/32
1902 Red Seal <$VALUE
4x5 1-1000 <$850
3x10-20 1-800 <$850
1902 Date Back
4x5 1-3400 <$400
3x10-20 1-3360 <$400
1902 Plain Back
3x10-20 3361-10518 <$400
1929 Small Size
10 Type 1 1-1752 <$275
20 Type 1 1-485 <$275
Total Issue $817,220
Out at close $75,000
Large out at close $3,660
Ch 4984 assumed circulation
****
6438 Wyoming
CITIZENS NB OF
TUNKHANNOCK
{{ 4 L 8 S }}
Chartered 9/24/02
1902 Red Seal <$VALUE
3x10-20 1-3762 <$400
1902 Date Back
3x10-20 1-4540 <$200
1902 Plain Back
3x10-20 4541-14664 <$200
1929 Small Size
10 Type 1 1-1550 <$110
20 Type 1 1-404 <$125
10 Type 2 1-2400 <$125
20 Type 2 1-888 <$125
Total Issue $1,104,540
Out in 1935 $48,310
Large out 1935 $1,640
****

***

835 Wyoming
WYOMING NB OF TUNKHANNOCK
{{ 10 L 16 S }}
Chartered 2/23/65
Original Series <$VALUE
3x1-2 1-1800 <$400/$1000
4x5 1-2750 <$450
3x10-20 1-2240 <$750/$1250
Series 1875
3x1-2 1-400 <$400/$1000
4x5 1-2361 <$450
3x10-20 1-2000 <$750/$1250
Brown Back
3x10-20 1-11893 <$275
1902 Red Seal
3x10-20 1-3800 <$300
1902 Date Back
3x10-20 1-8700 <$135
1902 Plain Back
3x10-20 8701-27989 <$135
1929 Small Size
10 Type 1 1-3040 <$65
20 Type 1 1-924 <$75
10 Type 2 1-4716 <$75
20 Type 2 1-1644 <$75
Total Issue $2,882,640
Out in 1935 $96,450
Large out 1935 $6,330

***

9803 Northumberland
TURBOTVILLE NB, TURBOTVILLE
{{ 3 L 4 S }}
Chartered 6/10
1902 Date Back <$VALUE
4x5 1-1100 <$300
3x10-20 1-1690 <$300
1902 Plain Back
4x5 1101-6005 <$300
3x10-20 1691-4614 <$300
1929 Small Size
5 Type 1 1-846 <$200
10 Type 1 1-496 <$200
20 Type 1 1-140 <$200
5 Type 2 1-1466 <$225
10 Type 2 1-789 <$225
20 Type 2 1-235 <$225
Total Issue $442,660
Out in 1935 $21,200
Large out 1935 $1,410

***

6574 Allegheny
FNB OF TURTLE CREEK
{{ 4 L 9 S }}
Chartered 1/03
Liquidated 3/15/32
1902 Red Seal <$VALUE
3x10-20 1-2520 <$650
1902 Date Back
3x10-20 1-4680 <$325
1902 Plain Back
3x10-20 4681-14829 <$325
1929 Small Size
10 Type 1 1-932 <$175
20 Type 1 1-263 <$175
Total Issue $954,930
Out at close $42,440
Large out at close $5,010

***

6568 Allegheny
NB OF TURTLE CREEK
{{ UNREPORTED }}
Chartered 1/3/03
Liquidated 1/2/07
1902 Red Seal <$VALUE
3x10-20 1-1956 <$1500
Total Issue $97,800
Out in 1910 $5,160

***

6516 Blair
BLAIR COUNTY NB OF TYRONE
Chartered 12/1/02
Closed 10/8/32
2nd title: Blair County NB & TC 1/30/28
FIRST TITLE {{ 9 L }}
1902 Red Seal <$VALUE
4x5 1-6230 <$250
3x10-20 1-5108 <$250
1902 Date Back
4x5 1-8350 <$125
3x10-20 1-6200 <$125
1902 Plain Back
4x5 8351-25698 <$125
3x10-20 6201-17629 <$125
SECOND TITLE {{ 1 L 12 S }}
1902 Plain Back
3x10-20 1-2350 <$150
1929 Small Size
10 Type 1 1-2435 <$100
20 Type 1 1-661 <$100
Total Issue $2,118,330
Out at close $100,000
Large out at close $8,090
Ch 4355 assumed circulation

***

6499 Blair
FARMERS & MERCHANTS NB OF TYRONE
{{ 10 L 4 S }}
Chartered 11/22/02
Receivership 12/12/30
1902 Red Seal <$VALUE
4x5 1-4025 <$250
3x10-20 1-3040 <$250
1902 Date Back
4x5 1-6750 <$125
3x10-20 1-4030 <$125
1902 Plain Back
4x5 6751-26621 <$125
3x10-20 4031-18065 <$125
1929 Small Size
5 Type 1 1-2053 <$175
10 Type 1 1-864 <$175
20 Type 1 1-281 <$175
Total Issue $1,815,320
Out at close $100,000
Large out at close $11,300

***

F Blair County NB of Tyrone
SEE Ch 4355
FNB of Tyrone

***

4355 Blair
FNB OF TYRONE
Chartered 1890
2nd title: F Blair County NB of Tyrone 10/8/32
FIRST TITLE {{ 15 L 4 S }}
Brown Back <$VALUE
4x5 1-15437 <$200
3x10-20 1-5280 <$200
1882 Date Back
4x5 1-1908 <$200
3x10-20 1-1124 <$200
1902 Date Back
4x5 1-6600 <$100
3x10-20 1-4860 <$100
1902 Plain Back
4x5 6601-25740 <$100
3x10-20 4861-17810 <$100
1929 Small Size
5 Type 1 1-3568 <$100
10 Type 1 1-1704 <$100
20 Type 1 1-484 <$100
SECOND TITLE {{ 16 S }}
1929 Small Size
5 Type 1 1-834 <$45
10 Type 1 1-528 <$50
20 Type 1 1-178 <$60
5 Type 2 1-11400 <$45
10 Type 2 1-5737 <$50
20 Type 2 1-1908 <$60
Total Issue $2,570,350
Out in 1935 $197,250
Large out 1935 $10,990
Outstanding includes Ch 6516

***

9505 Bradford
FNB OF ULSTER
{{ 2 L 4 S }}
Chartered 8/09
1902 Date Back <$VALUE
3x10-20 1-2550 <$500
1902 Plain Back
3x10-20 2551-7025 <$500
1929 Small Size
10 Type 1 1-764 <$250
20 Type 1 1-204 <$250
10 Type 2 1-1121 <$250
20 Type 2 1-330 <$250
Total Issue $439,380
Out in 1935 $25,000
Large out 1935 $390

***

8739 Potter
GRANGE NB OF POTTER COUNTY AT ULYSSES
{{ 2 L 2 S }}
Chartered 6/07
1902 Red Seal <$VALUE
4x5 1-625 <$1000
3x10-20 1-500 <$1000
1902 Date Back
4x5 1-1775 <$600
3x10-20 1-1270 <$600
1902 Plain Back
4x5 1776-5575 <$600
3x10-20 1271-3625 <$600
1929 Small Size
5 Type 1 1-732 <$400
10 Type 1 1-430 <$400
20 Type 1 1-108 <$400
5 Type 2 1-796 <$400
10 Type 2 1-535 <$400
20 Type 2 1-204 <$400
Total Issue $404,380
Out in 1935 $21,500
Large out 1935 $1,000

***

110 Erie
FNB OF UNION MILLS, UNION CITY
{{ 1 L }}
Chartered 10/23/63
Receivership 3/24/83
Original Series <$VALUE
4x5 1-4750 <$1000
Series 1875
4x5 1-3615 <$1000
Total Issue $167,300
Out in 1916 $1,130

***

8879 Erie
HOME NB OF UNION CITY
{{ 3 L 2U + 11 S }}
Chartered 9/07
Receivership 1/19/32
1902 Red Seal <$VALUE
3x10-20 1-1500 <$600
1902 Date Back
3x10-20 1-3500 <$275
1902 Plain Back
3x10-20 3501-11851 <$275
1929 Small Size
10 Type 1 1-1356 <$100
20 Type 1 1-380 <$100
5 Type 2 1-300 <$100
10 Type 2 1-1456 <$100
20 Type 2 1-492 <$100
Total Issue $820,410
Out in 1935 $48,400
Large out 1935 $2,405

***

5131 Erie
NB OF UNION CITY
{{ 3 L 11 S }}
Organized 5/5/98
Liquidated 5/18/34
Brown Back <$VALUE
3x10-20 1-4250 <$350
1882 Date Back
3x10-20 1-8800 <$350
1882 Value Back
3x10-20 8801-10450 <$350
1902 Plain Back
3x10-20 1-14620 <$175
1929 Small Size
10 Type 1 1-2898 <$85
20 Type 1 1-744 <$100
10 Type 2 1-42 <$135
20 Type 2 1-50 <$135
Total Issue $1,730,580
Out at close $93,820
Large out 1935 $4,460
Ch 14093 assumed circulation

***

14093 Erie
NB OF UNION CITY
{{ U + 2 S }}
Chartered 4/34
1929 Small Size <$VALUE
5 Type 2 1-8676 <$350
Total Issue $43,380
Out in 1935 $28,410
Large out 1935 $4,460
Outstanding includes Ch 5131

***

270 Fayette
FNB OF UNIONTOWN
{{ 2 L }}
Organized 2/20/64
Receivership 1/19/15
Original Series <$VALUE
4x5 1-3500 <$750
3x10-20 1-2000 <$850/$1500
Series 1875
3x10-20 1-1680 <$850/$1500
Brown Back
50-100 1-931 <$1250/$1500
1902 Red Seal
50-100 1-1027 <$2250/$2500
1902 Date Back
50-100 1-1200 <$500/$600
3x50-100 1-2291 <$500/$600
Total Issue $1,300,450
Out at close $99,930

***

681 Fayette
NB OF FAYETTE COUNTY, UNIONTOWN
{{ 12 L 12 S }}
Organized 12/19/64
Receivership 10/12/31
Original Series <$VALUE
4x5 1-3250 <$400
3x10-20 1-1700 <$750/$1250
Series 1875
3x10-20 1-2700 <$750/$1250
Brown Back
3x10-20 1-9464 <$225
1902 Red Seal
3x10-20 1-3800 <$225
1902 Date Back
3x10-20 1-8800 <$100
1902 Plain Back
3x10-20 8801-24220 <$100
3x50-100 1-1327 <$350/$400
1929 Small Size
50 Type 1 1-415 <$150
100 Type 1 1-127 <$200
Total Issue $2,691,650
Out at close $200,000
Large out at close $40,800

***

5034 Fayette
SECOND NB OF UNIONTOWN
{{ 10 L 21 S }}
Chartered 1896
Brown Back <$VALUE
3x10-20 1-2600 <$250
1882 Date Back
3x10-20 1-8095 <$250
1902 Plain Back
3x10-20 1-18516 <$100
1929 Small Size
10 Type 1 1-6900 <$35
20 Type 1 1-2172 <$45
10 Type 2 1-8527 <$35
20 Type 2 1-2484 <$45
Total Issue $2,270,140
Out in 1935 $294,900
Large out 1935 $8,620
Outstanding includes Ch 12500

***

12500 Fayette
UNIONTOWN NB & TC, UNIONTOWN
{{ 9 L 3 S }}
Chartered 2/24
Liquidated 9/20/30
1902 Plain Back <$VALUE
4x5 1-50700 <$125
1929 Small Size
5 Type 1 1-6280 <$175
Total Issue $1,202,400
Out at close $113,400
Large out at close $9,580

***

8190 Fayette
FNB OF VANDERBILT
{{ 2 L 2 S }}
Chartered 4/06
Receivership 8/4/30
1902 Red Seal <$VALUE
3x10-20 1-860 <$750
1902 Date Back
3x10-20 1-2530 <$400
1902 Plain Back
3x10-20 2531-7284 <$400
1929 Small Size
10 Type 1 1-261 <$350
20 Type 1 1-55 <$350
Total Issue $429,460
Out at close $25,000
Large out at close $5,280

***

7816 Westmoreland
CITIZENS NB OF VANDERGRIFT
{{ 3 L 4 S }}
Chartered 7/05
Receivership 10/13/31
1902 Red Seal <$VALUE
3x10-20 1-700 <$650
1902 Date Back
3x10-20 1-3060 <$325
1902 Plain Back
3x10-20 3061-8223 <$325
1929 Small Size
10 Type 1 1-583 <$200
20 Type 1 1-129 <$200
Total Issue $496,610
Out at close $26,960
Large out at close $2,900

***

5080 Westmoreland
FNB OF VANDERGRIFT
{{ 1 L }}
Chartered 7/8/97
Liquidated 5/15/02
Brown Back <$VALUE
3x10-20 1-534 <$1250
Total Issue $26,700
Out at close $10,100

***

4877 Allegheny
FNB OF VERONA
{{ 3 L 7 S }}
Organized 2/24/93
Receivership 8/23/33
Brown Back <$VALUE
4x5 1-4725 <$450
50-100 1-768 <$1250/$1500
1882 Date Back
4x5 1-2220 <$450
50-100 1-300 <$1250/$1500
3x50-100 1-52 <$1250/$1500
1902 Date Back
3x10-20 1-1500 <$275
1902 Plain Back
3x10-20 1501-10743 <$275
1929 Small Size
10 Type 1 1-1350 <$135
20 Type 1 1-364 <$150
Total Issue $973,930
Out at close $50,000
Large out at close $3,430

***

11834 Lawrence
FNB OF VOLANT
{{ 4 S }}
Chartered 9/20
1929 Small Size <$VALUE
5 Type 1 1-692 <$225
10 Type 1 1-282 <$225
5 Type 2 1-2866 <$225
10 Type 2 1-1360 <$225
Total Issue $65,610
Out in 1935 $19,650

***

14112 Lawrence
FNB IN WAMPUM
{{ UNREPORTED }}
Chartered 4/34
1929 Small Size <$VALUE
5 Type 2 1-280 <$850
10 Type 2 1-100 <$850
Total Issue $2,400
Out in 1935 $11,250
Large out 1935 $1,280
Outstanding includes Ch 6664

***

6664 Lawrence
FNB OF WAMPUM
{{ 1 L 2 S }}
Chartered 3/03
Liquidated 9/1/34
1902 Red Seal <$VALUE
3x10-20 1-730 <$1500
1902 Date Back
3x10-20 1-1170 <$850
1902 Plain Back
3x10-20 1171-3079 <$850
1929 Small Size
10 Type 1 1-310 <$600
20 Type 1 1-102 <$600
10 Type 2 1-175 <$600
20 Type 2 1-56 <$600
Total Issue $224,160
Out at close $10,500
Large out 1935 $280
Ch 14112 assumed circulation

***

2226 Warren
CITIZENS NB OF WARREN
{{ 11 L 6 S }}
Chartered 3/1/75
Receivership 6/4/31
Original Series <$VALUE
3x1 2 1-800 <$400/$1000
4x5 1-1150 <$450
Series 1875
3x1-2 1-660 <$400/$1000
4x5 1-11751 <$450
Brown Back
4x5 1-7460 <$225
3x10-20 1-4130 <$225
1882 Date Back
4x5 1-5936 <$225
3x10-20 1-5148 <$225
1902 Date Back
4x5 1-2500 <$100
3x10-20 1-2000 <$100
1902 Plain Back
4x5 2501-18765 <$100
3x10-20 2001-12356 <$100
1929 Small Size
5 Type 1 1-2112 <$100
10 Type 1 1-967 <$100
20 Type 1 1-278 <$100
Total Issue $2,144,980
Out at close $96,220
Large out at close $9,770

***

520 Warren
FNB OF WARREN
{{ 14 L 22 S }}
Organized 8/20/64
Original Series <$VALUE
3xI-2 1-3340 <$350/$1000
4x5 1-4750 <$400
3x10-20 1-2000 <$750/$1250
Series 1875
3x1-2 1-100 <$350/$1000
4x5 1-1830 <$400
3x10-20 1-1720 <$750/$1250
Brown Back
4x5 1-12880 <$200
3x10-20 1-7183 <$200
1902 Red Seal
4x5 1-3750 <$200
3x10-20 1-2600 <$200
1902 Date Back
4x5 1-7500 <$85
3x10-20 1-5480 <$85
1902 Plain Back
4x5 7501-23815 <$85
3x10-20 5481-16780 <$85
1929 Small Size
5 Type 1 1-3912 <$40
10 Type 1 1-1850 <$45
20 Type 1 1-498 <$50
5 Type 2 1-5516 <$40
10 Type 2 1-2688 <$45
20 Type 2 1-792 <$50
Total Issue $2,830,270
Out in 1935 $97,400
Large out 1935 $7,295

***

4879 Warren
WARREN NB, WARREN
{{ 31 L 50+ S }}
Chartered 1893
Brown Back <$VALUE
4x5 1-15425 <$150
3x10-20 1-15420 <$150/$175
1882 Date Back
4x5 1-15415 <$150
3x10-20 1-10341 <$150/$175
1902 Date Back
4x5 1-10500 <$65
4x10 1-10500 <$65
1902 Plain Back
4x5 10501-111261 <$65
4x10 10501-87613 <$65
1929 Small Size
5 Type 1 1-35820 <$25
10 Type 1 1-17950 <$30
5 Type 2 1-59172* <$25
10 Type 2 1-33993 <$35
* 14581-14586 not issued
Total Issue $10,421,950
Out in 1935 $636,150
Large out 1935 $19,670

***

3383 Washington
CITIZENS NB OF WASHINGTON
{{ 14 L 50+ S }}
Chartered 1885
Brown Back <$VALUE
3x10-20 1-4023 <$225
1902 Red Seal
4x5 1-4750 <$225
3x10-20 1-5300 <$225
1902 Date Back
4x5 1-17500 <$85
3x10-20 1-12740 <$85
1902 Plain Back
4x5 17501-113609 <$85
3x10-20 12741-75751 <$85
1929 Small Size
5 Type 1 1-32568 <$20
10 Type 1 1-16194 <$25
20 Type 1 1-3732 <$35
5 Type 2 1-49978 <$20
10 Type 2 1-27331 <$25
20 Type 2 1-10431 <$35
Total Issue $9,749,220
Out in 1935 $972,750
Large out 1935 $19,530

***

4181 Washington
FARMERS & MECHANICS NB OF WASHINGTON
{{ UNREPORTED }}
Chartered 12/19/89
Liquidated 7/1/01
Brown Back <$VALUE
3x10-20 1-3785 <$1000
Total Issue $189,250
Out in 1910 $3,180

***

586 Washington
FNB OF WASHINGTON
{{ 18 L }}
Chartered 11/64
Liquidated 4/16/27
Original Series <$VALUE
4x5 1-5500 <$400
3x10-20 1-3000 <$750/$1250
Series 1875
4x5 1-2730 <$400
3x10-20 1-2850 <$750/$1250
Brown Back
3x10-20 1-7780 <$200
50-100 1-2590 <$1250/$1500
1902 Red Seal
4x5 1-11250 <$200
3x10-20 1-3750 <$200
50-100 1-2734 <$2250/$2500
1902 Date Back
4x5 1-30000 <$85
3x10-20 1-19200 <$85
50-100 1-220 <$300/$350
3x50-100 1-600 <$300/$350
1902 Plain Back
4x5 30001-81555 <$85
3x10-20 19201-56831 <$85
Total Issue $6,712,850
Out at close $394,650

***

9901 Washington
PEOPLES NB OF WASHINGTON
{{ 3 L 20 S }}
Chartered 12/10
1902 Date Back <$VALUE
3x10-20 1-2800 <$275
1902 Plain Back
3x10-20 2801-7048 <$275
1929 Small Size
10 Type 1 1-1740 <$50
20 Type 1 1-512 <$60
10 Type 2 1-2853 <$50
20 Type 2 1-1020 <$60
Total Issue $567,170
Out in 1935 $100,000
Large out 1935 $1,150

10027 Erie
ENSWORTH NB OF WATERFORD
{{ 0 L 3 S }}
Chartered 6/11
1902 Date Back <$VALUE
3x10-20 1-800 <$600
1902 Plain Back
3x10-20 801-2046 <$600
1929 Small Size
10 Type 1 1-290 <$300
20 Type 1 1-97 <$300
Total Issue $131,340
Out in 1935 $9,850
Large out 1935 $430

3459 Northumberland
FARMERS NB OF WATSONTOWN
{{ 5 L 10 S }}
Chartered 1886
Brown Back <$VALUE
3x10-20 1-4524 <$350
1902 Red Seal
3x10-20 1-1400 <$375
1902 Date Back
3x10-20 1-4300 <$175
1902 Plain Back
3x10-20 4301-13586 <$175
1929 Small Size
10 Type 1 1-1678 <$100
20 Type 1 1-408 <$100
10 Type 2 1-2871 <$100
20 Type 2 1-610 <$100
Total Issue $1,166,050
Out in 1935 $53,420
Large out 1935 $2,740

2483 Northumberland
WATSONTOWN NB, WATSONTOWN
{{ 4 L 11 S }}
Chartered 6/17/80
Series 1875 <$VALUE
3x10-20 1-5860 <$750/$1250
Brown Back
3x10-20 1-4200 <$350
1882 Date Back
3x10-20 1-5500 <$350
1882 Value Back
3x10-20 5501-7979 <$350
1902 Plain Back
3x10-20 1-8007 <$175
1929 Small Size
10 Type 1 1-1844 <$100
20 Type 1 1-502 <$100
10 Type 2 1-2557 <$110
20 Type 2 1-794 <$125
Total Issue $1,514,630
Out in 1935 $58,200
Large out 1935 $3,120

12504 Delaware
MAIN LINE NB OF WAYNE
{{ 4 L }}
Chartered 3/24
Receivership 10/12/31
1902 Plain Back <$VALUE
4x5 1-16177 <$1000
Total Issue $323,540
Out at close $2,135

5832 Franklin
CITIZENS NB OF WAYNESBORO
Chartered 5/23/01
2nd title: Citizens NB & TC 4/1/29
FIRST TITLE {{ 10 L }}
Brown Back <$VALUE
3x10-20 1-4000 <$250
1882 Date Back
3x10-20 1-8400* <$250
1882 Value Back
3x10-20 8801-14384* <$250
* 8401-8800 not marked
1902 Plain Back
4x5 1-86916 <$100
SECOND TITLE {{ 18 S }}
1929 Small Size
5 Type 1 1-29668 <$40
5 Type 2 1-50554 <$40
Total Issue $3,797,030
Out in 1935 $206,000
Large out 1935 $7,570

11866 Franklin
FNB IN WAYNESBORO
Chartered 11/20 as NB of Waynesboro, under which there was no issue. Issuing title adopted 12/31/20.
2nd title: FNB & TC in Waynesboro 12/31/26
FIRST TITLE {{ 8 L }}
1902 Plain Back <$VALUE
3x10-20 1-32396 <$125
SECOND TITLE {{ 5 L 31 S }}
1902 Plain Back
3x10-20 1-10652 <$125
1929 Small Size
10 Type 1 1-8598 <$40
20 Type 1 1-2060 <$50
10 Type 2 1-9441 <$40
20 Type 2 1-2510 <$50
Total Issue $3,060,090
Out in 1935 $263,850
Large out 1935 $11,700
Outstanding includes Ch 4445

244 Franklin
FNB OF WAYNESBORO
{{ 1 L }}
Chartered 2/9/64
Liquidated 1/28/95
Original Series <$VALUE
4x5 1-2600 <$650
3x10-20 1-1550 <$850/$1500
Series 1875
3x10-20 1-1168 <$850/$1500
Brown Back
3x10-20 1-1214 <$600
Total Issue $249,600
Out in 1910 $1,705

4445 Franklin
PEOPLES NB OF WAYNESBORO
{{ 5 L }}
Chartered 1890
Closed 12/31/20
Brown Back <$VALUE
4x5 1-9750 <$250
3x10-20 1-3940 <$250
1882 Date Back
4x5 1-843 <$250
3x10-20 1-1691 <$250
1902 Date Back
3x10-20 1-6600 <$150
1902 Plain Back
3x10-20 6601-12132 <$150
Total Issue $1,100,010
Out at close $98,600
Ch 11866 assumed circulation

6105 Greene
AMERICAN NB OF WAYNESBURG
{{ 6 L }}
Chartered 1/25/02
Liquidated 3/28/21
1902 Red Seal <$VALUE
4x5 1-12075 <$350
3x10-20 1-10070 <$350
1902 Date Back
4x5 1-17000 <$175
3x10-20 1-11700 <$175
1902 Plain Back
4x5 17001-28062 <$175
3x10-20 11701-17778 <$175
Total Issue $2,195,140
Out at close $182,750

4267 Greene
CITIZENS NB OF WAYNESBURG
{{ 10 L }}
Organized 1/15/90
Receivership 8/17/27
Brown Back <$VALUE
3x10-20 1-7185 <$250
1882 Date Back
3x10-20 1-477 <$250
1902 Date Back
4x5 1-10250 <$100
3x10-20 1-8000 <$100
1902 Plain Back
4x5 10251-47955 <$100
3x10-20 8001-30567 <$100
Total Issue $2,870,550
Out at close $275,000
Outstanding includes Ch 5085

839 Greene
FARMERS & DROVERS NB OF WAYNESBURG
{{ 4 L }}
Chartered 2/25/65
Receivership 12/12/06
Original Series <$VALUE
3x1-2 1-1000 <$400/$1000
4x5 1-1950 <$500
3x10-20 1-2260 <$750/$1250
Series 1875
4x5 1-350 <$500
3x10-20 1-1880 <$750/$1250
50-100 1-594 <$3500
Brown Back
4x5 1-6486 <$350
3x10-20 1-1498 <$350
1902 Red Seal
4x5 1-1420 <$350
3x10-20 1-834 <$350
Total Issue $966,200
Out in 1916 $6,477

305 Greene
FNB OF WAYNESBURG
{{ UNREPORTED }}
Organized 3/5/64
Receivership 5/15/78
Original Series <$VALUE
4x5 1-2000 <$1250
3x10-20 1-962 <$1500/$2000
Total Issue $88,100
Out in 1916 $725

13134 Greene
FNB & TC OF WAYNESBURG
{{ 23 S }}
Chartered 10/27
1929 Small Size <$VALUE
5 Type 1 1-4880 <$25
10 Type 1 1-3456 <$30
20 Type 1 1-958 <$40
5 Type 2 1-15588 <$25
10 Type 2 1-7705 <$30
20 Type 2 1-2710 <$40
Total Issue $677,910
Out in 1935 $250,000

5085 Greene
PEOPLES NB OF WAYNESBURG
{{ 4 L }}
Chartered 1897
Closed 6/18/23
Brown Back <$VALUE
3x10-20 1-4550 <$350
1882 Date Back
3x10-20 1-6100 <$350
1882 Value Back
3x10-20 6101-6914 <$350
1902 Plain Back
3x10-20 1-6764 <$250
Total Issue $911,400
Out at close $98,300
Ch 4267 assumed circulation

13873 Greene
UNION NB OF WAYNESBURG
{{ 14 S }}
Chartered 12/33
1929 Small Size <$VALUE
5 Type 2 1-33756 <$60
10 Type 2 1-17388 <$60
Total Issue $342,660
Out in 1935 $187,560

6108 Carbon
FNB OF WEATHERLY
{{ 3 L 11 S }}
Chartered 1/28/02
1902 Red Seal <$VALUE
4x5 1-1465 <$450
3x10-20 1-1134 <$450
1902 Date Back
4x5 1-4550 <$200
3x10-20 1-2900 <$200
1902 Plain Back (dated 1901)
4x5 4551-9050 <$200
3x10-20 2901-5320 <$200
1902 Plain Back (dated 1921)
4x5 1-5890 <$200
3x10-20 1-4333 <$200
1929 Small Size
5 Type 1 1-2868 <$100
10 Type 1 1-2036 <$100
20 Type 1 1-466 <$100
5 Type 2 1-6910 <$100
10 Type 2 1-3897 <$100
20 Type 2 1-1048 <$100
Total Issue $1,226,050
Out in 1935 $66,880
Large out 1935 $2,250

6937 Westmoreland
FNB OF WEBSTER
{{ 3 L }}
Chartered 8/03
Receivership 8/8/27
1902 Red Seal <$VALUE
3x10-20 1-1600 <$600
1902 Date Back
3x10-20 1-2660 <$300
1902 Plain Back
3x10-20 2661-6710 <$300
Total Issue $415,500
Out at close $24,100

7112 Indiana
FNB OF WEHRUM
{{ UNREPORTED }}
Chartered 1/29/04
Liquidated 10/18/04
1902 Red Seal <$VALUE
3x10-20 1-146 <$2000
Total Issue $7,300
Out in 1910 $360

10214 Carbon
WEISSPORT NB, WEISSPORT
{{ 2 L 3 S }}
Chartered 6/12
1902 Date Back <$VALUE
4x5 1-1350 <$375
4x10 1-1275 <$375
1902 Plain Back
4x5 1351-7208 <$375
4x10 1276-5471 <$375
1929 Small Size
5 Type 1 1-1568 <$250
10 Type 1 1-610 <$250
5 Type 2 1-2366 <$250
10 Type 2 1-1452 <$250
Total Issue $472,990
Out in 1935 $18,150
Large out 1935 $1,110

328 Tioga
FNB OF WELLSBOROUGH
{{ 12 L 19 S }}
Chartered 3/64
Original Series <$VALUE
3x1-2 1-3100 <$350/$1000
4x5 1-8775 <$400
Series 1875
4x5 1-7745 <$400
Brown Back
3x10-20 1-2000 <$225/$250
50-100 1-1720 <$1250/$1500
1902 Red Seal
3x10-20 1-6300 <$250
50-100 1-450 <$2250/$2500
1902 Date Back
3x10-20 1-15500 <$100
50-100 1-200 <$350/$400
1902 Plain Back
3x10-20 15501-47272 <$100
1929 Small Size
10 Type 1 1-5696 <$50
20 Type 1 1-1528 <$60
10 Type 2 1-6454 <$60
20 Type 2 1-1576 <$60
Total Issue $4,101,180
Out in 1935 $169,550
Large out 1935 $11,420

3938 Tioga
WELLSBOROUGH NB, WELLSBOROUGH
{{ UNREPORTED }}
Chartered 11/10/88
Liquidated 8/6/97
Brown Back <$VALUE
4x5 1-2234 <$1250
Total Issue $44,680
Out in 1910 $230

8498 York
WELLSVILLE NB, WELLSVILLE
{{ 2 L 3 S }}
Chartered 1/07
1902 Red Seal <$VALUE
4x5 1-150 <$1000
3x10-20 1-140 <$1000
1902 Date Back
4x5 1-1250 <$500
3x10-20 1-1000 <$500
1902 Plain Back
4x5 1251-3550 <$500
3x10-20 1001-2468 <$500
1929 Small Size
5 Type 1 1-588 <$275
10 Type 1 1-434 <$275
20 Type 1 1-128 <$275
5 Type 2 1-1008 <$300
10 Type 2 1-580 <$300
20 Type 2 1-166 <$300
Total Issue $277,600
Out in 1935 $24,350
Large out 1935 $490

8131 Berks
WERNERSVILLE NB, WERNERSVILLE
Chartered 3/06
2nd title: Wernersville NB & TC 2/18/29
FIRST TITLE {{ 16 L }}
1902 Red Seal <$VALUE
3x10-20 1-687 <$400
1902 Date Back
3x10-20 1-3940 <$200
1902 Plain Back
3x10-20 3941-12600 <$200
SECOND TITLE {{ 10 S }}
1929 Small Size
10 Type 1 1-1366 <$125
20 Type 1 1-416 <$125
10 Type 2 1-1513 <$150
20 Type 2 1-395 <$150
Total Issue $819,260
Out in 1935 $50,000
Large out 1935 $2,450

11993 Washington
CITIZENS NB OF WEST ALEXANDER
{{ 0 L 4 S }}
Organized 5/24/21
Receivership 7/16/34
1902 Plain Back <$VALUE
3x10-20 1-2983 <$750
1929 Small Size
10 Type 1 1-644 <$175
20 Type 1 1-200 <$175
10 Type 2 1-364 <$200
20 Type 2 1-82 <$200
Total Issue $217,070
Out at close $25,000
Large out at close $1,700
Outstanding includes Ch 5948

8954 Washington
PEOPLES NB OF WEST ALEXANDER
{{ 5 L 11 S }}
Chartered 11/07
1902 Red Seal <$VALUE
3x10-20 1-195 <$450
1902 Date Back
3x10-20 1-2790 <$225
1902 Plain Back
3x10-20 2791-14627 <$225
1929 Small Size
10 Type 1 1-2150 <$85
20 Type 1 1-600 <$100
10 Type 2 1-2340 <$100
20 Type 2 1-535 <$100
Total Issue $976,200
Out in 1935 $75,000
Large out 1935 $3,000

5948 Washington
WEST ALEXANDER NB, WEST ALEXANDER
{{ 4 L }}
Chartered 8/27/01
Liquidated 8/18/21
Brown Back <$VALUE
3x10-20 1-1020 <$350
1882 Date Back
3x10-20 1-2190 <$350
1882 Value Back
3x10-20 2191-3483 <$350
Total Issue $225,150
Out at close $25,000
Ch 11993 assumed circulation

2857 Chester
FARMERS NB OF WEST CHESTER
{{ 1 L }}
Chartered 1/11/83
Liquidated 5/3/09
Brown Back <$VALUE
3x10-20 1-3278 <$1500
1902 Red Seal
4x5 1-4245 <$1500
3x10-20 1-2582 <$1500
Total Issue $377,900
Out in 1910 $8,765

148 Chester
FNB OF WEST CHESTER
{{ 16 L 2U + 27 S }}
Chartered 12/63
Original Series <$VALUE
4x5 1-4500 <$600
3x10-20 1-2100 <$850/$1500
50-100 1-1300 <$4000
Series 1875
4x5 1-2600 <$600
3x10-20 1-2000 <$850/$1500
50-100 1-360 <$4000
Brown Back
3x10-20 1-7105 <$400
50-100 1-1771 <$1750/$2000
1902 Red Seal
4x5 1-6000 <$400
3x10-20 1-5800 <$400
50-100 1-1000 <$2250/$2500
1902 Date Back
4x5 1-16000 <$175
3x10-20 1-10100 <$175
50-100 1-200 <$650/$750
3x50-100 1-240 <$650/$750
1902 Plain Back
4x5 16001-61305 <$175
3x10-20 10101-31943 <$175
1929 Small Size
5 Type 1 1-8350 <$40
10 Type 1 1-3892 <$50
20 Type 1 1-1474 <$60
5 Type 2 1-8882 <$40
10 Type 2 1-4946 <$50
20 Type 2 1-1884 <$60
Total Issue $5,482,600
Out in 1935 $194,150
Large out 1935 $12,680

552 Chester
NB OF CHESTER COUNTY, WEST CHESTER
Chartered 10/64
2nd title: NB of Chester County & TC 2/1/30
FIRST TITLE {{ 22 L 2 S }}
Original Series <$VALUE
4x5 1-3000 <$600
3x10-20 1-4200 <$850/$1500
50-100 1-1250 <$4000
Series 1875
4x5 1-2000 <$600
3x10-20 1-1400 <$850/$1500
50-100 1-911 <$4000
Brown Back
3x10-20 1-11768 <$400
50-100 1-2656 <$1500/$1750
1902 Red Seal
4x5 1-9500 <$400
3x10-20 1-4200 <$400
50-100 1-450 <$2250/$2500
1902 Date Back
4x5 1-17500* <$175
3x10-20 1-11600 <$175
50-100 1-800 <$500/$600
1902 Plain Back
4x5 17751-58820* <$175
3x10-20 11601-33111 <$175
3x50-100 1-824 <$500/$600
* 17501-17750 not marked
1929 Small Size
5 Type 1 1-2266 <$175
10 Type 1 1-1146 <$175
20 Type 1 1-384 <$175
50 Type 1 1-44 <$350
100 Type 1 1-14 <$400
SECOND TITLE {{ U + 22 S }}
1929 Small Size
5 Type 1 1-4126 <$100
10 Type 1 1-1876 <$100
20 Type 1 1-628 <$100
50 Type 1 1-162 <$225
100 Type 1 1-62 <$325
5 Type 2 1-9088 <$100
10 Type 2 1-5527 <$100
20 Type 2 1-1455 <$100
Total Issue $6,048,130
Out in 1935 $220,000
Large out 1935 $14,735

8890 Montgomery
PEOPLES NB OF WEST CONSHOHOCKEN
{{ 1 L }}
Chartered 9/07
Liquidated 12/31/23
1902 Red Seal <$VALUE
3x10-20 1-800 <$1000
1902 Date Back
3x10-20 1-2510 <$600
1902 Plain Back
3x10-20 2511-5391 <$600
Total Issue $309,550
Out at close $24,400

6373 Allegheny
FNB OF WEST ELIZABETH
{{ UNREPORTED }}
Chartered 8/9/02
Receivership 10/17/14
1902 Red Seal <$VALUE
4x5 1-1650 <$1000
3x10-20 1-1160 <$1000
1902 Date Back
4x5 1-2200 <$750
3x10-20 1-1410 <$750
Total Issue $205,500
Out in 1916 $6,595

CONDITION affects Value. The Values shown are for notes in FINE condition.

249 Mercer
FNB OF WEST GREENVILLE
Chartered 2/64
2nd title: FNB of
Greenville 2/26/83
FIRST TITLE {{ 0 L }}
Original Series <$VALUE
3x1-2 1-3000 <$750/$1500
4x5 1-5500 <$850
3x10-20 1-1550<$1000/$1500
Series 1875
3x10-20 1-1658<$1000/$1500
SECOND TITLE {{ 9 L 18 S }}
Brown Back
3x10-20 1-6696 <$275
1902 Red Seal
3x10-20 1-5400 <$300
50-100 1-400 <$2250/$2500
1902 Date Back
3x10-20 1-9200 <$150
50-100 1-300 <$400/$500
1902 Plain Back
3x10-20 9201-30369 <$150
1929 Small Size
5 Type 1 1-3988 <$60
10 Type 1 1-3544 <$60
20 Type 1 1-408 <$65
5 Type 2 1-9222 <$75
10 Type 2 1-5036 <$75
Total Issue $2,991,360
Out in 1935 $104,350
Large out 1935 $7,915

2669 Chester
NB OF WEST GROVE
Chartered 1882
2nd title: NB & TC of
West Grove 1/13/26
FIRST TITLE {{ 3 L }}
Series 1875 <$VALUE
3x10-20 1-1556<$1250/$1750
1902 Red Seal
3x10-20 1-3460 <$650
1902 Date Back
3x10-20 1-4780 <$300
1902 Plain Back
4x5 1-9666 <$300
3x10-20 4781-8718 <$300
SECOND TITLE {{ 2 L 10 S }}
1902 Plain Back
4x5 1-9809 <$300
1929 Small Size
5 Type 1 1-11238 <$175
5 Type 2 1-34188 <$175
Total Issue $1,584,280
Out in 1935 $96,640
Large out 1935 $2,640

6913 Mercer
FNB OF WEST MIDDLESEX
{{ 2 L U + 5 S }}
Chartered 8/03
1902 Red Seal <$VALUE
3x10-20 1-1700 <$850
1902 Date Back
3x10-20 1-2270 <$400
1902 Plain Back
3x10-20 2271-7089 <$400
1929 Small Size
10 Type 1 1-790 <$175
20 Type 1 1-214 <$175
10 Type 2 1-606 <$175
20 Type 2 1-175 <$175
Total Issue $522,090
Out in 1935 $21,400
Large out 1935 $1,040

5010 Westmoreland
FNB OF WEST NEWTON
{{ 5 L 10 S }}
Chartered 1895
Brown Back <$VALUE
4x5 1-3875 <$350
3x10-20 1-3630 <$350
1882 Date Back
4x5 1-4215 <$350
3x10-20 1-2829 <$350
1902 Plain Back
4x5 1-8892 <$200
3x10-20 1-6205 <$200
1929 Small Size
5 Type 1 1-1740 <$125
10 Type 1 1-944 <$125
20 Type 1 1-272 <$125
5 Type 2 1-2224 <$135
10 Type 2 1-1573 <$135
20 Type 2 1-401 <$135
Total Issue $1,149,190
Out in 1935 $49,450
Large out 1935 $2,340

8938 York
INDUSTRIAL NB OF
WEST YORK
{{ 7 L 18 S }}
Chartered 11/07
1902 Red Seal <$VALUE
3x10-20 1-1400 <$450
1902 Date Back
3x10-20 1-4640 <$200
1902 Plain Back
3x10-20 4641-20993 <$200
1929 Small Size
10 Type 1 1-3950 <$65
20 Type 1 1-1202 <$75
10 Type 2 1-5249 <$75
20 Type 2 1-1656 <$75
Total Issue $1,586,500
Out in 1935 $122,750
Large out 1935 $3,240

9513 Tioga
FARMERS & TRADERS NB OF
WESTFIELD
{{ 2 L 5 S }}
Chartered 8/09
1902 Date Back <$VALUE
4x5 1-2000 <$450
3x10-20 1-1600 <$450
1902 Plain Back
4x5 2001-6640 <$450
3x10-20 1601-4323 <$450
1929 Small Size
5 Type 1 1-1012 <$200
10 Type 1 1-490 <$200
20 Type 1 1-144 <$200
5 Type 2 1-1152 <$225
10 Type 2 1-636 <$225
20 Type 2 1-204 <$225
Total Issue $442,190
Out in 1935 $24,690
Large out 1935 $1,260

12933 Elk
WILCOX NB, WILCOX
{{ 1 L 2 S }}
Chartered 5/26
Receivership 10/27/31
1902 Plain Back <$VALUE
4x10 1-1552 <$750
1929 Small Size
10 Type 1 1-602 <$400
Total Issue $98,200
Out at close $20,000
Large out at close $850

30 Luzerne
FNB OF WILKES-BARRE*
{{ 28 L 41 S }}
Chartered 7/63
Liquidated 6/20/82
*Reorganized as Ch 2736
which retook Ch 30 5/31/11
Original Series <$VALUE
4x5 1-7100 <$400
3x10-20 1-5500 <$750/$1250
50-100 1-1460 <$3500
Series 1875
4x5 1-3930 <$400
3x10-20 1-4018 <$750/$1250
50-100 1-400 <$3500
1902 Date Back
3x10-20 1-21000 <$75
1902 Plain Back
3x10-20 21001-120868 <$75
1929 Small Size
10 Type 1 1-26310 <$20
20 Type 1 1-7104 <$30
10 Type 2 1-33595 <$20
20 Type 2 1-9062 <$30
Total Issue $9,967,170
Out in 1935 $607,195
Large out 1935 $26,335
Outstanding includes Ch 2736

2736 Luzerne
FNB OF WILKES-BARRE
{{ 6 L }}
Chartered 1882
RETOOK Ch 30 5/31/11
Brown Back <$VALUE
4x5 1-3750 <$275
3x10-20 1-26169 <$275
50-100 1-1439 <$1250/$1500
1902 Red Seal
4x5 1-8750 <$300
3x10-20 1-20250 <$300
1902 Date Back
4x5 1-10750 <$150
3x10-20 1-17500 <$150
Total Issue $3,876,800
Out in 1911 $375,000

9235 Luzerne
LUZERNE COUNTY NB OF
WILKES-BARRE
{{ 9 L }}
Chartered 9/08
Liquidated 7/14/23
1902 Date Back <$VALUE
4x5 1-40000 <$150
3x10-20 1-30800 <$150
1902 Plain Back
4x5 40001-89220 <$150
3x10-20 30801-60582 <$150
Total Issue $4,813,500
Out at close $377,950

13852 Luzerne
MINERS NB OF WILKES-BARRE
{{ 50+ S }}
Chartered 11/29/33
1929 Small Size <$VALUE
5 Type 2 1-181706 <$20
10 Type 2 1-126118 <$20
20 Type 2 1-76181 <$30
Total Issue $3,693,330
Out in 1935 $1,854,300

104 Luzerne
SECOND NB OF WILKES-BARRE
{{ 23 L 41 S }}
Chartered 10/63
Original Series <$VALUE
4x5 1-10061 <$375
4x10 1-11450 <$750
2x20-50-100 1-1422
<$1250/$3500/$3500
Series 1875
4x5 1-6500 <$375
4x10 1-10805 <$750
2x20-50-100 1-100
<$1250/$3500/$3500
Brown Back
4x5 1-46054 <$150
3x10-20 1-24225 <$150/$200
50-100 1-364 <$1250/$1500
1902 Red Seal
4x5 1-28500 <$150
4x10 1-5875 <$150
3x10-20 1-18400 <$150/$200
1902 Date Back
4x5 1-53750 <$60
4x10 1-43750 <$65
3x10-20 1-1300 <$65
1902 Plain Back
4x5 53751-211500 <$60
4x10 43751-157055 <$65
3x10-20 1301-2900 <$65
1929 Small Size
5 Type 1 1-39096 <$20
10 Type 1 1-20386 <$20
20 Type 1 1-2376 <$30
5 Type 2 1-74560 <$20
10 Type 2 1-35929 <$20
20 Type 2 1-12155 <$30
Total Issue $19,736,080
Out in 1935 $774,380
Large out 1935 $33,255

732 Luzerne
WYOMING NB OF
WILKES-BARRE
{{ 16 L 33 S }}
Chartered 1/19/65
Original Series <$VALUE
4x5 1-2500 <$400
3x10-20 1-2100 <$750/$1250
50-100 1-1202 <$3500
Series 1875
4x5 1-625 <$400
3x10-20 1-1791 <$750/$1250
50-100 1-211 <$3500
Brown Back
4x5 1-5708 <$175
3x10-20 1-4999 <$175/$200
50-100 1-353 <$1250/$1500
1902 Red Seal
4x5 1-4050 <$175
3x10-20 1-2830 <$175/$225
50-100 1-150 <$2250/$2500
1902 Date Back
4x5 1-14000 <$85
3x10-20 1-8900 <$85
50-100 1-200 <$400/$450
1902 Plain Back
4x5 14001-47365 <$85
3x10-20 8901-27769 <$85
1929 Small Size
5 Type 1 1-10080 <$25
10 Type 1 1-7038 <$25
20 Type 1 1-2106 <$25
5 Type 2 1-39612 <$25
10 Type 2 1-18913 <$25
20 Type 2 1-572715 <$25
Total Issue $4,975,940
Out in 1935 $388,560
Large out 1935 $8,060

5265 Allegheny
CENTRAL NB OF WILKINSBURG
{{ 4 L 3 S }}
Chartered 3/14/00
Closed 7/16/30
Brown Back <$VALUE
3x10-20 1-4700 <$350
1882 Date Back
3x10-20 1-8200 <$350
1882 Value Back
3x10-20 8201-11529 <$350
1902 Plain Back
3x10-20 1-15040 <$165
1929 Small Size
10 Type 1 1-1075 <$150
20 Type 1 1-239 <$150
Total Issue $1,656,630
Out at close $96,700
Large out at close $16,890
Ch 4728 assumed circulation

13823 Allegheny
FNB AT WILKINSBURG
{{ 18 S }}
Chartered 10/33
1929 Small Size <$VALUE
5 Type 2 1-7100 <$60
10 Type 2 1-11725 <$60
20 Type 2 1-5830 <$65
Total Issue $269,350
Out in 1935 $156,050

4728 Allegheny
FNB OF WILKINSBURG
{{ 9 L 26 S }}
Organized 4/2/92
Receivership 12/5/33
Brown Back <$VALUE
3x10-20 1-2820 <$275
1882 Date Back
3x10-20 1-1033 <$275
1902 Date Back
3x10-20 1-1260* <$135
1902 Plain Back
3x10-20 1461-26458* <$135
* 1261-1460 not marked
1929 Small Size
10 Type 1 1-8640 <$30
20 Type 1 1-2108 <$40
10 Type 2 1-3639 <$35
20 Type 2 1-320 <$50
Total Issue $2,334,200
Out at close $400,000
Large out at close $113,100
Outstanding includes Ch 5265

9392 Blair
FARMERS & MERCHANTS NB OF
WILLIAMSBURG
{{ 4 L 9 S }}
Chartered 4/09
1902 Date Back <$VALUE
3x10-20 1-2560 <$400
1902 Plain Back
3x10-20 2561-6850 <$400
1929 Small Size
10 Type 1 1-752 <$175
20 Type 1 1-172 <$175
10 Type 2 1-854 <$200
20 Type 2 1-142 <$200
Total Issue $419,640
Out in 1935 $22,700
Large out 1935 $1,470

6971 Blair
FNB OF WILLIAMSBURG
{{ 3 L 12 S }}
Chartered 9/03
Liquidated 7/18/34
1902 Red Seal <$VALUE
3x10-20 1-1420 <$600
1902 Date Back
3x10-20 1-3300 <$300
1902 Plain Back
3x10-20 3301-11528 <$300
1929 Small Size
10 Type 1 1 1384 <$125
20 Type 1 1-368 <$125
10 Type 2 1-378 <$150
20 Type 2 1-200 <$150
Total Issue $782,380
Out at close $50,000
Large out 1935 $3,090
Ch 14182 assumed circulation

14182 Blair
FNB OF WILLIAMSBURG
{{ 1 S }}
Chartered 6/34
1929 Small Size <$VALUE
10 Type 2 1-890 <$600
20 Type 2 1-258 <$600
Total Issue $14,060
Out in 1935 $48,650
Large out 1935 $3,090
Outstanding includes Ch 6971

2139 Lycoming
CITY NB OF WILLIAMSPORT
{{ 2 L }}
Chartered 3/17/74
Receivership 5/4/86
Original Series <$VALUE
4x5 1-1625 <$750
4x20 1-625 <$1500
50-100 1-250 <$3500
Series 1875
4x5 1-3250 <$750
4x20 1-225 <$1500
50-100 1-302 <$3500
Total Issue $248,300
Out in 1916 $855

175 Lycoming
FNB OF WILLIAMSPORT
{{ 18 L 3U + 24 S }}
Organized 11/18/63
Original Series <$VALUE
4x5 1-7400 <$400
4x10 1-7975 <$750
Series 1875
4x10 1-7400 <$750
Brown Back
3x10-20 1-6795 <$200
50-100 1-3955 <$1250/$1500
1902 Red Seal
4x5 1-11000 <$200
50-100 1-13000<$2250/$2500
1902 Date Back
4x5 1-22750 <$75
3x10-20 1-16900 <$80
1902 Plain Back
4x5 22751-79725 <$75
3x10-20 16901-52626 <$80
1929 Small Size
5 Type 1 1-12626 <$35
10 Type 1 1-6056 <$35
20 Type 1 1-1716 <$45
5 Type 2 1-13866 <$35
10 Type 2 1-6644 <$35
20 Type 2 1-1869 <$45
Total Issue $7,913,010
Out in 1935 $227,810
Large out 1935 $17,860

734 Lycoming
LUMBERMAN'S NB OF
WILLIAMSPORT
{{ UNREPORTED }}
Chartered 1/20/65
Liquidated 12/31/89
Original Series <$VALUE
4x5 1-2750 <$1250
3x10-20 1-2100<$1500/$2000
Series 1875
4x5 1-315 <$1250
3x10-20 1-1926<$1500/$2000
Brown Back
50-100 1-182 <$2500
Total Issue $289,900
Out in 1910 $1,730

2227 Lycoming
LYCOMING NB OF
WILLIAMSPORT
{{ 8 L }}
Chartered 3/1/75
Liquidated 12/31/26
Original Series <$VALUE
4x5 1-4500 <$450
Series 1875
4x5 1-5481 <$450
50-50 1-1239 <$3500
Brown Back
3x10-20 1-9700 <$250
1882 Date Back
3x10-20 1-6824 <$250
1902 Date Back
3x10-20 1-3000 <$150
1902 Plain Back
3x10-20 3001-13913 <$150
Total Issue $1,845,370
Out at close $94,800

3705 Lycoming
MERCHANTS NB OF
WILLIAMSPORT
{{ UNREPORTED }}
Chartered 5/14/87
Liquidated 4/24/00
Brown Back <$VALUE
4x5 1-600 <$1250
3x10-20 1-1741 <$1250
Total Issue $99,050
Out in 1910 $1,110

1505 Lycoming
WEST BRANCH NB OF
WILLIAMSPORT
{{ 14 L }}
Chartered 1865
Liquidated 12/31/26
Original Series <$VALUE
4x5 1-5600 <$450
3x10-20 1-1375 <$750/$1250
Series 1875
4x5 1-3500 <$450
3x10-20 1-2625 <$750/$1250
Brown Back
3x10-20 1-6834 <$300
50-100 1-1961 <$1250/$1500
1902 Red Seal
3x10-20 1-3600 <$300
50-100 1-1200 <$2250/$2500
1902 Date Back
3x10-20 1-20200 <$135
50-100 1-500 <$400/$500
3x50-100 1-1142 <$400/$500
1902 Plain Back
3x10-20 20201-67715 <$135
Total Issue $5,084,100
Out at close $500,000

Williamsport NB, Williamsport
SEE Ch 1464
Jersey Shore NB, Jersey Shore

5000 Allegheny
EAST PITTSBURGH NB OF
WILMERDING
Chartered 1895
2nd title: FNB of
Wilmerding 7/9/23
FIRST TITLE {{ 2 L }}
Brown Back <$VALUE
3x10-20 1-5380 <$500
50-100 1-890 <$1250/$1500
1882 Date Back
3x10-20 1-6295 <$500
50-100 1-160 <$1250/$1500
3x50-100 1-73 <$1250/$1500
1902 Date Back
3x10-20 1-1500 <$250
3x50-100 1-300 <$400/$500
1902 Plain Back
3x10-20 1501-7100 <$250
SECOND TITLE
{{4U + 14 L 6U+ 50+ S }}
1902 Plain Back
3x10-20 1-17618 <$100
1929 Small Size
10 Type 1 1-6724 <$25
20 Type 1 1-1930 <$40
10 Type 2 1-8282 <$30
20 Type 2 1-2366 <$45
Total Issue $2,835,580
Out in 1935 $245,400
Large out 1935 $10,260
Outstanding includes Ch 6325

FNB of Wilmerding
SEE Ch 5000
East Pittsburgh NB of
Wilmerding

6325 Allegheny
WILMERDING NB, WILMERDING
{{ 4 L }}
Chartered 6/30/02
Closed 7/9/23
1902 Red Seal <$VALUE
3x10-20 1-4600 <$500
1902 Date Back
3x10-20 1-6800 <$250
1902 Plain Back (dated 1902)
3x10-20 6801-12400 <$250
1902 Plain Back (dated 1922)
3x10-20 1-1376 <$250
Total Issue $918,800
Out at close $72,500
Ch 5000 assumed circulation

CONDITION affects Value. The Values shown are for notes in FINE condition.

****

6794 Allegheny
FNB OF WILSON
Chartered 5/03
2nd title: FNB of Clairton 1/16/22
FIRST TITLE {{ 1 L }}
1902 Red Seal <$VALUE
3x10-20 1-1466 <$1250
1902 Date Back
3x10-20 1-2480 <$650
1902 Plain Back
3x10-20 2481-4190 <$650
SECOND TITLE {{ 1 L 9 S }}
1902 Plain Back
3x10-20 1-3079 <$500
1929 Small Size
10 Type 1 1-1120 <$125
20 Type 1 1-256 <$125
10 Type 2 1-2258 <$125
20 Type 2 1-574 <$125
Total Issue $568,730
Out in 1935 $48 350
Large out 1935 $1,260
****

7334 Clearfield
BITUMINOUS NB OF WINBURNE
{{ 5 L 2 S }}
Chartered 7/04
Liquidated 11/14/30
1902 Red Seal <$VALUE
4x5 1-2325 <$650
3x10-20 1-2070 <$650
1902 Date Back
4x5 1-4300 <$350
3x10-20 1-3220 <$350
1902 Plain Back
4x5 4301-13972 <$350
3x10-20 3221-9186 <$350
1929 Small Size
5 Type 1 1-763 <$350
10 Type 1 1-360 <$350
20 Type 1 1-102 <$350
Total Issue $945,470
Out at close $44,450
Large out at close $6,900
****

14082 Somerset
CITIZENS NB IN WINDBER
{{ 1 S }}
Chartered 3/34
1929 Small Size <$VALUE
5 Type 2 1-696 <$600
10 Type 2 1-495 <$600
20 Type 2 1-90 <$600
Total Issue $10,230
Out in 1935 $53,430
Large out 1935 $3,430
Outstanding includes Ch 6848
****

6848 Somerset
CITIZENS NB OF WINDBER
{{ 6 L 11 S }}
Chartered 6/03
Liquidated 6/2/34
1902 Red Seal <$VALUE
4x5 1-2200 <$400
3x10-20 1-1730 <$400
1902 Date Back
4x5 1-5200 <$200
3x10-20 1-3390 <$200
1902 Plain Back
4x5 5201-23639 <$200
3x10-20 3391-15821 <$200
1929 Small Size
5 Type 1 1-4064 <$100
10 Type 1 1-2178 <$100
20 Type 1 1-528 <$115
5 Type 2 1-444 <$175
10 Type 2 1-260 <$175
20 Type 2 1-60 <$175
Total Issue $1,716,310
Out at close $66,790
Large out 1935 $3,430
Ch 14082 assumed circulation
****

5242 Somerset
WINDBER NB, WINDBER
{{ UNREPORTED }}
Chartered 1/5/00
Liquidated 11/1/09
Brown Back <$VALUE
4x5 1-6150 <$1000
3x10-20 1-4470 <$1000
1882 Date Back
4x5 1-1880 <$1000
3x10-20 1-931 <$1000
Total Issue $430,650
Out in 1910 $41,990
****

****

12063 York
FNB OF WINDSOR
{{ 4 L 5 S }}
Chartered 12/21
1902 Plain Back <$VALUE
3x10-20 1-3300 <$450
1929 Small Size
10 Type 1 1-830 <$225
20 Type 1 1-220 <$225
10 Type 2 1-925 <$250
20 Type 2 1-235 <$250
Total Issue $255,150
Out in 1935 $24,500
Large out 1935 $710
****

10951 Beaver
FNB OF WOODLAWN
Chartered 2/17
Liquidated 11/24/31
2nd title: Aliquippa NB, Aliquippa 3/29/28
FIRST TITLE {{ 5 L }}
1902 Plain Back <$VALUE
3x10-20 1-18800 <$350
SECOND TITLE {{ 3 L 4 S }}
1902 Plain Back
4x5 1-5042 <$350
1929 Small Size
5 Type 1 1-8806 <$200
Total Issue $1,305,020
Out at close $69,405
Large out at close $7,060
****

246 York
FNB OF WRIGHTSVILLE
{{ 14 L 22 S }}
Chartered 2/64
Original Series <$VALUE
4x5 1-2700 <$500
4x10 1-3200 <$750
3x20-50 1-800 <$1250/$3500
Series 1875
4x5 1-2178 <$500
4x10 1-1806 <$750
3x20-50 1-389 <$1250/$3500
Brown Back
4x5 1-3750 <$300
3x10-20 1-6357 <$300
50-100 1-430 <$1250/$1500
1902 Red Seal
3x10-20 1-5800 <$300
1902 Date Back
3x10-20 1-8000 <$150
1902 Plain Back
4x5 1-26445 <$150
3x10-20 8001-24368 <$150
1929 Small Size
10 Type 1 1-4598 <$60
20 Type 1 1-1254 <$70
10 Type 2 1-5558 <$60
20 Type 2 1-1525 <$70
Total Issue $3,435,680
Out in 1935 $146,150
Large out 1935 $7,750
****

5339 Bradford
FNB OF WYALUSING
{{ UNREPORTED }}
Chartered 5/8/00
Receivership 3/28/14
Brown Back <$VALUE
4x5 1-1575 <$1000
3x10-20 1-1590 <$1000
1882 Date Back
4x5 1-1440 <$1000
3x10-20 1-1131 <$1000
Total Issue $196,350
Out in 1916 $4,225
****

10606 Bradford
NB OF WYALUSING
{{ 3 L 8 S }}
Chartered 9/14
1902 Date Back <$VALUE
3x10-20 1-1450 <$300
1902 Plain Back
3x10-20 1451-10288 <$300
1929 Small Size
10 Type 1 1-1592 <$125
20 Type 1 1-388 <$125
10 Type 2 1-2311 <$150
20 Type 2 1-659 <$150
Total Issue $692,770
Out in 1935 $48,750
Large out 1935 $1,530
****

8517 Luzerne
FNB OF WYOMING
{{ 5 L 10 S }}
Chartered 1/07
1902 Red Seal <$VALUE
4x5 1-1362 <$450
3x10-20 1-1090 <$450
1902 Date Back
4x5 1-5125 <$225
3x10-20 1-3720 <$225

1902 Plain Back
4x5 5126-17166 <$225
3x10-20 3721-11344 <$225
1929 Small Size
5 Type 1 1-2346 <$100
10 Type 1 1-1298 <$100
20 Type 1 1-314 <$125
5 Type 2 1-4296 <$125
10 Type 2 1-2004 <$125
20 Type 2 1-648 <$125
Total Issue $1,232,680
Out in 1935 $47,720
Large out 1935 $1,950
****

4207 Bucks
YARDLEY NB, YARDLEY
{{ 9 L 12 S }}
Organized 10/25/89
Receivership 3/7/34
Brown Back <$VALUE
4x5 1-10015 <$300
3x10-20 1-6770 <$300
1882 Date Back
3x10-20 1-971 <$300
1902 Date Back
3x10-20 1-8700 <$200
1902 Plain Back
3x10-20 8701-28428 <$200
1929 Small Size
10 Type 1 1-3180 <$100
20 Type 1 1-814 <$100
10 Type 2 1-912 <$135
20 Type 2 1-366 <$135
Total Issue $2,313,670
Out at close $100,000
Large out at close $5,550
****

13950 Bucks
YARDLEY NB, YARDLEY
{{ 5 S }}
Chartered 1/34
1929 Small Size <$VALUE
5 Type 2 1-7786 <$250
10 Type 2 1-4057 <$250
Total Issue $79,500
Large out 1935 $36,600
****

9706 York
CENTRAL NB OF YORK
Chartered 3/10
2nd title: Central NB & TC 4/9/31
FIRST TITLE {{ 8 L 3 S }}
1902 Date Back <$VALUE
4x5 1-4500 <$150
3x10-20 1-3480 <$150
1902 Plain Back
4x5 4501-23895 <$150
3x10-20 3481-14762 <$150
1929 Small Size
5 Type 1 1-3768 <$75
10 Type 1 1-1796 <$75
20 Type 1 1-494 <$75
SECOND TITLE {{ 16 S }}
1929 Small Size
5 Type 1 1-2818 <$40
10 Type 1 1-1642 <$40
20 Type 1 1-372 <$50
5 Type 2 1-7754 <$40
10 Type 2 1-4219 <$40
20 Type 2 1-875 <$50
Total Issue $1,822,240
Out in 1935 $119,380
Large out 1935 $3,470
****

2958 York
DROVERS & MECHANICS NB OF YORK
{{ 10 L 17 S }}
Chartered 1883
Brown Back <$VALUE
3x10-20 1-7040 <$275
1902 Red Seal
3x10-20 1-5800 <$275
1902 Date Back
3x10-20 1-8100 <$125
1902 Plain Back
3x10-20 8101-25930 <$125
1929 Small Size
10 Type 1 1-3096 <$40
20 Type 1 1-848 <$50
10 Type 2 1-4540 <$50
20 Type 2 1-1356 <$60
Total Issue $2,298,540
Out in 1935 $98,250
Large out 1935 $2,390
****

2228 York
FARMERS NB OF YORK
{{ 4 L }}
Chartered 3/1/75
Liquidated 3/14/14
Original Series <$VALUE
4x5 1-4000 <$600
3x10-20 1-2000 <$750/$1250

Series 1875
4x5 1-19105 <$600
3x10-20 1-4452 <$750/$1250
Brown Back
3x10-20 1-10300 <$350
1882 Date Back
3x10-20 1-5624 <$350
Total Issue $1,580,900
Out in 1914 $50,060
****

197 York
FNB OF YORK
{{ 26 L 50+ S }}
Chartered 1/64
Original Series <$VALUE
4x5 1-10750 <$400
4x10 1-7875 <$750
3x20-50 1-500 <$1250/$3500
Series 1875
4x5 1-3508 <$400
4x10 1-4869 <$750
3x20-50 1-1023<$1250/$3500
Brown Back
4x5 1-6720 <$200
3x10-20 1-7196 <$200
50-100 1-494 <$1250/$1500
1902 Red Seal
4x5 1-12250 <$200
3x10-20 1-6512 <$200
50-100 1-2629 <$2250/$2500
1902 Date Back
4x5 1-33250 <$75
3x10-20 1-19400 <$85
50-100 1-200 <$450/$500
3x50-100 1-1300 <$450/$500
1902 Plain Back
4x5 33251-56750 <$75
3x10-20 19401-82834 <$85
1929 Small Size
10 Type 1 1-15604 <$25
20 Type 1 1-3950 <$35
10 Type 2 1-15799 <$25
20 Type 2 1-4065 <$35
Total Issue $8,246,180
Out in 1935 $421,500
Large out 1935 $25,890
****

2303 York
WESTERN NB OF YORK
{{ 14 L 37 S }}
Chartered 10/8/75
Series 1875 <$VALUE
4x5 1-7500 <$500
50-50 1-3100 <$3500
Brown Back
4x5 1-13250 <$250
50-100 1-3860 <$1250/$1500
1882 Date Back
4x5 1-3787 <$250
3x10-20 1-14841 <$250
50-100 1-161 <$1250/$1500
1902 Plain Back
4x5 1-3750 <$100
3x10-20 1-39213 <$100
1929 Small Size
10 Type 1 1-6674 <$40
20 Type 1 1-1844 <$50
10 Type 2 1-9786 <$40
20 Type 2 1-2724 <$50
Total Issue $4,955,650
Out in 1935 $191,450
Large out 1935 $14,600
****

694 York
YORK COUNTY NB OF YORK
{{ 24 L 42 S }}
Chartered 1/65
Original Series <$VALUE
4x5 1-15350 <$400
3x10-20 1-4500 <$750/$1250
50-100 1-346 <$3500
Series 1875
4x5 1-2500 <$400
3x10-20 1-6500 <$750/$1250
Brown Back
3x10-20 1-21770 <$200
1902 Red Seal
3x10-20 1-7700 <$250
1902 Date Back
4x5 1-27750 <$100
3x10-20 1-16300 <$100
1902 Plain Back
4x5 27751-85680 <$100
3x10-20 16301-52107 <$100
1929 Small Size
5 Type 1 1-4594 <$25
10 Type 1 1-12022 <$25
20 Type 1 1-726 <$40
10 Type 2 1-21008* <$30
* 13111-13116 not issued
Total Issue $7,907,630
Out in 1935 $248,320
Large out 1935 $18,650
****

****

604 York
YORK NB, YORK
Chartered 12/64
2nd title: York NB & TC 3/1/27
FIRST TITLE {{ 21 L }}
Original Series <$VALUE
4x5 1-18000 <$400
3x10-20 1-8800 <$750/$1250
50-100 1-600 <$3500
Series 1875
4x5 1-12250 <$400
3x10-20 1-7940 <$750/$1250
50-100 1-1100 <$3500
Brown Back
4x5 1-18254 <$200
3x10-20 1-16737 <$200
50-100 1-600 <$1250/$1500
1902 Red Seal
4x5 1-11250 <$250
3x10-20 1-9000 <$250
1902 Date Back
4x5 1-4250 <$75
3x10-20 1-3500 <$85
1902 Plain Back
4x5 4251-47276 <$75
3x10-20 3501-28017 <$85
SECOND TITLE {{4 L U + 50+ S}}
1902 Plain Back
4x5 1-19445 <$100
1929 Small Size
5 Type 1 1-28774 <$20
10 Type 1 1-7774 <$25
5 Type 2 1-60622 <$20
10 Type 2 1-27038 <$25
Total Issue $8,302,350
Out in 1935 $388,160
Large out 1935 $18,630
****

7856 Adams
FNB OF YORK SPRINGS
{{ 3 L 6 S }}
Chartered 8/05
1902 Red Seal <$VALUE
3x10-20 1-1100 <$700
1902 Date Back
3x10-20 1-2080 <$350
1902 Plain Back
3x10-20 2081-6141 <$350
1929 Small Size
10 Type 1 1-672 <$175
20 Type 1 1-182 <$175
10 Type 2 1-578 <$200
20 Type 2 1-132 <$200
Total Issue $432,630
Out in 1935 $25,000
Large out 1935 $1,620
****

8165 Warren
FNB OF YOUNGSVILLE
{{ 3 L 5 S }}
Chartered 4/06
Liquidated 11/17/31
1902 Red Seal <$VALUE
3x10-20 1-1400 <$600
1902 Date Back
4x5 1-4950 <$300
3x10-20 1-2720 <$300
1902 Plain Back
4x5 4951-13709 <$300
3x10-20 2721-8396 <$300
1929 Small Size
5 Type 1 1-1200 <$200
10 Type 1 1-623 <$200
20 Type 1 1-170 <$200
Total Issue $857,760
Out at close $47,960
Large out at close $3,920
****

6500 Westmoreland
FNB OF YOUNGWOOD
{{ 3 L 6 S }}
Chartered 11/22/02
1902 Red Seal <$VALUE
3x10-20 1-1026 <$650
50-100 1-170 <$2250/$2500
1902 Date Back
3x10-20 1-1950 <$325
50-100 1-80 <$750/$850
1902 Plain Back
3x10-20 1951-6428 <$325
1929 Small Size
10 Type 1 1-696 <$175
20 Type 1 1-192 <$175
10 Type 2 1-1042 <$200
20 Type 2 1-298 <$200
Total Issue $491,380
Out in 1935 $24,600
Large out 1935 $960
****

****

6141 Butler
FNB OF ZELIENOPLE
{{ 4 L 8 S }}
Chartered 2/28/02
Liquidated 8/17/34
1902 Red Seal <$VALUE
3x10-20 1-2550 <$500
1902 Date Back
3x10-20 1-3700 <$250
1902 Plain Back (dated 1902)
3x10-20 3701-6367 <$250
1902 Plain Back (dated 1922)
3x10-20 1-4547 <$250
1929 Small Size
10 Type 1 1-1110 <$125
20 Type 1 1-286 <$135
10 Type 2 1-560 <$175
20 Type 2 1-183 <$175
Total Issue $783,380
Out at close $37,880
Large out at close $2,560
****

7409 Butler
PEOPLES NB OF ZELIENOPLE
{{ 7 L 2U + 11 S }}
Chartered 9/04
Liquidated 8/17/34
1902 Red Seal <$VALUE
3x10-20 1-2180 <$500
1902 Date Back
3x10-20 1-4440 <$225
1902 Plain Back
3x10-20 4441-13586 <$225
1929 Small Size
10 Type 1 1-1344 <$125
20 Type 1 1-360 <$135
10 Type 2 1-1065 <$150
20 Type 2 1-200 <$150
Total Issue $926,790
Out at close $48,450
Large out at close $3,460
****

<$VALUEs are for notes in FINE condition. Value changes by approximately 25% for a change of one full grade.

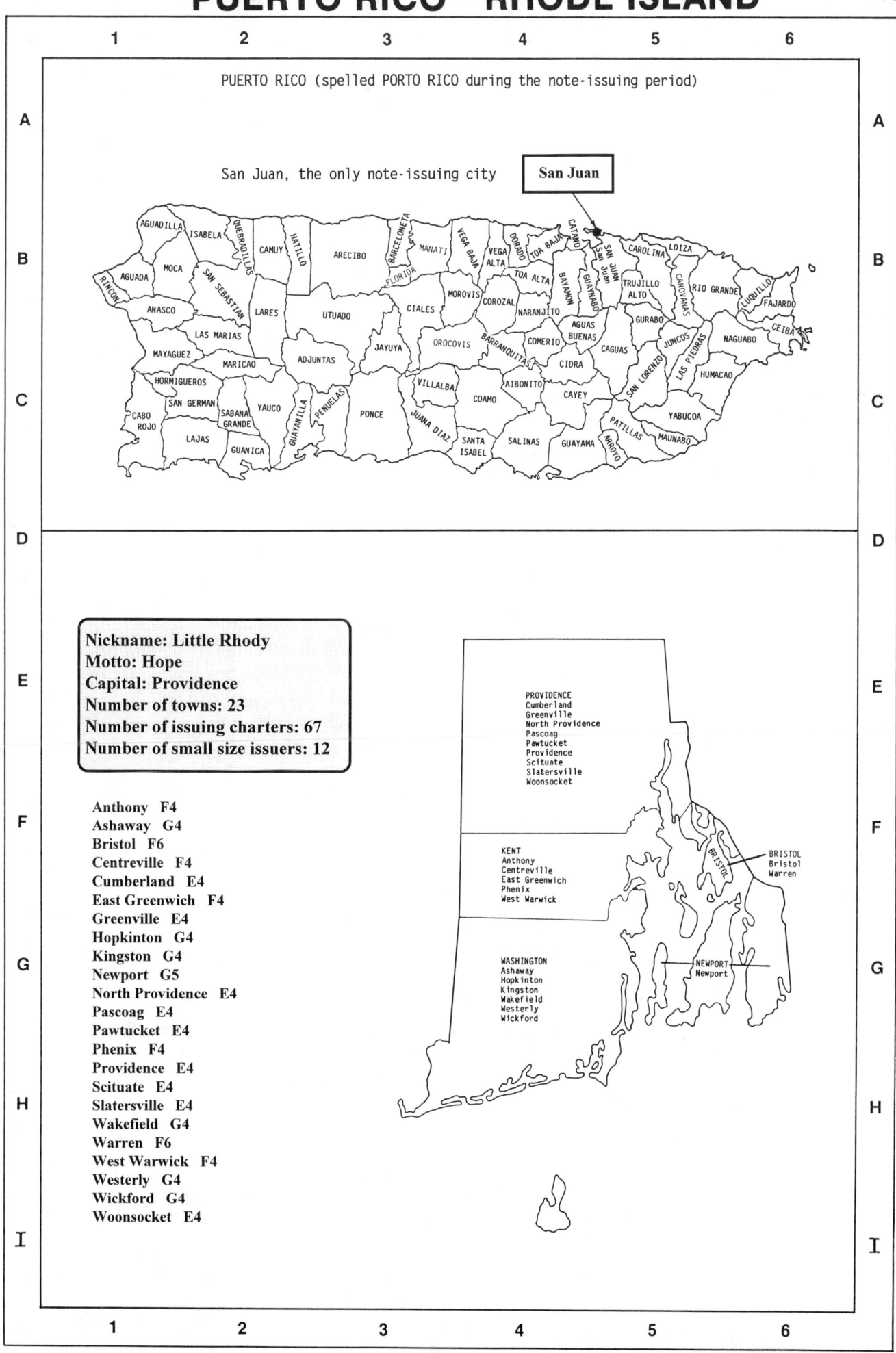

PUERTO RICO (spelled PORTO RICO during the note-issuing period)

San Juan, the only note-issuing city

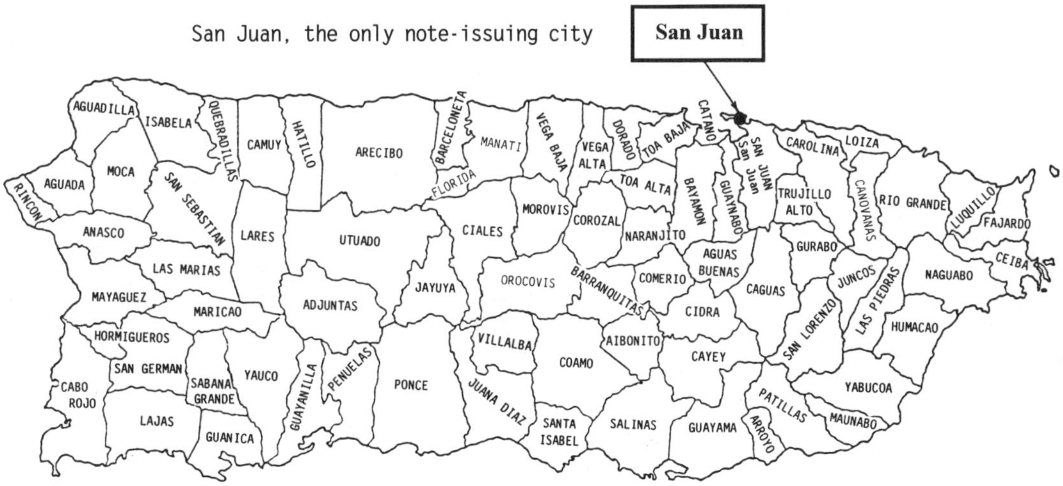

Nickname: Little Rhody
Motto: Hope
Capital: Providence
Number of towns: 23
Number of issuing charters: 67
Number of small size issuers: 12

Anthony F4
Ashaway G4
Bristol F6
Centreville F4
Cumberland E4
East Greenwich F4
Greenville E4
Hopkinton G4
Kingston G4
Newport G5
North Providence E4
Pascoag E4
Pawtucket E4
Phenix F4
Providence E4
Scituate E4
Slatersville E4
Wakefield G4
Warren F6
West Warwick F4
Westerly G4
Wickford G4
Woonsocket E4

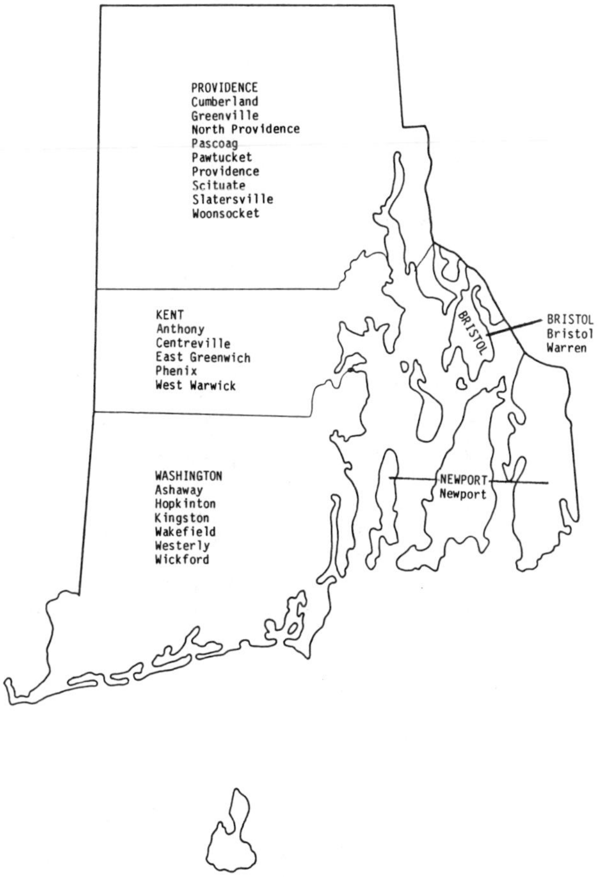

PORTO RICO

6484 San Juan
FNB OF PORTO RICO AT SAN JUAN
{{ 12 L }}
Chartered 11/10/02
Liquidated 9/8/11
TERRITORIAL ISSUES
1902 Red Seal <$VALUE
3x10-20 1-2400 <$60,000
50-100 1-847 <$65,000
1902 Date Back
3x10-20 1-1019 <$60,000
50-100 1-22 <$65,000
Total Issue $301,300
Out in 1920 $23,990

CONDITION affects Value. The Values shown are for notes in FINE condition.

RHODE ISLAND

1161 Kent
COVENTRY NB OF ANTHONY
{{ 3 L }}
Chartered 1865
Liquidated 4/17/85
Original Series <$VALUE
3x1-2 1-1900 <$500/$1250
4x5 1-3900 <$600
3x10-20 1-2100 <$850/$1250
Series 1875
3x1-2 1-660 <$500/$1250
4x5 1-3000 <$600
3x10-20 1-1568 <$850/$1250
Total Issue $334,200
Out at close $89,000
Out in 1910 $1,929

1150 Washington
ASHAWAY NB, ASHAWAY
{{ 9 L U + 13 S }}
Chartered 1865
Original Series <$VALUE
3x1-2 1-3900 <$400/$1000
4x5 1-3050 <$500
4x10 1-2225 <$650
Series 1875
3x1-2 1-102 <$400/$1000
4x5 1-1350 <$500
4x10 1-1375 <$650
Brown Back
4x5 1-4871 <$450
3x10-20 1-1525 <$450
1902 Red Seal
4x5 1-850 <$750
3x10-20 1-700 <$750
1902 Date Back
4x5 1-2550 <$275
3x10-20 1-1820 <$275
1902 Plain Back
4x5 2551-6680 <$275
3x10-20 1821-4018 <$275
1929 Small Size
5 Type 1 1-910 <$225
10 Type 1 1-498 <$225
20 Type 1 1-132 <$225
5 Type 2 1-968 <$250
10 Type 2 1-449 <$250
20 Type 2 1-204 <$250
Total Issue $898,610
Out in 1935 $25,000
Large out 1935 $2,410

1292 Bristol
FNB OF BRISTOL
{{ 4 L }}
Chartered 6/16/65
Liquidated 12/17/00
Original Series <$VALUE
3x1-2 1-2200 <$400/$1000
4x5 1-3700 <$500
3x10-20 1-1150 <$750/$1000
Series 1875
3x1-2 1-600 <$400/$1000
4x5 1-4200 <$500
3x10-20 1-722 <$750/$1000
Brown Back
4x5 1-4145 <$500
3x10-20 1-1349 <$500
Total Issue $415,950
Out at close $27,264
Out in 1910 $3,013

1562 Bristol
N EAGLE B OF BRISTOL
{{ 2 L }}
Chartered 9/18/65
Liquidated 12/17/00
Original Series <$VALUE
4x5 1-1950 <$850
3x10-20 1-725 <$1000/$1500
Series 1875
4x5 1-2417 <$850
3x10-20 1-764 <$1000/$1500
<$1000/$1500
Brown Back
4x5 1-2799 <$750
3x10-20 1-875 <$750
Total Issue $261,520
Out at close $20,415
Out in 1910 $1,700

1284 Kent
CENTREVILLE NB OF WARWICK, CENTREVILLE
Chartered 1865
2nd Title:Centreville NB of Warwick, West Warwick appears on small size notes
FIRST TITLE {{ 6 L }}
Original Series <$VALUE
3x1-2 1-2830 <$400/$1000
4x5 1-3500 <$500
3x10-20 1-2000 <$750/$1250
Series 1875
3x10-20 1-2940 <$750/$1250
Brown Back
3x10-20 1-5840 <$500
1902 Red Seal
3x10-20 1-1900 <$750
1902 Date Back
3x10-20 1-4700 <$300
1902 Plain Back
3x10-20 4701-11983 <$300
SECOND TITLE {{ 11 S }}
1929 Small Size
10 Type 1 1-1312 <$200
20 Type 1 1-362 <$225
5 Type 2 1-324 <$250
10 Type 2 1-1565 <$250
20 Type 2 1-475 <$250
Total Issue $1,466,230
Out in 1935 $50,000
Large out 1935 $3,075

1404 Providence
CUMBERLAND NB, CUMBERLAND
{{ 2 L }}
Chartered 1865
Liquidated 6/5/85
Original Series <$VALUE
3x1-2 1-3940 <$650/$1250
4x5 1-3150 <$750
3x10-20 1-2300<$1000/$1500
50-100 1-338 <$4000
Series 1875
4x5 1-3035 <$750
3x10-20 1-2560<$1000/$1500
Total Issue $437,100
Out at close $106,200
Out in 1910 $1,863

1405 Kent
GREENWICH NB, EAST GREENWICH
{{ UNREPORTED }}
Chartered 7/8/65
Liquidated 4/30/00
Original Series <$VALUE
4x5 1-2800 <$1250
3x10-20 1-510 <$1500/$2000
Series 1875
4x5 1-4000 <$1250
3x10-20 1-536 <$1500/$2000
Brown Back
4x5 1-4826 <$1250
Total Issue $284,820
Out at close $17,100
Out in 1910 $935

1498 Providence
N EXCHANGE B OF GREENVILLE
{{ 13 L }}
Chartered 1865
Liquidated 7/20/28
Original Series <$VALUE
3x1-2 1-5600 <$350/$850
4x5 1-3775 <$375
3x10-20 1-2710 <$600/$1000
50-100 1-220 <$4000
Series 1875
4x5 1-3405 <$375
3x10-20 1-2220 <$500/$850
50-100 1-322 <$4000
Brown Back
4x5 1-4254 <$300
3x10-20 1-2632 <$300/$350
50-100 1-309 <$1250/$1500
1902 Red Seal
3x10-20 1-1460 <$750
1902 Date Back
3x10-20 1-3900 <$250
1902 Plain Back
3x10-20 3901-8178 <$250
Total Issue $1,244,330
Out at close $37,500

1054 Washington
FNB OF HOPKINTON
{{ 11 L }}
Chartered 1865
Liquidated 5/25/14
Original Series <$VALUE
3x1-2 1-2400 <$350/$850
4x5 1-1750 <$375
3x10-20 1-2280 <$600/$1000
Series 1875
3x1-2 1-100 <$350/$850
4x5 1-960 <$375
3x10-20 1-2278 <$500/$850
Brown Back
4x5 1-12653 <$350
3x10-20 1-3914 <$350
1902 Red Seal
3x10-20 1-2850 <$750
1902 Date Back
3x10-20 1-4139 <$275
Total Issue $1,092,810
Out at close $66,000
Out in 1914 $52,475

1158 Washington
N LANDHOLDERS B OF KINGSTON
{{ 4 L }}
Chartered 5/17/65
Liquidated 4/10/05
Original Series <$VALUE
3x1-2 1-8080 <$400/$1000
4x5 1-3700 <$500
3x10-20 1-1850 <$750/$1250
Series 1875
4x5 1-3250 <$500
3x10-20 1-1500 <$650/$1000
Brown Back
3x10-20 1-8538 <$450
50-100 1-105 <$1250/$1500
Total Issue $789,550
Out at close $30,000
Out in 1910 $7,002

1546 Newport
AQUIDNECK NB OF NEWPORT
Chartered 1865
2nd title:Aquidneck N Exchange B & Savings Co of Newport
FIRST TITLE {{ 32 L }}
Original Series <$VALUE
3x1-2 1-11400 <$250/$750
4x5 1-7675 <$275
3x10-20 1-1300 <$550/$1000
50-100 1-316 <$4000
Series 1875
4x5 1-7560 <$275
3x10-20 1-2600 <$450/$850
50-100 1-600 <$4000
Brown Back
4x5 1-25419 <$175
3x10-20 1-10236 <$175/$200
1902 Red Seal
4x5 1-6250 <$500
3x10-20 1-3900 <$500
1902 Date Back
4x5 1-16500 <$75
3x10-20 1-14168 <$75
1902 Plain Back
4x5 16501-45767 <$75
3x10-20 14169-33258 <$75
SECOND TITLE {{ 19 L 42 S }}
1902 Plain Back
4x5 1-46405 <$75
1929 Small Size
5 Type 1 1-39578 <$35
5 Type 2 1-50948 <$35
Total Issue $6,982,700
Out in 1935 $150,000
Large out 1935 $19,770
Outstanding includes Ch 1565

Aquidneck N Exchange B & Savings Co of Newport
See Ch 1546
Aquidneck NB of Newport

1021 Newport
FNB OF NEWPORT
{{ 5 L }}
Chartered 4/17/65
Liquidated 9/7/05
Original Series <$VALUE
3x1-2 1-1200 <$400/$1000
4x5 1-4100 <$500
3x10-20 1-1700 <$750/$1250
50-100 1-300 <$4000
Series 1875
4x5 1-4455 <$500
3x10-20 1-1688 <$650/$1000
50-100 1-100 <$4000
Brown Back
4x5 1-21841 <$450
3x10-20 1-7874 <$450
1902 Red Seal
4x5 1-685 <$650
3x10-20 1-506 <$650
Total Issue $1,276,020
Out at close $120,000
Out in 1910 $12,065

1532 Newport
NB OF RHODE ISLAND, NEWPORT
{{ 9 L }}
Chartered 8/21/65
Liquidated 5/3/00
Original Series <$VALUE
3x1-2 1-6140 <$350/$850
4x5 1-6100 <$400
3x10-20 1-400 <$600/$1000
50-50 1-100 <$4000
Series 1875
4x5 1-4390 <$400
3x10-20 1-1998 <$500/$850
Brown Back
4x5 1-25300 <$350
Total Issue $876,400
Out at close $83,700
Out in 1910 $4,384

1565 Newport
N EXCHANGE B OF NEWPORT
{{ 18 L }}
Chartered 1865
Closed 2/6/26
Original Series <$VALUE
3x1-2 1-6800 <$250/$750
4x5 1-5200 <$275
3x10-20 1-1590 <$500/$1000
Series 1875
4x5 1-5000 <$275
3x10-20 1-1340 <$450/$850
Brown Back
4x5 1-12432 <$225
3x10-20 1-6860 <$225/$275
1902 Red Seal
4x5 1-4400 <$500
3x10-20 1-2840 <$500
1902 Date Back
4x5 1-8630 <$125
3x10-20 1-6488 <$125
1902 Plain Back
4x5 8631-23066 <$125
3x10-20 6489-15834 <$125
Total Issue $2,459,160
Out at close $100,000
Ch 1546 assumed circulation

1492 Newport
NEWPORT NB, NEWPORT
{{ 50+ L 16 S }}
Chartered 1865
Original Series <$VALUE
3x1-2 1-5700 <$250/$750
4x5 1-3700 <$250
3x10-20 1-1850 <$500/$1000
50-100 1-300 <$4000
Series 1875
3x1-2 1-83 <$250/$750
4x5 1-2482 <$250
3x10-20 1-2075 <$450/$850
50-100 1-169 <$4000
Brown Back
4x5 1-9627 <$175
3x10-20 1-8254 <$175/$225
50-100 1-635 <$1250/$1500
1902 Red Seal
4x5 1-5050 <$500
3x10-20 1-2610 <$500
1902 Date Back
4x5 1-9000 <$75
3x10-20 1-6000 <$75
50-100 1-190 <$350/$400
3x50-100 1-237 <$350/$400
1902 Plain Back
4x5 9001-27185 <$75
3x10-20 6001-17193 <$75
3x50-100 238-429<$350/$400
1929 Small Size
5 Type 1 1-2348 <$125
10 Type 1 1-1458 <$125
20 Type 1 1-436 <$135
50 Type 1 1-114 <$300
100 Type 1 1-36 <$400
5 Type 2 1-11172 <$135
Total Issue $3,212,145
Out in 1935 $110,000
Large out 1935 $8,515

2554 Newport
UNION NB OF NEWPORT
{{ 11 L }}
Chartered 1881
Liquidated 10/17/12
Series 1875 <$VALUE
4x5 1-10575 <$350
3x10-20 1-13093 <$450/$850
Brown Back
4x5 1-3100 <$350
3x10-20 1-3560 <$350
1882 Date Back
4x5 1-2130 <$450
3x10-20 1-1763 <$450
Total Issue $1,236,900
Out at close $47,000

1616 Providence
PACIFIC NB OF NORTH PROVIDENCE
{{ 12 L }}
Chartered 12/9/65
Liquidated 3/8/00
2nd title:Pacific NB of Pawtucket 1/12/89
Original Series <$VALUE
3x1-2 1-15600 <$300/$850
4x5 1-7975 <$350
3x10-20 1-830 <$500/$1000
Series 1875
3x1-2 1-3190 <$300/$850
4x5 1-10100 <$350
3x10-20 1-4103 <$450/$850
Brown Back
4x5 1-2300 <$350
3x10-20 1-720 <$350
50-100 1-67 <$1250/$1500
SECOND TITLE {{ 1 L }}
Brown Back
4x5 1-15102 <$650
Total Issue $1,096,190
Out at close $95,015
Out in 1910 $5,802

856 Providence
SLATER NB OF NORTH PROVIDENCE
Chartered 3/3/65
Liquidated 3/31/00
2nd title:Slater NB of Pawtucket 2/7/85
FIRST TITLE {{ 16 L }}
Original Series <$VALUE
3x1-2 1-10500 <$300/$850
4x5 1-9000 <$350
3x10-20 1-1650 <$600/$1000
50-100 1-300 <$4000
Series 1875
3x1-2 1-3860 <$300/$850
4x5 1-5000 <$350
3x10-20 1-7902 <$500/$850
50-100 1-200 <$4000
SECOND TITLE {{ 4 L }}
Brown Back
3x10-20 1-14777 <$500
Total Issue $1,643,250
Out at close $196,840
Out in 1910 $10,572

1512 Providence
PASCOAG NB, PASCOAG
{{ 4 L }}
Chartered 8/9/65
Liquidated 6/6/01
Original Series <$VALUE
3x1-2 1-1200 <$500/$1000
4x5 1-2550 <$600
3x10-20 1-1690 <$750/$1250
Series 1875
4x5 1-5245 <$600
3x10-20 1-1400 <$750/$1000
Brown Back
4x5 1-1000 <$500
3x10-20 1-8757 <$500
Total Issue $774,250
Out at close $100,000
Out in 1910 $5,765

<$VALUEs are for notes in FINE condition. Value changes by approximately 25% for a change of one full grade.

****
843 Providence
FNB OF PAWTUCKET
{{ 16 L }}
Chartered 2/27/65
Liquidated 3/8/00
Original Series <$VALUE
3x1-2 1-10000 <$350/$850
4x5 1-7500 <$350
3x10-20 1-4800 <$600/$1000
50-100 1-320 <$4000
500 1-44 <$150,000
Series 1875
3x1-2 1-5430 <$350/$850
4x5 1-3750 <$350
3x10-20 1-3190 <$500/$850
50-100 1-965 <$4000
500 1-75 <$150,000
Brown Back
4x5 1-18471 <$300
Total Issue $1,323,320
Out at close $97,478
Out in 1910 $7,011
****
Pacific NB of Pawtucket
SEE Ch 1616
Pacific NB of
North Providence
****
Slater NB of Pawtucket
SEE Ch 856
Slater NB of North Providence
****
1460 Kent
PHENIX NB, PHENIX
{{ UNREPORTED }}
Chartered 7/17/65
Liquidated 8/30/00
Original Series <$VALUE
4x5 1-2050 <$1250
3x10-20 1-1850<$1500/$2000
Series 1875
4x5 1-2000 <$1250
3x10-20 1-1490<$1500/$2000
Brown Back
3x10-20 1-2150 <$1250
Total Issue $355,500
Out at close $26,470
Out in 1910 $1,820
****
1472 Providence
AMERICAN NB OF PROVIDENCE
{{ 26 L }}
Chartered 7/20/65
Liquidated 2/12/06
Original Series <$VALUE
3x1-2 1-34900 <$250/$750
4x5 1-31725 <$275
3x10-20 1-7000 <$500/$1000
50-100 1-800 <$4000
500-1000 1-50
<$150,000/$250,000
Series 1875
3x1-2 1-11000 <$250/$750
4x5 1-29661 <$275
3x10-20 1-9801 <$450/$850
Brown Back
4x5 1-26075 <$175
3x10-20 1-13642 <$175/$225
1902 Red Seal
4x5 1-2850 <$500
3x10-20 1-2148 <$500
Total Issue $3,860,270
Out at close $343,700
Out in 1910 $47,757
****
2913 Providence
ATLANTIC NB OF PROVIDENCE
{{ 3 L }}
Organized 4/3/83
Receivership 4/16/13
Brown Back <$VALUE
4x5 1-13250 <$500
3x10-20 1-4212 <$500
1902 Red Seal
4x5 1-5850 <$750
3x10-20 1-4340 <$750
1902 Date Back
4x5 1-10923 <$400
3x10-20 1-6947 <$400
Total Issue $1,375,410
Out at close $180,100
Out in 1916 $16,435
****
1328 Providence
BLACKSTONE CANAL NB OF
PROVIDENCE
{{ 50+ L U + 50+ S }}
Chartered 1865
Original Series <$VALUE
3x1-2 1-5000 <$250/$750
4x5 1-4100 <$275
3x10-20 1-2900 <$500/$1000
50-100 1-550 <$4000
500 1-40 <$150,000
Series 1875
3x1-2 1-6990 <$250/$750
4x5 1-9250 <$275
3x10-20 1-6646 <$450/$850
50-100 1-1000 <$4000
500 1-30 <$150,000
Brown Back
4x5 1-59176 <$175
3x10-20 1-18522 <$175/$225
50-100 1-300 <$1250/$1500
1902 Red Seal
4x5 1-9250 <$500
3x10-20 1-7200 <$500
1902 Date Back
4x5 1-32415 <$75
3x10-20 1-24634 <$75
1902 Plain Back
4x5 32416-127077 <$75
3x10-20 24635-88027 <$75
1929 Small Size
5 Type 1 1-15530* <$30
10 Type 1 1-8788** <$35
20 Type 1 1-2912*** <$45
5 Type 2 1-33866 <$30
10 Type 2 1-16859 <$35
20 Type 2 1-3855 <$50
* 6347-7316 not issued
** 2973-3456 not issued
*** 812-1158 not issued
Total Issue $12,372,120
Out in 1935 $500,000
Large out 1935 $23,923
****
1429 Providence
CITY NB OF PROVIDENCE
{{ 1 L }}
Chartered 7/12/65
Liquidated 1/17/00
Original Series <$VALUE
4x5 1-8250 <$850
3x10-20 1-7000<$1000/$1250
50-100 1-700 <$4000
Series 1875
4x5 1-2500 <$850
3x10-20 1-2997<$1000/$1250
50-100 1-1409 <$4000
Brown Back
4x5 1-25633 <$750
Total Issue $1,543,860
Out at close $230,340
Out in 1910 $6,890
****
13981 Providence
COLUMBUS NB OF PROVIDENCE
{{ 16 S }}
Chartered 2/34
1929 Small Size <$VALUE
5 Type 2 1-9400 <$175
10 Type 2 1-4810 <$175
20 Type 2 1-1445 <$175
Total Issue $124,000
Out in 1935 $74,150
****
1319 Providence
COMMERCIAL NB OF
PROVIDENCE
{{ 7 L }}
Chartered 6/21/65
Liquidated 6/6/03
Original Series <$VALUE
4x5 1-14200 <$350
3x10-20 1-4101 <$500/$1000
20 4102-6601 <$1000
50-100 1-1568 <$4000
Series 1875
4x5 1-34276 <$350
3x10-20 1-13939 <$450/$850
Brown Back
4x5 1-32131 <$300
3x10-20 1-7040 <$300
Total Issue $3,151,340
Out at close $62,187
Out in 1910 $16,360
****
1002 Providence
FIFTH NB OF PROVIDENCE
{{ 7 L }}
Chartered 4/12/65
Liquidated 9/5/01
Original Series <$VALUE
3x1-2 1-16550 <$350/$850
4x5 1-10950 <$375
3x10-20 1-2870 <$500/$1000
50-100 1-650 <$4000
Series 1875
3x1-2 1-882 <$350/$850
4x5 1-11327 <$375
3x10-20 1-4592 <$450/$850
50-100 1-650 <$4000
Brown Back
4x5 1-4535 <$300
3x10-20 1-2748 <$300
50-100 1-782 <$1250/$1500
Total Issue $1,386,200
Out at close $59,200
Out in 1910 $9,616
****
134 Providence
FNB OF PROVIDENCE
{{ 32 L }}
Chartered 11/28/63
Liquidated 6/24/04
Original Series <$VALUE
3x1-2 1-23000 <$250/$750
4x5 1-27000 <$275
4x10 1-9500 <$500
2x20-50-100 1-950
<$1000/$4000/$4000
Series 1875
3x1-2 1-13280 <$250/$750
4x5 1-15000 <$275
4x10 1-9345 <$450
2x20-50-100 1-500
<$850/$4000/$4000
Brown Back
4x5 1-46272 <$150
3x10-20 1-14728 <$150/$200
50-100 1-500 <$1250/$1500
1902 Red Seal
3x10-20 1-1945 <$500
Total Issue $3,884,790
Out at close $146,150
Out in 1910 $25,868
****
772 Providence
FOURTH NB OF PROVIDENCE
{{ 11 L }}
Chartered 1/31/65
Liquidated 7/17/07
Original Series <$VALUE
3x1-2 1-16000 <$250/$750
4x5 1-18075 <$275
3x10-20 1-3700 <$500/$1000
50-100 1-290 <$4000
Series 1875
3x1-2 1-2000 <$250/$750
4x5 1-12400 <$275
3x10-20 1-7966 <$450/$850
50-100 1-226 <$4000
Brown Back
4x5 1-14825 <$200
3x10-20 1-9500 <$200/$250
1902 Red Seal
4x5 1-4615 <$500
3x10-20 1-2458 <$500
Total Issue $2,350,900
Out at close $150,000
Out in 1910 $26,231
****
1126 Providence
GLOBE NB OF PROVIDENCE
{{ 8 L }}
Chartered 5/9/65
Liquidated 7/12/99
Original Series <$VALUE
3x1-2 1-6000 <$350/$850
4x5 1-19500 <$450
3x10-20 1-7700 <$600/$1000
50-100 1-300 <$4000
Series 1875
4x5 1-16250 <$450
Brown Back
4x5 1-35696 <$400
Total Issue $1,888,920
Out at close $130,580
Out in 1910 $10,298
****
1369 Providence
LIME ROCK NB OF
PROVIDENCE
{{ 1 L }}
Chartered 6/7/65
Liquidated 11/27/94
Original Series <$VALUE
3x1-2 1-1400 <$750/$1500
4x5 1-7000 <$850
3x10-20 1-3000<$1250/$1750
Series 1875
4x5 1-12707 <$850
3x10-20 1-2600<$1250/$1750
Brown Back
4x5 1-3000 <$750
3x10-20 1-2359 <$750
Total Issue $859,090
Out at close $48,908
Out in 1910 $3,537
****
1283 Providence
MANUFACTURERS NB OF
PROVIDENCE
{{ 25 L }}
Chartered 6/16/65
Liquidated 12/30/99
Original Series <$VALUE
3x1-2 1-25100 <$250/$750
4x5 1-24700 <$275
3x10-20 1-5630 <$500/$1000
50-100 1-534 <$4000
Series 1875
3x1-2 1-17998 <$250/$750
4x5 1-11750 <$275
3x10-20 1-8689 <$450/$850
Brown Back
4x5 1-7400 <$200
3x10-20 1-3049 <$200/$250
Total Issue $2,040,990
Out at close $68,093
Out in 1910 $9,730
****
1007 Providence
MECHANICS NB OF
PROVIDENCE
{{ 50+ L 50+ S }}
Chartered 4/14/65
Original Series <$VALUE
3x1-2 1-7200 <$250/$750
4x5 1-15500 <$250
3x10-20 1-10100<$500/$1000
50-100 1-350 <$4000
Series 1875
3x1-2 1-11500 <$250/$750
4x5 1-11440 <$250
3x10-20 1-9698 <$450/$850
Brown Back
4x5 1-58750 <$175
3x10-20 1-34400 <$175/$225
1902 Red Seal
4x5 1-17750 <$500
3x10-20 1-7900 <$500
50-100 1-1200 <$1750/$2000
1902 Date Back
4x5 1-38665 <$75
3x10-20 1-21200 <$75
50-100 1-450 <$300/$350
3x50-100 1-4875 <$300/$350
1902 Plain Back
4x5 38666-104014 <$75
3x10-20 21201-49587 <$75
3x50-100 4876-5893
<$300/$350
1929 Small Size
5 Type 1 1-14326 <$35
10 Type 1 1-6376 <$40
20 Type 1 1-1728 <$50
50 Type 1 1-498 <$165
100 Type 1 1-156 <$225
5 Type 2 1-4920 <$45
10 Type 2 1-1845 <$50
20 Type 2 1-595 <$65
Total Issue $12,917,730
Out in 1935 $250,000
Large out 1935 $38,590
****
1131 Providence
MERCHANTS NB OF
PROVIDENCE
{{ 50+ L }}
Chartered 1865
Closed 5/15/26
Original Series <$VALUE
3x1-2 1-2000 <$250/$750
4x5 1-13500 <$250
3x10-20 1-5500 <$500/$1000
50-100 1-1620 <$4000
500 1-50 <$150,000
Series 1875
3x1-2 1-2000 <$250/$750
4x5 1-8459 <$250
3x10-20 1-11899 <$450/$850
50-100 1-800 <$4000
Brown Back
4x5 1-102718 <$175
3x10-20 1-26939 <$175/$225
1902 Red Seal
4x5 1-25050 <$500
3x10-20 1-16780 <$500
1902 Date Back
4x5 1-85330 <$75
3x10-20 1-56468 <$75
1902 Plain Back
4x5 85331-231903 <$75
3x10-20 56469-151072 <$75
Total Issue $18,650,100
Out in 1926 $1,000,000
Ch 1302 assumed circulation
****
1366 Providence
NB OF COMMERCE OF
PROVIDENCE
Chartered 1865
2nd title:NB of Commerce &
TC 1/21/31
FIRST TITLE {{ 39 L 10 S }}
Original Series <$VALUE
3x1-2 1-15400 <$250/$750
4x5 1-19000 <$250
3x10-20 1-13098<$500/$1000
50-100 1-1594 <$4000
500-1000 1-80
<$150,000/$250,000
Series 1875
3x1-2 1-5900 <$250/$750
4x5 1-40804 <$250
3x10-20 1-16683 <$450/$850
50-100 1-300 <$4000
Brown Back
4x5 1-9000 <$175
3x10-20 1-6605 <$175/$225
1902 Red Seal
3x10-20 1-1700 <$500
1902 Date Back
4x5 1-25500 <$75
3x10-20 1-18200 <$75
1902 Plain Back
4x5 25501-79180 <$75
3x10-20 18201-51171 <$75
1929 Small Size
5 Type 1 1-5826 <$100
10 Type 1 1-2740 <$100
20 Type 1 1-880 <$100
SECOND TITLE {{ 48 S }}
1929 Small Size
5 Type 1 1-12422 <$30
10 Type 1 1-6112 <$35
20 Type 1 1-1284 <$45
5 Type 2 1-55994 <$30
10 Type 2 1-5374 <$35
20 Type 2 1-2349 <$45
Total Issue $9,652,060
Out in 1934 $545,250
****
1036 Providence
NB OF NORTH AMERICA,
PROVIDENCE
{{ 13 L }}
Chartered 4/17/65
Liquidated 6/14/04
Original Series <$VALUE
4x5 1-23750 <$275
3x10-20 1-13468<$500/$1000
50-100 1-800 <$4000
500 1-106 <$150,000
Series 1875
3x1-2 1-10000 <$250/$750
4x5 1-39750 <$275
3x10-20 1-10000 <$450/$850
Brown Back
4x5 1-34642 <$250
3x10-20 1-12592 <$250/$300
Total Issue $3,988,840
Out at close $66,598
Out in 1910 $24,060
****
1030 Providence
N EAGLE B OF PROVIDENCE
{{ 12 L }}
Chartered 4/17/65
Liquidated 9/5/01
Original Series <$VALUE
3x1-2 1-5700 <$275/$750
4x5 1-30350 <$300
3x10-20 1-8478 <$500/$1000
50-100 1-540 <$4000
Series 1875
3x1-2 1-11500 <$275/$750
4x5 1-12976 <$300
3x10-20 1-6659 <$450/$850
Brown Back
4x5 1-25871 <$250
3x10-20 1-4547 <$250/$300
Total Issue $2,535,140
Out at close $110,480
Out in 1910 $14,373
****
1339 Providence
N EXCHANGE B OF
PROVIDENCE
{{ 50+ L }}
Chartered 1865
Liquidated 6/4/26
Original Series <$VALUE
3x1-2 1-2000 <$250/$750
4x5 1-8000 <$250
3x10-20 1-2130 <$500/$1000
50-100 1-170 <$4000
Series 1875
3x1-2 1-12164 <$250/$750
4x5 1-47961 <$250
3x10-20 1-700 <$450/$850
Brown Back
4x5 1-136932 <$175
3x10-20 1-16674 <$175/$225
1902 Red Seal
4x5 1-18000 <$500
3x10-20 1-12000 <$500
1902 Date Back
4x5 1-45250 <$75
3x10-20 1-29800 <$75
1902 Plain Back
4x5 45251-142069 <$75
3x10-20 29801-83289 <$75
Total Issue $12,922,070
Out at close $1,000,000
****
1151 Providence
OLD NB OF PROVIDENCE
{{ 16 L }}
Chartered 5/15/65
Liquidated 7/20/06
Original Series <$VALUE
3x1-2 1-21200 <$250/$750
4x5 1-15270 <$275
3x10-20 1-7781 <$500/$1000
50-100 1-337 <$4000
Series 1875
3x1-2 1-3000 <$250/$750
4x5 1-17745 <$275
3x10-20 1-6072 <$450/$850
Brown Back
4x5 1-17041 <$200
3x10-20 1-7421 <$200/$250
1902 Red Seal
4x5 1-2690 <$500
3x10-20 1-1989 <$500
Total Issue $2,389,620
Out at close $187,350
Out in 1910 $25,745
****
948 Providence
PHENIX NB OF PROVIDENCE
{{ 50+ L 50+ S }}
Chartered 3/28/65
Original Series <$VALUE
3x1-2 1-23700 <$250/$750
4x5 1-11450 <$250
3x10-20 1-5920 <$500/$1000
50-100 1-1309 <$4000
Series 1875
3x1-2 1-12280 <$250/$750
4x5 1-17212 <$250
3x10-20 1-5674 <$450/$850
Brown Back
4x5 1-11547 <$175
3x10-20 1-4159 <$175/$225
1902 Red Seal
4x5 1-4400 <$500
3x10-20 1-3140 <$500
1902 Date Back
4x5 1-15000 <$75
3x10-20 1-10700 <$75
1902 Plain Back
4x5 15001-98540 <$75
3x10-20 10701-62666 <$75
1929 Small Size
5 Type 1 1-17230 <$35
10 Type 1 1-9448 <$45
20 Type 1 1-2038 <$50
5 Type 2 1-28058 <$35
10 Type 2 1-16935 <$45
20 Type 2 1-4680 <$50
Total Issue $9,048,760
Out in 1935 $450,000
Large out 1935 $24,690
****

****

1302 Providence
PROVIDENCE NB, PROVIDENCE
{{ 50+ L 50+ S }}
Chartered 1865
Original Series <$VALUE
4x5 1-3900 <$250
3x10-20 1-3300 <$500/$1000
50-100 1-1450 <$4000
Series 1875
4x5 1-700 <$250
3x10-20 1-6195 <$450/$850
50-100 1-2146 <$4000
Brown Back
4x5 1-500 <$150
3x10-20 1-1040 <$150/$200
50-100 1-16922<$1250/$1500
1902 Red Seal
4x5 1-7500 <$500
3x10-20 1-2500 <$500
50-100 1-4600 <$1750/$2000
1902 Date Back
4x5 1-36165 <$75
3x10-20 1-19200 <$75
50-100 1-445 <$300/$350
3x50-100 1-1740 <$300/$350
1902 Plain Back
4x5 36166-159070 <$75
3x10-20 19201-97318 <$75
3x50-100 1741-2294 <$300/$350
1929 Small Size
5 Type 1 1-58736 <$30
10 Type 1 1-31272 <$35
20 Type 1 1-7978 <$45
5 Type 2 1-72070 <$30
10 Type 2 1-39353 <$35
20 Type 2 1-9518 <$45
Total Issue $18,899,000
Out in 1935 $1,500,000
Large out 1935 $75,120
Outstanding includes Ch 1131

****

13901 Providence
RHODE ISLAND HOSPITAL NB OF PROVIDENCE
{{ 4U + 50+ S }}
Chartered 12/33
1929 Small Size <$VALUE
5 Type 2 1-54450 <$75
10 Type 2 1-142690 <$75
20 Type 2 1-21858 <$75
50 Type 2 1-1690 <$350
100 Type 2 1-1611 <$400
Total Issue $2,381,910
Out in 1935 $1,603,750

****

983 Providence
RHODE ISLAND NB OF PROVIDENCE
{{ 12 L }}
Chartered 4/6/65
Liquidated 9/5/01
Original Series <$VALUE
3x1-2 1-17600 <$275/$750
4x5 1-26300 <$300
3x10-20 1-8000 <$550/$1000
50-100 1-100 <$4000
100-100 1-60 <$4000
500 1-40 <$150,000
Series 1875
3x1-2 1-4500 <$275/$750
4x5 1-19143 <$300
3x10-20 1-8200 <$500/$850
50-50 1-300 <$4000
Brown Back
4x5 1-22320 <$250
3x10-20 1-4039 <$250/$300
Total Issue $2,549,710
Out at close $63,027
Out in 1910 $13,959

****

1506 Providence
ROGER WILLIAMS NB OF PROVIDENCE
{{ 9 L }}
Chartered 8/7/65
Liquidated 1/30/00
Original Series <$VALUE
4x5 1-4085 <$750
3x10-20 1-2189 <$850/$1250
50-100 1-1360 <$4000
Series 1875
4x5 1-12755 <$750
3x10-20 1-2086 <$850/$1250
50-100 1-95 <$4000
Brown Back
4x5 1-13080 <$600
Total Issue $1,030,400
Out at close $54,590
Out in 1910 $4,510

****

565 Providence
SECOND NB OF PROVIDENCE
{{ 13 L }}
Chartered 11/9/64
Liquidated 9/5/01
Original Series <$VALUE
3x1-2 1-16000 <$250/$750
4x5 1-33000 <$275
3x10-20 1-4050 <$500/$1000
50-100 1-500 <$4000
Series 1875
3x1-2 1-2000 <$250/$750
4x5 1-21020 <$275
Brown Back
3x10-20 1-7853 <$200/$250
Total Issue $1,840,550
Out at close $108,980
Out in 1910 $12,415

****

636 Providence
THIRD NB OF PROVIDENCE
{{ 5 L }}
Chartered 12/20/64
Liquidated 1/25/00
Original Series <$VALUE
3x1-2 1-6600 <$350/$850
4x5 1-19600 <$500
3x10-20 1-7900 <$600/$1000
50-100 1-200 <$4000
Series 1875
4x5 1-8500 <$500
3x10-20 1-6400 <$500/$850
Brown Back
4x5 1-13438 <$350
3x10-20 1-2900 <$300/$350
Total Issue $1,753,760
Out at close $55,864
Out in 1910 $9,706

****

1396 Providence
TRADERS NB OF PROVIDENCE
{{ UNREPORTED }}
Chartered 7/7/65
Liquidated 7/1/96
Original Series <$VALUE
4x5 1-6670 <$1250
4x10 1-3375 <$1500
Series 1875
4x5 1-6996 <$1250
4x10 1-3875 <$1500
Brown Back
4x5 1-5028 <$1250
3x10-20 1-1644 <$1250
Total Issue $746,080
Out at close $49,507
Out in 1910 $2,955

****

5925 Providence
UNITED NB OF PROVIDENCE
{{ 18 L }}
Chartered 7/30/01
Liquidated 2/14/16
Brown Back <$VALUE
4x5 1-16065 <$175
3x10-20 1-11474 <$175/$225
1882 Date Back
4x5 1-24695 <$275
3x10-20 1-16621 <$275/$325
Total Issue $2,219,950
Out in 1916 $119,230

****

1173 Providence
WEYBOSSET NB OF PROVIDENCE
{{ 6 L }}
Chartered 5/20/65
Liquidated 7/26/04
Original Series <$VALUE
3x1-2 1-7125 <$350/$850
4x5 1-10500 <$450
3x10-20 1-4990 <$600/$1000
50-100 1-700 <$4000
Series 1875
3x1-2 1-3895 <$350/$850
4x5 1-16746 <$450
3x10-20 1-4759 <$500/$850
Brown Back
4x5 1-18714 <$300
3x10-20 1-5188 <$300/$350
Total Issue $1,826,150
Out at close $56,769
Out in 1910 $11,421

****

1552 Providence
SCITUATE NB, SCITUATE
{{ 1 L }}
Chartered 9/7/65
Liquidated 1/11/88
Original Series <$VALUE
3x1-2 1-1640 <$750/$1500
4x5 1-2600 <$1000
3x10-20 1-1000<$1250/$1750
Series 1875
4x5 1-2050 <$1000
3x10-20 1-812 <$1250/$1750
Brown Back
4x5 1-772 <$850
3x10-20 1-155 <$850
Total Issue $214,990
Out at close $35,018
Out in 1910 $946

****

1035 Providence
FNB OF SMITHFIELD, SLATERSVILLE
{{ 8 L 13 S }}
Chartered 1865
Original Series <$VALUE
3x1-2 1-6700 <$350/$850
4x5 1-4100 <$400
3x10-20 1-1380 <$600/$1000
Series 1875
3x1-2 1-1900 <$350/$850
4x5 1-3485 <$400
3x10-20 1-1742 <$500/$850
Brown Back
4x5 1-4097 <$350
3x10-20 1-4253 <$350/$400
1902 Red Seal
3x10-20 1-1050 <$750
1902 Date Back
3x10-20 1-5000 <$275
1902 Plain Back
3x10-20 5001-23216 <$275
1929 Small Size
10 Type 1 1-1938 <$150
20 Type 1 1-770 <$150
10 Type 2 1-3422 <$175
20 Type 2 1-971 <$175
Total Issue $2,181,010
Out in 1935 $100,000
Large out 1935 $5,330

****

1554 Washington
N EXCHANGE B OF WAKEFIELD
{{ 3 L }}
Chartered 1865
Liquidated 10/27/77
Original Series <$VALUE
3x1-2 1-1200 <$600/$1250
4x5 1-1200 <$700
3x10-20 1-1063 <$850/$1250
Total Issue $83,150
Out at close $34,650
Out in 1910 $500

****

1206 Washington
WAKEFIELD NB OF WAKEFIELD
{{ 3 L }}
Chartered 6/2/65
Liquidated 7/1/90
Original Series <$VALUE
3x1-2 1-3200 <$600/$1250
4x5 1-2925 <$700
3x10-20 1-1760 <$850/$1250
Series 1875
3x1-2 1-380 <$600/$1250
4x5 1-2705 <$700
3x10-20 1-1510 <$850/$1250
Brown Back
4x5 1-2484 <$500
3x10-20 1-1264 <$500
Total Issue $406,880
Out at close $59,249
Out in 1910 $1,914

****

673 Bristol
FNB OF WARREN
{{ 7 L }}
Chartered 12/30/64
Liquidated 8/24/04
Original Series <$VALUE
3x1-2 1-4340 <$350/$850
4x5 1-5250 <$375
3x10-20 1-1800 <$500/$1000
Series 1875
3x1-2 1-1000 <$350/$850
4x5 1-3000 <$375
3x10-20 1-700 <$450/$850
Brown Back
4x5 1-4795 <$300
3x10-20 1-3601 <$300/$350
Total Issue $596,650
Out at close $50,000
Out in 1910 $5,596

****

1008 Bristol
N HOPE B OF WARREN
{{ 8 L }}
Chartered 4/14/65
Liquidated 8/24/04
Original Series <$VALUE
3x1-2 1-4900 <$350/$850
4x5 1-6750 <$375
3x10-20 1-1748 <$500/$1000
50-100 1-100 <$4000
Series 1875
4x5 1-5685 <$375
3x10-20 1-1600 <$450/$850
Brown Back
4x5 1-5757 <$300
3x10-20 1-2871 <$300/$350
Total Issue $714,290
Out at close $32,500
Out in 1910 $5,692

****

1419 Bristol
N WARREN B, WARREN
{{ 9 L }}
Chartered 7/11/65
Liquidated 8/24/04
Original Series <$VALUE
3x1-2 1-6400 <$350/$850
4x5 1-4525 <$375
3x10-20 1-2970 <$500/$1000
50-100 1-100 <$4000
Series 1875
4x5 1-4500 <$375
3x10-20 1-2200 <$450/$850
Brown Back
4x5 1-6850 <$300
3x10-20 1-3977 <$300/$350
Total Issue $821,850
Out at close $49,300
Out in 1910 $5,891

****

Centreville NB of Warwick, West Warwick
SEE Ch 1284
Centreville NB of Warwick, Centreville

****

823 Washington
N NIANTIC B OF WESTERLY
{{ 11 L }}
Chartered 2/18/65
Liquidated 1/11/05
Original Series <$VALUE
3x1-2 1-1800 <$350/$850
4x5 1-8100 <$350
3x10-20 1-4750 <$500/$1000
50-100 1-350 <$4000
Series 1875
4x5 1-6000 <$350
3x10-20 1-5102 <$450/$850
Brown Back
4x5 1-13937 <$300
3x10-20 1-12592 <$300/$350
Total Issue $1,744,440
Out at close $50,000
Out in 1910 $15,006

****

1169 Washington
N PHENIX B OF WESTERLY
{{ 3 L }}
Chartered 5/18/65
Liquidated 8/15/01
Original Series <$VALUE
3x1-2 1-4600 <$600/$1250
4x5 1-5900 <$700
3x10-20 1-2120 <$850/$1250
50-100 1-154 <$4000
Series 1875
3x1-2 1-2840 <$600/$1250
4x5 1-5000 <$700
3x10-20 1-2520 <$850/$1250
Brown Back
4x5 1-7813 <$500
3x10-20 1-4891 <$500
Total Issue $911,110
Out at close $54,226
Out in 1910 $5,993

****

952 Washington
WASHINGTON NB OF WESTERLY
{{ 12 L }}
Chartered 3/29/65
Liquidated 1/23/04
Original Series <$VALUE
3x1-2 1-1000 <$350/$850
4x5 1-4500 <$350
3x10-20 1-3900 <$500/$1000
50-100 1-100 <$4000
Series 1875
3x1-2 1-1000 <$350/$850
4x5 1-4695 <$350
3x10-20 1-2436 <$450/$850
Brown Back
4x5 1-6837 <$300
3x10-20 1-9418 <$300/$350
Total Issue $1,133,340
Out at close $50,000
Out in 1910 $10,057

****

1592 Washington
WICKFORD NB, WICKFORD
{{ 5 L }}
Chartered 10/17/65
Liquidated 2/20/02
Original Series <$VALUE
3x1-2 1-4250 <$400/$1000
4x5 1-3475 <$500
3x10-20 1-950 <$650/$1000
50-100 1-225 <$4000
Series 1875
3x1-2 1-1600 <$400/$1000
4x5 1-8070 <$500
3x10-20 1-1158 <$600/$1000
50-100 1-50 <$4000
Brown Back
4x5 1-2341 <$350
3x10-20 1-2347 <$350/$400
Total Issue $570,970
Out at close $27,890
Out in 1910 $3,808

****

970 Providence
CITIZENS NB OF WOONSOCKET
{{ 15 L }}
Chartered 4/1/65
Receivership 9/18/28
Original Series <$VALUE
3x1-2 1-1000 <$250/$750
4x5 1-1300 <$275
3x10-20 1-2215 <$500/$1000
50-100 1-50 <$4000
Series 1875
3x10-20 1-2277 <$500/$850
Brown Back
4x5 1-4900 <$250
3x10-20 1-4738 <$250/$300
1902 Red Seal
4x5 1-2325 <$650
3x10-20 1-1330 <$650
1902 Date Back
4x5 1-8150 <$200
3x10-20 1-6140 <$200
1902 Plain Back
4x5 8151-27129 <$200
3x10-20 6141-18841 <$200
Total Issue $2,195,630
Out at close $63,027
Out at close $99,980

****

1402 Providence
FNB OF WOONSOCKET
{{ 2 L }}
Chartered 7/7/65
Liquidated 2/6/02
Original Series <$VALUE
3x1-2 1-2560 <$600/$1250
4x5 1-2400 <$750
3x10-20 1-2810<$1000/$1250
Series 1875
3x1-2 1-2160 <$600/$1250
4x5 1-3200 <$750
3x10-20 1-2244<$1000/$1250
Brown Back
4x5 1-16989 <$600
3x10-20 1-7210 <$600
Total Issue $1,088,580
Out at close $52,137
Out in 1910 $5,922

****

1423 Providence
N GLOBE B OF WOONSOCKET
{{ 8 L }}
Chartered 1865
Liquidated 1/12/29
Original Series <$VALUE
3x1-2 1-3000 <$400/$1000
4x5 1-1975 <$400
3x10-20 1-1023 <$600/$1000
Series 1875
4x5 1-2000 <$400
3x10-20 1-2833 <$500/$850
Brown Back
3x10-20 1-9967 <$400
1902 Red Seal
3x10-20 1-3000 <$750
1902 Date Back
3x10-20 1-9300 <$300
1902 Plain Back
3x10-20 9301-26942 <$300
Total Issue $2,282,750
Out at close $100,000

****

1409 Providence
N UNION B OF WOONSOCKET
{{ 10 L }}
Chartered 1865
Liquidated 5/4/15
Original Series <$VALUE
3x1-2 1-890 <$300/$800
4x5 1-2850 <$350
3x10-20 1-2220 <$500/$1000
50-100 1-631 <$4000
Series 1875
3x1-2 1-2000 <$300/$800
4x5 1-4410 <$350
3x10-20 1-2462 <$450/$850
50-100 1-100 <$4000
Brown Back
4x5 1-18909 <$350
3x10-20 1-8275 <$350/$400
1902 Red Seal
3x10-20 1-5500 <$650
1902 Date Back
3x10-20 1-12862 <$250
Total Issue $2,213,430
Out in 1915 $102,600

****

1421 Providence
PRODUCERS NB OF WOONSOCKET
{{ 17 L }}
Chartered 1865
Liquidated 1/16/26
Original Series <$VALUE
4x5 1-3825 <$275
3x10-20 1-3100 <$500/$1000
50-100 1-450 <$4000
Series 1875
4x5 1-2000 <$275
3x10-20 1-4914 <$450/$850
50-100 1-300 <$4000
Brown Back
3x10-20 1-25296 <$250/$300
1902 Red Seal
3x10-20 1-8000 <$500
1902 Date Back
4x5 1-6830 <$125
3x10-20 1-16500 <$125
1902 Plain Back
4x5 6831-27110 <$125
3x10-20 16501-34757 <$125
Total Issue $4,574,550
Out at close $200,000

****

1058 Providence
WOONSOCKET NB, WOONSOCKET
{{ 6 L }}
Chartered 4/26/65
Liquidated 7/19/00
Original Series <$VALUE
3x1-2 1-3600 <$400/$1000
4x5 1-3325 <$400
3x10-20 1-2130 <$600/$1000
50-100 1-1100 <$4000
Series 1875
3x1-2 1-1160 <$400/$1000
4x5 1-2190 <$400
3x10-20 1-2071 <$500/$850
50-100 1-1011 <$4000
Brown Back
4x5 1-13558 <$400
3x10-20 1-8825 <$400
50-100 1-941 <$1250/$1500
Total Issue $1,514,360
Out at close $200,000
Out in 1910 $9,312

****

<$VALUEs are for notes in FINE condition. Value changes by approximately 25% for a change of one full grade.

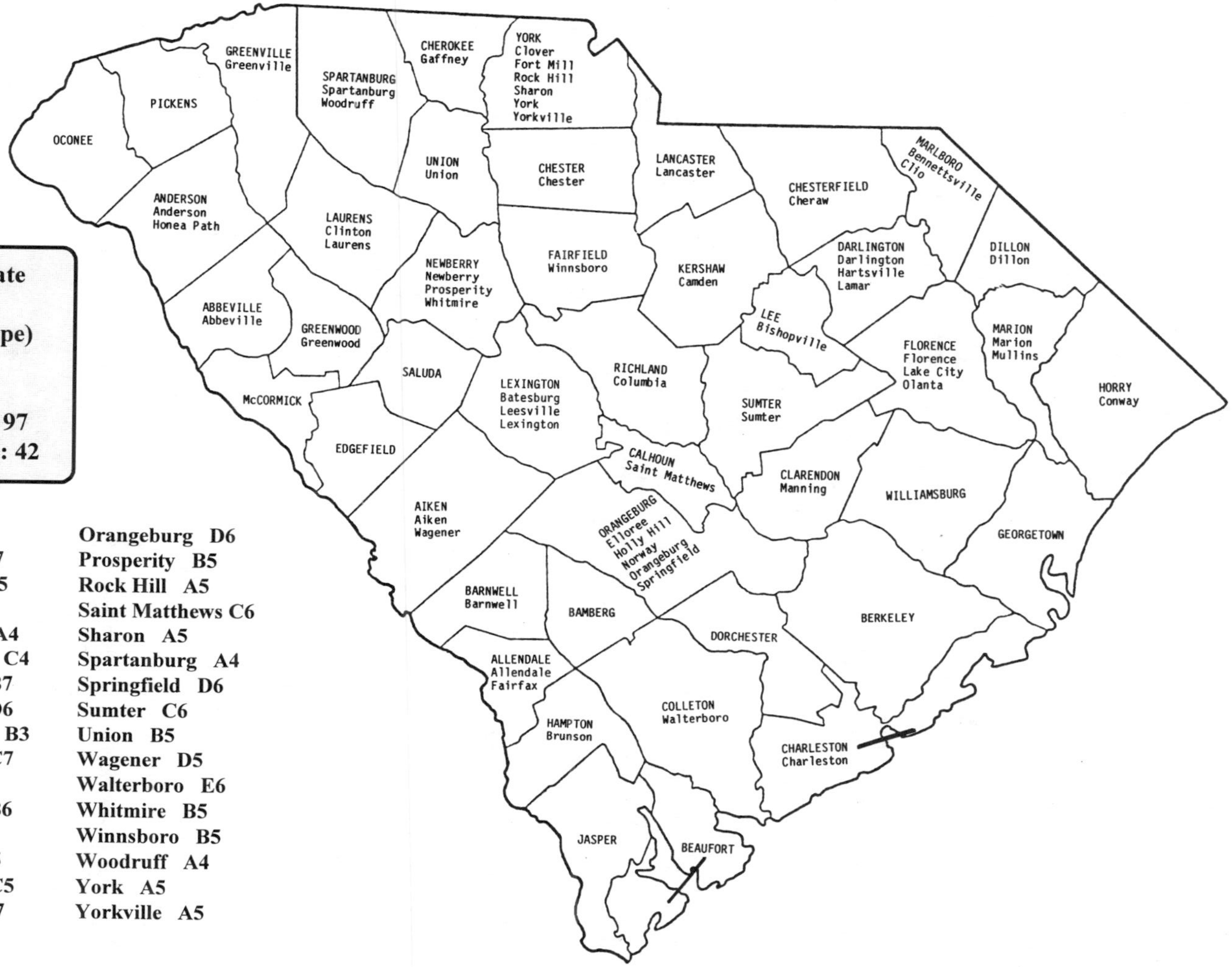

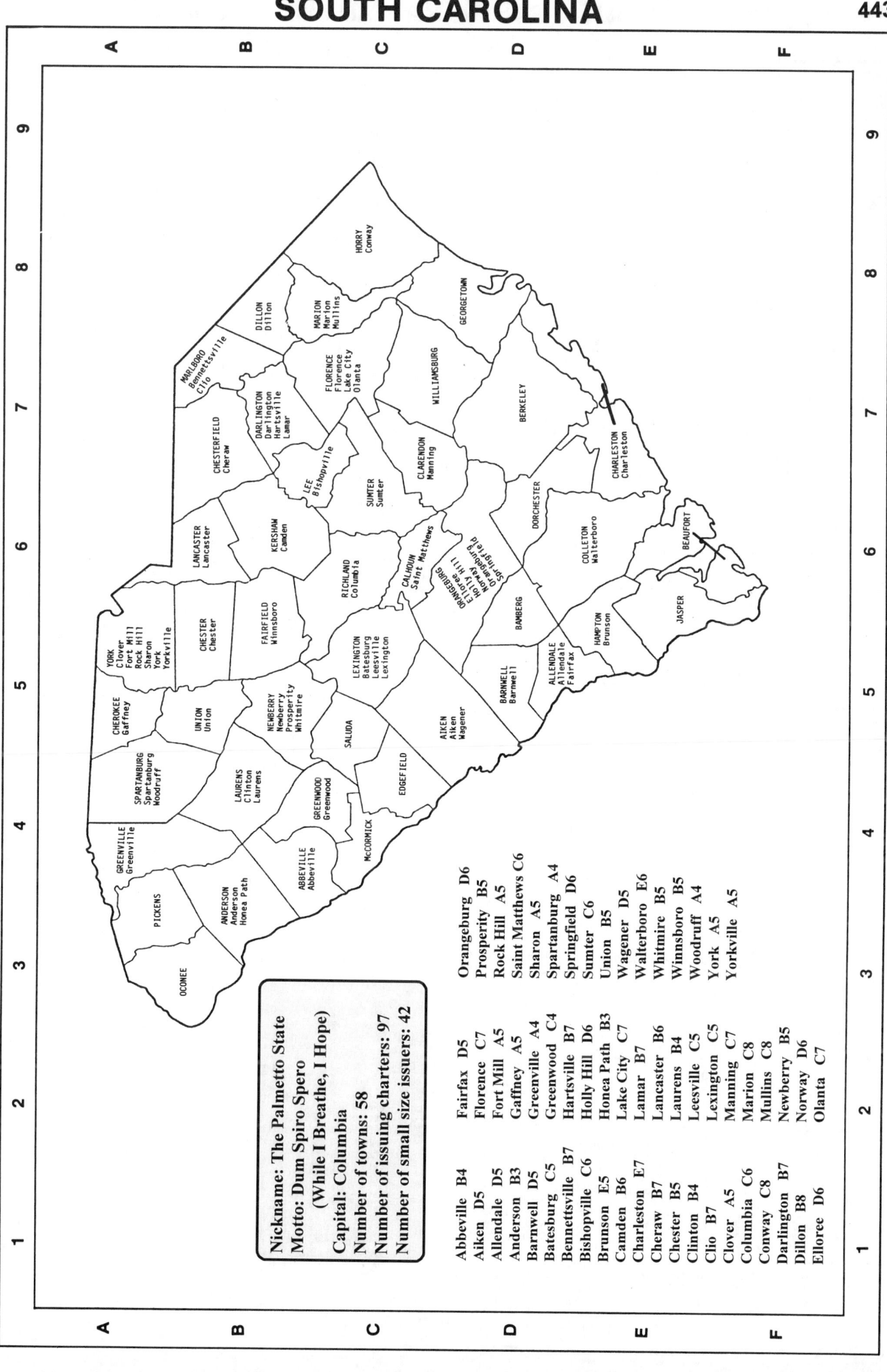

Nickname: The Palmetto State
Motto: Dum Spiro Spero
(While I Breathe, I Hope)
Capital: Columbia
Number of towns: 58
Number of issuing charters: 97
Number of small size issuers: 42

Abbeville B4
Aiken D5
Allendale D5
Anderson B3
Barnwell D5
Batesburg C5
Bennettsville B7
Bishopville C6
Brunson E5
Camden B6
Charleston E7
Cheraw B7
Chester B5
Clinton B4
Clio B7
Clover A5
Columbia C6
Conway C8
Darlington B7
Dillon B8
Elloree D6
Fairfax D5
Florence C7
Fort Mill A5
Gaffney A5
Greenville A4
Greenwood C4
Hartsville B7
Holly Hill D6
Honea Path B3
Lake City C7
Lamar B7
Lancaster B6
Laurens B4
Leesville C5
Lexington C5
Manning C7
Marion C8
Mullins C8
Newberry B5
Norway D6
Olanta C7
Orangeburg D6
Prosperity B5
Rock Hill A5
Saint Matthews C6
Sharon A5
Spartanburg A4
Springfield D6
Sumter C6
Union B5
Wagener D5
Walterboro E6
Whitmire B5
Winnsboro B5
Woodruff A4
York A5
Yorkville A5

3421 Abbeville
NB OF ABBEVILLE
{{ 3 L }}
Organized 10/16/85
Receivership 2/7/25
Brown Back <$VALUE
4x5 1-736 <$1500
3x10-20 1-2023 <$1500
1902 Red Seal
3x10-20 1-640 <$3500
1902 Date Back
3x10-20 1-4210 <$750
1902 Plain Back
3x10-20 4211-4296 <$750
Total Issue $362,670
Out at close $16,850

9650 Aiken
FNB OF AIKEN
{{ 5 L }}
Chartered 1/10
Liquidated 6/17/24
1902 Date Back <$VALUE
4x5 1-4300 <$500
3x10-20 1-3400 <$500
1902 Plain Back
4x5 4301-10149 <$500
3x10-20 3401-6962 <$500
Total Issue $551,080
Out at close $50,000

11111 Allendale
FNB OF ALLENDALE
{{ 1 L }}
Organized 11/30/17
Receivership 12/3/24
1902 Plain Back <$VALUE
4x5 1-2865 <$1500
Total Issue $57,300
Out at close $9,600

9104 Anderson
CITIZENS NB OF ANDERSON
{{ 5 L }}
Chartered 4/08
Liquidated 4/19/28
1902 Red Seal <$VALUE
4x5 1-625 <$3500
3x10-20 1-500 <$3500
1902 Date Back
4x5 1-5275 <$500
3x10-20 1-4620 <$500
1902 Plain Back
4x5 5276-9880 <$500
3x10-20 4621-7543 <$500
Total Issue $612,250
Out in 1927 $36,300

2072 Anderson
NB OF ANDERSON
{{ 2 L }}
Chartered 12/20/72
Liquidated 9/1/91
Original Series <$VALUE
4x5 1-1225 <$4000
3x10-20 1-950 <$4500/$6000
Series 1875
4x5 1-822 <$4000
3x10-20 1-1490<$4500/$6000
Total Issue $162,940
Out in 1910 $740

11287 Barnwell
FNB OF BARNWELL
{{ 2 L }}
Organized 1/9/19
Receivership 12/3/24
1902 Plain Back <$VALUE
4x5 1-12477 <$1000
3x10-20 1-940 <$1000
Total Issue $296,540
Out at close $48,800

10815 Lexington
CITIZENS NB OF BATESBURG
{{ 1 L }}
Chartered 1/16
Liquidated 8/15/17
1902 Plain Back <$VALUE
4x5 1-770 <$1500
3x10-20 1-591 <$1500
Total Issue $44,950
Out at close $30,000
Ch 5595 assumed circulation

5595 Lexington
FNB OF BATESBURG
{{ 6 L 7 S }}
Chartered 10/13/00
Liquidated 6/28/30
Brown Back <$VALUE
4x5 1-1575 <$1250
3x10-20 1-1240 <$1250
1882 Date Back
4x5 1-3100 <$1250
3x10-20 1-2440 <$1250
1882 Value Back
4x5 3101-7250 <$1250
3x10-20 2441-4660 <$1250
1902 Plain Back
4x5 1-13525 <$400
3x10-20 1-8538 <$400
1929 Small Size
5 Type 1 1-1277 <$275
10 Type 1 1-702 <$250
20 Type 1 1-145 <$275
Total Issue $1,266,730
Out at close $100,000
Large out at close $19,520
Outstanding includes Ch 10815

6385 Marlboro
PLANTERS NB OF BENNETTSVILLE
{{ 11 L 1 S }}
Chartered 8/02
Liquidated 4/22/30
1902 Red Seal <$VALUE
4x5 1-3915 <$3500
3x10-20 1-3234 <$3500
1902 Date Back
4x5 1-9800 <$350
3x10-20 1-7400 <$350
1902 Plain Back
4x5 9801-29806 <$350
3x10-20 7401-20211 <$350
1929 Small Size
5 Type 1 1-1219 <$600
10 Type 1 1-439 <$600
20 Type 1 1-30 <$600
Total Issue $1,913,180
Out at close $96,600
Large out at close $30,090

10263 Lee
FNB OF BISHOPVILLE
{{ 4 L 0 S }}
Organized 8/28/12
Receivership 1/18/30
1902 Date Back <$VALUE
4x5 1-2430 <$600
3x10-20 1-1948 <$600
1902 Plain Back
4x5 2431-12699 <$600
3x10-20 1949-8647 <$600
1929 Small Size
5 Type 1 1-256 <$750
10 Type 1 1-179 <$750
20 Type 1 1-25 <$750
Total Issue $707,750
Out at close $44,900
Large out at close $23,480

10832 Hampton
FNB OF BRUNSON
{{ 3 L }}
Organized 3/7/16
Receivership 2/20/29
1902 Plain Back <$VALUE
4x10 1-5901 <$850
Total Issue $236,040
Out at close $16,400

9083 Kershaw
FNB OF CAMDEN
{{ 12 L 14 S }}
Chartered 3/08
1902 Red Seal <$VALUE
4x5 1-1000 <$3500
3x10-20 1-800 <$3500
1902 Date Back
4x5 1-4550 <$350
3x10-20 1-3520 <$350
1902 Plain Back
4x5 4551-15023 <$350
3x10-20 3521-10374 <$350
1929 Small Size
5 Type 1 1-1966 <$150
10 Type 1 1-1032 <$150
20 Type 1 1-252 <$150
5 Type 2 1-3954 <$175
10 Type 2 1-1951 <$175
20 Type 2 1-612 <$200
Total Issue $1,081,820
Out in 1935 $50,000
Large out 1935 $2,550

Atlantic NB of Charleston
SEE Ch 10708
Germania NB of Charleston

2044 Charleston
B OF CHARLESTON N BANKING ASSOC, CHARLESTON
Chartered 9/10/72
2nd title:South Carolina NB of Charleston 3/1/26
FIRST TITLE {{ 40 L }}
Original Series <$VALUE
3x1-2 1-3000 <$4500/$6000
4x5 1-8000 <$3500
3x10-20 1-5241<$4500/$6000
50-100 1-453 <$15,000
Series 1875
4x5 1-1550 <$3500
3x10-20 1-1496<$4500/$6000
Brown Back
4x5 1-18500 <$700
3x10-20 1-23660 <$700
1882 Date Back
4x5 1-18500 <$700
3x10-20 1-10442 <$700
1902 Date Back
4x5 1-18250 <$75
3x10-20 1-11300 <$75/$85
1902 Plain Back
4x5 18251-139503 <$75
3x10-20 11301-93595<$75/$85
SECOND TITLE {{19 L U+50+ S}}
1902 Plain Back
4x5 1-58837 <$75
3x10-20 1-32105 <$75/$85
1929 Small Size
5 Type 1 1-42234 <$35
10 Type 1 1-21636 <$40
20 Type 1 1-5968 <$50
5 Type 2 1-63884 <$40
10 Type 2 1-35600 <$45
20 Type 2 1-9670 <$60
Total Issue $17,318,160
Out in 1935 $1,000,000
Large out 1935 $49,070

10543 Charleston
COMMERCIAL NB OF CHARLESTON
{{ UNREPORTED }}
Organized 5/5/14
Liquidated 2/15/23
1902 Date Back <$VALUE
4x5 1-1525 <$1000
3x10-20 1-1233 <$1000
Total Issue $92,150
Out at close $240

1622 Charleston
FNB OF CHARLESTON
{{ 22 L }}
Chartered 1865
Closed 2/27/26
Original Series <$VALUE
4x5 1-4750 <$3500
3x10-20 1-12000<$4500/$6000
Series 1875
3x10-20 1-4000<$4500/$6000
50-100 1-1325 <$15,000
Brown Back
3x10-20 1-11603 <$750
1902 Red Seal
3x10-20 1-5350 <$3000
1902 Date Back
3x10-20 1-21200 <$75/$85
1902 Plain Back
3x10-20 21201-47386<$75/$85
Total Issue $4,310,700
Out in 1926 $200,000
Ch 1621 assumed circulation

10708 Charleston
GERMANIA NB OF CHARLESTON
Chartered 2/15
Liquidated 1/13/34
2nd title:Atlantic NB of Charleston 5/25/18
FIRST TITLE {{ 0 L }}
1902 Date Back <$VALUE
4x5 1-2000 <$1000
3x10-20 1-1600 <$1000
1902 Plain Back
4x5 2001-5000 <$1000
3x10-20 1601-3600 <$1000
SECOND TITLE {{ 12 L }}
1902 Plain Back
4x5 1-14300 <$300
3x10-20 1-21076 <$300
Total Issue $1,619,800
Out at close $9,370

Peoples FNB of Charleston
SEE Ch 1621
Peoples NB of Charleston

1621 Charleston
PEOPLES NB OF CHARLESTON
Chartered 1865
Liquidated 3/1/30
2nd title:Peoples FNB 2/27/26
FIRST TITLE {{ 35 L }}
Original Series <$VALUE
4x5 1-2856 <$3500
4x10 1-6665 <$4500
4x20 1-2226 <$6000
Series 1875
4x5 1-100 <$3500
4x10 1-750 <$4500
4x20 1-776 <$6000
Brown Back
4x5 1-13980 <$700
3x10-20 1-13970 <$700
1902 Red Seal
4x5 1-8300 <$3000
3x10-20 1-5080 <$3000
1902 Date Back
4x5 1-40750 <$75
3x10-20 1-31700 <$75/$85
1902 Plain Back
4x5 40751-120222 <$75
3x10-20 31701-76636<$75/$85
SECOND TITLE {{ 15 L 15 S }}
1902 Plain Back
4x5 1-49433 <$75
3x10-20 1-36541 <$75/$85
1929 Small Size
5 Type 1 1-9902 <$125
10 Type 1 1-4617 <$125
20 Type 1 1-1075 <$135
Total Issue $11,749,010
Out in 1929 $959,560
Large out at close $268,700
Outstanding includes Ch 1622

South Carolina NB of Charleston
SEE Ch 2044
B of Charleston N Banking Association, Charleston

9342 Chesterfield
FNB OF CHERAW
{{ 5 L }}
Organized 2/4/09
Receivership 11/14/28
1902 Date Back <$VALUE
4x5 1-3475 <$450
3x10-20 1-2680 <$450
1902 Plain Back
4x5 3476-13465 <$450
3x10-20 2681-9227 <$450
Total Issue $730,650
Out at close $50,000

1804 Chester
NB OF CHESTER
{{ 1 L }}
Chartered 3/22/71
Liquidated 3/2/91
Original Series <$VALUE
4x5 1-3500 <$4000
3x10-20 1-1400<$4500/$6000
Series 1875
4x5 1-4000 <$4000
3x10-20 1-3208<$4500/$6000
Total Issue $380,400
Out in 1910 $1,580

8471 Chester
N EXCHANGE B OF CHESTER
{{ 14 L 10 S }}
Organized 12/4/06
Receivership 3/9/33
1902 Red Seal <$VALUE
4x10 1-4375 <$3500
1902 Date Back
4x10 1-14150 <$275
1902 Plain Back
4x10 14151-42617 <$275
1929 Small Size
10 Type 1 1-4747 <$175
Total Issue $2,164,500
Out at close $100,000
Large out at close $5,750

10663 Chester
PEOPLES NB OF CHESTER
{{ U + 38 S }}
Chartered 12/14
1929 Small Size <$VALUE
5 Type 1 1-3410 <$60
5 Type 2 1-15078 <$60
Total Issue $177,690
Out in 1935 $50,000

8041 Laurens
FNB OF CLINTON
{{ 8 L 6 S }}
Organized 1/8/06
Receivership 1/27/31
1902 Red Seal <$VALUE
4x5 1-1150 <$3500
3x10-20 1-1180 <$3500
1902 Date Back
4x5 1-4700 <$350
3x10-20 1-3840 <$350
1902 Plain Back
4x5 4701-24628 <$350
3x10-20 3841-16903 <$350
1929 Small Size
5 Type 1 1-1773 <$250
10 Type 1 1-904 <$250
20 Type 1 1-263 <$250
Total Issue $1,558,700
Out at close $100,000
Large out at close $13,170

11153 Marlboro
FNB OF CLIO
{{ UNREPORTED }}
Chartered 3/18
Liquidated 6/22/25
1902 Plain Back <$VALUE
4x5 1-3125 <$1500
3x10-20 1-1664 <$1500
Total Issue $145,700
Out at close $25,000

11439 York
FNB OF CLOVER
{{ 2 L 8 S }}
Chartered 8/19
1902 Plain Back <$VALUE
4x5 1-5025 <$1250
3x10-20 1-2695 <$1250
1929 Small Size
5 Type 1 1-918 <$250
10 Type 1 1-452 <$250
20 Type 1 1-146 <$250
5 Type 2 1-1332 <$275
10 Type 2 1-828 <$275
20 Type 2 1-264 <$275
Total Issue $327,650
Out in 1935 $25,000
Large out at close $790

1680 Richland
CAROLINA NB OF COLUMBIA
{{ 15 L }}
Organized 5/68
Liquidated 1/12/26
Original Series <$VALUE
3x10-20 1-4900<$4500/$6000
50-100 1-1000 <$15,000
Series 1875
3x10-20 1-400 <$4500/$6000
50-100 1-608 <$15,000
Brown Back
4x5 1-11705 <$750
3x10-20 1-6171 <$750
50-100 1-2638 <$3500/$4000
1902 Red Seal
4x5 1-1750 <$3000
3x10-20 1-1400 <$3000
1902 Date Back
4x5 1-20415 <$125
3x10-20 1-14734 <$125
1902 Plain Back
4x5 20416-48105 <$125
3x10-20 14735-31536 <$125
Total Issue $4,088,450
Out in 1925 $189,700

1765 Richland
CENTRAL NB OF COLUMBIA
{{ UNREPORTED }}
Chartered 1/13/71
Liquidated 2/25/02
Original Series <$VALUE
4x5 1-2000 <$3500
3x10-20 1-1300<$4500/$6000
50-50 1-400 <$15,000
Series 1875
3x10-20 1-500 <$4500/$6000
50-50 1-2003 <$15,000
Brown Back
4x5 1-1498 <$2000
3x10-20 1-963 <$2000
50-100 1-950 <$3500/$4000
Total Issue $590,910
Out in 1910 $6,070

12412 Richland
COLUMBIA NB, COLUMBIA
{{ 17 L 12 S }}
Chartered 7/23
Liquidated 7/1/30
1902 Plain Back <$VALUE
4x5 1-55994 <$125
3x10-20 1-39345 <$125
1929 Small Size
10 Type 1 1-4215 <$150
20 Type 1 1-1100 <$150
Total Issue $3,472,030
Out at close $473,850
Large out at close $88,950

13720 Richland
FNB OF COLUMBIA
{{ 14 S }}
Chartered 6/33
1929 Small Size <$VALUE
5 Type 2 1-33016 <$100
10 Type 2 1-9330 <$100
20 Type 2 1-2320 <$100
Total Issue $304,780
Out in 1935 $50,000

Liberty NB of South Carolina at Columbia
SEE Ch 9687
Union NB of Columbia

6871 Richland
N LOAN & EXCHANGE B OF COLUMBIA
{{ 35 L 27 S }}
Organized 7/4/03
Receivership 7/5/33
1902 Red Seal <$VALUE
4x5 1-13000 <$3000
3x10-20 1-13950 <$3000
1902 Date Back
4x5 1-34250 <$85
3x10-20 1-25200 <$100
1902 Plain Back
4x5 34251-106029 <$85
3x10-20 25201-68302 <$100
1929 Small Size
5 Type 1 1-13761 <$50
10 Type 1 1-7346 <$50
20 Type 1 1-1669 <$60
Total Issue $7,547,050
Out at close $390,000
Large out at close $27,140

10315 Richland
N STATE B OF COLUMBIA
{{ 12 L }}
Chartered 1/13
Liquidated 12/3/29
1902 Date Back <$VALUE
4x5 1-11330 <$200
3x10-20 1-8768 <$200
1902 Plain Back
4x5 11331-40430 <$200
3x10-20 8769-27585 <$200
Total Issue $2,187,850
Out at close $14,825

8133 Richland
PALMETTO NB OF COLUMBIA
{{ 32 L }}
Chartered 3/06
Liquidated 9/11/23
1902 Red Seal <$VALUE
4x5 1-10155 <$3000
3x10-20 1-8138 <$3000
1902 Date Back
4x5 1-33000 <$85
3x10-20 1-24800 <$85/$100
1902 Plain Back
4x5 33001-129720 <$85
3x10-20 24801-86280 <$85/$100
Total Issue $7,518,400
Out in 1922 $980,350

****
10597 Richland
PEOPLES NB OF COLUMBIA
{{ 4 L }}
Chartered 8/14
Closed 4/12/19
1902 Plain Back <$VALUE
4x5 1-4800 <$375
3x10-20 1-3242 <$375
Total Issue $258,100
Out at close $100,000
Ch 9687 assumed circulation
****
9687 Richland
UNION NB OF COLUMBIA
Organized 2/10/10
Receivership 3/4/26
2nd title:Liberty NB of South Carolina at Columbia 4/12/19
FIRST TITLE {{ 6 L }}
1902 Date Back <$VALUE
4x5 1-9500 <$225
3x10-20 1-10100 <$225
1902 Plain Back
4x5 9501-19750 <$225
3x10-20 10101-15900 <$225
SECOND TITLE {{ 7 L }}
1902 Plain Back
4x5 1-25950 <$225
3x10-20 1-17345 <$225
Total Issue $2,576,250
Out in 1923 $325,000
Outstanding includes Ch 10597
****
10536 Horry
CONWAY NB, CONWAY
{{ 5 L 9 S }}
Chartered 5/14
1902 Date Back <$VALUE
4x5 1-2665 <$400
3x10-20 1-2134 <$400
1902 Plain Back
4x5 2666-11893 <$400
3x10-20 2135-7989 <$400
1929 Small Size
5 Type 1 1-1698 <$175
10 Type 1 1-1210 <$175
20 Type 1 1-224 <$175
5 Type 2 1-3812 <$200
10 Type 2 1-2220 <$200
20 Type 2 1-516 <$200
Total Issue $839,310
Out in 1935 $50,000
Large out 1935 $2,435
****
9690 Horry
FNB OF CONWAY
{{ UNREPORTED }}
Chartered 3/10
Liquidated 5/8/14
1902 Date Back <$VALUE
4x5 1-1390 <$1500
3x10-20 1-1060 <$1500
Total Issue $80,800
Out in 1914 $12,940
****
10537 Horry
PEOPLES NB OF CONWAY
{{ 5 L 7 S }}
Chartered 5/14
1902 Date Back <$VALUE
3x10-20 1-700 <$400
1902 Plain Back
3x10-20 701-5134 <$400
1929 Small Size
10 Type 1 1-806 <$250
20 Type 1 1-194 <$250
10 Type 2 1-2231 <$250
20 Type 2 1-600 <$250
Total Issue $362,650
Out in 1935 $25,000
Large out 1935 $1,190
****
9999 Darlington
CAROLINA NB OF DARLINGTON
{{ 10 L }}
Organized 4/14/11
Receivership 11/2/28
1902 Date Back <$VALUE
4x5 1-3475 <$325
3x10-20 1-2750 <$325
1902 Plain Back
4x5 3476-21000 <$325
3x10-20 2751-13161 <$325
Total Issue $1,078,050
Out at close $85,500
****

****
2512 Darlington
DARLINGTON NB, DARLINGTON
{{ UNREPORTED }}
Chartered 3/26/81
Liquidated 2/10/87
Series 1875 <$VALUE
4x5 1-3199 <$5000
Total Issue $63,980
Out in 1910 $335
****
10908 Dillon
FNB OF DILLON
{{ 2 L }}
Chartered 9/16
Liquidated 5/21/29
1902 Plain Back <$VALUE
4x5 1-2370 <$1250
4x10 1-1810 <$1250
Total Issue $119,800
Out at close $2,500
****
10679 Orangeburg
FNB OF ELLOREE
{{ 4 L 3 S }}
Chartered 1/15
Liquidated 9/30/31
1902 Date Back <$VALUE
4x10 1-1000 <$600
1902 Plain Back
4x10 1001-14516 <$600
1929 Small Size
10 Type 1 1-1607 <$450
Total Issue $677,060
Out at close $50,000
Large out at close $4,100
****
10979 Allendale
FNB OF FAIRFAX
{{ 1 L }}
Organized 4/3/17
Liquidated 5/15/25
1902 Plain Back <$VALUE
4x10 1-4225 <$1500
Total Issue $169,000
Out at close $25,000
****
9747 Florence
FNB OF FLORENCE
{{ 8 L }}
Organized 3/23/10
Receivership 5/22/25
1902 Date Back <$VALUE
4x5 1-12600 <$325
3x10-20 1-10000 <$325
1902 Plain Back
4x5 12601-34735 <$325
3x10-20 10001-24131 <$325
Total Issue $1,901,250
Out at close $174,000
****
9941 York
FNB OF FORT MILL
{{ 4 L 4 S }}
Organized 2/21/11
Receivership 10/1/31
1902 Date Back <$VALUE
4x5 1-2075 <$500
3x10-20 1-1880 <$500
1902 Plain Back
4x5 2076-10159 <$500
3x10-20 1881-7305 <$500
1929 Small Size
5 Type 1 1-1014 <$350
10 Type 1 1-509 <$350
20 Type 1 1-141 <$350
Total Issue $646,310
Out at close $40,000
Large out at close $3,540
****
FNB of Gaffney
SEE Ch 5064
NB of Gaffney
****
10655 Cherokee
MERCHANTS & PLANTERS NB OF GAFFNEY
{{ 10 L 18 S }}
Chartered 11/14
1902 Date Back <$VALUE
3x10-20 1-1500 <$275
1902 Plain Back
4x5 1-20909 <$275
3x10-20 1501-14343 <$275

1929 Small Size
5 Type 1 1-4042 <$100
10 Type 1 1-2246 <$100
20 Type 1 1-600 <$100
5 Type 2 1-8348 <$100
10 Type 2 1-4590 <$100
20 Type 2 1-1170 <$100
Total Issue $1,574,390
Out in 1935 $125,000
Large out 1935 $4,360
****
5064 Cherokee
NB OF GAFFNEY
Organized 3/11/97
Receivership 2/17/30
2nd title:FNB of Gaffney 7/6/14
FIRST TITLE {{ 2 L }}
Brown Back <$VALUE
4x5 1-1550 <$1250
3x10-20 1-740 <$1250
1882 Date Back
4x5 1-2426 <$1250
3x10-20 1-1885 <$1250
SECOND TITLE {{ 3 L 1 S }}
1882 Date Back
4x5 1-1820 <$1000
3x10-20 1-1465 <$1000
1902 Plain Back
4x5 1-6993 <$500
3x10-20 1-4354 <$500
1929 Small Size
5 Type 1 1-474 <$500
10 Type 1 1-160 <$500
20 Type 1 1-9 <$500
Total Issue $702,880
Out at close $37,495
Large out at close $12,595
****
5004 Greenville
CITY NB OF GREENVILLE
{{ 5 L }}
Chartered 1895
Liquidated 9/21/18
Brown Back <$VALUE
3x10-20 1-3200 <$1000
50-100 1-1186 <$3500/$4000
1882 Date Back
3x10-20 1-5748 <$850
50-100 1-200 <$3500/$4000
3x50-100 1-178<$3500/$4000
1902 Date Back
4x5 1-1000 <$350
3x10-20 1-800 <$350
1902 Plain Back
4x5 1001-3055 <$350
3x10-20 801-1684 <$350
Total Issue $845,100
Out at close $92,500
Ch 8766 assumed circulation
****
FNB of Greenville
SEE Ch 1935
NB of Greenville
****
9190 Greenville
FOURTH NB OF GREENVILLE
{{ 2 L }}
Chartered 7/08
Liquidated 3/25/19
1902 Date Back <$VALUE
4x5 1-6350 <$500
4x10 1-8775 <$500
1902 Plain Back
4x5 6351-9942 <$500
4x10 8776-11493 <$500
Total Issue $658,560
Out at close $100,000
****
1935 Greenville
NB OF GREENVILLE
Chartered 2/14/72
2nd title:FNB of Greenville 1/25/12
FIRST TITLE {{ 8 L }}
Original Series <$VALUE
4x5 1-3250 <$3500
3x10-20 1-1000<$4500/$6000
Series 1875
4x5 1-2750 <$3500
3x10-20 1-4922<$4500/$6000
Brown Back
3x10-20 1-11100 <$750
1882 Date Back
3x10-20 1-3476 <$750
SECOND TITLE {{ 12 L 31 S }}
1902 Date Back
4x10 1-7750 <$175
1902 Plain Back
4x10 7751-32704 <$175

1929 Small Size
10 Type 1 1-7170 <$60
10 Type 2 1-13657 <$60
Total Issue $3,019,830
Out in 1935 $200,000
Large out 1935 $5,560
****
8766 Greenville
NORWOOD NB OF GREENVILLE
{{ 16 L }}
Chartered 6/07
Liquidated 3/13/26
1902 Red Seal <$VALUE
3x10-20 1-2500 <$3500
1902 Date Back
4x5 1-4775 <$150
3x10-20 1-11400 <$150
1902 Plain Back
4x5 4776-29350 <$150
3x10-20 11401-44666 <$150
Total Issue $2,945,300
Out in 1922 $400,000
Outstanding includes 5004
****
10635 Greenville
PEOPLES NB OF GREENVILLE
{{ 0 L 22 S }}
Chartered 10/14
1902 Date Back <$VALUE
4x10 1-1392 <$1500
1929 Small Size
5 Type 1 1-3484 <$80
10 Type 1 1-2350 <$80
5 Type 2 1-20854 <$85
10 Type 2 1-11427 <$85
Total Issue $519,740
Out in 1935 $200,000
Large out 1935 $55
****
11499 Greenville
WOODSIDE NB OF GREENVILLE
{{ 6 L 2 S }}
Chartered 10/19
Liquidated 11/25/29
1902 Plain Back <$VALUE
4x5 1-38741 <$400
1929 Small Size
5 Type 1 1-516 <$500
Total Issue $790,300
Out at close $83,400
****
7027 Greenwood
FNB OF GREENWOOD
Organized 9/16/03
Receivership 5/16/30
2nd title:N Loan & Exchange B of Greenwood 5/6/07
FIRST TITLE {{ 0 L }}
1902 Red Seal <$VALUE
4x5 1-1240 <$3500
3x10-20 1-1697 <$3500
SECOND TITLE {{ 10 L 3 S }}
1902 Red Seal
3x10-20 1-1500 <$3500
1902 Date Back
3x10-20 1-11500 <$225
1902 Plain Back
3x10-20 11501-31376 <$225
1929 Small Size
10 Type 1 1-905 <$350
20 Type 1 1-173 <$350
Total Issue $1,828,510
Out at close $100,000
Large out at close $28,440
****
N Loan & Exchange B of Greenwood
SEE Ch 7027
FNB of Greenwood
****
10137 Darlington
FNB OF HARTSVILLE
{{ 2 L }}
Organized 11/3/11
Liquidated 1/18/27
1902 Date Back <$VALUE
4x5 1-850 <$850
3x10-20 1-780 <$850
1902 Plain Back
4x5 851-5490 <$850
3x10-20 781-3487 <$850
Total Issue $284,150
Out at close $25,000
****
10680 Orangeburg
FNB OF HOLLY HILL
{{ 2 L 4 S }}
Chartered 1/15
1902 Date Back <$VALUE
4x10 1-625 <$800

1902 Plain Back
4x10 626-7201 <$800
1929 Small Size
10 Type 1 1-1352 <$350
10 Type 2 1-2280 <$350
Total Issue $391,960
Out in 1935 $23,380
Large out 1935 $1,070
****
12381 Anderson
NB OF HONEA PATH
{{ 1 L 2 S }}
Chartered 12/22
Liquidated 4/8/30
1902 Plain Back <$VALUE
3x10-20 1-2903 <$1500
1929 Small Size
10 Type 1 1-223 <$750
20 Type 1 1-14 <$750
Total Issue $160,210
Out at close $19,840
Large out at close $5,790
****
10681 Florence
FARMERS & MERCHANTS NB OF LAKE CITY
{{ 4 L }}
Organized 12/26/14
Receivership 10/18/26
1902 Date Back <$VALUE
4x5 1-1500 <$600
3x10-20 1-1400 <$600
1902 Plain Back
4x5 1501-22175 <$600
3x10-20 1401-11600 <$600
Total Issue $1,018,500
Out at close $97,600
****
11080 Darlington
LAMAR NB, LAMAR
{{ UNREPORTED }}
Organized 9/5/17
Receivership 11/9/28
1902 Plain Back <$VALUE
4x5 1-14627 <$1500
Total Issue $292,540
Out at close $25,000
****
7858 Lancaster
FNB OF LANCASTER
{{ 4 L }}
Chartered 8/05
Liquidated 5/15/22
1902 Red Seal <$VALUE
3x10-20 1-1125 <$3500
1902 Date Back
4x5 1-3550 <$600
3x10-20 1-3130 <$600
1902 Plain Back
4x5 3551-8145 <$600
3x10-20 3131-5750 <$600
Total Issue $506,650
Out at close $50,000
****
10605 Laurens
ENTERPRISE NB OF LAURENS
{{ UNREPORTED }}
Chartered 8/14
Liquidated 3/20/24
1902 Date Back <$VALUE
3x10-20 1-896 <$2000
Total Issue $44,800
Out at close $100
****
10652 Laurens
LAURENS NB, LAURENS
{{ UNREPORTED }}
Organized 10/22/14
Receivership 2/15/28
1902 Date Back <$VALUE
3x10-20 1-949 <$2000
Total Issue $47,450
Out at close $19,750
****
3540 Laurens
NB OF LAURENS
{{ 1 L }}
Chartered 7/24/86
Liquidated 7/10/06
Brown Back <$VALUE
3x10-20 1-1884 <$3000
Total Issue $94,200
Out in 1910 $2,360
****
9057 Lexington
NB OF LEESVILLE
{{ 14 L 8 S }}
Chartered 3/08
Liquidated 9/30/31
1902 Red Seal <$VALUE
3x10-20 1-600 <$3500

1902 Date Back
3x10-20 1-2560 <$325
1902 Plain Back
3x10-20 2561-6650 <$325
1929 Small Size
10 Type 1 1-377 <$400
20 Type 1 1-102 <$400
Total Issue $397,360
Out at close $25,000
Large out at close $4,110
****
9296 Lexington
HOME NB OF LEXINGTON
{{ 10 L 1 S }}
Chartered 12/08
Liquidated 7/15/30
1902 Date Back <$VALUE
3x10-20 1-3430 <$350
1902 Plain Back
3x10-20 3431-7547 <$350
1929 Small Size
10 Type 1 1-206 <$600
20 Type 1 1-33 <$600
Total Issue $393,670
Out at close $24,030
Large out at close $7,710
****
11155 Clarendon
FNB OF MANNING
{{ 1 L }}
Organized 2/23/18
Receivership 12/14/27
1902 Plain Back <$VALUE
3x10-20 1-3892 <$1000
Total Issue $194,600
Out at close $25,000
****
10085 Marion
MARION NB, MARION
{{ 12 L 2U + 10 S }}
Chartered 9/11
1902 Date Back <$VALUE
4x5 1-7000 <$250
3x10-20 1-6000 <$250
1902 Plain Back
4x5 7001-29403 <$250
3x10-20 6001-18133 <$250
1929 Small Size
5 Type 1 1-3760 <$150
10 Type 1 1-2196 <$150
20 Type 1 1-612 <$150
5 Type 2 1-7380 <$150
10 Type 2 1-4080 <$150
20 Type 2 1-1332 <$150
Total Issue $1,917,050
Out in 1935 $100,000
Large out 1935 $5,615
****
9876 Marion
FNB OF MULLINS
{{ 4 L 2 S }}
Organized 9/10
Receivership 12/14/31
1902 Date Back <$VALUE
4x5 1-2000 <$650
3x10-20 1-1760 <$650
1902 Plain Back
4x5 2001-7380 <$650
3x10-20 1761-4870 <$650
1929 Small Size
5 Type 1 1-643 <$500
10 Type 1 1-337 <$500
20 Type 1 1-91 <$500
Total Issue $441,530
Out at close $24,400
Large out at close $3,110
****
1844 Newberry
NB OF NEWBERRY
{{ 12 L }}
Chartered 7/6/71
Receivership 7/1/29
Original Series <$VALUE
4x5 1-3750 <$3500
3x10-20 1-2600<$4500/$6000
Series 1875
4x5 1-1500 <$3500
3x10-20 1-4121<$4500/$6000
Brown Back
3x10-20 1-4380 <$1250
1882 Date Back
4x5 1-1845 <$1250
3x10-20 1-3904 <$1250
1902 Date Back
4x5 1-5600 <$300
4x10 1-4850 <$300
1902 Plain Back
4x5 5601-25196 <$300
4x10 4851-21116 <$300
Total Issue $2,240,710
Out at close $36,100
****

11189 Orangeburg
FARMERS NB OF NORWAY
{{ 1 L }}
Chartered 6/18
Liquidated 1/20/31
1902 Plain Back <$VALUE
4x5 1-7770 <$1500
Total Issue $155,400
Out at close $585

10748 Florence
FNB OF OLANTA
{{ 3 L }}
Chartered 6/15
Liquidated 1/31/28
1902 Plain Back <$VALUE
4x5 1-5480 <$800
3x10-20 1-3292 <$800
Total Issue $274,200
Out at close $25,000

10650 Orangeburg
EDISTO NB OF ORANGEBURG
{{ 6 L 12 S }}
Organized 10/14
Receivership 1/23/34
1902 Date Back <$VALUE
3x10-20 1-2000 <$350
1902 Plain Back
4x5 1-24863 <$350
3x10-20 2001-13434 <$350
1929 Small Size
5 Type 1 1-4216 <$175
10 Type 1 1-2042 <$175
20 Type 1 1-568 <$175
Total Issue $1,486,120
Out at close $110,000
Large out at close $6,895

13918 Orangeburg
FNB IN ORANGEBURG
{{ 4 S }}
Chartered 12/33
1929 Small Size <$VALUE
5 Type 2 1-20352 <$350
Total Issue $101,760
Out in 1935 $50,000

5269 Orangeburg
FNB OF ORANGEBURG
{{ UNREPORTED }}
Chartered 3/00
Liquidated 6/1/01
Brown Back <$VALUE
3x10-20 1-600 <$2500
Total Issue $30,000
Out in 1910 $690

Orangeburg NB, Orangeburg
SEE Ch 10674
Peoples NB of Orangeburg

10674 Orangeburg
PEOPLES NB OF ORANGEBURG
Organized 12/24/14
Receivership 4/9/31
2nd title: Orangeburg NB 1/12/21
FIRST TITLE {{ 1 L }}
1902 Date Back <$VALUE
4x5 1-2500 <$1000
3x10-20 1-2000 <$1000
1902 Plain Back
4x5 2501-9200 <$1000
3x10-20 2001-6140 <$1000
SECOND TITLE {{ 5 L }}
1902 Plain Back
4x5 1-12100 <$400
3x10-20 1-8322 <$400
Total Issue $1,149,100
Out in 1926 $118,000

6994 Newberry
PEOPLES NB OF PROSPERITY
{{ UNREPORTED }}
Chartered 10/03
Liquidated 7/9/25
1902 Red Seal <$VALUE
3x10-20 1-820 <$5000
1902 Date Back
3x10-20 1-460 <$2000
1902 Plain Back
3x10-20 461-988 <$2000
Total Issue $90,400
Out in 1931 $670
Ch 12774 assumed circulation

3616 York
FNB OF ROCK HILL
{{ UNREPORTED }}
Chartered 1/11/87
Liquidated 8/31/98
Brown Back <$VALUE
4x5 1-3706 <$2500
Total Issue $74,120
Out in 1910 $440

5134 York
N UNION B OF ROCK HILL
{{ 12 L }}
Chartered 1898
Liquidated 7/1/30
Brown Back <$VALUE
4x5 1-4500 <$1250
3x10-20 1-7300 <$1250
1882 Date Back
4x5 1-19750 <$1250
3x10-20 1-15900 <$1250
1882 Value Back
4x5 19751-24500 <$1250
3x10-20 15901-18800 <$1250
1902 Plain Back
4x5 1-18436 <$300
4x10 1-9965 <$300
Total Issue $2,652,320
Out at close $7,550

9407 York
PEOPLES NB OF ROCK HILL
{{ 14 L U + 16 S }}
Chartered 5/09
1902 Date Back <$VALUE
4x5 1-9250 <$300
3x10-20 1-9680 <$300
1902 Plain Back
4x5 9251-30307 <$300
3x10-20 9681-22611 <$300
1929 Small Size
5 Type 1 1-4572 <$125
10 Type 1 1-2204 <$125
20 Type 1 1-524 <$125
5 Type 2 1-11362 <$135
10 Type 2 1-5822 <$135
20 Type 2 1-1582 <$135
Total Issue $2,215,640
Out in 1935 $100,000
Large out 1935 $4,600

10651 Calhoun
SAINT MATTHEWS NB, SAINT MATTHEWS
{{ 1 L }}
Chartered 10/14
Liquidated 5/18/27
1902 Date Back <$VALUE
4x10 1-2160 <$1500
Total Issue $86,400
Out at close $210

9533 York
FNB OF SHARON
{{ 7 L 7 S }}
Chartered 9/09
1902 Date Back <$VALUE
4x5 1-2325 <$450
4x10 1-2325 <$450
1902 Plain Back
4x5 2326-8118 <$450
4x10 2326-6629 <$450
1929 Small Size
5 Type 1 1-1402 <$300
10 Type 1 1-720 <$300
5 Type 2 1-2738 <$300
10 Type 2 1-1319 <$300
Total Issue $539,660
Out in 1935 $25,000
Large out 1935 $1,080

6658 Spartanburg
AMERICAN NB OF SPARTANBURG
{{ 7 L 6 S }}
Chartered 3/03
Closed 8/17/31
1902 Red Seal <$VALUE
3x10-20 1-5725 <$3500
1902 Date Back
3x10-20 1-11400 <$300
1902 Plain Back
3x10-20 11401-29634 <$300
1929 Small Size
10 Type 1 1-1616 <$250
20 Type 1 1-441 <$250
Total Issue $1,917,830
Out at close $100,000
Large out at close $13,420

4996 Spartanburg
CENTRAL NB OF SPARTANBURG
{{ 31 L 38 S }}
Organized 4/17/95
Receivership 8/8/33
Brown Back <$VALUE
4x5 1-5250 <$850
3x10-20 1-11600 <$850
1882 Date Back
4x5 1-30855 <$850
3x10-20 1-20849 <$850
1902 Date Back
4x5 1-5000 <$85
3x10-20 1-6000 <$100
1902 Plain Back
4x5 5001-80961 <$85
3x10-20 6001-54770 <$100
1929 Small Size
5 Type 1 1-16033 <$50
10 Type 1 1-7850 <$50
20 Type 1 1-1716 <$60
Total Issue $7,860,180
Out at close $385,560
Large out at close $27,780

14211 Spartanburg
COMMERCIAL NB OF SPARTANBURG
{{ 50+ S }}
Chartered 6/34
1929 Small Size <$VALUE
5 Type 2 1-4210 <$100
10 Type 2 1-1675 <$100
20 Type 2 1-830 <$125
Total Issue $54,400
Out in 1935 $50,000

FNB of Spartanburg
SEE Ch 1848
NB of Spartanburg

1848 Spartanburg
NB OF SPARTANBURG
Chartered 7/15/71
Receivership 6/30/32
2nd title:FNB of Spartanburg 4/25/03
FIRST TITLE {{ 1 L }}
Original Series <$VALUE
3x1-2 1-1000 <$4500/$6000
4x5 1-1700 <$3500
3x10-20 1-1420<$4500/$6000
Series 1875
4x5 1-1205 <$3500
3x10-20 1-3428<$4500/$6000
Brown Back
3x10-20 1-4276 <$2000
SECOND TITLE {{ 37 L 21 S }}
Brown Back
3x10-20 1-16500 <$850
1882 Date Back
3x10-20 1-18938 <$850
1902 Date Back
4x5 1-26750 <$85
3x10-20 1-21900 <$100
1902 Plain Back
4x5 26751-101647 <$85
3x10-20 21901-69628 <$100
1929 Small Size
5 Type 1 1-6271 <$75
10 Type 1 1-2941 <$75
20 Type 1 1-852 <$85
Total Issue $8,322,370
Out at close $299,995
Large out at close $34,265
Outstanding includes Ch 6658

10586 Orangeburg
FNB OF SPRINGFIELD
{{ 5 L 1 S }}
Chartered 7/14
Liquidated 5/6/30
1902 Date Back <$VALUE
4x5 1-625 <$500
4x10 1-625 <$500
1902 Plain Back
4x5 626-10573 <$500
4x10 626-8510 <$500
1929 Small Size
5 Type 1 1-784 <$500
10 Type 1 1-271 <$500
Total Issue $591,640
Out at close $50,000
Large out at close $10,390

10129 Sumter
CITY NB OF SUMTER
{{ 7 L 0 S }}
Organized 1/10/12
Liquidated 3/25/30
1902 Date Back <$VALUE
4x5 1-6400 <$400
3x10-20 1-5300 <$400
1902 Plain Back
4x5 6401-14555 <$400
3x10-20 5301-10845 <$400
1929 Small Size
5 Type 1 1-370 <$750
10 Type 1 1-95 <$750
20 Type 1 1-5 <$750
Total Issue $850,750
Out at close $32,350
Large out at close $14,950

FNB of Sumter
SEE Ch 3809
Simonds NB of Sumter

3082 Sumter
NB OF SUMTER
{{ UNREPORTED }}
Chartered 11/26/83
Receivership 8/24/87
Brown Back <$VALUE
3x10-20 1-310 <$2500
Total Issue $15,500
Out in 1915 $60

10670 Sumter
NB OF SUMTER
{{ 10 L 1 S }}
Chartered 12/14
Liquidated 12/30/29
1902 Plain Back <$VALUE
4x5 1-41537 <$275
4x10 1-28419 <$275
1929 Small Size
5 Type 1 1-1167 <$500
10 Type 1 1-529 <$500
Total Issue $2,034,250
Out at close $200,000
Large out at close $144,640

10660 Sumter
NB OF SOUTH CAROLINA OF SUMTER
{{ 19 L U + 50+ S }}
Chartered 12/14
1902 Date Back <$VALUE
3x10-20 1-6000 <$150
1902 Plain Back
4x5 1-32330 <$150
3x10-20 6001-43390 <$150
1929 Small Size
5 Type 1 1-14892 <$65
10 Type 1 1-6292 <$65
20 Type 1 1-1786 <$75
5 Type 2 1-36098* <$65
10 Type 2 1-10128 <$65
20 Type 2 1-3816 <$75
* 12763-12768 not issued
Total Issue $4,212,760
Out in 1935 $300,000
Large out 1935 $27,830

3809 Sumter
SIMONDS NB OF SUMTER
Chartered 1887
Liquidated 9/30/31
2nd title:FNB of Sumter 4/24/96
FIRST TITLE {{ 0 L }}
Brown Back <$VALUE
4x5 1-2766 <$2500
SECOND TITLE {{ 8 L 4 S }}
Brown Back
3x10-20 1-1875 <$1500
1902 Red Seal
3x10-20 1-250 <$3500
1902 Date Back
3x10-20 1-6050 <$375
1902 Plain Back
3x10-20 6051-14342 <$375
1929 Small Size
5 Type 1 1-4061 <$350
Total Issue $1,000,500
Out at close $50,000
Large out at close $6,325

9742 Union
CITIZENS NB OF UNION
{{ 4 L }}
Chartered 4/10
Liquidated 6/30/26
1902 Date Back <$VALUE
3x10-20 1-3700 <$600
1902 Plain Back
3x10-20 3701-6338 <$600
Total Issue $316,900
Out at close $25,000

2060 Union
MERCHANTS & PLANTERS NB OF UNION
{{ 4 L }}
Chartered 10/22/72
Liquidated 2/22/20
Original Series <$VALUE
3x1-2 1-1800 <$4500/$6000
4x5 1-3350 <$3500
Series 1875
3x1-2 1-640 <$4500/$6000
4x5 1-7536 <$3500
Brown Back
4x5 1-2500 <$1750
3x10-20 1-1000 <$1750
1882 Date Back
4x5 1-484 <$1750
3x10-20 1-322 <$1750
1902 Date Back
3x10-20 1-1560 <$600
1902 Plain Back
3x10-20 1561-1724 <$600
Total Issue $441,900
Out at close $15,000

10485 Aiken
FNB OF WAGENER
{{ UNREPORTED }}
Organized 2/11/14
Receivership 2/9/29
1902 Date Back <$VALUE
4x5 1-410* <$1500
4x10 1-420** <$1500
1902 Plain Back
4x5 661-1756* <$1500
4x10 671-1387** <$1500
* 411-660 not marked
** 421-670 not marked
Total Issue $90,600
Out at close $6,250

9849 Colleton
FNB OF WALTERBORO
{{ 10 L }}
Chartered 9/10
Liquidated 3/5/27
1902 Date Back <$VALUE
4x10 1-3225 <$300
1902 Plain Back
4x10 3226-16459 <$300
Total Issue $658,360
Out at close $75,000

6102 Newberry
FNB OF WHITMIRE
{{ UNREPORTED }}
Chartered 1/21/02
Liquidated 1/1/07
1902 Red Seal <$VALUE
3x10-20 1-377 <$5000
Total Issue $18,850
Out in 1910 $690

2087 Fairfield
WINNSBORO NB, WINNSBORO
{{ UNREPORTED }}
Chartered 3/1/73
Liquidated 3/2/96
Original Series <$VALUE
3x1-2 1-1800 <$4500/$6000
4x5 1-2600 <$3500
4x10 1-500 <$4500
Series 1875
3x1-2 1-343 <$4500/$6000
4x5 1-3450 <$3500
4x10 1-2475 <$4500
Brown Back
3x10-20 1-660 <$2500
Total Issue $283,715
Out in 1910 $1,201

10593 Spartanburg
FNB OF WOODRUFF
{{ UNREPORTED }}
Organized 7/24/14
Receivership 11/10/33
1902 Date Back <$VALUE
3x10-20 1-580 <$1500
Total Issue $29,000
Out at close $80

FNB of York
SEE Ch 6931
FNB of Yorkville

6931 York
FNB OF YORKVILLE
Chartered 8/03
Liquidated 1/7/20
2nd title:FNB of York 9/7/17
FIRST TITLE {{ 1 L }}
1902 Red Seal <$VALUE
3x10-20 1-1350 <$4000
1902 Date Back
3x10-20 1-3980 <$1500
1902 Plain Back
3x10-20 3981-4063 <$1500
SECOND TITLE {{ 0 L }}
1902 Plain Back
3x10-20 1-154 <$2000
Total Issue $278,350
Out at close $12,500

CONDITION affects Value. The Values shown are for notes in FINE condition.

<$VALUEs are for notes in **FINE** condition. Value changes by approximately **25%** for a change of one full grade.

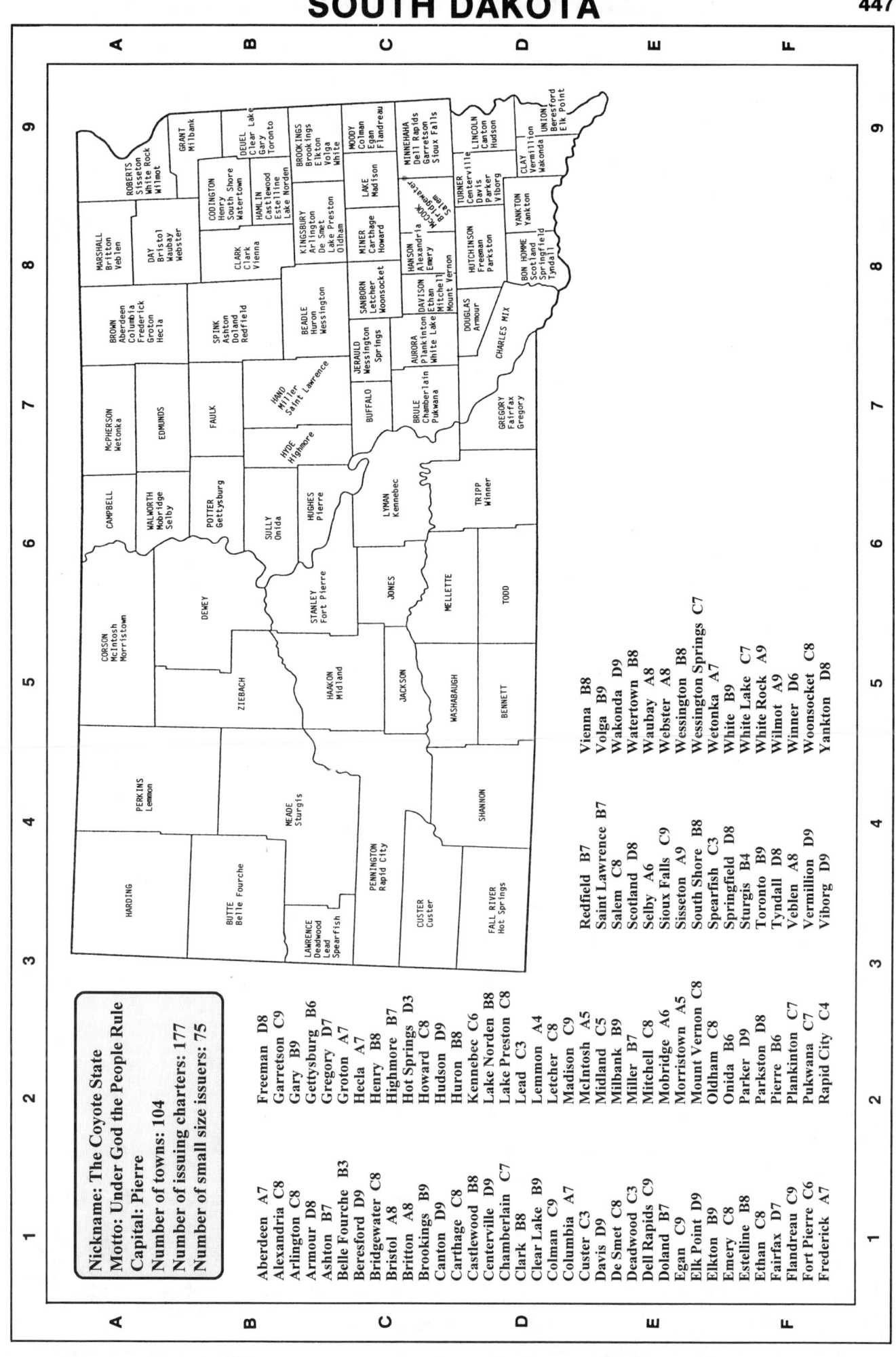

Nickname: The Coyote State
Motto: Under God the People Rule
Capital: Pierre
Number of towns: 104
Number of issuing charters: 177
Number of small size issuers: 75

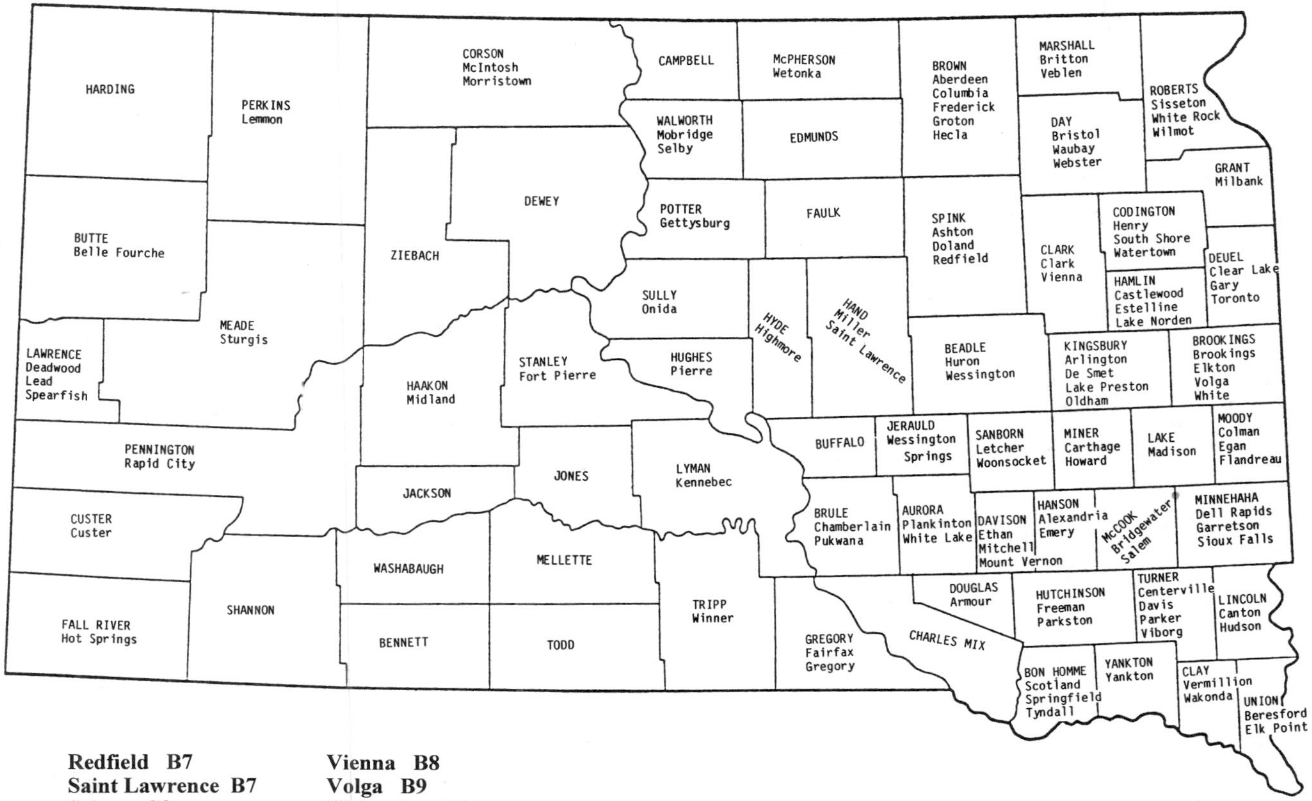

Aberdeen A7
Alexandria C8
Arlington C8
Armour D8
Ashton B7
Belle Fourche B3
Beresford D9
Bridgewater C8
Bristol A8
Britton A8
Brookings B9
Canton D9
Carthage C8
Castlewood B8
Centerville D9
Chamberlain C7
Clark B8
Clear Lake B9
Colman C9
Columbia A7
Custer C3
Davis D9
De Smet C8
Deadwood C3
Dell Rapids C9
Doland B7
Egan C9
Elk Point D9
Elkton B9
Emery C8
Estelline B8
Ethan C8
Fairfax D7
Flandreau C9
Fort Pierre C6
Frederick A7
Freeman D8
Garretson C9
Gary B9
Gettysburg B6
Gregory D7
Groton A7
Hecla A7
Henry B8
Highmore B7
Hot Springs D3
Howard C8
Hudson D9
Huron B8
Kennebec C6
Lake Norden B8
Lake Preston C8
Lead C3
Lemmon A4
Letcher C8
Madison C9
McIntosh A5
Midland C5
Milbank B9
Miller B7
Mitchell C8
Mobridge A6
Morristown A5
Mount Vernon C8
Oldham C8
Onida B6
Parker D9
Parkston D8
Pierre B6
Plankinton C7
Pukwana C7
Rapid City C4
Redfield B7
Saint Lawrence B7
Salem C8
Scotland D8
Selby A6
Sioux Falls C9
Sisseton A9
South Shore B8
Spearfish C3
Springfield D8
Sturgis B4
Toronto B9
Tyndall D8
Veblen A8
Vermillion D9
Viborg D9
Vienna B8
Volga B9
Wakonda D9
Watertown B8
Waubay A8
Webster A8
Wessington B8
Wessington Springs C7
Wetonka A7
White B9
White Lake C7
White Rock A9
Wilmot A9
Winner D6
Woonsocket C8
Yankton D8

3326 Brown
ABERDEEN NB, ABERDEEN
Chartered 3/85
TERRITORIAL ISSUES {{ 2 L }}
Brown Back <$VALUE
4x5 1-1815 <$5000
STATE ISSUES {{ 13 L }}
Brown Back
4x5 1816-4992 <$1250
3x10-20 1-1686 <$1250
1902 Red Seal
3x10-20 1-1700 <$1500
1902 Date Back
3x10-20 1-3400 <$250
1902 Plain Back
3x10-20 3401-8578 <$250
Total Issue $698,040
Out in 1935 $3,255

8642 Brown
DAKOTA NB OF ABERDEEN
{{ 12 L }}
Chartered 4/07
Liquidated 6/24/29
1902 Red Seal <$VALUE
3x10-20 1-1275 <$1500
1902 Date Back
3x10-20 1-1600 <$250
1902 Plain Back
3x10-20 1601-7156 <$250
Total Issue $421,550
Out at close $45,850

2980 Brown
FNB OF ABERDEEN
Chartered 1883
2nd title: FNB & TC 4/17/30
FIRST TITLE
TERRITORIAL ISSUES {{ 0 L }}
Brown Back <$VALUE
4x5 1-2250 <$5000
STATE ISSUES {{ 12 L 4 S }}
Brown Back
4x5 2251-4109 <$1250
3x10-20 1-784 <$1250
1902 Red Seal
3x10-20 1-2000 <$1500
1902 Date Back
3x10-20 1-3540 <$250
1902 Plain Back
3x10-20 3541-9148 <$250
1929 Small Size
10 Type 1 1-618 <$250
20 Type 1 1-210 <$250
SECOND TITLE {{ 7 S }}
1929 Small Size
10 Type 1 1-360 <$175
20 Type 1 1-134 <$175
10 Type 2 1-993 <$200
20 Type 2 1-233 <$200
Total Issue $793,330
Out in 1935 $50,000
Large out 1935 $3,630

3932 Brown
NORTHWESTERN NB OF ABERDEEN
{{ UNREPORTED }}
Chartered 10/22/88
Liquidated 1/15/92
TERRITORIAL ISSUES
Brown Back <$VALUE
4x5 1-1250 <$6000
STATE ISSUES
Brown Back
4x5 1251-1775 <$3000
Total Issue $35,500
Out in 1910 $260

5918 Hanson
FNB OF ALEXANDRIA
{{ 4 L }}
Organized 7/16/01
Receivership 6/23/24
Brown Back <$VALUE
3x10-20 1-1000 <$1500
1882 Date Back
3x10-20 1-1260 <$600
1882 Value Back
3x10-20 1261-2157 <$600
1902 Plain Back
4x10 1-971 <$400
Total Issue $196,690
Out at close $24,400

10187 Hanson
SECURITY NB OF ALEXANDRIA
{{ 8 L }}
Organized 4/13/12
Liquidated 3/19/29
1902 Date Back <$VALUE
4x10 1-1725* <$450
1902 Plain Back
4x10 1876-6356* <$450
* 1726-1875 not marked
Total Issue $254,240
Out at close $30,000

13286 Kingsbury
FNB IN ARLINGTON
{{ 6 S }}
Chartered 2/29
1929 Small Size <$VALUE
5 Type 1 1-816 <$200
10 Type 1 1-476 <$200
20 Type 1 1-150 <$200
5 Type 2 1-902 <$225
10 Type 2 1-461 <$225
20 Type 2 1-102 <$225
Total Issue $82,200
Out in 1935 $24,650

5916 Kingsbury
FNB OF ARLINGTON
{{ 10 L }}
Chartered 7/01
Liquidated 3/4/29
Brown Back <$VALUE
4x5 1-830 <$1500
3x10-20 1-628 <$1500
1882 Date Back
4x5 1-1525 <$600
3x10-20 1-1100 <$600
1882 Value Back
4x5 1526-4150 <$600
3x10-20 1101-2809 <$600
1902 Plain Back
3x10-20 1-3470 <$300
Total Issue $444,950
Out at close $50,000

8012 Douglas
FNB OF ARMOUR
{{ UNREPORTED }}
Chartered 12/18/05
Liquidated 9/2/07
1902 Red Seal <$VALUE
3x10-20 1-280 <$3500
Total Issue $14,000
Out in 1910 $2,430

3437 Spink
FNB OF ASHTON
{{ UNREPORTED }}
Chartered 1/19/86
Liquidated 3/6/88
TERRITORIAL ISSUES
Brown Back <$VALUE
3x10-20 1-250 <$6000
Total Issue $12,500
Out in 1910 $80

6561 Butte
FNB OF BELLE FOURCHE
{{ 6 L 2 S }}
Organized 12/8/02
Receivership 11/6/31
1902 Red Seal <$VALUE
3x10-20 1-440 <$2000
1902 Date Back
3x10-20 1-660 <$450
1902 Plain Back
3x10-20 661-1230 <$450
1929 Small Size
10 Type 1 1-116 <$500
20 Type 1 1-11 <$500
Total Issue $91,780
Out at close $6,320
Large out at close $1,190

10813 Union
FNB OF BERESFORD
{{ 8 L 9 S }}
Chartered 1/16
1902 Plain Back <$VALUE
4x5 1-3520 <$350
3x10-20 1-2221 <$350
1929 Small Size
5 Type 1 1-794 <$175
10 Type 1 1-392 <$175
20 Type 1 1-116 <$175
5 Type 2 1-70 <$200
10 Type 2 1-65 <$200
20 Type 2 1-20 <$200
Total Issue $244,110
Out in 1935 $20,000
Large out 1935 $2,085

7426 McCook
FARMERS NB OF BRIDGEWATER
{{ 1 L 2 S }}
Organized 9/28/04
Receivership 8/24/31
1902 Red Seal <$VALUE
3x10-20 1-365 <$2500
1902 Date Back
3x10-20 1-560 <$1000
1902 Plain Back
3x10-20 561-1065 <$1000
1929 Small Size
10 Type 1 1-94 <$600
20 Type 1 1-13 <$600
Total Issue $78,700
Out at close $6,500
Large out at close $1,160

6925 McCook
FNB OF BRIDGEWATER
{{ 1 L }}
Organized 7/23/03
Receivership 7/18/24
1902 Red Seal <$VALUE
3x10-20 1-362 <$2500
1902 Date Back
3x10-20 1-460* <$1000
1902 Plain Back
3x10-20 561-797* <$1000
* 461-560 not marked
Total Issue $57,950
Out at close $6,200

8480 Day
FNB OF BRISTOL
{{ 1 L }}
Organized 12/21/06
Receivership 11/17/15
1902 Red Seal <$VALUE
4x10 1-300 <$2500
1902 Date Back
4x10 1-2053 <$1000
Total Issue $94,120
Out at close $25,000

13460 Marshall
FNB IN BRITTON
{{ 19 S }}
Chartered 4/30
Closed 3/30/35
1929 Small Size <$VALUE
5 Type 1 1-420 <$125
10 Type 1 1-294 <$125
20 Type 1 1-66 <$125
5 Type 2 1-1500 <$150
10 Type 2 1-605 <$150
20 Type 2 1-125 <$150
Total Issue $54,210
Out in 1935 $25,000

6073 Marshall
FNB OF BRITTON
{{ 4 L 1 S }}
Chartered 12/01
Liquidated 4/30/30
Brown Back <$VALUE
3x10-20 1-1740 <$1500
1882 Date Back
3x10-20 1-1900 <$850
1882 Value Back
3x10-20 1901-3058 <$850
1902 Plain Back
3x10-20 1-1981 <$500
1929 Small Size
10 Type 1 1-248 <$500
20 Type 1 1-19 <$500
Total Issue $356,110
Out at close $29,000
Large out at close $11,840

6462 Brookings
FARMERS NB OF BROOKINGS
{{ 4 L }}
Organized 8/29/02
Receivership 12/3/26
1902 Red Seal <$VALUE
3x10-20 1-1262 <$1750
1902 Date Back
3x10-20 1-3000 <$500
1902 Plain Back
3x10-20 3001-7564 <$500
Total Issue $441,300
Out at close $49,200

3087 Brookings
FNB OF BROOKINGS
Organized 11/15/83
Receivership 2/9/24
TERRITORIAL ISSUES {{ 0 L }}
Brown Back <$VALUE
4x5 1-1375 <$5000
STATE ISSUES {{ 11 L }}
Brown Back
4x5 1376-3042 <$1250
3x10-20 1-252 <$1250
1902 Red Seal
3x10-20 1-545 <$1500
1902 Date Back
3x10-20 1-2600 <$225
1902 Plain Back
3x10-20 2601-8838 <$225
Total Issue $542,590
Out at close $98,500

2830 Lincoln
FNB OF CANTON
Organized 11/3/82
Receivership 12/13/33
TERRITORIAL ISSUES {{ 0 L }}
Brown Back <$VALUE
4x5 1-1600 <$5000
STATE ISSUES {{ 10 L 12 S }}
Brown Back
4x5 1601-3351 <$1250
3x10-20 1-197 <$1250
1902 Red Seal
3x10-20 1-615 <$1500
1902 Date Back
3x10-20 1-1140* <$200
1902 Plain Back
3x10-20 1271-6800* <$200
* 1141-1270 not marked
1929 Small Size
10 Type 1 1-952 <$135
20 Type 1 1-264 <$135
Total Issue $536,420
Out at close $50,000
Large out at close $6,480

4637 Lincoln
NB OF CANTON
{{ UNREPORTED }}
Chartered 9/25/91
Liquidated 2/1/96
Brown Back <$VALUE
3x10-20 1-416 <$3500
Total Issue $20,800
Out in 1910 $150

10833 Miner
FNB OF CARTHAGE
{{ 3 L }}
Organized 3/20/16
Receivership 2/12/24
1902 Plain Back <$VALUE
3x10-20 1-2152 <$750
Total Issue $107,600
Out at close $25,000

6000 Hamlin
FNB OF CASTLEWOOD
{{ 3 L }}
Organized 10/2/01
Receivership 2/19/24
Brown Back <$VALUE
4x5 1-500 <$2000
3x10-20 1-840 <$2000
1882 Date Back
4x5 1-1725 <$1000
3x10-20 1-1240 <$1000
1882 Value Back
4x5 1726-2990 <$1000
3x10-20 1241-1943 <$1000
1902 Plain Back
3x10-20 1-386 <$750
Total Issue $228,250
Out at close $24,600

5477 Turner
FNB OF CENTERVILLE
{{ 7 L 8 S }}
Chartered 6/30/00
Brown Back <$VALUE
3x10-20 1-1350 <$1500
1882 Date Back
3x10-20 1-1550* <$500
1882 Value Back
3x10-20 1751-2153* <$500
* 1551-1750 not marked
1902 Plain Back
3x10-20 1-1937 <$350
1929 Small Size
10 Type 1 1-580 <$175
20 Type 1 1-170 <$200
5 Type 2 1-120 <$200
Total Issue $327,800
Out in 1935 $25,000
Large out 1935 $1,625

8550 Brule
BRULE NB OF CHAMBERLAIN
{{ 3 L }}
Chartered 2/07
Liquidated 9/3/19
1902 Red Seal <$VALUE
3x10-20 1-180 <$2000
1902 Date Back
3x10-20 1-3800 <$650
1902 Plain Back
3x10-20 3801-4898 <$650
Total Issue $253,900
Out at close $50,000

4282 Brule
CHAMBERLAIN NB, CHAMBERLAIN
{{ UNREPORTED }}
Organized 4/8/90
Receivership 9/30/93
Brown Back <$VALUE
4x5 1-788 <$4000
Total Issue $15,760
Out in 1915 $125

2911 Brule
FNB OF CHAMBERLAIN
{{ UNREPORTED }}
Chartered 3/31/83
Liquidated 2/6/92
TERRITORIAL ISSUES
Brown Back <$VALUE
3x10-20 1-570 <$6000
STATE ISSUES
Brown Back
3x10-20 571-574 <$4000
Total Issue $28,700
Out in 1910 $100

13483 Brule
FNB & TC OF CHAMBERLAIN
{{ 20 S }}
Chartered 7/30
Closed 8/31/35
1929 Small Size <$VALUE
5 Type 1 1-208 <$125
10 Type 1 1-398 <$125
20 Type 1 1-76 <$125
5 Type 2 1-1068 <$125
10 Type 2 1-520 <$125
20 Type 2 1-110 <$125
Total Issue $51,980
Out in 1935 $22,750

9301 Brule
WHITBECK NB OF CHAMBERLAIN
{{ 10 L }}
Organized 11/14/08
Receivership 7/14/26
1902 Date Back <$VALUE
3x10-20 1-3800 <$275
1902 Plain Back
3x10-20 3801-7611 <$275
Total Issue $380,550
Out at close $50,000

6409 Clark
CLARK COUNTY NB OF CLARK
{{ 8 L 5 S }}
Chartered 9/02
1902 Red Seal <$VALUE
3x10-20 1-700 <$1750
1902 Date Back
3x10-20 1-860 <$350
1902 Plain Back
3x10-20 861-3577 <$350
1929 Small Size
10 Type 1 1-502 <$250
20 Type 1 1-140 <$250
10 Type 2 1-483 <$275
20 Type 2 1-139 <$275
Total Issue $268,380
Out in 1935 $25,000
Large out 1935 $1,750

3479 Clark
FNB OF CLARK
Chartered 4/1/86
Liquidated 11/1/97
TERRITORIAL ISSUES {{ 0 L }}
Brown Back <$VALUE
3x10-20 1-445 <$5000
STATE ISSUES {{ 1 L }}
Brown Back
3x10-20 446-1007 <$3000
Total Issue $50,350
Out in 1910 $510

12877 Deuel
DEUEL COUNTY NB OF CLEAR LAKE
{{ 1 L 9 S }}
Chartered 1/26
1902 Plain Back <$VALUE
4x5 1-1390 <$1250
1929 Small Size
5 Type 1 1-1346 <$165
5 Type 2 1-5812 <$175
Total Issue $97,240
Out in 1935 $25,000
Large out 1935 $180

6357 Deuel
FNB OF CLEAR LAKE
{{ 3 L }}
Organized 6/28/02
Receivership 5/25/25
1902 Red Seal <$VALUE
3x10-20 1-600 <$2000
1902 Date Back
3x10-20 1-1880 <$650
1902 Plain Back
3x10-20 1881-3698 <$650
Total Issue $214,900
Out at close $25,000

6688 Moody
FNB OF COLMAN
{{ 8 L }}
Organized 2/20/03
Receivership 8/19/26
1902 Red Seal <$VALUE
4x5 1-1425 <$1500
3x10-20 1-960 <$1500
1902 Date Back
4x5 1-1550 <$225
3x10-20 1-1140 <$225
1902 Plain Back
4x5 1551-3940 <$225
3x10-20 1141-2560 <$225
Total Issue $283,300
Out at close $24,500

3352 Brown
FNB OF COLUMBIA
{{ UNREPORTED }}
Chartered 6/12/85
Liquidated 11/26/88
TERRITORIAL ISSUES
Brown Back <$VALUE
4x5 1-893 <$6000
Total Issue $17,860
Out in 1910 $120

4448 Custer
FNB OF CUSTER CITY
{{ 1 L }}
Organized 9/27/90
Receivership 11/17/31
Brown Back <$VALUE
3x10-20 1-1470 <$3000
1882 Date Back
3x10-20 1-199 <$1500
1902 Date Back
3x10-20 1-860 <$1250
1902 Plain Back
3x10-20 861-1772 <$1250
Total Issue $172,050
Out at close $960

11457 Turner
FNB OF DAVIS
{{ 1 L 1 S }}
Chartered 9/19
Liquidated 1/12/32
1902 Plain Back <$VALUE
3x10-20 1-635 <$1500
1929 Small Size
10 Type 1 1-132 <$600
20 Type 1 1-21 <$600
Total Issue $42,190
Out at close $8,000
Large out 1935 $340
Ch 13589 assumed circulation

5355 Kingsbury
De SMET NB, De SMET
{{ 4 L }}
Organized 5/1/90
Receivership 7/6/26
Brown Back <$VALUE
3x10-20 1-1790 <$2000
1882 Date Back
3x10-20 1-1420 <$850
1882 Value Back
3x10-20 1421-2173 <$850
1902 Plain Back
3x10-20 1-1174 <$450
Total Issue $256,850
Out at close $23,800

<$VALUEs are for notes in FINE condition. Value changes by approximately 25% for a change of one full grade.

****
3435 Kingsbury
FNB OF De SMET
{{ UNREPORTED }}
Chartered 1/16/86
Liquidated 9/14/92
TERRITORIAL ISSUES
Brown Back <$VALUE
50-100 1-141 <$10,000
STATE ISSUES
Brown Back
50-100 142-178 <$6000
Total Issue $26,700
All notes reportedly redeemed
****
4983 Lawrence
AMERICAN NB OF DEADWOOD
{{ 1 L }}
Chartered 12/29/94
Liquidated 6/30/05
Brown Back <$VALUE
3x10-20 1-2905 <$3500
Total Issue $145,250
Out in 1910 $5,150
****
3552 Lawrence
DEADWOOD NB, DEADWOOD
Chartered 8/30/86
Liquidated 6/7/94
TERRITORIAL ISSUES {{ 0 L }}
Brown Back <$VALUE
4x5 1-2200 <$6000
STATE ISSUES {{ 1 L }}
Brown Back
4x5 2201-3737 <$3500
Total Issue $74,740
Out in 1910 $515
****
2391 Lawrence
FNB OF DEADWOOD
Chartered 7/25/78
TERRITORIAL ISSUES {{ 6 L }}
Series 1875 <$VALUE
4x5 1-6776 <$6000
STATE ISSUES {{ 18 L 12 S }}
Series 1875
4x5 6777-9578 <$4000
Brown Back
3x10-20 1-8725 <$1500
1882 Date Back
3x10-20 1-10400 <$650
1882 Value Back
3x10-20 10401-12389 <$650
1902 Plain Back
3x10-20 1-10401 <$325
1929 Small Size
10 Type 1 1-2174 <$175
20 Type 1 1-634 <$185
10 Type 2 1-1223 <$200
20 Type 2 1-229 <$200
Total Issue $1,990,640
Out in 1935 $75,000
Large out 1935 $9,440
****
2461 Lawrence
MERCHANTS NB OF DEADWOOD
Chartered 3/4/80
Liquidated 6/8/94
TERRITORIAL ISSUES {{ 2 L }}
Series 1875 <$VALUE
4x5 1-2850 <$6000
3x10-20 1-680 <$6000
STATE ISSUES {{ 1 L }}
Series 1875
4x5 2851-3110 <$4500
3x10-20 681-1170 <$4500
Total Issue $120,700
Out in 1910 $895
****
3508 Minnehaha
FNB OF DELL RAPIDS
Organized 4/21/86
Receivership 9/26/25
TERRITORIAL ISSUES {{ 0 L }}
Brown Back <$VALUE
4x5 1-1300 <$5000
STATE ISSUES {{ 20 L }}
Brown Back
4x5 1301-4720 <$1250
3x10-20 1-1922 <$1250
1902 Red Seal
3x10-20 1-1100 <$1500
1902 Date Back
3x10-20 1-4040 <$135
1902 Plain Back
3x10-20 4041-8155 <$135
Total Issue $653,250
Out at close $59,500
****

****
9693 Minnehaha
HOME NB OF DELL RAPIDS
{{ 25 L 4 S }}
Chartered 3/10
Liquidated 1/13/31
1902 Date Back <$VALUE
4x5 1-3150 <$125
3x10-20 1-2550 <$125
1902 Plain Back
4x5 3151-8920 <$125
3x10-20 2551-6408 <$125
1929 Small Size
5 Type 1 1-664 <$300
10 Type 1 1-321 <$300
20 Type 1 1-70 <$325
Total Issue $546,380
Out at close $50,000
Large out at close $10,540
****
3522 Spink
FNB OF DOLAND
Chartered 6/21/86
Liquidated 2/15/97
2nd title: Merchants NB of
Redfield 1895
FIRST TITLE
TERRITORIAL ISSUES {{ 1 L }}
Brown Back <$VALUE
4x5 1-1025 <$5000
STATE ISSUES {{ 1 L }}
Brown Back
4x5 1026-1881 <$3000
SECOND TITLE {{ 0 L }}
Brown Back
4x5 1-318 <$3000
Total Issue $43,980
Out in 1910 $340
****
7252 Moody
FNB OF EGAN
{{ 8 L 6 S }}
Organized 4/23/04
Receivership 10/10/32
1902 Red Seal <$VALUE
3x10-20 1-1200 <$1500
1902 Date Back
3x10-20 1-1680 <$350
1902 Plain Back
3x10-20 1681-4458 <$350
1929 Small Size
10 Type 1 1-425 <$250
20 Type 1 1-99 <$275
Total Issue $320,280
Out at close $25,000
Large out at close $2,750
****
5901 Union
FNB OF ELK POINT
{{ 5 L 1 S }}
Organized 6/22/01
Receivership 12/16/30
Brown Back <$VALUE
3x10-20 1-870 <$1750
1882 Date Back
3x10-20 1-1370 <$850
1882 Value Back
3x10-20 1371-2385 <$850
1902 Plain Back
3x10-20 1-1938 <$650
1929 Small Size
10 Type 1 1-278 <$600
20 Type 1 1-48 <$600
Total Issue $282,090
Out at close $25,000
Large out at close $5,530
****
6368 Brookings
FNB OF ELKTON
{{ 4 L }}
Organized 7/19/02
Receivership 12/3/26
1902 Red Seal <$VALUE
3x10-20 1-1122 <$2000
1902 Date Back
3x10-20 1-1600 <$600
1902 Plain Back
3x10-20 1601-3636 <$600
Total Issue $237,900
Out at close $25,000
****
11812 Hanson
SECURITY NB OF EMERY
{{ 8 L 9 S }}
Chartered 8/20
1902 Plain Back <$VALUE
4x5 1-1349 <$600
1929 Small Size
5 Type 1 1-616 <$300
Total Issue $45,460
Out in 1935 $5,000
Large out 1935 $210
****

****
11689 Hamlin
FARMERS NB OF ESTELLINE
{{ 3 S }}
Chartered 4/20 as Farmers
NB of South Shore, under
which there was no issue.
Issuing title adopted
2/13/28.
1929 Small Size <$VALUE
5 Type 2 1-1992 <$450
10 Type 2 1-1044 <$450
20 Type 2 1-240 <$450
Total Issue $25,200
Out in 1935 $25,000
****
13549 Davison
FNB OF ETHAN
{{ 1 S }}
Chartered 5/21/31
1929 Small Size <$VALUE
5 Type 2 1-710 <$600
10 Type 2 1-280 <$600
20 Type 2 1-80 <$600
Total Issue $7,950
Out in 1935 $4,950
****
12325 Gregory
FARMERS NB OF FAIRFAX
{{ 6 L }}
Organized 2/3/23
Liquidated 4/26/29
1902 Plain Back <$VALUE
3x10-20 1-2648 <$375
Total Issue $132,400
Out at close $50,000
Outstanding includes Ch 8711
Ch 13302 assumed circulation
****
13302 Gregory
FARMERS NB OF FAIRFAX
{{ 4 S }}
Organized 3/9/29
Receivership 8/26/31
1929 Small Size <$VALUE
10 Type 1 1-211 <$300
20 Type 1 1-45 <$325
Total Issue $18,060
Out at close $25,000
Outstanding includes Ch 12325
and Ch 8711
****
8711 Gregory
FNB OF FAIRFAX
{{ UNREPORTED }}
Chartered 5/07
Liquidated 1/22/23
1902 Red Seal <$VALUE
4x5 1-160 <$3000
3x10-20 1-128 <$3000
1902 Date Back
4x5 1-500 <$1250
3x10-20 1-400 <$1250
1902 Plain Back
4x5 501-3800 <$1250
3x10-20 401-2136 <$1250
Total Issue $192,400
Out at close $50,000
Ch 12325 assumed circulation
****
5854 Moody
FNB OF FLANDREAU
{{ 7 L 9 S }}
Organized 5/29/01
Receivership 11/3/32
Brown Back <$VALUE
3x10-20 1-1340 <$1250
1882 Date Back
3x10-20 1-2500 <$500
1882 Value Back
3x10-20 2501-3951 <$500
1902 Plain Back
3x10-20 1-2819 <$350
1929 Small Size
10 Type 1 1-600 <$150
20 Type 1 1-187 <$175
Total Issue $463,940
Out at close $39,700
Large out at close $4,990
****
4237 Stanley
FNB OF FORT PIERRE
{{ UNREPORTED }}
Chartered 2/19/90
Liquidated 8/28/94
Brown Back <$VALUE
4x5 1-1153 <$4000
Total Issue $23,060
Out in 1910 $150
****

****
9587 Stanley
FORT PIERRE NB,
FORT PIERRE
{{ 1 L 5 S }}
Chartered 11/09
1902 Date Back <$VALUE
4x5 1-850 <$1000
3x10-20 1-720 <$1000
1902 Plain Back
4x5 851-2010 <$1000
3x10-20 721-1363 <$1000
1929 Small Size
5 Type 1 1-357 <$325
10 Type 1 1-183 <$325
20 Type 1 1-60 <$325
Total Issue $137,240
Out in 1935 $10,000
Large out 1935 $545
****
8624 Brown
FNB OF FREDERICK
{{ 12 L }}
Chartered 4/07
1902 Red Seal <$VALUE
3x10-20 1-800 <$1750
1902 Date Back
3x10-20 1-1610 <$200
1902 Plain Back
3x10-20 1611-3586 <$200
Total Issue $219,300
Out in 1935 $1,295
****
6181 Hutchinson
FNB OF FREEMAN
{{ 1 L 3 S }}
Chartered 3/02
1902 Red Seal <$VALUE
3x10-20 1-400 <$2500
1902 Date Back
3x10-20 1-560 <$1250
1902 Plain Back (dated 1902)
3x10-20 561-576 <$1250
1902 Plain Back (dated 1922)
3x10-20 1-349 <$1250
1929 Small Size
10 Type 1 1-145 <$600
20 Type 1 1-29 <$600
Total Issue $78,430
Out in 1935 $6,300
Large out 1935 $620
****
7755 Minnehaha
FNB OF GARRETSON
{{ 2 L }}
Organized 5/3/05
Liquidated 12/14/34
1902 Red Seal <$VALUE
3x10-20 1-260 <$2500
1902 Date Back
3x10-20 1-580 <$850
1902 Plain Back
3x10-20 581-1116 <$850
Total Issue $68,800
Out at close $490
****
9393 Deuel
FNB OF GARY
{{ 2 L 7 S }}
Organized 3/1/09
Receivership 12/11/33
1902 Date Back <$VALUE
3x10-20 1-1950 <$600
1902 Plain Back
3x10-20 1951-4607 <$600
1929 Small Size
10 Type 1 1-458 <$200
20 Type 1 1-126 <$200
10 Type 2 1-18 <$275
20 Type 2 1-10 <$275
Total Issue $273,330
Out at close $24,750
Large out at close $2,040
****
10846 Deuel
NB OF GARY
{{ 2 L 2 S }}
Chartered 5/16
Liquidated 1/24/31
1902 Plain Back <$VALUE
4x5 1-650 <$650
3x10-20 1-2628 <$650
1929 Small Size
10 Type 1 1-196 <$400
20 Type 1 1-43 <$400
Total Issue $161,320
Out at close $25,000
Large out at close $8,490
****

****
8776 Potter
FNB OF GETTYSBURG
Chartered 7/07
2nd title: Potter County
NB of Gettysburg 3/29/30
FIRST TITLE {{ 3 L 3 S }}
1902 Red Seal <$VALUE
4x10 1-250 <$2000
1902 Date Back
4x10 1-1150* <$650
1902 Plain Back
4x10 1351-5423* <$650
* 1151-1350 not marked
1929 Small Size
10 Type 1 1-524 <$400
SECOND TITLE {{ 2 S }}
1929 Small Size
10 Type 1 1-446 <$500
10 Type 2 1-1260 <$500
Total Issue $297,720
Out in 1935 $25,000
Large out 1935 $1,260
****
Potter County NB of
Gettysburg
SEE Ch 8776
FNB of Gettysburg
****
8600 Gregory
FNB OF GREGORY
{{ 2 L }}
Organized 2/22/07
Receivership 4/12/23
1902 Red Seal <$VALUE
4x10 1-450 <$2000
1902 Date Back
4x10 1-2500 <$650
1902 Plain Back
4x10 2501-4631 <$650
Total Issue $203,240
Out at close $25,000
****
9377 Gregory
GREGORY NB, GREGORY
{{ 4 L }}
Organized 3/23/09
Receivership 11/25/25
1902 Date Back <$VALUE
3x10-20 1-3700 <$500
1902 Plain Back
3x10-20 3701-7884 <$500
Total Issue $394,200
Out at close $48,500
****
7885 Brown
FNB OF GROTON
{{ 7 L 6 S }}
Chartered 8/05
Liquidated 4/1/35
1902 Red Seal <$VALUE
3x10-20 1-750 <$2000
1902 Date Back
3x10-20 1-840 <$400
1902 Plain Back
3x10-20 841-3685 <$400
1929 Small Size
10 Type 1 1-546 <$200
20 Type 1 1-168 <$200
10 Type 2 1-229 <$225
20 Type 2 1-65 <$225
Total Issue $278,260
Out in 1935 $25,000
Large out 1935 $1,390
****
9679 Brown
FNB OF HECLA
{{ 4 L 4 S }}
Chartered 2/10
1902 Date Back <$VALUE
4x10 1-1175 <$500
1902 Plain Back
4x10 1176-2608 <$500
1929 Small Size
10 Type 1 1-556 <$275
Total Issue $137,680
Out in 1935 $15,000
Large out 1935 $720
****
10416 Codington
FNB OF HENRY
{{ UNREPORTED }}
Chartered 7/13
Liquidated 11/2/17
1902 Date Back <$VALUE
3x10-20 1-620 <$1500
1902 Plain Back
3x10-20 621-694 <$1500
Total Issue $34,700
Out at close $12,500
****

****
7794 Hyde
FNB OF HIGHMORE
{{ 5 L 8 S }}
Chartered 6/05
1902 Red Seal <$VALUE
3x10-20 1-900 <$2000
1902 Date Back
3x10-20 1-1750 <$500
1902 Plain Back
3x10-20 1751-4839 <$500
1929 Small Size
10 Type 1 1-542 <$175
20 Type 1 1-140 <$175
10 Type 2 1-636 <$200
20 Type 2 1-128 <$200
Total Issue $345,190
Out in 1935 $25,000
Large out 1935 $1,360
****
4370 Fall River
FNB OF HOT SPRINGS
{{ UNREPORTED }}
Organized 7/15/90
Receivership 8/17/93
Brown Back <$VALUE
4x5 1-913 <$4000
Total Issue $18,260
Out in 1915 $85
****
6339 Fall River
HOT SPRINGS NB,
HOT SPRINGS
{{ 1 L }}
Organized 7/14/02
Receivership 11/27/07
1902 Red Seal <$VALUE
3x10-20 1-1070 <$4000
Total Issue $53,500
Out in 1915 $1,220
****
9166 Fall River
PEOPLES NB OF HOT SPRINGS
{{ 1 L }}
Organized 5/23/08
Receivership 1/15/25
1902 Date Back <$VALUE
3x10-20 1-795 <$2000
1902 Plain Back
3x10-20 796-1011 <$2000
Total Issue $50,550
Out at close $5,950
****
6585 Miner
FNB OF HOWARD
{{ 3 L }}
Organized 11/29/02
Receivership 11/24/25
1902 Red Seal <$VALUE
3x10-20 1-420 <$2000
1902 Date Back
3x10-20 1-560 <$750
1902 Plain Back
3x10-20 561-1398 <$750
Total Issue $90,000
Out at close $12,500
****
7335 Lincoln
FNB OF HUDSON
{{ 7 L 9 S }}
Chartered 7/04
1902 Red Seal <$VALUE
3x10-20 1-387 <$1500
1902 Date Back
3x10-20 1-2200 <$300
1902 Plain Back
3x10-20 2201-5748 <$300
1929 Small Size
10 Type 1 1-622 <$165
20 Type 1 1-208 <$165
10 Type 2 1-307 <$200
20 Type 2 1-55 <$200
Total Issue $373,200
Out in 1935 $30,000
Large out 1935 $1,740
****
2989 Beadle
BEADLE COUNTY NB OF HURON
{{ UNREPORTED }}
Chartered 6/30/83
Liquidated 2/26/91
TERRITORIAL ISSUES
Brown Back <$VALUE
3x10-20 1-1020 <$6000
STATE ISSUES
Brown Back
3x10-20 1021-1091 <$3500
Total Issue $54,550
Out in 1910 $250
****

8781 Beadle
CITY NB OF HURON
{{ 2 L }}
Organized 6/3/07
Receivership 6/10/24
1902 Red Seal <$VALUE
3x10-20 1-775 <$2500
1902 Date Back
3x10-20 1-3400 <$600
1902 Plain Back
3x10-20 3401-7054 <$600
Total Issue $391,450
Out at close $39,000

2819 Beadle
FNB OF HURON
Organized 5/19/82
Receivership 3/14/24
TERRITORIAL ISSUES {{ 1 L }}
Brown Back <$VALUE
4x5 1-2425 <$5000
STATE ISSUES {{ 3 L }}
Brown Back
4x5 2426-5189 <$1500
3x10-20 1-282 <$1500
1902 Red Seal
50-100 1-526 <$6500
1902 Date Back
50-100 1-300 <$750/$850
1902 Plain Back
3x50-100 1-134 <$750/$850
Total Issue $275,280
Out at close $29,000

3267 Beadle
HURON NB, HURON
{{ UNREPORTED }}
Organized 11/21/84
Receivership 1/7/92
TERRITORIAL ISSUES
Brown Back <$VALUE
4x5 1-1850 <$6000
STATE ISSUES
Brown Back
4x5 1851-2230 <$3500
Total Issue $44,600
Out in 1915 $255

8841 Beadle
NB OF HURON
{{ 6 L 12 S }}
Chartered 8/07
Closed 8/31/35
1902 Red Seal <$VALUE
3x10-20 1-1300 <$1500
1902 Date Back
3x10-20 1-3200 <$350
1902 Plain Back
3x10-20 3201-9020 <$350
1929 Small Size
10 Type 1 1-980 <$150
20 Type 1 1-292 <$150
10 Type 2 1-1058 <$175
20 Type 2 1-243 <$175
Total Issue $625,280
Out in 1935 $50,000
Large out 1935 $3,830

3636 Beadle
NB OF DAKOTA, HURON
{{ UNREPORTED }}
Chartered 2/15/87
Liquidated 4/18/96
TERRITORIAL ISSUES
Brown Back <$VALUE
4x5 1-1025 <$6000
STATE ISSUES
Brown Back
4x5 1026-1995 <$3500
Total Issue $39,900
Out in 1910 $280

10098 Lyman
FNB OF KENNEBEC
{{ 4 L }}
Organized 9/20/11
Receivership 6/20/27
1902 Date Back <$VALUE
3x10-20 1-1420 <$600
1902 Plain Back
3x10-20 1421-4053 <$600
Total Issue $202,650
Out at close $24,700

10714 Hamlin
FNB OF LAKE NORDEN
{{ 3 L }}
Organized 3/3/15
Receivership 10/5/26
1902 Plain Back <$VALUE
4x5 1-3285 <$750
3x10-20 1-2029 <$750
Total Issue $167,150
Out at close $35,000

13221 Hamlin
FNB & TC OF LAKE NORDEN
{{ 6 S }}
Chartered 7/28 as Lake Norden NB, under which there was no issue. Issuing title adopted 9/20/30.
1929 Small Size <$VALUE
5 Type 1 1-398 <$200
10 Type 1 1-202 <$200
20 Type 1 1-62 <$225
5 Type 2 1-1156 <$250
10 Type 2 1-581 <$250
20 Type 2 1-155 <$250
Total Issue $46,190
Out in 1935 $23,000

10758 Kingsbury
FNB OF LAKE PRESTON
{{ 2 L }}
Organized 7/24/15
Receivership 3/28/24
1902 Plain Back <$VALUE
4x5 1-2250 <$1250
3x10-20 1-1542 <$1250
Total Issue $122,100
Out at close $24,200

4631 Lawrence
FNB OF LEAD
{{ 10 L 16 S }}
Chartered 1891
Brown Back <$VALUE
4x5 1-4000 <$1250
3x10-20 1-1690 <$1250
1882 Date Back
4x5 1-947 <$600
3x10-20 1-744 <$600
1902 Date Back
3x10-20 1-2140 <$225
1902 Plain Back
3x10-20 2141-8150 <$225
1929 Small Size
10 Type 1 1-1140 <$100
20 Type 1 1-334 <$100
10 Type 2 1-1265 <$150
20 Type 2 1-291 <$175
Total Issue $755,090
Out in 1935 $50,000
Large out 1935 $3,410

FNB in Lemmon
SEE Ch 12857
New FNB in Lemmon

9269 Perkins
FNB OF LEMMON
{{ 4 L }}
Organized 10/16/08
Receivership 4/2/25
1902 Date Back <$VALUE
3x10-20 1-2150 <$600
1902 Plain Back
3x10-20 2151-4259 <$600
Total Issue $212,950
Out at close $25,000

12857 Perkins
NEW FNB IN LEMMON
Chartered 12/25
2nd title: FNB in Lemmon 7/1/29
FIRST TITLE {{ 3 L }}
1902 Plain Back <$VALUE
3x10-20 1-1395 <$600
SECOND TITLE {{ 8 S }}
1929 Small Size
10 Type 1 1-616 <$165
20 Type 1 1-210 <$165
10 Type 2 1-2550 <$185
20 Type 2 1-595 <$185
Total Issue $169,310
Out in 1935 $50,000
Large out 1935 $510

9188 Sanborn
FNB OF LETCHER
{{ 4 L 11 S }}
Organized 5/25/08
Receivership 9/27/32
1902 Date Back <$VALUE
3x10-20 1-1275 <$400
1902 Plain Back
3x10-20 1276-3983 <$400
1929 Small Size
10 Type 1 1-414 <$175
20 Type 1 1-99 <$175
Total Issue $235,870
Out at close $25,000
Large out at close $3,170

3151 Lake
CITIZENS NB OF MADISON
{{ UNREPORTED }}
Organized 4/10/84
Receivership 12/12/94
TERRITORIAL ISSUES
Brown Back <$VALUE
4x5 1-1325 <$6000
STATE ISSUES
Brown Back
4x5 1326-2026 <$3500
Total Issue $40,520
Out in 1915 $320

3149 Lake
FNB OF MADISON
Organized 3/29/84
Receivership 5/21/25
TERRITORIAL ISSUES {{ 0 L }}
Brown Back <$VALUE
4x5 1-1337 <$5000
STATE ISSUES {{ 3 L }}
Brown Back
4x5 1338-3687 <$1500
3x10-20 1-300 <$1500
1902 Red Seal
3x10-20 1-1290 <$2000
1902 Date Back
3x10-20 1-1750 <$600
1902 Plain Back
3x10-20 1751-4033 <$600
Total Issue $354,890
Out at close $30,895

10636 Lake
LAKE COUNTY NB OF MADISON
{{ 9 L }}
Organized 10/2/14
Receivership 8/29/28
1902 Date Back <$VALUE
4x5 1-1750 <$300
3x10-20 1-1400 <$300
1902 Plain Back
4x5 1751-9705 <$300
3x10-20 1401-6510 <$300
Total Issue $519,600
Out at close $65,000

3597 Lake
MADISON NB, MADISON
{{ UNREPORTED }}
Organized 11/29/86
Receivership 6/23/88
TERRITORIAL ISSUES
Brown Back <$VALUE
4x5 1-589 <$6000
Total Issue $11,780
Out in 1915 $70

9283 Corson
FNB OF McINTOSH
{{ 1 L }}
Organized 10/16/08
Receivership 3/1/24
1902 Date Back <$VALUE
3x10-20 1-2070 <$1000
1902 Plain Back
3x10-20 2071-4058 <$1000
Total Issue $202,900
Out at close $23,300

10637 Haakon
FNB OF MIDLAND
{{ 0 L 5 S }}
Chartered 10/14
1902 Plain Back <$VALUE
4x5 1-4050 <$1500
1929 Small Size
5 Type 1 1-1142 <$350
5 Type 2 1-2538 <$350
Total Issue $127,950
Out in 1935 $12,000
Large out 1935 $940

13407 Grant
FARMERS & MERCHANTS NB IN MILBANK
{{ 11 S }}
Chartered 12/29
Closed 3/30/35
1929 Small Size <$VALUE
10 Type 1 1-1350 <$150
10 Type 2 1-1258 <$175
Total Issue $93,580
Out in 1935 $25,000
Outstanding includes Ch 8693

Farmers & Merchants NB of Milbank
SEE Ch 8698
Merchants NB of Milbank

6473 Grant
FNB OF MILBANK
{{ 10 L }}
Organized 10/16/02
Receivership 11/15/26
1902 Red Seal <$VALUE
3x10-20 1-370 <$1500
1902 Date Back
3x10-20 1-960 <$250
1902 Plain Back
3x10-20 961-4266 <$250
Total Issue $231,800
Out at close $38,500

8698 Grant
MERCHANTS NB OF MILBANK
Organized 4/27/07
Liquidated 1/28/30
2nd title: Farmers & Merchants NB 1/28/20
FIRST TITLE {{ 3 L }}
1902 Red Seal <$VALUE
4x5 1-250 <$2000
4x10 1-250 <$2000
1902 Date Back
4x5 1-1050 <$600
4x10 1-1000 <$600
1902 Plain Back
4x5 1051-1150 <$600
4x10 1001-1100 <$600
SECOND TITLE {{ 7 L 0 S }}
1902 Plain Back
4x10 1-1425 <$350
1929 Small Size
10 Type 1 1-30 <$750
Total Issue $140,800
Out at close $10,400
Large out 1935 $1,090
Ch 13407 assumed circulation

6789 Hand
FNB OF MILLER
{{ 9 L }}
Chartered 5/03
1902 Red Seal <$VALUE
3x10-20 1-1425 <$2000
1902 Date Back
3x10-20 1-2350 <$300
1902 Plain Back
3x10-20 2351-6222 <$300
Total Issue $382,350
Out in 1935 $4,560

2645 Davison
FNB OF MITCHELL
Organized 2/8/82
Receivership 10/23/23
TERRITORIAL ISSUES {{ 0 L }}
Series 1875 <$VALUE
4x10 1-1030 <$6500
STATE ISSUES {{ 20 L }}
Series 1875
4x10 1031-1897 <$4000
Brown Back
3x10-20 1-1880 <$1250
1882 Date Back
3x10-20 1-6200* <$400
1882 Value Back
3x10-20 6601-11249* <$400
* 6201-6600 not marked
1902 Plain Back
3x10-20 1-1536 <$125
Total Issue $809,130
Out at close $99,000

3578 Davison
MITCHELL NB, MITCHELL
Chartered 1886
TERRITORIAL ISSUES {{ 0 L }}
Brown Back <$VALUE
3x10-20 1-370 <$5000
STATE ISSUES {{ 25 L 30 S }}
Brown Back
3x10-20 371-2501 <$850
1902 Red Seal
3x10-20 1-1600 <$1500
1902 Date Back
3x10-20 1-6100 <$150
1902 Plain Back
3x10-20 6101-16240 <$150
1929 Small Size
10 Type 1 1-2010 <$75
20 Type 1 1-490 <$85
10 Type 2 1-2628 <$100
20 Type 2 1-384 <$100
Total Issue $1,230,410
Out in 1935 $100,000
Large out 1935 $7,660

7455 Davison
WESTERN NB OF MITCHELL
{{ 17 L }}
Organized 9/12/04
Receivership 2/27/24
1902 Red Seal <$VALUE
3x10-20 1-2212 <$1500
1902 Date Back
4x5 1-5750 <$200
3x10-20 1-5000 <$200
1902 Plain Back
4x5 5751-13660 <$200
3x10-20 5001-10020 <$200
Total Issue $884,800
Out at close $93,400

13467 Walworth
FNB IN MOBRIDGE
{{ 7 S }}
Chartered 5/30
Closed 3/30/35
1929 Small Size <$VALUE
5 Type 1 1-924 <$200
10 Type 1 1-472 <$200
20 Type 1 1-118 <$200
5 Type 2 1-1272 <$200
10 Type 2 1-648 <$200
Total Issue $83,040
Out in 1935 $20,000
Outstanding includes Ch 10744

10744 Walworth
FNB OF MOBRIDGE
{{ 10 L 4 S }}
Chartered 6/15
Liquidated 7/22/30
1902 Plain Back <$VALUE
4x5 1-5652 <$250
3x10-20 1-3242 <$250
1929 Small Size
5 Type 1 1-252 <$275
10 Type 1 1-130 <$275
20 Type 1 1-26 <$275
Total Issue $293,620
Out at close $25,000
Large out 1935 $2,630
Ch 13467 assumed circulation

11590 Walworth
SECURITY NB OF MOBRIDGE
{{ 1 L 0 S }}
Organized 12/5/19
Receivership 9/11/31
1902 Plain Back <$VALUE
3x10-20 1-1985 <$1000
1929 Small Size
10 Type 1 1-350 <$500
20 Type 1 1-93 <$500
Total Issue $131,410
Out at close $25,000
Large out at close $3,390

9817 Corson
FNB OF MORRISTOWN
{{ 2 L }}
Organized 5/11/10
Receivership 5/24/24
1902 Date Back <$VALUE
3x10-20 1-1610 <$1000
1902 Plain Back
3x10-20 1611-3571 <$1000
Total Issue $178,550
Out at close $25,000

7582 Davison
FNB OF MOUNT VERNON
{{ 3 L }}
Chartered 1/05
Liquidated 2/28/29
1902 Red Seal <$VALUE
3x10-20 1-364 <$2500
1902 Date Back
3x10-20 1-1600 <$750
1902 Plain Back
3x10-20 1601-4347 <$750
Total Issue $235,550
Out at close $24,050

10256 Kingsbury
FNB OF OLDHAM
{{ 7 L }}
Organized 8/30/12
Receivership 1/3/25
1902 Date Back <$VALUE
4x5 1-1015 <$250
3x10-20 1-814 <$250
1902 Plain Back
4x5 1016-3280 <$250
3x10-20 815-2174 <$250
Total Issue $174,300
Out at close $25,000

12662 Kingsbury
OLDHAM NB, OLDHAM
{{ 10 S }}
Chartered 3/25
1929 Small Size <$VALUE
5 Type 1 1-680 <$160
10 Type 1 1-406 <$160
20 Type 1 1-150 <$175
5 Type 2 1-746 <$185
10 Type 2 1-192 <$185
20 Type 2 1-120 <$200
Total Issue $70,810
Out in 1935 $25,000

11585 Sully
FNB OF ONIDA
{{ 1 L }}
Organized 1/17/20
Receivership 2/12/24
1902 Plain Back <$VALUE
3x10-20 1-1490 <$1250
Total Issue $74,500
Out at close $24,700

3675 Turner
FNB OF PARKER
Chartered 1887
TERRITORIAL ISSUES {{ 1 L }}
Brown Back <$VALUE
4x5 1-900 <$5000
STATE ISSUES {{ 4 L 9 S }}
Brown Back
4x5 901-3374 <$1500
50-100 1-298 <$5000
1902 Red Seal
3x10-20 1-500 <$2000
1902 Date Back
3x10-20 1-1400 <$400
1902 Plain Back
3x10-20 1401-3692 <$400
1929 Small Size
10 Type 1 1-546 <$175
20 Type 1 1-150 <$200
10 Type 2 1-196 <$225
20 Type 2 1-60 <$225
Total Issue $375 700
Out in 1935 $25,000
Large out 1935 $1,790

7662 Hutchinson
FNB OF PARKSTON
{{ 5 L 11 S }}
Chartered 3/05
1902 Red Seal <$VALUE
3x10-20 1-760 <$2000
1902 Date Back
3x10-20 1-1550 <$500
1902 Plain Back
3x10-20 1551-4065 <$500
1929 Small Size
10 Type 1 1-458 <$150
20 Type 1 1-126 <$150
10 Type 2 1-583 <$175
20 Type 2 1-132 <$175
Total Issue $292,320
Out in 1935 $25,000
Large out 1935 $3,340

14252 Hughes
FNB IN PIERRE
{{ 5 S }}
Chartered 8/34
1929 Small Size <$VALUE
10 Type 2 1-980 <$350
20 Type 2 1-510 <$350
Total Issue $20,000
Out in 1935 $20,000

2941 Hughes
FNB OF PIERRE
Organized 3/29/83
Liquidated 12/31/34
TERRITORIAL ISSUES {{ 0 L }}
Brown Back <$VALUE
4x5 1-1537 <$5000
STATE ISSUES {{ 17 L 14 S }}
Brown Back
4x5 1538-3225 <$1500
3x10-20 1-223 <$1500
1902 Red Seal
3x10-20 1-1400 <$1500
1902 Date Back
3x10-20 1-3400 <$275
1902 Plain Back
3x10-20 3401-9312 <$275
1929 Small Size
10 Type 1 1-988 <$150
20 Type 1 1-292 <$150
10 Type 2 1-521 <$175
20 Type 2 1-50 <$175
Total Issue $711,780
Out at close $50,000
Large out at close $4,070

4279 Hughes
NB OF COMMERCE OF PIERRE
{{ 12 L }}
Organized 2/13/90
Receivership 2/11/25
Brown Back <$VALUE
3x10-20 1-3095 <$1500
1882 Date Back
3x10-20 1-1164 <$850
1902 Date Back
3x10-20 1-4800 <$275
1902 Plain Back
3x10-20 4801-10102 <$275
Total Issue $718,050
Out at close $79,500

4104 Hughes
PIERRE NB, PIERRE
Chartered 1889
TERRITORIAL ISSUES {{ 0 L }}
Brown Back <$VALUE
3x10-20 1-250 <$5000
STATE ISSUES {{ 13 L 16 S }}
Brown Back
3x10-20 251-1490 <$1500
1882 Date Back
3x10-20 1-79 <$1000
1902 Date Back
3x10-20 1-3200 <$350
1902 Plain Back
3x10-20 3201-9220 <$350
1929 Small Size
10 Type 1 1-1156 <$150
20 Type 1 1-304 <$150
10 Type 2 1-607 <$175
20 Type 2 1-292 <$175
Total Issue $657,200
Out in 1935 $50,000
Large out 1935 $3,470

3130 Aurora
FNB OF PLANKINTON
{{ UNREPORTED }}
Chartered 2/29/84
Liquidated 10/21/85
TERRITORIAL ISSUES
Brown Back <$VALUE
3x10-20 1-225 <$5000
Total Issue $11,250
Out in 1910 $50

9958 Brule
FNB OF PUKWANA
{{ 8 L 13 S }}
Chartered 3/11
1902 Date Back <$VALUE
4x5 1-1260 <$300
4x10 1-1220 <$300
1902 Plain Back
4x5 1261-4710 <$300
4x10 1221-3643 <$300
1929 Small Size
5 Type 1 1-840 <$135
10 Type 1 1-546 <$135
5 Type 2 1-1460 <$175
10 Type 2 1-768 <$175
Total Issue $312,860
Out in 1935 $25,000
Large out 1935 $1,625

3401 Pennington
BLACK HILLS NB OF RAPID CITY
{{ UNREPORTED }}
Organized 10/23/85
Receivership 7/13/94
TERRITORIAL ISSUES
Brown Back <$VALUE
3x10-20 1-810 <$6000
STATE ISSUES
Brown Back
3x10-20 811-1404 <$4000
Total Issue $70,200
Out in 1915 $310

3237 Pennington
FNB OF RAPID CITY
Chartered 8/84
TERRITORIAL ISSUES {{ 0 L }}
Brown Back <$VALUE
4x5 1-1462 <$5000
TATE ISSUES {{ 7 L 7 S }}
Brown Back
4x5 1463-3617 <$1750
3x10-20 1-275 <$1750
1902 Red Seal
3x10-20 1-1770 <$2000
1902 Date Back
3x10-20 1-2700 <$400
1902 Plain Back
3x10-20 2701-12220 <$400
1929 Small Size
10 Type 1 1-1162 <$200
20 Type 1 1-296 <$225
10 Type 2 1-1021 <$225
20 Type 2 1-170 <$250
Total Issue $904,440
Out in 1935 $50,000
Large out 1935 $3,940

14099 Pennington
RAPID CITY NB, RAPID CITY
{{ 16 S }}
Chartered 4/34
1929 Small Size <$VALUE
5 Type 2 1-2930 <$225
10 Type 2 1-1715 <$225
Total Issue $31,800
Out in 1935 $25,000

American NB of Redfield
SEE Ch 8125
German American NB of Redfield

3398 Spink
FNB OF REDFIELD
{{ UNREPORTED }}
Organized 10/2/85
Receivership 1/11/95
TERRITORIAL ISSUES
Brown Back <$VALUE
4x5 1-1087 <$5000
STATE ISSUES
Brown Back
4x5 1088-1923 <$4000
Total Issue $38,460
Out in 1915 $300

8125 Spink
GERMAN AMERICAN NB OF REDFIELD
Organized 2/16/06
Receivership 12/12/30
2nd title: American NB of Redfield 2/14/18
FIRST TITLE {{ 0 L }}
1902 Red Seal <$VALUE
4x5 1-300 <$3000
3x10-20 1-240 <$3000
1902 Date Back
4x5 1-850 <$1500
3x10-20 1-680 <$1500
1902 Plain Back
4x5 851-950 <$1500
3x10-20 681-720 <$1500
SECOND TITLE {{ 4 L 4 S }}
1902 Plain Back
3x10-20 1-4487 <$500
1929 Small Size
10 Type 1 1-395 <$375
20 Type 1 1-86 <$375
Total Issue $331,370
Out at close $40,000
Large out at close $9,840

Merchants NB of Redfield
SEE Ch 3522
FNB of Doland

6256 Spink
REDFIELD NB, REDFIELD
{{ 5 L 7 S }}
Chartered 5/13/02
Liquidated 4/1/35
1902 Red Seal <$VALUE
3x10-20 1-900 <$2000
1902 Date Back
3x10-20 1-1160* <$500
1902 Plain Back (dated 1902)
3x10-20 1321-1850* <$500
* 1161-1320 not marked
1902 Plain Back (dated 1922)
3x10-20 1-1099 <$500
1929 Small Size
10 Type 1 1-314 <$200
20 Type 1 1-106 <$200
10 Type 2 1-326 <$250
20 Type 2 1-55 <$275
Total Issue $228,370
Out in 1935 $17,000
Large out 1935 $1,100

12547 Hand
FNB OF SAINT LAWRENCE
{{ 7 L 2 S }}
Chartered 6/24
Liquidated 7/1/32
1902 Plain Back <$VALUE
3x10-20 1-1514 <$400
1929 Small Size
10 Type 1 1-392 <$400
20 Type 1 1-101 <$400
Total Issue $111,340
Out at close $25,000
Large out at close $3,070

5898 McCook
FNB OF SALEM
{{ 9 L }}
Organized 7/5/01
Receivership 1/16/25
Brown Back <$VALUE
3x10-20 1-1040 <$1500
1882 Date Back
3x10-20 1-1800 <$600
1882 Value Back
3x10-20 1801-2524 <$600
1902 Plain Back
3x10-20 1-776 <$350
Total Issue $217,000
Out at close $24,500

12784 McCook
McCOOK COUNTY NB OF SALEM
{{ 40 S }}
Chartered 7/25
1929 Small Size <$VALUE
20 Type 1 1-260 <$150
20 Type 2 1-56 <$150
Total Issue $32,320
Out in 1935 $25,000

7048 Bon Homme
FNB OF SCOTLAND
{{ UNREPORTED }}
Organized 11/28/03
Receivership 2/4/07
1902 Red Seal <$VALUE
3x10-20 1-452 <$4000
Total Issue $22,600
Out in 1915 $510

9376 Walworth
FNB OF SELBY
{{ 7 L 7 S }}
Chartered 4/09
1902 Date Back <$VALUE
4x5 1-1500* <$400
3x10-20 1-1200** <$400
1902 Plain Back
4x5 1651-4082* <$400
3x10-20 1281-2652** <$400
* 1501-1650 not marked
** 1201-1280 not marked
1929 Small Size
5 Type 1 1-830 <$225
10 Type 1 1-212 <$225
20 Type 1 1-106 <$225
Total Issue $264,580
Out in 1935 $20,000
Large out 1935 $1,420

9915 Minnehaha
AMERICAN NB OF SIOUX FALLS
{{ 1 L }}
Chartered 1/11
Liquidated 2/8/12
1902 Date Back <$VALUE
3x10-20 1-1225 <$850
Total Issue $61,250
Out in 1912 $34,650

3586 Minnehaha
CITIZENS NB OF SIOUX FALLS
{{ 1 L }}
Chartered 11/8/86
Liquidated 4/24/88
TERRITORIAL ISSUES
Brown Back <$VALUE
4x5 1-588 <$6000
Total Issue $11,760
Out in 1910 $65

2843 Minnehaha
DAKOTA NB OF SIOUX FALLS
{{ UNREPORTED }}
Organized 12/19/82
Receivership 1/20/97
TERRITORIAL ISSUES
Brown Back <$VALUE
3x10-20 1-565 <$6000
STATE ISSUES
Brown Back
3x10-20 566-861 <$3500
Total Issue $43,050
Out in 1915 $230

2465 Minnehaha
FNB OF SIOUX FALLS
{{ UNREPORTED }}
Chartered 3/15/80
Receivership 3/11/86
TERRITORIAL ISSUES
Series 1875 <$VALUE
4x5 1-1737 <$6500
Total Issue $34,740
Out in 1915 $245

3393 Minnehaha
MINNEHAHA NB OF SIOUX FALLS
Chartered 1885
TERRITORIAL ISSUES {{ 0 L }}
Brown Back <$VALUE
3x10-20 1-1390 <$5000
STATE ISSUES {{ 2 L }}
Brown Back
3x10-20 1391-4374 <$2000
1902 Red Seal
50-100 1-1025 <$6500
1902 Date Back
50-100 1-600 <$850/$1000
3x50-100 1-784 <$850/$1000
Total Issue $658,450
Out in 1935 $6,040

10592 Minnehaha
SECURITY NB OF SIOUX FALLS
Chartered 7/14
2nd title: Security NB & TC 2/12/30
FIRST TITLE {{ 21 L }}
1902 Date Back <$VALUE
3x10-20 1-2000 <$150
1902 Plain Back
3x10-20 2001-18723 <$150
SECOND TITLE {{ 50+ S }}
1929 Small Size
10 Type 1 1-2561 <$65
20 Type 1 1-1656 <$70
Total Issue $1,288,530
Out in 1935 $100,000
Large out 1935 $8,585

2823 Minnehaha
SIOUX FALLS NB, SIOUX FALLS
Organized 11/14/82
Receivership 1/24/24
TERRITORIAL ISSUES {{ 1 L }}
Brown Back <$VALUE
4x5 1-2750 <$5000
STATE ISSUES {{ 2 L }}
Brown Back
4x5 2751-6455 <$1750
50-100 1-136 <$5000
1902 Red Seal
50-100 1-1020 <$6500
1902 Date Back
50-100 1-600 <$850/$1000
3x50-100 1-794 <$850/$1000
Total Issue $591,000
Out at close $74,250

4629 Minnehaha
UNION NB OF SIOUX FALLS
{{ UNREPORTED }}
Chartered 9/11/91
Liquidated 7/1/99
Brown Back <$VALUE
4x5 1-3569 <$3000
Total Issue $71,380
Out in 1910 $540

6395 Roberts
CITIZENS NB OF SISSETON
Organized 8/18/02
Receivership 1/5/33
2nd title:Citizens Security NB of Sisseton 5/14/26
FIRST TITLE {{ 4 L }}
1902 Red Seal <$VALUE
3x10-20 1-810 <$1500
1902 Date Back
4x5 1-2650 <$500
3x10-20 1-2160 <$500
1902 Plain Back
4x5 2651-6669 <$500
3x10-20 2161-4553 <$500
SECOND TITLE {{ 1 L 3 S }}
1902 Plain Back
4x5 1-2289 <$600
1929 Small Size
5 Type 1 1-3047 <$325
Total Issue $538,720
Out at close $39,760
Large out at close $4,260

Citizens Security NB of Sisseton
SEE Ch 6395
Citizens NB of Sisseton

5428 Roberts
FNB OF SISSETON
{{ 5 L 7 S }}
Organized 5/22/00
Receivership 10/1/31
Brown Back <$VALUE
3x10-20 1-620 <$1500
1882 Date Back
3x10-20 1-2100* <$650
1882 Value Back
3x10-20 2401-2998* <$650
* 2101-2400 not marked
1902 Plain Back
3x10-20 1-4884 <$325
1929 Small Size
10 Type 1 1-674 <$200
20 Type 1 1-199 <$200
Total Issue $489,420
Out at close $55,000
Large out at close $8,715

Roberts County NB of Sisseton
SEE Ch 6185
FNB of White Rock

7686 Codington
FNB OF SOUTH SHORE
{{ UNREPORTED }}
Chartered 4/05
Liquidated 12/31/17
1902 Red Seal <$VALUE
3x10-20 1-600 <$3000
1902 Date Back
3x10-20 1-607 <$1500
Total Issue $60,350
Out at close $10,000

8248 Lawrence
AMERICAN NB OF SPEARFISH
{{ UNREPORTED }}
Chartered 6/06
Liquidated 12/27/27
1902 Red Seal <$VALUE
3x10-20 1-187 <$4000
1902 Date Back
3x10-20 1-740 <$1500
1902 Plain Back
3x10-20 741-1147 <$1500
Total Issue $66,700
Out at close $6,250

4874 Lawrence
FNB OF SPEARFISH
{{ UNREPORTED }}
Chartered 3/6/93
Liquidated 9/3/95
Brown Back <$VALUE
4x5 1-756 <$4000
Total Issue $15,120
Out in 1910 $120

8942 Bon Homme
FNB OF SPRINGFIELD
{{ 1 L }}
Organized 10/2/07
Receivership 11/28/23
1902 Red Seal <$VALUE
4x5 1-250 <$2500
3x10-20 1-200 <$2500
1902 Date Back
4x5 1-1100 <$1000
3x10-20 1-780 <$1000
1902 Plain Back
4x5 1101-2456 <$1000
3x10-20 781-1564 <$1000
Total Issue $142,320
Out at close $17,750

6990 Meade
COMMERCIAL NB OF STURGIS
{{ 2 L 10 S }}
Chartered 10/03
1902 Red Seal <$VALUE
3x10-20 1-1256 <$2000
1902 Date Back
3x10-20 1-1900 <$600
1902 Plain Back
3x10-20 1901-4694 <$600
1929 Small Size
10 Type 1 1-620 <$175
20 Type 1 1-162 <$175
10 Type 2 1-158 <$225
20 Type 2 1-15 <$225
Total Issue $356,020
Out in 1935 $20,000
Large out 1935 $1,630

3739 Meade
FNB OF STURGIS
{{ UNREPORTED }}
Chartered 6/29/87
Liquidated 2/15/97
TERRITORIAL ISSUES
Brown Back <$VALUE
4x5 1-900 <$6000
STATE ISSUES
Brown Back
4x5 901-2182 <$3500
Total Issue $43,640
Out in 1910 $350

6381 Deuel
FNB OF TORONTO
{{ 3 L }}
Organized 7/8/02
Receivership 4/3/28
1902 Red Seal <$VALUE
3x10-20 1-620 <$2000
1902 Date Back
3x10-20 1-1790 <$650
1902 Plain Back
3x10-20 1791-4237 <$650
Total Issue $242,850
Out at close $24,300

6792 Bon Homme
FNB OF TYNDALL
{{ 14 L 17 S }}
Organized 5/6/03
Receivership 7/2/32
1902 Red Seal <$VALUE
3x10-20 1-1350 <$1500
1902 Date Back
3x10-20 1-1770 <$350
1902 Plain Back
3x10-20 1771-4139 <$350
1929 Small Size
10 Type 1 1-313 <$150
20 Type 1 1-82 <$175
Total Issue $303,070
Out at close $25,000
Large out at close $5,230

9858 Marshall
FNB OF VEBLEN
{{ 9 L }}
Organized 8/16/10
Receivership 9/18/26
1902 Date Back <$VALUE
3x10-20 1-1080* <$375
* 1055-1056 not issued
1902 Plain Back
3x10-20 1081-1318 <$375
Total Issue $65,800
Out at close $9,700

FNB in Vermillion
SEE Ch 13346
FNB & TC of Vermillion

4603 Clay
FNB OF VERMILLION
{{ 2 L }}
Chartered 1891
Liquidated 8/1/29
Brown Back <$VALUE
4x5 1-2125 <$1750
3x10-20 1-550 <$1750
1882 Date Back
4x5 1-241 <$1250
3x10-20 1-164 <$1250
1902 Date Back
3x50-100 1-214 <$1000/$1250
1902 Plain Back
3x50-100 215-227 <$1000/$1250
Total Issue $139,770
Out at close $12,250

13346 Clay
FNB & TC OF VERMILLION
Chartered 6/29
2nd title: FNB in Vermillion 2/28/34
FIRST TITLE {{ 13 S }}
1929 Small Size <$VALUE
10 Type 2 1-3732 <$125
20 Type 2 1-1248 <$150
SECOND TITLE {{ 0 S }}
1929 Small Size
10 Type 2 1-169 <$500
20 Type 2 1-30 <$500
Total Issue $64,570
Out in 1935 $43,550

****
7352 Clay
VERMILLION NB, VERMILLION
{{ 2 L }}
Chartered 8/04
Liquidated 8/1/29
1902 Red Seal <$VALUE
3x10-20 1-1412 <$2500
1902 Date Back
3x10-20 1-2150 <$750
1902 Plain Back
3x10-20 2151-5148 <$750
Total Issue $328,000
Out at close $9,560
****
13589 Turner
SECURITY NB OF VIBORG
{{ 7 S }}
Chartered 1/32
1929 Small Size <$VALUE
10 Type 1 1-50 <$225
20 Type 1 1-13 <$225
10 Type 2 1-252 <$225
20 Type 2 1-65 <$225
Total Issue $8,380
Out in 1935 $7,800
Outstanding includes Ch 11457
****
11558 Clark
FARMERS NB OF VIENNA
{{ 2 L 18 S }}
Chartered 12/19 as FNB of Garden City, under which there was no issue. Issuing title adopted 12/13/22.
1902 Plain Back <$VALUE
4x10 1-2019 <$750
1929 Small Size
10 Type 1 1-970 <$110
10 Type 2 1-409 <$110
Total Issue $143,050
Out in 1935 $25,000
Large out 1935 $1,360
****
7597 Clark
FNB OF VIENNA
{{ UNREPORTED }}
Chartered 2/05
Liquidated 2/2/20
1902 Red Seal <$VALUE
3x10-20 1-600 <$3000
1902 Date Back
3x10-20 1-750 <$1500
1902 Plain Back
3x10-20 751-953 <$1500
Total Issue $77,650
Out at close $12,500
****
6099 Brookings
FNB OF VOLGA
{{ 4 L 5 S }}
Chartered 1/02
Brown Back <$VALUE
4x5 1-350 <$1750
3x10-20 1-300 <$1750
1882 Date Back
4x5 1-550 <$800
3x10-20 1-380 <$800
1882 Value Back
4x5 551-640 <$800
3x10-20 381-457 <$800
1902 Plain Back
4x5 1-1432 <$600
1929 Small Size
5 Type 1 1-784 <$300
Total Issue $109,810
Out in 1935 $6,250
Large out 1935 $490
****
7968 Clay
FNB OF WAKONDA
{{ UNREPORTED }}
Chartered 11/1/05
Liquidated 1/8/07
1902 Red Seal <$VALUE
3x10-20 1-210 <$4000
Total Issue $10,500
Out in 1910 $1,960
****
3349 Codington
CITIZENS NB OF WATERTOWN
Chartered 1885
Liquidated 1/3/33
TERRITORIAL ISSUES {{ 2 L }}
Brown Back <$VALUE
4x5 1-1250 <$5000
STATE ISSUES {{ 2 L 7 S }}
Brown Back
4x5 1251-3060 <$1750
3x10-20 1-274 <$1750
1902 Red Seal
50-100 1-552 <$6500
1902 Date Back
50-100 1-600 <$850/$1000
3x50-100 1-560 <$850/$1000
1902 Plain Back
3x50-100 561-713 <$850/$1000
1929 Small Size
50 Type 1 1-109 <$400
100 Type 1 1-26 <$500
Total Issue $474,250
Out at close $50,000
Large out at close $10,895
****
F Citizens NB of Watertown
SEE Ch 2935
FNB of Watertown
****
2935 Codington
FNB OF WATERTOWN
Chartered 4/83
2nd title: FNB & TC 1/17/30
3rd title: F Citizens NB 1/3/33
FIRST TITLE
TERRITORIAL ISSUES {{ 0 L }}
Brown Back <$VALUE
4x5 1-1337 <$5000
STATE ISSUES {{ 13 L }}
Brown Back
4x5 1338-3721 <$1250
3x10-20 1-330 <$1250
1902 Red Seal
3x10-20 1-2050 <$1500
1902 Date Back
3x10-20 1-5400 <$175
1902 Plain Back
3x10-20 5401-16431 <$175
SECOND TITLE {{ 20 S }}
1929 Small Size
10 Type 1 1-1814 <$90
20 Type 1 1-576 <$100
THIRD TITLE {{ 3 S }}
1929 Small Size
10 Type 1 1-324 <$250
20 Type 1 1-72 <$250
10 Type 2 1-816 <$200
20 Type 2 1-250 <$200
Total Issue $1,234,170
Out in 1935 $100,000
Large out 1935 $8,570
****
7504 Codington
SECURITY NB OF WATERTOWN
{{ 8 L }}
Chartered 12/04
Liquidated 6/22/26
1902 Red Seal <$VALUE
3x10-20 1-1612 <$1500
1902 Date Back
3x10-20 1-3900 <$200
1902 Plain Back
3x10-20 3901-12584 <$200
Total Issue $709,800
Out at close $100,000
****
3414 Codington
WATERTOWN NB, WATERTOWN
{{ UNREPORTED }}
Chartered 11/25/85
Liquidated 7/10/96
TERRITORIAL ISSUES
Brown Back <$VALUE
3x10-20 1-420 <$5000
STATE ISSUES
Brown Back
3x10-20 421-690 <$3000
Total Issue $34,500
Out in 1910 $470
****
6124 Day
FNB OF WAUBAY
{{ 1 L }}
Organized 1/31/02
Receivership 8/20/26
1902 Red Seal <$VALUE
3x10-20 1-400 <$3000
1902 Date Back
3x10-20 1-560 <$1250
1902 Plain Back (dated 1902)
3x10-20 561-622 <$1250
1902 Plain Back (dated 1922)
3x10-20 1-192 <$1250
Total Issue $60,700
Out at close $6,250
****
8559 Day
FARMERS & MERCHANTS NB OF WEBSTER
{{ 8 L 9 S }}
Organized 10/27/06
Receivership 10/15/31
1902 Red Seal <$VALUE
4x5 1-556 <$1750
4x10 1-556 <$1750
1902 Date Back
4x5 1-3200 <$350
4x10 1-2950 <$350
1902 Plain Back
4x5 3201-9855 <$350
4x10 2951-8433 <$350
1929 Small Size
5 Type 1 1-1253 <$175
10 Type 1 1-569 <$175
Total Issue $639,510
Out at close $50,000
Large out at close $6,710
****
6502 Day
FNB OF WEBSTER
{{ 2 L }}
Organized 11/19/02
Receivership 1/2/24
1902 Red Seal <$VALUE
3x10-20 1-400 <$2500
1902 Date Back
3x10-20 1-1510 <$750
1902 Plain Back
3x10-20 1511-3058 <$750
Total Issue $172,900
Out at close $24,700
****
8325 Beadle
FNB OF WESSINGTON
{{ UNREPORTED }}
Chartered 8/06
Liquidated 12/20/26
1902 Red Seal <$VALUE
3x10-20 1-700 <$3000
1902 Date Back
3x10-20 1-1690 <$1000
1902 Plain Back
3x10-20 1691-4021 <$1000
Total Issue $236,050
Out at close $25,000
****
6446 Jerauld
FNB OF WESSINGTON SPRINGS
{{ 3 L }}
Organized 9/25/02
Receivership 2/5/23
1902 Red Seal <$VALUE
3x10-20 1-900 <$2500
1902 Date Back
3x10-20 1-1800* <$650
1902 Plain Back
4x5 1-2495 <$650
3x10-20 2041-3820* <$650
* 1801-2040 not marked
Total Issue $285,900
Out at close $39,300
****
11441 McPherson
FNB OF WETONKA
{{ 8 L }}
Chartered 8/19
Liquidated 1/18/27
1902 Plain Back <$VALUE
4x5 1-7845 <$375
Total Issue $156,900
Out at close $25,000
****
7134 Brookings
FARMERS NB OF WHITE
{{ UNREPORTED }}
Chartered 2/04
Liquidated 1/7/13
1902 Red Seal <$VALUE
3x10-20 1-620 <$4000
1902 Date Back
3x10-20 1-764 <$1500
Total Issue $69,200
Out at close $12,500
Ch 6294 assumed circulation
****
6294 Brookings
FNB OF WHITE
{{ 2 L 16 S }}
Chartered 6/9/02
1902 Red Seal <$VALUE
3x10-20 1-400 <$3000
1902 Date Back
3x10-20 1-1180* <$1250
1902 Plain Back (dated 1902)
3x10-20 1311-2590* <$1250
* 1181-1310 not marked
1902 Plain Back (dated 1922)
3x10-20 1-1462 <$1250
1929 Small Size
10 Type 1 1-486 <$250
20 Type 1 1-136 <$250
10 Type 2 1-479 <$300
20 Type 2 1-165 <$300
Total Issue $276,170
Out in 1935 $25,000
Large out 1935 $2,350
Outstanding includes Ch 7134
****
8291 Aurora
FNB OF WHITE LAKE
{{ 2 L 2 S }}
Organized 6/22/06
Receivership 11/11/33
1902 Red Seal <$VALUE
3x10-20 1-400 <$3000
1902 Date Back
3x10-20 1-680 <$1000
1902 Plain Back
3x10-20 681-1643 <$1000
1929 Small Size
10 Type 1 1-231 <$500
20 Type 1 1-42 <$500
Total Issue $121,050
Out at close $10,000
Large out at close $1,010
****
8332 Aurora
UNITED STATES NB OF WHITE LAKE
{{ 1 L }}
Chartered 8/17/06
Liquidated 7/24/07
1902 Red Seal <$VALUE
4x5 1-100 <$5000
3x10-20 1-86 <$5000
Total Issue $6,300
All notes reportedly redeemed
Census confirms one note
****
6185 Roberts
FNB OF WHITE ROCK
Chartered 4/02
2nd title:Roberts County NB of Sisseton 8/12/33
FIRST TITLE {{ 2 L U + 7 S }}
1902 Red Seal <$VALUE
4x5 1-1225 <$3000
3x10-20 1-940 <$3000
1902 Date Back
4x5 1-1400 <$1000
3x10-20 1-1100 <$1000
1902 Plain Back (dated 1902)
4x5 1401-2760 <$1000
3x10-20 1101-1957 <$1000
1902 Plain Back (dated 1922)
4x5 1-1811 <$1000
3x10-20 1-1096 <$1000
1929 Small Size
5 Type 1 1-716 <$225
10 Type 1 1-348 <$225
20 Type 1 1-102 <$225
SECOND TITLE {{ 1 S }}
1929 Small Size
5 Type 2 1-994 <$500
10 Type 2 1-527 <$500
20 Type 2 1-85 <$500
Total Issue $382,110
Out in 1935 $25,000
Large out 1935 $1,760
****
11399 Wilmot
FNB OF WILMOT
{{ 6 S }}
Chartered 7/19
1929 Small Size <$VALUE
5 Type 1 1-84 <$225
10 Type 1 1-64 <$225
20 Type 1 1-106 <$225
5 Type 2 1-140 <$250
10 Type 2 1-90 <$250
20 Type 2 1-25 <$275
Total Issue $21,180
Out in 1935 $15,000
****
11119 Tripp
FNB OF WINNER
{{ 1 L }}
Organized 12/15/17
Receivership 1/31/23
1902 Plain Back <$VALUE
3x10-20 1-1172 <$1500
Total Issue $58,600
Out at close $18,400
****
5946 Sanborn
CITIZENS NB OF WOONSOCKET
Organized 8/6/01
Receivership 7/23/26
2nd title:FNB of Woonsocket 4/27/14
FIRST TITLE {{ 4 L }}
Brown Back <$VALUE
3x10-20 1-500 <$1500
1882 Date Back
3x10-20 1-969 <$650
SECOND TITLE {{ 1 L }}
1882 Date Back
3x10-20 1-700 <$1500
1882 Value Back
3x10-20 701-1615 <$1500
1902 Plain Back
3x10-20 1-642 <$1000
Total Issue $186,300
Out at close $15,000
****
FNB of Woonsocket
SEE Ch 5946
Citizens NB of Woonsocket
****
9445 Yankton
DAKOTA NB OF YANKTON
{{ 13 L 7 S }}
Chartered 6/09
Liquidated 9/30/31
1902 Date Back <$VALUE
50-100 1-600 <$500/$600
3x50-100 1-1280 <$500/$600
1902 Plain Back
3x50-100 1281-1551 <$500/$600
1929 Small Size
50 Type 1 1-175 <$450
100 Type 1 1-39 <$600
Total Issue $553,650
Out at close $100,000
Large out at close $30,950
Ch 2068 assumed circulation
****
F Dakota NB & TC of Yankton
SEE Ch 2068
FNB of Yankton
****
2068 Yankton
FNB OF YANKTON
Chartered 12/7/72
2nd title: F Dakota NB & TC 1/25/32
FIRST TITLE
TERRITORIAL ISSUES {{ 15 L }}
Original Series <$VALUE
3x1-2 1-1500 <$4000/$6000
4x5 1-3000 <$4000
Series 1875
4x5 1-5976 <$4000
STATE ISSUES {{ 6 L }}
Brown Back
3x10-20 1-1130 <$1500
1882 Date Back
3x10-20 1-2117 <$650
1902 Date Back
3x50-100 1-935 <$500/$600
1902 Plain Back
3x50-100 936-991 <$500/$600
SECOND TITLE {{ 0 S }}
1929 Small Size
10 Type 1 1-35 <$750
20 Type 1 1-24 <$750
Total Issue $602,100
Out in 1935 $50,000
Large out 1935 $13,570
Outstanding includes Ch 9445
****
4613 Yankton
YANKTON NB, YANKTON
{{ 1 L }}
Chartered 8/13/91
Liquidated 4/13/09
Brown Back <$VALUE
4x5 1-3478 <$2500
50-100 1-1200 <$5000
Total Issue $249,560
Out in 1910 $30,160
****

CONDITION affects Value. The Values shown are for notes in FINE condition.

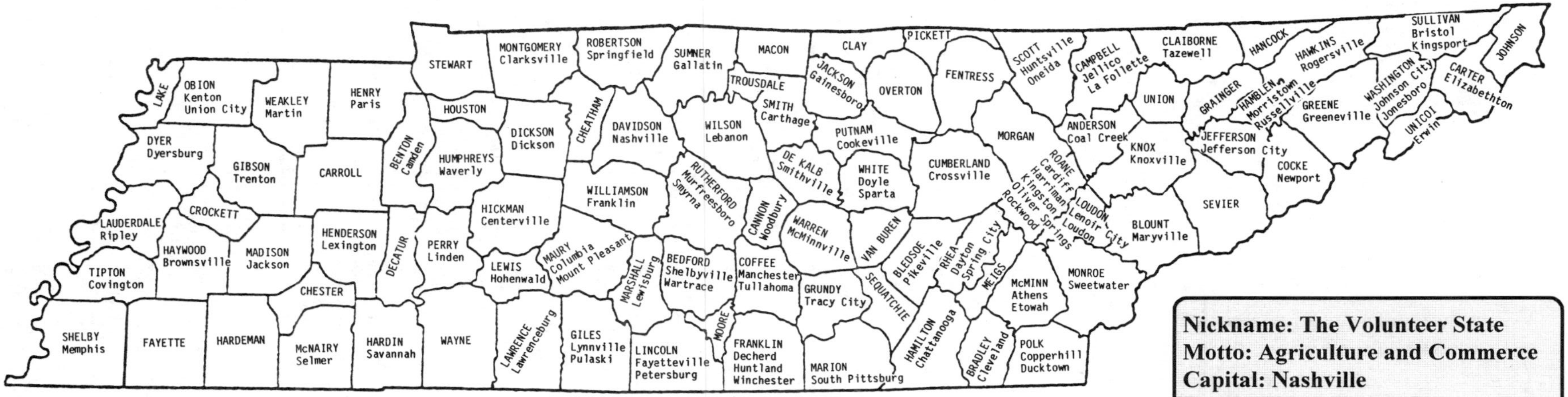

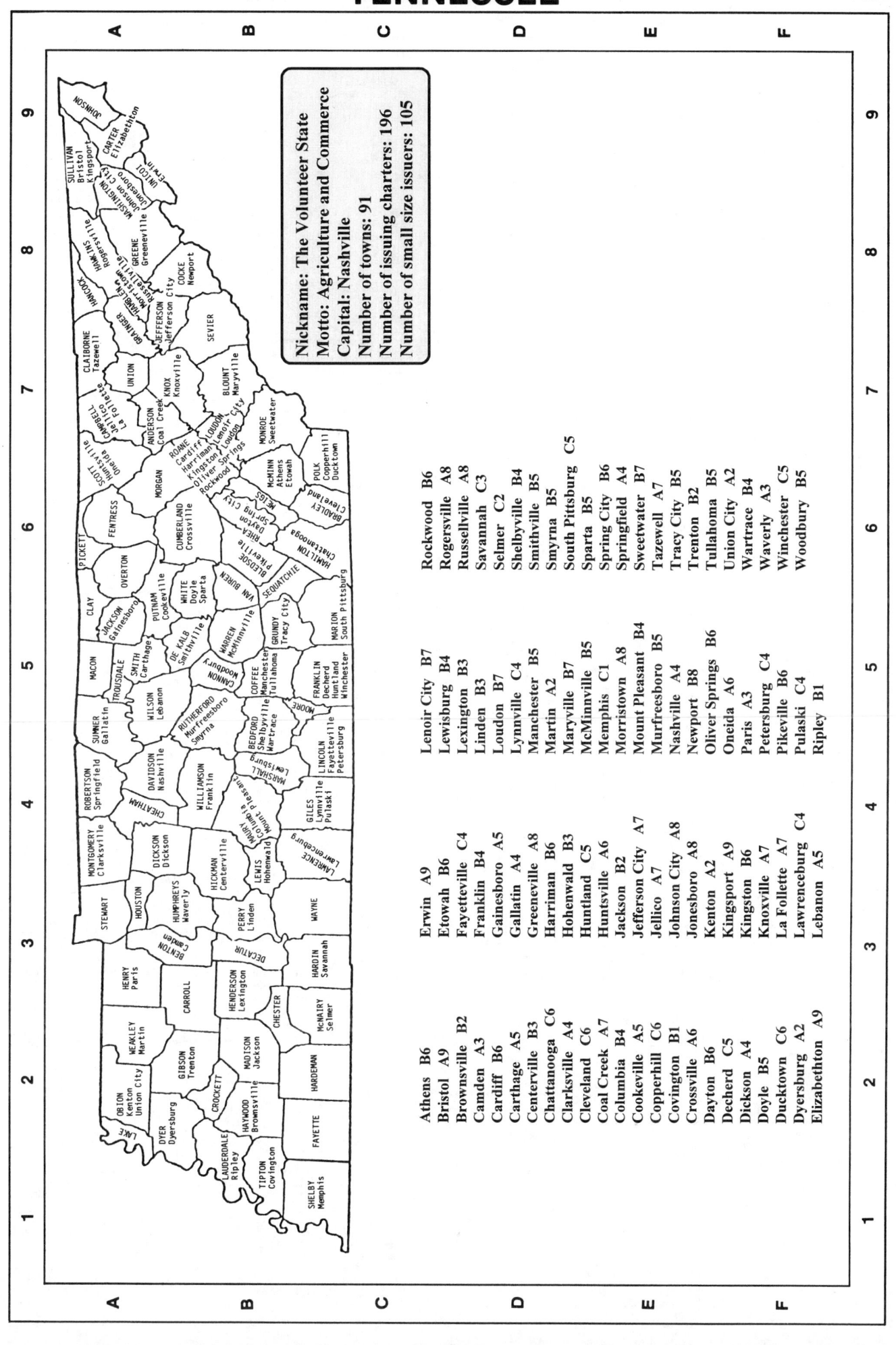

Nickname: The Volunteer State
Motto: Agriculture and Commerce
Capital: Nashville
Number of towns: 91
Number of issuing charters: 196
Number of small size issuers: 105

Athens B6
Bristol A9
Brownsville B2
Camden A3
Cardiff B6
Carthage A5
Centerville B3
Chattanooga C6
Clarksville A4
Cleveland C6
Coal Creek A7
Columbia B4
Cookeville A5
Copperhill C6
Covington B1
Crossville A6
Dayton B6
Decherd C5
Dickson A4
Doyle B5
Ducktown C6
Dyersburg A2
Elizabethton A9
Erwin A9
Etowah B6
Fayetteville C4
Franklin B4
Gainesboro A5
Gallatin A4
Greeneville A8
Harriman B6
Hohenwald B3
Huntland C5
Huntsville A6
Jackson B2
Jefferson City A7
Jellico A7
Johnson City A8
Jonesboro A8
Kenton A2
Kingsport A9
Kingston B6
Knoxville A7
La Follette A7
Lawrenceburg C4
Lebanon A5
Lenoir City B7
Lewisburg B4
Lexington B3
Linden B3
Loudon B7
Lynnville C4
Manchester B5
Martin A2
Maryville B7
McMinnville B5
Memphis C1
Morristown A8
Mount Pleasant B4
Murfreesboro B5
Nashville A4
Newport B8
Oliver Springs B6
Oneida A6
Paris A3
Petersburg C4
Pikeville B6
Pulaski C4
Ripley B1
Rockwood B6
Rogersville A8
Russellville A8
Savannah C3
Selmer C2
Shelbyville B4
Smithville B5
Smyrna B5
South Pittsburg C5
Sparta B5
Spring City B6
Springfield A4
Sweetwater B7
Tazewell A7
Tracy City B5
Trenton B2
Tullahoma B5
Union City A2
Wartrace B4
Waverly A3
Winchester C5
Woodbury B5

****

10735 McMinn
CITIZENS NB OF ATHENS
{{ 7 L 10 S }}
Chartered 5/15
1902 Date Back <$VALUE
4x10 1-1250 <$350
1902 Plain Back
4x5 1-17130 <$350
4x10 1251-13170 <$350
1929 Small Size
5 Type 1 1-5130 <$175
10 Type 1 1-2468 <$175
5 Type 2 1-6264 <$175
10 Type 2 1-3432 <$175
Total Issue $1,237,020
Out in 1935 $50,000
Large out 1935 $1,470

****

3341 McMinn
FNB OF ATHENS
{{ 8 L 12 S }}
Chartered 1885
Brown Back <$VALUE
3x10-20 1-3301 <$750
1902 Red Seal
3x10-20 1-2450 <$1000
1902 Date Back
3x10-20 1-5600 <$350
1902 Plain Back
3x10-20 5601-22926 <$350
1929 Small Size
10 Type 1 1-3056 <$150
20 Type 1 1-834 <$150
10 Type 2 1-5053 <$150
20 Type 2 1-1192 <$150
Total Issue $1,791,660
Out in 1935 $100,000
Large out 1935 $4,670

****

13640 Sullivan
FNB IN BRISTOL
{{ 16 S }}
Chartered 10/32
1929 Small Size <$VALUE
10 Type 1 1-1034 <$100
20 Type 1 1-356 <$100
10 Type 2 1-8317 <$100
20 Type 2 1-4280 <$100
Total Issue $273,530
Out in 1935 $250,000
Outstanding includes Ch 2796

****

2167 Sullivan
FNB OF BRISTOL
{{ 1 L }}
Chartered 8/12/74
Liquidated 7/10/76
Original Series <$VALUE
3x1-2 1-1500 <$2000/$3000
4x5 1-1875 <$2000
Series 1875
4x5 1-175 <$2000
Total Issue $48,500
Out in 1910 $241

****

FNB of Bristol
SEE Ch 2796
NB of Bristol

****

2796 Sullivan
NB OF BRISTOL
Chartered 1882
Liquidated 11/29/32
2nd title:FNB of Bristol 5/04
FIRST TITLE {{ 0 L }}
Brown Back <$VALUE
50-100 1-971 <$2500/$3000
1902 Red Seal
50-100 1-77 <$4000/$5000
SECOND TITLE {{ 21 L 31 S }}
1902 Red Seal
50-100 1-1540 <$4000/$5000
1902 Date Back
50-100 1-860 <$500/$600
3x50-100 1-1100 <$500/$600
1902 Plain Back
3x10-20 1-42514 <$165
1929 Small Size
10 Type 1 1-6850 <$100
20 Type 1 1-1786 <$100
Total Issue $3,543,220
Out at close $250,000
Large out 1935 $11,590
Ch 13640 assumed circulation

****

6042 Haywood
FNB OF BROWNSVILLE
{{ 1 L }}
Chartered 12/5/01
Liquidated 9/20/17
Brown Back <$VALUE
3x10-20 1-1000 <$1500
1882 Date Back
3x10-20 1-2338 <$1500
Total Issue $166,900
Out at close $25,000

****

8506 Benton
FNB OF CAMDEN
{{ 2 L }}
Chartered 1/07
Liquidated 1/13/25
1902 Red Seal <$VALUE
3x10-20 1-790 <$2000
1902 Date Back
3x10-20 1-1470* <$1000
1902 Plain Back
3x10-20 1591-3414* <$1000
* 1471-3410 not marked
Total Issue $210,200
Out at close $21,500

****

4303 Roane
FNB OF CARDIFF
{{ UNREPORTED }}
Chartered 5/8/90
Liquidated 5/25/91
Brown Back <$VALUE
4x5 1-613 <$2500
Total Issue $12,260
Out in 1910 $115

****

7928 Smith
FNB OF CARTHAGE
{{ UNREPORTED }}
Chartered 9/05
Liquidated 2/20/18
1902 Red Seal <$VALUE
3x10-20 1-1000 <$2500
1902 Date Back
3x10-20 1-1610 <$1500
1902 Plain Back
3x10-20 1611-1886 <$1500
Total Issue $144,300
Out at close $24,700

****

9827 Hickman
CITIZENS NB OF CENTERVILLE
{{ UNREPORTED }}
Organized 5/31/10
Receivership 10/28/24
1902 Date Back <$VALUE
3x10-20 1-920* <$1500
1902 Plain Back
3x10-20 981-1422* <$1500
* 921-980 not marked
Total Issue $71,100
Out at close $7,700

****

3288 Hickman
FNB OF CENTERVILLE
{{ 1 L 5 S }}
Chartered 1885
Brown Back <$VALUE
4x5 1-3003 <$1750
3x10-20 1-337 <$1750
1902 Red Seal
3x10-20 1-425 <$2000
1902 Date Back
3x10-20 1-1200* <$1000
1902 Plain Back
3x10-20 1401-2846* <$1000
*1201-1400 not marked
1929 Small Size
10 Type 1 1-1240 <$350
20 Type 1 1-400 <$350
10 Type 2 1-2207 <$350
20 Type 2 1-671 <$350
Total Issue $398,350
Out in 1935 $50,000
Large out 1935 $960

****

7817 Hamilton
AMERICAN NB OF CHATTANOOGA
{{ 1 L }}
Chartered 7/05
Liquidated 1/3/11
1902 Red Seal <$VALUE
4x5 1-7650 <$1000
3x10-20 1-5740 <$1000
1902 Date Back
4x5 1-5857 <$600
3x10-20 1-4357 <$600
Total Issue $774,990
Out in 1911 $120,945

****

3691 Hamilton
CHATTANOOGA NB, CHATTANOOGA
{{ UNREPORTED }}
Chartered 5/2/87
Liquidated 6/30/05
Brown Back <$VALUE
4x5 1-8525 <$1500
50-100 1-1929 <$2500/$3000
Total Issue $459,850
Out in 1910 $17,785

****

9176 Hamilton
CITIZENS NB OF CHATTANOOGA
{{ 5 L }}
Chartered 7/08
Liquidated 10/3/16
1902 Date Back <$VALUE
4x5 1-27500 <$250
3x10-20 1-22600 <$250
1902 Plain Back
4x5 27501-30245 <$250
3x10-20 22601-24230 <$250
Total Issue $1,816,400
Out in 1916 $283,695

****

1746 Hamilton
CITY NB OF CHATTANOOGA
{{ UNREPORTED }}
Chartered 12/5/70
Liquidated 9/10/74
Original Series <$VALUE
3x1-2 1-600 <$2000/$3000
4x5 1-2250 <$2000
3x10-20 1-2260<$2500/$3000
Total Issue $161,000
Out in 1910 $572

****

13746 Hamilton
COMMERCIAL NB OF CHATTANOOGA
{{ 33 S }}
Chartered 8/33
1929 Small Size <$VALUE
5 Type 2 1-37288 <$45
10 Type 2 1-18890 <$45
20 Type 2 1-7249 <$50
Total Issue $520,320
Out in 1935 $186,100

****

1606 Hamilton
FNB OF CHATTANOOGA
{{ 38 L 50+ S }}
Organized 10/25/65
Receivership 1/3/34
Original Series <$VALUE
3x1-2 1-5900 <$1000/$2000
4x5 1-6715 <$1000
3x10-20 1-3950<$1500/$2000
3x50-100 1-300<$5000/$7000
Series 1875
4x5 1-1500 <$1000
3x10-20 1-4400<$1500/$2000
Brown Back
4x5 1-2860 <$350
3x10-20 1-9939 <$350
1902 Red Seal
4x5 1-12000 <$400
3x10-20 1-11500 <$400
1902 Date Back
4x5 1-52000 <$75
3x10-20 1-43000 <$75
1902 Plain Back
4x5 52001-252162 <$75
3x10-20 43001-174436 <$75
1929 Small Size
5 Type 1 1-76519 <$35
10 Type 1 1-38837 <$35
20 Type 1 1-11620 <$45
50 Type 1 1-2002 <$100
100 Type 1 1-674 <$150
Total Issue $22,845,680
Out at close $1,570,320
Large out at close $51,105

****

4060 Hamilton
FOURTH NB OF CHATTANOOGA
{{ UNREPORTED }}
Chartered 6/28/89
Liquidated 8/10/93
Brown Back <$VALUE
3x10-20 1-1559 <$1500
Total Issue $77,950
Out in 1910 $420

****

7848 Hamilton
HAMILTON NB OF CHATTANOOGA
{{ 40 L 50+ S }}
Chartered 7/05
1902 Red Seal <$VALUE
4x5 1-10035 <$400
3x10-20 1-8186 <$400
1902 Date Back
4x5 1-71750 <$75
3x10-20 1-54400 <$75
1902 Plain Back
4x5 71751-412892 <$75
3x10-20 54401-259339 <$75
1929 Small Size
5 Type 1 1-91940 <$20
10 Type 1 1-50160 <$20
20 Type 1 1-16010 <$30
5 Type 2 1-129880 <$20
10 Type 2 1-75584 <$20
20 Type 2 1-23775 <$30
Total Issue $31,404,530
Out in 1935 $2,000,000
Large out 1935 $160,755

****

4456 Hamilton
MERCHANTS NB OF CHATTANOOGA
{{ UNREPORTED }}
Chartered 11/3/90
Liquidated 9/24/92
Brown Back <$VALUE
3x10-20 1-1150 <$1500
Total Issue $57,500
Out in 1910 $450

****

2559 Hamilton
THIRD NB OF CHATTANOOGA
{{ 1 L }}
Chartered 9/2/81
Liquidated 7/1/02
Series 1875 <$VALUE
3x10-20 1-6690<$1500/$2000
Brown Back
3x10-20 1-308 <$1000
Total Issue $349,900
Out in 1910 $3,510

****

2720 Montgomery
CLARKSVILLE NB, CLARKSVILLE
{{ 3 L 4 S }}
Chartered 1882
Brown Back <$VALUE
4x5 1-6827 <$750
50-100 1-115 <$2500/$3000
1902 Red Seal
50-100 1-917 <$4000/$5000
1902 Date Back
50-100 1-900 <$750/$850
3x50-100 1-1660 <$750/$850
1902 Plain Back
3x50-100 1661-2093 <$750/$850
1929 Small Size
5 Type 1 1-358 <$300
10 Type 1 1-160 <$300
20 Type 1 1-22 <$300
50 Type 1 1-252 <$400
100 Type 1 1-84 <$500
5 Type 2 1-264 <$350
10 Type 2 1-110 <$350
20 Type 2 1-125 <$350
Total Issue $1,103,490
Out in 1935 $100,000
Large out 1935 $13,840

****

3241 Montgomery
FARMERS & MERCHANTS NB OF CLARKSVILLE
{{ 2 L }}
Chartered 8/25/84
Liquidated 10/19/93
Brown Back <$VALUE
3x10-20 1-1221* <$2000
* 850-900 not issued
Total Issue $58,500
Out in 1910 $530

****

1603 Montgomery
FNB OF CLARKSVILLE
{{ 11 L 16 S }}
Chartered 1865
Original Series <$VALUE
3x1-2 1-2920 <$1250/$2000
4x5 1-2500 <$1500
3x10-20 1-2300<$1500/$2000
Series 1875
4x5 1-395 <$1500
3x10-20 1-1152<$1500/$2000
Brown Back
3x10-20 1-4197 <$600
1902 Red Seal
4x10 1-2250 <$750
50-100 1-266 <$4000/$5000
1902 Date Back
4x10 1-6550 <$175
50-100 1-200 <$500/$600
3x50-100 1-320 <$500/$600
1902 Plain Back
4x10 6551-25497 <$175
1929 Small Size
10 Type 1 1-5856 <$125
10 Type 2 1-7529 <$125
Total Issue $2,141,380
Out in 1935 $100,000
Large out 1935 $6,600

****

1666 Bradley
CLEVELAND NB, CLEVELAND
{{ 14 L 22 S }}
Chartered 1867
Original Series <$VALUE
3x1-2 1-2000 <$1250/$2000
4x5 1-1500 <$1250
3x10-20 1-3900<$1500/$2000
Series 1875
3x10-20 1-4180<$1500/$2000
Brown Back
50-100 1-3211 <$2500/$3000
1902 Red Seal
4x5 1-3750 <$600
3x10-20 1-1000 <$600
1902 Date Back
4x5 1-10750 <$175
3x10-20 1-9300 <$175
1902 Plain Back
4x5 10751-39532 <$175
3x10-20 9301-27589 <$175
1929 Small Size
5 Type 1 1-6478 <$100
10 Type 1 1-3638 <$100
20 Type 1 1-918 <$110
5 Type 2 1-12372 <$110
10 Type 2 1-6712 <$110
20 Type 2 1-1860 <$125
Total Issue $3,909,700
Out in 1935 $150,000
Large out 1935 $9,450

****

10028 Anderson
FNB OF COAL CREEK
{{ 3 L U + 5 S }}
Chartered 6/11
1902 Date Back <$VALUE
3x10-20 1-1870 <$750
1902 Plain Back
3x10-20 1871-6644 <$750
1929 Small Size
10 Type 1 1-1158 <$350
20 Type 1 1-332 <$400
10 Type 2 1-2604 <$400
20 Type 2 1-636 <$400
Total Issue $480,280
Out in 1935 $50,000
Large out 1935 $1,110

****

1713 Maury
FNB OF COLUMBIA
{{ UNREPORTED }}
Chartered 9/27/70
Liquidated 7/14/85
Original Series <$VALUE
3x1-2 1-3220 <$1500/$2500
4x5 1-1750 <$1500
3x10-20 1-1600<$2000/$2500
Series 1875
4x5 1-3075 <$1500
3x10-20 1-1250<$2000/$2500
Total Issue $255,100
Out in 1910 $1,598

****

4849 Maury
MAURY NB OF COLUMBIA
{{ 21 L 18 S }}
Chartered 1893
Liquidated 2/27/33
Brown Back <$VALUE
4x5 1-3000 <$400
3x10-20 1-5210 <$400
1882 Date Back
4x5 1-3405 <$350
3x10-20 1-2064 <$350
1902 Date Back
4x5 1-6500 <$150
3x10-20 1-5920 <$150
1902 Plain Back
4x5 6501-35420 <$150
3x10-20 5921-22918 <$150
1929 Small Size
5 Type 1 1-5632 <$125
10 Type 1 1-2774 <$110
20 Type 1 1-785 <$125
Total Issue $2,775,700
Out at close $134,520
Large out at close $12,180

****

7870 Maury
PHOENIX NB OF COLUMBIA
{{ 12 L 17 S }}
Organized 8/8/05
Receivership 11/11/31
1902 Red Seal <$VALUE
4x5 1-2500 <$750
3x10-20 1-2000 <$750
1902 Date Back
4x5 1-9400 <$175
3x10-20 1-7140 <$175
1902 Plain Back
4x5 9401-32522 <$175
3x10-20 7141-21699 <$175
1929 Small Size
5 Type 1 1-3709 <$125
10 Type 1 1-1729 <$110
20 Type 1 1-480 <$125
Total Issue $2,158,000
Out at close $120,560
Large out at close $13,500

****

2568 Maury
SECOND NB OF COLUMBIA
{{ 1 L }}
Organized 10/3/81
Receivership 5/19/93
Series 1875 <$VALUE
3x10-20 1-1999<$2000/$2500
Total Issue $99,950
Out in 1916 $430

****

9692 Putnam
COOKEVILLE NB, COOKEVILLE
{{ UNREPORTED }}
Chartered 3/10
Liquidated 12/16/10
1902 Date Back <$VALUE
4x5 1-205 <$2000
3x10-20 1-178 <$2000
Total Issue $13,000
Out in 1911 $7,470

****

9667 Putnam
FNB OF COOKEVILLE
{{ 4 L 6 S }}
Chartered 2/10
1902 Date Back <$VALUE
3x10-20 1-3600 <$500
1902 Plain Back
3x10-20 3601-11230 <$500
1929 Small Size
10 Type 1 1-1436 <$225
20 Type 1 1-414 <$250
10 Type 2 1-2177 <$250
20 Type 2 1-523 <$250
Total Issue $729,570
Out in 1935 $50,000
Large out 1935 $2,620

****

9027 Polk
FNB OF POLK COUNTY AT COPPERHILL
{{ 6 L 2 S }}
Chartered 2/08
1902 Red Seal <$VALUE
3x10-20 1-420 <$2000
1902 Date Back
3x10-20 1-2110 <$650
1902 Plain Back
3x10-20 2111-6628 <$650
1929 Small Size
10 Type 1 1-782 <$500
20 Type 1 1-210 <$500
10 Type 2 1-702 <$500
20 Type 2 1-237 <$500
Total Issue $436,280
Out in 1935 $25,000
Large out 1935 $1,450

****

10491 Tipton
FNB OF COVINGTON
{{ 3 L }}
Chartered 2/14
Liquidated 4/1/19
1902 Date Back <$VALUE
3x10-20 1-2400 <$750
1902 Plain Back
3x10-20 2401-3726 <$650
Total Issue $186,300
Out at close $60,000

****

****
9809 Cumberland
FNB OF CROSSVILLE
{{ 2 L 5 S }}
Chartered 7/10
1902 Date Back <$VALUE
4x5 1-1115 <$850
3x10-20 1-854 <$850
1902 Plain Back
4x5 1116-3285 <$850
3x10-20 855-2312 <$850
1929 Small Size
5 Type 1 1-1130 <$300
10 Type 1 1-682 <$300
20 Type 1 1-198 <$300
5 Type 2 1-3854 <$300
10 Type 2 1-1915 <$300
20 Type 2 1-498 <$300
Total Issue $328,260
Out in 1935 $49,995
Large out 1935 $1,045
****
5679 Rhea
AMERICAN NB OF DAYTON
{{ 2 L 2 S }}
Chartered 1/15/01
Receivership 11/14/31
Brown Back <$VALUE
3x10-20 1-900 <$1250
1882 Date Back
3x10-20 1-1180 <$1250
1882 Value Back
3x10-20 1181-2279 <$1250
1902 Plain Back
3x10-20 1-3456 <$850
1929 Small Size
10 Type 1 1-515 <$500
20 Type 1 1-133 <$500
Total Issue $378,610
Out at close $23,920
Large out at close $2,920
****
4362 Rhea
FNB OF DAYTON
{{ UNREPORTED }}
Organized 7/10/90
Receivership 10/25/93
Brown Back <$VALUE
4x5 1-450 <$2000
3x10-20 1-155 <$2000
Total Issue $16,750
Out in 1916 $45
****
7397 Franklin
FNB OF FRANKLIN COUNTY AT DECHERD
{{ 5 L 9 S }}
Chartered 9/04
1902 Red Seal <$VALUE
3x10-20 1-550 <$1250
1902 Date Back
3x10-20 1-2210 <$400
1902 Plain Back
3x10-20 2211-9369 <$400
1929 Small Size
5 Type 1 1-1664 <$200
10 Type 1 1-1214 <$200
20 Type 1 1-286 <$200
5 Type 2 1-3698 <$200
10 Type 2 1-2054 <$200
20 Type 2 1-563 <$200
Total Issue $703,320
Out in 1935 $50,000
Large out 1935 $1,920
****
8292 Dickson
CITIZENS NB OF DICKSON
{{ 3 L 4 S }}
Organized 6/14/06
Receivership 11/3/33
1902 Red Seal <$VALUE
3x10-20 1-1200 <$1500
1902 Date Back
3x10-20 1-2250* <$500
1902 Plain Back
3x10-20 2551-8574* <$500
* 2251-2550 not marked
1929 Small Size
10 Type 1 1-1139 <$300
20 Type 1 1-309 <$300
Total Issue $594,120
Out at close $37,495
Large out at close $2,695
****

****
10577 Dickson
DICKSON NB, DICKSON
{{ UNREPORTED }}
Chartered 7/14
Liquidated 1/4/15
1902 Date Back <$VALUE
3x10-20 1-300 <$1500
Total Issue $15,000
Out in 1915 $6,550
****
6930 Dickson
FNB OF DICKSON
{{ 4 L 10 S }}
Chartered 8/03
1902 Red Seal <$VALUE
3x10-20 1-980 <$1500
1902 Date Back
3x10-20 1-3010 <$450
1902 Plain Back
3x10-20 3011-13454 <$450
1929 Small Size
10 Type 1 1-1986 <$175
20 Type 1 1-546 <$200
5 Type 2 1-312 <$200
10 Type 2 1-2085 <$200
20 Type 2 1-432 <$200
Total Issue $937,430
Out in 1935 $60,000
Large out 1935 $3,005
****
10190 White
FNB OF DOYLE
{{ 3 L 3 S }}
Chartered 5/12
Liquidated 4/2/31
1902 Date Back <$VALUE
3x10-20 1-1360 <$600
1902 Plain Back
3x10-20 1361-5682 <$600
1929 Small Size
10 Type 1 1-409 <$400
20 Type 1 1-95 <$400
Total Issue $320,040
Out at close $22,660
Large out at close $3,690
****
9565 Polk
FNB OF DUCKTOWN
{{ UNREPORTED }}
Chartered 10/09
Liquidated 5/2/17
1902 Date Back <$VALUE
3x10-20 1-720* <$2000
* 721-735 not marked
Total Issue $36,750
Out at close $5,860
****
F-Citizens NB of Dyersburg
SEE Ch 5263
FNB of Dyersburg
****
5263 Dyer
FNB OF DYERSBURG
Chartered 3/9/00
2nd title:F-Citizens NB of Dyersburg 10/17/24
FIRST TITLE {{ 7 L }}
Brown Back <$VALUE
4x5 1-2500 <$500
3x10-20 1-3750 <$500
1882 Date Back
4x5 1-7850 <$500
3x10-20 1-5660 <$500
1882 Value Back
4x5 7851-12395 <$500
3x10-20 5661-7884 <$500
1902 Plain Back
4x5 1-7950 <$200
3x10-20 1-5320 <$200
SECOND TITLE {{ 50+ L 44 S }}
1902 Plain Back
4x5 1-7440 <$135
3x10-20 1-5467 <$135
1929 Small Size
5 Type 1 1-4464 <$75
10 Type 1 1-2188 <$75
20 Type 1 1-658 <$85
5 Type 2 1-6436 <$85
10 Type 2 1-3325 <$85
20 Type 2 1-876 <$85
Total Issue $2,153,860
Out in 1935 $100,000
Large out 1935 $6,000
****

****
9558 Carter
FNB OF ELIZABETHTON
{{ 5 L 4 S }}
Organized 8/31/09
Receivership 10/19/31
1902 Date Back <$VALUE
4x10 1-1675 <$350
1902 Plain Back
4x5 1-6866 <$350
4x10 1676-9457 <$350
1929 Small Size
5 Type 1 1-2284 <$300
10 Type 1 1-1019 <$300
Total Issue $645,260
Out at close $50,000
Large out at close $3,800
****
10976 Carter
HOLSTON NB OF ELIZABETHTON
{{ 8 L 3 S }}
Organized 3/6/17
Receivership 6/14/32
1902 Plain Back <$VALUE
4x5 1-7830 <$250
3x10-20 1-5536 <$250
1929 Small Size
5 Type 1 1-1267 <$400
10 Type 1 1-625 <$400
20 Type 1 1-157 <$400
Total Issue $527,750
Out at close $25,420
Large out at close $4,355
****
10583 Unicoi
ERWIN NB, ERWIN
{{ 6 S }}
Chartered 7/14
1929 Small Size <$VALUE
5 Type 1 1-862 <$300
10 Type 1 1-364 <$300
20 Type 1 1-140 <$300
5 Type 2 1-1828 <$300
10 Type 2 1-755 <$300
20 Type 2 1-260 <$325
Total Issue $86,390
Out at close $25,000
****
9720 Unicoi
FNB OF ERWIN
{{ UNREPORTED }}
Chartered 4/10
Liquidated 8/30/19
1902 Date Back <$VALUE
4x10 1-875 <$1500
1902 Plain Back
4x10 876-932 <$1500
Total Issue $37,280
Out at close $6,250
****
9162 McMinn
FNB OF ETOWAH
{{ 4 L 4 S }}
Organized 2/27/08
Receivership 6/21/32
1902 Date Back <$VALUE
3x10-20 1-4400 <$450
1902 Plain Back
3x10-20 4401-13611 <$450
1929 Small Size
10 Type 1 1-1201 <$350
20 Type 1 1-306 <$350
Total Issue $789,330
Out at close $49,580
Large out at close $4,850
****
3702 Lincoln
ELK NB OF FAYETTEVILLE
{{ 1 L }}
Chartered 5/9/87
Liquidated 2/19/07
Brown Back <$VALUE
4x5 1-2874 <$1500
3x10-20 1-510 <$1500
Total Issue $82,980
Out in 1910 $2,950
****
8555 Lincoln
ELK NB OF FAYETTEVILLE
{{ 9 L 15 S }}
Organized 1/31/07
Receivership 3/30/34
1902 Red Seal <$VALUE
4x5 1-1100 <$700
3x10-20 1-960 <$700
1902 Date Back
4x5 1-5600 <$175
3x10-20 1-4280 <$175

1902 Plain Back
4x5 5601-19920 <$175
3x10-20 4281-13144 <$175
1929 Small Size
5 Type 1 1-3288 <$125
10 Type 1 1-1614 <$110
20 Type 1 1-474 <$125
5 Type 2 1-720 <$150
10 Type 2 1-584 <$150
20 Type 2 1-170 <$160
Total Issue $1,390,800
Out at close $73,950
Large out at close $5,460
****
10198 Lincoln
FARMERS NB OF FAYETTEVILLE
{{ 3 L U + 15 S }}
Organized 4/18/12
Receivership 4/16/34
1902 Date Back <$VALUE
3x10-20 1-1030 <$450
1902 Plain Back
3x10-20 1031-9929 <$450
1929 Small Size
10 Type 1 1-1712 <$150
20 Type 1 1-398 <$150
10 Type 2 1-1103 <$150
20 Type 2 1-190 <$165
Total Issue $661,760
Out at close $50,000
Large out at close $2,420
****
2114 Lincoln
FNB OF FAYETTEVILLE
{{ 6 L 11 S }}
Chartered 6/27/73
Receivership 4/9/34
Original Series <$VALUE
4x5 1-600 <$1500
3x10-20 1-700 <$1750/$2000
Series 1875
3x10-20 1-1242<$1750/$2000
Brown Back
3x10-20 1-2410 <$500
1882 Date Back
4x5 1-1480 <$500
3x10-20 1-1363 <$500
1902 Date Back
4x5 1-1500 <$275
3x10-20 1-1200 <$275
1902 Plain Back
4x5 1501-13753 <$275
3x10-20 1201-8439 <$275
1929 Small Size
5 Type 1 1-2888 <$175
10 Type 1 1-1324 <$175
20 Type 1 1-360 <$175
5 Type 2 1-1090 <$200
10 Type 2 1-999 <$200
20 Type 2 1-120 <$200
Total Issue $1,251,480
Out at close $60,000
Large out at close $3,030
****
13948 Lincoln
UNION NB OF FAYETTEVILLE
{{ 10 S }}
Chartered 1/34
1929 Small Size <$VALUE
5 Type 2 1-8302 <$175
10 Type 2 1-3948 <$175
20 Type 2 1-1218 <$175
Total Issue $105,350
Out in 1935 $51,200
****
3062 Williamson
FARMERS NB OF FRANKLIN
{{ UNREPORTED }}
Chartered 1883
Liquidated 1/24/85
Brown Back <$VALUE
4x5 1-587 <$2000
Total Issue $11,740
Out in 1910 $80
****
8443 Williamson
HARPETH NB OF FRANKLIN
{{ 6 L 7 S }}
Chartered 11/06
1902 Red Seal <$VALUE
4x5 1-1462 <$850
4x10 1-1487 <$850
1902 Date Back
4x5 1-3600* <$300
4x10 1-3500** <$300
1902 Plain Back
4x5 3851-18598* <$300
4x10 3701-14602** <$300
* 3601-3850 not marked
** 3501-3700 not marked

1929 Small Size
5 Type 1 1-5290 <$200
10 Type 1 1-2844 <$200
5 Type 2 1-5430 <$200
10 Type 2 1-2325 <$200
Total Issue $1,424,440
Out in 1935 $37,160
Large out 1935 $2,700
****
1834 Williamson
NB OF FRANKLIN
{{ 17 L }}
Chartered 6/7/71
Receivership 10/18/26
Original Series <$VALUE
3x1-2 1-1800 <$1250/$2000
4x5 1-3500 <$1250
Series 1875
4x5 1-8400 <$1250
Brown Back
3x10-20 1-7950 <$400
1882 Date Back
3x10-20 1-1855 <$350
1902 Date Back
3x10-20 1-5600 <$175
1902 Plain Back
3x10-20 5601-17682 <$175
Total Issue $1,621,350
Out at close $96,600
****
5536 Jackson
FNB OF GAINESBORO
{{ UNREPORTED }}
Chartered 8/13/00
Liquidated 11/10/03
Brown Back <$VALUE
3x10-20 1-421 <$2500
Total Issue $21,050
Out in 1910 $1,260
****
F & Peoples NB of Gallatin
SEE Ch 5545
Peoples NB of Gallatin
****
1707 Sumner
FNB OF GALLATIN
{{ UNREPORTED }}
Chartered 9/14/70
Liquidated 10/1/75
Original Series <$VALUE
4x5 1-3450 <$2500
Total Issue $69,000
Out in 1910 $315
****
4236 Sumner
FNB OF GALLATIN
{{ UNREPORTED }}
Organized 2/17/90
Liquidated 1/3/16
Brown Back <$VALUE
4x5 1-3375 <$1500
50-100 1-360 <$3000/$3500
1882 Date Back
4x5 1-459 <$1500
50-100 1-84 <$3000/$3500
1902 Date Back
4x5 1-2032 <$1250
50-100 1-334 <$1500/$2000
3x50-100 1-122<$1500/$2000
Total Issue $264,520
Out at close $50,000
Ch 5545 assumed circulation
****
5545 Sumner
PEOPLES NB OF GALLATIN
Chartered 8/20/00
2nd title:F & Peoples NB of Gallatin 1/22/16
FIRST TITLE {{ 3 L }}
Brown Back <$VALUE
4x5 1-1410 <$500
50-100 1-392 <$2500/$3000
1882 Date Back
4x5 1-3065 <$500
50-100 1-160 <$2500/$3000
3x50-100 1-260<$2500/$3000
SECOND TITLE {{ 10 L 13 S }}
1882 Value Back
4x5 1-2835 <$500
3x10-20 1-2146 <$500
1902 Plain Back
4x5 1-11485 <$200
3x10-20 1-8438 <$200
1929 Small Size
5 Type 1 1-4240 <$125
10 Type 1 1-2328 <$125
20 Type 1 1-572 <$150
5 Type 2 1-6558 <$150
10 Type 2 1-3617 <$150
20 Type 2 1-874 <$150

Total Issue $1,474,860
Out in 1935 $79,550
Large out 1935 $2,835
Outstanding includes Ch 4236
****
13482 Greene
CITIZENS NB OF GREENEVILLE
{{ 4 S }}
Chartered 7/25/30
Receivership 6/3/33
1929 Small Size <$VALUE
5 Type 1 1-1238 <$400
10 Type 1 1-763 <$400
20 Type 1 1-333 <$400
Total Issue $122,880
Out at close $75,000
****
4177 Greene
FNB OF GREENEVILLE
{{ 2 L 5 S }}
Chartered 12/14/89
Brown Back <$VALUE
4x5 1-3400 <$1000
3x10-20 1-780 <$1000
1882 Date Back
4x5 1-68 <$1000
3x10-20 1-111 <$1000
1902 Date Back
3x10-20 1-1400 <$650
1902 Plain Back
3x10-20 1401-4142 <$650
1929 Small Size
10 Type 1 1-606 <$350
20 Type 1 1-150 <$350
10 Type 2 1-709 <$350
20 Type 2 1-110 <$350
Total Issue $334,400
Out in 1935 $15,800
Large out 1935 $1,180
****
12031 Roane
FNB IN HARRIMAN
{{ 7 L 11 S }}
Chartered 10/21
1902 Plain Back <$VALUE
4x5 1-9309 <$225
3x10-20 1-6340 <$225
1929 Small Size
5 Type 1 1-4180 <$150
10 Type 1 1-2436 <$150
20 Type 1 1-598 <$175
5 Type 2 1-6480 <$175
10 Type 2 1-2892 <$175
20 Type 2 1-900 <$175
Total Issue $925,820
Out in 1935 $100,000
Large out 1935 $3,075
****
4501 Roane
FNB OF HARRIMAN
{{ 2 L }}
Chartered 1891
Liquidated 10/25/19
Brown Back <$VALUE
3x10-20 1-2269 <$1000
1902 Date Back
3x10-20 1-1660* <$650
1902 Plain Back
3x10-20 1902-2292* <$650
* 1661-1901 not marked
Total Issue $228,050
Out at close $25,000
****
11915 Roane
HARRIMAN NB, HARRIMAN
{{ 3 L 2 S }}
Chartered 1/21
Liquidated 8/3/31
1902 Plain Back <$VALUE
4x5 1-25455 <$500
1929 Small Size
5 Type 1 1-4198 <$500
Total Issue $635,040
Out at close $42,500
Large out at close $2,330
****

CONDITION affects Value. The Values shown are for notes in FINE condition.

****

4654 Roane
MANUFACTURERS NB OF HARRIMAN
{{ 6 L }}
Chartered 1891
Liquidated 10/25/19
Brown Back <$VALUE
3x10-20 1-1400 <$500
50-100 1-703 <$2500/$3000
1882 Date Back
3x10-20 1-2522 <$500
1902 Date Back
3x10-20 1-3350 <$300
1902 Plain Back
3x10-20 3351-5706 <$300
Total Issue $586,850
Out at close $75,000

****

11985 Lewis
FNB OF HOHENWALD
{{ 0 L 6 S }}
Chartered 6/21
1902 Plain Back <$VALUE
3x10-20 1-5111 <$1250
1929 Small Size
10 Type 1 1-1142 <$300
20 Type 1 1-300 <$300
10 Type 2 1-1174 <$300
20 Type 2 1-315 <$300
Total Issue $378,110
Out in 1935 $35,000
Large out 1935 $1,460

****

8601 Franklin
FNB OF HUNTLAND
{{ 3 L 5 S }}
Chartered 3/07
1902 Red Seal <$VALUE
4x10 1-650 <$1500
1902 Date Back
4x10 1-2275 <$650
1902 Plain Back
4x10 2276-6558 <$650
1929 Small Size
10 Type 1 1-1022 <$300
10 Type 2 1-1776 <$300
Total Issue $367,400
Out in 1935 $20,000
Large out 1935 $830

****

10192 Scott
FNB OF HUNTSVILLE
{{ 0 L 1 S }}
Organized 5/4/12
Receivership 2/9/33
1902 Date Back <$VALUE
4x5 1-375 <$1500
3x10-20 1-600 <$1500
1902 Plain Back
4x5 376-1078 <$1500
3x10-20 601-988 <$1500
1929 Small Size
5 Type 1 1-282 <$750
10 Type 1 1-119 <$750
20 Type 1 1-24 <$750
Total Issue $89,440
Out at close $6,250
Large out at close $560

****

2168 Madison
FNB OF JACKSON
{{ 5U + 22 L 24 S }}
Chartered 8/17/74
Original Series <$VALUE
4x5 1-1350 <$1500
Series 1875
4x5 1-5901 <$1500
Brown Back
4x5 1-12875 <$350
3x10-20 1-4500 <$350
1882 Date Back
4x5 1-7559 <$350
3x10-20 1-5976 <$350
1902 Date Back
4x5 1-2500 <$150
3x10-20 1-3000 <$150
1902 Plain Back
4x5 2501-39960 <$150
3x10-20 3001-27078 <$150
1929 Small Size
5 Type 1 1-8792 <$100
10 Type 1 1-4540 <$100
20 Type 1 1-1198 <$100
5 Type 2 1-12445 <$100
10 Type 2 1-8403 <$100
20 Type 2 1-1557 <$100
Total Issue $4,112,915
Out in 1935 $200,000
Large out 1935 $10,780

****

12790 Madison
NB OF COMMERCE OF JACKSON
{{ 3 L 15 S }}
Chartered 7/25
1902 Plain Back <$VALUE
4x5 1-9087 <$350
4x10 1-4059 <$350
1929 Small Size
5 Type 1 1-7004 <$125
10 Type 1 1-3664 <$125
5 Type 2 1-10640 <$125
10 Type 2 1-5745 <$125
Total Issue $884,710
Out in 1935 $100,000
Large out 1935 $1,290

****

3576 Madison
SECOND NB OF JACKSON
{{ 10 L 16 S }}
Chartered 10/21/86
Brown Back <$VALUE
4x5 1-8700 <$600
3x10-20 1-3648 <$600
1902 Red Seal
4x5 1-1500 <$750
3x10-20 1-800 <$750
1902 Date Back
4x5 1-7500 <$200
3x10-20 1-5900 <$200
1902 Plain Back
4x5 7501-32632 <$200
3x10-20 5901-16287 <$200
1929 Small Size
5 Type 1 1-4536 <$125
10 Type 1 1-2380 <$125
20 Type 1 1-488 <$135
5 Type 2 1-6554 <$150
10 Type 2 1-3722 <$150
20 Type 2 1-1185 <$150
Total Issue $2,324,520
Out in 1935 $100,000
Large out 1935 $6,590

****

10334 Madison
SECURITY NB OF JACKSON
{{ 9 L U + 15 S }}
Organized 2/10/13
Liquidated 2/6/35
1902 Date Back <$VALUE
4x5 1-4350* <$200
3x10-20 1-3280** <$200
1902 Plain Back
4x5 4851-9850* <$200
3x10-20 3581-20956** <$200
* 4351-4850 not marked
** 3281-3580 not marked
1929 Small Size
10 Type 1 1-3128 <$125
20 Type 1 1-850 <$125
10 Type 2 1-681 <$150
20 Type 2 1-140 <$150
Total Issue $1,544,090
Out at close $99,995
Large out at close $6,365

****

11479 Jefferson
FNB OF JEFFERSON CITY
{{ 3 L 5 S }}
Chartered 10/19
1902 Plain Back <$VALUE
4x10 1-5837 <$600
1929 Small Size
10 Type 1 1-1510 <$350
10 Type 2 1-2657 <$350
Total Issue $350,650
Out in 1935 $25,000

****

7665 Campbell
FNB OF JELLICO
{{ 3 L 6 S }}
Chartered 3/05
1902 Red Seal <$VALUE
3x10-20 1-1100 <$1500
1902 Date Back
3x10-20 1-1970 <$600
1902 Plain Back
3x10-20 1971-6286 <$600
1929 Small Size
10 Type 1 1-758 <$275
20 Type 1 1-216 <$275
10 Type 2 1-721 <$325
20 Type 2 1-209 <$325
Total Issue $452,090
Out in 1935 $25,000
Large out 1935 $1,050

****

7636 Campbell
NB OF JELLICO
{{ 1 L }}
Chartered 3/05
Liquidated 1/1/19
1902 Red Seal <$VALUE
3x10-20 1-300 <$2000
1902 Date Back
3x10-20 1-1480 <$1000
1902 Plain Back
3x10-20 1481-2061 <$1000
Total Issue $118,050
Out at close $24,700

****

6236 Washington
CITY NB OF JOHNSON CITY
Chartered 5/2/02
Liquidated 9/26/32
2nd title:The Unaka & City NB 9/11/20
FIRST TITLE {{ 4 L }}
1902 Red Seal <$VALUE
4x5 1-2550 <$700
3x10-20 1-1920 <$700
1902 Date Back
4x5 1-3150 <$175
3x10-20 1-2680 <$175
1902 Plain Back
4x5 3151-10050 <$175
3x10-20 2681-6680 <$175
SECOND TITLE {{ 20 L 27 S }}
1902 Plain Back (dated 1902)
3x10-20 1-9400 <$135
1902 Plain Back (dated 1922)
4x5 1-43070 <$135
3x10-20 1-24267 <$135
1929 Small Size
5 Type 1 1-12548 <$75
10 Type 1 1-6191 <$75
20 Type 1 1-1689 <$85
Total Issue $4,177,330
Out at close $250,000
Large out at close $23,975
Outstanding includes Ch 5888
Ch 13635 assumed circulation

****

3951 Washington
FNB OF JOHNSON CITY
{{ UNREPORTED }}
Chartered 12/24/88
Receivership 11/13/94
Brown Back <$VALUE
3x10-20 1-497 <$2000
Total Issue $24,850
Out in 1916 $80

****

13635 Washington
HAMILTON NB OF JOHNSON CITY
{{ U + 14 S }}
Chartered 9/32
1929 Small Size <$VALUE
5 Type 1 1-1034 <$100
10 Type 1 1-778 <$100
20 Type 1 1-262 <$100
5 Type 2 1-4134 <$100
10 Type 2 1-3054 <$100
20 Type 2 1-720 <$100
Total Issue $174,750
Out in 1935 $100,000
Outstanding includes Ch 6236

****

11839 Washington
TENNESSEE NB OF JOHNSON CITY
{{ 12 L 12 S }}
Chartered 9/20
Liquidated 9/29/31
1902 Plain Back <$VALUE
3x10-20 1-31818 <$175
1929 Small Size
10 Type 1 1-3831 <$135
20 Type 1 1-1073 <$150
Total Issue $1,949,520
Out at close $160,140
Large out at close $17,970

****

5888 Washington
UNAKA NB OF JOHNSON CITY
{{ 10 L }}
Chartered 6/29/01
Liquidated 9/11/20
Brown Back <$VALUE
3x10-20 1-4750 <$450
1882 Date Back
3x10-20 1-7700 <$400
1882 Value Back
3x10-20 7701-11081 <$500
Total Issue $791,550
Out at close $21,000
Ch 6236 assumed circulation

****

Unaka & City NB of Johnson City
SEE Ch 6236
City NB of Johnson City

****

4715 Washington
FNB OF JONESBORO
{{ 5 L 5 S }}
Chartered 1892
Brown Back <$VALUE
4x5 1-2125 <$850
3x10-20 1-520 <$850
1882 Date Back
4x5 1-261 <$750
3x10-20 1-214 <$750
1902 Date Back
4x5 1-550 <$400
3x10-20 1-380 <$400
1902 Plain Back
4x5 551-5017 <$400
3x10-20 381-3145 <$400
1929 Small Size
5 Type 1 1-934 <$325
10 Type 1 1-540 <$325
20 Type 1 1-190 <$325
5 Type 2 1-1040 <$350
10 Type 2 1-644 <$350
20 Type 2 1-130 <$350
Total Issue $439,470
Out in 1935 $25,000
Large out 1935 $1,200

****

10404 Obion
FNB OF KENTON
{{ 1 L }}
Chartered 6/13
Liquidated 9/12/29
1902 Date Back <$VALUE
3x10-20 1-500 <$1500
1902 Plain Back
3x10-20 501-1276 <$1500
Total Issue $63,800
Out at close $5,350

****

10842 Sullivan
FNB OF KINGSPORT
{{ 3 L 11 S }}
Chartered 4/16
1902 Plain Back <$VALUE
3x10-20 1-6136 <$600
1929 Small Size
10 Type 1 1-3446 <$200
20 Type 1 1-900 <$200
10 Type 2 1-4704 <$200
20 Type 2 1-1272 <$200
Total Issue $694,040
Out in 1935 $100,000
Large out 1935 $1,270

****

12319 Roane
FNB OF KINGSTON
{{ 1 L 0 S }}
Organized 11/28/22
Receivership 12/24/31
1902 Plain Back <$VALUE
4x5 1-4622 <$1250
1929 Small Size
5 Type 1 1-1343 <$1000
Total Issue $132,730
Out at close $12,500

****

10327 Knox
AMERICAN NB OF KNOXVILLE
{{ 5 L }}
Chartered 2/13
Liquidated 12/26/22
1902 Date Back <$VALUE
3x10-20 1-5300 <$250
1902 Plain Back
3x10-20 5301-13116 <$250
Total Issue $655,800
Out at close $85,900
Ch 3837 assumed circulation

****

3837 Knox
CITY NB OF KNOXVILLE
{{ 29 L 15 S }}
Chartered 1/19/88
Receivership 3/9/32
Brown Back <$VALUE
3x10-20 1-24060 <$300
1902 Red Seal
4x10 1-7500 <$400
1902 Date Back
4x10 1-55000* <$75
1902 Plain Back
4x10 57001-213216* <$75
* 55001-57000 not marked
1929 Small Size
5 Type 1 1-24858 <$60
10 Type 1 1-10868 <$60
20 Type 1 1-3120 <$70
Total Issue $11,803,860
Out at close $400,000
Large out at close $53,290
Outstanding includes Ch 1032
Ch 2049 assumed circulation

****

2049 Knox
EAST TENNESSEE NB OF KNOXVILLE
Chartered 9/19/72
2nd title:Park NB of Knoxville 12/21/33
FIRST TITLE {{ 27 L 45 S }}
Original Series <$VALUE
3x1-2 1-2000 <$1250/$2000
4x5 1-2750 <$1250
3x10-20 1-800 <$1500/$2000
3x10-20 2551-2950 <$1500/$2000
20 801-2550 <$2000
Series 1875
3x10-20 1-2920<$1500/$2000
Brown Back
4x5 1-7500 <$300
3x10-20 1-18720 <$300/$350
1882 Date Back
4x5 1-8050 <$300
3x10-20 1-11442 <$300/$350
1902 Date Back
3x10-20 1-18500 <$75
1902 Plain Back
3x10-20 18501-107844 <$75
1929 Small Size
10 Type 1 1-30211 <$35
20 Type 1 1-8623 <$45
SECOND TITLE {{ 12 S }}
1929 Small Size
5 Type 1 1-636 <$100
10 Type 2 1-28410 <$100
20 Type 2 1-6775 <$100
Total Issue $10,787,500
Out in 1935 $1,000,000
Large out 1935 $54,820
Outstanding includes Ch 3837 and Ch 10327

****

391 Knox
FNB OF KNOXVILLE
{{ 1 L }}
Chartered 4/19/64
Liquidated 10/22/72
Original Series <$VALUE
3x1-2 1-1182 <$1500/$2500
4x5 1-1000 <$1500
3x10-20 1-1572<$2000/$2500
Total Issue $104,510
Out in 1910 $591

****

13539 Knox
HAMILTON NB OF KNOXVILLE
{{ U + 35 S }}
Chartered 4/31
1929 Small Size <$VALUE
5 Type 1 1-9240 <$25
10 Type 1 1-7702 <$25
20 Type 1 1-3066 <$35
5 Type 2 1-39234 <$25
10 Type 2 1-20687 <$25
20 Type 2 1-5952 <$35
Total Issue $1,629,320
Out in 1935 $488,300

****

4648 Knox
HOLSTON NB OF KNOXVILLE
Organized 10/13/91
Receivership 11/12/30
2nd title:Holston-Union NB of Knoxville 4/16/28
FIRST TITLE {{ 37 L }}
Brown Back <$VALUE
4x5 1-15875 <$300
3x10-20 1-9550 <$300/$350
1882 Date Back
4x5 1-9486 <$300
3x10-20 1-8261 <$300/$350
1902 Date Back
4x5 1-27000 <$65
3x10-20 1-21000 <$75
1902 Plain Back
4x5 27001-114521 <$65
3x10-20 21001-76928 <$75
SECOND TITLE {{ 6 L 10 S }}
1902 Plain Back
4x5 1-10709 <$150
3x10-20 1-6907 <$150
1929 Small Size
5 Type 1 1-14756 <$100
10 Type 1 1-7278 <$100
20 Type 1 1-1985 <$100
Total Issue $9,211,680
Out at close $750,000
Large out at close $132,735
Outstanding includes Ch 3708 and Ch 10401

****

Holston-Union NB of Knoxville
SEE Ch 4648
Holston NB of Knoxville

****

2658 Knox
MECHANICS NB OF KNOXVILLE
{{ 8 L }}
Chartered 4/12/82
Liquidated 8/23/07
Series 1875 <$VALUE
4x5 1-5545 <$850
50-100 1-554 <$5000/$7000
1902 Red Seal
3x10-20 1-4299 <$400
Total Issue $408,950
Out in 1910 $23,600

****

Park NB of Knoxville
SEE Ch 2049
East Tennessee NB of Knoxville

****

4102 Knox
STATE NB OF KNOXVILLE
{{ UNREPORTED }}
Chartered 8/28/89
Receivership 7/29/93
Brown Back <$VALUE
3x10-20 1-771 <$1500
Total Issue $38,550
Out in 1916 $130

****

3708 Knox
THIRD NB OF KNOXVILLE
{{ 18 L }}
Chartered 5/18/87
Closed 10/2/26
Brown Back <$VALUE
3x10-20 1-11140 <$300
1902 Red Seal
4x5 1-5000 <$400
4x10 1-3500 <$400
1902 Date Back
4x5 1-14850 <$85
4x10 1-13900 <$85
1902 Plain Back
4x5 14851-63958 <$85
4x10 13901-55135 <$85
Total Issue $4,281,560
Out at close $293,505
Ch 4648 assumed circulation

****

10401 Knox
UNION NB OF KNOXVILLE
{{ 23 L }}
Chartered 5/13
Liquidated 3/31/28
1902 Date Back <$VALUE
4x5 1-9500 <$65
3x10-20 1-8000 <$75
1902 Plain Back
4x5 9501-76295 <$65
3x10-20 8001-56717 <$75
Total Issue $4,361,750
Out at close $459,500
Ch 4648 assumed circulation

****

FNB of La Follette
SEE Ch 7225
NB of La Follette

****

7225 Campbell
NB OF La FOLLETTE
Chartered 4/04
2nd title:FNB of La Follette 10/31/23
FIRST TITLE {{ 0 L }}
1902 Red Seal <$VALUE
3x10-20 1-710 <$2000
1902 Date Back
3x10-20 1-1320 <$1000
1902 Plain Back
3x10-20 1321-2000 <$1000
SECOND TITLE {{ 1 L 7 S }}
1902 Plain Back
3x10-20 1-983 <$1000
1929 Small Size
10 Type 1 1-1010 <$225
20 Type 1 1-298 <$250
10 Type 2 1-2562 <$275
20 Type 2 1-685 <$275
Total Issue $320,330
Out in 1935 $50,000
Large out 1935 $340

****

****
12467 Campbell
PEOPLES NB OF La FOLLETTE
{{ 4 S }}
Chartered 12/23
1929 Small Size <$VALUE
5 Type 1 1-1656 <$350
10 Type 1 1-938 <$350
5 Type 2 1-6918 <$350
10 Type 2 1-3595 <$350
Total Issue $176,500
Out in 1935 $50,000
****
6093 Lawrence
FNB OF LAWRENCEBURG
{{ 8 L 7 S }}
Chartered 1/13/02
Brown Back <$VALUE
3x10-20 1-2450 <$600
1882 Date Back
3x10-20 1-4400 <$600
1882 Value Back
3x10-20 4401-7722 <$600
1902 Plain Back
3x10-20 1-6805 <$275
1929 Small Size
10 Type 1 1-1930 <$200
20 Type 1 1-538 <$225
10 Type 2 1-2819 <$225
20 Type 2 1-513 <$225
Total Issue $1,067,660
Out in 1935 $60,000
Large out 1935 $2,510
****
5754 Wilson
AMERICAN NB OF LEBANON
{{ 1 L }}
Chartered 3/25/01
Liquidated 1/7/29
Brown Back <$VALUE
3x10-20 1-1500 <$1000
1882 Date Back
3x10-20 1-2070 <$1000
1882 Value Back
3x10-20 2071-2870 <$1000
1902 Plain Back
3x10-20 1-2647 <$750
Total Issue $350,850
Out at close $20,200
****
8714 Wilson
LEBANON NB, LEBANON
{{ 4 L }}
Organized 4/13/07
Receivership 2/13/25
1902 Red Seal <$VALUE
3x10-20 1-940 <$1250
1902 Date Back
3x10-20 1-6100* <$450
1902 Plain Back
3x10-20 7101-14642* <$450
* 6101-7100 not marked
Total Issue $779,100
Out at close $78,600
****
1664 Wilson
NB OF LEBANON
{{ UNREPORTED }}
Chartered 10/13/66
Liquidated 8/30/86
Original Series <$VALUE
4x5 1-750 <$1750
3x10-20 1-1300<$2000/$2500
Series 1875
3x10-20 1-1067<$2000/$2500
Total Issue $133,350
Out in 1910 $620
****
1708 Wilson
SECOND NB OF LEBANON
{{ UNREPORTED }}
Chartered 9/17/70
Liquidated 9/18/89
Original Series <$VALUE
3x10-20 1-1300<$2000/$2500
Series 1875
3x10-20 1-1332<$2000/$2500
Total Issue $131,600
Out in 1910 $750
****
8673 Loudon
FNB OF LENOIR CITY
{{ 8 L 11 S }}
Chartered 5/07
1902 Red Seal <$VALUE
4x5 1-1300 <$1000
3x10-20 1-1105 <$1000
1902 Date Back
4x5 1-3450 <$300
3x10-20 1-2680 <$300
1902 Plain Back
4x5 3451-12454 <$300
3x10-20 2681-8669 <$300
1929 Small Size
5 Type 1 1-2812 <$175
10 Type 1 1-1830 <$175
20 Type 1 1-446 <$200
5 Type 2 1-5952 <$200
10 Type 2 1-3455 <$200
20 Type 2 1-1057 <$200
Total Issue $1,096,910
Out in 1935 $100,000
Large out 1935 $2,000
****
8934 Marshall
FNB OF LEWISBURG
{{ 10 L 20 S }}
Chartered 10/07
1902 Red Seal <$VALUE
4x10 1-1500 <$850
1902 Date Back
4x10 1-7575 <$250
1902 Plain Back
4x10 7576-25946 <$250
1929 Small Size
10 Type 1 1-4244 <$125
10 Type 2 1-5928 <$125
Total Issue $1,411,760
Out in 1935 $80,000
Large out 1935 $3,830
****
12324 Henderson
FNB OF LEXINGTON
{{ 0 L 5 S }}
Organized 2/8/23
1902 Plain Back <$VALUE
4x5 1-6587 <$1250
1929 Small Size
5 Type 1 1-3922 <$300
5 Type 2 1-8400 <$300
Total Issue $291,400
Out in 1935 $25,000
Large out 1935 $440
****
10181 Perry
FNB OF LINDEN
{{ 3 L 0 S }}
Chartered 4/12
1902 Date Back <$VALUE
4x5 1-1065 <$600
3x10-20 1-854 <$600
1902 Plain Back
4x5 1066-4467 <$600
3x10-20 855-2961 <$600
1929 Small Size
5 Type 1 1-984 <$600
10 Type 1 1-476 <$600
20 Type 1 1-152 <$600
5 Type 2 1-1016 <$600
10 Type 2 1-582 <$600
20 Type 2 1-214 <$600
Total Issue $328,890
Out in 1935 $25,000
Large out 1935 $1,370
****
12080 Loudon
FNB OF LOUDON
{{ 2 L 8 S }}
Chartered 12/21
1902 Plain Back <$VALUE
4x5 1-3750 <$600
3x10-20 1-2079 <$600
1929 Small Size
5 Type 1 1-1158 <$250
10 Type 1 1-956 <$250
20 Type 1 1-250 <$250
5 Type 2 1-3088 <$250
10 Type 2 1-1801 <$250
20 Type 2 1-528 <$250
Total Issue $345,060
Out in 1935 $50,000
Large out 1935 $700
****
8558 Giles
FNB OF LYNNVILLE
{{ UNREPORTED }}
Chartered 2/07
Liquidated 1/3/11
1902 Red Seal <$VALUE
4x5 1-250 <$2500
3x10-20 1-300 <$2500
1902 Date Back
4x5 1-65 <$1500
3x10-20 1-32 <$1500
Total Issue $22,900
Out in 1911 $4,560
****

****
5528 Coffee
FNB OF MANCHESTER
{{ 4 L 1 S }}
Chartered 8/2/00
Brown Back <$VALUE
3x10-20 1-620 <$1000
1882 Date Back
3x10-20 1-820 <$1000
1882 Value Back
3x10-20 821-1052 <$1000
1902 Plain Back
3x10-20 1-1037 <$500
1929 Small Size
10 Type 1 1-219 <$750
20 Type 1 1-57 <$750
Total Issue $155,430
Out in 1935 $6,250
Large out 1935 $560
****
9112 Weakley
CITY NB OF MARTIN
{{ 3 L }}
Chartered 4/08
Liquidated 5/15/20
1902 Red Seal <$VALUE
3x10-20 1-360 <$1250
1902 Date Back
3x10-20 1-4640 <$500
1902 Plain Back
3x10-20 4641-5968 <$500
Total Issue $316,400
Out at close $43,850
****
5617 Weakley
FNB OF MARTIN
{{ UNREPORTED }}
Chartered 11/8/00
Liquidated 4/30/06
Brown Back <$VALUE
50-100 1-128 <$3500/$4000
Total Issue $19,200
Out in 1910 $1,850
****
10542 Blount
FNB OF MARYVILLE
{{ 8 L 7 S }}
Organized 3/21/14
Receivership 1/13/33
1902 Date Back <$VALUE
4x10 1-1250 <$225
1902 Plain Back
4x10 1251-26956 <$225
1929 Small Size
10 Type 1 1-5476 <$175
Total Issue $1,406,800
Out at close $96,520
Large out at close $4,780
****
7834 Warren
AMERICAN NB OF McMINNVILLE
{{ UNREPORTED }}
Chartered 7/13/05
Liquidated 11/9/05
1902 Red Seal <$VALUE
3x10-20 1-750 <$2000
Total Issue $37,500
Out in 1910 $2,620
****
FNB of McMinnville
SEE Ch 2221
NB of McMinnville
****
2221 Warren
NB OF McMINNVILLE
Chartered 2/4/75
2nd title:FNB of McMinnville 1/20/05
FIRST TITLE {{ 0 L }}
Original Series <$VALUE
3x10-20 1-1300<$1500/$2000
Series 1875
3x10-20 1-2073<$1500/$2000
Brown Back
3x10-20 1-4901 <$1000
SECOND TITLE {{ 10 L 15 S }}
Brown Back
3x10-20 1-2000 <$500
1882 Date Back
3x10-20 1-4061 <$500
1902 Date Back
3x10-20 1-1000 <$175
1902 Plain Back
3x10-20 1001-24364 <$175
1929 Small Size
10 Type 1 1-5570 <$125
20 Type 1 1-1502 <$125
10 Type 2 1-7854 <$125
20 Type 2 1-2808 <$125
Total Issue $2,584,090
Out in 1935 $180,000
Large out 1935 $8,610
****
2593 Warren
PEOPLES NB OF McMINNVILLE
{{ 10 L 3 S }}
Chartered 1881
Liquidated 10/17/31
Series 1875 <$VALUE
3x10-20 1-2405<$1500/$2000
Brown Back
3x10-20 1-3050 <$500
1882 Date Back
3x10-20 1-3500 <$500
1882 Value Back
3x10-20 3501-6400 <$500
1902 Plain Back
3x10-20 1-6645 <$275
1929 Small Size
5 Type 1 1-1260 <$300
10 Type 1 1-880 <$300
20 Type 1 1-191 <$300
Total Issue $1,038,520
Out at close $52,420
Large out at close $7,740
****
Central-State NB of Memphis
SEE Ch 2127
State NB of Memphis
****
4307 Shelby
CONTINENTAL NB OF MEMPHIS
{{ 2 L }}
Chartered 5/9/90
Liquidated 4/25/99
Brown Back <$VALUE
3x10-20 1-2522 <$750
Total Issue $126,100
Out in 1910 $1,940
****
336 Shelby
FNB OF MEMPHIS
{{ U + 42 L 50+ S }}
Chartered 3/64
Original Series <$VALUE
3x1-2 1-3300 <$1250/$2500
4x5 1-1750 <$1250
3x10-20 1-2480<$1500/$2000
50-100 1-990 <$5000/$7000
Series 1875
3x1-2 1-1156 <$1250/$2500
4x5 1-360 <$1250
3x10-20 1-532 <$1500/$2000
50-100 1-344 <$5000/$7000
Brown Back
3x10-20 1-5112 <$350
50-100 1-1428 <$2500/$3000
1902 Red Seal
4x5 1-10000 <$400
3x10-20 1-3400 <$400
50-100 1-3533 <$4000/$5000
1902 Date Back
4x5 1-36750* <$65
3x10-20 1-22700 <$75
50-100 1-300 <$500/$600
3x50-100 1-1690 <$500/$600
1902 Plain Back
4x5 38751-89850 <$65
3x10-20 22701-53144 <$75
*36751-38750 not marked
1929 Small Size
10 Type 1 1-12514 <$25
20 Type 1 1-4144 <$35
50 Type 1 1-632 <$125
100 Type 1 1-224 <$175
10 Type 2 1-27135 <$25
20 Type 2 1-7376 <$35
Total Issue $8,697,620
Out in 1935 $1,000,000
Large out 1935 $37,424
Outstanding includes Ch 2127
****
2096 Shelby
FOURTH NB OF MEMPHIS
{{ UNREPORTED }}
Chartered 3/31/73
Liquidated 7/19/79
Original Series <$VALUE
4x5 1-2500 <$2000
3x10-20 1-650 <$2000/$2500
50-100 1-200 <$5000/$7000
Series 1875
3x10-20 1-558 <$5000/$7000
Total Issue $140,400
Out in 1910 $780
****

****
1636 Shelby
GERMAN NB OF MEMPHIS
{{ UNREPORTED }}
Chartered 1866
Liquidated 5/6/85
Original Series <$VALUE
3x1-2 1-2000 <$1500/$2500
4x5 1-1250 <$1500
3x10-20 1-1020<$2000/$2500
50-100 1-1218 <$5000/$7000
Series 1875
3x1-2 1-4610 <$1500/$2500
4x5 1-3750 <$1500
3x10-20 1-300 <$2000/$2500
50-100 1-886 <$5000/$7000
Total Issue $514,650
Out in 1910 $4,061
****
3633 Shelby
MEMPHIS NB OF MEMPHIS
{{ 2 L }}
Chartered 2/7/87
Liquidated 10/10/05
Brown Back <$VALUE
4x5 1-11650 <$750
50-100 1-574 <$2500/$3000
Total Issue $319,100
Out in 1910 $8,780
****
10540 Shelby
MERCANTILE NB OF MEMPHIS
{{ 5 L }}
Chartered 5/14
Liquidated 3/18/18
1902 Date Back <$VALUE
4x5 1-7500 <$300
3x10-20 1-10000 <$300
1902 Plain Back
4x5 7501-17125 <$300
3x10-20 10001-16751 <$300
Total Issue $1,180,050
Out at close $425,545
****
1407 Shelby
MERCHANTS NB OF MEMPHIS
{{ UNREPORTED }}
Chartered 7/8/65
Liquidated 8/30/73
Original Series <$VALUE
4x5 1-7300 <$1750
3x10-20 1-2496<$2000/$2500
Total Issue $270,800
Out in 1910 $2,275
****
9184 Shelby
NB OF MEMPHIS
{{ 13 L }}
Chartered 7/08
Liquidated 12/8/23
1902 Date Back <$VALUE
4x5 1-18500 <$125
3x10-20 1-13700 <$125
1902 Plain Back
4x5 18501-40970 <$125
3x10-20 13701-26855 <$125
Total Issue $2,162,150
Out at close $182,600
****
13681 Shelby
NB OF COMMERCE IN MEMPHIS
{{ 4 S }}
Chartered 4/33
1929 Small Size <$VALUE
50 Type 2 1-12800 <$350
100 Type 2 1-3600 <$600
Total Issue $1,000,000
Out in 1935 $1,000,000
****
5056 Shelby
NB OF COMMERCE OF MEMPHIS
{{ 6 L }}
Chartered 1/11/97
Liquidated 11/1/05
Brown Back <$VALUE
4x5 1-20965 <$400
3x10-20 1-17645 <$400
50-100 1-473 <$2500/$3000
Total Issue $1,372,500
Out in 1910 $52,330
****
12348 Shelby
SOUTHERN NB OF MEMPHIS
{{ 3 L }}
Chartered 4/23
Liquidated 2/5/25
1902 Plain Back <$VALUE
3x10-20 1-4140 <$400
Total Issue $207,000
Out at close $88,200
****

****
2127 Shelby
STATE NB OF MEMPHIS
Chartered 8/27/73
Closed 7/3/26
2nd title:Central-State NB of Memphis 5/1/12
FIRST TITLE {{ 12 L }}
Original Series <$VALUE
4x5 1-6150 <$1250
2x20-50-100 1-300 <$2000/$5000/$7000
Series 1875
4x5 1-5155 <$1250
2x20-50-100 1-1483 <$2000/$5000/$7000
Brown Back
4x5 1-27300 <$250
3x10-20 1-12300 <$250/$300
1882 Date Back
4x5 1-9590 <$250
3x10-20 1-5569 <$250/$300
SECOND TITLE {{ 11 L }}
1882 Date Back
3x10-20 1-3216 <$250/$300
1902 Date Back
3x10-20 1-15000 <$125
1902 Plain Back
3x10-20 15001-24324 <$125
Total Issue $3,573,120
Out at close $141,500
Ch 336 assumed circulation
****
1225 Shelby
TENNESSEE NB OF MEMPHIS
{{ UNREPORTED }}
Organized 6/5/65
Receivership 3/21/67
Original Series <$VALUE
4x5 1-2000 <$2500
3x10-20 1-1000<$2500/$3000
Total Issue $90,000
Out in 1916 $220
****
13349 Shelby
UNION PLANTERS NB & TC OF MEMPHIS
{{ 19U + 50+ S }}
Chartered 7/9/29
1929 Small Size <$VALUE
5 Type 1 1-48280 <$20
10 Type 1 1-16240 <$20
20 Type 1 1-5656 <$30
100 Type 1 1-3214 <$135
5 Type 2 1-165758 <$20
10 Type 2 1-81459 <$20
20 Type 2 1-16200 <$30
Total Issue $6,997,300
Out in 1935 $3,063,270
****
8025 Hamblen
CITY NB OF MORRISTOWN
Chartered 12/05
2nd title:Hamblen NB of Morristown 11/6/30
FIRST TITLE {{ 15 L 8 S }}
1902 Red Seal <$VALUE
4x5 1-4250 <$600
3x10-20 1-3900 <$600
1902 Date Back
4x5 1-11500 <$175
3x10-20 1-8500 <$175
1902 Plain Back
4x5 11501-40993 <$175
3x10-20 8501-25986 <$175
1929 Small Size
5 Type 1 1-3068 <$150
10 Type 1 1-1504 <$150
20 Type 1 1-498 <$150
SECOND TITLE {{ 9 S }}
1929 Small Size
5 Type 1 1-1880 <$150
10 Type 1 1-938 <$150
20 Type 1 1-308 <$150
5 Type 2 1-5072 <$150
10 Type 2 1-2519 <$150
20 Type 2 1-910 <$150
Total Issue $2,859,590
Out in 1935 $100,000
Large out 1935 $7,260
****

<$VALUEs are for notes in **FINE** condition. Value changes by approximately **25%** for a change of one full grade.

****
3432 Hamblen
FNB OF MORRISTOWN
{{ 11 L 10 S }}
Organized 1/4/86
Receivership 1/25/33
Brown Back <$VALUE
4x5 1-4600 <$600
3x10-20 1-1893 <$600
1902 Red Seal
3x10-20 1-1850 <$700
1902 Date Back
3x10-20 1-6900 <$200
1902 Plain Back
3x10-20 6901-19352 <$200
1929 Small Size
10 Type 1 1-2055 <$150
20 Type 1 1-576 <$165
Total Issue $1,439,170
Out at close $75,000
Large out at close $6,430
****
Hamblen NB of Morristown
SEE Ch 8025
City NB of Morristown
****
9319 Maury
FNB OF MOUNT PLEASANT
{{ 15 L 8 S }}
Chartered 1/09
1902 Date Back <$VALUE
3x10-20 1-4350 <$200
1902 Plain Back
3x10-20 4351-13140 <$200
1929 Small Size
10 Type 1 1-1716 <$175
20 Type 1 1-406 <$175
10 Type 2 1-1530 <$200
20 Type 2 1-490 <$200
Total Issue $833,780
Out in 1935 $40,000
Large out 1935 $3,150
****
1692 Rutherford
FNB OF MURFREESBORO
{{ 14 L 4 S }}
Organized 2/27/69
Receivership 2/1/32
Original Series <$VALUE
3x1-2 1-2000 <$1500/$2000
4x5 1-3200 <$1500
3x10-20 1-4700<$1750/$2000
Series 1875
4x5 1-2000 <$1500
3x10-20 1-1886<$1750/$2000
Brown Back
3x10-20 1-3821 <$450
1902 Date Back
3x10-20 1-4900 <$175
1902 Plain Back
3x10-20 4901-18385 <$175
1929 Small Size
10 Type 1 1-1820 <$300
20 Type 1 1-552 <$300
Total Issue $1,729,040
Out at close $86,540
Large out at close $12,580
****
2000 Rutherford
STONES RIVER NB OF
MURFREESBORO
{{ 6 L }}
Chartered 6/20/72
Liquidated 1/2/19
Original Series <$VALUE
3x1-2 1-1500 <$1500/$2000
4x5 1-3625 <$1500
Series 1875
4x5 1-6400 <$1500
Brown Back
4x5 1-3225 <$750
3x10-20 1-980 <$750
1882 Date Back
4x5 1-171 <$750
3x10-20 1-113 <$750
1902 Date Back
4x5 1-1700 <$400
3x10-20 1-1560 <$400
Total Issue $442,570
Out at close $37,495
****
3032 Davidson
AMERICAN NB OF NASHVILLE
{{ 50+ L 50+ S }}
Chartered 1883
Brown Back <$VALUE
4x5 1-1055 <$250
3x10-20 1-211 <$250/$300
50-100 1-1331 <$2500/$3000
1902 Red Seal
4x5 1-27465 <$400
3x10-20 1-18484 <$400
50-100 1-110 <$3000/$3500
1902 Date Back
4x5 1-69300 <$50
3x10-20 1-51600 <$65
50-100 1-240 <$400/$500
3x50-100 1-2758 <$400/$500
1902 Plain Back
4x5 69301-224985 <$50
3x10-20 51601-137162 <$65
3x50-100 2759-4611 <$400/$500
1929 Small Size
5 Type 1 1-79276 <$20
10 Type 1 1-42702 <$20
20 Type 1 1-14808 <$30
50 Type 1 1-2574 <$100
100 Type 1 1-970 <$150
5 Type 2 1-110758 <$20
10 Type 2 1-55451 <$20
20 Type 2 1-13620 <$30
Total Issue $23,720,110
Out in 1935 $3,000,000
Large out 1935 $67,900
Outstanding includes Ch 9659
****
9774 Davidson
BROADWAY NB OF NASHVILLE
{{ 15 L 29 S }}
Chartered 6/10
1902 Date Back <$VALUE
4x5 1-12850 <$100
3x10-20 1-9980 <$100
1902 Plain Back
4x5 12851-26718 <$100
3x10-20 9981-19779 <$100
1929 Small Size
5 Type 1 1-7718 <$40
10 Type 1 1-4694 <$40
20 Type 1 1-1012 <$50
5 Type 2 1-23794 <$40
10 Type 2 1-12765 <$40
20 Type 2 1-3498 <$50
Total Issue $2,474,510
Out in 1935 $300,000
Large out 1935 $4,210
****
3228 Davidson
COMMERCIAL NB OF NASHVILLE
{{ UNREPORTED }}
Organized 7/22/84
Receivership 4/6/93
Brown Back <$VALUE
50-100 1-775 <$2500/$3000
Total Issue $116,250
Out in 1916 $800
****
9659 Davidson
CUMBERLAND VALLEY NB OF
NASHVILLE
{{ 5 L }}
Chartered 2/10
Closed 1/20/21
1902 Date Back <$VALUE
4x5 1-8750 <$400
3x10-20 1-7600 <$400
1902 Plain Back
4x5 8751-14055 <$400
3x10-20 7601-10218 <$400
Total Issue $792,000
Out at close $124,200
Ch 3032 assumed circulation
****
150 Davidson
FNB OF NASHVILLE*
Chartered 12/63
Liquidated 7/8/12
*Consolidated with Ch 1669
which changed its title on
8/7/12 and then retook Ch 150
on 7/12/27.
2nd title: Fourth & FNB of
Nashville 7/12/27
Liquidated 10/10/32
FIRST TITLE {{ 10 L }}
Original Series <$VALUE
4x5 1-2750 <$850
4x10 1-3150 <$1500
3x20-50 1-2009<$2000/$5000
Series 1875
3x20-50 1-3090<$2000/$5000
Brown Back
4x5 1-20340 <$250
3x10-20 1-12012 <$250/$300
50-100 1-5328 <$2500/$3000
1902 Red Seal
4x5 1-13000 <$400
50-100 1-4000 <$4000/$5000
1902 Date Back
4x5 1-7340 <$100
50-100 1-1328 <$400/$500
SECOND TITLE {{ 36 L 50+ S }}
1902 Plain Back
4x5 1-52872 <$65
3x10-20 1-53535 <$75
1929 Small Size
5 Type 1 1-9962 <$25
10 Type 1 1-37682 <$25
20 Type 1 1-11935 <$35
Total Issue $10,880,060
Out at close $878,340
Large out at close $122,420
Outstanding includes Ch 1669
****
Fourth & FNB of Nashville
SEE Ch 150
FNB of Nashville
and see also Ch 1669
Fourth NB of Nashville
****
1669 Davidson
FOURTH NB OF NASHVILLE*
Organized 2/16/67
Consolidated with Ch 150
7/8/12
2nd title:Fourth & FNB of
Nashville 8/7/12
*RETOOK Ch 150 7/12/27
FIRST TITLE {{ 32 L }}
Original Series <$VALUE
4x5 1-1500 <$1000
4x10 1-2250 <$1250
3x20-50 1-5581<$2000/$5000
Series 1875
4x5 1-1250 <$1000
4x10 1-2250 <$1250
3x20-50 1-5198<$2000/$5000
Brown Back
4x5 1-3295 <$250
3x10-20 1-28654 <$250/$300
1902 Red Seal
4x5 1-7000 <$400
4x10 1-6500 <$400
1902 Date Back
4x5 1-31867 <$65
4x10 1-23879 <$65
SECOND TITLE {{ 36 L }}
1902 Date Back
4x5 1-56000 <$50
4x10 1-57500 <$60
1902 Plain Back
4x5 56001-287751 <$50
4x10 57501-222976 <$60
Total Issue $19,661,450
Out in 1927 $800,000
****
9532 Davidson
HERMITAGE NB OF NASHVILLE
Chartered 9/09
Liquidated 12/23/30
2nd title:Tennessee-
Hermitage NB 7/7/15
FIRST TITLE {{ 2 L }}
1902 Date Back <$VALUE
4x5 1-14885 <$400
3x10-20 1-10190 <$400
50-100 1-1000 <$650/$750
SECOND TITLE {{ 9 L 6 S }}
1902 Plain Back
4x5 1-19056 <$200
3x10-20 1-13795 <$200
1929 Small Size
5 Type 1 1-2094 <$175
10 Type 1 1-961 <$175
20 Type 1 1-282 <$175
Total Issue $2,182,390
Out at close $95,520
Large out at close $17,130
****
2200 Davidson
MECHANICS NB OF NASHVILLE
{{ 1 L }}
Chartered 10/31/74
Liquidated 1/13/80
Original Series <$VALUE
50-100 1-600 <$5000/$7000
Series 1875
50-100 1-216 <$5000/$7000
Total Issue $122,400
Out in 1910 $1,250
****
2513 Davidson
MERCHANTS NB OF NASHVILLE
{{ UNREPORTED }}
Chartered 1881
Liquidated 6/30/83
Series 1875 <$VALUE
3x10-20 1-3318<$2000/$2500
Total Issue $165,900
Out in 1910 $505
****
6729 Davidson
MERCHANTS NB OF NASHVILLE
{{ 2 L }}
Chartered 4/20/03
Liquidated 5/15/06
1902 Red Seal <$VALUE
4x5 1-1225 <$1000
3x10-20 1-7032 <$1000
Total Issue $376,100
Out in 1910 $26,910
****
771 Davidson
SECOND NB OF NASHVILLE
{{ UNREPORTED }}
Chartered 1/31/65
Liquidated 1/8/74
Original Series <$VALUE
4x5 1-3409 <$2000
3x10-20 1-1102<$2000/$2500
Total Issue $123,280
Out in 1910 $1,035
****
Tennessee-Hermitage NB of
Nashville
SEE Ch 9532
Hermitage NB of Nashville
****
13103 Davidson
THIRD NB IN NASHVILLE
{{ 3U + 22 S }}
Chartered 7/27
1929 Small Size <$VALUE
5 Type 1 1-10836 <$40
10 Type 1 1-5514 <$40
20 Type 1 1-1356 <$50
50 Type 1 1-68 <$200
5 Type 2 1-35988 <$40
10 Type 2 1-18742 <$40
20 Type 2 1-4745 <$50
Total Issue $1,301,300
Out in 1935 $388,100
****
1296 Davidson
THIRD NB OF NASHVILLE
{{ 5 L }}
Chartered 1865
Liquidated 2/20/84
Original Series <$VALUE
4x5 1-2500 <$850
3x10-20 1-1300<$1500/$2000
Series 1875
4x5 1-2090 <$850
3x10-20 1-4171<$1500/$2000
Total Issue $365,350
Out in 1910 $1,885
****
9632 Cocke
FNB OF NEWPORT
{{ 4 L 1 S }}
Organized 12/20/09
Receivership 12/4/30
1902 Date Back <$VALUE
4x5 1-3475 <$400
4x10 1-3475 <$400
1902 Plain Back
4x5 3476-12971 <$400
4x10 3476-11458 <$400
1929 Small Size
5 Type 1 1-1301 <$600
10 Type 1 1-628 <$600
Total Issue $794,450
Out at close $50,000
Large out at close $5,490
****
11998 Roane
TRI-COUNTY NB OF
OLIVER SPRINGS
{{ 0 L 3 S }}
Organized 6/22/21
Receivership 9/14/33
1902 Plain Back <$VALUE
4x10 1-1734 <$1500
1929 Small Size
10 Type 1 1-596 <$500
Total Issue $105,120
Out at close $10,000
Large out at close $300
****
FNB of Oneida
SEE Ch 8039
Scott County NB of Oneida
****
8039 Scott
SCOTT COUNTY NB OF ONEIDA
Chartered 1/06
2nd title:FNB of Oneida
4/25/19
FIRST TITLE {{ 1 L }}
1902 Red Seal <$VALUE
3x10-20 1-825 <$1500
1902 Date Back
3x10-20 1-1840 <$750
1902 Plain Back
3x10-20 1841-2620 <$750
SECOND TITLE {{ 1 L 5 S }}
1902 Plain Back
3x10-20 1-3389 <$750
1929 Small Size
10 Type 1 1-686 <$300
20 Type 1 1-194 <$300
10 Type 2 1-1140 <$300
20 Type 2 1-264 <$300
Total Issue $422,820
Out in 1935 $25,000
Large out 1935 $1,520
****
9334 Henry
FNB OF PARIS
{{ 8 L }}
Chartered 2/09
Liquidated 4/17/29
1902 Date Back <$VALUE
4x5 1-1450 <$200
3x10-20 1-1140 <$200
1902 Plain Back
4x5 1451-9965 <$200
3x10-20 1141-6849 <$200
Total Issue $541,750
Out at close $47,200
****
10306 Lincoln
FNB OF PETERSBURG
{{ 6 L 12 S }}
Chartered 1/13
1902 Date Back <$VALUE
4x10 1-850 <$300
1902 Plain Back
4x10 851-8237 <$300
1929 Small Size
10 Type 1 1-1820 <$150
10 Type 2 1-2373 <$165
Total Issue $462,410
Out in 1935 $30,000
Large out 1935 $550
****
10470 Bledsoe
FNB OF PIKEVILLE
{{ 2 L 2 S }}
Chartered 12/13
1902 Date Back <$VALUE
4x10 1-625 <$850
1902 Plain Back
4x10 626-2104 <$850
1929 Small Size
10 Type 1 1-946 <$500
10 Type 2 1-3541 <$500
Total Issue $176,330
Out in 1935 $30,000
Large out 1935 $190
****
4679 Giles
CITIZENS NB OF PULASKI
{{ 3 L }}
Chartered 1892
Liquidated 3/15/16
Brown Back <$VALUE
3x10-20 1-2960 <$850
1882 Date Back
3x10-20 1-458 <$850
1902 Date Back
3x10-20 1-1471 <$600
Total Issue $244,450
Out in 1916 $21,930
****
1990 Giles
GILES NB OF PULASKI
{{ 3 L }}
Chartered 5/31/72
Liquidated 1/12/92
Original Series <$VALUE
3x1-2 1-3000 <$1500/$2000
4x5 1-1800 <$1500
3x10-20 1-1380<$1750/$2000
Series 1875
4x5 1-301 <$1500
3x10-20 1-1723<$1750/$2000
Total Issue $212,170
Out in 1910 $1,205
****
1727 Giles
NB OF PULASKI
{{ 2 L }}
Chartered 1870
Liquidated 1/23/82
Original Series <$VALUE
3x1-2 1-3000 <$1500/$2000
4x5 1-2750 <$1500
3x10-20 1-800 <$1750/$2000
Series 1875
3x10-20 1-570 <$1750/$2000
Total Issue $138,500
Out in 1910 $697
****
6076 Giles
N PEOPLES B OF PULASKI
{{ 3 L }}
Chartered 1/2/02
Liquidated 3/15/16
Brown Back <$VALUE
3x10-20 1-1040 <$600
1882 Date Back
3x10-20 1-1077 <$600
Total Issue $105,850
Out in 1916 $11,440
****
2635 Giles
PEOPLES NB OF PULASKI
{{ UNREPORTED }}
Chartered 2/24/82
Liquidated 12/31/01
Series 1875 <$VALUE
3x10-20 1-1668<$2000/$2500
Total Issue $83,400
Out in 1910 $1,080
****
10449 Lauderdale
FNB OF RIPLEY
{{ 1 L 1 S }}
Chartered 9/25/13
Receivership 7/28/33
1902 Date Back <$VALUE
4x5 1-620 <$1000
4x10 1-515 <$1000
1902 Plain Back
4x5 621-3558 <$1000
4x10 516-3512 <$1000
1929 Small Size
5 Type 1 1-589 <$750
10 Type 1 1-311 <$750
Total Issue $247,970
Out at close $10,020
Large out at close $920
****
12264 Roane
CITY NB OF ROCKWOOD
{{ 2 L }}
Chartered 10/22
Liquidated 11/29/27
1902 Plain Back <$VALUE
4x5 1-6923 <$750
Total Issue $138,460
Out at close $9,910
****
4169 Roane
FNB OF ROCKWOOD
{{ 3 L 10 S }}
Chartered 12/3/89
Receivership 10/30/34
Brown Back <$VALUE
4x5 1-2300 <$850
3x10-20 1-2520 <$850
1882 Date Back
4x5 1-480 <$750
3x10-20 1-375 <$750
1902 Date Back
3x10-20 1-3600 <$400
1902 Plain Back
3x10-20 3601-12132 <$400
1929 Small Size
10 Type 1 1-1618 <$175
20 Type 1 1-404 <$200
20 Type 2 1-927 <$200
Total Issue $971,050
Out at close $50,000
Large out at close $3,050
****
12257 Roane
ROCKWOOD NB, ROCKWOOD
{{ 4 L 4 S }}
Chartered 10/22
Closed 2/19/32
1902 Plain Back <$VALUE
4x5 1-5765 <$450
3x10-20 1-4378 <$450
1929 Small Size
5 Type 1 1-1631 <$275
10 Type 1 1-811 <$275
20 Type 1 1-214 <$275
Total Issue $457,470
Out at close $50,000
Large out at close $2,360
****
4015 Hawkins
ROGERSVILLE NB,
ROGERSVILLE
{{ UNREPORTED }}
Chartered 4/22/89
Liquidated 1/5/99
Brown Back <$VALUE
3x10-20 1-1025 <$2000
Total Issue $51,250
Out in 1910 $930
****

10508 Hamblen
FNB OF RUSSELLVILLE
{{ 2 L }}
Chartered 4/14
Liquidated 5/4/21
1902 Date Back <$VALUE
3x10-20 1-700 <$1000
1902 Plain Back
3x10-20 701-1883 <$1000
Total Issue $94,150
Out at close $18,700

8889 Hardin
FNB OF SAVANNAH
{{ 6 L 2U + 6 S }}
Chartered 9/07
1902 Red Seal <$VALUE
4x5 1-750 <$850
3x10-20 1-600 <$850
1902 Date Back
4x5 1-1875 <$350
3x10-20 1-1500 <$350
1902 Plain Back
4x5 1876-7102 <$350
3x10-20 1501-4510 <$350
1929 Small Size
5 Type 1 1-1094 <$250
10 Type 1 1-544 <$250
20 Type 1 1-188 <$250
5 Type 2 1-2472 <$250
10 Type 2 1-1068 <$250
20 Type 2 1-264 <$250
Total Issue $528,880
Out in 1935 $30,000
Large out 1935 $1,810

8836 McNairy
FNB OF SELMER
{{ 1 L 3 S }}
Organized 8/6/07
1902 Red Seal <$VALUE
4x5 1-187 <$2000
3x10-20 1-150 <$2000
1902 Date Back
4x5 1-650 <$1000
3x10-20 1-520 <$1000
1902 Plain Back
4x5 651-1754 <$1000
3x10-20 521-1146 <$1000
1929 Small Size
5 Type 1 1-355 <$500
10 Type 1 1-189 <$500
20 Type 1 1-51 <$500
Total Issue $131,730
Out in 1935 $7,500
Large out 1935 $390

10785 Bedford
FARMERS NB OF SHELBYVILLE
Chartered 9/15
2nd title:FNB of Shelbyville 5/29/31
FIRST TITLE {{ 6 L 9 S }}
1902 Plain Back <$VALUE
3x10-20 1-19953 <$225
1929 Small Size
10 Type 1 1-1974 <$175
20 Type 1 1-508 <$175
SECOND TITLE {{ 10 S }}
1929 Small Size
10 Type 1 1-1138 <$150
20 Type 1 1-366 <$150
10 Type 2 1-3833 <$150
20 Type 2 1-1159 <$150
Total Issue $1,350,760
Out in 1935 $100,000
Large out 1935 $6,050

FNB of Shelbyville
SEE Ch 10785
Farmers NB of Shelbyville

2198 Bedford
NB OF SHELBYVILLE
{{ UNREPORTED }}
Chartered 10/29/74
Receivership 12/13/89
Original Series <$VALUE
3x10-20 1-900 <$2000/$2500
Series 1875
3x10-20 1-702 <$2000/$2500
Total Issue $80,100
Out in 1916 $395

3530 Bedford
PEOPLES NB OF SHELBYVILLE
{{ 12 L 12 S }}
Chartered 7/12/86
Brown Back <$VALUE
4x5 1-11318 <$500
3x10-20 1-3481 <$500
1902 Red Seal
3x10-20 1-1600 <$750
1902 Date Back
3x10-20 1-7800 <$175
1902 Plain Back
3x10-20 7801-24414 <$175
1929 Small Size
10 Type 1 1-3050 <$150
20 Type 1 1-838 <$150
10 Type 2 1-3815 <$150
20 Type 2 1-895 <$150
Total Issue $2,040,720
Out in 1935 $100,000
Large out 1935 $6,635

13056 Dekalb
FNB OF SMITHVILLE
{{ U + 1 L 3 S }}
Chartered 4/27
1902 Plain Back <$VALUE
4x5 1-2885 <$1000
1929 Small Size
5 Type 1 1-2830 <$500
5 Type 2 1-6522 <$500
Total Issue $175,210
Out in 1935 $20,000
Large out 1935 $250

9807 Rutherford
FNB OF SMYRNA
{{ 0 L 4 S }}
Chartered 7/10
1902 Date Back <$VALUE
4x5 1-615 <$1250
3x10-20 1-494 <$1250
1902 Plain Back
4x5 616-1462 <$1250
3x10-20 495-1041 <$1250
1929 Small Size
5 Type 1 1-337 <$500
10 Type 1 1-193 <$500
20 Type 1 1-49 <$500
Total Issue $108,860
Out in 1935 $6,250
Large out 1935 $250

3660 Marion
FNB OF SOUTH PITTSBURG
{{ 5 L 14 S }}
Chartered 3/29/87
Brown Back <$VALUE
3x10-20 1-1465 <$650
1902 Red Seal
3x10-20 1-1400 <$750
1902 Date Back
3x10-20 1-2550 <$300
1902 Plain Back
3x10-20 2551-14500 <$300
1929 Small Size
10 Type 1 1-3428 <$125
20 Type 1 1-876 <$135
10 Type 2 1-4912 <$150
20 Type 2 1-1272 <$150
Total Issue $1,253,610
Out in 1935 $100,000
Large out 1935 $4,240

7912 White
AMERICAN NB OF SPARTA
{{ 2 L }}
Chartered 9/05
Liquidated 5/22/23
1902 Red Seal <$VALUE
3x10-20 1-2150 <$1250
1902 Date Back
3x10-20 1-3440 <$600
1902 Plain Back
3x10-20 3441-7335 <$600
Total Issue $474,250
Out at close $50,000

3614 White
FNB OF SPARTA
{{ 8 L 12 S }}
Chartered 1/5/87
Brown Back <$VALUE
4x5 1-5283 <$650
3x10-20 1-2942 <$650
1902 Red Seal
3x10-20 1-2000 <$750
1902 Date Back
3x10-20 1-7200 <$250
1902 Plain Back
3x10-20 7201-23817 <$250
1929 Small Size
10 Type 1 1-2850 <$150
20 Type 1 1-758 <$150
10 Type 2 1-4089 <$165
20 Type 2 1-940 <$175
Total Issue $1,865,260
Out in 1935 $100,000
Large out 1935 $5,750

9470 Rhea
FNB OF SPRING CITY
{{ 2 L }}
Chartered 7/09
Liquidated 8/1/16
1902 Date Back <$VALUE
3x10-20 1-1080* <$1250
* 1081-1115 not marked
Total Issue $55,750
Out in 1916 $10,300

12639 Robertson
FNB OF SPRINGFIELD
{{ 1 L 11 S }}
Chartered 2/25
1902 Plain Back <$VALUE
3x10-20 1-3789 <$850
1929 Small Size
10 Type 1 1-1584 <$150
20 Type 1 1-430 <$175
10 Type 2 1-2387 <$175
20 Type 2 1-557 <$175
Total Issue $371,100
Out in 1935 $50,000
Large out 1935 $1,590

6189 Robertson
PEOPLES NB OF SPRINGFIELD
{{ 1 L }}
Chartered 4/4/02
Liquidated 11/14/17
1902 Red Seal <$VALUE
3x10-20 1-3200 <$1250
1902 Date Back
3x10-20 1-7000 <$750
1902 Plain Back
3x10-20 7001-8329 <$750
Total Issue $576,450
Out at close $100,000

2019 Robertson
SPRINGFIELD NB,
SPRINGFIELD
{{ UNREPORTED }}
Chartered 7/24/72
Liquidated 11/14/17
Original Series <$VALUE
3x10-20 1-1680<$2500/$3000
Series 1875
3x10-20 1-1594<$2500/$3000
Brown Back
50-100 1-751 <$2500/$3000
1902 Date Back
3x50-100 1-189<$1250/$1500
Total Issue $323,600
Out at close $24,100

11202 Monroe
FNB OF SWEETWATER
{{ 4 L 3 S }}
Organized 1/21/18
Receivership 12/17/30
1902 Plain Back <$VALUE
4x5 1-7905 <$750
4x10 1-5145 <$750
1929 Small Size
5 Type 1 1-1075 <$600
10 Type 1 1-545 <$600
Total Issue $428,850
Out at close $40,000
Large out at close $3,630

7740 Claiborne
CLAIBORNE NB OF TAZEWELL
{{ UNREPORTED }}
Chartered 5/05
Liquidated 12/1/19
1902 Red Seal <$VALUE
3x10-20 1-900 <$2000
1902 Date Back
3x10-20 1-1670 <$1250
1902 Plain Back
3x10-20 1671-2303 <$1250
Total Issue $160,150
Out at close $24,600

7314 Grundy
FNB OF TRACY CITY
{{ 3 L 5 S }}
Chartered 6/04
1902 Red Seal <$VALUE
3x10-20 1-1340 <$1500
1902 Date Back
3x10-20 1-1700 <$650
1902 Plain Back
3x10-20 1701-6001 <$650
1929 Small Size
10 Type 1 1-760 <$350
20 Type 1 1-212 <$350
10 Type 2 1-1133 <$350
20 Type 2 1-260 <$350
Total Issue $454,620
Out in 1935 $25,000
Large out 1935 $1,080

12438 Gibson
CITIZENS NB OF TRENTON
{{ 3 L 10 S }}
Chartered 9/23
1902 Plain Back <$VALUE
3x10-20 1-8355 <$500
1929 Small Size
10 Type 1 1-2336 <$150
20 Type 1 1-654 <$175
10 Type 2 1-3066 <$175
20 Type 2 1-1149 <$175
Total Issue $690,030
Out in 1935 $75,000
Large out 1935 $640

8406 Gibson
FNB OF TRENTON
{{ 1 L }}
Chartered 10/06
Liquidated 6/1/18
1902 Red Seal <$VALUE
4x5 1-400 <$1500
3x10-20 1-320 <$1500
1902 Date Back
4x5 1-4050 <$650
3x10-20 1-3020 <$650
1902 Plain Back
4x5 4051-5375 <$650
3x10-20 3021-3899 <$650
Total Issue $326,450
Out at close $55,000

3107 Coffee
FNB OF TULLAHOMA
{{ 3 L 6 S }}
Chartered 1884
Brown Back <$VALUE
50-100 1-1155 <$2500/$3000
1902 Red Seal
4x10 1-1250 <$850
50-100 1-360 <$4000/$5000
1902 Date Back
4x10 1-3275 <$400
50-100 1-100 <$1000/$1250
3x50-100 1-110<$1000/$1250
1902 Plain Back
4x10 3276-13806 <$400
1929 Small Size
10 Type 1 1-2788 <$200
10 Type 2 1-3941 <$225
Total Issue $1,078,680
Out in 1935 $39,810
Large out 1935 $3,210

4020 Coffee
TRADERS NB OF TULLAHOMA
{{ 6 L 9 S }}
Chartered 4/27/89
Brown Back <$VALUE
4x5 1-4561 <$500
3x10-20 1-2886 <$500
1902 Date Back
3x10-20 1-3540 <$275
1902 Plain Back
3x10-20 3541-12175 <$275
1929 Small Size
10 Type 1 1-1496 <$150
20 Type 1 1-416 <$175
10 Type 2 1-1459 <$175
20 Type 2 1-548 <$175
Total Issue $999,550
Out in 1935 $49,995
Large out 1935 $3,245

4442 Obion
FARMERS & MERCHANTS NB
OF UNION CITY
{{ UNREPORTED }}
Chartered 10/11/90
Liquidated 1/10/94
Brown Back <$VALUE
50-100 1-253 <$2500/$3000
Total Issue $37,950
Out in 1910 $700

3919 Obion
FNB OF UNION CITY
{{ 2 L }}
Chartered 8/4/88
Liquidated 1/10/10
Brown Back <$VALUE
4x5 1-3645 <$850
50-100 1-437 <$2500/$3000
1902 Date Back
3x10-20 1-1232 <$650
Total Issue $200,050
Out in 1910 $29,680

9629 Obion
OLD NB OF UNION CITY
{{ 6 L 10 S }}
Chartered 1/10
1902 Date Back <$VALUE
3x10-20 1-4840 <$275
1902 Plain Back
3x10-20 4841-13150 <$275
1929 Small Size
10 Type 1 1-1900 <$150
20 Type 1 1-484 <$165
10 Type 2 1-2677 <$175
20 Type 2 1-644 <$175
Total Issue $869,230
Out in 1935 $75,000
Large out 1935 $2,480

9239 Obion
THIRD NB OF UNION CITY
{{ 4 L 10 S }}
Chartered 9/08
1902 Date Back <$VALUE
3x10-20 1-6300 <$325
1902 Plain Back
3x10-20 6301-10564 <$325
1929 Small Size
10 Type 1 1-1488 <$150
20 Type 1 1-446 <$165
10 Type 2 1-3149 <$175
20 Type 2 1-753 <$175
Total Issue $717,550
Out in 1935 $80,000
Large out 1935 $1,620

9627 Bedford
FNB OF WARTRACE
{{ 1 L }}
Organized 1/6/10
Receivership 12/22/15
1902 Date Back <$VALUE
3x10-20 1-1606 <$1500
Total Issue $80,300
Out in 1916 $15,180

9331 Humphreys
CITIZENS NB OF WAVERLY
{{ UNREPORTED }}
Chartered 2/09
Liquidated 2/1/19
1902 Date Back <$VALUE
3x10-20 1-1604 <$1500
Total Issue $80,200
Out at close $12,200

5963 Humphreys
FNB OF WAVERLY
{{ UNREPORTED }}
Chartered 9/12/01
Liquidated 2/1/09
Brown Back <$VALUE
50-100 1-151 <$3000/$3500
Total Issue $22,650
Out in 1910 $3,850

8631 Franklin
AMERICAN NB OF WINCHESTER
{{ UNREPORTED }}
Chartered 4/3/07
Liquidated 3/1/09
1902 Red Seal <$VALUE
4x5 1-293 <$2500
4x10 1-326 <$2500
Total Issue $18,900
Out in 1910 $3,640

8640 Franklin
FARMERS NB OF WINCHESTER
{{ 3 L 7 S }}
Chartered 4/07
1902 Red Seal <$VALUE
3x10-20 1-440 <$1250
1902 Date Back
3x10-20 1-3340 <$450
1902 Plain Back
3x10-20 3341-8706 <$450
1929 Small Size
10 Type 1 1-946 <$225
20 Type 1 1-288 <$225
10 Type 2 1-1344 <$250
20 Type 2 1-400 <$250
Total Issue $570,060
Out in 1935 $35,000
Large out 1935 $1,550

9089 Cannon
FNB OF WOODBURY
{{ UNREPORTED }}
Chartered 4/08
Liquidated 6/30/19
1902 Red Seal <$VALUE
4x5 1-506 <$2500
3x10-20 1-405 <$2500
1902 Date Back
4x5 1-1050 <$1500
3x10-20 1-800 <$1500
1902 Plain Back
4x5 1051-1676 <$1500
3x10-20 801-1251 <$1500
Total Issue $126,440
Out at close $24,990

CONDITION affects Value. The Values shown are for notes in FINE condition.

1 2 3 4 5 6 7 8 9

A B C D E F

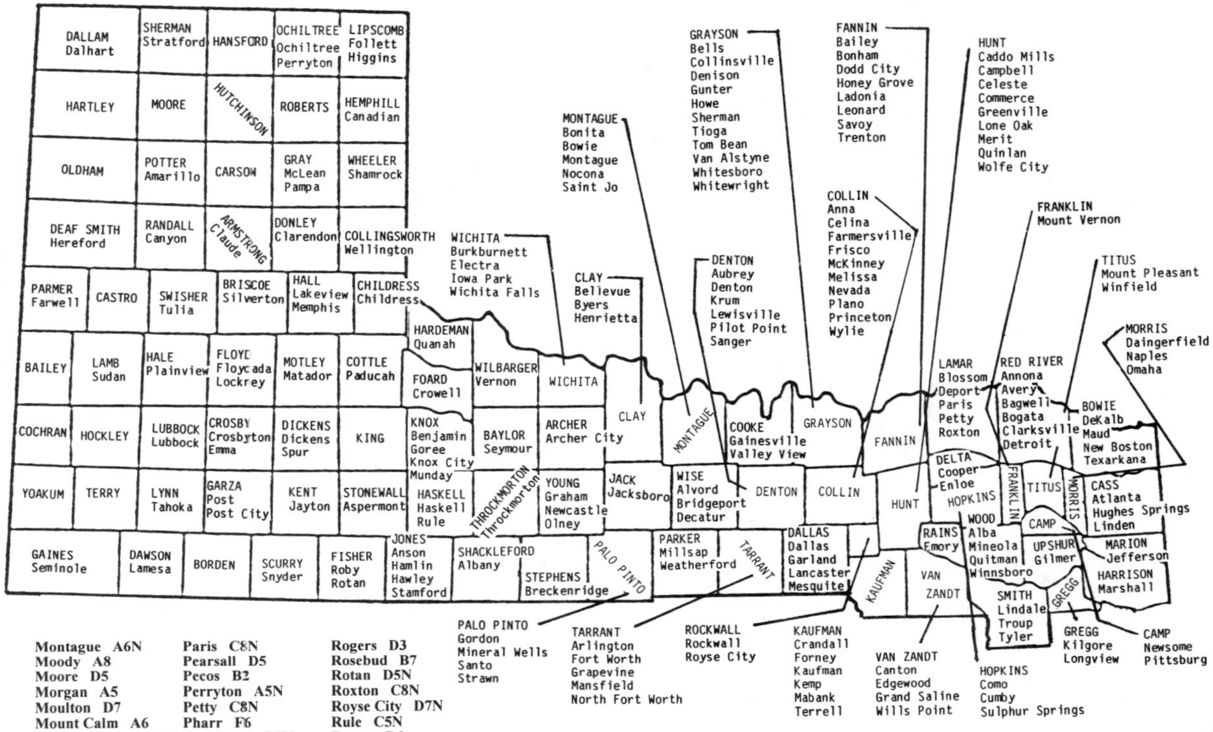

** Towns in the northern segment of the map are identified by a suffix letter 'N'.

Abilene B5
Alba C8N
Albany C6N
Alpine C3
Alvarado B6
Alvin D8
Alvord C7N
Amarillo A4N
Anderson C7
Angleton D8
Anna B8N
Annona C8N
Anson C5N
Aransas Pass E7
Archer City C6N
Arlington D6N
Aspermont C5N
Athens B7
Atlanta C9N
Aubrey B7N
Austin C6
Avery C8N
Bagwell C8N
Bailey A8N
Baird B5
Ballinger B5
Bardwell A7
Bartlett D3
Bastrop E4
Bay City D7
Beaumont C9
Beeville D6
Bellevue B6N
Bells A7N
Bellville C7
Belton D3
Benjamin C5N
Bertram C6
Big Spring B4
Blanco C6
Blooming Grove A8
Blossom C8N
Blum A6
Bogata C8N
Bonham A8N
Bonita A6N
Bowie A6N
Brady B5
Breckenridge D6N
Brenham C7
Bridgeport C7N
Bronte B4
Brownsville F6
Brownwood B5
Bryan C7
Buda C6
Burkburnett B6N
Burnet C6
Byers B6N
Bynum A6
Caddo Mills A8N
Caldwell C7
Calvert B7
Cameron C7
Campbell A8N
Canadian A5N
Canton D8N
Canyon B4N
Carthage B8
Celeste A8N
Celina B8N
Center B8
Center Point C5
Childress B5N
Cisco A5
Clarendon B5N
Clarksville C8N
Claude B4N
Cleburne B6
Cleveland C8
Clifton A5
Clyde B5
Coleman B5
Collinsville A7N
Colorado B4
Comanche B6
Commerce A8N
Como D8N
Conroe C8
Coolidge A9
Cooper C8N
Corpus Christi E6
Corsicana A8
Cotulla E5
Covington A6
Crandall D7N
Crawford A8
Cresson A6
Crockett B8
Crosbyton C4N
Cross Plains B5
Crowell C5N
Cuero D7
Cumby D8N
Daingerfield B9N
Dalhart A4N
Dallas C7N
Dawson A8
De Leon B6
Decatur C7N
DeKalb C9N
Del Rio C4
Denison A7N
Denton B7N
Deport C8N
Detroit C8N
Devine D5
Dickens C5N
Dickinson D9
Dodd City A8N
Dublin B6
Eagle Lake D7
Eagle Pass D5
Eastland A5
Edgewood D8N
Edinburg F6
Edna D7
El Campo D7
El Paso B1
Eldorado C4
Electra B6N
Elgin E4
Emma C4N
Emory C8N
Enloe C8N
Ennis A7
Fabens B1
Fairfield B7
Falfurrias F6
Falls City D6
Farmersville B8N
Farwell B4N
Fayetteville D8
Ferris A7
Flatonia D8
Floresville D6
Floydada B5N
Follett A5N
Forney D7N
Fort Stockton C3
Fort Worth D6N
Franklin B7
Frankston B7
Freeport D8
Frisco B8N
Frost A8
Gainesville C7N
Galveston D9
Ganado D7
Garland C7N
Gatesville B6
George West E6
Georgetown D4
Giddings C7
Gilmer C8N
Glen Rose A6
Goldthwaite B6
Goliad D7
Gonzales D6
Gordon D6N
Goree C5N
Gorman A5
Graham C6N
Granbury A6
Grand Saline D8N
Grandview B6
Granger D4
Grapevine D6N
Greenville A8N
Gregory E7
Groesbeck A9
Groveton B8
Gunter A7N
Hallettsville D7
Hamilton B6
Hamlin C5N
Haskell C5N
Hawley C5N
Hearne B7
Hebbronville F6
Hemphill B9
Hempstead C7
Henderson B8
Henrietta B6N
Hereford B4N
Hico B6
Higgins A5N
Hillsboro A6
Holland D3
Hondo D5
Honey Grove A8N
Houston C8
Howe A7N
Hubbard A6
Hughes Springs C9N
Huntsville C8
Hutto D4
Iowa Park B6N
Italy A7
Itasca A6
Jacksboro C6N
Jacksonville B8
Jasper B9
Jayton C5N
Jefferson C9N
Karnes City D6
Kaufman D7N
Kemp D7N
Kenedy D6
Kerens A8
Kilgore D9N
Killeen D3
Kingsbury D6
Kingsville E6
Knox City C5N
Kosse A9
Krum B7N
La Coste D5
La Feria F6
La Grange D8
Ladonia A8N
Lakeview B5N
Lamesa C4N
Lampasas B6
Lancaster C7N
Laredo E5
Leonard A8N
Lewisville B7N
Lindale D8N
Linden C9N
Lipan A6
Livingston C8
Llano C6
Lockhart C6
Lockney B5N
Lometa B6
Lone Oak A8N
Longview D9N
Lorena A8
Lott B7
Lovelady B8
Lubbock C4N
Lufkin B8
Luling C6
Mabank D7N
Madisonville B7
Malakoff B7
Manor C6
Mansfield D6N
Marble Falls C6
Marfa C2
Marlin B7
Marshall D9N
Mart A8
Mason C5
Matador B5N
Maud C9N
May B5
McGregor A8
McKinney B8N
McLean A5N
Melissa B8N
Memphis B5N
Menard C5
Mercedes F6
Meridian A5
Merit A8N
Merkel B5
Mertzon B4
Mesquite C7N
Mexia A9
Midland B3
Midlothian A7
Miles B5
Millsap C7N
Mineola C8N
Mineral Wells D6N
Mission F6
Montague A6N
Moody A8
Moore D5
Morgan A5
Moulton D7
Mount Calm A6
Mount Pleasant B9N
Mount Vernon B9N
Munday C5N
Nacogdoches B8
Naples B9N
Navasota C7
Nederland C9
Nevada B8N
New Boston C9N
New Braunfels C6
Newcastle C6N
Newsome D9N
Nixon D6
Nocona A6N
Normangee B7
North Fort Worth D6N
Oakville E6
Ochiltree A5N
Odessa B3
Olney C6N
Omaha B9N
Orange C9
Ozona C4
Paducah B5N
Paint Rock B5
Palestine B7
Pampa A5N
Paris C8N
Pearsall D5
Pecos B2
Perryton A5N
Petty C8N
Pharr F6
Pilot Point B7N
Pittsburg D9N
Plainview B4N
Plano B8N
Pleasanton D6
Port Arthur D9
Port Lavaca D7
Port Neches D9
Post C4N
Post City C4N
Poth D6
Princeton B8N
Purdon A8
Putnam B5
Quanah B5N
Quinlan A8N
Quitman C8N
Ranger A5
Raymondville F6
Refugio E7
Richmond D8
Rio Grande F6
Rising Star A5
Robert Lee B4
Roby D5N
Rockdale C7
Rockport E7
Rockwall D7N
Rogers D3
Rosebud B7
Rotan D5N
Roxton C8N
Royse City D7N
Rule C5N
Runge D6
Rusk B8
Sabinal D5
Saint Jo A6N
San Angelo B4
San Antonio D6
San Augustine B9
San Marcos C6
San Saba B6
Sanger B7N
Santa Anna B5
Santo D6N
Savoy A8N
Schulenburg D8
Schwertner D4
Sealy C7
Seguin D6
Seminole C4N
Seymour C6N
Shamrock A5N
Sherman A7N
Shiner D7
Silverton B5N
Smithville E4
Snyder D5N
Sonora C4
Sour Lake C8
Spur C5N
Stamford C5N
Stanton B3
Stephenville B6
Sterling City B4
Stratford A4N
Strawn D6N
Sudan B4N
Sulphur Springs D8N
Sweetwater B4
Taft E7
Tahoka C4N
Taylor D4
Teague B7
Temple D3
Terrell D7N
Texarkana C9N
Texas City D9
Thorndale C7
Thornton A9
Throckmorton C6N
Timpson B8
Tioga A7N
Tolar A6
Tom Bean A7N
Toyah B2
Trenton A8N
Trinity B8
Troupe D8N
Tulia B4N
Turnersville B6
Tyler D8N
Uvalde D5
Valley Mills A5
Valley View C7N
Van Alstyne A7N
Velasco D8
Venus B6
Vernon B6N
Victoria D7
Waco A8
Walnut Springs A5
Waxahachie A7
Weatherford C7N
Wellington B5N
Weslaco F6
West A8
Wharton D7
Whitesboro A7N
Whitewright A7N
Whitney A6
Wichita Falls B6N
Wills Point D8N
Winfield B9N
Winnsboro C8N
Wolfe City A8N
Wortham B7
Wylie B8N
Yoakum D7
Yorktown D7

1 2 3 4 5 6 7 8 9

A B C D E F

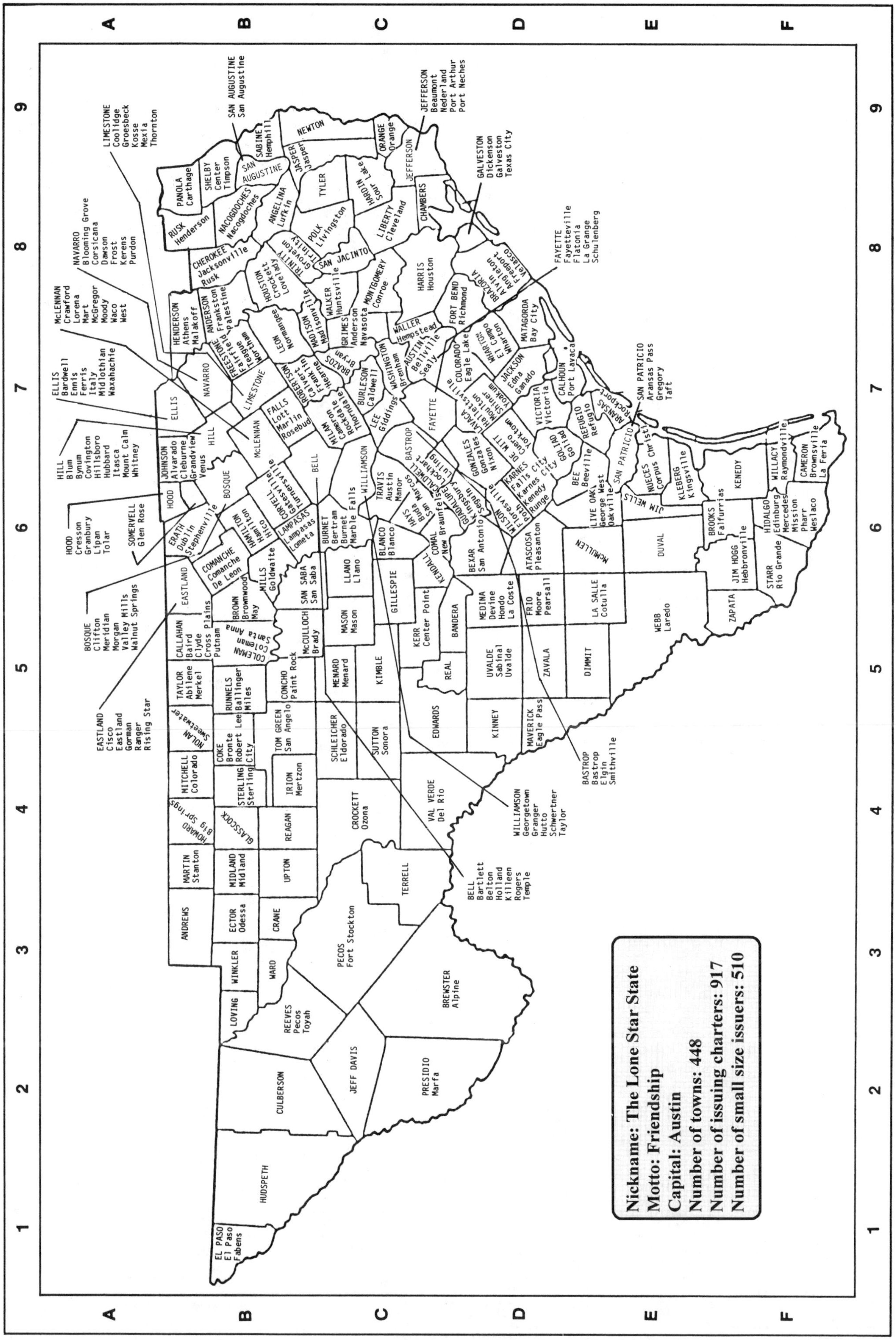

Nickname: The Lone Star State
Motto: Friendship
Capital: Austin
Number of towns: 448
Number of issuing charters: 917
Number of small size issuers: 510

3336 Taylor
ABILENE NB, ABILENE
{{ UNREPORTED }}
Chartered 4/21/85
Liquidated 5/3/98
Brown Back <$VALUE
3x10-20 1-1817 <$2500
Total Issue $90,850
Out in 1910 $740

7028 Taylor
AMERICAN NB OF ABILENE
{{ 1 L }}
Chartered 10/03
Receivership 1/18/05
1902 Red Seal <$VALUE
3x10-20 1-1744 <$2500
Total Issue $87,200
Out in 1916 $1,220

13727 Taylor
CITIZENS NB IN ABILENE
{{ 6 S }}
Chartered 7/33
1929 Small Size <$VALUE
5 Type 2 1-5686 <$300
10 Type 2 1-2290 <$300
20 Type 2 1-825 <$300
Total Issue $67,830
Out in 1935 $99,985
Large out 1935 $2,335
Outstanding includes Ch 6476

6476 Taylor
CITIZENS NB OF ABILENE
{{ 7 L 12 S }}
Chartered 10/30/02
Liquidated 8/19/33
1902 Red Seal <$VALUE
4x5 1-1172 <$1500
3x10-20 1-1820 <$1500
1902 Date Back
4x5 1-6050 <$400
3x10-20 1-3840 <$400
1902 Plain Back
4x5 6051-13729 <$400
3x10-20 3841-8979 <$400
1929 Small Size
5 Type 1 1-4812 <$150
10 Type 1 1-3186 <$150
20 Type 1 1-652 <$150
Total Issue $1,251,730
Out at close $182,665
Large out 1935 $2,335
Ch 13727 assumed circulation

7944 Taylor
COMMERCIAL NB OF ABILENE
{{ 2 L }}
Chartered 10/05
Liquidated 5/10/13
1902 Red Seal <$VALUE
3x10-20 1-2100 <$1500
1902 Date Back
3x10-20 1-3347 <$750
Total Issue $272,350
Out in 1913 $41,350

4166 Taylor
FARMERS & MERCHANTS NB OF ABILENE
{{ 9 L 16 S }}
Chartered 11/30/89
Brown Back <$VALUE
3x10-20 1-5150 <$750
1882 Date Back
3x10-20 1-1256 <$650
1902 Date Back
3x10-20 1-7200 <$250
1902 Plain Back
3x10-20 7201-23618 <$250
1929 Small Size
10 Type 1 1-3128 <$85
20 Type 1 1-794 <$100
5 Type 2 1-312 <$110
10 Type 2 1-3398 <$110
20 Type 2 1-844 <$125
Total Issue $1,836,580
Out in 1935 $84,550
Large out 1935 $5,195

3195 Taylor
FNB OF ABILENE
{{ UNREPORTED }}
Chartered 5/26/84
Liquidated 3/25/98
Brown Back <$VALUE
3x10-20 1-1856 <$2500
Total Issue $92,800
Out in 1910 $740

6896 Wood
ALBA NB, ALBA
{{ 3 L 1 S }}
Chartered 7/03
Liquidated 5/19/31
1902 Red Seal <$VALUE
3x10-20 1-1150 <$1500
1902 Date Back
3x10-20 1-2190 <$600
1902 Plain Back
3x10-20 2191-5259 <$600
1929 Small Size
10 Type 1 1-279 <$650
20 Type 1 1-52 <$650
Total Issue $343,430
Out at close $12,540
Large out at close $2,560

5680 Shackleford
ALBANY NB, ALBANY
{{ 2 L 2 S }}
Chartered 1/15/01
Closed 1/24/33
Brown Back <$VALUE
3x10-20 1-870 <$1250
1882 Date Back
3x10-20 1-1370* <$1250
1882 Value Back
3x10-20 1671-1844* <$1250
* 1371-1670 not marked
1902 Plain Back
3x10-20 1-1391 <$750
1929 Small Size
10 Type 1 1-347 <$500
20 Type 1 1-93 <$500
Total Issue $237,230
Out at close $12,495
Large out at close $1,065
Ch 3248 assumed circulation

3248 Shackleford
FNB OF ALBANY
{{ 6 L 14 S }}
Chartered 1884
Brown Back <$VALUE
4x5 1-5658 <$1000
3x10-20 1-891 <$1000
1902 Red Seal
4x5 1-962 <$1500
3x10-20 1-890 <$1500
1902 Date Back
4x5 1-5750* <$300
3x10-20 1-4480** <$300
1902 Plain Back
4x5 6101-11650* <$300
3x10-20 4761-17568** <$300
* 5751-6100 not marked
** 4481-4760 not marked
1929 Small Size
10 Type 1 1-2456 <$125
20 Type 1 1-726 <$150
5 Type 2 1-192 <$150
10 Type 2 1-5201 <$150
20 Type 2 1-1285 <$150
Total Issue $1,646,000
Out in 1935 $80,405
Large out 1935 $6,090
Outstanding includes Ch 5680

7214 Brewster
FNB OF ALPINE
{{ 7 L 12 S }}
Chartered 4/04
1902 Red Seal <$VALUE
3x10-20 1-500 <$1500
1902 Date Back
3x10-20 1-5600 <$350
1902 Plain Back
3x10-20 5601-18340 <$350
1929 Small Size
10 Type 1 1-2284 <$150
20 Type 1 1-612 <$150
10 Type 2 1-3495 <$150
20 Type 2 1-924 <$150
Total Issue $1,205,910
Out in 1935 $72,800
Large out 1935 $5,000

12289 Brewster
STATE NB OF ALPINE
{{ 3 L 10 S }}
Chartered 1/23
Liquidated 12/15/34
1902 Plain Back <$VALUE
3x10-20 1-2980 <$400
1929 Small Size
10 Type 1 1-1568 <$175
20 Type 1 1-454 <$200
10 Type 2 1-2140 <$200
20 Type 2 1-435 <$200
Total Issue $327,660
Out at close $40,450
Large out at close $1,080

3644 Johnson
FNB OF ALVARADO
{{ 2 L 1 S }}
Chartered 3/10/87
Liquidated 12/20/29
Brown Back <$VALUE
3x10-20 1-1816 <$1500
1902 Red Seal
3x10-20 1-375 <$2000
1902 Date Back
3x10-20 1-3600 <$750
1902 Plain Back
3x10-20 3601-5455 <$750
1929 Small Size
10 Type 1 1-128 <$650
20 Type 1 1-25 <$650
Total Issue $392,980
Out at close $18,750
Large out at close $8,070

7070 Brazoria
FNB OF ALVIN
{{ UNREPORTED }}
Chartered 12/21/03
Liquidated 1/31/06
1902 Red Seal <$VALUE
50-100 1-62 <$7500
Total Issue $9,300
Out in 1910 $550

6067 Wise
ALVORD NB, ALVORD
{{ UNREPORTED }}
Chartered 12/27/01
Liquidated 1/16/09
Brown Back <$VALUE
4x5 1-550 <$2500
3x10-20 1-444 <$2500
1882 Date Back
4x5 1-45 <$2500
Total Issue $34,100
Out in 1910 $3,600

8071 Wise
FARMERS & MERCHANTS NB OF ALVORD
{{ UNREPORTED }}
Chartered 1/06
Liquidated 1/29/12
1902 Red Seal <$VALUE
3x10-20 1-325 <$3000
1902 Date Back
3x10-20 1-233 <$2000
Total Issue $27,900
Out in 1912 $3,700

4710 Potter
AMARILLO NB, AMARILLO
{{ 6 L 11 S }}
Chartered 1892
Liquidated 4/3/35
Brown Back <$VALUE
4x5 1-3000 <$1000
3x10-20 1-3400 <$1000
1882 Date Back
4x5 1-2520 <$850
3x10-20 1-2007 <$850
50-100 1-503 <$3500/$4000
1902 Date Back
3x10-20 1-4300 <$300
3x50-100 1-200 <$500/$600
1902 Plain Back
3x10-20 4301-20569 <$300
1929 Small Size
10 Type 1 1-3066 <$150
20 Type 1 1-802 <$150
10 Type 2 1-2805 <$175
20 Type 2 1-496 <$175
Total Issue $1,852,820
Out at close $55,640
Large out at close $6,560

4214 Potter
FNB OF AMARILLO
{{ 11 L 16 S }}
Chartered 1890
Brown Back <$VALUE
3x10-20 1-10620 <$1000
1882 Date Back
3x10-20 1-1707 <$650
1902 Date Back
3x10-20 1-14900* <$200
1902 Plain Back
3x10-20 15901-66618* <$200
* 14901-15900 not marked
1929 Small Size
10 Type 1 1-10060 <$100
20 Type 1 1-2610 <$125
10 Type 2 1-6807 <$125
20 Type 2 1-1443 <$125
Total Issue $4,960,980
Out in 1935 $156,850
Large out 1935 $13,870

6865 Potter
NB OF COMMERCE, AMARILLO
{{ 5 L 5 S }}
Organized 6/26/03
Receivership 9/5/33
1902 Red Seal <$VALUE
4x5 1-1550 <$1250
3x10-20 1-1200 <$1250
1902 Date Back
4x5 1-5700 <$300
3x10-20 1-4400 <$300
1902 Plain Back
4x5 5701-20546 <$300
3x10-20 4401-13495 <$300
1929 Small Size
5 Type 1 1-1836 <$200
10 Type 1 1-864 <$200
20 Type 1 1-272 <$200
Total Issue $1,316,230
Out at close $17,895
Large out at close $5,235

7337 Grimes
FNB OF ANDERSON
{{ 4 L 6 S }}
Chartered 7/04
1902 Red Seal <$VALUE
3x10-20 1-300 <$1500
1902 Date Back
3x10-20 1-1960 <$500
1902 Plain Back
3x10-20 1961-5771 <$500
1929 Small Size
10 Type 1 1-722 <$250
20 Type 1 1-198 <$250
10 Type 2 1-1065 <$250
20 Type 2 1-252 <$250
Total Issue $386,320
Out in 1935 $29,650
Large out 1935 $1,740

14204 Brazoria
FNB OF ANGLETON
{{ 3 S }}
Chartered 6/34
1929 Small Size <$VALUE
5 Type 2 1-2080 <$450
10 Type 2 1-1092 <$450
20 Type 2 1-324 <$450
Total Issue $27,800
Out in 1935 $25,000

12867 Collin
FNB OF ANNA
{{ 1 L 5 S }}
Chartered 1/26
1902 Plain Back <$VALUE
3x10-20 1-750 <$2000
1929 Small Size
10 Type 1 1-310 <$300
20 Type 1 1-102 <$300
10 Type 2 1-3175 <$300
20 Type 2 1-877 <$300
Total Issue $117,630
Out in 1935 $35,000
Large out 1935 $330

7257 Red River
FNB OF ANNONA
{{ 1 L 2U + 2 S }}
Chartered 5/04
1902 Red Seal <$VALUE
3x10-20 1-400 <$2500
1902 Date Back
3x10-20 1-2580 <$1000
1902 Plain Back
3x10-20 2581-5220 <$1000
1929 Small Size
10 Type 1 1-128 <$400
20 Type 1 1-40 <$400
10 Type 2 1-707 <$400
20 Type 2 1-161 <$400
Total Issue $303,770
Out in 1935 $8,900
Large out 1935 $850

8897 Jones
FARMERS & MERCHANTS NB OF ANSON
{{ UNREPORTED }}
Chartered 9/07
Liquidated 12/23/10
1902 Red Seal <$VALUE
3x10-20 1-400 <$3000
1902 Date Back
3x10-20 1-188 <$2000
Total Issue $29,400
Out in 1911 $5,350

6091 Jones
FNB OF ANSON
{{ 2 L 4 S }}
Chartered 1/11/02
Brown Back <$VALUE
3x10-20 1-1720 <$1250
1882 Date Back
3x10-20 1-4200 <$850
1882 Value Back
3x10-20 4201-4914 <$850
1902 Plain Back
3x10-20 1-2320 <$750
1929 Small Size
10 Type 1 1-602 <$300
20 Type 1 1-168 <$300
10 Type 2 1-1119 <$300
20 Type 2 1-336 <$300
Total Issue $521,890
Out in 1935 $19,300
Large out 1935 $840

4438 San Particio
FNB OF ARANSAS PASS, ARANSAS PASS
Chartered 1890
2nd title:FNB of Rockport 2/25/03
FIRST TITLE {{ 1 L }}
Brown Back <$VALUE
3x10-20 1-1047 <$1500
SECOND TITLE {{ 3 L 4 S }}
Brown Back
3x10-20 1-670 <$1250
1882 Date Back
3x10-20 1-149 <$1250
1902 Date Back
4x10 1-1550 <$600
1902 Plain Back
4x10 1551-6840 <$600
1929 Small Size
10 Type 1 1-1346 <$350
10 Type 2 1-1915 <$350
Total Issue $466,810
Out in 1935 $24,250
Large out 1935 $1,580

10274 San Particio
FNB OF ARANSAS PASS
{{ 2 L U + 2 S }}
Organized 8/29/12
1902 Date Back <$VALUE
4x5 1-400 <$750
3x10-20 1-340 <$750
1902 Plain Back
4x5 401-1520 <$750
3x10-20 341-918 <$750
1929 Small Size
5 Type 1 1-308 <$500
10 Type 1 1-153 <$500
20 Type 1 1-39 <$500
Total Issue $99,400
Out in 1935 $2,950
Large out 1935 $380

5711 Archer
FNB OF ARCHER CITY
{{ UNREPORTED }}
Chartered 2/12/01
Liquidated 12/31/04
Brown Back <$VALUE
3x10-20 1-257 <$3000
Total Issue $12,850
Out in 1910 $600

7345 Tarrant
ARLINGTON NB, ARLINGTON
{{ 1 L }}
Chartered 7/04
Liquidated 7/31/19
1902 Red Seal <$VALUE
3x10-20 1-546 <$2500
1902 Date Back
3x10-20 1-4800 <$1500
1902 Plain Back
3x10-20 4801-6221 <$1500
Total Issue $338,350
Out at close $46,200

5806 Tarrant
CITIZENS NB OF ARLINGTON
{{ 2 L }}
Chartered 5/11/01
Receivership 11/6/15
Brown Back <$VALUE
3x10-20 1-1840 <$2000
1882 Date Back
3x10-20 1-2465 <$1500
Total Issue $215,250
Out in 1916 $16,640

5786 Stonewall
FNB OF ASPERMONT
{{ U + 0 L U + 2 S }}
Chartered 4/20/01
Brown Back <$VALUE
3x10-20 1-600 <$1500
1882 Date Back
3x10-20 1-1080 <$1500
1882 Value Back
3x10-20 1081-1139 <$1500
1902 Plain Back
3x10-20 1-806 <$1000
1929 Small Size
10 Type 1 1-289 <$500
20 Type 1 1-87 <$500
Total Issue $155,030
Out in 1935 $7,300
Large out 1935 $470

6400 Henderson
ATHENS NB, ATHENS
{{ 1 L 1 S }}
Chartered 8/26/02
Liquidated 4/8/31
1902 Red Seal <$VALUE
50-100 1-170 <$7500
1902 Date Back
50-100 1-120 <$2000
3x50-100 1-120 <$2000
1902 Plain Back
3x50-100 121-137 <$2000
1929 Small Size
50 Type 1 1-14 <$850
100 Type 1 1 <$1250
Total Issue $82,550
Out at close $5,950
Large out at close $2,650

4278 Henderson
FNB OF ATHENS
{{ 6 L 9 S }}
Chartered 1890
Brown Back <$VALUE
3x10-20 1-1560 <$1000
1882 Date Back
3x10-20 1-1199 <$750
1902 Date Back
3x10-20 1-5340 <$350
1902 Plain Back
3x10-20 5341-13975 <$350
1929 Small Size
10 Type 1 1-2129 <$200
20 Type 1 1-608 <$200
Total Issue $1,037,400
Out in 1935 $45,800
Large out 1935 $2,700

7694 Cass
ATLANTA NB, ATLANTA
{{ 4 L 8 S }}
Chartered 4/05
1902 Red Seal <$VALUE
3x10-20 1-1400 <$1500
1902 Date Back
3x10-20 1-2650* <$500
1902 Plain Back
3x10-20 3151-8407* <$500
* 2651-3150 not marked
1929 Small Size
10 Type 1 1-1702 <$225
20 Type 1 1-450 <$225
10 Type 2 1-2286 <$225
20 Type 2 1-595 <$225
Total Issue $681,230
Out in 1935 $49,000
Large out 1935 $1,590

4922 Cass
FNB OF ATLANTA
{{ 6 L 6 S }}
Chartered 1893
Brown Back <$VALUE
3x10-20 1-1770 <$1000
1882 Date Back
3x10-20 1-805 <$750
1902 Date Back
3x10-20 1-4000 <$400
1902 Plain Back
3x10-20 4001-14225 <$400
1929 Small Size
10 Type 1 1-1518 <$300
20 Type 1 1-412 <$300
10 Type 2 1-2449 <$325
20 Type 2 1-615 <$325
Total Issue $1,017,310
Out in 1935 $48,300
Large out 1935 $3,750

7495 Denton
FNB OF AUBREY
{{ UNREPORTED }}
Chartered 11/04
Liquidated 4/14/13
1902 Red Seal <$VALUE
4x5 1-1900 <$3000
3x10-20 1-1480 <$3000
1902 Date Back
4x5 1-680 <$2000
3x10-20 1-516 <$2000
Total Issue $151,400
Out in 1913 $17,800

4322 Travis
AMERICAN NB OF AUSTIN
{{ 27 L 38 S }}
Chartered 1890
Brown Back <$VALUE
3x10-20 1-12980 <$750
1882 Date Back
3x10-20 1-237 <$400
50-100 1-490 <$3500/$4000
1902 Date Back
4x5 1-7500* <$125
3x10-20 1-6000 <$125
3x50-100 1-1000 <$450/$500
1902 Plain Back
4x5 8501-131995* <$125
3x10-20 6001-8000 <$125
* 7501-8500 not marked
1929 Small Size
5 Type 1 1-40896 <$65
5 Type 2 1-84570 <$65
Total Issue $5,673,980
Out in 1935 $227,200
Large out 1935 $15,830

4308 Travis
AUSTIN NB, AUSTIN
{{ 31 L 44 S }}
Chartered 1890
Brown Back <$VALUE
3x10-20 1-15610 <$750
1882 Date Back
3x10-20 1-2839 <$400
1902 Date Back
3x10-20 1-31000 <$125
1902 Plain Back
3x10-20 31001-68952 <$125
1929 Small Size
10 Type 1 1-9022 <$50
20 Type 1 1-2372 <$60
5 Type 2 1-312 <$60
10 Type 2 1-13642 <$60
20 Type 2 1-3168 <$65
Total Issue $5,397,350
Out in 1935 $263,950
Large out 1935 $17,375

3289 Travis
CITY NB OF AUSTIN
{{ 2 L }}
Chartered 1/14/85
Liquidated 9/15/05
Brown Back <$VALUE
3x10-20 1-4629 <$1250
1902 Red Seal
3x10-20 1-311 <$1500
Total Issue $247,000
Out in 1910 $6,420

2118 Travis
FNB OF AUSTIN
{{ 1 L }}
Chartered 7/17/73
Liquidated 2/15/06
Original Series <$VALUE
4x5 1-1000 <$4000
3x10-20 1-500 <$5000/$6000
Series 1875
4x5 1-600 <$4000
3x10-20 1-2410<$5000/$6000
Brown Back
50-100 1-1671*<$4000/$4500
*1029-1120 not issued
Total Issue $414,350
Out in 1910 $21,265

2617 Travis
STATE NB OF AUSTIN
{{ 10 L }}
Organized 1/3/82
Receivership 11/20/26
Series 1875 <$VALUE
3x10-20 1-3489<$5000/$6000
Brown Back
50-100 1-733 <$4000/$4500
1882 Date Back
4x5 1-4250 <$450
4x10 1-4050 <$450
50-100 1-900 <$3500/$4000
1882 Value Back
4x5 4251-9255 <$500
4x10 4051-7445 <$500
1902 Plain Back
3x10-20 1-5790 <$250
Total Issue $1,191,800
Out at close $98,600

10638 Red River
FNB OF AVERY
{{ 2 L 2 S }}
Chartered 10/14
Liquidated 1/12/32
1902 Date Back <$VALUE
3x10-20 1-500 <$750
1902 Plain Back
3x10-20 501-3880 <$750
1929 Small Size
10 Type 1 1-403 <$450
20 Type 1 1-101 <$450
Total Issue $230,300
Out at close $19,160
Large out at close $2,330
Ch 13428 assumed circulation

10657 Red River
FNB OF BAGWELL
{{ 1 L 0 S }}
Chartered 11/14
Liquidated 1/20/30
1902 Date Back <$VALUE
3x10-20 1-500 <$1500
1902 Plain Back
3x10-20 501-1974 <$1500
1929 Small Size
10 Type 1 1-62 <$750
20 Type 1 1-2 <$750
Total Issue $102,660
Out at close $7,230
Large out at close $3,290

12741 Fannin
FNB OF BAILEY
{{ 1 S }}
Chartered 5/25
1929 Small Size <$VALUE
5 Type 1 1-168 <$500
10 Type 1 1-106 <$500
20 Type 1 1-32 <$500
5 Type 2 1-2554 <$500
10 Type 2 1-1515 <$500
20 Type 2 1-310 <$500
Total Issue $49,360
Out in 1935 $19,200

3286 Callahan
FNB OF BAIRD
{{ 4 L 6 S }}
Chartered 1885
Brown Back <$VALUE
3x10-20 1-3739 <$1000
1902 Red Seal
3x10-20 1-950 <$1500
1902 Date Back
3x10-20 1-2000 <$500
1902 Plain Back
3x10-20 2001-6035 <$500
1929 Small Size
10 Type 1 1-818 <$250
20 Type 1 1-214 <$250
10 Type 2 1-1089 <$250
20 Type 2 1-264 <$250
Total Issue $627,130
Out in 1935 $24,250
Large out 1935 $1,490

5493 Callahan
HOME NB OF BAIRD
{{ 3 L }}
Chartered 7/10/00
Liquidated 6/8/22
Brown Back <$VALUE
50-100 1-230 <$4000/$4500
1882 Date Back
3x10-20 1-4000 <$750
50-100 1-240 <$3500/$4000
3x50-100 1-60 <$3500/$4000
1882 Value Back
3x10-20 4001-5137 <$750
1902 Plain Back
3x10-20 1-1090 <$500
3x50-100 1-86 <$1250/$1500
Total Issue $418,350
Out at close $50,000

4193 Runnels
BALLINGER NB, BALLINGER
{{ UNREPORTED }}
Chartered 1/4/90
Liquidated 3/14/96
Brown Back <$VALUE
50-100 1-342 <$5000
Total Issue $51,300
Out in 1910 $700

6757 Runnels
CITIZENS NB OF BALLINGER
{{ 1 L }}
Chartered 4/03
Liquidated 11/1/09
1902 Red Seal <$VALUE
4x5 1-4300 <$2000
3x10-20 1-3200 <$2000
1902 Date Back
4x5 1-1160 <$1250
3x10-20 1-466 <$1250
Total Issue $292,500
Out in 1910 $53,045

3533 Runnels
FNB OF BALLINGER
{{ 6 L 10 S }}
Chartered 7/15/86
Brown Back <$VALUE
3x10-20 1-1493 <$1000
1902 Red Seal
3x10-20 1-275 <$1500
1902 Date Back
4x5 1-8600 <$350
3x10-20 1-7160 <$350
1902 Plain Back
4x5 8601-11125 <$350
3x10-20 7161-8757 <$350
1929 Small Size
5 Type 1 1-2170 <$150
10 Type 1 1-1304 <$150
20 Type 1 1-382 <$150
5 Type 2 1-8292 <$150
10 Type 2 1-3996 <$150
20 Type 2 1-912 <$150
Total Issue $1,037,590
Out in 1935 $95,600
Large out 1935 $2,480

10678 Ellis
FNB OF BARDWELL
{{ 1 L 1 S }}
Chartered 1/15
Liquidated 4/24/33
1902 Date Back <$VALUE
3x50-100 1-410 <$1500
1902 Plain Back
3x50-100 411-512 <$1500
1929 Small Size
50 Type 1 1-80 <$650
100 Type 1 1-7 <$750
Total Issue $156,200
Out at close $19,400
Large out at close $2,250
Ch 13667 assumed circulation

7317 Bell
BARTLETT NB OF BARTLETT
{{ 7 L 12 S }}
Chartered 6/04
Liquidated 12/27/34
1902 Red Seal <$VALUE
3x10-20 1-460 <$1500
1902 Date Back
3x10-20 1-5100 <$300
1902 Plain Back
3x10-20 5101-16680 <$300
1929 Small Size
10 Type 1 1-2060 <$150
20 Type 1 1-620 <$150
10 Type 2 1-2862 <$150
20 Type 2 1-721 <$150
Total Issue $1,098,040
Out at close $70,000
Large out at close $3,390

5422 Bell
FNB OF BARTLETT
{{ 6 L 10 S }}
Chartered 6/13/00
Brown Back <$VALUE
50-100 1-240 <$4000/$4500
1882 Date Back
50-100 1-260 <$3500/$4000
3x50-100 1-846<$3500/$4000
1902 Plain Back
3x10-20 1-8359 <$375
1929 Small Size
10 Type 1 1-2740* <$175
20 Type 1 1-1034** <$175
10 Type 2 1-2942 <$200
20 Type 2 1-958 <$200
* 460-1234 not issued
** 116-422 not issued
Total Issue $958,170
Out in 1935 $72,950
Large out 1935 $2,980

4093 Bastrop
FNB OF BASTROP
{{ 2 L 2 S }}
Chartered 8/15/89
Brown Back <$VALUE
3x10-20 1-1480 <$1500
1882 Date Back
3x10-20 1 <$1500
1902 Date Back
3x10-20 1-1250 <$750
1902 Plain Back
3x10-20 1251-2743 <$750
1929 Small Size
10 Type 1 1-486* <$400
20 Type 1 1-150** <$400
10 Type 2 1-414 <$400
20 Type 2 1-164 <$400
* 207-304 not issued
** 37-104 not issued
Total Issue $251,740
Out in 1935 $10,800
Large out 1935 $810

7753 Matagorda
BAY CITY NB, BAY CITY
{{ 2 L }}
Chartered 5/20/05
Liquidated 10/1/07
1902 Red Seal <$VALUE
3x10-20 1-380 <$2500
Total Issue $19,000
Out in 1910 $2,420

6062 Matagorda
FNB OF BAY CITY
{{ 5 L 15 S }}
Chartered 12/26/01
Brown Back <$VALUE
3x10-20 1-1100 <$1000
1882 Date Back
3x10-20 1-2090* <$750
1882 Value Back
3x10-20 2391-3633* <$800
* 2091-2390 not marked
1902 Plain Back
3x10-20 1-2620 <$400
1929 Small Size
10 Type 1 1-2272 <$100
20 Type 1 1-538 <$110
10 Type 2 1-5696 <$125
20 Type 2 1-1753 <$125
Total Issue $660,550
Out in 1935 $96,200
Large out 1935 $1,820

5825 Jefferson
AMERICAN NB OF BEAUMONT
{{ 10 L }}
Chartered 5/21/01
Brown Back <$VALUE
3x10-20 1-7300 <$1000
1882 Date Back
3x10-20 1-7000 <$500
1882 Value Back
3x10-20 7001-12100 <$500
1902 Plain Back
3x10-20 1-6161 <$275
Total Issue $1,278,050
Out in 1935 $3,930

5201 Jefferson
BEAUMONT NB, BEAUMONT
{{ U + 1 L }}
Chartered 6/29/99
Liquidated 11/2/05
Brown Back <$VALUE
3x10-20 1-1375 <$1500
Total Issue $68,750
Out in 1910 $3,050

5841 Jefferson
CITIZENS NB OF BEAUMONT
{{ UNREPORTED }}
Chartered 5/31/01
Receivership 8/20/03
Brown Back <$VALUE
3x10-20 1-796 <$2000
Total Issue $39,800
Out in 1916 $310

9357 Jefferson
COMMERCIAL NB OF BEAUMONT
{{ 1 L }}
Chartered 3/09
Liquidated 9/19/10
1902 Date Back <$VALUE
3x10-20 1-5587 <$1000
Total Issue $279,350
Out at close $200,000

4017 Jefferson
FNB OF BEAUMONT
{{ 16 L 15 S }}
Chartered 4/23/89
Brown Back <$VALUE
3x10-20 1-13250 <$850
1902 Date Back
3x10-20 1-14300 <$150
1902 Plain Back
3x10-20 14301-54802 <$150
1929 Small Size
10 Type 1 1-2810 <$85
20 Type 1 1-706 <$100
10 Type 2 1-2914 <$100
20 Type 2 1-835 <$100
Total Issue $3,701,760
Out in 1935 $88,800
Large out 1935 $15,190
Outstanding includes Ch 6338

6338 Jefferson
GULF NB OF BEAUMONT
{{ 4 L }}
Chartered 7/14/02
Closed 7/16/19
1902 Red Seal <$VALUE
3x10-20 1-6540 <$1500
1902 Date Back
4x5 1-11000 <$500
3x10-20 1-7500 <$500
1902 Plain Back
4x5 11001-16455 <$500
3x10-20 7501-10302 <$500
Total Issue $1,171,200
Out at close $150,000
Ch 4017 assumed circulation

4866 Bee
COMMERCIAL NB OF BEEVILLE
{{ 5 L 10 S }}
Chartered 1893
Brown Back <$VALUE
3x10-20 1-1290 <$1000
1882 Date Back
3x10-20 1-2723 <$750
1902 Date Back
3x10-20 1-2400 <$400
1902 Plain Back
3x10-20 2401-9611 <$400
1929 Small Size
10 Type 1 1-1420 <$175
20 Type 1 1-372 <$175
10 Type 2 1-1985 <$175
20 Type 2 1-585 <$175
Total Issue $842,590
Out in 1935 $48,100
Large out 1935 $2,990

4238 Bee
FNB OF BEEVILLE
{{ 4 L 11 S }}
Chartered 1890
Brown Back <$VALUE
3x10-20 1-1480 <$1000
1882 Date Back
3x10-20 1-821 <$750
1902 Date Back
3x10-20 1-4540 <$400
1902 Plain Back
3x10-20 4541-10154 <$400
1929 Small Size
10 Type 1 1-1480 <$175
20 Type 1 1-410 <$175
10 Type 2 1-2016 <$175
20 Type 2 1-468 <$175
Total Issue $790,270
Out in 1935 $49,400
Large out 1935 $2,540

8672 Clay
FNB OF BELLEVUE
{{ 4 L U + 6 S }}
Chartered 5/07
Liquidated 6/30/34
1902 Red Seal <$VALUE
4x5 1-750 <$1500
3x10-20 1-600 <$1500
1902 Date Back
4x5 1-2675 <$500
3x10-20 1-2040 <$500
1902 Plain Back
4x5 2676-8438 <$500
3x10-20 2041-5394 <$500
1929 Small Size
5 Type 1 1-1330 <$250
10 Type 1 1-710 <$250
20 Type 1 1-198 <$250
5 Type 2 1-206 <$250
10 Type 2 1-287 <$250
20 Type 2 1-60 <$250
Total Issue $594,820
Out at close $27,400
Large out at close $1,570

7524 Grayson
FNB OF BELLS
{{ 3 L 4 S }}
Chartered 12/04
1902 Red Seal <$VALUE
3x10-20 1-1000 <$1500
1902 Date Back
3x10-20 1-1720 <$500
1902 Plain Back
3x10-20 1721-5288 <$500
1929 Small Size
10 Type 1 1-630 <$350
20 Type 1 1-170 <$350
10 Type 2 1-1230 <$350
20 Type 2 1-366 <$350
Total Issue $392,220
Out in 1935 $20,000
Large out 1935 $1,020

4241 Austin
FNB OF BELLVILLE
{{ 5 L 12 S }}
Chartered 1890
Brown Back <$VALUE
3x10-20 1-1390 <$1000
1882 Date Back
3x10-20 1-24 <$750
1902 Date Back
3x10-20 1-1800 <$400
1902 Plain Back
3x10-20 1801-8466 <$400
1929 Small Size
10 Type 1 1-1340 <$175
20 Type 1 1-390 <$175
10 Type 2 1-2332 <$175
20 Type 2 1-514 <$175
Total Issue $654,800
Out in 1935 $49,200
Large out 1935 $2,330

3295 Bell
BELTON NB, BELTON
{{ 1 L }}
Chartered 1/27/85
Liquidated 12/10/04
Brown Back <$VALUE
4x5 1-8158 <$1250
3x10-20 1-560 <$1250
Total Issue $191,160
Out in 1910 $2,610

7509 Bell
BELTON NB, BELTON
{{ 2 L 4 S }}
Organized 11/12/04
Receivership 11/13/33
1902 Red Seal <$VALUE
3x10-20 1-1175 <$2000
1902 Date Back
3x10-20 1-2550* <$500
1902 Plain Back
3x10-20 2651-6766* <$500
* 2551-2650 not marked
1929 Small Size
10 Type 1 1-717 <$300
20 Type 1 1-197 <$300
Total Issue $463,710
Out at close $24,640
Large out at close $1,750

4167 Bell
CITIZENS NB OF BELTON
{{ UNREPORTED }}
Chartered 11/30/89
Liquidated 7/1/91
Brown Back <$VALUE
3x10-20 1-245 <$3000
Total Issue $12,250
Out in 1910 $10

13810 Bell
FARMERS NB OF BELTON
{{ 2 S }}
Chartered 10/33
1929 Small Size <$VALUE
5 Type 2 1-7880 <$400
Total Issue $39,400
Out in 1935 $18,000

2735 Bell
FNB OF BELTON
{{ UNREPORTED }}
Chartered 6/7/82
Liquidated 1/6/86
Series 1875 <$VALUE
3x10-20 1-674 <$6000/$6500
Total Issue $33,700
Out in 1910 $170

8518 Bell
PEOPLES NB OF BELTON
{{5 L 2U + 6 S}}
Chartered 1/07
1902 Red Seal <$VALUE
3x10-20 1-550 <$1500
1902 Date Back
3x10-20 1-4900 <$375
1902 Plain Back
3x10-20 4901-13230 <$375
1929 Small Size
10 Type 1 1-1530 <$175
20 Type 1 1-412 <$200
5 Type 2 1-1776 <$200
10 Type 2 1-1072 <$200
20 Type 2 1-380 <$200
Total Issue $857,390
Out in 1935 $41,750
Large out 1935 $3,120

7669 Knox
FNB OF BENJAMIN
{{2 L}}
Chartered 3/05
Liquidated 4/25/29
1902 Red Seal <$VALUE
3x10-20 1-460 <$2000
1902 Date Back
3x10-20 1-2760 <$750
1902 Plain Back
3x10-20 2761-6052 <$750
Total Issue $325,600
Out at close $18,750

11519 Burnet
FNB OF BERTRAM
{{2 L}}
Chartered 11/19
Liquidated 2/15/28
1902 Plain Back <$VALUE
4x5 1-3570 <$1250
3x10-20 1-2157 <$1250
Total Issue $179,250
Out at close $24,150

13984 Howard
FNB IN BIG SPRING
{{3 S}}
Chartered 2/34
1929 Small Size <$VALUE
5 Type 2 1-6170 <$350
10 Type 2 1-4449 <$350
Total Issue $75,340
Out in 1935 $98,550
Large out 1935 $4,540
Outstanding includes Ch 4306
and Ch 6668

4306 Howard
FNB OF BIG SPRING
{{6 L 8 S}}
Chartered 1890
Liquidated 3/19/34
Brown Back <$VALUE
3x10-20 1-3420 <$1250
1882 Date Back
3x10-20 1-702 <$1250
1902 Date Back
3x10-20 1-3800 <$500
1902 Plain Back
3x10-20 3801-12286 <$500
1929 Small Size
10 Type 1 1-1688 <$275
20 Type 1 1-476 <$275
10 Type 2 1-187 <$300
20 Type 2 1-30 <$300
Total Issue $981,270
Out at close $46,710
Large out at close $3,000
Ch 13984 assumed circulation

12543 Howard
STATE NB OF BIG SPRING
{{2 L 6 S}}
Chartered 5/24
1902 Plain Back <$VALUE
3x10-20 1-4338 <$850
1929 Small Size
10 Type 1 1-1742 <$300
20 Type 1 1-508 <$300
10 Type 2 1-2823 <$300
20 Type 2 1-682 <$300
Total Issue $424,250
Out in 1935 $41,550
Large out 1935 $1,380

6668 Howard
WEST TEXAS NB OF
BIG SPRING
{{5 L 10 S}}
Chartered 3/03
Liquidated 3/19/34
1902 Red Seal <$VALUE
3x10-20 1-2700 <$2000
1902 Date Back
3x10-20 1-4580 <$600
1902 Plain Back
3x10-20 4581-13656 <$600
1929 Small Size
10 Type 1 1-1878 <$225
20 Type 1 1-456 <$225
10 Type 2 1-467 <$225
20 Type 2 1-40 <$225
Total Issue $990,670
Out at close $46,850
Large out at close $2,240
Ch 13984 assumed circulation

8134 Blanco
BLANCO NB, BLANCO
{{2 L 2U + 10 S}}
Chartered 3/06
1902 Red Seal <$VALUE
3x10-20 1-700 <$2000
1902 Date Back
3x10-20 1-1590 <$750
1902 Plain Back
3x10-20 1591-4753 <$750
1929 Small Size
10 Type 1 1-698 <$175
20 Type 1 1-200 <$175
5 Type 2 1-324 <$175
10 Type 2 1-720 <$175
20 Type 2 1-236 <$175
Total Issue $352,070
Out in 1935 $25,000
Large out 1935 $1,435

7055 Navarro
CITIZENS NB OF
BLOOMING GROVE
{{0 L 1 S}}
Chartered 12/03
Liquidated 8/10/31
1902 Red Seal <$VALUE
50-100 1-140 <$7500
1902 Date Back
50-100 1-120 <$1500
3x50-100 1-570 <$1500
1902 Plain Back
3x50-100 571-709 <$1500
1929 Small Size
50 Type 1 1-63 <$750
100 Type 1 1-8 <$850
Total Issue $239,950
Out at close $24,700
Large out 1935 $3,200
Ch 13555 assumed circulation

13555 Navarro
FNB IN BLOOMING GROVE
{{ UNREPORTED }}
Organized 6/4/31
Receivership 11/10/33
1929 Small Size <$VALUE
50 Type 1 1-25 <$850
100 Type 1 1-6 <$1000
Total Issue $11,100
Out at close $21,800
Outstanding includes Ch 7055

4768 Navarro
FNB OF BLOOMING GROVE
{{ UNREPORTED }}
Chartered 6/29/92
Liquidated 6/30/00
Brown Back <$VALUE
3x10-20 1-668 <$3000
Total Issue $33,400
Out in 1910 $570

5733 Lamar
FNB OF BLOSSOM
{{2 L}}
Chartered 3/5/01
Liquidated 4/20/27
Brown Back <$VALUE
3x10-20 1-800 <$2000
1882 Date Back
3x10-20 1-1763 <$2000
1902 Plain Back
3x10-20 1-1208 <$1500
Total Issue $188,550
Out at close $10,900

6069 Hill
FNB OF BLUM
{{1 L}}
Chartered 12/28/01
Liquidated 5/11/12
Brown Back <$VALUE
3x10-20 1-1640 <$1500
1882 Date Back
3x10-20 1-839 <$1500
Total Issue $123,950
Out in 1912 $14,730

10639 Red River
BOGATA NB, BOGATA
{{2 L}}
Chartered 10/14
Liquidated 3/28/25
1902 Date Back <$VALUE
4x10 1-1250 <$850
1902 Plain Back
4x10 1251-4411 <$850
Total Issue $176,440
Out at close $21,400
Ch 10483 assumed circulation

10483 Red River
FNB OF BOGATA
{{2 L 4 S}}
Chartered 2/14
1902 Plain Back <$VALUE
4x5 1-5827 <$850
1929 Small Size
5 Type 1 1-3122 <$350
5 Type 2 1-9216 <$350
Total Issue $256,280
Out in 1935 $23,370
Large out 1935 $820
Outstanding includes Ch 10639

4540 Fannin
BONHAM NB, BONHAM
{{ UNREPORTED }}
Chartered 3/27/91
Liquidated 11/20/95
Brown Back <$VALUE
50-100 1-150 <$5000
Total Issue $22,500
Out in 1910 $600

5146 Fannin
FANNAN COUNTY NB OF
BONHAM
{{3 L}}
Chartered 1898
Liquidated 10/2/18
Brown Back <$VALUE
3x10-20 1-1300 <$1000
50-100 1-280 <$4000/$4500
1882 Date Back
3x10-20 1-3948 <$650
50-100 1-200 <$3500/$4000
3x50-100 1-316<$3500/$4000
Total Issue $413,400
Out at close $49,395

3094 Fannin
FNB OF BONHAM
{{7 L}}
Chartered 1883
Brown Back <$VALUE
3x10-20 1-4404 <$1000
1902 Red Seal
50-100 1-727 <$7500
1902 Date Back
3x10-20 1-4000 <$250
50-100 1-1000 <$500/$600
3x50-100 1-800 <$500/$600
1902 Plain Back
3x10-20 4001-18072 <$250
Total Issue $1,582,850
Out in 1935 $6,960

10163 Montague
FNB OF BONITA
{{1 L}}
Chartered 3/12
Liquidated 2/28/30
1902 Date Back <$VALUE
3x10-20 1-1620 <$1000
1902 Plain Back
3x10-20 1621-4259 <$1000
Total Issue $212,950
Out at close $1,980

4785 Montague
CITY NB OF BOWIE
{{8 L 2 S}}
Chartered 1892
Liquidated 11/12/30
Brown Back <$VALUE
4x5 1-3050 <$1000
3x10-20 1-1350 <$1000
1882 Date Back
4x5 1-862 <$650
3x10-20 1-703 <$650
1902 Date Back
4x5 1-2100 <$350
3x10-20 1-1820 <$350
1902 Plain Back
4x5 2101-5465 <$350
3x10-20 1821-3843 <$350
1929 Small Size
5 Type 1 1-399 <$500
10 Type 1 1-169 <$500
20 Type 1 1-46 <$500
Total Issue $509,970
Out at close $18,280
Large out at close $4,200

4265 Montague
FNB OF BOWIE
{{5 L 8 S}}
Chartered 1890
Brown Back <$VALUE
3x10-20 1-2170 <$1000
1882 Date Back
3x10-20 1-115 <$850
1902 Date Back
3x10-20 1-2270 <$350
1902 Plain Back
3x10-20 2271-10461 <$350
1929 Small Size
10 Type 1 1-1542 <$250
20 Type 1 1-450 <$250
10 Type 2 1-1383 <$250
20 Type 2 1-646 <$250
Total Issue $810,570
Out in 1935 $41,150
Large out 1935 $2,440

8330 Montague
NB OF BOWIE
{{3 L}}
Chartered 8/06
Liquidated 4/15/20
1902 Red Seal <$VALUE
4x10 1-1700 <$1500
1902 Date Back
4x10 1-6325 <$600
1902 Plain Back
4x10 6326-8896 <$600
Total Issue $423,840
Out at close $22,500

7827 McCulloch
BRADY NB, BRADY
{{6 L 10 S}}
Chartered 7/05
1902 Red Seal <$VALUE
3x10-20 1-2150 <$1500
1902 Date Back
3x10-20 1-4500 <$400
1902 Plain Back
3x10-20 4501-12912 <$400
1929 Small Size
10 Type 1 1-1474 <$175
20 Type 1 1-388 <$175
10 Type 2 1-2996 <$175
20 Type 2 1-782 <$175
Total Issue $933,700
Out in 1935 $50,000
Large out 1935 $2,770

8573 McCulloch
COMMERCIAL NB OF BRADY
{{3 L 2U + 12 S}}
Chartered 3/07
1902 Red Seal <$VALUE
4x5 1-750 <$1500
3x10-20 1-630 <$1500
1902 Date Back
4x5 1-3930 <$500
3x10-20 1-3035 <$500
1929 Small Size
5 Type 1 1-832 <$150
10 Type 1 1-832 <$150
20 Type 1 1-418 <$150
5 Type 2 1-8326 <$150
10 Type 2 1-3810 <$150
20 Type 2 1-810 <$150
Total Issue $497,820
Out in 1935 $76,270
Large out 1935 $1,370

4198 McCulloch
FNB OF BRADY
{{ UNREPORTED }}
Organized 1/7/90
Receivership 6/13/93
Brown Back <$VALUE
50-100 1-126 <$5000
Total Issue $18,900
Out at close $10,800
All notes reportedly redeemed

14027 Stephens
FNB IN BRECKENRIDGE
{{1 S}}
Chartered 2/34
1929 Small Size <$VALUE
10 Type 2 1-296 <$750
20 Type 2 1-117 <$750
Total Issue $5,300
Out in 1935 $10,000
Large out 1935 $1,160
Outstanding includes Ch 7422

7422 Stephens
FNB OF BRECKENRIDGE
{{1 L 2 S}}
Chartered 10/04
Liquidated 3/29/34
1902 Red Seal <$VALUE
3x10-20 1-1400 <$2000
1902 Date Back
3x10-20 1-1260 <$1250
1902 Plain Back
3x10-20 1261-2827 <$1250
1929 Small Size
10 Type 1 1-309 <$500
20 Type 1 1-96 <$500
Total Issue $241,410
Out at close $9,760
Large out 1935 $1,160
Ch 14027 assumed circulation

13678 Washington
FARMERS NB IN BRENHAM
{{2 S}}
Chartered 4/33
1929 Small Size <$VALUE
5 Type 2 1-5360 <$400
Total Issue $26,800
Out in 1935 $50,000
Large out 1935 $3,480
Outstanding includes Ch 10860

10860 Washington
FARMERS NB OF BRENHAM
{{6 L 30 S}}
Chartered 6/16
Liquidated 5/29/33
1902 Plain Back <$VALUE
4x10 1-18393 <$350
1929 Small Size
10 Type 1 1-4604 <$75
Total Issue $1,011,960
Out at close $50,000
Large out 1935 $3,480
Ch 13676 assumed circulation

3015 Washington
FNB OF BRENHAM
{{12 L 21 S}}
Chartered 1883
Brown Back <$VALUE
3x10-20 1-3902 <$1000
1902 Red Seal
3x10-20 1-1690 <$1250
1902 Date Back
3x10-20 1-10300 <$200
1902 Plain Back
3x10-20 10301-32421 <$200
1929 Small Size
10 Type 1 1-4030 <$60
20 Type 1 1-1160 <$75
10 Type 2 1-4256 <$75
20 Type 2 1-1171 <$75
Total Issue $2,347,630
Out in 1935 $98,920
Large out 1935 $7,770

8731 Wise
FNB OF BRIDGEPORT
{{3 L 6 S}}
Chartered 6/07
1902 Red Seal <$VALUE
3x10-20 1-400 <$1500
1902 Date Back
3x10-20 1-1240* <$600
1902 Plain Back
3x10-20 1341-5640* <$600
* 1241-1340 not marked
1929 Small Size
10 Type 1 1-1120 <$275
20 Type 1 1-316 <$275
10 Type 2 1-1703 <$275
20 Type 2 1-510 <$275
Total Issue $434,350
Out in 1935 $28,600
Large out 1935 $1,630

8641 Coke
FNB OF BRONTE
{{ UNREPORTED }}
Chartered 4/13/07
Liquidated 9/28/09
1902 Red Seal <$VALUE
3x10-20 1-189 <$3000
1902 Date Back
3x10-20 1-50 <$2000
Total Issue $11,950
Out in 1910 $3,170

12792 Cameron
FNB IN BROWNSVILLE
{{5 L 11 S}}
Chartered 7/25
Liquidated 1/12/32
1902 Plain Back <$VALUE
3x10-20 1-9853 <$400
1929 Small Size
10 Type 1 1-3774 <$135
20 Type 1 1-1108 <$135
Total Issue $852,050
Out at close $129,430
Large out at close $19,545
Outstanding includes Ch 4577
Ch 7002 assumed circulation

4577 Cameron
FNB OF BROWNSVILLE
{{7 L}}
Chartered 1891
Liquidated 10/20/25
Brown Back <$VALUE
4x5 1-4275 <$1000
3x10-20 1-3300 <$1000
1882 Date Back
4x5 1-2111 <$450
3x10-20 1-1729 <$450
1902 Date Back
3x10-20 1-6300 <$300
1902 Plain Back
3x10-20 6301-15395 <$300
Total Issue $1,148,920
Out at close $69,645
Ch 12792 assumed circulation

7002 Cameron
MERCHANTS NB OF
BROWNSVILLE
{{10 L 14 S}}
Organized 10/1/03
Receivership 3/28/32
1902 Red Seal <$VALUE
3x10-20 1-4875 <$1250
1902 Date Back
3x10-20 1-10500 <$200
1902 Plain Back
3x10-20 10501-41906 <$200
1929 Small Size
10 Type 1 1-4129 <$100
20 Type 1 1-1146 <$100
Total Issue $2,724,310
Out at close $249,995
Large out at close $22,620
Outstanding includes Ch 12792

12236 Cameron
STATE NB OF BROWNSVILLE
{{5 L 31 S}}
Chartered 7/22
1902 Plain Back <$VALUE
3x10-20 1-13686 <$400
1929 Small Size
10 Type 1 1-6680 <$75
20 Type 1 1-1852 <$85
10 Type 2 1-11849 <$85
20 Type 2 1-3373 <$85
Total Issue $1,493,290
Out in 1935 $250,000
Large out 1935 $5,230

CONDITION affects Value. The Values shown are for notes in FINE condition.

****
4695 Brown
BROWNWOOD NB, BROWNWOOD
Chartered 1892
2nd title: FNB in Brownwood 8/30/19
FIRST TITLE {{ 6 L }}
Brown Back <$VALUE
3x10-20 1-7930 <$1000
1882 Date Back
3x10-20 1-2121 <$500
1902 Date Back
3x10-20 1-6400 <$300
1902 Plain Back
3x10-20 6401-9600 <$300
SECOND TITLE {{ 3 L 4 S }}
1902 Plain Back
3x50-100 1-1656 <$650/$750
1929 Small Size
50 Type 1 1-314 <$250
100 Type 1 1-106 <$300
50 Type 2 1-186 <$400
100 Type 2 1-67 <$500
Total Issue $1,570,350
Out in 1935 $99,400
Large out 1935 $9,550
****
14273 Brown
CITIZENS NB AT BROWNWOOD
{{ 3 S }}
Chartered 9/34
1929 Small Size <$VALUE
10 Type 2 1-1424 <$400
20 Type 2 1-465 <$400
50 Type 2 1-183 <$500
Total Issue $32,690
Out in 1935 $99,995
Large out 1935 $4,805
Outstanding includes Ch 13588
****
13588 Brown
CITIZENS NB IN BROWNWOOD
{{ 2U + 10 S }}
Organized 12/5/31
Liquidated 3/4/35
1929 Small Size <$VALUE
10 Type 1 1-918 <$150
20 Type 1 1-234 <$150
10 Type 2 1-3992 <$150
20 Type 2 1-1536 <$150
Total Issue $153,800
Out at close $78,205
Outstanding includes Ch 8312
Ch 14273 assumed circulation
****
8312 Brown
CITIZENS NB OF BROWNWOOD
{{ 8 L 10 S }}
Chartered 7/06
Liquidated 3/15/32
1902 Red Seal <$VALUE
3x10-20 1-3500 <$1250
1902 Date Back
3x10-20 1-8300 <$275
1902 Plain Back
3x10-20 8301-25801 <$275
1929 Small Size
10 Type 1 1-1836 <$150
20 Type 1 1-572 <$150
Total Issue $1,643,850
Out at close $71,015
Large out 1935 $4,805
Ch 13588 assumed circulation
****
4344 Brown
CITY NB OF BROWNWOOD
{{ UNREPORTED }}
Organized 6/17/90
Liquidated 3/16/97
2nd title:Merchants NB of Brownwood 12/19/94
FIRST TITLE
Brown Back <$VALUE
4x5 1-732 <$2500
3x10-20 1-645 <$2500
SECOND TITLE
Brown Back
3x10-20 1-89 <$2500
Total Issue $51,340
Out in 1910 $400
****
9812 Brown
COGGIN NB OF BROWNWOOD
{{ 2 L 2 S }}
Chartered 7/10
Receivership 4/27/32
1902 Date Back <$VALUE
3x10-20 1-3660 <$850
1902 Plain Back
3x10-20 3661-7273 <$850
1929 Small Size
10 Type 1 1-357 <$400
20 Type 1 1-91 <$400
Total Issue $395,990
Out at close $20,190
Large out at close $3,290
****
FNB in Brownwood
SEE Ch 4695
Brownwood NB, Brownwood
****
2937 Brown
FNB OF BROWNWOOD
{{ UNREPORTED }}
Chartered 4/28/83
Liquidated 7/1/98
Brown Back <$VALUE
3x10-20 1-1955 <$2000
Total Issue $97,750
Out in 1910 $900
****
Merchants NB of Brownwood
SEE Ch 4344
City NB of Brownwood
****
City NB of Bryan
SEE Ch 4070
Merchants & Planters NB of Bryan
****
3446 Brazos
FNB OF BRYAN
{{ 10 L 9 S }}
Chartered 1886
Brown Back <$VALUE
3x10-20 1-3666 <$1000
1902 Red Seal
4x5 1-3500 <$1250
3x10-20 1-1300 <$1250
1902 Date Back
4x5 1-8250 <$225
3x10-20 1-6200 <$225
1902 Plain Back
4x5 8251-23904 <$225
3x10-20 6201-17020 <$225
1929 Small Size
5 Type 1 1-4212 <$150
10 Type 1 1-2402 <$150
20 Type 1 1-552 <$150
5 Type 2 1-8692 <$150
10 Type 2 1-4389 <$150
20 Type 2 1-1140 <$150
Total Issue $2,094,250
Out in 1935 $98,050
Large out 1935 $5,450
****
4070 Brazos
MERCHANTS & PLANTERS NB OF BRYAN
Chartered 7/6/89
2nd title:City NB of Bryan 4/25/02
FIRST TITLE {{ 0 L }}
Brown Back <$VALUE
3x10-20 1-2466 <$1250
SECOND TITLE {{ 6 L 7 S }}
Brown Back
3x10-20 1-2100 <$1000
1882 Date Back
3x10-20 1-455 <$700
1902 Date Back
3x10-20 1-4500 <$300
1902 Plain Back
3x10-20 4501-14174 <$300
1929 Small Size
50 Type 2 1-1942 <$300
100 Type 2 1-889 <$400
Total Issue $1,145,750
Out in 1935 $150,790
Large out 1935 $3,940
****
12241 Hays
FARMERS NB OF BUDA
{{ 1 L }}
Chartered 7/22
Liquidated 11/15/27
1902 Plain Back <$VALUE
3x10-20 1-2588 <$2000
Total Issue $129,400
Out at close $26,400
****
13668 Wichita
FNB IN BURKBURNETT
{{ 2U + 1 S }}
Chartered 3/33
1929 Small Size <$VALUE
5 Type 2 1-932 <$500
10 Type 2 1-539 <$500
Total Issue $10,050
Out in 1935 $39,500
Large out 1935 $4,070
Outstanding includes Ch 8706
****
8706 Wichita
FNB OF BURKBURNETT
{{ 9 L 13 S }}
Organized 5/15/07
Liquidated 4/25/33
1902 Red Seal <$VALUE
3x10-20 1-300 <$1250
1902 Date Back
3x10-20 1-2840 <$300
1902 Plain Back
3x10-20 2841-23367 <$300
1929 Small Size
10 Type 1 1-3045 <$150
20 Type 1 1-892 <$150
Total Issue $1,473,090
Out at close $93,580
Large out 1935 $4,070
Ch 13668 assumed circulation
****
6966 Burnet
BURNET NB, BURNET
{{ 3 L 4 S }}
Organized 9/15/03
Receivership 2/18/32
1902 Red Seal <$VALUE
4x5 1-1100 <$1500
3x10-20 1-826 <$1500
1902 Date Back
4x5 1-1875 <$600
3x10-20 1-1560 <$600
1902 Plain Back
4x5 1876-6531 <$600
3x10-20 1561-4606 <$600
1929 Small Size
5 Type 1 1-803 <$300
10 Type 1 1-383 <$300
20 Type 1 1-129 <$300
Total Issue $486,770
Out at close $29,035
Large out at close $2,255
****
3007 Burnet
FNB OF BURNET
{{ UNREPORTED }}
Chartered 7/18/83
Liquidated 5/22/93
Brown Back <$VALUE
50-100 1-268 <$4000
Total Issue $40,200
Out in 1910 $350
****
8787 Clay
FNB OF BYERS
{{ 3 L 5 S }}
Chartered 7/07
1902 Red Seal <$VALUE
3x10-20 1-190 <$1500
1902 Date Back
3x10-20 1-1480 <$600
1902 Plain Back
3x10-20 1481-6296 <$600
1929 Small Size
10 Type 1 1-908 <$300
20 Type 1 1-220 <$300
10 Type 2 1-1086 <$300
20 Type 2 1-240 <$300
Total Issue $420,840
Out in 1935 $24,200
Large out 1935 $930
****
10549 Hill
FNB OF BYNUM
{{ UNREPORTED }}
Chartered 5/14
1902 Date Back <$VALUE
4x5 1-150 <$2500
3x10-20 1-135 <$2500
Total Issue $9,750
Out at close $15
****
9637 Hunt
FNB OF CADDO MILLS
{{ UNREPORTED }}
Chartered 1/10
Liquidated 12/31/10
1902 Date Back <$VALUE
3x10-20 1-161 <$2500
Total Issue $8,050
Out in 1911 $2,350
****
6607 Burleson
CALDWELL NB, CALDWELL
{{ 7 L 10 S }}
Chartered 2/03
1902 Red Seal <$VALUE
4x5 1-850 <$1500
3x10-20 1-700 <$1500
1902 Date Back
4x5 1-3600 <$350
3x10-20 1-2790 <$350
1902 Plain Back
4x5 3601-18445 <$350
3x10-20 2791-13231 <$350
1929 Small Size
10 Type 1 1-2778 <$150
20 Type 1 1-804 <$175
10 Type 2 1-3410 <$175
20 Type 2 1-1061 <$175
Total Issue $1,400,930
Out in 1935 $97,745
Large out 1935 $5,800
****
6614 Burleson
FNB OF CALDWELL
{{ UNREPORTED }}
Chartered 2/6/03
Liquidated 7/6/06
1902 Red Seal <$VALUE
3x10-20 1-1057 <$2500
Total Issue $52,850
Out in 1910 $4,760
****
3742 Robertson
FNB OF CALVERT
{{ 1 L }}
Chartered 7/1/87
Liquidated 1/12/11
Brown Back <$VALUE
3x10-20 1-2778 <$2000
1902 Red Seal
3x10-20 1-250 <$2500
1902 Date Back
3x10-20 1-638 <$1000
Total Issue $183,300
Out in 1911 $13,120
****
5484 Milam
CITIZENS NB OF CAMERON
{{ 10 L 18 S }}
Chartered 7/6/00
Brown Back <$VALUE
3x10-20 1-1500 <$1000
1882 Date Back
3x10-20 1-7040 <$500
1882 Value Back
3x10-20 7041-10240 <$500
1902 Plain Back
3x10-20 1-13213 <$250
1929 Small Size
10 Type 1 1-3068 <$85
20 Type 1 1-834 <$100
10 Type 2 1-3890* <$100
20 Type 2 1-966 <$100
* 2461-2466 not issued
Total Issue $1,589,970
Out in 1935 $97,550
Large out 1935 $6,240
****
13731 Milam
FNB IN CAMERON
{{ UNREPORTED }}
Chartered 7/33
1929 Small Size <$VALUE
10 Type 2 1-1779 <$500
20 Type 2 1-540 <$500
Total Issue $28,590
Out in 1935 $53,150
Large out 1935 $4,800
Outstanding includes Ch 4086
****
4086 Milam
FNB OF CAMERON
{{ 6 L 10 S }}
Chartered 8/2/89
Liquidated 8/29/33
Brown Back <$VALUE
50-100 1-714 <$3500/$4000
1882 Date Back
50-100 1-24 <$3500/$4000
1902 Date Back
3x10-20 1-6500 <$300
1902 Plain Back
3x10-20 6501-18423 <$300
1929 Small Size
10 Type 1 1-2044 <$165
20 Type 1 1-575 <$165
Total Issue $1,223,490
Out at close $69,560
Large out 1935 $4,800
Ch 13731 assumed circulation
****
7348 Hunt
CAMPBELL NB, CAMPBELL
{{ 1 L }}
Chartered 8/04
Liquidated 12/31/13
1902 Red Seal <$VALUE
3x10-20 1-1230 <$2500
1902 Date Back
3x10-20 1-1605 <$1250
Total Issue $141,750
Out in 1914 $4,540
****
10473 Hunt
CAMPBELL N EXCHANGE B, CAMPBELL
{{ 2 L }}
Chartered 1/14
Liquidated 7/9/20
1902 Date Back <$VALUE
3x10-20 1-600 <$1250
1902 Plain Back
3x10-20 601-1629 <$1250
Total Issue $81,450
Out at close $29,000
****
6826 Hemphill
FNB OF CANADIAN
{{ 2 L }}
Chartered 6/03
1902 Red Seal <$VALUE
3x10-20 1-1528 <$2000
1902 Date Back
3x10-20 1-3190 <$850
1902 Plain Back
3x10-20 3191-4922 <$850
Total Issue $322,350
Out in 1935 $1,310
****
8891 Van Zandt
FNB OF CANTON
{{ 0 L 2 S }}
Chartered 9/07
1902 Red Seal <$VALUE
3x10-20 1-200 <$3000
1902 Date Back
3x10-20 1-1580 <$1500
1902 Plain Back
3x10-20 1581-3021 <$1500
1929 Small Size
10 Type 1 1-312 <$450
20 Type 1 1-104 <$450
10 Type 2 1-396 <$500
20 Type 2 1-150 <$500
Total Issue $199,210
Out in 1935 $9,450
Large out 1935 $520
****
7961 Randall
CANYON NB, CANYON
{{ 1 L }}
Chartered 10/05
Liquidated 4/12/12
1902 Red Seal <$VALUE
4x10 1-1630 <$2000
50-100 1-142 <$7500
1902 Date Back
4x10 1-1166 <$1250
50-100 1-99 <$1750/$2000
Total Issue $147,990
Out in 1912 $32,900
****
14090 Randall
FNB IN CANYON
{{ U + 6 S }}
Chartered 4/34
1929 Small Size <$VALUE
5 Type 2 1-80 <$400
10 Type 2 1-180 <$400
Total Issue $2,200
Out in 1935 $28,425
Large out 1935 $3,425
Outstanding includes Ch 5238
****
FNB of Canyon
SEE Ch 5238
Stockmen's NB of Canyon
****
5238 Randall
STOCKMEN'S NB OF CANYON
Chartered 12/26/99
Liquidated 5/31/34
2nd title: FNB of Canyon 7/10/03
FIRST TITLE {{ 1 L }}
Brown Back <$VALUE
4x5 1-1357 <$1250
3x10-20 1-1030 <$1250
SECOND TITLE {{ 6 L 6 S }}
Brown Back
3x10-20 1-1000 <$1000
50-100 1-1018 <$3500/$4000
1882 Date Back
3x10-20 1-5400 <$600
1882 Value Back
3x10-20 5401-6256 <$600
1902 Plain Back
3x10-20 1-6697 <$400
1929 Small Size
10 Type 1 1-1520 <$250
20 Type 1 1-414 <$250
10 Type 2 1-811 <$250
20 Type 2 1-214 <$250
Total Issue $1,082,260
Out at close $45,110
Large out at close $3,890
Ch 14090 assumed circulation
****
6197 Panola
FNB OF CARTHAGE
{{ 2 L 2 S }}
Chartered 4/8/02
1902 Red Seal <$VALUE
4x5 1-300 <$2000
3x10-20 1-400 <$2000
1902 Date Back
4x5 1-1050 <$750
3x10-20 1-840 <$750
1902 Plain Back (dated 1902)
4x5 1051-1560 <$750
3x10-20 841-1139 <$750
1902 Plain Back (dated 1922)
3x10-20 1-1011 <$750
1929 Small Size
10 Type 1 1-394 <$450
20 Type 1 1-114 <$450
10 Type 2 1-299 <$500
20 Type 2 1-100 <$500
Total Issue $207,010
Out in 1935 $12,200
Large out 1935 $680
****
6152 Panola
MERCHANTS & FARMERS NB OF CARTHAGE
{{ UNREPORTED }}
Chartered 3/10/02
Liquidated 4/11/10
1902 Red Seal <$VALUE
3x10-20 1-479 <$3000
Total Issue $23,950
Out in 1910 $3,750
****
5324 Hunt
FNB OF CELESTE
{{ 4 L 5 S }}
Chartered 5/3/00
Brown Back <$VALUE
3x10-20 1-2200 <$1250
1882 Date Back
3x10-20 1-3760 <$1250
1882 Value Back
3x10-20 3761-3969 <$1250
1902 Plain Back
3x10-20 1-4197 <$750
1929 Small Size
10 Type 1 1-940 <$450
20 Type 1 1-260 <$450
10 Type 2 1-1578 <$500
20 Type 2 1-429 <$500
Total Issue $630,260
Out in 1935 $30,000
Large out 1935 $2,080
****
6046 Collin
FNB OF CELINA
{{ UNREPORTED }}
Chartered 12/13/01
Liquidated 11/6/09
Brown Back <$VALUE
3x10-20 1-1540 <$2500
1882 Date Back
3x10-20 1-185 <$2500
Total Issue $86,250
Out in 1910 $14,770
****
7249 Shelby
FARMERS NB OF CENTER
{{ 2 L }}
Chartered 5/04
Liquidated 12/21/15
1902 Red Seal <$VALUE
3x10-20 1-1200 <$2000
1902 Date Back
3x10-20 1-1810 <$1250
1902 Plain Back
3x10-20 1811-1817 <$1250
Total Issue $150,850
Out in 1916 $15,370
****
5971 Shelby
FNB OF CENTER
{{ 3 L }}
Chartered 9/20/01
Receivership 12/3/24
Brown Back <$VALUE
3x10-20 1-3160 <$1000
1882 Date Back
3x10-20 1-3900 <$1000
1882 Value Back
3x10-20 3901-6666 <$1000
1902 Plain Back
3x10-20 1-2248 <$650
Total Issue $603,700
Out at close $48,900
****

****
6040 Kerr
FNB OF CENTER POINT
{{ UNREPORTED }}
Chartered 12/3/01
Liquidated 10/13/08
Brown Back <$VALUE
3x10-20 1-1819 <$3500
Total Issue $90,950
Out in 1910 $8,180
****
6024 Childress
CHILDRESS NB, CHILDRESS
{{ UNREPORTED }}
Chartered 11/18/01
Liquidated 5/8/09
Brown Back <$VALUE
3x10-20 1-688 <$2500
Total Issue $34,400
Out in 1910 $4,800
****
5992 Childress
CITY NB OF CHILDRESS
{{ 3 L }}
Chartered 10/4/01
Liquidated 12/31/20
Brown Back <$VALUE
3x10-20 1-1520 <$1000
1882 Date Back
3x10-20 1-7600 <$700
1882 Value Back
3x10-20 7601-12758 <$700
Total Issue $713,900
Out at close $90,250
****
12666 Childress
FNB IN CHILDRESS
{{ 9 S }}
Chartered 3/25
1929 Small Size <$VALUE
5 Type 1 1-712 <$200
10 Type 1 1-550 <$200
20 Type 1 1-170 <$200
5 Type 2 1-4440 <$200
10 Type 2 1-2565 <$200
20 Type 2 1-530 <$200
Total Issue $133,210
Out in 1935 $41,100
****
4571 Childress
FNB OF CHILDRESS
{{ UNREPORTED }}
Chartered 1891
Liquidated 12/19/10
2nd title:Quanah NB, Quanah 12/14/97
FIRST TITLE
Brown Back <$VALUE
50-100 1-194 <$5000
SECOND TITLE
Brown Back
50-100 1-280 <$5000
1882 Date Back
50-100 1-3 <$5000
Total Issue $71,550
Out in 1911 $4,800
****
11357 Eastland
AMERICAN NB OF CISCO
{{ 2 L }}
Chartered 5/19
Liquidated 8/15/21
1902 Plain Back <$VALUE
4x5 1-3370 <$850
3x10-20 1-3172 <$850
3x50-100 1-140<$1000/$1250
Total Issue $261,000
Out at close $86,800
****
6115 Eastland
CITIZENS NB OF CISCO
{{ 1 L }}
Chartered 1/3/02
Liquidated 1/1/18
1902 Red Seal <$VALUE
3x10-20 1-1400 <$2000
1902 Date Back
3x10-20 1-2090 <$1000
1902 Plain Back
3x10-20 2091-2472 <$1000
Total Issue $193,600
Out at close $23,600
****
4134 Eastland
FNB OF CISCO
{{ UNREPORTED }}
Chartered 10/3/89
Liquidated 1/29/97
Brown Back <$VALUE
3x10-20 1-582 <$2500
Total Issue $29,100
Out in 1910 $360
****

****
7360 Eastland
MERCHANTS & FARMERS NB, CISCO
{{ 1 L }}
Chartered 8/04
Liquidated 11/12/15
1902 Red Seal <$VALUE
3x10-20 1-2400 <$2000
1902 Date Back
3x10-20 1-3835 <$1000
Total Issue $311,750
Out in 1916 $28,850
****
5463 Donley
FNB OF CLARENDON
{{ 3 L 9 S }}
Chartered 6/27/00
Brown Back <$VALUE
3x10-20 1-1950 <$1000
1882 Date Back
3x10-20 1-4140 <$750
1882 Value Back
3x10-20 4141-5797 <$750
1902 Plain Back
3x10-20 1-6911 <$600
1929 Small Size
10 Type 1 1-1580 <$150
20 Type 1 1-412 <$175
10 Type 2 1-2461 <$175
20 Type 2 1-636 <$175
Total Issue $914,470
Out in 1935 $48,650
Large out 1935 $2,610
****
10643 Red River
CITY NB OF CLARKSVILLE
{{ 1 L }}
Organized 10/8/14
Receivership 3/9/25
1902 Date Back <$VALUE
4x10 1-828 <$1500
Total Issue $33,120
Out at close $90
****
13974 Red River
FNB IN CLARKSVILLE
{{ U + 3 S }}
Chartered 1/34
1929 Small Size <$VALUE
5 Type 2 1-2996 <$350
10 Type 2 1-1032 <$350
Total Issue $25,300
Out in 1935 $24,800
****
3973 Red River
FNB OF CLARKSVILLE
{{ 2 L 1 S }}
Chartered 2/1/89
Receivership 3/1/34
Brown Back <$VALUE
3x10-20 1-1525 <$1750
1902 Date Back
3x10-20 1-2340* <$1000
* 2275,2276,2309,2311 not issued
1902 Plain Back
3x10-20 2341-2965 <$1000
1929 Small Size
10 Type 1 1-123 <$750
20 Type 1 1-14 <$750
Total Issue $233,310
Out at close $1,540
Large out at close $1,040
****
13428 Red River
RED RIVER NB IN CLARKSVILLE
{{ 3U + 1 S }}
Chartered 2/30
1929 Small Size <$VALUE
5 Type 1 1-250 <$400
10 Type 1 1-25 <$400
20 Type 1 1-30 <$400
Total Issue $12,600
Out in 1935 $10,095
Large out 1935 $4,655
Outstanding includes Ch 10638 and Ch 4982
****
4982 Red River
RED RIVER NB OF CLARKSVILLE
{{ 6 L 2 S }}
Chartered 1894
Liquidated 4/8/30
Brown Back <$VALUE
3x10-20 1-3500 <$1500
50-100 1-213 <$3500/$4000
1882 Date Back
3x10-20 1-3900 <$1250
50-100 1-160 <$3500/$4000
3x50-100 1-209<$3500/$4000
1902 Date Back
4x5 1-4000 <$450
3x10-20 1-3000 <$450
1902 Plain Back
4x5 4001-10376 <$450
3x10-20 3001-6941 <$450
1929 Small Size
5 Type 1 1-696 <$450
10 Type 1 1-295 <$450
20 Type 1 1-27 <$450
Total Issue $1,074,590
Out at close $53,400
Large out at close $15,130
Ch 13428 assumed circulation
****
7123 Armstrong
FNB OF CLAUDE
{{ 3 L U + 5 S }}
Chartered 2/04
1902 Red Seal <$VALUE
3x10-20 1-1156 <$1500
1902 Date Back
3x10-20 1-2230 <$600
1902 Plain Back
3x10-20 2231-6005 <$600
1929 Small Size
10 Type 1 1-796 <$300
20 Type 1 1-190 <$300
10 Type 2 1-1512 <$300
20 Type 2 1-324 <$300
Total Issue $450,210
Out in 1935 $22,830
Large out 1935 $1,030
****
6791 Johnson
CITIZENS NB OF CLEBURNE
{{ UNREPORTED }}
Chartered 5/19/03
Liquidated 10/10/05
1902 Red Seal <$VALUE
3x10-20 1-861 <$2500
Total Issue $43,050
Out in 1910 $1,870
****
13107 Johnson
CITY NB OF CLEBURNE
{{ 3 L U + 14 S }}
Chartered 7/27
1902 Plain Back <$VALUE
3x10-20 1-4120 <$500
1929 Small Size
10 Type 1 1-3416 <$85
20 Type 1 1-924 <$100
10 Type 2 1-5068 <$100
20 Type 2 1-1509 <$100
Total Issue $602,700
Out in 1935 $97,550
Large out 1935 $1,210
****
4386 Johnson
FARMERS & MERCHANTS NB OF CLEBURNE
{{ 9 L }}
Organized 5/26/90
Receivership 5/11/27
Brown Back <$VALUE
50-100 1-2520 <$3500/$4000
1882 Date Back
4x5 1-1215 <$600
1902 Date Back
4x5 1-5500 <$250
50-100 1-667 <$500/$600
3x50-100 1-880 <$500/$600
1902 Plain Back
4x5 5501-27751 <$250
3x50-100 881-965<$500/$600
Total Issue $1,298,620
Out at close $98,250
****
2982 Johnson
FNB OF CLEBURNE
{{ UNREPORTED }}
Chartered 6/20/83
Liquidated 1/5/99
Brown Back <$VALUE
4x5 1-5093 <$1500
Total Issue $101,860
Out in 1910 $855
****
10411 Johnson
HOME NB OF CLEBURNE
{{ 6 L }}
Organized 6/7/13
Receivership 12/28/25
1902 Date Back <$VALUE
4x5 1-4325 <$300
3x10-20 1-3500 <$300
1902 Plain Back
4x5 4326-17065 <$300
3x10-20 3501-12430 <$300
Total Issue $962,800
Out at close $46,750
****

****
4035 Johnson
NB OF CLEBURNE
{{ 5 L }}
Chartered 5/16/89
Receivership 10/27/21
Brown Back <$VALUE
4x5 1-3750 <$1000
50-100 1-1583 <$3500/$4000
1902 Date Back
4x5 1-7900 <$350
3x10-20 1-6200 <$350
1902 Plain Back
4x5 7901-10904 <$350
3x10-20 6201-8276 <$350
Total Issue $944,330
Out at close $74,995
****
10276 Liberty
FNB OF CLEVELAND
{{ 1 L 3 S }}
Chartered 10/12
1902 Date Back <$VALUE
3x10-20 1-500 <$1250
1902 Plain Back
3x10-20 501-1390 <$1250
1929 Small Size
10 Type 1 1-314 <$400
20 Type 1 1-106 <$400
10 Type 2 1-1357 <$400
20 Type 2 1-253 <$400
Total Issue $119,690
Out in 1935 $19,350
Large out 1935 $500
****
7245 Bosque
FNB OF CLIFTON
{{ 4 L }}
Chartered 5/04
Liquidated 12/30/10
1902 Red Seal <$VALUE
4x5 1-1250 <$2000
3x10-20 1-2700 <$2000
1902 Date Back
4x5 1-1080 <$600
3x10-20 1-568 <$600
Total Issue $210,000
Out in 1911 $32,995
****
8780 Callahan
CLYDE NB, CLYDE
{{ 1 L 19 S }}
Organized 6/5/07
Receivership 11/14/33
1902 Red Seal <$VALUE
3x10-20 1-190 <$2500
1902 Date Back
3x10-20 1-1080 <$1250
1902 Plain Back
3x10-20 1081-1624 <$1250
1929 Small Size
10 Type 1 1-164 <$150
20 Type 1 1-35 <$150
Total Issue $104,740
Out at close $6,300
Large out at close $720
****
8106 Callahan
FNB OF CLYDE
{{ UNREPORTED }}
Chartered 2/06
Liquidated 2/29/16
1902 Red Seal <$VALUE
3x10-20 1-300 <$2500
1902 Date Back
3x10-20 1-504 <$1500
Total Issue $40,200
Out in 1916 $4,310
****
4683 Coleman
COLEMAN NB, COLEMAN
{{ 8 L }}
Chartered 1892
Liquidated 3/15/32
Brown Back <$VALUE
3x10-20 1-1620 <$1000
1882 Date Back
3x10-20 1-450 <$700
1902 Date Back
3x10-20 1-4900 <$300
1902 Pla150in Back
3x10-20 4901-27857 <$300
Total Issue $1,496,350
Out at close $7,300
****
13595 Coleman
FIRST COLEMAN NB OF COLEMAN
{{ 6U + 10 S }}
Chartered 2/32
1929 Small Size <$VALUE
5 Type 1 1-1638 <$125
10 Type 1 1-830 <$125
20 Type 1 1-212 <$125
5 Type 2 1-10380 <$125
10 Type 2 1-5331 <$125
20 Type 2 1-1492 <$125
Total Issue $259,430
Out in 1935 $78,850
****
3433 Coleman
FNB OF COLEMAN
{{ 5 L }}
Chartered 1886
Liquidated 3/15/32
Brown Back <$VALUE
3x10-20 1-2122 <$1000
1902 Red Seal
3x10-20 1-350 <$1500
1902 Date Back
3x10-20 1-7600 <$350
1902 Plain Back
3x10-20 7601-18129 <$350
Total Issue $1,030,050
Out at close $5,065
****
6300 Grayson
FNB OF COLLINSVILLE
{{ 1 L }}
Chartered 6/12/02
Liquidated 3/21/11
1902 Red Seal <$VALUE
3x10-20 1-2240 <$2500
1902 Date Back
3x10-20 1-912 <$1250
Total Issue $157,600
Out in 1911 $26,900
****
4395 Mitchell
CITIZENS NB OF COLORADO
{{ UNREPORTED }}
Chartered 8/14/90
Liquidated 11/3/91
Brown Back <$VALUE
3x10-20 1-300 <$2500
Total Issue $15,000
Out in 1910 $110
****
5276 Mitchell
CITY NB OF COLORADO
{{ 2 L 4 S }}
Chartered 4/4/00
Brown Back <$VALUE
3x10-20 1-1200 <$1250
1882 Date Back
3x10-20 1-1660 <$1000
1882 Value Back
3x10-20 1661-1836 <$1000
1902 Plain Back
3x10-20 1-2249 <$750
1929 Small Size 450
10 Type 1 1-674 <$450
20 Type 1 1-200 <$450
5 Type 2 1-324 <$450
10 Type 2 1-2023 <$450
20 Type 2 1-504 <$450
Total Issue $360,620
Out in 1935 $39,250
Large out 1935 $2,425
Outstanding includes Ch 13562
****
13562 Mitchell
COLORADO NB IN COLORADO
{{ UNREPORTED }}
Chartered 7/31
Closed 2/27/32
1929 Small Size <$VALUE
10 Type 1 1-71 <$750
20 Type 1 1-17 <$750
Total Issue $6,300
Out at close $22,120
Outstanding includes Ch 2801
Ch 5276 assumed circulation
****
2801 Mitchell
COLORADO NB, COLORADO
{{ 3 L 3 S }}
Chartered 1882
Liquidated 9/1/31
Brown Back <$VALUE
4x5 1-5498 <$1250
3x10-20 1-1468 <$1250
1902 Red Seal
3x10-20 1-2950 <$1500
1902 Date Back
3x10-20 1-5400 <$500
1902 Plain Back
3x10-20 5401-8791 <$500
1929 Small Size
10 Type 1 1-447 <$400
20 Type 1 1-158 <$400
Total Issue $816,190
Out at close $25,000
Large out 1935 $2,880
Ch 13562 assumed circulation
****

****
2893 Mitchell
FNB OF COLORADO
{{ UNREPORTED }}
Chartered 2/27/83
Liquidated 1/9/94
Brown Back <$VALUE
3x10-20 1-1597 <$2500
Total Issue $79,850
Out in 1910 $410
****
4950 Mitchell
PEOPLES NB OF COLORADO
{{ UNREPORTED }}
Chartered 4/5/94
Liquidated 7/22/95
Brown Back <$VALUE
3x10-20 1-237 <$3000
Total Issue $11,850
Out in 1910 $70
****
4246 Comanche
COMANCHE NB, COMANCHE
{{ 6 L 9 S }}
Chartered 1890
Brown Back <$VALUE
3x10-20 1-3502 <$1000
1902 Date Back
3x10-20 1-3800 <$400
1902 Plain Back
3x10-20 3801-12019 <$400
1929 Small Size
10 Type 1 1-1522 <$200
20 Type 1 1-370 <$225
10 Type 2 1-2917 <$225
20 Type 2 1-494 <$225
Total Issue $950,820
Out in 1935 $48,900
Large out 1935 $3,670
****
7105 Comanche
FARMERS & MERCHANTS NB OF COMANCHE
{{ 3 L }}
Chartered 1/04
Liquidated 12/11/17
1902 Red Seal <$VALUE
3x10-20 1-1910 <$1500
1902 Date Back
3x10-20 1-4160 <$500
1902 Plain Back
3x10-20 4161-4733 <$500
Total Issue $332,150
Out at close $49,200
****
3561 Comanche
FNB OF COMANCHE
{{ 6 L }}
Chartered 9/17/86
Liquidated 12/7/27
Brown Back <$VALUE
3x10-20 1-3177 <$1250
1902 Red Seal
3x10-20 1-1000 <$1500
1902 Date Back
3x10-20 1-4700 <$350
1902 Plain Back
3x10-20 4701-18762 <$350
Total Issue $1,146,950
Out at close $87,945
****
4021 Hunt
COMMERCE NB, COMMERCE
Chartered 4/29/89
2nd title:FNB of Commerce 7/25/03
FIRST TITLE {{ 0 L }}
Brown Back <$VALUE
3x10-20 1-1359 <$1500
SECOND TITLE {{ 3 L }}
Brown Back
3x10-20 1401-2994 <$1000
1902 Date Back
3x10-20 1-4700 <$600
1902 Plain Back
3x10-20 4701-9145 <$600
Total Issue $604,900
Out in 1935 $1,915
Outstanding includes Ch 6224
****
FNB of Commerce
SEE Ch 4021
Commerce NB, Commerce
****

<$VALUEs are for notes in **FINE** condition. Value changes by approximately **25%** for a change of one full grade.

6224 Hunt
PLANTERS & MERCHANTS NB
OF COMMERCE
{{ UNREPORTED }}
Chartered 4/22/02
Liquidated 3/15/27
1902 Red Seal <$VALUE
3x10-20 1-890 <$2500
1902 Date Back
3x10-20 1-1820 <$1500
1902 Plain Back (dated 1902)
3x10-20 1821-2269 <$1500
1902 Plain Back (dated 1922)
3x10-20 1-862 <$1500
Total Issue $201,050
Out at close $12,195
Ch 4021 assumed circulation

9931 Hopkins
FNB OF COMO
{{ UNREPORTED }}
Organized 2/11/11
Receivership 3/7/16
1902 Date Back <$VALUE
3x10-20 1-853 <$2000
Total Issue $42,650
Out in 1916 $6,940

12809 Montgomery
FNB IN CONROE
{{ 8 S }}
Chartered 8/25
1929 Small Size <$VALUE
5 Type 1 1-1250 <$200
10 Type 1 1-690 <$200
20 Type 1 1-204 <$200
5 Type 2 1-5316 <$200
10 Type 2 1-2796 <$200
20 Type 2 1-564 <$200
Total Issue $169,200
Out in 1935 $41,710

6394 Montgomery
FNB OF CONROE
{{ UNREPORTED }}
Chartered 8/23/02
Liquidated 11/1/04
1902 Red Seal <$VALUE
3x10-20 1-179 <$3000
Total Issue $8,950
Out in 1910 $530

7231 Limestone
FNB OF COOLIDGE
{{ 8 L 13 S }}
Chartered 4/04
1902 Red Seal <$VALUE
4x5 1-600 <$1250
3x10-20 1-580 <$1250
1902 Date Back
4x5 1-4750 <$275
3x10-20 1-3580 <$275
1902 Plain Back
4x5 4751-19505 <$275
3x10-20 3581-12769 <$275
1929 Small Size
5 Type 1 1-3454 <$150
10 Type 1 1-1706 <$150
20 Type 1 1-516 <$150
5 Type 2 1-5822 <$150
10 Type 2 1-3082 <$150
20 Type 2 1-1005 <$150
Total Issue $1,417,480
Out in 1935 $73,100
Large out 1935 $2,845

5533 Delta
DELTA NB OF COOPER
{{ 4 L 7 S }}
Chartered 8/11/00
Brown Back <$VALUE
3x10-20 1-750 <$1250
1882 Date Back
3x10-20 1-3800* <$750
1882 Value Back
3x10-20 3981-5432* <$750
* 3801-3980 not marked
1902 Plain Back
3x10-20 1-4879 <$500
1929 Small Size
10 Type 1 1-1208 <$275
20 Type 1 1-310 <$275
10 Type 2 1-2040 <$300
20 Type 2 1-435 <$300
Total Issue $691,830
Out in 1935 $36,550
Large out 1935 $2,140

10626 Delta
FARMERS NB OF COOPER
{{ 1 L }}
Organized 9/24/14
Receivership 1/28/21
1902 Date Back <$VALUE
3x10-20 1-1000 <$1000
1902 Plain Back
3x10-20 1001-2938 <$1000
Total Issue $146,900
Out at close $21,500

13046 Delta
FNB IN COOPER
{{ 12 S }}
Chartered 3/27
1929 Small Size <$VALUE
5 Type 1 1-2728 <$125
10 Type 1 1-1372 <$125
20 Type 1 1-402 <$125
5 Type 2 1-3112 <$125
10 Type 2 1-2133 <$125
20 Type 2 1-516 <$125
Total Issue $259,610
Out in 1935 $48,750

4500 Delta
FNB OF COOPER
{{ 4 L }}
Chartered 1891
Liquidated 4/28/27
Brown Back <$VALUE
3x10-20 1-1870 <$1000
1882 Date Back
3x10-20 1-1698 <$850
1902 Date Back
3x10-20 1-5200 <$500
1902 Plain Back
3x10-20 5201-13068 <$500
Total Issue $831,800
Out at close $47,600

7668 Nueces
CITY NB OF CORPUS CHRISTI
Chartered 3/05
Receivership 11/11/31
2nd title: City NB & TC of
Corpus Christi 11/20/28
FIRST TITLE {{ 10 L }}
1902 Red Seal <$VALUE
3x10-20 1-1410 <$1000
1902 Date Back
3x10-20 1-8400 <$225
1902 Plain Back
3x10-20 8401-21075 <$225
SECOND TITLE {{ 2 L 8 S }}
1902 Plain Back
4x5 1-7901 <$250
1929 Small Size
5 Type 1 1-17744 <$150
Total Issue $1,814,590
Out at close $195,440
Large out at close $12,965

4423 Nueces
CORPUS CHRISTI NB,
CORPUS CHRISTI
{{ 6 L }}
Chartered 1890
Brown Back <$VALUE
3x10-20 1-3870 <$1000
1882 Date Back
3x10-20 1-1971 <$650
1902 Date Back
3x10-20 1-8000 <$350
1902 Plain Back
3x10-20 8001-16552 <$350
Total Issue $1,119,650
Out in 1935 $3,840

12235 Nueces
STATE NB OF
CORPUS CHRISTI
{{ 18 S }}
Chartered 7/22
1929 Small Size <$VALUE
5 Type 1 1-1034 <$75
10 Type 1 1-2468 <$75
20 Type 1 1-830 <$85
5 Type 2 1-9694 <$75
10 Type 2 1-5350 <$75
20 Type 2 1-1185 <$85
Total Issue $404,370
Out at close $142,500

3915 Navarro
CITY NB OF CORSICANA
{{ 3 L }}
Chartered 7/27/88
Liquidated 2/2/15
Brown Back <$VALUE
3x10-20 1-6120 <$1000
1902 Date Back
3x10-20 1-7375* <$500
* 6001-6800 not issued
Total Issue $634,750
Out at close $70,500
Ch 3645 assumed circulation

3645 Navarro
CORSICANA NB, CORSICANA
{{ 9 L 13 S }}
Chartered 3/12/87
Closed 6/2/31
Brown Back <$VALUE
3x10-20 1-3034 <$1000
1902 Red Seal
3x10-20 1-450 <$1250
1902 Date Back
3x10-20 1-10000 <$250
1902 Plain Back
3x10-20 10001-48612 <$250
1929 Small Size
10 Type 1 1-3624 <$100
20 Type 1 1-1007 <$100
Total Issue $2,943,080
Out in 1935 $197,840
Large out 1935 $26,280
Outstanding includes Ch 3915
Ch 3506 assumed circulation

3506 Navarro
FNB OF CORSICANA
{{ 16 L 23 S }}
Chartered 1886
Brown Back <$VALUE
50-100 1-1308 <$3500/$4000
1902 Red Seal
50-100 1-367 <$7500
1902 Date Back
4x5 1-6250 <$125
3x10-20 1-5000 <$125
50-100 1-1700 <$400/$450
3x50-100 1-1200 <$400/$450
1902 Plain Back
4x5 6251-60243 <$125
3x10-20 5001-38393 <$125
1929 Small Size
5 Type 1 1-16986 <$65
10 Type 1 1-9226 <$65
20 Type 1 1-2024 <$70
5 Type 2 1-43390 <$65
10 Type 2 1-23950 <$65
20 Type 2 1-6048 <$70
Total Issue $5,814,440
Out in 1935 $489,500
Large out 1935 $26,390
Outstanding includes Ch 3645

11022 Navarro
STATE NB OF CORSICANA
{{ 13 L 36 S }}
Chartered 6/17
1902 Plain Back <$VALUE
4x5 1-29736 <$150
3x10-20 1-24673 <$150
3x50-100 1-887 <$400/$450
1929 Small Size
10 Type 1 1-2798 <$75
20 Type 1 1-684 <$85
50 Type 1 1-380 <$135
100 Type 1 1-118 <$200
5 Type 2 1-10622 <$80
10 Type 2 1-5893 <$80
20 Type 2 1-5077 <$85
Total Issue $2,692,460
Out in 1935 $300,000
Large out 1935 $8,810

14302 La Salle
STOCKMENS NB IN COTULLA
{{ 1 S }}
Chartered 11/34
1929 Small Size <$VALUE
10 Type 2 1-1480 <$650
20 Type 2 1-510 <$650
Total Issue $25,000
Out in 1935 $25,000

7243 La Salle
STOCKMENS NB OF COTULLA
{{ 5 L 8 S }}
Chartered 5/04
Liquidated 1/8/35
1902 Red Seal <$VALUE
3x10-20 1-2600 <$1500
1902 Date Back
3x10-20 1-5500 <$400
1902 Plain Back
3x10-20 5501-14940 <$400
1929 Small Size
10 Type 1 1-1738 <$225
20 Type 1 1-498 <$225
10 Type 2 1-1837 <$250
20 Type 2 1-465 <$250
Total Issue $1,068,710
Out at close $54,130
Large out at close $3,610

7147 Hill
FNB OF COVINGTON
{{ UNREPORTED }}
Chartered 2/23/04
Liquidated 9/30/07
1902 Red Seal <$VALUE
3x10-20 1-263 <$3000
Total Issue $13,150
Out in 1910 $1,100

5938 Kaufman
CITIZENS NB OF CRANDALL
{{ 4 L 5 S }}
Chartered 8/01
Brown Back <$VALUE
3x10-20 1-1700 <$1000
1882 Date Back
3x10-20 1-2330 <$750
1882 Value Back
3x10-20 2331-3907 <$750
1902 Plain Back
3x10-20 1-2970 <$500
1929 Small Size
10 Type 1 1-734 <$350
20 Type 1 1-228 <$350
5 Type 2 1-1894 <$350
10 Type 2 1-1033 <$350
20 Type 2 1-305 <$350
Total Issue $526,150
Out in 1935 $24,550
Large out 1935 $1,750

5824 Kaufman
FNB OF CRANDALL
{{ 2 L 1 S }}
Chartered 5/21/01
Liquidated 1/15/30
Brown Back <$VALUE
3x10-20 1-1400 <$1250
1882 Date Back
3x10-20 1-2500 <$1000
1882 Value Back
3x10-20 2501-3677 <$1000
1902 Plain Back
3x10-20 1-3226 <$750
1929 Small Size
10 Type 1 1-118 <$650
20 Type 1 1-12 <$650
Total Issue $423,670
Out at close $17,920

10400 McLennan
FNB OF CRAWFORD
{{ 1 L }}
Organized 5/19/13
Receivership 7/16/21
1902 Date Back <$VALUE
3x10-20 1-900 <$1500
1902 Plain Back
3x10-20 901-982 <$1500
Total Issue $49,100
Out at close $6,900

8965 Hood
CRESSON NB, CRESSON
{{ 2 L }}
Chartered 12/07
Liquidated 8/27/14
1902 Red Seal <$VALUE
3x10-20 1-200 <$2000
1902 Date Back
3x10-20 1-1862 <$1250
Total Issue $103,100
Out in 1914 $22,850

5953 Houston
FARMERS & MERCHANTS NB OF
CROCKETT
{{ 1 L }}
Chartered 8/29/01
Liquidated 3/1/04
Brown Back <$VALUE
3x10-20 1-387 <$2000
Total Issue $19,350
Out in 1910 $730

4684 Houston
FNB OF CROCKETT
{{ 7 L 8 S }}
Chartered 1892
Brown Back <$VALUE
3x10-20 1-6260 <$1000
1882 Date Back
3x10-20 1-3241 <$500
1902 Date Back
3x10-20 1-6700 <$300
1902 Plain Back
3x10-20 6701-15850 <$300
1929 Small Size
5 Type 1 1-2002 <$175
10 Type 1 1-678 <$175
20 Type 1 1-234 <$175
5 Type 2 1-7428 <$175
10 Type 2 1-4890 <$175
20 Type 2 1-1285 <$175
Total Issue $1,508,110
Out in 1935 $98,500
Large out 1935 $22,650

Citizens NB of Crosbyton
SEE Ch 8515
FNB of Emma

9989 Crosby
FNB OF CROSBYTON
{{ 1 L 0 S }}
Chartered 4/11
Liquidated 1/30/30
1902 Date Back <$VALUE
3x10-20 1-1740 $1250
1902 Plain Back
3x10-20 1741-3540 <$1250
1929 Small Size
10 Type 1 1-84 <$750
20 Type 1 1-5 <$750
Total Issue $182,640
Out at close $10,220
Large out at close $4,580
Ch 8515 assumed circulation

8583 Callahan
FARMERS NB OF
CROSS PLAINS
{{ 1 L 1 S }}
Chartered 3/07
Receivership 6/13/31
1902 Red Seal <$VALUE
3x10-20 1-189 <$2500
1902 Date Back
3x10-20 1-800* <$1500
1902 Plain Back
3x10-20 901-1836* <$1500
* 801-900 not marked
1929 Small Size
10 Type 1 1-143 <$750
20 Type 1 1-19 <$750
Total Issue $112,110
Out at close $6,300
Large out at close $780

6402 Foard
FNB OF CROWELL
{{ UNREPORTED }}
Chartered 8/29/02
Liquidated 8/1/05
1902 Red Seal <$VALUE
3x10-20 1-245 <$3000
Total Issue $12,250
Out in 1910 $650

9178 Foard
FOARD COUNTY NB OF
CROWELL
{{ UNREPORTED }}
Chartered 7/08
Liquidated 12/11/09
1902 Date Back <$VALUE
3x10-20 1-179 <$2000
Total Issue $8,950
Out in 1910 $2,900

14164 De Witt
BUCHEL NB IN CUERO
{{ U + 2 S }}
Chartered 5/34
1929 Small Size <$VALUE
10 Type 2 1-1932 <$500
20 Type 2 1-684 <$500
Total Issue $33,000
Out in 1935 $25,000

8562 De Witt
BUCHEL NB OF CUERO
{{ 3 L U + 3 S }}
Chartered 2/07
Liquidated 7/24/34
1902 Red Seal <$VALUE
3x10-20 1-652 <$1500
1902 Date Back
3x10-20 1-2750* <$500
1902 Plain Back
3x10-20 3151-7201* <$500
* 2751-3150 not marked
1929 Small Size
10 Type 1 1-652 <$350
20 Type 1 1-180 <$350
10 Type 2 1-428 <$350
20 Type 2 1-90 <$350
Total Issue $489,350
Out at close $23,500
Large out at close $2,320

4140 De Witt
FNB OF CUERO
{{ 1 L }}
Chartered 10/15/89
Liquidated 2/8/07
Brown Back <$VALUE
3x10-20 1-2625 <$1500
Total Issue $131,250
Out in 1910 $8,970

5719 Hopkins
FNB OF CUMBY
{{ 2 L }}
Chartered 2/16/01
Liquidated 1/20/16
Brown Back <$VALUE
3x10-20 1-2850 <$1250
1882 Date Back
3x10-20 1-4717 <$1000
Total Issue $378,350
Out in 1916 $31,255

7096 Morris
CITIZENS NB OF
DAINGERFIELD
{{ 1 L 1 S }}
Chartered 1/04
Liquidated 12/27/33
1902 Red Seal <$VALUE
3x10-20 1-500 <$2000
1902 Date Back
3x10-20 1-1000 <$1000
1902 Plain Back
3x10-20 1001-2098 <$1000
1929 Small Size
10 Type 1 1-259 <$600
20 Type 1 1-53 <$600
Total Issue $151,800
Out at close $7,500
Large out at close $740

4701 Morris
NB OF DAINGERFIELD
{{ 5 L 9 S }}
Chartered 1892
Brown Back <$VALUE
3x10-20 1-1470 <$1000
1882 Date Back
3x10-20 1-1224 <$650
1902 Date Back
3x10-20 1-2800 <$300
1902 Plain Back
3x10-20 2801-11341 <$300
1929 Small Size
10 Type 1 1-1540 <$150
20 Type 1 1-422 <$150
10 Type 2 1-2507 <$150
20 Type 2 1-612 <$150
Total Issue $882,100
Out in 1935 $48,650
Large out 1935 $3,210

7977 Dallam
DALHART NB, DALHART
{{ 1 L }}
Chartered 11/05
Liquidated 9/10/12
1902 Red Seal <$VALUE
3x10-20 1-887 <$2000
1902 Date Back
3x10-20 1-872 <$1000
Total Issue $87,950
Out at close $23,500
Ch 6762 assumed circulation

14199 Dallam
FNB IN DALHART
{{ 1 S }}
Chartered 6/34
1929 Small Size <$VALUE
5 Type 2 1-1640 <$600
10 Type 2 1-1030 <$600
20 Type 2 1-435 <$600
Total Issue $27,200
Out in 1935 $25,000

CONDITION affects Value. The Values shown are for notes in FINE condition.

****
6762 Dallam
FNB OF DALHART
{{ 6 L 11 S }}
Organized 3/3/03
Receivership 6/25/34
1902 Red Seal <$VALUE
3x10-20 1-2200 <$1250
1902 Date Back
3x10-20 1-5100 <$250
1902 Plain Back
3x10-20 5101-17270 <$250
1929 Small Size
10 Type 1 1-2132 <$100
20 Type 1 1-632 <$110
5 Type 2 1-1118 <$125
10 Type 2 1-750 <$125
20 Type 2 1-240 <$125
Total Issue $1,195,150
Out at close $68,690
Large out at close $5,670
Outstanding includes Ch 7977
****
American Exchange NB of Dallas
SEE Ch 3623
N Exchange B of Dallas
****
3132 Dallas
AMERICAN NB OF DALLAS
{{ 5 L }}
Chartered 3/4/84
Liquidated 9/23/05
Brown Back <$VALUE
3x10-20 1-9197 <$850
50-100 1-920 <$3500/$4000
1902 Red Seal
3x10-20 1-2808 <$1250
Total Issue $738,250
Out in 1910 $21,710
****
4213 Dallas
BANKERS & MERCHANTS NB OF DALLAS
{{ 1 L }}
Organized 1/21/90
Receivership 2/6/93
Brown Back <$VALUE
3x10-20 1-1301 <$1500
Total Issue $65,050
Out in 1916 $270
****
4127 Dallas
CENTRAL NB OF DALLAS
{{ UNREPORTED }}
Chartered 9/25/89
Liquidated 8/3/93
Brown Back <$VALUE
50-100 1-462 <$4500
Total Issue $69,300
Out in 1910 $400
****
2455 Dallas
CITY NB OF DALLAS
{{ 50+ L U + 6 S }}
Chartered 2/17/80
Closed 12/31/29
Series 1875 <$VALUE
4x5 1-6000 <$4000
3x10-20 1-6883<$5000/$6000
Brown Back
3x10-20 1-15600 <$750
1882 Date Back
4x5 1-78750* <$400
3x10-20 1-64200** <$400
1882 Value Back
4x5 86751-116247* <$450
3x10-20 67201-83887**<$450
* 78751-86750 not marked
** 64201-67200 not marked
1902 Plain Back
4x5 1-189650 <$50
3x10-20 1-133230 <$60
3x50-100 1-320 <$300/$350
1929 Small Size
5 Type 1 1-6526 <$175
10 Type 1 1-3863 <$150
20 Type 1 1-815 <$175
Total Issue $18,823,300
Out at close $969,580
Large out at close $444,220
Outstanding includes Ch 10965
Ch 3623 assumed circulation
****
8664 Dallas
COMMONWEALTH NB OF DALLAS
{{ 6 L }}
Chartered 4/07
Liquidated 7/2/14
1902 Red Seal <$VALUE
3x10-20 1-11000 <$1000
1902 Date Back
3x10-20 1-28163 <$200
Total Issue $1,958,150
Out at close $454,900
Ch 10564 assumed circulation
****
3008 Dallas
DALLAS NB, DALLAS
{{ UNREPORTED }}
Chartered 7/18/83
Liquidated 5/8/86
Brown Back <$VALUE
3x10-20 1-785 <$2500
Total Issue $39,250
Out in 1910 $300
****
11749 Dallas
DALLAS NB, DALLAS
{{ 18 L 2U + 16 S }}
Chartered 6/20
Liquidated 2/10/31
1902 Plain Back <$VALUE
4x5 1-32535 <$100
3x10-20 1-20322 <$100
1929 Small Size
5 Type 1 1-11247 <$50
10 Type 1 1-5547 <$50
20 Type 1 1-1456 <$60
Total Issue $2,511,570
Out at close $400,940
Large out at close $28,690
****
FNB in Dallas
SEE Ch 3623
N Exchange B of Dallas
****
2157 Dallas
FNB OF DALLAS
{{ 1 L }}
Chartered 7/16/74
Receivership 6/8/78
Original Series <$VALUE
4x5 1-1500 <$5000
Series 1875
4x5 1-665 <$5000
Total Issue $43,300
Out in 1916 $430
****
3664 Dallas
FOURTH NB OF DALLAS
{{ UNREPORTED }}
Chartered 3/31/87
Liquidated 2/10/94
2nd title:State NB of Dallas 2/4/92
FIRST TITLE
Brown Back <$VALUE
50-100 1-539 <$5000
SECOND TITLE
Brown Back
50-100 1-201 <$5000
Total Issue $111,000
Out in 1910 $800
****
7113 Dallas
GASTON NB OF DALLAS
{{ 1 L }}
Chartered 1/04
Liquidated 1/1/09
1902 Red Seal <$VALUE
3x10-20 1-6000 <$1750
50-100 1-2067 <$7500
1902 Date Back
3x10-20 1-1288 <$850
50-100 1-46 <$1250/$1500
Total Issue $681,350
Out in 1910 $190,960
****
13743 Dallas
MERCANTILE NB AT DALLAS
{{ 28 S }}
Chartered 8/33
1929 Small Size <$VALUE
10 Type 2 1-20309 <$50
20 Type 2 1-5638 <$60
50 Type 2 1-4793 <$175
100 Type 2 1-1234 <$225
Total Issue $678,900
Out in 1935 $435,250
****
4707 Dallas
MERCANTILE NB OF DALLAS
{{ UNREPORTED }}
Chartered 3/14/92
Liquidated 2/27/97
Brown Back <$VALUE
50-100 1-414 <$5000
Total Issue $62,100
Out in 1910 $1,450
****
12707 Dallas
MERCANTILE NB OF DALLAS
{{ 6 L }}
Chartered 4/25
Liquidated 2/1/29
1902 Plain Back <$VALUE
3x10-20 1-24404 <$250
3x50-100 1-3403 <$500/$600
Total Issue $2,070,950
Out at close $582,600
****
10331 Dallas
MERCHANTS NB OF DALLAS
{{ 2 L }}
Chartered 2/13
Liquidated 10/5/15
1902 Date Back <$VALUE
3x10-20 1-11137 <$600
Total Issue $556,850
Out at close $212,100
****
5078 Dallas
NB OF DALLAS
{{ 1 L }}
Chartered 7/1/97
Liquidated 4/9/00
Brown Back <$VALUE
4x5 1-1862 <$1500
Total Issue $37,240
Out in 1910 $415
****
3985 Dallas
NB OF COMMERCE OF DALLAS
{{ 4 L 6 S }}
Chartered 3/8/89
Brown Back <$VALUE
3x10-20 1-4481 <$1000
1902 Date Back
50-100 1-800 <$650/$750
3x50-100 1-1120 <$650/$750
1902 Plain Back
3x50-100 1121-2063 <$650/$750
1929 Small Size
50 Type 1 1-462 <$250
100 Type 1 1-134 <$300
5 Type 2 1-3140 <$175
10 Type 2 1-1795 <$175
20 Type 2 1-455 <$175
Total Issue $1,122,350
Out in 1935 $136,250
Large out 1935 $12,850
****
3623 Dallas
N EXCHANGE B OF DALLAS
Chartered 1/25/87
2nd title:American Exchange NB of Dallas 7/29/05
3rd title:FNB in Dallas 12/31/29
FIRST TITLE {{ 3 L }}
Brown Back <$VALUE
4x5 1-2500 <$750
3x10-20 1-8085 <$750
50-100 1-3535 <$3500/$4000
SECOND TITLE {{34 L U+21 S}}
Brown Back
4x5 1-2265 <$750
3x10-20 1-12585 <$750
1902 Red Seal
4x5 1-22500 <$1000
3x10-20 1-6000 <$1000
1902 Date Back
4x5 1-85500* <$50
3x10-20 1-72200** <$60
1902 Plain Back
4x5 89501-377941* <$50
3x10-20 76201-241590**<$60
3x50-100 1-5117 <$300/$350
* 85501-89500 not marked
** 72201-76200 not marked
1929 Small Size
5 Type 1 1-18860 <$20
10 Type 1 1-8230 <$20
20 Type 1 1-2770 <$30
50 Type 1 1-1426 <$100
100 Type 1 1-474 <$150
THIRD TITLE {{2U + 50+ S }}
1929 Small Size
5 Type 1 1-73260 <$15
10 Type 1 1-39140 <$20
20 Type 1 1-11092 <$30
50 Type 1 1-2374 <$85
100 Type 1 1-870 <$135
5 Type 2 1-106230 <$20
10 Type 2 1-63230 <$25
20 Type 2 1-14325 <$35
Total Issue $33,992,210
Out in 1935 $2,405,555
Large out 1935 $157,705
Outstanding includes Ch 2455
****
4415 Dallas
NINTH NB OF DALLAS
{{ UNREPORTED }}
Chartered 9/90
Receivership 7/16/91
Brown Back <$VALUE
50-100 1-300 <$5000
Total Issue $45,000
Out in 1916 $100
****
3834 Dallas
NORTH TEXAS NB AT DALLAS
{{ 1 L }}
Chartered 1/6/88
Liquidated 7/13/93
Brown Back <$VALUE
50-100 1-630 <$3500/$4000
Total Issue $94,500
Out in 1910 $1,450
****
12736 Dallas
NORTH TEXAS NB IN DALLAS
{{ 12 L U + 18 S }}
Chartered 5/25
Closed 12/28/29
1902 Plain Back <$VALUE
4x5 1-53645 <$125
3x10-20 1-29189 <$125
3x50-100 1-1884 <$400/$500
1929 Small Size
5 Type 1 1-2448 <$85
10 Type 1 1-1222 <$85
20 Type 1 1-426 <$100
50 Type 1 1-222 <$150
100 Type 1 1-72 <$200
Total Issue $3,311,030
Out at close $885,580
Large out at close $577,900
Ch 12186 assumed circulation
****
12186 Dallas
REPUBLIC NB OF DALLAS
Chartered 4/22
2nd title:Republic NB & TC of Dallas 7/18/28
FIRST TITLE {{ 24 L }}
1902 Plain Back <$VALUE
4x5 1-106278 <$60
3x10-20 1-82474 <$70
SECOND TITLE {{ 12 L 50+ S }}
1902 Plain Back
4x5 1-19422 <$60
3x10-20 1-11643 <$70
1929 Small Size
5 Type 1 1-113374 <$15
10 Type 1 1-58928 <$20
20 Type 1 1-17860 <$30
5 Type 2 1-292832 <$20
10 Type 2 1-159191 <$25
20 Type 2 1-35455 <$35
50 Type 2 1-3170 <$165
100 Type 2 1-1995 <$200
Total Issue $20,423,120
Out in 1935 $2,780,500
Large out 1935 $53,135
Outstanding includes Ch 12736
****
10564 Dallas
SECURITY NB OF DALLAS
{{ 20 L }}
Chartered 6/14
Liquidated 10/6/21
1902 Date Back <$VALUE
4x5 1-37500 <$60
3x10-20 1-30000 <$70
1902 Plain Back
4x5 37501-176460 <$60
3x10-20 30001-120937 <$70
Total Issue $9,576,050
Out at close $1,989,100
Outstanding includes Ch 8664
Ch 11996 assumed circulation
****
11996 Dallas
SOUTHWEST NB OF DALLAS
{{ 8 L }}
Chartered 7/21
Liquidated 6/25/25
1902 Plain Back <$VALUE
4x5 1-21370 <$150
4x10 1-15435 <$150
3x10-20 1-23468 <$150
Total Issue $2,218,200
Out at close $219,890
Outstanding includes Ch 10564
****
State NB of Dallas
SEE Ch 3664
Fourth NB of Dallas
****
10965 Dallas
TENISON NB OF DALLAS
{{ 5 L }}
Chartered 3/17
Liquidated 5/11/20
1902 Plain Back <$VALUE
4x5 1-19665 <$300
3x10-20 1-12854 <$300
Total Issue $1,036,000
Out at close $368,900
Ch 2455 assumed circulation
****
7052 Dallas
TEXAS NB OF DALLAS
{{ 2 L }}
Chartered 12/5/03
Liquidated 7/31/05
1902 Red Seal <$VALUE
3x10-20 1-5491 <$1250
Total Issue $274,550
Out in 1910 $21,140
****
9341 Dallas
TRINITY NB OF DALLAS
{{ UNREPORTED }}
Chartered 2/09
Liquidated 12/11/09
1902 Date Back <$VALUE
4x5 1-1010 <$1500
3x10-20 1-889 <$1500
Total Issue $64,650
Out in 1910 $26,010
****
9245 Dallas
UNION NB OF DALLAS
{{ 1 L }}
Chartered 9/08
Liquidated 5/28/10
1902 Date Back <$VALUE
4x5 1-5990 <$750
3x10-20 1-4436 <$750
Total Issue $341,600
Out in 1910 $143,500
****
10694 Navarro
FNB OF DAWSON
{{ 3 L U + 6 S }}
Chartered 2/15
1902 Date Back <$VALUE
4x5 1-415 <$500
3x10-20 1-334 <$500
1902 Plain Back
4x5 416-6219 <$500
3x10-20 335-3715 <$500
1929 Small Size
5 Type 1 1-1274 <$200
10 Type 1 1-616 <$200
20 Type 1 1-168 <$200
5 Type 2 1-3262 <$200
10 Type 2 1-1996 <$200
20 Type 2 1-588 <$200
Total Issue $453,500
Out in 1935 $49,170
Large out 1935 $2,690
Outstanding includes Ch 11239
****
11239 Navarro
LIBERTY NB OF DAWSON
{{ 3 L 6 S }}
Chartered 9/18
Closed 3/17/32
1902 Plain Back <$VALUE
3x10-20 1-7201 <$500
1929 Small Size
10 Type 1 1-1219 <$175
20 Type 1 1-319 <$200
Total Issue $471,470
Out at close $49,580
Large out at close $2,970
Ch 10694 assumed circulation
****
8449 Bowie
FNB OF De KALB
{{ UNREPORTED }}
Chartered 12/1/06
Liquidated 8/20/09
1902 Red Seal <$VALUE
4x10 1-291 <$3500
Total Issue $11,640
Out in 1910 $2,040
****
7553 Comanche
FARMERS & MERCHANTS NB OF De LEON
{{ 4 L 2U + 6 S }}
Chartered 1/05
1902 Red Seal <$VALUE
4x5 1-750 <$1500
3x10-20 1-1602 <$1500
1902 Date Back
4x5 1-3950* <$400
3x10-20 1-2660** <$400
1902 Plain Back
4x5 4101-11608* <$400
3x10-20 2781-7282** <$400
* 3951-4100 not marked
** 2661-2780 not marked
1929 Small Size
5 Type 1 1-1600 <$200
10 Type 1 1-756 <$200
20 Type 1 1-210 <$200
5 Type 2 1-3610 <$200
10 Type 2 1-2554 <$200
20 Type 2 1-660 <$200
Total Issue $866,710
Out in 1935 $48,900
Large out 1935 $2,210
****
5660 Comanche
FNB OF De LEON
{{ 2 L }}
Chartered 12/31/00
Liquidated 9/2/19
Brown Back <$VALUE
4x5 1-1225 <$1000
3x10-20 1-1110 <$1000
1882 Date Back
4x5 1-2100 <$750
3x10-20 1-1520 <$750
1882 Value Back
4x5 2101-2715 <$800
3x10-20 1521-1912 <$800
Total Issue $229,900
Out at close $20,400
****
5665 Wise
CITY NB OF DECATUR
{{ 5 L }}
Chartered 1/3/01
Receivership 10/25/30
Brown Back <$VALUE
3x10-20 1-2550 <$1000
1882 Date Back
3x10-20 1-4500 <$700
1882 Value Back
3x10-20 4501-6758 <$700
1902 Plain Back
3x10-20 1-6401 <$350
Total Issue $785,450
Out at close $43,550
****
13623 Wise
FNB IN DECATUR
{{ 2U + 5 S }}
Chartered 6/32
1929 Small Size <$VALUE
10 Type 1 1-366 <$250
20 Type 1 1-90 <$250
10 Type 2 1-3049 <$250
20 Type 2 1-691 <$250
Total Issue $77,070
Out in 1935 $48,200
Large out 1935 $2,980
Outstanding includes Ch 2940
****
2940 Wise
FNB OF DECATUR
{{ 7 L 5 S }}
Chartered 1883
Liquidated 9/13/32
Brown Back <$VALUE
3x10-20 1-2551 <$1000
1902 Red Seal
3x10-20 1-2500 <$1250
1902 Date Back
3x10-20 1-4700 <$250
1902 Plain Back
3x10-20 4701-13583 <$250
1929 Small Size
10 Type 1 1-1355 <$250
20 Type 1 1-364 <$250
Total Issue $1,056,680
Out at close $45,860
Large out 1935 $2,980
Ch 13623 assumed circulation
****
4116 Wise
WISE COUNTY NB OF DECATUR
{{ UNREPORTED }}
Chartered 9/11/89
Liquidated 9/7/99
Brown Back <$VALUE
3x10-20 1-875 <$2000
Total Issue $43,750
Out in 1910 $640
****

****
7433 Val Verde
DEL RIO NB, DEL RIO
{{ 10 L 14 S }}
Chartered 10/04
1902 Red Seal <$VALUE
3x10-20 1-580 <$1500
1902 Date Back
4x5 1-7550 <$250
3x10-20 1-6260 <$250
1902 Plain Back
4x5 7551-25147 <$250
3x10-20 6261-17947 <$250
1929 Small Size
5 Type 1 1-4270 <$125
10 Type 1 1-2266 <$125
20 Type 1 1-498 <$125
5 Type 2 1-7164 <$125
10 Type 2 1-3444 <$125
20 Type 2 1-1092 <$125
Total Issue $1,845,210
Out in 1935 $96,570
Large out 1935 $5,740
****
5294 Val Verde
FNB OF DEL RIO
{{ 8 L 3 S }}
Chartered 4/20/00
Liquidated 12/10/32
Brown Back <$VALUE
3x10-20 1-1450 <$1000
1882 Date Back
3x10-20 1-5600 <$600
1882 Value Back
3x10-20 5601-7798 <$600
1902 Plain Back
4x5 1-33186 <$225
1929 Small Size
5 Type 1 1-6082 <$300
Total Issue $1,308,580
Out at close $15,720
Large out at close $4,610
****
12728 Grayson
CITIZENS NB OF DENISON
{{ 1 L 18 S }}
Chartered 5/25
1902 Plain Back <$VALUE
3x10-20 1-1744 <$750
1929 Small Size
10 Type 1 1-3134 <$60
20 Type 1 1-856 <$60
5 Type 2 1-16882 <$65
10 Type 2 1-6070 <$65
20 Type 2 1-2160 <$70
Total Issue $566,270
Out in 1935 $150,000
Large out 1935 $7,090
Outstanding includes Ch 4447
****
2099 Grayson
FNB OF DENISON
{{ 1 L }}
Chartered 4/7/73
Liquidated 4/30/94
Original Series <$VALUE
3x1-2 1-760 <$4500/$15,000
4x5 1-1250 <$4500
3x10-20 1-1200<$5000/$6000
Series 1875
4x5 1-3855 <$4500
3x10-20 1-1437<$5000/$6000
Brown Back
3x10-20 1-407 <$1500
Total Issue $258,100
Out in 1910 $1,961
****
4447 Grayson
NB OF DENISON
{{ 7 L }}
Chartered 1890
Closed 7/31/28
Brown Back <$VALUE
4x5 1-13620 <$1000
3x10-20 1-4512 <$1000
1882 Date Back
4x5 1-1505 <$600
3x10-20 1-1136 <$600
1902 Date Back
3x10-20 1-6300 <$250
1902 Plain Back
3x10-20 6301-21753 <$250
Total Issue $1,672,550
Out at close $98,355
Ch 12728 assumed circulation
****
3058 Grayson
STATE NB OF DENISON
{{ 15 L 15 S }}
Chartered 1883
Brown Back <$VALUE
3x10-20 1-3576 <$1000
1902 Red Seal
3x10-20 1-2775 <$1250
1902 Date Back
4x5 1-8250 <$150
3x10-20 1-6400 <$150
1902 Plain Back
4x5 8251-26495 <$150
3x10-20 6401-18358 <$150
1929 Small Size
5 Type 1 1-4238 <$75
10 Type 1 1-2308 <$75
20 Type 1 1-534 <$85
5 Type 2 1-6342 <$75
10 Type 2 1-3830 <$75
20 Type 2 1-1212 <$85
Total Issue $2,189,300
Out in 1935 $95,650
Large out 1935 $6,205
****
4708 Denton
DENTON COUNTY NB, DENTON
{{ 6 L 12 S }}
Chartered 1892
Brown Back <$VALUE
3x10-20 1-1510 <$1000
1882 Date Back
3x10-20 1-412 <$650
1902 Date Back
3x10-20 1-3300* <$300
1902 Plain Back
3x10-20 3351-12440* <$300
* 3301-3350 not marked
1929 Small Size
10 Type 1 1-1704 <$125
20 Type 1 1-424 <$150
10 Type 2 1-2693 <$150
20 Type 2 1-820 <$150
Total Issue $914,550
Out in 1935 $48,400
Large out 1935 $2,390
****
2949 Denton
EXCHANGE NB OF DENTON
{{ 3 L }}
Organized 5/7/83
Receivership 12/26/28
Brown Back <$VALUE
4x5 1-3996 <$1250
50-100 1-94 <$3500/$4000
1902 Red Seal
50-100 1-450 <$7500
1902 Date Back
4x5 1-1915 <$400
50-100 1-500 <$750/$850
1902 Plain Back
4x5 1916-9769 <$400
Total Issue $431,900
Out at close $24,095
****
2812 Denton
FNB OF DENTON
{{ 3 L }}
Organized 10/30/82
Receivership 8/15/28
Brown Back <$VALUE
4x5 1-2238 <$1250
3x10-20 1-790 <$1250
1902 Red Seal
3x10-20 1-665 <$1500
1902 Date Back
3x10-20 1-3000 <$400
1902 Plain Back
3x10-20 3001-9008 <$400
Total Issue $567,910
Out at close $37,500
****
6430 Lamar
FNB OF DEPORT
{{ 3 L 4 S }}
Chartered 9/20/02
1902 Red Seal <$VALUE
3x10-20 1-700 <$1500
1902 Date Back
3x10-20 1-3010 <$450
1902 Plain Back
3x10-20 3011-6688 <$450
1929 Small Size
10 Type 1 1-766 <$300
20 Type 1 1-222 <$300
10 Type 2 1-1200 <$325
20 Type 2 1-252 <$325
Total Issue $459,040
Out in 1935 $24,010
Large out 1935 $790
****
4682 Red River
FNB OF DETROIT
{{ 3 L }}
Chartered 1892
Liquidated 1/14/29
Brown Back <$VALUE
3x10-20 1-2340 <$1000
1882 Date Back
3x10-20 1-734 <$750
1902 Date Back
4x5 1-2650 <$400
3x10-20 1-2240 <$400
1902 Plain Back
4x5 2651-5655 <$400
3x10-20 2241-4032 <$400
Total Issue $468,400
Out at close $20,650
****
7212 Medina
ADAMS NB OF DEVINE
{{ 5 L 8 S }}
Chartered 4/04
Liquidated 5/29/34
1902 Red Seal <$VALUE
3x10-20 1-2062 <$1250
1902 Date Back
3x10-20 1-3500 <$350
1902 Plain Back
3x10-20 3501-11740 <$350
1929 Small Size
10 Type 1 1-1558 <$225
20 Type 1 1-394 <$225
10 Type 2 1-929 <$225
20 Type 2 1-145 <$225
Total Issue $843,050
Out at close $48,400
Large out at close $3,480
****
8303 Dickens
FNB OF DICKENS
{{ UNREPORTED }}
Chartered 7/06
Liquidated 3/26/13
1902 Red Seal <$VALUE
3x10-20 1-288 <$3000
1902 Date Back
3x10-20 1-197 <$2000
Total Issue $24,250
Out in 1913 $2,550
****
12855 Galveston
FNB OF DICKINSON
{{ 2 L 2 S }}
Chartered 11/25
Receivership 12/18/33
1902 Plain Back <$VALUE
4x5 1-5514 <$850
1929 Small Size
5 Type 1 1-2841 <$500
Total Issue $195,510
Out at close $25,000
Large out at close $710
****
5728 Fannin
FNB OF DODD CITY
{{ 2 L 2 S }}
Chartered 2/27/01
Brown Back <$VALUE
3x10-20 1-750 <$1250
1882 Date Back
3x10-20 1-980* <$1250
1882 Value Back
3x10-20 1181-1435* <$1250
* 981-1180 not marked
1902 Plain Back
3x10-20 1-999 <$1000
1929 Small Size
10 Type 1 1-316 <$500
20 Type 1 1-102 <$500
10 Type 2 1-91 <$500
20 Type 2 1-20 <$500
Total Issue $191,710
Out in 1935 $9,700
Large out 1935 $640
****
5836 Erath
CITIZENS NB OF DUBLIN
{{ 3 L }}
Chartered 5/28/01
Liquidated 5/1/28
Brown Back <$VALUE
3x10-20 1-900 <$1250
1882 Date Back
3x10-20 1-3900 <$1000
1882 Value Back
3x10-20 3901-6200 <$1000
1902 Plain Back
3x10-20 1-5066 <$500
Total Issue $608,300
Out at close $47,100
****
4865 Erath
DUBLIN NB, DUBLIN
{{ 2 L 4 S }}
Chartered 1893
Brown Back <$VALUE
3x10-20 1-1520 <$1250
1882 Date Back
3x10-20 1-634 <$1000
1902 Date Back
3x10-20 1-2010 <$600
1902 Plain Back
3x10-20 2011-3279 <$600
1929 Small Size
10 Type 1 1-546 <$350
20 Type 1 1-176 <$350
10 Type 2 1-1116 <$350
20 Type 2 1-314 <$350
Total Issue $342,970
Out in 1935 $23,000
Large out 1935 $1,800
****
4062 Erath
FNB OF DUBLIN
{{ UNREPORTED }}
Chartered 7/1/89
Receivership 4/22/95
Brown Back <$VALUE
4x5 1-1161 <$2000
Total Issue $23,220
Out in 1916 $140
****
7534 Colorado
FNB OF EAGLE LAKE
{{ 0 L U + 3 S }}
Chartered 12/04
1902 Red Seal <$VALUE
50-100 1-132 <$7500
1902 Date Back
50-100 1-500 <$2000
3x50-100 1-160 <$2000
1902 Plain Back
3x50-100 161-260 <$2000
1929 Small Size
10 Type 1 1-132 <$400
50 Type 1 1-96 <$500
100 Type 1 1-30 <$600
Total Issue $214,520
Out in 1935 $32,600
Large out 1935 $2,250
****
5181 Maverick
BORDER NB OF EAGLE PASS
{{ 7 L }}
Chartered 2/27/99
Liquidated 1/21/22
Brown Back <$VALUE
3x10-20 1-4900 <$1250
1882 Date Back
3x10-20 1-7150 <$1000
1882 Value Back
3x10-20 7151-9013 <$1000
1902 Plain Back
3x10-20 1-4742 <$500
Total Issue $932,750
Out at close $81,300
****
4490 Maverick
FNB OF EAGLE PASS
{{ 6 L 10 S }}
Chartered 1890
Brown Back <$VALUE
3x10-20 1-4630 <$1000
1882 Date Back
3x10-20 1-584 <$1000
1902 Date Back
50-100 1-667 <$750/$850
3x50-100 1-1897 <$750/$850
1902 Plain Back
3x50-100 1898-2336 <$750/$850
1929 Small Size
50 Type 1 1-282 <$300
100 Type 1 1-96 <$350
5 Type 2 1-6530 <$200
10 Type 2 1-4244 <$200
20 Type 2 1-1100 <$200
Total Issue $1,184,040
Out in 1935 $145,150
Large out 1935 $11,410
****
5060 Maverick
SIMPSON NB OF EAGLE PASS
{{ UNREPORTED }}
Chartered 3/1/97
Liquidated 3/4/99
Brown Back <$VALUE
4x5 1-324 <$2500
3x10-20 1-524 <$2500
Total Issue $32,680
Out in 1910 $635
****
11258 Eastland
AMERICAN NB OF EASTLAND
{{ U + 0 L }}
Chartered 10/18
Liquidated 5/16/21
1902 Plain Back <$VALUE
4x5 1-4195 <$750
Total Issue $83,900
Out at close $25,500
****
7183 Eastland
CITY NB OF EASTLAND
{{ UNREPORTED }}
Chartered 3/04
Liquidated 1/25/21
1902 Red Seal <$VALUE
3x10-20 1-356 <$3000
1902 Date Back
3x10-20 1-1000 <$1500
1902 Plain Back
3x10-20 1001-1552 <$1500
Total Issue $95,400
Out at close $10,800
****
4466 Eastland
EASTLAND NB, EASTLAND
{{ UNREPORTED }}
Chartered 11/14/90
Liquidated 2/1/99
Brown Back <$VALUE
4x5 1-1848 <$2000
Total Issue $36,960
Out in 1910 $250
****
10624 Van Zandt
FNB OF EDGEWOOD
{{ 3 L 4 S }}
Organized 9/21/14
1902 Date Back <$VALUE
3x10-20 1-860 <$600
1902 Plain Back
4x5 1-7250 <$600
3x10-20 861-4529 <$600
1929 Small Size
5 Type 1 1-1080 <$350
10 Type 1 1-612 <$350
20 Type 1 1-166 <$350
5 Type 2 1-1584 <$350
10 Type 2 1-804 <$350
20 Type 2 1-336 <$350
Total Issue $483,170
Out in 1935 $23,980
Large out 1935 $1,160
****
13315 Hidalgo
FNB OF EDINBURG
{{ 4U + 8 S }}
Chartered 5/29
Liquidated 6/20/34
1929 Small Size <$VALUE
5 Type 1 1-622 <$200
10 Type 1 1-606 <$200
20 Type 1 1-148 <$200
50 Type 1 1-32 <$400
5 Type 2 1-1590 <$225
10 Type 2 1-600 <$225
20 Type 2 1-105 <$225
Total Issue $98,430
Out in 1935 $24,025
Ch 14124 assumed circulation
****
8123 Jackson
ALLEN NB OF EDNA
{{ 1 L }}
Chartered 3/06
Liquidated 12/31/21
1902 Red Seal <$VALUE
3x10-20 1-340 <$2500
1902 Date Back
3x10-20 1-2010 <$1250
1902 Plain Back
3x10-20 2011-3188 <$1250
Total Issue $176,400
Out at close $29,000
****
6112 Wharton
FNB OF EL CAMPO
{{ 6 L 15 S }}
Chartered 1/31/02
1902 Red Seal <$VALUE
3x10-20 1-1000 <$1500
1902 Date Back
3x10-20 1-3700 <$300
1902 Plain Back (dated 1902)
3x10-20 3701-8941 <$300
1902 Plain Back (dated 1922)
3x10-20 1-9793 <$300
1929 Small Size
10 Type 1 1-2840 <$100
20 Type 1 1-800 <$100
5 Type 2 1-4896 <$100
10 Type 2 1-3420 <$100
20 Type 2 1-1140 <$100
Total Issue $1,334,580
Out in 1935 $94,590
Large out 1935 $5,090
****
7530 El Paso
AMERICAN NB OF EL PASO
{{ 1 L }}
Chartered 12/04
Liquidated 12/31/12
1902 Red Seal <$VALUE
3x10-20 1-7500 <$1500
1902 Date Back
3x10-20 1-5502 <$1000
Total Issue $650,100
Out in 1913 $75,300
****
10974 El Paso
BORDER NB OF EL PASO
{{ 6 L }}
Chartered 4/17
Liquidated 3/25/24
1902 Plain Back <$VALUE
3x10-20 1-23062 <$350
Total Issue $1,153,100
Out at close $177,980
****
7514 El Paso
CITY NB OF EL PASO
{{ 14 L }}
Organized 10/14/04
Receivership 5/8/24
1902 Red Seal <$VALUE
3x10-20 1-3575 <$1250
1902 Date Back
4x5 1-23250 <$150
3x10-20 1-18400 <$150
1902 Plain Back
4x5 23251-67585 <$150
3x10-20 18401-44087 <$150
3x50-100 1-1443 <$400/$500
Total Issue $4,095 550
Out at close $442,050
****
10140 El Paso
COMMERCIAL NB OF EL PASO
{{ 1 L }}
Chartered 2/12
Liquidated 2/21/17
1902 Date Back <$VALUE
4x5 1-4650 <$750
3x10-20 1-3740 <$750
1902 Plain Back
4x5 4651-7160 <$750
3x10-20 3741-5251 <$750
Total Issue $405,750
Out at close $110,600
****
3608 El Paso
EL PASO NB OF TEXAS, EL PASO
{{ UNREPORTED }}
Chartered 12/22/86
Receivership 9/2/93
Brown Back <$VALUE
3x10-20 1-1665 <$1500
Total Issue $83,250
Out in 1916 $450
****
12769 El Paso
EL PASO NB, EL PASO
{{ 5 L 2U + 31 S }}
Chartered 6/25
1902 Plain Back <$VALUE
4x5 1-7815 <$350
3x10-20 1-4664 <$350
1929 Small Size
5 Type 1 1-9404 <$40
10 Type 1 1-4838 <$40
20 Type 1 1-1302 <$50
5 Type 2 1-20222 <$40
10 Type 2 1-12004 <$40
20 Type 2 1-2986 <$50
Total Issue $1,399,010
Out in 1935 $250,350
Large out 1935 $2,460
****

CONDITION affects Value. The Values shown are for notes in FINE condition.

2532 El Paso
FNB OF EL PASO
{{ 50+ L 29 S }}
Organized 5/25/81
Receivership 9/4/31
Series 1875 <$VALUE
3x10-20 1-6226<$5000/$6000
Brown Back
4x5 1-7500 <$750
3x10-20 1-6431 <$750
50-100 1-2473 <$3500/$4000
1882 Date Back
4x5 1-50000 <$300
3x10-20 1-29800 <$300
50-100 1-1400 <$3500/$4000
3x50-100 1-1440<$3500/$4000
1882 Value Back
4x5 50001-91000 <$400
3x10-20 29801-55600 <$400
1902 Plain Back
4x5 1-79655 <$100
4x10 1-37918 <$100
3x10-20 1-34768 <$100
1929 Small Size
5 Type 1 1-18926 <$40
10 Type 1 1-8920 <$40
20 Type 1 1-2748 <$50
Total Issue $12,604,760
Out at close $700,000
Large out at close $84,370

5239 El Paso
LOWDON NB OF EL PASO
{{ 1 L }}
Chartered 12/26/99
Liquidated 1/1/05
Brown Back <$VALUE
3x10-20 1-3084 <$1250
Total Issue $154,200
Out in 1910 $6,650

9155 El Paso
NB OF COMMERCE OF EL PASO
{{ UNREPORTED }}
Chartered 6/08
Liquidated 7/15/10
1902 Date Back <$VALUE
4x5 1-6425 <$1000
3x10-20 1-4726 <$1000
Total Issue $364,800
Out in 1910 $176,650

7075 El Paso
N EXCHANGE B OF EL PASO
{{ 1 L }}
Chartered 12/26/03
Liquidated 1/1/05
1902 Red Seal <$VALUE
3x10-20 1-1093 <$1500
Total Issue $54,650
Out in 1910 $2,580

2521 El Paso
STATE NB OF EL PASO
{{ 12 L 23 S }}
Chartered 1881
Series 1875 <$VALUE
4x5 1-4854 <$4000
3x10-20 1-94 <$5000/$6000
Brown Back
3x10-20 1-860 <$750
1882 Date Back
3x10-20 1-5300 <$350
1882 Value Back
3x10-20 5301-7580 <$450
1902 Plain Back
3x10-20 1-4752 <$150
1929 Small Size
10 Type 1 1-4542 <$40
20 Type 1 1-1446 <$50
10 Type 2 1-7663 <$40
20 Type 2 1-2410 <$50
Total Issue $1,332,250
Out in 1935 $205,770
Large out 1935 $3,220

8575 Schleicher
FNB OF ELDORADO
{{ 1 L 4 S }}
Chartered 3/07
1902 Red Seal <$VALUE
3x10-20 1-315 <$1500
1902 Date Back
3x10-20 1-2120 <$750
1902 Plain Back
3x10-20 2121-5252 <$750
1929 Small Size
10 Type 1 1-620 <$350
20 Type 1 1-206 <$350
10 Type 2 1-600 <$375
20 Type 2 1-219 <$375
Total Issue $350,650
Out in 1935 $20,000
Large out 1935 $1,000

10050 Wichita
FNB OF ELECTRA
{{ 2 L }}
Chartered 7/11
Liquidated 4/15/29
1902 Date Back <$VALUE
3x10-20 1-2080 <$650
1902 Plain Back
3x10-20 2081-6885 <$650
Total Issue $344,250
Out at close $21,500

8156 Bastrop
ELGIN NB, ELGIN
{{ 3 L 4 S }}
Chartered 4/06
1902 Red Seal <$VALUE
3x10-20 1-950 <$1500
1902 Date Back
3x10-20 1-2090 <$500
1902 Plain Back
3x10-20 2091-5923 <$500
1929 Small Size
10 Type 1 1-722 <$300
20 Type 1 1-190 <$300
10 Type 2 1-1062 <$300
20 Type 2 1-305 <$300
Total Issue $426,490
Out in 1935 $25,000
Large out 1935 $1,710

4410 Bastrop
FNB OF ELGIN
Chartered 1890
2nd title:FNB of Giddings
4/91
FIRST TITLE {{ 0 L }}
Brown Back <$VALUE
3x10-20 1-225 <$1500
SECOND TITLE {{ 1 L 3 S }}
Brown Back
4x5 1-1850 <$1250
3x10-20 1-750 <$1250
1882 Date Back
4x5 1-183 <$1250
3x10-20 1-64 <$1250
1902 Date Back
3x10-20 1-1150* <$650
1902 Plain Back
3x10-20 1311-2728* <$650
* 1151-1310 not marked
1929 Small Size
10 Type 1 1-422 <$400
20 Type 1 1-118 <$400
10 Type 2 1-350 <$400
20 Type 2 1-139 <$400
Total Issue $274,770
Out in 1935 $14,450
Large out 1935 $1,190

8515 Crosby
FNB OF EMMA
Chartered 1/07
2nd title:Citizens NB of
Crosbyton 4/22/11
FIRST TITLE {{ 0 L }}
1902 Red Seal <$VALUE
3x10-20 1-300 <$2500
1902 Date Back
3x10-20 1-265 <$1500
SECOND TITLE {{ 1 L 4 S }}
1902 Date Back
3x10-20 1-720 <$850
1902 Plain Back
3x10-20 721-2268 <$850
1929 Small Size
10 Type 1 1-626 <$350
20 Type 1 1-152 <$350
10 Type 2 1-1362 <$350
20 Type 2 1-340 <$350
Total Issue $217,870
Out in 1935 $22,500
Large out 1935 $1,230
Outstanding includes Ch 9989

6814 Rains
FNB OF EMORY
{{ 1 L 1 S }}
Chartered 6/03
1902 Red Seal <$VALUE
3x10-20 1-400 <$2500
1902 Date Back
3x10-20 1-860 <$1250
1902 Plain Back
3x10-20 861-1622 <$1250
1929 Small Size
10 Type 1 1-263 <$600
20 Type 1 1-71 <$600
Total Issue $125,400
Out in 1935 $7,250
Large out 1935 $1,400

6271 Delta
FNB OF ENLOE
{{ 2 L }}
Chartered 5/24/02
Liquidated 4/25/23
1902 Red Seal <$VALUE
3x10-20 1-900 <$1500
1902 Date Back
3x10-20 1-2130 <$750
1902 Plain Back (dated 1902)
3x10-20 2131-4062 <$750
1902 Plain Back (dated 1922)
3x10-20 1-276 <$750
Total Issue $261,900
Out at close $17,900

13667 Ellis
CITIZENS NB IN ENNIS
{{ UNREPORTED }}
Chartered 3/33
1929 Small Size <$VALUE
10 Type 2 1-457 <$600
20 Type 2 1-85 <$600
Total Issue $6,270
Out in 1935 $49,760
Large out 1935 $5,970
Outstanding includes Ch 7331
and Ch 10678

7331 Ellis
CITIZENS NB OF ENNIS
{{ 5 L 40 S }}
Chartered 7/04
Liquidated 4/26/33
1902 Red Seal <$VALUE
3x10-20 1-1470 <$1500
1902 Date Back
3x10-20 1-2300 <$350
1902 Plain Back
3x10-20 2301-14170 <$350
1929 Small Size
10 Type 1 1-2895 <$75
20 Type 1 1-732 <$85
Total Issue $1,043,540
Out at close $97,720
Large out at close $6,240
Ch 13667 assumed circulation

2939 Ellis
ENNIS NB, ENNIS
{{ 4 L }}
Chartered 1883
Liquidated 11/6/22
Brown Back <$VALUE
4x5 1-5103 <$1000
50-100 1-104 <$3500/$4000
1902 Red Seal
3x10-20 1-1250 <$1500
1902 Date Back
3x10-20 1-9000 <$400
1902 Plain Back
3x10-20 9001-15454 <$400
Total Issue $952,860
Out at close $36,400
Ch 12110 assumed circulation

12110 Ellis
FNB OF ENNIS
{{ 3 L 3 S }}
Organized 1/16/22
Receivership 2/11/30
1902 Plain Back <$VALUE
3x10-20 1-10385 <$500
1929 Small Size
10 Type 1 1-795 <$300
20 Type 1 1-149 <$300
Total Issue $584,830
Out at close $100,000
Large out at close $35,370
Outstanding includes Ch 2939

3532 Ellis
PEOPLES NB OF ENNIS
{{ 1 L }}
Chartered 7/13/86
Liquidated 1/31/14
Brown Back <$VALUE
3x10-20 1-1701 <$1250
1902 Red Seal
3x10-20 1-250 <$1500
1902 Date Back
3x10-20 1-3352 <$650
Total Issue $265,150
Out in 1914 $23,630

11700 El Paso
FNB OF FABENS
{{ 4 S }}
Chartered 5/20
1929 Small Size <$VALUE
5 Type 2 1-3228 <$350
10 Type 2 1-2744 <$350
50 Type 2 1-1396 <$450
Total Issue $71,500
Out in 1935 $42,000

4291 Freestone
FNB OF FAIRFIELD
{{ UNREPORTED }}
Chartered 4/22/90
Liquidated 12/28/91
Brown Back <$VALUE
50-100 1-90 <$4000
Total Issue $13,500
Out in 1910 $200

14072 Brooks
FNB IN FALFURRIAS
{{ UNREPORTED }}
Chartered 3/34
1929 Small Size <$VALUE
5 Type 2 1-240 <$750
10 Type 2 1-125 <$750
Total Issue $2,450
Out in 1935 $25,120
Large out 1935 $1,770
Outstanding includes Ch 11792

11792 Brooks
FNB OF FALFURRIAS
{{ 2 L 6 S }}
Chartered 7/20
Liquidated 4/28/34
1902 Plain Back <$VALUE
3x10-20 1-4035 <$750
1929 Small Size
10 Type 1 1-1259 <$300
20 Type 1 1-326 <$300
Total Issue $316,410
Out at close $37,590
Large out 1935 $1,770
Ch 14072 assumed circulation

8606 Karnes
FALLS CITY NB, FALLS CITY
{{ 4 L 3 S }}
Chartered 3/07
1902 Red Seal <$VALUE
4x10 1-262 <$1500
1902 Date Back
4x10 1-1650* <$500
1902 Plain Back
4x10 1801-5582* <$500
* 1651-1800 not marked
1929 Small Size
10 Type 1 1-894 <$400
10 Type 2 1-1404 <$400
Total Issue $301,440
Out in 1935 $16,310
Large out 1935 $960

6011 Collin
FARMERS & MERCHANTS NB OF
FARMERSVILLE
{{ 4 L }}
Chartered 11/5/01
Liquidated 4/12/27
Brown Back <$VALUE
3x10-20 1-1040 <$1000
1882 Date Back
3x10-20 1-5600 <$650
1882 Value Back
3x10-20 5601-9717 <$650
1902 Plain Back
3x10-20 1-4876 <$500
Total Issue $781,650
Out at close $59,600

3624 Collin
FNB OF FARMERSVILLE
{{ 1 L }}
Chartered 1/27/87
Receivership 8/6/30
Brown Back <$VALUE
3x10-20 1-1628 <$1250
1902 Red Seal
3x10-20 1-200 <$1500
1902 Date Back
3x10-20 1-2800* <$600
1902 Plain Back
3x10-20 3301-4158* <$600
Total Issue $299,300
Out at close $5,500

8431 Parmer
FNB OF FARWELL
{{ UNREPORTED }}
Chartered 11/06
Liquidated 12/20/10
1902 Red Seal <$VALUE
4x5 1-200 <$3000
3x10-20 1-100 <$3000
50-100 1-20 <$7500
1902 Date Back
4x5 1-100 <$2000
3x10-20 1-19 <$2000
50-100 1-4 <$2500
Total Issue $16,660
Out in 1911 $2,800

10954 Fayette
FARMERS NB OF
FAYETTEVILLE
{{ 4 L 5 S }}
Chartered 2/17
1902 Plain Back <$VALUE
3x10-20 1-3209 <$450
1929 Small Size
10 Type 1 1-548 <$300
20 Type 1 1-136 <$300
10 Type 2 1-994 <$300
20 Type 2 1-217 <$300
Total Issue $223,930
Out in 1935 $25,000
Large out 1935 $2,370

6553 Ellis
CITIZENS NB OF FERRIS
{{ 1 L }}
Chartered 12/26/02
Liquidated 2/10/05
1902 Red Seal <$VALUE
3x10-20 1-246 <$2500
Total Issue $12,300
Out in 1910 $590

6376 Ellis
FERRIS NB, FERRIS
{{ 2 L 1 S }}
Chartered 8/12/02
Liquidated 1/23/31
1902 Red Seal <$VALUE
3x10-20 1-856 <$1500
1902 Date Back
3x10-20 1-2980* <$600
* 2811 not issued
1902 Plain Back
3x10-20 2981-4847 <$600
1929 Small Size
10 Type 1 1-249 <$500
20 Type 1 1-35 <$500
Total Issue $304,240
Out at close $13,130
Large out at close $2,570

4179 Fayette
FNB OF FLATONIA
{{ UNREPORTED }}
Chartered 12/16/89
Liquidated 8/10/16
Brown Back <$VALUE
4x10 1-1546 <$2000
50-100 1-575 <$4500
1902 Date Back
4x10 1-3750* <$1000
1902 Plain Back
4x10 4001-4118* <$1000
* 3751-4000 not marked
Total Issue $312,810
Out in 1916 $46,700

8519 Wilson
CITY NB OF FLORESVILLE
{{ 4 L 6 S }}
Chartered 1/07
Closed 1/8/32
1902 Red Seal <$VALUE
3x10-20 1-1500 <$1250
1902 Date Back
3x10-20 1-3800 <$350
1902 Plain Back
3x10-20 3801-11748 <$350
1929 Small Size
10 Type 1 1-1134 <$200
20 Type 1 1-281 <$200
Total Issue $764,160
Out at close $50,000
Large out at close $4,540
Ch 6320 assumed circulation

F City NB of Floresville
SEE Ch 6320
FNB of Floresville

6320 Wilson
FNB OF FLORESVILLE
Chartered 6/25/02
2nd title: F City NB of
Floresville 11/8/32
FIRST TITLE {{ 6 L 3 S }}
1902 Red Seal <$VALUE
3x10-20 1-1950 <$1250
1902 Date Back
3x10-20 1-3790 <$350
1902 Plain Back
3x10-20 3791-11716 <$350
1929 Small Size
10 Type 1 1-1182 <$250
20 Type 1 1-400 <$250
SECOND TITLE {{ U + 3 S }}
1929 Small Size
10 Type 1 1-452 <$250
20 Type 1 1-96 <$250
10 Type 2 1-621 <$250
20 Type 2 1-91 <$250
Total Issue $848,890
Out in 1935 $54,560
Large out 1935 $5,610
Outstanding includes Ch 8519

7045 Floyd
FNB OF FLOYDADA
{{ 2 L 3 S }}
Chartered 11/03
1902 Red Seal <$VALUE
3x10-20 1-388 <$2000
1902 Date Back
3x10-20 1-1320* <$1000
1902 Plain Back
3x10-20 1441-3380* <$1000
* 1321-1440 not marked
1929 Small Size
10 Type 1 1-876 <$450
20 Type 1 1-253 <$450
Total Issue $271,320
Out in 1935 $23,810
Large out 1935 $660

12101 Lipscomb
FOLLETT NB, FOLLETT
{{ 0 L 4 S }}
Chartered 1/22
1902 Plain Back <$VALUE
3x10-20 1-819 <$1500
1929 Small Size
10 Type 1 1-586 <$300
20 Type 1 1-164 <$300
10 Type 2 1-1113 <$325
20 Type 2 1-230 <$325
Total Issue $111,520
Out in 1935 $22,000
Large out 1935 $510

6078 Kaufman
CITY NB OF FORNEY
{{ 3 L 1 S }}
Chartered 1/2/02
Liquidated 3/31/30
Brown Back <$VALUE
3x10-20 1-1200 <$1000
1882 Date Back
3x10-20 1-3360 <$850
1882 Value Back
3x10-20 3361-4334 <$850
1902 Plain Back
4x5 1-9778 <$500
1929 Small Size
5 Type 1 1-726 <$500
Total Issue $494,040
Out at close $21,730
Large out at close $1,950

9369 Kaufman
FARMERS NB OF FORNEY
{{ 7 L 8 S }}
Chartered 3/09
1902 Date Back <$VALUE
3x10-20 1-5700 <$250
1902 Plain Back
3x10-20 5701-24736 <$250
1929 Small Size
10 Type 1 1-1958 <$150
20 Type 1 1-602 <$150
10 Type 2 1-2236 <$150
20 Type 2 1-648 <$150
Total Issue $1,461,840
Out in 1935 $52,805
Large out 1935 $5,655

4014 Kaufman
NB OF FORNEY
{{ 1 L }}
Chartered 4/18/89
Liquidated 3/31/09
Brown Back <$VALUE
3x10-20 1-4518 <$1250
Total Issue $225,900
Out in 1910 $16,575

9848 Pecos
FNB OF FORT STOCKTON
{{ 2 L 2 S }}
Chartered 9/10
Receivership 10/13/31
1902 Date Back <$VALUE
3x10-20 1-1560 <$650
1902 Plain Back
3x10-20 1561-6109 <$650
1929 Small Size
10 Type 1 1-552 <$400
20 Type 1 1-133 <$400
Total Issue $354,530
Out at close $24,340
Large out at close $2,620

4848 Tarrant
AMERICAN NB OF FORT WORTH
{{ 5 L }}
Chartered 1893
Closed 3/15/19
Brown Back <$VALUE
3x10-20 1-11240 <$750
1882 Date Back
3x10-20 1-7006 <$400
1902 Date Back
3x50-100 1-1446 <$600/$750
Total Issue $1,273,800
Out at close $146,245
Ch 4004 assumed circulation

2359 Tarrant
CITY NB OF FORT WORTH
{{ 1 L }}
Chartered 5/28/77
Receivership 4/10/95
Series 1875 <$VALUE
4x5 1-11675 <$4000
Total Issue $233,500
Out in 1916 $1,225

4004 Tarrant
FARMERS AND MECHANICS NB OF FORT WORTH
{{ 8 L }}
Chartered 3/30/89
Closed 2/2/27
Brown Back <$VALUE
4x5 1-6865 <$750
50-100 1-4593 <$3500/$4000
1902 Date Back
4x5 1-20000 <$200
3x10-20 1-12900 <$200
50-100 1-667 <$400/$500
3x50-100 1-400 <$400/$500
1902 Plain Back
4x5 20001-80780 <$200
3x10-20 12901-49196 <$200
Total Issue $5,101,700
Out at close $437,100
Outstanding includes Ch 4848
Ch 3131 assumed circulation

2349 Tarrant
FNB OF FORT WORTH
{{ 19 L }}
Chartered 3/21/77
Series 1875 <$VALUE
4x5 1-8146 <$4000
3x10-20 1-1687<$5000/$6000
Brown Back
3x10-20 1-5650 <$750
1882 Date Back
3x10-20 1-35391 <$400
1902 Plain Back
3x50-100 1-7889 <$400/$500
Total Issue $4,271,570
Out in 1935 $33,265

3131 Tarrant
FORT WORTH NB, FORT WORTH
{{ 50+ L 50+ S }}
Chartered 1884
Brown Back <$VALUE
4x5 1-1075 <$750
3x10-20 1-8468 <$750
1902 Red Seal
4x5 1-7000 <$1000
3x10-20 1-8500 <$1000
1902 Date Back
4x5 1-39000 <$50
3x10-20 1-28900 <$60
1902 Plain Back
4x5 39001-215990 <$50
3x10-20 28901-136328 <$60
3x50-100 1-3188 <$350/$400
1929 Small Size
5 Type 1 1-68694 <$15
10 Type 1 1-36392 <$20
20 Type 1 1-9750 <$30
50 Type 1 1-2196 <$100
100 Type 1 1-712 <$150
5 Type 2 1-28152 <$20
10 Type 2 1-12937 <$25
20 Type 2 1-3255 <$35
Total Issue $19,778,670
Out in 1935 $1,322,670
Large out 1935 $85,020
Outstanding includes Ch 4004 and Ch 4848

3631 Tarrant
MERCHANTS NB OF FORT WORTH
{{ UNREPORTED }}
Chartered 2/1/87
Liquidated 8/15/93
Brown Back <$VALUE
50-100 1-656 <$5000
Total Issue $98,400
Out in 1910 $1,300

4946 Tarrant
N LIVESTOCK B OF FORT WORTH
{{ UNREPORTED }}
Chartered 3/28/94
Liquidated 11/1/97
Brown Back <$VALUE
3x10-20 1-1144 <$2500
Total Issue $57,200
Out in 1910 $870

3221 Tarrant
STATE NB OF FORT WORTH
{{ 3 L }}
Chartered 1884
Liquidated 3/3/14
Brown Back <$VALUE
3x10-20 1-3925 <$1000
50-100 1-2941 <$3500/$4000
1902 Red Seal
3x10-20 1-8000 <$1250
1902 Date Back
3x10-20 1-9280 <$400
Total Issue $1,501,400
Out in 1914 $111,190

Stockyards NB of Fort Worth
SEE Ch 6822
Stockyards NB of North Fort Worth

12371 Tarrant
TEXAS NB OF FORT WORTH
{{ 12 L 6 S }}
Organized 5/3/23
Receivership 2/4/30
1902 Plain Back <$VALUE
4x5 1-58505 <$175
3x10-20 1-37673 <$175
1929 Small Size
5 Type 1 1-4429 <$175
10 Type 1 1-2621 <$175
20 Type 1 1-420 <$175
Total Issue $3,394,280
Out at close $484,940
Large out at close $150,610

2689 Tarrant
TRADERS NB OF FORT WORTH
{{ 3 L }}
Chartered 1882
Liquidated 2/26/16
Series 1875 <$VALUE
4x10 1-4289 <$5000
1902 Red Seal
3x10-20 1-1900 <$1500
1902 Date Back
3x10-20 1-3903 <$500
Total Issue $461,710
Out in 1916 $27,200

7165 Tarrant
WESTERN NB OF FORT WORTH
{{ 5 L }}
Chartered 3/04
Liquidated 10/1/15
1902 Red Seal <$VALUE
3x10-20 1-19000 <$1250
1902 Date Back 1500
3x10-20 1-30189 <$350
Total Issue $2,459,450
Out at close $342,900

7838 Robertson
FNB OF FRANKLIN
{{ 6 L U + 8 S }}
Chartered 7/05
1902 Red Seal <$VALUE
4x5 1-900 <$1500
3x10-20 1-720 <$1500
1902 Date Back
4x5 1-3300 <$350
3x10-20 1-2520 <$350
1902 Plain Back
4x5 3301-11930 <$350
3x10-20 2521-8052 <$350
1929 Small Size
5 Type 1 1-1708 <$175
10 Type 1 1-1016 <$175
20 Type 1 1-272 <$175
5 Type 2 1-4068 <$175
10 Type 2 1-1932 <$175
20 Type 2 1-528 <$200
Total Issue $890,260
Out in 1935 $45,060
Large out 1935 $2,485

7623 Anderson
FNB OF FRANKSTON
{{ UNREPORTED }}
Chartered 2/23/05
Liquidated 12/21/08
1902 Red Seal <$VALUE
3x10-20 1-288 <$3000
Total Issue $14,400
Out in 1910 $2,080

10420 Brazoria
FREEPORT NB, FREEPORT
{{ 3 L 3 S }}
Chartered 7/13
1902 Date Back <$VALUE
4x5 1-625 <$650
3x10-20 1-410 <$650
3x50-100 1-50 <$850/$1000
1902 Plain Back
4x5 626-2250 <$650
3x10-20 411-1512 <$650
1929 Small Size
5 Type 1 1-524 <$400
10 Type 1 1-274 <$400
20 Type 1 1-94 <$400
5 Type 2 1-586 <$400
10 Type 2 1-363 <$400
20 Type 2 1-140 <$400
Total Issue $185,900
Out in 1935 $12,500
Large out 1935 $740

6346 Collin
FNB OF FRISCO
{{ 1 L }}
Chartered 7/19/02
Receivership 12/31/28
1902 Red Seal <$VALUE
3x10-20 1-1500 <$1500
1902 Date Back
3x10-20 1-2320 <$650
1902 Plain Back
3x10-20 2321-6423 <$650
Total Issue $396,150
Out at close $24,550

6968 Navarro
FNB OF FROST
{{ 2 L 2 S }}
Chartered 9/03
Liquidated 2/22/31
1902 Red Seal <$VALUE
3x10-20 1-1340 <$2000
1902 Date Back
3x10-20 1-2730 <$1000
1902 Plain Back
3x10-20 2731-7343 <$1000
1929 Small Size
10 Type 1 1-330 <$500
20 Type 1 1-105 <$500
Total Issue $466,550
Out at close $42,990
Large out at close $26,690

13507 Navarro
FROST NB, FROST
{{ U + 5 S }}
Chartered 12/30 as Frost NB of Frost under which there was no issue. Issuing title adopted 1/20/31.
1929 Small Size <$VALUE
5 Type 2 1-5118 <$250
10 Type 2 1-2604 <$250
20 Type 2 1-816 <$250
Total Issue $67,950
Out in 1935 $28,900

2836 Cooke
FNB OF GAINESVILLE
{{ 6 L }}
Chartered 1882
Closed 2/27/31
Brown Back <$VALUE
3x10-20 1-3561 <$1000
1902 Red Seal
3x10-20 1-2620 <$1250
1902 Date Back
3x10-20 1-12083 <$350
Total Issue $913,200
Out at close $7,630
Ch 6292 assumed circulation

2802 Cooke
GAINESVILLE NB, GAINESVILLE
{{ 1 L }}
Chartered 10/21/82
Liquidated 6/2/02
Brown Back <$VALUE
3x10-20 1-1370 <$1500
50-100 1-773 <$3500/$4000
Total Issue $184,450
Out in 1910 $3,640

6292 Cooke
LINDSAY NB OF GAINESVILLE
{{ 5 L }}
Chartered 6/6/02
Liquidated 9/19/33
1902 Red Seal <$VALUE
4x5 1-2520 <$1250
50-100 1-300 <$7500
1902 Date Back
4x5 1-4830 <$350
3x10-20 1-5100 <$350
50-100 1-300 <$650/$750
1902 Plain Back
4x5 4831-11525 <$350
3x10-20 5101-9073 <$350
Total Issue $900,150
Out at close $8,930
Outstanding includes Ch 2836

3229 Cooke
RED RIVER NB OF GAINESVILLE
{{ UNREPORTED }}
Chartered 7/25/84
Liquidated 12/30/03
Brown Back <$VALUE
3x10-20 1-2626 <$2500
Total Issue $131,300
Out in 1910 $2,000

4321 Galveston
AMERICAN NB OF GALVESTON
{{ 7 L }}
Chartered 5/28/90
Liquidated 12/19/94
Brown Back <$VALUE
4x5 1-1311 <$750
3x10-20 1-1203 <$750
Total Issue $86,370
Out in 1910 $780

8899 Galveston
CITY NB OF GALVESTON
{{ 9 L 3U + 29 S }}
Chartered 9/07
1902 Red Seal <$VALUE
3x10-20 1-2000 <$1000
1902 Date Back
3x10-20 1-9300 <$175
1902 Plain Back
3x10-20 9301-31962 <$175
1929 Small Size
10 Type 1 1-5790 <$40
20 Type 1 1-1512 <$40
10 Type 2 1-10299 <$40
20 Type 2 1-3196 <$40
Total Issue $2,393,850
Out in 1935 $190,900
Large out 1935 $9,650
Outstanding includes Ch 4153

1566 Galveston
FNB OF GALVESTON
{{ 18 L 23 S }}
Chartered 1865
Original Series <$VALUE
4x5 1-8350 <$4000
3x10-20 1-4960<$5000/$6000
Series 1875
4x5 1-1450 <$4000
3x10-20 1-4328<$5000/$6000
Brown Back
4x5 1-1625 <$750
3x10-20 1-7233 <$750
1902 Red Seal
3x10-20 1-5700 <$1000
1902 Date Back
3x10-20 1-16700 <$125
1902 Plain Back
3x10-20 16701-46423 <$125
1929 Small Size
5 Type 1 1-3248 <$50
10 Type 1 1-4946 <$45
20 Type 1 1-1306 <$50
5 Type 2 1-11544 <$50
10 Type 2 1-6732 <$50
20 Type 2 1-1600 <$60
Total Issue $4,368,660
Out in 1935 $187,990
Large out 1935 $16,740

4153 Galveston
GALVESTON NB, GALVESTON
{{ 5 L }}
Chartered 11/8/89
Liquidated 10/16/11
Brown Back <$VALUE
4x5 1-2280 <$1000
3x10-20 1-5960 <$1000
1882 Date Back
3x10-20 1-45 <$750
1902 Date Back
3x10-20 1-1410 <$350
Total Issue $416,350
Out at close $71,700

8068 Galveston
MERCHANTS NB OF GALVESTON
{{ UNREPORTED }}
Chartered 1/27/06
Liquidated 11/24/06
1902 Red Seal <$VALUE
4x5 1-415 <$2000
3x10-20 1-344 <$2000
Total Issue $25,500
Out in 1910 $3,305

1642 Galveston
NB OF TEXAS, GALVESTON
{{ 5 L }}
Chartered 3/9/66
Liquidated 3/19/90
Original Series <$VALUE
3x1-2 1-4280<$4500/$15,000
4x5 1-3380 <$4000
2x10-20-50 1-1050 <$5000/$6000/$15,000
Series 1875
2x10-20-50 1-1106 <$5000/$6000/$15,000
Brown Back
4x5 1-1150 <$1000
Total Issue $306,040
Out in 1910 $2,203

12475 Galveston
UNITED STATES NB OF GALVESTON
{{ 29 L 50+ S }}
Chartered 12/23
1902 Plain Back <$VALUE
4x5 1-67552 <$75
3x10-20 1-45357 <$100
3x50-100 1-3151 <$350/$400
1929 Small Size
5 Type 1 1-34190 <$30
10 Type 1 1-18540 <$35
20 Type 1 1-5294 <$45
50 Type 1 1-610 <$125
100 Type 1 1-172 <$175
5 Type 2 1-14166 <$30
10 Type 2 1-4890 <$35
20 Type 2 1-1370 <$45
Total Issue $7,613,350
Out in 1935 $544,640
Large out 1935 $43,450

10076 Jackson
FNB OF GANADO
{{ UNREPORTED }}
Chartered 9/8/11
Liquidated 4/2/18
1902 Date Back <$VALUE
3x10-20 1-980 <$1500
1902 Plain Back
3x10-20 981-1053 <$1500
Total Issue $52,650
Out at close $12,500

7140 Dallas
CITIZENS NB OF GARLAND
Chartered 2/04
Liquidated 1/20/31
2nd title: FNB of Garland 6/16/19
FIRST TITLE {{ 2 L }}
1902 Red Seal <$VALUE
4x5 1-2675 <$1500
3x10-20 1-1850 <$1500
1902 Date Back
4x5 1-4200 <$500
3x10-20 1-3140 <$500
1902 Plain Back
4x5 4201-6100 <$500
3x10-20 3141-4140 <$500
SECOND TITLE {{ 3 L 4 S }}
1902 Plain Back
4x5 1-10234 <$400
3x10-20 1-4558 <$400
1929 Small Size
5 Type 1 1-920 <$250
10 Type 1 1-411 <$250
20 Type 1 1-140 <$250
Total Issue $976,640
Out at close $43,510
Large out at close $8,310

FNB of Garland
SEE Ch 7140
Citizens NB of Garland

7989 Dallas
NB OF GARLAND
Chartered 11/05
2nd title:State NB of Garland 1/23/13
FIRST TITLE {{ 2 L }}
1902 Red Seal <$VALUE
4x5 1-1500 <$1500
3x10-20 1-1300 <$1500
1902 Date Back
4x5 1-2340 <$500
3x10-20 1-1723 <$500
SECOND TITLE {{8 L U + 16 S}}
1902 Date Back
4x5 1-4900 <$250
3x10-20 1-3220 <$250
1902 Plain Back
4x5 4901-24916 <$250
3x10-20 3221-16317 <$250
1929 Small Size
5 Type 1 1-4586 <$100
10 Type 1 1-2454 <$100
20 Type 1 1-592 <$100
5 Type 2 1-8580 <$125
10 Type 2 1-4877 <$125
20 Type 2 1-1352 <$125
Total Issue $2,016,690
Out in 1935 $96,400
Large out 1935 $2,650

State NB of Garland
SEE Ch 7989
NB of Garland

4388 Coryell
CITIZENS NB OF GATESVILLE
{{ UNREPORTED }}
Chartered 8/5/90
Liquidated 7/1/91
Brown Back <$VALUE
3x10-20 1-235 <$2500
Total Issue $11,750
Out in 1910 $80

4732 Coryell
CITY NB OF GATESVILLE
{{ UNREPORTED }}
Organized 4/23/92
Receivership 5/29/97
Brown Back <$VALUE
4x5 1-1270 <$2500
Total Issue $25,400
Out in 1916 $165

8928 Coryell
FARMERS NB OF GATESVILLE
{{ UNREPORTED }}
Chartered 10/23/07
Liquidated 10/3/08
1902 Red Seal <$VALUE
3x10-20 1-174 <$3000
Total Issue $8,700
Out in 1910 $1,810

4097 Coryell
FNB OF GATESVILLE
{{ 7 L 13 S }}
Chartered 8/21/89
Brown Back <$VALUE
3x10-20 1-4162 <$1000
1902 Date Back
3x10-20 1-3710 <$300
1902 Plain Back
3x10-20 3711-20838 <$300
1929 Small Size
10 Type 1 1-3128 <$125
20 Type 1 1-810 <$125
10 Type 2 1-4833 <$150
20 Type 2 1-1416 <$150
Total Issue $1,611,530
Out in 1935 $83,200
Large out 1935 $5,330

6150 Coryell
GATESVILLE NB, GATESVILLE
{{ 3 L 5 S }}
Chartered 3/10/02
1902 Red Seal <$VALUE
3x10-20 1-650 <$1500
1902 Date Back
3x10-20 1-2520 <$450
1902 Plain Back (dated 1902)
3x10-20 2521-3722 <$450
1902 Plain Back (dated 1922)
3x10-20 1-2555 <$450
1929 Small Size
10 Type 1 1-702 <$250
20 Type 1 1-222 <$250
10 Type 2 1-1321 <$250
20 Type 2 1-285 <$250
Total Issue $434,020
Out in 1935 $20,900
Large out 1935 $1,060

12919 Live Oak
FNB OF GEORGE WEST
{{ 3 L 3 S }}
Chartered 5/26
Liquidated 4/16/34
1902 Plain Back <$VALUE
3x10-20 1-3322 <$1250
1929 Small Size
10 Type 1 1-1344 <$650
20 Type 1 1-328 <$650
Total Issue $286,100
Out at close $48,380
Large out at close $2,960

4294 Williamson
FNB OF GEORGETOWN
{{ 4 L 17 S }}
Chartered 1890
Brown Back <$VALUE
50-100 1-594 <$3500/$4000
1882 Date Back
50-100 1-252 <$3500/$4000
1902 Date Back
50-100 1-800 <$600/$750
3x50-100 1-650 <$600/$750
1902 Plain Back
3x50-100 651-848<$600/$750
1929 Small Size
5 Type 1 1-6092 <$85
10 Type 1 1-3026 <$85
5 Type 2 1-11026 <$85
10 Type 2 1-6102 <$85
Total Issue $939,370
Out in 1935 $98,150
Large out 1935 $3,550

FNB of Giddings
SEE Ch 4410
FNB of Elgin

5741 Upshur
FARMERS & MERCHANTS NB OF GILMER
{{ 7 L 6 S }}
Chartered 3/14/01
Brown Back <$VALUE
3x10-20 1-3600 <$1000
1882 Date Back
3x10-20 1-4000 <$650
1882 Value Back
3x10-20 4001-6300 <$650
1902 Plain Back
3x10-20 1-6348 <$350
1929 Small Size
10 Type 1 1-1578 <$225
20 Type 1 1-442 <$225
5 Type 2 1-324 <$250
10 Type 2 1-2532 <$250
20 Type 2 1-715 <$250
Total Issue $1,001,360
Out in 1935 $48,150
Large out 1935 $5,455

5288 Upshur
FNB OF GILMER
{{ 4 L 5 S }}
Chartered 4/13/00
Brown Back <$VALUE
3x10-20 1-1430 <$1000
1882 Date Back
3x10-20 1-3340 <$750
1882 Value Back
3x10-20 3341-3471 <$750
1902 Plain Back
3x10-20 1-3608 <$500
1929 Small Size
10 Type 1 1-872 <$275
20 Type 1 1-234 <$275
10 Type 2 1-1108 <$275
20 Type 2 1-324 <$300
Total Issue $523,410
Out in 1935 $24,650
Large out 1935 $1,880

5795 Somervell
FNB OF GLEN ROSE
{{ 1 L }}
Chartered 5/4/01
Liquidated 6/26/28
Brown Back <$VALUE
3x10-20 1-920 <$2000
1882 Date Back
3x10-20 1-867 <$2000
1902 Plain Back
3x10-20 1-562 <$1500
Total Issue $117,450
Out at close $4,300

4687 Mills
FNB OF GOLDTHWAITE
{{ 1 L }}
Chartered 1/23/92
Liquidated 2/26/01
Brown Back <$VALUE
3x10-20 1-714 <$2500
Total Issue $35,700
Out in 1910 $3,955

6092 Mills
GOLDTHWAITE NB, GOLDTHWAITE
{{ 6 L }}
Chartered 1/13/02
Liquidated 5/22/24
Brown Back <$VALUE
3x10-20 1-500 <$1000
1882 Date Back
3x10-20 1-1960 <$650
1882 Value Back
3x10-20 1961-2830 <$650
1902 Plain Back
3x10-20 1-746 <$500
Total Issue $203,800
Out at close $23,500

7548 Goliad
COMMERCIAL NB OF GOLIAD
{{ 1 L }}
Chartered 1/05
Liquidated 8/27/18
1902 Red Seal <$VALUE
3x10-20 1-700 <$2000
1902 Date Back
3x10-20 1-1850 <$1000
1902 Plain Back
3x10-20 1851-2132 <$1000
Total Issue $141,600
Out at close $24,100

4565 Goliad
FNB OF GOLIAD
{{ 6 L 11 S }}
Chartered 1891
Brown Back <$VALUE
3x10-20 1-1290 <$1000
1882 Date Back
3x10-20 1-1453 <$750
1902 Date Back
3x10-20 1-3300 <$350
1902 Plain Back
3x10-20 3301-10885 <$350
1929 Small Size
10 Type 1 1-1512 <$150
20 Type 1 1-392 <$175
5 Type 2 1-324 <$175
10 Type 2 1-2011 <$175
20 Type 2 1-526 <$175
Total Issue $851,410
Out in 1935 $63,050
Large out 1935 $18,795

8392 Gonzales
FARMERS NB OF GONZALES
{{ 7 L 14 S }}
Organized 9/13/06
Receivership 11/4/32
1902 Red Seal <$VALUE
3x10-20 1-500 <$1250
1902 Date Back
3x10-20 1-2690* <$300
1902 Plain Back
3x10-20 2991-14581* <$300
* 2691-2990 not marked
1929 Small Size
10 Type 1 1-2444 <$100
20 Type 1 1-575 <$125
Total Issue $969,690
Out at close $97,240
Large out at close $8,280

6277 Gonzales
GONZALES NB, GONZALES
{{ UNREPORTED }}
Chartered 5/26/02
Liquidated 4/15/05
1902 Red Seal <$VALUE
3x10-20 1-445 <$2500
Total Issue $22,250
Out in 1910 $1,260

5759 Palo Pinto
FNB OF GORDON
{{ 1 L 0 S }}
Chartered 3/27/01
Brown Back <$VALUE
3x10-20 1-500 <$2500
1882 Date Back
3x10-20 1-860 <$2000
1882 Value Back
3x10-20 861-984 <$2000
1902 Plain Back
3x10-20 1-716 <$1500
1929 Small Size
10 Type 1 1-241 <$750
20 Type 1 1-51 <$750
Total Issue $130,580
Out in 1935 $6,250
Large out 1935 $390

8200 Knox
FNB OF GOREE
{{ 1 L 1 S }}
Chartered 5/06
Liquidated 3/2/32
1902 Red Seal <$VALUE
3x10-20 1-200 <$2500
1902 Date Back
3x10-20 1-1020 <$1500
1902 Plain Back
3x10-20 1021-1990 <$1500
1929 Small Size
10 Type 1 1-157 <$750
20 Type 1 1-23 <$750
Total Issue $121,680
Out at close $5,590
Large out at close $670

7410 Eastland
FNB OF GORMAN
{{ 3 L 5 S }}
Chartered 9/04
1902 Red Seal <$VALUE
3x10-20 1-1400 <$1500
1902 Date Back
3x10-20 1-2800 <$650
1902 Plain Back
3x10-20 2801-7961 <$650
1929 Small Size
10 Type 1 1-898 <$300
20 Type 1 1-256 <$300
10 Type 2 1-1114 <$300
20 Type 2 1-350 <$300
Total Issue $570,790
Out in 1935 $30,000
Large out 1935 $1,950

4418 Young
BECKHAM NB OF GRAHAM
Chartered 1890
2nd title:FNB in Graham 1/19/21
FIRST TITLE {{ 1 L }}
Brown Back <$VALUE
4x5 1-1575 <$1250
3x10-20 1-2490 <$1250
1882 Date Back
4x5 1-427 <$1000
3x10-20 1-286 <$1000
1902 Date Back
4x5 1-2425 <$650
3x10-20 1-1940 <$650
1902 Plain Back
4x5 2426-2975 <$650
3x10-20 1941-2280 <$650
SECOND TITLE {{ 1 L 12 S }}
1902 Plain Back
4x5 1-3679 <$650
3x10-20 1-2182 <$650
1929 Small Size
10 Type 1 1-708 <$150
20 Type 1 1-240 <$150
5 Type 2 1-30128 <$150
10 Type 2 1-636 <$150
20 Type 2 1-132 <$175
Total Issue $765,940
Out in 1935 $96,350
Large out 1935 $1,920

FNB in Graham
SEE Ch 4418
Beckham NB of Graham

4391 Young
FNB OF GRAHAM
{{ UNREPORTED }}
Chartered 8/11/90
Liquidated 3/4/95
Brown Back <$VALUE
3x10-20 1-450 <$2500
Total Issue $22,500
Out in 1910 $100

5897 Young
GRAHAM NB, GRAHAM
{{ 3 L 7 S }}
Chartered 7/8/01
Brown Back <$VALUE
4x5 1-450 <$1250
3x10-20 1-710 <$1250
1882 Date Back
4x5 1-725 <$850
3x10-20 1-880 <$850
1882 Value Back
4x5 726-1325 <$850
3x10-20 881-1161 <$850
1902 Plain Back
4x5 1-2672 <$500
3x10-20 1-1653 <$500
1929 Small Size
5 Type 1 1-2192 <$225
10 Type 1 1-1212 <$225
20 Type 1 1-350 <$225
5 Type 2 1-3132 <$225
10 Type 2 1-1572 <$225
20 Type 2 1-420 <$250
Total Issue $485,400
Out in 1935 $47,240
Large out 1935 $1,040

5808 Hood
CITY NB OF GRANBURY
{{ 3 L }}
Chartered 5/11/01
Liquidated 12/20/28
Brown Back <$VALUE
3x10-20 1-800 <$1000
1882 Date Back
4x5 1-1150* <$850
3x10-20 1-920** <$850
1882 Value Back
4x5 1401-3050* <$850
3x10-20 1121-1960** <$850
* 1151-1400 not marked
** 921-1120 not marked
1902 Plain Back
4x5 1-3885 <$500
3x10-20 1-2404 <$500
Total Issue $396,900
Out at close $4,570

3727 Hood
FNB OF GRANBURY
{{ 10 L 12 S }}
Chartered 6/18/87
Brown Back <$VALUE
3x10-20 1-4877 <$1000
1902 Red Seal
50-100 1-640 <$7500
1902 Date Back
4x5 1-7850* <$250
3x10-20 1-9299 <$250
50-100 1-500 <$500/$650
3x50-100 1-500 <$500/$650
1902 Plain Back
4x5 8351-25022* <$250
* 7851-8350 not marked
1929 Small Size
5 Type 1 1-3976 <$125
10 Type 1 1-2324 <$125
20 Type 1 1-648 <$125
5 Type 2 1-3376 <$150
10 Type 2 1-1610 <$150
20 Type 2 1-622 <$150
Total Issue $1,887,140
Out in 1935 $57,220
Large out 1935 $7,220

8884 Van Zandt
CITIZENS NB OF GRAND SALINE
{{ UNREPORTED }}
Chartered 9/07
Liquidated 1/20/12
1902 Red Seal <$VALUE
3x10-20 1-225 <$3000
1902 Date Back
3x10-20 1-251 <$2000
Total Issue $23,800
Out in 1912 $3,710

5722 Van Zandt
FNB OF GRAND SALINE
{{ UNREPORTED }}
Chartered 2/19/01
Liquidated 12/15/02
Brown Back <$VALUE
3x10-20 1-250 <$3000
Total Issue $12,500
Out in 1910 $530

5696 Van Zandt
NB OF GRAND SALINE
{{ 4 L }}
Chartered 1/29/01
Liquidated 8/15/27
Brown Back <$VALUE
3x10-20 1-2400 <$1000
1882 Date Back
3x10-20 1-4240 <$750
1882 Value Back
3x10-20 4241-6349 <$750
1902 Plain Back
3x10-20 1-4706 <$500
Total Issue $672,750
Out at close $43,200
Ch 12745 assumed circulation

12745 Van Zandt
STATE NB OF GRAND SALINE
{{ 2 L 9 S }}
Chartered 5/25
1902 Plain Back <$VALUE
3x10-20 1-1763 <$650
1929 Small Size
10 Type 1 1-1842 <$200
20 Type 1 1-452 <$200
10 Type 2 1-2895 <$200
20 Type 2 1-678 <$200
Total Issue $295,420
Out in 1935 $50,000
Large out 1935 $2,520
Outstanding includes Ch 5696

7269 Johnson
FARMERS & MERCHANTS NB OF GRANDVIEW
{{ 3 L }}
Chartered 5/04
Liquidated 1/27/31
1902 Red Seal <$VALUE
3x10-20 1-1650 <$1500
1902 Date Back
3x10-20 1-3350 <$500
1902 Plain Back
3x10-20 3351-7450 <$500
Total Issue $455,000
Out at close $3,110

4389 Johnson
FNB OF GRANDVIEW
{{ 5 L 7 S }}
Chartered 1890
Brown Back <$VALUE
3x10-20 1-2790 <$1000
1882 Date Back
4x5 1-605 <$1000
3x10-20 1-371 <$1000
1902 Date Back
4x5 1-2750 <$400
4x10 1-2750 <$400
1902 Plain Back
4x5 2751-11018 <$400
4x10 2751-9392 <$400
1929 Small Size
5 Type 1 1-2704 <$225
10 Type 1 1-1062 <$225
5 Type 2 1-4308 <$225
10 Type 2 1-2400 <$225
Total Issue $956,570
Out in 1935 $37,510
Large out 1935 $2,380

6361 Williamson
FNB OF GRANGER
{{ 1 L 1 S }}
Chartered 7/31/02
1902 Red Seal <$VALUE
4x5 1-500 <$2000
3x10-20 1-400 <$2000
1902 Date Back
4x5 1-1175 <$1000
3x10-20 1-940 <$1000
1902 Plain Back
4x5 1176-2403 <$1000
3x10-20 941-1667 <$1000
1929 Small Size
5 Type 1 1-420 <$600
10 Type 1 1-212 <$600
20 Type 1 1-72 <$600
5 Type 2 1-6 <$600
10 Type 2 1-18 <$600
20 Type 2 1-30 <$600
Total Issue $196,180
Out in 1935 $8,750
Large out 1935 $800

11642 Williamson
GRANGER NB, GRANGER
{{ 1 L 2 S }}
Chartered 3/20
1902 Plain Back <$VALUE
4x5 1-4417 <$1000
1929 Small Size
5 Type 1 1-1374 <$500
5 Type 2 1-3028 <$500
Total Issue $144,700
Out in 1935 $10,000
Large out 1935 $390

8318 Tarrant
FARMERS NB OF GRAPEVINE
{{ 4 L }}
Chartered 8/06
Liquidated 12/28/27
1902 Red Seal <$VALUE
3x10-20 1-340 <$1500
1902 Date Back
3x10-20 1-4150 <$500
1902 Plain Back
3x10-20 4151-11527 <$500
Total Issue $593,350
Out at close $9,570

5439 Tarrant
GRAPEVINE NB, GRAPEVINE
{{ 2 L }}
Chartered 6/19/00
Liquidated 12/31/18
Brown Back <$VALUE
3x10-20 1-500 <$1500
1882 Date Back
3x10-20 1-2700* <$1250
1882 Value Back
3x10-20 2901-3343* <$1250
* 2701-2900 not marked
Total Issue $192,150
Out at close $25,000

12708 Tarrant
TARRANT COUNTY NB OF GRAPEVINE
{{ U + 6 S }}
Chartered 5/25
1929 Small Size <$VALUE
5 Type 1 1-832 <$300
10 Type 1 1-418 <$300
20 Type 1 1-106 <$300
5 Type 2 1-4654 <$300
10 Type 2 1-2570 <$300
20 Type 2 1-600 <$300
Total Issue $123,730
Out in 1935 $38,650

5035 Hunt
CITY NB OF GREENVILLE
{{ UNREPORTED }}
Chartered 3/6/96
Liquidated 12/21/98
Brown Back <$VALUE
3x10-20 1-322 <$2000
Total Issue $16,100
Out in 1910 $330

7510 Hunt
COMMERCIAL NB OF GREENVILLE
{{ 8 L }}
Organized 11/24/04
Receivership 4/6/25
1902 Red Seal <$VALUE
3x10-20 1-4800 <$1250
1902 Date Back
3x10-20 1-11600 <$200
1902 Plain Back
3x10-20 11601-29338 <$200
Total Issue $1,706,900
Out at close $149,995

2998 Hunt
FNB OF GREENVILLE
{{ 10 L }}
Organized 6/30/83
Receivership 1/11/28
Brown Back <$VALUE
3x10-20 1-3230 <$1000
1902 Red Seal
3x10-20 1-4785 <$1250
1902 Date Back
3x10-20 1-13600 <$200
1902 Plain Back
3x10-20 13601-36870 <$200
Total Issue $2,244,250
Out at close $138,545

3646 Hunt
GREENVILLE NB, GREENVILLE
{{ UNREPORTED }}
Chartered 3/12/87
Liquidated 3/3/07
Brown Back <$VALUE
50-100 1-1535 <$4000
Total Issue $230,250
Out in 1910 $15,400

<$VALUEs are for notes in FINE condition. Value changes by approximately 25% for a change of one full grade.

****
8581 Hunt
GREENVILLE N EXCHANGE B, GREENVILLE
{{ 18 L 26 S }}
Chartered 3/07
1902 Red Seal <$VALUE
3x10-20 1-3200 <$1250
1902 Date Back
4x5 1-18400 <$125
3x10-20 1-14400 <$125
1902 Plain Back
4x5 18401-57249 <$125
3x10-20 14401-38527 <$125
1929 Small Size
5 Type 1 1-7612 <$50
10 Type 1 1-4354 <$50
20 Type 1 1-1238 <$60
5 Type 2 1-16892 <$50
10 Type 2 1-8424 <$50
20 Type 2 1-2460 <$65
Total Issue $4,087,390
Out in 1935 $200,000
Large out 1935 $11,115
****
3016 Hunt
HUNT COUNTY NB, GREENVILLE
{{ UNREPORTED }}
Chartered 1883
Liquidated 1/22/84
Brown Back <$VALUE
3x10-20 1-360 <$2000
Total Issue $18,000
Out in 1910 $130
****
10241 San Particio
FNB OF GREGORY
{{ 4 L 0 S }}
Chartered 8/12
1902 Date Back <$VALUE
4x5 1-1110 <$600
4x10 1-1120 <$600
1902 Plain Back
4x5 1111-1983 <$600
4x10 1121-1699 <$600
1929 Small Size
5 Type 1 1-465 <$750
10 Type 1 1-243 <$750
Total Issue $136,150
Out in 1935 $6,150
Large out 1935 $470
****
14126 Limestone
CITIZENS NB IN GROESBECK
{{ UNREPORTED }}
Chartered 4/34
1929 Small Size <$VALUE
5 Type 2 1-610 <$750
10 Type 2 1-299 <$750
20 Type 2 1-114 <$750
Total Issue $8,360
Out in 1935 $15,000
Large out 1935 $760
Outstanding includes Ch 6461
****
6461 Limestone
CITIZENS NB OF GROESBECK
{{ 1 L 1 S }}
Chartered 10/16/02
Liquidated 6/18/34
1902 Red Seal <$VALUE
3x10-20 1-945 <$2000
1902 Date Back
3x10-20 1-1320 <$750
1902 Plain Back
3x10-20 1321-2700 <$750
1929 Small Size
10 Type 1 1-470 <$500
20 Type 1 1-138 <$500
Total Issue $227,010
Out at close $13,920
Large out 1935 $760
Ch 14126 assumed circulation
****
4269 Limestone
GROESBECK NB, GROESBECK
{{ UNREPORTED }}
Organized 3/22/90
Receivership 8/22/03
Brown Back <$VALUE
4x5 1-2450 <$2000
50-100 1-67 <$4000
Total Issue $59,050
Out in 1916 $520
****
14104 Trinity
FNB IN GROVETON
{{ 1 S }}
Chartered 4/34
1929 Small Size <$VALUE
5 Type 2 1-2050 <$750
10 Type 2 1-1200 <$750
Total Issue $22,250
Out in 1935 $47,600
Large out 1935 $4,850
Outstanding includes Ch 6329
****
6329 Trinity
FNB OF GROVETON
{{ 7 L 11 S }}
Chartered 7/5/02
Liquidated 5/14/34
1902 Red Seal <$VALUE
3x10-20 1-1080 <$1500
1902 Date Back
3x10-20 1-5300 <$300
1902 Plain Back
3x10-20 5301-15662 <$300
1929 Small Size
10 Type 1 1-2026 <$175
20 Type 1 1-568 <$175
10 Type 2 1-1108 <$200
20 Type 2 1-232 <$200
Total Issue $1,042,540
Out at close $62,230
Large out 1935 $4,850
Ch 14104 assumed circulation
****
6404 Grayson
FNB OF GUNTER
{{ 1 L }}
Chartered 8/30/02
Liquidated 11/15/05
1902 Red Seal <$VALUE
4x5 1-835 <$3500
3x10-20 1-831 <$3500
Total Issue $58,250
Out in 1910 $2,250
****
FNB of Hallettsville
SEE Ch 4338
Lavaca County NB of Hallettsville
****
4338 Lavaca
LAVACA COUNTY NB OF HALLETTSVILLE
Chartered 1890
2nd title:FNB of Hallettsville 5/22/10
FIRST TITLE {{ 1 L }}
Brown Back <$VALUE
3x10-20 1-1610 <$1250
1882 Date Back
3x10-20 1-190 <$1000
SECOND TITLE {{ 5 L 9 S }}
1902 Date Back
3x10-20 1-4900 <$300
1902 Plain Back
3x10-20 4901-12416 <$300
1929 Small Size
10 Type 1 1-1378 <$150
20 Type 1 1-380 <$175
5 Type 2 1-312 <$200
10 Type 2 1-1554 <$200
20 Type 2 1-279 <$200
Total Issue $861,760
Out in 1935 $59,050
Large out 1935 $5,205
****
4451 Hamilton
HAMILTON NB, HAMILTON
{{ 4 L 4 S }}
Chartered 1890
Brown Back <$VALUE
4x5 1-3050 <$1000
3x10-20 1-1150 <$1000
1882 Date Back
4x5 1-415 <$1000
3x10-20 1-317 <$1000
1902 Date Back
3x10-20 1-1760 <$500
1902 Plain Back
4x5 1-2685 <$500
3x10-20 1761-4145 <$500
1929 Small Size
5 Type 1 1-866 <$350
10 Type 1 1-534 <$350
20 Type 1 1-162 <$350
5 Type 2 1-1338 <$350
10 Type 2 1-801 <$350
20 Type 2 1-264 <$350
Total Issue $501,040
Out in 1935 $24,350
Large out 1935 $1,825
****
12700 Jones
FARMERS & MERCHANTS NB OF HAMLIN
{{ 2 S }}
Chartered 4/25
1929 Small Size <$VALUE
10 Type 2 1-1392 <$500
20 Type 2 1-402 <$500
Total Issue $21,960
Out in 1935 $37,120
Outstanding includes Ch 8252
****
8252 Jones
FNB OF HAMLIN
{{ 5 L 7 S }}
Chartered 6/06
Liquidated 5/19/34
1902 Red Seal <$VALUE
3x10-20 1-800 <$1500
1902 Date Back
3x10-20 1-3260 <$300
1902 Plain Back
3x10-20 3261-10715 <$300
1929 Small Size
10 Type 1 1-1284 <$200
20 Type 1 1-340 <$200
10 Type 2 1-644 <$200
20 Type 2 1-250 <$200
Total Issue $705,030
Out at close $39,150
Large out 1935 $2,080
Ch 12700 assumed circulation
****
8427 Jones
HAMLIN NB, HAMLIN
{{ UNREPORTED }}
Chartered 11/5/06
Liquidated 8/1/07
1902 Red Seal <$VALUE
3x10-20 1-210 <$2500
Total Issue $10,500
Out in 1910 $750
****
7825 Haskell
FARMERS NB OF HASKELL
{{ UNREPORTED }}
Chartered 7/05
Liquidated 2/12/13
1902 Red Seal <$VALUE
3x10-20 1-1100 <$2000
1902 Date Back
3x10-20 1-1060 <$1000
Total Issue $108,000
Out in 1913 $12,000
****
4333 Haskell
FNB OF HASKELL
{{ UNREPORTED }}
Chartered 6/4/90
Liquidated 6/18/95
Brown Back <$VALUE
4x5 1-1291 <$2500
Total Issue $25,820
Out in 1910 $215
****
4474 Haskell
HASKELL NB, HASKELL
{{ 4 L 5 S }}
Chartered 1890
Liquidated 6/29/34
Brown Back <$VALUE
4x5 1-3625 <$1000
3x10-20 1-1420 <$1000
1882 Date Back
4x5 1-363 <$1000
3x10-20 1-314 <$1000
1902 Date Back
4x5 1-1800 <$400
3x10-20 1-1440 <$400
1902 Plain Back
4x5 1801-6107 <$400
3x10-20 1441-3956 <$400
1929 Small Size
5 Type 1 1-904 <$250
10 Type 1 1-458 <$250
20 Type 1 1-158 <$250
5 Type 2 1-602 <$275
10 Type 2 1-245 <$275
20 Type 2 1-132 <$275
Total Issue $568,060
Out at close $25,000
Large out at close $2,150
Ch 14149 assumed circulation
****
14149 Haskell
HASKELL NB, HASKELL
{{ 2U + 4 S }}
Chartered 5/34
1929 Small Size <$VALUE
5 Type 2 1-930 <$350
10 Type 2 1-493 <$350
20 Type 2 1-172 <$375
Total Issue $13,020
Out in 1935 $25,060
Large out 1935 $2,030
Outstanding includes Ch 4474
****
8535 Jones
FNB OF HAWLEY
{{ UNREPORTED }}
Chartered 2/07
Liquidated 1/25/13
1902 Red Seal <$VALUE
3x10-20 1-200 <$3000
1902 Date Back
3x10-20 1-250 <$2000
Total Issue $22,500
Out in 1913 $2,750
****
4976 Robertson
FNB OF HEARNE
{{ 1 L }}
Organized 7/5/94
Receivership 1/21/21
Brown Back <$VALUE
3x10-20 1-1190 <$1750
1882 Date Back
3x10-20 1-752 <$1500
1902 Date Back
3x10-20 1-1490 <$1000
Total Issue $171,600
Out at close $10,900
****
12995 Jim Hogg
FNB OF HEBBRONVILLE
{{ 14 S }}
Chartered 10/26
1929 Small Size <$VALUE
5 Type 1 1-3274 <$150
10 Type 1 1-1736 <$150
20 Type 1 1-594 <$150
5 Type 2 1-5292 <$175
10 Type 2 1-3168 <$175
20 Type 2 1-888 <$175
Total Issue $349,560
Out in 1935 $74,470
****
13526 Sabine
FNB IN HEMPHILL
{{ 2 S }}
Organized 1/26/31
Liquidated 8/15/33
1929 Small Size <$VALUE
5 Type 1 1-450 <$500
10 Type 1 1-200 <$500
20 Type 1 1-69 <$500
Total Issue $33,780
Out at close $18,880
Outstanding includes Ch 8526
****
8526 Sabine
FNB OF HEMPHILL
{{ 2 L 2 S }}
Chartered 1/07
Liquidated 5/21/31
1902 Red Seal <$VALUE
3x10-20 1-687 <$1500
1902 Date Back
3x10-20 1-1820 <$500
1902 Plain Back
3x10-20 1821-5860 <$500
1929 Small Size
10 Type 1 1-343 <$500
20 Type 1 1-107 <$500
Total Issue $360,770
Out at close $17,490
Large out 1935 $1,480
Ch 13526 assumed circulation
****
4905 Waller
FARMERS NB OF HEMPSTEAD
{{ 4 L }}
Organized 4/15/93
Receivership 2/7/25
Brown Back <$VALUE
50-100 1-410 <$3500/$4000
1882 Date Back
4x5 1-1000 <$850
4x10 1-982 <$850
50-100 1-139 <$3500/$4000
1902 Date Back
4x5 1-1450 <$400
4x10 1-1500 <$400
1902 Plain Back
4x5 1451-7887 <$400
4x10 1501-6355 <$400
Total Issue $553,570
Out at close $49,195
****
13443 Rusk
CITIZENS NB OF HENDERSON
{{ 3U + 14 S }}
Chartered 3/30
1929 Small Size <$VALUE
5 Type 1 1-3732 <$85
10 Type 1 1-2024 <$85
20 Type 1 1-536 <$100
5 Type 2 1-8128 <$100
10 Type 2 1-3412 <$100
20 Type 2 1-901 <$100
Total Issue $390,500
Out in 1935 $58,500
****
6780 Rusk
FARMERS & MERCHANTS NB OF HENDERSON
{{ 4 L 2 S }}
Organized 5/8/03
Receivership 2/24/30
1902 Red Seal <$VALUE
3x10-20 1-1200 <$1250
1902 Date Back
3x10-20 1-2190* <$350
1902 Plain Back
3x10-20 2321-16185* <$350
* 2191-2320 not marked
1929 Small Size
10 Type 1 1-789 <$400
20 Type 1 1-125 <$400
Total Issue $931,590
Out at close $100,000
Large out at close $37,660
****
6176 Rusk
FNB OF HENDERSON
{{ 4 L 8 S }}
Chartered 3/27/02
1902 Red Seal <$VALUE
3x10-20 1-2200 <$1250
1902 Date Back
4x5 1-2900 <$300
3x10-20 1-3240 <$300
1902 Plain Back (dated 1902)
4x5 2901-6550 <$300
3x10-20 3241-5319 <$300
1902 Plain Back (dated 1922)
4x5 1-17484 <$300
1929 Small Size
5 Type 1 1-7528 <$175
5 Type 2 1-18060 <$175
Total Issue $1,172,770
Out in 1935 $44,440
Large out 1935 $2,875
****
4068 Clay
FARMERS NB OF HENRIETTA
{{ 1 L }}
Chartered 7/3/80
Receivership 11/18/03
Brown Back <$VALUE
3x10-20 1-2363 <$3000
50-100 1-96 <$5000
Total Issue $61,660
Out in 1916 $505
****
3022 Clay
HENRIETTA NB, HENRIETTA
{{ UNREPORTED }}
Organized 8/3/83
Receivership 8/17/87
Brown Back <$VALUE
4x5 1-956 <$3500
Total Issue $19,120
Out in 1916 $150
****
FNB of Hereford
SEE Ch 5604
Hereford NB, Hereford
****
5604 Deaf Smith
HEREFORD NB, HEREFORD
Chartered 10/23/00
2nd title:FNB of Hereford 2/17/06
FIRST TITLE {{ 0 L }}
Brown Back <$VALUE
3x10-20 1-335 <$1500
SECOND TITLE {{ 7 L 9 S }}
Brown Back
3x10-20 1-1700 <$1000
1882 Date Back
3x10-20 1-3700 <$600
1882 Value Back
3x10-20 3701-5819 <$600
1902 Plain Back
3x10-20 1-6282 <$300
1929 Small Size
10 Type 1 1-1640 <$150
20 Type 1 1-378 <$175
10 Type 2 1-1505 <$200
20 Type 2 1-423 <$200
Total Issue $874,070
Out in 1935 $32,670
Large out 1935 $2,630
****
6812 Deaf Smith
WESTERN NB OF HEREFORD
{{ 4 L 5 S }}
Chartered 6/03
Liquidated 5/26/31
1902 Red Seal <$VALUE
3x10-20 1-2412 <$1250
1902 Date Back
3x10-20 1-3600 <$350
1902 Plain Back
3x10-20 3601-12196 <$350
1929 Small Size
10 Type 1 1-780 <$250
20 Type 1 1-213 <$250
Total Issue $802,760
Out at close $44,000
Large out at close $6,480
****
4366 Hamilton
FNB OF HICO
{{ 1 L }}
Chartered 1890
Brown Back <$VALUE
4x5 1-2825 <$1500
3x10-20 1-600 <$1500
1882 Date Back
4x5 1-142 <$1250
3x10-20 1-102 <$1250
1902 Date Back
3x10-20 1-959 <$1000
Total Issue $142,390
Out in 1935 $630
****
7157 Hamilton
HICO NB, HICO
{{ 4 L 4 S }}
Chartered 3/04
Liquidated 12/1/33
1902 Red Seal <$VALUE
3x10-20 1-760 <$1500
1902 Date Back
3x10-20 1-3550 <$500
1902 Plain Back
3x10-20 3551-7815 <$500
1929 Small Size
10 Type 1 1-759 <$350
20 Type 1 1-213 <$350
Total Issue $499,850
Out at close $26,410
Large out at close $2,470
****
8249 Lipscomb
CITIZENS NB OF HIGGINS
Chartered 6/06
2nd title:FNB in Higgins 5/1/29
FIRST TITLE {{ 2 L }}
1902 Red Seal <$VALUE
3x10-20 1-688 <$2500
1902 Date Back
3x10-20 1-360 <$1000
1902 Plain Back
3x10-20 361-940 <$1000
SECOND TITLE {{ 2 S }}
1929 Small Size
10 Type 1 1-210 <$500
20 Type 1 1-56 <$500
5 Type 2 1-108 <$500
Total Issue $101,260
Out in 1935 $6,250
Large out 1935 $275
****
8179 Lipscomb
FNB OF HIGGINS
{{ 1 L }}
Chartered 4/06
Liquidated 12/17/28
1902 Red Seal <$VALUE
3x10-20 1-300 <$2500
1902 Date Back
3x10-20 1-660 <$1500
1902 Plain Back
3x10-20 661-1273 <$1500
Total Issue $78,650
Out at close $6,150
****
FNB of Higgins
SEE Ch 8249
Citizens NB of Higgins
****
4900 Hill
CITIZENS NB OF HILLSBORO
{{ 9 L 20 S }}
Chartered 1893
Brown Back <$VALUE
3x10-20 1-4200 <$1000
1882 Date Back
3x10-20 1-3507 <$600
1902 Date Back
3x10-20 1-7000 <$150
1902 Plain Back
3x10-20 7001-34462 <$150
1929 Small Size
10 Type 1 1-6420 <$50
20 Type 1 1-1686 <$60
10 Type 2 1-3404 <$50
20 Type 2 1-735 <$60
Total Issue $2,744,710
Out in 1935 $89,320
Large out 1935 $8,570
Outstanding includes Ch 3786
****

3762 Hill
FARMERS NB OF HILLSBORO
{{ 6 L 8 S }}
Chartered 7/27/87
Liquidated 4/24/31
Brown Back <$VALUE
3x10-20 1-1539 <$1000
1902 Red Seal
3x10-20 1-200 <$1250
1902 Date Back
3x10-20 1-5800 <$250
1902 Plain Back
3x10-20 5801-24153 <$250
1929 Small Size
10 Type 1 1-1663 <$175
20 Type 1 1-430 <$175
Total Issue $1,445,980
Out at close $87,020
Large out at close $12,500

3046 Hill
HILL COUNTY NB OF HILLSBORO
{{ UNREPORTED }}
Chartered 9/14/83
Liquidated 4/5/98
Brown Back <$VALUE
4x5 1-3006 <$2000
Total Issue $60,120
Out in 1910 $495

3786 Hill
STURGIS NB OF HILLSBORO
{{ 3 L }}
Chartered 9/8/87
Liquidated 8/9/12
Brown Back <$VALUE
3x10-20 1-2181 <$1250
1902 Red Seal
3x10-20 1-500 <$1500
1902 Date Back
3x10-20 1-5075 <$500
Total Issue $387,800
Out at close $97,400
Ch 4900 assumed circulation

8008 Bell
FNB OF HOLLAND
{{ 1 L 2 S }}
Chartered 12/05
1902 Red Seal <$VALUE
3x10-20 1-260 <$2000
1902 Date Back
3x10-20 1-760* <$1000
1902 Plain Back
3x10-20 961-1729* <$1000
* 761-960 not marked
1929 Small Size
10 Type 1 1-238 <$450
20 Type 1 1-62 <$450
Total Issue $121,170
Out in 1935 $6,250
Large out 1935 $440

5765 Medina
FNB OF HONDO
{{ 4 L 4 S }}
Chartered 4/3/01
Brown Back <$VALUE
3x10-20 1-2300 <$1000
1882 Date Back
3x10-20 1-3400 <$850
1882 Value Back
3x10-20 3401-5400 <$850
1902 Plain Back
3x10-20 1-5320 <$500
1929 Small Size
10 Type 1 1-1355 <$350
20 Type 1 1-378 <$375
5 Type 2 1-61 <$400
Total Issue $777,965
Out in 1935 $27,480
Large out 1935 $3,075

13416 Fannin
FNB IN HONEY GROVE
{{ U + 7 S }}
Chartered 1/30
1929 Small Size <$VALUE
5 Type 1 1-1450 <$250
10 Type 1 1-796 <$250
20 Type 1 1-224 <$250
5 Type 2 1-3290 <$250
10 Type 2 1-1759 <$250
20 Type 2 1-502 <$250
Total Issue $162,220
Out in 1935 $50,000
Large out 1935 $3,750
Outstanding includes Ch 2867

2867 Fannin
FNB OF HONEY GROVE
{{ 4 L 1 S }}
Chartered 1883
Liquidated 2/20/30
Brown Back <$VALUE
3x10-20 1-6476 <$1250
1902 Red Seal
3x10-20 1-2300 <$1500
1902 Date Back
4x5 1-5280 <$400
3x10-20 1-3670 <$400
1902 Plain Back
4x5 5281-13375 <$400
3x10-20 3671-8819 <$400
1929 Small Size
5 Type 1 1-645 <$500
10 Type 1 1-258 <$500
20 Type 1 1-71 <$500
Total Issue $1,190,600
Out at close $50,000
Large out 1935 $3,750
Ch 13416 assumed circulation

4112 Fannin
PLANTERS NB OF HONEY GROVE
{{ 3 L }}
Chartered 9/6/89
Receivership 12/6/26
Brown Back <$VALUE
3x10-20 1-2535 <$1250
1902 Date Back
3x10-20 1-3200 <$600
1902 Plain Back
3x10-20 3201-4723 <$600
Total Issue $362,900
Out at close $18,400

10617 Fannin
STATE NB OF HONEY GROVE
{{ UNREPORTED }}
Organized 9/14/14
Receivership 3/19/30
1902 Date Back <$VALUE
3x10-20 1-982 <$1250
Total Issue $49,100
Out at close $310

9226 Harris
AMERICAN NB OF HOUSTON
{{ 2 L }}
Chartered 8/08
Liquidated 7/1/10
1902 Date Back <$VALUE
4x5 1-7250 <$600
3x10-20 1-4746 <$500
Total Issue $382,300
Out in 1910 $241,700

13943 Harris
CITY NB OF HOUSTON
{{ 24 S }}
Chartered 1/34
1929 Small Size <$VALUE
5 Type 2 1-30078 <$50
10 Type 2 1-13947 <$50
20 Type 2 1-6434 <$50
Total Issue $418,540
Out in 1935 $219,700

3517 Harris
COMMERCIAL NB OF HOUSTON
{{ 11 L }}
Chartered 7/1/86
Liquidated 3/1/12
Brown Back <$VALUE
4x5 1-4395 <$850
50-100 1-4170 <$3500/$4000
1902 Red Seal
4x5 1-7500 <$1000
3x10-20 1-2800 <$1000
1902 Date Back
4x5 1-13195 <$150
3x10-20 1-12171 <$150
Total Issue $1,875,850
Out in 1912 $298,550

13683 Harris
FNB IN HOUSTON
{{ U + 50+ S }}
Chartered 5/33
1929 Small Size <$VALUE
5 Type 2 1-133304 <$20
10 Type 2 1-61589 <$20
20 Type 2 1-16671 <$30
Total Issue $1,615,830
Out in 1935 $1,669,840
Large out 1935 $120,640
Outstanding includes Ch 1644

1644 Harris
FNB OF HOUSTON
{{ 50+ L 50+ S }}
Chartered 1866
Liquidated 6/21/33
Original Series <$VALUE
4x5 1-1500 <$7500
3x10-20 1-2900<$5000/$6000
50-100 1-184 <$15,000
Series 1875
4x5 1-202 <$7500
3x10-20 1-343 <$5000/$6000
Brown Back
50-100 1-267 <$3500/$4000
1902 Red Seal
50-100 1-327 <$7500
1902 Date Back
4x5 1-122000 <$50
4x10 1-97000 <$60
50-100 1-3661 <$400/$500
3x50-100 1-7214 <$400/$500
1902 Plain Back
4x5 122001-427289 <$50
4x10 97001-271849 <$60
3x10-20 1-76114 <$60
3x50-100 7215-10412 <$400/$500
1929 Small Size
5 Type 1 1-50456 <$15
10 Type 1 1-25886 <$20
20 Type 1 1-8584 <$30
50 Type 1 1-1983 <$125
100 Type 1 1-774 <$200
Total Issue $31,846,700
Out at close $2,000,000
Large out 1935 $120,640
Ch 13683 assumed circulation

12062 Harris
GUARANTY NB OF HOUSTON
{{ 10 L 4 S }}
Chartered 12/21
Closed 1/2/30
1902 Plain Back <$VALUE
3x10-20 1-28911 <$150
1929 Small Size
10 Type 1 1-1228 <$300
20 Type 1 1-404 <$300
Total Issue $1,567,710
Out at close $271,260
Large out at close $149,100
Ch 12055 assumed circulation

12840 Harris
HARRISBURG NB OF HOUSTON
{{ 4 S }}
Chartered 10/25 as Harrisburg NB, Harrisburg, under which there was no issue. Issuing title adopted 1/27/28.
1929 Small Size <$VALUE
5 Type 2 1-8388 <$375
10 Type 2 1-4666 <$375
Total Issue $88,600
Out in 1935 $30,050

9353 Harris
HOUSTON N EXCHANGE B, HOUSTON
Chartered 3/09
2nd title:Houston NB 9/14/23
FIRST TITLE {{ 14 L }}
1902 Date Back <$VALUE
3x10-20 1-17200* <$100
1902 Plain Back
3x10-20 18201-58200* <$100
* 17201-18200 not marked
SECOND TITLE {{ 5 L 26 S }}
1902 Plain Back
3x50-100 1-5442 <$350/$450
1929 Small Size
50 Type 1 1-2696 <$85
100 Type 1 1-834 <$135
5 Type 2 1-324 <$50
50 Type 2 1-1912 <$175
100 Type 2 1-713 <$225
Total Issue $5,748,220
Out in 1935 $829,320
Large out 1935 $45,560

4028 Harris
HOUSTON NB, HOUSTON
{{ 1 L }}
Chartered 5/7/89
Liquidated 3/28/09
Brown Back <$VALUE
3x10-20 1-2877 <$1250
Total Issue $143,850
Out in 1910 $10,670

Houston NB, Houston
SEE Ch 9353
Houston N Exchange B, Houston

8645 Harris
LUMBERMENS NB OF HOUSTON
Chartered 4/07
2nd title: Second NB of Houston 1/15/23
FIRST TITLE {{ 21 L }}
1902 Red Seal <$VALUE
4x5 1-7200 <$1000
3x10-20 1-5820 <$1000
1902 Date Back
4x5 1-38000 <$125
3x10-20 1-29200 <$125
1902 Plain Back
4x5 38001-92750 <$125
3x10-20 29201-63600 <$125
SECOND TITLE {{ 4 L 4U+50+ S }}
1902 Plain Back
4x5 1-5190 <$200
3x10-20 1-7143 <$200
1929 Small Size
5 Type 1 1-25778 <$15
10 Type 1 1-17378 <$20
20 Type 1 1-5510 <$30
5 Type 2 1-76704 <$15
10 Type 2 1-34410* <$20
20 Type 2 1-11975 <$30
* 14011-14016 not issued
Total Issue $9,375,230
Out in 1935 $818,785
Large out 1935 $17,685

5858 Harris
MERCHANTS NB OF HOUSTON
{{ 7 L }}
Chartered 6/11/01
Liquidated 5/31/10
Brown Back <$VALUE
3x10-20 1-5300 <$850
50-100 1-540 <$3500/$4000
1882 Date Back
4x5 1-1755 <$400
3x10-20 1-467 <$400
Total Issue $404,450
Out in 1910 $116,150

10225 Harris
NB OF COMMERCE OF HOUSTON
{{ 38 L 50+ S }}
Chartered 7/12
1902 Date Back <$VALUE
3x10-20 1-27000 <$60
1902 Plain Back
3x10-20 27001-115307 <$60
1929 Small Size
10 Type 1 1-27436 <$20
20 Type 1 1-6864 <$30
10 Type 2 1-58878 <$20
20 Type 2 1-16929 <$30
Total Issue $9,162,550
Out in 1935 $968,200
Large out 1935 $27,420

8288 Harris
N CITY B OF HOUSTON
{{ 3 L }}
Chartered 7/2/06
Liquidated 5/25/09
1902 Red Seal <$VALUE
4x5 1-7250 <$1000
3x10-20 1-5300 <$1000
1902 Date Back
4x5 1-1030 <$450
3x10-20 1-631 <$450
Total Issue $462,150
Out in 1910 $102,090

2092 Harris
N EXCHANGE B OF HOUSTON
{{ 3 L }}
Chartered 3/17/73
Liquidated 9/10/80
Original Series <$VALUE
3x1-2 1-1000<$4500/$15,000
4x5 1-750 <$4000
2x20-50-100 1-160
<$6000/$15,000/$15,000
Series 1875
3x1-2 1-202 <$4500/$15,000
4x5 1-929 <$4000
Total Issue $69,990
Out in 1910 $430

4463 Harris
PLANTERS & MERCHANTS NB OF HOUSTON
{{ 2 L }}
Chartered 11/11/90
Liquidated 11/7/07
Brown Back <$VALUE
4x5 1-5985 <$1500
3x10-20 1-2072 <$1500
50-100 1-2909 <$3500/$4000
Total Issue $659,650
Out in 1910 $56,720

12055 Harris
PUBLIC NB OF HOUSTON
Organized 11/7/21
Receivership 12/13/32
2nd title: Public NB & TC of Houston 6/13/29
FIRST TITLE {{ 12 L }}
1902 Plain Back <$VALUE
4x5 1-20045 <$150
3x10-20 1-13976 <$150
SECOND TITLE {{ 50+ S }}
1929 Small Size
5 Type 1 1-22403 <$15
10 Type 1 1-11973 <$20
20 Type 1 1-3431 <$30
Total Issue $2,901,890
Out at close $290,275
Outstanding includes Ch 12062

13925 Harris
SAN JACINTO NB OF HOUSTON
{{ U + 8 S }}
Chartered 1/34
1929 Small Size <$VALUE
5 Type 2 1-11898 <$250
10 Type 2 1-6216 <$250
Total Issue $121,650
Out in 1935 $97,750

Second NB of Houston
SEE Ch 8645
Lumbermens NB of Houston

10152 Harris
SOUTH TEXAS COMMERCIAL NB OF HOUSTON
{{ 31 L 5U + 50+ S }}
Chartered 3/12
1902 Date Back <$VALUE
4x5 1-56500 <$50
3x10-20 1-46000 <$60
1902 Plain Back
4x5 56501-151635 <$50
3x10-20 46001-109077 <$60
1929 Small Size
5 Type 1 1-22154 <$15
10 Type 1 1-10737 <$20
20 Type 1 1-4781 <$30
50 Type 1 1-1873 <$90
100 Type 1 1-962 <$140
Total Issue $11,508,210
Out in 1935 $1,322,100
Large out 1935 $21,600

4350 Harris
SOUTH TEXAS NB OF HOUSTON
{{ 8 L }}
Chartered 1890
Liquidated 3/1/12
Brown Back <$VALUE
4x5 1-15150 <$850
50-100 1-1385 <$3500/$4000
1882 Date Back
4x5 1-1820 <$450
1902 Date Back
4x5 1-10509 <$200
4x10 1-10633 <$200
Total Issue $1,182,650
Out in 1912 $253,740

12070 Harris
STATE NB OF HOUSTON
{{ 10 L 50+ S }}
Chartered 12/21
1902 Plain Back <$VALUE
3x10-20 1-31034 <$150
1929 Small Size
10 Type 1 1-19706 <$25
20 Type 1 1-5478 <$35
10 Type 2 1-25195 <$25
20 Type 2 1-8490 <$35
Total Issue $3,813,170
Out in 1935 $495,610
Large out 1935 $10,210

9712 Harris
UNION NB OF HOUSTON
{{ 50+ L 50+ S }}
Chartered 3/10
1902 Date Back <$VALUE
4x5 1-34250 <$50
3x10-20 1-27000 <$60
1902 Plain Back
4x5 34251-195692 <$50
3x10-20 27001-128040 <$60
1929 Small Size
5 Type 1 1-25114 <$20
10 Type 1 1-14080 <$20
20 Type 1 1-5096 <$30
5 Type 2 1-67514 <$20
10 Type 2 1-46095 <$20
20 Type 2 1-10650 <$30
Total Issue $13,537,100
Out in 1935 $763,250
Large out 1935 $41,850

5670 Grayson
FARMERS NB OF HOWE
{{ 3 L 2 S }}
Chartered 1/7/01
Receivership 10/8/30
Brown Back <$VALUE
3x10-20 1-2340 <$1250
1882 Date Back
3x10-20 1-2720 <$850
1882 Value Back
3x10-20 2721-3866 <$850
1902 Plain Back
3x10-20 1-3880 <$500
1929 Small Size
10 Type 1 1-409 <$400
20 Type 1 1-67 <$450
Total Issue $536,880
Out at close $29,995
Large out at close $5,635

5681 Grayson
FNB OF HOWE
{{ UNREPORTED }}
Chartered 1/15/01
Liquidated 2/1/02
Brown Back <$VALUE
3x10-20 1-131 <$3000
Total Issue $6,550
Out in 1910 $340

7407 Hill
FARMERS NB OF HUBBARD
{{ UNREPORTED }}
Chartered 9/23/04
Liquidated 6/24/09
1902 Red Seal <$VALUE
3x10-20 1-360 <$2500
Total Issue $18,000
Out in 1910 $2,660

5008 Hill
FNB OF HUBBARD
{{ 6 L 9 S }}
Chartered 1895
Brown Back <$VALUE
3x10-20 1-1240 <$1000
1882 Date Back
3x10-20 1-5611 <$600
1902 Plain Back
3x10-20 1-9176 <$350
1929 Small Size
10 Type 1 1-1540 <$150
20 Type 1 1-380 <$150
10 Type 2 1-2968 <$175
20 Type 2 1-636 <$175
Total Issue $981,750
Out in 1935 $48,850
Large out 1935 $3,100

6922 Cass
FNB OF HUGHES SPRINGS
{{ 3 L 5 S }}
Chartered 8/03
1902 Red Seal <$VALUE
3x10-20 1-870 <$1500
1902 Date Back
3x10-20 1-2600 <$500
1902 Plain Back
3x10-20 2601-9987 <$500
1929 Small Size
10 Type 1 1-1358 <$250
20 Type 1 1-358 <$250
10 Type 2 1-1601 <$275
20 Type 2 1-385 <$275
Total Issue $691,000
Out in 1935 $32,200
Large out 1935 $1,600

****
FNB of Huntsville
SEE Ch 4208
Gibbs NB of Huntsville
****
4208 Walker
GIBBS NB OF HUNTSVILLE
Chartered 1890
2nd title:FNB of Huntsville 1/19/23
FIRST TITLE {{ 3 L }}
Brown Back <$VALUE
4x5 1-4100 <$1250
4x10 1-889 <$1250
50-100 1-666 <$3500/$4000
1882 Date Back
4x5 1-473 <$1000
1902 Date Back
3x10-20 1-3200 <$450
1902 Plain Back
3x10-20 3201-7500 <$450
SECOND TITLE {{ 2 L 7 S }}
1902 Plain Back
3x10-20 1-4261 <$450
1929 Small Size
10 Type 1 1-1602 <$200
20 Type 1 1-422 <$200
10 Type 2 1-2640 <$225
20 Type 2 1-828 <$225
Total Issue $1,004,690
Out in 1935 $47,560
Large out 1935 $3,330
****
9625 Williamson
HUTTO NB, HUTTO
{{ 2 L 1 S }}
Chartered 1/10
Liquidated 7/30/30
1902 Date Back <$VALUE
3x10-20 1-2350 <$600
1902 Plain Back
3x10-20 2351-6255 <$600
1929 Small Size
10 Type 1 1-257 <$600
20 Type 1 1-46 <$600
Total Issue $333,690
Out at close $23,080
Large out at close $4,990
****
5589 Wichita
FNB OF IOWA PARK
{{ 2 L 2 S }}
Chartered 10/2/00
Liquidated 6/27/32
Brown Back <$VALUE
3x10-20 1-1450 <$1250
1882 Date Back
3x10-20 1-2450 <$1000
1882 Value Back
3x10-20 2451-3393 <$1000
1902 Plain Back
3x10-20 1-3892 <$650
1929 Small Size
10 Type 1 1-641 <$500
20 Type 1 1-181 <$500
Total Issue $496,930
Out at close $21,160
Large out at close $2,320
****
6471 Ellis
CITIZENS NB OF ITALY
{{ UNREPORTED }}
Chartered 10/25/02
Liquidated 12/11/05
1902 Red Seal <$VALUE
3x10-20 1-966 <$2500
Total Issue $48,300
Out in 1910 $1,820
****
5663 Ellis
FNB OF ITALY
{{ 6 L 9 S }}
Chartered 1/2/01
Brown Back <$VALUE
4x5 1-1600 <$1000
3x10-20 1-1840 <$1000
1882 Date Back
4x5 1-4600 <$600
3x10-20 1-3100 <$600
1882 Value Back
4x5 4601-7000 <$600
3x10-20 3101-4660 <$600
1902 Plain Back
3x10-20 1-6732 <$250
1929 Small Size
10 Type 1 1-1688 <$150
20 Type 1 1-412 <$150
10 Type 2 1-2112 <$175
20 Type 2 1-494 <$175
Total Issue $1,015,320
Out in 1935 $40,630
Large out 1935 $3,140
****

****
4924 Hill
CITIZENS NB OF ITASCA
{{ UNREPORTED }}
Chartered 7/28/93
Liquidated 12/23/97
Brown Back <$VALUE
3x10-20 1-525 <$2000
Total Issue $26,250
Out in 1910 $440
****
4461 Hill
FNB OF ITASCA
{{ 5 L 9 S }}
Chartered 1890
Brown Back <$VALUE
3x10-20 1-2940 <$1000
1882 Date Back
3x10-20 1-811 <$750
1902 Date Back
3x10-20 1-3540 <$400
1902 Plain Back
3x10-20 3541-12667 <$400
1929 Small Size
10 Type 1 1-1528 <$225
20 Type 1 1-426 <$225
10 Type 2 1-2637 <$225
20 Type 2 1-575 <$225
Total Issue $1,001,570
Out in 1935 $48,700
Large out 1935 $3,100
****
5749 Hill
ITASCA NB, ITASCA
{{ 10 L 4 S }}
Chartered 3/20/01
Receivership 1/2/32
Brown Back <$VALUE
3x10-20 1-2000 <$850
1882 Date Back
3x10-20 1-2810 <$600
1882 Value Back
3x10-20 2811-4400 <$600
1902 Plain Back
3x10-20 1-6043 <$250
1929 Small Size
10 Type 1 1-1278 <$300
20 Type 1 1-383 <$300
Total Issue $744,790
Out at close $59,100
Large out at close $4,940
****
5761 Jack
CITIZENS NB OF JACKSBORO
{{ UNREPORTED }}
Chartered 3/29/01
Liquidated 12/19/01
Brown Back <$VALUE
3x10-20 1-200 <$2500
Total Issue $10,000
Out in 1910 $210
****
4483 Jack
FNB OF JACKSBORO
{{ 10 L 12 S }}
Chartered 1890
Brown Back <$VALUE
3x10-20 1-3520 <$1000
1882 Date Back
3x10-20 1-498 <$600
1902 Date Back
3x10-20 1-7850 <$200
1902 Plain Back
3x10-20 7851-33171 <$200
1929 Small Size
5 Type 1 1-2411 <$150
10 Type 1 1-1660 <$150
20 Type 1 1-831 <$150
Total Issue $2,131,100
Out in 1935 $31,855
Large out 1935 $6,855
****
7814 Jack
JACKSBORO NB, JACKSBORO
{{ 2 L 2 S }}
Chartered 6/05
1902 Red Seal <$VALUE
4x5 1-755 <$1500
3x10-20 1-544 <$1500
1902 Date Back
4x5 1-1825 <$600
3x10-20 1-1360 <$600
1902 Plain Back
4x5 11826-5064 <$600
3x10-20 1361-3429 <$600
1929 Small Size
5 Type 1 1-794 <$400
10 Type 1 1-368 <$400
20 Type 1 1-116 <$400
5 Type 2 1-1328 <$400
10 Type 2 1-828 <$400
20 Type 2 1-276 <$400
Total Issue $395,290
Out in 1935 $18,750
Large out 1935 $1,010
****
6883 Cherokee
CITIZENS NB OF JACKSONVILLE
{{ UNREPORTED }}
Chartered 7/15/03
Liquidated 9/16/04
1902 Red Seal <$VALUE
50-100 1-172 <$7500
Total Issue $25,800
Out in 1910 $2,450
****
5581 Cherokee
FNB OF JACKSONVILLE
{{ 9 L 11 S }}
Chartered 9/21/00
Brown Back <$VALUE
3x10-20 1-4100 <$1000
1882 Date Back
3x10-20 1-7700 <$600
1882 Value Back
3x10-20 7701-9787 <$600
1902 Plain Back
3x10-20 1-9486 <$250
1929 Small Size
10 Type 1 1-2404 <$125
20 Type 1 1-672 <$125
10 Type 2 1-4347 <$125
20 Type 2 1-975 <$125
Total Issue $1,456,500
Out in 1935 $60,800
Large out 1935 $5,430
****
10478 Jasper
CITIZENS NB OF JASPER
{{ 5 S }}
Chartered 1/14
1929 Small Size <$VALUE
5 Type 1 1-964 <$250
10 Type 1 1-468 <$250
20 Type 1 1-150 <$250
50 Type 1 1-24 <$400
100 Type 1 1-12 <$600
5 Type 2 1-714 <$250
10 Type 2 1-295 <$250
20 Type 2 1-120 <$250
Total Issue $98,320
Out in 1935 $25,000
****
6134 Jasper
FNB OF JASPER
{{ UNREPORTED }}
Chartered 2/24/02
Liquidated 1/13/14
1902 Red Seal <$VALUE
3x10-20 1-400 <$2500
1902 Date Back
3x10-20 1-265 <$1500
Total Issue $33,250
Out in 1914 $3,710
****
9845 Kent
FNB OF JAYTON
{{ 1 L 1 S }}
Chartered 9/10
Receivership 6/8/32
1902 Date Back <$VALUE
3x10-20 1-1520 <$1000
1902 Plain Back
3x10-20 1521-3070 <$1000
1929 Small Size
10 Type 1 1-281 <$650
20 Type 1 1-48 <$650
Total Issue $176,120
Out at close $9,400
Large out at close $270
****
8770 Marion
COMMERCIAL NB OF JEFFERSON
{{ 2 L 1 S }}
Organized 6/12/07
Receivership 2/12/30
1902 Red Seal <$VALUE
3x10-20 1-375 <$1500
1902 Date Back
3x10-20 1-1860 <$600
1902 Plain Back
3x10-20 1861-6969 <$600
1929 Small Size
10 Type 1 1-252 <$500
20 Type 1 1-16 <$500
Total Issue $384,240
Out at close $27,200
Large out at close $10,160
****

****
1777 Marion
NB OF JEFFERSON
{{ 1 L }}
Chartered 1/28/71
Receivership 6/24/96
Original Series <$VALUE
4x5 1-1000 <$4000
3x10-20 1-1600<$5000/$6000
50-100 1-1200 <$15,000
Series 1875
3x10-20 1-400 <$5000/$6000
50-100 1-48 <$15,000
Brown Back
50-100 1-270 <$4000
Total Issue $347,700
Out in 1916 $1,595
****
4721 Marion
STATE NB OF JEFFERSON
{{ UNREPORTED }}
Chartered 4/2/92
Liquidated 12/30/93
Brown Back <$VALUE
3x10-20 1-260 <$2500
Total Issue $13,000
Out in 1910 $120
****
8565 Karnes
CITY NB OF KARNES CITY
{{ UNREPORTED }}
Chartered 2/26/07
Liquidated 9/29/08
1902 Red Seal <$VALUE
3x10-20 1-174 <$3000
Total Issue $8,700
Out in 1910 $1,880
****
5614 Karnes
KARNES COUNTY NB OF KARNES CITY
{{ 3 L 4 S }}
Chartered 11/2/00
Brown Back <$VALUE
4x5 1-950 <$1250
3x10-20 1-680 <$1250
1882 Date Back
4x5 1-2250 <$1000
3x10-20 1-1740 <$1000
1882 Value Back
4x5 2251-3255 <$1000
3x10-20 1741-2347 <$1000
1902 Plain Back
4x5 1-3405 <$600
3x10-20 1-1980 <$600
1929 Small Size
5 Type 1 1-1036 <$300
10 Type 1 1-482 <$300
20 Type 1 1-142 <$300
5 Type 2 1-1338 <$300
10 Type 2 1-840 <$300
20 Type 2 1-298 <$300
Total Issue $500,640
Out in 1935 $24,400
Large out 1935 $1,710
****
4492 Kaufman
CITIZENS NB OF KAUFMAN
{{ UNREPORTED }}
Chartered 1890
Liquidated 12/5/10
Brown Back <$VALUE
3x10-20 1-2060 <$1500
1882 Date Back
3x10-20 1-419 <$1250
Total Issue $123,950
Out in 1911 $8,770
****
10757 Kaufman
FARMERS & MERCHANTS NB OF KAUFMAN
{{ 4 L 10 S }}
Chartered 7/15
1902 Plain Back <$VALUE
3x10-20 1-8502 <$500
1929 Small Size
10 Type 1 1-2346 <$200
20 Type 1 1-686 <$200
10 Type 2 1-5202 <$200
20 Type 2 1-1119 <$200
Total Issue $722,580
Out in 1935 $75,000
Large out 1935 $820
****
3836 Kaufman
FNB OF KAUFMAN
{{ 5 L 6 S }}
Chartered 1/18/88
Liquidated 6/16/31
Brown Back <$VALUE
3x10-20 1-1830 <$1000
1902 Red Seal
3x10-20 1-500 <$1500
1902 Date Back
3x10-20 1-4500 <$450
1902 Plain Back
3x10-20 4501-20461 <$450
1929 Small Size
10 Type 1 1-1947 <$350
20 Type 1 1-494 <$350
Total Issue $1,315,650
Out at close $97,020
Large out at close $10,770
****
5932 Kaufman
FNB OF KEMP
{{ 3 L 3 S }}
Chartered 8/3/01
Brown Back <$VALUE
3x10-20 1-500 <$1250
1882 Date Back
3x10-20 1-2380 <$1000
1882 Value Back
3x10-20 2381-2619 <$1000
1902 Plain Back
3x10-20 1-2380 <$600
1929 Small Size
10 Type 1 1-670 <$500
20 Type 1 1-162 <$500
10 Type 2 1-807 <$500
20 Type 2 1-204 <$500
Total Issue $346,740
Out in 1935 $18,200
Large out 1935 $750
****
12182 Karnes
FNB OF KENEDY
{{ 2 L 5 S }}
Chartered 4/22
Closed 3/22/32
1902 Plain Back <$VALUE
3x10-20 1-5666 <$650
1929 Small Size
10 Type 1 1-1101 <$300
20 Type 1 1-311 <$300
Total Issue $386,680
Out at close $49,160
Large out 1935 $2,550
Ch 12187 assumed circulation
****
12187 Karnes
FIRST-NICHOLS NB OF KENEDY
{{ 8 S }}
Chartered 4/22 as Nichols NB of Kenedy, under which there was no issue. Issuing title adopted 3/22/32
1929 Small Size <$VALUE
10 Type 1 1-1106 <$150
20 Type 1 1-264 <$150
10 Type 2 1-5261 <$175
20 Type 2 1-1294 <$175
Total Issue $176,530
Out in 1935 $80,700
Outstanding includes Ch 12182
****
8013 Karnes
KENEDY NB, KENEDY
{{ 2 L }}
Chartered 12/05
Liquidated 8/23/12
1902 Red Seal <$VALUE
3x10-20 1-700 <$2000
1902 Date Back
3x10-20 1-899 <$1000
Total Issue $79,950
Out in 1912 $20,900
****
7529 Navarro
FNB OF KERENS
{{ 3 L 4 S }}
Chartered 12/04
Liquidated 1/18/33
1902 Red Seal <$VALUE
3x10-20 1-300 <$1500
1902 Date Back
3x10-20 1-3600 <$500
1902 Plain Back
3x10-20 3601-7946 <$500
1929 Small Size
10 Type 1 1-749 <$350
20 Type 1 1-198 <$350
Total Issue $481,000
Out at close $23,680
Large out 1935 $1,010
Ch 13656 assumed circulation
****

****
13656 Navarro
FNB OF KERENS
{{ 2U + 3 S }}
Chartered 1/33
1929 Small Size <$VALUE
10 Type 1 1-128 <$350
20 Type 1 1-42 <$350
10 Type 2 1-3516 <$350
20 Type 2 1-900 <$350
Total Issue $65,880
Out in 1935 $47,070
Large out 1935 $1,010
Outstanding includes Ch 7529
****
12698 Gregg
KILGORE NB OF KILGORE
{{ 1 L 7 S }}
Chartered 4/25
1902 Plain Back <$VALUE
4x5 1-7181 <$850
1929 Small Size
5 Type 1 1-6814 <$200
5 Type 2 1-20054 <$200
Total Issue $448,310
Out in 1935 $36,150
Large out 1935 $475
****
5750 Bell
FNB OF KILLEEN
{{ 4 L }}
Chartered 3/20/01
Brown Back <$VALUE
3x10-20 1-520 <$1000
1882 Date Back
3x10-20 1-6610 <$650
1882 Value Back
3x10-20 6611-8009 <$750
1902 Plain Back
3x10-20 1-3752 <$400
Total Issue $614,050
Out in 1935 $7,545
****
10266 Guadalupe
FNB OF KINGSBURY
{{ 2 L }}
Organized 8/15/12
Receivership 1/10/29
1902 Date Back <$VALUE
3x10-20 1-500 <$1000
1902 Plain Back
3x10-20 501-1217 <$1000
Total Issue $60,850
Out at close $6,250
****
12968 Kleberg
FNB OF KINGSVILLE
{{ 4 L 10 S }}
Chartered 7/26
1902 Plain Back <$VALUE
4x5 1-4992 <$400
1929 Small Size
5 Type 1 1-6298 <$200
10 Type 1 1-344 <$200
20 Type 1 1-98 <$200
5 Type 2 1-4656 <$200
10 Type 2 1-2664 <$200
20 Type 2 1-600 <$200
Total Issue $383,100
Out in 1935 $50,000
Large out 1935 NONE*
* Census confirms large size
****
7953 Knox
FNB OF KNOX CITY
{{ 2 L 3 S }}
Chartered 10/05
Liquidated 4/15/33
1902 Red Seal <$VALUE
3x10-20 1-700 <$1500
1902 Date Back
3x10-20 1-360 <$600
1902 Plain Back
3x10-20 361-3338 <$600
1929 Small Size
10 Type 1 1-565 <$400
20 Type 1 1-159 <$400
Total Issue $254,880
Out at close $17,080
Large out at close $1,220
****
9205 Limestone
FNB OF KOSSE
{{ 2 L }}
Chartered 7/08
Liquidated 3/27/29
1902 Date Back <$VALUE
3x10-20 1-3210 <$600
1902 Plain Back
3x10-20 3211-7107 <$600
Total Issue $355,350
Out at close $22,800
****

10418 Denton
FNB OF KRUM
{{ UNREPORTED }}
Chartered 7/13
Liquidated 7/30/15
1902 Date Back <$VALUE
3x10-20 1-257 <$2000
Total Issue $12,850
Out in 1915 $5,150

10189 Medina
La COSTE NB, La COSTE
{{ 3 L 5 S }}
Chartered 5/12
1902 Date Back <$VALUE
3x10-20 1-1350 <$600
1902 Plain Back
3x10-20 1351-5094 <$600
1929 Small Size
10 Type 1 1-688 <$300
20 Type 1 1-182 <$300
10 Type 2 1-1419 <$300
20 Type 2 1-238 <$300
Total Issue $336,770
Out in 1935 $24,500
Large out 1935 $1,310

12747 Cameron
FNB OF La FERIA
{{ 4 S }}
Chartered 5/25
1929 Small Size <$VALUE
50 Type 1 1-208 <$400
20 Type 2 1-565 <$350
Total Issue $73,700
Out in 1935 $50,000

3906 Fayette
FNB OF La GRANGE
{{ 10 L 10 S }}
Chartered 7/9/88
Brown Back <$VALUE
3x10-20 1-1414 <$1000
1902 Red Seal
3x10-20 1-150 <$1250
1902 Date Back
3x10-20 1-4600 <$225
1902 Plain Back
3x10-20 4601-12411 <$225
1929 Small Size
10 Type 1 1-1504 <$150
20 Type 1 1-402 <$150
10 Type 2 1 2541 <$150
20 Type 2 1-770 <$150
Total Issue $878,040
Out in 1935 $58,800
Large out 1935 $4,880

4311 Fannin
FNB OF LADONIA
{{ U + 4 L }}
Organized 4/26/90
Receivership 12/26/30
Brown Back <$VALUE
4x5 1-8775 <$1000
3x10-20 1-3960 <$1000
1882 Date Back
4x5 1-229 <$750
3x10-20 1-67 <$750
1902 Date Back
4x5 1-1000 <$400
50-100 1-1000 <$650/$750
3x50-100 1-736 <$650/$750
1902 Plain Back
4x5 1001-12224 <$400
Total Issue $959,910
Out at close $8,430

5739 Fannin
LADONIA NB, LADONIA
{{ UNREPORTED }}
Chartered 3/11/01
Liquidated 2/3/06
Brown Back <$VALUE
3x10-20 1-460 <$2000
Total Issue $23,000
Out in 1910 $970

4515 Fannin
WELDON NB OF LADONIA
{{ 1 L }}
Chartered 2/4/91
Liquidated 6/15/98
Brown Back <$VALUE
3x10-20 1-778 <$2500
Total Issue $38,900
Out in 1910 $420

12835 Hall
FNB OF LAKEVIEW
{{ 4 S }}
Chartered 10/25
1929 Small Size <$VALUE
5 Type 1 1-540 <$400
10 Type 1 1-246 <$400
20 Type 1 1-76 <$400
5 Type 2 1-2038 <$400
10 Type 2 1-982 <$400
20 Type 2 1-310 <$400
Total Issue $66,290
Out in 1935 $19,400

11163 Dawson
FNB OF LAMESA
{{ 0 L 1 S }}
Chartered 3/18
1902 Plain Back <$VALUE
4x5 1-1335 <$2000
3x10-20 1-716 <$2000
1929 Small Size
5 Type 1 1-352 <$600
10 Type 1 1-176 <$600
20 Type 1 1-64 <$600
Total Issue $91,300
Out in 1935 $6,250
Large out 1935 $230

3261 Lampasas
FNB OF LAMPASAS
{{ 3 L 1 S }}
Chartered 1884
Brown Back <$VALUE
4x5 1-2625 <$1250
3x10-20 1-2292 <$1250
1902 Red Seal
3x10-20 1-1850 <$1500
1902 Date Back
3x10-20 1-4200 <$500
1902 Plain Back
3x10-20 4201-8926 <$500
1929 Small Size
5 Type 2 1-1510 <$500
10 Type 2 1-1028 <$500
Total Issue $723,730
Out in 1935 $12,355
Large out 1935 $2,655

5645 Lampasas
LAMPASAS NB, LAMPASAS
{{ UNREPORTED }}
Chartered 12/00
Liquidated 5/19/03
Brown Back <$VALUE
3x10-20 1-370 <$2500
Total Issue $18,500
Out in 1910 $610

7572 Lampasas
PEOPLES NB OF LAMPASAS
{{ 3 L 4 S }}
Chartered 1/05
1902 Red Seal <$VALUE
3x10-20 1-1500 <$1500
1902 Date Back
3x10-20 1-4300 <$500
1902 Plain Back
3x10-20 4301-9269 <$500
1929 Small Size
5 Type 1 1-4034 <$300
10 Type 1 1-1513 <$300
20 Type 1 1-479 <$300
Total Issue $583,330
Out in 1935 $22,785
Large out 1935 $2,235

11423 Dallas
FNB OF LANCASTER
{{ 2 L 4 S }}
Chartered 8/19
1902 Plain Back <$VALUE
4x5 1-8540 <$600
3x10-20 1-5811 <$600
1929 Small Size
5 Type 1 1-1216 <$300
10 Type 1 1-554 <$300
20 Type 1 1-164 <$300
5 Type 2 1-1600 <$300
10 Type 2 1-957 <$300
20 Type 2 1-270 <$300
Total Issue $573,720
Out in 1935 $25,000
Large out 1935 $1,250

FNB of Laredo
SEE Ch 2486
Milmo NB of Laredo

5001 Webb
LAREDO NB, LAREDO
{{ 16 L 22 S }}
Chartered 1895
Brown Back <$VALUE
3x10-20 1-7300 <$1000
1882 Date Back
3x10-20 1-6690 <$600
1902 Date Back
3x10-20 1-2000 <$200
1902 Plain Back
3x10-20 2001-35849 <$200
1929 Small Size
10 Type 1 1-5250 <$85
20 Type 1 1-1428 <$100
10 Type 2 1-7562 <$100
20 Type 2 1-2458 <$100
Total Issue $3,103,090
Out in 1935 $193,050
Large out 1935 $15,630

2486 Webb
MILMO NB OF LAREDO
Chartered 7/1/80
Receivership 11/30/31
2nd title:FNB of Laredo
1/14/24
FIRST TITLE {{ 4 L }}
Series 1875 <$VALUE
4x5 1-4150 <$4000
3x10-20 1-2400<$5000/$6000
50-100 1-381 <$15,000
Brown Back
50-100 1-560 <$3500/$4000
1882 Date Back
50-100 1-500 <$3500/$4000
3x50-100 1-1315<$3500/$4000
1902 Plain Back
3x50-100 1-855 <$600/$750
SECOND TITLE {{ 3 L 9 S }}
1902 Plain Back
4x10 1-3370 <$350
3x10-20 1-3514 <$350
1929 Small Size
10 Type 1 1-1758 <$150
20 Type 1 1-709 <$175
Total Issue $1,462,710
Out at close $110,520
Large out at close $19,520

4146 Webb
RIO GRANDE NB OF LAREDO
{{ UNREPORTED }}
Chartered 10/28/89
Receivership 10/3/91
Brown Back <$VALUE
50-100 1-156 <$5000
Total Issue $23,400
Out in 1916 $150

5109 Fannin
FNB OF LEONARD
{{ 3 L 0 S }}
Chartered 1898
Liquidated 2/11/30
Brown Back <$VALUE
3x10-20 1-4150 <$1500
1882 Date Back
3x10-20 1-4640 <$1000
1882 Value Back
3x10-20 4641-5143 <$1000
1902 Plain Back
3x10-20 1-7679 <$400
1929 Small Size
10 Type 1 1-334 <$650
20 Type 1 1-41 <$650
Total Issue $873,560
Out at close $42,890
Large out at close $18,380

12382 Fannin
LEONARD NB, LEONARD
{{ 3 L 9 S }}
Chartered 5/23
1902 Plain Back <$VALUE
4x5 1-4835 <$450
3x10-20 1-3985 <$450
1929 Small Size
5 Type 1 1-2176 <$175
10 Type 1 1-1142 <$175
20 Type 1 1-338 <$175
5 Type 2 1-3770 <$200
10 Type 2 1-2253 <$200
20 Type 2 1-708 <$200
Total Issue $525,850
Out in 1935 $49,400
Large out 1935 $1,430

7144 Denton
FNB OF LEWISVILLE
{{ 3 L 4 S }}
Chartered 2/04
1902 Red Seal <$VALUE
4x5 1-1245 <$1500
3x10-20 1-1017 <$1500
1902 Date Back
4x5 1-2300 <$450
3x10-20 1-1740 <$450
1902 Plain Back
4x5 2301-7630 <$450
3x10-20 1741-4772 <$450
1929 Small Size
5 Type 1 1-1026 <$300
10 Type 1 1-508 <$300
20 Type 1 1-138 <$300
5 Type 2 1-1552 <$300
10 Type 2 1-892 <$300
20 Type 2 1-264 <$300
Total Issue $566,730
Out in 1935 $24,450
Large out 1935 $1,670

7956 Smith
FNB OF LINDALE
{{ UNREPORTED }}
Chartered 10/05
Liquidated 2/5/12
1902 Red Seal <$VALUE
4x5 1-615 <$3000
3x10-20 1-694 <$3000
1902 Date Back
4x5 1-800 <$2000
3x10-20 1-536 <$2000
Total Issue $89,800
Out in 1912 $12,500

10476 Cass
FNB OF LINDEN
{{ U + 4 S }}
Chartered 1/14
1929 Small Size <$VALUE
10 Type 1 1-472 <$350
20 Type 1 1-138 <$350
10 Type 2 1-1813 <$350
20 Type 2 1-560 <$350
Total Issue $74,210
Out in 1935 $29,200

10598 Hood
FNB OF LIPAN
{{ 1 L 6 S }}
Chartered 8/14
1902 Date Back <$VALUE
3x10-20 1-750 <$850
1902 Plain Back
3x10-20 751-5282 <$850
1929 Small Size
10 Type 1 1-832 <$250
20 Type 1 1-224 <$250
10 Type 2 1-1056 <$250
20 Type 2 1-324 <$250
Total Issue $357,940
Out in 1935 $23,600
Large out 1935 $1,040

6169 Polk
CITIZENS NB OF LIVINGSTON
Chartered 3/24/02
2nd title:FNB of Livingston
4/18/10
FIRST TITLE {{ 0 L }}
1902 Red Seal <$VALUE
3x10-20 1-478 <$2000
SECOND TITLE {{ 1 L 2 S }}
1902 Date Back
3x10-20 1-1640 <$850
1902 Plain Back (dated 1902)
3x10-20 1641-2056 <$850
1902 Plain Back (dated 1922)
3x10-20 1-1201 <$850
1929 Small Size
10 Type 1 1-527 <$500
20 Type 1 1-142 <$500
Total Issue $235,410
Out in 1935 $12,150
Large out 1935 $410

FNB of Livingston
SEE Ch 6169
Citizens NB of Livingston

4316 Llano
FNB OF LLANO
{{ UNREPORTED }}
Organized 5/20/90
Receivership 2/28/94
Brown Back <$VALUE
3x10-20 1-494 <$2500
Total Issue $24,700
Out in 1916 $150

7119 Llano
HOME NB OF LLANO
{{ 1 L }}
Organized 1/16/04
Receivership 4/18/23
1902 Red Seal <$VALUE
3x10-20 1-795 <$2000
1902 Date Back
3x10-20 1-2430 <$1000
1902 Plain Back
3x10-20 2431-2652 <$1000
Total Issue $172,350
Out at close $14,700

4371 Llano
IRON CITY NB OF LLANO
{{ 1 L }}
Chartered 7/15/90
Liquidated 4/14/96
Brown Back <$VALUE
3x10-20 1-581 <$2500
Total Issue $29,050
Out in 1910 $320

5853 Llano
LLANO NB, LLANO
{{ 1 L }}
Chartered 6/7/01
Receivership 4/18/23
Brown Back <$VALUE
3x10-20 1-500 <$2000
1882 Date Back
3x10-20 1-960 <$2000
1882 Value Back
3x10-20 961-977 <$2000
1902 Plain Back
3x10-20 1-114 <$1500
Total Issue $79,550
Out at close $4,800

13934 Caldwell
FIRST-LOCKHART NB, LOCKHART
{{ U + 2 S }}
Chartered 1/34
1929 Small Size <$VALUE
10 Type 2 1-1427 <$500
20 Type 2 1-372 <$500
Total Issue $21,710
Out in 1935 $49,200
Large out 1935 $5,960
Outstanding includes Ch 4030
and Ch 5491

4030 Caldwell
FNB OF LOCKHART
{{ 5 L 4 S }}
Chartered 5/10/89
Liquidated 2/20/34
Brown Back <$VALUE
3x10-20 1-1370 <$1000
50-100 1-191 <$3500/$4000
1902 Date Back
3x10-20 1-1800 <$350
1902 Plain Back
3x10-20 1801-5275 <$350
1929 Small Size
10 Type 1 1-727 <$250
20 Type 1 1-190 <$250
Total Issue $427,320
Out at close $23,260
Large out at close $2,280
Ch 13934 assumed circulation

5491 Caldwell
LOCKHART NB, LOCKHART
{{ 2 L 2 S }}
Chartered 7/10/00
Liquidated 2/20/34
Brown Back <$VALUE
50-100 1-300 <$3500/$4000
1882 Date Back
50-100 1-640 <$3500/$4000
3x50-100 1-39 <$3500/$4000
1902 Plain Back
3x50-100 1-311 <$850/$1000
1929 Small Size
50 Type 1 1-85 <$500
100 Type 1 1-17 <$600
Total Issue $264,200
Out at close $23,200
Large out at close $19,700
Ch 13934 assumed circulation

9126 Floyd
FNB OF LOCKNEY
{{ 1 L 2 S }}
Chartered 5/08
1902 Date Back <$VALUE
3x10-20 1-1200 <$1000
1902 Plain Back
3x10-20 1201-2908 <$1000
1929 Small Size
10 Type 1 1-312 <$500
20 Type 1 1-106 <$500
10 Type 2 1-428 <$500
20 Type 2 1-61 <$500
Total Issue $182,340
Out in 1935 $9,600
Large out 1935 $310

9193 Floyd
LOCKNEY NB, LOCKNEY
{{ UNREPORTED }}
Chartered 7/15/08
Liquidated 9/15/08
1902 Date Back <$VALUE
3x10-20 1-125 <$2500
Total Issue $6,250
Out at close $6,250
All notes reportedly redeemed

10323 Lampasas
FNB OF LOMETA
{{ 3 L 0 S }}
Organized 1/11/13
Receivership 8/18/30
1902 Date Back <$VALUE
4x10 1-1700 <$600
1902 Plain Back
4x10 1701-8007 <$600
1929 Small Size
10 Type 1 1-473 <$750
Total Issue $348,660
Out at close $24,100
Large out at close $3,780

7657 Hunt
FARMERS NB OF LONE OAK
{{ 2 L }}
Chartered 3/05
Liquidated 12/3/25
1902 Red Seal <$VALUE
3x10-20 1-340 <$3000
1902 Date Back
3x10-20 1-2960 <$2000
1902 Plain Back
3x10-20 2961-6468 <$2000
Total Issue $340,400
Out at close $14,700

6605 Hunt
FNB OF LONE OAK
{{ UNREPORTED }}
Chartered 2/03
Liquidated 3/3/13
1902 Red Seal <$VALUE
3x10-20 1-456 <$3500
1902 Date Back
3x10-20 1-221 <$2500
Total Issue $33,850
Out in 1913 $3,900

6043 Gregg
CITIZENS NB OF LONGVIEW
{{ 3 L }}
Chartered 12/5/01
Liquidated 12/31/24
Brown Back <$VALUE
3x10-20 1-2520 <$1250
1882 Date Back
3x10-20 1-4300 <$850
1882 Value Back
3x10-20 4301-7430 <$850
1902 Plain Back
3x10-20 1-2220 <$450
Total Issue $608,500
Out at close $37,395

4077 Gregg
FNB OF LONGVIEW
{{ 6 L 15 S }}
Chartered 7/19/89
Brown Back <$VALUE
3x10-20 1-3408 <$1000
1902 Date Back
3x10-20 1-4600 <$300
1902 Plain Back
3x10-20 4601-14902 <$300
1929 Small Size
10 Type 1 1-3094 <$100
20 Type 1 1-822 <$100
10 Type 2 1-5648 <$125
20 Type 2 1-1735 <$125
Total Issue $1,290,960
Out in 1935 $86,850
Large out 1935 $4,130

***
12411 Gregg
REMBERT NB OF LONGVIEW
{{ 3 L 16 S }}
Chartered 7/23
1902 Plain Back <$VALUE
4x5 1-8535 <$400
1929 Small Size
5 Type 1 1-17830 <$125
5 Type 2 1-46478 <$125
Total Issue $937,990
Out in 1935 $87,200
Large out 1935 $1,015
***
8621 McLennan
FNB OF LORENA
{{ UNREPORTED }}
Organized 3/15/07
Receivership 1/23/28
1902 Red Seal <$VALUE
4x10 1-325 <$3000
1902 Date Back
4x10 1-1450 <$1500
1902 Plain Back
4x10 1451-2723 <$1500
Total Issue $121,920
Out at close $7,500
***
6223 Falls
FNB OF LOTT
{{ 4 L 4 S }}
Chartered 4/22/02
Liquidated 6/20/33
1902 Red Seal <$VALUE
3x10-20 1-600 <$1500
1902 Date Back
3x10-20 1-2900 <$400
1902 Plain Back (dated 1902)
3x10-20 2901-5820 <$400
1902 Plain Back (dated 1922)
3x10-20 1-3635 <$400
1929 Small Size
10 Type 1 1-958 <$350
20 Type 1 1-306 <$350
Total Issue $596,950
Out at close $28,820
Large out at close $3,200
***
8742 Houston
FNB OF LOVELADY
{{ 0 L 1 S }}
Chartered 6/07
1902 Red Seal <$VALUE
3x10-20 1-200 <$3000
1902 Date Back
3x10-20 1-700* <$1500
1902 Plain Back
3x10-20 701-1515* <$1500
* 701-760 not marked
1929 Small Size
10 Type 1 1-273 <$750
20 Type 1 1-74 <$750
Total Issue $111,010
Out in 1935 $6,050
Large out 1935 $330
***
8208 Lubbock
CITIZENS NB OF LUBBOCK
{{ 1 L 6 S }}
Chartered 5/06
1902 Red Seal <$VALUE
50-100 1-125 <$7500
1902 Date Back
50-100 1-575 <$1500
3x50-100 1-300 <$1500
1902 Plain Back
3x50-100 301-538 <$1500
1929 Small Size
5 Type 1 1-1038 <$300
10 Type 1 1-314 <$300
20 Type 1 1-106 <$300
50 Type 1 1-190 <$400
100 Type 1 1-64 <$500
5 Type 2 1-2810 <$300
10 Type 2 1-1230 <$300
20 Type 2 1-350 <$300
Total Issue $430,950
Out in 1935 $88,600
Large out 1935 $3,700
***
6195 Lubbock
FNB OF LUBBOCK
{{ 1 L }}
Chartered 4/7/02
Liquidated 2/13/15
1902 Red Seal <$VALUE
3x10-20 1-2400 <$2000
1902 Date Back
3x10-20 1-3376 <$1000
Total Issue $288,800
Out in 1915 $27,900
***

***
12683 Lubbock
LUBBOCK NB, LUBBOCK
{{ 10 S }}
Chartered 4/25
1929 Small Size <$VALUE
5 Type 1 1-830 <$200
10 Type 1 1-416 <$200
20 Type 1 1-212 <$200
50 Type 1 1-84 <$400
100 Type 1 1-42 <$500
5 Type 2 1-1714 <$225
10 Type 2 1-1085 <$225
20 Type 2 1-185 <$225
Total Issue $148,820
Out in 1935 $52,000
***
6009 Angelina
ANGELINA COUNTY NB OF LUFKIN
{{ UNREPORTED }}
Chartered 11/2/01
Liquidated 7/6/12
Brown Back <$VALUE
3x10-20 1-800 <$2000
1882 Date Back
3x10-20 1-241 <$2000
Total Issue $52,050
Out in 1912 $9,950
***
5797 Angelina
LUFKIN NB, LUFKIN
{{ 6 L 12 S }}
Chartered 5/6/01
Brown Back <$VALUE
3x10-20 1-1410 <$1000
1882 Date Back
3x10-20 1-6710 <$650
1882 Value Back
3x10-20 6711-10210 <$650
1902 Plain Back
3x10-20 1-9478 <$300
1929 Small Size
10 Type 1 1-2380 <$150
20 Type 1 1-692 <$150
10 Type 2 1-4802 <$150
20 Type 2 1-1159 <$150
Total Issue $1,351,940
Out in 1935 $72,300
Large out 1935 $4,990
***
13919 Caldwell
FNB IN LULING
{{ 7 S }}
Chartered 12/33
1929 Small Size <$VALUE
5 Type 2 1-8904 <$225
10 Type 2 1-5064 <$225
20 Type 2 1-1200 <$225
Total Issue $119,160
Out in 1935 $70,920
***
4266 Caldwell
FNB OF LULING
{{ UNREPORTED }}
Chartered 3/20/90
Liquidated 12/23/93
Brown Back <$VALUE
50-100 1-132 <$5000
Total Issue $19,800
Out in 1910 $100
***
6422 Kaufman
FNB OF MABANK
{{ 2 L 5 S }}
Chartered 9/15/02
1902 Red Seal <$VALUE
3x10-20 1-500 <$1500
1902 Date Back
3x10-20 1-2670 <$600
1902 Plain Back
3x10-20 2671-7126 <$600
1929 Small Size
10 Type 1 1-760 <$300
20 Type 1 1-230 <$300
10 Type 2 1-1335 <$300
20 Type 2 1-230 <$300
Total Issue $472,450
Out in 1935 $25,000
Large out 1935 $1,550
***
6356 Madison
FNB OF MADISONVILLE
{{ 1 L 2 S }}
Chartered 7/28/02
1902 Red Seal <$VALUE
3x10-20 1-400 <$2000
1902 Date Back
3x10-20 1-1220 <$850
1902 Plain Back
3x10-20 1221-2973 <$850
1929 Small Size
10 Type 1 1-396 <$400
20 Type 1 1-118 <$400
10 Type 2 1-607 <$400
20 Type 2 1-144 <$400
Total Issue $215,520
Out in 1935 $12,200
Large out 1935 $700
***
10403 Henderson
FNB OF MALAKOFF
{{ 1 L 1 S }}
Chartered 6/13
1902 Date Back <$VALUE
3x10-20 1-800 <$1500
1902 Plain Back
3x10-20 801-1688 <$1000
1929 Small Size
10 Type 1 1-250 <$600
20 Type 1 1-77 <$600
Total Issue $108,640
Out in 1935 $5,910
Large out 1935 $530
***
7146 Travis
FARMERS NB OF MANOR
{{ UNREPORTED }}
Organized 2/6/04
Receivership 11/26/26
1902 Red Seal <$VALUE
50-100 1-304 <$7500
1902 Date Back
50-100 1-280 <$2000
3x50-100 1-466 <$2000
Total Issue $204,100
Out at close $24,750
***
7201 Tarrant
FNB OF MANSFIELD
{{ 3 L }}
Chartered 4/6/04
Receivership 5/25/27
1902 Red Seal <$VALUE
4x5 1-475 <$1500
3x10-20 1-390 <$1500
1902 Date Back
4x5 1-925 <$500
3x10-20 1-940 <$500
1902 Plain Back
4x5 926-4455 <$500
3x10-20 941-1300 <$500
Total Issue $183,100
Out at close $12,200
***
4545 Burnet
FNB OF MARBLE FALLS
{{ 2 L }}
Chartered 1891
Liquidated 6/25/23
Brown Back <$VALUE
4x5 1-2750 <$1500
3x10-20 1-520 <$1500
1882 Date Back
4x5 1-201 <$1500
3x10-20 1-176 <$1500
1902 Date Back
3x10-20 1-980 <$750
1902 Plain Back
3x10-20 981-1735 <$750
Total Issue $180,570
Out at close $11,400
***
8674 Presidio
MARFA NB, MARFA
{{ 6 L 2U + 12 S }}
Chartered 5/07
1902 Red Seal <$VALUE
3x10-20 1-260 <$1250
1902 Date Back
3x10-20 1-4900 <$350
1902 Plain Back
3x10-20 4901-16998 <$350
1929 Small Size
10 Type 1 1-2004 <$175
20 Type 1 1-558 <$175
10 Type 2 1-3666 <$200
20 Type 2 1-980 <$200
Total Issue $1,106,360
Out in 1935 $67,000
Large out 1935 $3,890
***
4706 Falls
FNB OF MARLIN
{{ 8 L 15 S }}
Chartered 1892
Brown Back <$VALUE
3x10-20 1-8760 <$1000
1882 Date Back
3x10-20 1-2839 <$600
1902 Date Back
3x10-20 1-4400 <$225
1902 Plain Back
3x10-20 4401-21942 <$225
1929 Small Size
10 Type 1 1-3178 <$100
20 Type 1 1-782 <$125
10 Type 2 1-4390 <$125
20 Type 2 1-1278 <$125
Total Issue $2,031,030
Out in 1935 $97,600
Large out 1935 $5,260
***
Marlin-Citizens NB of Marlin
SEE Ch 5606
Marlin NB, Marlin
***
5606 Falls
MARLIN NB, MARLIN
Chartered 10/24/00
Receivership 3/1/33
2nd title: Marlin-Citizens NB 2/9/31
FIRST TITLE {{ 8 L 4 S }}
Brown Back <$VALUE
3x10-20 1-1700 <$1000
1882 Date Back
3x10-20 1-6500 <$600
1882 Value Back
3x10-20 6501-10638 <$650
1902 Plain Back
3x10-20 1-12631 <$300
1929 Small Size
10 Type 1 1-1646 <$225
20 Type 1 1-470 <$225
SECOND TITLE {{ 4 S }}
1929 Small Size
10 Type 1 1-1053 <$200
20 Type 1 1-231 <$200
Total Issue $1,494,510
Out at close $93,700
Large out at close $7,460
***
3113 Harrison
FNB OF MARSHALL
{{ 7 L 17 S }}
Chartered 1884
Brown Back <$VALUE
3x10-20 1-3880 <$1000
1902 Red Seal
50-100 1-1100 <$7500
1902 Date Back
4x10 1-5000 <$250
50-100 1-500 <$500/$600
3x50-100 1-580 <$500/$600
1902 Plain Back
4x10 5001-17973 <$250
3x50-100 581-930<$500/$600
1929 Small Size
10 Type 1 1-4852 <$60
10 Type 2 1-10192 <$70
Total Issue $1,778,460
Out in 1935 $95,600
Large out 1935 $7,140
***
4101 Harrison
MARSHALL NB, MARSHALL
{{ 10 L 14 S }}
Chartered 8/27/89
Brown Back <$VALUE
3x10-20 1-5813 <$850
1902 Date Back
3x10-20 1-7600 <$175
1902 Plain Back
3x10-20 7601-24793 <$175
1929 Small Size
10 Type 1 1-3406 <$85
20 Type 1 1-810 <$100
10 Type 2 1-5446 <$100
20 Type 2 1-1147 <$100
Total Issue $1,909,260
Out in 1935 $98,400
Large out 1935 $4,500
***
12703 Harrison
STATE NB OF MARSHALL
{{ 3 L 16 S }}
Chartered 4/25
1902 Plain Back <$VALUE
4x5 1-4639 <$400
4x10 1-3118 <$400
1929 Small Size
5 Type 1 1-5058 <$100
10 Type 1 1-2800 <$100
5 Type 2 1-12012 <$100
10 Type 2 1-7104 <$100
Total Issue $668,340
Out in 1935 $97,720
Large out 1935 $920
***
7546 McLennan
FARMERS & MERCHANTS NB OF MART
{{ 5 L 2U + 8 S }}
Chartered 1/05
1902 Red Seal <$VALUE
3x10-20 1-2100 <$1250
1902 Date Back
3x10-20 1-3900 <$350
1902 Plain Back
3x10-20 3901-11037 <$350
1929 Small Size
10 Type 1 1-1442 <$200
20 Type 1 1-346 <$200
10 Type 2 1-2382 <$200
20 Type 2 1-450 <$200
Total Issue $817,710
Out in 1935 $38,550
Large out 1935 $1,990
***
5850 McLennan
FNB OF MART
{{ 6 L 9 S }}
Chartered 6/6/01
Brown Back <$VALUE
3x10-20 1-3500 <$1000
1882 Date Back
3x10-20 1-4340 <$700
1882 Value Back
3x10-20 4341-7010 <$750
1902 Plain Back
3x10-20 1-6042 <$325
1929 Small Size
10 Type 1 1-1498 <$175
20 Type 1 1-454 <$200
10 Type 2 1-2900 <$200
20 Type 2 1-884 <$200
Total Issue $1,018,640
Out in 1935 $47,350
Large out 1935 $2,790
***
4378 Mason
CITIZENS NB OF MASON
{{ UNREPORTED }}
Chartered 7/24/90
Liquidated 8/23/97
2nd title:FNB of Mason 9/91
FIRST TITLE
Brown Back <$VALUE
3x10-20 1-235 <$2500
SECOND TITLE
Brown Back
50-100 1-89 <$5000
Total Issue $25,100
Out in 1910 $470
***
FNB of Mason
SEE Ch 4378
Citizens NB of Mason
***
7098 Mason
GERMAN-AMERICAN NB OF MASON
Chartered 1/04
2nd title:Mason NB, Mason 5/31/18
FIRST TITLE {{ 1 L }}
1902 Red Seal <$VALUE
3x10-20 1-340 <$2000
1902 Date Back
3x10-20 1-2150 <$850
1902 Plain Back
3x10-20 2151-2590 <$850
SECOND TITLE {{ 3 L 4 S }}
1902 Plain Back
3x10-20 1-3382 <$450
1929 Small Size
10 Type 1 1-720 <$250
20 Type 1 1-170 <$250
10 Type 2 1-1577 <$275
20 Type 2 1-280 <$275
Total Issue $400,570
Out in 1935 $23,900
Large out 1935 $1,150
***
Mason NB, Mason
SEE Ch 7098
German-American NB of Mason
***
11002 Motley
FNB OF MATADOR
{{ 6 S }}
Chartered 5/17
Liquidated 5/1/35
1929 Small Size <$VALUE
5 Type 1 1-794 <$300
10 Type 1 1-286 <$300
20 Type 1 1-66 <$300
5 Type 2 1-1216 <$300
10 Type 2 1-545 <$300
20 Type 2 1-160 <$300
Total Issue $63,630
Out at close $11,700
***
10182 Bowie
MAUD NB, MAUD
{{ UNREPORTED }}
Chartered 4/12
Liquidated 5/20/26
1902 Date Back <$VALUE
3x10-20 1-600 <$1500
1902 Plain Back
3x10-20 601-1256 <$1500
Total Issue $62,800
Out at close $6,500
***
8327 Brown
FNB OF MAY
{{ 1 L 4 S }}
Chartered 8/06
Liquidated 12/31/33
1902 Red Seal <$VALUE
3x10-20 1-750 <$2000
1902 Date Back
3x10-20 1-1960 <$850
1902 Plain Back
3x10-20 1961-6271 <$850
1929 Small Size
10 Type 1 1-794 <$350
20 Type 1 1-202 <$350
Total Issue $422,930
Out at close $24,160
Large out at close $1,740
***
5504 McLennan
CITIZENS NB OF McGREGOR
{{ UNREPORTED }}
Chartered 7/18/00
Receivership 2/8/04
Brown Back <$VALUE
3x10-20 1-913 <$2000
Total Issue $45,650
Out in 1916 $350
***
4076 McLennan
FNB OF McGREGOR
{{ 4 L 6 S }}
Chartered 7/16/89
Brown Back <$VALUE
3x10-20 1-2672 <$1000
1902 Date Back
3x10-20 1-3650 <$500
1902 Plain Back
3x10-20 3651-9814 <$500
1929 Small Size
10 Type 1 1-1124 <$300
20 Type 1 1-302 <$300
5 Type 2 1-111 <$300
10 Type 2 1-899 <$300
20 Type 2 1-212 <$300
Total Issue $729,355
Out in 1935 $23,365
Large out 1935 $2,365
***
7599 McLennan
McGREGOR NB, McGREGOR
{{ 1 L }}
Chartered 2/6/05
Liquidated 3/31/06
1902 Red Seal <$VALUE
3x10-20 1-280 <$2500
Total Issue $14,000
Out in 1910 $1,150
***
14236 Collin
CENTRAL NB OF McKINNEY
{{ 3 S }}
Chartered 7/34
1929 Small Size <$VALUE
5 Type 2 1-3014 <$400
10 Type 2 1-2268 <$400
20 Type 2 1-560 <$400
50 Type 2 1-53 <$650
100 Type 2 1-36 <$750
Total Issue $55,200
Out in 1935 $50,000
***
2909 Collin
COLLIN COUNTY NB OF McKINNEY
{{ 14 L 18 S }}
Chartered 1883
Brown Back <$VALUE
3x10-20 1-6952 <$850
1902 Red Seal
3x10-20 1-9600 <$1000
1902 Date Back
4x5 1-16330 <$175
3x10-20 1-11400 <$175
1902 Plain Back
4x5 16331-52245 <$175
3x10-20 11401-34636 <$175
1929 Small Size
5 Type 1 1-6424 <$85
10 Type 1 1-3168 <$85
20 Type 1 1-926 <$100
5 Type 2 1-12556 <$100
10 Type 2 1-5521 <$100
20 Type 2 1-1325 <$100
Total Issue $4,242,710
Out in 1935 $116,950
Large out 1935 $11,190
***

****
2729 Collin
FNB OF McKINNEY
{{5L 1S}}
Organized 5/8/82
Receivership 3/19/30
Series 1875 <$VALUE
3x10-20 1-1638<$5000/$6000
1902 Red Seal
3x10-20 1-1620 <$1250
1902 Date Back
3x10-20 1-5300 <$300
1902 Plain Back
3x10-20 5301-13677 <$300
1929 Small Size
10 Type 1 1-514 <$400
20 Type 1 1-25 <$400
Total Issue $880,590
Out at close $45,320
Large out at close $13,820
****
7413 Gray
FNB OF McLEAN
{{1L}}
Chartered 9/29/04
Liquidated 3/30/09
1902 Red Seal <$VALUE
3x10-20 1-598 <$3000
Total Issue $29,900
Out in 1910 $4,180
****
10008 Collin
MELISSA NB, MELISSA
{{2L U+4S}}
Chartered 5/11
Liquidated 12/27/34
1902 Date Back <$VALUE
3x10-20 1-2045 <$850
1902 Plain Back
3x10-20 2046-6586 <$850
1929 Small Size
5 Type 1 1-104 <$350
10 Type 1 1-738 <$350
20 Type 1 1-234 <$350
5 Type 2 1-1468 <$350
10 Type 2 1-669 <$350
20 Type 2 1-150 <$350
Total Issue $421,810
Out at close $25,000
Large out at close $1,210
****
6107 Hall
FNB OF MEMPHIS
{{5L 3U+15S}}
Chartered 1/27/02
1902 Red Seal <$VALUE
3x10-20 1-2550 <$1250
1902 Date Back
3x10-20 1-4000 <$300
1902 Plain Back (dated 1902)
3x10-20 4001-7098 <$300
1902 Plain Back (dated 1922)
4x5 1-6534 <$300
3x10-20 1-4562 <$300
1929 Small Size
5 Type 1 1-4664 <$125
10 Type 1 1-2418 <$125
20 Type 1 1-570 <$125
5 Type 2 1-5284 <$150
10 Type 2 1-2770 <$150
20 Type 2 1-560 <$150
Total Issue $1,259,900
Out in 1935 $78,970
Large out 1935 $5,040
Outstanding includes Ch 8005
****
8005 Hall
HALL COUNTY NB OF MEMPHIS
{{6L 6S}}
Chartered 12/05
Closed 7/3/33
1902 Red Seal <$VALUE
3x10-20 1-660 <$1250
1902 Date Back
3x10-20 1-3710 <$300
1902 Plain Back
3x10-20 3711-12760 <$300
1929 Small Size
10 Type 1 1-1377 <$225
20 Type 1 1-400 <$250
Total Issue $801,620
Out at close $47,950
Large out at close $4,150
Ch 6107 assumed circulation
****
10044 Menard
FNB OF MENARD
{{ UNREPORTED }}
Chartered 6/11
Liquidated 3/16/14
1902 Date Back <$VALUE
3x10-20 1-439 <$2000
Total Issue $21,950
Out in 1914 $5,230
****

****
11879 Hidalgo
FNB OF MERCEDES
{{5L 10S}}
Chartered 11/20
1902 Plain Back <$VALUE
4x5 1-10665 <$400
3x10-20 1-7002 <$400
1929 Small Size
5 Type 1 1-4342 <$175
10 Type 1 1-2198 <$175
20 Type 1 1-476 <$200
5 Type 2 1-5438 <$200
10 Type 2 1-2820 <$200
20 Type 2 1-561 <$200
Total Issue $949,270
Out in 1935 $64,190
Large out 1935 $3,490
****
4016 Bosque
FNB OF MERIDIAN
{{ UNREPORTED }}
Chartered 4/22/89
Liquidated 4/24/26
Brown Back <$VALUE
50-100 1-562 <$5000
1902 Date Back
3x10-20 1-2200* <$1500
* 2169 not issued
1902 Plain Back
3x10-20 2201-2799 <$1500
Total Issue $224,200
Out at close $8,700
****
7378 Hunt
FNB OF MERIT
{{ UNREPORTED }}
Chartered 8/04
Liquidated 4/15/30
1902 Red Seal <$VALUE
3x10-20 1-360 <$2500
1902 Date Back
3x10-20 1-920 <$1500
1902 Plain Back
3x10-20 921-1706 <$1500
1929 Small Size
10 Type 1 1-59 <$750
20 Type 1 1-6 <$750
Total Issue $107,560
Out at close $5,890
Large out at close $1,680
****
7481 Taylor
FARMERS & MERCHANTS NB OF MERKEL
{{1L 2S}}
Chartered 11/04
1902 Red Seal <$VALUE
3x10-20 1-300 <$2000
1902 Date Back
3x10-20 1-1180 <$1000
1902 Plain Back
3x10-20 1181-1954 <$1000
1929 Small Size
10 Type 1 1-219 <$500
20 Type 1 1-61 <$500
Total Issue $133,610
Out in 1935 $6,100
Large out 1935 $300
****
5661 Taylor
FNB OF MERKEL
{{1L}}
Chartered 12/31/00
Liquidated 7/10/11
Brown Back <$VALUE
3x10-20 1-2950 <$1500
1882 Date Back
3x10-20 1-1339 <$1250
Total Issue $214,450
Out in 1911 $35,100
****
7466 Taylor
MERKEL NB, MERKEL
{{ UNREPORTED }}
Chartered 11/4/04
Liquidated 11/26/07
1902 Red Seal <$VALUE
3x10-20 1-222 <$2500
Total Issue $11,100
Out in 1910 $1,220
****
10052 Taylor
SOUTHERN NB OF MERKEL
{{ UNREPORTED }}
Chartered 7/11
Liquidated 7/25/13
1902 Date Back <$VALUE
3x10-20 1-1248 <$1500
Total Issue $62,400
Out in 1913 $29,250
****

****
9810 Irion
FNB OF MERTZON
{{ UNREPORTED }}
Chartered 7/10
1902 Date Back <$VALUE
3x10-20 1-900 <$1500
1902 Plain Back
3x10-20 901-1709 <$1500
1929 Small Size
10 Type 1 1-269 <$750
20 Type 1 1-64 <$750
Total Issue $109,270
Out in 1935 $6,000
Large out 1935 $200
****
6140 Dallas
FNB OF MESQUITE
{{1L 4S}}
Chartered 2/27/02
1902 Red Seal <$VALUE
4x5 1-790 <$2000
3x10-20 1-584 <$2000
1902 Date Back
4x5 1-2725 <$850
3x10-20 1-2060 <$850
1902 Plain Back (dated 1902)
4x5 2726-4215 <$850
3x10-20 2061-2931 <$850
1902 Plain Back (dated 1922)
4x5 1-3039 <$850
3x10-20 1-1892 <$850
1929 Small Size
5 Type 1 1-1000 <$350
10 Type 1 1-544 <$350
20 Type 1 1-160 <$350
5 Type 2 1-1770 <$350
10 Type 2 1-1202 <$350
20 Type 2 1-285 <$375
Total Issue $539,640
Out in 1935 $24,500
Large out 1935 $1,410
****
5697 Limestone
CITIZENS NB OF MEXIA
{{ UNREPORTED }}
Chartered 1/29/01
Liquidated 4/6/03
Brown Back <$VALUE
4x5 1-225 <$2500
3x10-20 1-256 <$2500
Total Issue $17,300
Out in 1910 $545
****
11964 Limestone
CITY NB OF MEXIA
{{5L 12S}}
Chartered 4/21
1902 Plain Back <$VALUE
3x10-20 1-14059 <$300
1929 Small Size
10 Type 1 1-3438 <$125
20 Type 1 1-850 <$125
10 Type 2 1-1352 <$150
20 Type 2 1-390 <$150
Total Issue $1,032,550
Out in 1935 $44,760
Large out 1935 $3,110
****
3014 Limestone
FNB OF MEXIA
{{1L}}
Chartered 1883
Liquidated 3/22/19
Brown Back <$VALUE
4x5 1-3297 <$1500
50-100 1-86 <$5000
1902 Red Seal
3x10-20 1-600 <$2000
1902 Date Back
3x10-20 1-1439 <$1000
Total Issue $180,790
Out at close $11,900
****
12190 Limestone
PRENDERGAST-SMITH NB OF MEXIA
{{14S}}
Chartered 5/22
1929 Small Size <$VALUE
5 Type 1 1-1898 <$125
10 Type 1 1-940 <$125
20 Type 1 1-284 <$125
5 Type 2 1-4062 <$150
10 Type 2 1-1960 <$150
20 Type 2 1-595 <$150
Total Issue $199,230
Out in 1935 $100,000
****

****
4368 Midland
FNB OF MIDLAND
{{4L 2S}}
Chartered 1890
Brown Back <$VALUE
3x10-20 1-2820 <$1500
1882 Date Back
3x10-20 1-297 <$1250
1902 Date Back
3x10-20 1-2290 <$750
1902 Plain Back
3x10-20 2291-3979 <$750
1929 Small Size
10 Type 1 1-564 <$600
20 Type 1 1-120 <$600
10 Type 2 1-423 <$600
20 Type 2 1-127 <$600
Total Issue $409,810
Out in 1935 $12,650
Large out 1935 $1,200
****
Midland NB, Midland
SEE Ch 6410
Odessa NB, Odessa
****
8568 Ellis
FARMERS NB OF MIDLOTHIAN
{{ UNREPORTED }}
Chartered 2/26/07
Liquidated 2/20/09
1902 Red Seal <$VALUE
3x10-20 1-197 <$3000
Total Issue $9,850
Out in 1910 $1,640
****
13670 Ellis
FNB IN MIDLOTHIAN
{{3S}}
Chartered 3/33
1929 Small Size <$VALUE
10 Type 2 1-2004 <$450
20 Type 2 1-504 <$450
Total Issue $30,120
Out in 1935 $23,450
Large out 1935 $730
Outstanding includes Ch 7775
****
7775 Ellis
FNB OF MIDLOTHIAN
{{3L 3S}}
Chartered 5/05
Liquidated 4/4/33
1902 Red Seal <$VALUE
3x10-20 1-560 <$1500
1902 Date Back
3x10-20 1-3160 <$450
1902 Plain Back
3x10-20 3161-7653 <$450
1929 Small Size
10 Type 1 1-718 <$400
20 Type 1 1-188 <$400
Total Issue $476,290
Out at close $20,020
Large out 1935 $730
Ch 13670 assumed circulation
****
6935 Runnels
MILES NB, MILES
{{ UNREPORTED }}
Chartered 8/03
Liquidated 12/15/23
1902 Red Seal <$VALUE
3x10-20 1-456 <$2500
1902 Date Back
3x10-20 1-1220 <$1500
1902 Plain Back
3x10-20 1221-1848 <$1500
Total Issue $115,200
Out at close $12,000
****
7414 Runnels
RUNNELS COUNTY NB OF MILES
{{1L}}
Chartered 9/04
Liquidated 2/11/11
1902 Red Seal <$VALUE
3x10-20 1-455 <$3000
Total Issue $22,750
Out in 1911 $3,400
****
12687 Parker
FNB OF MILLSAP
{{2L 2S}}
Chartered 4/25
Liquidated 5/10/32
1902 Plain Back <$VALUE
3x10-20 1-882 <$1250
1929 Small Size
10 Type 1 1-245 <$650
20 Type 1 1-64 <$650
Total Issue $66,480
Out at close $6,240
Large out at close $560
****

****
5127 Wood
FNB OF MINEOLA
{{5L 10S}}
Chartered 1898
Brown Back <$VALUE
3x10-20 1-1070 <$1000
1882 Date Back
4x5 1-3500 <$700
3x10-20 1-2960 <$700
1882 Value Back
4x5 3501-4535 <$750
3x10-20 2961-3625 <$750
1902 Plain Back
4x5 1-9230 <$350
3x10-20 1-5839 <$350
1929 Small Size
5 Type 1 1-2300 <$150
10 Type 1 1-1230 <$150
20 Type 1 1-322 <$150
5 Type 2 1-4008 <$150
10 Type 2 1-1908 <$150
20 Type 2 1-648 <$175
Total Issue $1,035,520
Out in 1935 $46,130
Large out 1935 $2,430
****
8037 Wood
MINEOLA NB, MINEOLA
{{ UNREPORTED }}
Chartered 1/06
Liquidated 1/5/10
1902 Red Seal <$VALUE
3x10-20 1-460 <$2500
1902 Date Back
3x10-20 1-80 <$1500
Total Issue $27,000
Out in 1910 $6,260
****
12734 Palo Pinto
CITY NB OF MINERAL WELLS
{{2L 15S}}
Chartered 5/25
1902 Plain Back <$VALUE
3x10-20 1-4023 <$650
1929 Small Size
10 Type 1 1-2506 <$125
20 Type 1 1-650 <$125
10 Type 2 1-4823 <$125
20 Type 2 1-1896 <$125
Total Issue $515,660
Out in 1935 $100,000
Large out 1935 $1,070
****
5511 Palo Pinto
FNB OF MINERAL WELLS
{{6L 4S}}
Chartered 7/20/00
Liquidated 6/9/31
Brown Back <$VALUE
4x5 1-1830 <$1000
3x10-20 1-1408 <$1000
1882 Date Back
4x5 1-3375 <$600
3x10-20 1-2330 <$600
1882 Value Back
4x5 3376-4925 <$600
3x10-20 2331-3190 <$600
1902 Plain Back
4x5 1-10140 <$300
3x10-20 1-5596 <$300
1929 Small Size
5 Type 1 1-1272 <$250
10 Type 1 1-668 <$250
20 Type 1 1-156 <$250
Total Issue $944,560
Out at close $41,165
Large out at close $6,665
****
12669 Palo Pinto
STATE NB OF MINERAL WELLS
{{4L 16S}}
Chartered 4/25
1902 Plain Back <$VALUE
3x10-20 1-8931 <$400
1929 Small Size
10 Type 1 1-3442 <$125
20 Type 1 1-900 <$125
10 Type 2 1-4872 <$150
20 Type 2 1-1500 <$150
Total Issue $839,790
Out in 1935 $99,680
Large out 1935 $2,750
****
10090 Hidalgo
FNB OF MISSION
{{3L 5S}}
Chartered 10/11
1902 Date Back <$VALUE
3x10-20 1-495* <$650
1902 Plain Back
3x10-20 856-4523* <$650
* 496-855 not marked

1929 Small Size
10 Type 1 1-678 <$350
20 Type 1 1-200 <$350
10 Type 2 1-1363 <$350
20 Type 2 1-212 <$375
Total Issue $308,700
Out in 1935 $23,850
Large out 1935 $1,780
****
3165 Montague
FNB OF MONTAGUE
{{ UNREPORTED }}
Chartered 4/24/84
Liquidated 3/7/98
Brown Back <$VALUE
3x10-20 1-935 <$2500
Total Issue $46,750
Out in 1910 $500
****
5774 McLennan
FNB OF MOODY
{{4L 8S}}
Chartered 4/11/01
Brown Back <$VALUE
3x10-20 1-720 <$1250
1882 Date Back
3x10-20 1-4900 <$850
1882 Value Back
3x10-20 4901-7440 <$850
1902 Plain Back
3x10-20 1-6116 <$400
1929 Small Size
10 Type 1 1-1506 <$225
20 Type 1 1-404 <$225
10 Type 2 1-2599 <$250
20 Type 2 1-471 <$250
Total Issue $888,050
Out in 1935 $42,600
Large out 1935 $3,260
****
8817 Frio
MOORE NB, MOORE
{{4L 1S}}
Chartered 8/07
Liquidated 12/23/30
1902 Red Seal <$VALUE
4x5 1-555 <$1500
3x10-20 1-444 <$1500
1902 Date Back
4x5 1-3575 <$400
3x10-20 1-2580 <$400
1902 Plain Back
4x5 3576-10452 <$400
3x10-20 2581-6832 <$400
1929 Small Size
5 Type 1 1-402 <$600
10 Type 1 1-209 <$600
20 Type 1 1-55 <$600
Total Issue $615,140
Out at close $21,640
Large out at close $4,210
****
6247 Bosque
FNB OF MORGAN
{{1L}}
Chartered 5/8/02
Receivership 11/13/24
1902 Red Seal <$VALUE
4x5 1-1250 <$1500
3x10-20 1-1100 <$1500
1902 Date Back
4x5 1-2025 <$750
3x10-20 1-1600 <$750
1902 Plain Back
4x5 2026-4870 <$750
3x10-20 1601-3303 <$750
Total Issue $342,550
Out at close $25,000
****
5399 Lavaca
FNB OF MOULTON
{{ UNREPORTED }}
Chartered 6/4/00
Liquidated 1/30/01
Brown Back <$VALUE
3x10-20 1-125 <$3500
Total Issue $6,250
Out in 1910 $240
****
13669 Hill
FNB IN MOUNT CALM
{{ UNREPORTED }}
Chartered 3/33
1929 Small Size <$VALUE
5 Type 2 1-1188 <$650
10 Type 2 1-828 <$650
Total Issue $14,220
Out in 1935 $25,910
Large out 1935 $1,460
Outstanding includes Ch 10297
****

10297 Hill
FNB OF MOUNT CALM
{{2L 6S}}
Chartered 12/12
Liquidated 7/17/33
1902 Date Back <$VALUE
3x10-20 1-1500 <$600
1902 Plain Back
3x10-20 1501-9128 <$600
1929 Small Size
10 Type 1 1-1358 <$300
20 Type 1 1-448 <$300
Total Issue $591,640
Out at close $40,940
Large out 1935 $1,690
Ch 13669 assumed circulation

4722 Titus
FNB OF MOUNT PLEASANT
{{U+4L}}
Chartered 1892
Liquidated 1/15/29
Brown Back <$VALUE
3x10-20 1-3790 <$1000
1882 Date Back
3x10-20 1-1703 <$750
1902 Date Back
3x10-20 1-3100 <$400
1902 Plain Back
3x10-20 3101-11317 <$400
Total Issue $840,500
Out at close $42,645

6139 Titus
MERCHANTS & PLANTERS NB OF MOUNT PLEASANT
Chartered 2/27/02
Liquidated 5/12/24
2nd title:State NB of Mount Pleasant 1/25/15
FIRST TITLE {{0L}}
1902 Red Seal <$VALUE
3x10-20 1-810 <$1500
1902 Date Back
3x10-20 1-5031 <$750
SECOND TITLE {{1L}}
1902 Date Back
3x10-20 1-1000 <$500
1902 Plain Back (dated 1902)
3x10-20 1001-4910 <$500
1902 Plain Back (dated 1922)
3x10-20 1-1934 <$500
Total Issue $634,250
Out at close $59,300

State NB of Mount Pleasant
SEE Ch 6139
Merchants & Planters NB of Mount Pleasant

5409 Franklin
FNB OF MOUNT VERNON
{{2L 6S}}
Chartered 6/7/00
Brown Back <$VALUE
3x10-20 1-870 <$1250
1882 Date Back
3x10-20 1-2090 <$1000
1902 Plain Back
3x10-20 1-1481 <$600
1929 Small Size
10 Type 1 1-504 <$300
20 Type 1 1-192 <$300
10 Type 2 1-2818 <$300
20 Type 2 1-505 <$300
Total Issue $313,610
Out in 1935 $41,550
Large out 1935 $2,260
Outstanding includes Ch 7674

7674 Franklin
MERCHANTS & PLANTERS NB OF MOUNT VERNON
{{3L 3S}}
Chartered 3/05
Closed 6/1/32
1902 Red Seal <$VALUE
3x10-20 1-400 <$1500
1902 Date Back
3x10-20 1-2700 <$400
1902 Plain Back
3x10-20 2701-7900 <$400
1929 Small Size
10 Type 1 1-665 <$400
20 Type 1 1-194 <$400
Total Issue $478,180
Out at close $30,000
Large out at close $2,890
Ch 5409 assumed circulation

8215 Knox
CITIZENS NB OF MUNDAY
{{ UNREPORTED }}
Chartered 5/06
Liquidated 12/30/11
1902 Red Seal <$VALUE
3x10-20 1-300 <$2500
1902 Date Back
3x10-20 1-161 <$1500
Total Issue $23,050
Out at close $5,950
Ch 7106 assumed circulation

7106 Knox
FNB OF MUNDAY
{{3L 3S}}
Chartered 1/04
Liquidated 3/1/32
1902 Red Seal <$VALUE
3x10-20 1-520 <$1500
1902 Date Back
3x10-20 1-2350 <$450
1902 Plain Back
3x10-20 2351-7024 <$450
1929 Small Size
10 Type 1 1-540 <$400
20 Type 1 1-164 <$400
Total Issue $429,280
Out at close $26,250
Large out at close $2,320
Outstanding includes Ch 8215

5991 Nacogdoches
COMMERCIAL NB OF NACOGDOCHES
{{1L}}
Chartered 10/14/01
Liquidated 2/28/10
Brown Back <$VALUE
3x10-20 1-830 <$2000
1882 Date Back
3x10-20 1-100 <$2000
Total Issue $46,500
Out in 1910 $8,850

4405 Nacogdoches
FNB OF NACOGDOCHES
{{ UNREPORTED }}
Chartered 8/28/90
Liquidated 12/30/99
Brown Back <$VALUE
3x10-20 1-672 <$2000
Total Issue $33,600
Out in 1910 $360

6627 Nacogdoches
STONE FORT NB OF NACOGDOCHES
{{2L U+10S}}
Chartered 2/03
1902 Red Seal <$VALUE
3x10-20 1-1200 <$2000
1902 Date Back
3x10-20 1-3160 <$850
1902 Plain Back
3x10-20 3161-4671 <$850
1929 Small Size
5 Type 1 1-12680 <$200
5 Type 2 1-38304 <$225
Total Issue $877,470
Out in 1935 $87,850
Large out 1935 $860

7194 Morris
MORRIS COUNTY NB OF NAPLES
{{4L 7S}}
Chartered 3/04
1902 Red Seal <$VALUE
3x10-20 1-550 <$1250
1902 Date Back
3x10-20 1-1400* <$350
1902 Plain Back
3x10-20 1601-8258* <$350
* 1401-1600 not marked
1929 Small Size
10 Type 1 1-1244 <$200
20 Type 1 1-336 <$200
10 Type 2 1-1960 <$200
20 Type 2 1-638 <$200
Total Issue $587,720
Out in 1935 $39,000
Large out 1935 $2,230
Outstanding includes Ch 8585

8585 Morris
NAPLES NB, NAPLES
{{3L}}
Chartered 3/07
Liquidated 2/23/16
1902 Red Seal <$VALUE
3x10-20 1-300 <$1250
1902 Date Back
3x10-20 1-3003 <$500
Total Issue $165,150
Out at close $27,700
Ch 7194 assumed circulation

5190 Grimes
CITIZENS NB OF NAVASOTA
{{4L 3S}}
Chartered 4/29/99
Liquidated 11/29/32
Brown Back <$VALUE
4x5 1-1225 <$1000
3x10-20 1-630 <$1000
1882 Date Back
4x5 1-2693 <$750
3x10-20 1-2144 <$750
1902 Plain Back
3x10-20 1-4155 <$400
1929 Small Size
10 Type 1 1-690 <$350
20 Type 1 1-193 <$350
Total Issue $489,370
Out at close $26,280
Large out at close $3,930
Ch 4253 assumed circulation

4253 Grimes
FNB OF NAVASOTA
{{6L 9S}}
Chartered 1890
Brown Back <$VALUE
3x10-20 1-1590 <$1000
1882 Date Back
3x10-20 1-902 <$750
1902 Date Back
3x10-20 1-5250 <$350
1902 Plain Back
3x10-20 5251-13741 <$350
1929 Small Size
10 Type 1 1-2033 <$200
20 Type 1 1-529 <$200
Total Issue $997,110
Out in 1935 $42,850
Large out 1935 $8,280
Outstanding includes Ch 5190

6596 Jefferson
FNB OF NEDERLAND
{{ UNREPORTED }}
Chartered 1/28/03
Receivership 1/26/05
1902 Red Seal <$VALUE
3x10-20 1-217 <$4000
Total Issue $10,850
Out at close $7,000
All notes reportedly redeemed

5721 Collin
FNB OF NEVADA
{{5L 2S}}
Chartered 2/16/01
Liquidated 2/20/34
Brown Back <$VALUE
4x5 1-1330 <$1000
3x10-20 1-908 <$1000
1882 Date Back
4x5 1-2225 <$750
3x10-20 1-1760 <$750
1882 Value Back
4x5 2226-3465 <$750
3x10-20 1761-2392 <$750
1902 Plain Back
4x5 1-3692 <$400
3x10-20 1-2120 <$400
1929 Small Size
5 Type 1 1-1072 <$400
10 Type 1 1-518 <$400
20 Type 1 1-154 <$400
5 Type 2 1-108 <$450
10 Type 2 1-65 <$450
20 Type 2 1-51 <$450
Total Issue $524,670
Out at close $20,880
Large out at close $2,830

5636 Bowie
FNB OF NEW BOSTON
{{2L 3S}}
Chartered 12/11/00
Brown Back <$VALUE
3x10-20 1-620 <$1250
1882 Date Back
3x10-20 1-1300 <$1000
1882 Value Back
3x10-20 1301-1348 <$1000
1902 Plain Back
4x5 1-3023 <$600
1929 Small Size
5 Type 1 1-1660 <$400
5 Type 2 1-11172 <$400
Total Issue $264,520
Out in 1935 $30,000
Large out 1935 $910
Outstanding includes Ch 8522

8522 Bowie
NEW BOSTON NB, NEW BOSTON
{{1L 0S}}
Chartered 1/07
Closed 1/22/31
1902 Red Seal <$VALUE
3x10-20 1-324 <$2500
1902 Date Back
3x10-20 1-1300 <$1000
1902 Plain Back
3x10-20 1301-2254 <$1000
1929 Small Size
10 Type 1 1-149 <$650
20 Type 1 1-13 <$650
Total Issue $139,400
Out at close $7,260
Large out at close $900
Ch 5636 assumed circulation

7924 Comal
COMAL NB OF NEW BRAUNFELS
{{ UNREPORTED }}
Chartered 9/27/05
Liquidated 9/25/08
1902 Red Seal <$VALUE
3x10-20 1-1272 <$2500
Total Issue $63,600
Out in 1910 $7,670

4295 Comal
FNB OF NEW BRAUNFELS
{{3L 4S}}
Chartered 1890
Brown Back <$VALUE
3x10-20 1-3510 <$1250
1882 Date Back
3x10-20 1-552 <$1000
1902 Date Back
3x10-20 1-2800* <$500
1902 Plain Back
3x10-20 3301-6986* <$500
* 2801-3300 not marked
1929 Small Size
100 Type 2 1-1141 <$450
Total Issue $666,500
Out in 1935 $101,230
Large out 1935 $1,930

10472 Young
FNB OF NEWCASTLE
{{1L 0S}}
Chartered 12/13
Liquidated 3/17/30
1902 Date Back <$VALUE
3x10-20 1-400 <$2000
1902 Plain Back
3x10-20 401-1390 <$2000
1929 Small Size
10 Type 1 1-60 <$1250
20 Type 1 1-3 <$1250
Total Issue $73,460
Out at close $5,830
Large out at close $1,970

10661 Camp
FNB OF NEWSOME
{{1L}}
Chartered 12/14
Liquidated 2/12/27
1902 Plain Back <$VALUE
3x10-20 1-3108 <$1250
Total Issue $155,400
Out at close $19,900

10682 Gonzales
FNB OF NIXON
{{2L}}
Chartered 1/15
Liquidated 8/11/25
1902 Plain Back <$VALUE
3x10-20 1-5677 <$1000
Total Issue $283,850
Out at close $29,950

8610 Montague
CITY NB OF NOCONA
{{1L}}
Chartered 3/07
Liquidated 8/29/12
1902 Red Seal <$VALUE
3x10-20 1-750 <$2000
1902 Date Back
3x10-20 1-1171 <$750
Total Issue $96,050
Out in 1912 $22,160

7617 Montague
FARMERS & MERCHANTS NB OF NOCONA
{{4L 4U+6S}}
Chartered 2/05
1902 Red Seal <$VALUE
3x10-20 1-1440 <$1250
1902 Date Back
4x5 1-2900 <$350
3x10-20 1-3170 <$350
1902 Plain Back
4x5 2901-8297 <$350
3x10-20 3171-6580 <$350
1929 Small Size
5 Type 1 1-826 <$200
10 Type 1 1-246 <$200
20 Type 1 1-84 <$200
5 Type 2 1-5800 <$200
10 Type 2 1-2837 <$200
20 Type 2 1-873 <$200
Total Issue $691,510
Out in 1935 $46,455
Large out 1935 $2,055

4621 Montague
FNB OF NOCONA
{{ UNREPORTED }}
Chartered 8/29/91
Liquidated 2/10/97
Brown Back <$VALUE
4x5 1-1472 <$2500
Total Issue $29,440
Out in 1910 $245

5338 Montague
NB OF NOCONA
Chartered 5/7/00
Receivership 3/25/21
2nd title: Nocona NB 12/23/04
FIRST TITLE {{1L}}
Brown Back <$VALUE
3x10-20 1-1328 <$1250
SECOND TITLE {{4L}}
Brown Back
3x10-20 1-2100 <$1000
1882 Date Back
3x10-20 1-3800* <$750
1882 Value Back
3x10-20 4001-5833* <$750
* 3801-4000 not marked
1902 Plain Back
3x10-20 1-468 <$400
Total Issue $486,450
Out at close $32,295

Nocona NB, Nocona
SEE Ch 5338
NB of Nocona

11959 Montague
PEOPLES NB OF NOCONA
{{6S}}
Chartered 4/21
1929 Small Size <$VALUE
10 Type 1 1-622 <$250
20 Type 1 1-212 <$250
10 Type 2 1-2949 <$250
20 Type 2 1-640 <$250
Total Issue $105,050
Out in 1935 $39,850

10275 Leon
FNB OF NORMANGEE
{{2L 4S}}
Chartered 10/12
1902 Date Back <$VALUE
3x10-20 1-700 <$600
1902 Plain Back
3x10-20 701-4952 <$600
1929 Small Size
10 Type 1 1-770 <$300
20 Type 1 1-190 <$300
10 Type 2 1-1528 <$300
20 Type 2 1-265 <$300
Total Issue $337,180
Out in 1935 $20,150
Large out 1935 $1,550

8287 Tarrant
EXCHANGE NB OF NORTH FORT WORTH
{{ UNREPORTED }}
Chartered 7/06
Liquidated 5/6/14
1902 Red Seal <$VALUE
3x10-20 1-460 <$2500
1902 Date Back
3x10-20 1-1825 <$1500
Total Issue $114,250
Out in 1914 $31,000

6822 Tarrant
STOCKYARDS NB OF NORTH FORT WORTH
Chartered 6/03
Liquidated 12/31/34
2nd title:Stockyards NB of Fort Worth 1/23/11
FIRST TITLE {{1L}}
1902 Red Seal <$VALUE
3x10-20 1-1520 <$2000
1902 Date Back
4x5 1-1225 <$750
3x10-20 1-2335 <$750
SECOND TITLE {{8L 9S}}
1902 Date Back
4x5 1-15250 <$175
3x10-20 1-10500 <$175
1902 Plain Back
4x5 15251-22840 <$175
3x10-20 10501-15672 <$175
1929 Small Size
5 Type 1 1-4488 <$125
10 Type 1 1-2693 <$125
20 Type 1 1-713 <$125
Total Issue $1,839,430
Out at close $45,320
Large out at close $4,125

8807 Live Oak
FNB OF OAKVILLE
{{ UNREPORTED }}
Chartered 7/07
Liquidated 3/27/19
1902 Red Seal <$VALUE
3x10-20 1-500 <$3000
1902 Date Back
3x10-20 1-396 <$2000
Total Issue $44,800
Out at close $5,700

8769 Ochiltree
FNB OF OCHILTREE
Chartered 6/07
2nd title: FNB of Perryton 9/20/19
FIRST TITLE {{0L}}
1902 Red Seal <$VALUE
3x10-20 1-240 <$1500
1902 Date Back
3x10-20 1-820 <$1000
SECOND TITLE {{2L 1S}}
1902 Plain Back
4x5 1-3122 <$600
1929 Small Size
5 Type 1 1-1000 <$600
5 Type 2 1-2362 <$600
Total Issue $157,250
Out in 1935 $7,500
Large out 1935 $490

8911 Ochiltree
OCHILTREE NB, OCHILTREE
{{ UNREPORTED }}
Chartered 10/11/07
Liquidated 7/20/09
1902 Red Seal <$VALUE
4x5 1-145 <$2500
3x10-20 1-120 <$2500
1902 Date Back
3x10-20 1-7 <$2000
Total Issue $9,250
Out in 1910 $2,950

8169 Ector
CITIZENS NB OF ODESSA
{{3L 3S}}
Organized 3/29/06
Receivership 5/19/31
1902 Red Seal <$VALUE
3x10-20 1-1225 <$1500
1902 Date Back
3x10-20 1-2650* <$500
1902 Plain Back
3x10-20 2891-9217* <$500
* 2651-2890 not marked
1929 Small Size
10 Type 1 1-616 <$350
20 Type 1 1-210 <$350
Total Issue $584,260
Out at close $32,360
Large out at close $4,300

<$VALUEs are for notes in FINE condition. Value changes by approximately 25% for a change of one full grade.

13608 Ector
FNB OF ODESSA
{{ 3 S }}
Chartered 3/32
1929 Small Size <$VALUE
10 Type 1 1-316 <$350
20 Type 1 1-104 <$350
10 Type 2 1-1983 <$350
20 Type 2 1-516 <$350
Total Issue $61,590
Out in 1935 $23,900

6410 Ector
ODESSA NB, ODESSA
Chartered 9/6/02
2nd title:Midland NB, Midland 8/03
FIRST TITLE {{ 0 L }}
1902 Red Seal <$VALUE
3x10-20 1-137 <$2500
SECOND TITLE {{ 4 L 9 S }}
1902 Red Seal
3x10-20 1-2155 <$2500
1902 Date Back
4x5 1-1250 <$600
3x10-20 1-4040 <$600
1902 Plain Back
4x5 1251-10196 <$600
3x10-20 4041-9795 <$600
1929 Small Size
5 Type 1 1-2462 <$250
10 Type 1 1-1370 <$250
20 Type 1 1-380 <$250
5 Type 2 1-4780 <$250
10 Type 2 1-2550 <$250
20 Type 2 1-596 <$250
Total Issue $1,071,250
Out in 1935 $58,350
Large out 1935 $2,350

8925 Ector
WESTERN NB OF ODESSA
{{ UNREPORTED }}
Chartered 10/22/07
Liquidated 1/1/08
1902 Red Seal <$VALUE
3x10-20 1-200 <$3000
Total Issue $10,000
Out in 1910 $1,870

12676 Young
CITY NB OF OLNEY
{{ 9 S }}
Chartered 4/25
Liquidated 7/25/35
1929 Small Size <$VALUE
5 Type 1 1-1186 <$150
10 Type 1 1-762 <$150
20 Type 1 1-224 <$150
5 Type 2 1-5952 <$150
10 Type 2 1-2736 <$150
20 Type 2 1-756 <$150
Total Issue $180,420
Out in 1935 $56,150

8982 Young
FNB OF OLNEY
{{ U + 4 L 5U + 9 S }}
Chartered 1/08
1902 Red Seal <$VALUE
4x10 1-250 <$1500
1902 Date Back
4x10 1-1350 <$400
1902 Plain Back
4x10 1351-14280 <$400
1929 Small Size
10 Type 1 1-3216 <$150
10 Type 2 1-6480 <$150
Total Issue $838,960
Out in 1935 $48,010
Large out 1935 $2,190

10426 Morris
FNB OF OMAHA
{{ UNREPORTED }}
Chartered 7/30/13
Liquidated 11/29/16
1902 Date Back <$VALUE
3x10-20 1-452 <$2000
Total Issue $22,600
Out at close $7,500

13661 Orange
FNB IN ORANGE
{{ UNREPORTED }}
Chartered 2/33
1929 Small Size <$VALUE
10 Type 2 1-169 <$750
20 Type 2 1-55 <$750
Total Issue $2,790
Out in 1935 $92,890
Large out 1935 $3,690
Outstanding includes Ch 4118

4118 Orange
FNB OF ORANGE
{{ 6 L 22 S }}
Chartered 9/12/89
Liquidated 3/31/33
Brown Back <$VALUE
3x10-20 1-1300 <$1000
50-100 1-287 <$3500/$4000
1882 Date Back
3x10-20 1-219 <$650
1902 Date Back
3x10-20 1-2400 <$250
1902 Plain Back
3x10-20 2401-12754 <$250
1929 Small Size
10 Type 1 1-9779 <$100
20 Type 1 1-2552 <$100
Total Issue $1,649,680
Out at close $264,400
Large out 1935 $3,690
Ch 13661 assumed circulation

6050 Orange
ORANGE NB, ORANGE
{{ 5 L 9 S }}
Chartered 12/16/01
Brown Back <$VALUE
3x10-20 1-3260 <$1000
1882 Date Back
3x10-20 1-2720 <$650
1882 Value Back
3x10-20 2721-6111 <$650
1902 Plain Back
3x10-20 1-5795 <$300
1929 Small Size
10 Type 1 1-1616 <$150
20 Type 1 1-388 <$150
10 Type 2 1-2124 <$150
20 Type 2 1-604 <$150
Total Issue $935,140
Out in 1935 $48,400
Large out 1935 $3,530

7748 Crockett
OZONA NB, OZONA
{{ 3 L 4 S }}
Chartered S/05
1902 Red Seal <$VALUE
50-100 1-398 <$7500
1902 Date Back
50-100 1-300 <$850/$1000
3x50-100 1-1598<$850/$1000
1902 Plain Back
3x50-100 1599-1985 <$850/$1000
1929 Small Size
50 Type 1 1-234 <$450
100 Type 1 1-76 <$600
5 Type 2 1-1050 <$400
10 Type 2 1-735 <$400
20 Type 2 1-95 <$400
Total Issue $731,250
Out in 1935 $73,250
Large out 1935 $8,100

10230 Cottle
FNB OF PADUCAH
{{ 2 L 6 S }}
Chartered 7/12
1902 Date Back <$VALUE
3x10-20 1-1400 <$600
1902 Plain Back
3x10-20 1401-9000 <$600
1929 Small Size
10 Type 1 1-1414 <$225
20 Type 1 1-320 <$225
10 Type 2 1-2116 <$225
20 Type 2 1-732 <$225
Total Issue $609,040
Out in 1935 $38,650
Large out 1935 $1,080

8306 Concho
FNB OF PAINT ROCK
{{ UNREPORTED }}
Chartered 7/06
Liquidated 11/18/10
1902 Red Seal <$VALUE
4x5 1-375 <$3500
3x10-20 1-330 <$3500
1902 Date Back
4x5 1-185 <$3000
3x10-20 1-124 <$3000
Total Issue $33,900
Out in 1911 $4,900

12556 Anderson
EAST TEXAS NB OF PALESTINE
{{ 12 S }}
Chartered 7/24
1929 Small Size <$VALUE
5 Type 1 1-1042 <$125
10 Type 1 1-1146 <$125
20 Type 1 1-862 <$125
5 Type 2 1-12298 <$125
10 Type 2 1-7505 <$125
20 Type 2 1-1776 <$125
Total Issue $375,520
Out in 1935 $146,650

3694 Anderson
FNB OF PALESTINE
{{ U + 9 L 9 S }}
Chartered 5/5/87
Brown Back <$VALUE
4x5 1-2025 <$1000
50-100 1-416 <$3500/$4000
1902 Red Seal
50-100 1-62 <$7500
1902 Date Back
4x5 1-4350 <$200
50-100 1-1100 <$500/$600
3x50-100 1-330 <$500/$600
1902 Plain Back
4x5 4351-38005 <$200
1929 Small Size
5 Type 1 1-11876 <$150
5 Type 2 1-25596 <$150
Total Issue $1,604,060
Out in 1935 $70,010
Large out 1935 $5,780

4436 Anderson
PALESTINE NB, PALESTINE
{{ 1 L }}
Chartered 1890
Liquidated 1/21/13
Brown Back <$VALUE
4x5 1-2805 <$1250
3x10-20 1-730 <$1250
1882 Date Back
3x10-20 1-474 <$1000
1902 Date Back
3x10-20 1-1720 <$750
Total Issue $202,300
Out in 1913 $26,045

7170 Anderson
ROYALL NB OF PALESTINE
{{ 8 L 13 S }}
Chartered 3/04
1902 Red Seal <$VALUE
3x10-20 1-1265 <$1250
1902 Date Back
3x10-20 1-11000 <$250
1902 Plain Back
3x10-20 11001-28471 <$250
1929 Small Size
10 Type 1 1-3332 <$110
20 Type 1 1-826 <$125
10 Type 2 1-6780 <$125
20 Type 2 1-1596 <$135
Total Issue $1,885,560
Out in 1935 $94,890
Large out 1935 $5,050

9142 Gray
FNB OF PAMPA
{{ 1 L 1 S }}
Organized 10/8/07
Liquidated 4/15/35
1902 Date Back <$VALUE
3x10-20 1-840 <$1500
1902 Plain Back
3x10-20 841-1825 <$1500
1929 Small Size
10 Type 1 1-264 <$600
20 Type 1 1-64 <$600
Total Issue $114,770
Out at close $5,800
Large out at close $360

8542 Lamar
AMERICAN NB OF PARIS
{{ 7 L 7 S }}
Chartered 2/07
Receivership 3/9/31
1902 Red Seal <$VALUE
3x10-20 1-2700 <$1000
1902 Date Back
3x10-20 1-12900 <$200
1902 Plain Back
3x10-20 12901-27254 <$200
1929 Small Size
10 Type 1 1-1502 <$175
20 Type 1 1-473 <$175
Total Issue $1,644,580
Out at close $94,960
Large out at close $12,840

4411 Lamar
CITY NB OF PARIS
{{ 13 L }}
Chartered 1890
Liquidated 8/31/26
Brown Back <$VALUE
3x10-20 1-21420 <$850
1882 Date Back
3x10-20 1-4291 <$500
1902 Date Back
4x5 1-16000 <$150
4x10 1-15000 <$150
1902 Plain Back
4x5 16001-40717 <$150
4x10 15001-31430 <$150
Total Issue $3,357,090
Out at close $33,600

3638 Lamar
FNB OF PARIS
{{ 16 L 25 S }}
Chartered 2/19/87
Brown Back <$VALUE
3x10-20 1-3682 <$850
1902 Red Seal
4x5 1-5000 <$1000
50-100 1-1420 <$7500
1902 Date Back
4x5 1-22250 <$100
50-100 1-2600 <$400/$500
3x50-100 1-3108 <$400/$500
1902 Plain Back
4x5 22251-108672 <$100
3x50-100 3109-3964 <$400/$500
1929 Small Size
5 Type 1 1-16216 <$60
50 Type 1 1-550 <$125
100 Type 1 1-212 <$175
5 Type 2 1-32152 <$60
Total Issue $4,990,980
Out in 1935 $252,500
Large out 1935 $22,545

5079 Lamar
PARIS NB, PARIS
{{ 1 L }}
Chartered 7/6/97
Liquidated 3/13/07
Brown Back <$VALUE
4x5 1-3435 <$1000
3x10-20 1-6070 <$1000
Total Issue $372,200
Out in 1910 $19,050

13572 Frio
PEARSALL NB IN PEARSALL
{{ U + 2 S }}
Organized 8/14/31
Liquidated 3/10/34
1929 Small Size <$VALUE
5 Type 1 1-204 <$400
10 Type 1 1-96 <$400
20 Type 1 1-32 <$400
Total Issue $15,720
Out at close $29,840
Outstanding includes Ch 6989

6989 Frio
PEARSALL NB, PEARSALL
{{ 6 L 10 S }}
Chartered 10/03
Liquidated 10/6/31
1902 Red Seal <$VALUE
4x5 1-3640 <$1250
3x10-20 1-2926 <$1250
1902 Date Back
4x5 1-7150 <$250
3x10-20 1-5420 <$250
1902 Plain Back
4x5 7151-22663 <$250
3x10-20 5421-14963 <$250
1929 Small Size
5 Type 1 1-1815 <$150
10 Type 1 1-848 <$150
20 Type 1 1-269 <$150
Total Issue $1,558,120
Out at close $67,280
Large out 1935 $5,560
Ch 13572 assumed circulation

8771 Reeves
FNB OF PECOS
{{ 5 L 7 S }}
Chartered 6/07
1902 Red Seal <$VALUE
4x10 1-500 <$2000
1902 Date Back
4x5 1-5000 <$500
4x10 1-3800 <$500
1902 Plain Back
4x5 5001-14295 <$500
4x10 3801-13512 <$500
1929 Small Size
5 Type 1 1-2716 <$300
10 Type 1 1-1388 <$300
20 Type 1 1-264 <$300
5 Type 2 1-3880 <$300
10 Type 2 1-2191 <$300
20 Type 2 1-528 <$300
Total Issue $1,094,690
Out in 1935 $48,600
Large out 1935 $2,635

FNB of Perryton
SEE Ch 8769
FNB of Ochiltree

10647 Lamar
CITIZENS NB OF PETTY
{{ UNREPORTED }}
Chartered 10/14
Receivership 11/24/26
1902 Date Back <$VALUE
3x10-20 1-392 <$2000
Total Issue $19,600
Out at close $80

5569 Lamar
FNB OF PETTY
{{ UNREPORTED }}
Chartered 9/4/00
Liquidated 1/14/14
Brown Back <$VALUE
3x10-20 1-1200 <$2000
1882 Date Back
3x10-20 1-772 <$2000
Total Issue $98,600
Out in 1914 $12,760

10169 Hidalgo
FNB OF PHARR
{{ 2 L 3U + 2 S }}
Organized 3/21/12
Receivership 11/12/31
1902 Date Back <$VALUE
4x5 1-1065 <$650
3x10-20 1-854 <$650
1902 Plain Back
4x5 1066-5834 <$650
3x10-20 855-3555 <$650
1929 Small Size
5 Type 1 1-646 <$400
10 Type 1 1-294 <$400
20 Type 1 1-92 <$400
Total Issue $342,490
Out at close $24,160
Large out at close $3,120

4777 Denton
PILOT POINT NB, PILOT POINT
{{ 1 L 2 S }}
Chartered 1892
Brown Back <$VALUE
3x10-20 1-1720 <$2500
50-100 1-380 <$5000
1882 Date Back
3x10-20 1-358 <$2500
50-100 1-21 <$5000
1902 Date Back
3x10-20 1-1600 <$1750
1902 Plain Back
3x10-20 1601-3334 <$1750
1929 Small Size
10 Type 1 1-468 <$750
20 Type 1 1-130 <$750
10 Type 2 1-687 <$750
20 Type 2 1-230 <$750
Total Issue $385,900
Out in 1935 $15,050
Large out 1935 $990

4863 Camp
FNB OF PITTSBURG
{{ 2 L 2 S }}
Organized 2/7/93
Liquidated 2/14/31
Brown Back <$VALUE
50-100 1-944 <$3500/$4000
1882 Date Back
50-100 1-460 <$3500/$4000
3x50-100 1-51 <$3500/$4000
1902 Date Back
3x50-100 1-1650 <$750/$850
1902 Plain Back
3x50-100 1651-2167 <$750/$850
1929 Small Size
50 Type 1 1-184 <$500
100 Type 1 1-35 <$600
Total Issue $841,300
Out at close $93,450
Large out at close $32,650

7376 Camp
PITTSBURG NB, PITTSBURG
{{ 7 L 8 S }}
Chartered 8/04
1902 Red Seal <$VALUE
3x10-20 1-1622 <$1250
1902 Date Back
3x10-20 1-4540 <$400
1902 Plain Back
3x10-20 4541-21092 <$400
1929 Small Size
10 Type 1 1-1420 <$250
20 Type 1 1-394 <$250
10 Type 2 1-2242 <$250
20 Type 2 1-828 <$250
Total Issue $1,307,160
Out in 1935 $45,850
Large out 1935 $4,970

9081 Hale
CITIZENS NB OF PLAINVIEW
{{ 2 L }}
Chartered 3/08
Liquidated 12/5/19
1902 Red Seal <$VALUE
3x10-20 1-750 <$1500
1902 Date Back
3x10-20 1-6200 <$500
1902 Plain Back
3x10-20 6201-9113 <$500
Total Issue $493,150
Out at close $84,100

5475 Hale
FNB OF PLAINVIEW
{{ 2 L 1 S }}
Chartered 6/30/00
Receivership 12/29/30
Brown Back <$VALUE
3x10-20 1-1400 <$1250
1882 Date Back
3x10-20 1-2700 <$1000
1882 Value Back
3x10-20 2701-3017 <$1000
1902 Plain Back
4x5 1-3565 <$600
3x10-20 1-2219 <$600
1929 Small Size
5 Type 1 1-339 <$600
10 Type 1 1-149 <$600
20 Type 1 1-30 <$600
Total Issue $425,810
Out at close $19,980
Large out at close $2,900

9802 Hale
THIRD NB OF PLAINVIEW
{{ 4 L }}
Chartered 6/10
Receivership 9/16/31
1902 Date Back <$VALUE
4x10 1-2000 <$350
50-100 1-500 <$650/$750
3x50-100 1-383 <$650/$750
1902 Plain Back
4x10 2001-14930 <$350
Total Issue $767,950
Out at close $5,160

5692 Collin
FARMERS & MERCHANTS NB OF PLANO
{{ 2 L }}
Chartered 1/23/01
Liquidated 12/16/20
Brown Back <$VALUE
3x10-20 1-2610 <$1000
1882 Date Back
3x10-20 1-4900 <$850
1882 Value Back
3x10-20 4901-7239 <$850
Total Issue $492,450
Out at close $49,995

13511 Collin
FNB OF PLANO
{{ U + 5 S }}
Chartered 12/30
1929 Small Size <$VALUE
5 Type 1 1-3734 <$250
5 Type 2 1-19258 <$250
Total Issue $208,310
Out in 1935 $32,000

3764 Collin
PLANO NB, PLANO
{{ 5 L 3 S }}
Chartered 7/28/87
Liquidated 2/3/31
Brown Back <$VALUE
3x10-20 1-4709 <$1000
1902 Red Seal
3x10-20 1-1000 <$1250
1902 Date Back
3x10-20 1-9700 <$300
1902 Plain Back
3x10-20 9701-23025 <$300
1929 Small Size
10 Type 1 1-609 <$300
20 Type 1 1-182 <$300
Total Issue $1,495,080
Out at close $44,300
Large out at close $10,440

****
8103 Atascosa
FNB OF PLEASANTON
{{1L 2S}}
Chartered 2/06
Liquidated 1/24/33
1902 Red Seal <$VALUE
4x5 1-200 <$2000
3x10-20 1-160 <$2000
1902 Date Back
4x5 1-1400 <$850
3x10-20 1-1120 <$850
1902 Plain Back
4x5 1401-3000 <$850
3x10-20 1121-2159 <$850
1929 Small Size
5 Type 1 1-414 <$500
10 Type 1 1-213 <$500
20 Type 1 1-68 <$500
Total Issue $213,310
Out at close $10,410
Large out at close $950
****
5485 Jefferson
FNB OF PORT ARTHUR
{{6L 18S}}
Chartered 7/7/00
Brown Back <$VALUE
3x10-20 1-5100 <$1000
1882 Date Back
3x10-20 1-6300* <$600
1882 Value Back
3x10-20 6701-10500* <$600
* 6301-6700 not marked
1902 Plain Back
3x10-20 1-13452 <$300
1929 Small Size
10 Type 1 1-3116 <$75
20 Type 1 1-836 <$100
10 Type 2 1-5009 <$100
20 Type 2 1-1214 <$100
Total Issue $1,814,250
Out in 1935 $84,300
Large out 1935 $7,410
****
5367 Calhoun
FNB OF PORT LAVACA
{{3L}}
Chartered 5/24/00
Liquidated 5/30/23
Brown Back <$VALUE
3x10-20 1-500 <$1500
1882 Date Back
3x10-20 1-836 <$1500
1902 Plain Back
3x10-20 1-224 <$850
Total Issue $78,000
Out at close $7,000
****
11799 Jefferson
FNB OF PORT NECHES
{{1L 3S}}
Chartered 7/20
1902 Plain Back <$VALUE
4x5 1-10998 <$1000
1929 Small Size
5 Type 1 1-3846 <$350
5 Type 2 1-8184 <$350
Total Issue $376,260
Out in 1935 $21,285
Large out 1935 $710
****
FNB of Post
SEE Ch 9485
FNB of Post City
****
9485 Garza
FNB OF POST CITY
Chartered 7/09
2nd title:FNB of Post
2/13/33
FIRST TITLE {{3L 3S}}
1902 Date Back <$VALUE
4x5 1-1850 <$500
3x10-20 1-1480 <$500
1902 Plain Back
4x5 1851-11664 <$500
3x10-20 1481-7522 <$500
1929 Small Size
5 Type 1 1-2016 <$350
10 Type 1 1-1110 <$350
20 Type 1 1-314 <$350
SECOND TITLE {{1S}}
1929 Small Size
5 Type 2 1-4572 <$400
10 Type 2 1-2328 <$400
20 Type 2 1-528 <$400
Total Issue $830,840
Out in 1935 $48,930
Large out 1935 $1,395
****

****
10320 Wilson
FNB OF POTH
{{1L 2S}}
Chartered 1/13
1902 Date Back <$VALUE
3x10-20 1-500 <$1500
1902 Plain Back
3x10-20 501-1086 <$1500
1929 Small Size
10 Type 1 1-312 <$600
20 Type 1 1-106 <$600
10 Type 2 1-154 <$600
20 Type 2 1-38 <$600
Total Issue $88,040
Out in 1935 $13,400
Large out 1935 $530
****
8611 Collin
FNB OF PRINCETON
{{ UNREPORTED }}
Chartered 3/07
Liquidated 8/15/10
1902 Red Seal <$VALUE
3x10-20 1-317 <$3000
Total Issue $15,850
Out in 1910 $5,695
****
10927 Navarro
FNB OF PURDON
{{2L 2S}}
Chartered 12/16
1902 Plain Back <$VALUE
4x5 1-5705 <$850
3x10-20 1-3433 <$850
1929 Small Size
5 Type 1 1-591 <$500
10 Type 1 1-366 <$500
20 Type 1 1-71 <$500
Total Issue $333,960
Out in 1935 $20,510
Large out 1935 $810
****
9749 Callahan
FNB OF PUTNAM
{{ UNREPORTED }}
Chartered 5/10
Liquidated 3/7/11
1902 Date Back <$VALUE
4x5 1-130 <$2000
3x10-20 1-85 <$2000
Total Issue $6,850
Out in 1911 $2,950
****
9906 Hardeman
CITIZENS NB OF QUANAH
{{1L}}
Chartered 12/10
Liquidated 8/25/17
1902 Date Back <$VALUE
3x10-20 1-2100 <$850
1902 Plain Back
3x10-20 2101-2977 <$850
Total Issue $148,850
Out at close $50,000
****
4361 Hardeman
CITY NB OF QUANAH
{{ UNREPORTED }}
Organized 7/9/90
Receivership 12/15/94
Brown Back <$VALUE
50-100 1-273 <$5000
Total Issue $40,950
Out in 1916 $400
****
12307 Hardeman
FNB IN QUANAH
{{3L 6S}}
Chartered 1/23
1902 Plain Back <$VALUE
4x5 1-19314 <$450
1929 Small Size
5 Type 1 1-2312 <$250
10 Type 1 1-1060 <$250
20 Type 1 1-284 <$250
5 Type 2 1-2774 <$250
10 Type 2 1-1423 <$250
20 Type 2 1-371 <$250
Total Issue $588,840
Out in 1935 $41,700
Large out 1935 $340
****
4144 Hardeman
FNB OF QUANAH
{{ UNREPORTED }}
Chartered 10/24/89
Liquidated 1/12/92
Brown Back <$VALUE
3x10-20 1-285 <$3000
Total Issue $14,250
Out in 1910 $60
****

****
Quanah NB, Quanah
SEE Ch 4571
FNB of Childress
****
5972 Hardeman
STATE NB OF QUANAH
{{ UNREPORTED }}
Chartered 9/20/01
Liquidated 11/20/02
Brown Back <$VALUE
50-100 1-99 <$5000
Total Issue $14,850
Out in 1910 $800
****
11970 Hunt
FNB OF QUINLAN
{{3L}}
Chartered 5/21
Liquidated 12/10/25
1902 Plain Back <$VALUE
4x5 1-2210 <$1250
Total Issue $44,200
Out at close $6,950
****
10646 Wood
FNB OF QUITMAN
{{ UNREPORTED }}
Chartered 10/14
1902 Date Back <$VALUE
3x10-20 1-530 <$2000
Total Issue $26,500
Large out 1935 $140
****
8072 Eastland
FNB OF RANGER
{{2L}}
Chartered 1/06
Receivership 3/2/21
1902 Red Seal <$VALUE
3x10-20 1-1100 <$3500
1902 Date Back
3x10-20 1-2120 <$2500
1902 Plain Back
3x10-20 2121-3439 <$2500
Total Issue $226,950
Out at close $22,400
****
12789 Willacy
FNB OF RAYMONDVILLE
{{2S}}
Chartered 7/25
1929 Small Size <$VALUE
5 Type 2 1-1420 <$600
10 Type 2 1-671 <$600
20 Type 2 1-252 <$600
Total Issue $18,850
Out in 1935 $11,300
****
12462 Refugio
FNB OF REFUGIO
{{8S}}
Chartered 11/23
1929 Small Size <$VALUE
5 Type 1 1-2000 <$175
10 Type 1 1-1200 <$175
20 Type 1 1-128 <$200
5 Type 2 1-426 <$200
10 Type 2 1-280 <$200
Total Issue $152,290
Out in 1935 $21,650
****
10350 Fort Bend
FNB OF RICHMOND
{{3L 4S}}
Chartered 3/13
1902 Date Back <$VALUE
3x10-20 1-1400 <$500
1902 Plain Back
3x10-20 1401-5513 <$500
1929 Small Size
10 Type 1 1-796 <$325
20 Type 1 1-214 <$325
10 Type 2 1-1041 <$350
20 Type 2 1-384 <$350
Total Issue $367,180
Out in 1935 $24,350
Large out 1935 $1,790
****
11591 Starr
FNB OF RIO GRANDE
{{1L 2S}}
Chartered 1/20
Liquidated 3/22/33
1902 Plain Back <$VALUE
3x10-20 1-960 <$1500
1929 Small Size
10 Type 1 1-588 <$600
20 Type 1 1-217 <$600
Total Issue $109,320
Out at close $21,280
Large out at close $500
****

****
7906 Eastland
FNB OF RISING STAR
{{2L 2S}}
Organized 8/24/05
Receivership 3/12/30
1902 Red Seal <$VALUE
3x10-20 1-1100 <$3500
1902 Date Back
3x10-20 1-2220 <$2000
1902 Plain Back
3x10-20 2221-6615 <$2000
1929 Small Size
10 Type 1 1-208 <$1000
20 Type 1 1-42 <$1000
Total Issue $403,270
Out at close $23,860
Large out at close $6,940
****
8659 Coke
FNB OF ROBERT LEE
{{1L}}
Chartered 4/07
Liquidated 12/4/19
1902 Red Seal <$VALUE
3x10-20 1-249 <$3500
1902 Date Back
3x10-20 1-680 <$2500
1902 Plain Back
3x10-20 681-729 <$2500
Total Issue $48,900
Out at close $6,000
****
5865 Fisher
FNB OF ROBY
{{1L}}
Chartered 6/18/01
Liquidated 3/15/22
Brown Back <$VALUE
3x10-20 1-770 <$2000
1882 Date Back
3x10-20 1-1080 <$1750
1882 Value Back
3x10-20 1081-1454 <$1750
1902 Plain Back
3x10-20 1-150 <$1500
Total Issue $118,700
Out at close $10,000
****
4175 Milam
FNB OF ROCKDALE
{{2L 2S}}
Chartered 12/11/89
Liquidated 3/22/32
Brown Back <$VALUE
3x10-20 1-2348 <$1500
1902 Date Back
3x10-20 1-1700 <$750
1902 Plain Back
3x10-20 1701-3781 <$750
1929 Small Size
10 Type 1 1-337 <$500
20 Type 1 1-94 <$500
Total Issue $337,950
Out at close $17,820
Large out at close $2,460
****
FNB of Rockport
SEE Ch 4438
FNB of Aransas Pass,
Aransas Pass
****
6679 Rockwall
CITIZENS NB OF ROCKWALL
{{1L}}
Chartered 3/03
Liquidated 3/30/15
1902 Red Seal <$VALUE
3x10-20 1-1980 <$2000
1902 Date Back
3x10-20 1-2614 <$1000
Total Issue $229,700
Out in 1915 $21,790
****
4717 Rockwall
FARMERS & MERCHANTS NB OF
ROCKWALL
{{ UNREPORTED }}
Chartered 3/30/92
Liquidated 7/11/92
Brown Back <$VALUE
3x10-20 1-235 <$3000
Total Issue $11,750
Out in 1910 $160
****
8204 Rockwall
FARMERS NB OF ROCKWALL
{{3L 0S}}
Chartered 5/06
Liquidated 4/4/30
1902 Red Seal <$VALUE
3x10-20 1-900 <$2000
1902 Date Back
3x10-20 1-2480 <$500

1902 Plain Back
3x10-20 2481-12032 <$500
1929 Small Size
10 Type 1 1-156 <$600
20 Type 1 1-45 <$600
Total Issue $661,360
Out at close $17,990
Large out 1935 $2,485
Ch 13402 assumed circulation
****
13402 Rockwall
FNB IN ROCKWALL
{{4S}}
Chartered 12/29
1929 Small Size <$VALUE
10 Type 1 1-516 <$375
20 Type 1 1-136 <$375
5 Type 2 1-1313 <$375
10 Type 2 1-921 <$400
20 Type 2 1-264 <$400
Total Issue $68,335
Out in 1935 $22,485
Large out 1935 $2,485
Outstanding includes Ch 8204
****
3890 Rockwall
FNB OF ROCKWALL
{{ UNREPORTED }}
Chartered 5/29/88
Receivership 7/20/92
Brown Back <$VALUE
3x10-20 1-820 <$3000
Total Issue $41,000
Out in 1916 $200
****
4911 Rockwall
ROCKWALL COUNTY NB,
ROCKWALL
{{ UNREPORTED }}
Chartered 6/1/93
Liquidated 1/14/96
Brown Back <$VALUE
3x10-20 1-307 <$3000
Total Issue $15,350
Out in 1910 $90
****
6703 Rockwall
ROCKWALL NB, ROCKWALL
{{ UNREPORTED }}
Chartered 3/30/03
Liquidated 11/2/03
1902 Red Seal <$VALUE
50-100 1-44 <$7500
Total Issue $6,600
Out in 1910 $800
****
5704 Bell
FNB OF ROGERS
{{4L 8S}}
Chartered 2/6/01
Brown Back <$VALUE
3x10-20 1-600 <$1250
1882 Date Back
3x10-20 1-4900* <$850
1882 Value Back
3x10-20 5101-7340* <$850
* 4901-5100 not marked
1902 Plain Back
3x10-20 1-6360 <$600
1929 Small Size
10 Type 1 1-1538 <$200
20 Type 1 1-446 <$225
10 Type 2 1-2288 <$225
20 Type 2 1-629 <$225
Total Issue $896,280
Out in 1935 $48,300
Large out 1935 $2,290
****
5513 Falls
FNB OF ROSEBUD
{{3L 4S}}
Chartered 7/23/00
Brown Back <$VALUE
3x10-20 1-2500 <$1500
1882 Date Back
3x10-20 1-3900 <$1500
1882 Value Back
3x10-20 3901-5284 <$1500
1902 Plain Back
3x10-20 1-5178 <$1000
1929 Small Size
10 Type 1 1-1324 <$600
20 Type 1 1-324 <$600
10 Type 2 1-676 <$600
20 Type 2 1-185 <$600
Total Issue $776,880
Out in 1935 $26,660
Large out 1935 $2,610
****

****
8066 Falls
PLANTERS NB OF ROSEBUD
{{1L 2S}}
Chartered 1/06
1902 Red Seal <$VALUE
3x10-20 1-480 <$2500
1902 Date Back
3x10-20 1-1900 <$1500
1902 Plain Back
3x10-20 1901-3638 <$1500
1929 Small Size
10 Type 1 1-368 <$650
20 Type 1 1-118 <$650
10 Type 2 1-289 <$650
20 Type 2 1-93 <$650
Total Issue $246,890
Out in 1935 $10,850
Large out 1935 $850
****
8693 Fisher
FNB OF ROTAN
{{1L 2S}}
Chartered 5/07
1902 Red Seal <$VALUE
4x10 1-500 <$2000
1902 Date Back
4x10 1-2175 <$850
1902 Plain Back
4x10 2176-5121 <$850
1929 Small Size
10 Type 1 1-764 <$500
10 Type 2 1-986 <$500
Total Issue $280,540
Out in 1935 $11,500
Large out 1935 $730
****
5710 Lamar
FNB OF ROXTON
{{3L 2S}}
Chartered 2/12/01
Brown Back <$VALUE
3x10-20 1-1200 <$1250
1882 Date Back
3x10-20 1-1710 <$1000
1882 Value Back
3x10-20 1711-2541 <$1000
1902 Plain Back
3x10-20 1-2430 <$600
1929 Small Size
10 Type 1 1-628 <$400
20 Type 1 1-150 <$400
10 Type 2 1-1056 <$400
20 Type 2 1-228 <$400
Total Issue $379,350
Out in 1935 $16,400
Large out 1935 $1,230
****
6551 Rockwall
FNB OF ROYSE CITY
{{2L 1S}}
Chartered 12/23/02
Receivership 2/11/30
1902 Red Seal <$VALUE
3x10-20 1-658 <$2000
1902 Date Back
3x10-20 1-1910 <$850
1902 Plain Back
3x10-20 1911-3602 <$850
1929 Small Size
10 Type 1 1-106 <$600
20 Type 1 1-7 <$600
Total Issue $220,200
Out at close $12,500
Large Out at close $5,350
****
8242 Haskell
FNB OF RULE
{{2L 3S}}
Chartered 5/06
Liquidated 4/14/33
1902 Red Seal <$VALUE
3x10-20 1-400 <$2000
1902 Date Back
3x10-20 1-1280 <$750
1902 Plain Back
3x10-20 1281-6656 <$750
1929 Small Size
10 Type 1 1-802 <$350
20 Type 1 1-248 <$350
Total Issue $430,680
Out at close $28,740
Large out at close $1,900
****

******

6522 Karnes
RUNGE NB, RUNGE
{{ 2 L }}
Chartered 12/6/02
Liquidated 4/12/26
1902 Red Seal <$VALUE
4x5 1-303 <$2000
50-100 1-300 <$7500
1902 Date Back
4x5 1-1825* <$850
50-100 1-85 <$1250
3x50-100 1-284 <$1250
1902 Plain Back
4x5 2076-4375* <$850
* 1826-2075 not marked
Total Issue $222,310
Out at close $18,890

******

4346 Cherokee
FNB OF RUSK
{{ 4 L }}
Chartered 1890
Liquidated 4/16/20
Brown Back <$VALUE
3x10-20 1-1240 <$1250
1882 Date Back
3x10-20 1-120 <$850
1902 Date Back
3x10-20 1-3500 <$500
1902 Plain Back
3x10-20 3501-5091 <$500
Total Issue $322,550
Out at close $45,700

******

7807 Uvalde
SABINAL NB, SABINAL
{{ 5 L 3 S }}
Chartered 6/05
Liquidated 12/10/32
1902 Red Seal <$VALUE
3x10-20 1-1350 <$1250
1902 Date Back
3x10-20 1-3660* <$350
1902 Plain Back
3x10-20 3901-12061* <$350
* 3661-3900 not marked
1929 Small Size
10 Type 1 1-1224 <$300
20 Type 1 1-320 <$300
Total Issue $782,390
Out at close $47,360
Large out at close $4,420

******

8402 Montague
CITIZENS NB OF SAINT JO
{{ 3 L 1 S }}
Chartered 10/06
Liquidated 2/17/31
1902 Red Seal <$VALUE
4x10 1-859 <$1500
1902 Date Back
4x10 1-850 <$600
1902 Plain Back
4x10 851-2683 <$600
1929 Small Size
10 Type 1 1-206 <$600
Total Issue $154,040
Out at close $6,870
Large out at close $1,070

******

5325 Montague
FNB OF SAINT JO
{{ 5 L 4 S }}
Chartered 5/3/00
Brown Back <$VALUE
3x10-20 1-2440 <$1000
1882 Date Back
3x10-20 1-2390 <$700
1882 Value Back
3x10-20 2391-3362 <$750
1902 Plain Back
3x10-20 1-3823 <$400
1929 Small Size
5 Type 1 1-1122 <$300
10 Type 1 1-566 <$300
20 Type 1 1-170 <$300
5 Type 2 1-1746 <$300
10 Type 2 1-960 <$300
20 Type 2 1-324 <$300
Total Issue $594,080
Out in 1935 $30,000
Large out 1935 $1,450

******

10664 Tom Green
CENTRAL NB OF SAN ANGELO
{{ 14 L 31 S }}
Chartered 12/14
1902 Plain Back <$VALUE
3x10-20 1-84227 <$175
1929 Small Size
10 Type 1 1-16382 <$60
20 Type 1 1-4562 <$65
10 Type 2 1-26924 <$65
20 Type 2 1-6682 <$75
Total Issue $6,144,590
Out in 1935 $484,700
Large out 1935 $19,240
Outstanding includes Ch 6807

******

4659 Tom Green
CITIZENS NB OF SAN ANGELO
{{ 1 L }}
Chartered 12/91
Receivership 9/9/96
Brown Back <$VALUE
3x10-20 1-897 <$1750
Total Issue $44,850
Out in 1916 $360

******

2767 Tom Green
CONCHO NB OF SAN ANGELO
Chartered 1882
2nd title:FNB of San Angelo 10/13/02
FIRST TITLE {{ 3 L }}
Series 1875 <$VALUE
4x5 1-5569 <$4000
3x10-20 1-432 <$5000/$6000
1902 Red Seal
3x10-20 1-34 <$1500
SECOND TITLE {{ 10 L 20 S }}
1902 Red Seal
4x5 1-1500 <$1250
3x10-20 1-2300 <$1250
1902 Date Back
4x5 1-12000 <$200
3x10-20 1-9000 <$200
1902 Plain Back
4x5 12001-42680 <$200
3x10-20 9001-26863 <$200
1929 Small Size
5 Type 1 1-7104 <$100
10 Type 1 1-3486 <$100
20 Type 1 1-992 <$100
5 Type 2 1-11354 <$100
10 Type 2 1-6334 <$100
20 Type 2 1-1836 <$100
Total Issue $3,174,580
Out in 1935 $152,300
Large out 1935 $8,350

******

FNB of San Angelo
SEE Ch 2767
Concho NB of San Angelo

******

6807 Tom Green
LANDON NB OF SAN ANGELO
Chartered 6/03
Closed 9/13/19
2nd title:Western NB of San Angelo 1/25/05
FIRST TITLE {{ 0 L }}
1902 Red Seal <$VALUE
4x5 1-585 <$2500
3x10-20 1-466 <$2500
SECOND TITLE {{ 2 L }}
1902 Red Seal
4x5 1-1750 <$2000
3x10-20 1-760 <$2000
1902 Date Back
4x5 1-7650 <$600
3x10-20 1-5660 <$600
1902 Plain Back
4x5 7651-11250 <$600
3x10-20 5661-7493 <$600
Total Issue $707,650
Out at close $100,000
Ch 10664 assumed circulation

******

3260 Tom Green
SAN ANGELO NB, SAN ANGELO
{{ 4 L 2 S }}
Organized 10/1/84
Liquidated 3/25/32
Brown Back <$VALUE
4x5 1-6439 <$1000
3x10-20 1-687 <$1000
1902 Red Seal
3x10-20 1-1050 <$1250
1902 Date Back
3x10-20 1-2450 <$400
1902 Plain Back
3x10-20 2451-5812 <$400
1929 Small Size
10 Type 1 1-480 <$400
20 Type 1 1-131 <$400
Total Issue $550,750
Out at close $24,995
Large out at close $3,885

******

Western NB of San Angelo
SEE Ch 6807
Landon NB of San Angelo

******

4525 Bexar
ALAMO NB OF SAN ANTONIO
{{ 25 L U + 44 S }}
Chartered 1891
Brown Back <$VALUE
4x5 1-5000 <$1000
3x10-20 1-5000 <$1000
50-100 1-3534 <$3500/$4000
1882 Date Back
4x5 1-8555 <$750
3x10-20 1-3339 <$750
50-100 1-72 <$3500/$4000
1902 Date Back
4x5 1-18500* <$200
3x10-20 1-18700** <$200
1902 Plain Back
4x5 20501-74717* <$200
3x10-20 20301-53976** <$200
* 18501-20500 not marked
** 18701-20300 not marked
1929 Small Size
5 Type 1 1-20410 <$100
10 Type 1 1-9986 <$100
20 Type 1 1-2374 <$100
5 Type 2 1-22188 <$110
10 Type 2 1-8300 <$125
20 Type 2 1-2647 <$135
Total Issue $7,165,310
Out in 1935 $433,655
Large out 1935 $20,355

******

14283 Bexar
BEXAR COUNTY NB OF SAN ANTONIO
{{ U + 10 S }}
Chartered 10/34
1929 Small Size <$VALUE
5 Type 2 1-15280 <$300
10 Type 2 1-7440 <$300
20 Type 2 1-2460 <$300
Total Issue $200,000
Out in 1935 $188,700

******

5217 Bexar
CITY NB OF SAN ANTONIO
{{ 18 L }}
Chartered 9/1/99
Liquidated 8/29/29
Brown Back <$VALUE
4x5 1-4100 <$750
50-100 1-860 <$3500/$4000
1882 Date Back
4x5 1-7450 <$400
50-100 1-740 <$3500/$4000
3x50-100 1-626 <$3500/$4000
1882 Value Back
4x5 7451-7900 <$450
1902 Plain Back
3x50-100 1-12704 <$350/$400
Total Issue $3,812,500
Out at close $989,250
Outstanding includes Ch 10793

******

12162 Bexar
COMMERCIAL NB OF SAN ANTONIO
{{ U + 10 L 23 S }}
Organized 4/4/22
Liquidated 11/20/34
1902 Plain Back <$VALUE
4x5 1-22750 <$200
3x10-20 1-16778 <$200
1929 Small Size
5 Type 1 1-13310 <$40
10 Type 1 1-7268 <$40
20 Type 1 1-1804 <$50
5 Type 2 1-1522 <$60
10 Type 2 1-670 <$60
Total Issue $2,360,070
Out at close $300,000
Large out at close $9,220

******

4748 Bexar
FIFTH NB OF SAN ANTONIO
{{ UNREPORTED }}
Chartered 6/2/92
Liquidated 5/29/95
Brown Back <$VALUE
3x10-20 1-902 <$2000
Total Issue $45,100
Out in 1910 $800

******

5179 Bexar
FROST NB OF SAN ANTONIO
{{ 29 L 24 S }}
Chartered 2/20/99
Brown Back <$VALUE
4x5 1-9415 <$850
3x10-20 1-14243 <$850
1882 Date Back
4x5 1-31000 <$350
3x10-20 1-24300 <$350
1882 Value Back
4x5 31001-43350 <$400
3x10-20 24301-31040 <$400
1902 Plain Back
4x5 1-148465 <$100
3x50-100 1-7010 <$350/$400
1929 Small Size
5 Type 1 1-54914 <$50
50 Type 1 1-2810 <$125
100 Type 1 1-1032 <$175
5 Type 2 1-53838 <$50
Total Issue $11,419,610
Out in 1935 $1,146,700
Large out 1935 $5,445
Outstanding includes Ch 3738

******

10148 Bexar
GROOS NB OF SAN ANTONIO
{{ 12 L 22 S }}
Chartered 2/12
1902 Date Back <$VALUE
4x5 1-7410 <$175
4x10 1-7420 <$175
1902 Plain Back
4x5 7411-43343 <$175
4x10 7421-35091 <$175
1929 Small Size
5 Type 1 1-15264 <$65
10 Type 1 1-7520 <$65
5 Type 2 1-26834 <$65
10 Type 2 1-13400 <$65
Total Issue $3,447,790
Out in 1935 $245,900
Large out 1935 $8,515

******

3738 Bexar
LOCKWOOD NB OF SAN ANTONIO
{{ 8 L }}
Chartered 6/28/87
Closed 2/16/29
Brown Back <$VALUE
50-100 1-1230 <$3500/$4000
1902 Red Seal
50-100 1-467 <$7500
1902 Date Back
4x5 1-5000 <$225
4x10 1-2500 <$225
50-100 1-1200 <$400/$500
3x50-100 1-320 <$400/$500
1902 Plain Back
4x5 5001-12215 <$225
4x10 2501-9460 <$225
Total Issue $1,137,250
Out at close $97,400
Ch 5179 assumed circulation

******

6956 Bexar
NB OF COMMERCE, SAN ANTONIO
{{ 23 L U + 50+ S }}
Chartered 9/03
1902 Red Seal <$VALUE
3x10-20 1-4100 <$1000
50-100 1-2167 <$7500
1902 Date Back
4x5 1-24500 <$60
3x10-20 1-14600 <$75
50-100 1-1500 <$350/$450
3x50-100 1-1000 <$350/$450
1902 Plain Back
4x5 24501-28500 <$60
3x10-20 14601-109256 <$75
1929 Small Size
5 Type 1 1-22 <$75
10 Type 1 1-18596 <$40
20 Type 1 1-4992 <$45
10 Type 2 1-26212 <$40
20 Type 2 1-8160 <$45
Total Issue $9,178,630
Out in 1935 $590,200
Large out 1935 $32,940

******

13578 Bexar
NB OF FORT SAM HOUSTON AT SAN ANTONIO
{{ 3U + 10 S }}
Chartered 11/13/31
1929 Small Size <$VALUE
5 Type 1 1-2052 <$250
10 Type 1 1-522 <$250
20 Type 1 1-262 <$250
5 Type 2 1-10764 <$250
10 Type 2 1-5460 <$250
20 Type 2 1-1920 <$250
Total Issue $271,140
Out in 1935 $106,750

******

1657 Bexar
SAN ANTONIO NB, SAN ANTONIO
{{ 30 L 32 S }}
Chartered 1866
Original Series <$VALUE
3x1-2 1-1000 <$4500/$15,000
4x5 1-875 <$4000
4x10 1-1400 <$5000
3x20-50 1-1260 <$6000/$15,000
Series 1875
4x10 1-2000 <$5000
3x20-50 1-288 <$6000/$15,000
Brown Back
3x10-20 1-2641 <$750
50-100 1-728 <$3500/$4000
1902 Red Seal
4x5 1-10000 <$1000
4x10 1-6500 <$1000
3x10-20 1-1400 <$1000
1902 Date Back
4x5 1-30170 <$60
4x10 1-30165 <$75
1902 Plain Back
4x5 30171-115433 <$60
4x10 30166-98833 <$75
1929 Small Size
5 Type 1 1-22658 <$40
10 Type 1 1-12302 <$45
5 Type 2 1-27446 <$40
10 Type 2 1-13779 <$45
Total Issue $9,054,890
Out in 1935 $366,150
Large out 1935 $24,025

******

10793 Bexar
STATE NB OF SAN ANTONIO
{{ 6 L }}
Chartered 10/15
Liquidated 12/24/21
1902 Plain Back <$VALUE
3x10-20 1-27028 <$225
3x50-100 1-2000 <$500/$600
Total Issue $1,851,400
Out at close $443 350
Ch 5217 assumed circulation

******

3298 Bexar
TEXAS NB OF SAN ANTONIO
{{ 1 L }}
Organized 1/31/85
Receivership 8/10/93
Brown Back <$VALUE
3x10-20 1-1136 <$2000
Total Issue $56,800
Out in 1916 $290

******

2883 Bexar
TRADERS NB OF SAN ANTONIO
{{ UNREPORTED }}
Chartered 2/14/83
Liquidated 4/29/89
Brown Back <$VALUE
3x10-20 1-813 <$2000
Total Issue $40,650
Out in 1910 $340

******

7316 Bexar
WOODS NB OF SAN ANTONIO
{{ 3 L }}
Chartered 6/04
Receivership 11/9/07
1902 Red Seal <$VALUE
3x10-20 1-5942 <$1250
Total Issue $297,100
Out in 1916 $5,640

******

6214 San Augustine
FNB OF SAN AUGUSTINE
{{ 3 L 2 S }}
Chartered 4/17/02
1902 Red Seal <$VALUE
3x10-20 1-1300 <$1500
1902 Date Back
3x10-20 1-4540 <$600
1902 Plain Back (dated 1902)
3x10-20 4541-4660 <$600
1902 Plain Back (dated 1922)
3x10-20 1-1474 <$600
1929 Small Size
10 Type 1 1-450 <$400
20 Type 1 1-140 <$400
10 Type 2 1-753 <$400
20 Type 2 1-193 <$400
Total Issue $426,890
Out in 1935 $16,250
Large out 1935 $1,850

******

6245 San Augustine
SAN AUGUSTINE NB, SAN AUGUSTINE
{{ UNREPORTED }}
Chartered 5/7/02
Liquidated 2/10/05
1902 Red Seal <$VALUE
3x10-20 1-173 <$3000
Total Issue $8,650
Out in 1910 $320

******

3346 Hays
FNB OF SAN MARCOS
{{ 4 L 4 S }}
Chartered 1885
Brown Back <$VALUE
4x5 1-550 <$1250
3x10-20 1-1784 <$1250
1902 Red Seal
4x5 1-1000 <$1500
50-100 1-547 <$7500
1902 Date Back
4x5 1-3400 <$350
50-100 1-300 <$650/$750
3x50-100 1-640 <$650/$750
1902 Plain Back
4x5 3401-17054 <$350
3x50-100 641-786 <$650/$750
1929 Small Size
5 Type 1 1-2292 <$300
50 Type 1 1-124 <$400
100 Type 1 1-51 <$500
Total Issue $921,390
Out in 1935 $40,310
Large out 1935 $4,750

******

Glover NB of San Marcos
SEE Ch 3344
NB of San Marcos

******

3344 Hays
NB OF SAN MARCOS
Chartered 5/25/85
Liquidated 10/20/09
2nd title:Glover NB of San Marcos 10/87
3rd title:Wood NB of San Marcos 5/12/05
FIRST TITLE {{ 0 L }}
Brown Back <$VALUE
3x10-20 1-241 <$2000
SECOND TITLE {{ 1 L }}
Brown Back
3x10-20 1-1069 <$2000
THIRD TITLE {{ 1 L }}
1902 Red Seal
3x10-20 1-410 <$2000
Total Issue $86,000
Out in 1910 $7,630

******

Wood NB of San Marcos
SEE Ch 3344
NB of San Marcos

******

7700 San Saba
FNB OF SAN SABA
{{ 1 L }}
Chartered 4/05
Liquidated 2/15/29
1902 Red Seal <$VALUE
3x10-20 1-600 <$2000
1902 Date Back
3x10-20 1-2100 <$850
1902 Plain Back
3x10-20 2101-3835 <$850
Total Issue $221,750
Out at close $14,150

******

9781 San Saba
SAN SABA NB, SAN SABA
{{ 2 L }}
Chartered 6/10
1902 Date Back <$VALUE
3x10-20 1-2510 <$750
1902 Plain Back
3x10-20 1-5272 <$750
Total Issue $263,600
Out in 1935 $580

******

<$VALUEs are for notes in FINE condition. Value changes by approximately 25% for a change of one full grade.

****
7886 Denton
FNB OF SANGER
{{4L 4S}}
Chartered 8/05
1902 Red Seal <$VALUE
4x5 1-1120 <$1500
3x10-20 1-720 <$1500
1902 Date Back
4x5 1-2150 <$500
3x10-20 1-1660 <$500
1902 Plain Back
4x5 2151-7196 <$500
3x10-20 1661-4588 <$500
1929 Small Size
5 Type 1 1-1050 <$300
10 Type 1 1-574 <$300
20 Type 1 1-184 <$300
5 Type 2 1-1778 <$300
10 Type 2 1-835 <$300
20 Type 2 1-264 <$300
Total Issue $542,260
Out in 1935 $24,445
Large out 1935 $1,515
****
8690 Denton
SANGER NB, SANGER
{{1L 0S}}
Chartered 5/07
Liquidated 5/15/30
1902 Red Seal <$VALUE
3x10-20 1-300 <$2000
1902 Date Back
3x10-20 1-850 <$1000
1902 Plain Back
3x10-20 851-1842 <$1000
1929 Small Size
10 Type 1 1-55 <$750
20 Type 1 1-13 <$750
Total Issue $111,960
Out at close $6,660
Large out at close $2,000
****
8109 Coleman
FNB OF SANTA ANNA
{{1L}}
Organized 1/29/06
Liquidated 1/9/34
1902 Red Seal <$VALUE
3x10-20 1-240 <$2000
1902 Date Back
3x10-20 1-1280 <$1000
1902 Plain Back
3x10-20 1281-1976 <$1000
Total Issue $110,800
Out at close $410
****
8176 Palo Pinto
FNB OF SANTO
{{4L 4S}}
Chartered 4/06
1902 Red Seal <$VALUE
3x10-20 1-500 <$1500
1902 Date Back
3x10-20 1-2600 <$400
1902 Plain Back
3x10-20 2601-6673 <$400
1929 Small Size
10 Type 1 1-798 <$350
20 Type 1 1-252 <$350
5 Type 2 1-2232 <$350
10 Type 2 1-324 <$375
20 Type 2 1-72 <$400
Total Issue $452,610
Out in 1935 $23,680
Large out 1935 $1,480
****
7645 Fannin
FNB OF SAVOY
{{1L}}
Chartered 3/05
Receivership 6/30/09
1902 Red Seal <$VALUE
3x10-20 1-618 <$3500
Total Issue $30,900
Out in 1916 $570
****
8034 Fayette
FNB OF SCHULENBURG
{{1L 4S}}
Chartered 1/06
1902 Red Seal <$VALUE
3x10-20 1-687 <$2000
1902 Date Back
3x10-20 1-1470 <$850
1902 Plain Back
3x10-20 1471-4798 <$850
1929 Small Size
10 Type 1 1-668 <$300
20 Type 1 1-200 <$300
10 Type 2 1-675 <$300
20 Type 2 1-138 <$300
Total Issue $347,840
Out in 1935 $25,000
Large out 1935 $1,580
****
10956 Williamson
FNB OF SCHWERTNER
{{3L 4S}}
Chartered 2/17
1902 Plain Back <$VALUE
3x10-20 1-2299 <$450
1929 Small Size
10 Type 1 1-750 <$300
20 Type 1 1-202 <$300
10 Type 2 1-1741 <$300
20 Type 2 1-340 <$300
Total Issue $208,400
Out in 1935 $25,000
Large out 1935 $980
****
10398 Austin
FARMERS NB OF SEALY
{{1L}}
Chartered 5/13
Closed 6/22/21
1902 Date Back <$VALUE
3x10-20 1-1100 <$1000
1902 Plain Back
3x10-20 1101-2563 <$1000
Total Issue $128,150
Out at close $24,300
Ch 6390 assumed circulation
****
6390 Austin
SEALY NB, SEALY
{{2L}}
Chartered 8/19/02
Liquidated 2/15/26
1902 Red Seal <$VALUE
3x10-20 1-940 <$1500
1902 Date Back
3x10-20 1-1360 <$600
1902 Plain Back
3x10-20 1361-5072 <$600
Total Issue $300,600
Out at close $43,700
Outstanding includes Ch 10398
****
5097 Guadalupe
FNB OF SEGUIN
{{3L U+3S}}
Chartered 1897
Brown Back <$VALUE
50-100 1-650 <$3500/$4000
1882 Date Back
50-100 1-55 <$3500/$4000
1902 Plain Back
3x50-100 1-157 <$850/$1000
1929 Small Size
5 Type 1 1-734 <$350
10 Type 1 1-366 <$350
50 Type 1 1-69 <$450
100 Type 1 1-9 <$600
5 Type 2 1-2820 <$350
10 Type 2 1-1960 <$350
Total Issue $248,780
Out in 1935 $49,300
Large out 1935 $1,950
****
8465 Gaines
SEMINOLE NB, SEMINOLE
{{ UNREPORTED }}
Chartered 12/06
Liquidated 3/20/14
1902 Red Seal <$VALUE
3x10-20 1-238 <$3500
1902 Date Back
3x10-20 1-357 <$2500
Total Issue $29,750
Out in 1914 $4,180
****
5904 Baylor
DAVIS NB OF SEYMOUR
{{ UNREPORTED }}
Chartered 7/15/01
Liquidated 1/30/04
Brown Back <$VALUE
3x10-20 1-400 <$2500
Total Issue $20,000
Out in 1910 $670
****
7482 Baylor
FARMERS NB OF SEYMOUR
{{1L 2S}}
Chartered 11/04
1902 Red Seal <$VALUE
3x10-20 1-600 <$2000
1902 Date Back
3x10-20 1-1800 <$750
1902 Plain Back
3x10-20 1801-3719 <$750
1929 Small Size
10 Type 1 1-585 <$400
20 Type 1 1-116 <$400
Total Issue $264,970
Out in 1935 $10,250
Large out 1935 $540
****
4263 Baylor
FNB OF SEYMOUR
{{4L 4S}}
Chartered 1890
Brown Back <$VALUE
3x10-20 1-2070 <$1000
1882 Date Back
3x10-20 1-403 <$1000
1902 Date Back
4x5 1-1725* <$400
4x10 1-1700** <$400
1902 Plain Back
4x5 1926-7124* <$400
4x10 1901-5581** <$400
* 1726-1925 not marked
** 1701-1900 not marked
1929 Small Size
5 Type 1 1-1802 <$300
10 Type 1 1-766 <$300
5 Type 2 1-3720 <$300
10 Type 2 1-1716 <$300
Total Issue $625,150
Out in 1935 $24,400
Large out 1935 $1,170
****
7306 Wheeler
FNB OF SHAMROCK
{{1L}}
Chartered 6/04
1902 Red Seal <$VALUE
50-100 1-120 <$10,000
1902 Date Back
50-100 1-280 <$5000
3x50-100 1-131 <$5000
Total Issue $92,750
Out in 1935 $150
****
5864 Grayson
COMMERCIAL NB OF SHERMAN
{{3L}}
Chartered 6/18/01
Liquidated 3/2/11
Brown Back <$VALUE
3x10-20 1-4800 <$1000
1882 Date Back
3x10-20 1-1327 <$750
Total Issue $306,350
Out in 1911 $52,295
****
10607 Grayson
COMMERCIAL NB OF SHERMAN
{{4L}}
Chartered 9/14
Liquidated 10/31/29
1902 Date Back <$VALUE
3x10-20 1-5000 <$300
1902 Plain Back
4x5 1-29075 <$300
3x10-20 5001-33273 <$300
Total Issue $2,245,150
Out at close $164,350
Ch 3159 assumed circulation
****
5192 Grayson
GRAYSON COUNTY NB OF SHERMAN
{{ UNREPORTED }}
Chartered 5/15/99
Liquidated 2/5/07
Brown Back <$VALUE
3x10-20 1-2713 <$2000
Total Issue $135,650
Out in 1910 $6,650
****
3159 Grayson
MERCHANTS & PLANTERS NB OF SHERMAN
{{26L 40S}}
Chartered 1884
Brown Back <$VALUE
3x10-20 1-5130 <$850
1902 Red Seal
4x5 1-12250 <$1000
3x10-20 1-8200 <$1000
1902 Date Back
4x5 1-26750 <$100
3x10-20 1-21800 <$100
1902 Plain Back
4x5 26751-96327 <$100
3x10-20 21801-66255 <$100
1929 Small Size
5 Type 1 1-27704 <$50
10 Type 1 1-14080 <$50
20 Type 1 1-3962 <$60
5 Type 2 1-24064 <$50
10 Type 2 1-10562 <$60
20 Type 2 1-3332 <$65
Total Issue $8,594,730
Out in 1935 $342,925
Large out 1935 $27,375
Outstanding includes Ch 10607
****
5628 Lavaca
FNB OF SHINER
{{28L 6S}}
Chartered 11/19/00
Brown Back <$VALUE
4x5 1-1335 <$750
3x10-20 1-1036 <$750
1882 Date Back
4x5 1-3250 <$600
3x10-20 1-2420 <$600
1882 Value Back
4x5 3251-4490 <$600
3x10-20 2421-3080 <$600
1902 Plain Back
4x5 1-4148 <$350
3x10-20 1-2799 <$350
1929 Small Size
5 Type 1 1-1154 <$250
10 Type 1 1-724 <$250
20 Type 1 1-192 <$250
5 Type 2 1-1844 <$250
10 Type 2 1-990 <$250
20 Type 2 1-164 <$275
Total Issue $668,710
Out in 1935 $39,300
Large out 1935 $3,740
****
8816 Briscoe
FNB OF SILVERTON
{{1L 1S}}
Organized 6/13/07
Receivership 6/5/33
1902 Red Seal <$VALUE
3x10-20 1-225 <$2500
1902 Date Back
3x10-20 1-1200 <$1000
1902 Plain Back
3x10-20 1201-1909 <$1000
1929 Small Size
10 Type 1 1-225 <$750
20 Type 1 1-53 <$750
Total Issue $126,560
Out at close $7,260
Large out at close $680
****
7041 Bastrop
FNB OF SMITHVILLE
{{1L 2S}}
Organized 11/11/03
Receivership 10/7/31
1902 Red Seal <$VALUE
3x10-20 1-435 <$2000
1902 Date Back
3x10-20 1-1870 <$850
1902 Plain Back
3x10-20 1871-5816 <$850
1929 Small Size
10 Type 1 1-414 <$500
20 Type 1 1-112 <$500
Total Issue $350,830
Out at close $23,320
Large out at close $4,230
****
5580 Scurry
FNB OF SNYDER
{{3L}}
Chartered 9/19/00
Liquidated 8/15/28
Brown Back <$VALUE
3x10-20 1-1460 <$1000
1882 Date Back
3x10-20 1-3150* <$750
1882 Value Back
3x10-20 3451-4643* <$750
* 3151-3450 not marked
1902 Plain Back
3x10-20 1-4018 <$450
Total Issue $506,050
Out at close $31,750
****
7635 Scurry
SNYDER NB, SNYDER
{{4L 6S}}
Chartered 3/05
Liquidated 11/13/34
1902 Red Seal <$VALUE
4x5 1-1000 <$1250
3x10-20 1-1073 <$1250
1902 Date Back
4x5 1-3850 <$350
3x10-20 1-3040 <$350
1902 Plain Back
4x5 3851-11071 <$350
3x10-20 3041-7777 <$350
1929 Small Size
5 Type 1 1-1748 <$250
10 Type 1 1-856 <$250
20 Type 1 1-246 <$250
5 Type 2 1-2464 <$250
10 Type 2 1-1414 <$250
20 Type 2 1-290 <$250
Total Issue $849,500
Out at close $39,650
Large out 1935 $2,250
Ch 14270 assumed circulation
****
14270 Scurry
SNYDER NB, SNYDER
{{1S}}
Chartered 9/34
1929 Small Size <$VALUE
5 Type 2 1-860 <$650
10 Type 2 1-446 <$650
20 Type 2 1-192 <$650
Total Issue $12,600
Out in 1935 $40,000
Large out 1935 $2,250
Outstanding includes Ch 7635
****
5466 Sutton
FNB OF SONORA
{{7L 17S}}
Chartered 6/28/00
Brown Back <$VALUE
4x5 1-1000 $1000
3x10-20 1-1150 <$1000
1882 Date Back
4x5 1-4550 <$700
3x10-20 1-3700 <$700
1882 Value Back
4x5 4551-6706 <$700
3x10-20 3701-4966 <$700
1902 Plain Back
4x5 1-14405 <$350
3x10-20 1-7666 <$350
1929 Small Size
5 Type 1 1-4068 <$150
10 Type 1 1-2220 <$150
20 Type 1 1-732 <$150
5 Type 2 1-7136 <$150
10 Type 2 1-3770 <$150
20 Type 2 1-1207 <$150
Total Issue $1,571,920
Out in 1935 $97,550
Large out 1935 $4,265
****
11021 Hardin
CITIZENS NB OF SOUR LAKE
{{3L 11S}}
Chartered 6/17
1902 Plain Back <$VALUE
4x5 1-9562 <$850
3x10-20 1-6847 <$850
1929 Small Size
5 Type 1 1-2078 <$350
10 Type 1 1-1170 <$350
20 Type 1 1-300 <$350
5 Type 2 1-3170 <$350
10 Type 2 1-2113 <$350
20 Type 2 1-469 <$350
Total Issue $748,490
Out in 1935 $50,000
Large out 1935 $2,005
****
6810 Hardin
FNB OF SOUR LAKE
{{1L}}
Chartered 6/1/03
Liquidated 1/10/05
1902 Red Seal <$VALUE
3x10-20 1-737 <$3500
Total Issue $36,850
Out in 1910 $1,760
****
6856 Hardin
SOUR LAKE NB, SOUR LAKE
{{ UNREPORTED }}
Chartered 6/26/03
Liquidated 10/8/03
1902 Red Seal <$VALUE
3x10-20 1-250 <$3500
Total Issue $12,500
Out in 1910 $690
****
10703 Dickens
CITY NB OF SPUR
{{1L 0S}}
Organized 2/14/15
Receivership 10/7/30
1902 Date Back <$VALUE
3x10-20 1-800 <$1500
1902 Plain Back
3x10-20 801-2109 <$1500
1929 Small Size
10 Type 1 1-139 <$1000
20 Type 1 1-19 <$1000
Total Issue $116,070
Out at close $9,040
Large out at close $1,430
****
9611 Dickens
SPUR NB, SPUR
{{3L 5S}}
Chartered 12/09
Liquidated 2/26/34
1902 Date Back <$VALUE
4x5 1-2450 <$600
3x10-20 1-1960 <$600
1902 Plain Back
4x5 2451-7159 <$600
3x10-20 1961-4804 <$600
1929 Small Size
5 Type 1 1-1090 <$400
10 Type 1 1-584 <$400
20 Type 1 1-170 <$400
5 Type 2 1-3828 <$400
10 Type 2 1-3811 <$400
20 Type 2 1-523 <$400
Total Issue $539,230
Out at close $73,250
Large out at close $1,440
****
7640 Jones
CITIZENS NB OF STAMFORD
{{1L}}
Chartered 3/05
Liquidated 1/8/20
1902 Red Seal <$VALUE
3x10-20 1-1400 <$2000
1902 Date Back
3x10-20 1-3200 <$850
1902 Plain Back
3x10-20 3201-3388 <$850
Total Issue $239,400
Out at close $29,700
****
13598 Jones
FNB IN STAMFORD
{{4U+5S}}
Chartered 2/32
1929 Small Size <$VALUE
5 Type 1 1-314 <$300
10 Type 1 1-318 <$300
20 Type 1 1-106 <$300
5 Type 2 1-2378 <$300
10 Type 2 1-1269 <$300
20 Type 2 1-294 <$300
Total Issue $71,700
Out in 1935 $24,700
Outstanding includes Ch 5560
****
5560 Jones
FNB OF STAMFORD
{{5L 4S}}
Chartered 8/28/00
Liquidated 2/25/32
Brown Back <$VALUE
3x10-20 1-2760 <$1000
1882 Date Back
4x5 1-8250 <$650
3x10-20 1-5800 <$650
1882 Value Back
4x5 8251-11135 <$650
3x10-20 5801-7541 <$650
1902 Plain Back
4x5 1-9980 <$300
3x10-20 1-6027 <$300
1929 Small Size
5 Type 1 1-2077 <$300
10 Type 1 1-976 <$300
20 Type 1 1-269 <$300
Total Issue $1,391,850
Out at close $67,300
Large out at close $6,840
Ch 13598 assumed circulation
****
8094 Martin
FNB OF STANTON
{{3L 4S}}
Chartered 2/06
1902 Red Seal <$VALUE
3x10-20 1-950 <$1500
1902 Date Back
3x10-20 1-2150 <$500
1902 Plain Back
3x10-20 2151-6784 <$500
1929 Small Size
10 Type 1 1-732 <$300
20 Type 1 1-222 <$300
10 Type 2 1-1324 <$300
20 Type 2 1-343 <$300
Total Issue $477,360
Out in 1935 $25,000
Large out 1935 $1,410
****

****
9053 Martin
HOME NB OF STANTON
{{2L 0S}}
Chartered 3/08
Liquidated 6/28/30
1902 Red Seal <$VALUE
3x10-20 1-200 <$1500
1902 Date Back
3x10-20 1-2280 <$500
1902 Plain Back
3x10-20 2281-7040 <$500
1929 Small Size
10 Type 1 1-246 <$600
20 Type 1 1-51 <$600
Total Issue $382,880
Out at close $20,740
Large out at close $4,910
****
8112 Martin
STANTON NB, STANTON
{{ UNREPORTED }}
Chartered 2/28/06
Liquidated 4/20/06
1902 Red Seal <$VALUE
3x10-20 1-126 <$3000
Total Issue $6,300
All notes reportedly redeemed
****
4081 Erath
ERATH COUNTY NB OF STEPHENVILLE
{{1L}}
Chartered 7/25/89
Liquidated 3/15/92
Brown Back <$VALUE
50-100 1-111 <$5000
Total Issue $16,650
Out in 1910 $200
****
12730 Erath
FARMERS-FIRST NB OF STEPHENVILLE
{{3L 15S}}
Chartered 5/25
1902 Plain Back <$VALUE
3x10-20 1-7404 <$400
1929 Small Size
10 Type 1 1-3096 <$150
20 Type 1 1-922 <$150
10 Type 2 1-5833 <$150
20 Type 2 1-1311 <$150
Total Issue $751,150
Out in 1935 $85,600
Large out 1935 $2,430
****
8054 Erath
FARMERS NB OF STEPHENVILLE
{{2L}}
Chartered 1/06
Liquidated 1/10/22
1902 Red Seal <$VALUE
3x10-20 1-1400 <$1500
1902 Date Back
3x10-20 1-4500 <$600
1902 Plain Back
3x10-20 4501-8065 <$600
Total Issue $473,250
Out at close $44,100
****
4095 Erath
FNB OF STEPHENVILLE
{{3L}}
Chartered 8/16/89
Liquidated 1/10/22
Brown Back <$VALUE
4x5 1-3375 <$1000
3x10-20 1-1440 <$1000
1902 Date Back
3x10-20 1-5100 <$400
1902 Plain Back
3x10-20 5100-10487 <$400
Total Issue $663,850
Out at close $69,900
****
9813 Sterling
FNB OF STERLING CITY
{{3L 2S}}
Chartered 7/10
1902 Date Back <$VALUE
3x10-20 1-1560* <$1000
1902 Plain Back
3x10-20 1721-3690* <$1000
* 1561-1720 not marked
1929 Small Size
10 Type 1 1-504 <$500
20 Type 1 1-130 <$500
10 Type 2 1-577 <$500
20 Type 2 1-178 <$500
Total Issue $239,670
Out in 1935 $14,200
Large out 1935 $8,200
****

****
FNB of Stratford
SEE Ch 8018
Stratford NB, Stratford
****
8018 Sherman
STRATFORD NB, STRATFORD
Chartered 12/05
Liquidated 11/10/13
2nd title:FNB of Stratford 12/8/06
FIRST TITLE {{1L}}
1902 Red Seal <$VALUE
4x5 1-105 <$3000
3x10-20 1-88 <$3000
SECOND TITLE {{0L}}
1902 Red Seal
4x5 1-150 <$3000
4x10 1-150 <$3000
1902 Date Back
4x5 1-258 <$2000
4x10 1-220 <$2000
Total Issue $29,460
Out in 1914 $2,840
****
10229 Palo Pinto
FNB OF STRAWN
{{1L 2S}}
Chartered 7/12
1902 Date Back <$VALUE
3x10-20 1-1095 <$1250
1902 Plain Back
3x10-20 1096-2913 <$1250
1929 Small Size
10 Type 1 1-398 <$450
20 Type 1 1-118 <$450
10 Type 2 1-542 <$500
20 Type 2 1-99 <$500
Total Issue $191,090
Out in 1935 $12,150
Large out 1935 $510
****
12775 Palo Pinto
STRAWN NB, STRAWN
{{7S}}
Chartered 6/25
1929 Small Size <$VALUE
5 Type 1 1-1630 <$300
10 Type 1 1-864 <$300
20 Type 1 1-250 <$300
5 Type 2 1-2198 <$350
10 Type 2 1-975 <$350
20 Type 2 1-310 <$350
Total Issue $157,680
Out in 1935 $25,250
****
12725 Lamb
FNB OF SUDAN
{{3S}}
Chartered 5/25
1929 Small Size <$VALUE
5 Type 2 1-2494 <$450
10 Type 2 1-1791 <$450
20 Type 2 1-747 <$450
Total Issue $45,320
Out in 1935 $22,350
****
3989 Hopkins
CITY NB OF SULPHUR SPRINGS
{{8L 14S}}
Chartered 3/13/89
Brown Back <$VALUE
3x10-20 1-8226 <$1000
1902 Date Back
3x10-20 1-8700 <$250
1902 Plain Back
3x10-20 8701-23293 <$250
1929 Small Size
10 Type 1 1-2758 <$100
20 Type 1 1-762 <$125
5 Type 2 1-324 <$125
10 Type 2 1-6183 <$125
20 Type 2 1-1453 <$150
Total Issue $1,925,380
Out in 1935 $97,950
Large out 1935 $5,245
****
12845 Hopkins
FNB IN SULPHUR SPRINGS
{{1L 8S}}
Chartered 11/25
Liquidated 1/10/33
1902 Plain Back <$VALUE
3x10-20 1-4322 <$850
1929 Small Size
10 Type 1 1-2839 <$175
20 Type 1 1-852 <$200
Total Issue $488,680
Out at close $50,000
Large out at close $4,280
Outstanding includes Ch 3466
Ch 13663 assumed circulation
****

****
3466 Hopkins
FNB OF SULPHUR SPRINGS
{{3L}}
Chartered 1886
Liquidated 12/24/25
Brown Back <$VALUE
3x10-20 1-2769 <$1000
1902 Red Seal
3x10-20 1-450 <$1250
1902 Date Back
3x10-20 1-3500 <$400
1902 Plain Back
3x10-20 3501-5721 <$400
Total Issue $447,000
Out at close $23,700
Ch 12845 assumed circulation
****
13653 Hopkins
FNB OF SULPHUR SPRINGS
{{2S}}
Chartered 12/32
Liquidated 12/3/34
1929 Small Size <$VALUE
10 Type 1 1-184 <$500
20 Type 1 1-64 <$500
10 Type 2 1-98 <$500
Total Issue $19,700
Out at close $52,570
Large out at close $2,570
Outstanding includes Ch 12845
****
11468 Nolan
CITY NB OF SWEETWATER
{{3L}}
Chartered 10/19
Liquidated 6/5/31
1902 Plain Back <$VALUE
4x5 1-7950 <$650
3x10-20 1-6988 <$650
Total Issue $508,400
Out at close $2,950
****
5781 Nolan
FNB OF SWEETWATER
{{3L}}
Chartered 4/18/01
Receivership 12/14/31
Brown Back <$VALUE
3x10-20 1-740 <$1500
1882 Date Back
3x10-20 1-2430 <$1250
1882 Value Back
3x10-20 2431-2897 <$1250
1902 Plain Back
3x10-20 1-1044 <$850
Total Issue $234,050
Out at close $1,060
****
12309 Particio
FNB OF TAFT
{{2L 4S}}
Chartered 1/23
1902 Plain Back <$VALUE
4x5 1-1175 <$1000
1929 Small Size
5 Type 2 1-9540* <$400
10 Type 2 1-5052 <$400
* 7513-7518 not issued
Total Issue $121,690
Out in 1935 $47,895
Large out 1935 $95
****
8597 Lynn
FNB OF TAHOKA
{{1L 1S}}
Chartered 3/07
1902 Red Seal <$VALUE
3x10-20 1-300 <$2500
1902 Date Back
3x10-20 1-910 <$1500
1902 Plain Back
3x10-20 911-3232 <$1500
1929 Small Size
10 Type 1 1-396 <$600
20 Type 1 1-118 <$600
10 Type 2 1-372 <$650
20 Type 2 1-110 <$650
Total Issue $220,440
Out in 1935 $12,500
Large out 1935 $210
****
5275 Williamson
CITY NB OF TAYLOR
{{5L 13S}}
Chartered 4/3/00
Brown Back <$VALUE
3x10-20 1-960 <$1000
1882 Date Back
3x10-20 1-4300 <$600
1882 Value Back
3x10-20 4301-5203 <$600
1902 Plain Back
3x10-20 1-6609 <$400
1929 Small Size
10 Type 1 1-2370 <$100
20 Type 1 1-568 <$125
10 Type 2 1-4780 <$125
20 Type 2 1-1425 <$125
Total Issue $925,260
Out in 1935 $97,800
Large out 1935 $2,800
****
F-Taylor NB of Taylor
SEE Ch 3027
FNB of Taylor
****
3027 Williamson
FNB OF TAYLOR
Chartered 1883
2nd title:F-Taylor NB 7/27/31
FIRST TITLE {{4L 3S}}
Brown Back <$VALUE
3x10-20 1-3719 <$1000
1902 Red Seal
50-100 1-625 <$7500
1902 Date Back
50-100 1-1300 <$650/$750
3x50-100 1-1400 <$650/$750
1902 Plain Back
3x50-100 1401-1790 <$650/$750
1929 Small Size
50 Type 1 1-252 <$400
100 Type 1 1-56 <$500
SECOND TITLE {{6S}}
1929 Small Size
50 Type 1 1-126 <$400
100 Type 1 1-54 <$500
10 Type 2 1-1759 <$300
20 Type 2 1-560 <$300
Total Issue $1,130,390
Out in 1935 $146,600
Large out 1935 $15,110
Outstanding includes Ch 3859
****
3859 Williamson
TAYLOR NB, TAYLOR
{{0L 3S}}
Chartered 3/26/88
Closed 7/27/31
Brown Back <$VALUE
3x10-20 1-2680 <$1500
50-100 1-282 <$3500/$4000
1902 Red Seal
50-100 1-250 <$7500
1902 Date Back
50-100 1-600 <$1500
3x50-100 1-500 <$1500
1902 Plain Back
3x50-100 501-681 <$1500
1929 Small Size
50 Type 1 1-90 <$500
100 Type 1 1-10 <$600
Total Issue $507,050
Out at close $34,800
Large out at close $10,500
Ch 3027 assumed circulation
****
8195 Freestone
FNB OF TEAGUE
{{5L U+8S}}
Chartered 4/06
1902 Red Seal <$VALUE
4x5 1-1450 <$1250
3x10-20 1-1160 <$1250
1902 Date Back
4x5 1-3750 <$300
3x10-20 1-2700 <$300
1902 Plain Back
4x5 3751-13800 <$300
3x10-20 2701-9098 <$300
1929 Small Size
5 Type 1 1-2410 <$150
10 Type 1 1-1126 <$150
20 Type 1 1-310 <$175
5 Type 2 1-3948 <$175
10 Type 2 1-2220 <$175
20 Type 2 1-540 <$175
Total Issue $1,047,700
Out in 1935 $49,460
Large out 1935 $3,520
****
13067 Freestone
TEAGUE NB, TEAGUE
{{7L 7S}}
Chartered 5/2/27
1902 Plain Back <$VALUE
4x5 1-8356 <$250
1929 Small Size
5 Type 1 1-8654 <$175
10 Type 1 1-398 <$175
20 Type 1 1-74 <$175
5 Type 2 1-6442 <$175
10 Type 2 1-3299* <$175
20 Type 2 1-936 <$175
* 2191-2196 not issued
Total Issue $543,360
Out in 1935 $58,600
Large out 1935 $650
****

****
4404 Bell
BELL COUNTY NB OF TEMPLE
{{ UNREPORTED }}
Chartered 8/90
Receivership 2/19/92
Brown Back <$VALUE
3x10-20 1-255 <$2500
Total Issue $12,750
Out in 1916 $110
****
6317 Bell
CITY NB OF TEMPLE
{{3L 3S}}
Chartered 6/24/02
Liquidated 6/5/31
1902 Red Seal <$VALUE
3x10-20 1-1700 <$1250
1902 Date Back
3x10-20 1-3340* <$400
1902 Plain Back
3x10-20 3541-11505* <$400
* 3341-3540 not marked
1929 Small Size
10 Type 1 1-704 <$350
20 Type 1 1-213 <$350
Total Issue $728,050
Out at close $42,750
Large out at close $7,050
****
3227 Bell
FNB OF TEMPLE
{{4L}}
Chartered 1884
Liquidated 6/25/28
Brown Back <$VALUE
3x10-20 1-2664 <$1000
1902 Red Seal
3x10-20 1-2200 <$1250
1902 Date Back
3x10-20 1-5000 <$350
1902 Plain Back
3x10-20 5001-8260 <$350
Total Issue $656,200
Out at close $6,700
****
3858 Bell
TEMPLE NB, TEMPLE
{{1L}}
Chartered 3/24/88
Liquidated 3/29/06
Brown Back <$VALUE
3x10-20 1-2188 <$1500
Total Issue $109,400
Out in 1910 $2,570
****
American NB of Terrell
SEE Ch 4990
Harris NB of Terrell
****
3816 Kaufman
FIRST NB OF TERRELL
{{8L 3S}}
Chartered 11/23/87
Liquidated 4/5/30
Brown Back <$VALUE
4x5 1-12200 <$1000
3x10-20 1-4100 <$1000
1902 Red Seal
4x10 1-1250 <$1250
1902 Date Back
4x5 1-14400 <$250
4x10 1-12875 <$250
1902 Plain Back
4x5 14401-56455 <$250
4x10 12876-45753 <$250
1929 Small Size
5 Type 1 1-3087 <$300
10 Type 1 1-1375 <$300
Total Issue $3,633,330
Out at close $173,655
Large out at close $28,805
****
4990 Kaufman
HARRIS NB OF TERRELL
Chartered 1895
2nd title: American NB of Terrell 1/17/03
FIRST TITLE {{2L}}
Brown Back <$VALUE
3x10-20 1-3463 <$1250
50-100 1-179 <$3500/$4000
SECOND TITLE {{6L 14S}}
Brown Back
3x10-20 1-5500 <$1000
1882 Date Back
3x10-20 1-11606 <$600
1902 Date Back
3x10-20 1-12600 <$250
1902 Plain Back
3x10-20 12601-37001 <$250
1929 Small Size
10 Type 1 1-6122 <$85
20 Type 1 1-1710 <$100
10 Type 2 1-12768 <$100
20 Type 2 1-3036 <$100
Total Issue $3,666,270
Out in 1935 $189,830
Large out 1935 $7,760
****
7392 Bowie
CITY NB OF TEXARKANA
{{3L}}
Chartered 9/04
Liquidated 12/2/16
1902 Red Seal <$VALUE
3x10-20 1-5300 <$1500
1902 Date Back
3x10-20 1-7400 <$400
1902 Plain Back
3x10-20 7401-8135 <$400
Total Issue $671,750
Out at close $98,995
****
3065 Bowie
FNB OF TEXARKANA
{{ UNREPORTED }}
Organized 10/26/83
Receivership 4/1/95
Brown Back <$VALUE
3x10-20 1-1190 <$2500
Total Issue $59,500
Out in 1916 $220
****
3998 Bowie
INTERSTATE NB OF TEXARKANA
{{ UNREPORTED }}
Chartered 3/26/89
Liquidated 1/15/96
Brown Back <$VALUE
3x10-20 1-1290 <$2500
Total Issue $64,500
Out in 1910 $680
****
3785 Bowie
TEXARKANA NB, TEXARKANA
{{15L 32S}}
Chartered 9/5/87
Brown Back <$VALUE
4x5 1-545 <$1000
50-100 1-1091 <$3500/$4000
1902 Red Seal
4x5 1-500 <$1250
3x10-20 1-1330 <$1250
1902 Date Back
4x5 1-15250 <$200
3x10-20 1-10900 <$200
1902 Plain Back
4x5 15251-42254 <$200
3x10-20 10901-29855 <$200
1929 Small Size
5 Type 1 1-23268 <$65
10 Type 1 1-11808 <$65
20 Type 1 1-2948 <$75
5 Type 2 1-9498 <$65
10 Type 2 1-5526 <$65
20 Type 2 1-1200 <$75
Total Issue $4,475,910
Out in 1935 $219,940
Large out 1935 $8,830
****
9936 Galveston
FNB OF TEXAS CITY
{{0L 1S}}
Chartered 2/11
Liquidated 6/27/32
1902 Date Back <$VALUE
3x10-20 1-720 <$1500
1902 Plain Back
3x10-20 721-2344 <$1500
1929 Small Size
10 Type 1 1-262 <$750
20 Type 1 1-49 <$750
Total Issue $138,800
Out at close $9,460
Large out at close $1,220
Ch 10040 assumed circulation
****

CONDITION affects Value. The Values shown are for notes in FINE condition.

****

10040 Galveston
TEXAS CITY NB, TEXAS CITY
{{ 2 L U + 6 S }}
Chartered 6/11
1902 Date Back <$VALUE
3x10-20 1-2540 <$750
1902 Plain Back
3x10-20 2541-6121 <$750
1929 Small Size
10 Type 1 1-854 <$300
20 Type 1 1-254 <$300
10 Type 2 1-1769 <$300
20 Type 2 1-360 <$300
Total Issue $412,660
Out in 1935 $33,250
Large out 1935 $2,060
Outstanding includes Ch 9936

****

5882 Milam
FNB OF THORNDALE
{{ 3 L 3 S }}
Chartered 6/26/01
Liquidated 2/23/33
Brown Back <$VALUE
3x10-20 1-520 <$1000
1882 Date Back
3x10-20 1-1300* <$750
1882 Value Back
3x10-20 1501-3200* <$750
* 1301-1500 not marked
1902 Plain Back
3x10-20 1-4014 <$500
1929 Small Size
10 Type 1 1-569 <$450
20 Type 1 1-159 <$450
Total Issue $439,920
Out at close $23,680
Large out at close $2,950

****

8538 Limestone
FNB OF THORNTON
{{ 4 L 5 S }}
Chartered 2/07
1902 Red Seal <$VALUE
3x10-20 1-300 <$1500
1902 Date Back
3x10-20 1-2470 <$400
1902 Plain Back
3x10-20 2471-6698 <$400
1929 Small Size
10 Type 1 1-830 <$250
20 Type 1 1-220 <$250
10 Type 2 1-900 <$250
20 Type 2 1-191 <$250
Total Issue $438,920
Out in 1935 $25,000
Large out 1935 $1,420

****

6001 Throckmorton
FNB OF THROCKMORTON
{{ 7 L 7 S }}
Chartered 10/28/01
Brown Back <$VALUE
4x5 1-430 <$1000
3x10-20 1-348 <$1000
1882 Date Back
4x5 1-2400* <$650
3x10-20 1-1920** <$650
1882 Value Back
4x5 2551-6230* <$650
3x10-20 2041-4326** <$650
* 2401-2550 not marked
** 1921-2040 not marked
1902 Plain Back
4x5 1-5745 <$300
3x10-20 1-3887 <$300
1929 Small Size
5 Type 1 1-2156 <$200
10 Type 1 1-1148 <$200
20 Type 1 1-324 <$200
5 Type 2 1-3474 <$200
10 Type 2 1-1640 <$200
20 Type 2 1-409 <$200
Total Issue $890,540
Out in 1935 $39,600
Large out 1935 $3,450

****

6177 Shelby
FNB OF TIMPSON
{{ UNREPORTED }}
Chartered 3/27/02
Liquidated 5/20/10
1902 Red Seal <$VALUE
3x10-20 1-491 <$3500
Total Issue $24,550
Out in 1910 $4,600

****

7714 Grayson
FNB OF TIOGA
{{ UNREPORTED }}
Chartered 4/05
Liquidated 5/12/11
1902 Red Seal <$VALUE
3x10-20 1-858 <$3500
1902 Date Back
3x10-20 1-388 <$2000
Total Issue $62,300
Out in 1911 $13,640

****

8001 Hood
FNB OF TOLAR
{{ UNREPORTED }}
Chartered 12/8/05
Liquidated 1/16/07
1902 Red Seal <$VALUE
3x10-20 1-137 <$3500
Total Issue $6,850
Out in 1910 $860

****

11019 Grayson
FNB OF TOM BEAN
{{ 0 L 5 S }}
Chartered 6/17
1902 Plain Back <$VALUE
4x5 1-5167 <$1500
3x10-20 1-3220 <$1500
1929 Small Size
5 Type 1 1-1084 <$600
10 Type 1 1-590 <$600
20 Type 1 1-164 <$600
5 Type 2 1-1710 <$600
10 Type 2 1-882 <$600
20 Type 2 1-292 <$600
Total Issue $375,150
Out in 1935 $21,250
Large out 1935 $880

****

8355 Reeves
FNB OF TOYAH
{{ UNREPORTED }}
Chartered 9/06
Liquidated 12/10/12
1902 Red Seal <$VALUE
3x10-20 1-288 <$3500
1902 Date Back
3x10-20 1-442 <$2000
Total Issue $36,500
Out in 1913 $4,700

****

5737 Fannin
FNB OF TRENTON
{{ 2 L 2 S }}
Chartered 3/9/01
Brown Back <$VALUE
3x10-20 1-700 <$1500
1882 Date Back
3x10-20 1-1680 <$1250
1882 Value Back
3x10-20 1681-1759 <$1250
1902 Plain Back
3x10-20 1-1287 <$750
1929 Small Size
10 Type 1 1-312 <$500
20 Type 1 1-106 <$500
10 Type 2 1-418 <$500
20 Type 2 1-69 <$500
Total Issue $224,300
Out in 1935 $8,650
Large out 1935 $820

****

13706 Trinity
FNB OF TRINITY
{{ 2U + 0 S }}
Chartered 6/33
1929 Small Size <$VALUE
5 Type 2 1-1620 <$500
10 Type 2 1-696 <$500
20 Type 2 1-264 <$500
Total Issue $20,340
Out in 1935 $14,480
Large out 1935 $420
Outstanding includes Ch 10078

****

10078 Trinity
TRINITY NB, TRINITY
{{ 0 L 2U + 2 S }}
Chartered 9/5/11
Liquidated 7/28/33
1902 Date Back <$VALUE
3x10-20 1-920 <$1000
1902 Plain Back
3x10-20 921-1887 <$1000
1929 Small Size
10 Type 1 1-217 <$400
20 Type 1 1-45 <$400
Total Issue $112,770
Out at close $7,140
Large out 1935 $420
Ch 13706 assumed circulation

****

6212 Smith
FNB OF TROUPE
{{ 2 L U + 3 S }}
Chartered 4/17/02
1902 Red Seal <$VALUE
3x10-20 1-400 <$1500
1902 Date Back
3x10-20 1-2120 <$500
1902 Plain Back (dated 1902)
3x10-20 2121-3588 <$500
1902 Plain Back (dated 1922)
4x5 1-8989 <$500
1929 Small Size
5 Type 1 1-4014 <$300
5 Type 2 1-8712 <$300
Total Issue $543,160
Out in 1935 $18,650
Large out 1935 $1,050

****

FNB of Tulia
SEE Ch 6298
Tulia NB, Tulia

****

6298 Swisher
TULIA NB, TULIA
Chartered 6/11/02
2nd title:FNB of Tulia
4/18/06
FIRST TITLE {{ 0 L }}
1902 Red Seal <$VALUE
3x10-20 1-310 <$2000
SECOND TITLE {{ 5 L 5 S }}
1902 Red Seal
3x10-20 1-1610 <$1500
1902 Date Back
3x10-20 1-3700 <$400
1902 Plain Back
3x10-20 3701-12434 <$400
1929 Small Size
10 Type 1 1-1678 <$300
20 Type 1 1-412 <$300
10 Type 2 1-718 <$300
20 Type 2 1-285 <$300
Total Issue $880,700
Out in 1935 $28,050
Large out 1935 $3,050

****

8843 Coryell
FNB OF TURNERSVILLE
{{ UNREPORTED }}
Chartered 8/22/07
Liquidated 2/26/08
1902 Red Seal <$VALUE
3x10-20 1-125 <$3500
Total Issue $6,250
Out in 1910 $1,200

****

5343 Smith
CITIZENS NB OF TYLER
{{ 13 L 28 S }}
Chartered 5/9/00
Brown Back <$VALUE
3x10-20 1-2200 <$850
50-100 1-1060 <$3500/$4000
1882 Date Back
3x10-20 1-12300 <$450
50-100 1-300 <$3500/$4000
1882 Value Back
3x10-20 12301-15965 <$500
1902 Plain Back
4x5 1-28406 <$175
3x10-20 1-18128 <$175
1929 Small Size
5 Type 1 1-11762 <$65
10 Type 1 1-6310 <$65
20 Type 1 1-1536 <$75
5 Type 2 1-23628 <$65
10 Type 2 1-12792 <$65
20 Type 2 1-3168 <$75
Total Issue $3,811,970
Out in 1935 $241,400
Large out 1935 $9,585

****

4353 Smith
CITY NB OF TYLER
{{ 1 L }}
Organized 7/2/90
Receivership 10/17/96
Brown Back <$VALUE
3x10-20 1-992 <$1500
Total Issue $49,600
Out in 1916 $235

****

7515 Smith
FARMERS & MERCHANTS NB OF TYLER
{{ UNREPORTED }}
Chartered 12/16/04
Liquidated 11/30/07
1902 Red Seal <$VALUE
3x10-20 1-3326 <$2000
Total Issue $116,300
Out in 1910 $19,160

****

3651 Smith
FNB OF TYLER
{{ 1 L }}
Chartered 3/21/87
Receivership 12/17/96
Brown Back <$VALUE
4x5 1-7546 <$1250
Total Issue $150,920
Out in 1916 $845

****

6234 Smith
JESTER NB OF TYLER
{{ 1 L }}
Chartered 5/1/02
Liquidated 5/23/11
1902 Red Seal <$VALUE
3x10-20 1-3000 <$1500
1902 Date Back
3x10-20 1-3514 <$850
Total Issue $325,700
Out in 1911 $62,850

****

13110 Smith
PEOPLES NB OF TYLER
{{ U + 1 L 5 S }}
Chartered 7/30/27
1902 Plain Back <$VALUE
4x5 1-1269 <$600
3x10-20 1-1926 <$600
1929 Small Size
5 Type 1 1-4598 <$175
10 Type 1 1-2580 <$175
20 Type 1 1-706 <$175
5 Type 2 1-20502 <$175
10 Type 2 1-11485 <$175
20 Type 2 1-3336 <$175
Total Issue $783,220
Out in 1935 $154,150
Large out 1935 $735

****

4747 Smith
TYLER NB, TYLER
{{ UNREPORTED }}
Chartered 6/1/92
Liquidated 12/31/98
Brown Back <$VALUE
50-100 1-352 <$5000
Total Issue $52,800
Out in 1910 $1,300

****

6831 Uvalde
COMMERCIAL NB OF UVALDE
{{ 5 L 8 S }}
Chartered 6/03
Liquidated 11/16/33
1902 Red Seal <$VALUE
3x10-20 1-2925 <$1250
1902 Date Back
3x10-20 1-5700 <$350
1902 Plain Back
3x10-20 5701-14978 <$350
1929 Small Size
10 Type 1 1-1669 <$175
20 Type 1 1-468 <$200
Total Issue $1,051,450
Out at close $51,110
Large out at close $4,370

****

4517 Uvalde
FNB OF UVALDE
{{ UNREPORTED }}
Chartered 2/10/91
Liquidated 7/31/96
Brown Back <$VALUE
3x10-20 1-514 <$2500
Total Issue $25,700
Out in 1910 $310

****

5175 Uvalde
UVALDE NB, UVALDE
{{ 1 L }}
Chartered 2/4/99
Liquidated 1/17/19
Brown Back <$VALUE
3x10-20 1-2450 <$1250
1882 Date Back
3x10-20 1-3026 <$1000
Total Issue $273,800
Out at close $31,250

****

9148 Bosque
FNB OF VALLEY MILLS
{{ 1 L }}
Chartered 5/08
Liquidated 4/2/29
1902 Date Back <$VALUE
3x10-20 1-1225 <$2000
1902 Plain Back
3x10-20 1226-2234 <$2000
Total Issue $111,700
Out at close $7,500

****

7731 Cooke
FNB OF VALLEY VIEW
{{ 2 L 5 S }}
Chartered 5/05
1902 Red Seal <$VALUE
3x10-20 1-360 <$2500
1902 Date Back
3x10-20 1-860 <$1500
1902 Plain Back
3x10-20 861-1642 <$1500
1929 Small Size
10 Type 1 1-580 <$500
20 Type 1 1-170 <$500
10 Type 2 1-1240 <$500
20 Type 2 1-293 <$500
Total Issue $173,560
Out in 1935 $24,300
Large out 1935 $850

****

7016 Grayson
FARMERS NB OF VAN ALSTYNE
{{ UNREPORTED }}
Chartered 10/22/03
Liquidated 7/30/07
1902 Red Seal <$VALUE
4x5 1-1680 <$2500
3x10-20 1-1228 <$2500
Total Issue $95,000
Out in 1910 $6,660

****

4289 Grayson
FNB OF VAN ALSTYNE
{{ 2 L 4 S }}
Chartered 1890
Brown Back <$VALUE
3x10-20 1-2130 <$1250
1882 Date Back
3x10-20 1-211 <$1000
1902 Date Back
3x10-20 1-3000 <$500
1902 Plain Back
3x10-20 3001-4688 <$500
1929 Small Size
10 Type 1 1-580 <$300
20 Type 1 1-150 <$300
10 Type 2 1-1127 <$300
20 Type 2 1-265 <$300
Total Issue $420,820
Out in 1935 $18,150
Large out 1935 $1,340

****

4662 Brazoria
VELASCO NB, VELASCO
{{ UNREPORTED }}
Chartered 12/8/91
Liquidated 3/3/04
Brown Back <$VALUE
3x10-20 1-894 <$3000
Total Issue $44,700
Out in 1910 $1,390

****

7798 Johnson
FARMERS & MERCHANTS NB OF VENUS
{{ UNREPORTED }}
Chartered 5/30/05
Liquidated 9/15/34
1902 Red Seal <$VALUE
3x10-20 1-300 <$3500
1902 Date Back
3x10-20 1-1160 <$2000
1902 Plain Back
3x10-20 1161-1359 <$2000
Total Issue $82,950
Out at close $340
Outstanding includes Ch 5549

****

5549 Johnson
FNB OF VENUS
{{ UNREPORTED }}
Chartered 8/23/00
Closed 6/16/21
Brown Back <$VALUE
3x10-20 1-500 <$3000
1882 Date Back
3x10-20 1-1000* <$2500
* 701-1000 not marked
Total Issue $75,000
Out at close $2,125

****

4033 Wilbarger
FNB OF VERNON
{{ UNREPORTED }}
Chartered 5/13/89
Receivership 8/12/93
Brown Back <$VALUE
4x5 1-2153 <$2500
Total Issue $43,060
Out in 1916 $305

****

7010 Wilbarger
HERRING NB OF VERNON
{{ 3 L 2U + 13 S }}
Chartered 10/03
1902 Red Seal <$VALUE
3x10-20 1-1100 <$1250
1902 Date Back
4x5 1-4875 <$400
3x10-20 1-4100 <$400
1902 Plain Back
4x5 4876-19015 <$400
3x10-20 4101-12766 <$400
1929 Small Size
5 Type 1 1-3102 <$100
10 Type 1 1-1502 <$100
20 Type 1 1-440 <$100
5 Type 2 1-12158 <$125
10 Type 2 1-6114 <$125
20 Type 2 1-1692 <$125
Total Issue $1,465,350
Out in 1935 $98,600
Large out 1935 $3,550

****

4130 Wilbarger
STATE NB OF VERNON
{{ UNREPORTED }}
Chartered 9/27/89
Receivership 9/24/94
Brown Back <$VALUE
4x5 1-2197 <$2000
Total Issue $43,940
Out in 1916 $245

****

5203 Wilbarger
WAGGONER NB OF VERNON
{{ 5 L 9 S }}
Chartered 7/3/99
Brown Back <$VALUE
4x5 1-2450 <$1000
3x10-20 1-3070 <$1000
1882 Date Back
4x5 1-4150 <$850
3x10-20 1-3080 <$850
1882 Value Back
4x5 4151-5450 <$850
3x10-20 3081-3780 <$850
1902 Plain Back
3x10-20 1-7290 <$400
1929 Small Size
10 Type 1 1-2466 <$150
20 Type 1 1-636 <$150
10 Type 2 1-5123 <$150
20 Type 2 1-1692 <$150
Total Issue $1,174,350
Out in 1935 $97,645
Large out 1935 $2,365

****

4184 Victoria
FNB OF VICTORIA
{{ 8 L }}
Chartered 12/20/89
Liquidated 4/15/13
Brown Back <$VALUE
4x5 1-2775 <$1000
3x10-20 1-5560 <$1000
1882 Date Back
4x5 1-1680 <$600
3x10-20 1-179 <$600
1902 Date Back
4x5 1-3680 <$300
3x10-20 1-2269 <$300
Total Issue $563,100
Out in 1913 $77,695

****

CONDITION affects Value. The Values shown are for notes in FINE condition.

****
10360 Victoria
VICTORIA NB, VICTORIA
{{ 23 L 40 S }}
Chartered 4/13
1902 Date Back <$VALUE
3x10-20 1-15000* <$175
3x50-100 1-1800 <$450/$500
1902 Plain Back
4x5 1-61499 <$175
3x10-20 17501-66583* <$175
* 15001-17500 not marked
1929 Small Size
5 Type 1 1-19996 <$60
10 Type 1 1-10896 <$60
20 Type 1 1-2842 <$70
5 Type 2 1-32866 <$60
10 Type 2 1-15194 <$65
20 Type 2 1-6576 <$75
Total Issue $7,051,480
Out in 1935 $484,600
Large out 1935 $27,975
****
3901 McLennan
AMERICAN NB OF WACO
{{ UNREPORTED }}
Chartered 6/21/88
Liquidated 6/24/90
Brown Back <$VALUE
50-100 1-346 <$5000
Total Issue $51,900
Out in 1910 $500
****
Central NB of Waco
SEE Ch 10220
Central Texas Exchange NB of Waco
****
10220 McLennan
CENTRAL TEXAS EXCHANGE NB OF WACO
Chartered 7/12
Closed 12/31/24
2nd title:Central NB of Waco 1/31/20
FIRST TITLE {{ 5 L }}
1902 Date Back <$VALUE
3x10-20 1-11000 <$225
3x50-100 1-3000 <$400/$500
1902 Plain Back
3x10-20 11001-22700 <$225
SECOND TITLE {{ 8 L }}
1902 Plain Back
3x10-20 1-21245 <$200
3x50-100 1-1620 <$400/$500
Total Issue $3,352,250
Out at close $500,000
Ch 2189 assumed circulation
****
9828 McLennan
CENTRAL TEXAS NB OF WACO
{{ 1 L }}
Chartered 8/10
Liquidated 7/3/12
1902 Date Back <$VALUE
4x5 1-8950 <$600
3x10-20 1-7130 <$600
Total Issue $535,500
Out in 1912 $211,960
****
3135 McLennan
CITIZENS NB OF WACO
{{ 13 L 30 S }}
Chartered 1884
Brown Back <$VALUE
3x10-20 1-5702 <$750
1902 Red Seal
50-100 1-1374 <$7500
1902 Date Back
4x5 1-10250 <$175
3x10-20 1-5600 <$175
50-100 1-1000 <$400/$500
3x50-100 1-1260 <$400/$500
1902 Plain Back
4x5 10251-46164 <$175
3x10-20 5601-26831 <$175
3x50-100 1261-1663 <$400/$500
1929 Small Size
5 Type 1 1-6600 <$40
10 Type 1 1-3066 <$40
20 Type 1 1-878 <$50
50 Type 1 1-360 <$125
100 Type 1 1-118 <$175
5 Type 2 1-5270 <$50
10 Type 2 1-3901 <$50
20 Type 2 1-825 <$60
Total Issue $4,069,760
Out in 1935 $219,840
Large out 1935 $16,070
****
8818 McLennan
EXCHANGE NB OF WACO
{{ 2 L }}
Chartered 8/07
Liquidated 7/3/12
1902 Red Seal <$VALUE
4x5 1-1125 <$1250
3x10-20 1-1050 <$1250
1902 Date Back
4x5 1-8785 <$600
3x10-20 1-6500 <$600
Total Issue $575,700
Out in 1912 $154,890
****
4349 McLennan
FARMERS & MERCHANTS NB OF WACO
{{ UNREPORTED }}
Chartered 6/25/90
Liquidated 7/1/98
Brown Back <$VALUE
3x10-20 1-1283 <$1500
Total Issue $64,150
Out in 1910 $605
****
FNB of Waco
SEE Ch 2189
Waco NB, Waco
****
11140 McLennan
LIBERTY NB OF WACO
{{ 10 L 21 S }}
Chartered 2/18
Receivership 6/3/32
1902 Plain Back <$VALUE
3x10-20 1-57019 <$250
1929 Small Size
10 Type 1 1-6387 <$75
20 Type 1 1-1937 <$85
Total Issue $3,466,610
Out at close $229,850
Large out at close $25,070
****
6572 McLennan
N CITY B OF WACO
{{ 10 L 3U + 14 S }}
Chartered 1/03
1902 Red Seal <$VALUE
3x10-20 1-5500 <$1000
1902 Date Back
3x10-20 1-7600 <$200
1902 Plain Back
3x10 20 7601-25331 <$200
1929 Small Size
10 Type 1 1-3234 <$85
20 Type 1 1-848 <$100
5 Type 2 1-324 <$100
10 Type 2 1-4479 <$100
20 Type 2 1-1478 <$100
Total Issue $1,913,320
Out in 1935 $97,550
Large out 1935 $6,605
****
4309 McLennan
PROVIDENT NB OF WACO
{{ UNREPORTED }}
Organized 3/31/90
Receivership 3/26/27
Brown Back <$VALUE
50-100 1-1754 <$4000
1882 Date Back
50-100 1-125 <$4000
1902 Date Back
50-100 1-1330 <$850/$1000
3x50-100 1-540 <$850/$1000
1902 Plain Back
3x50-100 541-592<$850/$1000
Total Issue $629,350
Out at close $50,000
****
2189 McLennan
WACO NB, WACO
Chartered 9/24/74
2nd title:FNB of Waco 2/89
FIRST TITLE {{ 1 L }}
Original Series <$VALUE
3x10-20 1-1800<$5000/$6000
Series 1875
3x10-20 1-238 <$5000/$6000
SECOND TITLE {{ 29 L 44 S }}
Series 1875
3x10-20 1-1562<$5000/$6000
Brown Back
50-100 1-1310 <$3500/$4000
1882 Date Back
3x10-20 1-23949 <$350
50-100 1-1500 <$3500/$4000
3x50-100 1-33 <$3500/$4000
1902 Date Back
3x50-100 1-9000 <$350/$400
1902 Plain Back
4x5 1-49755 <$100
3x10-20 1-36581 <$100
1929 Small Size
5 Type 1 1-43882 <$25
10 Type 1 1-19754 <$30
20 Type 1 1-5528 <$40
5 Type 2 1-30746 <$25
10 Type 2 1-13435 <$35
20 Type 2 1-3250 <$45
Total Issue $10,399,490
Out in 1935 $461,695
Large out 1935 $58,190
Outstanding includes Ch 10220
****
8130 Bosque
FNB OF WALNUT SPRINGS
{{ UNREPORTED }}
Chartered 3/06
Liquidated 12/30/09
1902 Red Seal <$VALUE
3x10-20 1-1100 <$3500
1902 Date Back
3x10-20 1-401 <$2500
Total Issue $75,050
Out in 1910 $15,680
****
13516 Ellis
CITIZENS NB IN WAXAHACHIE
{{ 5U + 18 S }}
Chartered 12/30
1929 Small Size <$VALUE
5 Type 1 1-3080 <$60
10 Type 1 1-1402 <$60
20 Type 1 1-442 <$60
5 Type 2 1-13656 <$70
10 Type 2 1-7404 <$70
20 Type 2 1-2028 <$70
Total Issue $412,440
Out in 1935 $138,190
****
3212 Ellis
CITIZENS NB OF WAXAHACHIE
{{ 14 L 7 S }}
Chartered 1884
Liquidated 3/16/31
Brown Back <$VALUE
3x10-20 1-2830 <$850
1902 Red Seal
3x10-20 1-3000 <$1000
1902 Date Back
3x10-20 1-13400 <$200
1902 Plain Back
3x10-20 13401-27609 <$200
1929 Small Size
10 Type 1 1-1448 <$200
20 Type 1 1-387 <$200
Total Issue $1,805,270
Out at close $84,030
Large out at close $12,970
****
2974 Ellis
FNB OF WAXAHACHIE
{{ UNREPORTED }}
Chartered 6/12/83
Liquidated 8/3/05
Brown Back <$VALUE
3x10-20 1-2591 <$1500
1902 Red Seal
3x10-20 1-415 <$2000
Total Issue $150,300
Out in 1910 $3,070
****
4379 Ellis
WAXAHACHIE NB, WAXAHACHIE
{{ 14 L }}
Chartered 1890
Liquidated 3/7/27
Brown Back <$VALUE
4x5 1-1000 <$1000
50-100 1-1387 <$3500/$4000
1882 Date Bak
4x5 1-2495 <$650
50-10 1-403 <$3500/$4000
1902 Date Back
4x5 1-11050 <$200
4x10 1-11050 <$200
1902 Plain Back
4x5 11051-59318 <$200
4x10 11051-45800 <$200
Total Issue $3,356,760
Out at close $177,400
****
2723 Parker
CITIZENS NB OF WEATHERFORD
{{ 9 L 16 S }}
Chartered 6/10/82
Series 1875 <$VALUE
3x10-20 1-3470<$5000/$6000
1902 Red Seal
3x10-20 1-4240 <$1250
1902 Date Back
3x10-20 1-7600 <$250
1902 Plain Back
3x10-20 7601-25300 <$250
1929 Small Size
10 Type 1 1-3200 <$85
20 Type 1 1-802 <$100
10 Type 2 1-5998 <$100
20 Type 2 1-1571 <$100
Total Issue $2,030,140
Out in 1935 $94,400
Large out 1935 $6,090
****
2477 Parker
FNB OF WEATHERFORD
{{ 5 L 12 S }}
Chartered 5/15/80
Series 1875 <$VALUE
3x10-20 1-2408<$5000/$6000
Brown Back
3x10-20 1-4040 <$1000
1882 Date Back
3x10-20 1-8800 <$650
1882 Value Back
3x10-20 8801-12463 <$750
1902 Plain Back
3x10-20 1-13794 <$350
1929 Small Size
10 Type 1 1-3186 <$125
20 Type 1 1-856 <$150
5 Type 2 1-324 <$150
10 Type 2 1-3699 <$150
20 Type 2 1-1188 <$150
Total Issue $1,301,800
Out in 1935 $96,000
Large out 1935 $7,375
****
3975 Parker
MERCHANTS & FARMERS NB OF WEATHERFORD
{{ 1 L }}
Chartered 2/7/89
Liquidated 12/31/08
Brown Back <$VALUE
3x10-20 1-10034 <$1250
Total Issue $501,700
Out in 1910 $33,960
****
9805 Collingsworth
CITY NB OF WELLINGTON
{{ UNREPORTED }}
Chartered 7/10
Liquidated 1/25/16
1902 Date Back <$VALUE
3x10-20 1-3790 <$1000
1902 Plain Back
3x10-20 3791-3795 <$1000
Total Issue $189,750
Out in 1916 $31,700
****
13249 Collingsworth
FNB IN WELLINGTON
{{ 3U + 8 S }}
Chartered 10/28
1929 Small Size <$VALUE
5 Type 1 1-540 <$300
10 Type 1 1-272 <$300
20 Type 1 1-64 <$300
5 Type 2 1-2334 <$300
10 Type 2 1-1174 <$300
20 Type 2 1-310 <$300
Total Issue $69,810
Out in 1935 $18,900
****
8102 Collingsworth
FNB OF WELLINGTON
{{ UNREPORTED }}
Chartered 2/06
Liquidated 12/26/28
1902 Red Seal <$VALUE
4x5 1-252 <$2500
3x10-20 1-183 <$2500
1902 Date Back
4x5 1-850 <$1250
3x10-20 1-680 <$1250
1902 Plain Back
4x5 851-1233 <$1250
3x10-20 681-935 <$1250
Total Issue $85,600
Out at close $655
****
12641 Hidalgo
FNB OF WESLACO
{{ 2 L 3 S }}
Organized 10/27/24
1902 Plain Back <$VALUE
4x5 1-6167 <$600
1929 Small Size
5 Type 1 1-3480 <$350
5 Type 2 1-6680 <$350
Total Issue $261,140
Out in 1935 $18,150
Large out 1935 $720
****
5543 McLennan
FNB OF WEST
{{ UNREPORTED }}
Chartered 8/17/00
Receivership 3/27/06
Brown Back <$VALUE
3x10-20 1-369 <$2500
Total Issue $18,450
Out in 1916 $110
****
8239 McLennan
NB OF WEST
{{ 4 L 8 S }}
Organized 5/18/06
Liquidated 10/9/34
1902 Red Seal <$VALUE
3x10-20 1-687 <$1500
1902 Date Back
3x10-20 1-3560 <$400
1902 Plain Back
3x10-20 3561-12540 <$400
1929 Small Size
10 Type 1 1-1476 <$250
20 Type 1 1-444 <$275
10 Type 2 1-213 <$300
20 Type 2 1-70 <$300
Total Issue $806,720
Out at close $50,000
Large out at close $2,900
****
13935 McLennan
WEST NB, WEST
{{ 2U + 3 S }}
Chartered 1/34
1929 Small Size <$VALUE
5 Type 2 1-6852 <$350
10 Type 2 1-2280 <$350
20 Type 2 1-756 <$350
Total Issue $72,180
Out in 1935 $46,680
****
4903 Wharton
FNB OF WHARTON
{{ UNREPORTED }}
Chartered 4/20/93
Liquidated 10/14/93
Brown Back <$VALUE
50-100 1-75 <$5000
Total Issue $11,250
Out in 1910 $250
****
6313 Wharton
WHARTON NB, WHARTON
{{ UNREPORTED }}
Chartered 6/21/02
Liquidated 4/30/18
1902 Red Seal <$VALUE
3x10-20 1-520 <$3500
1902 Date Back
3x10-20 1-488 <$2000
Total Issue $50,400
Out in 1915 $6,300
****
10634 Grayson
CITY NB OF WHITESBORO
Chartered 10/14
2nd title:Whitesboro NB 1/25/30
FIRST TITLE {{ 3 L 2 S }}
1902 Date Back <$VALUE
3x10-20 1-1000 <$400
1902 Plain Back
3x10-20 1001-9801 <$400
1929 Small Size
10 Type 1 1-616 <$300
20 Type 1 1-210 <$300
SECOND TITLE {{ 6 S }}
1929 Small Size
10 Type 1 1-942 <$275
20 Type 1 1-224 <$275
10 Type 2 1-1298 <$300
20 Type 2 1-259 <$300
Total Issue $653,770
Out in 1935 $26,630
Large out 1935 $2,330
****
5847 Grayson
FNB OF WHITESBORO
{{ 3 L 1 S }}
Chartered 5/31/01
Liquidated 1/30/30
Brown Back <$VALUE
3x10-20 1-1750 <$1000
1882 Date Back
3x10-20 1-2450 <$850
1882 Value Back
3x10-20 2451-4050 <$850
1902 Plain Back
3x10-20 1-3519 <$450
1929 Small Size
10 Type 1 1-222 <$500
20 Type 2 1-32 <$500
Total Issue $483,110
Out at close $30,000
Large out at close $12,840
****
Whitesboro NB, Whitesboro
SEE Ch 10634
City NB of Whitesboro
****
4692 Grayson
FNB OF WHITEWRIGHT
{{ 8 L 14 S }}
Chartered 1892
Brown Back <$VALUE
3x10-20 1-5740 <$850
1882 Date Back
3x10-20 1-3011 <$500
1902 Date Back
3x10-20 1-5800 <$225
1902 Plain Back
3x10-20 5801-23640 <$225
1929 Small Size
10 Type 1 1-3424 <$125
20 Type 1 1-892 <$125
10 Type 2 1-4223 <$125
20 Type 2 1-1121 <$125
Total Issue $1,996,680
Out in 1935 $79,050
Large out 1935 $4,540
****
6915 Grayson
PLANTERS NB OF WHITEWRIGHT
{{ 7 L 9 S }}
Chartered 8/03
Liquidated 2/10/32
1902 Red Seal <$VALUE
3x10-20 1-5500 <$1250
1902 Date Back
3x10-20 1-7800 <$250
1902 Plain Back
3x10-20 7801-25492 <$250
1929 Small Size
10 Type 1 1-2141 <$150
20 Type 1 1-531 <$175
Total Issue $1,741,780
Out at close $95,200
Large out at close $10,470
****
7915 Hill
CITIZENS NB OF WHITNEY
{{ 2 L }}
Chartered 9/05
Liquidated 2/11/27
1902 Red Seal <$VALUE
3x10-20 1-400 <$1500
1902 Date Back
3x10-20 1-4240 <$500
1902 Plain Back
3x10-20 4241-9624 <$500
Total Issue $501,200
Out at close $40,000
Ch 7875 assumed circulation
****
13649 Hill
FNB IN WHITNEY
{{ 2 S }}
Chartered 12/32
1929 Small Size <$VALUE
5 Type 1 1-148 <$500
10 Type 1 1-72 <$500
20 Type 1 1-32 <$500
5 Type 2 1-960 <$500
10 Type 2 1-576 <$500
20 Type 2 1-132 <$500
Total Issue $25,800
Out in 1935 $46,340
Large out 1935 $1,960
Outstanding includes Ch 7875 and Ch 7915
****

<$VALUEs are for notes in FINE condition. Value changes by approximately 25% for a change of one full grade.

****
7875 Hill
FNB OF WHITNEY
{{ 1 L 4 S }}
Chartered 8/05
Liquidated 1/10/33
1902 Red Seal <$VALUE
4x5 1-300 <$2000
3x10-20 1-220 <$2000
1902 Date Back
4x5 1-1200* <$750
3x10-20 1-960** <$750
1902 Plain Back
4x5 1351-4935* <$750
3x10-20 1081-3416** <$750
* 1201-1350 not marked
** 961-1080 not marked
1929 Small Size
5 Type 1 1-1860 <$400
10 Type 1 1-958 <$400
20 Type 1 1-259 <$400
Total Issue $430,860
Out at close $44,730
Large out 1935 $1,960
Ch 13649 assumed circulation
****
City NB of Commerce of Wichita Falls
SEE Ch 4248
City NB of Wichita Falls
****
4248 Wichita
CITY NB OF WICHITA FALLS
Chartered 1890
Liquidated 7/1/33
2nd title:City NB of Commerce of Wichita Falls 5/3/20
3rd title:City NB of Wichita Falls 1/17/23
FIRST TITLE {{ 6 L }}
Brown Back <$VALUE
3x10-20 1-5565 <$850
1882 Date Back
3x10-20 1-1246 <$500
1902 Date Back
4x5 1-2500 <$175
3x10-20 1-19200 <$175
1902 Plain Back
4x5 2501-26250 <$175
3x10-20 19201-31400 <$175
SECOND TITLE {{ 8 L }}
1902 Plain Back
4x5 1-67500 <$150
3x10-20 1-37500 <$150
THIRD TITLE {{ 22 L 50+ S }}
1902 Plain Back
4x5 1-91315 <$100
3x10-20 1-65171 <$100
3x50-100 1-1760 <$350/$400
1929 Small Size
5 Type 1 1-22520 <$20
10 Type 1 1-11539 <$25
20 Type 1 1-3828 <$35
50 Type 1 1-1310 <$100
100 Type 1 1-424 <$165
Total Issue $13,660,100
Out in 1935 $446,510
Large out 1935 $41,400
Outstanding includes Ch 10547
Ch 13665 assumed circulation
****
FNB of Wichita Falls
SEE Ch 3200
Panhandle NB of Wichita Falls
****
10547 Wichita
NB OF COMMERCE OF WICHITA FALLS
{{ 1 L }}
Chartered 5/14
Closed 5/3/20
1902 Date Back <$VALUE
3x10-20 1-2900 <$500
1902 Plain Back
3x10-20 2901-13483 <$500
Total Issue $674,150
Out at close $300,000
Ch 4248 assumed circulation
****
3200 Wichita
PANHANDLE NB OF WICHITA FALLS
Chartered 1884
2nd title:FNB of Wichita Falls 10/27/03
FIRST TITLE {{ 1 L }}
Brown Back <$VALUE
3x10-20 1-2869 <$3000
50-100 1-983 <$6000
SECOND TITLE {{ 16 L 50+ S }}
Brown Back
50-100 1-90 <$3500/$4000
1902 Red Seal
3x10-20 1-2750 <$1000
1902 Date Back
4x5 1-5500 <$100
3x10-20 1-9400 <$100
1902 Plain Back
4x5 5501-48500 <$100
3x10-20 9401-88031 <$100
1929 Small Size
10 Type 1 1-22820 <$25
20 Type 1 1-6658 <$35
10 Type 2 1-53254 <$25
20 Type 2 1-17900 <$35
Total Issue $8,872,150
Out in 1935 $888,700
Large out 1935 $19,410
****
11762 Wichita
SECURITY NB OF WICHITA FALLS
{{ 8 L 16 S }}
Chartered 6/12/20
Receivership 11/14/33
1902 Plain Back <$VALUE
3x10-20 1-26488 <$200
1929 Small Size
10 Type 1 1-3186 <$85
20 Type 1 1-1028 <$85
Total Issue $1,638,920
Out at close $169,290
Large out at close $15,180
****
13676 Wichita
WICHITA NB OF WICHITA FALLS
{{ 18 S }}
Chartered 4/33
1929 Small Size <$VALUE
5 Type 2 1-22728 <$60
10 Type 2 1-10663 <$60
20 Type 2 1-4074 <$70
50 Type 2 1-699 <$350
100 Type 2 1-384 <$400
Total Issue $375,100
Out in 1935 $167,500
****
5018 Van Zandt
FNB OF WILLS POINT
{{ 2 L 2 S }}
Chartered 1895
Brown Back <$VALUE
4x5 1-1725 <$1750
3x10-20 1-650 <$1750
1882 Date Back
4x5 1-897 <$1500
3x10-20 1-689 <$1500
1902 Plain Back
3x10-20 1-2318 <$1250
1929 Small Size
10 Type 1 1-390 <$600
20 Type 1 1-128 <$600
10 Type 2 1-96 <$600
20 Type 2 1-45 <$600
Total Issue $275,910
Out in 1935 $12,255
Large out 1935 $1,895
Outstanding includes Ch 6071
****
6071 Van Zandt
VAN ZANDT COUNTY NB OF WILLS POINT
{{ 1 L }}
Chartered 12/28/01
Closed 4/7/31
Brown Back <$VALUE
3x10-20 1-2100 <$2000
1882 Date Back
3x10-20 1-3000 <$1750
1882 Value Back
3x10-20 3201-3374* <$1750
* 3001-3200 not marked
Total Issue $273,700
Out at close $1,270
Ch 5018 assumed circulation
****
10488 Titus
FNB OF WINFIELD
{{ 1 L }}
Chartered 2/14
Liquidated 5/2/24
1902 Date Back <$VALUE
3x10-20 1-500* <$750
1902 Plain Back
3x10-20 701-7032* <$750
* 501-700 not marked
Total Issue $351,600
Out at close $46,500
****
6168 Wood
FARMERS NB OF WINNSBORO
{{ 1 L }}
Chartered 3/21/02
Liquidated 12/31/06
1902 Red Seal <$VALUE
3x10-20 1-2090 <$2500
Total Issue $104,500
Out in 1910 $6,920
****
5674 Wood
FNB OF WINNSBORO
{{ 6 L 8 S }}
Chartered 1/10/01
Brown Back <$VALUE
3x10-20 1-4250 <$1000
1882 Date Back
3x10-20 1-8000 <$600
1882 Value Back
3x10-20 8001-9471 <$650
1902 Plain Back
3x10-20 1-5764 <$350
1929 Small Size
10 Type 1 1-1386 <$200
20 Type 1 1-414 <$225
10 Type 2 1-3088 <$250
20 Type 2 1-637 <$250
Total Issue $1,150,710
Out in 1935 $48,650
Large out 1935 $3,930
****
8178 Hunt
CITIZENS NB OF WOLFE CITY
{{ 2 L }}
Chartered 4/06
Liquidated 11/1/13
1902 Red Seal <$VALUE
3x10-20 1-400 <$1500
1902 Date Back
3x10-20 1-2130 <$850
Total Issue $126,500
Out in 1914 $18,600
****
13199 Hunt
WOLFE CITY NB IN WOLFE CITY
{{ 2U + 14 S }}
Chartered 4/28
1929 Small Size <$VALUE
5 Type 1 1-484 <$300
10 Type 1 1-402 <$300
20 Type 1 1-94 <$300
5 Type 2 1-2340 <$300
10 Type 2 1-1369 <$300
20 Type 2 1-396 <$300
Total Issue $83,230
Out in 1935 $25,000
****
3984 Hunt
WOLFE CITY NB, WOLFE CITY
{{ 4 L }}
Chartered 3/8/89
Liquidated 6/22/28
Brown Back <$VALUE
3x10-20 1-4745 <$1000
1902 Date Back
3x10-20 1-7300 <$400
1902 Plain Back
3x10-20 7301-13022 <$400
Total Issue $888,350
Out at close $43,350
****
6686 Freestone
FNB OF WORTHAM
{{ 2 L 8 S }}
Chartered 3/03
1902 Red Seal <$VALUE
3x10-20 1-500 <$2000
1902 Date Back
3x10-20 1-1300 <$850
1902 Plain Back
3x10-20 1301-3723 <$850
1929 Small Size
10 Type 1 1-2290 <$300
20 Type 1 1-590 <$300
5 Type 2 1-1112 <$300
10 Type 2 1-3073 <$300
20 Type 2 1-840 <$300
Total Issue $472,440
Out in 1935 $58,400
Large out 1935 $920
****
5483 Collin
FNB OF WYLIE
{{ UNREPORTED }}
Chartered 7/2/00
Liquidated 5/31/22
Brown Back <$VALUE
3x10-20 1-940 <$2000
1882 Date Back
3x10-20 1-1560 <$2000
1882 Value Back
3x10-20 1561-1787 <$2000
1902 Plain Back
3x10-20 1-320 <$1500
Total Issue $152,350
Out at close $6,500
****
4363 Lavaca
FNB OF YOAKUM
{{ UNREPORTED }}
Chartered 7/10/90
Liquidated 5/18/07
Brown Back <$VALUE
3x10-20 1-1270 <$2500
Total Issue $63,500
Out in 1910 $2,490
****
8694 Lavaca
YOAKUM NB, YOAKUM
{{ 4 L U + 11 S }}
Chartered 5/07
1902 Red Seal <$VALUE
3x10-20 1-1625 <$1500
1902 Date Back
3x10-20 1-4500 <$400
1902 Plain Back
3x10-20 4501-12173 <$400
1929 Small Size
10 Type 1 1-2144 <$250
20 Type 1 1-560 <$250
10 Type 2 1-3467 <$250
20 Type 2 1-776 <$250
Total Issue $935,930
Out in 1935 $79,250
Large out 1935 $3,600
****
6987 De Witt
FNB OF YORKTOWN
{{ 3 L 6 S }}
Chartered 10/03
1902 Red Seal <$VALUE
3x10-20 1-670 <$1500
1902 Date Back
3x10-20 1-1300* <$600
1902 Plain Back
3x10-20 1801-2633* <$600
* 1301-1800 not marked
1929 Small Size
10 Type 1 1-378 <$350
20 Type 1 1-118 <$350
10 Type 2 1-3823 <$350
20 Type 2 1-1170 <$350
Total Issue $263,620
Out in 1935 $49,200
Large out 1935 $730
****

UTAH

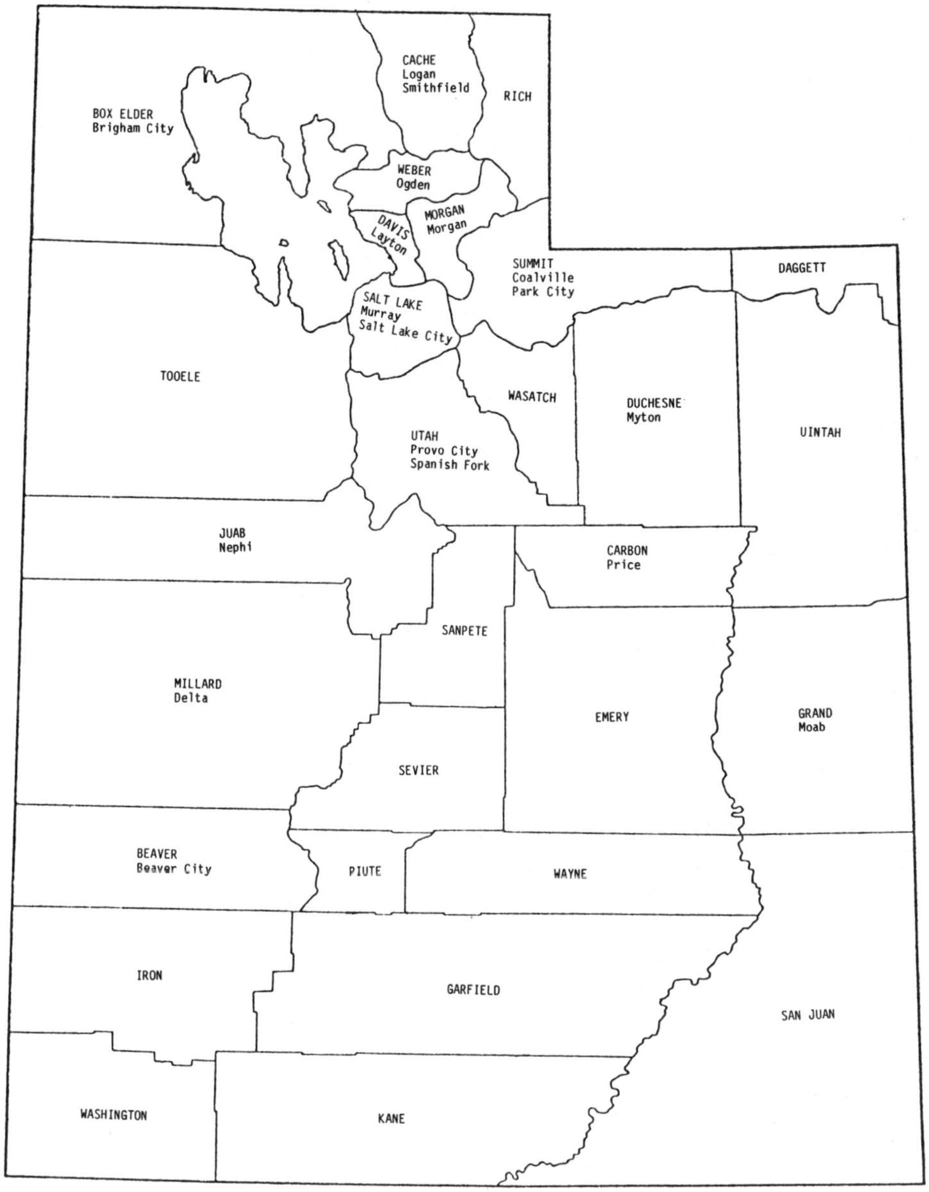

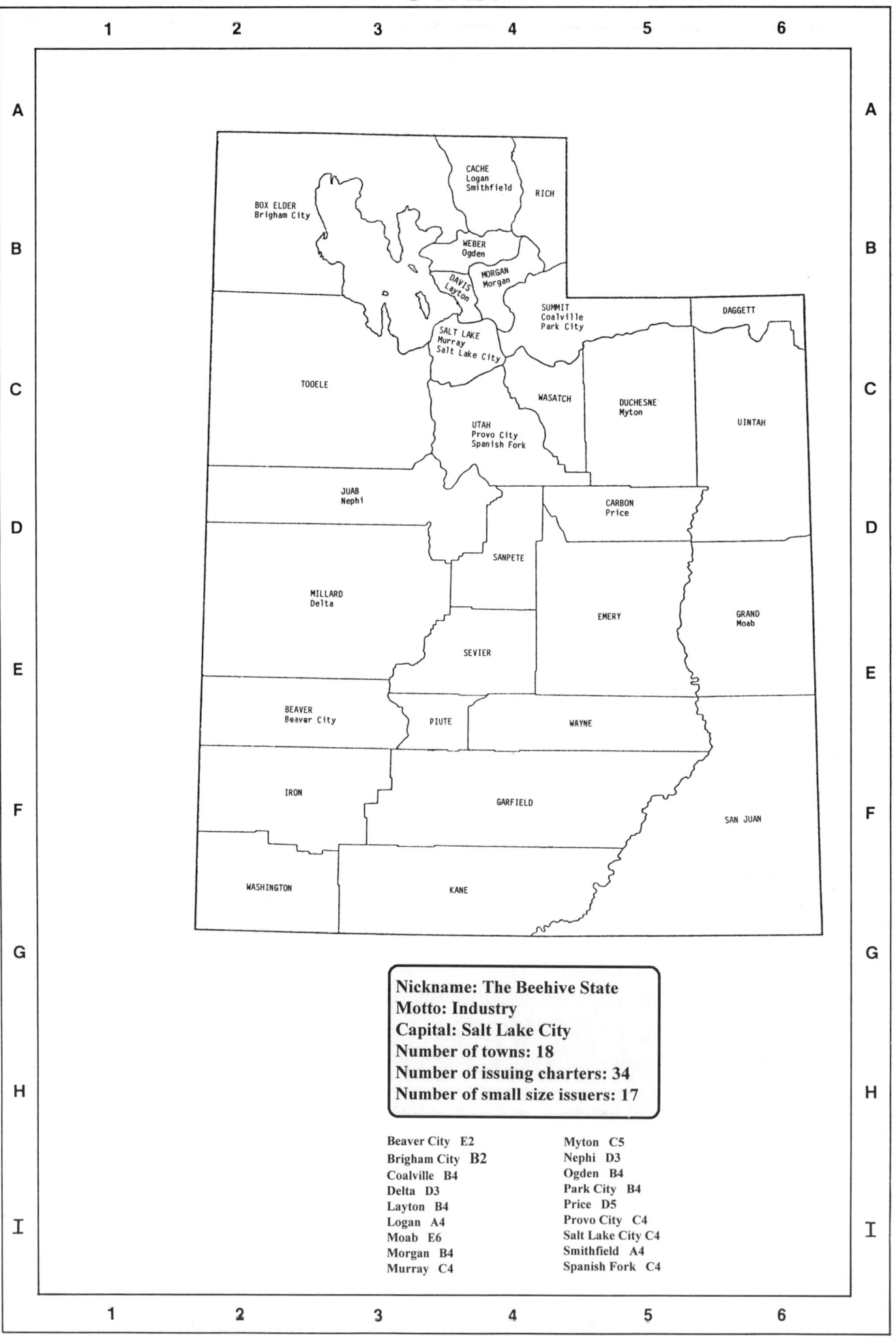

Nickname: The Beehive State
Motto: Industry
Capital: Salt Lake City
Number of towns: 18
Number of issuing charters: 34
Number of small size issuers: 17

Beaver City E2
Brigham City B2
Coalville B4
Delta D3
Layton B4
Logan A4
Moab E6
Morgan B4
Murray C4
Myton C5
Nephi D3
Ogden B4
Park City B4
Price D5
Provo City C4
Salt Lake City C4
Smithfield A4
Spanish Fork C4

9119 Beaver
FNB OF BEAVER CITY
{{ UNREPORTED }}
Chartered 4/08
Liquidated 5/1/22
1902 Date Back <$VALUE
4x5 1-987 <$3000
3x10-20 1-1030 <$3000
1902 Plain Back
3x10-20 1031-1078 <$3000
Total Issue $62,860
Out at close $6,800

6036 Box Elder
FNB OF BRIGHAM CITY
{{ 9 L 3 S }}
Chartered 11/30/01
Brown Back <$VALUE
4x5 1-325 <$1500
3x10-20 1-440 <$1500
1882 Date Back
4x5 1-1125 <$1250
3x10-20 1-900 <$1250
1882 Value Back
4x5 1126-2375 <$1500
3x10-20 901-1600 <$1500
1902 Plain Back
4x5 1-2265 <$750
3x10-20 1-1512 <$750
1929 Small Size
5 Type 1 1-804 <$500
10 Type 1 1-412 <$500
20 Type 1 1-116 <$500
5 Type 2 1-876 <$550
10 Type 2 1-444 <$550
20 Type 2 1-132 <$550
Total Issue $355,120
Out in 1935 $19,070
Large out 1935 $1,530

7696 Summit
FNB OF COALVILLE
{{ 3 L 11 S }}
Chartered 4/05
1902 Red Seal <$VALUE
3x10-20 1-1000 <$6000
1902 Date Back-
3x10-20 1-1970 <$1250
1902 Plain Back
3x10-20 1971-5380 <$1250
1929 Small Size
5 Type 1 1-620 <$350
10 Type 1 1-420 <$350
20 Type 1 1-160 <$350
5 Type 2 1-3926 <$400
10 Type 2 1-1926 <$400
20 Type 2 1-409 <$400
Total Issue $429,070
Out in 1935 $41,540
Large out 1935 $1,190

11529 Millard
FNB OF DELTA
{{ UNREPORTED }}
Organized 11/17/19
Liquidated 4/25/22 1902
Plain Back <$VALUE
3x10-20 1-632 <$3000
Total Issue $31,600
Out at close $11,300

7685 Davis
FNB OF LAYTON
{{ 2 L 8 S }}
Chartered 4/04
1902 Red Seal <$VALUE
3x10-20 1-1150 <$6000
1902 Date Back
3x10-20 1-1870 <$1250
1902 Plain Back
3x10-20 1871-6176 <$1250
1929 Small Size
10 Type 1 1-784 <$400
20 Type 1 1-198 <$400
10 Type 2 1-738 <$450
20 Type 2 1-290 <$450
Total Issue $450,280
Out in 1935 $25,000
Large out 1935 $1,620

4670 Cache
FNB OF LOGAN
Chartered 1891
TERRITORIAL ISSUES {{ 0 L }}
Brown Back <$VALUE
3x10-20 1-490 <$6000
STATE ISSUES {{ 7 L 26 S }}
Brown Back
3x10-20 491-1440 <$1250
1882 Date Back
3x10-20 1-851 <$1000
1902 Date Back
3x10-20 1-1940 <$400
1902 Plain Back
3x10-20 1941-17141 <$400
1929 Small Size
10 Type 1 1-2878 <$150
20 Type 1 1-758 <$175
10 Type 2 1-1132 <$200
20 Type 2 1-390 <$200
Total Issue $1,254,360
Out in 1935 $53,180
Large out 1935 $4,310

10925 Grand
FNB OF MOAB
{{ 4 L 12 S }}
Chartered 12/16
1902 Plain Back <$VALUE
4x5 1-8567 <$850
3x10-20 1-5556 <$850
1929 Small Size
5 Type 1 1-2002 <$350
10 Type 1 1-942 <$350
20 Type 1 1-266 <$350
5 Type 2 1-2500 <$400
10 Type 2 1-1488 <$400
20 Type 2 1-384 <$400
Total Issue $632,700
Out in 1935 $39,970
Large out 1935 $2,470

6958 Morgan
FNB OF MORGAN
{{ 4 L 1 S }}
Chartered 9/03
1902 Red Seal <$VALUE
3x10-20 1-1264 <$6000
1902 Date Back
3x10-20 1-1900 <$850
1902 Plain Back
3x10-20 1901-5999 <$850
1929 Small Size
10 Type 1 1-366 <$850
20 Type 1 1-90 <$850
Total Issue $395,910
Out in 1935 $4,575
Large out 1935 $1,515

6558 Salt Lake
FNB OF MURRAY
{{ 7 L 18 S }}
Chartered 12/29/02
1902 Red Seal <$VALUE
3x10-20 1-1050 <$6000
1902 Date Back
3x10-20 1-6000 <$600
1902 Plain Back
3x10-20 6001-23159 <$600
1929 Small Size
10 Type 1 1-2838 <$225
20 Type 1 1-852 <$250
10 Type 2 1-884 <$250
20 Type 2 1-221 <$275
Total Issue $1,496,230
Out in 1935 $47,945
Large out 1935 $5,275

11702 Duchesne
FNB OF MYTON
{{ UNREPORTED }}
Organized 4/10/20
Receivership 2/24/22
1902 Plain Back <$VALUE
4x5 1-200 <$4000
Total Issue $4,000
Out at close $2,500

3537 Juab
FNB OF NEPHI
Chartered 7/22/86
Receivership 2/5/35
TERRITORIAL ISSUES {{ 0 L }}
Brown Back <$VALUE
4x5 1-2250 <$6000
STATE ISSUES {{ 8 L }}
Brown Back
4x5 2251-4724 <$1500
3x10-20 1-1984 <$1500
1902 Red Seal
4x5 1-825 <$6000
3x10-20 1-670 <$6000
1902 Date Back
4x5 1-3900 <$500
3x10-20 1-2620 <$500
1902 Plain Back
4x5 3901-10262 <$500
3x10-20 2621-6700 <$500
Total Issue $783,920
Out at close $3,315

8508 Juab
NEPHI NB, NEPHI
{{ 6 L U + 4 S }}
Organized 11/21/06
Liquidated 1/26/32
1902 Red Seal <$VALUE
4x5 1-1225 <$6000
4x10 1-1275 <$6000
1902 Date Back
4x5 1-3750 <$500
4x10 1-3500 <$500
1902 Plain Back
4x5 3751-13725 <$500
4x10 3501-11379 <$500
1929 Small Size
5 Type 1 1-2131 <$500
10 Type 1 1-810 <$500
Total Issue $917,690
Out at close $42,740
Large out at close $3,990

3139 Weber
COMMERCIAL NB OF OGDEN
Chartered 1884
Liquidated 7/31/25
TERRITORIAL ISSUES {{ 1 L }}
Brown Back <$VALUE
3x10-20 1-3520 <$6000
STATE ISSUES {{ 8 L }}
Brown Back
3x10-20 3521-5395 <$1250
1902 Red Seal
3x10-20 1-1800 <$6000
1902 Date Back
3x10-20 1-5000 <$350
1902 Plain Back
3x10-20 5001-16014 <$350
Total Issue $1,160,450
Out at close $89,600

2597 Weber
FNB OF OGDEN
Chartered 1881
2nd title: F & Utah NB 10/2/22
3rd title: F Utah NB 1/18/23
4th title: FNB 1/19/26
5th title: F Security B of Utah N Assoc 2/24/34
FIRST TITLE
TERRITORIAL ISSUES {{ 0 L }}
Series 1875 <$VALUE
3x10-20 1-1280 <$6000/$8500
50-100 1-834 <$20,000
STATE ISSUES {{ 13 L }}
Series 1875
3x10-20 1281-2167 <$4500/$6500
Brown Back
3x10-20 1-6075 <$1000
1882 Date Back
4x5 1-10000** <$850
3x10-20 1-7100* <$850
1882 Value Back
4x5 10501-19975** <$1000
3x10-20 7501-13239* <$1000
** 10001-10500 not marked
* 7001-7500 not marked

1902 Plain Back
3x10-20 1-2700 <$300
SECOND TITLE {{ 1 L }}
1902 Plain Back
3x10-20 1-5000 <$500
THIRD TITLE {{ 6 L }}
1902 Plain Back
3x10-20 1-16441 <$400
FOURTH TITLE {{ 14 L 50+ S }}
1902 Plain Back
3x10-20 1-23148 <$275
1929 Small Size
10 Type 1 1-15030 <$65
20 Type 1 1-3612 <$65
10 Type 2 1-9264 <$65
20 Type 2 1-1896 <$75
FIFTH TITLE {{ 8 S }}
1929 Small Size
10 Type 2 1-1560 <$150
20 Type 2 1-709 <$150
Total Issue $5,458,680
Out in 1935 $361,060
Large out 1935 $26,110
Outstanding includes Ch 2880

NB of Commerce of Ogden
SEE Ch 7296
Pingree NB of Ogden

7296 Weber
PINGREE NB OF OGDEN
Chartered 6/04
Liquidated 6/10/30
2nd title: NB of Commerce of Ogden 10/25/20
FIRST TITLE {{ 7 L }}
1902 Red Seal <$VALUE
3x10-20 1-7700 <$6000
1902 Date Back
3x10-20 1-12000 <$400
1902 Plain Back
3x10-20 12001-20200 <$400
SECOND TITLE {{ 6 L 7 S }}
1902 Plain Back
3x10-20 1-22672 <$450
1929 Small Size
10 Type 1 1-2234 <$275
20 Type 1 1-538 <$275
Total Issue $2,727,200
Out in 1930 $212,675
Large out at close $46,905

2880 Weber
UTAH NB OF OGDEN
Chartered 1883
Closed 10/2/22
TERRITORIAL ISSUES {{ 2 L }}
Brown Back <$VALUE
3x10-20 1-1100 <$5000
50-100 1-800 <$15,000
STATE ISSUES {{ 12 L }}
Brown Back
3x10-20 1181-1207 <$1250
1902 Red Seal
3x10-20 1-2750 <$6000
1902 Date Back
3x10-20 1-11200 <$300
1902 Plain Back
3x10-20 11201-35207 <$300
Total Issue $2,078,200
Out in 1922 $500,000
Ch 2597 assumed circulation

4564 Summit
FNB OF PARK CITY
Organized 4/16/91
Liquidated 2/9/34
TERRITORIAL ISSUES {{ 1 L }}
Brown Back <$VALUE
4x5 1-1600 <$6000
STATE ISSUES {{ 7 L }}
Brown Back
4x5 1601-4470 <$1500
3x10-20 1-2252 <$1500
1882 Date Back
4x5 1-1274 <$1250
3x10-20 1-934 <$1250
1902 Date Back
4x5 1-1950 <$750
3x10-20 1-1960 <$750
1902 Plain Back
4x5 1951-7910 <$750
3x10-20 1961-5699 <$750
Total Issue $717,330
Out at close $2,725

6012 Carbon
FNB OF PRICE
{{ 8 L U + 14 S }}
Chartered 11/5/01
Brown Back <$VALUE
4x5 1-1050 <$1250
3x10-20 1-2940 <$1250
1882 Date Back
4x5 1-2450 <$1250
3x10-20 1-2900 <$1250
1882 Value Back
4x5 2451-5680 <$1250
3x10-20 2901-4771 <$1250
1902 Plain Back
4x5 1-5365 <$650
3x10-20 1-4083 <$650
1929 Small Size
5 Type 1 1-1816 <$350
10 Type 1 1-1026 <$350
20 Type 1 1-296 <$350
5 Type 2 1-3994 <$350
10 Type 2 1-1956 <$350
20 Type 2 1-480 <$350
Total Issue $1,032,290
Out in 1935 $48,900
Large out 1935 $3,435

2641 Utah
FNB OF PROVO CITY
{{ UNREPORTED }}
Chartered 3/2/82
Liquidated 6/30/00
TERRITORIAL ISSUES
Series 1875 <$VALUE
3x10-20 1-1340 <$8500
STATE ISSUES
Series 1875
3x10-20 1341-1475 <$6000
Total Issue $73,750
Out in 1910 $640

4486 Utah
NB OF COMMERCE, PROVO CITY
{{ UNREPORTED }}
Chartered 12/18/90
Liquidated 1/2/94
TERRITORIAL ISSUES
Brown Back <$VALUE
3x10-20 1-350 <$7500
Total Issue $17,500
Out in 1910 $190

4432 Salt Lake
AMERICAN NB OF SALT LAKE CITY
{{ UNREPORTED }}
Chartered 10/7/90
Liquidated 2/24/94
TERRITORIAL ISSUES
Brown Back <$VALUE
4x5 1-3276 <$6500
50-100 1-55 <$12,500
Total Issue $73,770
Out in 1910 $475

4051 Salt Lake
COMMERCIAL NB OF SALT LAKE CITY
Chartered 6/12/89
Liquidated 5/6/09
TERRITORIAL ISSUES {{ 0 L }}
Brown Back <$VALUE
3x10-20 1-2360 <$6000
STATE ISSUES {{ 3 L }}
Brown Back
3x10-20 2361-16250 <$1250
1882 Date Back
3x10-20 1-1287 <$1250
Total Issue $877,350
Out in 1910 $85,160

9403 Salt Lake
CONTINENTAL NB OF SALT LAKE CITY
Chartered 5/09
2nd title: Continental NB & TC of Salt Lake City 1/17/31
FIRST TITLE {{ 22 L 15 S }}
1902 Date Back <$VALUE
4x5 1-20500 <$250
3x10-20 1-15000 <$250
1902 Plain Back
4x5 20501-101758 <$250
3x10-20 15001-66407 <$250
1929 Small Size
5 Type 1 1-13172 <$75
10 Type 1 1-6054 <$80
20 Type 1 1-1666 <$90
SECOND TITLE {{ 50+ S }}
1929 Small Size
5 Type 1 1-12320 <$60
10 Type 1 1-7264 <$70
20 Type 1 1-1444 <$75
5 Type 2 1-32288 <$70
10 Type 2 1-18510 <$70
20 Type 2 1-4500 <$85
Total Issue $7,729,090
Out in 1935 $454,250
Large out 1935 $33,545
Outstanding includes Ch 4310

2059 Salt Lake
DESERET NB OF SALT LAKE CITY
Chartered 10/21/72
2nd title: FNB of Salt Lake City 4/5/32
TERRITORIAL ISSUES {{ 31 L }}
Original Series <$VALUE
3x1-2 1-1000 <$5000/$10,000
4x5 1-1000 <$5000
3x10-20 1-1100 <$6500/$8500
50-100 1-800 <$25,000
Series 1875
4x5 1-275 <$5000
3x10-20 1-1250 <$6500/$8500
50-100 1-2569 <$25,000
Brown Back
3x10-20 1-5000 <$3000
50-100 1-1700 <$15,000
STATE ISSUES {{2U+50 L 50+S}}
Brown Back
4x5 1-21300 <$750
3x10-20 5001-23680 <$750
50-100 1701-2200 <$3500
1882 Date Back
4x5 1-18432 <$650
3x10-20 1-10927 <$650
50-100 1-73 <$3500
1902 Date Back
4x5 1-13750 <$175
3x10-20 1-11000 <$175
1902 Plain Back
4x5 13751-79275 <$175
3x10-20 11001-76147 <$175
1929 Small Size
5 Type 1 1-16570 <$65
10 Type 1 1-8502 <$65
20 Type 1 1-2310 <$75
SECOND TITLE {{ U + 45 S }}
1929 Small Size
5 Type 1 1-3094 <$65
10 Type 1 1-2576 <$65
20 Type 1 1-630 <$75
5 Type 2 1-46618 <$65
10 Type 2 1-19757 <$65
20 Type 2 1-7199 <$75
Total Issue $11,094,180
Out in 1935 $619,570
Large out 1935 $47,285
Outstanding includes Ch 9652

FNB of Salt Lake City
SEE Ch 2059
Deseret NB of Salt Lake City

<$VALUEs are for notes in **FINE** condition. Value changes by approximately **25%** for a change of one full grade.

****
1695 Salt Lake
FNB OF UTAH,
SALT LAKE CITY
{{ UNREPORTED }}
Organized 11/2/69
Receivership 12/10/74
TERRITORIAL ISSUES
Original Series <$VALUE
3x1-2 1-1000 <$6000/$8500
4x5 1-2660 <$6000
2x20-50-100 1-507
<$8500/$20,000/$20,000
Total Issue $154,530
Out in 1916 $681
****
1646 Salt Lake
MINERS NB OF
SALT LAKE CITY
{{ 2 L }}
Chartered 3/28/66
Liquidated 12/2/69
TERRITORIAL ISSUES
Original Series <$VALUE
3x1-2 1-2136 <$5000/$7500
4x5 1-950 <$5000
3x10-20 1-690 <$6500/$8500
3x20-50 1-727
<$8500/$20,000
Total Issue $135,500
Out in 1910 $686
****
4310 Salt Lake
NB OF THE REPUBLIC AT
SALT LAKE CITY
Chartered 1890
Closed 9/30/22
TERRITORIAL ISSUES {{ 0 L }}
Brown Back <$VALUE
3x10-20 1-2160 <$6000
STATE ISSUES {{ 10 L }}
Brown Back
4x5 1-7000 <$850
3x10-20 2161-19560 <$850
1882 Date Back
4x5 1-5380 <$750
3x10-20 1-2469 <$750
1902 Date Back
3x10-20 1-19500 <$375
1902 Plain Back
3x10-20 19501-40944 <$375
Total Issue $3,396,250
Out at close $296,900
Ch 9403 assumed circulation
****
10308 Salt Lake
N CITY B OF
SALT LAKE CITY
{{ 6 L }}
Organized 11/19/12
Receivership 2/3/22
1902 Date Back <$VALUE
3x10-20 1-12500 <$500
1902 Plain Back
3x10-20 12501-28838 <$500
Total Issue $1,441,900
Out at close $243,300
****

****
9652 Salt Lake
N COPPER B OF
SALT LAKE CITY
Chartered 2/10
Closed 4/5/32
2nd title: Security NB
4/10/31
FIRST TITLE {{ 21 L 42 S }}
1902 Date Back <$VALUE
4x5 1-29000 <$325
3x10-20 1-20000 <$325
50-100 1-600 <$1250
3x50-100 1-1000 <$1250
1902 Plain Back
4x5 29001-54100 <$325
3x10-20 20001-37190 <$325
1929 Small Size
5 Type 1 1-12568 <$100
10 Type 1 1-5656 <$100
20 Type 1 1-1672 <$110
SECOND TITLE {{ 18 S }}
1929 Small Size
5 Type 1 1-5633 <$125
10 Type 1 1-2401 <$125
20 Type 1 1-660 <$135
Total Issue $4,590,790
Out at close $516,750
Large out at close $17,250
****
1921 Salt Lake
SALT LAKE CITY NB OF UTAH
{{ 3 L }}
Chartered 1/12/72
Liquidated 2/21/76
TERRITORIAL ISSUES
Original Series <$VALUE
3x1-2 1-4120 <$5000/$8500
4x5 1-2750 <$5000
3x10-20 1-500 <$6500/$8500
Series 1875
4x5 1-380 <$5000
Total Issue $108,200
Out in 1910 $744
****
Security NB, Salt Lake City
SEE Ch 9652
N Copper B of Salt Lake City
****
3306 Salt Lake
UNION NB OF
SALT LAKE CITY
{{ UNREPORTED }}
Chartered 2/19/85
Liquidated 3/23/94
TERRITORIAL ISSUES
Brown Back <$VALUE
4x5 1-1200 <$6000
3x10-20 1-2032 <$6000
Total Issue $125,600
Out in 1910 $990
****

****
4341 Salt Lake
UTAH NB OF SALT LAKE CITY
Chartered 1890
2nd title: Utah State NB
4/30/12
FIRST TITLE
TERRITORIAL ISSUES {{ 0 L }}
Brown Back <$VALUE
4x5 1-1250 <$6000
3x10-20 1-1660 <$6000
STATE ISSUES {{ 8 L }}
Brown Back
4x5 1251-6850 <$1000
3x10-20 1661-7400 <$1000
1882 Date Back
4x5 1-2765 <$1000
3x10-20 1-2098 <$1000
1902 Date Back
4x5 1-5017 <$375
SECOND TITLE {{ 21 L 50+ S }}
1902 Date Back
4x5 5018-22500 <$300
3x10-20 1-16000 <$300
1902 Plain Back
4x5 22501-92125 <$300
3x10-20 16001-58244 <$300
1929 Small Size
5 Type 1 1-9274 <$85
10 Type 1 1-5786 <$85
20 Type 1 1-1790 <$100
50 Type 1 1-208 <$650
5 Type 2 1-27864 <$85
10 Type 2 1-15282 <$85
20 Type 2 1-4097 <$100
Total Issue $7,173,410
Out in 1935 $410,420
Large out 1935 $23,470
****
Utah State NB, Salt Lake City
SEE Ch 4341
Utah NB of Salt Lake City
****
10135 Cache
COMMERCIAL NB OF
SMITHFIELD
{{ 3 L 4 S }}
Chartered 1/12
1902 Date Back <$VALUE
3x10-20 1-1460 <$1000
1902 Plain Back
3x10-20 1461-5536 <$1000
1929 Small Size
10 Type 1 1-764 <$500
20 Type 1 1-190 <$500
10 Type 2 1-777 <$550
20 Type 2 1-207 <$500
Total Issue $357,350
Out in 1935 $24,650
Large out 1935 $1,050
****

****
9111 Utah
FNB OF SPANISH FORK
{{ 3 L 2 S }}
Organized 3/25/08
Liquidated 8/21/30
1902 Date Back <$VALUE
3x10-20 1-1500 <$2000
1902 Plain Back
3x10-20 1501-5527 <$2000
1929 Small Size
10 Type 1 1-284 <$1250
20 Type 1 1-37 <$1250
Total Issue $297,830
Out at close $19,600
Large out at close $4,510
****

CONDITION affects Value. The Values shown are for notes in FINE condition.

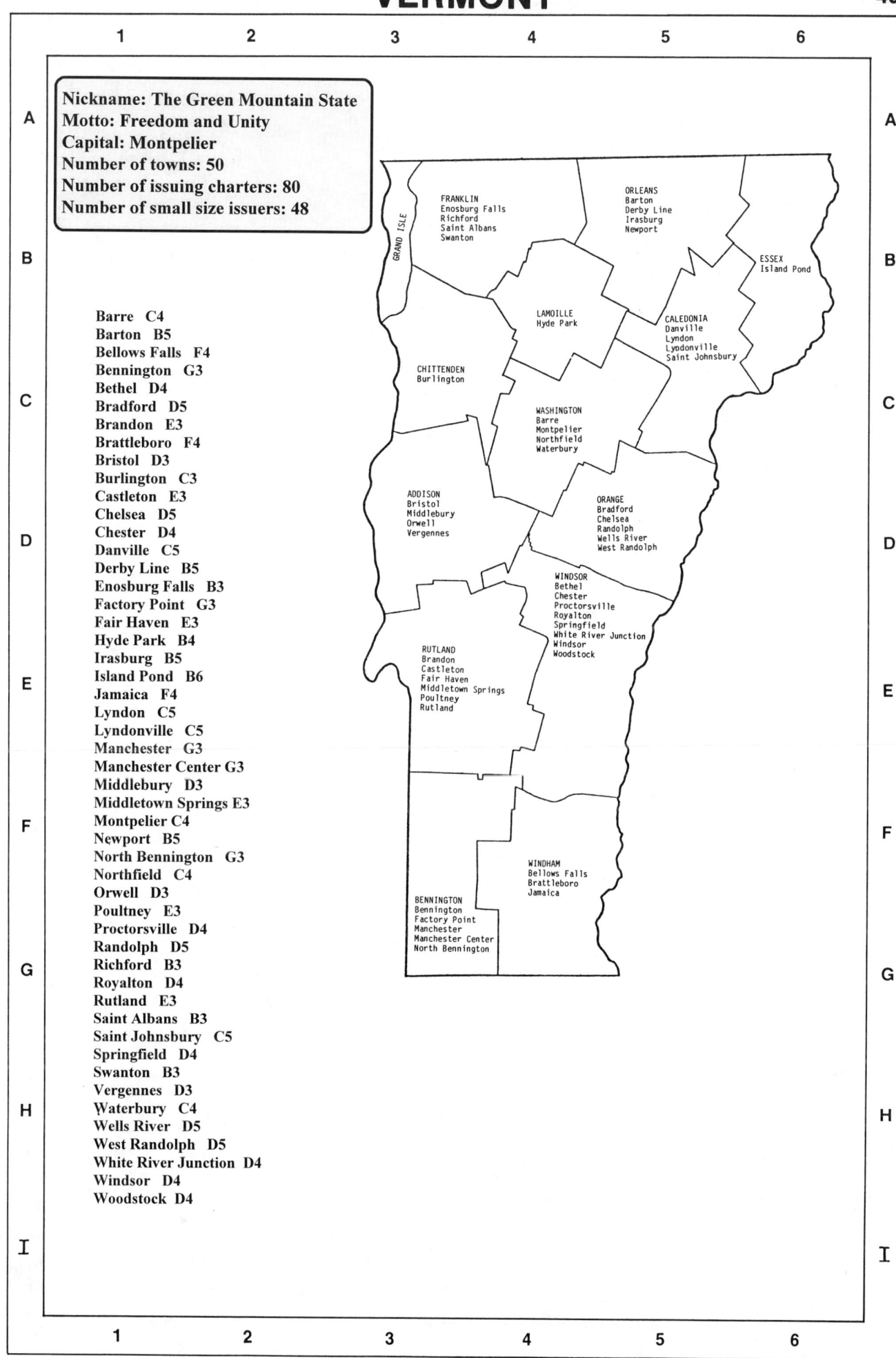

Nickname: The Green Mountain State
Motto: Freedom and Unity
Capital: Montpelier
Number of towns: 50
Number of issuing charters: 80
Number of small size issuers: 48

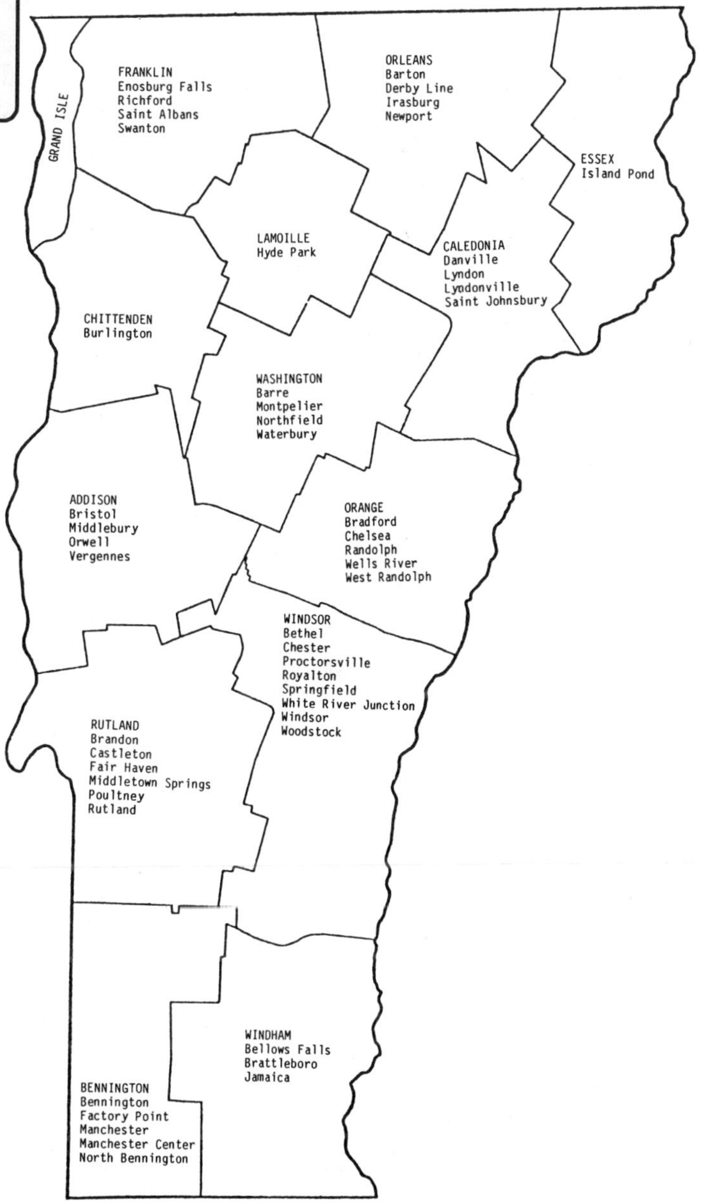

Barre C4
Barton B5
Bellows Falls F4
Bennington G3
Bethel D4
Bradford D5
Brandon E3
Brattleboro F4
Bristol D3
Burlington C3
Castleton E3
Chelsea D5
Chester D4
Danville C5
Derby Line B5
Enosburg Falls B3
Factory Point G3
Fair Haven E3
Hyde Park B4
Irasburg B5
Island Pond B6
Jamaica F4
Lyndon C5
Lyndonville C5
Manchester G3
Manchester Center G3
Middlebury D3
Middletown Springs E3
Montpelier C4
Newport B5
North Bennington G3
Northfield C4
Orwell D3
Poultney E3
Proctorsville D4
Randolph D5
Richford B3
Royalton D4
Rutland E3
Saint Albans B3
Saint Johnsbury C5
Springfield D4
Swanton B3
Vergennes D3
Waterbury C4
Wells River D5
West Randolph D5
White River Junction D4
Windsor D4
Woodstock D4

2109 Washington
NB OF BARRE
{{ 10 L }}
Chartered 5/17/73
Liquidated 4/5/13
Original Series <$VALUE
3x1-2 1-1000 <$400/$1250
4x5 1-2500 <$450
3x10-20 1-2500 <$850/$1500
Series 1875
4x5 1-9967 <$450
3x10-20 1-700 <$850/$1500
Brown Back
4x5 1-19125 <$400
50-100 1-1510 <$3000/$3500
1882 Date Back
4x5 1-4900 <$400
50-100 1-820 <$3000/$3500
3x50-100 1-103
<$3000/$3500
Total Issue $1,270,090
Out in 1913 $48,850

7068 Washington
PEOPLES NB OF BARRE
{{ 12 L 31 S }}
Chartered 12/03
1902 Red Seal <$VALUE
4x5 1-3770 <$450
3x10-20 1-3437 <$450
1902 Date Back
4x5 1-9450 <$175
3x10-20 1-6920 <$175
1902 Plain Back
4x5 9451-16850 <$175
3x10-20 6921-22869 <$175
1929 Small Size
10 Type 1 1-3956 <$60
20 Type 1 1-1136 <$60
10 Type 2 1-8139 <$65
20 Type 2 1-2151 <$75
Total Issue $2,225,790
Out in 1935 $200,000
Large out 1935 $2,990

2290 Orleans
BARTON NB, BARTON
{{ 2 L }}
Chartered 7/30/75
Liquidated 3/15/09
Series 1875 <$VALUE
3x10-20 1-6420<$1000/$1500
Brown Back
3x10-20 1-6360 <$750
1882 Date Back
3x10-20 1-159 <$750
Total Issue $646,950
Out in 1910 $16,855

1653 Windham
NB OF BELLOWS FALLS
{{ 16 L 19 S }}
Organized 6/12/66
Receivership 1/15/34
Original Series <$VALUE
3x1-2 1-6000 <$350/$1000
4x5 1-4700 <$450
3x10-20 1-1100 <$850/$1500
Series 1875
3x1-2 1-1060 <$350/$1000
4x5 1-4162 <$450
3x10-20 1-1236 <$850/$1500
Brown Back
4x5 1-13856 <$400
3x10-20 1-6668 <$400
1902 Red Seal
4x5 1-3300 <$450
3x10-20 1-2280 <$450
1902 Date Back
4x5 1-7400 <$175
3x10-20 1-5420 <$175
1902 Plain Back
4x5 7401-25120 <$175
3x10-20 5421-16996 <$175
1929 Small Size
5 Type 1 1-3912 <$75
10 Type 1 1-1814 <$75
20 Type 1 1-468 <$90
5 Type 2 1-404 <$110
10 Type 2 1-145 <$125
20 Type 2 1-25 <$135
Total Issue $2,781,750
Out at close $99,250
Large out at close $8,350

13894 Windham
WINDHAM NB OF
BELLOWS FALLS
{{ 3 S }}
Chartered 12/33
1929 Small Size <$VALUE
5 Type 2 1-5050 <$350
Total Issue $25,250
Out in 1935 $25,000

2395 Bennington
BENNINGTON COUNTY NB OF
BENNINGTON
Chartered 8/17/78
2nd title:County NB of
Bennington 8/7/18
FIRST TITLE {{ 16 L }}
Series 1875 <$VALUE
4x5 1-19504 <$400
Brown Back
4x5 1-7850 <$400
3x10-20 1-6192 <$400
1882 Date Back
4x5 1-9100* <$400
3x10-20 1-5860** <$400
1882 Value Back
4x5 9601-12675* <$650
3x10-20 6261-7958** <$650
* 9101-9600 not marked
** 5861-6260 not marked
SECOND TITLE {{ 7 L 21 S }}
1902 Plain Back
4x5 1-15270 <$150
3x10-20 1-10547 <$150
1929 Small Size
5 Type 1 1-3774 <$60
10 Type 1 1-1890 <$60
20 Type 1 1-500 <$65
5 Type 2 1-10182 <$65
10 Type 2 1-4920 <$65
20 Type 2 1-1187 <$75
Total Issue $2,751,300
Out in 1935 $150,000
Large out 1935 $6,340

130 Bennington
FNB OF BENNINGTON
{{ 14 L 20 S }}
Chartered 10/10/63
Original Series <$VALUE
3x1-2 1-2000 <$400/$1000
4x5 1-5000 <$450
4x10 1-2500 <$750
Series 1875
4x5 1-2874 <$450
4x10 1-2385 <$750
Brown Back
4x5 1-13914 <$400
3x10-20 1-7870 <$400
1902 Red Seal
4x5 1-4900 <$450
3x10-20 1-4240 <$450
1902 Date Back
4x5 1-9500 <$175
3x10-20 1-6880 <$175
1902 Plain Back
4x5 9501-25188 <$175
3x10-20 6881-20415 <$175
1929 Small Size
10 Type 1 1-3006 <$75
20 Type 1 1-768 <$80
10 Type 2 1-4085 <$100
20 Type 2 1-1190 <$100
Total Issue $3,206,340
Out in 1935 $110,000
Large out 1935 $7,490

962 Windsor
N WHITE RIVER B OF BETHEL
{{ 9 L 4 S }}
Chartered 3/31/65
Liquidated 11/13/33
Original Series <$VALUE
3x1-2 1-4500 <$500/$1250
4x5 1-6000 <$600
3x10-20 1-3000 <$850/$1500
Series 1875
3x1-2 1-1920 <$500/$1250
4x5 1-4450 <$600
3x10-20 1-800 <$850/$1500
Brown Back
4x5 1-10077 <$500
3x10-20 1-4207 <$500
1902 Red Seal
4x5 1-4025 <$600
50-100 1-820 <$3500/$4000
1902 Date Back
4x5 1-4100 <$300
50-100 1-280 <$750/$850
3x50-100 1-549 <$750/$850
1902 Plain Back
4x5 4101-14694 <$300
3x50-100 550-716<$750/$850
1929 Small Size
5 Type 1 1-1815 <$275
50 Type 1 1-92 <$450
100 Type 1 1-32 <$600
Total Issue $1,664,620
Out at close $50,000
Large out at close $6,850

7267 Orange
BRADFORD NB, BRADFORD
{{ 4 L U+6 S }}
Organized 5/4/04
1902 Red Seal <$VALUE
3x10-20 1-620 <$800
1902 Date Back
3x10-20 1-2230 <$350
1902 Plain Back
3x10-20 2231-6273 <$350
1929 Small Size
10 Type 1 1-626 <$250
20 Type 1 1-172 <$250
10 Type 2 1-933 <$275
20 Type 2 1-220 <$275
Total Issue $416,580
Out in 1935 $25,000
Large out 1935 $1,270

404 Rutland
BRANDON NB, BRANDON
{{ 10 L 15 S }}
Organized 3/26/64
Receivership 11/7/33
Original Series <$VALUE
3x1-2 1-5000 <$500/$1250
4x5 1-9250 <$500
3x10-20 1-3600 <$850/$1500
Series 1875
3x1-2 1-3980 <$500/$1250
4x5 1-2250 <$500
3x10-20 1-2876 <$850/$1500
Brown Back
3x10-20 1-7338 <$400
1902 Red Seal
4x5 1-2400 <$450
3x10-20 1-4740 <$450
1902 Date Back
4x5 1-8450 <$175
3x10-20 1-5460 <$175
1902 Plain Back
4x5 8451-26160 <$175
3x10-20 5461-17154 <$175
1929 Small Size
5 Type 1 1-3232 <$100
10 Type 1 1-1782 <$100
20 Type 1 1-502 <$110
5 Type 2 1-956 <$150
10 Type 2 1-400 <$150
20 Type 2 1-40 <$150
Total Issue $2,905,200
Out at close $99,995
Large out at close $8,655

278 Rutland
FNB OF BRANDON
{{ 9 L 13 S }}
Chartered 2/64
Original Series <$VALUE
3x1-2 1-4500 <$500/$1250
4x5 1-3125 <$500
3x10-20 1-1600 <$850/$1500
3x50-100 1-470 <$6000
Series 1875
3x1-2 1-2750 <$500/$1250
4x5 1-1500 <$500
3x10-20 1-2000 <$850/$1500
3x50-100 1-100 <$6000
Brown Back
4x5 1-22222 <$400
3x10-20 1-921 <$400
1902 Red Seal
4x5 1-2950 <$450
3x10-20 1-1740 <$450
1902 Date Back
4x5 1-9750 <$175
3x10-20 1-7000 <$175
1902 Plain Back
4x5 9751-22971 <$175
3x10-20 7001-15215 <$175
1929 Small Size
5 Type 1 1-2906 <$100
10 Type 1 1-1368 <$100
20 Type 1 1-336 <$125
5 Type 2 1-3944 <$150
10 Type 2 1-2292 <$150
20 Type 2 1-684 <$150
Total Issue $2,573,810
Out in 1935 $75,000
Large out 1935 $6,210

470 Windham
FNB OF BRATTLEBORO
{{ UNREPORTED }}
Organized 6/30/64
Receivership 6/19/80
Original Series <$VALUE
4x5 1-13000 <$1500
3x10-20 1-5500<$1750/$2000
Series 1875
3x10-20 1-966 <$1750/$2000
Total Issue $583,300
Out in 1916 $3,610

2305 Windham
PEOPLES NB OF BRATTLEBORO
{{ 14 L }}
Chartered 10/16/75
Closed 1/2/23
Series 1875 <$VALUE
3x1-2 1-2000 <$375/$1000
4x5 1-5587 <$450
3x10-20 1-3046 <$850/$1500
Brown Back
4x5 1-6650 <$350
3x10-20 1-7205 <$350/$400
1882 Date Back
4x5 1-8040 <$350
3x10-20 1-5289 <$350/$400
1902 Date Back
4x5 1-8425 <$175
3x10-20 1-5472 <$175
Total Issue $1,634,640
Out at close $99,995
Ch 1430 assumed circulation

1430 Windham
VERMONT NB OF BRATTLEBORO
Chartered 5/12/65
2nd title:Vermont-Peoples
NB 1/2/23
FIRST TITLE {{ 9 L }}
Original Series <$VALUE
3x1-2 1-2000 <$400/$1000
4x5 1-4050 <$450
3x10-20 1-3460 <$850/$1500
50-100 1-202 <$6000
Series 1875
4x5 1-2035 <$450
3x10-20 1-2930 <$850/$1500
Brown Back
4x5 1-4670 <$400
3x10-20 1-17043 <$400
1902 Red Seal
4x6 1-7250 <$450
3x10-20 1-4900 <$450
1902 Date Back
4x5 1-11750 <$165
3x10-20 1-8800 <$165
1902 Plain Back
4x5 11751-24000 <$165
3x10-20 8801-16900 <$165
SECOND TITLE {{ 12 L 30 S }}
1902 Plain Back
4x5 1-22903 <$125
3x10-20 1-15269 <$125
1929 Small Size
5 Type 1 1-9128 <$50
10 Type 1 1-4312 <$50
20 Type 1 1-1148 <$60
5 Type 2 1-13188 <$75
10 Type 2 1-6889 <$75
20 Type 2 1-1953 <$85
Total Issue $5,207,770
Out in 1935 $250,000
Large out 1935 $14,585
Outstanding includes Ch 2305

6252 Addison
FNB OF BRISTOL
{{ 2 L 5 S }}
Chartered 5/12/02
1902 Red Seal <$VALUE
3x10-20 1-1800 <$1250
1902 Date Back
3x10-20 1-2020 <$650
1902 Plain Back (dated 1902)
3x10-20 2021-3780 <$650
1902 Plain Back (dated 1922)
3x10-20 1-2448 <$650
1929 Small Size
10 Type 1 1-684 <$250
20 Type 1 1-194 <$250
10 Type 2 1-782 <$275
20 Type 2 1-155 <$275
Total Issue $476,640
Out in 1935 $25,000
Large out 1935 $860

861 Chittenden
FNB OF BURLINGTON
{{ UNREPORTED }}
Chartered 3/6/65
Liquidated 10/15/70
Original Series <$VALUE
4x5 1-4410 <$1500
3x10-20 1-3200<$1750/$2000
50-100 1-200 <$6000
Total Issue $278,200
Out in 1910 $2,575

1698 Chittenden
HOWARD NB OF BURLINGTON
Chartered 1870
2nd title:Howard NB & TC
3/12/31
FIRST TITLE {{ 30 L 10 S }}
Original Series <$VALUE
4x5 1-5250 <$400
3x10-20 1-3900 <$850/$1500
Series 1875
4x5 1-4000 <$400
3x10-20 1-2611 <$850/$1500
Brown Back
4x5 1-28500 <$250
3x10-20 1-14600 <$250/$300
1882 Date Back
4x5 1-4655 <$250
3x10-20 1-3706 <$250/$300
1902 Date Back
4x5 1-17750 <$85
4x10 1-17840* <$85
1902 Plain Back
4x5 17751-101641 <$85
4x10 18841-83308 <$85
* 17841-18840 not marked
1929 Small Size
5 Type 1 1-14768 <$60
10 Type 1 1-7354 <$60
SECOND TITLE {{ 50+ S }}
1929 Small Size
5 Type 1 1-11336 <$40
10 Type 1 1-5148 <$40
5 Type 2 1-50248 <$50
10 Type 2 1-29436 <$50
Total Issue $9,532,930
Out in 1935 $500,000
Large out 1935 $18,435

1197 Chittenden
MERCHANTS NB OF
BURLINGTON
{{ 16 L 21 S }}
Chartered 1865
Original Series <$VALUE
3x1-2 1-19940 <$350/$1000
4x5 1-16650 <$450
3x10-20 1-4881 <$850/$1500
50-100 1-1067 <$6000
Series 1875
4x5 1-19465 <$450
3x10-20 1-11500<$850/$1500
50-100 1-1842 <$6000
Brown Back
4x5 1-112043 <$250
3x10-20 1-13939 <$250/$300
50-100 1-876 <$3000/$3500
1902 Red Seal
4x5 1-4500 <$350
3x10-20 1-3200 <$350
50-100 1-100 <$3500/$4000
1902 Date Back
4x5 1-9250 <$100
3x10-20 1-6300 <$100
50-100 1-300 <$650/$750
1902 Plain Back
4x5 9251-35056 <$100
3x10-20 6301-21376 <$100
1929 Small Size
5 Type 1 1-4702 <$60
10 Type 1 1-2692 <$60
20 Type 1 1-662 <$70
5 Type 2 1-7408 <$100
10 Type 2 1-4190 <$100
20 Type 2 1-1189 <$110
Total Issue $7,726,270
Out in 1935 $149,995
Large out 1935 $19,565

1598 Rutland
CASTLETON NB, CASTLETON
{{ 1 L }}
Chartered 10/21/65
Liquidated 1/22/92
Original Series <$VALUE
4x5 1-1625 <$2000
3x10-20 1-1050<$2000/$2500
Series 1875
4x5 1-2050 <$2000
3x10-20 1-816 <$2000/$2500
Brown Back
4x5 1-597 <$1500
3x10-20 1-518 <$1500
Total Issue $204,640
Out in 1910 $990

2120 Orange
FNB OF CHELSEA
{{ 2 L }}
Chartered 7/19/73
Liquidated 6/10/93
Original Series <$VALUE
3x1-2 1-1900 <$850/$1500
4x5 1-2750 <$850
3x10-20 1-950 <$1000/$1500
Series 1875
3x1-2 1-340 <$850/$1500
4x5 1-6716 <$850
3x10-20 1-3441<$1000/$1500
Total Issue $420,070
Out in 1910 $1,974

4929 Orange
NB OF ORANGE COUNTY AT
CHELSEA
{{ 4 L 8 S }}
Organized 9/9/93
Receivership 1/17/34
Brown Back <$VALUE
4x5 1-6750 <$600
50-100 1-887 <$3000/$3500
1882 Date Back
4x5 1-2425 <$600
50-100 1-300 <$3000/$3500
3x50-100 1-84 <$3000/$3500
1902 Date Back
3x10-20 1-1500 <$350
1902 Plain Back
3x10-20 1501-9340 <$350
1929 Small Series
10 Type 1 1-1298 <$165
20 Type 1 1-382 <$175
10 Type 2 1-68 <$250
20 Type 2 1-30 <$250
Total Issue $974,550
Out at close $49,995
Large out at close $2,515

1004 Orange
ORANGE COUNTY NB OF
CHELSEA
{{ 1 L }}
Chartered 4/12/65
Liquidated 1/14/73
Original Series <$VALUE
3x1-2 1-1000 <$1500/$2000
4x5 1-3250 <$1500
3x10-20 1-2312<$1750/$2000
50-100 1-100 <$6000
Total Issue $200,600
Out in 1910 $1,798

4380 Windsor
NB OF CHESTER
{{ 1 L 4 S }}
Chartered 1890
Brown Back <$VALUE
3x10-20 1-1920 <$1250
1882 Date Back
3x10-20 1-119 <$1250
1902 Date Back
3x10-20 1-920 <$850
1902 Plain Back
3x10-20 921-2619 <$850
1929 Small Size
10 Type 1 1-608 <$300
20 Type 1 1-158 <$300
10 Type 2 1-688 <$325
20 Type 2 1-125 <$325
Total Issue $297,720
Out in 1935 $25,000
Large out 1935 $710

CONDITION affects Value. The Values shown are for notes in FINE condition.

****
1576 Caledonia
CALEDONIA NB OF DANVILLE
{{ 13 L 17 S }}
Chartered 1865
Original Series <$VALUE
3x1-2 1-4650 <$450/$1500
4x5 1-5125 <$450
3x10-20 1-1100 <$850/$1500
Series 1875
3x1-2 1-250 <$450/$1500
4x5 1-3400 <$450
3x10-20 1-920 <$850/$1500
Brown Back
4x5 1-13296 <$400
3x10-20 1-2571 <$400
1902 Red Seal
4x5 1-3750 <$450
3x10-20 1-2800 <$450
1902 Date Back
4x5 1-7350 <$175
3x10-20 1-5880 <$175
1902 Plain Back
4x5 7351-26898 <$175
3x10-20 5881-18194 <$175
1929 Small Size
5 Type 1 1-4108 <$75
10 Type 1 1-1834 <$75
20 Type 1 1-488 <$85
5 Type 2 1-5038 <$100
10 Type 2 1-3210 <$100
20 Type 2 1-905 <$110
Total Issue $2,720,360
Out in 1935 $100,000
Large out 1935 $5,500
****
1368 Orleans
NB OF DERBY LINE
{{ 12 L 9 S }}
Chartered 1865
Original Series <$VALUE
3x1-2 1-3000 <$450/$1250
4x5 1-4100 <$500
3x10-20 1-3300 <$850/$1500
Series 1875
3x10-20 1-3384 <$850/$1500
Brown Back
3x10-20 1-5736 <$450
1902 Red Seal
4x5 1-1575 <$500
3x10-20 1-910 <$500
1902 Date Back
4x5 1-11500 <$200
3x10-20 1-9020 <$200
1902 Plain Back
4x5 11501-25815 <$200
3x10-20 9021-16227 <$200
1929 Small Size
5 Type 1 1-2522 <$160
10 Type 1 1-1182 <$150
20 Type 1 1-374 <$150
5 Type 2 1-4284 <$175
10 Type 2 1-2004 <$175
20 Type 2 1-564 <$175
Total Issue $2,366,850
Out in 1935 $67,500
Large out 1935 $5,050
****
13986 Franklin
ENOSBURG FALLS NB,
ENOSBURG FALLS
{{ 2 S }}
Chartered 2/34
1929 Small Size <$VALUE
5 Type 2 1-2670 <$500
10 Type 2 1-1345 <$500
Total Issue $26,800
Out in 1935 $15,400
****
7614 Franklin
FNB OF ENOSBURG FALLS
{{ 2 L 3 S }}
Organized 2/11/05
Receivership 2/26/34
1902 Red Seal <$VALUE
3x10-20 1-800 <$1250
1902 Date Back
3x10-20 1-1770* <$650
1902 Plain Back
3x10-20 1891-5130* <$650
* 1771-1890 not marked
1929 Small Size
10 Type 1 1-526 <$400
20 Type 1 1-140 <$400
5 Type 2 1-222 <$400
10 Type 2 1-147 <$400
20 Type 2 1-10 <$400
Total Issue $347,640
Out at close $19,995
Large out at close $795
****

****
3080 Bennington
FACTORY POINT NB,
FACTORY POINT
Chartered 1883
2nd title:Factory Point NB
of Manchester Center 1903
FIRST TITLE {{ 1 L }}
Brown Back <$VALUE
3x10-20 1-2264 <$1500
SECOND TITLE {{ 9 L 11 S }}
1902 Red Seal
4x5 1-4000 <$1000
3x10-20 1-2500 <$1000
1902 Date Back
4x5 1-6450 <$350
3x10-20 1-4380 <$350
1902 Plain Back
4x5 6451-21165 <$350
3x10-20 4381-13212 <$350
1929 Small Size
5 Type 1 1-2996 <$175
10 Type 1 1-1384 <$175
20 Type 1 1-374 <$175
5 Type 2 1-4418 <$200
10 Type 2 1-2404 <$200
20 Type 2 1-696 <$200
Total Issue $1,679,950
Out in 1935 $72,350
Large out 1935 $3,900
****
2422 Rutland
ALLEN NB OF FAIR HAVEN
{{ 8 L 8 S }}
Chartered 4/12/79
Series 1875 <$VALUE
4x5 1-13709 <$600
Brown Back
4x5 1-2950 <$450
3x10-20 1-2160 <$450
1882 Date Back
4x5 1-3250 <$450
3x10-20 1-2560 <$450
1882 Value Back
4x5 3251-4747 <$650
3x10-20 2561-3378 <$650
1902 Plain Back
4x5 1-19411 <$200
1929 Small Size
5 Type 1 1-1384 <$150
10 Type 1 1-794 <$150
20 Type 1 1-234 <$165
5 Type 2 1-1562 <$200
10 Type 2 1-1018 <$200
20 Type 2 1-204 <$200
Total Issue $1,232,550
Out in 1935 $38,800
Large out 1935 $2,430
****
344 Rutland
FNB OF FAIR HAVEN
{{ 12 L 6 S }}
Chartered 3/64
Original Series <$VALUE
4x5 1-4750 <$600
3x10-20 1-1300 <$850/$1500
Series 1875
3x10-20 1-2344 <$850/$1500
Brown Back
3x10-20 1-3867 <$400
1902 Red Seal
3x10-20 1-1500 <$450
1902 Date Back
3x10-20 1-2850 <$200
1902 Plain Back
3x10-20 2851-7005 <$200
1929 Small Size
10 Type 1 1-788 <$225
20 Type 1 1-222 <$225
10 Type 2 1-1101 <$250
20 Type 2 1-237 <$250
Total Issue $985,470
Out in 1935 $29,795
Large out 1935 $3,085
****
1163 Lamoille
LAMOILLE COUNTY NB OF
HYDE PARK
{{ 7 L }}
Chartered 1865
Liquidated 1/24/24
Original Series <$VALUE
3x1-2 1-6990 <$500/$1250
4x5 1-4650 <$600
3x10-20 1-2000 <$850/$1500
Series 1875
3x1-2 1-600 <$500/$1250
4x5 1-4900 <$600
3x10-20 1-3089 <$850/$1500
Brown Back
4x5 1-12733 <$500
3x10-20 1-3950 <$500

1902 Red Seal
3x10-20 1-3800 <$600
1902 Date Back
3x10-20 1-9300 <$300
1902 Plain Back
3x10-20 9301-11911 <$300
Total Issue $1,721,110
Out at close $49,500
****
1541 Orleans
IRASBURG NB OF ORLEANS AT
IRASBURG
{{ UNREPORTED }}
Chartered 8/29/65
Liquidated 3/17/75
Original Series <$VALUE
3x1-2 1-1500 <$1250/$2000
4x5 1-2900 <$1500
3x10-20 1-943 <$1750/$2000
Total Issue $112,900
Out in 1910 $747
****
4275 Essex
ISLAND POND NB,
ISLAND POND
{{ 5 L 11 S }}
Organized 2/22/90
Brown Back <$VALUE
3x10-20 1-5120 <$850
1882 Date Back
3x10-20 1-927 <$850
1902 Date Back
3x10-20 1-4400 <$450
1902 Plain Back
3x10-20 4401-10306 <$450
1929 Small Size
10 Type 1 1-884 <$175
20 Type 1 1-264 <$175
10 Type 2 1-2850 <$200
20 Type 2 1-919 <$200
Total Issue $949,250
Out in 1935 $55,000
Large out 1935 $1,520
****
1564 Windham
WEST RIVER NB OF JAMAICA
{{ 1 L }}
Chartered 1865
Liquidated 8/17/85
Original Series <$VALUE
3x1-2 1-2000 <$1000/$2000
4x5 1-4500 <$1000
3x10-20 1-1300<$1250/$2000
Series 1875
3x1-2 1-1160 <$1000/$2000
4x5 1-2474 <$1000
3x10-20 1-906 <$1250/$2000
Total Issue $265,580
Out in 1910 $1,323
****
1140 Caledonia
NB OF LYNDON
{{ 6 L }}
Chartered 5/15/65
Liquidated 9/27/04
Original Series <$VALUE
3x1-2 1-4000 <$600/$1500
4x5 1-2500 <$650
3x10-20 1-2200 <$850/$1500
Series 1875
3x1-2 1-4220 <$600/$1500
4x5 1-3415 <$650
3x10-20 1-1570 <$850/$1500
Brown Back
3x10-20 1-3462 <$500
Total Issue $521,000
Out in 1910 $4,437
****
3158 Caledonia
LYNDONVILLE NB,
LYNDONVILLE
{{ 6 L }}
Chartered 1884
Liquidated 12/30/22
Brown Back <$VALUE
4x5 1-14725 <$650
3x10-20 1-1600 <$650
1902 Red Seal
4x5 1-2875 <$750
3x10-20 1-2300 <$750
1902 Date Back
4x5 1-7000 <$375
3x10-20 1-5000 <$375
1902 Plain Back
4x5 7001-14157 <$375
3x10-20 5001-9543 <$375
Total Issue $1,307,290
Out at close $74,100
****

****
1488 Bennington
BATTENKILL NB OF
MANCHESTER
{{ 1 L }}
Chartered 1865
Liquidated 3/21/85
Original Series <$VALUE
3x1-2 1-3800 <$1000/$2000
4x5 1-2800 <$1000
3x10-20 1-1380<$1250/$2000
Series 1875
3x1-2 1-340 <$1000/$2000
4x5 1-500 <$1000
3x10-20 1-1976<$1250/$2000
Total Issue $254,500
Out in 1910 $1,290
****
Factory Point NB of
Manchester Center
SEE Ch 3080
Factory Point NB,
Factory Point
****
1195 Addison
NB OF MIDDLEBURY
{{ 16 L 5U + 14 S }}
Chartered 1865
Original Series <$VALUE
4x5 1-4500 <$450
3x10-20 1-2200 <$750/$1500
50-100 1-1100 <$6000
Series 1875
4x5 1-2985 <$450
3x10-20 1-3474 <$750/$1500
50-100 1-100 <$6000
Brown Back
4x5 1-13550 <$350
3x10-20 1-14041 <$350
50-100 1-1100 <$3000/$3500
1902 Red Seal
4x5 1-7000 <$350
3x10-20 1-3300 <$350
50-100 1-300 <$3500/$4000
1902 Date Back
4x5 1-14250 <$135
3x10-20 1-8300 <$135
50-100 1-300 <$650/$750
3x50-100 1-300 <$650/$750
1902 Plain Back
4x5 14251-34594 <$135
3x10-20 8301-21288 <$135
3x50-100 301-457<$650/$750
1929 Small Size
5 Type 1 1-1582 <$100
10 Type 1 1-1090 <$100
20 Type 1 1-370 <$100
50 Type 1 1-130 <$350
100 Type 1 1-48 <$500
5 Type 2 1-1650 <$135
10 Type 2 1-585 <$135
20 Type 2 1-252 <$150
Total Issue $4,261,180
Out in 1935 $100,000
Large out 1935 $10,415
****
3150 Rutland
GRAY NB OF
MIDDLETOWN SPRINGS
{{ UNREPORTED }}
Chartered 4/9/84
Liquidated 9/20/93
Brown Back <$VALUE
3x10-20 1-1394 <$1500
Total Issue $69,700
Out in 1910 $260
****
748 Washington
FNB OF MONTPELIER
{{ 12 L 17 S }}
Chartered 1/24/65
Original Series <$VALUE
3x1-2 1-6000 <$500/$1000
4x5 1-7800 <$600
4x10 1-4750 <$750
3x20-50 1-400 <$1500/$6000
Series 1875
4x5 1-593 <$600
4x10 1-3944 <$750
3x20-50 1-1188<$1500/$6000
Brown Back
4x5 1-11907 <$450
3x10-20 1-1580 <$450
1902 Red Seal
3x10-20 1-3900 <$500
1902 Date Back
3x10-20 1-8400 <$250
1902 Plain Back
3x10-20 8401-24942 <$250

1929 Small Size
10 Type 1 1-2828 <$100
20 Type 1 1-760 <$115
5 Type 2 1-324 <$135
10 Type 2 1-3456 <$135
20 Type 2 1-751 <$135
Total Issue $2,792,100
Out in 1935 $100,000
Large out 1935 $8,005
****
857 Washington
MONTPELIER NB, MONTPELIER
{{ 16 L 16 S }}
Chartered 3/3/65
Liquidated 1/29/35
Original Series <$VALUE
3x1-2 1-9000 <$450/$1000
4x5 1-9000 <$500
3x10-20 1-6850 <$750/$1500
50-100 1-150 <$6000
Series 1875
4x5 1-9250 <$500
3x10-20 1-6930 <$750/$1500
Brown Back
4x5 1-20103 <$400
3x10-20 1-11929 <$400
1902 Red Seal
4x5 1-6300 <$450
3x10-20 1-4180 <$450
1902 Date Back
4x5 1-11250 <$175
3x10-20 1-9100 <$175
1902 Plain Back
4x5 11251-40007 <$175
3x10-20 9101-26428 <$175
1929 Small Size
5 Type 1 1-4934 <$100
10 Type 1 1-2696 <$100
20 Type 1 1-724 <$110
5 Type 2 1-2880 <$125
10 Type 2 1-1100 <$125
20 Type 2 1-100 <$150
Total Issue $5,000,610
Out at close $88,620
Large out at close $14,220
****
2263 Orleans
NB OF NEWPORT
{{ 10 L 13 S }}
Chartered 3/17/75
Original Series <$VALUE
3x10-20 1-1800 <$850/$1500
Series 1875
3x10-20 1-2531 <$850/$1500
Brown Back
3x10-20 1-5600 <$400
1882 Date Back
3x10-20 1-5945 <$400
1902 Date Back
4x5 1-1500 <$200
4x10 1-1500 <$200
1902 Plain Back
4x5 1501-20257 <$200
4x10 1501-15510 <$200
1929 Small Size
5 Type 1 1-4218 <$110
10 Type 1 1-2546 <$110
5 Type 2 1-9246 <$135
10 Type 2 1-3997 <$135
Total Issue $2,184,840
Out in 1935 $74,400
Large out 1935 $3,880
****
194 Bennington
FNB OF NORTH BENNINGTON
{{ 16 L 3U + 20 S }}
Chartered 1/64
Original Series <$VALUE
3x1-2 1-8940 <$400/$1000
4x5 1-14250 <$500
4x10 1-12125 <$750
3x20-50 1-1680<$1500/$6000
Series 1875
4x5 1-12915 <$500
4x10 1-5480 <$750
Brown Back
4x5 1-35730 <$300
3x10-20 1-3111 <$350
1902 Red Seal
4x5 1-7950 <$350
3x10-20 1-6220 <$350
1902 Date Back
4x5 1-11750 <$150
3x10-20 1-8200 <$150
1902 Plain Back
4x5 11751-40962 <$150
3x10-20 8201-25256 <$150
1929 Small Size
5 Type 1 1-5562 <$70
10 Type 1 1-2984 <$70
20 Type 1 1-688 <$85
5 Type 2 1-7576 <$100
10 Type 2 1-4500 <$100
20 Type 2 1-1116 <$100

Total Issue $5,432,850
Out in 1935 $150,000
Large out 1935 $16,345
****
1638 Washington
NORTHFIELD NB, NORTHFIELD
{{ 6 L 6 S }}
Chartered 1866
Original Series <$VALUE
3x1-2 1-1600 <$500/$1500
4x5 1-4000 <$650
3x10-20 1-1900 <$850/$1500
Series 1875
3x1-2 1-2180 <$500/$1500
4x5 1-2500 <$650
3x10-20 1-1880 <$850/$1500
Brown Back
3x10-20 1-5500 <$500
1902 Red Seal
3x10-20 1-1500 <$600
1902 Date Back
3x10-20 1-3940 <$300
1902 Plain Back
3x10-20 3941-9116 <$300
1929 Small Size
10 Type 1 1-768 <$200
20 Type 1 1-228 <$200
10 Type 2 1-789 <$250
20 Type 2 1-168 <$250
Total Issue $1,228,390
Out in 1935 $30,000
Large out 1935 $3,880
****
228 Addison
FNB OF ORWELL
{{ 7 L 18 S }}
Chartered 2/64
Original Series <$VALUE
3x1-2 1-4200 <$500/$1250
4x5 1-3700 <$600
3x10-20 1-2200 <$750/$1500
Series 1875
3x1-2 1-480 <$500/$1250
4x5 1-425 <$600
3x10-20 1-2000 <$750/$1500
Brown Back
4x5 1-4714 <$450
3x10-20 1-4832 <$450
1902 Red Seal
4x5 1-2600 <$500
3x10-20 1-1920 <$500
1902 Date Back
4x5 1-3175 <$275
3x10-20 1-2360 <$275
1902 Plain Back
4x5 3176-11124 <$275
3x10-20 2361-7787 <$275
1929 Small Size
5 Type 1 1-1932 <$100
10 Type 1 1-872 <$100
20 Type 1 1-248 <$110
5 Type 2 1-2982 <$135
10 Type 2 1-1459 <$135
20 Type 2 1-419 <$150
Total Issue $1,589,530
Out in 1935 $50,000
Large out 1935 $4,600
****
9824 Rutland
CITIZENS NB OF POULTNEY
{{ 5 L 8 S }}
Organized 2/2/10
Liquidated 11/2/34
1902 Date Back <$VALUE
3x10-20 1-4640 <$400
1902 Plain Back
3x10-20 4641-13705 <$400
1929 Small Size
10 Type 1 1-1348 <$135
20 Type 1 1-400 <$150
10 Type 2 1-77 <$200
20 Type 2 1-25 <$200
Total Issue $815,400
Out at close $29,690
Large out at close $190
Ch 14234 assumed circulation
****
13261 Rutland
FNB IN POULTNEY
{{ UNREPORTED }}
Organized 11/12/28
Receivership 6/20/30
1902 Plain Back <$VALUE
3x10-20 1-469 <$1000
1929 Small Size
10 Type 1 1-504 <$600
20 Type 1 1-92 <$600
Total Issue $64,730
Out at close $48,435
Large out at close $8,105
Outstanding includes Ch 2545
****

2545 Rutland
FNB OF POULTNEY
{{ 6 L }}
Chartered 1881
Liquidated 3/5/29
Series 1875 <$VALUE
4x5 1-7245 <$650
3x10-20 1-430 <$850/$1500
Brown Back
4x5 1-1250 <$500
3x10-20 1-3000 <$500
1882 Date Back
4x5 1-4250 <$500
3x10-20 1-3080 <$500
1882 Value Back
4x5 4251-7995 <$650
3x10-20 3081-5233 <$650
1902 Plain Back
4x5 1-5611 <$300
3x10-20 1-3955 <$300
Total Issue $1,072,920
Out at close $38,045
Ch 13261 assumed circulation

1200 Rutland
NB OF POULTNEY
{{ 1 L }}
Organized 5/31/65
Receivership 4/7/79
Original Series <$VALUE
4x5 1-10275 <$2000
Series 1875
4x5 1-2070 <$2000
Total Issue $246,900
Out in 1910 $1,440

14234 Rutland
POULTNEY NB, POULTNEY
{{ 5 S }}
Chartered 7/34
1929 Small Size <$VALUE
5 Type 2 1-196 <$400
10 Type 2 1-105 <$400
Total Issue $2,030
Out in 1935 $25,000
Outstanding includes Ch 9824

1383 Windsor
N BLACK RIVER B OF PROCTORSVILLE
{{ 3 L 6 S }}
Organized 5/22/65
Receivership 12/5/33
Original Series <$VALUE
3x1-2 1-1000 <$850/$2000
4x5 1-2500 <$1000
3x10-20 1-400 <$1250/$2000
Series 1875
4x5 1-500 <$1000
3x10-20 1-1297<$1250/$2000
Brown Back
3x10-20 1-2348 <$1000
1902 Red Seal
3x10-20 1-740 <$1250
1902 Date Back
3x10-20 1-1850 <$500
1902 Plain Back
3x10-20 1851-4648 <$500
1929 Small Size
10 Type 1 1-560 <$250
20 Type 1 1-148 <$250
5 Type 2 1-84 <$300
10 Type 2 1-30 <$300
Total Issue $589,450
Out at close $25,000
Large out at close $2,300

Randolph NB of Randolph
SEE Ch 2274
Randolph NB of West Randolph

11615 Franklin
RICHFORD NB, RICHFORD
{{ 6 L 10 S }}
Chartered 2/20
1902 Plain Back <$VALUE
4x5 1-7300 <$325
4x10 1-6394 <$325
1929 Small Size
5 Type 1 1-2652 <$165
10 Type 1 1-1310 <$165
5 Type 2 1-3630 <$185
10 Type 2 1-2584 <$185
Total Issue $603,910
Out in 1935 $50,000
Large out 1935 $1,050

1673 Windsor
NB OF ROYALTON
{{ 3 L }}
Chartered 1867
Liquidated 1/10/82
Original Series <$VALUE
3x1-2 1-2260 <$750/$1500
3x10-20 1-4165<$1000/$2000
Total Issue $219,550
Out in 1910 $994

1700 Rutland
BAXTER NB OF RUTLAND
Organized 8/10/70
2nd title:Central NB of Rutland 4/18/28
FIRST TITLE {{ 10 L }}
Original Series <$VALUE
3x1-2 1-7000 <$375/$1000
4x5 1-11500 <$450
3x10-20 1-4500 <$750/$1500
Series 1875
4x5 1-12386 <$450
3x10-20 1-8760 <$750/$1500
Brown Back
4x5 1-5000 <$350
3x10-20 1-27500 <$350
1882 Date Back
4x5 1-1856 <$350
3x10-20 1-377 <$350
1902 Date Back
3x10-20 1-5600 <$175
1902 Plain Back
3x10-20 5601-20233 <$175
SECOND TITLE {{ 1 L 13 S }}
1902 Plain Back
3x10-20 1-844 <$400
1929 Small Size
10 Type 1 1-2566 <$80
20 Type 1 1-708 <$90
10 Type 2 1-2609 <$125
20 Type 2 1-784 <$125
Total Issue $4,041,230
Out in 1935 $100,000
Large out 1935 $9,610

Central NB of Rutland
SEE Ch 1700
Baxter NB of Rutland

2950 Rutland
CLEMENT NB OF RUTLAND
{{ 11 L 17 S }}
Organized 4/21/83
Brown Back <$VALUE
4x5 1-5590 <$400
3x10-20 1-4494 <$400
1902 Red Seal
3x10-20 1-2900 <$450
1902 Date Back
3x10-20 1-9800 <$165
1902 Plain Back
3x10-20 9801-27444 <$165
1929 Small Size
10 Type 1 1-2834 <$75
20 Type 1 1-724 <$80
10 Type 2 1-3165 <$100
20 Type 2 1-684 <$100
Total Issue $2,155,950
Out in 1935 $100,000
Large out 1935 $4,540

2905 Rutland
KILLINGTON NB OF RUTLAND
{{ 3 L 6 S }}
Chartered 1883
Brown Back <$VALUE
4x5 1-7222 <$650
3x10-20 1-5732 <$650
1902 Red Seal
50-100 1-1760 <$3500/$4000
1902 Date Back
50-100 1-1100 <$850/$1000
3x50-100 1-2100<$850/$1000
1902 Plain Back
3x50-100 2101-2600 <$850/$1000
1929 Small Size
50 Type 1 1-290 <$300
100 Type 1 1-106 <$400
5 Type 2 1-240 <$200
20 Type 2 1-30 <$225
Total Issue $1,662,440
Out in 1935 $100,000
Large out 1935 $8,300

3311 Rutland
MERCHANTS NB OF RUTLAND
{{ UNREPORTED }}
Organized 2/25/85
Receivership 3/26/00
Brown Back <$VALUE
4x5 1-4511 <$2000
3x10-20 1-760 <$2000
Total Issue $128,220
Out in 1916 $455

1450 Rutland
NB OF RUTLAND
{{ 7 L }}
Chartered 1865
Liquidated 1/13/85
Original Series <$VALUE
3x1-2 1-24000 <$400/$1250
4x5 1-15595 <$500
3x10-20 1-7595 <$750/$1500
50-100 1-735 <$6000
Series 1875
3x1-2 1-3800 <$400/$1250
4x5 1-7645 <$500
3x10-20 1-6644 <$750/$1500
50-100 1-300 <$6000
Total Issue $1,471,000
Out in 1910 $6,970

820 Rutland
RUTLAND COUNTY NB, RUTLAND
{{ 9 L 10 S }}
Chartered 2/18/65
Original Series <$VALUE
3x1-2 1-6000 <$400/$1000
4x5 1-5250 <$500
3x10-20 1-3010 <$750/$1500
50-100 1-730 <$6000
Series 1875
3x1-2 1-1440 <$400/$1000
4x5 1-10430 <$500
3x10-20 1-3972 <$750/$1500
50-100 1-60 <$6000
Brown Back
4x5 1-10601 <$400
3x10-20 1-6216 <$400
1902 Red Seal
4x5 1-1875 <$450
3x10-20 1-1550 <$450
1902 Date Back
4x5 1-3500 <$175
3x10-20 1-2800 <$175
1902 Plain Back
4x5 3501-10540 <$175
3x10-20 2801-7734 <$175
1929 Small Size
5 Type 1 1-1566 <$150
10 Type 1 1-746 <$150
20 Type 1 1-232 <$165
5 Type 2 1-2614 <$175
10 Type 2 1-1238 <$175
20 Type 2 1-321 <$200
Total Issue $2,205,170
Out in 1935 $50,000
Large out 1935 $7,040

269 Franklin
FNB OF SAINT ALBANS
{{ UNREPORTED }}
Organized 2/20/64
Receivership 4/22/84
Original Series <$VALUE
4x5 1-2000 <$1250
4x10 1-4125 <$1500
Series 1875
4x10 1-1674 <$1500
Brown Back
3x10-20 1-604 <$1250
Total Issue $302,160
Out in 1916 $1,740

1583 Franklin
VERMONT NB OF SAINT ALBANS
{{ 1 L }}
Organized 10/11/65
Receivership 8/9/83
Original Series <$VALUE
4x5 1-5000 <$1000
3x10-20 1-5000<$1500/$2000
Series 1875
4x5 1-1500 <$1000
3x10-20 1-1266<$1500/$2000
Total Issue $443,300
Out in 1916 $2,230

13800 Franklin
WELDEN NB IN SAINT ALBANS
{{ 4 S }}
Chartered 10/33
1929 Small Size <$VALUE
5 Type 2 1-2976 <$275
10 Type 2 1-2955 <$275
20 Type 2 1-1300 <$275
Total Issue $70,430
Out in 1935 $47,200

3482 Franklin
WELDEN NB OF SAINT ALBANS
{{ 6 L 7 S }}
Organized 2/17/86
Receivership 12/28/33
Brown Back <$VALUE
4x5 1-900 <$500
3x10-20 1-4756 <$500
1902 Red Seal
3x10-20 1-1400 <$500
1902 Date Back
4x5 1-4433 <$200
3x10-20 1-3470 <$200
1902 Plain Back
4x5 4434-13750 <$200
3x10-20 3471-9317 <$200
1929 Small Size
5 Type 1 1-1938 <$175
10 Type 1 1-943 <$175
20 Type 1 1-260 <$185
Total Issue $1,212,570
Out at close $49,400
Large out at close $2,500

489 Caledonia
FNB OF SAINT JOHNSBURY
{{ 16 L 27 S }}
Chartered 7/64
Original Series <$VALUE
3x1-2 1-5000 <$350/$1000
4x5 1-7100 <$400
3x10-20 1-9280 <$750/$1500
50-100 1-1900 <$6000
Series 1875
3x1-2 1-7000 <$350/$1000
4x5 1-7375 <$400
3x10-20 1-5500 <$750/$1500
Brown Back
4x5 1-9081 <$300
3x10-20 1-15651 <$300
50-100 1-567 <$3000/$3500
1902 Red Seal
4x5 1-12300 <$300
3x10-20 1-10480 <$300
1902 Date Back
4x5 1-14250 <$110
3x10-20 1-10900 <$110
1902 Plain Back
4x5 14251-50198 <$110
3x10-20 10901-33672 <$110
1929 Small Size
5 Type 1 1-7414 <$50
10 Type 1 1-3730 <$50
20 Type 1 1-974 <$55
5 Type 2 1-10316 <$65
10 Type 2 1-5637 <$65
20 Type 2 1-1716 <$70
Total Issue $6,585,650
Out in 1935 $200,000
Large out 1935 $14,040

2295 Caledonia
MERCHANTS NB OF SAINT JOHNSBURY
{{ 9 L 12 S }}
Chartered 9/2/75
Series 1875 <$VALUE
4x5 1-12969 <$450
3x10-20 1-3733 <$750/$1500
Brown Back
4x5 1-14100 <$350
3x10-20 1-15410 <$350
1882 Date Back
4x5 1-12265 <$350
3x10-20 1-7421 <$350
1902 Date Back
4x5 1-2500 <$165
3x10-20 1-2000 <$165
1902 Plain Back
4x5 2501-12250 <$165
3x10-20 2001-7939 <$165
1929 Small Size
5 Type 1 1-2414 <$100
10 Type 1 1-1182 <$100
20 Type 1 1-292 <$110
5 Type 2 1-2758 <$135
10 Type 2 1-360 <$135
Total Issue $2,974,090
Out in 1935 $64,105
Large out 1935 $5,985

122 Windsor
FNB OF SPRINGFIELD
{{ 16 L 22 S }}
Chartered 5/30/63
Original Series <$VALUE
3x1-2 1-4200 <$400/$1000
4x5 1-8750 <$450
3x10-20 1-2700 <$750/$1500
50-100 1-300 <$6000
Series 1875
4x5 1-1895 <$450
3x10-20 1-1352 <$750/$1500
50-100 1-186 <$6000
Brown Back
4x5 1-5473 <$300
3x10-20 1-1718 <$300
50-100 1-40 <$3000/$3500
1902 Red Seal
3x10-20 1-6700 <$350
1902 Date Back
4x10 1-5150* <$135
3x10-20 1-4300 <$135
1902 Plain Back
4x10 5851-47264* <$135
* 5151-5850 not marked
1929 Small Size
10 Type 1 1-9622 <$65
10 Type 2 1-3139 <$75
Total Issue $3,760,030
Out in 1935 $100,000
Large out 1935 $9,450

4258 Franklin
FERRIS NB OF SWANTON
{{ UNREPORTED }}
Chartered 3/14/90
Liquidated 4/18/90
Brown Back <$VALUE
4x5 1-562 <$1500
Total Issue $11,240
All notes reportedly redeemed

1634 Franklin
N UNION B OF SWANTON
{{ 1 L }}
Chartered 1866
Liquidated 4/28/85
Original Series <$VALUE
4x5 1-3850 <$1250
4x10 1-2000 <$1500
Series 1875
4x5 1-2245 <$1250
4x10 1-985 <$1500
Total Issue $241,300
Out in 1910 $1,070

4943 Franklin
PEOPLES NB OF SWANTON
{{ 1 L }}
Organized 3/7/94
Receivership 8/18/04
Brown Back <$VALUE
4x5 1-2685 <$1250
3x10-20 1-1363 <$1250
Total Issue $121,850
Out in 1916 $820

2475 Addison
FARMERS NB OF VERGENNES
{{ 4 L }}
Chartered 4/29/80
Receivership 4/13/01
Series 1875 <$VALUE
4x5 1-11620 <$650
Brown Back
3x10-20 1-138 <$600
Total Issue $239,300
Out in 1916 $890

1364 Addison
NB OF VERGENNES
{{ 18 L 24 S }}
Chartered 1865
Original Series <$VALUE
3x1-2 1-6500 <$400/$1000
4x5 1-700 <$450
3x10-20 1-2300 <$750/$1500
50-100 1-434 <$6000
Series 1875
4x5 1-4135 <$450
3x10-20 1-856 <$750/$1500
50-100 1-244 <$6000
Brown Back
4x5 1-17980 <$300
3x10-20 1-6250 <$300
50-100 1-1498 <$3000/$3500
1902 Red Seal
4x5 1-4100 <$350
3x10-20 1-2690 <$350
50-100 1-210 <$3500/$4000
1902 Date Back
4x5 1-10600 <$135
3x10-20 1-7580 <$135
50-100 1-200 <$650/$750
3x50-100 1-400 <$650/$750
1902 Plain Back
4x5 10601-33555 <$135
3x10-20 7581-20390 <$135
3x50-100 401-685<$650/$750
1929 Small Size
5 Type 1 1-4220 <$65
10 Type 1 1-1756 <$65
20 Type 1 1-560 <$75
50 Type 1 1-172 <$500
100 Type 1 1-44 <$600
5 Type 2 1-4082 <$85
10 Type 2 1-2150 <$85
20 Type 2 1-600 <$90
Total Issue $3,955,420
Out in 1935 $150,000
Large out 1935 $9,550

1462 Washington
WATERBURY NB, WATERBURY
{{ 2 L }}
Chartered 1865
Liquidated 10/1/11
Original Series <$VALUE
4x5 1-5050 <$1000
3x10-20 1-1367<$1250/$2000
Series 1875
4x5 1-2750 <$1000
3x10-20 1-2000<$1250/$2000
Brown Back
4x5 1-1100 <$850
3x10-20 1-4066 <$850
1902 Red Seal
3x10-20 1-1190 <$1000
1902 Date Back
3x10-20 1-796 <$600
Total Issue $648,950
Out in 1912 $4,350

1406 Orange
NB OF NEWBURY, WELLS RIVER
Chartered 1865
2nd title: NB of Newbury at Wells River 5/20/05
FIRST TITLE {{ 12 L }}
Original Series <$VALUE
3x1-2 1-7260 <$500/$1250
4x5 1-4600 <$600
3x10-20 1-3550 <$850/$1500
3x50-100 1-340 <$6000
Series 1875
4x5 1-5148 <$600
3x10-20 1-6114 <$850/$1500
50-100 1-146 <$6000
Brown Back
4x5 1-12500 <$300
3x10-20 1-19000 <$300
SECOND TITLE {{ 27 L 36 S }}
1902 Red Seal
4x5 1-9750 <$350
4x10 1-3125 <$350
3x10-20 1-4900 <$350
1902 Date Back
4x5 1-23500 <$125
4x10 1-17250 <$125
3x10-20 1-3500 <$125
1902 Plain Back
4x5 23501-87773 <$125
4x10 18501-65523* <$125
* 17257-18500 not marked
1929 Small Size
5 Type 1 1-16786 <$40
10 Type 1 1-6996 <$40
5 Type 2 1-27934 <$45
10 Type 2 1-17512 <$45
Total Issue $8,390,470
Out in 1935 $300,000
Large out 1935 $15,500

2274 Orange
RANDOLPH NB OF WEST RANDOLPH
Chartered 6/7/75
2nd title:Randolph NB of Randolph 5/21/95
FIRST TITLE {{ 0 L }}
Original Series <$VALUE
4x5 1-1500 <$1500
3x10-20 1-600 <$1750/$2000
Series 1875
4x5 1-5482 <$1500
3x10-20 1-1171<$1750/$2000
SECOND TITLE {{ 1 L }}
Brown Back
3x10-20 1-2421 <$1000
1882 Date Back
3x10-20 1-1394 <$1000
1902 Date Back
3x50-100 1-400 <$850/$1000
1902 Plain Back
3x50-100 401-438<$850/$1000
Total Issue $528,440
Out in 1935 $2,265

****

9108 Windsor
HARTFORD NB OF
WHITE RIVER JUNCTION
{{ 1 L }}
Chartered 4/08
Liquidated 7/15/14

1902 Red Seal		<$VALUE
4x5	1-500	<$1500
3x10-20	1-400	<$1500
1902 Date Back		
4x5	1-1185	<$1000
3x10-20	1-942	<$1000
Total Issue		$100,800
Out in 1914		$15,050

****

3484 Windsor
NB OF
WHITE RIVER JUNCTION
Chartered 1886
2nd title:FNB of White River Junction 1/20/10
FIRST TITLE **{{ 8 L }}**

Brown Back		<$VALUE
4x5	1-18675	<$500
3x10-20	1-4180	<$500
1902 Red Seal		
4x5	1-2000	<$600
3x10-20	1-1600	<$600
1902 Date Back		
4x5	1-1443	<$250
3x10-20	1-1444	<$250

SECOND TITLE **{{ 11 L 20 S }}**

1902 Date Back		
4x10	1-10050	<$175
1902 Plain Back		
4x10	10051-33480	<$175
1929 Small Size		
10 Type 1	1-5683	<$75
Total Issue		$2,483,740
Out in 1935		$100,000
Large out 1935		$5,175

****

816 Windsor
ASCUTNEY NB OF WINDSOR
{{ UNREPORTED }}
Chartered 2/18/65
Liquidated 10/19/80

Original Series		<$VALUE
3x1-2	1-1500	<$1250/$2000
4x5	1-4390	<$1250
3x10-20	1-1650	<$1500/$2000
Series 1875		
3x10-20	1-1304	<$1500/$2000
Total Issue		$243,000
Out in 1910		$1,460

****

7721 Windsor
STATE NB OF WINDSOR
{{ 1 L }}
Organized 3/25/05
Receivership 12/11/33

1902 Red Seal		<$VALUE
3x10-20	1-1100	<$1250
1902 Date Back		
3x10-20	1-2340*	<$750
1902 Plain Back		
3x10-20	2541-5960*	<$750

* 2341-2540 not marked

Total Issue	$353,000
Out at close	$900

****

3257 Windsor
WINDSOR NB, WINDSOR
{{ UNREPORTED }}
Chartered 10/18/84
Liquidated 2/24/91

Brown Back		<$VALUE
3x10-20	1-897	<$1500
Total Issue		$44,850
Out in 1910		$245

****

1133 Windsor
WOODSTOCK NB, WOODSTOCK
{{ U + 17 L 8 S }}
Chartered 1865

Original Series			<$VALUE
3x1-2	1-5000		<$450/$1000
4x5	1-12000		<$500
3x10-20	1-3300		<$750/$1500
50-100	1-370		<$6000
Series 1875			
3x1-2	1-3820		<$450/$1000
4x5	1-10895		<$500
3x10-20	1-2578		<$750/$1500
50-100	1-688		<$6000
Brown Back			
4x5	1-24305		<$300
3x10-20	1-10460		<$300
1902 Red Seal			
4x5	1-2500		<$400
3x10-20	1-4600		<$400
1902 Date Back			
4x5	1-10750		<$135
3x10-20	1-4600		<$135
1902 Plain Back			
4x5	10751-22189		<$135
3x10-20	4601-11191		<$135
1929 Small Size			
5	Type 1	1-1522	<$135
10	Type 1	1-716	<$135
20	Type 1	1-218	<$150
5	Type 2	1-2516	<$175
10	Type 2	1-1264	<$175
20	Type 2	1-396	<$175
Total Issue			$3,394,950
Out in 1935			$50,000
Large out 1935			$8,885

****

<$VALUEs are for notes in **FINE** condition. Value changes by approximately **25%** for a change of one full grade.

VIRGINIA

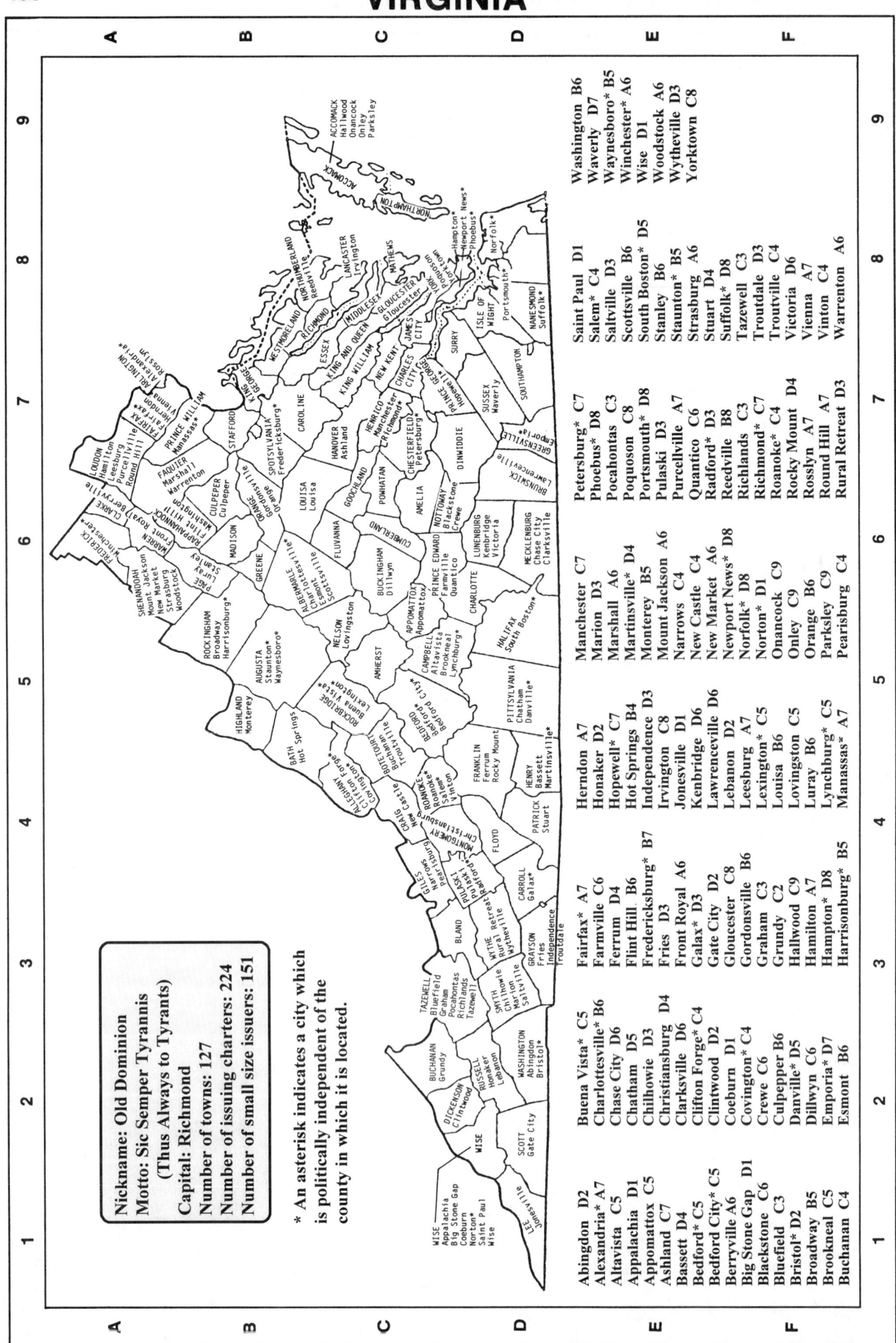

Nickname: Old Dominion
Motto: Sic Semper Tyrannis
(Thus Always to Tyrants)
Capital: Richmond
Number of towns: 127
Number of issuing charters: 224
Number of small size issuers: 151

* An asterisk indicates a city which is politically independent of the county in which it is located.

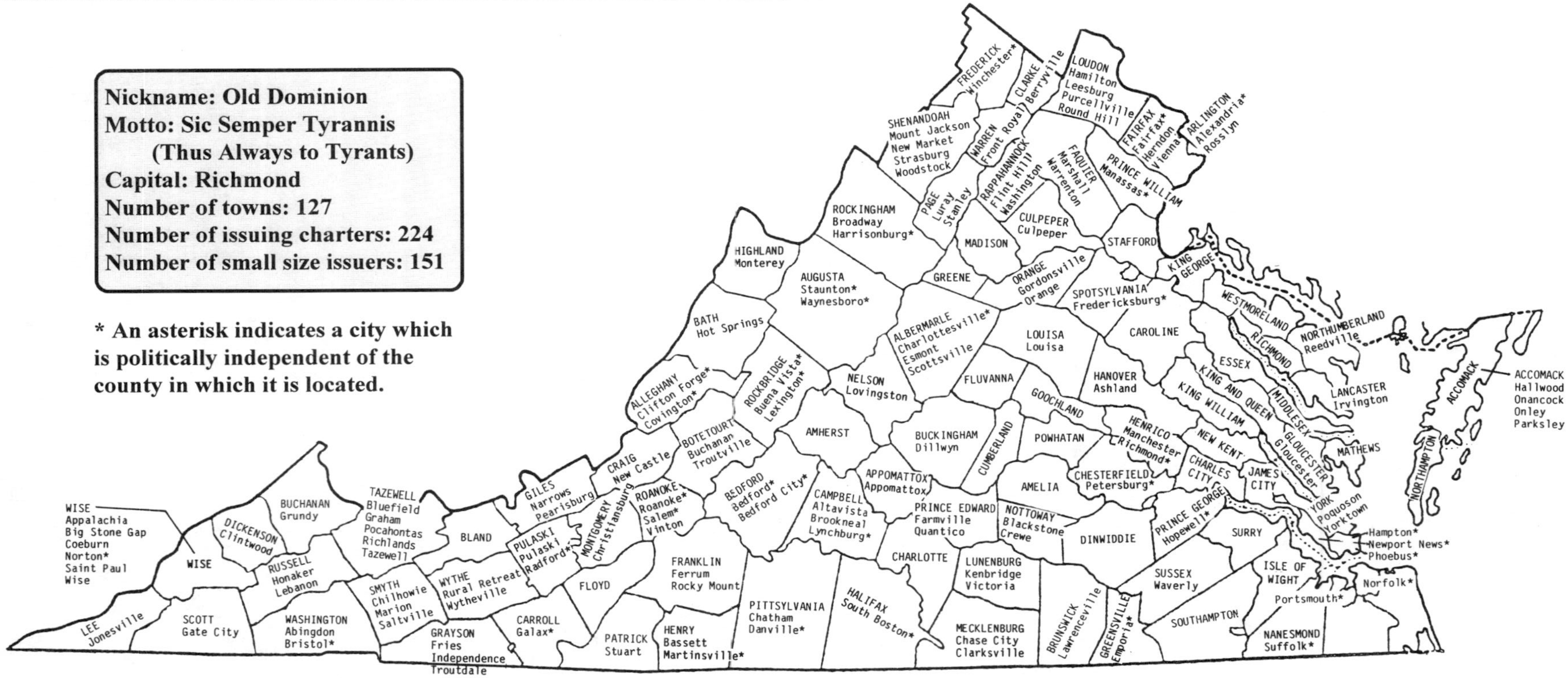

Abingdon D2
Alexandria* A7
Altavista C5
Appalachia D1
Appomattox C5
Ashland C7
Bassett D4
Bedford* C5
Bedford City* C5
Berryville A6
Big Stone Gap D1
Blackstone C6
Bluefield C3
Bristol* D2
Broadway B5
Brookneal C5
Buchanan C4

Buena Vista* C5
Charlottesville* B6
Chase City D6
Chatham D5
Chilhowie D3
Christiansburg D4
Clarksville D6
Clifton Forge* C4
Clintwood D2
Coeburn D1
Covington* C4
Crewe C6
Culpepper B6
Danville* D5
Dillwyn C6
Emporia* D7
Esmont B6

Fairfax* A7
Farmville C6
Ferrum D4
Flint Hill B6
Fredericksburg* B7
Fries D3
Front Royal A6
Galax* D3
Gate City D2
Gloucester C8
Gordonsville B6
Graham C3
Grundy C2
Hallwood C9
Hamilton A7
Hampton* D8
Harrisonburg* B5

Herndon A7
Honaker D2
Hopewell* C7
Hot Springs B4
Independence D3
Irvington C8
Jonesville D1
Kenbridge D6
Lawrenceville D6
Lebanon D2
Leesburg A7
Lexington* C5
Louisa B6
Lovingston C5
Luray B6
Lynchburg* C5
Manassas* A7

Manchester C7
Marion D3
Marshall A6
Martinsville* D4
Monterey B5
Mount Jackson A6
Narrows C4
New Castle C4
New Market A6
Newport News* D8
Norfolk* D8
Norton* D1
Onancock C9
Onley C9
Orange B6
Parksley C9
Pearisburg C4

Petersburg* C7
Phoebus* D8
Pocahontas C3
Poquoson C8
Portsmouth* D8
Pulaski D3
Purcellville A7
Quantico C6
Radford* D3
Reedville B8
Richlands C3
Richmond* C7
Roanoke* C4
Rocky Mount D4
Rosslyn A7
Round Hill A7
Rural Retreat D3

Saint Paul D1
Salem* C4
Saltville D3
Scottsville B6
South Boston* D5
Stanley B6
Staunton* B5
Strasburg A6
Stuart D4
Suffolk* D8
Tazewell C3
Troutdale D3
Troutville C4
Victoria D6
Vienna A7
Vinton C4
Warrenton A6

Washington B6
Waverly D7
Waynesboro* B5
Winchester* A6
Wise D1
Woodstock A6
Wytheville D3
Yorktown C8

****

5150 Washington
FNB OF ABINGDON
{{ 14 L 20 S }}
Organized 10/3/98
Liquidated 4/16/35
Brown Back <$VALUE
4x5 1-6375 <$500
3x10-20 1-3900 <$500
1882 Date Back
4x5 1-6550 <$500
3x10-20 1-5100 <$500
1882 Value Back
4x5 6551-8355 <$500
3x10-20 5101-6392 <$500
1902 Plain Back
4x5 1-101735 <$200
1929 Small Size
5 Type 1 1-27812 <$85
5 Type 2 1-25626 <$85
Total Issue $3,806,390
Out in 1935 $200,000
Large out 1935 $8,785

****

8819 Washington
PEOPLES NB OF ABINGDON
{{ 6 L }}
Chartered 8/07
Liquidated 5/31/26
1902 Red Seal <$VALUE
4x5 1-800 <$850
3x10-20 1-650 <$850
1902 Date Back
4x5 1-3600 <$400
3x10-20 1-2780 <$400
1902 Plain Back
4x5 3601-15600 <$400
3x10-20 2781-11012 <$400
Total Issue $911,100
Out at close $100,000

****

7093 Independent City
ALEXANDRIA NB, ALEXANDRIA
{{ 10 L 15 S }}
Chartered 1/04
1902 Red Seal <$VALUE
3x10-20 1-6000 <$650
1902 Date Back
3x10-20 1-9000 <$275
1902 Plain Back
3x10-20 9001-33744 <$275
1929 Small Size
10 Type 1 1-5490 <$100
20 Type 1 1-1460 <$100
10 Type 2 1-7794 <$100
20 Type 2 1-2424 <$100
Total Issue $2,618,220
Out in 1935 $150,000
Large out 1935 $530

****

1716 Independent City
CITIZENS NB OF ALEXANDRIA
{{ 12 L 21 S }}
Chartered 10/8/70
Original Series <$VALUE
4x5 1-1250 <$1250
3x10-20 1-2700<$1500/$2000
Series 1875
3x10-20 1-3214<$1500/$2000
Brown Back
3x10-20 1-5500 <$500
50-100 1-530 <$3500/$4000
1882 Date Back
3x10-20 1-1854 <$500
50-100 1-171 <$3500/$4000
1902 Date Back
3x10-20 1-8700 <$200
1902 Plain Back
3x10-20 8701-48583 <$200
1929 Small Size
10 Type 1 1-7366 <$85
20 Type 1 1-1936 <$85
10 Type 2 1-9720 <$100
20 Type 2 1-2868 <$100
Total Issue $4,051,540
Out in 1935 $200,000
Large out 1935 $5,970

****

651 Independent City
FNB OF ALEXANDRIA
{{ 10 L 14 S }}
Chartered 12/64
Original Series <$VALUE
4x5 1-3550 <$1250
3x10-20 1-2100<$1500/$2000
Series 1875
3x10-20 1-2880<$1500/$2000
Brown Back
3x10-20 1-7457 <$500
1902 Red Seal
3x10-20 1-3400 <$600
1902 Date Back
3x10-20 1-6600* <$250
1902 Plain Back
3x10-20 7101-28819* <$250
* 6601-7100 not marked
1929 Small Size
10 Type 1 1-3686 <$85
20 Type 1 1-940 <$100
10 Type 2 1-5207 <$110
20 Type 2 1-1476 <$125
Total Issue $2,026,500
Out in 1935 $100,000
Large out 1935 $5,550

****

9295 Campbell
FNB OF ALTAVISTA
{{ 5 L 10 S }}
Chartered 12/08
1902 Date Back <$VALUE
4x5 1-4100 <$500
3x10-20 1-3120 <$500
1902 Plain Back
4x5 4101-15295 <$500
3x10-20 3121-10630 <$500
1929 Small Size
5 Type 1 1-2194 <$200
10 Type 1 1-1216 <$200
20 Type 1 1-344 <$225
5 Type 2 1-3936 <$250
10 Type 2 1-2028 <$250
20 Type 2 1-636 <$250
Total Issue $1,070,140
Out in 1935 $50,000
Large out 1935 $1,870

****

9379 Wise
FNB OF APPALACHIA
{{ 3 L 12 S }}
Chartered 4/09
1902 Date Back <$VALUE
3x10-20 1-4880 <$600
1902 Plain Back
3x10-20 4881-20102 <$600
1929 Small Size
10 Type 1 1-3158 <$200
20 Type 1 1-856 <$200
10 Type 2 1-6267 <$200
20 Type 2 1-1368 <$200
Total Issue $1,387,330
Out in 1935 $100,000
Large out 1935 $3,590

****

11205 Appomattox
FARMERS NB OF APPOMATTOX
{{ 2 L 8 S }}
Organized 6/22/18
1902 Plain Back <$VALUE
3x10-20 1-6933 <$750
1929 Small Size
10 Type 1 1-1956 <$275
20 Type 1 1-444 <$275
10 Type 2 1-2868 <$300
20 Type 2 1-882 <$300
Total Issue $563,610
Out in 1935 $50,000
Large out 1935 $1,510

****

11978 Hanover
FNB OF ASHLAND
{{ 4 L 4 S }}
Chartered 6/21
1902 Plain Back <$VALUE
4x5 1-6257 <$500
1929 Small Size
5 Type 1 1-2264 <$350
5 Type 2 1-10776 <$375
Total Issue $246,940
Out in 1935 $25,000
Large out 1935 $780

****

11976 Henry
FNB OF BASSETT
{{ 5 L 10 S }}
Chartered 6/21
1902 Plain Back <$VALUE
3x10-20 1-13074 <$500
1929 Small Size
10 Type 1 1-3938 <$200
20 Type 1 1-900 <$200
10 Type 2 1-5901 <$200
20 Type 2 1-2028 <$200
Total Issue $1,097,550
Out in 1935 $100,000
Large out 1935 $2,690

****

11328 Independent City
PEOPLES NB OF BEDFORD
{{ 4 L 12 S }}
Chartered 4/19
1902 Plain Back <$VALUE
4x5 1-12351 <$500
3x10-20 1-8402 <$500
1929 Small Size
10 Type 1 1-2156 <$150
20 Type 1 1-590 <$165
10 Type 2 1-4596 <$175
20 Type 2 1-1404 <$175
Total Issue $941,320
Out in 1935 $100,000
Large out 1935 $2,230

****

4257 Independent City
FNB OF BEDFORD CITY
{{ UNREPORTED }}
Organized 3/13/90
Receivership 5/2/96
Brown Back <$VALUE
4x5 1-1602 <$2000
Total Issue $32,040
Out in 1915 $190

****

7338 Clarke
FNB OF BERRYVILLE
{{ 0 L 2 S }}
Chartered 7/04
1902 Red Seal <$VALUE
3x10-20 1-440 <$2500
1902 Date Back
3x10-20 1-910* <$1500
1902 Plain Back
3x10-20 1011-2429* <$1500
* 911-1010 not marked
1929 Small Size
10 Type 1 1-293 <$600
20 Type 1 1-92 <$600
Total Issue $172,070
Out in 1935 $8,000
Large out 1935 $270

****

11765 Wise
FNB OF BIG STONE GAP
{{ 2 L 8 S }}
Chartered 6/20
1902 Plain Back <$VALUE
3x10-20 1-6171 <$1000
1929 Small Size
10 Type 1 1-1618 <$500
20 Type 1 1-400 <$500
10 Type 2 1-3042 <$500
20 Type 2 1-768 <$500
Total Issue $499,410
Out in 1935 $50,000
Large out 1935 $1,200

****

9224 Nottoway
FNB OF BLACKSTONE
{{ 8 L 13 S }}
Chartered 8/08
1902 Date Back <$VALUE
4x6 1-5400 <$300
4x10 1-5100 <$300
1902 Plain Back
4x5 5401-26477 <$300
4x10 5101-22809 <$300
1929 Small Size
5 Type 1 1-6634 <$110
10 Type 1 1-3418 <$110
5 Type 2 1-11364 <$125
10 Type 2 1-6336 <$125
Total Issue $1,966,180
Out in 1934 $97,250
Large out 1935 $3,895

****

Twin City NB of Bluefield
SEE Ch 7782
FNB of Graham

****

4477 Independent City
DOMINION NB OF BRISTOL
{{ 16 L 34 S }}
Chartered 1890
Brown Back <$VALUE
4x5 1-1250 <$500
3x10-20 1-3700 <$500
50-100 1-540 <$3500/$4000
1882 Date Back
4x5 1-1675 <$500
3x10-20 1-1225 <$500
50-100 1-25 <$3500/$4000
1902 Date Back
3x10-20 1-8300 <$175
1902 Plain Back
3x10-20 8301-47012 <$175
1929 Small Size
10 Type 1 1-8290 <$50
20 Type 1 1-3222 <$60
10 Type 2 1-9487 <$60
20 Type 2 1-4911 <$65
Total Issue $3,817,230
Out in 1935 $300,000
Large out 1935 $10,800

****

6666 Rockingham
FNB OF BROADWAY
{{ 0 L 1 S }}
Chartered 3/03
1902 Red Seal <$VALUE
3x10-20 1-450 <$2500
1902 Date Back
3x10-20 1-760 <$1500
1902 Plain Back
3x10-20 761-1620 <$1500
1929 Small Size
10 Type 1 1-242 <$750
20 Type 1 1-62 <$750
Total Issue $125,460
Out in 1935 $6,250
Large out 1935 $440

****

10835 Campbell
FNB OF BROOKNEAL
{{ 1 L }}
Chartered 3/16
Liquidated 1/11/27
1902 Plain Back <$VALUE
3x10-20 1-4028 <$850
Total Issue $201,400
Out at close $25,000

****

11960 Campbell
PEOPLES NB OF BROOKNEAL
{{ 1 L }}
Organized 8/7/20
Receivership 10/31/30
1902 Plain Back <$VALUE
3x10-20 1-584 <$1500
Total Issue $29,200
Out at close $490

****

9375 Botetourt
BUCHANAN NB, BUCHANAN
{{ 5 L 10 S }}
Chartered 4/09
1902 Date Back <$VALUE
3x10-20 1-2450 <$400
1902 Plain Back
3x10-20 2451-14513 <$400
1929 Small Size
10 Type 1 1-2130 <$200
20 Type 1 1-528 <$200
10 Type 2 1-3554 <$200
20 Type 2 1-687 <$225
Total Issue $966,090
Out in 1935 $60,000
Large out 1935 $2,130

****

4460 Botetourt
FNB OF BUCHANAN
{{ UNREPORTED }}
Chartered 11/8/90
Liquidated 9/30/99
Brown Back <$VALUE
3x10-20 1-704 <$2000
Total Issue $35,200
Out in 1910 $620

****

4314 Independent City
FNB OF BUENA VISTA
Chartered 1890
2nd title: FNB of Lexington 5/95
FIRST TITLE {{ 0 L }}
Brown Back <$VALUE
3x10-20 1-490 <$2000
SECOND TITLE {{ 5 L 10 S }}
Brown Back
4x5 1-1975 <$750
3x10-20 1-1160 <$750
1882 Date Back
4x5 1-742 <$750
3x10-20 1-524 <$750
1902 Date Back
3x10-20 1-3700 <$400
1902 Plain Back
3x10-20 3701-12805 <$400
1929 Small Size
10 Type 1 1-1686 <$200
20 Type 1 1-456 <$200
10 Type 2 1-2664 <$200
20 Type 2 1-588 <$225
Total Issue $997,570
Out in 1935 $50,000
Large out 1935 $730

****

9890 Independent City
FNB OF BUENA VISTA
{{ 1 L 1 S }}
Chartered 11/10
1902 Date Back <$VALUE
3x10-20 1-1500 <$1000
1902 Plain Back
3x10-20 1501-3605 <$1000
1929 Small Size
10 Type 1 1-454 <$650
20 Type 1 1-140 <$650
10 Type 2 1-504 <$650
20 Type 2 1-120 <$650
Total Issue $231,730
Out in 1935 $12,500
Large out 1935 $100

****

9246 Independent City
ALBEMARLE NB OF CHARLOTTESVILLE
{{ UNREPORTED }}
Chartered 10/08
Liquidated 9/24/14
1902 Date Back <$VALUE
3x10-20 1-2327 <$1000
Total Issue $116,350
Out at close $25,000
Ch 2594 assumed circulation

****

1468 Independent City
CHARLOTTESVILLE NB, CHARLOTTESVILLE
{{ UNREPORTED }}
Organized 7/19/65
Receivership 10/28/75
Original Series <$VALUE
4x5 1-7496 <$2000
3x10-20 1-2611<$2500/$3000
Total Issue $280,470
Out in 1910 $1,570

****

1742 Independent City
CITIZENS NB OF CHARLOTTESVILLE
{{ UNREPORTED }}
Chartered 12/1/70
Liquidated 4/27/74
Original Series <$VALUE
4x5 1-2685 <$2000
4x10 1-1018 <$2500
Total Issue $94,420
Out in 1910 $480

****

11517 Independent City
FARMERS & MERCHANTS NB OF CHARLOTTESVILLE
{{ 3 L }}
Chartered 11/19
Closed 4/10/26
1902 Plain Back <$VALUE
3x10-20 1-12896 <$500
Total Issue $644,800
Out at close $100,000
Ch 10618 assumed circulation

****

6005 Independent City
JEFFERSON NB OF CHARLOTTESVILLE
{{ 3 L }}
Chartered 10/01
Liquidated 1/11/17
Brown Back <$VALUE
3x10-20 1-1170 <$850
1882 Date Back
3x10-20 1-8100 <$850
1882 Value Back
3x10-20 8101-9398 <$850
Total Issue $528,400
Out in 1916 $97,800
Ch 2594 assumed circulation

****

10618 Independent City
NB OF CHARLOTTESVILLE
Chartered 9/14
2nd title: NB & TC at Charlottesville 6/30/28
FIRST TITLE {{ 11 L }}
1902 Date Back <$VALUE
4x5 1-4750 <$175
3x10-20 1-4000 <$175
1902 Plain Back
4x5 4751-5550 <$175
3x10-20 4001-83471 <$175
SECOND TITLE {{ 4 L 36 S }}
1902 Plain Back
3x10-20 1-9032 <$175
1929 Small Size
10 Type 1 1-17750 <$50
20 Type 1 1-4566 <$55
10 Type 2 1-9488 <$55
20 Type 2 1-2445 <$65
Total Issue $6,492,850
Out in 1935 $250,000
Large out 1935 $19,440
Outstanding includes Ch 11517

****

2594 Independent City
PEOPLES NB OF CHARLOTTESVILLE
{{ 19 L 36 S }}
Chartered 1881
Series 1875 <$VALUE
3x10-20 1-2486<$1500/$2000
Brown Back
3x10-20 1-1300 <$500
1882 Date Back
3x10-20 1-9900 <$500
1882 Value Back
3x10-20 9901-25800 <$500
1902 Plain Back
3x10-20 1-44792 <$150
1929 Small Size
10 Type 1 1-16458 <$40
20 Type 1 1-3670 <$50
10 Type 2 1-34289 <$40
20 Type 2 1-10276 <$50
Total Issue $5,695,190
Out in 1935 $600,000
Large out 1935 $14,750
Outstanding includes Ch 9246 and Ch 6005

****

9291 Mecklenburg
FNB OF CHASE CITY
{{ 4 L 4 S }}
Organized 6/23/08
Receivership 10/13/31
1902 Date Back <$VALUE
4x5 1-5600 <$500
3x10-20 1-4240 <$500
1902 Plain Back
4x5 5601-17779 <$500
3x10-20 4241-12358 <$500
1929 Small Size
5 Type 1 1-1298 <$300
10 Type 1 1-639 <$300
20 Type 1 1-168 <$300
Total Issue $1,070,920
Out at close $50,000
Large out at close $5,580

****

10821 Pittsylvania
FNB OF CHATHAM
{{ 2 L 0 S }}
Chartered 2/16
Liquidated 5/24/30
1902 Plain Back <$VALUE
4x5 1-9740 <$750
3x10-20 1-3250 <$750
1929 Small Size
5 Type 1 1-794 <$750
Total Issue $381,120
Out at close $25,000
Large out at close $3,080

****

8875 Smyth
NB OF CHILHOWIE
{{ 3 L 3 S }}
Chartered 9/07
1902 Red Seal <$VALUE
3x10-20 1-562 <$1500
1902 Date Back
3x10-20 1-2180 <$600
1902 Plain Back
3x10-20 2181-6377 <$600
1929 Small Size
10 Type 1 1-782 <$375
20 Type 1 1-232 <$375
10 Type 2 1-1140 <$400
20 Type 2 1-252 <$400
Total Issue $438,150
Out in 1935 $25,000
Large out 1935 $1,110

****

7937 Montgomery
FNB OF CHRISTIANSBURG
{{ 5 L 11 S }}
Chartered 10/05
1902 Red Seal <$VALUE
3x10-20 1-400 <$1000
1902 Date Back
3x10-20 1-3380 <$500
1902 Plain Back
4x5 1-15332 <$500
3x10-20 3381-14920 <$500
1929 Small Size
5 Type 1 1-4682 <$175
10 Type 1 1-2216 <$175
20 Type 1 1-556 <$175
5 Type 2 1-8392 <$200
10 Type 2 1-5268 <$200
20 Type 2 1-1332 <$200
Total Issue $1,534,060
Out in 1935 $100,000
Large out 1935 $3,720

****

1658 Mecklenburg
FNB OF CLARKSVILLE
{{ UNREPORTED }}
Chartered 8/6/66
Liquidated 10/13/70
Original Series <$VALUE
4x5 1-450 <$2500
3x10-20 1-360 <$2500/$3000
Total Issue $27,000
Out in 1910 $85

9177 Independent City
CLIFTON FORGE NB, CLIFTON FORGE
{{ 14 L U + 17 S }}
Organized 6/4/08
Liquidated 8/11/34
1902 Date Back <$VALUE
3x10-20 1-10900 <$150
1902 Plain Back
3x10-20 10901-31528 <$150
1929 Small Size
10 Type 1 1-3502 <$85
20 Type 1 1-904 <$100
10 Type 2 1-1607 <$110
20 Type 2 1-527 <$125
Total Issue $1,921,610
Out at close $100,000
Large out at close $4,840
Ch 14180 assumed circulation

6008 Independent City
FNB OF CLIFTON FORGE
{{ 22 L 20 S }}
Chartered 11/01
Brown Back <$VALUE
3x10-20 1-3600 <$450
1882 Date Back
3x10-20 1-4140 <$400
1882 Value Back
3x10-20 4141-12090 <$400
1902 Plain Back
3x10-20 1-13426 <$150
1929 Small Size
10 Type 1 1-3488 <$75
20 Type 1 1-928 <$75
10 Type 2 1-4939 <$75
20 Type 2 1-1449 <$80
Total Issue $1,854,810
Out in 1935 $100,000
Large out 1935 $5,100

8362 Dickenson
CITIZENS NB OF CLINTWOOD
{{ UNREPORTED }}
Chartered 9/06
Liquidated 9/23/10
1902 Red Seal <$VALUE
4x10 1-325 <$2500
1902 Date Back
4x10 1-60 <$2000
Total Issue $15,400
Out in 1911 $2,540

6899 Wise
FNB OF COEBURN
{{ 5 L 2U + 12 S }}
Organized 7/21/03
Receivership 2/27/34
1902 Red Seal <$VALUE
3x10-20 1-1507 <$1000
1902 Date Back
3x10-20 1-2050 <$400
1902 Plain Back
3x10-20 2051-18475 <$400
1929 Small Size
10 Type 1 1-3054 <$165
20 Type 1 1-900 <$175
10 Type 2 1-493 <$200
20 Type 2 1-98 <$200
Total Issue $1,297,230
Out at close $100,000
Large out at close $4,880

5326 Independent City
CITIZENS NB OF COVINGTON
{{ 10 L 14 S }}
Chartered 5/3/00
Brown Back <$VALUE
3x10-20 1-3300 <$500
1882 Date Back
3x10-20 1-7900* <$500
* 7875-7876 not issued
1882 Value Back
3x10-20 7901-8037 <$500
1902 Plain Back
4x5 1-51626 <$225
1929 Small Size
5 Type 1 1-11812 <$100
10 Type 1 1-1956 <$100
5 Type 2 1-15370 <$100
10 Type 2 1-6952 <$100
Total Issue $2,245,360
Out in 1935 $125,000
Large out 1935 $3,470

4503 Independent City
COVINGTON NB, COVINGTON
{{ 11 L 17 S }}
Chartered 1891
Brown Back <$VALUE
4x5 1-2875 <$500
3x10-20 1-3620 <$500
1882 Date Back
4x5 1-2690 <$500
3x10-20 1-1628 <$500
1902 Date Back
4x5 1-8175 <$225
3x10-20 1-6650 <$225
1902 Plain Back
4x5 8176-25369 <$225
3x10-20 6651-17859 <$225
1929 Small Size
5 Type 1 1-4524 <$85
10 Type 1 1-2444 <$85
20 Type 1 1-556 <$100
5 Type 2 1-7524 <$110
10 Type 2 1-4320 <$110
20 Type 2 1-1056 <$110
Total Issue $2,230,750
Out in 1935 $100,000
Large out 1935 $4,270

9455 Nottoway
FNB OF CREWE
{{ 4 L 10 S }}
Organized 6/10/09
Liquidated 5/31/34
1902 Date Back <$VALUE
4x5 1-2175 <$500
3x10-20 1-1730 <$500
1902 Plain Back
4x5 2176-11558 <$500
3x10-20 1731-8104 <$500
1929 Small Size
5 Type 1 1-2402 <$175
10 Type 1 1-1244 <$175
20 Type 1 1-340 <$185
5 Type 2 1-1128 <$200
10 Type 2 1-504 <$200
20 Type 2 1-120 <$225
Total Issue $836,940
Out at close $50,000
Large out at close $2,490
Ch 14052 assumed circulation

14052 Nottoway
NB OF CREWE
{{ 3 S }}
Chartered 3/34
1929 Small Size <$VALUE
5 Type 2 1-2462 <$400
10 Type 2 1-1657 <$400
20 Type 2 1-516 <$400
Total Issue $39,200
Out in 1935 $50,000
Outstanding includes Ch 9455

5591 Culpepper
CULPEPER NB, CULPEPER
{{ 5 L 13 S }}
Chartered 10/3/00
Brown Back <$VALUE
4x5 1-1525 <$650
4x10 1-400 <$650
3x10-20 1-1040 <$650
1882 Date Back
4x5 1-4700* <$650
4x10 1-3775** <$650
3x10-20 1-100 <$650
1882 Value Back
4x5 4851-7791* <$650
* 4701-4850 not marked
** 3776-6065 not marked
1902 Plain Back
3x10-20 1-6737 <$375
1929 Small Size
10 Type 1 1-2796 <$85
20 Type 1 1-764 <$100
10 Type 2 1-6110 <$100
20 Type 2 1-1439 <$100
Total Issue $1,188,090
Out in 1935 $100,000
Large out 1935 $2,680

3570 Culpepper
FARMERS NB OF CULPEPER
{{ UNREPORTED }}
Chartered 10/14/86
Liquidated 7/12/97
Brown Back <$VALUE
3x10-20 1-720 <$2000
Total Issue $36,000
Out in 1910 $400

5394 Culpepper
SECOND NB OF CULPEPER
{{ 5 L 10 S }}
Chartered 6/2/00
Brown Back <$VALUE
3x10-20 1-720 <$650
1882 Date Back
4x5 1-2400 <$650
3x10-20 1-2470 <$650
1882 Value Back
4x5 2401-5020 <$650
3x10-20 2471-3820 <$650
1902 Plain Back
4x5 1-11632 <$375
3x10-20 1-7731 <$375
1929 Small Size
5 Type 1 1-4630 <$100
10 Type 1 1-2328 <$100
20 Type 1 1-704 <$110
5 Type 2 1-8226 <$125
10 Type 2 1-5398 <$125
20 Type 2 1-1152 <$125
Total Issue $1,427,800
Out in 1935 $100,000
Large out 1935 $3,775

9343 Independent City
AMERICAN NB OF DANVILLE
Organized 1/9/09
2nd title: American NB & TC of Danville 1/12/29
FIRST TITLE {{ 8 L }}
1902 Date Back <$VALUE
3x10-20 1-10900 <$175
1902 Plain Back
4x5 1-40815 <$175
3x10-20 10901-43766 <$175
SECOND TITLE {{ 2 L 2U + 29 S }}
1902 Plain Back
4x5 1-5785 <$200
3x10-20 1-2538 <$200
1929 Small Size
5 Type 1 1-13324 <$35
10 Type 1 1-6380 <$40
20 Type 1 1-2190 <$45
5 Type 2 1-26856 <$35
10 Type 2 1-13178 <$40
20 Type 2 1-5388 <$45
Total Issue $4,666,340
Out in 1935 $300,000
Large out 1935 $9,820

1609 Independent City
FNB OF DANVILLE
{{ UNREPORTED }}
Chartered 11/14/65
Liquidated 9/30/68
Original Series <$VALUE
4x5 1-1000 <$2500
3x10-20 1-500 <$2500/$3000
Total Issue $45,000
Out in 1910 $215

FNB of Danville
SEE Ch 1985
Planters NB of Danville

9475 Independent City
NB OF DANVILLE
{{ 5 L }}
Chartered 7/09
Liquidated 6/12/17
1902 Date Back <$VALUE
4x5 1-14150 <$300
3x10-20 1-10920 <$300
1902 Plain Back
4x5 14151-17679 <$300
3x10-20 10921-13385 <$300
Total Issue $1,022,830
Out at close $175,000

1985 Independent City
PLANTERS NB OF DANVILLE
Chartered 5/18/72
2nd title:FNB of Danville 8/1/99
FIRST TITLE {{ 4 L }}
Original Series <$VALUE
4x5 1-3000 <$1250
3x10-20 1-1000<$1500/$2000
Series 1875
4x5 1-3308 <$1250
3x10-20 1-2694<$1500/$2000
Brown Back
4x5 1-1675 <$750
3x10-20 1-1326 <$750
SECOND TITLE {{ 16 L 31 S }}
Brown Back
4x5 1-4250 <$500
3x10-20 1-2400 <$500
50-100 1-1566 <$3500/$4000
1882 Date Back
4x5 1-6670 <$500
3x10-20 1-5028 <$500
50-100 1-200 <$3500/$4000
1902 Date Back
4x5 1-9000 <$125
3x10-20 1-8700 <$125
1902 Plain Back
4x5 9001-69174 <$125
3x10-20 8701-47149 <$125
1929 Small Size
5 Type 1 1-13458 <$40
10 Type 1 1-6378 <$35
20 Type 1 1-1654 <$45
5 Type 2 1-24734 <$45
10 Type 2 1-11844 <$40
20 Type 2 1-2865 <$50
Total Issue $6,290,600
Out in 1935 $275,000
Large out 1935 $12,340

10156 Independent City
VIRGINIA NB OF DANVILLE
{{ 1 L }}
Chartered 3/12
Liquidated 1/12/15
1902 Date Back <$VALUE
3x10-20 1-5923 <$750
Total Issue $296,150
Out in 1910 $49,000

11480 Buckingham
FNB OF DILLWYN
{{ 1 L }}
Organized 9/11/19
Liquidated 12/23/26
1902 Plain Back <$VALUE
4x5 1-2165 <$1000
Total Issue $43,300
Out in 1925 $24,400

12240 Independent City
CITIZENS NB OF EMPORIA
{{ 5 L 8 S }}
Chartered 7/22
1902 Plain Back <$VALUE
4x5 1-7441 <$400
4x10 1-6277 <$400
1929 Small Size
5 Type 1 1-3562 <$175
10 Type 1 1-1544 <$175
5 Type 2 1-7320 <$175
10 Type 2 1-4032 <$175
Total Issue $676,320
Out in 1935 $50,000
Large out 1935 $1,080

8688 Independent City
FNB OF EMPORIA
{{ 7 L 10 S }}
Chartered 5/07
1902 Red Seal <$VALUE
4x5 1-500 <$850
3x10-20 1-480 <$850
1902 Date Back
4x5 1-4300 <$350
3x10-20 1-3390 <$350
1902 Plain Back
4x5 4301-15920 <$350
3x10-20 3391-11115 <$350
1929 Small Size
5 Type 1 1-2360 <$150
10 Type 1 1-1242 <$150
20 Type 1 1-326 <$175
5 Type 2 1-3876 <$175
10 Type 2 1-1980 <$175
20 Type 2 1-576 <$200
Total Issue $1,143,290
Out in 1935 $50,000
Large out 1935 $2,210
Outstanding includes Ch 9732

9732 Independent City
PLANTERS NB OF EMPORIA
{{ UNREPORTED }}
Chartered 4/10
Liquidated 3/2/14
1902 Date Back <$VALUE
3x10-20 1-1424 <$1500
Total Issue $71,200
Out at close $25,000
Ch 8688 assumed circulation

8003 Albemarle
ESMONT NB, ESMONT
{{ 4 L 4 S }}
Organized 11/28/05
Liquidated 10/10/33
1902 Red Seal <$VALUE
4x5 1-900 <$1000
3x10-20 1-720 <$1000
1902 Date Back
4x5 1-2050 <$600
3x10-20 1-1500 <$600
1902 Plain Back
4x5 2051-6927 <$600
3x10-20 1501-4469 <$600
1929 Small Size
5 Type 1 1-999 <$400
10 Type 1 1-464 <$400
20 Type 1 1-130 <$400
Total Issue $489,400
Out at close $25,000
Large out at close $1,760

6389 Independent City
NB OF FAIRFAX
{{ 9 L 11 S }}
Chartered 8/02
1902 Red Seal <$VALUE
3x10-20 1-1100 <$850
1902 Date Back
3x10-20 1-2350 <$300
1902 Plain Back
3x10-20 2351-13190 <$300
1929 Small Size
10 Type 1 1-1828 <$135
20 Type 1 1-502 <$160
5 Type 2 1-91 <$225
10 Type 2 1-2664 <$200
20 Type 2 1-710 <$200
Total Issue $925,715
Out in 1935 $50,000
Large out 1935 $2,745

5683 Prince Edward
FNB OF FARMVILLE
{{ 6 L 14 S }}
Chartered 1/18/01
Brown Back <$VALUE
3x10-20 1-3200 <$750
1882 Date Back
3x10-20 1-6900 <$750
1882 Value Back
3x10-20 6901-10652 <$750
1902 Plain Back
3x10-20 1-10634 <$400
1929 Small Size
10 Type 1 1-2518 <$125
20 Type 1 1-662 <$135
10 Type 2 1-4206 <$165
20 Type 2 1-1238 <$175
Total Issue $1,521,640
Out in 1935 $75,000
Large out 1935 $3,450

9222 Prince Edward
PEOPLES NB OF FARMVILLE
{{ 4 L 15 S }}
Chartered 8/08
1902 Date Back <$VALUE
3x10-20 1-5300 <$450
1902 Plain Back
3x10-20 5301-16145 <$450
1929 Small Size
10 Type 1 1-2576 <$100
20 Type 1 1-738 <$110
10 Type 2 1-3816 <$125
20 Type 2 1-1260 <$125
Total Issue $1,113,730
Out in 1935 $75,000
Large out 1935 $2,460

12311 Franklin
FNB OF FERRUM
{{ 3 L 2 S }}
Organized 12/28/22
1902 Plain Back <$VALUE
3x10-20 1-3278 <$750
1929 Small Size
5 Type 1 1-106 <$500
10 Type 1 1-916 <$500
20 Type 1 1-250 <$500
5 Type 2 1-1044 <$500
10 Type 2 1-606 <$500
20 Type 2 1-204 <$500
100 Type 2 1-72 <$1000
Total Issue $274,600
Out in 1935 $25,000
Large out 1935 $790

11797 Rappahannock
FNB OF FLINT HILL
{{ 2 L 4 S }}
Organized 4/13/20
1902 Plain Back <$VALUE
3x10-20 1-1615 <$850
1929 Small Size
10 Type 1 1-522 <$400
20 Type 1 1-158 <$400
10 Type 2 1-1422 <$400
20 Type 2 1-327 <$400
Total Issue $151,790
Out in 1935 $25,000
Large out 1935 $450

5268 Independent City
CONWAY, GORDON & GARNETT NB OF FREDERICKSBURG
{{ 3 L }}
Chartered 3/23/00
Liquidated 11/20/12
Brown Back <$VALUE
4x5 1-4000 <$1250
3x10-20 1-2800 <$1250
1882 Date Back
4x5 1-2155 <$1250
3x10-20 1-1513 <$1250
Total Issue $338,750
Out in 1913 $22,450

1582 Independent City
NB OF FREDERICKSBURG
{{ 6 L 10 S }}
Chartered 1865
Original Series <$VALUE
4x5 1-3775 <$1250
3x10-20 1-2420<$1500/$2000
Series 1875
4x5 1-735 <$1250
3x10-20 1-264 <$1500/$2000
Brown Back
4x5 1-5609 <$500
3x10-20 1-1633 <$500
1902 Red Seal
4x5 1-1330 <$600
3x10-20 1-1068 <$600
1902 Date Back
4x5 1-4575 <$300
3x10-20 1-3160 <$300
1902 Plain Back
4x5 4576-14794 <$300
3x10-20 3161-9705 <$300
1929 Small Size
5 Type 1 1-2298 <$150
10 Type 1 1-1192 <$150
20 Type 1 1-318 <$150
5 Type 2 1-3620 <$175
10 Type 2 1-2207 <$175
20 Type 2 1-528 <$175
Total Issue $1,506,710
Out in 1935 $50,000
Large out 1935 $3,930

13603 Independent City
PLANTERS NB IN FREDERICKSBURG
{{ 5U + 12 S }}
Chartered 3/32
1929 Small Size <$VALUE
5 Type 1 1-1176 <$100
10 Type 1 1-614 <$100
20 Type 1 1-222 <$100
5 Type 2 1-11268 <$110
10 Type 2 1-5644 <$110
20 Type 2 1-1542 <$125
Total Issue $242,380
Out in 1935 $78,750

10325 Independent City
PLANTERS NB OF FREDERICKSBURG
{{ 7 L U + 10 S }}
Organized 2/4/13
Liquidated 4/23/32
1902 Date Back <$VALUE
4x5 1-3650 <$225
3x10-20 1-2740 <$225
1902 Plain Back
4x5 3651-19225 <$225
3x10-20 2741-12862 <$225
1929 Small Size
5 Type 1 1-2469 <$150
10 Type 1 1-1261 <$150
20 Type 1 1-308 <$165
Total Issue $1,214,290
Out at close $75,000
Large out at close $5,750

12290 Grayson
FNB OF FRIES
{{ 1 L 3 S }}
Chartered 1/23
1902 Plain Back <$VALUE
4x5 1-3562 <$850
1929 Small Size
5 Type 1 1-2764 <$500
5 Type 2 1-10320 <$500
Total Issue $205,760
Out in 1935 $30,000
Large out 1935 $350

****
2967 Warren
FRONT ROYAL NB,
FRONT ROYAL
{{ 4 L }}
Organized 4/10/83
Liquidated 1/20/30
Brown Back <$VALUE
3x10-20 1-1916 <$850
1902 Red Seal
3x10-20 1-645 <$1000
1902 Date Back
3x10-20 1-3810 <$500
1902 Plain Back
3x10-20 3811-8596 <$500
Total Issue $557,850
Out at close $7,840
****

8791 Independent City
FNB OF GALAX
{{ 3 L 4 S }}
Chartered 7/07
1902 Red Seal <$VALUE
4x5 1-556 <$1250
4x10 1-556 <$1250
1902 Date Back
4x5 1-1750 <$600
4x10 1-1700 <$600
1902 Plain Back
4x5 1751-7235 <$600
4x10 1701-5539 <$600
1929 Small Size
5 Type 1 1-1568 <$400
10 Type 1 1-788 <$400
5 Type 2 1-3312 <$400
10 Type 2 1-1896 <$400
Total Issue $529,460
Out in 1935 $25,000
Large out 1935 $1,080
****

F & Peoples NB of Gate City
SEE Ch 13502
Peoples NB in Gate City
****

7208 Scott
FNB OF GATE CITY
{{ 4 L 3 S }}
Chartered 4/04
Closed 8/15/32
1902 Red Seal <$VALUE
4x5 1-1225 <$1250
3x10-20 1-980 <$1250
1902 Date Back
4x5 1-2050 <$500
3x10-20 1-1500 <$500
1902 Plain Back
4x5 2051-6994 <$500
3x10-20 1501-4792 <$500
1929 Small Size
5 Type 1 1-864 <$375
10 Type 1 1-440 <$375
20 Type 1 1-136 <$375
Total Issue $521,620
Out at close $28,500
Large out at close $2,620
Ch 13502 assumed circulation
****

13502 Scott
PEOPLES NB IN GATE CITY
Chartered 11/30
2nd title:F & Peoples NB
of Gate City 8/15/32
FIRST TITLE {{ 2 S }}
1929 Small Size <$VALUE
10 Type 1 1-212 <$400
20 Type 1 1-64 <$400
SECOND TITLE {{ 2 S }}
1929 Small Size
10 Type 1 1-246 <$400
20 Type 1 1-86 <$400
5 Type 2 1-301 <$400
10 Type 2 1-1912 <$400
20 Type 2 1-422 <$400
Total Issue $74,545
Out in 1935 $50,000
Outstanding includes Ch 7135
and Ch 7208
****

7135 Scott
PEOPLES NB OF GATE CITY
{{ 7 L 3 S }}
Chartered 2/04
Liquidated 5/21/31
1902 Red Seal <$VALUE
3x10-20 1-1300 <$1250
1902 Date Back
3x10-20 1-1750 <$500
1902 Plain Back
3x10-20 1751-5946 <$500
1929 Small Size
10 Type 1 1-431 <$375
20 Type 1 1-109 <$375
Total Issue $401,240
Out at close $25,000
Large out at close $3,715
Ch 13502 assumed circulation
****

10658 Gloucester
FNB OF GLOUCESTER
{{ 4 L 4 S }}
Chartered 11/14
Liquidated 3/23/32
1902 Date Back <$VALUE
4x5 1-1000 <$650
3x10-20 1-800 <$650
1902 Plain Back
4x5 1001-8761 <$650
3x10-20 801-5248 <$650
1929 Small Size
5 Type 1 1-1094 <$375
10 Type 1 1-554 <$375
20 Type 1 1-157 <$375
Total Issue $522,520
Out at close $35,000
Large out at close $2,915
****

10287 Orange
NB OF GORDONSVILLE
{{ 2 L 4 S }}
Chartered 11/12
1902 Date Back <$VALUE
4x5 1-500 <$750
3x10-20 1-420 <$750
1902 Plain Back
4x5 501-5425 <$750
3x10-20 421-3283 <$750
1929 Small Size
5 Type 1 1-1194 <$350
10 Type 1 1-550 <$350
20 Type 1 1-172 <$350
5 Type 2 1-1580 <$350
10 Type 2 1-693 <$350
20 Type 2 1-252 <$375
Total Issue $381,980
Out in 1935 $25,000
Large out 1935 $960
****

7734 Tazewell
AMERICAN NB OF GRAHAM
Chartered 5/11/05
Moved to Bluefield, W Va on
2/21/06 with change of
title to: American NB of
Bluefield, WEST VIRGINIA
Liquidated 5/1/09
FIRST TITLE (VA) {{ 1 L }}
1902 Red Seal <$VALUE
4x5 1-425 <$1500
3x10-20 1-336 <$1500
SECOND TITLE (WV) {{ 1 L }}
1902 Red Seal
4x5 1-2920 <$1500
3x10-20 1-2191 <$1500
Total Issue $193,250
Out in 1910 $22,170
****

7782 Tazewell
FNB OF GRAHAM
Organized 5/13/05
Receivership 8/22/32
2nd title: Twin City NB of
Bluefield 7/25/24
FIRST TITLE {{ 3 L }}
1902 Red Seal <$VALUE
4x5 1-1715 <$1000
3x10-20 1-1514 <$1000
1902 Date Back
4x5 1-4100 <$500
3x10-20 1-3020 <$500
1902 Plain Back
4x5 4101-10850 <$500
3x10-20 3021-7010 <$500
SECOND TITLE {{ 3 L 4 S }}
1902 Plain Back
4x5 1-4483 <$600
3x10-20 1-3291 <$600
1929 Small Size
5 Type 1 1-2013 <$350
10 Type 1 1-983 <$350
20 Type 1 1-262 <$375
Total Issue $1,082,520
Out at close $49,100
Large out at close $4,160
****

11698 Buchanan
FNB OF GRUNDY
{{ 3 L 2 S }}
Organized 4/19/20
Receivership 12/13/29
1902 Plain Back <$VALUE
3x10-20 1-8020 <$500
1929 Small Size
10 Type 1 1-232 <$600
20 Type 1 1-20 <$600
Total Issue $417,320
Out at close $50,000
Large out at close $33,680
****

****
7659 Accomack
HALLWOOD NB, HALLWOOD
{{ 3 L 5 S }}
Organized 3/2/05
1902 Red Seal <$VALUE
3x10-20 1-400 <$1250
1902 Date Back
3x10-20 1-700 <$500
1902 Plain Back
3x10-20 701-4877 <$500
1929 Small Size
10 Type 1 1-754 <$300
20 Type 1 1-194 <$300
10 Type 2 1-968 <$300
20 Type 2 1-171 <$300
Total Issue $345,470
Out in 1935 $25,000
Large out 1935 $1,090
****

9861 Loudon
FARMERS & MERCHANTS NB OF
HAMILTON
{{ 2 L 5 S }}
Chartered 9/10
1902 Date Back <$VALUE
3x10-20 1-1895 <$650
1902 Plain Back
3x10-20 1896-7262 <$650
1929 Small Size
10 Type 1 1-924 <$300
20 Type 1 1-216 <$300
10 Type 2 1-1092 <$325
20 Type 2 1-293 <$350
Total Issue $461,240
Out in 1935 $25,000
Large out 1935 $510
****

13775 Independent City
CITIZENS NB OF HAMPTON
{{ 7 S }}
Chartered 9/33
1929 Small Size <$VALUE
5 Type 2 1-19404 <$175
10 Type 2 1-10152 <$175
20 Type 2 1-3048 <$175
50 Type 2 1-528 <$600
100 Type 2 1-252 <$750
Total Issue $311,100
Out in 1935 $200,000
Outstanding includes Ch 6842
****

6842 Independent City
FNB OF HAMPTON
{{ 5 L 7 S }}
Organized 4/23/03
Liquidated 11/6/33
1902 Red Seal <$VALUE
4x5 1-2700 <$750
3x10-20 1-2040 <$750
1902 Date Back
4x5 1-4550* <$375
3x10-20 1-3280** <$375
1902 Plain Back
4x5 4801-15930* <$375
3x10-20 3441-10769** <$375
* 4551-4800 not marked
** 3281-3440 not marked
1929 Small Size
5 Type 1 1-2300 <$175
10 Type 1 1-1238 <$175
20 Type 1 1-336 <$175
5 Type 2 1-300 <$225
10 Type 2 1-229 <$225
20 Type 2 1-25 <$250
Total Issue $1,200,940
Out at close $50,000
Large out at close $2,845
Ch 13775 assumed circulation
****

6778 Independent City
MERCHANTS NB OF HAMPTON
{{ 7 L 21 S }}
Chartered 5/03
1902 Red Seal <$VALUE
4x5 1-3080 <$750
3x10-20 1-2280 <$750
1902 Date Back
4x5 1-4600* <$275
3x10-20 1-3200** <$275
1902 Plain Back
4x5 4851-21710* <$275
3x10-20 3361-14996** <$275
* 4601-4850 not marked
** 3201-3360 not marked
1929 Small Size
5 Type 1 1-4646 <$65
10 Type 1 1-2578 <$65
20 Type 1 1-706 <$75
5 Type 2 1-8638 <$70
10 Type 2 1-4575 <$70
20 Type 2 1-975 <$85
Total Issue $1,846,820
Out in 1935 $1,000,000
Large out 1935 $3,790
****

****
1572 Independent City
FNB OF HARRISONBURG
{{ 11 L 19 S }}
Chartered 1865
Original Series <$VALUE
4x5 1-4250 <$1250
3x10-20 1-2175<$1500/$2000
Series 1875
3x10-20 1-1131<$1500/$2000
Brown Back
3x10-20 1-5495 <$600
1902 Red Seal
3x10-20 1-3000 <$650
1902 Date Back
3x10-20 1-13900 <$175
1902 Plain Back
3x10-20 13901-50103 <$175
1929 Small Size
10 Type 1 1-4426 <$85
20 Type 1 1-1130 <$85
10 Type 2 1-7139 <$100
20 Type 2 1-1815 <$100
Total Issue $3,689,050
Out in 1935 $150,000
Large out 1935 $11,550
****

11694 Independent City
NB OF HARRISONBURG
{{ 11 L 16 S }}
Chartered 5/20
1902 Plain Back <$VALUE
3x10-20 1-24699 <$225
1929 Small Size
10 Type 1 1-4862 <$85
20 Type 1 1-1378 <$90
10 Type 2 1-5830 <$90
20 Type 2 1-1732 <$90
Total Issue $1,784,970
Out in 1935 $150,000
Large out 1935 $5,370
****

5261 Independent City
ROCKINGHAM NB OF
HARRISONBURG
{{ 7 L 20 S }}
Chartered 2/00
Brown Back <$VALUE
3x10-20 1-2950 <$650
1882 Date Back
3x10-20 1-5400 <$650
1882 Value Back
3x10-20 5401-6677 <$650
1902 Plain Back
3x10-20 1-14016 <$275
1929 Small Size
10 Type 1 1-3692 <$85
20 Type 1 1-1064 <$90
10 Type 2 1-7475 <$90
20 Type 2 1-2579 <$90
Total Issue $1,657,680
Out in 1935 $150,000
Large out 1935 $4,440
****

9635 Fairfax
NB OF HERNDON
{{ 3 L U + 6 S }}
Organized 10/25/09
Receivership 1/10/35
1902 Date Back <$VALUE
3x10-20 1-2260 <$600
1902 Plain Back
3x10-20 2261-7688 <$600
1929 Small Size
10 Type 1 1-920 <$275
20 Type 1 1-242 <$275
10 Type 2 1-902 <$300
20 Type 2 1-250 <$325
Total Issue $482,660
Out at close $24,500
Large out at close $1,250
****

10252 Russell
FNB OF HONAKER
{{ 1 L 3 S }}
Organized 8/5/12
Receivership 3/26/34
1902 Date Back <$VALUE
3x10-20 1-1340 <$850
1902 Plain Back
3x10-20 1341-5785 <$850
1929 Small Size
10 Type 1 1-708 <$450
20 Type 1 1-184 <$450
10 Type 2 1-576 <$500
20 Type 2 1-86 <$500
Total Issue $361,290
Out at close $25,000
Large out at close $2,400
****

****
10866 Independent City
NB OF HOPEWELL
{{ 1 L }}
Chartered 6/16
Liquidated 2/21/24
1902 Plain Back <$VALUE
3x10-20 1-2668 <$1000
Total Issue $133,400
Out at close $25,000
****

8722 Bath
BATH COUNTY NB OF
HOT SPRINGS
{{ U + 11 L 15 S }}
Chartered 6/07
1902 Red Seal <$VALUE
4x10 1-825 <$650
1902 Date Back
4x10 1-5750 <$200
1902 Plain Back
4x10 5751-20561 <$200
1929 Small Size
10 Type 1 1-2918 <$135
10 Type 2 1-5328 <$150
Total Issue $1,083,800
Out in 1935 $50,000
Large out 1935 $2,090
****

10834 Grayson
GRAYSON COUNTY NB OF
INDEPENDENCE
{{ 3 L 8 S }}
Chartered 3/16
1902 Plain Back <$VALUE
3x10-20 1-5547 <$500
1929 Small Size
10 Type 1 1-1216 <$200
20 Type 1 1-296 <$200
10 Type 2 1-2522 <$200
20 Type 2 1-648 <$225
Total Issue $424,010
Out in 1935 $50,000
Large out 1935 $2,380
Outstanding includes Ch 11990
****

5290 Lancaster
LANCASTER NB OF IRVINGTON
{{ 4 L 5 S }}
Chartered 4/14/00
Brown Back <$VALUE
3x10-20 1-2040 <$850
1882 Date Back
3x10-20 1-1660* <$850
1882 Value Back
3x10-20 1761-2632* <$850
* 1661-1760 not marked
1902 Plain Back
3x10-20 1-3499 <$500
1929 Small Size
10 Type 1 1-812 <$350
20 Type 1 1-206 <$350
10 Type 2 1-1020 <$400
20 Type 2 1-175 <$400
Total Issue $495,690
Out in 1935 $25,000
Large out 1935 $1,140
****

8384 Lee
PEOPLES NB OF JONESVILLE
{{ UNREPORTED }}
Chartered 10/06
Liquidated 1/31/11
1902 Red Seal <$VALUE
4x5 1-300 <$2000
3x10-20 1-240 <$2000
1902 Date Back
4x5 1-160 <$1500
3x10-20 1-159 <$1500
Total Issue $29,150
Out in 1911 $5,850
****

9924 Lee
POWELL VALLEY NB OF
JONESVILLE
{{ 2 L 5 S }}
Chartered 1/11
1902 Date Back <$VALUE
4x5 1-750 <$850
3x10-20 1-620 <$850
1902 Plain Back
4x5 751-2340 <$850
3x10-20 621-1545 <$850
1929 Small Size
5 Type 1 1-420 <$400
10 Type 1 1-212 <$400
20 Type 1 1-72 <$425
5 Type 2 1-74 <$500
10 Type 2 1-120 <$500
20 Type 2 1-10 <$500
Total Issue $159,780
Out in 1935 $10,000
Large out 1935 $480
****

****
12251 Lunenburg
FNB OF KENBRIDGE
{{ 3 L }}
Chartered 9/22
Liquidated 3/10/26
1902 Plain Back <$VALUE
4x5 1-7625 <$600
Total Issue $152,500
Out at close $40,000
****

9433 Brunswick
FNB OF LAWRENCEVILLE
{{ 3 L }}
Chartered 6/09
Liquidated 7/5/27
1902 Date Back <$VALUE
4x5 1-2750 <$500
3x10-20 1-2260 <$500
1902 Plain Back
4x5 2751-9670 <$500
3x10-20 2261-6813 <$500
Total Issue $534,050
Out at close $40,000
****

6886 Russell
CITIZENS NB OF LEBANON
Chartered 7/03
2nd title:FNB of Lebanon
7/1/07
FIRST TITLE {{ 0 L }}
1902 Red Seal <$VALUE
3x10-20 1-428 <$1500
SECOND TITLE {{ 4 L 8 S }}
1902 Red Seal
3x10-20 1-440 <$850
1902 Date Back
3x10-20 1-5600* <$375
1902 Plain Back
3x10-20 5901-16249* <$375
* 5601-5900 not marked
1929 Small Size
10 Type 1 1-1808 <$175
20 Type 1 1-514 <$185
10 Type 2 1-2589 <$200
20 Type 2 1-670 <$200
Total Issue $1,065,300
Out in 1935 $60,000
Large out 1935 $3,420
****

FNB of Lebanon
SEE Ch 6886
Citizens NB of Lebanon
****

1738 Loudon
LOUDOUN NB OF LEESBURG
{{ 13 L 17 S }}
Chartered 11/28/70
Original Series <$VALUE
4x5 1-750 <$1250
3x10-20 1-2520<$1500/$2000
50-100 1-60 <$8500
Series 1875
4x5 1-260 <$1250
3x10-20 1-2998<$1500/$2000
50-100 1-336 <$8500
Brown Back
3x10-20 1-8620 <$500
1882 Date Back
4x5 1-1475 <$500
3x10-20 1-1439 <$500
1902 Date Back
4x5 1-6200 <$225
3x10-20 1-4980 <$225
1902 Plain Back
4x5 6201-26400 <$225
3x10-20 4981-18697 <$225
1929 Small Size
5 Type 1 1-3852 <$85
10 Type 1 1-2338 <$85
20 Type 1 1-634 <$90
5 Type 2 1-6672 <$100
10 Type 2 1-4440 <$100
20 Type 2 1-1044 <$110
Total Issue $2,781,360
Out in 1935 $100,000
Large out 1935 $3,210
****

CONDITION affects Value. The Values shown are for notes in FINE condition.

3917 Loudon
PEOPLES NB OF LEESBURG
{{ 8 L 13 S }}
Chartered 1888
Brown Back <$VALUE
3x10-20 1-8195 <$650
1902 Date Back
3x10-20 1-10700 <$275
1902 Plain Back
3x10-20 10701-30724 <$275
1929 Small Size
5 Type 1 1-3502 <$100
10 Type 1 1-2738 <$100
20 Type 1 1-674 <$125
5 Type 2 1-6464 <$125
10 Type 2 1-3401 <$125
20 Type 2 1-1128 <$135
Total Issue $2,385,060
Out in 1935 $100,000
Large out 1935 $5,440

FNB of Lexington
SEE Ch 4314
FNB of Buena Vista

7173 Independent City
PEOPLES NB OF LEXINGTON
{{ 4 L 10 S }}
Chartered 3/04
1902 Red Seal <$VALUE
3x10-20 1-1322 <$1000
1902 Date Back
3x10-20 1-2160 <$450
1902 Plain Back
3x10-20 2161-7366 <$450
1929 Small Size
10 Type 1 1-2604 <$150
20 Type 1 1-748 <$175
10 Type 2 1-3944 <$175
20 Type 2 1-984 <$185
Total Issue $739,520
Out in 1935 $75,000
Large out 1935 $1,290

10968 Louisa
FNB OF LOUISA
{{ 4 L }}
Organized 3/24/17
Receivership 8/30/33
1902 Plain Back <$VALUE
4x5 1-8950 <$500
3x10-20 1-6162 <$500
Total Issue $487,100
Out at close $2,095

11957 Nelson
FNB OF NELSON COUNTY AT LOVINGSTON
{{ 5 L 6 S }}
Chartered 4/21
1902 Plain Back <$VALUE
4x5 1-24557 <$450
1929 Small Size
5 Type 1 1-7486 <$225
5 Type 2 1-17844 <$225
Total Issue $804,940
Out in 1935 $50,000
Large out 1935 $1,630

6031 Page
FNB OF LURAY
{{ 5 L 5 S }}
Organized 10/16/01
Brown Back <$VALUE
4x5 1-1025 <$1000
3x10-20 1-800 <$1000
1882 Date Back
4x5 1-1825 <$1000
3x10-20 1-1280 <$1000
1882 Value Back
4x5 1826-3375 <$1000
3x10-20 1281-2137 <$1000
1902 Plain Back
4x5 1-2990 <$500
3x10-20 1-1906 <$500
1929 Small Size
5 Type 1 1-1118* <$275
10 Type 1 1-580** <$275
20 Type 1 1-174*** <$275
5 Type 2 1-1340 <$325
10 Type 2 1-734 <$325
20 Type 2 1-276 <$325
* 726-778 not issued
** 368-390 not issued
*** 103-118 not issued
Total Issue $493,840
Out in 1935 $25,000
Large out 1935 $1,730

6206 Page
PAGE VALLEY NB OF LURAY
{{ 4 L 5 S }}
Chartered 4/02
1902 Red Seal <$VALUE
4x5 1-875 <$1000
3x10-20 1-640 <$1000
1902 Date Back
4x5 1-2050 <$500
3x10-20 1-1400 <$500
1902 Plain Back (dated 1902)
4x5 2051-3750 <$500
3x10-20 1401-2300 <$500
1902 Plain Back (dated 1922)
4x5 1-2652 <$500
3x10-20 1-1475 <$500
1929 Small Size
5 Type 1 1-1100 <$300
10 Type 1 1-504 <$300
20 Type 1 1-140 <$325
5 Type 2 1-1600 <$350
10 Type 2 1-847 <$350
20 Type 2 1-260 <$350
Total Issue $468,000
Out in 1935 $25,000
Large out 1935 $1,685

7308 Independent City
AMERICAN NB OF LYNCHBURG
{{ 1 L }}
Chartered 6/04
Liquidated 2/17/13
1902 Red Seal <$VALUE
4x5 1-6500 <$1000
3x10-20 1-5800 <$1000
1902 Date Back
4x5 1-12770 <$650
3x10-20 1-9589 <$650
Total Issue $1,154,850
Out in 1913 $125,685

1558 Independent City
FNB OF LYNCHBURG
{{ 27 L 45 S }}
Chartered 1865
Original Series <$VALUE
4x5 1-5250 <$1000
3x10-20 1-4500<$1250/$2000
Series 1875
4x5 1-2595 <$1000
3x10-20 1-1768<$1250/$2000
Brown Back
50-100 1-2882 <$3500/$4000
1902 Red Seal
4x5 1-8250 <$450
3x10-20 1-5400 <$450
1902 Date Back
4x5 1-14750 <$85
3x10-20 1-33300 <$85
1902 Plain Back
3x10-20 33301-127090 <$85
1929 Small Size
5 Type 1 1-15080 <$40
10 Type 1 1-7610 <$40
20 Type 1 1-4624 <$50
5 Type 2 1-55378 <$40
10 Type 2 1-51355 <$40
20 Type 2 1-21492 <$50
Total Issue $10,671,260
Out in 1935 $1,000,000
Large out 1935 $18,590

1522 Independent City
LYNCHBURG NB, LYNCHBURG
Chartered 1865
2nd title:Lynchburg NB & TC 4/21/28
FIRST TITLE {{ 31 L }}
Original Series <$VALUE
4x5 1-7500 <$1000
Series 1875
4x5 1-11515 <$1000
3x20-50 1-690 <$2000/$8500
Brown Back
3x10-20 1-9157 <$500
50-100 1-2315 <$3500/$4000
1902 Red Seal
3x10-20 1-8000 <$450
1902 Date Back
4x5 1-33165* <$85
3x10-20 1-21900** <$85
1902 Plain Back
4x5 361-136205* <$85
3x10-20 23401-140686**<$85
* 33166-36165 not marked
** 21901-23400 not marked
SECOND TITLE {{ 8 L 50+ S }}
1902 Plain Back
3x10-20 1-23096 <$100
1929 Small Size
10 Type 1 1-36202 <$30
20 Type 1 1-10150 <$40
10 Type 2 1-46669 <$30
20 Type 2 1-13399 <$40
Total Issue $16,699,290
Out in 1935 $600,000
Large out 1935 $25,520
Outstanding includes 2506

2506 Independent City
N EXCHANGE B OF LYNCHBURG
{{ 7 L }}
Chartered 1881
Liquidated 4/8/13
Series 1875 <$VALUE
3x10-20 1-6522<$1500/$2000
Brown Back
3x10-20 1-16000 <$500
1882 Date Back
3x10-20 1-13413 <$500
Total Issue $1,796,750
Out at close $250,000
Ch 1522 assumed circulation

2760 Independent City
PEOPLES NB OF LYNCHBURG
{{ 26 L 41 S }}
Chartered 1882
Series 1875 <$VALUE
3x10-20 1-12768<$1250/$2000
1902 Red Seal
3x10-20 1-13000 <$450
1902 Date Back
4x5 1-29415 <$85
3x10-20 1-22100 <$85
1902 Plain Back
4x5 29416-117440 <$85
3x10-20 22101-85018 <$85
1929 Small Size
5 Type 1 1-23446 <$30
10 Type 1 1-12738 <$30
20 Type 1 1-3046 <$40
5 Type 2 1-42194 <$30
10 Type 2 1-21600 <$30
20 Type 2 1-6648 <$40
Total Issue $10,281,210
Out in 1935 $500,000
Large out 1935 $32,140

5032 Independent City
NB OF MANASSAS
{{ 5 L 5 S }}
Chartered 1896
Brown Back <$VALUE
3x10-20 1-2790 <$850
1882 Date Back
3x10-20 1-1401 <$850
1902 Plain Back
3x10-20 1-4764 <$500
1929 Small Size
10 Type 1 1-796 <$325
20 Type 1 1-196 <$325
10 Type 2 1-1604 <$350
20 Type 2 1-396 <$350
Total Issue $542,990
Out in 1935 $22,500
Large out 1935 $1,530

6748 Independent City
PEOPLES NB OF MANASSAS
{{ 5 L 7 S }}
Chartered 5/03
1902 Red Seal <$VALUE
3x10-20 1-1790 <$1000
1902 Date Back
3x10-20 1-2510 <$500
1902 Plain Back
3x10-20 2511-9074 <$500
1929 Small Size
10 Type 1 1-1044 <$275
20 Type 1 1-278 <$275
10 Type 2 1-1824 <$300
20 Type 2 1-432 <$300
Total Issue $666,080
Out in 1935 $30,000
Large out 1935 $1,890

9663 Henrico
MANCHESTER NB, MANCHESTER
Chartered 2/10
Liquidated 5/10/18
2nd title: Manchester NB of Richmond 10/25/12
FIRST TITLE {{ 1 L }}
1902 Date Back <$VALUE
4x5 1-4121 <$850
4x10 1-3955 <$850
SECOND TITLE {{ 1 L }}
1902 Date Back
4x10 1-6750 <$600
1902 Plain Back
4x10 6751-9722 <$600
Total Issue $629,500
Out at close $100,000

6839 Smyth
MARION NB, MARION
{{ 6 L 14 S }}
Chartered 6/03
1902 Red Seal <$VALUE
3x10-20 1-2056 <$850
1902 Date Back
3x10-20 1-3180 <$375
1902 Plain Back
3x10-20 3181-16099 <$375
1929 Small Size
10 Type 1 1-3708 <$100
20 Type 1 1-874 <$110
10 Type 2 1-7638 <$125
20 Type 2 1-2050 <$125
Total Issue $1,352,490
Out in 1935 $135,000
Large out 1935 $3,490
Outstanding includes Ch 11718

11718 Smyth
PEOPLES NB OF MARION
{{ 2 L }}
Chartered 5/20
Closed 3/11/25
1902 Plain Back <$VALUE
3x10-20 1-5476 <$650
Total Issue $273,800
Out at close $70,000
Ch 6839 assumed circulation

10253 Faquier
MARSHALL NB, MARSHALL
Chartered 9/13/12
2nd title: Marshall NB & TC 9/7/28
FIRST TITLE {{ 4 L }}
1902 Date Back <$VALUE
3x10-20 1-800 <$350
1902 Plain Back
3x10-20 801-5811 <$350
SECOND TITLE {{ 2 L 14 S }}
1902 Plain Back
3x10-20 1-1835 <$400
1929 Small Size
5 Type 1 1-418 <$110
10 Type 1 1-3348 <$100
20 Type 1 1-918 <$100
5 Type 2 1-7300 <$100
10 Type 2 1-3816 <$100
20 Type 2 1-1104 <$100
Total Issue $802,620
Out in 1935 $100,000
Large out 1935 $2,150

7206 Independent City
FNB OF MARTINSVILLE
{{ 6 L 11 S }}
Chartered 4/04
1902 Red Seal <$VALUE
4x5 1-2250 <$850
3x10-20 1-1860 <$850
1902 Date Back
4x5 1-3700 <$400
3x10-20 1-2820 <$400
1902 Plain Back
4x5 3701-20511 <$400
3x10-20 2821-14252 <$400
1929 Small Size
5 Type 1 1-4696 <$165
10 Type 1 1-2596 <$150
20 Type 1 1-646 <$165
5 Type 2 1-7464 <$175
10 Type 2 1-4569 <$175
20 Type 2 1-1536 <$175
Total Issue $1,748,710
Out in 1935 $100,000
Large out 1935 $3,390

9847 Independent City
PEOPLES NB OF MARTINSVILLE
{{ 5 L 7 S }}
Chartered 9/10
Liquidated 2/15/32
1902 Date Back <$VALUE
4x5 1-6330 <$450
3x10-20 1-4968 <$450
1902 Plain Back
4x5 6331-23905 <$450
3x10-20 4969-15056 <$450
1929 Small Size
5 Type 1 1-2577 <$225
10 Type 1 1-1214 <$225
20 Type 1 1-339 <$250
Total Issue $1,421,730
Out at close $80,000
Large out at close $4,730

9043 Highland
FNB OF HIGHLAND AT MONTEREY
{{ 4 L }}
Chartered 2/08
Liquidated 9/2/29
1902 Red Seal <$VALUE
4x10 1-875 <$1000
1902 Date Back
4x10 1-2550 <$500
1902 Plain Back
4x10 2551-8334 <$500
Total Issue $368,360
Out at close $20,400

3209 Shenandoah
MOUNT JACKSON NB, MOUNT JACKSON
{{ 12 L 7 S }}
Chartered 1884
Liquidated 4/29/32
Brown Back <$VALUE
3x10-20 1-4058 <$650
1902 Red Seal
3x10-20 1-2000 <$850
1902 Date Back
3x10-20 1-4050 <$350
1902 Plain Back
3x10-20 4051-11527 <$350
1929 Small Size
10 Type 1 1-1021 <$200
20 Type 1 1-272 <$225
Total Issue $973,150
Out at close $50,000
Large out at close $6,760

11444 Giles
FNB OF NARROWS
{{ 4 L 8 S }}
Chartered 9/19
1902 Plain Back <$VALUE
3x10-20 1-9120 <$600
1929 Small Size
10 Type 1 1-1728 <$300
20 Type 1 1-474 <$300
10 Type 2 1-3159 <$300
20 Type 2 1-849 <$300
Total Issue $665,130
Out in 1935 $50,000
Large out 1935 $1,890

10993 Craig
FNB OF NEW CASTLE
{{ 4 L 6 S }}
Chartered 5/17
1902 Plain Back <$VALUE
3x10-20 1-4209 <$650
1929 Small Size
10 Type 1 1-754 <$350
20 Type 1 1-200 <$350
10 Type 2 1-1259 <$350
20 Type 2 1-408 <$350
Total Issue $300,440
Out in 1935 $25,000
Large out 1935 $1,190

10568 Shenandoah
FNB OF NEW MARKET
{{ 1 L }}
Chartered 6/14
Liquidated 12/1/18
1902 Date Back <$VALUE
3x10-20 1-700 <$1250
1902 Plain Back
3x10-20 701-1163 <$1250
Total Issue $58,150
Out at close $20,000

4635 Independent City
FNB OF NEWPORT NEWS
{{ 12 L 22 S }}
Organized 9/14/91
Brown Back <$VALUE
4x5 1-14000 <$500
3x10-20 1-5240 <$500
1882 Date Back
4x5 1-2664 <$500
3x10-20 1-2334 <$500
1902 Date Back
3x10-20 1-6100 <$175
1902 Plain Back
3x10-20 6101-40298 <$175
1929 Small Size
10 Type 1 1-8614 <$65
20 Type 1 1-2154 <$75
10 Type 2 1-21145 <$75
20 Type 2 1-5202 <$75
Total Issue $3,817,690
Out in 1935 $300,000
Large out 1935 $5,810

11364 Independent City
N MECHANICS B OF NEWPORT NEWS
{{ 4 L }}
Chartered 5/19
Liquidated 11/5/24
1902 Plain Back <$VALUE
4x5 1-35525 <$400
Total Issue $710,500
Out at close $100,000

6781 Independent City
NEWPORT NEWS NB, NEWPORT NEWS
{{ 1 L }}
Chartered 5/14/03
Liquidated 12/14/08
1902 Red Seal <$VALUE
4x5 1-4755 <$1000
3x10-20 1-3697 <$1000
Total Issue $279,950
Out in 1910 $14,915

11028 Independent City
SCHMELZ NB OF NEWPORT NEWS
{{ 10 L 12 S }}
Organized 6/25/17
Liquidated 3/18/32
1902 Plain Back <$VALUE
4x5 1-46940 <$250
3x10-20 1-30739 <$250
1929 Small Size
5 Type 1 1-7474 <$100
10 Type 1 1-3478 <$100
20 Type 1 1-818 <$115
Total Issue $3,006,810
Out in 1930 $200,000
Large out at close $15,500

4743 Independent City
CITY NB OF NORFOLK
{{ 2 L }}
Chartered 5/24/92
Liquidated 9/28/03
Brown Back <$VALUE
4x5 1-28488 <$850
3x10-20 1-5502 <$850
Total Issue $844,860
Out in 1910 $13,235

1137 Independent City
EXCHANGE NB OF NORFOLK
{{ 2 L }}
Organized 5/13/65
Receivership 4/9/85
Original Series <$VALUE
3x1-2 1-2000 <$2500/$6000
4x5 1-6050 <$1500
3x10-20 1-4400<$2000/$2500
50-100 1-460 <$8500
Series 1875
4x5 1-5700 <$1500
3x10-20 1-4996<$2000/$2500
50-100 1-390 <$8500
Total Issue $842,300
Out in 1915 $4,162

271 Independent City
FNB OF NORFOLK
{{ UNREPORTED }}
Organized 2/23/64
Receivership 6/3/74
Original Series <$VALUE
4x5 1-2375 <$2500
4x10 1-2395 <$3000
Total Issue $143,300
Out in 1915 $1,155

CONDITION affects Value. The Values shown are for notes in FINE condition.

6032 Independent City
NB OF COMMERCE OF NORFOLK
Chartered 11/01
Closed 10/9/33
2nd title: Norfolk NB of Commerce & Trusts 1/7/27
FIRST TITLE {{ 31 L }}
Brown Back <$VALUE
3x10-20 1-34200 <$400
1882 Date Back
3x10-20 1-119000 <$400
1882 Value Back
3x10-20 119001-181936<$400
1902 Plain Back
3x10-20 1-97886 <$75
SECOND TITLE {{ 13 L 50+ S }}
1902 Plain Back
3x10-20 1-45562 <$85
1929 Small Size
10 Type 1 1-45369 <$25
20 Type 1 1-12820 <$35
Total Issue $22,239,740
Out at close $2,000,000
Large out at close $122,190
Outstanding includes Ch 3368
Ch 9885 assumed circulation

NB of Commerce of Norfolk
SEE Ch 9885
Virginia NB of Norfolk

3368 Independent City
NORFOLK NB, NORFOLK
{{ 27 L }}
Organized 8/1/85
Closed 1/7/27
Brown Back <$VALUE
4x5 1-3575 <$400
3x10-20 1-31986 <$400
1902 Red Seal
4x5 1-24000 <$400
3x10-20 1-14900 <$400
1902 Date Back
4x5 1-84830 <$100
3x10-20 1-64400 <$100
1902 Plain Back
4x5 84831-259238 <$100
3x10-20 64401-180236 <$100
Total Issue $17,092,360
Out in 1926 $983,400
Ch 6032 assumed circulation

Norfolk NB of Commerce & Trusts, Norfolk
SEE Ch 6032
NB of Commerce of Norfolk

1704 Independent City
PEOPLES NB OF NORFOLK
{{ UNREPORTED }}
Chartered 1870
Liquidated 7/31/78
Original Series <$VALUE
4x5 1-500 <$2000
3x10-20 1-3686<$2500/$3000
Total Issue $194,300
Out in 1910 $470

Seaboard Citizens NB of Norfolk
SEE Ch 10194
Seaboard NB of Norfolk

10194 Independent City
SEABOARD NB OF NORFOLK
Chartered 5/12
2nd title: Seaboard Citizens NB 6/30/28
FIRST TITLE {{ 15 L }}
1902 Date Back <$VALUE
3x10-20 1-17700 <$75
1902 Plain Back
4x5 1-103319 <$75
3x10-20 17701-135207 <$75
SECOND TITLE {{ 31 L 50+ S }}
1902 Plain Back
4x5 1-22266 <$75
3x10-20 1-14775 <$75
1929 Small Size
5 Type 1 1-59710 <$20
10 Type 1 1-38666 <$20
20 Type 1 1-12344 <$20
5 Type 2 1-172671* <$20
10 Type 2 1-82187 <$20
20 Type 2 1-2508 <$30
* 93607-93612 not issued
Total Issue $17,338,695
Out in 1935 $1,500,000
Large out 1935 $35,950

9885 Independent City
VIRGINIA NB OF NORFOLK
Chartered 11/10
2nd title: NB of Commerce of Norfolk 10/9/33
FIRST TITLE {{29 L 2U+21 S}}
1902 Date Back <$VALUE
4x5 1-45750 <$85
3x10-20 1-35300 <$85
1902 Plain Back
4x5 45751-148670 <$85
3x10-20 35301-101272 <$85
1929 Small Size
5 Type 1 1-24722 <$40
10 Type 1 1-12490 <$40
20 Type 1 1-3224 <$50
5 Type 2 1-11052 <$40
10 Type 2 1-4992 <$40
20 Type 2 1-1260 <$50
SECOND TITLE {{ 20 S }}
1929 Small Size
5 Type 2 1-85548* <$30
10 Type 2 1-79217 <$40
20 Type 2 1-17261 <$40
* 1747-1752 not issued
Total Issue $11,610,420
Out in 1935 $2,000,000
Large out 1935 $19,290
Outstanding includes Ch 6032

6235 Independent City
FNB OF NORTON
{{ 6 L 9 S }}
Chartered 5/02
1902 Red Seal <$VALUE
4x5 1-1285 <$850
3x10-20 1-1046 <$850
1902 Date Back
4x5 1-4300 <$375
3x10-20 1-3220 <$375
1902 Plain Back (dated 1902)
4x5 4301-12150 <$375
4x5 3221-7980 <$375
1902 Plain Back (dated 1922)
4x5 1-10757 <$375
3x10-20 1-8390 <$375
1929 Small Size
10 Type 1 1-3410 <$175
20 Type 1 1-924 <$175
10 Type 2 1-5325 <$200
20 Type 2 1-1912 <$200
Total Issue $1,761,610
Out in 1935 $100,000
Large out 1935 $3,185

9746 Independent City
NB OF NORTON
{{ 4 L 27 S }}
Organized 4/25/10
Receivership 3/31/31
1902 Date Back <$VALUE
3x10-20 1-2240 <$450
1902 Plain Back
3x10-20 2241-11680 <$450
1929 Small Size
10 Type 1 1-893 <$125
20 Type 1 1-223 <$125
Total Issue $664,340
Out at close $50,000
Large out at close $6,160

13878 Accomack
FNB IN ONANCOCK
{{ UNREPORTED }}
Chartered 12/33
1929 Small Size <$VALUE
10 Type 2 1-1420 <$650
20 Type 2 1-314 <$650
Total Issue $20,480
Out in 1935 $50,000
Outstanding includes Ch 4940

4940 Accomack
FNB OF ONANCOCK
{{ 4 L 7 S }}
Organized 12/27/93
Liquidated 4/10/34
Brown Back <$VALUE
3x10-20 1-1190 <$1000
1882 Date Back
3x10-20 1-3291 <$1000
1902 Date Back
3x10-20 1-1200 <$600
1902 Plain Back
3x10-20 1201-9776 <$600
1929 Small Size
10 Type 1 1-1328 <$250
20 Type 1 1-358 <$250
10 Type 2 1-431 <$275
20 Type 2 1-150 <$275
Total Issue $842,800
Out in 1934 $50,000
Large out at close $3,010
Ch 13878 assumed circulation

7258 Accomack
FARMERS & MERCHANTS NB OF ONLEY
{{ 6 L 9 S }}
Organized 5/6/04
Liquidated 6/20/35
1902 Red Seal <$VALUE
4x5 1-2610 <$750
3x10-20 1-1906 <$750
1902 Date Back
4x5 1-4050 <$400
3x10-20 1-2720 <$400
1902 Plain Back
4x5 4051-13451 <$400
3x10-20 2721-8756 <$400
1929 Small Size
5 Type 1 1-1948 <$200
10 Type 1 1-962 <$200
20 Type 1 1-286 <$200
5 Type 2 1-874 <$225
10 Type 2 1-380 <$225
20 Type 2 1-108 <$250
Total Issue $1,015,130
Out in 1935 $50,000
Large out 1935 $2,965

5532 Orange
AMERICAN NB OF ORANGE
{{ UNREPORTED }}
Chartered 8/10/00
Liquidated 1/8/01
Brown Back <$VALUE
4x5 1-415 <$2000
3x10-20 1-344 <$2000
Total Issue $25,500
Out in 1910 $500

7150 Orange
CITIZENS NB OF ORANGE
{{ 11 L 19 S }}
Chartered 2/04
1902 Red Seal <$VALUE
3x10-20 1-1426 <$650
1902 Date Back
3x10-20 1-2120 <$250
1902 Plain Back
3x10-20 2121-20365 <$250
1929 Small Size
10 Type 1 1-6120 <$75
20 Type 1 1-1758 <$85
10 Type 2 1-15194 <$100
20 Type 2 1-3170 <$100
Total Issue $1,883,050
Out in 1935 $225,000
Large out 1935 $4,280

5438 Orange
NB OF ORANGE
{{ 7 L 16 S }}
Chartered 6/18/00
Brown Back <$VALUE
3x10-20 1-1800 <$750
1882 Date Back
3x10-20 1-2060 <$750
1882 Value Back
3x10-20 2061-6720 <$750
1902 Plain Back
3x10-20 1-14625 <$350
1929 Small Size
10 Type 1 1-3270 <$85
20 Type 1 1-818 <$100
5 Type 2 1-324 <$100
10 Type 2 1-5613 <$100
20 Type 2 1-1844 <$100
Total Issue $1,546,240
Out in 1935 $100,000
Large out 1935 $3,825

6246 Accomack
PARKSLEY NB, PARKSLEY
{{ 7 L 9 S }}
Organized 3/8/02
1902 Red Seal <$VALUE
4x5 1-2175 <$750
3x10-20 1-1380 <$750
50-100 1-400 <$3000/$3500
1902 Date Back
4x5 1-4500* <$375
3x10-20 1-3080** <$375
1902 Plain Back (dated 1902)
4x5 5001-9720* <$375
3x10-20 3481-5987** <$375
* 4501-5000 not marked
** 3081-3480 not marked
1902 Plain Back (dated 1922)
4x5 1-7137 <$375
3x10-20 1-4210 <$375
1929 Small Size
5 Type 1 1-2572 <$175
10 Type 1 1-1292 <$175
20 Type 1 1-326 <$200
5 Type 2 1-2746 <$200
10 Type 2 1-1653 <$200
20 Type 2 1-475 <$200
Total Issue $1,253,050
Out in 1935 $60,000
Large out 1935 $3,580

8091 Giles
FNB OF PEARISBURG
{{ 6 L 6 S }}
Chartered 2/06
Liquidated 8/17/31
1902 Red Seal <$VALUE
3x10-20 1-1700 <$850
1902 Date Back
3x10-20 1-7500 <$450
1902 Plain Back
4x5 1-9750 <$450
3x10-20 7501-23987 <$450
1929 Small Size
5 Type 1 1-2803 <$275
10 Type 1 1-1320 <$275
20 Type 1 1-416 <$275
Total Issue $1,692,560
Out at close $100,000
Large out at close $7,840

13792 Independent City
CITIZENS NB OF PETERSBURG
{{ 10 S }}
Chartered 10/33
1929 Small Size <$VALUE
5 Type 2 1-15060 <$125
10 Type 2 1-8074 <$125
20 Type 2 1-2610 <$125
Total Issue $208,240
Out in 1935 $93,800

1769 Independent City
COMMERCIAL NB OF PETERSBURG
{{ UNREPORTED }}
Chartered 1/16/71
Liquidated 1/14/79
Original Series <$VALUE
4x5 1-2150 <$2000
3x10-20 1-2200<$2500/$3000
50-100 1-200 <$8500
Series 1875
3x10-20 1-936 <$2500/$3000
Total Issue $229,800
Out in 1910 $1,550

FNB & TC of Petersburg
SEE Ch 3515
NB of Petersburg

1378 Independent City
FNB OF PETERSBURG
{{ UNREPORTED }}
Organized 7/1/65
Receivership 9/25/73
Original Series <$VALUE
4x5 1-2900 <$2000
3x10-20 1-2350<$2500/$3000
50-100 1-150 <$8500
Total Issue $198,000
Out in 1915 $1,520

1548 Independent City
MERCHANTS NB OF PETERSBURG
{{ UNREPORTED }}
Organized 9/1/65
Receivership 9/25/73
Original Series <$VALUE
4x5 1-5330 <$2000
3x10-20 1-3232<$2500/$3000
50-100 1-734 <$8500
Total Issue $378,300
Out in 1915 $2,390

3515 Independent City
NB OF PETERSBURG
Organized 5/18/86
Receivership 11/16/33
2nd title:FNB & TC of Petersburg 9/30/31
FIRST TITLE {{ 19 L 9 S }}
Brown Back <$VALUE
4x5 1-6211 <$450
3x10-20 1-990 <$450
1902 Red Seal
3x10-20 1-2940 <$450
1902 Date Back
3x10-20 1-10200 <$75
1902 Plain Back
3x10-20 10201-123814 <$75
1929 Small Size
10 Type 1 1-8856 <$65
20 Type 1 1-2680 <$75
SECOND TITLE {{ 21 S }}
1929 Small Size
10 Type 1 1-4841 <$50
20 Type 1 1-1458 <$60
Total Issue $7,829,800
Out at close $692,200
Large out at close $81,375
Outstanding includes Ch 7709

7709 Independent City
VIRGINIA NB OF PETERSBURG
{{ 31 L U + 23 S }}
Chartered 4/05
Closed 9/30/31
1902 Red Seal <$VALUE
50-100 1-3652 <$3000/$3500
1902 Date Back
4x5 1-33000 <$75
3x10-20 1-8800 <$75
50-100 1-2700 <$500/$600
3x50-100 1-1900 <$500/$600
1902 Plain Back
4x5 33001-108500 <$75
3x10-20 8801-188800 <$75
1929 Small Size
5 Type 1 1-14504 <$40
10 Type 1 1-21061 <$40
20 Type 1 1-2850 <$50
Total Issue $15,078,580
Out at close $1,000,000
Large out at close $112,540
Ch 3515 assumed circulation

12267 Independent City
OLD POINT NB OF PHOEBUS
{{ 3 L 6 S }}
Chartered 11/22
1902 Plain Back <$VALUE
4x5 1-5685 <$800
3x10-20 1-4090 <$800
1929 Small Size
5 Type 1 1-2582 <$350
10 Type 1 1-1294 <$350
20 Type 1 1-370 <$350
5 Type 2 1-4336 <$350
10 Type 2 1-2724 <$350
20 Type 2 1-732 <$350
Total Issue $581,260
Out in 1935 $50,000
Large out 1935 $1,450

7847 Pocahontas
FNB OF POCAHONTAS
{{ 2 L }}
Chartered 7/05
Liquidated 3/10/27
1902 Red Seal <$VALUE
3x10-20 1-1700 <$1250
1902 Date Back
3x10-20 1-3560 <$750
1902 Plain Back
3x10-20 3561-9501 <$750
Total Issue $560,050
Out at close $35,000

12092 York
FNB OF POQUOSON
{{ 2 L 2 S }}
Chartered 1/22
1902 Plain Back <$VALUE
4x5 1-11422 <$750
1929 Small Size
5 Type 1 1-3930 <$450
5 Type 2 1-8184 <$450
Total Issue $387,260
Out in 1935 $25,000
Large out 1935 $710

11381 Independent City
AMERICAN NB OF PORTSMOUTH
{{ 15 L 25 S }}
Chartered 6/19
1902 Plain Back <$VALUE
4x5 1-105129 <$135
3x10-20 1-67671 <$135
1929 Small Size
5 Type 1 1-23430 <$40
10 Type 1 1-13040 <$40
20 Type 1 1-3378 <$50
5 Type 2 1-24918 <$40
10 Type 2 1-10810 <$40
20 Type 2 1-3480 <$50
Total Issue $7,679,080
Out in 1935 $250,000
Large out 1935 $18,090

9300 Independent City
FNB OF PORTSMOUTH
{{ 8 L }}
Organized 12/9/08
Liquidated 1/15/30
1902 Date Back <$VALUE
3x10-20 1-8800 <$200
1902 Plain Back
3x10-20 8801-59102 <$200
Total Issue $2,955,100
Out at close $86,350

11387 Pulaski
PEOPLES NB OF PULASKI
{{ 6 L 15 S }}
Chartered 6/19
1902 Plain Back <$VALUE
4x5 1-19377 <$250
3x10-20 1-6462 <$250
1929 Small Size
5 Type 1 1-5966 <$85
10 Type 1 1-2186 <$85
20 Type 1 1-704 <$100
5 Type 2 1-9836 <$100
10 Type 2 1-3583 <$100
20 Type 2 1-1120 <$100
Total Issue $1,212,670
Out in 1935 $100,000
Large out 1935 $2,985

4071 Pulaski
PULASKI NB, PULASKI
{{ 8 L 17 S }}
Chartered 1889
Brown Back <$VALUE
4x5 1-1774 <$750
3x10-20 1-1012 <$750
1902 Date Back
4x5 1-2050 <$225
3x10-20 1-1640 <$225
1902 Plain Back
4x5 2051-33701 <$225
3x10-20 1641-19939 <$225
1929 Small Size
5 Type 1 1-6788 <$65
10 Type 1 1-3814 <$65
20 Type 1 1-1032 <$85
5 Type 2 1-13138 <$85
10 Type 2 1-7483 <$85
20 Type 2 1-1405 <$85
Total Issue $2,481,990
Out in 1935 $150,000
Large out 1935 $6,600

6018 Loudon
PURCELLVILLE NB, PURCELLVILLE
{{ 5 L 6 S }}
Chartered 11/01
Brown Back <$VALUE
4x5 1-2480 <$850
3x10-20 1-1808 <$850
1882 Date Back
4x5 1-4350 <$850
3x10-20 1-3000 <$850
1882 Value Back
4x5 4351-8960 <$850
3x10-20 3001-5114 <$850
1902 Plain Back
4x5 1-21249 <$450
1929 Small Size
5 Type 1 1-7422 <$225
5 Type 2 1-17052 <$225
Total Issue $1,307,800
Out in 1935 $50,000
Large out 1935 $2,945

12477 Prince Edward
FNB OF QUANTICO
{{ U + 9 S }}
Chartered 12/23
1929 Small Size <$VALUE
5 Type 1 1-1162 <$175
10 Type 1 1-818 <$175
20 Type 1 1-196 <$175
5 Type 2 1-1656 <$200
10 Type 2 1-960 <$200
20 Type 2 1-276 <$200
Total Issue $130,860
Out in 1935 $25,000

<$VALUEs are for notes in FINE condition. Value changes by approximately 25% for a change of one full grade.

***

11690 Independent City
FARMERS & MERCHANTS NB OF RADFORD
{{ 2 L 6 S }}
Chartered 4/20
Closed 6/28/32
1902 Plain Back <$VALUE
3x10-20 1-9965 <$650
1929 Small Size
10 Type 1 1-1496 <$300
20 Type 1 1-439 <$300
Total Issue $640,690
Out at close $60,000
Large out at close $3,930
Ch 6782 assumed circulation

***

F & Merchants NB of Radford
SEE Ch 6782
FNB of Radford

***

6782 Independent City
FNB OF RADFORD
Chartered 5/03
2nd title: F & Merchants NB of Radford 6/28/32
FIRST TITLE {{ 1 L 1 S }}
1902 Red Seal <$VALUE
3x10-20 1-800 <$1250
1902 Date Back
3x10-20 1-1400 <$750
1902 Plain Back
3x10-20 1401-3637 <$750
1929 Small Size
10 Type 1 1-314 <$300
20 Type 1 1-106 <$300
SECOND TITLE {{ 9 S }}
1929 Small Size
10 Type 1 1-944 <$200
20 Type 1 1-254 <$200
10 Type 2 1-5325 <$200
20 Type 2 1-1576 <$200
Total Issue $425,300
Out in 1935 $100,000
Large out 1935 $1,820
Outstanding includes Ch 11690

***

10827 Northumberland
COMMONWEALTH NB OF REEDVILLE
{{ 1 L }}
Organized 1/6/16
Receivership 2/16/21
1902 Plain Back <$VALUE
4x10 1-2182 <$1000
Total Issue $87,280
Out at close $23,700

***

10850 Tazewell
FNB OF RICHLANDS
{{ 2 L 7 S }}
Chartered 5/16
1902 Plain Back <$VALUE
4x5 1-7253 <$600
3x10-20 1-5238 <$600
1929 Small Size
5 Type 1 1-1920 <$225
10 Type 1 1-1044 <$225
20 Type 1 1-308 <$225
5 Type 2 1-2412 <$250
10 Type 2 1-1896 <$250
20 Type 2 1-504 <$250
Total Issue $605,260
Out in 1935 $40,000
Large out 1935 $1,200

***

10857 Tazewell
RICHLANDS NB, RICHLANDS
{{ 2 L 4 S }}
Chartered 5/16
1902 Plain Back <$VALUE
4x5 1-4233 <$750
4x10 1-3316 <$750
1929 Small Size
5 Type 1 1-1494 <$350
10 Type 1 1-726 <$350
5 Type 2 1-3048 <$350
10 Type 2 1-1644 <$350
Total Issue $337,360
Out in 1934 $21,000
Large out 1935 $510

***

5229 Independent City
AMERICAN NB OF RICHMOND
{{ 45 L }}
Organized 11/1/99
Liquidated 12/29/28
Brown Back <$VALUE
4x5 1-27215 <$400
3x10-20 1-20114 <$400
1882 Date Back
4x5 1-74830 <$350
3x10-20 1-58468 <$350
1882 Value Back
4x5 74831-112830 <$400
3x10-20 58469-80468 <$400
1902 Plain Back
4x5 1-90334 <$65
3x10-20 1-59348 <$65
Total Issue $12,604,080
Out in 1924 $185,000

***

10344 Independent City
BROADWAY NB OF RICHMOND
{{ 7 L }}
Chartered 3/13
Liquidated 4/9/29
1902 Date Back <$VALUE
4x5 1-4500* <$175
3x10-20 1-3600** <$175
1902 Plain Back
4x5 5251-31525* <$175
3x10-20 4201-19972** <$175
* 4501-5250 not marked
** 3601-4200 not marked
Total Issue $1,629,100
Out in 1922 $189,500

***

10080 Independent City
CENTRAL NB OF RICHMOND
{{ 30 L 50+ S }}
Chartered 9/11
1902 Date Back <$VALUE
4x5 1-5330 <$85
3x10-20 1-4268 <$85
1902 Plain Back
4x5 5331-93907 <$85
3x10-20 4269-69736 <$85
1929 Small Size
5 Type 1 1-43782* <$20
10 Type 1 1-23274** <$20
20 Type 1 1-6686*** <$30
5 Type 2 1-36568 <$20
10 Type 2 1-17649 <$20
20 Type 2 1-5005 <$30
* 24934-28614 not issued
** 12072-13766 not issued
*** 3370-4136 not issued
Total Issue $9,032,420
Out in 1935 $500,000
Large out 1935 $26,085

***

1570 Independent City
FARMERS NB OF RICHMOND
{{ UNREPORTED }}
Chartered 9/28/65
Liquidated 10/22/66
Original Series <$VALUE
4x5 1-500 <$2000
4x10 1-1325 <$2500
3x20-50 1-200 <$3000/$8500
Total Issue $85,000
Out in 1910 $1,590

***

1111 Independent City
FNB OF RICHMOND
{{ 50+ L }}
Chartered 4/24/65
Original Series <$VALUE
4x5 1-12825 <$1000
3x10-20 1-9130 <$1500/$2000
3x50-100 1-720 <$8500
Series 1875
3x10-20 1-14182<$1500/$2000
3x50-100 1-40 <$8500
Brown Back
4x5 1-11500 <$400
3x10-20 1-31800 <$400
1902 Red Seal
4x5 1-30750 <$400
4x10 1-16250 <$400
3x10-20 1-10500 <$400
1902 Date Back
4x5 1-116500 <$65
4x10 1-113500 <$65
3x10-20 1-16468 <$65
1902 Plain Back
4x5 116501-238741 <$65
4x10 113501-204969 <$65
Total Issue $19,019,080
Out in 1935 $59,005
Outstanding includes Ch 1125 and Ch 1754

***

Manchester NB of Richmond
SEE Ch 9663
Manchester NB, Manchester

***

1754 Independent City
MERCHANTS NB OF RICHMOND
{{ 10 L }}
Chartered 12/17/70
Closed 2/27/26
Original Series <$VALUE
4x5 1-5500 <$1250
3x10-20 1-2400<$1500/$2000
Series 1875
4x5 1-3500 <$1250
3x10-20 1-3766<$1500/$2000
50-100 1-1338 <$8500
Brown Back
4x5 1-14250 <$500
3x10-20 1-16300 <$500
50-100 1-2342 <$3500/$4000
1882 Date Back
4x5 1-2900 <$450
3x10-20 1-2873 <$450
1902 Date Back
4x5 1-22240 <$175
3x10-20 1-17914 <$175
Total Issue $3,682,450
Out in 1922 $50,500
Ch 1111 assumed circulation

***

1125 Independent City
NB OF VIRGINIA, RICHMOND
{{ 14 L }}
Chartered 1865
Liquidated 9/2/12
Original Series <$VALUE
4x5 1-19000 <$1250
Series 1875
4x5 1-12000 <$1250
50-100 1-680 <$8500
Brown Back
4x5 1-18455 <$500
3x10-20 1-16034 <$500
50-100 1-1575 <$3500/$4000
1902 Red Seal
4x5 1-15863 <$450
3x10-20 1-12288 <$450
1902 Date Back
4x5 1-34421 <$110
3x10-20 1-26649 <$110
Total Issue $5,081,580
Out at close $873,500
Ch 1111 assumed circulation

***

1155 Independent City
N EXCHANGE B OF RICHMOND
{{ UNREPORTED }}
Chartered 5/15/65
Liquidated 12/5/67
Original Series <$VALUE
4x5 1-4765 <$2000
3x10-20 1-1632<$2500/$3000
50-100 1-24 <$8500
Total Issue $180,500
Out in 1910 $440

***

N State & City B of Richmond
SEE Ch 8666
N State B of Richmond

***

8666 Independent City
N STATE B OF RICHMOND
Chartered 4/07
Liquidated 8/17/22
2nd title: N State & City B of Richmond 7/1/10
FIRST TITLE {{ 2 L }}
1902 Red Seal <$VALUE
4x5 1-8750 <$650
4x10 1-8750 <$650
1902 Date Back
4x5 1-5557 <$350
4x10 1-1302 <$350
SECOND TITLE {{ 11 L }}
1902 Date Back
4x5 1-38150 <$200
4x10 1-38050 <$200
1902 Plain Back
4x5 38151-62650 <$200
4x10 38051-57050 <$200
Total Issue $4,223,220
Out in 1921 $407,500

***

1628 Independent City
PLANTERS NB OF RICHMOND
{{ 17 L }}
Chartered 1/66
Liquidated 2/27/26
Original Series <$VALUE
4x5 1-5510 <$1250
4x10 1-4910 <$1500
3x20-50 1-1575<$2000/$8500
Series 1875
4x10 1-4704 <$1500
3x20-50 1-1948<$2000/$8500
Brown Back
4x5 1-37898 <$500
3x10-20 1-9793 <$500
50-100 1-2247 <$3500/$4000
1902 Red Seal
4x5 1-6500 <$500
3x10-20 1-4400 <$500
1902 Date Back
4x5 1-37000 <$135
3x10-20 1-31500 <$135
1902 Plain Back
4x5 37001-40646 <$135
3x10-20 31501-33552 <$135
Total Issue $5,201,780
Out at close $150,000

***

10532 Independent City
AMERICAN NB OF ROANOKE
{{ 10 L }}
Chartered 5/14
Closed 6/29/29
1902 Date Back <$VALUE
3x10-20 1-4000* <$165
1902 Plain Back
3x10-20 6001-64269* <$165
* 4001-6000 not marked
Total Issue $3,213,450
Out at close $296,950
Ch 11817 assumed circulation

***

4531 Independent City
CITIZENS NB OF ROANOKE
{{ 1 L }}
Chartered 3/10/91
Liquidated 4/4/92
Brown Back <$VALUE
4x5 1-1274 <$1500
Total Issue $25,480
Out in 1910 $135

***

8152 Independent City
CITY NB OF ROANOKE
{{ 4 L }}
Chartered 3/06
Liquidated 1/12/15
1902 Red Seal <$VALUE
4x5 1-5000 <$650
3x10-20 1-4900 <$650
1902 Date Back
4x5 1-6630 <$300
3x10-20 1-15567 <$300
Total Issue $1,255,950
Out in 1915 $106,700

***

Colonial-American NB of Roanoke
SEE Ch 11817
Colonial NB of Roanoke

***

11817 Independent City
COLONIAL NB OF ROANOKE
Chartered 8/20
2nd title:Colonial-American NB of Roanoke 6/29/29
FIRST TITLE {{ 11 L }}
1902 Plain Back <$VALUE
3x10-20 1-61187 <$175
SECOND TITLE {{ 36 S }}
1929 Small Size
10 Type 1 1-29126 <$35
20 Type 1 1-8150 <$45
10 Type 2 1-54494 <$35
20 Type 2 1-14756 <$45
Total Issue $6,625,090
Out in 1935 $1,000,000
Large out 1935 $21,445
Outstanding includes Ch 11191 and Ch 10532

***

4026 Independent City
COMMERCIAL NB OF ROANOKE
{{ 1 L }}
Chartered 5/4/89
Liquidated 2/16/97
Brown Back <$VALUE
3x10-20 1-1240 <$1500
Total Issue $62,000
Out in 1910 $540

***

2737 Independent City
FNB OF ROANOKE
Chartered 1882
2nd title:FN Exchange B of Roanoke 12/31/25
FIRST TITLE {{ 15 L }}
Series 1875 <$VALUE
3x10-20 1-3260<$1500/$2000
1902 Red Seal
3x10-20 1-9800 <$450
1902 Date Back
3x10-20 1-32500 <$85
1902 Plain Back
3x10-20 32501-89899 <$85
SECOND TITLE {{ 17 L 50+ S }}
1902 Plain Back
3x10-20 1-62022 <$85
1929 Small Size
10 Type 1 1-33798 <$20
20 Type 1 1-9288 <$30
10 Type 2 1-59593 <$20
20 Type 2 1-14594 <$30
Total Issue $12,279,300
Out in 1935 $1,000,000
Large out 1935 $41,005
Outstanding includes Ch 4027

***

FN Exchange B of Roanoke
SEE Ch 2737
FNB of Roanoke

***

11191 Independent City
LIBERTY NB OF ROANOKE
{{ 1 L }}
Chartered 6/18
Closed 11/13/20
1902 Plain Back <$VALUE
3x10-20 1-1162 <$750
Total Issue $58,100
Out at close $50,000
Ch 11817 assumed circulation

***

4027 Independent City
N EXCHANGE B OF ROANOKE
{{ 15 L }}
Chartered 1889
Closed 12/31/25
Brown Back <$VALUE
3x10-20 1-17720 <$500
1902 Date Back
3x10-20 1-36000 <$100
1902 Plain Back
3x10-20 36001-101655 <$100
Total Issue $5,968,750
Out at close $500,000
Ch 2737 assumed circulation

***

6798 Independent City
PEOPLES NB OF ROANOKE
{{ UNREPORTED }}
Chartered 5/23/03
Liquidated 2/21/06
1902 Red Seal <$VALUE
3x10-20 1-2637 <$1250
Total Issue $131,850
Out in 1910 $6,530

***

2907 Independent City
ROANOKE NB, ROANOKE
{{ UNREPORTED }}
Chartered 3/24/83
Liquidated 9/16/86
Brown Back <$VALUE
3x10-20 1-304 <$1500
Total Issue $15,200
Out in 1910 $50

***

6685 Franklin
FNB OF ROCKY MOUNT
{{ 3 L }}
Chartered 3/03
Liquidated 10/1/26
1902 Red Seal <$VALUE
3x10-20 1-2160 <$1250
1902 Date Back
3x10-20 1-4240 <$450
1902 Plain Back
3x10-20 4241-11088 <$450
Total Issue $662,400
Out at close $50,000
Ch 8984 assumed circulation

***

8984 Franklin
PEOPLES NB OF ROCKY MOUNT
{{ 11 L 17 S }}
Chartered 1/08
1902 Red Seal <$VALUE
4x10 1-250 <$850
1902 Date Back
4x10 1-3325 <$225
1902 Plain Back
4x5 1-17304 <$225
4x10 3326-18259 <$225
1929 Small Size
5 Type 1 1-7258 <$100
10 Type 1 1-4324 <$100
5 Type 2 1-15804 <$100
10 Type 2 1-8339 <$100
Total Issue $1,726,030
Out in 1935 $125,000
Large out 1935 $7,025
Outstanding includes Ch 6685

***

8389 Arlington
ARLINGTON NB OF ROSSLYN
{{ UNREPORTED }}
Chartered 10/06
Liquidated 1/12/14
1902 Red Seal <$VALUE
3x10-20 1-800 <$2000
1902 Date Back
3x10-20 1-2024 <$1000
Total Issue $141,200
Out in 1914 $13,070

***

11569 Loudon
ROUND HILL NB, ROUND HILL
{{ 2 L 8 S }}
Chartered 12/19
1902 Plain Back <$VALUE
3x10-20 1-3764 <$800
1929 Small Size
10 Type 1 1-1274 <$250
20 Type 1 1-358 <$275
10 Type 2 1-1871 <$300
20 Type 2 1-436 <$300
Total Issue $355,030
Out in 1935 $40,000
Large out 1935 $820

***

10061 Wythe
FNB OF RURAL RETREAT
{{ 5 L 9 S }}
Chartered 8/1/11
Liquidated 6/14/33
1902 Date Back <$VALUE
3x10-20 1-1450 <$750
1902 Plain Back
3x10-20 1451-9131 <$750
1929 Small Size
10 Type 1 1-1348 <$250
20 Type 1 1-358 <$275
Total Issue $580,390
Out at close $50,000
Large out at close $3,260

***

8547 Wise
SAINT PAUL NB, SAINT PAUL
{{ 9 L U + 18 S }}
Chartered 2/07
1902 Red Seal <$VALUE
4x5 1-300 <$600
4x10 1-300 <$600
1902 Date Back
4x5 1-1750 <$200
4x10 1-1675 <$200
1902 Plain Back
4x5 1751-17109 <$200
4x10 1676-14921 <$200
1929 Small Size
5 Type 1 1-6654 <$75
10 Type 1 1-3386 <$75
5 Type 2 1-14436 <$85
10 Type 2 1-7932 <$85
Total Issue $1,511,300
Out in 1935 $100,000
Large out 1935 $3,390

***

1824 Independent City
FARMERS NB OF SALEM
{{ 8 L 14 S }}
Chartered 5/23/71
Original Series <$VALUE
4x5 1-3750 <$1500
Series 1875
4x5 1-4051 <$1500
Brown Back
4x5 1-4825 <$750
3x10-20 1-2810 <$750
1882 Date Back
4x5 1-1420 <$750
3x10-20 1-1960 <$750
1902 Date Back
4x5 1-2600 <$300
3x10-20 1-1960 <$300
1902 Plain Back
4x5 2601-16519 <$300
3x10-20 1961-11181 <$300
1929 Small Size
5 Type 1 1-4308 <$125
10 Type 1 1-2350 <$125
20 Type 1 1-616 <$150
5 Type 2 1-7022 <$150
10 Type 2 1-3502 <$150
20 Type 2 1-1164 <$150
Total Issue $1,793,870
Out in 1935 $100,000
Large out 1935 $4,435

***

11265 Smyth
FNB OF SALTVILLE
{{ 3 L 8 S }}
Chartered 11/18
1902 Plain Back <$VALUE
3x10-20 1-7945 <$650
1929 Small Size
10 Type 1 1-1702 <$225
20 Type 1 1-450 <$250
10 Type 2 1-2168 <$250
20 Type 2 1-595 <$250
Total Issue $586,950
Out in 1935 $50,000
Large out 1935 $1,450

***

5725 Albemarle
SCOTTSVILLE NB, SCOTTSVILLE
{{ 3 L 8 S }}
Chartered 2/01
Liquidated 1/22/35
Brown Back <$VALUE
4x5 1-1390 <$850
3x10-20 1-1114 <$850
1882 Date Back
4x5 1-1575 <$850
3x10-20 1-1200 <$850
1882 Value Back
4x5 1576-2845 <$850
3x10-20 1201-1853 <$850
1902 Plain Back
4x5 1-2643 <$500
3x10-20 1-1680 <$500
1929 Small Size
5 Type 1 1-1366 <$225
10 Type 1 1-644 <$225
20 Type 1 1-214 <$225
5 Type 2 1-1780 <$250
10 Type 2 1-767 <$250
20 Type 2 1-325 <$250
Total Issue $498,280
Out in 1935 $50,000
Large out 1935 $1,230

8414 Independent City
BOSTON NB OF SOUTH BOSTON
{{ 16 L 10 S }}
Organized 10/10/06
Receivership 7/10/31
1902 Red Seal <$VALUE
4x5 1-1125 <$600
3x10-20 1-800 <$600
1902 Date Back
4x5 1-4800 <$200
3x10-20 1-3960 <$200
1902 Plain Back
4x5 4801-34149 <$200
3x10-20 3961-30717 <$200
1929 Small Size
10 Type 1 1-3737 <$125
20 Type 1 1-1050 <$135
Total Issue $2,631,550
Out at close $200,000
Large out at close $20,370

5872 Independent City
FNB OF SOUTH BOSTON
{{ 3 L }}
Chartered 6/01
Liquidated 1/12/26
Brown Back <$VALUE
3x10-20 1-1750 <$750
1882 Date Back
3x10-20 1-2381 <$750
Total Issue $206,550
Out at close $680

Planters & Merchants FNB of South Boston
SEE Ch 8643
Planters & Merchants NB of South Boston

8643 Independent City
PLANTERS & MERCHANTS NB OF SOUTH BOSTON
Organized 3/15/07
Receivership 10/10/31
2nd title: Planters & Merchants FNB of South Boston 1/26/26
FIRST TITLE {{ 10 L }}
1902 Red Seal <$VALUE
4x5 1-2900 <$600
3x10-20 1-2320 <$600
1902 Date Back
4x5 1-9915 <$200
3x10-20 1-7634 <$200
1902 Plain Back
4x5 9916-23666 <$200
3x10-20 7635-16620 <$200
SECOND TITLE {{ 2 L 9 S }}
1902 Plain Back
4x10 1-7791 <$275
1929 Small Size
10 Type 1 1-3693 <$150
Total Issue $2,011,540
Out at close $100,000
Large out at close $10,370

10973 Page
FARMERS & MERCHANTS NB OF STANLEY
{{ 3 L 8 S }}
Chartered 4/17
1902 Plain Back <$VALUE
3x10-20 1-5014 <$600
1929 Small Size
10 Type 1 1-1598 <$175
20 Type 1 1-410 <$200
10 Type 2 1-3579 <$200
20 Type 2 1-780 <$200
Total Issue $447,170
Out in 1935 $50,000
Large out 1935 $1,210

2269 Independent City
AUGUSTA NB OF STAUNTON
{{ 9 L 17 S }}
Chartered 5/24/75
Original Series <$VALUE
4x5 1-500 <$1250
3x10-20 1-400 <$2500/$3000
Series 1875
4x5 1-1250 <$1250
3x10-20 1-6475<$2500/$3000
Brown Back
3x10-20 1-8700 <$500
1882 Date Back
3x10-20 1-7431 <$500
1902 Date Back
3x50-100 1-1340 <$175
1902 Plain Back
3x10-20 1-7712 <$175
1929 Small Size
10 Type 1 1-3214 <$75
20 Type 1 1-824 <$85
10 Type 2 1-4202 <$85
20 Type 2 1-1374 <$85
Total Issue $2,267,120
Out in 1935 $100,000
Large out 1935 $4,705

1585 Independent City
FNB OF STAUNTON
{{ UNREPORTED }}
Chartered 10/12/65
Liquidated 1/23/75
Original Series <$VALUE
4x5 1-3035 <$2000
3x10-20 1-1400<$2500/$3000
Total Issue $130,700
Out in 1910 $750

1620 Independent City
N VALLEY B OF STAUNTON
{{ 13 L 20 S }}
Chartered 1865
Original Series <$VALUE
4x5 1-7550 <$1250
3x10-20 1-5600<$1500/$2000
Series 1875
4x5 1-2500 <$1250
3x10-20 1-848 <$1500/$2000
Brown Back
4x5 1-3100 <$600
3x10-20 1-3845 <$600
50-100 1-465 <$3500/$4000
1902 Red Seal
3x10-20 1-3100 <$600
1902 Date Back
4x5 1-5000 <$150
3x10-20 1-9100 <$150
1902 Plain Back
4x5 5001-25610 <$150
3x10-20 9101-20100 <$150
1929 Small Size
5 Type 1 1-18094 <$75
5 Type 2 1-66780 <$75
Total Issue $3,396,320
Out in 1935 $200,000
Large out 1935 $7,530

6903 Independent City
STAUNTON NB, STAUNTON
Chartered 7/03
2nd title:Staunton NB & TC 5/29/28
FIRST TITLE {{ 6 L }}
1902 Red Seal <$VALUE
3x10-20 1-2725 <$750
1902 Date Back
3x10-20 1-6700 <$300
1902 Plain Back
3x10-20 6701-20723 <$300
SECOND TITLE {{ 1 L 11 S }}
1902 Plain Back
3x10-20 1-1341 <$350
1929 Small Size
10 Type 1 1-2532 <$110
20 Type 1 1-676 <$125
5 Type 1 1-324 <$125
10 Type 1 1-3660 <$125
20 Type 1 1-1260 <$125
Total Issue $1,535,910
Out in 1934 $81,000
Large out 1935 $3,895

FNB of Strasburg
SEE Ch 8746
Peoples NB of Strasburg

8753 Shenandoah
MASSANUTTEN NB OF STRASBURG
{{ 3 L 4U + 14 S }}
Chartered 6/07
Liquidated 2/23/35
1902 Red Seal <$VALUE
4x5 1-140 <$1250
3x10-20 1-131 <$1250
1902 Date Back
4x5 1-1500 <$500
3x10-20 1-1160 <$500
1902 Plain Back
4x5 1501-10442 <$500
3x10-20 1161-7006 <$500
1929 Small Size
5 Type 1 1-1978 <$175
10 Type 1 1-1116 <$175
20 Type 1 1-322 <$175
5 Type 2 1-3014 <$200
10 Type 2 1-1402 <$200
20 Type 2 1-330 <$200
Total Issue $769,120
Out in 1935 $50,000
Large out 1935 $1,900

8746 Shenandoah
PEOPLES NB OF STRASBURG
Chartered 6/07
2nd title: FNB of Strasburg 1/10/28
FIRST TITLE {{ 4 L }}
1902 Red Seal <$VALUE
4x5 1-175 <$850
3x10-20 1-140 <$850
1902 Date Back
4x5 1-1350 <$400
3x10-20 1-1070 <$400
1902 Plain Back
4x5 1351-8945 <$400
3x10-20 1071-5953 <$400
SECOND TITLE {{ 8 S }}
1929 Small Size
5 Type 1 1-2152 <$175
10 Type 1 1-1206 <$175
20 Type 1 1-338 <$175
5 Type 2 1-3500 <$200
10 Type 2 1-1644 <$200
20 Type 2 1-444 <$200
Total Issue $707,350
Out in 1935 $50,000
Large out 1935 $1,055

11901 Patrick
FNB OF STUART
{{ 3 L 10 S }}
Chartered 12/20
1902 Plain Back <$VALUE
4x5 1-7278 <$600
3x10-20 1-4203 <$600
1929 Small Size
5 Type 1 1-2094 <$175
10 Type 1 1-1146 <$175
20 Type 1 1-308 <$175
5 Type 2 1-4440 <$200
10 Type 2 1-2004 <$200
20 Type 2 1-516 <$200
Total Issue $576,810
Out in 1935 $50,000
Large out 1935 $1,510

4047 Independent City
FNB OF SUFFOLK
{{ UNREPORTED }}
Chartered 5/25/89
Liquidated 2/12/91
Brown Back <$VALUE
4x5 1-325 <$2000
3x10-20 1-125 <$2000
Total Issue $12,750
Out in 1910 $125

9733 Independent City
NB OF SUFFOLK
{{ 15 L 28 S }}
Chartered 4/10
1902 Date Back <$VALUE
4x5 1-9000 <$150
3x10-20 1-7600 <$150
1902 Plain Back
4x5 9001-82518 <$150
3x10-20 7601-51139 <$150
1929 Small Size
5 Type 1 1-17118 <$60
10 Type 1 1-8436 <$60
20 Type 1 1-2262 <$65
5 Type 2 1-20964 <$65
10 Type 2 1-10303 <$65
20 Type 2 1-3530 <$65
Total Issue $5,776,900
Out in 1935 $250,000
Large out 1935 $9,280

11533 Tazewell
FARMERS NB OF TAZEWELL
{{ 2 L 0 S }}
Chartered 12/19
Liquidated 2/21/30
1902 Plain Back <$VALUE
3x10-20 1-8972 <$650
1929 Small Size
10 Type 1 1-179 <$650
20 Type 1 1-86 <$650
Total Issue $469,660
Out at close $50,000
Large out at close $36,490

6123 Tazewell
TAZEWELL NB, TAZEWELL
{{ 4 L 10 S }}
Chartered 2/02
1902 Red Seal <$VALUE
4x5 1-3050 <$750
3x10-20 1-2690 <$750
1902 Date Back
4x5 1-4650 <$375
3x10-20 1-3460 <$375
1902 Plain Back (dated 1902)
4x5 4651-9175 <$375
3x10-20 3461-6178 <$375
1902 Plain Back (dated 1922)
3x10-20 1-7501 <$375
1929 Small Size
5 Type 1 1-3040 <$150
10 Type 1 1-1498 <$150
20 Type 1 1-434 <$150
5 Type 2 1-4680 <$175
10 Type 2 1-2796 <$175
20 Type 2 1-696 <$175
Total Issue $1,361,390
Out in 1935 $60,000
Large out 1935 $3,620

11990 Grayson
FNB OF TROUTDALE
{{ 5 L 1 S }}
Chartered 7/21
Closed 6/30/32
1902 Plain Back <$VALUE
4x5 1-9622 <$350
1929 Small Size
5 Type 1 1-2253 <$600
Total Issue $260,030
Out at close $25,000
Large out at close $1,660
Ch 10834 assumed circulation

9764 Botetourt
FNB OF TROUTVILLE
{{ 2 L 0 3 }}
Chartered 6/10
1902 Date Back <$VALUE
4x5 1-1915 <$650
3x10-20 1-1730 <$650
1902 Plain Back
4x5 1916-7523 <$650
3x10-20 1731-5119 <$650
1929 Small Size
5 Type 1 1-1276 <$225
10 Type 1 1-628 <$225
20 Type 1 1-158 <$225
5 Type 2 1-2058 <$250
10 Type 2 1-1169 <$250
20 Type 2 1-336 <$250
Total Issue $530,030
Out in 1935 $25,000
Large out 1935 $980

12183 Lunenburg
FNB OF VICTORIA
{{ 2 L 2 S }}
Organized 4/14/22
Receivership 2/9/32
1902 Plain Back <$VALUE
4x5 1-11270 <$650
1929 Small Size
5 Type 1 1-2814 <$400
Total Issue $309,820
Out at close $25,000
Large out at close $1,210

11764 Fairfax
VIENNA NB, VIENNA
{{ 1 L }}
Chartered 6/20
Liquidated 6/29/29
1902 Plain Back <$VALUE
3x10-20 1-1873 <$750
Total Issue $93,650
Out at close $8,300

11911 Roanoke
FNB OF VINTON
{{ 1 L }}
Chartered 1/21
Liquidated 4/30/25
1902 Plain Back <$VALUE
3x10-20 1-312 <$1000
Total Issue $15,600
Out at close $5,000

6126 Fauquier
FAUQUIER NB OF WARRENTON
{{ 4 L 8 S }}
Chartered 2/02
1902 Red Seal <$VALUE
3x10-20 1-1010 <$750
1902 Date Back
3x10-20 1-4900 <$375
1902 Plain Back (dated 1902)
3x10-20 4901-9041 <$375
1902 Plain Back (dated 1922)
3x10-20 1-7222 <$375
1929 Small Size
10 Type 1 1-2344 <$125
20 Type 1 1-630 <$135
10 Type 2 1-2131 <$150
20 Type 2 1-475 <$150
Total Issue $1,110,700
Out in 1935 $62,500
Large out 1935 $2,960

9642 Fauquier
PEOPLES NB OF WARRENTON
{{ 4 L 9 S }}
Chartered 1/10
1902 Date Back <$VALUE
3x10-20 1-4600 <$375
1902 Plain Back
3x10-20 4601-14456 <$375
1929 Small Size
10 Type 1 1-1756 <$135
20 Type 1 1-458 <$150
10 Type 2 1-2484 <$165
20 Type 2 1-624 <$165
Total Issue $920,440
Out in 1935 $50,000
Large out 1935 $1,790

6443 Rappahannock
RAPPAHANNOCK NB OF WASHINGTON
{{ 0 L 2 S }}
Chartered 9/02
1902 Red Seal <$VALUE
3x10-20 1-620 <$1500
1902 Date Back
3x10-20 1-820 <$850
1902 Plain Back
3x10-20 821-2152 <$850
1929 Small Size
10 Type 1 1-426 <$450
20 Type 1 1-138 <$450
10 Type 2 1-972 <$500
20 Type 2 1-195 <$500
Total Issue $194,340
Out in 1934 $17,200
Large out 1935 $600

10914 Sussex
FNB OF WAVERLY
{{ 1 L }}
Organized 10/2/16
Liquidated 8/1/27
1902 Plain Back <$VALUE
4x5 1-4455 <$750
3x10-20 1-2590 <$750
Total Issue $218,600
Out at close $25,000

7587 Independent City
FNB OF WAYNESBORO
{{ 4 L 15 S }}
Chartered 2/05
1902 Red Seal <$VALUE
3x10-20 1-1160 <$650
1902 Date Back
3x10-20 1-2200 <$325
1902 Plain Back
3x10-20 2201-8270 <$325
1929 Small Size
10 Type 1 1-3540 <$85
20 Type 1 1-1042 <$100
10 Type 2 1-5040 <$100
20 Type 2 1-1212 <$100
Total Issue $883,580
Out in 1935 $100,000
Large out 1935 $2,020

9261 Independent City
WAYNESBORO NB, WAYNESBORO
{{ 3 L }}
Chartered 10/08
Liquidated 5/14/28
1902 Date Back <$VALUE
3x10-20 1-1100* <$450
1902 Plain Back
3x10-20 1301-5190* <$450
* 1101-1300 not marked
Total Issue $259,500
Out in 1927 $38,700

6084 Independent City
FARMERS & MERCHANTS NB OF WINCHESTER
Chartered 1/02
2nd title: Farmers & Merchants NB & TC 1/23/28
FIRST TITLE {{ 15 L }}
Brown Back <$VALUE
4x5 1-6100 <$450
3x10-20 1-4560 <$450
1882 Date Back
4x5 1-7100* <$400
3x10-20 1-4960** <$400
1882 Value Back
4x5 7501-22630* <$400
3x10-20 5281-14047** <$400
* 7101-7500 not marked
** 4961-5280 not marked
1902 Plain Back
4x5 1-33084 <$135
3x10-20 1-20367 <$135
SECOND TITLE {{ 4 L 14 S }}
1902 Plain Back
4x5 1-6493 <$165
3x10-20 1-5591 <$165
1929 Small Size
5 Type 1 1-6606 <$65
10 Type 1 1-3034 <$65
20 Type 1 1-964 <$75
5 Type 2 1-4792 <$85
10 Type 2 1-2933 <$85
20 Type 2 1-733 <$85
Total Issue $4,158,240
Out in 1935 $100,000
Large out 1935 $10,095

1635 Independent City
SHENANDOAH VALLEY NB OF WINCHESTER
{{ 15 L 23 S }}
Chartered 1866
Original Series <$VALUE
4x5 1-4700 <$1500
3x10-20 1-2340<$1750/$2500
Series 1875
3x10-20 1-2729<$1750/$2500
Brown Back
3x10-20 1-5986 <$600
1902 Red Seal
3x10-20 1-4350 <$700
1902 Date Back
3x10-20 1-16800 <$175
1902 Plain Back
4x5 1-4978 <$175
3x10-20 16801-63240 <$175
1929 Small Size
5 Type 1 1-9034 <$75
10 Type 1 1-4664 <$75
20 Type 1 1-1288 <$75
5 Type 2 1-9478 <$85
10 Type 2 1-5316 <$85
20 Type 2 1-1995 <$85
Total Issue $4,971,680
Out in 1935 $150,000
Large out 1935 $13,550

10611 Wise
FNB OF WISE
{{ 1 L 1 S }}
Chartered 9/14 as Wise Co NB of Wise, under which there was no issue. Issuing title adopted 1/9/24.
1902 Plain Back <$VALUE
4x5 1-1751 <$850
1929 Small Size
5 Type 1 1-986 <$600
Total Issue $64,600
Out in 1935 $5,000
Large out 1935 $150

<$VALUEs are for notes in FINE condition. Value changes by approximately 25% for a change of one full grade.

****

5449 Shenandoah

SHENANDOAH NB OF WOODSTOCK

{{ 1 L }}

Chartered 6/25/00

Liquidated 2/23/35

Brown Back		<$VALUE
4x5	1-470	<$1000
3x10-20	1-376	<$1000
1882 Date Back		
4x5	1-900	<$1000
3x10-20	1-700	<$1000
1882 Value Back		
4x5	901-1140	<$1000
3x10-20	701-825	<$1000
1902 Plain Back		
4x5	1-1095	<$750
3x10-20	1-706	<$750
Total Issue		$149,450
Out at close		$500

****

9012 Wythe

FNB OF WYTHEVILLE

Chartered 2/08

2nd title:FN Farmers B of Wytheville 12/31/30

FIRST TITLE **{{ 10 L 4 S }}**

1902 Red Seal		<$VALUE
3x10-20	1-500	<$750
1902 Date Back		
3x10-20	1-4500	<$300
1902 Plain Back		
3x10-20	4501-19876	<$300
1929 Small Size		
10 Type 1	1-1644	<$250
20 Type 1	1-470	<$250
SECOND TITLE **{{ 13 S }}**		
1929 Small Size		
10 Type 1	1-1356	<$150
20 Type 1	1-306	<$165
10 Type 2	1-16823	<$165
20 Type 2	1-2826	<$165
Total Issue		$1,516,670
Out in 1935		$200,000
Large out 1935		$6,340

****

FN Farmers B of Wytheville

SEE Ch 9012
FNB of Wytheville

****

12599 Wythe

WYTHE COUNTY NB OF WYTHEVILLE

{{ 11 S }}

Organized 10/16/24

1929 Small Size		<$VALUE
5 Type 1	1-1972	<$150
10 Type 1	1-842	<$150
5 Type 2	1-8064	<$150
10 Type 2	1-4044	<$150
Total Issue		$190,440
Out in 1935		$50,000

****

11554 York

FNB OF YORKTOWN

{{ 4 L 5 S }}

Organized 12/2/19

1902 Plain Back		<$VALUE
4x5	1-1576	<$600
1929 Small Size		
5 Type 1	1-4326	<$300
5 Type 2	1-10824	<$300
Total Issue		$499,260
Out in 1935		$25,000
Large out 1935		$900

****

CONDITION affects Value. The Values shown are for notes in FINE condition.

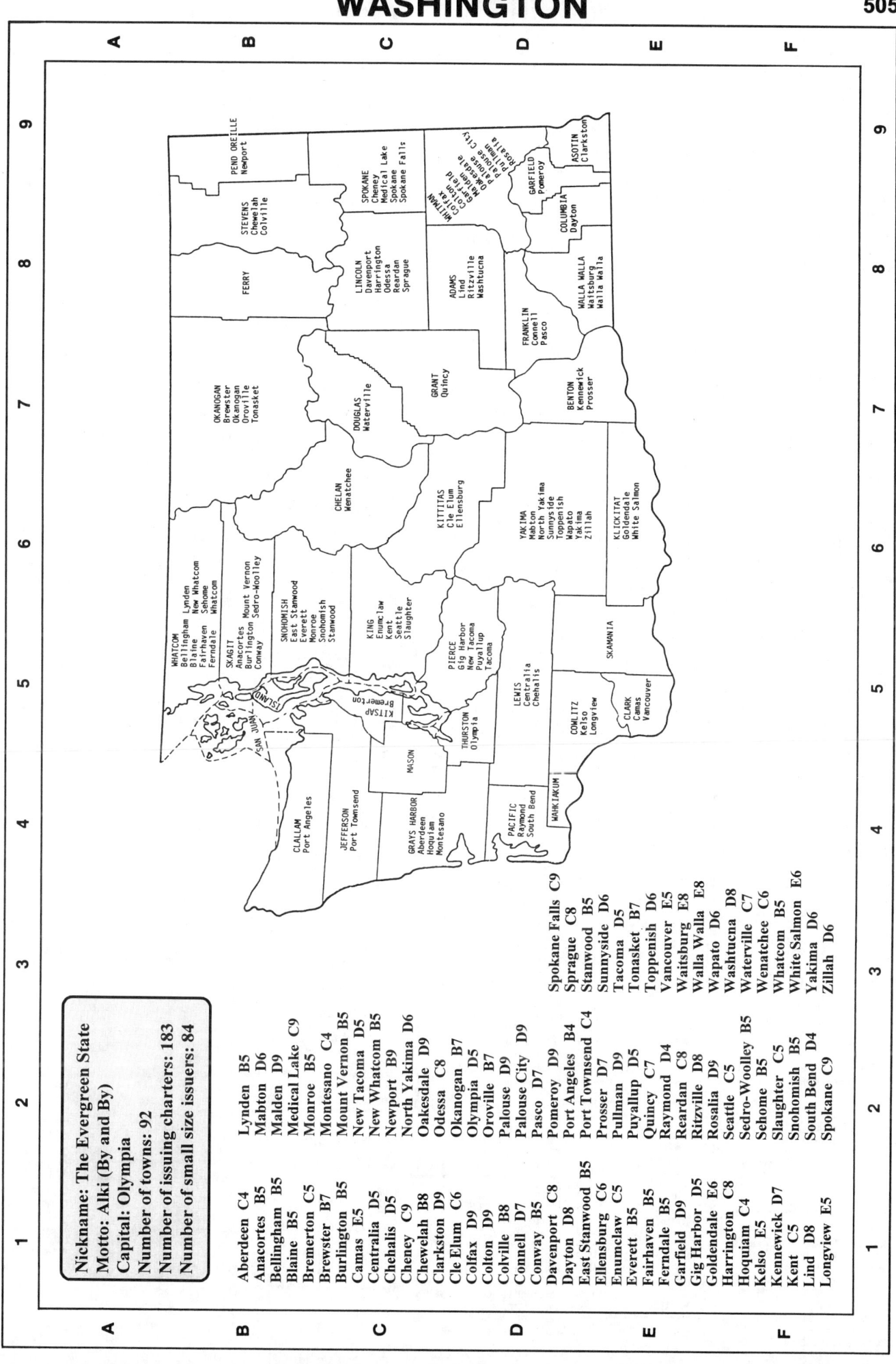

Nickname: The Evergreen State
Motto: Alki (By and By)
Capital: Olympia
Number of towns: 92
Number of issuing charters: 183
Number of small size issuers: 84

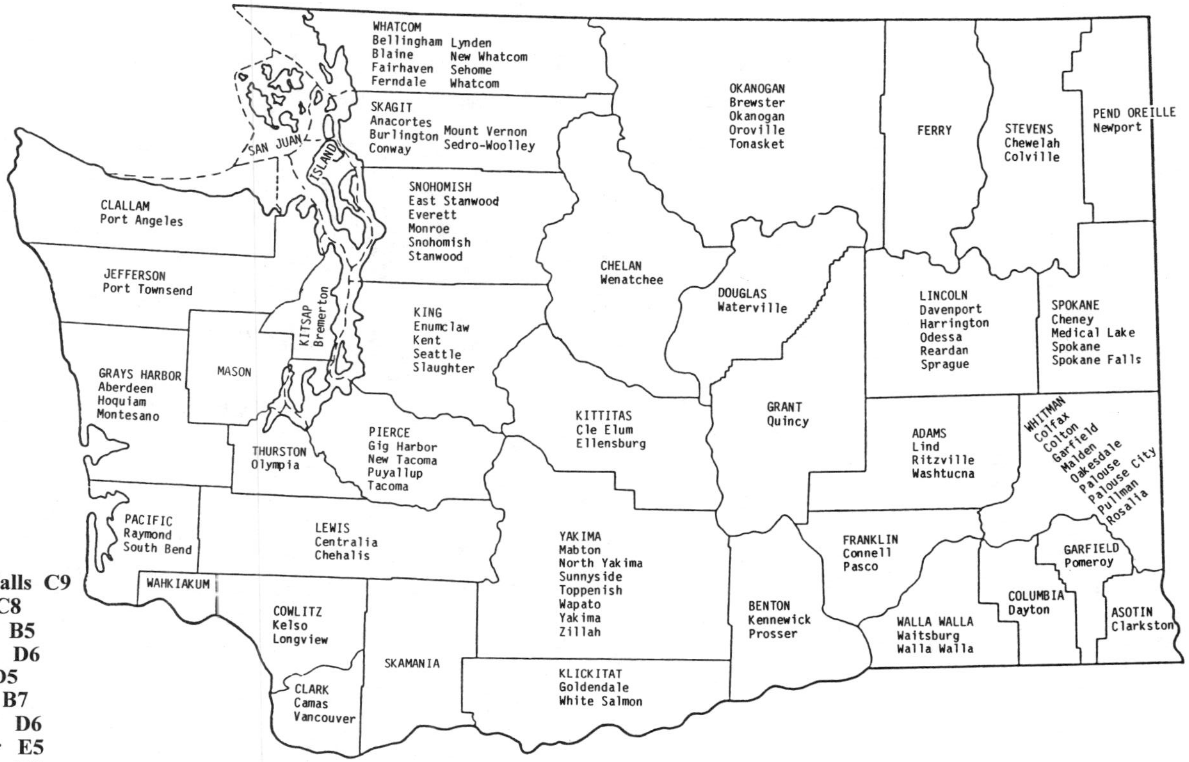

Aberdeen C4
Anacortes B5
Bellingham B5
Blaine B5
Bremerton C5
Brewster B7
Burlington B5
Camas E5
Centralia D5
Chehalis D5
Cheney C9
Chewelah B8
Clarkston D9
Cle Elum C6
Colfax D9
Colton D9
Colville B8
Connell D7
Conway B5
Davenport C8
Dayton D8
East Stanwood B5
Ellensburg C6
Enumclaw C5
Everett B5
Fairhaven B5
Ferndale B5
Garfield D9
Gig Harbor D5
Goldendale E6
Harrington C8
Hoquiam C4
Kelso E5
Kennewick D7
Kent C5
Lind D8
Longview E5
Lynden B5
Mabton D6
Malden D9
Medical Lake C9
Monroe B5
Montesano C4
Mount Vernon B5
New Tacoma D5
New Whatcom B5
Newport B9
North Yakima D6
Oakesdale D9
Odessa C8
Okanogan B7
Olympia D5
Oroville B7
Palouse D9
Palouse City D9
Pasco D7
Pomeroy D9
Port Angeles B4
Port Townsend C4
Prosser D7
Pullman D9
Puyallup D5
Quincy C7
Raymond D4
Reardan C8
Ritzville D8
Rosalia D9
Seattle C5
Sedro-Woolley B5
Sehome B5
Slaughter C5
Snohomish B5
South Bend D4
Spokane C9
Spokane Falls C9
Sprague C8
Stanwood B5
Sunnyside D6
Tacoma D5
Tonasket B7
Toppenish D6
Vancouver E5
Waitsburg E8
Walla Walla E8
Wapato D6
Washtucna D8
Waterville C7
Wenatchee C6
Whatcom B5
White Salmon E6
Yakima D6
Zillah D6

****
13091 Grays Harbor
AMERICAN NB OF ABERDEEN
{{ 5 L 18 S }}
Chartered 6/27
Liquidated 12/4/31
1902 Plain Back <$VALUE
3x10-20 1-11329 <$400
1929 Small Size
10 Type 1 1-6886 <$100
20 Type 1 1-2046 <$100
Total Issue $1,225,130
Out at close $336,020
Large out at close $8,780
****
11751 Grays Harbor
ABERDEEN NB, ABERDEEN
Organized 5/22/20
Receivership 12/11/31
2nd title: FNB in Aberdeen 4/14/25
FIRST TITLE {{ 0 L }}
1902 Plain Back <$VALUE
4x5 1-1600 <$1500
3x10-20 1-1400 <$1500
SECOND TITLE {{ 2 L 7 S }}
1902 Plain Back
4x5 1-5077 <$750
3x10-20 1-3546 <$750
1929 Small Size
5 Type 1 1-2628 <$250
10 Type 1 1-1238 <$225
20 Type 1 1-333 <$250
Total Issue $573,920
Out at close $97,660
Large out at close $5,290
****
FNB in Aberdeen
SEE Ch 11751
Aberdeen NB, Aberdeen
****
4407 Grays Harbor
FNB OF ABERDEEN
{{ UNREPORTED }}
Chartered 9/1/90
Liquidated 10/12/95
Brown Back <$VALUE
4x5 1-1384 <$3000
Total Issue $27,680
Out in 1910 $235
****
12704 Grays Harbor
GRAYS HARBOR NB OF ABERDEEN
{{ 5 L 20 S }}
Chartered 4/25
Liquidated 1/29/34
1902 Plain Back <$VALUE
4x5 1-10952 <$450
3x10-20 1-7116 <$450
1929 Small Size
5 Type 1 1-7526 <$75
10 Type 1 1-4037 <$75
20 Type 1 1-981 <$85
Total Issue $1,160,560
Out at close $154,100
Large out at close $4,220
Ch 4375 assumed circulation
****
9535 Grays Harbor
UNITED STATES NB OF ABERDEEN
{{ UNREPORTED }}
Chartered 9/09
Liquidated 12/31/13
1902 Date Back <$VALUE
4x5 1-1295 <$1500
3x10-20 1-992 <$1500
Total Issue $75,500
Out in 1914 $13,335
****
4458 Skagit
FNB OF ANACORTES
{{ UNREPORTED }}
Organized 11/6/90
Receivership 3/6/95
Brown Back <$VALUE
4x5 1-1174 <$3500
Total Issue $23,480
Out in 1916 $185
****
7474 Whatcom
BELLINGHAM NB, BELLINGHAM
{{ 10 L 18 S }}
Chartered 11/04
1902 Red Seal <$VALUE
3x10-20 1-3850 <$1500
1902 Date Back
3x10-20 1-7100 <$275
1902 Plain Back
3x10-20 7101-22456 <$275
1929 Small Size
10 Type 1 1-3810 <$100
20 Type 1 1-1286 <$110
10 Type 2 1-4124 <$125
20 Type 2 1-690 <$125
Total Issue $1,753,260
Out in 1935 $200,000
Large out 1935 $6,040
****
7372 Whatcom
FNB OF BELLINGHAM
{{ 5 L 2U + 33 S }}
Chartered 8/04
1902 Red Seal <$VALUE
3x10-20 1-2025 <$1500
1902 Date Back
3x10-20 1-5100 <$400
1902 Plain Back
3x10-20 5101-10727 <$400
1929 Small Size
5 Type 1 1-5232 <$50
10 Type 1 1-11200 <$50
20 Type 1 1-2612 <$60
5 Type 2 1-29376 <$60
10 Type 2 1-10439 <$60
20 Type 2 1-3700 <$60
Total Issue $2,105,270
Out in 1935 $500,000
Large out 1935 $2,860
****
9070 Whatcom
NORTHWESTERN NB OF BELLINGHAM
{{ 2 L 4 S }}
Chartered 3/08
1902 Red Seal <$VALUE
3x10-20 1-740 <$1500
1902 Date Back
3x10-20 1-2240 <$750
1902 Plain Back
3x10-20 2241-4007 <$750
1929 Small Size
10 Type 2 1-6767 <$400
Total Issue $305,020
Out in 1935 $50,000
Large out 1935 $900
****
4471 Whatcom
BLAINE NB, BLAINE
{{ UNREPORTED }}
Chartered 11/20/90
Liquidated 11/5/94
Brown Back <$VALUE
3x10-20 1-431 <$3500
Total Issue $21,550
Out in 1910 $150
****
4470 Whatcom
FNB OF BLAINE
{{ UNREPORTED }}
Chartered 11/20/90
Liquidated 3/9/92
Brown Back <$VALUE
50-100 1-78 <$5000
Total Issue $11,700
All notes reportedly redeemed
****
9280 Kitsap
FNB OF BREMERTON
{{ 2 L 13 S }}
Organized 9/15/08
Liquidated 4/2/34
1902 Date Back <$VALUE
3x10-20 1-1820 <$750
1902 Plain Back
3x10-20 1821-4029 <$750
1929 Small Size
10 Type 1 1-2052 <$150
20 Type 1 1-3061 <$165
Total Issue $355,180
Out at close $100,000
Ch 4375 assumed circulation
****
9170 Okanogan
FNB OF BREWSTER
{{ 1 L 4 S }}
Chartered 6/08
1902 Date Back <$VALUE
3x10-20 1-875 <$1250
1902 Plain Back
3x10-20 876-3304 <$1250
1929 Small Size
10 Type 1 1-462 <$450
20 Type 1 1-130 <$450
10 Type 2 1-412 <$500
20 Type 2 1-138 <$500
Total Issue $215,400
Out in 1935 $15,900
Large out 1935 $690
****
10648 Skagit
BURLINGTON NB, BURLINGTON
{{ 2 L }}
Chartered 10/14
Closed 2/23/26
1902 Plain Back <$VALUE
4x5 1-3180 <$850
3x10-20 1-2094 <$850
Total Issue $168,300
Out at close $24,100
Ch 9808 assumed circulation
****
9808 Skagit
FNB OF BURLINGTON
{{ 2 L 8 S }}
Chartered 7/10
1902 Date Back <$VALUE
3x10-20 1-720 <$750
1902 Plain Back
3x10-20 721-3504 <$750
1929 Small Size
10 Type 1 1-1470 <$175
20 Type 1 1-358 <$175
10 Type 2 1-2243 <$200
20 Type 2 1-531 <$200
Total Issue $339,410
Out in 1935 $50,000
Large out 1935 $1,970
Outstanding includes Ch 10648
****
10686 Clark
FNB OF CAMAS
Chartered 1/15
2nd title: Clark County NB of Vancouver 4/26/33
FIRST TITLE {{ 3 L 5 S }}
1902 Plain Back <$VALUE
3x10-20 1-7764 <$500
1929 Small Size
10 Type 1 1-1366 <$300
20 Type 1 1-402 <$300
SECOND TITLE {{ 7 S }}
1929 Small Size
10 Type 2 1-6480 <$200
20 Type 2 1-1580 <$200
Total Issue $614,800
Out in 1935 $100,000
Large out 1935 $2,250
****
13099 Lewis
FNB IN CENTRALIA
{{ 2 L 8 S }}
Chartered 7/1/27
Liquidated 12/15/31
1902 Plain Back <$VALUE
3x10-20 1-4249 <$750
1929 Small Size
10 Type 1 1-1925 <$225
20 Type 1 1-520 <$250
Total Issue $390,350
Out at close $95,720
Large out at close $4,030
****
4439 Lewis
FNB OF CENTRALIA
{{ 1 L }}
Chartered 10/10/90
Liquidated 2/1/94
Brown Back <$VALUE
4x5 1-1026 <$2500
Total Issue $20,520
Out in 1910 $230
****
8736 Lewis
UNITED STATES NB OF CENTRALIA
{{ 3 L }}
Organized 6/10/07
Receivership 9/21/14
1902 Red Seal <$VALUE
4x5 1-2625 <$1500
3x10-20 1-2100 <$1500
1902 Date Back
4x5 1-5705 <$600
3x10-20 1-3672 <$600
Total Issue $455,200
Out in 1916 $21,725
****
9389 Lewis
CHEHALIS NB, CHEHALIS
Chartered 4/09
Liquidated 4/9/32
2nd title: FNB in Chehalis 9/4/20
FIRST TITLE {{ 0 L }}
1902 Date Back <$VALUE
3x10-20 1-1660* <$1500
1902 Plain Back
3x10-20 2061-3350* <$1500
* 1661-2060 not marked
SECOND TITLE {{ 1 L 6 S }}
1902 Plain Back
3x10-20 1-4791 <$1500
1929 Small Size
10 Type 1 1-915 <$350
20 Type 1 1-273 <$350
Total Issue $494,710
Out at close $47,140
Large out at close $3,950
****
FNB in Chehalis
SEE Ch 9389
Chehalis NB, Chehalis
****
4203 Lewis
FNB OF CHEHALIS
{{ UNREPORTED }}
Chartered 1/10/90
Liquidated 11/6/99
Brown Back <$VALUE
3x10-20 1-806 <$3000
Total Issue $40,300
Out in 1910 $380
****
4542 Spokane
FNB OF CHENEY
{{ UNREPORTED }}
Organized 4/1/91
Receivership 6/27/96
Brown Back <$VALUE
4x5 1-1404 <$3000
Total Issue $28,080
Out in 1916 $110
****
9080 Spokane
NB OF CHENEY, CHENEY
{{ 3 L }}
Chartered 3/08
Closed 2/27/28
1902 Red Seal <$VALUE
3x10-20 1-200 <$2000
1902 Date Back
3x10-20 1-2160 <$600
1902 Plain Back
3x10-20 2161-5289 <$600
Total Issue $274,450
Out at close $25,000
Ch 9144 assumed circulation
****
9144 Spokane
SECURITY NB OF CHENEY
{{ 4 L 6 S }}
Chartered 5/08
Liquidated 12/30/33
1902 Date Back <$VALUE
4x10 1-3145 <$450
1902 Plain Back
4x10 3146-9437 <$450
1929 Small Size
5 Type 1 1-5589 <$225
Total Issue $545,150
Out at close $28,940
Large out at close $2,990
Outstanding includes Ch 9080
****
8789 Stevens
FNB OF CHEWELAH
{{ 3 L U + 8 S }}
Chartered 7/07
1902 Red Seal <$VALUE
3x10-20 1-185 <$2000
1902 Date Back
3x10-20 1-2250 <$600
1902 Plain Back
3x10-20 2251-6132 <$600
1929 Small Size
10 Type 1 1-670 <$225
20 Type 1 1-172 <$225
10 Type 2 1-810 <$275
20 Type 2 1-145 <$300
Total Issue $387,690
Out in 1935 $25,000
Large out 1935 $1,390
****
6742 Asotin
FNB OF CLARKSTON
{{ 3 L }}
Organized 3/16/03
Receivership 2/12/24
1902 Red Seal <$VALUE
3x10-20 1-400 <$2000
1902 Date Back
3x10-20 1-680 <$750
1902 Plain Back
3x10-20 681-3756 <$750
Total Issue $207,800
Out at close $50,000
****
10469 Kittitas
FNB OF CLE ELUM
{{ 1 L 7 S }}
Chartered 12/13
1902 Date Back <$VALUE
3x10-20 1-500 <$1500
1902 Plain Back
3x10-20 501-1353 <$1500
1929 Small Size
10 Type 1 1-664 <$350
20 Type 1 1-318 <$350
10 Type 2 1-1564 <$375
20 Type 2 1-324 <$400
Total Issue $167,770
Out in 1935 $50,000
Large out 1935 $300
****
7095 Whitman
COLFAX NB, COLFAX
{{ 17 L 23 S }}
Chartered 1/04
Liquidated 1/30/32
1902 Red Seal <$VALUE
3x10-20 1-7750 <$1500
1902 Date Back
3x10-20 1-14500 <$175
1902 Plain Back
3x10-20 14501-44814 <$175
1929 Small Size
10 Type 1 1-3567 <$65
20 Type 1 1-1047 <$75
Total Issue $2,967,860
Out at close $200,000
Large out at close $23,010
****
10511 Whitman
FARMERS NB OF COLFAX
{{ 16 S }}
Organized 4/4/14
1929 Small Size <$VALUE
5 Type 1 1-3952 <$75
10 Type 1 1-2248 <$75
20 Type 1 1-552 <$85
5 Type 2 1-6540 <$100
10 Type 2 1-3360 <$100
20 Type 2 1-768 <$100
Total Issue $401,340
Out in 1935 $100,000
****
3076 Whitman
FNB OF COLFAX
Chartered 11/14/83
Liquidated 6/30/05
TERRITORIAL ISSUES {{ 1 L }}
Brown Back <$VALUE
3x10-20 1-830 <$15,000
STATE ISSUES {{ 0 L }}
Brown Back
3x10-20 831-2758 <$2500
1902 Red Seal
3x10-20 1-369 <$3000
Total Issue $156,350
Out in 1910 $3,010
****
3119 Whitman
SECOND NB OF COLFAX
Chartered 2/6/84
Liquidated 1/16/04
TERRITORIAL ISSUES {{ 0 L }}
Brown Back <$VALUE
3x10-20 1-630 <$12,500
STATE ISSUES {{ 1 L }}
Brown Back
3x10-20 631-1772 <$2500
Total Issue $88,600
Out in 1910 $1,280
****
4788 Whitman
FNB OF COLTON
{{ UNREPORTED }}
Chartered 8/4/92
Liquidated 1/25/00
Brown Back <$VALUE
3x10-20 1-652 <$3500
Total Issue $32,600
Out in 1910 $300
****
8104 Stevens
FNB OF COLVILLE
{{ 7 L 6 S }}
Organized 2/3/06
Receivership 10/8/31
1902 Red Seal <$VALUE
3x10-20 1-767 <$1500
1902 Date Back
3x10-20 1-5040 <$450
1902 Plain Back
3x10-20 5041-14194 <$450
1929 Small Size
10 Type 1 1-931 <$300
20 Type 1 1-256 <$325
Total Issue $834,630
Out at close $60,000
Large out at close $7,470
****
8958 Franklin
CONNELL NB, CONNELL
{{ UNREPORTED }}
Chartered 12/07
Liquidated 12/15/09
1902 Red Seal <$VALUE
3x10-20 1-187 <$4000
1902 Date Back
3x10-20 1-28 <$3000
Total Issue $10,750
Out in 1910 $3,710
****
11984 Skagit
FNB OF CONWAY
{{ 2 L 5 S }}
Organized 6/14/21
Receivership 7/27/34
1902 Plain Back <$VALUE
3x10-20 1-3233 <$1250
1929 Small Size
5 Type 1 1-1410 <$400
10 Type 1 1-652 <$400
5 Type 2 1-436 <$450
10 Type 2 1-249 <$450
Total Issue $247,740
Out at close $25,000
Large out at close $760
****
4002 Lincoln
BIG BEND NB OF DAVENPORT
{{ UNREPORTED }}
Chartered 3/28/89
Receivership 11/25/04
TERRITORIAL ISSUES
Brown Back <$VALUE
4x5 1-625 <$15,000
STATE ISSUES
Brown Back
4x5 626-2744 <$3500
50-100 1-106 <$5000
Total Issue $70,780
Out in 1916 $660
****
7527 Lincoln
DAVENPORT NB, DAVENPORT
{{ 2 L }}
Organized 12/22/04
Receivership 11/12/25
1902 Red Seal <$VALUE
3x10-20 1-1180 <$2000
1902 Date Back
3x10-20 1-2690 <$1000
1902 Plain Back
3x10-20 2691-4410 <$1000
Total Issue $279,500
Out at close $23,100
****
9443 Columbia
BROUGHTON NB OF DAYTON
{{ 5 L U + 14 S }}
Chartered 6/09
1902 Date Back <$VALUE
4x5 1-2125 <$500
3x10-20 1-1620 <$500
1902 Plain Back
4x5 2126-9110 <$500
3x10-20 1621-6347 <$500
1929 Small Size
5 Type 1 1-1796 <$175
10 Type 1 1-1412 <$175
20 Type 1 1-360 <$185
5 Type 2 1-4512 <$200
10 Type 2 1-2056 <$200
20 Type 2 1-510 <$225
Total Issue $734,670
Out in 1935 $50,000
Large out 1935 $1,800

4473 Columbia
CITIZENS NB OF DAYTON
{{ UNREPORTED }}
Chartered 11/24/90
Liquidated 3/11/99
Brown Back <$VALUE
3x10-20 1-680 <$3000
Total Issue $34,000
Out in 1910 $440
****

2772 Columbia
COLUMBIA NB OF DAYTON
Chartered 1882
TERRITORIAL ISSUES {{ 0 L }}
Brown Back <$VALUE
4x5 1-4250 <$12,500
STATE ISSUES {{ 5 L 8 S }}
Brown Back
4x5 4251-6478 <$1500
3x10-20 1-267 <$1500
1902 Red Seal
3x10-20 1-2120 <$1500
1902 Date Back
3x10-20 1-5200 <$500
1902 Plain Back
3x10-20 5201-14329 <$500
1929 Small Size
10 Type 1 1-1700 <$175
20 Type 1 1-476 <$200
10 Type 2 1-727 <$225
20 Type 2 1-260 <$250
Total Issue $1,136,950
Out in 1935 $50,000
Out in 1935 $4,720

8090 Columbia
DAYTON NB, DAYTON
{{ UNREPORTED }}
Chartered 2/14/06
Liquidated 8/27/07
1902 Red Seal <$VALUE
3x10-20 1-250 <$3500
Total Issue $12,500
Out in 1910 $1,600

2520 Columbia
FNB OF DAYTON
{{ UNREPORTED }}
Chartered 4/21/81
Liquidated 3/24/86
TERRITORIAL ISSUES
Series 1875 <$VALUE
4x5 1-2018 <$15,000
Total Issue $40,360
Out in 1910 $360

3799 Columbia
NB OF DAYTON
{{ UNREPORTED }}
Chartered 10/5/87
Liquidated 11/21/88
TERRITORIAL ISSUES
Brown Back <$VALUE
3x10-20 1-225 <$15,000
Total Issue $11,250
Out in 1910 $80

13439 Snohomish
NB OF EAST STANWOOD
{{ 4 S }}
Chartered 3/30
1929 Small Size <$VALUE
5 Type 1 1-1070 <$400
10 Type 1 1-532 <$400
5 Type 2 1-2352 <$400
10 Type 2 1-1464 <$400
Total Issue $90,420
Out in 1935 $23,580

3867 Kittitas
ELLENSBURG NB, ELLENSBURG
Chartered 4/14/88
Receivership 7/18/96
2nd title: Kittitas Valley NB of Ellensburg 10/95
FIRST TITLE {{ 2 L }}
TERRITORIAL ISSUES
Brown Back <$VALUE
4x5 1-825 <$12,500
STATE ISSUES {{ 0 L }}
Brown Back
4x5 826-1949 <$3000
SECOND TITLE {{ 1 L }}
Brown Back
4x5 1-165 <$3000
Total Issue $42,280
Out in 1916 $335

3037 Kittitas
FNB OF ELLENSBURG
{{ UNREPORTED }}
Chartered 1883
Liquidated 8/9/84
TERRITORIAL ISSUES
Brown Back <$VALUE
3x10-20 1-270 <$15,000
Total Issue $13,500
Out in 1910 $30

Kittitas Valley NB of Ellensburg
SEE Ch 3867
Ellensnurg NB, Ellensburg

11045 Kittitas
NB OF ELLENSBURG
{{ 4 L 6 S }}
Organized 6/2/17
Receivership 11/10/33
1902 Plain Back <$VALUE
4x5 1-8690 <$500
3x10-20 1-5784 <$500
1929 Small Size
5 Type 1 1-1846 <$275
10 Type 1 1-851 <$275
20 Type 1 1-242 <$275
Total Issue $598,480
Out at close $50,000
Large out at close $2,650

9079 Kittitas
WASHINGTON NB OF ELLENSBURG
{{ 7 L 15 S }}
Chartered 3/08
1902 Red Seal <$VALUE
3x10-20 1-360 <$1500
1902 Date Back
3x10-20 1-4400 <$350
1902 Plain Back
3x10-20 4401-19082 <$350
1929 Small Size
10 Type 1 1-2643 <$100
20 Type 1 1-723 <$110
Total Issue $1,217,440
Out in 1935 $54,090
Large out 1935 $5,440

12114 King
FNB OF ENUMCLAW
{{ 3 L }}
Chartered 2/22
1929 Small Size <$VALUE
5 Type 2 1-5110 <$450
10 Type 2 1-2480 <$450
20 Type 2 1-850 <$450
Total Issue $67,350
Out in 1935 $50,000

6053 Snohomish
AMERICAN NB OF EVERETT
{{ 2 L }}
Chartered 12/19/01
Liquidated 1/16/09
Brown Back <$VALUE
3x10-20 1-4828 <$1500
Total Issue $241,400
Out in 1910 $33,060

Citizens Security NB of Everett
SEE Ch 11693
Security NB of Everett

4738 Snohomish
EVERETT NB, EVERETT
{{ 2 L }}
Chartered 5/12/92
Liquidated 1/12/01
Brown Back <$VALUE
4x5 1-4082 <$1750
3x10-20 1-182 <$1750
Total Issue $90,740
Out in 1910 $1,155

4686 Snohomish
FNB OF EVERETT
{{ 9 L 28 S }}
Chartered 1892
Brown Back <$VALUE
3x10-20 1-5190 <$1000
1882 Date Back
3x10-20 1-9389 <$850
1902 Date Back
3x10-20 1-9500 <$175
1902 Plain Back
3x10-20 9501-17135 <$175
1929 Small Size
10 Type 1 1-1056 <$50
20 Type 1 1-3974 <$60
Total Issue $2,125,940
Out in 1935 $269,380
Large out 1935 $6,890

4796 Snohomish
PUGET SOUND NB OF EVERETT
{{ UNREPORTED }}
Organized 9/23/92
Receivership 8/7/95
Brown Back <$VALUE
4x5 1-1004 <$3500
Total Issue $20,080
Out in 1916 $120

11693 Snohomish
SECURITY NB OF EVERETT
Chartered 4/20
2nd title: Citizens Security NB of Everett 4/20/29
3rd title: Security NB of Everett 5/27/32
FIRST TITLE {{ 6 L }}
1902 Plain Back <$VALUE
4x5 1-50642* <$275
* 48756-49755 not issued
SECOND TITLE {{ 10 S }}
1929 Small Size
5 Type 1 1-9976 <$85
10 Type 1 1-3032 <$85
20 Type 1 1-712 <$85
THIRD TITLE {{ 14 S }}
1929 Small Size
5 Type 1 1-418 <$85
10 Type 1 1-620 <$85
20 Type 1 1-212 <$85
5 Type 2 1-12404 <$75
10 Type 2 1-5841 <$75
20 Type 2 1-2004 <$75
Total Issue $1,795,170
Out in 1935 $200,000

5243 Whatcom
CITIZENS NB OF FAIRHAVEN
{{ 1 L }}
Chartered 1/10/00
Liquidated 8/26/01
Brown Back <$VALUE
3x10-20 1-304 <$3500
Total Issue $15,200
Out in 1910 $160

4387 Whatcom
FAIRHAVEN NB, FAIRHAVEN
{{ UNREPORTED }}
Chartered 8/2/90
Liquidated 10/10/96
Brown Back <$VALUE
4x5 1-1203 <$3500
Total Issue $24,060
Out in 1910 $220

4171 Whatcom
FNB OF FAIRHAVEN
Chartered 12/4/89
Receivership 9/19/96
2nd title: Bennett NB of New Whatcom 11/93
FIRST TITLE {{ 0 L }}
Brown Back <$VALUE
4x5 1-560 <$3500
3x10-20 1-181 <$3500
SECOND TITLE {{ 1 L }}
Brown Back
4x5 1-580 <$3500
Total Issue $31,850
Out in 1916 $205

11667 Whatcom
FNB OF FERNDALE
{{ 6 S }}
Chartered 4/20
1929 Small Size <$VALUE
5 Type 1 1-204 <$350
10 Type 1 1-212 <$350
20 Type 1 1-104 <$375
5 Type 2 1-1412 <$400
10 Type 2 1-725 <$400
20 Type 2 1-144 <$400
Total Issue $48,510
Out in 1935 $25,000

9185 Whitman
GARFIELD NB, GARFIELD
{{ 2 L 2U + 2 S }}
Chartered 7/08
Liquidated 6/26/31
1902 Date Back <$VALUE
4x5 1-765 <$850
3x10-20 1-610 <$850
1902 Plain Back
4x5 766-4912 <$850
3x10-20 611-3088 <$850
1929 Small Size
5 Type 1 1-370 <$400
10 Type 1 1-205 <$400
20 Type 1 1-59 <$450
Total Issue $283,120
Out at close $17,815
Large out at close $2,945

12231 Whitman
STATE NB OF GARFIELD
{{ 5 S }}
Chartered 7/22
1929 Small Size <$VALUE
5 Type 2 1-5690 <$325
10 Type 2 1-2865 <$325
20 Type 2 1-990 <$325
Total Issue $76,900
Out in 1935 $50,000

13057 Pierce
FNB OF GIG HARBOR
{{ 1 S }}
Organized 1/26/27
Receivership 8/18/33
1929 Small Size <$VALUE
5 Type 1 1-363 <$750
10 Type 1 1-216 <$750
20 Type 1 1-64 <$750
50 Type 1 1-20 <$1250
Total Issue $37,530
Out at close $24,460

4031 Klickitat
FNB OF GOLDENDALE
{{ UNREPORTED }}
Chartered 5/11/89
Liquidated 12/17/96
TERRITORIAL ISSUES
Brown Back <$VALUE
4x5 1-625 <$15,000
STATE ISSUES
Brown Back
4x5 626-1826 <$3500
Total Issue $36,520
Out in 1910 $295

9210 Lincoln
FNB OF HARRINGTON
{{ 1 L }}
Chartered 7/10/08
Receivership 8/6/24
1902 Date Back <$VALUE
4x5 1-3460 <$850
3x10-20 1-3150 <$850
1902 Plain Back
4x5 3461-5265 <$850
3x10-20 3151-4353 <$850
Total Issue $322,950
Out at close $19,200

9182 Spokane
FNB OF HILLYARD
{{ 2 L 2 S }}
Chartered 7/08
Liquidated 4/29/31
1902 Date Back <$VALUE
3x10-20 1-1075 <$750
1902 Plain Back
3x10-20 1076-4620 <$750
1929 Small Size
10 Type 1 1-305 <$500
20 Type 1 1-84 <$500
Total Issue $259,380
Out at close $19,590
Large out at close $3,060

4427 Grays Harbor
FNB OF HOQUIAM
{{ 8 L 19 S }}
Organized 9/22/90
Receivership 11/6/31
Brown Back <$VALUE
3x10-20 1-2960 <$1250
1882 Date Back
3x10-20 1-328 <$1250
1902 Date Back
3x10-20 1-3200 <$275
1902 Plain Back
3x10-20 3201-18567 <$275
1929 Small Size
10 Type 1 1-5441 <$100
20 Type 1 1-1527 <$100
Total Issue $1,602,450
Out at close $294,000
Large out at close $13,270

4390 Grays Harbor
HOQUIAM NB, HOQUIAM
{{ UNREPORTED }}
Chartered 8/8/90
Liquidated 7/18/93
Brown Back <$VALUE
3x10-20 1-355 <$3000
Total Issue $17,750
Out in 1910 $120

8639 Cowlitz
FNB OF KELSO
{{ 13 L 1 S }}
Organized 2/1/07
Receivership 12/29/31
1902 Red Seal <$VALUE
4x5 1-650 <$1250
3x10-20 1-520 <$1250
1902 Date Back
4x5 1-1600 <$275
3x10-20 1-1190 <$275
1902 Plain Back
4x5 1601-7991 <$275
3x10-20 1191-5067 <$275
1929 Small Size
5 Type 1 1-584 <$500
10 Type 1 1-296 <$500
20 Type 1 1-83 <$500
Total Issue $497,410
Out at close $24,280
Large out at close $2,950

8948 Benton
FNB OF KENNEWICK
{{ 2 L 3 S }}
Organized 9/6/07
1902 Red Seal <$VALUE
3x10-20 1-188 <$1750
1902 Date Back
3x10-20 1-2410 <$650
1902 Plain Back
3x10-20 2411-6151 <$650
1929 Small Size
10 Type 1 1-783 <$400
20 Type 1 1-200 <$400
Total Issue $387,930
Out in 1935 $25,000
Large out 1935 $1,770

10174 King
FNB OF KENT
{{ 1 L 4 S }}
Chartered 4/12
1902 Date Back <$VALUE
4x5 1-800 <$1250
3x10-20 1-680 <$1250
1902 Plain Back
4x5 801-1990 <$1250
3x10-20 681-1327 <$1250
1929 Small Size
5 Type 1 1-418 <$400
10 Type 1 1-190 <$400
20 Type 1 1-64 <$425
5 Type 2 1-1482 <$425
10 Type 2 1-996 <$425
20 Type 2 1-276 <$450
Total Issue $160,660
Out in 1935 $25,000
Large out 1935 $510

12217 King
KENT NB, KENT
{{ 5 S }}
Chartered 6/22
1929 Small Size <$VALUE
5 Type 1 1-622 <$275
10 Type 1 1-316 <$275
20 Type 1 1-106 <$275
5 Type 2 1-2640 <$300
10 Type 2 1-1558 <$300
20 Type 2 1-396 <$300
Total Issue $87,040
Out in 1935 $40,000

9101 Adams
FNB OF LIND
{{ 0 L 2 S }}
Organized 3/3/08
1902 Red Seal <$VALUE
4x5 1-250 <$2500
3x10-20 1-200 <$2500
1902 Date Back
4x5 1-850 <$1500
3x10-20 1-680 <$1500
1902 Plain Back
4x5 851-2440 <$1500
3x10-20 681-1583 <$1500
1929 Small Size
5 Type 1 1-418 <$600
10 Type 1 1-212 <$600
20 Type 1 1-70 <$600
5 Type 2 1-78 <$600
10 Type 2 1-72 <$600
20 Type 2 1-45 <$600
Total Issue $178,620
Out in 1935 $10,000
Large out 1935 $450

12392 Cowlitz
FNB OF LONGVIEW
{{ 10 S }}
Chartered 6/23 as Longview NB, under which there was no issue. Issuing title adopted 1/2/26.
1929 Small Size <$VALUE
5 Type 1 1-3602 <$165
10 Type 1 1-2198 <$150
5 Type 2 1-4828 <$200
10 Type 2 1-1945 <$185
Total Issue $283,530
Out in 1935 $50,000

11808 Whatcom
FNB OF LYNDEN
{{ 2 L 5 S }}
Chartered 8/20
1902 Plain Back <$VALUE
3x10-20 1-5026 <$850
1929 Small Size
10 Type 1 1-1324 <$275
20 Type 1 1-340 <$300
10 Type 2 1-653 <$350
20 Type 2 1-165 <$375
Total Issue $381,370
Out in 1935 $25,000
Large out 1935 $1,570

9757 Yakima
FNB OF MABTON
{{ UNREPORTED }}
Chartered 5/10
Liquidated 6/15/12
1902 Date Back <$VALUE
4x5 1-220 <$2500
3x10-20 1-169 <$2500
Total Issue $12,850
Out at close $5,950

9351 Whitman
FNB OF MALDEN
{{ UNREPORTED }}
Chartered 3/09
Liquidated 1/4/13
1902 Date Back <$VALUE
3x10-20 1-547 <$2500
Total Issue $27,350
Out in 1913 $5,050

9030 Spokane
FNB OF MEDICAL LAKE
{{ 2 L 4 S }}
Chartered 1/27/08
1902 Red Seal <$VALUE
4x5 1-500 <$4000
3x10-20 1-400 <$4000
1902 Date Back
4x5 1-1750 <$2500
3x10-20 1-1300 <$2500
1902 Plain Back
4x5 1751-6230 <$2500
3x10-20 1301-4112 <$2500
1929 Small Size
5 Type 1 1-882 <$750
10 Type 1 1-420 <$750
20 Type 1 1-118 <$750
5 Type 2 1-1560 <$750
10 Type 2 1-758 <$750
20 Type 2 1-204 <$750
Total Issue $445,480
Out in 1935 $25,000
Large out 1935 $1,460

9372 Snohomish
FNB OF MONROE
{{ 0 L 3 S }}
Chartered 3/09
1902 Date Back <$VALUE
4x10 1-1075 <$1500
1902 Plain Back
4x10 1076-2631 <$1500
1929 Small Size
10 Type 1 1-526 <$500
10 Type 2 1-759 <$500
Total Issue $144,390
Out in 1935 $25,000
Large out 1935 $1,480
Outstanding includes Ch 9478

<$VALUEs are for notes in FINE condition. Value changes by approximately 25% for a change of one full grade.

****

9478 Snohomish
MONROE NB, MONROE
{{2L U+4S}}
Chartered 7/09
Liquidated 10/4/32
1902 Date Back <$VALUE
3x10-20 1-900 <$750
1902 Plain Back
3x10-20 901-4648 <$750
1929 Small Size
10 Type 1 1-536 <$350
20 Type 1 1-131 <$375
Total Issue $280,280
Out at close $22,840
Large out at close $1,870
Ch 9372 assumed circulation

****

FNB in Montesano
SEE Ch 5472
Montesano NB, Montesano

****

4779 Grays Harbor
FNB OF MONTESANO
{{ UNREPORTED }}
Chartered 7/18/92
Liquidated 8/20/94
Brown Back <$VALUE
3x10-20 1-292 <$3500
Total Issue $14,600
Out in 1910 $150

****

5472 Grays Harbor
MONTESANO NB, MONTESANO
Chartered 6/30/00
2nd title: FNB in Montesano 2/1/30
FIRST TITLE {{6L 4S}}
Brown Back <$VALUE
3x10-20 1-800 <$1250
1882 Date Back
3x10-20 1-1700 <$1250
1882 Value Back
3x10-20 1701-2323 <$1250
1902 Plain Back
4x5 1-3475 <$450
3x10-20 1-3677 <$450
1929 Small Size
5 Type 1 1-830 <$350
10 Type 1 1-416 <$350
20 Type 1 1-146 <$350
SECOND TITLE {{U+1S}}
1929 Small Size
5 Type 1 1-858 <$400
10 Type 1 1-326 <$400
20 Type 1 1-114 <$400
50 Type 1 1-32 <$650
100 Type 1 1-7 <$750
5 Type 2 1-224 <$450
10 Type 2 1-297 <$450
20 Type 2 1-50 <$450
Total Issue $554,750
Out in 1935 $31,160
Large out 1935 $1,700

****

4529 Skagit
FNB OF MOUNT VERNON
{{3L}}
Chartered 1891
Brown Back <$VALUE
50-100 1-754 <$3000/$3500
1882 Date Back
50-100 1-218 <$3000/$3500
1902 Date Back
3x10-20 1-2460 <$450
1902 Plain Back
3x10-20 2461-3860 <$450
Total Issue $548,800
Out in 1935 $1,190

****

10602 Skagit
MOUNT VERNON NB, MOUNT VERNON
{{2L}}
Chartered 8/14
Closed 5/4/29
1902 Plain Back <$VALUE
4x5 1-6019 <$600
4x10 1-4985 <$600
Total Issue $319,780
Out in 1934 $1,330
Ch 12154 assumed circulation

****

<$VALUEs are for notes in FINE condition. Value changes by approximately 25% for a change of one full grade.

****

12154 Skagit
SKAGIT NB OF MOUNT VERNON
{{9S}}
Chartered 4/22
Liquidated 2/13/34
1929 Small Size <$VALUE
5 Type 1 1-624 <$150
10 Type 1 1-624 <$150
20 Type 1 1-572 <$160
5 Type 2 1-198 <$175
10 Type 2 1-258 <$175
20 Type 2 1-30 <$200
Total Issue $128,970
Out at close $98,990
Outstanding includes Ch 10602

****

Bellingham Bay NB of New Whatcom
SEE Ch 3976
Bellingham Bay NB of Sehome

****

Bennett NB of New Whatcom
SEE Ch 4171
FNB of Fairhaven

****

Columbia NB of New Whatcom
SEE Ch 4351
Columbia NB of Sehome

****

2924 Pierce
TACOMA NB, NEW TACOMA
{{ UNREPORTED }}
Organized 4/13/83
Receivership 12/14/94
2nd title: Tacoma NB, Tacoma 1887
TERRITORIAL ISSUES
FIRST TITLE
Brown Back <$VALUE
3x10-20 1-325 <$12,500
SECOND TITLE
Brown Back
3x10-20 326-1355 <$12,500
STATE ISSUES
Brown Back
3x10-20 1356-2467 <$2500
Total Issue $120,350
Out in 1916 $600

****

8828 Pend Oreille
FNB OF NEWPORT
{{ UNREPORTED }}
Chartered 8/07
Liquidated 9/10/13
1902 Red Seal <$VALUE
4x5 1-150 <$3000
3x10-20 1-127 <$3000
1902 Date Back
4x5 1-1237 <$2000
3x10-20 1-886 <$2000
Total Issue $78,390
Out at close $24,190

****

3355 Yakima
FNB OF NORTH YAKIMA
Chartered 1885
2nd title:FNB of Yakima 11/24/19
3rd title: Yakima FNB 2/21/30
FIRST TITLE
TERRITORIAL ISSUES {{0L}}
Brown Back <$VALUE
3x10-20 1-695 <$12,500
STATE ISSUES {{0L}}
Brown Back
3x10-20 696-2163 <$2000
1902 Red Seal
3x10-20 1-3325 <$2000
1902 Date Back
3x10-20 1-7000 <$1000
1902 Plain Back
3x10-20 7001-10200 <$1000
SECOND TITLE {{2L 2S}}
1902 Plain Back
3x10-20 1-12395 <$650
1929 Small Size
10 Type 1 1-1232 <$250
20 Type 1 1-418 <$250
THIRD TITLE {{31S}}
1929 Small Size
10 Type 1 1-7196 <$50
20 Type 1 1-2278 <$60
5 Type 2 1-324 <$100
10 Type 2 1-14382 <$65
20 Type 2 1-3848 <$70
Total Issue $2,455,750
Out in 1935 $500,000
Large out 1935 $8,405
Outstanding includes Ch 3862

****

3862 Yakima
YAKIMA NB OF NORTH YAKIMA
Chartered 4/2/88
Closed 2/21/30
2nd title: Yakima NB, Yakima 1/25/18
FIRST TITLE
TERRITORIAL ISSUES {{0L}}
Brown Back <$VALUE
3x10-20 1-320 <$12,500
STATE ISSUES {{1L}}
Brown Back
3x10-20 321-2361 <$1500
1902 Red Seal
3x10-20 1-500 <$1500
1902 Date Back
3x10-20 1-3600 <$750
1902 Plain Back
3x10-20 3601-4601 <$750
SECOND TITLE {{2L 0S}}
1902 Plain Back
4x10 1-9494 <$500
1929 Small Size
10 Type 1 1-492 <$750
Total Issue $782,330
Out at close $49,995
Large out at close $20,475
Ch 3355 assumed circulation

****

4122 Whitman
FNB OF OAKESDALE
{{ UNREPORTED }}
Chartered 9/16/89
Liquidated 2/1/97
TERRITORIAL ISSUES
Brown Back <$VALUE
3x10-20 1-250 <$12,500
STATE ISSUES
Brown Back
3x10-20 251-653 <$3500
Total Issue $32,650
Out in 1910 $190

****

9150 Whitman
NB OF OAKESDALE
{{2L}}
Organized 4/25/08
Receivership 12/21/26
1902 Date Back <$VALUE
3x10-20 1-2080 <$1000
1902 Plain Back
3x10-20 2081-5098 <$1000
Total Issue $254,900
Out at close $25,000

****

9052 Lincoln
FNB OF ODESSA
{{ UNREPORTED }}
Chartered 3/08
Liquidated 2/16/11
1902 Red Seal <$VALUE
4x5 1-155 <$3000
3x10-20 1-125 <$3000
1902 Date Back
4x5 1-95 <$2000
3x10-20 1-68 <$2000
Total Issue $14,650
Out in 1911 $6,250

****

9411 Okanogan
FNB OF OKANOGAN
{{2L 3U+5S}}
Organized 4/3/09
1902 Date Back <$VALUE
4x5 1-1100 <$850
3x10-20 1-820 <$850
1902 Plain Back
4x5 1101-8888 <$850
3x10-20 821-5837 <$850
1929 Small Size
5 Type 1 1-1808 <$300
10 Type 1 1-1002 <$300
20 Type 1 1-270 <$300
5 Type 2 1-840 <$325
10 Type 2 1-475 <$325
20 Type 2 1-105 <$325
Total Issue $627,420
Out in 1935 $29,995
Large out 1935 $2,315

****

4297 Thurston
CAPITAL NB OF OLYMPIA
{{5L 16S}}
Chartered 1890
Liquidated 1/30/34
Brown Back <$VALUE
3x10-20 1-7080 <$2250
1882 Date Back
3x10-20 1-325 <$2250
1902 Date Back
3x10-20 1-5800 <$750
1902 Plain Back
3x10-20 5801-19836 <$750
1929 Small Size
10 Type 1 1-2841 <$350
20 Type 1 1-676 <$350
Total Issue $1,613,630
Out at close $95,980
Large out at close $6,880
Ch 4375 assumed circulation

****

3024 Thurston
FNB OF OLYMPIA
{{ UNREPORTED }}
Organized 8/11/83
Receivership 2/17/97
TERRITORIAL ISSUES
Brown Back <$VALUE
3x10-20 1-760 <$15,000
STATE ISSUES
Brown Back
3x10-20 761-1635 <$3500
Total Issue $81,750
Out in 1916 $410

****

5652 Thurston
OLYMPIA NB, OLYMPIA
{{2L}}
Chartered 12/24/00
Receivership 2/3/32
Brown Back <$VALUE
3x10-20 1-2350 <$2500
1882 Date Back
3x10-20 1-1860 <$2500
1882 Value Back
3x10-20 1861-3134 <$2500
1902 Plain Back
3x10-20 1-3876 <$1000
Total Issue $468,000
Out in 1922 $97,800

****

8279 Okanogan
FNB OF OROVILLE
{{2L}}
Chartered 6/2/06
Receivership 2/8/26
1902 Red Seal <$VALUE
4x5 1-360 <$2000
3x10-20 1-290 <$2000
1902 Date Back
4x5 1-1850* <$1000
3x10-20 1-1340** <$1000
1902 Plain Back
4x5 2051-4900* <$1000
3x10-20 1501-3240** <$1000
* 1851-2150 not marked
** 1341-1500 not marked
Total Issue $281,700
Out at close $24,400

****

Farmers NB of Palouse
SEE Ch 9499
NB of Palouse

****

9499 Whitman
NB OF PALOUSE
Chartered 8/09
Liquidated 7/31/26
2nd title: Farmers NB of Palouse 12/10/19
FIRST TITLE {{1L}}
1902 Date Back <$VALUE
3x10-20 1-3350 <$1000
1902 Plain Back
3x10-20 3351-5090 <$1000
SECOND TITLE {{2L}}
1902 Plain Back
4x5 1-12816 <$850
Total Issue $510,820
Out at close $36,345

****

12184 Whitman
SECURITY NB OF PALOUSE
{{7S}}
Organized 4/11/22
1929 Small Size <$VALUE
5 Type 1 1-1880 <$225
10 Type 1 1-872 <$225
20 Type 1 1-268 <$225
5 Type 2 1-2716 <$250
10 Type 2 1-1393 <$250
20 Type 2 1-223 <$250
Total Issue $172,850
Out in 1935 $50,000

****

4186 Whitman
FNB OF PALOUSE CITY
{{ UNREPORTED }}
Chartered 12/21/89
Liquidated 12/17/94
Brown Back <$VALUE
3x10-20 1-698 <$3500
Total Issue $34,900
Out in 1910 $300

****

9265 Franklin
FNB OF PASCO
{{2L}}
Organized 8/22/08
Receivership 11/21/25
1902 Date Back <$VALUE
4x5 1-2625 <$850
3x10-20 1-2700 <$850
1902 Plain Back
4x5 2626-8235 <$850
3x10-20 2701-6222 <$850
Total Issue $475,800
Out at close $42,800

****

11416 Garfield
FARMERS NB OF POMEROY
{{0L 2S}}
Organized 7/19/19
Receivership 5/19/31
1902 Plain Back <$VALUE
3x10-20 1-2579 <$1500
1929 Small Size
10 Type 1 1-290 <$500
20 Type 1 1-55 <$500
Total Issue $152,950
Out at close $20,000
Large out at close $3,020

****

3460 Garfield
FNB OF POMEROY
{{ UNREPORTED }}
Chartered 2/27/86
Liquidated 1/11/98
TERRITORIAL ISSUES
Brown Back <$VALUE
3x10-20 1-450 <$12,500
STATE ISSUES
Brown Back
3x10-20 451-850 <$3000
Total Issue $42,500
Out in 1910 $430

****

6074 Callam
CAIN NB OF PORT ANGELES
Chartered 12/31/01
2nd title: Citizens NB of Port Angeles 4/04
3rd title: FNB in Port Angeles 12/30/20
FIRST TITLE {{0L}}
Brown Back <$VALUE
3x10-20 1-195 <$2500
SECOND TITLE {{1L}}
Brown Back
3x10-20 1-300 <$1500
1882 Date Back
3x10-20 1-580 <$1500
1882 Value Back
3x10-20 581-1500 <$1500
THIRD TITLE {{2L 15S}}
1902 Plain Back
3x10-20 1-4462 <$750
1929 Small Size
10 Type 1 1-2438 <$110
20 Type 1 1-680 <$125
10 Type 2 1-4067 <$135
20 Type 2 1-1262 <$150
Total Issue $616,140
Out in 1935 $100,000
Large out 1935 $1,590

****

Citizens NB of Port Angeles
SEE Ch 6074
Cain NB of Port Angeles

****

FNB in Port Angeles
SEE Ch 6074
Cain NB of Port Angeles

****

4315 Callam
FNB OF PORT ANGELES
{{ UNREPORTED }}
Organized 5/19/90
Receivership 4/26/95
Brown Back <$VALUE
3x10-20 1-553 <$3000
Total Issue $22,900
Out in 1916 $150

****

13351 Jefferson
AMERICAN NB OF PORT TOWNSEND
Organized 6/13/29
2nd title: F American NB of Port Townsend 12/7/31
FIRST TITLE {{1S}}
1929 Small Size <$VALUE
5 Type 1 1-828 <$400
10 Type 1 1-416 <$400
20 Type 1 1-138 <$400
SECOND TITLE {{3S}}
1929 Small Size
5 Type 1 1-440 <$300
10 Type 1 1-382 <$300
20 Type 1 1-62 <$300
5 Type 2 1-2928 <$300
10 Type 2 1-1392 <$300
20 Type 2 1-396 <$300
Total Issue $146,400
Out in 1935 $50,000
Outstanding includes Ch 2948

****

F American NB of Port Townsend
SEE Ch 13351
American NB of Port Townsend

****

2948 Jefferson
FNB OF PORT TOWNSEND
Chartered 1883
Liquidated 12/2/31
TERRITORIAL ISSUES {{0L}}
Brown Back <$VALUE
3x10-20 1-775 <$12,500
STATE ISSUES {{3L 2S}}
Brown Back
3x10-20 776-2088 <$1500
1902 Red Seal
3x10-20 1-625 <$1500
1902 Date Back
3x10-20 1-1820 <$600
1902 Plain Back
3x10-20 1821-3362 <$600
1929 Small Size
10 Type 1 1-245 <$500
20 Type 1 1-33 <$500
Total Issue $322,410
Out at close $10,875
Large out 1935 $1,385
Ch 13351 assumed circulation

****

4290 Jefferson
PORT TOWNSEND NB, PORT TOWNSEND
{{ UNREPORTED }}
Chartered 4/18/90
Receivership 10/3/93
Brown Back <$VALUE
3x10-20 1-758 <$3000
Total Issue $37,900
Out in 1916 $180

****

9417 Benton
BENTON COUNTY NB OF PROSSER
{{ UNREPORTED }}
Chartered 5/09
Liquidated 4/28/13
1902 Date Back <$VALUE
4x5 1-328 <$2000
3x10-20 1-252 <$2000
Total Issue $19,160
Out in 1913 $4,210

****

7489 Benton
FNB OF PROSSER
{{ UNREPORTED }}
Chartered 11/25/04
Liquidated 1/1/06
1902 Red Seal <$VALUE
3x10-20 1-143 <$3500
Total Issue $7,150
Out in 1910 $520

****

4699 Whitman
FNB OF PULLMAN
{{6L 15S}}
Organized 2/20/92
Brown Back <$VALUE
4x5 1-1330 <$1500
3x10-20 1-2858 <$1500
1882 Date Back
4x5 1-1565 <$1500
3x10-20 1-1233 <$1500
1902 Date Back
4x5 1-2050 <$300
3x10-20 1-1500 <$300
1902 Plain Back
4x5 2051-5820 <$300
3x10-20 1501-11604 <$300
1929 Small Size
5 Type 1 1-3036 <$110
10 Type 1 1-1348 <$110
20 Type 1 1-344 <$135
5 Type 2 1-4102 <$160
10 Type 2 1-2357 <$160
20 Type 2 1-650 <$175
Total Issue $1,229,370
Out in 1935 $75,000
Large out 1935 $4,210

****

****
4224 Pierce
FNB OF PUYALLUP
{{ UNREPORTED }}
Chartered 2/1/90
Liquidated 1/1/96
Brown Back <$VALUE
4x5 1-2188 <$3500
Total Issue $43,760
Out in 1910 $300
****
9102 Grant
FNB OF QUINCY
{{ UNREPORTED }}
Chartered 4/08
Liquidated 5/15/13
1902 Red Seal <$VALUE
4x5 1-150 <$3500
3x10-20 1-125 <$3500
1902 Date Back
4x5 1-250 <$2000
3x10-20 1-164 <$2000
Total Issue $22,450
Out in 1913 $4,345
****
11672 Pacific
FNB OF RAYMOND
{{ 2 L 6 S }}
Organized 3/23/20
Receivership 2/3/32
1902 Plain Back <$VALUE
3x10-20 1-7042 <$850
1929 Small Size
10 Type 1 1-910 <$275
20 Type 1 1-252 <$300
Total Issue $436,940
Out at close $48,860
Large out at close $4,700
****
13444 Lincoln
FNB OF REARDAN
{{ U + 10 S }}
Organized 3/26/30
1929 Small Size <$VALUE
5 Type 1 1-1704 <$175
10 Type 1 1-940 <$175
20 Type 1 1-230 <$175
5 Type 2 1-2640 <$200
10 Type 2 1-1353 <$200
20 Type 2 1-247 <$225
Total Issue $166,790
Out in 1935 $50,000
****
5751 Adams
FNB OF RITZVILLE
{{ 3 L 15 S }}
Chartered 3/21/01
Brown Back <$VALUE
4x5 1-1150 <$1500
3x10-20 1-1080 <$1500
1882 Date Back
4x5 1-1750 <$1500
3x10-20 1-1360 <$1500
1882 Value Back
4x5 1751-2555 <$1500
3x10-20 1361-1805 <$1500
1902 Plain Back
4x5 1-3360 <$650
3x10-20 1-2072 <$650
1929 Small Size
5 Type 1 1-3434 <$135
10 Type 1 1-1782 <$135
20 Type 1 1-436 <$160
5 Type 2 1-862 <$200
10 Type 2 1-475 <$200
20 Type 2 1-80 <$225
Total Issue $662,070
Out in 1935 $50,000
Large out 1935 $2,885
Outstanding includes Ch 8743
****
8743 Adams
PIONEER NB OF RITZVILLE
{{ 1 L }}
Chartered 6/07
Liquidated 1/28/20
1902 Red Seal <$VALUE
4x5 1-800 <$2000
3x10-20 1-640 <$2000
1902 Date Back
4x5 1-2350 <$1000
3x10-20 1-1820 <$1000
1902 Plain Back
4x5 2351-3235 <$1000
3x10-20 1821-2175 <$1000
Total Issue $221,450
Out at close $30,000
Ch 5751 assumed circulation
****

****
9273 Whitman
WHITMAN COUNTY NB OF ROSALIA
{{ 2 L 9 S }}
Organized 9/28/08
Receivership 4/25/34
1902 Date Back <$VALUE
3x10-20 1-2650 <$750
1902 Plain Back
3x10-20 2651-8860 <$750
1929 Small Size
10 Type 1 1-1005 <$275
20 Type 1 1-313 <$300
Total Issue $540,860
Out at close $43,000
Large out at close $2,910
****
13581 King
BALLARD FNB OF SEATTLE
{{ 3 S }}
Chartered 12/31
Liquidated 6/10/33
1929 Small Size <$VALUE
5 Type 1 1-842 <$400
10 Type 1 1-425 <$400
Total Issue $50,760
Out at close $49,820
****
4124 King
BOSTON NB OF SEATTLE
{{ UNREPORTED }}
Chartered 9/19/89
Liquidated 8/8/03
TERRITORIAL ISSUES
Brown Back <$VALUE
3x10-20 1-1000 <$12,500
STATE ISSUES
Brown Back
3x10-20 1001-4318 <$2500
Total Issue $215,900
Out in 1910 $3,280
****
9662 King
CITIZENS NB OF SEATTLE
{{ UNREPORTED }}
Chartered 2/10
Liquidated 8/29/14
2nd title: Mercantile NB of Seattle 1/20/12
FIRST TITLE
1902 Date Back <$VALUE
3x10-20 1-1732 <$1500
SECOND TITLE
1902 Date Back
3x10-20 1-5262 <$1500
Total Issue $349,700
Out at close $146,945
****
4397 King
COMMERCIAL NB OF SEATTLE
{{ UNREPORTED }}
Chartered 8/15/90
Liquidated 12/29/94
Brown Back <$VALUE
3x10-20 1-927 <$3000
Total Issue $46,350
Out in 1910 $530
****
9798 King
DEXTER HORTON NB OF SEATTLE
{{ 1 L }}
Chartered 6/10
Closed 3/10/24
1902 Date Back <$VALUE
3x10-20 1-7564 <$1000
Total Issue $378,200
Out at close $49,500
Ch 11280 assumed circulation
****
Dexter Horton NB of Seattle
SEE Ch 11280
Union NB of Seattle
****
2783 King
FNB OF SEATTLE
Chartered 1882
Closed 10/31/29
TERRITORIAL ISSUES {{ 0 L }}
Brown Back <$VALUE
3x10-20 1-1740 <$12,500
STATE ISSUES {{ 3 L 2 S }}
Brown Back
3x10-20 1741-5944 <$1250
1902 Red Seal
50-100 1-1768 <$6500
1902 Date Back
50-100 1-1500 <$500/$600
3x50-100 1-900 <$500/$600
1902 Plain Back
3x50-100 901-1255<$500/$600
1929 Small Size
5 Type 1 1-89* <$500
10 Type 1 1-25 <$500
20 Type 1 1-5** <$500
*C000089A-F000089A canceled
**B000005A-F000005A canceled
Total Issue $1,105,800
Out at close $100,000
Large out at close $95,350
****
FNB of Seattle
SEE Ch 11280
Union NB of Seattle
****
F Seattle Dexter Horton NB of Seattle
SEE Ch 11280
Union NB of Seattle
****
Mercantile NB of Seattle
SEE Ch 9662
Citizens NB of Seattle
****
2985 King
MERCHANTS NB OF SEATTLE
{{ UNREPORTED }}
Organized 6/23/83
Receivership 6/19/95
TERRITORIAL ISSUES
Brown Back <$VALUE
3x10-20 1-805 <$12,500
STATE ISSUES
Brown Back
3x10-20 806-2332 <$2500
Total Issue $116,600
Out in 1916 $630
****
4375 King
NB OF COMMERCE OF SEATTLE
{{ 8 L 24 S }}
Chartered 1890
Brown Back <$VALUE
4x5 1-13775 <$1000
50-100 1-7277 <$2500/$3000
1882 Date Back
50-100 1-279 <$2500/$3000
1902 Date Back
4x5 1-5000 <$175
50-100 1-4000 <$400/$450
1902 Plain Back
3x50-100 1-1754 <$400/$450
1929 Small Size
50 Type 1 1-2808 <$150
100 Type 1 1-1011 <$200
Total Issue $3,996,400
Out in 1935 $1,309,800
Large out 1935 $37,810
Outstanding includes Ch 10026 Ch 12704, Ch 9280, and Ch 4297
****
10026 King
N CITY B OF SEATTLE
{{ 5 L }}
Chartered 6/11
Closed 2/23/29
1902 Date Back <$VALUE
3x10-20 1-8000 <$350
1902 Plain Back
3x10-20 8001-11075 <$350
Total Issue $553,750
Out at close $50,000
Ch 4375 assumed circulation
****
13230 King
PACIFIC NB OF SEATTLE
{{ 6 L 44 S }}
Chartered 8/28
1902 Plain Back <$VALUE
3x10-20 1-10849 <$275/$300
1929 Small Size
10 Type 1 1-27040 <$40
20 Type 1 1-6496 <$50
10 Type 2 1-57004 <$40
20 Type 2 1-52674 <$50
Total Issue $4,567,890
Out in 1935 $1,656,300
Large out 1935 $2,900
****
2966 King
PUGET SOUND NB OF SEATTLE
Chartered 1883
Liquidated 5/14/10
TERRITORIAL ISSUES {{ 1 L }}
Brown Back <$VALUE
4x5 1-2275 <$15,000
50-100 1-197 <$20,000
STATE ISSUES {{ 0 L }}
Brown Back
4x5 2276-3105 <$3000
50-100 198-1774 <$5000
1902 Red Seal
50-100 1-2060 <$6500
1902 Date Back
50-100 1-116 <$1750/$2000
Total Issue $654,600
Out in 1910 $86,700
****
4229 King
SEATTLE NB, SEATTLE
{{ 33 L }}
Chartered 1890
Closed 10/31/29
Brown Back <$VALUE
4x5 1-18550 <$1000
50-100 1-5070 <$2500/$3000
1882 Date Back
4x5 1-2985 <$850
50-100 1-465 <$2500/$3000
1902 Date Back
50-100 1-5000 <$350/$400
3x50-100 1-16000<$350/$400
1902 Plain Back
3x50-100 16001-24978 <$350/$400
Total Issue $8,255,450
Out at close $1,999,995
Ch 11280 assumed circulation
****
11280 King
UNION NB OF SEATTLE
Chartered 12/18
2nd title: Dexter Horton NB of Seattle 5/19/24
3rd ttile: F Seattle Dexter Horton NB, Seattle 10/31/29
4th title: FNB of Seattle 10/31/31
FIRST TITLE {{ 6 L }}
1902 Plain Back <$VALUE
3x10-20 1-15000 <$250
SECOND TITLE {{ 24 L 8 S }}
1902 Plain Back
3x10-20 1-152240 <$75/$85
1929 Small Size
10 Type 1 1-5488 <$100
20 Type 1 1-1846 <$100
THIRD TITLE {{ 50+ S }}
1929 Small Size
10 Type 1 1-63836 <$30
20 Type 1 1-23886 <$40
FOURTH TITLE {{ 50+ S }}
1929 Small Size
10 Type 1 1-61250 <$30
20 Type 1 1-21398 <$40
10 Type 2 1-229862 <$30
20 Type 2 1-80750 <$40
Total Issue $25,765,660
Out in 1935 $7,000,000
Large out 1935 $181,650
Outstanding includes Ch 2783, Ch 4229, and Ch 9798
****
12153 King
UNIVERSITY NB OF SEATTLE
{{ 12 L 39 S }}
Chartered 4/22
1902 Plain Back <$VALUE
4x5 1-31570 <$135
3x10-20 1-15135 <$135/$150
1929 Small Size
5 Type 1 1-9658 <$40
10 Type 1 1-4624 <$40
20 Type 1 1-2404 <$50
5 Type 2 1-19758 <$40
10 Type 2 1-10818 <$40
20 Type 2 1-3468 <$50
Total Issue $2,520,140
Out in 1935 $400,000
Large out 1935 $6,495
****
4059 King
WASHINGTON NB OF SEATTLE
Chartered 6/27/89
Liquidated 6/25/06
TERRITORIAL ISSUES {{ 0 L }}
Brown Back <$VALUE
3x10-20 1-500 <$12,500
STATE ISSUES {{ 1 L }}
Brown Back
3x10-20 501-2949 <$2000
Total Issue $147,450
Out in 1910 $4,420
****
7908 Skagit
FNB OF SEDRO-WOOLLEY
{{ 2 L }}
Organized 8/31/05
Receivership 2/23/32
1902 Red Seal <$VALUE
3x10-20 1-850 <$2000
1902 Date Back
3x10-20 1-1900 <$1000
1902 Plain Back
3x10-20 1901-5204 <$1000
Total Issue $302,700
Out at close $1,730
****

****
3976 Whatcom
BELLINGHAM BAY NB OF SEHOME
{{ UNREPORTED }}
Chartered 2/7/89
Receivership 12/5/95
2nd title: Bellingham Bay NB of New Whatcom 5/7/91
FIRST TITLE
TERRITORIAL ISSUES
Brown Back <$VALUE
3x10-20 1-300 <$15,000
STATE ISSUES
Brown Back
3x10-20 301-344 <$3500
SECOND TITLE
Brown Back
3x10-20 1-396 <$3500
Total Issue $37,000
Out in 1916 $180
****
4351 Whatcom
COLUMBIA NB OF SEHOME
{{ UNREPORTED }}
Organized 6/28/90
Receivership 6/27/93
2nd title: Columbia NB of New Whatcom 5/19/91
FIRST TITLE
Brown Back <$VALUE
4x5 1-450 <$3500
3x10-20 1-310 <$3500
SECOND TITLE
Brown Back
4x5 1-612 <$3500
Total Issue $36,740
Out in 1916 $195
****
4457 King
FNB OF SLAUGHTER
{{ UNREPORTED }}
Chartered 11/3/90
Liquidated 10/25/93
Brown Back <$VALUE
3x10-20 1-355 <$3500
Total Issue $17,750
Out in 1910 $140
****
3887 Snohomish
FNB OF SNOHOMISH
Chartered 5/28/88
TERRITORIAL ISSUES {{ 0 L }}
Brown Back <$VALUE
4x5 1-800 <$15,000
STATE ISSUES {{ 2 L 3 S }}
Brown Back
4x5 801-3410 <$2000
3x10-20 1-489 <$2000
1902 Red Seal
3x10-20 1-125 <$2500
1902 Date Back
3x10-20 1-1320 <$1000
1902 Plain Back
3x10-20 1321-2883 <$1000
1929 Small Size
10 Type 1 1-314 <$450
20 Type 1 1-106 <$450
10 Type 2 1-241 <$500
20 Type 2 1-51 <$500
Total Issue $278,040
Out in 1935 $12,500
Large out 1935 $1,190
****
4526 Snohomish
SNOHOMISH NB, SNOHOMISH
{{ UNREPORTED }}
Chartered 3/3/91
Liquidated 2/25/97
Brown Back <$VALUE
4x5 1-1588 <$3500
Total Issue $31,760
Out in 1910 $295
****
4467 Pacific
FNB OF SOUTH BEND
{{ UNREPORTED }}
Organized 11/15/90
Receivership 8/17/95
Brown Back <$VALUE
3x10-20 1-449 <$3000
Total Issue $22,450
Out in 1916 $170
****

****
12418 Spokane
BROTHERHOODS CO-OPERATIVE NB OF SPOKANE
Organized 7/3/23
Liquidated 3/19/29
2nd title: City NB of Spokane 12/1/28
FIRST TITLE {{ 8 L }}
1902 Plain Back <$VALUE
4x5 1-47099 <$200
SECOND TITLE {{ 0 L }}
1902 Plain Back
4x5 1-2363 <$600
Total Issue $989,240
Out at close $200,000
****
City NB of Spokane
SEE Ch 12418
Brotherhoods Co-Operative NB of Spokane
****
Exchange NB of Spokane
SEE Ch 4044
Exchange NB of Spokane Falls
****
Fidelity NB of Spokane
SEE Ch 3528
FNB of Sprague
****
FNB of Hillyard, Spokane
SEE Ch 9182
FNB of Hillyard
****
13331 Spokane
FNT & SAVINGS B OF SPOKANE
{{ 30 S }}
Chartered 5/29
1929 Small Size <$VALUE
10 Type 1 1-14580 <$40
20 Type 1 1-3784 <$50
10 Type 2 1-1026 <$50
20 Type 2 1-397 <$60
Total Issue $1,347,080
Out in 1935 $250,000
Outstanding includes Ch 3528
****
9589 Spokane
NB OF COMMERCE OF SPOKANE
{{ 3 L }}
Chartered 11/09
Liquidated 3/4/15
1902 Date Back <$VALUE
4x5 1-8670 <$450
3x10-20 1-7230 <$450
Total Issue $534,900
Out in 1915 $95,850
****
4668 Spokane
OLD NB OF SPOKANE
Organized 11/28/91
2nd title: Old NB & Union TC of Spoakne 4/5/26
FIRST TITLE {{ 46 L }}
Brown Back <$VALUE
3x10-20 1-14860 <$850
1882 Date Back
3x10-20 1-35000 <$750
1902 Date Back
3x10-20 1-46000 <$50/$60
1902 Plain Back
4x5 1-157504 <$50
3x10-20 46001-122883 <$50/$60
SECOND TITLE {{ 27 L 50+ S }}
1902 Plain Back
4x5 1-65978 <$50
3x10-20 1-40071 <$50/$60
1929 Small Size
5 Type 1 1-55337 <$25
10 Type 1 1-26718 <$25
20 Type 1 1-7953 <$35
Total Issue $19,327,890
Out in 1935 $524,255
Large out 1935 $61,975
****
Old NB & Union TC of Spokane
SEE Ch 4668
Old NB of Spokane
****
Traders NB of Spokane
SEE Ch 3409
Traders NB of Spokane Falls
****

4025 Spokane
BROWNE NB OF SPOKANE FALLS
Chartered 5/4/89
Receivership 2/8/95
TERRITORIAL ISSUES {{ 0 L }}
Brown Back <$VALUE
4x5 1-1250 <$12,500
STATE ISSUES {{ 1 L }}
Brown Back
4x5 1251-2796 <$3000
Total Issue $55,920
Out in 1916 $425

4005 Spokane
CITIZENS NB OF SPOKANE FALLS
Chartered 4/8/89
Receivership 12/13/94
TERRITORIAL ISSUES {{ 1 L }}
Brown Back <$VALUE
3x10-20 1-750 <$12,500
STATE ISSUES {{ 0 L }}
Brown Back
3x10-20 751-1453 <$3000
Total Issue $72,650
Out in 1916 $470

4044 Spokane
EXCHANGE NB OF SPOKANE FALLS
Organized 5/4/89
Receivership 1/18/29
2nd title: Exchange NB of Spokane 1/16/07
FIRST TITLE
TERRITORIAL ISSUES {{ 0 L }}
Brown Back <$VALUE
4x5 1-1250 <$12,500
STATE ISSUES {{ 1 L }}
Brown Back
4x5 1251-7741 <$2000
3x10-20 1-2761 <$2000
SECOND TITLE {{ 50+ L }}
Brown Back
50-100 1-4500 <$2500/$3000
1882 Date Back
50-100 1-1005 <$2500/$3000
1902 Date Back
4x5 1-66000 <$50
3x10-20 1-39000 <$50/$60
1902 Plain Back
4x5 66001-153490 <$50
3x10 20 39001 163820 <$50/$60
Total Issue $12,379,420
Out at close $980,800

2805 Spokane
FNB OF SPOKANE FALLS
{{ UNREPORTED }}
Organized 10/24/82
Receivership 11/20/93
TERRITORIAL ISSUES
Brown Back <$VALUE
4x5 1-3050 <$12,500
STATE ISSUES
Brown Back
4x5 3051-3862 <$3000
3x10-20 1-617 <$3000
Total Issue $108,090
Out in 1916 $935

3838 Spokane
SPOKANE NB OF SPOKANE FALLS
{{ UNREPORTED }}
Chartered 1/24/88
Receivership 2/3/91
TERRITORIAL ISSUES
Brown Back <$VALUE
4x5 1-1650 <$12,500
STATE ISSUES
Brown Back
4x5 1651-1821 <$3000
Total Issue $36,420
Out in 1916 $325

3409 Spokane
TRADERS NB OF SPOKANE FALLS
Chartered 1885
Liquidated 8/5/14
2nd title: Traders NB of Spokane 1/27/93
FIRST TITLE
TERRITORIAL ISSUES {{ 0 L }}
Brown Back <$VALUE
4x5 1-3450 <$12,500
STATE ISSUES {{ 0 L }}
Brown Back
4x5 3451-5374 <$2500
SECOND TITLE {{ 5 L }}
Brown Back
3x10-20 1-5183 <$1250
1902 Red Seal
3x10-20 1-8100 <$1500
1902 Date Back
3x10-20 1-23980 <$400
Total Issue $1,711,480
Out in 1914 $358,750

4277 Spokane
WASHINGTON NB OF SPOKANE FALLS
{{ UNREPORTED }}
Chartered 4/2/90
Liquidated 7/30/94
Brown Back <$VALUE
3x10-20 1-1590 <$3000
Total Issue $79,500
Out in 1910 $570

3528 Lincoln
FNB OF SPRAGUE
Chartered 7/7/86
Closed 7/9/29
2nd title: Fidelity NB of Spokane 5/13/96
FIRST TITLE
TERRITORIAL ISSUES {{ 0 L }}
Brown Back <$VALUE
4x5 1-1075 <$12,500
STATE ISSUES {{ 0 L }}
Brown Back
4x5 1076-2475 <$2500
SECOND TITLE {{ 8 L }}
Brown Back
3x10-20 1-3033 <$1000
1902 Red Seal
3x10-20 1-4900 <$1250
1902 Date Back
3x10-20 1-12500 <$175
1902 Plain Back
3x10-20 12501-59586 <$175
Total Issue $3,425,450
Out at close $500,000
Large out 1935 $16,920
Ch 13331 assumed circulation

11935 Snohomish
FNB OF STANWOOD
{{ U + 10 S }}
Chartered 2/21
1929 Small Size <$VALUE
5 Type 1 1-1710 <$225
10 Type 1 1-834 <$225
20 Type 1 1-252 <$225
5 Type 2 1-3946 <$250
10 Type 2 1-2194 <$250
20 Type 2 1-650 <$275
Total Issue $186,250
Out in 1935 $64,750

8481 Yakima
FNB OF SUNNYSIDE
Chartered 12/06
2nd title: The FNB of Sunnyside 11/2/29
FIRST TITLE {{ 2 L }}
1902 Red Seal <$VALUE
3x10-20 1-875 <$2000
1902 Date Back
3x10-20 1-1890 <$850
1902 Plain Back
3x10-20 1891-5611 <$850
SECOND TITLE {{ 10 S }}
1929 Small Size
10 Type 1 1-1240 <$250
20 Type 1 1-372 <$275
10 Type 2 1-2100 <$275
20 Type 2 1-399 <$300
Total Issue $474,720
Out in 1935 $50,000
Large out 1935 $1,290

12667 Pierce
BROTHERHOOD-COOPERATIVE NB OF TACOMA
Organized 12/27/24
Receivership 2/2/32
2nd title: Washington NB in the City of Tacoma 5/12/30
FIRST TITLE {{ 7 L 5 S }}
1902 Plain Back <$VALUE
4x5 1-47729 <$250
1929 Small Size
5 Type 1 1-9200 <$250
SECOND TITLE {{ 4 S }}
1929 Small Size
5 Type 1 1-7064 <$250
Total Issue $1,442,500
Out at close $191,960
Large out at close $7,360

4069 Pierce
CITIZENS NB OF TACOMA
{{ UNREPORTED }}
Chartered 7/6/89
Liquidated 7/27/95
TERRITORIAL ISSUES
Brown Back <$VALUE
3x10-20 1-500 <$12,500
STATE ISSUES
Brown Back
3x10-20 501-1071 <$3000
Total Issue $53,550
Out in 1910 $425

4623 Pierce
COLUMBIA NB OF TACOMA
{{ UNREPORTED }}
Organized 9/2/91
Receivership 10/30/95
Brown Back <$VALUE
3x10-20 1-1694 <$3000
Total Issue $84,700
Out in 1916 $285

6006 Pierce
LUMBERMEN'S NB OF TACOMA
{{ UNREPORTED }}
Chartered 10/31/01
Liquidated 6/28/05
Brown Back <$VALUE
4x5 1-500 <$3000
3x10-20 1-1401 <$3000
50-100 1-379 <$4000
Total Issue $140,900
Out in 1910 $6,810

3172 Pierce
MERCHANTS NB OF TACOMA
Organized 5/2/84
Receivership 6/23/93
TERRITORIAL ISSUES {{ 1 L }}
Brown Back <$VALUE
3x10-20 1-1235 <$12,500
STATE ISSUES {{ 0 L }}
Brown Back
3x10-20 1236-1954 <$3000
Total Issue $97,700
Out in 1916 $490

3789 Pierce
NB OF COMMERCE OF TACOMA
Chartered 9/14/87
Liquidated 8/30/13
TERRITORIAL ISSUES {{ 0 L }}
Brown Back <$VALUE
3x10-20 1-1280 <$12,500
STATE ISSUES {{ 7 L }}
Brown Back
3x10-20 1281-11626 <$1000
1902 Red Seal
4x5 1-3000 <$1250
4x10 1-2000 <$1250
1902 Date Back
4x5 1-9185 <$250
4x10 1-6778 <$250
Total Issue $1,176,120
Out at close $200,000
Ch 3417 assumed circulation

NB of Tacoma
SEE Ch 3417
Pacific NB of Tacoma

4426 Pierce
NB OF THE REPUBLIC, TACOMA
{{ UNREPORTED }}
Chartered 9/30/90
Liquidated 10/1/92
Brown Back <$VALUE
3x10-20 1-1172 <$3000
Total Issue $58,650
Out in 1910 $350

3417 Pierce
PACIFIC NB OF TACOMA
Chartered 1885
2nd title: NB of Tacoma 9/2/13
FIRST TITLE
TERRITORIAL ISSUES {{ 1 L }}
Brown Back <$VALUE
4x5 1-2000 <$12,500
STATE ISSUES {{ 9 L }}
Brown Back
4x5 2001-3550 <$1000
3x10-20 1-6111 <$1000
1902 Red Seal
3x10-20 1-8750 <$1250
1902 Date Back
3x10-20 1-11945 <$200
SECOND TITLE {{ 36 L 50+ S }}
1902 Date Back
4x5 1-12500 <$60
3x10-20 1-10000 <$60
1902 Plain Back
4x5 12501-17500 <$60
3x10-20 10001-120714 <$60
1929 Small Size
10 Type 1 1-17550 <$25
20 Type 1 1-4848 <$35
10 Type 2 1-27047 <$25
20 Type 2 1-8165 <$35
Total Issue $9,865,530
Out in 1935 $700,000
Large out 1935 $36,960
Outstanding includes Ch 3789

12292 Pierce
PUGET SOUND NB OF TACOMA
{{ 2 L 27 S }}
Chartered 1/23
1902 Plain Back <$VALUE
3x10-20 1-10774 <$650
1929 Small Size
10 Type 1 1-9042 <$60
20 Type 1 1-2470 <$65
10 Type 2 1-6161 <$75
20 Type 2 1-3390 <$75
Total Issue $1,507,030
Out in 1935 $300,000
Large out 1935 $4,600

Tacoma NB, Tacoma
SEE Ch 2924
Tacoma NB, New Tacoma

Washington NB in the City of Tacoma
SEE Ch 12667
Brotherhood-Cooperative NB of Tacoma

4018 Pierce
WASHINGTON NB OF TACOMA
{{ UNREPORTED }}
Chartered 4/23/89
Receivership 8/26/93
TERRITORIAL ISSUES
Brown Back <$VALUE
3x10-20 1-500 <$12,500
STATE ISSUES
Brown Back
3x10-20 501-1591 <$3000
Total Issue $79,550
Out in 1916 $470

10407 Okanogan
FNB OF TONASKET
{{ 3 L 0 S }}
Organized 4/26/13
Liquidated 5/26/34
1902 Date Back <$VALUE
3x10-20 1-400* <$850
1902 Plain Back
3x10-20 501-1212* <$850
* 401-500 not marked
1929 Small Size
10 Type 1 1-216 <$850
20 Type 1 1-34 <$850
Total Issue $77,640
Out at close $5,650
Large out at close $380

14166 Okanogan
FNB OF TONASKET
{{ UNREPORTED }}
Chartered 5/34
1929 Small Size <$VALUE
10 Type 2 1-405 <$850
20 Type 2 1-140 <$850
Total Issue $6,850
Out in 1935 $6,250

7767 Yakima
FNB OF TOPPENISH
{{ 1 L 2 S }}
Chartered 6/05
1902 Red Seal <$VALUE
3x10-20 1-300 <$3000
1902 Date Back
3x10-20 1-720 <$2000
1902 Plain Back
3x10-20 721-1565 <$2000
1929 Small Size
10 Type 1 1-222 <$700
20 Type 1 1-45 <$750
Total Issue $111,970
Out in 1935 $6,250
Large out 1935 $440

8987 Clark
CITIZENS NB OF VANCOUVER
{{ 1 L }}
Chartered 1/08
Liquidated 2/24/10
1902 Red Seal <$VALUE
3x10-20 1-1500 <$2500
1902 Date Back
3x10-20 1-224 <$1500
Total Issue $86,200
Out in 1910 $34,050

Clark County NB of Vancouver
SEE Ch 10686
FNB of Camas

3031 Clark
FNB OF VANCOUVER
{{ UNREPORTED }}
Organized 8/15/83
Receivership 4/20/01
TERRITORIAL ISSUES
Brown Back <$VALUE
3x10-20 1-600 <$12,500
STATE ISSUES
Brown Back
3x10-20 601-2075 <$3000
Total Issue $103,750
Out in 1916 $610

9646 Clark
UNITED STATES NB OF VANCOUVER
{{ 6 L 12 S }}
Organized 1/11/10
Receivership 2/5/34
1902 Date Back <$VALUE
3x10-20 1-8600 <$350
1902 Plain Back
3x10-20 8601-25038 <$350
1929 Small Size
10 Type 1 1-2752 <$125
20 Type 1 1-699 <$135
Total Issue $1,500,900
Out at close $100,000
Large out at close $5,910

6013 Clark
VANCOUVER NB, VANCOUVER
{{ 8 L U + 15 S }}
Chartered 11/5/01
Liquidated 8/7/34
Brown Back <$VALUE
3x10-20 1-3160 <$1000
1882 Date Back
3x10-20 1-8300 <$1000
1882 Value Back
3x10-20 8301-13600 <$1000
1902 Plain Back
3x10-20 1-10665 <$300
1929 Small Size
10 Type 1 1-2698 <$125
20 Type 1 1-814 <$135
10 Type 2 1-362 <$200
20 Type 2 1-69 <$200
Total Issue $1,635,810
Out at close $70,070
Large out at close $6,340
Ch 14186 assumed circulation

13137 Clark
WASHINGTON NB OF VANCOUVER
{{ 18 S }}
Chartered 11/1/27
1929 Small Size <$VALUE
5 Type 2 1-12444 <$85
10 Type 2 1-6104 <$85
20 Type 2 1-1914 <$85
Total Issue $161,540
Out in 1935 $89,860

4681 Walla Walla
FNB OF WAITSBURG
{{ UNREPORTED }}
Chartered 1/13/92
Liquidated 6/25/98
Brown Back <$VALUE
4x5 1-1660 <$3500
Total Issue $33,200
All notes reportedly redeemed

8895 Walla Walla
FNB OF WAITSBURG
{{ 4 L 6 S }}
Chartered 9/07
1902 Red Seal <$VALUE
4x10 1-468 <$1500
1902 Date Back
4x10 1-1500 <$600
1902 Plain Back
4x10 1501-2350 <$600
3x10-20 1-6675 <$600
1929 Small Size
10 Type 1 1-1200 <$250
20 Type 1 1-288 <$250
10 Type 2 1-2056 <$275
20 Type 2 1-376 <$300
Total Issue $581,110
Out in 1935 $50,000
Large out 1935 $1,990

3956 Walla Walla
BAKER-BOYER NB OF WALLA WALLA
Chartered 1/8/89
TERRITORIAL ISSUES {{ 0 L }}
Brown Back <$VALUE
3x10-20 1-750 <$15,000
STATE ISSUES {{ 3 L 5 S }}
Brown Back
3x10-20 751-4770 <$1500
1882 Date Back
3x10-20 1-98 <$1500
1902 Date Back
3x10-20 1-4200 <$600
1902 Plain Back
3x10-20 4201-9885 <$600
1929 Small Size
20 Type 1 1-1038 <$350
20 Type 2 1-903 <$375
Total Issue $880,270
Out in 1935 $100,000
Large out 1935 $3,140

2380 Walla Walla
FNB OF WALLA WALLA
Chartered 3/18/78
TERRITORIAL ISSUES {{ 1 L }}
Series 1875 <$VALUE
4x5 1-18750 <$15,000
STATE ISSUES {{ 13 L }}
Series 1875
4x5 8751-21229 <$6500
Brown Back
4x5 1-3300 <$1250
3x10-20 1-2900 <$1250
1882 Date Back
4x5 1-7500 <$1250
3x10-20 1-5800 <$1250
1882 Value Back
4x5 7501-9147 <$1250
3x10-20 5801-6743 <$1250
1902 Plain Back
4x5 1-46446 <$400
Total Issue $2,084,590
Out in 1935 $9,710

9068 Walla Walla
THIRD NB OF WALLA WALLA
{{ UNREPORTED }}
Chartered 3/08
Liquidated 3/17/28
1902 Red Seal <$VALUE
3x10-20 1-750 <$3000
1902 Date Back
3x10-20 1-2490 <$1500
1902 Plain Back
3x10-20 2491-5079 <$1500
Total Issue $291,450
Out at close $22,950

9129 Yakima
FNB OF WAPATO
{{ 1 L 3 S }}
Chartered 5/08
1902 Date Back <$VALUE
3x10-20 1-880 <$1500
1902 Plain Back
3x10-20 881-1779 <$1500
1929 Small Size
10 Type 1 1-480 <$500
20 Type 1 1-118 <$500
10 Type 2 1-896 <$500
20 Type 2 1-182 <$500
Total Issue $144,510
Out in 1935 $25,000
Large out 1935 $440

CONDITION affects Value. The Values shown are for notes in FINE condition.

****

9054 Adams
FNB OF WASHTUCNA
{{ UNREPORTED }}
Chartered 3/08
Liquidated 2/17/26

1902 Red Seal		<$VALUE
4x5	1-750	<$3000
3x10-20	1-600	<$3000
1902 Date Back		
4x5	1-2300	<$1500
3x10-20	1-1610	<$1500
1902 Plain Back		
4x5	2301-5450	<$1500
3x10-20	1611-3524	<$1500
Total Issue		$330,200
Out at close		$11,750

****

4532 Douglas
FNB OF WATERVILLE
{{ 1 L }}
Chartered 3/10/91
Liquidated 2/24/98

Brown Back		<$VALUE
4x5	1-1745	<$3000
Total Issue		$34,900
Out in 1910		$350

****

8064 Chelan
FNB OF WENATCHEE
{{ 8 L 21 S }}
Chartered 1/06

1902 Red Seal			<$VALUE
4x5		1-410	<$1500
3x10-20		1-330	<$1500
1902 Date Back			
4x5		1-3425	<$350
3x10-20		1-2600	<$350
1902 Plain Back			
4x5		3426-15910	<$350
3x10-20		2601-10790	<$350
1929 Small Size			
5	Type 1	1-3884	<$110
10	Type 1	1-1918	<$100
20	Type 1	1-506	<$125
5	Type 2	1-5292	<$135
10	Type 2	1-3168	<$135
20	Type 2	1-816	<$135
Total Issue			$1,249,180
Out in 1935			$100,000
Large out 1935			$4,725

****

4099 Whatcom
FNB OF WHATCOM
{{ UNREPORTED }}
Chartered 8/26/89
Receivership 6/27/93
TERRITORIAL ISSUES

Brown Back		<$VALUE
3x10-20	1-250	<$15,000
STATE ISSUES		
Brown Back		
3x10-20	251-387	<$3500
Total Issue		$19,350
Out in 1916		$110

****

10000 Klickitat
FNB OF WHITE SALMON
{{ UNREPORTED }}
Chartered 4/11
Liquidated 6/1/16

1902 Date Back		<$VALUE
3x10-20	1-1106	<$3000
Total Issue		$55,300
Out in 1916		$12,100

****

2876 Yakima
FNB OF YAKIMA
{{ UNREPORTED }}
Chartered 1883
Liquidated 6/30/85
TERRITORIAL ISSUES

Brown Back		<$VALUE
3x10-20	1-402	<$15,000
Total Issue		$20,100
Out in 1910		$90

****

FNB of Yakima
SEE Ch 3355
FNB of North Yakima

****

Yakima FNB, Yakima
SEE Ch 3355
FNB of North Yakima

****

Yakima NB, Yakima
SEE Ch 3862
Yakima NB of North Yakima

****

****

9576 Yakima
FNB OF ZILLAH
{{ UNREPORTED }}
Organized 9/30/09
Receivership 12/2/31

1902 Date Back			<$VALUE
3x10-20		1-800	<$2500
1902 Plain Back			
3x10-20		801-1543	<$2500
1929 Small Size			
10	Type 1	1-144	<$1250
20	Type 1	1-16	<$1250
Total Issue			$87,710
Out at close			$6,250
Large out at close			$660

****

<$VALUEs are for notes in **FINE** condition. Value changes by approximately **25%** for a change of one full grade.

WEST VIRGINIA

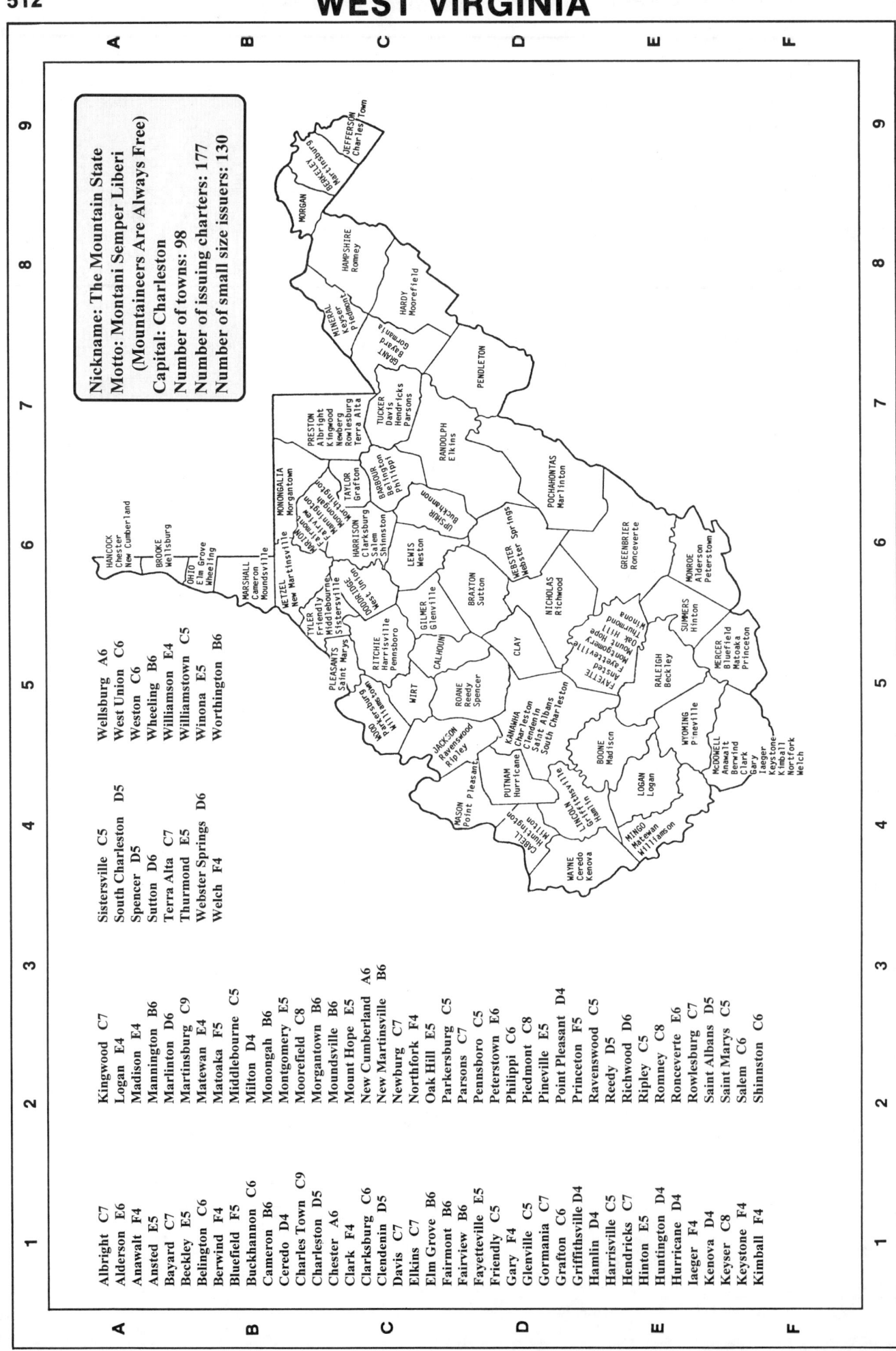

Albright C7	Kingwood C7	Sistersville C5	Wellsburg A6
Alderson E6	Logan E4	South Charleston D5	West Union C6
Anawalt F4	Madison E4	Spencer D5	Weston C6
Ansted E5	Mannington B6	Sutton D6	Wheeling B6
Bayard C7	Marlinton D6	Terra Alta C7	Williamson E4
Beckley E5	Martinsburg C9	Thurmond E5	Williamstown C5
Belington C6	Matewan E4	Webster Springs D6	Winona E5
Berwind F4	Matoaka F5	Welch F4	Worthington B6
Bluefield F5	Middlebourne C5		
Buckhannon C6	Milton D4		
Cameron B6	Monongah B6		
Ceredo D4	Montgomery E5		
Charles Town C9	Moorefield C8		
Charleston D5	Morgantown B6		
Chester A6	Moundsville B6		
Clark F4	Mount Hope E5		
Clarksburg C6	New Cumberland A6		
Clendenin D5	New Martinsville B6		
Davis C7	Newburg C7		
Elkins C7	Northfork F4		
Elm Grove B6	Oak Hill E5		
Fairmont B6	Parkersburg C5		
Fairview B6	Parsons C7		
Fayetteville E5	Pennsboro C5		
Friendly C5	Peterstown E6		
Gary F4	Philippi C6		
Glenville C5	Piedmont C8		
Gormania C7	Pineville E5		
Grafton C6	Point Pleasant D4		
Griffithsville D4	Princeton F5		
Hamlin D4	Ravenswood C5		
Harrisville C5	Reedy D5		
Hendricks C7	Richwood D6		
Hinton E5	Ripley C5		
Huntington D4	Romney C8		
Hurricane D4	Ronceverte E6		
Iaeger F4	Rowlesburg C7		
Kenova D4	Saint Albans D5		
Keyser C8	Saint Marys C5		
Keystone F4	Salem C6		
Kimball F4	Shinnston C6		

Nickname: The Mountain State
Motto: Montani Semper Liberi
(Mountaineers Are Always Free)
Capital: Charleston
Number of towns: 98
Number of issuing charters: 177
Number of small size issuers: 130

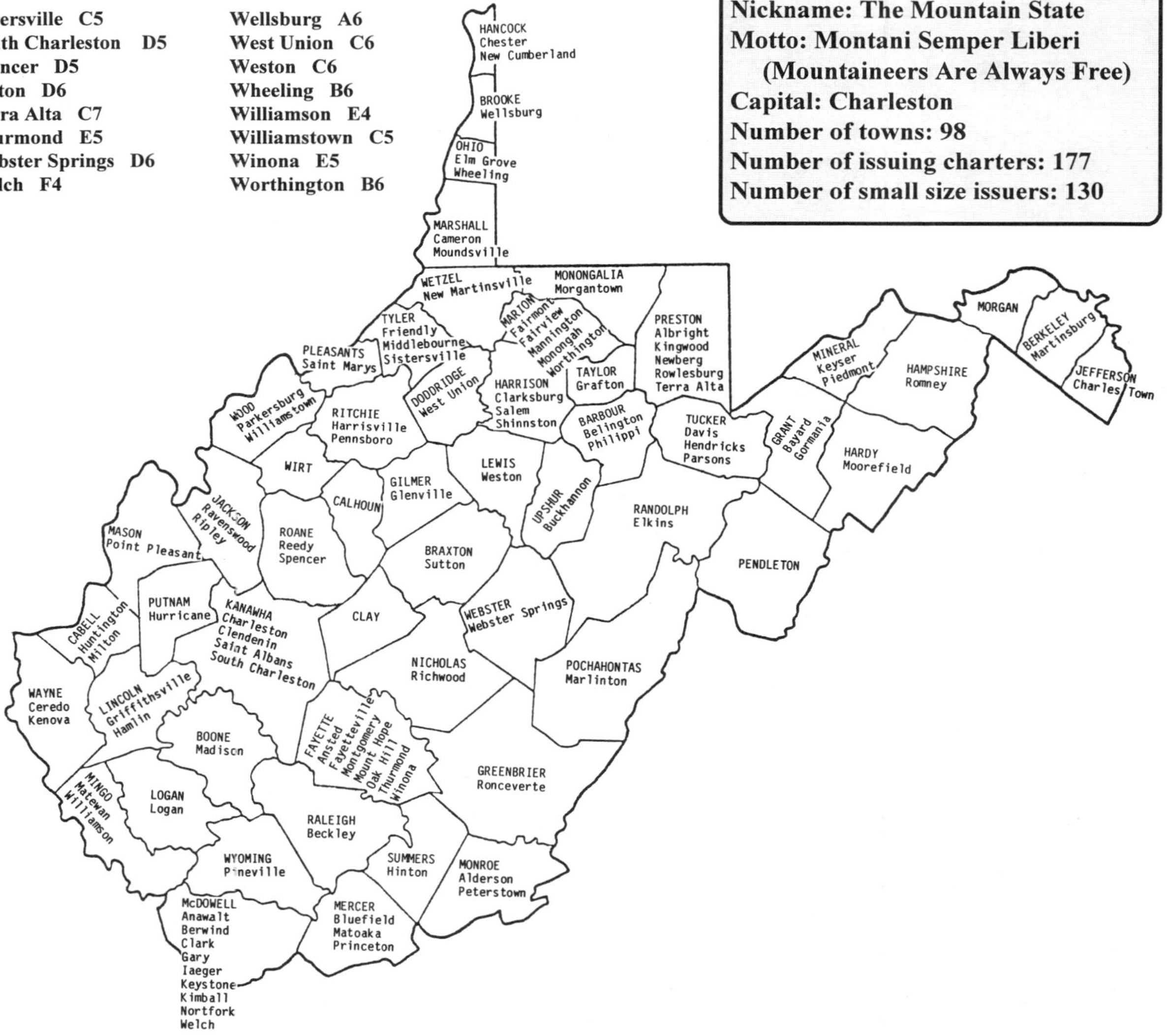

10480 Preston
FNB OF ALBRIGHT
{{ 4 L U + 4 S }}
Organized 11/7/13
1902 Date Back <$VALUE
4x5 1-650 <$400
3x10-20 1-720 <$400
1902 Plain Back
4x5 651-5884 <$400
3x10-20 721-3723 <$400
1929 Small Size
5 Type 1 1-852 <$300
10 Type 1 1-408 <$300
20 Type 1 1-128 <$300
5 Type 2 1-988 <$325
10 Type 2 1-663 <$325
20 Type 2 1-204 <$325
Total Issue $384,880
Out in 1935 $25,000
Large out 1935 $1,000

9523 Monroe
ALDERSON NB, ALDERSON
{{ 2 L 1 S }}
Organized 7/19/09
Receivership 9/28/31
1902 Date Back <$VALUE
4x5 1-1200 <$600
3x10-20 1-940 <$600
1902 Plain Back
4x5 1201-3840 <$600
3x10-20 941-2491 <$600
1929 Small Size
5 Type 1 1-371 <$500
10 Type 1 1-159 <$500
20 Type 1 1-49 <$500
Total Issue $227,900
Out at close $12,135
Large out at close $1,485

5903 Monroe
FNB OF ALDERSON
{{ 7 L 12 S }}
Chartered 7/13/01
Brown Back <$VALUE
4x5 1-1580 <$600
3x10-20 1-1268 <$600
1882 Date Back
4x5 1-5200 <$550
3x10-20 1-4060 <$550
1882 Value Back
4x5 5201-7600 <$600
3x10-20 4061-7881 <$600
1902 Plain Back
4x5 1-11027 <$300
3x10-20 1-6989 <$300
1929 Small Size
5 Type 1 1-3816 <$150
10 Type 1 1-1760 <$150
20 Type 1 1-548 <$165
5 Type 2 1-7692 <$185
10 Type 2 1-3408 <$185
20 Type 2 1-984 <$185
Total Issue $1,589,100
Out in 1935 $71,100
Large out 1935 $5,300

10392 McDowell
FNB OF ANAWALT
{{ 2 L 2 S }}
Organized 5/2/13
Receivership 10/15/31
1902 Date Back <$VALUE
3x10-20 1-1380 <$650
1902 Plain Back
3x10-20 1381-7387 <$650
1929 Small Size
10 Type 1 1-600 <$450
20 Type 1 1-179 <$450
Total Issue $426,830
Out at close $24,640
Large out at close $2,110

8904 Fayette
ANSTED NB, ANSTED
{{ 6 L 4 S }}
Organized 9/11/07
Liquidated 2/28/35
1902 Red Seal <$VALUE
3x10-20 1-462 <$850
1902 Date Back
3x10-20 1-2810 <$400
1902 Plain Back
3x10-20 2811-9255 <$400
1929 Small Size
10 Type 1 1-1164 <$275
20 Type 1 1-308 <$275
Total Issue $592,650
Out at close $24,170
Large out at close $2,020

11664 Grant
BAYARD NB, BAYARD
{{ 2 L 2 S }}
Organized 2/23/20
Receivership 4/28/32
1902 Plain Back <$VALUE
3x10-20 1-4327 <$650
1929 Small Size
10 Type 1 1-571 <$450
20 Type 1 1-143 <$450
Total Issue $267,770
Out at close $25,000
Large out at close $1,440

10589 Raleigh
BECKLEY NB, BECKLEY
Chartered 7/14
2nd title:Beckley N Exchange B 4/5/32
FIRST TITLE {{ 6 L 2 S }}
1902 Date Back <$VALUE
3x10-20 1-1000 <$350
1902 Plain Back
3x10-20 1001-20784 <$350
1929 Small Size
10 Type 1 1-2414 <$275
20 Type 1 1-706 <$275
SECOND TITLE {{ 9 S }}
1929 Small Size
5 Type 1 1-736 <$165
10 Type 1 1-712 <$165
20 Type 1 1-178 <$165
5 Type 2 1-10308 <$185
10 Type 2 1-4968 <$185
20 Type 2 1-1284 <$185
Total Issue $1,481,820
Out in 1935 $90,730
Large out 1935 $3,490

Beckley N Exchange B, Beckley
SEE Ch 10589
Beckley NB, Beckley

6735 Raleigh
FNB OF BECKLEY
{{ UNREPORTED }}
Chartered 4/21/03
Liquidated 8/27/07
1902 Red Seal <$VALUE
3x10-20 1-521 <$2000
Total Issue $26,050
Out in 1910 $1,930

9038 Raleigh
PEOPLES NB OF BECKLEY
{{ UNREPORTED }}
Chartered 2/08
Liquidated 1/21/10
1902 Red Seal <$VALUE
3x10-20 1-470 <$2000
Total Issue $23,500
Out in 1910 $4,170

6634 Barbour
BELINGTON NB, BELINGTON
{{ UNREPORTED }}
Chartered 2/17/03
Liquidated 8/6/06
1902 Red Seal <$VALUE
3x10-20 1-876 <$2000
Total Issue $43,800
Out in 1910 $2,570

6618 Barbour
CITIZENS NB OF BELINGTON
{{ 4 L }}
Chartered 2/03
Liquidated 3/28/25
1902 Red Seal <$VALUE
3x10-20 1-2800 <$1000
1902 Date Back
3x10-20 1-3580 <$500
1902 Plain Back
3x10-20 3581-8210 <$500
Total Issue $550,500
Out at close $30,000

6619 Barbour
FNB OF BELINGTON
{{ 4 L 5 S }}
Organized 2/4/03
Receivership 10/13/31
1902 Red Seal <$VALUE
4x5 1-1795 <$1000
3x10-20 1-1582 <$1000
1902 Date Back
4x5 1-3250 <$450
3x10-20 1-2340 <$450
1902 Plain Back
4x5 3251-10648 <$450
3x10-20 2341-7237 <$450
1929 Small Size
5 Type 1 1-860 <$225
10 Type 1 1-426 <$225
20 Type 1 1-133 <$225
Total Issue $757,130
Out at close $39,340
Large out at close $6,710

9909 McDowell
BERWIND NB, BERWIND
{{ 1 L }}
Chartered 12/10
Liquidated 7/1/14
1902 Date Back <$VALUE
4x5 1-1605 <$1000
3x10-20 1-1252 <$1000
Total Issue $94,700
Out in 1914 $20,500

7734 Mercer
AMERICAN NB OF BLUEFIELD*
Chartered 5/11/05
Liquidated 5/1/09
*1st title and location: American NB of Graham, VA
Moved to WV 2/21/06
FIRST TITLE (VA) {{ 1 L }}
1902 Red Seal <$VALUE
4x5 1-425 <$1500
3x10-20 1-336 <$1500
SECOND TITLE (WV) {{ 1 L }}
1902 Red Seal
4x5 1-2920 <$1500
3x10-20 1-2191 <$1500
Total Issue $193,250
Out in 1910 $22,170

11109 Mercer
BLUEFIELD NB, BLUEFIELD
Chartered 12/17
2nd title:Flat Top NB of Bluefield 5/2/32
FIRST TITLE {{ 8 L 6 S }}
1902 Plain Back <$VALUE
4x5 1-33684 <$275
3x10-20 1-19197 <$275
1929 Small Size
5 Type 1 1-6160 <$175
10 Type 1 1-3060 <$175
20 Type 1 1-868 <$175
SECOND TITLE {{ 12 S }}
1929 Small Size
5 Type 1 1-726 <$150
10 Type 1 1-368 <$150
20 Type 1 1-160 <$150
5 Type 2 1-11618 <$165
10 Type 2 1-6965 <$165
20 Type 2 1-2100 <$165
Total Issue $2,338,890
Out in 1935 $150,150
Large out 1935 $11,180
Outstanding includes Ch 6647

4643 Mercer
FNB OF BLUEFIELD
{{ 7 L 14 S }}
Chartered 1891
Brown Back <$VALUE
4x5 1-2300 <$650
3x10-20 1-4510 <$650
1882 Date Back
4x5 1-1315 <$600
3x10-20 1-1030 <$600
1902 Date Back
3x10-20 1-4500 <$275
1902 Plain Back
3x10-20 4501-12182 <$275
1929 Small Size
10 Type 1 1-1404 <$150
20 Type 1 1-402 <$150
10 Type 2 1-2522 <$165
20 Type 2 1-743 <$175
Total Issue $1,130,960
Out in 1935 $41,800
Large out 1935 $2,610

6674 Mercer
FLAT TOP NB OF BLUEFIELD
{{ 11 L 15 S }}
Chartered 3/03
Closed 5/2/32
1902 Red Seal <$VALUE
3x10-20 1-5200 <$750
1902 Date Back
3x10-20 1-9300 <$375
1902 Plain Back
3x10-20 9301-30918 <$375
1929 Small Size
10 Type 1 1-2668 <$165
20 Type 1 1-744 <$175
Total Issue $2,055,260
Out at close $100,000
Large out at close $9,730
Ch 11109 assumed circulation

Flat Top NB of Bluefield
SEE Ch 11109
Bluefield NB, Bluefield

13646 Upshur
CENTRAL NB OF BUCKHANNON
{{ 50+ S }}
Chartered 11/32
1929 Small Size <$VALUE
5 Type 1 1-1040 <$125
10 Type 1 1-316 <$125
20 Type 1 1-104 <$125
5 Type 2 1-2040 <$125
10 Type 2 1-1428 <$125
20 Type 2 1-456 <$125
Total Issue $98,060
Out in 1935 $49,150

4760 Upshur
TRADERS NB OF BUCKHANNON
{{ 6 L 8 S }}
Organized 4/14/92
Liquidated 6/11/34
Brown Back <$VALUE
4x5 1-4250 <$600
3x10-20 1-2420 <$600
1882 Date Back
4x5 1-1633 <$600
3x10-20 1-1200 <$600
1902 Date Back
4x5 1-1950 <$300
3x10-20 1-1580 <$300
1902 Plain Back
4x5 1951-9190 <$300
3x10-20 1581-7206 <$300
1929 Small Size
5 Type 1 1-1041 <$200
10 Type 1 1-512 <$200
20 Type 1 1-157 <$225
Total Issue $923,550
Out at close $49,340
Large out at close $5,140

6020 Marshall
FNB OF CAMERON
{{ 6 L 12 S }}
Chartered 11/13/01
Brown Back <$VALUE
3x10-20 1-3200 <$600
1882 Date Back
3x10-20 1-3640* <$600
1882 Value Back
3x10-20 3891-6396* <$600
* 3641-3890 not marked
1902 Plain Back
3x10-20 1-5363 <$350
1929 Small Size
10 Type 1 1-1256 <$135
20 Type 1 1-322 <$150
10 Type 2 1-1524 <$175
20 Type 2 1-354 <$200
Total Issue $884,270
Out in 1935 $46,900
Large out 1935 $3,100

4775 Wayne
FNB OF CEREDO
{{ 5 L 14 S }}
Chartered 1892
Brown Back <$VALUE
3x10-20 1-1840 <$600
1882 Date Back
3x10-20 1-2213 <$600
1902 Date Back
3x10-20 1-2260 <$350
1902 Plain Back
3x10-20 2261-10950 <$350
1929 Small Size
10 Type 1 1-1580 <$110
20 Type 1 1-412 <$110
10 Type 2 1-2306 <$135
20 Type 2 1-594 <$135
Total Issue $929,330
Out in 1935 $49,000
Large out 1935 $3,490

1868 Jefferson
FNB OF JEFFERSON AT CHARLES TOWN
{{ 3 L }}
Chartered 9/1/71
Liquidated 5/7/03
Original Series <$VALUE
4x5 1-1100 <$750
3x10-20 1-1510 <$850/$1500
Series 1875
4x5 1-250 <$750
3x10-20 1-2253 <$850/$1500
Brown Back
3x10-20 1-1850 <$650
Total Issue $307,650
Out in 1910 $2,680

7270 Jefferson
N CITIZENS B OF CHARLES TOWN
{{ 6 L 8 S }}
Organized 5/16/04
Receivership 12/19/33
1902 Red Seal <$VALUE
3x10-20 1-2900 <$750
1902 Date Back
3x10-20 1-4340 <$350
1902 Plain Back
3x10-20 4341-13839 <$350
1929 Small Size
10 Type 1 1-1523 <$185
20 Type 1 1-416 <$225
Total Issue $978,250
Out at close $50,000
Large out at close $3,040

3236 Kanawha
CHARLESTON NB, CHARLESTON
{{ U + 50+ L 50+ S }}
Chartered 1884
Brown Back <$VALUE
4x5 1-8925 <$300
3x10-20 1-9742 <$300/$350
1902 Red Seal
4x5 1-8000 <$350
3x10-20 1-10000 <$350/$400
1902 Date Back
4x5 1-46165 <$100
3x10-20 1-35334 <$100
1902 Plain Back
4x5 46166-147537 <$100
3x10-20 35335-102924 <$100
1929 Small Size
5 Type 1 1-43430 <$40
10 Type 1 1-20184 <$40
20 Type 1 1-6012 <$50
5 Type 2 1-71376 <$40
10 Type 2 1-39492 <$40
20 Type 2 1-12144 <$55
Total Issue $13,652,600
Out in 1935 $968,140
Large out 1935 $47,965
Outstanding includes Ch 4412, and Ch 4667

4412 Kanawha
CITIZENS NB OF CHARLESTON
{{ 8 L }}
Chartered 1890
Closed 3/30/29
Brown Back <$VALUE
4x5 1-2500 <$350
3x10-20 1-7945 <$350/$400
1882 Date Back
4x5 1-1135 <$350
3x10-20 1-2597 <$350/$400
1902 Date Back
3x10-20 1-8800 <$175
1902 Plain Back
3x10-20 8801-32851 <$175
Total Issue $2,242,350
Out at close $119,550
Ch 3236 assumed circulation

1795 Kanawha
FNB OF CHARLESTON
{{ 1 L }}
Chartered 2/23/71
Liquidated 10/2/75
Original Series <$VALUE
3x1-2 1-2040 <$2000/$4000
4x5 1-5490 <$1500
Total Issue $120,000
Out in 1910 $633

4667 Kanawha
KANAWHA NB OF CHARLESTON
{{ 16 L 5 S }}
Chartered 1891
Closed 11/15/30
Brown Back <$VALUE
3x10-20 1-15600 <$300/$350
1882 Date Back
3x10-20 1-8944 <$250/$300
1902 Date Back
3x10-20 1-14200 <$125
1902 Plain Back
3x10-20 14201-64884 <$125
1929 Small Size
10 Type 1 1-3657 <$200
20 Type 1 1-948 <$225
Total Issue $4,804,580
Out at close $250,000
Large out at close $39,640
Ch 3236 assumed circulation

13509 Kanawha
NB OF COMMERCE OF CHARLESTON
{{ 36 S }}
Chartered 12/30
1929 Small Size <$VALUE
5 Type 1 1-6868 <$40
10 Type 1 1-3742 <$45
20 Type 1 1-1286 <$55
5 Type 2 1-19116 <$50
10 Type 2 1-9660 <$50
20 Type 2 1-2796 <$60
Total Issue $832,980
Out in 1935 $189,800

8569 Kanawha
N CITY B OF CHARLESTON
{{ 2 L }}
Chartered 2/07
Liquidated 3/31/15
1902 Red Seal <$VALUE
4x5 1-1750 <$600
3x10-20 1-1400 <$600
1902 Date Back
4x5 1-10060 <$350
3x10-20 1-6974 <$350
Total Issue $654,900
Out in 1915 $79,000

6984 Hancock
FNB OF CHESTER
{{ 5 L 6 S }}
Organized 10/9/03
Receivership 12/22/32
1902 Red Seal <$VALUE
3x10-20 1-2400 <$850
1902 Date Back
3x10-20 1-4540 <$400
1902 Plain Back
3x10-20 4541-13691 <$400
1929 Small Size
10 Type 1 1-1359 <$250
20 Type 1 1-364 <$275
Total Issue $929,770
Out at close $50,000
Large out at close $3,540

10157 McDowell
CLARK NB, CLARK
{{ 1 L 4 S }}
Chartered 3/12
Closed 6/30/32
1902 Date Back <$VALUE
3x10-20 1-1900 <$600
1902 Plain Back
3x10-20 1901-7469 <$600
1929 Small Size
10 Type 1 1-718 <$300
20 Type 1 1-168 <$300
Total Issue $436,690
Out at close $24,750
Large out at close $2,010
Ch 8309 assumed circulation

7029 Harrison
EMPIRE NB OF CLARKSBURG
{{ 17 L 31 S }}
Organized 9/19/03
1902 Red Seal <$VALUE
3x10-20 1-14300 <$400/$450
1902 Date Back
3x10-20 1-23900 <$150
1902 Plain Back
3x10-20 23901-71681 <$150
1929 Small Size
5 Type 1 1-5792 <$40
10 Type 1 1-6096 <$45
20 Type 1 1-1492 <$55
5 Type 2 1-12898 <$50
10 Type 2 1-7077 <$50
20 Type 2 1-2164 <$60
Total Issue $5,196,150
Out in 1935 $211,700
Large out 1935 $14,680

CONDITION affects Value. The Values shown are for notes in FINE condition.

****
1530 Harrison
MERCHANTS NB OF
WEST VIRGINIA, CLARKSBURG
{{ 11 L 8 S }}
Chartered 1865
Original Series <$VALUE
4x5 1-1500 <$600
3x10-20 1-3180 <$850/$1500
Series 1875
4x5 1-96 <$600
3x10-20 1-2162 <$850/$1500
Brown Back
3x10-20 1-6231 <$400
1902 Red Seal
3x10-20 1-3600 <$500
1902 Date Back
3x10-20 1-7400 <$175
1902 Plain Back
3x10-20 7401-23279 <$175
1929 Small Size
5 Type 1 1-1732 <$160
10 Type 1 1-2530 <$160
20 Type 1 1-676 <$175
5 Type 2 1-3526 <$200
10 Type 2 1-2489 <$200
20 Type 2 1-632 <$200
Total Issue $2,294,560
Out in 1935 $98,250
Large out 1935 $6,240
****
4569 Harrison
TRADERS NB OF CLARKSBURG
{{ 3 L }}
Chartered 5/9/91
Liquidated 4/10/05
Brown Back <$VALUE
4x5 1-9785 <$500
3x10-20 1-4890 <$500
Total Issue $440,200
Out in 1910 $13,175
****
7681 Harrison
UNION NB OF CLARKSBURG
{{ 32 L 39 S }}
Organized 4/5/05
1902 Red Seal <$VALUE
4x5 1-12400 <$450
3x10-20 1-9140 <$450
1902 Date Back
4x5 1-26000 <$100
3x10-20 1-18900 <$100
1902 Plain Back
4x5 26001-128676 <$100
3x10-20 18901-86879 <$100
1929 Small Size
5 Type 1 1-18886 <$40
10 Type 1 1-10286 <$40
20 Type 1 1-2578 <$50
5 Type 2 1-29038 <$40
10 Type 2 1-16645 <$50
20 Type 2 1-5352 <$60
Total Issue $9,534,250
Out in 1935 $500,000
Large out 1935 $20,245
****
7275 Kanawha
FNB OF CLENDENIN
{{ 2 L 2 S }}
Chartered 5/04
Liquidated 9/30/31
1902 Red Seal <$VALUE
3x10-20 1-356 <$1000
1902 Date Back
3x10-20 1-940 <$500
1902 Plain Back
3x10-20 941-4962 <$500
1929 Small Size
10 Type 1 1-458 <$450
20 Type 1 1-127 <$450
Total Issue $308,620
Out at close $13,590
Large out at close $2,280
****
4828 Tucker
NB OF DAVIS
{{ 2 L 3 S }}
Organized 12/20/92
Brown Back <$VALUE
4x5 1-2350 <$750
3x10-20 1-900 <$750
1882 Date Back
4x5 1-177 <$750
3x10-20 1-693 <$750
1902 Date Back
3x10-20 1-120 <$500
1902 Plain Back
3x10-20 121-2701 <$500
1929 Small Size
10 Type 1 1-312 <$325
20 Type 1 1-104 <$325
10 Type 2 1-446 <$350
20 Type 2 1-89 <$350
Total Issue $302,680
Out in 1935 $12,050
Large out 1935 $1,020
****
12483 Randolph
CITIZENS NB OF ELKINS
{{ 0 L 5 S }}
Chartered 1/24
1902 Plain Back <$VALUE
4x5 1-1015 <$1250
4x10 1-862 <$1250
1929 Small Size
5 Type 1 1-1358 <$250
10 Type 1 1-790 <$250
5 Type 2 1-3272 <$275
10 Type 2 1-2292 <$275
20 Type 2 1-468 <$275
Total Issue $191,560
Out in 1935 $50,000
Large out 1935 $40
****
4718 Randolph
ELKINS NB, ELKINS
{{ 3 L 6 S }}
Organized 3/21/92
Liquidated 4/16/34
Brown Back <$VALUE
4x5 1-1525 <$750
3x10-20 1-1040 <$750
1882 Date Back
4x5 1-382 <$750
3x10-20 1-289 <$750
1902 Date Back
4x5 1-1750 <$600
3x10-20 1-1400 <$600
1902 Plain Back
4x5 1751-6235 <$600
3x10-20 1401-4087 <$600
1929 Small Size
5 Type 1 1-948 <$350
10 Type 1 1-467 <$350
20 Type 1 1-168 <$350
Total Issue $510,260
Out at close $25,000
Large out at close $1,430
Ch 14002 assumed circulation
****
8376 Randolph
PEOPLES NB OF ELKINS
{{ 2 L 3 S }}
Organized 8/25/06
Liquidated 4/16/34
1902 Red Seal <$VALUE
4x5 1-410 <$1500
3x10-20 1-331 <$1500
1902 Date Back
4x5 1-1400 <$750
3x10-20 1-1040 <$750
1902 Plain Back
4x5 1401-3270 <$750
3x10-20 1041-2247 <$750
1929 Small Size
5 Type 1 1-500 <$400
10 Type 1 1-250 <$400
20 Type 1 1-84 <$425
5 Type 2 1-204 <$400
10 Type 2 1-100 <$425
20 Type 2 1-15 <$450
Total Issue $244,900
Out at close $11,600
Large out at close $320
Ch 14002 assumed circulation
****
7060 Randolph
RANDOLPH NB OF ELKINS
{{ UNREPORTED }}
Chartered 12/10/03
Liquidated 12/31/04
1902 Red Seal <$VALUE
3x10-20 1-160 <$2500
Total Issue $8,000
Out in 1910 $320
****
14002 Randolph
TYGARTS VALLEY NB OF
ELKINS
{{ 26 S }}
Chartered 2/34
1929 Small Size <$VALUE
5 Type 2 1-5266 <$165
10 Type 2 1-2857 <$200
20 Type 2 1-610 <$200
Total Issue $67,100
Out in 1935 $75,000
Large out 1935 $1,550
Outstanding includes Ch 4718
and Ch 8376
****
8983 Ohio
FNB OF ELM GROVE
Chartered 1/08
2nd title:FNB & TC of
Elm Grove 7/29/20
FIRST TITLE {{ 1 L }}
1902 Red Seal <$VALUE
3x10-20 1-200 <$850
1902 Date Back
3x10-20 1-2600 <$400
1902 Plain Back
3x10-20 2601-3820 <$400
SECOND TITLE {{ 4 L 16 S }}
1902 Plain Back
3x10-20 1-13735 <$300
1929 Small Size
10 Type 1 1-2986 <$110
20 Type 1 1-890 <$110
10 Type 2 1-3095 <$125
20 Type 2 1-794 <$125
Total Issue $1,220,540
Out in 1935 $98,300
Large out 1935 $3,750
****
13811 Marion
FNB IN FAIRMONT
{{ 22 S }}
Chartered 10/33
1929 Small Size <$VALUE
5 Type 2 1-25192 <$65
10 Type 2 1-14169 <$65
20 Type 2 1-4620 <$70
Total Issue $360,050
Out in 1935 $193,750
****
961 Marion
FNB OF FAIRMONT
{{ 14 L }}
Chartered 3/31/65
Liquidated 9/16/15
Original Series <$VALUE
4x5 1-6750 <$600
3x10-20 1-550 <$850/$1500
Series 1875
4x5 1-5845 <$600
Brown Back
4x5 1-21023 <$325
3x10-20 1-2943 <$325/$375
1902 Red Seal
4x5 1-4100 <$375
3x10-20 1-2560 <$375/$400
1902 Date Back
4x5 1-15075 <$175
3x10-20 1-11475 <$175
Total Issue $1,932,260
Out at close $167,300
****
9462 Marion
NB OF FAIRMONT
{{ 31 L 36 S }}
Organized 6/19/09
Receivership 11/13/33
1902 Date Back <$VALUE
4x5 1-28500 <$100
3x10-20 1-22400 <$100
1902 Plain Back
4x5 28501-105907 <$100
3x10-20 22401-73060 <$100
1929 Small Size
5 Type 1 1-14892 <$40
10 Type 1 1-8372 <$45
20 Type 1 1-2222 <$55
5 Type 2 1-2952 <$45
10 Type 2 1-708 <$55
20 Type 2 1-246 <$65
Total Issue $7,013,620
Out at close $400,000
Large out at close $24,795
****
9645 Marion
PEOPLES NB OF FAIRMONT
Organized 1/10/10
Receivership 12/16/30
2nd title:Union NB of
Fairmont 11/27/29
FIRST TITLE {{ 22 L 3 S }}
1902 Date Back <$VALUE
4x5 1-15500 <$100
3x10-20 1-12000 <$100
1902 Plain Back
4x5 15501-56670 <$100
3x10-20 12001-38490 <$100
1929 Small Size
5 Type 1 1-1524 <$200
10 Type 1 1-778 <$200
20 Type 1 1-260 <$200
SECOND TITLE {{ 5 S }}
1929 Small Size
5 Type 1 1-2002 <$175
10 Type 1 1-843 <$175
20 Type 1 1-261 <$175
Total Issue $3,323,460
Out at close $194,960
Large out at close $27,440
****
Union NB of Fairmont
SEE Ch 9645
Peoples NB of Fairmont
****
10219 Marion
FNB OF FAIRVIEW
{{ 3 L 3 S }}
Chartered 6/25/12
Receivership 10/13/31
1902 Date Back <$VALUE
3x10-20 1-1750 <$400
1902 Plain Back
3x10-20 1751-7029 <$400
1929 Small Size
10 Type 1 1-377 <$350
20 Type 1 1-201 <$350
Total Issue $398,190
Out at close $29,460
Large out at close $3,570
****
8345 Fayette
FAYETTE COUNTY NB OF
FAYETTEVILLE
{{ 3 L 8 S }}
Chartered 8/06
1902 Red Seal <$VALUE
4x5 1-765 <$750
3x10-20 1-634 <$750
1902 Date Back
4x5 1-2200 <$375
3x10-20 1-1680 <$375
1902 Plain Back
4x5 2201-10501 <$375
3x10-20 1681-7296 <$375
1929 Small Size
5 Type 1 1-2524 <$200
10 Type 1 1-1306 <$200
20 Type 1 1-384 <$200
5 Type 2 1-4634 <$225
10 Type 2 1-2513 <$225
20 Type 2 1-660 <$225
Total Issue $883,480
Out in 1935 $48,800
Large out 1935 $855
****
5434 Fayette
FAYETTEVILLE NB,
FAYETTEVILLE
{{ 1 L }}
Chartered 6/16/00
Liquidated 9/15/06
Brown Back <$VALUE
4x5 1-855 <$1250
3x10-20 1-693 <$1250
Total Issue $51,750
Out in 1910 $1,570
****
5814 Tyler
FNB OF FRIENDLY
{{ UNREPORTED }}
Chartered 5/15/01
Receivership 7/25/08
Brown Back <$VALUE
3x10-20 1-1714 <$2000
Total Issue $85,700
Out in 1916 $1,010
****
8333 McDowell
GARY NB, GARY
{{ 4 L 2 S }}
Chartered 8/06
Liquidated 3/14/31
1902 Red Seal <$VALUE
4x5 1-725 <$1000
4x10 1-725 <$1000
1902 Date Back
4x5 1-2475* <$400
4x10 1-2475* <$400
1902 Plain Back
4x5 2576-13566* <$400
4x10 2576-11762** <$400
* 2476-2575 not marked
** 2476-2575 not marked
1929 Small Size
5 Type 1 1-1545 <$400
10 Type 1 1-842 <$400
Total Issue $882,170
Out at close $31,160
Large out 1935 $3,580
Ch 13505 assumed circulation
****
13505 McDowell
GARY NB, GARY
{{ UNREPORTED }}
Organized 12/3/30
Receivership 10/15/31
1929 Small Size <$VALUE
5 Type 1 1-684 <$750
10 Type 1 1-390 <$750
Total Issue $43,920
Out at close $47,180
Large out at close $3,580
Outstanding includes Ch 8333
****
5939 Gilmer
FNB OF GLENVILLE
{{ UNREPORTED }}
Chartered 8/14/01
Liquidated 4/24/06
Brown Back <$VALUE
4x5 1-400 <$2000
3x10-20 1-320 <$2000
Total Issue $24,000
Out in 1910 $1,225
****
8751 Grant
FNB OF GORMANIA
{{ 2 L 2 S }}
Organized 4/11/07
Liquidated 1/19/32
1902 Red Seal <$VALUE
4x5 1-550 <$1500
3x10-20 1-440 <$1500
1902 Date Back
4x5 1-2375 <$750
3x10-20 1-1860 <$750
1902 Plain Back
4x5 2376-7583 <$750
3x10-20 1861-4906 <$750
1929 Small Size
5 Type 1 1-592 <$500
10 Type 1 1-281 <$500
20 Type 1 1-84 <$500
Total Issue $474,660
Out at close $16,660
Large out at close $2,250
****
2445 Taylor
FNB OF GRAFTON
{{ 13 L 16 S }}
Chartered 12/29/79
Series 1875 <$VALUE
4x5 1-6750 <$600
3x10-20 1-4818 <$850/$1500
Brown Back
3x10-20 1-6600 <$350
1882 Date Back
3x10-20 1-8300* <$350
1882 Value Back
3x10-20 8801-11755* <$350
* 8301-8800 not marked
1902 Plain Back
3x10-20 1-7094 <$200
1929 Small Size
10 Type 1 1-2446 <$100
20 Type 1 1-816 <$100
10 Type 2 1-18 <$150
Total Issue $1,897,410
Out in 1935 $116,425
Large out 1935 $4,875
****
10097 Lincoln
OIL FIELD NB OF
GRIFFITHSVILLE
{{ 6 L 6 S }}
Chartered 10/11
1902 Date Back <$VALUE
4x5 1-1400 <$600
3x10-20 1-1135 <$600
1902 Plain Back
4x5 1401-6592 <$600
3x10-20 1136-4114 <$600
1929 Small Size
5 Type 1 1-1132 <$500
10 Type 1 1-528 <$500
20 Type 1 1-168 <$500
5 Type 2 1-1520 <$500
10 Type 2 1-982 <$500
20 Type 2 1-190 <$500
Total Issue $444,560
Out in 1935 $24,150
Large out 1935 $1,550
****
8171 Lincoln
LINCOLN NB OF HAMLIN
{{ 1 L 2 S }}
Chartered 4/06
1902 Red Seal <$VALUE
3x10-20 1-300 <$1250
1902 Date Back
3x10-20 1-760* <$750
1902 Plain Back
3x10-20 811-1565* <$750
* 761-810 not marked
1929 Small Size
10 Type 1 1-235 <$500
20 Type 1 1-60 <$500
Total Issue $114,550
Out in 1935 $6,590
Large out 1935 $830
****
6790 Ritchie
FNB OF HARRISVILLE
{{ 2 L }}
Chartered 5/03
Liquidated 1/31/24
1902 Red Seal <$VALUE
3x10-20 1-2685 <$1250
1902 Date Back
3x10-20 1-3400 <$650
1902 Plain Back
3x10-20 3401-7125 <$650
Total Issue $490,500
Out at close $50,000
****
7845 Tucker
FNB OF HENDRICKS
{{ 3 L 2 S }}
Chartered 7/05
Liquidated 12/15/31
1902 Red Seal <$VALUE
4x5 1-850 <$1000
3x10-20 1-690 <$1000
1902 Date Back
4x5 1-3675 <$500
3x10-20 1-2720 <$500
1902 Plain Back
4x5 3676-11757 <$500
3x10-20 2721-7818 <$500
1929 Small Size
5 Type 1 1-495 <$450
10 Type 1 1-251 <$450
20 Type 1 1-76 <$450
Total Issue $716,570
Out at close $18,355
Large out at close $4,005
****
10348 Summers
CITIZENS NB OF HINTON
{{ 4 L 4 S }}
Chartered 3/13
Liquidated 12/14/31
1902 Date Back <$VALUE
4x5 1-1000 <$350
3x10-20 1-800 <$350
1902 Plain Back
4x5 1001-11083 <$350
3x10-20 801-7624 <$350
1929 Small Size
5 Type 1 1-1498 <$250
10 Type 1 1-703 <$250
20 Type 1 1-226 <$250
Total Issue $717,100
Out at close $44,410
Large out at close $4,180
Ch 5562 assumed circulation
****
5562 Summers
FNB OF HINTON
{{ 8 L 22 S }}
Chartered 8/29/00
Brown Back <$VALUE
4x5 1-3400 <$450
3x10-20 1-2680 <$450
1002 Date Back
4x5 1-4450 <$450
3x10-20 1-3040 <$450
1882 Value Back
4x5 4451-7285 <$450
3x10-20 3041-4578 <$450
1902 Plain Back
4x5 1-11534 <$225
3x10-20 1-7781 <$225
1929 Small Size
5 Type 1 1-9166 <$65
10 Type 1 1-5220 <$65
20 Type 1 1-1256 <$75
5 Type 2 1-24514 <$85
10 Type 2 1-12345 <$85
20 Type 2 1-3064 <$85
Total Issue $2,242,530
Out in 1935 $209,750
Large out 1935 $6,235
Outstanding includes Ch 10348
****
7998 Summers
NB OF SUMMERS OF HINTON
{{ 8 L 16 S }}
Chartered 12/05
1902 Red Seal <$VALUE
3x10-20 1-4400 <$500
1902 Date Back
4x5 1-7250 <$200
3x10-20 1-5500 <$200
1902 Plain Back
4x5 7251-27917 <$200
3x10-20 5501-19418 <$200
1929 Small Size
5 Type 1 1-4862 <$85
10 Type 1 1-2588 <$85
20 Type 1 1-690 <$85
5 Type 2 1-6506 <$100
10 Type 2 1-4587 <$100
20 Type 2 1-1284 <$100
Total Issue $2,237,260
Out in 1935 $96,650
Large out 1935 $4,770
****

****

9598 Cabell
AMERICAN NB OF HUNTINGTON
{{ 2 L }}
Chartered 12/09
Liquidated 12/31/13
1902 Date Back <$VALUE
3x10-20 1-6156 <$450
Total Issue $307,800
Out in 1914 $46,870

****

4607 Cabell
COMMERCIAL NB OF
HUNTINGTON
Chartered 1891
Closed: 7/12/24
2nd title:Huntington NB
1/94
FIRST TITLE {{ 1 L }}
Brown Back <$VALUE
4x5 1-2041 <$500
SECOND TITLE {{ 17 L }}
Brown Back
4x5 1-9500 <$300
3x10-20 1-5700 <$300/$350
1882 Date Back
4x5 1-4576 <$250
3x10-20 1-1023 <$250/$300
1902 Date Back
4x5 1-4850 <$100
3x10-20 1-3680 <$100
1902 Plain Back
4x5 4851-68655 <$100
3x10-20 3681-46208 <$100
Total Issue $4,341,990
Out at close $689,995
Ch 3106 assumed circulation

****

F Huntington NB, Huntington
SEE Ch 3106
FNB of Huntington

****

3106 Cabell
FNB OF HUNTINGTON
Chartered 1884
2nd title:F Huntington NB
7/12/24
FIRST TITLE {{ 8 L }}
Brown Back <$VALUE
4x5 1-11100 <$300
3x10-20 1-1978 <$300
1902 Red Seal
3x10-20 1-9500 <$350/$400
1902 Date Back
3x10-20 1-40500 <$100
1902 Plain Back
3x10-20 40501-114700 <$100
SECOND TITLE {{ 50+ L 50+ S }}
1902 Plain Back
4x5 1-121110 <$60
3x10-20 1-66849 <$60/$75
3x50-100 1-1814 <$500/$650
1929 Small Size
5 Type 1 1-59608 <$20
10 Type 1 1-30512 <$25
20 Type 1 1-8912 <$35
5 Type 2 1-106050 <$20
10 Type 2 1-43021 <$25
Total Issue $18,397,910
Out in 1935 $1,395,590
Large out 1935 $68,195
Outstanding includes Ch 4607

****

Huntington NB, Huntington
SEE Ch 4607
Commercial NB of Huntington

****

7359 Cabell
WEST VIRGINIA NB OF
HUNTINGTON
{{ 3 L }}
Chartered 8/11/04
Liquidated 4/17/09
1902 Red Seal <$VALUE
4x5 1-5450 <$750
3x10-20 1-3074 <$750
50-100 1-529 <$4000
Total Issue $342,050
Out in 1910 $42,060

****

11670 Putnam
HURRICANE NB, HURRICANE
{{ 4 L }}
Chartered 12/14
Liquidated 5/14/27
1902 Plain Back <$VALUE
4x10 1-7373 <$750
Total Issue $294,920
Out at close $50,000

****

11268 McDowell
FNB OF IAEGER
{{ 3 L 1 S }}
Organized 10/15/18
Receivership 6/25/30
1902 Plain Back <$VALUE
3x10-20 1-5237 <$500
1929 Small Size
10 Type 1 1-277 <$600
20 Type 1 1-78 <$600
Total Issue $287,830
Out at close $25,000
Large out at close $4,720

****

12372 McDowell
TUG RIVER NB OF IAEGER
{{ 2 L }}
Organized 5/5/23
Liquidated 1/23/28
1902 Plain Back <$VALUE
3x10-20 1-2768 <$650
Total Issue $138,400
Out at close $24,270

****

9913 Wayne
FNB OF KENOVA
{{ 3 L 12 S }}
Chartered 12/10
1902 Date Back <$VALUE
3x10-20 1-3140* <$450
1902 Plain Back
3x10-20 3341-10902* <$450
* 3141-3340 not marked
1929 Small Size
10 Type 1 1-1210 <$165
20 Type 1 1-372 <$165
10 Type 2 1-1458 <$185
20 Type 2 1-400 <$185
Total Issue $684,920
Out in 1935 $29,610
Large out 1935 $1,990

****

6205 Mineral
FNB OF KEYSER
{{ 5 L 10 S }}
Chartered 4/12/02
Receivership 12/8/33
1902 Red Seal <$VALUE
3x10-20 1-3420 <$650
1902 Date Back
3x10-20 1-6550 <$275
1902 Plain Back (dated 1902)
3x10-20 6551-11369 <$275
1902 Plain Back (dated 1922)
3x10-20 1-7376 <$275
1929 Small Size
10 Type 1 1-1834 <$165
20 Type 1 1-474 <$175
Total Issue $1,275,170
Out at close $58,680
Large out at close $4,770

****

13831 Mineral
NB OF KEYSER
{{ 14 S }}
Chartered 11/33
1929 Small Size <$VALUE
10 Type 2 1-9356 <$150
20 Type 2 1-2980 <$150
Total Issue $153,160
Out in 1935 $88,700

****

10369 McDowell
FNB OF KEYSTONE
{{ 6 L 10 S }}
Chartered 4/13
1902 Date Back <$VALUE
4x5 1-1780 <$350
3x10-20 1-1468 <$350
1902 Plain Back
4x5 1781-11014 <$350
3x10-20 1469-7290 <$350
1929 Small Size
5 Type 1 1-1888 <$175
10 Type 1 1-1048 <$175
20 Type 1 1-288 <$175
5 Type 2 1-4360 <$200
10 Type 2 1-2300 <$200
20 Type 2 1-540 <$200
Total Issue $794,460
Out in 1935 $37,700
Large out 1935 $1,760

****

11502 McDowell
FNB OF KIMBALL
{{ 1 L 0 S }}
Organized 8/26/19
Liquidated 8/14/30
1902 Plain Back <$VALUE
4x5 1-6433 <$850
1929 Small Size
5 Type 1 1-469 <$750
Total Issue $142,730
Out at close $9,940
Large out 1935 $220
Ch 13484 assumed circulation

****

13484 McDowell
KIMBALL NB, KIMBALL
{{ 10 S }}
Chartered 8/30
1929 Small Size <$VALUE
5 Type 1 1-2160 <$175
5 Type 2 1-12984 <$200
Total Issue $129,720
Out in 1935 $22,700
Outstanding includes Ch 11502

****

6332 Preston
KINGWOOD NB, KINGWOOD
{{ UNREPORTED }}
Chartered 7/10/02
Receivership 6/23/31
1902 Red Seal <$VALUE
3x10-20 1-500 <$2000
1902 Date Back
3x10-20 1-760 <$1500
1902 Plain Back
3x10-20 761-1430 <$1500
Total Issue $96,500
Out at close $560

****

1608 Preston
NB OF KINGWOOD
{{ UNREPORTED }}
Chartered 11/14/65
Liquidated 10/21/86
Original Series <$VALUE
4x5 1-3775 <$2000
3x10-20 1-2500 <$2000/$2500
Series 1875
3x10-20 1-3342 <$2000/$2500
Brown Back
3x10-20 1-254 <$2000
Total Issue $380,300
Out in 1910 $2,315

****

FNB of Logan
SEE Ch 8136
Logan NB, Logan

****

8136 Logan
LOGAN NB, LOGAN
Organized 2/19/06
Receivership 2/1/34
2nd title:FNB of Logan
1/15/09
FIRST TITLE {{ 1 L }}
1902 Red Seal <$VALUE
3x10-20 1-962 <$1250
SECOND TITLE {{ 3 L 2 S }}
1902 Date Back
4x10 1-3125 <$450
1902 Plain Back
4x10 3126-6493 <$450
1929 Small Size
10 Type 1 1-820 <$400
10 Type 2 1-143 <$400
Total Issue $358,450
Out at close $12,500
Large out at close $600

****

13954 Logan
NB OF LOGAN
{{ 8 S }}
Chartered 1/34
1929 Small Size <$VALUE
5 Type 2 1-12276 <$165
10 Type 2 1-6168 <$175
Total Issue $123,060
Out in 1935 $81,910

****

Boone NB of Madison
SEE Ch 6510
Madison NB, Madison

****

6510 Boone
MADISON NB, MADISON
Chartered 11/28/02
2nd title:Boone NB of
Madison 5/31/29
FIRST TITLE {{ 5 L }}
1902 Red Seal <$VALUE
3x10-20 1-720 <$850
1902 Date Back
3x10-20 1-5200 <$400
1902 Plain Back
3x10-20 5201-15217 <$400
SECOND TITLE {{ 10 S }}
1929 Small Size
10 Type 1 1-2126 <$175
20 Type 1 1-542 <$175
10 Type 2 1-6779 <$200
20 Type 2 1-1674 <$200
Total Issue $1,090,720
Out in 1935 $79,050
Large out 1935 $2,330

****

5012 Marion
FNB OF MANNINGTON
{{ 9 L 6 S }}
Chartered 1895
Liquidated 8/17/32
Brown Back <$VALUE
4x5 1-5600 <$500
3x10-20 1-3420 <$500
1882 Date Back
4x5 1-4215 <$450
3x10-20 1-3047 <$450
1902 Date Back
4x5 1-1000 <$250
3x10-20 1-800 <$250
1902 Plain Back
4x5 1001-12114 <$250
3x10-20 801-7193 <$250
1929 Small Size
5 Type 1 1-1844 <$225
10 Type 1 1-783 <$225
20 Type 1 1-218 <$225
Total Issue $1,250,040
Out at close $52,890
Large out at close $5,025

****

13783 Pocahontas
FNB IN MARLINTON
{{ 1 S }}
Chartered 9/33
1929 Small Size <$VALUE
5 Type 2 1-4416 <$600
Total Issue $22,080
Out in 1935 $24,610
Large out 1935 $1,250
Outstanding includes Ch 6538

****

6538 Pocahontas
FNB OF MARLINTON
{{ 3 L 4 S }}
Chartered 12/17/02
Liquidated 12/30/33
1902 Red Seal <$VALUE
4x5 1-1240 <$850
3x10-20 1-1000 <$850
1902 Date Back
4x5 1-2025 <$400
3x10-20 1-1500 <$400
1902 Plain Back
4x5 2026-6921 <$400
3x10-20 1501-4349 <$400
1929 Small Size
5 Type 1 1-900 <$250
10 Type 1 1-486 <$250
20 Type 1 1-168 <$250
5 Type 2 1-406 <$275
10 Type 2 1-160 <$275
20 Type 2 1-35 <$300
Total Issue $511,320
Out at close $23,750
Large out 1935 $1,250
Ch 13783 assumed circulation

****

4811 Berkeley
CITIZENS NB OF
MARTINSBURG
{{ 11 L 18 S }}
Chartered 1892
Brown Back <$VALUE
4x5 1-3500 <$400
3x10-20 1-6620 <$400
1882 Date Back
4x5 1-2820 <$400
3x10-20 1-2794 <$400
1902 Date Back
4x5 1-3900 <$200
3x10-20 1-2920 <$200
1902 Plain Back
4x5 3901-23283 <$200
3x10-20 2921-15831 <$200
1929 Small Size
5 Type 1 1-4410 <$85
10 Type 1 1-2446 <$85
20 Type 1 1-492 <$100
5 Type 2 1-5494 <$110
10 Type 2 1-2895 <$110
20 Type 2 1-830 <$125
Total Issue $2,265,430
Out in 1935 $83,600
Large out 1935 $5,115

****

1524 Berkeley
NB OF MARTINSBURG
{{ 2 L }}
Chartered 8/12/65
Liquidated 5/31/02
Original Series <$VALUE
4x5 1-1625 <$850
3x10-20 1-2500<$1000/$1500
Series 1875
4x5 1-315 <$850
3x10-20 1-2114<$1000/$1500
Brown Back
3x10-20 1-3331 <$600
Total Issue $436,050
Out in 1910 $4,905

****

6283 Berkeley
OLD NB OF MARTINSBURG
{{ 12 L 22 S }}
Chartered 5/31/02
1902 Red Seal <$VALUE
3x10-20 1-5700 <$500
1902 Date Back
3x10-20 1-9100 <$175
1902 Plain Back
3x10-20 9101-31363 <$175
1929 Small Size
5 Type 1 1-8348 <$50
10 Type 1 1-6396 <$50
20 Type 1 1-1742 <$65
5 Type 2 1-11744 <$60
10 Type 2 1-7321 <$65
20 Type 2 1-1890 <$75
Total Issue $2,866,120
Out in 1935 $221,350
Large out 1935 $3,950

****

2144 Berkeley
PEOPLES NB OF MARTINSBURG
{{ 2 L }}
Chartered 5/5/74
Liquidated 9/2/01
Original Series <$VALUE
3x1-2 1-1000 <$2000/$4000
4x5 1-2500 <$850
Series 1875
4x5 1-7434 <$850
Brown Back
4x5 1-1946 <$600
3x10-20 1-1332 <$600
Total Issue $309,200
Out in 1910 $2,324

****

10370 Mingo
MATEWAN NB, MATEWAN
{{ 4 L 12 S }}
Chartered 4/13
1902 Date Back <$VALUE
3x10-20 1-860 <$350
1902 Plain Back
3x10-20 861-10278 <$350
1929 Small Size
10 Type 1 1-1846 <$165
20 Type 1 1-488 <$175
10 Type 2 1-3885 <$200
20 Type 2 1-986 <$200
Total Issue $741,770
Out in 1935 $48,650
Large out 1935 $1,620

****

11264 Mercer
FNB OF MATOAKA
{{ 3 L }}
Organized 11/7/18
Receivership 3/3/25
1902 Plain Back <$VALUE
4x5 1-5510 <$450
3x10-20 1-3518 <$450
Total Issue $286,100
Out at close $50,000

****

12839 Mercer
MATOAKA NB, MATOAKA
{{ 1 L 4 S }}
Chartered 10/25
Liquidated 6/21/32
1902 Plain Back <$VALUE
3x10-20 1-1807 <$750
1929 Small Size
10 Type 1 1-774 <$300
20 Type 1 1-211 <$300
Total Issue $162,110
Out at close $18,770
Large out at close $1,160

****

6170 Tyler
FNB OF MIDDLEBOURNE
{{ 2 L 2 S }}
Chartered 3/24/02
Liquidated 7/15/31
1902 Red Seal <$VALUE
3x10-20 1-1540 <$850
1902 Date Back
3x10-20 1-1810 <$500
1902 Plain Back (dated 1902)
3x10-20 1811-3078 <$500
1902 Plain Back (dated 1922)
3x10-20 1-2322 <$500
1929 Small Size
10 Type 1 1-373 <$400
20 Type 1 1-115 <$400
Total Issue $383,180
Out at close $21,330
Large out at close $490

****

12765 Cabell
MILTON NB, MILTON
{{ 3 L }}
Chartered 6/25
Liquidated 6/28/29
1902 Plain Back <$VALUE
4x5 1-8174 <$500
Total Issue $163,480
Out at close $50,000

****

7545 Marion
FNB OF MONONGAH
{{ 3 L 4 S }}
Organized 12/31/04
1902 Red Seal <$VALUE
4x5 1-1150 <$850
3x10-20 1-920 <$850
1902 Date Back
4x5 1-2200 <$400
3x10-20 1-1600 <$400
1902 Plain Back
4x5 2201-7557 <$400
3x10-20 1601-4762 <$400
1929 Small Size
5 Type 1 1-922 <$250
10 Type 1 1-426 <$250
20 Type 1 1-126 <$250
5 Type 2 1-1800 <$275
10 Type 2 1-822 <$275
20 Type 2 1-204 <$275
Total Issue $547,880
Out in 1935 $25,000
Large out 1935 $1,470

****

9740 Fayette
MERCHANTS NB OF
MONTGOMERY
{{ 5 L 11 S }}
Chartered 4/10
1902 Date Back <$VALUE
4x5 1-1565 <$275
3x10-20 1-1254 <$275
1902 Plain Back
4x5 1566-11907 <$275
3x10-20 1255-8260 <$275
1929 Small Size
5 Type 1 1-2534 <$125
10 Type 1 1-1230 <$125
20 Type 1 1-350 <$125
5 Type 2 1-5036 <$150
10 Type 2 1-2949 <$150
20 Type 2 1-744 <$150
Total Issue $912,510
Out in 1935 $50,000
Large out 1935 $1,920

****

5691 Fayette
MONTGOMERY NB, MONTGOMERY
{{ 10 L 18 S }}
Chartered 1/25/01
Brown Back <$VALUE
3x10-20 1-1260 <$450
1882 Date Back
3x10-20 1-4800* <$450
1882 Value Back
3x10-20 5161-8860* <$450
* 4801-5160 not marked
1902 Plain Back
3x10-20 1-15696 <$225
1929 Small Size
5 Type 1 1-524 <$100
10 Type 1 1-3596 <$100
20 Type 1 1-1024 <$100
5 Type 2 1-8076 <$110
10 Type 2 1-4176 <$110
20 Type 2 1-1032 <$110
Total Issue $1,747,940
Out in 1935 $95,140
Large out 1935 $2,130

****

CONDITION affects Value. The Values shown are for notes in FINE condition.

***
3029 Hardy
SOUTH BRANCH VALLEY NB OF MOOREFIELD
{{ 9 L 19 S }}
Chartered 1883
Brown Back <$VALUE
4x5 1-6330 <$600
3x10-20 1-1378 <$600
1902 Red Seal
3x10-20 1-2450 <$700
1902 Date Back
3x10-20 1-7900 <$250
1902 Plain Back
3x10-20 7901-24091 <$250
1929 Small Size
10 Type 1 1-2784 <$100
20 Type 1 1-824 <$100
10 Type 2 1-3440 <$110
20 Type 2 1-871 <$125
Total Issue $1,840,290
Out in 1935 $83,300
Large out 1935 $6,230

***
5583 Monongalia
CITIZENS NB OF MORGANTOWN
{{ 4 L }}
Chartered 9/22/00
Liquidated 3/17/20
Brown Back <$VALUE
3x10-20 1-8350 <$600
1882 Date Back
3x10-20 1-13300 <$600
1882 Value Back
3x10-20 13301-18206 <$600
Total Issue $1,327,800
Out at close $141,400

***
1502 Monongalia
MERCHANTS NB OF WEST VIRGINIA, MORGANTOWN
{{ 2 L }}
Chartered 8/3/65
Liquidated 10/4/88
Original Series <$VALUE
4x5 1-4925 <$850
3x10-20 1-1600<$1250/$1500
Series 1875
4x5 1-4510 <$850
3x10-20 1-1912<$1250/$1500
Brown Back
4x5 1-1194 <$750
3x10-20 1-631 <$750
Total Issue $419,730
Out in 1910 $2,495

***
2458 Monongalia
SECOND NB OF MORGANTOWN
{{ 6 L 6 S }}
Chartered 2/24/80
Receivership 11/11/31
Series 1875 <$VALUE
3x10-20 1-2924<$1000/$1500
Brown Back
3x10-20 1-5980 <$500
1882 Date Back
3x10-20 1-6500* <$500
1882 Value Back
3x10-20 6901-9304* <$500
* 6501-6900 not marked
1902 Plain Back
3x10-20 1-10832 <$300
1929 Small Size
10 Type 1 1-1395 <$225
20 Type 1 1-403 <$225
Total Issue $1,584,060
Out at close $77,780
Large out at close $9,020

***
14142 Marshall
FNB AT MOUNDSVILLE
{{ 2 S }}
Chartered 5/34
1929 Small Size <$VALUE
10 Type 2 1-996 <$500
20 Type 2 1-262 <$500
Total Issue $15,200
Out in 1935 $50,000
Large out 1935 $3,300
Outstanding includes Ch 5717

***
5717 Marshall
FNB OF MOUNDSVILLE
{{ 7 L 10 S }}
Chartered 2/15/01
Liquidated 6/21/34
Brown Back <$VALUE
3x10-20 1-3360 <$500
1882 Date Back
3x10-20 1-4120 <$500
1882 Value Back
3x10-20 4121-6477 <$500
1902 Plain Back
3x10-20 1-6534 <$250
1929 Small Size
10 Type 1 1-1398 <$200
20 Type 1 1-392 <$200
10 Type 2 1-404 <$225
20 Type 2 1-50 <$250
Total Issue $954,510
Out at close $49,600
Large out 1935 $3,300
Ch 14142 assumed circulation

***
11049 Fayette
FNB OF MOUNT HOPE
{{ 2 L 11 S }}
Chartered 8/17
1902 Plain Back <$VALUE
3x10-20 1-4805 <$600
1929 Small Size
10 Type 1 1-1670 <$175
20 Type 1 1-444 <$175
10 Type 2 1-3552 <$200
20 Type 2 1-960 <$200
Total Issue $448,450
Out in 1935 $46,730
Large out 1935 $610

***
6582 Hancock
FNB OF NEW CUMBERLAND
{{ 3 L }}
Organized 12/9/02
Receivership 11/21/27
1902 Red Seal <$VALUE
4x5 1-2380 <$1000
3x10-20 1-1828 <$1000
1902 Date Back
4x5 1-4350* <$500
3x10-20 1-2920** <$500
1902 Plain Back
4x5 4601-13305* <$500
3x10-20 3081-8614** <$500
* 4351-4600 not marked
** 2921-3080 not marked
Total Issue $835,800
Out at close $50,000

***
5266 Wetzel
FNB OF NEW MARTINSVILLE
{{ 9 L 10 S }}
Chartered 3/21/00
Brown Back <$VALUE
4x5 1-4050 <$500
3x10-20 1-3160 <$500
1882 Date Back
4x5 1-3300 <$500
3x10-20 1-2420 <$500
1882 Value Back
4x5 3301-5030 <$500
3x10-20 2421-3436 <$500
1902 Plain Back
4x5 1-6698 <$250
3x10-20 1-4457 <$250
1929 Small Size
5 Type 1 1-2038 <$150
10 Type 1 1-1042 <$150
20 Type 1 1-258 <$150
5 Type 2 1-2074 <$175
10 Type 2 1-1220 <$175
20 Type 2 1-412 <$175
Total Issue $1,053,640
Out in 1935 $48,850
Large out 1935 $3,000

***
7626 Preston
FNB OF NEWBURG
{{ 3 L 2 S }}
Organized 1/23/05
Receivership 10/30/31
1902 Red Seal <$VALUE
4x5 1-1246 <$1000
3x10-20 1-880 <$1000
1902 Date Back
4x5 1-2275 <$500
3x10-20 1-1670 <$500
1902 Plain Back
4x5 2276-7328 <$500
3x10-20 1671-4641 <$500
1929 Small Size
5 Type 1 1-571 <$500
10 Type 1 1-299 <$500
20 Type 1 1-89 <$500
Total Issue $493,280
Out at close $24,460
Large out at close $3,710

***
F Clark NB of Northfork
SEE Ch 8309
FNB of Northfork

***
8309 McDowell
FNB OF NORTHFORK
Chartered 7/06
2nd title:F Clark NB of Northfork 6/30/32
FIRST TITLE {{ 6 L 6 S }}
1902 Red Seal <$VALUE
3x10-20 1-1975 <$850
1902 Date Back
3x10-20 1-4620 <$375
1902 Plain Back
3x10-20 4621-28606 <$375
1929 Small Size
10 Type 1 1-3172 <$275
20 Type 1 1-850 <$275
SECOND TITLE {{ 6 S }}
1929 Small Size
5 Type 1 1-562 <$250
10 Type 1 1-190 <$250
5 Type 2 1-11026 <$250
10 Type 2 1-6667 <$250
Total Issue $1,971,430
Out in 1935 $85,450
Large out 1935 $5,270
Outstanding includes Ch 10157

***
12075 Fayette
OAK HILL NB, OAK HILL
{{ 5 L 8 S }}
Organized 11/25/21
Liquidated 3/19/34
1902 Plain Back <$VALUE
4x5 1-6035 <$400
3x10-20 1-4781 <$400
1929 Small Size
5 Type 1 1-2390 <$250
10 Type 1 1-1300 <$250
20 Type 1 1-366 <$275
Total Issue $553,370
Out at close $34,680
Large out at close $1,670

***
2649 Wood
CITIZENS NB OF PARKERSBURG
{{ 16 L 12 S }}
Chartered 1882
Closed 6/15/35
Series 1875 <$VALUE
3x10-20 1-6615 <$850/$1500
Brown Back
3x10-20 1-5900 <$350/$400
1882 Date Back
3x10-20 1-6700* <$300/$350
1882 Value Back
3x10-20 7101-12796* <$300/$350
* 6701-7100 not marked
1902 Plain Back
3x10-20 1-10635 <$150
1929 Small Size
10 Type 1 1-2826 <$100
20 Type 1 1-808 <$100
10 Type 2 1-3312 <$110
20 Type 2 1-900 <$110
Total Issue $2,114,940
Out at close $99,820
Large out at close $7,000

***
5320 Wood
FARMERS & MECHANICS NB OF PARKERSBURG
{{ 4 L }}
Chartered 5/1/00
Liquidated 2/15/17
Brown Back <$VALUE
3x10-20 1-7800 <$500
1882 Date Back
3x10-20 1-7500 <$500
1882 Value Back
3x10-20 7501-8142 <$500
Total Issue $797,100
Out at close $98,800
Ch 180 assumed circulation

***
180 Wood
FNB OF PARKERSBURG
{{ 22 L 22 S }}
Organized 12/15/63
Liquidated 12/31/32
Original Series <$VALUE
3x1-2 1-500 <$2000/$4000
4x5 1-5000 <$600
3x10-20 1-3700 <$850/$1500
Series 1875
3x10-20 1-2300 <$850/$1500
Brown Back
3x10-20 1-11829 <$350
1902 Red Seal
3x10-20 1-13000 <$400
1902 Date Back
4x5 1-17250 <$100
3x10-20 1-12300 <$100
1902 Plain Back
4x5 17251-82825 <$100
3x10-20 12301-50559 <$100
1929 Small Size
5 Type 1 1-11987 <$60
10 Type 1 1-6136 <$60
20 Type 1 1-1601 <$70
Total Issue $6,748,290
Out at close $428,255
Large out at close $372,220
Outstanding includes Ch 5320, and Ch 864

***
1427 Wood
PARKERSBURG NB, PARKERSBURG
{{ 16 L 31 S }}
Chartered 1865
Original Series <$VALUE
4x5 1-6350 <$600
3x10-20 1-2752 <$850/$1500
Series 1875
4x5 1-2249 <$600
3x10-20 1-3764 <$850/$1500
Brown Back
3x10-20 1-10997 <$350/$375
1902 Red Seal
3x10-20 1-5300 <$375/$425
1902 Date Back
3x10-20 1-10300 <$125
1902 Plain Back
3x10-20 10301-35146 <$125
1929 Small Size
10 Type 1 1-4560 <$40
20 Type 1 1-1248 <$50
10 Type 2 1-3419 <$45
20 Type 2 1-1385 <$55
Total Issue $3,555,180
Out in 1935 $141,595
Large out 1935 $11,735

***
13621 Wood
PEOPLES NB OF PARKERSBURG
{{ 14 S }}
Organized 5/12/32
1929 Small Size <$VALUE
5 Type 2 1-23632 <$100
10 Type 2 1-12863 <$100
20 Type 2 1-3960 <$100
Total Issue $325,990
Out in 1935 $198,200

***
864 Wood
SECOND NB OF PARKERSBURG
{{ 12 L }}
Chartered 3/7/65
Closed 4/30/27
Original Series <$VALUE
4x5 1-7580 <$600
3x10-20 1-2667 <$850/$1500
Series 1875
4x5 1-2500 <$600
3x10-20 1-1816 <$850/$1500
Brown Back
3x10-20 1-10853 <$350/$400
1902 Red Seal
3x10-20 1-5360 <$375/$425
1902 Date Back
3x10-20 1-11400 <$150
1902 Plain Back
3x10-20 11401-31780 <$150
Total Issue $2,825,400
Out at close $149,000
Ch 180 assumed circulation

***
9610 Tucker
FNB OF PARSONS
{{ 4 L 7 S }}
Chartered 12/09
1902 Date Back <$VALUE
4x5 1-1650 <$375
3x10-20 1-1400 <$375
1902 Plain Back
4x5 1651-6622 <$375
3x10-20 1401-4364 <$375
1929 Small Size
5 Type 1 1-876 <$200
10 Type 1 1-522 <$200
20 Type 1 1-134 <$200
5 Type 2 1-1194 <$225
10 Type 2 1-538 <$225
20 Type 2 1-160 <$225
Total Issue $438,870
Out in 1935 $24,550
Large out 1935 $1,210

***
7246 Ritchie
CITIZENS NB OF PENNSBORO
{{ 4 L 1 S }}
Chartered 5/04
Closed 11/23/29
1902 Red Seal <$VALUE
3x10-20 1-1350 <$750
1902 Date Back
3x10-20 1-1920 <$375
1902 Plain Back
3x10-20 1921-8786 <$375
1929 Small Size
10 Type 1 1-170 <$600
20 Type 1 1-12 <$600
Total Issue $518,440
Out at close $50,000
Large out at close $38,360
Ch 7191 assumed circulation

***
F-Citizens NB of Pennsboro
SEE Ch 7191
FNB of Pennsboro

***
7191 Ritchie
FNB OF PENNSBORO
Chartered 3/04
Liquidated 12/31/31
2nd title:F-Citizens NB 11/23/29
FIRST TITLE {{ 4 L 2 S }}
1902 Red Seal <$VALUE
3x10-20 1-1300 <$750
1902 Date Back
3x10-20 1-1880 <$375
1902 Plain Back
3x10-20 1881-9213 <$375
1929 Small Size
10 Type 1 1-622 <$300
20 Type 1 1-208 <$300
SECOND TITLE {{ 4 S }}
1929 Small Size
10 Type 1 1-784 <$250
20 Type 1 1-243 <$250
Total Issue $664,130
Out at close $82,230
Large out at close $12,910
Outstanding includes Ch 7246

***
9721 Monroe
FNB OF PETERSTOWN
{{ 2 L 5 S }}
Chartered 4/10
1902 Date Back <$VALUE
3x10-20 1-1830 <$600
1902 Plain Back
3x10-20 1831-6311 <$600
1929 Small Size
10 Type 1 1-702 <$250
20 Type 1 1-192 <$250
10 Type 2 1-1380 <$275
20 Type 2 1-311 <$275
Total Issue $400,730
Out in 1935 $25,000
Large out 1935 $1,410

***
6377 Barbour
CITIZENS NB OF PHILIPPI
{{ 4 L 4 S }}
Chartered 8/12/02
Receivership 10/30/31
1902 Red Seal <$VALUE
3x10-20 1-1250 <$750
1902 Date Back
4x5 1-3550 <$375
3x10-20 1-2400 <$375
1902 Plain Back
4x5 3551-11201 <$375
3x10-20 2401-7347 <$375
1929 Small Size
5 Type 1 1-1043 <$275
10 Type 1 1-529 <$275
20 Type 1 1-147 <$275
Total Issue $734,540
Out at close $39,400
Large out at close $3,750

***
14053 Barbour
FNB IN PHILIPPI
{{ 6 S }}
Chartered 3/34
1929 Small Size <$VALUE
5 Type 2 1-1550 <$400
10 Type 2 1-576 <$400
20 Type 2 1-190 <$400
Total Issue $17,310
Out in 1935 $40,000
Large out 1935 $2,410
Outstanding includes Ch 6302

***
6302 Barbour
FNB OF PHILIPPI
{{ 5 L 6 S }}
Chartered 6/13/02
Liquidated 8/11/34
1902 Red Seal <$VALUE
3x10-20 1-2370 <$650
1902 Date Back
3x10-20 1-3400 <$300
1902 Plain Back
3x10-20 3401-10283 <$300
1929 Small Size
10 Type 1 1-1039 <$200
20 Type 1 1-329 <$225
Total Issue $734,470
Out at close $32,200
Large out 1935 $2,410
Ch 14053 assumed circulation

***
4088 Mineral
DAVIS NB OF PIEDMONT
{{ 7 L 8 S }}
Chartered 8/3/89
Liquidated 7/15/33
Brown Back <$VALUE
3x10-20 1-3722 <$500
50-100 1-266 <$4000
1882 Date Back
3x10-20 1-393 <$500
1902 Date Back
4x5 1-3875 <$250
3x10-20 1-3480 <$250
1902 Plain Back
4x5 3876-14122 <$250
3x10-20 3481-10153 <$250
1929 Small Size
5 Type 1 1-1737 <$175
10 Type 1 1-1062 <$175
20 Type 1 1-245 <$200
Total Issue $1,180,970
Out at close $46,400
Large out at close $2,400
Ch 3629 assumed circulation

***
3629 Mineral
FNB OF PIEDMONT
{{ 12 L 20 S }}
Chartered 2/1/87
Brown Back <$VALUE
4x5 1-6250 <$450
3x10-20 1-2140 <$450
1902 Red Seal
4x5 1-1300 <$500
3x10-20 1-1160 <$500
1902 Date Back
4x5 1-6800 <$200
3x10-20 1-5640 <$200
1902 Plain Back
4x5 6801-23108 <$200
3x10-20 5641-15860 <$200
1929 Small Size
5 Type 1 1-3108 <$75
10 Type 1 1-1602 <$75
20 Type 1 1-516 <$85
5 Type 2 1-8604 <$100
10 Type 2 1-3924 <$100
20 Type 2 1-1140 <$100
Total Issue $1,927,500
Out in 1935 $118,680
Large out 1935 $4,690
Outstanding includes Ch 4088

***
1883 Mineral
NB OF PIEDMONT
{{ 1 L }}
Chartered 9/21/71
Liquidated 10/14/86
Original Series <$VALUE
4x5 1-500 <$1250
3x10-20 1-1100<$1500/$1750
Series 1875
4x5 1-1000 <$1250
3x10-20 1-1502<$1500/$1750
Total Issue $160,100
Out in 1910 $645

***
8749 Wyoming
CITIZENS NB OF PINEVILLE
{{ 1 L }}
Chartered 6/18/07
Receivership 7/16/17
1902 Red Seal <$VALUE
4x5 1-350 <$1500
3x10-20 1-280 <$1500
1902 Date Back
4x5 1-2300 <$750
3x10-20 1-1820 <$750
1902 Plain Back
4x5 2301-2715 <$750
3x10-20 1821-2035 <$750
Total Issue $177,050
Out at close $24,500

***
CONDITION affects Value. The Values shown are for notes in FINE condition.

7672 Wyoming
FNB OF PINEVILLE
{{ 3 L 1 S }}
Organized 3/6/05
Receivership 5/1/30
1902 Red Seal <$VALUE
4x5 1-425 <$1000
3x10-20 1-310 <$1000
1902 Date Back
4x5 1-2125 <$500
3x10-20 1-1600 <$500
1902 Plain Back
4x5 2126-7764 <$500
3x10-20 1601-5023 <$500
1929 Small Size
5 Type 1 1-335 <$600
10 Type 1 1-167 <$600
20 Type 1 1-36 <$600
Total Issue $454,820
Out at close $25,000
Large out at close $5,570

13231 Mason
CITIZENS NB OF POINT PLEASANT
{{ 24 S }}
Chartered 8/28
1929 Small Size <$VALUE
5 Type 1 1-3556 <$75
10 Type 1 1-2034 <$75
20 Type 1 1-40 <$85
5 Type 2 1-8134 <$100
10 Type 2 1-4240 <$100
20 Type 2 1-1100 <$100
Total Issue $338,590
Out in 1935 $79,850

Merchants NB of Point Pleasant
SEE Ch 1504
Merchants NB of West Virginia at Point Pleasant

1504 Mason
MERCHANTS NB OF WEST VIRGINIA AT POINT PLEASANT
Organized 7/18/65
Liquidated 11/5/29
2nd title:Merchants NB of Point Pleasant 9/03
FIRST TITLE {{ 3 L }}
Original Series <$VALUE
4x5 1-8100 <$600
3x10-20 1-3100 <$850/$1500
Series 1875
4x5 1-1975 <$600
3x10-20 1-1154 <$850/$1500
Brown Back
4x5 1-2834 <$500
3x10-20 1-3423 <$500
SECOND TITLE {{ 7 L }}
Brown Back
3x10-20 1-699 <$500
1902 Red Seal
3x10-20 1-3700 <$600
1902 Date Back
4x5 1-6715 <$200
3x10-20 1-4100 <$200
1902 Plain Back
4x5 6716-22004 <$200
3x10-20 4101-14167 <$200
Total Issue $2,010,410
Out at close $30,330

5701 Mason
POINT PLEASANT NB, POINT PLEASANT
{{ 5 L 8 S }}
Chartered 2/4/01
Brown Back <$VALUE
4x5 1-1765 <$500
3x10-20 1-1294 <$500
1882 Date Back
4x5 1-2000 <$500
3x10-20 1-1480 <$500
1882 Value Back
4x5 2001-3320 <$500
3x10-20 1481-2245 <$500
1902 Plain Back
4x5 1-3929 <$275
3x10-20 1-2340 <$275
1929 Small Size
5 Type 1 1-998 <$175
10 Type 1 1-548 <$175
20 Type 1 1-162 <$175
5 Type 2 1-1728 <$200
10 Type 2 1-1029 <$200
20 Type 2 1-255 <$200
Total Issue $580,520
Out in 1935 $28,750
Large out 1935 $2,070

8219 Mercer
FNB OF PRINCETON
{{ 5 L 5 S }}
Chartered 5/06
Liquidated 3/19/32
1902 Red Seal <$VALUE
4x5 1-1830 <$600
3x10-20 1-1368 <$600
1902 Date Back
4x5 1-4300 <$300
3x10-20 1-3120 <$300
1902 Plain Back
4x5 4301-15002 <$300
3x10-20 3121-10178 <$300
1929 Small Size
5 Type 1 1-1776 <$250
10 Type 1 1-842 <$250
20 Type 1 1-248 <$250
Total Issue $1,047,500
Out at close $46,090
Large out at close $3,795

10759 Jackson
FNB OF RAVENSWOOD
{{ UNREPORTED }}
Chartered 8/15
Liquidated 5/28/31
1929 Small Size <$VALUE
5 Type 1 1-42 <$850
10 Type 1 1-93 <$850
20 Type 1 1 <$1000
Total Issue $6,960
Out at close $4,370

10285 Roane
FNB OF REEDY
{{ 2 L 2U + 10 S }}
Chartered 10/12
1902 Date Back <$VALUE
4x5 1-825 <$600
3x10-20 1-660 <$600
1902 Plain Back
4x5 826-3455 <$600
3x10-20 661-2334 <$600
1929 Small Size
5 Type 1 1-606 <$185
10 Type 1 1-316 <$185
20 Type 1 1-96 <$200
5 Type 2 1-534 <$225
10 Type 2 1-441 <$225
20 Type 2 1-92 <$250
Total Issue $243,380
Out in 1935 $16,300
Large out 1935 $730

13627 Nicholas
CHERRY RIVER NB OF RICHWOOD
{{ U + 10 S }}
Chartered 7/32 as Cherry River NB, Richwood, under which there was no issue. Issuing title adopted 10/21/32.
1929 Small Size <$VALUE
5 Type 1 1-940 <$200
10 Type 1 1-580 <$200
5 Type 2 1-4942 <$200
10 Type 2 1-2524 <$200
Total Issue $112,950
Out in 1935 $48,575
Large out 1935 $825
Outstanding includes Ch 8434

8434 Nicholas
FNB OF RICHWOOD
{{ 4 L 3 S }}
Organized 10/17/06
Liquidated 10/28/32
1902 Red Seal <$VALUE
3x10-20 1-990 <$850
1902 Date Back
3x10-20 1-2190 <$425
1902 Plain Back
3x10-20 2191-7195 <$425
1929 Small Size
10 Type 1 1-402 <$350
20 Type 1 1-90 <$350
50 Type 1 1-17 <$850
100 Type 1 1 <$1250
Total Issue $449,870
Out at close $22,425
Large out 1935 $825
Ch 13627 assumed circulation

10762 Jackson
FNB OF RIPLEY
{{ 5 L 8 S }}
Organized 7/31/15
Receivership 1/19/32
1902 Plain Back <$VALUE
3x10-20 1-5737 <$375
1929 Small Size
10 Type 1 1-852 <$200
20 Type 1 1-264 <$200
10 Type 2 1-4575 <$225
20 Type 2 1-1099 <$225
Total Issue $437,380
Out in 1935 $70,000
Large out 1935 $2,840

9766 Hampshire
FNB OF ROMNEY
{{ 5 L 16 S }}
Chartered 6/10
1902 Date Back <$VALUE
3x10-20 1-3950 <$300
1902 Plain Back
4x5 1-7910 <$300
3x10-20 3951-10165 <$300
1929 Small Size
5 Type 1 1-1814 <$100
10 Type 1 1-1126 <$100
20 Type 1 1-336 <$110
5 Type 2 1-1644 <$135
10 Type 2 1-1606 <$135
20 Type 2 1-456 <$150
Total Issue $862,150
Out in 1935 $50,000
Large out 1935 $2,580

5280 Greenbrier
FNB OF RONCEVERTE
{{ 5 L 6 S }}
Chartered 4/10/00
Liquidated 11/28/33
Brown Back <$VALUE
3x10-20 1-3200 <$500
1882 Date Back
3x10-20 1-4300 <$450
1882 Value Back
3x10-20 4301-6281 <$450
1902 Plain Back
3x10-20 1-7850 <$275
1929 Small Size
10 Type 1 1-1690 <$175
20 Type 1 1-456 <$200
Total Issue $1,022,670
Out at close $45,200
Large out at close $3,350

6226 Greenbrier
RONCEVERTE NB, RONCEVERTE
{{ 3 L 6 S }}
Chartered 4/23/02
1902 Red Seal <$VALUE
3x10-20 1-1840 <$700
1902 Date Back
3x10-20 1-2100 <$350
1902 Plain Back (dated 1902)
3x10-20 2101-4120 <$350
1902 Plain Back (dated 1922)
3x10-20 1-2869 <$350
1929 Small Size
10 Type 1 1-884 <$175
20 Type 1 1-220 <$175
10 Type 2 1-1097 <$200
20 Type 2 1-252 <$200
Total Issue $536,900
Out in 1935 $25,000
Large out 1935 $1,470

9288 Preston
FNB OF ROWLESBURG
{{ UNREPORTED }}
Organized 12/9/08
Receivership 7/31/12
1902 Date Back <$VALUE
3x10-20 1-721 <$1500
Total Issue $36,050
Out in 1916 $980

10250 Preston
PEOPLES NB OF ROWLESBURG
{{ 3 L 5 S }}
Organized 8/8/12
1902 Date Back <$VALUE
4x5 1-1365 <$400
3x10-20 1-1094 <$400
1902 Plain Back
4x5 1366-6454 <$400
3x10-20 1095-4106 <$400
1929 Small Size
5 Type 1 1-1006 <$225
10 Type 1 1-466 <$225
20 Type 1 1-162 <$225
5 Type 2 1-1020 <$250
10 Type 2 1-635 <$250
20 Type 2 1-100 <$250
Total Issue $425,410
Out in 1935 $24,550
Large out 1935 $1,980

9640 Kanawha
FNB OF SAINT ALBANS
{{ 2 L U + 4 S }}
Organized 12/29/09
Receivership 12/18/33
1902 Date Back <$VALUE
3x10-20 1-1460 <$600
1902 Plain Back
3x10-20 1461-5460 <$600
1929 Small Size
10 Type 1 1-690 <$300
20 Type 1 1-184 <$300
10 Type 2 1-45 <$350
20 Type 2 1-25 <$350
Total Issue $337,430
Out at close $19,000
Large out at close $250

5226 Pleasants
FNB OF SAINT MARYS
{{ 8 L 14 S }}
Chartered 10/26/99
Brown Back <$VALUE
3x10-20 1-2050 <$400
1882 Date Back
3x10-20 1-3000* <$400
1882 Value Back
3x10-20 3201-4597* <$400
* 3001-3200 not marked
1902 Plain Back
3x10-20 1-12241 <$225
1929 Small Size
10 Type 1 1-2840 <$125
20 Type 1 1-754 <$125
10 Type 2 1-2544 <$150
20 Type 2 1-957 <$150
Total Issue $1,249,860
Out in 1935 $98,350
Large out 1935 $3,650

7250 Harrison
FNB OF SALEM
{{ 5 L 8 S }}
Organized 4/18/04
Liquidated 4/3/35
1902 Red Seal <$VALUE
3x10-20 1-3350 <$650
1902 Date Back
4x5 1-4650 <$300
3x10-20 1-3600 <$300
1902 Plain Back
4x5 4651-16179 <$300
3x10-20 3601-10662 <$300
1929 Small Size
5 Type 1 1-2252 <$150
10 Type 1 1-1274 <$150
20 Type 1 1-336 <$165
5 Type 2 1-1114 <$200
10 Type 2 1-382 <$200
20 Type 2 1-75 <$225
Total Issue $1,219,390
Out at close $31,950
Large out at close $3,460

9453 Harrison
FNB OF SHINNSTON
{{ 4 L }}
Organized 6/14/09
Receivership 5/22/29
1902 Date Back <$VALUE
4x5 1-3950 <$400
3x10-20 1-2920 <$400
1902 Plain Back
4x5 3951-13095 <$400
3x10-20 2921-8658 <$400
Total Issue $694,800
Out at close $44,400

5028 Tyler
FARMERS & PRODUCERS NB OF SISTERSVILLE
Chartered 1895
2nd title:Union NB of Sistersville 7/3/22
FIRST TITLE {{ 4 L }}
Brown Back <$VALUE
4x5 1-9990 <$500
3x10-20 1-1000 <$500
50-100 1-1648 <$4000
1882 Date Back
4x5 1-6350 <$500
3x10-20 1-3960 <$500
50-100 1-17 <$4000
1882 Value Back
4x5 6351-6424 <$500
3x10-20 3961-4053 <$500
1902 Plain Back
3x10-20 1-7300 <$300
SECOND TITLE {{ 10 L 24 S }}
1902 Plain Back
3x10-20 1-15785 <$165
1929 Small Size
10 Type 1 1-4630 <$85
20 Type 1 1-1222 <$85
10 Type 2 1-5485 <$100
20 Type 2 1-1569 <$100
Total Issue $2,495,600
Out in 1935 $154,945
Large out 1935 $11,495
Outstanding includes Ch 6548

5027 Tyler
FNB OF SISTERSVILLE
{{ 6 L }}
Chartered 1895
Liquidated 6/30/21
Brown Back <$VALUE
4x5 1-11775 <$400
3x10-20 1-5690 <$400
1882 Date Back
4x5 1-6888 <$400
3x10-20 1-4492 <$400
1902 Plain Back
4x5 1-5305 <$250
3x10-20 1-3378 <$250
Total Issue $1,157,360
Out at close $98,300

6548 Tyler
PEOPLES NB OF SISTERSVILLE
{{ 2 L }}
Chartered 12/22/02
Closed 7/3/22
1902 Red Seal <$VALUE
3x10-20 1-4820 <$750
1902 Date Back
3x10-20 1-5800 <$400
1902 Plain Back
3x10-20 5801-10540 <$400
Total Issue $768,000
Out at close $73,400
Ch 5028 assumed circulation

Union NB of Sistersville
SEE Ch 5028
Farmers & Producers NB of Sistersville

11340 Kanawha
FNB OF SOUTH CHARLESTON
{{ 4 L U + 6 S }}
Chartered 4/19
1902 Plain Back <$VALUE
4x5 1-2428 <$400
4x10 1-1709 <$400
1929 Small Size
5 Type 1 1-1456 <$250
10 Type 1 1-796 <$250
5 Type 2 1-5628 <$250
10 Type 2 1-2700 <$250
Total Issue $263,500
Out in 1935 $28,830
Large out 1935 $580

10127 Roane
FNB OF SPENCER
{{ 5 L 9 S }}
Chartered 1/12
1902 Date Back <$VALUE
4x5 1-2700 <$275
4x10 1-2600 <$275
1902 Plain Back
4x5 2701-11507 <$275
4x10 2601-9885 <$275
1929 Small Size
5 Type 1 1-2736 <$150
10 Type 1 1-1472 <$150
5 Type 2 1-4936 <$175
10 Type 2 1-2710 <$175
Total Issue $847,120
Out in 1935 $49,300
Large out 1935 $4,130

6213 Braxton
FNB OF SUTTON
{{ UNREPORTED }}
Chartered 4/17/02
Receivership 8/29/14
1902 Red Seal <$VALUE
4x5 1-950 <$1500
3x10-20 1-2240 <$1500
1902 Date Back
4x5 1-485 <$1000
3x10-20 1-3177 <$1000
Total Issue $299,550
Out in 1916 $14,620

9604 Braxton
HOME NB OF SUTTON
{{ 8 L 14 S }}
Chartered 12/09
1902 Date Back <$VALUE
4x5 1-4050 <$225
3x10-20 1-3120 <$225
1902 Plain Back
4x5 4051-14861 <$225
3x10-20 3121-9170 <$225
1929 Small Size
5 Type 1 1-2274 <$110
10 Type 1 1-1178 <$110
20 Type 1 1-318 <$125
5 Type 2 1-1974 <$135
10 Type 2 1-1005 <$135
20 Type 2 1-310 <$150
Total Issue $958,900
Out in 1935 $47,350
Large out 1935 $2,490

6999 Preston
FNB OF TERRA ALTA
{{ 3 L U + 16 S }}
Organized 8/4/03
Receivership 10/20/31
1902 Red Seal <$VALUE
4x5 1-1290 <$1250
3x10-20 1-1034 <$1250
1902 Date Back
4x5 1-2175 <$600
3x10-20 1-1600 <$600
1902 Plain Back
4x5 2176-7247 <$600
3x10-20 1601-4669 <$600
1929 Small Size
5 Type 1 1-776 <$175
10 Type 1 1-482 <$175
20 Type 1 1-136 <$175
5 Type 2 1-1308 <$175
10 Type 2 1-516 <$175
20 Type 2 1-188 <$175
Total Issue $539,870
Out in 1935 $24,700
Large out 1935 $1,710

8998 Fayette
NB OF THURMOND
{{ 3 L 4 S }}
Organized 12/30/07
Receivership 2/18/31
1902 Red Seal <$VALUE
3x10-20 1-370 <$1000
1902 Date Back
3x10-20 1-1600 <$500
1902 Plain Back
3x10-20 1601-9720 <$500
1929 Small Size
10 Type 1 1-917 <$350
20 Type 1 1-248 <$350
Total Issue $589,280
Out at close $48,500
Large out at close $5,870

8360 Webster
FNB OF WEBSTER SPRINGS
{{ 1 L 2 S }}
Organized 6/30/06
Receivership 4/9/34
1902 Red Seal <$VALUE
3x10-20 1-300 <$1500
1902 Date Back
3x10-20 1-720 <$1000
1902 Plain Back
3x10-20 721-1419 <$1000
1929 Small Size
10 Type 1 1-228 <$500
20 Type 1 1-44 <$500
Total Issue $104,910
Out at close $6,250
Large out at close $590

14013 Webster
WEBSTER SPRINGS NB, WEBSTER SPRINGS
{{ 4 S }}
Chartered 2/34
1929 Small Size <$VALUE
5 Type 2 1-3982 <$500
10 Type 2 1-2244 <$500
Total Issue $42,350
Out in 1935 $25,000

<$VALUEs are for notes in FINE condition. Value changes by approximately 25% for a change of one full grade.

9048 McDowell
FNB OF WELCH
{{4 L 5 S}}
Chartered 3/08
Liquidated 6/30/30
1902 Red Seal <$VALUE
3x10-20 1-375 <$750
1902 Date Back
3x10-20 1-3000* <$350
1902 Plain Back
3x10-20 3201-24811* <$350
* 3001-3200 not marked
1929 Small Size
10 Type 1 1-1155 <$250
20 Type 1 1-333 <$250
Total Issue $1,368,560
Out at close $74,920
Large out at close $15,400

13512 McDowell
McDOWELL COUNTY NB IN WELCH
{{21 S}}
Chartered 12/30
1929 Small Size <$VALUE
5 Type 1 1-7046 <$85
10 Type 1 1-4090 <$85
20 Type 1 1-1134 <$85
5 Type 2 1-32458 <$100
10 Type 2 1-17150 <$100
20 Type 2 1-4008 <$100
Total Issue $1,006,810
Out in 1935 $195,800
Large out 1935 $4,470
Outstanding includes Ch 9071

9071 McDowell
McDOWELL COUNTY NB OF WELCH
{{7 L 11 S}}
Organized 2/20/08
Receivership 10/25/32
1902 Red Seal <$VALUE
4x5 1-2000 <$600
3x10-20 1-1600 <$600
1902 Date Back
4x5 1-9050 <$250
3x10-20 1-6800 <$250
1902 Plain Back
4x5 9051-34115 <$250
3x10-20 6801-22625 <$250
1929 Small Size
5 Type 1 1-2772 <$165
10 Type 1 1-1420 <$165
20 Type 1 1-353 <$175
Total Issue $2,144,270
Out at close $97,120
Large out 1935 $4,470
Ch 13512 assumed circulation

1387 Brooke
FNB OF WELLSBURG
{{ UNREPORTED }}
Chartered 7/1/65
Liquidated 6/24/71
Original Series <$VALUE
4x5 1-3600 <$2000
3x10-20 1-486 <$2250/$2500
Total Issue $96,300
Out in 1910 $615

1884 Brooke
WELLSBURG NB, WELLSBURG
{{8 L 12 S}}
Chartered 9/25/71
Liquidated 12/17/35
Original Series <$VALUE
4x5 1-3250 <$600
3x10-20 1-3100 <$850/$1500
Series 1875
3x10-20 1-1995 <$850/$1500
Brown Back
3x10-20 1-5850 <$400
1882 Date Back
3x10-20 1-2795 <$400
1902 Date Back
4x10 1-6875 <$200
1902 Plain Back
4x10 6876-34176 <$200
1929 Small Size
10 Type 1 1-5430 <$110
10 Type 2 1-430 <$150
Total Issue $2,449,140
Out in 1935 $44,010
Large out 1935 $5,360

14295 Brooke
WELLSBURG NB, WELLSBURG
{{3 S}}
Chartered 10/34
1929 Small Size <$VALUE
5 Type 2 1-4744 <$400
10 Type 2 1-2653 <$400
Total Issue $50,250
Out in 1935 $50,000

13881 Doddridge
FNB IN WEST UNION
{{4 S}}
Chartered 12/33
1929 Small Size <$VALUE
5 Type 2 1-2484 <$300
10 Type 2 1-1212 <$300
20 Type 2 1-336 <$325
Total Issue $31,260
Out in 1935 $49,000
Large out 1935 $3,000
Outstanding includes Ch 6424

6424 Doddridge
FNB OF WEST UNION
{{3 L 6 S}}
Chartered 9/16/02
Liquidated 2/5/34
1902 Red Seal <$VALUE
3x10-20 1-1332 <$800
1902 Date Back
3x10-20 1-4340 <$400
1902 Plain Back
3x10-20 4341-11700 <$400
1929 Small Size
10 Type 1 1-1296 <$225
20 Type 1 1-328 <$250
Total Issue $768,720
Out at close $47,000
Large out 1935 $3,000
Ch 13881 assumed circulation

1607 Lewis
N EXCHANGE B OF WESTON
{{8 L 5 S}}
Organized 10/23/65
Liquidated 9/15/32
Original Series <$VALUE
3x1-2 1-400 <$2000/$4000
4x5 1-3050 <$650
3x10-20 1-2520<$1000/$1250
Series 1875
3x10-20 1-2360<$1000/$1250
Brown Back
3x10-20 1-4372 <$500
1902 Red Seal
3x10-20 1-1600 <$600
1902 Date Back
4x5 1-4600 <$225
3x10-20 1-2960 <$225
1902 Plain Back
4x5 4601-15495 <$225
3x10-20 2961-9373 <$225
1929 Small Size
5 Type 1 1-1465 <$250
10 Type 1 1-786 <$250
20 Type 1 1-177 <$200
Total Issue $1,496,500
Out at close $58,680
Large out at close $7,540

13634 Lewis
WESTON NB, WESTON
{{12 S}}
Chartered 9/32
1929 Small Size <$VALUE
5 Type 1 1-1232 <$125
10 Type 1 1-832 <$125
20 Type 1 1-316 <$125
5 Type 2 1-6684 <$150
10 Type 2 1-3410 <$150
20 Type 2 1-740 <$150
Total Issue $207,120
Out in 1935 $85,250

10455 Ohio
CITIZENS NB OF WHEELING
{{3 L}}
Chartered 10/13
Liquidated 4/29/16
1902 Date Back <$VALUE
3x10-20 1-4000 <$450
1902 Plain Back
3x10-20 4001-4122 <$450
Total Issue $206,100
Out in 1916 $76,280

360 Ohio
FNB OF WHEELING
{{2 L}}
Chartered 4/2/64
Liquidated 4/22/75
Original Series <$VALUE
3x1-2 1-2000 <$2000/$4000
4x5 1-6250 <$850
3x10-20 1-4380<$1250/$1750
Total Issue $354,000
Out in 1910 $2,315

1343 Ohio
MERCHANTS NB OF WEST VIRGINIA, WHEELING
{{2 L}}
Chartered 6/26/65
Liquidated 7/7/74
Original Series <$VALUE
4x5 1-10550 <$850
3x10-20 1-9100<$1250/$1750
Total Issue $666,000
Out in 1910 $4,210

1424 Ohio
NB OF WEST VIRGINIA, WHEELING
{{24 L 50+ S}}
Chartered 1865
Original Series <$VALUE
4x5 1-9250 <$600
3x10-20 1-2900 <$850/$1500
Series 1875
4x5 1-2500 <$600
3x10-20 1-1600 <$850/$1500
Brown Back
3x10-20 1-5339 <$275/$325
1902 Red Seal
3x10-20 1-13500 <$300/$350
1902 Date Back
3x10-20 1-35300* <$75
1902 Plain Back
3x10-20 37301-121913* <$75
* 35301-37300 not marked
1929 Small Size
10 Type 1 1-14428 <$35
20 Type 1 1-4104 <$45
10 Type 2 1-7800 <$40
20 Type 2 1-2766 <$50
Total Issue $8,989,080
Out in 1935 $438,060
Large out 1935 $23,690

5164 Ohio
N EXCHANGE B OF WHEELING
{{U + 50+ L 2U + 50+ S}}
Chartered 12/29/98
Brown Back <$VALUE
4x5 1-23750 <$225
3x10-20 1-21100 <$225/$275
1882 Date Back
4x5 1-38500 <$200
3x10-20 1-29200 <$200/$250
1882 Value Back
4x5 38501-52580 <$200
3x10-20 29201-37303 <$200/$250
1902 Plain Back
4x5 1-83839 <$40
3x10-20 1-54017 <$50/$60
1929 Small Size
5 Type 1 1-20668 <$20
10 Type 1 1-10250 <$20
20 Type 1 1-2292 <$30
5 Type 2 1-29356 <$20
10 Type 2 1-14557 <$25
20 Type 2 1-3880 <$35
Total Issue $10,704,410
Out in 1935 $423,280
Large out 1935 $29,115

1594 Ohio
N SAVINGS B OF WHEELING
{{ UNREPORTED }}
Chartered 10/18/65
Liquidated 1/7/69
Original Series <$VALUE
4x5 1-2500 <$1500
3x10-20 1-992 <$1750/$2000
Total Issue $99,600
Out in 1910 $495

6830 Mingo
FNB OF WILLIAMSON
{{9 L 11 S}}
Organized 6/3/03
1902 Red Seal <$VALUE
3x10-20 1-1270 <$700
1902 Date Back
3x10-20 1-3860* <$275
1902 Plain Back
3x10-20 4361-25838* <$275
* 3861-4360 not marked
1929 Small Size
10 Type 1 1-3805 <$150
20 Type 1 1-987 <$150
Total Issue $1,702,140
Out in 1935 $48,400
Large out 1935 $4,560

10067 Mingo
NB OF COMMERCE OF WILLIAMSON
{{6 L 14 S}}
Chartered 8/11
1902 Date Back <$VALUE
3x10-20 1-4000 <$275
1902 Plain Back
3x10-20 4001-24830 <$275
1929 Small Size
10 Type 1 1-3532 <$100
20 Type 1 1-994 <$100
10 Type 2 1-6771 <$100
20 Type 2 1-1937 <$110
Total Issue $1,679,150
Out in 1935 $93,900
Large out 1935 $4,170

11483 Wood
FARMERS & MECHANICS NB OF WILLIAMSTOWN
{{4 L 4 S}}
Organized 10/1/19
1902 Plain Back <$VALUE
4x5 1-2893 <$375
3x10-20 1-2017 <$375
1929 Small Size
5 Type 1 1-690 <$275
10 Type 1 1-412 <$275
20 Type 1 1-126 <$275
5 Type 2 1-936 <$300
10 Type 2 1-742 <$300
20 Type 2 1-132 <$300
Total Issue $233,990
Out in 1935 $20,000
Large out 1935 $720

6233 Wood
WILLIAMSTOWN NB, WILLIAMSTOWN
{{2 L}}
Chartered 4/29/02
Receivership 11/23/16
1902 Red Seal <$VALUE
3x10-20 1-2000 <$850
1902 Date Back
3x10-20 1-2250 <$500
1902 Plain Back
3x10-20 2251-2434 <$500
Total Issue $221,700
Out at close $29,300

9850 Fayette
WINONA NB, WINONA
{{3 L U + 4 S}}
Chartered 9/10
1902 Date Back <$VALUE
4x5 1-1115 <$400
3x10-20 1-902 <$400
1902 Plain Back
4x5 1116-6716 <$400
3x10-20 903-4278 <$400
1929 Small Size
5 Type 1 1-1238 <$275
10 Type 1 1-676 <$275
20 Type 1 1-174 <$275
5 Type 2 1-1566 <$300
10 Type 2 1-839 <$300
20 Type 2 1-318 <$300
Total Issue $469,380
Out in 1935 $24,300
Large out 1935 $630

10450 Marion
FNB OF WORTHINGTON
{{3 L 4 S}}
Chartered 9/25/13
Receivership 3/31/31
1902 Date Back <$VALUE
4x5 1-950 <$450
3x10-20 1-760 <$450
1902 Plain Back
4x5 951-7330 <$450
3x10-20 761-4525 <$450
1929 Small Size
5 Type 1 1-683 <$275
10 Type 1 1-305 <$275
20 Type 1 1-72 <$300
Total Issue $420,280
Out at close $29,220
Large out at close $3,550

CONDITION affects Value. The Values shown are for notes in FINE condition.

WISCONSIN

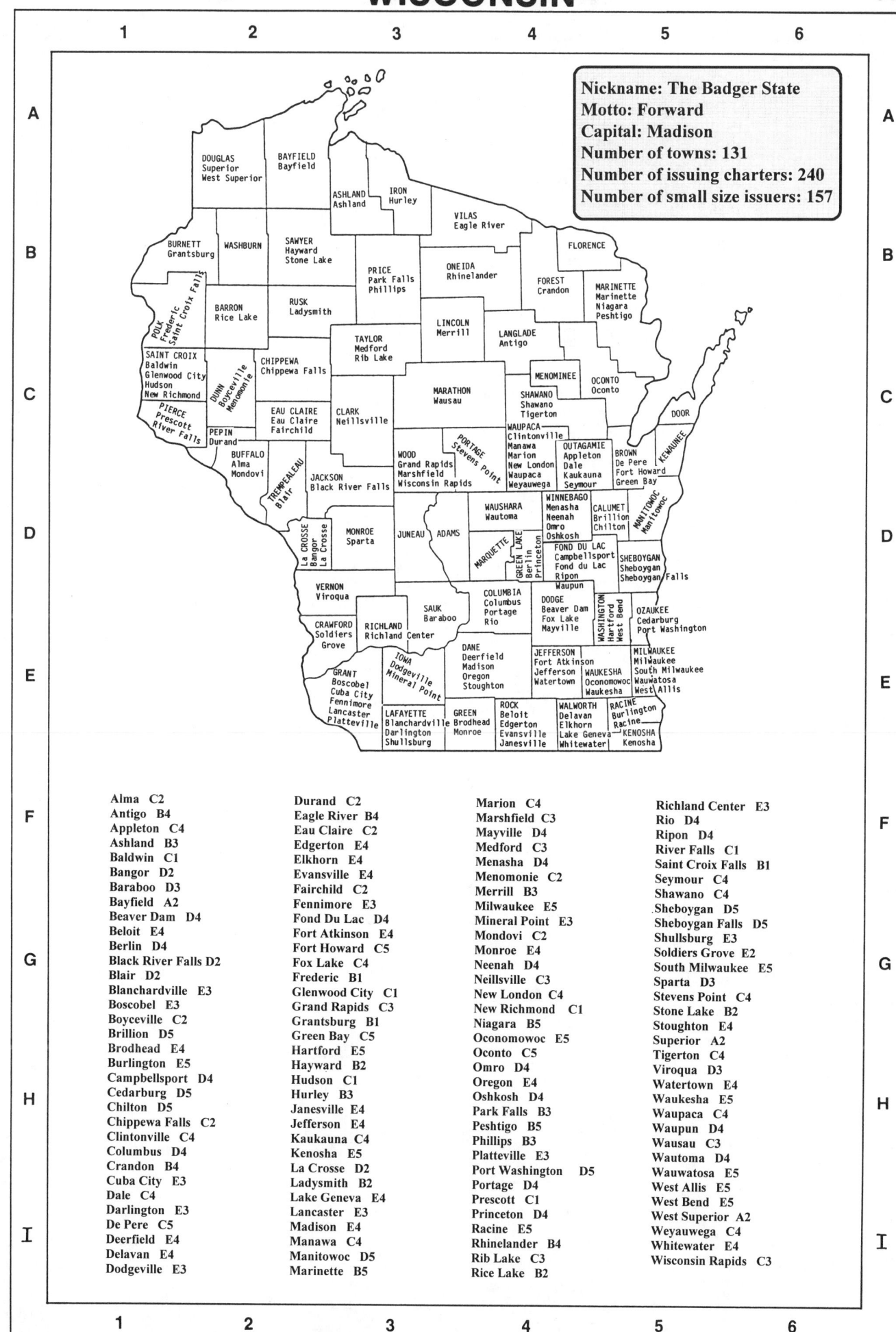

Nickname: The Badger State
Motto: Forward
Capital: Madison
Number of towns: 131
Number of issuing charters: 240
Number of small size issuers: 157

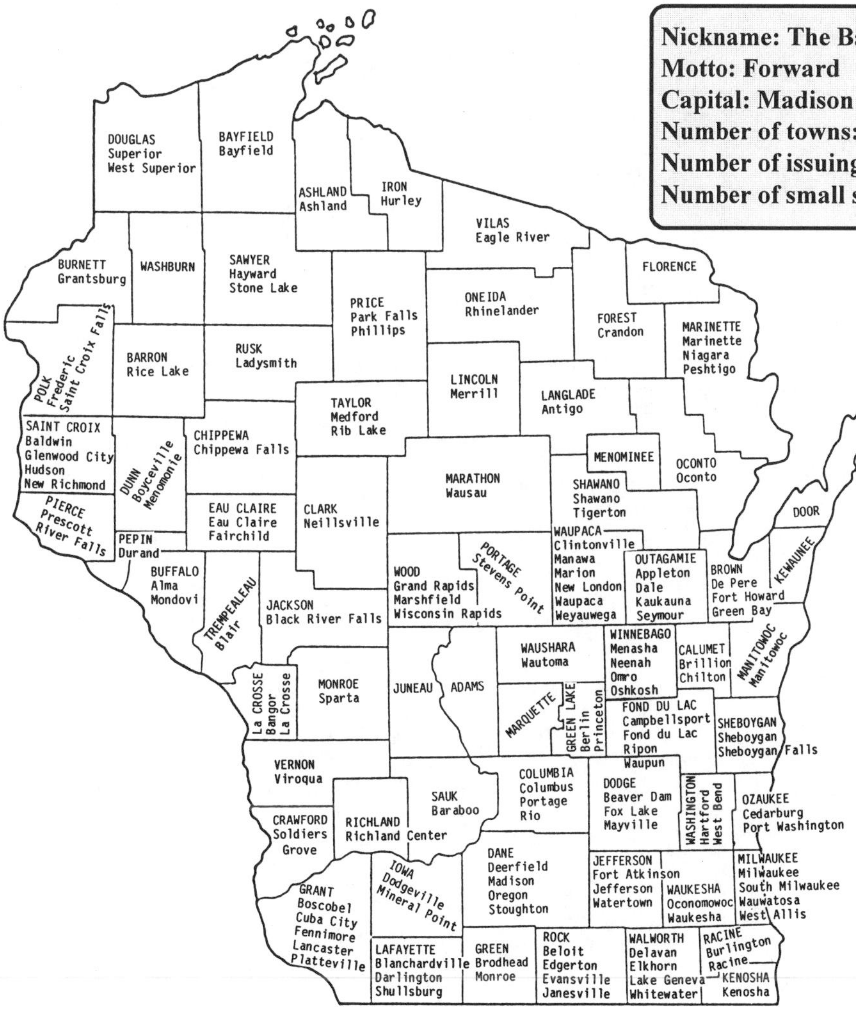

Alma C2
Antigo B4
Appleton C4
Ashland B3
Baldwin C1
Bangor D2
Baraboo D3
Bayfield A2
Beaver Dam D4
Beloit E4
Berlin D4
Black River Falls D2
Blair D2
Blanchardville E3
Boscobel E3
Boyceville C2
Brillion D5
Brodhead E4
Burlington E5
Campbellsport D4
Cedarburg D5
Chilton D5
Chippewa Falls C2
Clintonville C4
Columbus D4
Crandon B4
Cuba City E3
Dale C4
Darlington E3
De Pere C5
Deerfield E4
Delavan E4
Dodgeville E3
Durand C2
Eagle River B4
Eau Claire C2
Edgerton E4
Elkhorn E4
Evansville E4
Fairchild C2
Fennimore E3
Fond Du Lac D4
Fort Atkinson E4
Fort Howard C5
Fox Lake C4
Frederic B1
Glenwood City C1
Grand Rapids C3
Grantsburg B1
Green Bay C5
Hartford E5
Hayward B2
Hudson C1
Hurley B3
Janesville E4
Jefferson E4
Kaukauna C4
Kenosha E5
La Crosse D2
Ladysmith B2
Lake Geneva E4
Lancaster E3
Madison E4
Manawa C4
Manitowoc D5
Marinette B5
Marion C4
Marshfield C3
Mayville D4
Medford C3
Menasha D4
Menomonie C2
Merrill B3
Milwaukee E5
Mineral Point E3
Mondovi C2
Monroe E4
Neenah D4
Neillsville C3
New London C4
New Richmond C1
Niagara B5
Oconomowoc E5
Oconto C5
Omro D4
Oregon E4
Oshkosh D4
Park Falls B3
Peshtigo B5
Phillips B3
Platteville E3
Port Washington D5
Portage D4
Prescott C1
Princeton D4
Racine E5
Rhinelander B4
Rib Lake C3
Rice Lake B2
Richland Center E3
Rio D4
Ripon D4
River Falls C1
Saint Croix Falls B1
Seymour C4
Shawano C4
Sheboygan D5
Sheboygan Falls D5
Shullsburg E3
Soldiers Grove E2
South Milwaukee E5
Sparta D3
Stevens Point C4
Stone Lake B2
Stoughton E4
Superior A2
Tigerton C4
Viroqua D3
Watertown E4
Waukesha E5
Waupaca C4
Waupun D4
Wausau C3
Wautoma D4
Wauwatosa E5
West Allis E5
West Bend E5
West Superior A2
Weyauwega C4
Whitewater E4
Wisconsin Rapids C3

****
8338 Buffalo
FNB OF ALMA
{{ 3 L }}
Organized 5/16/06
Receivership 11/7/24
1902 Red Seal <$VALUE
3x10-20 1-390 <$1250
1902 Date Back
3x10-20 1-1560* <$600
1902 Plain Back
3x10-20 1761-2988* <$600
* 1561-1760 not marked
Total Issue $168,900
Out at close $24,995
****
5143 Langlade
FNB OF ANTIGO
{{ 14 L 10 S }}
Organized 8/31/98
Receivership 5/31/34
Brown Back <$VALUE
4x5 1-2375 <$350
3x10-20 1-1300 <$350
1882 Date Back
4x5 1-4700* <$350
3x10-20 1-3580** <$350
1882 Value Back
4x5 5101-6998* <$350
3x10-20 3901-4955** <$350
* 4701-5100 not marked
** 3581-3900 not marked
1902 Plain Back
4x5 1-12030 <$175
3x10-20 1-8281 <$175
1929 Small Size
5 Type 1 1-3436 <$125
10 Type 1 1-1638 <$125
20 Type 1 1-424 <$135
5 Type 2 1-168 <$150
Total Issue $1,407,940
Out at close $98,950
Large out at close $6,360
****
5942 Langlade
LANGLADE NB OF ANTIGO
{{ 12 L 15 S }}
Organized 8/1/01
Receivership 5/31/34
Brown Back <$VALUE
4x5 1-675 <$400
3x10-20 1-550 <$400
1882 Date Back
4x5 1-2550* <$400
3x10-20 1-1900** <$400
1882 Value Back
4x5 2701-6735* <$400
3x10-20 2021-4533** <$400
* 2551-2700 not marked
** 1901-2020 not marked
1902 Plain Back
4x5 1-9840 <$200
3x10-20 1-6846 <$200
1929 Small Size
5 Type 1 1-3308 <$100
10 Type 1 1-1558 <$100
20 Type 1 1-364 <$100
5 Type 2 1-2080 <$110
10 Type 2 1-910 <$110
20 Type 2 1-124 <$135
Total Issue $1,199,830
Out at close $100,000
Large out at close $4,765
****
1650 Outgamie
APPLETON NB OF APPLETON
{{ UNREPORTED }}
Chartered 4/18/66
Liquidated 1/21/68
Original Series <$VALUE
3x1-2 1-1500 <$2500/$4000
4x5 1-1875 <$2500
Total Issue $45,000
Out in 1910 $593
****
4937 Outgamie
CITIZENS NB OF APPLETON
{{ 13 L 14 S }}
Organized 6/1/93
Liquidated 12/16/31
Brown Back <$VALUE
3x10-20 1-8600 <$300
1882 Date Back
3x10-20 1-4861 <$300
1902 Date Back
3x10-20 1-4000 <$175
1902 Plain Back
3x10-20 4001-29109 <$175
1929 Small Size
10 Type 1 1-3263 <$75
20 Type 1 1-918 <$85
Total Issue $2,434,440
Out at close $200,000
Large out at close $21,060
Ch 1749 assumed circulation
****
2565 Outgamie
COMMERCIAL NB OF APPLETON
{{ 12 L }}
Chartered 9/24/81
Closed 9/30/19
Series 1875 <$VALUE
3x10-20 1-6884<$1250/$2000
Brown Back
3x10-20 1-6800 <$300
1882 Date Back
3x10-20 1-9400 <$300
1882 Value Back
3x10-20 9401-12200 <$300
Total Issue $1,294,200
Out at close $145,050
Ch 1749 assumed circulation
****
1749 Outgamie
FNB OF APPLETON
{{ 28 L 50+ S }}
Chartered 12/13/70
Original Series <$VALUE
3x1-2 1-2420 <$500/$1000
4x5 1-5125 <$500
Series 1875
4x5 1-4661 <$500
Brown Back
4x5 1-11125 <$200
3x10-20 1-3350 <$200/$250
1882 Date Back
4x5 1-3165 <$200
3x10-20 1-1075 <$200
1902 Date Back
3x10-20 1-12000 <$85
1902 Plain Back
4x10 1-42946 <$85
3x10-20 12001-13400 <$85
1929 Small Size
10 Type 1 1-14498 <$30
10 Type 2 1-8686 <$30
Total Issue $4,059,450
Out in 1934 $499,995
Large out 1935 $23,596
Outstanding includes Ch 2565, and Ch 4937
****
1820 Outgamie
MANUFACTURERS NB OF APPLETON
{{ 3 L }}
Chartered 5/17/71
Liquidated 10/10/85
Original Series <$VALUE
3x1-2 1-2300 <$1250/$2000
4x5 1-3175 <$1250
Series 1875
4x5 1-4242 <$1250
Total Issue $159,840
Out in 1910 $1,058
****
3196 Ashland
ASHLAND NB, ASHLAND
{{ 7 L 9 S }}
Organized 5/3/84
Receivership 2/13/33
Brown Back <$VALUE
3x10-20 1-2977 <$500
1902 Red Seal
50-100 1-980 <$6000/$6500
1902 Date Back
50-100 1-500 <$600/$700
3x50-100 1-1630 <$600/$700
1902 Plain Back
3x50-100 1631-1949 <$600/$700
1929 Small Size
50 Type 1 1-243 <$250
100 Type 1 1-54 <$350
Total Issue $963,400
Out at close $99,400
Large out at close $17,850
****
3590 Ashland
FNB OF ASHLAND
{{ 3 L }}
Chartered 11/15/86
Liquidated 6/8/98
Brown Back <$VALUE
4x5 1-5473 <$1000
Total Issue $109,460
Out in 1910 $890
****
3607 Ashland
NORTHERN NB OF ASHLAND
{{ 8 L 8 S }}
Organized 11/20/86
Receivership 2/13/33
Brown Back <$VALUE
4x5 1-8750 <$500
50-100 1-1460 <$4000/$5000
1902 Red Seal
50-100 1-600 <$6000/$6500
1902 Date Back
50-100 1-900 <$500/$600
3x50-100 1-1339 <$500/$600
1902 Plain Back
3x50-100 1340-1665 <$500/$600
1929 Small Size
5 Type 1 1-260 <$200
10 Type 1 1-96 <$200
20 Type 1 1-47 <$200
50 Type 1 1-220 <$225
100 Type 1 1-52 <$275
Total Issue $1,151,650
Out at close $99,100
Large out at close $18,190
****
13870 Ashland
UNION NB OF ASHLAND
{{ 6 S }}
Chartered 12/33
1929 Small Size <$VALUE
5 Type 2 1-3464 <$225
10 Type 2 1-1840 <$225
20 Type 2 1-1208 <$225
Total Issue $59,880
Out in 1935 $50,000
****
10106 Saint Croix
FNB OF BALDWIN
{{ 3 L 11 S }}
Chartered 11/11
1902 Date Back <$VALUE
4x5 1-515 <$600
3x10-20 1-414 <$600
1902 Plain Back
4x5 516-2300 <$600
3x10-20 415-1579 <$600
1929 Small Size
5 Type 1 1-638 <$175
10 Type 1 1-368 <$175
20 Type 1 1-140 <$200
5 Type 2 1-1060 <$225
10 Type 2 1-467 <$225
20 Type 2 1-59 <$225
Total Issue $194,120
Out in 1935 $25,000
Large out 1935 $900
****
13202 La Crosse
FNB OF BANGOR
{{ 3 L 9 S }}
Chartered 5/1/28
1902 Plain Back <$VALUE
4x5 1-721 <$600
3x10-20 1-415 <$600
1929 Small Size
5 Type 1 1-1212 <$175
10 Type 1 1-652 <$175
20 Type 1 1-182 <$200
5 Type 2 1-1194 <$200
10 Type 2 1-695 <$200
20 Type 2 1-195 <$225
Total Issue $149,310
Out in 1935 $50,000
Large out 1935 $330
****
2079 Sauk
FNB OF BARABOO
{{ UNREPORTED }}
Chartered 1/31/73
Liquidated 11/27/80
Original Series <$VALUE
3x1-2 1-1500 <$2500/$4000
4x5 1-1875 <$2500
Series 1875
3x1-2 1-140 <$2500/$4000
4x5 1-1290 <$2500
Total Issue $71,500
Out in 1910 $458
****
3609 Sauk
FNB OF BARABOO
Organized 12/8/86
Receivership 9/11/33
2nd title:FNB & TC 12/31/29
FIRST TITLE {{ 12 L 2 S }}
Brown Back <$VALUE
3x10-20 1-2949 <$400
1902 Red Seal
3x10-20 1-600 <$500
1902 Date Back
3x10-20 1-5900 <$200
1902 Plain Back
3x10-20 5901-18492 <$200
1929 Small Size
10 Type 1 1-1232 <$150
20 Type 1 1-418 <$150
SECOND TITLE {{ 11 S }}
1929 Small Size
10 Type 1 1-1373 <$100
20 Type 1 1-320 <$100
Total Issue $1,346,910
Out at close $150,000
Large out at close $7,420
****
7158 Bayfield
FNB OF BAYFIELD
{{ 5 L 6 S }}
Chartered 3/04
1902 Red Seal <$VALUE
4x5 1-1125 <$900
3x10-20 1-786 <$900
1902 Date Back
4x5 1-1850 <$450
3x10-20 1-1300 <$450
1902 Plain Back
4x5 1851-5237 <$450
3x10-20 1301-3308 <$450
1929 Small Size
5 Type 1 1-824 <$250
10 Type 1 1-410 <$250
20 Type 1 1-116 <$250
5 Type 2 1-384 <$300
10 Type 2 1-315 <$300
20 Type 2 1-50 <$300
Total Issue $401,250
Out in 1935 $25,000
Large out 1935 $1,380
****
American NB of Beaver Dam
SEE Ch 4602
German NB of Beaver Dam
****
3270 Dodge
FNB OF BEAVER DAM
{{ UNREPORTED }}
Chartered 11/29/84
Liquidated 11/12/04
Brown Back <$VALUE
3x10-20 1-1481 <$2000
Total Issue $74,050
Out in 1910 $1,790
****
4602 Dodge
GERMAN NB OF BEAVER DAM
Chartered 1891
2nd title:American NB of Beaver Dam 3/29/18
FIRST TITLE {{ 7 L }}
Brown Back <$VALUE
4x5 1-3625 <$600
3x10-20 1-1260 <$600
1882 Date Back
4x5 1-1011 <$500
3x10-20 1-713 <$500
1902 Date Back
4x5 1-4200 <$350
3x10-20 1-3120 <$350
SECOND TITLE {{ 9 L 18 S }}
1902 Plain Back
4x5 4201-6700 <$250
3x10-20 3121-4600 <$250
1902 Plain Back (new plate)
[Plate Date Mar 29, 1918]
3x10-20 1-10984 <$250
1929 Small Size
10 Type 1 1-2172 <$60
20 Type 1 1-656 <$70
10 Type 2 1-1982 <$70
20 Type 2 1-580 <$80
Total Issue $1,341,670
Out in 1935 $100,000
Large out 1935 $6,600
****
851 Dodge
NB OF BEAVER DAM
{{ 1 L }}
Chartered 3/65
Liquidated 12/24/84
Original Series <$VALUE
3x1-2 1-1000 <$2000/$3500
4x5 1-6250 <$2000
Series 1875
4x5 1-2910 <$2000
Total Issue $188,200
Out in 1910 $1,399
****
7462 Dodge
OLD NB OF BEAVER DAM
{{ 8 L 18 S }}
Chartered 11/04
1902 Red Seal <$VALUE
3x10-20 1-2900 <$600
1902 Date Back
3x10-20 1-5200 <$225
1902 Plain Back
3x10-20 5201-14859 <$225
1929 Small Size
5 Type 1 1-2222 <$60
10 Type 1 1-1798 <$65
20 Type 1 1-474 <$75
5 Type 2 1-2246 <$75
10 Type 2 1-1511 <$75
20 Type 2 1-555 <$85
Total Issue $1,156,810
Out in 1935 $100,000
Large out 1935 $3,950
****
836 Rock
BELOIT NB, BELOIT
{{ 1 L }}
Chartered 2/23/65
Liquidated 10/2/73
Original Series <$VALUE
3x1-2 1-960 <$2000/$3500
4x5 1-2805 <$2000
Total Issue $60,900
Out in 1910 $634
****
2407 Rock
CITIZENS NB OF BELOIT
{{ UNREPORTED }}
Chartered 1/21/79
Liquidated 3/22/86
Series 1875 <$VALUE
3x10-20 1-743 <$3500/$4000
Total Issue $37,150
Out in 1910 $150
****
2163 Rock
FNB OF BELOIT
{{ 1 L }}
Chartered 8/4/74
Liquidated 6/30/87
Original Series <$VALUE
4x5 1-2250 <$2000
Series 1875
4x5 1-1790 <$2000
Total Issue $80,800
Out in 1910 $475
****
2725 Rock
SECOND NB OF BELOIT
{{ 6 L 6 S }}
Chartered 1882
Series 1875 <$VALUE
4x5 1-3850 <$1000
50-100 1-348<$9000/$10,000
1902 Red Seal
50-100 1-860 <$6000/$6500
1902 Date Back
50-100 1-300 <$650/$750
3x50-100 1-600 <$650/$750
1902 Plain Back
3x50-100 1-447 <$650/$750
1929 Small Size
50 Type 1 1-150 <$350
100 Type 1 1-28 <$400
Total Issue $626,750
Out in 1935 $35,000
Large out 1935 $4,740
****
4641 Green Lake
BERLIN NB, BERLIN
{{ 1 L }}
Organized 10/8/91
Receivership 11/17/04
Brown Back <$VALUE
3x10-20 1-1203 <$1500
Total Issue $60,150
Out in 1915 $920
****
400 Green Lake
FNB OF BERLIN
{{ 2 L }}
Chartered 4/25/64
Liquidated 1/25/70
Original Series <$VALUE
3x1-2 1-900 <$2000/$3500
4x5 1-1975 <$2000
Total Issue $44,000
Out in 1910 $368
****
4620 Green Lake
FNB OF BERLIN
{{ 28 L 19 S }}
Chartered 1891
Brown Back <$VALUE
4x5 1-3475 <$300
3x10-20 1-1160 <$300/$350
1882 Date Back
4x5 1-253 <$300
3x10-20 1-196 <$300/$350
1902 Date Back
3x10-20 1-1200* <$100
1902 Plain Back
3x10-20 1401-3743* <$100
* 1201-1400 not marked
1929 Small Size
10 Type 1 1-1636 <$65
20 Type 1 1-454 <$75
10 Type 2 1-934 <$100
20 Type 2 1-304 <$100
Total Issue $497,570
Out in 1935 $50,000
Large out 1935 $2,075
****
3897 Jackson
FNB OF BLACK RIVER FALLS
{{ 7 L 4 S }}
Chartered 1888
Liquidated 4/26/33
Brown Back <$VALUE
4x5 1-2524 <$1500
3x10-20 1-435 <$1500
1902 Red Seal
4x5 1-150 <$2000
4x10 1-150 <$2000
1902 Date Back
4x5 1-950 <$650
4x10 1-900 <$650
1902 Plain Back
4x5 951-1752 <$650
4x10 901-1555 <$650
1929 Small Size
5 Type 1 1-407 <$500
10 Type 1 1-205 <$500
Total Issue $202,980
Out at close $12,500
Large out at close $1,350
****
10667 Trempealeau
FNB OF BLAIR
{{ 5 L 6 S }}
Chartered 12/14
Liquidated 2/29/32
1902 Date Back <$VALUE
4x5 1-500 <$500
3x10-20 1-420 <$500
1902 Plain Back
4x5 501-3615 <$500
3x10-20 421-2356 <$500
1929 Small Size
5 Type 1 1-481 <$300
10 Type 1 1-246 <$300
20 Type 1 1-64 <$325
Total Issue $226,970
Out at close $25,000
Large out at close $2,110
****
11114 Lafayette
FNB OF BLANCHARDVILLE
{{ 4 L 6 S }}
Organized 12/6/17
1902 Plain Back <$VALUE
4x5 1-9818 <$600
1929 Small Size
5 Type 1 1-2718 <$300
5 Type 2 1-5568 <$300
Total Issue $305,740
Out in 1935 $25,000
Large out 1935 $780
****
1771 Grant
FNB OF BOSCOBEL
{{ 2 L }}
Chartered 1/17/71
Liquidated 1/21/79
Original Series <$VALUE
3x1-2 1-1500 <$1500/$2500
4x5 1-2875 <$1500
Series 1875
4x5 1-1625 <$1500
Total Issue $97,500
Out in 1910 $745
****
11128 Dunn
FNB OF BOYCEVILLE
{{ 1 L }}
Organized 12/8/17
Receivership 1/18/27
1902 Plain Back <$VALUE
3x10-20 1-1824 <$1250
Total Issue $91,200
Out at close $24,700
****

CONDITION affects Value. The Values shown are for notes in FINE condition.

7224 Calumet
FNB OF BRILLION
{{ 8 L 15 S }}
Chartered 4/04
Liquidated 3/28/33
1902 Red Seal <$VALUE
3x10-20 1-1036 <$600
1902 Date Back
3x10-20 1-1460 <$250
1902 Plain Back
3x10-20 1461-6638 <$250
1929 Small Size
10 Type 1 1-936 <$100
20 Type 1 1-247 <$100
Total Issue $469,500
Out at close $50,000
Large out at close $4,830

1710 Green
FNB OF BRODHEAD
{{ UNREPORTED }}
Chartered 9/20/70
Liquidated 6/24/75
Original Series <$VALUE
3x1-2 1-1400 <$2500/$4000
4x5 1-2995 <$2500
Total Issue $66,900
Out in 1910 $388

11783 Racine
BURLINGTON NB, BURLINGTON
{{ 8 L 26 S }}
Chartered 7/20
1902 Plain Back <$VALUE
4x5 1-40584 <$175
1929 Small Size
5 Type 1 1-12080 <$35
5 Type 2 1-10750 <$35
10 Type 2 1-3830 <$40
Total Issue $1,266,130
Out in 1935 $85,000
Large out 1935 $3,080

1933 Racine
FNB OF BURLINGTON
{{ 3 L }}
Chartered 2/3/72
Liquidated 12/19/91
Original Series <$VALUE
3x1-2 1-1780 <$1250/$2000
4x5 1-3275 <$1250
Series 1875
4x5 1-4949 <$1250
Total Issue $173,380
Out in 1910 $1,119

6222 Fond du Lac
FNB OF CAMPBELLSPORT
{{ UNREPORTED }}
Chartered 4/22/02
Liquidated 3/6/09
1902 Red Seal <$VALUE
4x5 1-505 <$2500
3x10-20 1-360 <$2500
Total Issue $28,100
Out in 1910 $4,130

1415 Ozaukee
FNB OF CEDARBURG
{{ UNREPORTED }}
Chartered 7/11/65
Liquidated 3/23/68
Original Series <$VALUE
4x5 1-1950 <$2500
3x10-20 1-1020<$3500/$4000
Total Issue $90,000
Out in 1910 $355

5933 Calumet
CHILTON NB, CHILTON
{{ 7 L 9 S }}
Organized 7/31/01
Receivership 12/7/33
Brown Back <$VALUE
3x10-20 1-2700 <$650
1882 Date Back
4x5 1-2730 <$600
3x10-20 1-1720 <$600
1882 Value Back
4x5 2731-4810 <$600
3x10-20 1721-2874 <$600
1902 Plain Back
4x5 1-4039 <$300
3x10-20 1-2838 <$300
1929 Small Size
5 Type 1 1-1619 <$150
10 Type 1 1-758 <$150
20 Type 1 1-202 <$175
Total Issue $715,870
Out at close $49,400
Large out at close $2,970

2125 Chippewa
FNB OF CHIPPEWA FALLS
{{ 13 L 12 S }}
Chartered 8/73
Original Series <$VALUE
3x1-2 1-1420 <$500/$1000
4x5 1-1875 <$500
Series 1875
4x5 1-5263 <$500
Brown Back
3x10-20 1-9060 <$375
1882 Date Back
3x10-20 1-3006 <$375
1902 Date Back
3x10-20 1-3000 <$225
1902 Plain Back
3x10-20 3001-13359 <$225
1929 Small Size
10 Type 1 1-2080 <$100
20 Type 1 1-590 <$100
10 Type 2 1-883 <$135
20 Type 2 1-225 <$150
Total Issue $1,637,240
Out in 1935 $50,000
Large out 1935 $7,310

3778 Chippewa
LUMBERMEN'S NB OF CHIPPEWA FALLS
{{ 7 L 14 S }}
Chartered 1887
Brown Back <$VALUE
3x10-20 1-2676 <$600
1902 Red Seal
4x5 1-2000 <$750
3x10-20 1-1200 <$750
1902 Date Back
4x5 1-3950 <$350
3x10-20 1-3020 <$350
1902 Plain Back
4x5 3951-10870 <$350
3x10-20 3021-7993 <$350
1929 Small Size
5 Type 1 1-2152 <$85
10 Type 1 1-1002 <$85
20 Type 1 1-284 <$100
5 Type 2 1-1574 <$135
10 Type 2 1-680 <$135
20 Type 2 1-240 <$150
Total Issue $1,029,080
Out in 1935 $50,000
Large out 1935 $4,210

6273 Waupaca
FNB OF CLINTONVILLE
{{ 12 L 10 S }}
Organized 5/19/02
Receivership 8/16/33
1902 Red Seal <$VALUE
4x5 1-1265 <$600
3x10-20 1-1014 <$600
1902 Date Back
4x5 1-3200 <$250
3x10-20 1-2460 <$250
1902 Plain Back
4x5 3201-11050 <$250
3x10-20 2461-7544 <$250
1929 Small Size
5 Type 1 1-1590 <$125
10 Type 1 1-1267 <$125
20 Type 1 1-403 <$150
Total Issue $846,280
Out at close $100,000
Large out at close $4,230

178 Columbia
FNB OF COLUMBUS
{{ 6 L 19 S }}
Chartered 1863
Original Series <$VALUE
4x5 1-4750 <$1000
Series 1875
4x5 1-3110 <$1000
Brown Back
3x10-20 1-1163 <$750
1902 Red Seal
3x10-20 1-785 <$850
1902 Date Back
3x10-20 1-1550 <$400
1902 Plain Back
3x10-20 1551-3851 <$400
1929 Small Size
10 Type 1 1-1236 <$135
20 Type 1 1-328 <$150
5 Type 2 1-192 <$175
10 Type 2 1-598 <$175
20 Type 2 1-161 <$200
Total Issue $570,830
Out in 1935 $50,000
Large out 1935 $2,355

12814 Forest
CRANDON NB, CRANDON
{{ 4 L 7 S }}
Chartered 9/25
1902 Plain Back <$VALUE
3x10-20 1-1223 <$600
1929 Small Size
10 Type 1 1-588 <$175
20 Type 1 1-160 <$175
10 Type 2 1-447 <$200
20 Type 2 1-87 <$200
Total Issue $121,840
Out in 1935 $15,000
Large out 1935 $580

9387 Forest
FNB OF CRANDON
{{ 4 L }}
Organized 3/16/09
Receivership 5/29/25
1902 Date Back <$VALUE
3x10-20 1-2040 <$500
1902 Plain Back
3x10-20 2041-5059 <$500
Total Issue $252,950
Out at close $45,200

5632 Grant
FNB OF CUBA CITY
{{ 3 L }}
Chartered 11/26/00
Liquidated 4/17/28
Brown Back <$VALUE
3x10-20 1-550 <$850
1882 Date Back
3x10-20 1-1570 <$850
1882 Value Back
3x10-20 1571-2292 <$850
1902 Plain Back
3x10-20 1-1830 <$600
Total Issue $233,600
Out at close $25,000

8118 Outgamie
FNB OF DALE
{{ 3 L U + 2 S }}
Organized 2/26/06
Liquidated 9/10/34
1902 Red Seal <$VALUE
3x10-20 1-210 <$1500
1902 Date Back
3x10-20 1-660 <$750
1902 Plain Back
3x10-20 661-1319 <$750
1929 Small Size
10 Type 1 1-186 <$250
20 Type 1 1-36 <$250
Total Issue $91,930
Out at close $7,000
Large out at close $380

3308 Lafayette
CITIZENS NB OF DARLINGTON
{{ 6 L 10 S }}
Chartered 1885
Brown Back <$VALUE
4x5 1-3003 <$650
50-100 1-159 <$4000/$5000
1902 Red Seal
3x10-20 1-1500 <$750
1902 Date Back
3x10-20 1-2700 <$300
1902 Plain Back
3x10-20 2701-8222 <$300
1929 Small Size
10 Type 1 1-984 <$150
20 Type 1 1-258 <$150
10 Type 2 1-847 <$175
20 Type 2 1-234 <$175
Total Issue $673,160
Out in 1935 $50,000
Large out 1935 $3,230

14184 Lafayette
FNB AT DARLINGTON
{{ 10 S }}
Chartered 6/34
1929 Small Size <$VALUE
5 Type 2 1-4100 <$200
10 Type 2 1-1895 <$200
20 Type 2 1-655 <$200
Total Issue $52,550
Out in 1935 $50,000

3161 Lafayette
FNB OF DARLINGTON
{{ 12 L 14 S }}
Organized 3/20/84
Receivership 6/25/34
Brown Back <$VALUE
3x10-20 1-1154 <$400
1902 Red Seal
3x10-20 1-2050 <$500
1902 Date Back
4x5 1-3030 <$200
3x10-20 1-2000 <$200
1902 Plain Back
4x5 3031-13260 <$200
3x10-20 2001-8496 <$200
1929 Small Size
5 Type 1 1-2374 <$75
10 Type 1 1-1080 <$85
20 Type 1 1-296 <$100
5 Type 2 1-538 <$100
10 Type 2 1-214 <$100
Total Issue $1,026,570
Out at close $74,500
Large out at close $4,830

2133 Brown
FNB OF DePERE
{{ 1 L }}
Chartered 1/16/74
Liquidated 8/17/76
Original Series <$VALUE
3x1-2 1-800 <$2000/$3500
4x5 1-1785 <$3500
Total Issue $39,700
Out in 1910 $149

6469 Brown
NB OF DePERE
{{ 12 L 10 S }}
Organized 10/6/02
Receivership 2/16/32
1902 Red Seal <$VALUE
3x10-20 1-1900 <$500
1902 Date Back
3x10-20 1-3000 <$200
1902 Plain Back
3x10-20 3001-15032 <$200
1929 Small Size
10 Type 1 1-1574 <$165
20 Type 1 1-498 <$175
Total Issue $1,000,800
Out at close $100,000
Large out at close $11,570

11577 Dane
FNB OF DEERFIELD
{{ UNREPORTED }}
Chartered 1/20
Liquidated 10/15/30
1902 Plain Back <$VALUE
4x5 1-2060 <$1500
Total Issue $41,200
Out at close $330

1248 Walworth
NB OF DELAVAN
{{ UNREPORTED }}
Chartered 1865
Original Series <$VALUE
4x5 1-1900 <$2500
3x10-20 1-780 <$3500/$4000
Series 1875
4x5 1-860 <$2500
Total Issue $94,200
Out in 1910 $770

6698 Iowa
FNB OF DODGEVILLE
{{ 8 L 13 S }}
Chartered 3/03
1902 Red Seal <$VALUE
4x5 1-1925 <$600
3x10-20 1-1710 <$600
1902 Date Back
4x5 1-3750 <$250
3x10-20 1-2540 <$250
1902 Plain Back
4x5 3751-15735 <$250
3x10-20 2541-10611 <$250
1929 Small Size
5 Type 1 1-2883 <$125
10 Type 1 1-1440 <$125
20 Type 1 1-361 <$150
Total Issue $1,185,460
Out in 1934 $50,000
Large out 1935 $1,445

13529 Pepin
FNB IN DURAND
{{ U + 5 S }}
Organized 2/24/31
Liquidated 5/24/34
1929 Small Size <$VALUE
5 Type 1 1-506 <$325
10 Type 1 1-276 <$325
20 Type 1 1-70 <$350
Total Issue $40,140
Out at close $40,000
Outstanding includes Ch 10791
Ch 14095 assumed circulation

10791 Pepin
FNB OF DURAND
{{ 3 L 6 S }}
Chartered 10/15
Liquidated 4/2/31
1902 Plain Back <$VALUE
4x5 1-4618 <$600
3x10-20 1-1932 <$600
1929 Small Size
5 Type 1 1-657 <$300
10 Type 1 1-315 <$300
20 Type 1 1-81 <$300
Total Issue $237,290
Out at close $40,000
Large out 1935 $1,630
Ch 13529 assumed circulation

14095 Pepin
SECURITY NB OF DURAND
{{ U + 0 S }}
Chartered 4/34
1929 Small Size <$VALUE
10 Type 2 1-30 <$750
Total Issue $300
Out in 1935 $20,000
Outstanding includes Ch 13529
and Ch 10791

12124 Vilas
FNB OF EAGLE RIVER
{{ 2 L 12 S }}
Organized 1/22
1902 Plain Back <$VALUE
4x5 1-8317 <$1000
1929 Small Size
5 Type 1 1-2852 <$250
5 Type 2 1-5462 <$250
Total Issue $279,210
Out in 1935 $25,000
Large out 1935 $720

13645 Eau Claire
AMERICAN NB & TC OF EAU CLAIRE
{{ 14 S }}
Chartered 11/32
1929 Small Size <$VALUE
10 Type 1 1-1226 <$100
20 Type 1 1-414 <$100
10 Type 2 1-2264 <$125
20 Type 2 1-385 <$125
Total Issue $153,580
Out in 1935 $100,000

2759 Eau Claire
EAU CLAIRE NB, EAU CLAIRE
{{ 24 L 10 S }}
Organized 7/17/82
Liquidated 7/9/31
Series 1875 <$VALUE
3x10-20 1-3015<$1000/$1250
1902 Red Seal
3x10-20 1-6100 <$250/$300
1902 Date Back
4x5 1-11500 <$100
3x10-20 1-4600 <$100
1902 Plain Back
4x5 11501-30765 <$100
3x10-20 4601-16126 <$100
1929 Small Size
5 Type 1 1-2557 <$150
10 Type 1 1-1254 <$150
20 Type 1 1-344 <$150
Total Issue $2,070,580
Out at close $150,000
Large out at close $20,850

2069 Eau Claire
FNB OF EAU CLAIRE
{{ 3 L }}
Chartered 12/12/72
Liquidated 3/30/78
Original Series <$VALUE
3x1-2 1-1900 <$1250/$2000
4x5 1-2775 <$1250
Series 1875
4x5 1-845 <$1250
Total Issue $81,900
Out in 1910 $510

8281 Eau Claire
UNION NB OF EAU CLAIRE
{{ 27 L 33 S }}
Chartered 6/06
1902 Red Seal <$VALUE
4x5 1-3050 <$200
4x10 1-1650 <$200
3x10-20 1-1380 <$200/$250
50-100 1-60 <$6000/$6500
1902 Date Back
4x5 1-12250 <$75
4x10 1-10500 <$75
3x10-20 1-500 <$75
3x50-100 1-400 <$350/$400
1902 Plain Back
4x5 12251-41327 <$75
4x10 10501-30280 <$75
1929 Small Size
5 Type 1 1-9778 <$35
10 Type 1 1-5128 <$35
5 Type 2 1-13232 <$40
10 Type 2 1-6528 <$40
Total Issue $3,100,200
Out in 1935 $150,000
Large out 1935 $13,020

7040 Rock
FNB OF EDGERTON
{{ 6 L 12 S }}
Organized 10/30/03
Liquidated 1/20/34
1902 Red Seal <$VALUE
3x10-20 1-656 <$750
1902 Date Back
3x10-20 1-2800 <$300
1902 Plain Back
3x10-20 2801-9175 <$300
1929 Small Size
5 Type 1 1-116 <$150
10 Type 1 1-1068 <$150
20 Type 1 1-261 <$165
Total Issue $590,430
Out at close $50,000
Large out at close $4,620

13932 Rock
NB OF EDGERTON
{{ 6 S }}
Chartered 1/34
1929 Small Size <$VALUE
5 Type 2 1-3280 <$350
10 Type 2 1-1200 <$350
Total Issue $28,400
Out in 1935 $25,000

873 Walworth
FNB OF ELKHORN
{{ 8 L U + 9 S }}
Chartered 1865
Original Series <$VALUE
4x5 1-7175 <$1000
Series 1875
4x5 1-3145 <$1000
Brown Back
4x5 1-4890 <$850
50-100 1-100 <$4000/$5000
1902 Red Seal
3x10-20 1-395 <$750
1902 Date Back
3x10-20 1-2000 <$375
1902 Plain Back
3x10-20 2001-6809 <$375
1929 Small Size
10 Type 1 1-1088 <$200
20 Type 1 1-278 <$200
10 Type 2 1-232 <$250
20 Type 2 1-55 <$275
Total Issue $781,460
Out in 1935 $50,000
Large out 1935 $6,880

1729 Rock
FNB OF EVANSVILLE
{{ 1 L }}
Chartered 10/31/70
Liquidated 1/9/75
Original Series <$VALUE
3x1-2 1-1500 <$2000/$3500
4x5 1-2225 <$2000
Total Issue $52,000
Out in 1910 $383

7264 Eau Claire
FNB OF FAIRCHILD
{{ 1 L 1 S }}
Organized 5/9/04
Receivership 8/18/31
1902 Red Seal <$VALUE
3x10-20 1-500 <$2500
1902 Date Back
3x10-20 1-720 <$1500
1902 Plain Back
3x10-20 721-1498 <$1500
1929 Small Size
10 Type 1 1-131 <$750
20 Type 1 1-23 <$750
Total Issue $110,520
Out at close $10,000
Large out at close $1,820

****

13599 Grant
FNB IN FENNIMORE
{{ 5 S }}
Chartered 2/32
1929 Small Size <$VALUE
10 Type 1 1-356 <$300
20 Type 1 1-86 <$300
10 Type 2 1-304 <$325
20 Type 2 1-100 <$350
Total Issue $36,720
Out in 1935 $37,500
Outstanding includes Ch 9522

****

9522 Grant
FNB OF FENNIMORE
{{ 6 L 7 S }}
Organized 5/17/09
Liquidated 3/12/32
1902 Date Back <$VALUE
4x5 1-1515 <$400
3x10-20 1-1214 <$400
1902 Plain Back
4x5 1516-4550 <$400
3x10-20 1215-3108 <$400
1929 Small Size
5 Type 1 1-692 <$300
10 Type 1 1-364 <$300
20 Type 1 1-114 <$300
Total Issue $302,680
Out at close $50,000
Large out 1935 $1,870
Ch 13599 assumed circulation

****

6015 Fond du Lac
COMMERCIAL NB OF FOND DU LAC
{{ 28 L 50+ S }}
Organized 10/20/01
Receivership 1/2/34
Brown Back <$VALUE
3x10-20 1-5600 <$275
1882 Date Back
4x5 1-6750* <$225
3x10-20 1-3500** <$225
1882 Value Back
4x5 7751-18940* <$275
3x10-20 4301-11089** <$275
* 6751-7750 not marked
** 3501-4300 not marked
1902 Plain Back
4x5 1-26618 <$100
3x10-20 1-19905 <$100
1929 Small Size
5 Type 1 1-12196 <$20
10 Type 1 1-6724 <$25
20 Type 1 1-1800 <$35
5 Type 2 1-594 <$30
10 Type 2 1-260 <$35
Total Issue $3,731,750
Out at close $372,450
Large out at close $15,990

****

F-Fond du Lac NB, Fond du Lac
SEE Ch 555
FNB of Fond du Lac

****

555 Fond du Lac
FNB OF FOND DU LAC
Chartered 1864
2nd title: F-Fond du Lac NB 8/31/18
FIRST TITLE {{ 4 L }}
Original Series <$VALUE
3x1-2 1-5400 <$850/$1750
4x5 1-3900 <$1000
3x10-20 1-800 <$1250/$2000
Series 1875
3x1-2 1-360 <$850/$1750
4x5 1-995 <$1000
3x10-20 1-793 <$1250/$2000
Brown Back
3x10-20 1-2558 <$750
1902 Red Seal
3x10-20 1-1400 <$850
1902 Date Back
3x10-20 1-2700 <$300
SECOND TITLE {{ 27 L 50+ S }}
1902 Plain Back
3x10-20 1-35704 <$100
1929 Small Size
10 Type 1 1-9256 <$30
20 Type 1 1-2434 <$40
10 Type 2 1-3279 <$30
20 Type 2 1-1114 <$40
Total Issue $3,226,960
Out in 1935 $300,000
Large out 1935 $29,710
Outstanding includes Ch 3685

****

3685 Fond du Lac
FOND DU LAC NB OF FOND DU LAC
{{ 12 L }}
Chartered 1887
Liquidated 8/31/18
Brown Back <$VALUE
3x10-20 1-4360 <$400
1902 Red Seal
3x10-20 1-2200 <$500
1902 Date Back
3x10-20 1-13269 <$175
Total Issue $991,450
Out at close $169,995
Ch 555 assumed circulation

****

157 Jefferson
FNB OF FORT ATKINSON
{{ 9 L 10 S }}
Chartered 1863
Original Series <$VALUE
3x1-2 1-3000 <$750/$1750
4x5 1-6250 <$750
Series 1875
4x5 1-3885 <$750
Brown Back
4x5 1-4897 <$500
3x10-20 1-510 <$500
1902 Red Seal
3x10-20 1-1920 <$600
1902 Date Back
3x10-20 1-3100 <$300
1902 Plain Back
3x10-20 3101-9704 <$300
1929 Small Size
10 Type 1 1-1178 <$200
20 Type 1 1-338 <$200
10 Type 2 1-1027 <$225
20 Type 2 1-165 <$250
Total Issue $1,047,150
Out in 1935 $50,000
Large out 1935 $5,580

****

4783 Brown
McCARTNEY NB OF FORT HOWARD
Organized 6/30/92 4
Receivership 5/29/31
2nd title:McCartney NB of Green Bay 1/29/10
FIRST TITLE {{ 4 L }}
Brown Back <$VALUE
3x10-20 1-6125 <$800
1882 Date Back
3x10-20 1-2613 <$750
SECOND TITLE {{ 17 L 14 S }}
1882 Date Back
3x10-20 1-4533 <$250/$300
1902 Date Back
3x10-20 1-8000 <$125
1902 Plain Back
3x10-20 8001-39617 <$125
1929 Small Size
10 Type 1 1-3454 <$65
20 Type 1 1-1024 <$75
Total Issue $2,974,520
Out at close $250,000
Large out at close $33,365

****

426 Dodge
FNB OF FOX LAKE
{{ 3 L }}
Chartered 5/16/64
Liquidated 1/14/90
Original Series <$VALUE
3x1-2 1-5000 <$1250/$2000
4x5 1-5750 <$1250
Series 1875
4x5 1-3310 <$1250
Brown Back
4x5 1-4415 <$1000
Total Issue $294,500
Out in 1910 $2,592

****

8491 Polk
FNB OF FREDERIC
{{ 3 L 5 S }}
Organized 12/10/06
Receivership 11/17/31
1902 Red Seal <$VALUE
3x10-20 1-507 <$1500
1902 Date Back
3x10-20 1-1610 <$750
1902 Plain Back
3x10-20 1611-4565 <$750
1929 Small Size
10 Type 1 1-342 <$400
20 Type 1 1-92 <$400
Total Issue $285,160
Out at close $24,700
Large out at close $3,760

****

11083 Saint Croix
FARMERS NB OF GLENWOOD CITY
{{ 4 L 1 S }}
Organized 9/1/17
Receivership 8/22/30
1902 Plain Back <$VALUE
4x5 1-5317 <$750
1929 Small Size
5 Type 1 1-822 <$750
Total Issue $131,000
Out at close $24,700
Large out at close $2,680

****

10330 Wood
CITIZENS NB OF GRAND RAPIDS
Organized 12/30/12
Receivership 12/22/31
2nd title:Citizens NB of Wisconsin Rapids 11/11/20
FIRST TITLE {{ 10 L }}
1902 Date Back <$VALUE
4x5 1-3165 <$250
3x10-20 1-2534 <$250
1902 Plain Back
4x5 3166-7665 <$250
3x10-20 2535-5174 <$250
SECOND TITLE {{ 6 L 8 S }}
1902 Plain Back
4x5 1-10845 <$300
3x10-20 1-6701 <$300
1929 Small Size
5 Type 1 1-2006 <$200
10 Type 1 1-1032 <$200
20 Type 1 1-263 <$200
Total Issue $1,117,610
Out at close $82,240
Large out at close $10,970

****

1998 Wood
FNB OF GRAND RAPIDS
Chartered 6/18/72
2nd title:FNB of Wisconsin Rapids 9/23/20
FIRST TITLE {{ 19 L }}
Original Series <$VALUE
3x1-2 1-1800 <$600/$1250
4x5 1-2600 <$650
Series 1875
4x5 1-5155 <$650
Brown Back
3x10-20 1-2810 <$400
1882 Date Back
3x10-20 1-1121 <$400
1902 Date Back
3x10-20 1-4100 <$175
1902 Plain Back
3x10-20 4101-10000 <$175
SECOND TITLE {{ 7 L 38 S }}
1902 Plain Back
3x10-20 1-18329 <$250
1929 Small Size
10 Type 1 1-4713 <$50
20 Type 1 1-1280 <$60
Total Issue $2,213,480
Out in 1935 $100,000
Large out 1935 $11,870

****

4639 Wood
WOOD COUNTY NB OF GRAND RAPIDS
Organized 8/27/91
2nd title:Wood County NB of Wisconsin Rapids 11/13/20
FIRST TITLE {{ 10 L }}
Brown Back <$VALUE
4x5 1-4625 <$400
3x10-20 1-1820 <$400
1882 Date Back
4x5 1-2640 <$350
3x10-20 1-2074 <$350
1902 Date Back
3x10-20 1-4200 <$225
1902 Plain Back
3x10-20 4201-8100 <$225
SECOND TITLE {{ 3 L 31 S }}
1902 Plain Back
3x10-20 1-8452 <$350
1929 Small Size
10 Type 1 1-2178 <$50
20 Type 1 1-622 <$60
10 Type 2 1-825 <$75
20 Type 2 1-145 <$100
Total Issue $1,384,070
Out in 1935 $50,000
Large out 1935 $6,220

****

8444 Burnett
FNB OF GRANTSBURG
{{ 2 L 10 S }}
Chartered 11/06
1902 Red Seal <$VALUE
3x10-20 1-195 <$1500
1902 Date Back
3x10-20 1-700 <$850
1902 Plain Back
3x10-20 701-2290 <$850
1929 Small Size
10 Type 1 1-542 <$400
20 Type 1 1-140 <$400
10 Type 2 1-378 <$450
20 Type 2 1-135 <$450
Total Issue $180,050
Out in 1935 $25,000
Large out 1935 $1,420

****

3884 Brown
CITIZENS NB OF GREEN BAY
{{ 20 L }}
Chartered 1888
Closed 8/7/26
Brown Back <$VALUE
4x5 1-9410 <$300
3x10-20 1-4716 <$300/$350
1902 Red Seal
4x5 1-1500 <$300
3x10-20 1-1400 <$300/$350
1902 Date Back
4x5 1-11500 <$100
3x10-20 1-8800 <$100
1902 Plain Back
4x5 11501-40500 <$100
3x10-20 8801-19949 <$100
Total Issue $2,331,450
Out at close $200,000
Ch 2132 assumed circulation

****

1009 Brown
CITY NB OF GREEN BAY
{{ UNREPORTED }}
Chartered 4/14/65
Liquidated 11/29/73
Original Series <$VALUE
4x5 1-1000 <$2500
3x10-20 1-740 <$3500/$4000
Total Issue $57,000
Out in 1910 $535

****

874 Brown
FNB OF GREEN BAY
{{ 2 L }}
Chartered 3/65
Liquidated 10/19/77
Original Series <$VALUE
3x1-2 1-3240 <$1500/$2500
4x5 1-3550 <$1500
Series 1875
4x5 1-1040 <$1500
Total Issue $108,000
Out in 1910 $930

****

Kellogg-Citizens NB of Green Bay
SEE Ch 2132
Kellogg NB of Green Bay

****

2132 Brown
KELLOGG NB OF GREEN BAY
Chartered 1/19/74
2nd title:Kellogg-Citizens NB of Green Bay 8/7/26
FIRST TITLE {{ 14 L }}
Original Series <$VALUE
4x5 1-2250 <$5000
Series 1875
4x5 1-4090 <$4500
Brown Back
3x10-20 1-4940 <$350
1882 Date Back
3x10-20 1-3558 <$350
1902 Date Back
3x50-100 1-1860 <$450/$500
1902 Plain Back
3x50-100 1861-1958 <$450/$500
SECOND TITLE {{ 5 L 31 S }}
1902 Plain Back
3x10-20 1-5468 <$200
1929 Small Size
10 Type 1 1-5694 <$35
20 Type 1 1-1518 <$45
10 Type 2 1-5154 <$40
20 Type 2 1-961 <$50
Total Issue $1,909,160
Out in 1935 $260,000
Large out 1935 $21,080
Outstanding includes Ch 3884

****

McCartney NB of Green Bay
SEE Ch 4783
McCartney NB of Fort Howard

****

1819 Brown
NB OF COMMERCE OF GREEN BAY
{{ 1 L }}
Chartered 5/17/71
Liquidated 1/12/75
Original Series <$VALUE
4x5 1-3445 <$2000
3x10-20 1-600 <$3000/$3500
Total Issue $98,900
Out in 1910 $600

****

8671 Washington
FNB OF HARTFORD
{{ 12 L 12 S }}
Chartered 5/07
1902 Red Seal <$VALUE
4x5 1-600 <$600
3x10-20 1-480 <$600
1902 Date Back
4x5 1-3325 <$250
3x10-20 1-2280 <$250
1902 Plain Back
4x5 3326-10080 <$250
3x10-20 2281-6711 <$250
1929 Small Size
5 Type 1 1-1670 <$200
10 Type 1 1-784 <$200
20 Type 1 1-234 <$200
5 Type 2 1-1420 <$200
10 Type 2 1-716 <$200
20 Type 2 1-192 <$225
Total Issue $716,470
Out in 1935 $50,000
Large out 1935 $2,510

****

7831 Sawyer
FNB OF HAYWARD
{{ 2 L }}
Organized 6/9/05
Receivership 3/29/24
1902 Red Seal <$VALUE
4x5 1-325 <$1500
3x10-20 1-290 <$1500
1902 Date Back
4x5 1-800 <$850
3x10-20 1-620 <$850
1902 Plain Back
4x5 801-1410 <$850
3x10-20 621-942 <$850
Total Issue $96,300
Out at close $9,600

****

95 Saint Croix
FNB OF HUDSON
{{ 6 L 11 S }}
Chartered 1863
Original Series <$VALUE
4x5 1-5325 <$1000
Series 1875
4x5 1-2700 <$1000
Brown Back
4x5 1-5533 <$750
3x10-20 1-913 <$750
1902 Red Seal
3x10-20 1-2260 <$850
1902 Date Back
3x10-20 1-3900 <$400
1902 Plain Back
3x10-20 3901-8827 <$400
1929 Small Size
10 Type 1 1-998 <$200
20 Type 1 1-286 <$200
10 Type 2 1-1281 <$225
20 Type 2 1-293 <$250
Total Issue $984,030
Out in 1935 $50,000
Large out 1935 $5,020

****

4304 Iron
FNB OF HURLEY
{{ 1 L }}
Chartered 5/9/90
Liquidated 2/19/95
Brown Back <$VALUE
4x5 1-1195 <$1500
Total Issue $23,900
Out in 1910 $210

****

11594 Iron
HURLEY NB, HURLEY
{{ 4 L 6 S }}
Organized 1/30/20
Receivership 6/21/32
1902 Plain Back <$VALUE
4x5 1-20063 <$500
1929 Small Size
5 Type 1 1-3922 <$275
Total Issue $518,920
Out at close $50,000
Large out at close $3,000

****

83 Rock
FNB OF JANESVILLE
{{ 1 L }}
Chartered 9/63
Liquidated 6/30/82
Original Series <$VALUE
4x5 1-3000 <$2500
4x10 1-6000 <$3000
Series 1875
4x5 1-487 <$2500
4x10 1-789 <$3000
Total Issue $341,300
Out in 1910 $2,265

****

2748 Rock
FNB OF JANESVILLE
{{ 6 L 16 S }}
Organized 5/23/82
Brown Back <$VALUE
3x10-20 1-4389 <$650
1902 Red Seal
3x10-20 1-2300 <$750
1902 Date Back
3x10-20 1-5500 <$375
1902 Plain Back
3x10-20 5501-14745 <$375
1929 Small Size
10 Type 1 1-3316 <$75
20 Type 1 1-910 <$85
10 Type 2 1-4799 <$85
20 Type 2 1-1277 <$90
Total Issue $1,453,390
Out in 1935 $200,000
Large out 1935 $4,160

****

749 Rock
ROCK COUNTY NB OF JANESVILLE
{{ 12 L 10 S }}
Chartered 1865
Original Series <$VALUE
3x1-2 1-4600 <$600/$1250
4x5 1-5250 <$650
3x10-20 1-700 <$1250/$1750
Series 1875
3x1-2 1-260 <$600/$1250
4x5 1-4800 <$650
3x10-20 1-1398<$1250/$1750
Brown Back
4x5 1-2220 <$400
3x10-20 1-1116 <$400
1902 Red Seal
4x5 1-2025 <$500
3x10-20 1-1640 <$500
1902 Date Back
4x5 1-1250 <$250
3x10-20 1-1000 <$250
1902 Plain Back
4x5 1251-42684 <$250
3x10-20 1001-2780 <$250
1929 Small Size
5 Type 1 1-11548 <$100
5 Type 2 1-8092 <$100
Total Issue $1,932,480
Out in 1935 $100,000
Large out 1935 $46,235

****

1076 Jefferson
NB OF JEFFERSON
{{ UNREPORTED }}
Chartered 4/28/65
Liquidated 8/26/75
Original Series <$VALUE
4x5 1-5124 <$2500
Total Issue $102,480
Out in 1910 $860

****

3641 Outgamie
FNB OF KAUKAUNA
{{ 7 L 3 S }}
Chartered 1887
Liquidated 12/18/31
Brown Back <$VALUE
4x5 1-4050 <$650
3x10-20 1-1233 <$650
1902 Red Seal
3x10-20 1-800 <$750
1902 Date Back
3x10-20 1-3800 <$375
1902 Plain Back
3x10-20 3801-9103 <$375
1929 Small Size
10 Type 1 1-843 <$400
20 Type 1 1-212 <$400
Total Issue $713,820
Out at close $50,000
Large out at close $6,100

****

****
212 Kenosha
FNB OF KENOSHA
{{ 10 L 31 S }}
Chartered 1864
Original Series <$VALUE
4x5 1-5000 <$850
Series 1875
4x5 1-2670 <$850
Brown Back
4x5 1-4548 <$500
3x10-20 1-489 <$500
1902 Red Seal
4x5 1-1900 <$600
3x10-20 1-1380 <$600
1902 Date Back
4x5 1-6300 <$300
3x10-20 1-3800 <$300
1902 Plain Back
4x5 6301-15215 <$300
3x10-20 3801-11138 <$300
1929 Small Size
5 Type 1 1-7160 <$50
10 Type 1 1-3750 <$50
20 Type 1 1-982 <$60
5 Type 2 1-5506 <$50
10 Type 2 1-3055 <$60
20 Type 2 1-1220 <$75
Total Issue $1,877,130
Out in 1935 $290,000
Large out 1935 $4,960
****
12351 Kenosha
UNITED STATES NB OF KENOSHA
Organized 3/31/23
Receivership 11/15/32
2nd title:United States NB & TC of Kenosha 11/1/28
FIRST TITLE {{ 8 L }}
1902 Plain Back <$VALUE
4x5 1-8628 <$300
3x10-20 1-8625 <$300
SECOND TITLE {{ 4 L 18 S }}
1902 Plain Back
3x10-20 1-1758 <$350
1929 Small Size
5 Type 1 1-5947 <$100
10 Type 1 1-2775 <$100
20 Type 1 1-713 <$110
Total Issue $1,122,180
Out at close $175,000
Large out at close $7,550
****
7347 La Crosse
BATAVIAN NB OF La CROSSE
{{ 19 L 23 S }}
Chartered 7/04
1902 Red Seal <$VALUE
3x10-20 1-15000 <$350/$400
1902 Date Back
3x10-20 1-20500* <$150
1902 Plain Back
3x10-20 22501-49459* <$150
* 20501-22500 not marked
1929 Small Size
20 Type 1 1-3000 <$75
Total Issue $3,582,950
Out in 1933 $300,000
Large out 1935 $14,970
****
1313 La Crosse
FNB OF La CROSSE
{{ UNREPORTED }}
Organized 6/30/65
Receivership 4/11/76
Original Series <$VALUE
4x5 1-4225 <$2500
Total Issue $84,500
Out in 1915 $705
****
2344 La Crosse
La CROSSE NB, La CROSSE
{{ 50+ L }}
Chartered 12/1/76
Liquidated 7/1/96
Series 1875 <$VALUE
3x1-2 1-500 <$450/$900
3x10-20 1-3525<$1250/$1750
Total Issue $178,750
Out in 1910 $2,112
****
5047 La Crosse
NB OF La CROSSE
{{ 24 L 50+ S }}
Chartered 1896
Brown Back <$VALUE
3x10-20 1-21600 <$250/$300
1882 Date Back
3x10-20 1-15047 <$225/$275
1902 Plain Back
3x10-20 1-53539 <$100
1929 Small Size
10 Type 1 1-10398 <$30
20 Type 1 1-2814 <$35
10 Type 2 1-6 <$100
Total Issue $5,470,920
Out in 1935 $250,000
Large out 1935 $29,850
****
3412 La Crosse
UNION NB OF La CROSSE
{{ UNREPORTED }}
Chartered 11/20/85
Liquidated 12/9/89
Brown Back <$VALUE
4x5 1-1884 <$2000
Total Issue $37,680
Out in 1910 $295
****
5535 Rusk
FNB OF LADYSMITH
{{ 1 L }}
Organized 8/13/00
Receivership 6/2/05
Brown Back <$VALUE
4x5 1-325 <$1500
3x10-20 1-151 <$1500
Total Issue $14,050
Out in 1915 $275
****
7966 Rusk
LADYSMITH NB, LADYSMITH
{{ 3 L }}
Chartered 10/05
Liquidated 10/24/10
1902 Red Seal <$VALUE
3x10-20 1-500 <$1250
1902 Date Back
3x10-20 1-583 <$750
Total Issue $54,150
Out at close $25,000
****
11826 Rusk
PIONEER NB OF LADYSMITH
{{ 3 L 8 S }}
Chartered 8/23/20
1902 Plain Back <$VALUE
4x5 1-5117 <$750
1929 Small Size
5 Type 1 1-5745* <$300
* 437-2036 not issued
Total Issue $226,690
Out in 1935 $20,000
Large out 1935 $565
****
5592 Walworth
FARMERS NB OF LAKE GENEVA
{{ 6 L 9 S }}
Organized 9/4/00
Receivership 1/5/34
Brown Back <$VALUE
3x10-20 1-1800 <$650
1882 Date Back
3x10-20 1-3040 <$600
1882 Value Back
3x10-20 3041-4686 <$600
1902 Plain Back
3x10-20 1-5461 <$350
1929 Small Size
10 Type 1 1-1192 <$200
20 Type 1 1-312 <$200
10 Type 2 1-277 <$225
20 Type 2 1-90 <$250
Total Issue $710,880
Out at close $50,000
Large out at close $3,620
****
3125 Walworth
FNB OF LAKE GENEVA
{{ 6 L 9 S }}
Chartered 1884
Brown Back <$VALUE
4x5 1-3852 <$700
50-100 1-357 <$4000/$5000
1902 Red Seal
4x5 1-1585 <$850
50-100 1-382 <$6000/$6500
1902 Date Back
4x5 1-2500 <$350
50-100 1-280 <$600/$750
3x50-100 1-494 <$600/$750
1902 Plain Back
4x5 2501-12430 <$350
3x50-100 495-637<$600/$750
1929 Small Size
5 Type 1 1-1966 <$200
50 Type 1 1-106 <$250
100 Type 1 1-34 <$375
5 Type 2 1-40 <$300
50 Type 2 1-15 <$1000
Total Issue $781,570
Out in 1935 $50,000
Large out 1935 $3,185
****
7007 Grant
FNB OF LANCASTER
{{ 1 L }}
Chartered 10/03
Liquidated 11/24/13
1902 Red Seal <$VALUE
3x10-20 1-857 <$2000
1902 Date Back
3x10-20 1-985 <$1250
Total Issue $92,100
Out in 1914 $13,070
****
9153 Dane
COMMERCIAL NB OF MADISON
{{ 16 L 16 S }}
Chartered 5/08
Liquidated 2/28/33
1902 Date Back <$VALUE
3x10-20 1-16700 <$125
1902 Plain Back
3x10-20 16701-41113 <$125
1929 Small Size
10 Type 1 1-3622 <$100
20 Type 1 1-975 <$100
Total Issue $2,389,970
Out at close $200,000
Large out at close $19,870
****
144 Dane
FNB OF MADISON
{{ 29 L 50+ S }}
Chartered 1863
Original Series <$VALUE
3x1-2 1-140 <$650/$1500
4x5 1-4465 <$750
3x10-20 1-2300<$1250/$1750
Series 1875
3x10-20 1-368 <$1250/$1750
Brown Back
3x10-20 1-3993 <$250/$300
1902 Red Seal
3x10-20 1-3550 <$275/$325
1902 Date Back
3x10-20 1-14800 <$100
1902 Plain Back
3x10-20 14801-54843 <$100
1929 Small Size
10 Type 1 1-15780 <$25
20 Type 1 1-3800 <$35
10 Type 2 1-14506 <$25
20 Type 2 1-3645 <$35
Total Issue $4,963,460
Out in 1935 $1,000,000
Large out 1935 $16,620
****
8710 Waupaca
FNB OF MANAWA
{{ 12 L 8 S }}
Organized 2/16/07
Receivership 3/14/34
1902 Red Seal <$VALUE
4x5 1-250 <$750
3x10-20 1-200 <$750
1902 Date Back
4x5 1-1400 <$300
3x10-20 1-1050 <$300
1902 Plain Back
4x5 1401-4362 <$300
3x10-20 1051-2841 <$300
1929 Small Size
5 Type 1 1-746 <$250
10 Type 1 1-356 <$250
20 Type 1 1-98 <$250
5 Type 2 1-234 <$300
10 Type 2 1-90 <$300
20 Type 2 1-25 <$300
Total Issue $302,360
Out at close $25,000
Large out at close $1,660
****
FNB in Manitowoc
SEE Ch 4975
NB of Manitowoc
****
852 Manitowoc
FNB OF MANITOWOC
{{ UNREPORTED }}
Chartered 3/1/65
Liquidated 12/26/91
Original Series <$VALUE
3x1-2 1-1500 <$2500/$4000
4x5 1-5500 <$2500
Series 1875
4x5 1-2985 <$2500
Brown Back
4x5 1-1520 <$1500
Total Issue $207,600
Out in 1910 $1,647
****
4975 Manitowoc
NB OF MANITOWOC
Chartered 1894
2nd title:FNB in Manitowoc 1/22/23
FIRST TITLE {{ U + 10 L }}
Brown Back <$VALUE
4x5 1-8350 <$500
3x10-20 1-3300 <$500
1882 Date Back
4x5 1-4194 <$450
3x10-20 1-3093 <$450
1902 Date Back
4x5 1-2500 <$175
3x10-20 1-2000 <$175
1902 Plain Back
4x5 2501-11800 <$175
3x10-20 2001-7720 <$175
SECOND TITLE {{ 14 L 28 S }}
1902 Plain Back
4x5 1-9195 <$150
3x10-20 1-6415 <$150
1929 Small Size
5 Type 1 1-5862 <$50
10 Type 1 1-2878 <$50
20 Type 1 1-772 <$60
5 Type 2 1-4378 <$60
10 Type 2 1-2712 <$60
20 Type 2 1-440 <$75
Total Issue $2,196,170
Out in 1935 $200,000
Large out 1935 $9,280
****
4123 Marinette
FNB OF MARINETTE
{{ 10 L 19 S }}
Chartered 1889
Brown Back <$VALUE
3x10-20 1-4320 <$400
1882 Date Back
3x10-20 1-770 <$350
1902 Date Back
4x5 1-6550 <$200
4x10 1-5150 <$200
1902 Plain Back
4x5 6551-21983 <$200
4x10 5151-17526 <$200
1929 Small Size
5 Type 1 1-4898 <$65
10 Type 1 1-2316 <$65
5 Type 2 1-5314 <$75
10 Type 2 1-2949 <$75
Total Issue $1,737,160
Out in 1935 $100,000
Large out 1935 $4,780
****
4137 Marinette
STEPHENSON NB OF MARINETTE
{{ 16 L 28 S }}
Chartered 1889
Brown Back <$VALUE
4x5 1-8832 <$300
3x10-20 1-3418 <$300
1902 Date Back
3x10-20 1-6800 <$150
1902 Plain Back
3x10-20 6801-18926 <$150
1929 Small Size
10 Type 1 1-3688 <$50
20 Type 1 1-956 <$60
10 Type 2 1-3132 <$60
20 Type 2 1-1068 <$65
Total Issue $1,682,520
Out in 1935 $200,000
Large out 1935 $5,930
****
14130 Waupaca
FNB IN MARION
{{ 3 S }}
Chartered 5/34
1929 Small Size <$VALUE
5 Type 2 1-1526 <$500
10 Type 2 1-1041 <$500
Total Issue $18,040
Out in 1935 $50,000
Outstanding includes Ch 12286
****
12286 Waupaca
FNB OF MARION
{{ 4 L 9 S }}
Organized 12/12/22
Liquidated 6/27/34
1902 Plain Back <$VALUE
4x5 1-4722 <$500
4x10 1-3799 <$500
1929 Small Size
5 Type 1 1-2236 <$200
10 Type 1 1-1104 <$200
5 Type 2 1-1572 <$225
10 Type 2 1-816 <$225
Total Issue $395,740
Out at close $50,000
Large out 1935 $1,180
Ch 14130 assumed circulation
****
5437 Wood
AMERICAN NB OF MARSHFIELD
{{ 13 L 20 S }}
Organized 6/7/00
Receivership 5/23/34
Brown Back <$VALUE
3x10-20 1-3000 <$350
1882 Date Back
3x10-20 1-2340 <$300
1882 Value Back
3x10-20 2341-3664 <$350
1902 Plain Back
3x10-20 1-14858 <$175
1929 Small Size
10 Type 1 1-3331 <$65
20 Type 1 1-978 <$75
Total Issue $1,393,320
Out at close $150,000
Large out at close $7,320
****
14125 Wood
CITIZENS NB OF MARSHFIELD
{{ 7 S }}
Chartered 4/34
1929 Small Size <$VALUE
10 Type 2 1-4630 <$300
20 Type 2 1-1510 <$300
Total Issue $76,500
Out in 1935 $75,000
****
4573 Wood
FNB OF MARSHFIELD
{{ 8 L 10 S }}
Organized 5/18/91
Receivership 12/22/32
Brown Back <$VALUE
4x5 1-3975 <$500
3x10-20 1-2320 <$500
1882 Date Back
4x5 1-1690 <$450
3x10-20 1-856 <$450
1902 Date Back
3x10-20 1-3600 <$250
1902 Plain Back
3x10-20 3601-20689 <$250
1929 Small Size
10 Type 1 1-2814 <$175
20 Type 1 1-747 <$175
Total Issue $1,565,030
Out at close $147,180
Large out at close $14,260
****
10653 Dodge
FNB OF MAYVILLE
{{ 3 L 7 S }}
Organized 9/19/14
Receivership 3/23/34
1902 Date Back <$VALUE
4x5 1-1000 <$600
3x10-20 1-800 <$600
1902 Plain Back
4x5 1001-8168 <$600
3x10-20 801-5441 <$600
1929 Small Size
5 Type 1 1-1532 <$250
10 Type 1 1-791 <$250
20 Type 1 1-236 <$250
Total Issue $557,150
Out at close $50,000
Large out at close $2,570
****
5695 Taylor
FNB OF MEDFORD
{{ 10 L 27 S }}
Organized 12/3/00
Liquidated 1/11/33
Brown Back <$VALUE
3x10-20 1-2180 <$400
1882 Date Back
3x10-20 1-1500 <$400
1882 Value Back
3x10-20 1501-2395 <$400
1902 Plain Back
3x10-20 1-3686 <$200
1929 Small Size
10 Type 1 1-804 <$65
20 Type 1 1-238 <$75
Total Issue $489,850
Out at close $50,000
Large out at close $6,300
****
3724 Winnebago
FNB OF MENASHA
{{ 12 L 18 S }}
Chartered 1887
Brown Back <$VALUE
4x5 1-7097 <$350
3x10-20 1-2194 <$350
1902 Red Seal
3x10-20 1-800 <$400
1902 Date Back
3x10-20 1-5500 <$175
1902 Plain Back
3x10-20 5501-15858 <$175
1929 Small Size
10 Type 1 1-2779 <$75
20 Type 1 1-894 <$85
Total Issue $1,358,560
Out in 1935 $75,000
Large out 1935 $3,965
****
1714 Winnebago
NB OF MENASHA
{{ 2 L }}
Chartered 9/30/70
Liquidated 4/26/79
Original Series <$VALUE
3x1-2 1-1660 <$1500/$2500
4x5 1-3085 <$1500
Series 1875
4x5 1-1420 <$1500
Total Issue $98,400
Out in 1910 $677
****
2851 Dunn
FNB OF MENOMONIE
{{ 24 L 26 S }}
Organized 12/23/82
Brown Back <$VALUE
3x10-20 1-2030 <$300/$350
1902 Red Seal
3x10-20 1-2100 <$300/$350
1902 Date Back
3x10-20 1-3600 <$125
1902 Plain Back
3x10-20 3601-18195 <$125
1929 Small Size
10 Type 1 1-4570 <$50
20 Type 1 1-1198 <$60
10 Type 2 1-933 <$50
20 Type 2 1-326 <$60
Total Issue $1,550,060
Out in 1935 $100,000
Large out 1935 $9,910
****
10176 Lincoln
CITIZENS NB OF MERRILL
{{ 12 L 16 S }}
Chartered 4/12
Liquidated 4/20/33
1902 Date Back <$VALUE
3x10-20 1-4400 <$200
1902 Plain Back
3x10-20 4401-15585 <$200
1929 Small Size
10 Type 1 1-2302 <$100
20 Type 1 1-507 <$100
Total Issue $983,010
Out at close $150,000
Large out at close $8,910
****
3704 Lincoln
FNB OF MERRILL
{{ 1 L }}
Chartered 5/12/87
Liquidated 3/27/97
Brown Back <$VALUE
4x5 1-2319 <$1500
Total Issue $46,380
Out in 1910 $445
****
4736 Lincoln
NB OF MERRILL
{{ 6 L }}
Chartered 1892
Liquidated 4/14/12
Brown Back <$VALUE
3x10-20 1-8420 <$650
1882 Date Back
3x10-20 1-2887 <$600
Total Issue $565,350
Out in 1912 $27,400
****
Bay View NB of Milwaukee
SEE Ch 12816
Mechanics NB of Milwaukee
****
4816 Milwaukee
CENTRAL NB OF MILWAUKEE
{{ 1 L }}
Chartered 11/10/92
Liquidated 8/17/98
Brown Back <$VALUE
3x10-20 1-1840 <$1250
Total Issue $92,000
Out in 1910 $1,410
****

64 Milwaukee
FNB OF MILWAUKEE*
Chartered 8/63
Liquidated 5/31/82
***Reorganized as Ch 2715 which retook Ch 64 5/31/11**
2nd title: F Wisconsin NB of Milwaukee 7/1/19
FIRST TITLE **{{ 12 L }}**
Original Series <$VALUE
4x5 1-7250 <$850
4x10 1-3760 <$1500
3x20-100 1-700 <$2500/$10,000
Series 1875
4x5 1-4940 <$850
4x10 1-2625 <$1500
1902 Date Back
4x5 1-78000 <$125
3x10-20 1-56000 <$125
1902 Plain Back
4x5 78001-103000 <$125
3x10-20 56001-66600 <$125
SECOND TITLE **{{50+ L 50+ S}}**
1902 Plain Back (dated 1902)
4x5 1-87500 <$50
3x10-20 1-45000 <$60
1902 Plain Back (dated 1922)
4x5 1-134801 <$50
3x10-20 1-96821 <$60
1929 Small Size
5 Type 1 1-100286 <$15
10 Type 1 1-118464 <$20
20 Type 1 1-39598* <$30
5 Type 2 1-100928** <$15
10 Type 2 1-69345 <$20
20 Type 2 1-25100 <$30
* 37345 not issued
** 40069-40074 not issued
Total Issue $32,966,140
Out in 1935 $947,070
Large out 1935 $148,125
Outstanding includes Ch 4817 Ch 2715, and Ch 6853

2715 Milwaukee
FNB OF MILWAUKEE
{{ 16 L }}
Chartered 1882
RETOOK Ch 64 5/31/11
Brown Back <$VALUE
4x5 1-24000 <$300
3x10-20 1-13205 <$300
1902 Red Seal
4x5 1-33000 <$350
3x10-20 1-32300 <$350
1902 Date Back
4x5 1-51000 <$125
3x10-20 1-40000 <$125
Total Issue $6,435,250
Out in 1911 $500,000

F Wisconsin NB of Milwaukee
SEE Ch 64
FNB of Milwaukee

6853 Milwaukee
GERMANIA NB OF MILWAUKEE
Chartered 6/03
Liquidated 9/22/32
2nd title:NB of Commerce of Milwaukee 6/1/18
FIRST TITLE **{{ 12 L }}**
1902 Red Seal <$VALUE
4x5 1-7705 <$400
3x10-20 1-4068 <$400
50-100 1-1400 <$6000/$6500
1902 Date Back
4x5 1-18500* <$200
3x10-20 1-12000** <$200
50-100 1-200 <$450/$500
3x50-100 1-317 <$450/$500
1902 Plain Back
4x5 19751-23585* <$200
3x10-20 13001-14900** <$200
SECOND TITLE **{{ 28 L 50+ S }}**
1902 Plain Back
4x5 1-87702 <$65
3x10-20 1-63683 <$75
1929 Small Size
5 Type 1 1-32416 <$15
10 Type 1 1-13353 <$20
20 Type 1 1-3592 <$30
Total Issue $9,036,340
Out at close $1,000,000
Large out at close $62,950
Ch 64 assumed circulation

12628 Milwaukee
GRAND & SIXTH NB OF MILWAUKEE
Chartered 1/25
Liquidated 10/18/32
2nd title: Sixth Wisconsin NB of Milwaukee 9/24/28
FIRST TITLE **{{ 4 L }}**
1902 Plain Back <$VALUE
4x5 1-15909 <$300
SECOND TITLE **{{ 3 L 27 S }}**
1902 Plain Back
4x5 1-4014 <$300
1929 Small Size
5 Type 1 1-13546 <$50
Total Issue $804,840
Out at close $200,000
Large out at close $3,310

5458 Milwaukee
MARINE NB OF MILWAUKEE
Chartered 6/26/00
2nd title:Marine N Exchange B of Milwaukee 7/31/30
FIRST TITLE **{{ 50+ L 16 S }}**
Brown Back <$VALUE
4x5 1-17150 <$175
3x10-20 1-14040 <$175/$225
1882 Date Back
4x5 1-24415 <$150
3x10-20 1-19334 <$150/$175
1882 Value Back
4x5 24416-41785 <$175
3x10-20 19335-28475 <$175/$225
1902 Plain Back
4x5 1-78401 <$50
3x10-20 1-53955 <$60
1929 Small Size
5 Type 1 1-15382 <$50
10 Type 1 1-7280 <$50
20 Type 1 1-2080 <$60
SECOND TITLE **{{ 50+ S }}**
1929 Small Size
5 Type 1 1-40592 <$15
10 Type 1 1-19968 <$20
20 Type 1 1-6815 <$30
Total Issue $11,951,720
Out in 1935 $1,263,335
Large out 1935 $64,745
Outstanding includes Ch 1003

Marine N Exchange B of Milwaukee
SEE Ch 5458
Marine NB of Milwaukee

12816 Milwaukee
MECHANICS NB OF MILWAUKEE
Chartered 9/25
Liquidated 10/18/32
2nd title:Bay View NB of Milwaukee 4/26/30
FIRST TITLE **{{ 7 L 4 S }}**
1902 Plain Back <$VALUE
4x5 1-19237 <$300
1929 Small Size
5 Type 1 1-4092 <$300
SECOND TITLE **{{ 12 S }}**
1929 Small Size
5 Type 1 1-9676 <$125
Total Issue $797,780
Out at close $200,000
Large out at close $2,965

1438 Milwaukee
MERCHANTS NB OF MILWAUKEE
{{ 1 L }}
Chartered 7/14/65
Liquidated 6/14/70
Original Series <$VALUE
4x5 1-1000 <$2500
3x10-20 1-1420 <$3500/$4000
Total Issue $91,000
Out in 1910 $560

1017 Milwaukee
MILWAUKEE NB OF WISCONSIN MILWAUKEE
{{ 12 L }}
Chartered 4/65
Liquidated 8/29/12
Original Series <$VALUE
4x5 1-7450 <$650
3x10-20 1-3000 <$1250/$1750
20 3001-4500 <$1750
Series 1875
4x5 1-3750 <$650
3x10-20 1-7212 <$1250/$1750
Brown Back
3x10-20 1-16231 <$350
1902 Red Seal
3x10-20 1-12000 <$350
1902 Date Back
3x10-20 1-11233 <$175
Total Issue $2,737,800
Out in 1912 $425,550

NB of Commerce of Milwaukee
SEE Ch 6853
Germania NB of Milwaukee

1483 Milwaukee
N CITY B OF MILWAUKEE
{{ UNREPORTED }}
Chartered 7/25/65
Liquidated 2/24/75
Original Series <$VALUE
4x5 1-1650 <$2500
3x10-20 1-1196 <$3500/$4000
Total Issue $92,800
Out in 1910 $680

1003 Milwaukee
N EXCHANGE B OF MILWAUKEE
{{ 43 L 50+ S }}
Chartered 4/65
Closed 7/31/30
Original Series <$VALUE
4x5 1-10100 <$650
3x10-20 1-1930 <$1250/$1750
Series 1875
4x5 1-7500 <$650
3x10-20 1-3950 <$1250/$1750
Brown Back
4x5 1-3375 <$200
3x10-20 1-15135 <$200/$250
50-100 1-3437 <$4000/$5000
1902 Red Seal
3x10-20 1-13600 <$200/$250
1902 Date Back
3x10-20 1-26000 <$65
1902 Plain Back
3x10-20 26001-70783 <$65
1929 Small Size
10 Type 1 1-10276 <$25
20 Type 1 1-2863 <$35
Total Issue $7,165,070
Out at close $500,000
Large out at close $95,100
Ch 5458 assumed circulation

12564 Milwaukee
NORTHWESTERN NB OF MILWAUKEE
{{ 12 L 9 S }}
Chartered 7/24
Liquidated 2/14/33
1902 Plain Back <$VALUE
4x5 1-12662 <$165
1929 Small Size
5 Type 1 1-10021 <$150
Total Issue $551,670
Out at close $182,120
Large out at close $1,940

Sixth Wisconsin NB of Milwaukee
SEE Ch 12628
Grand & Sixth NB of Milwaukee

4817 Milwaukee
WISCONSIN NB OF MILWAUKEE
{{ 50+ L }}
Chartered 11/12/92
Closed 7/1/19
Brown Back <$VALUE
3x10-20 1-73000 <$175/$225
1882 Date Back
3x10-20 1-43343 <$150/$200
1902 Date Back
3x10-20 1-81320 <$65
1902 Plain Back
3x10-20 81321-83461 <$65
Total Issue $9,990,200
Out at close $665,995
Ch 64 assumed circulation

3203 Iowa
FNB OF MINERAL POINT
{{ UNREPORTED }}
Organized 6/10/84
Receivership 10/12/09
Brown Back <$VALUE
3x10-20 1-2184 <$2000
1902 Red Seal
3x10-20 1-790 <$2500
1902 Date Back
3x10-20 1-94 <$1500
Total Issue $153,400
Out in 1915 $2,750

5779 Buffalo
FNB OF MONDOVI
{{ 6 L 6 S }}
Chartered 4/01
Brown Back <$VALUE
4x5 1-700 <$750
3x10-20 1-580 <$750
1882 Date Back
4x5 1-700 <$700
3x10-20 1-540 <$700
1882 Value Back
4x5 701-835 <$700
3x10-20 541-740 <$700
1902 Plain Back
4x5 1-1150 <$400
3x10-20 1-649 <$400
1929 Small Size
5 Type 1 1-387 <$350
10 Type 1 1-206 <$350
20 Type 1 1-73 <$375
Total Issue $184,880
Out in 1935 $12,500
Large out 1935 $650

230 Green
FNB OF MONROE
{{ 13 L U + 20 S }}
Chartered 1864
Original Series <$VALUE
3x1-2 1-1000 <$750/$1500
4x5 1-7950 <$750
Series 1875
4x5 1-5745 <$750
Brown Back
4x5 1-9126 <$400
3x10-20 1-944 <$400
1902 Red Seal
3x10-20 1-2600 <$500
1902 Date Back
3x10-20 1-6100* <$200
1902 Plain Back
3x10-20 6601-17867* <$200
* 6101-6600 not marked
1929 Small Size
10 Type 1 1-2828 <$75
20 Type 1 1-866 <$85
10 Type 2 1-2120 <$85
20 Type 2 1-341 <$100
Total Issue $1,833,590
Out in 1935 $150,000
Large out 1935 $7,610

FNB of Neenah
SEE Ch 1602
NB of Neenah

2603 Winnebago
MANUFACTURERS NB OF NEENAH
{{ 7 L }}
Chartered 12/16/81
Liquidated 11/28/01
Series 1875 <$VALUE
4x5 1-7973 <$600
3x10-20 1-729 <$1250/$1750
Total Issue $195,910
Out in 1910 $2,795

1602 Winnebago
NB OF NEENAH
Chartered 1865
2nd title: FNB of Neenah 10/12/05
FIRST TITLE **{{ 0 L }}**
Original Series <$VALUE
4x5 1-4175 <$1500
3x10-20 1-510 <$2500/$3000
Series 1875
4x5 1-4150 <$1500
3x10-20 1-958 <$2500/$3000
Brown Back
3x10-20 1-4536 <$1250
SECOND TITLE **{{ 2 L 12 S }}**
1902 Red Seal
50-100 1-450 <$6000/$6500
1902 Date Back
50-100 1-934 <$1000/$1250
3x50-100 1-451 <$1000/$1250
1929 Small Size
50 Type 1 1-269 <$200
100 Type 1 1-81 <$250
Total Issue $916,350
Out in 1932 $125,000
Large out 1935 $3,815

6034 Winnebago
N MANUFACTURERS B OF NEENAH
{{ 13 L 18 S }}
Chartered 11/01
Brown Back <$VALUE
3x10-20 1-4100 <$300
1882 Date Back
3x10-20 1-4600* <$275
1882 Value Back
3x10-20 5201-8257* <$300
* 4601-5200 not marked
1902 Plain Back
4x5 1-6241 <$175
1929 Small Size
10 Type 1 1-2162 <$65
20 Type 1 1-640 <$75
10 Type 2 1-1042 <$100
20 Type 2 1-324 <$100
Total Issue $1,153,320
Out in 1935 $100,000
Large out 1935 $4,290

14200 Clark
FNB AT NEILLSVILLE
{{ 5 S }}
Chartered 6/34
1929 Small Size <$VALUE
10 Type 2 1-2610 <$500
Total Issue $26,100
Out in 1935 $25,000

9606 Clark
FNB OF NEILLSVILLE
{{ 6 L U + 7 S }}
Organized 9/28/09
Receivership 10/26/33
1902 Date Back <$VALUE
4x5 1-3100* <$350
3x10-20 1-2380** <$350
1902 Plain Back
4x5 3301-10235* <$350
3x10-20 2541-7040** <$350
* 3100-3300 not marked
** 2381-2540 not marked
1929 Small Size
5 Type 1 1-1455 <$200
10 Type 1 1-728 <$200
20 Type 1 1-182 <$200
Total Issue $665,870
Out at close $50,000
Large.out at close $2,990

5013 Waupaca
FNB OF NEW LONDON
{{ 4 L 7 S }}
Chartered 7/22/95
Liquidated 5/31/33
Brown Back <$VALUE
4x5 1-2375 <$800
3x10-20 1-800 <$800
1882 Date Back
4x5 1-800 <$750
3x10-20 1-594 <$750
1902 Plain Back
3x10-20 1-1683 <$500
1929 Small Size
5 Type 1 1-786 <$300
10 Type 1 1-474 <$300
20 Type 1 1-32 <$325
Total Issue $273,210
Out at close $42,500
Large out at close $1,190

11412 Saint Croix
FNB OF NEW RICHMOND
{{ 6 L 7 S }}
Chartered 8/19
1902 Plain Back <$VALUE
4x5 1-8337 <$400
1929 Small Size
5 Type 1 1-2596 <$250
5 Type 2 1-5244 <$275
Total Issue $270,840
Out in 1935 $25,000
Large out 1935 $1,110

11051 Marinette
FNB OF NIAGARA
{{ 4 L 4 S }}
Chartered 8/5/17
1902 Plain Back <$VALUE
4x5 1-3317 <$750
1929 Small Size
5 Type 1 1-2066 <$400
5 Type 2 1-4070 <$400
Total Issue $148,670
Out in 1935 $25,000
Large out 1935 $80

5505 Waukesha
FNB OF OCONOMOWOC
{{ U + 8 L 8 S }}
Organized 7/3/00
Receivership 2/4/32
Brown Back <$VALUE
3x10-20 1-1400 <$450
1882 Date Back
4x5 1-2330* <$400
3x10-20 1-1460** <$400
1882 Value Back
4x5 2631-3680* <$400
3x10-20 1701-2320** <$400
* 2331-2630 not marked
** 1461-1700 not marked
1902 Plain Back
3x10-20 1-7765 <$200
1929 Small Size
10 Type 1 1-1735 <$150
20 Type 1 1-450 <$150
Total Issue $805,950
Out at close $100,000
Large out 1935 $4,690
Ch 13616 assumed circulation

13616 Waukesha
OCONOMOWOC NB, OCONOMOWOC
{{ 7 S }}
Chartered 5/32
1929 Small Size <$VALUE
10 Type 1 1-316 <$225
20 Type 1 1-106 <$225
10 Type 2 1-1405 <$225
20 Type 2 1-321 <$250
Total Issue $52,150
Out in 1935 $75,000
Outstanding includes Ch 5505

5521 Oconto
CITIZENS NB OF OCONTO
{{ 12 L 8 S }}
Organized 12/28/00
Liquidated 9/5/34
Brown Back <$VALUE
3x10-20 1-3300 <$400
1882 Date Back
3x10-20 1-4140 <$400
1882 Value Back
3x10-20 4141-4530 <$400
1902 Plain Back
3x10-20 1-5168 <$225
1929 Small Size
10 Type 1 1-1166 <$175
20 Type 1 1-306 <$200
Total Issue $756,580
Out in 1934 $50,000
Large out 1935 $2,810
Ch 14233 assumed circulation

3541 Oconto
OCONTO NB, OCONTO
{{ 7 L 7 S }}
Organized 7/15/86
Receivership 8/3/31
Brown Back <$VALUE
4x5 1-3321 <$600
3x10-20 1-531 <$600
1902 Red Seal
3x10-20 1-300 <$750
1902 Date Back
3x10-20 1-1460 <$350
1902 Plain Back
3x10-20 1461-6412 <$350
1929 Small Size
10 Type 1 1-907 <$250
20 Type 1 1-227 <$250
Total Issue $510,230
Out at close $60,000
Large out at close $6,450

5566 Winnebago
FNB OF OMRO
{{ 3 L }}
Chartered 8/31/00
Liquidated 1/30/09
Brown Back <$VALUE
4x5 1-1250 <$1000
3x10-20 1-858 <$1000
Total Issue $67,900
Out in 1910 $9,210

10620 Dane
FNB OF OREGON
{{ 4 L 3 S }}
Organized 5/25/14
Receivership 10/25/33
1902 Plain Back <$VALUE
3x10-20 1-2815 <$750
1929 Small Size
10 Type 1 1-256 <$500
20 Type 1 1-62 <$500
Total Issue $163,550
Out at close $12,500
Large out at close $1,130

****
9347 Winnebago
CITY NB OF OSHKOSH
{{ 26 L 16 S }}
Organized 1/9/09
Receivership 1/31/33
1902 Date Back <$VALUE
4x5 1-14000 <$100
3x10-20 1-10100 <$100
1902 Plain Back
4x5 14001-42093 <$100
3x10-20 10101-28346 <$100
1929 Small Size
5 Type 1 1-5751 <$75
10 Type 1 1-3006 <$75
20 Type 1 1-737 <$85
Total Issue $2,700,490
Out at close $165,000
Large out at close $16,030
****
1568 Winnebago
COMMERCIAL NB OF OSHKOSH
{{ UNREPORTED }}
Chartered 9/25/65
Liquidated 11/22/71
Original Series <$VALUE
4x5 1-3605 <$2500
3x10-20 1-450 <$3500/$4000
Total Issue $94,600
Out in 1910 $655
****
5557 Winnebago
COMMERCIAL NB OF OSHKOSH
{{ 26 L }}
Chartered 8/25/00
Liquidated 11/1/19
Brown Back <$VALUE
4x5 1-9065 <$175
3x10-20 1-6674 <$175/$225
1882 Date Back
4x5 1-13250 <$175
3x10-20 1-8800 <$175/$225
1882 Value Back
4x5 13251-18400 <$200
3x10-20 8801-11330
<$200/$250
Total Issue $1,449,500
Out in 1919 $191,500
****
FNB in Oshkosh
SEE Ch 6604
Old NB of Oshkosh
****
218 Winnebago
FNB OF OSHKOSH
{{ 2 L }}
Chartered 1/64
Liquidated 2/24/83
Original Series <$VALUE
4x5 1-6750 <$1250
Series 1875
4x5 1-5425 <$1250
Total Issue $243,500
Out in 1910 $1,350
****
4196 Winnebago
GERMAN NB OF OSHKOSH
{{ 4 L }}
Chartered 1/7/90
Liquidated 4/6/09
Brown Back <$VALUE
4x5 1-4930 <$700
3x10-20 1-3308 <$700
1882 Date Back
4x5 1-586 <$650
3x10-20 1-135 <$650
Total Issue $282,490
Out in 1910 $32,930
****
2877 Winnebago
NB OF OSHKOSH
{{ 1 L }}
Chartered 2/10/83
Liquidated 2/1/03
Brown Back <$VALUE
3x10-20 1-4596 <$1250
Total Issue $229,800
Out in 1910 $4,200
****
4508 Winnebago
N UNION B OF OSHKOSH
{{ 8 L }}
Chartered 1/20/91
Liquidated 2/20/09
Brown Back <$VALUE
4x5 1-15719 <$250
3x10-20 1-8638 <$250/$300
Total Issue $746,280
Out in 1910 $27,580
****
Old-Commercial NB of Oshkosh
SEE Ch 6604
Old NB of Oshkosh
****
6604 Winnebago
OLD NB OF OSHKOSH
Chartered 2/03
2nd title:Old-Commercial NB 11/1/19
3rd title:FNB in Oshkosh 9/15/25
FIRST TITLE {{ 4 L }}
1902 Red Seal <$VALUE
3x10-20 1-4300 <$275/$325
1902 Date Back
3x10-20 1-6500 <$125
1902 Plain Back
3x10-20 6501-7500 <$125
SECOND TITLE {{ 7 L }}
1902 Plain Back
3x10-20 1-22000 <$125
THIRD TITLE {{12 L 50+ S}}
1902 Plain Back
3x10-20 1-24687 <$85
1929 Small Size
10 Type 1 1-14580 <$20
20 Type 1 1-4374 <$30
10 Type 2 1-11855* <$20
20 Type 2 1-3192 <$30
* 5989 - 6000 not issued
Total Issue $4,506,300
Out in 1935 $500,000
Large out 1935 $15,190
****
13806 Winnebago
OSHKOSH NB, OSHKOSH
{{ 16 S }}
Chartered 10/16/33
1929 Small Size <$VALUE
5 Type 2 1-12100 <$65
10 Type 2 1-9439 <$65
20 Type 2 1-4270 <$70
Total Issue $240,290
Out in 1935 $200,000
****
1787 Winnebago
UNION NB OF OSHKOSH
{{ UNREPORTED }}
Chartered 2/9/71
Liquidated 1/23/91
Original Series <$VALUE
4x5 1-7000 <$2000
3x10-20 1-1000<$2500/$3000
Series 1875
4x5 1-1588 <$2000
3x10-20 1-995 <$2500/$3000
Total Issue $271,510
Out in 1910 $1,520
****
10489 Price
FNB OF PARK FALLS
{{ 5 L 10 S }}
Chartered 2/14
1902 Date Back <$VALUE
4x5 1-410 <$500
3x10-20 1-336 <$500
1902 Plain Back
4x5 411-3026 <$500
3x10-20 337-1931 <$500
1929 Small Size
5 Type 1 1-1136 <$200
10 Type 1 1-720 <$200
20 Type 1 1-164 <$200
5 Type 2 1-1054 <$225
10 Type 2 1-652 <$225
20 Type 2 1-215 <$225
Total Issue $270,120
Out in 1935 $50,000
Large out 1935 $1,020
****
5658 Marinette
PESHTIGO NB, PESHTIGO
{{ 5 L 7 S }}
Chartered 12/29/00
Brown Back <$VALUE
3x10-20 1-800 <$700
1882 Date Back
3x10-20 1-500* <$700
1882 Value Back
3x10-20 601-739* <$700
* 501-600 not marked
1902 Plain Back
3x10-20 1-921 <$500
1929 Small Size
10 Type 1 1-261 <$250
20 Type 1 1-64 <$250
Total Issue $146,340
Out in 1935 $10,000
Large out 1935 $780
****
13487 Price
FNB IN PHILLIPS
{{ 2U + 7 S }}
Chartered 8/30
1929 Small Size <$VALUE
5 Type 1 1-548 <$200
10 Type 1 1-170 <$200
5 Type 2 1-92 <$200
10 Type 2 1-142 <$225
Total Issue $28,520
Out in 1935 $25,000
Outstanding includes Ch 7434
****
7434 Price
FNB OF PHILLIPS
{{ 4 L 6 S }}
Chartered 10/04
Liquidated 6/24/31
1902 Red Seal <$VALUE
3x10-20 1-626 <$1250
1902 Date Back
3x10-20 1-1660 <$600
1902 Plain Back
3x10-20 1661-4655 <$600
1929 Small Size
10 Type 1 1-314 <$300
20 Type 1 1-106 <$300
Total Issue $295,610
Out at close $25,000
Large out 1935 $1,160
Ch 13487 assumed circulation
****
4650 Grant
FNB OF PLATTEVILLE
{{ 7 L 8 S }}
Chartered 1891
Brown Back <$VALUE
4x5 1-4350 <$600
3x10-20 1-1750 <$600
1882 Date Back
4x5 1-1068 <$600
3x10-20 1-763 <$600
1902 Date Back
3x10-20 1-2100 <$300
1902 Plain Back
3x10-20 2101-8076 <$300
1929 Small Size
10 Type 1 1-1140 <$200
20 Type 1 1-308 <$200
10 Type 2 1-610 <$225
20 Type 2 1-119 <$225
Total Issue $751,650
Out in 1935 $50,000
Large out 1935 $3,440
****
9419 Ozaukee
FNB OF PORT WASHINGTON
{{ 5 L U + 9 S }}
Organized 3/6/09
1902 Date Back <$VALUE
3x10-20 1-3600 <$500
1902 Plain Back
3x10-20 3601-9569 <$500
1929 Small Size
5 Type 1 1-1352 <$200
10 Type 1 1-936 <$200
20 Type 1 1-210 <$225
5 Type 2 1-1746* <$225
10 Type 2 1-552 <$225
* 517-522 not issued
Total Issue $614,590
Out in 1935 $50,000
Large out 1935 $2,600
****
4234 Columbia
FNB OF PORTAGE
{{ 11 L 14 S }}
Organized 2/8/90
Brown Back <$VALUE
4x5 1-5144 <$400
3x10-20 1-1657 <$400
1902 Date Back
4x5 1-10177* <$200
3x10-20 1-2900** <$200
1902 Plain Back
4x5 * <$200
3x10-20 3301-9177** <$200
*Total issue of 10177 sheets
Break between types not known
** 2901-3300 not marked
1929 Small Size
5 Type 1 1-2074 <$125
10 Type 1 1-1256 <$125
20 Type 1 1-346 <$125
5 Type 2 1-1170 <$175
10 Type 2 1-459 <$175
20 Type 2 1-70 <$175
Total Issue $1,039,060
Out in 1935 $50,000
Large out 1935 $4,100
****
10522 Pierce
FNB OF PRESCOTT
{{ 2 L 6 S }}
Chartered 4/14
1902 Plain Back <$VALUE
3x10-20 1-1838 <$1000
1929 Small Size
10 Type 1 1-558 <$300
20 Type 1 1-146 <$300
10 Type 2 1-820 <$300
20 Type 2 1-115 <$300
Total Issue $153,400
Out in 1935 $25,000
Large out 1935 $830
****
13904 Green Lake
FARMERS-MERCHANTS NB IN PRINCETON
{{ 5 S }}
Chartered 12/33
1929 Small Size <$VALUE
5 Type 2 1-3920 <$300
10 Type 2 1-2135 <$300
20 Type 2 1-650 <$300
Total Issue $53,950
Out in 1935 $40,000
****
5978 Green Lake
FNB OF PRINCETON
{{ 6 L }}
Organized 7/25/01
Receivership 2/21/24
Brown Back <$VALUE
4x5 1-400 <$500
3x10-20 1-300 <$500
1882 Date Back
4x5 1-900 <$450
3x10-20 1-700 <$450
1882 Value Back
4x5 901-1110 <$500
3x10-20 701-833 <$500
Total Issue $86,850
Out in 1918 $15,000
****
10938 Racine
AMERICAN NB OF RACINE
{{ 1 L }}
Chartered 1/17
Liquidated 8/24/23
1902 Plain Back <$VALUE
4x5 1-3865 <$1000
Total Issue $77,300
Out at close $20,000
****
457 Racine
FNB OF RACINE
Organized 5/16/64
2nd title:FNB & TC 9/27/29
FIRST TITLE {{ 8 L }}
Original Series
3x1-2 1-3000 <$650/$1500
4x5 1-2750 <$750
3x10-20 1-1650<$1250/$1750
Series 1875
4x5 1-930 <$750
3x10-20 1-1170<$1250/$1750
Brown Back
3x10-20 1-3949 <$400
1902 Red Seal
4x5 1-3775 <$400
3x10-20 1-3020 <$400
1902 Date Back
4x5 1-9554 <$175
3x10-20 1-6705 <$175
SECOND TITLE {{ 50+ S }}
1929 Small Size
10 Type 1 1-2548 <$20
20 Type 1 1-1124 <$30
10 Type 2 1-12850 <$20
20 Type 2 1-10510 <$30
Total Issue $1,808,340
Out in 1935 $500,000
Large out 1935 $9,728
Outstanding includes Ch 1802, and Ch 10938
****
1802 Racine
MANUFACTURERS NB OF RACINE
{{ 12 L }}
Chartered 3/16/71
Closed 9/27/29
Original Series <$VALUE
3x1-2 1-2500 <$650/$1250
4x5 1-5985 <$750
3x10-20 1-456 <$1250/$1750
Series 1875
4x5 1-3000 <$750
3x10-20 1-4581<$1250/$1750
Brown Back
4x5 1-13850 <$400
3x10-20 1-7460 <$400
1882 Date Back
4x5 1-2307 <$400
3x10-20 1-1860 <$400
1902 Date Back
4x5 1-8250 <$175
3x10-20 1-6300 <$175
1902 Plain Back
4x5 8251-9755 <$175
3x10-20 6301-7326 <$175
Total Issue $1,794,590
Out at close $9,219
Outstanding includes Ch 10938
Ch 457 assumed circulation
****
2557 Racine
UNION NB OF RACINE
{{ 2 L }}
Chartered 9/1/81
Liquidated 9/15/00
Series 1875 <$VALUE
3x10-20 1-4239<$2500/$3000
Total Issue $211,950
Out in 1910 $2,380
****
4312 Oneida
FNB OF RHINELANDER
{{ 5 L 11 S }}
Chartered 1890
Brown Back <$VALUE
4x5 1-2725 <$700
3x10-20 1-1400 <$700
1882 Date Back
4x5 1-285 <$700
3x10-20 1-153 <$700
1902 Date Back
4x5 1-2400 <$400
3x10-20 1-1860 <$400
1902 Plain Back
4x5 2401-8899 <$400
3x10-20 1861-6152 <$400
1929 Small Size
5 Type 1 1-1418 <$150
10 Type 1 1-846 <$150
20 Type 1 1-254 <$150
5 Type 2 1-1506 <$175
10 Type 2 1-754 <$175
20 Type 2 1-101 <$175
Total Issue $764,300
Out in 1935 $50,000
Large out 1935 $3,315
****
11646 Oneida
ONEIDA NB OF RHINELANDER
{{ 5 L 8 S }}
Chartered 3/20
Liquidated 3/14/32
1902 Plain Back <$VALUE
3x10-20 1-11505 <$400
1929 Small Size
10 Type 1 1-1458 <$200
20 Type 1 1-469 <$200
Total Issue $719,010
Out at close $100,000
Large out at close $10,180
****
6711 Taylor
FNB OF RIB LAKE
{{ 5 L 9 S }}
Chartered 4/03
1902 Red Seal <$VALUE
3x10-20 1-770 <$1250
1902 Date Back
3x10-20 1-900 <$600
1902 Plain Back
3x10-20 901-3663 <$600
1929 Small Size
10 Type 1 1-544 <$250
20 Type 1 1-148 <$275
10 Type 2 1-421 <$300
20 Type 2 1-64 <$300
Total Issue $277,540
Out in 1935 $25,000
Large out 1935 $1,530
****
6663 Barron
FNB OF RICE LAKE
{{ 4 L U + 25 S }}
Chartered 3/03
1902 Red Seal <$VALUE
4x5 1-650 <$1250
3x10-20 1-460 <$1250
1902 Date Back
4x5 1-2850 <$600
3x10-20 1-2130 <$600
1902 Plain Back
4x5 2851-9113 <$600
3x10-20 2131-6156 <$600
1929 Small Size
5 Type 1 1-1512 <$150
10 Type 1 1-716 <$150
20 Type 1 1-194 <$150
5 Type 2 1-1156 <$150
10 Type 2 1-652 <$150
20 Type 2 1-222 <$150
Total Issue $654,400
Out in 1935 $50,000
Large out 1935 $3,240
****
7901 Richland
FNB OF RICHLAND CENTER
{{ 8 L }}
Organized 8/7/05
Receivership 11/26/28
1902 Red Seal <$VALUE
4x5 1-625 <$750
3x10-20 1-500 <$750
1902 Date Back
4x5 1-2600 <$350
3x10-20 1-1940 <$350
1902 Plain Back
4x5 2601-8710 <$350
3x10-20 1941-5978 <$350
Total Issue $510,600
Out at close $49,300
****
8632 Columbia
FNB OF RIO
{{ 1 L 0 S }}
Chartered 4/07
Liquidated 2/18/32
1902 Red Seal <$VALUE
4x5 1-156 <$2500
4x10 1-156 <$2500
1902 Date Back
4x5 1-550 <$1500
4x10 1-500 <$1500
1902 Plain Back
4x5 551-1226 <$1500
4x10 501-1015 <$1500
1929 Small Size
5 Type 1 1-219 <$1000
10 Type 1 1-88 <$1000
Total Issue $86,330
Out at close $6,250
Large out at close $450
****
American NB of Ripon
SEE Ch 4305
German NB of Ripon
****
425 Fond du Lac
FNB OF RIPON
{{ 27 L 50+ S }}
Chartered 1864
Original Series <$VALUE
4x5 1-5450 <$650
Series 1875
4x5 1-2545 <$650
Brown Back
3x10-20 1-4378 <$250/$275
1902 Red Seal
3x10-20 1-4800 <$250/$275
1902 Date Back
3x10-20 1-5300 <$85
1902 Plain Back
3x10-20 5301-16635 <$85
1929 Small Size
10 Type 1 1-5906 <$20
20 Type 1 1-1684 <$30
10 Type 2 1-4846 <$20
20 Type 2 1-1474 <$30
Total Issue $2,084,930
Out in 1935 $250,000
Large out 1935 $13,205
Outstanding includes Ch 4305
****
4305 Fond du Lac
GERMAN NB OF RIPON
Chartered 1890
Closed 3/18/30
2nd title:American NB of Ripon 6/1/18
FIRST TITLE {{ 15 L }}
Brown Back <$VALUE
4x5 1-6950 <$350
3x10-20 1-2260 <$350
1882 Date Back
4x5 1-875 <$350
3x10-20 1-550 <$350
1902 Date Back
4x5 1-5000 <$150
3x10-20 1-3800 <$150
1902 Plain Back
4x5 5001-6700 <$150
3x10-20 3801-4860 <$150
SECOND TITLE {{ 6 L 3 S }}
1902 Plain Back
4x5 1-13647 <$275
3x10-20 1-6938 <$275
1929 Small Size
5 Type 1 1-1123 <$450
10 Type 1 1-437 <$450
20 Type 1 1-63 <$450
Total Issue $1,361,310
Out at close $100,000
Large out at close $32,770
Ch 425 assumed circulation
****

****
3146 Fond du Lac
RIPON NB, RIPON
{{ UNREPORTED }}
Chartered 1884
Liquidated 2/7/85
Brown Back <$VALUE
4x5 1-810 <$2000
Total Issue $16,200
Out in 1910 $100
****
7087 Pierce
FNB OF RIVER FALLS
{{ 1 L }}
Chartered 1/04
1902 Red Seal <$VALUE
4x5 1-325 <$2500
3x10-20 1-270 <$2500
1902 Date Back
4x5 1-500 <$1500
3x10-20 1-380 <$1500
1902 Plain Back
4x5 501-815 <$1500
3x10-20 381-586 <$1500
Total Issue $65,600
Out in 1935 $315
****
11526 Polk
FNB OF SAINT CROIX FALLS
{{ 1 L }}
Chartered 11/19
1902 Plain Back <$VALUE
4x5 1-900 <$1250
3x10-20 1-1276 <$1250
Total Issue $81,800
Out in 1935 $580
****
6575 Outgamie
FNB OF SEYMOUR
{{ 7 L 12 S }}
Chartered 1/10/03
1902 Red Seal <$VALUE
3x10-20 1-1590 <$750
1902 Date Back
3x10-20 1-1850 <$375
1902 Plain Back
3x10-20 1851-5428 <$375
1929 Small Size
10 Type 1 1-622 <$125
20 Type 1 1-210 <$125
10 Type 2 1-619 <$165
20 Type 2 1-95 <$175
Total Issue $421,510
Out in 1935 $30,000
Large out 1935 $1,700
****
5469 Shawano
FNB OF SHAWANO
{{ 12 L 12 S }}
Organized 5/19/00
Liquidated 2/27/35
Brown Back <$VALUE
4x5 1-1475 <$400
3x10-20 1-980 <$400
1882 Date Back
4x5 1-2825 <$400
3x10-20 1-1980 <$400
1882 Value Back
4x5 2826-4500 <$400
3x10-20 1981-2857 <$400
1902 Plain Back
4x5 1-5185 <$200
3x10-20 1-3512 <$200
1929 Small Size
5 Type 1 1-1869 <$125
10 Type 1 1-1184 <$125
20 Type 1 1-328 <$125
Total Issue $757,120
Out at close $100,000
Large out at close $5,110
Outstanding includes Ch 6403
****
6403 Shawano
GERMAN-AMERICAN NB OF SHAWANO
Chartered 8/02
Closed 2/19/32
2nd title:Wisconsin NB of Shawano 7/19/18
FIRST TITLE {{ 6 L }}
1902 Red Seal <$VALUE
4x5 1-1005 <$650
3x10-20 1-813 <$650
1902 Date Back
4x5 1-1500 <$300
3x10-20 1-1110 <$300
1902 Plain Back
4x5 1501-1975 <$300
3x10-20 1111-1390 <$300
SECOND TITLE {{ 6 L 4 S }}
1902 Plain Back
4x5 1-18961 <$250
1929 Small Size
5 Type 1 1-3931 <$300
Total Issue $666,900
Out at close $50,000
Large out at close $3,190
Ch 5469 assumed circulation
****
Wisconsin NB of Shawano
SEE Ch 6403
German-American NB of Shawano
****
2123 Sheboygan
FNB OF SHEBOYGAN
{{ UNREPORTED }}
Chartered 7/30/73
Liquidated 1/14/79
Original Series <$VALUE
3x1-2 1-1500 <$2500/$4000
4x5 1-2875 <$2500
Series 1875
4x5 1-1165 <$2500
Total Issue $88,300
Out in 1910 $535
****
11150 Sheboygan
SECURITY NB OF SHEBOYGAN
{{ 36 S }}
Chartered 2/7/18
1929 Small Size <$VALUE
5 Type 1 1-4908 <$35
10 Type 1 1-1628 <$45
20 Type 1 1-420 <$50
5 Type 2 1-14650 <$45
10 Type 2 1-7450 <$50
20 Type 2 1-2390 <$60
Total Issue $490,870
Out in 1935 $100,000
****
5947 Sheboygan
DAIRYMEN'S NB OF SHEBOYGAN FALLS
{{ 2 L }}
Chartered 8/01
Liquidated 8/15/10
Brown Back <$VALUE
3x10-20 1-1200 <$1500
1882 Date Back
3x10-20 1-64 <$1500
Total Issue $63,200
Out in 1910 $16,600
****
4055 Lafayette
FNB OF SHULLSBURG
{{ 10 L 9 S }}
Organized 5/23/89
Receivership 10/27/33
Brown Back <$VALUE
3x10-20 1-1220 <$500
1882 Date Back
3x10-20 1-46 <$500
1902 Date Back
3x10-20 1-3200* <$275
1902 Plain Back
3x10-20 3701-9605* <$275
* 3201-3700 not marked
1929 Small Size
5 Type 1 1-362 <$200
10 Type 1 1-813 <$200
20 Type 1 1-253 <$200
Total Issue $633,550
Out at close $4,430
****
13308 Crawford
FNB OF SOLDIERS GROVE
{{ 7 S }}
Chartered 4/1/29
Liquidated 3/26/34
1929 Small Size <$VALUE
5 Type 1 1-440 <$600
10 Type 1 1-350 <$600
20 Type 1 1-114 <$600
5 Type 2 1-162 <$600
10 Type 2 1-90 <$600
20 Type 2 1-10 <$600
Total Issue $49,790
Out at close $25,000
****
4893 Milwaukee
SOUTH MILWAUKEE NB, SOUTH MILWAUKEE
{{ 2 L }}
Chartered 3/27/93
Liquidated 7/1/97
Brown Back <$VALUE
3x10-20 1-1077 <$1250
Total Issue $53,850
Out in 1910 $1,090
****
11463 Monroe
FARMERS NB OF SPARTA
{{ 6 L 6 S }}
Organized 7/30/19
1902 Plain Back <$VALUE
4x5 1-16303 <$350
1929 Small Size
5 Type 1 1-4356 <$250
5 Type 2 1-3906 <$250
Total Issue $476,270
Out in 1935 $25,000
Large out 1935 $1,455
****
1115 Monroe
FNB OF SPARTA
{{ 2 L }}
Chartered 1865
Liquidated 9/14/78
Original Series <$VALUE
3x1-2 1-2400 <$1500/$2500
4x5 1-2375 <$1500
3x10-20 1-500 <$2000/$2500
Series 1875
4x5 1-1025 <$1500
3x10-20 1-108 <$2000/$2500
Total Issue $110,400
Out in 1910 $785
****
4912 Portage
CITIZENS NB OF STEVENS POINT
{{ 27 L 20 S }}
Chartered 4/27/93
Brown Back <$VALUE
4x5 1-4850 <$300
3x10-20 1-2280 <$300/$350
1882 Date Back
4x5 1-3630 <$300
3x10-20 1-2402 <$300/$350
1902 Date Back
4x5 1-2415 <$150
3x10-20 1-1934 <$150
1902 Plain Back
4x5 2416-14425 <$150
3x10-20 1935-9784 <$150
1929 Small Size
5 Type 1 1-2684 <$50
10 Type 1 1-1582 <$50
20 Type 1 1-436 <$60
5 Type 2 1-2800 <$50
10 Type 2 1-1180 <$65
20 Type 2 1-260 <$85
Total Issue $1,440,160
Out in 1935 $100,000
Large out 1935 $5,870
****
3001 Portage
FNB OF STEVENS POINT
{{ 12 L 16 S }}
Chartered 1883
Brown Back <$VALUE
3x10-20 1-1386 <$500
1902 Red Seal
3x10-20 1-1910 <$500
1902 Date Back
3x10-20 1-4200 <$250
1902 Plain Back
3x10-20 4201-12930 <$250
1929 Small Size
10 Type 1 1-1540 <$110
20 Type 1 1-454 <$125
10 Type 2 1-1777 <$135
20 Type 2 1-394 <$150
Total Issue $983,830
Out in 1935 $75,000
Large out 1935 $5,250
****
10322 Sawyer
FNB OF STONE LAKE
{{ 5 L 4 S }}
Organized 1/24/13
Receivership 12/12/33
1902 Date Back <$VALUE
4x5 1-415 <$500
3x10-20 1-334 <$500
1902 Plain Back
4x5 416-2062 <$500
3x10-20 335-1299 <$500
1929 Small Size
5 Type 1 1-746 <$300
10 Type 1 1-364 <$300
20 Type 1 1-108 <$325
5 Type 2 1-376 <$350
10 Type 2 1-103 <$350
Total Issue $166,280
Out at close $25,000
Large out at close $1,080
****
9304 Dane
CITIZENS NB OF STOUGHTON
{{ 5 L 7 S }}
Organized 11/25/03
Receivership 1/10/34
1902 Date Back <$VALUE
3x10-20 1-3900 <$400
1902 Plain Back
3x10-20 3901-10430 <$400
1929 Small Size
10 Type 1 1-1065 <$200
20 Type 1 1-313 <$200
Total Issue $622,960
Out at close $50,000
Large out at close $2,360
****
5222 Dane
FNB OF STOUGHTON
{{ 15 L 14 S }}
Chartered 10/11/99
Brown Back <$VALUE
4x5 1-2225 <$400
3x10-20 1-1160 <$400
1882 Date Back
4x5 1-3050 <$375
3x10-20 1-2320 <$375
1882 Value Back
4x5 3051-4353 <$400
3x10-20 2321-3066 <$400
1902 Plain Back
4x5 1-5390 <$175
3x10-20 1-3760 <$175
1929 Small Size
5 Type 1 1-1684 <$85
10 Type 1 1-798 <$85
20 Type 1 1-226 <$100
5 Type 2 1-764 <$100
10 Type 2 1-843 <$100
20 Type 2 1-230 <$100
Total Issue $781,030
Out in 1935 $50,000
Large out 1935 $2,790
****
2653 Douglas
FNB OF SUPERIOR
{{ 1 L }}
Chartered 1882
Liquidated 5/16/85
Series 1875 <$VALUE
4x5 1-1430 <$2000
Total Issue $28,600
Out in 1910 $175
****
FNB of the City of Superior
SEE Ch 3926
FNB of West Superior
****
9140 Douglas
UNITED STATES NB OF SUPERIOR
{{ 4 L 26 S }}
Organized 5/13/08
Liquidated 5/22/34
1902 Date Back <$VALUE
4x5 1-2650 <$500
3x10-20 1-2040 <$500
1902 Plain Back
4x5 2651-5236 <$500
3x10-20 2041-3565 <$500
1929 Small Size
5 Type 1 1-2254 <$60
10 Type 1 1-1950 <$60
20 Type 1 1-444 <$75
5 Type 2 1-132 <$100
Total Issue $521,530
Out at close $170,000
Large out at close $1,820
Ch 14109 assumed circulation
****
14150 Shawano
FNB IN TIGERTON
{{ 9 S }}
Chartered 5/34
1929 Small Size <$VALUE
5 Type 2 1-4218 <$250
10 Type 2 1-2140 <$250
20 Type 2 1-438 <$275
Total Issue $51,250
Out in 1935 $50,000
****
5446 Shawano
FNB OF TIGERTON
{{ 12 L 6 S }}
Organized 6/9/00
Receivership 6/4/34
Brown Back <$VALUE
3x10-20 1-1700 <$400
1882 Date Back
3x10-20 1-1410 <$400
1882 Value Back
3x10-20 1411-2027 <$400
1902 Plain Back
3x10-20 1-2266 <$200
1929 Small Size
10 Type 1 1-754 <$250
20 Type 1 1-170 <$250
10 Type 2 1-242 <$275
20 Type 2 1-60 <$300
Total Issue $368,910
Out at close $39,500
Large out at close $1,780
****
8529 Vernon
FNB OF VIROQUA
{{ 6 L 13 S }}
Organized 1/4/07
Liquidated 5/8/34
1902 Red Seal <$VALUE
4x5 1-1200 <$750
3x10-20 1-1020 <$750
1902 Date Back
4x5 1-3150 <$400
3x10-20 1-2040 <$400
1902 Plain Back
4x5 3151-9910 <$400
3x10-20 2041-6398 <$400
1929 Small Size
5 Type 1 1-1464 <$150
10 Type 1 1-710 <$150
20 Type 1 1-200 <$150
5 Type 2 1-944 <$175
10 Type 2 1-380 <$175
20 Type 2 1-65 <$175
Total Issue $713,440
Out at close $49,995
Large out 1935 $2,870
Ch 14058 assumed circulation
****
9003 Jefferson
MERCHANTS NB OF WATERTOWN
{{ 16 L U + 31 S }}
Chartered 1/08
1902 Red Seal <$VALUE
4x5 1-1500 <$250
4x10 1-1500 <$250
1902 Date Back
4x5 1-11500 <$125
4x10 1-10750 <$135
1902 Plain Back
4x5 11501-40281 <$125
4x10 10751-33324 <$135
1929 Small Size
5 Type 1 1-8424 <$20
10 Type 1 1-4910 <$25
5 Type 2 1-9460 <$20
10 Type 2 1-4237 <$25
Total Issue $2,865,570
Out in 1935 $200,000
Large out 1935 $9,175
****
1010 Jefferson
WISCONSIN NB OF WATERTOWN
{{ 7 L 6 S }}
Organized 2/27/65
Receivership 3/26/34
Original Series <$VALUE
4x5 1-2150 <$1000
3x10-20 1-1300<$1500/$2000
Series 1875
4x5 1-1580 <$1000
3x10-20 1-490 <$1500/$2000
Brown Back
3x10-20 1-1344 <$500
1902 Red Seal
3x10-20 1-1400 <$650
1902 Date Back
3x10-20 1-2300 <$300
1902 Plain Back
3x10-20 2301-6363 <$300
1929 Small Size
5 Type 1 1-570 <$250
10 Type 1 1-692 <$250
20 Type 1 1-220 <$250
5 Type 2 1-180 <$275
10 Type 2 1-50 <$275
Total Issue $705,870
Out at close $40,000
Large out at close $3,800
****
1159 Waukesha
FARMERS NB OF WAUKESHA
{{ UNREPORTED }}
Chartered 5/17/65
Liquidated 11/25/66
Original Series <$VALUE
4x5 1-4500 <$2500
Total Issue $90,000
Out in 1910 $440
****
2647 Waukesha
N EXCHANGE B OF WAUKESHA
{{ 26 L 37 S }}
Organized 2/14/82
Receivership 1/27/33
Series 1875 <$VALUE
4x5 1-5447 <$650
3x10-20 1-65 <$1250/$1750
Brown Back
3x10-20 1-2000 <$350
1882 Date Back
3x10-20 1-4500 <$300
1882 Value Back
3x10-20 4501-12538 <$325
1902 Plain Back
3x10-20 1-17790 <$125
1929 Small Size
10 Type 1 1-4196 <$45
20 Type 1 1-1084 <$50
Total Issue $2,110,430
Out at close $200,000
Large out at close $14,220
****
1086 Waukesha
WAUKESHA NB, WAUKESHA
{{ 15 L 23 S }}
Chartered 1865
Original Series <$VALUE
4x5 1-4425 <$750
Series 1875
4x5 1-7000 <$750
Brown Back
50-100 1-4045 <$4000/$5000
1902 Red Seal
50-100 1-1700 <$6000/$6500
1902 Date Back
50-100 1-800 <$350/$450
3x50-100 1-3664 <$350/$450
1902 Plain Back
3x50-100 3665-4619
<$350/$450
1929 Small Size
10 Type 1 1-3499 <$35
20 Type 1 1-608 <$45
50 Type 1 1-569 <$110
100 Type 1 1-195 <$160
Total Issue $2,935,600
Out in 1935 $300,000
Large out 1935 $25,260
****
FNB of Waupaca
SEE Ch 4414
Waupaca County NB of Waupaca
****
14063 Waupaca
FNB OF WAUPACA
{{ 6 S }}
Chartered 3/34
1929 Small Size <$VALUE
5 Type 2 1-4940 <$350
10 Type 2 1-2450 <$350
20 Type 2 1-770 <$350
Total Issue $64,600
Out in 1935 $50,000
****
4424 Waupaca
NB OF WAUPACA
Organized 9/6/90
Receivership 3/26/34
2nd title:Old NB of Waupaca 1/17/07
FIRST TITLE {{ 2 L }}
Brown Back <$VALUE
4x5 1-2183 <$600
3x10-20 1-382 <$600
SECOND TITLE {{ 7 L 13 S }}
Brown Back
4x5 1-200 <$600
3x10-20 1-158 <$600
1882 Date Back
4x5 1-205 <$600
1902 Date Back
4x5 1-1625 <$300
3x10-20 1-1220 <$300
1902 Plain Back
4x5 1626-4347 <$300
3x10-20 1221-2829 <$300
1929 Small Size
5 Type 1 1-960 <$125
10 Type 1 1-720 <$125
20 Type 1 1-186 <$125
5 Type 2 1-490 <$150
10 Type 2 1-214 <$165
20 Type 2 1-20 <$175
Total Issue $406,460
Out at close $50,000
Large out at close $1,970
****
Old NB of Waupaca
SEE Ch 4424
NB of Waupaca
****

****

4414 Waupaca
WAUPACA COUNTY NB OF
WAUPACA
Chartered 9/90
Liquidated 6/17/10
 2nd title:FNB of Waupaca
 5/3/06
FIRST TITLE {{ 1 L }}
Brown Back <$VALUE
 3x10-20 1-1165 <$1500
SECOND TITLE {{ 0 L }}
Brown Back
 3x10-20 1-301 <$2000
Total Issue $73,300
Out in 1910 $10,750

****

3391 Fond du Lac
FNB OF WAUPUN
{{ 3 L }}
Chartered 9/8/85
Liquidated 9/1/05
Brown Back <$VALUE
 4x5 1-8426 <$850
 3x10-20 1-623 <$850
Total Issue $199,670
Out in 1910 $4,885

****

7898 Fond du Lac
NB OF WAUPUN
{{ 8 L 3U + 7 S }}
Chartered 9/05
1902 Red Seal <$VALUE
 4x5 1-1750 <$650
 3x10-20 1-1300 <$650
1902 Date Back
 4x5 1-3000 <$300
 3x10-20 1-2040 <$300
1902 Plain Back
 4x5 3001-8843 <$300
 3x10-20 2041-6120 <$300
1929 Small Size
 5 Type 1 1-1544 <$200
 10 Type 1 1-742 <$200
 20 Type 1 1-224 <$200
 5 Type 2 1-1562 <$250
 10 Type 2 1-935 <$250
 20 Type 2 1-240 <$250
Total Issue $722,540
Out in 1935 $50,000
Large out 1935 $2,480

****

American NB of Wausau
SEE Ch 4744
N German-American B of Wausau

****

2820 Marathon
FNB OF WAUSAU
{{ 27 L 50+ S }}
Chartered 10/5/82
Liquidated 4/26/33
Brown Back <$VALUE
 3x10-20 1-2480 <$300
1902 Red Seal
 3x10-20 1-8050 <$300
1902 Date Back
 3x10-20 1-13700 <$100
1902 Plain Back
 4x5 1-24411 <$100
 3x10-20 13701-27634 <$100
1929 Small Size
 5 Type 1 1-11645 <$25
 10 Type 1 1-2731 <$25
 20 Type 1 1-849 <$35
Total Issue $3,011,510
Out at close $350,000
Large out at close $9,755

****

4744 Marathon
N GERMAN-AMERICAN B OF
WAUSAU
Chartered 1892
Liquidated 4/3/33
 2nd title:American NB
 2/1/18
FIRST TITLE {{ 9 L }}
Brown Back <$VALUE
 3x10-20 1-11920 <$500
1882 Date Back
 3x10-20 1-4826 <$450
1902 Date Back
 3x10-20 1-8000 <$175
1902 Plain Back
 3x10-20 8001-10000 <$175
SECOND TITLE {{ 12 L 28 S }}
1902 Plain Back
 4x5 1-25119 <$175
 4x10 1-18104 <$175
1929 Small Size
 5 Type 1 1-10162 <$40
 10 Type 1 1-5832 <$40
Total Issue $3,218,620
Out at close $350,000
Large out at close $13,850

****

7136 Waushara
FNB OF WAUTOMA
{{ UNREPORTED }}
Chartered 2/04
Liquidated 3/26/13
1902 Red Seal <$VALUE
 3x10-20 1-300 <$2500
1902 Date Back
 3x10-20 1-425 <$1500
Total Issue $36,250
Out in 1913 $7,300

****

8689 Milwaukee
FNB OF WAUWATOSA
{{ 7 L 13 S }}
Chartered 5/07
Liquidated 5/18/35
1902 Red Seal <$VALUE
 3x10-20 1-700 <$750
1902 Date Back
 3x10-20 1-1960 <$300
1902 Plain Back
 3x10-20 1961-14904 <$300
1929 Small Size
 5 Type 1 1-3446 <$125
 10 Type 1 1-1656 <$125
 20 Type 1 1-436 <$125
 5 Type 2 1-1802 <$150
 10 Type 2 1-715 <$150
 20 Type 2 1-205 <$165
Total Issue $1,055,520
Out in 1935 $50,000
Large out 1935 $5,170

****

6908 Milwaukee
FNB OF WEST ALLIS
{{ 14 L 22 S }}
Organized 6/27/03
Receivership 2/9/34
1902 Red Seal <$VALUE
 3x10-20 1-1100 <$350
1902 Date Back
 3x10-20 1-1350 <$165
1902 Plain Back
 3x10-20 1351-18415 <$165
1929 Small Size
 10 Type 1 1-3454 <$50
 20 Type 1 1-992 <$60
 10 Type 2 1-1127 <$60
 20 Type 2 1-105 <$65
Total Issue $1,315,400
Out at close $148,560
Large out at close $6,110

****

11060 Washington
FNB OF WEST BEND
{{ 6 L 18 S }}
Chartered 8/17
1902 Plain Back <$VALUE
 4x5 1-10670 <$300
 3x10-20 1-6727 <$300
1929 Small Size
 5 Type 1 1-2664 <$75
 10 Type 1 1-1270 <$75
 20 Type 1 1-338 <$85
 5 Type 2 1-4986 <$100
 10 Type 2 1-2633 <$100
 20 Type 2 1-714 <$100
Total Issue $811,970
Out in 1935 $100,000
Large out 1935 $2,280

****

3926 Douglas
FNB OF WEST SUPERIOR
Chartered 1888
 2nd title:FNB of the City
 of Superior 1/18/90
FIRST TITLE {{ 0 L }}
Brown Back <$VALUE
 3x10-20 1-484 <$1500
SECOND TITLE {{ 14 L 28 S }}
Brown Back
 3x10-20 1-11758 <$375
1902 Date Back
 3x10-20 1-9000 <$150
1902 Plain Back
 3x10-20 9001-27871 <$150
1929 Small Size
 10 Type 1 1-4586 <$50
 20 Type 1 1-1230 <$60
 10 Type 2 1-3104 <$50
 20 Type 2 1-974 <$65
Total Issue $2,748,930
Out in 1935 $200,000
Large out 1935 $11,665

****

4399 Douglas
KEYSTONE NB OF SUPERIOR,
WEST SUPERIOR
{{ UNREPORTED }}
Organized 8/16/90
Receivership 8/15/95
Brown Back <$VALUE
 4x5 1-500 <$2000
 3x10-20 1-1271 <$2000
Total Issue $73,550
Out in 1915 $490

****

4878 Douglas
NORTHWESTERN NB OF
SUPERIOR,
WEST SUPERIOR
{{ UNREPORTED }}
Chartered 5/2/93
Liquidated 10/7/02
Brown Back <$VALUE
 3x10-20 1-6329 <$1500
Total Issue $316,450
Out in 1910 $5,630

****

4680 Douglas
SUPERIOR NB OF
WEST SUPERIOR
{{ UNREPORTED }}
Organized 1/13/92
Receivership 8/6/95
Brown Back <$VALUE
 4x5 1-1906 <$2000
 3x10-20 1-885 <$2000
Total Issue $82,370
Out in 1915 $435

****

7470 Waupaca
FNB OF WEYAUWEGA
{{ 12 L 4 S }}
Chartered 11/04
Liquidated 7/14/31
1902 Red Seal <$VALUE
 3x10-20 1-300 <$500
1902 Date Back
 3x10-20 1-560 <$200
1902 Plain Back
 3x10-20 561-3342 <$200
1929 Small Size
 10 Type 1 1-351 <$375
 20 Type 1 1-90 <$375
Total Issue $213,960
Out at close $25,000
Large out at close $3,250

****

2925 Walworth
CITIZENS NB OF WHITEWATER
{{ 2 L }}
Chartered 4/13/83
Liquidated 1/9/94
Brown Back <$VALUE
 4x5 1-3924 <$1250
Total Issue $78,480
Out in 1910 $570

****

124 Walworth
FNB OF WHITEWATER
{{ 17 L 16 S }}
Chartered 1863
Liquidated 6/27/31
Original Series <$VALUE
 3x1-2 1-3000 <$650/$1500
 4x5 1-5625 <$750
Series 1875
 3x1-2 1-1000 <$650/$1500
 4x5 1-6120 <$750
Brown Back
 4x5 1-13844 <$350
 3x10-20 1-1864 <$350
1902 Red Seal
 3x10-20 1-4600 <$375
1902 Date Back
 3x10-20 1-5400 <$150
1902 Plain Back
 3x10-20 5401-15947 <$150
1929 Small Size
 10 Type 1 1-1310 <$85
 20 Type 1 1-378 <$100
Total Issue $1,776,290
Out at close $100,000
Large out at close $22,470

****

****

Citizens NB of
Wisconsin Rapids
SEE Ch 10330
Citizens NB of Grand Rapids

****

FNB of Wisconsin Rapids
SEE Ch 1998
FNB of Grand Rapids

****

Wood County NB of
Wisconsin Rapids
SEE Ch 4639
Wood County NB of
Grand Rapids

****

CONDITION affects Value. The Values shown are for notes in FINE condition.

<$VALUEs are for notes in **FINE** condition. Value changes by approximately **25%** for a change of one full grade.

Nickname: The Equality State
Motto: Equal Rights
Capital: Cheyenne
Number of towns: 31
Number of issuing charters: 51
Number of small size issuers: 23

Basin B6
Buffalo C7
Casper D7
Cheyenne E9
Cody B5
Douglas D8
Evanston E4
Green River E5
Greybull B6
Guernsey D8
Kemmerer D4
Lander D5
Laramie E8
Laramie City E8
Lovell B6
Lusk C8
Manville C8
Meeteetse B5
Newcastle C8
Powell B5
Rawlins E7
Rock River E8
Rock Springs E5
Saratoga E7
Sheridan B7
Shoshoni D5
Sundance B8
Thermopolis C5
Torrington D9
Wheatland D8
Worland C6

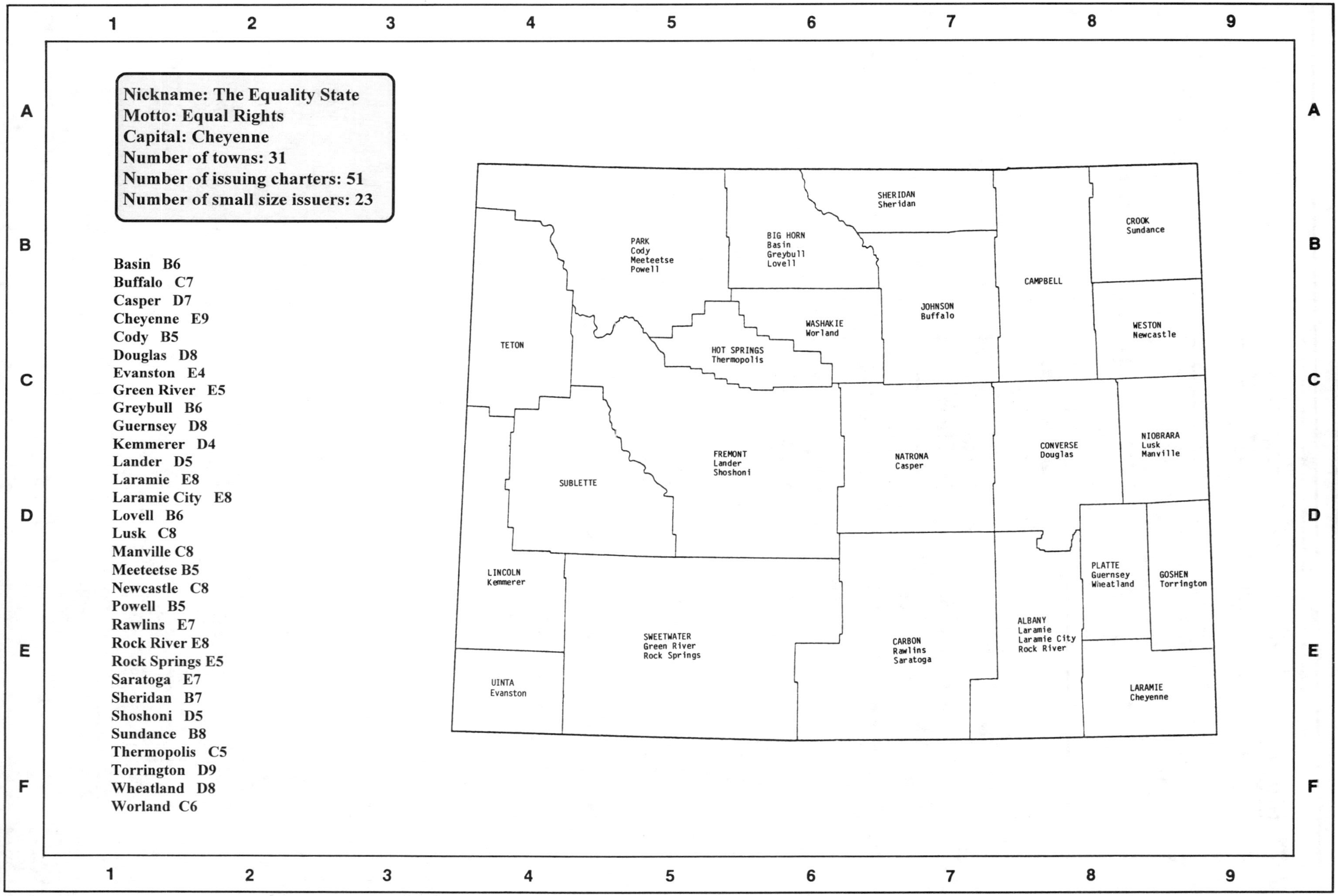

****
10858 Big Horn
FNB OF BASIN
{{ 3 L }}
Organized 5/15/16
Receivership 6/14/24
1902 Plain Back <$VALUE
4x10 1-3784 <$1500
Total Issue $151,360
Out at close $33,800
****
3299 Johnson
FNB OF BUFFALO
Chartered 1885
TERRITORIAL ISSUES {{ 0 L }}
Brown Back <$VALUE
3x10-20 1-485 <$7500
STATE ISSUES {{ 11 L 17 S }}
Brown Back
3x10-20 486-2844 <$2500
1902 Red Seal
3x10-20 1-3745 <$5000
1902 Date Back
3x10-20 1-5200 <$750
1902 Plain Back
3x10-20 5201-11127 <$750
1929 Small Size
10 Type 1 1-1178 <$325
20 Type 1 1-338 <$325
5 Type 2 1-324 <$425
10 Type 2 1-2112 <$425
20 Type 2 1-398 <$450
Total Issue $1,027,740
Out in 1935 $50,000
Large out 1935 $2,775
****
6850 Natrona
CASPER NB, CASPER
{{ 15 L 32 S }}
Chartered 6/03
1902 Red Seal <$VALUE
3x10-20 1-1232 <$4500
1902 Date Back
3x10-20 1-4200 <$350
1902 Plain Back
3x10-20 4291-17272 <$350
1929 Small Size
10 Type 1 1-2540 <$185
20 Type 1 1-674 <$200
10 Type 2 1-3241 <$250
20 Type 2 1-899 <$275
Total Issue $1,208,870
Out in 1935 $100,000
Large out 1935 $3,660
****
11683 Natrona
CITIZENS NB OF CASPER
{{ 5 L }}
Chartered 4/20
Liquidated 4/19/27
1902 Plain Back <$VALUE
3x10-20 1-9844 <$650
Total Issue $492,000
Out at close $100,000
****
11490 Natrona
NB OF COMMERCE OF CASPER
{{ 2 L }}
Chartered 10/19
Liquidated 7/18/24
1902 Plain Back <$VALUE
3x10-20 1-9320 <$1500
Total Issue $466,000
Out at close $125,000
****
7083 Natrona
STOCKMEN'S NB OF CASPER
{{ 9 L }}
Chartered 1/04
Liquidated 2/11/28
1902 Red Seal <$VALUE
3x10-20 1-2512 <$4500
1902 Date Back
3x10-20 1-3740 <$450
1902 Plain Back
3x10-20 3741-10580 <$450
Total Issue $654,600
Out at close $50,000
****
10533 Natrona
WYOMING NB OF CASPER
{{ 13 L 39 S }}
Chartered 5/14
1902 Date Back <$VALUE
3x10-20 1-750* <$350
1902 Plain Back
3x10-20 871-18126* <$350
* 751-870 not marked
1929 Small Size
10 Type 1 1-2734 <$165
20 Type 1 1-596 <$185
10 Type 2 1-4179 <$185
20 Type 2 1-1311 <$185
Total Issue $1,209,870
Out in 1935 $100,000
Large out 1935 $5,950
****

****
11380 Laramie
AMERICAN NB OF CHEYENNE
{{ 23 L U + 31 S }}
Chartered 6/19
1902 Plain Back <$VALUE
4x5 1-12375 <$350
3x10-20 1-10011 <$300
1929 Small Size
5 Type 1 1-3394 <$165
10 Type 1 1-2034 <$165
20 Type 1 1-458 <$185
5 Type 2 1-4686 <$275
10 Type 2 1-2340 <$275
20 Type 2 1-734 <$300
Total Issue $1,088,380
Out in 1935 $100,000
Large out 1935 $3,970
****
3416 Laramie
CHEYENNE NB, CHEYENNE
{{ UNREPORTED }}
Chartered 12/2/85
Receivership 12/5/91
TERRITORIAL ISSUES
Brown Back <$VALUE
3x10-20 1-1090 <$7500
STATE ISSUES
Brown Back
3x10-20 1091-1161 <$4500
Total Issue $58,050
Out in 1915 $300
****
8089 Laramie
CITIZENS NB OF CHEYENNE
{{ 8 L }}
Organized 1/15/06
Receivership 7/21/24
1902 Red Seal <$VALUE
3x10-20 1-2400 <$4500
1902 Date Back
3x10-20 1-7500 <$500
1902 Plain Back
3x10-20 7501-16395 <$500
Total Issue $939,750
Out at close $96,395
****
1800 Laramie
FNB OF CHEYENNE
Chartered 3/7/71
Receivership 7/9/24
TERRITORIAL ISSUES {{ 2 L }}
Original Series <$VALUE
4x5 1-2500 <$6500
3x10-20 1-800 <$7500
Series 1875
4x5 1-665 <$6500
3x10-20 1-1656 <$7500
STATE ISSUES {{ 19 L }}
Brown Back
3x10-20 1-8900 <$1500
1882 Date Back
3x10-20 1-1399 <$1500
1902 Date Back
4x5 1-5250 <$350
3x10-20 1-4300 <$300
1902 Plain Back
4x5 5251-19945 <$350
3x10-20 4301-15946 <$300
Total Issue $1,897,250
Out at close $190,600
****
2652 Laramie
STOCK GROWERS NB OF
CHEYENNE
Chartered 1882
TERRITORIAL ISSUES {{ 3 L }}
Series 1875 <$VALUE
4x5 1-4650 <$6500
3x10-20 1-900 <$7500
STATE ISSUES {{ 34 L }}
Series 1875
4x5 4651-9685 <$2500
3x10-20 901-2296 <$3000
Brown Back
4x5 1-3575 <$1500
3x10-20 1-3120 <$1500
1882 Date Back
4x5 1-6930* <$1250
3x10-20 1-5228** <$1250
1882 Value Back
4x5 7431-8837** <$1250
3x10-20 5629-6720* <$1250
** 6931-7430 not marked
* 5229-5628 not marked
1902 Plain Back
4x5 1-2720 <$350
Total Issue $1,103,140
Out in 1935 $4,420
****

****
7319 Park
FNB OF CODY
{{ 5 L 10 S }}
Chartered 6/04
1902 Red Seal <$VALUE
3x10-20 1-480 <$6000
1902 Date Back
3x10-20 1-2160* <$1250
1902 Plain Back
3x10-20 2401-3795* <$1250
* 2161-2400 not marked
1929 Small Size
10 Type 1 1-616** <$500
20 Type 1 1-198*** <$500
10 Type 2 1-416 <$600
20 Type 2 1-130 <$650
** 231-314 not issued
*** 43-104 not issued
Total Issue $268,750
Out in 1935 $25,000
Large out 1935 $970
****
8020 Park
SHOSHONE NB OF CODY
{{ 6 L 12 S }}
Chartered 12/05
1902 Red Seal <$VALUE
3x10-20 1-700 <$5000
1902 Date Back
3x10-20 1-2050 <$1000
1902 Plain Back
3x10-20 2051-5272 <$1000
1929 Small Size
10 Type 1 1-630 <$500
20 Type 1 1-182 <$525
10 Type 2 1-735 <$550
20 Type 2 1-170 <$650
Total Issue $368,990
Out in 1935 $25,000
Large out 1935 $1,330
****
8087 Converse
DOUGLAS NB, DOUGLAS
{{ 11 L 18 S }}
Chartered 2/06
1902 Red Seal <$VALUE
3x10-20 1-1275 <$5000
1902 Date Back
3x10-20 1-3500 <$650
1902 Plain Back
3x10-20 3501-10528 <$650
1929 Small Size
10 Type 1 1-1142 <$300
20 Type 1 1-358 <$300
10 Type 2 1-1932 <$350
20 Type 2 1-528 <$400
Total Issue $731,510
Out in 1935 $50,000
Large out 1935 $2,950
****
3556 Converse
FNB OF DOUGLAS
Chartered 1886
Liquidated 12/15/23
TERRITORIAL ISSUES {{ 0 L }}
Brown Back <$VALUE
4x5 1-525 <$7500
3x10-20 1-430 <$7500
STATE ISSUES {{ 7 L }}
Brown Back
4x5 526-750 <$3000
3x10-20 431-1945 <$3000
1902 Red Seal
3x10-20 1-2375 <$5000
1902 Date Back
3x10-20 1-5100 <$650
1902 Plain Back
3x10-20 5101-11008 <$650
Total Issue $781,400
Out in 1923 $73,500
****
8612 Uinta
EVANSTON NB, EVANSTON
{{ 6 L 23 S }}
Chartered 3/07
1902 Red Seal <$VALUE
3x10-20 1-1275 <$5000
1902 Date Back
3x10-20 1-4100 <$750
1902 Plain Back
3x10-20 4101-12044 <$750
1929 Small Size
10 Type 1 1-1366 <$200
20 Type 1 1-370 <$225
10 Type 2 1-1520 <$250
20 Type 2 1-404 <$300
Total Issue $815,590
Out in 1935 $50,000
Large out 1935 $2,690
****

****
8534 Uinta
FNB OF EVANSTON
{{ 1 L 17 S }}
Chartered 2/07
1902 Red Seal <$VALUE
3x10-20 1-1000 <$5000
1902 Date Back
3x10-20 1-4000 <$1250
1902 Plain Back
3x10-20 4001-12504 <$1250
1929 Small Size
10 Type 1 1-1338 <$250
20 Type 1 1-360 <$250
5 Type 2 1-312 <$400
10 Type 2 1-1511 <$300
20 Type 2 1-435 <$325
Total Issue $824,050
Out in 1935 $50,000
Large out 1935 $2,635
****
10698 Sweetwater
FNB OF GREEN RIVER
{{ 9 L 37 S }}
Chartered 2/15
1902 Date Back <$VALUE
3x10-20 1-1300 <$650
1902 Plain Back
3x10-20 1301-12421 <$650
1929 Small Size
10 Type 1 1-2360 <$225
20 Type 1 1-604 <$225
10 Type 2 1-1095 <$275
20 Type 2 1-190 <$350
Total Issue $849,880
Out in 1935 $40,000
Large out 1935 $3,160
****
10810 Big Horn
FNB OF GREYBULL
{{ 4 L 10 S }}
Chartered 12/15
1902 Plain Back <$VALUE
4x10 1-3514 <$1500
1929 Small Size
10 Type 1 1-1084 <$600
10 Type 2 1-2159 <$650
Total Issue $227,190
Out in 1935 $25,000
Large out 1935 $660
****
5295 Platte
FNB OF GUERNSEY
{{ UNREPORTED }}
Chartered 4/20/00
Liquidated 5/1/01
Brown Back <$VALUE
4x5 1-400 <$4000
3x10-20 1-362 <$4000
Total Issue $26,100
Out in 1910 $595
****
5480 Lincoln
FNB OF KEMMERER
{{ 24 L 43 S }}
Chartered 7/2/00
Brown Back <$VALUE
3x10-20 1-1560 <$1500
1882 Date Back
3x10-20 1-3400 <$1250
1882 Value Back
3x10-20 3401-7800 <$1250
1902 Plain Back
3x10-20 1-11712 <$300
1929 Small Size
10 Type 1 1-2556 <$175
20 Type 1 1-680 <$175
10 Type 2 1-1913 <$250
20 Type 2 1-323 <$300
Total Issue $1,314,150
Out in 1935 $30,000
Large out 1935 $6,560
****
4720 Fremont
FNB OF LANDER
{{ 16 L 17 S }}
Chartered 1892
Brown Back <$VALUE
3x10-20 1-2130 <$1500
1882 Date Back
3x10-20 1-1547 <$1250
1902 Date Back
3x10-20 1-2100 <$400
1902 Plain Back
3x10-20 2101-8140 <$400
1929 Small Size
10 Type 1 1-1148 <$200
20 Type 1 1-328 <$250
10 Type 2 1-1613 <$250
20 Type 2 1-535 <$250
Total Issue $725,920
Out in 1935 $50,000
Large out 1935 $3,890
****

****
4989 Albany
FNB OF LARAMIE
{{ 17 L 50+ S }}
Chartered 1895
Brown Back <$VALUE
3x10-20 1-3900 <$1500
1882 Date Back
3x10-20 1-5512 <$1250
1902 Date Back
3x10-20 1-2000 <$350
1902 Plain Back
3x10-20 2001-15532 <$350
1929 Small Size
10 Type 1 1-2536 <$165
20 Type 1 1-788 <$165
10 Type 2 1-2016 <$225
20 Type 2 1-765 <$250
Total Issue $1,529,380
Out in 1935 $100,000
Large out 1935 $5,250
****
3615 Albany
ALBANY COUNTY NB OF
LARAMIE CITY
Chartered 1887
2nd title: Albany NB of
Laramie 1/18/18
TERRITORIAL ISSUES {{ 0 L }}
Brown Back <$VALUE
3x10-20 1-780 <$6000
STATE ISSUES {{ 3 L }}
Brown Back
3x10-20 781-3568 <$2500
1902 Red Seal
3x10-20 1-2600 <$5000
1902 Date Back
3x10-20 1-6800 <$650
1902 Plain Back
3x10-20 6801-8500 <$650
SECOND TITLE {{ 11 L 50+ S }}
1902 Plain Back
3x10-20 1-13365 <$300
1929 Small Size
10 Type 1 1-2786 <$165
20 Type 1 1-698 <$165
10 Type 2 1-489 <$250
20 Type 2 1-89 <$350
Total Issue $1,659,240
Out in 1935 $50,000
Large out 1935 $5,450
****
2518 Albany
LARAMIE NB OF
LARAMIE CITY
Chartered 4/18/81
Liquidated 3/15/95
2nd title: Laramie NB of
Laramie 2/8/92
TERRITORIAL ISSUES {{ 0 L }}
Series 1875 <$VALUE
3x10-20 1-1630 <$7500
STATE ISSUES {{ 0 L }}
Series 1875
3x10-20 1631-1684 <$4000
SECOND TITLE {{ 1 L }}
Series 1875
3x10-20 1-431 <$4000
Total Issue $105,750
Out in 1910 $750
****
2110 Albany
WYOMING NB OF
LARAMIE CITY
Chartered 5/17/73
Liquidated 3/7/95
2nd title: Wyoming NB of
Laramie 1/28/92
TERRITORIAL ISSUES {{ 7 L }}
Original Series <$VALUE
3x1-2 1-1000<$6000/$10,000
4x5 1-1875 <$6000
Series 1875
4x5 1-4350 <$6000
STATE ISSUES {{ 1 L }}
Series 1875
4x5 4351-4841 <$3500
SECOND TITLE {{ 1 L }}
Series 1875
3x10-20 1-209 <$4000
Brown Back
3x10-20 1-274 <$3000
Total Issue $163,470
Out in 1910 $1,300
****

****
10844 Big Horn
FNB OF LOVELL
{{ U + 12 S }}
Chartered 5/16
1929 Small Size <$VALUE
5 Type 1 1-622 <$400
10 Type 1 1-210 <$400
20 Type 1 1-64 <$500
50 Type 1 1-10 <$1000
100 Type 1 1-6 <$1250
5 Type 2 1-2298 <$450
10 Type 2 1-1030 <$450
20 Type 2 1-135 <$600
Total Issue $70,030
Out in 1935 $30,000
****
11390 Niobrara
FNB OF LUSK
{{ UNREPORTED }}
Organized 6/23/19
Receivership 2/7/24
1902 Plain Back <$VALUE
4x5 1-3550 <$2500
3x10-20 1-2182 <$1500
Total Issue $180,100
Out at close $48,500
****
11352 Niobrara
FNB OF MANVILLE
{{ 1 L }}
Organized 5/1/19
Receivership 12/11/23
1902 Plain Back <$VALUE
3x10-20 1-1786 <$2500
Total Issue $89,300
Out at close $25,000
****
6340 Park
FNB OF MEETEETSE
{{ 7 L 3 S }}
Chartered 7/02
1902 Red Seal <$VALUE
4x5 1-353 <$6000
3x10-20 1-295 <$6000
1902 Date Back
4x5 1-600 <$1000
3x10-20 1-480 <$1000
1902 Plain Back
4x5 601-1278 <$1000
3x10-20 481-906 <$1000
1929 Small Size
5 Type 1 1-266 <$1250
10 Type 1 1-138 <$1250
20 Type 1 1-41 <$1250
Total Issue $113,850
Out in 1935 $6,250
Large out 1935 $430
****
7198 Weston
FNB OF NEWCASTLE
{{ 2 L }}
Organized 3/23/04
Receivership 6/12/24
1902 Red Seal <$VALUE
3x10-20 1-1075 <$6000
1902 Date Back
3x10-20 1-1800 <$2000
1902 Plain Back
3x10-20 1801-3822 <$2000
Total Issue $244,850
Out at close $24,300
****
10265 Park
FNB OF POWELL
{{ 6 L 15 S }}
Chartered 9/12
1902 Date Back <$VALUE
3x10-20 1-1280 <$750
1902 Plain Back
3x10-20 1281-6215 <$750
1929 Small Size
10 Type 1 1-744 <$350
20 Type 1 1-246 <$350
10 Type 2 1-1152 <$375
20 Type 2 1-213 <$450
Total Issue $400,690
Out in 1935 $35,000
Large out 1935 $1,850
****
10565 Park
POWELL NB, POWELL
{{ 6 L }}
Organized 6/12/14
Liquidated 2/2/29
1902 Date Back <$VALUE
3x10-20 1-500 <$750
1902 Plain Back
3x10-20 501-2712 <$750
Total Issue $135,600
Out at close $2,740
****

4320 Carbon
FNB OF RAWLINS
Chartered 1890
TERRITORIAL ISSUES {{ 1 L }}
Brown Back <$VALUE
3x10-20 1-375 <$6500
STATE ISSUES {{ 18 L 44 S }}
Brown Back
3x10-20 376-4405 <$1500
1882 Date Back
3x10-20 1-447 <$1250
1902 Date Back
4x5 1-3350 <$300
3x10-20 1-2150 <$300
1902 Plain Back
4x5 3351-17060 <$300
3x10-20 2151-11320 <$300
1929 Small Size
5 Type 1 1-3512 <$165
10 Type 1 1-1982 <$165
20 Type 1 1-528 <$175
5 Type 2 1-5294 <$200
10 Type 2 1-2847 <$200
20 Type 2 1-772 <$250
Total Issue $1,507,820
Out in 1935 $100,000
Large out 1935 $4,540

5413 Carbon
RAWLINS NB, RAWLINS
{{ 20 L 50 + S }}
Chartered 6/9/00
Brown Back <$VALUE
3x10-20 1-3000 <$1500
1882 Date Back
3x10-20 1-4500 <$1250
1882 Value Back
3x10-20 4501-5804 <$1250
1902 Plain Back
3x10-20 1-8101 <$300
1929 Small Size
10 Type 1 1-3568 <$165
20 Type 1 1-954 <$165
10 Type 2 1-2056 <$200
20 Type 2 1-680 <$250
Total Issue $1,207,970
Out in 1935 $100,000
Large out 1935 $5,100

9557 Carbon
STOCKGROWERS NB OF RAWLINS
{{ 11 L }}
Chartered 10/09
Liquidated 10/28/24
1902 Date Back <$VALUE
3x10-20 1-6300 <$450
1902 Plain Back
3x10-20 6301-13561 <$450
Total Issue $678,050
Out at close $75,000

11342 Albany
FNB OF ROCK RIVER
{{UNREPORTED }}
Organized 4/24/19
Receivership 6/14/23
1902 Plain Back <$VALUE
3x10-20 1-770 <$2500
Total Issue $38,500
Out at close $13,700

3920 Sweetwater
FNB OF ROCK SPRINGS
Chartered 1888
Liquidated 11/7/27
TERRITORIAL ISSUES {{ 0 L }}
Brown Back <$VALUE
3x10-20 1-320 <$7500
STATE ISSUES {{ 8 L }}
Brown Back
3x10-20 321-4205 <$1750
1902 Date Back
4x5 1-5150 <$600
3x10-20 1-3640 <$550
1902 Plain Back
4x5 5151-12350 <$600
3x10-20 3641-15490 <$550
Total Issue $1,231,750
Out in 1927 $98,800

4755 Sweetwater
ROCK SPRINGS NB, ROCK SPRINGS
{{ 16 L 45 S }}
Chartered 1892
Brown Back <$VALUE
3x10-20 1-3490 <$1500
1882 Date Back
3x10-20 1-1801 <$1250
1902 Date Back
4x5 1-3625 <$450
3x10-20 1-2750 <$350
1902 Plain Back
4x5 3626-5275 <$450
3x10-20 2751-17091 <$350
1929 Small Size
10 Type 1 1-2602 <$175
20 Type 1 1-602 <$175
10 Type 2 1-3634 <$200
20 Type 2 1-1272 <$200
Total Issue $1,514,740
Out in 1935 $90,000
Large out 1935 $4,825

8961 Carbon
FNB OF SARATOGA
{{ U + 0 L }}
Chartered 12/07
Liquidated 7/1/10
1902 Red Seal <$VALUE
4x10 1-250 <$6000
1902 Date Back
4x10 1-85 <$4000
Total Issue $13,400
Out in 1910 $4,860

4604 Sheridan
FNB OF SHERIDAN
{{ 12 L 50+ S }}
Chartered 1891
Brown Back <$VALUE
3x10-20 1-1240 <$1750
1882 Date Back
3x10-20 1-236 <$1500
1902 Date Back
3x10-20 1-2550 <$450
1902 Plain Back
3x10-20 2551-16232 <$450
1929 Small Size
10 Type 1 1-2562 <$165
20 Type 1 1-684 <$165
10 Type 2 1-2189 <$200
20 Type 2 1-615 <$200
Total Issue $1,155,390
Out in 1935 $100,000
Large out 1935 $4,730

8275 Sheridan
SHERIDAN NB, SHERIDAN
{{ 12 L }}
Chartered 6/06
Liquidated 3/10/28
1902 Red Seal <$VALUE
3x10-20 1-1100 <$5000
1902 Date Back
3x10-20 1-4100 <$500
1902 Plain Back
3x10-20 4101-9749 <$500
Total Issue $542,450
Out at close $49,995

7978 Fremont
FNB OF SHOSHONI
{{ 1 L }}
Chartered 11/05
Liquidated 11/29/24
1902 Red Seal <$VALUE
3x10-20 1-825 <$6000
1902 Date Back
3x10-20 1-1900* <$2000
1902 Plain Back
3x10-20 2031-4174* <$2000
* 1901-2030 not marked
Total Issue $249,950
Out at close $25,000

8232 Fremont
WIND RIVER NB OF SHOSHONI
{{ UNREPORTED }}
Chartered 5/23/06
Liquidated 7/18/08
1902 Red Seal <$VALUE
3x10-20 1-215 <$7500
Total Issue $10,750
Out in 1910 $1,660

4343 Crook
FNB OF SUNDANCE
{{ UNREPORTED }}
Organized 6/16/90
Receivership 10/11/93
TERRITORIAL ISSUES
Brown Back <$VALUE
4x5 1-305 <$12,500
3x10-20 1-126 <$12,500
STATE ISSUES
Brown Back
3x10-20 127-253 <$10,000
Total Issue $18,750
Out in 1915 $100

12638 Hot Springs
FNB IN THERMOPOLIS
{{ 4 L 20 S }}
Chartered 2/25
1902 Plain Back <$VALUE
3x10-20 1-2395 <$1250
1929 Small Size
10 Type 1 1-1146 <$300
20 Type 1 1-342 <$300
5 Type 2 1-312 <$350
10 Type 2 1-1431 <$350
20 Type 2 1-359 <$350
Total Issue $252,600
Out in 1935 $50,000
Large out 1935 $2,135
Outstanding includes Ch 5949

5949 Hot Springs
FNB OF THERMOPOLIS
{{ 5 L }}
Chartered 8/27/01
Liquidated 2/21/25
Brown Back <$VALUE
3x10-20 1-620 <$1750
1882 Date Back
3x10-20 1-910 <$1500
1882 Value Back
3x10-20 911-3279 <$1500
1902 Plain Back
3x10-20 1-2093 <$750
Total Issue $299,600
Out in 1925 $50,000
Ch 12638 assumed circulation

9289 Goshen
FNB OF TORRINGTON
{{ 2 L }}
Chartered 10/6/08
Receivership 12/16/24
1902 Date Back <$VALUE
3x10-20 1-720 <$2000
1902 Plain Back
3x10-20 721-1152 <$2000
Total Issue $57,600
Out at close $6,100

8432 Platte
FNB OF WHEATLAND
{{ UNREPORTED }}
Chartered 11/10/06
Liquidated 8/1/08
1902 Red Seal <$VALUE
3x10-20 1-727 <$6500
Total Issue $36,350
Out in 1910 $6,290

8253 Washakie
FNB OF WORLAND
{{ 2 L }}
Chartered 6/06
Liquidated 12/29/24
1902 Red Seal <$VALUE
3x10-20 1-400 <$6000
1902 Date Back
3x10-20 1-820 <$2000
1902 Plain Back
3x10-20 821-1659 <$2000
Total Issue $102,950
Out at close $10,000

CONDITION affects Value. The Values shown are for notes in FINE condition.

Chapter 5

UNCUT SHEETS OF NATIONAL BANK NOTES

This chapter studies and evaluates uncut sheets of national bank notes, and presents a census of approximately 2000 sheets known to have survived.

National bank notes were sent to the banks as uncut sheets. In most banks the notes were cut apart by a teller, a clerk, or some other employee. The aunt of the author's wife worked in the First National Bank of Homestead, Pennsylvania where one of her duties was to make up the bank's weekly payroll. She recalled separating sheets of large size notes with shears. An elderly gentleman whose father had been Cashier of the First National Bank of Kansas, Ohio told the author about his boyhood chore of separating notes using a paper cutter. The irregular edges on some notes show that they were separated by tearing against the edge of a teller's counter. Happily, a number of sheets have survived for us to collect in uncut form.

Several different sheet formats were used for large size nationals. Most $1 and $2 nationals were issued in sheets containing three $1 and one $2. This layout, shown in Figure 1, is designated in the listings as "3x1-2". Four banks issued sheets containing two $1 and two $2 notes. These banks were: Merchants NB of Bangor, Maine (Ch 1437), The City NB of Manchester, New Hampshire (Ch 1520), Washington County NB of Greenwich, New York (Ch 1266), and West Chester County NB of Peekskill, New York (Ch 1422).

All large size $5 notes were issued in sheets of four notes. This layout, shown in Figure 2, is designated in the listings as "4x5". Many $50 and $100 large size notes were issued in sheets of two notes. This layout, shown in Figure 3, is designated in the listings as "50-100". In a few instances large size notes were issued as "sheets" of just one note. Most large size $10 and $20 notes were issued in sheets containing three $10 and one $20. This layout, shown in Figure 4, is designated as "3x10-20".

Figure 1. Most $1 and $2 nationals were printed as sheets of three $1 and one $2.

Figure 2. The four notes have the same serial number, but different plate position letters.

Figure 4. The 3x10-20 format was used for most large size $10 and $20 notes.

Figure 3. The 50-100 format used for Brown Backs

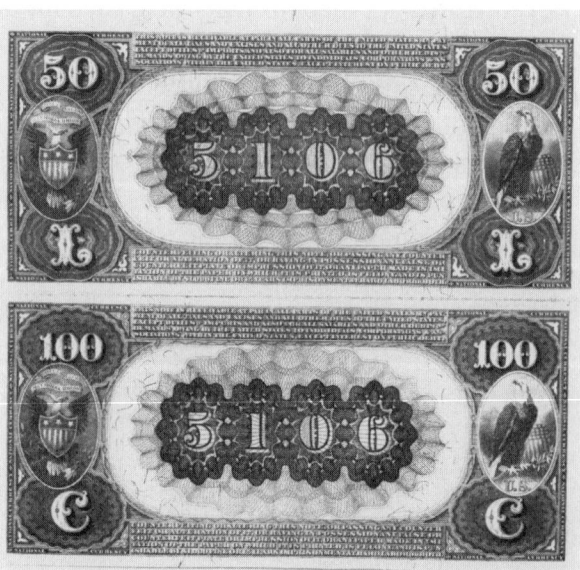

Figure 5. Back of unique 50-100 Brown Back sheet

Figure 6. A small fraction of the large size $10 notes were issued in the 4x10 format.

Small size notes were issued in sheets of six notes, all the same denomination. On Type 1 notes the serial numbers on all six notes are the same, but the prefix letters are different. For example, the six notes of a "#1 sheet" have serials A000001A, B000001A, C000001A, D000001A, E000001A, and F000001A. For Type 1 notes the listings in this guide give the range of sheet serial numbers. The number of notes issued is six times the number of sheets issued. Thus for example, if the listing reads

5 Type 1 1-100 <$150

then **100 sheets** of Type 1 $5 notes were issued, a total of **600 notes**.

Figure 7. A Type 1 sheet. The serial numbers are the same. The prefix letters are different.

On Type 2 notes the serial numbers are different for each note in a sheet. For example, the six notes of the first sheet carried the serials A000001, A000002, A000003, A000004, A000005, and A000006. For Type 2 notes the listings in this guide give the range of note serial numbers. For example, if the listing reads

5 Type 2 1-606 <$125

then **606 notes** were issued (**101 sheets**) with serials from A00000l to A000606.

The census which follows reveals that a majority of the surviving uncut sheets of small size notes are the first sheets issued to the bank. And therein hangs a tale, told first by William A. Philpott, Jr. (1971). The survival of so many serial number one sheets can be traced to George H. Blake, a pioneer paper money collector. Mr. Blake had friends in the right places, at the Redemption Bureau and the Comptroller's Office. He acted as an agent for the famous Colonel E. H. R. Green. Colonel Green was the son of Hetty Green, known as "The Witch of Wall Street" for her ruthless ways in the securities trade. Colonel Green is best known among collectors as the person who acquired the sheet of 24 cent airmail inverts. In an age when parents gave their sons model trains to play with, Hetty gave her son the Baltimore and Ohio Railroad Co. to "play with".

In 1929 the change to small size notes began. George Blake suggested to Colonel Green that acquiring the serial number one uncut sheets of the new small size notes would be a fascinating project. Colonel Green agreed. Through a contact at the Treasury, Mr. Blake would learn when a bank placed its initial order for small size notes. He then wrote to the bank offering a premium for the number one sheets. His buying price was $37.50 for sheets of six $5 notes, $66 for sheets of six $10 notes, and $125 for sheets of six $20 notes.

As soon as the sheets reached Mr. Blake he delivered them to Colonel Green. What price did Colonel Green pay? He paid $50 for the five dollar sheets, $80 for the tens and $145 for the twenties. Blake's efforts continued through the note issuing period and he purchased both Type 1 and Type 2 sheets.

Figure 8. A Type 2 sheet. The six notes have different serial numbers and no suffix letter.

When Colonel Green's estate was administered there was little collector interest in the sheets. Mr. Philpott and a few others bought sheets at 15 percent over face. The remainder of the sheets were turned in to the New York Federal Reserve Bank, at face value. The New York Bank sent a list to each of the other 11 Federal Reserve District Banks, suggesting they offer sheets to their member national banks at face value, as a good will gesture. The Dallas Federal Reserve Bank contacted Mr. Philpott advising that he could have any or all of the Texas number one sheets at face value. In Mr. Phipott's words, "Again, I heaved a sigh, signed another large note or two at my bank, and rescued another score or so of uncut Texas sheets." Thus, it was through the efforts of Blake, Green, and Philpott that hundreds of number one uncut sheets were preserved for collectors.

Hoards of Uncut Sheets

Several notable hoards of uncut sheets have surfaced. Over ninety uncut small size sheets have survived from The First National Bank of Cassopolis, Michigan (Charter 1812). The First National Bank in Reno, Nevada (Charter 7038) evidently preserved its entire final shipment of nationals, as over forty uncut sheets are recorded. The Lawndale National Bank of Chicago, Illinois (Charter 11247) provided a sizable hoard of uncut sheets, both large size and small size. The First National Bank of Clifton, Kansas has provided collectors with nearly twenty uncut sheets of large size notes, eight of them 1902 Red Seals. Fifteen sets of $5, $10, and $20 sheets, with serial numbers one through fifteen, have survived from The Boatmen's National Bank of St Louis, Missouri (Charter 12916).

Aubree Bebee uncovered a hoard of twenty two uncut sheets of $5 Brown Backs issued to the St Paul, Nebraska NB (Charter 3129). This $440 made up over half of the circulation outstanding on the bank in 1910, some thirteen years after the bank liquidated. The sheets were in pristine condition and several have been cut.

The most electrifying hoard of uncut sheets surfaced at the 1966 Central States Show where dealer Joe Welles of Topeka, Kansas sold four sheets of $5 1902 Red Seals issued to The First National Bank of Fairbanks, Alaska. He sold the sheets for $1000 each. All four of the sheets have now been cut. A single note from one of the sheets sold for $13,750 in 1993. Joe Welles kept a fifth sheet for himself, but later sold it to John J. Ford, Jr. That sheet (serial 1065) is still intact (Ford 1978).

For many years the author and Charles A. Dean have tracked uncut sheets of nationals. The census which follows lists over 2000 sheets which entered the numismatic market in uncut form. The demand for single notes has resulted in many sheets being cut. **These are listed with a double asterisk following the serial number (e.g. 1069**).** The purpose of listing these now-cut sheets is to save future researchers from the trap of "discovering" an "unreported" sheet in some ancient auction catalog or pricelist. For some 1929 Type 2 sheets the serial number range is given (e.g. 1-6). For Type 2 sheets with longer serial numbers, the serial number of the top note is given, followed by two dashes (e.g. 90001--).

The census includes 10 Original Series and 8 Series 1875 sheets. In Series 1882 sheets there are 58 Brown Backs, 7 Date Backs, and 3 Value Backs. The Series 1902 count is 43 Red Seals, 34 Date Backs, and 263 Plain Backs. The census includes over 1500 small size sheets, almost equally divided between Type 1 and Type 2.

The listing is alphabetic by state, alphabetic by town name, and numerical by charter number. A number in parentheses following the town name indicates a second or higher title. The types are abbreviated. For example, 82BB refers to 1882 Brown Back, and a Series 1929 Type 1 sheet is indicated by 29-1.

The surviving uncut sheets are typically found in About Uncirculated condition. Such a sheet may have been folded lightly or show other signs of handling but is otherwise in new condition. The valuations which follow refer to uncut sheets in About Uncirculated condition.

Some sheet combinations are unknown to collectors, and the values assigned are simply educated guesses about potential values.

VALUES: UNCUT SHEETS OF NATIONAL BANK NOTES

Format/Series	**Original/Series 1875**		
3x1-2	$10,000		
4x5	$10,000		
3x10-20	$15,000		
50-100	$125,000		
	1882 Brown Back	**1882 Date Back**	**1882 Value Back**
4x5	$3000	$3500	$10,000
3x10-20	$3500	$4000	$10,000
50-100	$30,000	$30,000	$150,000
	1902 Red Seal	**1902 Date Back**	**1902 Plain Back**
4x5	$3500	$2000	$1500
4x10	$4000	$2000	$2000
3x10-20	$4000	$2000	$1500
50-100	$50,000	$10,000	Not Issued
3x50-100	Not Issued	$10,000	$10,000
	1929 Type 1	**1929 Type 2**	
6x5	$600	$750	
6x10	$600	$750	
6x20	$650	$850	
6x50	$5000	$7500	
6x100	$6000	$10,000	

State/Town	Charter	Denom	Type	Serial
ALASKA				
FAIRBANKS	7718	5	02RS	1054**
FAIRBANKS	7718	5	02RS	1061**
FAIRBANKS	7718	5	02RS	1064**
FAIRBANKS	7718	5	02RS	1065
FAIRBANKS	7718	5	02RS	1069**
FAIRBANKS	7718	5	02RS	750
FAIRBANKS	7718	5	02PB	6000
FAIRBANKS	7718	5	29-2	2017-22
Total Sheets: 8				
ALABAMA				
ALEXANDER CITY	7417	5	29-1	5
ANNISTON	3041	10	29-2	1-6
ANNISTON	3041	20	29-2	1-6
BIRMINGHAM	13358	5	29-1	1
BIRMINGHAM	13358	5	29-2	1-6
DECATUR(2)	10336	5	29-1	1
DECATUR(2)	10336	10	29-1	1
DECATUR(2)	10336	5	29-1	2
EUTAW	3931	20	29-2	1-6
MOBILE	13414	5	29-1	1
MOBILE	13414	10	29-1	1
OPELIKA	9550	20	29-1	1
OPELIKA	9550	5	29-2	1-6
OPELIKA	9550	10	29-2	1-6
SLOCOMB	7940	5	29-1	1
Total Sheets: 15				
ARKANSAS				
BATESVILLE	7556	3x10-20	02PB	5566
BATESVILLE	7556	5	02PB	
BERRYVILLE	10406	5	29-1	1
BERRYVILLE	10406	10	29-2	1-6
EL DORADO	7046	10	29-2	1-6
EL DORADO	7046	20	29-2	1-6
FAYETTEVILLE	7346	20	29-2	1-6
FORDYCE	9501	10	29-2	1-6
GURDON	13210	5	29-2	5863-68
GURDON	13210	5	29-2	5869-74
GURDON	13210	5	29-2	5875-80
HELENA	13520	5	29-1	1
LAKE VILLAGE	13632	5	29-1	1
NEWARK	9022	10	29-2	1-6
SILOAM SPRINGS	13274	5	02PB	325
SILOAM SPRINGS	13274	5	02PB	352**
STUTTGART	10459	5	02PB	3300
Total Sheets: 17				
ARIZONA				
PRESCOTT	13262	5	29-1	1
Total Sheets: 1				
CALIFORNIA				
ANAHEIM(2)	10228	20	29-1	1
ANTIOCH	9892	10	29-2	1-6
ANTIOCH	9892	20	29-2	1-6
AZUSA	8065	5	29-1	1
BAKERSFIELD(2)	10357	10	29-1	1
BAKERSFIELD(2)	10357	100	29-1	1
BAKERSFIELD(2)	10357	20	29-1	1
BAKERSFIELD(2)	10357	5	29-1	1
BAKERSFIELD(2)	10357	20	29-2	1-6
BANNING	9459	5	29-1	1
BANNING	9459	10	29-2	1-6
BANNING	9459	5	29-2	1-6
BREA	13877	5	29-2	2575-80
BREA	13877	5	29-2	2815-20
CALISTOGA	9551	10	29-2	1-6
CALISTOGA	9551	20	29-2	1-6
CHICO	13711	10	29-2	1-6
CHICO	13711	5	29-2	1-6
CORCORAN	9546	5	29-2	1-6
CORONA	7867	10	29-2	3151--
CORONA	7867	5	29-2	7891--
COVINA	5830	5	82BB	560
COVINA	8222	10	29-2	1-6
COVINA	8222	20	29-2	1-6
GLENDORA	8652	20	29-1	1
GLENDORA	8652	20	29-2	1-6
LOMA LINDA	13332	5	29-2	13-18
LOMA LINDA	13332	5	29-2	7-12
LOS ANGELES	12545	5	29-1	5
McCLOUD	9479	10	29-2	1-6
McCLOUD	9479	5	29-2	1-6
McFARLAND	10387	5	29-1	1
MERCED	13028	5	29-2	1-6
MONTEREY	7058	20	29-2	1-6
OAKDALE	7502	5	29-1	6
ONTARIO	6268	5	29-1	1
ORANGE COVE	11616	5	29-2	1-6
PACIFIC GROVE	13375	20	29-1	1
PACIFIC GROVE	13375	10	29-2	1-6
PACIFIC GROVE	13375	20	29-2	1-6
PALO ALTO	13212	20	29-1	1**
PALO ALTO	13212	5	29-1	1**
PALO ALTO	13212	10	29-2	1-6
PALO ALTO	13212	20	29-2	1-6
PALO ALTO	13212	5	29-2	1-6
PASADENA	10167	5	29-1	1
PASADENA	10167	10	29-2	1-6
PLEASANTON	9897	10	29-1	1**
PLEASANTON	9897	20	29-1	1
PLEASANTON	9897	5	29-1	1
PLEASANTON	9897	20	29-2	1-6
REDDING	10100	5	29-2	1-6
REDWOOD CITY	7279	10	29-2	1-6
REDWOOD CITY	7279	20	29-2	1-6
RIVERSIDE(2)	8377	20	29-2	1-6
RIVERSIDE(2)	8377	5	29-2	1-6
SACRAMENTO	10107	5	02PB	97088
SACRAMENTO	10107	5	29-2	1-6
SAN DIMAS	10068	20	29-1	1
SAN DIMAS	10068	5	29-1	1
SAN FERNANDO	10273	10	29-1	1
SAN FRANCISCO(2)	3555	3x10-20	02RS	
SAN FRANCISCO(2)	3555	5	02RS	
SAN JOSE	13338	10	29-2	1-6
SAN JOSE	13338	20	29-2	1-6
SAN JOSE	13338	5	29-2	1-6
SAN MARINO	13335	5	29-1	55
SAN MARINO	13335	10	29-2	1-6
SAN MARINO	13335	20	29-2	1-6
SAN MARINO	13335	5	29-2	1-6
TUSTIN	10134	10	29-1	1
TUSTIN	10134	20	29-1	1
TUSTIN	10134	5	29-2	1-6
WEED	9873	20	29-1	1**
WEED	9873	5	29-1	1**
WEED	9873	5	29-2	1-6
WHITTIER(2)	7999	5	29-1	1
WINTERS	13312	10	29-1	1
WINTERS	13312	20	29-1	1
WINTERS	13312	5	29-1	1
WINTERS	13312	20	29-2	1-6
WINTERS	13312	5	29-2	1-6
WOODLAKE	10309	3x10-20	02PB	3
YREKA	13340	10	29-2	1-6
YREKA	13340	20	29-2	1-6
YREKA	13340	5	29-2	1-6
Total Sheets: 86				
COLORADO				
BRUSH	6437	5	29-1	1
CARBONDALE	9009	5	29-1	
CEDAREDGE	10272	10	29-2	1-6
COLORADO CITY	6238	3x10-20	02PB	
COLORADO SPRINGS	2179	5	29-1	333
COLORADO SPRINGS(2)	6238	10	29-1	1
DENVER	3269	10	29-1	2
DENVER	7408	3x10-20	02PB	89999
DENVER	7408	3x10-20	02PB	90000
DENVER	7408	10	29-1	555
DENVER	7408	20	29-1	1
DENVER	12517	5	02PB	
DENVER	12517	5	29-1	4444
DENVER	13098	10	29-1	1
DENVER	13098	5	29-1	1
EADS	8412	20	29-1	1
EADS	14213	10	29-2	1-6
EADS	14213	20	29-2	1-6
EADS	14213	5	29-2	1-6
FORT COLLINS	2622	10	29-1	1
FORT COLLINS	5503		02PB	
JOHNSTOWN	8636	10	29-1	
LONGMONT	7839	10	29-1	
LONGMONT	7839	20	29-1	
PUEBLO	1833	3x50-100	02PB	4664**
WRAY	8752	10	29-1	
Total Sheets: 26				
CONNECTICUT				
BRIDGEPORT(4)	335	5	29-1	
DANBURY	943	5	29-1	1**
DANIELSON(3)	1360	5	02PB	9286
DANIELSON(3)	1360	5	02PB	9287
DANIELSON(3)	1360	5	29-1	1
GREENWICH	8243	3x10-20	02RS	1115
HARTFORD	13038	10	02PB	2
HARTFORD	13038	10	02PB	5
HARTFORD	13038	5	02PB	6**
HARTFORD	13038	5	02PB	7
HARTFORD	13038	5	02PB	8
HARTFORD	13038	5	02PB	9
HARTFORD(2)	13038	10	29-1	2
HARTFORD(2)	13038	5	29-1	3
LITCHFIELD	709	3x10-20	02PB	24393
MERIDEN	720	10	29-2	1-6
MERIDEN	720	20	29-2	1-6
MIDDLETOWN(2)	1216	5	29-1	1
MIDDLETOWN	1340	3x10-20	02PB	32251
NEW HAVEN(2)	2	10	29-1	1000
NEW HAVEN(2)	2	20	29-1	1000
NEW HAVEN(2)	2	5	29-1	1000
NEW HAVEN(2)	2	10	29-2	1-6
NEW HAVEN(2)	2	5	29-2	1-6**
NEW HAVEN	1128	5	29-1	1128
NEW HAVEN(2)	1202	5	29-1	1202
NEW LONDON	978	10	29-1	1
NEW LONDON	978	10	29-2	1-6
STAMFORD(2)	4	20	29-1	40
STAMFORD(3)	4	10	29-1	1
STAMFORD(3)	4	10	29-1	200
STAMFORD(3)	4	5	29-1	5
STAMFORD(3)	4	5	29-1	6
WATERBURY	780	5	29-1	1
WATERBURY	780	5	29-2	1-6
Total Sheets: 35				
DELAWARE				
DAGSBORO	8972	10	29-2	1-6**
Total Sheets: 1				
DISTRICT OF COLUMBIA				
WASHINGTON(3)	1069	3x10-20	02PB	180500
WASHINGTON(3)	1069	3x10-20	02PB	180700
WASHINGTON(3)	1069	10	29-1	2
WASHINGTON	2382	3x10-20	82BB	
WASHINGTON	7446	3x10-20	02RS	1000
WASHINGTON	13782	5	29-2	90001--
WASHINGTON	13782	5	29-2	99997--
Total Sheets: 7				
FLORIDA				
BARTOW	13389	10	29-2	1-6
BROOKSVILLE	9891	3x10-20	02DB	1
BROOKSVILLE	9891	3x10-20	02PB	10293
BROOKSVILLE	13320	5	29-2	1-6
HOMESTEAD	13641	5	29-1	1
JACKSONVILLE	10136	10	02PB	46310
JACKSONVILLE	10136	5	02PB	46843
JACKSONVILLE	10136	5	02PB	46844
LAKE CITY	7540	5	29-2	3793--
LAKE CITY	7540	5	29-2	3817--
LAKELAND	13370	5	29-1	1
LAKELAND	13370	10	29-2	1-6
LAKELAND	13370	5	29-2	1-6
LIVE OAK	6055	20	29-2	1-6
MIAMI	6370	10	29-1	1
MIAMI	6370	20	29-1	1
MIAMI	6370	50	29-1	1
PALATKA	13214	5	29-1	1**
SARASOTA	13352	10	29-1	1
SARASOTA	13352	10	29-1	3
SARASOTA	13352	5	29-2	1-6
SARASOTA	13352	20	29-2	1-6
WINTER HAVEN	13383	5	29-2	1-6
Total Sheets: 23				
GEORGIA				
GAINESVILLE	3983	10	29-2	2437-42
GAINESVILLE	3983	10	29-2	2485-90
JACKSON	13897	10	29-2	1-6
JACKSON	13897	20	29-2	1-6
JACKSON	13897	5	29-2	1-6
JACKSON	13897	5	29-2	1-6
MACON	8990	5	02RS	
MADISON	7300	10	29-2	1-6
MONTICELLO	9346	5	29-1	1**
SANDERSVILLE	7934	3x10-20	02DB	1404
TIFTON	8350	10	29-1	1
WAYNESBORO	7899	5	29-1	1
Total Sheets: 12				
IDAHO				
BOISE	10751	3x10-20	02DB	2
COEUR D'ALENE	13288	10	29-1	1
IDAHO FALLS	6982	5	29-1	1
REXBURG	7133	5	02RS	1**
REXBURG	7133	3x10-20	02DB	2223
REXBURG	7133	5	02PB	2661
Total Sheets: 6				
ILLINOIS				
ARENZVILLE	9183	5	29-1	1
ATLANTA	2283	3x10-20	1875	531
BARRINGTON	11283	3x10-20	02PB	
BELLEVILLE	13236	10	29-1	1
BELLEVILLE	13236	20	29-1	1
BELLEVILLE	13236	5	29-1	1
BRIDGEPORT	8347	5	29-1	1
CHICAGO	1867	5	1875	715
CHICAGO	3503	3x10-20	82BB	221
CHICAGO	3698	5	02DB	
CHICAGO	4605	5	02PB	321039
CHICAGO	5106	50-100	82BB	6400
CHICAGO	9010	5	02DB	14106
CHICAGO(2)	10237	10	29-1	1

State/Town	Charter	Denom	Type	Serial
CHICAGO	10247	3x10-20	02PB	3
CHICAGO	10247	3x10-20	02PB	7373
CHICAGO	10247	3x10-20	02PB	7387
CHICAGO	10247	3x10-20	02PB	7388
CHICAGO	10247	3x10-20	02PB	7396
CHICAGO	10247	3x10-20	02PB	7398
CHICAGO	10247	5	02PB	9646
CHICAGO	10247	5	02PB	9731
CHICAGO	10247	5	02PB	9734
CHICAGO	10247	5	02PB	9744
CHICAGO	10247	5	02PB	9745
CHICAGO	10247	5	02PB	9748
CHICAGO	10247	5	29-2	13-18
CHICAGO	10247	10	29-2	13-18
CHICAGO	10247	10	29-2	25-30
CHICAGO	10247	10	29-2	31-37
CHICAGO	10247	10	29-2	37-42
CHICAGO	10247	20	29-2	13-18
CHICAGO	10247	20	29-2	25-30
CHICAGO	10247	20	29-2	37-42
CHICAGO	10247	20	29-2	43-48
CHICAGO(2)	10337	5	02PB	
CHICAGO(2)	11737	10	29-1	1
CHICAGO	12227	5	02PB	77631
CHICAGO	12227	5	02PB	77632
CHICAGO	12227	5	02PB	77635
CHICAGO	12227	5	02PB	77636
CHICAGO	12227	5	02PB	77639
CHICAGO	13684	10	29-2	
CICERO	11662	5	02PB	1232
COLUMBIA	13805	10	29-2	1-6
FLORA	1961	5	29-2	1-6**
GRANITE CITY(2)	6564	20	29-1	1
GRANITE CITY(2)	6564	5	29-1	1
GRANITE CITY(2)	6564	5	29-1	2
GRANITE CITY(2)	6564	5	29-2	1-6
HEGEWISCH	8605	3x10-20	02PB	2463
HEGEWISCH	8605	5	02PB	3850**
HENRY	7049	20	29-2	1-6
HIGHLAND	6653	5	02RS	A286336
JACKSONVILLE	511	3x1-2	ORIG	1
JACKSONVILLE	511	3x10-20	82BB	1**
KINMUNDY	6143	10	29-2	1-6
MARISSA	13735	10	29-2	1-6
MARISSA	13735	20	29-2	1-6
NEW DOUGLAS	13696	10	29-2	1-6
O'FALLON	6924	10	29-2	1-6
PEKIN	9788	10	29-1	1
PEORIA(2)	3214	10	29-2	1-6
PEORIA(2)	3214	20	29-2	1-6
PEORIA(2)	3214	5	29-2	1-6
PERU	13577	5	29-1	1
RAMSEY	9895	20	29-1	1
ROCKFORD	13652	50	29-1	1
ROCKFORD	13652	10	29-2	1-6
ROCKFORD	13652	10	29-2	1135--
ROCKFORD	13652	20	29-2	1-6
SAINT ELMO	9388	5	29-2	1-6**
SHELBYVILLE	2128	5	82BB	1006
SMITHTON	13525	10	29-1	1
STAUNTON	10173	5	29-1	1
STREATOR	2681	3x10-20	1875	2681
SUMNER	6907	20	29-2	1-6
SYCAMORE(2)	1896	20	29-1	
WATERLOO	10180	5	29-2	1-6
WITT	13650	20	29-1	1
WOOD RIVER	11876	5	02PB	5
Total Sheets: 81				
INDIANA				
BLUFFTON(2)	13305	20	29-1	1
BLUFFTON(2)	13305	5	29-1	1**
BLUFFTON	13317	10	29-1	1
CRAWFORDSVILLE	571	5	29-1	1
EAST CHICAGO	13531	5	29-1	1
EAST CHICAGO	13532	5	0	
GREENSBURG	1890	10	29-1	1
GREENSBURG	1890	20	29-1	1
GREENSBURG	1890	5	29-1	1
INDIANAPOLIS	55	3x1-2	1875	1567
INDIANAPOLIS	984	3x10-20	02PB	
JEFFERSONVILLE	956	5	29-1	2
JEFFERSONVILLE	956	5	29-1	3
KNIGHTSTOWN	872	5	29-1	1
LINTON	14258	10	29-2	1-6
LOGANSPORT	13580	10	29-1	1
MARION	4189	5	29-1	1**
MARION	13717	5	29-2	1-6
NEW CASTLE	804	3x1-2	ORIG	1532
POSEYVILLE	8149	5	29-1	1**
POSEYVILLE	13503	20	29-1	1
POSEYVILLE	13503	5	29-1	1**
RICHMOND	17	5	29-1	1
RICHMOND	17	5	29-2	1-6
SEYMOUR	1002	5	29-1	1**
VINCENNES	1873	3x10-20	82BB	4227
VINCENNES	1873	3x10-20	02PB	5144
VINCENNES	1873	5	02PB	7716
WHITING	6526	3x10-20	02PB	8876**
Total Sheets: 29				
IOWA				
BEDFORD	5165	5	82BB	12006
CLINTON	994	10	29-1	1
CLINTON	994	5	29-1	3
CLINTON	2469	5	29-1	5989
COUNCIL BLUFFS	9306	5	29-2	1-6
DES MOINES	13321	10	29-1	1
DES MOINES	13321	20	29-1	1
DES MOINES	13321	5	29-1	1
DES MOINES	13321	10	29-2	1-6
DES MOINES	13321	20	29-2	1-6
GRINNELL	13473	10	29-1	1
GRINNELL	13473	20	29-1	1
GRINNELL	13473	5	29-1	1
HARVEY	6936	5	29-2	1-6
KNOXVILLE	1986	5	02PB	6078
NEWTON	13609	5	29-1	1
SIOUX CITY	5022	10	29-2	6325--
SIOUX CITY	5022	10	29-2	6337-42
SIOUX CITY	5022	10	29-2	6349--
SIOUX CITY	5022	10	29-2	6355--
SIOUX CITY	5022	10	29-2	6427-32
THORNTON	8340	5	29-1	1
TIPTON	13232	5	29-1	1
TOLEDO	13073	5	29-1	1
VILLISCA	14041	5	29-2	1-6**
VILLISCA	14041	10	29-2	1-6**
WATERLOO	792	5	29-1	1
Total Sheets: 27				
KANSAS				
CLIFTON	7178	3x10-20	02RS	1171
CLIFTON	7178	3x10-20	02RS	1172
CLIFTON	7178	3x10-20	02RS	1173
CLIFTON	7178	3x10-20	02RS	1174
CLIFTON	7178	3x10-20	02RS	1175
CLIFTON	7178	3x10-20	02RS	1176
CLIFTON	7178	3x10-20	02RS	1177
CLIFTON	7178	3x10-20	02RS	1178
CLIFTON	7178	3x10-20	02DB	218
CLIFTON	7178	3x10-20	02DB	219
CLIFTON	7178	3x10-20	02DB	220
CLIFTON	7178	3x10-20	02DB	221
CLIFTON	7178	3x10-20	02DB	222
CLIFTON	7178	3x10-20	02DB	223
CLIFTON	7178	3x10-20	02DB	224
CLIFTON	7178	3x10-20	02DB	225
CLIFTON	7178	3x10-20	02DB	226
CLIFTON	7178	3x10-20	02PB	1707
COFFEYVILLE	6797	10	29-2	1-6
COLBY	13076	5	02PB	10
COLBY	13076	5	02PB	12
COLBY	13076	5	02PB	13
COLBY	13076	5	02PB	14
COLBY	13076	5	29-2	11215--
COLBY	13076	5	29-2	11233--
COLBY	13076	5	29-2	11371--
COLBY	13076	5	29-2	11395
COLDWATER	6767	10	29-2	1-6
COLDWATER	6767	5	29-2	1-6
DEXTER	9225	3x10-20	02DB	1**
DEXTER	9225	3x10-20	02DB	429**
DEXTER	9225	3x10-20	02DB	430
DEXTER	9225	3x10-20	02DB	431
DEXTER	9225	3x10-20	02DB	432
DEXTER	9225	3x10-20	02DB	433
DEXTER	9225	3x10-20	02DB	434
DIGHTON	9773	20	29-1	1**
DIGHTON	9773	10	29-2	1-6
DIGHTON	9773	5	29-2	1-6
EDNA	7590	10	29-2	721-726
ERIE	3963	5	82BB	302
FORT LEAVENWORTH	8796	5	29-1	1
HUTCHINSON	3180	3x10-20	82BB	1
HUTCHINSON	3180	3x10-20	02RS	1
HUTCHINSON	3180	3x10-20	02DB	1
INDEPENDENCE	13492	5	29-1	1
KANSAS CITY	6311	3x10-20	02PB	32955
KANSAS CITY	6311	5	02PB	58625
KANSAS CITY	9309	3x10-20	02DB	1
KANSAS CITY	9309	5	29-1	1905
KANSAS CITY	13801	10	29-2	
KANSAS CITY	13801	5	29-2	
LAWRENCE	3584	10	29-1	1
LEROY	6149	10	29-2	1-6
LEROY	6149	20	29-2	1-6
LIBERAL	13406	5	29-1	1
LIBERAL	13406	10	29-2	1-6
MANKATO(2)	6817	10	29-1	1**
MANKATO(2)	6817	5	29-1	1
OAKLEY	10041	5	29-1	1
OBERLIN	4642	10	29-1	1**
OSBORNE	3472	10	29-1	1**
PARSONS	1951	3x10-20	82BB	4594
PARSONS	1951	3x10-20	82BB	4596**
PITTSBURG	3463	5	02PB	14603
SAINT JOHN	7844	10	29-2	1-6
SAINT JOHN	7844	20	29-2	1-6
SCOTT CITY	8808	20	29-2	1-6
THAYER	9465	10	29-2	1-6
THAYER	9465	20	29-2	1-6
TOPEKA	11398	20	29-1	1**
WAVERLY	6101	5	29-2	1-6
WINFIELD	3218	10	29-2	4807--
WINFIELD	3218	20	29-2	1603--
Total Sheets: 74				
KENTUCKY				
ADAIRVILLE	8814	10	29-2	1-6
ASHLAND	3944	5	82BB	1948
FLEMING	11988	5	29-2	1-6
HARLAN	12295	3x10-20	02PB	
HARRODSBURG	13612	10	29-1	1
HARRODSBURG	13612	5	29-1	1
JACKSON	9320	5	29-1	
LOUISVILLE	2062	3x1-2	ORIG	14
LOUISVILLE	2062	3x1-2	ORIG	16
PIKEVILLE	7030	5	02RS	1
PIKEVILLE	7030	10	29-2	1-6
PIKEVILLE	7030	20	29-2	1-6
PIKEVILLE	7030	5	29-2	1-6
PROVIDENCE	9708	20	29-1	1
WILMORE	9880	5	29-1	1
Total Sheets: 15				
LOUISIANA				
DE RIDDER	14168	5	29-2	1-6
GRETNA	13732	10	29-2	1-6
GRETNA	13732	5	29-2	1-6
LAKE PROVIDENCE	6291	10	29-2	1-6
LAKE PROVIDENCE	6291	20	29-2	1-6
LAKE PROVIDENCE	6291	5	29-2	1-6
MONROE	13655	10	29-2	1-6
MONROE	13655	20	29-2	1-6
SHREVEPORT	3600	5	29-1	1
SHREVEPORT	13648	100	29-1	1
SHREVEPORT	13648	5	29-1	1
SHREVEPORT	13648	50	29-1	1
SHREVEPORT	13648	5	29-2	1-6
SHREVEPORT	13648	5	29-2	133-138
SHREVEPORT	13648	5	29-2	157-162
SHREVEPORT	13648	5	29-2	187-192
SHREVEPORT	13648	5	29-2	37-42
SHREVEPORT	13648	5	29-2	79-84
SHREVEPORT	13648	5	29-2	85-90
SHREVEPORT	13648	5	29-2	91-96
Total Sheets: 20				
MAINE				
AUGUSTA(2)	498	10	29-1	1
AUGUSTA(2)	498	20	29-1	1
AUGUSTA(2)	498	5	29-1	1
AUGUSTA(2)	498	10	29-2	1-6
BATH	494	10	29-1	1
BATH	494	5	29-1	1
LEWISTON	330	5	02PB	58151
PORTLAND	941	5	29-1	12891
PORTLAND	941	5	29-1	7
PORTLAND	4128	5	29-1	1
PORTLAND	4128	5	29-2	1-6
Total Sheets: 11				
MARYLAND				
BALTIMORE	814	5	02DB	
BALTIMORE	5984	5	02PB	34700
BRUNSWICK	8244	5	29-1	1
FEDERALSBURG	10210	20	29-1	1
LA PLATA	8456	5	29-1	1
LEONARDTOWN	6606	10	29-2	25-30
LEONARDTOWN	6606	10	29-2	7-12
LEONARDTOWN	6606	20	29-2	13-18
LEONARDTOWN	6606	20	29-2	19-24
OAKLAND	13776	5	29-2	1-6
Total Sheets: 10				
MASSACHUSETTS				
BEVERLY	969	5	29-1	1**
BOSTON	379	5	02RS	24732
BOSTON	615	5	02RS	2603
BOSTON	684	3x10-20	02PB	
BOSTON	684	5	02PB	
BOSTON(2)	1527	5	29-2	30823-8
BOSTON	2112	3x1-2	1875	2840
BOSTON(2)	2304	5	82BB	35807
BOSTON	11903	5	02PB	111030
BOSTON	12336	3x10-20	02PB	106199
BOSTON	12336	5	02PB	183201
BUZZARDS BAY	13222	5	29-1	1
CONWAY	895	5	29-1	1

State/Town	Charter	Denom	Type	Serial
DANVERS	7452	3x10-20	02PB	6734
FAIRHAVEN	490	10	29-1	1
FAIRHAVEN	490	20	29-1	1
FAIRHAVEN	490	5	29-1	3
FAIRHAVEN	490	5	29-2	1-6
HAVERHILL	633	10	29-1	
HAVERHILL	633	5	29-1	
LAWRENCE	1014	5	29-1	
LENOX	4013	5	02PB	5874
MALDEN	588	10	29-1	1
MALDEN	588	5	29-1	1
MALDEN	588	5	29-2	
NEW BEDFORD	261	10	29-1	1
NEW BEDFORD	261	20	29-1	1
NEW BEDFORD	261	5	29-2	1-6
NEWTON	13252	5	29-1	2222
SHELBURNE FALLS	1144	5	29-2	1-6
SPRINGFIELD	2435	5	02PB	78130
SPRINGFIELD	2435	10	29-1	2
SPRINGFIELD	2435	5	29-1	2
SPRINGFIELD	2435	5	29-1	3
SPRINGFIELD	2435	5	29-1	4
SPRINGFIELD(3)	4907	10	29-1	2
SPRINGFIELD(3)	4907	5	29-1	3
WESTBORO	421	5	29-1	1

Total Sheets: 38

MICHIGAN

ANN ARBOR(2)	2714	10	29-1	1
ANN ARBOR(2)	2714	20	29-1	1
ANN ARBOR(2)	2714	5	29-1	1
CASSOPOLIS	1812	10	29-1	10
CASSOPOLIS	1812	10	29-1	11
CASSOPOLIS	1812	10	29-1	246
CASSOPOLIS	1812	10	29-1	7
CASSOPOLIS	1812	10	29-1	8
CASSOPOLIS	1812	10	29-1	9
CASSOPOLIS	1812	20	29-1	2
CASSOPOLIS	1812	20	29-1	64
CASSOPOLIS	1812	20	29-1	65
CASSOPOLIS	1812	20	29-1	66
CASSOPOLIS	1812	20	29-1	67
CASSOPOLIS	1812	20	29-1	69
CASSOPOLIS	1812	20	29-1	71
CASSOPOLIS	1812	5	29-1	1
CASSOPOLIS	1812	5	29-1	10
CASSOPOLIS	1812	5	29-1	200
CASSOPOLIS	1812	5	29-1	202
CASSOPOLIS	1812	5	29-1	203
CASSOPOLIS	1812	5	29-1	204
CASSOPOLIS	1812	5	29-1	205
CASSOPOLIS	1812	5	29-1	206
CASSOPOLIS	1812	5	29-1	207
CASSOPOLIS	1812	5	29-1	208
CASSOPOLIS	1812	5	29-1	209
CASSOPOLIS	1812	5	29-1	210
CASSOPOLIS	1812	5	29-1	212
CASSOPOLIS	1812	5	29-1	213
CASSOPOLIS	1812	5	29-1	214
CASSOPOLIS	1812	5	29-1	217
CASSOPOLIS	1812	5	29-1	218
CASSOPOLIS	1812	5	29-1	219
CASSOPOLIS	1812	5	29-1	220
CASSOPOLIS	1812	5	29-1	221
CASSOPOLIS	1812	5	29-1	222
CASSOPOLIS	1812	5	29-1	223
CASSOPOLIS	1812	5	29-1	224
CASSOPOLIS	1812	5	29-1	225
CASSOPOLIS	1812	5	29-1	226
CASSOPOLIS	1812	5	29-1	322
CASSOPOLIS	1812	5	29-1	327
CASSOPOLIS	1812	5	29-1	328
CASSOPOLIS	1812	5	29-1	329
CASSOPOLIS	1812	5	29-1	330
CASSOPOLIS	1812	5	29-1	332
CASSOPOLIS	1812	5	29-1	333
CASSOPOLIS	1812	5	29-1	339**
CASSOPOLIS	1812	5	29-1	340
CASSOPOLIS	1812	5	29-1	351
CASSOPOLIS	1812	5	29-1	356
CASSOPOLIS	1812	5	29-1	357
CASSOPOLIS	1812	5	29-1	358
CASSOPOLIS	1812	5	29-1	359
CASSOPOLIS	1812	5	29-1	360
CASSOPOLIS	1812	5	29-1	361
CASSOPOLIS	1812	5	29-1	362
CASSOPOLIS	1812	5	29-1	363
CASSOPOLIS	1812	5	29-1	364
CASSOPOLIS	1812	5	29-1	367
CASSOPOLIS	1812	5	29-1	368
CASSOPOLIS	1812	5	29-1	369
CASSOPOLIS	1812	5	29-1	370
CASSOPOLIS	1812	5	29-1	371
CASSOPOLIS	1812	5	29-1	372
CASSOPOLIS	1812	5	29-1	373
CASSOPOLIS	1812	5	29-1	377
CASSOPOLIS	1812	5	29-1	378
CASSOPOLIS	1812	5	29-1	379
CASSOPOLIS	1812	5	29-1	380
CASSOPOLIS	1812	5	29-1	381
CASSOPOLIS	1812	5	29-1	382
CASSOPOLIS	1812	5	29-1	383
CASSOPOLIS	1812	5	29-1	384
CASSOPOLIS	1812	5	29-1	385
CASSOPOLIS	1812	5	29-1	386
CASSOPOLIS	1812	5	29-1	387
CASSOPOLIS	1812	5	29-1	388
CASSOPOLIS	1812	5	29-1	389
CASSOPOLIS	1812	5	29-1	390
CASSOPOLIS	1812	5	29-1	391
CASSOPOLIS	1812	5	29-1	392
CASSOPOLIS	1812	5	29-1	393
CASSOPOLIS	1812	5	29-1	394
CASSOPOLIS	1812	5	29-1	395
CASSOPOLIS	1812	5	29-1	396
CASSOPOLIS	1812	5	29-1	397
CASSOPOLIS	1812	5	29-1	398
CASSOPOLIS	1812	5	29-1	399
CASSOPOLIS	1812	5	29-1	400
CASSOPOLIS	1812	5	29-1	418
CASSOPOLIS	1812	5	29-1	419
CASSOPOLIS	1812	5	29-1	428
CASSOPOLIS	1812	5	29-1	5
CASSOPOLIS	1812	5	29-1	6
CASSOPOLIS	1812	5	29-1	7
CASSOPOLIS	1812	5	29-1	8
COLDWATER	1235	5	29-1	1**
DEARBORN	12989	20	29-1	1
DETROIT(2)	10527	3x10-20	02PB	100000
DETROIT(2)	10527	3x10-20	02PB	66666
DETROIT(2)	10527	3x10-20	02PB	77777
DETROIT(2)	10527	3x10-20	02PB	88888
DETROIT(2)	10527	3x10-20	02PB	99999
DETROIT(2)	10527	3x50-100	02PB	8888
DETROIT(2)	10527	5	02PB	111111
DETROIT(2)	10527	5	02PB	111113
DETROIT(2)	10527	5	02PB	127565
DETROIT(2)	10527	10	29-1	1
DETROIT(2)	10527	10	29-1	33333
DETROIT(2)	10527	100	29-1	1
DETROIT(2)	10527	100	29-1	888
DETROIT(2)	10527	20	29-1	1
DETROIT(2)	10527	20	29-1	11111
DETROIT(2)	10527	5	29-1	1
DETROIT(2)	10527	5	29-1	66666
DETROIT(2)	10527	50	29-1	1
DETROIT(2)	10527	50	29-1	3333
DETROIT(3)	10527	10	29-1	1
DETROIT(3)	10527	10	29-1	10527
DETROIT(3)	10527	100	29-1	1
DETROIT(3)	10527	20	29-1	1
DETROIT(3)	10527	5	29-1	1**
DETROIT(3)	10527	5	29-1	10527
DETROIT(3)	10527	50	29-1	1
DETROIT(4)	10527	10	29-1	1
DETROIT(4)	10527	100	29-1	1
DETROIT(4)	10527	20	29-1	1
DETROIT(4)	10527	5	29-1	1
DETROIT(4)	10527	5	29-1	5
DETROIT(4)	10527	50	29-1	1
EVART	12561	10	29-1	1
EVART	12561	20	29-1	1
EVART	12561	5	29-1	1
GRAND RAPIDS	2460	3x10-20	82BB	
GRAND RAPIDS	2460	5	82BB	55
GRAND RAPIDS	2460	5	02PB	
GRAND RAPIDS	2611	3x10-20	02PB	9560
GRAND RAPIDS	2611	3x10-20	02PB	9562
GRAND RAPIDS	2611	5	02PB	18816
GRAND RAPIDS	2611	5	02PB	18818
GRAND RAPIDS	2611	5	02PB	18820
GRAND RAPIDS	3293	5	02PB	76815
MARQUETTE	12027	5	29-2	1-6
MOUNT CLEMENS	12971	5	02PB	1
MOUNT CLEMENS	12971	5	02PB	1002
MOUNT CLEMENS	12971	5	02PB	1003
NILES	13307	10	29-1	4444
YPSILANTI	155	5	29-1	363

Total Sheets: 150

MINNESOTA

APPLETON	8813	5	29-1	1
DODGE CENTER	6623	10	29-2	1-6
DODGE CENTER	6623	20	29-2	1-6
DULUTH	6520	10	29-2	1-6
LITCHFIELD	13486	20	29-1	1**
LONG PRAIRIE	7080	10	29-2	1-6
MADISON	13561	10	29-2	
MADISON	13561	20	29-2	
MINNEAPOLIS	13108	5	29-2	1-6
OLIVIA	13081	5	29-1	1
ROCHESTER	579	10	29-1	1
SAINT PAUL	11741	3x10-20	02PB	
STARBUCK	9596	5	29-1	1
WORTHINGTON	8989	5	29-1	1

Total Sheets: 14

MISSISSIPPI

COLUMBUS(2)	10738	5	29-2	1-6
COLUMBUS(2)	10738	5	29-2	17437--
COLUMBUS(2)	10738	5	29-2	17467--
COLUMBUS(2)	10738	5	29-2	17485--
COLUMBUS(2)	10738	5	29-2	17779--
COLUMBUS(2)	10738	5	29-2	17833--
COLUMBUS(2)	10738	5	29-2	17839--
COLUMBUS(2)	10738	5	29-2	17845--
COLUMBUS(2)	10738	5	29-2	17929--
COLUMBUS(2)	10738	5	29-2	17935--
LAUREL	6681	10	29-1	1
LAUREL	6681	20	29-1	1
LAUREL	6681	5	29-1	1
LAUREL	6681	10	29-2	1-6
LAUREL	6681	20	29-2	1-6
LAUREL	6681	5	29-2	1-6
MOSS POINT	8593	5	29-2	1-6
VICKSBURG(2)	3430	5	29-1	1

Total Sheets: 18

MISSOURI

BRAYMER	7351	10	29-1	1
BRAYMER	7351	5	29-1	1
CALIFORNIA	1712	3x10-20	82BB	1**
CALIFORNIA	1712	3x10-20	02DB	1
CALIFORNIA	1712	10	29-1	1
CAMERON	4259	3x10-20	02PB	3958
CLINTON	7806	3x10-20	02RS	1
CLINTON	8509	5	29-1	1
COLUMBIA	1467	10	02PB	21226
COLUMBIA	1467	10	29-1	1
COLUMBIA	1467	20	29-1	1
KANSAS CITY	3544	3x10-20	82BB	11125**
KANSAS CITY	5138	5	82BB	2074
KING CITY	6383	10	29-2	1-6
KING CITY	6383	20	29-2	1-6
MONETT	5973	20	29-1	1
NORTH KANSAS CITY	13690	20	29-2	55-60
PEIRCE CITY(2)	4225	5	29-2	2377-82
PEIRCE CITY(2)	4225	5	29-2	2383-88
PEIRCE CITY(2)	4225	5	29-2	2395--
PEIRCE CITY(2)	4225	5	29-2	2401-06
PEIRCE CITY(2)	4225	5	29-2	2407-12
PEIRCE CITY(2)	4225	5	29-2	2389-94
PEIRCE CITY(2)	4225	5	29-2	2401-06
PEIRCE CITY(2)	4225	5	29-2	2413-18
PEIRCE CITY(2)	4225	5	29-2	2419-24
PEIRCE CITY(2)	4225	5	29-2	2449-54
SAINT CHARLES	260	10	29-1	1
SAINT CHARLES	260	10	29-2	1-6
SAINT CHARLES	260	20	29-2	1-6
SAINT JOSEPH(2)	9042	10	29-1	1
SAINT JOSEPH(2)	9042	5	29-1	1
SAINT LOUIS(2)	170	3x10-20	02PB	95196
SAINT LOUIS	4048	5	82BB	26262
SAINT LOUIS	4178	5	02PB	444444
SAINT LOUIS	5788	3x10-20	82BB	11683
SAINT LOUIS	7808	5	02RS	3379
SAINT LOUIS	12916	10	29-1	1
SAINT LOUIS	12916	10	29-1	10
SAINT LOUIS	12916	10	29-1	11
SAINT LOUIS	12916	10	29-1	12
SAINT LOUIS	12916	10	29-1	13
SAINT LOUIS	12916	10	29-1	14
SAINT LOUIS	12916	10	29-1	15
SAINT LOUIS	12916	10	29-1	2
SAINT LOUIS	12916	10	29-1	3
SAINT LOUIS	12916	10	29-1	4
SAINT LOUIS	12916	10	29-1	5
SAINT LOUIS	12916	10	29-1	6
SAINT LOUIS	12916	10	29-1	7
SAINT LOUIS	12916	10	29-1	8
SAINT LOUIS	12916	10	29-1	9
SAINT LOUIS	12916	20	29-1	1
SAINT LOUIS	12916	20	29-1	10
SAINT LOUIS	12916	20	29-1	11
SAINT LOUIS	12916	20	29-1	12
SAINT LOUIS	12916	20	29-1	13
SAINT LOUIS	12916	20	29-1	14
SAINT LOUIS	12916	20	29-1	15
SAINT LOUIS	12916	20	29-1	2
SAINT LOUIS	12916	20	29-1	3
SAINT LOUIS	12916	20	29-1	4
SAINT LOUIS	12916	20	29-1	5
SAINT LOUIS	12916	20	29-1	6
SAINT LOUIS	12916	20	29-1	7
SAINT LOUIS	12916	20	29-1	8
SAINT LOUIS	12916	20	29-1	9
SAINT LOUIS	12916	5	29-1	1
SAINT LOUIS	12916	5	29-1	11
SAINT LOUIS	12916	5	29-1	12

State/Town	Charter	Denom	Type	Serial
SAINT LOUIS	12916	5	29-1	13
SAINT LOUIS	12916	5	29-1	14
SAINT LOUIS	12916	5	29-1	15
SAINT LOUIS	12916	5	29-1	2
SAINT LOUIS	12916	5	29-1	3
SAINT LOUIS	12916	5	29-1	4
SAINT LOUIS	12916	5	29-1	5
SAINT LOUIS	12916	5	29-1	6
SAINT LOUIS	12916	5	29-1	7
SAINT LOUIS	12916	5	29-1	8
SAINT LOUIS	12916	5	29-1	9
SALEM	7921	20	29-2	1-6
SALEM	7921	20	29-2	1-6
WARRENSBURG	5156	5	29-1	1
WEST PLAINS	5036	5	82BB	1208
WEST PLAINS	5036	5	82DB	169
WINDSOR	9519	20	29-1	1**
Total Sheets: 87				
MONTANA				
CONRAD	9759	10	29-1	1
GEYSER	10952	3x10-20	02PB	1610
GLASGOW	7990	5	29-2	1-6
HELENA	4396	5	29-1	1
HELENA(2)	4396	10	29-1	1
LEWISTOWN	12608	5	29-1	1
WHITEFISH	8589	10	29-1	1**
WHITEFISH	8589	20	29-1	1
WHITEFISH	8589	10	29-2	1-6
WHITEFISH	8589	20	29-2	1-6
WHITEFISH	8589	5	29-2	1-6
WHITEHALL	11024	3x10-20	02PB	1655
Total Sheets: 12				
NEBRASKA				
ATKINSON	6489	3x10-20	02PB	3933
BEATRICE	3081	10	29-2	2353-58
BELDEN	10025	5	29-1	1
BENEDICT	8105	10	29-1	1
BRADSHAW	8097	10	29-2	1-6
CAMBRIDGE	6506	10	29-2	547-552
CAMBRIDGE	6506	10	29-2	571-576
CAMBRIDGE	6506	10	29-2	577-582
EMERSON	7425	20	29-2	1-6
FREMONT	13408	20	29-1	1
FREMONT	13408	5	29-1	1
GRAND ISLAND	9395	10	29-1	1
GRAND ISLAND	9395	20	29-1	
GRAND ISLAND	9395	5	29-1	1
KIMBALL	13420	10	29-1	1
KIMBALL	13420	5	29-1	1
KIMBALL	13420	10	29-2	2857-62
KIMBALL	13420	20	29-2	895-900
LEIGH	9831	10	29-1	
LEIGH	9831	5	29-1	
LINCOLN	2750	5	1875	384
MCCOOK	8823	10	29-1	1
MCCOOK	8823	20	29-1	1
MCCOOK	8823	20	29-1	6
OAKDALE	13339	10	29-1	1
OAKDALE	13339	20	29-1	1
OAKDALE	13339	5	29-1	1
OMAHA	2978	10	29-1	131
OVERTON	13446	10	29-2	1-6
OVERTON	13446	20	29-2	1-6
OVERTON	13446	5	29-2	1-6
PILGER	5941	5	82VB	4515
PILGER	13453	5	29-1	1**
PILGER	13453	5	29-1	2
PILGER	13453	5	29-1	3
PILGER	13453	5	29-2	1-6
RANDOLPH	7421	10	29-1	1
SAINT PAUL	3129	5	82BB	2607
SAINT PAUL	3129	5	82BB	2608
SAINT PAUL	3129	5	82BB	2609
SAINT PAUL	3129	5	82BB	2610
SAINT PAUL	3129	5	82BB	2611
SAINT PAUL	3129	5	82BB	2612
SAINT PAUL	3129	5	82BB	2613
SAINT PAUL	3129	5	82BB	2614
SAINT PAUL	3129	5	82BB	2615
SAINT PAUL	3129	5	82BB	2616
SAINT PAUL	3129	5	82BB	2617
SAINT PAUL	3129	5	82BB	2618
SAINT PAUL	3129	5	82BB	2619
SAINT PAUL	3129	5	82BB	2620
SAINT PAUL	3129	5	82BB	2621
SAINT PAUL	3129	5	82BB	2622
SAINT PAUL	3129	5	82BB	2623
SAINT PAUL	3129	5	82BB	2624
SAINT PAUL	3129	5	82BB	2625
SAINT PAUL	3129	5	82BB	2626
SAINT PAUL	3129	5	82BB	2627
SAINT PAUL	3129	5	82BB	2628
SCHUYLER	3152	5	82BB	1582
SIDNEY	13425	10	29-1	1
SIDNEY	13425	20	29-1	1
SIDNEY	13425	5	29-1	1
SOUTH OMAHA	9908	5	29-2	1-6
STANTON	7836	10	29-2	1-6
STANTON	7836	20	29-2	1-6
STANTON	7836	5	29-2	1-6
TEKAMAH	4324	3x10-20	02PB	17547
TEKAMAH	4324	10	29-1	1
TILDEN	9217	20	29-1	1
TILDEN	10011	20	29-1	1
WYMORE	14282	20	29-2	1-6
YORK	2683	3x10-20	02RS	1**
YORK	2683	5	02RS	1**
YORK	2683	3x10-20	02PB	1
Total Sheets: 75				
NEVADA				
ELY	9310	10	29-2	1-6
ELY	9310	20	29-2	1-6
MCGILL	9452	10	29-2	1-6
MCGILL	9452	20	29-2	1-6**
RENO(2)	7038	10	29-2	6463--
RENO(2)	7038	10	29-2	6475-80
RENO(2)	7038	10	29-2	6481--
RENO(2)	7038	10	29-2	6487-92
RENO(2)	7038	5	29-2	12613--
RENO(2)	7038	5	29-2	12619--
RENO(2)	7038	5	29-2	12625--
RENO(2)	7038	5	29-2	12631--
RENO(2)	7038	5	29-2	12637--
RENO(2)	7038	5	29-2	12643--
RENO(2)	7038	5	29-2	12649--
RENO(2)	7038	5	29-2	12655--
RENO(2)	7038	5	29-2	12661--
RENO(2)	7038	5	29-2	12667--
RENO(2)	7038	5	29-2	12674--
RENO(2)	7038	5	29-2	12679--
RENO(2)	7038	5	29-2	12685--
RENO(2)	7038	5	29-2	12691--
RENO(2)	7038	5	29-2	12697--
RENO(2)	7038	5	29-2	12703--
RENO(2)	7038	5	29-2	12709--
RENO(2)	7038	5	29-2	12715--
RENO(2)	7038	5	29-2	12721--
RENO(2)	7038	5	29-2	12727--
RENO(2)	7038	5	29-2	12733--
RENO(2)	7038	5	29-2	12739--
RENO(2)	7038	5	29-2	12745--
RENO(2)	7038	5	29-2	12751--
RENO(2)	7038	5	29-2	12757--
RENO(2)	7038	5	29-2	12769--
RENO(2)	7038	5	29-2	12775--
RENO(2)	7038	5	29-2	12781--
RENO(2)	7038	5	29-2	12787--
RENO(2)	7038	5	29-2	12793--
RENO(2)	7038	5	29-2	12799--
RENO(2)	7038	5	29-2	12805--
RENO(2)	7038	5	29-2	12811--
RENO(2)	7038	5	29-2	12817--
RENO(2)	7038	5	29-2	12877--
RENO(2)	7038	5	29-2	12895--
RENO(2)	7038	5	29-2	12907--
RENO(2)	7038	5	29-2	12913--
RENO(2)	7038	5	29-2	12919--
RENO(2)	7038	5	29-2	12925--
RENO(2)	7038	5	29-2	12925--
RENO(2)	7038	5	29-2	12931--
RENO(2)	7038	5	29-2	12955**
RENO(2)	7038	5	29-2	12967--
RENO(2)	7038	5	29-2	12973--
RENO(2)	7038	5	29-2	12979--
RENO(2)	7038	5	29-2	12985--
RENO(2)	7038	5	29-2	12991--
RENO(2)	7038	5	29-2	12997--
RENO(2)	7038	5	29-2	13003--
RENO(2)	7038	5	29-2	13009--
RENO(2)	7038	5	29-2	13015--
RENO(2)	7038	5	29-2	13027--
RENO(2)	7038	5	29-2	13039--
RENO(2)	7038	5	29-2	13045--
RENO(2)	7038	5	29-2	13051--
RENO(2)	7038	5	29-2	13057--
RENO(2)	7038	5	29-2	13063--
RENO(2)	7038	5	29-2	1363--
RENO(2)	7038	5	29-2	1627--
Total Sheets: 68				
NEW HAMPSHIRE				
BERLIN	14100	10	29-2	1-6
CONCORD	318	3x1-2	ORIG	3091
DOVER	5274	5	82BB	1
GORHAM	9001	10		
GORHAM	9001	5		
KEENE	559	5	29-1	
LEBANON	808	5	29-2	1-6
NASHUA	2240	10	29-1	
NASHUA	2240	20	29-1	
NASHUA	2240	5	29-1	
PETERBOROUGH	1179	10	29-1	
PETERBOROUGH	1179	20	29-1	392
PETERBOROUGH	1179	20	29-1	393
PETERBOROUGH	1179	5	29-1	
WINCHESTER	887	5	29-1	1
Total Sheets: 15				
NEW JERSEY				
BEACH HAVEN	11658	10	29-1	1
BEACH HAVEN	11658	20	29-1	1
BEACH HAVEN	11658	5	29-1	1
BEACH HAVEN	11658	10	29-2	1-6
BEACH HAVEN	11658	20	29-2	1-6
BEACH HAVEN	11658	5	29-2	1-6
BERLIN	9779	5	29-1	3
BERLIN	9779	5	29-1	5
BERLIN	9779	5	29-1	7
BRANCHVILLE	13855	5	29-2	1-6
BRIDGETON	9498	10	29-1	
BURLINGTON	1222	5	02RS	3718
CAMDEN	13203	10	29-1	1
CLIFTON	11983	5	29-2	33991--
ELIZABETH	11744	3x10-20	02PB	
FAIRVIEW	12465	5	02PB	352
FREEHOLD	452	10	29-1	1
FREEHOLD	452	10	29-2	1-6
HILLSDALE	12902	5	02PB	
JERSEY CITY	374	3x1-2	ORIG	13783
JERSEY CITY	374	3x10-20	02PB	
JERSEY CITY	374	3x10-20	02PB	78650
JERSEY CITY	374	3x10-20	02PB	78651
JERSEY CITY	374	5	02PB	120909
JERSEY CITY	374	5	02PB	120910
JERSEY CITY	374	5	02PB	120911
JERSEY CITY	12939	5	02PB	4361
JERSEY CITY	12939	5	02PB	5801
JERSEY CITY	12939	5	29-1	11111
KEARNY	13537	5	29-1	1
MEDFORD	1191	5	29-1	1
MERCHANTVILLE(3)	8323	5	29-2	1-6
METUCHEN	7754	5	02RS	474
MONTCLAIR(2)	9339	10	29-1	1
NEW BRUNSWICK	587	10	29-1	1
NEW BRUNSWICK	587	20	29-1	1
NEW BRUNSWICK	587	5	29-1	1
NEWARK	2040	3x10-20	82BB	7014
PASSAIC	12834	5	02PB	6016
PASSAIC	12834	5	02PB	6017
PASSAIC	12834	5	02PB	6017
PATERSON	810	10	29-1	2
PATERSON	810	20	29-1	2
PATERSON	12726	3x10-20	02PB	
PLAINFIELD	447	10	29-1	1
PLAINFIELD	447	5	29-1	1
PLAINFIELD	13174	5	29-1	3
PLAINFIELD	13629	10	29-1	1**
PLEASANTVILLE	6508	10	29-1	346
PLEASANTVILLE	6508	5	29-1	
RAMSEY(2)	9367	10	29-2	37-42
RIVERSIDE	12984	10	29-1	1
ROEBLING	11620	5	29-1	824
SECAUCUS	9380	5	29-1	1
TENAFLY	8614	5	02DB	253
TRENTON	281	5	02PB	138805
TRENTON	13039	5	29-2	45691--
TUCKAHOE	14189	10	29-2	1-6
TUCKAHOE	14189	20	29-2	1-6
UNION CITY(2)	9867	5	29-1	1
WOODBINE	12977	10	29-2	1459-64
WOODBINE	12977	10	29-2	3313--
WOODBINE	12977	5	29-2	3049-54
WOODBINE	12977	5	29-2	3055--
WOODBINE	12977	5	29-2	3067-72
WOODBINE	12977	5	29-2	3085-90
WOODBINE	12977	5	29-2	3283--
WOODBINE	12977	5	29-2	3301-06
WOODBINE	12977	5	29-2	3307-12
WOODBINE	12977	5	29-2	3313-18
WOODBINE	12977	5	29-2	3337-42
WOODBRIDGE	8299	3x10-20	02RS	510
WOODBRIDGE	8299	5	02RS	574
WOODBRIDGE	8299	3x10-20	02PB	
WOODBRIDGE	8299	5	02PB	
WOODBRIDGE(2)	8299	5	29-1	200**
WOODBURY	1199	20	29-2	7-12
Total Sheets: 77				
NEW MEXICO				
BELEN	6597	5	29-1	1
BELEN	6597	5	29-1	3
SANTA FE	1750	5	29-1	1
SILVER CITY	8132	10	29-2	1-6
Total Sheets: 4				

State/Town	Charter	Denom	Type	Serial
NEW YORK				
ALBANY	267	3x10-20	82BB	6146
ARCADE	10410	10	29-2	1-6
ARCADE	10410	20	29-2	1-6
ARGYLE	13521	10	29-1	1
ARGYLE	13521	5	29-1	1
BABYLON (2)	10358	5	29-1	1
BATAVIA	340	5	02PB	
BATAVIA	340	10	29-1	340
BATAVIA	340	5	29-1	163
BATAVIA	340	10	29-2	1-6
BATAVIA	340	20	29-2	1-6
BATAVIA	340	5	29-2	1-6
BATAVIA	340	5	29-2	4699--
BELLEROSE	13234	10	29-2	1-6
BELLEROSE	13234	20	29-2	1-6
BELLEROSE	13234	5	29-2	1-6
BINGHAMTON	202	5	02PB	
BROCKPORT	382	10	29-1	1
BROCKPORT	13965	10	29-2	
BUFFALO	13219	5	29-1	1
BUFFALO	13219	5	29-1	10
BUFFALO	13219	5	29-1	4
CALEDONIA	5648	3x10-20	02PB	
CALLICOON	13590	5	29-1	1
CANAJOHARIE	1257	10	29-2	1-6
CANAJOHARIE	1257	20	29-2	1-6
CANAJOHARIE	1257	5	29-2	1-6
CANAJOHARIE	13876	5	29-2	1-6
CANDOR	353	10	29-1	1
CANDOR	353	20	29-1	1
CANDOR	353	5	29-1	1
CANDOR	353	20	29-2	1-6
CHAMPLAIN	316	10	29-1	1
CHAMPLAIN	316	20	29-1	1**
CHAMPLAIN	316	5	29-1	1
CHAPPAQUA	12746	20	29-1	2
CHAPPAQUA	12746	5	29-1	2
CHERRY CREEK	10481	10	02PB	3128
CHERRY CREEK	10481	5	02PB	
CHERRY CREEK	10481	5	02PB	4063
CHERRY CREEK	10481	5	02PB	4067
CHERRY CREEK	10481	5	02PB	4068
CHERRY CREEK	10481	5	02PB	4353
CHERRY CREEK	10481	10	29-1	
CHERRY CREEK	10481	10	29-1	
CHERRY CREEK	10481	10	29-1	12
COBLESKILL	461	10	29-2	1-6
COBLESKILL	461	20	29-2	1-6
COBLESKILL	461	5	29-2	1-6
COOPERSTOWN	223	10	29-1	2
COOPERSTOWN	223	10	29-1	3
COOPERSTOWN	223	20	29-1	1
COOPERSTOWN	223	20	29-1	2
COOPERSTOWN	223	5	29-1	3
DUNKIRK	2619	5	02PB	22693
DUNKIRK	2916	3x10-20	02PB	22784
EAST ROCHESTER	10141	10	29-2	1-6
EAST ROCHESTER	10141	20	29-2	1-6
ELMIRA (2)	149	20	29-2	1-6
FALCONER	5407	3x10-20	02PB	
FALCONER	5407	3x10-20	02PB	2477
FAR ROCKAWAY	9271	5	29-2	15385--
FAR ROCKAWAY	9271	5	29-2	15397--
FLORAL PARK	12449	5	29-1	7460
FORESTVILLE	10444	3x10-20	02PB	3361
FORESTVILLE	10444	5	02PB	5221**
FORESTVILLE	10444	10	29-1	2
FORESTVILLE	10444	20	29-1	1
FREDONIA	9019	3x10-20	02PB	11458
FREDONIA	9019	3x10-20	02PB	11460
FREDONIA	9019	3x10-20	02PB	11462
FREDONIA	9019	10	29-1	2
FREDONIA	9019	20	29-1	1
FREDONIA	9019	5	29-2	23683--
FREEPORT	7703	5	02RS	1**
FREEPORT	7703	5	02PB	1972
FREEPORT(2)	7703	3x10-20	02PB	1
FREEPORT(2)	7703	10	29-1	1
FREEPORT(2)	7703	5	29-1	1
GENESEO	886	5	29-1	1
GLEN HEAD	13126	5	29-1	1
GLEN HEAD	13126	5	29-2	1-6
GRANVILLE	7255	10	29-2	1-6
GRANVILLE	7255	20	29-2	1-6
GRANVILLE	7255	5	29-2	1-6
HAMPTON BAYS	12987	3x10-20	02PB	2792
HARRISON	12601	10	29-2	1-6
HORSEHEADS	8301	10	29-2	1-6**
HORSEHEADS	8301	20	29-2	1-6
HUDSON FALLS(2)	6470	10	29-2	1-6
JAMESTOWN	548	3x10-20	02PB	10582
JAMESTOWN	8453	3x10-20	02PB	
JAMESTOWN	8453	10	29-1	3
JAMESTOWN	9748	3x10-20	02PB	10198
JAMESTOWN	9748	3x10-20	02PB	9485
JAMESTOWN	9748	5	02PB	
JAMESTOWN	9748	5	02PB	
JAMESTOWN	9748	5	29-1	
JAMESTOWN	9748	5	29-1	3382
LACKAWANNA	6964	20	29-2	1-6
LANCASTER	11912	3x10-20	02PB	
LIBERTY	10037	10	29-2	1-6
LIVINGSTON MANOR	10043	5	29-2	1-6
LONG BEACH	13074	5	02PB	3
LONG BEACH	13074	5	02PB	5
LONG BEACH	13074	5	02PB	6
LONG BEACH	13074	5	29-1	1
LYNBROOK(2)	8923	10	29-1	1
LYNBROOK(2)	8923	5	29-1	1
LYNBROOK(2)	8923	5	29-1	10
LYNBROOK(2)	8923	5	29-1	100
LYNBROOK(2)	8923	5	29-1	11
LYNBROOK(2)	8923	5	29-1	20
LYNBROOK(2)	8923	5	29-1	22
LYNBROOK(2)	8923	5	29-1	30
LYNBROOK(2)	8923	5	29-1	33
LYNBROOK(2)	8923	5	29-1	40
LYNBROOK(2)	8923	5	29-1	44
LYNBROOK(2)	8923	5	29-1	50
LYNBROOK(2)	8923	5	29-1	55
LYNBROOK(2)	8923	5	29-1	60
LYNBROOK(2)	8923	5	29-1	66
LYNBROOK(2)	8923	5	29-1	70
LYNBROOK(2)	8923	5	29-1	77
LYNBROOK(2)	8923	5	29-1	80
LYNBROOK(2)	8923	5	29-1	88
LYNBROOK(2)	8923	5	29-1	90
LYNBROOK(2)	8923	5	29-1	99
LYONS	1027	10	29-1	1
LYONS	1027	5	29-1	1
LYONS	1027	5	29-1	2
MAMARONECK	13592	10	29-1	1
MAMARONECK	13592	10	29-1	2
MAMARONECK	13592	5	29-1	
MILLERTON	2661	5	29-2	
MINEOLA	13404	10	29-1	1
MINEOLA	13404	5	29-1	
MOHAWK	1130	5	29-1	1
MONTGOMERY	13559	5	29-1	1
MORAVIA	99	3x10-20	02RS	660
MORAVIA	99	5	02RS	1
MORAVIA	99	10	29-2	1-6
MORAVIA	99	20	29-2	1-6
MORAVIA	99	5	29-2	1-6
MOUNT MORRIS	1416	3x1-2	ORIG	600
NEW BERLIN	10199	10	29-2	1-6
NEW YORK	29	10	29-1	1
NEW YORK	29	10	29-1	2
NEW YORK	29	20	29-1	1
NEW YORK	29	5	29-1	1
NEW YORK	29	10	29-2	1-6
NEW YORK	29	5	29-2	1-6
NEW YORK	733	10	82BB	
NEW YORK	891	10	02PB	981202
NEW YORK	891	10	02PB	981205
NEW YORK	891	5	02PB	A274501
NEW YORK	891	5	02PB	A274503
NEW YORK	891	10	29-1	1
NEW YORK	891	20	29-1	1
NEW YORK	1080	3x1-2	1875	6388
NEW YORK	1461	5	29-1	22853
NEW YORK	2370	5	29-1	40000
NEW YORK(2)	6198	10	29-2	1-6
NEW YORK	6284	5	02RS	781**
NEW YORK	8926	10	02PB	13602
NEW YORK	8926	5	02PB	7619
NEW YORK	9955	10	02PB	115511
NEW YORK	9955	10	02PB	51838
NEW YORK(2)	9955	5	29-2	7-12
NEW YORK(2)	11034	5	29-1	
NEW YORK(2)	11034	5	29-2	1-6
NEW YORK(2)	11844	10	02PB	23
NEW YORK(2)	11844	5	02PB	7
NEW YORK(2)	11844	5	02PB	8
NEW YORK(2)	11844	5	02PB	9
NEW YORK	12214	5	02PB	4
NEW YORK	12214	5	02PB	5
NEW YORK	12550	10	02PB	1754
NEW YORK	12550	10	02PB	1756
NEW YORK	12892	5	29-2	1-6
NEW YORK	12897	5	02PB	2770
NEW YORK	13149	10	29-1	1
NEW YORK	13149	20	29-1	1
NEW YORK	13149	5	29-1	1
NEW YORK	13237	3x10-20	02PB	10
NEW YORK	13237	3x10-20	02PB	11
NEW YORK	13237	3x10-20	02PB	15
NEW YORK	13237	3x10-20	02PB	26
NEW YORK	13237	3x10-20	02PB	3
NEW YORK	13237	3x10-20	02PB	30
NEW YORK	13237	3x10-20	02PB	4
NEW YORK	13237	3x10-20	02PB	5
NEW YORK	13237	5	02PB	10
NEW YORK	13237	5	02PB	13
NEW YORK	13237	5	02PB	17
NEW YORK	13237	5	02PB	2
NEW YORK	13237	5	02PB	20
NEW YORK	13237	5	02PB	21
NEW YORK	13237	5	02PB	24
NEW YORK	13237	5	02PB	25
NEW YORK	13237	5	02PB	3
NEW YORK	13237	5	02PB	30
NEW YORK	13237	5	02PB	33
NEW YORK	13237	5	02PB	4
NEW YORK	13237	5	02PB	55
NEW YORK	13237	5	02PB	6
NEW YORK	13237	10	29-1	1
NEW YORK	13237	10	29-1	2
NEW YORK	13237	10	29-1	4
NEW YORK	13237	20	29-1	1
NEW YORK	13237	5	29-1	11
NEW YORK	13237	5	29-1	2
NEW YORK	13237	5	29-1	9
NEW YORK	13260	5	29-1	1234
NEW YORK	13292	3x10-20	02PB	25
NEW YORK	13295	5	29-1	
NEW YORK(2)	13334	5	29-1	11
NEW YORK(2)	13334	5	29-1	22
NEW YORK(2)	13334	5	29-1	30
NEW YORK(2)	13334	5	29-1	33
NEW YORK(2)	13334	5	29-1	40
NEW YORK(2)	13334	5	29-1	77
NEW YORK(2)	13334	5	29-1	90
NEW YORK(2)	13334	5	29-1	99
NEWARK	349	10	29-1	
ODESSA	13493	20	29-1	1
ODESSA	13493	5	29-1	1
PAINTED POST	13664	10	29-1	1
PAINTED POST	13664	5	29-1	1
PALMYRA	295	5	82BB	
PALMYRA	295	5	02PB	
PINE BUSH	9940	20	29-2	1-6
REMSEN	6482	5	29-1	1
RIPLEY	6386	3x10-20	02PB	5444
ROCHESTER(2)	8026	3x10-20	02PB	39000
ROSLYN	13326	20	29-1	1
SAINT JOHNSVILLE	375	10	29-2	1-6
SAINT JOHNSVILLE	375	20	29-2	1-6
SALEM	7588	10	29-2	1-6
SCARSDALE(2)	11708	5	29-2	1-6
SCARSDALE(2)	11708	5	29-2	64849--
SILVER CREEK	10159	3x10-20	02PB	7692
SILVER CREEK	10159	3x10-20	02PB	7750
SILVER CREEK	10159	3x10-20	02PB	7751
SILVER CREEK	10159	5	02PB	13036
SILVER CREEK	10159	10	29-1	1
SILVER CREEK	10159	5	29-1	1
SILVER CREEK	10159	10	29-2	1-6
SILVER CREEK	10159	20	29-2	1-6
SILVER CREEK	10258	3x10-20	02PB	16785
SILVER SPRINGS	6148	5	29-2	1-6
SOUTH OTSELIC	7774	10	29-2	1-6
SYRACUSE	13393	10	29-1	1
SYRACUSE	13393	10	29-1	2
SYRACUSE	13393	5	29-1	2
SYRACUSE	13393	5	29-2	1-6
TANNERSVILLE	11057	3x10-20	02PB	2344
TANNERSVILLE	11057	3x10-20	02PB	3004
THERESA	8158	20	29-2	1-6
TROY	7612	10	29-1	1
TROY	7612	5	29-1	1
TROY	7612	10	29-2	1-6
WASHINGTONVILLE	9065	5	29-1	
WATERLOO	368	10	29-2	13-18
WESTFIELD	3166	5	02PB	
WESTFIELD	12476	5	02PB	9220
WINDHAM	13962	5	29-2	1-6
WINDHAM	13962	5	29-2	1573--
WINDHAM	13962	5	29-2	1579--
WINDHAM	13962	5	29-2	1591--
WINDHAM	13962	5	29-2	1597--
Total Sheets: 271				
NORTH CAROLINA				
ALBEMARLE	11091	20	29-1	1
GASTONIA	7536	3x10-20	02PB	11062
HENDERSON	7564	5	29-1	1
HENDERSON	13636	10	29-1	1
HENDERSON	13636	5	29-1	1
MONROE	8712	10	29-1	1
Total Sheets: 6				
NORTH DAKOTA				
BISMARCK	13398	10	29-1	1
BISMARCK	13398	20	29-1	1
BISMARCK	13398	5	29-1	1
BISMARCK	13398	10	29-2	1-6
BISMARCK	13398	20	29-2	1-6

State/Town	Charter	Denom	Type	Serial
CARSON	13454	5	29-1	1
COOPERSTOWN	13362	5	29-2	
MOTT	9489	20	29-2	
NEW ENGLAND	9776	5	29-2	1-6
VALLEY CITY	13385	10	29-1	1
VALLEY CITY	13385	5	29-1	1
WALHALLA	9133	5	29-1	1
WALHALLA	9133	5	29-1	73
Total Sheets: 13				
OHIO				
ARCANUM	9255	3x10-20	02DB	429
BELLAIRE	7327	20	29-2	1-6
BEVERLY	133	3x1-2	ORIG	1686
BRADFORD	9163	20	29-2	1-6
BUCYRUS	443	10	29-1	1
BUCYRUS	443	10	29-1	3
BUCYRUS	443	20	29-1	1
CAMBRIDGE	6566	3x10-20	02PB	12749
CAMBRIDGE	6566	10	29-2	1-6
CAMBRIDGE	6566	20	29-2	1-6
CANTON	76	10	29-1	9999
CINCINNATI(2)	2524	5	29-1	12200
CINCINNATI(2)	2798	5	82BB	
CINCINNATI	3642	3x10-20	02RS	1
CLEVELAND	786	5	02PB	119422
CLEVELAND	11862	5	02PB	291901
CLEVELAND(2)	11862	5	02PB	10
CLEVELAND(2)	11862	5	02PB	2
COLUMBUS	5065	5	02PB	1
COLUMBUS	5065	10	29-2	1-6
COLUMBUS	7745	20	29-2	1-6
COLUMBUS	9282	3x10-20	02PB	13301
CRESTLINE	5099	5	82BB	1384
DAYTON	2678	5	02PB	2641
DAYTON(2)	2678	5	02PB	
DEFIANCE	13457	10	29-1	1
DELAWARE	13535	20	29-1	1
DELAWARE	13535	10	29-2	1-6
DELAWARE	13535	20	29-2	1-6
FINDLAY(2)	36	3x10-20	02PB	1
FOSTORIA	9192	20	29-2	1-6
FREMONT	5	3x10-20	02PB	**
GEORGETOWN	2705	10	29-2	25-30
GEORGETOWN	5996	10	29-2	1-6
GEORGETOWN	5996	20	29-2	1-6
GREENFIELD	10105	20	29-2	1-6
GREENFIELD	10105	5	29-2	1-6
GREENVILLE	1092	10	29-2	1-6
HILLSBORO	9243	10	29-2	1-6
HILLSBORO	9243	20	29-2	1-6
HILLSBORO	9243	5	29-2	1-6
IRONTON	98	5	29-2	1-6
LANCASTER	9547	50	29-1	99
LONDON	10373	5	29-1	1
MARIETTA	13971	10	29-2	1-6
MARIETTA	13971	20	29-2	1-6
MARIETTA	13971	5	29-2	1-6
MARION	6308	3x10-20	02PB	30963
MARION	11831	5	02PB	24841
MARION	11831	5	02PB	24842
NEW LEXINGTON	13596	5	29-1	1
OXFORD	6059	5	29-1	1**
PIQUA(2)	1006	3x10-20	02PB	10605
PORTSMOUTH	68	10	29-2	1-6
PORTSMOUTH	68	5	29-2	1-6
PORTSMOUTH	13832	20	29-2	1-6
PORTSMOUTH	13832	5	29-2	1-6**
SAINT CLAIRSVILLE	315	5	29-1	1
SAINT CLAIRSVILLE	13922	10	29-2	1-6
SAINT CLAIRSVILLE	13922	5	29-2	1-6
SALEM	43	10	29-2	1-6
TOLEDO	91	10	29-2	1-6
TOLEDO	91	20	29-2	1-6
TOLEDO	91	5	29-2	1-6
TOLEDO	14030	10	29-2	1-6
TOLEDO	14030	20	29-2	1-6
WAPAKONETA	3157	10	29-2	5263-68
WASH. COURT HOUSE	13490	10	29-1	1
WASH. COURT HOUSE	13490	5	29-1	2
WASH. COURT HOUSE	13490	10	29-2	2863--
WASH. COURT HOUSE	13490	10	29-2	2869--
WASH. COURT HOUSE	13490	10	29-2	2887--
WASH. COURT HOUSE	13490	10	29-2	2899--
WOOSTER	828	10	29-1	1
WOOSTER	7670	10	29-2	1-6
WOOSTER	7670	20	29-2	1-6
WOOSTER	7670	5	29-2	1-6
XENIA	2932	5	29-2	3199--
YOUNGSTOWN	3	3x10-20	02PB	89519
YOUNGSTOWN	3	5	02PB	137333
YOUNGSTOWN	3	10	29-1	1
YOUNGSTOWN	3	10	29-1	2
YOUNGSTOWN	3	10	29-1	3
YOUNGSTOWN	3	20	29-1	2
YOUNGSTOWN	3	5	29-1	1
YOUNGSTOWN	3	5	29-1	2
YOUNGSTOWN	3	5	29-1	3
Total Sheets: 87				
OKLAHOMA				
BLAIR	12130	5	29-2	2059--
EL RENO	4830	10	29-1	1
EL RENO	5985	10	29-1	1
EL RENO	5985	5	29-1	1
EL RENO	5985	20	29-2	1-6
HENNESSEY	10209	5	29-1	1
MARLOW	5724	5	82BB	1
MUSKOGEE	12890	20	29-2	13-18
PAWHUSKA	13527	5	29-2	1-6
SEMINOLE	9514	10	29-2	1-6
SEMINOLE	9514	20	29-2	1-6
SHAWNEE	5115	3x10-20	82VB	9256
WAGONER	5016	10	29-1	1
WAKITA	5982	3x10-20	82BB	1185
Total Sheets: 14				
OREGON				
BEND	13093	10	29-1	1
BEND	13093	20	29-1	1
BEND	13093	5	29-1	1
BEND	13093	10	29-2	1-6
BEND	13093	5	29-2	1-6
CONDON	7059	10	29-2	1-6
CONDON	7059	20	29-2	1-6
DALLAS	7472	10	29-2	1-6
DALLAS	7472	20	29-2	1-6
FOREST GROVE	8036	10	29-1	1
FOREST GROVE	8036	10	29-2	1-6
HOOD RIVER	7272	10	29-2	1-6
HOOD RIVER	7272	20	29-2	1-6
LA GRANDE	13602	10	29-1	1
LA GRANDE	13602	20	29-1	1
LA GRANDE	13602	5	29-2	1-6
NEWBERG	9358	10	29-1	1
NEWBERG	9358	20	29-1	1
ONTARIO	9348	5	29-1	1
PENDLETON	13576		29-1	1
PENDLETON	13576	20	29-2	1-6
PORTLAND	13299	20	29-1	1
PORTLAND	13299	5	29-1	1
PRAIRIE CITY	9763	10	29-1	1
PRAIRIE CITY	9763	5	29-1	1
WALLOWA	9002	10	29-2	1-6
WALLOWA	9002	20	29-2	1-6
WALLOWA	9002	5	29-2	1-6**
Total Sheets: 28				
PENNSYLVANIA				
ALEXANDRIA	11263	10	29-2	3019--
ALEXANDRIA	11263	10	29-2	3055--
ALEXANDRIA	11263	20	29-2	1-6
ALEXANDRIA	11263	20	29-2	865--
BROOKVILLE	3051	100	29-1	41
CANONSBURG	13813	10	29-2	1-6
CANONSBURG	13813	20	29-2	1-6
CECIL	14094	10	29-2	1-6**
CECIL	14094	20	29-2	1-6
CHARLEROI	13585	10	29-1	1
CHARLEROI	13585	20	29-1	1
CHARLEROI	13585	5	29-1	1
CHERRY TREE	7000	10	29-2	1-6
CHERRY TREE	7000	20	29-2	1-6
CHESTER	332	10	29-1	1
CLAIRTON	6495	5	02RS	226**
CLEARFIELD	13998	10	29-2	1-6
CLEARFIELD	13998	20	29-2	1-6
CLEARFIELD	13998	5	29-2	4705--
CONNELLSVILLE	13491	10	29-1	
COPLAY	9113	20	29-2	1-6
CORRY	4823	10	29-2	1-6
CRAFTON	6010	5	29-2	1-6
DONORA	13644	10	29-1	1
DONORA	13644	20	29-1	1
DONORA	13644	5	29-1	1
DONORA	13644	20	29-2	1-6
EAST BERLIN	14091	5	29-2	1-6
EASTON	1171	5	02PB	80990
EASTON	1233	20	29-1	1
EDENBURG	6182	10	29-2	1-6
EDENBURG	6182	20	29-2	1-6
ELLWOOD CITY	8678	10	29-2	1-6
ELLWOOD CITY	8678	20	29-2	1-6
ELLWOOD CITY	8678	5	29-2	1-6
FAWN GROVE	9385	10	29-2	1-6**
FREEPORT	13826	10	29-2	1-6
FREEPORT	13826	20	29-2	1-6
GREENVILLE	2251	10	29-2	1-6
HOOVERSVILLE	6250	10	29-2	1-6
HOOVERSVILLE	6250	20	29-2	1-6
HOOVERSVILLE	14156	20	29-2	1-6
HOOVERSVILLE	14156	5	29-2	1-6
INTERCOURSE	9216		29-	
JERSEY SHORE	13107	5	29-1	
LANCASTER	683	10	29-1	1
LANCASTER	683	5	29-1	1
LANCASTER	2634	3x10-20	1875	3762
LEBANON	240	5	29-1	
LEWISTOWN	1579	3x10-20	02PB	
LEWISTOWN	1579	10	29-1	1
LEWISTOWN	1579	5	29-1	1
LEWISTOWN	1579	10	29-2	1-6
LEWISTOWN	1579	5	29-2	1-6
LOCK HAVEN	507	5	29-2	1-6
LYKENS	11062	3x10-20	02PB	
MAHANOY CITY	567	5	29-2	1-6
MANOR	6456	20	29-2	1-6
MARIETTA	25	10	29-1	1
MCALISTERVILLE	9526	3x10-20	02PB	6775
MCALISTERVILLE	9526	10	29-1	1
MCALISTERVILLE	9526	20	29-1	1
MCALISTERVILLE	9526	10	29-2	1-6
MCALISTERVILLE	9526	10	29-2	13-18
MCALISTERVILLE	9526	10	29-2	7-12
MCALISTERVILLE	9526	20	29-2	1-6
MCKEESPORT	4625	5	02PB	50510
MCKEESPORT	4625	5	29-1	7594
MCKEESPORT	4625	5	29-1	7595
MECHANICSBURG	326	10	29-2	1-6
MECHANICSBURG	326	20	29-2	1-6
MECHANICSBURG	326	5	29-2	1-6
MERCER	392	10	29-1	2
MOSCOW	9340	5	29-1	1**
MOSCOW	9340	5	29-2	1-6
MOUNT HOLLY SPRINGS	8493	10	29-2	1-6
MOUNT HOLLY SPRINGS	8493	5	29-2	1-6
MOUNTVILLE	3808	10	29-1	622
MOUNTVILLE	3808	5	29-1	10
MOUNTVILLE	3808	5	29-1	3
PHILADELPHIA	1	3x10-20	02RS	2501
PHILADELPHIA	1	5	02RS	1
PHILADELPHIA	1	5	02DB	1
PHILADELPHIA	1	5	02DB	39341
PHILADELPHIA	1	5	02DB	40151
PHILADELPHIA	1	5	02DB	50281
PHILADELPHIA	1	5	29-1	11111
PHILADELPHIA	1	5	29-1	12345
PHILADELPHIA	1	20	29-2	1-6
PHILADELPHIA	1	20	29-2	1-6
PHILADELPHIA	213	5	29-1	1
PHILADELPHIA	213	10	29-2	1-6
PHILADELPHIA	234	3x1-2	ORIG	4574
PHILADELPHIA	413	3x10-20	82BB	1848
PHILADELPHIA	539	3x10-20	02DB	
PHILADELPHIA	539	10	29-1	1
PHILADELPHIA	539	20	29-1	1
PHILADELPHIA	539	5	29-1	1
PHILADELPHIA	539	5	29-1	4
PHILADELPHIA	539	5	29-1	5
PHILADELPHIA	539	5	29-1	539
PHILADELPHIA(2)	570	3x10-20	02PB	1
PHILADELPHIA(2)	570	5	02PB	1
PHILADELPHIA	592	5	02DB	122264
PHILADELPHIA	7522	5	29-1	6
PHILADELPHIA	7929	5	02RS	358
PHILADELPHIA	13032	5	29-1	1
PHILADELPHIA	13325	20	29-1	2
PHILADELPHIA	13325	5	29-1	1
PHILADELPHIA	13325	5	29-1	2
PITTSBURGH(2)	252	3x10-20	02PB	116882
PITTSBURGH	685	5	29-1	44444
PITTSBURGH	685	5	29-1	88888
PITTSBURGH	4883	3x10-20	82DB	802
PITTSBURGH	6301	5	02PB	1888881
PITTSBURGH	6301	5	29-1	1
PITTSBURGH	6301	5	29-1	3
PITTSBURGH	6301	5	29-1	6
PITTSBURGH	6301	5	29-1	9
PITTSBURGH	14271	5	29-2	1-6
PORTLAND	136 06	5	29-1	
RIMERSBURG	6676	10	29-2	1-6
RIMERSBURG	6676	20	29-2	1-6
RIMERSBURG	6676	5	29-2	1-6
ROYERSFORD	3551	5	02PB	13798**
SAINT MARYS	6589	3x10-20	02PB	29762
SAINT MARYS	6589	5	02PB	45510
SCENERY HILL	7262	20	29-2	1-6
SCHUYLKILL HAVEN	5216	10	02PB	8596
SCRANTON	77	10	29-1	2
SHENANDOAH	4546	3x10-20	02PB	25899
SHIPPENSBURG	6946	3x10-20	02PB	11751
SPRING GROVE(2)	6536	5	29-2	7543---
SPRINGDALE	8320	5	29-1	1**
TOPTON	8223	10	29-2	1-6
TOPTON	8223	10	29-2	2179--
TOPTON	8223	10	29-2	2185--
TOPTON	8223	10	29-2	2197--
TOPTON	8223	10	29-2	2209--
TOPTON	8223	10	29-2	2221--

State/Town	Charter	Denom	Type	Serial
TOPTON	8223	10	29-2	2227--
TOPTON	8223	10	29-2	2233--
TOPTON	8223	20	29-2	445-450
UNION CITY	8879	10	29-2	1-6
UNION CITY	8879	20	29-2	1-6
UNION CITY	14093	5	29-2	8653--**
WEST CHESTER	148	10	29-1	1
WEST CHESTER	148	5	29-1	
WEST CHESTER	552	10	29-1	1
WEST MIDDLESEX	6913	10	29-2	1-6
WEST MIDDLESEX	6913	20	29-2	1-6
WILLIAMSPORT	175	10	29-1	1
WILLIAMSPORT	175	5	29-1	
WILLIAMSPORT	175	20	29-2	1-6
WILLIAMSPORT	175	5	29-2	1-6
WILLIAMSPORT	175	5	29-2	7-12
WILMERDING(2)	5000	20	29-1	2
WILMERDING(2)	5000	3x10-20	02PB	17609
WILMERDING(2)	5000	3x10-20	02PB	17612
WILMERDING(2)	5000	3x10-20	02PB	17615
WILMERDING(2)	5000	3x10-20	02PB	17617
WILMERDING(2)	5000	10	29-1	11
WILMERDING(2)	5000	10	29-1	12
WILMERDING(2)	5000	10	29-1	2
WILMERDING(2)	5000	10	29-1	6
WILMERDING(2)	5000	10	29-1	7
WILMERDING(2)	5000	10	29-2	19-24
YORK	604	5	29-1	
YORK	9706	5	29-1	1
YORK	9706	10	29-2	1-6
ZELIENOPLE	7409	10	29-2	1-6
ZELIENOPLE	7409	20	29-2	1-6
Total Sheets: 172				
RHODE ISLAND				
ASHAWAY	1150	5	29-1	1
PROVIDENCE	1328	5	29-1	1
PROVIDENCE	1328	5	29-2	1-6
PROVIDENCE	13901	10	29-2	13-18
PROVIDENCE	13901	100	29-2	1-6
PROVIDENCE	13901	20	29-2	7-12
PROVIDENCE	13901	5	29-2	31-36
Total Sheets: 7				
SOUTH CAROLINA				
CHARLESTON(2)	2044	5	29-1	1
CHARLESTON(2)	2044	5	29-2	1-6
CHESTER	10663	5	29-1	1
MARION	10085	10	29-1	1
MARION	10085	5	29-1	1
ROCK HILL	9407	10	29-1	1
SUMTER	10660	20	29-2	1-6
Total Sheets: 7				
SOUTH DAKOTA				
BRITTON	13460	10	29-1	1
BRITTON	13460	5	29-1	1
CHAMBERLAIN	13483	10	29-1	1
CHAMBERLAIN	13483	5	29-1	1
MOBRIDGE	13467	5	29-2	1-6
SELBY	9376	5	29-1	1
VIBORG	13589	10	29-1	1
Total Sheets: 7				
TENNESSEE				
COAL CREEK	10028	10	29-1	1
FAYETTEVILLE	10198	10	29-2	1-6
FAYETTEVILLE	10198	20	29-2	1-6**
JACKSON	2168	3x10-20	82DB	1348
JACKSON	2168	3x10-20	82DB	151
JACKSON	2168	5	82DB	1308
JACKSON	2168	5	82DB	463
JACKSON	2168	5	82DB	464
JACKSON	10334	20	29-2	1-6
JOHNSON CITY	13635	5	29-1	1
JOHNSON CITY	13635	20	29-2	1-6**
KNOXVILLE	13539	10	29-1	1
MEMPHIS	336	3x1-2	ORIG	
MEMPHIS	13349	100	29-1	1
MEMPHIS	13349	20	29-1	1
MEMPHIS	13349	10	29-2	1-6
MEMPHIS	13349	10	29-2	81385--
MEMPHIS	13349	10	29-2	81391--
MEMPHIS	13349	10	29-2	81403--
MEMPHIS	13349	10	29-2	81409--
MEMPHIS	13349	10	29-2	81415--
MEMPHIS	13349	10	29-2	81421--
MEMPHIS	13349	10	29-2	81445--
MEMPHIS	13349	20	29-2	1-6
MEMPHIS	13349	20	29-2	16141--
MEMPHIS	13349	20	29-2	16147--
MEMPHIS	13349	20	29-2	16153--
MEMPHIS	13349	20	29-2	16165--
MEMPHIS	13349	20	29-2	16171--
MEMPHIS	13349	20	29-2	16183--
MEMPHIS	13349	5	29-2	165661-
MEMPHIS	13349	5	29-2	165661-
MEMPHIS	13349	5	29-2	165697-
MEMPHIS	13349	5	29-2	165697-
MEMPHIS	13349	5	29-2	165709-
NASHVILLE	13103	10	29-1	1**
NASHVILLE	13103	20	29-1	1
NASHVILLE	13103	5	29-1	1
SAVANNAH	8889	10	29-2	1-6
SAVANNAH	8889	5	29-2	1-6
SMITHVILLE	13056	5	02PB	333
Total Sheets: 41				
TEXAS				
ANNONA	7257	10	29-1	1
ANNONA	7257	20	29-1	1
ARANSAS PASS	10274	5	29-1	1
ASPERMONT	5786	3x10-20	02PB	800
ASPERMONT	5786	10	29-1	1
BEAUMONT	5201	3x10-20	82BB	38
BELLEVUE	8672	10	29-2	1-6
BELTON	8518	10	29-2	1-6
BELTON	8518	20	29-2	1-6
BELTON	8518	5	29-2	1-6
BLANCO	8134	20	29-2	1-6**
BLANCO	8134	5	29-2	1-6
BRADY	8573	10	29-1	1
BRADY	8573	5	29-1	1
BROWNWOOD	13588	10	29-2	1-6
BROWNWOOD	13588	20	29-2	1-6
BURKBURNETT	13668	10	29-2	1-6
BURKBURNETT	13668	5	29-2	1-6
CANYON	14090	5	29-2	1-6
CLARKSVILLE	13428	10	29-1	1
CLARKSVILLE	13428	20	29-1	1
CLARKSVILLE	13428	5	29-1	1
CLARKSVILLE	13974	10	29-2	1-6
CLARKSVILLE	13974	5	29-2	1-6
CLAUDE	7123	10	29-2	1-6
CLEBURNE	13107	10	29-1	
COLEMAN	13595	10	29-1	1
COLEMAN	13595	20	29-1	1
COLEMAN	13595	5	29-1	1
COLEMAN	13595	10	29-2	1-6
COLEMAN	13595	20	29-2	1-6
COLEMAN	13595	5	29-2	1-6
CUERO	8562	10	29-2	1-6
CUERO	14164	20	29-2	1-6
DALLAS	2455	5	29-1	1
DALLAS	2455	5	29-1	2
DALLAS(2)	3623		29-1	
DALLAS(3)	3623	5	29-1	1
DALLAS(3)	3623	5	29-1	2
DALLAS	11749	10	29-1	1
DALLAS	11749	5	29-1	1
DALLAS	12736	5	29-1	1
DAWSON	10694	5	29-1	1
DE LEON	7553	10	29-2	1-6
DE LEON	7553	20	29-2	1-6
DECATUR	13623	10	29-1	1**
DECATUR	13623	10	29-2	1-6
DECATUR	13623	20	29-2	1-6
EAGLE LAKE	7534	10	29-1	1
EASTLAND	11258	5	02PB	
EDINBURG	13315	10	29-1	1
EDINBURG	13315	10	29-2	1-6
EDINBURG	13315	20	29-2	1-6
EDINBURG	13315	5	29-2	
EL PASO	12769	10	29-2	11767--
EL PASO	12769	5	29-2	18907--
EL PASO	12769	5	29-2	18931--
FLORESVILLE(2)	6320	10	29-1	1
FRANKLIN	7838	20	29-2	1-6
FRANKLIN	7838	5	29-2	1-6
FROST	13507	10	29-2	1-6
FROST	13507	5	29-2	1-6
GALVESTON	8899	10	29-2	13-18
GALVESTON	8899	10	29-2	7-12
GARLAND(2)	7989	10	29-2	1-6
GRAPEVINE	12708	5	29-1	1
GRAPEVINE	12708	5	29-2	1-6
HASKELL	14149	10	29-2	1-6
HASKELL	14149	20	29-2	1-6
HENDERSON	13443	10	29-1	1
HENDERSON	13443	20	29-1	1
HENDERSON	13443	10	29-2	1-6
HENDERSON	13443	20	29-2	1-6
HONEY GROVE	13416	5	29-1	1
HOUSTON(2)	8645	10	29-1	1**
HOUSTON(2)	8645	20	29-1	1
HOUSTON(2)	8645	10	29-2	1-6
HOUSTON(2)	8645	20	29-2	1-6
HOUSTON(2)	8645	5	29-2	1-6
HOUSTON	10152	10	29-1	1
HOUSTON	10152	100	29-1	1
HOUSTON	10152	20	29-1	1
HOUSTON	10152	5	29-1	1
HOUSTON	10152	50	29-1	1
HOUSTON	13683	20	29-2	1-6
HOUSTON	13925	10	29-2	1-6
HOUSTON	13925	5	29-2	1-6**
KERENS	13656	10	29-1	1
KERENS	13656	20	29-1	1
LADONIA	4311			
LINDEN	10476	10	29-1	1
LOCKHART	13934	10	29-2	1-6
LOCKHART	13934	20	29-2	1-6
MARFA	8674	10	29-2	1-6
MARFA	8674	20	29-2	1-6
MART	7546	10	29-2	1-6
MART	7546	20	29-2	1-6
MELISSA	10008	20	29-2	1-6
MEMPHIS	6107	10	29-1	1
MEMPHIS	6107	10	29-2	1-6
MEMPHIS	6107	20	29-2	1-6
MOUNT PLEASANT	4722	3x10-20	02PB	9284
NACOGDOCHES	6627	5	29-2	1-6
NOCONA	7617	10	29-1	1
NOCONA	7617	20	29-1	1
NOCONA	7617	5	29-1	1
NOCONA	7617	10	29-2	1-6
NOCONA	7617	5	29-2	1-6
OLNEY	8982		02PB	
OLNEY	8982	10	29-1	1
OLNEY	8982	10	29-1	3216
OLNEY	8982	10	29-2	1-6
OLNEY	8982	10	29-2	6379-84
OLNEY	8982	10	29-2	6385-90
OLNEY	8982	10	29-2	7-12
PALESTINE	3694	5	02PB	
PEARSALL	13572	10	29-1	1**
PEARSALL	13572	20	29-1	1
PHARR	10169	10	29-1	1
PHARR	10169	20	29-1	1
PHARR	10169	5	29-1	1
PLANO	13511	5	29-1	
SAN ANTONIO	4525	5	29-1	1
SAN ANTONIO	6956	5	29-1	1
SAN ANTONIO	12162	3x10-20	02PB	3374
SAN ANTONIO	13578	10	29-1	1
SAN ANTONIO	13578	20	29-1	1
SAN ANTONIO	13578	5	29-1	1
SAN ANTONIO	14283	5	29-2	1-6
SEGUIN	5097	5	29-1	551
STAMFORD	13598	5	29-1	1
STAMFORD	13598	10	29-2	1-6
STAMFORD	13598	20	29-2	1-6
STAMFORD	13598	5	29-2	1-6
TEAGUE	8195	5	29-2	3751--
TEXAS CITY	10040	20	29-1	1
TRINITY	10078	10	29-1	1**
TRINITY	10078	20	29-1	1
TRINITY	13706	10	29-2	1-6
TRINITY	13706	20	29-2	1-6
TROUPE	6212	5	29-2	1-6
TYLER	13110	5	02PB	
VERNON	7010	10	29-2	1-6
VERNON	7010	5	29-2	1-6
WACO	6572	10	29-2	1-6
WACO	6572	20	29-2	1-6
WACO	6572	5	29-2	1-6
WAXAHACHIE	13516	20	29-1	1
WAXAHACHIE	13516	5	29-1	1
WAXAHACHIE	13516	10	29-2	6757--
WAXAHACHIE	13516	20	29-2	1957-62
WAXAHACHIE	13516	5	29-2	13501--
WAXAHACHIE	13516	5	29-2	13513--
WAXAHACHIE	13516	5	29-2	13555--
WELLINGTON	13249	10	29-1	1**
WELLINGTON	13249	10	29-2	1-6
WELLINGTON	13249	20	29-2	1-6
WELLINGTON	13249	5	29-2	1-6
WEST	13935	10	29-2	1-6
WEST	13935	5	29-2	1-6
WOLFE CITY	13199	10	29-1	1**
WOLFE CITY	13199	10	29-2	1-6
WOLFE CITY	13199	20	29-2	1-6
WOLFE CITY	13199	5	29-2	1-6**
YOAKUM	8694	20	29-2	1-6
Total Sheets: 165				
UTAH				
PRICE	6012	10	29-2	
PRICE	6012	5	29-2	
SALT LAKE CITY	2059	5	02PB	76709
SALT LAKE CITY(2)	2059	10	29-1	1
SALT LAKE CITY(2)	2059	5	29-2	1-6
SALT LAKE CITY	9403	10	29-1	
SALT LAKE CITY	9403	5	29-1	1**
Total Sheets: 7				

VERMONT

State/Town	Charter	Denom	Type	Serial
BRADFORD	7267	10	29-2	1-6
BURLINGTON	1197	20	29-2	1-6
MIDDLEBURY	1195	10	29-1	1
MIDDLEBURY	1195	10	29-1	3
MIDDLEBURY	1195	5	29-1	1
MIDDLEBURY	1195	5	29-1	3
MIDDLEBURY	1195	5	29-2	1-6
NORTH BENNINGTON	194	10	29-1	1
NORTH BENNINGTON	194	5	29-1	1**
NORTH BENNINGTON	194	20	29-2	1-6
ORWELL	228	10	29-1	1**
ORWELL	228	5	29-2	1-6**
SPRINGFIELD	122	10	29-1	2
WOODSTOCK	1133	5	02PB	12600

Total Sheets: 14

VIRGINIA

State/Town	Charter	Denom	Type	Serial
CLIFTON FORGE	9177	10	29-2	1-6
COEBURN	6899	10	29-2	1-6
DANVILLE	9343	5	29-1	1
DANVILLE	9343	10	29-2	1-6
DANVILLE	9343	5	29-2	1-6
FREDERICKSBURG	10325	5	29-1	
FREDERICKSBURG	13603	10	29-1	2
FREDERICKSBURG	13603	20	29-1	1
FREDERICKSBURG	13603	20	29-1	2
FREDERICKSBURG	13603	5	29-1	2
FREDERICKSBURG	13603	10	29-2	1-6
HERNDON	9635	10	29-2	1-6
HOT SPRINGS	8722	10	02PB	8974
HOT SPRINGS	8722	5	02PB	
NORFOLK(2)	9885	10	29-2	1-6
NORFOLK(2)	9885	20	29-2	1-6
PETERSBURG	7709	5	29-1	1
QUANTICO	12477	5	29-1	
SAINT PAUL	8547	10	29-2	1-6
SAINT PAUL	8547	5	29-2	1-6
STRASBURG	8753	10	29-1	1
STRASBURG	8753	20	29-1	1
STRASBURG	8753	5	29-1	1**
STRASBURG	8753	10	29-2	1-6
STRASBURG	8753	20	29-2	1-6

Total Sheets: 25

WASHINGTON

State/Town	Charter	Denom	Type	Serial
BELLINGHAM	7372	10	29-2	1-6
BELLINGHAM	7372	20	29-2	1-6
BREMERTON	9280	10	29-1	1
CHEWELAH	8789	20	29-2	1-6
DAYTON	9443	5	29-1	1
GARFIELD	9185	20	29-1	1
GARFIELD	9185	5	29-1	1
MONROE	9478	10	29-1	1
OKANOGAN	9411	10	29-2	1-6
OKANOGAN	9411	20	29-2	1-6
OKANOGAN	9411	5	29-2	1-6
REARDAN	13444	10	29-1	1**
REARDAN	13444	5	29-1	1
STANWOOD	11935	5	29-1	1**
VANCOUVER	6013	3x10-20	82VB	11668
VANCOUVER	6013	10	29-2	1-6
VANCOUVER	6013	20	29-2	1-6
WENATCHEE	8064	5	29-1	1**

Total Sheets: 18

WEST VIRGINIA

State/Town	Charter	Denom	Type	Serial
ALBRIGHT	10480	3x10-20	02PB	1295
ALBRIGHT	10480	5	29-1	1
CHARLESTON	3236	5	02PB	145603
REEDY	10285	10	29-1	1
REEDY	10285	5	29-1	1**
REEDY	10285	10	29-2	1-6
RICHWOOD	13627	10	29-1	1
SAINT ALBANS	9640	10	29-2	1-6
SAINT ALBANS	9640	20	29-2	1-6
SOUTH CHARLESTON	11340		29-1	
TERRA ALTA	6999	10	29-2	1-6
TERRA ALTA	6999	20	29-2	1-6
TERRA ALTA	6999	5	29-2	1-6
WHEELING	5164	5	82BB	12000
WHEELING	5164	5	82BB	12006
WHEELING	5164	10	29-2	1-6
WHEELING	5164	5	29-2	1-6
WINONA	9850	10	29-1	1

Total Sheets: 18

WISCONSIN

State/Town	Charter	Denom	Type	Serial
BALDWIN	10106	5	29-1	1
COLUMBUS	178	5	29-2	1-6
DURAND	13529	5	29-1	1
DURAND	14095	10	29-2	1-6
EDGERTON	7040	5	29-1	
MANITOWOC	4975	5	02PB	3179
NEILLSVILLE	9606	10	29-1	
NEILLSVILLE	9606	5	29-1	1
OCONOMOWOC	5505	3x10-20	02PB	
PHILLIPS	13487	10	29-1	1
PHILLIPS	13487	5	29-1	1
PORT WASHINGTON	9419	5	29-1	1
PORTAGE	4234	5	02PB	1536
RICE LAKE	6663	10	29-2	1-6
RICE LAKE	6663	20	29-2	
SHEBOYGAN	11150	20	29-2	7-12
SUPERIOR	9140	5	29-1	
WATERTOWN	9003	10	29-2	1-6
WATERTOWN	9003	5	29-2	1-6
WAUPUN	7898	10	29-2	1-6
WAUPUN	7898	20	29-2	1-6
WAUPUN	7898	5	29-2	1-6
WAUSAU	2820	5	02PB	
WAUSAU	2820	5	02PB	20401**

Total Sheets: 24

WYOMING

State/Town	Charter	Denom	Type	Serial
CHEYENNE	2652	5	02PB	2664**
CHEYENNE	11380	10	29-1	842**
LOVELL	10844	5	29-1	1
SARATOGA	8961	10	02RS	2

Total Sheets: 4

Chapter 6

NATIONAL BANK NOTE ERRORS

with Harry E. Jones

This chapter deals with national bank notes that never should have left the Bureau of Engraving and Printing. We identify the different types of errors, explain how they came about, and evaluate them. A census of national bank note errors is included. Small size replacement nationals are discussed briefly. Although they are not errors, their existence stems directly from a recognized error.

National bank note errors present a fascinating challenge for collectors. Major errors are rare and expensive. The extensive collection of national bank notes errors formed by Albert A. Grinnell was dispersed over 50 years ago. A sizable portion of the error notes in our census carry the Grinnell pedigree, indicated by "AAG" and the lot number.

Most national bank errors were produced at the Bureau of Engraving and Printing. These include double denominations, inverted backs, engraving errors, and mismatched charter numbers. The major error occurring at the banks was application of inverted rubber stamped signatures.

Double Denomination Errors

A double denomination note is one whose face and back bear different denominations. Figure 1 shows a famous double denomination error - the face is a $100 Brown Back, and the back is a $50 Brown Back. Figure 2 shows the other half of this famous pair - the $50 face mated with a $100 back.

Double denomination notes are generally regarded to be the "king" of error note types. All double denomination nationals reported to date are large size notes.

Figure 1. This Albuquerque, New Mexico Territory note has a $100 face and a $50 back.

Figure 2. Sheet mate of the note above: $50 face and $100 back.

Double denomination notes occur when the sheet of notes is turned end for end between the printing of back and face. Figure 3 shows the relative positions of back and face for a normal sheet of \$10-\$10-\$10-\$20 nationals. Figure 4 shows the relative positions in a sheet with two double denomination notes. The backs are printed first. If the sheet is turned end for end before the face is printed, four error notes are produced: There is a \$10 face with an inverted \$20 back and a \$20 face with an inverted \$10 back. The two middle \$10 notes have inverted backs.

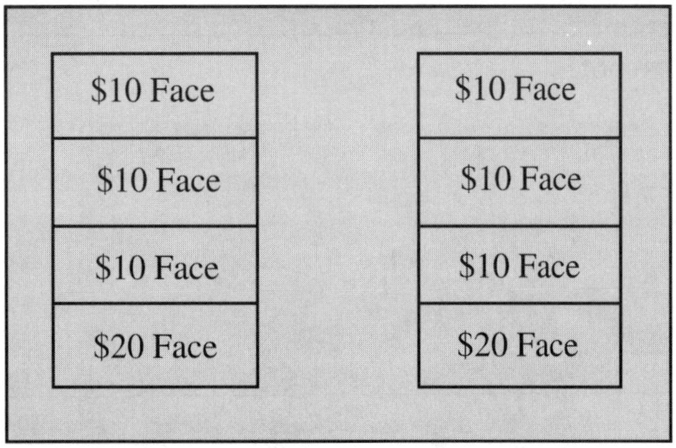

Figure 3. Relative positions of faces and backs on a normal \$10-\$10-\$10-\$20 sheet.

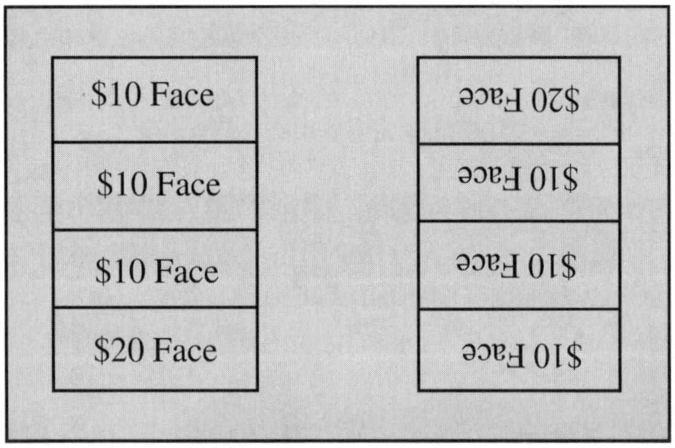

Figure 4. Relative positions of faces and backs on a double denomination \$10-\$10-\$10-\$20 sheet.

No double denomination small size nationals are known. Inverted backs are known for a few small size nationals. They also were the result of turning the sheet end for end between printing the back and face. Small size notes were printed as sheets of twelve notes of the same denomination, so inverted backs did not produce double denominations.

From the explanation just given it might seem that all large size double denomination notes would have inverted backs. However, the error census contains three double denomination nationals that do not have inverted backs. One of these is the 1902 Date Back \$10 Face/\$20 Back on the NB of Lumberton, North Carolina, Charter 10610. This error occurred when the 4x10 face plate was mated with the back plate used for the 3x10-20 format. The 3x10-20 sheets were issued first and the \$10 subjects made up positions A, B, and C. The 4x10 sheets were printed later and consisted of positions D, E, F, and G. The \$10 face on the error note is position G, which mates correctly with the bottom position \$20 back.

The other two banks with not-inverted back errors are more difficult to explain. One is lot 1737 of the Grinnell sale, a \$20 face/\$10 back 1882 Date Back on the German NB of Cincinnati, Ohio, Charter 2524. This can be explained in terms of a mismatch of the 3x10-20 face plate with a 4x10 back plate. Although the German NB did not use the 4x10 format many other banks did. The back plate for 1882 Date Backs was the same for all banks from all states, so a mismatch seems plausible.

The other not-inverted back is lot 1734 of the Grinnell sale, a \$10 face/\$20 back Original Series note on the NB of Middlebury, Vermont. It is repaired and laminated. It also may be homemade! The \$10/\$20 combination is possible only if the 3x10-20 face plate was mismatched with a 4x20 back plate. However, no Vermont banks used the 4x20 format.

Double Denomination Error Census

All of the following double denomination errors are from the Albert A. Grinnell collection. Lot numbers are indicated. Charter numbers are in parentheses.

Lot 1734 $10 Face/$20 Back Original Series NB of Middlebury, VT (1195) Fine. Back not inverted. Reinforced on back. Split and laminated

Lot 1735 $20 Face/$10 Back 1882 Brown Back FNB of Washington, NJ (860) XF

Lot 1736 $50 Face/$100 Back 1882 Brown Back FNB of Albuquerque, NM Terr (2614) and $100 Face/$50 Back. CU

Lot 1737 $20 Face/$10Back 1882 Date Back German NB of Cincinnati, OH (2524) Fine. Back not inverted. UL corner severed/resected

Lot 1738 $50 Face/$100 Back 1882 Date Back Columbia NB of Buffalo, NY (4731) and $100 Face/$50 Back. Unc

Lot 1739 $10 Face/$20 Back 1882 Value Back Lowry NB of Atlanta, GA (5318) and $20 Face/ $10 Back. Unc. The $20 Face/$10 Back was resold separately as Lot 4419.

Lot 1740 $10 Face/$20 Back 1882 Value Back Old NB of Zanesville, OH (5760) Unc. Serial 17022, V174210 Pos D. [The inverted back $10 notes also survive.]

Lot 1741 $10 Face/$20 Back 1882 Value Back FNB of Barry, IL (5771) and $20 Face/$10 Back Bank serial 4899. Unc

Lot 1742 $10 Face/$20 Back 1882 Value Back Citizens NB of Houghton, MI (5896). Unc

Lot 1743 $10 Face/$20 Back 1902 Date Back 2nd NB of Baltimore, MD (414) and $20 Face/ $10 Back. Unc

Lot 1744 $20 Face/$10 Back 1902 Date Back N City B of Chicago, IL (8532). VF

Lot 1745 $10 Face/$20 Back 1902 Date Back NB of Lumberton, NC (10610). Unc [Resold by NASCA 11/20/82 Lot 984]

Lot 1746 $10 Face/$20 Back 1902 Plain Back Great Falls NB, Great Falls, MT (4541) Fine

Lot 1747 $10 Face/$20 Back 1902 Plain Back FNB of Parkers Prairie, MN (6661). Unc and $20 Face/$10 Back. XF

Lot 1748 $10 Face/$20 Back 1902 Plain Back Northwestern NB of Grand Forks, ND (11142) VF

Lot 1749 $10 Face/$20 Back 1902 Date Back American NB of Paris, TX (8542) and $20 Face/ $10 Back. Unc, with tiny mended tears at top. The $10 Face/$20 Back was resold separately as Lot 4420.

Figure 5. This Parker's Prairie $10/$20 error is one of many attractions at the Higgins National Bank Note Museum in Okoboji, Iowa.

Values of Double Denomination Notes

Fine $5000 CU $8500

Inverted Back Errors

Large size nationals with inverted backs were produced along with double denomination errors. A 3x10-20 sheet which produced $10/$20 and $20/ $10 errors also contained two $10 notes with inverted backs. The bankers who recognized the double denomination errors and preserved them for collectors did not always appreciate the significance of the inverted backs which came with them. For example, the $10/$20 and $20/$10 errors from Parker's Prairie, Minnesota survived but not the accompanying pair of $10 inverted backs.

Small size inverted backs have turned up on several banks. All notes in the small size sheet have the same denomination so an error sheet has six notes with inverted backs. Bart (1994) illustrates many error notes, including some nationals.

Inverted Back Error Census

Grinnell pedigrees are denoted by "AAG" followed by the lot number. Prices realized at recent auctions are indicated.

$10 1882 Value Back Old NB of Zanesville, OH (5760). Serials 17022, V174210 Pos F. CU [Heritage Auctions, ANA 1996. Lot 6086]

$5 1902 PB Commercial NB of Shreveport, LA Vernon Treat. (3600). Duplicate Serial 145870 Pos L. Fine AAG 4415

$5 1929 Type 1 FNB at Pittsburgh, PA (252)

$5 1929 Type 1 North Broad NB of Philadelphia, PA (13325). Serial A000549A. AU [Currency Auctions of America 5/96 Lot 798 $1265]

$10 1929 Type 1 Lake Shore NB of Dunkirk, NY (2916)

$10 1929 Type 1 Peoples NB, Reynoldsville, PA (7620)

$10 1929 Type 1 Greenville N Exchange B Greenville, TX (8581). Serial A000992A. AU [Lyn Knight Memphis 1996 Lot 178 $1045

Figure 6. Inverted back, Greenville, TX.

$10 1929 Type 1 FNB of Plainfield, NJ (13629)

$10 1929 Type 2 FNB in Dallas, TX (3623) Serial A018702.

$10 1929 Type 2 Ohio NB of Columbus, OH (5065) Reconstructed sheet of 6 notes. Serials A013657-58-59-60-61-62. AAG 5772. [A013657 Lyn Knight Memphis 1996 Lot 180 Ch CU $1100]

Values of Inverted Back Errors

Large Size	**Fine $1500**	**CU $3000**
Small Size	**Fine $750**	**CU $1250**

Inverted Overprints

Three small size nationals are known with inverted overprints. Figure 7 shows the first of them, a $5 Type 1 on The Farmers and Merchants NB of Tyrone, PA (6499). This note has an invert of the black overprint.

Figure 7. The black overprint is inverted.

Figure 8 shows a $5 Type 1 on The FNB of Belleville, IL (2154) which sports an invert of the brown overprint.

A second example of an inverted brown overprint

Figure 8. The Treasury seal and serials are inverted.

is a $5 Type 1 on The Liberty NB & TC in New York, NY (12352). Serial D013934A

Values of Inverted Overprint Errors

Fine $2000 - $2500	CU $4000 - $5000

Mismatched Charter or Serial Numbers

There are many examples of mismatched serial numbers on issues of Silver Certificates and Federal Reserve Notes. Mismatched serial numbers or charter numbers on nationals are extremely rare.

$5 1902 Date Back. Lyons Treat. Mismatched charter overprint. NB of Savannah, GA. (3**406**) One overprinted number is incorrect (3**046**). Two notes in census. Serials 19988, B611695B Pos E and 20308, B612015B Pos E.

$5 1902 Date Back. Vernon McClung. Both overprinted charter numbers are incorrect (3557). The correct charter number is engraved at six positions on the border of the note. Mechanics and Metals NB of New York, NY (1250). Serials 283007, A774749B Pos S.

$10 1902 Date Back. Vernon McClung. Mismatched charter overprint. One overprinted number is incorrect (100**26**). FNB of Bay Shore, NY (100**29**). AU AAG 4412

$10 1929 Type 2 Mismatched Charter Overprint One of the charter numbers printed in brown is incorrect (**12**150). FNB of Tigerton, WI (**14**150). Fine. Research by Huntoon (1990) shows that this error is likely to have occurred on one note (plate position D) in sheets of $5, $10, and $20 notes.

Figure 9. Mismatched charter numbers.

$5 1929 Type 1 Mismatched serial numbers. The Millikin NB, Decatur, IL (5089) Serials C000001A/C001001A. XF.

Values of Mismatched Charters or Serials

Fine $2000	CU $3000

Obstruction Errors

A variety of errors can result when a fold or some extraneous piece of material obstructs part of the sheet during overprinting. Our census includes several examples.

$1 Series 1875. The Treasury seal and overprinted charter number are visible only as an albino embossing. The two serial numbers are present. FNB of Hyannis, MA (1107)

Figure 10. Treasury seal and charter number missing

$5 1902 Date Back. Lyons Roberts. Treasury seal missing. Boylston NB of Boston, MA (545). XF AAG 4408

$5 1902 Date Back. Part of seal and charter number overprint missing. Farmers and Merchants of Baltimore, MD (1337). Fine AAG 4409

$10 1929 Type 1. Bank title and Cashier signature missing. The Chase NB of New York, NY (2370) Serial B715852A.

$10 1929 Type 1 An uncut sheet of six notes shows three notes without the Treasury seal. Four notes lack complete serial numbers. An obstruction blocked part of the sheet during the overprinting. Chase NB, New York, NY (2370). Sheet serial number 18289.

$50 1929 Type 1 Treasury seal and right serial not printed. Merchants NB of Nebraska City, NE. (2536). Serial B000151A.

Values of Obstruction Errors
(value depends greatly on size of blocked area)

Fine $200 - $500 CU $300 - $1500

Treasury Seal/Serials on Back Errors

A few nationals are known with portions of the Treasury seal and/or serial numbers overprinted on the back. Such errors resulted from a fold which exposed part of the back of the sheet to the seal overprinting operation. Value: $1000 up.

$5 1882 Date Back. Tillman-Morgan. Part of seal on back. Charter number missing on Face, part showing on back. Chase NB of NY (2370) Fine. AAG 4406

$10 1902 Date Back. Lyons Roberts. Autographed by John Burke. FNB of Omaha, NE (209). Fine. AAG 4411

$20 1929 Type 1 Seal and serials on back. This error ended up with two serial numbers, A000821A and B000821A! The FNB of Fort Collins, CO (2622).

Figure 11. Treasury seal on back. Fort Collins, CO

$10 1929 Type 1 Seal and serial on back. It has serial F009248A on the face. The brown overprint on the back is rotated nearly 90 degrees. The NB of Cortland, NY (2272).

$20 1929 Type 1. Seal on back. The N City B of New York, NY (1461). Serial F042947A.

Value of Seal/Serials on Back Errors

$1000 and up

Shifted or Skewed Overprints

Improper positioning or a fold can produce a shifted or skewed overprint.

$10 1902 PB. Lyons Roberts. Seal, charter number and serial number shifted down. Lower serial number not printed on note. Union NB of Lewisburg, PA (784). VF AAG 4416

$5 1929 Type 1. Brown overprint shifted upwards. The Chase NB, New York, NY (2370) Serial E503019A

$10 1929 Type 1. Part of black overprint skewed. The FNB of Cincinnati, OH (24)

Figure 12. Skewed black overprint.

$20 1929 Type 1 Black overprint shifted upward. FNB of Gunnison, CO (2686) Serial C000129A [Lyn Knight Memphis 1996 Lot 179 XF/AU $825. A rare note even without the error]

$10 1929 Type 2. Brown overprint shifted upward. Farmers & Merchants NB of Matawan, NJ (6440). Serial A000739

Values of Shifted/Skewed Overprints

Fine $350 - $500 CU $750 - $1000

Offset Errors

Wet ink on the face of a sheet of nationals left an offset impression on the back of a sheet stacked on top of it. Three examples in our census.

$20 1902 Plain Back. Exchange NB of Leon, IA (5489). Serial 270, X411372D Pos B. Fine

Figure 13. Offset Treasury seal and charter number.

$20 1929 Type 1. New Alexandria NB, New Alexandria, PA (6580). Serial E000001A. AU.

$10 1929 Type 1. FNB of Syracuse, KS (8114) XF.

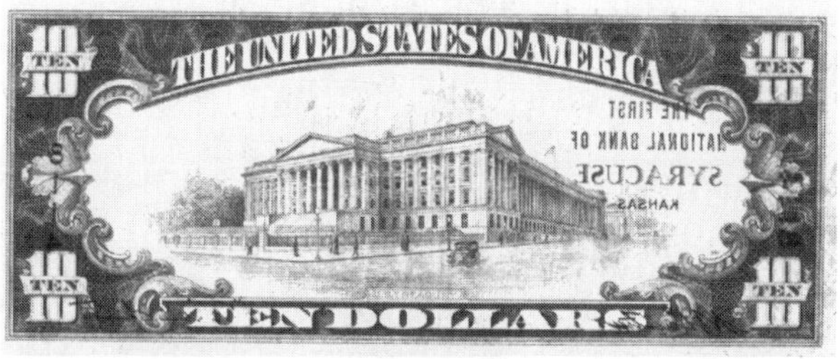

Figure 14. Offset of black overprint.

Values of Offset Errors
(depends on strength and size of offset)

$300 and up

Miscellaneous Bureau Errors

$20 1902 Date Back FNB of Oxnard, CA (9481) The Treasurer's name, Chas H. Treat, is engraved twice, with Register Vernon's name missing. A human error made by the engraver. Abt XF. This error involved only the $20 subject of the $10-10-10-20 sheets. The Comptroller's records show that sheets containing the error continued to be issued to the bank after the defect was discovered and the plate corrected. Huntoon (1995) shows a certified proof of the sheet containing this error. AAG 4413. Value: $5000 up.

$5 1902 Date Back Boylston NB of Boston, MA (545). The overprinted charter number is nearly vertical. Treasury seal is missing. Serials 5159, D126017 Pos H.

$5 1929 Type 1 Huge horizontal gutter. The Harriman NB & TC of the City of New York, NY (9955). Serial E015457A.

Figure 15. Huge gutter.

$5 1929 Type 1 Printed butterfly fold at lower right corner. Portion of President's signature printed on back. Charter 252. Serial F382292A. XF

Figure 16. Printed butterfly fold at lower right.

$5 1929 Type 2. Vertical Gutter. The FNB of Paterson, NJ (329). Serial A027577

$10 1929 Type 1. Butterfly corner fold. Wood County NB of Wisconsin Rapids, WI (4639) Serial F001641A.

$10 1929 Type 1. Missing brown overprint. Staten Island NB & TC of New York, NY (6198)

Figure 17. The brown overprint is missing.

$20 1929 Type 2. Partially turned digit in serial number. Hamilton NB of Chattanooga, TN (7848) Serial A013609. XF

Values: Fine $250 - $500 CU $500 - $1000

Errors Created at the Banks

National bank notes were shipped to the banks in uncut sheet form. On large size notes the banks applied the signatures of their officers and separated the notes. Errors during these two operations occurred often enough that collectors have been left with a variety of samples. Values are difficult to assess, ranging from less than a hundred dollar premium to several hundred dollars.

$5 1882 Date Back. Lyons Roberts. Bank signatures applied upside down at top of note. German NB of Cincinnati, OH (2524) Abt XF AAG 4407

$5 1902 Plain Back. Lyons Roberts. Bank signatures printed upside down at top of note. FNB of Kansas City, MO (3456). VF AAG 4414

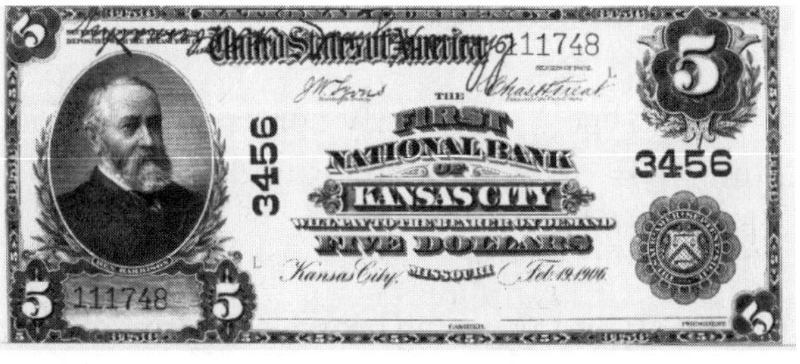

Figure 18. Inverted bank signatures.

$10 1902 Plain Back. Bank signatures shifted upward, above middle of note. The Virginia NB of Petersburg, VA (7709). Duplicate serials 172579, Pos J. VF

$10 1902 Plain Back. Cashier signature rubber stamped twice. FNB of Roanoke Rapids, NC (5767). Serials 3223, U911855E, Pos B. AU.

Values: Fine $250 up CU $500 up

Small Size Replacement Notes

Collectors of most types of United States paper money are familiar with the "star notes" used to replace errors detected during production. Although replacement notes are not errors, they came about as a result of an error detected during production. Defective sheets of small size nationals were replaced by sheets which had the serial numbers applied by hand, perhaps with a rubber stamp device. The serial numbers have a coarse, appearance and are sometimes underinked. Often they are not aligned properly. The illustration shows a small size replacement national. Note the slope of the serial numbers, which is slightly different for the two numbers.

Figure 19. Replacement national. The serial numbers are underinked and inclined at slightly different angles.

Small size replacement nationals are often overlooked by collectors and dealers because the differences are rather subtle. It is estimated that approximately one in every one thousand small size nationals is a replacement note. The relative obscurity of this variety gives it a premium value of $25 to $50 above the price of a non-replacement note.

Chapter 7

STOLEN AND COUNTERFEIT NATIONAL BANK NOTES

with Bob Cochran

This chapter deals briefly with two offbeat aspects of national bank notes: nationals that were stolen before being put into circulation, and counterfeit nationals.

Stolen National Bank Notes

With nearly 17 billion dollars worth of nationals being shipped from the Comptroller to the banks, it is easy to understand that some would end up being stolen. A list of Original Series and Series 1875 notes that were stolen before reaching their intended destinations was published by the Treasury and is shown below. A sizable fraction of these were stolen between 1867 and 1869 from the Office of the Comptroller. The thief was caught, tried, and convicted, but was set free upon appeal when it was determined that the indictment was defective. The original national bank act required the cashier and president or vice president to sign the notes before they became redeemable. This forced the thieves to forge the signatures of the bank officers. The fraudulent signatures allowed the government to refuse to redeem the notes. The Act of July 28, 1892 made national bank notes redeemable whether signed or not.

One shipment of notes has yielded most of the survivors known to collectors. A group of 450 sheets of $5 Original Series notes were stolen from The Osage National Bank of Osage, Iowa. The thieves "distressed" the notes before placing them in circulation to avoid calling attention to "new money". All of the half dozen or so examples the author has examined are well-used. Most are stamped "S" in red or purple, evidently applied by the Treasury when the notes were presented for redemption. At that time, stolen and counterfeit notes were refused and returned to the bank which sent them for redemption. Figure 1 shows a relatively high grade example of a stolen Osage note.

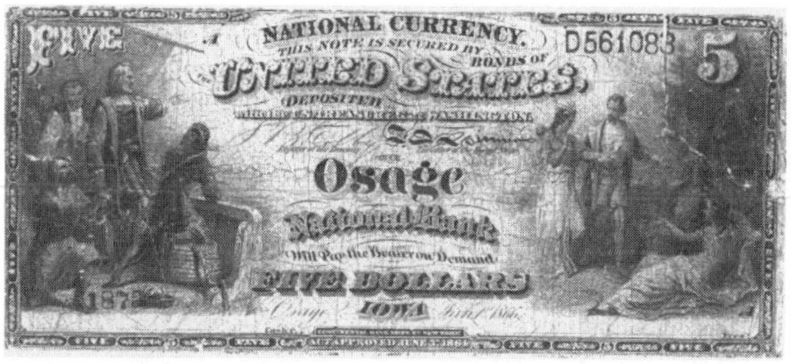

Figure 1. One of the stolen Osage, Iowa notes. Most are found stamped "S" many times.

Two notes are known to have survived from a group of 25 sheets stolen from the National Bank of Pontiac, Illinois. They are the rare Black Charter Number variety. Both were punch canceled when discovered, indicating that their stolen status was recognized.

Census of Stolen National Bank Notes

Stolen national bank notes are identified by location, bank title and charter number, denomination and series, and the range of bank serial numbers.

Albany, New York Merchants NB (1045)
$10 & $20 Series 1875 Serials 759-766

Atchison, Kansas First NB (1672)
$10 & $20 Original Series Serials 655-668

Barre, Vermont NB of Barre (2109)
$10 & $20 Original Series Serials 911-936

Boston, Massachusetts N Hide & Leather B (460)
$10 & $20 Original Series Serials 11919-11972

Jersey City, New Jersey First NB (374)
$50 & $100 Original Series Serials 671-750

Lynn, Massachusetts N City B (697)
$50 & $100 Original Series Serials 121-150

Milwaukee, Wisconsin First NB (64)
$5 Original Series Serials 13701-13750

New York, New York Third NB (87)
$10 & $20 Original Series Serials 9414-9428

Osage, Iowa Osage NB (1618)
$5 Original Series Serials 1751-2200

Pontiac, Illinois The NB of Pontiac (2141)
$5 Series 1875 Serials 741-765

Counterfeit National Bank Notes

Counterfeiting has been a 'side show' throughout the 300-year history of paper money in the United States. In the Colonial Era many notes carried the warning "'Tis Death To Counterfeit". British counterfeits of one Continental Currency issue caused its withdrawal and replacement. In the State Bank Era counterfeit notes were so prevalent that the public came to view all paper money with suspicion.

The counterfeiting of national bank notes was never a serious problem in the sense that it threatened to undermine the public's confidence in the notes.

Early in the National Bank Era, counterfeits were returned to the bank which submitted them for redemption. The Treasury began to confiscate counterfeits in 1874 when it took over the task of sorting notes sent for redemption. This greatly reduced the numbers which have survived in the hands of collectors. The Original Series counterfeits, once returned to the banks, are now subject to confiscation. Needless to say, collectors of these 'wannabes' hestitate to exhibit their holdings. Counterfeits of Series 1882 and Series 1902 nationals are seldom seen. Very few counterfeit small size nationals have been reported.

Counterfeit Detectors

Publications began in the Colonial Era to protect the public against counterfeits. The earliest counterfeit detectors took the form of broadsides circulated among merchants. As the use of paper money grew so did counterfeiting and the publications aimed at thwarting it. During the State Bank Era there were many monthly newspapers which listed counterfeits and banks whose notes were being accepted at various discounts from their face value.

In 1864 Laban Heath published the first of a series of counterfeit detectors. Heath received permission from the Treasury to publish partial plate impressions of genuine United States notes and national bank notes. The partial plates used by Heath were defaced by a wedge or line, as a safeguard against having his product used by counterfeiters. Figure 2 shows impressions from a Heath detector.

Figure 2. A plate from a Heath detector showing defaced partial impressions of genuine notes.

Some editions of Heath's publication have full impressions made from counterfeit plates seized by the Secret Service. They show the great skill of the persons who engraved the counterfeit plates.

A paperback publication "The National Counterfeit Detector" was published by Grant, Bushnell & Co. One of its principals, Edward D. Bushnell, was licensed by the Treasury to possess counterfeit United States currency. Upon his death in 1937, the Secret Service immediately confiscated his holdings.

Census of Counterfeit Notes

The census of counterfeits is arranged in order by denomination, state, town, and bank title. The correct charter number for the bank is in parentheses following the title. Some counterfeiters did not understand the significance of the charter number. As a consequence, counterfeits sometimes sport an incorrect charter number.

Details are given only for the more deceptive counterfeits. Unfortunately for the unwary or inexperienced the most deceptive counterfeits also are the ones encountered most often. These pretenders were made using engraved plates. Most are from the Original Series and Series 1875 issues. They survived in great numbers to haunt and intrigue collectors because they circulated before the Treasury began its policy of confiscation.

Very often the counterfeiters "distressed" their goods before attempting to circulate them. The idea was that a well-used note presumably had been accepted as genuine many times and would therefore receive less scrutiny.

If you encounter any note in the list which follows **assume it is counterfeit**. Very few genuine notes survived a competition against good counterfeits.

$1 Counterfeit

This is the rarest counterfeit denomination. It was created for only one bank and was a Series 1875 fabrication.

Massachusetts
Boston N Eagle B (993) Bank serial 3640 observed

$2 Counterfeits

Counterfeit lazy twos were circulated for nine banks, seven of them from New York. Some are quite good and still fool experienced dealers. All are Original Series.

New York
Kinderhook N Union B (929)
Linderpark N Union B Spurious, no such bank
New York Market NB (964)
New York Marine NB (1215)
New York Ninth NB (387)
New York Saint Nicholas NB (972)
[genuine deuces are known on Charter 972]
Peekskill Westchester County NB (1422)
[one confirmed genuine note in census]

Pennsylvania
Philadelphia Sixth NB (352)

Rhode Island
Newport NB of Rhode Island (1532)

$5 Counterfeits

There are a number of excellent forgeries of $5 Original Series. The most dangerous of these is on the Traders NB of Chicago, Illinois, a bank for which no genuine survivors have been confirmed. The hallmark of the Traders counterfeits, and others produced from the same master plate, is an incorrect plate date of May 10, 1865. Original Series $5 counterfeits are the denomination encountered most often and they are found on many different banks.

California
San Francisco 1882 Brown Back Nevada NB (5105)
Los Angeles 1882 Date Back First NB (2491)
Tulare 1902 Date Back NB of Tulare (10201)

Connecticut
Jewett City Original Series Jewett City NB (1478)
Norwalk Series 1882 Central NB (2342)
Counterfeits have incorrect charter number, 404

Suffield Series 1882 First NB (497)
Waterbury Series 1902 Citizens NB (791)

Idaho
Wallace 1902 Date Back Wallace NB (9134)

Illinois
Aurora Original Series First NB (38)
Canton Original Series First NB (415)
Cecil Original Series First NB
Spurious, no such bank
Chicago Original Series Central NB (2047)
Chicago Original Series First NB (8)
Chicago 1882 Brown Back Fort Dearborn NB (3698)
Chicago Original Series German NB (1784)
Chicago Original Series Merchants NB (642)
Deceptive. Plate date May 10, 1865 on counterfeit
Chicago Original Series NB of Illinois (1867)
Chicago Original Series Traders NB (966) Deceptive
Plate date is May 10, 1865 on counterfeit
Chicago Original Series Union NB (698) Deceptive
Plate date is May 10, 1865 on counterfeit
Galena Original Series First NB
Spurious, no such bank
Omaha 1902 Date Back First NB (10291)
Paxton Original Series First NB (1876)
Peru Original Series First NB (441) Deceptive
Plate date is May 10, 1865 on counterfeit
Quincy Series 1882 NB of Quincy (3752)
Serial 1633
Virginia Original Series Farmers NB (1472)
Deceptive Plate date May 10, 1865 on counterfeit

Kansas
Beloit 1902 Date Back German NB (6701)

Kentucky
Lebanon 1882 Brown Back Marion NB (2150)
Lexington 1882 Brown Back Fayette NB (1720)
Lexington Series 1875 N Exchange B (2393)
Owensboro 1902 Date Back United States NB (9456)

Louisiana
New Orleans 1882 Brown Back Union NB (1796)

Massachusetts
Boston Series 1875 Boylston NB (545)
Boston 1882 Brown Back Fourth NB (2277)
Boston Series 1875 Globe NB (936)
Boston Series 1875 Pacific NB (2373)
Dedham Series 1875 Dedham NB (659)
Fall River Series 1875 Pocasset NB (679)
Harwich 1882 Brown Back Cape Cod NB (713)
Holyoke 1902 Date Back Home NB (3128)
Leicester Series 1875 Leicester NB (913)
Lynn 1882 Brown Back First NB (638)
New Bedford Series 1875 First NB (261)
New Bedford Original Series Merchants NB (799)
Northampton Original Series First NB (383)
Southbridge Series 1875 Southbridge NB (934)
Waltham 1882 Brown Back Waltham NB (683)
Westfield Original Series Hampden NB (1367)

Michigan
Bay City 1882 Brown Back First NB (2853)
Flint 1882 Brown Back First NB (3361)
Grand Rapids 1882 Brown Back Old NB (2890)
Jackson 1882 Brown Back Peoples NB (1533)
Niles 1882 Brown Back Citizens NB (1886)

Minnesota
Albert Lea 1902 Date Back Citizens NB (6128)
Brainerd 1882 Date Back First NB (2590)

Missouri
Jefferson City Series 1929 First NB (9264)
Face plate 107 Notes have incorrect charter number (639)
Joplin 1882 Brown Back First NB (3841)
Plattsburg 1902 Date Back First NB (4215)
Wrong overprinted charter number (10231)
Springfield 1882 Brown Back N Exchange B (5082)
St Louis 1902 Date Back NB of Commerce (4178)
St Louis 1902 Plain Back NB of Commerce (4178)
St Louis Series 1929 First NB (170) Face plate 107. May have incorrect charter number (639)
St Louis 1882 Brown Back State NB (5172)

New Hampshire
Derry 1882 Brown Back Derry NB (499)

New Jersey
Morristown 1882 Brown Back N Iron B (1113)

New Mexico
Alamogordo Series 1902 Citizens NB (8315)

New York
Amsterdam Original Series Manufacturers NB (2239)
Castleton Original Series NB of Castleton (842)
Friendship 1882 Brown Back Citizens NB (2632)
Lockport Original Series Niagara County NB (639)
New York Series 1882 American Exchange NB (1394)
New York Series 1902 American Exchange NB (1394)
New York Series 1902 Chase NB (2370)
New York Series 1882 International NB Spurious, no such bank
New York Series 1902 First NB (29) Deceptive. Face and back printed on separate pieces of bond paper
New York 1902 Blue Seal Irving NB (345)
New York 1902 Date Back Mechanics & Metals NB (1250)
New York 1882 Brown Back NB of Commerce (733)
New York 1882 Brown Back N City B (1461)
New York 1902 Date Back N Park B (891)
Pawling Original Series NB of Pawling (1269) Deceptive. Bank signatures engraved on plate
Rome Original Series Fort Stanwix NB (1410)
Troy Original Series First NB (163)
Troy Original Series N State B (991) Deceptive Plate date is May 10, 1865 on counterfeit
Troy Series 1882 Fifth NB Spurious, no such bank

Ohio
Cincinnati 1882 Brown Back N State B Spurious, no such bank
Springfield Series 1875 Lagonda NB (2098)
Toledo Series 1929 First NB (91) Face plate 107 May have incorrect charter number (639)
Urbana Series 1929 Champaign NB (916) Face plate 107. May have incorrect charter number (639)

Youngstown Series 1902 Date Back First NB (2693) Deceptive. Photographic print, with blue coloring applied to seal and numbers.

Oklahoma
Bartlesville Series 1929 Union NB (9567)

Oregon
Portland Series 1902 United States NB (4514)

Pennsylvania
Hanover Original Series First NB (187)
Pittsburgh Series 1902 Exchange NB (1057)
Tamaqua Original Series First NB (1219) Deceptive. Incorrect charter number.

Rhode Island
Providence 1882 Brown back Commercial NB (1319)
Providence 1882 Brown Back Blackstone Canal NB. (1328) Counterfeits have incorrect charter number. (1131)

Tennessee
Knoxville 1902 Date Back Holston NB (4648)
Nashville Series 1902 Wisconsin NB Spurious, no such bank

Texas
Cleburne 1902 Date Back Home NB (10041)
Dallas Series 1929 Type 2 NB of Commerce (3985)
Hillsboro 1882 Brown Back Hill County NB (3046)

Vermont
Montpelier Series 1875 Montpelier NB (857)
St Johnsbury Series 1875 First NB (489)

Wisconsin
Milwaukee Series 1882 First NB (2715)

$10 Counterfeits

The production and issue of $10 Original Series notes for selected banks was suspended between October 14,1873 and June 29,1874. This was in response to the extensive counterfeiting of their notes.

Arizona
Phoenix Series 1882 Phoenix NB (4729)
Yuma 1902 Date Back First NB (7951)

California
El Centro Series 1902 El Centro NB (9349)

Los Angeles Series 1902 Farmers & Merchants NB (6617)
Los Angeles Series 1882 Los Angeles NB (2938)
Orange 1902 Date Back First NB (8181)
Pasadena 1902 Date Back Pasadena NB (3568)
Riverside 1902 Date Back NB of Riverside (8377)
San Francisco 1902 Date Back Anglo & London Paris NB (9174)
San Francisco Series 1902 B of California N Assoc (9655)
San Francisco 1902 Date Back Crocker NB (3555)
San Francisco Series 1882 Wells Fargo Nevada NB (5155)
San Francisco Series 1902 Germania NB (6592)
Santa Ana Series 1902 First NB (3520)

Illinois
Chicago Series 1902 First NB (2670)
Rockford Series 1902 Third NB (479)
Springfield Series 1902 Illinois NB (3548)

Indiana
Lafayette Original Series Lafayette NB (2213)
All counterfeits have bank serial 1496
Muncie Original Series Muncie NB (793)
All counterfeits have bank serial 1496
Richmond Original Series Richmond NB (2090)
All counterfeits have bank serial 1496
Vevay Original Series First NB (347)
All counterfeits have bank serial 1496

Kansas
Emporia Series 1902 Emporia NB (1985)
Wichita 1882 Date Back NB of Commerce (5169)

Kentucky
Louisville 1882 Date Back American NB (4956)

Louisiana
New Orleans Series 1882 Germania NB (1591)
New Orleans Series 1882 Hibernia NB (2086)
Opelousas 1902 Date Back Planters NB (9872)

Maryland
Baltimore Series 1902 NB of Commerce (4285)
Baltimore Series 1875 N Union B (1489)

Massachusetts
Athol Series 1882 Millers River NB (708)
Boston Series 1882 Eliot NB (536)
Boston Series 1902 Second NB (322)
New Bedford Series 1882 Mechanics NB (743)
Roxbury Series 1882 Peoples NB (595)
Worcester 1902 Date Back Mechanics NB (1135)

Michigan
Detroit Series 1882 First NB (2707)
Detroit Series 1882 Union NB (3487)
Monroe Series 1902 First NB (1587)

Minnesota
Minneapolis Series 1929 Northwestern NB (2006)

Mississippi
Jackson Series 1882 First NB (3332)

Missouri
Columbia 1902 Date Back Exchange NB (1467)

Montana
Butte Series 1902 Silver Bow NB (4283)

Nebraska
Omaha Series 1902 United States NB (2978)

New Jersey
Trenton Series 1902 First NB (281)

New Mexico
Carlsbad Series 1902 Carlsbad NB (6884)

New York
Albany Original Series Albany City NB (1291)
Auburn Original Series Auburn City NB (1285)
Buffalo Original Series Farmers & Manufacturers NB. Spurious, no such bank
Buffalo Series 1902 Marine NB (6184)
Ithaca Series 1882 Tompkins County NB (1561)
Kingston Series 1882 N Ulster County B (1050)
Lackawanna Series 1902 Lackawanna NB (6964)
Lockport Original Series First NB (211)
Incorrect plate date July 1, 1865
Newburgh Original Series Highland NB (1106)
Incorrect plate date July 1, 1865
New York Original Series American NB (750)
Incorrect plate date July 1, 1865
New York Series 1902 American Exchange B (1394)
New York Series 1902 B of New York, N Banking Assoc. (1393)

New York Series 1902 Chatham & Phenix NB (10778)
New York 1902 Red Seal Citizens Central NB (1290)
New York Original Series Croton NB (1556)
New York Series 1882 First NB (29)
New York 1902 Red Seal First NB (29)
New York Original Series Marine NB (1215)
New York Original Series Market NB (964)
New York Original Series Mechanics NB (1250)
New York Original Series Merchants NB (1370)
New York Original Series NB of Commerce (733)
New York Series 1882 NB of Commerce (733)
New York Original Series NB of the State of New York (1476)
New York Series 1902 N City B (1461)
New York 1902 Date Back N Park B (891)
New York Original Series Union NB (1278)
Incorrect plate date July 1, 1865
Ozone Park Series 1902 First NB (8865)
Deceptive. Counterfeits may have incorrect charter number
Poughkeepsie Original Series City NB (1305)
Poughkeepsie Original Series Farmers & Manufacturers NB (1305)
Poughkeepsie Original Series First NB (465)
Red Hook Original Series First NB (752)
Incorrect plate date Feb 26, 1865
Rochester Original Series Flour City NB (1362)
Incorrect plate date July 1, 1865
Rome Original Series Central NB (1376)
Incorrect plate date May 12, 1865
Syracuse Original Series Syracuse NB (1341)
Troy Original Series Mutual NB (992)
Waterford Original Series Saratoga County NB (1229)
Watkins Original Series Watkins NB (456)

Ohio
Cincinnati Series 1882 Third NB (2730)
Cleveland 1902 Date Back Central NB Savings & Trust Co (4318)
Cleveland Series 1929 Central United NB (4318)

Oklahoma
Chandler 1902 Date Back Union NB (6269)
Edmond 1902 Date Back First NB (6156)
Enid Series 1929 First NB (11584)
Lone Wolf Series 1902 First NB (10096)
Walters 1902 Date Back Walters NB (7811)

Oregon
Portland 1902 Date Back First NB (1553)

Pennsylvania
Ashley 1902 Date Back First NB (8656)
Philadelphia Original Series First NB (1)
Philadelphia Series 1882 Fourth Street NB (3557)
Philadelphia Series 1902 Fourth Street NB (3557)
Philadelphia Original Series Third NB (234)
Pittsburgh 1902 Date Back First NB (252)
Tyrone 1902 Date Back Blair County NB (6516)
Williamsport 1902 Date Back First NB (175)

Rhode Island
Providence Series 1902 Merchants NB (1131)

Texas
Atlanta Series 1902 First NB (3520)
Beaumont Series 1902 Gulf NB (6338)
Breckenridge Series 1902 First NB (7422)
Fort Stockton Series 1902 First NB (9848)
Fort Worth 1882 Brown Back NB of Fort Worth (3131)
Galveston Series 1929 United States NB (12475)
Staunton 1902 Date Back Home NB (9053)
Weatherford Series 1882 Merchants & Farmers NB (3975)

Virginia
Pearisburg 1902 Date Back First NB (8901)

Vermont
Vergennes Series 1882 NB of Vergennes (1364)

Washington
Bellingham Series 1902 First NB (7372)
Burlington Series 1902 First NB (9808)
Kent Series 1902 First NB (10174)

Wisconsin
Superior Series 1902 First NB (3926)

$20 Counterfeits

Counterfeits of the $20 Original Series notes are very deceptive. The master plate used to produce them was seized by the Secret Service. Some editions of Heath's counterfeit detector have impressions from this plate. The counterfeits show Chittenden as Register of the Treasury. Most of the genuine notes bear the engraved signature of Colby as Register of the Treasury.

Alabama
Talladega Series 1882 Isbell NB (4338)

California
Calexico Series 1902 First NB (9686)

Los Angeles Series 1929 Seaboard NB (12545) Very deceptive. Observed with incorrect charter numbers 15, 421. Serial E712048A
Los Angeles 1902 Date Back United States NB (7632)

Colorado
Grand Junction Mesa County NB (7766) A spurious issue with portrait of Washington

Connecticut
Portland Original Series First NB (1013)

Idaho
Payette Series 1902 First NB (5906) Deceptive Incorrect charter number (2532)

Illinois
Metropolis Series 1882 N State B (5254)

Indiana
Indianapolis Original Series First NB (55)
South Bend Series 1882 South Bend NB (1739)

Indian Territory [the only territorial counterfeit]
Marietta Series 1882 Marietta NB (5958)

Kentucky
Mayfield Series 1882 First NB (2245)

Maryland
Baltimore Series 1902 Second NB (414)

Massachusetts
Boston Series 1882 Fourth NB (2277)
Boston 1902 Date Back N Security B (1675)

Michigan
Grand Rapids Series 1902 Grand Rapids N City B (3293)

New York
Albany Series 1902 N Commercial B & Trust Co (1301)
Mohawk Series 1882 N Mohawk Valley B (1130)
New York Series 1902 American Exchange NB (1394)
New York Original Series Fourth NB (290)
New York Original Series First NB (29) All counterfeits dated July 19, 1865
New York Original Series Market NB (964) Chittenden is Register of Treasury on counterfeit
New York Original Series Merchants NB (1370) Chittenden is Register of Treasury on counterfeit
New York Original Series NB of Commerce (733) Chittenden is Register of Treasury on counterfeit
New York Original Series N Shoe & Leather B (917) Chittenden is Register of Treasury on counterfeit
New York Original Series Tradesmens NB (905) Chittenden is Register of Treasury on counterfeit
New York Series 1902 Chatham & Phenix NB (10778) Incorrect charter number overprinted (1077)
Utica Original Series City NB Spurious, no such bank
Utica Original Series Oneida NB (1392) Chittenden is Register of Treasury on counterfeit

Ohio
Cincinnati Series 1902 First NB (24)

Pennsylvania
Philadelphia Original Series Fourth NB (286)

South Dakota
Wessington Series 1902 First NB (8335)

Texas
Bowie Series 1882 First NB (4265)
Fort Worth Series 1902 Western NB (7165)
Hereford Series 1882 First NB (5604)
Pearsall Series 1902 Pearsall NB (6989)
San Angelo 1902 Date Back Central NB (10664) Very deceptive. Serial numbers are too thin and out of alignment.

Vermont
Barre Original Series NB of Barre (2109)

Wisconsin
Milwaukee Series 1882 Wisconsin NB (4817)

$50 Counterfeits

One master plate was used to produce excellent counterfeits of $50 Original Series notes for eight national banks, seven in New York City, and one in Buffalo, NY. The words "Deposited with the U. S. Treasurer at Washington" appear above the center of the face of the note. On genuine notes there is a flourish above and below the words "with the", as shown in Figure 3. The flourishes are missing on the counterfeits. On the back, the figure of "Justice" appears on the left side of the state seal of New York. A bandage covers the eyes of Justice on genuine notes, but not on the counterfeits. The bank officer signatures were engraved on the counterfeits, something that was not done for any genuine Original Series or Series 1875 notes.

Figure 3. Genuine $50 Original Series note showing flourishes above and below "with the".

New Jersey
Bridgeton 1882 Brown Back Bridgeton NB (2999)
Newark Series 1902 Merchants & Manufacturers NB (1818)

New York
Buffalo Original Series Third NB (850)
Chittenden is Register of Treasury on counterfeit
New York Original Series Central NB (376)
Bank officer signatures engraved on plate
New York Original Series Mechanics NB (1250)
Chittenden is Register of Treasury on counterfeit
New York Original Series Metropolitan NB (1121)
Chittenden is Register of Treasury on counterfeit
New York Original Series NB of Commerce (733)
Bank officer signatures engraved on plate
New York Original Series N Broadway B (687)
Bank officer signatures engraved on plate
New York Original Series Tradesmens NB (905)
Chittenden is Register of Treasury on counterfeit
New York Original Series Union NB (1278)
Chittenden is Register of Treasury on counterfeit

$100 Counterfeits

There are two groups of very deceptive counterfeits of $100 Original Series and Series 1875 nationals. They were printed from engraved plates.

Figure 4. Heath detector impression of Original Series $100.

Figure 4 shows the face of the more famous C-note imitation, as published in a Heath counterfeit detector. At the lower right, the words "The Union" and "Maintain It" appear next to America. On the counterfeits, the word "MAINTAIN" is misspelled "MAINIAIN", as shown in Figure 5. Often the missing top of the letter "T" has been added using pen or pencil! On genuine notes, water drips from both sides of the bow oar; on counterfeits from only one side. Counterfeits made from the same master plate showing these hallmarks were put into play for five banks:

Figure 5. Enlarged view showing the misspelling "MAINIAIN".

Massachusetts
Boston Original Series First NB (200)
New Bedford Original Series Merchants NB (799)

New York
New York Original Series Central NB (376)

Ohio
Cincinnati Original Series Ohio NB (630)

Pennsylvania
Wilkes-Barre Original Series Second NB (104)

The second dangerous $100 counterfeit appears to be a "corrected" version of those showing the "MAINIAIN" error. It also has one of the flaws noted above; water drips from only one side of the bow oar. On the back, the spacing of letters in the words "OTHER DEBTS" is uniform on genuine notes. On counterfeits, the letters "R" and "D" are joined at the base. The "D" is raised slightly above the "R". **There is one simple geometric test that will identify notes printed from this plate**: Lay a straightedge along the base of the words "with the U S Treasurer at Washington" so that it extends to Liberty at the right. On genuine notes the straightedge strikes Liberty's lips. On counterfeits it strikes her chin. The difference is quite noticeable. Counterfeits of this ilk were circulated for four banks:

Maryland
Baltimore Original Series N Exchange B (1109)

Massachusetts
Boston Original Series N Revere B (1295)
Pittsfield Original Series Pittsfield NB (1260)

Pennsylvania
Pittsburgh Series 1875 Pittsburgh NB of Commerce (668). This is the most dangerous of all the $100 counterfeits as it has the scalloped seal and is printed on fibre paper.

Chapter 8

TOWNS WITH NOTE-ISSUING NATIONAL BANKS

This chapter lists all towns which had note-issuing national banks. The order is alphabetic by town name and state abbreviation. Bank titles, charter numbers, and detailed information about the issued notes may be found in the state listings in Chapter 4.

Nationals from A to Z. Only the states of Illinois and Ohio had note-issuing national banks in towns beginning with all letters A through Z.

ABBEVILLE AL
LA
SC
ABERCROMBIE ND
ABERDEEN MD
MS
SD
WA
ABILENE KS
TX
ABINGDON IL
VA
ABINGTON MA
ABSECON NJ
ACHILLE OK
ACKERMAN MS
ACKLEY IA
ADA MN
OH
OK
ADAIR IA
ADAIRVILLE KY
ADAMS MA
MN
ND
NE
NY
ADAMSBURG PA
ADDINGTON OK
ADDISON NY
PA
ADEL GA
IA
ADENA OH
ADRIAN MI
MN
MO
AFTON IA
NY
OK
AIKEN SC
AINSWORTH NE
AITKIN MN
AKRON CO
IA
NY
OH
PA
ALACHUA FL
ALAMEDA CA
ALAMOGORDO NM
ALAMOSA CO
ALBA TX
ALBANY AL
GA
IL
MO
NY
OR
TX
ALBEMARLE NC
ALBERT LEA MN
ALBERTVILLE AL
ALBIA IA
ALBION IL
IN
MI
NE
NY
PA
ALBRIGHT WV
ALBUQUERQUE NM
ALDEN MN
ALDERSON WV
ALEDO IL
ALEX OK
ALEXANDER ND
ALEXANDER CITY AL
ALEXANDRIA IN
LA
MN
PA
SD
VA
ALEXANDRIA BAY NY
ALEXIS IL
ALGONA IA
ALGONAC MI
ALHAMBRA CA
ALIQUIPPA PA
ALLEGAN MI
ALLEGANY NY
ALLEGHENY PA
ALLEN NE
OK
ALLENDALE IL
NJ
SC
ALLENHURST NJ
ALLENTOWN NJ
PA
ALLENWOOD PA
ALLERTON IA
ALLIANCE NE
OH
ALMA KS
NE
WI
ALMENA KS
ALMONT MI
ALPENA MI
ALPHA MI
NJ
ALPINE TX
ALTA IA
ALTAMONT IL
NY
ALTAVISTA VA
ALTON IL
ALTONA IL
ALTOONA PA
ALTURAS CA
ALTUS OK
ALVA OK
ALVARADO TX
ALVIN TX
ALVORD TX
AMARILLO TX
AMBIA IN
AMBLER PA
AMBOY IL
MN
AMBRIDGE PA
AMBROSE ND
AMENIA NY
AMERICAN FALLS ID
AMERICUS GA
KS
AMES IA
AMESBURY MA
AMESVILLE OH
AMHERST MA
NE
AMITYVILLE NY
AMO IN
AMSTERDAM NY
ANACONDA MT
ANACORTES WA
ANADARKO OK
ANAHEIM CA
ANAMOOSE ND
ANAMOSA IA
ANAWALT WV
ANDALUSIA AL
ANDERSON IN
SC
TX
ANDES NY
ANDOVER MA
NY
ANGELICA NY
ANGLETON TX
ANGOLA IN
ANN ARBOR MI
ANNA IL
TX
ANNAPOLIS IL
MD
ANNISTON AL
ANNONA TX
ANNVILLE PA
ANOKA MN
NE
ANSLEY NE
ANSON TX
ANSONIA CT
OH
ANSTED WV
ANTELOPE MT
ANTHONY KS
RI
ANTIGO WI
ANTIOCH CA
ANTLER ND
ANTLERS OK
APACHE OK
APALACHICOLA FL
APOLLO PA
APPALACHIA VA
APPLETON MN
WI
APPLETON CITY MO
APPOMATTOX VA
ARANSAS PASS TX
ARAPAHO OK
ARAPAHOE NE
ARCADE NY
ARCADIA FL
IN
LA
ARCANUM OH
ARCATA CA
ARCHER CITY TX
ARCOLA IL
ARDMORE OK
PA
ARDSLEY NY
ARENDTSVILLE PA
ARENZVILLE IL
ARGOS IN
ARGYLE MN
NY
ARKADELPHIA AR
ARKANSAS CITY KS
ARLINGTON GA
IA
MA
NE
NJ
OR
SD
TX
ARMOUR SD
ARMSTRONG IA
ARNOLD PA
ARTESIA CA
NM
ARTHUR IL
ARVADA CO
ASBURY PARK NJ
ASHAWAY RI
ASHBURNHAM MA
ASHDOWN AR
ASHEBORO NC
ASHEVILLE NC
ASHFORD AL
ASHLAND AL
KS
KY
NE
OH
OR
PA
VA
WI
ASHLEY ND
PA
ASHTABULA OH
ASHTON ID
SD
ASPEN CO
ASPERMONT TX
ASPINWALL PA
ASSUMPTION IL
ASTORIA OR
ATCHISON KS
ATGLEN PA
ATHENA OR
ATHENS AL
GA
NY
OH
PA
TN
TX
ATHOL MA
ATKINSON NE
ATLANTA GA
IL
NY
TX
ATLANTIC IA
ATLANTIC CITY NJ
ATLANTIC
HIGHLANDS NJ
ATMORE AL
ATOKA OK
ATTALLA AL
ATTICA IN
KS
NY
ATTLEBORO MA
ATTLEBOROUGH MA
ATWATER MN
ATWOOD IL
KS
AUBREY TX
AUBURN AL
CA
IN
ME
NE
NY
PA
AUDUBON IA
AUGUSTA GA
IL
KS
KY
ME
AULT CO
AURELIA IA
AURORA IL
IN
MN
MO
NE
NY
OR
AUSTIN IL
MN
NV
PA
TX
AVA IL
AVELLA PA
AVERY TX
AVOCA MN
PA
AVON PARK FL
AVONDALE PA
AVONMORE PA
AYDEN NC
AYER MA
AYLESWORTH OK
AYRSHIRE IA
AZUSA CA
BABYLON NY
BAGLEY IA
MN
BAGWELL TX
BAILEY TX
BAINBRIDGE GA
NY
PA
BAIRD TX
BAKER MT
OR
BAKER CITY OR
BAKERSFIELD CA
BAKERTON PA
BALATON MN
BALDWIN NY
WI
BALDWINSVILLE NY
BALLINGER TX
BALLSTON SPA NY
BALLY PA
BALTIMORE MD
OH
BANCROFT IA
NE
BANDON OR
BANGOR ME
PA
WI
BANNING CA
BAR HARBOR ME
BARABOO WI
BARBERTON OH
BARBOURVILLE KY
BARDWELL KY
TX
BARKER NY
BARNARD KS
BARNEGAT NJ
BARNESBORO PA
BARNESVILLE GA
BARNESVILLE MN
OH
BARNUM MN
BARNWELL SC
BARRE MA
VT
BARRINGTON IL
BARRY IL
BARTLESVILLE OK
BARTLETT TX
BARTON MD
VT
BARTOW FL
BASIN WY
BASSETT VA
BASTROP TX
BATAVIA IL
NY
OH
BATESBURG SC
BATESVILLE AR
IN
OH
BATH ME
NY
PA
BATHGATE ND
BATON ROUGE LA
BATTLE CREEK MI
BATTLE LAKE MN
BAUDETTE MN
BAXTER SPRINGS KS
BAY CITY MI
TX
BAY POINT CA
BAY SHORE NY
BAYARD NE
WV
BAYFIELD WI
BAYONNE NJ
BAYSIDE NY
BAZILE MILLS NE
BEACH ND
BEACH HAVEN NJ
BEACON NY
BEALLSVILLE OH
BEARDSLEY MN
BEARDSTOWN IL
BEATRICE NE
BEATTYVILLE KY
BEAUMONT TX
BEAVER KS
PA
BEAVER CITY NE
UT
BEAVER CREEK MN
BEAVER DAM WI
BEAVER FALLS PA
BEAVER SPRINGS PA
BEAVERDALE PA
BECKLEY WV
BEDFORD IA
IN
PA
VA
BEDFORD CITY VA
BEECH CREEK PA
BEECHER IL
BEEMER NE
BEEVILLE TX
BEGGS OK
BEL AIR MD
BELDEN NE
NM
BELFAST ME
NY
BELFIELD ND
BELINGTON WV
BELLAIRE OH
BELLE FOURCHE SD
BELLE PLAINE IA
MN
BELLE VERNON PA
BELLEFONTAINE OH
BELLEFONTE PA
BELLEROSE NY
BELLEVILLE IL
KS
NJ
PA
BELLEVUE OH
PA
BELLEVUE TX
BELLFLOWER CA
BELLINGHAM WA
BELLMORE NY
BELLOWS FALLS VT
BELLPORT NY
BELLS TX
BELLVILLE TX
BELLWOOD PA
BELMAR NJ
BELMOND IA
BELMONT OH
BELOIT KS
WI
BELPRE OH
BELTON TX
BELVIDERE IL
NJ
BEMENT IL
BEMIDJI MN
BEND OR
BENDERSVILLE PA
BENEDICT NE
BENJAMIN TX
BENLD IL
BENNETTSVILLE SC
BENNINGTON OK
VT
BENSON MN
NC
PA
BENTLEYVILLE PA
BENTON AR
IL
PA
BENTON HARBOR MI
BENTONVILLE AR
BEREA KY
OH
BERESFORD SD
BERGENFIELD NJ
BERKELEY CA
BERLIN MD
NH
NJ
PA
WI
BERNARDSVILLE NJ
BERNVILLE PA
BERRYVILLE AR
VA
BERTHA MN
BERTHOUD CO
BERTRAM TX
BERTRAND NE
BERWICK PA
BERWIND WV
BERWYN IL
OK
PA
BESSEMER AL
MI
BETHANY MO
BETHEL CT
ME
OH
VT
BETHESDA OH
BETHLEHEM PA
BEVERLY MA
NJ
OH
BEVERLY HILLS CA
BICKNELL IN
BIDDEFORD ME
BIG LAKE MN
BIG RAPIDS MI
BIG RUN PA
BIG SPRING TX
BIG STONE GAP VA
BIG TIMBER MT
BIGGSVILLE IL
BIGLERVILLE PA
BILLINGS MT
OK
BILOXI MS
BINFORD ND
BINGHAMTON NY
BIOLA CA
BIRDSBORO PA
BIRDSEYE IN
BIRMINGHAM AL
BIRMINGHAM CT
MI
BISBEE AZ
ND
BISHOPVILLE SC
BISMARCK ND
BIWABIK MN
BIXBY OK
BLACK LICK PA
BLACK RIVER FALLS WI
BLACKDUCK MN
BLACKFOOT ID
BLACKSTONE MA
VA
BLACKWELL OK
BLACKWOOD NJ
BLAINE WA
BLAIR NE
OK
WI
BLAIRSTOWN NJ
BLAIRSVILLE PA
BLAKELY GA
BLANCHARD IA
OK
BLANCHARDVILLE WI
BLANCHESTER OH
BLANCO TX
BLANDINSVILLE IL
BLISS NY
BLISSFIELD MI
BLOCKTON IA
BLOOMFIELD IA
NE
NJ
BLOOMING GROVE TX
BLOOMING PRAIRIE MN
BLOOMINGTON IL
IN
BLOOMSBURG PA
BLOOMSBURY NJ
BLOSSBURG PA
BLOSSOM TX
BLUE BALL PA
BLUE EARTH MN
BLUE HILL NE
BLUE MOUND IL
BLUE RIDGE GA
BLUE RIDGE
SUMMIT PA
BLUEFIELD VA
WV
BLUFFTON IN
OH
BLUM TX
BOAZ AL
BODE IA
BOGALUSA LA
BOGATA TX
BOGOTA NJ
BOISE ID
BOISE CITY ID
OK
BOKCHITO OK
BOLIVAR MO
NY
PA
BOLTON LANDING NY
BONHAM TX
BONITA TX
BONNER SPRINGS KS
BONNERS FERRY ID
BOONE IA
BOONTON NJ
BOONVILLE IN
MO
NY
BOOTHBAY HARBOR ME
BORDENTOWN NJ
BOSCOBEL WI
BOSTON MA
BOSWELL IN
OK
PA
BOSWORTH MO
BOTTINEAU ND
BOULDER CO
BOULDER VALLEY MT
BOUND BROOK NJ
BOVEY MN
BOWBELLS ND
BOWDOINHAM ME

BOWERSTON OH
BOWIE TX
BOWLING GREEN KY
OH
BOWMAN ND
BOWMANVILLE IL
BOYCEVILLE WI
BOYD MN
BOYERTOWN PA
BOYNE CITY MI
BOYNTON OK
BOZEMAN MT
BRADDOCK PA
BRADENTON FL
BRADENTOWN FL
BRADFORD OH
PA
VT
BRADLEY BEACH NJ
BRADSHAW NE
BRADY TX
BRAGGS OK
BRAHAM MN
BRAIDWOOD IL
BRAINERD MN
BRAINTREE MA
BRAMAN OK
BRANCHVILLE NJ
BRANDON MN
VT
BRANTLEY AL
BRASHER FALLS NY
BRATTLEBORO VT
BRAWLEY CA
BRAYMER MO
BRAZIL IN
BREA CA
BRECKENRIDGE MN
TX
BREESE IL
BREMEN OH
BREMERTON WA
BRENHAM TX
BREWSTER MN
NY
WA
BRICELYN MN
BRIDGEHAMPTON NY
BRIDGEPORT AL
CT
IL
NE
OH
PA
TX
BRIDGETON NJ
BRIDGEVILLE PA
BRIDGEWATER SD
BRIDGTON ME
BRIGHAM CITY UT
BRIGHTON CO
IA
IL
BRILLION WI
BRINSMADE ND
BRISTOL CT
NH
PA
RI
SD
TN
VA
VT
BRISTOW NE
OK
BRITT IA
BRITTON SD
BROADWAY VA
BROCKPORT NY
BROCKTON MA
BROCKWAY PA
BROCKWAYVILLE PA
BRODHEAD WI
BROKEN ARROW OK
BROKEN BOW NE
OK
BRONSON MI
BRONTE TX
BRONXVILLE NY
BROOKFIELD MO
BROOKHAVEN MS
BROOKINGS SD
BROOKLINE MA
BROOKLYN CT

BROOKLYN IA
NY
BROOKNEAL VA
BROOKPORT IL
BROOKSVILLE FL
KY
BROOKVILLE IN
OH
PA
TX
BROWERVILLE MN
BROWN STATION NY
BROWNS VALLEY MN
BROWNSTOWN IL
IN
PA
BROWNSVILLE PA
TN
TX
NE
BROWNWOOD TX
BRUIN PA
BRUNDIDGE AL
BRUNSON SC
BRUNSWICK GA
MD
ME
MO
NE
BRUSH CO
BRUSHTON NY
BRYAN OH
TX
BRYN MAWR PA
BUCHANAN MI
VA
BUCKEYE CITY OH
BUCKHANNON WV
BUCKSPORT ME
BUCYRUS OH
BUDA TX
BUENA VISTA CO
GA
VA
BUFFALO KY
MN
ND
NY
OK
WY
BUFFALO CENTER IA
BUHL ID
BURBANK CA
BURGETTSTOWN PA
BURKBURNETT TX
BURLEY ID
BURLINGAME KS
BURLINGTON IA
KS
NC
NJ
VT
WA
WI
BURLINGTON JUNCTION MO
BURNET TX
BURNHAM PA
BURNS OR
BURNSIDE KY
PA
BURR OAK KS
MI
BURT IA
BURTON OH
BURWELL NE
BUSHNELL IL
BUTLER IN
MO
NJ
OH
PA
BUTTE MT
NE
BUXTON ND
BUZZARDS BAY MA
BYARS OK
BYERS TX
BYESVILLE OH
BYNUM TX
BYROMVILLE GA
CABOOL MO
CADDO OK
CADDO MILLS TX
CADIZ OH

CAINESVILLE MO
CAIRNBROOK PA
CAIRO IL
CALAIS ME
CALDWELL ID
KS
NJ
OH
TX
CALEDONIA IL
MN
NY
CALERA OK
CALEXICO CA
CALHOUN GA
CALIFON NJ
CALIFORNIA MO
PA
CALIPATRIA CA
CALISTOGA CA
CALLAWAY NE
CALLICOON NY
CALUMET MI
CALVERT TX
CALVIN OK
CAMAS WA
CAMBRIDGE IA
IL
MA
MD
MN
NE
NY
OH
VA
CAMBRIDGE CITY IN
CAMBRIDGE SPRINGS PA
CAMDEN AL
AR
ME
NJ
NY
OH
SC
TN
CAMERON MO
TX
WV
CAMP HILL PA
CAMPBELL CA
MN
MO
NE
TX
CAMPBELLSPORT WI
CAMPBELLSVILLE KY
CANAAN CT
CANADIAN OK
TX
CANAJOHARIE NY
CANAL DOVER OH
CANANDAIGUA NY
CANASTOTA NY
CANBY MN
OR
CANDO ND
CANDOR NY
CANEY KS
CANFIELD OH
CANNEL CITY KY
CANNELTON IN
CANNON FALLS MN
CANON CITY CO
CANONSBURG PA
CANTON IL
MA
MD
MO
MS
NY
OH
PA
SD
TX
CANYON TX
CANYON CITY OR
CAPAC MI
CAPE GIRARDEAU MO
CAPE MAY NJ
CAPE MAY COURT HOUSE NJ
CAPITOL HILL OK
CARBONDALE CO
IL

CARBONDALE PA
CARDIFF TN
CARDINGTON OH
CAREY OH
CARIBOU ME
CARLINVILLE IL
CARLISLE IN
KY
PA
CARLSBAD NM
CARLSTADT NJ
CARLTON MN
CARLYLE IL
CARMEL NY
CARMEN OK
CARMI IL
CARMICHAELS PA
CARNEGIE OK
PA
CARONDELET MO
CARPIO ND
CARRIER MILLS IL
CARRINGTON ND
CARROLL IA
NE
CARROLLTON GA
IL
KY
MO
OH
CARROLLTOWN PA
CARSON ND
CARSON CITY NV
CARTER MT
CARTERET NJ
CARTERSVILLE GA
CARTERVILLE IL
MO
CARTHAGE IL
MO
NY
OH
SD
TN
TX
CARUTHERS CA
CARUTHERSVILLE MO
CASEY IA
IL
CASHION OK
CASPER WY
CASPIAN MI
CASS LAKE MN
CASSANDRA PA
CASSELTON ND
CASSOPOLIS MI
CASSVILLE MO
CASTLE MT
CASTLE ROCK CO
CASTLE SHANNON PA
CASTLETON NY
VT
CASTLETON ON HUDSON NY
CASTLEWOOD SD
CATASAUQUA PA
CATAWISSA PA
CATLETTSBURG KY
CATLIN IL
CATO NY
CATONSVILLE MD
CATSKILL NY
CAVALIER ND
CAVE CITY KY
CAVERNA KY
CAWKER CITY KS
CAYUGA IN
CAZENOVIA NY
CECIL PA
CEDAR FALLS IA
CEDAR GROVE NJ
CEDAR RAPIDS IA
NE
CEDAR VALE KS
CEDARBURG WI
CEDAREDGE CO
CEDARHURST NY
CEDARTOWN GA
CELESTE TX
CELINA OH
TX
CEMENT OK
CENTER CO
TX

CENTER POINT IN
TX
CENTERBURG OH
CENTERVILLE CA
IA
IN
SD
TN
CENTRAL CITY CO
KY
NE
PA
CENTRAL PARK NY
CENTRAL SQUARE NY
CENTRAL VALLEY NY
CENTRALIA IL
KS
MO
OK
PA
WA
CENTRE HALL PA
CENTREVILLE MD
MI
OH
RI
CEREDO WV
CEYLON MN
CHADRON NE
CHADWICK IL
CHAFFEE MO
CHALFONT PA
CHALLIS ID
CHAMBERLAIN SD
CHAMBERSBURG PA
CHAMBERSBURGH PA
CHAMPAIGN IL
CHAMPLAIN NY
CHANDLER OK
CHANUTE KS
CHAPPAQUA NY
CHAPPELL NE
CHARDON OH
CHARITON IA
CHARLEROI PA
CHARLES CITY IA
CHARLES TOWN WV
CHARLESTON IL
SC
WV
CHARLESTOWN IN
MA
NH
CHARLOTTE MI
NC
CHARLOTTESVILLE VA
CHARTER OAK IA
CHARTIERS PA
CHASE CITY VA
CHASKA MN
CHATEAUGAY NY
CHATFIELD MN
CHATHAM VA
CHATSWORTH IL
CHATTANOOGA TN
CHEBOYGAN MI
CHECOTAH OK
CHEHALIS WA
CHELSEA IA
MA
OK
VT
CHELTENHAM PA
CHENEY WA
CHERAW SC
CHEROKEE IA
KS
OK
CHERRY CREEK NY
CHERRY TREE PA
CHERRY VALLEY NY
CHERRYVALE KS
CHERRYVILLE NC
CHESANING MI
CHESAPEAKE CITY MD
CHESTER IL
MT
NY
PA
SC
VT
WV
CHESTERHILL OH
CHESTERTOWN MD

CHETOPA KS
CHEVIOT OH
CHEWELAH WA
CHEYENNE WY
CHICAGO IL
CHICAGO HEIGHTS IL
CHICKASHA OK
CHICO CA
CHICOPEE MA
CHILDERSBURG AL
CHILDRESS TX
CHILHOWIE VA
CHILLICOTHE IL
MO
OH
CHILTON WI
CHINO CA
CHINOOK MT
CHIPLEY FL
CHIPPEWA FALLS WI
CHISHOLM MN
CHITTENANGO NY
CHOKIO MN
CHOWCHILLA CA
CHRISMAN IL
CHRISTIANA PA
CHRISTIANSBURG VA
CHRISTOPHER IL
CHURCHS FERRY ND
CHURDAN IA
CICERO IL
IN
CIMARRON KS
NM
CINCINNATI OH
CIRCLE MT
CIRCLEVILLE OH
CISCO TX
CITRONELLE AL
CLAIRTON PA
CLANTON AL
CLAREMONT CA
NH
CLAREMORE OK
CLARENCE IA
CLARENDON TX
CLARINDA IA
CLARINGTON OH
CLARION IA
PA
CLARK SD
WV
CLARKFIELD MN
CLARKS NE
CLARKS SUMMIT PA
CLARKSBURG WV
CLARKSDALE MS
CLARKSTON WA
CLARKSVILLE AR
OH
TN
TX
VA
CLATSKANIE OR
CLAUDE TX
CLAXTON GA
CLAY KY
CLAY CENTER KS
NE
CLAY CITY IN
KY
CLAYSBURG PA
CLAYSVILLE PA
CLAYTON MO
NJ
NM
NY
OK
CLE ELUM WA
CLEAR LAKE IA
SD
CLEAR SPRING MD
CLEARBROOK MN
CLEARFIELD IA
PA
CLEARWATER FL
CLEBURNE TX
CLEMENTON NJ
CLENDENIN WV
CLERMONT FL
CLEVELAND OH
OK
TN
TX
CLEVES OH

CLIFFSIDE PARK NJ
CLIFTON AZ
CO
IL
KS
NJ
TX
CLIFTON FORGE VA
CLIFTON HEIGHTS PA
CLIFTON SPRINGS NY
CLINTON CT
IA
IL
IN
KY
MA
MN
MO
NJ
NY
OK
SC
CLINTONVILLE PA
WI
CLINTWOOD VA
CLIO SC
CLOQUET MN
CLOSTER NJ
CLOVER SC
CLOVERDALE CA
IN
CLOVIS CA
NM
CLUTIER IA
CLYDE KS
NY
OH
TX
CLYMER PA
COACHELLA CA
COAL CITY IL
COAL CREEK TN
COALDALE PA
COALGATE OK
COALINGA CA
COALPORT PA
COALVILLE UT
COATESVILLE IN
PA
COBDEN IL
COBLESKILL NY
COCHRAN GA
COCHRANTON PA
COCKEYSVILLE MD
CODY WY
COEBURN VA
COEUR D'ALENE ID
COFFEE SPRINGS AL
COFFEEN IL
COFFEYVILLE KS
COHOES NY
COIN IA
COKATO MN
COLBERT OK
COLBY KS
COLCHESTER IL
COLD SPRING MN
NY
COLDWATER KS
MI
COLEBROOK NH
COLEMAN TX
COLERAINE MN
COLERIDGE NE
COLFAX IA
WA
COLLEGE CORNER OH
COLLEGE SPRINGS IA
COLLEGEVILLE PA
COLLINGSWOOD NJ
COLLINS MS
COLLINSVILLE AL
IL
OK
TX
COLLYER KS
COLMAN SD
COLONY KS
COLORADO TX
COLORADO CITY CO
COLORADO SPRINGS CO
COLQUITT GA

COLTON CA
WA
COLUMBIA AL
IL
KY
MO
MS
PA
SC
SD
TN
COLUMBIA CITY IN
COLUMBIANA OH
COLUMBUS GA
IN
KS
MS
MT
NE
OH
WI
COLUMBUS
JUNCTION IA
COLUSA CA
COLVILLE WA
COMANCHE OK
TX
COMMERCE GA
OK
TX
COMO TX
COMPTON CA
IL
CONCORD CA
MA
MI
NC
NH
CONCORDIA KS
CONDON OR
CONEWANGO
VALLEY NY
CONFLUENCE PA
CONNEAUT OH
CONNEAUT LAKE PA
CONNEAUTVILLE PA
CONNELL WA
CONNELLSVILLE PA
CONNERSVILLE IN
CONRAD IA
MT
CONROE TX
CONSHOHOCKEN PA
CONSTANTINE MI
CONVERSE IN
CONVOY OH
CONWAY AR
MA
NH
SC
WA
CONWAY SPRINGS KS
CONYERS GA
CONYNGHAM PA
COOKEVILLE TN
COOLIDGE TX
COOLVILLE OH
COON RAPIDS IA
COOPER TX
COOPERSBURG PA
COOPERSTOWN ND
NY
COPENHAGEN NY
COPLAY PA
COPPERHILL TN
COQUILLE OR
CORAL GABLES FL
CORAOPOLIS PA
CORBIN KY
CORCORAN CA
CORDELE GA
CORDELL OK
CORINTH MS
NY
CORNELIA GA
CORNING AR
IA
NY
CORNISH OK
CORNWALL NY
CORONA CA
NY
CORPUS CHRISTI TX
CORRY PA
CORSICANA TX
CORTEZ CO
CORTLAND NY
OH
CORUNNA MI
CORVALLIS OR
CORWITH IA
CORYDON IA
IN
COSHOCTON OH
COTTAGE GROVE OR
COTTON PLANT AR
COTTONWOOD ID
MN
COTTONWOOD
FALLS KS
COTULLA TX
COUDERSPORT PA
COULTERVILLE IL
COUNCIL BLUFFS IA
COUNCIL GROVE KS
COURTENAY ND
COVINA CA
COVINGTON GA
IN
KY
OH
TN
TX
VA
COWDEN IL
COWETA OK
COWGILL MO
COXSACKIE NY
COYLE OK
COZAD NE
CRAFTON PA
CRAIG CO
NE
CRANBURY NJ
CRANDALL TX
CRANDON WI
CRANFORD NJ
CRARY ND
CRAWFORD NE
TX
CRAWFORDSVILLE IN
CREEDE CO
CREEDMOOR NC
CREIGHTON NE
CRESCENT CITY IL
CRESCENT
HEIGHTS CA
CRESCO IA
CRESSON PA
TX
CRESSONA PA
CRESTLINE OH
CRESTON IA
CRETE NE
CREWE VA
CRIPPLE CREEK CO
CROCKETT CA
TX
CROFTON NE
CROGHAN NY
CROOKSTON MN
CROSBY MN
ND
CROSBYTON TX
CROSS PLAINS TX
CROSSVILLE IL
TN
CROSWELL MI
CROTON ON
HUDSON NY
CROWELL TX
CROWLEY LA
CROWN POINT IN
CROWS LANDING CA
CRYSTAL ND
CRYSTAL FALLS MI
CRYSTAL LAKE IA
CUBA IL
NY
CUBA CITY WI
CUCAMONGA CA
CUERO TX
CULBERTSON MT
CULLMAN AL
CULLOM IL
CULPEPPER VA
CULVER CITY CA
CUMBERLAND IA
CUMBERLAND MD
RI
CUMBY TX
CURTIS NE
CURWENSVILLE PA
CUSHING OK
CUSTER SD
CUSTER CITY OK
CUT BANK MT
CUTCHOGUE NY
CUTHBERT GA
CUTTER NM
CUYAHOGA FALLS OH
CYNTHIANA KY
DAGSBORO DE
DAHLGREN IL
DAINGERFIELD TX
DALE PA
WI
DALHART TX
DALLAS OR
PA
TX
DALLAS CITY IL
DALLASTOWN PA
DALTON GA
OH
DAMARISCOTTA ME
DANA IN
DANBURY CT
DANIELSON CT
DANIELSONVILLE CT
DANIELSVILLE PA
DANSVILLE NY
DANVERS IL
MA
DANVILLE IL
IN
KY
NE
PA
VA
VT
DARBY PA
DARDANELLE AR
DARLINGTON SC
WI
DAUPHIN PA
DAVENPORT IA
OK
WA
DAVID CITY NE
DAVIDSON OK
DAVIDSVILLE PA
DAVIS OK
SD
WV
DAWSON GA
MN
PA
TX
DAWSON SPRINGS KY
DAYTON IA
OH
PA
TN
WA
DAYTONA FL
DAYTONA BEACH FL
DE FUNIAK SPRINGS FL
DE KALB IL
DE LAND IL
DE LEON TX
DE PERE WI
DE RIDDER LA
DE SMET SD
DE WITT IA
DEADWOOD SD
DEARBORN MI
DECATUR AL
IL
IN
MI
NE
TX
NY
DECHERD TN
DECKERTOWN NJ
DECORAH IA
DEDHAM MA
DEEP RIVER CT
IA
DEER CREEK MN
DEER LODGE MT
DEER RIVER MN
DEERFIELD WI
DEERWOOD MN
DEFIANCE OH
DEKALB TX
DEL NORTE CO
DEL REY CA
DEL RIO TX
DELAND FL
DELANO CA
MN
DELAVAN IL
WI
DELAWARE OH
DELAWARE CITY DE
DELHI LA
NY
DELL RAPIDS SD
DELMAR DE
DELMONT PA
DELPHI IN
DELPHOS KS
OH
DELTA CO
OH
PA
UT
DEMING NM
DEMOPOLIS AL
DENISON IA
TX
DENNISON OH
DENTON MD
MT
TX
DENVER CO
PA
DEPEW OK
DEPORT TX
DEPOSIT NY
DEQUEEN AR
DERBY CT
DERBY LINE VT
DERRY NH
PA
DES MOINES IA
DES PLAINES IL
DETROIT MI
MN
TX
DETROIT LAKES MN
DEVILS LAKE ND
DEVINE TX
DEVOL OK
DEWEY OK
DEWITT AR
NE
DEXTER IA
KS
ME
MO
NY
DIAGONAL IA
DICKENS TX
DICKINSON ND
TX
DICKSON TN
DICKSON CITY PA
DIETERICH IL
DIGHTON KS
DIKE IA
DILLER NE
DILLON MT
SC
DILLONVALE OH
DILLSBORO IN
DILLSBURG PA
DILLWYN VA
DINUBA CA
DIVERNON IL
DIXON CA
IL
DODD CITY TX
DODGE NE
DODGE CENTER MN
DODGE CITY KS
DODGEVILLE WI
DOLAND SD
DOLGEVILLE NY
DOLORES CO
DOLTON IL
DONGOLA IL
DONORA PA
DOON IA
DORCHESTER MA
NE
DOTHAN AL
DOUGHERTY IA
DOUGLAS AZ
WY
DOVER DE
ME
NH
NJ
OH
PA
DOVER PLAINS NY
DOWAGIAC MI
DOWNERS GROVE IL
DOWNEY CA
DOWNINGTOWN PA
DOWNS KS
DOWNSVILLE NY
DOYLE TN
DOYLESTOWN PA
DOZIER AL
DRAKE ND
DRAYTON ND
DRESDEN OH
DRIGGS ID
DRY RIDGE KY
DRY RUN PA
DRYDEN NY
DUBLIN GA
IN
PA
TX
DUBOIS ID
PA
DUBOIS CITY PA
DUBUQUE IA
DUCKTOWN TN
DUCOR CA
DULUTH MN
DUMONT NJ
DUNBAR PA
DUNCAN OK
DUNCANNON PA
DUNDEE IL
NY
DUNELLEN NJ
DUNKERTON IA
DUNKIRK IN
NY
OH
DUNLAP IA
DUNMORE PA
DUNN NC
DUNNELL MN
DUQUESNE PA
DUQUOIN IL
DURAND MI
WI
DURANGO CO
DURANT OK
DURHAM NC
DUSHORE PA
DUSTIN OK
DWIGHT IL
DYER IN
DYERSBURG TN
DYERSVILLE IA
DYSART IA
EADS CO
EAGLE CO
EAGLE BEND MN
EAGLE GROVE IA
EAGLE LAKE TX
EAGLE PASS TX
EAGLE RIVER WI
EARLE AR
EARLVILLE IL
NY
EAST AURORA NY
EAST BERLIN PA
EAST BERNSTADT KY
EAST BRADY PA
EAST CAMBRIDGE MA
EAST CHICAGO IN
EAST CONEMAUGH PA
EAST ELY NV
EAST FAIRVIEW ND
EAST GRAND FORKS MN
EAST GREENVILLE PA
EAST GREENWICH RI
EAST HADDAM CT
EAST HAMPTON NY
EAST ISLIP NY
EAST JAFFREY NH
EAST LIVERPOOL OH
EAST MAUCH CHUNK PA
EAST NEWARK NJ
EAST NORTHPORT NY
EAST ORANGE NJ
EAST PALESTINE OH
EAST PEORIA IL
EAST PORT
CHESTER CT
EAST ROCHESTER NY
EAST ROCKAWAY NY
EAST SAGINAW MI
EAST SAINT LOUIS IL
EAST SETAUKET NY
EAST SMITHFIELD PA
EAST STANWOOD WA
EAST
STROUDSBURG PA
EAST WORCESTER NY
EASTHAMPTON MA
EASTLAND TX
EASTMAN GA
EASTON MD
PA
EASTPORT ME
EATON CO
OH
EATON RAPIDS MI
EATONTOWN NJ
EAU CLAIRE WI
EBENSBURG PA
ECONOMY PA
EDDY NM
EDDYVILLE KY
EDEN ME
EDENBURG PA
EDGARTOWN MA
EDGELEY ND
EDGERTON WI
EDGEWATER NJ
EDGEWOOD TX
EDINA MO
EDINBORO PA
EDINBURG IN
TX
EDMESTON NY
EDMOND KS
OK
EDMORE ND
EDNA KS
TX
EDWARDS NY
EDWARDSVILLE IL
PA
EFFINGHAM IL
EGAN SD
EGELAND ND
EL CAMPO TX
EL CENTRO CA
EL DORADO AR
KS
OK
EL MONTE CA
EL PASO IL
TX
EL RENO OK
ELBA AL
ELBERTON GA
ELBOW LAKE MN
ELDON IA
ELDORA IA
ELDORADO IL
TX
ELDORADO
SPRINGS MO
ELDRED PA
ELECTRA TX
ELGIN IL
MN
NE
OR
TX
ELIDA NM
ELIZABETH CO
NJ
PA
ELIZABETH CITY NC
ELIZABETHTON TN
ELIZABETHTOWN KY
PA
ELIZABETHVILLE PA
ELK CITY KS
OK
ELK POINT SD
ELK RIVER MN
ELKADER IA
ELKHART IN
ELKHORN WI
ELKIN NC
ELKINS WV
ELKINS PARK PA
ELKLAND PA
ELKO NV
ELKTON MD
SD
ELLENDALE ND
ELLENSBURG WA
ELLENVILLE NY
ELLICOTT CITY MD
ELLIOTT IA
ELLOREE SC
ELLSWORTH KS
ME
MN
PA
ELLWOOD CITY PA
ELM CREEK NE
ELM GROVE WV
ELMER NJ
ELMHURST IL
ELMIRA NY
ELMORE MN
OH
ELMSFORD NY
ELMWOOD NE
ELMWOOD PLACE OH
ELSINORE CA
ELVERSON PA
ELWOOD IN
NE
ELY MN
NV
ELYRIA OH
ELYSBURG PA
EMAUS PA
EMERSON NE
EMERY SD
EMERYVILLE CA
EMLENTON PA
EMMA TX
EMMETSBURG IA
EMMETT ID
EMMONS MN
EMORY TX
EMPORIA KS
VA
EMPORIUM PA
ENDERLIN ND
ENFIELD IL
ENGLEWOOD CO
IL
KS
NJ
ENGLISHTOWN NJ
ENID OK
ENLOE TX
ENNIS TX
ENOSBURG FALLS VT
ENSLEY AL
ENTERPRISE AL
OR
ENUMCLAW WA
EPHRATA PA
EQUALITY IL
ERICK OK
ERIE IL
KS
PA
ERSKINE MN
ERWIN TN
ESCANABA MI
ESCONDIDO CA
ESMONT VA
ESSEX CT
IA
ESTELLINE SD
ESTHERVILLE IA
ETHAN SD
ETNA PA
ETOWAH TN
EUDORA AR
EUFAULA AL
OK
EUGENE OR
EUGENE CITY OR
EUNICE LA
EUREKA CA
KS
NV

EUREKA SPRINGS AR
EUTAW AL
EVANS CITY PA
EVANSTON IL
WY
EVANSVILLE IN
WI
EVART MI
EVELETH MN
EVERETT PA
WA
EVERGREEN AL
EVERLY IA
EXCELSIOR
SPRINGS MO
EXCHANGE PA
EXETER CA
NE
NH
PA
EXIRA IA
EXPORT PA
EYOTA MN
FABENS TX
FACTORY POINT VT
FACTORYVILLE PA
FAIR HAVEN VT
FAIRBANKS AK
FAIRBURY IL
NE
FAIRCHANCE PA
FAIRCHILD WI
FAIRFAX MN
OK
SC
SD
VA
FAIRFIELD AL
CA
IA
ID
IL
ME
MT
NE
PA
TX
FAIRHAVEN MA
WA
FAIRLAND IN
FAIRMONT MN
NE
WV
FAIRMOUNT IL
ND
FAIRPORT NY
FAIRPORT HARBOR OH
FAIRVIEW MO
MT
NJ
OK
WV
FALCONER NY
FALFURRIAS TX
FALL RIVER MA
FALLS CITY NE
TX
FALLS CREEK PA
FALLS VILLAGE CT
FALMOUTH KY
MA
FAR ROCKAWAY NY
FARGO ND
FARIBAULT MN
FARMER CITY IL
FARMERSBURG IN
FARMERSVILLE IL
TX
FARMINGDALE NY
FARMINGTON IA
ME
MN
NH
NM
FARMLAND IN
FARMVILLE VA
FARNHAMVILLE IA
FARRAGUT IA
FARRELL PA
FARWELL TX
FAWN GROVE PA
FAYETTE AL
IA
FAYETTE CITY PA
FAYETTEVILLE AR
NC
NY
TN
TX
WV
FEDERALSBURG MD
FELICITY OH
FELTON DE
FENNIMORE WI
FENTON MI
FERDINAND IN
FERGUS FALLS MN
FERNANDINA FL
FERNDALE WA
FERRIS TX
FERRUM VA
FERTILE MN
FESSENDEN ND
FINDLAY IL
OH
FINGAL ND
FINLEY ND
FINLEYVILLE PA
FIRTH ID
FISHERS IN
FISHKILL NY
FISHKILL LANDING NY
FITCHBURG MA
FITZGERALD GA
FLAGSTAFF AZ
FLANDREAU SD
FLATONIA TX
FLEETWOOD PA
FLEISCHMANNS NY
FLEMING CO
KY
FLEMINGSBURG KY
FLEMINGTON NJ
FLINT MI
FLINT HILL VA
FLORA IL
IN
FLORAL PARK NY
FLORALA AL
FLORENCE AL
AZ
CA
CO
SC
FLORESVILLE TX
FLORIDA NY
FLOYD IA
FLOYDADA TX
FLUSHING MI
NY
OH
FOGELSVILLE PA
FOLEY MN
FOLLETT TX
FOND DU LAC WI
FONDA IA
NY
FONTANA CA
FONTANELLE IA
FORAKER OK
FORD CITY PA
FORDS NJ
FORDYCE AR
FOREST OH
FOREST CITY IA
NC
PA
FOREST GROVE OR
FOREST LAKE MN
FORESTVILLE NY
FORMAN ND
FORMOSO KS
FORNEY TX
FORREST IL
FORREST CITY AR
FORSYTH GA
MT
FORT ATKINSON WI
FORT BENTON MT
FORT BRAGG CA
FORT BRANCH IN
FORT COLLINS CO
FORT DODGE IA
FORT EDWARD NY
FORT FAIRFIELD ME
FORT GAINES GA
FORT GIBSON OK
FORT HOWARD WI
FORT KENT ME
FORT LAUDERDALE FL
FORT
LEAVENWORTH KS
FORT LEE NJ
FORT MADISON IA
FORT MEADE FL
FORT MILL SC
FORT MORGAN CO
FORT MYERS FL
FORT PAYNE AL
FORT PIERRE SD
FORT PLAIN NY
FORT SCOTT KS
FORT SILL OK
FORT SMITH AR
FORT STOCKTON TX
FORT SUMNER NM
FORT TOWSON OK
FORT VALLEY GA
FORT WAYNE IN
FORT WORTH TX
FORTVILLE IN
FOSS OK
FOSSTON MN
FOSTORIA OH
FOUNTAIN CO
FOWLER CA
CO
IN
KS
FOX LAKE WI
FOXBORO MA
FRACKVILLE PA
FRAMINGHAM MA
FRANCESTOWN NH
FRANCIS OK
FRANKFORD DE
FRANKFORT IN
KS
KY
NY
FRANKLIN IN
KY
LA
MA
NE
NH
NY
OH
PA
TN
TX
FRANKLIN SQUARE NY
FRANKLINVILLE NY
FRANKSTON TX
FRAZEE MN
FREDERIC WI
FREDERICA DE
FREDERICK MD
OK
SD
FREDERICKSBURG IA
PA
VA
FREDERICKTOWN OH
PA
FREDONIA KS
NY
PA
FREEBURG IL
FREEDOM PA
FREEHOLD NJ
FREELAND PA
FREELAND PARK IN
FREEMAN SD
FREEPORT IL
NY
OH
PA
TX
FREMONT IN
NE
OH
FRENCHTOWN NJ
FRESNO CA
MT
FRIEND NE
FRIENDLY WV
FRIENDSHIP NY
FRIENDSVILLE MD
FRIES VA
FRISCO TX
FRONT ROYAL VA
FROST TX
FROSTBURG MD
FRUITA CO
FRYBURG PA
FULDA MN
FULLERTON CA
NE
FULTON KY
MO
NY
FULTONVILLE NY
GADSDEN AL
GAFFNEY SC
GAGE OK
GAINESBORO TN
GAINESVILLE AL
FL
GA
NY
TX
GAITHERSBURG MD
GALAX VA
GALENA IL
KS
GALESBURG IL
GALETON PA
GALION OH
GALLATIN MO
TN
GALLIPOLIS OH
GALLITZIN PA
GALLUP NM
GALVA IA
IL
GALVESTON TX
GANADO TX
GAP PA
GARDEN CITY KS
GARDEN GROVE CA
IA
GARDENA CA
GARDINER ME
OR
GARDNER IL
MA
GARFIELD NJ
WA
GARLAND TX
GARNER IA
GARNETT KS
GARRETSON SD
GARRETT IL
PA
GARRETTSVILLE OH
GARRISON ND
GARY IN
SD
WV
GAS CITY IN
GASPORT NY
GASTONIA NC
GATE CITY VA
GATESVILLE TX
GAYLORD KS
GEARY OK
GENESEE ID
PA
GENESEO IL
NY
GENEVA AL
IL
NE
NY
OH
GENOA NE
NY
GENTRY AR
GEORGE IA
GEORGE WEST TX
GEORGETOWN CO
DC
DE
IL
KY
MA
OH
TX
GERALDINE MT
GERING NE
GERMANTOWN NY
OH
GETTYSBURG OH
PA
SD
GEYSER MT
GEYSERVILLE CA
GIBBON NE
GIBSLAND LA
GIBSON CITY IL
GIDDINGS TX
GIG HARBOR WA
GILBERT MN
GILL CO
GILLESPIE IL
GILMAN IL
GILMER TX
GILMORE CITY IA
GILROY CA
GIRARD KS
OH
PA
GIRARDVILLE PA
GLADBROOK IA
GLADSTONE MI
GLASCO KS
GLASGOW KY
MT
GLASSBORO NJ
GLASSPORT PA
GLEN CAMPBELL PA
GLEN HEAD NY
GLEN LYON PA
GLEN ROCK NJ
PA
GLEN ROSE TX
GLEN ULLIN ND
GLENCOE MN
GLENDALE CA
GLENDIVE MT
GLENDORA CA
GLENS FALLS NY
GLENSIDE PA
GLENVILLE WV
GLENWOOD IA
MN
GLENWOOD CITY WI
GLENWOOD
SPRINGS CO
GLIDDEN IA
GLOBE AZ
GLOUCESTER MA
VA
GLOUCESTER CITY NJ
GLOUSTER OH
GLOVERSVILLE NY
GOFF KS
GOLCONDA IL
GOLDEN CO
GOLDEN CITY MO
GOLDENDALE WA
GOLDFIELD IA
NV
GOLDSBORO NC
PA
GOLDTHWAITE TX
GOLIAD TX
GONIC NH
GONVICK MN
GONZALES TX
GOOD THUNDER MN
GOODHUE MN
GOODING ID
GOODLAND IN
KS
GOODRICH ND
GOODWATER AL
GORDON NE
TX
GORDONSVILLE VA
GOREE TX
GOREVILLE IL
GORHAM IL
NH
GORMAN TX
GORMANIA WV
GOSHEN IN
NY
GOTEBO OK
GOTHENBURG NE
GOUVERNEUR NY
GOWRIE IA
GRACEVILLE FL
MN
GRAETTINGER IA
GRAFTON IA
MA
ND
WV
GRAHAM CA
NC
TX
VA
GRANADA CO
GRANBURY TX
GRAND FORKS ND
GRAND GORGE NY
GRAND HAVEN MI
GRAND ISLAND NE
GRAND JUNCTION CO
GRAND MEADOW MN
GRAND RAPIDS MI
MN
WI
GRAND RIDGE IL
GRAND RIVER IA
GRAND SALINE TX
GRAND TOWER IL
GRANDFIELD OK
GRANDVIEW TX
GRANGER TX
GRANGEVILLE ID
GRANITE OK
GRANITE CITY IL
GRANITE FALLS MN
GRANT NE
GRANT CITY MO
GRANT PARK IL
GRANTHAM PA
GRANTS PASS OR
GRANTSBURG WI
GRANTSVILLE MD
GRANVILLE IL
NY
OH
GRAPEVINE TX
GRASS RANGE MT
GRASS VALLEY CA
GRATZ PA
GRAVETTE AR
GRAYSON KY
GRAYVILLE IL
GREAT BARRINGTON MA
GREAT BEND KS
GREAT FALLS MT
NH
GREAT NECK
STATION NY
GREELEY CO
NE
GREEN BAY WI
GREEN CASTLE IN
GREEN CITY MO
GREEN FOREST AR
GREEN LANE PA
GREEN RIVER WY
GREEN SPRING OH
GREENCASTLE IN
PA
GREENE IA
GREENEVILLE TN
GREENFIELD IA
IL
MA
OH
GREENLEAF KS
GREENPORT NY
GREENS FORK IN
GREENSBORO AL
GA
NC
GREENSBURG IN
KS
PA
GREENUP IL
KY
GREENVILLE AL
IL
KY
MI
MS
NC
OH
PA
RI
SC
TX
GREENWICH CT
NY
OH
GREENWOOD AR
IN
MS
GREENWOOD NE
NY
SC
GREGORY SD
TX
GRESHAM NE
GRETNA LA
GREY EAGLE MN
GREYBULL WY
GRIDLEY CA
IL
GRIFFIN GA
GRIFFIN CORNERS NY
GRIFFITHSVILLE WV
GRIGGSVILLE IL
GRINNELL IA
GRISWOLD IA
GROESBECK TX
GROTON NY
SD
GROVE OK
GROVE CITY OH
PA
GROVETON NH
TX
GRUNDY VA
GRUNDY CENTER IA
GUERNSEY WY
GUILFORD CT
ME
MS
GUNNISON CO
GUNTER TX
GUNTERSVILLE AL
GURDON AR
GUTHRIE OK
GUTHRIE CENTER IA
GUTTENBERG NJ
GUYMON OK
GYPSUM KS
HACKENSACK NJ
HACKETTSTOWN NJ
HADDON HEIGHTS NJ
HADDONFIELD NJ
HAGERMAN ID
NM
HAGERSTOWN IN
MD
HAILEY ID
HALEDON NJ
HALIFAX PA
HALLETTSVILLE TX
HALLOCK MN
HALLOWELL ME
HALLSTEAD PA
HALLWOOD VA
HALSTAD MN
HALSTEAD KS
HAMBURG IA
NJ
PA
HAMDEN NY
HAMILTON IL
KS
MO
MT
NY
OH
TX
VA
HAMILTON SQUARE NJ
HAMLET NC
HAMLIN TX
WV
HAMMOND IN
LA
NY
HAMPDEN ND
HAMPSTEAD MD
HAMPTON GA
IA
NE
VA
HAMPTON BAYS NY
HAMTRAMCK MI
HANCOCK MD
MI
MN
NY
HANFORD CA
HANKINSON ND
HANLEY FALLS MN
HANNAFORD ND

HANNIBAL MO
HANOVER NH
PA
HANSKA MN
HARDIN MT
HARDWICK CA
HARLAN IA
KY
HARLEM MT
HARLEYSVILLE PA
HARLOWTOWN MT
HARMONY MN
PA
HARPER KS
HARRAH OK
HARRIMAN TN
HARRINGTON DE
WA
HARRIS IA
HARRISBURG IL
OR
PA
HARRISON AR
NE
NJ
NY
OH
OK
HARRISONBURG VA
HARRISONVILLE MO
HARRISVILLE NY
PA
WV
HARRODSBURG KY
HART MI
HARTFORD AL
AR
CT
KS
KY
MI
WI
HARTFORD CITY IN
HARTINGTON NE
HARTLEY IA
HARTSDALE NY
HARTSELLE AL
HARTSHORNE OK
HARTSVILLE IN
SC
HARTWELL GA
HARTWICK NY
HARVARD NE
HARVEY IA
IL
ND
HARWICH MA
HASKELL OK
TX
HASTINGS MI
MN
NE
OK
PA
HASTINGS
UPON HUDSON NY
HATBORO PA
HATFIELD PA
HATTIESBURG MS
HATTON ND
HAVANA IL
NY
HAVELOCK IA
NE
HAVENSVILLE KS
HAVERHILL MA
HAVERSTRAW NY
HAVILAND OH
HAVRE MT
HAVRE DE GRACE MD
HAWARDEN IA
HAWKEYE IA
HAWKINSVILLE GA
HAWLEY MN
PA
TX
HAWTHORNE NJ
HAXTUN CO
HAY SPRINGS NE
HAYES CENTER NE
HAYNEVILLE AL
HAYS PA
HAYS CITY KS
HAYWARD CA

HAYWARD WI
HAZARD KY
HAZELHURST PA
HAZLETON PA
HEADLAND AL
HEALDSBURG CA
HEALDTON OK
HEARNE TX
HEAVENER OK
HEBBRONVILLE TX
HEBER SPRINGS AR
HEBRON ND
NE
HECLA SD
HEDRICK IA
HEGEWISCH IL
HEGINS PA
HELENA AR
MT
OK
HEMET CA
HEMINGFORD NE
HEMPHILL TX
HEMPSTEAD NY
TX
HENDERSON IA
KY
NC
NE
TX
HENDERSONVILLE NC
HENDRICKS MN
WV
HENNESSEY OK
HENNING MN
HENRIETTA TX
HENRY IL
SD
HENRYETTA OK
HEPPNER OR
HEREFORD TX
HERINGTON KS
HERKIMER NY
HERMAN MN
HERMANSVILLE MI
HERMINIE PA
HERMISTON OR
HERMON NY
HERMOSA BEACH CA
HERNDON PA
VA
HERON LAKE MN
HERRIN IL
HERSHEY PA
HETTINGER ND
HEUVELTON NY
HIAWATHA KS
HIBBING MN
HICKMAN KY
HICKORY NC
PA
HICKSVILLE NY
OH
HICO TX
HIGGINS TX
HIGGINSPORT OH
HIGH BRIDGE NJ
HIGH POINT NC
HIGHLAND IL
KS
NY
HIGHLAND FALLS NY
HIGHLAND PARK NJ
PA
HIGHMORE SD
HIGHTSTOWN NJ
HIGHWOOD MT
HILL CITY KS
HILLS MN
HILLSBORO IL
KS
ND
OH
OR
TX
HILLSBOROUGH NH
OH
HILLSDALE MI
NJ
HILLSIDE NJ
HINDSBORO IL
HINGHAM MA
HINSDALE IL
HINTON WV

HOBART NY
OK
HOBOKEN NJ
HOBSON MT
HODGENVILLE KY
HOHENWALD TN
HOISINGTON KS
HOLBROOK AZ
HOLCOMB NY
HOLDEN MO
HOLDENVILLE OK
HOLDREGE NE
HOLLAND IN
TX
HOLLAND PATENT NY
HOLLIDAYSBURG PA
HOLLIS OK
HOLLISTER CA
HOLLISTON MA
HOLLY CO
MI
HOLLY GROVE AR
HOLLY HILL SC
HOLLYWOOD CA
HOLSTEIN IA
HOLTON KS
HOLTVILLE CA
HOLYOKE CO
MA
HOMER IL
LA
NY
HOMER CITY PA
HOMESTEAD FL
PA
HOMINY OK
HONAKER VA
HONDO TX
HONEA PATH SC
HONESDALE PA
HONEY GROVE TX
HONEYBROOK PA
HONOLULU HI
HOOD RIVER OR
HOOPER NE
HOOPESTON IL
HOOSICK FALLS NY
HOOVERSVILLE PA
HOP BOTTOM PA
HOPE AR
IN
ND
NJ
NM
HOPEDALE IL
OH
HOPEWELL NJ
PA
VA
HOPKINS MN
MO
HOPKINSVILLE KY
HOPKINTON MA
RI
HOQUIAM WA
HORATIO AR
HORNELL NY
HORNELLSVILLE NY
HORSE CAVE KY
HORSEHEADS NY
HORTON KS
HOT SPRINGS AR
SD
VA
HOTCHKISS CO
HOUGHTON MI
HOULTON ME
HOUSTON PA
TX
HOUTZDALE PA
HOWARD KS
PA
SD
HOWE TX
HOWELL MI
HOXIE KS
HUBBARD IA
OH
TX
HUBBELL MI
HUDSON IA
MA
NY
OH

HUDSON SD
WI
HUDSON FALLS NY
HUGHES SPRINGS TX
HUGHESVILLE PA
HUGO CO
OK
HUGOTON KS
HULL IA
NY
HUMBOLDT IA
IL
KS
NE
HUME IL
HUMMELSTOWN PA
HUMPHREY NE
HUNTER ND
NY
HUNTINGBURG IN
HUNTINGDON PA
HUNTINGTON IN
NY
WV
HUNTINGTON BEACH CA
HUNTINGTON PARK CA
HUNTLAND TN
HUNTSVILLE AL
AR
TN
TX
HURLEY WI
HURON OH
SD
HURRICANE WV
HUSTONVILLE KY
HUTCHINSON KS
MN
HUTTIG AR
HUTTO TX
HYANNIS MA
HYATTSVILLE MD
HYDE PARK IL
MA
HYDE PARK VT
HYDRO OK
HYNDMAN PA
HYNES CA
IAEGER WV
IDA GROVE IA
IDABEL OK
IDAHO FALLS ID
IDAHO SPRINGS CO
ILION NY
IMOGENE IA
IMPERIAL CA
NE
INDEPENDENCE IA
KS
MO
OR
VA
INDIANA PA
INDIANAPOLIS IN
INDIANOLA IA
NE
INGLEWOOD CA
INTERCOURSE PA
INTERLAKEN NY
INTERNATIONAL
FALLS MN
INWOOD IA
NY
IOLA KS
IONA MN
IONIA MI
IOWA CITY IA
IOWA FALLS IA
IOWA PARK TX
IPSWICH MA
IRASBURG VT
IRETON IA
IRON MOUNTAIN MI
IRON RIVER MI
IRONTON MN
OH
IRONWOOD MI
IRVING IL
IRVING PARK IL
IRVINGTON NJ
NY
VA
IRVONA PA
IRWIN PA
ISANTI MN

ISHPEMING MI
ISLAND CITY OR
ISLAND POND VT
ISLIP NY
ISMAY MT
ITALY TX
ITASCA TX
ITHACA MI
NY
ITTA BENA MS
IUKA MS
IVANHOE MN
IVESDALE IL
JACKSBORO TX
JACKSON AL
GA
KY
MI
MN
MO
MS
OH
TN
JACKSON CENTER OH
JACKSONVILLE AL
FL
IL
TX
JAMAICA NY
VT
JAMESBURG NJ
JAMESPORT MO
JAMESTOWN CA
ND
NY
JANESVILLE WI
JASONVILLE IN
JASPER AL
FL
MN
MO
TX
JAYTON TX
JEANERETTE LA
JEANETTE PA
JEFFERSON GA
IA
NC
OH
PA
TX
WI
JEFFERSON CITY MO
TN
JEFFERSON PARK IL
JEFFERSONVILLE IN
NY
JELLICO TN
JENKINS KY
JENKINTOWN PA
JENNINGS LA
JERMYN PA
JEROME ID
PA
JERSEY CITY NJ
JERSEY SHORE PA
JERSEYVILLE IL
JESSUP PA
JESUP IA
JETMORE KS
JEWELL IA
JEWELL CITY KS
JEWETT OH
JEWETT CITY CT
JOHNSON NE
JOHNSON CITY TN
JOHNSONBURG PA
JOHNSTON CITY IL
JOHNSTOWN CO
NY
PA
JOLIET IL
JONESBORO AR
IL
TN
JONESVILLE VA
JOPLIN MO
JORDAN MN
NY
JOSEPH OR
JUDSONIA AR
JULESBURG CO
JUNCTION CITY KS
OR

JUNEAU AK
JUNIATA PA
KAHULUI HI
KALAMAZOO MI
KALIDA OH
KALISPELL MT
KANAWHA IA
KANE PA
KANKAKEE IL
KANORADO KS
KANSAS IL
OH
KANSAS CITY KS
MO
KARNES CITY TX
KASSON MN
KAUFMAN TX
KAUKAUNA WI
KAW CITY OK
KEANSBURG NJ
KEARNEY NE
KEARNY NJ
KEENE NH
KEESEVILLE NY
KEEWATIN MN
KEITHSBURG IL
KELLOGG ID
KELSO WA
KEMMERER WY
KEMP TX
KENBRIDGE VA
KENDALLVILLE IN
KENDRICK ID
KENEDY TX
KENEFIC OK
KENMARE ND
KENMORE NY
KENNEBEC SD
KENNEBUNK ME
KENNETT SQUARE PA
KENNEWICK WA
KENOSHA WI
KENOVA WV
KENSAL ND
KENSINGTON KS
KENT OH
WA
KENTON OH
TN
KEOKUK IA
KEOTA OK
KERENS TX
KERKHOVEN MN
KERMAN CA
KETCHIKAN AK
KETCHUM ID
KEWANEE IL
KEWANNA IN
KEY WEST FL
KEYPORT NJ
KEYSER WV
KEYSTONE WV
KEZAR FALLS ME
KIEFER OK
KIESTER MN
KILGORE TX
KILLEEN TX
KILLINGLY CT
KIMBALL NE
WV
KIMBALLTON IA
KINDERHOOK NY
KING CITY MO
KINGFISHER OK
KINGMAN KS
KINGS MOUNTAIN NC
KINGS PARK NY
KINGSBURG CA
KINGSBURY TX
KINGSLEY IA
KINGSPORT TN
KINGSTON NY
OH
OK
PA
RI
TN
KINGSVILLE TX
KINGWOOD WV
KINMUNDY IL
KINSLEY KS
KINSMAN OH
KINSTON NC
KIOWA KS

KIOWA OK
KIRKLIN IN
KIRKSVILLE MO
KIRKWOOD IL
KIRWIN KS
KITTANNING PA
KITZMILLERVILLE MD
KLAMATH FALLS OR
KLEMME IA
KNIGHTSTOWN IN
KNOB NOSTER MO
KNOX IN
ND
KNOX CITY TX
KNOXVILLE IA
IL
PA
TN
KOKOMO IN
KONAWA OK
KOPPEL PA
KOSSE TX
KRAMER ND
KRUM TX
KULM ND
KUTZTOWN PA
L'ANSE MI
L'ANSE CREUSE MI
LA COSTE TX
LA CROSSE KS
WI
LA FARGEVILLE NY
LA FAYETTE GA
LA FERIA TX
LA FOLLETTE TN
LA GRANDE OR
LA GRANGE GA
TX
LA HABRA CA
LA HARPE IL
KS
LA JARA CO
LA JUNTA CO
LA MOURE ND
LA PLATA MD
LA PORTE IN
LA RUE OH
LA VERNE CA
LACEYVILLE PA
LACKAWANNA NY
LACON IL
LACONA NY
LACONIA NH
TX
LADYSMITH WI
LAFAYETTE CO
IN
LA
LAGRANGE IN
MO
LAHAINA HI
LAHOMA OK
LAKE IL
LAKE ARIEL PA
LAKE ARTHUR LA
NM
LAKE BENTON MN
LAKE CHARLES LA
LAKE CITY CO
FL
IA
MN
SC
LAKE CRYSTAL MN
LAKE FOREST IL
LAKE GENEVA WI
LAKE GEORGE NY
LAKE HAMILTON FL
LAKE LINDEN MI
LAKE MILLS IA
LAKE NORDEN SD
LAKE PARK MN
LAKE PRESTON SD
LAKE PROVIDENCE LA
LAKE RONKONKOMA NY
LAKE VILLAGE AR
LAKE WILSON MN
LAKE WORTH FL
LAKEFIELD MN
LAKEHURST NJ
LAKELAND FL
LAKEPORT NH
LAKEVIEW OR
TX

LAKEWOOD NJ
NM
OH
LAKOTA ND
LAMAR AR
CO
MO
SC
LAMBERTON MN
LAMBERTVILLE NJ
LAMESA TX
LAMONT OK
LAMPASAS TX
LANARK IL
LANCASTER KY
MA
MN
MO
NH
NY
OH
PA
SC
TX
WI
LANDER WY
LANDISVILLE PA
LANESBORO MN
LANGDON ND
LANGHORNE PA
LANSDALE PA
LANSDOWNE PA
LANSFORD ND
PA
LANSING IA
MI
LANSINGBURGH NY
LAPEER MI
LAPORTE PA
LAPORTE CITY IA
LARAMIE WY
LARAMIE CITY WY
LARCHMONT NY
LAREDO TX
LARIMORE ND
LARNED KS
LAS ANIMAS CO
LAS CRUCES NM
LAS VEGAS NM
LASALLE IL
LATHROP MO
LATON CA
LATONIA KY
LATROBE PA
LAUREL DE
MD
MS
MT
NE
LAUREL SPRINGS NJ
LAURENS IA
SC
LAURINBURG NC
LAURIUM MI
LAVONIA GA
LAWLER IA
LAWRENCE KS
MA
NE
LAWRENCEBURG IN
KY
TN
LAWRENCEBURGH IN
LAWRENCEVILLE GA
IL
PA
VA
LAWTON MI
OK
LAYTON UT
LE MARS IA
LE ROY KS
MN
NY
LE SUEUR MN
LE SUEUR CENTER MN
LEAD SD
LEADVILLE CO
LEAKSVILLE NC
LEAVENWORTH KS
LEBANON IN
KS
KY
NH
LEBANON OH
OR
PA
TN
VA
LEE MA
LEECHBURG PA
LEEDS AL
MO
ND
LEESBURG FL
OK
VA
LEESPORT PA
LEESVILLE LA
SC
LEETONIA OH
LEGER OK
LEHIGH IA
OK
LEHIGHTON PA
LEICESTER MA
LEIGH NE
LEIPSIC OH
LEITCHFIELD KY
LELAND IL
LEMASTERS PA
LEMMON SD
LEMOORE CA
LEMOYNE PA
LENAPAH OK
LENOIR NC
LENOIR CITY TN
LENOX IA
MA
LEOMINSTER MA
LEON IA
LEONARD TX
LEONARDSVILLE NY
LEONARDTOWN MD
LEONIA NJ
LEOTI CITY KS
LERAYSVILLE PA
LERNA IL
LEROY IL
LESLIE AR
MI
LESTERSHIRE NY
LETCHER SD
LEWES DE
LEWIS KS
LEWISBURG PA
TN
LEWISTON ID
ME
LEWISTOWN IL
MT
PA
LEWISVILLE AR
IN
OH
TX
LEXINGTON IL
KY
NC
NE
OK
SC
TN
VA
LIBBY MT
LIBERAL KS
MO
LIBERTY IN
MO
NE
NY
PA
LIBERTYVILLE IL
LIDGERWOOD ND
LIGONIER PA
LILLINGTON NC
LILLY PA
LIMA IN
MT
OH
LIME SPRINGS IA
LIMERICK ME
LIMON CO
LINCOLN AL
AR
IL
KS
NE
PA
LINCOLN PARK MI
LINCOLNTON NC
LIND WA
LINDALE TX
LINDEN AL
NJ
TN
TX
LINDENHURST NY
LINDSAY CA
OK
LINDSBORG KS
LINEVILLE AL
IA
LINN CREEK MO
LINN GROVE IA
LINNTON OR
LINTON IN
ND
LIPAN TX
LISBON IA
ND
NY
LISLE NY
LITCHFIELD CT
IL
MN
NE
LITCHVILLE ND
LITITZ PA
LITTLE FALLS MN
NJ
NY
LITTLE FERRY NJ
LITTLE ROCK AR
IA
LITTLE YORK IL
LITTLEFORK MN
LITTLESTOWN PA
LITTLETON CO
NH
LIVE OAK FL
LIVERMORE CA
LIVERPOOL PA
LIVINGSTON IL
MT
NJ
TX
LIVINGSTON MANOR NY
LIVONIA NY
LLANO TX
LOCK HAVEN PA
LOCKHART TX
LOCKLAND OH
LOCKNEY TX
LOCKPORT IL
NY
LODGEPOLE NE
LODI CA
NJ
OH
LOGAN IA
KS
OH
UT
WV
LOGANSPORT IN
LOGANTON PA
LOMA LINDA CA
LOMETA TX
LONACONING MD
LONDON KY
OH
LONE OAK TX
LONE WOLF OK
LONG BEACH CA
NY
LONG BRANCH NJ
LONG ISLAND CITY NY
LONG PRAIRIE MN
LONGMONT CO
LONGTON KS
LONGVIEW TX
WA
LOOGOOTEE IN
LOOMIS NE
LORAIN OH
LORDSBURG CA
NM
LORENA TX
LORIMOR IA
LOS ALTOS CA
LOS ANGELES CA
LOS BANOS CA
LOS GATOS CA
LOST NATION IA
LOTT TX
LOUDON TN
LOUDONVILLE OH
LOUISA KY
VA
LOUISBURG KS
NC
LOUISIANA MO
LOUISVILLE GA
KY
OH
LOUP CITY NE
LOVELADY TX
LOVELAND CO
OH
LOVELL WY
LOVELOCK NV
LOVINGSTON VA
LOVINGTON IL
LOWELL IN
MA
MI
OH
LOWVILLE NY
LOYSVILLE PA
LUBBOCK TX
LUCAS KS
LUDINGTON MI
LUDLOW KY
MO
LUFKIN TX
LULING TX
LUMBERTON MS
NC
LURAY KS
VA
LUSK WY
LUTHER OK
LUVERNE AL
MN
LUXEMBURG MO
LUZERNE PA
LYKENS PA
LYLE MN
LYNBROOK NY
LYNCH NE
LYNCHBURG OH
VA
LYNDEN WA
LYNDHURST NJ
LYNDON KS
VT
LYNDONVILLE VT
LYNDORA PA
LYNN MA
LYNNVILLE IN
TN
LYONS GA
IA
KS
MI
NE
NY
LYONS FALLS NY
MABANK TX
MABEL MN
MABTON WA
MACEDON NY
MACHIAS ME
MACKINAW IL
MACKSBURG IA
MACOMB IL
MACON GA
MO
MADDOCK ND
MADELIA MN
MADERA CA
PA
MADILL OK
MADISON FL
GA
IL
IN
KS
ME
MN
NE
NJ
SD
WI
WV
MADISONVILLE KY
MADISONVILLE OH
TX
MAGDALENA NM
MAHAFFEY PA
MAHANOY CITY PA
MAHNOMEN MN
MAHOPAC NY
MAKOTI ND
MALAD CITY ID
MALAKOFF TX
MALDEN MA
WA
MALONE NY
MALTA IL
MT
OH
MALVERN AR
IA
PA
MAMARONECK NY
MANASQUAN NJ
MANASSAS VA
MANAWA WI
MANCHESTER IA
KY
MO
NH
OH
TN
VA
VT
MANCHESTER
CENTER VT
MANCOS CO
MANDAN ND
MANGUM OK
MANHASSET NY
MANHATTAN IL
KS
MANHEIM PA
MANILLA IA
MANISTEE MI
MANISTIQUE MI
MANITOWOC WI
MANKATO KS
MN
MANLIUS IL
MANNING IA
SC
MANNINGTON WV
MANNSVILLE OK
MANOR PA
TX
MANSFIELD AR
IL
LA
MA
OH
PA
TX
MANTUA OH
MANVILLE WY
MAPLETON MN
PA
MAPLEWOOD MO
MAQUOKETA IA
MAQUON IL
MARATHON IA
NY
MARBLE MN
MARBLE FALLS TX
MARBLEHEAD MA
MARCELINE MO
MARCELLUS NY
MARCUS IA
MARENGO IA
IL
MARFA TX
MARGARETVILLE NY
MARIANNA FL
MARICOPA CA
MARIENVILLE PA
MARIETTA GA
OH
OK
PA
MARINE IL
MARINE CITY MI
MARINER HARBOR NY
MARINETTE WI
MARION IA
IL
IN
KS
MARION NC
ND
NY
OH
SC
VA
WI
MARION CENTER PA
MARISSA IL
MARKED TREE AR
MARLBORO MA
NY
MARLBOROUGH MA
MARLIN TX
MARLINTON WV
MARLOW OK
MARMARTH ND
MARQUETTE MI
NE
MARS PA
MARSEILLES IL
MARSHALL AR
IL
MI
MN
MO
TX
VA
MARSHALLTOWN IA
MARSHFIELD MO
OR
WI
MART TX
MARTIN TN
MARTINEZ CA
MARTINSBURG PA
WV
MARTINSVILLE IL
IN
VA
MARYSVILLE CA
KS
PA
MARYVILLE MO
TN
MASCOUTAH IL
MASON MI
OH
TX
MASON CITY IA
IL
MASONTOWN PA
MASSENA NY
MASSILLON OH
MATADOR TX
MATAWAN NJ
MATEWAN WV
MATOAKA WV
MATTEAWAN NY
MATTHEWS IN
MATTITUCK NY
MATTOON IL
MAUCH CHUNK PA
MAUD OK
TX
MAY TX
MAYBROOK NY
MAYETTA KS
MAYFIELD KY
MAYS IN
MAYS LANDING NJ
MAYSVILLE GA
KY
OK
MAYTOWN PA
MAYVILLE ND
WI
MAZON IL
MEADE KS
MEADE CENTER KS
MEADVILLE PA
MEBANE NC
MECHANICSBURG OH
PA
MECHANICSVILLE MD
NY
MEDARYVILLE IN
MEDFORD MA
NJ
OK
OR
WI
MEDIA PA
MEDICAL LAKE WA
MEDICINE LODGE KS
MEDINA NY
OH
MEEKER CO
MEETEETSE WY
MELISSA TX
MELROSE MA
MN
NM
MELVIN IA
MEMPHIS MO
TN
TX
MENA AR
MENAHGA MN
MENARD TX
MENASHA WI
MENDON OH
MENDOTA IL
MENOMINEE MI
WI
MENTONE IN
MERCED CA
MERCEDES TX
MERCER PA
MERCERSBURG PA
MERCHANTVILLE NJ
MERIDEN CT
MERIDIAN ID
MS
TX
MERIT TX
MERKEL TX
MERRICK NY
MERRILL OR
WI
MERRIMAC MA
MERTZON TX
MESA AZ
MESHOPPEN PA
MESQUITE TX
METCALF IL
METHUEN MA
METROPOLIS IL
METUCHEN NJ
MEXIA TX
MEXICO MO
NY
MEYERSDALE PA
MIAMI FL
OK
MIAMI BEACH FL
MIAMISBURG OH
MICHIGAN CITY IN
MIDDLEBOROUGH MA
MIDDLEBOURNE WV
MIDDLEBURGH NY
PA
MIDDLEBURY VT
MIDDLEPORT NY
OH
MIDDLESBOROUGH KY
MIDDLETOWN CT
DE
IL
NY
OH
PA
MIDDLETOWN
SPRINGS VT
MIDDLEVILLE NY
MIDLAND MD
PA
SD
TX
MIDLAND CITY AL
MIDLOTHIAN TX
MIDWAY PA
MIFFLIN PA
MIFFLINBURG PA
MIFFLINTOWN PA
MILACA MN
MILAN MO
MILBANK SD
MILBURN OK
MILDRED PA
MILES TX
MILES CITY MT

MILFORD DE
IA
IL
MA
MI
NH
NJ
NY
OH
PA
MILL CREEK OK
MILLBROOK KS
MILLBURN NJ
MILLBURY MA
MILLEDGEVILLE GA
MILLEN GA
MILLER SD
MILLERSBURG OH
PA
MILLERSTOWN PA
MILLERSVILLE PA
MILLERTON NY
MILLHEIM PA
MILLINGTON MI
MILLSAP TX
MILLSBORO PA
MILLSTADT IL
MILLTOWN IN
NJ
MILLVILLE NJ
PA
MILNOR ND
MILROY IN
MILTON FL
IA
MA
ND
OR
PA
WV
MILWAUKEE WI
MINATARE NE
MINCO OK
MINDEN LA
NE
MINEOLA NY
TX
MINERAL POINT WI
MINERAL WELLS TX
MINERSVILLE PA
MINERVA OH
MINGO JUNCTION OH
MINNEAPOLIS KS
MN
MINNEOTA MN
MINNESOTA LAKE MN
MINNEWAUKAN ND
MINOA NY
MINONK IL
MINOOKA IL
MINOT ND
MINOTOLA NJ
MISHAWAKA IN
MISSION TX
MISSOULA MT
MISSOURI VALLEY IA
MITCHELL IN
NE
SD
MOAB UT
MOBERLY MO
MOBILE AL
MOBRIDGE SD
MOCANAQUA PA
MODESTO CA
MOHALL ND
MOHAWK NY
MOHNTON PA
MOLALLA OR
MOLINE IL
KS
MOMENCE IL
MONACA PA
MONDOVI WI
MONESSEN PA
MONETT MO
MONMOUTH IL
OR
MONONGAH WV
MONONGAHELA
CITY PA
MONROE IA
LA
MI
MONROE NC
NY
OH
WA
WI
MONROEVILLE AL
OH
MONROVIA CA
IN
MD
MONSON MA
MONTAGUE TX
MONTCLAIR NJ
MONTE VISTA CO
MONTEREY CA
IN
VA
MONTEREY PARK CA
MONTESANO WA
MONTEVIDEO MN
MONTEZUMA GA
IA
IN
MONTGOMERY AL
IN
MN
NY
PA
WV
MONTICELLO GA
IA
IL
IN
KY
NY
MONTOUR IA
MONTOUR FALLS NY
MONTOURSVILLE PA
MONTPELIER ID
IN
OH
VT
MONTROSE CO
PA
MOODY TX
MOORE MT
OK
TX
MOOREFIELD WV
MOORESTOWN NJ
MOORESVILLE IN
NC
MOORHEAD MN
MOOSE LAKE MN
MOOSUP CT
MORA MN
MORAVIA NY
MOREHEAD KY
MORENCI MI
MORGAN TX
UT
MORGAN CITY LA
MORGANFIELD KY
MORGANTON NC
MORGANTOWN IN
WV
MORRILL NE
MORRILTON AR
MORRIS IL
MN
NY
OK
MORRISON IL
TN
MORRISONVILLE IL
MORRISTOWN NJ
NY
SD
TN
MORRISVILLE NY
MORROW OH
MOSCOW ID
PA
MOSS POINT MS
MOTLEY MN
MOTORDALE MN
MOTT ND
MOULTON IA
TX
MOULTRIE GA
MOUND CITY IL
MOUND VALLEY KS
MOUNDS IL
OK
MOUNDSVILLE WV
MOUNT AIRY MD
NC
MOUNT AUBURN IL
MOUNT CALM TX
MOUNT CARMEL IL
PA
MOUNT CARROLL IL
MOUNT CLEMENS MI
MOUNT GILEAD OH
MOUNT HEALTHY OH
MOUNT HOLLY NJ
MOUNT HOLLY
SPRINGS PA
MOUNT HOPE KS
WV
MOUNT JACKSON VA
MOUNT JEWETT PA
MOUNT JOY PA
MOUNT KISCO NY
MOUNT MORRIS NY
PA
MOUNT OLIVE IL
NC
MOUNT ORAB OH
MOUNT PLEASANT IA
MI
OH
PA
TN
TX
MOUNT PROSPECT IL
MOUNT PULASKI IL
MOUNT RANIER MD
MOUNT SAVAGE MD
MOUNT STERLING IL
KY
OH
MOUNT UNION PA
MOUNT VERNON IL
IN
MO
NY
OH
SD
TX
WA
MOUNT
WASHINGTON OH
MOUNT WOLF PA
MOUNTAIN GROVE MO
MOUNTAIN HOME ID
MOUNTAIN LAKE MN
MOUNTAIN VIEW CA
OK
MOUNTVILLE PA
MOWEAQUA IL
MUIR MI
MULBERRY IN
MULBERRY GROVE IL
MULDROW OK
MULHALL OK
MULLAN ID
MULLICA HILL NJ
MULLINS SC
MUNCIE IN
MUNCY PA
MUNDAY TX
MUNFORDVILLE KY
MUNHALL PA
MUNICH ND
MUNISING MI
MURFREESBORO NC
TN
MURPHY NC
MURPHYSBORO IL
MURRAY KY
UT
MUSCATINE IA
MUSCOGEE OK
MUSKEGON MI
MUSKOGEE OK
MYERSTOWN PA
MYLO ND
MYSTIC CT
MYSTIC BRIDGE CT
MYSTIC RIVER CT
MYTON UT
McADOO PA
McALESTER OK
McALISTERVILLE PA
McARTHUR OH
McCLOUD CA
McCLURE PA
McCLUSKY ND
McCOMB CITY MS
McCONNELLSBURG PA
McCONNELSVILLE OH
McCOOK NE
McCUMBER ND
McCUNE KS
McDONALD PA
McDONOUGH GA
McFARLAND CA
McGHEE AR
McGILL NV
McGREGOR IA
TX
McHENRY ND
McINTOSH MN
SD
McKEES ROCKS PA
McKEESPORT PA
McKINNEY TX
McLEAN TX
McLEANSBORO IL
McLOUD OK
McMINNVILLE OR
TN
McPHERSON KS
McVEYTOWN PA
McVILLE ND
NACOGDOCHES TX
NAMPA ID
NANTICOKE PA
NANTUCKET MA
NANUET NY
NAPA CA
NAPER NE
NAPERVILLE IL
NAPLES TX
NAPOLEON ND
OH
NAPPANEE IN
NARA VISA NM
NARROWS VA
NARROWSBURG NY
NASH OK
NASHUA IA
NH
NASHVILLE AR
GA
IL
TN
NASHWAUK MN
NATCHEZ MS
NATICK MA
NATIONAL CITY CA
IL
NATOMA KS
NATRONA PA
NAUGATUCK CT
NAUVOO IL
NAVASOTA TX
NAZARETH PA
NEBO IL
NEBRASKA CITY NE
NECHE ND
NEDERLAND TX
NEEDLES CA
NEENAH WI
NEFFS OH
PA
NEGAUNEE MI
NEIHART MT
NEILLSVILLE WI
NELIGH NE
NELSON NE
NEODESHA KS
NEOGA IL
NEOSHO MO
NEPHI UT
NESCOPECK PA
NESQUEHONING PA
NESS CITY KS
NETCONG NJ
NEVADA IA
MO
TX
NEW ALBANY IN
MS
PA
NEW ALEXANDRIA PA
NEW BEDFORD MA
NEW BERLIN NY
PA
NEW BERN NC
NEW BERNE NC
NEW BETHLEHEM PA
NEW BLOOMFIELD PA
NEW BOSTON TX
NEW BRAUNFELS TX
NEW BREMEN OH
NEW BRIGHTON MN
NY
PA
NEW BRITAIN CT
NEW BROCKTON AL
NEW BRUNSWICK GA
NJ
NEW CANAAN CT
NEW CARLISLE IN
OH
NEW CASTLE IN
KY
ME
PA
VA
NEW CONCORD OH
NEW CUMBERLAND PA
WV
NEW DECATUR AL
NEW DOUGLAS IL
NEW DULUTH MN
NEW EGYPT NJ
NEW ENGLAND ND
NEW FLORENCE PA
NEW FREEDOM PA
NEW GERMANY MN
NEW HAMPTON IA
NEW HARMONY IN
NEW HARTFORD NY
NEW HAVEN CT
IL
PA
NEW HOLLAND OH
PA
NEW HOPE PA
NEW IBERIA LA
NEW KENSINGTON PA
NEW LEXINGTON OH
NEW LISBON OH
NEW LONDON CT
IA
OH
WI
NEW MARKET NH
VA
NEW MARTINSVILLE WV
NEW MATAMORAS OH
NEW MILFORD CT
PA
NEW ORLEANS LA
NEW PALTZ NY
NEW PARIS OH
NEW PHILADELPHIA OH
NEW POINT IN
NEW PRAGUE MN
NEW RICHMOND OH
WI
NEW ROADS LA
NEW ROCHELLE NY
NEW ROCKFORD ND
NEW SALEM ND
PA
NEW SHARON IA
NEW TACOMA WA
NEW TRIPOLI PA
NEW ULM MN
NEW VIENNA OH
NEW WHATCOM WA
NEW WILMINGTON PA
NEW WILSON OK
NEW WINDSOR MD
NEW YORK NY
NEW YORK CITY NY
NEWARK AR
DE
NJ
NY
OH
NEWARK VALLEY NY
NEWBERG OR
NEWBERRY SC
NEWBURG WV
NEWBURGH NY
NEWBURYPORT MA
NEWCASTLE TX
WY
NEWCOMERSTOWN OH
NEWDALE ID
NEWELL IA
NEWFOUNDLAND PA
NEWKIRK OK
NEWMAN CA
IL
NEWMAN GROVE NE
NEWNAN GA
NEWPORT AR
DE
IN
KY
NH
NY
PA
RI
TN
VT
WA
NEWPORT NEWS VA
NEWSOME TX
NEWTON IA
IL
KS
MA
NC
NJ
NEWTON FALLS OH
NEWTONVILLE MA
NEWTOWN PA
NEWVILLE AL
PA
NEZPERCE ID
NIAGARA WI
NIAGARA FALLS NY
NICHOLASVILLE KY
NICHOLS NY
NICHOLSON PA
NILES MI
OH
NIXON TX
NOBLE IL
OK
NOBLESVILLE IN
NOCONA TX
NOGALES AZ
NOKOMIS IL
NOME ND
NORA SPRINGS IA
NORCATUR KS
NORCO LA
NORFOLK NE
VA
NORMAL IL
NORMAN OK
NORMANGEE TX
NORRIS CITY IL
NORRISTOWN PA
NORTH ADAMS MA
NORTH ARLINGTON NJ
NORTH
ATTLEBOROUGH MA
NORTH AUBURN NE
NORTH BALTIMORE OH
NORTH BELLE
VERNON PA
NORTH BEND NE
OR
NORTH BENNINGTON VT
NORTH BERGEN NJ
NORTH BERWICK ME
NORTH CREEK NY
NORTH EAST MD
PA
NORTH EASTON MA
NORTH
FORT WORTH TX
NORTH GIRARD PA
NORTH GRANVILLE NY
NORTH
KANSAS CITY MO
NORTH MANCHESTER IN
NORTH
MERCHANTVILLE NJ
NORTH PLAINFIELD NJ
NORTH PLATTE NE
NORTH PROVIDENCE RI
NORTH ROSE NY
NORTH TONAWANDA NY
NORTH VERNON IN
NORTH WALES PA
NORTH
WHITE CREEK NY
NORTH YAKIMA WA
NORTHAMPTON MA
PA
NORTHBORO IA
NORTHBOROUGH MA
NORTHFIELD MN
VT
NORTHFORK WV
NORTHPORT NY
NORTHUMBERLAND PA
NORTHWOOD IA
ND
NORTON KS
VA
NORTONVILLE KS
NORWALK CT
OH
NORWAY IA
ME
MI
SC
NORWICH CT
NY
NORWOOD MA
OH
NOWATA OK
NUMIDIA PA
NUNDA NY
NUREMBURG PA
NUTLEY NJ
NYACK NY
O'FALLON IL
O'KEENE OK
O'NEILL NE
OAK HARBOR OH
OAK HILL WV
OAK PARK IL
OAKDALE CA
NE
PA
OAKES ND
OAKESDALE WA
OAKFORD IL
OAKLAND CA
IL
MD
ME
NE
OK
OAKLAND CITY IN
OAKLEY KS
OAKLYN NJ
OAKMONT PA
OAKVILLE TX
OBERLIN KS
OH
OBLONG IL
OCALA FL
OCEAN CITY NJ
OCEAN GROVE NJ
OCEAN PARK CA
OCEANSIDE CA
OCHILTREE TX
OCILLA GA
OCONOMOWOC WI
OCONTO WI
ODEBOLT IA
ODELL IL
ODESSA DE
MO
NY
TX
WA
ODIN IL
ODON IN
OELWEIN IA
OGALALLA NE
OGDEN IL
UT
OGDENSBURG NY
OIL CITY PA
OKANOGAN WA
OKAWVILLE IL
OKEANA OH
OKEMAH OK
OKLAHOMA CITY OK
OKMULGEE OK
OKOLONA MS
OKTAHA OK
OLANTA SC
OLATHE CO
KS
OLD FORGE NY
OLDHAM SD
OLEAN NY
OLEY PA
OLIN IA
OLIVE CA

ROCKFORD - STRAWBERRY POINT

ROCKFORD IA
IL
ROCKLAND MA
ME
MI
ROCKMART GA
ROCKPORT IN
MA
TX
ROCKVILLE CT
IN
MD
ROCKVILLE CENTRE NY
ROCKWALL TX
ROCKWELL IA
ROCKWELL CITY IA
ROCKWOOD PA
TN
ROCKY FORD CO
ROCKY MOUNT NC
VA
ROCKY RIVER OH
RODEO CA
ROEBLING NJ
ROFF OK
ROGERS AR
TX
ROGERS PARK IL
ROGERSVILLE TN
ROLAND IA
ROLETTE ND
ROLFE IA
ROLLA MO
ND
ROME GA
NY
PA
ROMEO MI
ROMNEY WV
ROMULUS NY
RONAN MT
RONCEVERTE WV
RONDOUT NY
ROODHOUSE IL
ROOSEVELT NJ
NY
ROSALIA WA
ROSCOE NY
PA
ROSEAU MN
ROSEBUD MT
TX
ROSEBURG OR
ROSEDALE IN
MS
ROSELLE NJ
ROSEMOUNT MN
ROSEVILLE CA
IL
OH
ROSLYN NY
ROSSLYN VA
ROSSVILLE IL
ROSWELL NM
ROTAN TX
ROUND HILL VA
ROUNDUP MT
ROUSES POINT NY
ROWLESBURG WV
ROXBURY NY
ROXTON TX
ROY MT
ROYAL IA
ROYAL OAK MI
ROYALTON MN
VT
ROYERSFORD PA
ROYSE CITY TX
RUGBY ND
RULE TX
RULO NE
RUMFORD ME
RUNGE TX
RUPERT ID
RURAL RETREAT VA
RURAL VALLEY PA
RUSH CITY MN
RUSH SPRINGS OK
RUSHFORD MN
RUSHMORE MN
RUSHVILLE IL
IN
NE
RUSK TX

RUSSELL KS
KY
RUSSELL SPRINGS KS
KY
RUSSELLTON PA
RUSSELLVILLE AL
AR
KY
TN
RUSSIAVILLE IN
RUSTON LA
RUTHERFORD NJ
RUTHTON MN
RUTHVEN IA
RUTLAND VT
RYAN OK
RYDER ND
RYE NY
SABETHA KS
SABINA OH
SABINAL TX
SAC CITY IA
SACO ME
MT
SACRAMENTO CA
SAEGERTOWN PA
SAGINAW MI
SAGUACHE CO
SAINT ALBANS VT
WV
SAINT ANNE IL
SAINT ANSGAR IA
SAINT ANTHONY ID
MN
SAINT AUGUSTINE FL
SAINT CHARLES IL
MN
MO
SAINT CLAIR MI
SAINT CLAIR
HEIGHTS MI
SAINT CLAIR SHORES MI
SAINT CLAIRSVILLE OH
SAINT CLOUD FL
MN
SAINT CROIX FALLS WI
SAINT EDWARD NE
SAINT ELMO IL
SAINT FRANCISVILLE IL
SAINT HELENA CA
SAINT HELENS OR
SAINT IGNACE MI
SAINT JAMES MN
NE
SAINT JO TX
SAINT JOHN KS
SAINT JOHNS MI
OR
SAINT JOHNSBURY VT
SAINT JOHNSVILLE NY
SAINT JOSEPH MI
MO
SAINT LAWRENCE SD
SAINT LOUIS MI
MO
SAINT MARIES ID
SAINT MARYS KS
OH
PA
WV
SAINT MATTHEWS SC
SAINT MICHAEL PA
SAINT PARIS OH
SAINT PAUL MN
NE
VA
SAINT PETER IL
MN
SAINT PETERSBURG FL
SAINT REGIS FALLS NY
SAINT THOMAS ND
SALAMANCA NY
SALEM IL
IN
MA
MO
NC
NJ
NY
OH
OR
SD
VA
WV

SALIDA CA
CO
SALINA KS
SALINAS CA
SALISBURY MA
MD
MO
NC
PA
SALLISAW OK
SALMON ID
SALT LAKE CITY UT
SALTSBURG PA
SALTVILLE VA
SALYERSVILLE KY
SAMSON AL
SAN ANGELO TX
SAN ANTONIO TX
SAN AUGUSTINE TX
SAN BERNARDINO CA
SAN DIEGO CA
SAN DIMAS CA
SAN FERNANDO CA
SAN FRANCISCO CA
SAN JACINTO CA
SAN JOAQUIN CA
SAN JOSE CA
SAN JUAN PR
SAN LEANDRO CA
SAN LUIS OBISPO CA
SAN MARCOS TX
SAN MARINO CA
SAN MATEO CA
SAN PEDRO CA
SAN RAFAEL CA
SAN SABA TX
SANBORN IA
ND
SANBORNTON NH
SAND SPRINGS OK
SANDERSVILLE GA
SANDOVAL IL
SANDPOINT ID
SANDSTONE MN
SANDUSKY OH
SANDWICH NH
SANDY HILL NY
SANDY SPRING MD
SANFORD FL
ME
NC
SANGER CA
TX
SANTA ANA CA
TX
SANTA BARBARA CA
SANTA CRUZ CA
SANTA FE NM
SANTA MARIA CA
SANTA MONICA CA
SANTA PAULA CA
SANTA ROSA CA
NM
SANTO TX
SAPULPA OK
SARANAC LAKE NY
SARASOTA FL
SARATOGA WY
SARATOGA SPRINGS NY
SARCOXIE MO
SARDINIA OH
SARDIS OH
SARGENT NE
SASAKWA OK
SAUGERTIES NY
SAUK CENTRE MN
SAULT STE MARIE MI
SAUSALITO CA
SAVANNA IL
SAVANNAH GA
MO
TN
SAVONA NY
SAVOY TX
SAXTON PA
SAYRE OK
PA
SAYVILLE NY
SCANDIA KS
SCAPPOOSE OR
SCARSDALE NY
SCENERY HILL PA
SCHAEFFERSTOWN PA
SCHELLBURG PA

SCHELLSBURG PA
SCHENECTADY NY
SCHENEVUS NY
SCHOHARIE NY
SCHOOLCRAFT MI
SCHULENBURG TX
SCHUYLER NE
SCHUYLERVILLE NY
SCHUYLKILL HAVEN PA
SCHWENKSVILLE PA
SCHWERTNER TX
SCIO OH
SCITUATE RI
SCOBEY MT
SCOTIA CA
SCOTLAND SD
SCOTT CITY KS
SCOTTDALE PA
SCOTTSBLUFF NE
SCOTTSBORO AL
SCOTTSVILLE KY
VA
SCRANTON ND
PA
SCRIBNER NE
SEA BRIGHT NJ
SEA ISLE CITY NJ
SEABRIGHT NJ
SEAFORD DE
SEALY TX
SEARSPORT ME
SEATTLE WA
SEBASTOPOL CA
SEBREE KY
SECAUCUS NJ
SECOR IL
SEDALIA MO
SEDAN KS
SEDGWICK CO
SEDRO-WOOLLEY WA
SEELEY CA
SEGUIN TX
SEHOME WA
SEILING OK
SELBY SD
SELBYVILLE DE
SELINS GROVE PA
SELINSGROVE PA
SELLERSVILLE PA
SELMA AL
CA
NC
SELMER TN
SEMINOLE OK
TX
SENECA IL
KS
MO
SENECA FALLS NY
SENECAVILLE OH
SENOIA GA
SENTINEL OK
SESSER IL
SEVEN MILE OH
SEVEN VALLEYS PA
SEWARD NE
PA
SEWICKLEY PA
SEYMOUR CT
IA
IN
MO
TX
WI
SHAKOPEE MN
SHAMOKIN PA
SHAMROCK TX
SHANNON CITY IA
SHARON ND
PA
SC
SHARON SPRINGS NY
SHARPSVILLE PA
SHATTUCK OK
SHAW MS
SHAWANO WI
SHAWNEE OK
SHAWNEETOWN IL
SHEBOYGAN WI
SHEBOYGAN FALLS WI
SHEFFIELD AL
IA
PA
SHELBINA MO

SHELBURN IN
SHELBURNE FALLS MA
SHELBY NC
NE
OH
SHELBYVILLE IL
IN
TN
SHELDON IA
ND
SHELLEY ID
SHELLMAN GA
SHELTON NE
SHENANDOAH IA
PA
SHERADEN PA
SHERBURN MN
SHERBURNE NY
SHERIDAN IN
OR
WY
SHERMAN TX
SHEYENNE ND
SHICKSHINNY PA
SHINER TX
SHINGLE HOUSE PA
WA
SHINNSTON WV
SHIPPENSBURG PA
SHIPPENSBURGH PA
SHIPPENVILLE PA
SHIRLEY IN
SHOEMAKERSVILLE PA
SHOSHONE ID
SHOSHONI WY
SHREVEPORT LA
SHULLSBURG WI
SIBLEY IA
SIDELL IL
SIDNEY IA
MT
NE
NY
OH
SIEGFRIED PA
SIERRA MADRE CA
SIGOURNEY IA
SILOAM SPRINGS AR
SILVER CITY NM
SILVER CREEK NY
SILVER SPRING MD
SILVER SPRINGS NY
SILVERTON CO
OR
TX
SING SING NY
SIOUX CENTER IA
SIOUX CITY IA
SIOUX FALLS SD
SIOUX RAPIDS IA
SIPESVILLE PA
SISSETON SD
SISTERSVILLE WV
SKANEATELES NY
SKIATOOK OK
SKOWHEGAN ME
SLATERSVILLE RI
SLATINGTON PA
SLAUGHTER WA
SLAYTON MN
SLEEPY EYE MN
SLEEPY EYE LAKE MN
SLIGO PA
SLIPPERY ROCK PA
SLOCOMB AL
SMETHPORT PA
SMITH CENTER KS
SMITH CENTRE KS
SMITHFIELD NC
OH
PA
UT
SMITHTON IL
PA
SMITHTOWN
BRANCH NY
SMITHVILLE TN
TX
SMYRNA DE
TN
SNOHOMISH WA
SNOW HILL MD
NC
SNYDER OK
TX

SOCORRO NM
SODUS NY
SOLDIER ID
SOLDIERS GROVE WI
SOLOMON KS
SOMERFIELD PA
SOMERS NY
SOMERS POINT NJ
SOMERSET KY
OH
PA
SOMERSWORTH NH
SOMERTON OH
SOMERVILLE MA
NJ
OH
SONOMA CA
SONORA CA
TX
SOPER OK
SOUDERTON PA
SOUR LAKE TX
SOUTH AMBOY NJ
SOUTH AUBURN NE
SOUTH BEND IN
WA
SOUTH BERWICK ME
SOUTH BETHLEHEM PA
SOUTH BOSTON VA
SOUTH
CHARLESTON OH
SOUTH
CHARLESTON WV
SOUTH CHICAGO IL
SOUTH DANVERS MA
SOUTH DEERFIELD MA
SOUTH EAST NY
SOUTH FALLSBURG NY
SOUTH FORK PA
SOUTH
FRAMINGHAM MA
SOUTH
GLENS FALLS NY
SOUTH HAVEN MI
SOUTH MCALESTER OK
SOUTH MILWAUKEE WI
SOUTH NORWALK CT
SOUTH OMAHA NE
SOUTH OTSELIC NY
SOUTH PASADENA CA
SOUTH PITTSBURG TN
SOUTH PLAINFIELD NJ
SOUTH PUEBLO CO
SOUTH RIVER NJ
SOUTH SAINT PAUL MN
SOUTH
SAN FRANCISCO CA
SOUTH SHORE SD
SOUTH SIOUX CITY NE
SOUTH WEYMOUTH MA
SOUTH WORCESTER NY
SOUTHAMPTON NY
SOUTHBRIDGE MA
SOUTHINGTON CT
SOUTHPORT CT
SPALDING NE
SPANGLER PA
SPANISH FORK UT
SPARTA GA
IL
TN
WI
SPARTANBURG SC
SPARTANSBURG PA
SPEARFISH SD
SPEARVILLE KS
SPENCER IA
IN
MA
NE
WV
SPIRIT LAKE IA
SPIRO OK
SPOKANE WA
SPOKANE FALLS WA
SPOKOGEE OK
SPRAGUE WA
SPRING CITY PA
TN
SPRING GROVE PA
SPRING LAKE NJ
SPRING MILLS PA
SPRING VALLEY IL
MN

SPRING VALLEY NY
OH
SPRINGDALE AR
PA
SPRINGFIELD IL
KY
MA
MN
MO
OH
OR
SC
SD
TN
VT
SPRINGVALE ME
SPRINGVILLE NY
PA
SPUR TX
SPURGEON IN
STAFFORD KS
STAFFORD SPRINGS CT
STAMFORD CT
NY
TX
STANFORD KY
STANLEY ND
VA
STANTON IA
MI
NE
TX
STANWOOD WA
STAPLES MN
STAPLETON NY
STARBUCK MN
STARKVILLE MS
STARKWEATHER ND
STATE CENTER IA
STATE COLLEGE PA
STATESBORO GA
STATESVILLE NC
STAUNTON IL
VA
STEAMBOAT
SPRINGS CO
STEELE MO
ND
STEELTON PA
STEELVILLE MO
STEPHEN MN
STEPHENVILLE TX
STERLING CO
IL
KS
NE
STERLING CITY TX
STERRETT OK
STEUBENVILLE OH
STEVENS POINT WI
STEVENSON AL
STEVENSVILLE MT
STEWARD IL
STEWARDSON IL
STEWARTSTOWN PA
STEWARTSVILLE MO
STEWARTVILLE MN
STIGLER OK
STILLWATER MN
OK
STILWELL OK
STOCKBRIDGE MA
STOCKPORT OH
STOCKTON CA
IL
KS
STONE KY
STONE LAKE WI
STONEBORO PA
STONEHAM MA
STONEWALL OK
STONINGTON CT
IL
STORM LAKE IA
STORY CITY IA
STOUGHTON WI
STOYSTOWN PA
STRASBURG PA
VA
STRATFORD OK
TX
STRAUSSTOWN PA
STRAWBERRY POINT IA

STRAWN IL
TX
STREATOR IL
STREETER ND
STROMSBURG NE
STRONG CITY KS
STRONGHURST IL
STROUD OK
STROUDSBURG PA
STUART IA
NE
OK
VA
STURGIS KY
MI
SD
STUTTGART AR
SUDAN TX
SUFFERN NY
SUFFIELD CT
SUFFOLK VA
SUGAR CITY CO
SUISUN CA
SULLIVAN IL
IN
SULPHUR OK
SULPHUR SPRINGS TX
SUMMERFIELD OH
SUMMERVILLE PA
SUMMIT MS
NJ
SUMNER IA
IL
SUMPTER OR
SUMTER SC
SUNBURY PA
SUNDANCE WY
SUNMAN IN
SUNNYSIDE WA
SUPERIOR NE
WI
SUSQUEHANNA PA
SUSQUEHANNA
DEPOT PA
SUSSEX NJ
SUTERSVILLE PA
SUTHERLAND IA
SUTTON NE
WV
SWANTON VT
SWANVILLE MN
SWARTHMORE PA
SWAYZEE IN
SWEA CITY IA
SWEDESBORO NJ
SWEET SPRINGS MO
SWEETWATER TN
TX
SWINEFORD PA
SWISSVALE PA
SYCAMORE IL
OH
SYKESVILLE MD
PA
SYLACAUGA AL
SYLVANIA GA
SYLVESTER GA
SYRACUSE KS
NE
NY
TABOR IA
TACOMA WA
TAFT CA
TX
TAHLEQUAH OK
TAHOKA TX
TALIHINA OK
TALLADEGA AL
TALLAHASSEE FL
TALLAPOOSA GA
TALLASSEE AL
TALLULAH LA
TALOGA OK
TAMA IA
TAMA CITY IA
TAMAQUA PA
TAMAROA IL
TAMPA FL
TAMPICO IL
TANNERSVILLE NY
TARBORO NC
TARENTUM PA
TARKIO MO
TARPON SPRINGS FL
TARRYTOWN NY
TAUNTON MA
TAYLOR ND
TX
TAYLORVILLE IL
TAZEWELL TN
VA
TEAGUE TX
TECUMSEH MI
NE
OK
TEKAMAH NE
TELFORD PA
TELL CITY IN
TELLURIDE CO
TEMPE AZ
TEMPLE OK
TX
TENAFLY NJ
TENNYSON IN
TERLTON OK
TERRA ALTA WV
TERRA BELLA CA
TERRAL OK
TERRE HAUTE IN
TERRE HILL PA
TERRELL TX
TERRIL IA
TEXARKANA AR
TX
TEXAS CITY TX
TEXHOMA OK
TEXICO NM
THAYER KS
THE DALLES OR
THERESA NY
THERMOPOLIS WY
THIEF RIVER FALLS MN
THOMAS OK
THOMASBORO IL
THOMASTON CT
ME
THOMASVILLE AL
GA
NC
THOMPSON CT
IA
ND
THOMPSONTOWN PA
THOMSON GA
THORNDALE TX
THORNTON IA
TX
THORNTOWN IN
THREE FORKS MT
THREE RIVERS MI
THREE SPRINGS PA
THROCKMORTON TX
THURMOND WV
THURMONT MD
TICONDEROGA NY
TIFFIN OH
TIFTON GA
TIGERTON WI
TILDEN NE
TILLAMOOK OR
TILTON NH
TIMBLIN PA
TIMPSON TX
TIOGA PA
TX
TIONESTA PA
TIPPECANOE CITY OH
TIPTON IA
IN
OK
TISBURY MA
TISHOMINGO OK
TITONKA IA
TITUSVILLE PA
TOBIAS NE
TOCCOA GA
TOLAR TX
TOLEDO IA
IL
OH
TOLLAND CT
TOLLEY ND
TOLUCA IL
TOM BEAN TX
TOMBSTONE AZ
TOMS RIVER NJ
TONASKET WA
TONAWANDA NY
TONKAWA OK
TONOPAH NV
TOPEKA KS
TOPPENISH WA
TOPTON PA
TORONTO KS
OH
SD
TORRANCE CA
TORRINGTON CT
WY
TOTTENVILLE NY
TOWANDA KS
PA
TOWER MN
TOWER CITY ND
PA
TOWNER ND
TOWNSEND MA
MT
TOWSON MD
TOYAH TX
TRACY MN
TRACY CITY TN
TRAER IA
TRAFALGAR IN
TRAFFORD PA
TRAFFORD CITY PA
TRANQUILITY CA
TRAVERSE CITY MI
TREMONT IL
PA
TRENTON IL
MO
NE
NJ
TN
TX
TREVORTON PA
TRINIDAD CO
TRINITY TX
TRIUMPH IL
TROPICO CA
TROUPE TX
TROUTDALE VA
TROUTVILLE VA
TROY AL
KS
NY
OH
PA
TRUMAN MN
TRUMANSBURG NY
TUCKAHOE NJ
NY
TUCSON AZ
TUCUMCARI NM
TULARE CA
TULIA TX
TULLAHOMA TN
TULLY NY
TULSA OK
TUNKHANNOCK PA
TUPELO MS
OK
TUPPER LAKE NY
TURBOTVILLE PA
TURLOCK CA
TURNERS FALLS MA
TURNERSVILLE TX
TURTLE CREEK PA
TURTLE LAKE ND
TUSCALOOSA AL
TUSCOLA IL
TUSCUMBIA AL
TUSTIN CA
TUTTLE ND
OK
TUXEDO NY
TWIN BRIDGES MT
TWIN FALLS ID
TWIN VALLEY MN
TWO HARBORS MN
TYLER MN
TX
VA
TYNDALL SD
TYRONE OK
PA
UHRICHSVILLE OH
UKIAH CA
ULEN MN
ULLIN IL
ULSTER PA
ULYSSES PA
UNADILLA NY
UNION NJ
NY
OR
SC
UNION BRIDGE MD
UNION CITY IN
MI
NJ
PA
TN
UNION POINT GA
UNION SPRINGS AL
NY
UNION
STOCK YARDS KS
UNIONTOWN KY
PA
UNIONVILLE MO
NY
UNIVERSITY PLACE NE
UPLAND CA
UPPER MARLBORO MD
UPPER SANDUSKY OH
URBANA IL
OH
UTICA MI
NE
NY
OH
UVALDE TX
UXBRIDGE MA
VACAVILLE CA
VALDOSTA GA
VALE OR
VALENTINE NE
VALIER MT
VALLEJO CA
VALLEY CITY ND
VALLEY FALLS KS
VALLEY JUNCTION IA
VALLEY MILLS TX
VALLEY STREAM NY
VALLEY VIEW TX
VALLIANT OK
VALPARAISO IN
VAN ALSTYNE TX
VAN BUREN AR
ME
VAN HOOK ND
VAN NUYS CA
VAN WERT OH
VANCOUVER WA
VANDALIA IL
VANDERBILT PA
VANDERGRIFT PA
VASSAR MI
VEBLEN SD
VEEDERSBURG IN
VELASCO TX
VENICE CA
VENTNOR CITY NJ
VENTURA CA
VENUS TX
VERDEN OK
VERGENNES VT
VERMILION IL
VERMILLION SD
VERNDALE MN
VERNON IN
NY
TX
VERO FL
VERONA PA
VERSAILLES KY
MO
OH
OK
VEVAY IN
VIAN OK
VIBORG SD
VICKSBURG MS
VICTOR CO
VICTORIA TX
VA
VICTORVILLE CA
VIDALIA GA
VIENNA GA
IL
SD
VA
VILLA GROVE IL
VILLE PLATTE LA
VILLISCA IA
VINCENNES IN
VINCENTOWN NJ
VINELAND NJ
VINITA OK
VINTON IA
VA
VIRGINIA IL
MN
VIROQUA WI
VISALIA CA
VOLANT PA
VOLGA SD
WABASH IN
WABASHA MN
WACO TX
WACONIA MN
WADDAMS GROVE IL
WADENA MN
WADESBORO NC
WADESVILLE IN
WADSWORTH OH
WAGENER SC
WAGONER OK
WAHOO NE
WAHPETON ND
WAILUKU HI
WAITSBURG WA
WAKARUSA IN
WAKEENEY KS
WAKEFIELD MA
MI
NE
RI
WAKITA OK
WAKONDA SD
WALDEN NY
WALDOBORO ME
WALDOBORO' ME
WALDRON AR
WALHALLA ND
WALKER MN
WALKILL NY
WALLA WALLA WA
WALLACE ID
WALLINGFORD CT
WALLINS CREEK KY
WALLOWA OR
WALNUT IL
WALNUT CREEK CA
WALNUT PARK CA
WALNUT RIDGE AR
WALNUT SPRINGS TX
WALSENBURG CO
WALTERBORO SC
WALTERS OK
WALTHAM MA
WALTHILL NE
WALTON NY
WALTONVILLE IL
WAMEGO KS
WAMPUM PA
WANETTE OK
WAPAKONETA OH
WAPANUCKA OK
WAPATO WA
WAPPINGERS FALLS NY
WARE MA
WAREHAM MA
WARNER NH
OK
WARREN IL
IN
MN
OH
PA
RI
WARRENSBURG MO
WARRENSBURGH NY
WARRENTON VA
WARSAW IL
IN
NC
NY
WARTRACE TN
WARWICK NY
WASECA MN
WASHINGTON
COURT HOUSE OH
WASHBURN ND
WASHINGTON DC
GA
IA
IN
KS
MO
WASHINGTON NC
NJ
OH
OK
PA
VA
WASHINGTON C. H. OH
WASHINGTONVILLE NY
WASHTUCNA WA
WATERBURY CT
VT
WATERFORD NY
PA
WATERLOO IA
IL
NY
WATERTOWN MA
NY
OH
SD
WI
WATERVILLE ME
MN
NY
WA
WATERVLIET MI
NY
WATKINS NY
WATONGA OK
WATSEKA IL
WATSONTOWN PA
WATSONVILLE CA
WAUBAY SD
WAUKEGAN IL
WAUKESHA WI
WAUKOMIS OK
WAUKON IA
WAUPACA WI
WAUPUN WI
WAURIKA OK
WAUSA NE
WAUSAU WI
WAUSEON OH
WAUTOMA WI
WAUWATOSA WI
WAVERLY IA
IL
KS
NY
OH
TN
VA
WAXAHACHIE TX
WAYCROSS GA
WAYLAND NY
WAYNE NE
PA
WAYNE CITY IL
WAYNESBORO GA
PA
VA
WAYNESBURG PA
WAYNESVILLE NC
OH
WAYNOKA OK
WEATHERFORD OK
TX
WEATHERLY PA
WEBB CITY MO
WEBBERS FALLS OK
WEBSTER MA
NY
PA
SD
WEBSTER CITY IA
WEBSTER SPRINGS WV
WEED CA
WEEDSPORT NY
WEEHAWKEN NJ
WEEPING WATER NE
WEHRUM PA
WEISER ID
WEISSPORT PA
WELCH WV
WELCOME MN
WELDON NC
WELEETKA OK
WELLESLEY MA
WELLINGTON CO
KS
OH
TX
WELLS MN
NY
WELLS RIVER VT
WELLSBOROUGH PA
WELLSBURG WV
WELLSTON MO
OH
OK
WELLSVILLE NY
OH
PA
WELSH LA
WENATCHEE WA
WENDELL ID
MN
WENONA IL
WERNERSVILLE PA
WESLACO TX
WESLEY IA
WESSINGTON SD
WESSINGTON
SPRINGS SD
WEST TX
WEST ALEXANDER PA
WEST ALLIS WI
WEST BADEN IN
WEST BEND WI
WEST CHESTER PA
WEST CONCORD MN
WEST
CONSHOHOCKEN PA
WEST DERRY NH
WEST ELIZABETH PA
WEST ENGLEWOOD NJ
WEST FRANKFORT IL
WEST GREENVILLE PA
WEST GROVE PA
WEST HEMPSTEAD NY
WEST HOBOKEN NJ
WEST JEFFERSON NC
WEST KILLINGLY CT
WEST LIBERTY KY
OH
WEST MERIDEN CT
WEST MIDDLESEX PA
WEST MILTON OH
WEST MINNEAPOLIS MN
WEST NEW YORK NJ
WEST NEWTON PA
WEST ORANGE NJ
WEST PALM BEACH FL
WEST PATERSON NJ
WEST PLAINS MO
WEST POINT GA
MS
NE
WEST RANDOLPH VT
WEST SALEM IL
WEST SENECA NY
WEST SUPERIOR WI
WEST TROY NY
WEST UNION IA
OH
WEST UNION WV
WEST WARWICK RI
WEST WINFIELD NY
WEST YORK PA
WESTBORO MA
WESTBROOK MN
WESTBURY NY
WESTERLY RI
WESTERNPORT MD
WESTERVELT IL
WESTERVILLE OH
WESTFIELD IL
MA
NJ
NY
PA
WESTHOPE ND
WESTMINSTER MA
MD
WESTMORELAND KS
WESTON OH
WV
WESTPORT CT
IN
NY
WESTVILLE IL
NJ
OK
WESTWOOD NJ
WETMORE KS
WETONKA SD
WETUMKA OK
WETUMPKA AL

WEWOKA OK
WEYAUWEGA WI
WEYMOUTH MA
WHARTON NJ
TX
WHAT CHEER IA
WHATCOM WA
WHEATLAND WY
WHEATON IL
MN
WHEELER OR
WHEELING WV
WHITE SD
WHITE CITY KS
WHITE HALL IL
MD
WHITE HOUSE
STATION NJ
WHITE LAKE SD
WHITE PIGEON MI
WHITE PLAINS NY
WHITE RIVER
JUNCTION VT
WHITE ROCK SD
WHITE SALMON WA
WHITE SULPHUR
SPRINGS MT
WHITEFISH MT
WHITEHALL MI
MT
NY
WHITELAND IN
WHITESBORO NY
TX
WHITESBURG KY
WHITESTONE NY
WHITESTOWN NY
WHITESVILLE NY
WHITEWATER WI
WHITEWRIGHT TX
WHITING IA
IN
WHITINSVILLE MA
WHITMAN MA
WHITMIRE SC
WHITNEY TX
WHITNEY POINT NY
WHITTIER CA
WIBAUX MT
WICHITA KS
WICHITA FALLS TX
WICKFORD RI
WICKLIFFE KY
WILBER NE
WILBURTON OK
WILCOX NE
PA
WILDWOOD NJ
WILKES BARRE PA
WILKINSBURG PA
WILKINSON IN
WILLIAMS IA
WILLIAMSBURG IN
KY
OH
PA
WILLIAMSON WV
WILLIAMSPORT MD
OH
PA
WILLIAMSTOWN MA
NJ
WV
WILLIMANTIC CT
WILLISTON ND
WILLITS CA
WILLMAR MN
WILLOUGHBY OH
WILLOW CITY ND
WILLOWS CA
WILLS POINT TX
WILLSBORO NY
WILMERDING PA
WILMETTE IL
WILMINGTON CA
DE
IL
NC
OH
WILMONT MN
WILMORE KY
WILMOT SD
WILSON NC
PA
WILSONVILLE IL

WILTON ND
NH
WIMBLEDON ND
WINAMAC IN
WINBURNE PA
WINCHENDON MA
WINCHESTER IL
IN
KY
MA
NH
OH
TN
VA
WINDBER PA
WINDER GA
WINDHAM CT
NY
WINDOM MN
WINDSOR CO
IL
MO
NY
PA
VT
WINFIELD IA
KS
TX
WINIFRED MT
WINNEBAGO MN
NE
WINNEMUCCA NV
WINNER SD
WINNSBORO SC
TX
WINONA MN
WV
WINSLOW AZ
IN
WINSTED CT
WINSTON NC
WINSTON-SALEM NC
WINTER GARDEN FL
WINTER HAVEN FL
WINTERS CA
WINTERSET IA
WINTHROP ME
MN
NY
WISCASSET ME
WISCONSIN RAPIDS WI
WISE VA
WISNER NE
WITT IL
WOBURN MA
WOLBACH NE
WOLCOTT NY
WOLF POINT MT
WOLFE CITY TX
WOLFEBORO NH
WOLFEBOROUGH NH
WOOD RIVER IL
NE
WOODBINE IA
MD
NJ
WOODBRIDGE NJ
WOODBURY NJ
TN
WOODHULL IL
WOODLAKE CA
WOODLAND CA
WOODLAWN IL
PA
WOODMERE NY
WOODRIDGE NY
WOODRUFF SC
WOODSFIELD OH
WOODSTOCK IL
MN
VA
VT
WOODSTOWN NJ
WOODSVILLE NH
WOODVILLE OK
WOODWARD OK
WOONSOCKET RI
SD
WOOSTER OH
WORCESTER MA
WORDEN IL
WORLAND WY
WORTHAM TX
WORTHINGTON MN
WV

WRAY CO
WRENTHAM MA
WRIGHTSVILLE GA
PA
WYALUSING PA
WYANDOTTE KS
MI
WYANET IL
WYCKOFF NJ
WYLIE TX
WYMORE NE
WYNDMERE ND
WYNNE AR
WYNNEWOOD OK
WYNOT NE
WYOMING DE
IA
IL
NY
PA
WYTHEVILLE VA
XENIA IL
OH
YAKIMA WA
YALE MI
OK
YANKTON SD
YARDLEY PA
YARDVILLE NJ
YARMOUTH MA
YATES ND
YATES CENTER KS
YAZOO CITY MS
YOAKUM TX
YONKERS NY
YORK NE
PA
SC
YORK SPRINGS PA
YORK VILLAGE ME
YORKTOWN TX
VA
YORKVILLE IL
SC
YOUNGSTOWN OH
YOUNGSVILLE PA
YOUNGWOOD PA
YPSILANTI MI
YREKA CA
YUBA CITY CA
YUKON OK
YUMA AZ
CO
ZANESVILLE OH
ZEIGLER IL
ZELIENOPLE PA
ZILLAH WA

Chapter 9

NATIONAL BANK TOWNS BY CHARTER NUMBER

This chapter lists the charter number of every note-issuing national bank in numerical order. Following the charter number is the name of the town and the abbreviation of the state in which the bank was located. Duplicate charter numbers indicate a change in the city name as it appears on the notes, or a change of location of the bank.

Many banks were located in territories during all or part of their note-issuing lifetimes. Territorial locations are listed under the appropriate state. In particular, Indian Territory and Oklahoma Territory banks are listed under Oklahoma, and Dakota Territory banks are listed under North Dakota or South Dakota. Bank titles and detailed information about the issued notes may be found in the state listings in Chapter 4.

Notes displaying the lowest and highest charter numbers that appear on national bank notes.

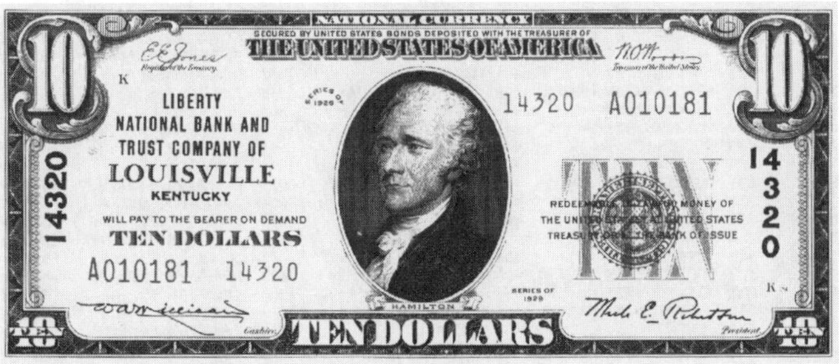

CHARTER NUMBERS 1 - 813

1 PHILADELPHIA PA
2 NEW HAVEN CT
3 YOUNGSTOWN OH
4 STAMFORD CT
5 FREMONT OH
6 SYRACUSE NY
7 CLEVELAND OH
8 CHICAGO IL
9 DAYTON OH
10 DAYTON OH
11 FORT WAYNE IN
12 ERIE PA
13 CLEVELAND OH
14 SPRINGFIELD MA
15 DAVENPORT IA
16 SANDUSKY OH
17 RICHMOND IN
18 IOWA CITY IA
19 PORTSMOUTH NH
20 CINCINNATI OH
21 CARLISLE PA
22 ANN ARBOR MI
23 LAFAYETTE IN
24 CINCINNATI OH
25 MARIETTA PA
26 WASHINGTON DC
27 AKRON OH
28 EVANSVILLE IN
29 NEW YORK NY
30 WILKES BARRE PA
31 HUNTINGDON PA
32 CINCINNATI OH
33 CAIRO IL
34 RONDOUT NY
35 FISHKILL LANDING NY
35 BEACON NY
36 FINDLAY OH
37 CENTERVILLE IN
38 AURORA IL
39 TOWANDA PA
40 AKRON OH
41 KENDALLVILLE IN
42 STRASBURG PA
43 SALEM OH
44 ANDERSON IN
45 ELLENVILLE NY
46 McCONNELSVILLE OH
47 TERRE HAUTE IN
48 PITTSBURGH PA
49 SCRANTON PA
50 FRANKLIN IN
51 JOHNSTOWN PA
52 NEWARK NJ
53 LODI OH
54 GIRARD PA
55 INDIANAPOLIS IN
56 HAMILTON OH
57 HOLLIDAYSBURG PA
58 BLUFFTON IN
59 TROY OH
60 NEWVILLE PA
61 BATH ME
62 NEW YORK NY
63 ROCKVILLE IN
64 MILWAUKEE WI
65 NORWICH CT
66 LYONS IA
66 CLINTON IA
67 COLUMBIA MO
68 PORTSMOUTH OH
69 KITTANNING PA
70 CAMBRIDGE CITY IN
71 ADAMS NY
72 OBERLIN OH
73 WATERTOWN NY
74 WARREN OH
75 DANSVILLE NY
76 CANTON OH
77 SCRANTON PA
78 FRANKLIN IN
79 WORCESTER MA
80 KEOKUK IA
81 FENTON MI
82 LAWRENCEBURG IN
83 JANESVILLE WI
84 NASHUA NH
85 MONMOUTH IL
86 GERMANTOWN OH
87 NEW YORK NY
88 WARSAW IN
89 SAINT LOUIS MO
90 UPPER SANDUSKY OH
91 TOLEDO OH
92 LOGAN OH
93 CINCINNATI OH
94 DELHI NY
94 PORT JERVIS NY
95 HUDSON WI
96 BARRE MA
97 DETROIT MI
98 IRONTON OH
99 MORAVIA NY
100 CADIZ OH
101 GREENFIELD OH
102 SENECA FALLS NY
103 SOUTH WORCESTER NY
104 WILKES BARRE PA
105 VALPARAISO IN
106 RAVENNA OH
107 OTTUMWA IA
108 ROCK ISLAND IL
109 LOUISVILLE KY
110 UNION CITY PA
111 MADISON IN
112 BANGOR ME
113 DANVILLE IL
114 LASALLE IL
115 MEADVILLE PA
116 DETROIT MI
117 MARION IA
118 CIRCLEVILLE OH
119 ELMIRA NY
120 UTICA NY
121 HARTFORD CT
122 SPRINGFIELD VT
123 COLUMBUS OH
124 WHITEWATER WI
125 READING PA
126 SOUTH BEND IN
127 CARDINGTON OH
128 CHILLICOTHE OH
129 WABASH IN
130 BENNINGTON VT
131 ZANESVILLE OH
132 POMEROY OH
133 BEVERLY OH
134 PROVIDENCE RI
135 BROWNSVILLE PA
136 GALLIPOLIS OH
137 LANCASTER OH
138 BETHLEHEM PA
139 SAINT LOUIS MO
140 SYRACUSE NY
141 CAMBRIDGE OH
142 MARIETTA OH
143 CONNEAUTVILLE PA
144 MADISON WI
145 HUNTINGTON IN
146 GOSHEN IN
147 OSKALOOSA IA
148 WEST CHESTER PA
149 ELMIRA NY
150 NASHVILLE TN
151 NEW BERLIN NY
152 DANVILLE IN
153 GENEVA OH
154 AUBURN ME
155 YPSILANTI MI
156 DORCHESTER MA
157 FORT ATKINSON WI
158 MARLBORO MA
159 SYRACUSE NY
160 MOLINE IL
161 ALLENTOWN PA
162 NEW ORLEANS LA
163 TROY NY
164 ZANESVILLE OH
165 BATH NY
166 ALBION NY
167 GENEVA NY
168 HILLSDALE MI
169 PENN YAN NY
170 SAINT LOUIS MO
171 SOUTH CHARLESTON OH
172 CIRCLEVILLE OH
173 OIL CITY PA
174 MIFFLINBURG PA
175 WILLIAMSPORT PA
176 PEORIA IL
177 WILMINGTON IL
178 COLUMBUS WI
179 CHITTENANGO NY
180 PARKERSBURG WV
181 SPRINGFIELD MA
182 LEAVENWORTH KS
183 ASHLAND OH
184 SANDY HILL NY
185 UTICA NY
186 ROCKVILLE CT
187 HANOVER PA
188 GRAFTON MA
189 FRANKLIN PA
190 WESTFIELD MA
191 KALAMAZOO MI
192 BRUNSWICK ME
193 HOBART NY
194 NORTH BENNINGTON VT
196 NEW LONDON CT
197 YORK PA
198 ALLEGHENY PA
199 ATTICA NY
200 BOSTON MA
201 HARRISBURG PA
202 BINGHAMTON NY
203 SAINT PAUL MN
204 BALTIMORE MD
205 SPRINGFIELD IL
206 ELKHART IN
207 PEORIA IL
208 NEW BRUNSWICK NJ
209 OMAHA NE
210 SANDUSKY OH
211 LOCKPORT NY
212 KENOSHA WI
213 PHILADELPHIA PA
214 BRIDGEPORT OH
215 NORWALK OH
216 MASSILLON OH
217 LEONARDSVILLE NY
218 OSHKOSH WI
219 GREENCASTLE IN
220 PAINESVILLE OH
221 PORTLAND ME
222 ITHACA NY
223 COOPERSTOWN NY
224 NORWICH CT
225 CHICAGO IL
226 CORTLAND NY
227 NEW HAVEN CT
228 ORWELL VT
229 MEDINA NY
230 MONROE WI
231 AUBURN NY
233 ATHENS OH
234 PHILADELPHIA PA
235 BUFFALO NY
236 CHICAGO IL
237 BRYAN OH
238 SPRINGFIELD OH
239 SKOWHEGAN ME
240 LEBANON PA
241 GALESBURG IL
242 IRONTON OH
243 DELAWARE OH
244 WAYNESBORO PA
245 MORRISVILLE NY
246 WRIGHTSVILLE PA
247 ALTOONA PA
248 TOLEDO OH
249 WEST GREENVILLE PA
249 GREENVILLE PA
250 WEST MERIDEN CT
250 MERIDEN CT
251 MYSTIC BRIDGE CT
252 PITTSBURGH PA
253 MILTON PA
254 NEW YORK CITY NY
255 OSWEGO NY
256 FALL RIVER MA
257 SIDNEY OH
258 MOUNT GILEAD OH
259 CANANDAIGUA NY
260 SAINT CHARLES MO
261 NEW BEDFORD MA
262 HORNELLSVILLE NY
262 HORNELL NY
263 SPRINGFIELD OH
264 LANSING MI
265 FRIENDSHIP NY
266 PLATTSBURGH NY
267 ALBANY NY
268 MERRIMAC MA
269 SAINT ALBANS VT
270 UNIONTOWN PA
271 NORFOLK VA
272 NORRISTOWN PA
273 OXFORD NY
274 DELPHOS OH
275 IONIA MI
276 CHICAGO IL
277 XENIA OH
278 BRANDON VT
279 NEWBURYPORT MA
280 COOPERSTOWN NY
281 TRENTON NJ
282 FRANKLIN NY
283 SAINT LOUIS MO
284 WASHINGTON OH
285 WHITEHALL NY
286 PHILADELPHIA PA
287 MARION OH
288 JAMESBURG NJ
289 RIPLEY OH
290 NEW YORK NY
291 PITTSBURGH PA
292 BALDWINSVILLE NY
293 BLOOMSBURG PA
294 GRAND RAPIDS MI
295 PALMYRA NY
296 OSWEGO NY
297 WAVERLY NY
298 SKOWHEGAN ME
299 MOUNT PLEASANT IA
300 CURWENSVILLE PA
301 HAVANA NY
302 ANDES NY
303 SKANEATELES NY
304 CLYDE NY
305 WAYNESBURG PA
306 BANGOR ME
307 NEW YORK NY
308 SPRINGFIELD MA
309 BUTLER PA
310 HALLOWELL ME
311 GETTYSBURG PA
312 MEDIA PA
313 INDIANA PA
314 WARWICK NY
315 SAINT CLAIRSVILLE OH
316 CHAMPLAIN NY
317 DUBUQUE IA
318 CONCORD NH
319 FREEPORT IL
320 CHICAGO IL
321 PLATTSBURGH NY
322 BOSTON MA
323 McGREGOR IA
324 NEWTOWN PA
325 DANVILLE PA
326 MECHANICSBURG PA
327 WINCHENDON MA
328 WELLSBOROUGH PA
329 PATERSON NJ
330 LEWISTON ME
331 LOWELL MA
332 CHESTER PA
333 LANCASTER PA
334 GREENPORT NY
335 BRIDGEPORT CT
336 MEMPHIS TN
337 CENTERVILLE IA
338 DOWNINGTOWN PA
339 BATAVIA IL
340 BATAVIA NY
341 NEW YORK NY
342 UNION SPRINGS NY
343 HAVANA NY
344 FAIR HAVEN VT
345 NEW YORK NY
346 VEVAY IN
347 LACON IL
348 LOWVILLE NY
349 NEWARK NY
350 RAVENNA OH
351 BURLINGTON IA
352 PHILADELPHIA PA
353 CANDOR NY
354 ROMEO MI
355 CHESTER PA
356 GREENSBURG IN
357 SELINS GROVE PA
358 WATKINS NY
358 PENN YAN NY
359 BOSTON MA
360 WHEELING WV
361 HARTFORD CT
362 NEWARK NJ
363 PERU IN
364 TARRYTOWN NY
365 WILMINGTON OH
366 MOUNT VERNON IN
367 AUGUSTA ME
368 WATERLOO NY
369 XENIA OH
370 VINCENTOWN NJ
371 COLUMBIA PA
372 WOODSTOCK IL
373 ALLENTOWN PA
374 JERSEY CITY NJ
375 SAINT JOHNSVILLE NY
376 NEW YORK NY
377 LA PORTE IN
378 CUYAHOGA FALLS OH
379 BOSTON MA
380 MECHANICSBURG PA
381 CUMBERLAND MD
382 BROCKPORT NY
383 NORTHAMPTON MA
384 NEW YORK NY
385 FREEPORT IL
386 MOUNT PLEASANT PA
387 NEW YORK NY
388 GRANVILLE OH
389 DES MOINES IA
390 MARQUETTE MI
391 KNOXVILLE TN
392 MERCER PA
393 AMHERST MA
394 WESTPORT CT
395 SOMERVILLE NJ
396 HUDSON NY
397 MIDDLETOWN CT
398 WASHINGTON IA
399 WOODSTOWN NJ
400 BERLIN WI
401 PORTSMOUTH NH
402 PORT CHESTER NY
403 ASHLAND PA
404 BRANDON VT
405 LANSING IA
406 AUGUSTA ME
407 SALEM MA
408 BOSTON MA
409 MOUNT CARROLL IL
410 BAY CITY MI
411 MARSHALLTOWN IA
412 AURORA NY
413 PHILADELPHIA PA
414 BALTIMORE MD
415 CANTON IL
416 NORTH EASTON MA
417 LAFAYETTE IN
418 NORTHAMPTON MA
419 GALION OH
420 COOPERSTOWN NY
420 ONEONTA NY
421 WESTBORO MA
422 VAN WERT OH
423 MINERSVILLE PA
424 QUINCY IL
425 RIPON WI
426 FOX LAKE WI
427 JEFFERSON OH
428 EASTHAMPTON MA
429 ROCKFORD IL
430 LANSDALE PA
431 CAMDEN NJ
432 PITTSBURGH PA
433 CAMBRIDGE MA
434 PONTIAC MI
435 GLEN ROCK PA
436 MANSFIELD OH
437 MAUCH CHUNK PA
438 ELYRIA OH
439 FALL RIVER MA
440 CLINTON MA
441 PERU IL
442 WORCESTER MA
443 BUCYRUS OH
444 NEW YORK CITY NY
445 RED BANK NJ
446 DAMARISCOTTA ME
447 PLAINFIELD NJ
448 PUTNAM CT
449 EAST CAMBRIDGE MA
450 WEST KILLINGLY CT
450 KILLINGLY CT
451 KINGSTON NY
452 FREEHOLD NJ
453 BUFFALO NY
454 CARONDELET MO
455 WORCESTER MA
456 WATKINS NY
457 RACINE WI
458 NORWICH CT
459 BELLEFONTE PA
460 BOSTON MA
461 COBLESKILL NY
462 ADAMS MA
464 WELLINGTON OH
465 POUGHKEEPSIE NY
466 CHICAGO IL
467 FORT PLAIN NY
468 NEWBURGH NY
469 MAUCH CHUNK PA
470 BRATTLEBORO VT
471 SING SING NY
471 OSSINING NY
472 DEPOSIT NY
473 WILMINGTON DE
474 GREENFIELD MA
475 BOSTON MA
476 WORCESTER MA
477 DECATUR IL
478 PITTSTON PA
479 ROCKFORD IL
480 MANSFIELD OH
481 HAVERHILL MA
482 ROCKFORD IL
483 CEDAR RAPIDS IA
484 HAVERHILL MA
485 DES MOINES IA
486 HARTFORD CT
487 ELIZABETH NJ
488 NEWTONVILLE MA
489 SAINT JOHNSBURY VT
490 FAIRHAVEN MA
491 GALESBURG IL
492 MOUNT PLEASANT OH
493 DECORAH IA
494 BATH ME
495 WARSAW IL
496 HASTINGS MN
497 SUFFIELD CT
498 AUGUSTA ME
499 DERRY NH
500 CEDAR RAPIDS IA
501 SMITHFIELD OH
502 SOUTH NORWALK CT
503 MONSON MA
504 WESTFIELD NY
505 BOSTON MA
506 LOWELL MA
507 LOCK HAVEN PA
508 CHICAGO IL
509 ROCKVILLE CT
510 WEYMOUTH MA
511 JACKSONVILLE IL
512 JOLIET IL
513 LEOMINSTER MA
514 BOSTON MA
515 BOSTON MA
516 YARMOUTH MA
517 QUINCY MA
518 BANGOR ME
519 ONEIDA NY
520 WARREN PA
521 PROVIDENCE PA
522 PHILADELPHIA PA
523 MIDDLETOWN NY
524 BOSTON MA
525 BOSTON MA
526 WASHINGTON DC
527 ROCHESTER NY
528 FRAMINGHAM MA
529 BOSTON MA
530 EATON OH
531 MORRIS IL
532 HALLOWELL ME
533 CHELSEA MA
534 GENESEO IL
535 ERIE PA
536 BOSTON MA
537 CHARLESTOWN NH
538 PHILADELPHIA PA
539 PHILADELPHIA PA
540 PHILADELPHIA PA
541 PHILADELPHIA PA
542 PHILADELPHIA PA
543 PHILADELPHIA PA
544 PHILADELPHIA PA
545 BOSTON MA
546 PHILADELPHIA PA
547 PHILADELPHIA PA
548 JAMESTOWN NY
549 GLOUCESTER MA
550 WINONA MN
551 BOSTON MA
552 WEST CHESTER PA
553 WINTHROP ME
554 BOSTON MA
555 FOND DU LAC WI
556 PHILADELPHIA PA
557 PHILADELPHIA PA
558 RANDOLPH MA
559 KEENE NH
560 PHILADELPHIA PA
561 PHILADELPHIA PA
562 NEW CASTLE PA
563 PHILADELPHIA PA
564 ANGELICA NY
565 PROVIDENCE RI
566 NORTHUMBERLAND PA
567 MAHANOY CITY PA
568 BERWICK PA
569 CORRY PA
570 PHILADELPHIA PA
571 CRAWFORDSVILLE IN
572 MILLBURY MA
573 DOYLESTOWN PA
574 MANCHESTER NH
575 COATESVILLE PA
576 FRANCESTOWN NH
577 ATTICA IN
578 BOSTON MA
579 ROCHESTER MN
580 HARRISBURG PA
581 INDIANAPOLIS IN
582 BOSTON MA
583 LANCASTER MA
583 CLINTON MA
584 NEWBURYPORT MA
585 MIDDLETOWN PA
586 WASHINGTON PA
587 NEW BRUNSWICK NJ
588 MALDEN MA
589 HAVERHILL MA
590 FALL RIVER MA
591 COLUMBUS OH
592 PHILADELPHIA PA
593 CHAMBERSBURGH PA
594 DANVERS MA
595 BOSTON MA
596 CLAREMONT NH
597 LANCASTER PA
598 MALONE NY
599 COLUMBUS OH
600 THREE RIVERS MI
601 BOSTON MA
602 PHILADELPHIA PA
603 BOSTON MA
604 YORK PA
605 CORRY PA
606 ERIE PA
607 TOLEDO OH
608 POTTSTOWN PA
609 BOSTON MA
610 PHILADELPHIA PA
611 GETTYSBURG PA
612 FALL RIVER MA
613 PITTSBURGH PA
614 CAMBRIDGE MA
615 BOSTON MA
616 SOUTH DANVERS MA
616 PEABODY MA
617 INDIANAPOLIS IN
618 SOUTH WEYMOUTH MA
619 PITTSBURGH PA
620 CINCINNATI OH
621 TROY NY
622 TITUSVILLE PA
623 PHILADELPHIA PA
624 HALLOWELL ME
625 BOSTON MA
626 HOPKINTON MA
627 WASHINGTON DC
628 WARE MA
629 BOSTON MA
630 CINCINNATI OH
631 NEW ULM MN
632 NEW BRIGHTON PA
633 HAVERHILL MA
634 SALEM MA
635 BOSTON MA
636 PROVIDENCE RI
637 EAST SAGINAW MI
638 LYNN MA
639 LOCKPORT NY
640 TROY NY
641 COLUMBIA PA
642 CHICAGO IL
643 BOSTON MA
644 HONESDALE PA
645 MYSTIC RIVER CT
646 BOSTON MA
647 SALEM MA
648 BROWNSVILLE PA
649 POTTSVILLE PA
650 NEWTON IA
651 ALEXANDRIA VA
652 KENT OH
653 YONKERS NY
654 BOSTON MA
655 LEBANON PA
656 PHILADELPHIA PA
657 NORWICH CT
658 BROOKLYN NY
659 POUGHKEEPSIE NY
660 SOUTHPORT CT
661 DOWNINGTOWN PA
662 RICHMOND ME
663 CANTON MA
664 CARBONDALE PA
665 BOSTON MA
666 NEW LONDON CT
667 MOUNT JOY PA
668 PITTSBURGH PA
669 DEDHAM MA
670 HARTFORD CT
671 WATERTOWN NY
672 BOSTON MA
673 WARREN RI
674 PHOENIXVILLE PA
675 PITTSBURGH PA
676 MARBLEHEAD MA
677 BOSTON MA
678 PITTSBURGH PA
679 FALL RIVER MA
680 LEBANON PA
681 UNIONTOWN PA
682 GEORGETOWN DC
683 LANCASTER PA
684 BOSTON MA
685 PITTSBURGH PA
686 STAFFORD SPRINGS CT
687 NEW YORK NY
688 WALTHAM MA
689 SHAMOKIN PA
690 NEW BEDFORD MA
691 SALEM MA
692 MUSCATINE IA
693 READING PA
694 YORK PA
695 JERSEY CITY NJ
696 READING PA
697 LYNN MA
698 CHICAGO IL
699 AURORA IN
700 PITTSBURGH PA
701 NEW ALBANY IN
702 FITCHBURG MA
703 QUINCY IL
704 SALEM MA
705 PITTSBURGH PA
706 AMENIA NY
707 PLYMOUTH PA
708 ATHOL MA
709 LITCHFIELD CT
710 MINNEAPOLIS MN
711 MILTON PA
712 HARWICH MA
713 CHICAGO IL
714 NANTUCKET MA
715 BATAVIA OH
716 BOSTON MA
717 BRISTOL PA
718 COVINGTON KY
719 MINNEAPOLIS MN
720 MERIDEN CT
721 TROY NY
722 PITTSBURGH PA
723 PHILADELPHIA PA
724 CHICAGO IL
725 SAINT PAUL MN
726 SALEM MA
727 PITTSBURGH PA
728 OXFORD PA
729 ITHACA NY
730 EVANSVILLE IN
731 CAMBRIDGE MA
732 WILKES BARRE PA
733 NEW YORK NY
734 WILLIAMSPORT PA
735 STONINGTON CT
736 PROVINCETOWN MA
737 WARSAW NY
738 FRANKLIN OH
739 ALBANY NY
740 GARDINER ME
741 NORTH EAST PA
742 WESTMINSTER MD
743 NEW BEDFORD MA
744 WALDOBORO' ME
745 LEWISBURG PA
746 WOBURN MA
747 NEW WINDSOR MD
748 MONTPELIER VT
749 JANESVILLE WI
750 NEW YORK NY
751 BURLINGTON IA
752 RED HOOK NY
753 LOWELL MA
754 NORWALK CT
755 PHILADELPHIA PA
756 HARTFORD CT
757 PITTSBURGH PA
758 CONCORD NH
759 KNOXVILLE IL
760 LEXINGTON KY
761 BATH ME
762 WATERVILLE ME
763 CHARLESTON IL
764 OXFORD MA
765 WORCESTER MA
766 TAUNTON MA
767 MARBLEHEAD MA
768 CLEARFIELD PA
769 WHITINSVILLE MA
770 CAMBRIDGE MA
771 NASHVILLE TN
772 PROVIDENCE RI
773 CLEVELAND OH
774 CLARION PA
775 NEW ALBANY IN
776 ALLEGHENY PA
776 PITTSBURGH PA
777 LOUISVILLE KY
778 BOSTON MA
779 PLYMOUTH MA
780 WATERBURY CT
781 LOWELL MA
782 BATH ME
783 INDIANAPOLIS IN
784 LEWISBURG PA
785 CAIRO IL
786 CLEVELAND OH
787 HILLSBOROUGH OH
788 LOUISVILLE KY
789 NEWTON MA
790 LOUISVILLE KY
791 WATERBURY CT
792 WATERLOO IA
793 MUNCIE IN
794 MARTINSVILLE IN
795 SEAFORD DE
796 NEW HAVEN CT
797 TREMONT PA
798 WATERVILLE ME
799 NEW BEDFORD MA
800 MANSFIELD OH
801 WEST WINFIELD NY
802 HOLLISTON MA
803 VICKSBURG MS
804 NEW CASTLE IN
805 TOWNSEND MA
806 BOSTON MA
807 CLEVELAND OH
808 LEBANON NH
809 TOLEDO OH
810 PATERSON NJ
811 ELMIRA NY
812 GRAND RAPIDS MI
813 CONSTANTINE MI

814 BALTIMORE MD
815 UNION CITY IN
816 WINDSOR VT
817 SALEM MA
818 CHICAGO IL
819 BLOOMINGTON IL
820 RUTLAND VT
821 OSWEGO NY
822 DOVER PLAINS NY
823 WESTERLY RI
824 GRAFTON MA
825 STURGIS MI
826 ANNAPOLIS MD
826 BALTIMORE MD
827 GALVA IL
828 WOOSTER OH
829 HAMILTON OH
830 SOUTH EAST NY
831 GALENA IL
832 QUINCY MA
833 CONCORD MA
834 SHIPPENSBURGH PA
835 TUNKHANNOCK PA
836 BELOIT WI
837 MUNCY PA
838 GONIC NH
839 WAYNESBURG PA
840 BELFAST ME
841 FREDONIA NY
842 CASTLETON NY
843 PAWTUCKET RI
844 CINCINNATI OH
845 MIDDLETOWN CT
846 DUBUQUE IA
847 BOSTON MA
848 DAVENPORT IA
849 WARREN IL
850 BUFFALO NY
851 BEAVER DAM WI
852 MANITOWOC WI
853 DELAWARE OH
854 PLUMER PA
855 CLEARFIELD PA
856 NORTH PROVIDENCE RI
856 PAWTUCKET RI
857 MONTPELIER VT
858 NEWARK OH
859 MARIETTA OH
860 WASHINGTON NJ
861 BURLINGTON VT
862 OWEGO NY
863 URBANA OH
864 PARKERSBURG WV
865 FORT WAYNE IN
866 MILFORD MA
867 BLAIRSVILLE PA
868 POTSDAM NY
869 INDIANAPOLIS IN
870 ERIE PA
871 MEADVILLE PA
872 KNIGHTSTOWN IN
873 ELKHORN WI
874 GREEN BAY WI
875 WASHINGTON DC
876 NEWTON NJ
877 KEENE NH
878 PORTLAND ME
879 TITUSVILLE PA
880 WATERVILLE ME
881 RAHWAY NJ
882 LAFAYETTE IN
883 ROCKFORD IL
884 GARDNER MA
885 LEE MA
886 GENESEO NY
887 WINCHESTER NH
888 NEWPORT NH
889 WINCHESTER IN
890 THOMASTON ME
891 NEW YORK NY
892 FLEMINGTON NJ
893 SARATOGA SPRINGS NY
894 KOKOMO IN
895 CONWAY MA
896 RAHWAY NJ
897 BROOKVILLE PA
898 DAYTON OH
899 GLOUCESTER MA
900 TIFFIN OH
901 FARMINGTON ME
902 DIXON IL
903 PRINCETON IL
904 TROY NY
905 NEW YORK NY
906 LEXINGTON KY
907 TIFFIN OH
908 MOUNT VERNON OH
909 RICHMOND ME
910 BRIDGEPORT CT
911 BARNESVILLE OH
912 MANHEIM PA
913 CHAMPAIGN IL
914 MALONE NY
915 SHAWNEETOWN IL
916 URBANA OH
917 NEW YORK NY
918 LEICESTER MA
919 PAWCATUCK CT
920 GREENFIELD MA
921 BRIDGEPORT CT
922 MOUNT PLEASANT IA
923 BROOKLYN NY
923 NEW YORK NY
924 FALL RIVER MA
925 NEWTON NJ
926 PITTSBURGH PA
927 BRIDGEPORT CT
928 BRIDGEPORT CT
929 KINDERHOOK NY
930 LAFAYETTE IN
931 NORWALK OH
932 BOSTON MA
933 RIPLEY OH
934 SOUTHBRIDGE MA
935 PORTSMOUTH OH
936 BOSTON MA
937 LE ROY NY
938 JAMESTOWN NY
939 GARDINER ME
940 TROY NY
941 PORTLAND ME
942 NORWALK CT
943 DANBURY CT
944 BOWDOINHAM ME
945 WAUKEGAN IL
946 KEENE NH
947 TAUNTON MA
948 PROVIDENCE RI
949 GENEVA NY
950 DES MOINES IA
951 FREEHOLD NJ
952 WESTERLY RI
953 NEW CASTLE ME
953 DAMARISCOTTA ME
954 BALLSTON SPA NY
955 KINGSTON NY
956 JEFFERSONVILLE IN
957 TAUNTON MA
958 PEABODY MA
959 SOUTH BERWICK ME
960 LOWELL MA
961 FAIRMONT WV
962 BETHEL VT
963 TROY NY
964 NEW YORK NY
965 NEW ALBANY IN
966 CHICAGO IL
967 MACOMB IL
968 FULTON NY
969 BEVERLY MA
970 WOONSOCKET RI
971 FISHKILL NY
972 NEW YORK NY
973 SALEM OH
974 BOSTON MA
975 ASHTABULA OH
976 CARMEL NY
977 IOWA CITY IA
978 NEW LONDON CT
979 GALENA IL
980 GLENS FALLS NY
981 PINE PLAINS NY
982 SPRINGFIELD MA
983 PROVIDENCE RI
984 INDIANAPOLIS IN
985 BOSTON MA
986 LOWELL MA
987 SPRINGFIELD MA
988 SPRINGFIELD MA
989 EVANSVILLE IN
990 HUDSON NY
991 TROY NY
992 TROY NY
993 BOSTON MA
994 CLINTON IA
995 WINCHESTER KY
996 PLYMOUTH MA
997 NEWPORT DE
998 NEW YORK NY
999 MAQUOKETA IA
1000 NEW YORK NY
1001 CENTRALIA IL
1002 PROVIDENCE RI
1003 MILWAUKEE WI
1004 CHELSEA VT
1005 CHARLESTOWN MA
1005 BOSTON MA
1006 PIQUA OH
1007 PROVIDENCE RI
1008 WARREN RI
1009 GREEN BAY WI
1010 WATERTOWN WI
1011 NEWBURYPORT MA
1012 TROY NY
1013 PORTLAND CT
1014 LAWRENCE MA
1015 BOSTON MA
1016 DENVER CO
1017 MILWAUKEE WI
1018 NORTHAMPTON MA
1019 OWEGO NY
1020 PITTSFIELD NH
1021 NEWPORT RI
1022 UXBRIDGE MA
1023 PORTLAND ME
1024 MATTOON IL
1025 PORTSMOUTH NH
1026 KINDERHOOK NY
1027 LYONS NY
1028 BOSTON MA
1029 BOSTON MA
1030 PROVIDENCE RI
1031 LOGANSPORT IN
1032 SEYMOUR IN
1033 MORRISON IL
1034 CONNERSVILLE IN
1035 SLATERSVILLE RI
1036 PROVIDENCE RI
1037 NEW LONDON CT
1038 STAMFORD CT
1039 LOCKPORT NY
1040 SAUGERTIES NY
1041 BATH ME
1042 PITTSFIELD IL
1043 DOVER NH
1044 WELLSVILLE OH
1045 ALBANY NY
1046 THORNTOWN IN
1047 NEWBURYPORT MA
1048 LAWRENCE MA
1049 SALISBURY MA
1049 AMESBURY MA
1050 KINGSTON NY
1051 MOUNT VERNON OH
1052 PORTSMOUTH NH
1053 SUSQUEHANNA DEPOT PA
1053 SUSQUEHANNA PA
1054 HOPKINTON RI
1055 SPRINGFIELD MA
1056 CHICOPEE MA
1057 PITTSBURGH PA
1058 WOONSOCKET RI
1059 MANCHESTER NH
1060 PORTLAND ME
1061 PIQUA OH
1062 STEUBENVILLE OH
1063 TECUMSEH MI
1064 LONDON OH
1065 JACKSON MI
1066 COLUMBUS IN
1067 NEW YORK NY
1068 NEW RICHMOND OH
1069 WASHINGTON DC
1070 MILFORD NH
1071 SANDWICH NH
1072 ROCHESTER NY
1073 WORCESTER MA
1074 BATAVIA NY
1075 NEW YORK NY
1076 JEFFERSON WI
1077 FITCHBURG MA
1078 DANVILLE PA
1079 BUCKSPORT ME
1080 NEW YORK NY
1081 GREENCASTLE PA
1082 PITTSFIELD MA
1083 GROTON NY
1084 ESSEX CT
1085 WRENTHAM MA
1086 WAUKESHA WI
1087 DOVER NH
1088 PORTSMOUTH OH
1089 BIDDEFORD ME
1090 ONEIDA NY
1091 HUDSON NY
1092 GREENVILLE OH
1093 ANSONIA CT
1094 ATHENS PA
1095 BANGOR ME
1096 BELVIDERE NJ
1097 BELVIDERE IL
1098 BIRMINGHAM CT
1098 DERBY CT
1099 BOSTON MA
1100 FORT WAYNE IN
1101 OSKALOOSA IA
1102 RICHMOND IN
1103 TERRE HAUTE IN
1104 ROCHESTER NY
1105 NEW YORK NY
1106 NEWBURGH NY
1107 HYANNIS MA
1108 WALDOBORO ME
1109 BALTIMORE MD
1110 FAYETTEVILLE NY
1111 RICHMOND VA
1112 SAINT LOUIS MO
1113 MORRISTOWN NJ
1114 CLINTON NJ
1115 SPARTA WI
1116 NEW YORK NY
1117 PEORIA IL
1118 BRUNSWICK ME
1119 HINGHAM MA
1120 RONDOUT NY
1120 KINGSTON NY
1121 NEW YORK NY
1122 CANAJOHARIE NY
1123 ALBANY NY
1125 RICHMOND VA
1126 PROVIDENCE RI
1127 SALEM NY
1128 NEW HAVEN CT
1129 ANDOVER MA
1130 MOHAWK NY
1131 PROVIDENCE RI
1132 DANBURY CT
1133 WOODSTOCK VT
1134 ORONO ME
1135 WORCESTER MA
1136 CHERRY VALLEY NY
1137 NORFOLK VA
1138 FREDERICK MD
1139 DEEP RIVER CT
1140 LYNDON VT
1141 BETHEL CT
1142 THOMASTON ME
1143 CUBA NY
1144 SHELBURNE FALLS MA
1145 HANOVER NH
1146 SPRINGFIELD OH
1147 EXETER NH
1148 NORRISTOWN PA
1149 KINGSTON NY
1150 ASHAWAY RI
1151 PROVIDENCE RI
1152 POTTSVILLE PA
1153 MANCHESTER NH
1154 OTTAWA IL
1155 RICHMOND VA
1156 NEW CASTLE PA
1157 RHINEBECK NY
1158 KINGSTON RI
1159 WAUKESHA WI
1160 WHITEHALL NY
1161 ANTHONY RI
1162 GLOUCESTER MA
1163 HYDE PARK VT
1164 STEUBENVILLE OH
1165 HARTFORD CT
1166 SHERBURNE NY
1167 CARTHAGE IL
1168 MOUNT HOLLY NJ
1169 WESTERLY RI
1170 STOCKBRIDGE MA
1171 EASTON PA
1172 CHILLICOTHE OH
1173 PROVIDENCE RI
1174 GARDINER ME
1175 NEW LONDON CT
1176 FRANKLIN PA
1177 MENDOTA IL
1178 FULTON NY
1179 PETERBOROUGH NH
1180 SOMERSWORTH NH
1181 MIDDLETOWN DE
1182 JERSEY CITY NJ
1183 GREAT FALLS NH
1183 SOMERSWORTH NH
1184 NEW BRITAIN CT
1185 CINCINNATI OH
1186 NEW PALTZ NY
1187 NORWICH CT
1188 MORRISTOWN NJ
1189 BINGHAMTON NY
1190 WILMINGTON DE
1191 MEDFORD NJ
1192 WAVERLY NY
1193 NEW MILFORD CT
1194 ROCKPORT MA
1195 MIDDLEBURY VT
1196 NEW YORK NY
1197 BURLINGTON VT
1198 CATSKILL NY
1199 WOODBURY NJ
1200 POULTNEY VT
1201 LYNN MA
1202 NEW HAVEN CT
1203 GREAT BARRINGTON MA
1204 STANFORD KY
1205 BATTLE CREEK MI
1206 WAKEFIELD RI
1207 BLACKSTONE MA
1207 FRANKLIN MA
1208 SAUGERTIES NY
1209 CAMDEN NJ
1210 NORTH ADAMS MA
1211 PORT DEPOSIT MD
1212 FONDA NY
1213 NEWBURGH NY
1214 FALLS VILLAGE CT
1215 NEW YORK NY
1216 MIDDLETOWN CT
1217 NEWARK NJ
1218 FORT EDWARD NY
1219 TAMAQUA PA
1220 NEWARK NJ
1221 DECKERTOWN NJ
1222 BURLINGTON NJ
1223 BROOKLYN NY
1224 NEW YORK CITY NY
1225 MEMPHIS TN
1226 SCHENECTADY NY
1227 SARATOGA SPRINGS NY
1228 CAMBRIDGE MA
1229 WATERFORD NY
1230 ZANESVILLE OH
1231 NEW YORK NY
1232 NEW YORK NY
1233 EASTON PA
1234 LIMA IN
1235 COLDWATER MI
1236 ELKTON MD
1237 SUNBURY PA
1238 LEBANON OH
1239 PHILLIPSBURG NJ
1240 SENECA FALLS NY
1241 LANCASTER OH
1242 EAST JAFFREY NH
1243 NEW HAVEN CT
1244 ANNAPOLIS MD
1245 NEW HAVEN CT
1246 HOLYOKE MA
1247 HOUGHTON MI
1248 DELAVAN WI
1249 NEW CANAAN CT
1250 NEW YORK NY
1251 NEWARK NJ
1252 BALTIMORE MD
1253 BALLSTON SPA NY
1254 KENNEBUNK ME
1255 SAVANNAH GA
1256 CORUNNA MI
1257 CANAJOHARIE NY
1258 SAINT PAUL MN
1259 HACKETTSTOWN NJ
1260 PITTSFIELD MA
1261 NEW YORK NY
1262 ALBANY NY
1263 SHELBYVILLE IN
1264 VERNON NY
1265 WEST TROY NY
1265 WATERVLIET NY
1266 GREENWICH NY
1267 FREDERICK MD
1268 MYSTIC CT
1269 PAWLING NY
1270 MILLVILLE NJ
1271 CAZENOVIA NY
1272 LAMBERTVILLE NJ
1273 LOCK HAVEN PA
1274 EDGARTOWN MA
1274 TISBURY MA
1275 NORTH WHITE CREEK NY
1275 CAMBRIDGE NY
1276 MIDDLETOWN NY
1277 CHILLICOTHE OH
1278 NEW YORK NY
1279 NORTHBOROUGH MA
1280 LOWELL MI
1281 ODESSA DE
1282 ROCHESTER NY
1283 PROVIDENCE RI
1284 CENTREVILLE RI
1284 WEST WARWICK RI
1285 AUBURN NY
1286 NYACK NY
1287 SYRACUSE NY
1288 FALL RIVER MA
1289 ALBANY NY
1290 NEW YORK NY
1291 ALBANY NY
1292 BRISTOL RI
1293 GLENS FALLS NY
1294 CATSKILL NY
1295 BOSTON MA
1296 NASHVILLE TN
1297 NEW YORK NY
1298 SCHUYLERVILLE NY
1299 BLOOMFIELD IA
1300 HARTFORD CT
1301 ALBANY NY
1302 PROVIDENCE RI
1303 BALTIMORE MD
1304 SOMERS NY
1305 POUGHKEEPSIE NY
1306 POUGHKEEPSIE NY
1307 AMSTERDAM NY
1308 UTICA NY
1309 RICHMOND KY
1310 NASHUA NH
1311 OWEGO NY
1312 POUGHKEEPSIE NY
1313 LA CROSSE WI
1314 CLINTON CT
1315 BRUNSWICK ME
1316 NEWARK NJ
1317 ORANGE NJ
1318 MASSILLON OH
1319 PROVIDENCE RI
1320 FALMOUTH MA
1321 HARTFORD CT
1322 ALLENTOWN PA
1323 DELHI NY
1324 NEW YORK NY
1325 BALTIMORE MD
1326 SALEM NJ
1327 TRENTON NJ
1328 PROVIDENCE RI
1329 LOWELL MA
1330 NEW MARKET NH
1331 AUSTIN NV
1332 DELAWARE CITY DE
1333 SANBORNTON NH
1333 TILTON NH
1334 HAMILTON NY
1335 AMSTERDAM NY
1336 BALTIMORE MD
1337 BALTIMORE MD
1338 HARTFORD CT
1339 PROVIDENCE RI
1340 MIDDLETOWN CT
1341 SYRACUSE NY
1342 SYRACUSE NY
1343 WHEELING WV
1344 LITTLE FALLS NY
1345 AUBURN NY
1346 BRIDGETON NJ
1347 COHOES NY
1348 FORT EDWARD NY
1348 NORTH GRANVILLE NY
1349 CHESTER NY
1350 AUBURN NY
1351 AUBURN NY
1352 NEW YORK NY
1353 DOVER NH
1354 NORWICH NY
1355 OSWEGO NY
1356 MOUNT HOLLY NJ
1357 NEW YORK NY
1358 NORWICH CT
1359 KALAMAZOO MI
1360 BROOKLYN CT
1360 DANIELSONVILLE CT
1360 DANIELSON CT
1361 WATERVILLE NY
1362 ROCHESTER NY
1363 PORT JERVIS NY
1364 VERGENNES VT
1365 ELGIN IL
1366 PROVIDENCE RI
1367 WESTFIELD MA
1368 DERBY LINE VT
1369 PROVIDENCE RI
1370 NEW YORK NY
1371 NEW YORK NY
1372 NEW YORK NY
1373 NEW YORK NY
1374 NEW YORK NY
1375 NEW YORK NY
1376 ROME NY
1377 HARTFORD CT
1378 PETERSBURG VA
1379 NORWICH CT
1380 POUGHKEEPSIE NY
1381 SAINT LOUIS MO
1382 MERIDEN CT
1383 PROCTORSVILLE VT
1384 BALTIMORE MD
1385 TOLLAND CT
1386 ABINGTON MA
1387 WELLSBURG WV
1388 NEW YORK NY
1389 NEW YORK NY
1390 WILMINGTON DE
1391 ELMIRA NY
1392 UTICA NY
1393 NEW YORK NY
1394 NEW YORK NY
1395 UTICA NY
1396 PROVIDENCE RI
1397 ROCHESTER NY
1398 COXSACKIE NY
1399 GOSHEN NY
1400 TOMS RIVER NJ
1401 SYRACUSE NY
1402 WOONSOCKET RI
1403 WINTERSET IA
1404 CUMBERLAND RI
1405 EAST GREENWICH RI
1406 WELLS RIVER VT
1407 MEMPHIS TN
1408 GOSHEN NY
1409 WOONSOCKET RI
1410 ROME NY
1411 CATASAUQUA PA
1412 FROSTBURG MD
1413 BALTIMORE MD
1414 ROME NY
1415 CEDARBURG WI
1416 MOUNT MORRIS NY
1417 NEBRASKA CITY NE
1418 LAWRENCEBURG IN
1419 WARREN RI
1420 WILMINGTON DE
1421 WOONSOCKET RI
1422 PEEKSKILL NY
1423 WOONSOCKET RI
1424 WHEELING WV
1425 CALAIS ME
1426 LANSINGBURGH NY
1427 PARKERSBURG WV
1428 ALTON IL
1429 PROVIDENCE RI
1430 BRATTLEBORO VT
1431 HAGERSTOWN MD
1432 BALTIMORE MD
1433 DETROIT MI
1434 EASTON MD
1436 ELIZABETH NJ
1437 BANGOR ME
1438 MILWAUKEE WI
1440 WAREHAM MA
1441 KEOKUK IA
1442 BOSTON MA
1443 NEW YORK CITY NY
1443 BROOKLYN NY
1444 HOBOKEN NJ
1445 ALTON IL
1446 ROCKLAND ME
1447 CADIZ OH
1448 LEAVENWORTH KS
1449 FREDERICK MD
1450 RUTLAND VT
1451 PORTLAND ME
1452 NEWARK NJ
1453 RUSHVILLE IL
1454 VINCENNES IN
1455 WAKEFIELD MA
1456 RUSHVILLE IN
1457 MADISON IN
1458 WHITESTOWN NY
1459 FRENCHTOWN NJ
1460 PHENIX RI
1461 NEW YORK NY
1462 WATERBURY VT
1463 UNADILLA NY
1464 JERSEY SHORE PA
1464 WILLIAMSPORT PA
1465 OTTAWA IL
1466 JEFFERSONVILLE IN
1467 COLUMBIA MO
1468 CHARLOTTESVILLE VA
1469 BOSTON MA
1470 HILLSDALE MI
1471 VIRGINIA IL
1472 PROVIDENCE RI
1473 MIDDLETOWN NY
1474 GLOVERSVILLE NY
1475 FAIRFIELD IA
1476 NEW YORK NY
1477 THOMPSON CT
1477 PUTNAM CT
1478 JEWETT CITY CT
1479 COUNCIL BLUFFS IA
1480 EAST HADDAM CT
1481 NORWICH CT
1482 HENRY IL
1483 MILWAUKEE WI
1484 WINCHESTER IL
1485 METHUEN MA
1486 WOLFEBOROUGH NH
1487 RED WING MN
1488 MANCHESTER VT
1489 BALTIMORE MD
1490 WATERTOWN NY
1491 BROOKLYN NY
1492 NEWPORT RI
1493 LANCASTER KY
1494 WINSTED CT
1495 EASTPORT ME
1496 PULASKI NY
1497 NEW YORK NY
1498 GREENVILLE RI
1499 NEW YORK NY
1500 CHESTERTOWN MD
1501 SAINT LOUIS MO
1502 MORGANTOWN WV
1503 MONTICELLO NY
1504 POINT PLEASANT WV
1505 WILLIAMSPORT PA
1506 PROVIDENCE RI
1507 WATERTOWN NY
1508 WATERTOWN NY
1509 ALBION NY
1510 SCHOHARIE NY
1511 PORTLAND ME
1512 PASCOAG RI
1513 BINGHAMTON NY
1514 STILLWATER MN
1515 MARSHALL MI
1516 MOUNT JOY PA
1517 VANDALIA IL
1518 MARSHALL MI
1519 CUMBERLAND MD
1520 MANCHESTER NH
1521 PAW PAW MI
1522 LYNCHBURG VA
1523 NORTH BERWICK ME
1524 MARTINSBURG WV
1525 CANASTOTA NY
1526 WESTMINSTER MD
1527 BOSTON MA
1528 SACO ME
1529 INDEPENDENCE MO
1530 CLARKSBURG WV
1531 ADAMS NY
1532 NEWPORT RI
1533 JACKSON MI
1534 LANSINGBURGH NY
1535 SACO ME
1536 NEWARK DE
1537 SELMA AL
1538 HASTINGS MN
1539 SAINT JOHNS MI
1540 DUBUQUE IA
1541 IRASBURG VT
1542 DETROIT MI
1543 BROOKLYN NY
1544 ALBION MI
1545 MIDDLETOWN OH
1546 NEWPORT RI
1547 CHARLOTTE NC
1548 PETERSBURG VA
1549 WISCASSET ME
1550 EAST SAGINAW MI
1551 WILLIAMSPORT MD
1552 SCITUATE RI
1553 PORTLAND OR
1554 WAKEFIELD RI
1555 PARIS IL
1556 NEW YORK NY
1557 RALEIGH NC
1558 LYNCHBURG VA
1559 ATLANTA GA
1560 HUNTSVILLE AL
1561 ITHACA NY
1562 BRISTOL RI
1563 JAMESTOWN NY
1564 JAMAICA VT
1565 NEWPORT RI
1566 GALVESTON TX
1567 DOVER DE
1568 OSHKOSH WI
1569 SYRACUSE NY
1570 RICHMOND VA
1571 HANNIBAL MO
1572 HARRISONBURG VA
1573 OWOSSO MI
1574 PONTIAC MI
1575 BIDDEFORD ME
1576 DANVILLE VT
1577 MUSCATINE IA
1578 WARREN OH
1579 LEWISTOWN PA
1580 SAINT JOSEPH MO
1581 INDEPENDENCE IA
1582 FREDERICKSBURG VA
1583 SAINT ALBANS VT
1584 BOONVILLE MO
1585 STAUNTON VA
1587 MONROE MI
1588 FLINT MI
1589 FREDERICK MD
1590 LAWRENCE KS
1591 NEW ORLEANS LA
1592 WICKFORD RI
1593 VINTON IA
1594 WHEELING WV
1595 MOBILE AL
1596 WESTMINSTER MD
1597 SHAKOPEE MN
1598 CASTLETON VT
1599 PADUCAH KY
1600 DANVILLE KY
1601 DANVILLE KY
1602 NEENAH WI
1603 CLARKSVILLE TN
1604 ATTLEBOROUGH MA
1605 ATLANTA GA
1606 CHATTANOOGA TN
1607 WESTON WV
1608 KINGWOOD WV
1609 DANVILLE VA
1610 JACKSON MS
1611 FORT MADISON IA
1612 KANSAS CITY MO
1613 AUGUSTA GA

1614 WINDHAM CT
1614 WILLIMANTIC CT
1615 HENDERSON KY
1616 NORTH PROVIDENCE RI
1616 PAWTUCKET RI
1617 MACON GA
1618 OSAGE IA
1619 BROOKVILLE IN
1620 STAUNTON VA
1621 CHARLESTON SC
1622 CHARLESTON SC
1623 MINNEAPOLIS MN
1624 NEW YORK NY
1625 DOWAGIAC MI
1626 NEW ORLEANS LA
1627 SEDALIA MO
1628 RICHMOND VA
1629 GRINNELL IA
1630 COLUMBUS GA
1631 FORT SMITH AR
1632 NEW BERNE NC
1633 OMAHA NE
1634 SWANTON VT
1635 WINCHESTER VA
1636 MEMPHIS TN
1637 PEKIN IL
1638 NORTHFIELD VT
1639 ATHENS GA
1640 SAVANNAH GA
1641 OLNEY IL
1642 GALVESTON TX
1643 WINONA MN
1644 HOUSTON TX
1645 LACONIA NH
1646 SALT LAKE CITY UT
1647 PHILADELPHIA PA
1648 LITTLE ROCK AR
1649 HELENA MT
1650 APPLETON WI
1651 DENVER CO
1652 CENTRAL CITY CO
1653 BELLOWS FALLS VT
1655 NEWPORT NY
1656 WILMINGTON NC
1657 SAN ANTONIO TX
1658 CLARKSVILLE VA
1659 SALEM NC
1660 TOPEKA KS
1661 FORT DODGE IA
1662 SPRINGFIELD IL
1663 POTTSVILLE PA
1664 LEBANON TN
1665 SAINT LOUIS MO
1666 CLEVELAND TN
1667 SAINT JOSEPH MO
1668 BOISE CITY ID
1668 BOISE ID
1669 NASHVILLE TN
1670 ILION NY
1671 DAVENPORT IA
1672 ATCHISON KS
1673 ROYALTON VT
1674 WARNER NH
1675 BOSTON MA
1676 HONEYBROOK PA
1677 SPRINGFIELD MO
1678 LAKE IL
1680 COLUMBIA SC
1681 PRINCETON NJ
1682 RALEIGH NC
1683 MANKATO MN
1684 COUNCIL BLUFFS IA
1685 SHARON PA
1686 FARIBAULT MN
1687 BANGOR ME
1688 HILLSBOROUGH NH
1689 CLEVELAND OH
1690 AUSTIN MN
1691 NEW YORK NY
1692 MURFREESBORO TN
1693 CHICAGO IL
1694 LEBANON KY
1695 SALT LAKE CITY UT
1696 LEON IA
1697 PORT HENRY NY
1698 BURLINGTON VT
1699 BOSTON MA
1700 RUTLAND VT
1701 SPRINGFIELD MO
1702 MAYSVILLE KY
1703 AUGUSTA GA
1704 NORFOLK VA
1705 STANFORD KY
1706 MONMOUTH IL
1707 GALLATIN TN
1708 LEBANON TN
1709 CHICAGO IL
1710 BRODHEAD WI
1711 SHELBINA MO
1712 CALIFORNIA MO
1713 COLUMBIA TN
1714 MENASHA WI
1715 SALEM IL
1716 ALEXANDRIA VA
1717 STERLING IL
1718 OTTAWA KS
1719 JACKSONVILLE IL
1720 LEXINGTON KY
1721 WATSEKA IL
1722 DECATUR MI
1723 TUSCOLA IL
1724 CHARITON IA
1725 SCHOOLCRAFT MI
1726 OTTUMWA IA
1727 PULASKI TN
1728 RICHMOND KY
1729 EVANSVILLE WI
1730 MUSKEGON MI
1731 LAPEER MI
1732 LAWRENCE KS
1733 SPRINGFIELD IL
1734 CHICAGO IL
1735 PALMYRA MO
1736 SELMA AL
1737 HIGHTSTOWN NJ
1738 LEESBURG VA
1739 SOUTH BEND IN
1740 LAKE CITY MN
1741 SAN FRANCISCO CA
1742 CHARLOTTESVILLE VA
1743 PHILADELPHIA PA
1744 BURLINGTON IA
1745 HASTINGS MI
1746 CHATTANOOGA TN
1747 NEW ORLEANS LA
1748 SOMERSET KY
1749 APPLETON WI
1750 SANTA FE NM
1751 PLEASANT HILL MO
1752 HOLLY MI
1753 KEESEVILLE NY
1754 RICHMOND VA
1755 LANARK IL
1756 FAYETTEVILLE NC
1757 SIOUX CITY IA
1758 CHARLOTTE MI
1759 HIGHTSTOWN NJ
1760 FRANKLIN KY
1761 NILES MI
1762 WASHINGTON IA
1763 FORT SCOTT KS
1764 MASON MI
1765 COLUMBIA SC
1766 RALEIGH NC
1767 SPRINGFIELD KY
1768 SAGINAW MI
1769 PETERSBURG VA
1770 COLUMBIA MO
1771 BOSCOBEL WI
1772 EVANSVILLE IN
1772 MOUNT VERNON NY
1773 SENECA IL
1773 MORRIS IL
1774 NEW ORLEANS LA
1775 SHAWNEETOWN IL
1776 OSCEOLA IA
1777 JEFFERSON TX
1778 NEW ORLEANS LA
1779 VANDALIA IL
1780 FLINT MI
1781 CHARLOTTE NC
1782 WINONA MN
1783 STILLWATER MN
1784 BELLEFONTAINE OH
1785 KEWANEE IL
1786 SIGOURNEY IA
1787 OSHKOSH WI
1788 DAYTON OH
1789 SAINT CLAIR MI
1790 RICHMOND KY
1791 BUSHNELL IL
1792 AURORA IL
1793 KANKAKEE IL
1794 SAINT PETER MN
1795 CHARLESTON WV
1796 NEW ORLEANS LA
1797 BALTIMORE MD
1798 LINCOLN NE
1799 ALBIA IA
1800 CHEYENNE WY
1801 DUBUQUE IA
1802 RACINE WI
1803 PARIS MO
1804 CHESTER SC
1805 KEITHSBURG IL
1806 POLO IL
1807 HARRODSBURG KY
1808 LEWISTOWN IL
1809 JEFFERSON CITY MO
1810 CHARLES CITY IA
1811 INDIANOLA IA
1812 CASSOPOLIS MI
1813 ANAMOSA IA
1814 MONTGOMERY AL
1815 ELKADER IA
1816 ROCKFORD IL
1817 MOBILE AL
1818 NEWARK NJ
1819 GREEN BAY WI
1820 APPLETON WI
1821 WINCHESTER IL
1822 GAINESVILLE AL
1823 SOUTH HAVEN MI
1824 SALEM VA
1825 NEW ORLEANS LA
1826 UNION CITY MI
1827 BOSTON MA
1828 OLATHE KS
1829 ALLEGAN MI
1830 SAINT ANTHONY MN
1830 MINNEAPOLIS MN
1831 NICHOLASVILLE KY
1832 BIG RAPIDS MI
1833 PUEBLO CO
1834 FRANKLIN TN
1835 VERSAILLES KY
1836 ATLANTIC IA
1837 PONTIAC IL
1838 BAXTER SPRINGS KS
1839 LAGRANGE MO
1840 WYANDOTTE KS
1841 GREENVILLE IL
1842 WINONA MN
1843 BUTLER MO
1844 NEWBERRY SC
1845 CHICAGO IL
1846 BROWNVILLE NE
1847 COVINGTON KY
1848 SPARTANBURG SC
1849 GRAND HAVEN MI
1850 MASON CITY IL
1851 CHARLESTON IL
1852 MARSEILLES IL
1853 TUSCALOOSA AL
1854 FRANKFORT IN
1855 NEBRASKA CITY NE
1856 WARRENSBURG MO
1857 PORT HURON MI
1858 SAINT LOUIS MO
1859 COVINGTON KY
1860 AUGUSTA GA
1861 NEWNAN GA
1862 GLENWOOD IA
1863 FARIBAULT MN
1864 PAOLA KS
1865 ROLLA MO
1866 SAINT JOSEPH MI
1867 CHICAGO IL
1868 CHARLES TOWN WV
1869 RUSHVILLE IN
1870 MARENGO IL
1871 KNOXVILLE IA
1872 MACOMB IL
1873 VINCENNES IN
1874 WEBSTER CITY IA
1875 KUTZTOWN PA
1875 READING PA
1876 PAXTON IL
1877 KNOB NOSTER MO
1878 INDIANAPOLIS IN
1879 PERU IN
1880 TAMA CITY IA
1880 TAMA IA
1881 DIXON IL
1882 JOLIET IL
1883 PIEDMONT WV
1884 WELLSBURG WV
1885 LITTLETON NH
1886 NILES MI
1887 OLEAN NY
1888 BLOOMINGTON IN
1889 ROCK ISLAND IL
1890 GREENSBURG IN
1891 PELLA IA
1892 BEDFORD IN
1893 WASHINGTON DC
1893 HAGERSTOWN MD
1894 GREENSBURG PA
1894 PITTSBURGH PA
1895 TOLEDO OH
1896 SYCAMORE IL
1897 NEWPORT IN
1898 NEW ORLEANS LA
1899 LINCOLN NE
1900 CYNTHIANA KY
1901 KANSAS CITY MO
1902 CHETOPA KS
1903 JACKSON OH
1904 PLYMOUTH OH
1905 HACKENSACK NJ
1906 DEFIANCE OH
1907 ROCHELLE IL
1908 LOUISVILLE KY
1909 AURORA IL
1910 OTTAWA KS
1911 OWATONNA MN
1912 WOOSTER OH
1913 WICHITA KS
1914 PLATTSMOUTH NE
1915 EMPORIA KS
1916 PLYMOUTH MI
1917 NAPOLEON OH
1918 EAST SAGINAW MI
1918 SAGINAW MI
1919 THREE RIVERS MI
1920 COSHOCTON OH
1921 SALT LAKE CITY UT
1922 ROCHELLE IL
1923 MILLERSBURG OH
1924 COLDWATER MI
1925 LIBERTY IN
1926 CLINTON IL
1927 FORT SCOTT KS
1928 GEORGETOWN DC
1928 WASHINGTON DC
1929 SHELBY OH
1930 MINERVA OH
1931 MONTICELLO KY
1932 SULLIVAN IN
1933 BURLINGTON WI
1934 NOKOMIS IL
1935 GREENVILLE SC
1936 PHOENIXVILLE PA
1937 NEW ORLEANS LA
1938 GLOVERSVILLE NY
1939 HOLYOKE MA
1940 CLINTON MO
1941 MOLINE IL
1942 CAMBRIDGE OH
1943 WYOMING IA
1944 BELLAIRE OH
1945 TOPEKA KS
1946 SCRANTON PA
1947 FORT DODGE IA
1948 PORTSMOUTH OH
1949 DELPHI IN
1950 FORT SMITH AR
1951 PARSONS KS
1952 ROCHESTER IN
1953 LANSING MI
1954 DULUTH MN
1955 DENVER CO
1956 NORWAY ME
1957 EL DORADO KS
1958 PORTSMOUTH OH
1959 RISING SUN IN
1960 HELENA MT
1961 FLORA IL
1962 LAWRENCE MA
1963 OWENTON KY
1964 BRAIDWOOD IL
1964 WILMINGTON IL
1965 HOLLY MI
1966 TRENTON MO
1967 LAFAYETTE IN
1968 PROPHETSTOWN IL
1969 OREGON IL
1970 DES MOINES IA
1971 SEDALIA MO
1972 WASHINGTON OH
1973 ADRIAN MI
1974 FREMONT NE
1975 DEER LODGE MT
1976 SIOUX CITY IA
1977 JUNCTION CITY KS
1978 CHICAGO IL
1979 BURLINGTON KS
1980 POMEROY OH
1981 NEW LONDON OH
1982 MANCHESTER OH
1983 EMPORIA KS
1984 GALION OH
1985 DANVILLE VA
1986 KNOXVILLE IA
1987 FAIRBURY IL
1988 RICHMOND IN
1989 QUAKER CITY OH
1990 PULASKI TN
1991 GEORGETOWN CO
1992 KEOKUK IA
1993 BOSTON MA
1994 SAN FRANCISCO CA
1995 KANSAS CITY MO
1996 MOUNT VERNON IL
1997 WILMINGTON OH
1998 GRAND RAPIDS WI
1998 WISCONSIN RAPIDS WI
1999 NEW PHILADELPHIA OH
2000 MURFREESBORO TN
2001 COUNCIL GROVE KS
2002 WINTERSET IA
2003 FAYETTEVILLE NC
2004 BEREA OH
2005 MANKATO MN
2006 MINNEAPOLIS MN
2007 LIBERTY IN
2008 LYONS MI
2008 IONIA MI
2009 AMERICUS GA
2010 ASHLAND KY
2011 KANSAS IL
2012 BELLE PLAINE IA
2013 CARTHAGE MO
2014 SACRAMENTO CA
2015 WEST UNION IA
2016 ELGIN IL
2017 MUIR MI
2018 SPRING CITY PA
2019 SPRINGFIELD TN
2020 SAINT PAUL MN
2021 SAINT CHARLES IL
2022 FARMINGTON NH
2023 MARSHALL MI
2024 SANTA FE NM
2025 MIDDLETOWN OH
2026 JEFFERSON OH
2027 BOZEMAN MT
2028 CLARINDA IA
2029 MONTGOMERY AL
2030 FERGUS FALLS MN
2031 ASHTABULA OH
2032 COLUMBUS JUNCTION IA
2033 BRIGHTON IA
2034 GARRETTSVILLE OH
2035 LIMA OH
2036 McARTHUR OH
2037 GREEN SPRING OH
2038 WASHINGTON DC
2039 HILLSBOROUGH OH
2040 NEWARK NJ
2041 ALLIANCE OH
2042 CARLINVILLE IL
2043 WASHINGTON IN
2044 CHARLESTON SC
2045 NEWARK NJ
2046 BUCHANAN MI
2047 CHICAGO IL
2048 CHICAGO IL
2049 KNOXVILLE TN
2050 BETHLEHEM PA
2051 BOONE IA
2052 MALTA OH
2053 MEDINA OH
2054 GREENVILLE MI
2055 JEFFERSON CITY MO
2056 NEW LEXINGTON OH
2057 LEBANON IN
2058 TURNERS FALLS MA
2059 SALT LAKE CITY UT
2060 UNION SC
2061 SANDUSKY OH
2062 LOUISVILLE KY
2063 PELLA IA
2064 ATLANTA GA
2065 BIRMINGHAM AL
2066 PRINCETON IN
2067 GOSHEN IN
2068 YANKTON SD
2069 EAU CLAIRE WI
2070 PADUCAH KY
2071 URBANA OH
2072 ANDERSON SC
2073 NORTHFIELD MN
2074 YONKERS NY
2075 GRIFFIN GA
2076 DOVER NJ
2077 STOCKTON CA
2078 CONSHOHOCKEN PA
2079 BARABOO WI
2080 MONTICELLO IA
2081 MUSKEGON MI
2082 ATCHISON KS
2083 NEWARK NJ
2084 ISHPEMING MI
2085 NEGAUNEE MI
2086 NEW ORLEANS LA
2087 WINNSBORO SC
2088 ROCHESTER MN
2089 BANGOR ME
2090 RICHMOND IN
2091 MEDINA OH
2092 HOUSTON TX
2093 PADUCAH KY
2094 MANHATTAN KS
2095 CENTREVILLE MI
2096 MEMPHIS TN
2097 ROCKLAND ME
2098 SPRINGFIELD OH
2099 DENISON TX
2100 PARIS IL
2101 MICHIGAN CITY IN
2102 CALDWELL OH
2103 BOSTON MA
2104 SANTA BARBARA CA
2105 HELENA MT
2106 MISSOULA MT
2107 NATICK MA
2108 WATERTOWN MA
2109 BARRE VT
2110 LARAMIE CITY WY
2110 LARAMIE WY
2111 BOSTON MA
2112 BOSTON MA
2113 ASHBURNHAM MA
2114 FAYETTEVILLE TN
2115 MARSHALLTOWN IA
2116 GRIGGSVILLE IL
2117 ELLENVILLE NY
2118 AUSTIN TX
2119 PLYMOUTH IN
2120 CHELSEA VT
2121 ASHLAND NE
2122 OWATONNA MN
2123 SHEBOYGAN WI
2124 DECATUR IL
2125 CHIPPEWA FALLS WI
2126 LINCOLN IL
2127 MEMPHIS TN
2128 SHELBYVILLE IL
2129 CENTRAL CITY CO
2130 RED OAK IA
2131 GREEN LANE PA
2132 GREEN BAY WI
2133 DE PERE WI
2134 PUEBLO CO
2135 CHARLOTTE NC
2136 BINGHAMTON NY
2137 BOYERTOWN PA
2138 ROCHESTER NH
2139 WILLIAMSPORT PA
2140 GOLDEN CO
2141 PONTIAC IL
2142 SCHWENKSVILLE PA
2143 HANCOCK MI
2144 MARTINSBURG WV
2145 BAY CITY MI
2146 EAST LIVERPOOL OH
2147 MATTOON IL
2148 WINCHESTER KY
2149 BOWLING GREEN KY
2150 LEBANON KY
2151 ONEONTA NY
2152 BROCKTON MA
2153 FITCHBURG MA
2154 BELLEVILLE IL
2155 ROCK ISLAND IL
2156 FARMER CITY IL
2157 DALLAS TX
2158 SAN JOSE CA
2159 KASSON MN
2160 STEUBENVILLE OH
2161 LOUISVILLE KY
2162 LESLIE MI
2163 BELOIT WI
2164 LOUISVILLE KY
2165 PRINCETON IL
2166 NEW ALBANY IN
2167 BRISTOL TN
2168 JACKSON TN
2169 RUSSELLVILLE KY
2170 STREATOR IL
2171 LOUISVILLE KY
2172 ATHOL MA
2173 SALEM IN
2174 JACKSONVILLE FL
2175 FAIRFIELD ME
2176 STREATOR IL
2177 CEDAR FALLS IA
2178 SPENCER IN
2179 COLORADO SPRINGS CO
2180 PRINCETON IN
2181 CENTREVILLE OH
2182 LISBON IA
2183 CROWN POINT IN
2184 LAGRANGE IN
2185 MOUNT STERLING KY
2186 ROMEO MI
2187 INDEPENDENCE IA
2188 EVANSVILLE IN
2189 WACO TX
2190 LAWRENCEBURG KY
2191 ALLERTON IA
2192 TOPEKA KS
2193 PETALUMA CA
2195 PITTSBURGH PA
2196 NEW CASTLE KY
2197 CENTERVILLE IA
2198 SHELBYVILLE TN
2199 GEORGETOWN CO
2200 NASHVILLE TN
2201 TELL CITY IN
2202 NEW CASTLE IN
2203 NEW LISBON OH
2204 ARCOLA IL
2205 MONMOUTH IL
2206 CAVERNA KY
2207 BOONVILLE IN
2208 MONTICELLO IN
2209 MORGANFIELD KY
2210 MIDDLEPORT OH
2211 CONSTANTINE MI
2212 OAKLAND IL
2213 LAFAYETTE IN
2214 MOUNT CLEMENS MI
2215 MONROE IA
2216 MOUNT STERLING KY
2217 YOUNGSTOWN OH
2218 LANCASTER MO
2219 BATESVILLE OH
2220 WAYNESVILLE OH
2221 McMINNVILLE TN
2222 McKEESPORT PA
2223 MONTROSE PA
2224 NUNDA NY
2225 BREWSTER NY
2226 WARREN PA
2227 WILLIAMSPORT PA
2228 YORK PA
2229 HAVERSTRAW NY
2230 RED OAK IA
2231 OAKLAND ME
2232 ATTLEBORO MA
2233 WHITEHALL NY
2234 MUNCIE IN
2235 ALLEGHENY PA
2236 PITTSBURGH PA
2237 PITTSBURGH PA
2238 AUBURN IN
2239 AMSTERDAM NY
2240 NASHUA NH
2241 MILLERSTOWN PA
2242 HAVANA IL
2243 PLAINFIELD NJ
2244 SHARON PA
2245 MAYFIELD KY
2246 CLINTON NJ
2247 MALVERN IA
2248 OAKLAND CA
2249 JENKINTOWN PA
2250 BRISTOL CT
2251 GREENVILLE PA
2252 MILLERSBURG PA
2253 HATBORO PA
2254 PRAIRIE CITY IL
2255 ORANGE MA
2256 MERCER PA
2257 RED BANK NJ
2258 MEYERSDALE PA
2259 DEXTER ME
2260 LEWISTON ME
2261 ALLEGHENY PA
2261 PITTSBURGH PA
2262 NEW BEDFORD MA
2263 NEWPORT VT
2264 GREENFIELD MA
2265 FITCHBURG MA
2266 OAKLAND CA
2267 PHILLIPS ME
2268 WINONA MN
2269 STAUNTON VA
2270 AUBURN ME
2271 BLOOMSBURY NJ
2272 CORTLAND NY
2273 WORCESTER MA
2274 WEST RANDOLPH VT
2274 RANDOLPH VT
2275 MILFORD MA
2276 NEWPORT KY
2277 BOSTON MA
2278 PITTSBURGH PA
2279 PITTSBURGH PA
2280 ASHLAND PA
2281 PITTSBURGH PA
2282 FRANKLIN OH
2283 ATLANTA IL
2284 WESTMINSTER MA
2284 GARDNER MA
2285 TARENTUM PA
2286 FREEPORT PA
2287 PEKIN IL
2288 SPENCER MA
2289 BOSTON MA
2290 BARTON VT
2291 PHILADELPHIA PA
2292 GLOUCESTER MA
2293 SLATINGTON PA
2294 GRANVILLE NY
2295 SAINT JOHNSBURY VT
2296 TOLEDO OH
2297 GEORGETOWN MA
2298 BEDFORD IA
2299 KEENE NH
2300 TRINIDAD CO
2301 PENNSBURG PA
2302 BELLEVUE OH
2303 YORK PA
2304 BOSTON MA
2305 BRATTLEBORO VT
2306 WATERVILLE ME
2307 DES MOINES IA
2308 LEHIGHTON PA
2309 EUFAULA AL
2310 PUEBLO CO
2311 CAMDEN ME
2312 WEBSTER MA
2313 KIRKWOOD IL
2314 CHARLOTTE NC
2315 CINCINNATI OH
2316 ROCHESTER MN
2317 PHILADELPHIA PA
2318 NEW ULM MN
2319 WINSTON NC
2320 BOONVILLE NY
2321 WILSON NC
2322 GREENSBORO NC
2323 FLEMINGSBURG KY
2324 PALMER MA
2325 MECHANICSBURG OH
2326 AFTON IA
2327 DUBUQUE IA
2328 JERSEYVILLE IL
2329 CONNELLSVILLE PA
2330 VIRGINIA IL
2331 FLEMINGTON NJ
2332 GENESEO IL
2333 SOUDERTON PA
2334 PENNSBURG PA
2335 HARMONY PA
2336 SMYRNA DE
2337 TOWANDA PA
2338 COLUMBUS GA
2339 LAMBERTVILLE NJ
2340 MILFORD DE
2341 CENTREVILLE MD
2342 NORWALK CT
2343 MOUNT HOLLY NJ
2344 LA CROSSE WI
2345 FRANKLINVILLE NY
2346 ANDERSON IN
2347 LAWRENCE MA
2348 WALDEN NY
2349 FORT WORTH TX
2350 YOUNGSTOWN OH
2351 DENVER CO
2352 BOULDER CO
2353 MORAVIA NY
2354 LAKE CITY CO
2355 BOULDER CO
2356 PLATTE CITY MO
2357 BEATRICE NE
2358 WASHINGTON DC
2359 FORT WORTH TX
2360 LEBANON OH
2361 ROCKVILLE IN
2362 MANCHESTER NH
2363 SHENANDOAH IA
2364 HAMBURG IA
2365 DETROIT MI
2366 QUAKERTOWN PA
2367 EATON RAPIDS MI
2368 ROME GA
2369 SULLIVAN IN
2370 NEW YORK NY
2371 ROCKLAND ME
2372 UNION CITY MI
2373 BOSTON MA
2374 RICHMOND KY
2375 KOKOMO IN
2376 OLEAN NY
2377 FARGO ND
2378 NYACK NY
2379 MILFORD MI
2380 WALLA WALLA WA
2381 SMYRNA DE
2382 WASHINGTON DC
2383 ROCHESTER NY
2384 ANNVILLE PA
2385 EASTON PA
2386 BLOOMINGTON IL
2387 CANNON FALLS MN
2388 WILLIMANTIC CT
2389 HUBBARD OH
2390 CARROLLTON IL
2391 DEADWOOD SD
2392 BROOKVILLE PA
2393 LEXINGTON KY
2394 GEORGETOWN CO
2395 BENNINGTON VT
2396 NORTH ADAMS MA
2397 DILLSBURG PA
2398 HOMER NY
2399 VINELAND NJ
2400 LITTLE FALLS NY
2401 ONEIDA NY
2402 MOUNT STERLING IL
2403 VALPARAISO IN
2404 MARLBOROUGH MA
2405 PENN YAN NY
2406 LITTLE FALLS NY
2407 BELOIT WI
2408 BURGETTSTOWN PA
2409 DANVILLE KY
2410 ROME NY
2411 NASHUA IA
2412 STOCKTON CA
2413 PRINCETON IL
2414 WINSTED CT

2415 PITTSBURGH PA
2416 CUMBERLAND MD
2417 OSKALOOSA IA
2418 JOHNSTOWN NY
2419 WINSTED CT
2420 LEADVILLE CO
2421 BATAVIA NY
2422 FAIR HAVEN VT
2423 COLUMBUS OH
2424 ATLANTA GA
2425 WINSTON NC
2426 LOWVILLE NY
2427 ABILENE KS
2428 BRADFORD PA
2429 WHITEHALL MI
2430 HOLYOKE MA
2431 ALAMEDA CA
2432 MEMPHIS MO
2433 SPRINGFIELD MA
2434 BISMARCK ND
2435 SPRINGFIELD MA
2436 LAS VEGAS NM
2437 ATTICA NY
2438 MONROEVILLE OH
2439 FORT WAYNE IN
2440 KANSAS CITY MO
2441 POLAND NY
2442 CARTHAGE NY
2443 FRANKLIN NH
2444 CADIZ OH
2445 GRAFTON WV
2446 OGDENSBURG NY
2447 CONCORD NH
2448 CAMDEN NY
2449 HILLSBORO OH
2450 CHICAGO IL
2451 CUBA NY
2452 LITITZ PA
2453 BALTIMORE MD
2454 LAS VEGAS NM
2455 DALLAS TX
2456 SANTA BARBARA CA
2457 BROWNSVILLE PA
2458 MORGANTOWN WV
2459 MOUNT GILEAD OH
2460 GRAND RAPIDS MI
2461 DEADWOOD SD
2462 PHILADELPHIA PA
2463 DUNDEE NY
2464 PARKESBURG PA
2465 SIOUX FALLS SD
2466 TITUSVILLE PA
2467 MAYSVILLE KY
2468 CLYDE NY
2469 CLINTON IA
2470 BRADFORD PA
2471 HOOSICK FALLS NY
2472 SALAMANCA NY
2473 READING PA
2474 BRYAN OH
2475 VERGENNES VT
2476 FORT BENTON MT
2476 GREAT FALLS MT
2477 WEATHERFORD TX
2478 RENO NV
2479 WARREN OH
2480 BELLEFONTAINE OH
2481 RISING SUN MD
2482 YOUNGSTOWN OH
2483 WATSONTOWN PA
2484 MARENGO IA
2485 SOUTH FRAMINGHAM MA
2486 LAREDO TX
2487 MIDDLEBURGH NY
2488 SAINT PARIS OH
2489 CANTON OH
2490 PENSACOLA FL
2491 LOS ANGELES CA
2492 SAGINAW MI
2493 RONDOUT NY
2494 WATERBURY CT
2495 CINCINNATI OH
2496 GRANVILLE OH
2497 LIMA OH
2498 CAMBRIDGE MD
2499 BALTIMORE MD
2500 KENTON OH
2501 KEWANEE IL
2502 ELKHART IN
2503 LASALLE IL
2504 BROCKTON MA
2505 CANTON PA
2506 LYNCHBURG VA
2507 NEW YORK NY
2508 HUNTINGTON IN
2509 TOMS RIVER NJ
2510 GOUVERNEUR NY
2511 CEDAR RAPIDS IA
2512 DARLINGTON SC
2513 NASHVILLE TN
2514 FARGO ND
2515 EPHRATA PA
2516 DEFIANCE OH
2517 GREENWICH NY
2518 LARAMIE CITY WY
2519 QUINCY IL
2520 DAYTON WA
2521 EL PASO TX
2522 HORNELLSVILLE NY
2522 HORNELL NY
2523 DENVER CO
2524 CINCINNATI OH
2525 PITTSFIELD MA
2526 KENNETT SQUARE PA
2527 ATLANTIC CITY NJ
2528 HASTINGS NE
2529 ZANESVILLE OH
2530 NEW HOLLAND PA
2531 HARRODSBURG KY
2532 EL PASO TX
2533 CRAWFORDSVILLE IN
2534 PLATTSBURGH NY
2535 SIOUX CITY IA
2536 NEBRASKA CITY NE
2538 SALINA KS
2539 MANISTEE MI
2540 CAMBRIDGE IL
2541 SOUTH PUEBLO CO
2541 PUEBLO CO
2542 CINCINNATI OH
2543 BAINBRIDGE NY
2544 EAST LIVERPOOL OH
2545 POULTNEY VT
2546 SOUTH PUEBLO CO
2546 PUEBLO CO
2547 DENTON MD
2548 VALLEY CITY ND
2549 CINCINNATI OH
2550 QUINCY MI
2551 MADISON NJ
2552 READING PA
2553 RICHBURG NY
2554 NEWPORT RI
2555 NEVADA IA
2556 INDIANAPOLIS IN
2557 RACINE WI
2558 GREENSBURG PA
2559 CHATTANOOGA TN
2560 CYNTHIANA KY
2561 BUTLER MO
2562 GREENSBURG PA
2563 LYNN MA
2564 GRAND FORKS ND
2565 APPLETON WI
2566 BUTTE MT
2567 CROOKSTON MN
2568 COLUMBIA TN
2569 MOORHEAD MN
2570 GRAND FORKS ND
2571 GLENCOE MN
2572 CAMBRIDGE IL
2573 HAMPTON IA
2574 MASON CITY IA
2575 XENIA OH
2576 OWENSBORO KY
2577 MANSFIELD OH
2578 JAMESTOWN ND
2579 CHARLES CITY IA
2580 JAMESTOWN ND
2581 NORRISTOWN PA
2582 UHRICHSVILLE OH
2583 DES MOINES IA
2584 DANVILLE IL
2585 MANDAN ND
2586 CRESTON IA
2587 PLYMOUTH NH
2588 NEW HAMPTON IA
2589 HIAWATHA KS
2590 BRAINERD MN
2591 DETROIT MI
2592 CARROLLTON KY
2593 McMINNVILLE TN
2594 CHARLOTTESVILLE VA
2595 STORM LAKE IA
2596 LOGANSPORT IN
2597 OGDEN UT
2598 NEW YORK NY
2599 WALLINGFORD CT
2600 LANCASTER NH
2601 CHICAGO IL
2602 STAMFORD NY
2603 NEENAH WI
2604 DAYTON OH
2605 COLUMBUS OH
2606 MANISTEE MI
2607 PONTIAC MI
2608 NEW YORK NY
2609 SALTSBURG PA
2610 SALAMANCA NY
2611 GRAND RAPIDS MI
2612 LAWRENCEBURGH IN
2613 KANSAS CITY MO
2614 ALBUQUERQUE NM
2615 SARATOGA SPRINGS NY
2616 CINCINNATI OH
2617 AUSTIN TX
2618 HUDSON MA
2619 DUNKIRK NY
2620 SPRINGFIELD OH
2621 OTTUMWA IA
2622 FORT COLLINS CO
2623 BALTIMORE MD
2624 WAHPETON ND
2625 LORAIN OH
2626 TARRYTOWN NY
2627 SOCORRO NM
2628 VAN WERT OH
2629 OLNEY IL
2630 PENDLETON OR
2631 DES MOINES IA
2632 FRIENDSHIP NY
2633 BATON ROUGE LA
2634 LANCASTER PA
2635 PULASKI TN
2636 APPLETON CITY MO
2637 DURANGO CO
2638 COLUMBUS MS
2639 TUCSON AZ
2640 CAWKER CITY KS
2641 PROVO CITY UT
2642 SEARSPORT ME
2643 SOUTH NORWALK CT
2644 NEWTON IA
2645 MITCHELL SD
2646 TOPEKA KS
2647 WAUKESHA WI
2648 FERGUS FALLS MN
2649 PARKERSBURG WV
2650 VALLEY CITY ND
2651 RICHFIELD SPRINGS NY
2652 CHEYENNE WY
2653 SUPERIOR WI
2654 KITTANNING PA
2655 CORNING NY
2656 WASHINGTON IA
2657 WATERTOWN NY
2658 KNOXVILLE TN
2659 BANGOR PA
2660 LEBANON IN
2661 MILLERTON NY
2662 CLEVELAND OH
2663 MAYSVILLE KY
2664 CINCINNATI OH
2665 OMAHA NE
2666 LARNED KS
2667 SELLERSVILLE PA
2668 NEW YORK NY
2669 WEST GROVE PA
2670 CHICAGO IL
2671 CONSHOHOCKEN PA
2672 PORTSMOUTH NH
2673 BROWNSVILLE PA
2674 STILLWATER MN
2675 WOODSTOCK IL
2676 BLOOMINGTON IL
2677 BISMARCK ND
2678 DAYTON OH
2679 SHENANDOAH IA
2680 RICHMOND IN
2681 STREATOR IL
2682 NEW HAVEN CT
2683 YORK NE
2684 WALNUT IL
2685 BARRE MA
2686 GUNNISON CO
2687 KENDALLVILLE IN
2688 SPRINGFIELD IL
2689 FORT WORTH TX
2690 CLEVELAND OH
2691 SALEM OH
2692 EVANSVILLE IN
2693 YOUNGSTOWN OH
2694 DENVER CO
2695 DAVENPORT IA
2696 CENTERVILLE IN
2697 SCRANTON PA
2698 AKRON OH
2699 WORCESTER MA
2700 STRASBURG PA
2701 FORT WAYNE IN
2702 DE KALB IL
2703 FREMONT OH
2704 VALPARAISO IN
2705 GEORGETOWN OH
2706 CRETE NE
2707 DETROIT MI
2708 FLUSHING MI
2709 STERLING IL
2710 MARIETTA PA
2711 PITTSBURGH PA
2712 McCONNELSVILLE OH
2713 KIRKSVILLE MO
2714 ANN ARBOR MI
2715 MILWAUKEE WI
2716 AKRON OH
2717 LAFAYETTE IN
2718 OBERLIN OH
2719 GENEVA OH
2720 CLARKSVILLE TN
2721 STUART IA
2722 COVINGTON KY
2723 WEATHERFORD TX
2724 BLAIR NE
2725 BELOIT WI
2726 NEWPORT KY
2727 TROY OH
2728 LE MARS IA
2729 McKINNEY TX
2730 CINCINNATI OH
2731 PHILADELPHIA PA
2732 HELENA MT
2733 LYONS IA
2734 CAMBRIDGE CITY IN
2735 BELTON TX
2736 WILKES BARRE PA
2737 ROANOKE VA
2738 IOWA CITY IA
2739 JOHNSTOWN PA
2740 CATLETTSBURG KY
2741 NASHUA NH
2742 TERRE HAUTE IN
2743 BATH ME
2744 HOLLIDAYSBURG PA
2745 PITTSBURGH PA
2746 FALLS CITY NE
2747 MICHIGAN CITY IN
2748 JANESVILLE WI
2749 HOULTON ME
2750 LINCOLN NE
2751 MONMOUTH IL
2752 MILES CITY MT
2753 MARION IA
2754 SOUTH CHARLESTON OH
2755 FRANKLINVILLE NY
2756 HEBRON NE
2757 HELENA MT
2758 ATCHISON KS
2759 EAU CLAIRE WI
2760 LYNCHBURG VA
2761 EAST SAGINAW MI
2762 ATLANTIC IA
2763 FORT DODGE IA
2764 COTTONWOOD FALLS KS
2765 CANANDAIGUA NY
2766 VILLISCA IA
2767 SAN ANGELO TX
2768 DULUTH MN
2769 FRANKLIN IN
2770 MARLBORO MA
2771 SEWARD NE
2772 DAYTON WA
2773 LUDINGTON MI
2774 NORFOLK NE
2775 OMAHA NE
2776 PINE BLUFF AR
2777 NEWTON KS
2778 SCHUYLER NE
2779 GRAND ISLAND NE
2780 WAHOO NE
2781 ALTOONA PA
2782 WICHITA KS
2783 SEATTLE WA
2784 LOUISVILLE KY
2785 LIMERICK ME
2786 WICHITA KS
2787 STROUDSBURG PA
2788 STANFORD KY
2789 HILLSBORO IL
2790 SAINT CLOUD MN
2791 MARYSVILLE KS
2792 CASSELTON ND
2793 GALVA IL
2794 STOCKTON CA
2795 MINNEAPOLIS MN
2796 BRISTOL TN
2797 BEL AIR MD
2798 CINCINNATI OH
2799 BRADDOCK PA
2800 ANOKA MN
2801 COLORADO TX
2802 GAINESVILLE TX
2803 BOZEMAN MT
2804 LASALLE IL
2805 SPOKANE FALLS WA
2806 KEARNEY NE
2807 COLUMBUS NE
2808 HOOPESTON IL
2809 FRANKFORT KS
2810 SANDUSKY OH
2811 RED CLOUD NE
2812 DENTON TX
2813 HELENA MT
2814 SOUTHINGTON CT
2815 WYOMING IL
2816 SALEM OR
2817 CIRCLEVILLE OH
2818 LE MARS IA
2819 HURON SD
2820 WAUSAU WI
2821 IOWA CITY IA
2822 HUMMELSTOWN PA
2823 SIOUX FALLS SD
2824 LEXINGTON IL
2825 PAWNEE CITY NE
2826 CHICAGO IL
2827 CORTLAND NY
2828 BRADDOCK PA
2829 CHAMPAIGN IL
2830 CANTON SD
2831 FOSTORIA OH
2832 HOT SPRINGS AR
2833 CRESTON IA
2834 TITUSVILLE PA
2835 SAINT LOUIS MO
2836 GAINESVILLE TX
2837 RIPLEY OH
2838 SANDY HILL NY
2839 AMERICUS GA
2840 GRAFTON ND
2841 CENTERVILLE IA
2842 PAINESVILLE OH
2843 SIOUX FALLS SD
2844 GREENSBURG IN
2845 ADAMS NY
2846 BOSTON MA
2847 ALPENA MI
2848 FREMONT NE
2849 CHRISTIANA PA
2850 WELLSVILLE NY
2851 MENOMONIE WI
2852 MAUCH CHUNK PA
2853 BAY CITY MI
2854 LARIMORE ND
2856 JESUP IA
2857 WEST CHESTER PA
2858 LAKE IL
2859 LIMA OH
2860 FORT PLAIN NY
2861 CAMBRIDGE OH
2862 MACON MO
2863 ELYRIA OH
2864 GAP PA
2865 BAKER CITY OR
2865 BAKER OR
2866 WELLINGTON OH
2867 HONEY GROVE TX
2868 OWENTON KY
2869 FULTONVILLE NY
2870 DETROIT MI
2871 CENTRAL CITY NE
2872 CAMBRIDGE OH
2873 TROY NY
2874 DAYTON OH
2875 FREEPORT IL
2876 YAKIMA WA
2877 OSHKOSH WI
2878 PEORIA IL
2879 WELLINGTON KS
2880 OGDEN UT
2881 MEXICO MO
2882 FELICITY OH
2883 SAN ANTONIO TX
2884 MARSHALL MO
2885 DELPHOS OH
2886 DES MOINES IA
2887 HOT SPRINGS AR
2888 LANCASTER KY
2889 LAWRENCEBURG IN
2890 GRAND RAPIDS MI
2891 WEST POINT MS
2892 SPRINGVILLE NY
2893 COLORADO TX
2894 CHICAGO IL
2895 OSKALOOSA IA
2896 GREEN CASTLE IN
2897 AURORA NE
2898 SAINT JOSEPH MO
2899 READING PA
2900 BOYERTOWN PA
2901 LEXINGTON KY
2902 DAVID CITY NE
2903 NORTH MANCHESTER IN
2904 CHESTER PA
2905 RUTLAND VT
2906 OXFORD PA
2907 ROANOKE VA
2908 BARNESVILLE OH
2909 McKINNEY TX
2910 WATERLOO IA
2911 CHAMBERLAIN SD
2912 WASHINGTON KS
2913 PROVIDENCE RI
2914 STANTON MI
2915 URBANA IL
2916 DUNKIRK NY
2917 HUSTONVILLE KY
2918 VINELAND NJ
2919 SEDALIA MO
2920 AMSTERDAM NY
2921 ASHLAND NE
2922 CINCINNATI OH
2923 SWEDESBORO NJ
2924 NEW TACOMA WA
2924 TACOMA WA
2925 WHITEWATER WI
2926 PAXTON IL
2927 GEORGETOWN KY
2928 ALBANY OR
2929 AMESBURY MA
2930 SILVERTON CO
2931 HENDERSON KY
2932 XENIA OH
2933 MORRIS MN
2934 FERGUS FALLS MN
2935 WATERTOWN SD
2936 CORNING IA
2937 BROWNWOOD TX
2938 LOS ANGELES CA
2939 ENNIS TX
2940 DECATUR TX
2941 PIERRE SD
2942 WEST LIBERTY OH
2943 SAINT PAUL MN
2944 BIG RAPIDS MI
2945 AURORA IL
2946 AKRON OH
2947 UNION OR
2948 PORT TOWNSEND WA
2949 DENTON TX
2950 RUTLAND VT
2951 PERU IL
2952 SENECA KS
2953 GRINNELL IA
2954 SABETHA KS
2955 TECUMSEH NE
2956 CLEVELAND OH
2957 MERIDIAN MS
2958 YORK PA
2959 SAINT PAUL MN
2960 FRIEND NE
2961 MONTEZUMA IA
2962 IDAHO SPRINGS CO
2963 AURORA IN
2964 FULLERTON NE
2965 HOMER IL
2966 SEATTLE WA
2967 FRONT ROYAL VA
2968 OWENTON KY
2969 DUBOIS CITY PA
2970 SAINT JOSEPH MO
2971 MARSHALLTOWN IA
2972 LEWISTON ID
2973 GARNETT KS
2974 WAXAHACHIE TX
2975 GUNNISON CO
2976 BROOKLYN NY
2976 NEW YORK NY
2977 ROCHESTER PA
2978 OMAHA NE
2979 PALMYRA MO
2980 ABERDEEN SD
2981 SALISBURY NC
2982 CLEBURNE TX
2983 TIPTON IA
2984 WEBSTER CITY IA
2985 SEATTLE WA
2986 BISMARCK ND
2987 VASSAR MI
2988 LINCOLN NE
2989 HURON SD
2990 SABETHA KS
2991 WILBER NE
2992 GREENVILLE OH
2993 CHILLICOTHE OH
2994 FAIRBURY NE
2995 ALEXANDRIA MN
2996 OWEGO NY
2997 EL PASO IL
2998 GREENVILLE TX
2999 BRIDGETON NJ
3000 ANOKA MN
3001 STEVENS POINT WI
3002 STRONG CITY KS
3003 BIGGSVILLE IL
3004 TIPPECANOE CITY OH
3005 CARTHAGE MO
3006 LIVINGSTON MT
3007 BURNET TX
3008 DALLAS TX
3009 SAINT CLOUD MN
3010 HAVRE DE GRACE MD
3011 NORWICH NY
3012 ALBIA IA
3013 BEDFORD IN
3014 MEXIA TX
3015 BRENHAM TX
3016 GREENVILLE TX
3017 AMES IA
3018 MARION KS
3019 MIDDLETOWN DE
3020 NAUGATUCK CT
3021 INDEPENDENCE KS
3022 HENRIETTA TX
3023 LEWISTON ID
3024 OLYMPIA WA
3025 PORTLAND OR
3026 PERRY IA
3027 TAYLOR TX
3028 DECATUR IN
3029 MOOREFIELD WV
3030 PUNXSUTAWNEY PA
3031 VANCOUVER WA
3032 NASHVILLE TN
3033 LEAVENWORTH KS
3034 CHARLOTTE MI
3035 EL DORADO KS
3037 ELLENSBURG WA
3038 OSWEGO KS
3039 SHAKOPEE MN
3040 MANASQUAN NJ
3041 ANNISTON AL
3042 ELIZABETHTOWN KY
3043 PETERSBURG IL
3044 CLARION PA
3045 SHAMOKIN PA
3046 HILLSBORO TX
3047 WATKINS NY
3048 GRISWOLD IA
3049 CHEROKEE IA
3050 SAN DIEGO CA
3051 BROOKVILLE PA
3052 LEXINGTON KY
3053 ROCKFORD IA
3054 PHOENIX AZ
3055 RED OAK IA
3056 SAN DIEGO CA
3057 MINDEN NE
3058 DENISON TX
3059 NORTH BEND NE
3060 SEWARD NE
3061 HOLTON KS
3062 FRANKLIN TN
3063 LANGHORNE PA
3064 PRINCETON KY
3065 TEXARKANA TX
3066 CONCORDIA KS
3067 QUARRYVILLE PA
3068 UNIONVILLE MO
3069 NEW ORLEANS LA
3070 PEORIA IL
3071 GREENE IA
3072 CLAY CENTER KS
3073 AYER MA
3074 CARROLLTON KY
3075 BOZEMAN MT
3076 COLFAX WA
3077 KINSMAN OH
3078 TOPEKA KS
3079 TARKIO MO
3080 FACTORY POINT VT
3080 MANCHESTER CENTER VT
3081 BEATRICE NE
3082 SUMTER SC
3083 SYRACUSE NE
3084 LOGANSPORT IN
3085 PHILADELPHIA PA
3086 HASTINGS NE
3087 BROOKINGS SD
3088 MUSKEGON MI
3089 BEDFORD PA
3090 CONCORDIA KS
3091 WELLINGTON KS
3092 WILLIAMSTOWN MA
3093 LA GRANGE GA
3094 BONHAM TX
3095 ISHPEMING MI
3096 GRAFTON ND
3097 BILLINGS MT
3098 MINNEAPOLIS MN
3099 HASTINGS NE
3100 WABASHA MN
3101 GRAND ISLAND NE
3102 SOUTH CHICAGO IL
3102 CHICAGO IL
3103 LOUISIANA MO
3104 KITTANNING PA
3105 WAVERLY IA
3106 HUNTINGTON WV
3107 TULLAHOMA TN
3108 YATES CENTER KS
3109 PLYMOUTH MI
3110 MILAN MO
3111 LOUISIANA MO
3112 CLARINDA IA
3113 MARSHALL TX
3114 ALAMOSA CO
3115 CLYDE KS
3116 NEW BRUNSWICK GA
3117 EXETER NE
3118 WAHOO NE
3119 COLFAX WA
3120 DILLON MT
3121 EXETER NE
3122 PRESCOTT AZ
3123 EAST SAGINAW MI
3124 SIOUX CITY IA
3125 LAKE GENEVA WI
3126 SAINT PAUL NE
3127 SHAKOPEE MN
3128 HOLYOKE MA
3129 SAINT PAUL NE
3130 PLANKINTON SD
3131 FORT WORTH TX
3132 DALLAS TX
3133 THREE RIVERS MI
3134 PEABODY KS
3135 WACO TX
3136 MODESTO CA
3137 UNIONVILLE MO
3138 GALESBURG IL
3139 OGDEN UT
3140 DUBUQUE IA
3141 SANDUSKY OH
3142 KETCHUM ID
3143 SHENANDOAH PA
3144 SUSQUEHANNA PA
3145 MINNEAPOLIS MN
3146 RIPON WI
3147 MALVERN PA
3148 EUREKA KS
3149 MADISON SD
3150 MIDDLETOWN SPRINGS VT
3151 MADISON SD
3152 SCHUYLER NE
3153 ROCK RAPIDS IA
3154 GRANVILLE NY
3155 SAUK CENTRE MN
3156 METROPOLIS IL
3157 WAPAKONETA OH
3158 LYNDONVILLE VT
3159 SHERMAN TX
3160 DEMING NM
3161 DARLINGTON WI
3162 YORK NE
3163 OMAHA NE
3164 KEYPORT NJ
3165 MONTAGUE TX
3166 WESTFIELD NY
3167 WASHINGTON KS
3168 CRANBURY NJ
3169 BISMARCK ND
3170 BURLINGTON KS
3171 MECHANICVILLE NY
3172 TACOMA WA
3173 DILLON MT
3174 PLATTSBURGH NY
3175 FORT SCOTT KS
3176 MERIDIAN MS
3177 FLUSHING OH
3178 GREELEY CO
3179 CHICAGO IL
3180 HUTCHINSON KS
3181 RED CLOUD NE
3182 DE WITT IA
3183 HERKIMER NY
3184 PORTLAND OR
3185 BIRMINGHAM AL
3186 HOMER NY
3187 ROCKVILLE MD
3188 FREMONT NE
3189 MISSOURI VALLEY IA
3190 BELVIDERE IL
3191 NEWARK OH
3192 WHAT CHEER IA
3193 MARATHON NY
3194 LEAVENWORTH KS
3195 ABILENE TX
3196 ASHLAND WI
3197 ALGONA IA
3198 LINCOLN PA
3199 HUTCHINSON KS
3200 WICHITA FALLS TX
3201 KEARNEY NE
3202 CLEVELAND OH
3203 MINERAL POINT WI
3204 LEOMINSTER MA
3205 CENTREVILLE MD
3206 MINNEAPOLIS MN
3207 STERLING KS
3208 HOLDREGE NE
3209 MOUNT JACKSON VA
3210 KALAMAZOO MI
3211 KALAMAZOO MI
3212 WAXAHACHIE TX
3213 EL DORADO KS
3214 PEORIA IL
3215 MOUNT PLEASANT MI
3216 GIRARD KS
3217 ITHACA MI
3218 WINFIELD KS
3219 GARDINER ME
3220 AMBLER PA
3221 FORT WORTH TX
3222 ALBUQUERQUE NM
3223 PALATKA FL
3224 WINONA MN
3225 GRUNDY CENTER IA
3226 PANORA IA

3227 TEMPLE TX
3228 NASHVILLE TN
3229 GAINESVILLE TX
3230 FAIRMONT NE
3231 BELOIT KS
3232 GREENPORT NY
3233 SAINT PAUL MN
3234 MILFORD OH
3235 CHEBOYGAN MI
3236 CHARLESTON WV
3237 RAPID CITY SD
3238 HUMBOLDT NE
3239 SAINT LOUIS MI
3240 SUTTON NE
3241 CLARKSVILLE TN
3242 HOWARD KS
3243 GREENVILLE MI
3244 SANDY HILL NY
3244 HUDSON FALLS NY
3245 SALEM NY
3246 BOULDER CO
3247 HALLOWELL ME
3248 ALBANY TX
3249 ELLSWORTH KS
3250 SALISBURY MD
3251 CONCORD MI
3252 IOWA FALLS IA
3253 MEDICINE LODGE KS
3254 PEORIA IL
3255 EMPORIUM PA
3256 MENOMINEE MI
3257 WINDSOR VT
3258 VICKSBURG MS
3259 NEW BRIGHTON PA
3260 SAN ANGELO TX
3261 LAMPASAS TX
3262 CROOKSTON MN
3263 INDEPENDENCE IA
3264 OVID MI
3265 HARPER KS
3266 PALATKA FL
3267 HURON SD
3268 MARYVILLE MO
3269 DENVER CO
3270 BEAVER DAM WI
3271 AUGUSTA ME
3272 CLEVELAND OH
3273 BOONE IA
3274 BUCYRUS OH
3275 MILES CITY MT
3276 STURGIS MI
3277 CHERRYVALE KS
3278 CHICAGO IL
3279 GALENA IL
3280 LAFAYETTE IN
3281 EVANSVILLE IN
3282 ALBANY NY
3283 LE ROY NY
3284 BROOKLYN IA
3285 FORT WAYNE IN
3286 BAIRD TX
3287 KNOXVILLE IL
3288 CENTERVILLE TN
3289 AUSTIN TX
3290 WINCHESTER KY
3291 RIPLEY OH
3292 PLUM CREEK NE
3292 LEXINGTON NE
3293 GRAND RAPIDS MI
3294 DIXON IL
3295 BELTON TX
3296 PEORIA IL
3297 NEWTON KS
3298 SAN ANTONIO TX
3299 BUFFALO WY
3300 LITTLE ROCK AR
3301 GRAND FORKS ND
3302 ARAPAHOE NE
3303 CENTRALIA IL
3304 WESTMORELAND KS
3306 SALT LAKE CITY UT
3307 MALONE NY
3308 DARLINGTON WI
3309 SALEM NY
3310 STEUBENVILLE OH
3311 RUTLAND VT
3312 GLOVERSVILLE NY
3313 ISLAND CITY OR
3314 BATTLE CREEK MI
3315 TIFFIN OH
3316 ALBION MI
3317 DANVILLE KY
3318 LITTLE ROCK AR
3319 OSBORNE KS
3320 SIBLEY IA
3321 FRESNO CA
3322 PARIS MO
3323 EARLVILLE IL
3324 COFFEYVILLE KS
3325 TRAVERSE CITY MI
3326 ABERDEEN SD
3327 JACKSONVILLE FL
3328 MOUNT VERNON OH
3329 SENECA FALLS NY
3330 FORT EDWARD NY
3331 JAMESTOWN ND
3332 JACKSON MS
3333 MIDDLETOWN NY
3334 HOUGHTON MI
3335 ELIZABETHTOWN PA
3336 ABILENE TX
3337 EMMETSBURG IA
3338 FRANKLIN IN
3339 ORD NE
3340 WEST POINT NE
3341 ATHENS TN
3342 ORLEANS NE
3343 NORTH AUBURN NE
3343 AUBURN NE
3344 SAN MARCOS TX
3345 CLAY CENTER KS
3346 SAN MARCOS TX
3347 NORFOLK NE
3348 RIVERSIDE CA
3349 WATERTOWN SD
3350 PAOLA KS
3351 WINFIELD KS
3352 COLUMBIA SD
3353 MINNEAPOLIS KS
3354 LONGMONT CO
3355 NORTH YAKIMA WA
3355 YAKIMA WA
3356 BEAVER FALLS PA
3357 DETROIT MI
3358 TOPTON PA
3359 NEW YORK CITY NY
3359 NEW YORK NY
3360 ARKANSAS CITY KS
3361 FLINT MI
3362 WARREN OH
3363 GREAT BEND KS
3364 STANTON NE
3365 NORTH ATTLEBOROUGH MA
3366 MALONE NY
3367 LANCASTER PA
3368 NORFOLK VA
3369 LINCOLN IL
3370 WEST POINT NE
3371 PHILADELPHIA PA
3372 CAMDEN NJ
3373 LOUP CITY NE
3374 SAINT MARYS KS
3375 WHITE SULPHUR SPRINGS MT
3376 PARIS IL
3377 ABINGDON IL
3378 SAINT JOHNS MI
3379 McCOOK NE
3380 GRANT CITY MO
3381 DANVILLE KY
3382 NEWNAN GA
3383 WASHINGTON PA
3384 ANTHONY KS
3385 ANTHONY KS
3386 BELLEVILLE KS
3387 MOORESTOWN NJ
3388 PONTIAC MI
3389 RALEIGH NC
3390 DORCHESTER NE
3391 WAUPUN WI
3392 WAYNE NE
3393 SIOUX FALLS SD
3394 ANTHONY KS
3395 WILMINGTON DE
3396 GRUNDY CENTER IA
3397 DEVILS LAKE ND
3398 REDFIELD SD
3399 McMINNVILLE OR
3400 HILLSBORO ND
3401 RAPID CITY SD
3402 PORTLAND OR
3403 GREENWOOD NE
3404 NEWPORT NH
3405 SALEM OR
3406 SAVANNAH GA
3407 FARMER CITY IL
3408 MOSCOW ID
3409 SPOKANE FALLS WA
3409 SPOKANE WA
3410 OWOSSO MI
3411 HILLSBORO ND
3412 LA CROSSE WI
3413 RICHMOND IN
3414 WATERTOWN SD
3415 NEW YORK NY
3416 CHEYENNE WY
3417 TACOMA WA
3418 ASHEVILLE NC
3419 BLUE HILL NE
3420 WEBSTER CITY IA
3421 ABBEVILLE SC
3422 PORTLAND OR
3423 PHILADELPHIA PA
3424 O'NEILL NE
3425 WASHINGTON DC
3426 DETROIT MN
3427 COUNCIL BLUFFS IA
3428 LUVERNE MN
3429 LYNN MA
3430 VICKSBURG MS
3431 HARPER KS
3432 MORRISTOWN TN
3433 COLEMAN TX
3434 WAMEGO KS
3435 DE SMET SD
3436 PARK RIVER ND
3437 ASHTON SD
3438 PEMBINA ND
3439 EAGLE GROVE IA
3440 STOCKTON KS
3441 THE DALLES OR
3442 BIRMINGHAM AL
3443 HALSTEAD KS
3444 NEW BRIGHTON NY
3445 BROKEN BOW NE
3446 BRYAN TX
3447 ELLSWORTH KS
3448 GARDEN CITY KS
3449 BROKEN BOW NE
3450 TRINIDAD CO
3451 ASBURY PARK NJ
3452 OPELIKA AL
3453 DULUTH MN
3454 KIRWIN KS
3455 MANNING IA
3456 KANSAS CITY MO
3457 CALUMET MI
3458 EUGENE CITY OR
3458 EUGENE OR
3459 WATSONTOWN PA
3460 POMEROY WA
3461 CINCINNATI OH
3462 SAINT AUGUSTINE FL
3463 PITTSBURG KS
3464 LINCOLN KS
3465 SPRING VALLEY IL
3466 SULPHUR SPRINGS TX
3467 SAINT JOHN KS
3468 PHILADELPHIA PA
3469 ORLANDO FL
3470 OCALA FL
3471 BOISE CITY ID
3471 BOISE ID
3472 OSBORNE KS
3473 NEWTON KS
3474 NORTH MANCHESTER IN
3475 PITTSBURG KS
3476 FREDERICK MD
3477 FINDLAY OH
3478 HAMMOND IN
3479 CLARK SD
3480 MUNCY PA
3481 ORD NE
3482 SAINT ALBANS VT
3483 INDIANOLA NE
3484 WHITE RIVER JUNCTION VT
3485 ASPEN CO
3486 ASTORIA OR
3487 DETROIT MI
3488 GRAND RAPIDS MI
3489 KANSAS CITY MO
3490 HIGH POINT NC
3491 PHILADELPHIA PA
3492 CONNEAUT OH
3493 FAIRFIELD NE
3494 POTTSTOWN PA
3495 NELSON NE
3496 NORTH PLATTE NE
3497 TAMPA FL
3498 PHILADELPHIA PA
3499 PASADENA CA
3500 CHICAGO IL
3501 ALLENTOWN NJ
3502 CHICAGO IL
3503 CHICAGO IL
3504 GRAND FORKS ND
3505 KENTON OH
3506 CORSICANA TX
3507 PHILADELPHIA PA
3508 DELL RAPIDS SD
3509 KINGMAN KS
3510 HAVERHILL MA
3511 OBERLIN KS
3512 COLBY KS
3513 LANSING MI
3514 DETROIT MI
3515 PETERSBURG VA
3516 OMAHA NE
3517 HOUSTON TX
3518 POMONA CA
3519 LEETONIA OH
3520 SANTA ANA CA
3521 McPHERSON KS
3522 DOLAND SD
3522 REDFIELD SD
3523 WEEPING WATER NE
3524 WICHITA KS
3525 GREAT FALLS MT
3526 KEARNEY NE
3527 SAN BERNARDINO CA
3528 SPRAGUE WA
3528 SPOKANE WA
3529 SUPERIOR NE
3530 SHELBYVILLE TN
3531 SALINA KS
3532 ENNIS TX
3533 BALLINGER TX
3534 THE DALLES OR
3535 WAPAKONETA OH
3536 PORTLAND OR
3537 NEPHI UT
3538 LOS ANGELES CA
3539 SILVER CITY NM
3540 LAURENS SC
3541 OCONTO WI
3542 NESS CITY KS
3543 JUNCTION CITY KS
3544 KANSAS CITY MO
3545 CLEVELAND OH
3546 SMITH CENTRE KS
3547 SAULT STE MARIE MI
3548 SPRINGFIELD IL
3549 FRANKLIN NE
3550 WORTHINGTON MN
3551 ROYERSFORD PA
3552 DEADWOOD SD
3553 BROOKLINE MA
3554 SILVER CITY NM
3555 SAN FRANCISCO CA
3556 DOUGLAS WY
3557 PHILADELPHIA PA
3558 SANTA ROSA CA
3559 KINGMAN KS
3560 ALBERT LEA MN
3561 COMANCHE TX
3562 MANKATO MN
3563 DOWNS KS
3564 WELLINGTON KS
3565 WELLSTON OH
3566 YAZOO CITY MS
3567 GREENLEAF KS
3568 PASADENA CA
3569 DOWNS KS
3570 CULPEPPER VA
3571 LINCOLN NE
3572 PASSAIC NJ
3573 COLTON CA
3574 CLAY CENTER NE
3575 WINNEMUCCA NV
3576 JACKSON TN
3577 LYONS KS
3578 MITCHELL SD
3579 TAYLORVILLE IL
3580 ALMA NE
3581 GALION OH
3582 FRANKFORT NY
3583 BRAZIL IN
3584 LAWRENCE KS
3585 ELLICOTT CITY MD
3586 SIOUX FALLS SD
3587 BIRMINGHAM AL
3588 TOWSON MD
3589 LINDSBORG KS
3590 ASHLAND WI
3591 JEWELL CITY KS
3592 SAN FRANCISCO CA
3593 CANTON IL
3594 MEDICINE LODGE KS
3595 SHREVEPORT LA
3596 DODGE CITY KS
3597 MADISON SD
3598 NEWTON MA
3599 STEELTON PA
3600 SHREVEPORT LA
3601 PHILLIPSBURG KS
3602 FARGO ND
3603 OMAHA NE
3604 PHILADELPHIA PA
3605 LIVINGSTON MT
3606 CINCINNATI OH
3607 ASHLAND WI
3608 EL PASO TX
3609 BARABOO WI
3610 COLUMBUS OH
3611 SOUTH OMAHA NE
3612 ATCHISON KS
3613 LINCOLN IL
3614 SPARTA TN
3615 LARAMIE CITY WY
3615 LARAMIE WY
3616 ROCK HILL SC
3617 SHEFFIELD AL
3618 SUTHERLAND IA
3619 BEAVER CITY NE
3620 WENONA IL
3621 ATLANTIC CITY NJ
3622 EUFAULA AL
3623 DALLAS TX
3624 FARMERSVILLE TX
3625 WASHINGTON DC
3626 DULUTH MN
3627 PONCA NE
3628 SOUTH AUBURN NE
3628 AUBURN NE
3629 PIEDMONT WV
3630 SMITH CENTER KS
3631 FORT WORTH TX
3632 STROUDSBURG PA
3633 MEMPHIS TN
3634 FORT SMITH AR
3635 MANHEIM PA
3636 HURON SD
3637 KANSAS CITY MO
3638 PARIS TX
3639 CINCINNATI OH
3640 BEARDSTOWN IL
3641 KAUKAUNA WI
3642 CINCINNATI OH
3643 CEDAR RAPIDS IA
3644 ALVARADO TX
3645 CORSICANA TX
3646 GREENVILLE TX
3647 CHICAGO IL
3648 GRASS VALLEY CA
3649 PRATT KS
3650 LANCASTER PA
3651 TYLER TX
3652 OGALALLA NE
3653 SUTTON NE
3654 CANFIELD OH
3655 LA GRANDE OR
3656 ABERDEEN MS
3657 RUSSELL KS
3658 CALDWELL KS
3659 RED LAKE FALLS MN
3660 SOUTH PITTSBURG TN
3661 GLENWOOD SPRINGS CO
3662 HELENA AR
3663 GADSDEN AL
3664 DALLAS TX
3665 PENDLETON OR
3666 MEDIA PA
3667 GREENSBURG KS
3668 NEW BRITAIN CT
3669 LISBON ND
3670 ROME GA
3671 NEW IBERIA LA
3672 CARTHAGE NY
3673 MAYVILLE ND
3674 RULO NE
3675 PARKER SD
3676 ARLINGTON OR
3677 CHICAGO IL
3678 TUSCALOOSA AL
3679 BIRMINGHAM AL
3680 JERSEY CITY NJ
3681 EDMESTON NY
3682 STATESVILLE NC
3683 WICHITA KS
3684 PHILADELPHIA PA
3685 FOND DU LAC WI
3686 CHILLICOTHE MO
3687 NORTON KS
3688 STARKVILLE MS
3689 SAINT PAUL MN
3690 DOVER ME
3691 CHATTANOOGA TN
3692 MONROE LA
3693 SEAFORD DE
3694 PALESTINE TX
3695 MEADE CENTER KS
3696 CANTON NY
3697 NEW BRUNSWICK NJ
3698 CHICAGO IL
3699 DECATUR AL
3700 NEW YORK NY
3701 NATCHEZ MS
3702 FAYETTEVILLE TN
3703 COLDWATER KS
3704 MERRILL WI
3705 WILLIAMSPORT PA
3706 KANSAS CITY KS
3707 CINCINNATI OH
3708 KNOXVILLE TN
3709 TRENTON NJ
3710 ASHLAND KS
3711 ATLANTA IL
3712 LIBERTY MO
3713 HARRISBURG PA
3714 DEVILS LAKE ND
3715 SAN JOSE CA
3716 WOODBURY NJ
3717 NEGAUNEE MI
3718 SPRINGFIELD MO
3719 PORTLAND OR
3720 OLATHE KS
3721 ALLIANCE OH
3722 GLENWOOD SPRINGS CO
3723 PHILADELPHIA PA
3724 MENASHA WI
3725 TOBIAS NE
3726 KANSAS CITY KS
3727 GRANBURY TX
3728 PHOENIX AZ
3729 FINDLAY OH
3730 DETROIT MI
3731 MINNEAPOLIS KS
3732 HASTINGS NE
3733 MERCED CA
3734 BIRMINGHAM AL
3735 CAIRO IL
3736 CLINTON IA
3737 KINGMAN KS
3738 SAN ANTONIO TX
3739 STURGIS SD
3740 MACON GA
3741 NORFOLK NE
3742 CALVERT TX
3743 MONROVIA CA
3744 HOBOKEN NJ
3745 MANKATO KS
3746 LEADVILLE CO
3747 SAULT STE MARIE MI
3748 CONCORDIA KS
3749 LAMAR CO
3750 PIQUA OH
3751 CIMARRON KS
3752 QUINCY IL
3753 BRUNSWICK GA
3754 HARRISONVILLE MO
3755 ATTICA IN
3756 WICHITA KS
3757 SAINT HELENA CA
3758 MILLBROOK KS
3758 HILL CITY KS
3759 KINSLEY KS
3760 KANSAS CITY MO
3761 ESCANABA MI
3762 HILLSBORO TX
3763 RENOVO PA
3764 PLANO TX
3765 GREENVILLE MS
3766 BRYN MAWR PA
3767 THOMASVILLE GA
3768 WATERBURY CT
3769 ALMA KS
3770 PEKIN IL
3771 NEW YORK NY
3772 LIMA OH
3773 MADISON NE
3774 HEPPNER OR
3775 RUSSELL SPRINGS KS
3776 WAKEENEY KS
3777 ABILENE KS
3778 CHIPPEWA FALLS WI
3779 SCANDIA KS
3779 BELLEVILLE KS
3780 SAN DIEGO CA
3781 DELAVAN IL
3782 MANHATTAN KS
3783 SNOW HILL MD
3784 MINNEAPOLIS MN
3785 TEXARKANA TX
3786 HILLSBORO TX
3787 PRATT KS
3788 CLARION IA
3789 TACOMA WA
3790 TOPEKA KS
3791 McPHERSON KS
3792 ASBURY PARK NJ
3793 KANSAS CITY MO
3794 HOWARD KS
3795 PAOLA KS
3796 CLARION IA
3797 CLAYTON NY
3798 SANFORD FL
3799 DAYTON WA
3800 PAINTED POST NY
3801 DAVID CITY NE
3802 ORLANDO FL
3803 McPHERSON KS
3804 ELLSWORTH ME
3805 JETMORE KS
3806 IRON MOUNTAIN MI
3807 HUMBOLDT KS
3808 MOUNTVILLE PA
3809 SUMTER SC
3810 HORTON KS
3811 DURHAM NC
3812 MANKATO KS
3813 OSAGE CITY KS
3814 ELLSWORTH ME
3815 OCALA FL
3816 TERRELL TX
3817 CANANDAIGUA NY
3818 SAN BERNARDINO CA
3819 CHANUTE KS
3820 TOLEDO OH
3821 DAYTON OH
3822 SIDNEY NY
3823 CHADRON NE
3824 CENTRALIA KS
3825 TROY OH
3826 SAN LUIS OBISPO CA
3827 PRESQUE ISLE ME
3828 SAN DIEGO CA
3829 HOMESTEAD PA
3830 MARIETTA GA
3831 LATROBE PA
3832 SOMERSET KY
3833 EL DORADO KS
3834 DALLAS TX
3835 FREDONIA KS
3836 KAUFMAN TX
3837 KNOXVILLE TN
3838 SPOKANE FALLS WA
3839 MOUNT PULASKI IL
3840 HAMILTON OH
3841 JOPLIN MO
3842 WASHINGTON IN
3843 GLASSBORO NJ
3844 LEOTI CITY KS
3845 SANTA MONICA CA
3846 JAMESTOWN NY
3847 CHICAGO IL
3848 SHELDON IA
3849 LAWRENCE KS
3850 BEAVER PA
3851 PRINEVILLE OR
3852 STAFFORD KS
3853 MEADE CENTER KS
3854 AURORA IL
3855 SEDAN KS
3856 HOPKINSVILLE KY
3857 McMINNVILLE OR
3858 TEMPLE TX
3859 TAYLOR TX
3860 GRAND JUNCTION CO
3861 HUTCHINSON KS
3862 NORTH YAKIMA WA
3862 YAKIMA WA
3863 KANSAS CITY MO
3864 VINCENNES IN
3865 WELLINGTON KS
3866 BOUND BROOK NJ
3867 ELLENSBURG WA
3868 ROCKLAND MA
3869 JACKSONVILLE FL
3870 FRESNO CA
3871 CEDAR FALLS IA
3872 ALBANY GA
3873 COLUMBIA PA
3874 PITTSBURGH PA
3875 HOLDREGE NE
3876 MIAMISBURG OH
3877 PORT ALLEGANY PA
3878 SOUTH AMBOY NJ
3879 CANON CITY CO
3880 BURR OAK KS
3881 LAWRENCE KS
3882 CHICAGO IL
3883 HARRINGTON DE
3884 GREEN BAY WI
3885 HAYS CITY KS
3886 SAINT IGNACE MI
3887 SNOHOMISH WA
3888 DIGHTON KS
3889 EATON OH
3890 ROCKWALL TX
3891 SAINT PAUL NE
3892 REDLANDS CA
3893 HAZLETON PA
3894 GAINESVILLE FL
3895 HAILEY ID
3896 BATTLE CREEK MI
3897 BLACK RIVER FALLS WI
3898 SPENCER IA
3899 TALLADEGA AL
3900 GARDEN CITY KS
3901 WACO TX
3902 HUGHESVILLE PA
3903 CONCORD NC
3904 KANSAS CITY MO
3905 BIRDSBORO PA
3906 LA GRANGE TX
3907 DALTON GA
3908 LEAVENWORTH KS
3909 TOPEKA KS
3910 LATROBE PA
3911 SAGINAW MI
3912 ENTERPRISE OR
3913 COLORADO SPRINGS CO
3914 STAFFORD SPRINGS CT
3915 CORSICANA TX
3916 HYDE PARK IL
3916 CHICAGO IL
3917 LEESBURG VA
3918 ARLINGTON OR
3919 UNION CITY TN
3920 ROCK SPRINGS WY
3921 GIBBON NE
3922 SALEM NJ
3923 BOSTON MA
3924 TOWER MN
3925 BUCHANAN MI
3926 WEST SUPERIOR WI
3926 SUPERIOR WI
3927 BROKEN BOW NE
3928 MARION KS
3929 TERRE HAUTE IN
3930 IDA GROVE IA
3931 EUTAW AL
3932 ABERDEEN SD
3933 BEL AIR MD
3934 DAVID CITY NE
3935 WABASH IN
3936 GLOUCESTER CITY NJ
3937 COLUMBUS GA
3938 WELLSBOROUGH PA
3939 WOOD RIVER NE
3940 SIOUX CITY IA
3941 EDEN ME
3941 BAR HARBOR ME
3942 LEXINGTON KY
3943 LONDON KY
3944 ASHLAND KY
3945 BERWYN PA
3946 TRENTON MO
3947 BESSEMER MI
3948 LAKE LINDEN MI
3949 LEADVILLE CO
3950 CLEVELAND OH
3951 JOHNSON CITY TN
3952 ROCKFORD IL
3953 HEPPNER OR
3954 STANFORD KY
3955 NANTICOKE PA
3956 WALLA WALLA WA
3957 TRENTON MO
3958 KEARNEY NE
3959 NEVADA MO
3960 ALBION NE
3961 SOUTH BETHLEHEM PA
3961 BETHLEHEM PA
3962 LITCHFIELD IL
3963 ERIE KS
3964 THOMASTON CT
3965 ANACONDA MT
3966 HILLSBORO OR
3967 FRANKLIN IN
3968 SIOUX CITY IA
3969 CARROLL IA
3970 LA CROSSE KS
3971 IRONWOOD MI
3972 INDEPENDENCE OR
3973 CLARKSVILLE TX
3974 FORT MADISON IA
3975 WEATHERFORD TX
3976 SEHOME WA
3976 NEW WHATCOM WA
3977 LAWRENCE MA
3978 NEW ORLEANS LA
3979 INDEPENDENCE OR
3980 MOUNT CARMEL PA
3981 FLORENCE AL
3982 PIPESTONE MN
3983 GAINESVILLE GA
3984 WOLFE CITY TX
3985 DALLAS TX
3986 EUGENE CITY OR
3987 LANCASTER PA
3988 LEBANON KY
3989 SULPHUR SPRINGS TX
3990 COATESVILLE PA
3991 PAOLA KS
3992 ARKANSAS CITY KS
3993 BIRMINGHAM AL
3994 MIDDLEBOROUGH MA
3995 MISSOULA MT
3996 HADDONFIELD NJ
3997 MAHANOY CITY PA
3998 TEXARKANA TX
3999 ELM CREEK NE
4000 MOBERLY MO
4001 DULUTH MN
4002 DAVENPORT WA
4003 HARRISBURG IL
4004 FORT WORTH TX
4005 SPOKANE FALLS WA
4006 OWENSBORO KY
4007 MONTROSE CO
4008 MANHATTAN KS
4009 MINOT ND
4010 HANNIBAL MO
4011 EAST STROUDSBURG PA
4012 CARTERSVILLE GA
4013 LENOX MA
4014 FORNEY TX

4015 ROGERSVILLE TN
4016 MERIDIAN TX
4017 BEAUMONT TX
4018 TACOMA WA
4019 MURPHYSBORO IL
4020 TULLAHOMA TN
4021 COMMERCE TX
4022 DAVENPORT IA
4023 POCATELLO ID
4024 NORTH PLATTE NE
4025 SPOKANE FALLS WA
4026 ROANOKE VA
4027 ROANOKE VA
4028 HOUSTON TX
4029 WISNER NE
4030 LOCKHART TX
4031 GOLDENDALE WA
4032 GARNETT KS
4033 VERNON TX
4034 LITTLE FALLS MN
4035 CLEBURNE TX
4036 CHANUTE KS
4037 LACONIA NH
4038 PANA IL
4039 MIFFLINTOWN PA
4040 BURLINGAME KS
4041 COLEBROOK NH
4042 SHELTON NE
4043 RAVENNA NE
4044 SPOKANE FALLS WA
4044 SPOKANE WA
4045 BOWLING GREEN OH
4046 EASTON MD
4047 SUFFOLK VA
4048 SAINT LOUIS MO
4049 HAGERSTOWN MD
4050 PHILADELPHIA PA
4051 SALT LAKE CITY UT
4052 GENEVA NE
4053 SAINT JOSEPH MO
4054 DAYTON OH
4055 SHULLSBURG WI
4056 BLOOMFIELD NJ
4057 LAMAR MO
4058 HERINGTON KS
4059 SEATTLE WA
4060 CHATTANOOGA TN
4061 ADAMS NY
4062 DUBLIN TX
4063 HYNDMAN PA
4064 FORT PAYNE AL
4066 CAMDEN AR
4067 HUNTSVILLE AL
4068 HENRIETTA TX
4069 TACOMA WA
4070 BRYAN TX
4071 PULASKI VA
4072 PATERSON NJ
4073 ENGLEWOOD IL
4074 CHELSEA MA
4075 CEDARTOWN GA
4076 McGREGOR TX
4077 LONGVIEW TX
4078 PAWNEE CITY NE
4079 CARROLLTON MO
4080 LIBERTY NE
4081 STEPHENVILLE TX
4082 MONROE LA
4083 BRUNSWICK MO
4084 DENVER CO
4085 CAMBRIDGE MD
4086 CAMERON TX
4087 OMAHA NE
4088 PIEDMONT WV
4089 AINSWORTH NE
4090 FRANKFORT KY
4091 FRANKFORT KY
4092 JEANETTE PA
4093 BASTROP TX
4094 ASHEVILLE NC
4095 STEPHENVILLE TX
4096 LOS ANGELES CA
4097 GATESVILLE TX
4098 SCOTTDALE PA
4099 WHATCOM WA
4100 SOMERSET PA
4101 MARSHALL TX
4102 KNOXVILLE TN
4103 ADAMS NY
4104 PIERRE SD
4105 ELMIRA NY
4106 WAHPETON ND
4107 WASHINGTON DC
4108 PUEBLO CO
4109 OURAY CO
4110 NELIGH NE
4111 CHILLICOTHE MO
4112 HONEY GROVE TX
4113 DENVER CO
4114 LAPORTE CITY IA
4115 DAWSON GA
4116 DECATUR TX
4117 LIVINGSTON MT
4118 ORANGE TX
4119 ATLANTIC HIGHLANDS NJ
4120 SANTA PAULA CA
4121 KOKOMO IN
4122 OAKESDALE WA
4123 MARINETTE WI
4124 SEATTLE WA
4125 MUSKEGON MI
4126 DURANGO CO
4127 DALLAS TX
4128 PORTLAND ME
4129 HARVARD NE
4130 VERNON TX
4131 AUSTIN MN
4132 TALLAHASSEE FL
4133 LOCKLAND OH
4134 CISCO TX
4135 FLORENCE AL
4136 PITTSBURG KS
4137 MARINETTE WI
4138 LONG BRANCH NJ
4139 DUNLAP IA
4140 CUERO TX
4141 ODESSA MO
4142 DUNCANNON PA
4143 LAKOTA ND
4144 QUANAH TX
4145 LOUISVILLE KY
4146 LAREDO TX
4147 KEYPORT NJ
4148 BEATRICE NE
4149 FROSTBURG MD
4150 SEDAN KS
4151 HAMILTON MO
4152 NEW YORK NY
4153 GALVESTON TX
4154 LAKE CHARLES LA
4155 PRIMGHAR IA
4156 MIDDLEBURGH PA
4157 INDEPENDENCE MO
4158 INDIANAPOLIS IN
4159 DENVER CO
4160 STEWARTSVILLE MO
4161 LEXINGTON NE
4162 ELKTON MD
4163 STERLING NE
4164 MARIETTA OH
4165 COZAD NE
4166 ABILENE TX
4167 BELTON TX
4168 GRANTS PASS OR
4169 ROCKWOOD TN
4170 GRANT NE
4171 FAIRHAVEN WA
4171 NEW WHATCOM WA
4172 SALIDA CO
4173 ALBION NE
4174 HOPKINS MO
4175 ROCKDALE TX
4176 RUSHVILLE NE
4177 GREENEVILLE TN
4178 SAINT LOUIS MO
4179 FLATONIA TX
4180 MONTGOMERY AL
4181 WASHINGTON PA
4182 FREEHOLD NJ
4183 SCRANTON PA
4184 VICTORIA TX
4185 BEATRICE NE
4186 PALOUSE CITY WA
4187 CHESTER IL
4188 PITTSFIELD ME
4189 MARION IN
4190 NILES OH
4191 POCOMOKE CITY MD
4192 PHILADELPHIA PA
4193 BALLINGER TX
4194 FORT BENTON MT
4195 WASHINGTON DC
4196 OSHKOSH WI
4197 CLYDE OH
4198 BRADY TX
4199 BRADFORD PA
4200 CATLETTSBURG KY
4201 MIDDLESBOROUGH KY
4202 BOSTON MA
4203 CHEHALIS WA
4204 HAZLETON PA
4205 DELTA PA
4206 BAKER CITY OR
4207 YARDLEY PA
4208 HUNTSVILLE TX
4209 SIOUX CITY IA
4210 WYMORE NE
4211 AMSTERDAM NY
4212 JOHNSTOWN PA
4213 DALLAS TX
4214 AMARILLO TX
4215 PLATTSBURG MO
4216 HOMER LA
4217 CLAY CITY KY
4218 BALTIMORE MD
4219 SAINT MARYS OH
4220 BESSEMER AL
4221 MANCHESTER IA
4222 PITTSBURGH PA
4223 POLAND NY
4224 PUYALLUP WA
4225 PEIRCE CITY MO
4226 ALLIANCE NE
4227 SOMERSET PA
4228 SAINT JOSEPH MO
4229 SEATTLE WA
4230 RIVERHEAD NY
4232 SAINT LOUIS MO
4233 EFFINGHAM IL
4234 PORTAGE WI
4235 SIOUX CITY IA
4236 GALLATIN TN
4237 FORT PIERRE SD
4238 BEEVILLE TX
4239 LEBANON OH
4240 STONEHAM MA
4241 BELLVILLE TX
4242 CREIGHTON NE
4243 MARYVILLE MO
4244 WASHINGTON DC
4245 YORK NE
4246 COMANCHE TX
4247 WASHINGTON DC
4248 WICHITA FALLS TX
4249 PENDLETON OR
4250 ANNISTON AL
4251 KANSAS CITY MO
4252 HOULTON ME
4253 NAVASOTA TX
4254 HOPEWELL NJ
4255 CLAYSVILLE PA
4256 FARGO ND
4257 BEDFORD CITY VA
4258 SWANTON VT
4259 CAMERON MO
4260 COVINGTON KY
4261 BENTON HARBOR MI
4262 SAINT LOUIS MO
4263 SEYMOUR TX
4264 DEL NORTE CO
4265 BOWIE TX
4266 LULING TX
4267 WAYNESBURG PA
4268 CORNING IA
4269 GROESBECK TX
4270 OMAHA NE
4271 LEBANON KY
4272 CHAMBERSBURG PA
4273 CLAYSVILLE PA
4274 BOONTON NJ
4275 ISLAND POND VT
4276 TECUMSEH NE
4277 SPOKANE FALLS WA
4278 ATHENS TX
4279 PIERRE SD
4280 PIERCE NE
4281 LAWRENCEBURG IN
4282 CHAMBERLAIN SD
4283 BUTTE MT
4284 JUNCTION CITY KS
4285 BALTIMORE MD
4286 MASSILLON OH
4287 TUCSON AZ
4288 CHERRYVALE KS
4289 VAN ALSTYNE TX
4290 PORT TOWNSEND WA
4291 FAIRFIELD TX
4292 WINSTON NC
4293 CANAL DOVER OH
4293 DOVER OH
4294 GEORGETOWN TX
4295 NEW BRAUNFELS TX
4296 WATERTOWN NY
4297 OLYMPIA WA
4298 ZANESVILLE OH
4299 CARLINVILLE IL
4300 LAWRENCE MA
4301 CORVALLIS OR
4302 NEW BRIGHTON MN
4303 CARDIFF TN
4304 HURLEY WI
4305 RIPON WI
4306 BIG SPRING TX
4307 MEMPHIS TN
4308 AUSTIN TX
4309 WACO TX
4310 SALT LAKE CITY UT
4311 LADONIA TX
4312 RHINELANDER WI
4313 MONMOUTH IL
4314 BUENA VISTA VA
4314 LEXINGTON VA
4315 PORT ANGELES WA
4316 LLANO TX
4317 SALINA KS
4318 CLEVELAND OH
4319 JACKSONVILLE AL
4320 RAWLINS WY
4321 GALVESTON TX
4322 AUSTIN TX
4323 BOULDER VALLEY MT
4324 TEKAMAH NE
4325 ROCKFORD IL
4326 ALBANY OR
4327 CHESTERTOWN MD
4328 EAST SAINT LOUIS IL
4329 PLATTE CITY MO
4330 NORTH WALES PA
4331 CANAL DOVER OH
4331 DOVER OH
4332 JACKSONVILLE FL
4333 HASKELL TX
4334 RICO CO
4335 NEW YORK NY
4336 IRONTON OH
4337 NEW ORLEANS LA
4338 HALLETTSVILLE TX
4339 PITTSBURGH PA
4340 OPELOUSAS LA
4341 SALT LAKE CITY UT
4342 KANKAKEE IL
4343 SUNDANCE WY
4344 BROWNWOOD TX
4345 HOLDREGE NE
4346 RUSK TX
4347 NORTH BALTIMORE OH
4348 GUTHRIE OK
4349 WACO TX
4350 HOUSTON TX
4351 SEHOME WA
4351 NEW WHATCOM WA
4352 PEN ARGYL PA
4353 TYLER TX
4354 WAYNE NE
4355 TYRONE PA
4356 GREENVILLE KY
4357 GRAND ISLAND NE
4358 DENVER CO
4359 MARSHALLTOWN IA
4360 SPRINGFIELD MO
4361 QUANAH TX
4362 DAYTON TN
4363 YOAKUM TX
4364 LAUREL MD
4365 ENGLEWOOD NJ
4366 HICO TX
4367 DELTA PA
4368 MIDLAND TX
4369 ROME GA
4370 HOT SPRINGS SD
4371 LLANO TX
4372 GRAND FORKS ND
4373 KING CITY MO
4374 BUTLER PA
4375 SEATTLE WA
4376 CHARTER OAK IA
4377 GASTONIA NC
4378 MASON TX
4379 WAXAHACHIE TX
4380 CHESTER VT
4381 KANSAS CITY KS
4381 KANSAS CITY MO
4382 DENVER CO
4383 GUTHRIE OK
4384 DICKINSON ND
4385 MUSCOGEE OK
4386 CLEBURNE TX
4387 FAIRHAVEN WA
4388 GATESVILLE TX
4389 GRANDVIEW TX
4390 HOQUIAM WA
4391 GRAHAM TX
4392 SEDALIA MO
4393 ARDMORE OK
4394 DEMOPOLIS AL
4395 COLORADO TX
4396 HELENA MT
4397 SEATTLE WA
4398 MUSKEGON MI
4399 WEST SUPERIOR WI
4400 MONMOUTH IL
4401 TEXARKANA AR
4402 OKLAHOMA CITY OK
4403 ASTORIA OR
4404 TEMPLE TX
4405 NACOGDOCHES TX
4406 HELENA MT
4407 ABERDEEN WA
4408 ORWIGSBURG PA
4409 AURORA MO
4410 ELGIN TX
4410 GIDDINGS TX
4411 PARIS TX
4412 CHARLESTON WV
4413 REED CITY MI
4414 WAUPACA WI
4415 DALLAS TX
4416 COLD SPRING NY
4417 TELLURIDE CO
4418 GRAHAM TX
4419 CANASTOTA NY
4420 ATLANTIC CITY NJ
4421 DULUTH MN
4422 GIRARDVILLE PA
4423 CORPUS CHRISTI TX
4424 WAUPACA WI
4425 JOPLIN MO
4426 TACOMA WA
4427 HOQUIAM WA
4428 DARBY PA
4429 VALDOSTA GA
4430 RICHMOND KY
4431 SIOUX CITY IA
4432 SALT LAKE CITY UT
4433 VIENNA IL
4434 GREAT FALLS MT
4435 LINCOLN NE
4436 PALESTINE TX
4437 GREELEY CO
4438 ARANSAS PASS TX
4438 ROCKPORT TX
4439 CENTRALIA WA
4440 TUCSON AZ
4441 CARTHAGE MO
4442 UNION CITY TN
4443 COLUMBUS OH
4444 CARLISLE PA
4445 WAYNESBORO PA
4446 PORT HURON MI
4447 DENISON TX
4448 CUSTER SD
4449 ANNA IL
4450 SAC CITY IA
4451 HAMILTON TX
4452 LA GRANDE OR
4453 TARENTUM PA
4454 MENOMINEE MI
4455 EDDY NM
4456 CHATTANOOGA TN
4457 SLAUGHTER WA
4458 ANACORTES WA
4459 FARMINGTON ME
4460 BUCHANAN VA
4461 ITASCA TX
4462 SEWICKLEY PA
4463 HOUSTON TX
4464 KANSAS CITY MO
4465 HICKMAN KY
4466 EASTLAND TX
4467 SOUTH BEND WA
4468 LAFAYETTE IN
4469 AURORA IL
4470 BLAINE WA
4471 BLAINE WA
4472 MIDDLEPORT OH
4473 DAYTON WA
4474 HASKELL TX
4475 WEBB CITY MO
4475 CARTERVILLE MO
4476 STREATOR IL
4477 BRISTOL VA
4478 TAMPA FL
4479 CORRY PA
4480 MOUNT CARMEL IL
4481 CONNELLSVILLE PA
4482 DANSVILLE NY
4483 JACKSBORO TX
4484 GENEVA NE
4485 SOCORRO NM
4486 PROVO CITY UT
4487 ARKANSAS CITY KS
4488 READING MA
4489 CHICAGO IL
4490 EAGLE PASS TX
4491 TICONDEROGA NY
4492 KAUFMAN TX
4493 EARLVILLE NY
4494 KANSAS CITY MO
4495 WALTON NY
4496 COCKEYSVILLE MD
4497 HOBART NY
4498 PUEBLO CO
4499 INDEPENDENCE KS
4500 COOPER TX
4501 HARRIMAN TN
4502 MARION IL
4503 COVINGTON VA
4504 FREMONT NE
4505 DUSHORE PA
4506 ASHTABULA OH
4507 LA JUNTA CO
4508 OSHKOSH WI
4509 LAKE BENTON MN
4510 SIOUX CITY IA
4511 ODEBOLT IA
4512 NEW YORK NY
4513 BANGOR PA
4514 PORTLAND OR
4515 LADONIA TX
4516 ATHENA OR
4517 UVALDE TX
4518 BALTIMORE MD
4519 PERRY NY
4520 JOLIET IL
4521 TUPELO MS
4522 WASHINGTON DC
4523 BERLIN NH
4524 NEW IBERIA LA
4525 SAN ANTONIO TX
4526 SNOHOMISH WA
4527 WHITE PIGEON MI
4528 HARTINGTON NE
4529 MOUNT VERNON WA
4530 BALTIMORE MD
4531 ROANOKE VA
4532 WATERVILLE WA
4533 BALTIMORE MD
4534 CHARLEROI PA
4535 RED BANK NJ
4536 LYONS IA
4537 BATHGATE ND
4538 REEDSVILLE PA
4539 TAMPA FL
4540 BONHAM TX
4541 GREAT FALLS MT
4542 CHENEY WA
4543 BLOOMSBURG PA
4544 JOHNSONBURG PA
4545 MARBLE FALLS TX
4546 SHENANDOAH PA
4547 MACON GA
4548 CATAWISSA PA
4549 NEW BRIGHTON PA
4550 SAINT THOMAS ND
4551 NAPERVILLE IL
4552 WAHPETON ND
4553 HOLSTEIN IA
4554 CORDELE GA
4555 FRANKLIN LA
4556 WINFIELD KS
4557 SOUTH SIOUX CITY NE
4558 FERNANDINA FL
4559 ASHLAND KY
4560 AVONDALE PA
4561 JAMESTOWN ND
4562 ADAMS MA
4563 FULTON KY
4564 PARK CITY UT
4565 GOLIAD TX
4566 FORT DODGE IA
4567 NEW YORK NY
4568 HIGH POINT NC
4569 CLARKSBURG WV
4570 CANONSBURG PA
4571 CHILDRESS TX
4571 QUANAH TX
4572 CASTLE MT
4573 MARSHFIELD WI
4574 SOCORRO NM
4575 SAINT LOUIS MO
4576 DECATUR IL
4577 BROWNSVILLE TX
4578 GRAND HAVEN MI
4579 COLUMBUS OH
4580 LYNN MA
4581 NEW YORK NY
4582 RUSSELLVILLE AR
4583 ARLINGTON NE
4584 MOSCOW ID
4585 TOLEDO OH
4586 KALISPELL MT
4587 MASON CITY IA
4588 AUBURN NE
4589 SOUTH OMAHA NE
4590 BIG TIMBER MT
4591 BRIDGEPORT AL
4592 INDEPENDENCE KS
4593 BILLINGS MT
4594 HAWARDEN IA
4595 MARSHALL MN
4596 AURORA IL
4597 HICKORY NC
4598 PINEVILLE KY
4599 OXFORD OH
4600 NEIHART MT
4601 PETERSON IA
4602 BEAVER DAM WI
4603 VERMILLION SD
4604 SHERIDAN WY
4605 CHICAGO IL
4606 LINCOLN NE
4607 HUNTINGTON WV
4608 GAITHERSBURG MD
4609 TABOR IA
4610 OAKLAND NE
4611 CAPE GIRARDEAU MO
4612 AUGUSTA KY
4613 YANKTON SD
4614 MARSHALL MN
4615 EMLENTON PA
4616 AUGUSTA KY
4617 ELBOW LAKE MN
4618 CAWKER CITY KS
4619 SAINT MARYS KS
4620 BERLIN WI
4621 NOCONA TX
4622 CALIFORNIA PA
4623 TACOMA WA
4624 ROSEBURG OR
4625 McKEESPORT PA
4626 SABETHA KS
4627 BARTOW FL
4628 ELIZABETH CITY NC
4629 SIOUX FALLS SD
4630 SIOUX CITY IA
4631 LEAD SD
4632 SOUTH OMAHA NE
4633 KNOXVILLE IA
4634 ABERDEEN MD
4635 NEWPORT NEWS VA
4636 PURCELL OK
4637 CANTON SD
4638 EAST GRAND FORKS MN
4639 GRAND RAPIDS WI
4639 WISCONSIN RAPIDS WI
4640 ARKANSAS CITY KS
4641 BERLIN WI
4642 OBERLIN KS
4643 BLUEFIELD WV
4644 BRECKENRIDGE MN
4645 NEW YORK NY
4646 BATAVIA IL
4647 MADISON ME
4648 KNOXVILLE TN
4649 PLYMOUTH MI
4650 PLATTEVILLE WI
4651 KALISPELL MT
4652 SEYMOUR IN
4653 LONGMONT CO
4654 HARRIMAN TN
4655 LITTLE FALLS MN
4656 LAFAYETTE IN
4657 WOOSTER OH
4658 PHILIPSBURG MT
4659 SAN ANGELO TX
4660 WHITMAN MA
4661 DEFIANCE OH
4662 VELASCO TX
4663 POMONA CA
4664 ARLINGTON MA
4665 STEWARTSTOWN PA
4666 CHICAGO IL
4667 CHARLESTON WV
4668 SPOKANE WA
4669 WELLS MN
4670 LOGAN UT
4671 CHARDON OH
4672 KEY WEST FL
4673 DAWSON PA
4674 MUNCIE IN
4675 ELWOOD IN
4676 NEW CASTLE PA
4677 CHARLES CITY IA
4678 NORTH VERNON IN
4679 PULASKI TN
4680 WEST SUPERIOR WI
4681 WAITSBURG WA
4682 DETROIT TX
4683 COLEMAN TX
4684 CROCKETT TX
4685 ANDERSON IN
4686 EVERETT WA
4687 GOLDTHWAITE TX
4688 VERNON IN
4689 HUNTSVILLE AL
4690 CALDWELL ID
4691 COLUMBUS GA
4692 WHITEWRIGHT TX
4693 MANCHESTER NH
4694 EAGLE GROVE IA
4695 BROWNWOOD TX
4696 ANAMOSA IA
4697 COLUMBUS OH
4698 IRWIN PA
4699 PULLMAN WA
4700 ESTHERVILLE IA
4701 DAINGERFIELD TX
4702 ALBERT LEA MN
4703 HOLYOKE MA
4704 VINITA OK
4705 GUTHRIE OK
4706 MARLIN TX
4707 DALLAS TX
4708 DENTON TX
4709 BUSHNELL IL
4710 AMARILLO TX
4711 SCHENECTADY NY
4712 NEW LONDON OH
4713 MOORHEAD MN
4714 POTTSTOWN PA
4715 JONESBORO TN
4716 CREEDE CO
4717 ROCKWALL TX
4718 ELKINS WV
4719 WESTFIELD NJ
4720 LANDER WY
4721 JEFFERSON TX
4722 MOUNT PLEASANT TX
4723 ARDMORE OK
4724 ORANGE NJ
4725 FORT WAYNE IN
4726 WILMINGTON NC
4727 MANKATO MN
4728 WILKINSBURG PA
4729 PHOENIX AZ
4730 DUQUESNE PA
4731 DANVILLE IL
4732 GATESVILLE TX
4733 ASPEN CO
4734 RATON NM
4735 ELGIN IL
4736 MERRILL WI
4737 DUQUOIN IL
4738 EVERETT WA
4739 MINNEAPOLIS MN
4740 LAKEPORT NH
4740 LACONIA NH
4741 BUFFALO NY
4742 SALINA KS
4743 NORFOLK VA
4744 WAUSAU WI
4745 WOODBINE IA
4746 DEMING NM
4747 TYLER TX
4748 SAN ANTONIO TX
4749 CHERRYVALE KS
4750 NEW DULUTH MN
4751 ROYERSFORD PA
4752 McDONALD PA
4753 LOWELL MA
4754 BELLE PLAINE IA
4755 ROCK SPRINGS WY
4756 PURCELL OK
4757 RIVERSIDE CA
4758 SPIRIT LAKE IA
4759 MARSHALL IL
4760 BUCKHANNON WV
4761 NORA SPRINGS IA
4762 CHARTIERS PA
4762 CARNEGIE PA
4763 WASHINGTON C. H. OH
4764 SOUTH BEND IN
4765 NEWPORT KY
4766 EAST ORANGE NJ
4767 EVANSTON IL
4768 BLOOMING GROVE TX
4769 MELROSE MA
4770 OKLAHOMA CITY OK
4771 SOMERVILLE MA
4772 CORTLAND OH
4773 WALLACE ID
4774 IPSWICH MA
4775 CEREDO WV
4776 DURANGO CO
4777 PILOT POINT TX
4778 HURON OH
4779 MONTESANO WA
4780 GUILFORD ME
4781 FORT FAIRFIELD ME
4782 CLEVELAND OH
4783 FORT HOWARD WI
4783 GREEN BAY WI
4784 DENISON IA
4785 BOWIE TX
4786 KANSAS CITY MO
4787 CHICAGO IL
4788 COLTON WA
4789 MARATHON IA
4790 KENDRICK ID
4791 PENDER NE
4792 SANDUSKY OH
4793 CLAREMONT NH
4794 IRETON IA
4795 LAURENS IA
4796 EVERETT WA
4797 SAINT CLOUD MN
4798 GALENA KS
4799 CANTON MD
4800 SHELBYVILLE IN
4801 MULBERRY IN
4802 LANGDON ND
4803 KALISPELL MT
4804 MURPHYSBORO IL
4805 URBANA OH
4806 BELFAST ME
4807 PRINCETON MN
4808 GENESEE ID
4809 MUNCIE IN
4810 GARNER IA
4811 MARTINSBURG WV
4812 GRAND FORKS ND
4813 PALATKA FL
4814 GLIDDEN IA
4815 CARTHAGE MO
4816 MILWAUKEE WI
4817 MILWAUKEE WI
4818 ELLWOOD CITY PA
4819 GLASGOW KY
4820 CRETE NE
4821 WADENA MN
4822 MIAMISBURG OH
4823 CORRY PA
4824 SANBORN IA
4825 GAS CITY IN
4826 MONTICELLO IL
4827 POCATELLO ID
4828 DAVIS WV
4829 BEMENT IL
4830 EL RENO OK
4831 APPLETON MN
4832 PHILIPSBURG PA

4833 HAVERHILL MA
4834 MALVERN IA
4835 ALEXANDRIA IN
4836 CLEARFIELD PA
4837 PENSACOLA FL
4838 TALLADEGA AL
4839 ARCANUM OH
4840 MUSKEGON MI
4841 ELKHART IN
4842 MEDINA OH
4843 PHILIPSBURG MT
4844 YORK VILLAGE ME
4845 CRIPPLE CREEK CO
4846 GLENS FALLS NY
4847 AUSTIN MN
4848 FORT WORTH TX
4849 COLUMBIA TN
4850 BELLE VERNON PA
4851 PRESCOTT AZ
4852 MUNCIE IN
4853 CADIZ OH
4854 KEWANEE IL
4855 NEW YORK NY
4856 HAGERSTOWN MD
4857 PATTON PA
4858 PORT HENRY NY
4859 SAINT JAMES MN
4860 NEWTON KS
4861 CONNELLSVILLE PA
4862 OKLAHOMA CITY OK
4863 PITTSBURG TX
4864 BELMONT OH
4865 DUBLIN TX
4866 BEEVILLE TX
4867 HICKSVILLE OH
4868 PORTLAND ME
4869 TONAWANDA NY
4870 MORRIS NY
4871 TOLUCA IL
4872 PRINCETON NJ
4873 NEEDLES CA
4874 SPEARFISH SD
4875 MOUNT PLEASANT PA
4876 McKEESPORT PA
4877 VERONA PA
4878 WEST SUPERIOR WI
4879 WARREN PA
4880 HEMPSTEAD NY
4881 HARTLEY IA
4882 NOBLESVILLE IN
4883 PITTSBURGH PA
4884 GIRARD OH
4885 OSAGE IA
4886 SAN DIEGO CA
4887 READING PA
4888 DUNKIRK IN
4889 FOREST CITY IA
4890 GOTHENBURG NE
4891 AUDUBON IA
4892 MOUNT PLEASANT PA
4893 SOUTH MILWAUKEE WI
4894 BEAVER FALLS PA
4895 DEWITT NE
4896 MOUNT AIRY NC
4897 CRESCO IA
4898 NEW YORK NY
4899 NIAGARA FALLS NY
4900 HILLSBORO TX
4901 VINCENNES IN
4902 BLANCHARD IA
4903 WHARTON TX
4904 CARBONDALE IL
4905 HEMPSTEAD TX
4906 BABYLON NY
4907 SPRINGFIELD MA
4908 REYNOLDSVILLE PA
4909 MERCER PA
4910 PITTSBURGH PA
4911 ROCKWALL TX
4912 STEVENS POINT WI
4913 NEW KENSINGTON PA
4914 MATTEAWAN NY
4914 BEACON NY
4915 ATHENS PA
4916 WADENA MN
4917 NEWPORT PA
4918 PITTSBURGH PA
4919 BLAIRSVILLE PA
4920 DECATUR IL
4921 WAUKON IA
4922 ATLANTA TX
4923 EPHRATA PA
4924 ITASCA TX
4925 LIBERTY NY
4926 FROSTBURG MD
4927 NORTH EAST PA
4928 OWATONNA MN
4929 CHELSEA VT
4930 NORMAL IL
4931 MINNEAPOLIS KS
4932 BIG TIMBER MT
4933 TRENTON MO
4934 CARMI IL
4935 YORK NE
4936 FAIRMONT MN
4937 APPLETON WI
4938 MEADVILLE PA
4939 SAINT JOSEPH MO
4940 ONANCOCK VA
4941 LEWISTOWN IL
4942 SOMERVILLE NJ
4943 SWANTON VT
4944 BRUNSWICK GA
4945 SALINA KS
4946 FORT WORTH TX
4947 WADESBORO NC
4948 COUDERSPORT PA
4949 TAMPA FL
4950 COLORADO TX
4951 MINNEAPOLIS MN
4952 JERSEYVILLE IL
4953 BAY CITY MI
4954 ROLFE IA
4955 LEBANON PA
4956 LOUISVILLE KY
4957 PHILLIPS ME
4958 FARMER CITY IL
4959 BARNESVILLE MN
4960 WILMINGTON NC
4961 AKRON OH
4962 SCHENEVUS NY
4963 WAYCROSS GA
4964 MARTINSVILLE IN
4965 HUNTINGDON PA
4966 LAKE CITY IA
4967 ALEXIS IL
4968 BOZEMAN MT
4969 KASSON MN
4970 YOUNGSTOWN OH
4971 COCHRANTON PA
4972 LAGRANGE IN
4973 FAIRFIELD ME
4974 GREENSBURG PA
4975 MANITOWOC WI
4976 HEARNE TX
4977 NILES OH
4978 NEW BETHLEHEM PA
4979 LEBANON PA
4980 BELVIDERE NJ
4981 EL DORADO KS
4982 CLARKSVILLE TX
4983 DEADWOOD SD
4984 TROY PA
4985 GRANVILLE NY
4986 MEDINA NY
4987 CLAREMORE OK
4988 WELLSVILLE NY
4989 LARAMIE WY
4990 TERRELL TX
4991 ALLEGHENY PA
4992 TRACY MN
4993 SAINT CLAIRSVILLE OH
4994 VANDALIA IL
4995 FORT SMITH AR
4996 SPARTANBURG SC
4997 WASHINGTON NC
4998 ALBION NY
4999 GRAYVILLE IL
5000 WILMERDING PA
5001 LAREDO TX
5002 SAINT LOUIS MO
5003 NEW YORK NY
5004 GREENVILLE SC
5005 RUTHERFORD NJ
5006 CLEVELAND OH
5007 BLOSSBURG PA
5008 HUBBARD TX
5009 FAIRFIELD IL
5010 WEST NEWTON PA
5011 FOREST CITY IA
5012 MANNINGTON WV
5013 NEW LONDON WI
5014 RIDGWAY PA
5015 MILES CITY MT
5016 WAGONER OK
5017 PITTSBURGH PA
5018 WILLS POINT TX
5019 DUBOIS PA
5020 BRITT IA
5021 ALEXANDRIA LA
5022 SIOUX CITY IA
5023 LAFAYETTE LA
5024 EUFAULA AL
5025 KANE PA
5026 MOUNT KISCO NY
5027 SISTERSVILLE WV
5028 SISTERSVILLE WV
5029 COLUMBUS OH
5030 ATLANTA GA
5031 GREENSBORO NC
5032 MANASSAS VA
5033 MAYFIELD KY
5034 UNIONTOWN PA
5035 GREENVILLE TX
5036 WEST PLAINS MO
5037 MECHANICVILLE NY
5038 TIONESTA PA
5039 STEUBENVILLE OH
5040 TIONESTA PA
5041 HOLTON KS
5042 BEAVER PA
5043 ELKLAND PA
5044 GROVE CITY PA
5045 ATLANTA GA
5046 WASHINGTON DC
5047 LA CROSSE WI
5048 GOLDSBORO NC
5049 ROBINSON IL
5050 SANFORD ME
5051 NEW BETHLEHEM PA
5052 SOUTH McALESTER OK
5053 WALDEN NY
5054 THOMPSON IA
5055 CHARLOTTE NC
5056 MEMPHIS TN
5057 MOUNT VERNON IL
5058 McDONALD PA
5059 JOHNSTOWN PA
5060 EAGLE PASS TX
5061 SUMMIT NJ
5062 EDWARDSVILLE IL
5063 WINDOM MN
5064 GAFFNEY SC
5065 COLUMBUS OH
5066 PHILIPSBURG PA
5067 ROCKVILLE IN
5068 PORT JEFFERSON NY
5069 CORAOPOLIS PA
5070 EAST SAINT LOUIS IL
5071 WINCHESTER MA
5072 SARANAC LAKE NY
5073 KITTANNING PA
5074 SALINAS CA
5075 ASHTABULA OH
5076 LOGANSPORT IN
5077 NAZARETH PA
5078 DALLAS TX
5079 PARIS TX
5080 VANDERGRIFT PA
5081 DECORAH IA
5082 SPRINGFIELD MO
5083 VINITA OK
5084 EBENSBURG PA
5085 WAYNESBURG PA
5086 MENDOTA IL
5087 FARGO ND
5088 VINTON IA
5089 DECATUR IL
5090 CLEVELAND OH
5091 PAULS VALLEY OK
5092 WOODSVILLE NH
5093 CATONSVILLE MD
5094 UNION CITY IN
5095 SHAWNEE OK
5096 SAN FRANCISCO CA
5097 SEGUIN TX
5098 EAST LIVERPOOL OH
5099 CRESTLINE OH
5100 FRANKLIN OH
5101 SENECA KS
5102 KUTZTOWN PA
5103 COSHOCTON OH
5104 ALMA KS
5105 SAN FRANCISCO CA
5106 CHICAGO IL
5107 KIRKSVILLE MO
5108 CLAYTON NY
5109 LEONARD TX
5110 ASHEVILLE NC
5111 CHICAGO IL
5112 NEW YORK NY
5113 CEDAR RAPIDS IA
5114 ELIZABETH PA
5115 SHAWNEE OK
5116 INDIANAPOLIS IN
5117 JUNEAU AK
5118 EASTON PA
5119 BLOOMINGTON IL
5120 WATERLOO IA
5121 WASHINGTON NJ
5122 DENTON MD
5123 LAKE MILLS IA
5124 GRANT PARK IL
5125 LIMA OH
5126 WYNNEWOOD OK
5127 MINEOLA TX
5128 CHECOTAH OK
5129 DURANT OK
5130 FORD CITY PA
5131 UNION CITY PA
5132 STANFORD KY
5133 NEW BLOOMFIELD PA
5134 ROCK HILL SC
5135 TRAER IA
5136 DOVER NJ
5137 ELMIRA NY
5138 KANSAS CITY MO
5139 MEDINA OH
5140 ELDORA IA
5141 HERKIMER NY
5142 McKEES ROCKS PA
5143 ANTIGO WI
5144 DRESDEN OH
5145 SIDNEY IA
5146 BONHAM TX
5147 MIFFLINTOWN PA
5148 LEWES DE
5149 MILFORD IL
5150 ABINGDON VA
5151 BRISTOL NH
5152 CLEVELAND OH
5153 HARRISBURG IL
5154 BUFFALO CENTER IA
5155 BOSTON MA
5156 WARRENSBURG MO
5157 LAKE CHARLES LA
5158 BOSTON MA
5159 OKLAHOMA CITY OK
5160 SPRINGFIELD OH
5161 LOUISVILLE KY
5162 FRESNO CA
5163 BOSTON MA
5164 WHEELING WV
5165 BEDFORD IA
5166 EAST GREENVILLE PA
5167 MISHAWAKA IN
5168 GREENSBORO NC
5169 WICHITA KS
5170 ROCHESTER PA
5171 TULSA OK
5172 SAINT LOUIS MO
5173 BEDFORD IN
5174 BUFFALO NY
5175 UVALDE TX
5176 HATTIESBURG MS
5177 HATTIESBURG MS
5178 ADDISON NY
5179 SAN ANTONIO TX
5180 COLUMBUS NE
5181 EAGLE PASS TX
5182 WILMINGTON NC
5183 COLEBROOK NH
5184 RED LION PA
5185 ROCKWELL CITY IA
5186 SAYVILLE NY
5187 BEDFORD IN
5188 ALTON IL
5189 GENOA NE
5190 NAVASOTA TX
5191 CLEVELAND OH
5192 SHERMAN TX
5193 RANTOUL IL
5194 CLEVELAND OH
5195 LOUISVILLE KY
5196 WAYLAND NY
5197 SCIO OH
5198 DELTA PA
5199 ROCKLAND MI
5200 ROCK VALLEY IA
5201 BEAUMONT TX
5202 ATHENS PA
5203 VERNON TX
5204 GLEN CAMPBELL PA
5205 RIDGEWOOD NJ
5206 STILLWATER OK
5207 HARLAN IA
5208 MILLVILLE NJ
5209 SPRINGFIELD MO
5210 MILFORD NY
5211 BLOOMSBURG PA
5212 MARIETTA OH
5213 LINCOLN NE
5214 SIDNEY OH
5215 PERTH AMBOY NJ
5216 SCHUYLKILL HAVEN PA
5217 SAN ANTONIO TX
5218 NAPOLEON OH
5219 MOBILE AL
5220 ROSWELL NM
5221 FRANKLIN PA
5222 STOUGHTON WI
5223 AMBOY IL
5224 PAWNEE OK
5225 PITTSBURGH PA
5226 SAINT MARYS WV
5227 SIEGFRIED PA
5227 NORTHAMPTON PA
5228 POTSDAM NY
5229 RICHMOND VA
5230 BARBERTON OH
5231 TORRINGTON CT
5232 LAKEWOOD NJ
5233 ARTHUR IL
5234 LANSFORD PA
5235 TORRINGTON CT
5236 MUSKOGEE OK
5237 NEW YORK NY
5238 CANYON TX
5239 EL PASO TX
5240 OIL CITY PA
5241 MYERSTOWN PA
5242 WINDBER PA
5243 FAIRHAVEN WA
5244 ALAMOGORDO NM
5245 NEWPORT PA
5246 CADDO OK
5247 MEDFORD MA
5248 NORMAN OK
5249 DOTHAN AL
5250 KANSAS CITY MO
5251 MOUNT GILEAD OH
5252 MIAMI OK
5253 MONESSEN PA
5254 METROPOLIS IL
5255 IRWIN PA
5256 SLAYTON MN
5257 PRINCETON KY
5258 GROVETON NH
5258 GORHAM NH
5259 McCONNELSVILLE OH
5260 RAHWAY NJ
5261 HARRISONBURG VA
5262 NEWCOMERSTOWN OH
5263 DYERSBURG TN
5264 CARROLLTON GA
5265 WILKINSBURG PA
5266 NEW MARTINSVILLE WV
5267 BRAZIL IN
5268 FREDERICKSBURG VA
5269 ORANGEBURG SC
5270 HOLDENVILLE OK
5271 MOUNT VERNON NY
5272 NEWKIRK OK
5273 TOLEDO IL
5274 DOVER NH
5275 TAYLOR TX
5276 COLORADO TX
5277 COLLEGE CORNER OH
5278 MONTPELIER IN
5279 EVANSTON IL
5280 RONCEVERTE WV
5281 WEEPING WATER NE
5282 NEWMAN GROVE NE
5283 COLORADO SPRINGS CO
5284 ALEXANDRIA BAY NY
5285 GEORGETOWN IL
5286 SYRACUSE NY
5287 IOLA KS
5288 GILMER TX
5289 LEWISTOWN PA
5290 IRVINGTON VA
5291 STONINGTON IL
5292 GARNETT KS
5293 MEXICO NY
5294 DEL RIO TX
5295 GUERNSEY WY
5296 SHERIDAN IN
5297 HOOPER NE
5298 DAVIS OK
5299 HOLLAND PATENT NY
5300 PETERSBURG IN
5301 WILMONT MN
5302 DAYTON IA
5303 HERRIN IL
5304 OGDEN IL
5305 CRYSTAL LAKE IA
5306 BELLEVILLE PA
5307 CONFLUENCE PA
5308 PENDER NE
5309 RIDGEFIELD CT
5310 BARTLESVILLE OK
5311 SMITHTON PA
5312 LOUISVILLE KY
5313 RIDGE FARM IL
5314 LEITCHFIELD KY
5315 MONTPELIER OH
5316 ASSUMPTION IL
5317 GROVETON NH
5318 ATLANTA GA
5319 MOULTON IA
5320 PARKERSBURG WV
5321 EAST BRADY PA
5322 PIPER CITY IL
5323 LUDLOW KY
5324 CELESTE TX
5325 SAINT JO TX
5326 COVINGTON VA
5327 OAKDALE PA
5328 KINGFISHER OK
5329 LOWELL OH
5330 STEWARTVILLE MN
5331 MIDLAND MD
5332 CUMBERLAND MD
5333 HIGH BRIDGE NJ
5334 GREENFIELD IA
5335 ENID OK
5336 HIGHLAND NY
5337 HUMPHREY NE
5338 NOCONA TX
5339 WYALUSING PA
5340 ROCKWOOD PA
5341 MONTPELIER OH
5342 ELDON IA
5343 TYLER TX
5344 MINERVA OH
5345 MARIETTA OK
5346 SAINT EDWARD NE
5347 STILLWATER OK
5348 MANISTIQUE MI
5349 CANEY KS
5350 CLEVELAND OH
5351 TARENTUM PA
5352 WEATHERFORD OK
5353 LYONS KS
5354 CHANDLER OK
5355 DE SMET SD
5356 EAST BRADY PA
5357 CARMI IL
5358 GUILFORD CT
5359 NORTONVILLE KS
5360 SKANEATELES NY
5361 PEORIA IL
5362 WEST CONCORD MN
5363 BELMAR NJ
5364 VALLEY CITY ND
5365 HOMESTEAD PA
5366 CLUTIER IA
5367 PORT LAVACA TX
5368 WAKEFIELD NE
5369 LOWELL IN
5370 MANTUA OH
5371 LORAIN OH
5372 DIKE IA
5373 GOLDFIELD IA
5374 EYOTA MN
5375 COOPERSTOWN ND
5376 FRANKFORT KY
5377 ELMORE MN
5378 TECUMSEH OK
5379 DUNCAN OK
5380 BERKELEY CA
5381 FLORENCE CO
5382 MOUNT STERLING OH
5383 HERON LAKE MN
5384 FULLERTON NE
5385 LAWRENCEVILLE IL
5386 ASHLAND KS
5387 PENN'S GROVE NJ
5388 WASHINGTON MO
5389 MILLVILLE PA
5390 SPRING VALLEY NY
5391 BUTLER PA
5392 SULLIVAN IN
5393 BLUE EARTH MN
5394 CULPEPPER VA
5395 SELMA CA
5396 CARROLLTON OH
5397 SUPERIOR NE
5398 ROSSVILLE IL
5399 MOULTON TX
5400 HARTINGTON NE
5401 NOWATA OK
5402 LOST NATION IA
5403 OCEAN GROVE NJ
5404 OAKLAND OK
5404 MADILL OK
5405 CLOQUET MN
5406 WINNEBAGO MN
5407 FALCONER NY
5408 FESSENDEN ND
5409 MOUNT VERNON TX
5410 TAYLORVILLE IL
5411 MAMARONECK NY
5412 CHELSEA IA
5413 RAWLINS WY
5414 WOODSFIELD OH
5415 DURAND MI
5416 CARLSTADT NJ
5417 ROFF OK
5418 OKMULGEE OK
5419 LOOMIS NE
5420 NEW LONDON IA
5421 FREDERICA DE
5422 BARTLETT TX
5423 FAIRMONT MN
5424 GUTHRIE CENTER IA
5425 ADA OH
5426 NEOGA IL
5427 TIFFIN OH
5428 SISSETON SD
5429 MESHOPPEN PA
5430 FOWLER IN
5431 CHICKASHA OK
5432 OWENSVILLE IN
5433 GRANITE CITY IL
5434 FAYETTEVILLE WV
5435 GREENSBURG IN
5436 STILLWATER OK
5437 MARSHFIELD WI
5438 ORANGE VA
5439 GRAPEVINE TX
5440 ELGIN NE
5441 MASONTOWN PA
5442 ARMSTRONG IA
5443 WICKLIFFE KY
5444 BATH PA
5445 HAVRE DE GRACE MD
5446 TIGERTON WI
5447 CHEROKEE KS
5448 UPPER SANDUSKY OH
5449 WOODSTOCK VA
5450 MORGANTON NC
5451 KINGS MOUNTAIN NC
5452 SOMERSET PA
5453 ADA MN
5454 FREEDOM PA
5455 LAKOTA ND
5456 LONG BEACH CA
5457 WESLEY IA
5458 MILWAUKEE WI
5459 PHILADELPHIA PA
5460 BLACKWELL OK
5461 GLADBROOK IA
5462 LEXINGTON OK
5463 CLARENDON TX
5464 GARDEN GROVE IA
5465 SYRACUSE NY
5466 SONORA TX
5467 DELTA CO
5469 SHAWANO WI
5470 SAINT ANNE IL
5471 UPPER MARLBORO MD
5472 MONTESANO WA
5473 HENNESSEY OK
5474 PONCA CITY OK
5475 PLAINVIEW TX
5476 BOSWELL IN
5477 CENTERVILLE SD
5478 TAHLEQUAH OK
5479 AYRSHIRE IA
5480 KEMMERER WY
5481 EMLENTON PA
5482 YALE MI
5483 WYLIE TX
5484 CAMERON TX
5485 PORT ARTHUR TX
5486 GLASGOW KY
5487 CARLSBAD NM
5488 HARVEY ND
5489 LEON IA
5490 ATLANTA GA
5491 LOCKHART TX
5492 PAWNEE OK
5493 BAIRD TX
5494 LOVINGTON IL
5495 ROSCOE PA
5496 MILFORD PA
5497 BROCKWAYVILLE PA
5497 BROCKWAY PA
5498 EMPORIA KS
5499 SEYMOUR CT
5500 MINNEWAUKAN ND
5501 GROVE CITY PA
5502 LEECHBURG PA
5503 FORT COLLINS CO
5504 McGREGOR TX
5505 OCONOMOWOC WI
5506 HAVENSVILLE KS
5507 CEDAR FALLS IA
5508 MANGUM OK
5509 BELLEVUE PA
5510 EL PASO IL
5511 MINERAL WELLS TX
5512 ALBANY GA
5513 ROSEBUD TX
5514 COON RAPIDS IA
5515 SARCOXIE MO
5516 CANEY KS
5517 LENOX IA
5518 FOREST CITY PA
5519 CHATSWORTH IL
5520 CROWLEY LA
5521 OCONTO WI
5522 PLAIN CITY OH
5523 CELINA OH
5524 RUSSIAVILLE IN
5525 ANNA IL
5526 LEWISVILLE IN
5527 JEANETTE PA
5528 MANCHESTER TN
5529 MADISON KS
5530 COVINGTON OH
5532 ORANGE VA
5533 COOPER TX
5534 ARCADIA FL
5535 LADYSMITH WI
5536 GAINESBORO TN
5537 SOUTH McALESTER OK
5538 HINDSBORO IL
5539 MILFORD IA
5540 HEDRICK IA
5541 RUTHVEN IA
5542 PARK RAPIDS MN
5543 WEST TX
5544 LATHROP MO
5545 GALLATIN TN
5546 PRYOR CREEK OK
5547 CHICKASHA OK
5548 CARLYLE IL
5549 VENUS TX
5550 HONOLULU HI
5551 CARRINGTON ND
5552 CHESTERHILL OH
5553 EVELETH MN
5554 BRIGHTON IA
5555 ROSEVILLE OH
5556 PHILLIPSBURG NJ
5557 OSHKOSH WI
5558 ORLEANS IN
5559 MOUNT HOPE KS
5560 STAMFORD TX
5561 SANDY SPRING MD
5562 HINTON WV
5563 ELIZABETHVILLE PA
5564 PLEASANTVILLE IA
5565 OIL CITY PA
5566 OMRO WI
5567 WILLISTON ND
5568 STAPLES MN
5569 PETTY TX
5570 ELLSWORTH MN
5571 GRAETTINGER IA
5572 GREENVILLE AL
5573 SHICKSHINNY PA
5574 MONTGOMERY PA
5575 WOODWARD OK
5576 DOUGHERTY IA
5577 DELTA OH
5578 EAST STROUDSBURG PA
5579 FARMINGTON IA
5580 SNYDER TX
5581 JACKSONVILLE TX
5582 BEMIDJI MN
5583 MORGANTOWN WV
5584 CHILLICOTHE IL
5585 WILLIAMS IA
5586 VICTOR CO
5587 ALVA OK
5588 WHITTIER CA
5589 IOWA PARK TX
5590 DURANT OK
5591 CULPEPPER VA
5592 LAKE GENEVA WI
5593 TROY AL
5594 SAINT JOSEPH MI
5595 BATESBURG SC
5596 SALLISAW OK
5597 TITONKA IA
5598 BOOTHBAY HARBOR ME
5599 MARS PA
5600 LEWISTON ID
5601 HALIFAX PA
5602 BETHESDA OH
5603 PENSACOLA FL
5604 HEREFORD TX
5605 HERMON NY
5606 MARLIN TX
5607 PETOSKEY MI
5608 CEDAR VALE KS
5609 DALLAS CITY IL
5610 PORT DEPOSIT MD
5611 RICHLAND IA
5612 NORMAN OK
5613 LUMBERTON MS
5614 KARNES CITY TX
5615 ASHLAND PA
5616 MELVIN IA
5617 MARTIN TN
5618 DILLONVALE OH
5619 CHADWICK IL
5620 ADA OK
5621 BLAIRSTOWN NJ
5622 BERLIN NH
5623 OAKLAND MD
5624 STERLING CO
5625 SHAMOKIN PA
5626 BLUFFTON OH
5627 BETHEL OH
5628 SHINER TX
5629 BROOKVILLE IN
5630 COBDEN IL
5631 AKRON NY
5632 CUBA CITY WI
5633 ADA OK
5634 CHILLICOTHE OH
5635 WAVERLY OH
5636 NEW BOSTON TX
5637 SWEA CITY IA
5638 DUNDEE IL
5639 NEW CARLISLE IN
5640 FREDERICKTOWN OH
5641 BYESVILLE OH
5642 COTTAGE GROVE OR

5643 BANCROFT IA
5644 FORSYTH GA
5645 LAMPASAS TX
5646 FAYETTE CITY PA
5647 COALGATE OK
5648 CALEDONIA NY
5649 NEW ORLEANS LA
5650 MARION OH
5651 LAURINBURG NC
5652 OLYMPIA WA
5653 CLEVELAND OH
5654 FULLERTON CA
5655 EUREKA KS
5656 MOUNTAIN VIEW OK
5657 ALLIANCE NE
5658 PESHTIGO WI
5659 HUDSON IA
5660 DE LEON TX
5661 MERKEL TX
5662 RYE NY
5663 ITALY TX
5664 THOMASVILLE AL
5665 DECATUR TX
5666 SAYRE PA
5667 BIG RUN PA
5668 ISHPEMING MI
5669 MORENCI MI
5670 HOWE TX
5671 HELENA MT
5672 INDIANAPOLIS IN
5673 ELKIN NC
5674 WINNSBORO TX
5675 CAZENOVIA NY
5676 HAVRE MT
5677 FAYETTEVILLE NC
5678 CLEVELAND OH
5679 DAYTON TN
5680 ALBANY TX
5681 HOWE TX
5682 STOYSTOWN PA
5683 FARMVILLE VA
5684 SAYRE PA
5685 BURT IA
5686 NAZARETH PA
5687 HOXIE KS
5688 SAN FRANCISCO CA
5689 MOUNT VERNON IL
5690 NELIGH NE
5691 MONTGOMERY WV
5692 PLANO TX
5693 GREENSBORO AL
5694 MINGO JUNCTION OH
5695 MEDFORD WI
5696 GRAND SALINE TX
5697 MEXIA TX
5698 LEXINGTON NC
5699 DE LAND IL
5700 WATERLOO IA
5701 POINT PLEASANT WV
5702 PUNXSUTAWNEY PA
5703 BURT IA
5704 ROGERS TX
5705 GREAT BEND KS
5706 LYLE MN
5707 GOWRIE IA
5708 GLASSPORT PA
5709 JACKSON GA
5710 ROXTON TX
5711 ARCHER CITY TX
5712 POINT PLEASANT BEACH NJ
5713 CLAYTON NM
5714 GENEVA AL
5715 PORT GIBSON MS
5716 OKLAHOMA CITY OK
5717 MOUNDSVILLE WV
5718 PENNINGTON NJ
5719 CUMBY TX
5720 TEMPE AZ
5721 NEVADA TX
5722 GRAND SALINE TX
5723 APOLLO PA
5724 MARLOW OK
5725 SCOTTSVILLE VA
5726 HOPE IN
5727 MARIENVILLE PA
5728 DODD CITY TX
5729 NATRONA PA
5730 SPRING LAKE NJ
5731 WYNNEWOOD OK
5732 TULSA OK
5733 BLOSSOM TX
5734 MONTGOMERY IN
5735 HOLDENVILLE OK
5736 PERKASIE PA
5737 TRENTON TX
5738 ESSEX IA
5739 LADONIA TX
5740 KINGFISHER OK
5741 GILMER TX
5742 DAYTON PA
5743 JEWELL IA
5744 LATROBE PA
5745 HIBBING MN
5746 TULLY NY
5747 ASHLAND OR
5748 SULPHUR OK
5749 ITASCA TX
5750 KILLEEN TX
5751 RITZVILLE WA
5752 SHREVEPORT LA
5753 FORT SILL OK
5753 LAWTON OK
5754 LEBANON TN
5755 LEHIGH OK
5756 TELL CITY IN
5757 COUNCIL GROVE KS
5758 WEATHERFORD OK
5759 GORDON TX
5760 ZANESVILLE OH
5761 JACKSBORO TX
5762 CLARINGTON OH
5763 JACKSONVILLE IL
5764 SAINT ANTHONY ID
5765 HONDO TX
5766 ELK CITY OK
5767 WELDON NC
5767 ROANOKE RAPIDS NC
5768 CRESSON PA
5769 ZANESVILLE OH
5770 O'NEILL NE
5771 BARRY IL
5772 LIDGERWOOD ND
5773 LITITZ PA
5774 MOODY TX
5775 CORWITH IA
5776 BALTIMORE MD
5777 ADAMSBURG PA
5777 BEAVER SPRINGS PA
5778 OELWEIN IA
5779 MONDOVI WI
5780 SAVANNAH MO
5781 SWEETWATER TX
5782 MOUNT CARMEL IL
5783 NEW YORK NY
5784 CARMICHAELS PA
5785 PLATTSBURG NY
5786 ASPERMONT TX
5787 ELMWOOD NE
5788 SAINT LOUIS MO
5789 IONIA MI
5790 KINGFISHER OK
5791 ATOKA OK
5792 HARTFORD KY
5793 SAINT EDWARD NE
5794 PARIS MO
5795 GLEN ROSE TX
5796 MEDFORD OK
5797 LUFKIN TX
5798 CANDO ND
5799 LEBANON KS
5800 RYAN OK
5801 MEYERSDALE PA
5802 HICKSVILLE OH
5803 ESSEX IA
5804 WATONGA OK
5805 CLEVELAND OH
5806 ARLINGTON TX
5807 ABBEVILLE LA
5808 GRANBURY TX
5809 TISHOMINGO OK
5810 KINSLEY KS
5811 MANGUM OK
5812 DANVILLE IL
5813 STRONGHURST IL
5814 FRIENDLY WV
5815 MALTA IL
5816 CASTLETON NY
5816 CASTLETON ON HUDSON NY
5817 ODEBOLT IA
5818 BARNESBORO PA
5819 BARBERTON OH
5020 IDAHO FALLS ID
5821 CLIFTON AZ
5822 ONTARIO OR
5823 BERLIN PA
5824 CRANDALL TX
5825 BEAUMONT TX
5826 REDWOOD FALLS MN
5827 GALLATIN MO
5828 WADSWORTH OH
5829 THURMONT MD
5830 COVINA CA
5831 WESTERNPORT MD
5832 WAYNESBORO PA
5833 MEYERSDALE PA
5834 OSBORNE KS
5835 DONORA PA
5836 DUBLIN TX
5837 NEW SALEM PA
5838 COUNCIL BLUFFS IA
5839 CAPE MAY NJ
5840 BOSTON MA
5841 BEAUMONT TX
5842 THORNTOWN IN
5843 PATTERSON LA
5844 SHREVEPORT LA
5845 INDIANAPOLIS IN
5846 SUFFERN NY
5847 WHITESBORO TX
5848 PITCAIRN PA
5849 WALDRON AR
5850 MART TX
5851 SOUTH GLENS FALLS NY
5852 JACKSON MN
5853 LLANO TX
5854 FLANDREAU SD
5855 CARROLLTOWN PA
5856 GILMAN IL
5857 GREENCASTLE PA
5858 HOUSTON TX
5859 ALEXANDRIA MN
5860 VINITA OK
5861 FARMINGTON ME
5862 PAULDING OH
5863 HANFORD CA
5864 SHERMAN TX
5865 ROBY TX
5866 WARREN MN
5867 GAINESVILLE NY
5868 LEHIGH IA
5869 NEWTON IL
5870 WADSWORTH OH
5871 KIRKSVILLE MO
5872 SOUTH BOSTON VA
5873 MANILLA IA
5874 HOOSICK FALLS NY
5875 SHAWNEE OK
5876 CHICAGO HEIGHTS IL
5877 MONTGOMERY AL
5878 MONACA PA
5879 MONACA PA
5880 CAMBRIDGE MD
5881 SOMERSET KY
5882 THORNDALE TX
5883 ROSEVILLE IL
5884 ATLANTIC CITY NJ
5885 OXFORD NC
5886 DEVILS LAKE ND
5887 O'KEENE OK
5888 JOHNSON CITY TN
5889 LAFAYETTE IN
5890 HARRISON AR
5891 VALLEY JUNCTION IA
5892 RUTHTON MN
5893 HOPE ND
5894 THIEF RIVER FALLS MN
5895 NORTHFIELD MN
5896 HOUGHTON MI
5897 GRAHAM TX
5898 SALEM SD
5899 ELLWOOD CITY PA
5900 BOWLING GREEN KY
5901 ELK POINT SD
5902 EUFAULA OK
5903 ALDERSON WV
5904 SEYMOUR TX
5905 ANADARKO OK
5906 PAYETTE ID
5907 ARGYLE MN
5908 HOUSTON PA
5909 DOTHAN AL
5910 WORTHINGTON MN
5911 CLEVELAND OK
5912 PRESCOTT IA
5913 JOHNSTOWN PA
5914 LAWTON OK
5915 HOBART OK
5916 ARLINGTON SD
5917 PAULDING OH
5918 ALEXANDRIA SD
5919 KNOX IN
5920 FREDERICKTOWN PA
5921 HACKENSACK NJ
5922 ARDMORE OK
5923 ANADARKO OK
5924 MARGARETVILLE NY
5925 PROVIDENCE RI
5926 SEABRIGHT NJ
5927 LOS ANGELES CA
5928 WOLCOTT NY
5929 DEQUEEN AR
5930 GEORGETOWN DE
5931 LOWELL IN
5932 KEMP TX
5933 CHILTON WI
5934 DYSART IA
5935 WETUMKA OK
5936 NORTHPORT NY
5937 PILGER NE
5938 CRANDALL TX
5939 GLENVILLE WV
5940 LAFAYETTE IN
5941 PILGER NE
5942 ANTIGO WI
5943 GRANTSVILLE MD
5944 MANSFIELD MA
5945 RIDGWAY PA
5946 WOONSOCKET SD
5947 SHEBOYGAN FALLS WI
5948 WEST ALEXANDER PA
5949 THERMOPOLIS WY
5950 WAPANUCKA OK
5951 SAPULPA OK
5952 BAXTER SPRINGS KS
5953 CROCKETT TX
5954 HOBART OK
5955 CHELSEA OK
5956 MONESSEN PA
5957 CARROLL NE
5958 MARIETTA OK
5959 CARLISLE KY
5960 BILLINGS OK
5961 PAWHUSKA OK
5962 ENSLEY AL
5963 WAVERLY TN
5964 PEPPERELL MA
5965 PUNXSUTAWNEY PA
5966 JENNINGS LA
5967 EUFAULA OK
5968 MONONGAHELA CITY PA
5969 CHOKIO MN
5970 ANDALUSIA AL
5971 CENTER TX
5972 QUANAH TX
5973 MONETT MO
5974 SCOTTDALE PA
5975 CORDELE GA
5976 HOTCHKISS CO
5977 SHERADEN PA
5978 PRINCETON WI
5979 CHARLES CITY IA
5980 NORTHWOOD ND
5981 PAULSBORO NJ
5982 WAKITA OK
5983 JACKSON AL
5984 BALTIMORE MD
5985 EL RENO OK
5986 EUREKA CA
5987 ABBEVILLE AL
5988 FERTILE MN
5989 IDAHO SPRINGS CO
5990 NEW YORK CITY NY
5991 NACOGDOCHES TX
5992 CHILDRESS TX
5993 LOS ANGELES CA
5994 WAILUKU HI
5995 BROKEN BOW NE
5996 GEORGETOWN OH
5997 DANA IN
5998 MATTHEWS IN
5999 NEW MATAMORAS OH
6000 CASTLEWOOD SD
6001 THROCKMORTON TX
6002 FORT GAINES GA
6003 MARQUETTE MI
6004 BAINBRIDGE GA
6005 CHARLOTTESVILLE VA
6006 TACOMA WA
6007 SECOR IL
6008 CLIFTON FORGE VA
6009 LUFKIN TX
6010 CRAFTON PA
6011 FARMERSVILLE TX
6012 PRICE UT
6013 VANCOUVER WA
6014 CHARITON IA
6015 FOND DU LAC WI
6016 ADENA OH
6017 HAMBURG IA
6018 PURCELLVILLE VA
6019 LARCHMONT NY
6020 CAMERON WV
6021 ANNISTON AL
6022 VERNDALE MN
6023 PITTSBURGH PA
6024 CHILDRESS TX
6025 PINCKNEYVILLE IL
6026 CASEY IL
6027 IMPERIAL CA
6028 ELIZABETHTOWN KY
6029 CEYLON MN
6030 LAS ANIMAS CO
6031 LURAY VA
6032 NORFOLK VA
6033 OSCEOLA IA
6034 NEENAH WI
6035 WHEATON MN
6036 BRIGHAM CITY UT
6037 DENVER PA
6038 LONG BRANCH NJ
6039 GOODLAND KS
6040 CENTER POINT TX
6041 MANILLA IA
6042 BROWNSVILLE TN
6043 LONGVIEW TX
6044 BAKERSFIELD CA
6045 PARKERS LANDING PA
6046 CELINA TX
6047 NEWNAN GA
6048 WAGONER OK
6049 HERNDON PA
6050 ORANGE TX
6051 SLATINGTON PA
6052 CORDELL OK
6053 EVERETT WA
6054 FULDA MN
6055 LIVE OAK FL
6056 RED OAK IA
6057 EATON CO
6058 SAYRE OK
6059 OXFORD OH
6060 OCEAN CITY NJ
6061 PONCA CITY OK
6062 BAY CITY TX
6063 POMEROY IA
6064 KENMARE ND
6065 LITTLE YORK IL
6066 PORT ALLEGANY PA
6067 ALVORD TX
6068 FAIRPORT HARBOR OH
6069 BLUM TX
6070 SHERIDAN IN
6071 WILLS POINT TX
6072 CHANUTE KS
6073 BRITTON SD
6074 PORT ANGELES WA
6075 NEWTON NC
6076 PULASKI TN
6077 LOWELL MA
6078 FORNEY TX
6079 BLUE RIDGE GA
6080 COON RAPIDS IA
6081 SANTA ROSA NM
6082 FITZGERALD GA
6083 RURAL VALLEY PA
6084 WINCHESTER VA
6085 BOTTINEAU ND
6086 OQUAWKA IL
6087 LE ROY NY
6088 LAKE CHARLES LA
6089 ALBANY IL
6090 HUNTINGDON PA
6091 ANSON TX
6092 GOLDTHWAITE TX
6093 LAWRENCEBURG TN
6094 CARTHAGE NY
6095 MARION NC
6096 MANSFIELD IL
6097 CHINOOK MT
6098 BARNESVILLE MN
6099 VOLGA SD
6100 PAINTSVILLE KY
6101 WAVERLY KS
6102 WHITMIRE SC
6103 COLUMBUS KS
6104 BOSTON MA
6105 WAYNESBURG PA
6106 SALISBURY PA
6107 MEMPHIS TX
6108 WEATHERLY PA
6109 SWISSVALE PA
6110 MARIANNA FL
6111 HENNESSEY OK
6112 EL CAMPO TX
6113 LEGER OK
6113 ALTUS OK
6114 POINT MARION PA
6115 CISCO TX
6116 WAVERLY IL
6117 TOWER CITY PA
6118 LITCHFIELD MN
6119 CAREY OH
6120 HILLSBORO KS
6121 VICKSBURG MS
6122 WASHINGTON IA
6123 TAZEWELL VA
6124 WAUBAY SD
6125 COLLINSVILLE IL
6126 WARRENTON VA
6127 KITTANNING PA
6128 ALBERT LEA MN
6129 MOUNT STERLING KY
6130 HUGO OK
6131 MINERSVILLE PA
6132 ORANGE CITY IA
6133 IVESDALE IL
6134 JASPER TX
6135 BOLIVAR PA
6136 BENTON IL
6137 GRAND JUNCTION CO
6138 COLLINSVILLE OK
6139 MOUNT PLEASANT TX
6140 MESQUITE TX
6141 ZELIENOPLE PA
6142 CHANDLER OK
6143 KINMUNDY IL
6144 MOUNT SAVAGE MD
6145 EMMETT ID
6146 ATHENS AL
6148 SILVER SPRINGS NY
6149 LE ROY KS
6150 GATESVILLE TX
6151 WILLMAR MN
6152 CARTHAGE TX
6153 PITTSBURG PA
6154 BENSON MN
6155 JERSEY SHORE PA
6156 EDMOND OK
6157 ROLLA ND
6158 JERMYN PA
6159 YUKON OK
6160 MOUNT STERLING KY
6161 CASHION OK
6162 BERWICK PA
6163 GEARY OK
6164 ELK CITY OK
6165 TREMONT PA
6166 TECUMSEH NE
6167 FULTON KY
6168 WINNSBORO TX
6169 LIVINGSTON TX
6170 MIDDLEBOURNE WV
6171 LINDSAY OK
6172 MONTICELLO IN
6173 TUSCALOOSA AL
6174 CARNEGIE PA
6175 FREELAND PA
6176 HENDERSON TX
6177 TIMPSON TX
6178 RIFLE CO
6179 SOUTH RIVER NJ
6180 SYLVESTER GA
6181 FREEMAN SD
6182 EDENBURG PA
6183 FARMINGTON NM
6184 BUFFALO NY
6185 WHITE ROCK SD
6185 SISSETON SD
6186 BUFFALO NY
6187 PORTALES NM
6188 GULFPORT MS
6189 SPRINGFIELD TN
6190 CARIBOU ME
6191 GREENUP IL
6192 GARRETT IL
6193 SHEFFIELD PA
6194 ROCKPORT IN
6195 LUBBOCK TX
6196 FRIENDSVILLE MD
6197 CARTHAGE TX
6198 PORT RICHMOND NY
6198 NEW YORK NY
6199 HILLS MN
6200 EVANSVILLE IN
6201 SIDNEY NE
6202 POCOMOKE CITY MD
6203 TYLER MN
6204 MINNESOTA LAKE MN
6205 KEYSER WV
6206 LURAY VA
6207 LOUISVILLE GA
6208 LONG PRAIRIE MN
6209 EBENSBURG PA
6210 COURTENAY ND
6211 PHILO IL
6212 TROUPE TX
6213 SUTTON WV
6214 SAN AUGUSTINE TX
6215 VALPARAISO IN
6216 PITTSBURGH PA
6217 FRANKFORT IN
6218 HANKINSON ND
6219 SAINT CHARLES IL
6220 EVERETT PA
6221 LYONS NE
6222 CAMPBELLSPORT WI
6223 LOTT TX
6224 COMMERCE TX
6225 DRAYTON ND
6226 RONCEVERTE WV
6227 PORT CLINTON OH
6228 PAW PAW IL
6229 PRATT KS
6230 SOUTH McALESTER OK
6230 McALESTER OK
6231 CAMDEN ME
6232 RALSTON OK
6233 WILLIAMSTOWN WV
6234 TYLER TX
6235 NORTON VA
6236 JOHNSON CITY TN
6237 SAINT CHARLES MN
6238 COLORADO CITY CO
6238 COLORADO SPRINGS CO
6239 YORKVILLE IL
6240 SCOTTSBLUFF NE
6241 OKMULGEE OK
6242 BURLINGTON JUNCTION MO
6243 BARNESVILLE GA
6244 STURGIS KY
6245 SAN AUGUSTINE TX
6246 PARKSLEY VA
6247 MORGAN TX
6248 LATONIA KY
6249 BURTON OH
6250 HOOVERSVILLE PA
6251 TIPTON IN
6252 BRISTOL VT
6253 NEW YORK NY
6254 WEWOKA OK
6255 FAIRMOUNT ND
6256 REDFIELD SD
6257 ARAPAHO OK
6258 BARTLESVILLE OK
6259 CAMPBELL MN
6260 BRISTOW OK
6261 KOKOMO IN
6262 BARBOURVILLE KY
6263 MOUNDS OK
6264 LEESVILLE LA
6265 CONNERSVILLE IN
6266 EAGLE BEND MN
6267 HOBART OK
6268 ONTARIO CA
6269 CHANDLER OK
6270 SUTERSVILLE PA
6271 ENLOE TX
6272 SAINT JOSEPH MO
6273 CLINTONVILLE WI
6274 APALACHICOLA FL
6275 CLIFTON HEIGHTS PA
6276 PERHAM MN
6277 GONZALES TX
6278 WILDWOOD NJ
6279 PRESTON MN
6280 DELPHOS OH
6281 LIGONIER PA
6282 GOTHENBURG NE
6283 MARTINSBURG WV
6284 NEW YORK NY
6285 HANLEY FALLS MN
6286 LARIMORE ND
6287 RUMFORD ME
6288 TUCUMCARI NM
6289 WARREN OH
6290 CHICAGO IL
6291 LAKE PROVIDENCE LA
6292 GAINESVILLE TX
6293 PLAINVIEW MN
6294 WHITE SD
6295 BURNS OR
6296 COLUMBIANA OH
6297 SNOW HILL MD
6298 TULIA TX
6299 COMANCHE OK
6300 COLLINSVILLE TX
6301 PITTSBURGH PA
6302 PHILIPPI WV
6303 POCAHONTAS IA
6304 TWO HARBORS MN
6305 NATCHEZ MS
6306 STROUD OK
6307 ANADARKO OK
6308 MARION OH
6309 WABASH IN
6310 MORRIS MN
6311 KANSAS CITY KS
6312 LEEDS ND
6313 WHARTON TX
6314 ELMWOOD PLACE OH
6315 MINOT ND
6316 SPRING VALLEY MN
6317 TEMPLE TX
6318 CLIFTON IL
6319 ENTERPRISE AL
6320 FLORESVILLE TX
6321 DAWSON MN
6322 NORWOOD OH
6323 PARIS KY
6324 WELEETKA OK
6325 WILMERDING PA
6326 YATES CENTER KS
6327 WASHBURN ND
6328 BENTON PA
6329 GROVETON TX
6330 SPRINGVILLE NY
6331 WELCOME MN
6332 KINGWOOD WV
6333 CALDWELL KS
6334 SOUTH BEND IN
6335 BRECKENRIDGE MN
6336 ALBANY GA
6337 CHURCHS FERRY ND
6338 BEAUMONT TX
6339 HOT SPRINGS SD
6340 MEETEETSE WY
6341 RUGBY ND
6342 CAMPBELLSVILLE KY
6343 HARRISONVILLE MO
6344 PERRYOPOLIS PA
6345 WELLSVILLE OH
6346 FRISCO TX
6347 POCATELLO ID
6348 SHERBURN MN
6349 PELICAN RAPIDS MN
6350 LERAYSVILLE PA
6351 WHITE PLAINS NY
6352 CASS LAKE MN
6353 WARREN OH
6354 MONROVIA IN
6355 DENVER CO
6356 MADISONVILLE TX
6357 CLEAR LAKE SD
6358 HOBART OK
6359 ATWOOD IL
6360 WELSH LA
6361 GRANGER TX
6362 ORRVILLE OH
6363 RATON NM
6364 TRUMAN MN
6365 MADILL OK
6366 CANBY MN
6367 NOWATA OK
6368 ELKTON SD
6369 JASPER MO
6370 MIAMI FL
6371 IRVINGTON NY
6372 DALTON OH
6373 WEST ELIZABETH PA
6374 DUBLIN GA
6375 PROPHETSTOWN IL
6376 FERRIS TX
6377 PHILIPPI WV
6378 VALENTINE NE
6379 ORRVILLE OH
6380 NEW DECATUR AL
6380 ALBANY AL
6380 DECATUR AL
6381 TORONTO SD
6382 NEOSHO MO
6383 KING CITY MO
6384 FALLS CREEK PA
6385 BENNETTSVILLE SC
6386 RIPLEY NY
6387 SLEEPY EYE LAKE MN
6387 SLEEPY EYE MN
6388 WEST BADEN IN
6389 FAIRFAX VA
6390 SEALY TX
6391 BELMONT OH
6392 WICHITA KS
6393 NEW ROCKFORD ND
6394 CONROE TX
6395 SISSETON SD
6396 WINDOM MN
6397 STARKWEATHER ND
6398 ELLENDALE ND
6399 BARTON MD
6400 ATHENS TX
6401 TWIN VALLEY MN
6402 CROWELL TX
6403 SHAWANO WI
6404 GUNTER TX
6405 BUTLER MO
6406 SOUTH McALESTER OK
6406 McALESTER OK
6407 CRARY ND
6408 NEW HAVEN PA
6408 CONNELLSVILLE PA
6409 CLARK SD
6410 ODESSA TX
6410 MIDLAND TX
6411 MOUNT UNION PA
6412 WESTBROOK MN
6413 MINNEOTA MN
6414 TAHLEQUAH OK
6415 WILBER NE
6416 SHAWNEE OK
6417 SAUK CENTRE MN
6418 WELSH LA
6419 MONTICELLO KY
6420 FINLEYVILLE PA
6421 TREMONT IL
6422 MABANK TX
6423 JOLIET IL
6424 WEST UNION WV
6425 NEW YORK NY
6426 SAN FRANCISCO CA
6427 NEW ROCHELLE NY
6428 NEW SALEM ND
6429 MINOT ND
6430 DEPORT TX
6431 ALBERT LEA MN
6432 TOLEDO IA
6433 MITCHELL IN
6434 STANTON IA
6435 RADCLIFFE IA
6436 RUSHFORD MN
6437 BRUSH CO
6438 TUNKHANNOCK PA
6439 TOMBSTONE AZ
6440 MATAWAN NJ
6441 NEW YORK NY

6442 GALLITZIN PA
6443 WASHINGTON VA
6444 STEWARTSTOWN PA
6445 HAWLEY PA
6446 WESSINGTON SPRINGS SD
6447 DOLGEVILLE NY
6448 CLARKFIELD MN
6449 MINNEAPOLIS MN
6450 NORMAN OK
6451 PARIS IL
6452 CONNELLSVILLE PA
6453 ETNA PA
6454 STEAMBOAT SPRINGS CO
6455 SANDUSKY OH
6456 MANOR PA
6457 OAKES ND
6458 CALDWELL OH
6459 ORTONVILLE MN
6460 GRAYVILLE IL
6461 GROESBECK TX
6462 BROOKINGS SD
6463 PAGE ND
6464 ANOKA NE
6465 QUAKERTOWN PA
6466 RAVENNA OH
6467 IVANHOE MN
6468 HENDRICKS MN
6469 DE PERE WI
6470 SANDY HILL NY
6470 HUDSON FALLS NY
6471 ITALY TX
6472 SUGAR CITY CO
6473 MILBANK SD
6474 FORMAN ND
6475 OMEMEE ND
6476 ABILENE TX
6477 OKEMAH OK
6478 BRICELYN MN
6479 CORINTH NY
6480 CLINTON IN
6481 ANAHEIM CA
6482 REMSEN NY
6483 SLIPPERY ROCK PA
6484 SAN JUAN PR
6485 ITHACA MI
6486 ENDERLIN ND
6487 DRYDEN NY
6488 McINTOSH MN
6489 ATKINSON NE
6490 ALVA OK
6491 CANYON CITY OR
6492 DETROIT MI
6493 OSCEOLA NE
6494 EL DORADO KS
6495 CLAIRTON PA
6496 DAWSON GA
6497 GOLDEN CO
6498 COLQUITT GA
6499 TYRONE PA
6500 YOUNGWOOD PA
6501 OSCEOLA MILLS PA
6502 WEBSTER SD
6503 BLOOMFIELD NE
6504 FARMLAND IN
6505 NEW LEXINGTON OH
6506 CAMBRIDGE NE
6507 HAYS PA
6508 PLEASANTVILLE NJ
6509 AUBURN IN
6510 MADISON WV
6511 BOYNTON OK
6512 BERLIN PA
6513 INDIANAPOLIS IN
6514 LIBERTYVILLE IL
6515 BUTLER OH
6516 TYRONE PA
6517 QUINTON OK
6518 MILTON ND
6519 MANKATO MN
6520 DULUTH MN
6521 MOUNTAIN HOME ID
6522 RUNGE TX
6523 JASPER MN
6524 NASHVILLE IL
6525 ATHENS GA
6526 WHITING IN
6527 VIRGINIA MN
6528 MASONTOWN PA
6529 DRESDEN OH
6530 CEDAR VALE KS
6531 LEHIGHTON PA
6532 MINNESOTA LAKE MN
6533 CAMBRIDGE SPRINGS PA
6534 MAUCH CHUNK PA
6535 CHICAGO IL
6536 SPRING GROVE PA
6537 LAKEFIELD MN
6538 MARLINTON WV
6539 FORT GIBSON OK
6540 HOLDENVILLE OK
6541 PAWNEE CITY NE
6542 TIFTON GA
6543 STEWARD IL
6544 WASECA MN
6545 LOS ANGELES CA
6546 RUSSELLVILLE KY
6547 SUMPTER OR
6548 SISTERSVILLE WV
6549 RIDGEWAY MO
6550 FONDA IA
6551 ROYSE CITY TX
6552 OSSINING NY
6553 FERRIS TX
6554 WAYNESVILLE NC
6555 KENMARE ND
6556 CASTLE ROCK CO
6557 TOWER CITY ND
6558 MURRAY UT
6559 BUFFALO ND
6560 SHARON PA
6561 BELLE FOURCHE SD
6562 STAPLETON NY
6563 GRAND RAPIDS MN
6564 GRANITE CITY IL
6565 LEIPSIC OH
6566 CAMBRIDGE OH
6567 PITTSBURG PA
6568 TURTLE CREEK PA
6569 RIMERSBURG PA
6570 TEMPLE OK
6571 BOYD MN
6572 WACO TX
6573 SOUTH FORK PA
6574 TURTLE CREEK PA
6575 SEYMOUR WI
6576 MONTEZUMA GA
6577 SHOSHONE ID
6578 MANNSVILLE OK
6579 GLOBE AZ
6580 NEW ALEXANDRIA PA
6581 PLEASANT UNITY PA
6582 NEW CUMBERLAND WV
6583 RENVILLE MN
6584 COTTONWOOD MN
6585 HOWARD SD
6586 LEROY IL
6587 HUNTINGTON NY
6588 OAKLAND MD
6589 SAINT MARYS PA
6590 COTTONWOOD FALLS KS
6591 NOGALES AZ
6592 SAN FRANCISCO CA
6593 EAST PALESTINE OH
6594 NEW CARLISLE OH
6595 CLARKSDALE MS
6596 NEDERLAND TX
6597 BELEN NM
6598 CRESCENT CITY IL
6599 NEW SALEM PA
6600 KEARNEY NE
6601 EDMORE ND
6602 VINITA OK
6603 BOSWELL PA
6604 OSHKOSH WI
6605 LONE OAK TX
6606 LEONARDTOWN MD
6607 CALDWELL TX
6608 CHATFIELD MN
6609 FAIRFIELD IL
6610 GRAFTON IA
6611 GILMORE CITY IA
6612 WALTERS OK
6613 PLATTSBURG NY
6614 CALDWELL TX
6615 HYNDMAN PA
6616 SANFORD NC
6616 LILLINGTON NC
6617 LOS ANGELES CA
6618 BELINGTON WV
6619 BELINGTON WV
6620 MOUNT GILEAD OH
6621 BARNESVILLE OH
6622 PIKEVILLE KY
6623 DODGE CENTER MN
6624 BRIDGEPORT OH
6625 CORYDON IN
6626 MIDWAY PA
6627 NACOGDOCHES TX
6628 DUNKIRK OH
6629 WYOMING IL
6630 ORISKANY FALLS NY
6631 ALDEN MN
6632 OAK HARBOR OH
6633 DOUGLAS AZ
6634 BELINGTON WV
6635 HANNIBAL MO
6636 BRIDGEVILLE PA
6637 IVANHOE MN
6638 STONEBORO PA
6639 PAULS VALLEY OK
6640 MOUNT PLEASANT OH
6641 WANETTE OK
6642 SMITHFIELD PA
6643 AUGUSTA KS
6644 ELGIN OR
6645 ALLENTOWN PA
6646 JACKSON MS
6647 CORDELL OK
6648 DALLASTOWN PA
6649 McLEANSBORO IL
6650 PRIMGHAR IA
6651 RENSSELAER IN
6652 DUNKIRK OH
6653 HIGHLAND IL
6654 CHESTER PA
6655 POND CREEK OK
6656 WESTON OH
6657 LOUDONVILLE OH
6658 SPARTANBURG SC
6659 KLEMME IA
6660 McLOUD OK
6661 PARKERS PRAIRIE MN
6662 SUMMERFIELD OH
6663 RICE LAKE WI
6664 WAMPUM PA
6665 PORTLAND PA
6666 BROADWAY VA
6667 MOUNT PLEASANT OH
6668 BIG SPRING TX
6669 TULSA OK
6670 LIBERTYVILLE IL
6671 PAONIA CO
6672 LINCOLN KS
6673 ASBURY PARK NJ
6674 BLUEFIELD WV
6675 LA RUE OH
6676 RIMERSBURG PA
6677 CHEROKEE OK
6678 OKLAHOMA CITY OK
6679 ROCKWALL TX
6680 PINE BLUFF AR
6681 LAUREL MS
6682 DODGE CENTER MN
6683 BOKCHITO OK
6684 GRAND RIDGE IL
6685 ROCKY MOUNT VA
6686 WORTHAM TX
6687 TOCCOA GA
6688 COLMAN SD
6689 WELEETKA OK
6690 LA MOURE ND
6691 MARISSA IL
6692 NETCONG NJ
6693 FERTILE MN
6694 MASSENA NY
6695 HOUTZDALE PA
6696 LAKE BENTON MN
6697 NEZPERCE ID
6698 DODGEVILLE WI
6699 NEW HARMONY IN
6700 FARRAGUT IA
6701 BELOIT KS
6702 KINGFISHER OK
6703 ROCKWALL TX
6704 CANNON FALLS MN
6705 DEEP RIVER IA
6706 PERRY AR
6707 ELMER NJ
6708 RED LION PA
6709 ADDISON PA
6710 LINDSAY OK
6711 RIB LAKE WI
6712 WIMBLEDON ND
6713 BROOKPORT IL
6714 ROSWELL NM
6715 NEW FREEDOM PA
6716 WASHINGTON DC
6717 MULDROW OK
6718 SELBYVILLE DE
6719 CARMEN OK
6720 LIBERAL KS
6721 MARTINSVILLE IL
6722 DUNKERTON IA
6723 CHICAGO IL
6724 EAST PEORIA IL
6725 PITTSBURG PA
6726 LAUREL DE
6727 HART MI
6728 MULLICA HILL NJ
6729 NASHVILLE TN
6730 LONG BEACH CA
6731 ROYALTON MN
6732 SOUTH SAINT PAUL MN
6733 BISBEE ND
6734 PANA IL
6735 BECKLEY WV
6736 FOSS OK
6737 CHURDAN IA
6738 DUNNELL MN
6739 SUMMERVILLE PA
6740 DANVERS IL
6741 GARRETT PA
6742 CLARKSTON WA
6743 HATTON ND
6744 LINCOLNTON NC
6745 MORRISONVILLE IL
6746 MONTROSE PA
6747 ORTONVILLE MN
6748 MANASSAS VA
6749 LONG BEACH CA
6750 LIME SPRINGS IA
6751 AUGUSTA IL
6752 ANTHONY KS
6753 HARRISON OK
6754 WEISER ID
6755 PRAIRIE CITY IA
6756 DERRY PA
6757 BALLINGER TX
6758 NEWPORT AR
6759 SHEFFIELD AL
6760 TIPTON IA
6761 SALISBURY MD
6762 DALHART TX
6763 AKRON OH
6764 DOON IA
6765 LOWELL IN
6766 WILLOW CITY ND
6767 COLDWATER KS
6768 BAKER CITY OR
6769 COLUMBIA KY
6770 ELMORE OH
6771 LOGAN IA
6772 FOUNTAIN CO
6773 SAINT LOUIS MO
6774 MIAMI FL
6775 BLOOMING PRAIRIE MN
6776 SHELBY NC
6777 ROSWELL NM
6778 HAMPTON VA
6779 LOVELAND OH
6780 HENDERSON TX
6781 NEWPORT NEWS VA
6782 RADFORD VA
6783 ROSEAU MN
6784 EMMONS MN
6785 PATCHOGUE NY
6786 GREENWOOD AR
6787 MAPLETON MN
6788 WELLS MN
6789 MILLER SD
6790 HARRISVILLE WV
6791 CLEBURNE TX
6792 TYNDALL SD
6793 COEUR D'ALENE ID
6794 WILSON PA
6794 CLAIRTON PA
6795 MADISON MN
6796 BRADDOCK PA
6797 COFFEYVILLE KS
6798 ROANOKE VA
6799 SHINGLE HOUSE PA
6800 FAYETTE CITY PA
6801 MORGAN CITY LA
6802 NEWARK NY
6803 AITKIN MN
6804 SPOKOGEE OK
6804 DUSTIN OK
6805 GENOA NE
6806 PITTSBURG PA
6807 SAN ANGELO TX
6808 PORTERVILLE CA
6809 NORTH TONAWANDA NY
6810 SOUR LAKE TX
6811 WOODSTOCK IL
6812 HEREFORD TX
6813 BAGLEY MN
6814 EMORY TX
6815 CAIRO IL
6816 LOVELAND OH
6817 MANKATO KS
6818 BEEMER NE
6819 TORONTO KS
6820 ONTONAGON MI
6821 FALL RIVER MA
6822 NORTH FORT WORTH TX
6822 FORT WORTH TX
6823 RIVERSIDE NJ
6824 POTOMAC IL
6825 OCALA FL
6826 CANADIAN TX
6827 GROVE CITY OH
6828 SAINT PAUL MN
6829 SHARPSVILLE PA
6830 WILLIAMSON WV
6831 UVALDE TX
6832 LIGONIER PA
6833 RIVERSIDE CA
6834 MAYFIELD KY
6835 CITRONELLE AL
6836 DENNISON OH
6837 OSAKIS MN
6838 BOONE IA
6839 MARION VA
6840 BALATON MN
6841 LOGAN KS
6842 HAMPTON VA
6843 DENNISON OH
6844 CARMEN OK
6845 CHESAPEAKE CITY MD
6846 PARAGOULD AR
6847 CANTON MS
6848 WINDBER PA
6849 COQUILLE OR
6850 CASPER WY
6851 CLINTON OK
6852 MACKSBURG IA
6853 MILWAUKEE WI
6854 WATERLOO IA
6855 OKMULGEE OK
6856 SOUR LAKE TX
6857 ELLIOTT IA
6858 NEW IBERIA LA
6859 HARRISVILLE PA
6860 MONTEVIDEO MN
6861 FINDLAY IL
6862 RUSHMORE MN
6863 NORWAY MI
6864 LOS ANGELES CA
6865 AMARILLO TX
6866 WISNER NE
6867 HENRYETTA OK
6868 BEGGS OK
6869 SAN DIEGO CA
6870 EXIRA IA
6871 COLUMBIA SC
6872 GLASGOW KY
6873 HANFORD CA
6874 HOLLIDAYSBURG PA
6875 CENTRALIA MO
6876 MOORESVILLE IN
6877 SUNBURY PA
6878 EAST BERLIN PA
6879 COWETA OK
6880 GREENE IA
6881 PLYMOUTH PA
6882 DILLSBORO IN
6883 JACKSONVILLE TX
6884 CARLSBAD NM
6885 CAMPBELL MO
6886 LEBANON VA
6887 COALPORT PA
6888 JACKSONVILLE FL
6889 FOSSTON MN
6890 WILBURTON OK
6891 CONNEAUT LAKE PA
6892 COSHOCTON OH
6893 CUSHING OK
6894 HODGENVILLE KY
6895 NEODESHA KS
6896 ALBA TX
6897 ELBA AL
6898 KNOX ND
6899 COEBURN VA
6900 CRAWFORD NE
6901 SCRIBNER NE
6902 LITTLE ROCK AR
6903 STAUNTON VA
6904 PETALUMA CA
6905 EDINBURG IN
6906 HENNING MN
6907 SUMNER IL
6908 WEST ALLIS WI
6909 DYER IN
6910 RAYMOND IL
6911 MUSKOGEE OK
6912 BUTLER NJ
6913 WEST MIDDLESEX PA
6914 NEODESHA KS
6915 WHITEWRIGHT TX
6916 BLACKWELL OK
6917 MINNEOTA MN
6918 LAKE CRYSTAL MN
6919 OROVILLE CA
6920 OPELOUSAS LA
6921 LE SUEUR CENTER MN
6922 HUGHES SPRINGS TX
6923 LAUREL MS
6924 O'FALLON IL
6925 BRIDGEWATER SD
6926 COWGILL MO
6927 GRANGEVILLE ID
6928 DURANT OK
6929 ELLSWORTH PA
6930 DICKSON TN
6931 YORKVILLE SC
6931 YORK SC
6932 HAMILTON KS
6933 GRAND MEADOW MN
6934 HALLOCK MN
6935 MILES TX
6936 HARVEY IA
6937 WEBSTER PA
6938 HOPEDALE OH
6939 CLARKS NE
6940 CLINTON OK
6941 SPENCER IA
6942 SHAMOKIN PA
6943 WATERTOWN OH
6944 BURGETTSTOWN PA
6945 SANTA MONICA CA
6946 SHIPPENSBURG PA
6947 STUART NE
6948 CLINTONVILLE PA
6949 HARRIS IA
6950 RINGTOWN PA
6951 ERIE IL
6952 CHARLESTOWN IN
6953 HULL IA
6954 RUSH CITY MN
6955 BURLINGTON KS
6956 SAN ANTONIO TX
6957 GLENWOOD SPRINGS CO
6958 MORGAN UT
6959 HARTFORD CITY IN
6960 BERNARDSVILLE NJ
6961 BESSEMER AL
6962 TRAFFORD CITY PA
6962 TRAFFORD PA
6963 HUMBOLDT KS
6964 WEST SENECA NY
6964 LACKAWANNA NY
6965 SYRACUSE NY
6966 BURNET TX
6967 GREENSBORO GA
6968 FROST TX
6969 CURWENSVILLE PA
6970 GAYLORD KS
6971 WILLIAMSBURG PA
6972 PERRY OK
6973 CARLTON MN
6974 DEMING NM
6975 REMSEN IA
6976 NEW CONCORD OH
6977 SHELDON ND
6978 EQUALITY IL
6979 EAST CONEMAUGH PA
6980 CALVIN OK
6981 OKLAHOMA CITY OK
6982 IDAHO FALLS ID
6983 MOUNT MORRIS PA
6984 CHESTER WV
6985 HUNTER ND
6986 DELPHI IN
6987 YORKTOWN TX
6988 OAKES ND
6989 PEARSALL TX
6990 STURGIS SD
6991 EVELETH MN
6992 JACKSON MN
6993 EL MONTE CA
6994 PROSPERITY SC
6995 BAGLEY IA
6996 HANCOCK MN
6997 MONTOURSVILLE PA
6998 ROCK FALLS IL
6999 TERRA ALTA WV
7000 CHERRY TREE PA
7001 GREENWICH OH
7002 BROWNSVILLE TX
7003 SWINEFORD PA
7004 FORT MORGAN CO
7005 NORTHUMBERLAND PA
7006 OTTAWA OH
7007 LANCASTER WI
7008 MOHALL ND
7009 ALLEGANY NY
7010 VERNON TX
7011 PLAINFIELD IN
7012 DRY RIDGE KY
7013 BATTLE CREEK MI
7014 WINTHROP MN
7015 SPARTA IL
7016 VAN ALSTYNE TX
7017 LODI OH
7018 BLAKELY GA
7019 TALOGA OK
7020 BIRMINGHAM AL
7021 SAINT JAMES MN
7022 WALSENBURG CO
7023 ANGOLA IN
7024 FRAZEE MN
7025 BEALLSVILLE OH
7026 MITCHELL NE
7027 GREENWOOD SC
7028 ABILENE TX
7029 CLARKSBURG WV
7030 PIKEVILLE KY
7031 COMPTON IL
7032 BARTLESVILLE OK
7033 HANCOCK MN
7034 MILTON FL
7035 PLYMOUTH OH
7036 POSEYVILLE IN
7037 GREENUP KY
7038 RENO NV
7039 PIKETON OH
7040 EDGERTON WI
7041 SMITHVILLE TX
7042 TISHOMINGO OK
7043 ARTESIA NM
7044 TROY AL
7045 FLOYDADA TX
7046 EL DORADO AR
7047 LAKE ARTHUR LA
7048 SCOTLAND SD
7049 HENRY IL
7050 HARTSHORNE OK
7051 LANSFORD PA
7052 DALLAS TX
7053 CALVIN OK
7054 STONEWALL OK
7055 BLOOMING GROVE TX
7056 ATGLEN PA
7057 SAN PEDRO CA
7058 MONTEREY CA
7059 CONDON OR
7060 ELKINS WV
7061 FONTANELLE IA
7062 MOBILE AL
7063 VISALIA CA
7064 NORTH EAST MD
7065 HUMBOLDT NE
7066 MARCELINE MO
7067 SPARTA GA
7068 BARRE VT
7069 PALO ALTO CA
7070 ALVIN TX
7071 ADA OK
7072 DALLAS OR
7073 OXFORD AL
7074 KALIDA OH
7075 EL PASO TX
7076 CECIL PA
7077 WHITE HALL IL
7078 CHRISTIANA PA
7079 MOMENCE IL
7080 LONG PRAIRIE MN
7081 ULEN MN
7082 ROCKY FORD CO
7083 CASPER WY
7084 SELMA AL
7085 SMOKEY HOLLOW OH
7086 MIDDLESBOROUGH KY
7087 RIVER FALLS WI
7088 VILLA GROVE IL
7089 ROCK RAPIDS IA
7090 RICES LANDING PA
7091 WAUSEON OH
7092 NEW PRAGUE MN
7093 ALEXANDRIA VA
7094 LIBERAL MO
7095 COLFAX WA
7096 DAINGERFIELD TX
7097 CULLMAN AL
7098 MASON TX
7099 BENNINGTON OK
7100 MADELIA MN
7101 GLENDIVE MT
7102 OLEAN NY
7103 POND CREEK OK
7104 POTEAU OK
7105 COMANCHE TX
7106 MUNDAY TX
7107 NEW YORK NY
7108 AURELIA IA
7109 LE ROY MN
7110 LOUISA KY
7111 CHRISMAN IL
7112 WEHRUM PA
7113 DALLAS TX
7114 COLFAX IA
7115 BROKEN ARROW OK
7116 BOWBELLS ND
7117 FAIRVIEW OK
7118 POTEAU OK
7119 LLANO TX
7120 COEUR D'ALENE ID
7121 WHITE HALL IL
7122 LOUISA KY
7123 CLAUDE TX
7124 GREENS FORK IN
7125 LARNED KS
7126 ALTA IA
7127 APACHE OK
7128 IONA MN
7130 GREENVILLE OH
7131 CALDWELL NJ
7132 COLUMBIA CITY IN
7133 REXBURG ID
7134 WHITE SD
7135 GATE CITY VA
7136 WAUTOMA WI
7137 LINN GROVE IA
7138 TEXARKANA AR
7139 EMAUS PA
7140 GARLAND TX
7141 MONTGOMERY AL
7142 CASSELTON ND
7143 LAKE PARK MN
7144 LEWISVILLE TX
7145 ALEDO IL
7146 MANOR TX
7147 COVINGTON TX
7148 LINDEN AL
7150 ORANGE VA
7151 STRAWN IL
7152 CUCAMONGA CA
7153 TAMPA FL
7154 PLEASANT HILL MO
7155 BICKNELL IN
7156 MILLERSTOWN PA
7157 HICO TX
7158 BAYFIELD WI
7159 LEGER OK
7159 ALTUS OK
7160 MOUNT AIRY MD
7161 CLINTON MN
7162 WESTHOPE ND
7163 MENA AR
7164 PAINTSVILLE KY
7165 FORT WORTH TX
7166 WYNDMERE ND
7167 KLAMATH FALLS OR
7168 HUMBOLDT IL
7169 NEW ROADS LA
7170 PALESTINE TX
7171 CRANFORD NJ
7172 PLAINS MT
7173 LEXINGTON VA
7174 WILLIAMSBURG KY
7175 COLUMBIA CITY IN
7176 NAPA CA
7177 PRAGUE OK
7178 CLIFTON KS
7179 SAINT LOUIS MO
7180 PORTLAND IN
7181 SPANGLER PA
7182 BISBEE AZ
7183 EASTLAND TX
7184 ELGIN MN
7185 FRANCIS OK
7186 ALBUQUERQUE NM
7187 NEW HOLLAND OH
7188 DUNN NC
7189 SIOUX RAPIDS IA
7190 MADISON FL
7191 PENNSBORO WV
7192 MEADE KS
7193 SWARTHMORE PA
7194 NAPLES TX
7195 OVERBROOK KS
7196 HALSTAD MN
7197 MILL CREEK OK
7198 NEWCASTLE WY
7199 LE SUEUR MN
7200 SHAW MS
7201 MANSFIELD TX
7202 SONORA CA
7203 NEW YORK NY
7204 ELWOOD NE
7205 ALBANY MO
7206 MARTINSVILLE VA
7207 LEXINGTON OK
7208 GATE CITY VA
7209 BERWYN OK
7210 VENTURA CA
7211 DELMAR DE
7212 DEVINE TX
7213 GRACEVILLE MN
7214 ALPINE TX
7215 PINEVILLE KY
7216 GREENWOOD MS
7217 STIGLER OK
7218 FREDONIA KS
7219 ALTURAS CA
7220 TALLAPOOSA GA
7221 LAMBERTON MN
7222 LYNDON KS
7223 ENGLISHTOWN NJ
7224 BRILLION WI
7225 LA FOLLETTE TN
7226 LA HARPE KS
7227 BROWERVILLE MN
7228 MONTE VISTA CO
7229 SAXTON PA
7230 SAINT ANTHONY ID
7231 COOLIDGE TX
7232 MANSFIELD LA
7233 PHILMONT NY
7234 OSNABROCK ND
7235 AMESVILLE OH
7236 ELGIN IL
7237 SOMERSET OH
7238 WEATHERFORD OK
7239 LINCOLN NE
7240 FORT SMITH AR
7241 LOOGOOTEE IN
7242 SEBREE KY
7243 COTULLA TX
7244 LAKEVIEW OR
7245 CLIFTON TX
7246 PENNSBORO WV
7247 LA FAYETTE GA
7248 MOUNT VERNON OH
7249 CENTER TX
7250 SALEM WV
7251 RAMONA OK
7252 EGAN SD
7253 QUINCY FL
7254 PRESTONBURG KY
7255 GRANVILLE NY
7256 VERSAILLES MO
7257 ANNONA TX
7258 ONLEY VA
7259 REDLANDS CA
7260 ODON IN
7261 LINEVILLE IA

7262 SCENERY HILL PA
7264 FAIRCHILD WI
7265 WILLIAMSTOWN NJ
7266 MERIDIAN MS
7267 BRADFORD VT
7268 DEER CREEK MN
7269 GRANDVIEW TX
7270 CHARLES TOWN WV
7271 BOLIVAR MO
7272 HOOD RIVER OR
7273 BELLE PLAINE MN
7274 LEWISTOWN MT
7275 CLENDENIN WV
7276 CATLIN IL
7277 LOUP CITY NE
7278 THOMAS OK
7279 REDWOOD CITY CA
7280 GALETON PA
7281 OLIVE HILL KY
7282 MOUNTAIN GROVE MO
7283 WATERVILLE MN
7284 BARBOURVILLE KY
7285 DODGE CITY KS
7286 TAMAQUA PA
7287 NORWAY IA
7288 MONTROSE CO
7289 DUNCAN OK
7290 STAPLETON NY
7291 LAKEWOOD NJ
7292 MORA MN
7293 NORMAN OK
7294 HAVELOCK IA
7295 FINGAL ND
7296 OGDEN UT
7297 WELLESLEY MA
7298 OBERLIN KS
7299 GUTHRIE OK
7300 MADISON GA
7301 PENDLETON OR
7302 BURR OAK KS
7303 EUREKA KS
7304 INWOOD IA
7305 COOPERSTOWN NY
7306 SHAMROCK TX
7307 RED WING MN
7308 LYNCHBURG VA
7309 COIN IA
7310 MILLSBORO PA
7311 CORNING AR
7312 EDINBORO PA
7313 PLAINVILLE KS
7314 TRACY CITY TN
7315 CARPIO ND
7316 SAN ANTONIO TX
7317 BARTLETT TX
7318 MOLINE KS
7319 CODY WY
7320 FORSYTH MT
7321 COALGATE OK
7322 AKRON IA
7323 EL DORADO AR
7324 FINLEY ND
7325 SPENCER NE
7326 CUMBERLAND IA
7327 BELLAIRE OH
7328 MANGUM OK
7329 NORFOLK NE
7330 UNION POINT GA
7331 ENNIS TX
7332 WILLOW CITY ND
7333 DODGE NE
7334 WINBURNE PA
7335 HUDSON SD
7336 MADERA CA
7337 ANDERSON TX
7338 BERRYVILLE VA
7339 WINDSOR IL
7340 BURWELL NE
7341 BROWNS VALLEY MN
7342 JASONVILLE IN
7343 GIRARD PA
7344 CORNWALL NY
7345 ARLINGTON TX
7346 FAYETTEVILLE AR
7347 LA CROSSE WI
7348 CAMPBELL TX
7349 NEW CUMBERLAND PA
7350 MOUNT OLIVE IL
7351 BRAYMER MO
7352 VERMILLION SD
7353 MARYSVILLE PA
7354 HARTSVILLE IN
7355 DILLER NE
7356 BELLWOOD PA
7357 MONROE IA
7358 CHICAGO IL
7359 HUNTINGTON WV
7360 CISCO TX
7361 VAN BUREN AR
7362 ROCKY MOUNT NC
7363 PARNASSUS PA
7363 NEW KENSINGTON PA
7364 BRANCHVILLE NJ
7365 GEORGETOWN IL
7366 FREEPORT PA
7367 PORTAGE PA
7368 CADDO OK
7369 SIOUX CENTER IA
7370 CLARKSVILLE OH
7371 THOMASVILLE AL
7372 BELLINGHAM WA
7373 BERTHA MN
7374 RUSHVILLE IN
7375 TELL CITY IN
7376 PITTSBURG TX
7377 CANDO ND
7378 MERIT TX
7379 MULBERRY GROVE IL
7380 INTERNATIONAL FALLS MN
7381 MONTPELIER ID
7382 HENDERSON IA
7383 CHERRYVALE KS
7384 SARGENT NE
7385 GOLCONDA IL
7386 CLEVELAND OK
7387 BRAHAM MN
7388 CALISTOGA CA
7389 BYARS OK
7390 FOWLER CA
7391 NEWTON FALLS OH
7392 TEXARKANA TX
7393 ANSLEY NE
7395 NEW BRIGHTON PA
7396 SHELBYVILLE IL
7397 DECHERD TN
7398 LUMBERTON NC
7399 SENECAVILLE OH
7400 MADERA PA
7401 SIOUX CITY IA
7402 FRANKLIN KY
7403 MASON OH
7404 DE FUNIAK SPRINGS FL
7405 HICKORY PA
7406 NANTICOKE PA
7407 HUBBARD TX
7408 DENVER CO
7409 ZELIENOPLE PA
7410 GORMAN TX
7411 LINTON IN
7412 KINGMAN KS
7413 McLEAN TX
7414 MILES TX
7415 LAFAYETTE IN
7416 GOFF KS
7417 ALEXANDER CITY AL
7418 SAN DIEGO CA
7419 BLACKFOOT ID
7420 CORNISH OK
7421 RANDOLPH NE
7422 BRECKENRIDGE TX
7423 GRACEVILLE FL
7424 HEADLAND AL
7425 EMERSON NE
7426 BRIDGEWATER SD
7427 CANBY MN
7428 CAMBRIDGE MN
7429 BRUNDIDGE AL
7430 CURWENSVILLE PA
7431 COMMERCE GA
7432 STIGLER OK
7433 DEL RIO TX
7434 PHILLIPS WI
7435 MEEKER CO
7436 FREEHOLD NJ
7437 FREELAND PARK IN
7438 BEARDSLEY MN
7439 GRINNELL IA
7440 PAWNEE IL
7441 BOZEMAN MT
7442 DAVIS OK
7443 MOUND CITY IL
7444 TONKAWA OK
7445 CONNELLSVILLE PA
7446 WASHINGTON DC
7447 NEW YORK NY
7448 CATAWISSA PA
7449 NORTH BEND NE
7450 NEW YORK NY
7451 SYLACAUGA AL
7452 DANVERS MA
7453 DUBOIS PA
7454 MUNCIE IN
7455 MITCHELL SD
7456 CLEVES OH
7457 LOUISVILLE KY
7458 JOHNSTON CITY IL
7459 FORT VALLEY GA
7460 JAMESPORT MO
7461 McCOMB CITY MS
7462 BEAVER DAM WI
7463 MONTEZUMA IN
7464 PIEDMONT AL
7465 JOHNSTOWN PA
7466 MERKEL TX
7467 UNION SPRINGS AL
7468 STATESBORO GA
7469 MONTOUR IA
7470 WEYAUWEGA WI
7471 FREDONIA PA
7472 DALLAS OR
7473 MOUNT JEWETT PA
7474 BELLINGHAM WA
7475 MARSHFIELD OR
7476 ARCADIA LA
7477 RANDOLPH NE
7478 EVANSVILLE IN
7479 LYONS NY
7480 SANTA MARIA CA
7481 MERKEL TX
7482 SEYMOUR TX
7483 WEST WINFIELD NY
7484 SYLACAUGA AL
7485 HUNTER NY
7486 BOWERSTON OH
7487 CLEVELAND OH
7488 SYKESVILLE PA
7489 PROSSER WA
7490 MORGANFIELD KY
7491 TRAFALGAR IN
7492 EDDYVILLE KY
7493 KENSINGTON KS
7494 JACKSON MO
7495 AUBREY TX
7496 TIPTON IN
7497 LAWRENCEBURG KY
7498 NEW ORLEANS LA
7499 BOKCHITO OK
7500 WESTVILLE IL
7501 ARVADA CO
7502 OAKDALE CA
7503 HAGERMAN NM
7504 WATERTOWN SD
7505 DELAWARE OH
7506 VILLISCA IA
7507 VICKSBURG MS
7508 CALEDONIA MN
7509 BELTON TX
7510 GREENVILLE TX
7511 STATE COLLEGE PA
7512 SHARON SPRINGS NY
7513 SHELBURN IN
7514 EL PASO TX
7515 TYLER TX
7516 LINEVILLE AL
7517 LANCASTER OH
7518 FOREST OH
7519 HYATTSVILLE MD
7520 OXFORD NE
7521 IOWA FALLS IA
7522 PHILADELPHIA PA
7523 BENTONVILLE AR
7524 BELLS TX
7525 CRYSTAL FALLS MI
7526 PRESTON ID
7527 DAVENPORT WA
7528 ECONOMY PA
7529 KERENS TX
7530 EL PASO TX
7531 HOT SPRINGS AR
7532 DELPHOS KS
7533 LITTLETON CO
7534 EAGLE LAKE TX
7535 SEDAN KS
7536 GASTONIA NC
7537 NEWBERG OR
7538 WITT IL
7539 ELDORADO IL
7540 LAKE CITY FL
7541 TRUMANSBURG NY
7542 NEW RICHMOND OH
7543 HOLLYWOOD CA
7544 CORBIN KY
7545 MONONGAH WV
7546 MART TX
7547 NOKOMIS IL
7548 GOLIAD TX
7549 CALHOUN GA
7550 WOBURN MA
7551 LINEVILLE AL
7552 ALBION MI
7553 DE LEON TX
7554 LOUISBURG NC
7555 EARLVILLE IL
7556 BATESVILLE AR
7557 EATON OH
7558 TALLADEGA AL
7559 McKEESPORT PA
7560 PITTSBURG PA
7561 LUCAS KS
7562 TERRE HAUTE IN
7563 MONROE NY
7564 HENDERSON NC
7565 MOULTRIE GA
7566 MELROSE MN
7567 COCHRAN GA
7568 WETUMPKA AL
7569 MUNICH ND
7570 SAINT LOUIS MO
7571 SALLISAW OK
7572 LAMPASAS TX
7573 BOSWORTH MO
7574 SPALDING NE
7575 NEWMAN IL
7576 DUNBAR PA
7577 BRIGHTON CO
7578 TOBIAS NE
7579 COFFEEN IL
7580 HAWKINSVILLE GA
7581 PITTSBURG PA
7582 MOUNT VERNON SD
7583 BLACKWELL OK
7584 COLUMBUS OH
7585 OLIN IA
7586 BELFAST ME
7587 WAYNESBORO VA
7588 SALEM NY
7589 BATTLE CREEK MI
7590 EDNA KS
7591 YUMA AZ
7592 HARTFORD AL
7593 MOREHEAD KY
7594 AVONMORE PA
7595 WORCESTER MA
7596 UTICA OH
7597 VIENNA SD
7598 CARBONDALE IL
7599 McGREGOR TX
7600 BROKEN ARROW OK
7601 EAST CHICAGO IN
7602 HORSE CAVE KY
7603 GOODHUE MN
7604 GREELEY CO
7605 MANCHESTER KY
7606 GOREVILLE IL
7607 NEW HAMPTON IA
7608 TWIN FALLS ID
7609 RIPPEY IA
7610 MAHAFFEY PA
7611 PAWNEE OK
7612 TROY NY
7613 BETHEL ME
7614 ENOSBURG FALLS VT
7615 PORTER OK
7616 GAINESVILLE GA
7617 NOCONA TX
7618 GRAND GORGE NY
7619 HOLDENVILLE OK
7620 REYNOLDSVILLE PA
7621 COLUMBUS OH
7622 GREELEY NE
7623 FRANKSTON TX
7624 EXPORT PA
7625 WOODSTOCK MN
7626 NEWBURG WV
7627 PERCY IL
7628 WAGONER OK
7629 OZARK AL
7630 FORT EDWARD NY
7631 BUCKEYE CITY OH
7632 LOS ANGELES CA
7633 KONAWA OK
7634 MALVERN AR
7635 SNYDER TX
7636 JELLICO TN
7637 FOWLER CO
7638 MOUNT VERNON OH
7639 BALTIMORE OH
7640 STAMFORD TX
7641 BLUE EARTH MN
7642 OAKMONT PA
7643 MANCHESTER MO
7644 HARLEM MT
7645 SAVOY TX
7646 GARDEN CITY KS
7647 CHISHOLM MN
7648 LOVELAND CO
7649 LOGAN OH
7650 HAMPDEN ND
7651 BOSWELL OK
7652 MORGANTOWN IN
7653 RICHMOND KY
7654 LOVELOCK NV
7655 ROCHESTER IN
7656 SENECA MO
7657 LONE OAK TX
7658 HANFORD CA
7659 HALLWOOD VA
7660 TRIUMPH IL
7661 MOUNT HEALTHY OH
7662 PARKSTON SD
7663 DICKINSON ND
7664 FLINT MI
7665 JELLICO TN
7666 ATOKA OK
7667 ANTLERS OK
7668 CORPUS CHRISTI TX
7669 BENJAMIN TX
7670 WOOSTER OH
7671 WESTERVILLE OH
7672 PINEVILLE WV
7673 WEST FRANKFORT IL
7674 MOUNT VERNON TX
7675 NORTH ATTLEBOROUGH MA
7676 HOUGHTON MI
7677 OKEMAH OK
7678 ROXBURY NY
7679 WHITNEY POINT NY
7680 FORREST IL
7681 CLARKSBURG WV
7682 CLARENCE IA
7683 GLASCO KS
7684 GOLDEN CITY MO
7685 LAYTON UT
7686 SOUTH SHORE SD
7687 EVERGREEN AL
7688 STEUBENVILLE OH
7689 MINOT ND
7690 OCEAN PARK CA
7691 SAN FRANCISCO CA
7692 SULLIVAN IL
7693 PORTLAND ND
7694 ATLANTA TX
7695 WAHPETON ND
7696 COALVILLE UT
7697 PURCELL OK
7698 DURHAM NC
7699 GLENS FALLS NY
7700 SAN SABA TX
7701 MEDFORD OR
7702 HALLSTEAD PA
7703 FREEPORT NY
7704 HOLLY CO
7705 MONROVIA CA
7706 CENTRALIA OK
7707 WOODVILLE OK
7708 PRINCETON MN
7709 PETERSBURG VA
7710 PEN ARGYL PA
7711 SARDIS OH
7712 GRAND TOWER IL
7713 SAN FRANCISCO CA
7714 TIOGA TX
7715 SAINT LOUIS MO
7716 NEWPORT PA
7717 COLUMBIA IL
7718 FAIRBANKS AK
7719 LODI CA
7720 LAS CRUCES NM
7721 WINDSOR VT
7722 TREVORTON PA
7723 MADILL OK
7724 WETUMKA OK
7725 FORT WAYNE IN
7726 BEECHER IL
7727 HANNAFORD ND
7728 BENLD IL
7729 CANTON MO
7730 SAINT PETERSBURG FL
7731 VALLEY VIEW TX
7732 LONACONING MD
7733 SAINT REGIS FALLS NY
7734 GRAHAM VA
7734 BLUEFIELD WV
7735 LANSDALE PA
7736 GUTHRIE CENTER IA
7737 UNIVERSITY PLACE NE
7738 TURLOCK CA
7739 MOWEAQUA IL
7740 TAZEWELL TN
7741 EXCELSIOR SPRINGS MO
7742 GLENWOOD MN
7743 ELKO NV
7744 ATHENS OH
7745 COLUMBUS OH
7746 JASPER AL
7747 HUGO OK
7748 OZONA TX
7749 ROCHESTER PA
7750 DAHLGREN IL
7751 BEATTYVILLE KY
7752 SHAWNEETOWN IL
7753 BAY CITY TX
7754 METUCHEN NJ
7755 GARRETSON SD
7756 TECUMSEH OK
7757 JASPER FL
7758 MARION IN
7759 POWHATAN POINT OH
7760 CORYDON IN
7761 WINAMAC IN
7762 LA GRANGE GA
7763 EAST HAMPTON NY
7764 MOTLEY MN
7765 JENNINGS LA
7766 GRAND JUNCTION CO
7767 TOPPENISH WA
7768 JEANERETTE LA
7769 McCLURE PA
7770 LUVERNE MN
7771 THOMAS OK
7772 HAWLEY MN
7773 CRAWFORDSVILLE IN
7774 SOUTH OTSELIC NY
7775 MIDLOTHIAN TX
7776 SACRAMENTO CA
7777 ALBANY GA
7778 CHIPLEY FL
7779 LEMOORE CA
7780 TALIHINA OK
7781 PORTSMOUTH OH
7782 GRAHAM VA
7782 BLUEFIELD VA
7783 LAMONT OK
7784 SILVERTON CO
7785 PECKVILLE PA
7786 MOUNT VERNON IN
7787 NEWARK OH
7788 SAPULPA OK
7789 ROGERS AR
7790 ROCK CREEK OH
7791 MIDDLETOWN IL
7792 JEANETTE PA
7793 WELLINGTON CO
7794 HIGHMORE SD
7795 TIFFIN OH
7796 SAINT PETERSBURG FL
7797 JACKSON MN
7798 VENUS TX
7799 HACKENSACK NJ
7800 SARDINIA OH
7801 ESCONDIDO CA
7802 FLORA IN
7803 HOLLYWOOD CA
7804 BOWLING GREEN KY
7805 BROOKVILLE IN
7806 CLINTON MO
7807 SABINAL TX
7808 SAINT LOUIS MO
7809 GRANADA CO
7810 TOLLEY ND
7811 WALTERS OK
7812 EAST HADDAM CT
7813 LESTERSHIRE NY
7814 JACKSBORO TX
7815 STOCKTON KS
7816 VANDERGRIFT PA
7817 CHATTANOOGA TN
7818 COLUMBUS OH
7819 MARION CENTER PA
7820 JAMESTOWN ND
7821 YORK NE
7822 HASKELL OK
7823 BUFFALO NY
7824 BATESVILLE IN
7825 HASKELL TX
7826 MIDDLETOWN PA
7827 BRADY TX
7828 EVERLY IA
7829 MENA AR
7830 FERDINAND IN
7831 HAYWARD WI
7832 FORT MORGAN CO
7833 RANDOLPH IA
7834 McMINNVILLE TN
7835 SPRINGVALE ME
7836 STANTON NE
7837 FORT COLLINS CO
7838 FRANKLIN TX
7839 LONGMONT CO
7840 OVID NY
7841 NEOGA IL
7842 MILBURN OK
7843 HAMPTON IA
7844 SAINT JOHN KS
7845 HENDRICKS WV
7846 McCUMBER ND
7847 POCAHONTAS VA
7848 CHATTANOOGA TN
7849 BERKELEY CA
7850 WHITESVILLE NY
7851 NEW BREMEN OH
7852 ADAMS ND
7853 LINN CREEK MO
7854 AVELLA PA
7855 ANTLER ND
7856 YORK SPRINGS PA
7857 MYLO ND
7858 LANCASTER SC
7859 HANCOCK MD
7860 FRACKVILLE PA
7861 WILCOX NE
7862 SIDNEY OH
7863 GOODLAND IN
7864 LELAND IL
7865 PERRY FL
7866 ROLETTE ND
7867 CORONA CA
7868 HUNTINGTON BEACH CA
7869 CLEAR LAKE IA
7870 COLUMBIA TN
7871 SLOCOMB AL
7872 EGELAND ND
7873 SHARPSVILLE PA
7874 SHIPPENVILLE PA
7875 WHITNEY TX
7876 NEW ORLEANS LA
7877 SAN LUIS OBISPO CA
7878 DOWNSVILLE NY
7879 BOTTINEAU ND
7880 SHELDON IA
7881 ATKINSON NE
7882 GOODLAND KS
7883 PAWHUSKA OK
7884 POLO MO
7885 GROTON SD
7886 SANGER TX
7887 PLUMVILLE PA
7888 SALIDA CO
7889 CARTERVILLE IL
7890 LONDON KY
7891 CANNEL CITY KY
7892 PAULS VALLEY OK
7893 KINGSTON OK
7894 SAN FRANCISCO CA
7895 REDONDO CA
7896 SPRING VALLEY OH
7897 NEW BERLIN PA
7898 WAUPUN WI
7899 WAYNESBORO GA
7900 LUDLOW MO
7901 RICHLAND CENTER WI
7902 HAGERSTOWN IN
7903 GILLESPIE IL
7904 ALAMOSA CO
7905 HATTON ND
7906 RISING STAR TX
7907 TOPEKA KS
7908 SEDRO-WOOLLEY WA
7909 LAWRENCEBURG IN
7910 NICHOLSON PA
7911 MARION KS
7912 SPARTA TN
7913 WILMINGTON NC
7914 EDGELEY ND
7915 WHITNEY TX
7916 WEST LIBERTY KY
7917 BIGLERVILLE PA
7918 CRYSTAL ND
7919 CAVE CITY KY
7920 HYDE PARK MA
7921 SALEM MO
7922 TERRE HAUTE IN
7923 COTTONWOOD ID
7924 NEW BRAUNFELS TX
7925 OVERTON NE
7926 CHICAGO IL
7927 HOMINY OK
7928 CARTHAGE TN
7929 PHILADELPHIA PA
7930 WARREN IN
7931 DANIELSVILLE PA
7932 DOTHAN AL
7933 FOLEY MN
7934 SANDERSVILLE GA
7935 BENSON PA
7936 WASHINGTON DC
7937 CHRISTIANSBURG VA
7938 DOTHAN AL
7939 BAYSIDE NY
7940 SLOCOMB AL
7941 FREEBURG IL
7942 KEY WEST FL
7943 KENSAL ND
7944 ABILENE TX
7945 CAPE MAY COURT HOUSE NJ
7946 SHELBYVILLE IN
7947 MONROE OH
7948 ENFIELD IL
7949 SHELBY NE
7950 STERRETT OK
7951 ATTALLA AL
7952 FAYETTEVILLE AR
7953 KNOX CITY TX
7954 METCALF IL
7955 TOWNER ND
7956 LINDALE TX
7957 EDGARTOWN MA
7958 WEST MINNEAPOLIS MN
7958 HOPKINS MN
7959 SHELBY NC
7960 ADRIAN MN
7961 CANYON TX
7962 COLBERT OK
7963 BUENA VISTA GA
7964 OWASSO OK
7965 LINDSAY CA
7966 LADYSMITH WI
7967 WAUKOMIS OK
7968 WAKONDA SD
7969 McDONOUGH GA
7970 WHITE CITY KS
7971 NORRIS CITY IL
7972 FAIRFAX OK
7973 STERLING CO
7974 MARTINSBURG PA
7975 HAYNEVILLE AL
7976 RAVIA OK
7977 DALHART TX
7978 SHOSHONI WY
7979 LYONS GA
7980 SANTA ANA CA
7981 IRVINGTON NJ
7982 MONTGOMERY NY
7983 COLLINGSWOOD NJ
7984 SOMERTON OH
7985 OPP AL
7986 MAYSVILLE GA
7987 GLENDALE CA
7988 RENWICK IA
7989 GARLAND TX
7990 GLASGOW MT
7991 BRANTLEY AL
7992 LUVERNE AL
7993 INDIANA PA
7994 QUITMAN GA
7995 BERTHOUD CO
7996 TERRAL OK
7997 SAN JACINTO CA
7998 HINTON WV
7999 WHITTIER CA
8000 FRANKLIN OH
8001 TOLAR TX
8002 LIVERMORE CA
8003 ESMONT VA
8004 PALISADES CO
8005 MEMPHIS TX
8006 HILLSBORO IL
8007 PEDRICKTOWN NJ
8008 HOLLAND TX
8009 BETHANY MO
8010 ERICK OK
8011 WELLSTON MO
8012 ARMOUR SD
8013 KENEDY TX
8014 FLORA IN
8015 CARRIER MILLS IL
8016 WEBB CITY MO
8017 CONVOY OH
8018 STRATFORD TX
8019 ROCK LAKE ND
8020 CODY WY
8021 SAINT JOSEPH MO
8022 BOONVILLE NY
8023 WRIGHTSVILLE GA
8024 WEBBERS FALLS OK
8025 MORRISTOWN TN
8026 ROCHESTER NY
8027 BLAIR NE
8028 SAMSON AL
8029 KRAMER ND
8030 PRAIRIE GROVE AR
8031 HAYES CENTER NE
8032 SPIRIT LAKE IA
8033 BERTHOUD CO
8034 SCHULENBURG TX
8035 EMMETSBURG IA
8036 FOREST GROVE OR
8037 MINEOLA TX
8038 WEST DERRY NH
8039 ONEIDA TN
8040 ESCONDIDO CA
8041 CLINTON SC
8042 STOCKPORT OH
8043 CASEY IL
8044 DWIGHT IL
8045 QUARRYVILLE PA
8046 WEST POINT GA
8047 PELLA IA
8048 JOSEPH OR
8049 HERMAN MN
8050 RAYMOND MN
8051 COLD SPRING MN
8052 WEWOKA OK
8053 NEW HAVEN IL
8054 STEPHENVILLE TX
8055 GLENDIVE MT
8056 HOLLIS OK
8057 MALVERN IA
8058 GREENWOOD NY
8059 ADAMS MN
8060 REMINGTON IN
8061 HOLLIS OK
8062 GERING NE
8063 ARTESIA CA
8064 WENATCHEE WA
8065 AZUSA CA
8066 ROSEBUD TX
8067 HARTSELLE AL
8068 GALVESTON TX
8069 OCEANSIDE CA
8071 ALVORD TX
8072 RANGER TX
8073 REDLANDS CA
8074 AZUSA CA
8075 PAYETTE ID
8076 OSKALOOSA IA
8077 GOODRICH ND
8078 FORT TOWSON OK
8079 FORT GIBSON OK
8080 SALMON ID
8081 NESS CITY KS
8082 ANTLERS OK
8083 McCONNELLSBURG PA
8084 HANKINSON ND

8085 COMPTON CA
8086 JONESBORO AR
8087 DOUGLAS WY
8088 AULT CO
8089 CHEYENNE WY
8090 DAYTON WA
8091 PEARISBURG VA
8092 TIOGA PA
8093 LITCHFIELD NE
8094 STANTON TX
8095 COLUMBIA AL
8096 OVERLY ND
8097 BRADSHAW NE
8098 RATON NM
8099 CASEY IA
8100 CORNING IA
8101 LAHAINA HI
8102 WELLINGTON TX
8103 PLEASANTON TX
8104 COLVILLE WA
8105 BENEDICT NE
8106 CLYDE TX
8107 MOUND VALLEY KS
8108 SAINT PAUL MN
8109 SANTA ANNA TX
8110 COVINGTON KY
8111 ROCHESTER NY
8112 STANTON TX
8113 GOTHENBURG NE
8114 SYRACUSE KS
8115 GREENUP IL
8116 LOVELAND CO
8117 LOS ANGELES CA
8118 DALE WI
8119 LITTLE ROCK IA
8120 RATON NM
8121 CHICAGO IL
8122 DETROIT MN
8123 EDNA TX
8124 McHENRY ND
8125 REDFIELD SD
8126 EL DORADO OK
8127 SAINT PARIS OH
8128 DUBLIN GA
8129 PEMBERTON NJ
8130 WALNUT SPRINGS TX
8131 WERNERSVILLE PA
8132 SILVER CITY NM
8133 COLUMBIA SC
8134 BLANCO TX
8135 BENTONVILLE AR
8136 LOGAN WV
8137 WAPANUCKA OK
8138 GUYMON OK
8139 WEISER ID
8140 FREDERICK OK
8141 SPRING GROVE PA
8142 NESS CITY KS
8143 REDONDO CA
8144 CEMENT OK
8145 ELK CITY KS
8146 ANDOVER NY
8147 WOLFEBORO NH
8148 LANSING MI
8149 POSEYVILLE IN
8150 SOUTH DEERFIELD MA
8151 PINE GROVE PA
8152 ROANOKE VA
8153 TUPPER LAKE NY
8154 AMO IN
8155 THOMASBORO IL
8156 ELGIN TX
8157 FRANKLINVILLE NY
8158 THERESA NY
8159 PRAGUE OK
8160 GREENVILLE NC
8161 JOHNSON NE
8162 TROY KS
8163 MORRIS IL
8164 DALLAS PA
8165 YOUNGSVILLE PA
8166 PRINCETON IN
8167 AULT CO
8168 CULBERTSON MT
8169 ODESSA TX
8170 FARGO ND
8171 HAMLIN WV
8172 GRESHAM NE
8173 TEXICO NM
8174 GIBSON CITY IL
8175 COOLVILLE OH
8176 SANTO TX
8177 KEOTA OK
8178 WOLFE CITY TX
8179 HIGGINS TX
8180 ULLIN IL
8181 ORANGE CA
8182 CENTERBURG OH
8183 HENDERSON NE
8184 LINCOLNTON NC
8185 BEAVER PA
8186 CROFTON NE
8187 LANSFORD ND
8188 MILFORD OH
8189 LEHIGH OK
8190 VANDERBILT PA
8191 ROSCOE NY
8192 KEWANNA IN
8193 GLOBE AZ
8194 MARINER HARBOR NY
8195 TEAGUE TX
8196 BENTLEYVILLE PA
8197 HARTFORD KS
8198 SUMNER IA
8199 HAMMOND IN
8200 GOREE TX
8201 DICKINSON ND
8202 FAIRFAX OK
8203 CHICKASHA OK
8204 ROCKWALL TX
8205 JULESBURG CO
8206 FREDERICK OK
8207 KAHULUI HI
8208 LUBBOCK TX
8209 HASTINGS OK
8210 HASTINGS OK
8211 BLOCKTON IA
8212 FINDLAY IL
8213 KONAWA OK
8214 NEWKIRK OK
8215 MUNDAY TX
8216 WESTFIELD IL
8217 CAMDEN AL
8218 TRENTON NE
8219 PRINCETON WV
8220 KIOWA KS
8221 NASHVILLE IL
8222 COVINA CA
8223 TOPTON PA
8224 LERNA IL
8225 CALDWELL ID
8226 MADDOCK ND
8227 HAMBURG NJ
8228 HARRISON OH
8229 CENTRAL CITY KY
8230 LIDGERWOOD ND
8231 ENID OK
8232 SHOSHONI WY
8233 PATTON PA
8234 BENTON IL
8235 SCRANTON PA
8236 MEDFORD OR
8237 GRAVETTE AR
8238 JUNIATA PA
8239 WEST TX
8240 BRONXVILLE NY
8241 BEMIDJI MN
8242 RULE TX
8243 GREENWICH CT
8244 BRUNSWICK MD
8245 FAIRCHANCE PA
8246 AURORA NE
8247 SEYMOUR IA
8248 SPEARFISH SD
8249 HIGGINS TX
8250 FITZGERALD GA
8251 WILMINGTON OH
8252 HAMLIN TX
8253 WORLAND WY
8254 NEW EGYPT NJ
8255 ALMENA KS
8256 OAKFORD IL
8257 INWOOD IA
8258 HAZARD KY
8259 WIBAUX MT
8260 CHRISTOPHER IL
8261 CONDON OR
8262 JEFFERSON IA
8263 REYNOLDSVILLE PA
8264 MILNOR ND
8265 BINFORD ND
8266 UPLAND CA
8267 HACKETTSTOWN NJ
8268 JAMAICA NY
8269 SPRINGFIELD MN
8270 DEWEY OK
8271 ELIZABETH CO
8273 PRESTON IA
8274 STOCKTON KS
8275 SHERIDAN WY
8276 KIRKSVILLE MO
8277 HUMBOLDT IA
8278 MARIETTA OK
8279 OROVILLE WA
8280 MILNOR ND
8281 EAU CLAIRE WI
8282 CEDAR RAPIDS NE
8283 CATASAUQUA PA
8284 MONTGOMERY AL
8285 HAMPTON NE
8286 STROMSBURG NE
8287 FORT WORTH TX
8288 HOUSTON TX
8289 RANSOM IL
8290 NORCATUR KS
8290 OBERLIN KS
8291 WHITE LAKE SD
8292 DICKSON TN
8293 ALLENDALE IL
8294 MAUD OK
8295 IMOGENE IA
8296 WINDSOR CO
8297 SANDY HILL NY
8297 HUDSON FALLS NY
8298 LITCHVILLE ND
8299 WOODBRIDGE NJ
8300 CAMDEN OH
8301 HORSEHEADS NY
8302 KITZMILLERVILLE MD
8303 DICKENS TX
8304 WANETTE OK
8305 AMERICUS GA
8306 PAINT ROCK TX
8307 HARPER KS
8308 HARPER KS
8309 NORTHFORK WV
8310 TEMPLE OK
8311 MIDLAND PA
8312 BROWNWOOD TX
8313 PAWHUSKA OK
8314 ARLINGTON GA
8315 ALAMOGORDO NM
8316 OLUSTEE OK
8317 MADISON NE
8318 GRAPEVINE TX
8319 BERLIN MD
8320 SPRINGDALE PA
8321 JACKSONVILLE FL
8322 COLERAINE MN
8323 MERCHANTVILLE NJ
8324 WILLISTON ND
8325 WESSINGTON SD
8326 LIVERPOOL PA
8327 MAY TX
8328 COLUMBUS NE
8329 BRIDGEPORT PA
8330 BOWIE TX
8331 BARDWELL KY
8332 WHITE LAKE SD
8333 GARY WV
8334 TOTTENVILLE NY
8335 SAINT JAMES NE
8335 WYNOT NE
8336 RUSH SPRINGS OK
8337 FAIRLAND IN
8338 ALMA WI
8339 NORTON KS
8340 THORNTON IA
8341 SANDPOINT ID
8342 GRANITE OK
8343 ARGYLE NY
8344 RICHLAND PA
8345 FAYETTEVILLE WV
8346 BOISE ID
8347 BRIDGEPORT IL
8348 ELIDA NM
8349 HELENA OK
8350 TIFTON GA
8351 RIDGEVILLE IN
8352 NEW LONDON IA
8353 BOSWELL OK
8354 ARDMORE OK
8355 TOYAH TX
8356 TARBORO NC
8357 ALMA KS
8358 FULTON MO
8359 SALISBURY MO
8360 WEBSTER SPRINGS WV
8362 CLINTWOOD VA
8364 PORTALES NM
8365 MACON GA
8366 COMANCHE OK
8367 GARNER IA
8368 MENTONE IN
8369 MOLINE KS
8370 NAMPA ID
8371 MORRISTOWN NY
8372 ALLEN NE
8373 NORTHWOOD IA
8374 SIDELL IL
8375 LAWTON OK
8376 ELKINS WV
8377 RIVERSIDE CA
8378 CHASKA MN
8379 ABILENE KS
8380 HAZELHURST PA
8381 TOWSON MD
8382 BELLEVILLE NJ
8383 JOHNSON NE
8384 JONESVILLE VA
8385 CENTRAL CITY NE
8386 MADISONVILLE KY
8387 UNION OR
8388 WHITEHALL NY
8389 ROSSLYN VA
8390 GUTTENBERG NJ
8391 TEXICO NM
8392 GONZALES TX
8393 MOUNT CARMEL PA
8394 CLOSTER NJ
8395 HOPE ND
8396 BARNARD KS
8397 MELROSE NM
8398 PEEKSKILL NY
8399 WELLINGTON KS
8400 MARQUETTE NE
8401 EDGEWATER NJ
8402 SAINT JO TX
8403 SANTA CRUZ CA
8404 COLLEGEVILLE PA
8405 LEMASTERS PA
8406 TRENTON TN
8407 CAINESVILLE MO
8408 NEW POINT IN
8409 KINGSBURG CA
8410 EXCHANGE PA
8411 SABINA OH
8412 EADS CO
8413 WOLBACH NE
8414 SOUTH BOSTON VA
8415 BLOOMINGTON IN
8416 GRANITE FALLS MN
8417 SHELLMAN GA
8418 PITTSBURG KS
8419 ABERCROMBIE ND
8420 BELPRE OH
8421 BLUE BALL PA
8422 GREENWOOD IN
8423 GLOUSTER OH
8424 RENO NV
8425 MILLSTADT IL
8426 GARY IN
8427 HAMLIN TX
8428 BLACK LICK PA
8429 ALBION IL
8430 HUTCHINSON KS
8431 FARWELL TX
8432 WHEATLAND WY
8433 CANON CITY CO
8434 RICHWOOD WV
8435 BEREA KY
8436 CORONA CA
8437 ROOSEVELT NJ
8437 CARTERET NJ
8438 CINCINNATI OH
8439 GLASGOW KY
8440 SHREVEPORT LA
8441 MIDDLEPORT OH
8442 RICEVILLE IA
8443 FRANKLIN TN
8444 GRANTSBURG WI
8445 LENOIR NC
8446 EAST MAUCH CHUNK PA
8447 COATESVILLE IN
8448 SANBORN ND
8449 DEKALB TX
8450 LILLY PA
8451 MADISONVILLE KY
8452 GREENSBORO GA
8453 JAMESTOWN NY
8454 BAYONNE NJ
8455 SAINT LOUIS MO
8456 LA PLATA MD
8457 MADISON IL
8458 MIDLAND CITY AL
8459 AMBRIDGE PA
8460 MONTGOMERY AL
8461 GREENWOOD IN
8462 GARFIELD NJ
8463 DEXTER NY
8464 CLEARFIELD PA
8465 SEMINOLE TX
8466 BERTRAND NE
8467 CONWAY SPRINGS KS
8468 LA HARPE IL
8469 BAZILE MILLS NE
8470 LAVONIA GA
8471 CHESTER SC
8472 OKLAHOMA CITY OK
8473 GREENFIELD IL
8474 NORWOOD MA
8475 TUTTLE OK
8476 WALKER MN
8477 NEWNAN GA
8478 CHEVIOT OH
8479 PORUM OK
8480 BRISTOL SD
8481 SUNNYSIDE WA
8482 MAQUON IL
8483 ROSELLE NJ
8484 RIVERTON NJ
8485 COLCHESTER IL
8486 IDABEL OK
8487 SAN FRANCISCO CA
8488 CARTHAGE OH
8489 HUGO CO
8490 ALHAMBRA CA
8491 FREDERIC WI
8492 EVANSVILLE IN
8493 MOUNT HOLLY SPRINGS PA
8494 AVOCA PA
8495 EUREKA SPRINGS AR
8496 ESCANABA MI
8497 BARNEGAT NJ
8498 WELLSVILLE PA
8499 NEW HOLLAND PA
8500 PITMAN NJ
8501 DUNELLEN NJ
8502 BRINSMADE ND
8503 NEW CASTLE PA
8504 SACRAMENTO CA
8505 NORWOOD OH
8506 CAMDEN TN
8507 LEBANON OH
8508 NEPHI UT
8509 CLINTON MO
8510 LONG BEACH CA
8511 CANAAN CT
8512 BOUND BROOK NJ
8513 SIDNEY NY
8514 NEW ALBANY MS
8515 EMMA TX
8515 CROSBYTON TX
8516 MOUNT VERNON NY
8517 WYOMING PA
8518 BELTON TX
8519 FLORESVILLE TX
8520 BRUSH CO
8521 GORDON NE
8522 NEW BOSTON TX
8523 STAPLES MN
8524 STRATFORD OK
8525 LONGTON KS
8526 HEMPHILL TX
8527 SENOIA GA
8528 VALE OR
8529 VIROQUA WI
8530 TONOPAH NV
8531 CANTON NY
8532 CHICAGO IL
8533 POLK NE
8534 EVANSTON WY
8535 HAWLEY TX
8536 JACKSON CENTER OH
8537 MEDARYVILLE IN
8538 THORNTON TX
8539 MOORE MT
8540 SAVANNA IL
8541 ALAMOSA CO
8542 PARIS TX
8543 GAGE OK
8544 SOUTH PASADENA CA
8545 IRON RIVER MI
8546 MILL CREEK OK
8547 SAINT PAUL VA
8548 AKRON CO
8550 CHAMBERLAIN SD
8551 FAIRMONT MN
8552 TULSA OK
8553 KIEFER OK
8554 FOREST GROVE OR
8555 FAYETTEVILLE TN
8556 OREGON CITY OR
8557 MADISONVILLE OH
8558 LYNNVILLE TN
8559 WEBSTER SD
8560 GADSDEN AL
8561 ELY NV
8562 CUERO TX
8563 LUTHER OK
8564 COVINGTON KY
8565 KARNES CITY TX
8566 ROCKAWAY NJ
8567 ORLEANS NE
8568 MIDLOTHIAN TX
8569 CHARLESTON WV
8570 GREEN CITY MO
8571 JEFFERSON NC
8571 WEST JEFFERSON NC
8572 COLORADO SPRINGS CO
8573 BRADY TX
8574 TILLAMOOK OR
8575 ELDORADO TX
8576 LYNDORA PA
8577 KAW CITY OK
8578 SYKESVILLE MD
8579 GEORGETOWN KY
8580 OCILLA GA
8581 GREENVILLE TX
8582 MAYS LANDING NJ
8583 CROSS PLAINS TX
8584 LAKE ARTHUR NM
8585 NAPLES TX
8586 HASTINGS UPON HUDSON NY
8587 SYKESVILLE MD
8588 BLANCHESTER OH
8589 WHITEFISH MT
8590 ALIQUIPPA PA
8591 SMETHPORT PA
8592 ELY MN
8593 MOSS POINT MS
8594 HOPE AR
8595 TONKAWA OK
8596 FORMOSO KS
8597 TAHOKA TX
8598 LAURIUM MI
8599 SCOTTSVILLE KY
8600 GREGORY SD
8601 HUNTLAND TN
8602 KANSAS CITY KS
8603 ALBIA IA
8604 LAWRENCEBURG KY
8605 HEGEWISCH IL
8606 FALLS CITY TX
8607 OBLONG IL
8608 COLTON CA
8609 TUPELO OK
8610 NOCONA TX
8611 PRINCETON TX
8612 EVANSTON WY
8613 HANCOCK NY
8614 TENAFLY NJ
8615 SEILING OK
8616 DUNCAN OK
8617 FORT SUMNER NM
8618 SAN BERNARDINO CA
8619 McADOO PA
8620 BRAZIL IN
8621 LORENA TX
8622 UNIONTOWN KY
8623 WESTFIELD NJ
8624 FREDERICK SD
8625 WILLIAMSBURG IN
8626 TULARE CA
8627 ARLINGTON NJ
8627 KEARNY NJ
8628 ROCKMART GA
8629 TAMAROA IL
8630 RIDGE FARM IL
8631 WINCHESTER TN
8632 RIO WI
8633 EDWARDSVILLE PA
8634 NEW YORK NY
8635 KALISPELL MT
8636 JOHNSTOWN CO
8637 ROODHOUSE IL
8638 KIOWA OK
8639 KELSO WA
8640 WINCHESTER TN
8641 BRONTE TX
8642 ABERDEEN SD
8643 SOUTH BOSTON VA
8644 MINCO OK
8645 HOUSTON TX
8646 DOWNINGTOWN PA
8647 IRVING IL
8648 MANLIUS IL
8649 BURLINGTON NC
8650 MILLTOWN IN
8651 KEARNEY NE
8652 GLENDORA CA
8653 SELINSGROVE PA
8654 MONROE LA
8655 GLASGOW MT
8656 ASHLEY PA
8657 LUDLOW MO
8658 EATON CO
8659 ROBERT LEE TX
8660 KANSAS CITY MO
8661 MILLBURN NJ
8662 CUTTER NM
8663 NARA VISA NM
8664 DALLAS TX
8665 NEW YORK NY
8666 RICHMOND VA
8667 HARVEY IL
8668 DAVENPORT OK
8669 LAUREL MT
8670 HERRIN IL
8671 HARTFORD WI
8672 BELLEVUE TX
8673 LENOIR CITY TN
8674 MARFA TX
8675 DELTA CO
8676 PORTER OK
8677 EUNICE LA
8678 ELLWOOD CITY PA
8679 DOLTON IL
8680 PEMBROKE GA
8681 TUCKAHOE NJ
8682 FAYETTEVILLE NC
8683 HARMONY MN
8684 CULLOM IL
8685 WALTHILL NE
8686 RHYOLITE NV
8687 SHATTUCK OK
8688 EMPORIA VA
8689 WAUWATOSA WI
8690 SANGER TX
8691 BURNS OR
8692 MARTINEZ CA
8693 ROTAN TX
8694 YOAKUM TX
8695 ORDWAY CO
8696 OBLONG IL
8697 BIWABIK MN
8698 MILBANK SD
8699 ADAIR IA
8700 MAYS IN
8701 LIMA OH
8702 BLANCHARD OK
8703 DETROIT MI
8704 BEVERLY NJ
8705 TORONTO OH
8706 BURKBURNETT TX
8707 SIERRA MADRE CA
8708 ELK CITY KS
8709 MORROW OH
8710 MANAWA WI
8711 FAIRFAX SD
8712 MONROE NC
8713 MANHATTAN IL
8714 LEBANON TN
8715 WAURIKA OK
8716 LAUREL MT
8717 CLIFTON SPRINGS NY
8718 FRESNO CA
8719 POPLARVILLE MS
8720 MINNEAPOLIS MN
8721 SHERIDAN OR
8722 HOT SPRINGS VA
8723 VASSAR MI
8723 MILLINGTON MI
8724 SLIPPERY ROCK PA
8725 CORNING IA
8726 MAHNOMEN MN
8727 CUSTER CITY OK
8728 ARCADIA FL
8729 GREY EAGLE MN
8730 CUSHING OK
8731 BRIDGEPORT TX
8732 MACKINAW IL
8733 ALTAMONT IL
8734 NEW ORLEANS LA
8735 BUENA VISTA CO
8736 CENTRALIA WA
8737 SCRANTON PA
8738 KANSAS CITY MO
8739 ULYSSES PA
8740 GENEVA IL
8741 MORROW OH
8742 LOVELADY TX
8743 RITZVILLE WA
8744 WAURIKA OK
8745 METROPOLIS IL
8746 STRASBURG VA
8747 WINAMAC IN
8748 BELMOND IA
8749 PINEVILLE WV
8750 CORVALLIS OR
8751 GORMANIA WV
8752 WRAY CO
8753 STRASBURG VA
8754 OLUSTEE OK
8755 PLATTEVILLE CO
8756 BATTLE LAKE MN
8757 ELK RIVER MN
8758 SESSER IL
8759 VERDEN OK
8760 HAY SPRINGS NE
8761 BELLEVUE PA
8762 ACKLEY IA
8763 SPRINGDALE AR
8764 SHARON PA
8765 HUNTSVILLE AL
8766 GREENVILLE SC
8767 CLOVIS NM
8768 RIALTO CA
8769 OCHILTREE TX
8769 PERRYTON TX
8770 JEFFERSON TX
8771 PECOS TX
8772 ASHEVILLE NC
8773 McVEYTOWN PA
8774 DENVER CO
8775 ALTUS OK
8776 GETTYSBURG SD
8777 WESTWOOD NJ
8778 DUNCANNON PA
8779 MILFORD NJ
8780 CLYDE TX
8781 HURON SD
8782 LAKEWOOD NM
8783 FREDERICKSBURG PA
8784 CLOVIS NM
8785 NAPPANEE IN
8786 FAYETTEVILLE AR
8787 BYERS TX
8788 THOMASVILLE NC
8789 CHEWELAH WA
8790 AFTON OK
8791 GALAX VA
8792 RUSSELL KY
8793 LAKE GEORGE NY
8794 ISLIP NY
8795 MUNHALL PA
8796 FORT LEAVENWORTH KS
8797 CREIGHTON NE
8798 CHICO CA
8799 WOODBINE MD
8800 ATLANTIC CITY NJ
8801 CROSSVILLE IL
8802 GAINESVILLE FL
8803 PLEASANTON KS
8804 DUBLIN IN
8805 CARLISLE IN
8806 OLYPHANT PA
8807 OAKVILLE TX
8808 SCOTT CITY KS
8809 WARNER OK
8810 MANSFIELD PA
8811 UTICA NE
8812 CURTIS NE
8813 APPLETON MN
8814 ADAIRVILLE KY
8815 ASPEN CO
8816 SILVERTON TX
8817 MOORE TX
8818 WACO TX
8819 ABINGDON VA
8820 SWAYZEE IN
8821 TURTLE LAKE ND
8822 MALAD CITY ID
8823 McCOOK NE
8824 ASPINWALL PA
8825 HOLLIS OK
8826 TORONTO OH
8827 LOS ANGELES CA
8828 NEWPORT WA
8829 LITTLE FALLS NJ
8830 BROOKSVILLE KY
8831 MANSFIELD PA
8832 EVANSVILLE IN
8833 LINDENHURST NY
8834 MARLBORO NY
8835 BIRDSEYE IN
8836 SELMER TN
8837 HENDERSONVILLE NC
8838 HIGHLAND FALLS NY
8839 TIPPECANOE CITY OH
8840 FRUITA CO
8841 HURON SD
8842 CHICAGO IL
8843 TURNERSVILLE TX
8844 GRAHAM NC
8845 LACEYVILLE PA
8846 SAINT FRANCISVILLE IL
8847 GRIFFIN CORNERS NY
8847 FLEISCHMANNS NY
8848 WASHINGTON GA
8849 TROY PA
8850 HIGHLAND FALLS NY
8851 LAWRENCE NE
8852 TEXHOMA OK
8853 CORONA NY
8854 EVANS CITY PA
8855 HOMER CITY PA
8856 LINEVILLE AL
8857 REEDLEY CA
8858 OLEY PA
8859 VERDEN OK
8860 POOLESVILLE MD
8861 WAURIKA OK
8862 LAWRENCEBURG KY
8863 BANCROFT NE
8864 BATESVILLE AR
8865 OZONE PARK NY
8866 MONTGOMERY PA
8867 PIKESVILLE MD
8868 LYNNVILLE IN
8869 AMERICAN FALLS ID
8870 LONG BEACH CA
8871 CAMBRIDGE CITY IN
8872 ROCKVILLE CENTRE NY
8873 AMITYVILLE NY
8874 FORT LEE NJ
8875 CHILHOWIE VA
8876 MORRIS OK
8877 CABOOL MO
8878 SUNMAN IN
8879 UNION CITY PA
8880 LORDSBURG NM
8881 McCLUSKY ND
8882 FARMINGDALE NY
8883 STAFFORD KS
8884 GRAND SALINE TX
8885 LINCOLN NE
8886 SHEYENNE ND
8888 HARRISON NE
8889 SAVANNAH TN
8890 WEST CONSHOHOCKEN PA
8891 CANTON TX
8892 PALESTINE IL
8893 CHATEAUGAY NY
8894 WASHINGTON GA
8895 WAITSBURG WA
8896 BUFFALO OK
8897 ANSON TX
8898 NAUVOO IL
8899 GALVESTON TX
8900 HAWKEYE IA
8901 SOMERFIELD PA
8902 CREEDMOOR NC
8903 BURNSIDE KY
8904 ANSTED WV
8905 SALYERSVILLE KY
8906 MULLAN ID
8907 RIVERSIDE CA
8908 BLANDINSVILLE IL

8909 LAFAYETTE CO
8910 FLORALA AL
8911 OCHILTREE TX
8912 ALBION IN
8913 BERNVILLE PA
8914 STEELVILLE MO
8915 GRISWOLD IA
8916 FAIRVIEW MO
8917 WIMBLEDON ND
8918 FRANKFORD DE
8919 BRUIN PA
8920 ONEONTA NY
8921 LUZERNE PA
8922 NEW YORK NY
8923 LYNBROOK NY
8924 HUGHESVILLE PA
8925 ODESSA TX
8926 NEW YORK NY
8927 WADESVILLE IN
8928 GATESVILLE TX
8929 HUNTINGBURG IN
8930 PALMERTON PA
8931 STATE CENTER IA
8932 EAST SAINT LOUIS IL
8933 LOCKPORT IL
8934 LEWISBURG TN
8935 SARANAC LAKE NY
8936 ESSEX CT
8937 LAKE FOREST IL
8938 WEST YORK PA
8939 FLEETWOOD PA
8940 TAYLORVILLE IL
8941 SPRINGFIELD OR
8942 SPRINGFIELD SD
8943 CLAY KY
8944 EL DORADO OK
8945 COVINGTON GA
8946 SLIGO PA
8947 JOPLIN MO
8948 KENNEWICK WA
8949 SOUTH OMAHA NE
8950 NEW SHARON IA
8951 SALIDA CO
8952 HUNTSVILLE AR
8953 ASHEBORO NC
8954 WEST ALEXANDER PA
8955 ROSEBURG OR
8956 TENNYSON IN
8957 WHITESTONE NY
8958 CONNELL WA
8959 BOGALUSA LA
8960 NEW MILFORD PA
8961 SARATOGA WY
8962 SCHAEFFERSTOWN PA
8963 SCOTTSBORO AL
8964 POTTSVILLE PA
8965 CRESSON TX
8966 FITZGERALD GA
8967 CORTEZ CO
8968 MOHNTON PA
8969 MECHANICSBURG PA
8970 HUBBARD IA
8971 SHENANDOAH IA
8972 DAGSBORO DE
8973 NEW ALBANY PA
8974 WETMORE KS
8975 CAMPBELL NE
8976 BOWMAN ND
8977 LUVERNE MN
8978 LEWISVILLE OH
8979 CASSVILLE MO
8980 ALACHUA FL
8981 ADEL IA
8982 OLNEY TX
8983 ELM GROVE WV
8984 ROCKY MOUNT VA
8985 ORBISONIA PA
8986 FAIRFIELD IA
8987 VANCOUVER WA
8988 DECATUR NE
8989 WORTHINGTON MN
8990 MACON GA
8991 HETTINGER ND
8992 AINSWORTH NE
8993 WHEATON MN
8994 ATOKA OK
8995 FAIRBURY NE
8996 OXFORD NC
8997 STEELE ND
8998 THURMOND WV
8999 MAYSVILLE OK
9000 MUNISING MI
9001 GORHAM NH
9002 WALLOWA OR
9003 WATERTOWN WI
9004 SIDNEY MT
9005 SHARON ND
9006 ROSEDALE IN
9007 PENSACOLA FL
9008 CHEROKEE OK
9009 CARBONDALE CO
9010 CHICAGO IL
9011 NEWKIRK OK
9012 WYTHEVILLE VA
9013 EAGLE CO
9014 CAMBRIDGE IA
9015 NORTHBORO IA
9016 GLEN ULLIN ND
9017 STORY CITY IA
9018 KANAWHA IA
9019 FREDONIA NY
9020 BOYNE CITY MI
9021 SALEM OR
9022 NEWARK AR
9023 MUSKOGEE OK
9024 CHARITON IA
9025 ALBION IL
9026 BROWNSTOWN PA
9027 COPPERHILL TN
9028 HAMBURG PA
9029 GREEN CITY MO
9030 MEDICAL LAKE WA
9031 MABEL MN
9032 MULHALL OK
9033 ADRIAN MN
9034 COOPERSBURG PA
9035 FORT MYERS FL
9036 LAMAR CO
9037 LITTLE ROCK AR
9038 BECKLEY WV
9039 JEFFERSON GA
9040 PONTOTOC MS
9041 PHILADELPHIA MS
9042 SAINT JOSEPH MO
9043 MONTEREY VA
9044 KINSTON NC
9045 SEDGWICK CO
9046 SULPHUR OK
9047 SAINT JOHNS OR
9048 WELCH WV
9049 JACKSONVILLE FL
9050 MILACA MN
9051 WINDER GA
9052 ODESSA WA
9053 STANTON TX
9054 WASHTUCNA WA
9055 PRATTVILLE AL
9056 AURORA NE
9057 LEESVILLE SC
9058 BENTLEYVILLE PA
9059 PRESTON MN
9060 EAST WORCESTER NY
9061 WHITE HOUSE STATION NJ
9062 WEST MILTON OH
9063 OLIVIA MN
9064 STEPHEN MN
9065 WASHINGTONVILLE NY
9066 UNION BRIDGE MD
9067 RALEIGH NC
9068 WALLA WALLA WA
9069 STRAWBERRY POINT IA
9070 BELLINGHAM WA
9071 WELCH WV
9072 GOLDSBORO PA
9073 FORT BRANCH IN
9074 CORDELE GA
9075 LANGDON ND
9076 SALISBURY NC
9077 FORT BRANCH IN
9078 GOLDFIELD NV
9079 ELLENSBURG WA
9080 CHENEY WA
9081 PLAINVIEW TX
9082 MARMARTH ND
9083 CAMDEN SC
9084 GREEN LANE PA
9085 KINSTON NC
9086 NORTH ATTLEBOROUGH MA
9087 HANCOCK MI
9088 MILLEN GA
9089 WOODBURY TN
9090 HOLLAND IN
9091 MANCHESTER OH
9092 AMHERST NE
9093 INGLEWOOD CA
9094 CORINTH MS
9095 MOUNT STERLING OH
9096 WARREN IL
9097 ENGLEWOOD KS
9098 CLINTON KY
9099 RICHLAND MI
9100 CORTEZ CO
9101 LIND WA
9102 QUINCY WA
9103 ISMAY MT
9104 ANDERSON SC
9105 ATLANTA GA
9106 NASHVILLE GA
9107 HEGINS PA
9108 WHITE RIVER JUNCTION VT
9109 ILION NY
9110 SPARTANSBURG PA
9111 SPANISH FORK UT
9112 MARTIN TN
9113 COPLAY PA
9114 BENDERSVILLE PA
9115 KIRKLIN IN
9116 KINGSLEY IA
9117 ROCKY FORD CO
9118 NATIONAL CITY IL
9119 BEAVER CITY UT
9120 WINDSOR CO
9121 PASADENA CA
9122 NORTH VERNON IN
9123 GREENSBORO NC
9124 WILMINGTON NC
9125 DIAGONAL IA
9126 LOCKNEY TX
9127 LEBANON OR
9128 CASTLE SHANNON PA
9129 WAPATO WA
9130 FACTORYVILLE PA
9131 DEER RIVER MN
9132 FELTON DE
9133 WALHALLA ND
9134 WALLACE ID
9135 WARRENSBURGH NY
9136 HIGHLAND KS
9137 SHELBINA MO
9138 WYMORE NE
9139 ARENDTSVILLE PA
9140 SUPERIOR WI
9141 SAN FRANCISCO CA
9142 PAMPA TX
9143 BROWNSTOWN IN
9144 CHENEY WA
9145 HAILEY ID
9146 HARRISBURG OR
9147 BLACKDUCK MN
9148 VALLEY MILLS TX
9149 NORTH EAST PA
9150 OAKESDALE WA
9151 FARMINGTON NM
9152 KNIGHTSTOWN IN
9153 MADISON WI
9154 CLINTONVILLE PA
9155 EL PASO TX
9156 DINUBA CA
9157 BURLINGAME KS
9158 DINUBA CA
9159 WINSLOW IN
9160 EDMOND KS
9161 MARION ND
9162 ETOWAH TN
9163 BRADFORD OH
9164 CHARLOTTE NC
9165 ROUNDUP MT
9166 HOT SPRINGS SD
9167 OROSI CA
9168 CEDAR RAPIDS IA
9169 MACOMB IL
9170 BREWSTER WA
9171 CROTON ON HUDSON NY
9172 KANSAS CITY MO
9173 VISALIA CA
9174 SAN FRANCISCO CA
9175 WESTPORT IN
9176 CHATTANOOGA TN
9177 CLIFTON FORGE VA
9178 CROWELL TX
9179 NEWARK OH
9180 PORTLAND OR
9181 BRIDGTON ME
9182 SPOKANE WA
9183 ARENZVILLE IL
9184 MEMPHIS TN
9185 GARFIELD WA
9186 JACKSON GA
9187 MINEOLA NY
9188 LETCHER SD
9189 CAYUGA IN
9190 GREENVILLE SC
9191 RUSHVILLE NE
9192 FOSTORIA OH
9193 LOCKNEY TX
9194 ANSONIA OH
9195 DELANO CA
9196 OKOLONA MS
9197 BONNER SPRINGS KS
9198 MOUNT PLEASANT PA
9199 RICHWOOD OH
9200 SHELTON NE
9201 MILTON OR
9202 RIEGELSVILLE PA
9203 FOREST CITY NC
9204 RIPLEY MS
9205 KOSSE TX
9206 MIDDLEPORT NY
9207 LITTLESTOWN PA
9208 MINOOKA IL
9209 SHIRLEY IN
9210 HARRINGTON WA
9211 NEW PARIS OH
9212 MACON GA
9213 MANASQUAN NJ
9214 RYDER ND
9215 HARDIN MT
9216 INTERCOURSE PA
9217 TILDEN NE
9218 ROCHESTER MI
9219 NEW YORK NY
9220 ALAMEDA CA
9221 HUDSON OH
9222 FARMVILLE VA
9223 ADAMS NE
9224 BLACKSTONE VA
9225 DEXTER KS
9226 HOUSTON TX
9227 AUBURN CA
9228 PENDLETON OR
9229 JERSEY CITY NJ
9230 TAMPICO IL
9231 ALLERTON IA
9232 HOISINGTON KS
9233 ELDORA IA
9234 KERMAN CA
9235 WILKES BARRE PA
9236 KANSAS CITY MO
9237 DE RIDDER LA
9238 MONROVIA MD
9239 UNION CITY TN
9240 AUBURN PA
9241 LOUISVILLE KY
9242 CARSON CITY NV
9243 HILLSBORO OH
9244 WAYNE NE
9245 DALLAS TX
9246 CHARLOTTESVILLE VA
9247 SHENANDOAH PA
9248 FOREST CITY PA
9249 HOWARD PA
9250 CENTER POINT IN
9251 ACKERMAN MS
9252 ELBERTON GA
9253 WASECA MN
9254 COLQUITT GA
9255 ARCANUM OH
9256 FAIRFIELD PA
9257 TELFORD PA
9258 CALLAWAY NE
9259 MILLERSVILLE PA
9260 CALIFON NJ
9261 WAYNESBORO VA
9262 GILBERT MN
9263 SANDPOINT ID
9264 BAINBRIDGE PA
9265 PASCO WA
9266 BOONVILLE IN
9267 MOUNTAIN LAKE MN
9268 BORDENTOWN NJ
9269 LEMMON SD
9270 HARLOWTOWN MT
9271 FAR ROCKAWAY NY
9272 SHOSHONE ID
9273 ROSALIA WA
9274 MENDON OH
9275 SPIRO OK
9276 UNION NY
9277 WYANET IL
9278 HOLYOKE CO
9279 WILKINSON IN
9280 BREMERTON WA
9281 HERMISTON OR
9282 COLUMBUS OH
9283 McINTOSH SD
9284 LOGAN OH
9285 CAPE MAY NJ
9286 BUTLER IN
9287 NOME ND
9288 ROWLESBURG WV
9289 TORRINGTON WY
9290 LEECHBURG PA
9291 CHASE CITY VA
9292 CIMARRON NM
9293 KANSAS IL
9294 CHICO CA
9295 ALTAVISTA VA
9296 LEXINGTON SC
9297 SAINT LOUIS MO
9298 MILFORD IA
9299 FORTVILLE IN
9300 PORTSMOUTH VA
9301 CHAMBERLAIN SD
9302 THOMSON GA
9303 BLOOMFIELD IA
9304 STOUGHTON WI
9305 GLOVERSVILLE NY
9306 COUNCIL BLUFFS IA
9307 CLAYSVILLE PA
9308 SANGER CA
9309 KANSAS CITY KS
9310 ELY NV
9311 KANSAS CITY MO
9312 LANDISVILLE PA
9313 PLAINVILLE CT
9314 LA GRANDE OR
9315 SPRINGFIELD MO
9316 TERRE HILL PA
9317 CANTON PA
9318 CRESSONA PA
9319 MOUNT PLEASANT TN
9320 JACKSON KY
9321 BEAVER CREEK MN
9322 EAST ISLIP NY
9323 COALINGA CA
9324 EARLE AR
9325 TREMONT IL
9326 WAPPINGERS FALLS NY
9327 DULUTH MN
9328 NORTH BEND OR
9329 MONTICELLO GA
9330 MERCERSBURG PA
9331 WAVERLY TN
9332 WALNUT RIDGE AR
9333 CALDWELL ID
9334 PARIS TN
9335 STATESVILLE NC
9336 VERSAILLES OH
9337 THREE FORKS MT
9338 WEST SALEM IL
9339 MONTCLAIR NJ
9340 MOSCOW PA
9341 DALLAS TX
9342 CHERAW SC
9343 DANVILLE VA
9344 PENBROOK PA
9345 LOGANTON PA
9346 MONTICELLO GA
9347 OSHKOSH WI
9348 ONTARIO OR
9349 EL CENTRO CA
9350 EL CENTRO CA
9351 MALDEN WA
9352 PATOKA IN
9353 HOUSTON TX
9354 LEWISVILLE AR
9355 BILLINGS MT
9356 SCOTTSVILLE KY
9357 BEAUMONT TX
9358 NEWBERG OR
9359 HUBBELL MI
9360 NEW YORK NY
9361 MOUNT WOLF PA
9362 DOVER PA
9363 BEND OR
9364 AKRON PA
9365 BOWLING GREEN KY
9366 PASADENA CA
9367 RAMSEY NJ
9368 WHEATON IL
9369 FORNEY TX
9370 EXETER CA
9371 GOODING ID
9372 MONROE WA
9373 PRAIRIE VIEW KS
9374 DULUTH MN
9375 BUCHANAN VA
9376 SELBY SD
9377 GREGORY SD
9378 HOLLISTER CA
9379 APPALACHIA VA
9380 SECAUCUS NJ
9381 MICHIGAN CITY IN
9382 NEVADA MO
9383 LEEDS MO
9383 KANSAS CITY MO
9384 NATOMA KS
9385 FAWN GROVE PA
9386 AMBROSE ND
9387 CRANDON WI
9388 SAINT ELMO IL
9389 CHEHALIS WA
9390 ANAMOOSE ND
9391 NORTH PLAINFIELD NJ
9392 WILLIAMSBURG PA
9393 GARY SD
9394 HIGGINSPORT OH
9394 WINCHESTER OH
9395 GRAND ISLAND NE
9396 COLUMBUS MT
9397 BRIGHTON IL
9398 HOPEDALE IL
9399 NICHOLS NY
9400 MINDEN NE
9401 CANNELTON IN
9402 BALLY PA
9403 SALT LAKE CITY UT
9404 KANSAS CITY MO
9405 WESTPORT NY
9406 GARDNER IL
9407 ROCK HILL SC
9408 McLEANSBORO IL
9409 MINNEAPOLIS MN
9410 EMERYVILLE CA
9411 OKANOGAN WA
9412 ANAMOOSE ND
9413 HADDON HEIGHTS NJ
9414 RIDGEWOOD NY
9415 WINDSOR NY
9416 ELDRED PA
9417 PROSSER WA
9418 SODUS NY
9419 PORT WASHINGTON WI
9420 LODI NJ
9421 ADRIAN MI
9422 LITITZ PA
9423 ROSEBURG OR
9424 SAN MATEO CA
9425 HOOPESTON IL
9426 FOXBORO MA
9427 CALLICOON NY
9428 WYOMING DE
9429 MECHANICSVILLE MD
9430 CAMBRIDGE SPRINGS PA
9431 ASHLAND OR
9432 SALMON ID
9433 LAWRENCEVILLE VA
9434 DEPOSIT NY
9435 SHAWNEETOWN IL
9436 McCOOK NE
9437 MERCED CA
9438 STEWARDSON IL
9439 RIDGWAY IL
9440 HAVRE MT
9441 HOPE NM
9442 MINNEAPOLIS MN
9443 DAYTON WA
9444 PARKTON MD
9445 YANKTON SD
9446 SPRINGFIELD OH
9447 CONRAD IA
9448 BRISTOW NE
9449 POLSON MT
9450 OKEANA OH
9451 PLATTEVILLE CO
9452 McGILL NV
9453 SHINNSTON WV
9454 STERLING CO
9455 CREWE VA
9456 OWENSBORO KY
9457 HENDRICKS MN
9458 MURPHY NC
9459 BANNING CA
9460 SAINT LOUIS MO
9461 MAYTOWN PA
9462 FAIRMONT WV
9463 PRINCETON IN
9464 SANDSTONE MN
9465 THAYER KS
9466 OMAHA NE
9467 CLAREMONT CA
9468 ARTESIA NM
9469 WHITE HALL MD
9470 SPRING CITY TN
9471 RALEIGH NC
9472 STANLEY ND
9473 GRATZ PA
9474 BEL AIR MD
9475 DANVILLE VA
9476 CONWAY NH
9477 CHALLIS ID
9478 MONROE WA
9479 McCLOUD CA
9480 FRYBURG PA
9481 OXNARD CA
9482 BROWN STATION NY
9483 SAN DIEGO CA
9484 BEACH ND
9485 POST CITY TX
9485 POST TX
9486 HAMILTON MT
9487 WEST UNION OH
9488 ARCADIA IN
9489 MOTT ND
9490 EDINA MO
9491 WENDELL ID
9492 WHITELAND IN
9493 WOODLAND CA
9494 BENTON AR
9495 LEESPORT PA
9496 VALE OR
9497 BURR OAK MI
9498 BRIDGETON NJ
9499 PALOUSE WA
9500 BATAVIA IL
9501 FORDYCE AR
9502 OAKLAND CA
9503 POINT MARION PA
9504 PLAINVIEW NE
9505 ULSTER PA
9506 PELL CITY AL
9507 SEVEN VALLEYS PA
9508 RALSTON PA
9509 L'ANSE MI
9510 AMBIA IN
9511 MILLHEIM PA
9512 NATIONAL CITY CA
9513 WESTFIELD PA
9514 SEMINOLE OK
9515 WILMINGTON CA
9516 UNADILLA NY
9517 IRONWOOD MI
9518 SEVEN MILE OH
9519 WINDSOR MO
9520 VALIER MT
9521 ELLENDALE ND
9522 FENNIMORE WI
9523 ALDERSON WV
9524 DRAKE ND
9525 ODIN IL
9526 McALISTERVILLE PA
9527 NOBLE IL
9528 LAPORTE PA
9529 RAVENA NY
9530 BLUE MOUND IL
9531 MOORESVILLE NC
9532 NASHVILLE TN
9533 SHARON SC
9534 ALBION PA
9535 ABERDEEN WA
9536 KINGSTON OH
9537 INDIANAPOLIS IN
9538 FULLERTON CA
9539 BELFIELD ND
9540 CLAY CITY IN
9541 HARLEYSVILLE PA
9542 WEST ORANGE NJ
9543 FREEDOM PA
9544 UNION NJ
9544 UNION CITY NJ
9545 WASHINGTON DC
9546 CORCORAN CA
9547 LANCASTER OH
9548 CHERRYVILLE NC
9549 CLEARFIELD IA
9550 OPELIKA AL
9551 CALISTOGA CA
9552 MILDRED PA
9553 BROOKVILLE OH
9554 NEW WILMINGTON PA
9555 DYERSVILLE IA
9556 NEGAUNEE MI
9557 RAWLINS WY
9558 ELIZABETHTON TN
9559 BELLEVILLE KS
9560 KANSAS CITY MO
9561 MAYSVILLE KY
9562 OAKLAND CITY IN
9563 PITSBURG OH
9564 OKLAHOMA CITY OK
9565 DUCKTOWN TN
9566 KELLOGG ID
9567 BARTLESVILLE OK
9568 CENTRALIA PA
9569 NEW YORK NY
9570 UPLAND CA
9571 HENDERSONVILLE NC
9572 SYCAMORE IL
9573 VALLEJO CA
9574 CUT BANK MT
9575 SAN FERNANDO CA
9576 ZILLAH WA
9577 MONTCLAIR NJ
9578 EAST ELY NV
9579 BOSTON MA
9580 ASHLAND AL
9581 SCOTTSBLUFF NE
9582 DIETERICH IL
9583 ANACONDA MT
9584 CAPITOL HILL OK
9585 SIOUX RAPIDS IA
9586 ENID OK
9587 FORT PIERRE SD
9588 NEWVILLE PA
9589 SPOKANE WA
9590 LINTON ND
9591 CRAIG NE
9592 FAYETTE IA
9593 EASTMAN GA
9594 LIBBY MT
9595 FOWLER KS
9596 STARBUCK MN
9597 BLACKWOOD NJ
9598 HUNTINGTON WV
9599 LORDSBURG CA
9599 LA VERNE CA
9600 JESSUP PA
9601 MINONK IL
9602 CATLETTSBURG KY
9603 JULESBURG CO
9604 SUTTON WV
9605 NEWARK NJ
9606 NEILLSVILLE WI
9607 BYROMVILLE GA
9608 YUMA AZ
9609 GARDINER ME
9610 PARSONS WV
9611 SPUR TX
9612 CALDWELL NJ
9613 CORNELIA GA
9614 CULLMAN AL
9615 REYNOLDS GA
9616 PONCA CITY OK
9617 ATLANTA GA
9618 VIENNA GA
9619 KIMBALLTON IA
9620 ALLEN OK
9621 WATSONVILLE CA
9622 BISMARCK ND
9623 BUTTE NE
9624 ODELL IL
9625 HUTTO TX
9626 FORT BRAGG CA
9627 WARTRACE TN
9628 JACKSONVILLE FL
9629 UNION CITY TN
9630 LOUISVILLE OH
9631 ELLENDALE ND
9632 NEWPORT TN
9633 CLARKSVILLE AR
9634 CORBIN KY
9635 HERNDON VA
9636 ROME GA
9637 CADDO MILLS TX
9638 HOPEWELL PA
9639 BALTIMORE MD
9640 SAINT ALBANS WV
9641 SANDERSVILLE GA
9642 WARRENTON VA
9643 BRUSHTON NY
9644 BELFAST NY
9645 FAIRMONT WV
9646 VANCOUVER WA
9647 HOP BOTTOM PA
9648 SEBASTOPOL CA
9649 ALEDO IL
9650 AIKEN SC
9651 CHELSEA MA
9652 SALT LAKE CITY UT
9653 MORRILL NE
9654 ITHACA MI
9655 SAN FRANCISCO CA
9656 NEW TRIPOLI PA
9657 DELAND FL
9658 TULSA OK
9659 NASHVILLE TN
9660 JEFFERSON PA
9661 EAST NEWARK NJ
9662 KEARNY NJ
9662 SEATTLE WA
9663 MANCHESTER VA
9663 RICHMOND VA
9664 ARLINGTON IA
9665 NAPER NE
9666 BAYARD NE
9667 COOKEVILLE TN
9668 GLENSIDE PA
9669 BRIDGEHAMPTON NY
9670 REDKEY IN
9671 WINNEBAGO NE
9672 MILLEDGEVILLE GA
9673 BRAWLEY CA
9674 MANCOS CO
9675 OSBORN OH
9676 WRAY CO
9677 KANSAS CITY MO
9678 PATTERSON PA
9678 MIFFLIN PA
9679 HECLA SD
9680 JEROME ID
9681 DOZIER AL
9682 CANNELTON IN
9683 SAN FRANCISCO CA
9684 REEDER ND
9685 VENTURA CA
9686 CALEXICO CA
9687 COLUMBIA SC
9688 REEDLEY CA
9689 PLAZA ND
9690 CONWAY SC
9691 FLUSHING NY
9692 COOKEVILLE TN
9693 DELL RAPIDS SD
9694 GERING NE
9695 GYPSUM KS
9696 OKMULGEE OK
9697 GILL CO
9698 YATES ND
9699 CLEAR SPRING MD
9700 COWDEN IL
9701 MUSKOGEE OK
9702 LAWRENCEVILLE PA
9703 DEERWOOD MN
9704 BRONSON MI
9705 CALEXICO CA
9706 YORK PA
9707 SAINT CLOUD FL
9708 PROVIDENCE KY
9709 WAYNOKA OK
9710 LINDSAY CA
9711 BRIDGEPORT NE
9712 HOUSTON TX
9713 WILLOWS CA
9714 LA MOURE ND
9715 SPENCER IN
9716 NORTH CREEK NY
9717 NEW YORK NY
9718 BANDON OR

9719 OLATHE CO
9720 ERWIN TN
9721 PETERSTOWN WV
9722 GLASGOW KY
9723 SHANNON CITY IA
9724 AURELIA IA
9725 DOWNERS GROVE IL
9726 ARGOS IN
9727 GRANTHAM PA
9728 COLLINS MS
9729 ALBANY GA
9730 OMAHA NE
9731 CRETE NE
9732 EMPORIA VA
9733 SUFFOLK VA
9734 GREENVILLE IL
9735 RICHMOND CA
9736 MASCOUTAH IL
9737 GRAND RIVER IA
9738 MALTA MT
9739 COALDALE PA
9740 MONTGOMERY WV
9741 LODGEPOLE NE
9742 UNION SC
9743 CENTER CO
9744 CHESTERTOWN MD
9745 SANTA CRUZ CA
9746 NORTON VA
9747 FLORENCE SC
9748 JAMESTOWN NY
9749 PUTNAM TX
9750 CHICAGO IL
9751 CORINTH MS
9752 MYERSTOWN PA
9753 SUMMIT MS
9754 NORTHWOOD ND
9755 HAMPSTEAD MD
9756 NOBLESVILLE IN
9757 MABTON WA
9758 UNION STOCK YARDS KS
9759 CONRAD MT
9760 NEWMAN CA
9761 MOUNT WASHINGTON OH
9762 IMPERIAL NE
9763 PRAIRIE CITY OR
9764 TROUTVILLE VA
9765 CROWS LANDING CA
9766 ROMNEY WV
9767 FAIRVIEW OK
9768 BREMEN OH
9769 ROCKWOOD PA
9770 HOLTVILLE CA
9771 FAIRFAX MN
9772 HAVELOCK NE
9773 DIGHTON KS
9774 NASHVILLE TN
9775 AMBOY MN
9776 NEW ENGLAND ND
9777 ADEL GA
9778 GARRISON ND
9779 BERLIN NJ
9780 RIDGEFIELD PARK NJ
9781 SAN SABA TX
9782 HAVRE MT
9783 GENESEE PA
9784 MONTEREY IN
9785 LYNCH NE
9786 SANDOVAL IL
9787 SCOTIA CA
9788 PEKIN IL
9789 SACO MT
9790 CHAPPELL NE
9791 HARLAN KY
9792 CROSWELL MI
9793 LAUREL NE
9794 SOLOMON KS
9795 VACAVILLE CA
9796 COLERIDGE NE
9797 DURANGO CO
9798 SEATTLE WA
9799 NEFFS OH
9800 SAN LEANDRO CA
9801 PONCA CITY OK
9802 PLAINVIEW TX
9803 TURBOTVILLE PA
9804 POLAND NY
9805 WELLINGTON TX
9806 McMINNVILLE OR
9807 SMYRNA TN
9808 BURLINGTON WA
9809 CROSSVILLE TN
9810 MERTZON TX
9811 LAKELAND FL
9812 BROWNWOOD TX
9813 STERLING CITY TX
9814 BUTLER PA
9815 RACINE OH
9816 WALTHILL NE
9817 MORRISTOWN SD
9818 LATON CA
9819 MARCUS IA
9820 SMITHTOWN BRANCH NY
9821 FLOYD IA
9822 OLEAN NY
9823 ROCKFORD IL
9824 POULTNEY VT
9825 YONKERS NY
9826 KEZAR FALLS ME
9827 CENTERVILLE TN
9828 WACO TX
9829 INDIANAPOLIS IN
9830 SILVER SPRING MD
9831 LEIGH NE
9832 RICHMOND KY
9833 BLAIRSTOWN NJ
9834 BATON ROUGE LA
9835 BOKCHITO OK
9836 ELMHURST IL
9837 RED LAKE FALLS MN
9838 CROSBY MN
9839 PHELPS NY
9840 LA JARA CO
9841 RED LODGE MT
9842 RUSSELLVILLE KY
9843 HODGENVILLE KY
9844 PASO ROBLES CA
9845 JAYTON TX
9846 PARKERSBURG IA
9847 MARTINSVILLE VA
9848 FORT STOCKTON TX
9849 WALTERBORO SC
9850 WINONA WV
9851 DICKSON CITY PA
9852 NEW CASTLE IN
9853 CRYSTAL LAKE IA
9854 HARTFORD MI
9855 STEVENSON AL
9856 OKLAHOMA CITY OK
9857 CATO NY
9858 VEBLEN SD
9859 SOMERVILLE OH
9860 COVINGTON IN
9861 HAMILTON VA
9862 EDWARDSVILLE PA
9863 PUNXSUTAWNEY PA
9864 RONAN MT
9865 OXFORD MS
9866 ALTAMONT NY
9867 WEST HOBOKEN NJ
9867 UNION CITY NJ
9868 DUNMORE PA
9869 MARCELLUS NY
9870 PELHAM GA
9871 SILOAM SPRINGS AR
9872 OPELOUSAS LA
9873 WEED CA
9874 BIRMINGHAM MI
9875 CLIFTON CO
9876 MULLINS SC
9877 ROSSVILLE IL
9878 ORANGE CA
9879 VIDALIA GA
9880 WILMORE KY
9881 KINGSTON OK
9882 SAN FRANCISCO CA
9883 HAMILTON IL
9884 CHEROKEE OK
9885 NORFOLK VA
9886 LAKE ARIEL PA
9887 DENVER CO
9888 HEAVENER OK
9889 TERRA BELLA CA
9890 BUENA VISTA VA
9891 BROOKSVILLE FL
9892 ANTIOCH CA
9893 BREESE IL
9894 PUENTE CA
9895 RAMSEY IL
9896 SAINT PETER IL
9897 PLEASANTON CA
9898 CLYMER PA
9899 DEER LODGE MT
9900 TICONDEROGA NY
9901 WASHINGTON PA
9902 ALIQUIPPA PA
9903 DELANO MN
9904 SANTA ANA CA
9905 ARDMORE PA
9906 QUANAH TX
9907 ENGLEWOOD CO
9908 SOUTH OMAHA NE
9909 BERWIND WV
9910 GEORGE IA
9911 LONGTON KS
9912 NEWARK NJ
9913 KENOVA WV
9914 LIVERMORE CA
9915 SIOUX FALLS SD
9916 WINSTON NC
9917 HILLSBORO OR
9918 PETALUMA CA
9919 HYNES CA
9920 MILBURN OK
9921 GENOA NY
9922 MOUNT AUBURN IL
9923 HILLSBORO OR
9924 JONESVILLE VA
9925 OXFORD AL
9926 OCALA FL
9927 NEWVILLE AL
9928 CHAFFEE MO
9929 WARSAW IL
9930 WILLIAMSBURG OH
9931 COMO TX
9932 SEYMOUR MO
9933 LOS BANOS CA
9934 MAYETTA KS
9935 ONTARIO CA
9936 TEXAS CITY TX
9937 NOBLE OK
9938 CHICKASHA OK
9939 NEW YORK NY
9940 PINE BUSH NY
9941 FORT MILL SC
9942 TULSA OK
9943 TULSA OK
9944 HYDRO OK
9945 CONCORD CA
9946 MARLOW OK
9947 OKMULGEE OK
9948 NOWATA OK
9949 NOWATA OK
9950 EAST AURORA NY
9951 LENAPAH OK
9952 ELK CITY OK
9953 AKRON OH
9954 KINGFISHER OK
9955 NEW YORK NY
9956 FLORIDA NY
9957 MARICOPA CA
9958 PUKWANA SD
9959 SAYRE OK
9960 OLUSTEE OK
9961 WAPAKONETA OH
9962 LAWTON OK
9963 EL DORADO OK
9964 GUYMON OK
9965 COLLINSVILLE OK
9966 ALHAMBRA CA
9967 TEMPLE OK
9968 CORDELL OK
9969 SKIATOOK OK
9970 STILWELL OK
9971 CORDELL OK
9972 CORDELL OK
9973 SALLISAW OK
9974 LAHOMA OK
9975 MULDROW OK
9976 SAYRE OK
9977 WATKINS NY
9978 KNOXVILLE PA
9979 LAUREL NE
9980 HARRAH OK
9981 CUSTER CITY OK
9982 TOWNSEND MT
9983 WELLSTON OK
9984 WAKEFIELD NE
9985 CLINTON OK
9986 DEWEY OK
9987 SHATTUCK OK
9988 GALLUP NM
9989 CROSBYTON TX
9990 CENTRAL VALLEY NY
9991 TERLTON OK
9992 VALLIANT OK
9993 CANADIAN OK
9994 WAUSA NE
9995 SENTINEL OK
9996 DELMONT PA
9997 SAGUACHE CO
9998 SHAWNEE OK
9999 DARLINGTON SC
10000 WHITE SALMON WA
10001 ADDINGTON OK
10002 HOMINY OK
10003 BRAMAN OK
10004 PARAGOULD AR
10005 POND CREEK OK
10006 GRANDFIELD OK
10007 STUART OK
10008 MELISSA TX
10009 MARSHFIELD MO
10010 CADDO OK
10011 TILDEN NE
10012 TISHOMINGO OK
10013 HOLDENVILLE OK
10014 YALE OK
10015 OKTAHA OK
10016 NORTH ROSE NY
10017 WAUSA NE
10018 HAYWARD CA
10019 MIAMI OK
10020 GEARY OK
10021 MADISON NE
10022 OAKLAND NE
10023 COLERIDGE NE
10024 FERNANDINA FL
10025 BELDEN NE
10026 SEATTLE WA
10027 WATERFORD PA
10028 COAL CREEK TN
10029 BAY SHORE NY
10030 DEXTER IA
10031 COWETA OK
10032 TYRONE OK
10033 BRUNSWICK NE
10034 STORM LAKE IA
10035 DEMOPOLIS AL
10036 PORT NORRIS NJ
10037 LIBERTY NY
10038 GREELEY CO
10039 KANSAS CITY MO
10040 TEXAS CITY TX
10041 OAKLEY KS
10042 EAST SMITHFIELD PA
10043 LIVINGSTON MANOR NY
10044 MENARD TX
10045 MATTOON IL
10046 HOLCOMB NY
10047 CANANDAIGUA NY
10048 MOUNT PROSPECT IL
10049 GIBSLAND LA
10050 ELECTRA TX
10051 CHECOTAH OK
10052 MERKEL TX
10053 CHINOOK MT
10054 BROOKLYN NY
10055 ELDORADO SPRINGS MO
10056 MERRILL OR
10057 FARMERSVILLE IL
10058 GETTYSBURG OH
10059 LEOMINSTER MA
10060 HUTTIG AR
10061 RURAL RETREAT VA
10062 JENKINS KY
10063 CHECOTAH OK
10064 DENVER CO
10065 LURAY KS
10066 CHILDERSBURG AL
10067 WILLIAMSON WV
10068 SAN DIMAS CA
10069 ORLANDO FL
10070 REDDING CA
10071 MONMOUTH OR
10072 COLUSA CA
10073 DOWAGIAC MI
10074 SPRINGFIELD MO
10075 KAW CITY OK
10076 GANADO TX
10077 COPENHAGEN NY
10078 TRINITY TX
10079 LITCHFIELD IL
10080 RICHMOND VA
10081 OSHKOSH NE
10082 PASADENA CA
10083 BOISE ID
10084 CORNWALL NY
10085 MARION SC
10086 DONGOLA IL
10087 ARKADELPHIA AR
10088 TAFT CA
10089 HAMPTON GA
10090 MISSION TX
10091 LOS GATOS CA
10092 PLACENTIA CA
10093 YUMA CO
10094 HASTINGS OK
10095 FREDERICK OK
10096 LONE WOLF OK
10097 GRIFFITHSVILLE WV
10098 KENNEBEC SD
10099 BURBANK CA
10100 REDDING CA
10101 NEW LONDON OH
10102 ASHFORD AL
10103 SAINT JOHNS OR
10103 PORTLAND OR
10104 KENEFIC OK
10105 GREENFIELD OH
10106 BALDWIN WI
10107 SACRAMENTO CA
10108 JEFFERSON PARK IL
10108 CHICAGO IL
10109 CENTRAL SQUARE NY
10110 EATONTOWN NJ
10111 NEWARK VALLEY NY
10112 GREENSBORO NC
10113 MUSKOGEE OK
10114 RED BLUFF CA
10115 BRISTOW OK
10116 CAVALIER ND
10117 CLAREMORE OK
10118 HOPE NJ
10119 GROVE OK
10120 DIXON CA
10121 INDIANAPOLIS IN
10122 PURDY MO
10123 JEFFERSON IA
10124 PARLIER CA
10125 TRENTON IL
10126 BARKER NY
10127 SPENCER WV
10128 BELLEVILLE PA
10129 SUMTER SC
10130 PERRY IA
10131 LINCOLN AL
10132 COAL CITY IL
10133 WINTERS CA
10134 TUSTIN CA
10135 SMITHFIELD UT
10136 JACKSONVILLE FL
10137 HARTSVILLE SC
10138 LESLIE AR
10139 SIOUX CITY IA
10140 EL PASO TX
10141 EAST ROCHESTER NY
10142 WESTFIELD NJ
10143 BENTON HARBOR MI
10144 MATTOON IL
10145 PLAINFIELD CT
10145 MOOSUP CT
10146 CORYDON IA
10147 HUTCHINSON MN
10148 SAN ANTONIO TX
10149 SUISUN CA
10150 ALAMEDA CA
10151 EDMOND OK
10152 HOUSTON TX
10153 MONROE LA
10154 IUKA MS
10155 WALKILL NY
10156 DANVILLE VA
10157 CLARK WV
10158 WESTVILLE OK
10159 SILVER CREEK NY
10160 HASKELL OK
10161 SPEARVILLE KS
10162 SOLDIER ID
10162 FAIRFIELD ID
10163 BONITA TX
10164 LEBANON OR
10165 BARRE MA
10166 GILROY CA
10167 PASADENA CA
10168 VAN NUYS CA
10169 PHARR TX
10170 WILBURTON OK
10171 EAST CHICAGO IN
10172 ROFF OK
10173 STAUNTON IL
10174 KENT WA
10175 LACONA NY
10176 MERRILL WI
10177 SAN RAFAEL CA
10178 DEWITT AR
10179 IRVING PARK IL
10179 CHICAGO IL
10180 WATERLOO IL
10181 LINDEN TN
10182 MAUD TX
10183 THREE SPRINGS PA
10184 HEALDSBURG CA
10185 SOUTHAMPTON NY
10186 MAZON IL
10187 ALEXANDRIA SD
10188 HERMINIE PA
10189 LA COSTE TX
10190 DOYLE TN
10191 NEWELL IA
10192 HUNTSVILLE TN
10193 ALEX OK
10194 NORFOLK VA
10195 ALMA KS
10196 YUKON OK
10197 MADERA CA
10198 FAYETTEVILLE TN
10199 NEW BERLIN NY
10200 RIVERDALE CA
10201 TULARE CA
10202 ENID OK
10203 CARMEN OK
10204 HEALDSBURG CA
10205 MARLOW OK
10206 MOUNT UNION PA
10207 WAUKON IA
10208 CLAREMONT CA
10209 HENNESSEY OK
10210 FEDERALSBURG MD
10211 THOMPSONTOWN PA
10212 LEWISTON ID
10213 CLOVIS CA
10214 WEISSPORT PA
10215 RAVENSWOOD IL
10216 HAMMOND NY
10217 ROCKWELL IA
10218 JUNCTION CITY OR
10219 FAIRVIEW WV
10220 WACO TX
10221 MERIDIAN ID
10222 STORY CITY IA
10223 STORM LAKE IA
10224 BRADLEY BEACH NJ
10225 HOUSTON TX
10226 CALVIN OK
10227 WAUKOMIS OK
10228 ANAHEIM CA
10229 STRAWN TX
10230 PADUCAH TX
10231 KANSAS CITY MO
10232 CLAYSBURG PA
10233 VENICE CA
10234 MULBERRY IN
10235 BATH NY
10236 PLANT CITY FL
10237 BOWMANVILLE IL
10237 CHICAGO IL
10238 TERRIL IA
10239 HEAVENER OK
10240 HOLLIS OK
10241 GREGORY TX
10242 HEMINGFORD NE
10243 MILTON IA
10244 DUNCAN OK
10245 BRADENTOWN FL
10245 BRADENTON FL
10246 ROME PA
10247 CHICAGO IL
10248 VENTNOR CITY NJ
10249 HOLLIS OK
10250 ROWLESBURG WV
10251 NESQUEHONING PA
10252 HONAKER VA
10253 MARSHALL VA
10254 EAST BERNSTADT KY
10255 BROKEN ARROW OK
10256 OLDHAM SD
10257 ANNAPOLIS IL
10258 SILVER CREEK NY
10259 SONOMA CA
10260 LOUISBURG NC
10261 MINNEAPOLIS MN
10262 TULSA OK
10263 BISHOPVILLE SC
10264 WITT IL
10265 POWELL WY
10266 KINGSBURY TX
10267 WILLIAMSPORT OH
10268 MAGDALENA NM
10269 ASHTON ID
10270 MACON GA
10271 CHINO CA
10272 CEDAREDGE CO
10273 SAN FERNANDO CA
10274 ARANSAS PASS TX
10275 NORMANGEE TX
10276 CLEVELAND TX
10277 WASHINGTON OK
10278 DRIGGS ID
10279 CUTHBERT GA
10280 COLLINSVILLE OK
10281 WALNUT CREEK CA
10282 OROVILLE CA
10283 MAYSVILLE OK
10284 JAMESTOWN CA
10285 REEDY WV
10286 MADILL OK
10287 GORDONSVILLE VA
10288 HOBART OK
10289 BETHEL CT
10290 ANDERSON IN
10291 OMAHA IL
10292 COACHELLA CA
10293 SELMA CA
10294 HAGERMAN ID
10295 CLINTON NY
10296 DIVERNON IL
10297 MOUNT CALM TX
10298 KEOTA OK
10299 YUBA CITY CA
10300 PORTLAND OR
10301 DUCOR CA
10302 ROME GA
10303 ROME GA
10304 TECUMSEH OK
10305 ROGERS PARK IL
10306 PETERSBURG TN
10307 GENEVA AL
10308 SALT LAKE CITY UT
10309 WOODLAKE CA
10310 GAINESVILLE FL
10311 SNYDER OK
10312 FOWLER CA
10313 PETERSBURG PA
10314 SASAKWA OK
10315 COLUMBIA SC
10316 WASHINGTON DC
10317 SNYDER OK
10318 ALLENDALE IL
10319 DES PLAINES IL
10320 POTH TX
10321 MUSKOGEE OK
10322 STONE LAKE WI
10323 LOMETA TX
10324 MOUNTAIN VIEW CA
10325 FREDERICKSBURG VA
10326 COLUMBIA MS
10327 KNOXVILLE TN
10328 OROSI CA
10329 LONG ISLAND CITY NY
10330 GRAND RAPIDS WI
10330 WISCONSIN RAPIDS WI
10331 DALLAS TX
10332 CUSHING OK
10333 CLAXTON GA
10334 JACKSON TN
10335 ORBISONIA PA
10336 DECATUR AL
10337 AUSTIN IL
10337 CHICAGO IL
10338 SUMMIT MS
10339 AFTON OK
10340 FAIRBURY NE
10341 BURLEY ID
10342 TULSA OK
10343 BENNINGTON OK
10344 RICHMOND VA
10345 EUGENE OR
10346 PANAMA CITY FL
10347 ACHILLE OK
10348 HINTON WV
10349 HENRYETTA OK
10350 RICHMOND TX
10351 FRANKFORT NY
10352 MERCED CA
10353 NEW FLORENCE PA
10354 HARLAN IA
10355 WAUKEGAN IL
10356 FORAKER OK
10357 BAKERSFIELD CA
10358 BABYLON NY
10359 ATTICA KS
10360 VICTORIA TX
10361 COLUMBUS MS
10362 JAMESTOWN CA
10363 BOSWELL OK
10364 HARDWICK CA
10365 VERMILION IL
10366 SOPER OK
10367 NORTH KANSAS CITY MO
10368 BLAIR OK
10369 KEYSTONE WV
10370 MATEWAN WV
10371 BODE IA
10372 ARCATA CA
10373 LONDON OH
10374 REDWOOD NY
10375 ADRIAN MO
10376 KEANSBURG NJ
10377 FAYETTE AL
10378 ORLAND CA
10379 WINTER HAVEN FL
10380 ACHILLE OK
10381 COLBERT OK
10382 IRONTON MN
10383 CLARKS SUMMIT PA
10384 HOLDEN MO
10385 AYLESWORTH OK
10386 FORT MEADE FL
10387 McFARLAND CA
10387 DELANO CA
10388 EUFAULA OK
10389 GOTEBO OK
10390 TOPEKA KS
10391 SAN DIEGO CA
10392 ANAWALT WV
10393 WINNEBAGO MN
10394 ARDMORE OK
10395 ROYAL IA
10396 TORRANCE CA
10397 BROWNSTOWN IL
10398 SEALY TX
10399 EAST SAINT LOUIS IL
10400 CRAWFORD TX
10401 KNOXVILLE TN
10402 KAW CITY OK
10403 MALAKOFF TX
10404 KENTON TN
10405 SCRANTON ND
10406 BERRYVILLE AR
10407 TONASKET WA
10408 AMES IA
10409 GREENCASTLE IN
10410 ARCADE NY
10411 CLEBURNE TX
10412 TROPICO CA
10412 GLENDALE CA
10413 KANSAS CITY MO
10414 SARASOTA FL
10415 FARRELL PA
10416 HENRY SD
10417 LYNDHURST NJ
10418 KRUM TX
10419 FISHERS IN
10420 FREEPORT TX
10421 ENTERPRISE AL
10422 GREEN FOREST AR
10423 NEW DECATUR AL
10423 ALBANY AL
10423 DECATUR AL
10424 BROKEN BOW OK
10425 EAST FAIRVIEW ND
10426 OMAHA TX
10427 RIVERBANK CA
10428 MASON CITY IA
10429 RUPERT ID
10430 WESTVILLE NJ
10431 TISHOMINGO OK
10432 PAISLEY OR
10433 WHITESBURG KY
10434 MORRILTON AR
10435 SAN DIEGO CA
10436 HAVILAND OH
10437 BRAGGS OK
10438 PLENTYWOOD MT
10439 JUDSONIA AR
10440 MINOTOLA NJ
10441 BOAZ AL
10442 HYDRO OK
10443 BAKER MT
10444 FORESTVILLE NY
10445 MOUNDS IL
10446 HEUVELTON NY
10447 HORATIO AR
10448 BOWLING GREEN KY
10449 RIPLEY TN
10450 WORTHINGTON WV
10451 PAIA HI
10452 STRAUSSTOWN PA
10453 GARDENA CA
10454 FRANCIS OK
10455 WHEELING WV
10456 JEFFERSONVILLE NY
10457 NEW BROCKTON AL
10458 GRANVILLE IL
10459 STUTTGART AR
10460 WAYNE CITY IL
10461 SONORA CA
10462 SEELEY CA
10463 JACKSON MS
10464 SKIATOOK OK
10465 CLOVERDALE IN
10466 REPUBLIC PA
10467 BIXBY OK
10468 TAHLEQUAH OK
10469 CLE ELUM WA
10470 PIKEVILLE TN
10471 CLAYTON NJ
10472 NEWCASTLE TX
10473 CAMPBELL TX
10474 SALLISAW OK
10475 SAINT PAUL MN
10476 LINDEN TX
10478 JASPER TX
10479 ATHENS OH
10480 ALBRIGHT WV
10481 CHERRY CREEK NY
10482 BEGGS OK
10483 BOGATA TX
10485 WAGENER SC
10486 ASHDOWN AR
10488 WINFIELD TX
10489 PARK FALLS WI
10491 COVINGTON TN
10492 NEBO IL
10493 RUSSELLTON PA
10494 BROOKHAVEN MS
10496 REYNOLDS ND
10497 MONTOUR FALLS NY
10498 WATERVLIET MI
10501 GALVA IA
10502 SMITHFIELD NC
10504 WASHINGTON DC
10506 LEWISTOWN PA
10507 LANESBORO MN
10508 RUSSELLVILLE TN
10511 COLFAX WA
10512 PUNTA GORDA FL
10513 ADA OK
10517 RUPERT ID
10522 PRESCOTT WI
10523 JACKSON MS
10525 TUCKAHOE NY
10526 PEARL RIVER NY
10527 DETROIT MI
10528 EUREKA CA
10529 BENTON HARBOR MI
10530 GREAT FALLS MT
10531 TUPELO OK
10532 ROANOKE VA
10533 CASPER WY
10534 LINNTON OR
10535 PENSACOLA FL
10536 CONWAY SC
10538 DURANT OK
10540 MEMPHIS TN
10541 FREDERICKSBURG IA

10542 MARYVILLE TN
10543 CHARLESTON SC
10544 MINDEN LA
10545 DAYTONA FL
10546 MARION NY
10547 WICHITA FALLS TX
10548 RINGLING OK
10549 BYNUM TX
10550 FORREST CITY AR
10551 PRINCETON IN
10552 SIDNEY MT
10554 ISANTI MN
10557 GREENSBURG KS
10558 CRAIG CO
10561 FORT GIBSON OK
10564 DALLAS TX
10565 POWELL WY
10567 CALEDONIA IL
10568 NEW MARKET VA
10569 EDWARDS NY
10570 ATWATER MN
10571 SANTA CRUZ CA
10573 VIAN OK
10574 NEW WILSON OK
10576 BILOXI MS
10577 DICKSON TN
10578 OCALA FL
10579 HOPE AR
10580 KASSON MN
10582 MARINE IL
10583 ERWIN TN
10586 SPRINGFIELD SC
10588 VILLE PLATTE LA
10589 BECKLEY WV
10590 JOHNSTOWN PA
10592 SIOUX FALLS SD
10593 WOODRUFF SC
10596 CROSBY ND
10597 COLUMBIA SC
10598 LIPAN TX
10599 LAWLER IA
10600 DETROIT MI
10601 ALPHA MI
10602 MOUNT VERNON WA
10603 KIESTER MN
10604 MANDAN ND
10605 LAURENS SC
10606 WYALUSING PA
10607 SHERMAN TX
10608 ROCKY MOUNT NC
10609 FORT-SMITH AR
10610 LUMBERTON NC
10611 WISE VA
10613 BOONVILLE IN
10614 GOLDSBORO NC
10616 KEWANNA IN
10617 HONEY GROVE TX
10618 CHARLOTTESVILLE VA
10619 CANBY OR
10619 AURORA OR
10620 OREGON WI
10623 GASPORT NY
10624 EDGEWOOD TX
10626 COOPER TX
10628 VAN BUREN ME
10629 MOUNT OLIVE NC
10630 ROCKY MOUNT NC
10631 CAPAC MI
10632 SAINT CLAIR HEIGHTS MI
10633 GOLDEN CITY MO
10634 WHITESBORO TX
10635 GREENVILLE SC
10636 MADISON SD
10637 MIDLAND SD
10638 AVERY TX
10639 BOGATA TX
10640 WINFIELD IA
10641 WESTERVELT IL
10643 CLARKSVILLE TX
10644 ATWOOD KS
10646 QUITMAN TX
10647 PETTY TX
10648 BURLINGTON WA
10649 PORUM OK
10650 ORANGEBURG SC
10651 SAINT MATTHEWS SC
10652 LAURENS SC
10653 MAYVILLE WI
10655 GAFFNEY SC
10657 BAGWELL TX
10658 GLOUCESTER VA
10660 SUMTER SC
10661 NEWSOME TX
10663 CHESTER SC
10664 SAN ANGELO TX
10665 ADA MN
10666 SCHELLBURG PA
10666 SCHELLSBURG PA
10667 BLAIR WI
10669 WORDEN IL
10670 SUMTER SC
10671 INDIANAPOLIS IN
10674 ORANGEBURG SC
10676 GARDINER OR
10677 LODI OH
10678 BARDWELL TX
10679 ELLOREE SC
10680 HOLLY HILL SC
10681 LAKE CITY SC
10682 NIXON TX
10684 SAINT ANSGAR IA
10686 CAMAS WA
10686 VANCOUVER WA
10687 CALIPATRIA CA
10688 ITTA BENA MS
10689 COMMERCE OK
10690 GORHAM IL
10692 MOUNT ORAB OH
10693 NAMPA ID
10694 DAWSON TX
10697 ATMORE AL
10698 GREEN RIVER WY
10700 CROWLEY LA
10703 SPUR TX
10704 CAIRNBROOK PA
10707 MARIETTA PA
10708 CHARLESTON SC
10709 STEVENSVILLE MT
10710 BAUDETTE MN
10711 CHEROKEE IA
10712 BLOOMSBURY NJ
10714 LAKE NORDEN SD
10715 HOBSON MT
10716 WOODHULL IL
10718 FREMONT IN
10720 CICERO IN
10721 McVILLE ND
10723 COTTON PLANT AR
10724 STREETER ND
10727 BONNERS FERRY ID
10731 YREKA CA
10734 HENDERSONVILLE NC
10735 ATHENS TN
10736 NASHWAUK MN
10738 COLUMBUS MS
10739 SELMA NC
10741 HEBRON ND
10742 RICHMOND MI
10744 MOBRIDGE SD
10745 ROSEDALE MS
10746 ARKANSAS CITY KS
10747 WINTHROP NY
10748 OLANTA SC
10750 ROGERS AR
10751 BOISE ID
10752 ONEIDA IL
10754 BLISS NY
10757 KAUFMAN TX
10758 LAKE PRESTON SD
10759 RAVENSWOOD WV
10762 RIPLEY WV
10763 CHICAGO IL
10764 HEMET CA
10765 HUTCHINSON KS
10766 TALLASSEE AL
10767 HARRISVILLE NY
10768 PINE BLUFF AR
10770 DOLORES CO
10771 SAINT MARIES ID
10775 ELVERSON PA
10777 STAUNTON IL
10778 NEW YORK NY
10779 MURRAY KY
10781 RED CREEK NY
10783 AITKIN MN
10784 CARUTHERSVILLE MO
10785 SHELBYVILLE TN
10786 HUGO CO
10791 DURAND WI
10793 SAN ANTONIO TX
10794 MARSHALL AR
10795 MARSHALL AR
10796 HARTFORD CT
10801 HARRISON AR
10803 GERALDINE MT
10805 WINDER GA
10807 WYNNE AR
10810 GREYBULL WY
10811 DRY RUN PA
10813 BERESFORD SD
10814 BUXTON ND
10815 BATESBURG SC
10816 LISLE NY
10817 STOCKTON CA
10819 DENTON MT
10821 CHATHAM VA
10823 ABSECON NJ
10824 SWANVILLE MN
10825 WASHINGTON DC
10826 AVON PARK FL
10827 REEDVILLE VA
10828 WILMETTE IL
10829 SYLVANIA GA
10830 GONVICK MN
10832 BRUNSON SC
10833 CARTHAGE SD
10834 INDEPENDENCE VA
10835 BROOKNEAL VA
10836 LAKE CHARLES LA
10837 ELYSBURG PA
10838 SCOBEY MT
10839 AMBRIDGE PA
10842 KINGSPORT TN
10844 LOVELL WY
10846 GARY SD
10847 RIDLEY PARK PA
10850 RICHLANDS VA
10851 HAMLET NC
10852 OTIS CO
10853 RECTOR AR
10856 ATHENS NY
10857 RICHLANDS VA
10858 BASIN WY
10860 BRENHAM TX
10861 WHITING IA
10862 BRANDON MN
10863 LEWIS KS
10864 ASHLEY ND
10865 WINONA MN
10866 HOPEWELL VA
10869 FAIRPORT NY
10870 SHREVEPORT LA
10875 ERICK OK
10878 WOODLAND CA
10879 SYLACAUGA AL
10886 GLADSTONE MI
10887 SNOW HILL NC
10891 OLIVE CA
10892 KANSAS CITY MO
10898 WENDELL MN
10901 AKRON CO
10902 AMERICUS KS
10903 KEEWATIN MN
10906 TULSA OK
10908 DILLON SC
10911 AVA IL
10912 DELHI LA
10914 WAVERLY VA
10915 BOONVILLE MO
10916 NAMPA ID
10920 RIRIE ID
10923 WALDEN NY
10925 MOAB UT
10927 PURDON TX
10930 CONEWANGO VALLEY NY
10931 SAN BERNARDINO CA
10935 MILLTOWN NJ
10936 PIPESTONE MN
10938 RACINE WI
10939 GRASS RANGE MT
10940 SAINT PAUL MN
10943 BRASHER FALLS NY
10945 MACON GA
10946 BREWSTER MN
10947 NEW VIENNA OH
10948 CROGHAN NY
10950 LEMASTERS PA
10951 WOODLAWN PA
10951 ALIQUIPPA PA
10952 GEYSER MT
10954 FAYETTEVILLE TX
10956 SCHWERTNER TX
10958 TAMPA FL
10959 ABBEVILLE AL
10960 POCASSET OK
10964 OLD FORGE NY
10965 DALLAS TX
10966 VAN HOOK ND
10968 LOUISA VA
10973 STANLEY VA
10974 EL PASO TX
10975 NEWDALE ID
10976 ELIZABETHTON TN
10977 UKIAH CA
10979 FAIRFAX SC
10980 MARION KS
10983 GREENWOOD AR
10984 FAIRFIELD CA
10986 RESERVE MT
10988 MODESTO CA
10990 GUNTERSVILLE AL
10991 ROY MT
10992 SCAPPOOSE OR
10993 NEW CASTLE VA
10995 CARTER MT
10997 FLINT MI
10998 FLORENCE AZ
11002 MATADOR TX
11005 VICTORVILLE CA
11006 WINIFRED MT
11008 TWIN BRIDGES MT
11009 CHICAGO IL
11010 WICHITA KS
11012 NOGALES AZ
11014 MALDEN MA
11015 NEW HOPE PA
11018 HEALDTON OK
11019 TOM BEAN TX
11020 WEEDSPORT NY
11021 SOUR LAKE TX
11022 CORSICANA TX
11023 BUFFALO MN
11024 WHITEHALL MT
11028 NEWPORT NEWS VA
11034 NEW YORK NY
11035 FARMERSBURG IN
11036 WOLF POINT MT
11037 KANSAS CITY MO
11038 LEESBURG FL
11039 EDWARDSVILLE IL
11041 DEL REY CA
11042 KASSON MN
11043 WAKARUSA IN
11044 VEEDERSBURG IN
11045 ELLENSBURG WA
11047 COLBY KS
11049 MOUNT HOPE WV
11051 NIAGARA WI
11052 TIPTON OK
11053 HAILEY ID
11054 BOVEY MN
11055 FRIENDSHIP NY
11056 BAXTER SPRINGS KS
11057 TANNERSVILLE NY
11059 WOODRIDGE NY
11060 WEST BEND WI
11062 LYKENS PA
11064 HARTSHORNE OK
11065 BUHL ID
11067 WOBURN MA
11069 KULM ND
11072 BELLMORE NY
11073 WEST PALM BEACH FL
11074 BAKER MT
11078 RAYMOND MT
11080 LAMAR SC
11082 HAMTRAMCK MI
11083 GLENWOOD CITY WI
11084 BOISE CITY OK
11085 HARLOWTOWN MT
11087 HICKSVILLE NY
11091 ALBEMARLE NC
11092 CHICAGO IL
11093 ARDMORE OK
11094 GARY IN
11096 FRESNO MT
11097 OPHEIM MT
11098 SCOBEY MT
11099 HAXTUN CO
11101 CIRCLE MT
11103 WINCHESTER MA
11105 CHESTER MT
11106 SILVERTON OR
11108 HUME IL
11109 BLUEFIELD WV
11110 NECHE ND
11111 ALLENDALE SC
11112 BATHGATE ND
11113 NASHVILLE AR
11114 BLANCHARDVILLE WI
11115 IRVONA PA
11119 WINNER SD
11120 FLAGSTAFF AZ
11121 LAKEVIEW OR
11122 MARKED TREE AR
11123 MARYSVILLE CA
11125 PROCTOR MN
11126 LODI CA
11127 LIBERTY PA
11128 BOYCEVILLE WI
11130 MESA AZ
11131 HIGHWOOD MT
11137 BOSTON MA
11140 WACO TX
11141 CLEVELAND OH
11142 GRAND FORKS ND
11144 CUBA IL
11148 LAFAYETTE IN
11150 SHEBOYGAN WI
11151 CHOWCHILLA CA
11152 CAMBRIDGE MA
11153 CLIO SC
11154 TOWANDA KS
11155 MANNING SC
11156 VERO FL
11159 TUCSON AZ
11161 SEBASTOPOL CA
11163 LAMESA TX
11164 GRIDLEY CA
11168 BRIDGEPORT AL
11169 LYNN MA
11173 ERSKINE MN
11177 BEAVER KS
11178 MINNEAPOLIS MN
11180 HEBER SPRINGS AR
11182 CALERA OK
11184 MAKOTI ND
11185 PETERSBURG ND
11188 COALDALE PA
11188 BEDFORD PA
11189 NORWAY SC
11191 ROANOKE VA
11193 PERRYVILLE MD
11196 MANSFIELD AR
11198 FIRTH ID
11200 SAINT HELENS OR
11201 RODEO CA
11202 SWEETWATER TN
11204 TIMBLIN PA
11205 APPOMATTOX VA
11206 VALLEJO CA
11207 BALTIMORE MD
11208 GRIDLEY IL
11210 SEYMOUR IA
11212 HASTINGS MN
11213 SPRING MILLS PA
11215 MONTGOMERY MN
11216 FREEPORT OH
11218 JORDAN MN
11224 AVOCA MN
11226 PARSHALL ND
11227 HASTINGS PA
11229 REIDSVILLE NC
11230 OKLAHOMA CITY OK
11233 REFORM AL
11236 WEBSTER MA
11239 DAWSON TX
11242 MONROE LA
11243 ANDES NY
11244 MAPLETON PA
11249 ROLAND IA
11251 GARDEN GROVE CA
11253 LONGMONT CO
11255 CONYERS GA
11257 BURNHAM PA
11258 EASTLAND TX
11259 COFFEE SPRINGS AL
11260 MARINE CITY MI
11262 LAKE VILLAGE AR
11263 ALEXANDRIA PA
11264 MATOAKA WV
11265 SALTVILLE VA
11267 PEQUOT MN
11268 IAEGER WV
11270 CHELSEA MA
11271 MOLALLA OR
11274 TWIN FALLS ID
11275 NORWALK OH
11276 DARDANELLE AR
11278 IDAHO FALLS ID
11280 SEATTLE WA
11281 TUSCUMBIA AL
11282 CLOVERDALE CA
11283 BARRINGTON IL
11284 WHITESBORO NY
11286 WARREN MN
11287 BARNWELL SC
11288 HANSKA MN
11289 JACKSON MI
11290 QUITMAN GA
11293 LAKE WILSON MN
11294 REDMOND OR
11295 COLLEGE SPRINGS IA
11297 ALEXANDER ND
11300 HUGOTON KS
11302 REDMOND OR
11304 FORT DODGE IA
11305 WAKEFIELD MI
11306 NASH OK
11307 FAIRFIELD MT
11308 HINSDALE IL
11312 WALNUT RIDGE AR
11314 PAWHUSKA OK
11315 STUART OK
11317 BEAVERDALE PA
11318 DOWNS KS
11319 BUFFALO NY
11320 DEXTER MO
11326 CROCKETT CA
11327 BAKERSFIELD CA
11328 BEDFORD VA
11330 CARUTHERS CA
11331 ALTONA IL
11332 PAYNESVILLE MN
11333 TOLUCA IL
11336 MUNFORDVILLE KY
11337 COLLINSVILLE AL
11338 TUTTLE ND
11339 BOSTON MA
11340 SOUTH CHARLESTON WV
11342 ROCK RIVER WY
11343 PANDORA OH
11344 KANSAS CITY MO
11345 AURORA MN
11347 BRAINTREE MA
11348 RUSSELL SPRINGS KY
11349 SAVONA NY
11350 ANTELOPE MT
11351 PERTH AMBOY NJ
11352 MANVILLE WY
11355 REMINGTON IN
11356 LANCASTER MN
11357 CISCO TX
11358 CHARLESTON IL
11359 PITTSBURG CA
11360 JAMESTOWN NY
11361 DUMONT NJ
11364 NEWPORT NEWS VA
11365 KERKHOVEN MN
11368 BERGENFIELD NJ
11369 PORT ROYAL PA
11370 JEFFERSON PA
11372 SWEET SPRINGS MO
11373 PORT ROYAL PA
11374 CHETOPA KS
11375 HEMPSTEAD NY
11376 CLEVELAND OH
11377 KANSAS CITY MO
11378 NAPOLEON ND
11380 CHEYENNE WY
11381 PORTSMOUTH VA
11383 SYCAMORE OH
11387 PULASKI VA
11388 SOUTHBRIDGE MA
11389 WINTER GARDEN FL
11390 LUSK WY
11392 CLEARBROOK MN
11393 SPRINGVILLE PA
11397 TONKAWA OK
11398 TOPEKA KS
11399 WILMOT SD
11401 LAKE CRYSTAL MN
11402 PERRYVILLE MO
11403 FORT KENT ME
11404 TUXEDO NY
11405 ATCHISON KS
11407 DAVIDSVILLE PA
11409 NUTLEY NJ
11410 WACONIA MN
11412 NEW RICHMOND WI
11413 HOOVERSVILLE PA
11416 POMEROY WA
11417 VALLEY CITY ND
11420 SAINT AUGUSTINE FL
11423 LANCASTER TX
11425 PASADENA CA
11428 FORDS NJ
11433 TRANQUILITY CA
11434 SHELLEY ID
11435 BUFFALO NY
11437 ROSEBUD MT
11439 CLOVER SC
11440 SMITHFIELD NC
11441 WETONKA SD
11442 ALBUQUERQUE NM
11443 FAIRMOUNT IL
11444 NARROWS VA
11445 HEADLAND AL
11448 UNIONVILLE NY
11450 JENNINGS LA
11451 FORT PAYNE AL
11454 CHESANING MI
11457 DAVIS SD
11458 RIGBY ID
11461 BEVERLY HILLS CA
11462 MACHIAS ME
11463 SPARTA WI
11468 SWEETWATER TX
11469 IRONWOOD MI
11472 KANSAS CITY MO
11473 FRESNO CA
11474 BALDWIN NY
11477 GASTONIA NC
11478 BELLEVILLE IL
11479 JEFFERSON CITY TN
11480 DILLWYN VA
11483 WILLIAMSTOWN WV
11484 SAN JOAQUIN CA
11485 TAHLEQUAH OK
11487 MONESSEN PA
11489 NIAGARA FALLS NY
11490 CASPER WY
11491 KANSAS CITY MO
11492 LIMA MT
11495 BERKELEY CA
11496 PARMA ID
11499 GREENVILLE SC
11502 KIMBALL WV
11504 LIMON CO
11507 OAK PARK IL
11508 DUBOIS ID
11509 FLORA IL
11511 EAST SETAUKET NY
11512 DAUPHIN PA
11513 AFTON NY
11515 CLANTON AL
11516 WALTONVILLE IL
11517 CHARLOTTESVILLE VA
11518 FREEPORT NY
11519 BERTRAM TX
11521 SHREVEPORT LA
11522 LOS ALTOS CA
11524 LOYSVILLE PA
11526 SAINT CROIX FALLS WI
11529 DELTA UT
11531 COLONY KS
11532 MOUNTAIN VIEW CA
11533 TAZEWELL VA
11535 DEVOL OK
11537 PARSONS KS
11538 BUFFALO KY
11539 PHILADELPHIA PA
11543 BOGOTA NJ
11544 SOMERSET KY
11545 LINDEN NJ
11547 CRYSTAL FALLS MI
11548 DAWSON SPRINGS KY
11549 PONTIAC MI
11550 MOTORDALE MN
11550 NEW GERMANY MN
11552 GOOD THUNDER MN
11553 RED BANK NJ
11554 YORKTOWN VA
11555 FARGO ND
11557 MURFREESBORO NC
11558 VIENNA SD
11559 PHOENIX AZ
11561 BAY POINT CA
11564 DENVER CO
11566 WILLITS CA
11569 ROUND HILL VA
11570 ELLWOOD CITY PA
11571 FLEMING CO
11572 CAMPBELL CA
11573 BLUFFTON OH
11576 OSWEGO KS
11577 DEERFIELD WI
11579 NASHWAUK MN
11580 CLARKSVILLE AR
11581 PINE CITY MN
11582 ROCKWELL CITY IA
11585 ONIDA SD
11586 HOWELL MI
11588 SHENANDOAH IA
11589 BOWLING GREEN KY
11590 MOBRIDGE SD
11591 RIO GRANDE TX
11592 PARIS AR
11593 ALLENWOOD PA
11594 HURLEY WI
11596 EAST SAINT LOUIS IL
11597 GRIFFIN GA
11598 KANSAS OH
11599 THOMPSON ND
11601 SALIDA CA
11603 LYNBROOK NY
11608 MARBLE MN
11611 BIG LAKE MN
11615 RICHFORD VT
11616 ORANGE COVE CA
11618 CLIFFSIDE PARK NJ
11620 ROEBLING NJ
11627 IVANHOE MN
11635 OPELIKA AL
11638 HOMER LA
11642 GRANGER TX
11643 PICTURE ROCKS PA
11646 RHINELANDER WI
11652 FOREST LAKE MN
11654 DAVIDSON OK
11655 NEW YORK NY
11656 MIDDLEVILLE NY
11657 HARTWICK NY
11658 BEACH HAVEN NJ
11662 CICERO IL
11664 BAYARD WV
11667 FERNDALE WA
11668 FARIBAULT MN
11669 MANSFIELD LA
11670 HURRICANE WV
11671 CONVERSE IN
11672 RAYMOND WA
11675 WADDAMS GROVE IL
11677 HETTINGER ND
11678 GEYSERVILLE CA
11679 ROCKFORD IL
11683 CASPER WY
11684 SUISUN CA
11687 FARMINGTON MN
11689 ESTELLINE SD
11690 RADFORD VA
11692 LOCK HAVEN PA
11693 EVERETT WA
11694 HARRISONBURG VA
11695 HARTWELL GA
11697 MEBANE NC
11698 GRUNDY VA
11700 FABENS TX
11701 DOWNEY CA
11702 MYTON UT
11703 LAKE HAMILTON FL
11707 GREAT BEND KS
11708 SCARSDALE NY
11712 WILTON ND
11714 CARROLLTON OH
11716 LAKE WORTH FL
11718 MARION VA
11726 BELLEFONTAINE OH
11727 HILLSIDE NJ
11728 RICHMOND KS
11730 WESTBURY NY
11731 ROCKFORD IL
11732 CULVER CITY CA
11734 WOODSTOWN NJ
11735 RAKE IA
11737 CHICAGO IL
11739 ROMULUS NY
11740 MENAHGA MN
11741 SAINT PAUL MN
11742 PORT LEYDEN NY
11743 CENTERVILLE CA
11744 ELIZABETH NJ
11745 LEWISTON ID
11748 HARTFORD AR
11749 DALLAS TX
11751 ABERDEEN WA
11753 ANNISTON AL
11754 OKAWVILLE IL
11755 LONG BEACH NY
11757 BAKERTON PA
11759 RIDGEWOOD NJ
11761 BARNUM MN
11762 WICHITA FALLS TX
11763 CARNEGIE OK
11764 VIENNA VA
11765 BIG STONE GAP VA
11766 FAIRFIELD AL
11767 WARSAW NC
11768 BUFFALO NY
11769 BIOLA CA
11772 LYNCHBURG OH
11774 WOODLAWN IL
11775 CLYDE KS
11776 ROSEMOUNT MN
11778 MINNEAPOLIS MN
11780 OKAWVILLE IL
11781 EMPORIA KS
11782 MILROY IN
11783 BURLINGTON WI
11784 EUREKA NV
11785 NEW HARTFORD NY
11789 REBERSBURG PA
11792 FALFURRIAS TX
11793 PALMYRA NJ
11795 RUSTON LA
11797 FLINT HILL VA
11798 LOUISBURG KS
11799 PORT NECHES TX
11801 KLAMATH FALLS OR
11802 CASPIAN MI
11808 LYNDEN WA
11809 SOUTH FALLSBURG NY
11810 DULUTH MN
11812 EMERY SD
11813 BLISSFIELD MI
11816 VALLEY FALLS KS
11817 ROANOKE VA
11818 SAINT CLOUD MN
11819 ALBERTVILLE AL
11820 ALBERTVILLE AL
11823 ANAHEIM CA
11825 LINCOLN AR
11826 LADYSMITH WI
11827 LA HABRA CA
11830 HARTFORD AR
11831 MARION OH
11833 CEDARTOWN GA
11834 VOLANT PA
11836 BUFFALO NY
11839 JOHNSON CITY TN
11841 SHOEMAKERSVILLE PA
11843 GREENVILLE MI
11844 NEW YORK NY
11845 LIVINGSTON IL
11846 RUSSELLVILLE AL
11847 SOUTH PLAINFIELD NJ
11848 ROSEAU MN
11849 SIPESVILLE PA
11852 BATTLE CREEK MI
11854 CEDARHURST NY
11855 COLLYER KS
11860 KANORADO KS
11861 MINNEAPOLIS MN
11862 CLEVELAND OH
11863 LITTLEFORK MN
11865 PITTSTON PA
11866 WAYNESBORO PA
11867 RIALTO CA
11868 ARLINGTON MA
11869 SANTA ANA CA
11870 BOAZ AL
11873 LONG BEACH CA
11875 SACRAMENTO CA

11876 WOOD RIVER IL
11879 MERCEDES TX
11880 CRESCENT HEIGHTS CA
11881 VALLEY STREAM NY
11882 HOMER IL
11883 BUFFALO NY
11887 RANDALL KS
11890 STONE KY
11892 PITCAIRN PA
11893 ROCHESTER NH
11895 BRAIDWOOD IL
11896 ARNOLD PA
11897 MALONE NY
11898 LAUREL MS
11899 SEWARD PA
11900 GALLUP NM
11901 STUART VA
11902 BURNSIDE PA
11903 BOSTON MA
11904 CENTRALIA IL
11905 BESSEMER AL
11907 FARNHAMVILLE IA
11908 PHILADELPHIA PA
11909 PALISADES PARK NJ
11910 SAEGERTOWN PA
11911 VINTON VA
11912 LANCASTER NY
11913 IDABEL OK
11915 HARRIMAN TN
11920 CHECOTAH OK
11921 CLERMONT FL
11922 ELSINORE CA
11923 CENTRALIA IL
11924 MANHASSET NY
11925 HUNTINGTON PARK CA
11927 MAYBROOK NY
11929 IRON MOUNTAIN MI
11932 MORRIS OK
11934 PALATINE IL
11935 STANWOOD WA
11936 LAWRENCEVILLE GA
11938 KOPPEL PA
11942 ALAMEDA CA
11944 PIKEVILLE KY
11947 FALMOUTH KY
11949 LITTLETON CO
11950 LEONIA NJ
11951 PELHAM NY
11952 GRANT PARK IL
11953 ROOSEVELT NY
11954 HERMANSVILLE MI
11955 ANDALUSIA AL
11956 PAINTED POST NY
11957 LOVINGSTON VA
11959 NOCONA TX
11960 BROOKNEAL VA
11961 ROSEVILLE CA
11964 MEXIA TX
11966 OSCEOLA MILLS PA
11967 CENTRAL CITY PA
11969 ROUSES POINT NY
11970 QUINLAN TX
11971 WILLSBORO NY
11973 SAINT LOUIS MO
11974 PROCTOR MN
11976 BASSETT VA
11977 HAMMOND LA
11978 ASHLAND VA
11981 NUMIDIA PA
11983 CLIFTON NJ
11984 CONWAY WA
11985 HOHENWALD TN
11988 FLEMING KY
11989 SAINT LOUIS MO
11990 TROUTDALE VA
11992 ROSEVILLE CA
11993 WEST ALEXANDER PA
11994 WILLOUGHBY OH
11995 NORTH BELLE VERNON PA
11996 DALLAS TX
11998 OLIVER SPRINGS TN
11999 CHICAGO IL
12000 COULTERVILLE IL
12001 CHICAGO IL
12002 PEAPACK-GLADSTONE NJ
12004 CHICAGO IL
12006 ONEONTA AL
12014 HACKENSACK NJ
12015 FAIRVIEW MT
12017 HAMDEN NY
12018 LISBON NY
12019 BELLEVILLE NJ
12020 FORT LAUDERDALE FL
12022 LAUREL SPRINGS NJ
12026 FARGO ND
12027 MARQUETTE MI
12028 SPURGEON IN
12029 JEROME PA
12031 HARRIMAN TN
12033 NORTH ARLINGTON NJ
12035 MOORE OK
12036 NORMAN OK
12043 TULSA OK
12047 MIAMI BEACH FL
12048 OKMULGEE OK
12055 HOUSTON TX
12056 PLACERVILLE CA
12057 WEST PALM BEACH FL
12058 EAST CHICAGO IN
12061 MONTEREY PARK CA
12062 HOUSTON TX
12063 WINDSOR PA
12064 WEST NEW YORK NJ
12065 DUNCAN OK
12066 SAINT LOUIS MO
12067 LAWTON OK
12070 HOUSTON TX
12071 ATLANTA NY
12073 ROSEDALE MS
12075 OAK HILL WV
12078 WELLSTON OK
12079 SAND SPRINGS OK
12080 LOUDON TN
12081 HELENA OK
12083 WALNUT RIDGE AR
12084 LAWTON MI
12089 TAHLEQUAH OK
12092 POQUOSON VA
12096 XENIA IL
12097 ZEIGLER IL
12098 JOHNSTOWN PA
12100 WINTER HAVEN FL
12101 FOLLETT TX
12104 DEPEW OK
12110 ENNIS TX
12112 LODI CA
12114 ENUMCLAW WA
12115 RICHFIELD MN
12115 MINNEAPOLIS MN
12117 PRYOR CREEK OK
12120 APACHE OK
12122 SYRACUSE NY
12123 NEW YORK NY
12124 EAGLE RIVER WI
12129 MARLOW OK
12130 BLAIR OK
12132 EVANSVILLE IN
12134 PURCELL OK
12140 DULUTH MN
12148 COYLE OK
12153 SEATTLE WA
12154 MOUNT VERNON WA
12155 ALTUS OK
12157 NORMAN OK
12159 NESCOPECK PA
12162 SAN ANTONIO TX
12164 WINDHAM NY
12172 PASO ROBLES CA
12176 WILMINGTON NC
12178 EAST SAINT LOUIS IL
12182 KENEDY TX
12183 VICTORIA VA
12184 PALOUSE WA
12186 DALLAS TX
12187 KENEDY TX
12188 MILL CREEK OK
12189 CONNEAUTVILLE PA
12190 MEXIA TX
12191 McCUNE KS
12192 CENTRE HALL PA
12196 DELPHOS OH
12197 PENBROOK PA
12198 HOLBROOK AZ
12201 SANTA ROSA CA
12202 WALLINS CREEK KY
12205 PASSAIC NJ
12208 KENMORE NY
12209 HERMOSA BEACH CA
12214 NEW YORK NY
12216 SAINT LOUIS MO
12217 KENT WA
12220 SAINT LOUIS MO
12222 CLARKSDALE MS
12227 CHICAGO IL
12231 GARFIELD WA
12235 CORPUS CHRISTI TX
12236 BROWNSVILLE TX
12238 LAMAR AR
12240 EMPORIA VA
12241 BUDA TX
12242 GERMANTOWN NY
12243 HARLAN KY
12244 ASHEVILLE NC
12248 LORIMOR IA
12251 KENBRIDGE VA
12252 NEW YORK NY
12255 JERSEY CITY NJ
12256 BURLEY ID
12257 ROCKWOOD TN
12259 LEAKSVILLE NC
12260 KANSAS CITY MO
12261 STATE COLLEGE PA
12263 CRANFORD NJ
12264 ROCKWOOD TN
12267 PHOEBUS VA
12268 MONTCLAIR NJ
12271 HERMOSA BEACH CA
12272 WYCKOFF NJ
12274 TARPON SPRINGS FL
12275 PALM BEACH FL
12277 MUSKOGEE OK
12278 WINSTON-SALEM NC
12279 SEA ISLE CITY NJ
12280 NEW YORK NY
12281 BLUE RIDGE SUMMIT PA
12282 MINNEAPOLIS MN
12284 NIAGARA FALLS NY
12285 CHICAGO IL
12286 MARION WI
12288 PONTIAC MI
12289 ALPINE TX
12290 FRIES VA
12291 HARRISON AR
12292 TACOMA WA
12293 ASHLAND KY
12294 WOODMERE NY
12295 HARLAN KY
12296 HOLLY GROVE AR
12300 NEW YORK NY
12304 ROARING SPRING PA
12307 QUANAH TX
12309 TAFT TX
12311 FERRUM VA
12313 BUFFALO NY
12314 GILLESPIE IL
12316 REDLANDS CA
12317 SPARTA GA
12319 KINGSTON TN
12320 BERKELEY CA
12324 LEXINGTON TN
12325 FAIRFAX SD
12328 BELLFLOWER CA
12329 CLAYTON MO
12332 YOUNGSTOWN OH
12333 CLAYTON MO
12336 BOSTON MA
12337 BUFFALO NY
12339 SHAWNEE OK
12340 GENTRY AR
12341 RICHMOND CA
12343 LOWELL MA
12344 NEW YORK NY
12346 WICHITA KS
12347 ROCKY RIVER OH
12348 MEMPHIS TN
12349 MOCANAQUA PA
12351 KENOSHA WI
12352 NEW YORK NY
12353 ONAGA KS
12355 BOLIVAR PA
12357 TWO HARBORS MN
12358 PAOLI PA
12362 LYNN MA
12363 NORTH GIRARD PA
12364 SOUTH SAN FRANCISCO CA
12371 FORT WORTH TX
12372 IAEGER WV
12373 JONESBORO IL
12375 JORDAN NY
12378 LITTLE FERRY NJ
12380 CAMP HILL PA
12381 HONEA PATH SC
12382 LEONARD TX
12383 PATERSON NJ
12385 PASADENA CA
12386 RIVERSIDE IL
12387 IRONWOOD MI
12389 SAINT LOUIS MO
12391 CHICAGO IL
12392 LONGVIEW WA
12393 DRAKE ND
12395 COKATO MN
12397 JERSEY CITY NJ
12398 NEW YORK NY
12400 STAMFORD CT
12401 DICKINSON ND
12402 WEST ENGLEWOOD NJ
12404 BARNESVILLE GA
12405 NEW BEDFORD MA
12406 NEW YORK NY
12407 BILLINGS MT
12410 LOS ANGELES CA
12411 LONGVIEW TX
12412 COLUMBIA SC
12414 PITTSBURGH PA
12418 SPOKANE WA
12419 NEW YORK NY
12420 RUSHVILLE IN
12426 BERWYN IL
12427 WHEELER OR
12430 SHEFFIELD IA
12433 GRASS VALLEY CA
12438 TRENTON TN
12441 SHAWNEE OK
12443 MOUNT RANIER MD
12444 EVANSVILLE IN
12445 BUFFALO NY
12446 CINCINNATI OH
12449 FLORAL PARK NY
12452 STEELE MO
12453 SAUSALITO CA
12454 LOS ANGELES CA
12455 AUBURN AL
12459 DICKSON CITY PA
12460 INWOOD NY
12461 FOREST CITY NC
12462 REFUGIO TX
12465 FAIRVIEW NJ
12466 MOUNT VERNON IN
12467 LA FOLLETTE TN
12471 NEFFS PA
12472 ARDMORE OK
12473 BELLPORT NY
12475 GALVESTON TX
12476 WESTFIELD NY
12477 QUANTICO VA
12478 HATTIESBURG MS
12483 ELKINS WV
12485 ALBUQUERQUE NM
12489 KINGS PARK NY
12491 SAINT LOUIS MO
12494 MACEDON NY
12496 NARROWSBURG NY
12497 FORT LEE NJ
12498 CARMEN OK
12500 UNIONTOWN PA
12502 TAYLOR ND
12503 MERRICK NY
12504 WAYNE PA
12506 SAINT LOUIS MO
12507 WADENA MN
12510 PLEASANTVILLE NJ
12511 MARTINEZ CA
12517 DENVER CO
12518 WEST MINNEAPOLIS MN
12518 HOPKINS MN
12521 OCEAN CITY NJ
12523 CROWLEY LA
12524 PERTH AMBOY NJ
12525 WOODHULL IL
12526 CHELTENHAM PA
12530 JENKINTOWN PA
12532 KENDALLVILLE IN
12533 HOPE AR
12536 MILES CITY MT
12537 NATCHEZ MS
12538 ROCHESTER NY
12540 BOSTON MA
12542 ANACONDA MT
12543 BIG SPRING TX
12544 POCAHONTAS IA
12545 LOS ANGELES CA
12546 DAYTONA BEACH FL
12547 SAINT LAWRENCE SD
12550 NEW YORK NY
12551 CUTCHOGUE NY
12552 HARRISON NE
12553 NEW YORK NY
12556 PALESTINE TX
12557 PORTLAND OR
12559 SOMERS POINT NJ
12560 PATERSON NJ
12561 EVART MI
12562 AUSTIN PA
12563 NUREMBURG PA
12564 MILWAUKEE WI
12567 DEDHAM MA
12568 HIBBING MN
12569 CARLSBAD NM
12570 NEWARK NJ
12571 LAKEHURST NJ
12572 WALNUT PARK CA
12573 PHILADELPHIA PA
12574 WHITE PLAINS NY
12578 KETCHIKAN AK
12579 SAN FRANCISCO CA
12581 WINSLOW AZ
12582 CHALFONT PA
12587 YAZOO CITY MS
12588 SAINT MICHAEL PA
12590 HAGERSTOWN MD
12591 ADA OK
12593 EAST NORTHPORT NY
12596 CARBONDALE IL
12598 HIGHLAND PARK NJ
12599 WYTHEVILLE VA
12601 HARRISON NY
12604 NEWARK NJ
12605 CHICAGO IL
12606 YARDVILLE NJ
12607 GREY EAGLE MN
12608 LEWISTOWN MT
12609 GLEN ROCK NJ
12613 PORTLAND OR
12614 BENSON NC
12616 WYANDOTTE MI
12621 OAKLYN NJ
12623 SAINT PETERSBURG FL
12624 FLORENCE CA
12628 MILWAUKEE WI
12630 WILSONVILLE IL
12634 LUVERNE MN
12635 CARTERSVILLE GA
12636 CRESTON IA
12637 PLANTSVILLE CT
12638 THERMOPOLIS WY
12639 SPRINGFIELD TN
12640 SAN RAFAEL CA
12641 WESLACO TX
12642 MONROEVILLE AL
12646 HAMILTON SQUARE NJ
12656 HEDRICK IA
12657 ROYAL OAK MI
12658 PLYMOUTH IL
12659 GREAT NECK STATION NY
12661 L'ANSE CREUSE MI
12661 SAINT CLAIR SHORES MI
12662 OLDHAM SD
12663 HAWTHORNE NJ
12665 OAKLAND CA
12666 CHILDRESS TX
12667 TACOMA WA
12669 MINERAL WELLS TX
12673 GRAHAM CA
12675 MONTCLAIR NJ
12676 OLNEY TX
12678 VISALIA CA
12683 LUBBOCK TX
12687 MILLSAP TX
12688 HERSHEY PA
12690 CLIFTON NJ
12694 HOISINGTON KS
12697 MASON MI
12698 KILGORE TX
12700 HAMLIN TX
12703 MARSHALL TX
12704 ABERDEEN WA
12705 HARTSDALE NY
12706 ALLENDALE NJ
12707 DALLAS TX
12708 GRAPEVINE TX
12720 CASSANDRA PA
12725 SUDAN TX
12726 PATERSON NJ
12728 DENISON TX
12730 STEPHENVILLE TX
12732 NORTH BERGEN NJ
12734 MINERAL WELLS TX
12736 DALLAS TX
12740 TOPEKA KS
12741 BAILEY TX
12745 GRAND SALINE TX
12746 CHAPPAQUA NY
12747 LA FERIA TX
12750 NUTLEY NJ
12751 SARASOTA FL
12754 BELLFLOWER CA
12755 LOS ANGELES CA
12764 FULLERTON CA
12765 MILTON WV
12769 EL PASO TX
12771 NEWARK NJ
12775 STRAWN TX
12776 LIDGERWOOD ND
12780 MOUNT VERNON IN
12784 SALEM SD
12787 SANTA MONICA CA
12788 PATCHOGUE NY
12789 RAYMONDVILLE TX
12790 JACKSON TN
12792 BROWNSVILLE TX
12793 ALMONT MI
12794 KANSAS CITY MO
12797 SOUTH PASADENA CA
12800 METHUEN MA
12801 HUGO OK
12802 SAN LEANDRO CA
12804 LOS ANGELES CA
12805 SHAMOKIN PA
12806 GUTTENBERG NJ
12809 CONROE TX
12813 EUDORA AR
12814 CRANDON WI
12816 MILWAUKEE WI
12818 EAST ROCKAWAY NY
12819 LONG BEACH CA
12820 BROOKFIELD MO
12823 ALPHA NJ
12825 NEW YORK NY
12826 UTICA MI
12828 RAHWAY NJ
12829 WEEHAWKEN NJ
12834 PASSAIC NJ
12835 LAKEVIEW TX
12836 LYONS FALLS NY
12839 MATOAKA WV
12840 HOUSTON TX
12845 SULPHUR SPRINGS TX
12846 NEW BRITAIN CT
12847 DETROIT MI
12848 WEST PATERSON NJ
12849 KNOXVILLE IA
12854 HALEDON NJ
12855 DICKINSON TX
12857 LEMMON SD
12860 PHILADELPHIA PA
12861 PROSPECT PARK NJ
12863 ALBANY GA
12867 ANNA TX
12873 CHICAGO IL
12874 NEW YORK NY
12875 WAHPETON ND
12877 CLEAR LAKE SD
12885 NEW YORK NY
12889 EXETER NH
12890 MUSKOGEE OK
12891 ALLENHURST NJ
12892 NEW YORK NY
12897 NEW YORK NY
12900 NEW YORK NY
12902 HILLSDALE NJ
12903 NORTH MERCHANTVILLE NJ
12905 CLEARWATER FL
12906 BIRMINGHAM AL
12909 BEVERLY HILLS CA
12911 NEWFOUNDLAND PA
12912 DERRY PA
12916 SAINT LOUIS MO
12918 MUSKOGEE OK
12919 GEORGE WEST TX
12921 KINGSTON PA
12922 SAINT PAUL MN
12923 TALLULAH LA
12924 RATON NM
12925 WEST SENECA NY
12931 PHILADELPHIA PA
12933 WILCOX PA
12934 CARNEGIE PA
12935 TOWANDA KS
12939 JERSEY CITY NJ
12941 MAHNOMEN MN
12944 ALGONAC MI
12945 CHICAGO IL
12947 MOOSE LAKE MN
12949 TRENTON NJ
12950 SHENANDOAH IA
12951 CENTRAL PARK NY
12953 PLYMOUTH MI
12954 WAVERLY NY
12955 MAPLEWOOD MO
12956 ELMSFORD NY
12959 BUFFALO MN
12960 GOODWATER AL
12961 PADUCAH KY
12962 UNION SPRINGS AL
12965 NEW YORK NY
12967 DALE PA
12968 KINGSVILLE TX
12971 MOUNT CLEMENS MI
12972 MINNEAPOLIS MN
12973 EAST PORT CHESTER CT
12975 FOGELSVILLE PA
12976 FONTANA CA
12977 WOODBINE NJ
12979 MEDFORD MA
12982 GRAYSON KY
12984 RIVERSIDE NJ
12987 HAMPTON BAYS NY
12989 DEARBORN MI
12991 NATIONAL CITY IL
12992 ARDSLEY NY
12993 MONTGOMERY AL
12995 HEBBRONVILLE TX
12996 VENTURA CA
12997 FRANKLIN SQUARE NY
12999 LINCOLN PARK MI
13001 BREA CA
13003 PHILADELPHIA PA
13006 LIVONIA NY
13008 CORAL GABLES FL
13016 SAN FRANCISCO CA
13017 LINCOLN NE
13018 DURANT OK
13020 SPIRIT LAKE IA
13021 MADILL OK
13023 PAINTSVILLE KY
13026 HATFIELD PA
13027 NEW YORK NY
13028 MERCED CA
13029 ESCONDIDO CA
13030 ELKINS PARK PA
13032 PHILADELPHIA PA
13034 HARRISON NJ
13035 NEW YORK NY
13037 INTERLAKEN NY
13038 HARTFORD CT
13039 TRENTON NJ
13044 SAN FRANCISCO CA
13045 NEW YORK NY
13046 COOPER TX
13047 WHARTON NJ
13056 SMITHVILLE TN
13057 GIG HARBOR WA
13067 TEAGUE TX
13068 SAVANNAH GA
13073 TOLEDO IA
13074 LONG BEACH NY
13075 DETROIT LAKES MN
13076 COLBY KS
13078 DULUTH MN
13081 OLIVIA MN
13084 NEW KENSINGTON PA
13087 AMBRIDGE PA
13089 BOLTON LANDING NY
13091 ABERDEEN WA
13092 ONTARIO CA
13093 BEND OR
13096 MINNEAPOLIS MN
13097 MOBILE AL
13098 DENVER CO
13099 CENTRALIA WA
13103 NASHVILLE TN
13104 WEST HEMPSTEAD NY
13105 NEW YORK NY
13106 HUTCHINSON KS
13107 CLEBURNE TX
13108 MINNEAPOLIS MN
13110 TYLER TX
13113 PHILADELPHIA PA
13116 DULUTH MN
13119 CHICAGO IL
13120 CAMDEN NJ
13121 MAHOPAC NY
13123 PASSAIC NJ
13126 GLEN HEAD NY
13129 LIVINGSTON NJ
13130 LAKE RONKONKOMA NY
13131 SAINT PAUL MN
13133 DUBLIN PA
13134 WAYNESBURG PA
13136 CEDAR GROVE NJ
13137 VANCOUVER WA
13142 JEFFERSON CITY MO
13144 WITT IL
13145 WEBSTER NY
13146 CHICAGO IL
13149 NEW YORK NY
13150 JEWETT OH
13151 LANSDOWNE PA
13153 PITTSBURGH PA
13154 CALDWELL OH
13155 PARAGOULD AR
13157 SANFORD FL
13160 GLEN LYON PA
13161 MOULTRIE GA
13162 JOPLIN MO
13171 SMITHFIELD OH
13174 PLAINFIELD NJ
13175 PHILADELPHIA PA
13177 EXETER PA
13180 PHILADELPHIA PA
13187 LOS ANGELES CA
13193 NEW YORK NY
13195 MOBILE AL
13196 HIGHLAND PARK PA
13197 JERSEY SHORE PA
13198 WEST UNION OH
13199 WOLFE CITY TX
13200 SANTA ANA CA
13202 BANGOR WI
13203 CAMDEN NJ
13205 BEECH CREEK PA
13209 LAFAYETTE LA
13210 GURDON AR
13212 PALO ALTO CA
13214 PALATKA FL
13215 POINT PLEASANT BEACH NJ
13216 CHICAGO IL
13217 SAN LEANDRO CA
13219 BUFFALO NY
13220 BUFFALO NY
13221 LAKE NORDEN SD
13222 BUZZARDS BAY MA
13223 ALBANY GA
13229 WYOMING NY
13230 SEATTLE WA
13231 POINT PLEASANT WV
13232 TIPTON IA
13234 BELLEROSE NY
13236 BELLEVILLE IL
13237 NEW YORK NY
13246 BOLIVAR NY
13247 WILTON NH
13249 WELLINGTON TX
13251 SOUDERTON PA
13252 NEWTON MA
13254 NEW YORK NY
13260 NEW YORK NY
13261 POULTNEY VT
13262 PRESCOTT AZ
13264 SAINT LOUIS MO
13268 UNIONVILLE MO
13273 CRESTLINE OH
13274 SILOAM SPRINGS AR
13280 McGHEE AR
13286 ARLINGTON SD
13288 COEUR D'ALENE ID
13289 WELLS NY
13292 NEW YORK NY
13293 LUDLOW MO
13294 PORTLAND OR
13295 NEW YORK NY
13296 NEW YORK NY
13297 MOORHEAD MN
13298 NEW BERN NC
13299 PORTLAND OR
13300 WEST PALM BEACH FL
13302 FAIRFAX SD
13303 DEER CREEK MN
13304 NEW YORK NY
13305 BLUFFTON IN
13307 NILES MI
13308 SOLDIERS GROVE WI
13312 WINTERS CA
13314 NANUET NY
13315 EDINBURG TX
13316 MINATARE NE
13317 BLUFFTON IN
13318 PAINESVILLE OH
13319 YONKERS NY
13320 BROOKSVILLE FL
13321 DES MOINES IA
13323 FARGO ND
13324 VALLEY CITY ND
13325 PHILADELPHIA PA
13326 ROSLYN NY
13328 GRAND RAPIDS MI
13329 CIMARRON KS
13330 ROCHESTER NY
13331 SPOKANE WA
13332 LOMA LINDA CA
13333 LINCOLN NE
13334 NEW YORK NY
13335 SAN MARINO CA
13336 NEW YORK NY
13338 SAN JOSE CA
13339 OAKDALE NE
13340 YREKA CA
13346 VERMILLION SD
13349 MEMPHIS TN
13350 NORTHFIELD MN
13351 PORT TOWNSEND WA
13352 SARASOTA FL
13353 LITTLE FALLS MN
13354 ASTORIA OR
13356 COLTON CA
13358 BIRMINGHAM AL
13359 LEEDS AL
13360 NEW YORK NY
13362 COOPERSTOWN ND
13363 ASBURY PARK NJ
13364 HACKENSACK NJ
13365 LA FARGEVILLE NY
13367 VERSAILLES MO
13368 VALLEJO CA
13370 LAKELAND FL
13373 CHICAGO HEIGHTS IL
13375 PACIFIC GROVE CA
13378 FRANKLIN IN
13380 SALINAS CA
13381 BLOSSBURG PA
13383 WINTER HAVEN FL
13385 VALLEY CITY ND
13388 DELAND FL
13389 BARTOW FL
13392 CONYNGHAM PA
13393 SYRACUSE NY
13394 SPENCER MA
13395 HYANNIS MA
13396 RED WING MN
13398 BISMARCK ND
13400 SIOUX RAPIDS IA
13402 ROCKWALL TX
13404 MINEOLA NY
13406 LIBERAL KS
13407 MILBANK SD

13408 FREMONT NE
13410 GLEN ULLIN ND
13411 WEBSTER MA
13412 GADSDEN AL
13414 MOBILE AL
13416 HONEY GROVE TX
13420 KIMBALL NE
13425 SIDNEY NE
13426 COZAD NE
13428 CLARKSVILLE TX
13432 LIGONIER PA
13435 ASHLAND NE
13437 WINTER HAVEN FL
13439 EAST STANWOOD WA
13441 BUFFALO NY
13443 HENDERSON TX
13444 REARDAN WA
13445 MATTITUCK NY
13446 OVERTON NE
13448 GEORGETOWN IL
13452 MOUNT OLIVE IL
13453 PILGER NE
13454 CARSON ND
13457 DEFIANCE OH
13458 CHARITON IA
13460 BRITTON SD
13467 MOBRIDGE SD
13472 SAVANNAH GA
13473 GRINNELL IA
13476 MINOA NY
13479 HODGENVILLE KY
13481 CLAYTON MO
13482 GREENEVILLE TN
13483 CHAMBERLAIN SD
13484 KIMBALL WV
13486 LITCHFIELD MN
13487 PHILLIPS WI
13490 WASHINGTON COURT HOUSE OH
13491 CONNELLSVILLE PA
13492 INDEPENDENCE KS
13493 ODESSA NY
13494 LEMOYNE PA
13501 GARRISON ND
13502 GATE CITY VA
13503 POSEYVILLE IN
13504 MOUNT VERNON MO
13505 GARY WV
13507 FROST TX
13509 CHARLESTON WV
13510 HOLLISTER CA
13511 PLANO TX
13512 WELCH WV
13513 MANISTIQUE MI
13514 LUXEMBURG MO
13515 HASTINGS NE
13516 WAXAHACHIE TX
13520 HELENA AR
13521 ARGYLE NY
13523 LENOIR NC
13524 NANTICOKE PA
13525 SMITHTON IL
13526 HEMPHILL TX
13527 PAWHUSKA OK
13529 DURAND WI
13530 HADDON HEIGHTS NJ
13531 EAST CHICAGO IN
13532 EAST CHICAGO IN
13533 GALLITZIN PA
13534 ASHDOWN AR
13535 DELAWARE OH
13537 KEARNY NJ
13539 KNOXVILLE TN
13540 LINDEN NJ
13542 NEW HARMONY IN
13547 ANOKA MN
13548 PLATTSBURG NY
13549 ETHAN SD
13550 FITZGERALD GA
13551 MERIDIAN MS
13553 GULFPORT MS
13554 AYDEN NC
13555 BLOOMING GROVE TX
13558 READING MA
13559 MONTGOMERY NY
13561 MADISON MN
13562 COLORADO TX
13563 SIDNEY NY
13564 DAWSON MN
13565 AURORA IL
13568 NELIGH NE
13569 CHARDON OH
13570 MIAMI FL
13571 NEW KENSINGTON PA
13572 PEARSALL TX
13573 LAKE CHARLES LA
13576 PENDLETON OR
13577 PERU IL
13578 SAN ANTONIO TX
13580 LOGANSPORT IN
13581 SEATTLE WA
13583 MONTOUR FALLS NY
13584 CARTHAGE NY
13585 CHARLEROI PA
13586 YOUNGSTOWN OH
13588 BROWNWOOD TX
13589 VIBORG SD
13590 CALLICOON NY
13592 MAMARONECK NY
13594 PORTLAND ND
13595 COLEMAN TX
13596 NEW LEXINGTON OH
13597 BLANDINSVILLE IL
13598 STAMFORD TX
13599 FENNIMORE WI
13600 PONTIAC MI
13601 ALMA KS
13602 LA GRANDE OR
13603 FREDERICKSBURG VA
13604 GLOUCESTER MA
13605 ROBINSON IL
13606 PORTLAND PA
13607 BESSEMER MI
13608 ODESSA TX
13609 NEWTON IA
13611 MENDOTA IL
13612 HARRODSBURG KY
13613 BURLINGTON NC
13615 STEWARTVILLE MN
13616 OCONOMOWOC WI
13617 ALLIANCE NE
13618 MANSFIELD PA
13619 SHENANDOAH PA
13620 LOUP CITY NE
13621 PARKERSBURG WV
13622 BAY CITY MI
13623 DECATUR TX
13624 LOVELAND CO
13625 ALTONA IL
13626 WILSON NC
13627 RICHWOOD WV
13628 BELVIDERE NJ
13629 PLAINFIELD NJ
13632 LAKE VILLAGE AR
13634 WESTON WV
13635 JOHNSON CITY TN
13636 HENDERSON NC
13637 FORREST CITY AR
13640 BRISTOL TN
13641 HOMESTEAD FL
13643 MARTINSVILLE IN
13644 DONORA PA
13645 EAU CLAIRE WI
13646 BUCKHANNON WV
13648 SHREVEPORT LA
13649 WHITNEY TX
13650 WITT IL
13651 GLASGOW KY
13652 ROCKFORD IL
13653 SULPHUR SPRINGS TX
13655 MONROE LA
13656 KERENS TX
13657 DURHAM NC
13658 LIGONIER PA
13661 ORANGE TX
13663 BENTLEYVILLE PA
13664 PAINTED POST NY
13666 STOCKTON IL
13667 ENNIS TX
13668 BURKBURNETT TX
13669 MOUNT CALM TX
13670 MIDLOTHIAN TX
13673 CASEY IL
13674 CHICAGO IL
13676 WICHITA FALLS TX
13677 ARDMORE OK
13678 BRENHAM TX
13679 TULSA OK
13680 BEL AIR MD
13681 MEMPHIS TN
13682 TOLEDO IL
13683 HOUSTON TX
13684 CHICAGO IL
13686 COLFAX IA
13688 NEW ORLEANS LA
13689 NEW ORLEANS LA
13690 NORTH KANSAS CITY MO
13692 PARK RAPIDS MN
13693 MENA AR
13695 FREEPORT IL
13696 NEW DOUGLAS IL
13699 SEWICKLEY PA
13700 LATROBE PA
13701 PITTSBURGH PA
13702 WATERLOO IA
13703 BIRMINGHAM MI
13704 NEW HAVEN CT
13706 TRINITY TX
13707 KNOXVILLE IA
13708 JACKSON MS
13709 EVANSTON IL
13710 PORTLAND ME
13711 CHICO CA
13713 CANNON FALLS MN
13715 LAKEWOOD OH
13716 PORTLAND ME
13717 MARION IN
13719 CONWAY AR
13720 COLUMBIA SC
13722 NATCHEZ MS
13725 SANDERSVILLE GA
13726 SAINT LOUIS MO
13727 ABILENE TX
13728 GADSDEN AL
13731 CAMERON TX
13732 GRETNA LA
13733 ATHOL MA
13735 MARISSA IL
13737 BATON ROUGE LA
13739 PONTIAC MI
13740 BRYAN OH
13741 JACKSON MI
13742 ORRVILLE OH
13743 DALLAS TX
13744 HOOPESTON IL
13745 BALTIMORE MD
13746 CHATTANOOGA TN
13747 FREDERICK MD
13748 CHERRY VALLEY NY
13750 NORWAY ME
13751 OKMULGEE OK
13752 HEADLAND AL
13756 ALTUS OK
13757 HENDERSON KY
13758 GRAND RAPIDS MI
13759 INDIANAPOLIS IN
13760 FREDERICK OK
13761 GREENSBORO NC
13763 PAINTSVILLE KY
13764 FARMINGTON NH
13765 McCONNELLSBURG PA
13766 HUMBOLDT IA
13767 LIMA OH
13768 PRESQUE ISLE ME
13770 McALESTER OK
13771 MEDFORD OR
13772 SCOTTDALE PA
13773 ELLICOTT CITY MD
13774 CLEVES OH
13775 HAMPTON VA
13776 OAKLAND MD
13777 PITTSFIELD ME
13780 WEBSTER MA
13781 JOHNSTOWN PA
13782 WASHINGTON DC
13783 MARLINTON WV
13784 MADELIA MN
13787 FORT BRAGG CA
13788 BEDFORD IN
13789 BESSEMER AL
13790 GRAND FORKS ND
13791 SANFORD NC
13792 PETERSBURG VA
13794 DERRY PA
13795 MASCOUTAH IL
13798 CHESTERTOWN MD
13799 GRAND RAPIDS MI
13800 SAINT ALBANS VT
13801 KANSAS CITY KS
13802 DENNISON OH
13803 SHARON PA
13804 CAIRO IL
13805 COLUMBIA IL
13806 OSHKOSH WI
13810 BELTON TX
13811 FAIRMONT WV
13812 HARRISVILLE PA
13813 CANONSBURG PA
13814 ALBUQUERQUE NM
13817 BOONE IA
13818 FORT WAYNE IN
13819 LEWISTON ID
13822 KINGSTON NY
13823 WILKINSBURG PA
13824 HUBBELL MI
13825 FLORIDA NY
13826 FREEPORT PA
13828 MIAMI BEACH FL
13829 CLAREMONT NH
13831 KEYSER WV
13832 PORTSMOUTH OH
13835 MILLBURY MA
13837 CHINOOK MT
13839 NORCO LA
13840 PORT DEPOSIT MD
13841 ROCHESTER MI
13842 HAMPTON IA
13843 FORT FAIRFIELD ME
13844 CALDWELL OH
13846 MERCER PA
13848 BELMAR NJ
13850 EAST PALESTINE OH
13852 WILKES BARRE PA
13853 HANCOCK MD
13855 BRANCHVILLE NJ
13856 DIXON IL
13857 HASTINGS MI
13858 BATTLE CREEK MI
13861 ROCHESTER NH
13862 SWAYZEE IN
13863 STRAUSSTOWN PA
13865 MONTICELLO IL
13866 BRADDOCK PA
13867 PARKTON MD
13868 BLAIRSVILLE PA
13870 ASHLAND WI
13871 ALBION PA
13873 WAYNESBURG PA
13876 CANAJOHARIE NY
13877 BREA CA
13878 ONANCOCK VA
13881 WEST UNION WV
13883 CARROLLTON OH
13884 FREDONIA PA
13886 SAVANNA IL
13887 NEW FREEDOM PA
13889 TUCKAHOE NY
13891 PONCA CITY OK
13892 NEOGA IL
13893 EDGEWATER NJ
13894 BELLOWS FALLS VT
13897 JACKSON GA
13899 BRYAN OH
13900 SOMERSET PA
13901 PROVIDENCE RI
13902 GRAND JUNCTION CO
13904 PRINCETON WI
13905 CAMBRIDGE OH
13906 BARBOURVILLE KY
13907 NEW FLORENCE PA
13908 RURAL VALLEY PA
13909 ANDOVER NY
13910 NEW EGYPT NJ
13911 GOUVERNEUR NY
13912 MONTPELIER OH
13914 BELLAIRE OH
13916 METUCHEN NJ
13918 ORANGEBURG SC
13919 LULING TX
13922 SAINT CLAIRSVILLE OH
13925 HOUSTON TX
13928 GREELEY CO
13929 ONTONAGON MI
13931 ISHPEMING MI
13932 EDGERTON WI
13934 LOCKHART TX
13935 WEST TX
13938 TERRE HAUTE IN
13939 HAWARDEN IA
13940 TARENTUM PA
13942 CONNEAUTVILLE PA
13943 HOUSTON TX
13945 PHILMONT NY
13946 GARFIELD NJ
13947 SCRANTON PA
13948 FAYETTEVILLE TN
13950 YARDLEY PA
13952 BUFFALO NY
13954 LOGAN WV
13956 MIDDLETOWN NY
13959 NEW YORK NY
13960 PINE BUSH NY
13962 WINDHAM NY
13965 BROCKPORT NY
13967 McKEESPORT PA
13968 MILTON FL
13969 COLLINGSWOOD NJ
13971 MARIETTA OH
13974 CLARKSVILLE TX
13979 FROSTBURG MD
13980 CONNEAUT LAKE PA
13981 PROVIDENCE RI
13982 HERNDON PA
13983 HENDERSON KY
13984 BIG SPRING TX
13986 ENOSBURG FALLS VT
13993 ALTAMONT IL
13994 HEGINS PA
13996 BELLAIRE OH
13998 CLEARFIELD PA
13999 BERWYN PA
14000 LITTLE ROCK AR
14001 CLATSKANIE OR
14002 ELKINS WV
14005 DURANT OK
14006 CLEMENTON NJ
14008 DE KALB IL
14010 EAST PEORIA IL
14011 DILLONVALE OH
14013 WEBSTER SPRINGS WV
14014 GUTTENBERG NJ
14019 KINGS PARK NY
14020 PERRY OK
14021 BOULDER CO
14023 KINGSTON PA
14024 CHARLESTON IL
14025 OXFORD NY
14026 OWENTON KY
14027 BRECKENRIDGE TX
14028 COUNCIL BLUFFS IA
14030 TOLEDO OH
14031 TOWER CITY PA
14032 LANSING MI
14033 WOBURN MA
14035 GRANVILLE IL
14039 STANFORD KY
14040 LENOX IA
14041 VILLISCA IA
14042 WINTHROP MN
14044 BRUNSWICK MD
14048 LYONS KS
14049 DOVER PA
14050 BRIDGEPORT OH
14051 EXPORT PA
14052 CREWE VA
14053 PHILIPPI WV
14055 GREENSBURG PA
14056 PINE BLUFF AR
14061 ELBERTON GA
14062 HILLSDALE MI
14063 WAUPACA WI
14065 NEVADA IA
14070 KOPPEL PA
14071 JEFFERSON PA
14072 FALFURRIAS TX
14075 FRANKLIN IN
14076 PARIS KY
14077 BRADFORD OH
14078 CHERRY CREEK NY
14079 OLYPHANT PA
14081 TUCUMCARI NM
14082 WINDBER PA
14083 SUPERIOR NE
14087 CHELSEA MA
14088 PALISADES PARK NJ
14089 STOYSTOWN PA
14090 CANYON TX
14091 EAST BERLIN PA
14092 CARUTHERSVILLE MO
14093 UNION CITY PA
14094 CECIL PA
14095 DURAND WI
14096 CAMDEN AR
14098 INDIANA PA
14099 RAPID CITY SD
14100 BERLIN NH
14102 IRON RIVER MI
14104 GROVETON TX
14105 SPRINGFIELD OH
14106 POCOMOKE CITY MD
14108 WALTERS OK
14110 CHICAGO IL
14111 GLADSTONE MI
14112 WAMPUM PA
14113 GOSHEN IN
14117 BEAVER FALLS PA
14118 LINCOLN IL
14121 MOUNT WOLF PA
14122 CLIFTON HEIGHTS PA
14123 CHARLEROI PA
14125 MARSHFIELD WI
14126 GROESBECK TX
14130 MARION WI
14133 LATROBE PA
14137 WOODSTOCK IL
14142 MOUNDSVILLE WV
14144 HOWELL MI
14146 FORT COLLINS CO
14149 HASKELL TX
14150 TIGERTON WI
14153 CARTERET NJ
14156 HOOVERSVILLE PA
14162 CLIFFSIDE PARK NJ
14163 GOODLAND KS
14164 CUERO TX
14166 TONASKET WA
14167 WEST CONCORD MN
14168 DE RIDDER LA
14169 SYKESVILLE PA
14170 BANGOR PA
14173 GOLCONDA IL
14177 SEA BRIGHT NJ
14181 GALLITZIN PA
14182 WILLIAMSBURG PA
14183 MINGO JUNCTION OH
14184 DARLINGTON WI
14187 IONIA MI
14189 TUCKAHOE NJ
14195 FORT MYERS FL
14199 DALHART TX
14200 NEILLSVILLE WI
14201 DELTA PA
14202 TORRANCE CA
14204 ANGLETON TX
14205 FOREST CITY PA
14211 SPARTANBURG SC
14213 EADS CO
14214 GREEN LANE PA
14219 ERIE PA
14220 MANKATO MN
14224 FORT KENT ME
14225 DELHI LA
14230 CORCORAN CA
14232 PAINESVILLE OH
14234 POULTNEY VT
14236 McKINNEY TX
14245 CHICAGO IL
14246 CHICAGO IL
14249 HANCOCK MI
14250 HAMBURG PA
14252 PIERRE SD
14257 CORDELE GA
14258 LINTON IN
14261 BETHESDA OH
14266 HAVERHILL MA
14270 SNYDER TX
14271 PITTSBURGH PA
14273 BROWNWOOD TX
14274 OIL CITY PA
14282 WYMORE NE
14283 SAN ANTONIO TX
14285 MOUNT OLIVE IL
14295 WELLSBURG WV
14297 LANARK IL
14302 COTULLA TX
14304 PAWHUSKA OK
14305 WEST NEW YORK NJ
14309 KEOKUK IA
14320 LOUISVILLE KY

BIBLIOGRAPHY

Anton, William T and Perlmutter, Morey **The Albert A. Grinnell Collection of United States Paper Money**. (1971)

Bart, Dr. Frederick J. **Comprehensive Catalog of United States Paper Money Errors** BNR Press, Port Clinton, OH (1994)

Blake, George H. **Issues of United States Paper Money**, (1908) Revised 1948

Bowen, Harold L. **State Bank Notes of Michigan** Havelet Advertising Services (1956)

Comptroller of Currency Report 1937 United States Government Printing Office, Washington (1938)

Congressional Record; Various dates

Dillistin, William H. **A Descriptive History of National Bank Notes, 1863-1935** Paterson, NJ (1956).

Donlon, William P. **United States Large Size Paper Money 1861-1923** Published by the author, (1968)

Ford, John J., Jr. Letter to the Editor **Bank Note Reporter**, March, 1978

Friedberg, Robert. **Paper Money of the United States** First Edition (1953) Appendix. Coin & Currency Publishing Institute, New York

Grinnell, Albert A. [See Anton, William T.]

Hessler, Gene **The Comprehensive Catalog of U.S. Paper Money** BNR Press, Port Clinton, OH (1996)

Hessler, Gene **U.S. Essay, Proof and Specimen Notes** BNR Press, Portage, OH (1979)

Huntoon, Peter **The Types of 1882 and 1902 National Bank Notes.** Paper Money Vol. 12, pp 13-18 (1973)

Huntoon, Peter **Territorials, A Guide to U.S. Territorial National Bank Notes** Society of Paper Money Collectors, Inc. (1980)

Huntoon, Peter **The Misdated 1902 Plate For The First National Bank of Arizona at Phoenix**. Paper Money Vol. 20, pp. 67-70 (1981)

Huntoon, Peter **Tigerton Wisconsin Series of 1929 Mismatched Number** Paper Money Vol 29 p 161 (1990)

Huntoon, Peter **United States Large Size National Bank Notes**. Society of Paper Money Collectors, Inc., Laramie, WY (1995)

Limpert, Frank Alvin. **United States Paper Money - Old Series** Third Edition Royal Oak, MI (1950)

McCulloch, Hugh **Men and Measures of Half a Century** Charles Scribners' Sons, New York, NY (1888)

Morris, Thomas F. **The First U. S. National Bank Notes**. The Essay-Proof Journal Vols. 79, 80(1963) and Vol. 81 (1964).

National-Bank Act, As Amended, and Other Laws Relating to National Banks. Government Printing Office 1908, 1918, et seq. Washington, DC

Philpott, William A., Jr. **Why No. 1 Sheets Are Not Too Rare**. Paper Money Vol. 10, pp. 16-17 (1971)

Van Belkum, Louis **National Banks of the Note-Issuing Pcriod 1863-1935** Hewitt Brothers, Chicago (1968)

Walton, Gerome **A History of Nebraska Banking and Paper Money** The Centennial, Lincoln, Nebraska (1978)

Warns, M. Owen (Ed), Huntoon, Peter, and Van Belkum, Louis **The National Bank Note Issues of 1929-1935** Society of Paper Money Collectors, Inc. (1970)

Criswell, Grover C. **Confederate and Southern States Currency** 4th Edition (1992) BNR Press Port Clinton, OH

Walter O. Woods **The Story of Uncle Sam's Money** Gregg Publishing, New York, NY (1932)

This guide contains data for over 12,000 banks. There are more than 300,000 note evaluations. Typos and other errors are inevitable, despite the best efforts of the author and others involved. Furthermore, the census of national bank notes is not static. Discoveries continue to present collectors with exciting new notes. The list below corrects a few typos detected during production, and updates the census, particularly the census of uncut sheets. Readers are urged to report errors and census changes to the author at P O Box 85 Oxford, OH 45056 (513)523-6861 or e-mail at 73717.3152@compuserve.com. (donc_kelly@compuserve.com). Thanks for your help.

Typos

p 96 City NB of New Britain Ch 12846 1902 Plain Back Value should be <$400
p 537 COLORADO Colorado City 6238 should read Colorado Springs(2) 6238
p 537 GEORGIA Jackson 13897 $5 29-2 1-6 entry appears twice
p 538 IOWA Waterloo 792 Delete entry
p 539 MINNESOTA Dodge Center 6623 Delete both entries
p 540 MISSOURI Salem 7921 $20 29-2 1-6 entry appears twice
p 540 NEW JERSEY Bridgeton 9498 Delete entry
p 540 NEW JERSEY Passaic 12834 $5 02 PB 6017 entry appears twice

Population Changes (revised population follows charter number)

p 88 FNB in Eads Ch 14213 **3U + 2 S**
p 89 FNB of Eads Ch 8412 **3L U + 11 S**
p 116 Overland NB of Boise Ch 10751 **U + 3 L**
p 130 FNB of Highland Ch 6653 **U + 9 L 14 S**
p 138 Illinois NB & TC of Rockford Ch 13652 **4U + 16 S**
p 138 FNB of Saint Elmo Ch 9388 **5 L 11 S**
p 149 Citizens NB of Greensburg Ch 1890 **8 L 3U + 7 S**
p 155 FNB of Richmond Ch 17 **12 L 2U + 14 S**
p 157 FNB of Vincennes Ch 1873 **3U + 25 L 3 S**
p 157 FNB of Whiting Ch 6526 **U + 6 L**
p 159 Bedford NB Ch 5165 **U + 9 L 12 S**
p 161 City NB of Clinton Ch 2469 **32 L U + 50+ S**
p 161 Clinton NB Ch 994 **14 L 2U + 14 S**
p 166 Marion County NB of Knoxville Ch 1986 **U + 9 L**
p 169 Newton NB Ch 13609 **U + 2 S**
p 172 NB of Toledo Ch 13073 **U + 18 S**
p 172 Nodaway Valley NB of Villisca Ch 14041 **U + 7 S**
p 188 Morgan County NB of Cannel City Ch 7891 **5 L 4 S**
p 190 Harlan NB Ch 12295 **U + 3 L 14 S**
p 203 Canal NB of Portland Ch 941 **29 L 2U + 37 S**
p 219 Merrimack NB of Haverhill Ch 633 **12 L 2U + 4 S**
p 222 Newton NB Ch 13252 **13 L U + 23 S**

p 239 FNB of Appleton Ch 8813 **4 L U + 11 S**
p 241 City NB of Duluth Ch 6520 **40 L U + 50+ S**
p 245 Klein NB of Madison Ch 13561 **U + 20 S**
p 253 F-Columbus NB Ch 10738 **10U + 50+ S**
p 257 Exchange NB of Columbia Ch 1467 **U + 23 L 2U + 21 S**
p 260 NB in North Kansas City Ch 13690 **U + 1 S**
p 260 FNB of Peirce City Ch 4225 **6 L 10U + 9 S**
p 261 American NB of Saint Joseph Ch 9042 **10 L 2U + 10 S**
p 261 NB of Commerce in Saint Louis Ch 4178 **U + 50 L**
p 262 FNB in St Louis Ch 170 **U + 22 L 50+ S**
p 266 FNB & TC of Helena Ch 4396 **U + 30 S**
p 273 Grand Island NB Ch 9395 **35 L 3U + 16 S**
p 292 Hillsdale NB Ch 12902 **U + 24 L 27 S**
p 292 FNB of Jersey City Ch 374 **7U + 50+ L 50+ S**
p 292 Labor NB of Jersey City Ch 12939 **3U + 8 L 4 S**
p 293 Burlington County NB of Medford Ch 1191 **9 L U + 18 S**
p 293 Metuchen NB Ch 7754 **U + 12 L 12 S**
p 294 FNB & TC of Montclair Ch 9339 **8 L U + 35 S**
p 296 Broadway NB of Paterson Ch 12726 **U + 11 L**
p 296 FNB of Plainfield Ch 447 **31 L 2U + 27 S**
p 298 FNB of Trenton Ch 281 **U + 50+ L**
p 299 FNB of Woodbridge **4U + 9L 0 S**
p 299 FNB & TC of Woodbury Ch 1199 **6 L U + 24 S**
p 301 FNB of Belen Ch 6597 **12 L 2U + 38 S**
p 302 FNB Of Santa Fe Ch 1750 **20 L U + 50+ S**
p 340 FNB of Henderson Ch 7564 **21 L U + 9 S**
p 344 Dakota NB & TC, Bismarck Ch 13398 **5U + 10 S**
p 362 Ohio NB of Lima Ch 3772 **2L**
p 369 Jefferson NB of Steubenville Ch 1062 **1L**
p 378 Citizens NB of El Reno Ch 5985 **6 L 3U + 31 S**
p 378 FNB of El Reno Ch 4830 **9 L U + 7 S**
p 384 Citizens-FNB of Pawhuska Ch 13527 **U + 16 S**
p 386 Shawnee NB Ch 5115 **U + 4 L 14 S**
p 393 United States NB of Newberg Ch 9358 **5 L 2U + 8 S**
p 401 FNB of Blue Ridge Summit Ch 12281 **2 L 6 S**
p 441 Blackstone Canal NB of Providence Ch 1328 **50+ L 2U + 50+ S**
p 444 South Carolina NB of Charleston Ch 2044 **19 L 2U + 50+ S**
p 448 FNB in Britton Ch 13460 **2U + 7 S**
p 448 FNB & TC of Chamberlain Ch 13483 **2U + 8 S**
p 450 FNB in Mobridge Ch 13467 **U + 1 S**
p 451 FNB of Selby Ch 9376 **7 L U + 1 S**
p 452 Security NB of Viborg Ch 13589 **U + 1 S**

p 489 FNB of Price Ch 6012 **8 L 2U + 14 S**
p 489 FNB of Salt Lake City Ch 2059 **2U + 45 S**
p 492 Merchants NB of Burlington Ch 1197 **15 L U + 21 S**
p 494 FNB of Springfield Ch 122 **16 L U + 22 S**
p 498 American NB & TC of Danville Ch 9343 **2 L 3U + 29 S**
p 502 Saint Paul NB Ch 8547 **9 L 3U + 18 S**
p 506 FNB of Bremerton Ch 9280 **2 L U + 7 S**
p 510 Vancouver NB Ch 6013 **U + 4 L 2U + 9 S**
p 513 FNB of Albright Ch 10480 **U + 4 L U + 4 S**
p 517 FNB of St Albans Ch 9640 **2 L 2U + 4 S**
p 517 FNB of Terra Alta Ch 6999 **3 L 3U + 16 S**
p 518 N Exchange B of Wheeling Ch 5164 **2U + 50+ L 2U + 50+ S**
p 520 FNB of Baldwin Ch 10106 **3 L U + 5 S**
p 521 FNB of Edgerton Ch 7040 **6 L U + 6 S**
p 524 FNB of Neillsville Ch 9606 **6 L 2U + 7 S**
p 525 FNB of Portage Ch 4234 **U + 7 L 14 S**
p 526 Security NB of Sheboygan Ch 11150 **U + 30 S**
p 526 United States NB of Superior Ch 9140 **4 L U + 20 S**
p 526 Merchants NB of Watertown Ch 9003 **16 L 2U + 31 S**

Uncut Sheets

p 538 MARYLAND Federalsburg Ch 10210 $20 29-1 Serial #1 has been cut
p 538 MASSACHUSETTS Athol Ch 13733 Add $5 29-2 1-6
p 539 MINNESOTA Madison Ch 13561 Add $10 29-2 Serials 1-6** has been cut
p 539 MINNESOTA Madison Ch 13561 Add $20 29-2 Serials 1-6
p 540 NEBRASKA Belden Ch 10025 Add $5 29-1 Serial 823; $20 29-1 Serial 66; $5 29-2 Serials 1-6
p 541 NEW YORK New York Ch 13237 $5 02 PB Serial #3 has been cut
p 542 PENNSYLVANIA McKeesport Ch 4625 Add $5 29-1 7593
p 544 VIRGINIA Danville Ch 9343 The three sheets listed are on the **second title**
p 544 VIRGINIA St Paul Ch 8547 Add $5 29-2 14125--14130
p 544 WISCONSIN Columbus Ch 178 $5 29-2 Serials 1-6** has been cut